CONTENTS (Cont.)

NOTE: *Overhaul* articles may include SERVICE BULLETINS. These bulletins include information which may also affect older units.

MANUAL TRANSMISSIONS

AXLE SHAFTS & TRANSFER CASES

**CHRYSLER CORP.
FORD MOTOR CO.
GENERAL MOTORS**

1993-94 MITCHELL® TRANSMISSION SERVICE & REPAIR

DOMESTIC CARS, LIGHT TRUCKS & VANS

The Leader in Professional Estimating and Repair Information.

Mitchell International

ACKNOWLEDGMENT

Mitchell International thanks the
domestic and import automobile and light truck
manufacturers, distributors, and dealers
for their generous cooperation and assistance
which make this manual possible.

MARKETING

Senior Vice President
David Peterson

Product Managers
Catherine Smith
Daniel D. Fleming

EDITORIAL

Vice President
Thomas Garrett

Manager, Annual Data Editorial
Thomas L. Landis

Manager, Special Product Editorial
Ronald E. Garrett

Senior Editors
Chuck Vedra
Ramiro Gutierrez
John M. Fisher
Tom L. Hall
James A. Hawes
Serge G. Pirino

Technical Editors
Scott A. Olsen
Bob Reel
David W. Himes
Alex A. Solis
Donald T. Pellettera
Michael C. May
Scott A. Tiner
James R. Warren
James D. Boxberger
Bobby R. Gifford
Linda M. Murphy
Tim P. Lockwood
Dave L. Skora
Donald Lawler
Wayne D. Charbonneau
Sal Caloca
Charles "Bud" Gardner
Dan Hankins
Robert L. Eller
Nick DiVerde
Trang Nguyen
Julia A. Kinneer

WIRING DIAGRAMS

Manager
Matthew M. Krimple

TECHNICAL LIBRARIAN

Charlotte Norris

PRODUCT SUPPORT

Manager
Eddie Santangelo

Senior Product Specialist
Robert L. Rothgery

Product Specialists
James A. Wafford
Stephen Hill
Jeffrey H. Lenzkes

GRAPHICS

Manager
Judie LaPierre
Supervisor
Ann Klimetz

Published By

MITCHELL INTERNATIONAL
9889 Willow Creek Road
P.O. Box 26260
San Diego, CA 92196-0260

ISBN 0-8470-1438-X

© 1994 Mitchell International
All Rights Reserved

Printed in U.S.A.

Customer Service Numbers:
Subscription/Billing Information:
1-800-648-8010 or 619-578-6550

Technical Information:
1-800-854-7030 or 619-578-6550

Or Write: P.O. Box 26260, San Diego, CA 92196-0260

APPLICATIONS & IDENTIFICATION

NOTE: Many vehicles imported by Chrysler use Mitsubishi built transmissions. Imported transmissions are identified as Chrysler for easier model identification.

1993-94 CHRYSLER CORP. PASSENGER CARS

Model (Body Code)	Transmission Number
AWD Passenger Cars	
Colt Vista AWD	W4A32
Laser AWD	W4A33
Summit Wagon AWD	W4A32
Talon AWD	W4A33
FWD Passenger Cars	
Acclaim (AA)	
2.5L	30TH
3.0L	31TH Or 41TE
Colt	
3-Speed	F3A21
4-Speed	F4A21/22
Colt Vista (2WD)	
1.8L	F4A22
2.4L	F4A23
Concorde	
3.3L & 3.5L	42LE
Daytona (AG)	
2.2L & 2.5L	30TH
3.3L	41TE
Dynasty (AC) (1993 Only)	
2.5L	30TH
3.0L & 3.3L	41TE
Eagle Vision	
3.3L & 3.5L	42LE
Fifth Ave (AY) (1993 Only)	
3.3L & 3.8L	41TE
Imperial (AY) (1993 Only)	
3.3L & 3.8L	41TE
Intrepid	
3.3L & 3.5L	42LE
Laser	
Non-Turbo	F4A22
Turbo	F4A33
Lebaron (AJ) Except Sedan	
2.5L	30TH
3.0L	41TE
Lebaron Sedan (AA)	
2.5L (1993 Only)	30TH
3.0L	31TH Or 41TE
LHS (1994 Only)	
3.3L & 3.5L	42LE
New Yorker (AC) (1993 Only)	
2.5L	30TH
3.0L & 3.3L	41TE
New Yorker (1994 Only)	
3.3L & 3.5L	42LE
Shadow (AP)	
2.2L & 2.5L	30TH
3.0L	41TE
Spirit (AA)	
2.5L	30TH
3.0L	31TH Or 41TE
Stealth	F4A33
Summit	
3-Speed	F3A21
4-Speed	F4A21/22
Summit Wagon (2WD)	
1.8L	F4A22
2.4L	F4A23
Sundance (AP)	
2.2L & 2.5L	30TH
3.0L	41TE
Talon	
Non-Turbo	F4A22
Turbo	F4A33

[1] – For repair information on this transmission, see MITCHELL® 1993-94 TRANSMISSION SERVICE & REPAIR for IMPORTED CARS, LIGHT TRUCKS & VANS.

1993-94 CHRYSLER CORP. LIGHT TRUCKS, VANS & JEEP

Model (Body Code)	Transmission Number
FWD Vans	
Caravan, Town & Country, Voyager (AS)	
2.5L	31TH
3.0L	31TH Or 41TE
3.3L Or 3.8L	41TE
3.3L Or 3.8L AWD	41AE
RWD & 4WD Vehicles	
Cherokee (XJ)	
2.5L (1994)	30RH
4.0L	
1993	AW4
1994	32RH
Dakota (AN)	
3.9L	42RH
5.2L	46RH
BR Series Pickup (1994)	
3.9L	42RH Or 32RH
5.2L	46RH Or 36RH
5.9L	
Gasoline (Except V10)	36RH Or 46RH
Gasoline (V10)	37RH Or 47RH
Diesel	37RH, 46RH or 47RH
D & W Series Pickup (1993)	
3.9L	42RH Or 32RH
5.2L	46RH Or 36RH
5.9L	
Gasoline	36RH Or 46RH
Diesel	37RH
Grand Cherokee (ZJ)	
4.0L	[1] AW4, 42RE Or 42RH
5.2L	46RH
Ramcharger	
5.2L	46RH Or 36RH
5.9L	46RH
Ram Van (AB)	
3.9L	42RH Or 32RH
5.2L	46RH Or 36RH
5.9L	46RH
Ram-50	
2WD	R4AC1
4WD	V4AC1
Wrangler (YJ)	
2.5L (1994)	30RH
4.0L	32RH

[1] – Earlier models used the Aisin Warner 4 transmission. Some models may use the 42RE and some models may use the 42RH. The 42RE is used with 4.0L engine only.

NOTE: Many vehicles imported by Chrysler use Mitsubishi built transmissions. Imported transmissions are identified as Chrysler for easier model identification.

1993-94 CHRYSLER CORP. PASSENGER CARS

Model (Body Code)	Transmission Number
AWD Passenger Cars	
Colt Vista AWD	[1] W5M31 Or W5M33
Eagle Summit Wagon AWD	[1] W5M31 Or W5M33
Laser AWD	[1] W5M33
Stealth	
1993	[2] W5MG1
1994	[2] W6MG1
Talon AWD	[1] W5M33
FWD Passenger Cars	
Acclaim (AA)	
2.5L	A-523
3.0L	A-543
Colt	[1] F5M21 Or F5M22
Colt Vista (2WD) 5-Speed	
1993 2.4L Only	[1] F5M31
1993-94 All Others	[1] F5M22
Daytona (AG)	
2.2L Turbo	A-568
2.5L	A-523
3.0L	A-543
Eagle Summit Wagon	
1993 2.4L Only	[1] F5M31
1993-94 All Others	[1] F5M22
Laser	
Non-Turbo	[1] F4M22
Turbo	[1] F5M33
Lebaron (AA & AJ)	
2.5L	A-523
3.0L	A-543
Shadow (AP)	
2.2L & 2.5L	A-523
3.0L	A-543
Spirit (AA)	
2.5L	A-523
3.0L	A-543
Stealth	[1] F5M33
Summit	[1] F5M21 Or F5M22
Sundance (AP)	
2.2L & 2.5L	A-523
3.0L	A-543
Talon	
Non-Turbo	[1] F4M22
Turbo	[1] F5M33

[1] – For repair information on this transmission, see MITCHELL® 1993-94 TRANSMISSION SERVICE & REPAIR for IMPORTED CARS, LIGHT TRUCKS & VANS.
[2] – Overhaul information is not available.

1993-94 CHRYSLER CORP. LIGHT TRUCKS, VANS & JEEP

Model (Body Code)	Transmission Number
FWD Light Trucks & Vans	
Caravan & Voyager (AS)	
2.5L	A-523
RWD & 4WD Vehicles	
Cherokee & Wagoneer (XJ)	
2.5L	AX5
4.0L	AX15
Dakota (AN)	
2.5L	NV3500
3.9L	AX15
5.2L	NV4500
D & W Series Pickup (AD)	
3.9L, 5.2L & 5.9L	NV4500
5.9L Diesel	[2] Getrag 360
BR Series Pickup	
3.9L, 5.2L & 5.9L	NV4500
Grand Cherokee (ZJ)	AX15
Ramcharger	
5.2L & 5.9L	NV4500
Ram Van (AB) 3.9L	AX15
Ram-50	
2WD	[1] R5M21
4WD	
2.4L	[1] V5M21
3.0L	[1] V5MT1
Wrangler (YJ)	AX15

[1] – For repair information on this transmission, see MITCHELL® 1993-94 TRANSMISSION SERVICE & REPAIR for IMPORTED CARS, LIGHT TRUCKS & VANS.
[2] – Used on 1993 vehicles only.

APPLICATIONS & IDENTIFICATION
Ford Motor Co. Automatic Transmissions

1993-94 FORD MOTOR CO. PASSENGER CARS

Model	Transmission Number
FWD Passenger Cars	
Aspire	ATX
Capri	4EAT
Continental	AXOD-E/AX4S
Escort	4EAT
Festiva	[1] ATX
Probe	
1993	4EAT
1994	CD4E Or 4EAT
Sable	AXOD-E/AX4S
Taurus	
1993 (Except SHO)	AXOD-E/AX4S
1994 (Including SHO)	AXOD-E/AX4S
Tempo	ATX/FLC
Topaz	ATX/FLC
Tracer	4EAT
RWD Passenger Cars	
Cougar	
1993	AOD
1994	AODE-W/4R70W
Crown Victoria	AOD-E
Grand Marquis	AOD-E
Mark VII	AOD-E
Mustang	
2.3L Engine	A4LD
3.8L Engine	AOD-E
5.0L Engine	
1993	AOD
1994	AOD-E
Thunderbird	
1993	AOD
1994	AODE-W/4R70W
Town Car	AOD-E

[1] – Identified in some manufacturer publications as 3HAT. For repair information, see FESTIVA ATX & GEO KF400 overhaul article.

1993-94 FORD MOTOR CO. LIGHT TRUCKS & VANS

Model	Transmission Number
Aerostar	A4LD
Bronco	
1993	AOD Or E4OD
1994	E4OD
"E" Series	
4.9L, 5.0L, 5.8L & 7.5L Engines	[1] AOD, C-6 Or E4OD
7.3L Diesel Engine	C6 Or E4OD
Explorer	A4LD
"F" Series	
4.9L, 5.0L, 5.8L & 7.5L Engines	[1] AOD, AODE-W/4R70W, C-6 Or E4OD
7.3L Diesel Engine	C6 Or E4OD
Ranger	A4LD
Villager	4F20E

[1] – AOD used on 1993 models only.

Ford Motor Co. Manual Transmissions

1993-94 FORD MANUAL TRANSMISSIONS

Model	Transmission
FWD Vehicles	
Aspire (1994)	MTX 5-Speed
Capri	
Non-Turbo	Mazda (F-Type) 5-Speed
Turbo	Mazda (G-Type) 5-Speed
Escort	
1.8L	Mazda (G-Type) 5-Speed
1.9L	Mazda (F-Type) 5-Speed
Festiva (1993)	MTX 5-Speed
Probe	
2.0L & 2.5L	Mazda (G-Type) 5-Speed
Taurus (SHO Only)	MTX IV 5-Speed
Tracer	
1.8L	Mazda (G-Type) 5-Speed
1.9L	Mazda (F-Type) 5-Speed
Tempo & Topaz	MTX III 5-Speed
RWD Passenger Cars	
Thunderbird Super Coupe	M5R2 5-Speed
Mustang	Borg Warner T5 5-Speed
Light Trucks & Vans	
Aerostar, Explorer & Ranger	Mazda M50D 5-Speed
Bronco 4WD, F150/250 Pickup	[1] Borg-Warner T-18 4-Speed
Bronco, & "F" Series	Mazda M50D 5-Speed
F350 & Super Duty	[2] ZF S5-42 5-Speed

[1] – Used on 1993 vehicles only.
[2] – Used on vehicles with Gross Vehicle Weight Rating GVWR over 8500 lbs. (3855 kg).

1993-94 GENERAL MOTORS PASSENGER CARS

Application (Body Code)	Transmission (RPO Code)
Buick	
Century (A)	
2.2L L4	3T40 (MD9)
3.1L V6 (1994)	4T60-E (M13)
3.3L V6 (1993)	3T40 (MD9) Or 4T60 (ME9)
LeSabre (H)	4T60-E (M13)
Park Avenue (C)	4T60-E (M13)
Regal (W)	4T60-E (M13)
Riviera (E) (1993 Only)	4T60-E (M13)
Roadmaster (B)	
1993	4L60 (MD8)
1994	4L60-E (M30)
Skylark (N)	
2.3L L4 & 3.3L V6	3T40 (MD9)
3.1L V6 (1994)	4T60-E (M13)
Cadillac	
Brougham (D)	
1993	4L60 (MD8)
1994	4L60-E (M30)
DeVille (C) (1993 Only)	4T60-E (M13)
Eldorado (E)	
4.6L V8 (1993-1994)	4T80-E (MH1)
4.9L V8 (1993)	4T60-E (M13)
Fleetwood (C) (1993 Only)	4T60-E (M13)
Fleetwood (D) (1994 Only)	4L60-E (M30)
Seville (K)	
4.6L V8	4T80-E (MH1)
4.9L V8	4T60-E (M13)
Chevrolet	
Beretta (L)	
All Except 3.1L V6	3T40 (MD9)
3.1L V6 (1994 Only)	4T60-E (M13)
Camaro (F)	
1993	4L60 (MD8)
1994	4L60-E (M30)
Caprice (B)	
1993	4L60 (MD8)
1994	4L60-E (M30)
Cavalier (J)	3T40 (MD9)
Corsica (L)	
2.3L L4 & 3.1L V6 (1993 Only)	3T40 (MD9)
3.1L V6 (1994 Only)	4T60-E (M13)
Corvette (Y)	
1993	4L60 (MD8)
1994	4L60-E (M30)
Lumina (W)	
2.5L L4	3T40 (MD9)
3.1L V6	3T40 (MD9) Or 4T60-E (M13)
3.4L V6	4T60-E (M13)
Geo	
Metro (M)	[1] 3-Speed MX1
Prizm (S)	
1.6L 3-Speed	[1] A131L
1.8L 4-Speed	[1] A245E
Storm (R) (1993 Only)	
1.6L (SOHC)	3-Speed KF400 (RMC)
1.8L (DOHC)	4-Speed JF403-E (RML)
Tracker (J1)	[2] 3-Speed 3L30/THM 180C (MD2)
Oldsmobile	
Achieva (N)	
1993	3T40 (MD9)
1994	
2.3L L4	3T40 (MD9)
3.1L V6	4T60-E (M13)
Cutlass Ciera (A)	
1993	
2.5L L4	3T40 (MD9)
3.3L V6	3T40 (MD9) Or 4T60 (ME9)
1994	
2.2L L4	3T40 (MD9)
3.1L V6	4T60-E (M13)

1993-94 GENERAL MOTORS PASSENGER CARS

Application (Body Code)	Transmission (RPO Code)
Oldsmobile (Cont.)	
Cutlass Cruiser (A)	
1993	
2.5L L4	3T40 (MD9)
3.3L V6	4T60 (ME9)
1994	
2.2L L4	3T40 (MD9)
3.1L V6	4T60-E (M13)
Cutlass Supreme (W)	
1993	4T60-E (M13)
1994	
3.1L V6	3T40 (MD9) Or 4T60-E (M13)
3.4L V6	4T60-E (M13)
Eighty-Eight (Royale) (H)	4T60-E (M13)
Ninety-Eight (Regency Elite & Touring Sedan) (C)	4T60-E (M13)
Pontiac	
Bonneville (H)	4T60-E (M13)
Firebird (F)	
1993	4L60 (MD8)
1994	4L60-E (M30)
Grand Am (N)	
1993	3T40 (MD9)
1994	
2.3L L4	3T40 (MD9) Or 4T60-E (M13)
3.1L V6	4T60-E (M13)
Grand Prix (W)	4T60-E (M13)
LeMans (T)	3T40 (M40/MD9)
Sunbird (J)	3T40 (MD9)
Saturn	
Coupe & Sedan	
Base A/T	MP6
Performance A/T	MP7

1993-94 GENERAL MOTORS LIGHT TRUCKS & VANS

Application (Body Code)	Transmission (RPO Code)
Chevrolet	
Astro Van (M)	4L60-E (M30)
"C" & "K" Series	4L60-E (M30) Or 4L80-E (MT1)
"G" Series Van	4L60-E (M30) Or 4L80-E (MT1)
"S" & "T" Series	[1] 3L30 3-Speed (MD2), [2] 4L60 4-Speed (MD8) Or 4L60-E 4-Speed (M30)
Lumina APV (U)	
3.1L Engine	3T40 (MD9) Or 4T60-E (M30)
3.8L Engine	4T60-E (M13)
"P" Series	4L80-E (MT1)
Suburban	4L60-E (M30) Or 4L80-E (MT1)
GMC	
Jimmy & Pickup	4L60-E (M30)
"P" Series	4L80-E (MT1)
Suburban	4L60-E (M30) Or 4L80-E (MT1)
Sierra, Suburban & Yukon	4L60-E (M30) Or 4L80-E (MT1)
Safari	4L60-E (M30)
Typhoon (1993 Only)	4L60 (MD8)
Vandura & Rally Van	4L60-E (M30) Or 4L80-E (MT1)
Oldsmobile	
Bravada (T)	4L60-E (M30)
Silhouette APV (U)	
3.1L Engine	3T40 (MD9)
3.8L Engine	4T60-E (M13)
Pontiac	
Trans Sport MPV (U)	
3.1L V6 Engine	3T40 (MD9)
3.8L V6 Engine	4T60-E (M13)

[1] – Used on Postal vehicles.
[2] – Used on 1993 2.5L models only.

[1] – For repair information on this transmission, see MITCHELL® 1993-94 TRANSMISSION SERVICE & REPAIR for IMPORTED CARS, LIGHT TRUCKS & VANS.

[2] – For repair information on this transmission, see MITCHELL® 1988-90 TRANSMISSION SERVICE & REPAIR for IMPORTED CARS, LIGHT TRUCKS & VANS.

1993-94 GENERAL MOTORS PASSENGER CARS

Application (Body Code)	Transmission (RPO Code)
Chevrolet	
Beretta (L)	
2.2L	5-Speed Isuzu (MR3)
2.3L & 3.1L	5-Speed NVT550 (MG2 & MV5)
Camaro (F)	
3.4L V6	5-Speed Borg Warner T5 (M49)
5.7L V8	6-Speed Borg Warner T56 (M29/MG5)
Cavalier (J)	
2.2L	5-Speed Isuzu 76mm (MK7)
3.1L	5-Speed NVT550 (MG2)
Corsica (L)	
2.2L	5-Speed Isuzu 76mm (MK7)
Corvette (Y)	6-Speed ZF S6-40 (ML9)
Oldsmobile	
Achieva (N)	
2.3L L4 (Quad-4 HO)	5-Speed NVT550 (MY5 & MV5)
All Other Engines	5-Speed Isuzu 76mm (M32)
Cutlass Supreme (W)	
3.4L V6 (1993 Only)	5-Speed Getrag 284 (M27)
Pontiac	
Firebird (F)	
3.4L V6	5-Speed Borg Warner T5 (M49)
5.7L V8	6-Speed Borg Warner T56 (M29/MG5)
Grand Am (N)	
2.3L L4 (VIN A)	5-Speed NVT550 (MV5)
All Others	5-Speed Isuzu 76mm (M32)
Grand Prix (W)	
3.4L V6	5-Speed Getrag 284 (M27)
LeMans (T)	
4-Speed	[1] F16 (MM4/M21)
5-Speed	[1] F16 (MM5/M79)
Sunbird (J)	
3.1L V6 (VIN T)	5-Speed NVT550 (MG2)
All Others	5-Speed Isuzu 76mm (MK7)
Geo	
Metro (M)	5-Speed Suzuki MX1 (MM5)
Prizm (S)	[1] 5-Speed (MM5)
Storm (R)	[1] 5-Speed Isuzu 76mm (MK7, MR3 & MT2)
Tracker (J1)	[1] 5-Speed (MM5)
Saturn	
Coupe & Sedan	
DOHC	5-Speed MP3
SOHC	5-Speed MP2

[1] – For repair information on this transmission, see MITCHELL® 1993-94 TRANSMISSION SERVICE & REPAIR for IMPORTED CARS, LIGHT TRUCKS & VANS.

1993-94 GENERAL MOTORS LIGHT TRUCKS & VANS

Application (Body Code)	[1] Transmission (RPO Code)
"C" & "K" Series	5-Speed 109mm (MT8)
	5-Speed NVG 5LM60 85mm (MG5)
	5-Speed NV 4500 117mm (MT8)
"P" Series	5-Speed NV 4500 117mm (MT8)
"S" & "T" Series	
2.5L L4	5-Speed Borg Warner T5 77mm (MW1)
2.8L V6	5-Speed 77mm (ML3)
4.3L V6	5-Speed NVG 5LM60 85mm (MY2)

[1] – Manual transmissions are identified by the total number of forward speeds and the measured distant between the centerlines of the mainshaft and countershaft.

MODEL IDENTIFICATION

Vehicle model can be identified by body code. Body code is the 5th character of Vehicle Identification Number (VIN), stamped on metal pad on top of left end of instrument panel, near windshield.

1993-94 GENERAL MOTORS PASSENGER CARS

Application	Body Code
Buick	
Century	"A"
LeSabre	"H"
Park Avenue	"C"
Regal	"W"
Riviera (1993)	"E"
Roadmaster	"B"
Skylark	"N"
Cadillac	
Brougham (1993)	"D"
DeVille (1993)	"C"
DeVille (1994)	"K"
Eldorado	"E"
Fleetwood (1993)	"C"
Fleetwood (1994)	"C"
Seville	"K"
Chevrolet	
Beretta	"L"
Camaro	"F"
Caprice	"B"
Cavalier	"J"
Corsica	"L"
Corvette	"Y"
Lumina	"W"
Geo	
Metro	"M"
Prizm	"S"
Storm	"R"
Tracker	"J"
Oldsmobile	
Achieva	"N"
Custom Cruiser	"B"
Cutlass Ciera	"A"
Cutlass Cruiser	"A"
Cutlass Supreme	"W"
Eighty-Eight	"H"
Ninety-Eight	"C"
Toronado (1993)	"E"
Trofeo (1993)	"E"
Pontiac	
Bonneville	"H"
Firebird	"F"
Grand Am	"N"
Grand Prix	"W"
LeMans	"T"
Sunbird	"J"
Saturn	"Z"

1993-94 GENERAL MOTORS LIGHT TRUCKS & VANS

Application	Body Code
Astro	
2WD	"M"
4WD	"L"
Blazer	
2WD	"S"
4WD	"T" & "K"
Bravada AWD	"T"
Jimmy	
2WD	"S"
4WD	"T"
Lumina APV	"U"
Parcel Van	"P"
Pickup	
2WD	"C"
4WD	"K"
Safari	
2WD	"M"
4WD	"L"
Silhouette	"U"
Sonoma	
2WD	"S"
4WD	"T"
Suburban	
2WD	"C"
4WD	"K"
Trans Sport	"U"
Typhoon 4WD (1993)	"T"
Van (Vandura & Rally Van)	"G"
Yukon 4WD	"K"

1993-94 TRANSFER CASES

Vehicle Application	Manual Trans.	Automatic Trans.	Transfer Case
CHRYSLER CORP.			
Caravan	....	41AE	Power Transfer Unit
Dakota	AX-15, NP2500 Or NV3500	42RH Or 46RH	NP 231
Pickup & Ramcharger	[1] G360 Or NV4500	32/42RH, 46/47RH Or 36/37RH	[2] NP 021, [3] 205, [4] 231 Or 241
Laser, Summit Wagon, Talon & Vista Wagon	W5M31 Or W5M33	W4A32 Or W4A33	AWD
Ram-50	V5M21 Or V5MT1	V4AC1	4WD
Town & Country	....	41AE	Power Transfer Unit
Voyager	....	41AE	Power Transfer Unit
FORD MOTOR CO.			
Aerostar	M50D	A4LD	Dana TC-28
Bronco	ZF S5-42 Or T18	AOD Or E4OD	Borg-Warner 1356
"F" Series	ZF S5-42 Or T18	AOD Or E4OD	Borg-Warner 1356
Explorer & Ranger	M50D	A4LD	Borg-Warner 1354
GENERAL MOTORS			
Chevrolet/GMC			
Astro, Bravada, Safari & Typhoon	....	4L60-E	Borg-Warner 4472
Jimmy & "T" Series	T5 Or 5LM60	4L60-E	NP 231 Or NP 233
"K"	GM 109, NV 4500 Or 5LM60	4L60-E Or 4L80-E	NP 241, B-W 4401 Or 4470
GEO			
Geo Tracker	MM5	3L30	[5] Geo
JEEP			
Cherokee & Wrangler	AX-5 Or AX-15	AW4, 30RH Or 32RH	NP 231 Or NP 242
Grand Cherokee	AX-15	AW4, 42RE, 42RH Or 46RH	NP 231, 242 Or 249

[1] – Used on 1993 Cummins diesel only.

[2] – Power take off (if equipped) used on 2WD pickup only.

[3] – Used on 1993 pickup and Ramcharger only.

[4] – Transfer case used on late 1994 pickup and Ramcharger vehicles is an NP 231 HD. It is similar to an NP 241 with an NP 231 extension housing assembly.

[5] – For repair information, see MITCHELL® 1993-94 TRANSMISSION SERVICE & REPAIR for IMPORTED CARS, LIGHT TRUCKS & VANS.

DESCRIPTION

Tool applications used in this manual are noted where applicable. These (usually specific tools) are used to perform a specific task during REMOVAL, INSTALLATION, OVERHAUL or TESTING of components.

For example: "Using Spline Adapter (J-28513) and Holding Wrench (J28514), tighten pinion nut until end play is taken up." Although other tools could be used, the tools referenced are those recommended by the vehicle manufacturer. Use these tools whenever possible.

In cases where a non-specific tool is mentioned, tool number will not be given. For example: "Place bearing insert in connecting rod and install guides on rod bolts. Compress piston rings using ring compressor." Since almost any piston ring compressor may be used, no specific tool number is listed.

The following descriptions show an example of the reference in text, the tool maker recommended by the manufacturer and the tool maker's address. Further information on tools and local suppliers can be obtained from the tool maker. It is also possible, for example, that a Kent-Moore tool may be cross-referenced to another tool maker. In this case it is important that the tools be exactly the same design and perform the same function.

CHRYSLER CORP. & JEEP

Chrysler Corp. tool applications mentioned in this manual will appear as follows: "Assemble pinion locating Spacer (SP-6030) over body of Arbor (SP-5385). Install shaft locating Sleeve (L-4507), Washer (C4656) and Compression Nut (SP-533)".

CHRYSLER CORP. & JEEP TOOL MANUFACTURER

Miller Special Tools
SPX Corporation
12842 Farmington Rd.
Livonia, Michigan 48150
Telephone (313) 522-6717
Fax (313) 522-6505

FORD MOTOR CO.

Ford tool applications mentioned in this manual will appear as follows: "Remove pinion bearing with Slide Hammer (T50T-100-A with attachment T58L-101-A). Remove bearing with Puller (T81P-3504-5)".

Ford tools are manufactured by Owatonna Tool Corporation (OTC). The number after the prefix is the basic tool part number. Any letters or numbers after the basic part number designate either a revised tool number or that the tool is part of a set.

FORD TOOL MANUFACTURER

OTC Tool & Equipment Division
SPX Corporation
655 Eisenhower Drive
Owatonna, MN 55060
Telephone (800) 533-5338
Fax (800) 283-8665

GENERAL MOTORS

General Motors tool applications mentioned in this manual will appear as follows: "Using Ball Joint Separator (J-36226) for "C" and "H" bodies or (J-29330) for all others, separate ball joint stud from steering knuckle".

The "J" in front of the tool number indicates it is a Kent-Moore tool. The set of numbers after the "J" give the basic tool number. Additional numbers or letters after the basic tool number designate an improved tool (-02,-03, -A. -C) or a tool that is part of a set (-2, -3, etc.). Tool numbers without additional characters indicate that the tool listed is a complete tool.

GENERAL MOTORS TOOL MANUFACTURER

Kent-Moore Tool
SPX Corporation
29784 Little Mack
Roseville, Michigan 48066-2298
Telephone (800) 345-2233
FAX (313) 578-7375

INTRODUCTION

Vehicles equipped with engine or transmission computers may require a relearn procedure after the vehicle battery is disconnected. Vehicle computers memorize and store vehicle operation patterns for optimum driveability and performance. When the vehicle battery is disconnected, this memory is lost. Default data is used until new data from each key start is stored. As the computer restores its memory from each new key start, driveability is restored.

Driveability problems may occur during the relearn stage. Depending on the vehicle and how it is equipped, the following driveability problems may exist:

- Rough or unstable idle.
- Hesitation or stumble.
- Rich or lean running.
- Poor fuel mileage.
- Harsh or poor transmission shift quality.

To accelerate relearn process after battery removal and installation, vehicle should be road tested in the following manner:

- Vehicle at normal operating temperature (cooling fan cycles).
- Accelerate at normal throttle position (20-50%).
- Cruise at light to medium throttle.
- Decelerate to a stop, downshifting and using brakes normally.

Manufacturers identify specific relearn procedures. See RELEARN PROCEDURES. Always complete the procedure before returning the vehicle to the customer.

RELEARN PROCEDURES

CHRYSLER CORP.

NOTE: If repairs other than battery replacement have been made to late model vehicles, always refer to appropriate verification tests in ENGINE PERFORMANCE of appropriate MITCHELL® manual.

Theft Alarm Relearn Procedure – 1) Theft alarm relearn is necessary whenever battery is disconnected or dead battery is boosted. If battery is connected or boosted without conducting relearn procedure, alarm system will enter power-up mode and vehicle will not start.
2) Before reconnecting battery or connecting booster, insert door key into driver side door lock. Connect battery cable(s) and cycle driver side door lock once. Vehicle may now be started. On some models, horn will sound 3 times to indicate theft system is activated.

NOTE: If Single Board Engine Controller or Powertrain Control Module (SBEC or PCM) is replaced, theft alarm system will not operate for minimum of 20 engine starts.

Shift Quality Quick-Learn Procedure – 1) This procedure quickly optimizes shift quality. Procedure must be performed after disconnecting battery or loss of voltage supply to Transaxle Control Module (TCM), replacing TCM, transaxle internal components, solenoid assembly or torque converter.
2) Chrysler's Diagnostic Readout Box (DRB) scan tool with proper cartridge must be used to perform shift quality quick-learn procedure. The following conditions must be met when performing shift quality quick-learn procedure: oil temperature must be greater than 60°F (16°C), brakes must be applied when indicated, engine speed greater than 500 RPM, throttle angle less than 3 degrees, gearshift must be moved only when indicated, gearshift must remain in overdrive as indicated until DRB indicates procedure is completed.
3) If unused replacement TCM is installed on vehicle with engine at normal operating temperature, shift quality quick-learn procedure will cause TCM to indicate a cold oil temperature. Oil temperature must be monitored with DRB.
4) If oil temperature is less than 60°F (16°C), allow engine to idle until oil temperature is greater than 60°F (16°C). If oil temperature is greater than 200°F (94°C), allow transaxle to cool until oil temperature is less than 200°F (94°C).
5) Connect DRB to data link connector, located near brake pedal at bottom of instrument panel. Using proper cartridge and DRB manufacture's instructions, move through program to enter 41TE/AE menu. Start vehicle. Select ADJUSTMENTS function.
6) Apply brakes. Select QUICK-LEARN function. Place gearshift in Neutral and then "OD" (overdrive) when indicated. Wait until TEST COMPLETE is indicated on DRB. Place gearshift in Park. Release brakes. Remove DRB.

Pinion Factor Procedure – 1) Pinion factor procedure must be performed if Transaxle Control Module (TCM) is replaced or changed from one vehicle to another. Procedure must be used to calibrate TCM for different equipment combinations to provide speedometer operation and correct readings. Failure to perform this procedure will result in no speedometer operation.

NOTE: It may be necessary to consult manufacturer to determine Final Drive Ration (FDR) number when performing pinion factor procedure.

2) Connect DRB to data link connector, located near brake pedal at bottom of instrument panel. Using proper cartridge and DRB manufacture's instructions, move through program to enter 41TE/AE menu. Select ADJUSTMENTS function.
3) Select PINION FACTOR function. Select appropriate Final Drive Ratio (FDR) number and then the tire size. Remove DRB. Road test vehicle and verify speedometer operation.

FORD MOTOR CO.

Vehicle Preparation – Ensure all components are connected. Ensure transmission fluid level is correct. Warm engine to normal operating temperature. If vehicle has been repaired, perform KOEO and Continuous Memory Code Self-Test and ensure fault codes are not present. See appropriate SELF-DIAGNOSTICS article in ENGINE PERFORMANCE.

Vehicle Driveability Relearn Procedure – Place automatic transmission in Park (A/T) or Neutral (M/T). Start engine and allow to idle for one minute. Drive vehicle for 10 miles or more to allow processor to relearn values for optimum performance.

AOD-E, AXOD & AXOD-E Transaxle Shift Relearn Procedure – With transaxle gear selector in Overdrive, moderately accelerate vehicle to 50 MPH for a minimum of 15 seconds. Transaxle should be in 4th gear. While holding speed steady, lightly apply and release brake for about 5 seconds. Stop and park vehicle for at least 20 seconds with gear selector in Drive. Repeat procedure 5 times.

E4OD Transmission Shift Relearn Procedure – 1) With gear selector in Drive, press Overdrive Cancel Switch (LED should light). Moderately accelerate vehicle to 40 MPH for a minimum of 15 seconds (30 seconds above 4000-ft. elevation). Transmission should be in 3rd gear.
2) While holding speed steady, press Overdrive Cancel Switch (LED should go off) and accelerate from 40 MPH to 50 MPH. Transmission should shift from 3rd gear to 4th gear. Hold speed steady for 15 seconds. While holding speed steady, lightly apply and release brakes enough to turn brake lights on. Maintain 50 MPH for about 5 seconds. Stop vehicle for a minimum of 20 seconds with transmission gear selector in Drive. Repeat procedure 5 times.

GENERAL MOTORS

Vehicle Driveability Relearn Procedure – General Motors does not provide a specific procedure for driveability relearn. If a vehicle battery was disconnected for facilitating repairs or a Powertrain Control Module (PCM) was replaced, driving the vehicle will enable the PCM to relearn driveability. Inform your customer that he/she may experience driveability different from what they are accustomed to until the PCM completes it's relearn function.

TP Sensor Learn (Corvette) – If a NEW TP sensor or throttle body is installed, EBTCM must learn new TP sensor idle position voltage. This procedure is necessary to ensure effective engine torque reduction during ASR operations. TP sensor learn procedure requires a Tech-1 scan tester or T-100 (CAMS) unit.
1) Turn ignition off. Connect Tech-1 scan tester with a Mass Storage cartridge. Turn ignition on. Select ABS/ASR feature from menu.
2) Select F5 (TP SENSR LEARN). Press up arrow to begin learn procedure. Wait for Tech-1 scan tester to indicate COMPLETE. Turn ignition off. Disconnect Tech-1 scan tester.

NOTE: Ensure accelerator and brake pedals are free from any obstructions while performing TP sensor/idle learn procedure. PCM will not perform learn function with accelerator pedal or brake pedal obstructions.

NOTE: TP sensor/idle learn procedure should be performed with A/C on and with A/C off due to engine load differences.

TP Sensor/Idle Learn (DeVille, Eldorado, Fleetwood & Seville 4.9L) – **1)** Ensure outside air temperature is greater than 50°F (10°C) to allow operation of A/C compressor. Start engine and allow to idle for 13 minutes. With engine running, enter diagnostics. See SELF-DIAGNOSTICS – CADILLAC 4.9L article.
2) Turn ignition off. Wait 20 seconds, then turn ignition on, with engine off. Reenter diagnostics. Repeat step **2)**.
3) Turn ignition off. Wait 20 seconds, then start engine. Apply brakes and place transmission in Drive. Turn Climate Control Panel (CCP) to OFF position and allow engine to idle for one minute.
4) Turn CCP to AUTO position and ensure A/C compressor engages. Allow engine to idle for one minute. Place transmission in Park and turn ignition off.

Cautions & Warnings

COMPRESSED NATURAL GAS SAFETY PRECAUTIONS

Observe the following safety precautions when working on any vehicle equipped to operate on natural gas fuel:

- DO NOT smoke or create sparks while servicing CNG fuel systems.
- Natural gas vapors at atmospheric pressure are lighter than air and will rise and disperse in open areas. In enclosed areas, natural gas vapor may collect and form a combustible mixture. If the vehicle is routinely placed in an enclosed area or if the facility is heated with open flame heaters, the area should be provided with adequate ventilation and/or a natural gas detection system. For long term storage, the manual shut-off valve and individual cylinder valves should be closed.
- Natural gas contains an odorant additive. If persistent natural gas odor is detected, a leak is indicated and should be located and repaired immediately.
- DO NOT return any vehicle to service that has been in an accident that may have damaged or dislocated any fuel system component until a thorough inspection and leak test has been made.
- DO NOT attempt to weld CNG fuel cylinders or any other part of fuel system.
- Any fuel system component, including the cylinders, that have been subjected to fire may not be returned to service due to reduced pressure capability.
- DO NOT use paint oven to cure paint repairs.
- DO NOT paint or undercoat any CNG fuel system component.
- Chrysler CNG fuel systems have a maximum capacity of 3000 psi compensated to a temperature of 70°F (21°C). Vehicles SHOULD ONLY be refueled using equipment incorporating temperature compensation to 70°F (21°C). Exceeding fuel system capacity will result in fuel system damage or personal injury.
- The fuel pressure regulator is under cooling system pressure. DO NOT attempt to remove hoses from regulator without relieving system pressure.
- DO NOT park vehicle near a source of excessive heat or open flame.

- DO NOT attempt to force open fuel filler valve. A sudden release of natural gas will occur, possibly causing an explosion.
- When replacing threaded fuel system components on General Motors vehicles, ALWAYS apply SWAK® anaerobic pipe sealant to new component threads except compression fittings.
- When replacing threaded fuel system components on Chrysler vehicles, a go/no-go tool MUST be used to check correct tightness of fittings.
- CNG fuel systems are under extremely high pressure. NEVER use steel, copper or brass tubing in place of stainless steel fuel tubes.
- NEVER use replacement fuel system components that are not manufactured to OEM standards.

TRANSMISSION FLUID

DEXRON-IIE

DEXRON-IIE is now the preferred fluid for all Hydra-Matic transmissions and transaxles. It will replace DEXRON-II. It is recommended wherever DEXRON-II was previously specified. It may be used in all General Motors automatic transmissions and transaxles produced since 1949. It may be mixed, in any ratio, in a transmission already filled with DEXRON or DEXRON-II without draining or flushing. Both fluids are fully compatible and may be substituted when necessary. DEXRON-IIE has the following advantages over DEXRON-II:

- Improved anti-foaming characteristics.
- Improved low temperature flow.
- Improved high temperature oxidation stability.

Before removing engine/transmission assembly on compressed natural gas powered vehicles, see COMPRESSED NATURAL GAS SAFETY PRECAUTIONS article in GENERAL INFORMATION.

WARNING: Before removing engine/transmission assembly on compressed natural gas powered vehicles, see COMPRESSED NATURAL GAS SAFETY PRECAUTIONS article in GENERAL INFORMATION.

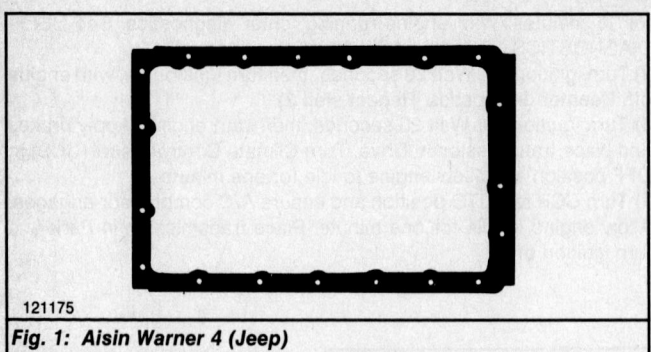

121175

Fig. 1: Aisin Warner 4 (Jeep)

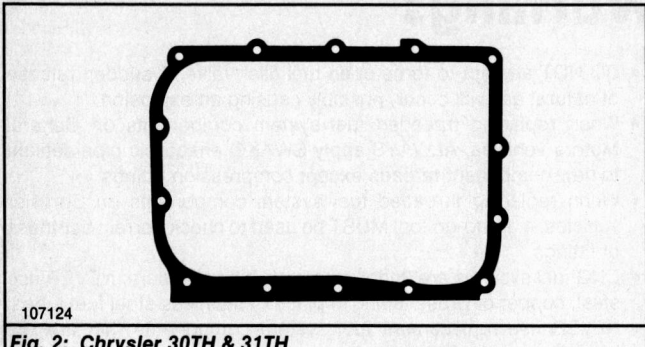

107124

Fig. 2: Chrysler 30TH & 31TH

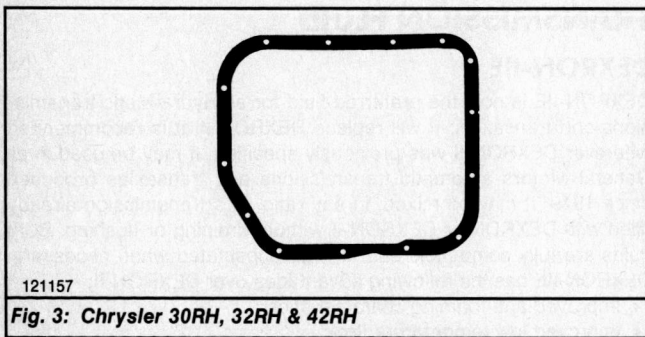

121157

Fig. 3: Chrysler 30RH, 32RH & 42RH

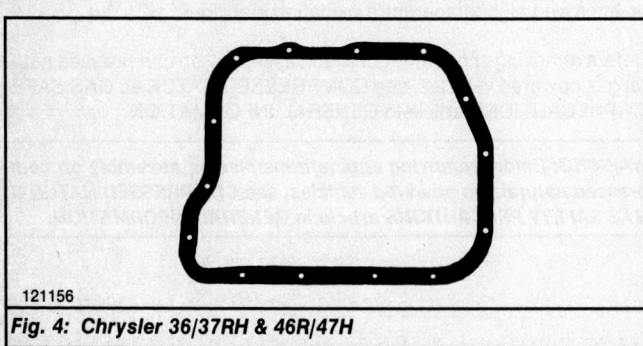

121156

Fig. 4: Chrysler 36/37RH & 46R/47H

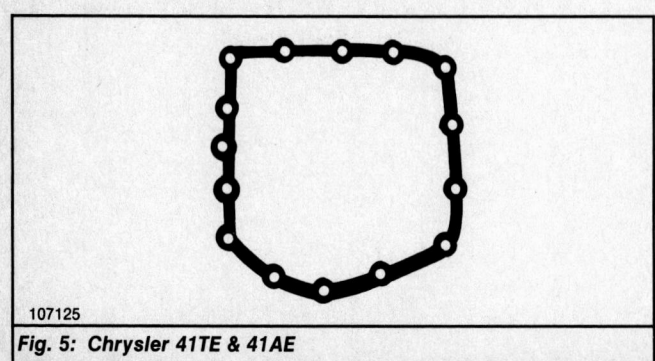

107125

Fig. 5: Chrysler 41TE & 41AE

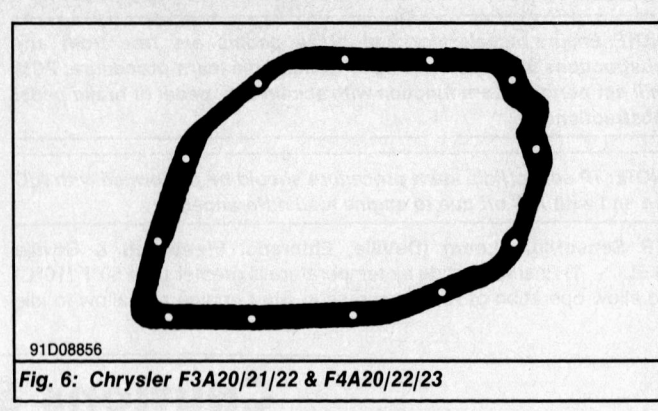

91D08856

Fig. 6: Chrysler F3A20/21/22 & F4A20/22/23

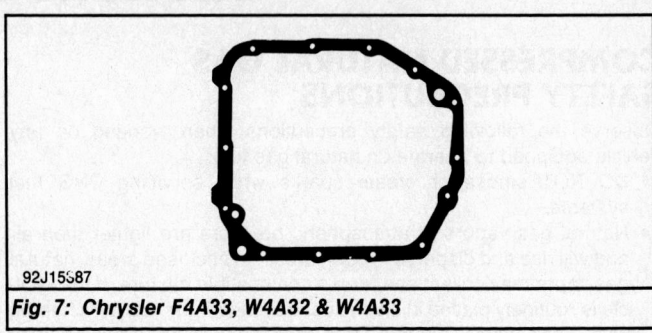

92J15587

Fig. 7: Chrysler F4A33, W4A32 & W4A33

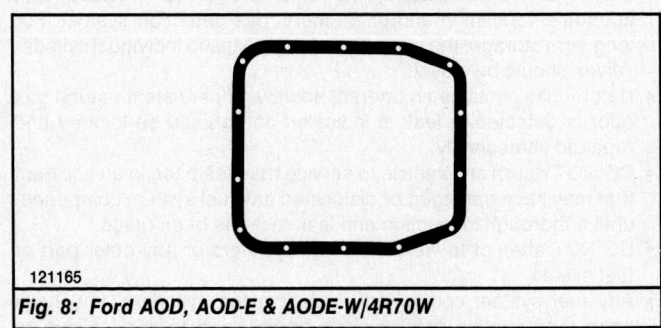

121165

Fig. 8: Ford AOD, AOD-E & AODE-W/4R70W

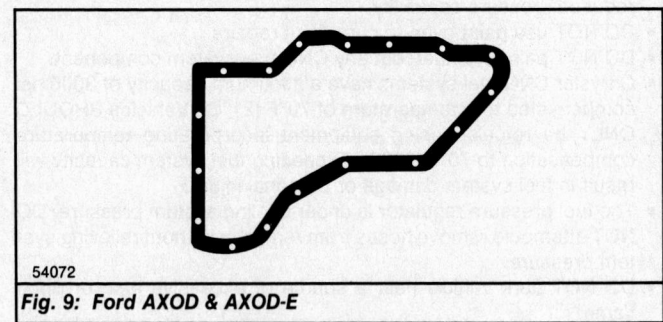

54072

Fig. 9: Ford AXOD & AXOD-E

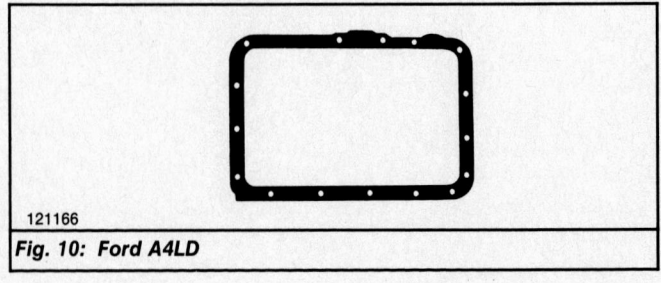

121166

Fig. 10: Ford A4LD

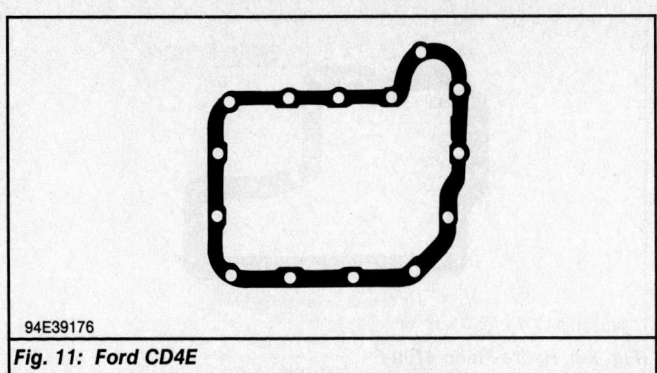

94E39176

Fig. 11: Ford CD4E

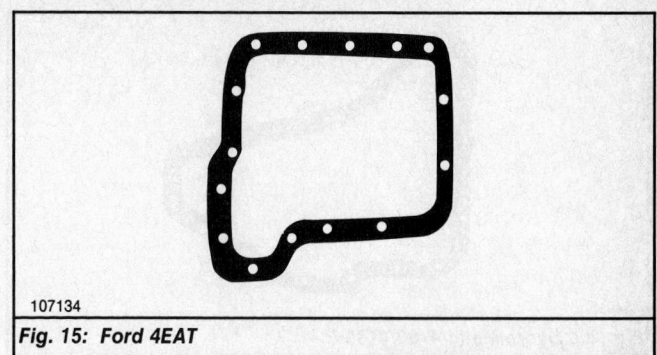

107134

Fig. 15: Ford 4EAT

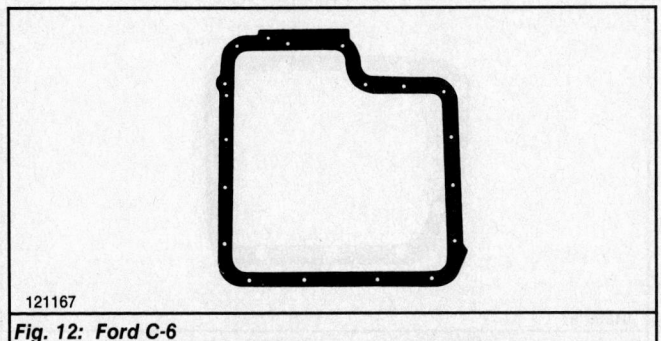

121167

Fig. 12: Ford C-6

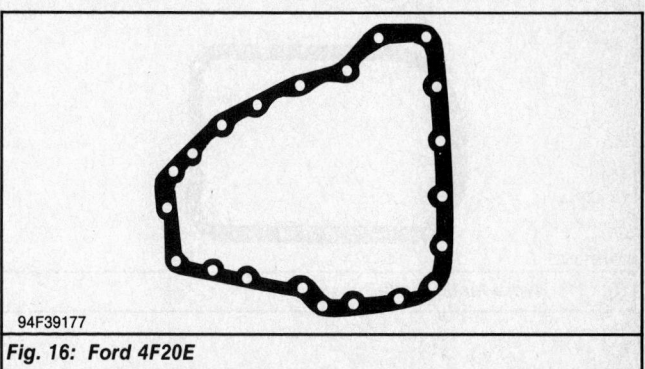

94F39177

Fig. 16: Ford 4F20E

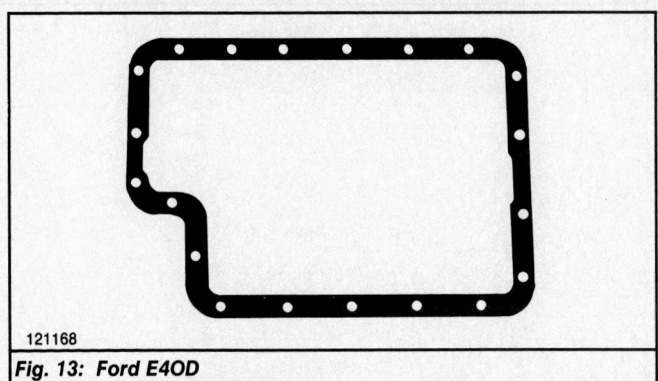

121168

Fig. 13: Ford E4OD

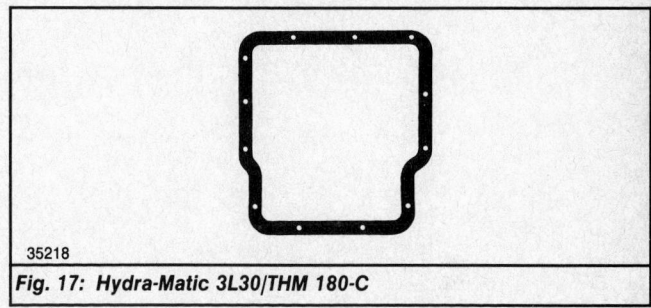

35218

Fig. 17: Hydra-Matic 3L30/THM 180-C

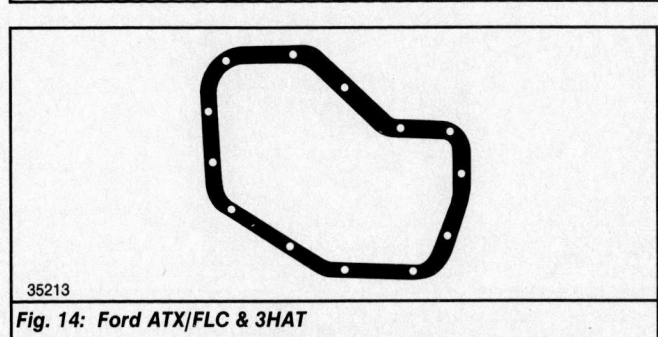

35213

Fig. 14: Ford ATX/FLC & 3HAT

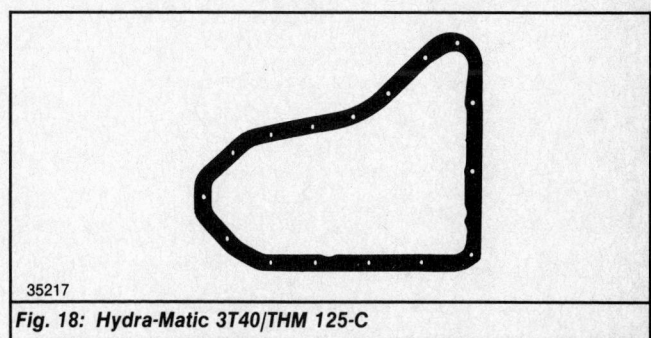

35217

Fig. 18: Hydra-Matic 3T40/THM 125-C

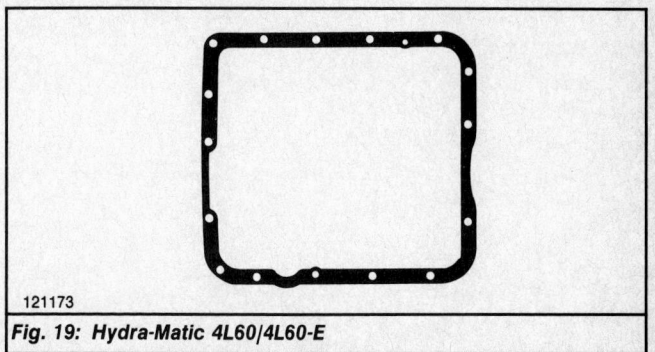

121173

Fig. 19: Hydra-Matic 4L60/4L60-E

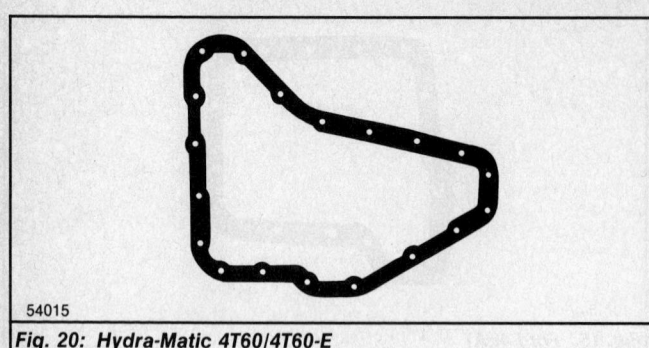

54015

Fig. 20: Hydra-Matic 4T60/4T60-E

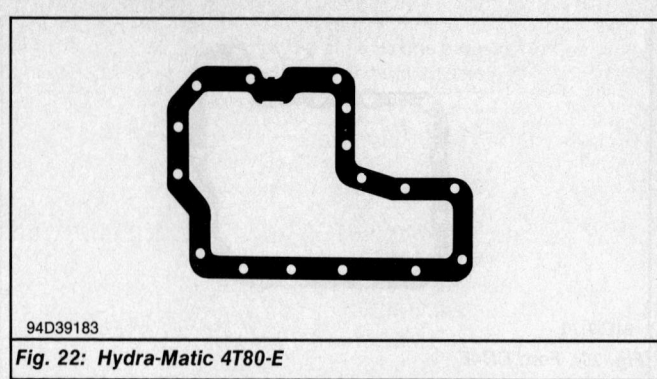

94D39183

Fig. 22: Hydra-Matic 4T80-E

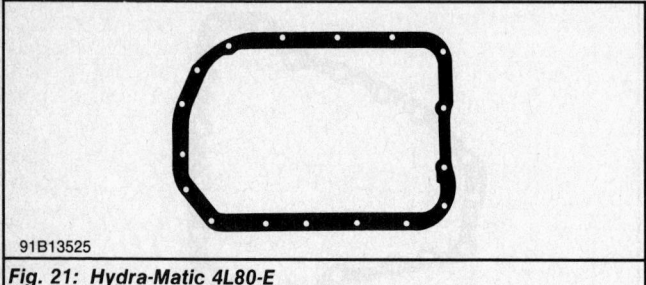

91B13525

Fig. 21: Hydra-Matic 4L80-E

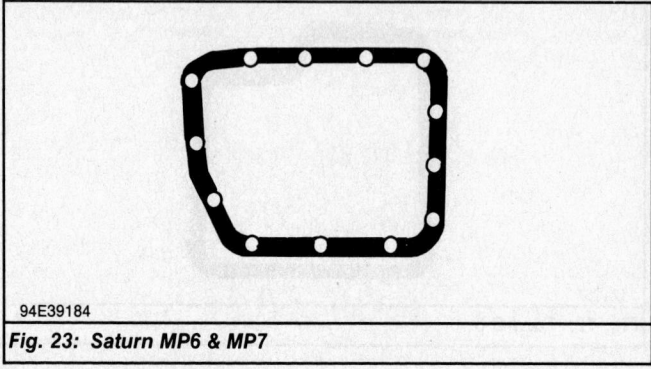

94E39184

Fig. 23: Saturn MP6 & MP7

NOTE: Latest changes and corrections represents a collection of last minute information and relevant technical service bulletins. Read this section and make notations in appropriate 1992 and earlier manuals for easy reference.

FORD MOTOR CO.
MANUAL TRANSMISSIONS

☞1 *1991-92 BORG WARNER T5 5-SPEED: EXPLODED VIEW OF SYNCRONIZER ASSEMBLIES* – Please note that the figure showing exploded view of syncronizer assemblies has been revised. The revised figure now identifies the insert retainer.

This revision applies to the following publication:
1992 DOMESTIC CARS, LIGHT TRUCKS & VANS TRANSMISSION SERVICE & REPAIR manual.
• 1991-92 – Page 4-23, Fig. 7.

This revision applies to the following publication:
1992 DOMESTIC CARS, LIGHT TRUCKS & VANS TRANSMISSION SERVICE & REPAIR manual.
• 1991-92 – Page 3-1047.

☞3 *1991-92 HYDRA-MATIC 4L80-E: DIRECT CLUTCH* — Callout number 12 on page 3-1157, Fig. 26 is not pointing at direct clutch housing. A callout on Fig. 27 incorrectly identifies the center support and race assembly. Please use the following revised figures.

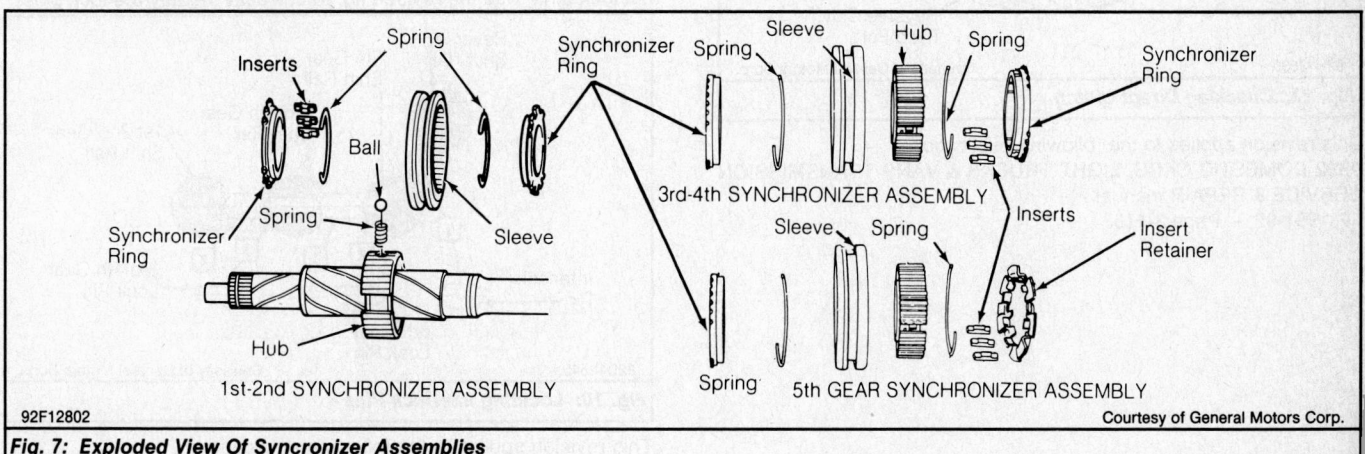

92F12802   Courtesy of General Motors Corp.

Fig. 7: Exploded View Of Syncronizer Assemblies

GENERAL MOTOR CORP.
AUTOMATIC TRANSMISSIONS

☞2 *1991-92 HYDRA-MATIC 3T40: INSTALLING DIRECT & FORWARD CLUTCH* – Please note that the direct and forward clutch assembly inspection procedure, step 12) and related fig. 40, have been revised as follows:

12) Install direct and forward clutch assemblies into case. Rotate clutch assemblies, without pushing down, until they drop into fully seated position in case. When correctly installed, case face-to-direct clutch housing distance should be 1 11/16". *See Fig. 40.*

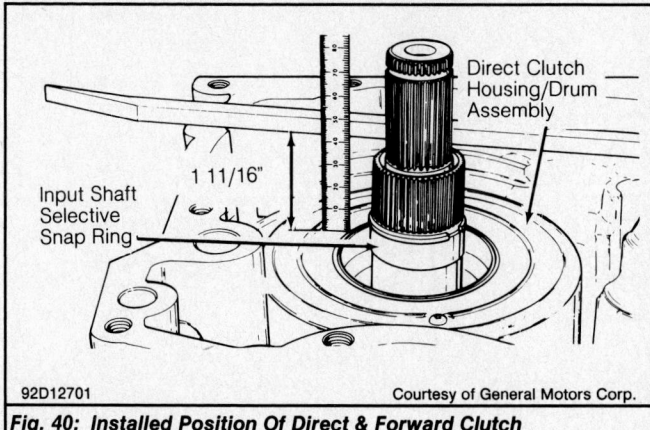

92D12701   Courtesy of General Motors Corp.

Fig. 40: Installed Position Of Direct & Forward Clutch

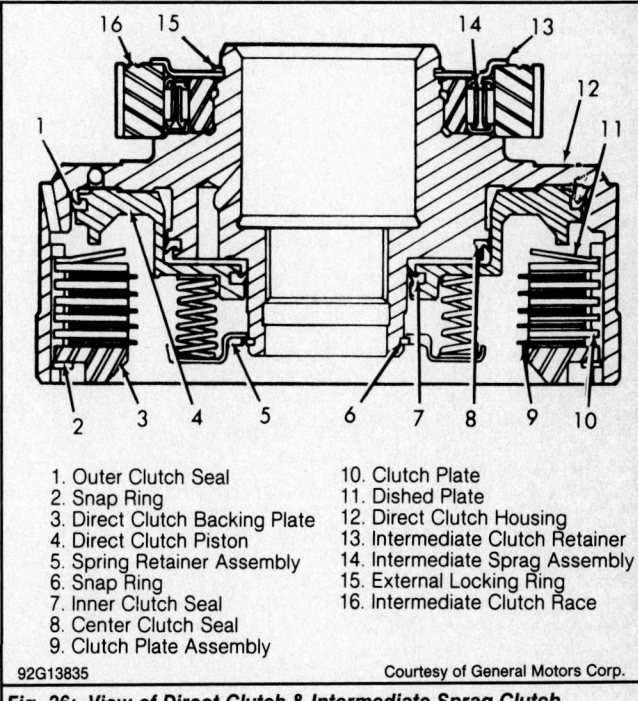

1. Outer Clutch Seal
2. Snap Ring
3. Direct Clutch Backing Plate
4. Direct Clutch Piston
5. Spring Retainer Assembly
6. Snap Ring
7. Inner Clutch Seal
8. Center Clutch Seal
9. Clutch Plate Assembly
10. Clutch Plate
11. Dished Plate
12. Direct Clutch Housing
13. Intermediate Clutch Retainer
14. Intermediate Sprag Assembly
15. External Locking Ring
16. Intermediate Clutch Race

92G13835   Courtesy of General Motors Corp.

Fig. 26: View of Direct Clutch & Intermediate Sprag Clutch

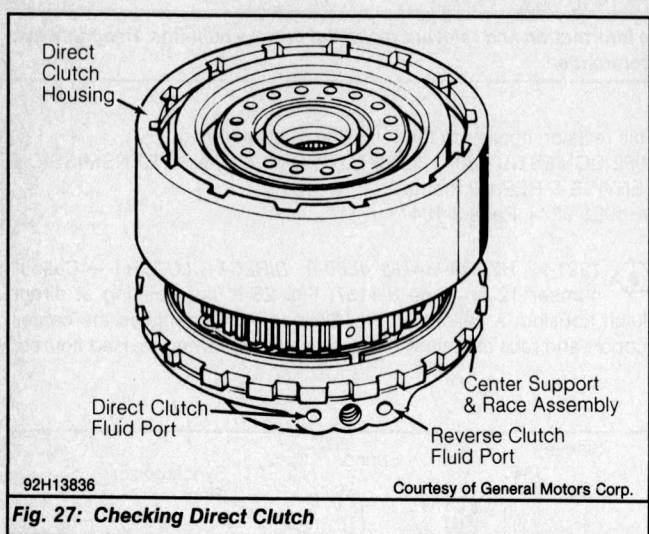

Direct Clutch Housing

Direct Clutch Fluid Port

Center Support & Race Assembly

Reverse Clutch Fluid Port

92H13836

Courtesy of General Motors Corp.

Fig. 27: Checking Direct Clutch

This revision applies to the following publication:
1992 DOMESTIC CARS, LIGHT TRUCKS & VANS TRANSMISSION SERVICE & REPAIR manual.
- 1991-92 – Page 3-1157.

MANUAL TRANSMISSIONS

4 > *1991-92 BORG WARNER T5 5-SPEED: EXPLODED VIEW OF SYNCRONIZER ASSEMBLIES* – Please note that the figure showing exploded view of syncronizer assemblies has been revised. The revised figure now identifies the insert retainer. See fig. 7 under FORD MOTOR CO., MANUAL TRANSMISSIONS: EXPLODED VIEW OF SYNCRONIZER ASSEMBLIES, in this article.

This revision applies to the following publication:
1992 DOMESTIC CARS, LIGHT TRUCKS & VANS TRANSMISSION SERVICE & REPAIR manual.
- 1991-92 – Page 4-23, Fig. 7.

5 > *1991-92 ISUZU 76 MM 5-SPEED: REVISED FIGURE CALLOUTS* – Fig. 10 on page 4-122 incorrectly identifies the shift rail lock pins. Use the revised fig. to correctly identify the lock pins.

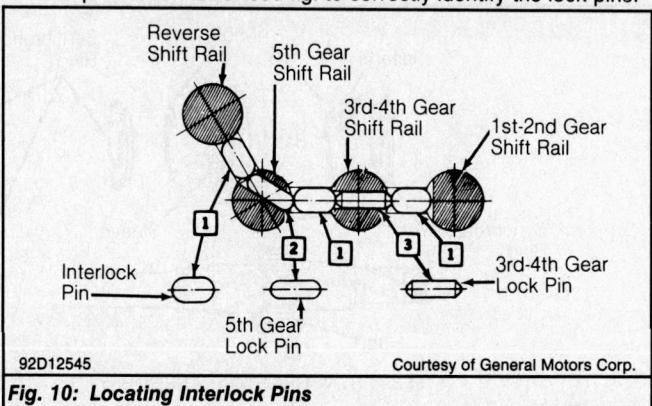

Reverse Shift Rail

5th Gear Shift Rail

3rd-4th Gear Shift Rail

1st-2nd Gear Shift Rail

Interlock Pin

5th Gear Lock Pin

3rd-4th Gear Lock Pin

92D12545

Courtesy of General Motors Corp.

Fig. 10: Locating Interlock Pins

This revision applies to the following publication:
1992 DOMESTIC CARS, LIGHT TRUCKS & VANS TRANSMISSION SERVICE & REPAIR manual.
- 1991-92 – Page 4-122, Fig. 10.

OIL CIRCUIT DIAGRAMS

OIL CIRCUIT DIAGRAMS
Aisin Warner 4

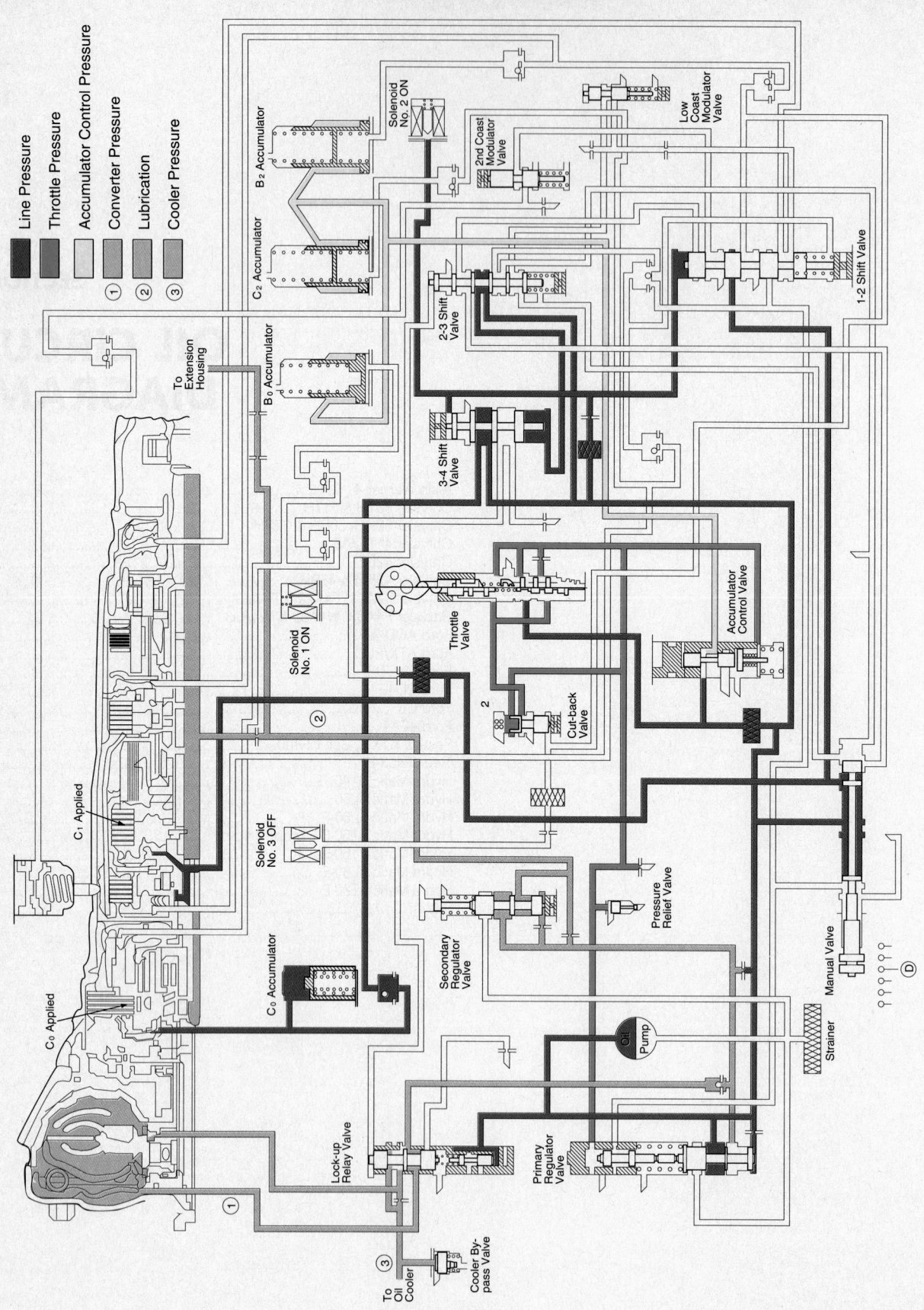

Fig. 1: "D" Range — 1st Gear

Courtesy of Chrysler Corp.

OIL CIRCUIT DIAGRAMS
Aisin Warner 4 (Cont.)

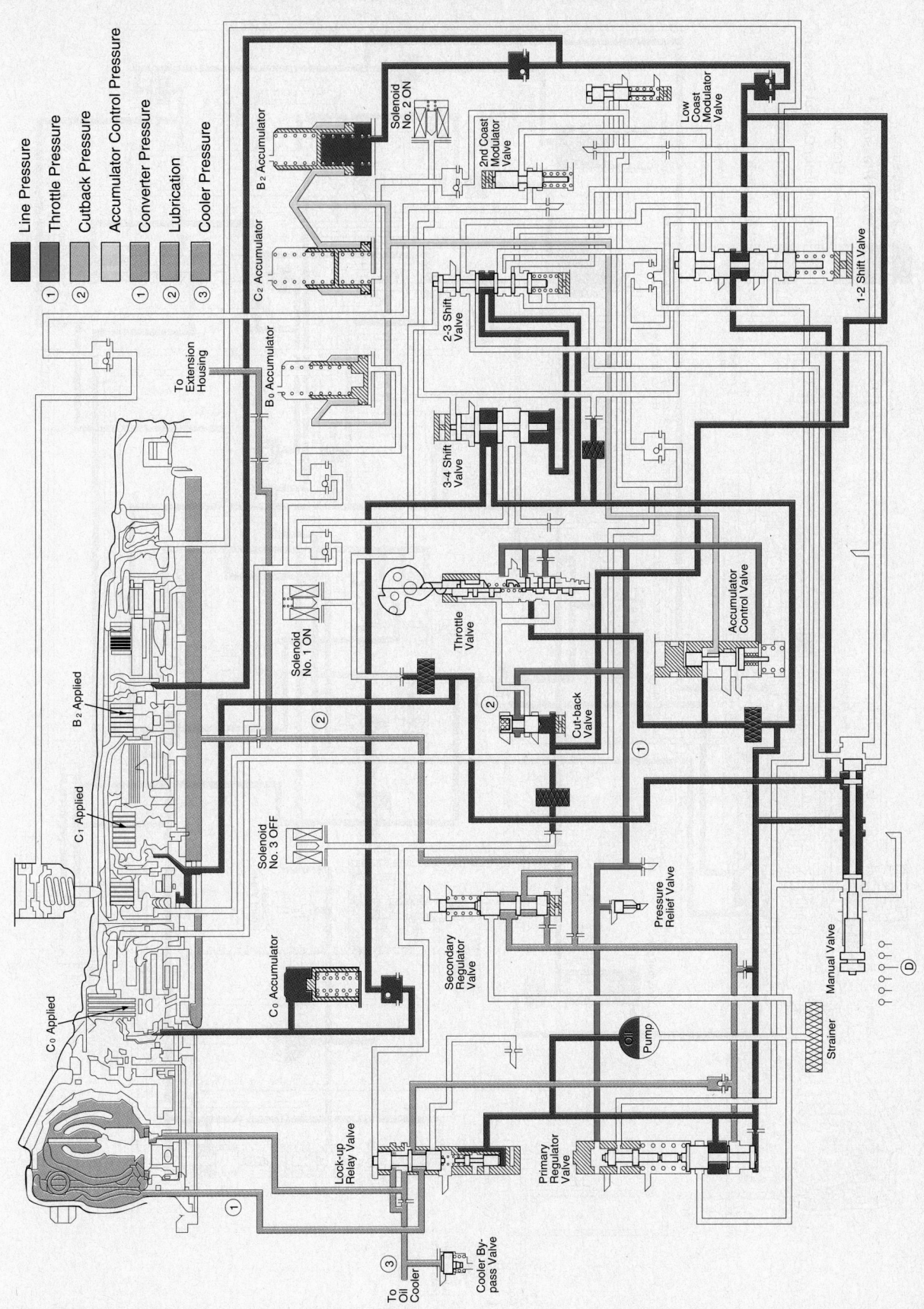

Fig. 2: "D" Range — 2nd Gear

Courtesy of Chrysler Corp.

OIL CIRCUIT DIAGRAMS
Aisin Warner 4 (Cont.)

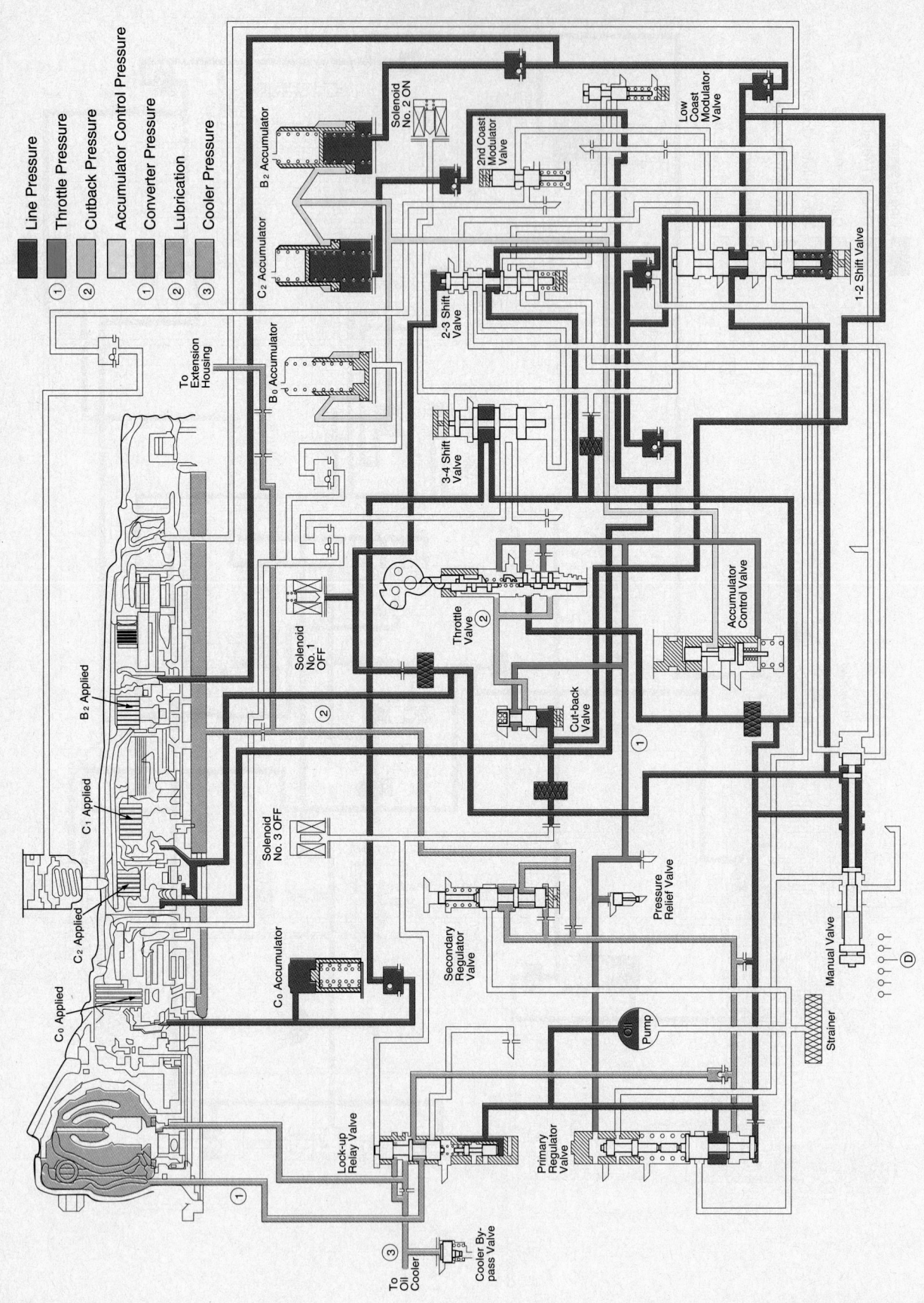

Fig. 3: "D" Range — 3rd Gear

Courtesy of Chrysler Corp.

OIL CIRCUIT DIAGRAMS
Aisin Warner 4 (Cont.)

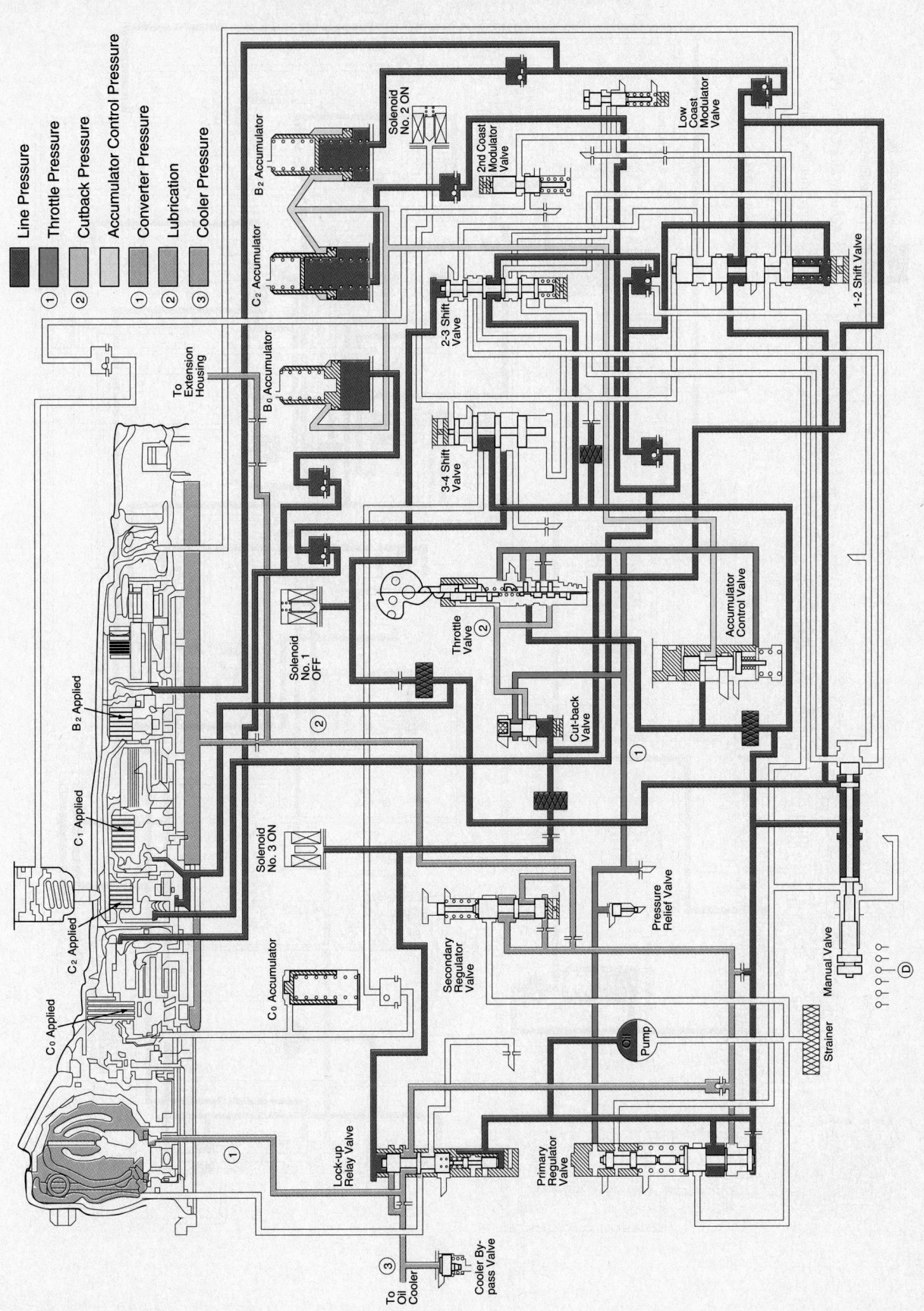

Fig. 4: "D" Range — Overdrive Gear (Lock-up On)

Courtesy of Chrysler Corp.

OIL CIRCUIT DIAGRAMS
Aisin Warner 4 (Cont.)

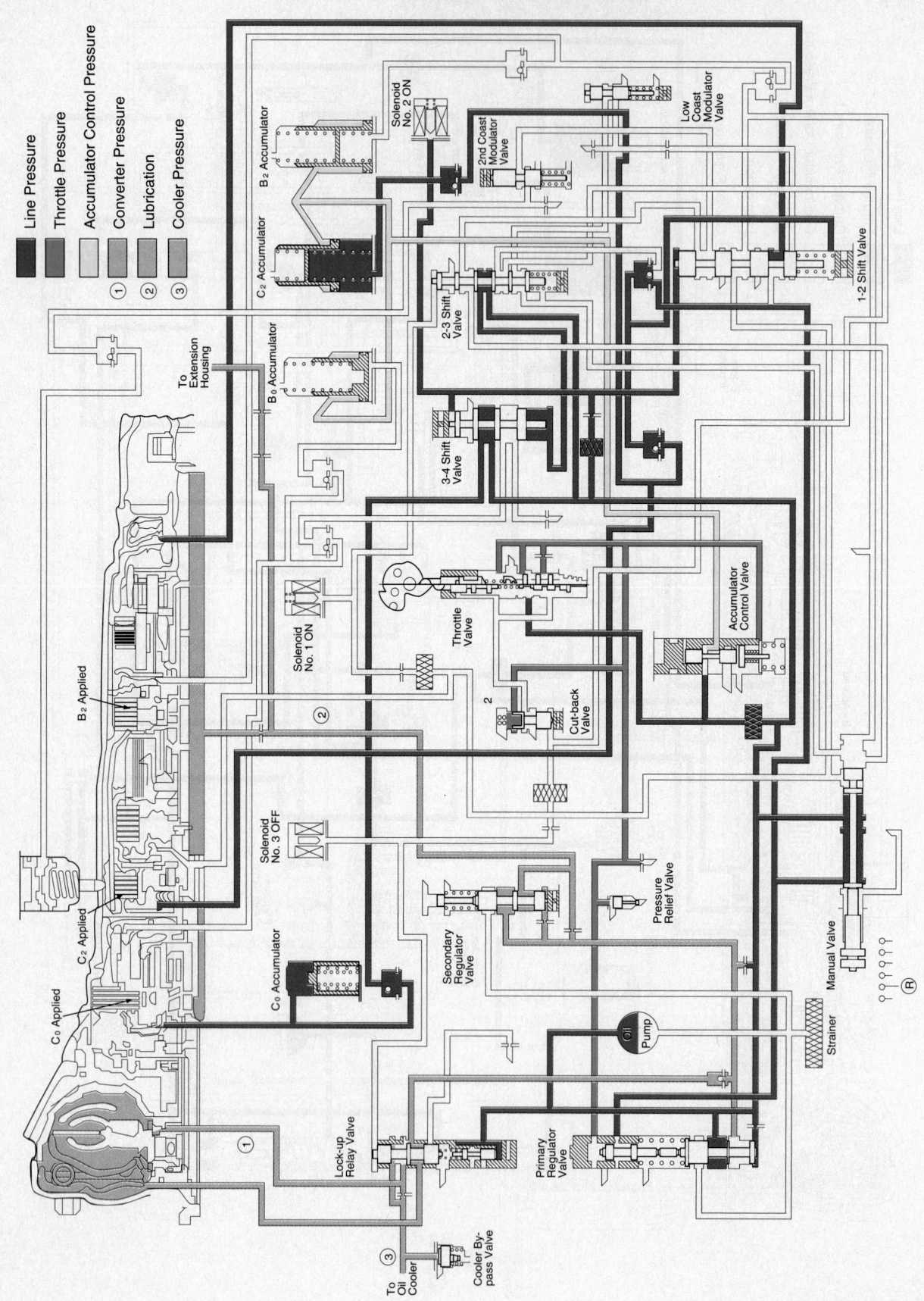

Fig. 5: "R" Range — Reverse Gear

Courtesy of Chrysler Corp.

OIL CIRCUIT DIAGRAMS
Aisin Warner 4 (Cont.)

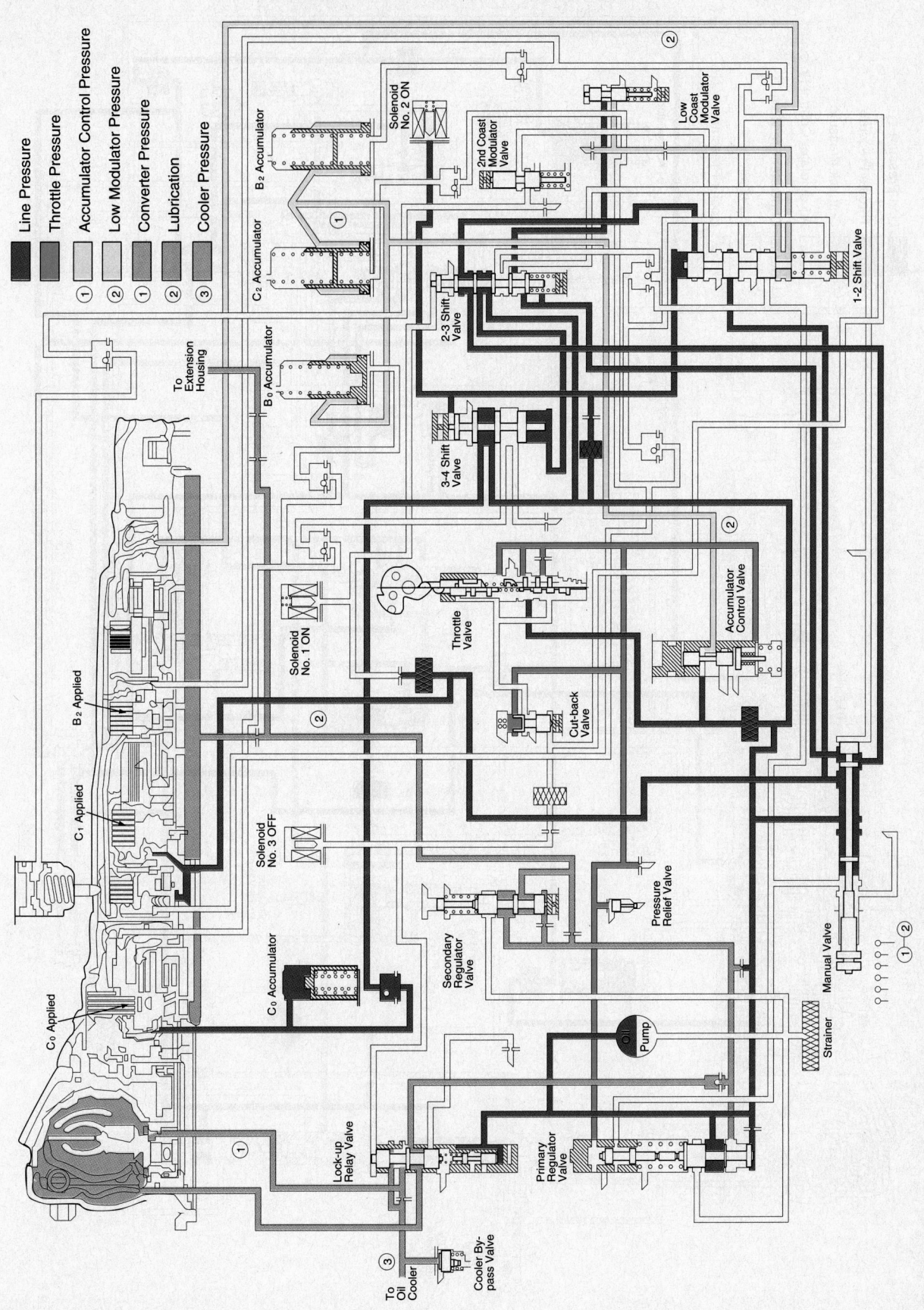

Fig. 6: "1-2" Range — 1st Gear

Courtesy of Chrysler Corp.

OIL CIRCUIT DIAGRAMS
Aisin Warner 4 (Cont.)

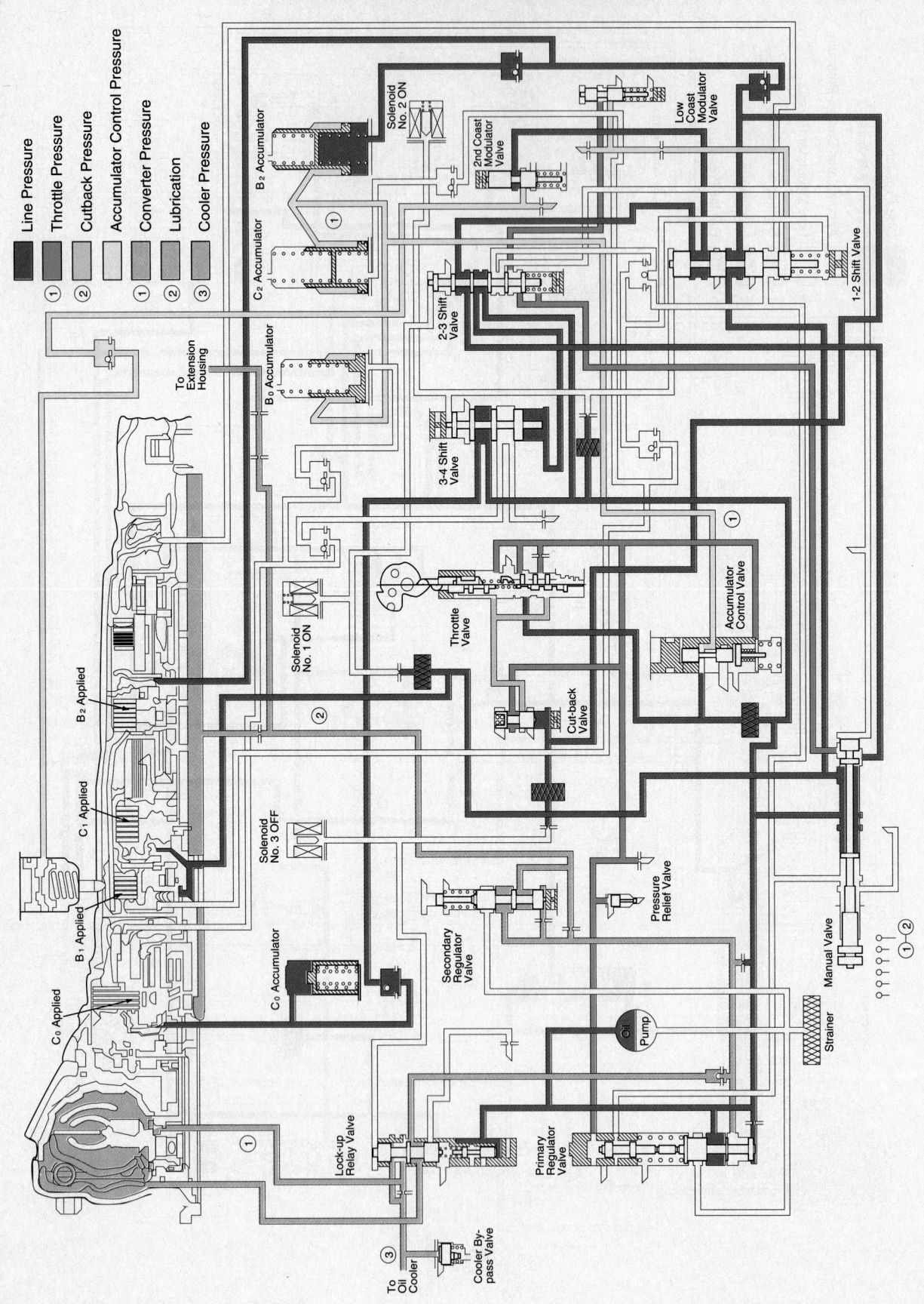

Fig. 7: "1-2" Range — 2nd Gear

Courtesy of Chrysler Corp.

OIL CIRCUIT DIAGRAMS
Chrysler 30TH & 31TH

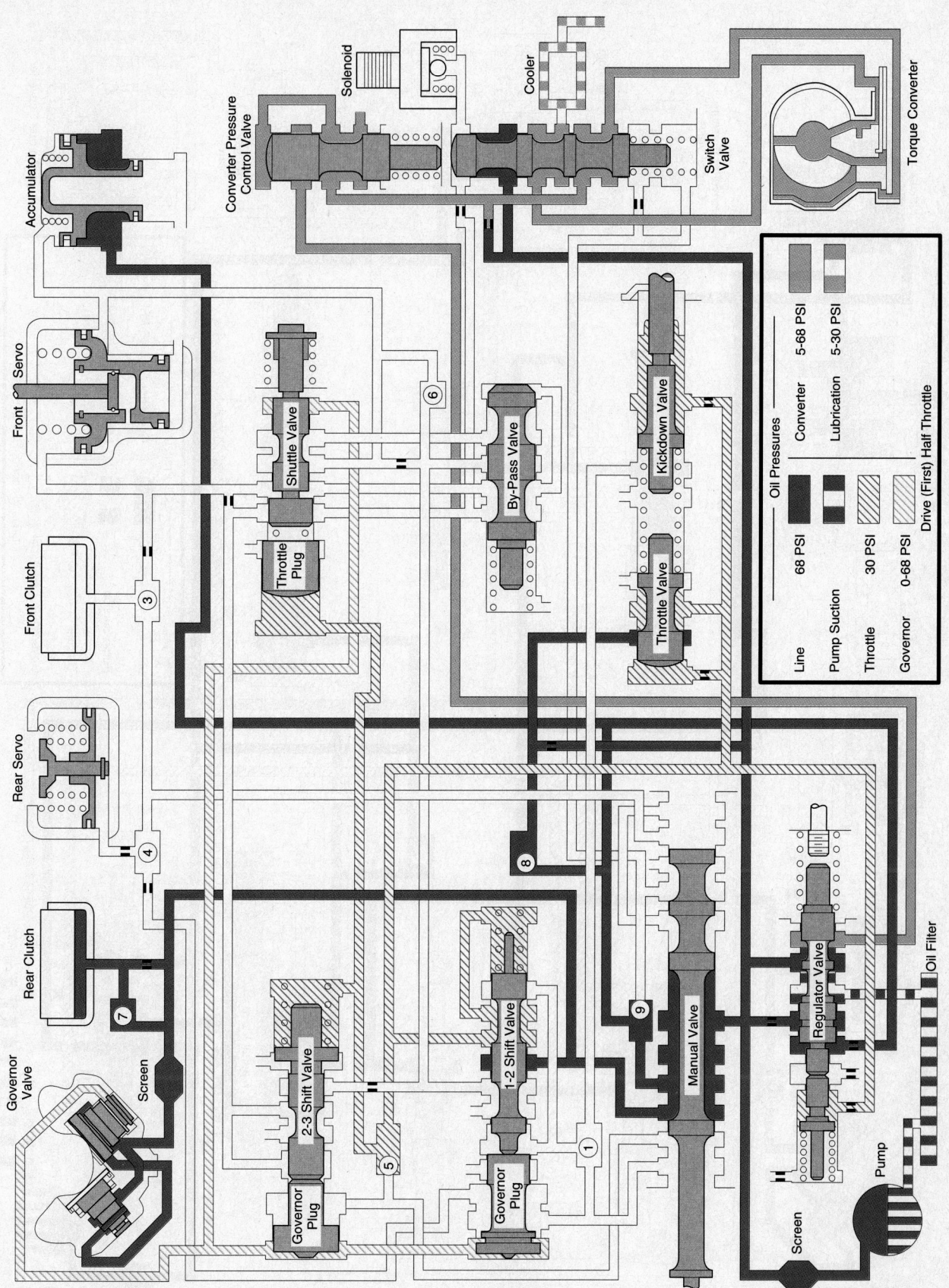

Fig. 1: "D" Range — 1st Gear (Half Throttle)

Courtesy of Chrysler Corp.

OIL CIRCUIT DIAGRAMS
Chrysler 30TH & 31TH (Cont.)

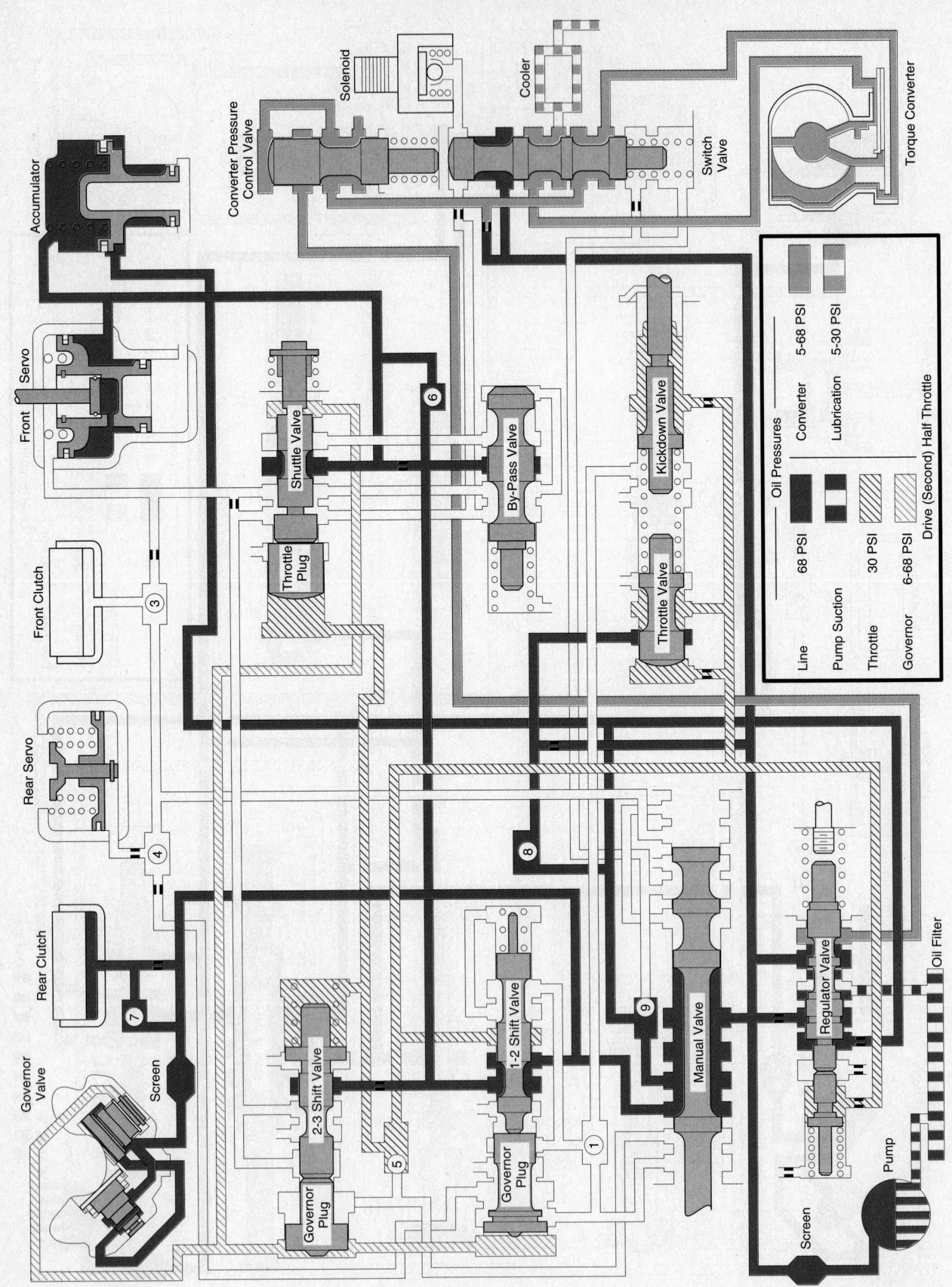

Fig. 2: "D" Range — 2nd Gear (Half Throttle)

Courtesy of Chrysler Corp.

OIL CIRCUIT DIAGRAMS
Chrysler 30TH & 31TH (Cont.)

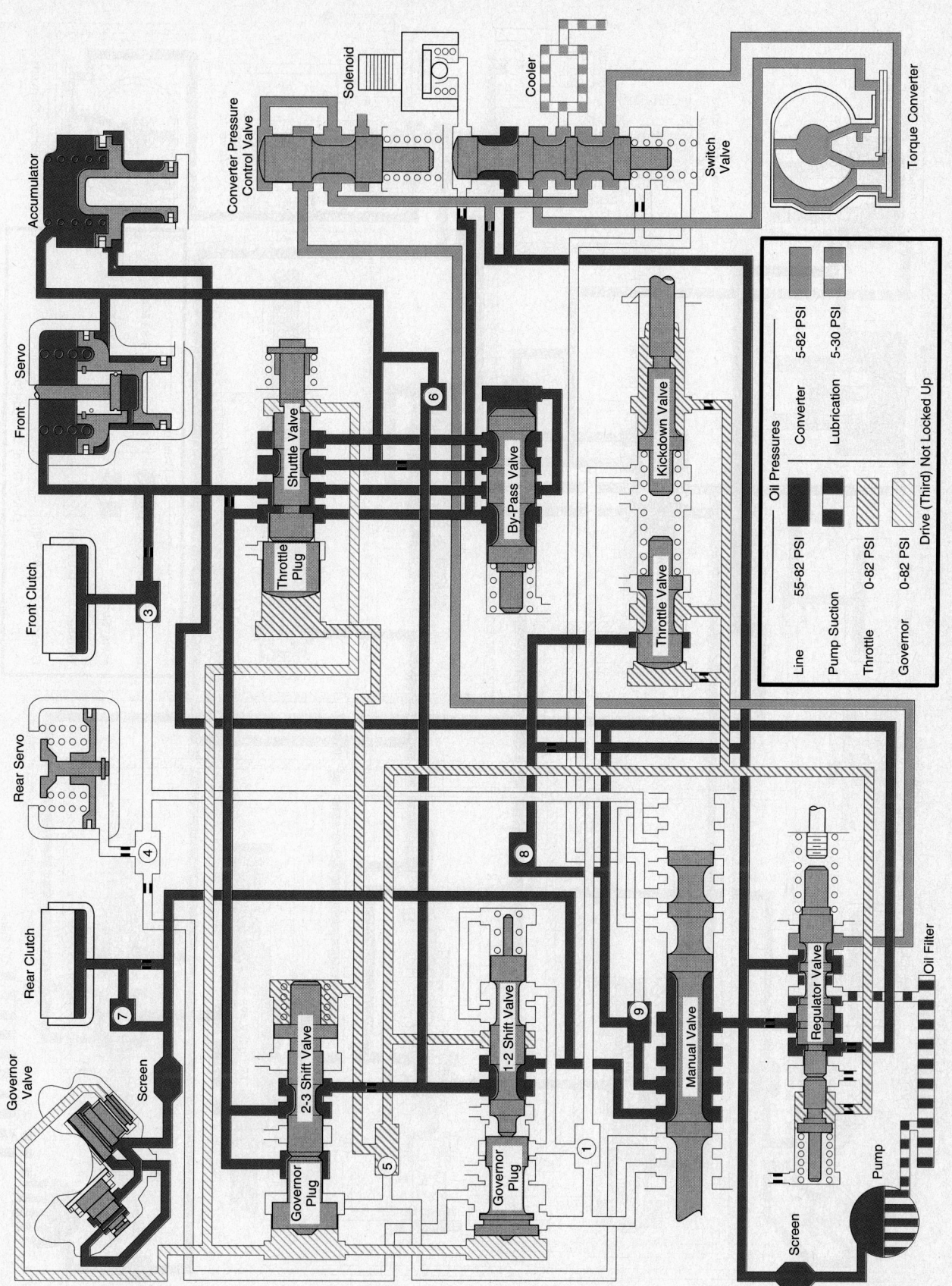

Fig. 3: "D" Range — 3rd Gear (Lock-Up Off)

Courtesy of Chrysler Corp.

OIL CIRCUIT DIAGRAMS
Chrysler 30TH & 31TH (Cont.)

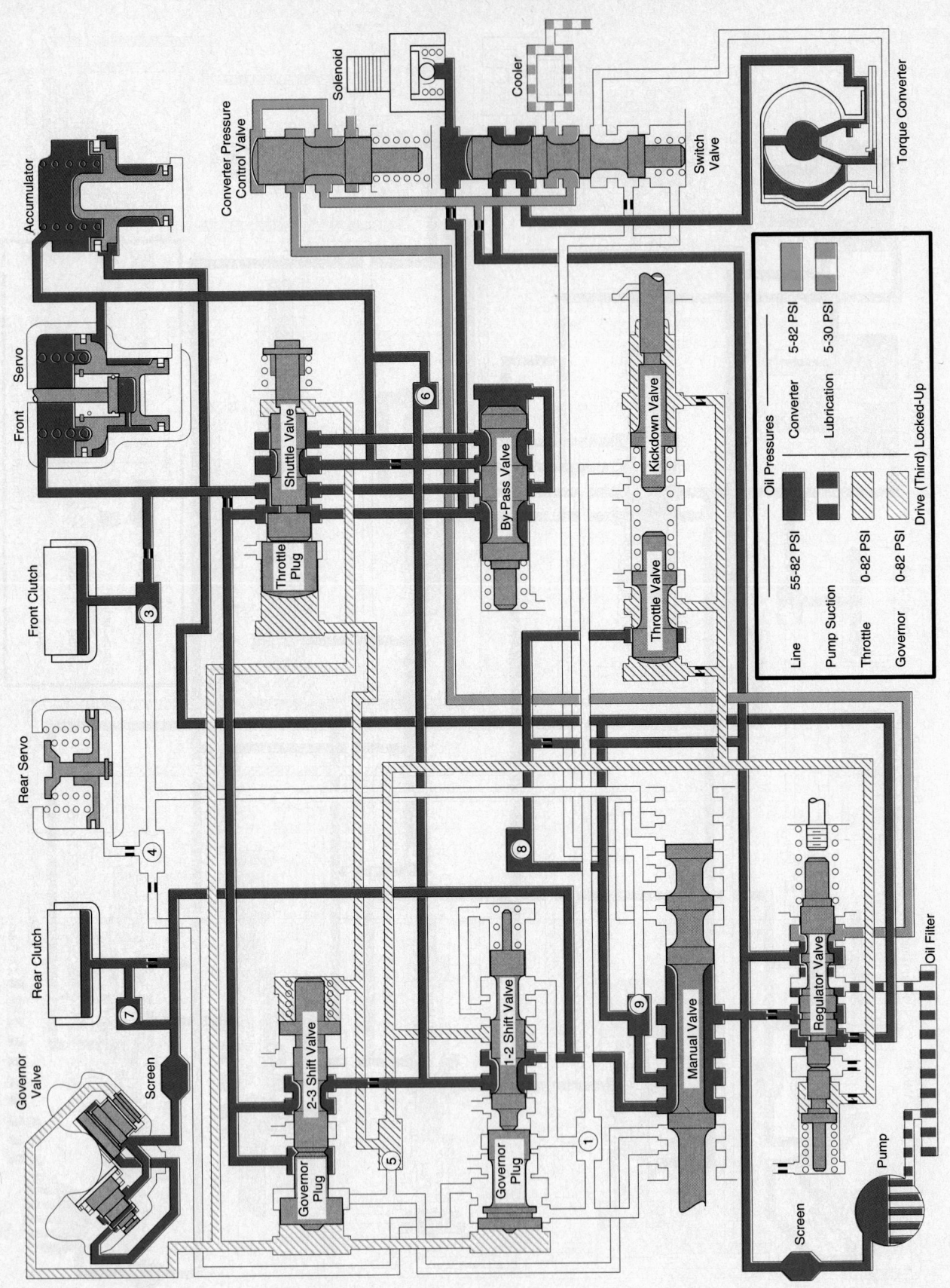

Fig. 4: "D" Range — 3rd Gear (Lock-Up On)

Courtesy of Chrysler Corp.

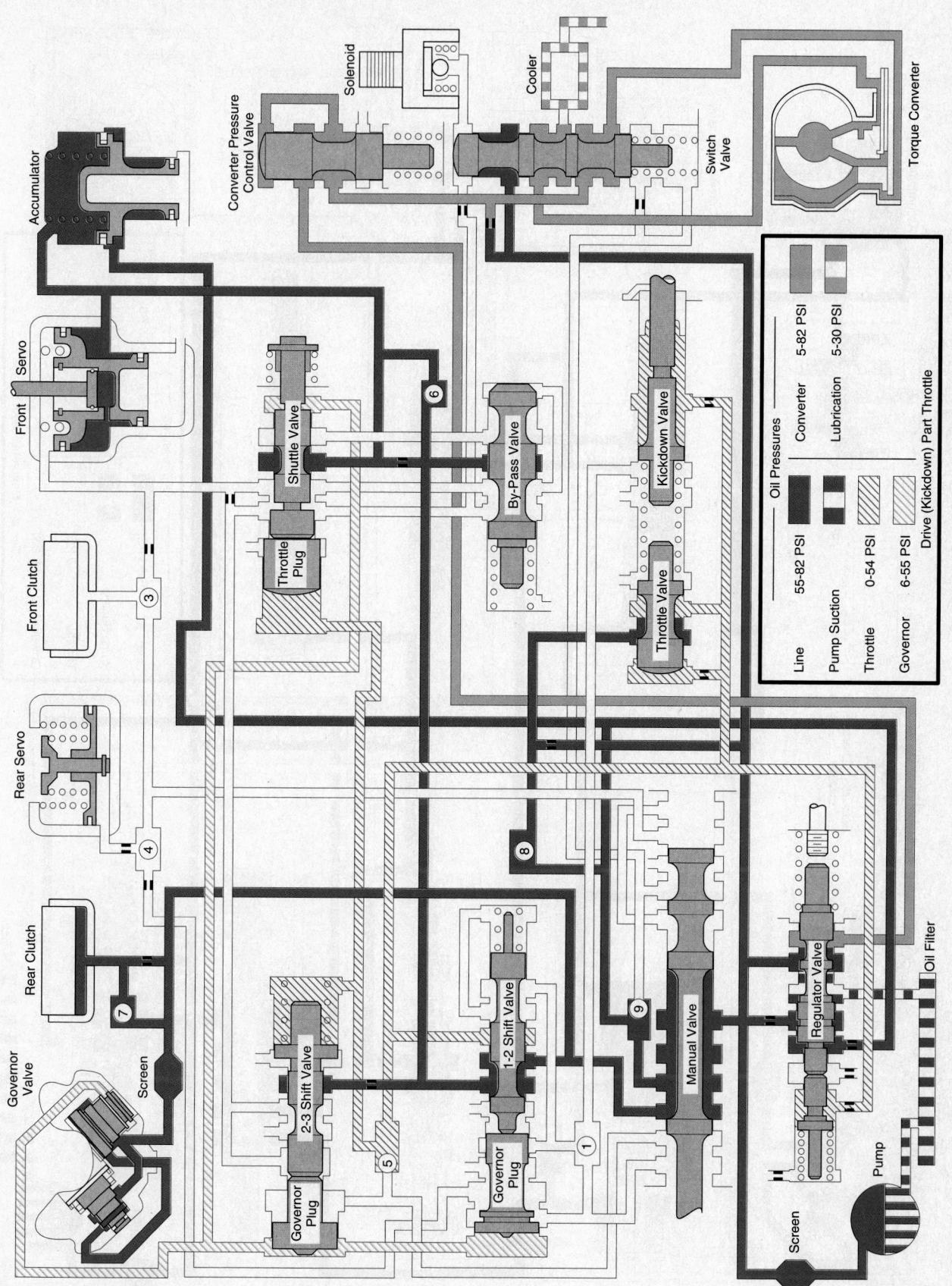

Fig. 5: "D" Range — Kickdown (Part Throttle)

Courtesy of Chrysler Corp.

OIL CIRCUIT DIAGRAMS
Chrysler 30TH & 31TH (Cont.)

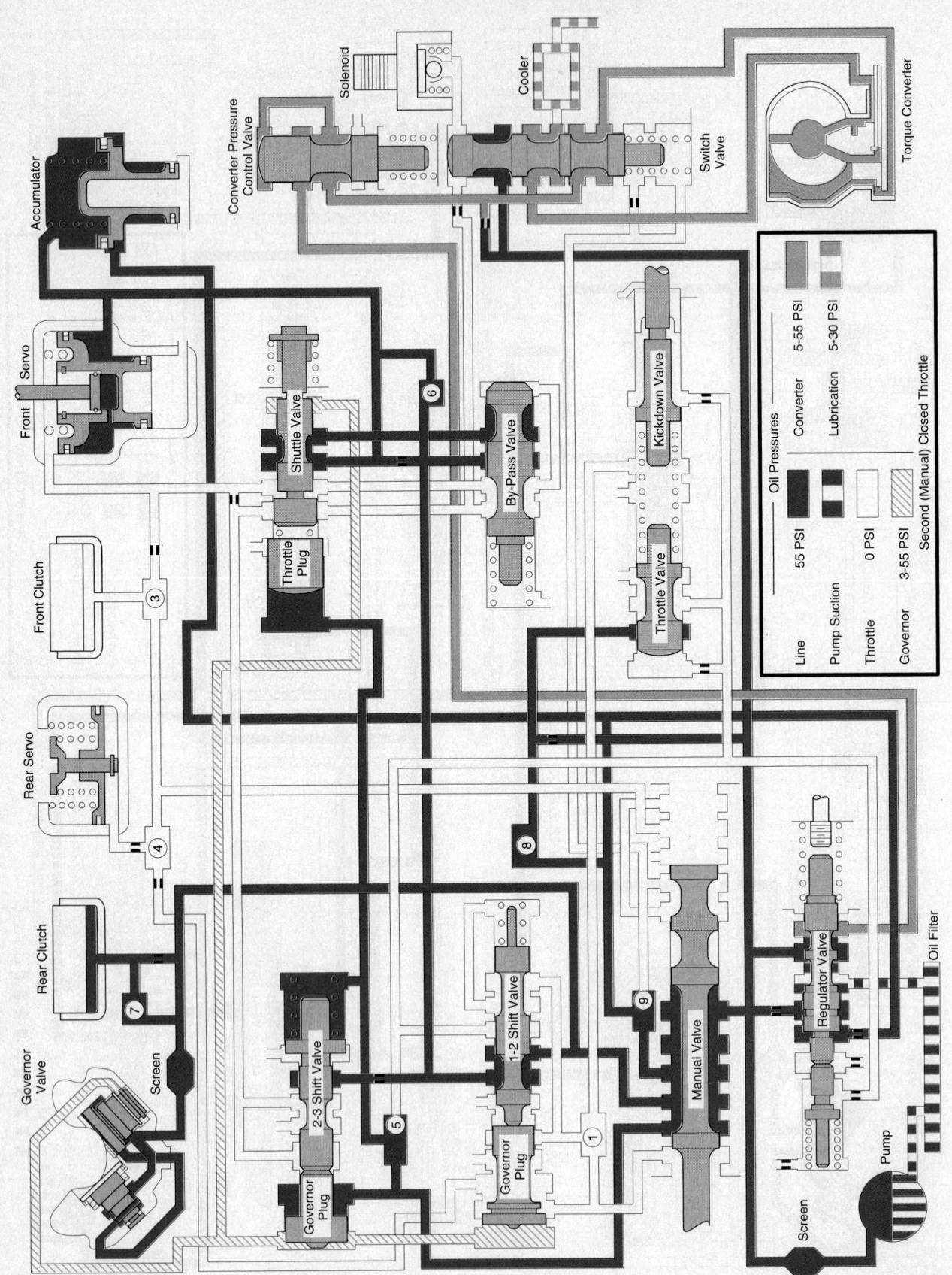

Fig. 6: "2" Range — 2nd Gear Manual Select (Closed Throttle)

Courtesy of Chrysler Corp.

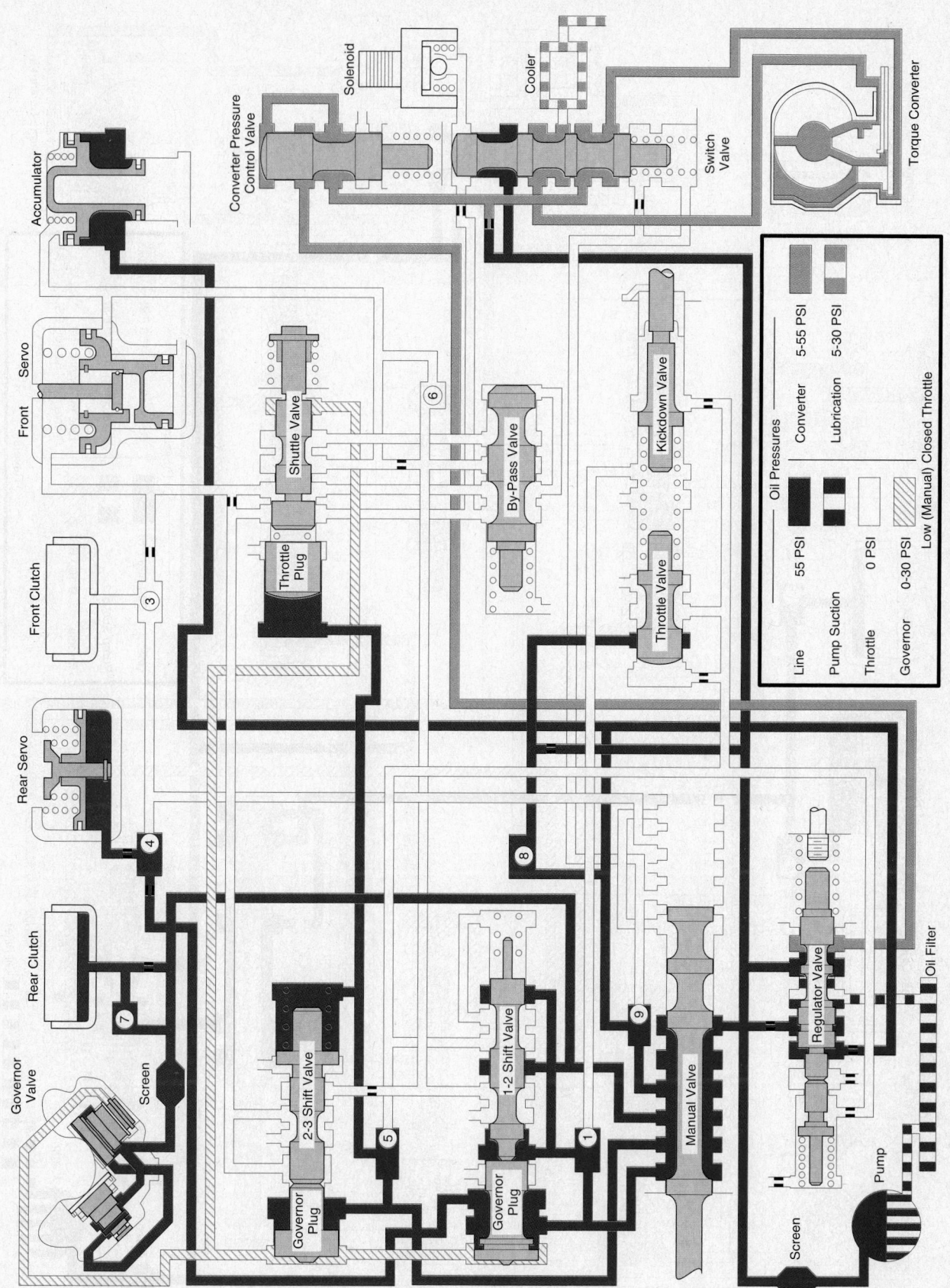

Fig. 7: "L" Range — 1st Gear Manual Select (Closed Throttle)

Courtesy of Chrysler Corp.

OIL CIRCUIT DIAGRAMS
Chrysler 30TH & 31TH (Cont.)

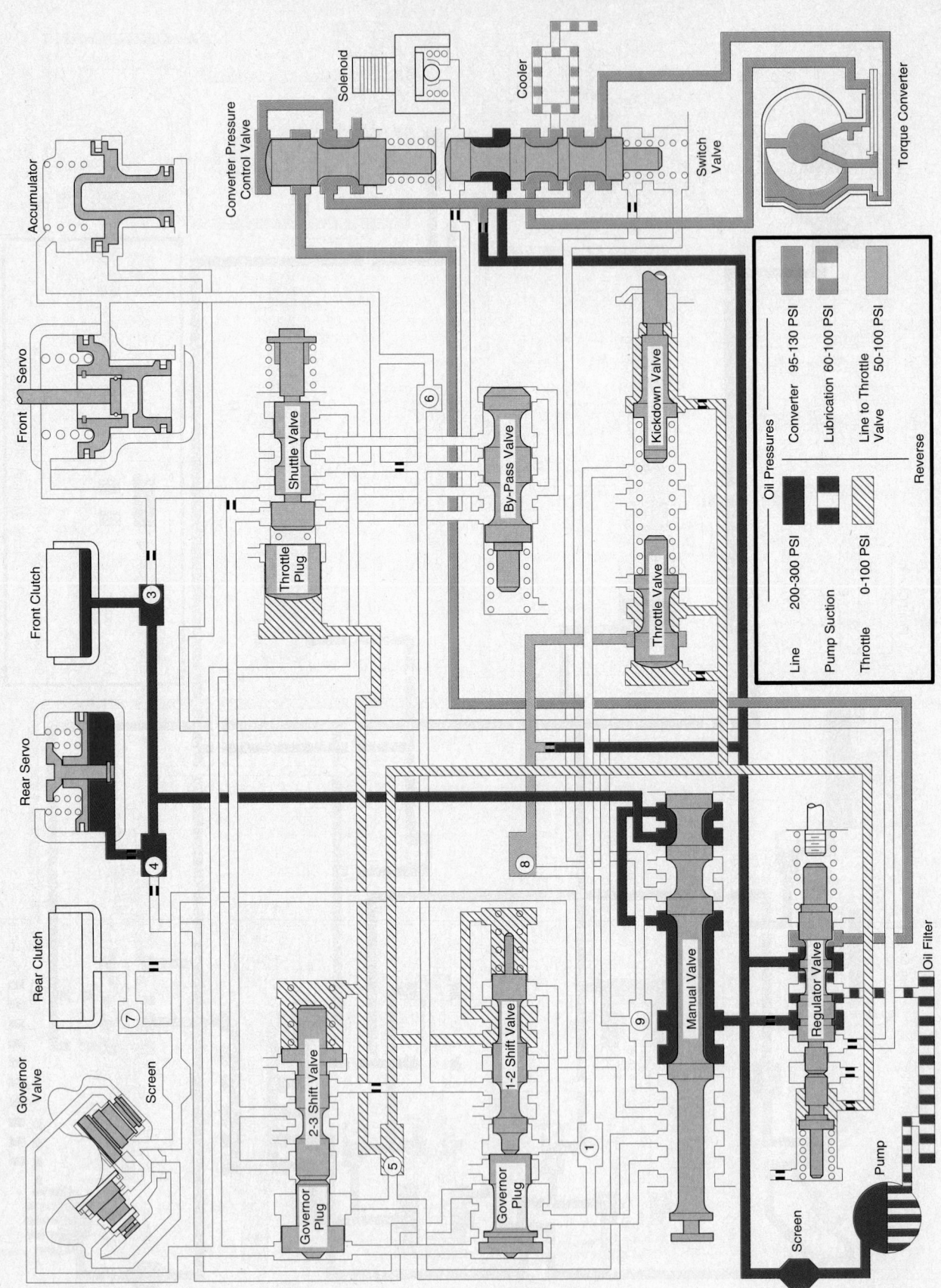

Fig. 8: "R" Range — Reverse Gear

Courtesy of Chrysler Corp.

OIL CIRCUIT DIAGRAMS
Chrysler 32RH, 36RH, & 37RH

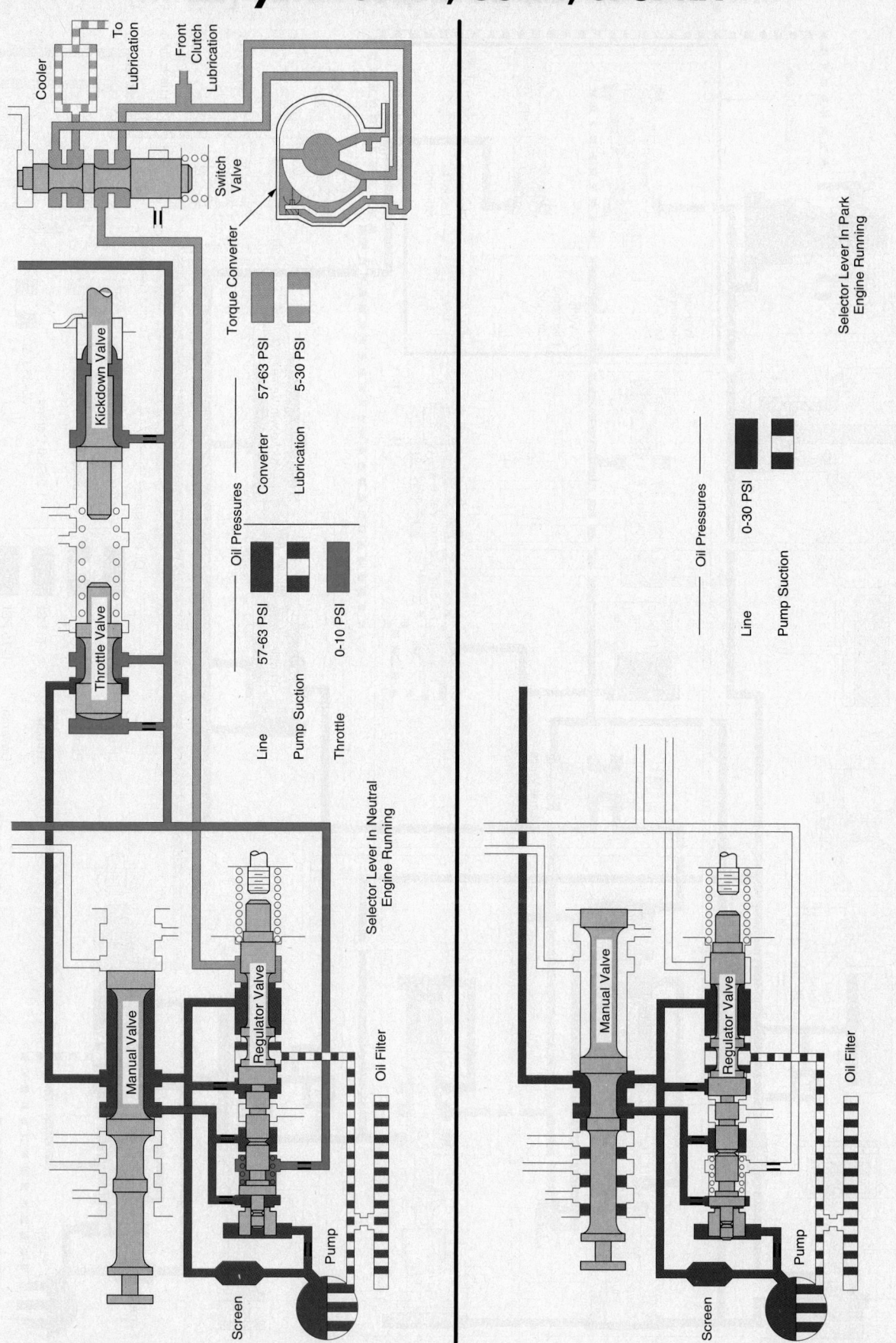

Fig. 1: "N" & "P" Range — Neutral & Park (Engine Running)

Courtesy of Chrysler Corp.

OIL CIRCUIT DIAGRAMS
Chrysler 32RH, 36RH, & 37RH (Cont.)

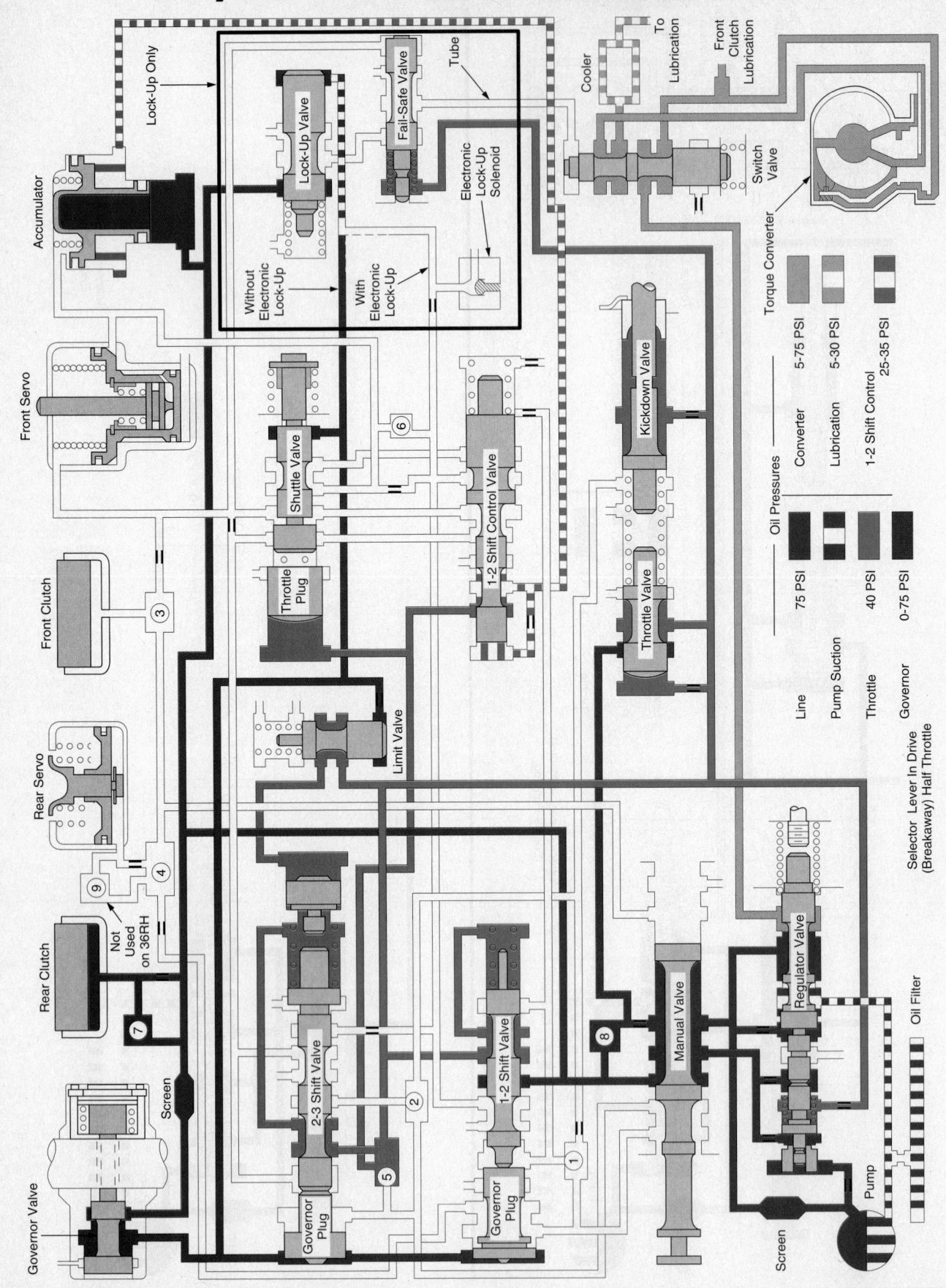

Fig. 2: "D" Range — Drive (Kickdown at Half Throttle)

Courtesy of Chrysler Corp.

OIL CIRCUIT DIAGRAMS
Chrysler 32RH, 36RH, & 37RH (Cont.)

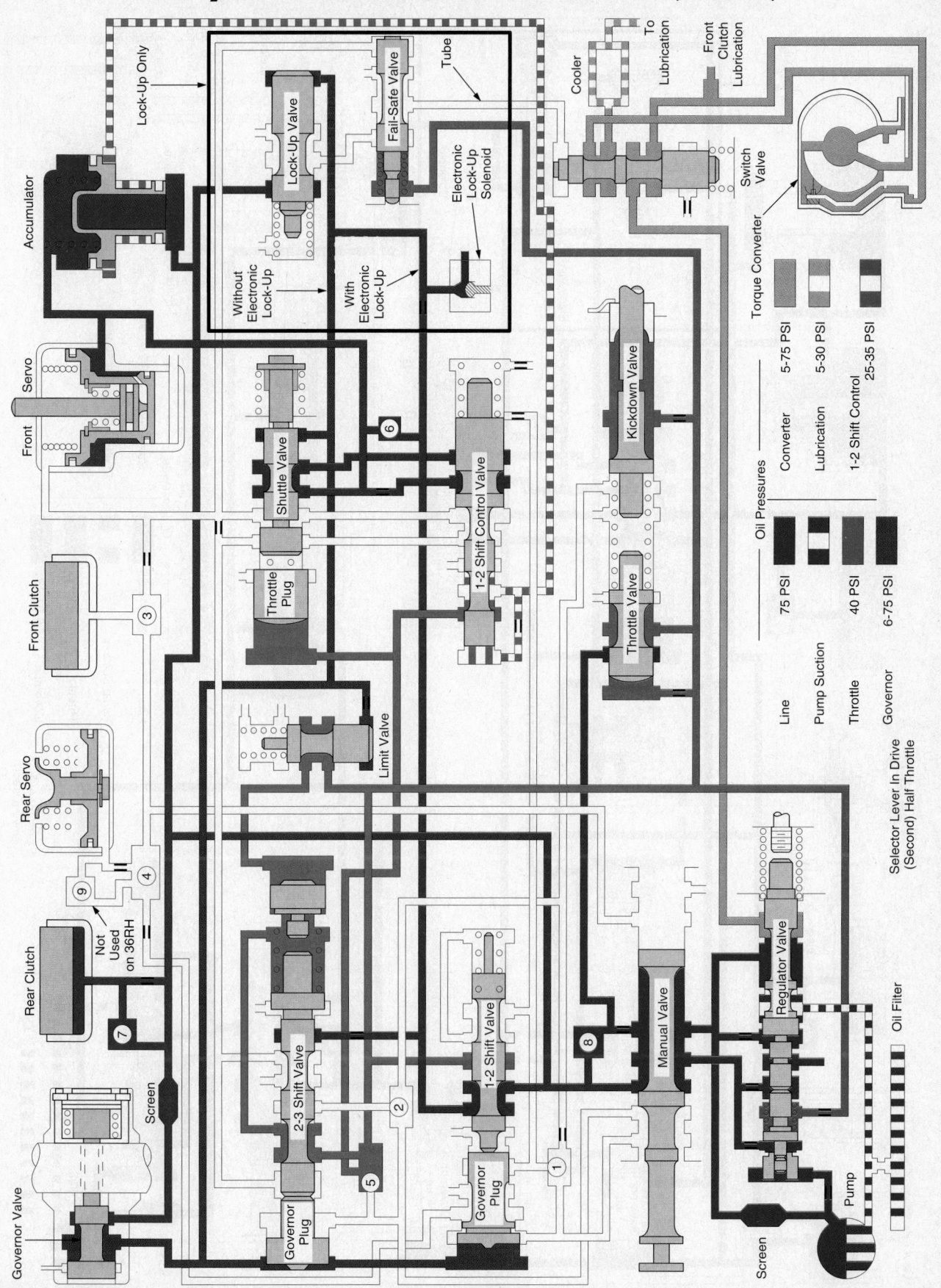

Fig. 3: "D" Range — 2nd Gear (Half Throttle)

Courtesy of Chrysler Corp.

OIL CIRCUIT DIAGRAMS
Chrysler 32RH, 36RH, & 37RH (Cont.)

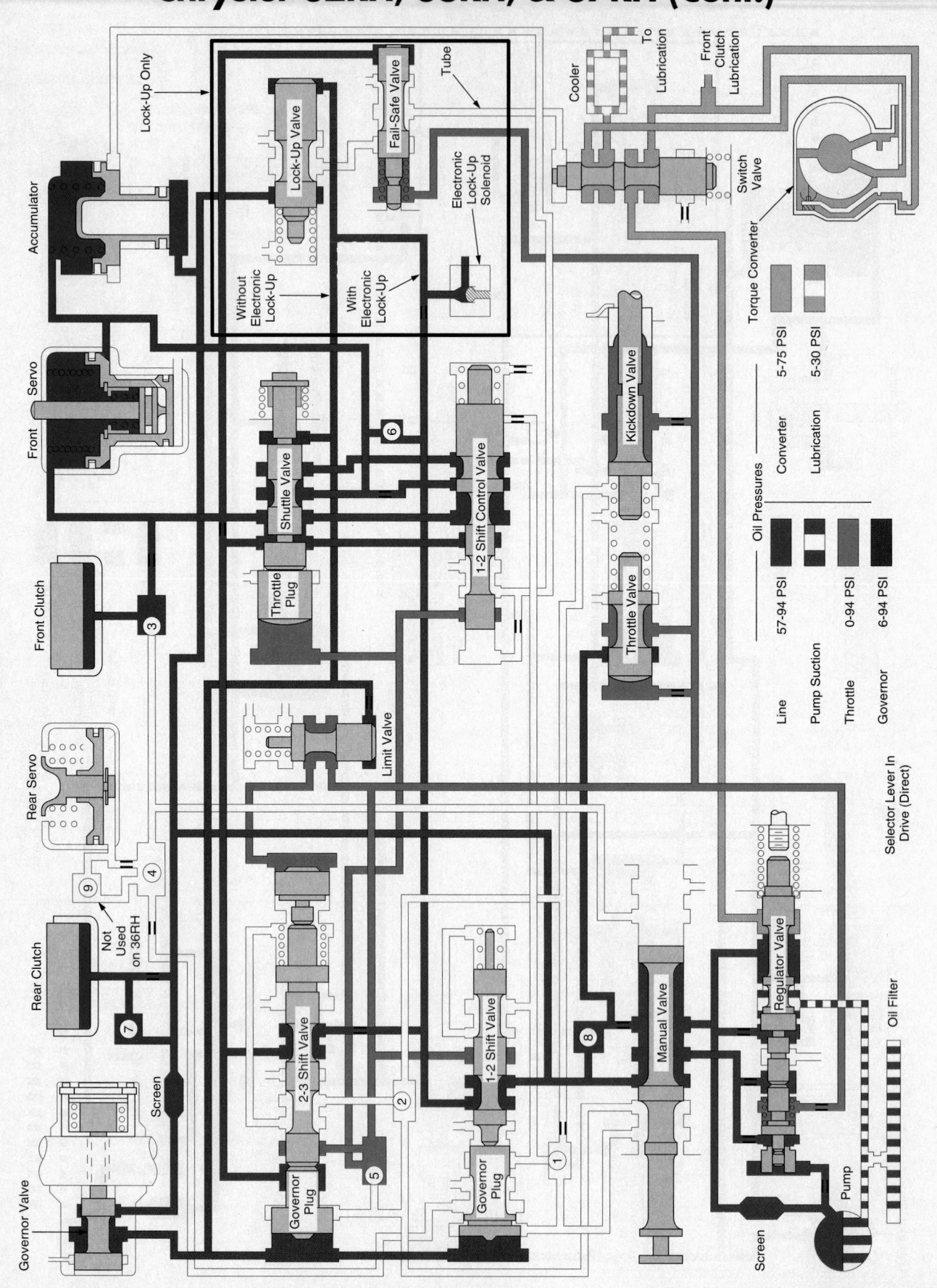

Fig. 4: "D" Range — Drive

Courtesy of Chrysler Corp.

OIL CIRCUIT DIAGRAMS
Chrysler 32RH, 36RH, & 37RH (Cont.)

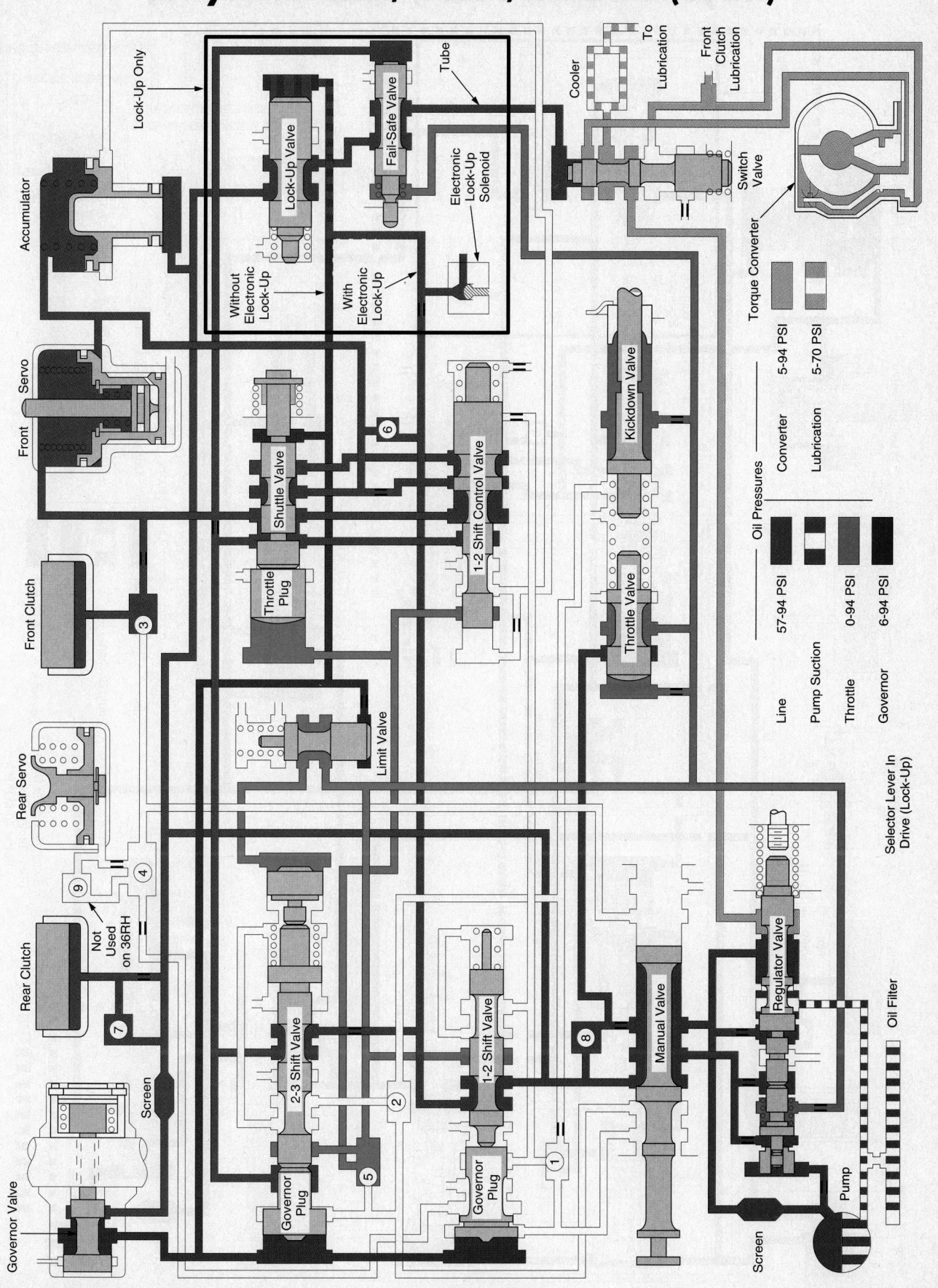

Fig. 5: "D" Range — Drive (Full Lock-Up)

Courtesy of Chrysler Corp.

OIL CIRCUIT DIAGRAMS
Chrysler 32RH, 36RH, & 37RH (Cont.)

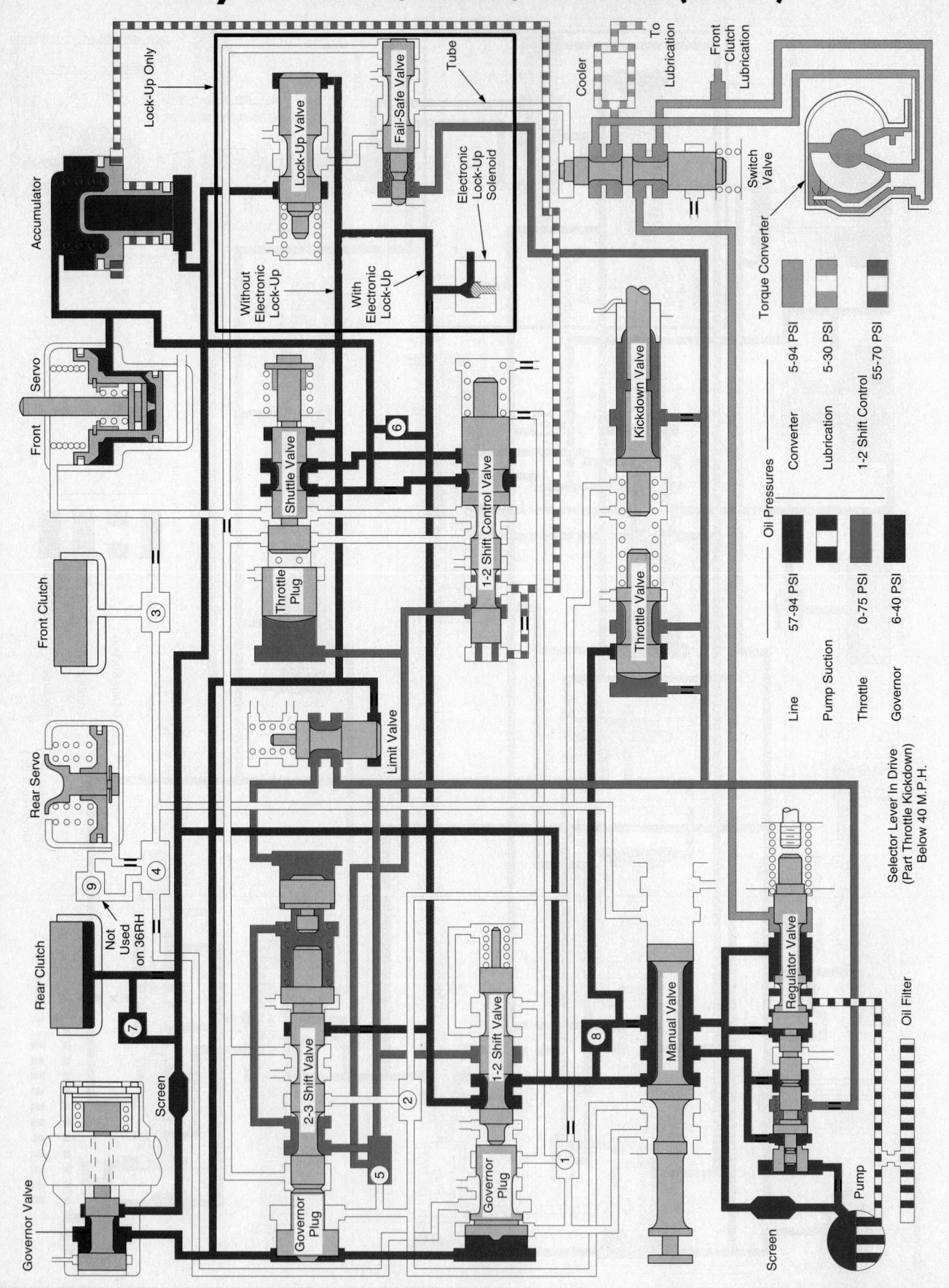

Fig. 6: "D" Range — Drive (Part Throttle Kickdown Below 40 MPH)

Courtesy of Chrysler Corp.

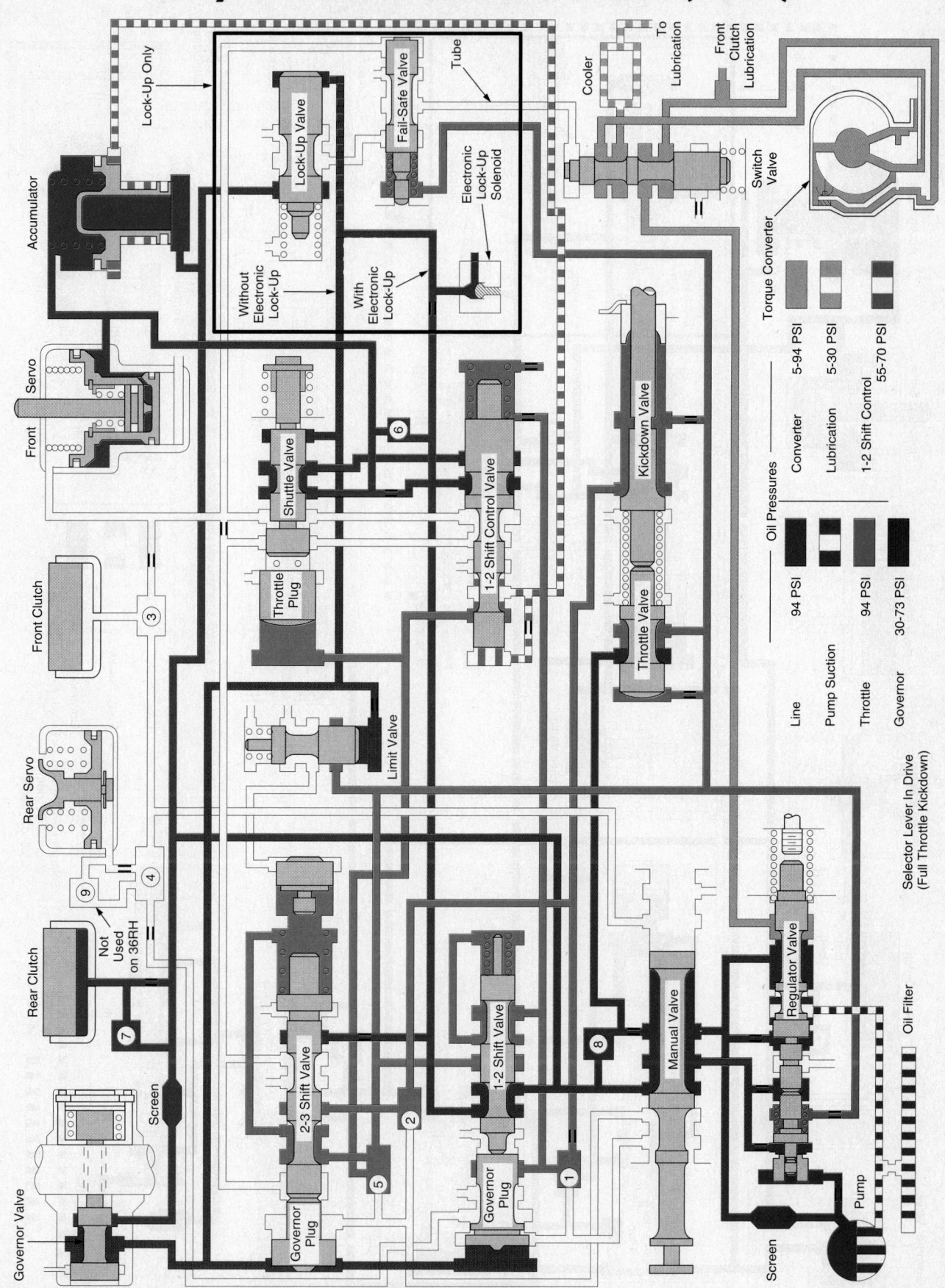

Fig. 7: "D" Range — Drive (Full Throttle Kickdown)

Courtesy of Chrysler Corp.

OIL CIRCUIT DIAGRAMS
Chrysler 32RH, 36RH, & 37RH (Cont.)

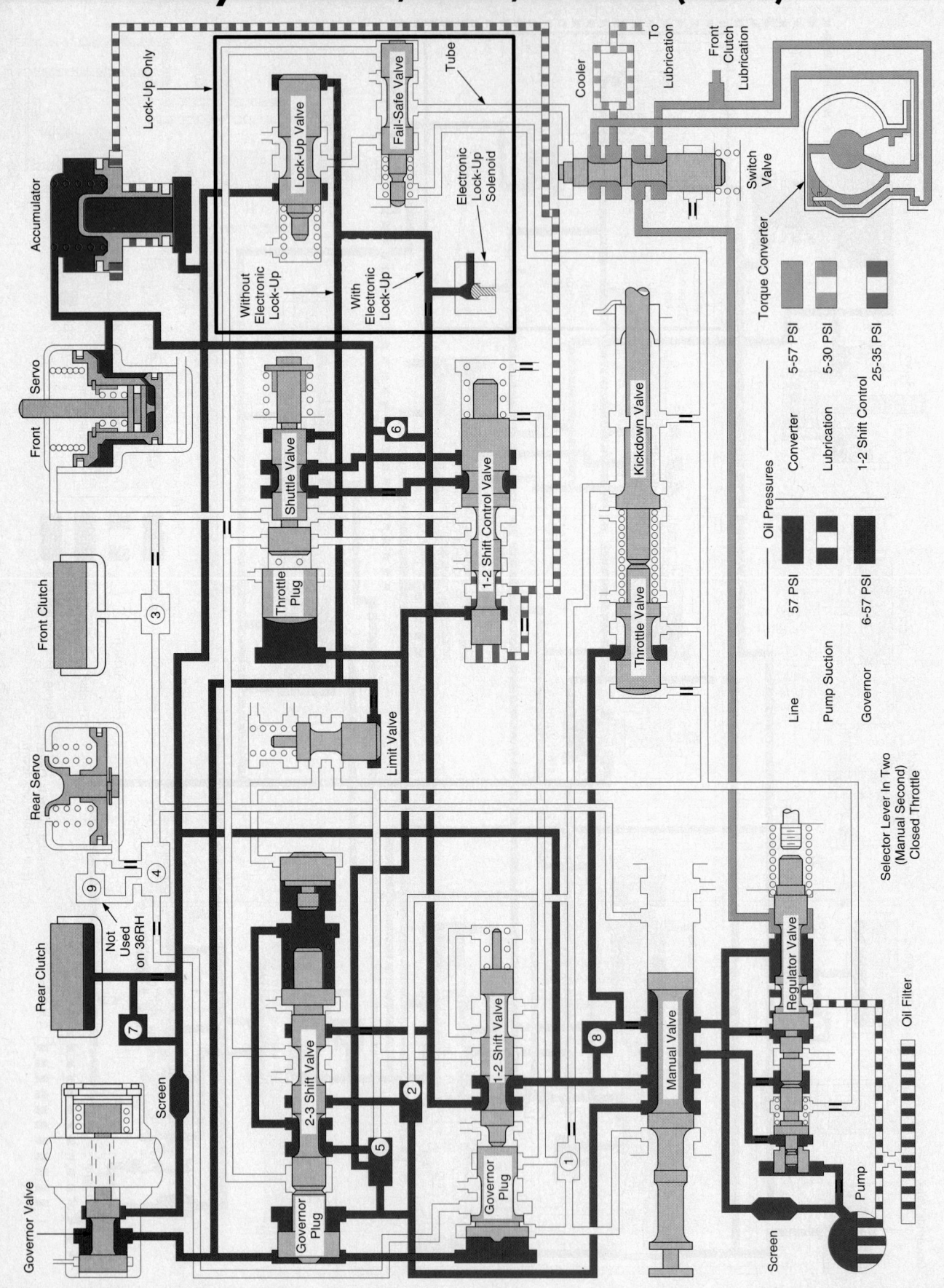

Fig. 8: "2" Range — 2nd Gear Manual Select (Closed Throttle)

Courtesy of Chrysler Corp.

OIL CIRCUIT DIAGRAMS
Chrysler 32RH, 36RH, & 37RH (Cont.)

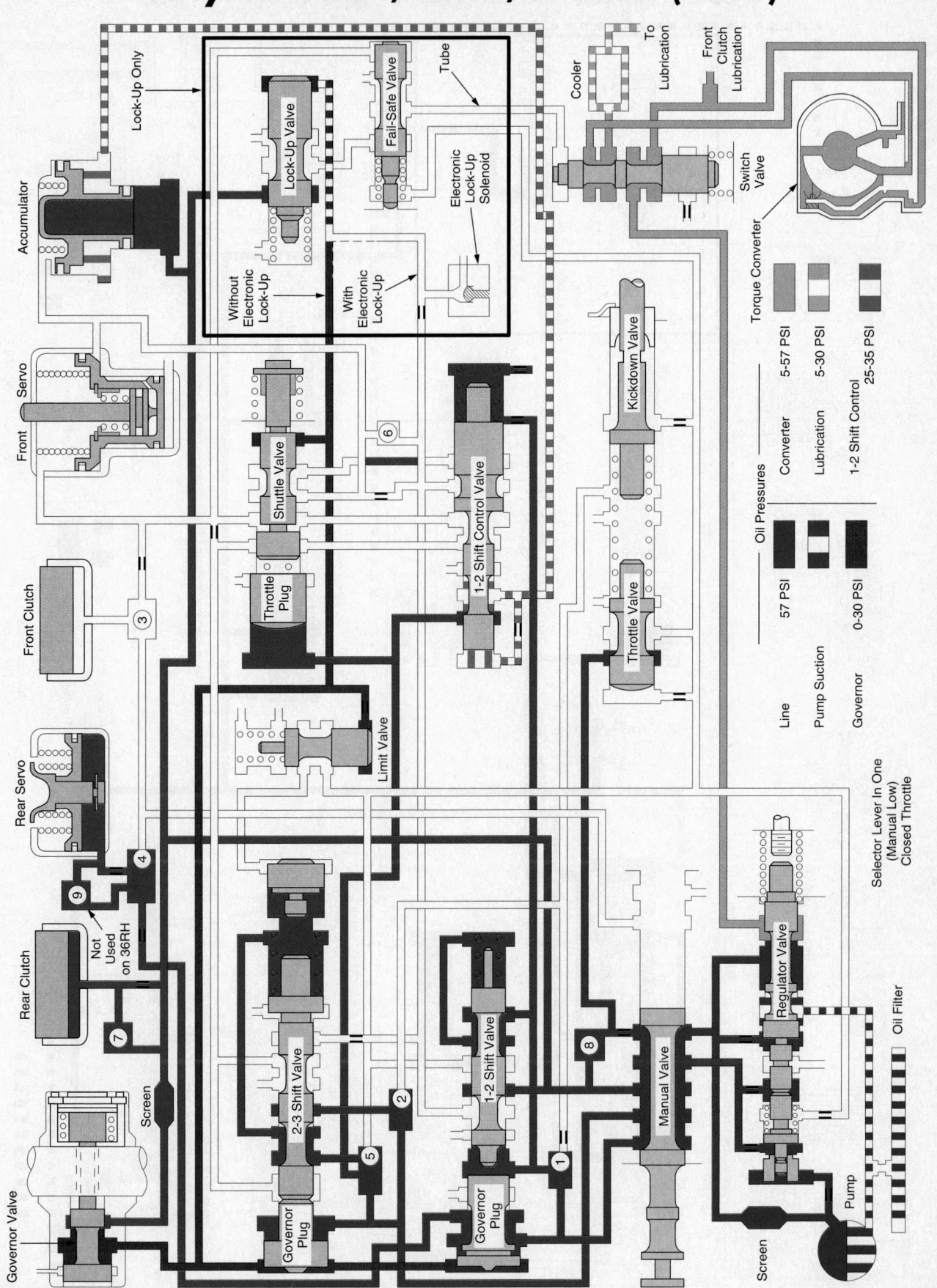

Fig. 9: "L" Range — 1st Gear Manual Select (Closed Throttle)

Courtesy of Chrysler Corp.

OIL CIRCUIT DIAGRAMS
Chrysler 32RH, 36RH, & 37RH (Cont.)

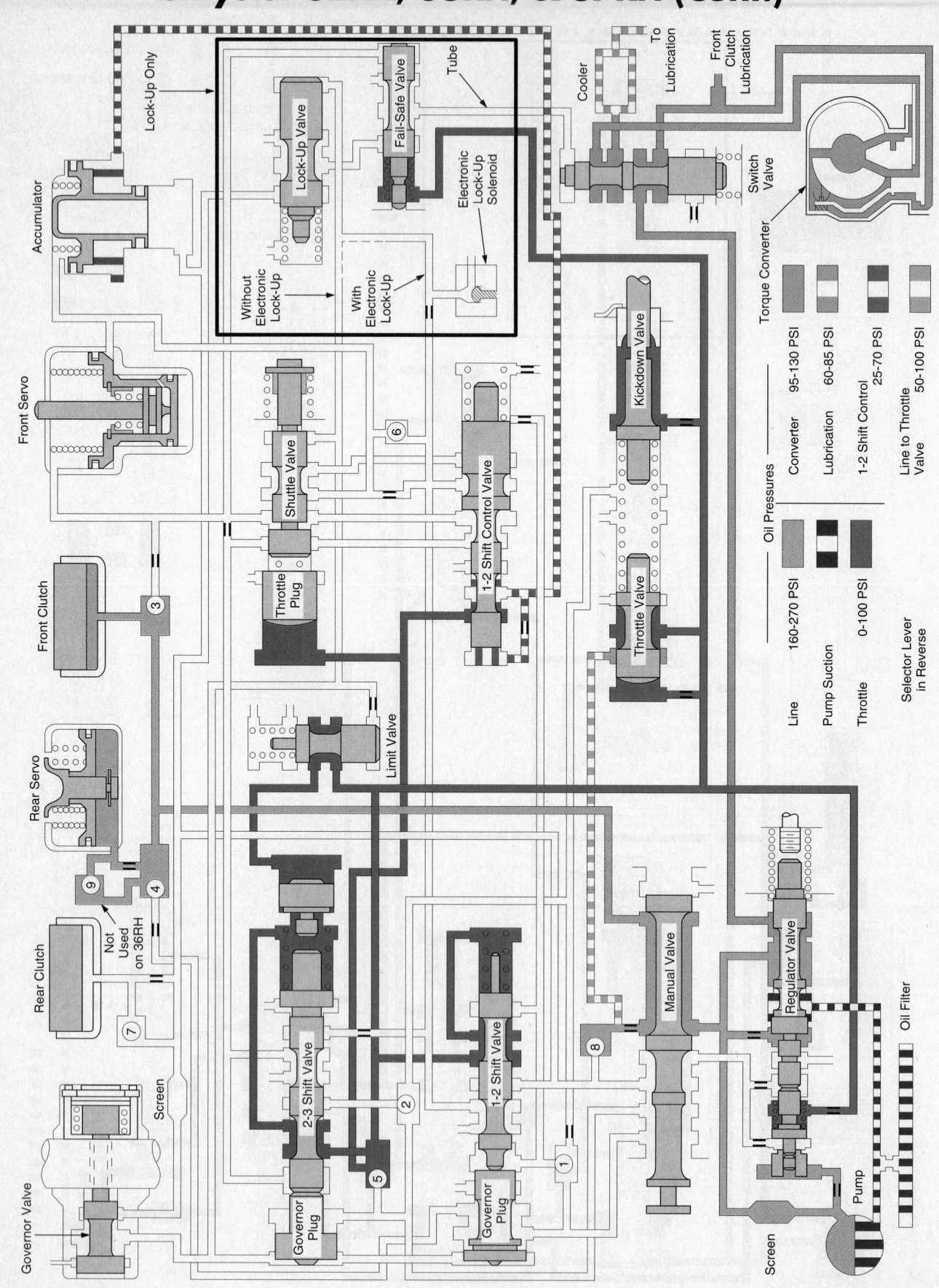

Fig. 10: "R" Range — Reverse

Courtesy of Chrysler Corp.

OIL CIRCUIT DIAGRAMS
Chrysler 41TE/AE

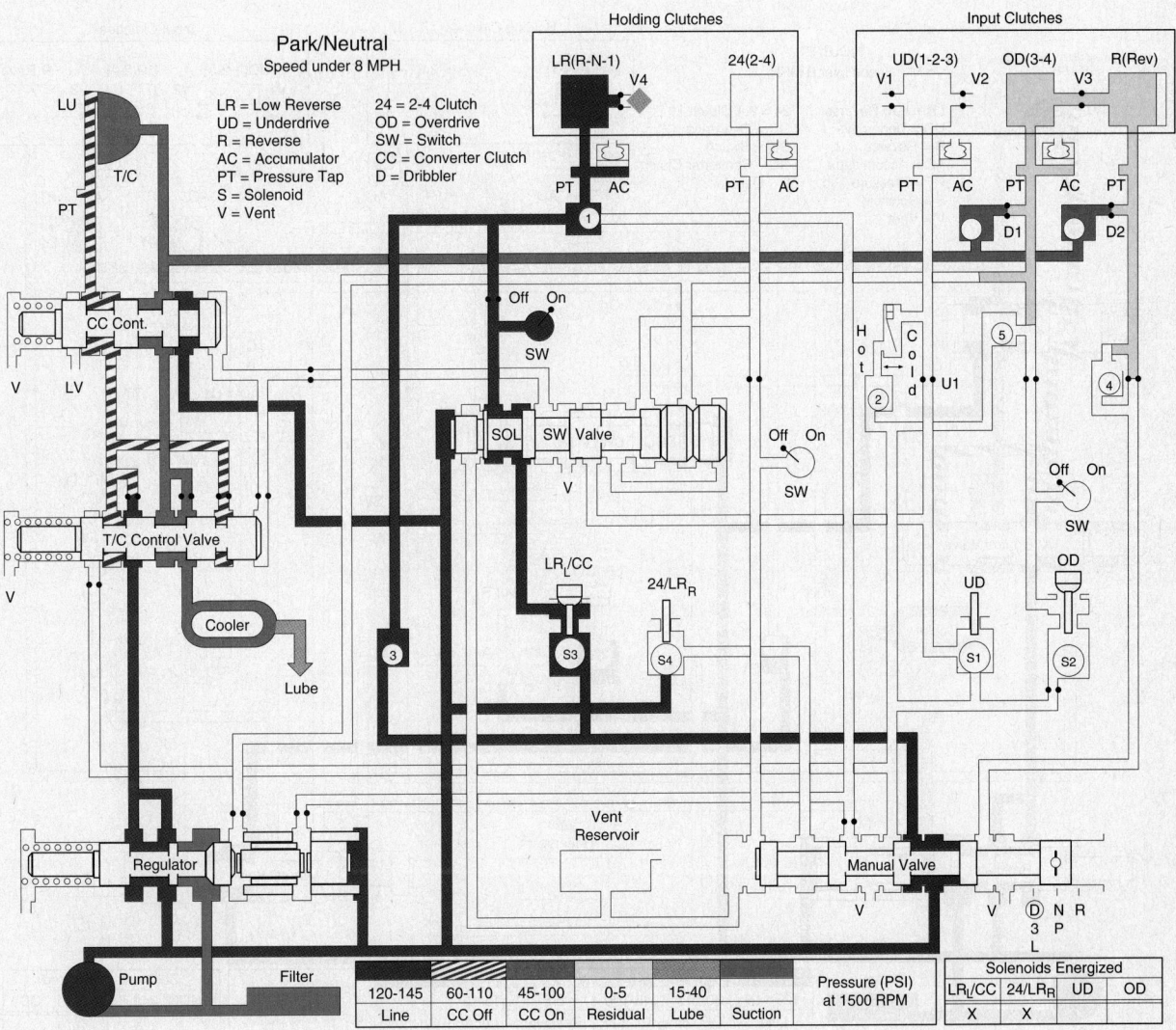

Park/Neutral
Speed under 8 MPH

LR = Low Reverse   24 = 2-4 Clutch
UD = Underdrive   OD = Overdrive
R = Reverse   SW = Switch
AC = Accumulator   CC = Converter Clutch
PT = Pressure Tap   D = Dribbler
S = Solenoid
V = Vent

Holding Clutches

Input Clutches

120-145	60-110	45-100	0-5	15-40	Suction	Pressure (PSI) at 1500 RPM
Line	CC Off	CC On	Residual	Lube		

Solenoids Energized			
LR$_L$/CC	24/LR$_R$	UD	OD
X	X		

Fig. 1: "P" & "N" Range — Park & Neutral

Courtesy of Chrysler Corp.

OIL CIRCUIT DIAGRAMS
Chrysler 41TE/AE (Cont.)

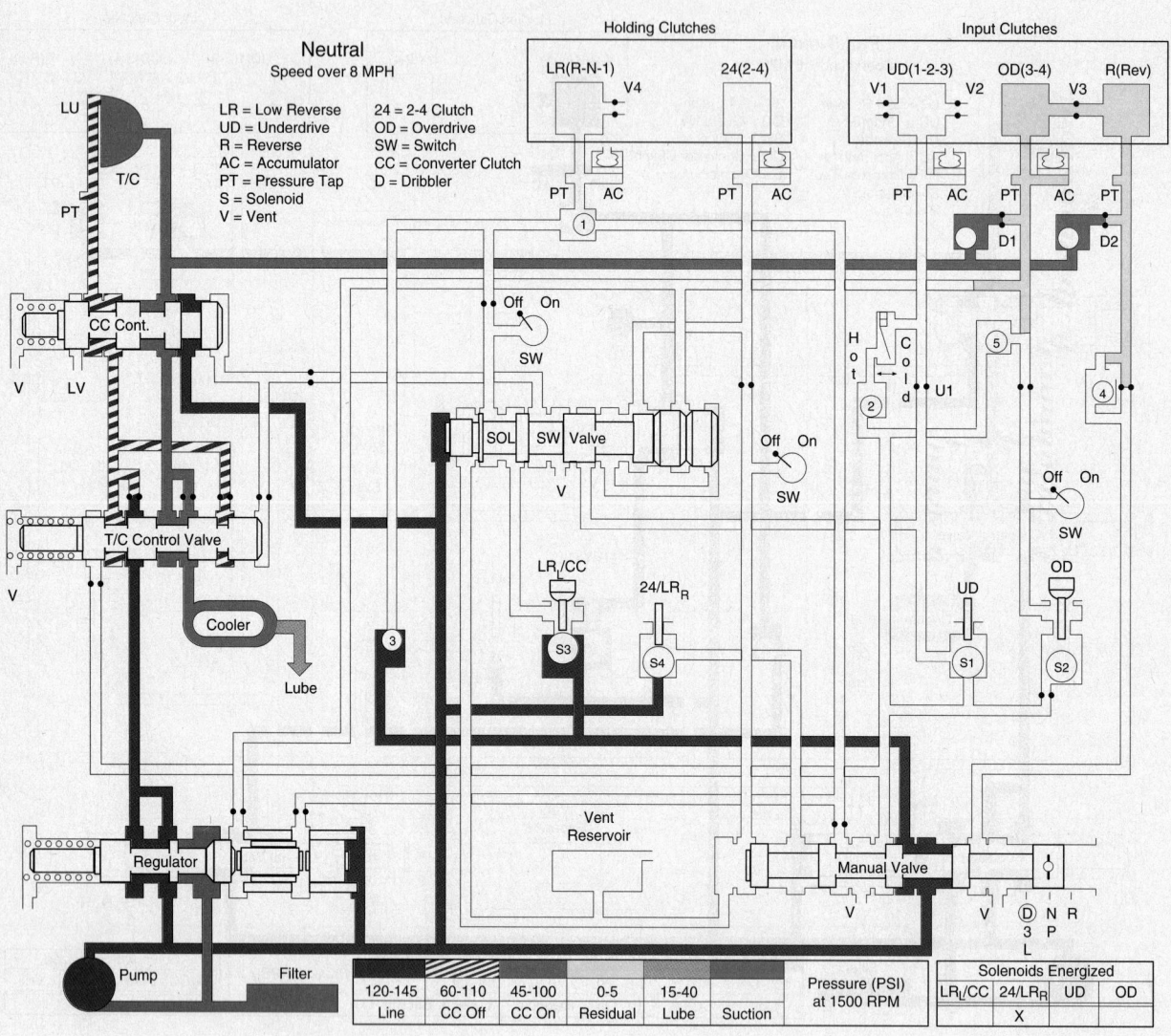

Neutral
Speed over 8 MPH

LR = Low Reverse   24 = 2-4 Clutch
UD = Underdrive   OD = Overdrive
R = Reverse   SW = Switch
AC = Accumulator   CC = Converter Clutch
PT = Pressure Tap   D = Dribbler
S = Solenoid
V = Vent

					Pressure (PSI) at 1500 RPM
120-145	60-110	45-100	0-5	15-40	
Line	CC Off	CC On	Residual	Lube	Suction

Solenoids Energized			
LR$_L$/CC	24/LR$_R$	UD	OD
	X		

Fig. 2: "N" Range — Neutral (Rolling Speed Greater Than 8 MPH)   Courtesy of Chrysler Corp.

OIL CIRCUIT DIAGRAMS
Chrysler 41TE/AE (Cont.)

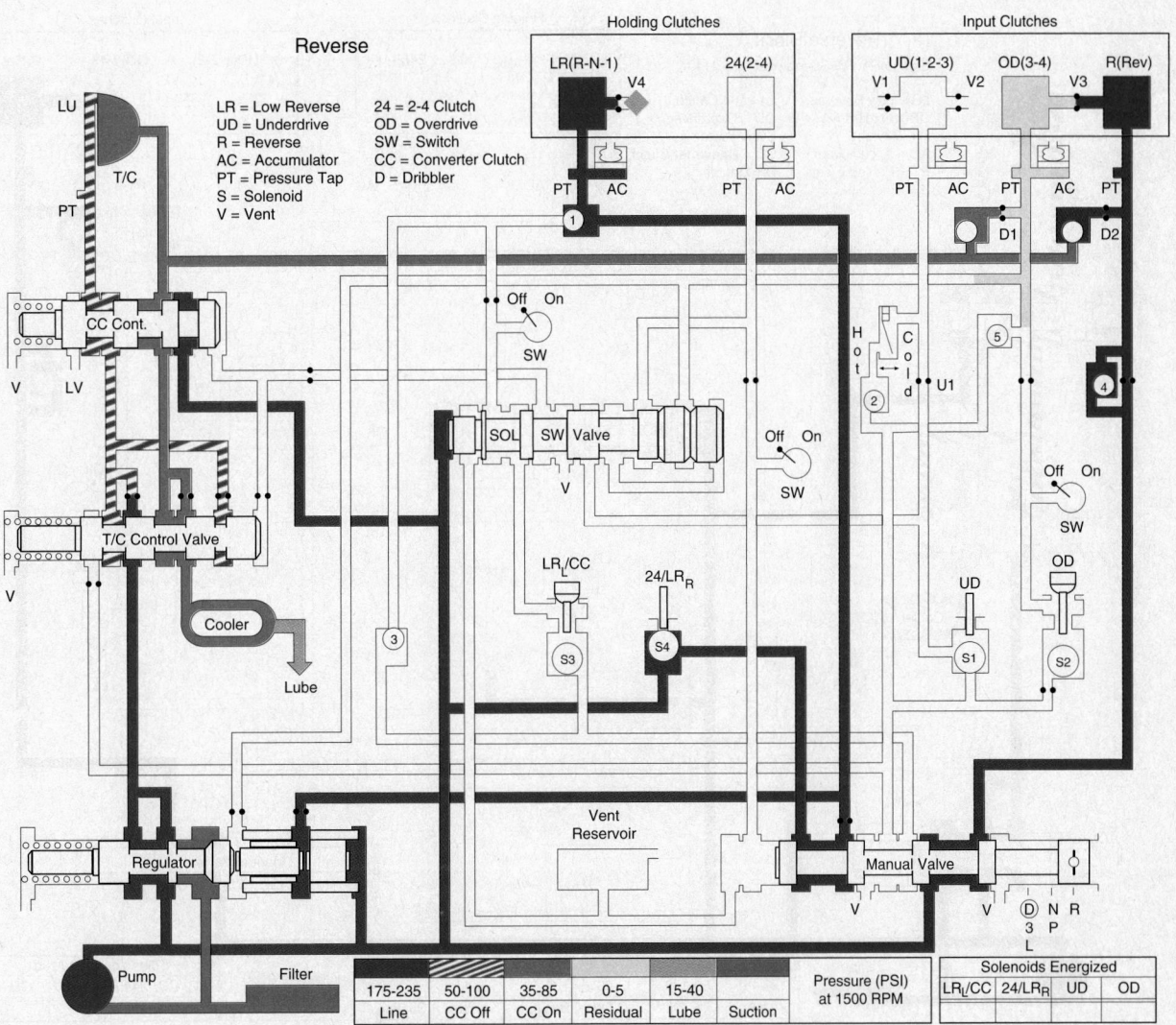

Reverse

LR = Low Reverse
UD = Underdrive
R = Reverse
AC = Accumulator
PT = Pressure Tap
S = Solenoid
V = Vent

24 = 2-4 Clutch
OD = Overdrive
SW = Switch
CC = Converter Clutch
D = Dribbler

Holding Clutches

LR(R-N-1)   24(2-4)

Input Clutches

UD(1-2-3)   OD(3-4)   R(Rev)

					Pressure (PSI) at 1500 RPM			
175-235	50-100	35-85	0-5	15-40	Suction			
Line	CC Off	CC On	Residual	Lube	Suction			

Solenoids Energized

LR_L/CC	24/LR_R	UD	OD

OIL CIRCUIT DIAGRAMS
Chrysler 41TE/AE (Cont.)

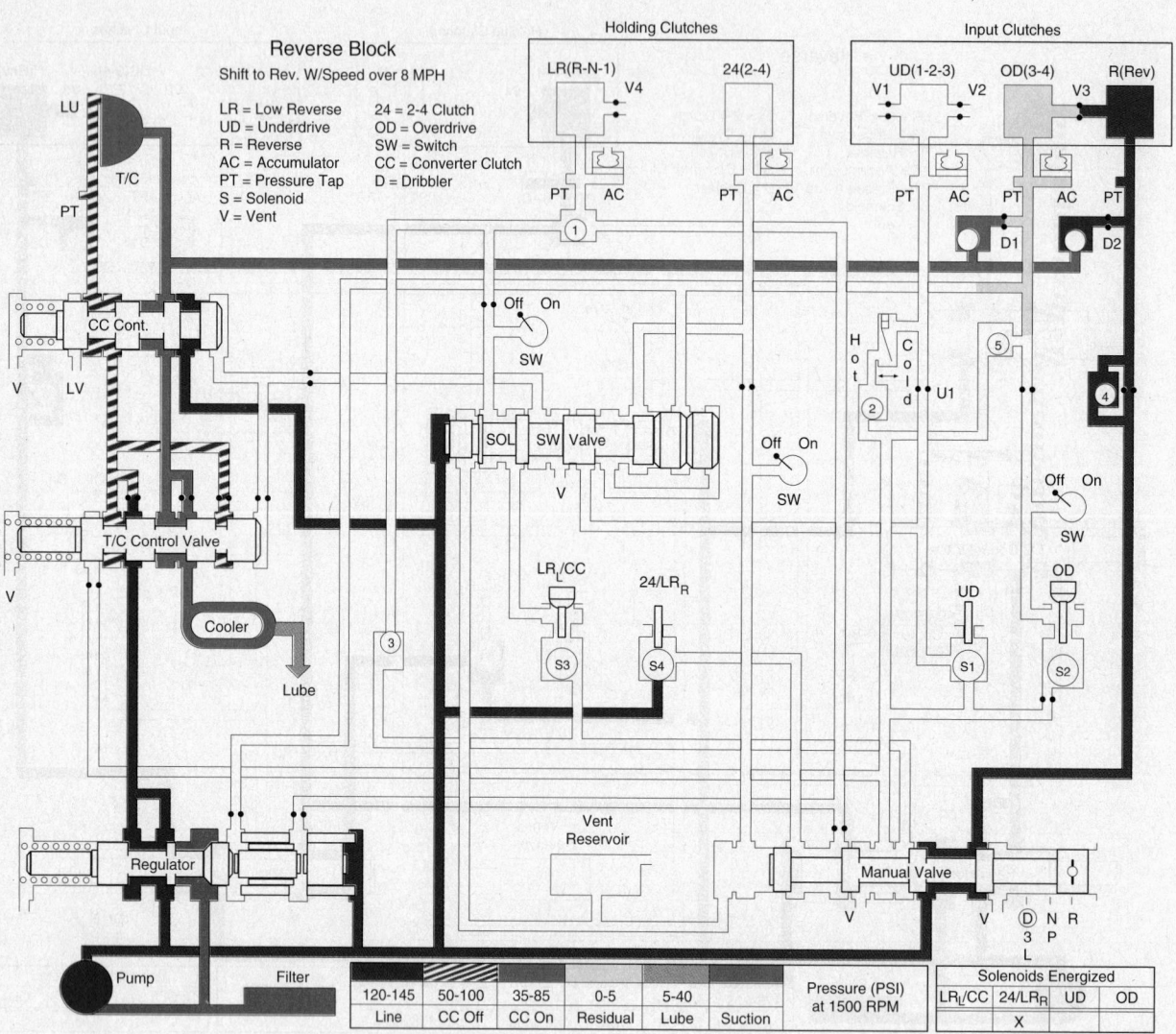

Reverse Block

Shift to Rev. W/Speed over 8 MPH

LR = Low Reverse 24 = 2-4 Clutch
UD = Underdrive OD = Overdrive
R = Reverse SW = Switch
AC = Accumulator CC = Converter Clutch
PT = Pressure Tap D = Dribbler
S = Solenoid
V = Vent

						Pressure (PSI) at 1500 RPM
120-145	50-100	35-85	0-5	5-40		
Line	CC Off	CC On	Residual	Lube	Suction	

Solenoids Energized			
LR$_L$/CC	24/LR$_R$	UD	OD
	X		

Fig. 4: "R" Range — Reverse Gear Blocked Out (When "R" Selected Above 8 MPH)   Courtesy of Chrysler Corp.

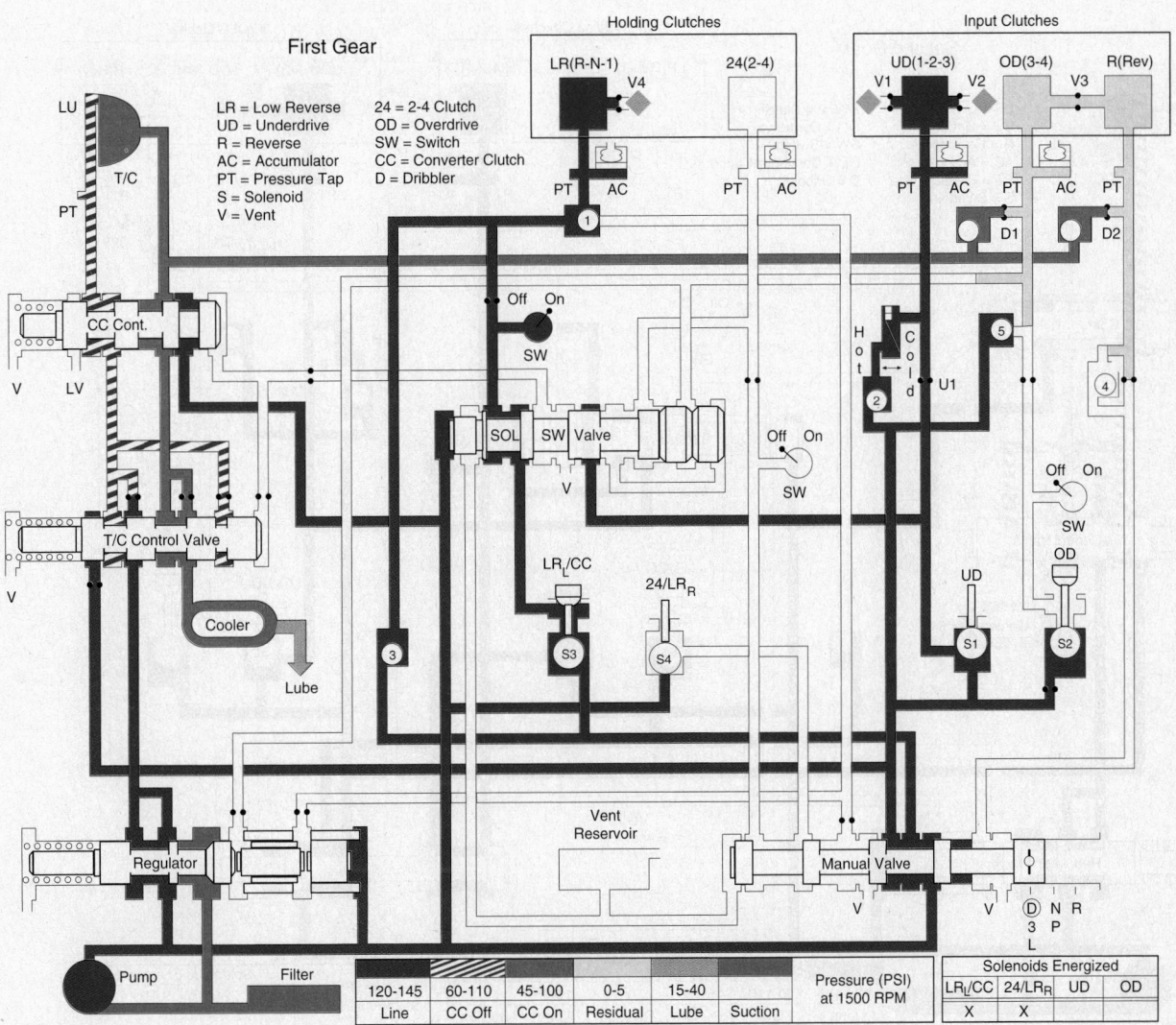

First Gear

LR = Low Reverse	24 = 2-4 Clutch
UD = Underdrive	OD = Overdrive
R = Reverse	SW = Switch
AC = Accumulator	CC = Converter Clutch
PT = Pressure Tap	D = Dribbler
S = Solenoid	
V = Vent	

Holding Clutches

Input Clutches

Pressure (PSI) at 1500 RPM					
120-145	60-110	45-100	0-5	15-40	
Line	CC Off	CC On	Residual	Lube	Suction

Solenoids Energized			
LR$_L$/CC	24/LR$_R$	UD	OD
X	X		

Fig. 5: "L" Range — 1st Gear

Courtesy of Chrysler Corp.

OIL CIRCUIT DIAGRAMS
Chrysler 41TE/AE (Cont.)

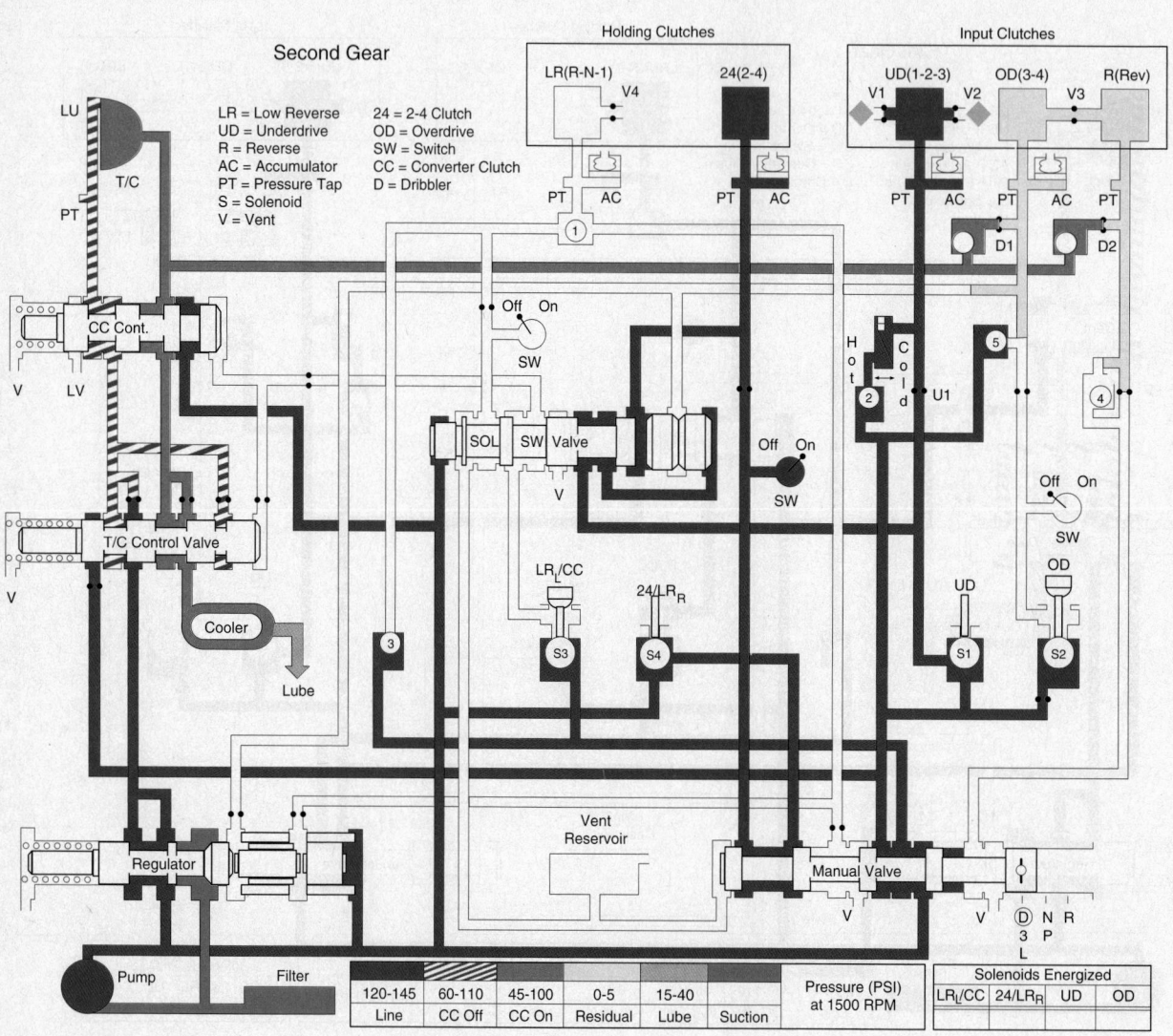

Second Gear

LR = Low Reverse
UD = Underdrive
R = Reverse
AC = Accumulator
PT = Pressure Tap
S = Solenoid
V = Vent

24 = 2-4 Clutch
OD = Overdrive
SW = Switch
CC = Converter Clutch
D = Dribbler

					Pressure (PSI) at 1500 RPM
120-145	60-110	45-100	0-5	15-40	
Line	CC Off	CC On	Residual	Lube	Suction

Solenoids Energized

LR$_L$/CC	24/LR$_R$	UD	OD

Fig. 6: "3" Range — 2nd Gear

Courtesy of Chrysler Corp.

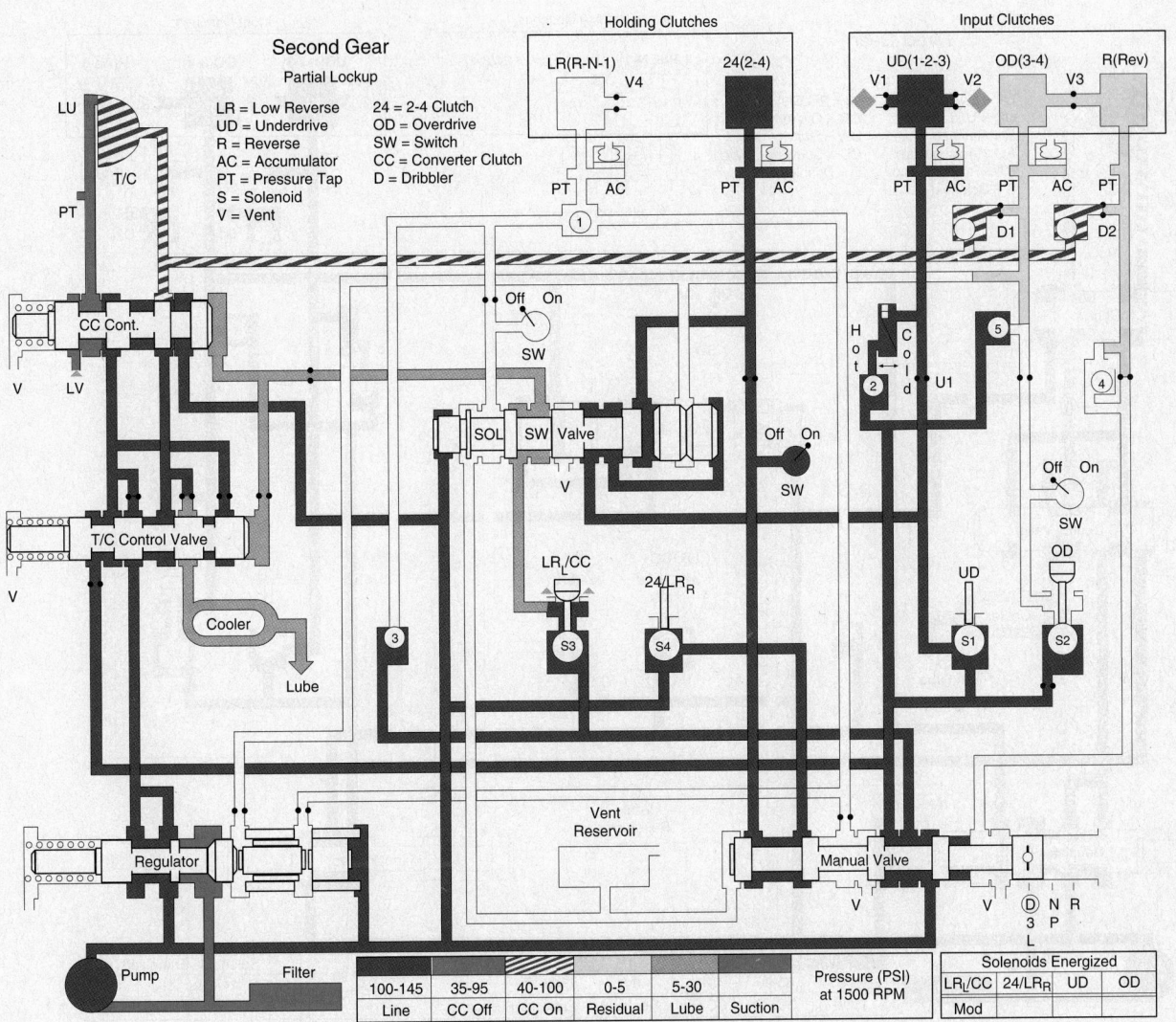

Second Gear
Partial Lockup

LR = Low Reverse
UD = Underdrive
R = Reverse
AC = Accumulator
PT = Pressure Tap
S = Solenoid
V = Vent

24 = 2-4 Clutch
OD = Overdrive
SW = Switch
CC = Converter Clutch
D = Dribbler

				Pressure (PSI) at 1500 RPM		Solenoids Energized		
100-145	35-95	40-100	0-5	5-30			LR$_L$/CC	24/LR$_R$	UD	OD
Line	CC Off	CC On	Residual	Lube	Suction		Mod			

Fig. 7: "3" Range — 2nd Gear (Partial Lock-Up)

Courtesy of Chrysler Corp.

OIL CIRCUIT DIAGRAMS
Chrysler 41TE/AE (Cont.)

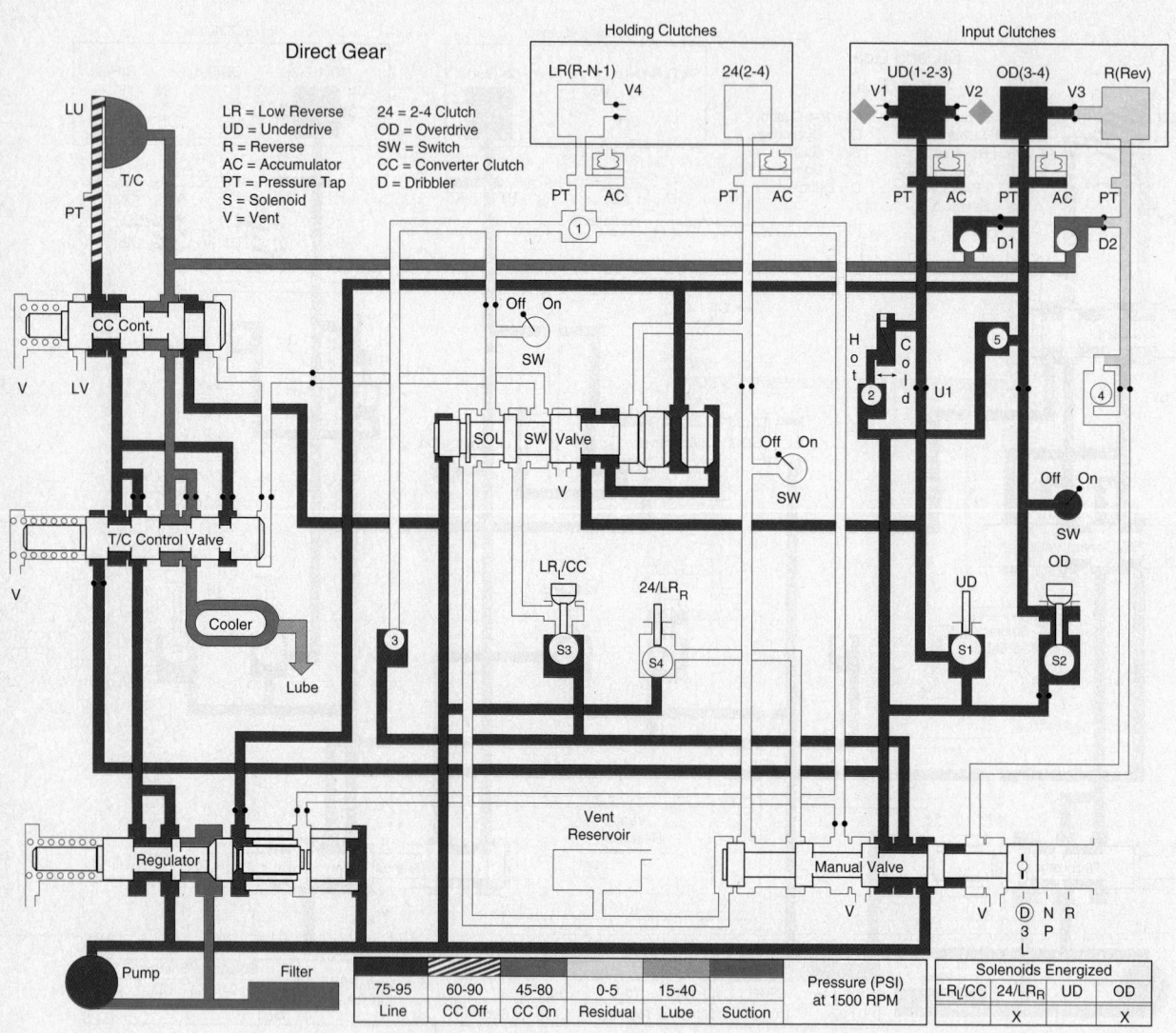

Fig. 8: "3" Range — Direct Gear

Courtesy of Chrysler Corp.

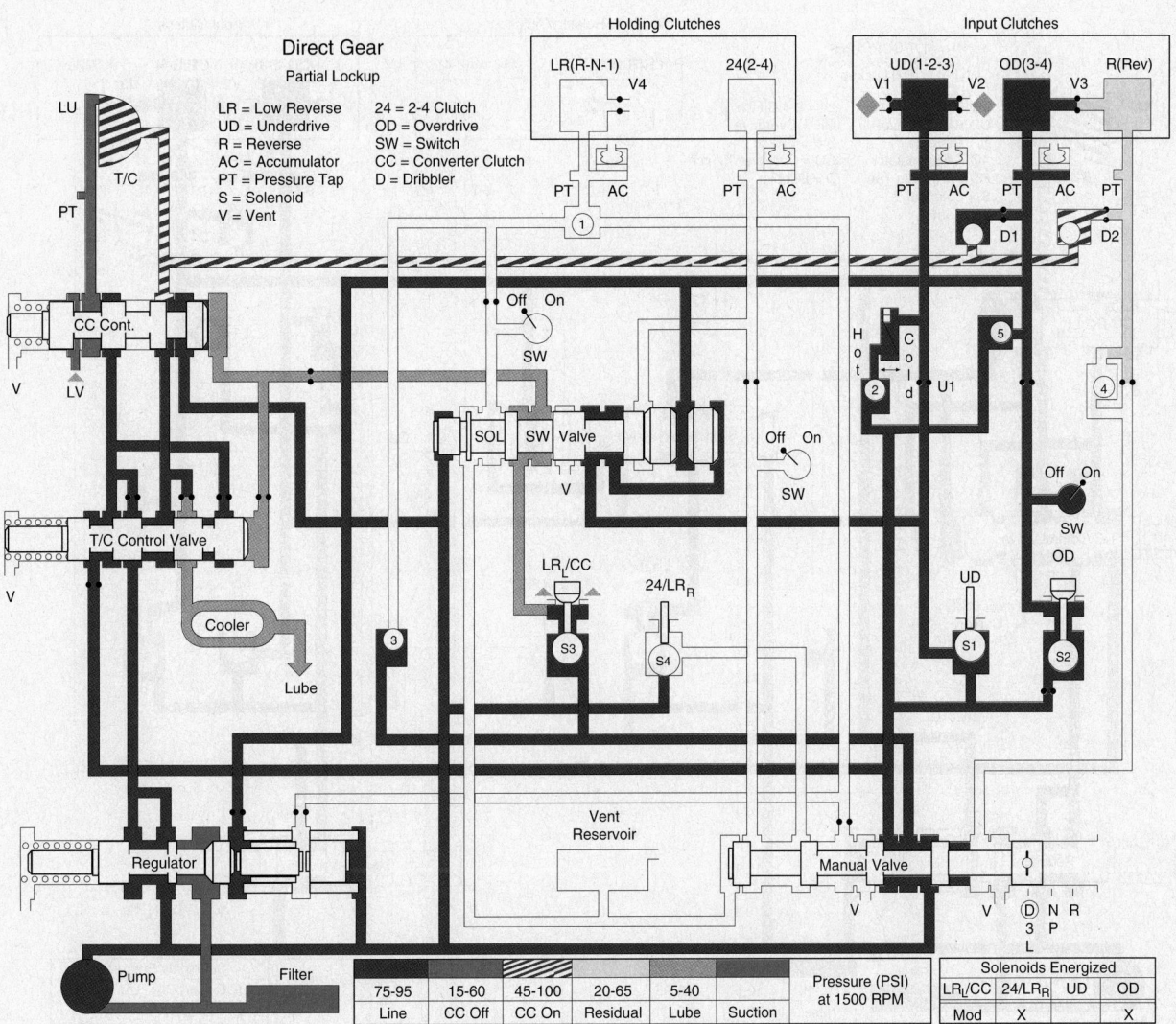

Direct Gear
Partial Lockup

LR = Low Reverse   24 = 2-4 Clutch
UD = Underdrive   OD = Overdrive
R = Reverse   SW = Switch
AC = Accumulator   CC = Converter Clutch
PT = Pressure Tap   D = Dribbler
S = Solenoid
V = Vent

				Pressure (PSI) at 1500 RPM			
75-95	15-60	45-100	20-65	5-40			
Line	CC Off	CC On	Residual	Lube	Suction		

Solenoids Energized			
LR$_L$/CC	24/LR$_R$	UD	OD
Mod	X		X

Fig. 9: "3" Range — Direct Gear (Partial Lock-Up)

Courtesy of Chrysler Corp.

OIL CIRCUIT DIAGRAMS
Chrysler 41TE/AE (Cont.)

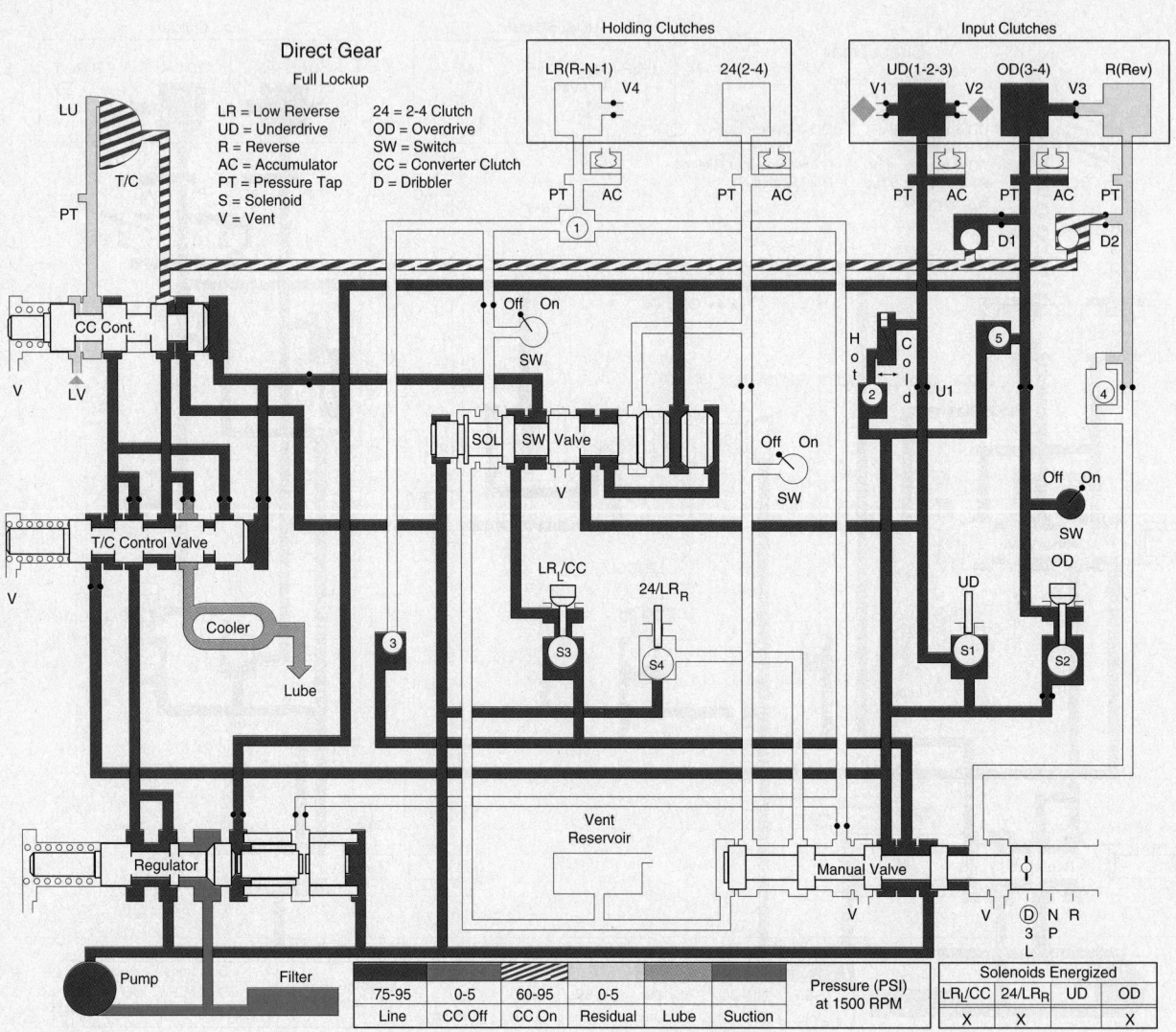

Fig. 10: "3" Range — Direct Gear (Full Lock-up)

Courtesy of Chrysler Corp.

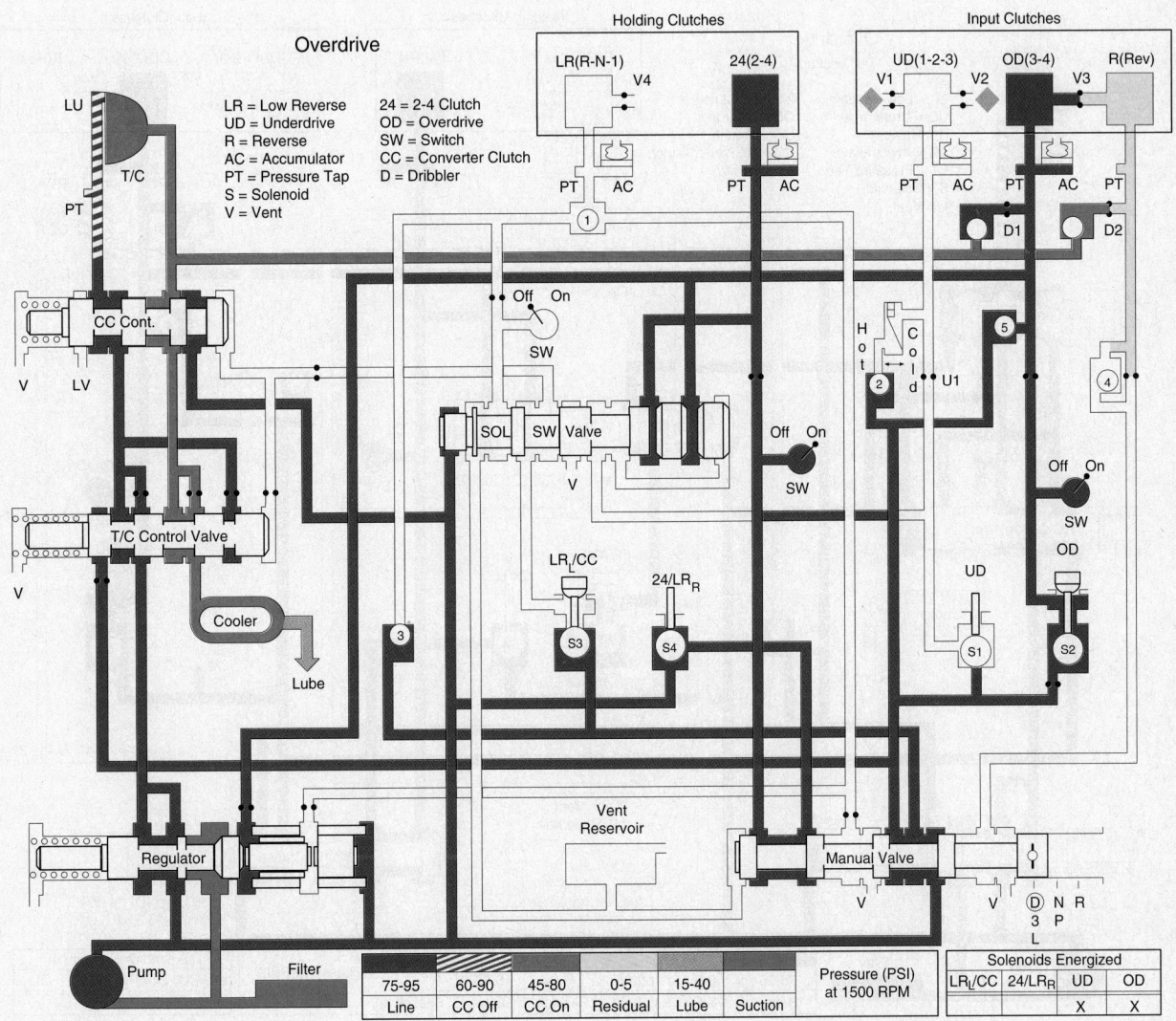

Fig. 11: "OD" Range — Overdrive Gear

Courtesy of Chrysler Corp.

OIL CIRCUIT DIAGRAMS
Chrysler 41TE/AE (Cont.)

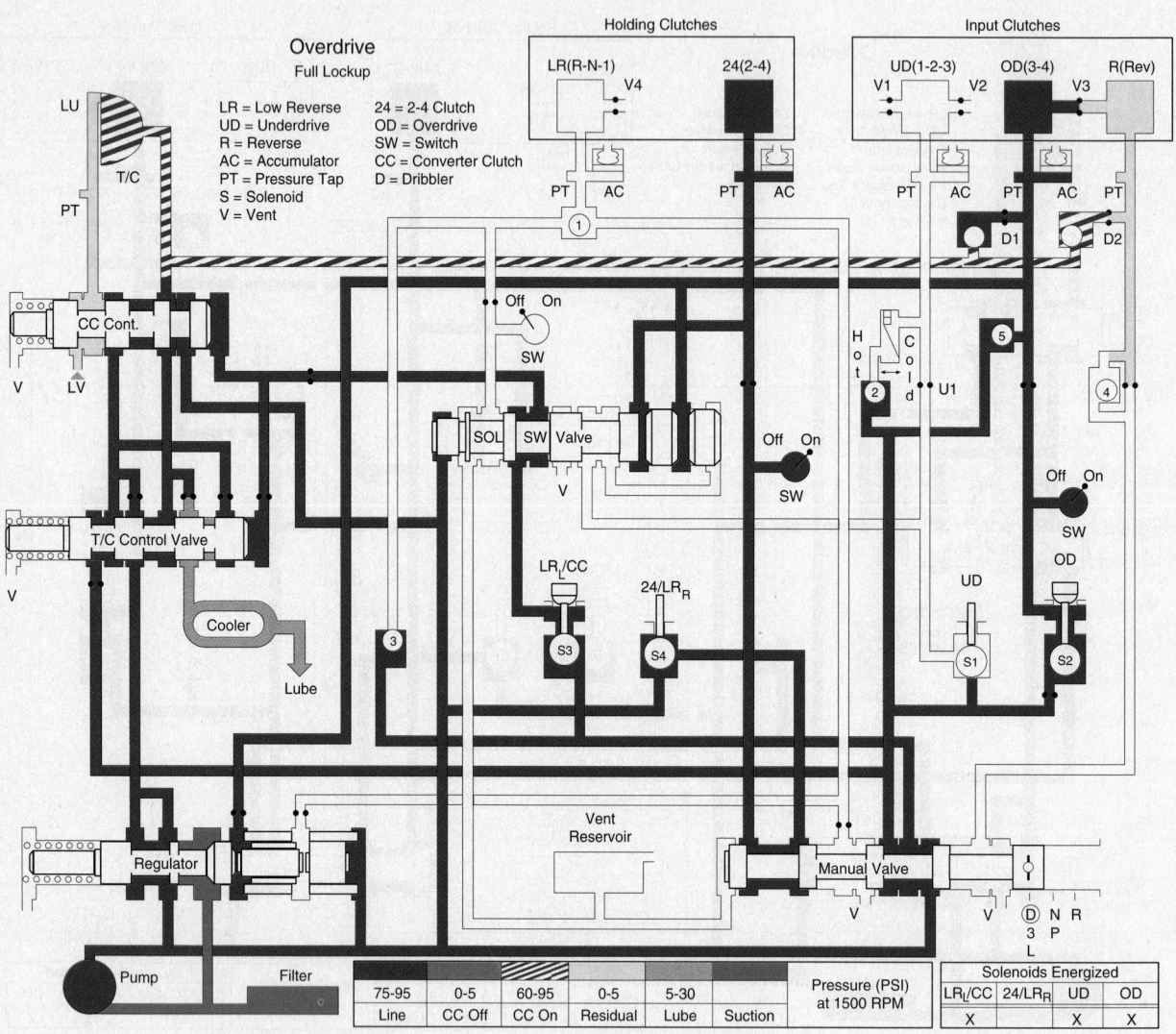

Fig. 12: "OD" Range — Overdrive Gear (Full Lock-Up)

Courtesy of Chrysler Corp.

OIL CIRCUIT DIAGRAMS
Chrysler 42LE

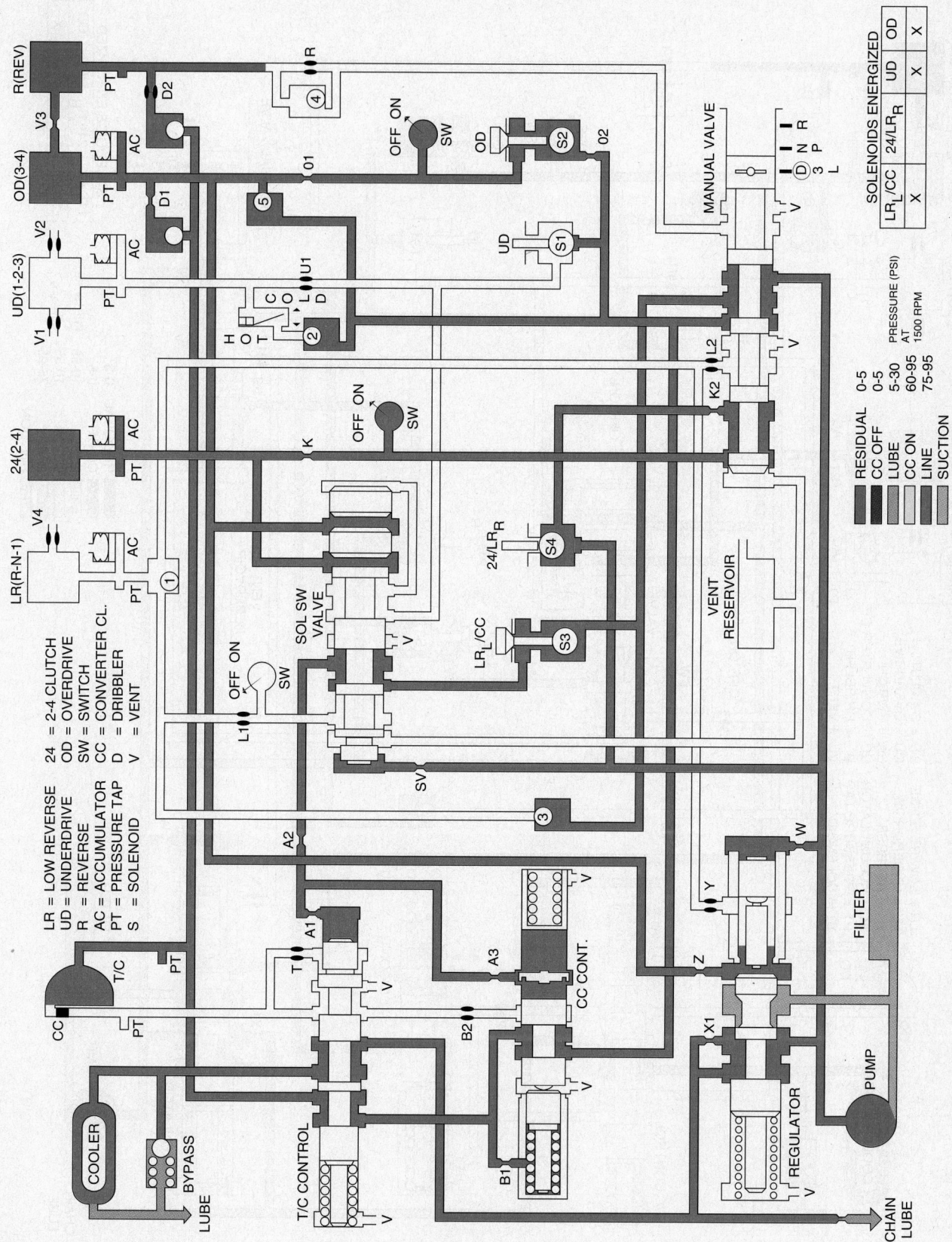

Fig. 1: "OD/D" Range — (Converter Clutch ON — Full Lock-Up)

Courtesy of Chrysler Corp.

OIL CIRCUIT DIAGRAMS
Chrysler 42LE (Cont.)

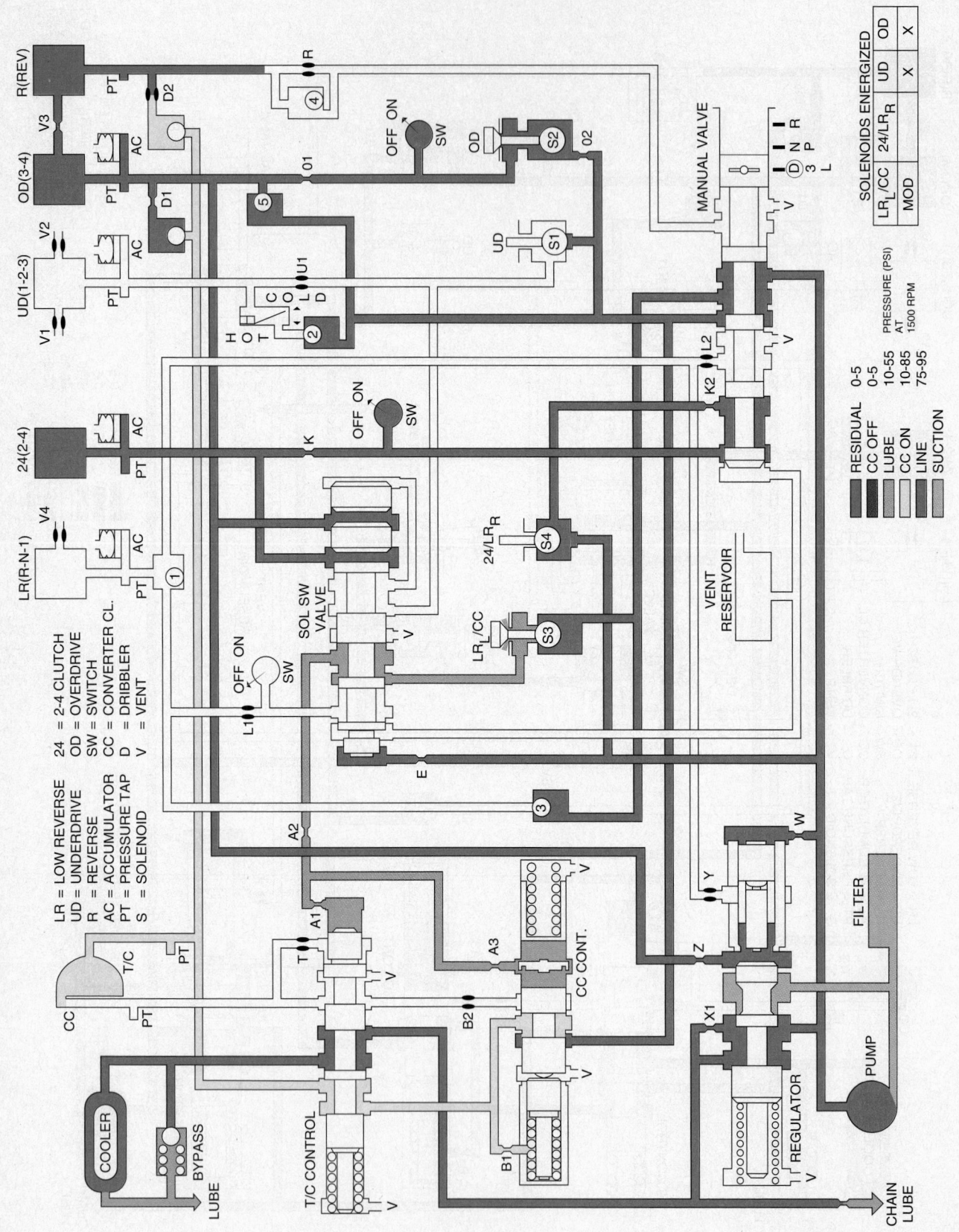

Fig. 2: "OD/D" Range — (Converter EMCC – Partial Lock-Up)

Courtesy of Chrysler Corp.

OIL CIRCUIT DIAGRAMS
Chrysler 42LE (Cont.)

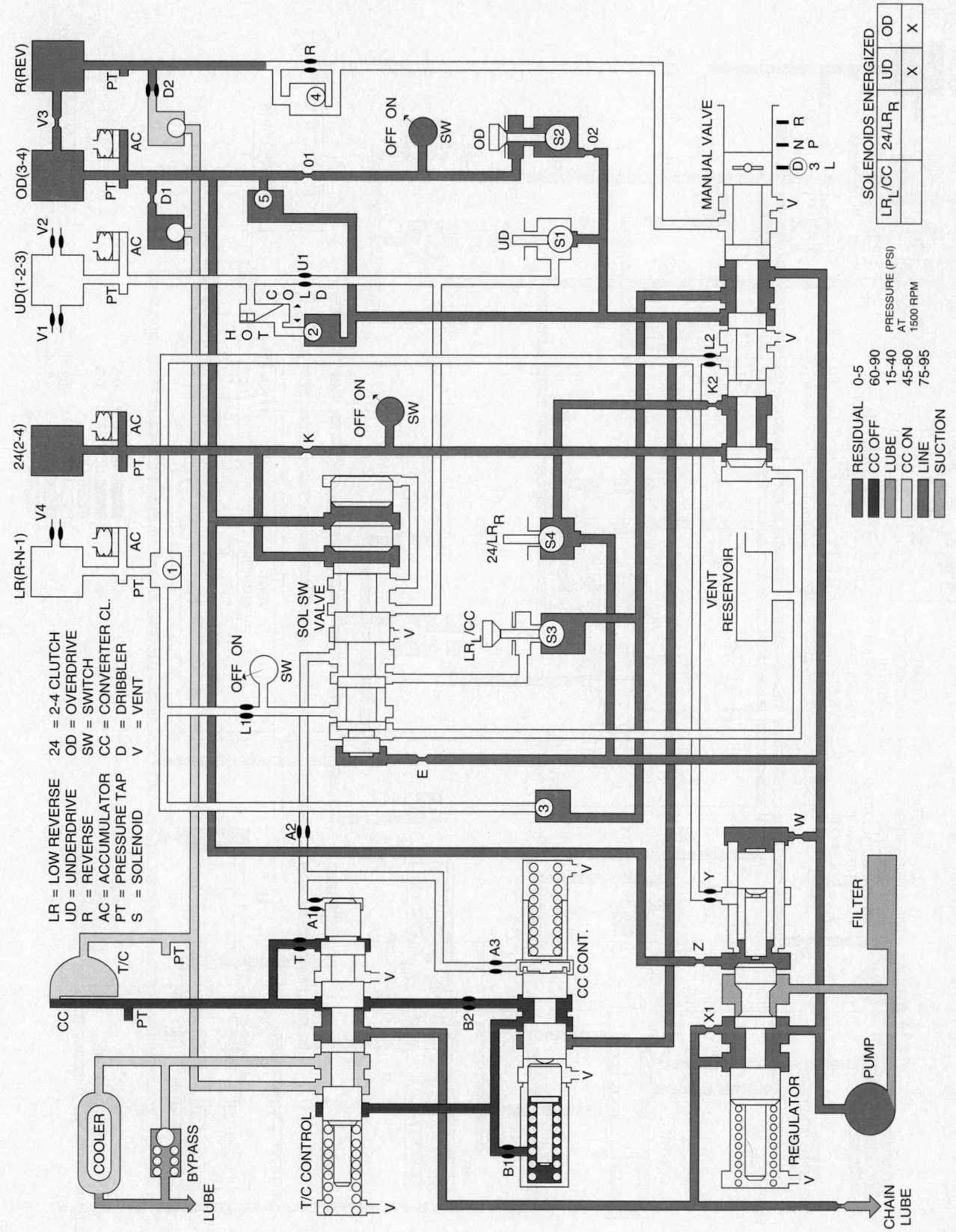

SOLENOIDS ENERGIZED

	LR_L/CC	$24/LR_R$	UD	OD
OD				X
		X	X	

PRESSURE (PSI)
AT
1500 RPM

RESIDUAL	0-5
CC OFF	60-90
LUBE	15-40
CC ON	45-80
LINE	75-95
SUCTION	

LR = LOW REVERSE
UD = UNDERDRIVE
R = REVERSE
AC = ACCUMULATOR
PT = PRESSURE TAP
S = SOLENOID

24 = 2-4 CLUTCH
OD = OVERDRIVE
SW = SWITCH
CC = CONVERTER CL.
D = DRIBBLER
V = VENT

Fig. 3: "OD/D" Range — Overdrive (Converter Clutch OFF)

Courtesy of Chrysler Corp.

OIL CIRCUIT DIAGRAMS
Chrysler 42LE (Cont.)

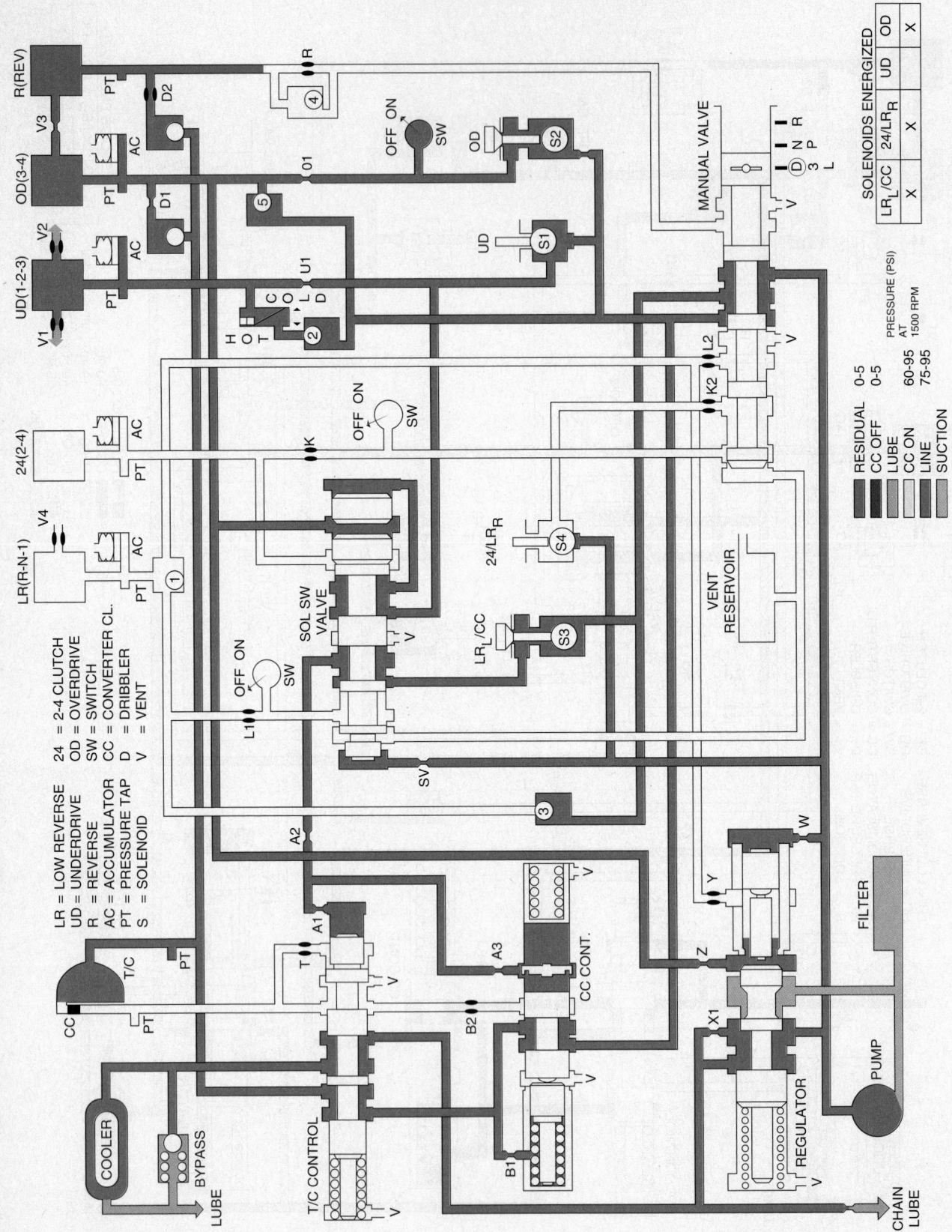

Fig. 4: "OD/D" Range — 3rd Gear (Converter Clutch ON — Full Lock-Up)

Courtesy of Chrysler Corp.

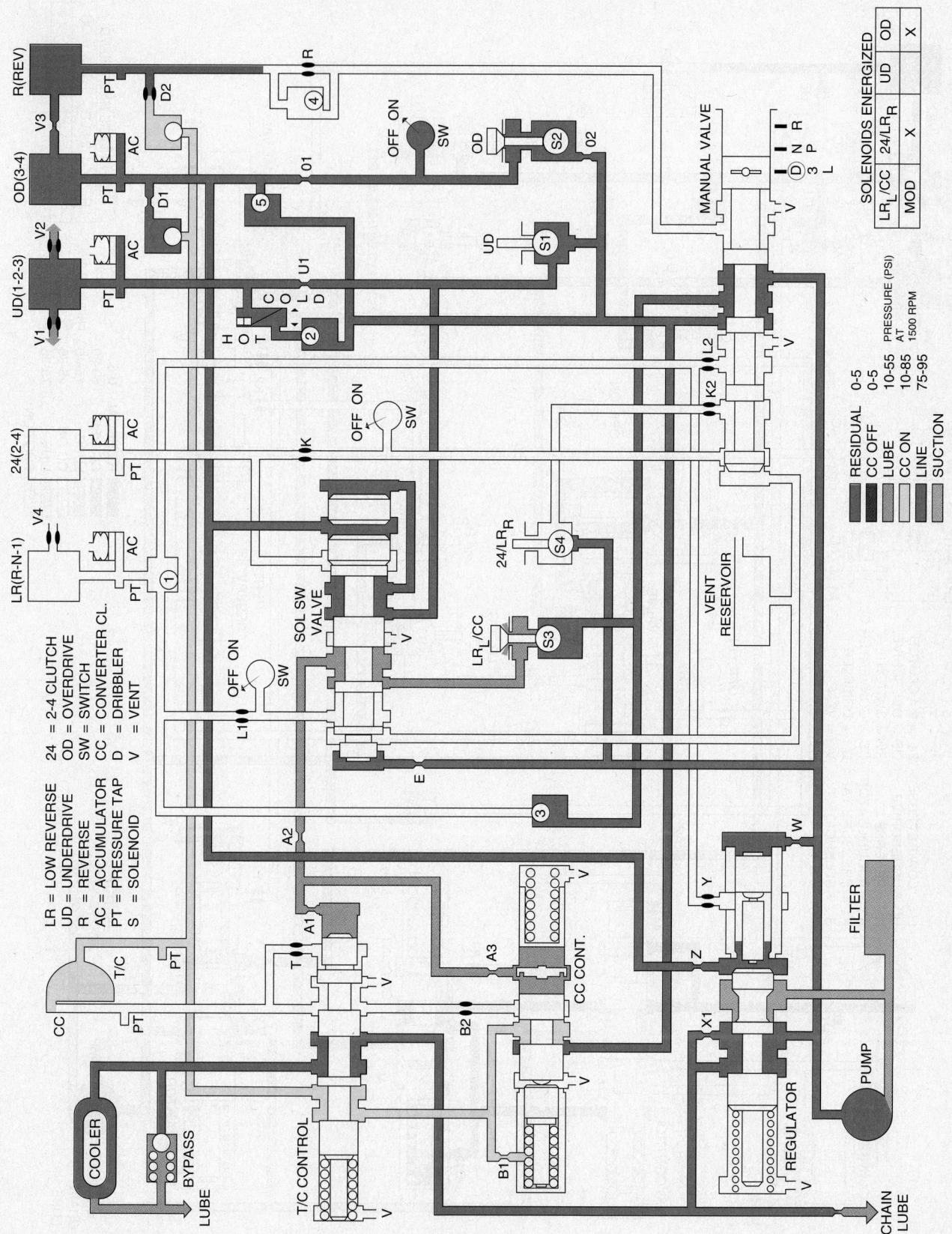

SOLENOIDS ENERGIZED		
	OD	X
	UD	
	24/LR_R	X
	LR_L/CC	X
	MOD	

PRESSURE (PSI)
AT
1500 RPM

RESIDUAL	0-5
CC OFF	0-5
LUBE	10-55
CC ON	10-85
LINE	75-95
SUCTION	

LR = LOW REVERSE
UD = UNDERDRIVE
R = REVERSE
AC = ACCUMULATOR
PT = PRESSURE TAP
S = SOLENOID

24 = 2-4 CLUTCH
OD = OVERDRIVE
SW = SWITCH
CC = CONVERTER CL.
D = DRIBBLER
V = VENT

Fig. 5: "OD/D" Range — 3rd Gear (Converter EMCC—Partial Lock-Up)

Courtesy of Chrysler Corp.

OIL CIRCUIT DIAGRAMS
Chrysler 42LE (Cont.)

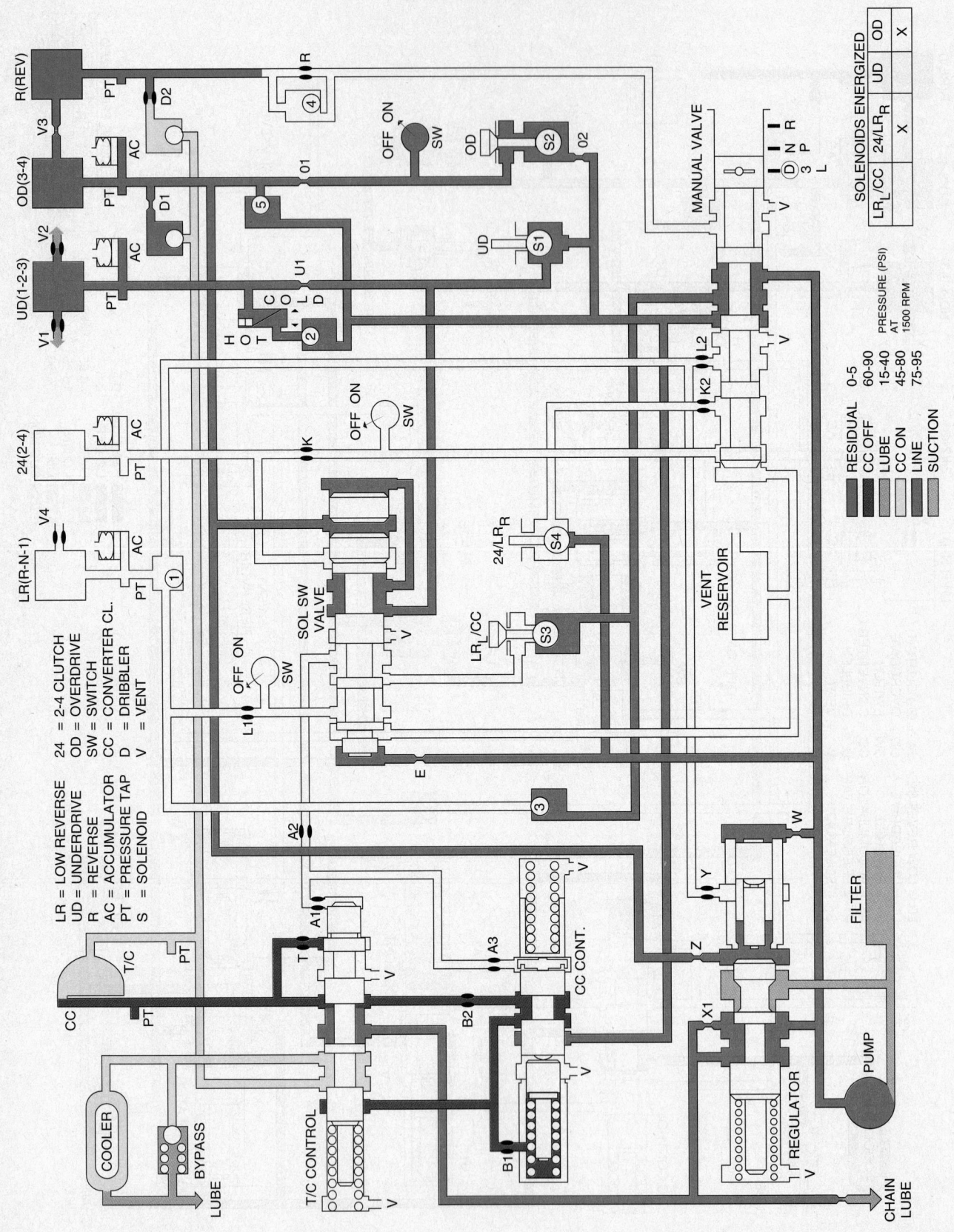

Fig. 6: "OD/D" Range — 3rd Gear (Converter Clutch OFF)

Courtesy of Chrysler Corp.

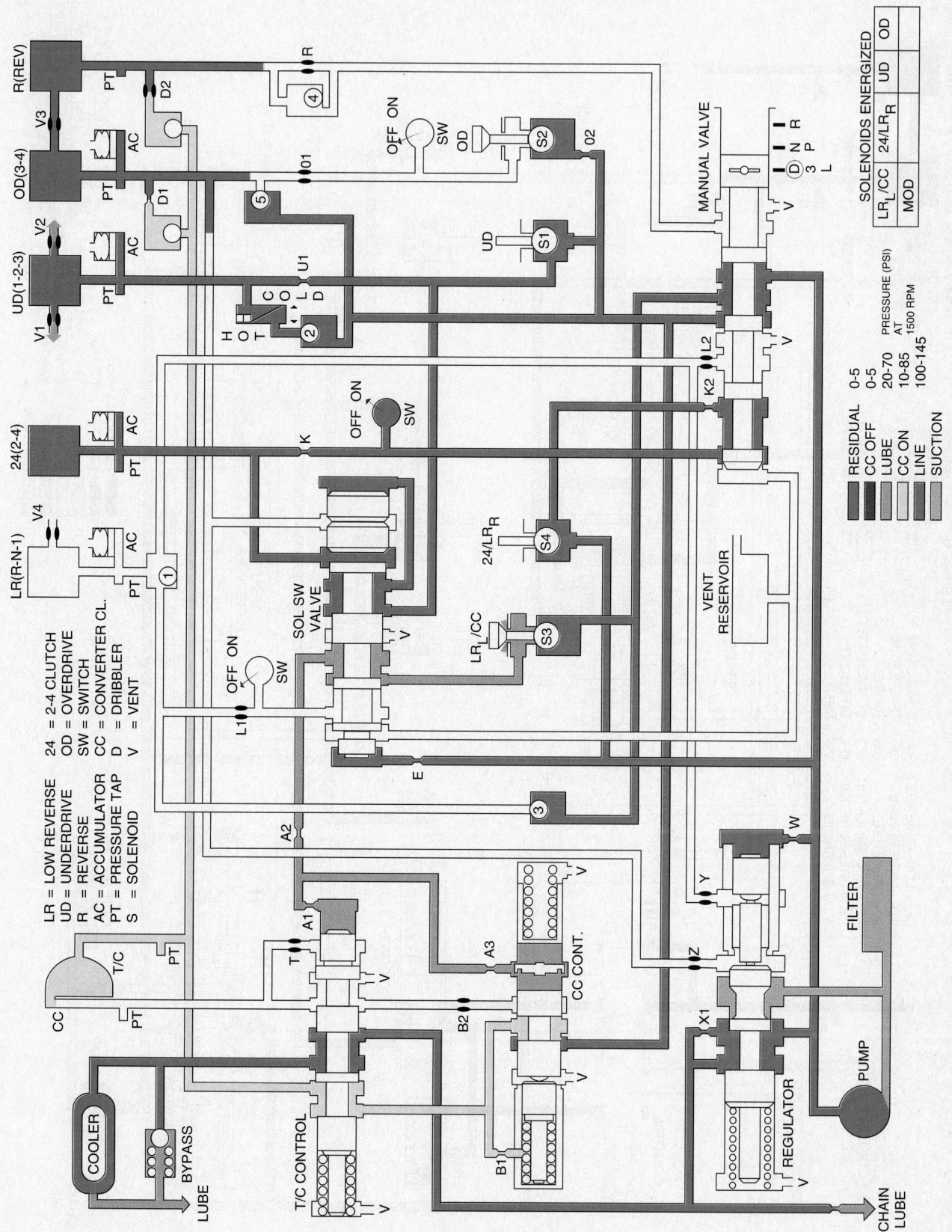

Fig. 7: "OD/D" Range — 2nd Gear (Converter EMCC)

Courtesy of Chrysler Corp.

OIL CIRCUIT DIAGRAMS
Chrysler 42LE (Cont.)

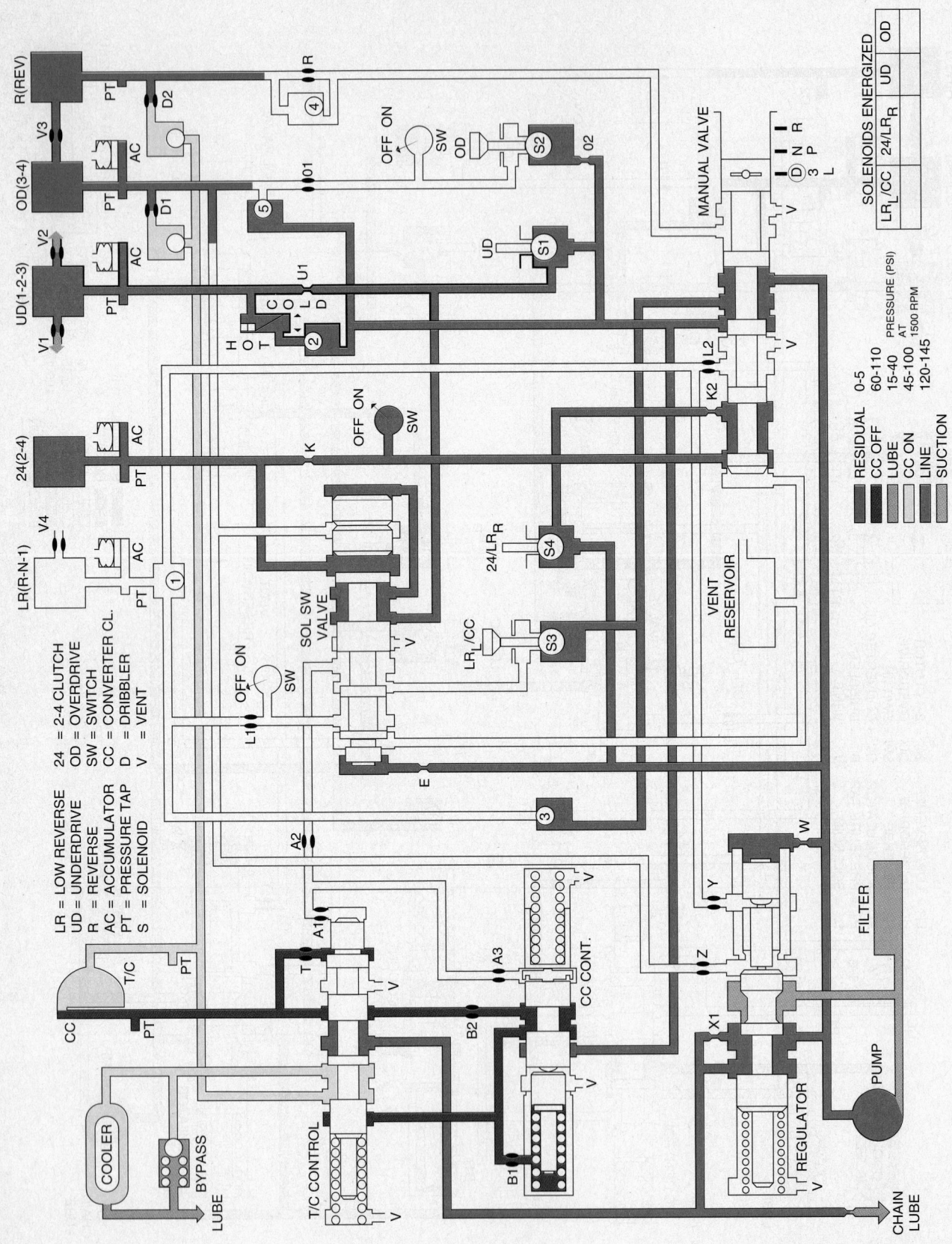

Fig. 8: "OD/D" Range — 2nd Gear

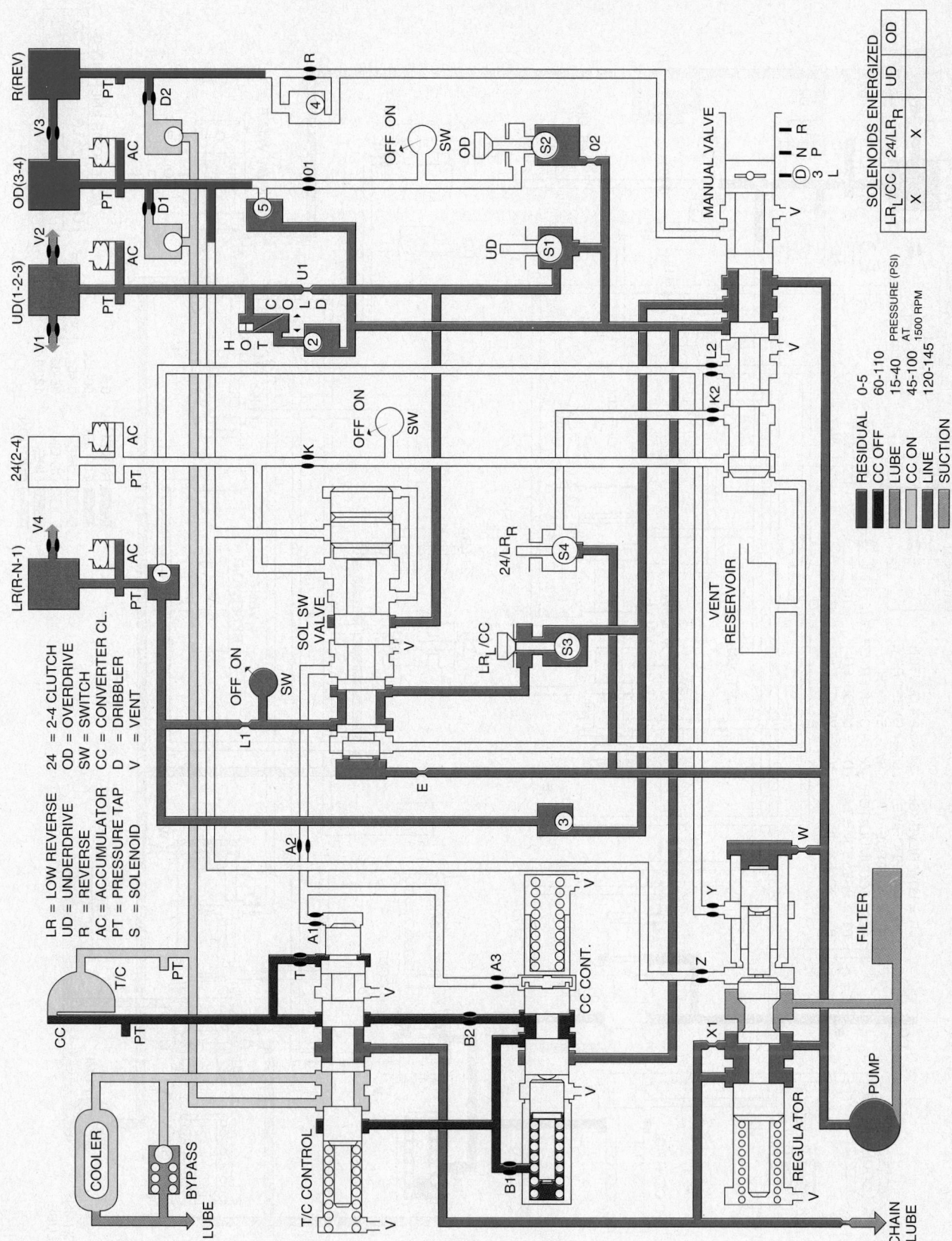

Fig. 9: "OD/D" Range — 1st Gear

Courtesy of Chrysler Corp.

OIL CIRCUIT DIAGRAMS
Chrysler 42LE (Cont.)

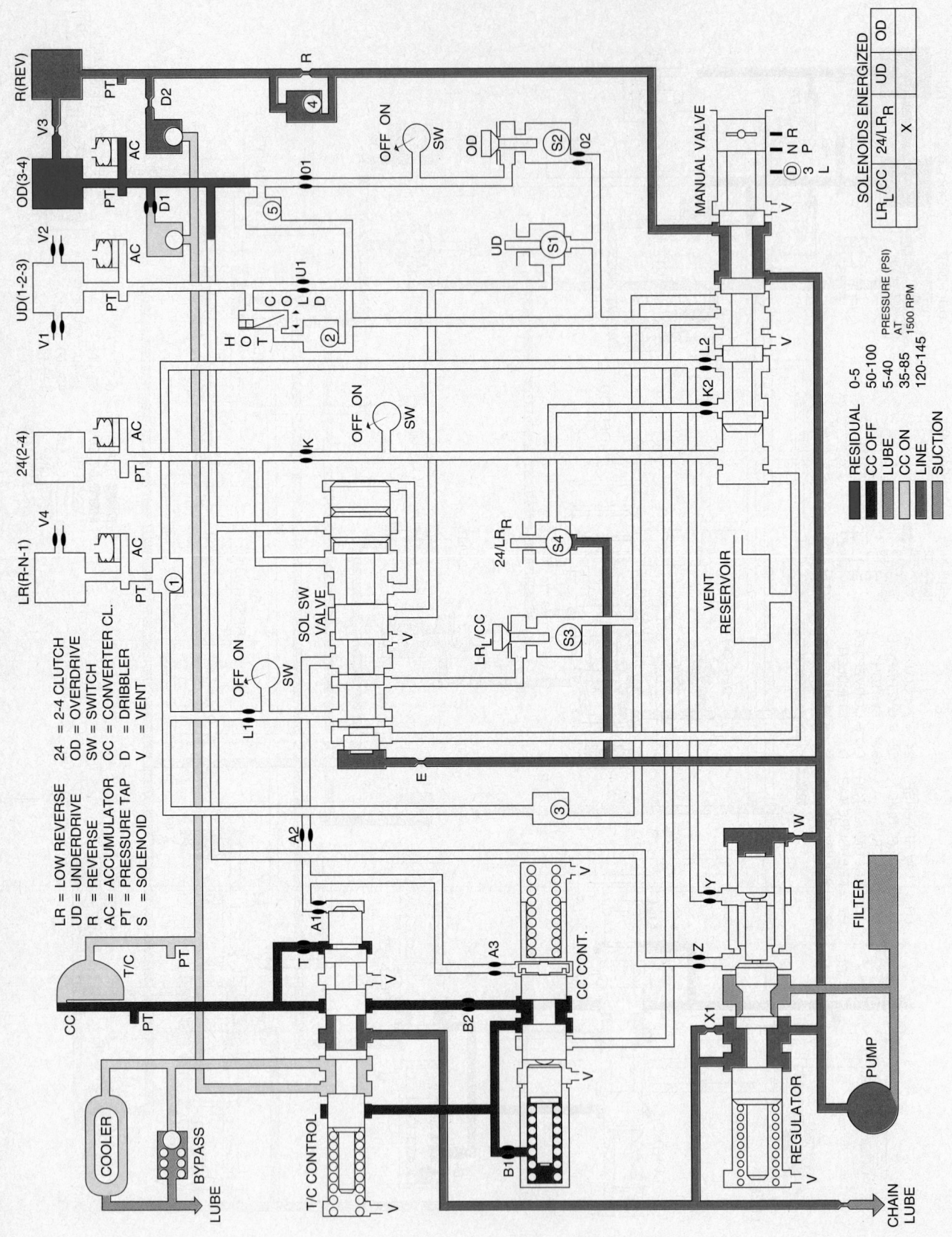

	SOLENOIDS ENERGIZED		
	LR$_L$/CC	24/LR$_R$	UD	OD
	X			

PRESSURE (PSI) AT 1500 RPM

RESIDUAL	0-5
CC OFF	50-100
LUBE	5-40
CC ON	35-85
LINE	120-145
SUCTION	

LR = LOW REVERSE 24 = 2-4 CLUTCH
UD = UNDERDRIVE OD = OVERDRIVE
R = REVERSE SW = SWITCH
AC = ACCUMULATOR CC = CONVERTER CL.
PT = PRESSURE TAP D = DRIBBLER
S = SOLENOID V = VENT

Fig. 10: "R" Range — "R" Selected With Speed Greater Than 8 MPH

Courtesy of Chrysler Corp.

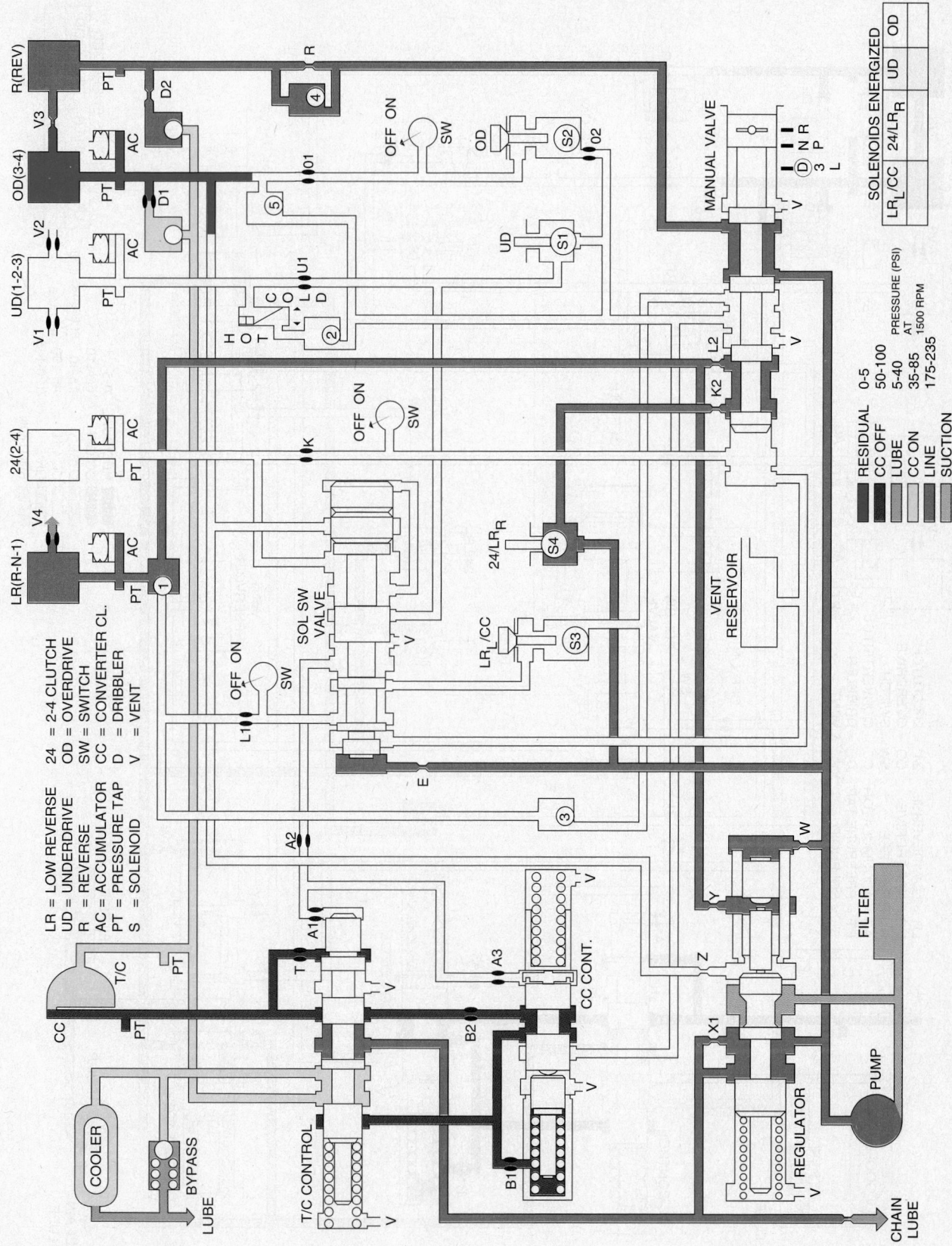

Fig. 11: "R" Range — Reverse

Courtesy of Chrysler Corp.

OIL CIRCUIT DIAGRAMS
Chrysler 42LE (Cont.)

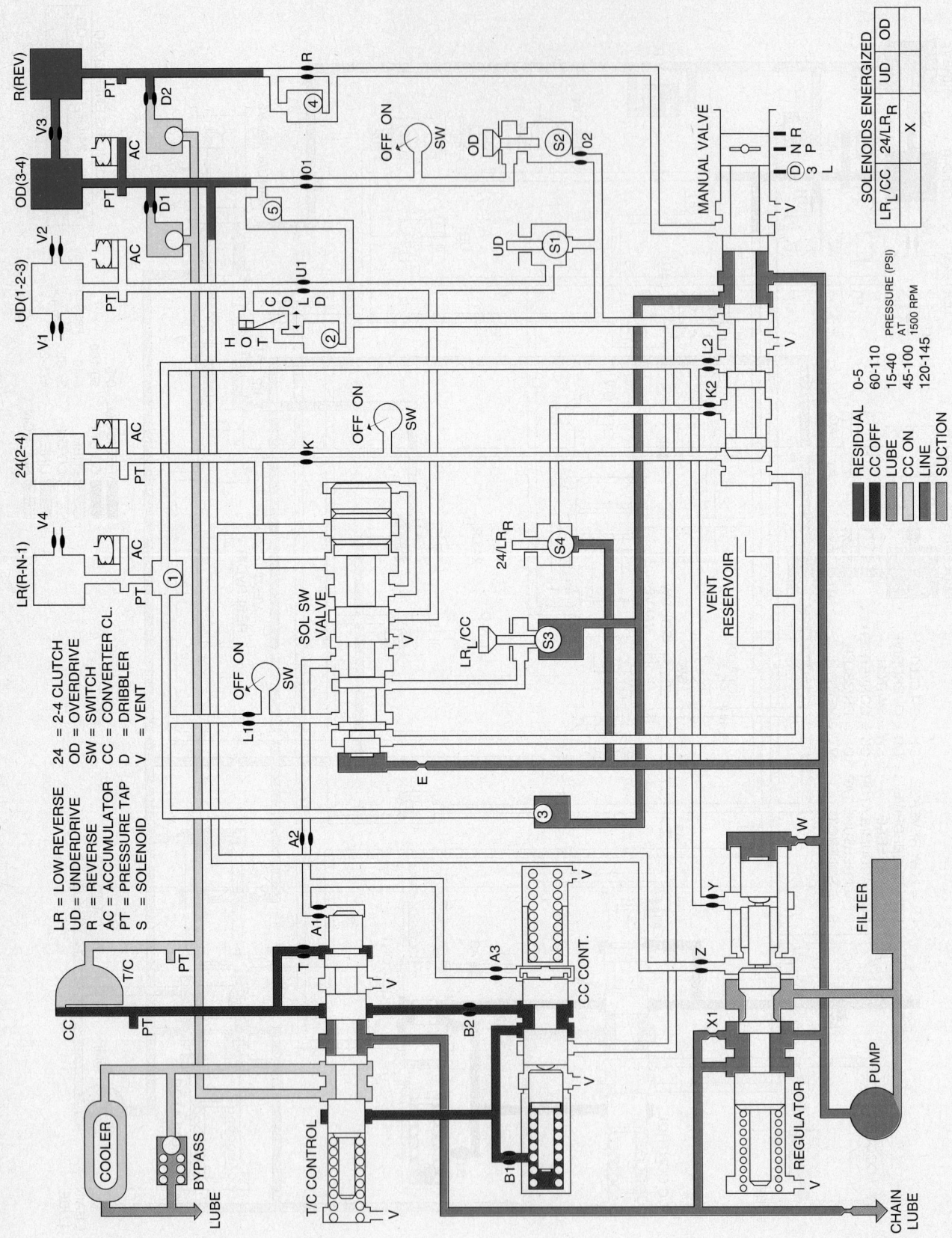

SOLENOIDS ENERGIZED			
LR$_L$/CC	24/LR$_R$	UD	OD
	X		

PRESSURE (PSI) AT 1500 RPM	
RESIDUAL	0-5
CC OFF	60-110
LUBE	15-40
CC ON	45-100
LINE	120-145
SUCTION	

LR = LOW REVERSE
UD = UNDERDRIVE
R = REVERSE
AC = ACCUMULATOR
PT = PRESSURE TAP
S = SOLENOID

24 = 2-4 CLUTCH
OD = OVERDRIVE
SW = SWITCH
CC = CONVERTER CL.
D = DRIBBLER
V = VENT

Fig. 12: "N" Range — Neutral (Speed Over 8 MPH)

Courtesy of Chrysler Corp.

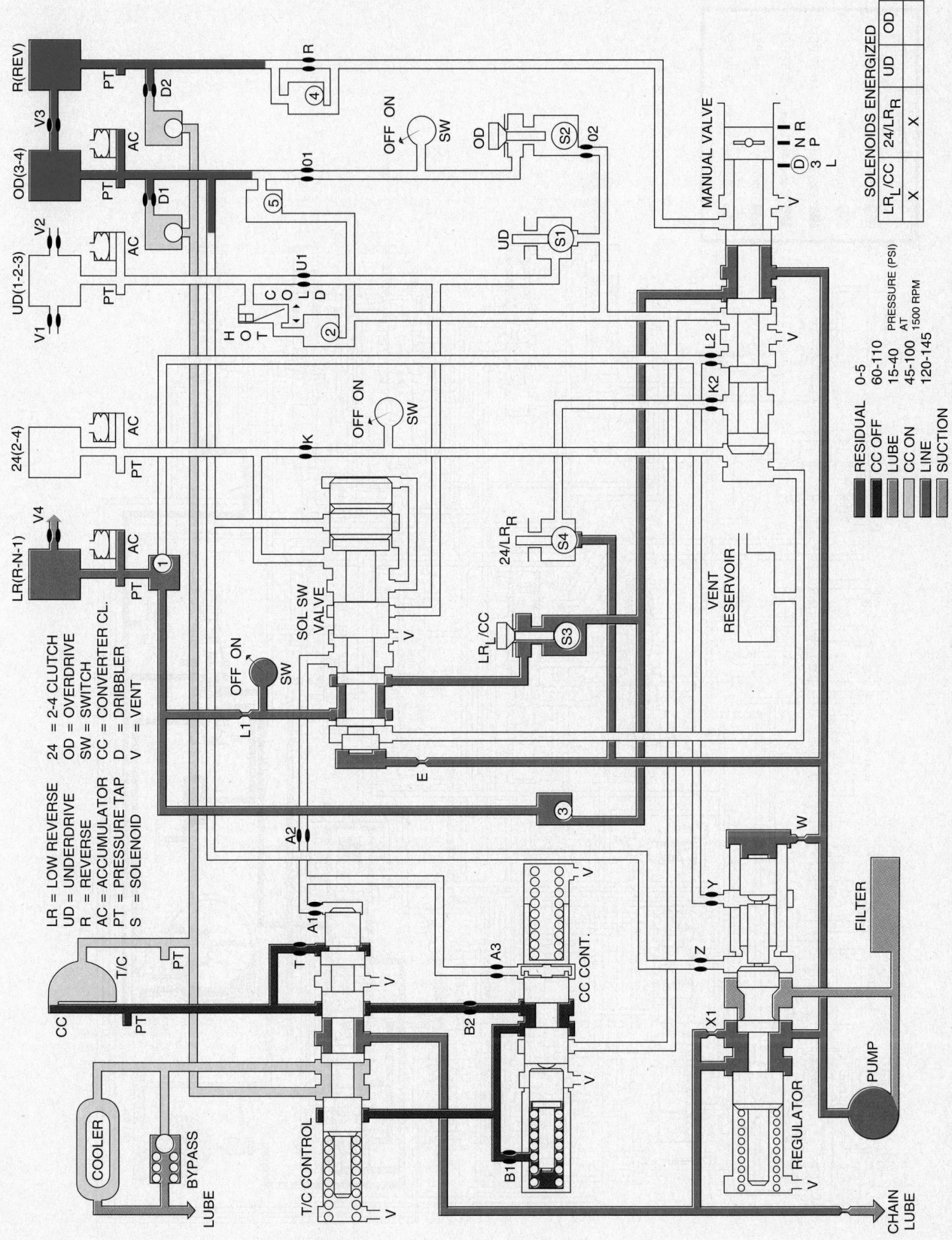

Fig. 13: "P" Or "N" Range — Speed Less Than 8 MPH

Courtesy of Chrysler Corp.

OIL CIRCUIT DIAGRAMS
Chrysler 42RH & 46RH

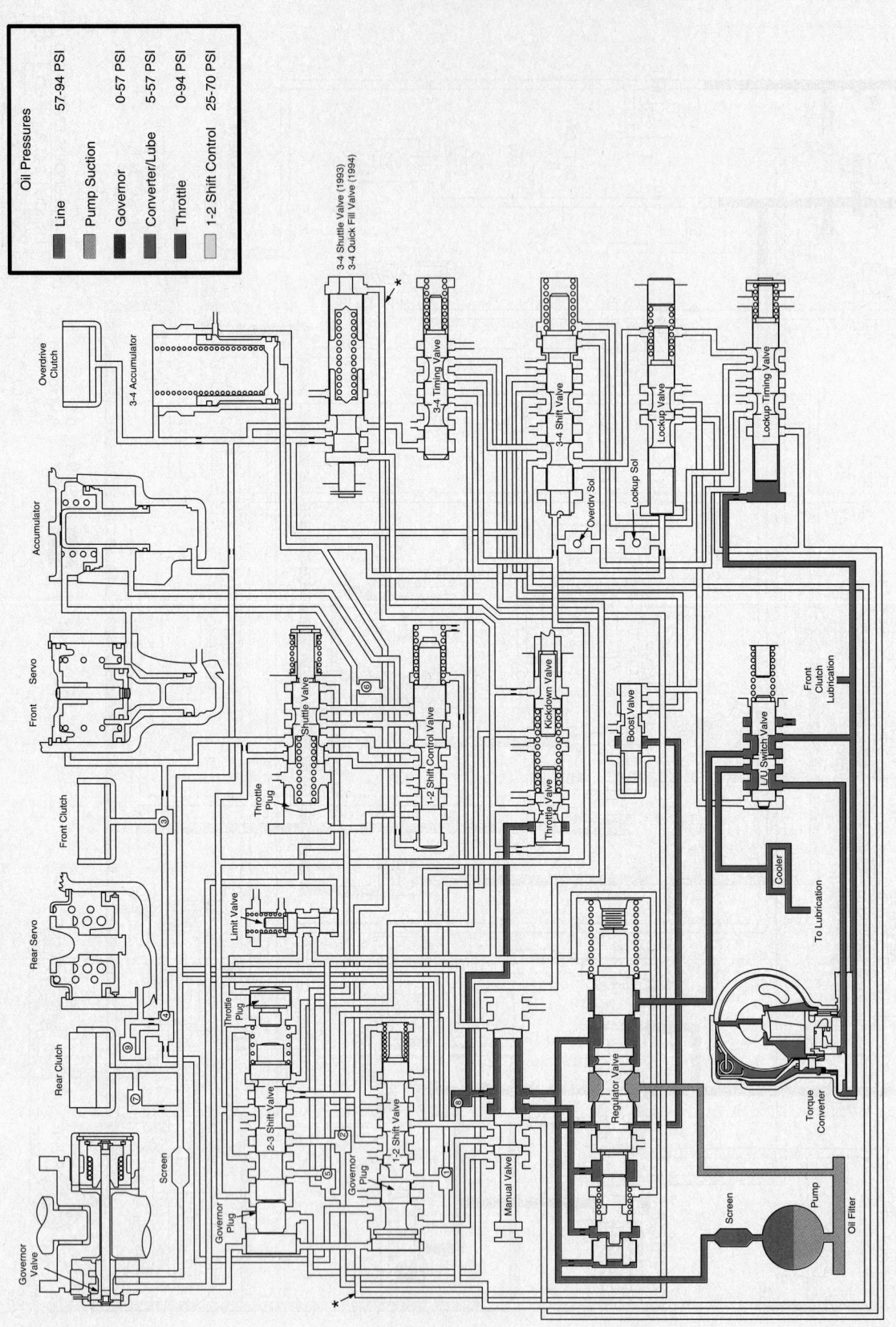

Oil Pressures

Line	57-94 PSI
Pump Suction	
Governor	0-57 PSI
Converter/Lube	5-57 PSI
Throttle	0-94 PSI
1-2 Shift Control	25-70 PSI

Note: this circuit may not be present on 1994 models

Fig. 1: "N" Range — Neutral

Courtesy of Chrysler Corp.

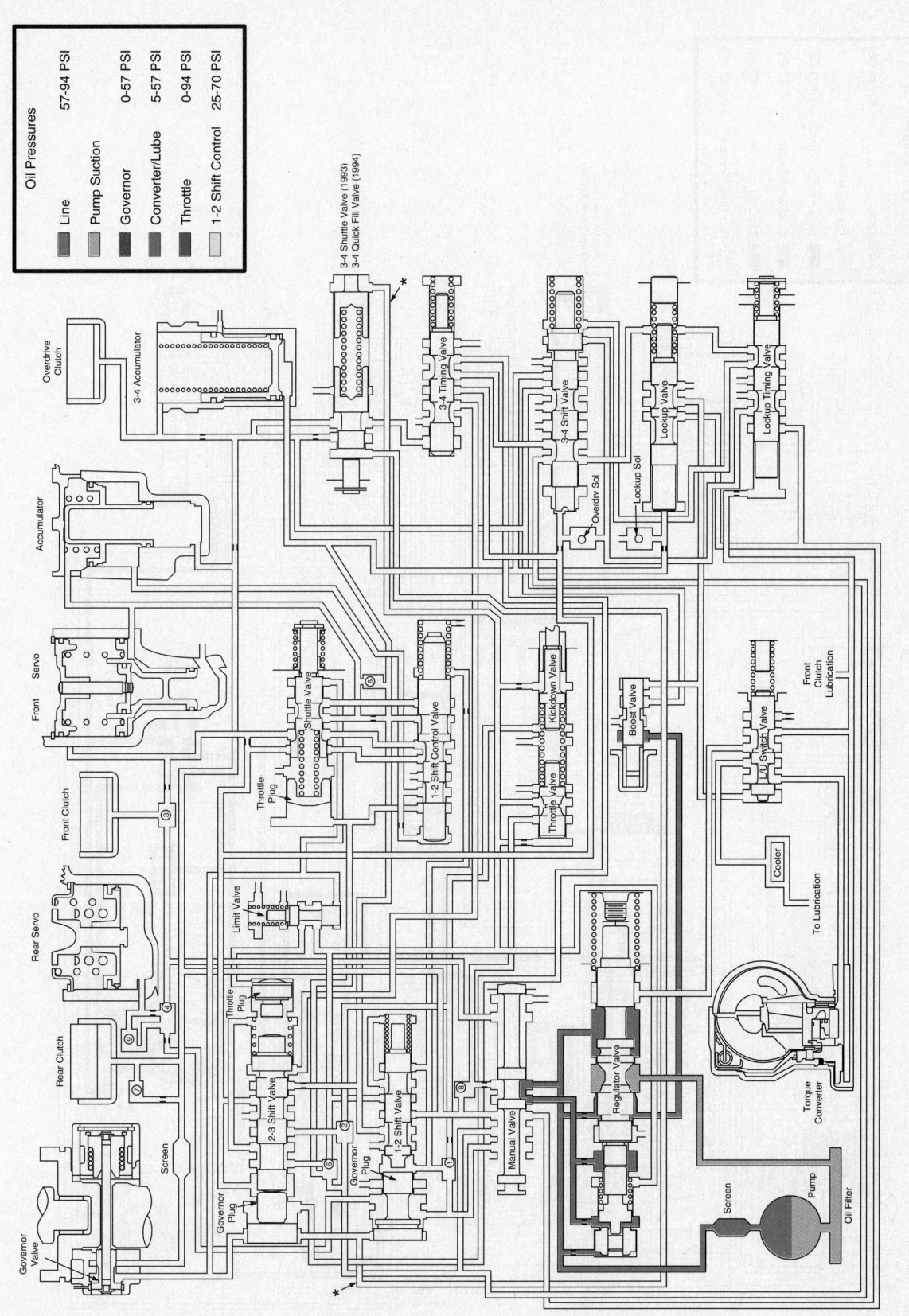

Note: this circuit may not be present on 1994 models

Fig. 2: "P" Range — Park

Courtesy of Chrysler Corp.

OIL CIRCUIT DIAGRAMS
Chrysler 42RH & 46RH (Cont.)

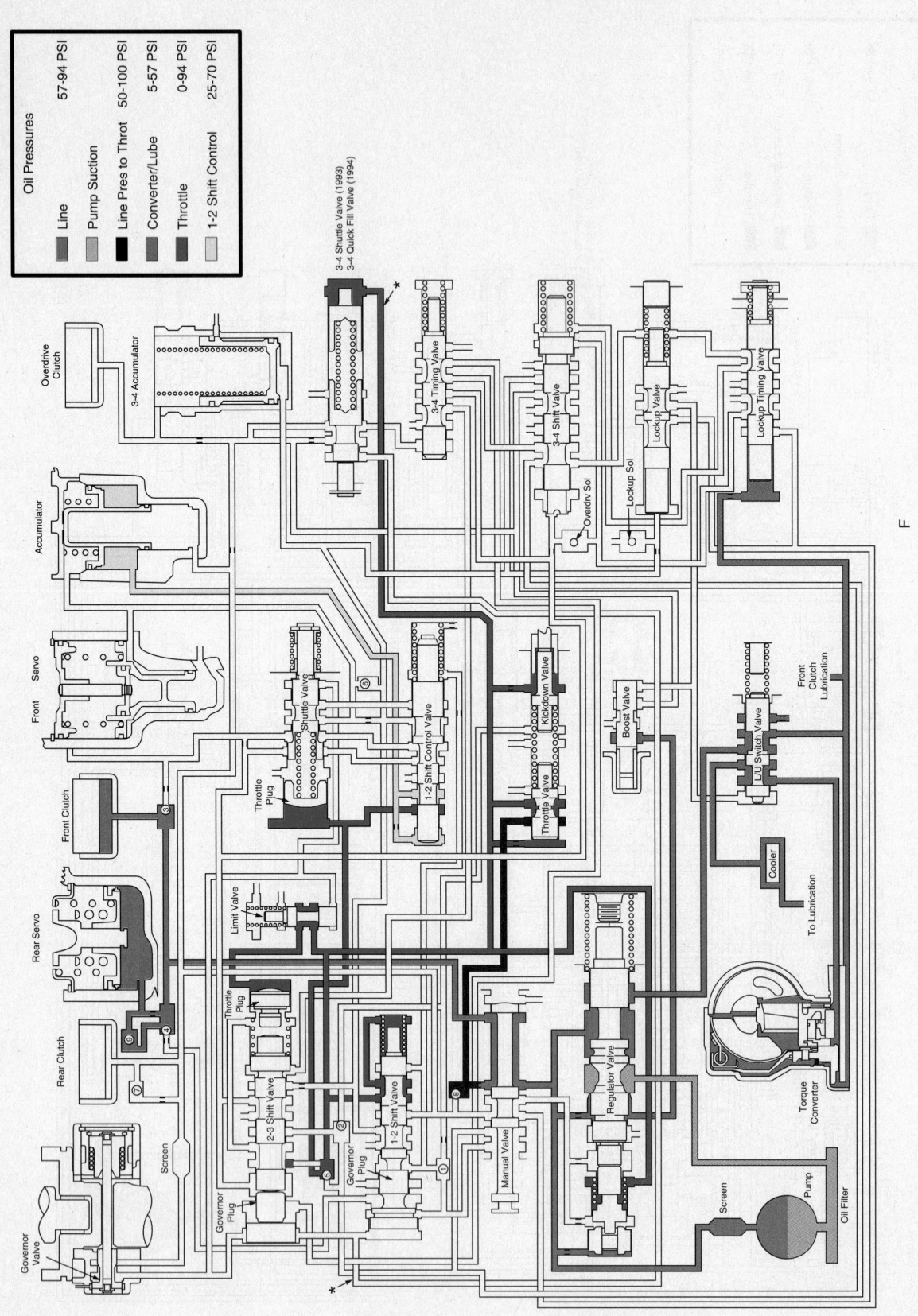

Note: this circuit may not be present on 1994 models

Fig. 3: "R" Range — Reverse

Courtesy of Chrysler Corp.

OIL CIRCUIT DIAGRAMS
Chrysler 42RH & 46RH (Cont.)

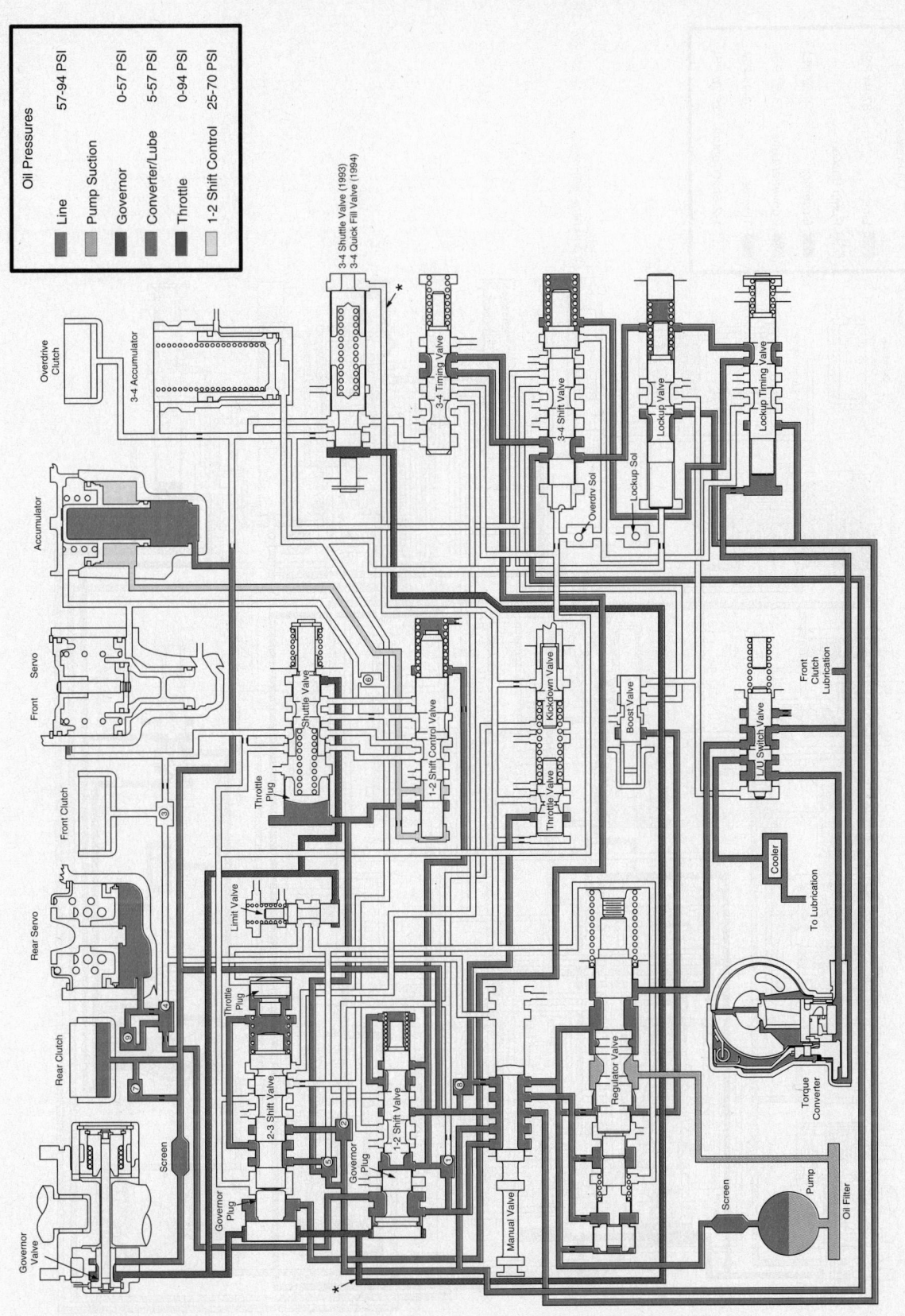

Note: this circuit may not be present on 1994 models

Fig. 4: "L" Range — Manual Select

Courtesy of Chrysler Corp.

OIL CIRCUIT DIAGRAMS
Chrysler 42RH & 46RH (Cont.)

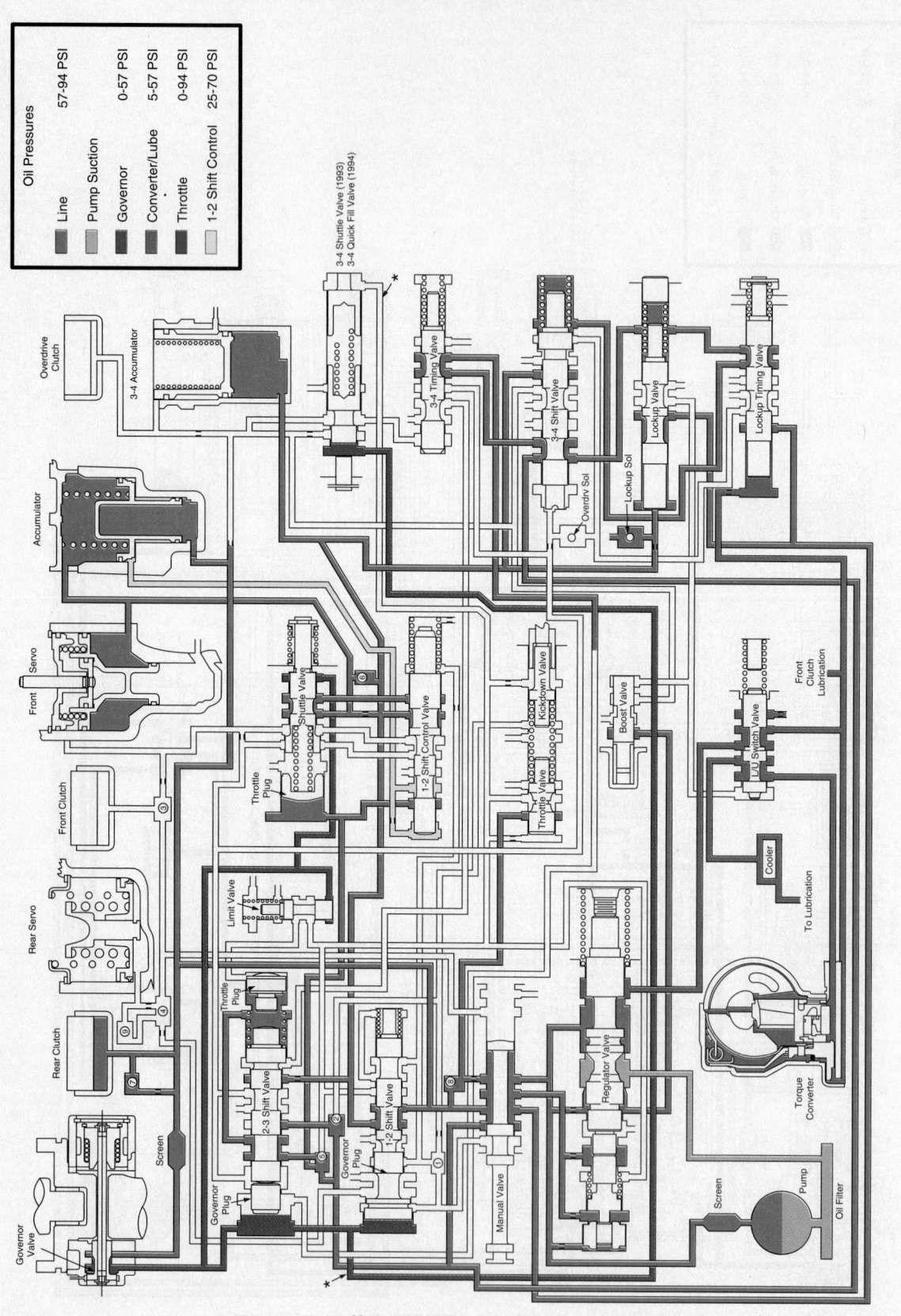

Note: this circuit may not be present on 1994 models

Fig. 5: "2" Range — Manual Select

Courtesy of Chrysler Corp.

OIL CIRCUIT DIAGRAMS
Chrysler 42RH & 46RH (Cont.)

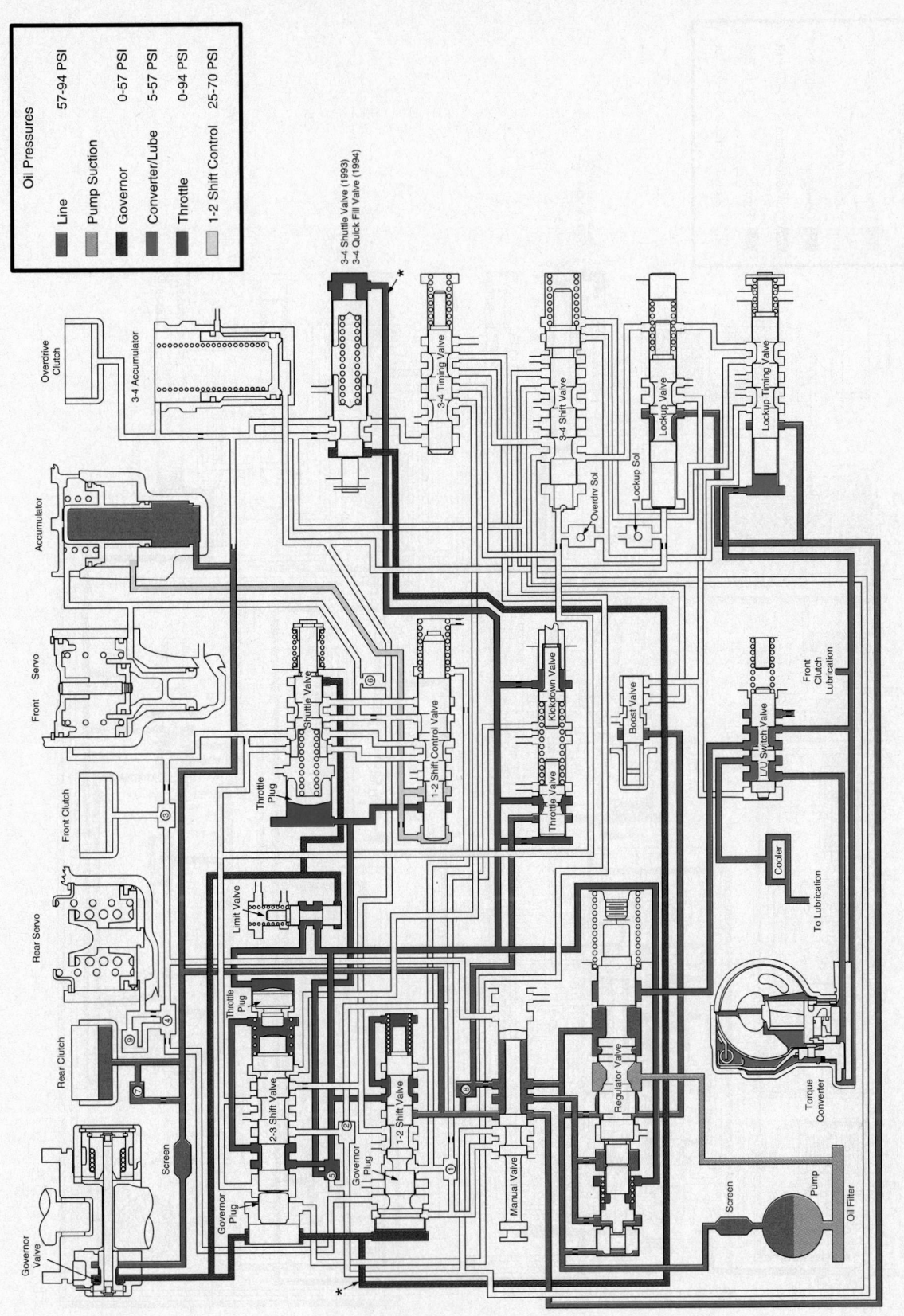

Note: this circuit may not be present on 1994 models

Fig. 6: "D" Range — 1st Gear

Courtesy of Chrysler Corp.

OIL CIRCUIT DIAGRAMS
Chrysler 42RH & 46RH (Cont.)

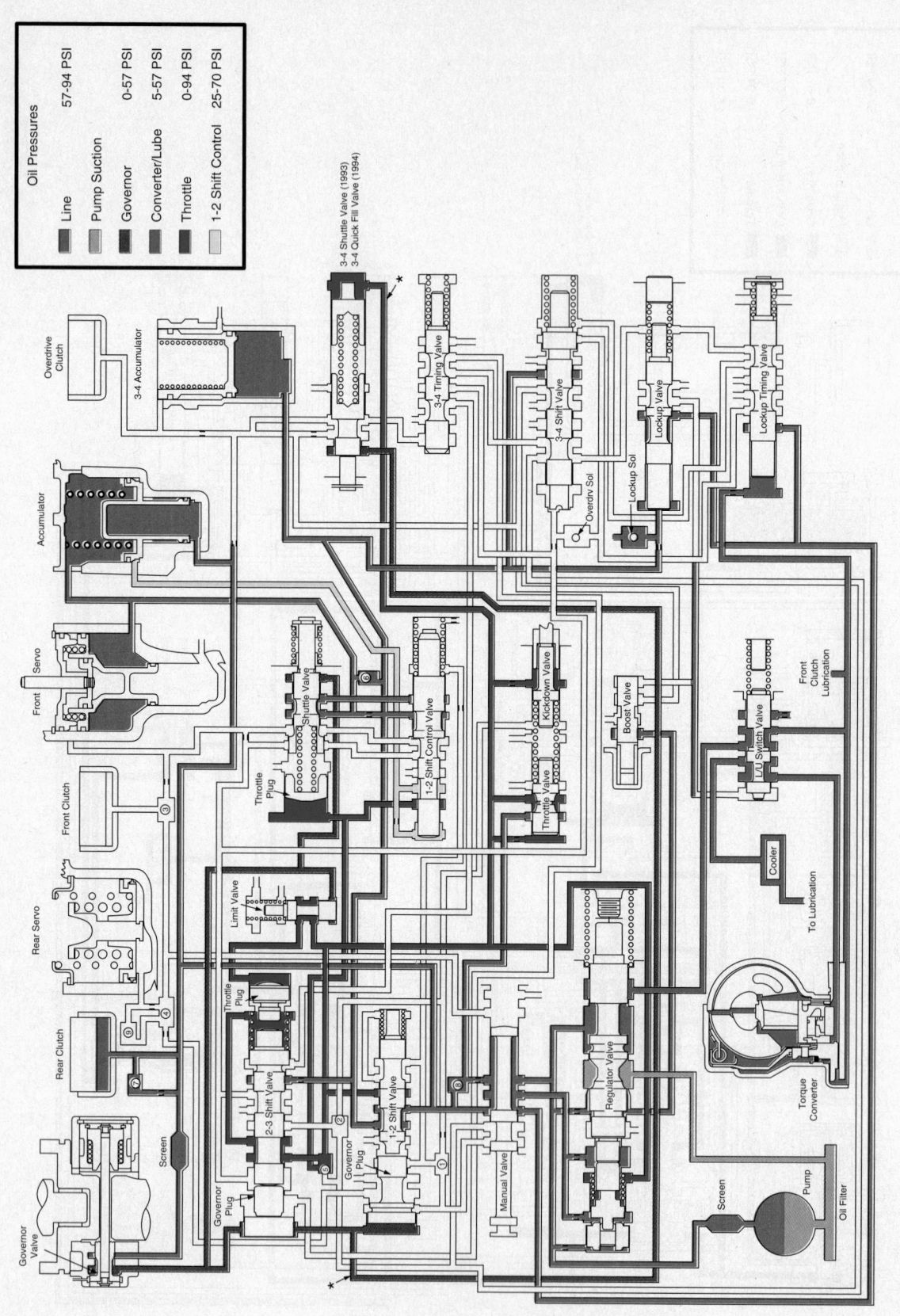

Note: this circuit may not be present on 1994 models

Fig. 7: "D" Range — 2nd Gear

Courtesy of Chrysler Corp.

OIL CIRCUIT DIAGRAMS
Chrysler 42RH & 46RH (Cont.)

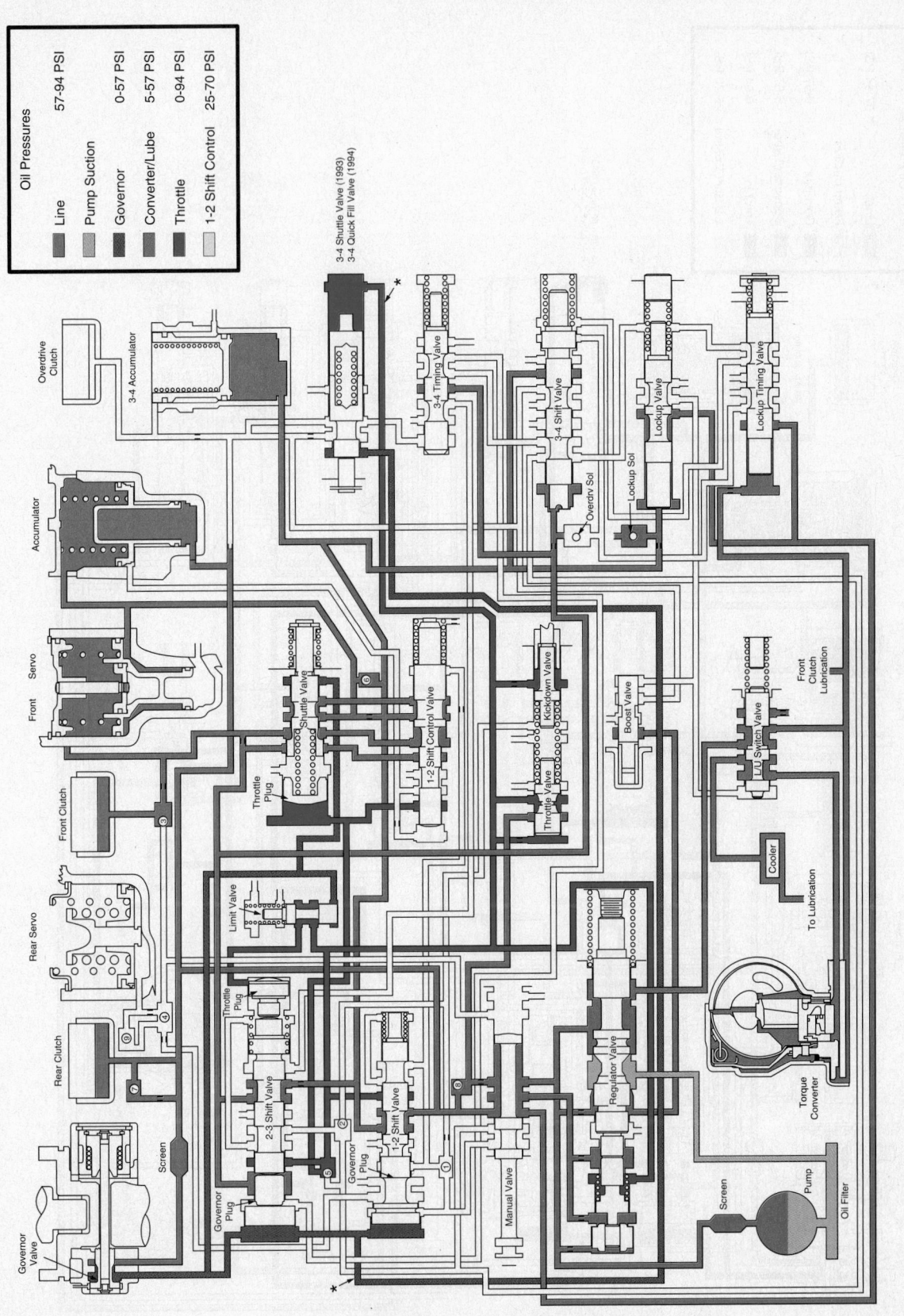

Note: this circuit may not be present on 1994 models

Fig. 8: "D" Range — 3rd Gear

Courtesy of Chrysler Corp.

OIL CIRCUIT DIAGRAMS
Chrysler 42RH & 46RH (Cont.)

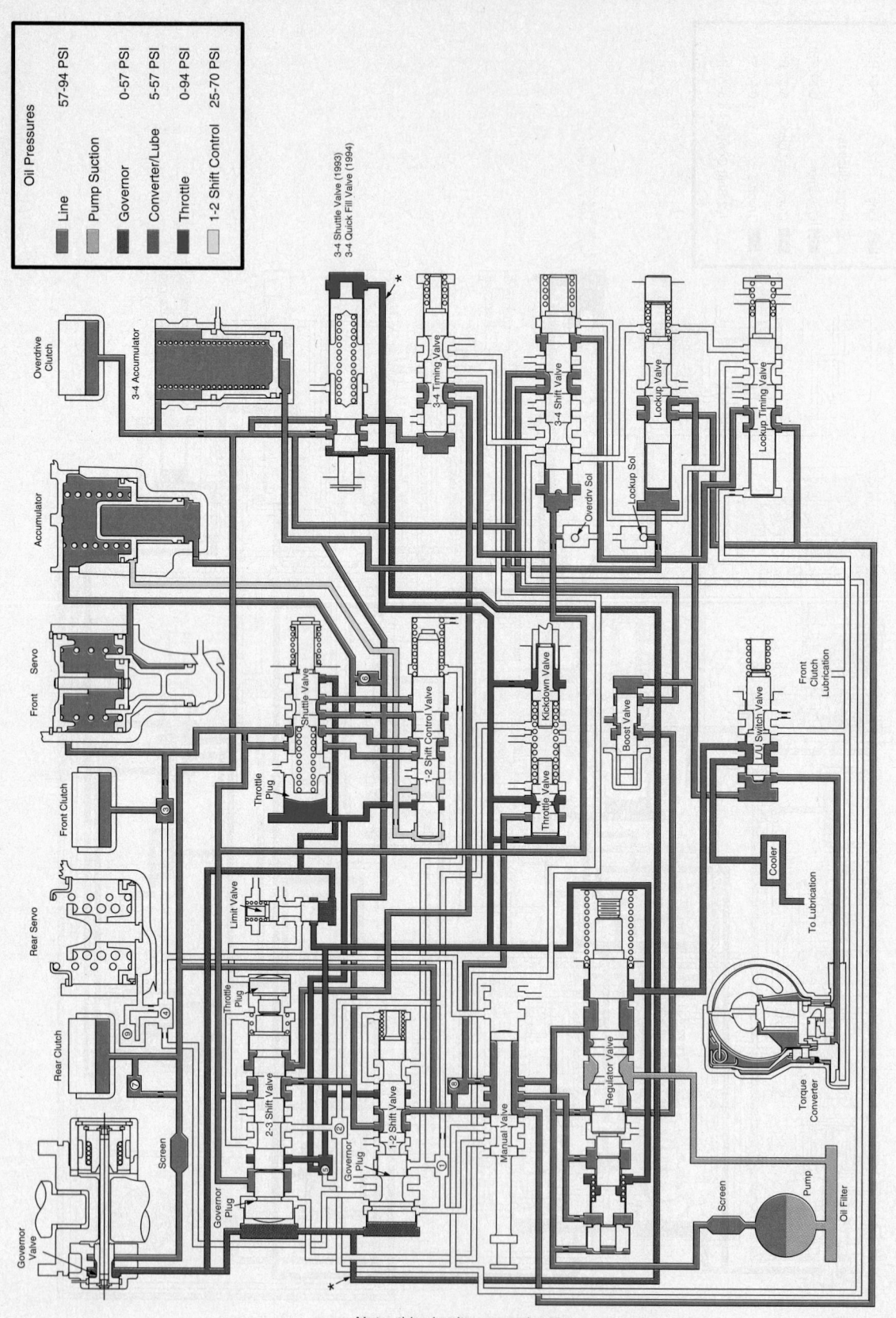

Oil Pressures

Line	57-94 PSI
Pump Suction	
Governor	0-57 PSI
Converter/Lube	5-57 PSI
Throttle	0-94 PSI
1-2 Shift Control	25-70 PSI

Note: this circuit may not be present on 1994 models

Fig. 9: "D" Range — 4th Gear Overdrive

Courtesy of Chrysler Corp.

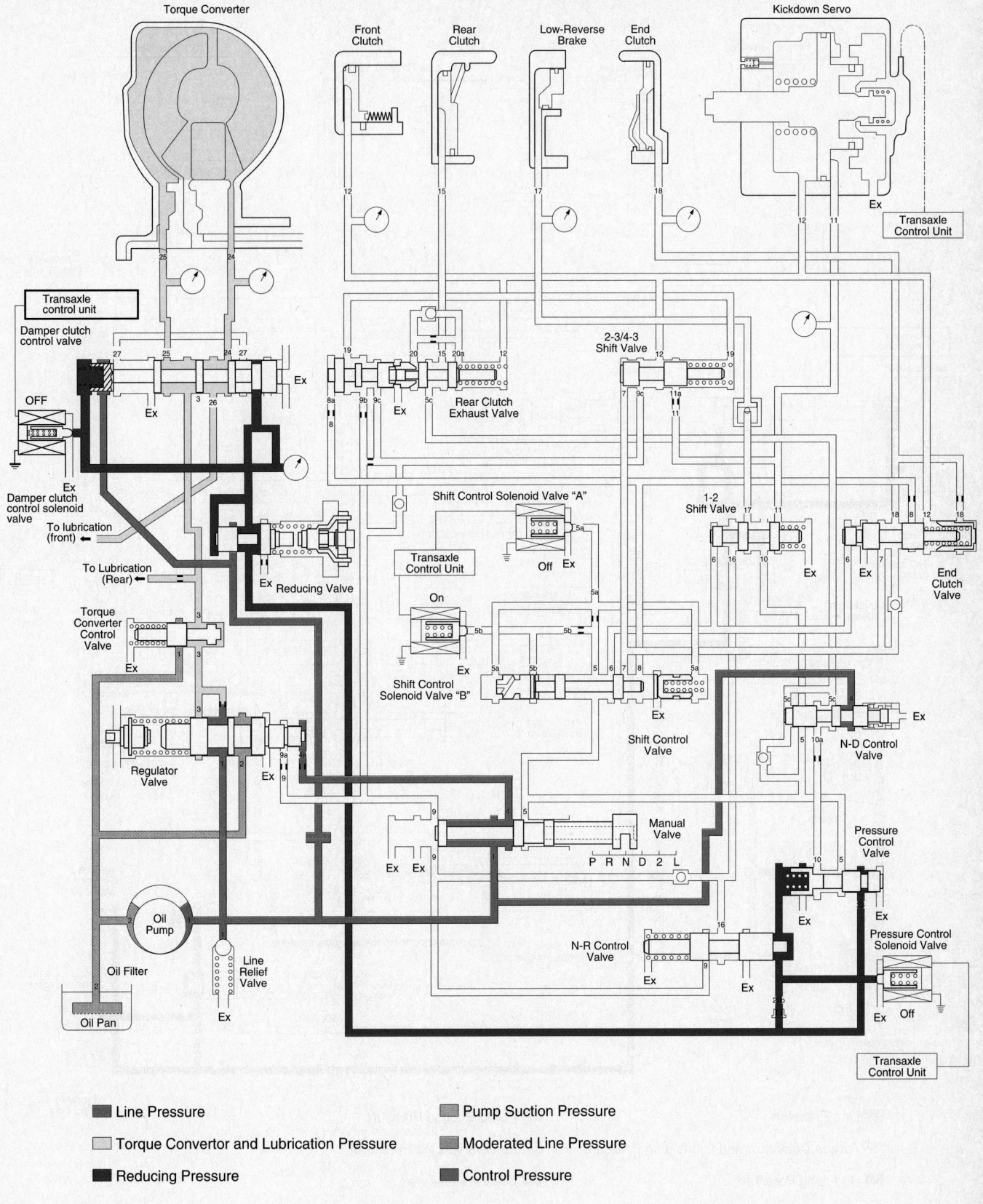

OIL CIRCUIT DIAGRAMS
Chrysler F4A21, F4A22 & F4A23 (Cont.)

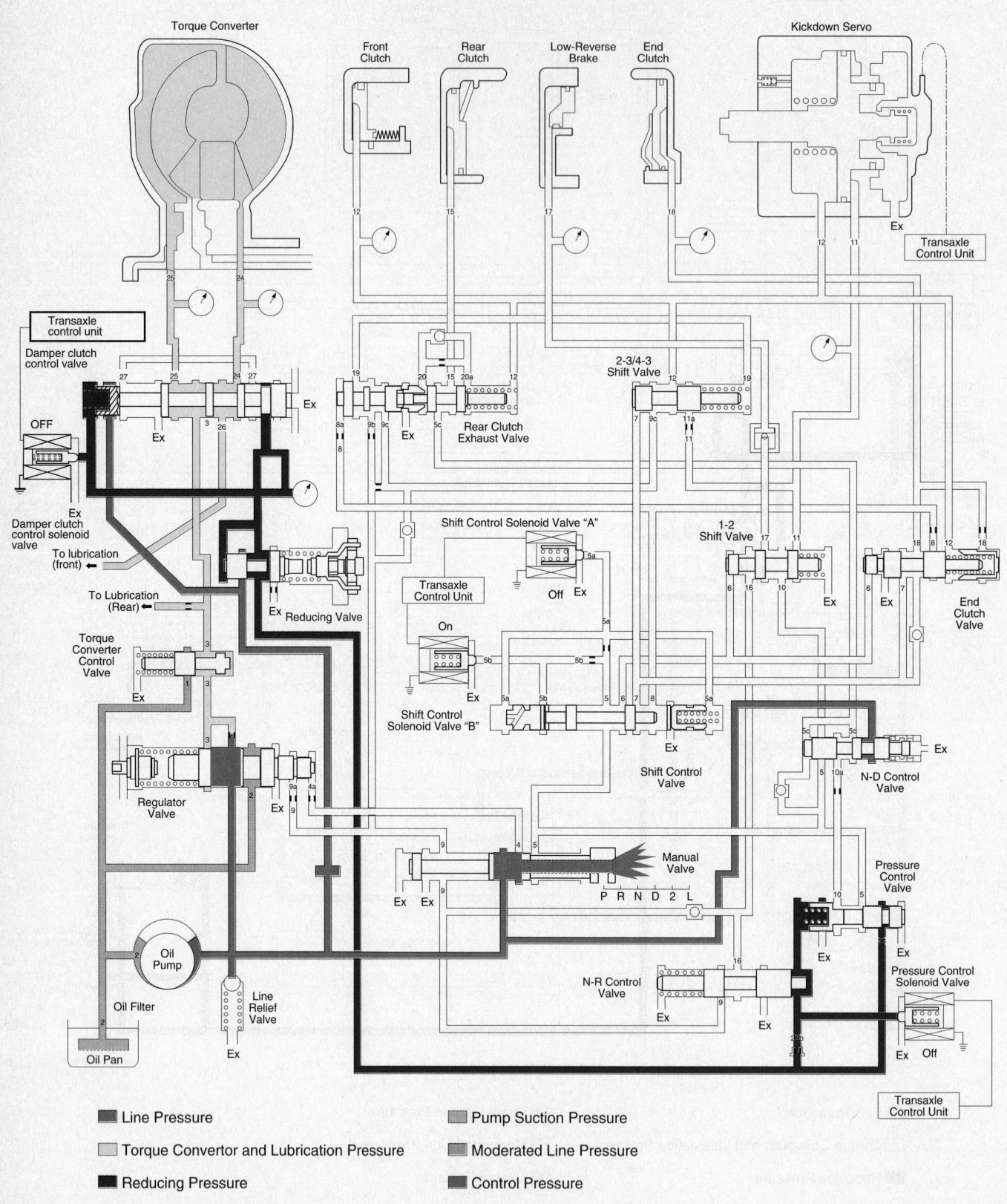

Fig. 2: "P" Range — Park

Courtesy of Chrysler Corp.

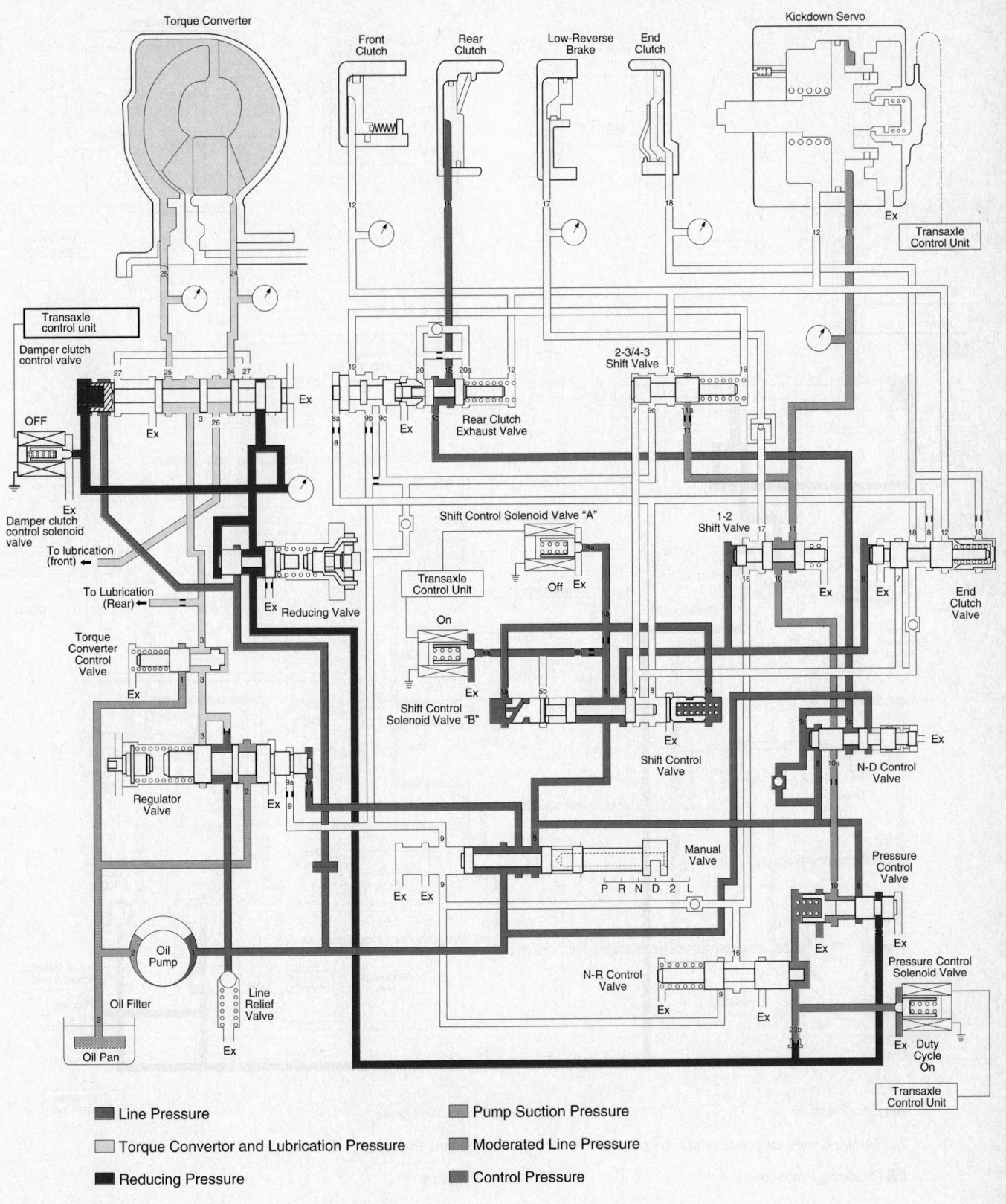

Fig. 3: "D" Range — Stopped At Idle

Courtesy of Chrysler Corp.

OIL CIRCUIT DIAGRAMS
Chrysler F4A21, F4A22 & F4A23 (Cont.)

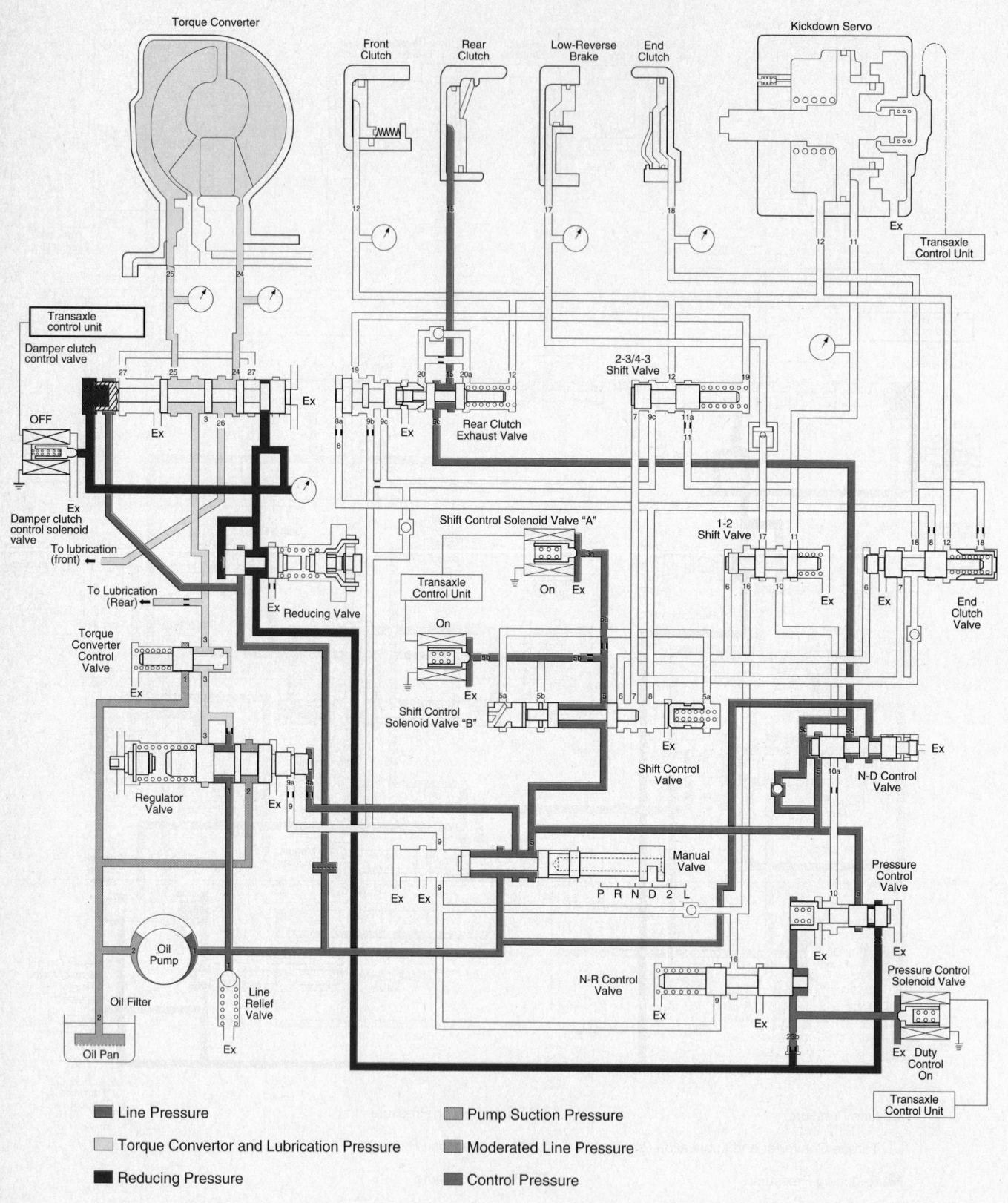

Fig. 4: "D" Range — 1st Gear

Courtesy of Chrysler Corp.

OIL CIRCUIT DIAGRAMS
Chrysler F4A21, F4A22 & F4A23 (Cont.)

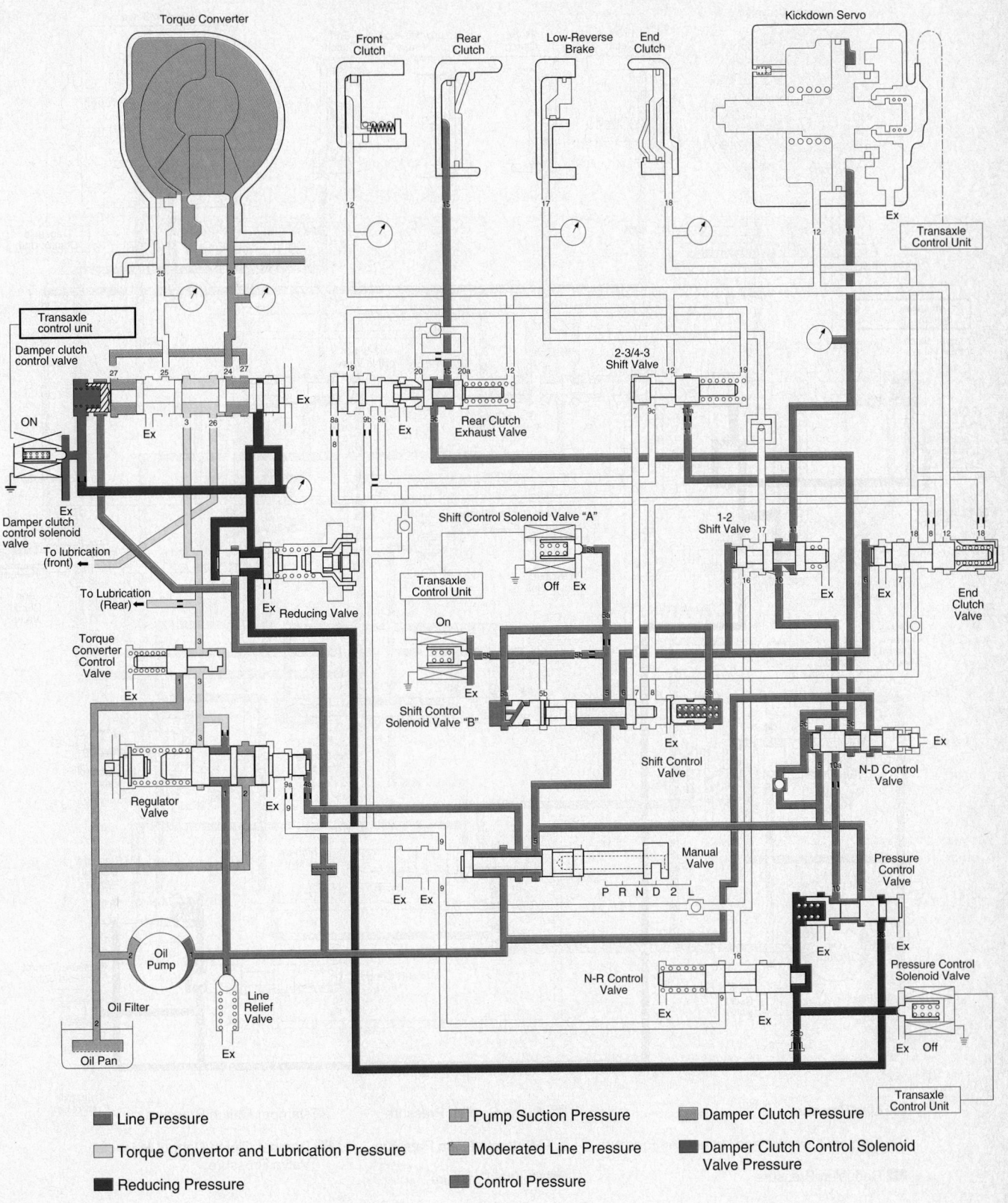

Line Pressure

Torque Convertor and Lubrication Pressure

Reducing Pressure

Pump Suction Pressure

Moderated Line Pressure

Control Pressure

Damper Clutch Pressure

Damper Clutch Control Solenoid Valve Pressure

Fig. 5: "D" Range — 2nd Gear

Courtesy of Chrysler Corp.

OIL CIRCUIT DIAGRAMS
Chrysler F4A21, F4A22 & F4A23 (Cont.)

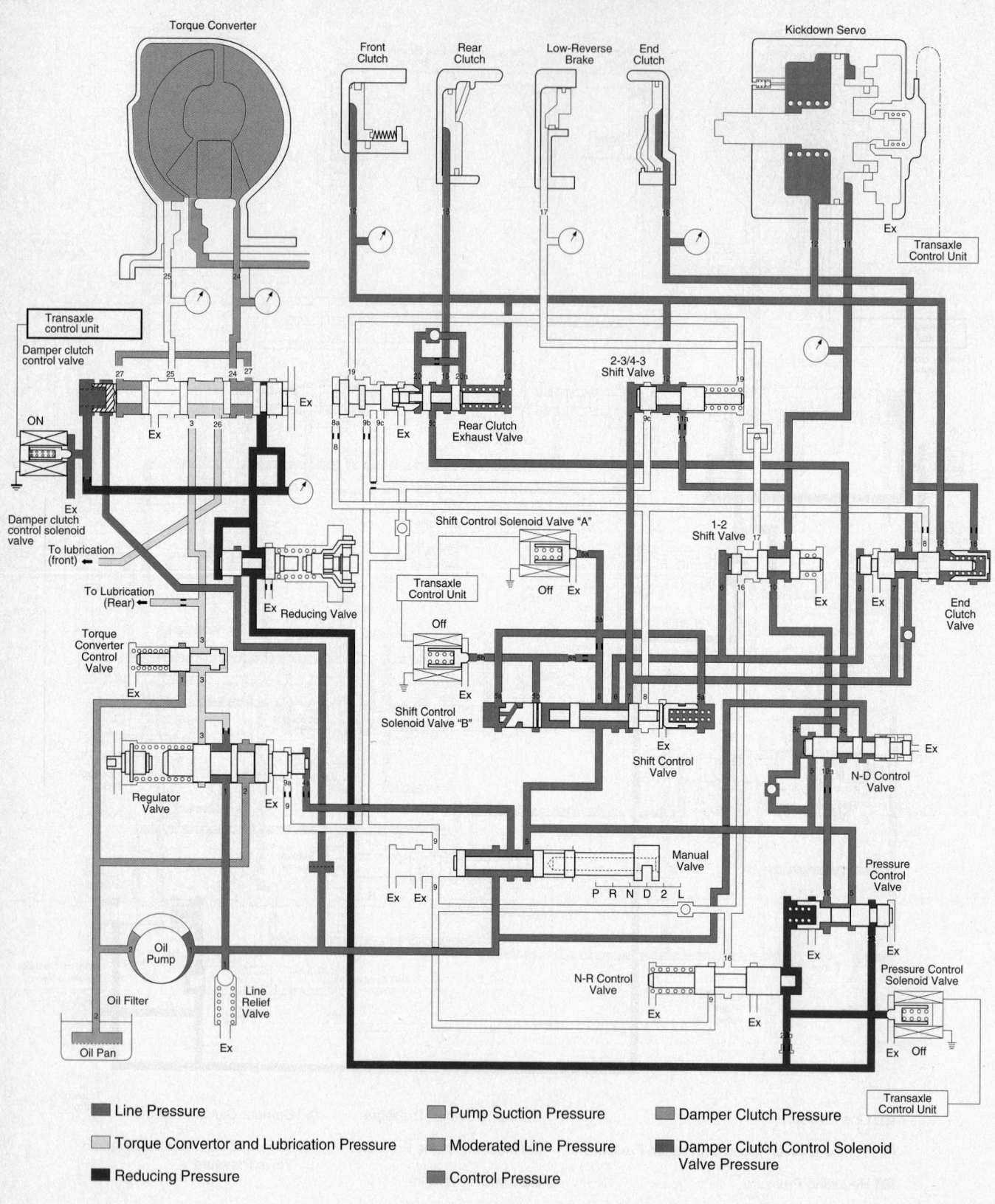

Fig. 6: "D" Range — 3rd Gear

Courtesy of Chrysler Corp.

OIL CIRCUIT DIAGRAMS
Chrysler F4A21, F4A22 & F4A23 (Cont.)

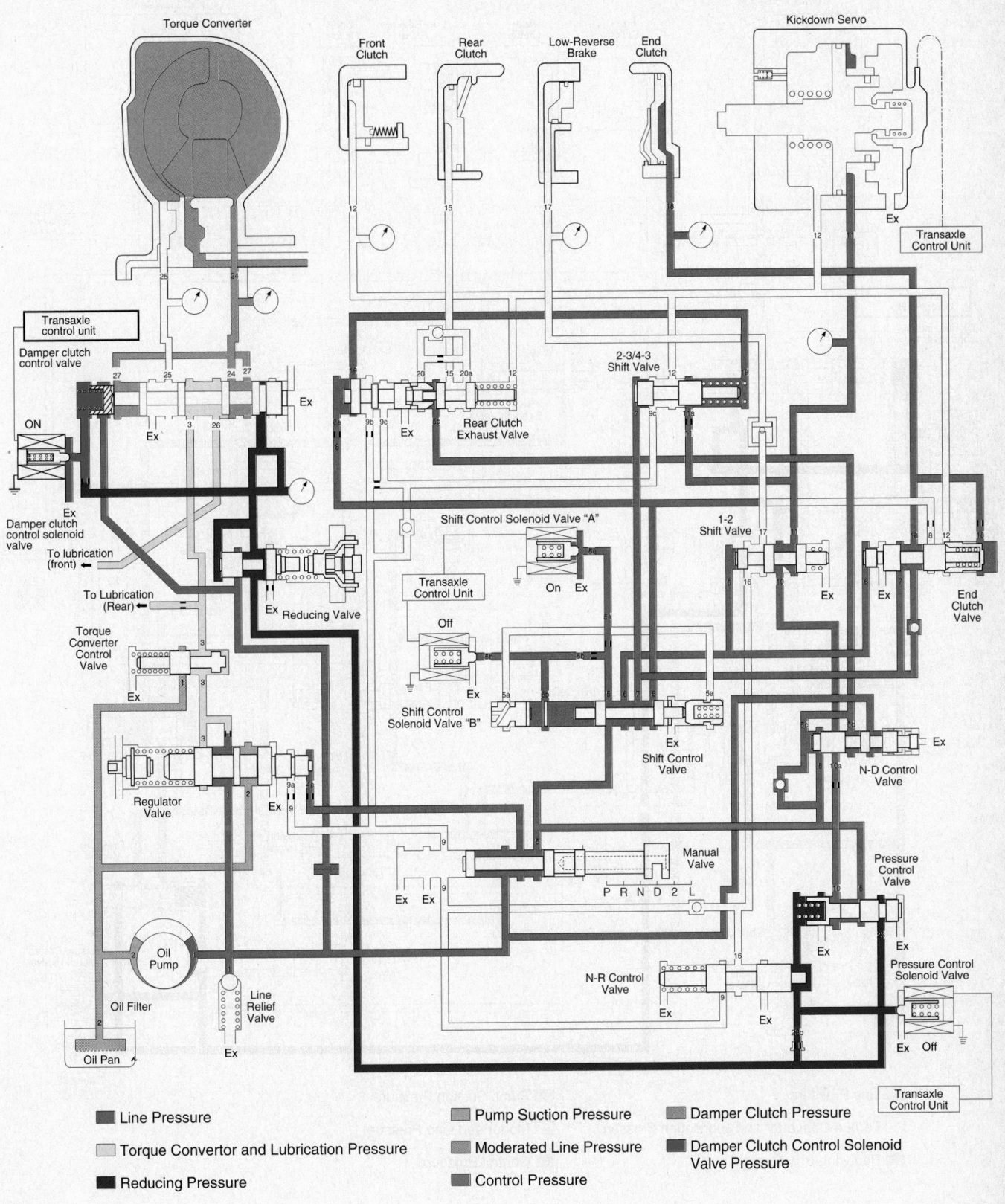

Fig. 7: "D" Range — 4th Gear

Courtesy of Chrysler Corp.

OIL CIRCUIT DIAGRAMS
Chrysler F4A21, F4A22 & F4A23 (Cont.)

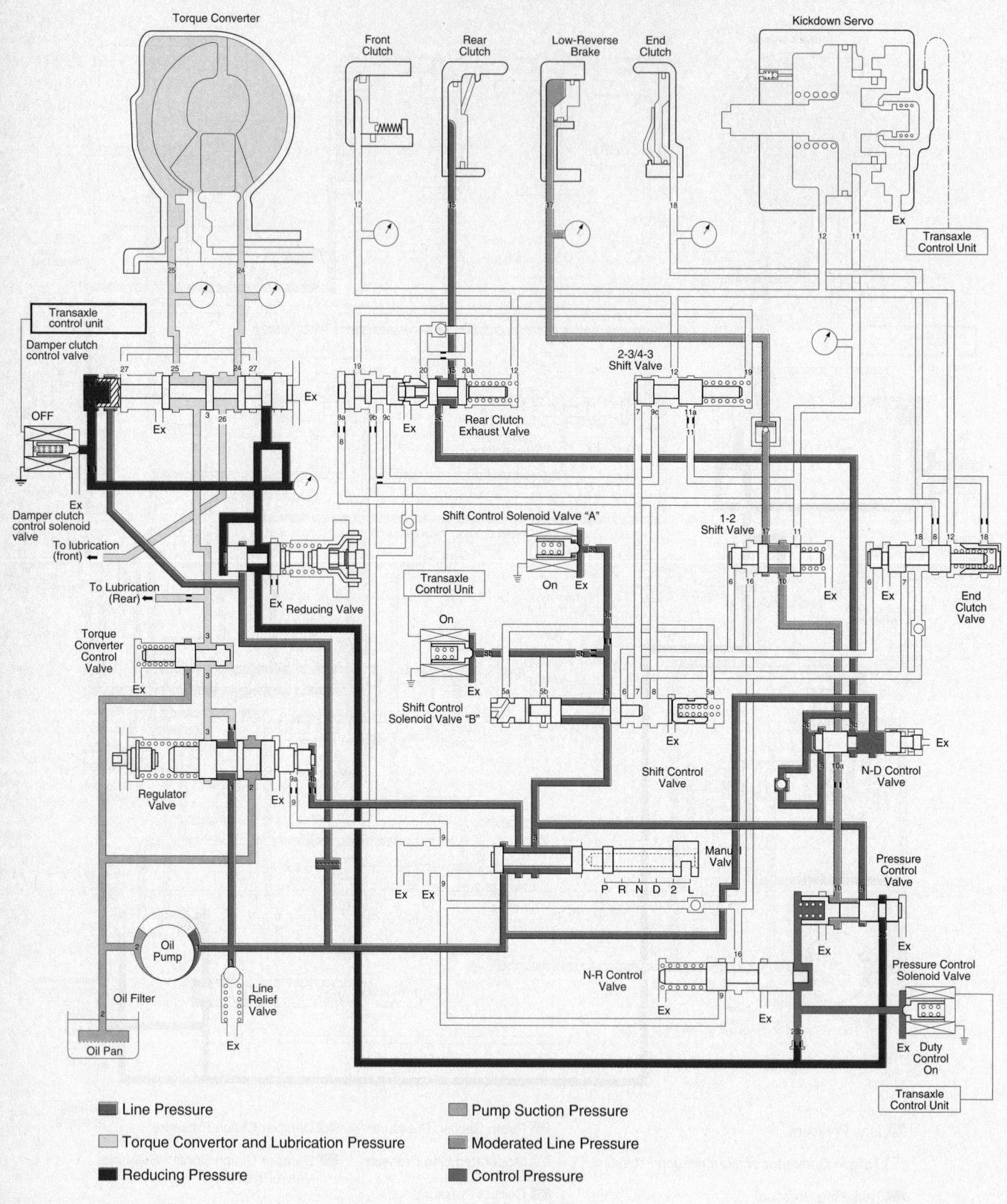

Fig. 8: "L" Range — 1st Gear

Courtesy of Chrysler Corp.

OIL CIRCUIT DIAGRAMS
Chrysler F4A21, F4A22 & F4A23 (Cont.)

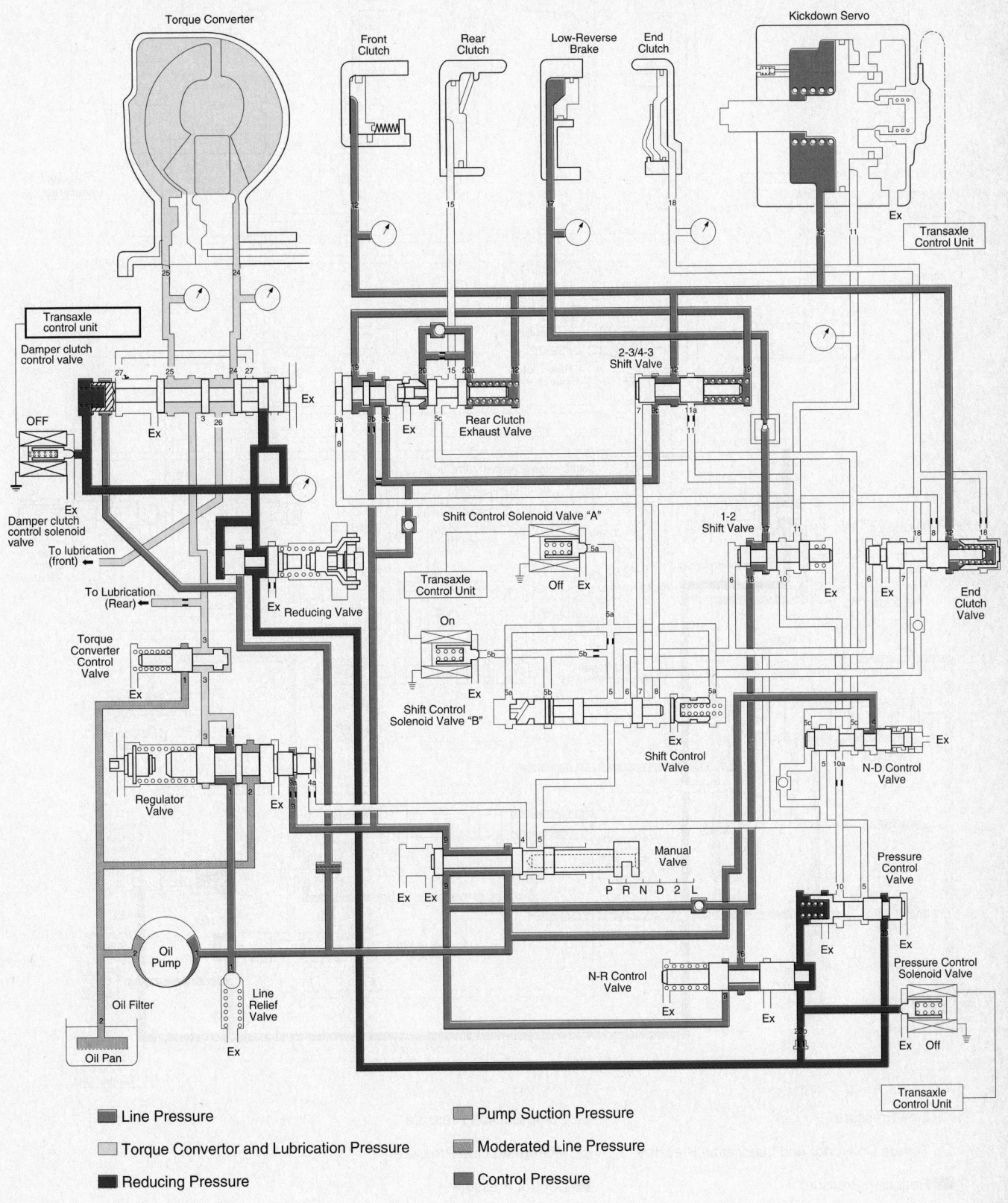

Fig. 9: "R" Range — Reverse

Courtesy of Chrysler Corp.

OIL CIRCUIT DIAGRAMS
Chrysler F4A33, W4A32 & W4A33

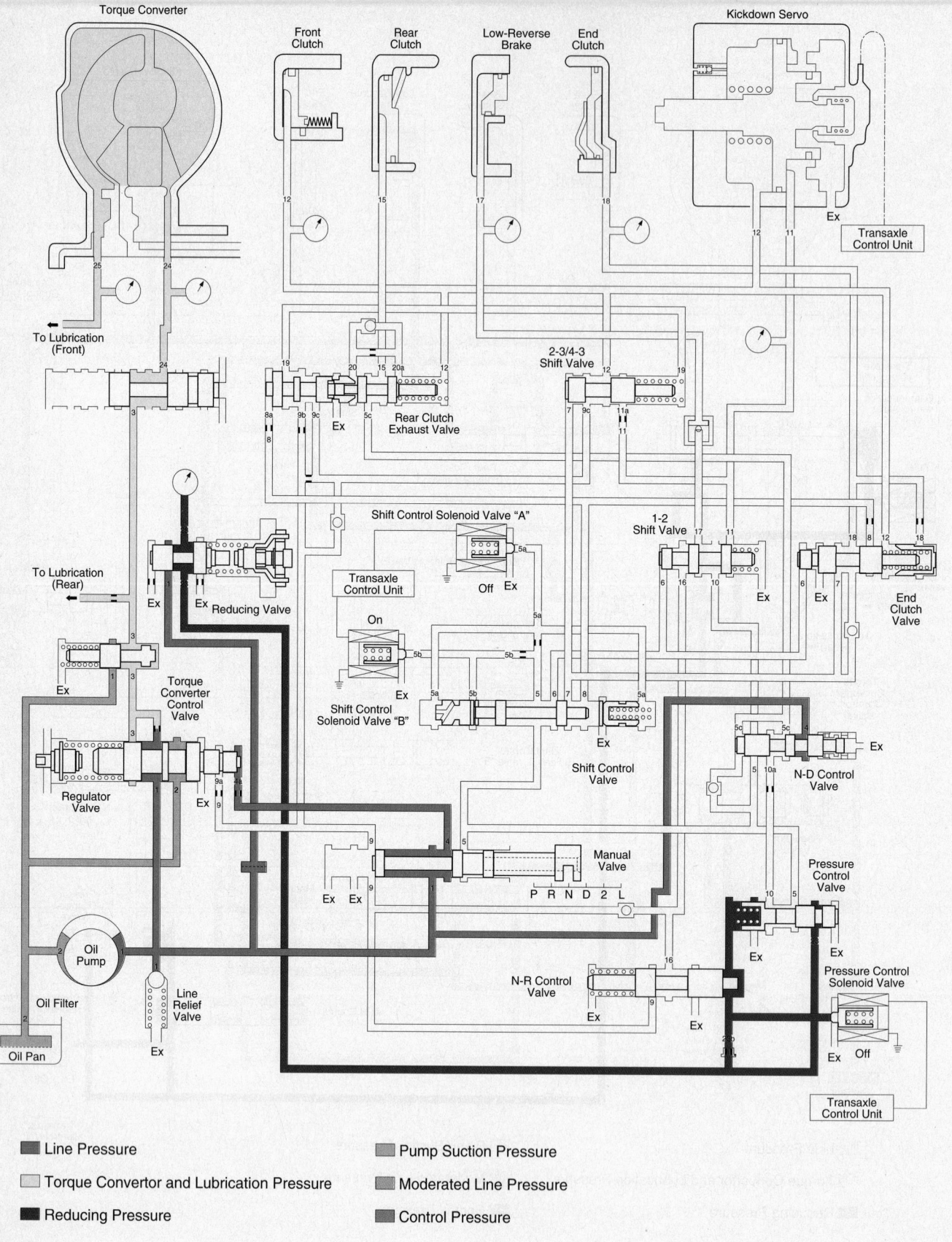

Fig. 1: "N" Range — Neutral

Courtesy of Chrysler Corp.

OIL CIRCUIT DIAGRAMS
Chrysler F4A33, W4A32 & W4A33 (Cont.)

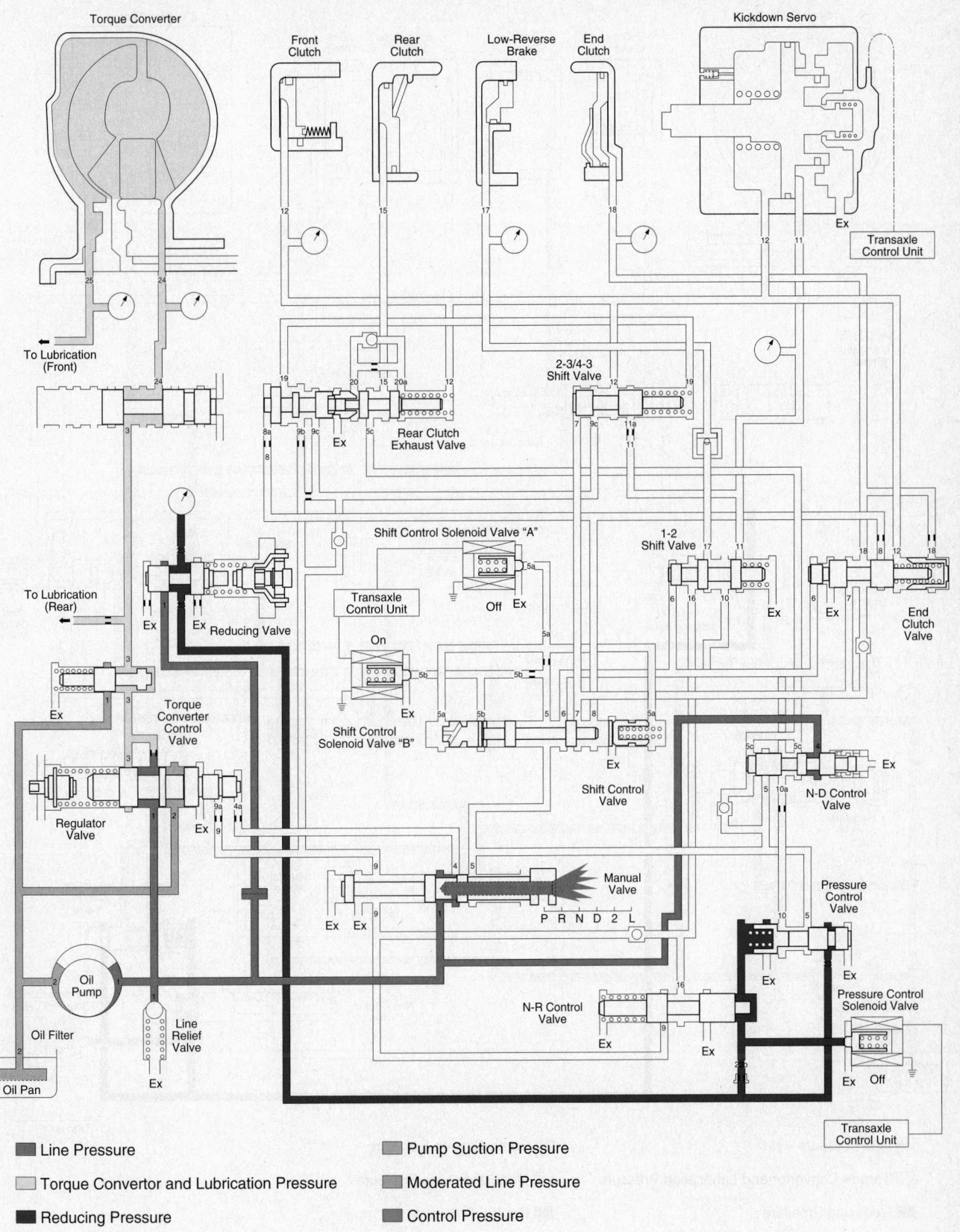

Fig. 2: "P" Range — Park

Courtesy of Chrysler Corp.

OIL CIRCUIT DIAGRAMS
Chrysler F4A33, W4A32 & W4A33 (Cont.)

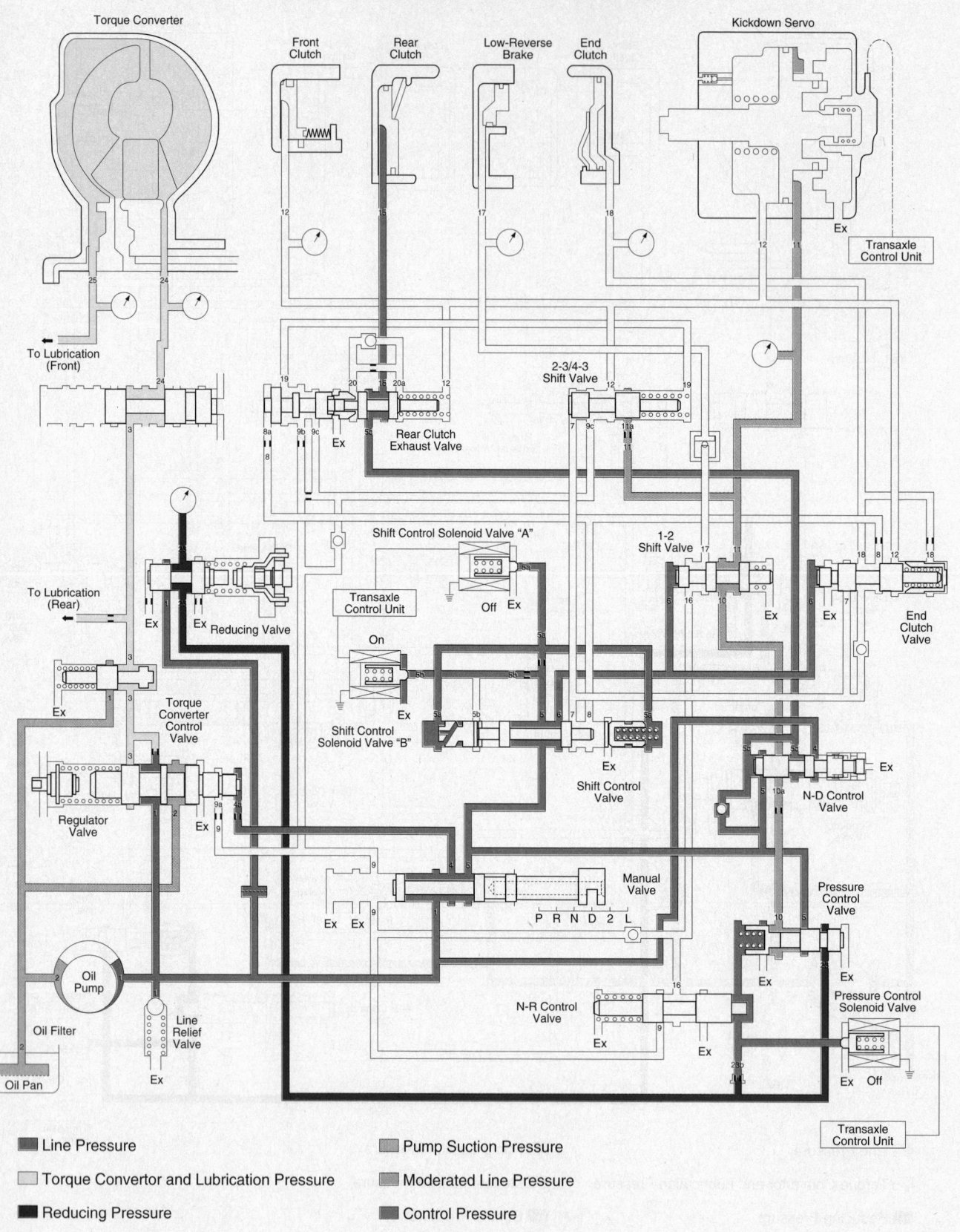

Fig. 3: "D" Range — Stopped At Idle

Courtesy of Chrysler Corp.

OIL CIRCUIT DIAGRAMS
Chrysler F4A33, W4A32 & W4A33 (Cont.)

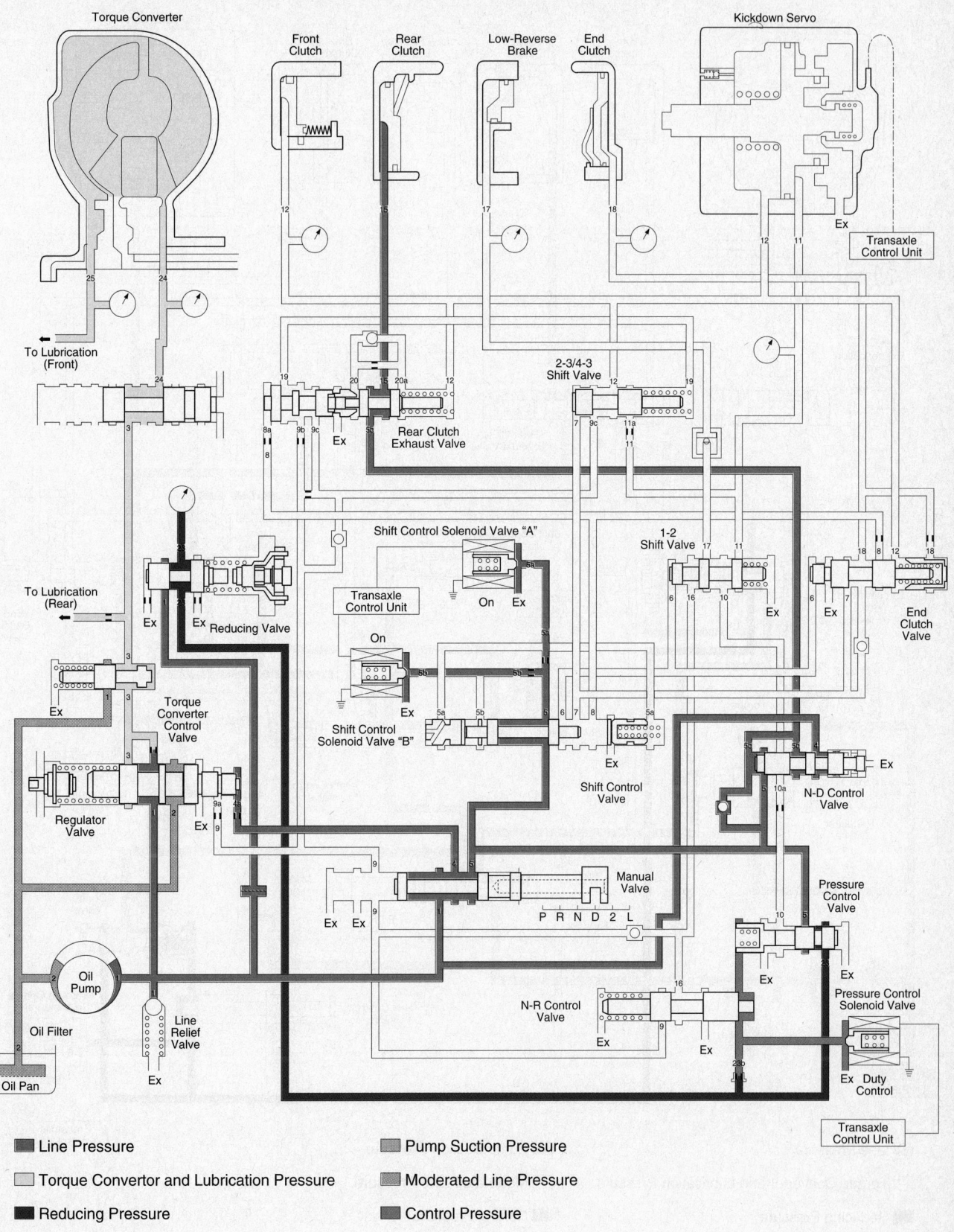

Line Pressure

Torque Convertor and Lubrication Pressure

Reducing Pressure

Pump Suction Pressure

Moderated Line Pressure

Control Pressure

Fig. 4: "D" Range — 1st Gear   Courtesy of Chrysler Corp.

OIL CIRCUIT DIAGRAMS
Chrysler F4A33, W4A32 & W4A33 (Cont.)

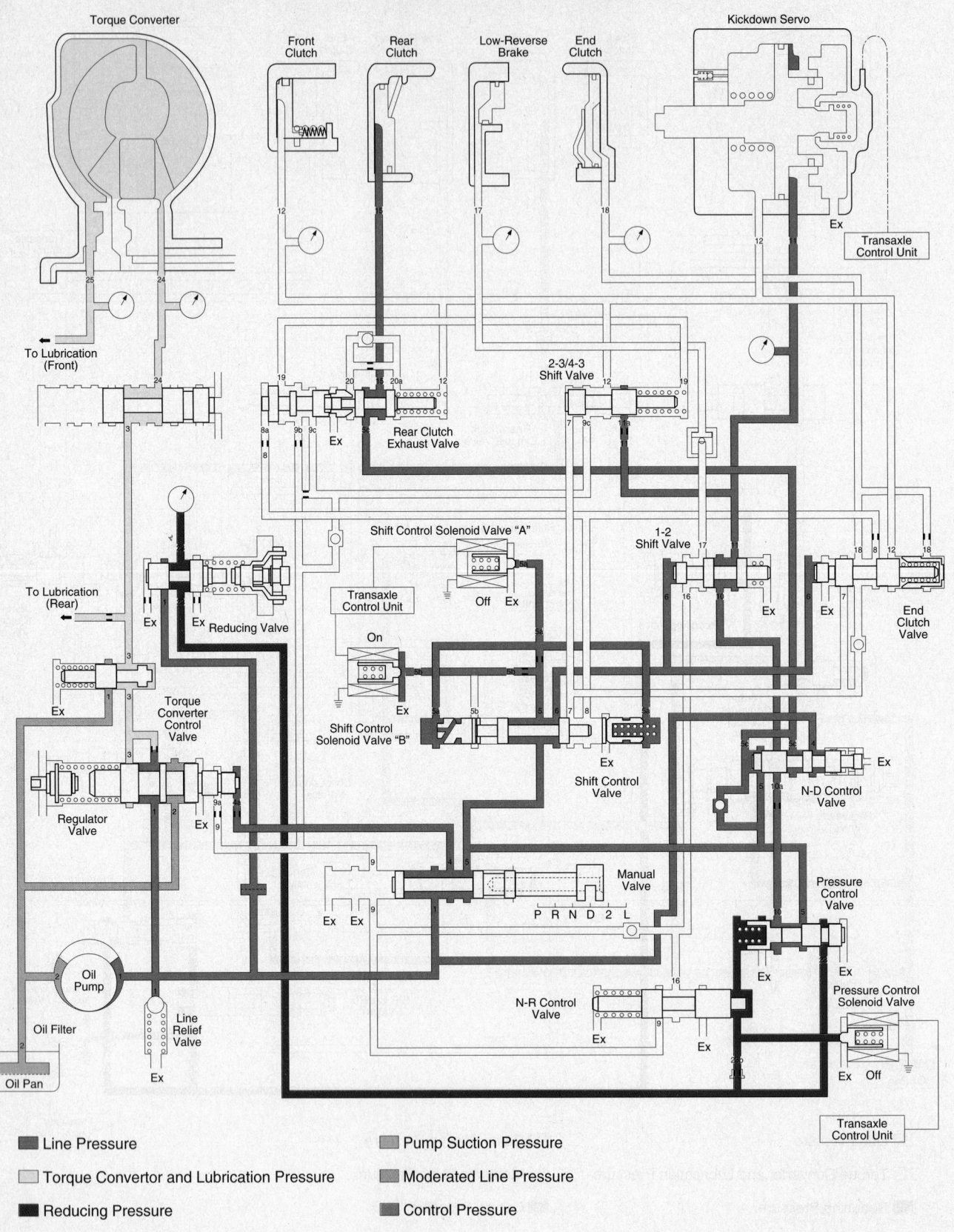

Fig. 5: "D" Range — 2nd Gear

Courtesy of Chrysler Corp.

OIL CIRCUIT DIAGRAMS
Chrysler F4A33, W4A32 & W4A33 (Cont.)

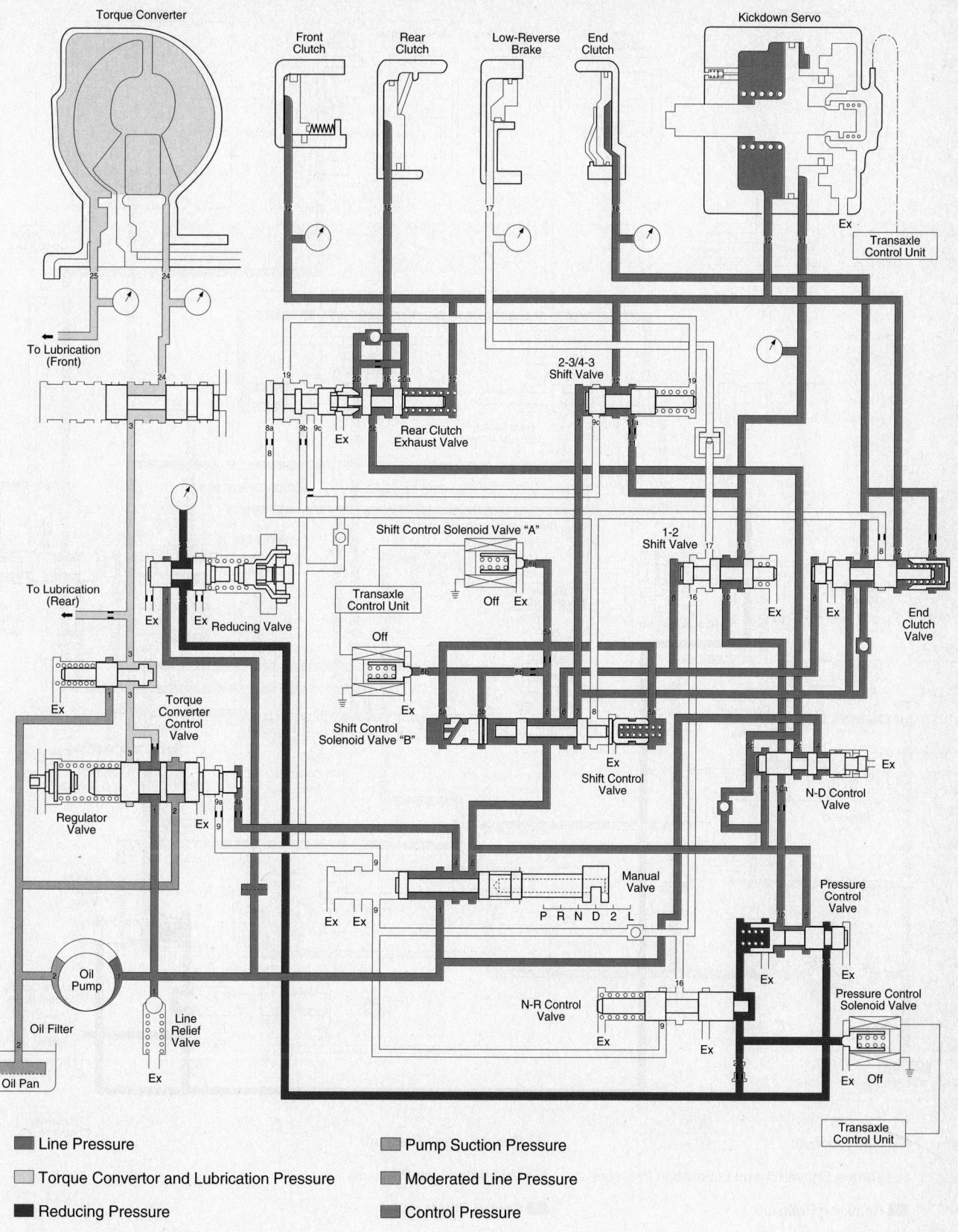

Line Pressure

Torque Convertor and Lubrication Pressure

Reducing Pressure

Pump Suction Pressure

Moderated Line Pressure

Control Pressure

Fig. 6: "D" Range — 3rd Gear   Courtesy of Chrysler Corp.

OIL CIRCUIT DIAGRAMS
Chrysler F4A33, W4A32 & W4A33 (Cont.)

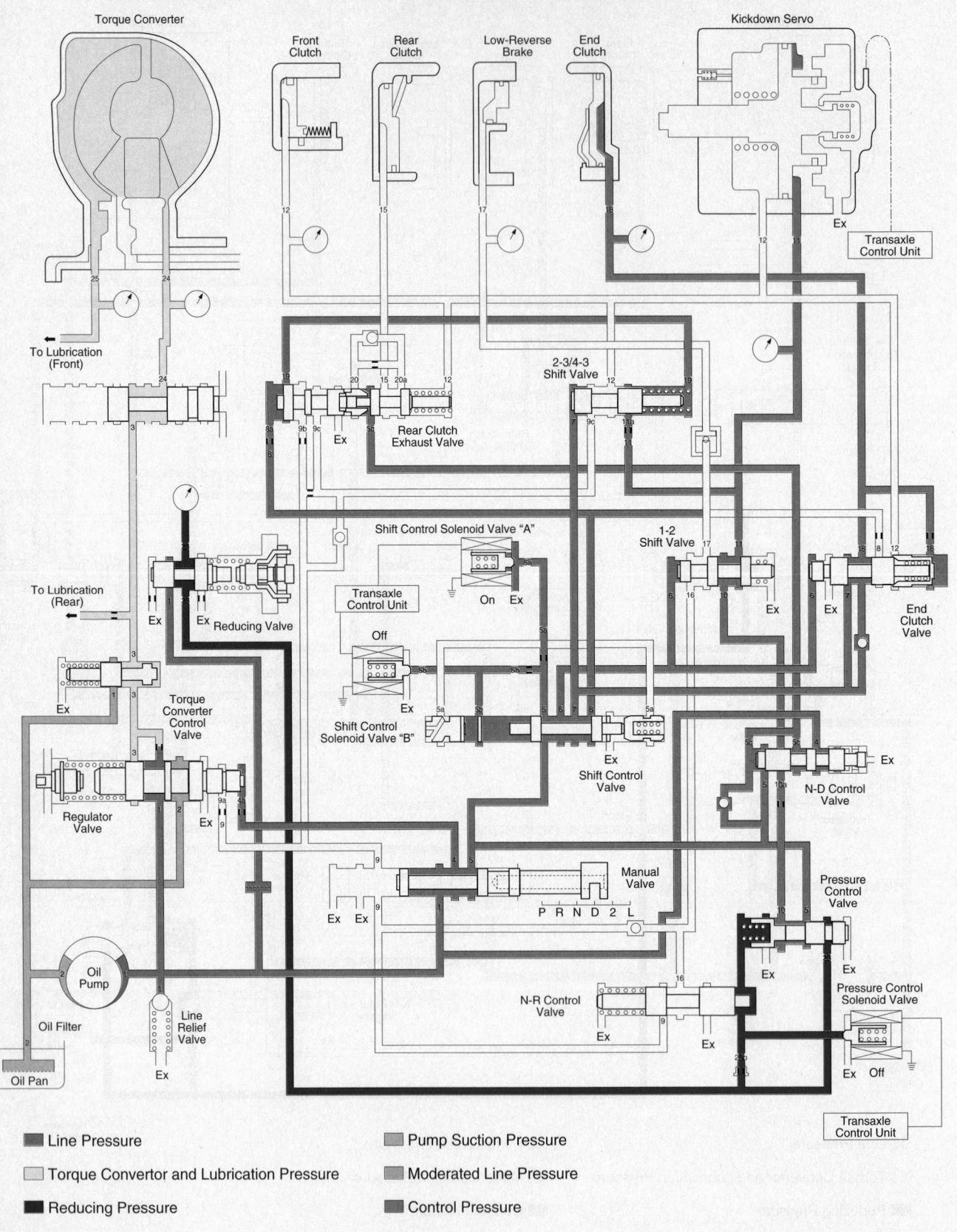

Fig. 7: "D" Range — 4th Gear

Courtesy of Chrysler Corp.

OIL CIRCUIT DIAGRAMS
Chrysler F4A33, W4A32 & W4A33 (Cont.)

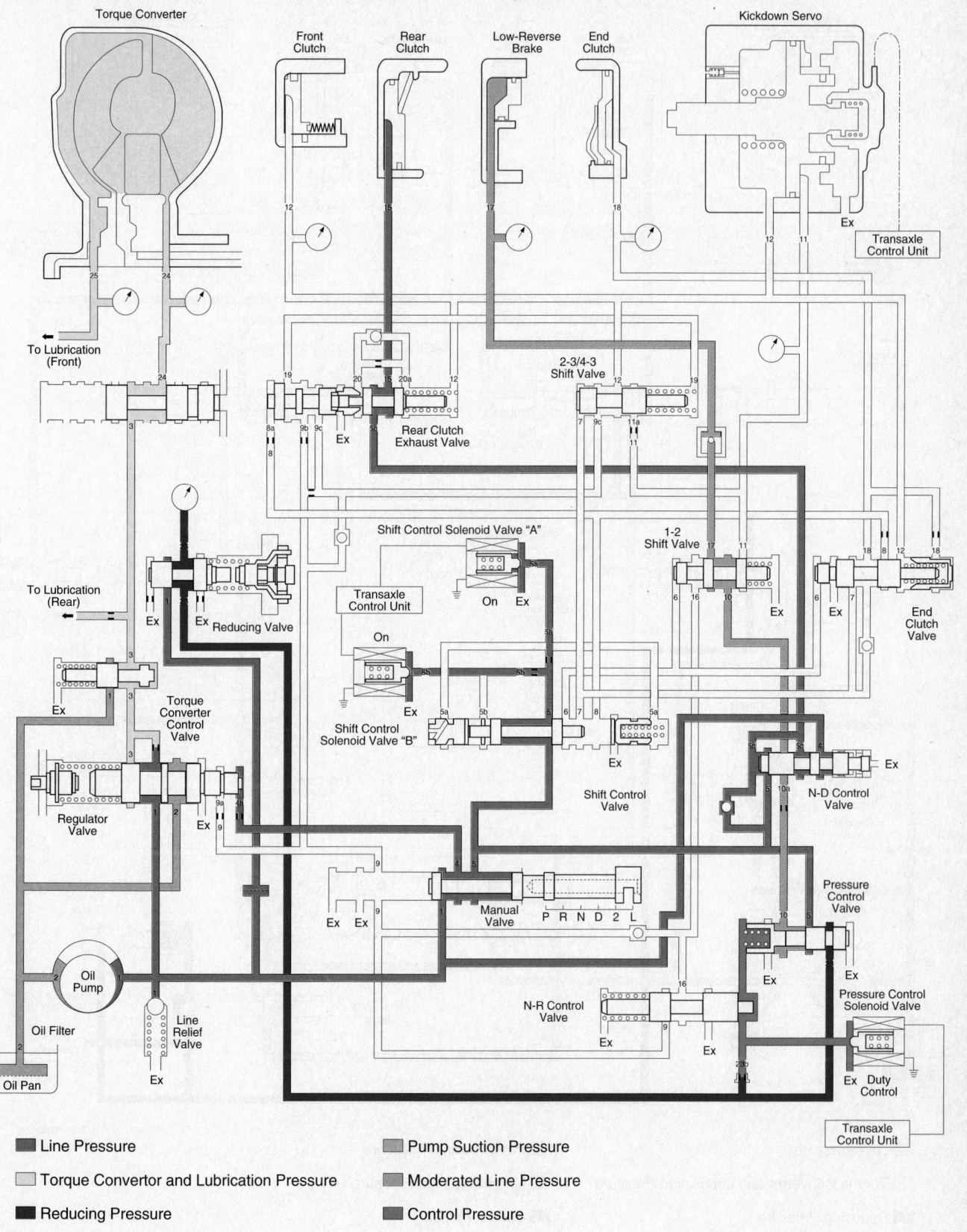

Fig. 8: "L" Range — 1st Gear

Courtesy of Chrysler Corp.

OIL CIRCUIT DIAGRAMS
Chrysler F4A33, W4A32 & W4A33 (Cont.)

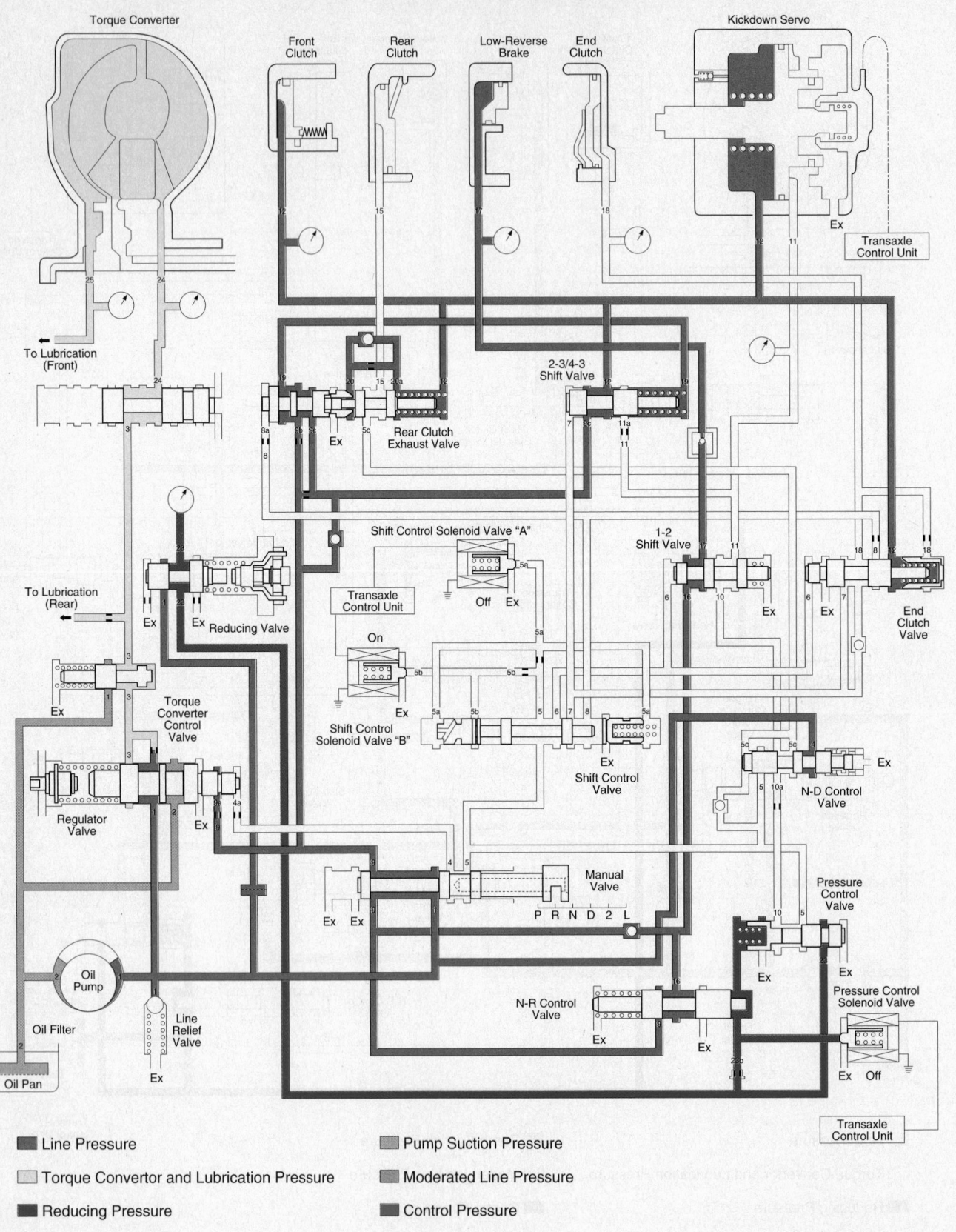

Fig. 9: "R" Range — Reverse

Courtesy of Chrysler Corp.

OIL CIRCUIT DIAGRAMS
Ford AOD

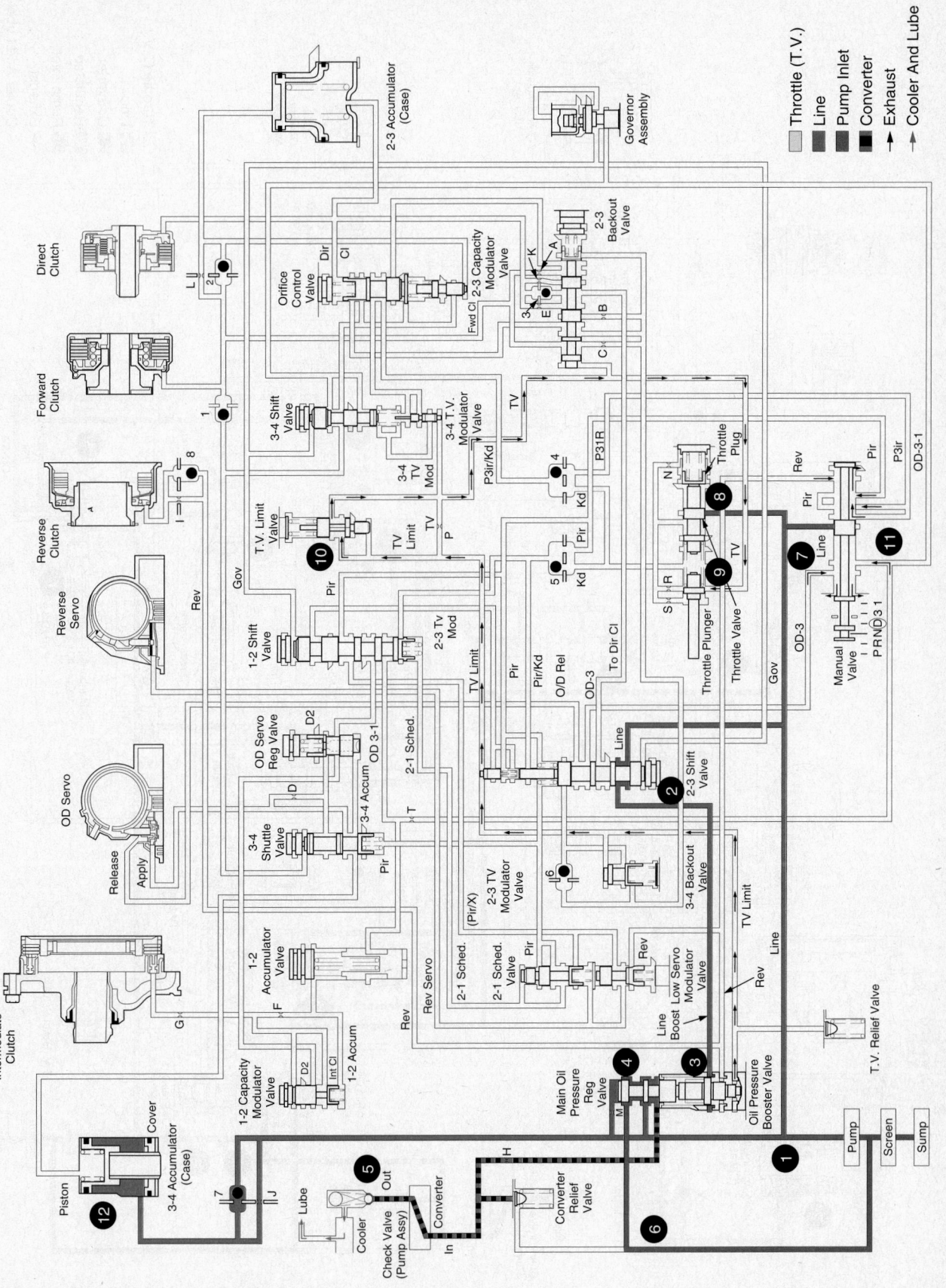

Fig. 1: "N" Range — Neutral (Closed Throttle)

Courtesy of Ford Motor Co.

OIL CIRCUIT DIAGRAMS
Ford AOD (Cont.)

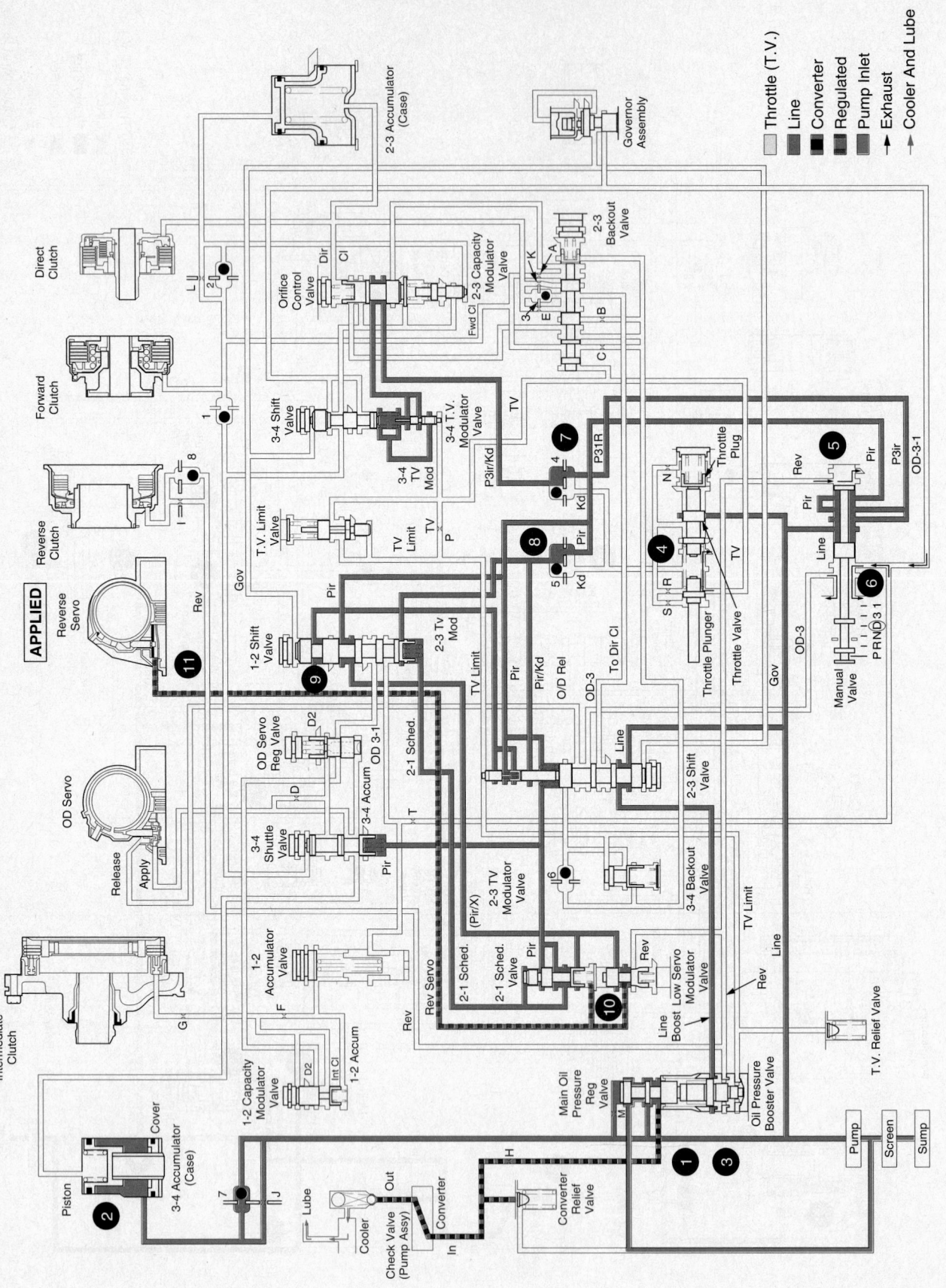

Fig. 2: "P" Range — Park (Closed Throttle)

Courtesy of Ford Motor Co.

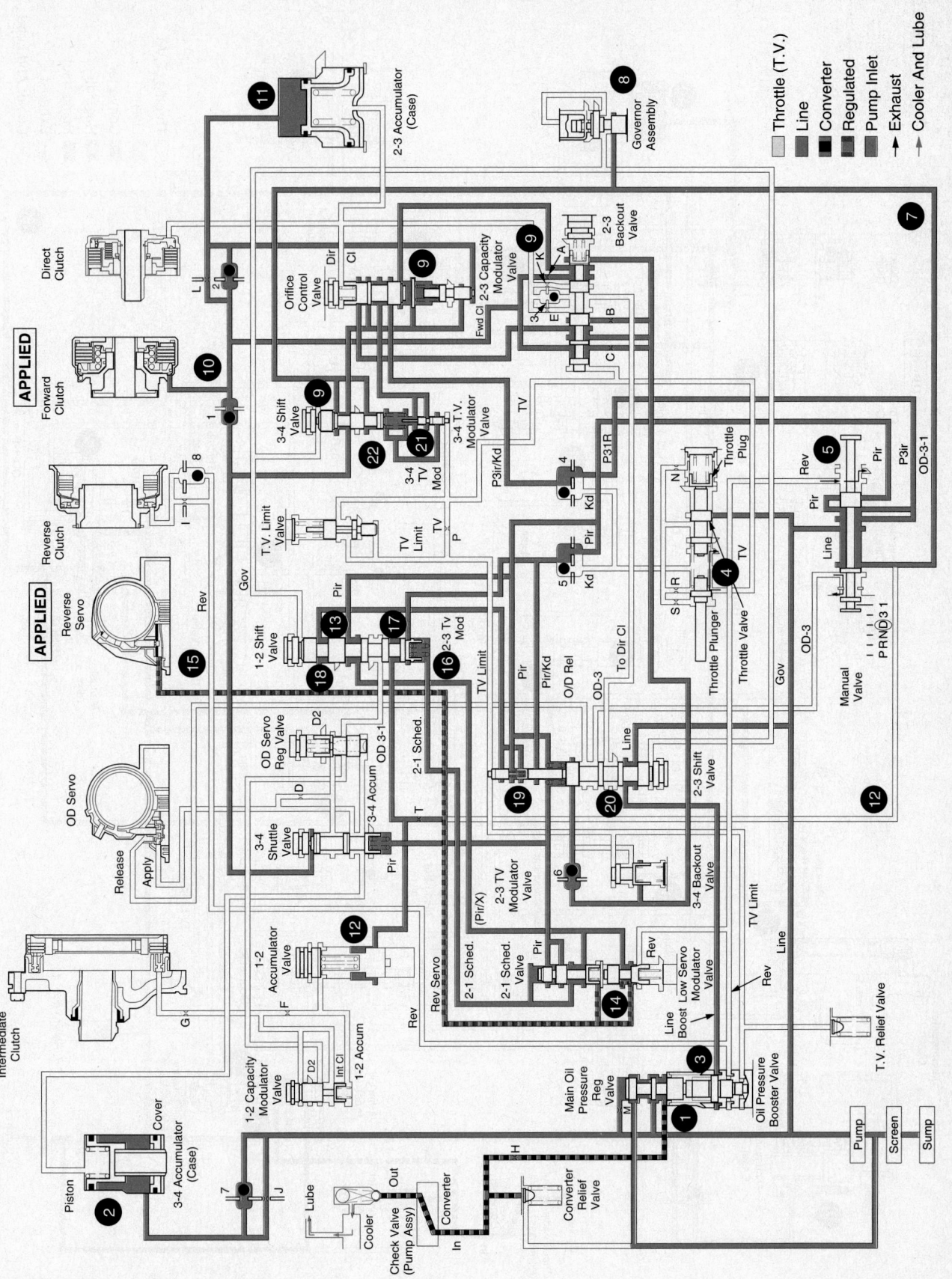

Fig. 3: "L" Range — 1st Gear Manual Select (Closed Throttle At Zero MPH)   Courtesy of Ford Motor Co.

OIL CIRCUIT DIAGRAMS
Ford AOD (Cont.)

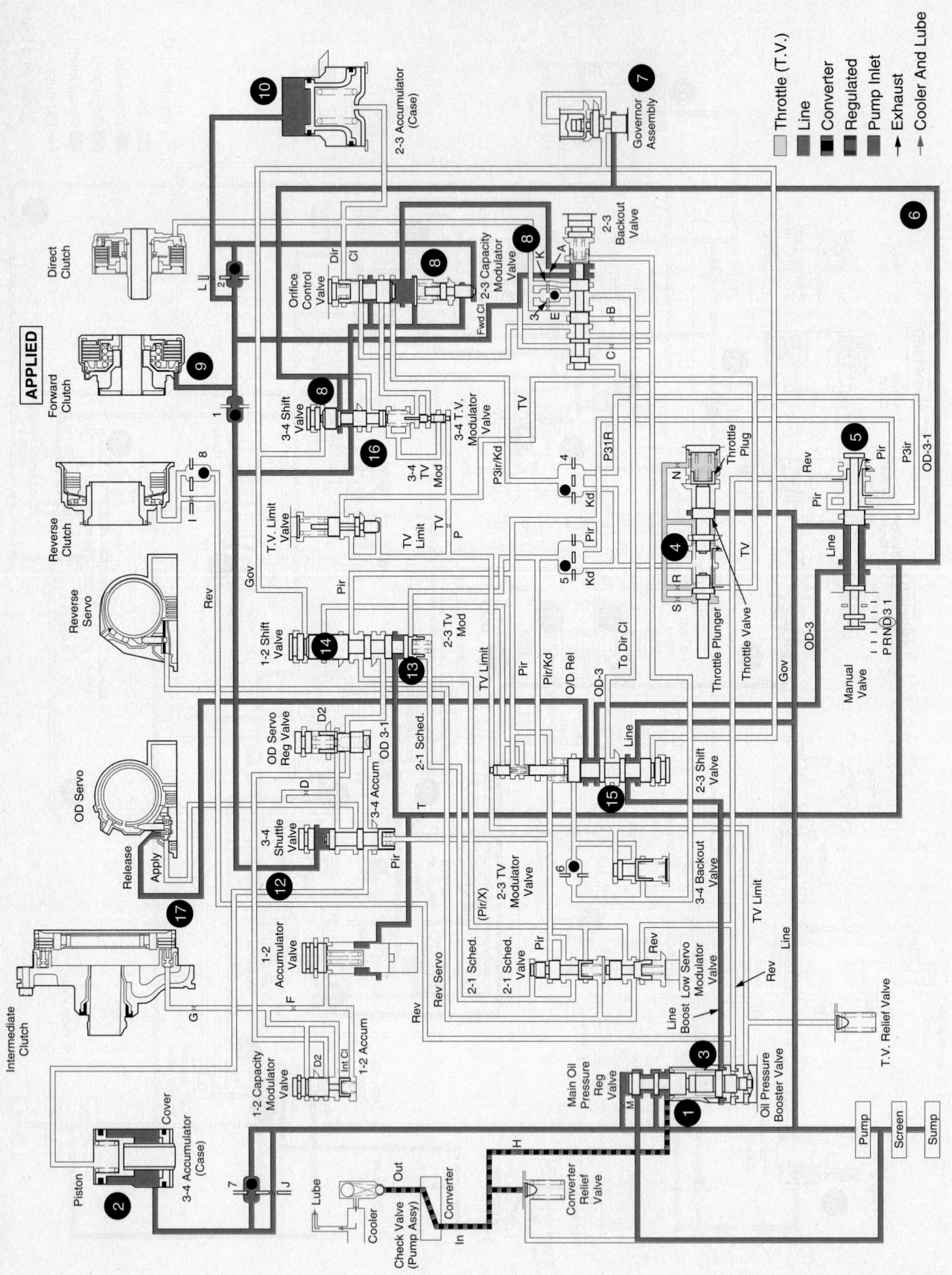

Fig. 4: "OD" Range — 1st Gear (Closed Throttle)

Courtesy of Ford Motor Co.

OIL CIRCUIT DIAGRAMS
Ford AOD (Cont.)

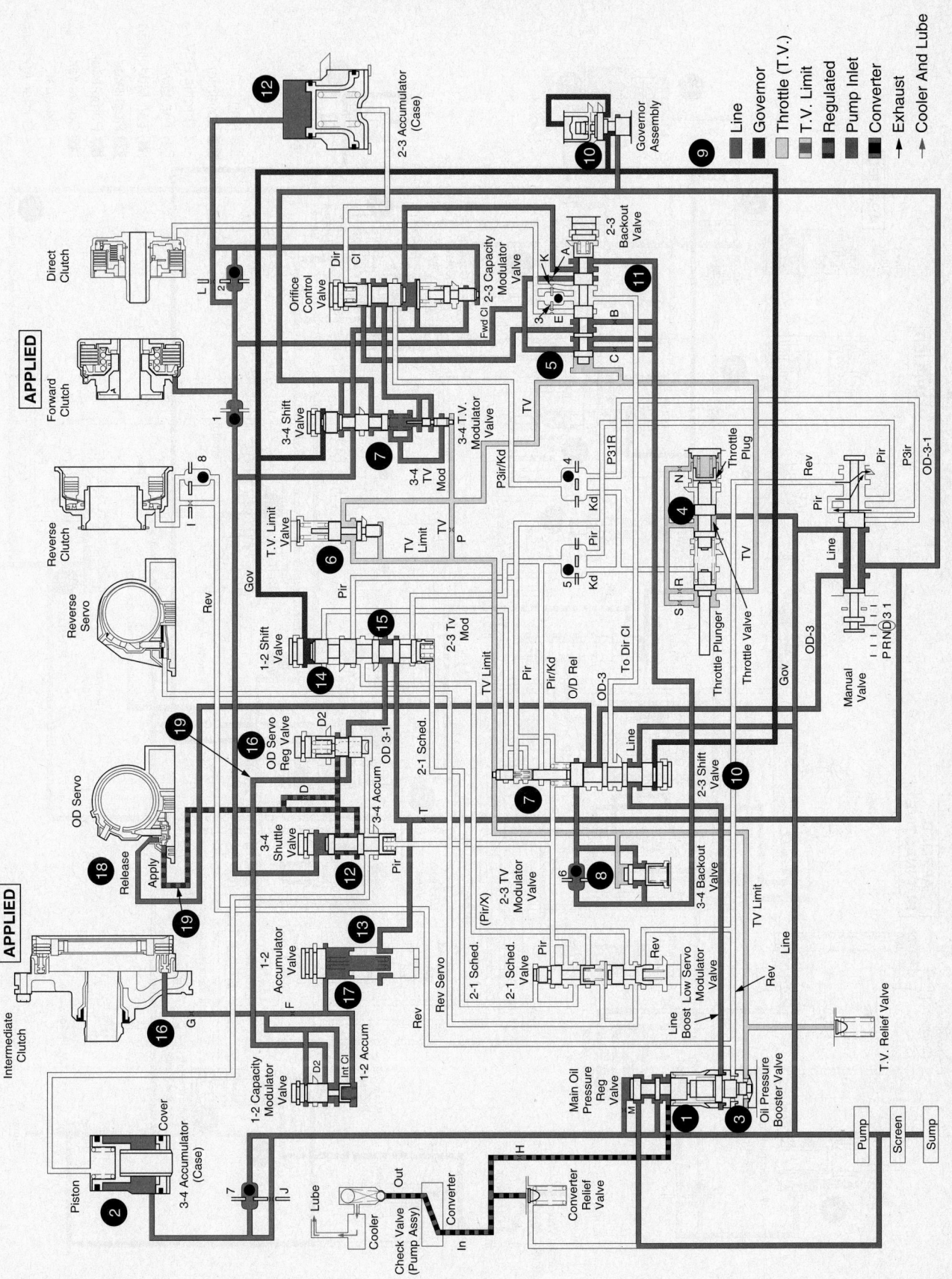

Fig. 5: "OD" Range — 2nd Gear (Part Throttle)

Courtesy of Ford Motor Co.

OIL CIRCUIT DIAGRAMS
Ford AOD (Cont.)

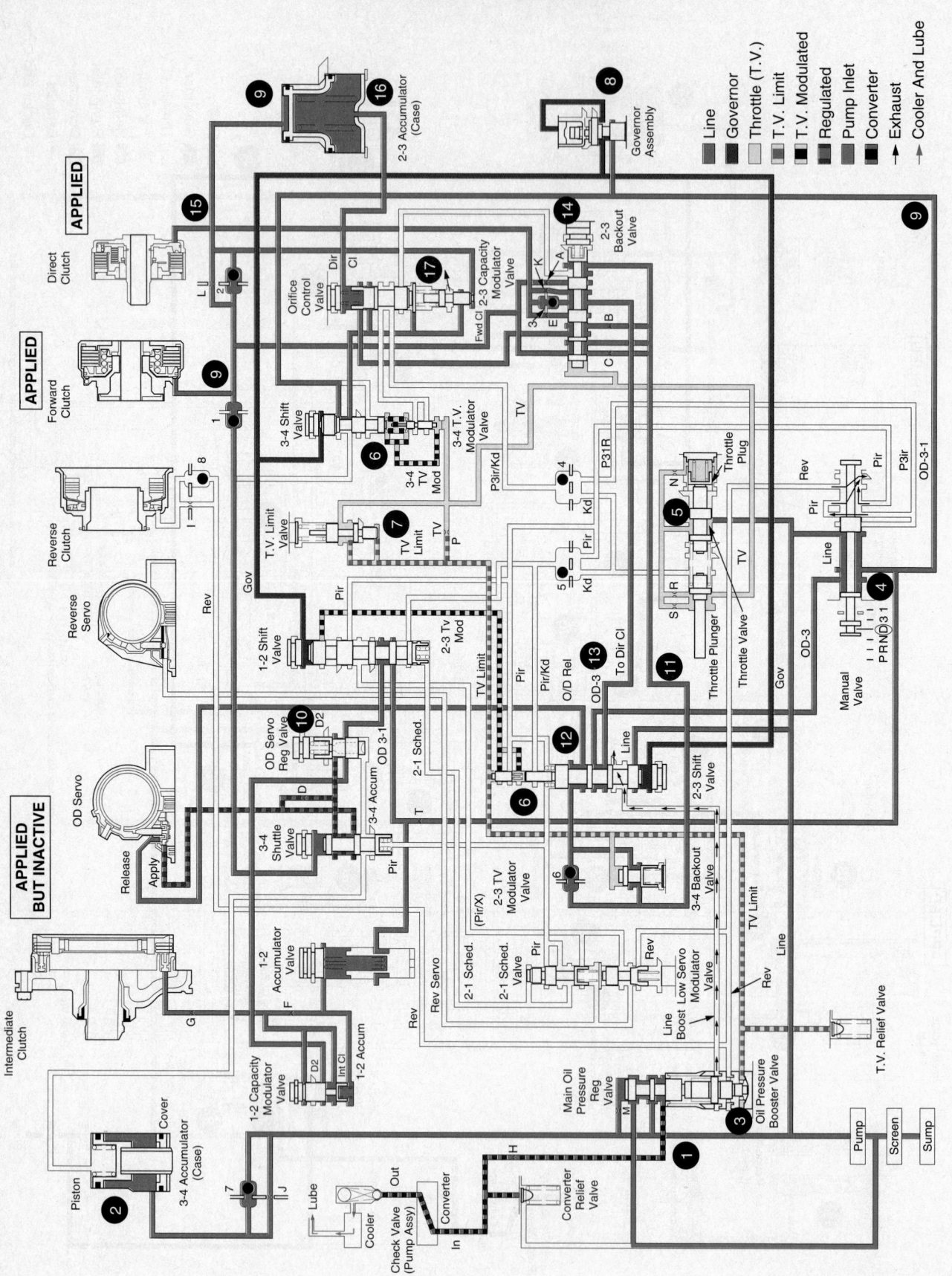

Fig. 6: "OD" Range — 3rd Gear (3/4 Throttle)

Courtesy of Ford Motor Co.

OIL CIRCUIT DIAGRAMS
Ford AOD (Cont.)

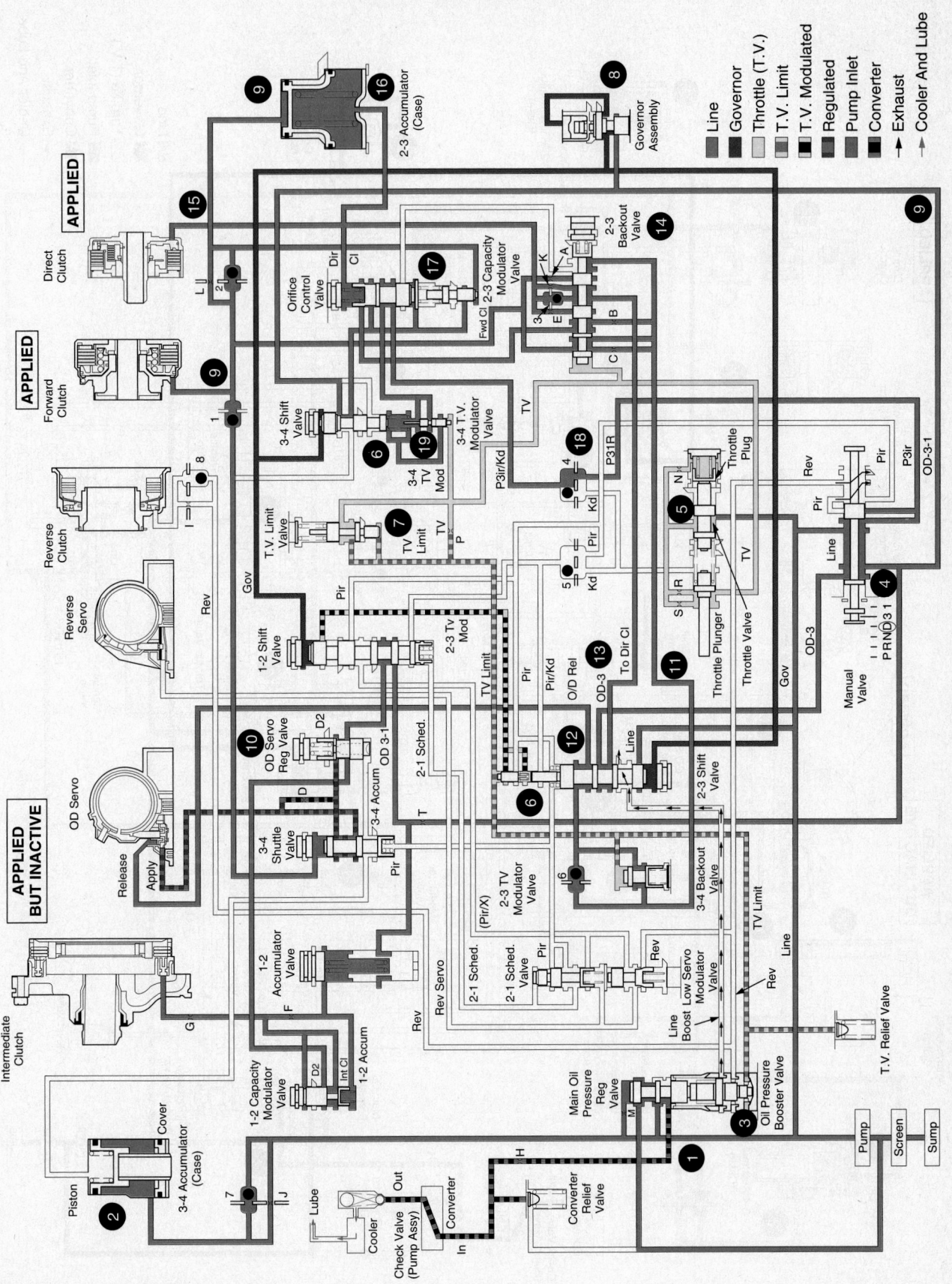

Fig. 7: "3" Range — 3rd Gear (3/4 Throttle)

Courtesy of Ford Motor Co.

OIL CIRCUIT DIAGRAMS
Ford AOD (Cont.)

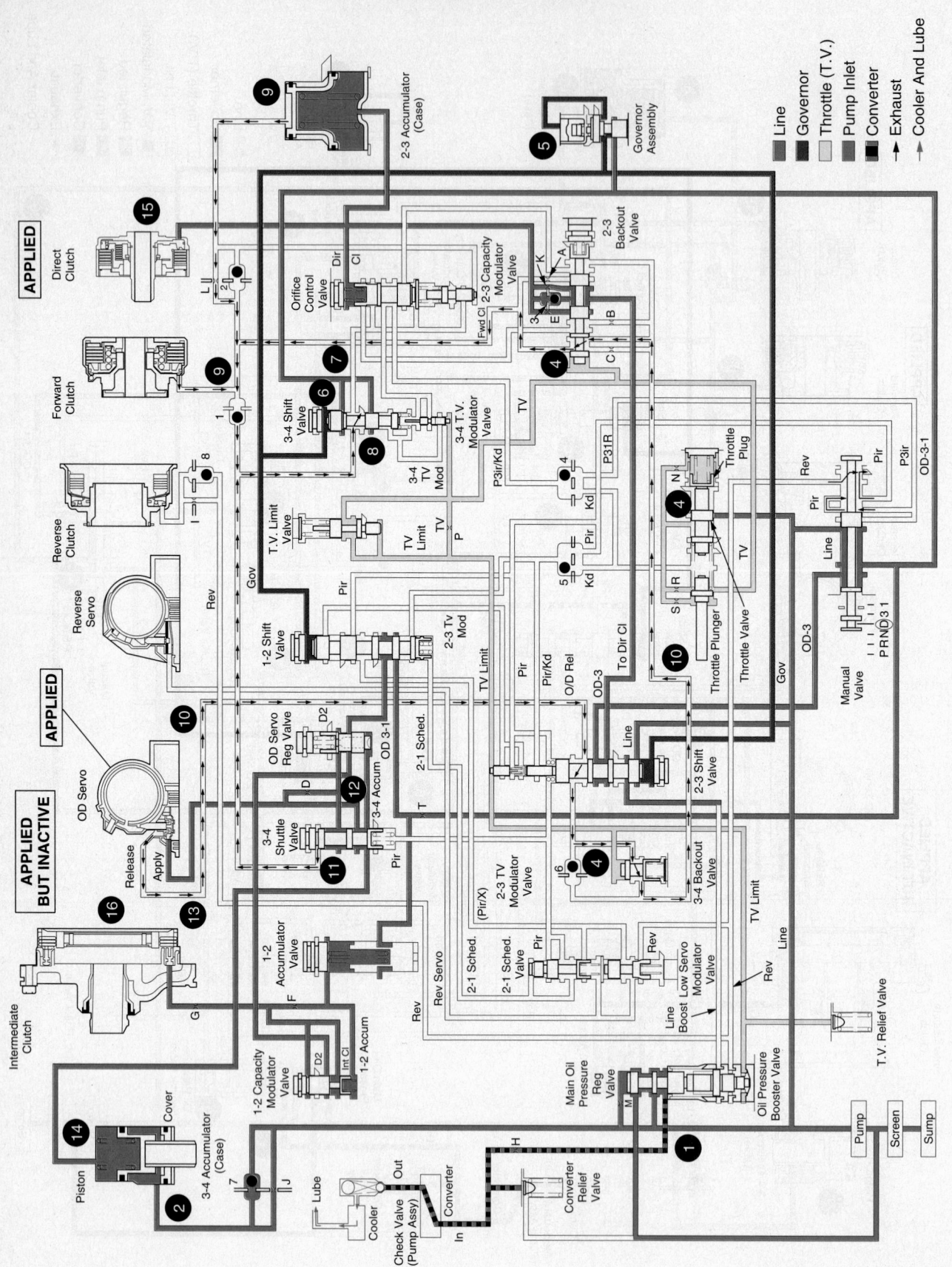

Fig. 8: "OD" Range — 4th Gear (Part Throttle)

Courtesy of Ford Motor Co.

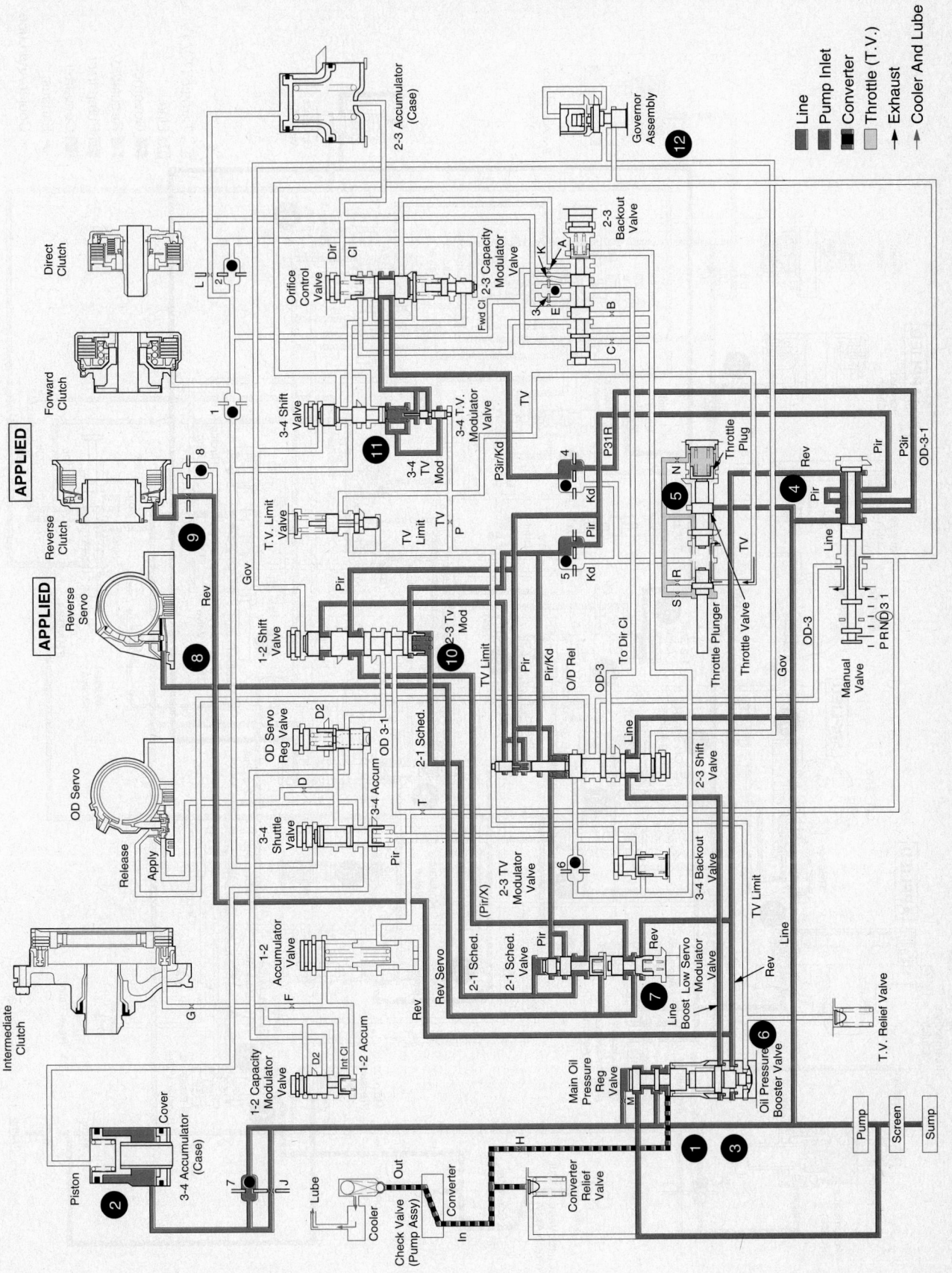

Fig. 9: "R" Range — Reverse (Closed Throttle)

Courtesy of Ford Motor Co.

OIL CIRCUIT DIAGRAMS
Ford AOD (Cont.)

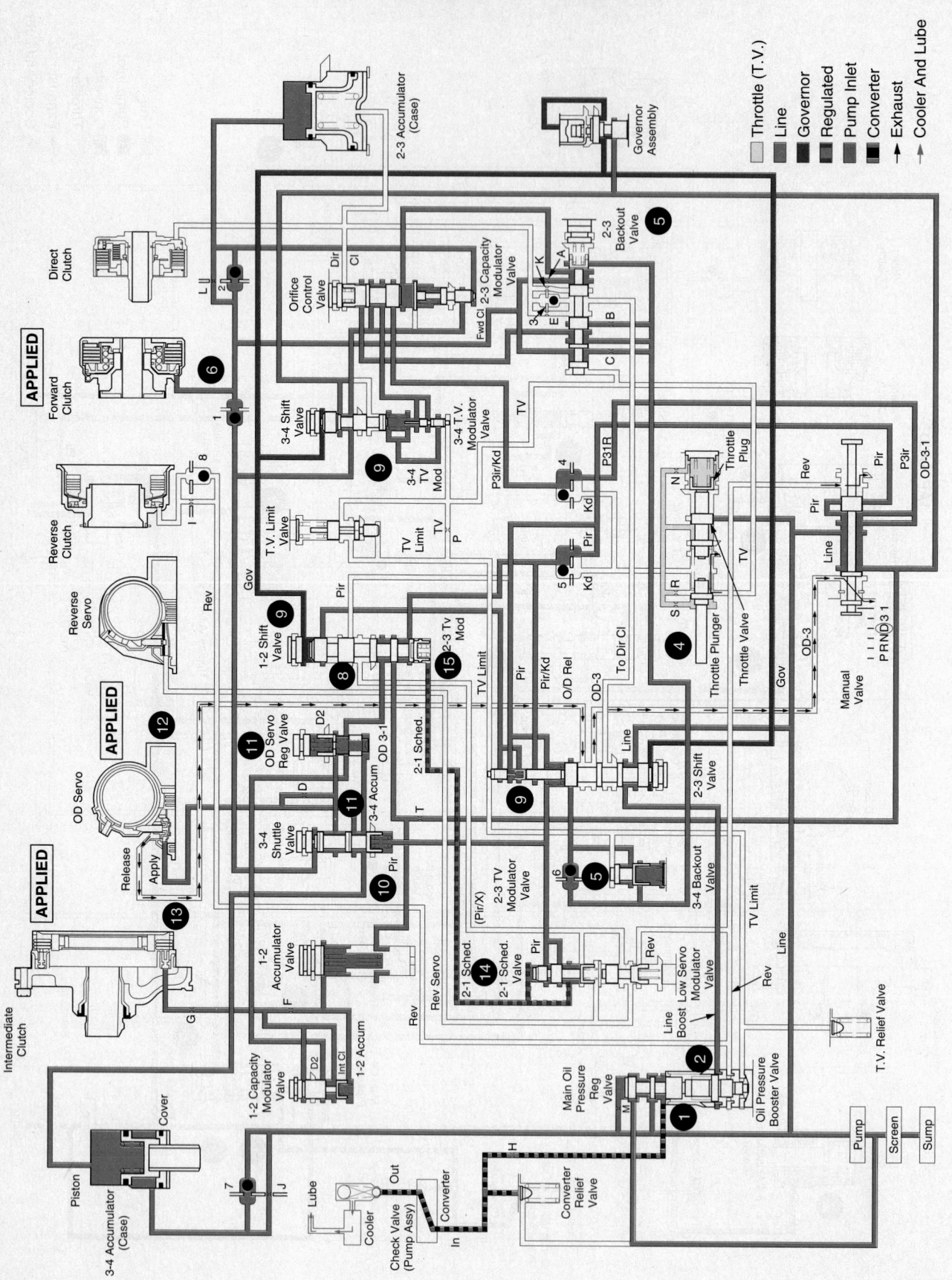

Fig. 10: "L" Range — 1st Gear Manual Select (Closed Throttle Above 2-1 Downshift MPH)   Courtesy of Ford Motor Co.

OIL CIRCUIT DIAGRAMS
Ford ATX/FLC

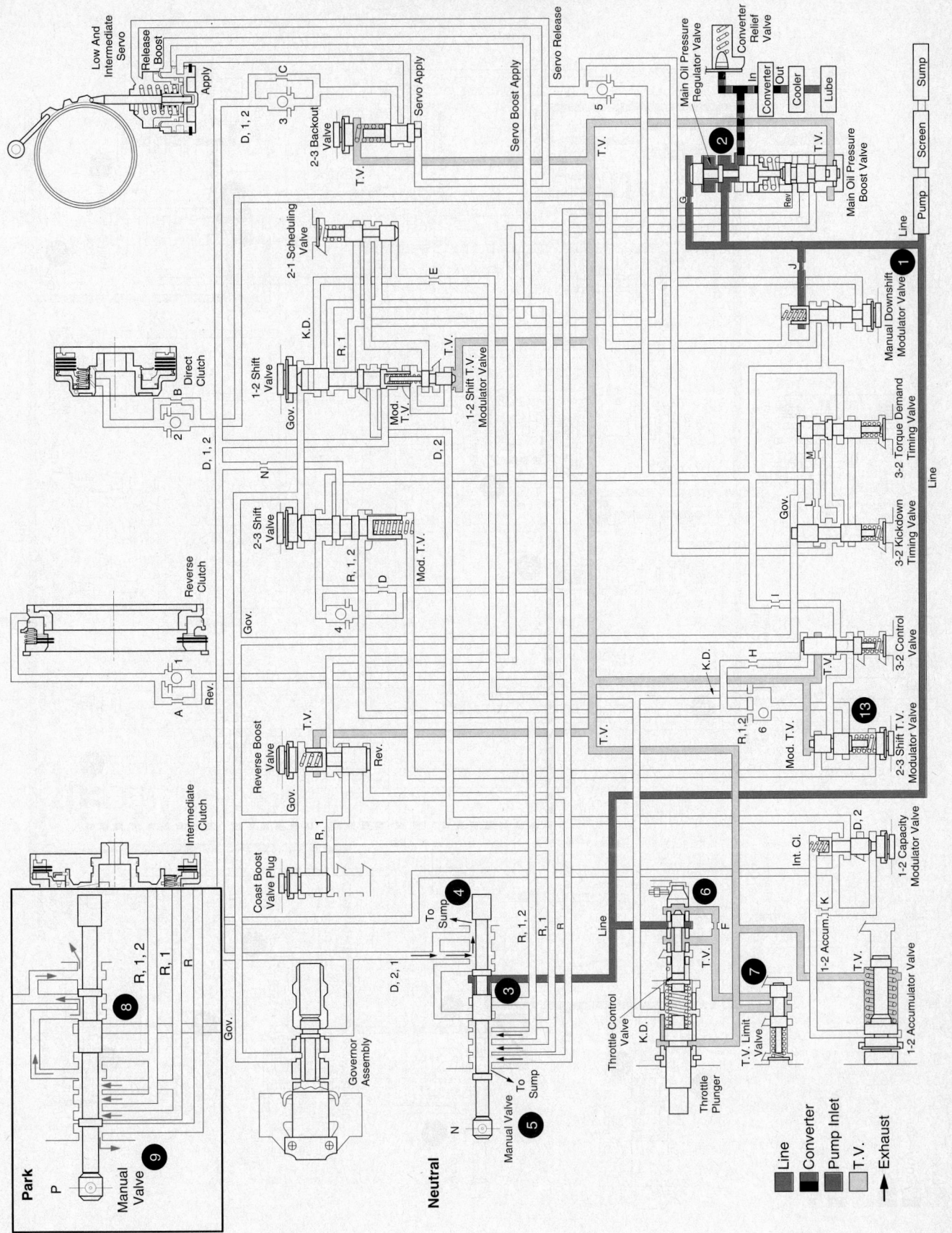

Fig. 1: "N" & "P" Range — Neutral Or Park (Light Throttle)

Courtesy of Ford Motor Co.

OIL CIRCUIT DIAGRAMS
Ford ATX/FLC (Cont.)

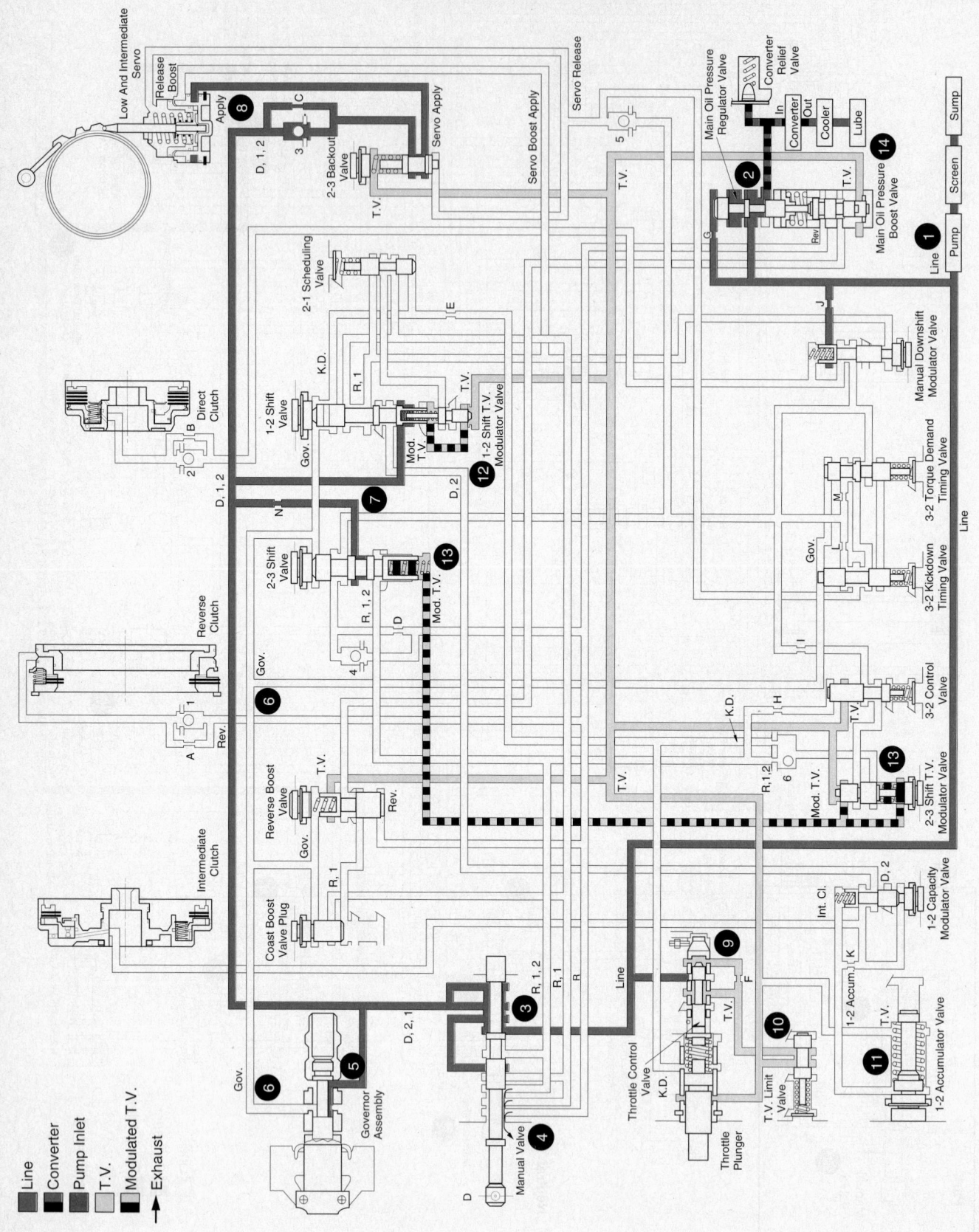

Fig. 2: "D" Range — 1st Gear   Courtesy of Ford Motor Co.

OIL CIRCUIT DIAGRAMS
Ford ATX/FLC (Cont.)

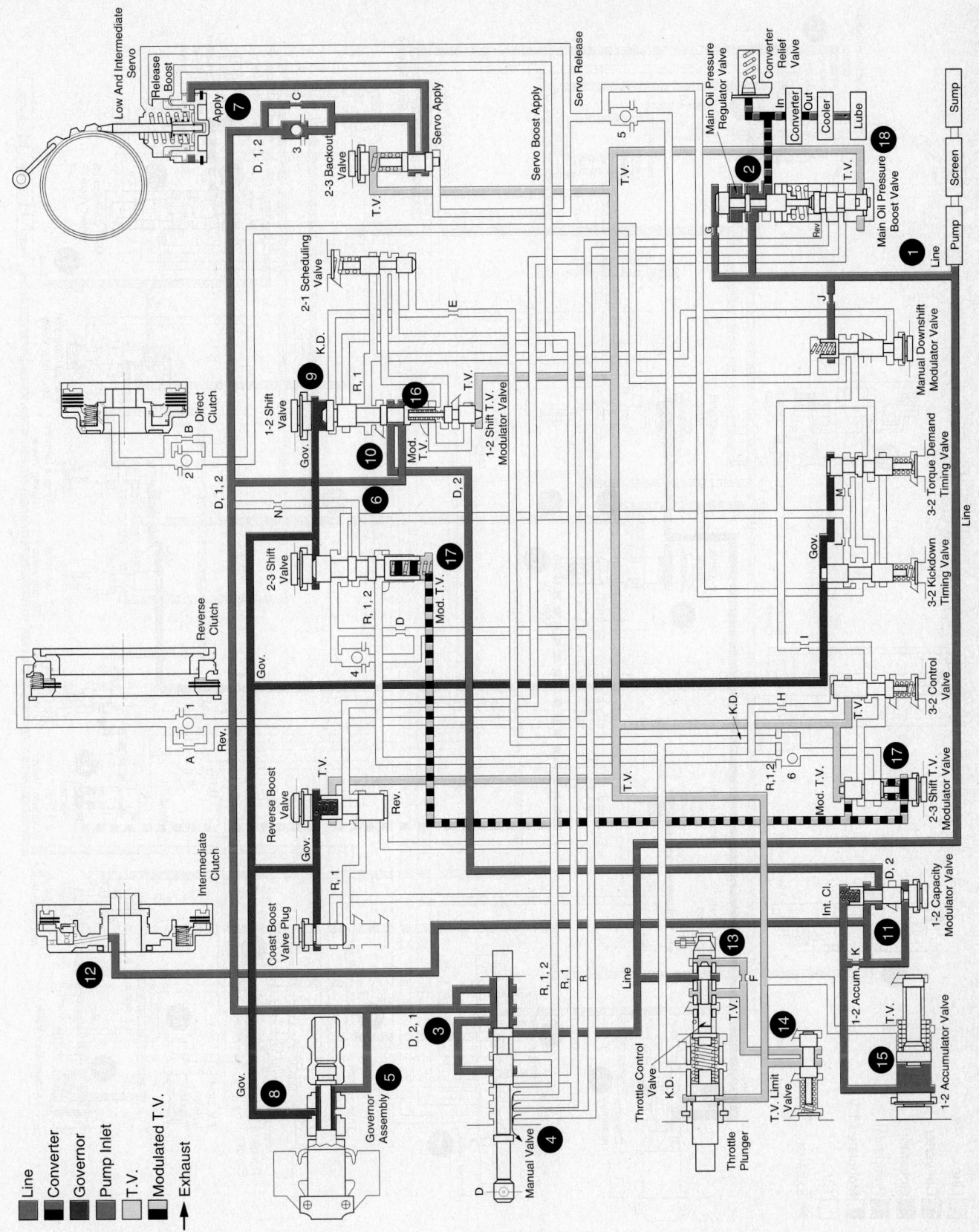

Fig. 3: "D" Range — 2nd Gear

Courtesy of Ford Motor Co.

OIL CIRCUIT DIAGRAMS
Ford ATX/FLC (Cont.)

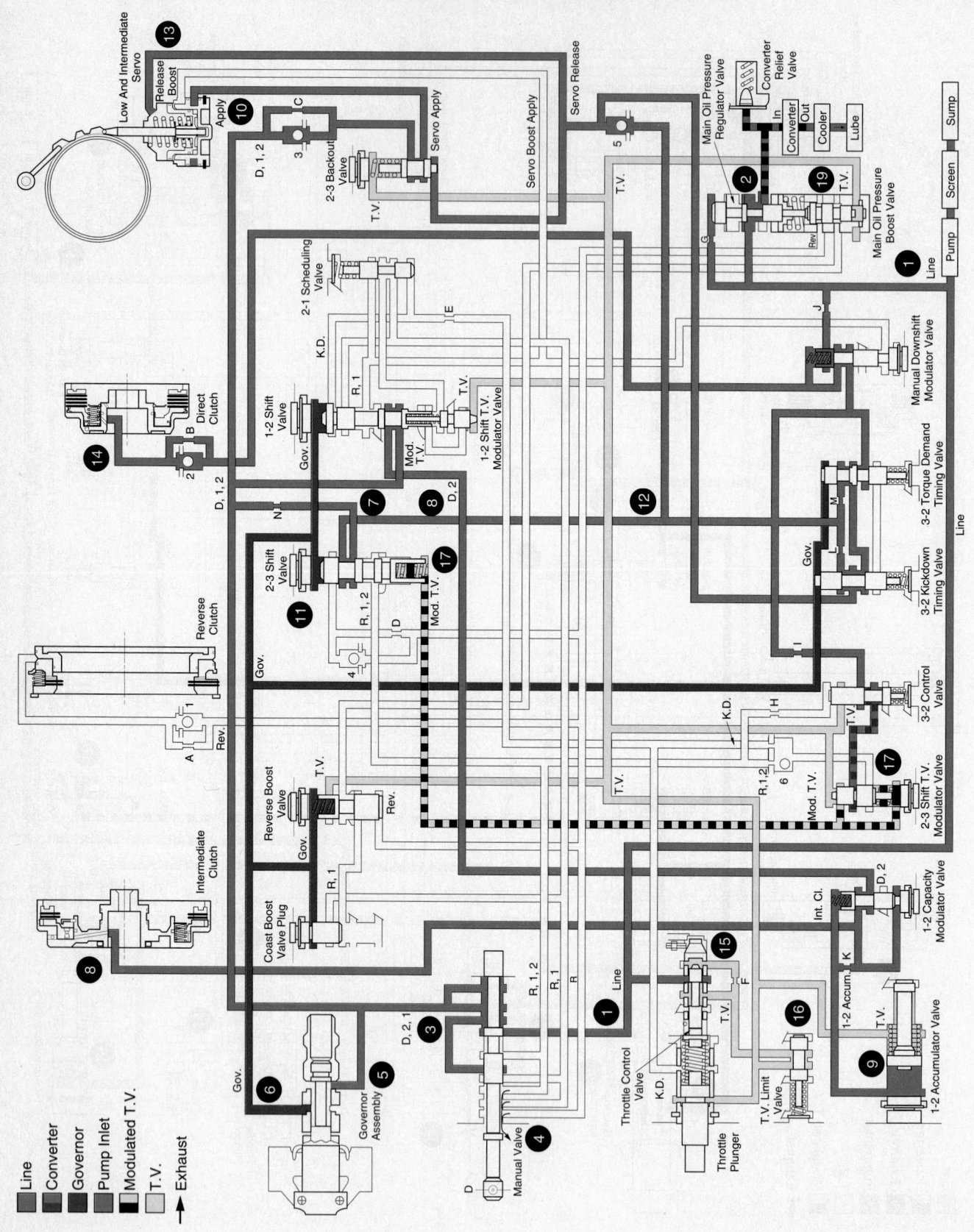

Fig. 4: "D" Range — 3rd Gear

Courtesy of Ford Motor Co.

OIL CIRCUIT DIAGRAMS
Ford ATX/FLC (Cont.)

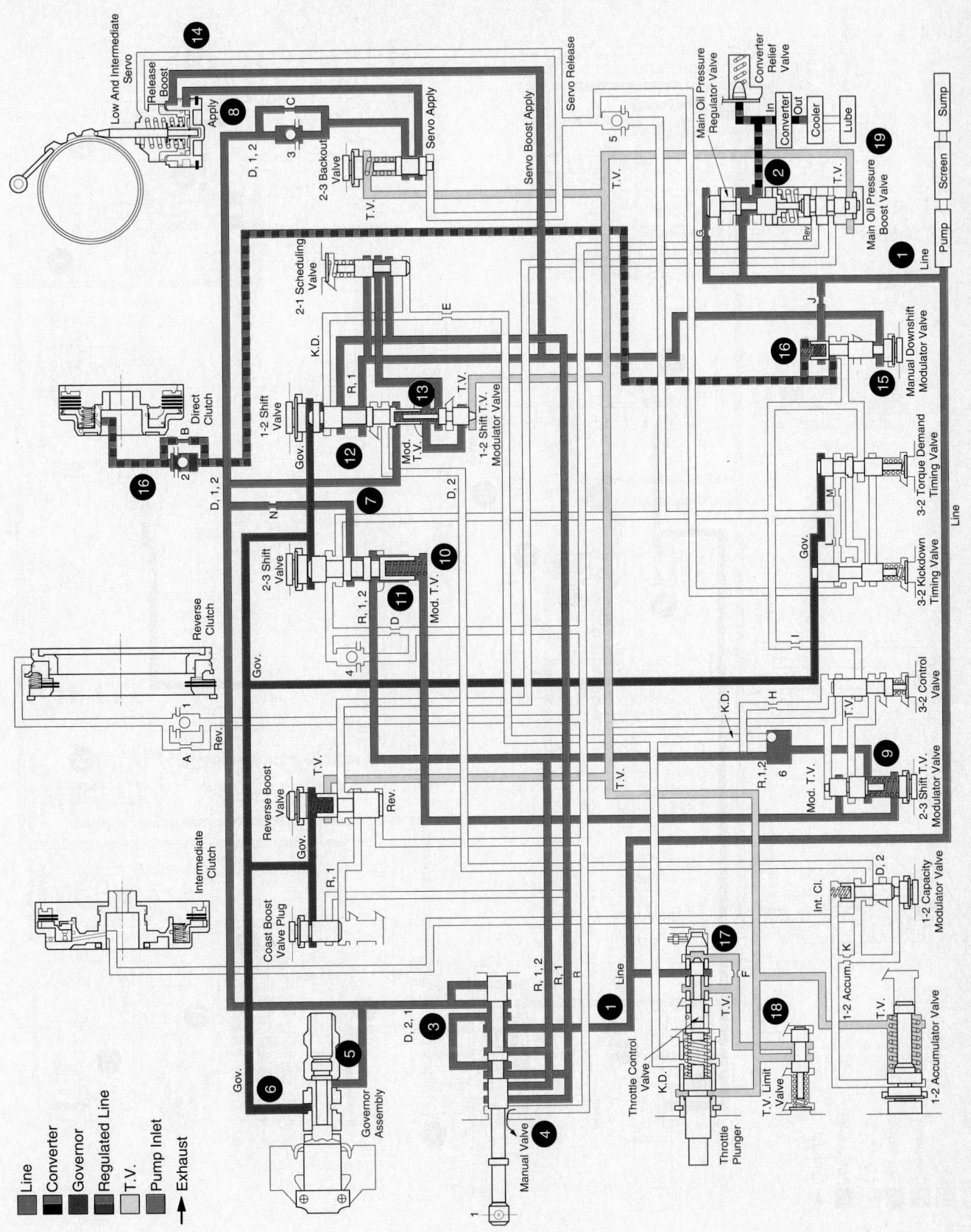

Fig. 5: "L" Range — 1st Gear (Manual Select)

Courtesy of Ford Motor Co.

OIL CIRCUIT DIAGRAMS
Ford ATX/FLC (Cont.)

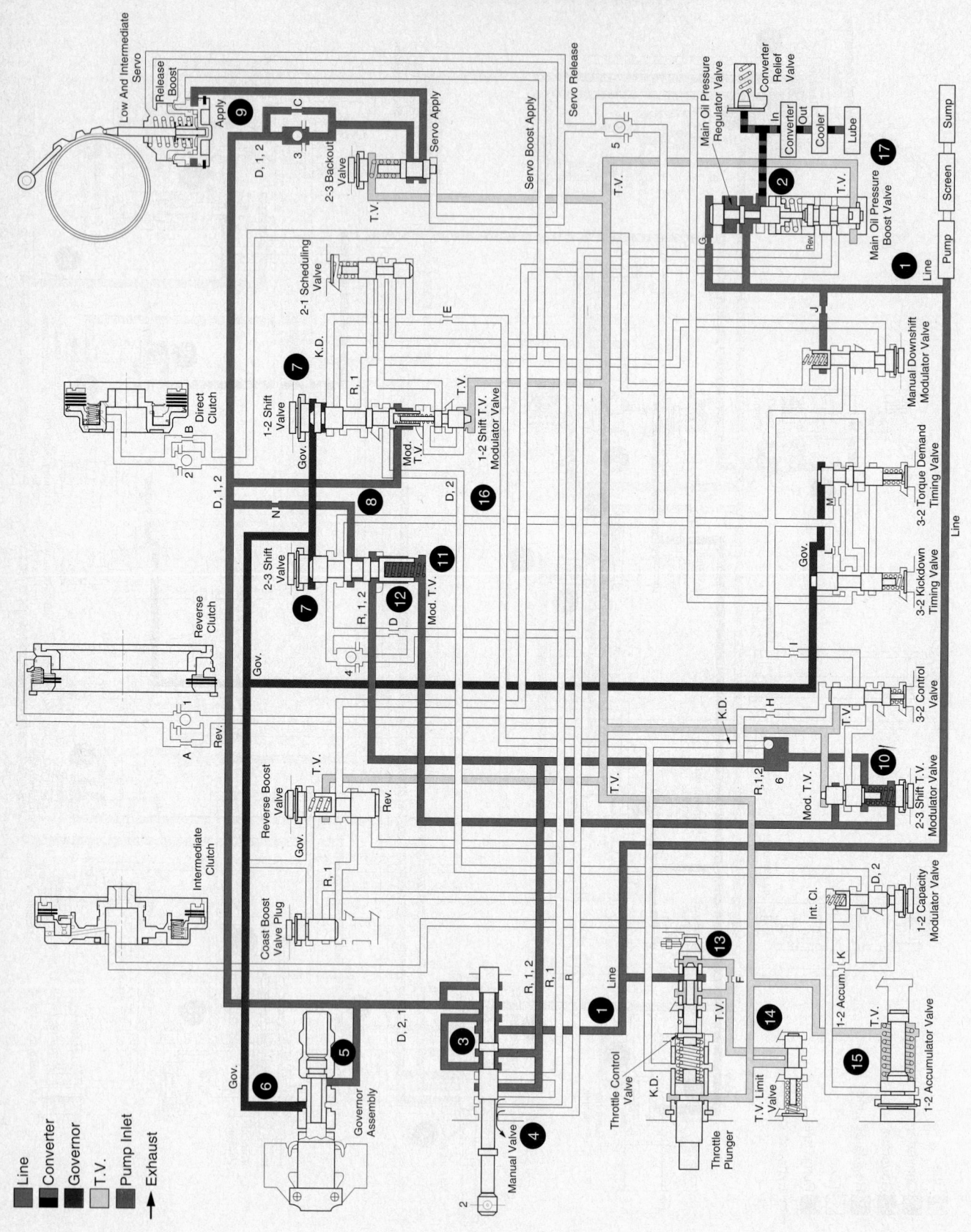

Fig. 6: "2" Range — 1st Gear

Courtesy of Ford Motor Co.

OIL CIRCUIT DIAGRAMS
Ford ATX/FLC (Cont.)

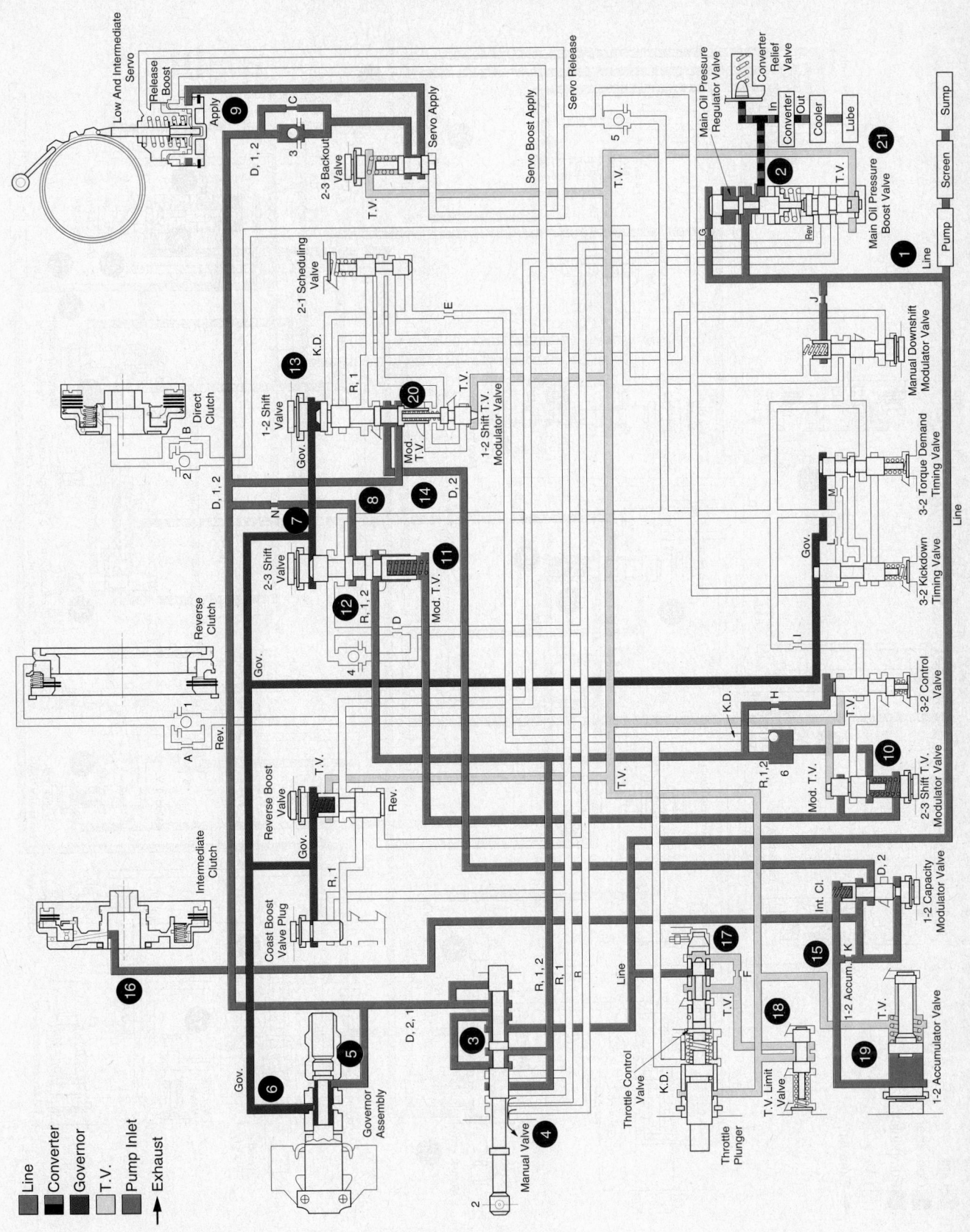

Fig. 7: "2" Range — 2nd Gear

Courtesy of Ford Motor Co.

OIL CIRCUIT DIAGRAMS
Ford ATX/FLC (Cont.)

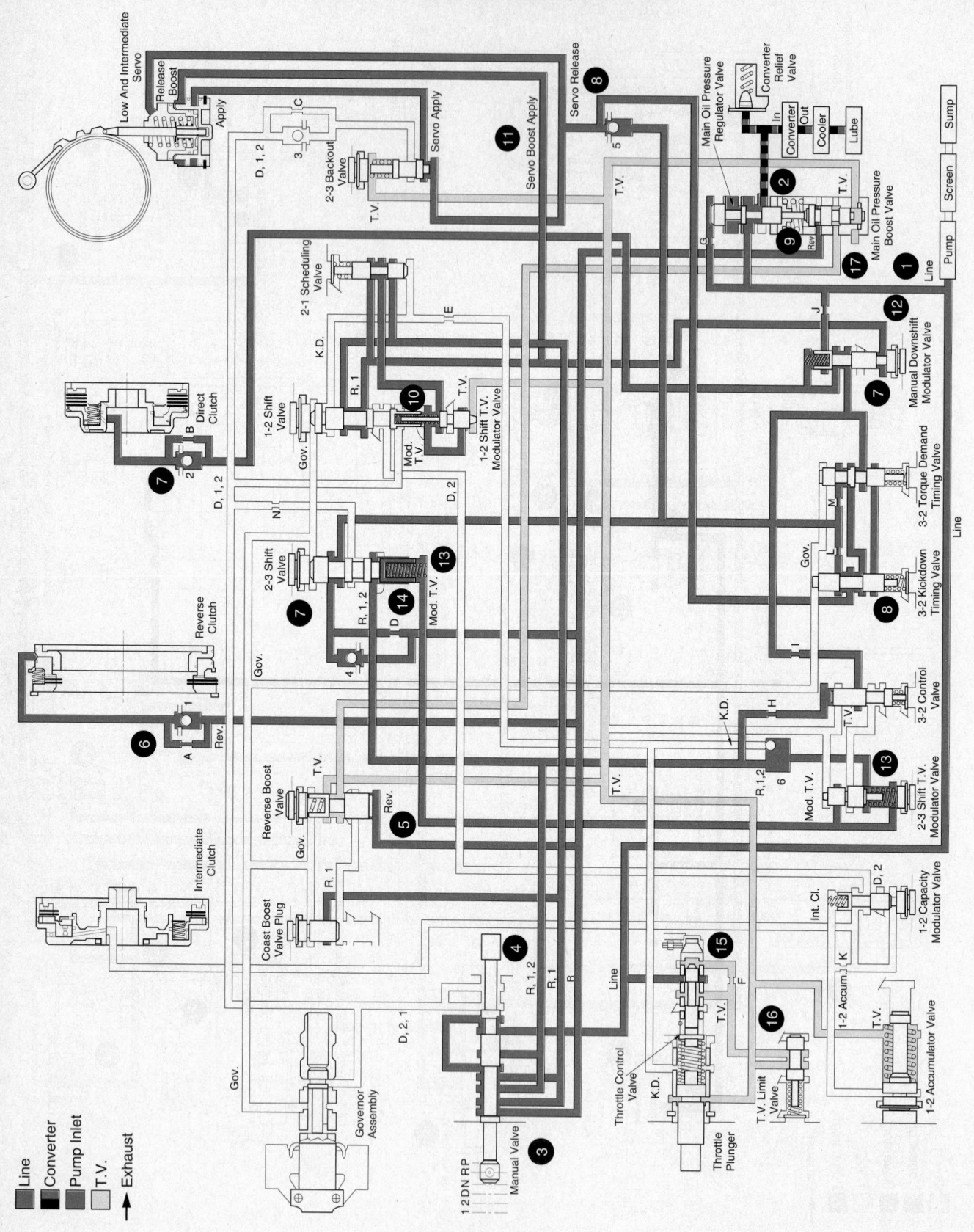

Fig. 8: "R" Range — Reverse

Courtesy of Ford Motor Co.

OIL CIRCUIT DIAGRAMS
Ford AXOD-E

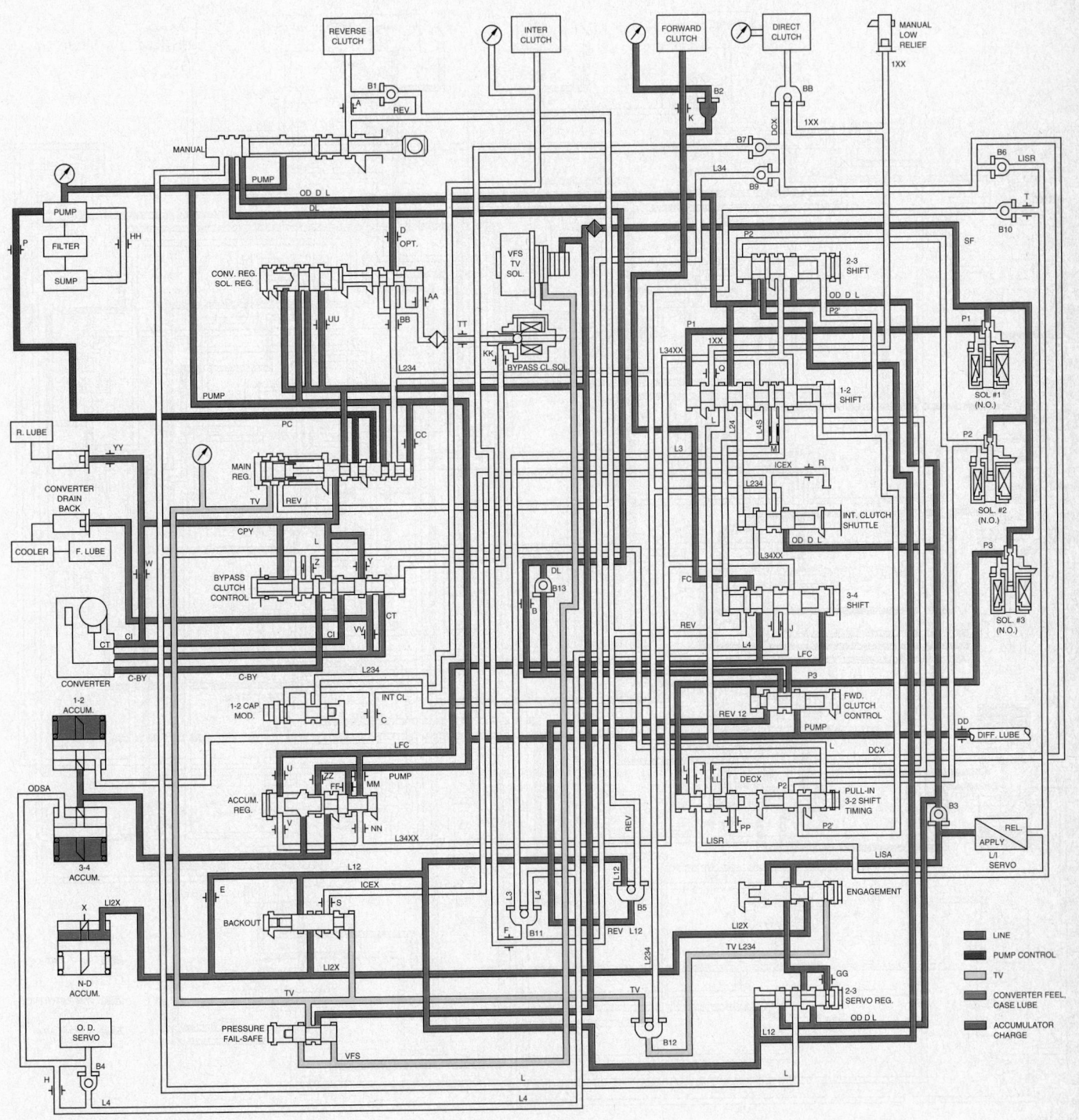

Fig. 1: *"D" Or "OD" Range — 1st Gear*

Courtesy of Ford Motor Co.

OIL CIRCUIT DIAGRAMS
Ford AXOD-E (Cont.)

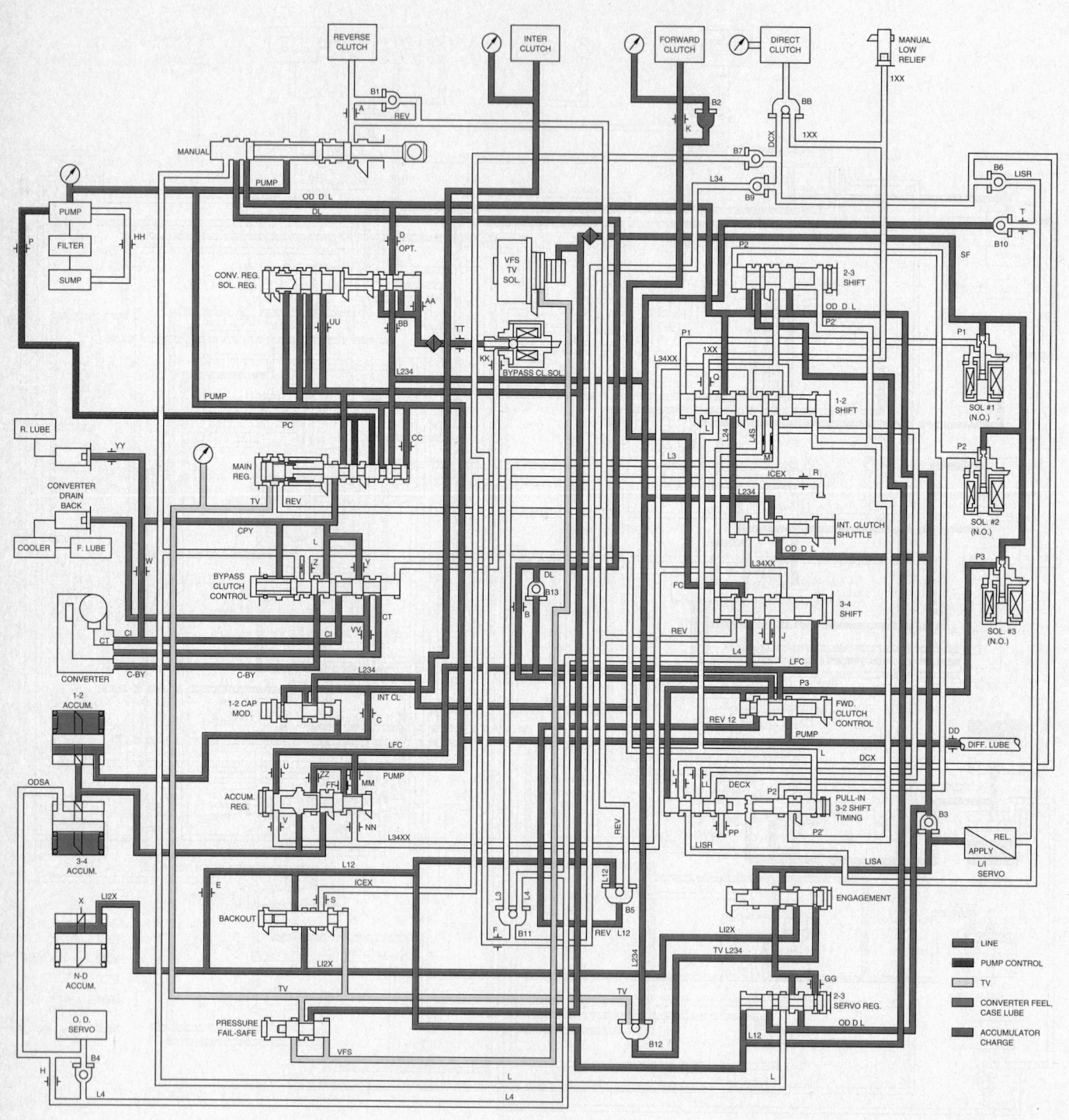

Fig. 2: "D" Or "OD" Range — 2nd Gear

Courtesy of Ford Motor Co.

OIL CIRCUIT DIAGRAMS
Ford AXOD-E (Cont.)

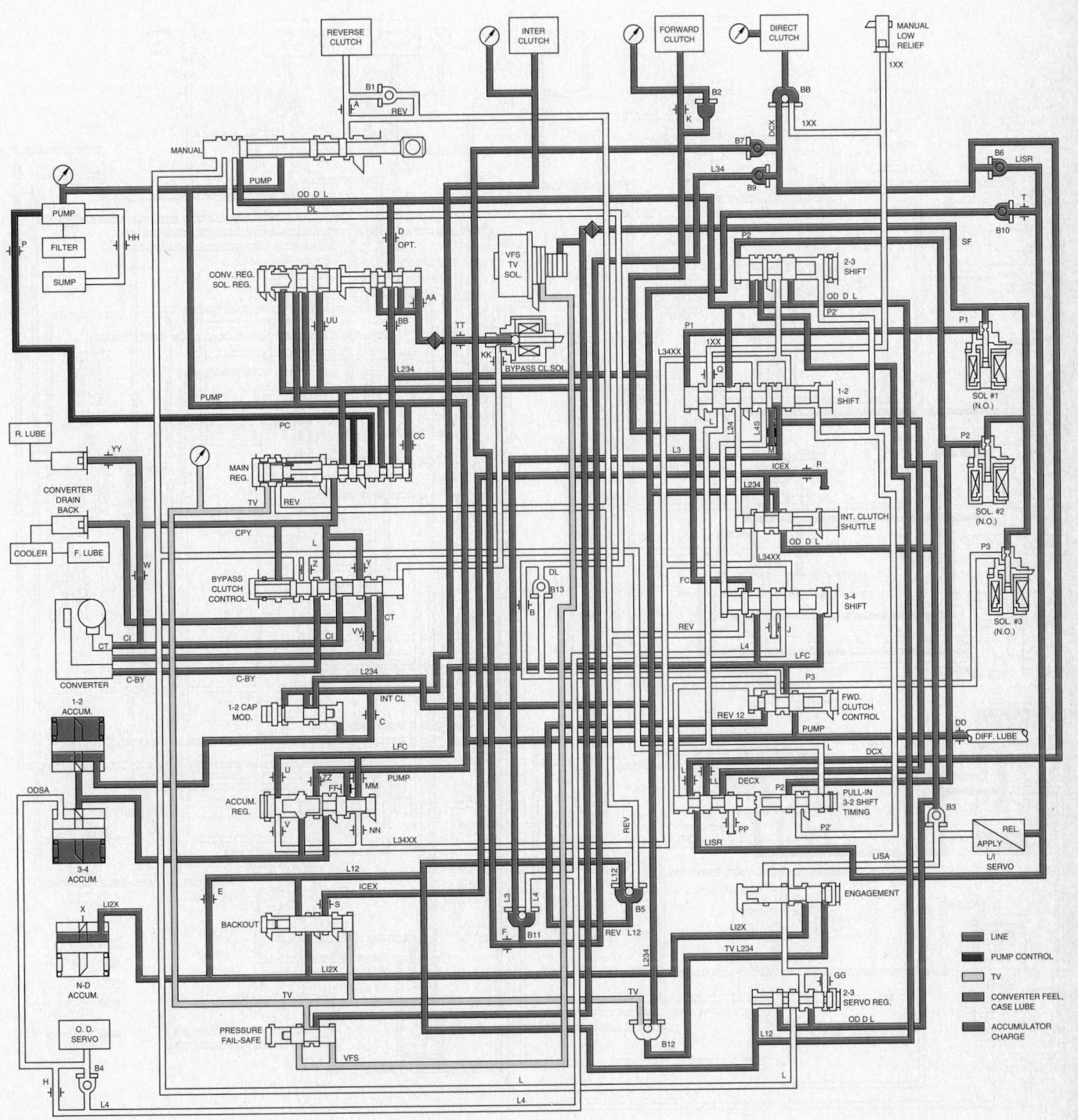

Fig. 3: *"OD" Range — 3rd Gear (Converter Clutch OFF)*

Courtesy of Ford Motor Co.

OIL CIRCUIT DIAGRAMS
Ford AXOD-E (Cont.)

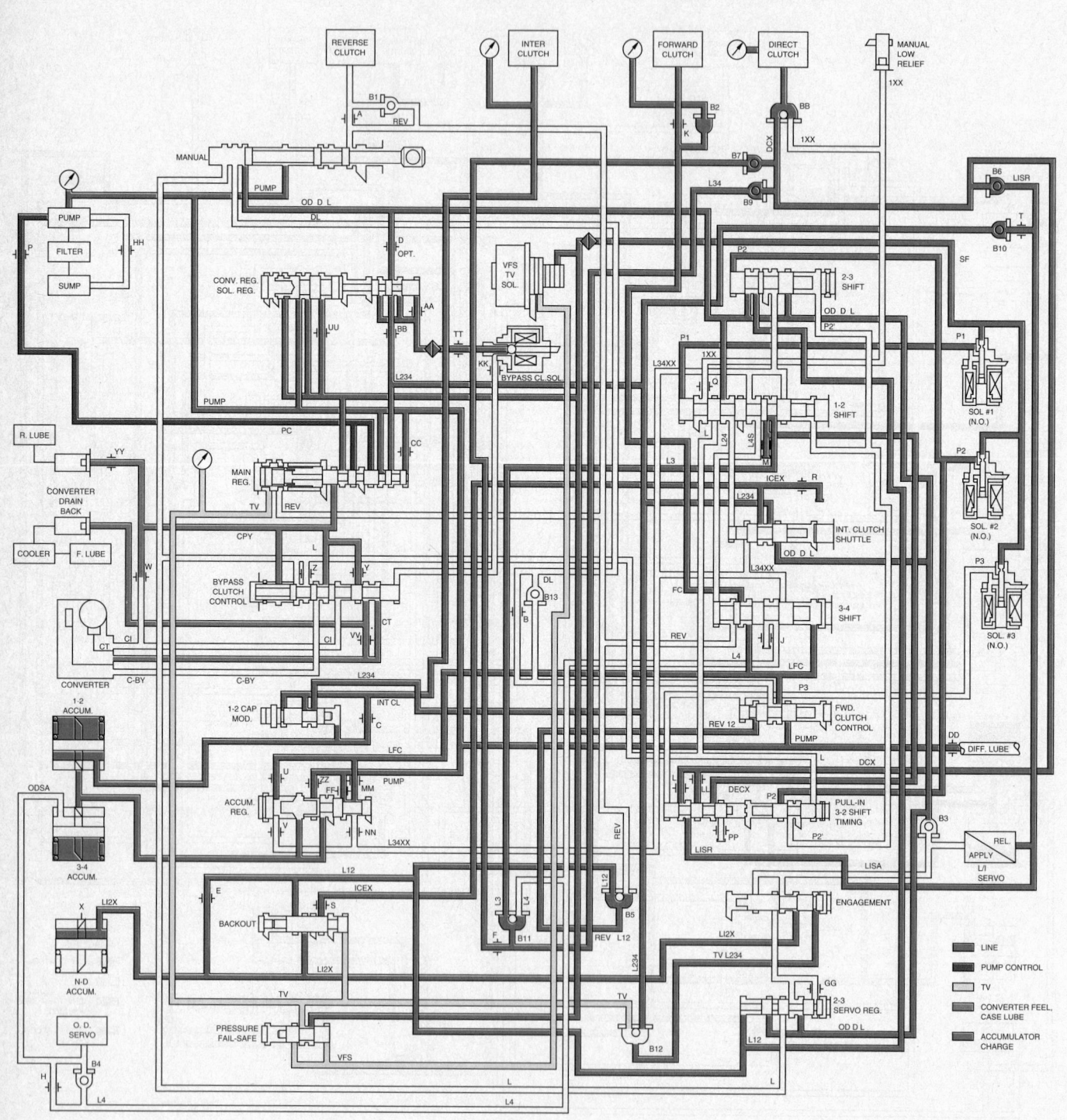

Fig. 4: "OD" Range — 3rd Gear (Converter Clutch ON)

Courtesy of Ford Motor Co.

OIL CIRCUIT DIAGRAMS
Ford AXOD-E (Cont.)

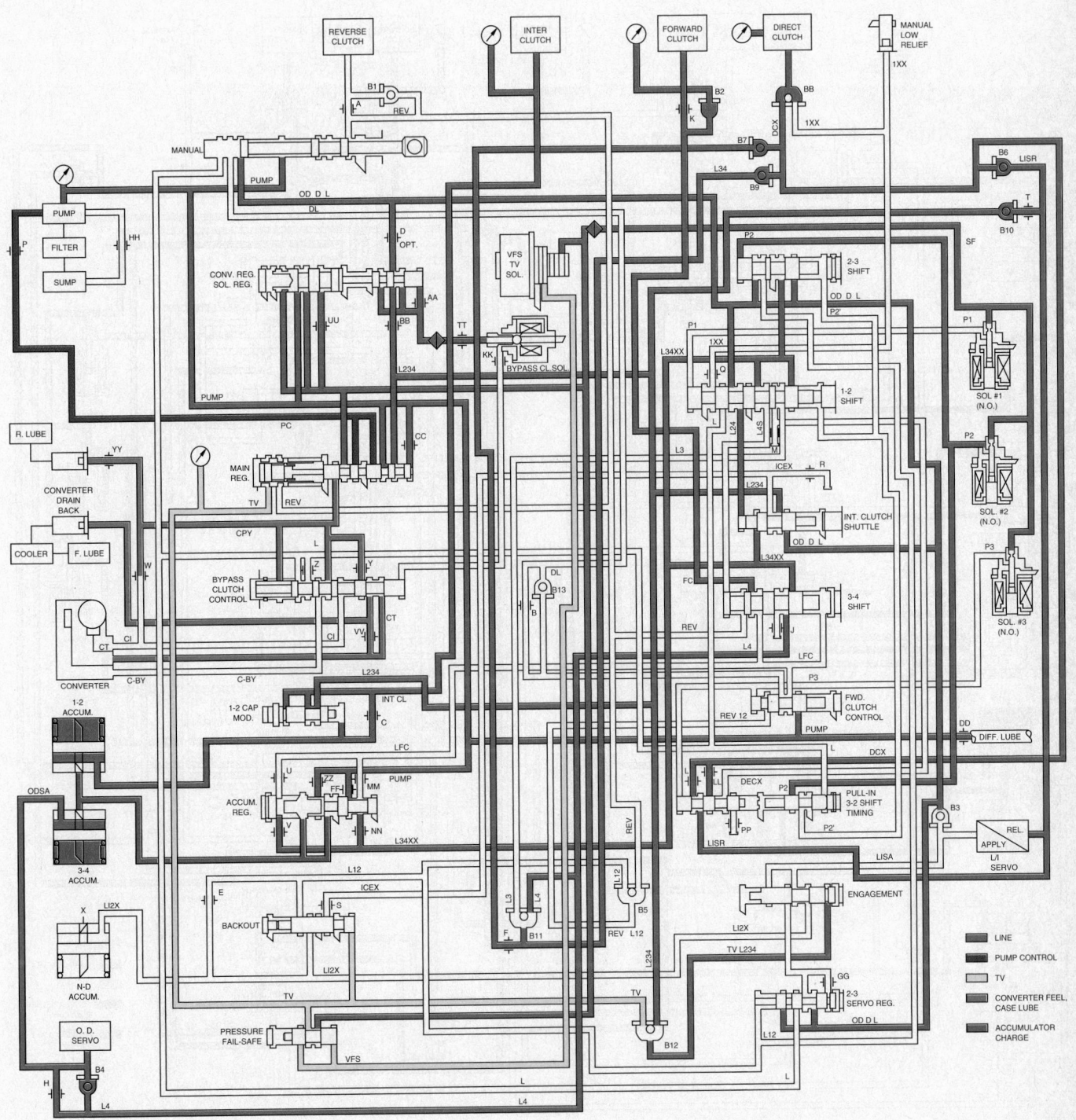

Fig. 5: "OD" Range — 4th Gear (Converter Clutch ON)

Courtesy of Ford Motor Co.

OIL CIRCUIT DIAGRAMS
Ford AXOD-E (Cont.)

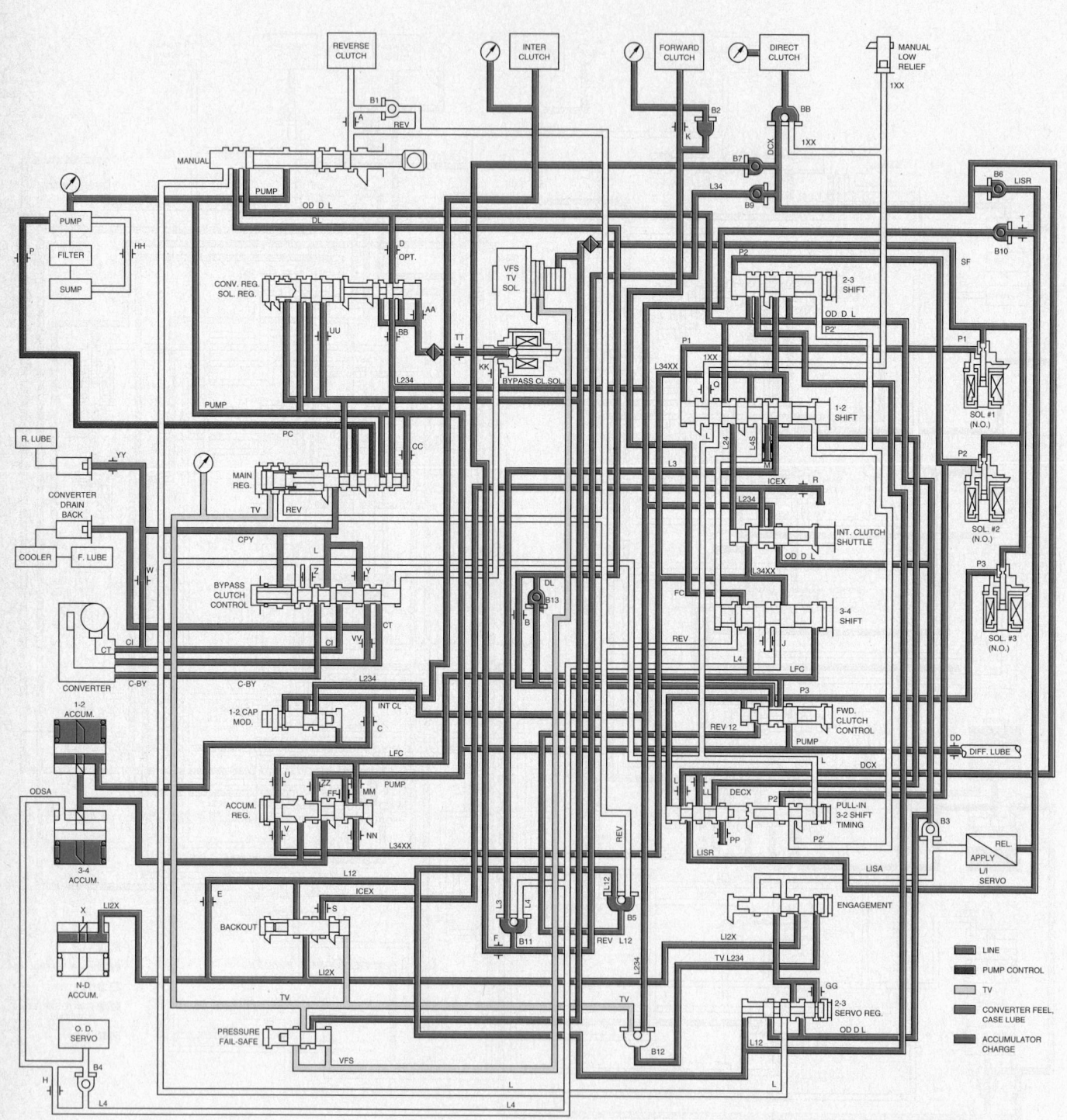

Fig. 6: "D" Range — 3rd Gear (Converter Clutch OFF)

Courtesy of Ford Motor Co.

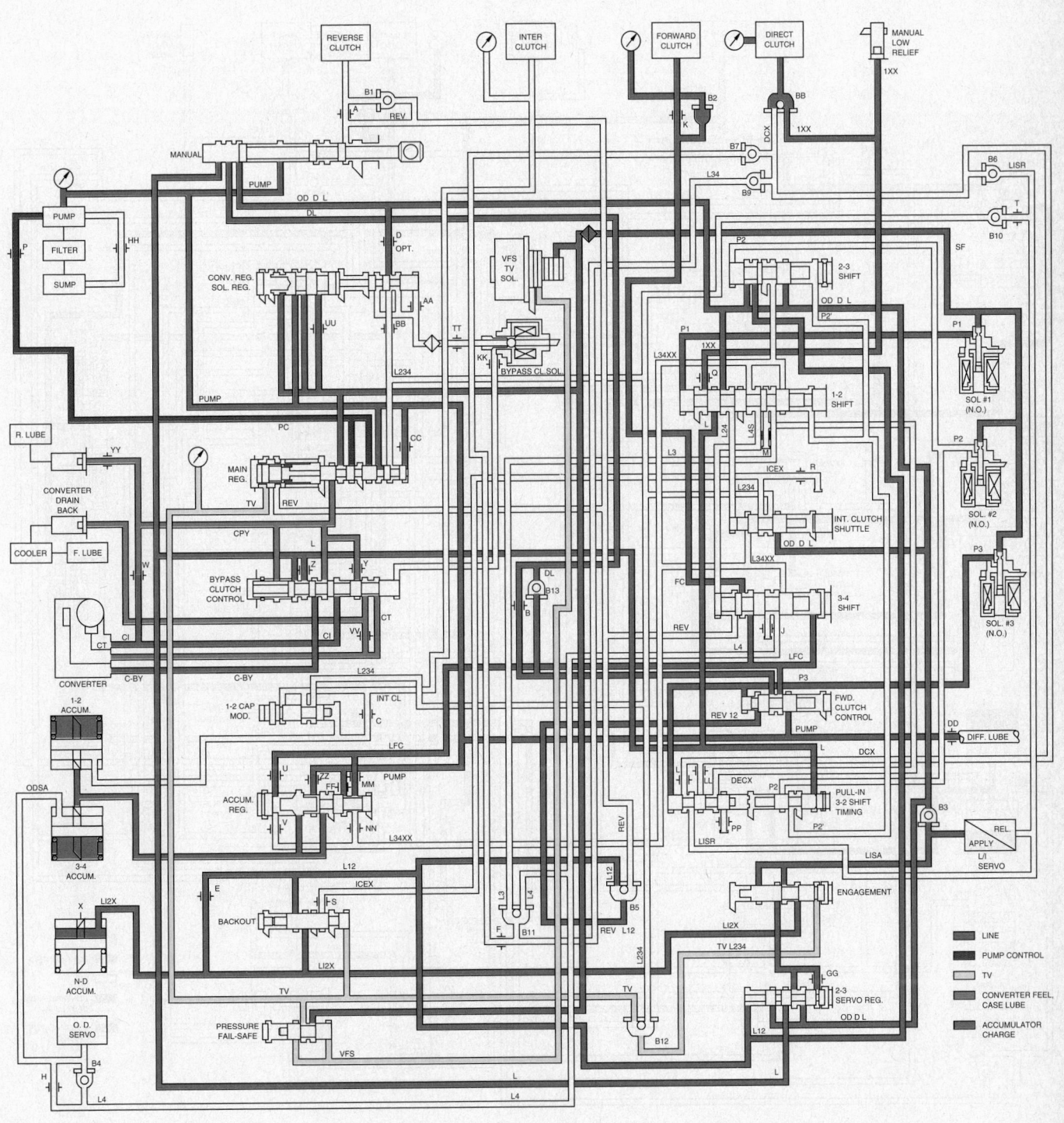

Fig. 7: "L" Range — 1st Gear (Manual Select)

Courtesy of Ford Motor Co.

OIL CIRCUIT DIAGRAMS
Ford AXOD-E (Cont.)

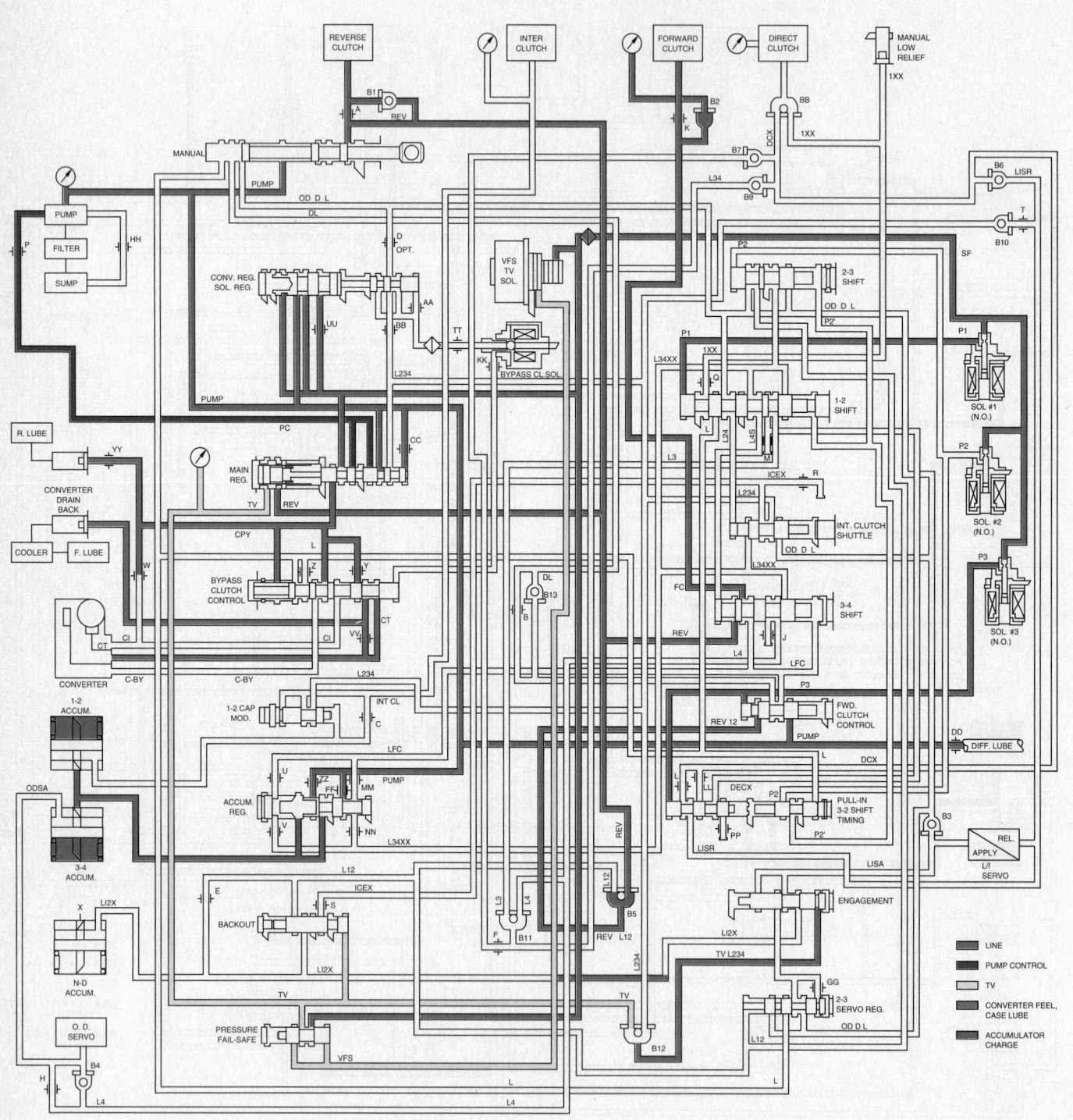

Fig. 8: "R" Range — Reverse Gear

Courtesy of Ford Motor Co.

OIL CIRCUIT DIAGRAMS
Ford CD4E

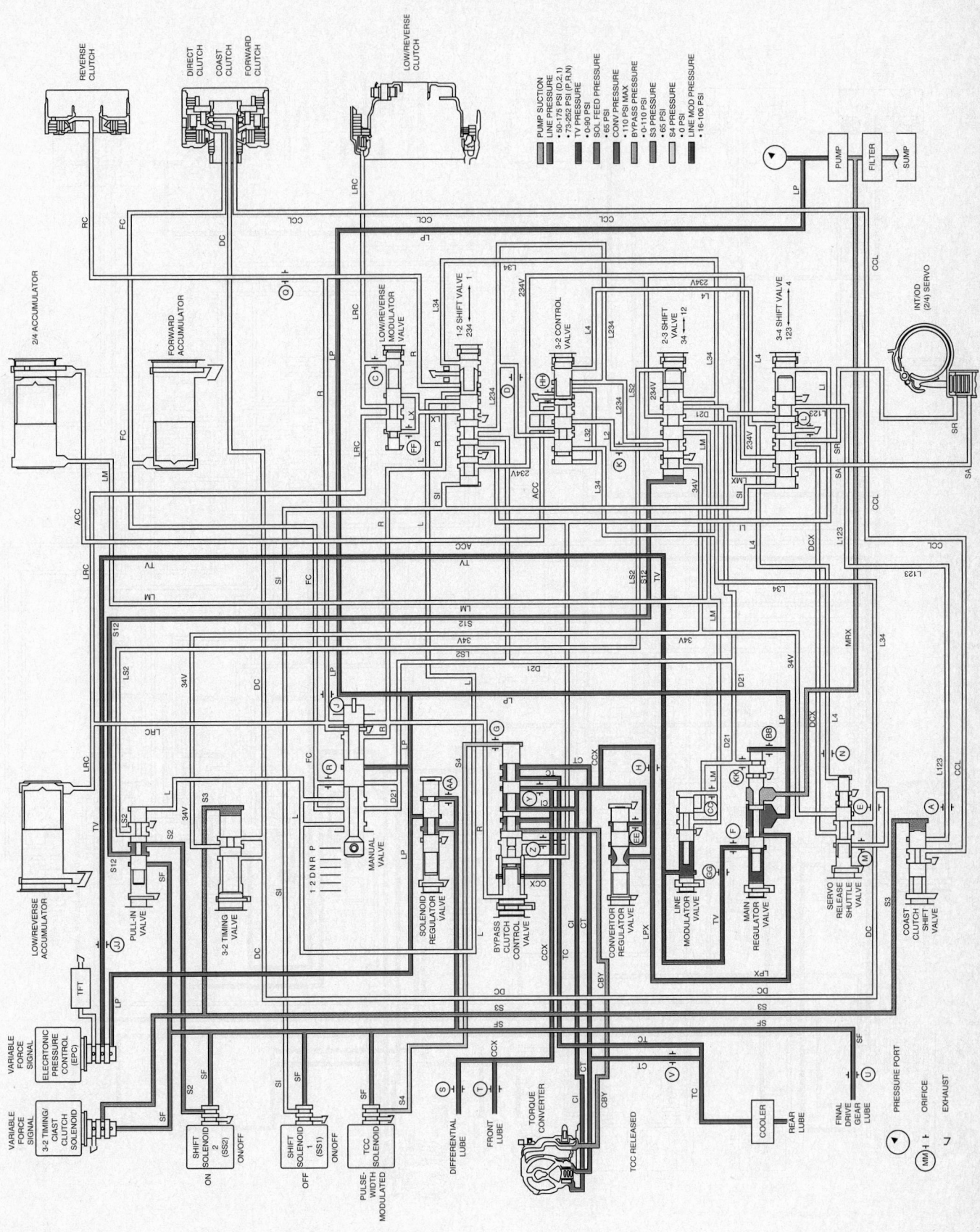

Fig. 1: "P" Or "N" Range — Park Or Neutral

Courtesy of Ford Motor Co.

OIL CIRCUIT DIAGRAMS
Ford CD4E (Cont.)

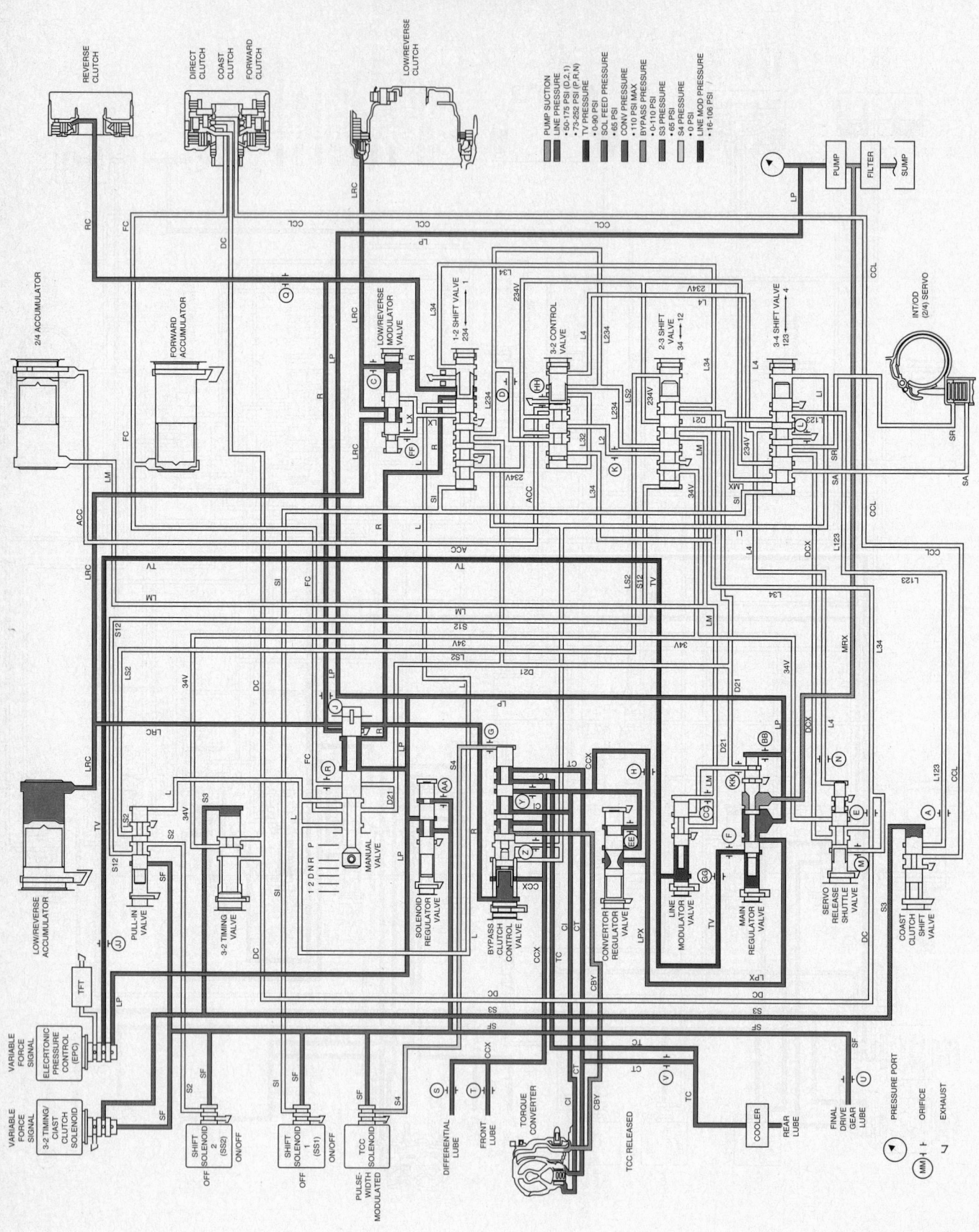

Fig. 2: "R" Range — Reverse Gear

Courtesy of Ford Motor Co.

OIL CIRCUIT DIAGRAMS
Ford CD4E (Cont.)

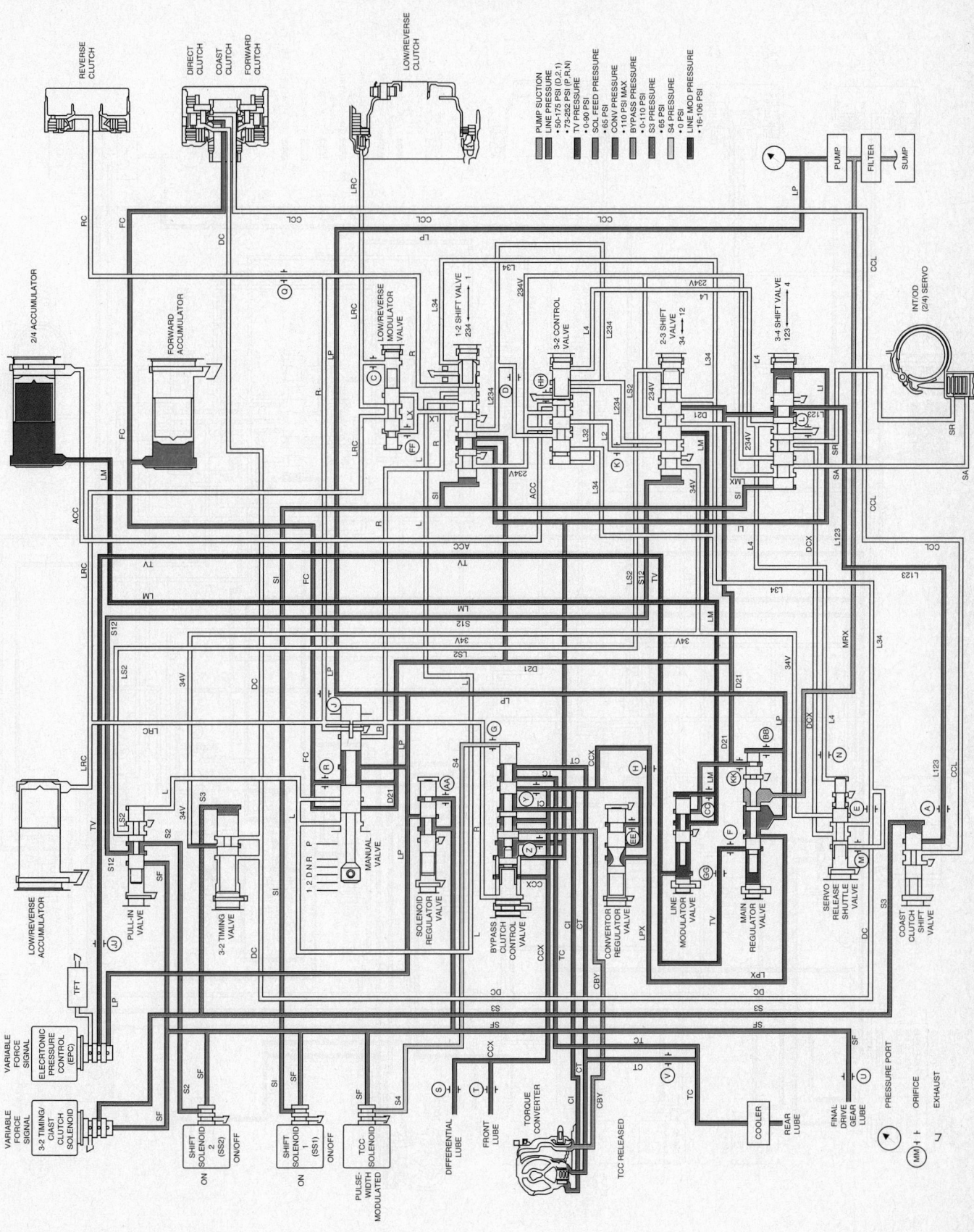

Fig. 3: "D" Or "2" Range — 1st Gear

Courtesy of Ford Motor Co.

OIL CIRCUIT DIAGRAMS
Ford CD4E (Cont.)

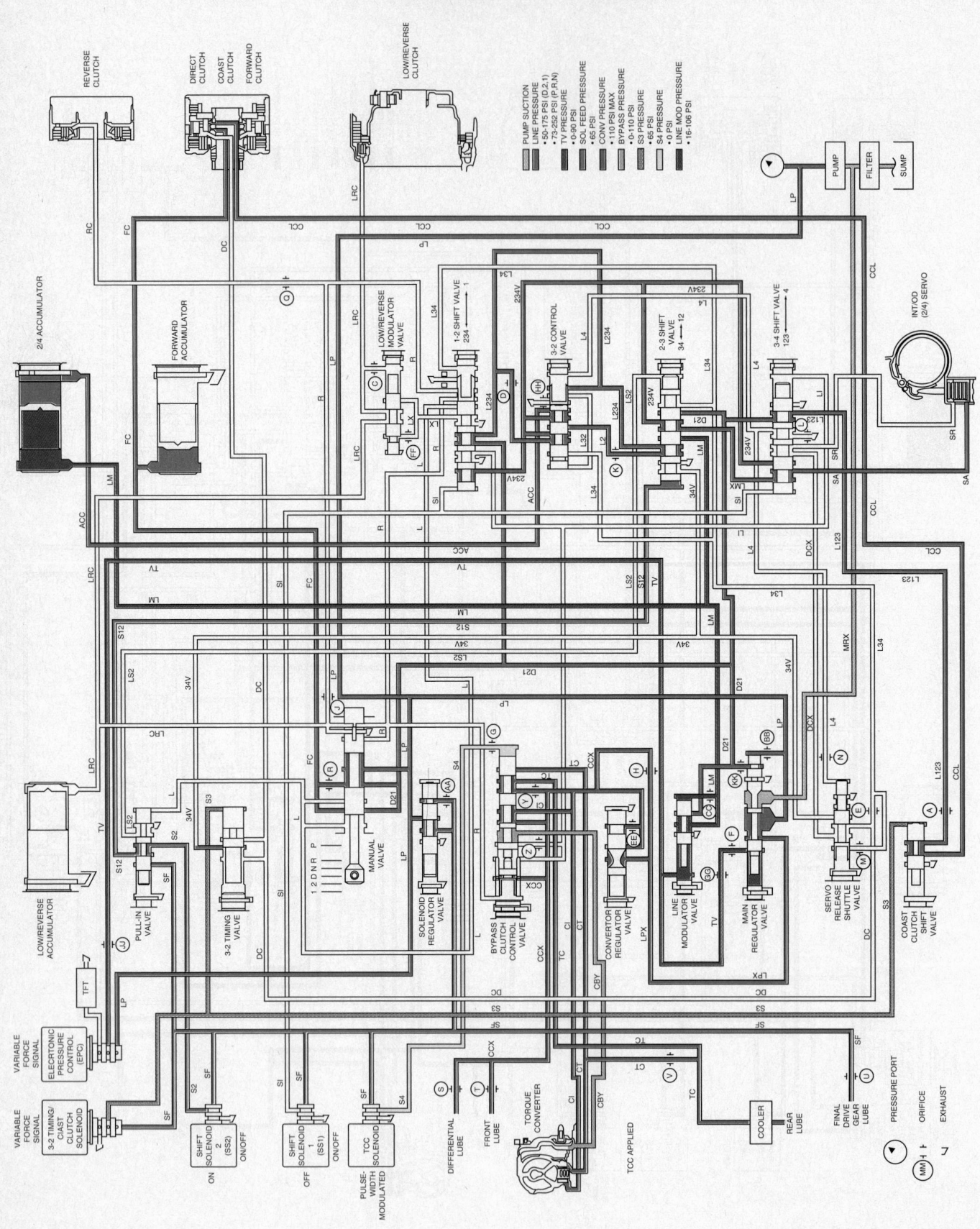

Fig. 4: "D" Or "2" Range — 2nd Gear

Courtesy of Ford Motor Co.

OIL CIRCUIT DIAGRAMS
Ford CD4E (Cont.)

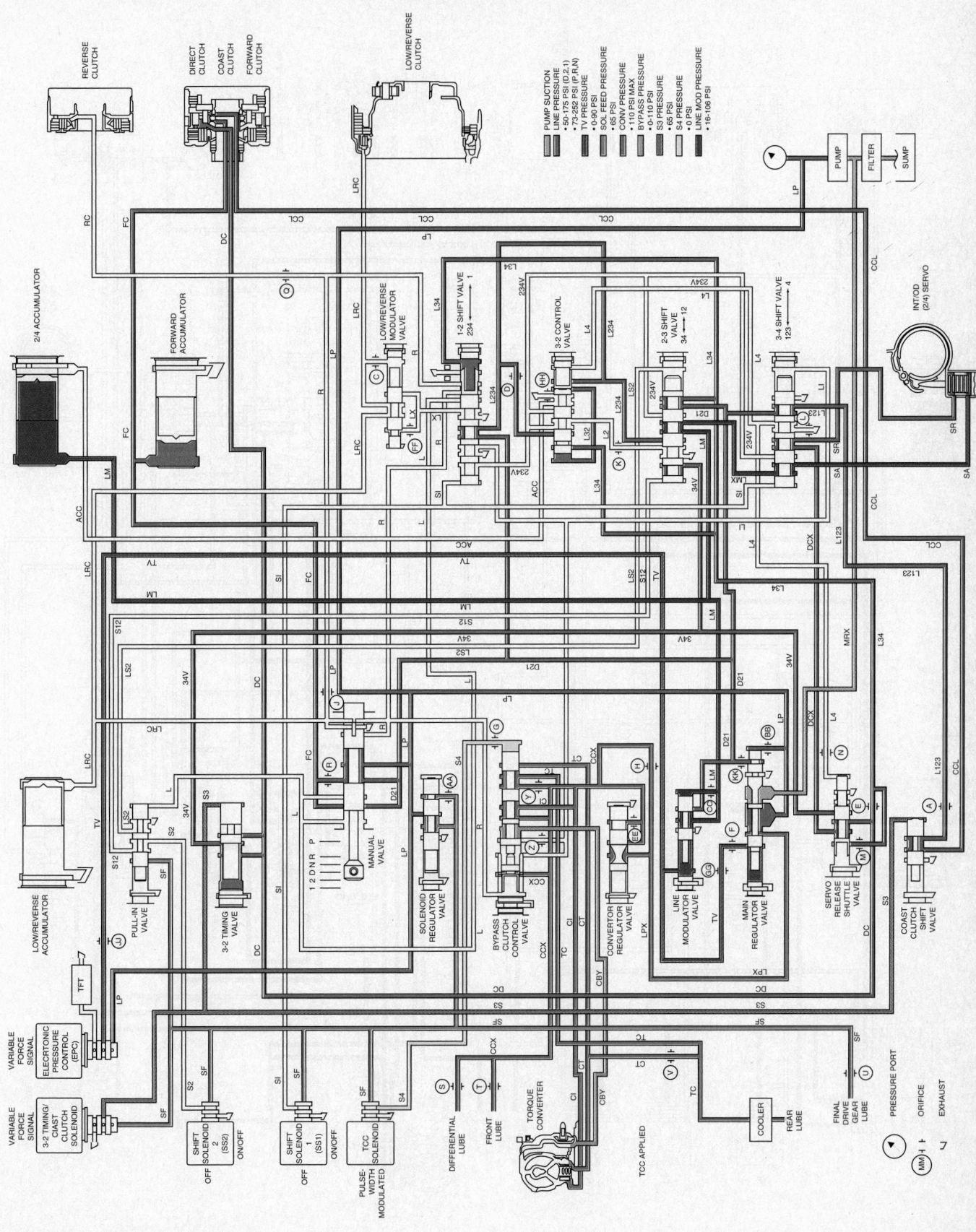

Fig. 5: "D" Or "2" Range — 3rd Gear

Courtesy of Ford Motor Co.

OIL CIRCUIT DIAGRAMS
Ford CD4E (Cont.)

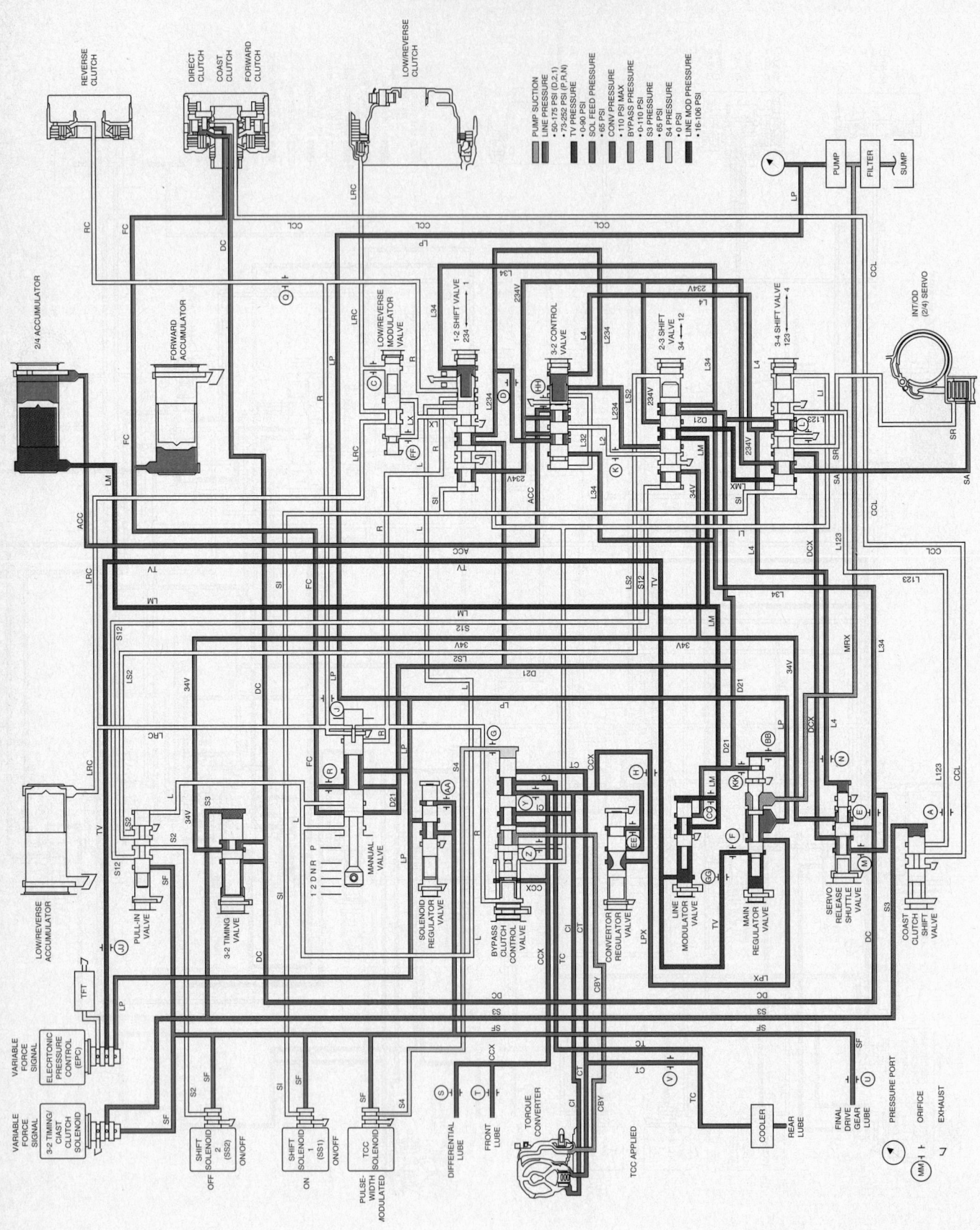

Fig. 6: "D" Range — 4th Gear

Courtesy of Ford Motor Co.

OIL CIRCUIT DIAGRAMS
Ford CD4E (Cont.)

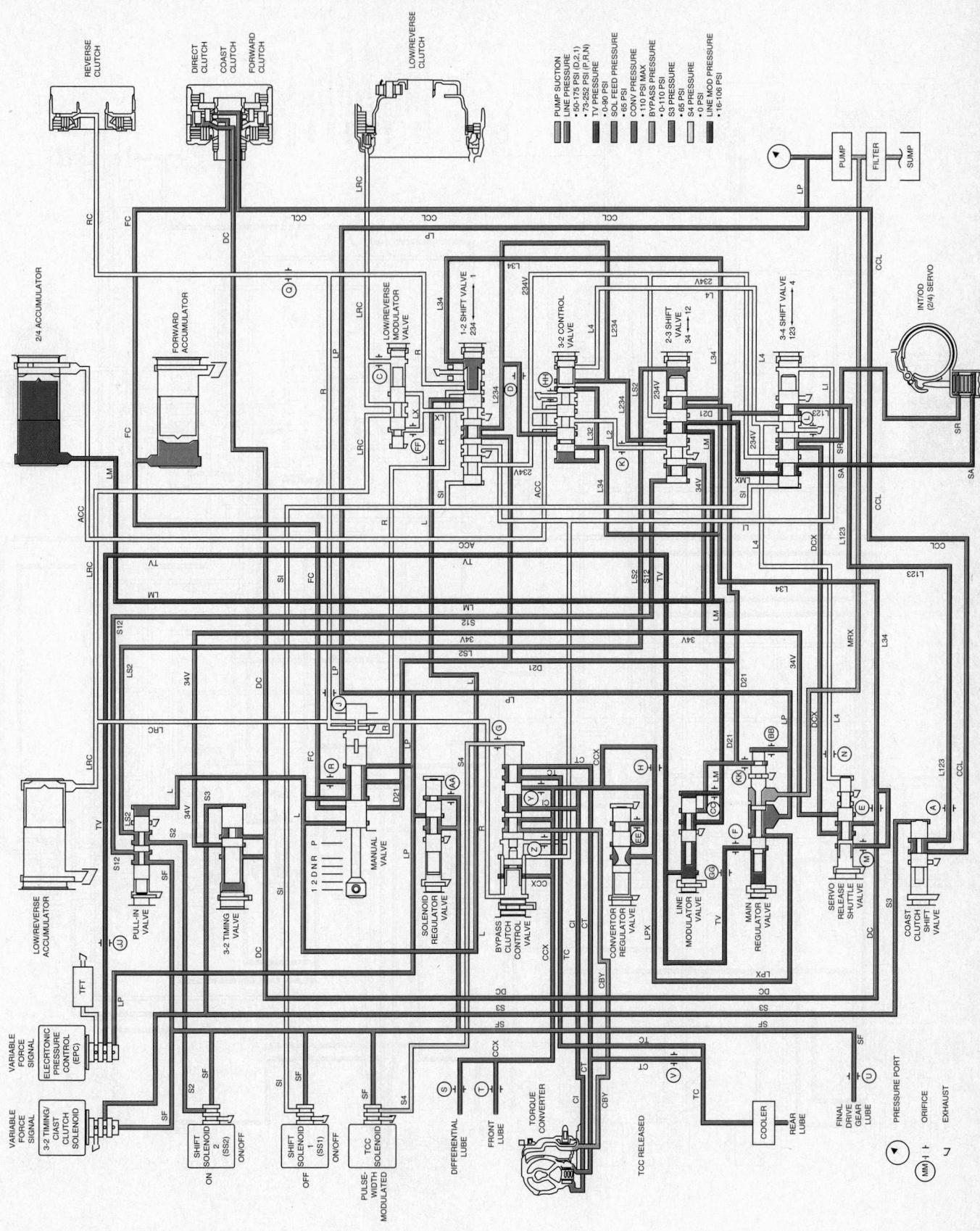

Fig. 7: "1" Range — 3rd Gear

Courtesy of Ford Motor Co.

OIL CIRCUIT DIAGRAMS
Ford CD4E (Cont.)

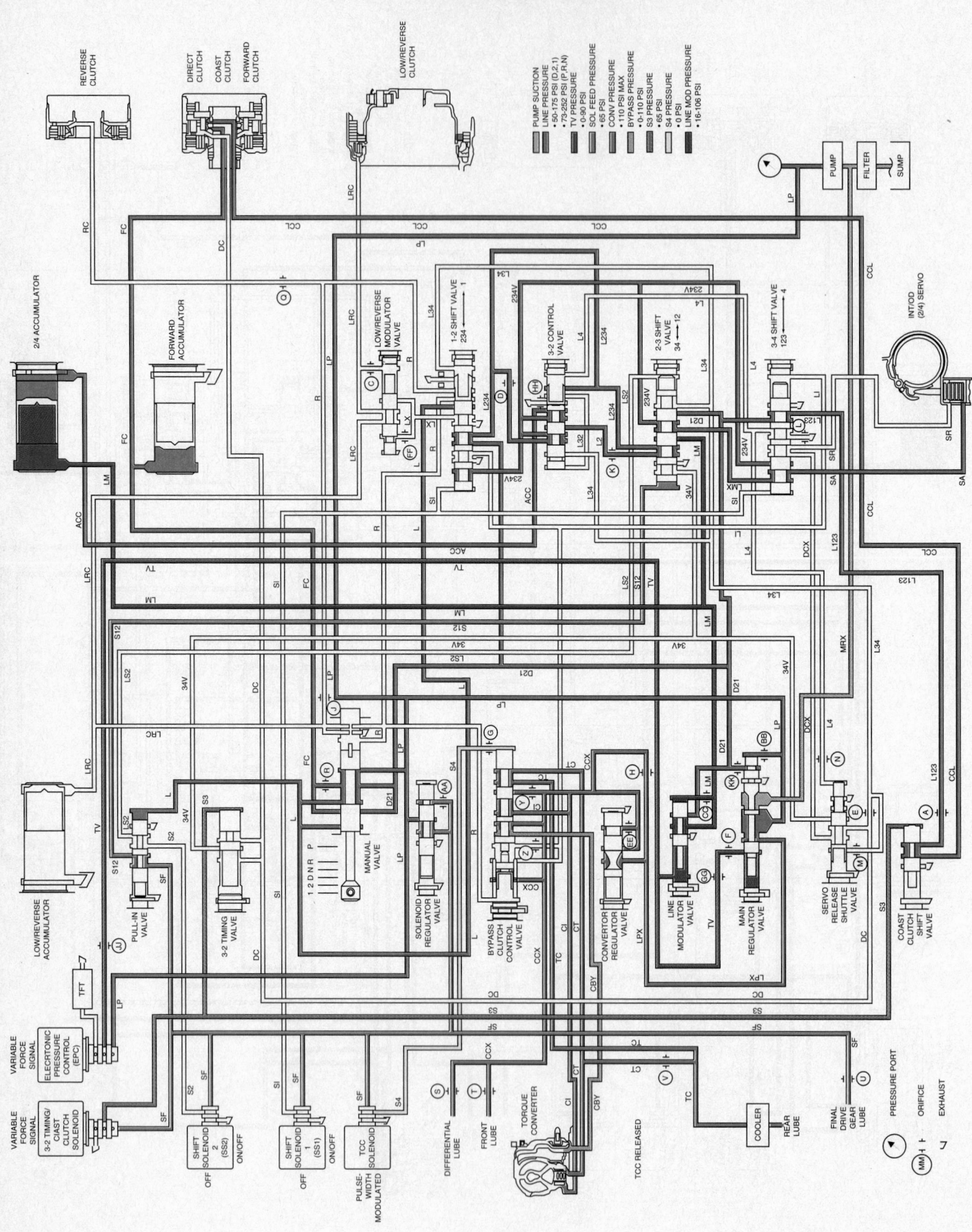

Fig. 8: "1" Range — 2nd Gear

Courtesy of Ford Motor Co.

OIL CIRCUIT DIAGRAMS
Ford CD4E (Cont.)

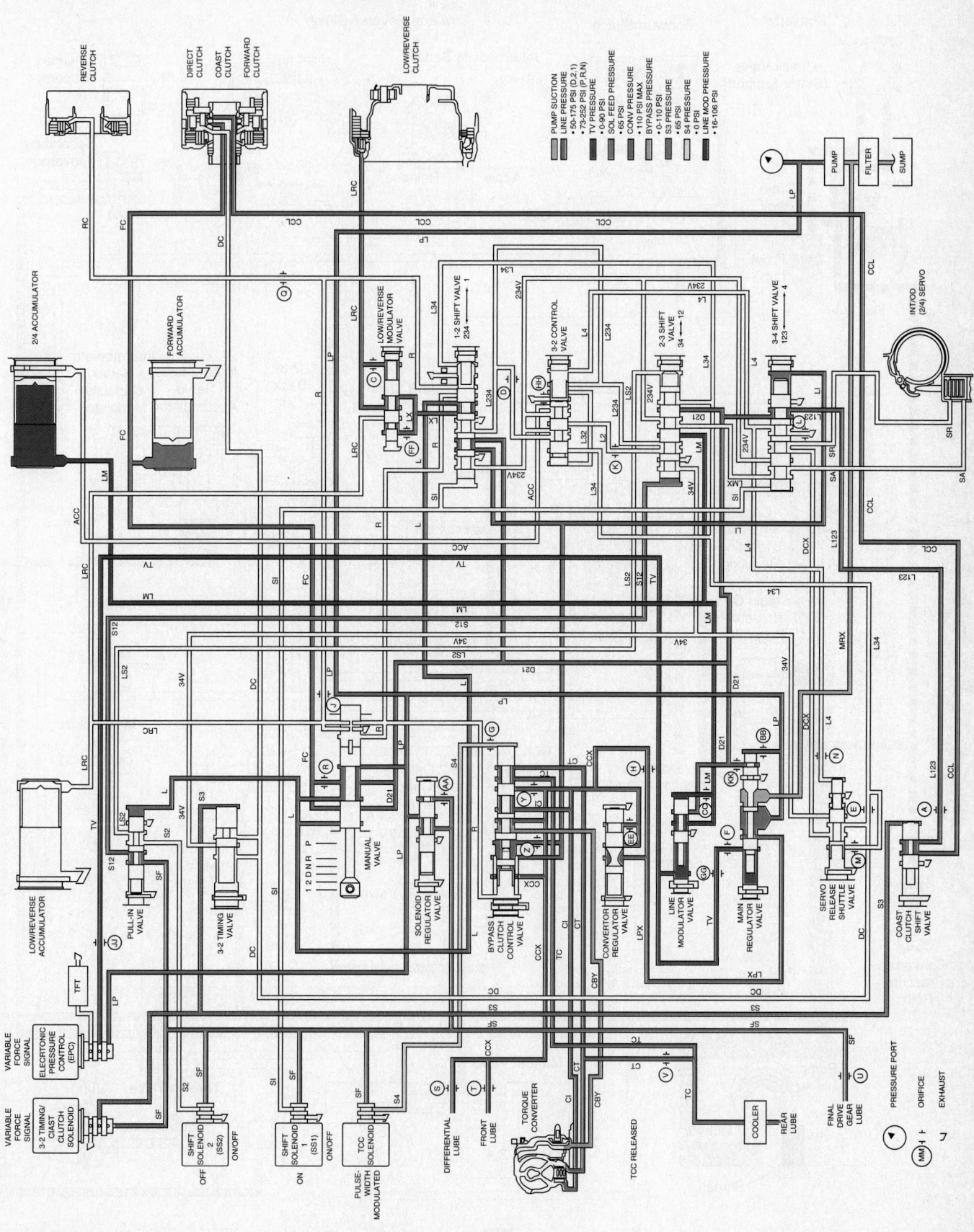

Fig. 9: "1" Range — 1st Gear

Courtesy of Ford Motor Co.

OIL CIRCUIT DIAGRAMS
Ford C6

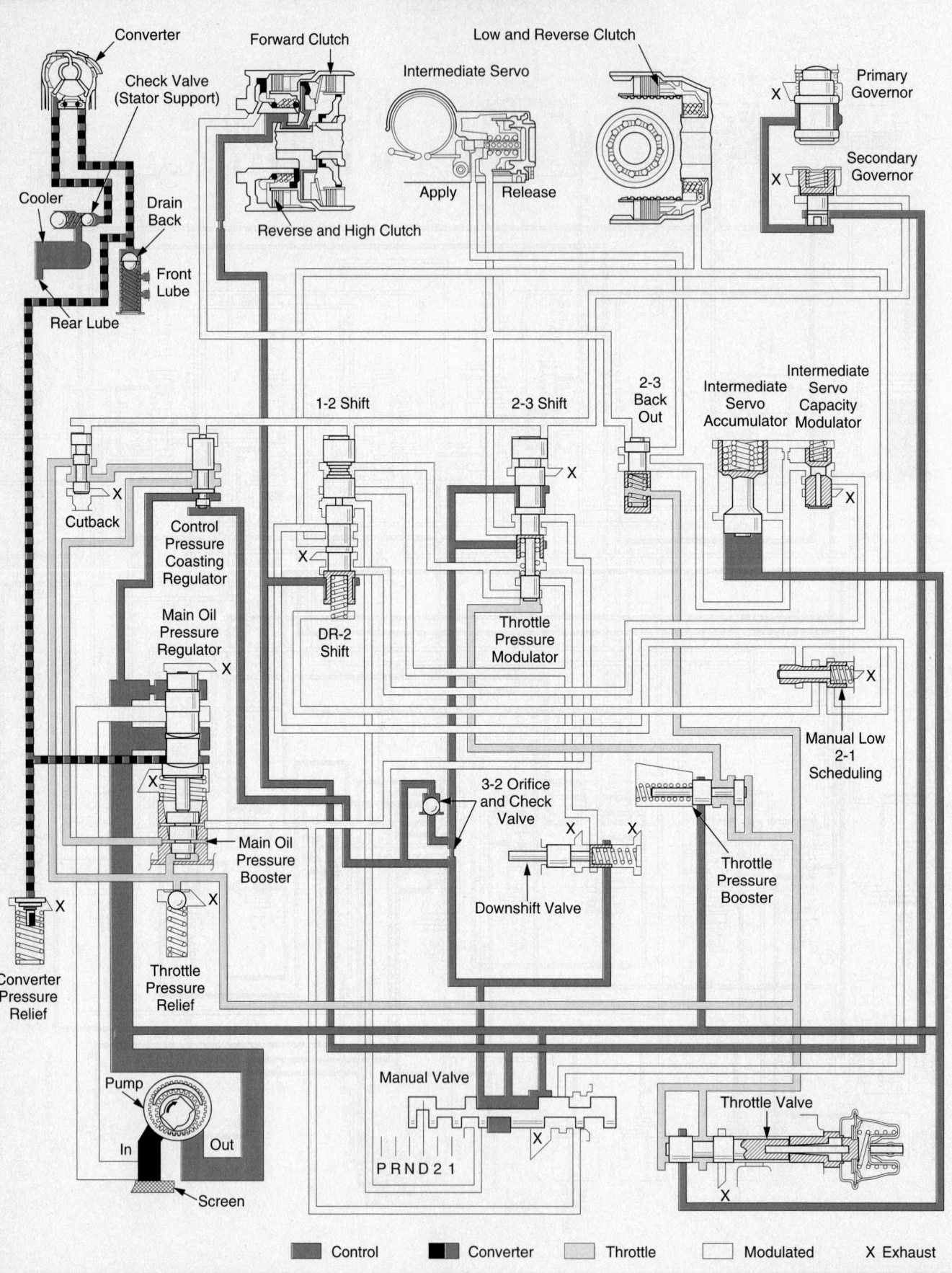

Fig. 1: "D" Range — Transmission Pressures At 14 Inches Of Vacuum — Courtesy of Ford Motor Co.

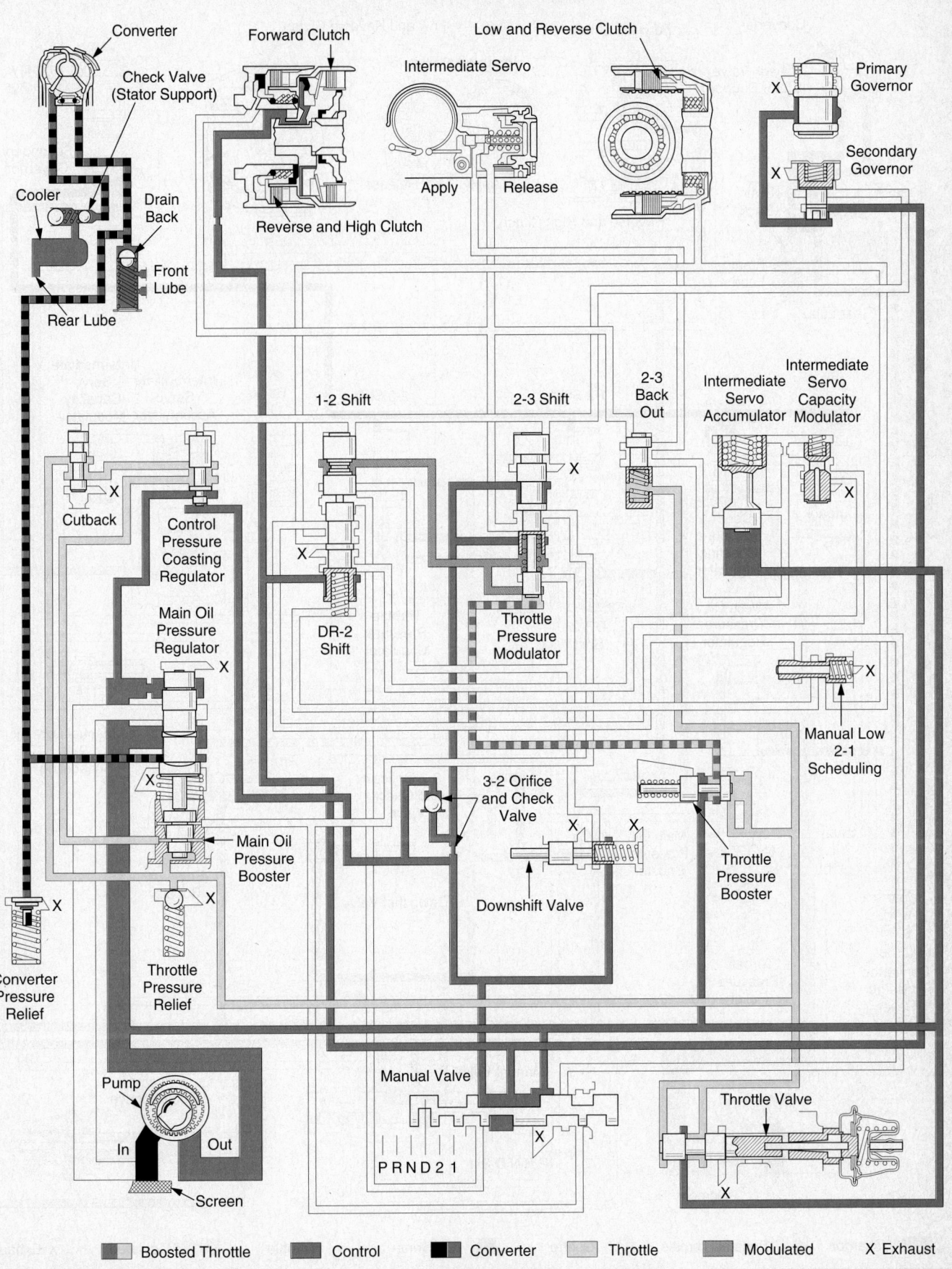

Fig. 2: "D" Range — Transmission Pressures At Less Than One Inch Of Vacuum

Courtesy of Ford Motor Co.

OIL CIRCUIT DIAGRAMS
Ford C6 (Cont.)

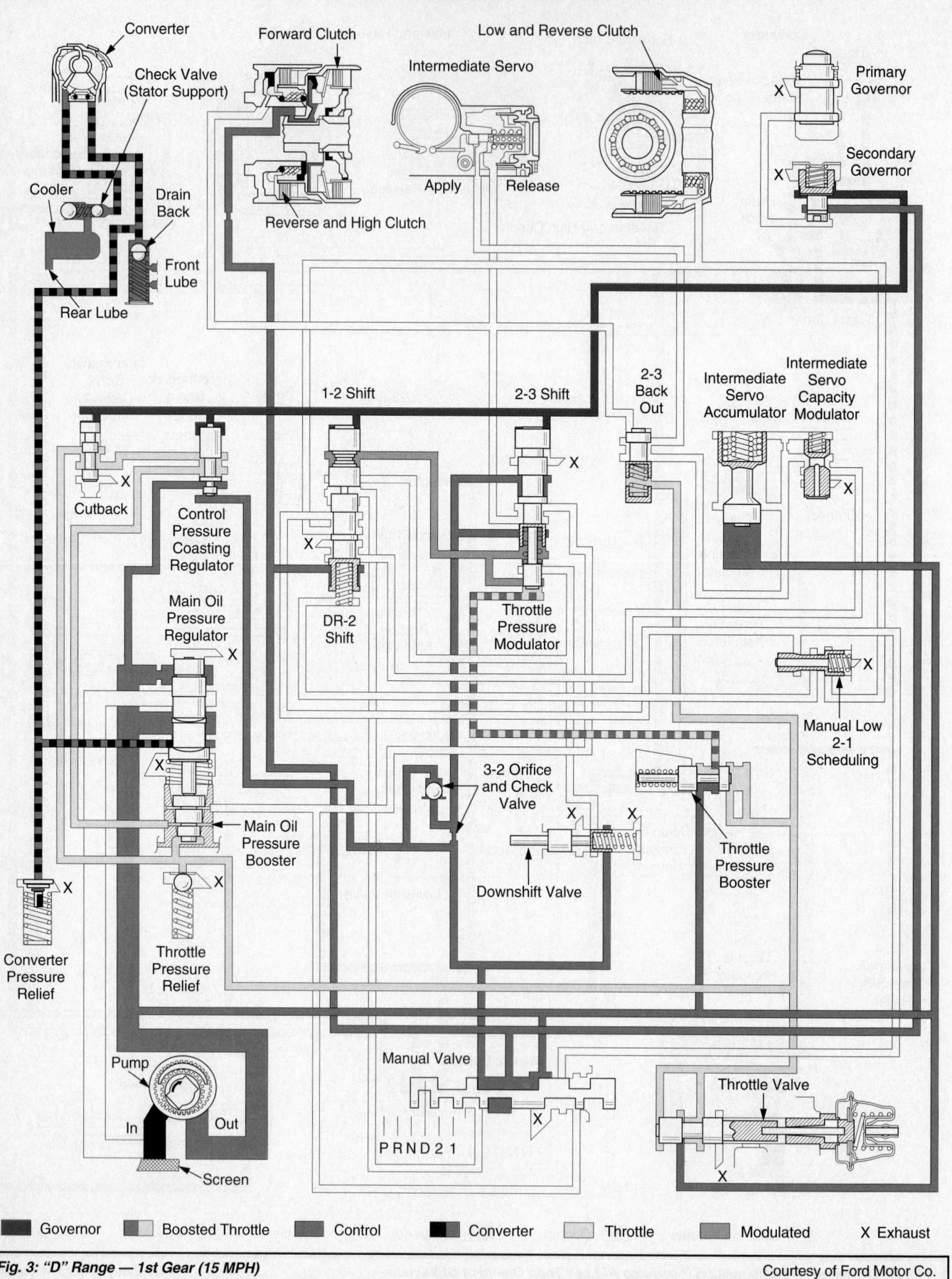

Converter

Check Valve (Stator Support)

Cooler

Drain Back

Front Lube

Rear Lube

Forward Clutch

Reverse and High Clutch

Intermediate Servo

Apply   Release

Low and Reverse Clutch

Primary Governor

Secondary Governor

1-2 Shift

2-3 Shift

2-3 Back Out

Intermediate Servo Accumulator

Intermediate Servo Capacity Modulator

Cutback

Control Pressure Coasting Regulator

Main Oil Pressure Regulator

DR-2 Shift

Throttle Pressure Modulator

Manual Low 2-1 Scheduling

Main Oil Pressure Booster

3-2 Orifice and Check Valve

Downshift Valve

Throttle Pressure Booster

Converter Pressure Relief

Throttle Pressure Relief

Pump

In   Out

Screen

Manual Valve

P R N D 2 1

Throttle Valve

Governor   Boosted Throttle   Control   Converter   Throttle   Modulated   X Exhaust

Fig. 3: "D" Range — 1st Gear (15 MPH)   Courtesy of Ford Motor Co.

OIL CIRCUIT DIAGRAMS
Ford C6 (Cont.)

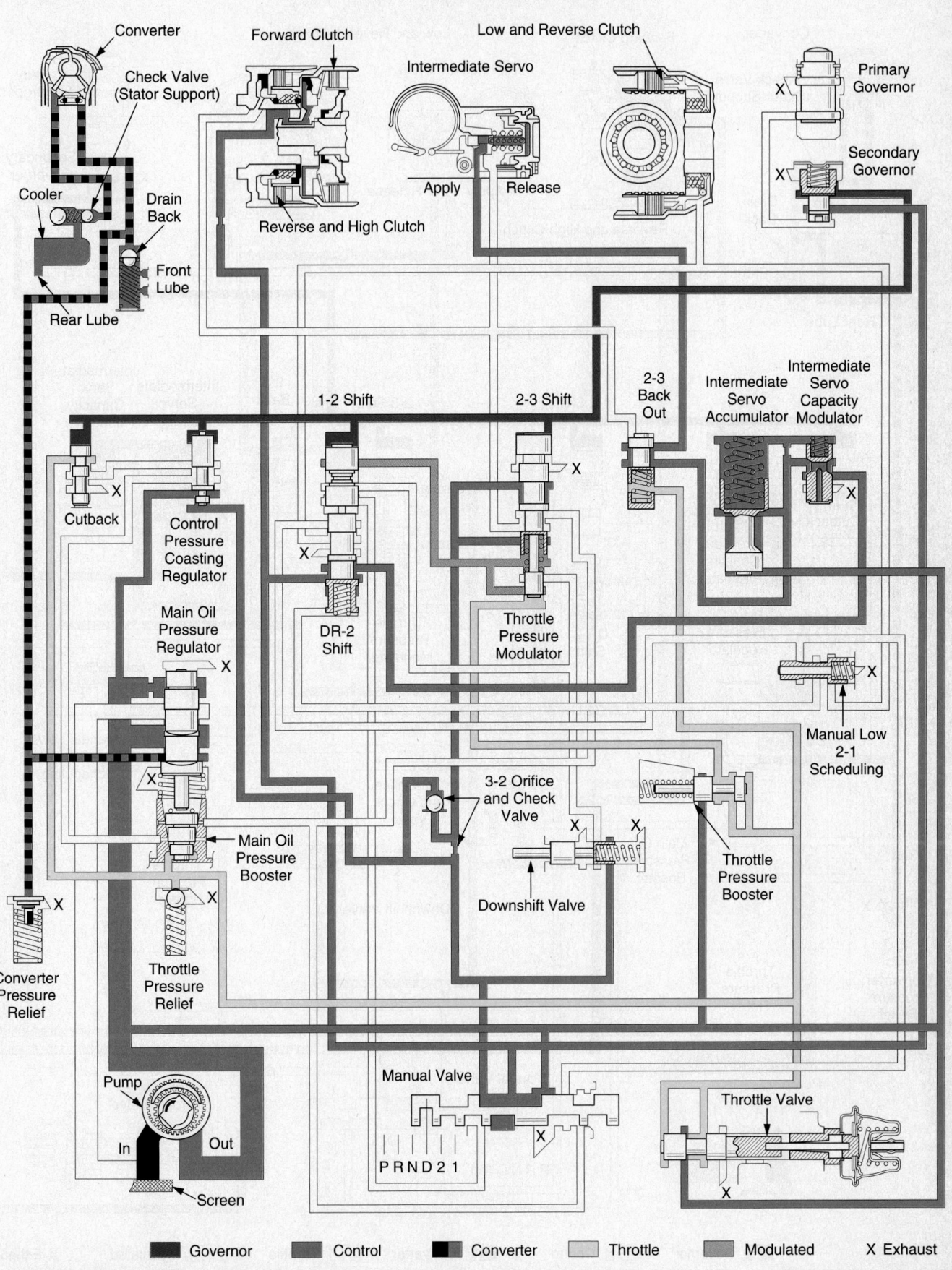

Converter

Check Valve (Stator Support)

Cooler

Drain Back

Front Lube

Rear Lube

Forward Clutch

Reverse and High Clutch

Intermediate Servo

Apply   Release

Low and Reverse Clutch

Primary Governor

Secondary Governor

Cutback

Control Pressure Coasting Regulator

Main Oil Pressure Regulator

Main Oil Pressure Booster

Converter Pressure Relief

Throttle Pressure Relief

1-2 Shift

DR-2 Shift

2-3 Shift

Throttle Pressure Modulator

2-3 Back Out

Intermediate Servo Accumulator

Intermediate Servo Capacity Modulator

Manual Low 2-1 Scheduling

3-2 Orifice and Check Valve

Downshift Valve

Throttle Pressure Booster

Pump

In   Out

Screen

Manual Valve

P R N D 2 1

Throttle Valve

Governor   Control   Converter   Throttle   Modulated   X Exhaust

Fig. 4: "D" Range — 2nd Gear (20 MPH)

Courtesy of Ford Motor Co.

OIL CIRCUIT DIAGRAMS
Ford C6 (Cont.)

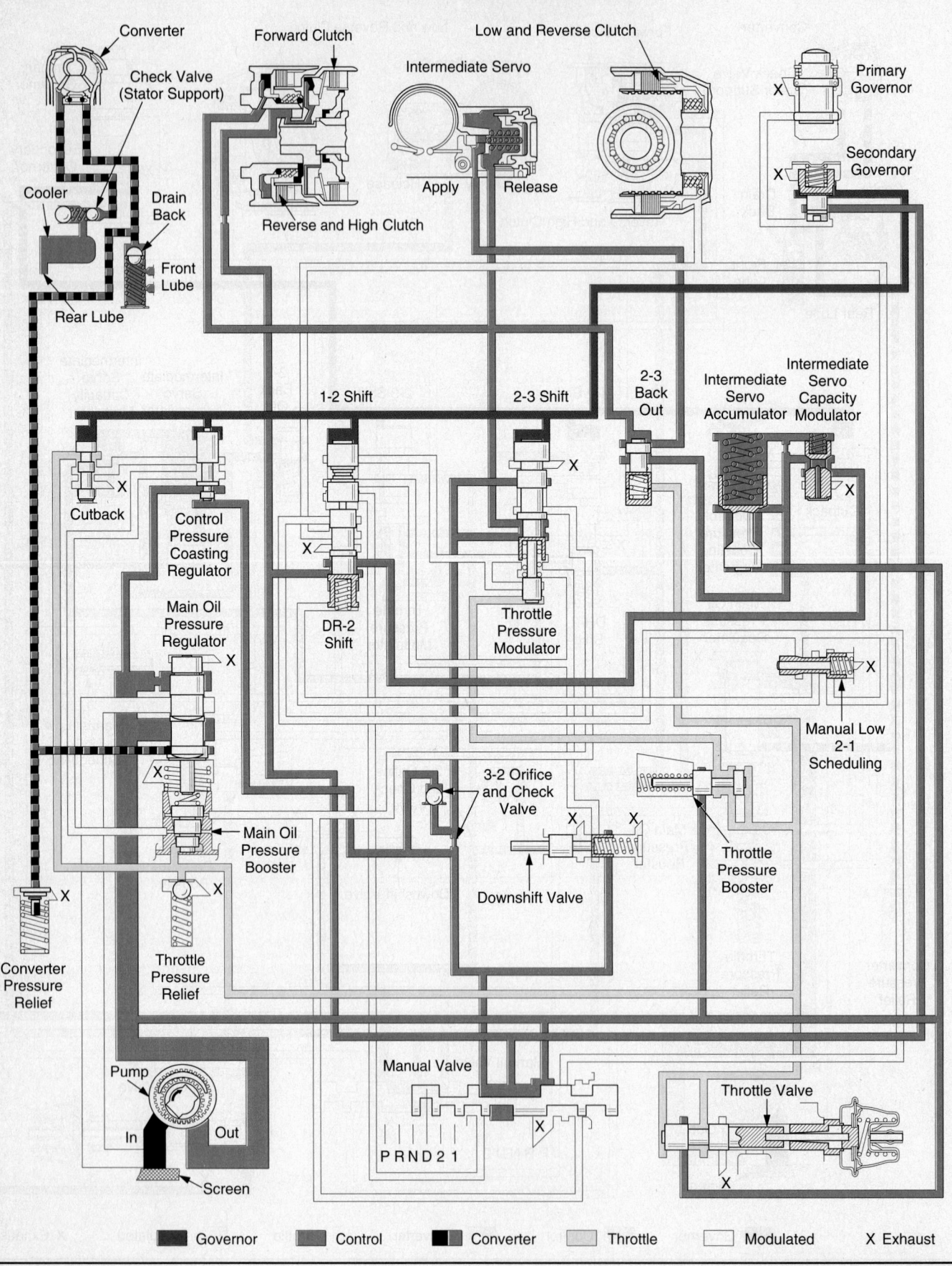

Fig. 5: "D" Range — High Gear

Courtesy of Ford Motor Co.

OIL CIRCUIT DIAGRAMS
Ford C6 (Cont.)

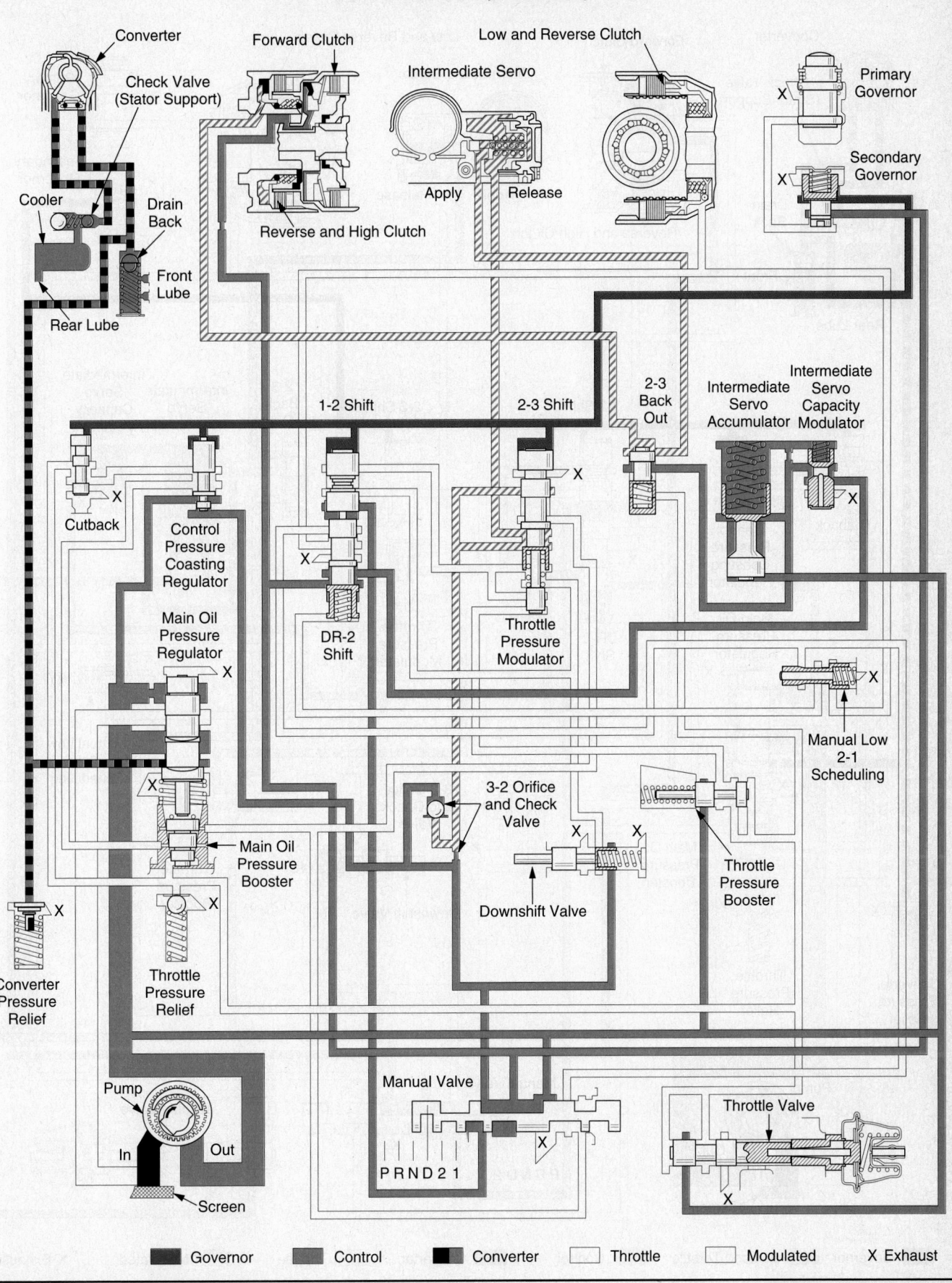

Fig. 6: "D" Range — 2-3 Shift (Back-Out)

Courtesy of Ford Motor Co.

OIL CIRCUIT DIAGRAMS
Ford C6 (Cont.)

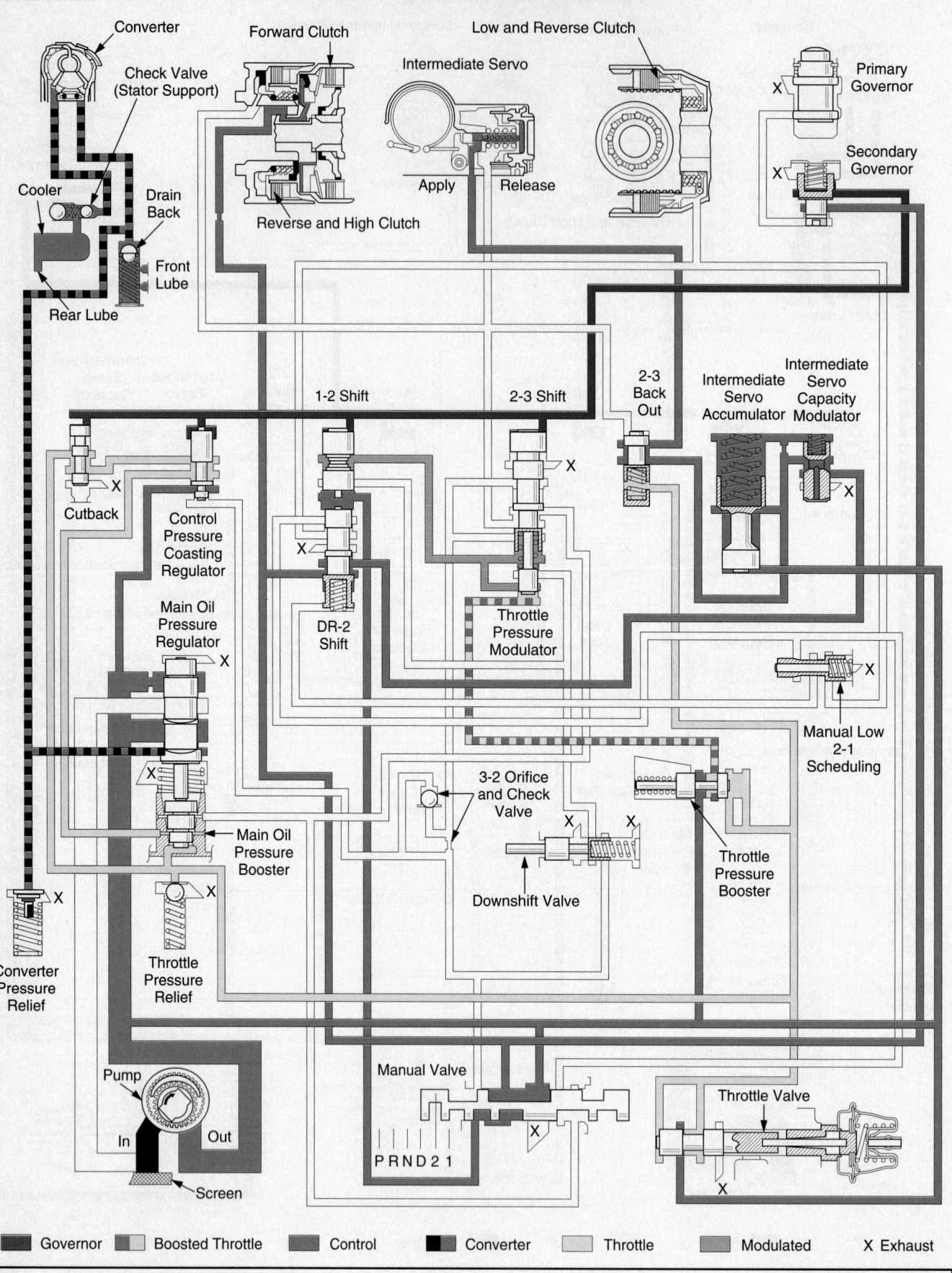

Converter

Check Valve
(Stator Support)

Cooler

Drain
Back

Rear Lube

Front
Lube

Forward Clutch

Reverse and High Clutch

Intermediate Servo

Apply   Release

Low and Reverse Clutch

Primary
Governor

Secondary
Governor

1-2 Shift

2-3 Shift

2-3
Back
Out

Intermediate
Servo
Accumulator

Intermediate
Servo
Capacity
Modulator

Cutback

Control
Pressure
Coasting
Regulator

Main Oil
Pressure
Regulator

DR-2
Shift

Throttle
Pressure
Modulator

Manual Low
2-1
Scheduling

Main Oil
Pressure
Booster

3-2 Orifice
and Check
Valve

Downshift Valve

Throttle
Pressure
Booster

Converter
Pressure
Relief

Throttle
Pressure
Relief

Pump

In   Out

Screen

Manual Valve

P R N D 2 1

Throttle Valve

| ■ Governor | ▨ Boosted Throttle | ▨ Control | ■ Converter | ▨ Throttle | ▨ Modulated | X Exhaust |

Fig. 7: "2" Range — 2nd Gear (Manual Select)   Courtesy of Ford Motor Co.

OIL CIRCUIT DIAGRAMS
Ford C6 (Cont.)

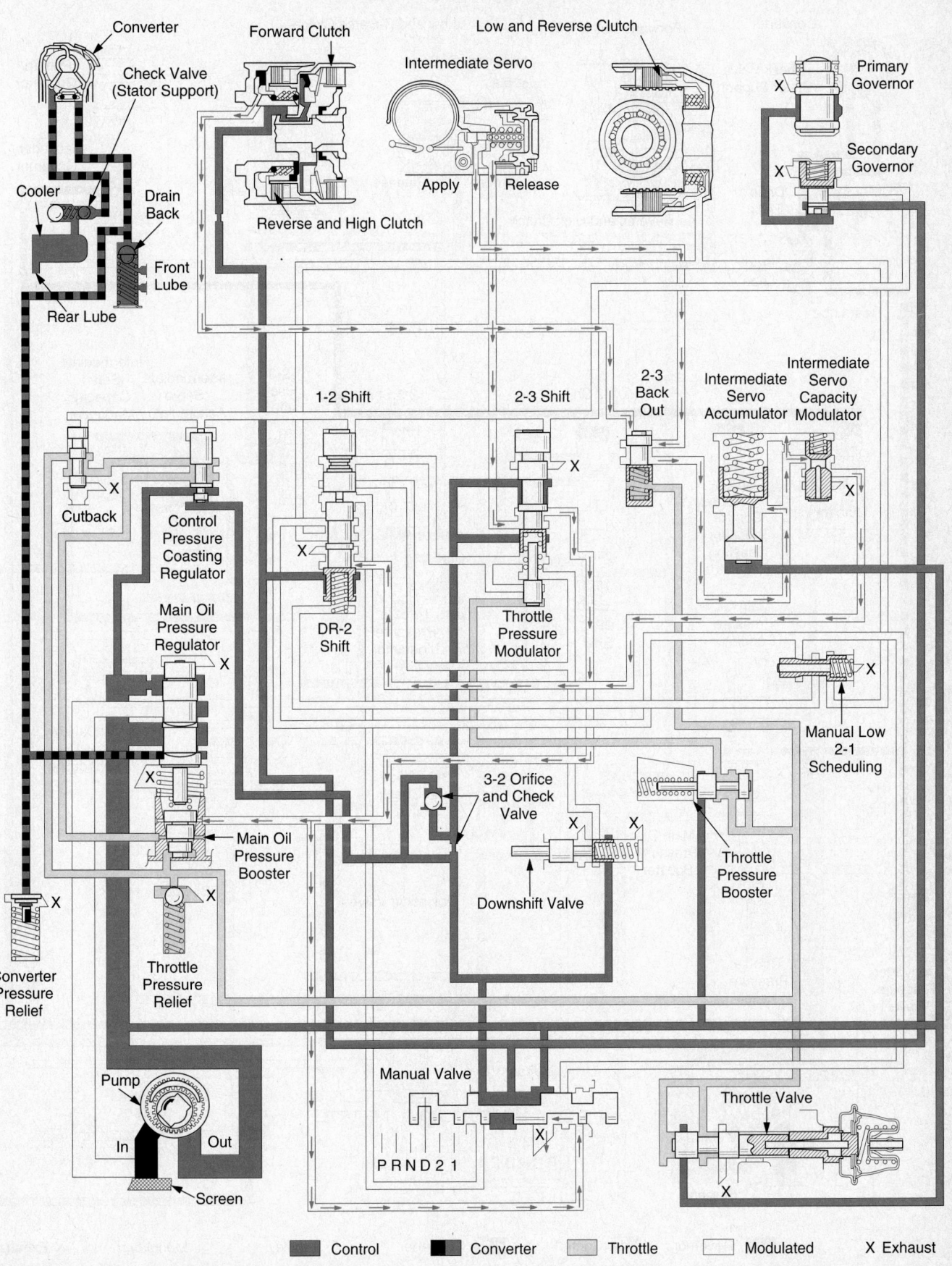

Converter

Forward Clutch

Low and Reverse Clutch

Check Valve
(Stator Support)

Intermediate Servo

Primary Governor

Cooler

Drain Back

Apply   Release

Secondary Governor

Rear Lube

Reverse and High Clutch

Front Lube

1-2 Shift

2-3 Shift

2-3 Back Out

Intermediate Servo Accumulator

Intermediate Servo Capacity Modulator

Cutback

Control Pressure Coasting Regulator

DR-2 Shift

Throttle Pressure Modulator

Manual Low 2-1 Scheduling

Main Oil Pressure Regulator

Main Oil Pressure Booster

3-2 Orifice and Check Valve

Throttle Pressure Booster

Converter Pressure Relief

Throttle Pressure Relief

Downshift Valve

Pump

Manual Valve

Throttle Valve

In   Out

Screen

P R N D 2 1

| Control | Converter | Throttle | Modulated | X Exhaust |

Fig. 8: "D" Range — 3-1 Downshift (Closed Throttle)

Courtesy of Ford Motor Co.

OIL CIRCUIT DIAGRAMS
Ford C6 (Cont.)

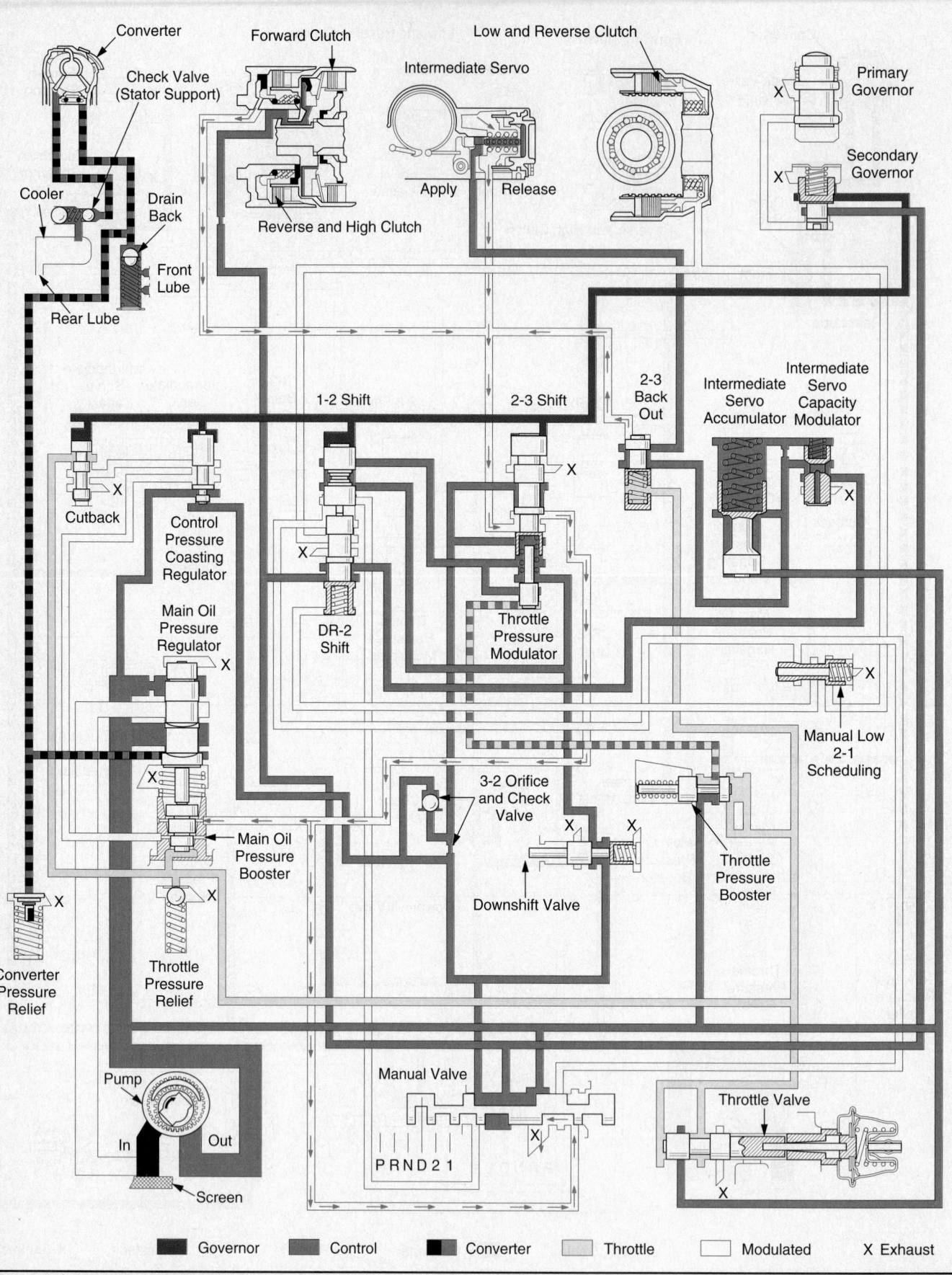

| | Governor | | Control | | Converter | | Throttle | | Modulated | X Exhaust |

Fig. 9: "D" Range — 3-2 Downshift

Courtesy of Ford Motor Co.

OIL CIRCUIT DIAGRAMS
Ford C6 (Cont.)

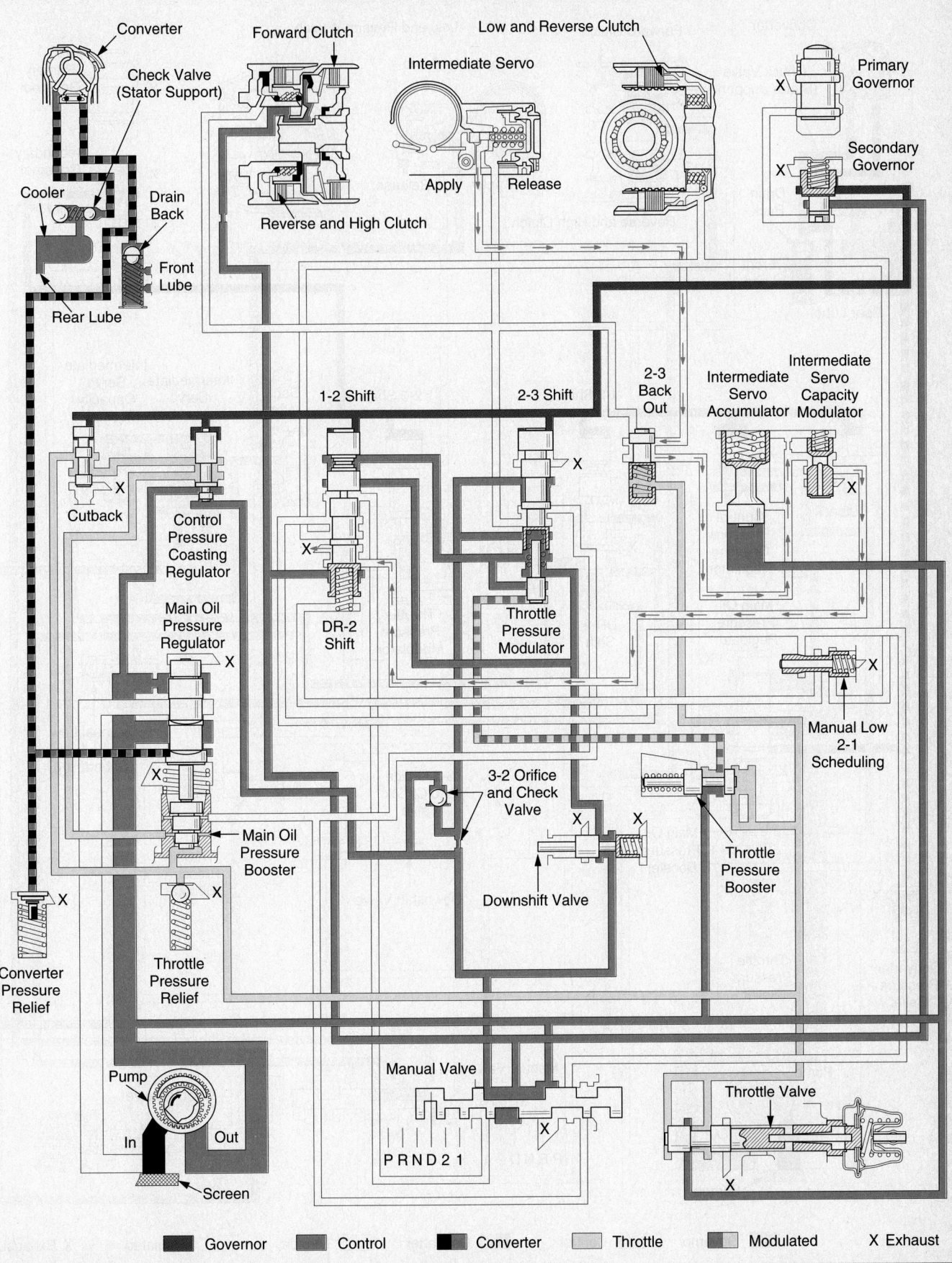

Fig. 10: "D" Range — Downshift To Low

Courtesy of Ford Motor Co.

OIL CIRCUIT DIAGRAMS
Ford C6 (Cont.)

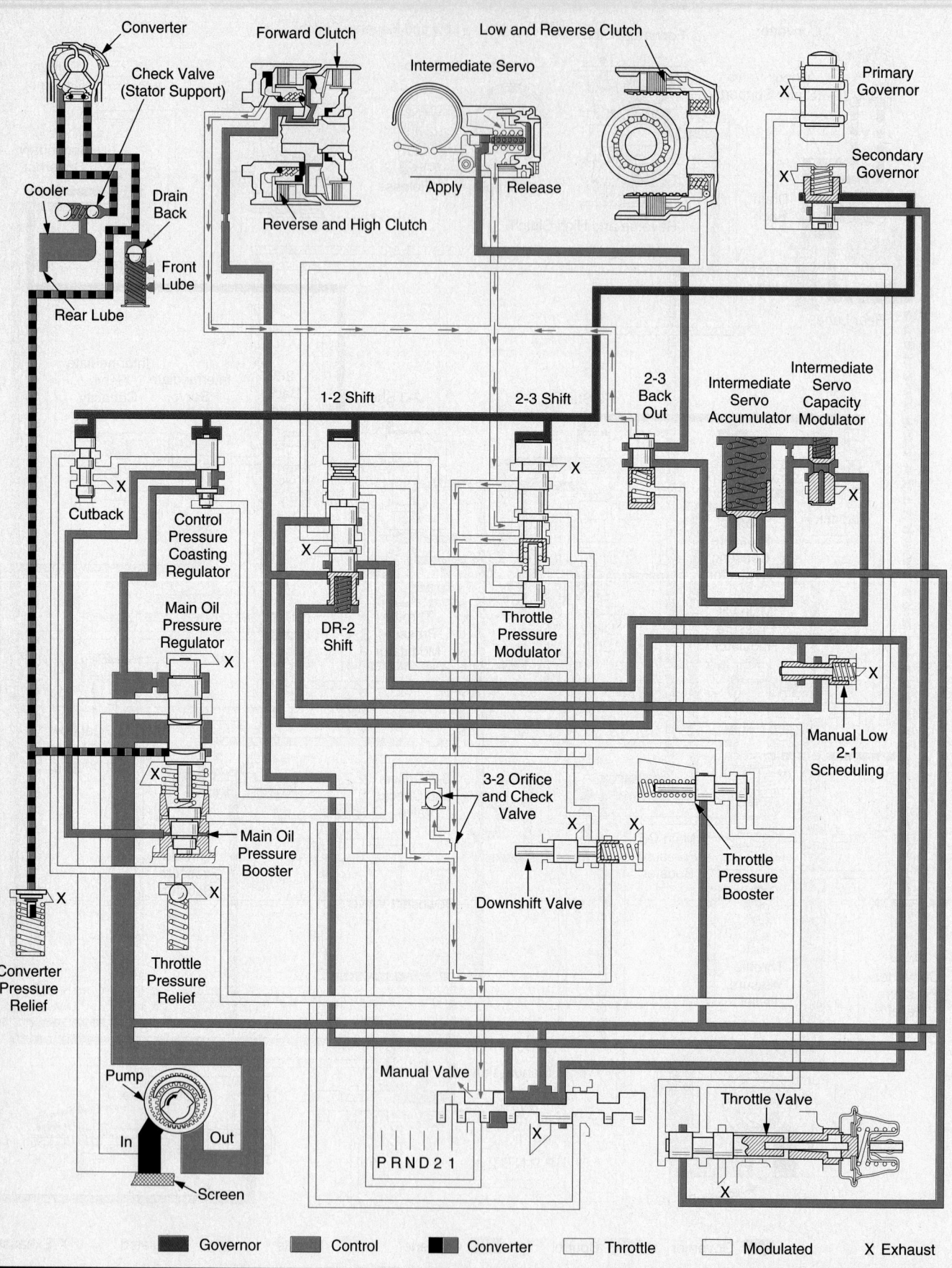

Fig. 11: "1" Range — Manual Downshift From "D"   Courtesy of Ford Motor Co.

OIL CIRCUIT DIAGRAMS
Ford C6 (Cont.)

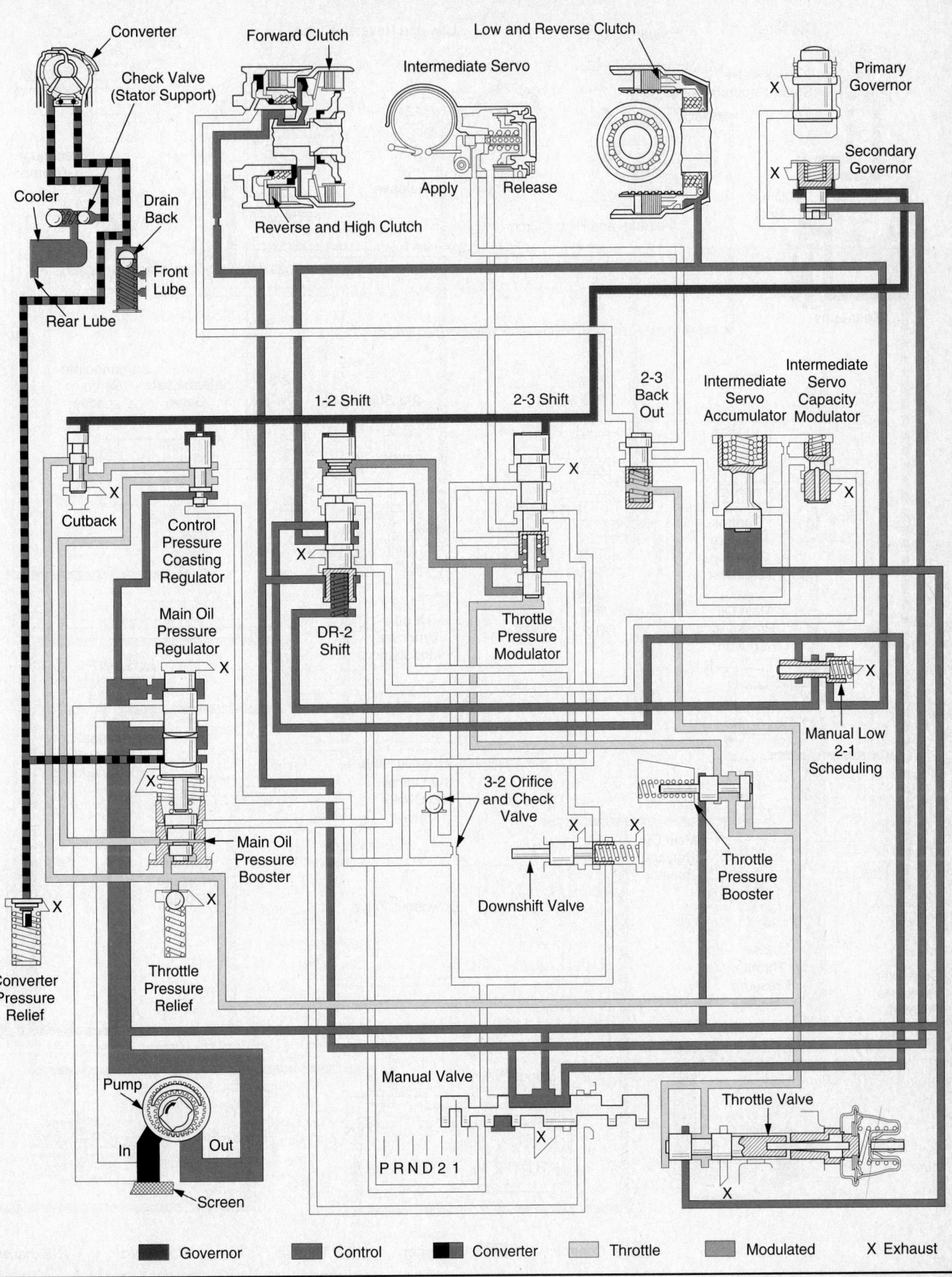

Converter

Check Valve (Stator Support)

Cooler

Drain Back

Front Lube

Rear Lube

Forward Clutch

Reverse and High Clutch

Low and Reverse Clutch

Intermediate Servo

Apply   Release

Primary Governor

Secondary Governor

1-2 Shift

2-3 Shift

2-3 Back Out

Intermediate Servo Accumulator

Intermediate Servo Capacity Modulator

Cutback

Control Pressure Coasting Regulator

Main Oil Pressure Regulator

DR-2 Shift

Throttle Pressure Modulator

Manual Low 2-1 Scheduling

Main Oil Pressure Booster

3-2 Orifice and Check Valve

Throttle Pressure Booster

Downshift Valve

Converter Pressure Relief

Throttle Pressure Relief

Pump

In   Out

Screen

Manual Valve

P R N D 2 1

Throttle Valve

| ▉ Governor | ▉ Control | ▉ Converter | ▉ Throttle | ▉ Modulated | X Exhaust |

Fig. 12: "1" Range — Manual Low Start

Courtesy of Ford Motor Co.

OIL CIRCUIT DIAGRAMS
Ford C6 (Cont.)

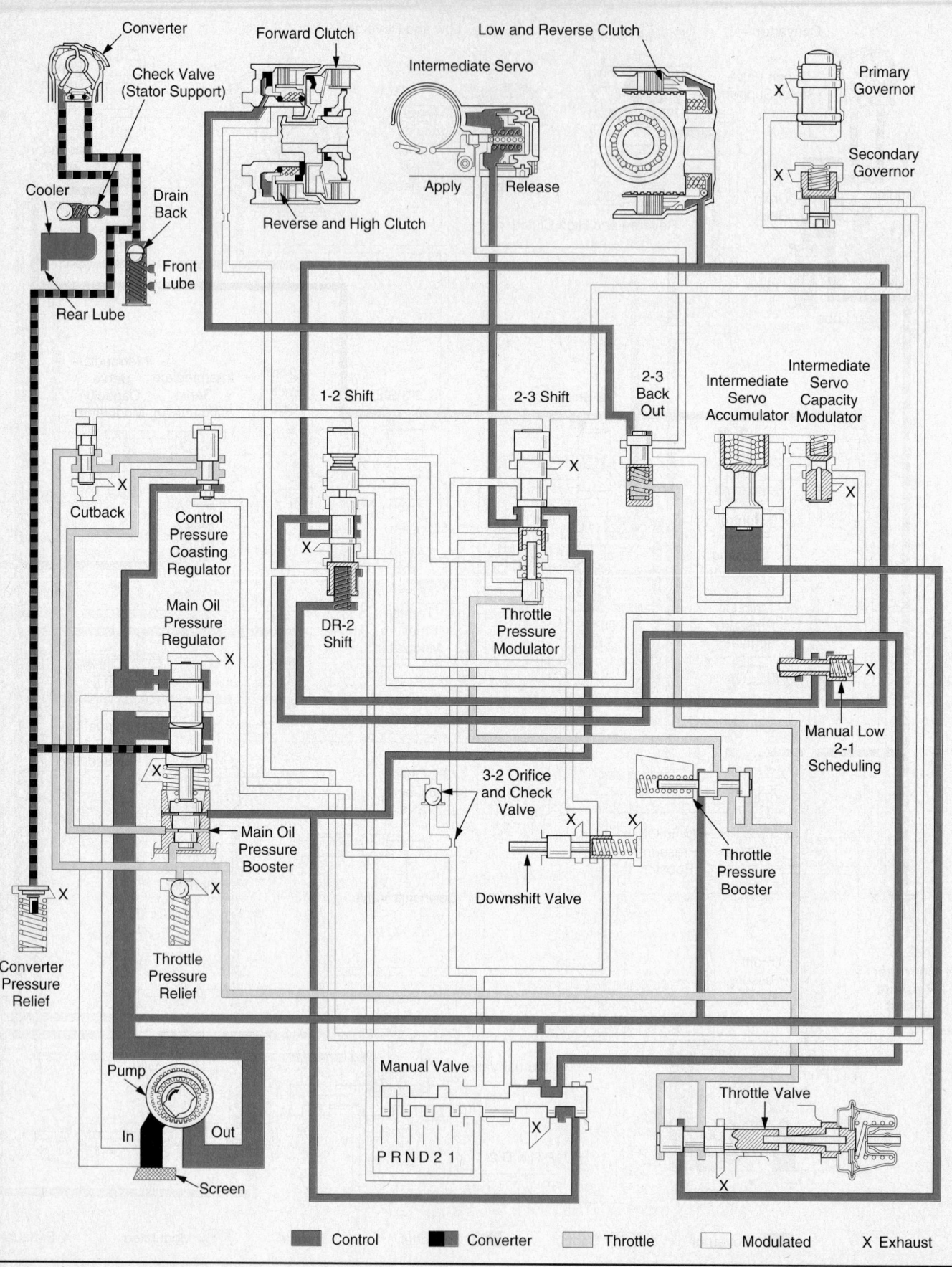

Fig. 13: "R" Range — Reverse

Courtesy of Ford Motor Co.

OIL CIRCUIT DIAGRAMS
Ford 4EAT

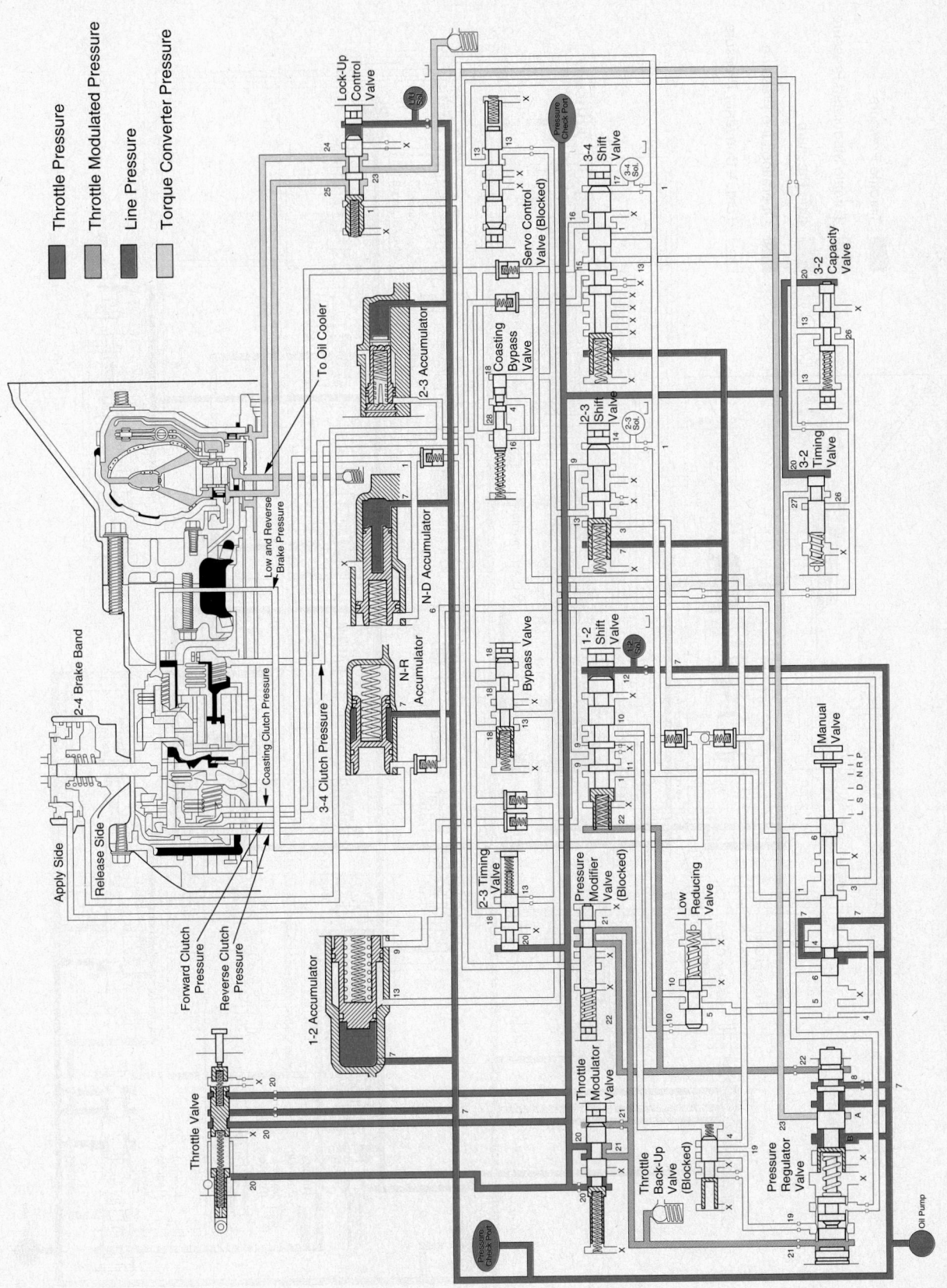

OIL CIRCUIT DIAGRAMS
Ford 4EAT (Cont.)

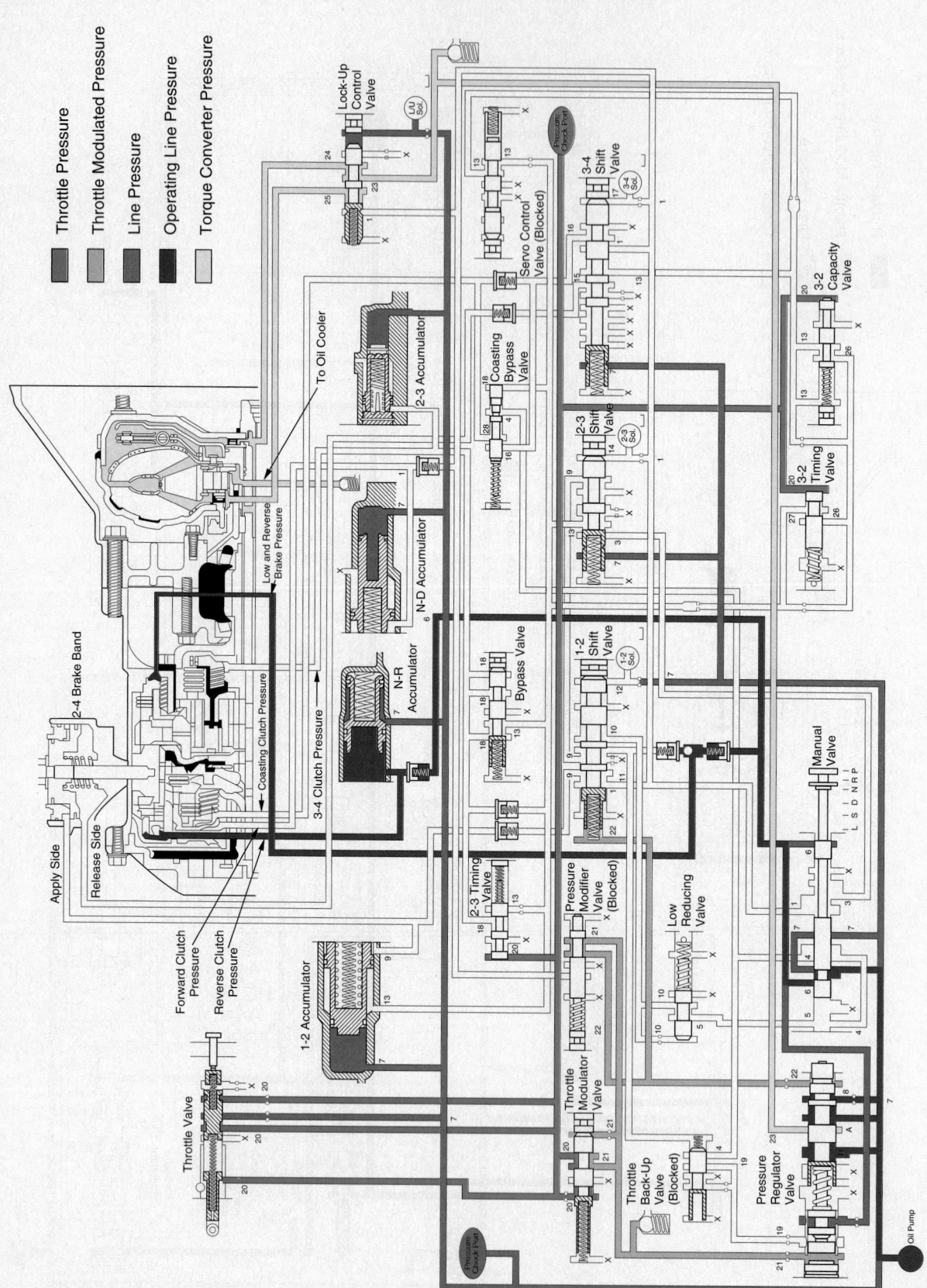

Fig. 2: "R" Range

Courtesy of Ford Motor Co.

OIL CIRCUIT DIAGRAMS
Ford 4EAT (Cont.)

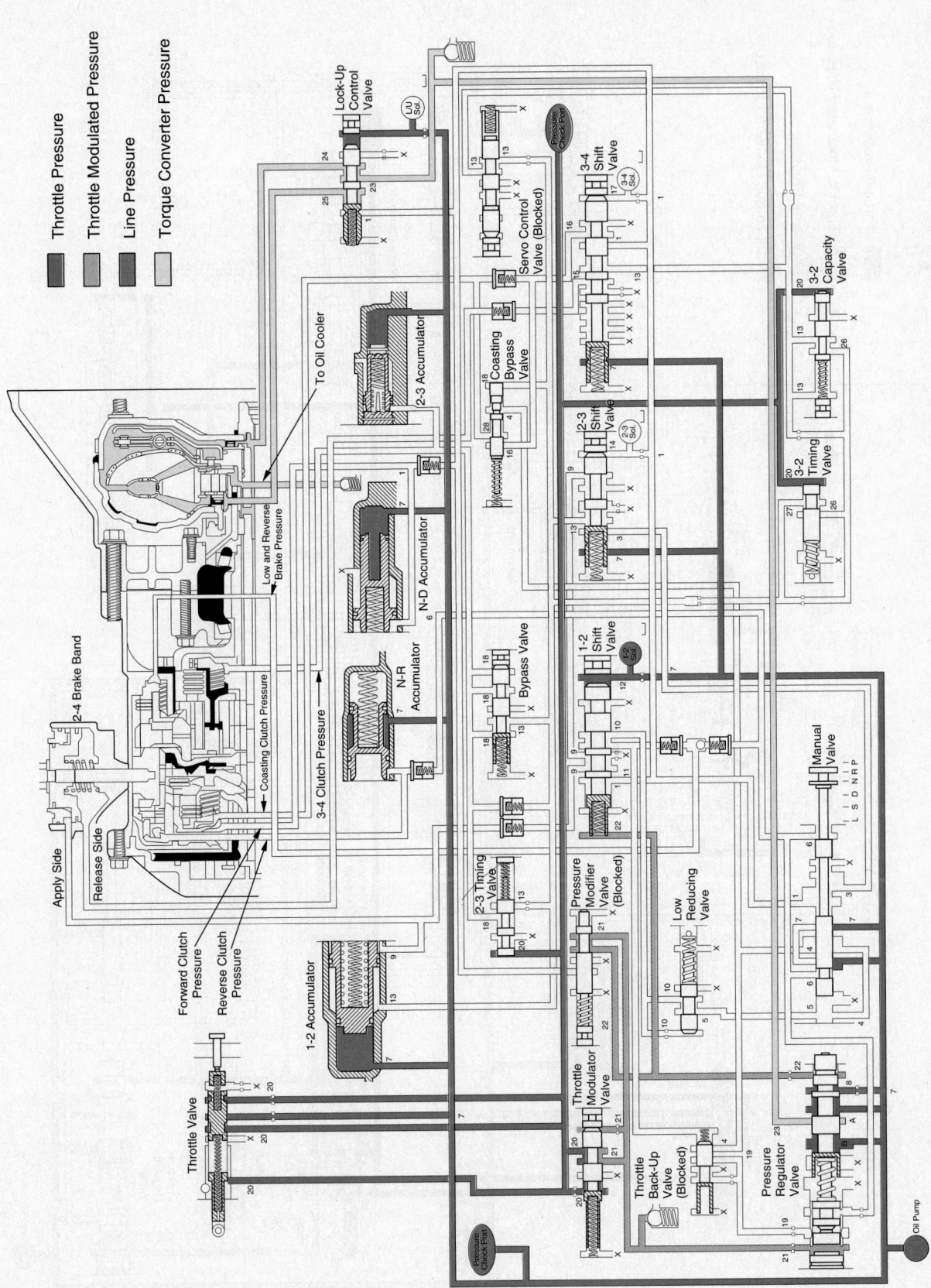

Fig. 3: "R" Range — Below 11 MPH

Courtesy of Ford Motor Co.

OIL CIRCUIT DIAGRAMS
Ford 4EAT (Cont.)

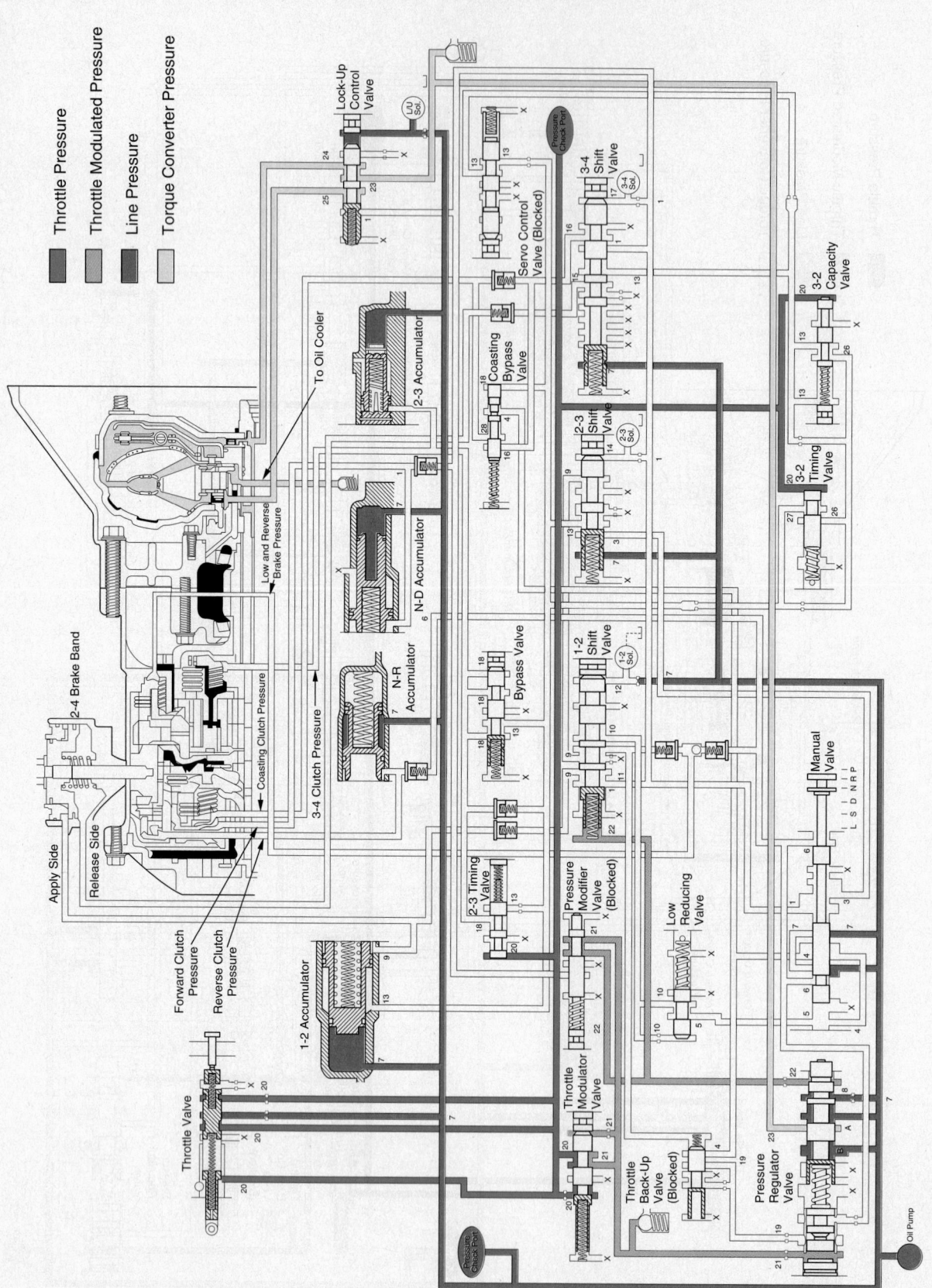

Fig. 4: "N" Range — Above 11 MPH

Courtesy of Ford Motor Co.

OIL CIRCUIT DIAGRAMS
Ford 4EAT (Cont.)

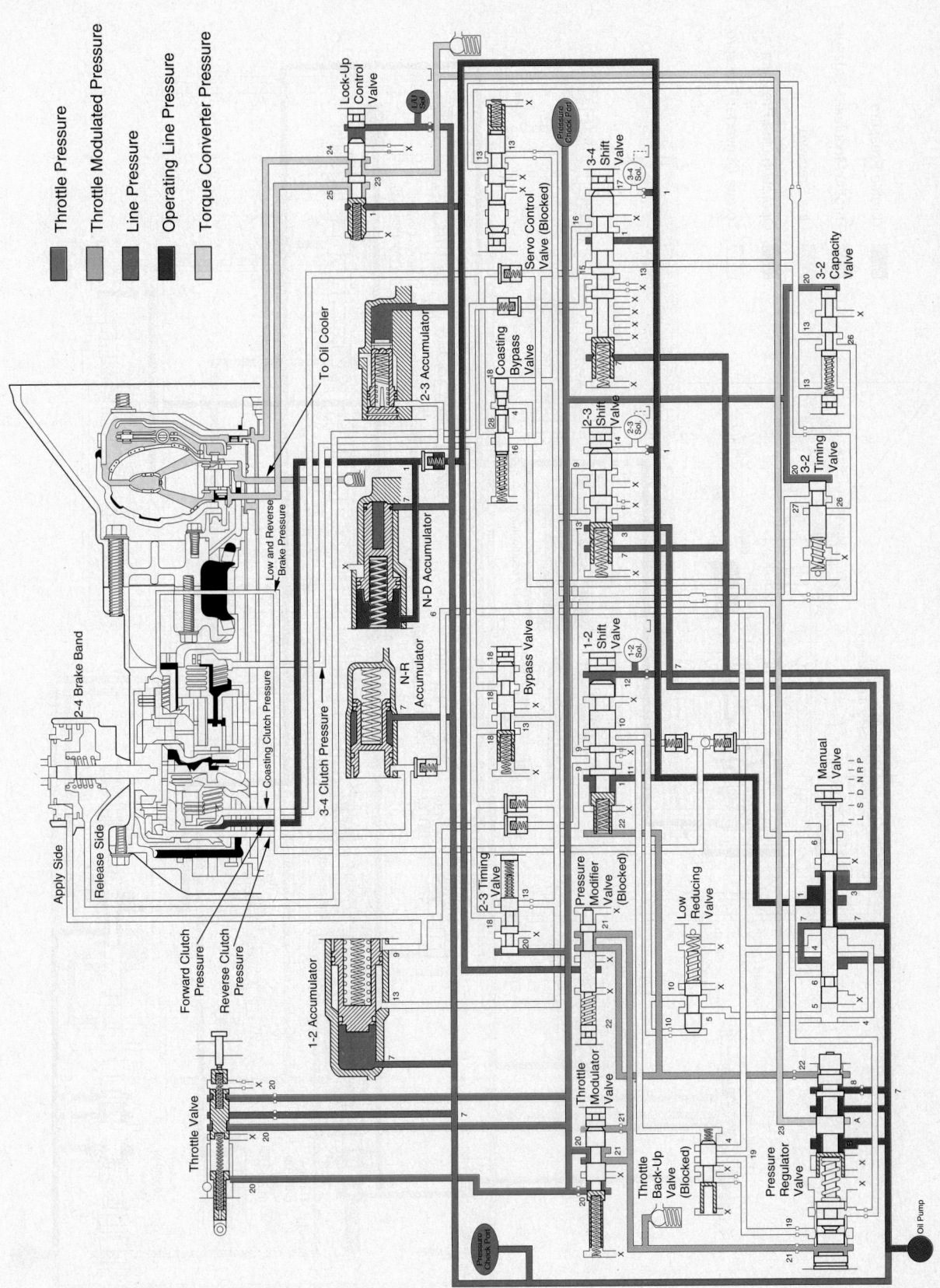

Fig. 5: "D" Range — 1st Gear

Courtesy of Ford Motor Co.

OIL CIRCUIT DIAGRAMS
Ford 4EAT (Cont.)

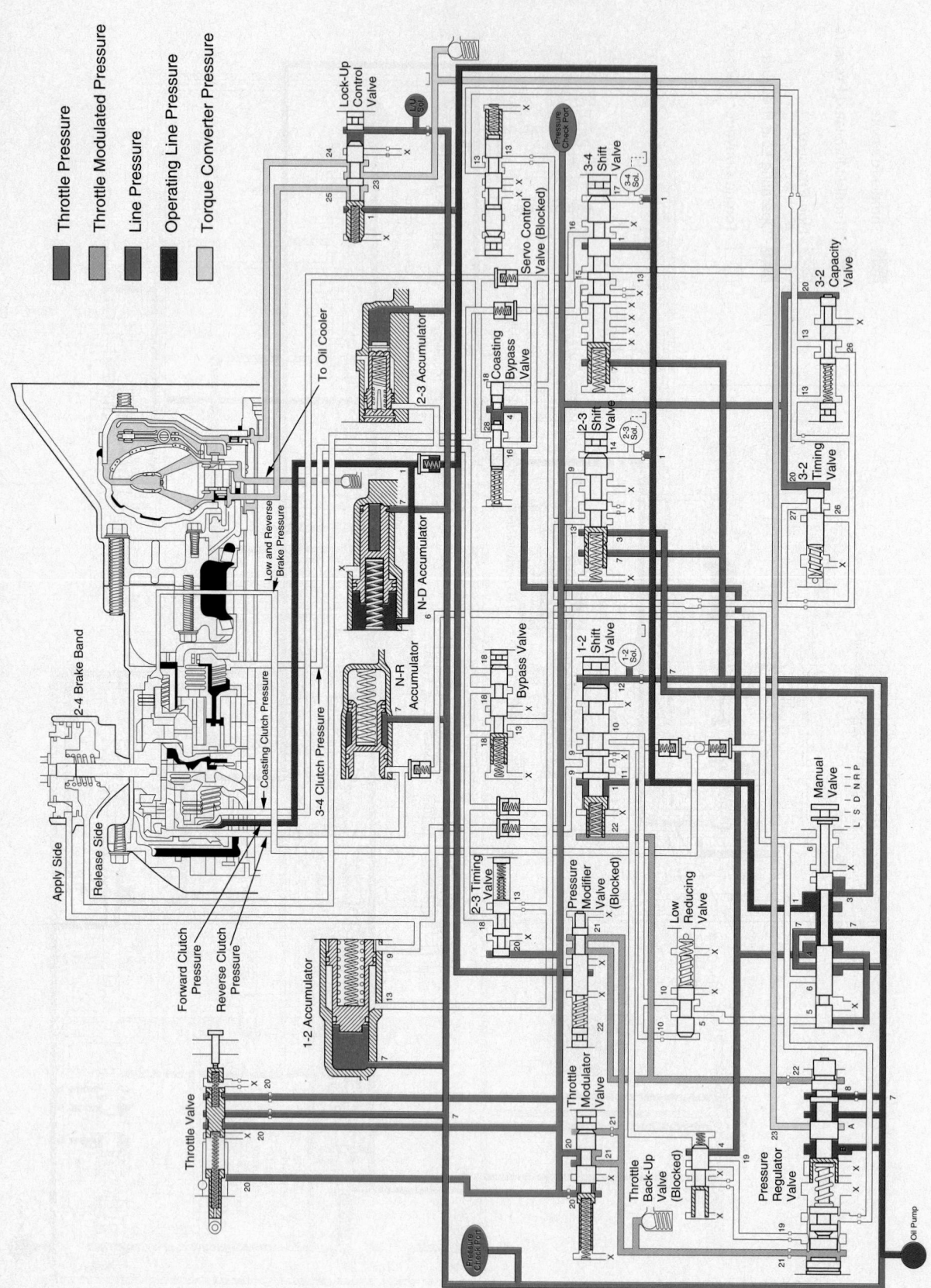

Fig. 6: "S" Range — 1st Gear

Courtesy of Ford Motor Co.

OIL CIRCUIT DIAGRAMS
Ford 4EAT (Cont.)

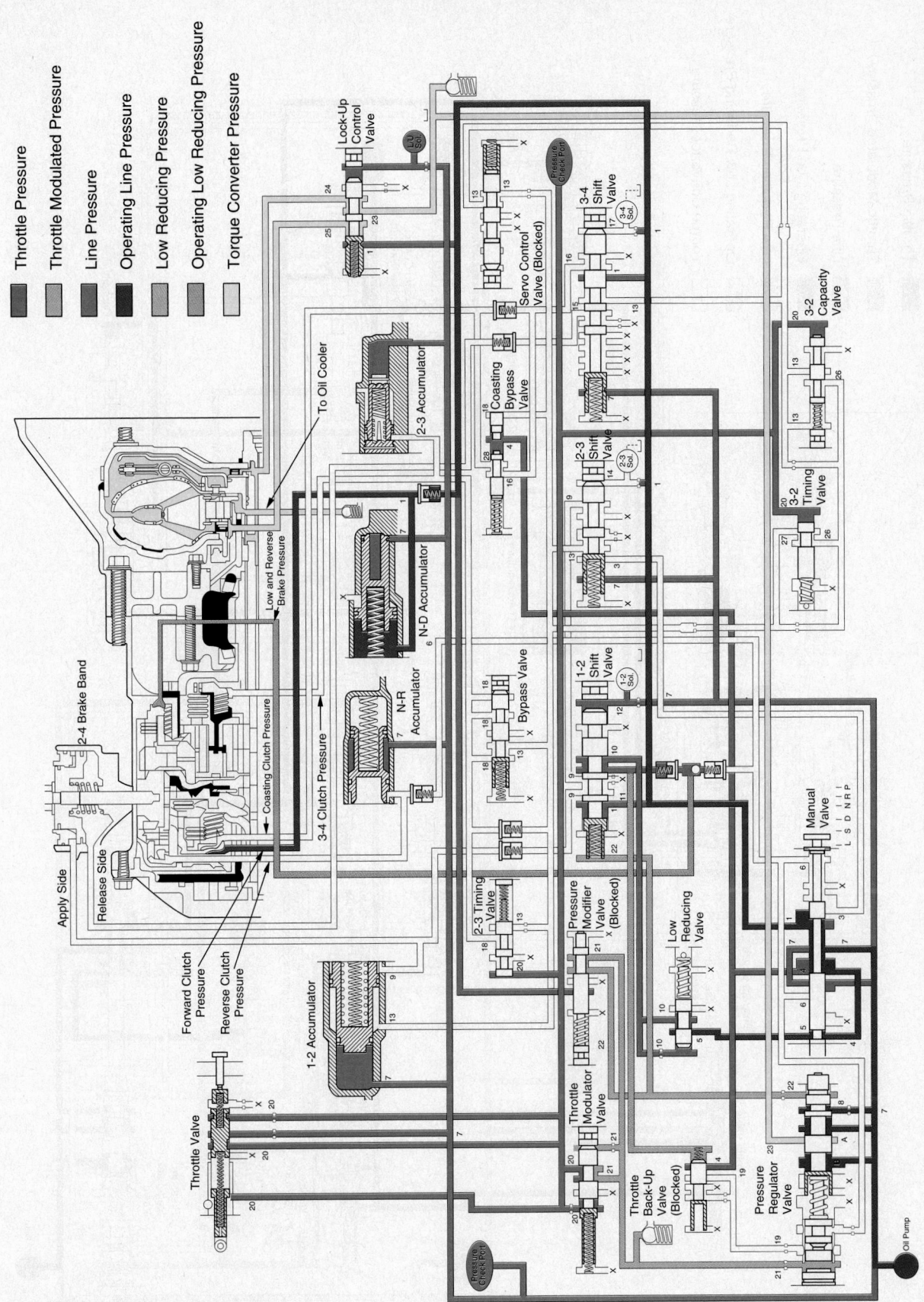

Fig. 7: "L" Range — 1st Gear

OIL CIRCUIT DIAGRAMS
Ford 4EAT (Cont.)

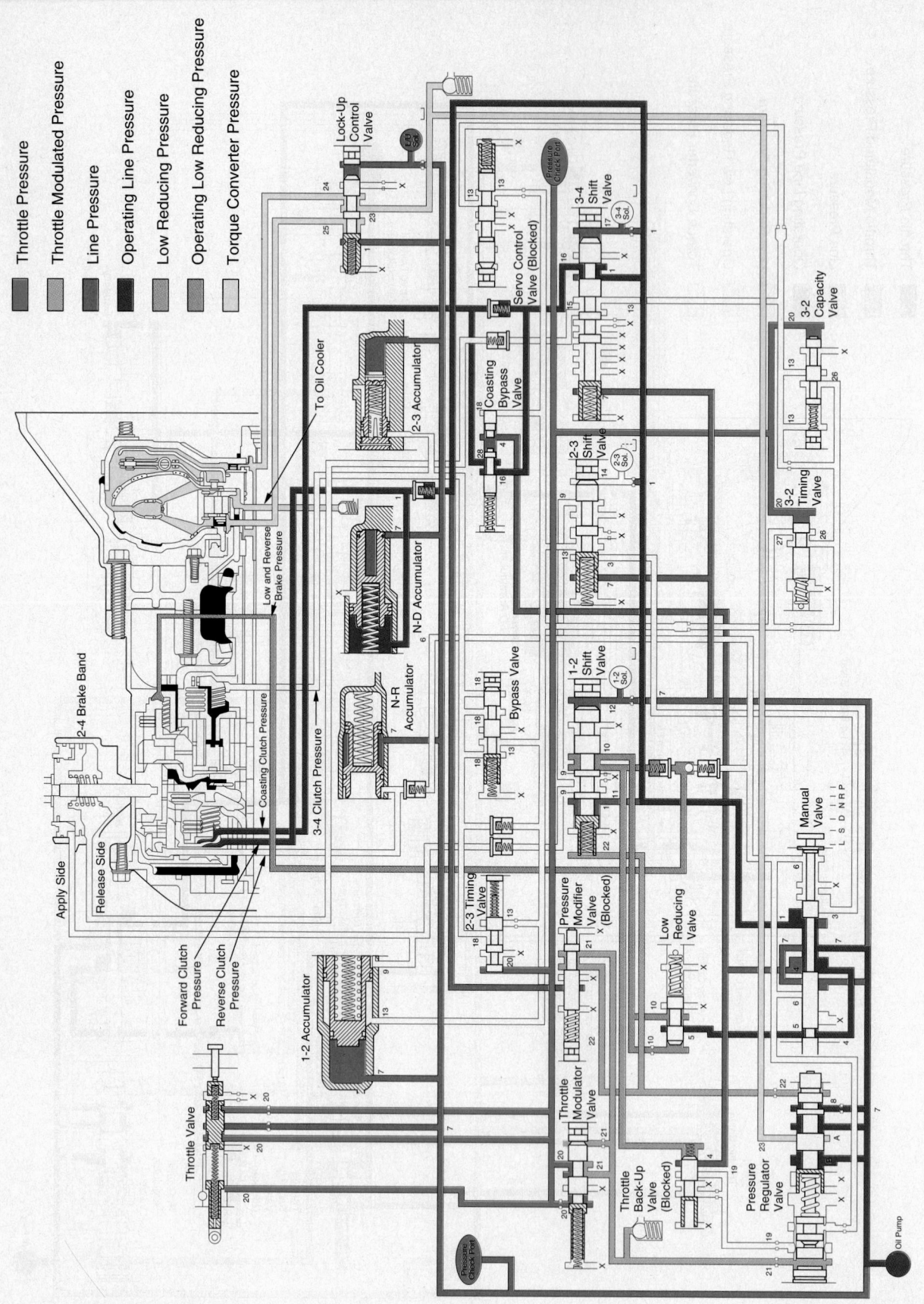

Fig. 8: "L" Range — 1st Gear (Hold)

Courtesy of Ford Motor Co.

OIL CIRCUIT DIAGRAMS
Ford 4EAT (Cont.)

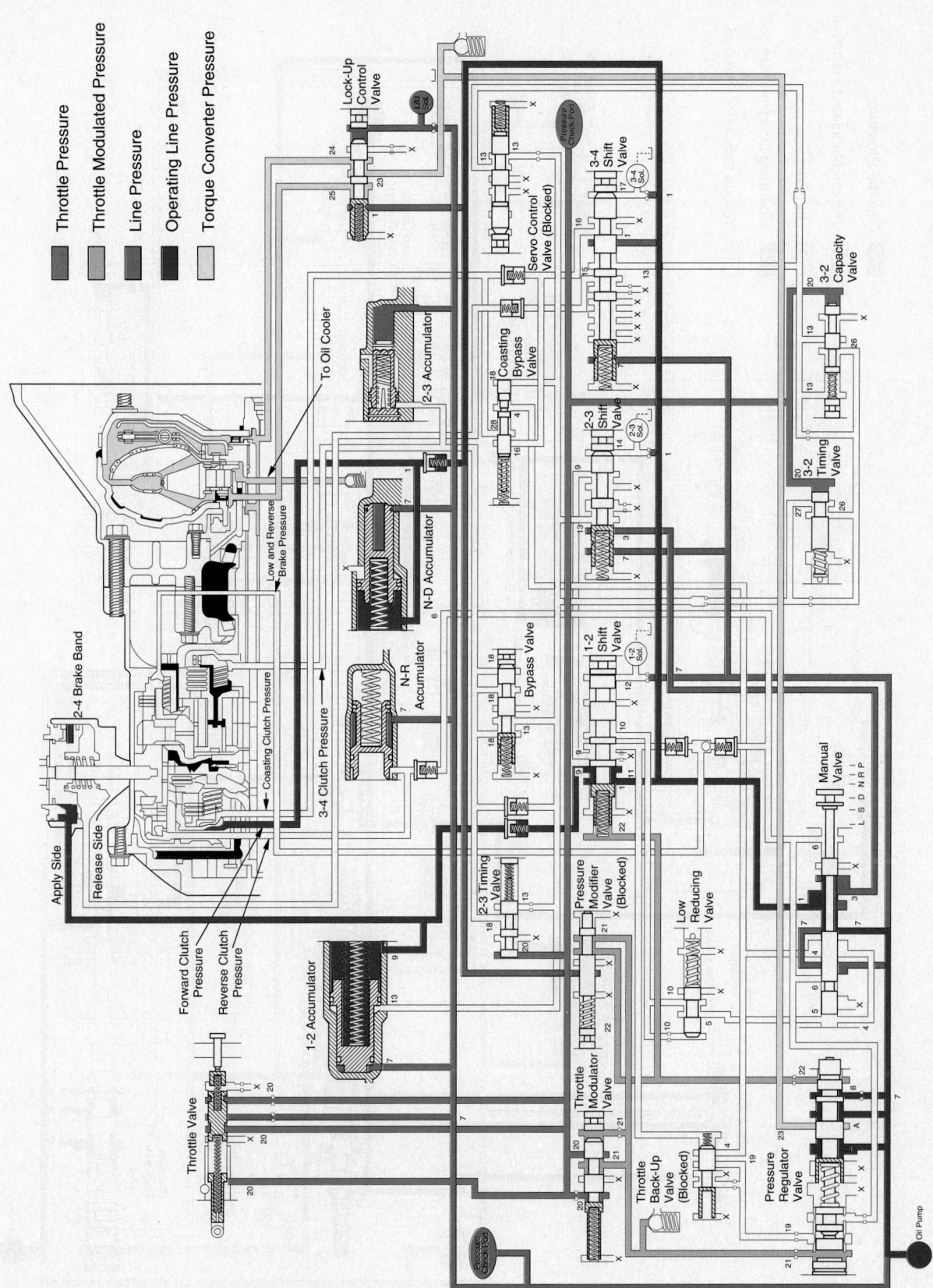

Fig. 9: "D" Range — 2nd Gear

Courtesy of Ford Motor Co.

OIL CIRCUIT DIAGRAMS
Ford 4EAT (Cont.)

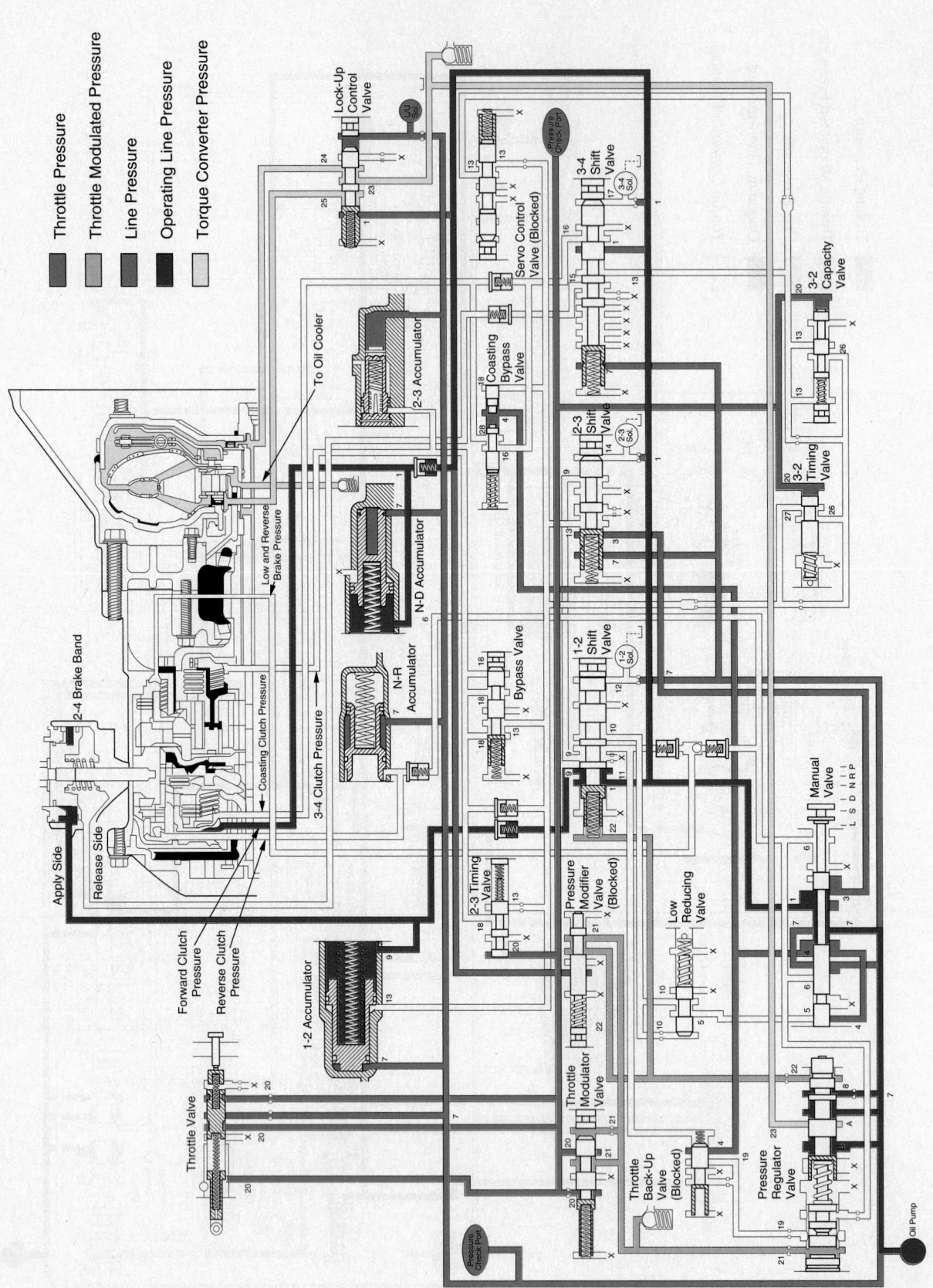

Fig. 10: "S" Range — 2nd Gear

Courtesy of Ford Motor Co.

OIL CIRCUIT DIAGRAMS
Ford 4EAT (Cont.)

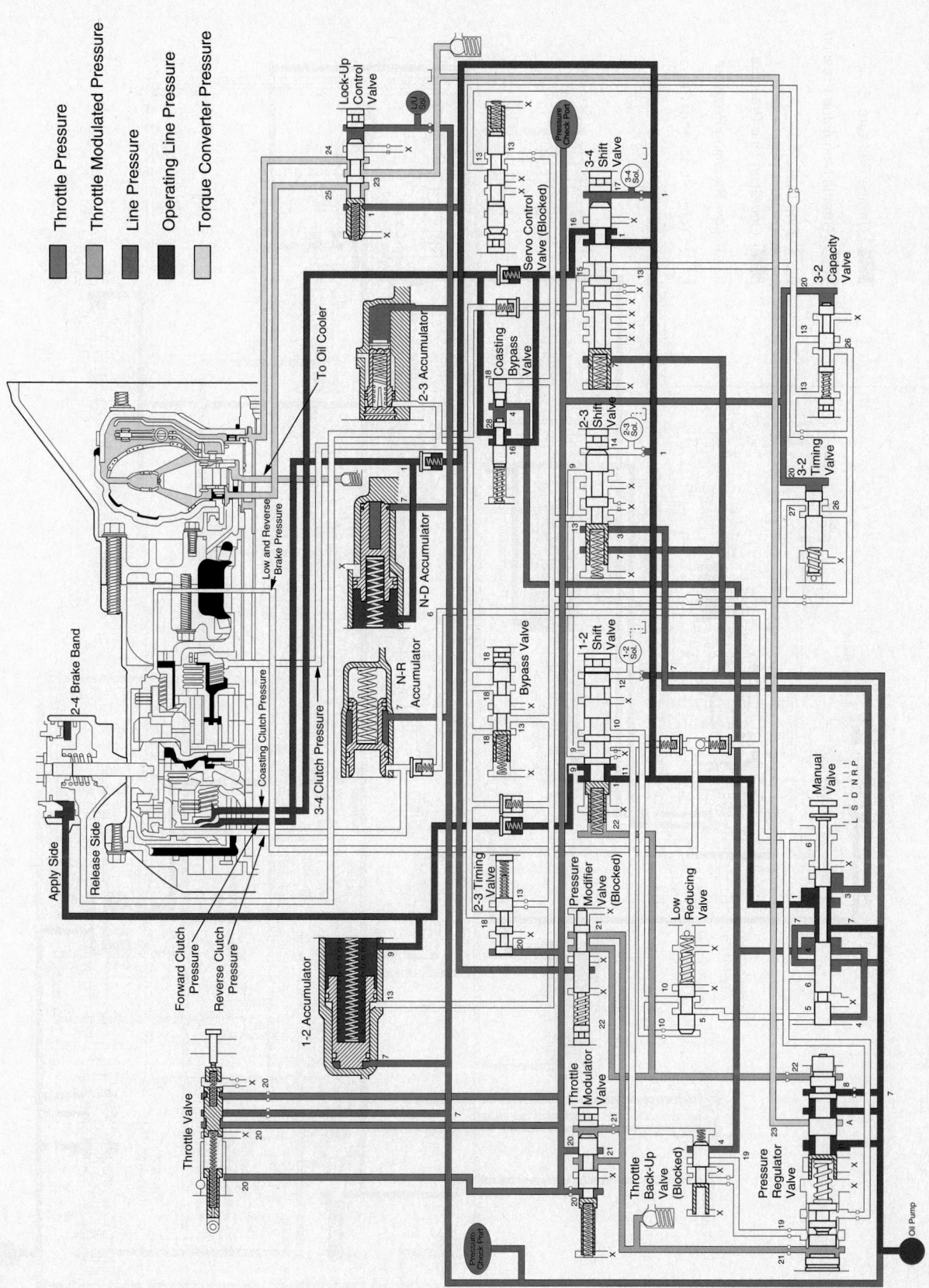

Fig. 11: "S" Range — 2nd Gear (Hold)

Courtesy of Ford Motor Co.

OIL CIRCUIT DIAGRAMS
Ford 4EAT (Cont.)

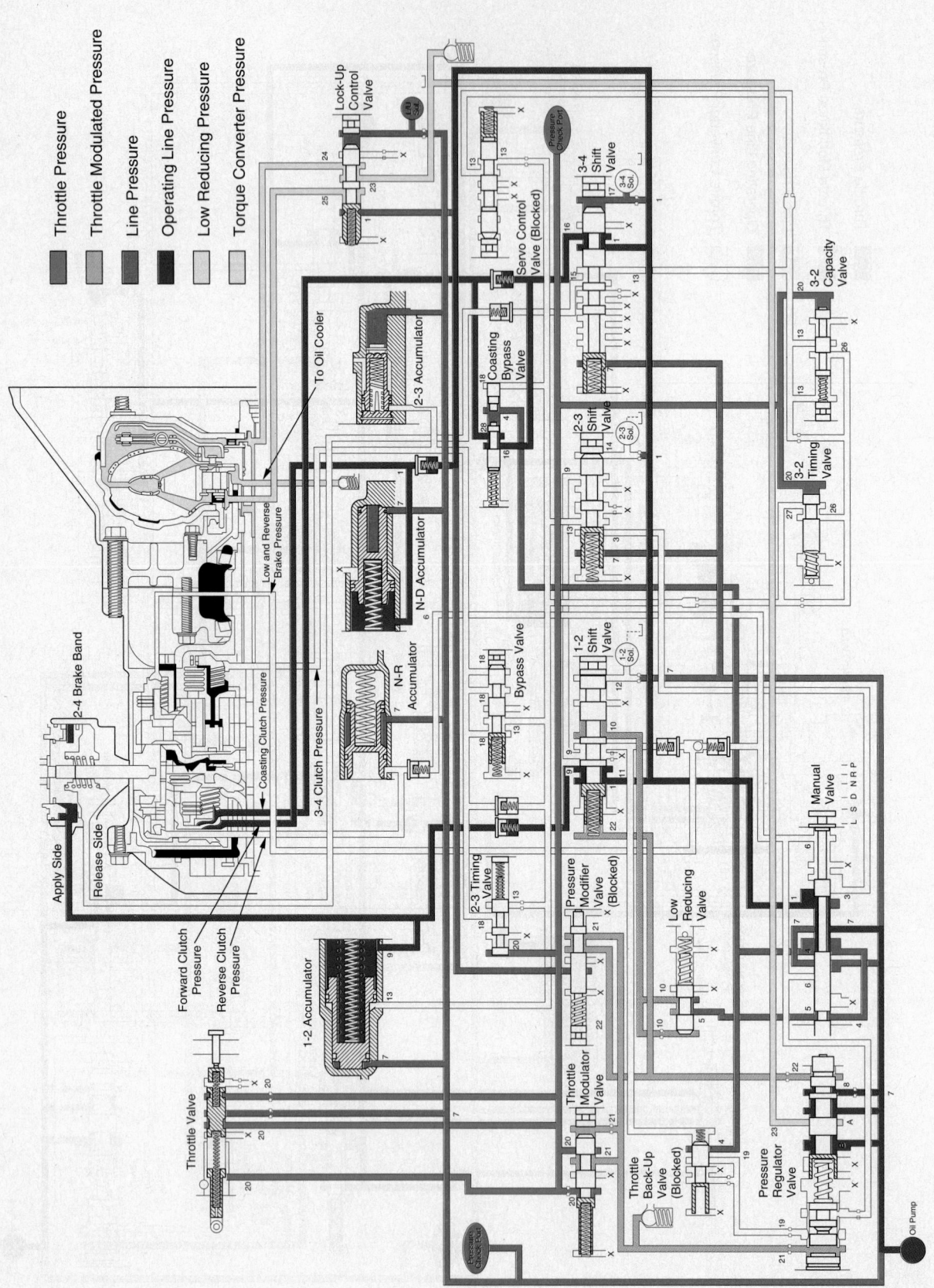

Fig. 12: "L" Range — 2nd Gear (Below 68 MPH)

Courtesy of Ford Motor Co.

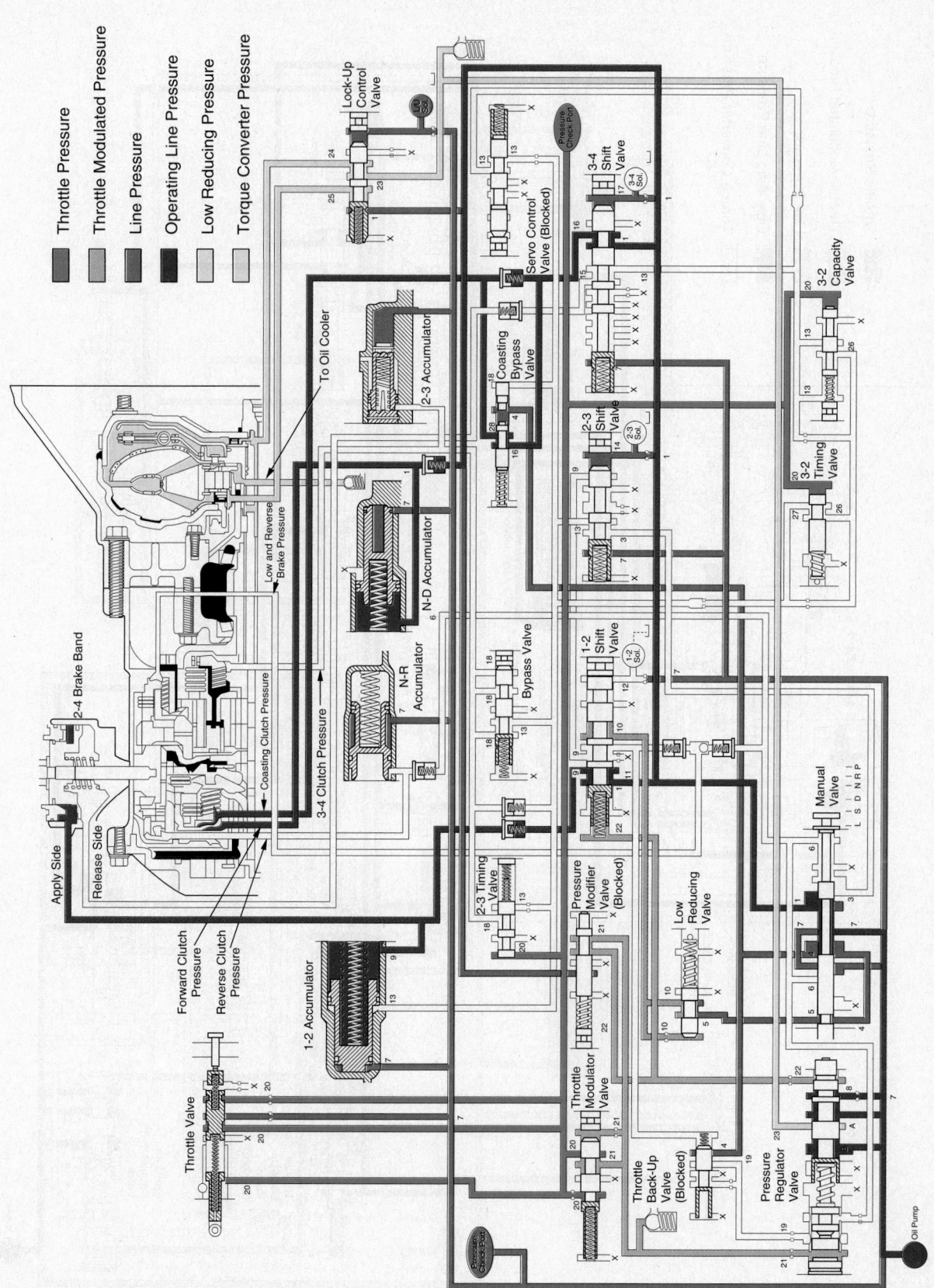

Fig. 13: "L" Range — 2nd Gear (Above 68 MPH)

Courtesy of Ford Motor Co.

OIL CIRCUIT DIAGRAMS
Ford 4EAT (Cont.)

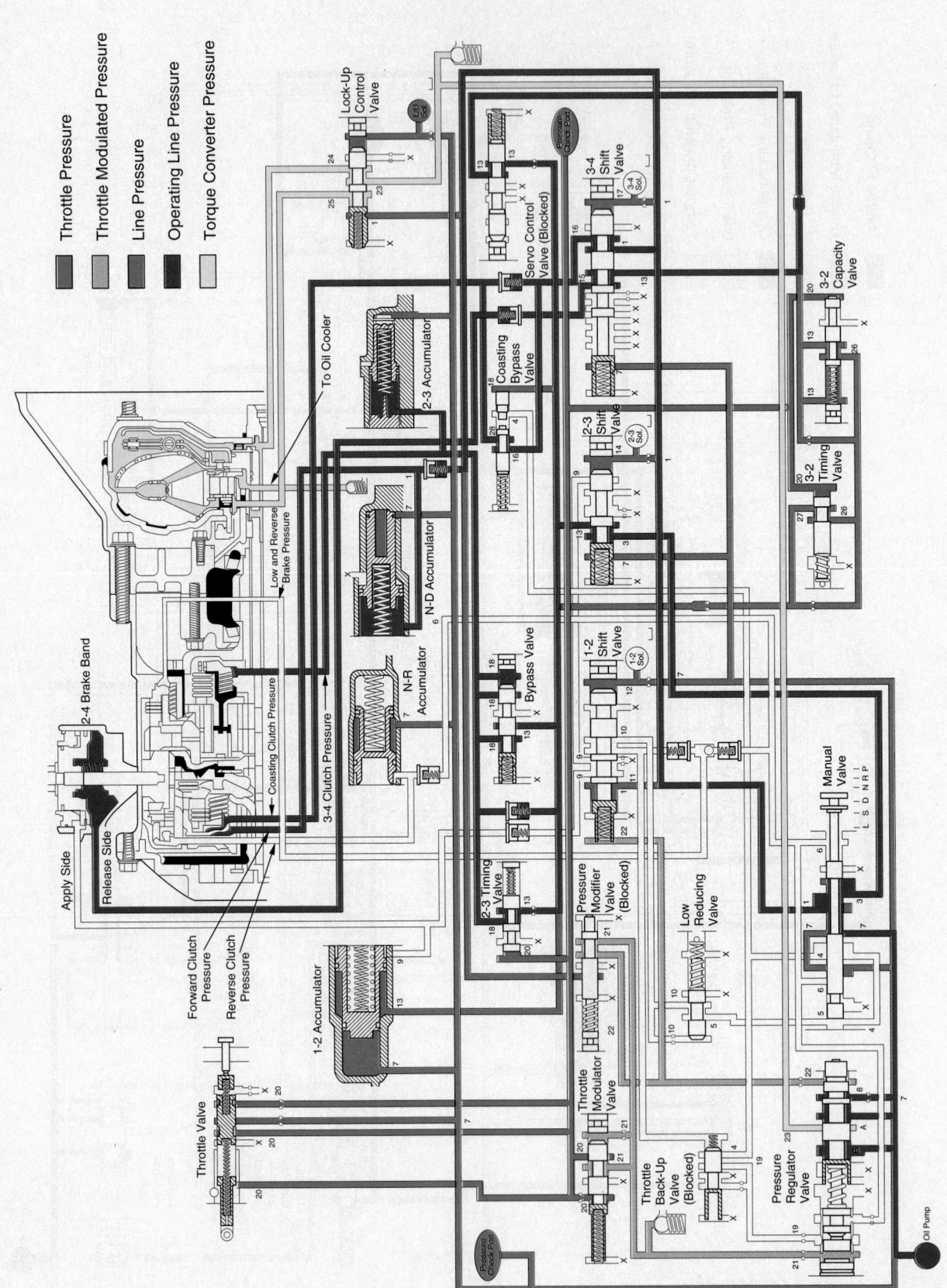

Fig. 14: "D" Range — 3rd Gear (Below 25 MPH)

Courtesy of Ford Motor Co.

OIL CIRCUIT DIAGRAMS
Ford 4EAT (Cont.)

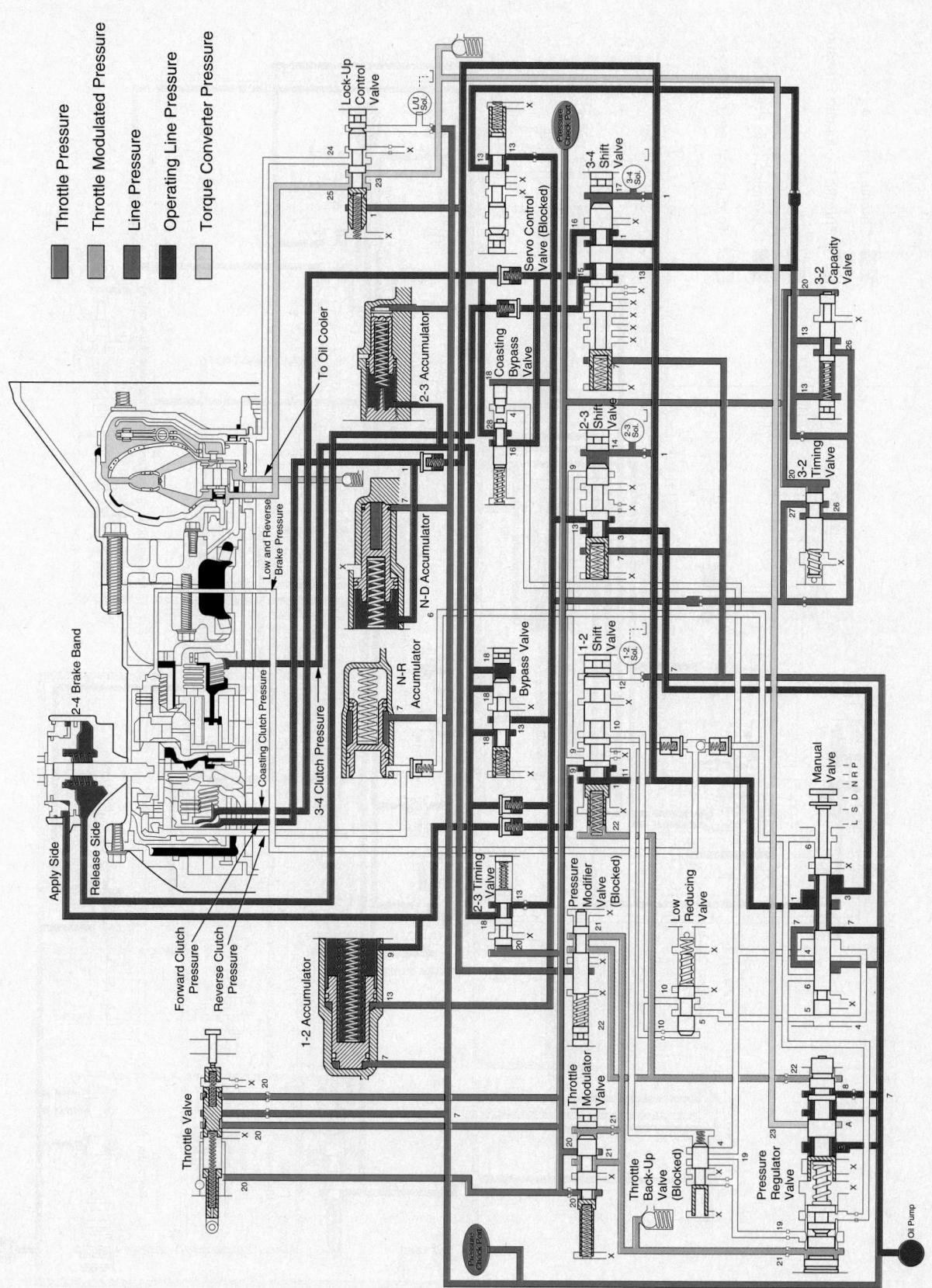

Fig. 15: "D" Range — 3rd Gear (Above 25 MPH — Lock-Up ON)

Courtesy of Ford Motor Co.

OIL CIRCUIT DIAGRAMS
Ford 4EAT (Cont.)

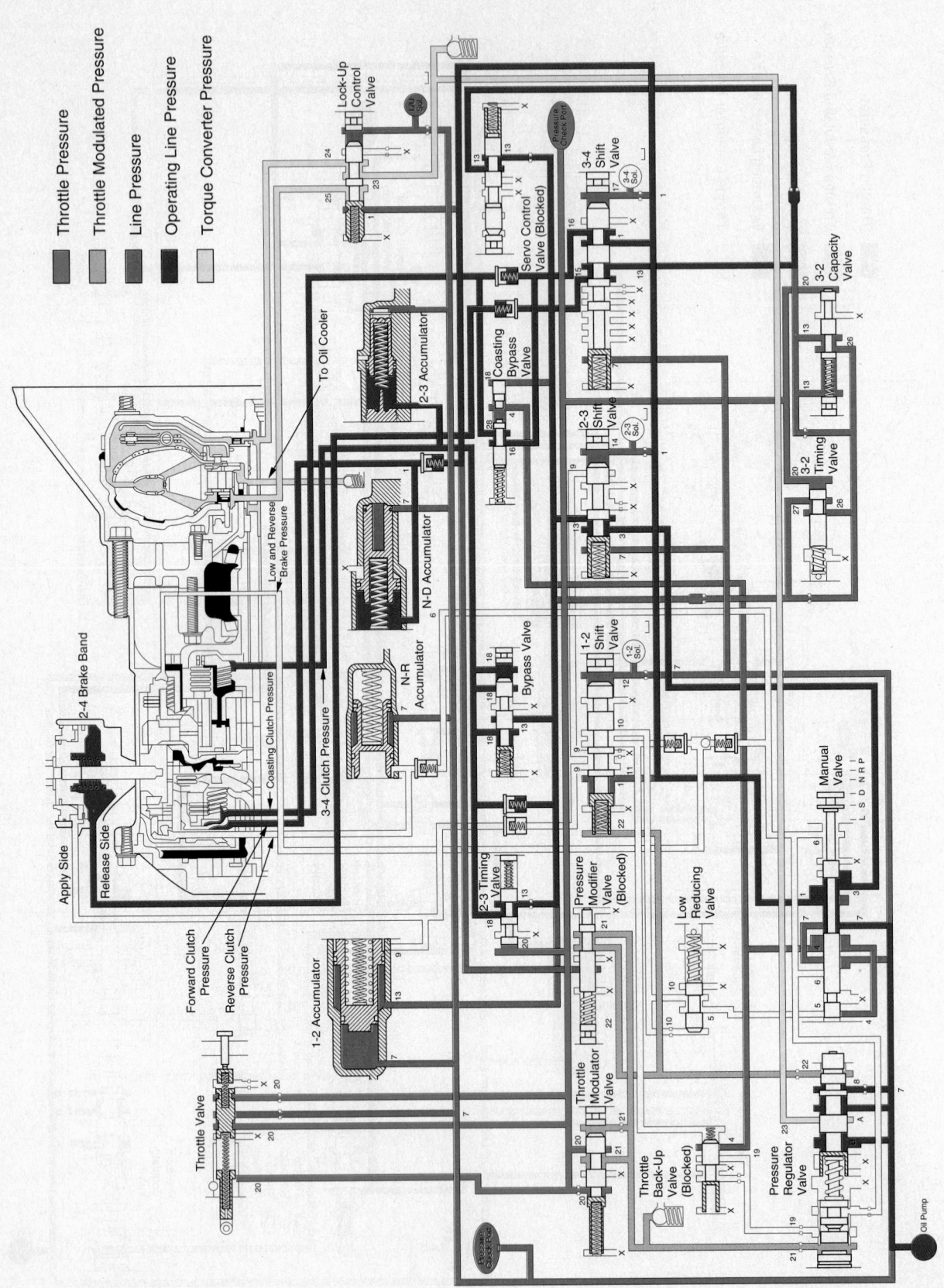

Fig. 16: "S" Range — 3rd Gear (Below 25 MPH)

Courtesy of Ford Motor Co.

OIL CIRCUIT DIAGRAMS
Ford 4EAT (Cont.)

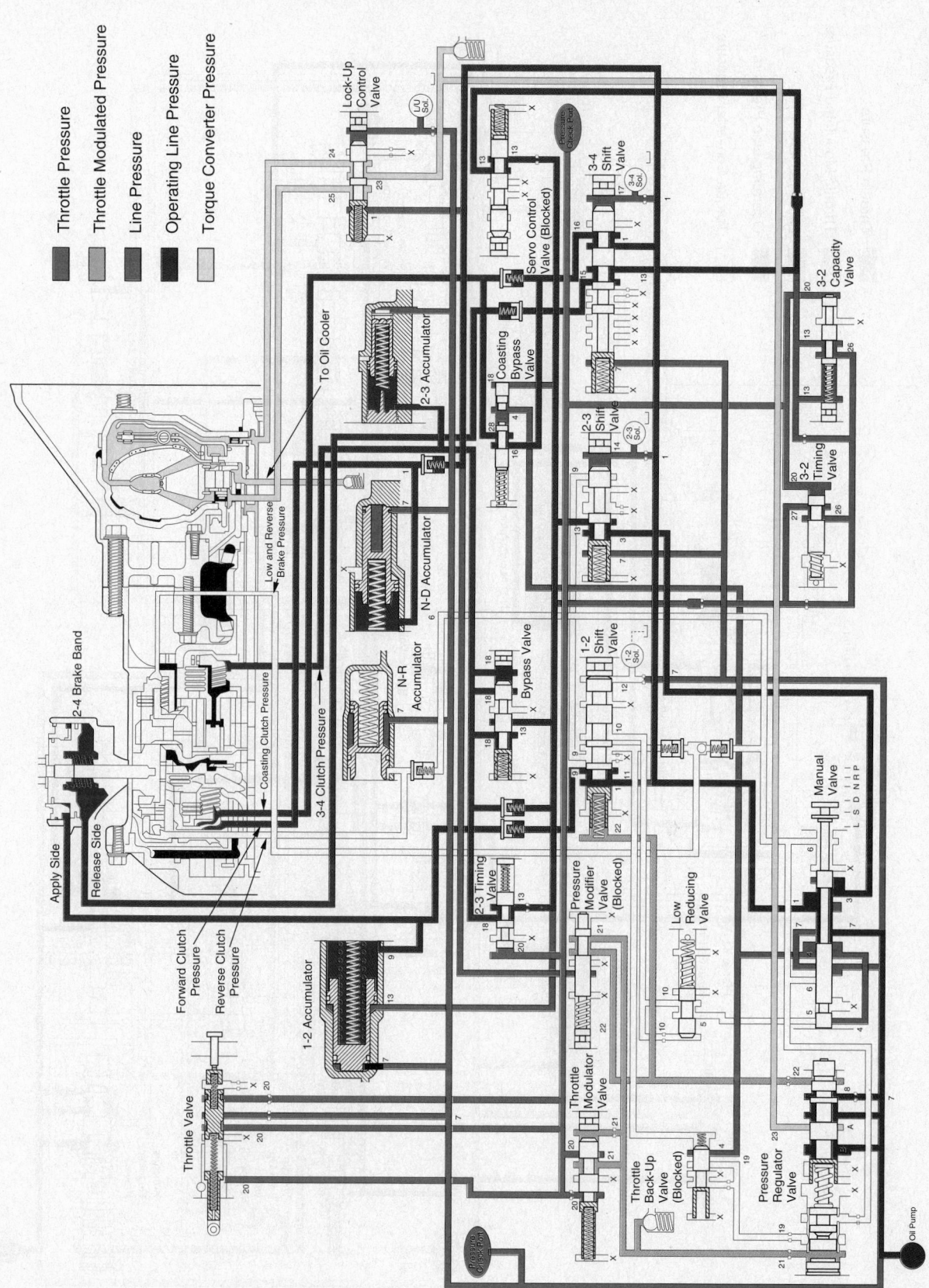

Fig. 17: "S" Range — 3rd Gear (Above 25 MPH)

Courtesy of Ford Motor Co.

OIL CIRCUIT DIAGRAMS
Ford 4EAT (Cont.)

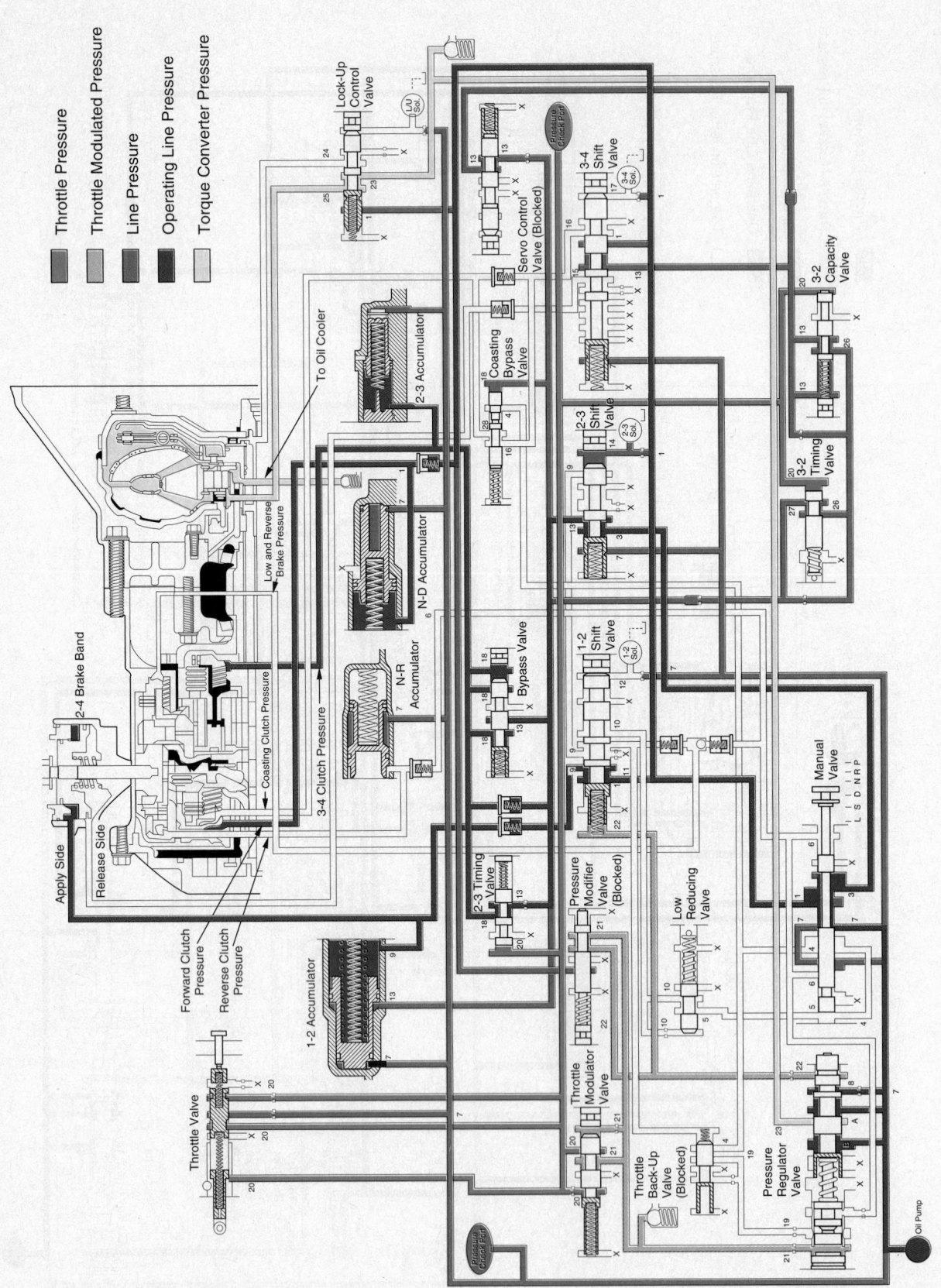

Fig. 18: "D" Range — Overdrive (Lock-Up ON)

Courtesy of Ford Motor Co.

OIL CIRCUIT DIAGRAMS
Festiva ATX & Geo KF400

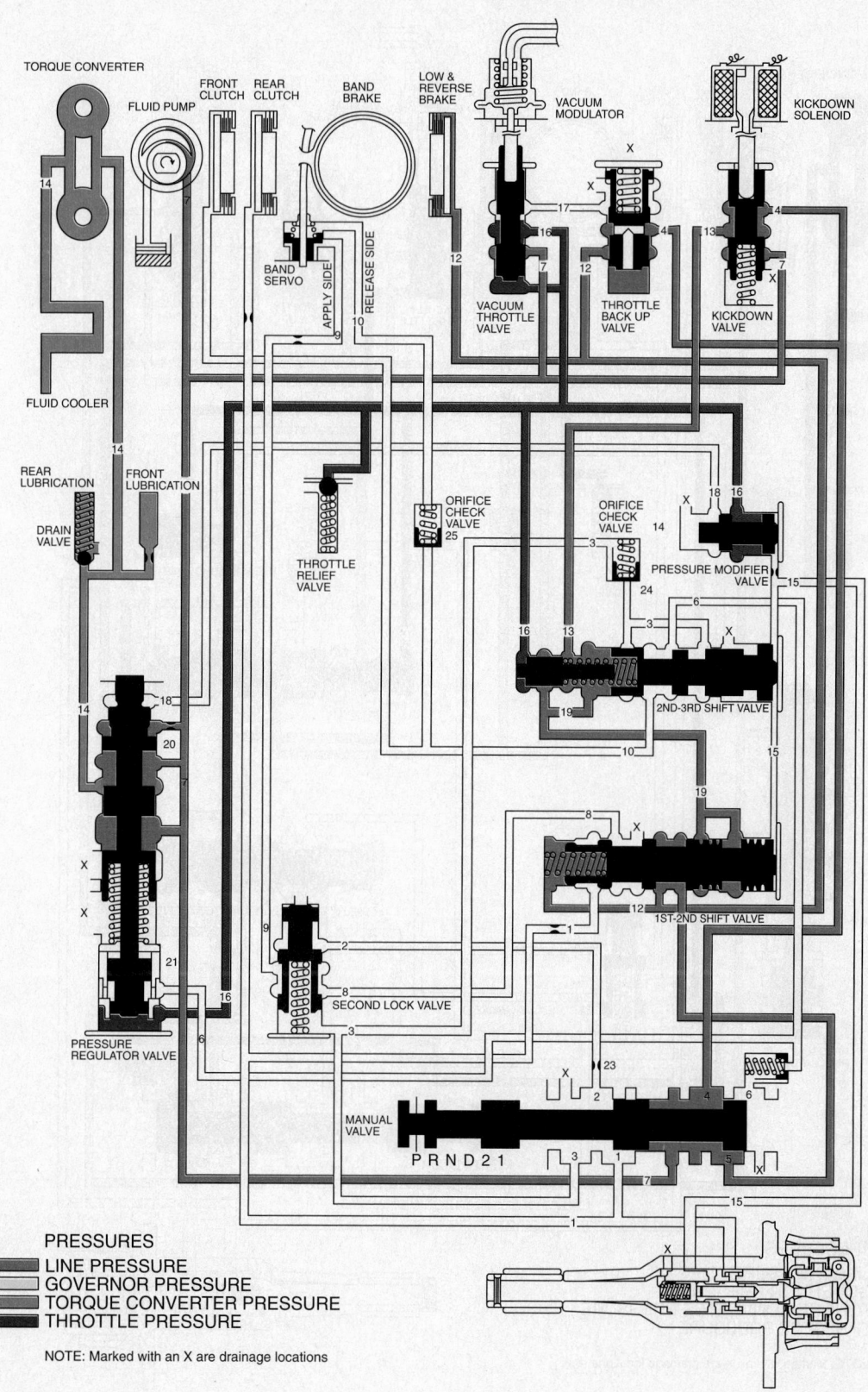

Fig. 1: "P" Range — Park

Courtesy of General Motors Corp.

OIL CIRCUIT DIAGRAMS
Festiva ATX & Geo KF400 (Cont.)

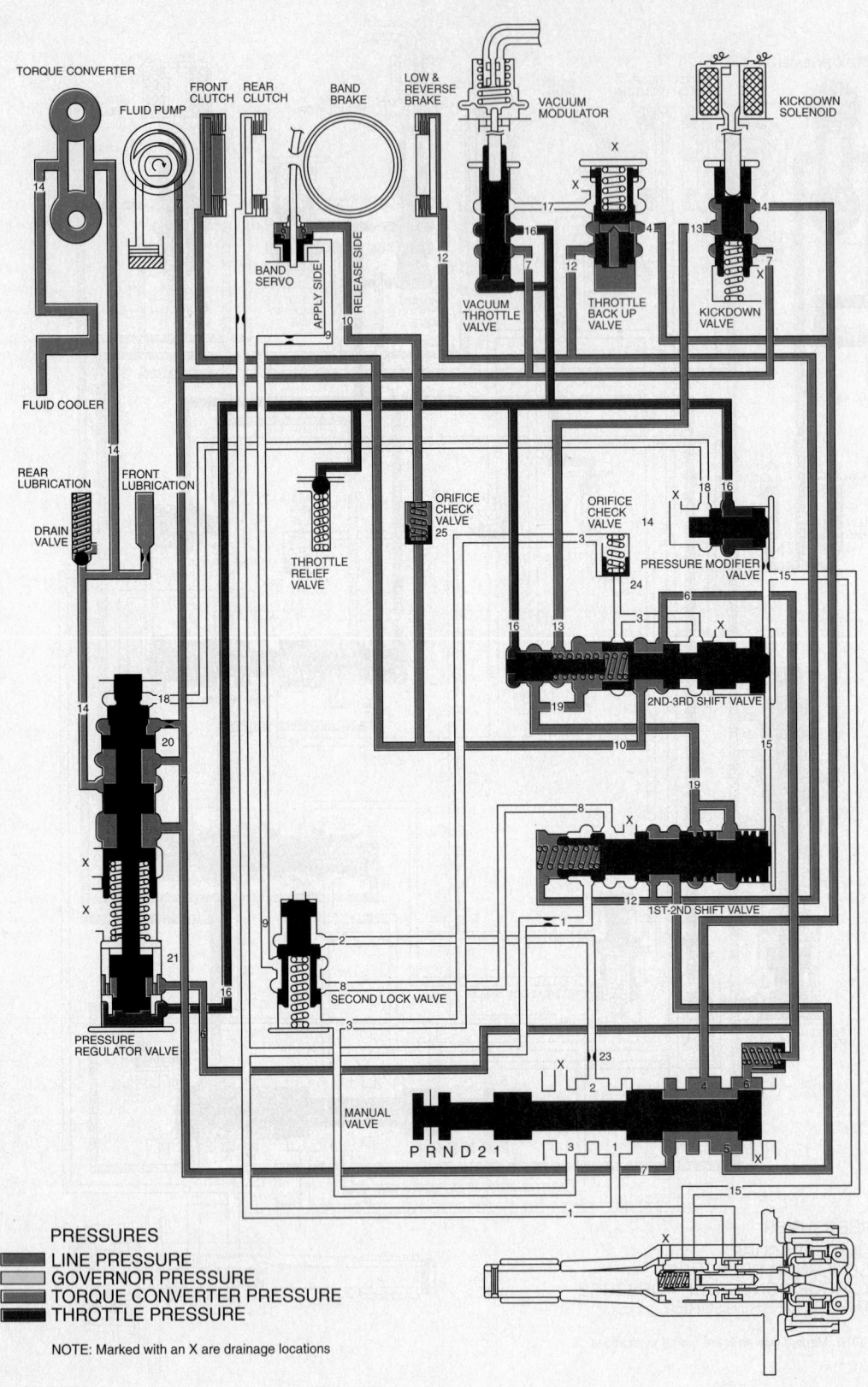

PRESSURES

- LINE PRESSURE
- GOVERNOR PRESSURE
- TORQUE CONVERTER PRESSURE
- THROTTLE PRESSURE

NOTE: Marked with an X are drainage locations

Fig. 2: "R" Range — Reverse

Courtesy of General Motors Corp.

OIL CIRCUIT DIAGRAMS
Festiva ATX & Geo KF400 (Cont.)

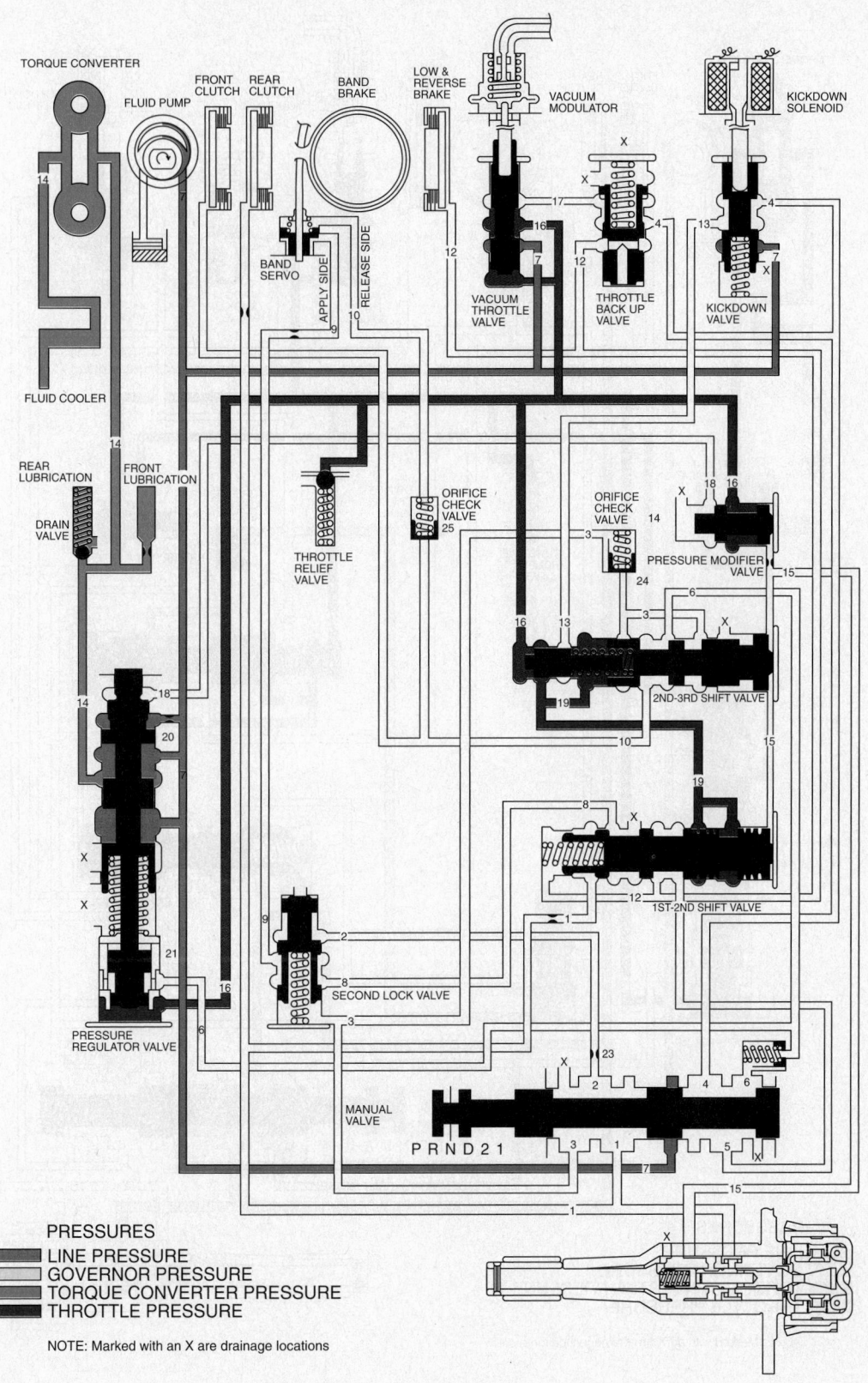

PRESSURES

- LINE PRESSURE
- GOVERNOR PRESSURE
- TORQUE CONVERTER PRESSURE
- THROTTLE PRESSURE

NOTE: Marked with an X are drainage locations

Fig. 3: "N" Range — Neutral　　　　　　　　　　　　Courtesy of General Motors Corp.

OIL CIRCUIT DIAGRAMS
Festiva ATX & Geo KF400 (Cont.)

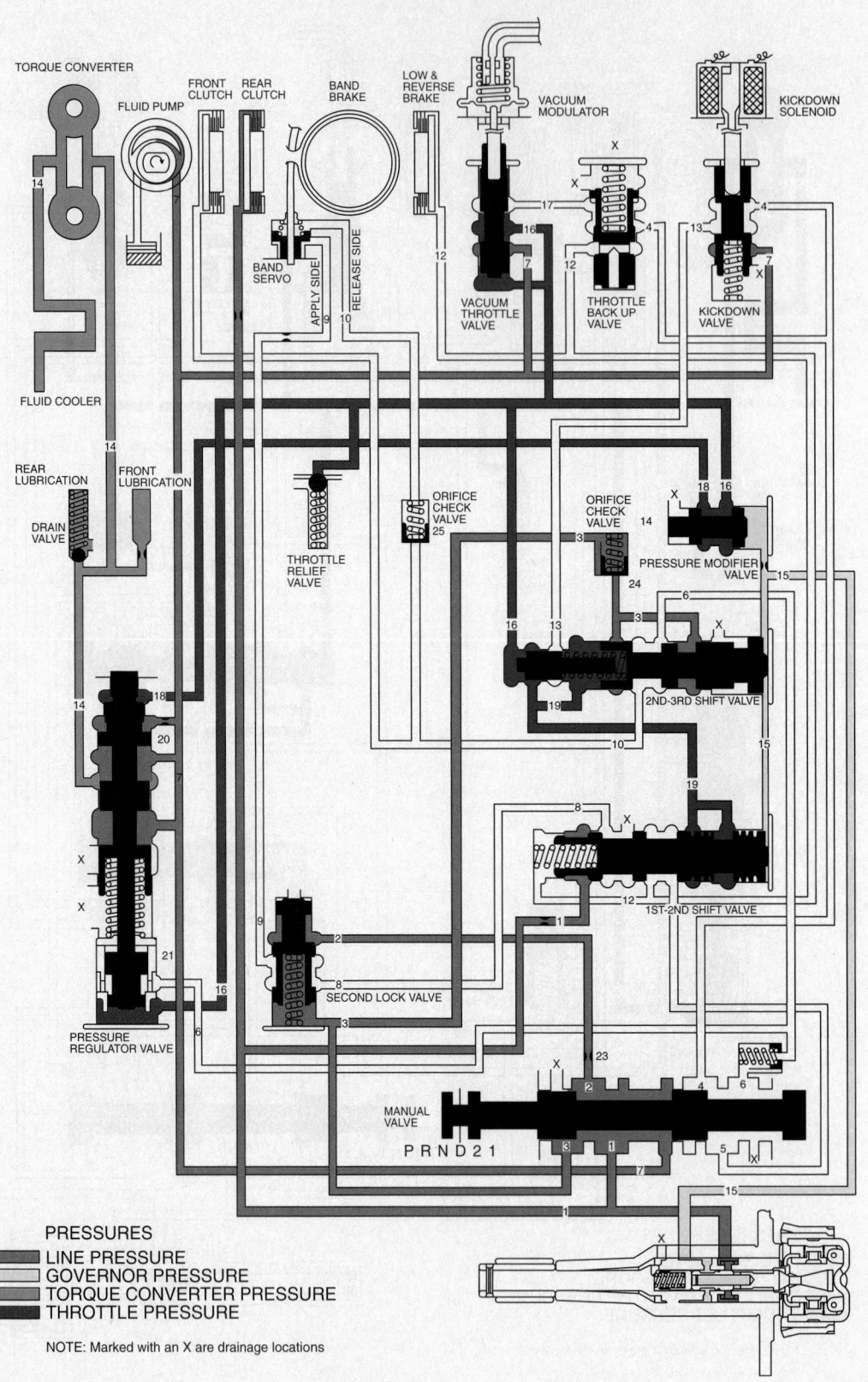

PRESSURES
- ██ LINE PRESSURE
- ░░ GOVERNOR PRESSURE
- ▓▓ TORQUE CONVERTER PRESSURE
- ██ THROTTLE PRESSURE

NOTE: Marked with an X are drainage locations

Fig. 4: "D" Range — 1st Gear

Courtesy of General Motors Corp.

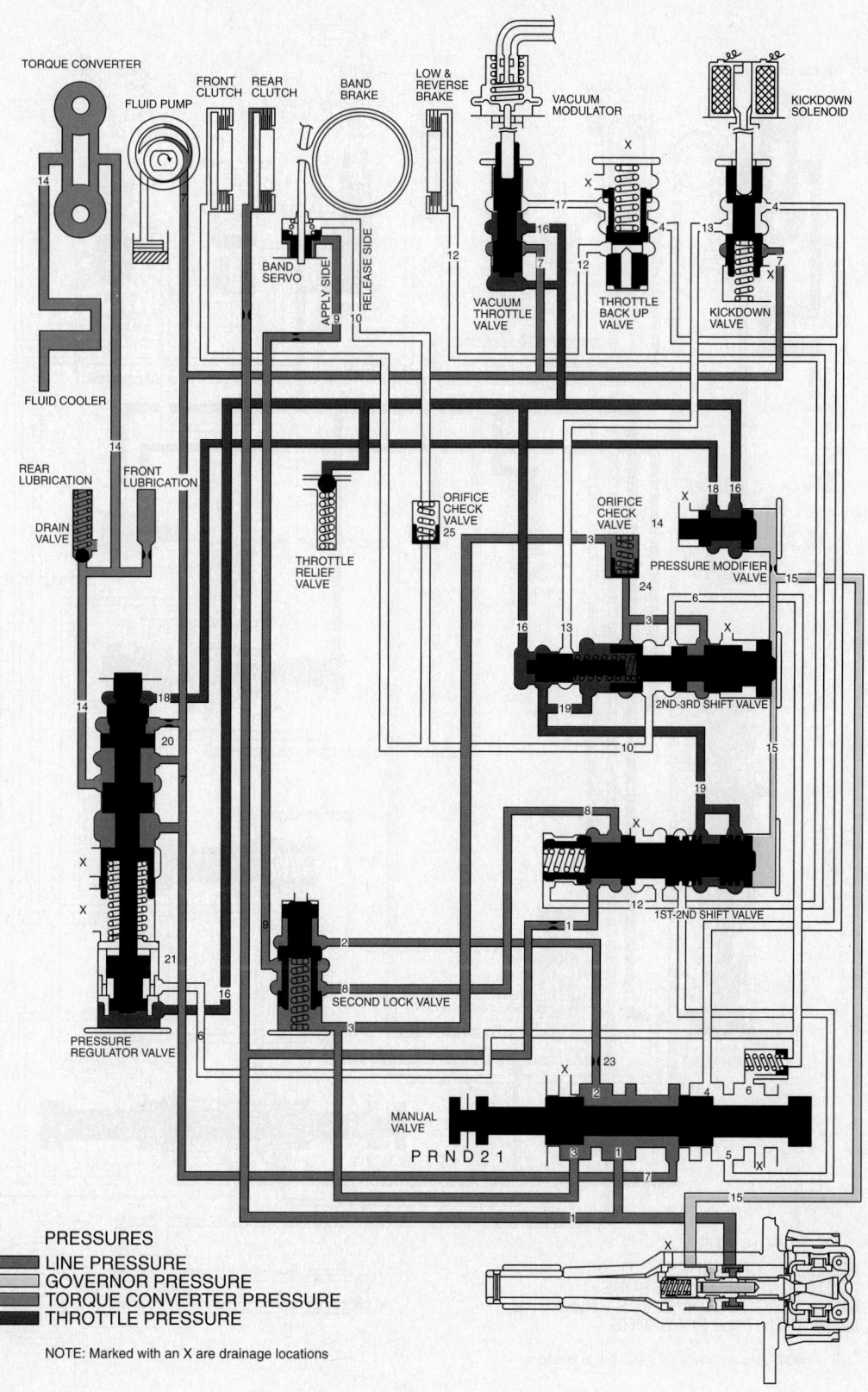

OIL CIRCUIT DIAGRAMS
Festiva ATX & Geo KF400 (Cont.)

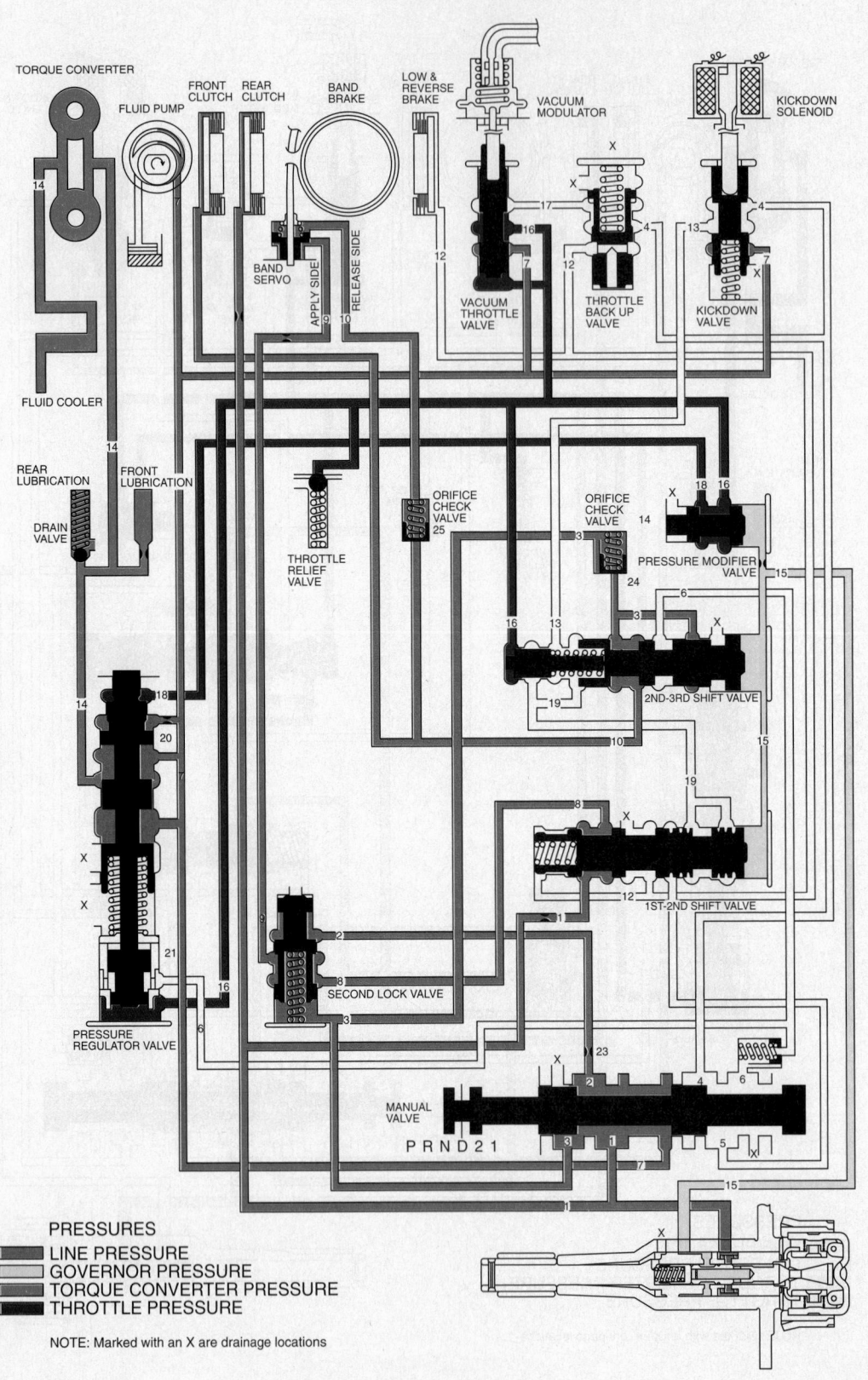

PRESSURES
- LINE PRESSURE
- GOVERNOR PRESSURE
- TORQUE CONVERTER PRESSURE
- THROTTLE PRESSURE

NOTE: Marked with an X are drainage locations

Fig. 6: "D" Range — 3rd Gear

Courtesy of General Motors Corp.

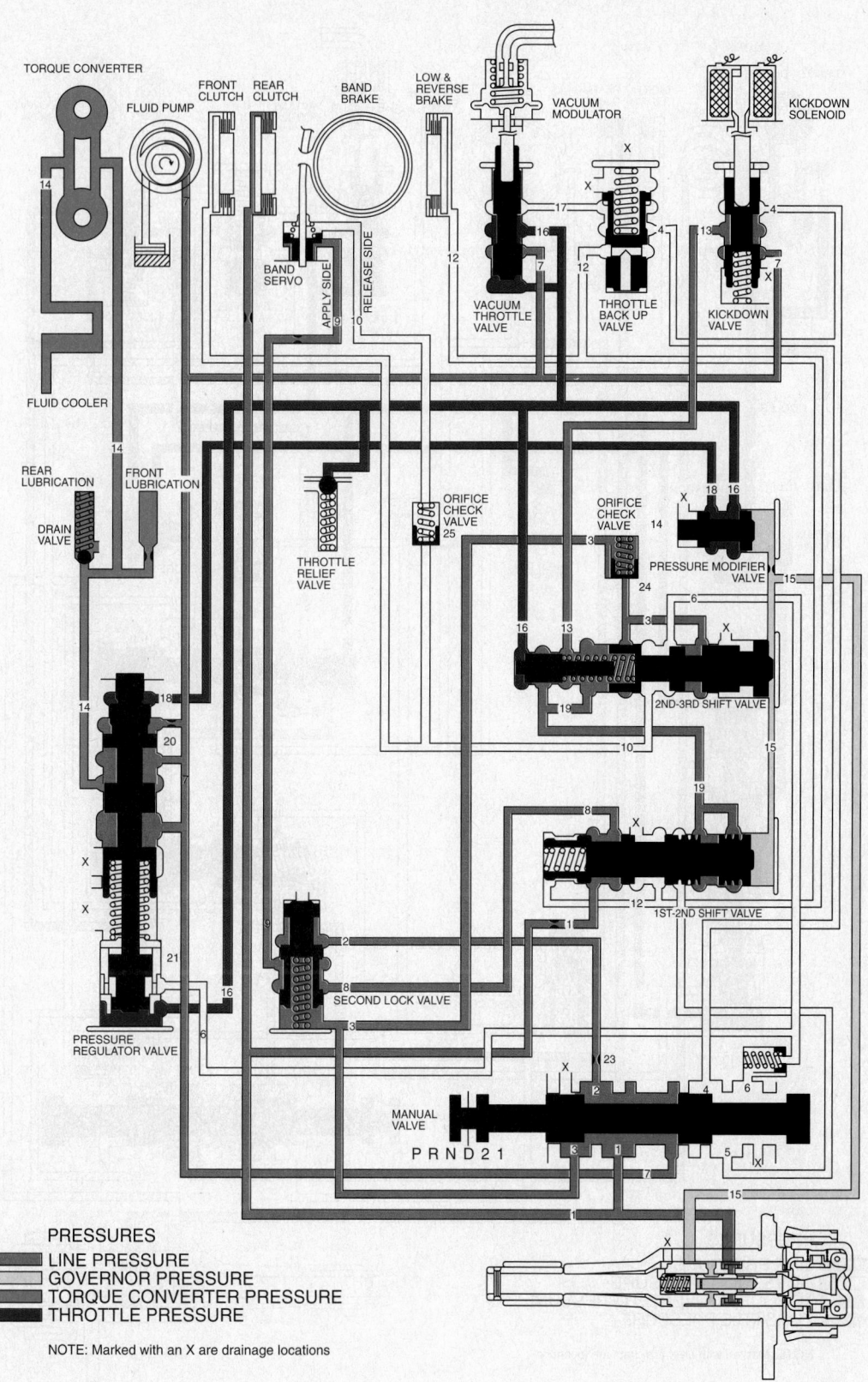

Fig. 7: "D" Range — Kickdown (Valves Shown in 2nd Position)

Courtesy of General Motors Corp.

OIL CIRCUIT DIAGRAMS
Festiva ATX & Geo KF400 (Cont.)

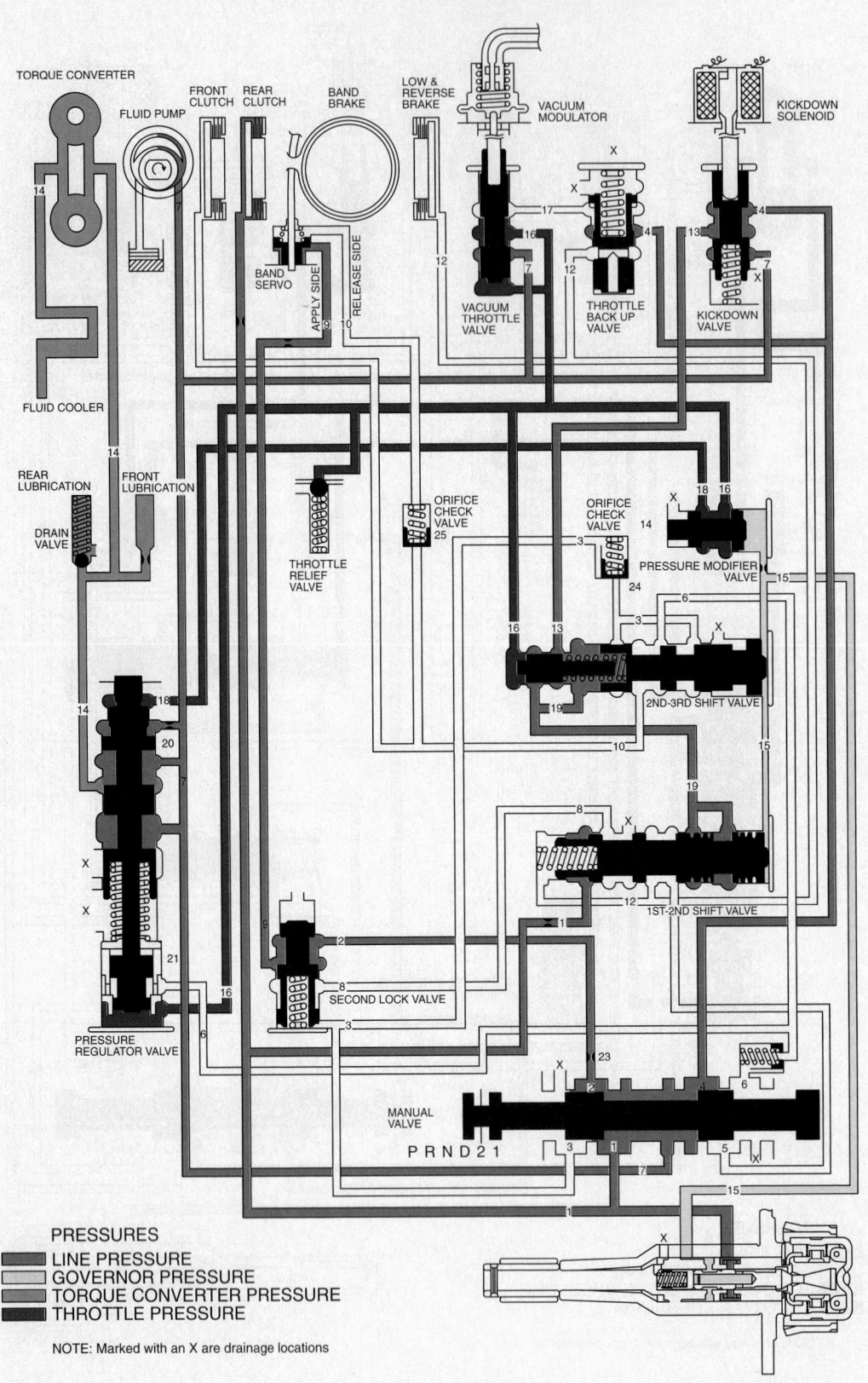

OIL CIRCUIT DIAGRAMS
Festiva ATX & Geo KF400 (Cont.)

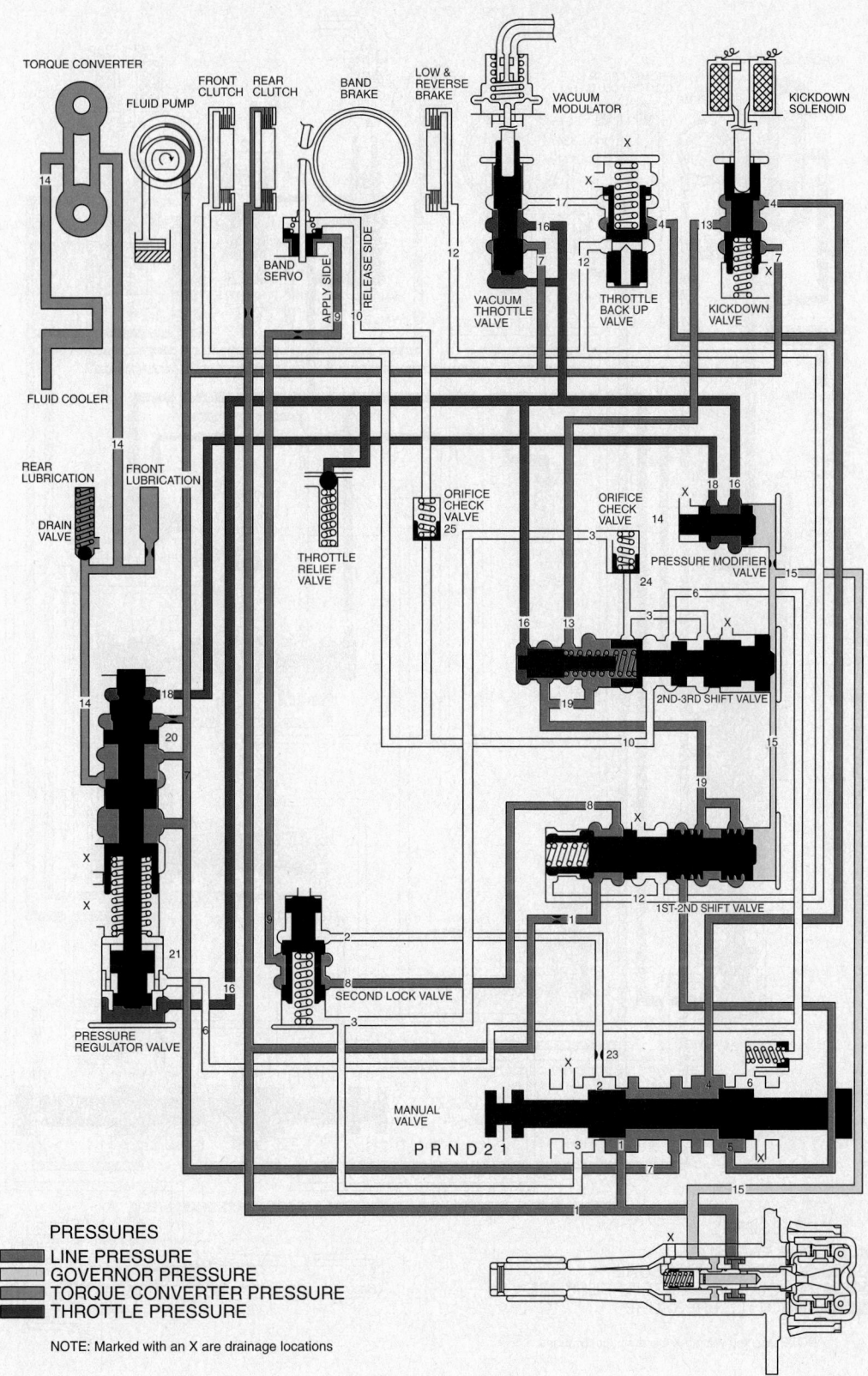

TORQUE CONVERTER

FLUID PUMP

FRONT CLUTCH

REAR CLUTCH

BAND BRAKE

LOW & REVERSE BRAKE

VACUUM MODULATOR

KICKDOWN SOLENOID

BAND SERVO

APPLY SIDE

RELEASE SIDE

VACUUM THROTTLE VALVE

THROTTLE BACK UP VALVE

KICKDOWN VALVE

FLUID COOLER

REAR LUBRICATION

FRONT LUBRICATION

DRAIN VALVE

THROTTLE RELIEF VALVE

ORIFICE CHECK VALVE

ORIFICE CHECK VALVE

PRESSURE MODIFIER VALVE

2ND-3RD SHIFT VALVE

1ST-2ND SHIFT VALVE

SECOND LOCK VALVE

PRESSURE REGULATOR VALVE

MANUAL VALVE

P R N D 2 1

PRESSURES

LINE PRESSURE
GOVERNOR PRESSURE
TORQUE CONVERTER PRESSURE
THROTTLE PRESSURE

NOTE: Marked with an X are drainage locations

Fig. 9: "1" Range — 2nd Gear   Courtesy of General Motors Corp.

OIL CIRCUIT DIAGRAMS
Festiva ATX & Geo KF400 (Cont.)

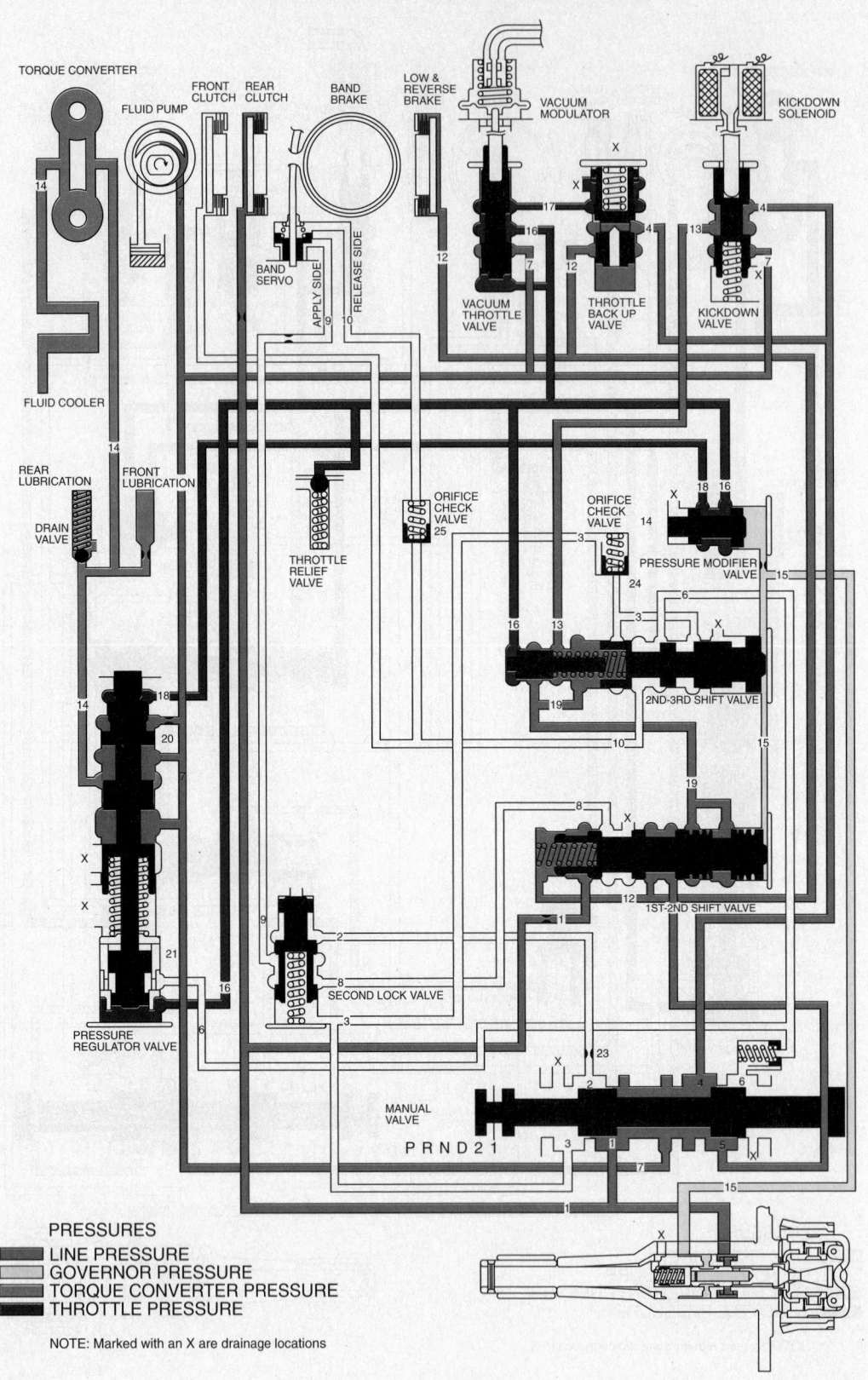

PRESSURES

LINE PRESSURE
GOVERNOR PRESSURE
TORQUE CONVERTER PRESSURE
THROTTLE PRESSURE

NOTE: Marked with an X are drainage locations

Fig. 10: "1" Range — Low Gear

Courtesy of General Motors Corp.

OIL CIRCUIT DIAGRAMS
Geo JF403-E

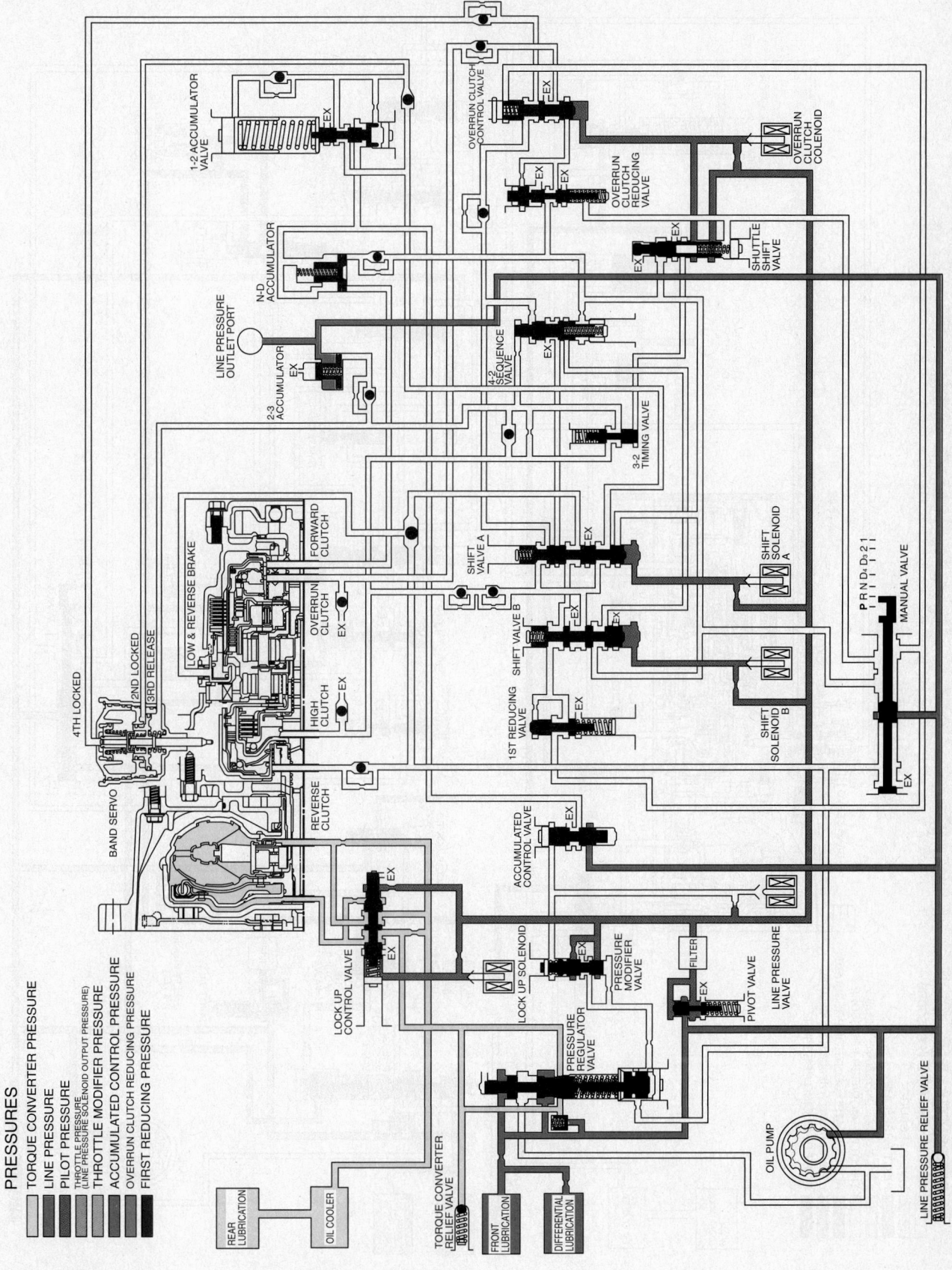

Fig. 1: "P" Range — Park

Courtesy of General Motors Corp.

OIL CIRCUIT DIAGRAMS
Geo JF403-E (Cont.)

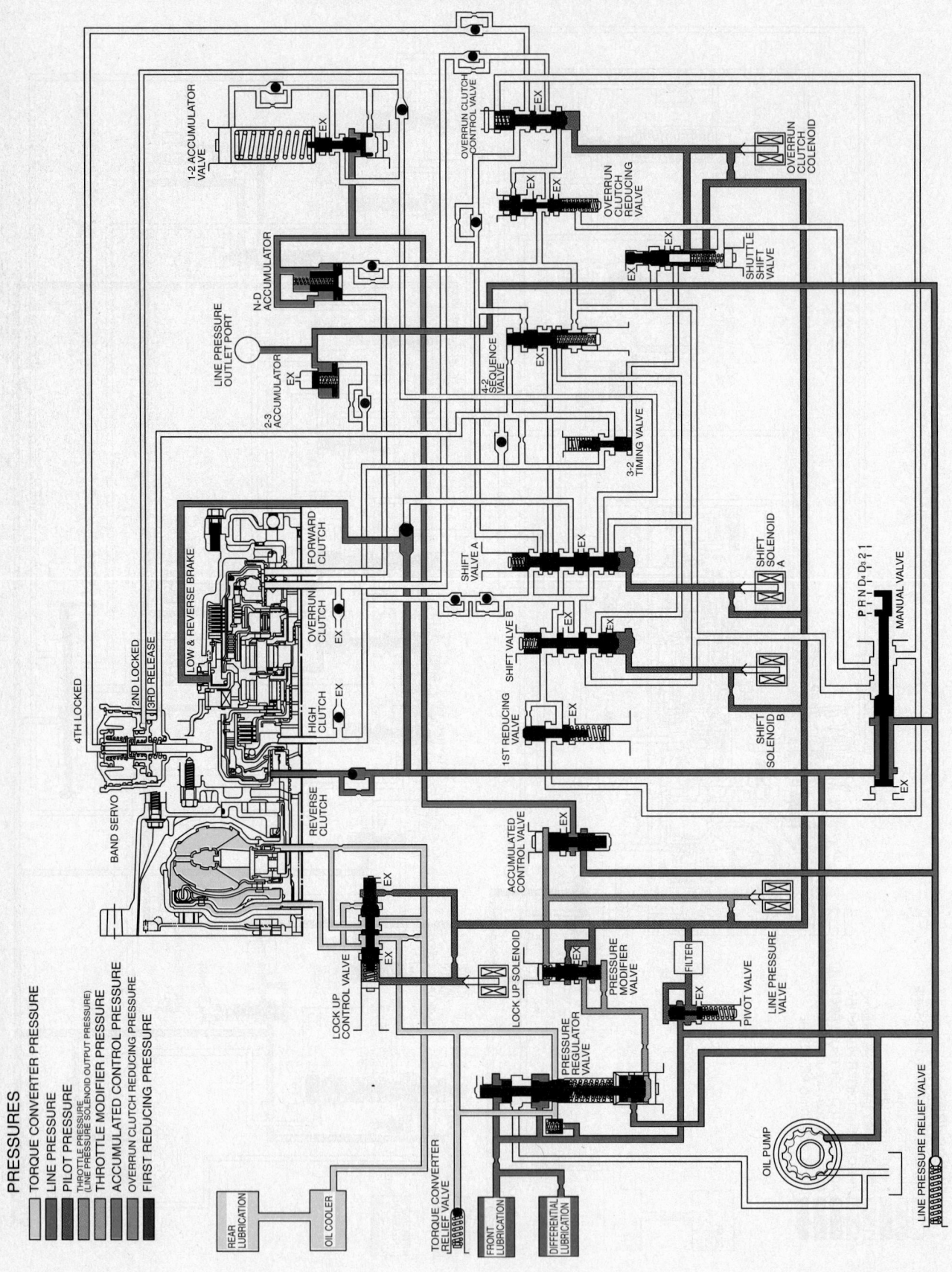

Fig. 2: "R" Range — Reverse

Courtesy of General Motors Corp.

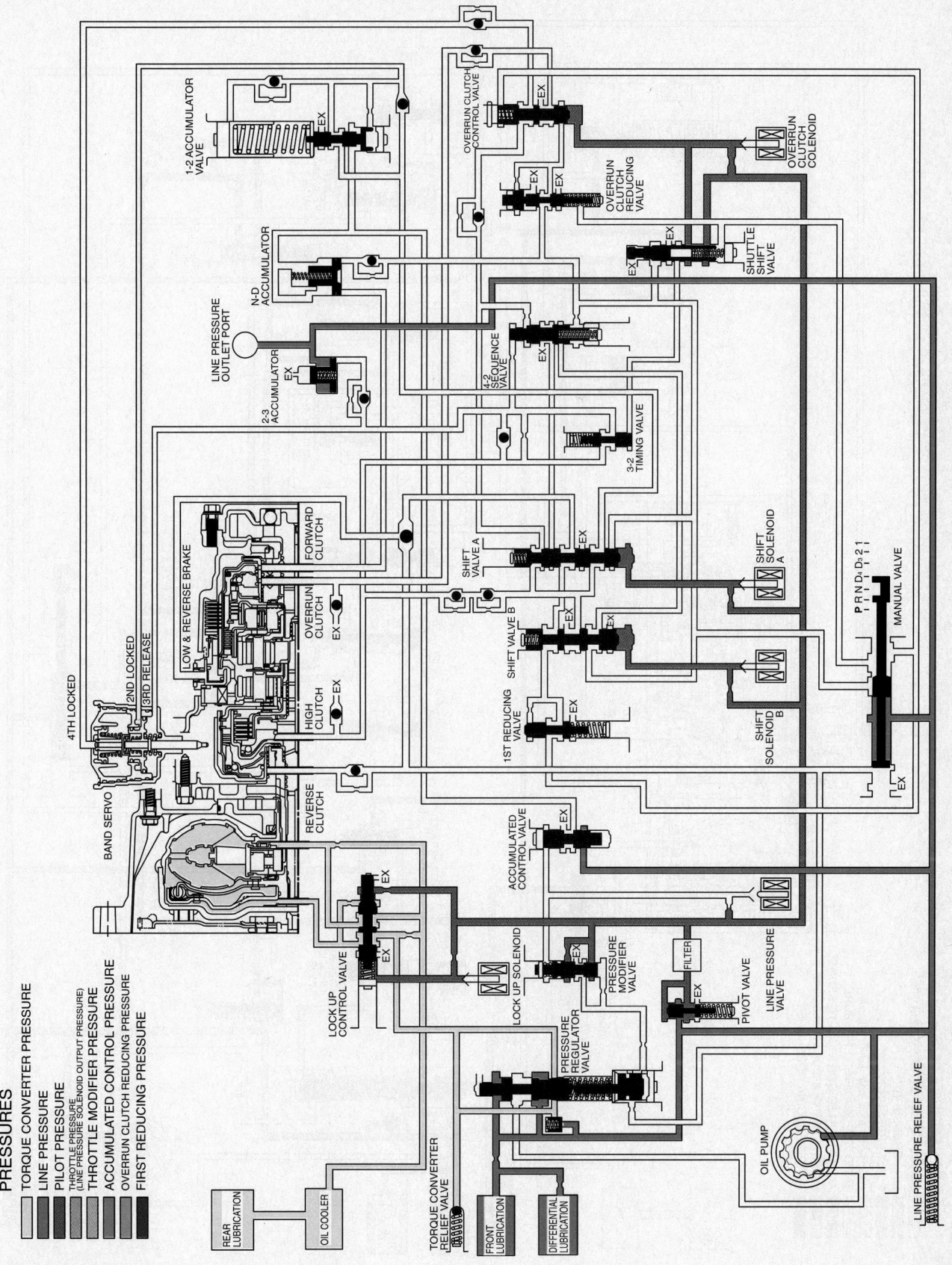

Fig. 3: "N" Range — Neutral

Courtesy of General Motors Corp.

OIL CIRCUIT DIAGRAMS
Geo JF403-E (Cont.)

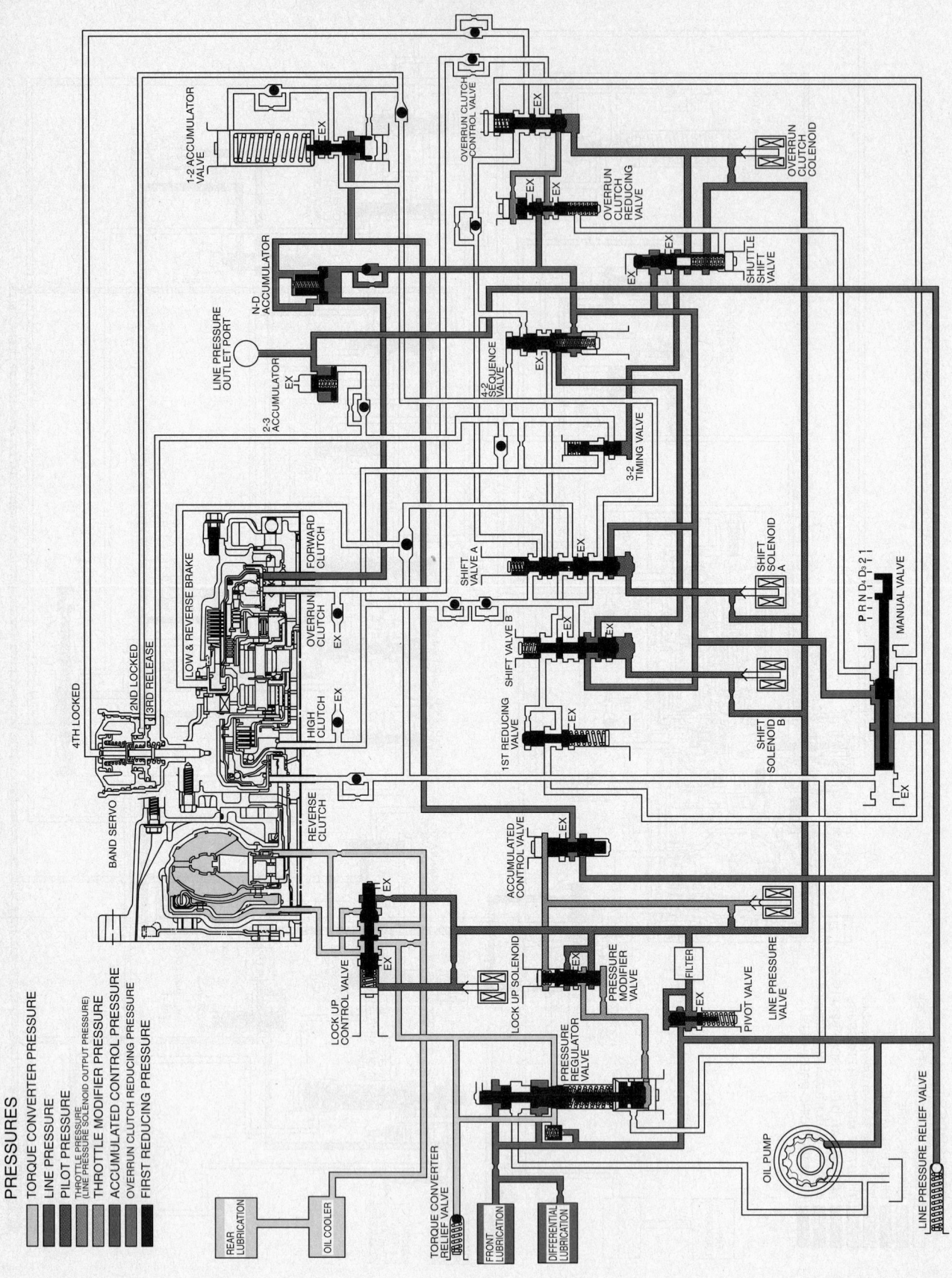

Fig. 4: "D4" & "D3" Range — 1st Gear

Courtesy of General Motors Corp.

OIL CIRCUIT DIAGRAMS
Geo JF403-E (Cont.)

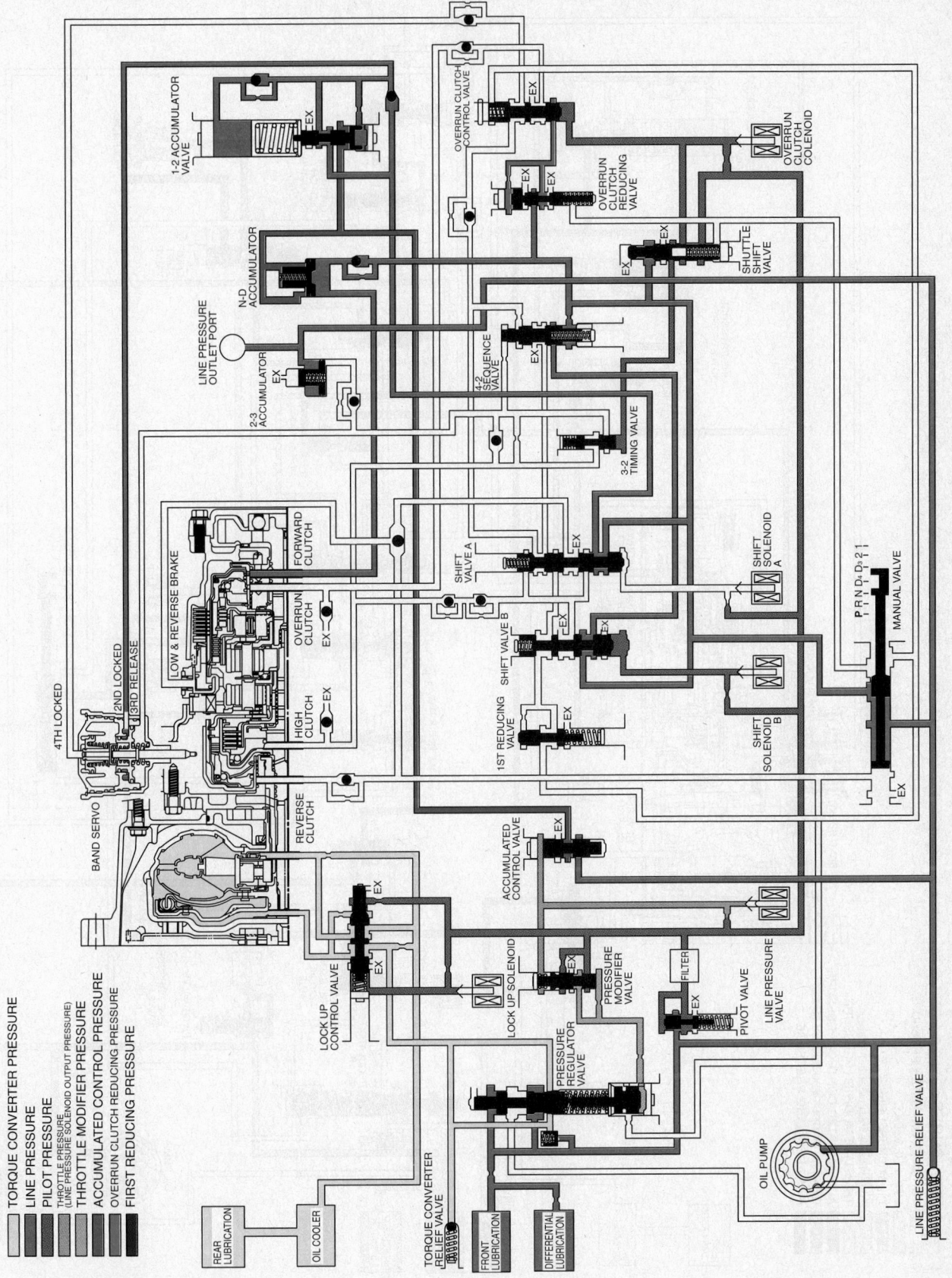

PRESSURES

TORQUE CONVERTER PRESSURE
LINE PRESSURE
PILOT PRESSURE
THROTTLE PRESSURE
(LINE PRESSURE SOLENOID OUTPUT PRESSURE)
THROTTLE MODIFIER PRESSURE
ACCUMULATED CONTROL PRESSURE
OVERRUN CLUTCH REDUCING PRESSURE
FIRST REDUCING PRESSURE

Fig. 5: "D4" & "D3" Range — 2nd Gear

Courtesy of General Motors Corp.

OIL CIRCUIT DIAGRAMS
Geo JF403-E (Cont.)

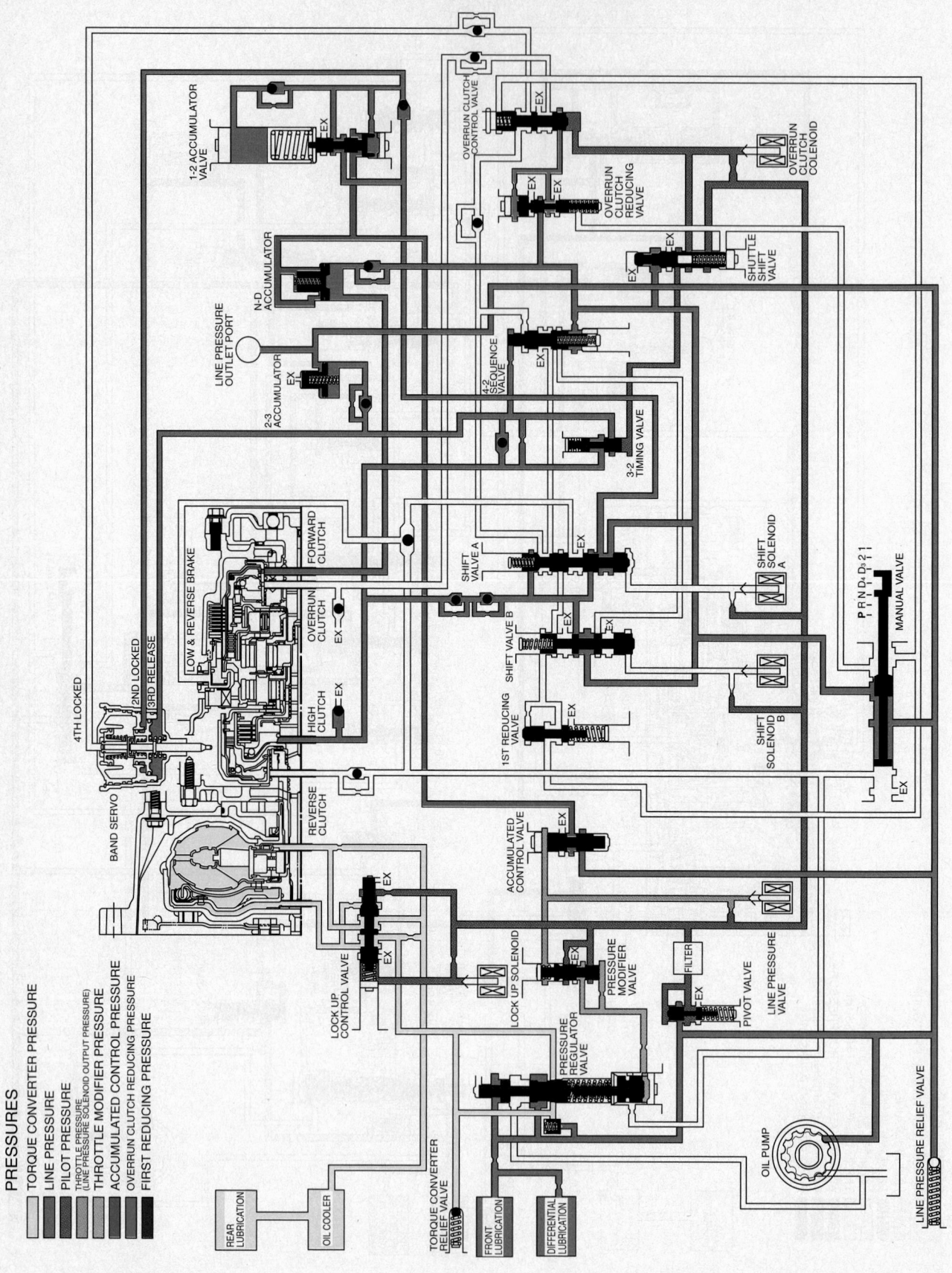

Fig. 6: "D4" & "D3" Range — 3rd Gear

Courtesy of General Motors Corp.

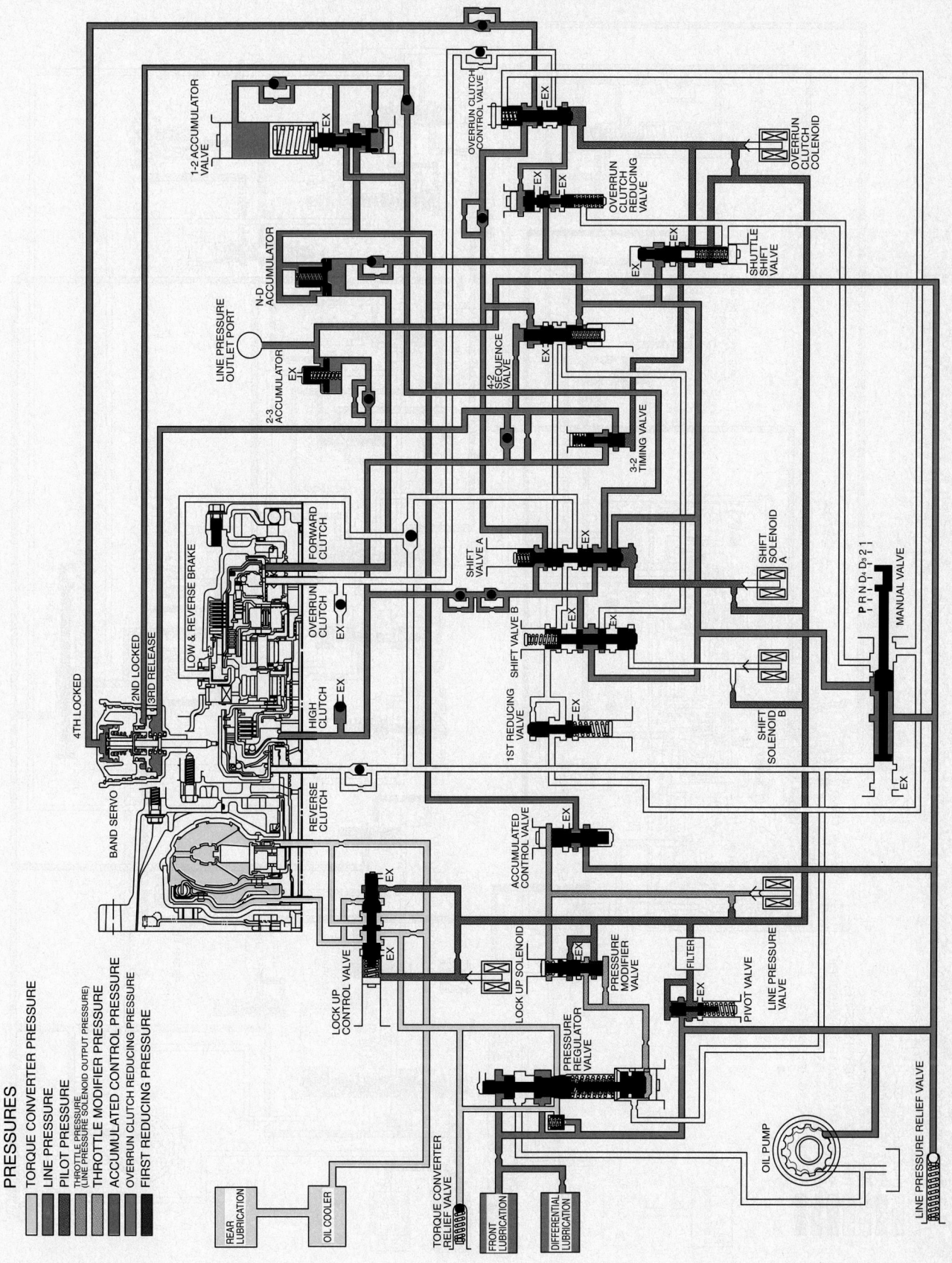

PRESSURES

- TORQUE CONVERTER PRESSURE
- LINE PRESSURE
- PILOT PRESSURE
- THROTTLE PRESSURE (LINE PRESSURE SOLENOID OUTPUT PRESSURE)
- ACCUMULATED CONTROL PRESSURE
- OVERRUN CLUTCH REDUCING PRESSURE
- FIRST REDUCING PRESSURE

Fig. 7: "D4" & "D3" Range — 4th Gear (TCC Off)

Courtesy of General Motors Corp.

OIL CIRCUIT DIAGRAMS
Geo JF403-E (Cont.)

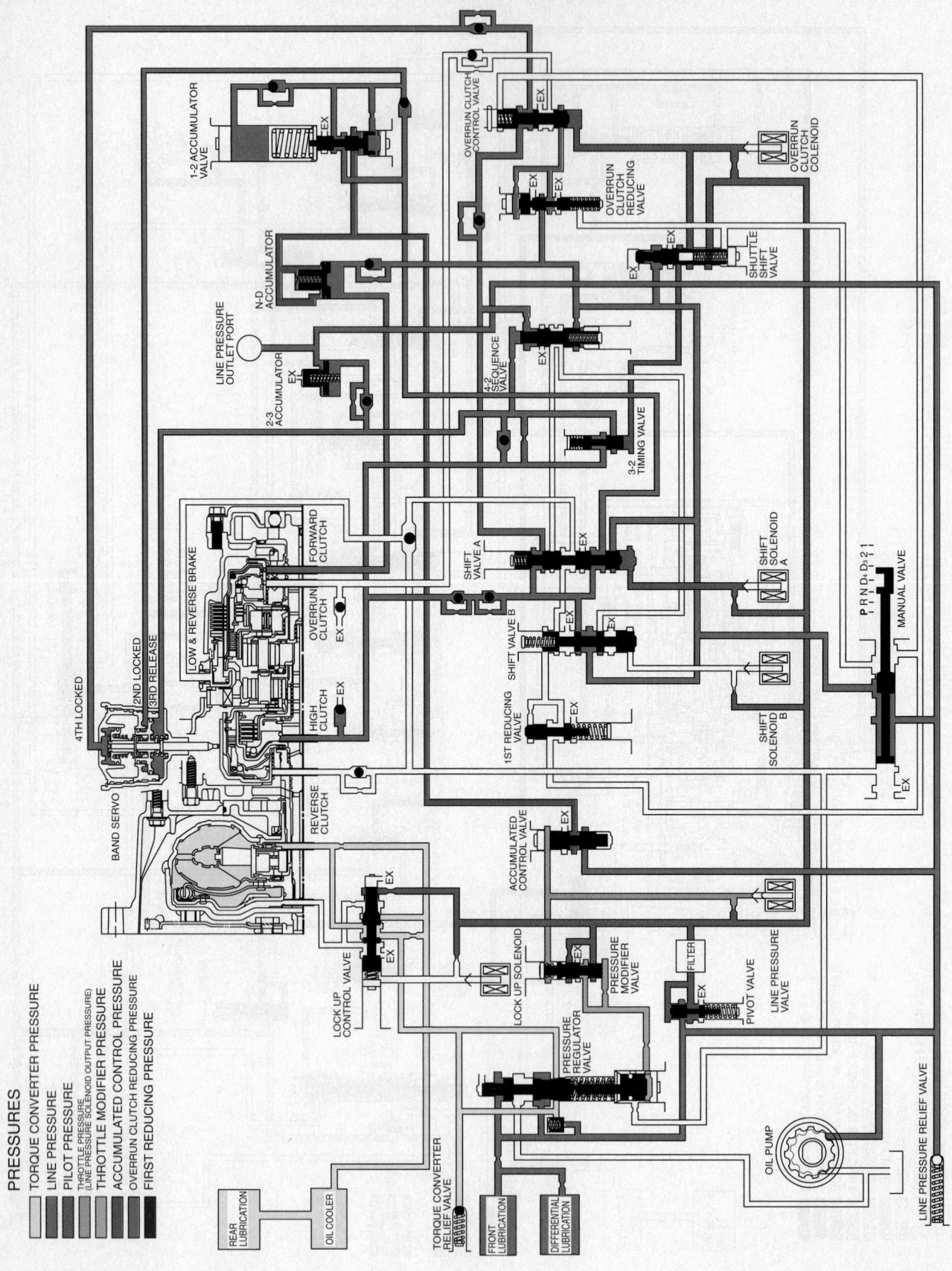

Fig. 8: "D4" & "D3" Range — 4th Gear (TCC On)

Courtesy of General Motors Corp.

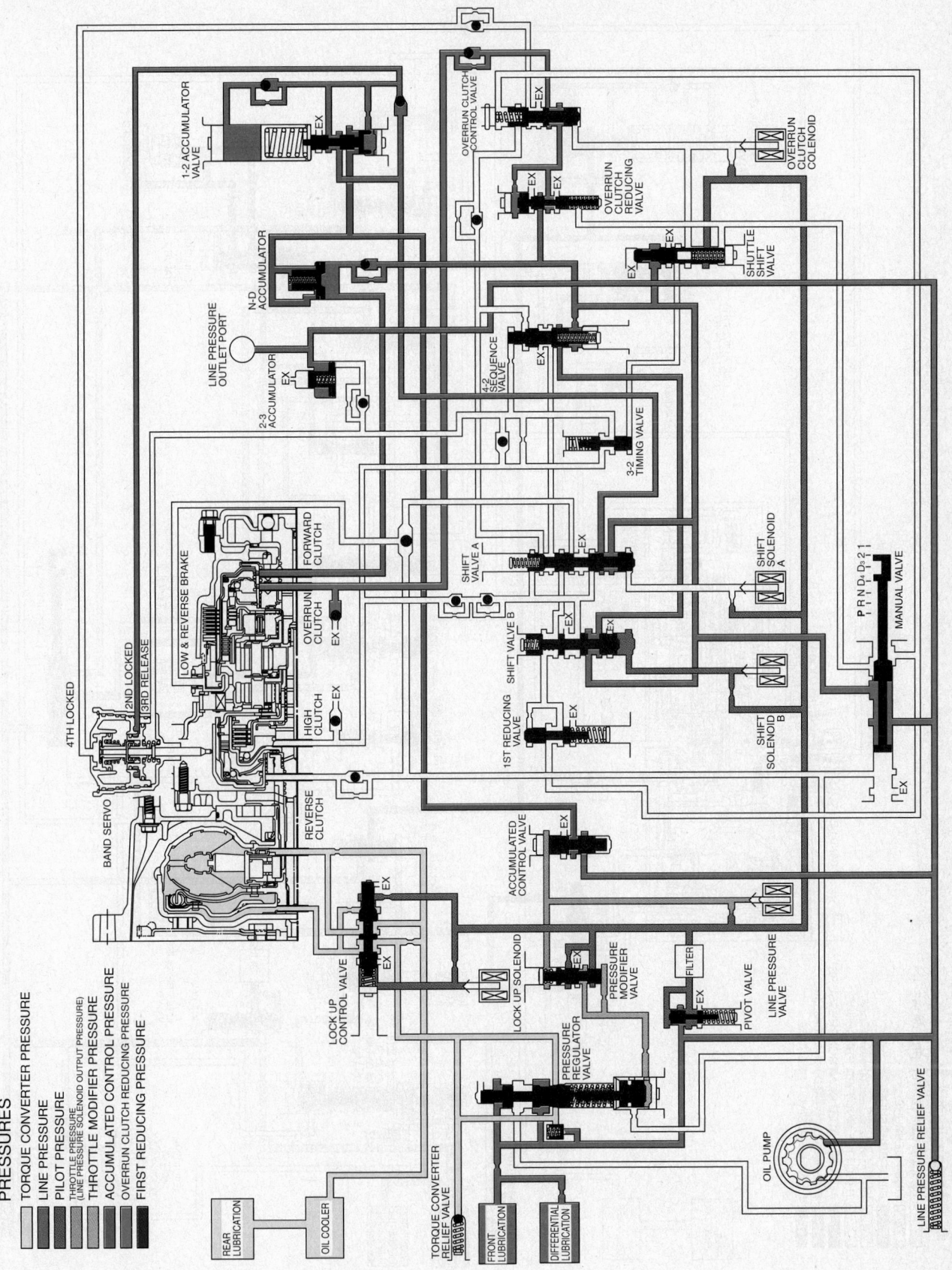

Fig. 9: "D3" Range — 2nd Gear (Overrun Clutch Engaged)

Courtesy of General Motors Corp.

OIL CIRCUIT DIAGRAMS
Geo JF403-E (Cont.)

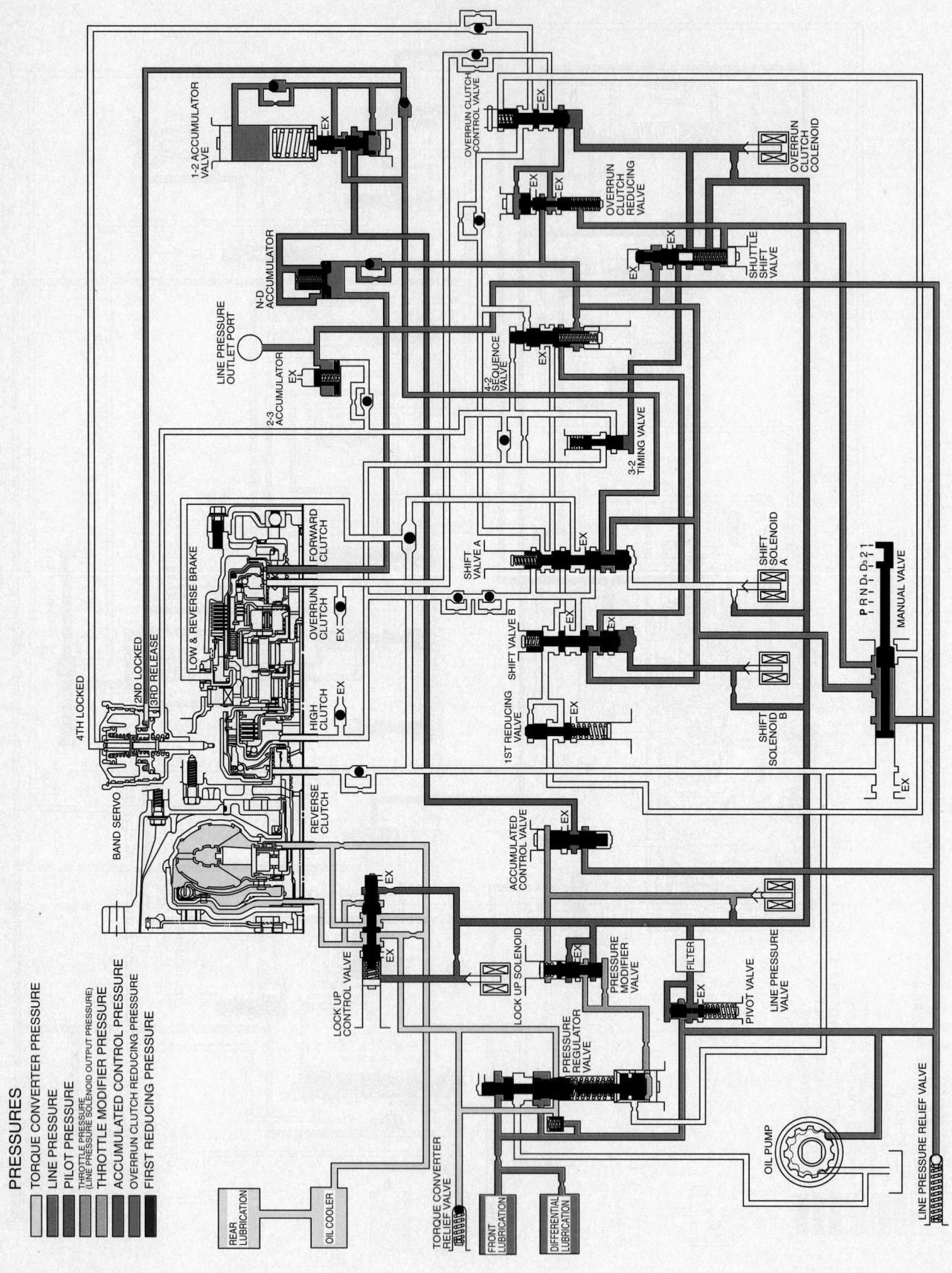

Fig. 10: "2" Range — 2nd Gear

Courtesy of General Motors Corp.

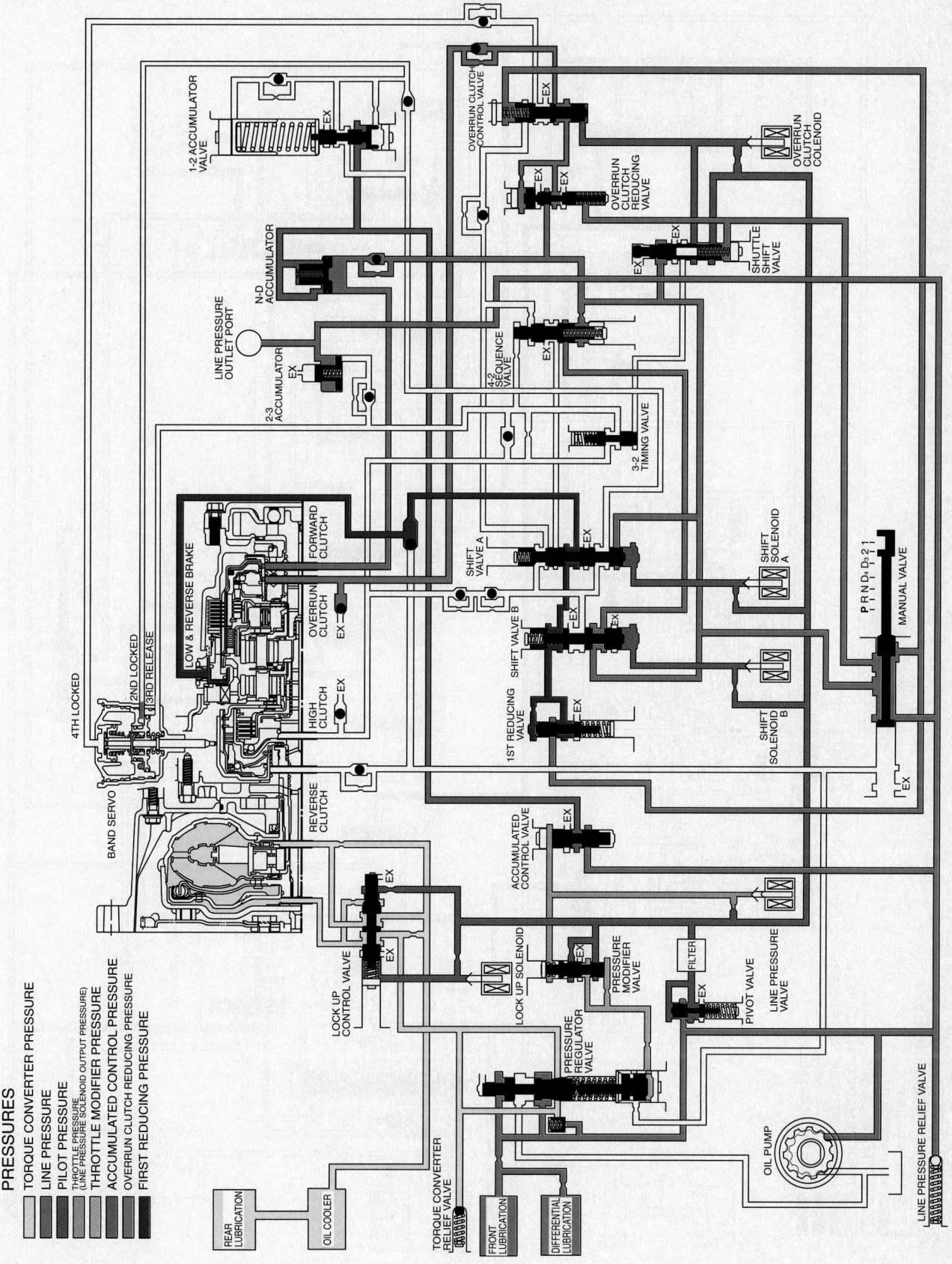

Fig. 11: "1" Range — 1st Gear

Courtesy of General Motors Corp.

OIL CIRCUIT DIAGRAMS
Geo JF403-E (Cont.)

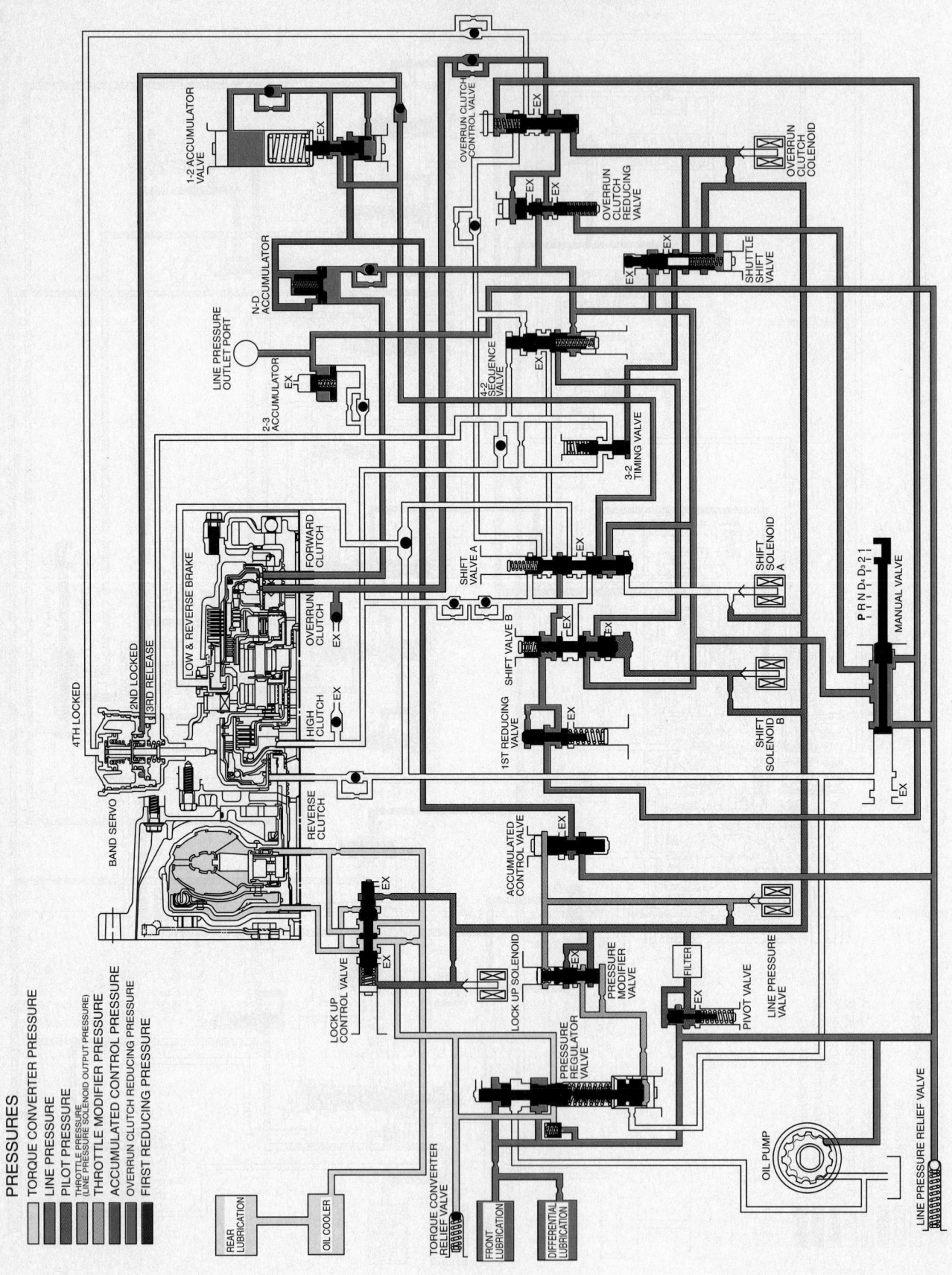

Fig. 12: "1" Range — 2nd dGear

Courtesy of General Motors Corp.

OIL CIRCUIT DIAGRAMS
Hydra-Matic 3T40

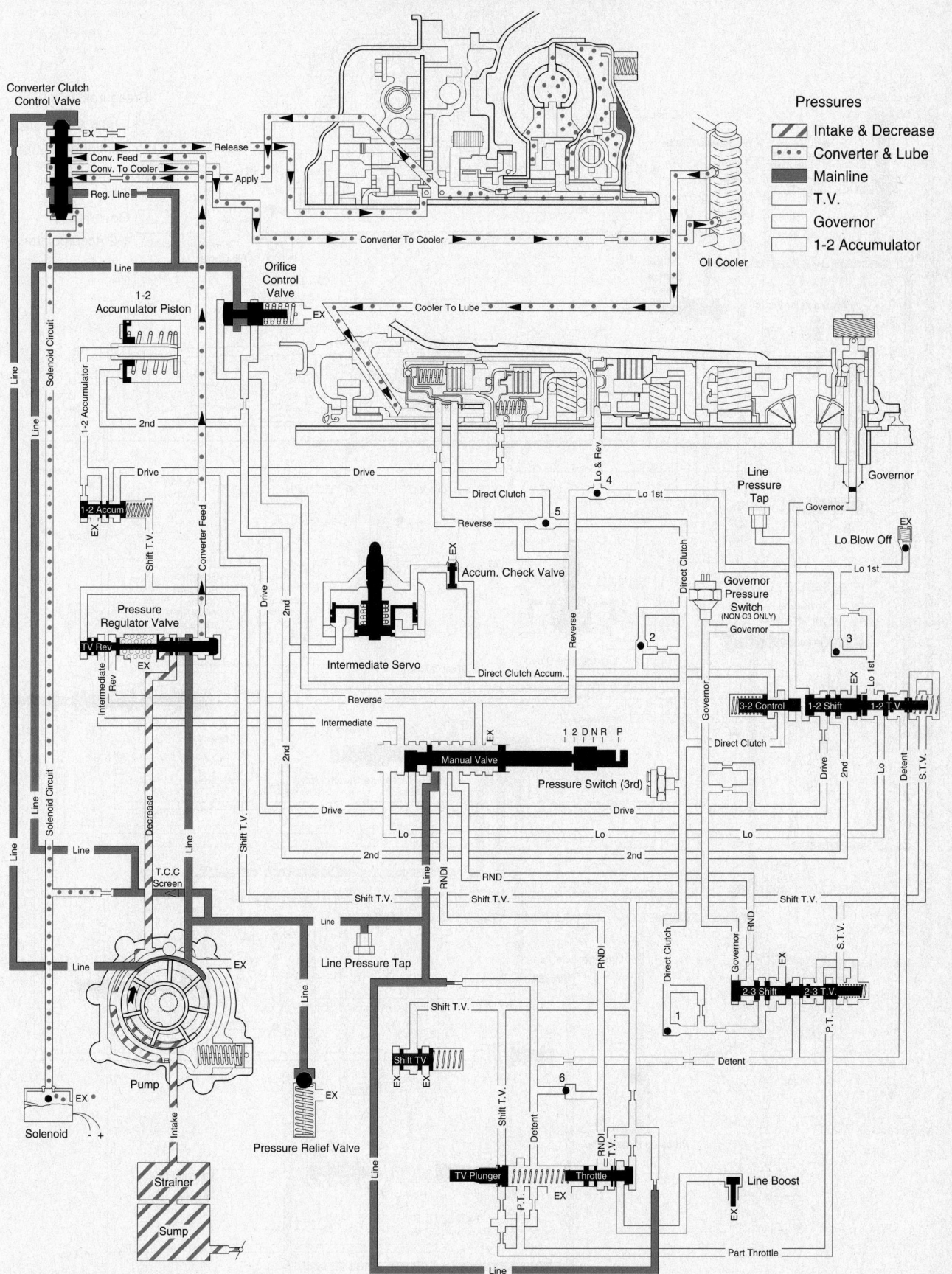

Pressures

- ▨ Intake & Decrease
- ⋯ Converter & Lube
- ▓ Mainline
- ☐ T.V.
- ☐ Governor
- ☐ 1-2 Accumulator

Fig. 1: Park — Engine Running   Courtesy of General Motors Corp.

OIL CIRCUIT DIAGRAMS
Hydra-Matic 3T40 (Cont.)

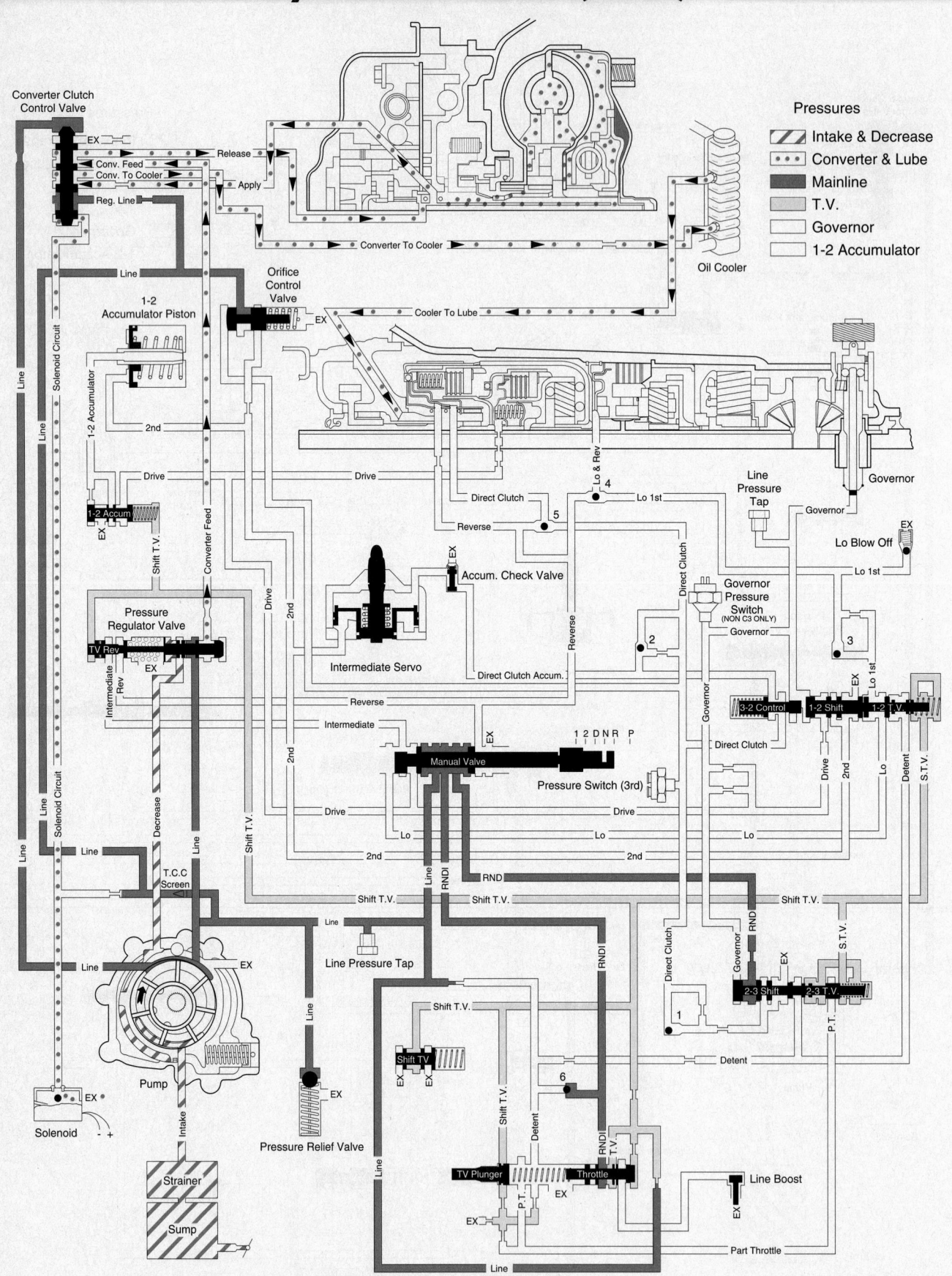

Fig. 2: Neutral — Engine Running

Courtesy of General Motors Corp.

OIL CIRCUIT DIAGRAMS
Hydra-Matic 3T40 (Cont.)

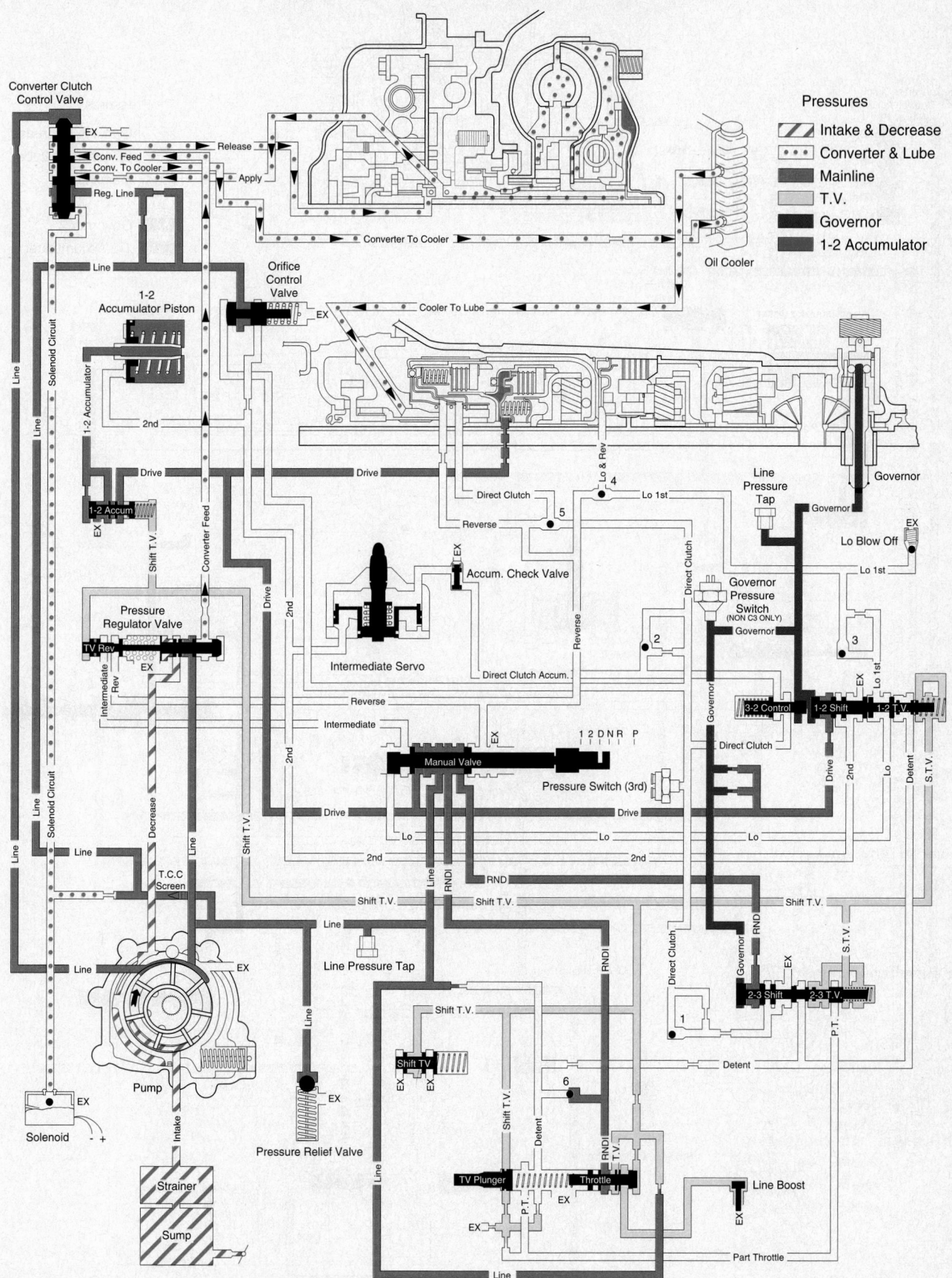

Pressures

- Intake & Decrease
- Converter & Lube
- Mainline
- T.V.
- Governor
- 1-2 Accumulator

Fig. 3: Drive Range — 1st Gear

Courtesy of General Motors Corp.

OIL CIRCUIT DIAGRAMS
Hydra-Matic 3T40 (Cont.)

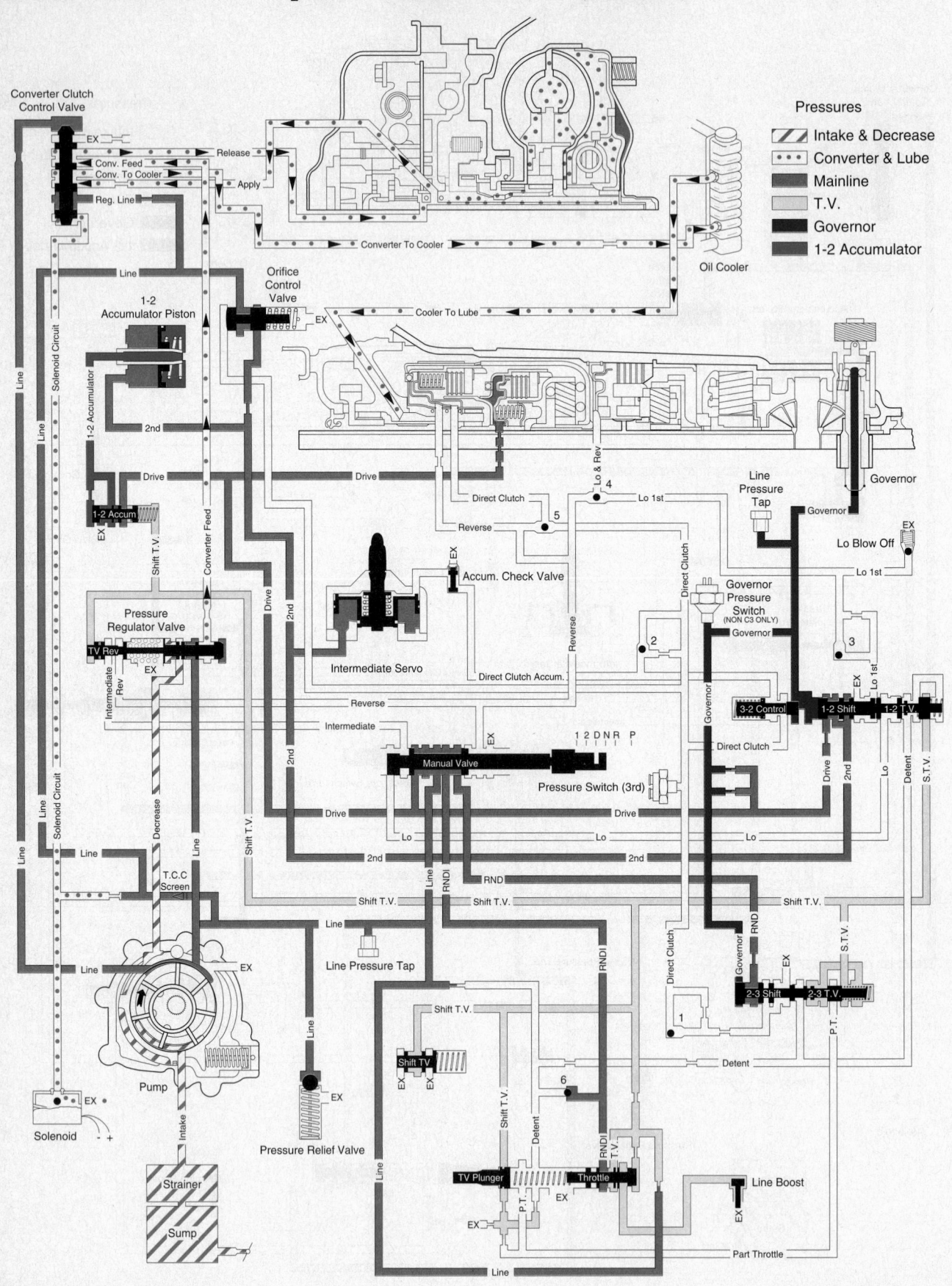

Pressures

▨	Intake & Decrease
⋯	Converter & Lube
▓	Mainline
░	T.V.
▉	Governor
▤	1-2 Accumulator

Fig. 4: Drive Range — 2nd Gear

Courtesy of General Motors Corp.

OIL CIRCUIT DIAGRAMS
Hydra-Matic 3T40 (Cont.)

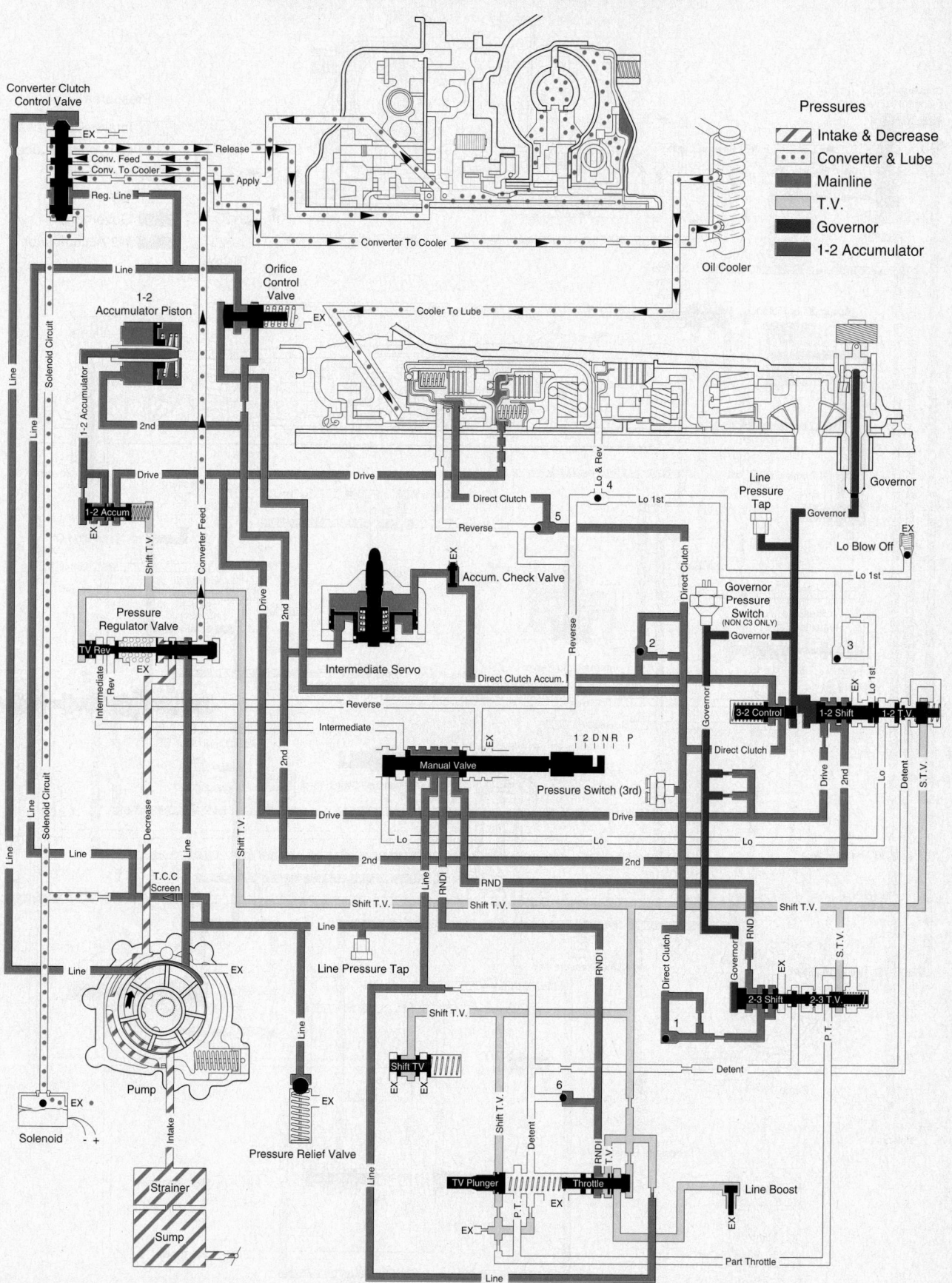

Pressures

▨	Intake & Decrease
⋯	Converter & Lube
▮	Mainline
▮	T.V.
▮	Governor
▮	1-2 Accumulator

Fig. 5: Drive Range — 3rd Gear (Converter Clutch Released)

Courtesy of General Motors Corp.

OIL CIRCUIT DIAGRAMS
Hydra-Matic 3T40 (Cont.)

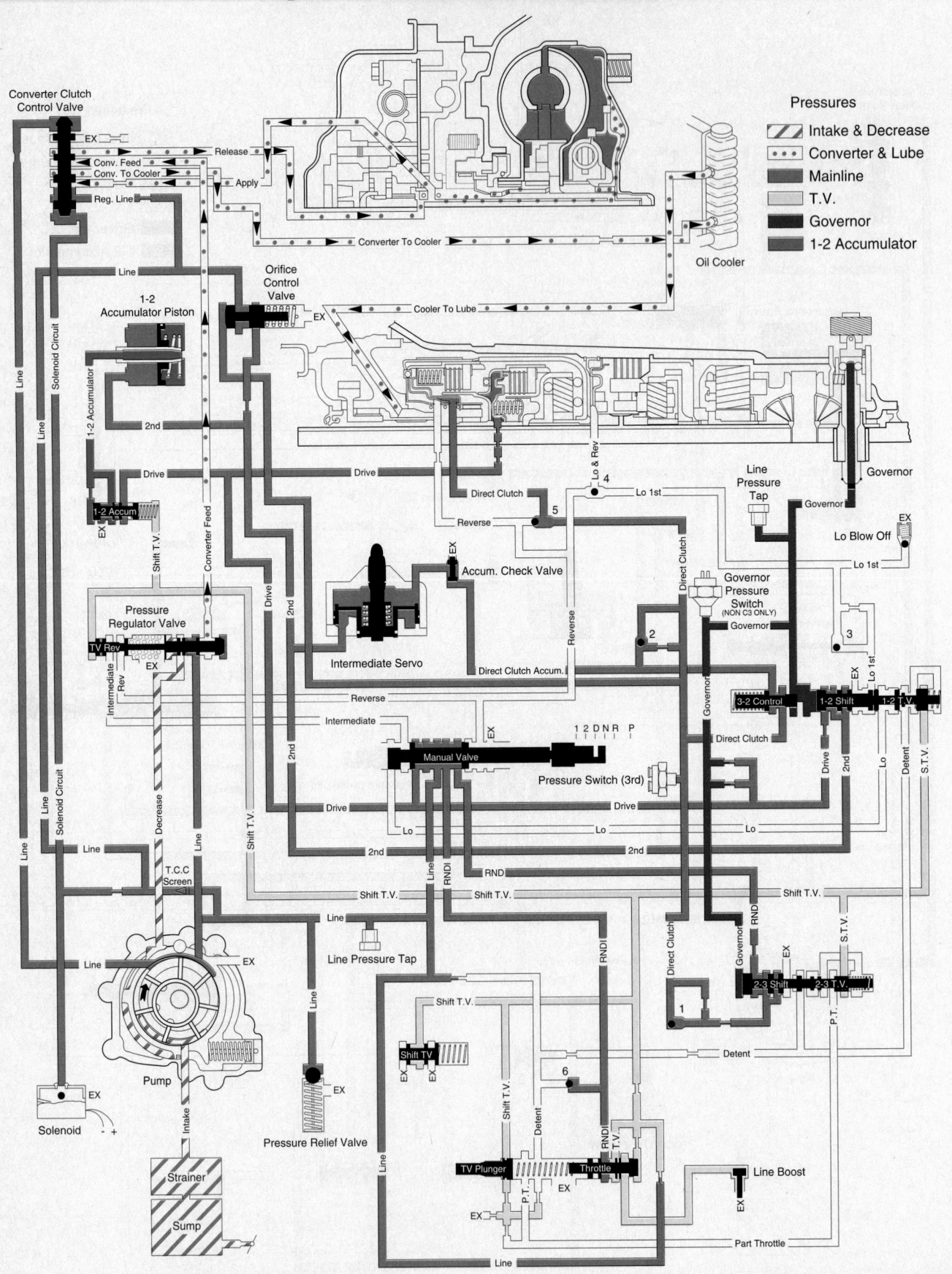

Fig. 6: Drive Range — 3rd Gear (Converter Clutch Applied)

Courtesy of General Motors Corp.

OIL CIRCUIT DIAGRAMS
Hydra-Matic 3T40 (Cont.)

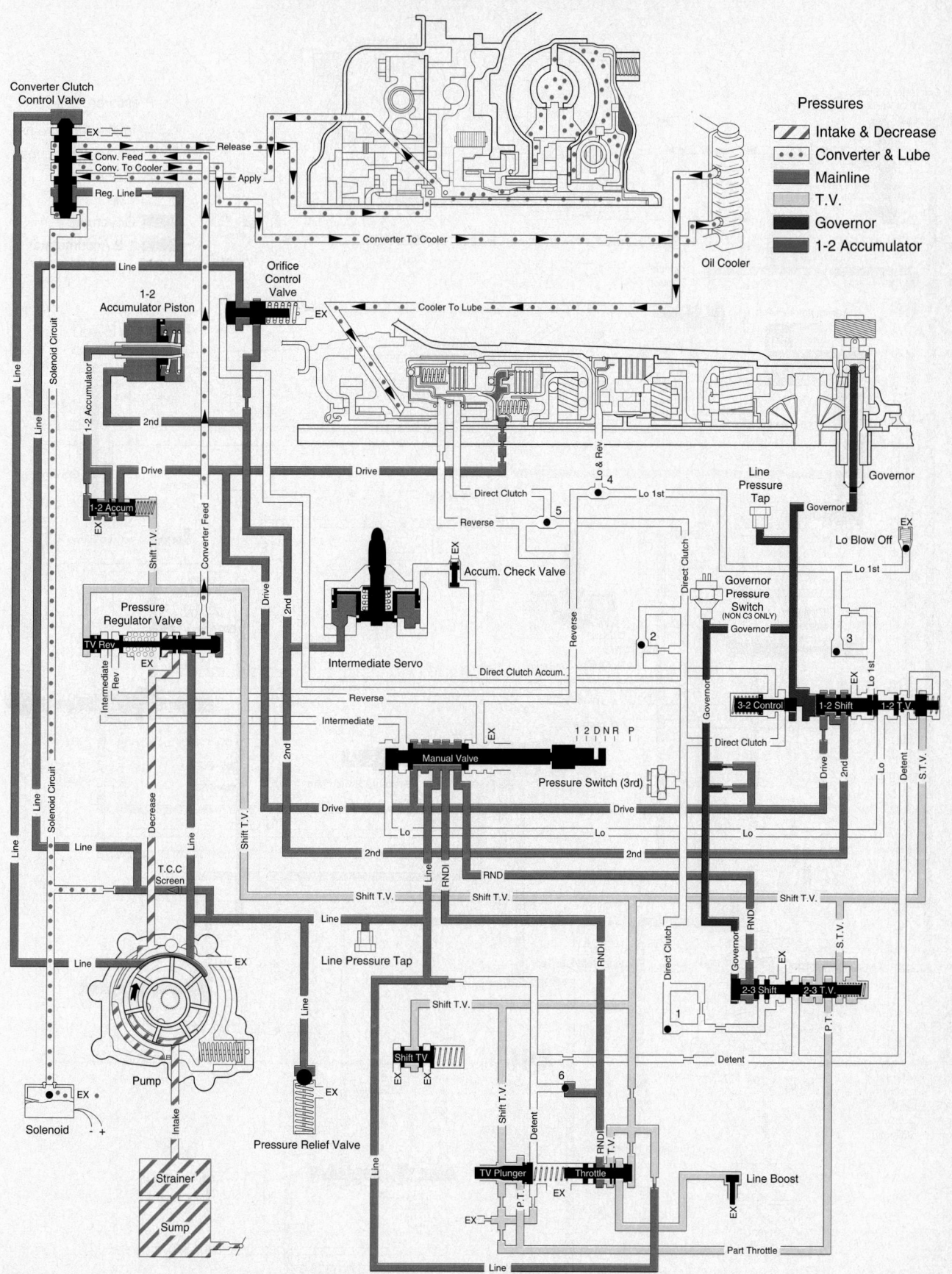

Fig. 7: Part Throttle 3-2 Downshift (Valves in 2nd Gear Position)

Courtesy of General Motors Corp.

OIL CIRCUIT DIAGRAMS
Hydra-Matic 3T40 (Cont.)

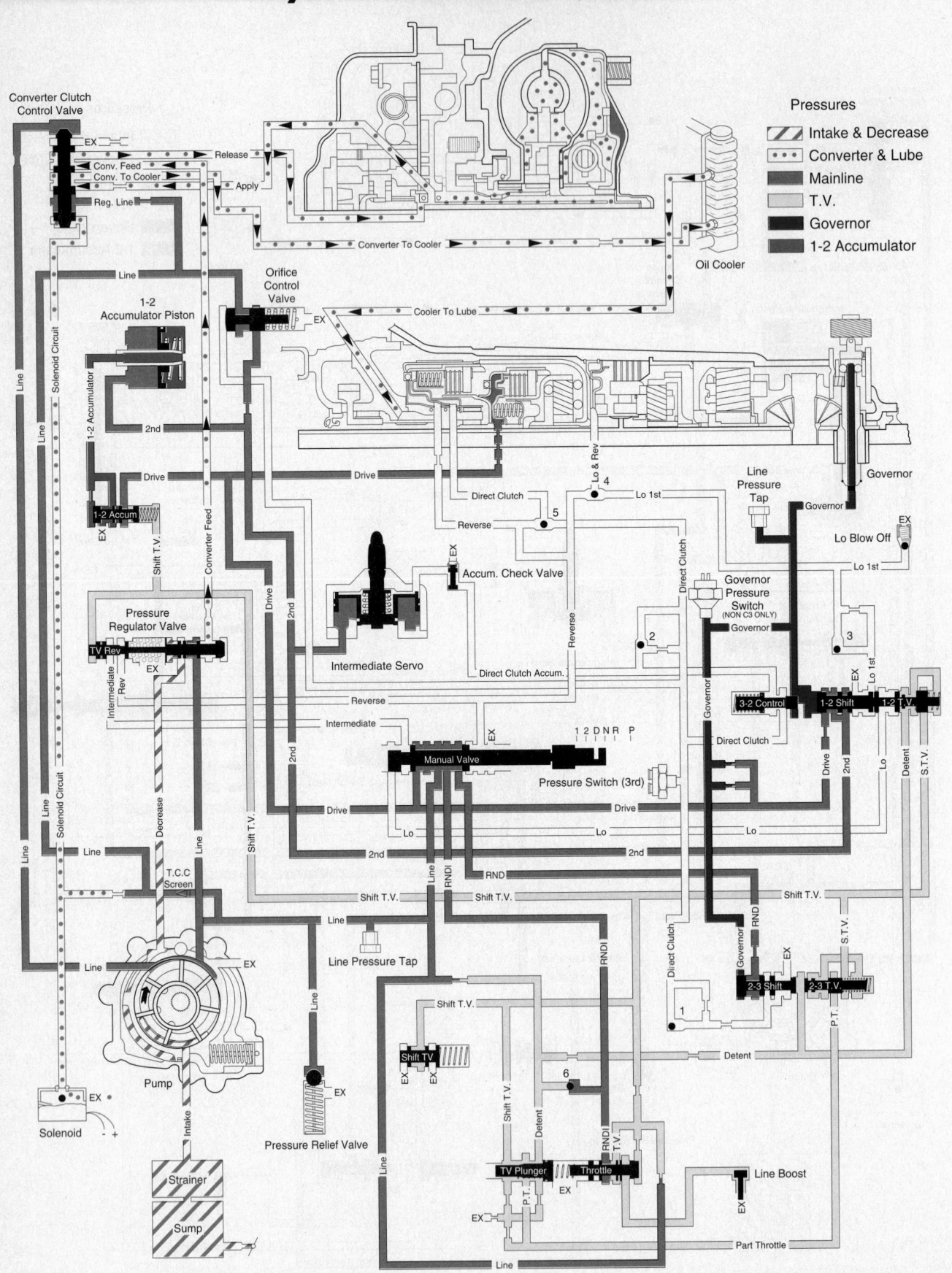

Fig. 8: Detent Downshift (Valves In 2nd Gear Position)

Courtesy of General Motors Corp.

OIL CIRCUIT DIAGRAMS
Hydra-Matic 3T40 (Cont.)

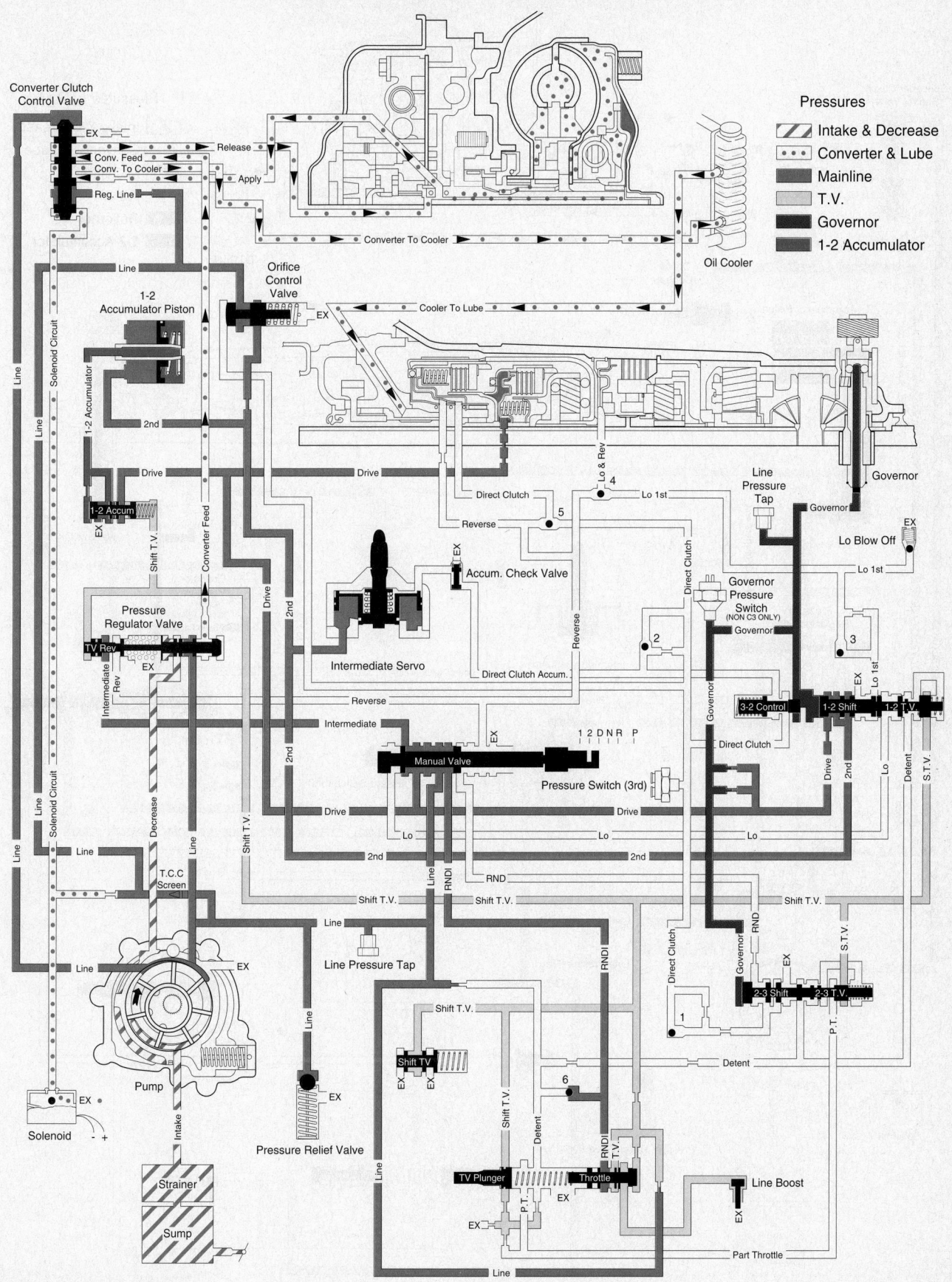

Fig. 9: Manual 2nd Gear

Courtesy of General Motors Corp.

OIL CIRCUIT DIAGRAMS
Hydra-Matic 3T40 (Cont.)

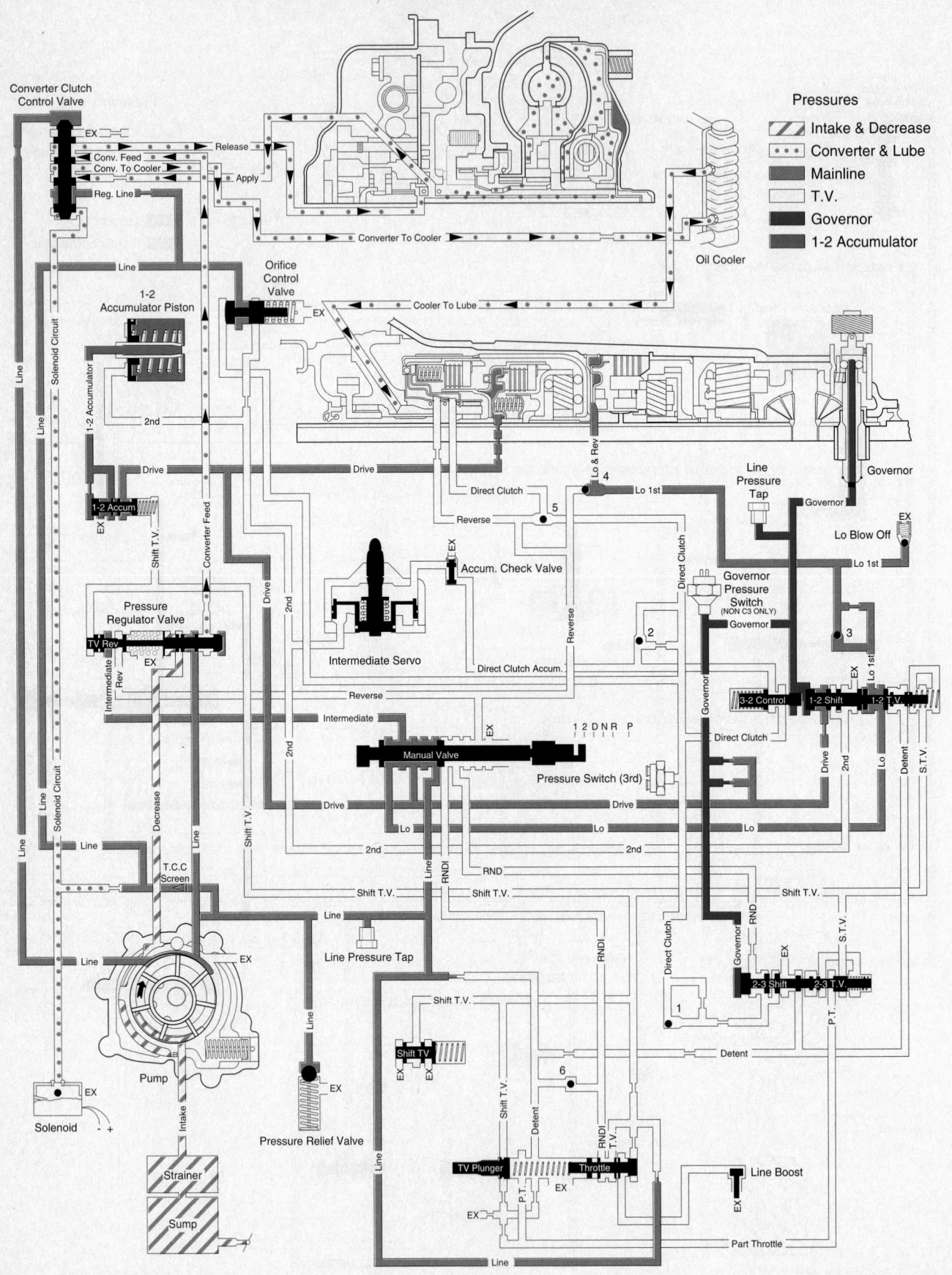

Fig. 10: Manual Low Gear

Courtesy of General Motors Corp.

OIL CIRCUIT DIAGRAMS
Hydra-Matic 3T40 (Cont.)

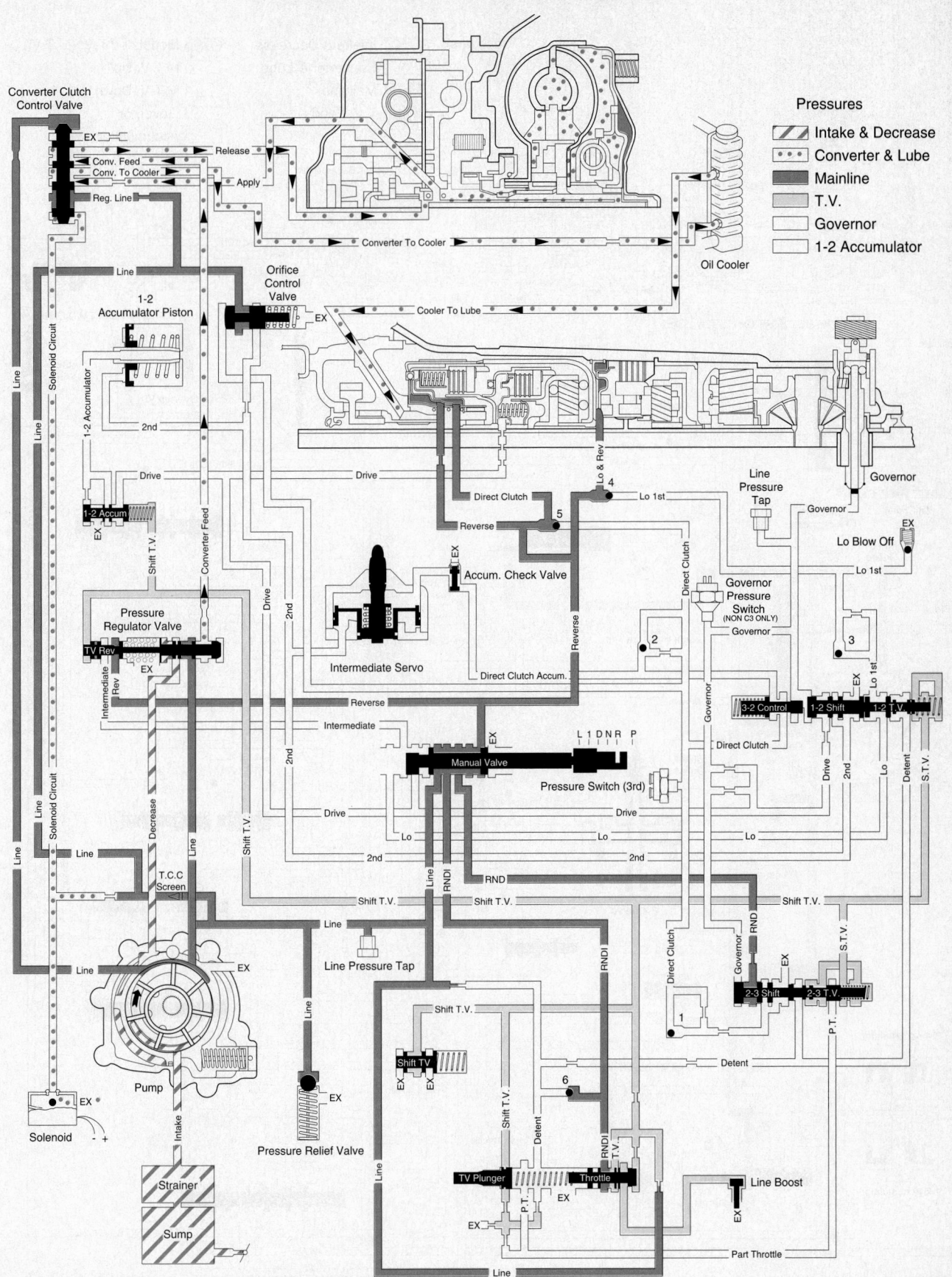

Pressures

- Intake & Decrease
- Converter & Lube
- Mainline
- T.V.
- Governor
- 1-2 Accumulator

Fig. 11: Reverse Gear

Courtesy of General Motors Corp.

OIL CIRCUIT DIAGRAMS
Hydra-Matic 4L60

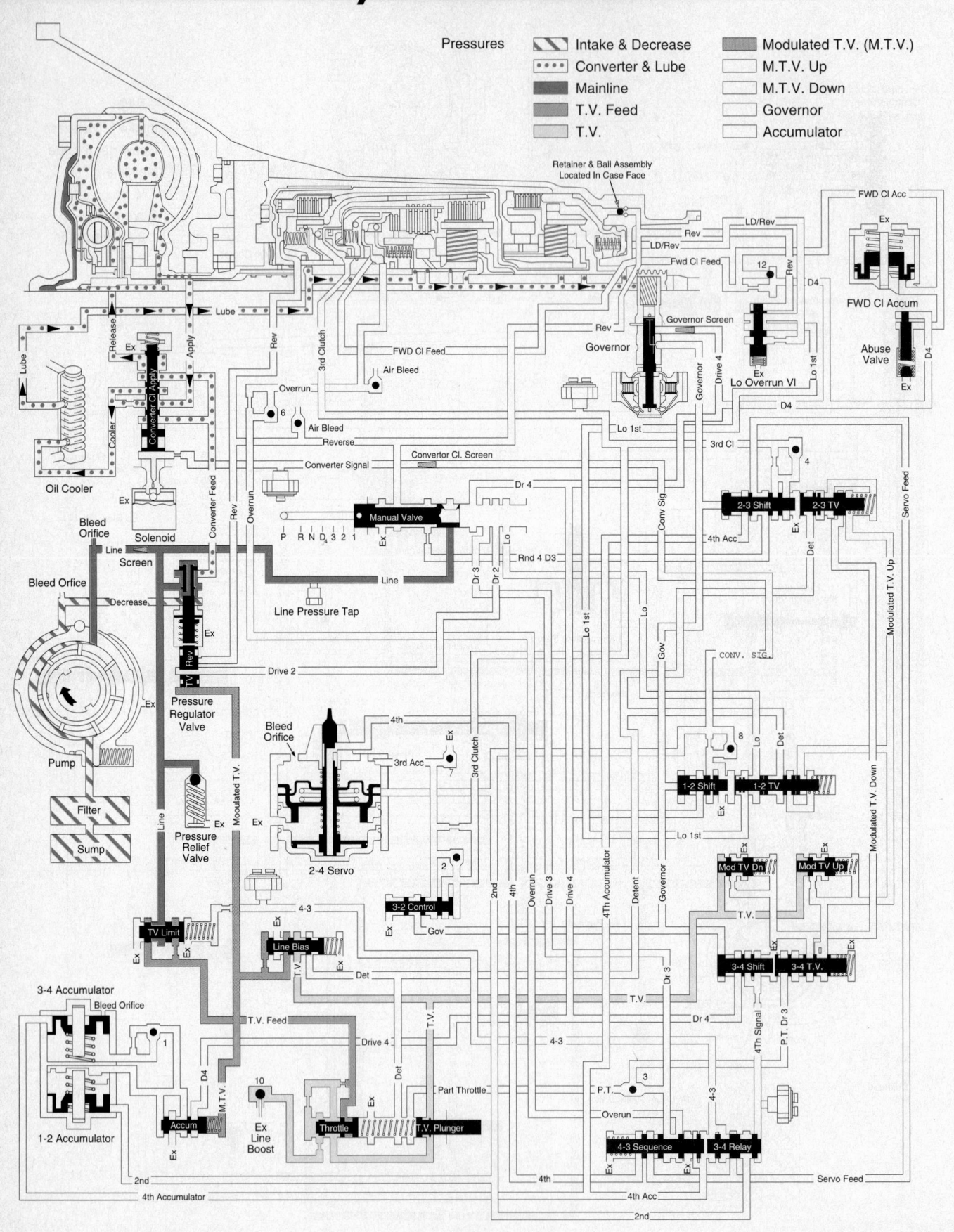

Fig. 1: Park — Engine Running

Courtesy of General Motors Corp.

OIL CIRCUIT DIAGRAMS
Hydra-Matic 4L60 (Cont.)

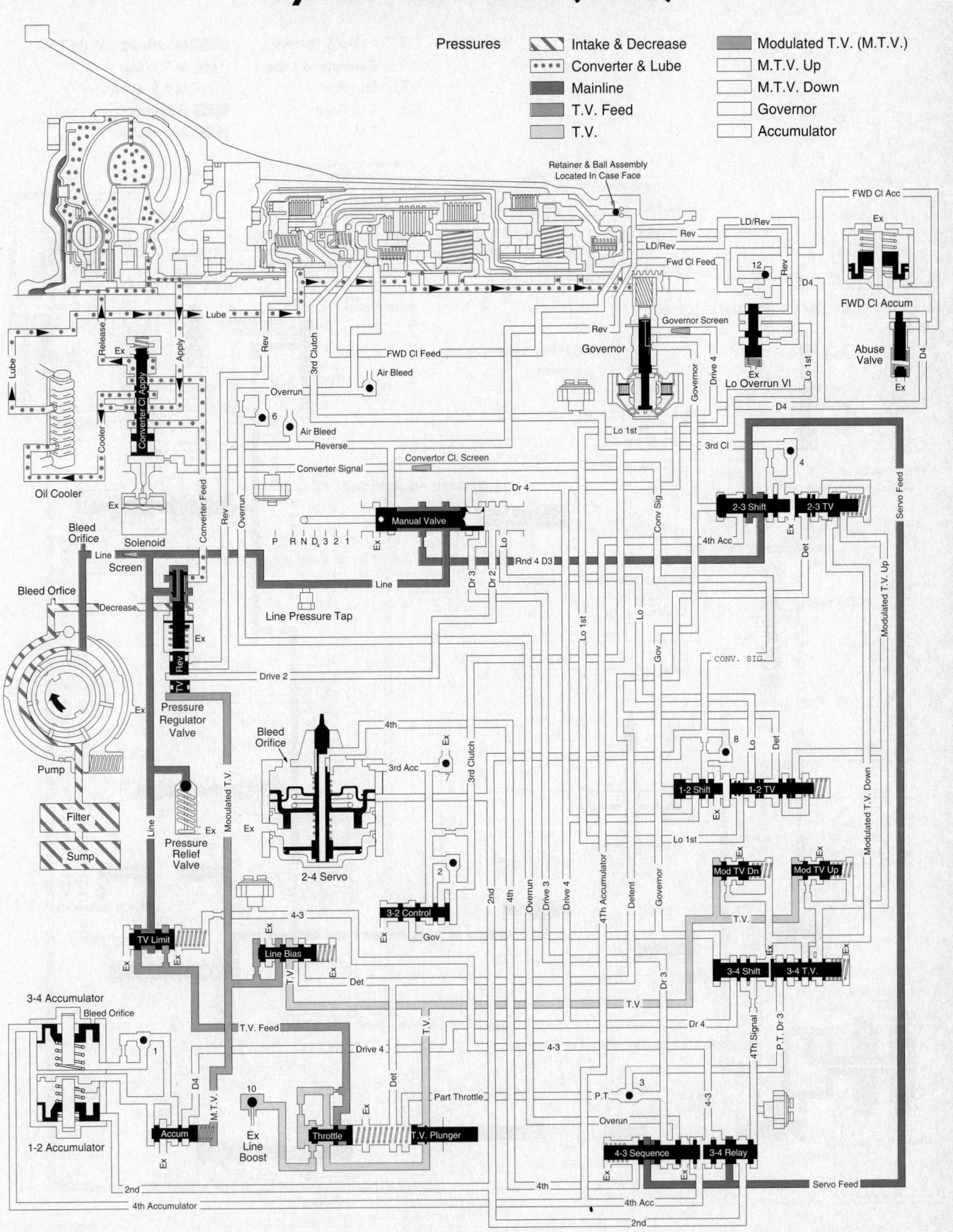

Fig. 2: Neutral — Engine Running

Courtesy of General Motors Corp.

OIL CIRCUIT DIAGRAMS
Hydra-Matic 4L60 (Cont.)

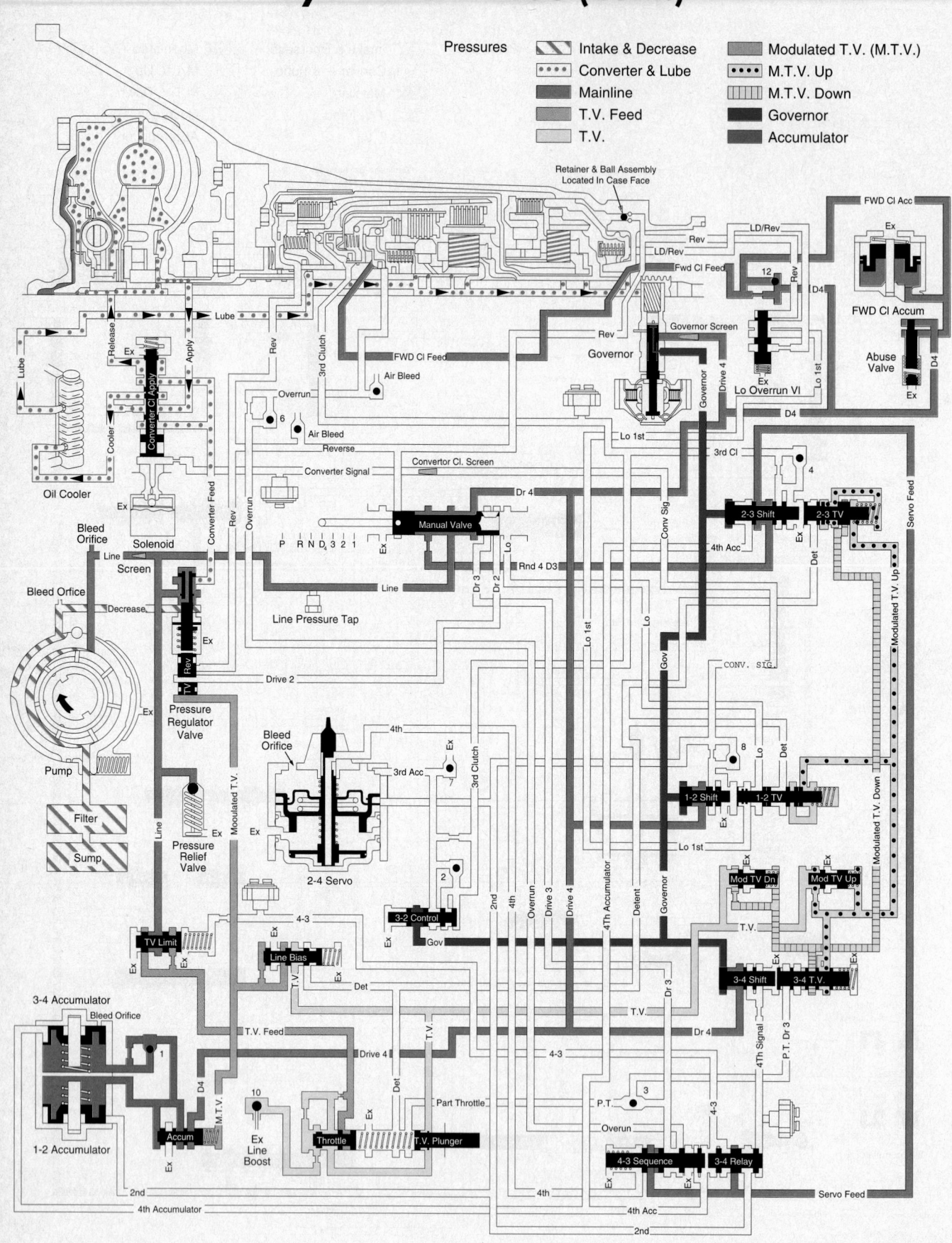

Fig. 3: D4 — 1st Gear

Courtesy of General Motors Corp.

OIL CIRCUIT DIAGRAMS
Hydra-Matic 4L60 (Cont.)

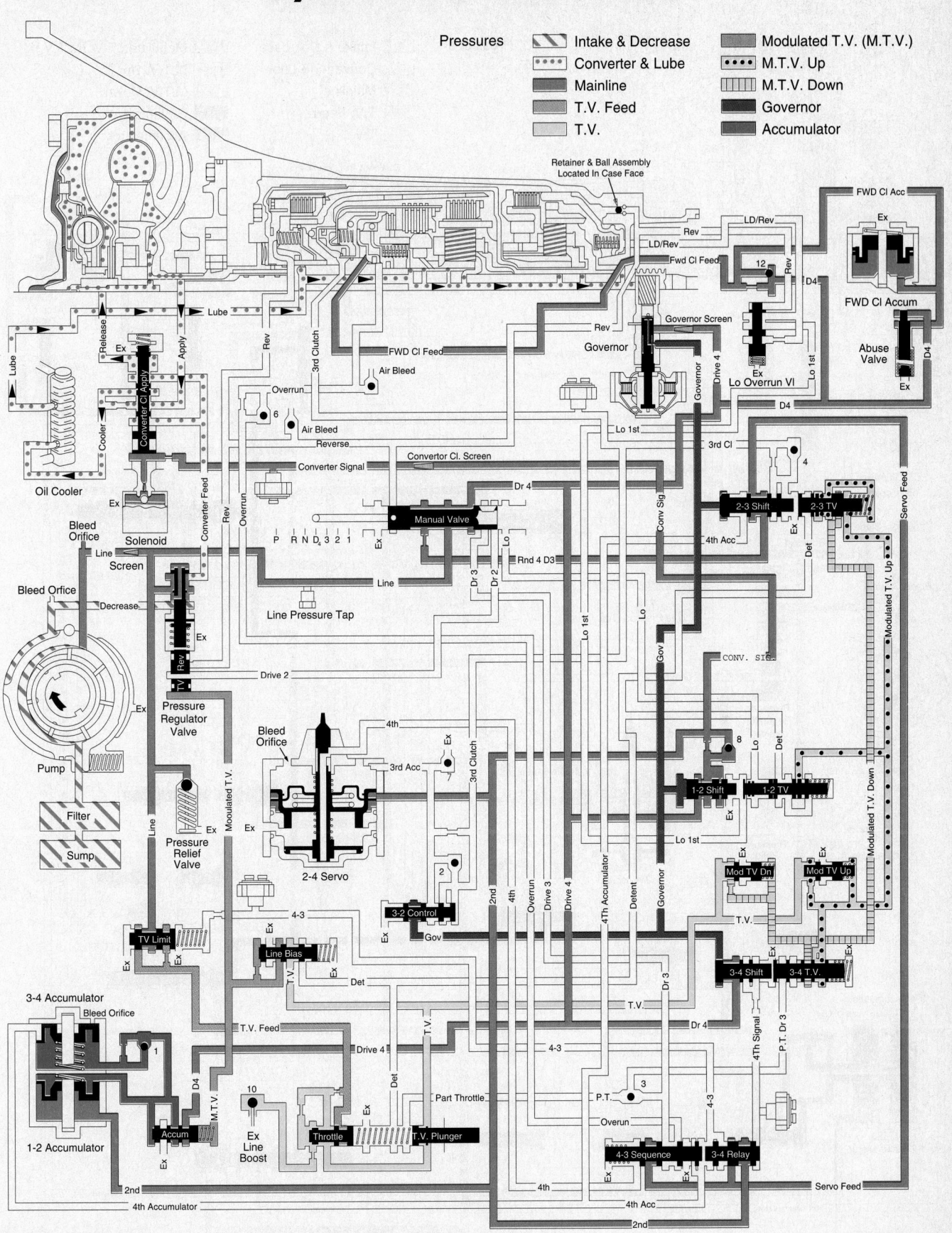

Fig. 4: D4 — 2nd Gear

Courtesy of General Motors Corp.

OIL CIRCUIT DIAGRAMS
Hydra-Matic 4L60 (Cont.)

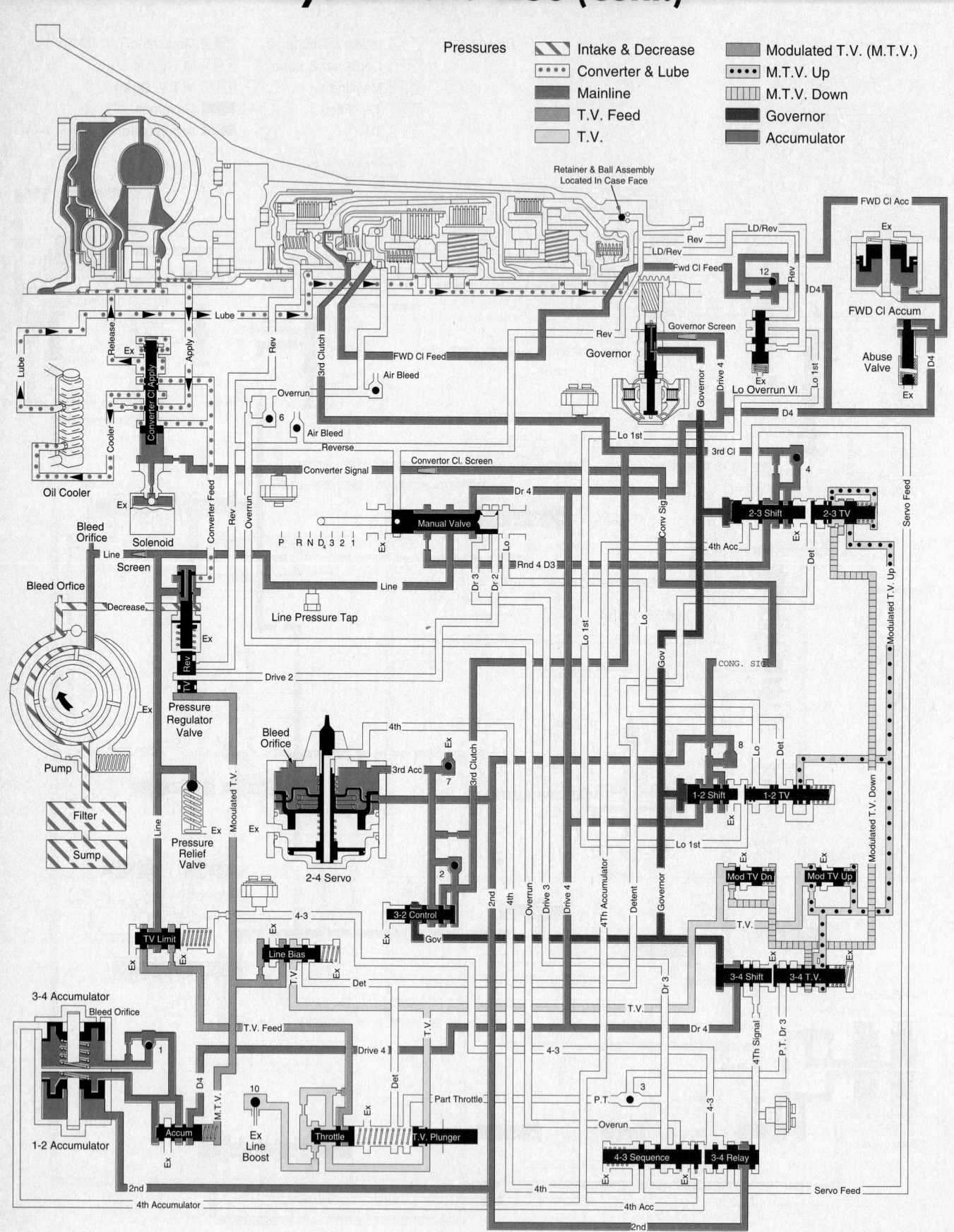

Fig. 5: D4 — 3rd Gear — Converter Clutch Applied

Courtesy of General Motors Corp.

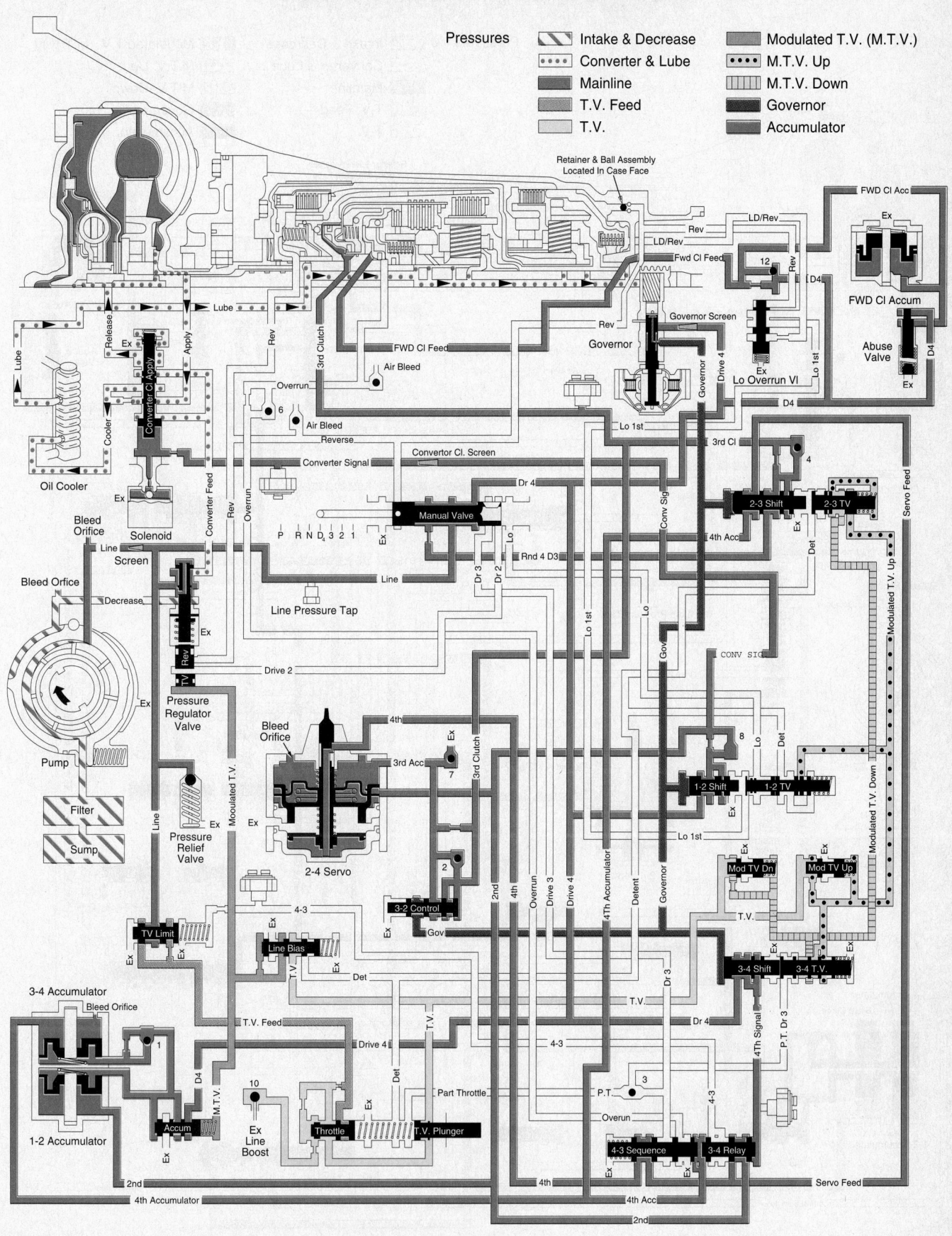

Fig. 6: D4 — Overdrive

Courtesy of General Motors Corp.

OIL CIRCUIT DIAGRAMS
Hydra-Matic 4L60 (Cont.)

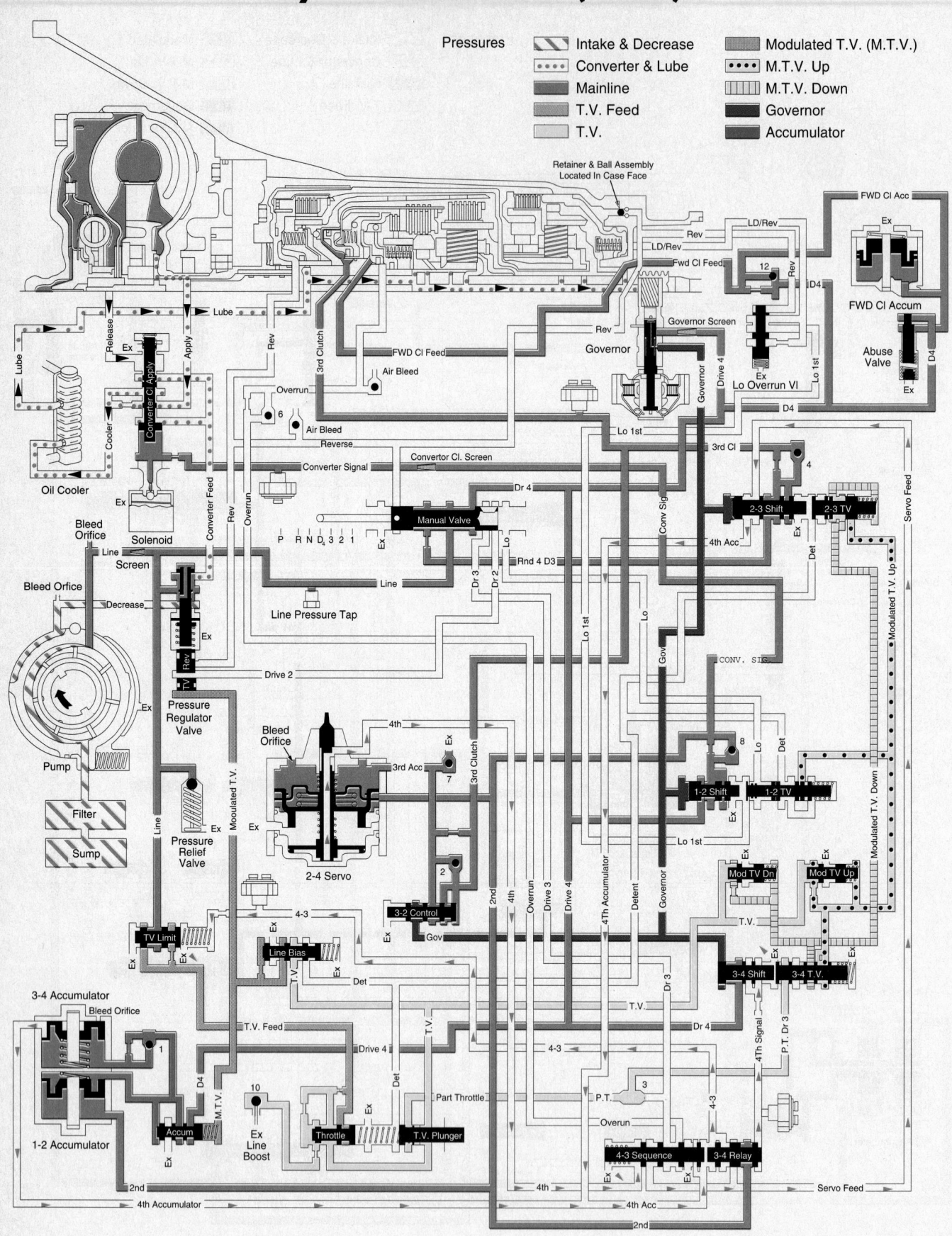

Fig. 7: Part Throttle 4-3 & Modulated Downshifts

Courtesy of General Motors Corp.

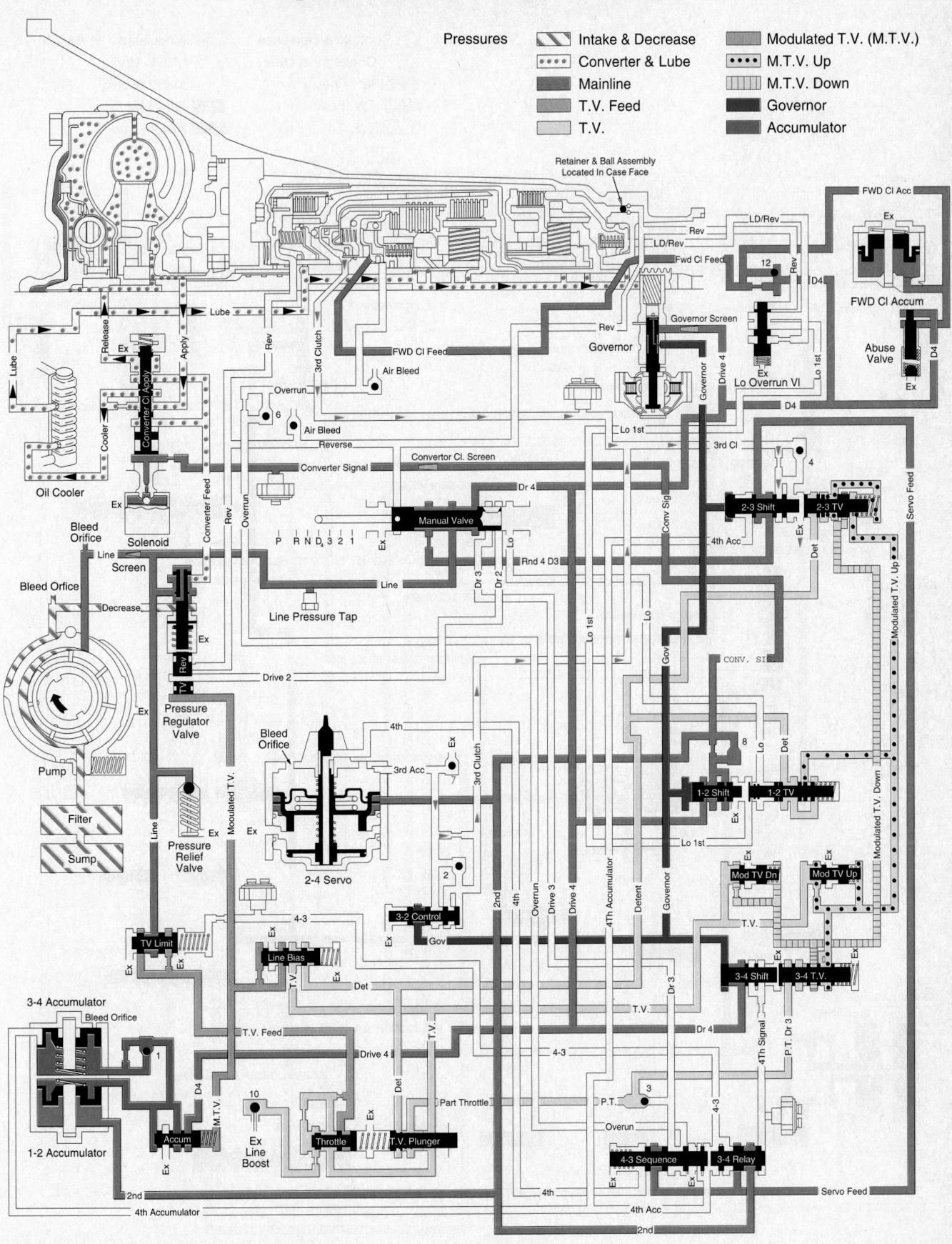

Fig. 8: Detent Downshifts Valves Shown In 2nd Gear Position

Courtesy of General Motors Corp.

OIL CIRCUIT DIAGRAMS
Hydra-Matic 4L60 (Cont.)

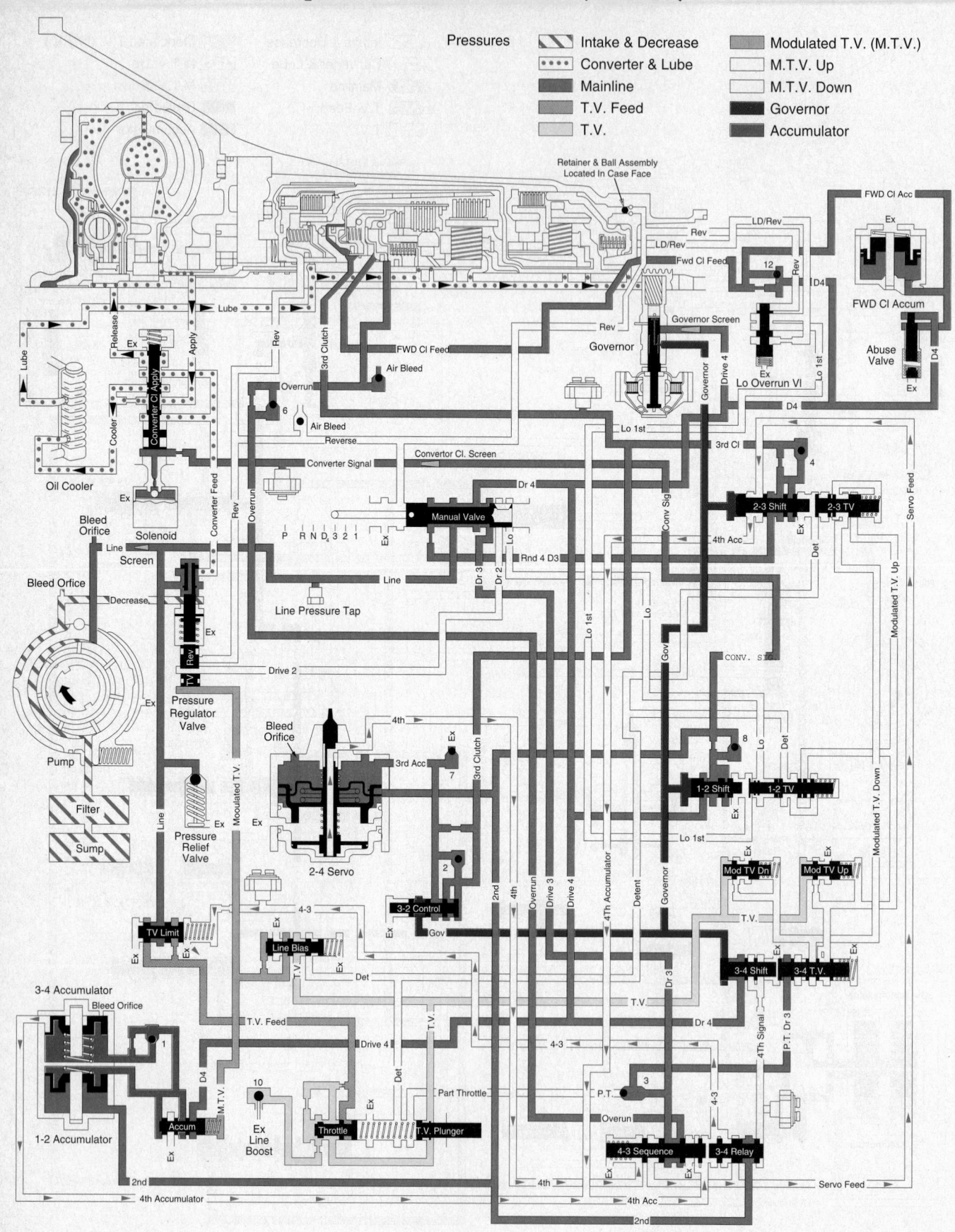

Fig. 9: Manual 3rd Gear

Courtesy of General Motors Corp.

OIL CIRCUIT DIAGRAMS
Hydra-Matic 4L60 (Cont.)

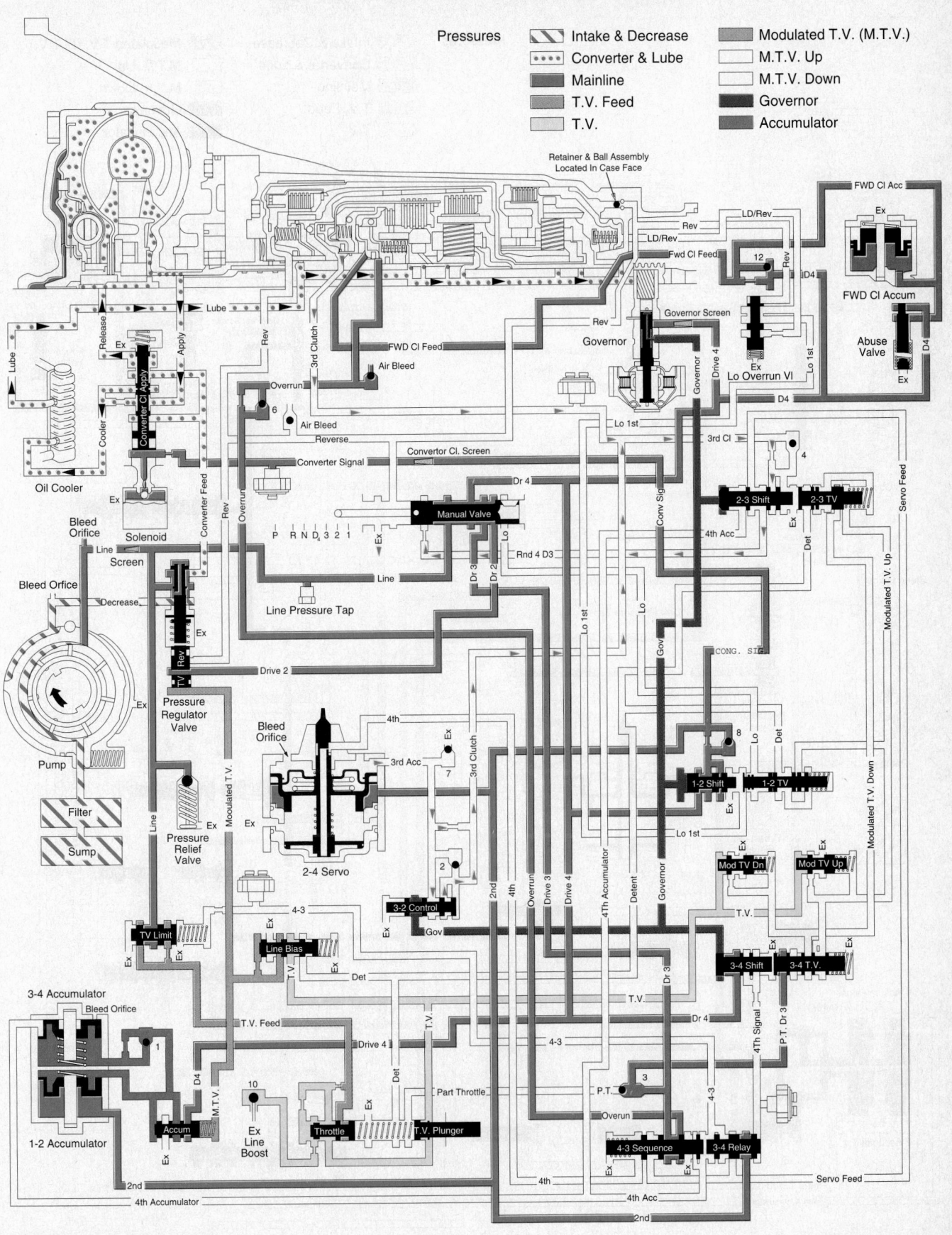

Fig. 10: Manual 2nd Gear

Courtesy of General Motors Corp.

OIL CIRCUIT DIAGRAMS
Hydra-Matic 4L60 (Cont.)

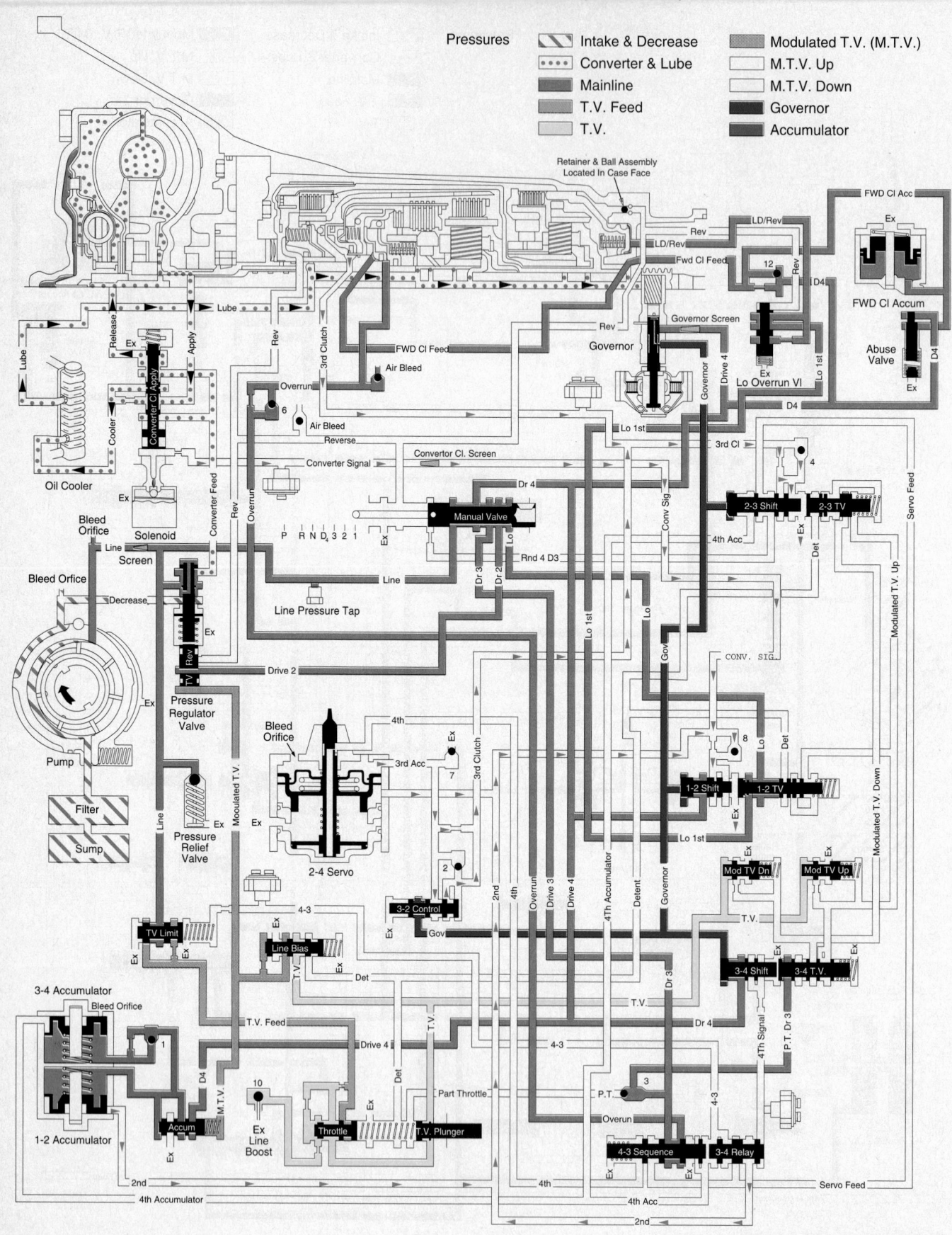

Fig. 11: Manual Low Gear

Courtesy of General Motors Corp.

OIL CIRCUIT DIAGRAMS
Hydra-Matic 4L60 (Cont.)

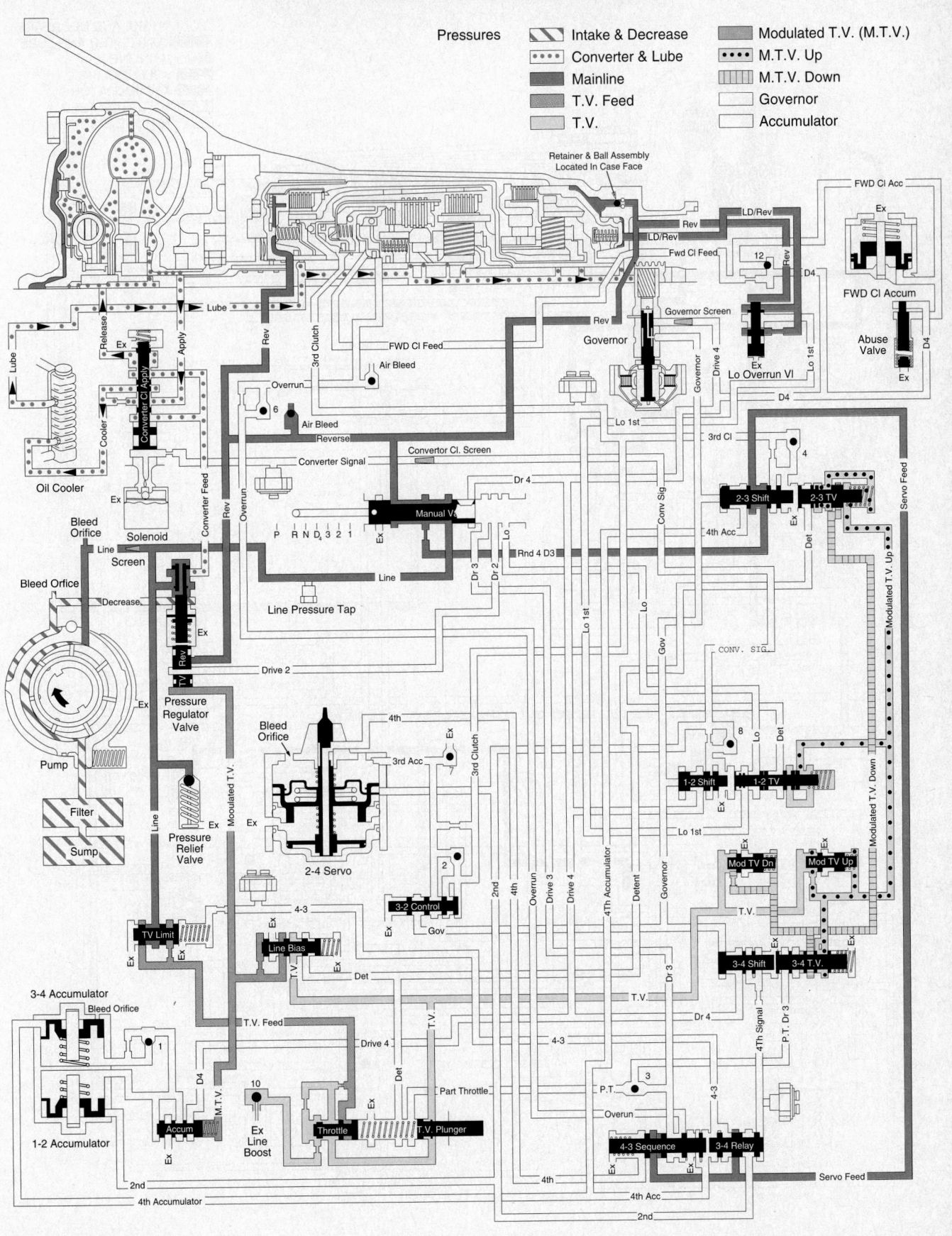

Fig. 12: Reverse Gear

Courtesy of General Motors Corp.

OIL CIRCUIT DIAGRAMS
Hydra-Matic 4L60-E

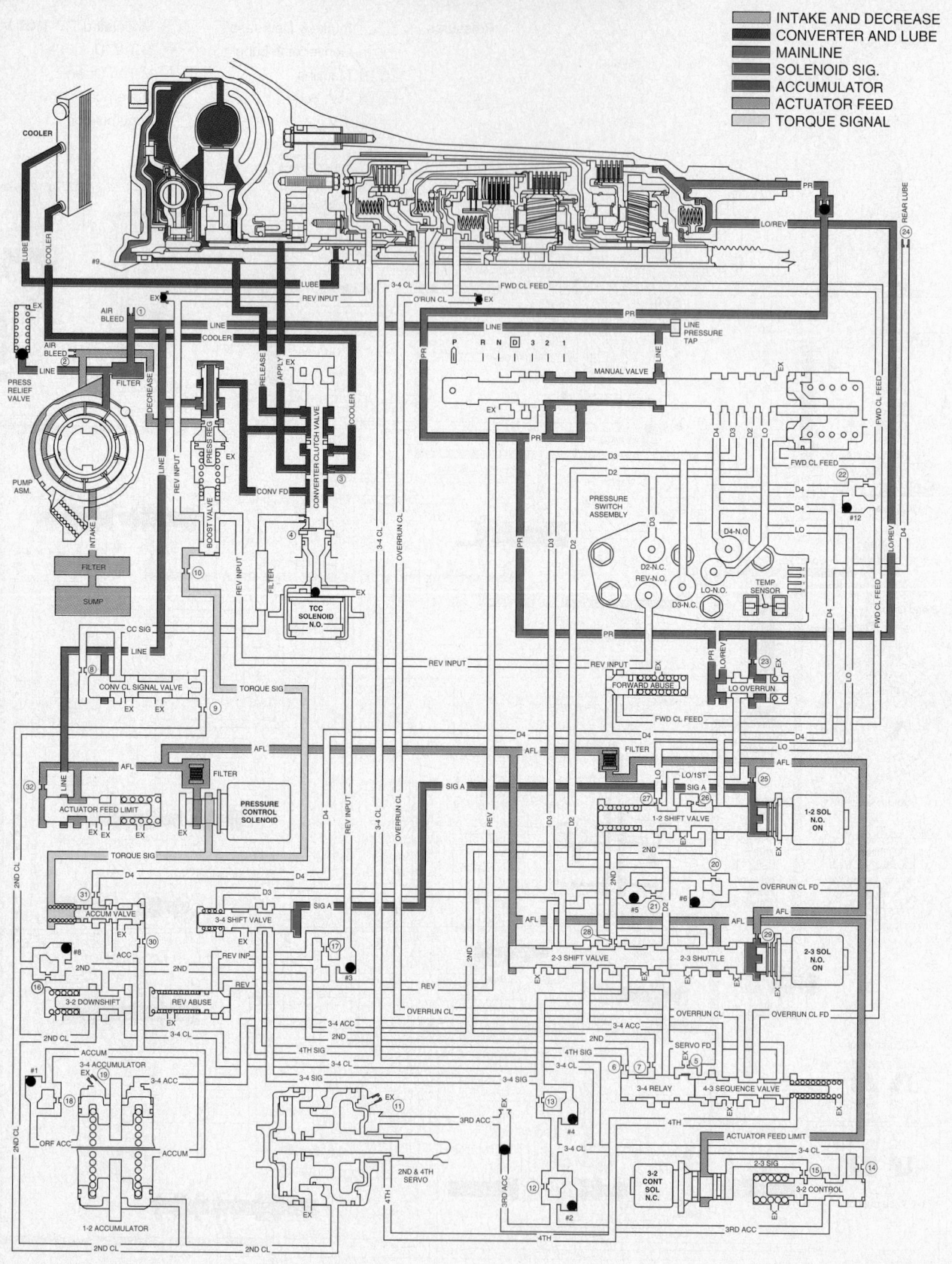

Fig. 1: "P" Range — Park

Courtesy of General Motors Corp.

OIL CIRCUIT DIAGRAMS
Hydra-Matic 4L60-E (Cont.)

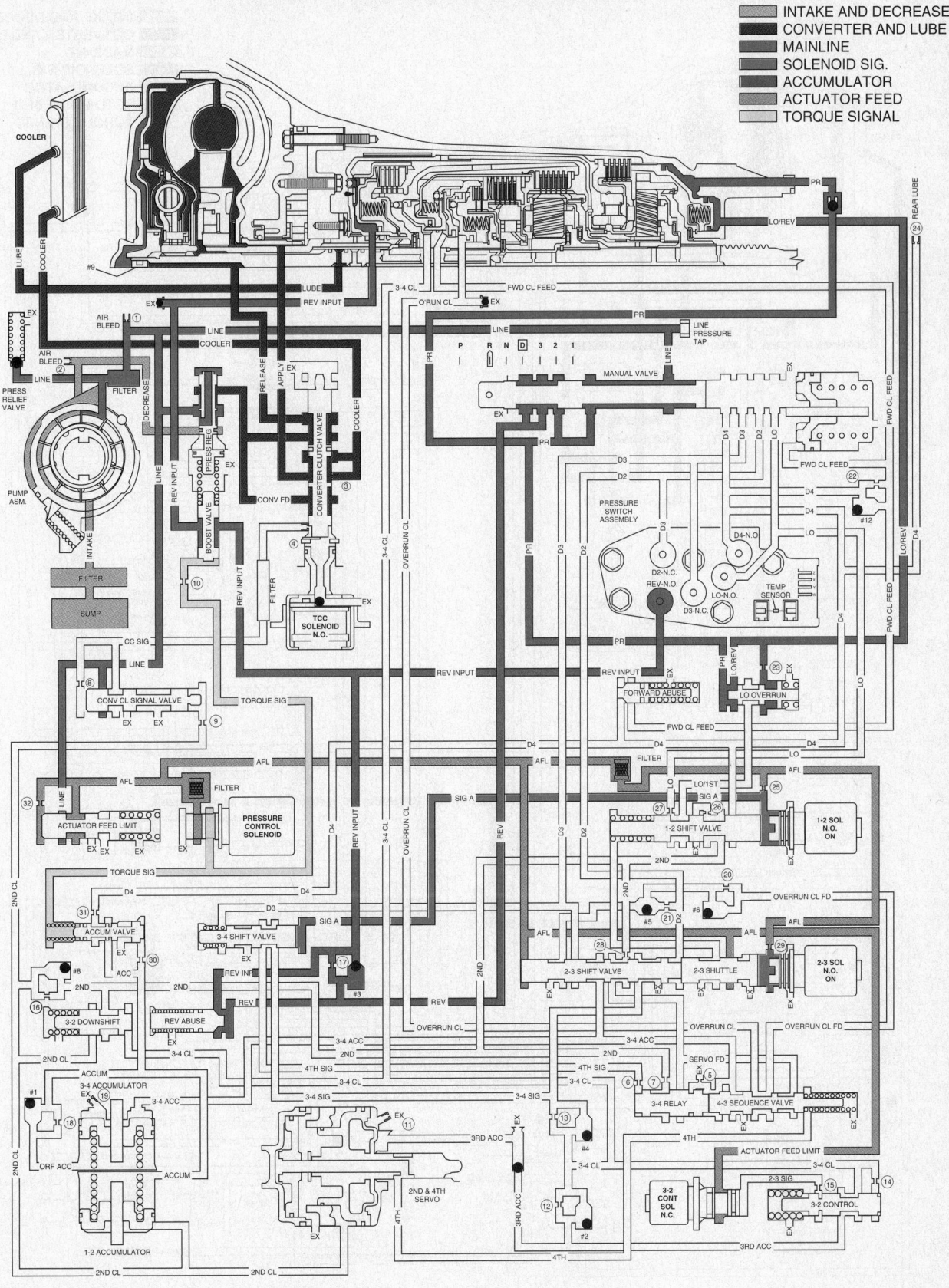

Fig. 2: "R" Range — Reverse

Courtesy of General Motors Corp.

OIL CIRCUIT DIAGRAMS
Hydra-Matic 4L60-E (Cont.)

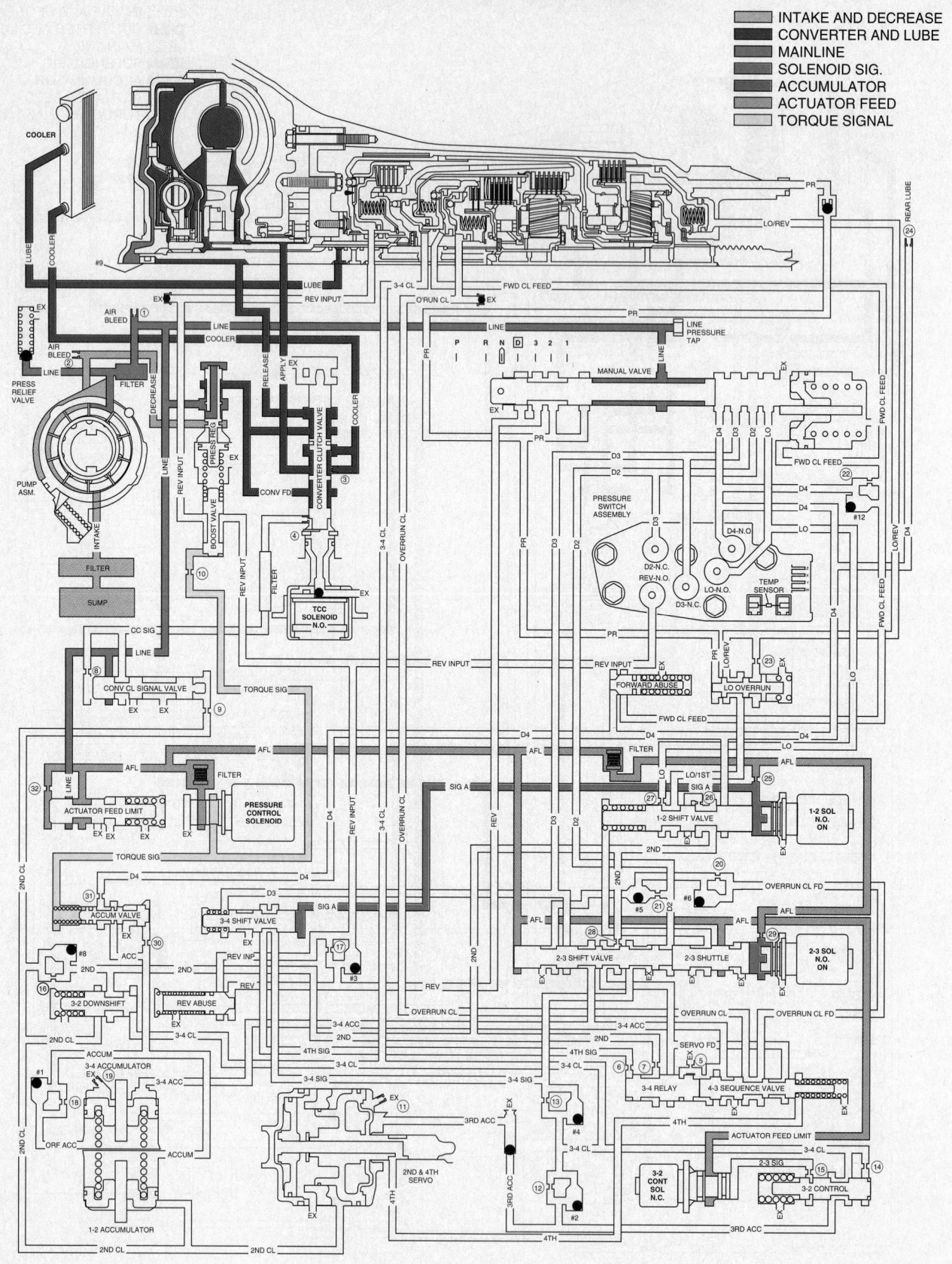

INTAKE AND DECREASE
CONVERTER AND LUBE
MAINLINE
SOLENOID SIG.
ACCUMULATOR
ACTUATOR FEED
TORQUE SIGNAL

Fig. 3: "N" Range — Neutral

Courtesy of General Motors Corp.

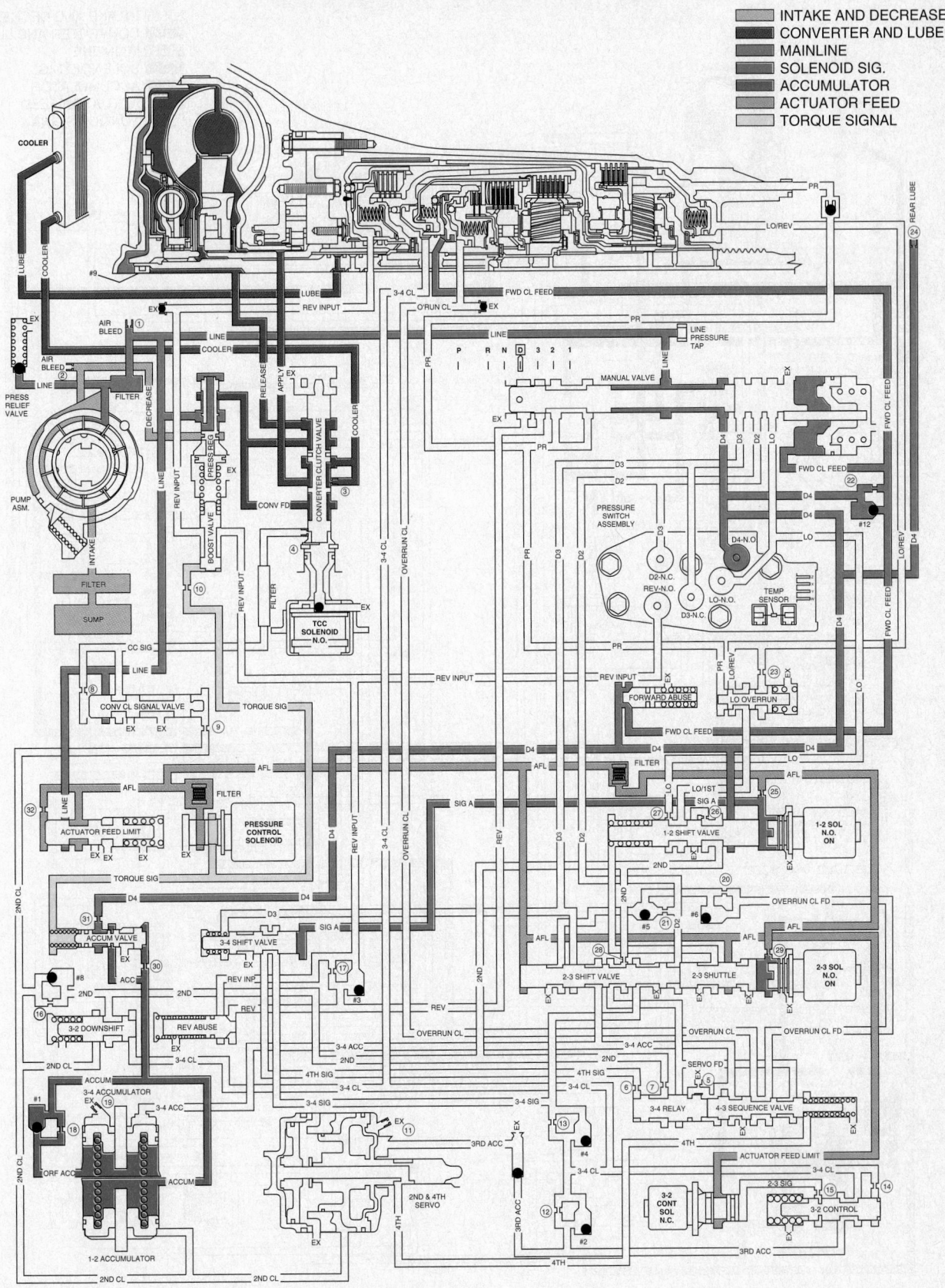

OIL CIRCUIT DIAGRAMS
Hydra-Matic 4L60-E (Cont.)

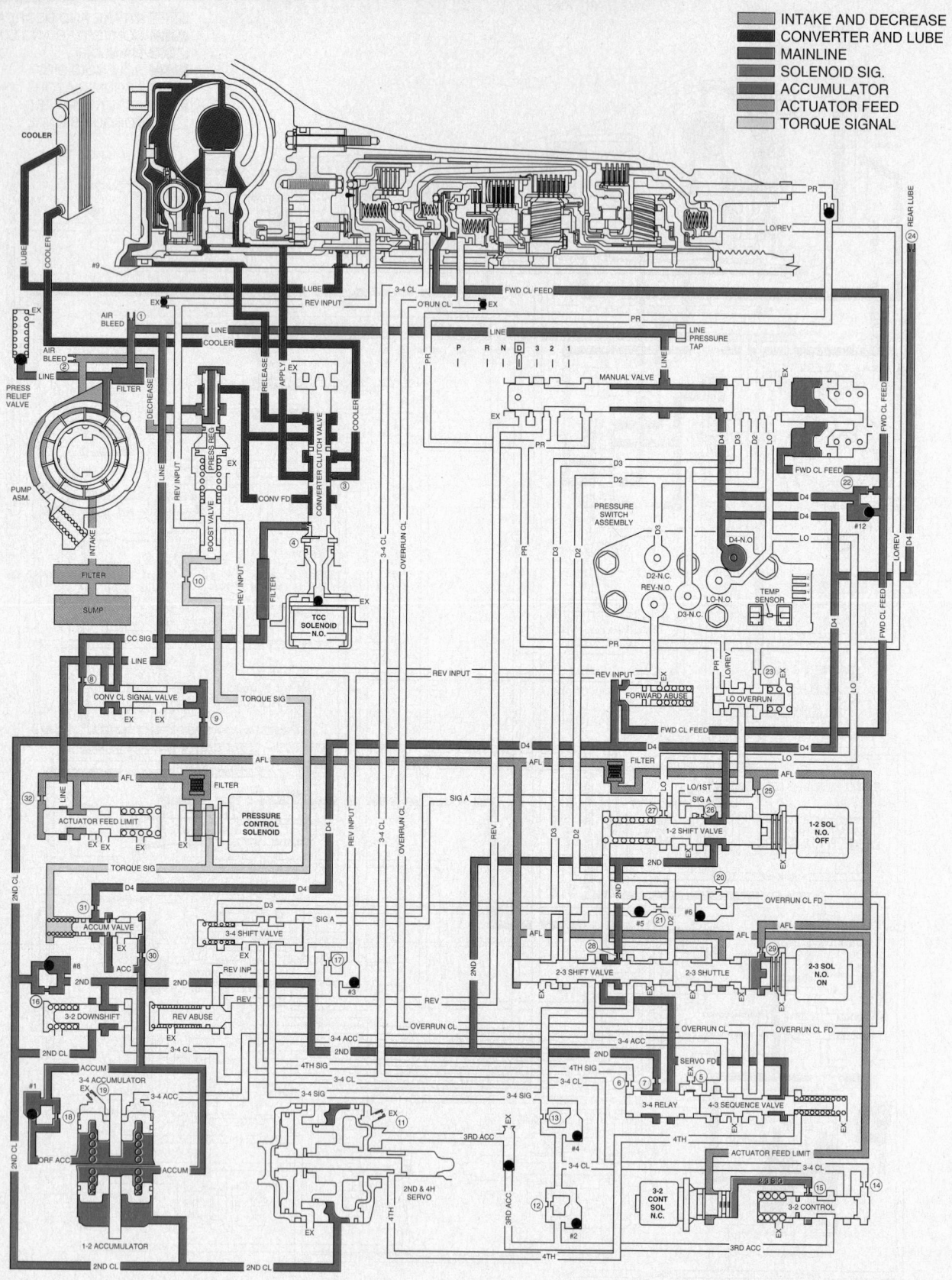

Fig. 5: "OD" Range — 2nd Gear

Courtesy of General Motors Corp.

OIL CIRCUIT DIAGRAMS
Hydra-Matic 4L60-E (Cont.)

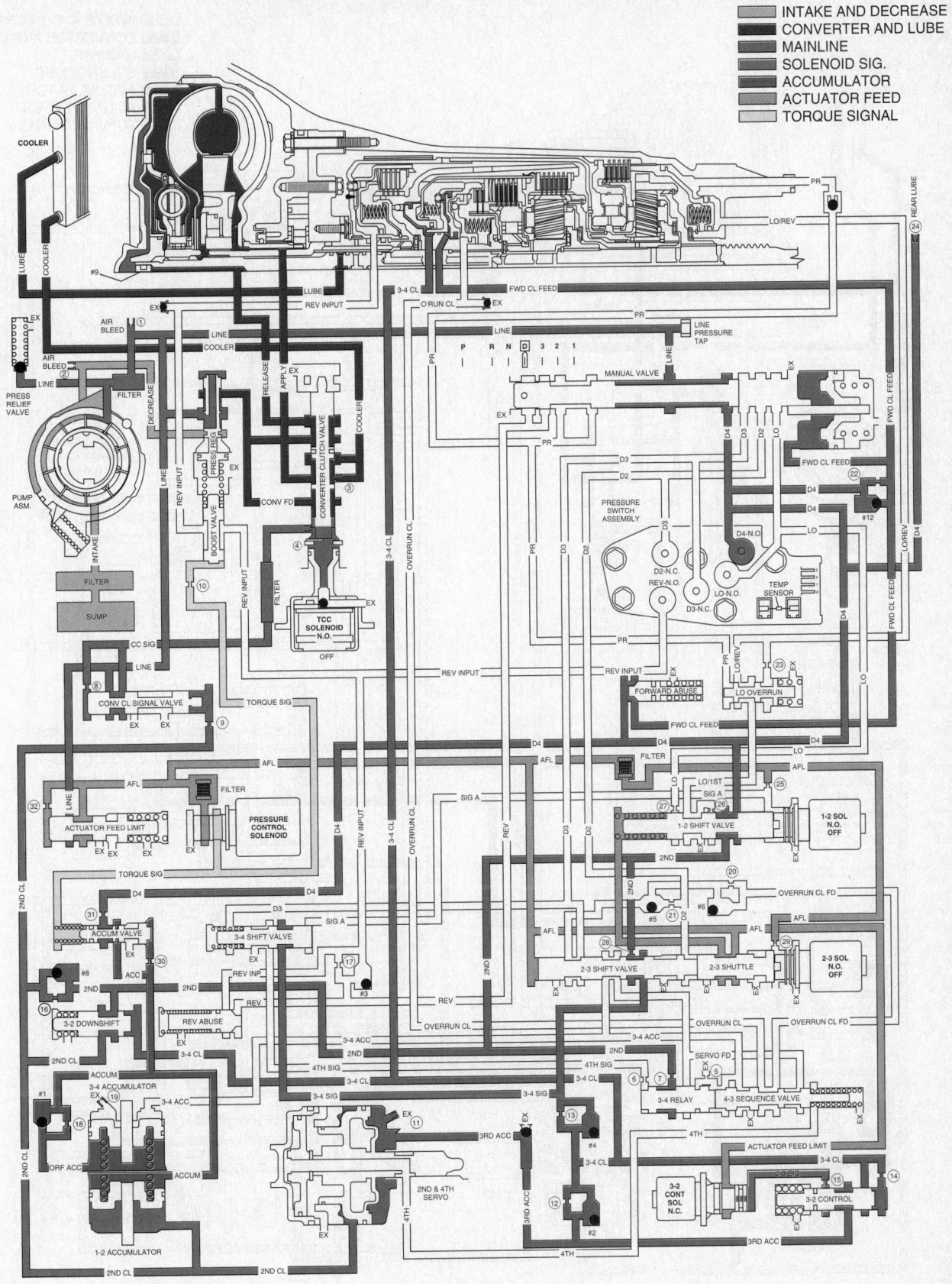

INTAKE AND DECREASE
CONVERTER AND LUBE
MAINLINE
SOLENOID SIG.
ACCUMULATOR
ACTUATOR FEED
TORQUE SIGNAL

Fig. 6: "OD" Range — 3rd Gear

Courtesy of General Motors Corp.

OIL CIRCUIT DIAGRAMS
Hydra-Matic 4L60-E (Cont.)

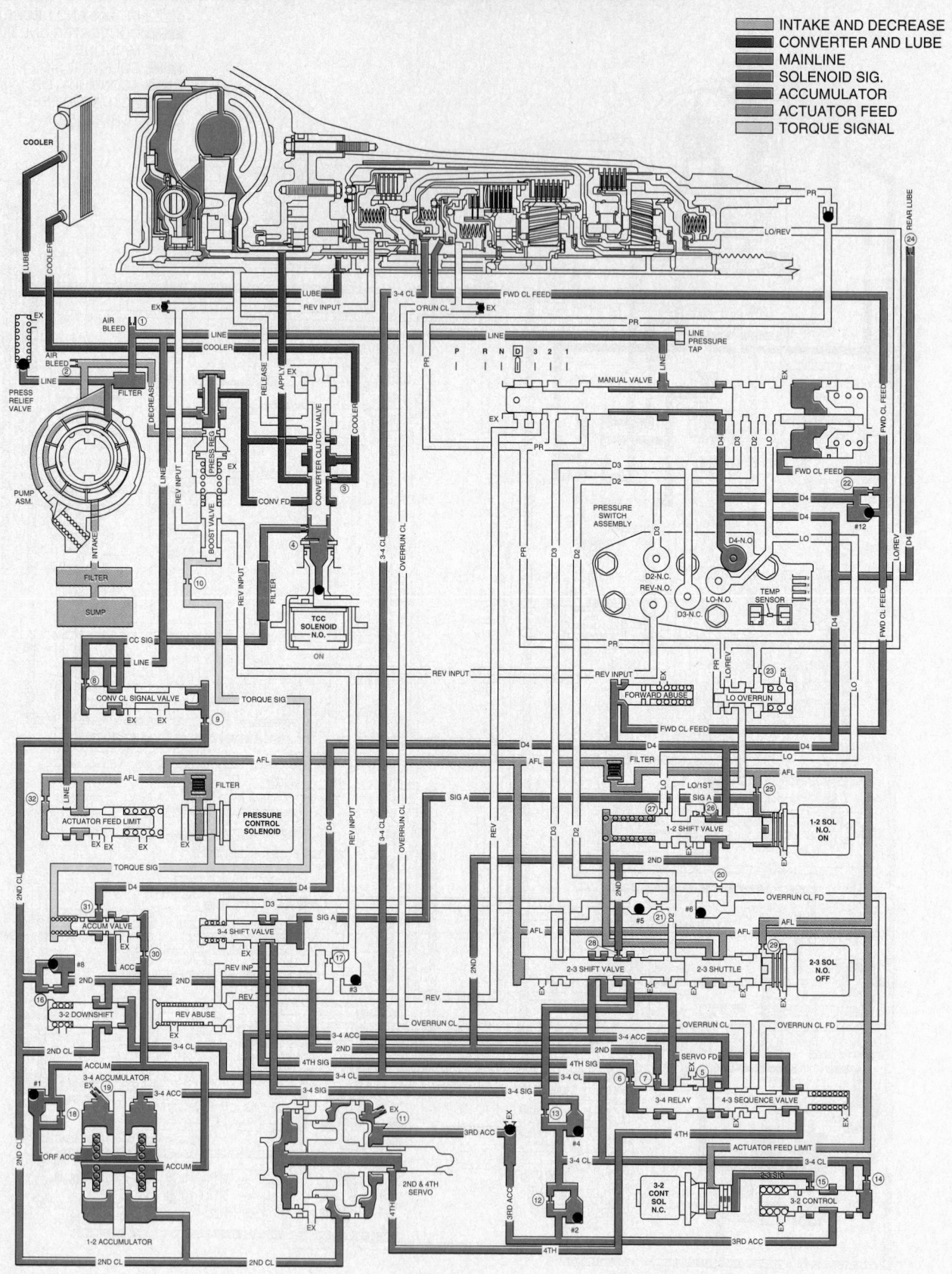

Fig. 7: "OD" Range — 4th Gear (TCC Applied)

Courtesy of General Motors Corp.

OIL CIRCUIT DIAGRAMS
Hydra-Matic 4L60-E (Cont.)

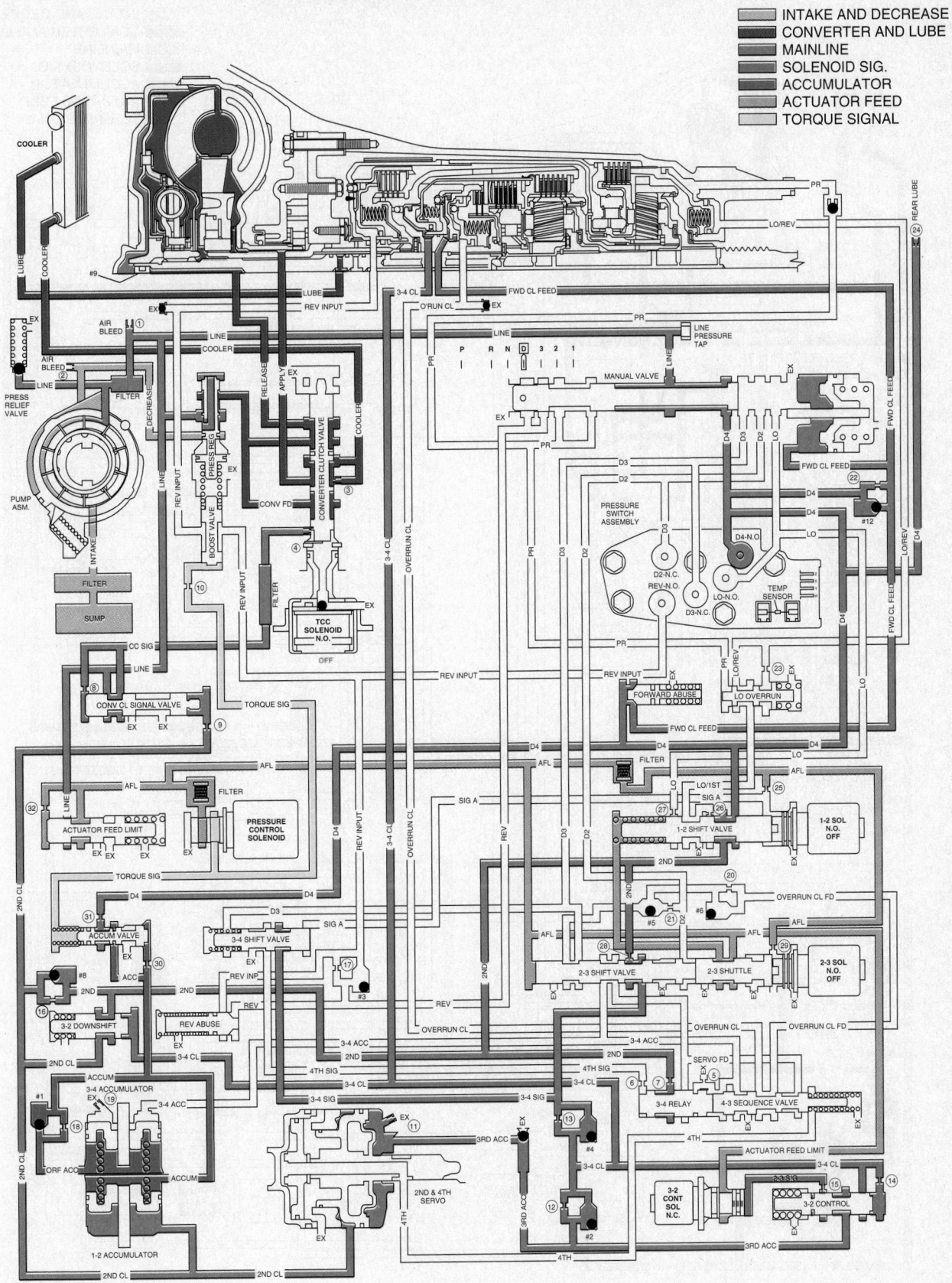

INTAKE AND DECREASE
CONVERTER AND LUBE
MAINLINE
SOLENOID SIG.
ACCUMULATOR
ACTUATOR FEED
TORQUE SIGNAL

Fig. 8: "OD" Range — 4-3 Downshift

Courtesy of General Motors Corp.

OIL CIRCUIT DIAGRAMS
Hydra-Matic 4L60-E (Cont.)

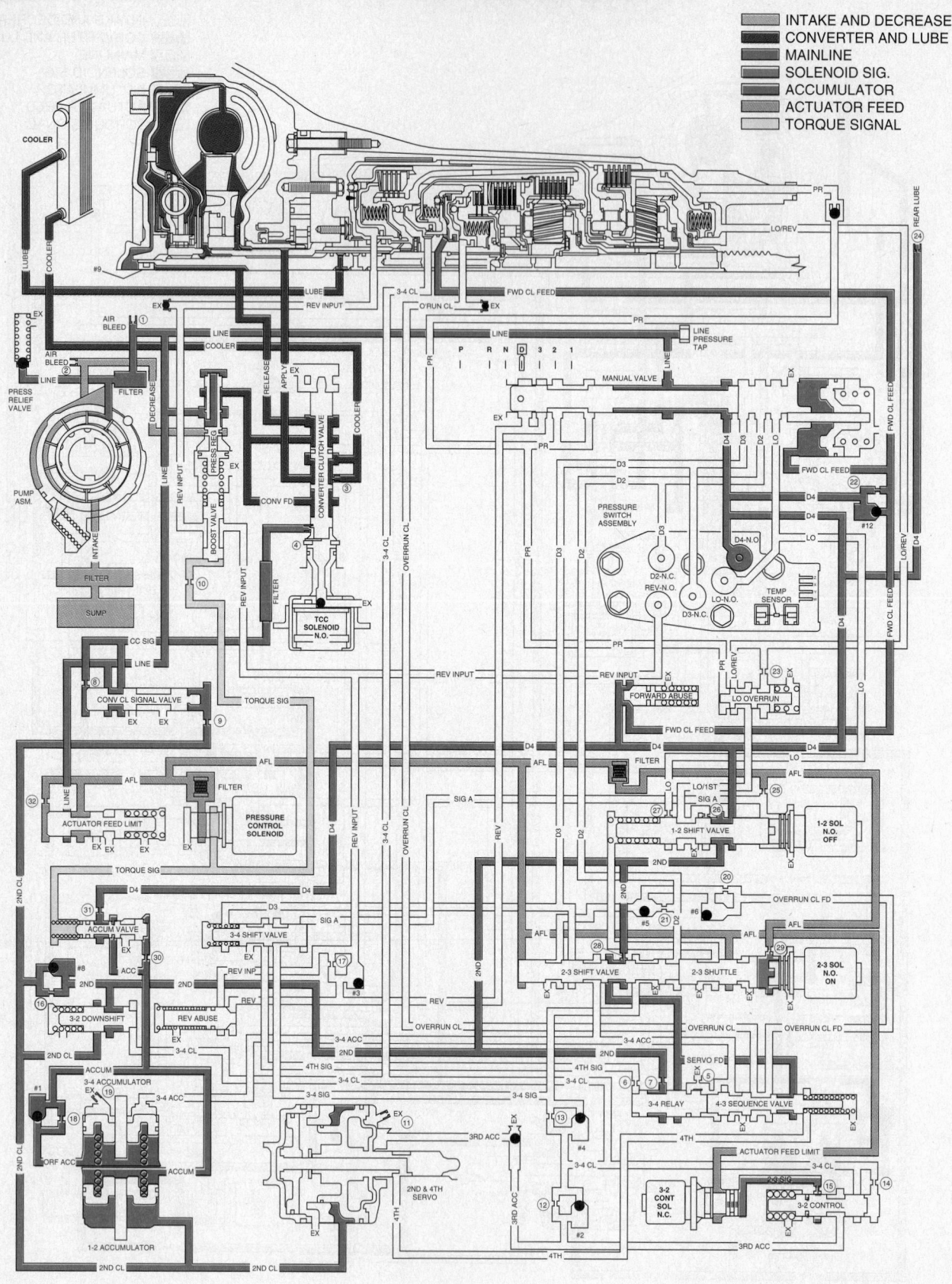

Fig. 9: "OD" Range — 3-2 Downshift

Courtesy of General Motors Corp.

OIL CIRCUIT DIAGRAMS
Hydra-Matic 4L60-E (Cont.)

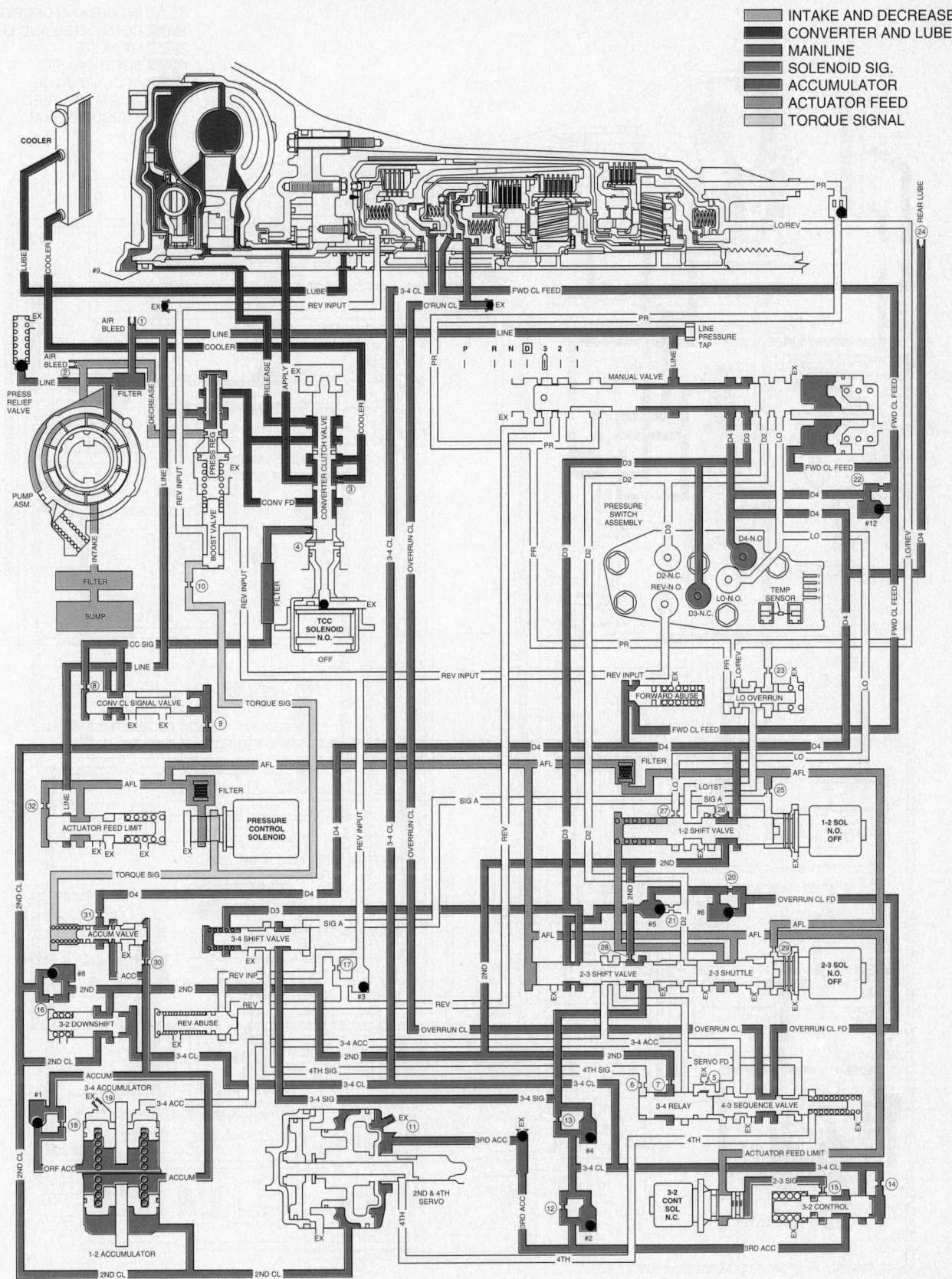

Legend:
- INTAKE AND DECREASE
- CONVERTER AND LUBE
- MAINLINE
- SOLENOID SIG.
- ACCUMULATOR
- ACTUATOR FEED
- TORQUE SIGNAL

Fig. 10: "3" Range — 3rd Gear (Manual Select)

Courtesy of General Motors Corp.

OIL CIRCUIT DIAGRAMS
Hydra-Matic 4L60-E (Cont.)

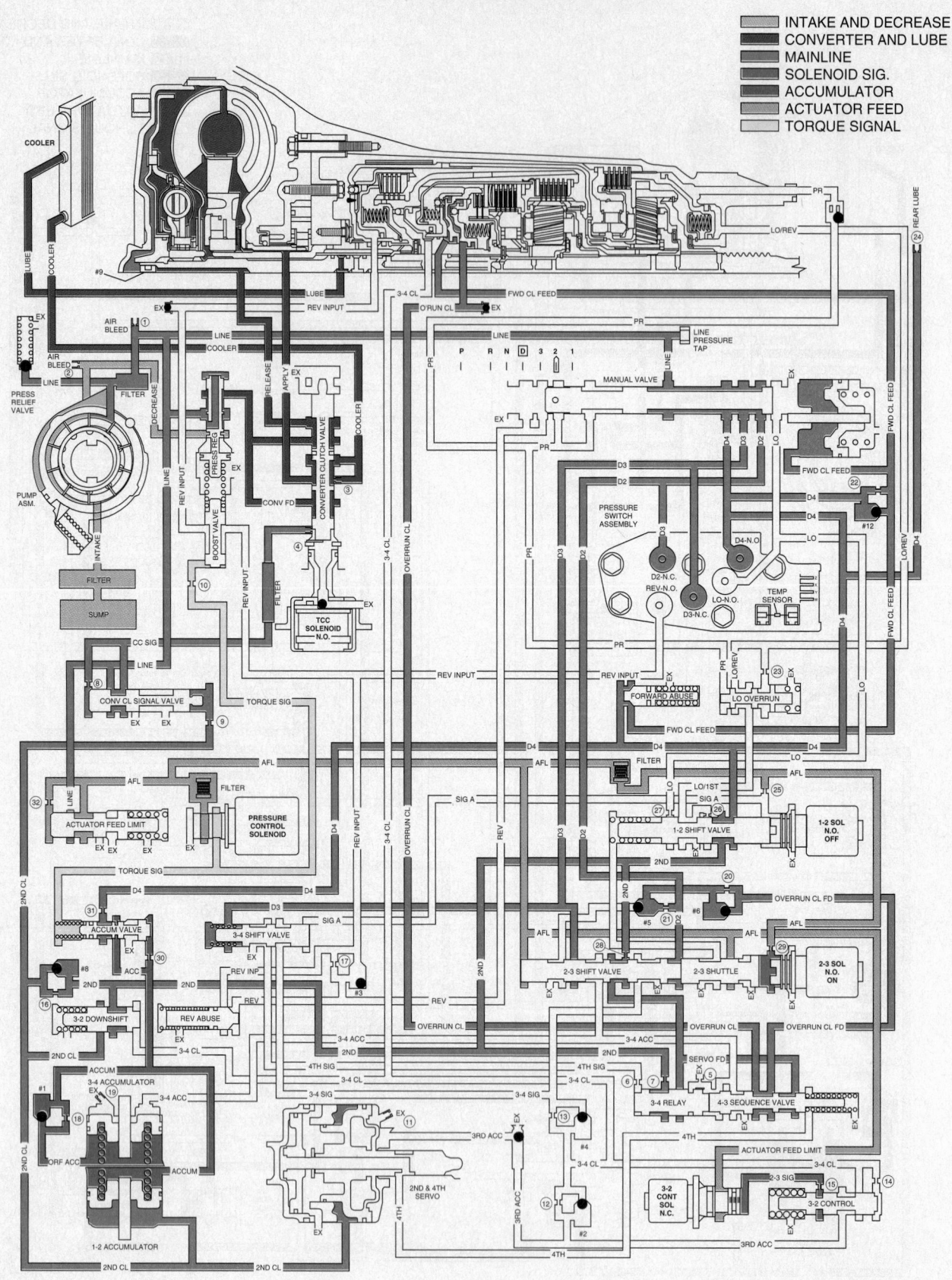

INTAKE AND DECREASE
CONVERTER AND LUBE
MAINLINE
SOLENOID SIG.
ACCUMULATOR
ACTUATOR FEED
TORQUE SIGNAL

Fig. 11: "2" Range — 2nd Gear (Manual Select)   Courtesy of General Motors Corp.

OIL CIRCUIT DIAGRAMS
Hydra-Matic 4L60-E (Cont.)

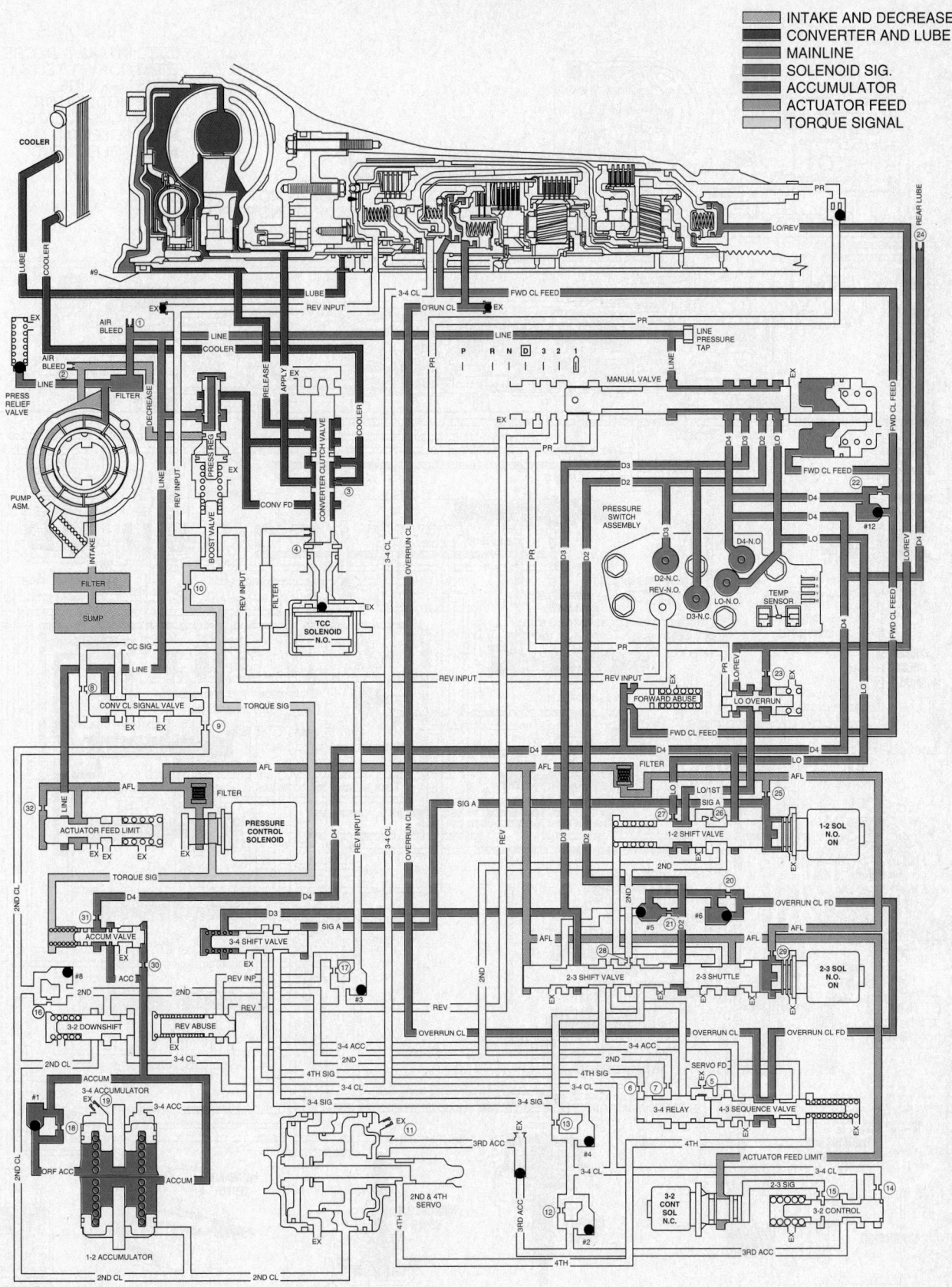

Fig. 12: "1" Range — 1st Gear (Manual Select)

Courtesy of General Motors Corp.

OIL CIRCUIT DIAGRAMS
Hydra-Matic 4T60-E Except 3.4L

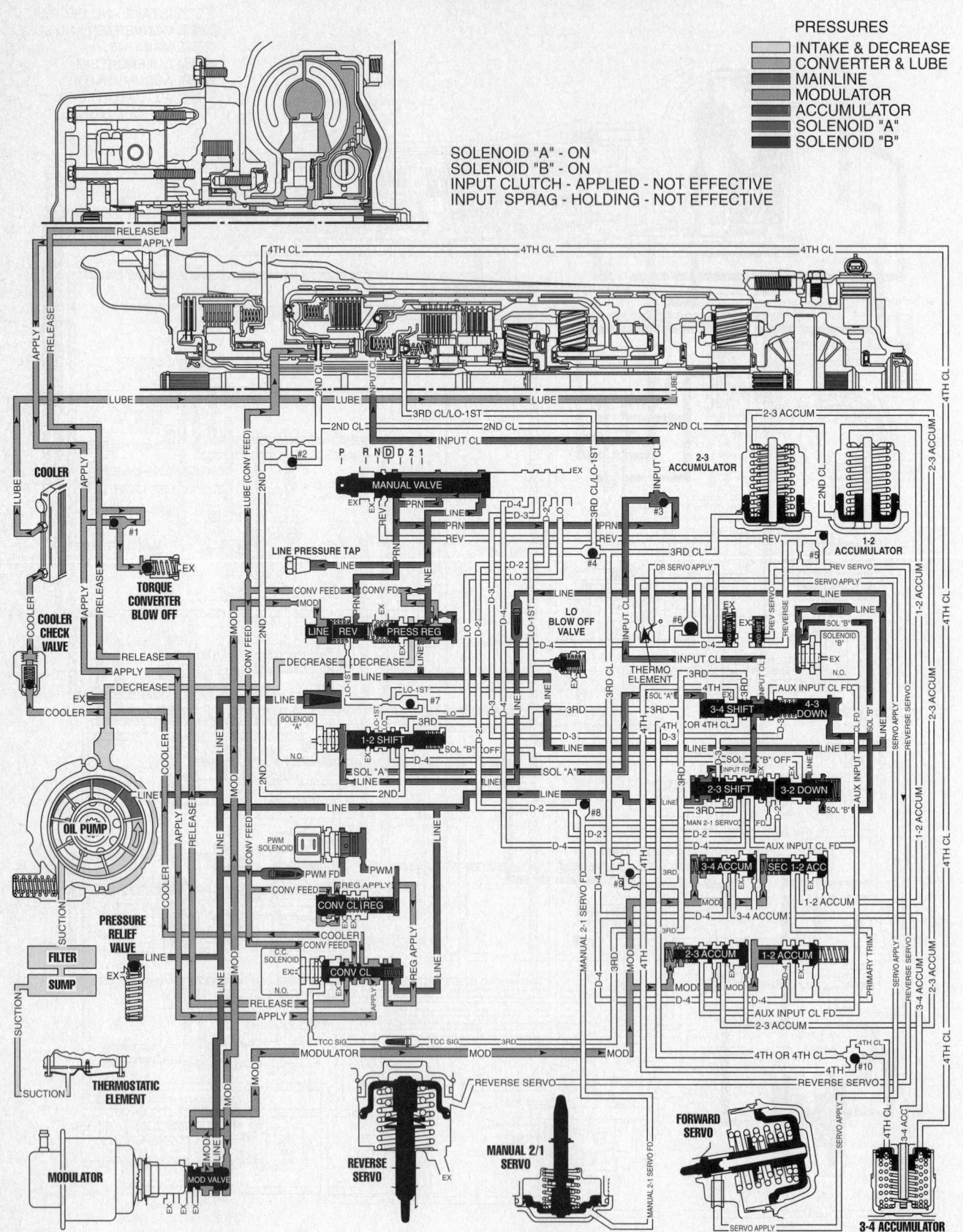

Fig. 1: "P" or "N" Range — Park or Neutral

Courtesy of General Motors Corp.

OIL CIRCUIT DIAGRAMS
Hydra-Matic 4T60-E Except 3.4L (Cont.)

1-203

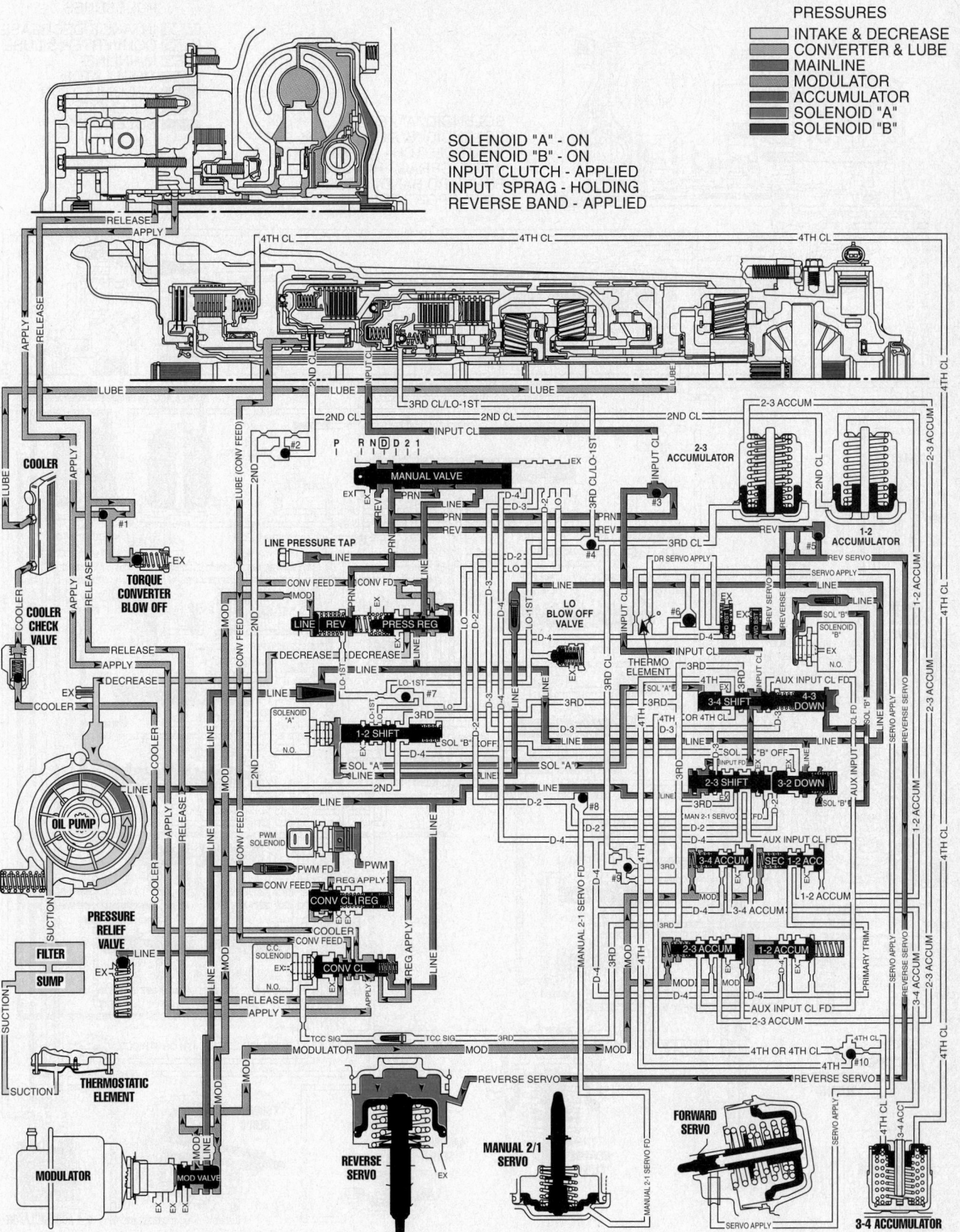

PRESSURES
- INTAKE & DECREASE
- CONVERTER & LUBE
- MAINLINE
- MODULATOR
- ACCUMULATOR
- SOLENOID "A"
- SOLENOID "B"

SOLENOID "A" - ON
SOLENOID "B" - ON
INPUT CLUTCH - APPLIED
INPUT SPRAG - HOLDING
REVERSE BAND - APPLIED

Fig. 2: "R" Range — Reverse

Courtesy of General Motors Corp.

OIL CIRCUIT DIAGRAMS
Hydra-Matic 4T60-E Except 3.4L (Cont.)

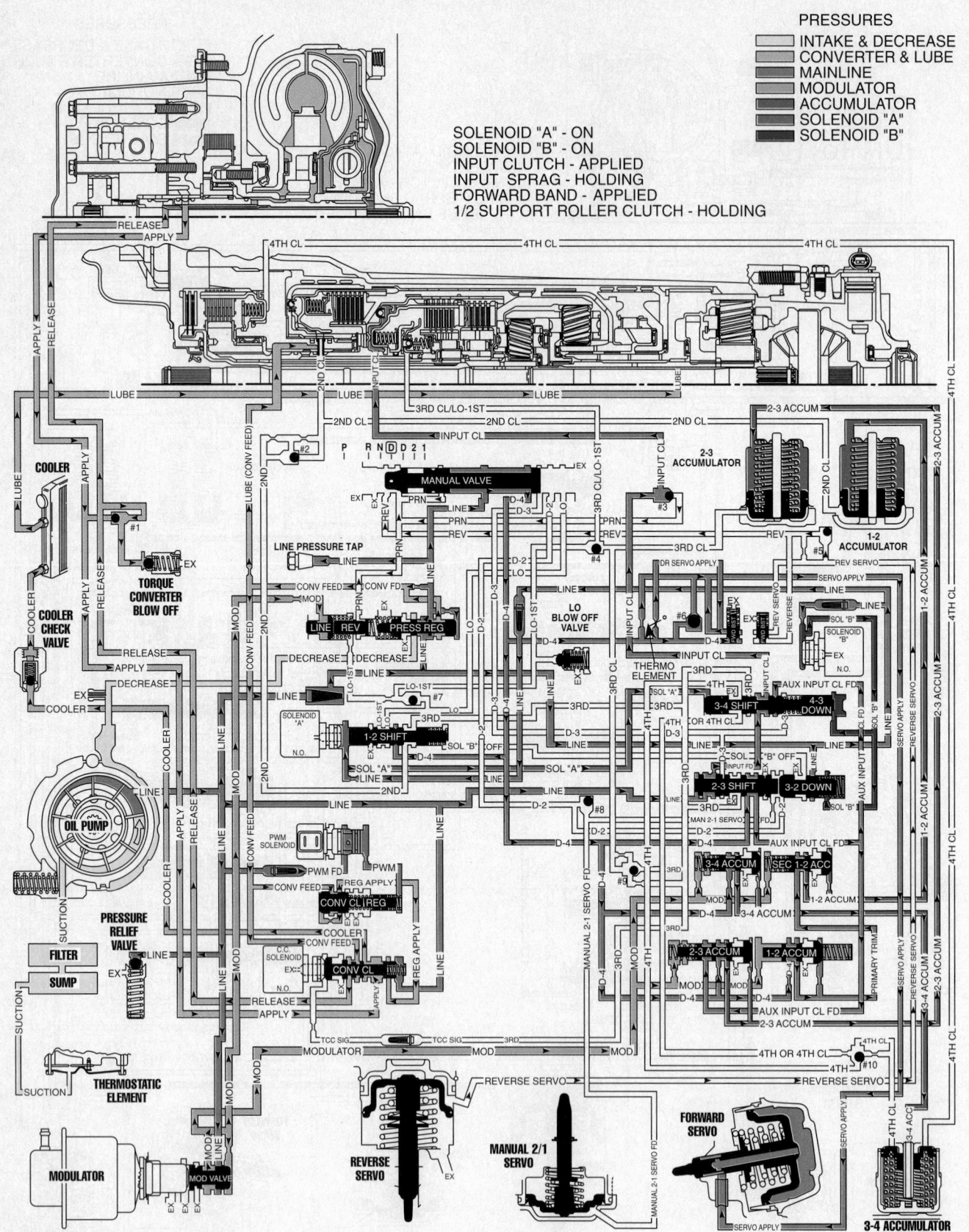

SOLENOID "A" - ON
SOLENOID "B" - ON
INPUT CLUTCH - APPLIED
INPUT SPRAG - HOLDING
FORWARD BAND - APPLIED
1/2 SUPPORT ROLLER CLUTCH - HOLDING

PRESSURES
INTAKE & DECREASE
CONVERTER & LUBE
MAINLINE
MODULATOR
ACCUMULATOR
SOLENOID "A"
SOLENOID "B"

Fig. 3: "OD" Range — 1st Gear

Courtesy of General Motors Corp.

OIL CIRCUIT DIAGRAMS
Hydra-Matic 4T60-E Except 3.4L (Cont.)

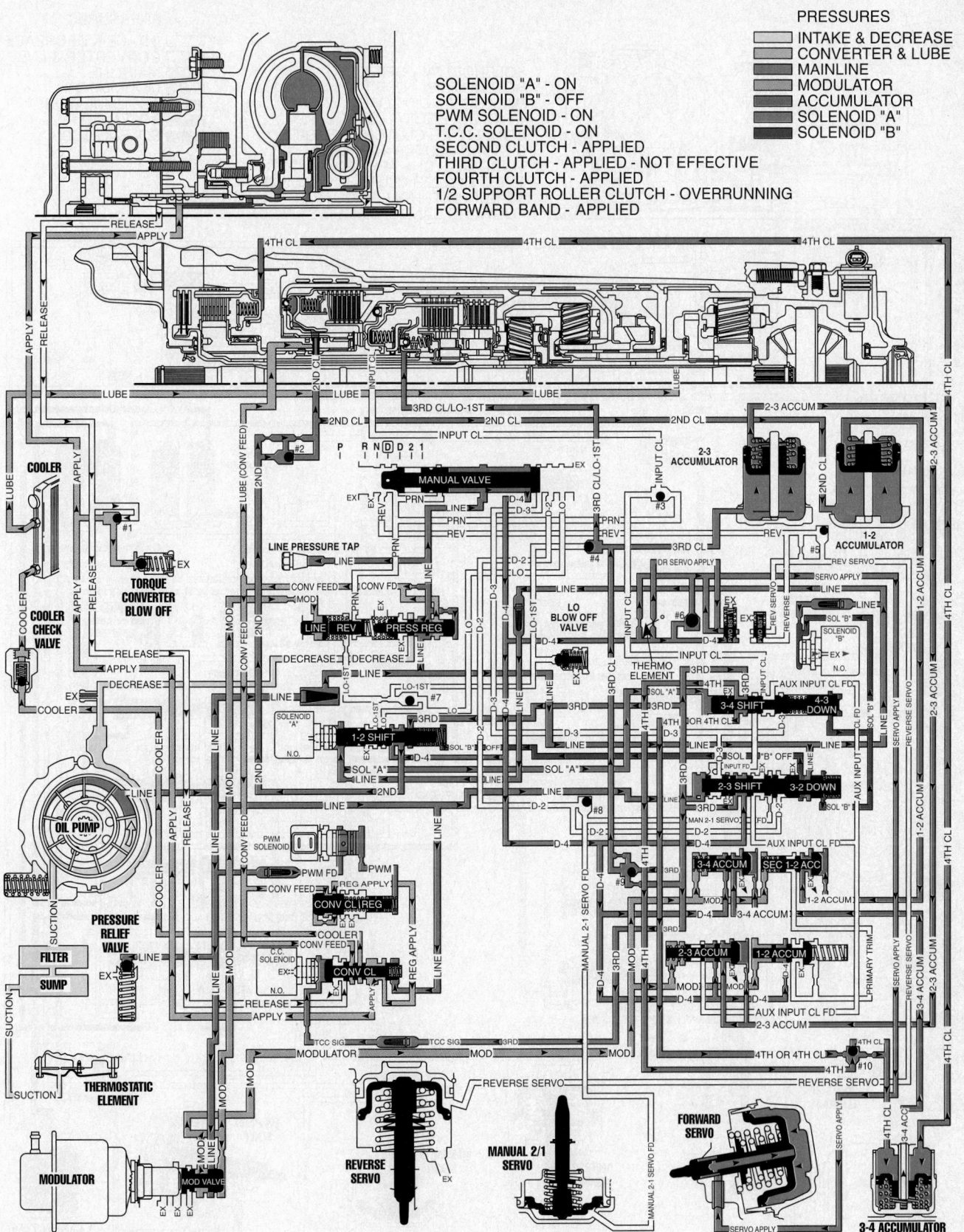

SOLENOID "A" - ON
SOLENOID "B" - OFF
PWM SOLENOID - ON
T.C.C. SOLENOID - ON
SECOND CLUTCH - APPLIED
THIRD CLUTCH - APPLIED - NOT EFFECTIVE
FOURTH CLUTCH - APPLIED
1/2 SUPPORT ROLLER CLUTCH - OVERRUNNING
FORWARD BAND - APPLIED

PRESSURES
INTAKE & DECREASE
CONVERTER & LUBE
MAINLINE
MODULATOR
ACCUMULATOR
SOLENOID "A"
SOLENOID "B"

Fig. 4: "OD" Range — 2nd Gear

Courtesy of General Motors Corp.

OIL CIRCUIT DIAGRAMS
Hydra-Matic 4T60-E Except 3.4L (Cont.)

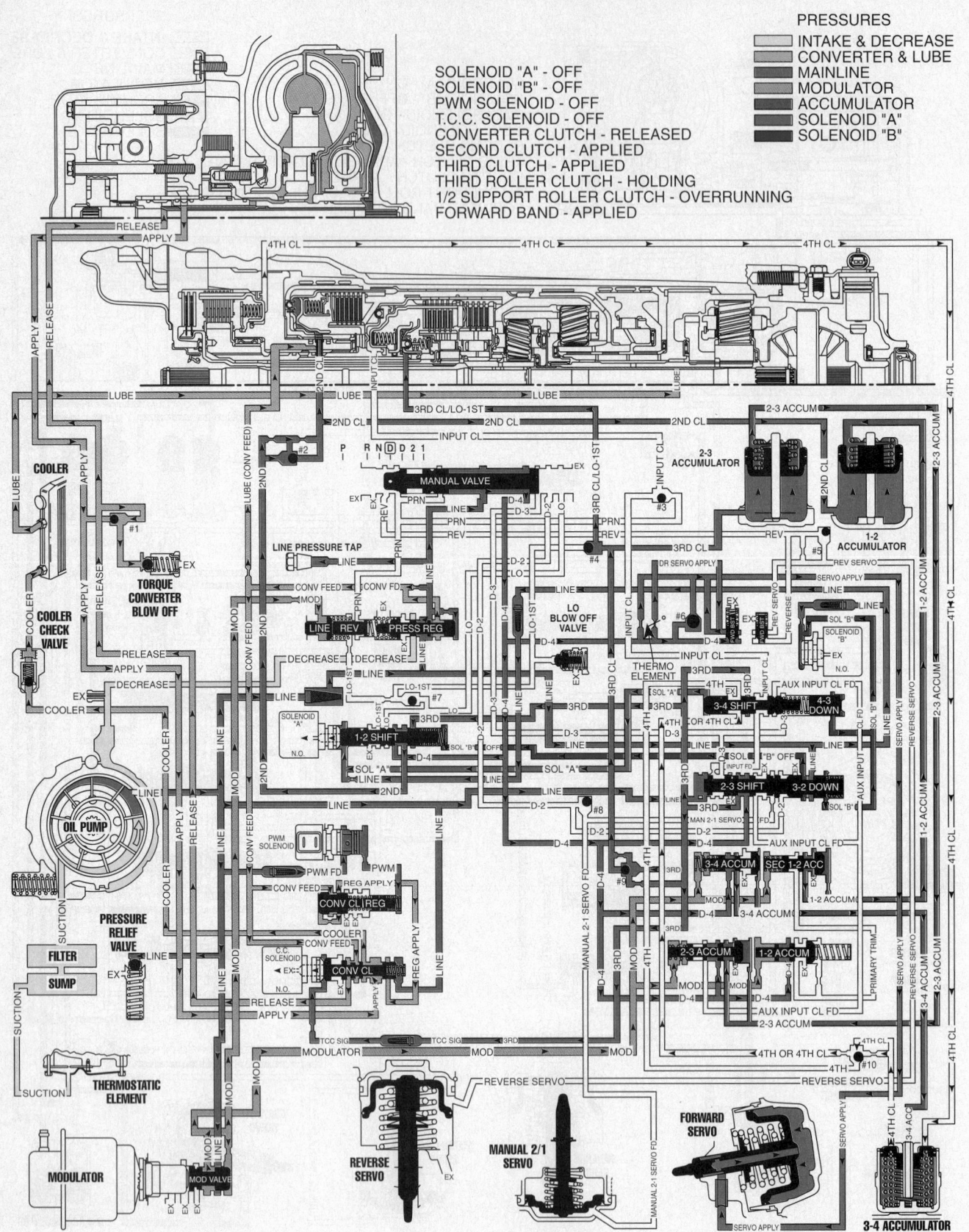

SOLENOID "A" - OFF
SOLENOID "B" - OFF
PWM SOLENOID - OFF
T.C.C. SOLENOID - OFF
CONVERTER CLUTCH - RELEASED
SECOND CLUTCH - APPLIED
THIRD CLUTCH - APPLIED
THIRD ROLLER CLUTCH - HOLDING
1/2 SUPPORT ROLLER CLUTCH - OVERRUNNING
FORWARD BAND - APPLIED

PRESSURES
INTAKE & DECREASE
CONVERTER & LUBE
MAINLINE
MODULATOR
ACCUMULATOR
SOLENOID "A"
SOLENOID "B"

Fig. 5: "OD" Range — 3rd Gear (TCC Off)

Courtesy of General Motors Corp.

OIL CIRCUIT DIAGRAMS
Hydra-Matic 4T60-E Except 3.4L (Cont.)

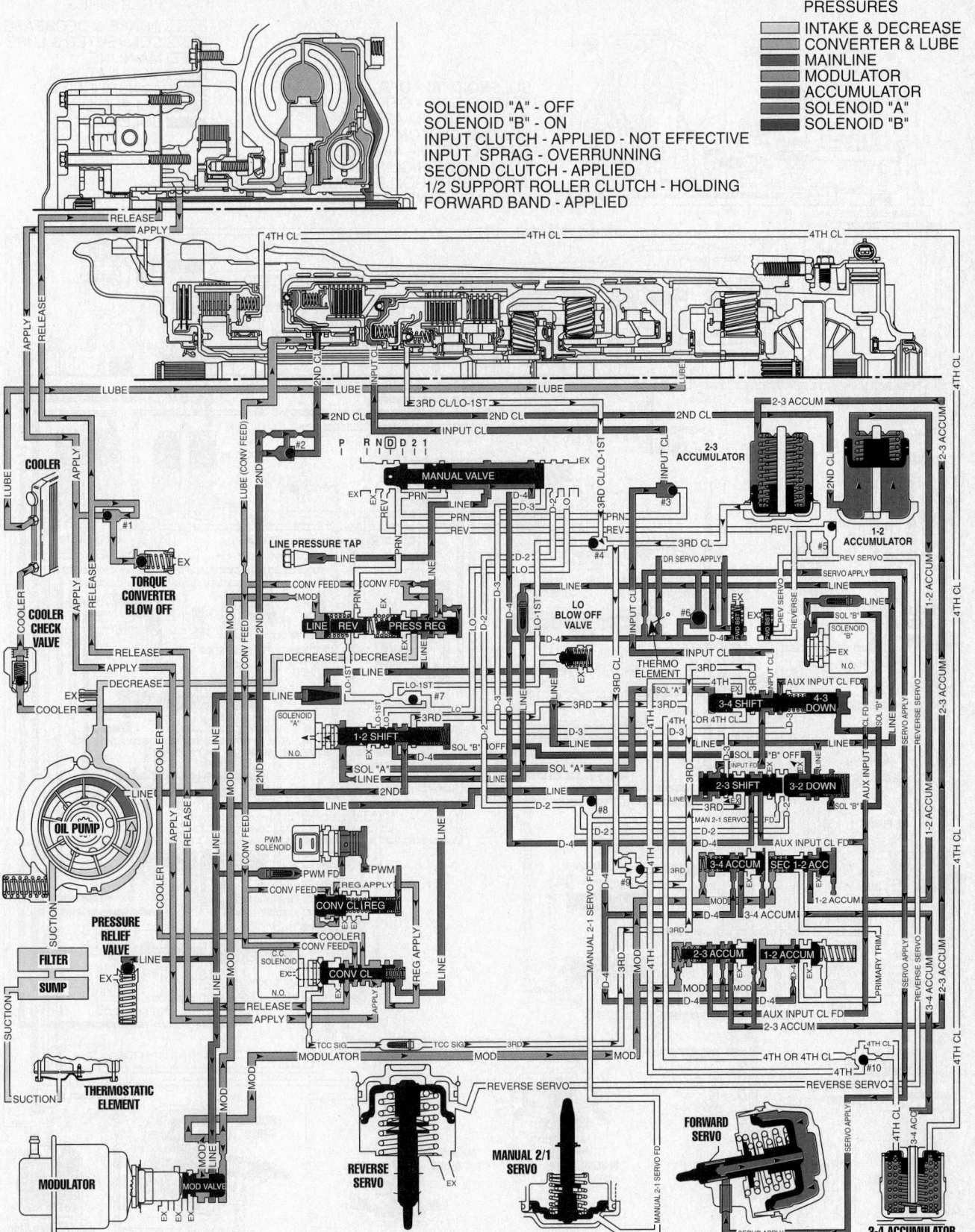

PRESSURES
- INTAKE & DECREASE
- CONVERTER & LUBE
- MAINLINE
- MODULATOR
- ACCUMULATOR
- SOLENOID "A"
- SOLENOID "B"

SOLENOID "A" - OFF
SOLENOID "B" - ON
INPUT CLUTCH - APPLIED - NOT EFFECTIVE
INPUT SPRAG - OVERRUNNING
SECOND CLUTCH - APPLIED
1/2 SUPPORT ROLLER CLUTCH - HOLDING
FORWARD BAND - APPLIED

Fig. 6: "OD" Range — 3rd Gear (TCC On)

Courtesy of General Motors Corp.

OIL CIRCUIT DIAGRAMS
Hydra-Matic 4T60-E Except 3.4L (Cont.)

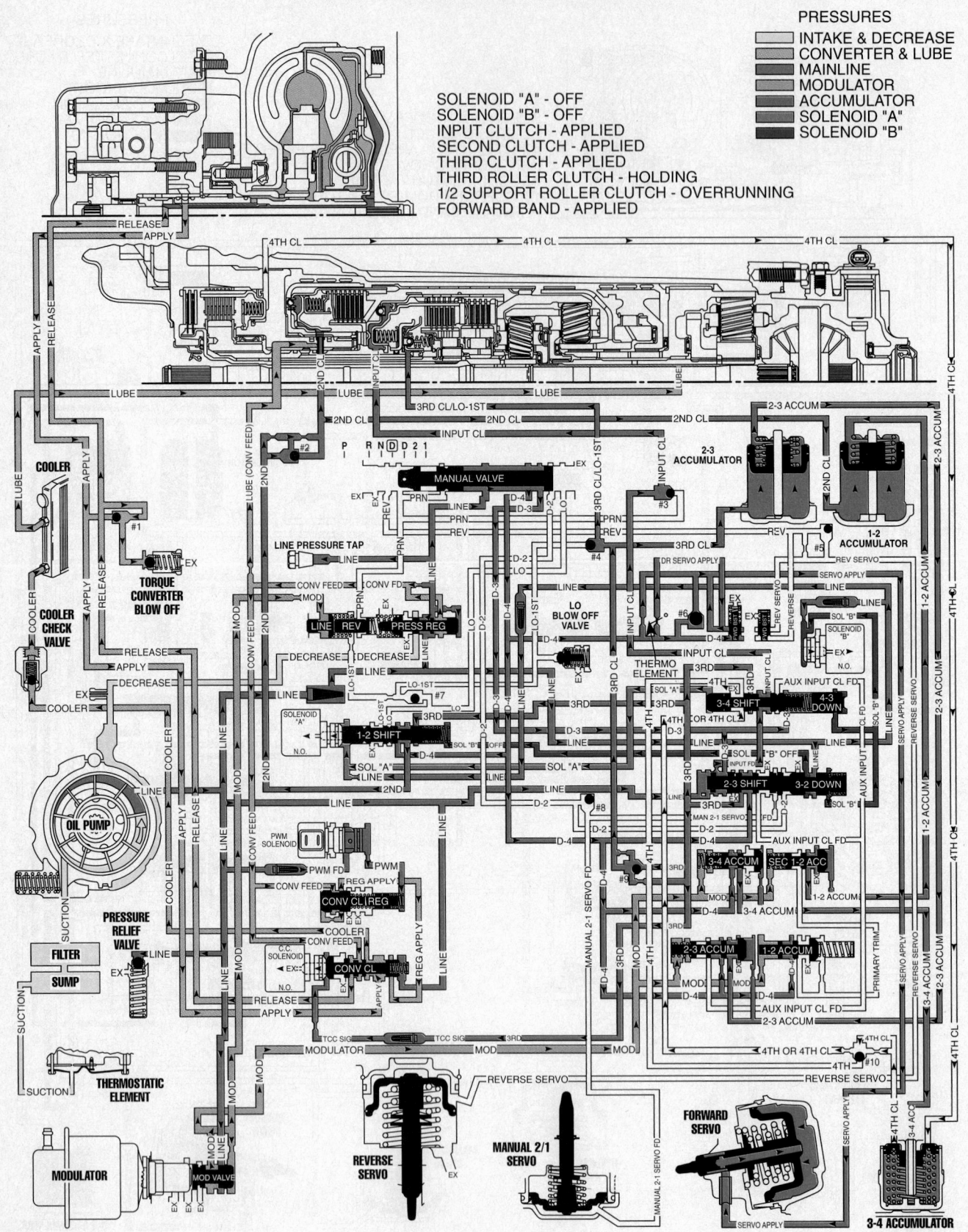

SOLENOID "A" - OFF
SOLENOID "B" - OFF
INPUT CLUTCH - APPLIED
SECOND CLUTCH - APPLIED
THIRD CLUTCH - APPLIED
THIRD ROLLER CLUTCH - HOLDING
1/2 SUPPORT ROLLER CLUTCH - OVERRUNNING
FORWARD BAND - APPLIED

PRESSURES
- INTAKE & DECREASE
- CONVERTER & LUBE
- MAINLINE
- MODULATOR
- ACCUMULATOR
- SOLENOID "A"
- SOLENOID "B"

Fig. 7: "OD" Range — 4th Gear (TCC On)

Courtesy of General Motors Corp.

OIL CIRCUIT DIAGRAMS
Hydra-Matic 4T60-E Except 3.4L

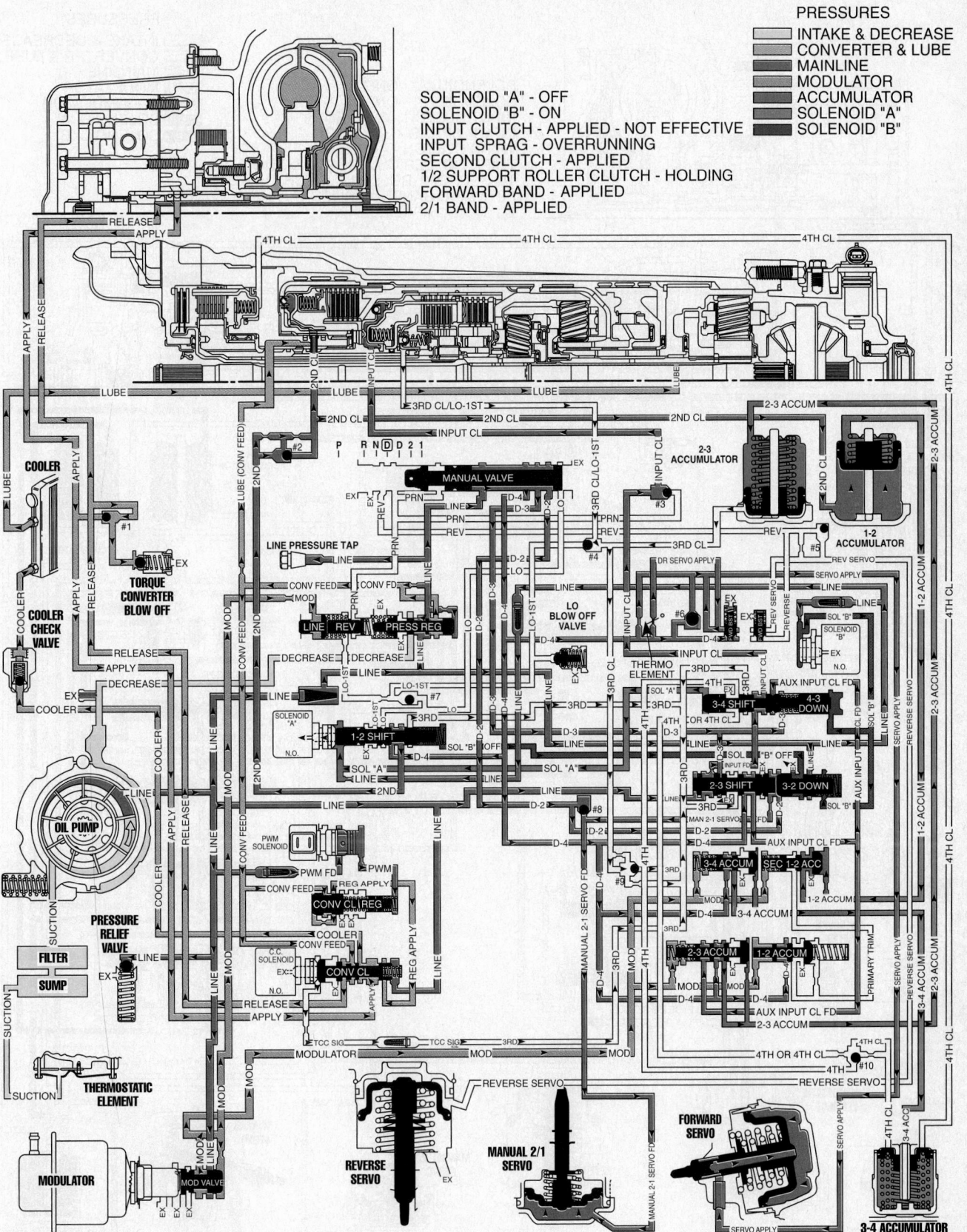

SOLENOID "A" - OFF
SOLENOID "B" - ON
INPUT CLUTCH - APPLIED - NOT EFFECTIVE
INPUT SPRAG - OVERRUNNING
SECOND CLUTCH - APPLIED
1/2 SUPPORT ROLLER CLUTCH - HOLDING
FORWARD BAND - APPLIED
2/1 BAND - APPLIED

PRESSURES

	INTAKE & DECREASE
	CONVERTER & LUBE
	MAINLINE
	MODULATOR
	ACCUMULATOR
	SOLENOID "A"
	SOLENOID "B"

Fig. 8: "OD" Range — 4-3 Downshift

Courtesy of General Motors Corp.

OIL CIRCUIT DIAGRAMS
Hydra-Matic 4T60-E Except 3.4L (Cont.)

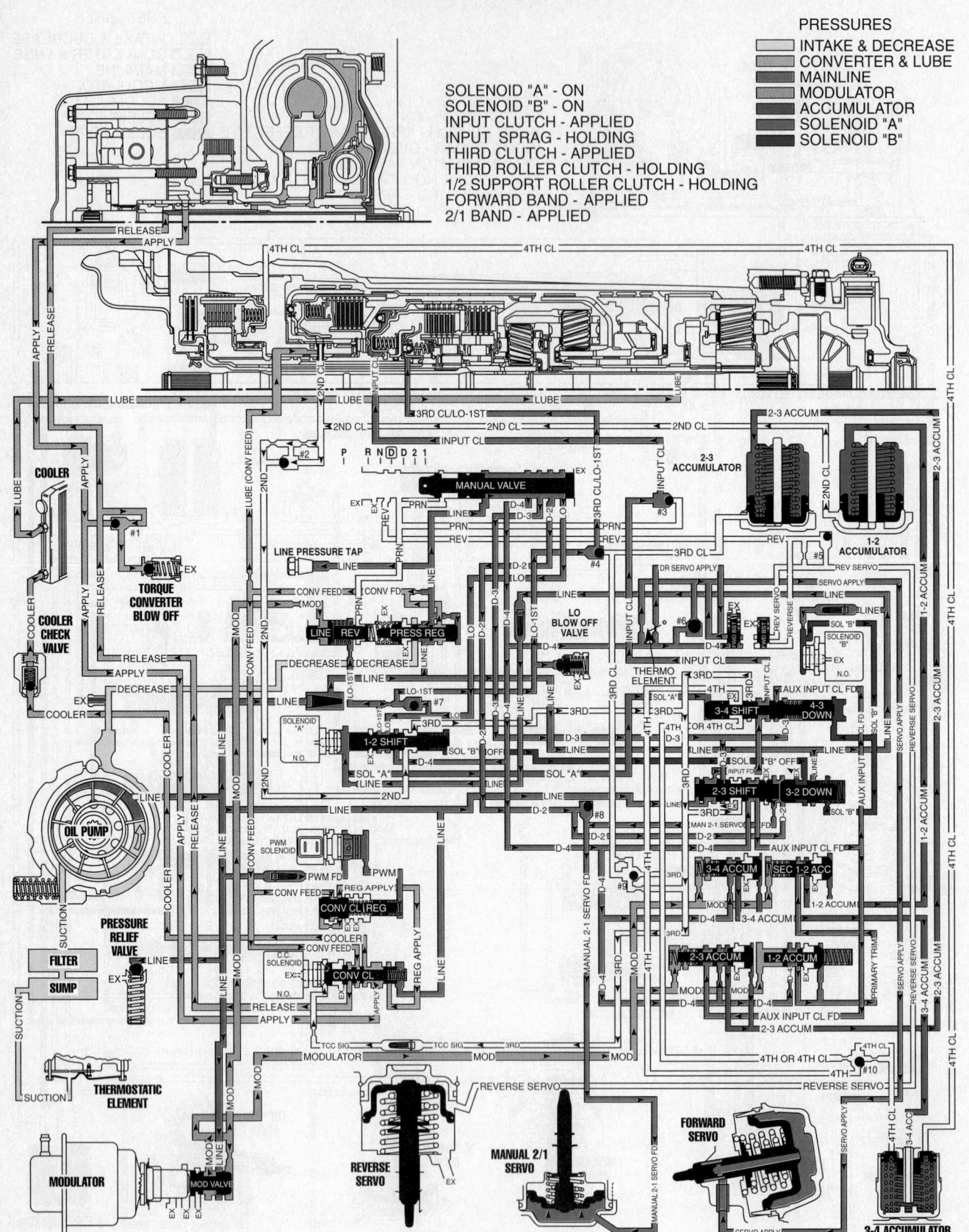

SOLENOID "A" - ON
SOLENOID "B" - ON
INPUT CLUTCH - APPLIED
INPUT SPRAG - HOLDING
THIRD CLUTCH - APPLIED
THIRD ROLLER CLUTCH - HOLDING
1/2 SUPPORT ROLLER CLUTCH - HOLDING
FORWARD BAND - APPLIED
2/1 BAND - APPLIED

PRESSURES
INTAKE & DECREASE
CONVERTER & LUBE
MAINLINE
MODULATOR
ACCUMULATOR
SOLENOID "A"
SOLENOID "B"

Fig. 9: "OD" Range — 3-2 Downshift

Courtesy of General Motors Corp.

Hydra-Matic 4T60-E Except 3.4L (Cont.)

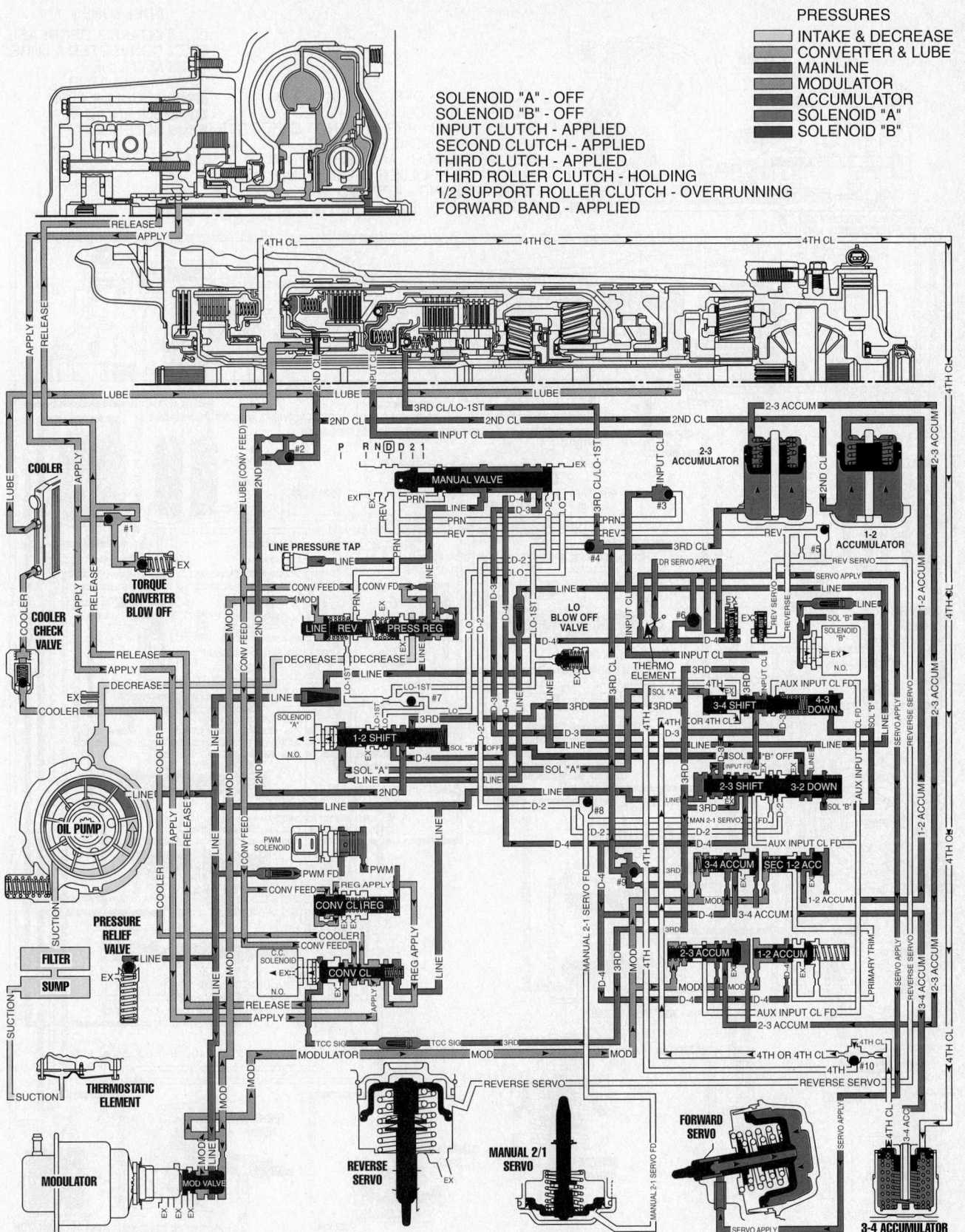

PRESSURES
- INTAKE & DECREASE
- CONVERTER & LUBE
- MAINLINE
- MODULATOR
- ACCUMULATOR
- SOLENOID "A"
- SOLENOID "B"

SOLENOID "A" - OFF
SOLENOID "B" - OFF
INPUT CLUTCH - APPLIED
SECOND CLUTCH - APPLIED
THIRD CLUTCH - APPLIED
THIRD ROLLER CLUTCH - HOLDING
1/2 SUPPORT ROLLER CLUTCH - OVERRUNNING
FORWARD BAND - APPLIED

Fig. 10: "D" Range — Manual Select 3rd Gear From "OD"

Courtesy of General Motors Corp.

OIL CIRCUIT DIAGRAMS
Hydra-Matic 4T60-E Except 3.4L (Cont.)

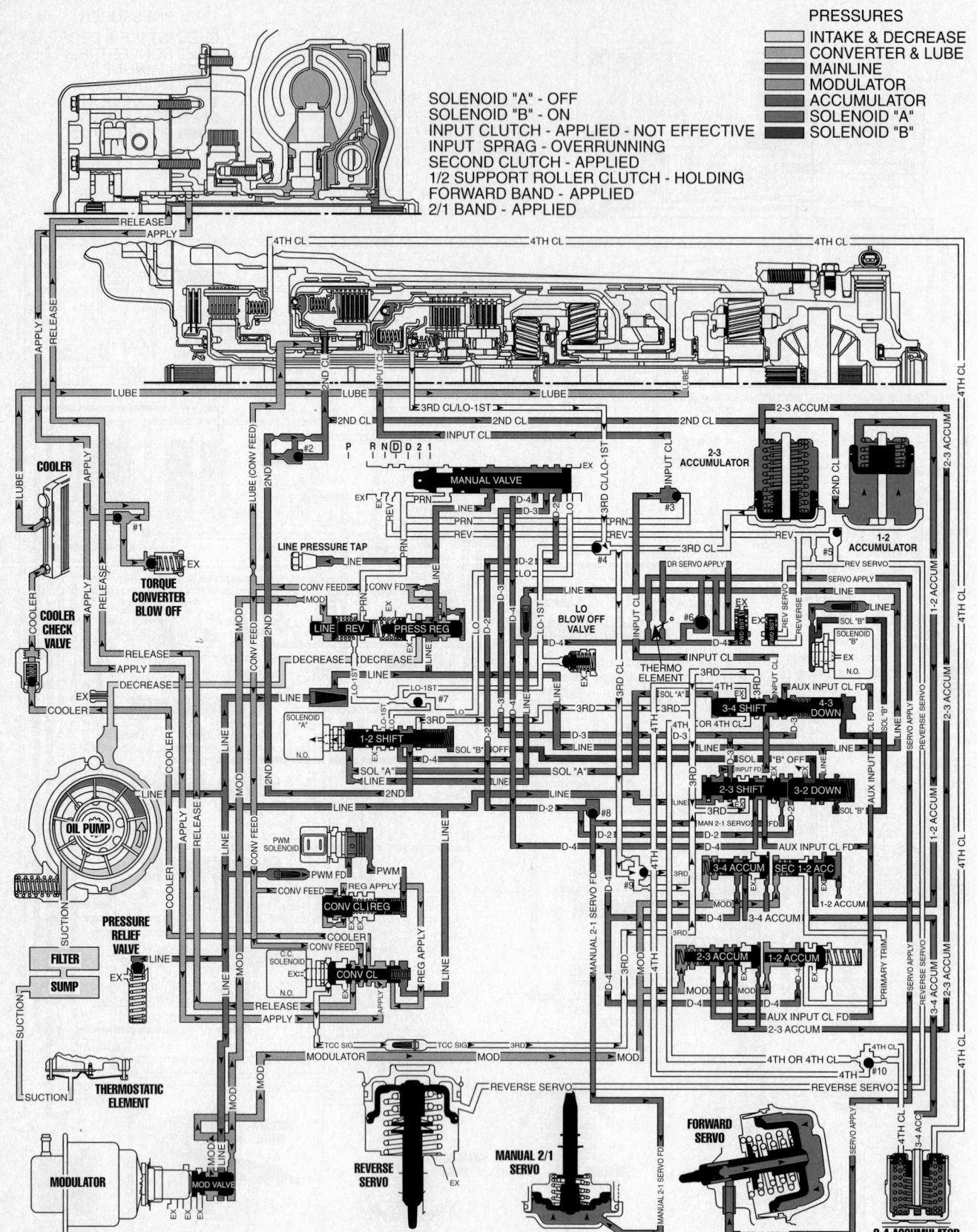

SOLENOID "A" - OFF
SOLENOID "B" - ON
INPUT CLUTCH - APPLIED - NOT EFFECTIVE
INPUT SPRAG - OVERRUNNING
SECOND CLUTCH - APPLIED
1/2 SUPPORT ROLLER CLUTCH - HOLDING
FORWARD BAND - APPLIED
2/1 BAND - APPLIED

PRESSURES
INTAKE & DECREASE
CONVERTER & LUBE
MAINLINE
MODULATOR
ACCUMULATOR
SOLENOID "A"
SOLENOID "B"

Fig. 11: "D" Range — Manual Select 2nd Gear From "D"

Courtesy of General Motors Corp.

OIL CIRCUIT DIAGRAMS
Hydra-Matic 4T60-E Except 3.4L (Cont.)

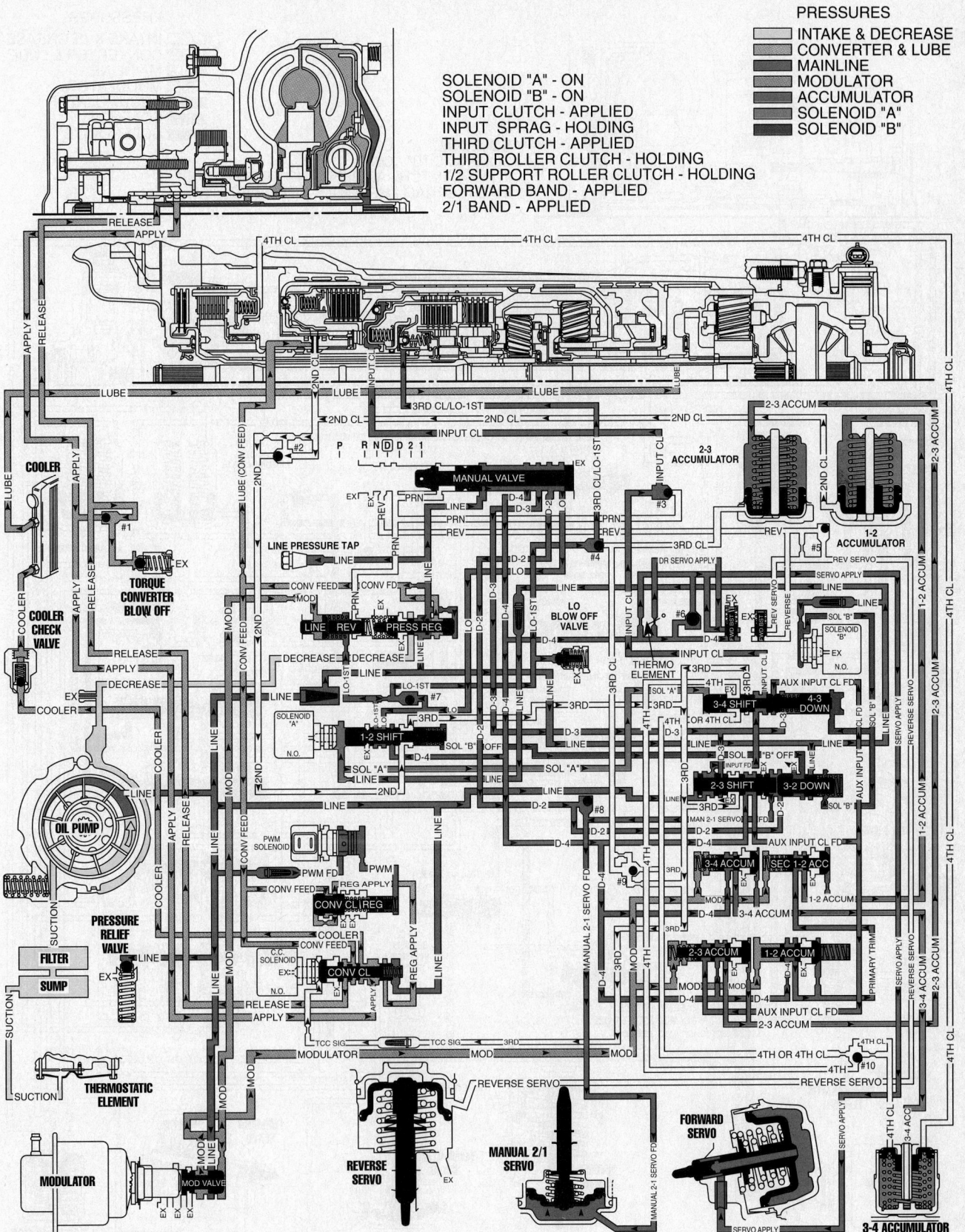

Fig. 12: "D" Range — Manual Select 1st Gear From 2nd

Courtesy of General Motors Corp.

OIL CIRCUIT DIAGRAMS
Hydra-Matic 4T60-E 3.4L

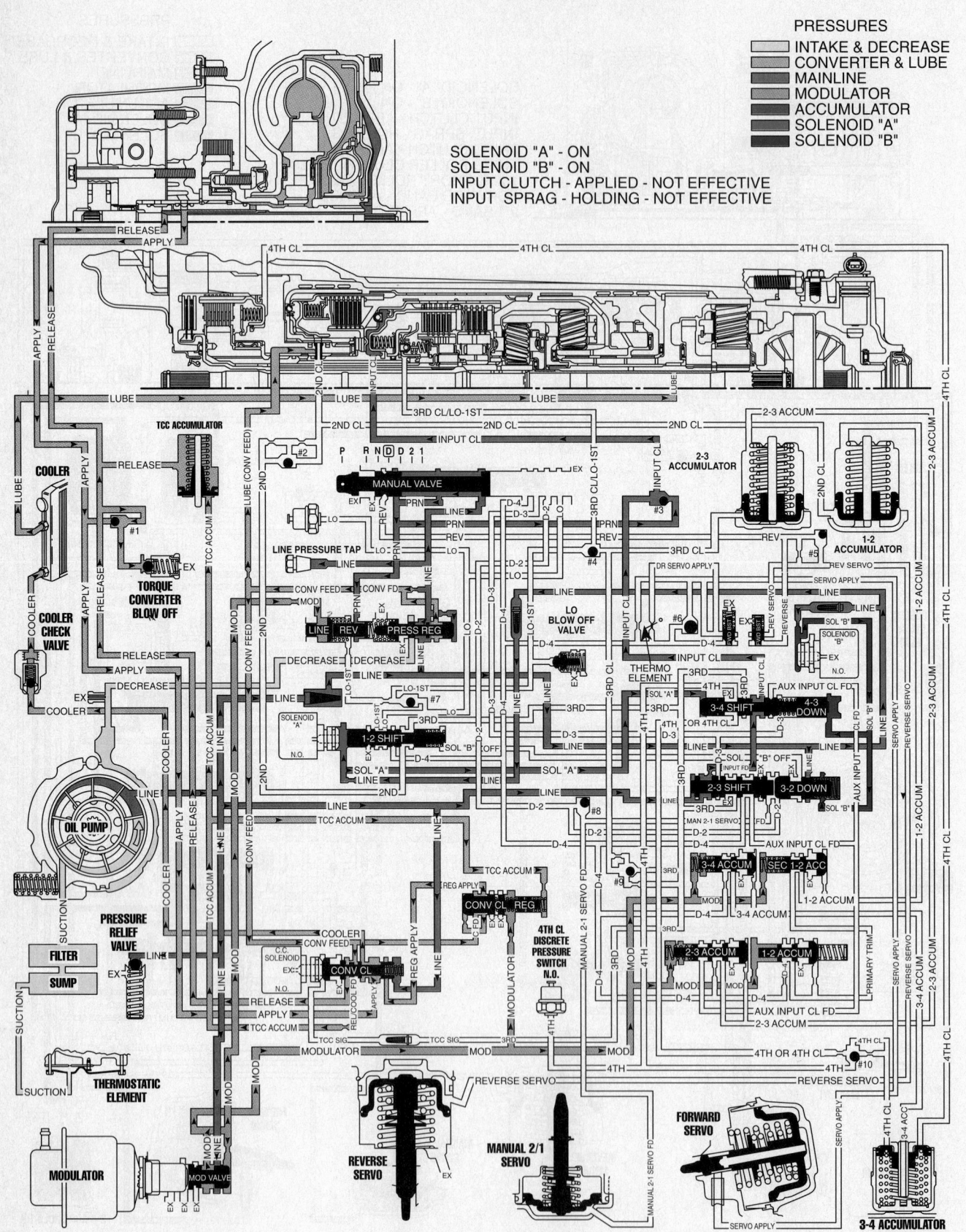

PRESSURES
- INTAKE & DECREASE
- CONVERTER & LUBE
- MAINLINE
- MODULATOR
- ACCUMULATOR
- SOLENOID "A"
- SOLENOID "B"

SOLENOID "A" - ON
SOLENOID "B" - ON
INPUT CLUTCH - APPLIED - NOT EFFECTIVE
INPUT SPRAG - HOLDING - NOT EFFECTIVE

Fig. 1: "P" or "N" Range — Park or Neutral

Courtesy of General Motors Corp.

OIL CIRCUIT DIAGRAMS
Hydra-Matic 4T60-E 3.4L (Cont.)

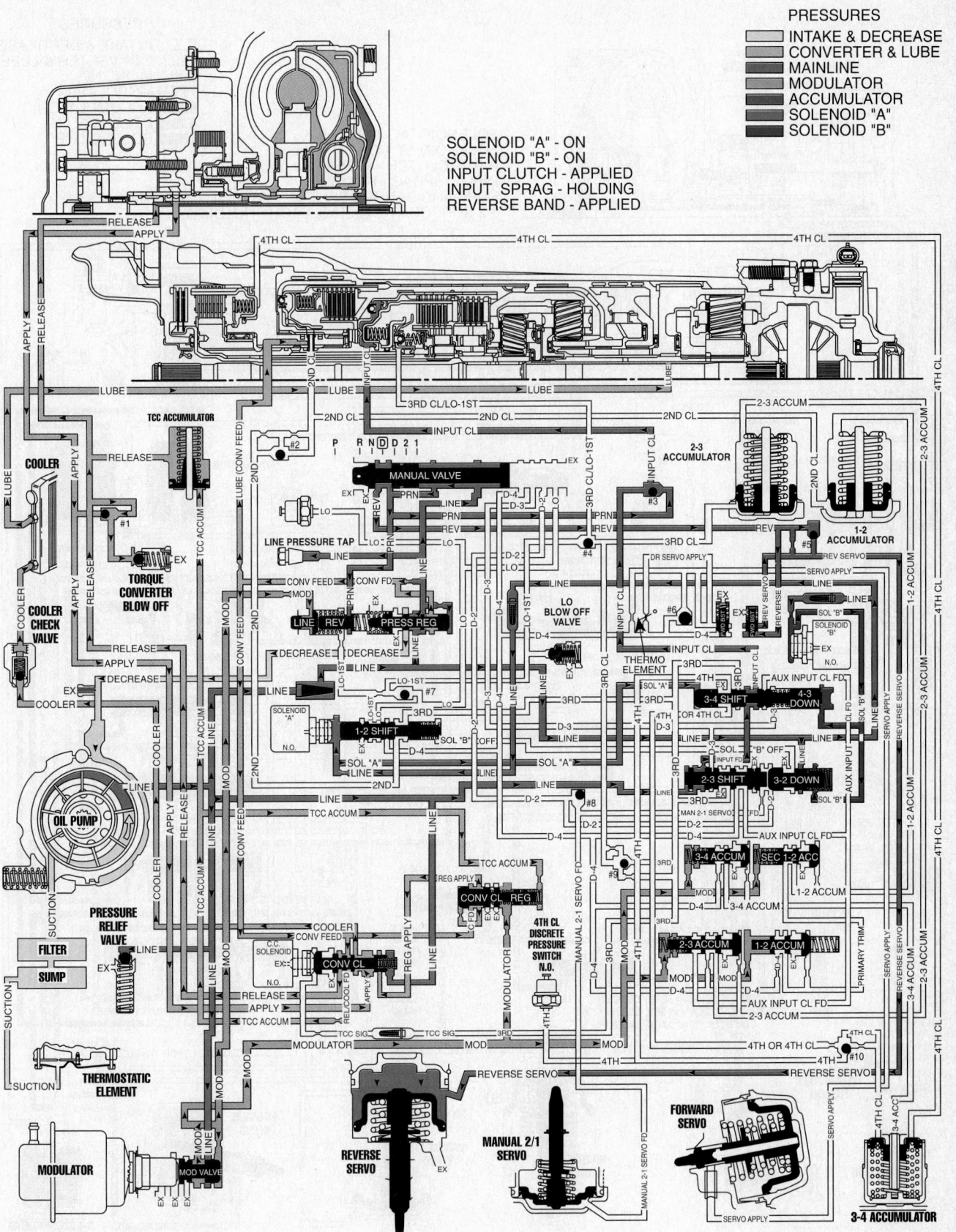

PRESSURES
- INTAKE & DECREASE
- CONVERTER & LUBE
- MAINLINE
- MODULATOR
- ACCUMULATOR
- SOLENOID "A"
- SOLENOID "B"

SOLENOID "A" - ON
SOLENOID "B" - ON
INPUT CLUTCH - APPLIED
INPUT SPRAG - HOLDING
REVERSE BAND - APPLIED

Fig. 2: "R" Range — Reverse

Courtesy of General Motors Corp.

OIL CIRCUIT DIAGRAMS
Hydra-Matic 4T60-E 3.4L (Cont.)

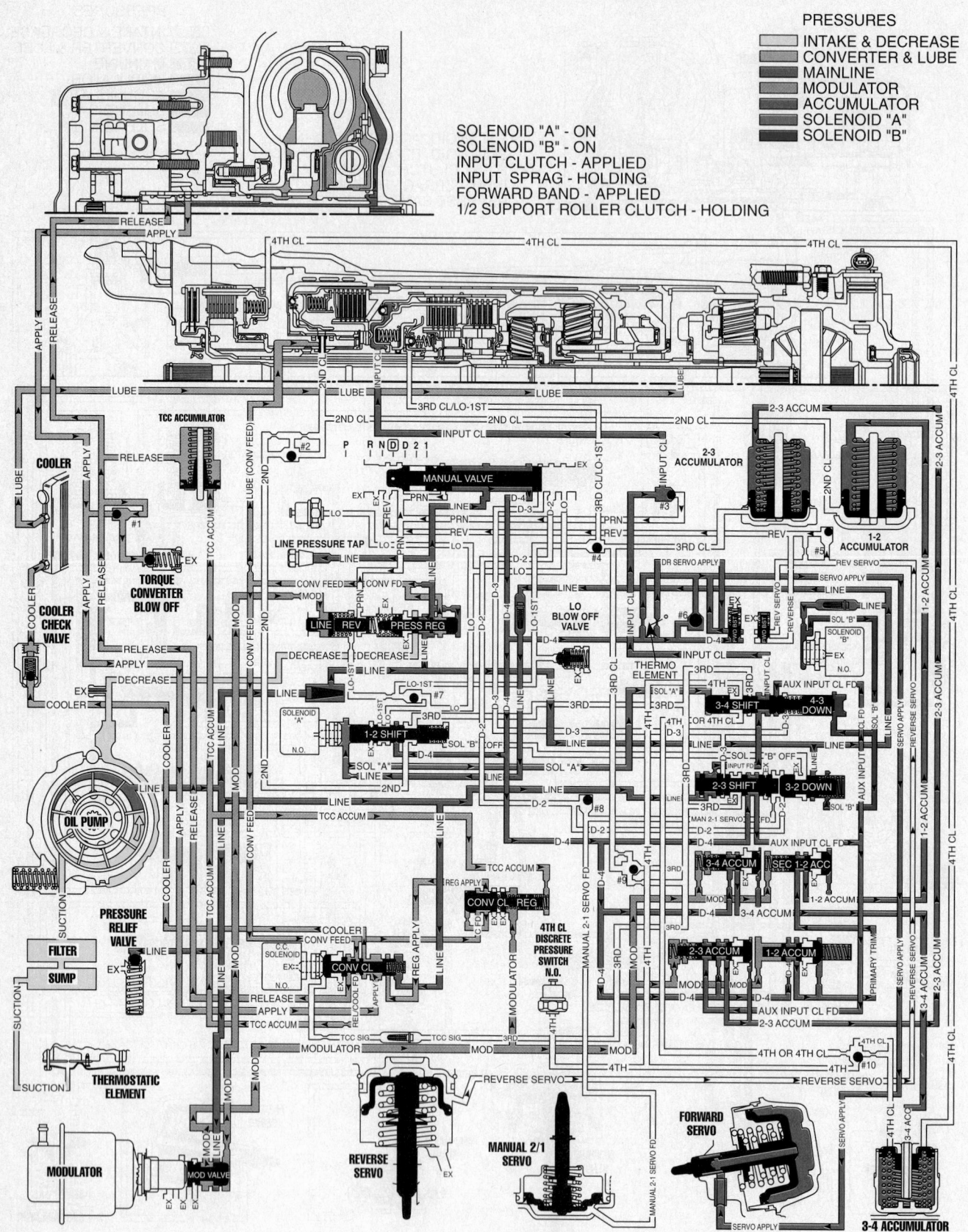

PRESSURES
- INTAKE & DECREASE
- CONVERTER & LUBE
- MAINLINE
- MODULATOR
- ACCUMULATOR
- SOLENOID "A"
- SOLENOID "B"

SOLENOID "A" - ON
SOLENOID "B" - ON
INPUT CLUTCH - APPLIED
INPUT SPRAG - HOLDING
FORWARD BAND - APPLIED
1/2 SUPPORT ROLLER CLUTCH - HOLDING

Fig. 3: "OD" Range — 1st Gear

Courtesy of General Motors Corp.

OIL CIRCUIT DIAGRAMS
Hydra-Matic 4T60-E 3.4L (Cont.)

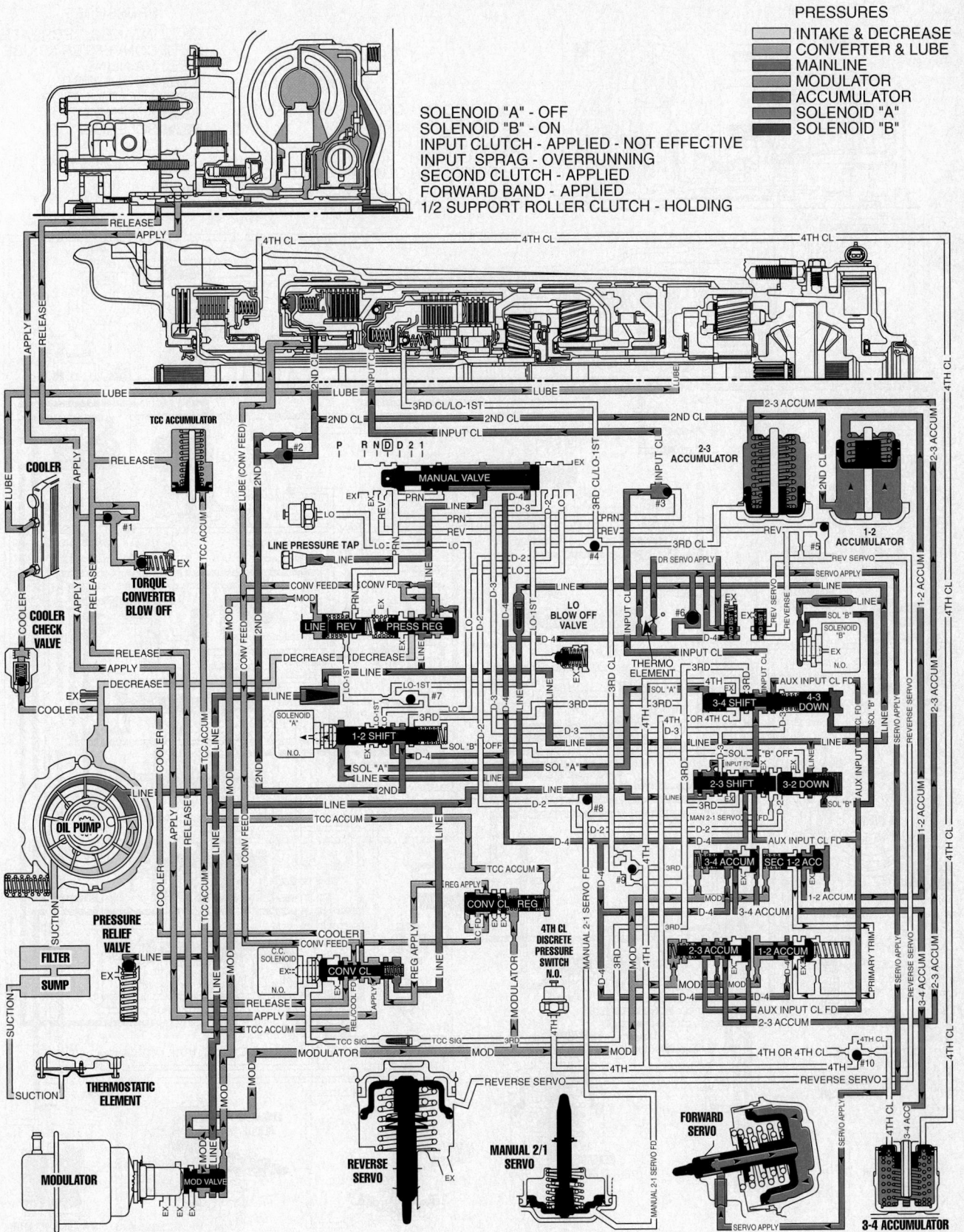

SOLENOID "A" - OFF
SOLENOID "B" - ON
INPUT CLUTCH - APPLIED - NOT EFFECTIVE
INPUT SPRAG - OVERRUNNING
SECOND CLUTCH - APPLIED
FORWARD BAND - APPLIED
1/2 SUPPORT ROLLER CLUTCH - HOLDING

PRESSURES
INTAKE & DECREASE
CONVERTER & LUBE
MAINLINE
MODULATOR
ACCUMULATOR
SOLENOID "A"
SOLENOID "B"

Fig. 4: "OD" Range — 2nd Gear

Courtesy of General Motors Corp.

OIL CIRCUIT DIAGRAMS
Hydra-Matic 4T60-E 3.4L (Cont.)

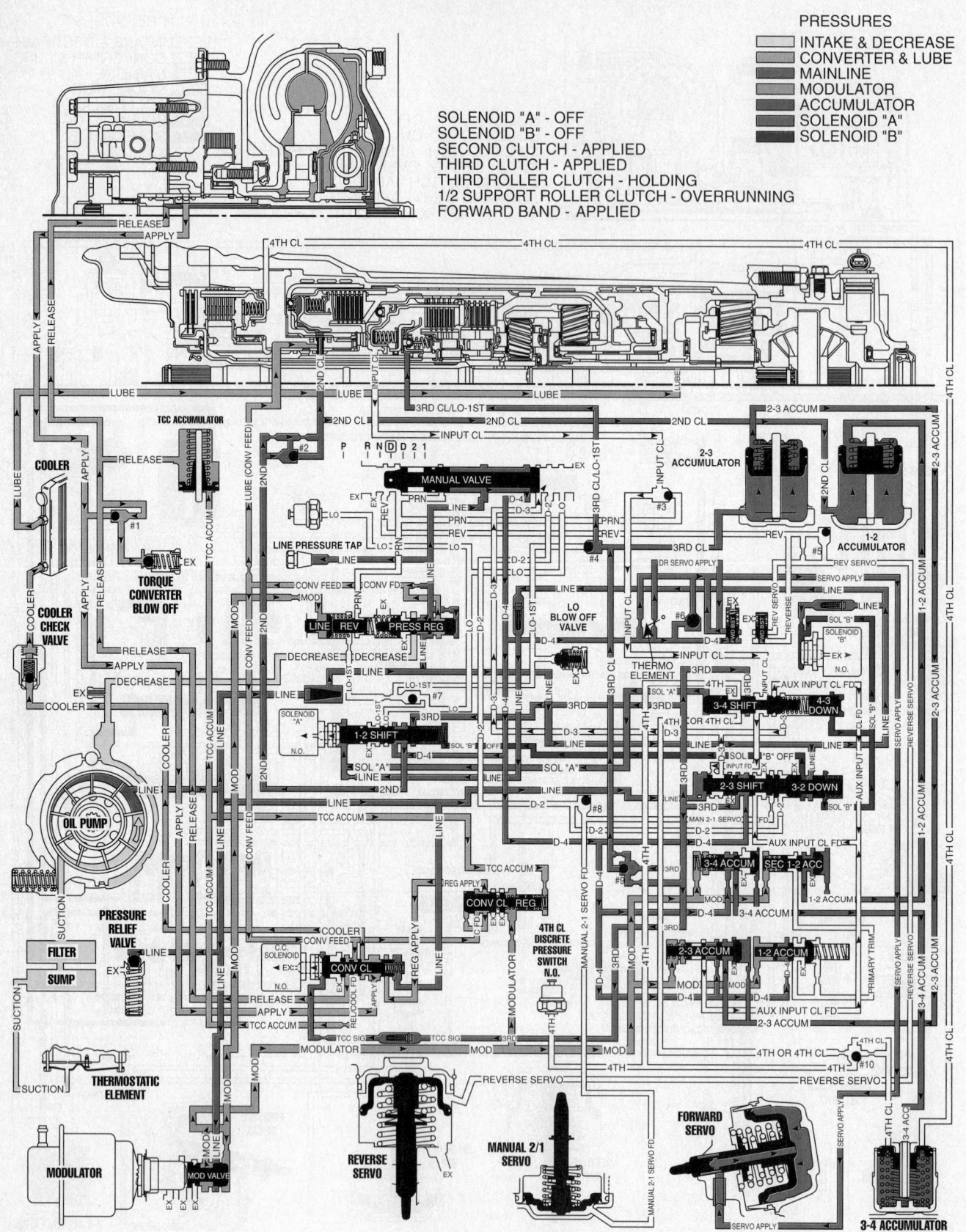

PRESSURES
- INTAKE & DECREASE
- CONVERTER & LUBE
- MAINLINE
- MODULATOR
- ACCUMULATOR
- SOLENOID "A"
- SOLENOID "B"

SOLENOID "A" - OFF
SOLENOID "B" - OFF
SECOND CLUTCH - APPLIED
THIRD CLUTCH - APPLIED
THIRD ROLLER CLUTCH - HOLDING
1/2 SUPPORT ROLLER CLUTCH - OVERRUNNING
FORWARD BAND - APPLIED

Fig. 5: "OD" Range — 3rd Gear (TCC Off)

Courtesy of General Motors Corp.

OIL CIRCUIT DIAGRAMS
Hydra-Matic 4T60-E 3.4L (Cont.)

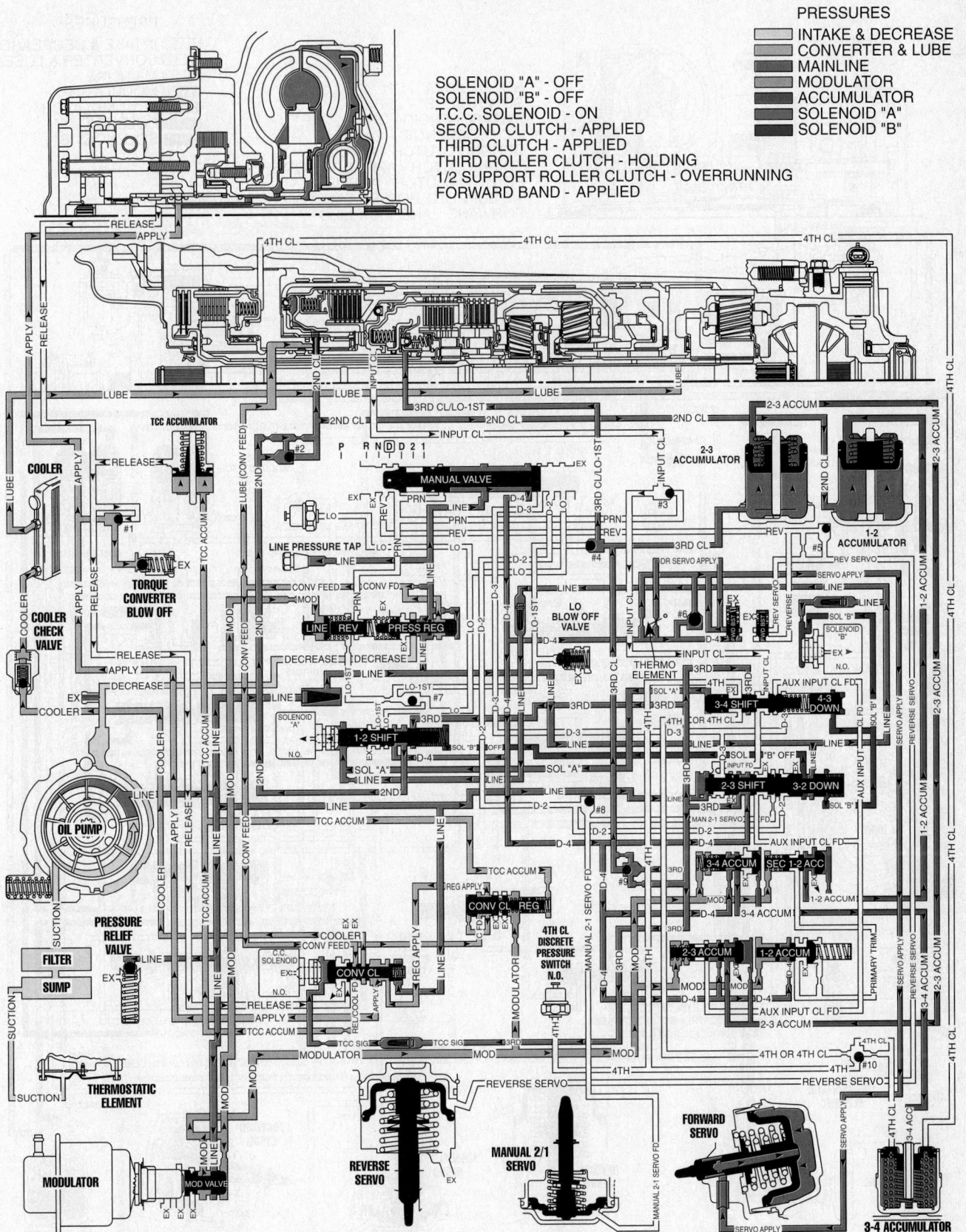

PRESSURES
- INTAKE & DECREASE
- CONVERTER & LUBE
- MAINLINE
- MODULATOR
- ACCUMULATOR
- SOLENOID "A"
- SOLENOID "B"

SOLENOID "A" - OFF
SOLENOID "B" - OFF
T.C.C. SOLENOID - ON
SECOND CLUTCH - APPLIED
THIRD CLUTCH - APPLIED
THIRD ROLLER CLUTCH - HOLDING
1/2 SUPPORT ROLLER CLUTCH - OVERRUNNING
FORWARD BAND - APPLIED

Fig. 6: "OD" Range — 3rd Gear (TCC On)

Courtesy of General Motors Corp.

OIL CIRCUIT DIAGRAMS
Hydra-Matic 4T60-E 3.4L (Cont.)

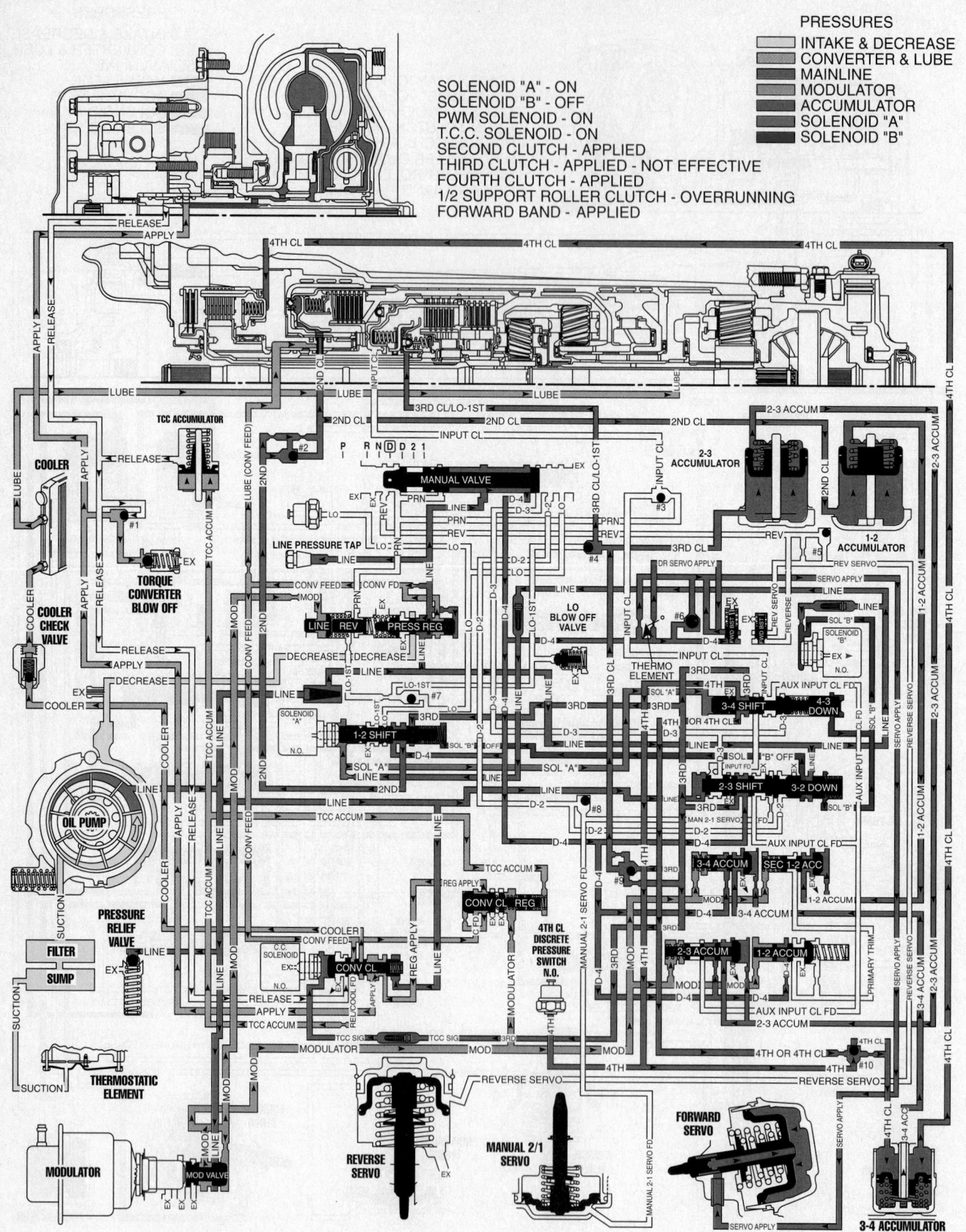

SOLENOID "A" - ON
SOLENOID "B" - OFF
PWM SOLENOID - ON
T.C.C. SOLENOID - ON
SECOND CLUTCH - APPLIED
THIRD CLUTCH - APPLIED - NOT EFFECTIVE
FOURTH CLUTCH - APPLIED
1/2 SUPPORT ROLLER CLUTCH - OVERRUNNING
FORWARD BAND - APPLIED

PRESSURES
INTAKE & DECREASE
CONVERTER & LUBE
MAINLINE
MODULATOR
ACCUMULATOR
SOLENOID "A"
SOLENOID "B"

Fig. 7: "OD" Range — 4th Gear (TCC On)

Courtesy of General Motors Corp.

OIL CIRCUIT DIAGRAMS
Hydra-Matic 4T60-E 3.4L (Cont.)

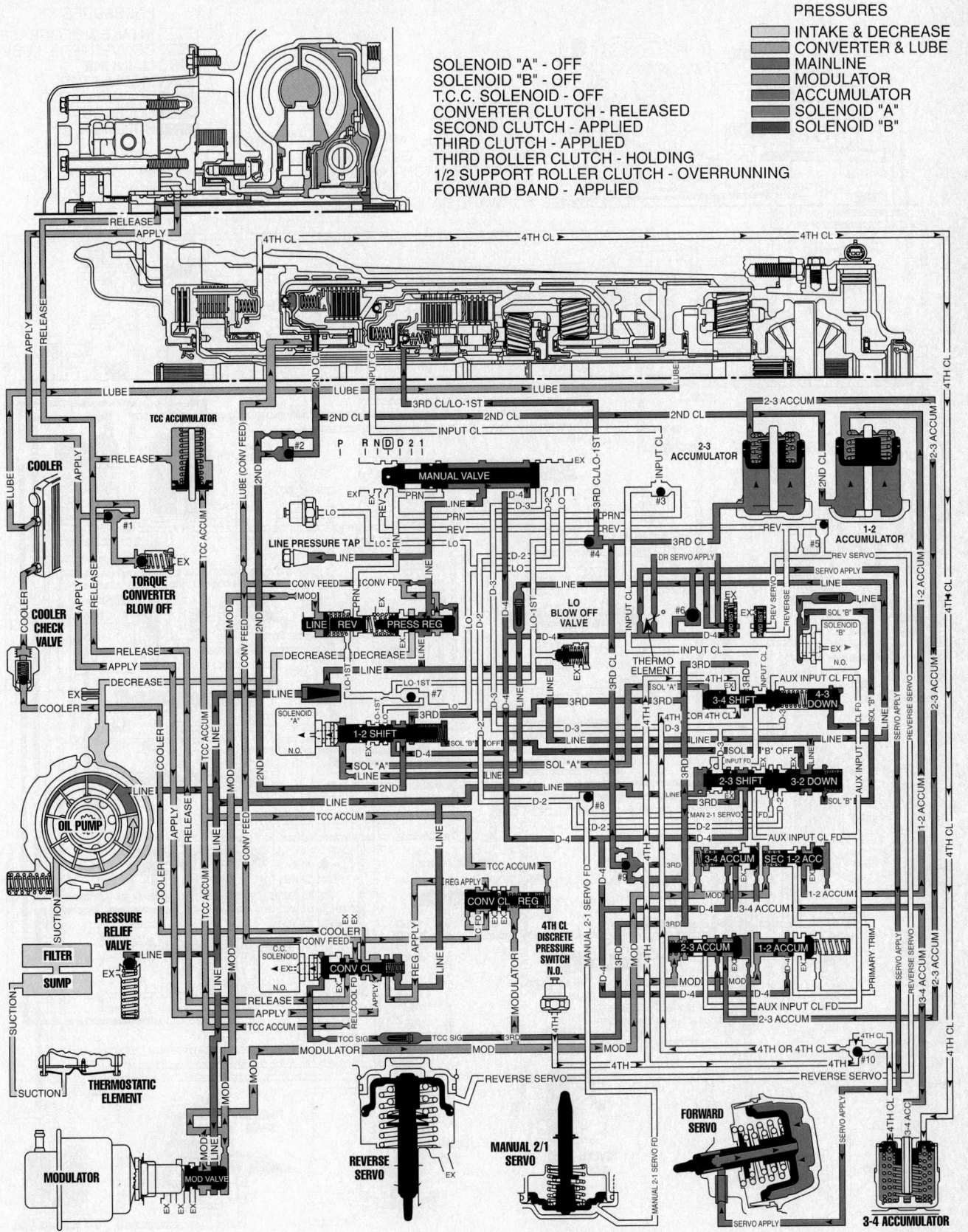

SOLENOID "A" - OFF
SOLENOID "B" - OFF
T.C.C. SOLENOID - OFF
CONVERTER CLUTCH - RELEASED
SECOND CLUTCH - APPLIED
THIRD CLUTCH - APPLIED
THIRD ROLLER CLUTCH - HOLDING
1/2 SUPPORT ROLLER CLUTCH - OVERRUNNING
FORWARD BAND - APPLIED

PRESSURES
INTAKE & DECREASE
CONVERTER & LUBE
MAINLINE
MODULATOR
ACCUMULATOR
SOLENOID "A"
SOLENOID "B"

Fig. 8: "OD" Range — 4-3 Downshift

Courtesy of General Motors Corp.

OIL CIRCUIT DIAGRAMS
Hydra-Matic 4T60-E 3.4L (Cont.)

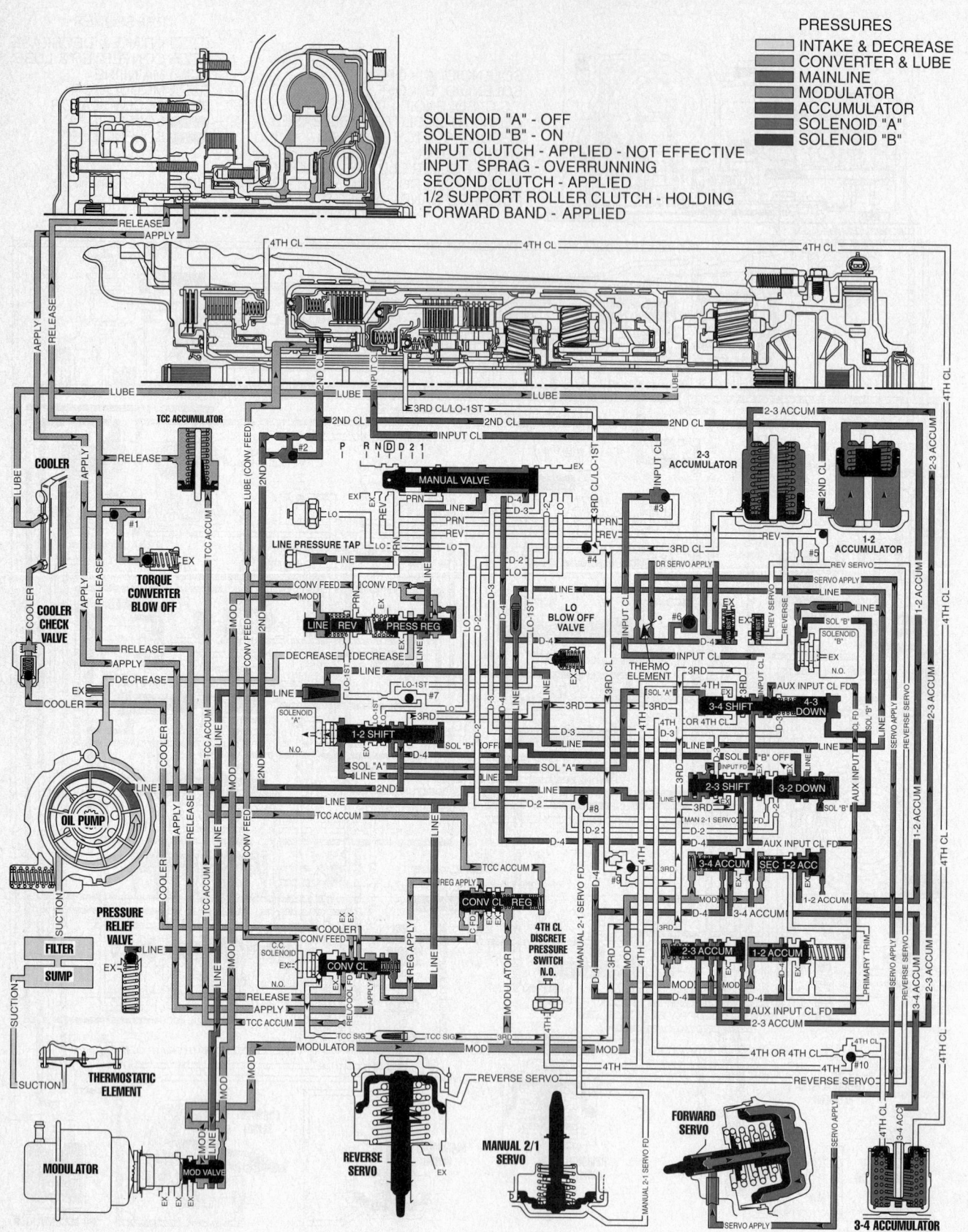

SOLENOID "A" - OFF
SOLENOID "B" - ON
INPUT CLUTCH - APPLIED - NOT EFFECTIVE
INPUT SPRAG - OVERRUNNING
SECOND CLUTCH - APPLIED
1/2 SUPPORT ROLLER CLUTCH - HOLDING
FORWARD BAND - APPLIED

PRESSURES
INTAKE & DECREASE
CONVERTER & LUBE
MAINLINE
MODULATOR
ACCUMULATOR
SOLENOID "A"
SOLENOID "B"

Fig. 9: "OD" Range — 3-2 Downshift

Courtesy of General Motors Corp.

OIL CIRCUIT DIAGRAMS
Hydra-Matic 4T60-E 3.4L (Cont.)

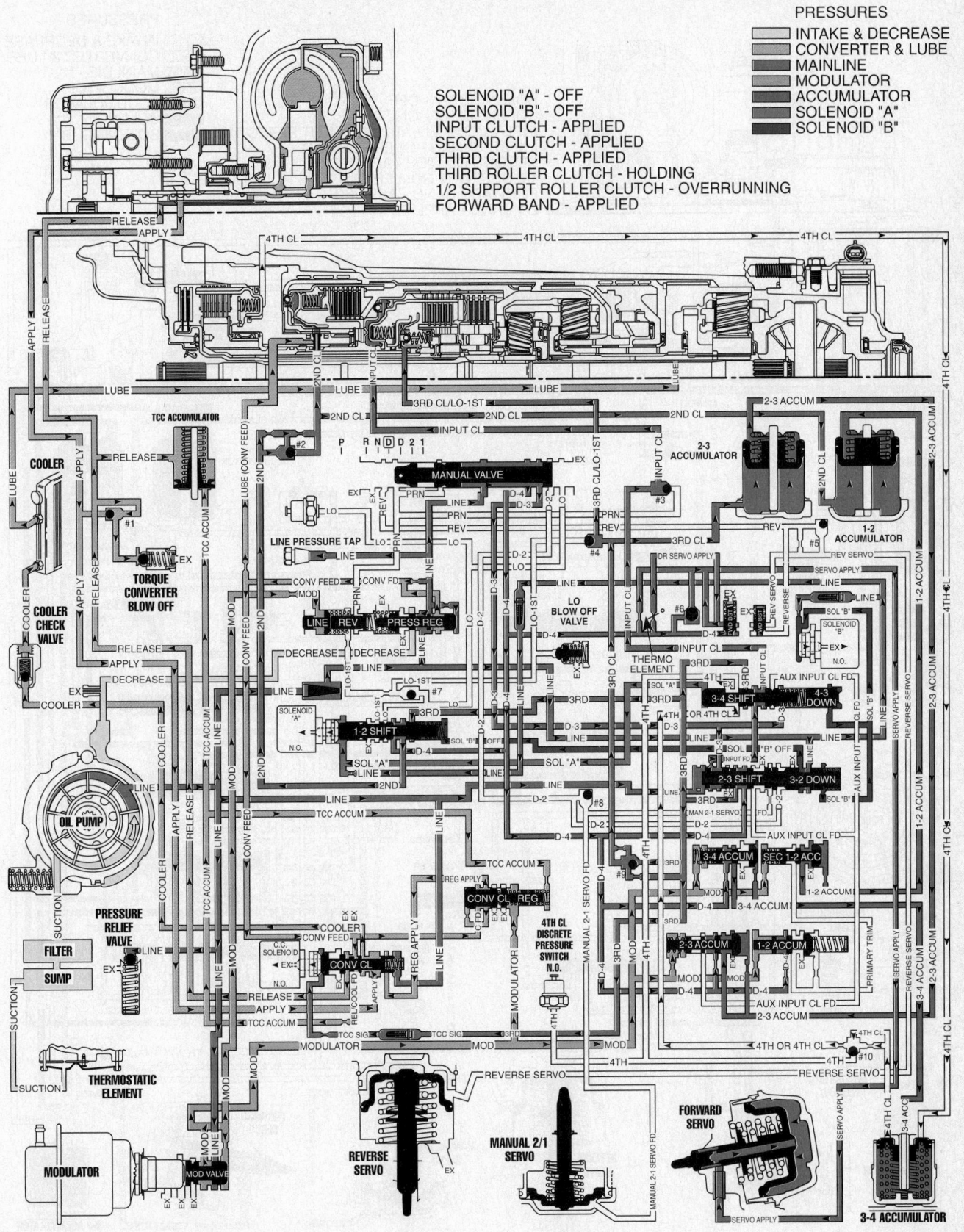

PRESSURES
- INTAKE & DECREASE
- CONVERTER & LUBE
- MAINLINE
- MODULATOR
- ACCUMULATOR
- SOLENOID "A"
- SOLENOID "B"

SOLENOID "A" - OFF
SOLENOID "B" - OFF
INPUT CLUTCH - APPLIED
SECOND CLUTCH - APPLIED
THIRD CLUTCH - APPLIED
THIRD ROLLER CLUTCH - HOLDING
1/2 SUPPORT ROLLER CLUTCH - OVERRUNNING
FORWARD BAND - APPLIED

Fig. 10: "D" Range — Manual Select 3rd Gear From "(OD)"   Courtesy of General Motors Corp.

OIL CIRCUIT DIAGRAMS
Hydra-Matic 4T60-E 3.4L (Cont.)

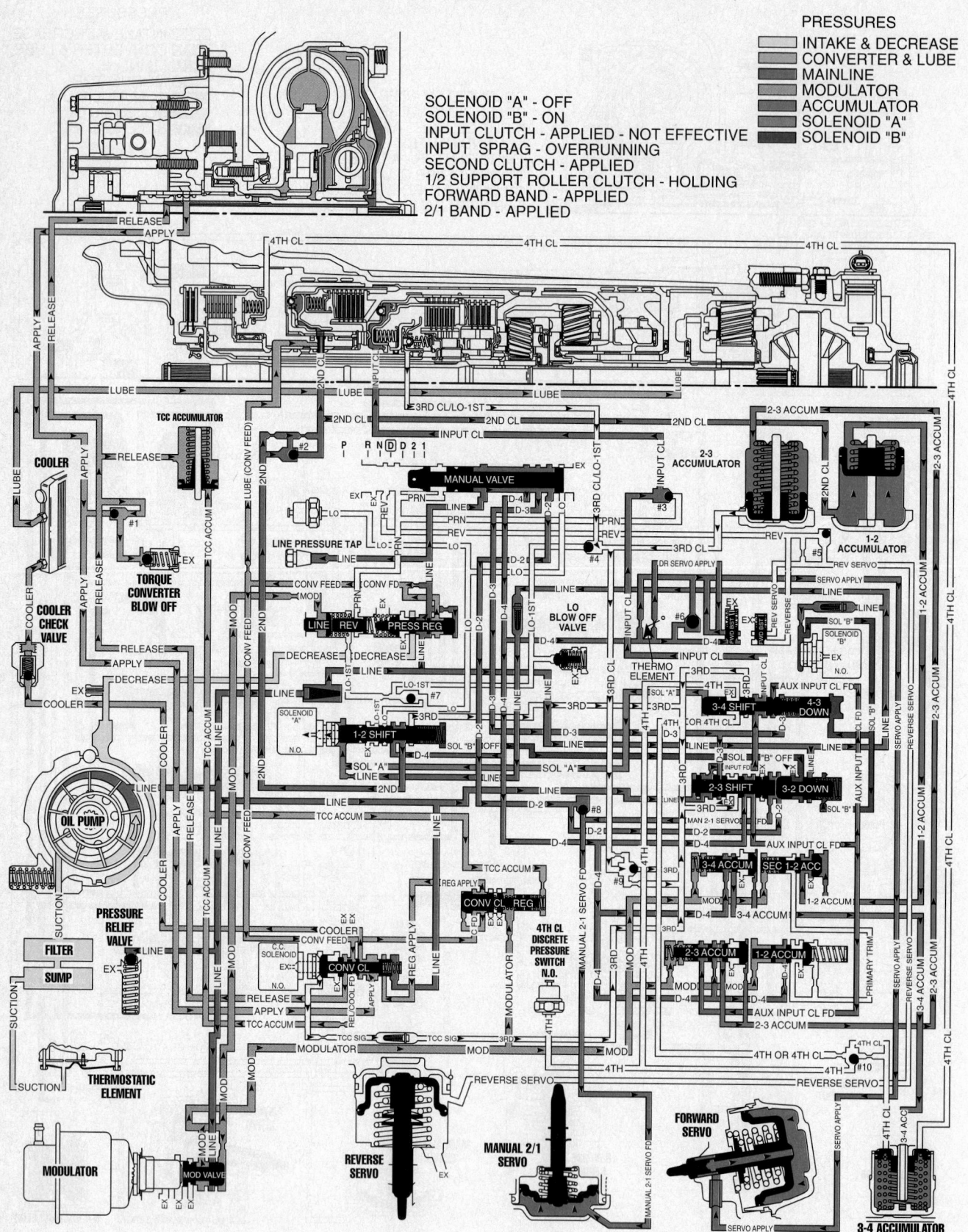

SOLENOID "A" - OFF
SOLENOID "B" - ON
INPUT CLUTCH - APPLIED - NOT EFFECTIVE
INPUT SPRAG - OVERRUNNING
SECOND CLUTCH - APPLIED
1/2 SUPPORT ROLLER CLUTCH - HOLDING
FORWARD BAND - APPLIED
2/1 BAND - APPLIED

PRESSURES
INTAKE & DECREASE
CONVERTER & LUBE
MAINLINE
MODULATOR
ACCUMULATOR
SOLENOID "A"
SOLENOID "B"

Fig. 11: "D" Range — Manual Select 2nd Gear From "D"

Courtesy of General Motors Corp.

OIL CIRCUIT DIAGRAMS
Hydra-Matic 4T60-E 3.4L (Cont.)

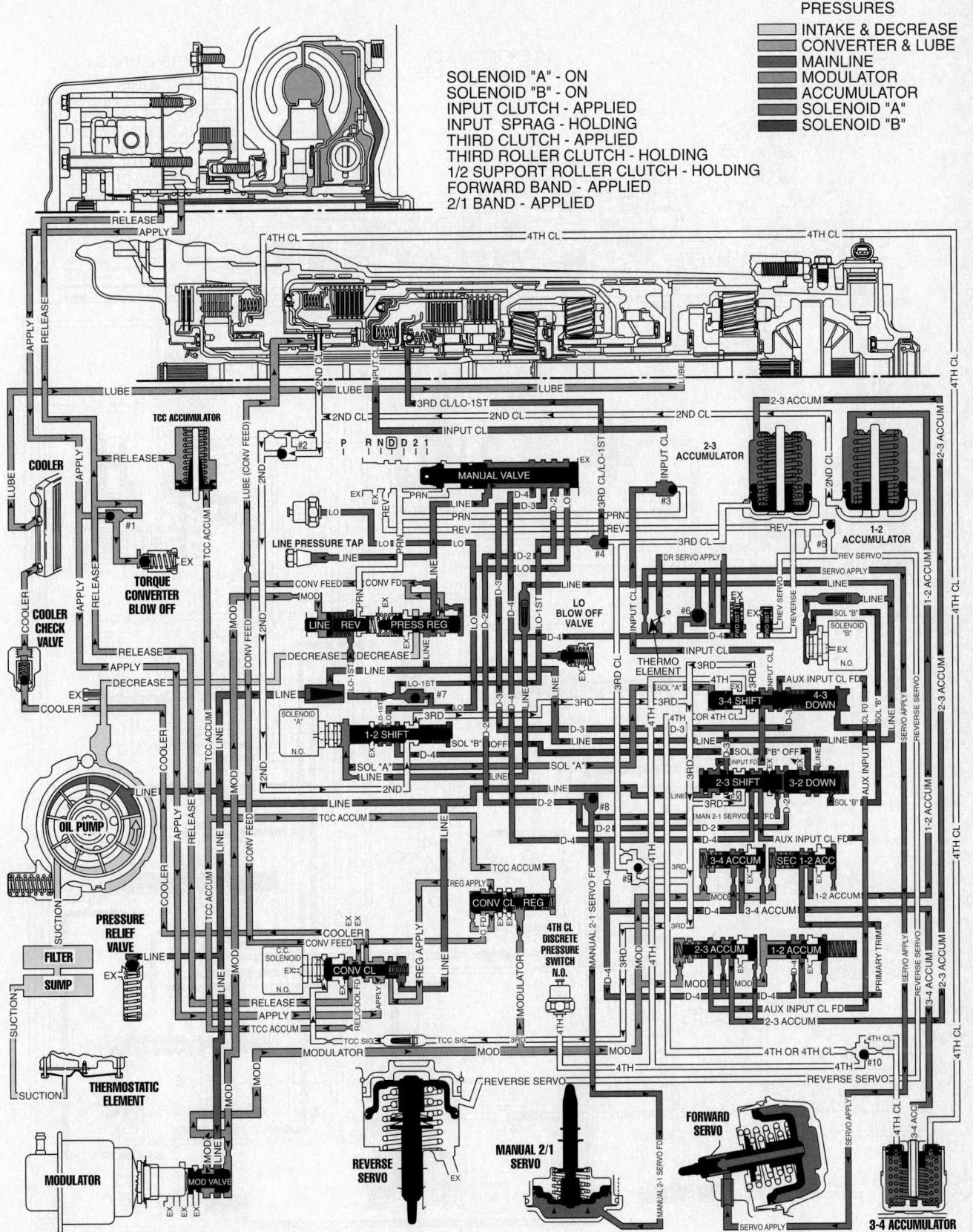

SOLENOID "A" - ON
SOLENOID "B" - ON
INPUT CLUTCH - APPLIED
INPUT SPRAG - HOLDING
THIRD CLUTCH - APPLIED
THIRD ROLLER CLUTCH - HOLDING
1/2 SUPPORT ROLLER CLUTCH - HOLDING
FORWARD BAND - APPLIED
2/1 BAND - APPLIED

PRESSURES
INTAKE & DECREASE
CONVERTER & LUBE
MAINLINE
MODULATOR
ACCUMULATOR
SOLENOID "A"
SOLENOID "B"

Fig. 12: "D" Range — Manual Select 1st Gear From 2nd

Courtesy of General Motors Corp.

OIL CIRCUIT DIAGRAMS
Hydra-Matic 4L80-E

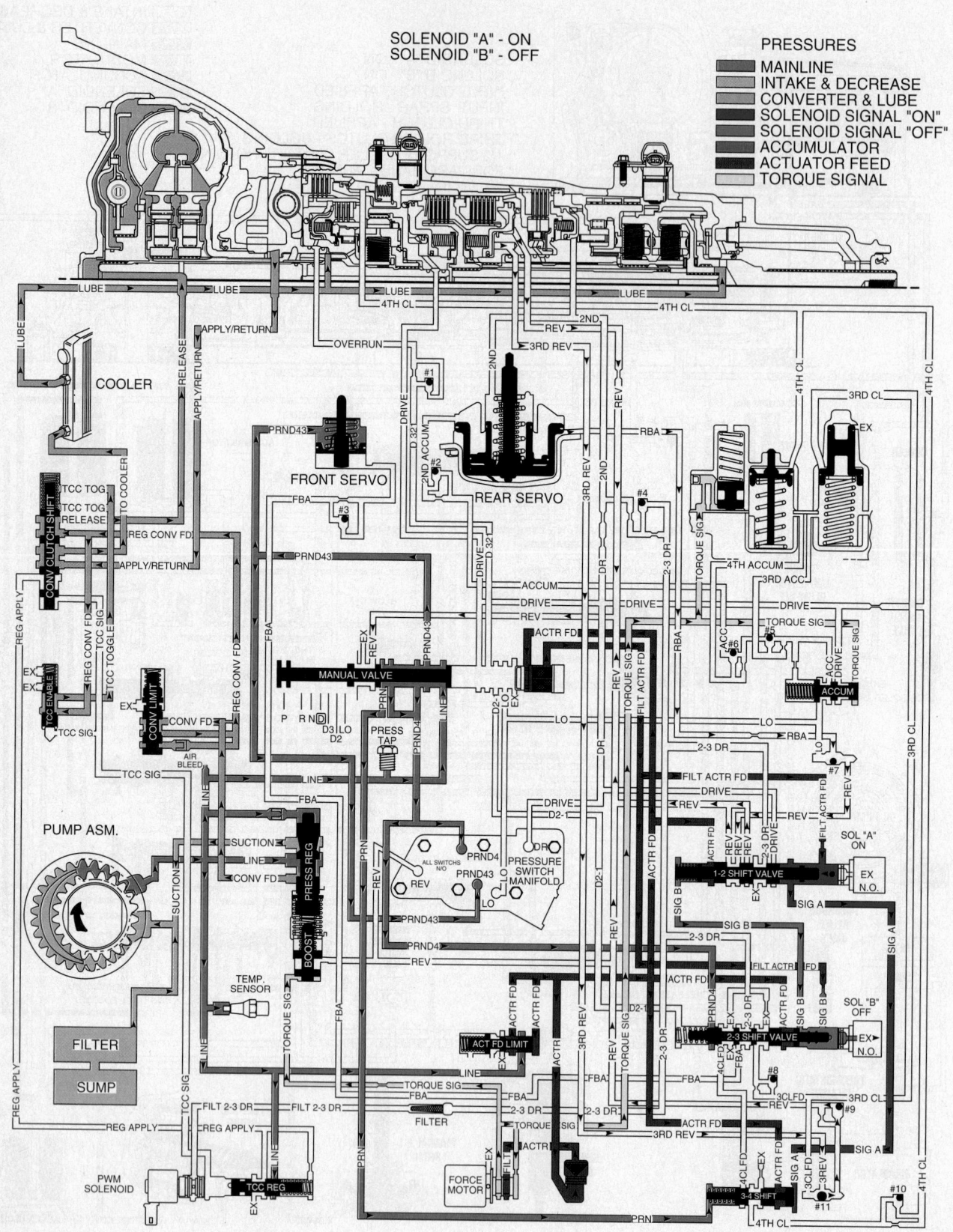

Fig. 1: "P" or "N" Range — Park or Neutral

Courtesy of General Motors Corp.

OIL CIRCUIT DIAGRAMS
Hydra-Matic 4L80-E (Cont.)

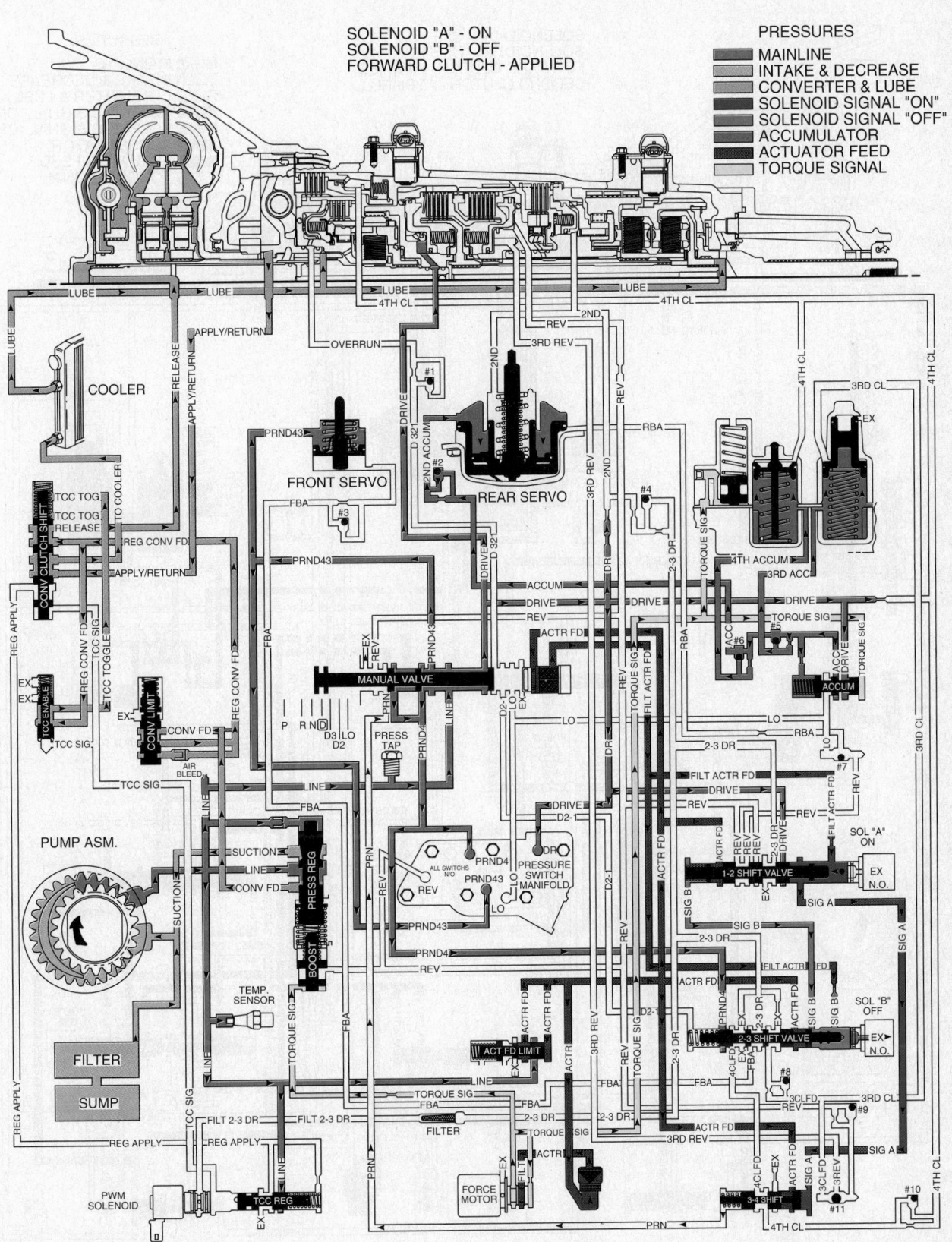

SOLENOID "A" - ON
SOLENOID "B" - OFF
FORWARD CLUTCH - APPLIED

PRESSURES
MAINLINE
INTAKE & DECREASE
CONVERTER & LUBE
SOLENOID SIGNAL "ON"
SOLENOID SIGNAL "OFF"
ACCUMULATOR
ACTUATOR FEED
TORQUE SIGNAL

Fig. 2: "OD" Range — 1st Gear

Courtesy of General Motors Corp.

OIL CIRCUIT DIAGRAMS
Hydra-Matic 4L80-E (Cont.)

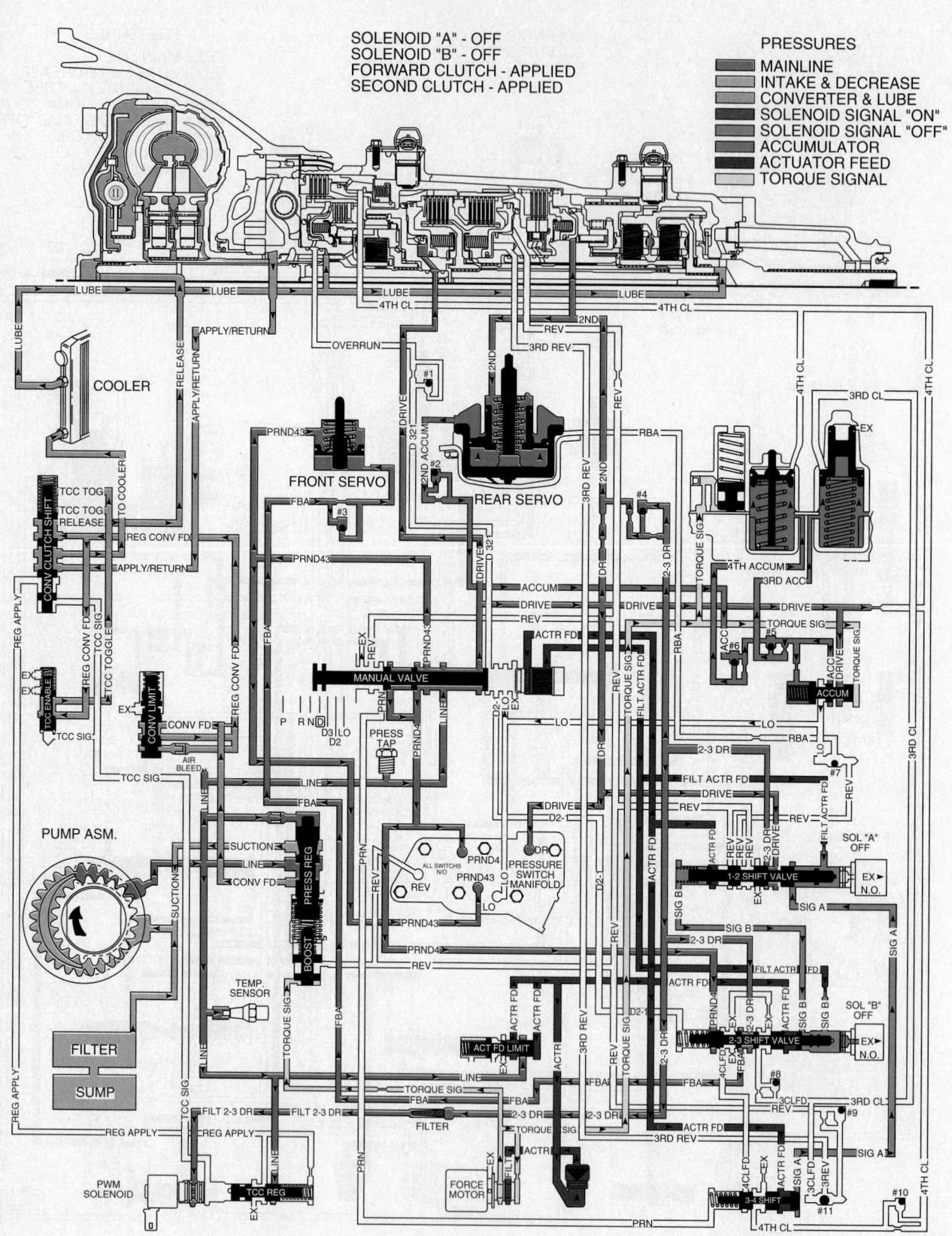

SOLENOID "A" - OFF
SOLENOID "B" - OFF
FORWARD CLUTCH - APPLIED
SECOND CLUTCH - APPLIED

PRESSURES
MAINLINE
INTAKE & DECREASE
CONVERTER & LUBE
SOLENOID SIGNAL "ON"
SOLENOID SIGNAL "OFF"
ACCUMULATOR
ACTUATOR FEED
TORQUE SIGNAL

Fig. 3: "OD" Range — 2nd Gear

Courtesy of General Motors Corp.

OIL CIRCUIT DIAGRAMS
Hydra-Matic 4L80-E (Cont.)

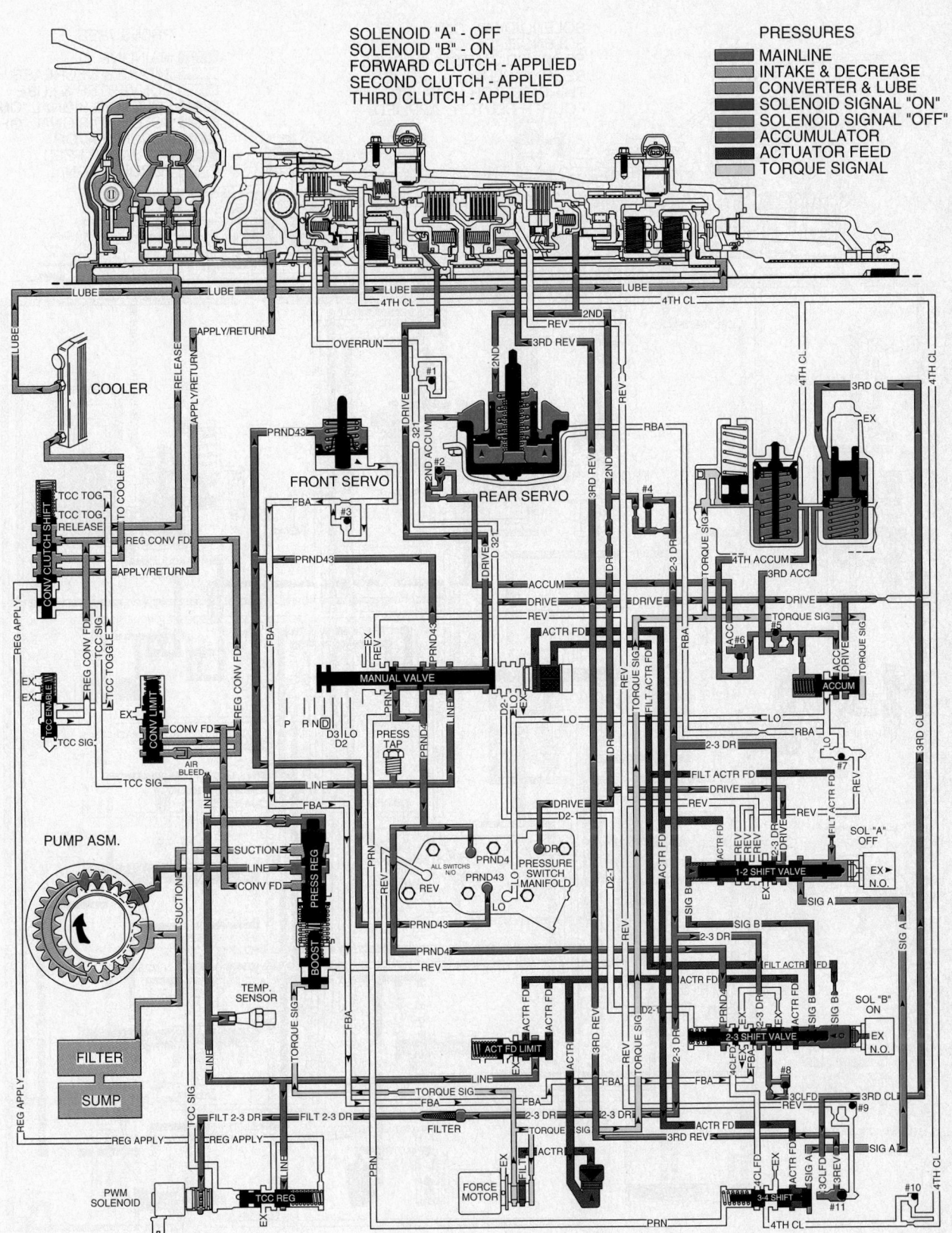

SOLENOID "A" - OFF
SOLENOID "B" - ON
FORWARD CLUTCH - APPLIED
SECOND CLUTCH - APPLIED
THIRD CLUTCH - APPLIED

PRESSURES
MAINLINE
INTAKE & DECREASE
CONVERTER & LUBE
SOLENOID SIGNAL "ON"
SOLENOID SIGNAL "OFF"
ACCUMULATOR
ACTUATOR FEED
TORQUE SIGNAL

Fig. 4: "OD" Range — 3rd Gear

Courtesy of General Motors Corp.

OIL CIRCUIT DIAGRAMS
Hydra-Matic 4L80-E (Cont.)

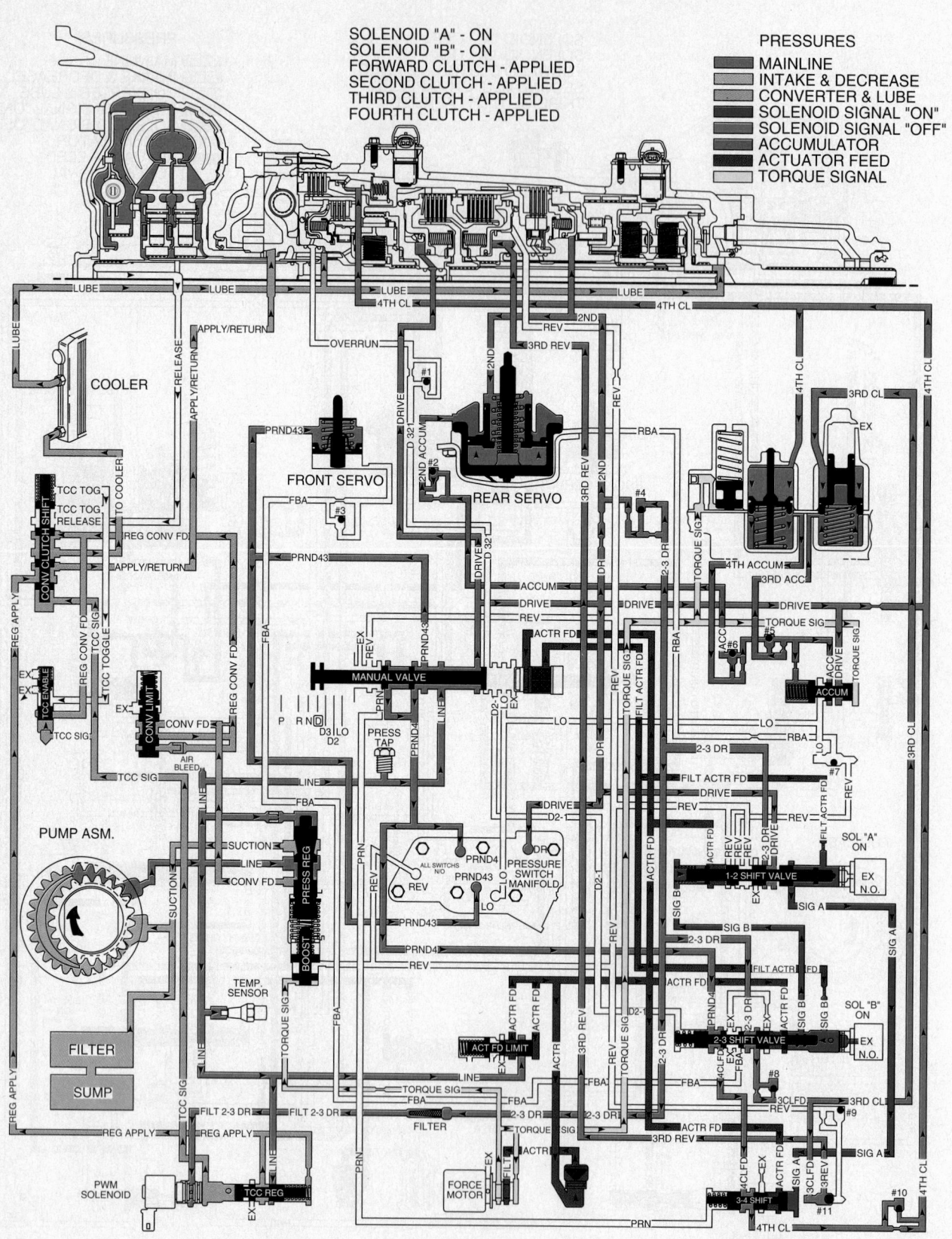

SOLENOID "A" - ON
SOLENOID "B" - ON
FORWARD CLUTCH - APPLIED
SECOND CLUTCH - APPLIED
THIRD CLUTCH - APPLIED
FOURTH CLUTCH - APPLIED

PRESSURES
MAINLINE
INTAKE & DECREASE
CONVERTER & LUBE
SOLENOID SIGNAL "ON"
SOLENOID SIGNAL "OFF"
ACCUMULATOR
ACTUATOR FEED
TORQUE SIGNAL

Fig. 5: "OD" Range — 4th Gear (TCC On)

Courtesy of General Motors Corp.

OIL CIRCUIT DIAGRAMS
Hydra-Matic 4L80-E (Cont.)

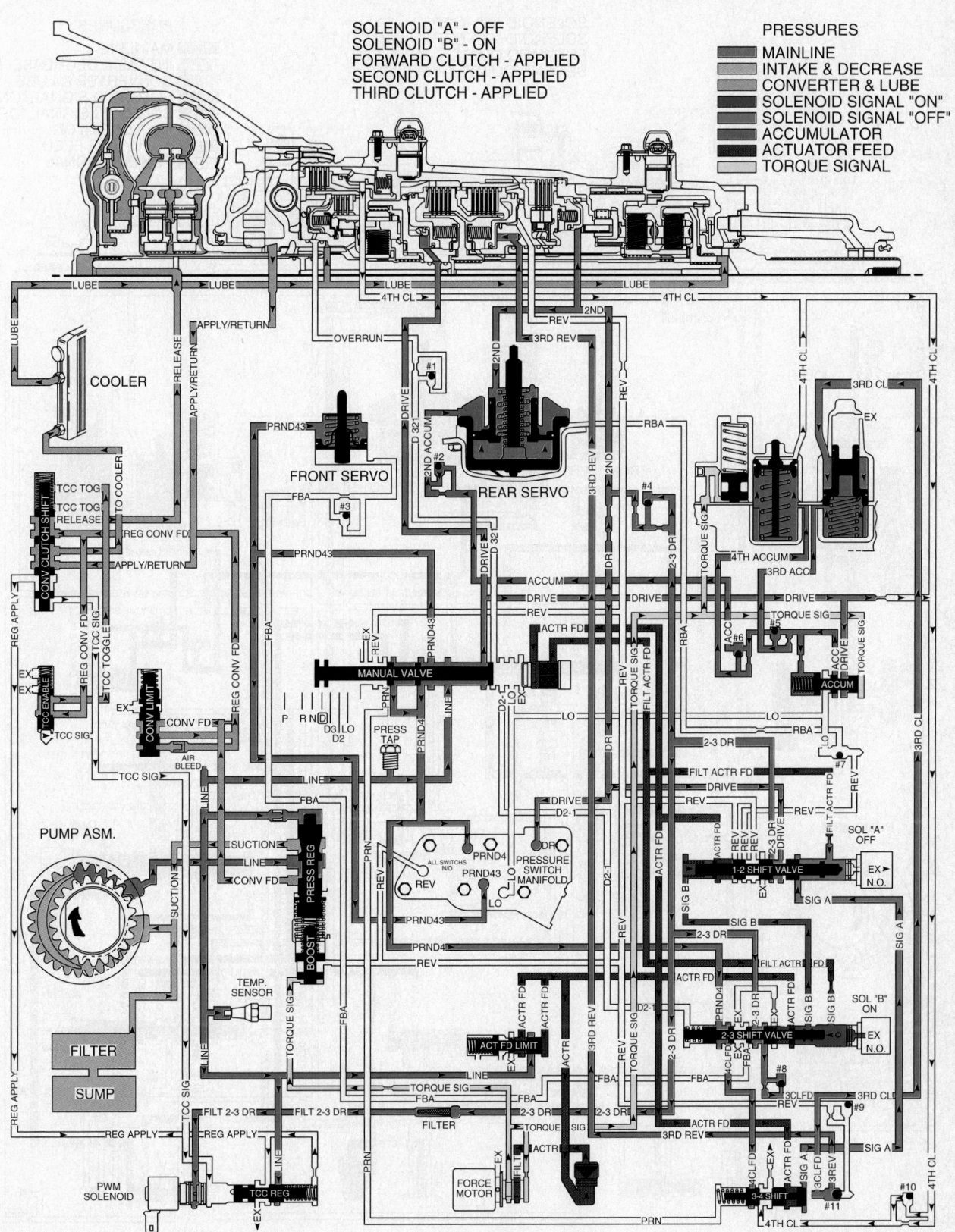

Fig. 6: 4-3 Downshift (Valves in 3rd Gear Position)

Courtesy of General Motors Corp.

OIL CIRCUIT DIAGRAMS
Hydra-Matic 4L80-E (Cont.)

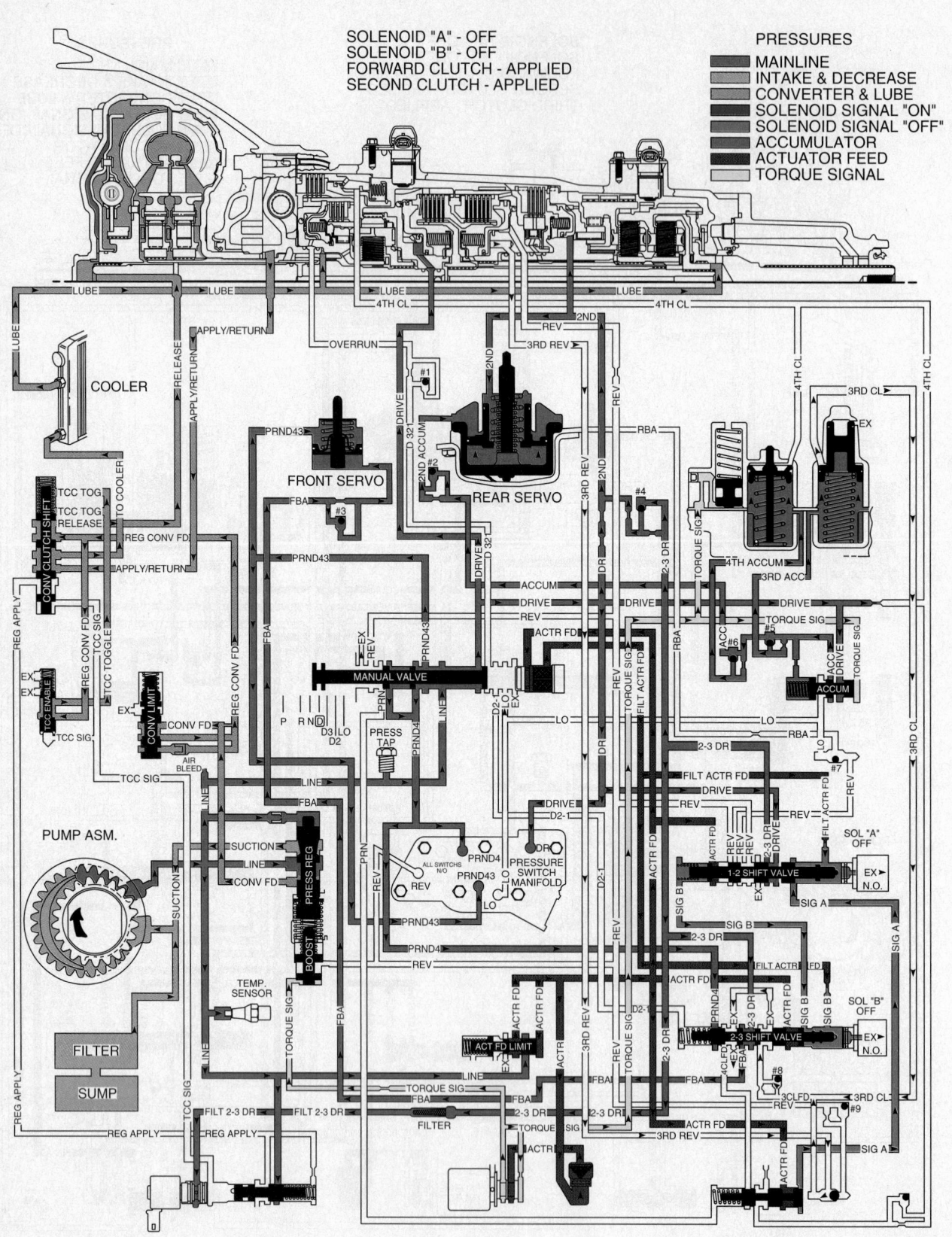

SOLENOID "A" - OFF
SOLENOID "B" - OFF
FORWARD CLUTCH - APPLIED
SECOND CLUTCH - APPLIED

PRESSURES
- MAINLINE
- INTAKE & DECREASE
- CONVERTER & LUBE
- SOLENOID SIGNAL "ON"
- SOLENOID SIGNAL "OFF"
- ACCUMULATOR
- ACTUATOR FEED
- TORQUE SIGNAL

Fig. 7: 3-2 Downshift (Valves in 2nd Gear Position)   Courtesy of General Motors Corp.

OIL CIRCUIT DIAGRAMS
Hydra-Matic 4L80-E (Cont.)

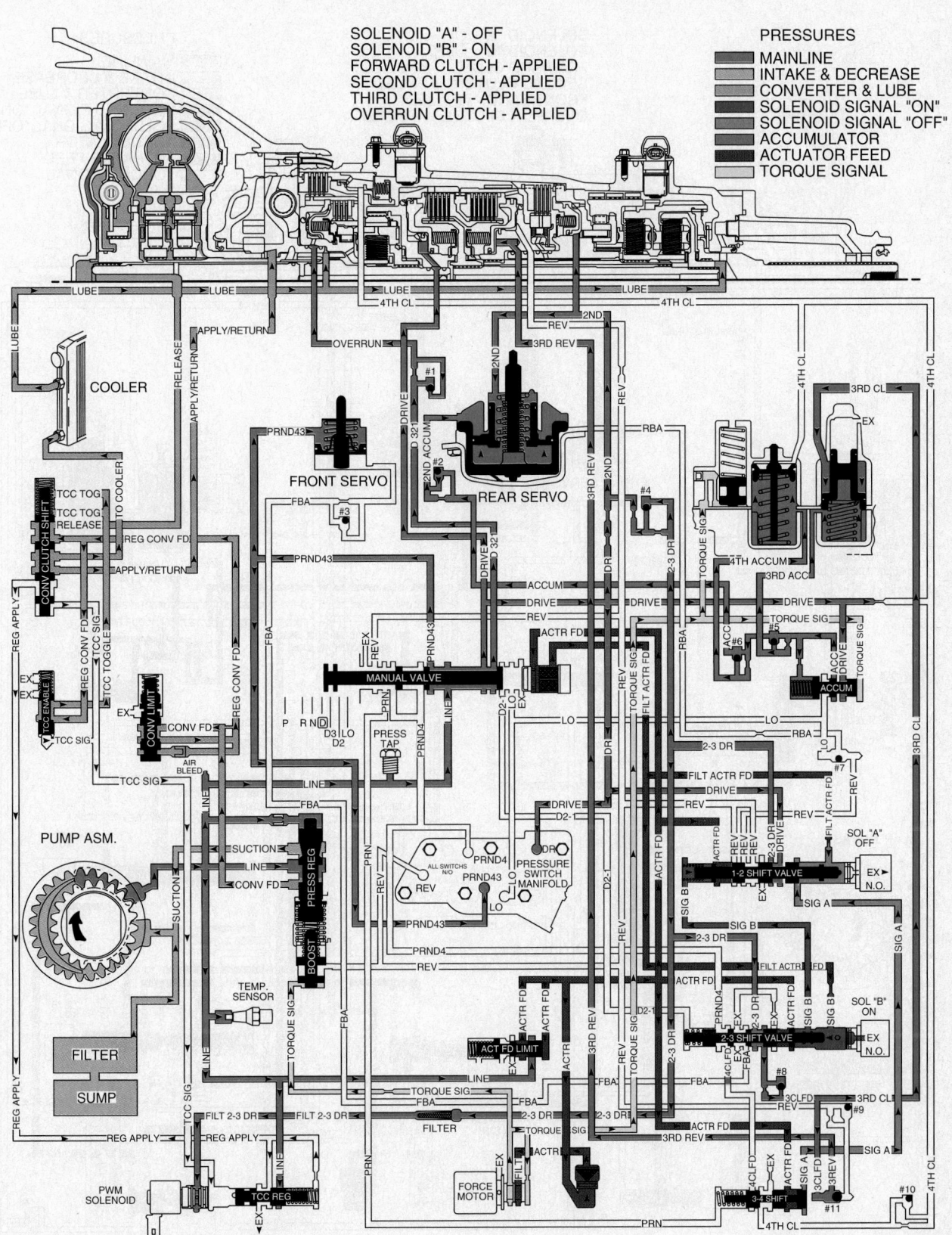

SOLENOID "A" - OFF
SOLENOID "B" - ON
FORWARD CLUTCH - APPLIED
SECOND CLUTCH - APPLIED
THIRD CLUTCH - APPLIED
OVERRUN CLUTCH - APPLIED

PRESSURES
MAINLINE
INTAKE & DECREASE
CONVERTER & LUBE
SOLENOID SIGNAL "ON"
SOLENOID SIGNAL "OFF"
ACCUMULATOR
ACTUATOR FEED
TORQUE SIGNAL

Fig. 8: "3" Range — 3rd Gear (Manual Select)

Courtesy of General Motors Corp.

OIL CIRCUIT DIAGRAMS
Hydra-Matic 4L80-E (Cont.)

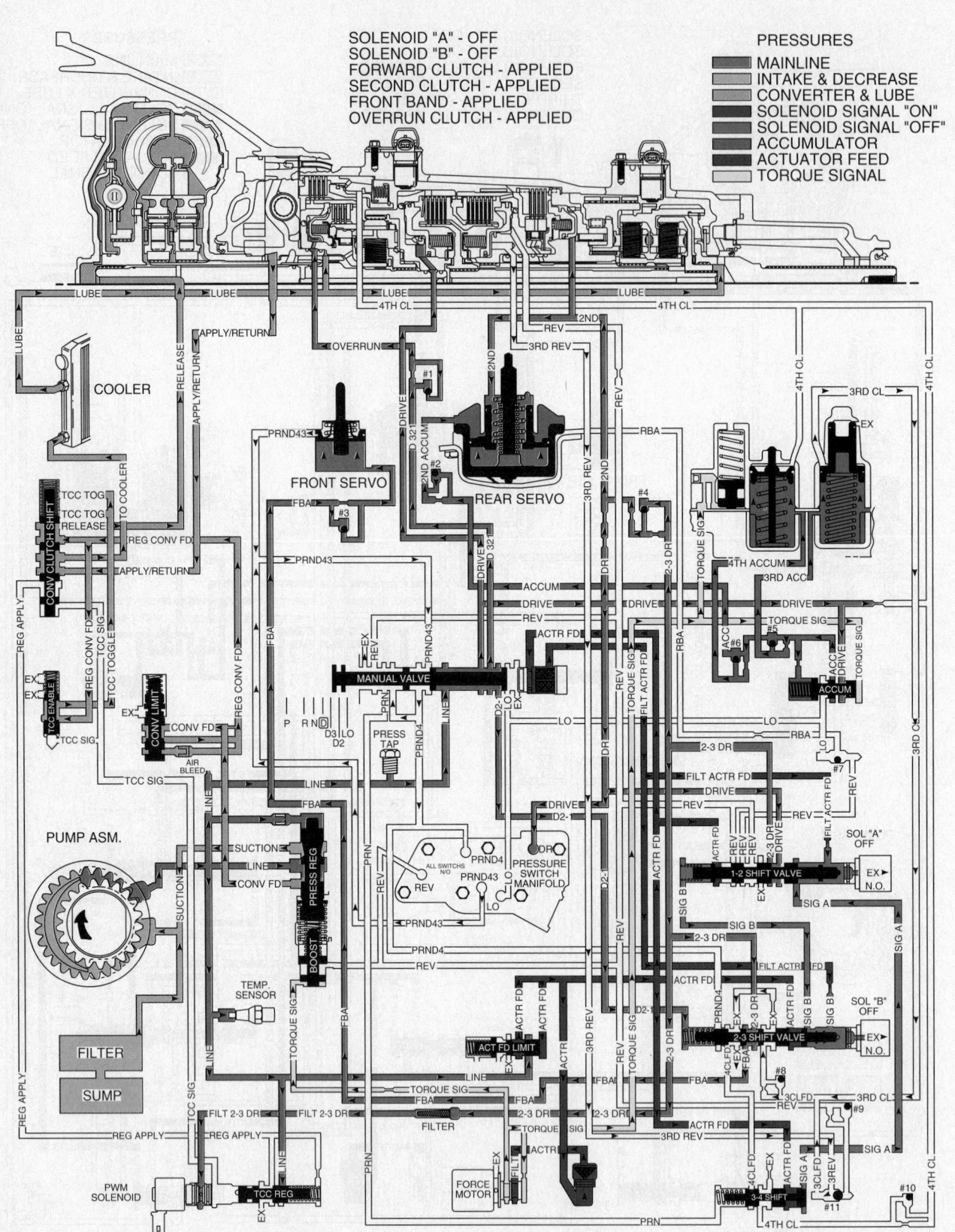

SOLENOID "A" - OFF
SOLENOID "B" - OFF
FORWARD CLUTCH - APPLIED
SECOND CLUTCH - APPLIED
FRONT BAND - APPLIED
OVERRUN CLUTCH - APPLIED

PRESSURES
- MAINLINE
- INTAKE & DECREASE
- CONVERTER & LUBE
- SOLENOID SIGNAL "ON"
- SOLENOID SIGNAL "OFF"
- ACCUMULATOR
- ACTUATOR FEED
- TORQUE SIGNAL

Fig. 9: "2" Range — 2nd Gear (Manual Select)

Courtesy of General Motors Corp.

OIL CIRCUIT DIAGRAMS
Hydra-Matic 4L80-E (Cont.)

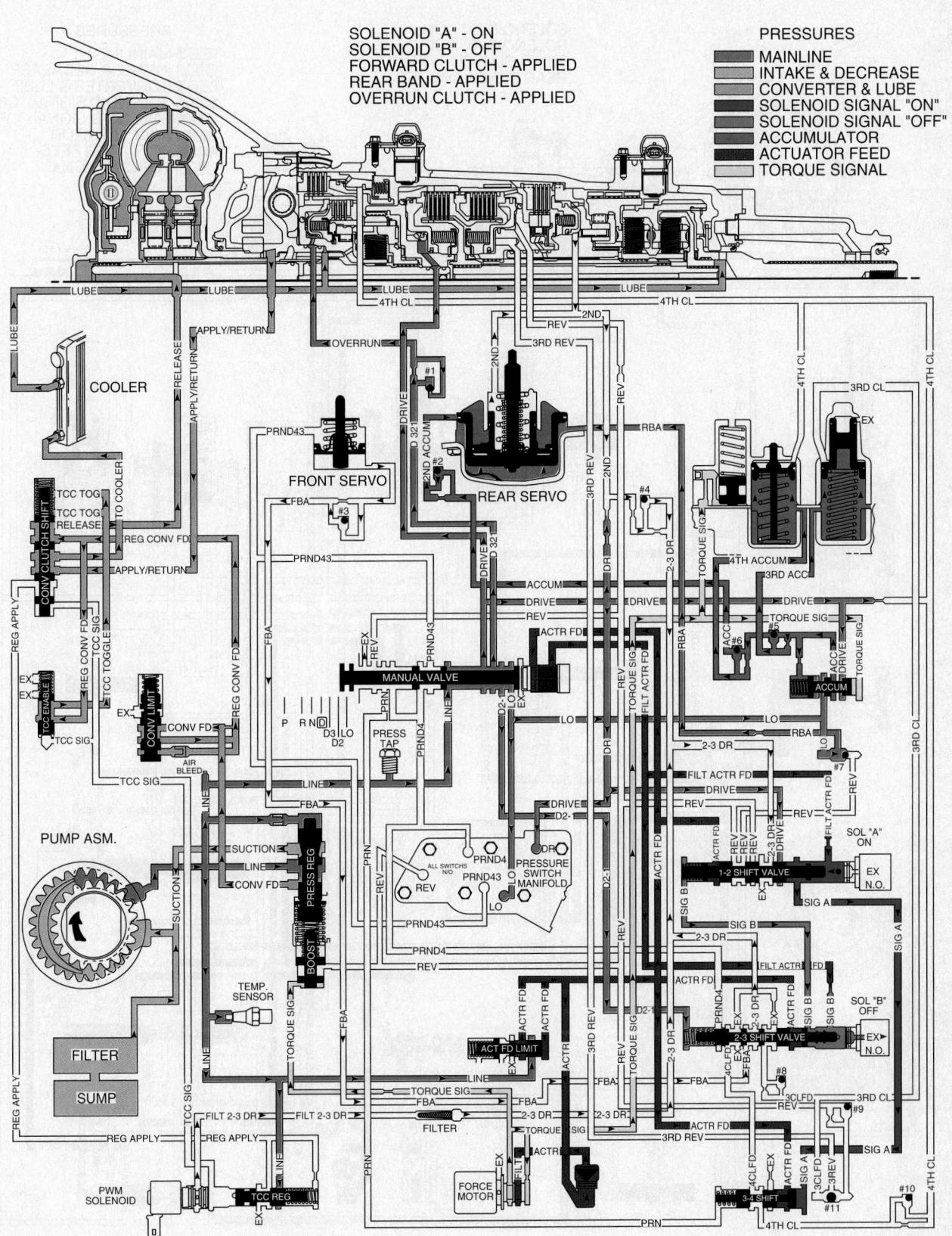

SOLENOID "A" - ON
SOLENOID "B" - OFF
FORWARD CLUTCH - APPLIED
REAR BAND - APPLIED
OVERRUN CLUTCH - APPLIED

PRESSURES
- MAINLINE
- INTAKE & DECREASE
- CONVERTER & LUBE
- SOLENOID SIGNAL "ON"
- SOLENOID SIGNAL "OFF"
- ACCUMULATOR
- ACTUATOR FEED
- TORQUE SIGNAL

Fig. 10: "1" Range — 1st Gear (Manual Select)

Courtesy of General Motors Corp.

OIL CIRCUIT DIAGRAMS
Hydra-Matic 4L80-E (Cont.)

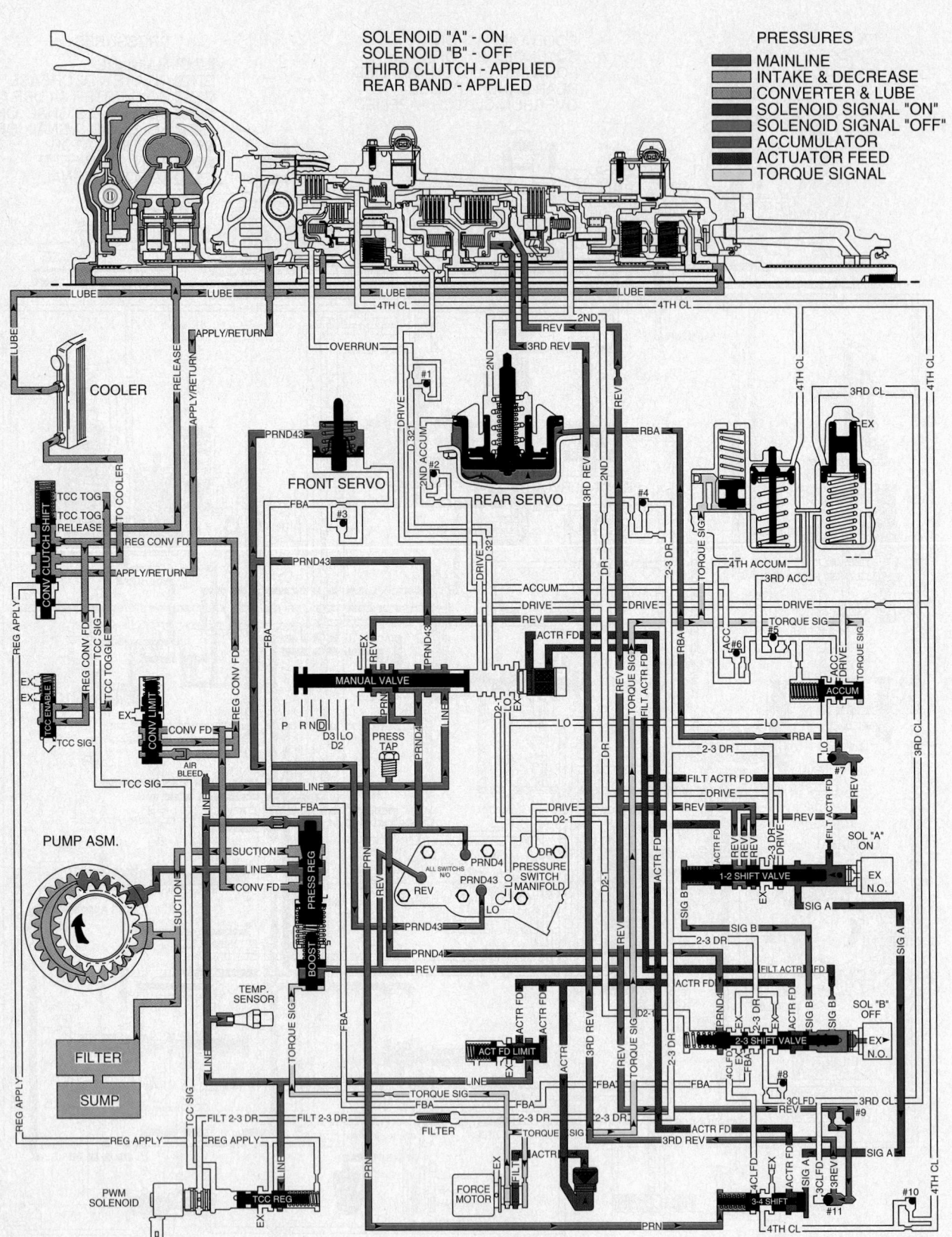

Fig. 11: "R" Range — Reverse

Courtesy of General Motors Corp.

OIL CIRCUIT DIAGRAMS
Hydra-Matic 4T80-E

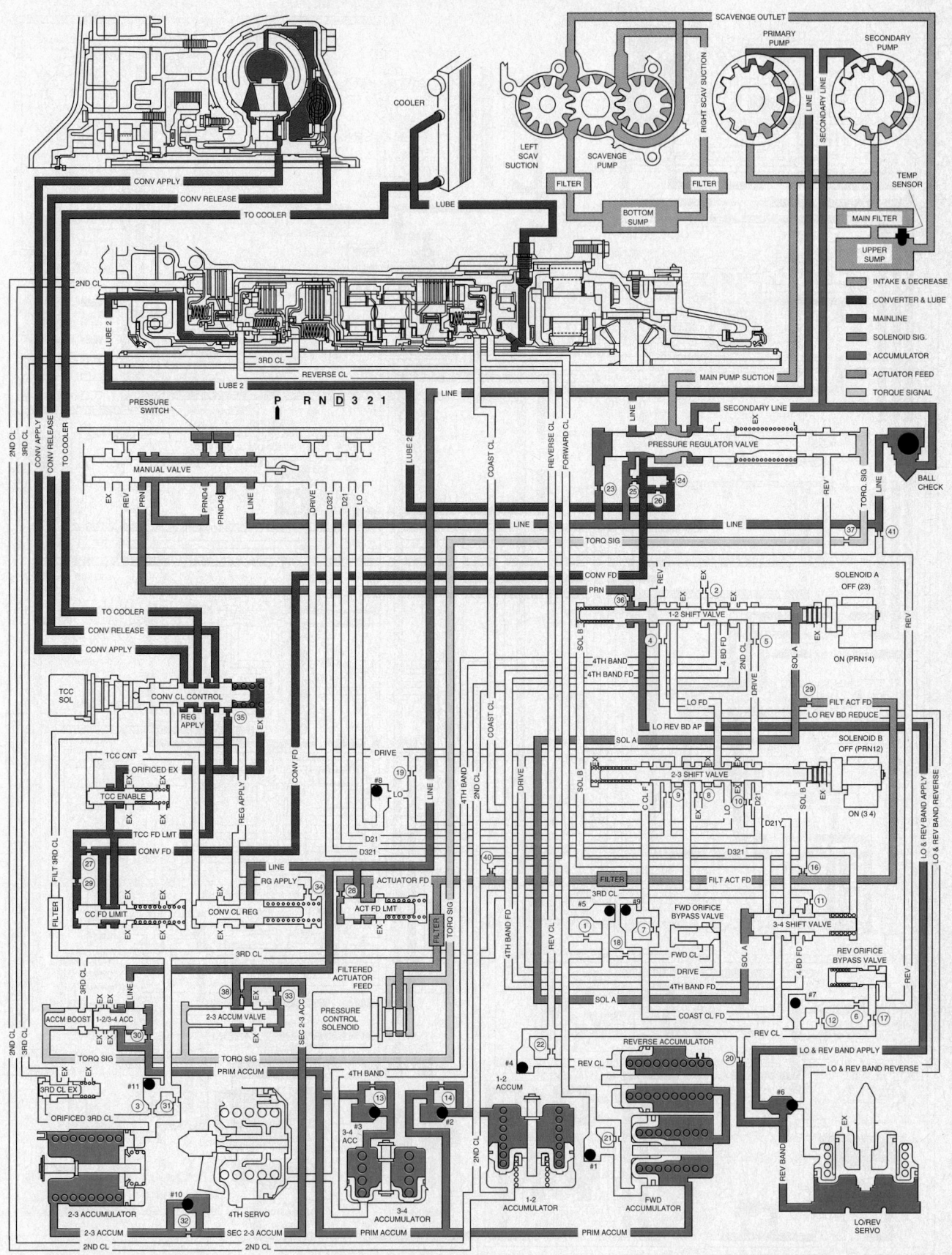

Fig. 1: "P" Range — Park

Courtesy of General Motors Corp.

OIL CIRCUIT DIAGRAMS
Hydra-Matic 4T80-E (Cont.)

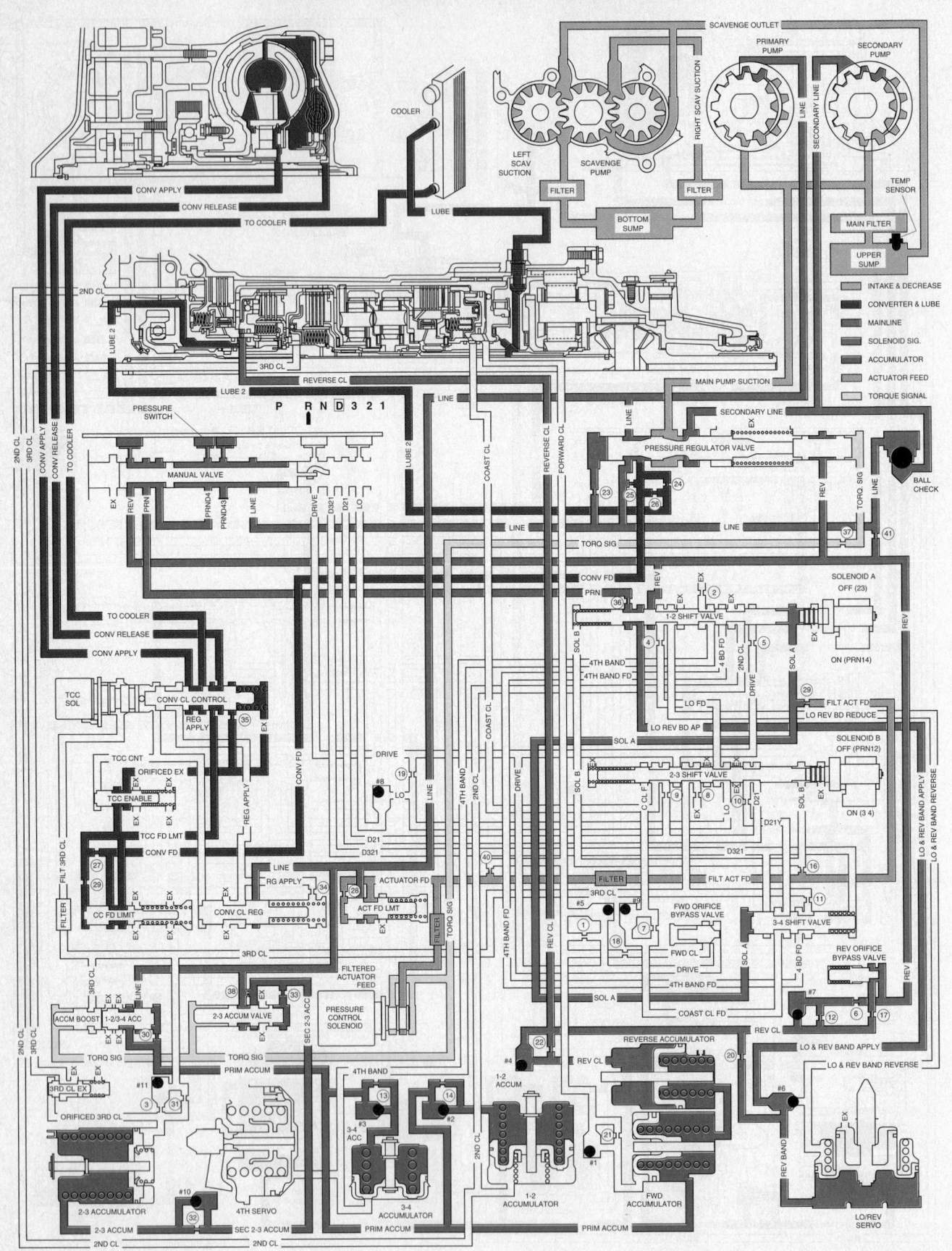

Fig. 2: "R" Range — Reverse

Hydra-Matic 4T80-E (Cont.)

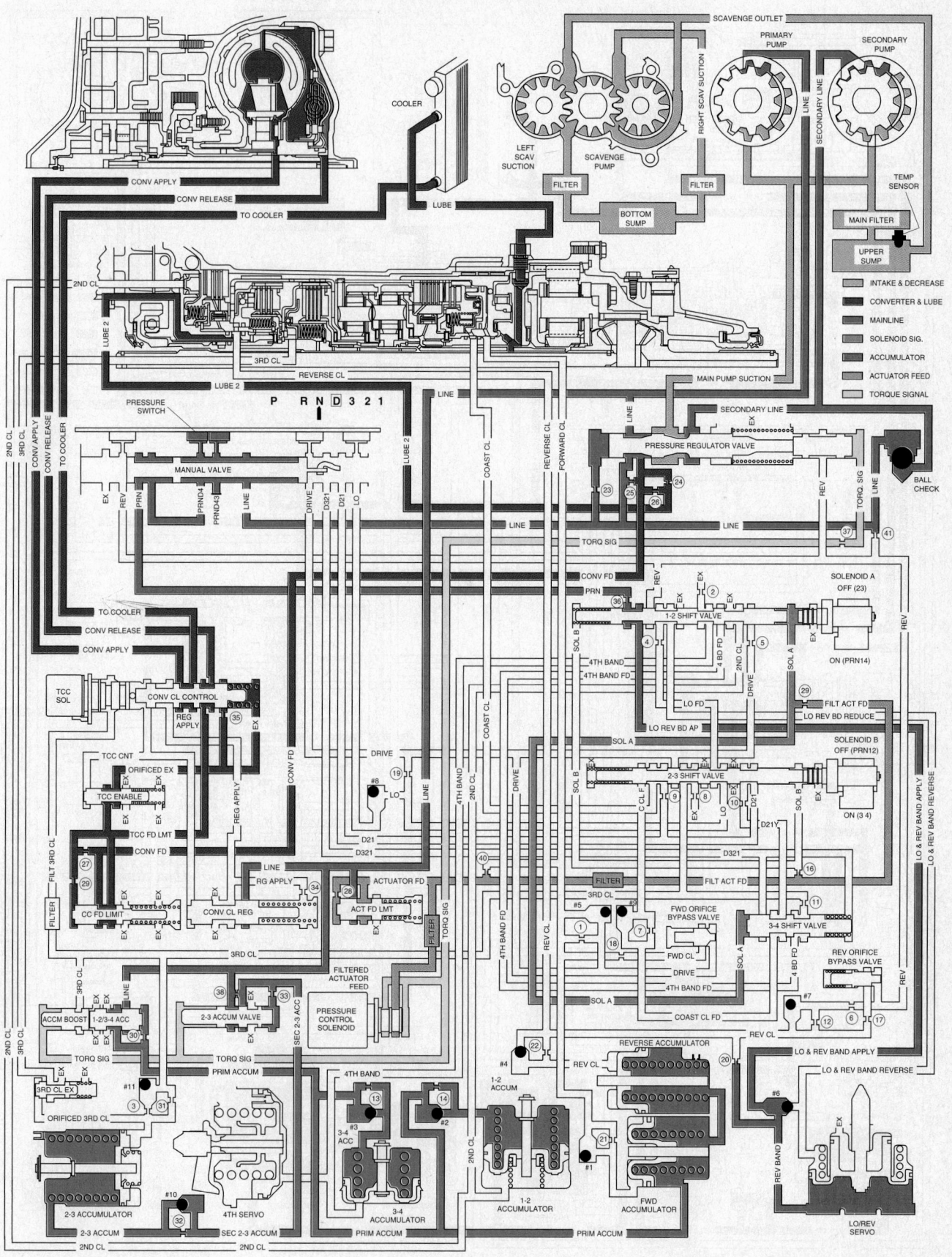

Fig. 3: "N" Range — Neutral

Courtesy of General Motors Corp.

OIL CIRCUIT DIAGRAMS
Hydra-Matic 4T80-E (Cont.)

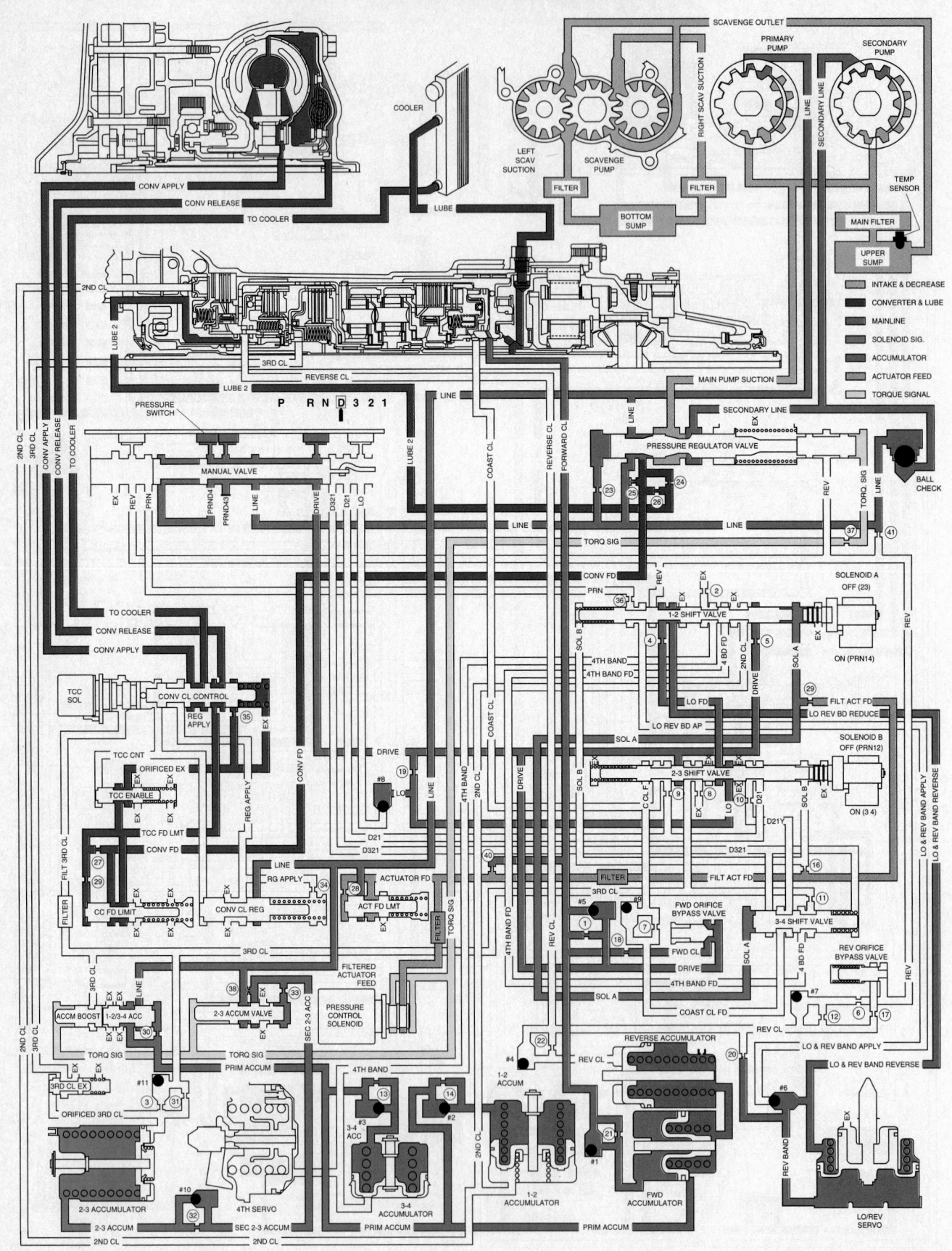

Fig. 4: "OD" Range — 1st Gear

Courtesy of General Motors Corp.

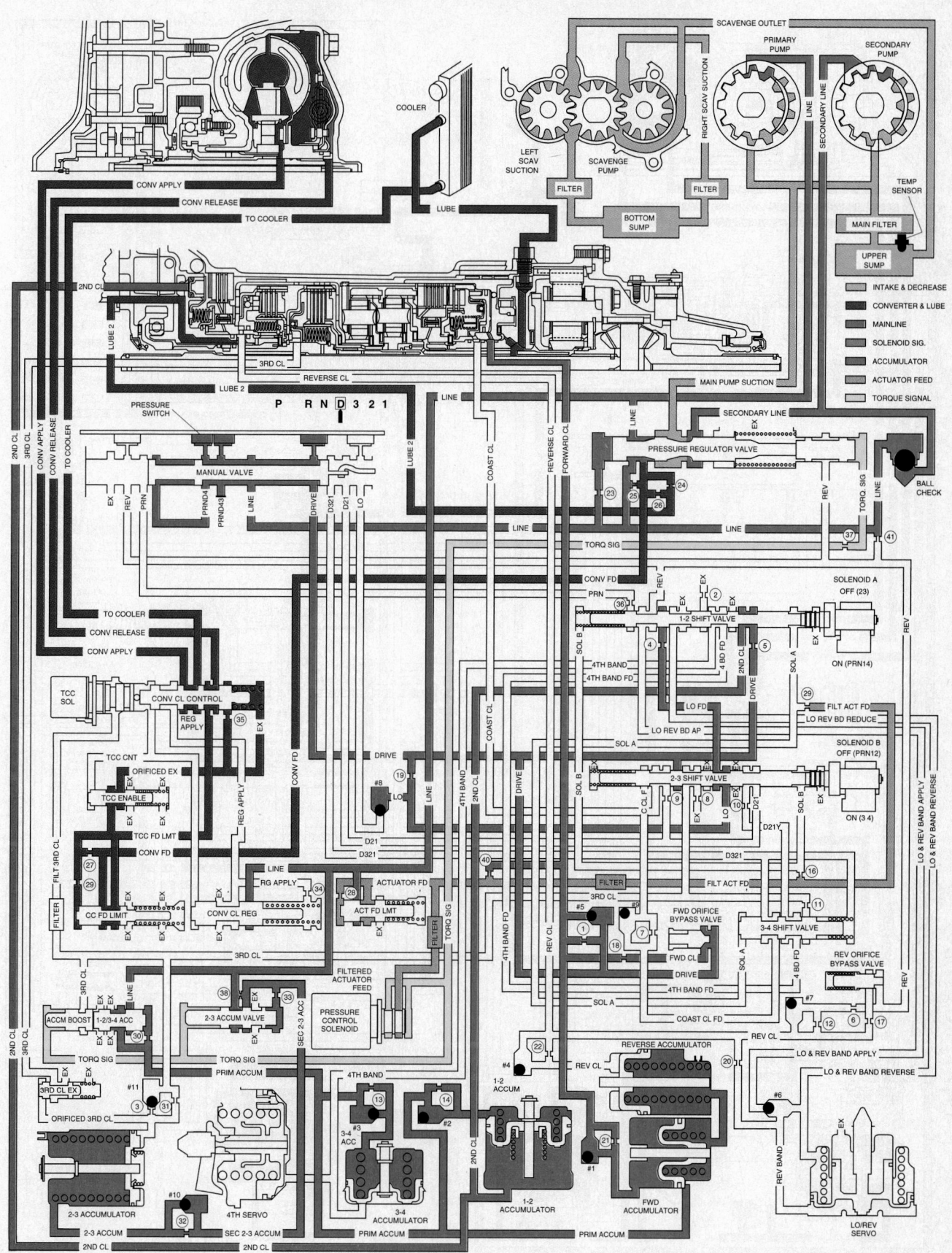

Fig. 5: "OD" Range — 2nd Gear

Courtesy of General Motors Corp.

OIL CIRCUIT DIAGRAMS
Hydra-Matic 4T80-E (Cont.)

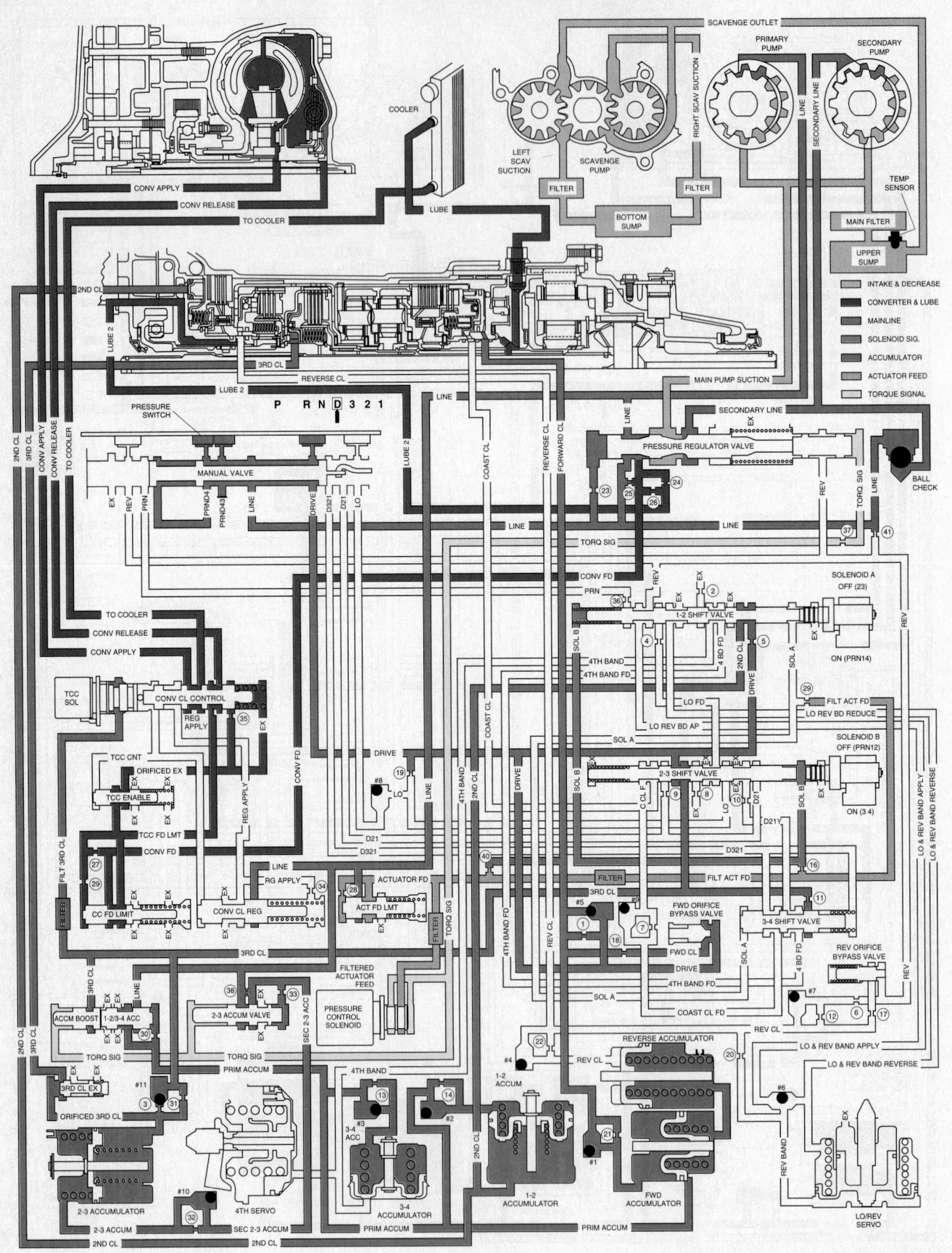

Fig. 6: "OD" Range — 3rd Gear

Courtesy of General Motors Corp.

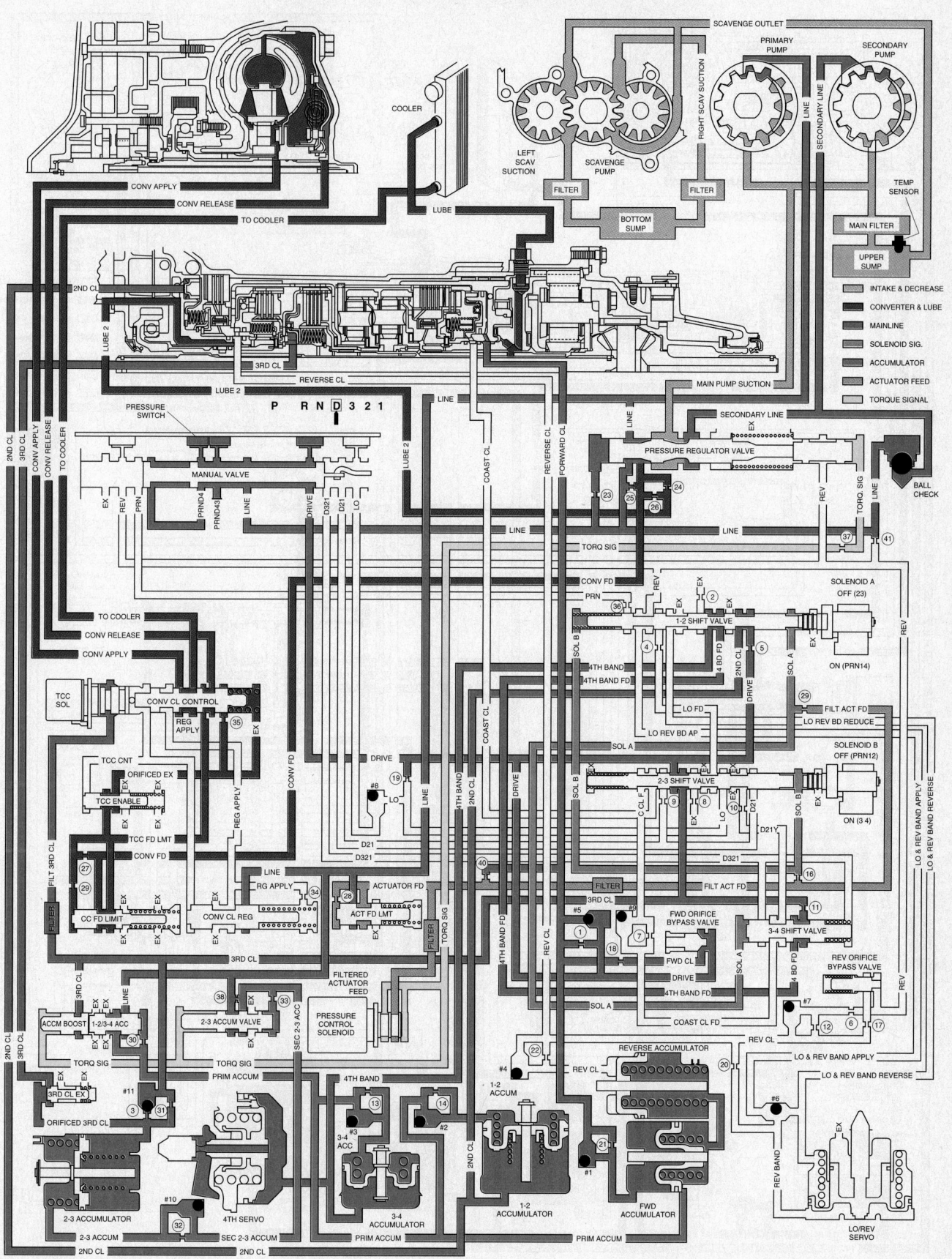

Fig. 7: "OD" Range — 4h Gear (TCC Off)

Courtesy of General Motors Corp.

OIL CIRCUIT DIAGRAMS
Hydra-Matic 4T80-E (Cont.)

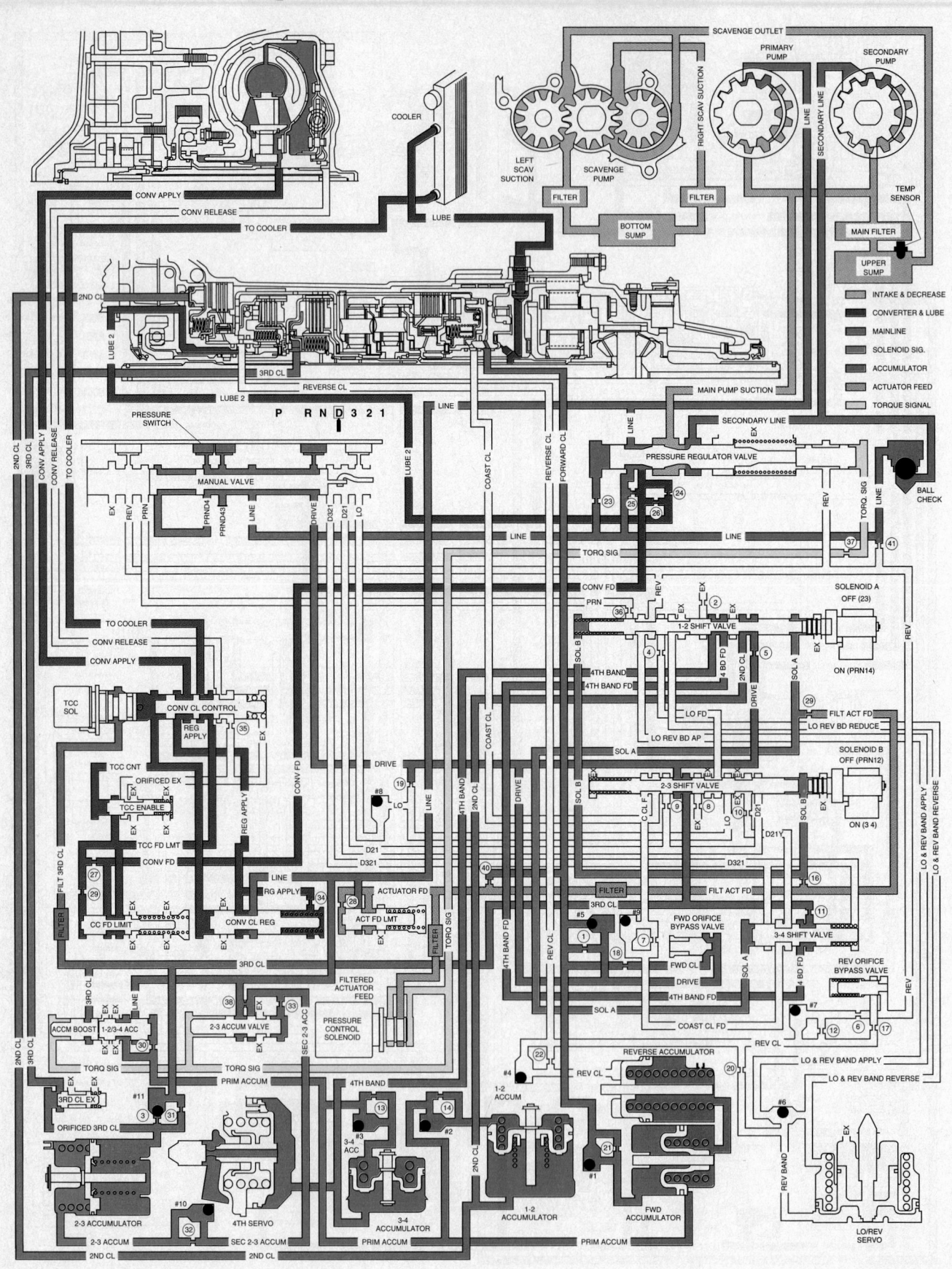

Fig. 8: "OD" Range — 4h Gear (TCC On)

Courtesy of General Motors Corp.

OIL CIRCUIT DIAGRAMS
Hydra-Matic 4T80-E (Cont.)

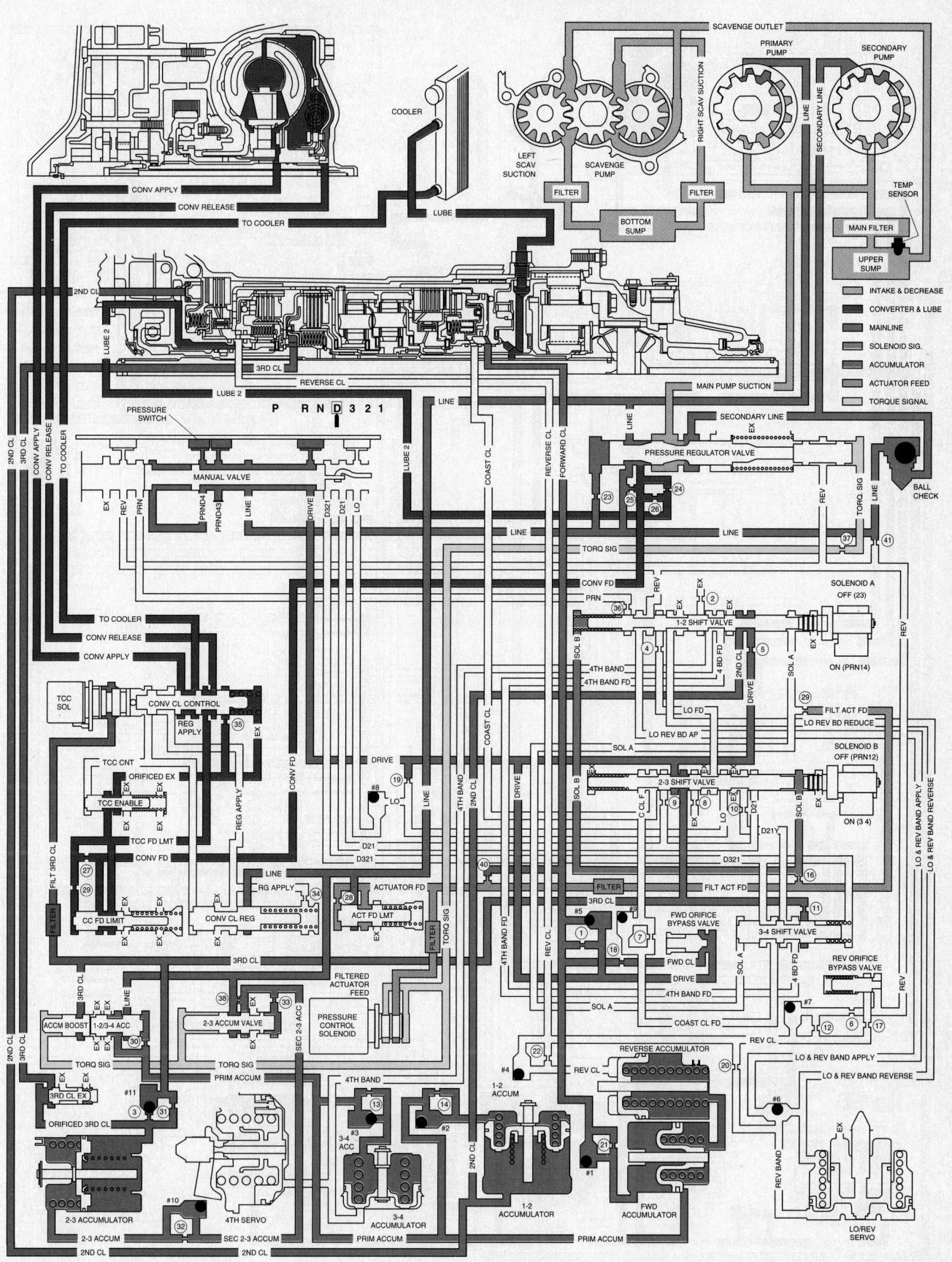

Fig. 9: "OD" Range — 4-3 Downshift

Courtesy of General Motors Corp.

OIL CIRCUIT DIAGRAMS
Hydra-Matic 4T80-E (Cont.)

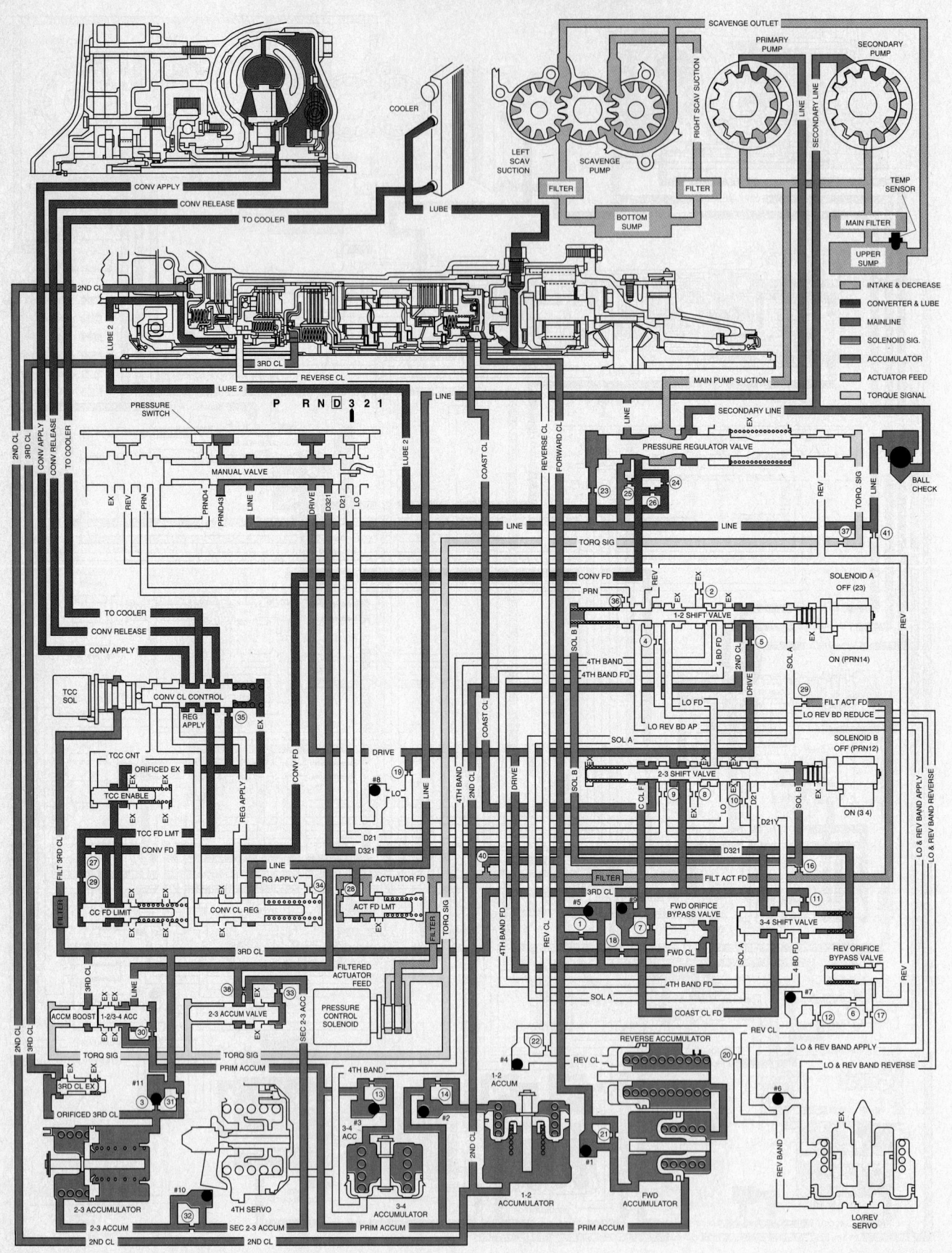

Fig. 10: "3" Range — 3rd Gear (Manual Select)

Courtesy of General Motors Corp.

OIL CIRCUIT DIAGRAMS
Hydra-Matic 4T80-E (Cont.)

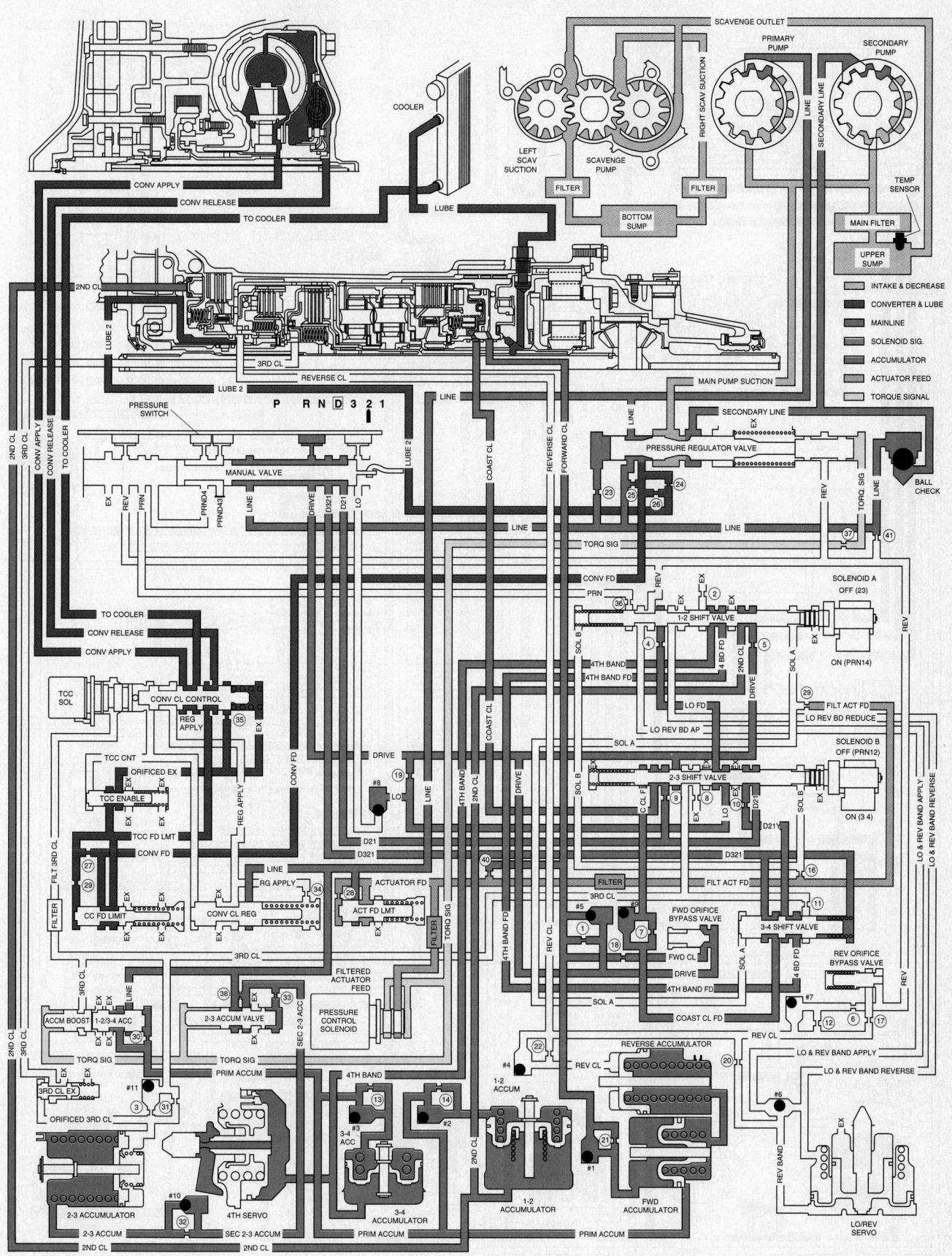

Fig. 11: "2" Range — 2nd Gear (Manual Select)

Courtesy of General Motors Corp.

OIL CIRCUIT DIAGRAMS
Hydra-Matic 4T80-E (Cont.)

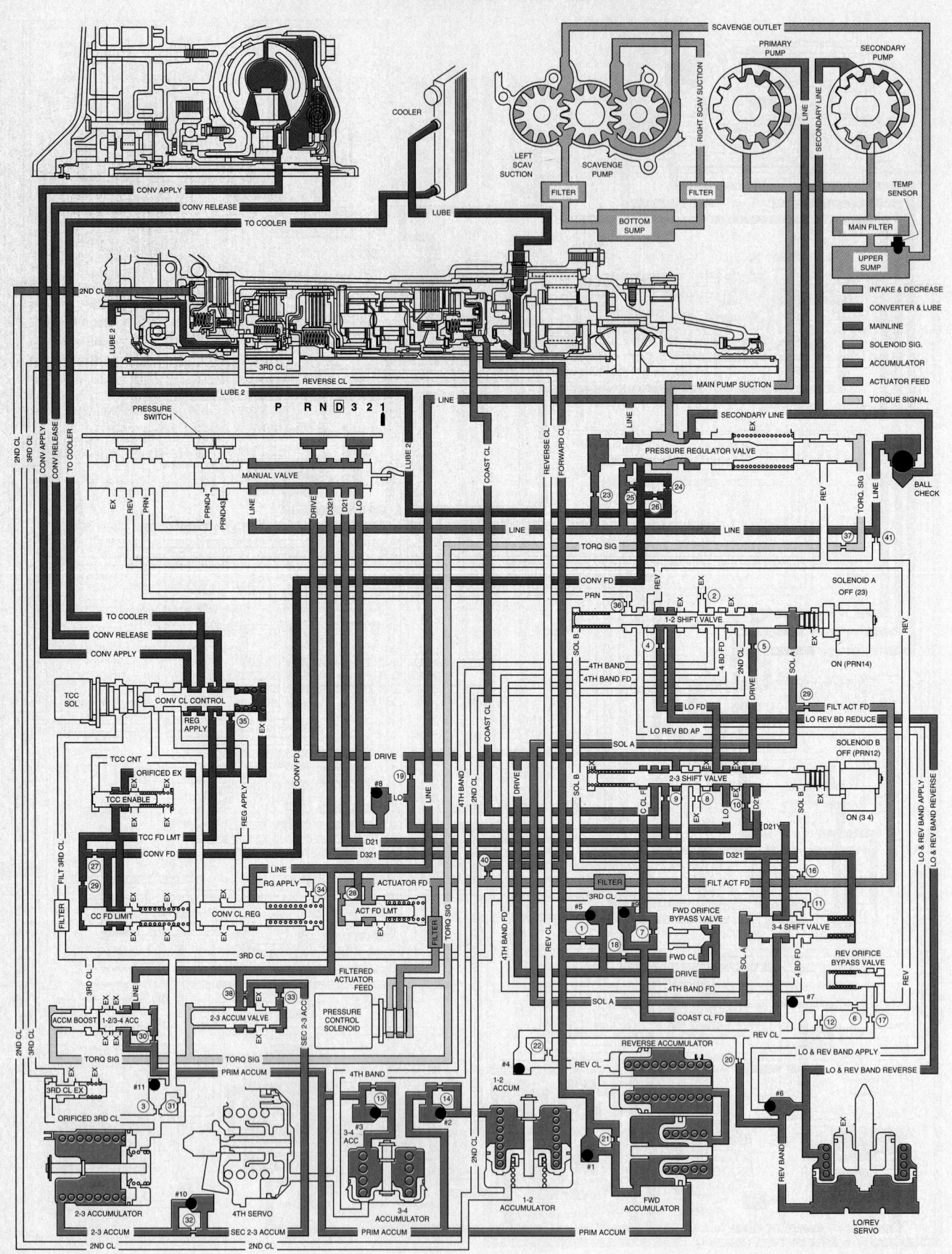

Fig. 12: "1" Range — 1st Gear (Manual Select)

Courtesy of General Motors Corp.

OIL CIRCUIT DIAGRAMS
Saturn

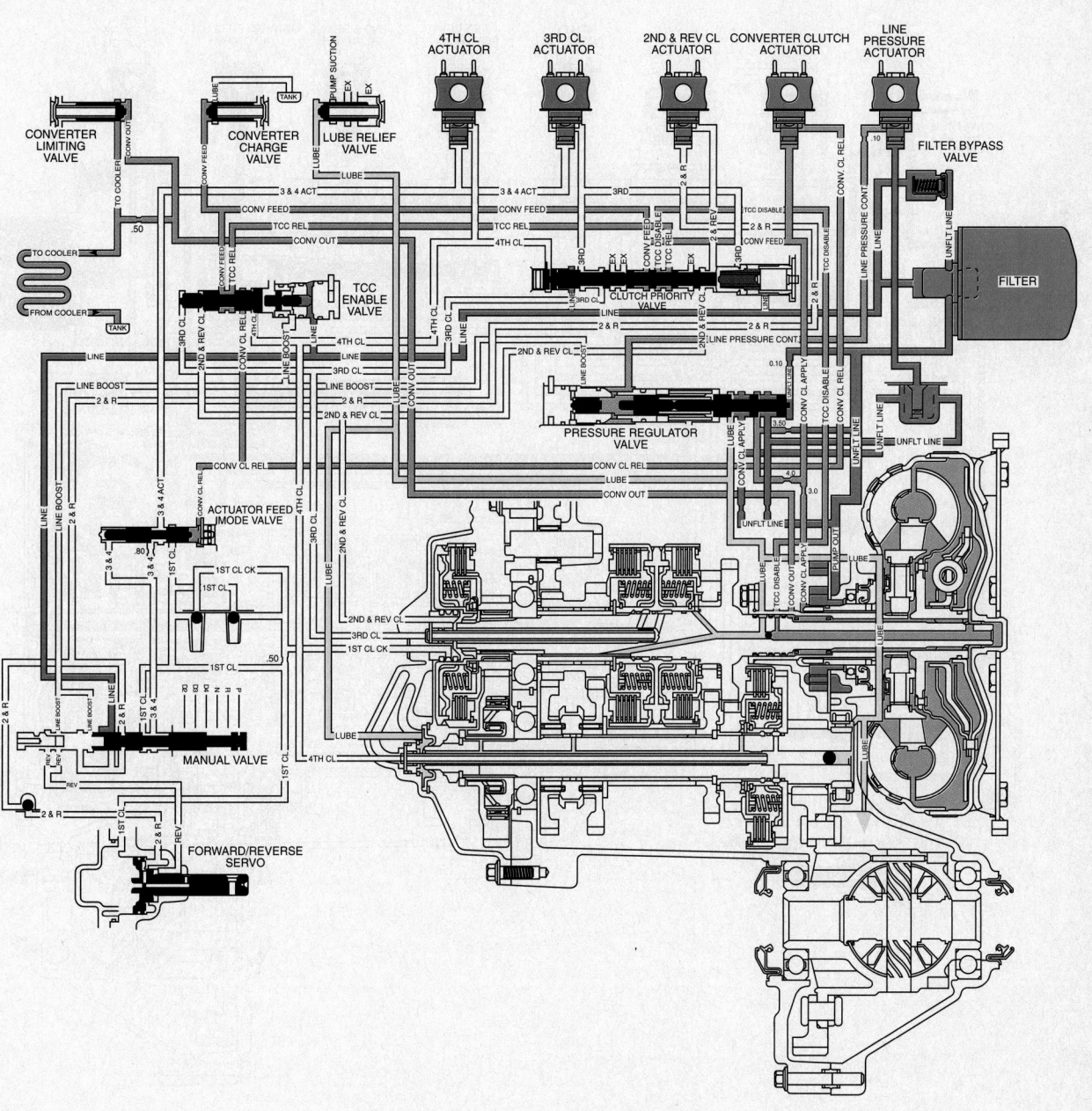

PRESSURES
- MAINLINE PRESSURE
- MODULATOR PRESSURE
- GOVERNOR PRESSURE
- DETENT REGULATED PRESSURE
- 1-2 ACCUMULATOR PRESSURE
- PUMP SUCTION
- CONVERTER OR LUBE

Fig. 1: "P" Range — Park

Courtesy of General Motors Corp.

OIL CIRCUIT DIAGRAMS
Saturn (Cont.)

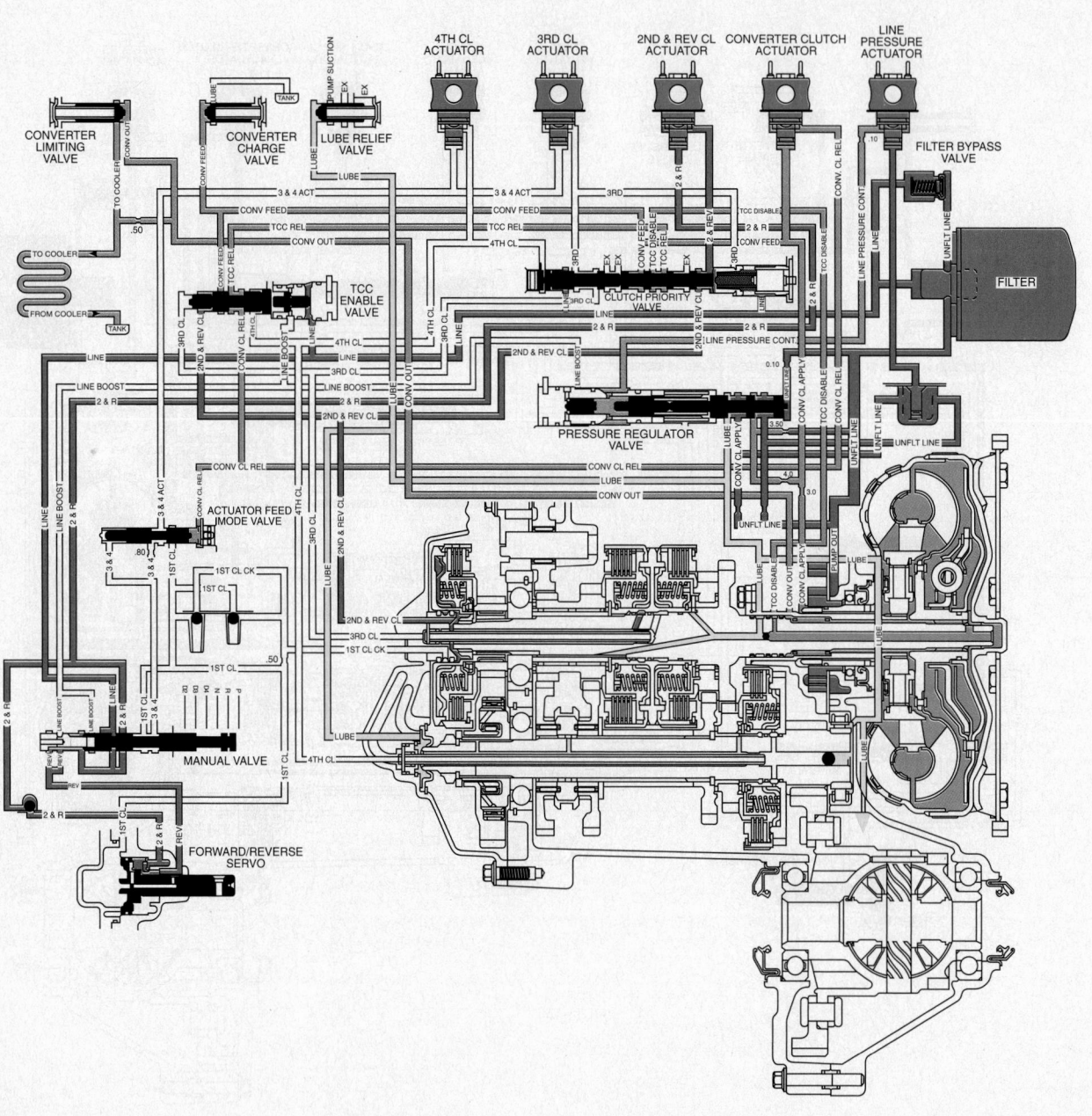

PRESSURES

	MAINLINE PRESSURE
	MODULATOR PRESSURE
	GOVERNOR PRESSURE
	DETENT REGULATED PRESSURE
	1-2 ACCUMULATOR PRESSURE
	PUMP SUCTION
	CONVERTER OR LUBE

Fig. 2: "R" Range — Reverse

Courtesy of General Motors Corp.

OIL CIRCUIT DIAGRAMS
Saturn (Cont.)

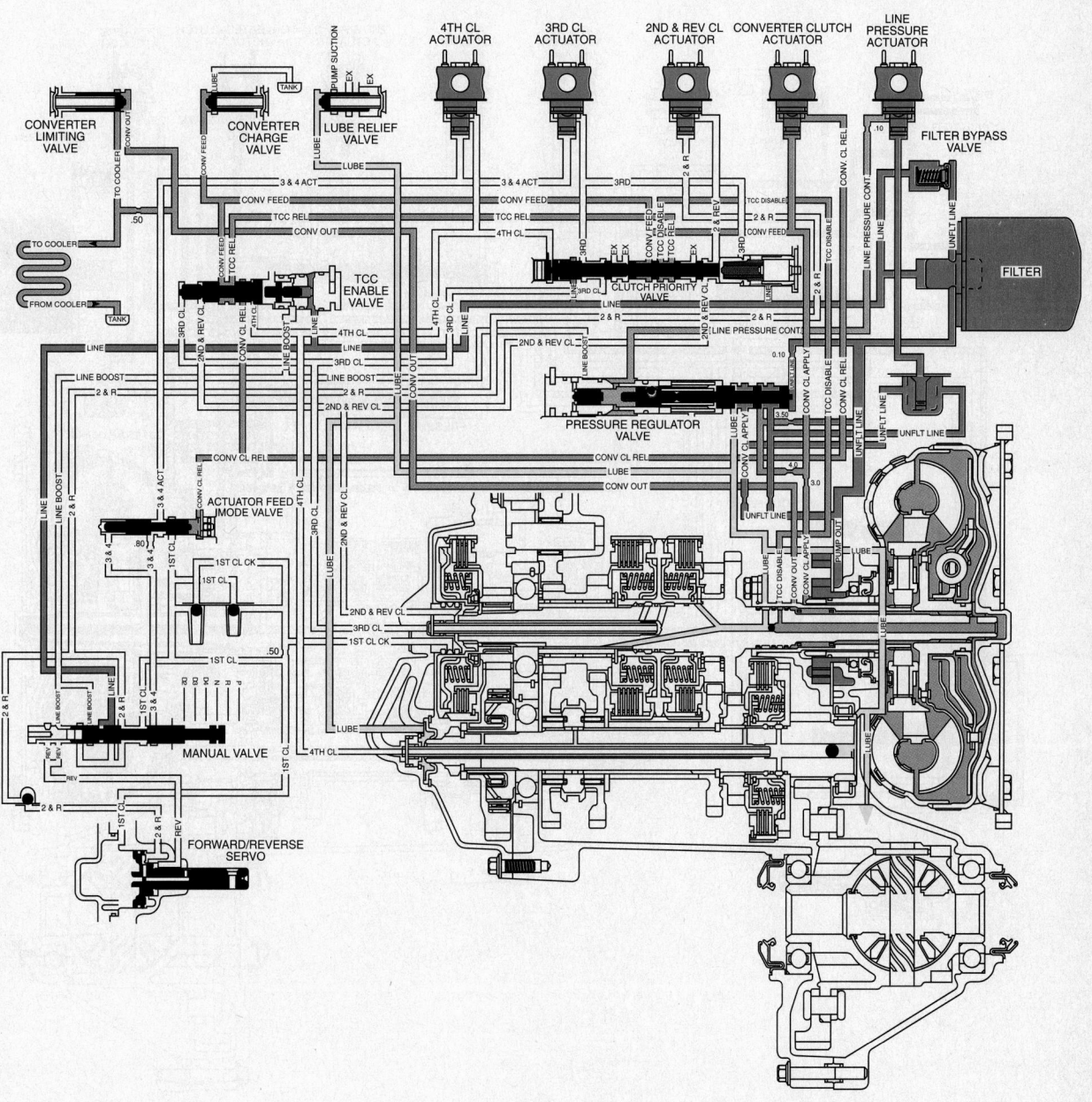

PRESSURES

■	MAINLINE PRESSURE
■	MODULATOR PRESSURE
■	GOVERNOR PRESSURE
■	DETENT REGULATED PRESSURE
■	1-2 ACCUMULATOR PRESSURE
□	PUMP SUCTION
■	CONVERTER OR LUBE

Fig. 3: "N" Range — Neutral

Courtesy of General Motors Corp.

OIL CIRCUIT DIAGRAMS
Saturn (Cont.)

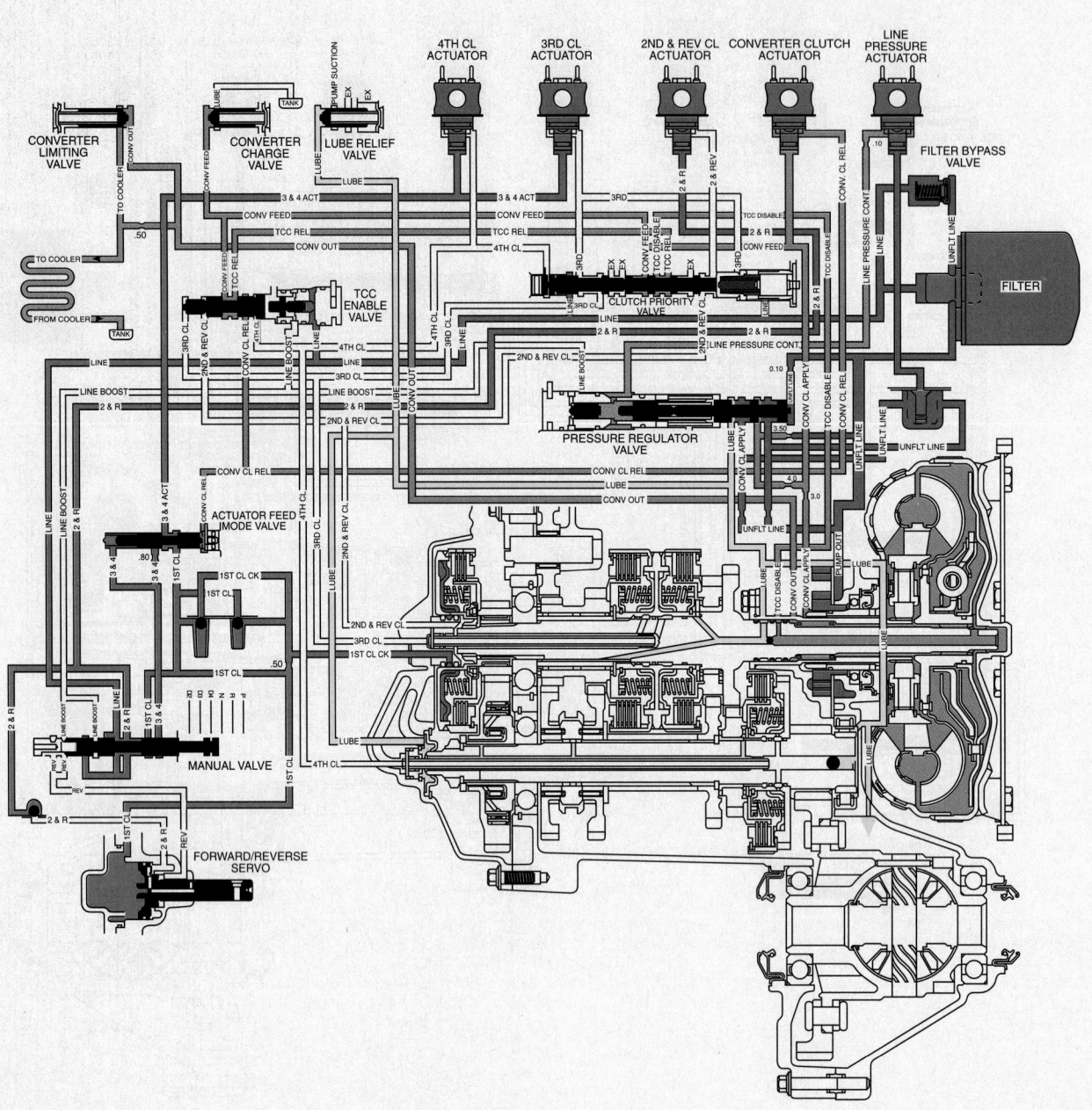

PRESSURES
- MAINLINE PRESSURE
- MODULATOR PRESSURE
- GOVERNOR PRESSURE
- DETENT REGULATED PRESSURE
- 1-2 ACCUMULATOR PRESSURE
- PUMP SUCTION
- CONVERTER OR LUBE

Fig. 4: "D3" or "D4" Range — 1st Gear

Courtesy of General Motors Corp.

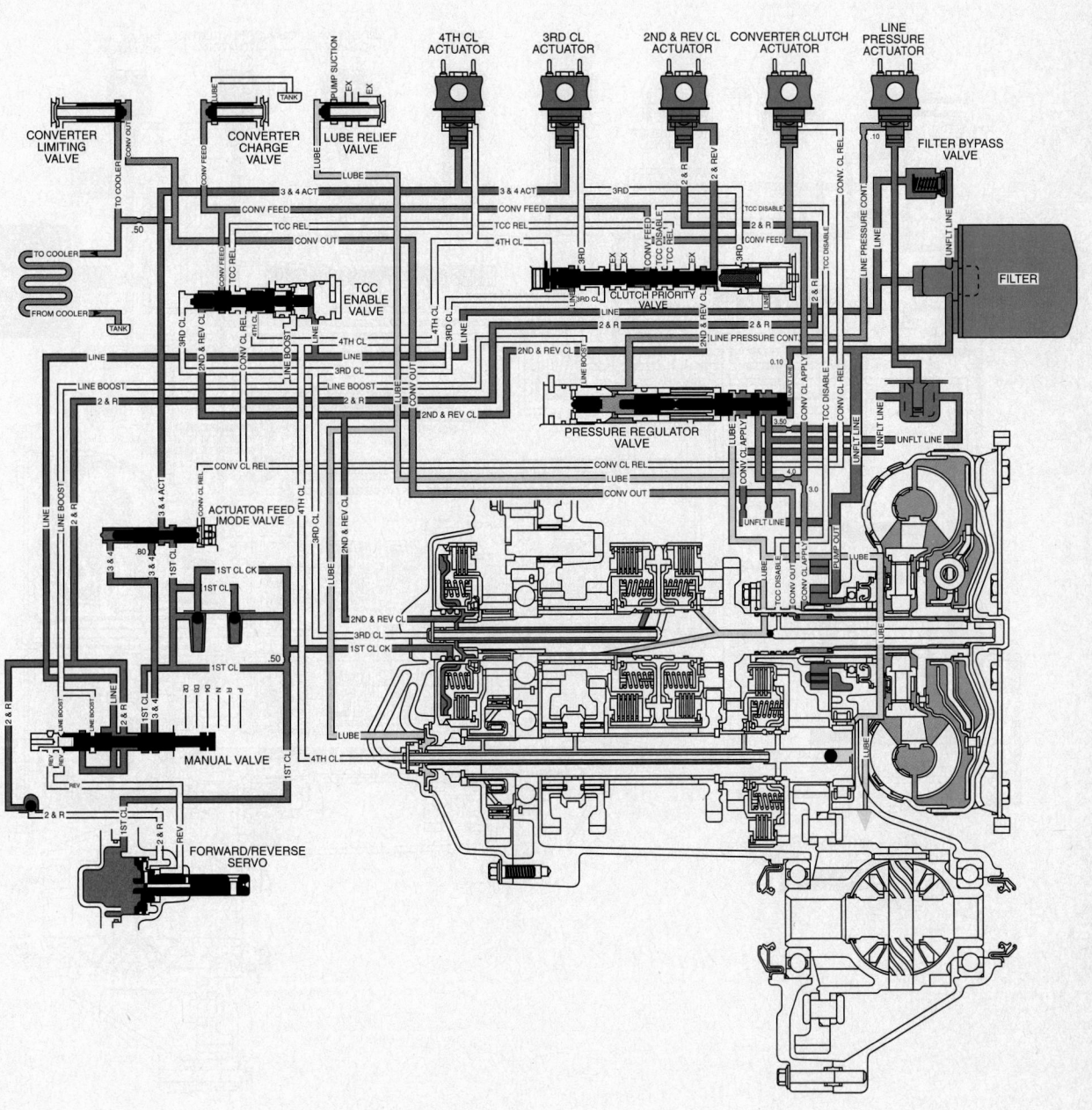

Fig. 5: "D3" or "D4" Range — 2nd Gear (TCC On)

Courtesy of General Motors Corp.

OIL CIRCUIT DIAGRAMS
Saturn (Cont.)

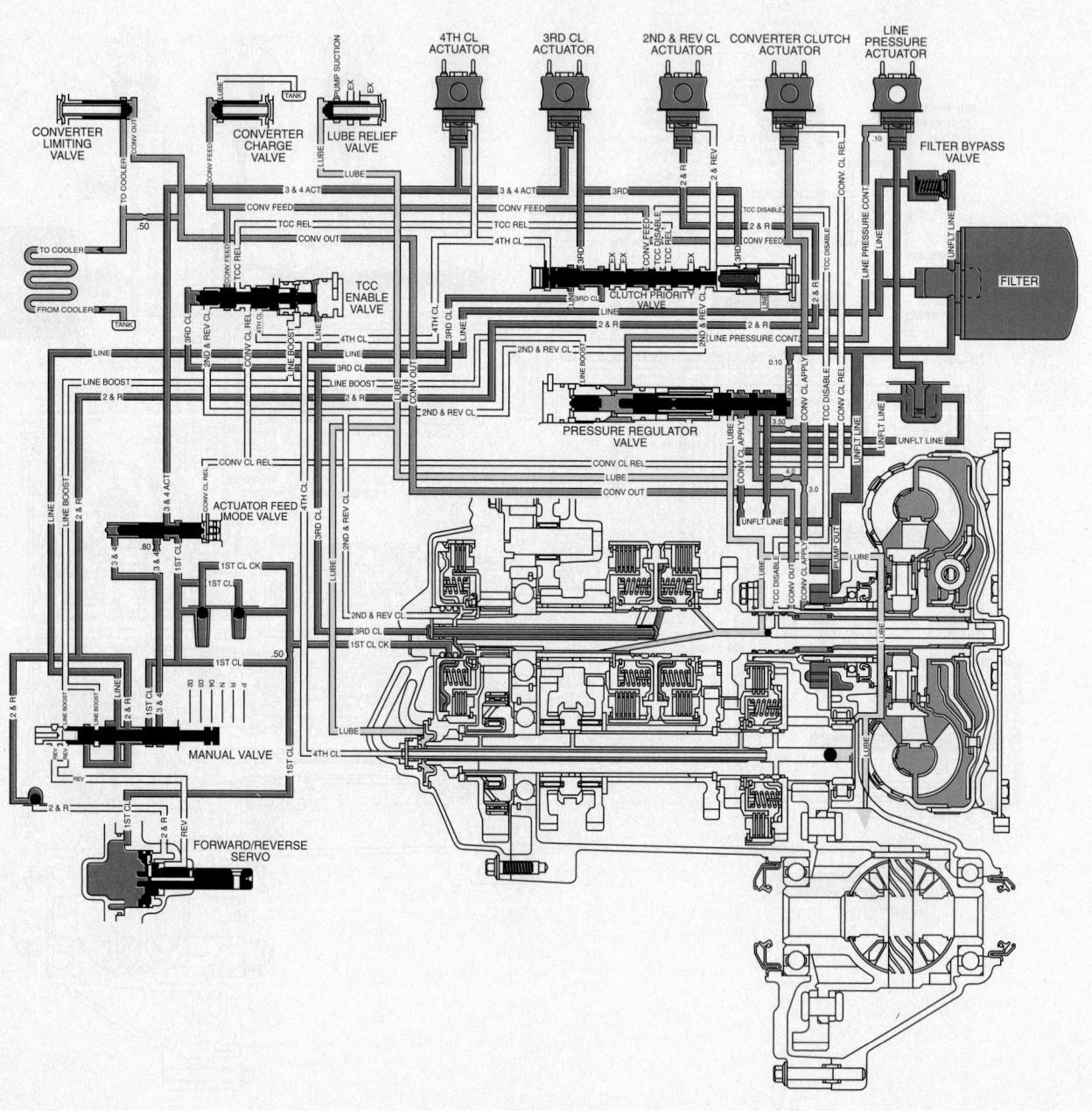

Fig. 6: "D3" or "D4" Range — 3rd Gear (TCC On)

Courtesy of General Motors Corp.

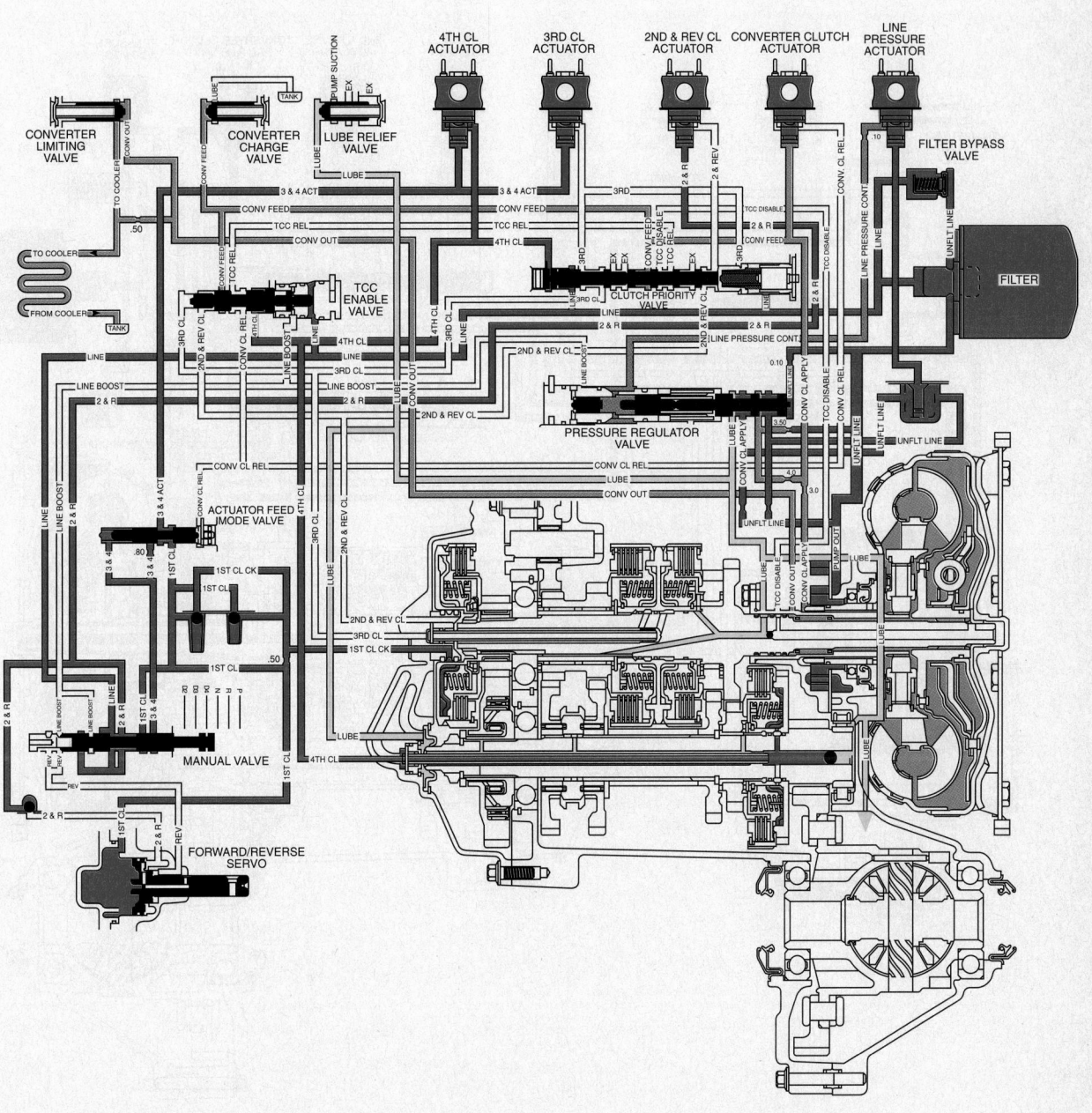

OIL CIRCUIT DIAGRAMS
Saturn (Cont.)

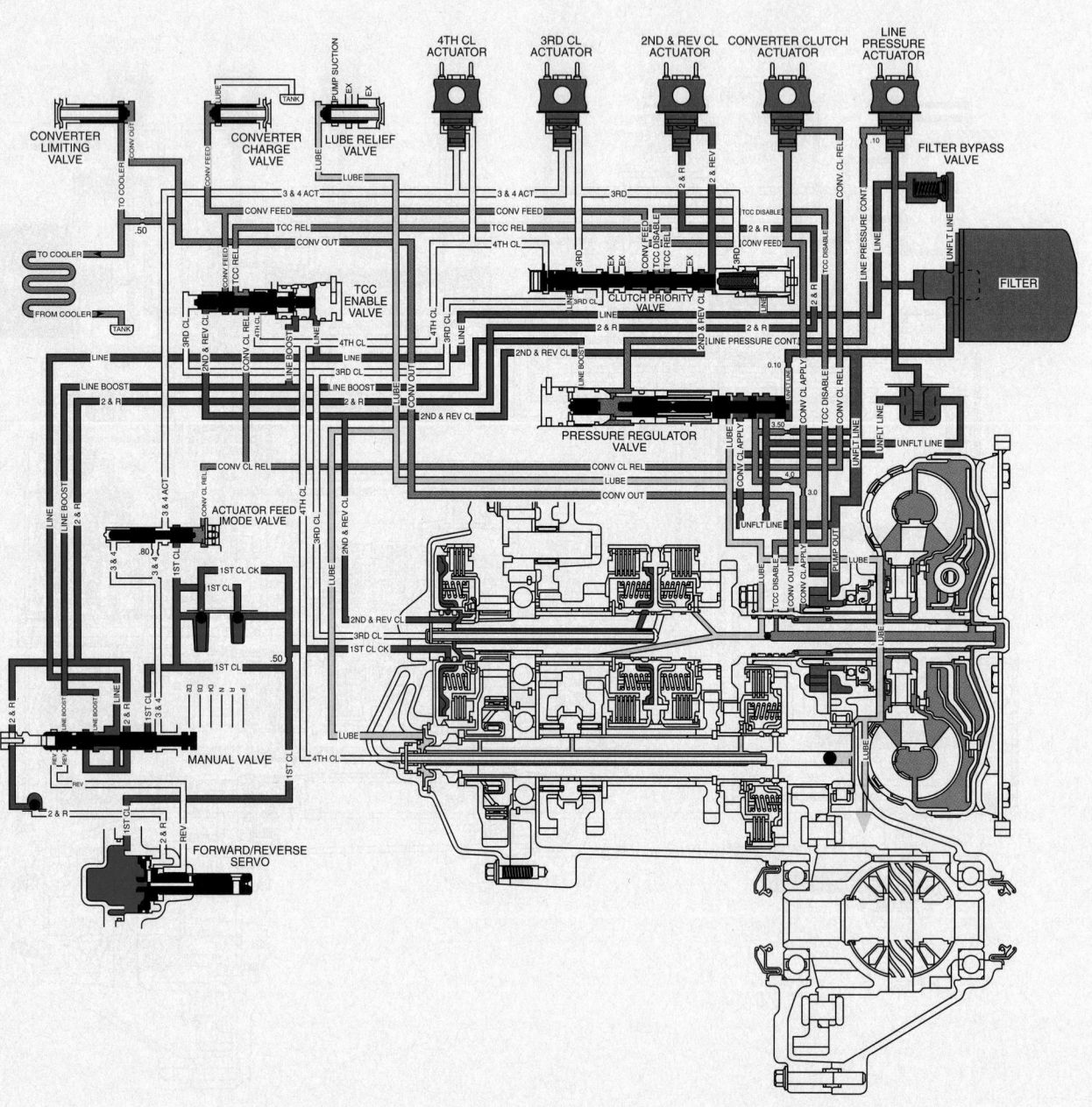

PRESSURES
- MAINLINE PRESSURE
- MODULATOR PRESSURE
- GOVERNOR PRESSURE
- DETENT REGULATED PRESSURE
- 1-2 ACCUMULATOR PRESSURE
- PUMP SUCTION
- CONVERTER OR LUBE

Fig. 8: "D2" Range — 2nd Gear

Courtesy of General Motors Corp.

OIL CIRCUIT DIAGRAMS
Saturn (Cont.)

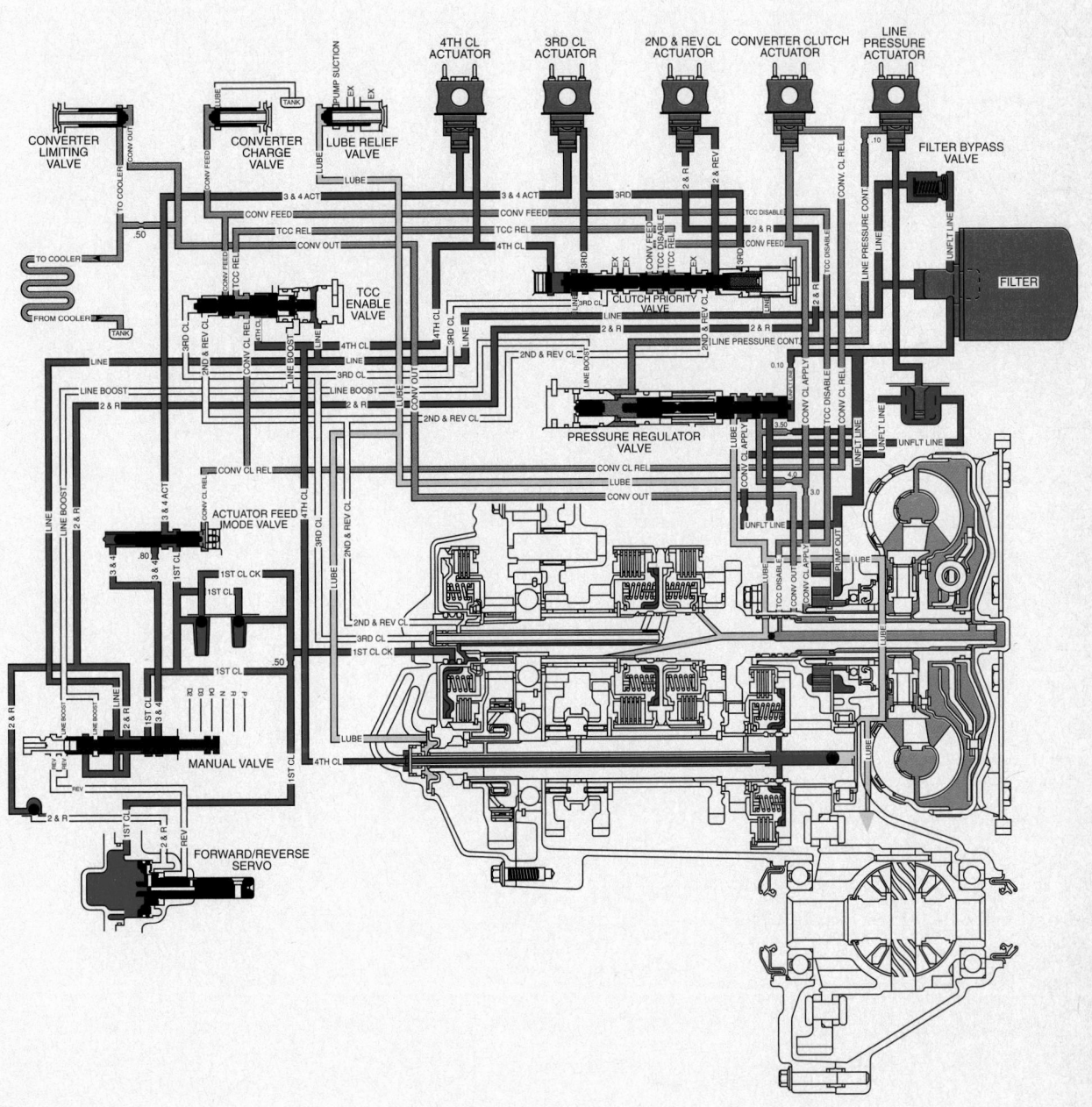

PRESSURES

- MAINLINE PRESSURE
- MODULATOR PRESSURE
- GOVERNOR PRESSURE
- DETENT REGULATED PRESSURE
- 1-2 ACCUMULATOR PRESSURE
- PUMP SUCTION
- CONVERTER OR LUBE

Fig. 9: "D4" Range — 4th Gear (TCC Off)

Courtesy of General Motors Corp.

TRANSMISSION SERVICING

Acclaim, Colt, Colt Vista, Daytona, Dynasty, Eagle Summit Wagon, Fifth Avenue, Imperial, Laser, LeBaron, New Yorker, Shadow, Spirit, Stealth, Summit, Sundance, Talon

APPLICATION

NOTE: For automatic transaxle applications, see appropriate table in APPLICATIONS & IDENTIFICATION.

LUBRICATION

SERVICE INTERVALS

Check fluid level whenever performing other underhood services. Draining, refilling and band adjustments are not required under normal driving conditions. Under heavy duty (severe service) conditions, change fluid, replace filter and adjust bands (if applicable) every 15,000 miles. On F3A21, F4A22, F4A33 and W4A33 units, change transaxle fluid and filter screen every 30,000 miles.

CHECKING FLUID LEVEL

Transaxle – 1) With vehicle on level ground, apply parking brake and run engine at curb idle for at least one minute. Move gear selector through all positions, ending in Park.

2) Fluid level should be between upper and lower marks on dipstick, depending on fluid temperature. Check condition of fluid for contamination and burned smell. DO NOT overfill. Fully seat dipstick.

CAUTION: If severe darkening of fluid and strong odor are noted, change fluid and filter, and adjust bands.

Transfer Case (Colt Vista AWD) – Check fluid level with dipstick. If oil level is low, fill through dipstick hole to a point between the 2 lines on dipstick.

Transfer Case (Stealth) – Lubricant level should be 1/2" below fill hole on side of transfer case.

Transfer Case (All Others) – Lubricant level should be to bottom of fill hole on side of transfer case.

RECOMMENDED FLUID

Transaxle – Use only Mopar ATF type 7176. Manufacturer does not recommend using any additives in transmission or differential.

Transfer Cases – On model 42LE transfer case, use SAE 75W-85 gear oil with API GL-4 rating or higher. On all other transfer cases, use Mopar ATF type 7176.

FLUID CAPACITY

NOTE: Transmission and converter assembly capacities given below are approximate. Correct fluid level should be determined by mark on dipstick.

TRANSMISSION REFILL CAPACITIES

Application	Qts. (L)
30TH & 31TH	
Overhaul [1]	
Except Fleet	8.9 (8.4)
Fleet	9.2 (8.7)
Service	4.0 (3.8)
41TE	
Overhaul [1]	9.9 (9.4)
Service	4.0 (3.8)
42LE	
Transaxle	
Overhaul [1]	9.9 (9.4)
Service	5.1 (4.8)
Differential	1.0 (.95)
F3A21 & F4A22	6.4 (6.1)
F4A33	7.4 (7.0)
W4A33	7.4 (7.0)

[1] – Fill capacity with converter empty.

DRAINING & REFILLING

30TH, 31TH, 41TE & 42LE – 1) Raise and support vehicle. Remove oil pan bolts necessary to gradually lower and drain pan at one corner. Remove oil filter screws, and remove filter. Adjustment of rear band can now be made (if required).

2) Install NEW filter and filter gasket or "O" ring (if equipped) on bottom of valve body, and tighten screws to 40 INCH lbs. (5 N.m). Clean pan with solvent, and blow dry using compressed air.

3) Install pan using RTV sealant to form gasket. Tighten pan bolts to 165 INCH lbs. (19 N.m). Lower vehicle, add 4 qts. (3.8L), 5.1 qts. (4.8L) on 42LE, of ATF and start engine. Allow to idle for at least 2 minutes.

4) With engine at curb idle and parking brake applied, move gear selector lever through all positions, ending in "P" position. Add enough fluid to bring level to 1/8" below ADD mark.

5) Recheck fluid level after transaxle has reached normal operating temperature. Add required amount of fluid. DO NOT overfill. Ensure dipstick is fully seated.

F3A21, F4A22, F4A33 & W4A33 – 1) Raise and support vehicle. Remove drain plug, and drain fluid. Remove pan, and check filter for clogging and damage. Replace if necessary.

2) Clean inside of pan and magnets (if equipped). Reinstall magnets in concave part of pan. Clean both gasket surfaces, and reinstall pan. Replace drain plug gasket, and reinstall plug. Fill transaxle with ATF. Tighten oil pan bolts to specification. See OIL PAN TORQUE SPECIFICATIONS table.

Transfer Case – Drain plug is located on bottom of transfer case. Change drain plug gasket whenever fluid is changed. On Colt Vista, refill through dipstick hole to a point between the 2 lines on dipstick. On Stealth, lubricant level should be 1/2" below fill hole on side of transfer case. On all other models, lubricant level should be to bottom of fill hole on side of transfer case.

OIL PAN TORQUE SPECIFICATIONS

Transmission	INCH Lbs. (N.m)
30TH, 31TH, 41TE & 42LE	168 (19)
F3A21, F4A22, F4A33 & W4A33	88-106 (10-12)

ADJUSTMENTS

KICKDOWN BAND (FRONT)

NOTE: 41TE and 42LE transaxles do not have bands.

NOTE: Kickdown band adjusting screw is located on left side (top front) of transaxle case.

30TH & 31TH – 1) Loosen adjusting screw lock nut, and back off 5 turns. After making sure adjusting screw turns freely in case, tighten screw to 72 INCH lbs. (8 N.m).

2) Back off screw 2 1/2 turns. Hold adjusting screw in this position and tighten lock nut to 35 ft. lbs. (47 N.m).

F3A21, F4A22, F4A33 & W4A33 – 1) Remove all dirt and grease around kickdown servo switch. Remove snap ring and kickdown servo switch.

2) To prevent servo piston from turning, install Restrainer Adapter (MD998918) and bolt to side of transaxle.

CAUTION: DO NOT push servo piston inward while installing adapter and servo wrench. Install adapter in brake pressure port by hand ONLY. DO NOT use wrench to tighten adapter.

3) Loosen lock nut to "V" channel of adjuster rod. Tighten inner section of Kickdown Service Adjustment Assembly (MD998916) until it contacts lock nut.

4) Install outer section of kickdown service adjustment assembly on lock nut. Rotate outer section to left and inner section to right to contact lock nut with inner section.

5) Using an INCH-pound torque wrench on inner section, tighten inner section to 89 INCH lbs. (10.0 N.m), and then loosen inner section. Tighten inner section to 44 INCH lbs. (5.0 N.m).

AUTOMATIC TRANSMISSION SERVICING
Chrysler Corp. Passenger Cars (Cont.)

2-3

CAUTION: Before tightening lock nut with torque wrench, tighten it by hand until it contacts piston. If torque wrench is used initially, lock nut and adjustment rod may rotate together.

6) Back off outer section 2 1/2 turns. Rotate outer section to right and inner section to left until inner section is free of lock nut.

7) Tighten lock nut by hand until it contacts piston. Using torque wrench, tighten lock nut to 18-23 ft. lbs. (25-32 N.m). Remove adapter and kickdown servo wrench. Install switch and snap ring.

LOW-REVERSE BAND (REAR)

NOTE: Low-reverse band adjusting screw is located on rear servo lever. It is not accessible unless valve body is removed.

30TH & 31TH – 1) Drain transaxle and remove oil pan. Loosen band adjusting screw lock nut about 5 turns. Ensure adjusting screw turns freely. Tighten adjusting screw to 41 INCH lbs. (5 N.m).

2) Back off adjusting screw 3 1/2 turns. Hold in this position and tighten lock nut to 120 INCH lbs. (14 N.m). Install oil pan and fill transaxle with fluid.

THROTTLE VALVE CABLE

30TH & 31TH – 1) Ensure engine idle speed is correct and engine is at normal operating temperature. Loosen adjustment bracket lock screw. Bracket must have both bracket alignment tabs touching transaxle cast surface. Tighten lock screw to 105 INCH lbs. (12 N.m).

2) Release cross-lock on cable assembly by pulling upward. Ensure adjustment is correct. Cable must be free to slide toward engine, against its stop, after cross-lock is released.

3) Move transaxle throttle control lever fully clockwise against its internal stop. Press cross-lock downward into locked position.

4) Move transaxle throttle lever counterclockwise. Slowly release it to ensure it will return to full clockwise position.

F3A21, F4A22, F4A33 & W4A33 – 1) On Colt Vista, turn ignition switch on (engine off) for 15-20 seconds. Ensure throttle valve is at standard idle opening.

2) On all other models, ensure throttle lever is in curb idle position. Engine must be at normal operating temperature.

3) On all models, raise throttle cable cover upward to expose nipple. Loosen lower cable bracket mounting bolt. Move lower cable bracket until distance between nipple and top of cover on throttle cable is .02-.06" (.5-1.5 mm).

4) Tighten lower cable bracket mounting bolt to 108-126 INCH lbs. (12-14 N.m). With throttle lever in wide open throttle position, pull cable upward to ensure some cable free play exists.

THROTTLE VALVE ROD (V6 ENGINE)

31TH – 1) Ensure engine idle speed is correct and engine is at normal operating temperature. Loosen adjustment swivel lock screw. Ensure swivel is free to slide along throttle rod. Disassemble and repair if necessary.

2) Move transaxle throttle pressure lever toward engine until it contacts internal stop. Tighten swivel lock screw to 100 INCH lbs. (11 N.m). Ensure linkage backlash is removed by preload spring.

SHIFT INTERLOCK CABLE

30TH, 31TH & 41TE – 1) When ignition switch is in LOCK or ACC position, console gearshift lever should be locked in Park position. When ignition switch is in OFF or RUN position, console gearshift lever should be unlocked and movable. Ignition key cannot be set to OFF or ACC position unless shift lever is in Park position.

2) If ignition switch binds or cannot be set to OFF position, or shift lever is difficult to move, console gearshift lever interlock lever requires adjustment.

3) With shift lever in Park position, remove shift knob. Leave release button on top of shift lever. Remove PRNDL plate from console by gently prying upward on all corners.

4) With shift lever in Park position, verify Green plunger on shift lever rod is in full up position. If Green plunger is not in full up position, adjust transmission shift linkage/cable. See SHIFT LINKAGE under ADJUSTMENTS.

5) Ensure cable slug is seated in interlock lever. Rotate ignition switch to ACC position. Loosen interlock lever adjusting nut to allow tension spring to center interlock lever on shift bracket assembly.

6) Tighten interlock lever adjusting nut to 25 INCH lbs. (3 N.m). Operate ignition switch and gearshift lever to verify correct adjustment. If adjustment is okay, install PRNDL plate and shift knob.

F3A21, F4A22, F4A33 & W4A33 – With ignition switch is in LOCK position, ensure console gearshift lever is locked in Park position. Remove console cover. Loosen nut securing cable housing. Lightly remove slack from cable and retighten cable housing nut. Install console.

42LE (Column Shift) – Push interlock cassette adjustment tab in until it stops. The adjustment tab will "click" as it moves into position. Ensure tab is fully depressed.

42LE (Floor Shift) – 1) Remove floor shift handle. Remove bezel from shift console. Remove driver's side kick panel from center console. Loosen adjustment nut on interlock lever. Place ignition key (lock cylinder) in RUN position.

2) Remove interlock cable from shift housing. Slide cable out of groove in interlock lever. With lock cylinder in OFF position and ignition key removed, cable core wire should not move when pulled.

3) With ignition key (lock cylinder) in RUN position, cable core should slide freely when pulled. Cable should return to bottomed out position when released. If cable core does not operate as indicated, cable is improperly installed or is kinked. Repair or replace cable as necessary.

4) Place shift lever in Park position. Slide interlock cable core wire into groove on adjustment lever. Ensure cable end seats in groove. Slip cable into housing until it snaps into place.

5) Ensure shift lever is in Park position. With ignition switch in OFF position, remove ignition key from lock cylinder. When adjustment nut on interlock lever is loosened, cable indexes itself to correct position. Tighten adjustment nut.

6) If interlock mechanism operates properly, install bezel on shift console. Install shift lever handle. Install driver's side kick panel to center console.

SHIFT LINKAGE

NOTE: Shift linkage on F3A21, F4A22, F4A33 and W4A33 transaxles do not require periodic adjustment.

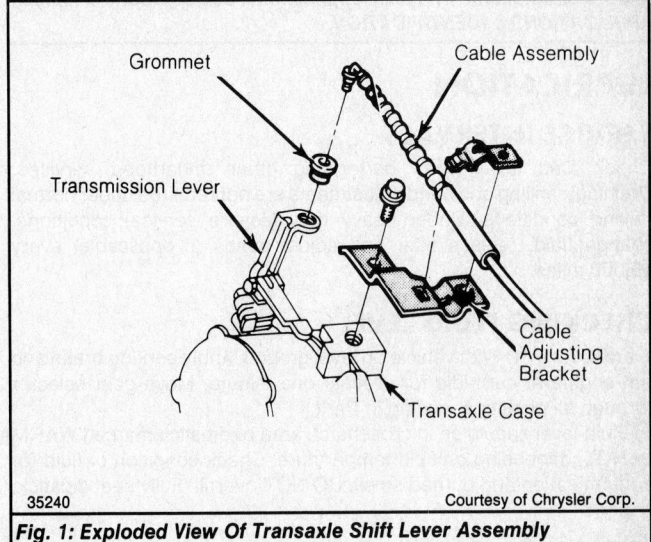

35240   Courtesy of Chrysler Corp.

Fig. 1: Exploded View Of Transaxle Shift Lever Assembly

2-4

AUTOMATIC TRANSMISSION SERVICING
Chrysler Corp. Passenger Cars (Cont.)

30TH, 31TH & 41TE – 1) Place shift selector in "P" position. Loosen lock bolt on cable adjusting bracket on transaxle. *See Fig. 1.* On column shift models, ensure preload adjustment spring engages fork on transaxle bracket.

2) On all models, pull shift lever by hand all the way to front detent position (Park). Tighten lock screw to 100 INCH lbs. (11 N.m). To check adjustment, gearshift lever should be within limits of hand lever gate stops when shifted through gear positions. Vehicle must only start in Park or Neutral.

42LE (Column Shift) – 1) Remove upper steering column shroud. Tilt steering column to full up position. Rotate cable adjuster to unlock position. Ensure transaxle shift lever is in Park (rearmost) position.

2) Place column shift lever in Park position. Remove ignition key. Adjust cable by rotating cable end so it locks in position. Install steering column shroud. Check for smooth operation. Vehicle must start only in Park or Neutral.

nsaxle and no slack exists in cable.

42LE (Floor Shift) – 1) Remove shifter handle and console bezel. Loosen nut on shifter cable adjuster. Rotate cable adjuster to unlock position. Ensure transaxle shift lever is in Park (rearmost) position.

2) Place shift lever in Park position. Remove ignition key. Tighten shifter cable adjuster lock nut. Install console bezel and shifter handle. Check for smooth operation. Vehicle must start only in Park or Neutral.

NEUTRAL SAFETY SWITCH

NOTE: On 41TE and 42LE transaxle's neutral safety function and back-up lights are controlled by Manual Lever Position Switch (MLPS). For further information, see appropriate CHRYSLER ELECTRONIC DIAGNOSIS article.

NOTE: 30TH and 31TH combination neutral safety and back-up light switch is screwed into side of transaxle case. Switch is not adjustable. Switch may be tested for continuity using the following method.

30TH & 31TH – 1) Center terminal of 3-terminal neutral safety and back-up light switch provides ground for starter solenoid circuit through shift lever in Park or Neutral positions only.

2) To test, remove wiring connector from switch and check for continuity between center pin of switch and case. Continuity should exist only when transmission is in Park or Neutral.

NOTE: Check shift linkage adjustment before replacing a switch that tests bad.

3) Back-up light switch circuit is through 2 outside terminals of switch. Continuity should exist between 2 terminals only when transmission is in reverse. No continuity should exist from either terminal to case.

4) To replace, unscrew switch from case (some fluid will escape). Place shift selector lever in Park, and then in Neutral position. Check to see that switch operating fingers are centered in switch opening in case. Install switch with NEW seal into case and tighten. Check transaxle fluid level.

F3A21, F4A22, F4A33 & W4A33 – 1) Place shift and manual control levers in Neutral. For adjustment, turn switch body in order to align small end of manual control lever with corresponding flange on switch body. Tighten switch mounting bolts to 84-108 INCH lbs. (10-12 N.m).

CAUTION: DO NOT drop switch body.

2) Loosen nut at end of transaxle control cable, and lightly pull in direction of switch. Tighten nut to 84-120 INCH lbs. (10-14 N.m).

3) Ensure selector lever is in Neutral. Ensure lever functions correctly at transaxle, in range corresponding to that indicated by selector lever.

INHIBITOR SWITCH

F4A22, F4A33 & W4A33 – Place selector lever in Neutral. Place manual control lever in Neutral. To adjust, rotate switch body so manual control lever .20" (5.0 mm) hole and switch body .20" (5.0 mm) hole are aligned.

Chrysler Corp. FWD Vans

Caravan, Town & Country, Voyager

APPLICATION

NOTE: For automatic transaxle applications, see appropriate table in APPLICATIONS & IDENTIFICATION.

LUBRICATION

SERVICE INTERVALS

Check fluid level when performing other underhood services. Draining, refilling and band adjustments are not required under normal driving conditions. Under heavy duty (severe service) conditions, change fluid, replace filter and adjust bands (if applicable) every 15,000 miles.

CHECKING FLUID LEVEL

Transaxle – 1) With vehicle on level ground, apply parking brake and run engine at curb idle for at least one minute. Move gear selector through all positions, ending in Park.

2) Fluid level should be in crosshatch area of dipstick marked WARM or HOT, depending on fluid temperature. Check condition of fluid for contamination and burned smell. DO NOT overfill. Fully seat dipstick.

FLUID CAPACITY

NOTE: Transmission and converter assembly capacities given below are approximate. Correct fluid level should be determined by mark on dipstick.

TRANSMISSION REFILL CAPACITIES

Application	Qts. (L)
31TH	
Overhaul [1]	
Except Fleet	8.9 (8.4)
Fleet	9.2 (8.7)
Service	4.0 (3.8)
41TE	
Overhaul	9.1 (8.6)
Service	4.0 (3.8)
Power Transfer Unit (PTU)	1.2 (1.1)

[1] – Fill capacity with converter empty.

DRAINING & REFILLING

31TH & 41TE – 1) Raise and support vehicle. Remove oil pan bolts necessary to gradually lower and drain pan at one corner. Remove oil filter screws, and remove filter. Adjustment of low-reverse (rear) band can now be made (if required).

AUTOMATIC TRANSMISSION SERVICING
Chrysler Corp. FWD Vans (Cont.)

2-5

2) Install NEW filter and filter gasket or "O" ring (if equipped) on bottom of valve body, and tighten screws to 40 INCH lbs. (5 N.m). Clean pan with solvent, and blow dry using compressed air.

3) Install pan using RTV sealant to form gasket. Tighten pan bolts to 165 INCH lbs. (19 N.m). Lower vehicle, add 4 qts. (3.8L) of ATF and start engine. Allow to idle for at least 2 minutes.

4) With engine at curb idle and parking brake applied, move gear selector lever through all positions, ending in "P" position. Add enough fluid to bring level to 1/8" below ADD mark.

5) Recheck fluid level after transaxle has reached normal operating temperature. Add required amount of fluid. DO NOT overfill. Ensure dipstick is fully seated.

ADJUSTMENTS

KICKDOWN BAND (FRONT)

NOTE: 41TE transaxle does not have bands.

31TH – 1) Kickdown band adjusting screw is located on left side (top front) of transaxle case. Loosen adjusting screw lock nut, and back off 5 turns. After making sure adjusting screw turns freely in case, tighten screw to 72 INCH lbs. (8 N.m).

2) Back off screw 2 1/2 turns. Hold adjusting screw in this position and tighten lock nut to 35 ft. lbs. (47 N m).

LOW-REVERSE BAND (REAR)

31TH – 1) Low-reverse band adjusting screw is located on rear servo lever. It is not accessible unless valve body is removed. Transmission oil pan must be removed to provide access to band adjusting screw.

2) Drain transmission and remove oil pan. Loosen band adjusting screw lock nut about 5 turns. Ensure adjusting screw turns freely. Tighten adjusting screw to 41 INCH lbs. (5 N.m).

3) Back off adjusting screw 3 1/2 turns. Hold in this position and tighten lock nut to 120 INCH lbs. (14 N.m). Install oil pan and fill transaxle with fluid.

THROTTLE VALVE ROD (V6 ENGINE)

31TH – 1) Ensure engine idle speed is correct and engine is at normal operating temperature. Loosen adjustment swivel lock screw. Ensure swivel is free to slide along throttle rod. Disassemble and repair if necessary.

2) Move transaxle throttle pressure lever toward engine until it contacts internal stop. Tighten swivel lock screw to 100 INCH lbs. (11 N.m). Ensure linkage backlash is removed by preload spring.

SHIFT LINKAGE

1) Place shift selector in "P" position. Loosen lock bolt on cable adjusting bracket on transaxle. *See Fig. 1.* Ensure preload adjustment spring engages fork on transaxle bracket.

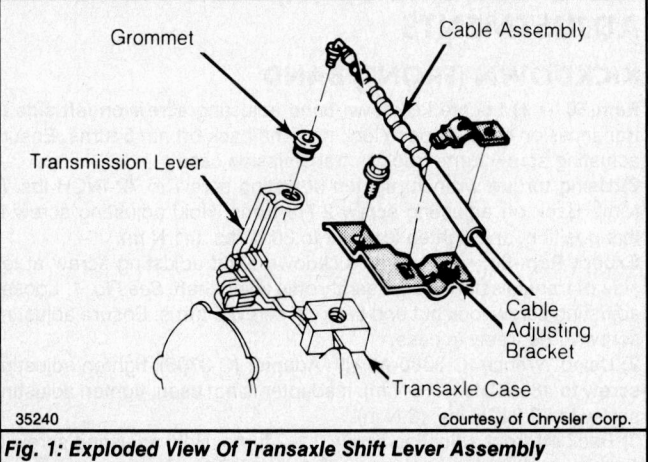

Grommet
Cable Assembly
Transmission Lever
Cable Adjusting Bracket
Transaxle Case
35240
Courtesy of Chrysler Corp.

Fig. 1: Exploded View Of Transaxle Shift Lever Assembly

2) Pull shift lever by hand all the way to front detent position (Park). Tighten lock screw to 100 lbs. (11 N.m). To check adjustment, gearshift lever should be within limits of hand lever gate stops when shifted through gear positions. Vehicle must only start in Park or Neutral.

CAUTION: Replace old plastic grommets with new ones if necessary to remove linkage cable from lever. Use pliers to snap new grommet into lever and rod into grommet.

NEUTRAL SAFETY SWITCH (31TH ONLY)

Combination neutral safety and back-up light switch is screwed into side of transmission/transaxle case. Switch is nonadjustable. Switch may be tested for continuity using following method.

Testing – 1) Center terminal of 3-terminal neutral safety and back-up light switch provides ground for starter solenoid circuit through shift lever in Park or Neutral positions only.

2) To test, remove wiring connector from switch and check for continuity between center pin of switch and case. Continuity should exist only when transmission/transaxle is in Park or Neutral.

NOTE: Check shift linkage adjustment before replacing a switch that tests bad.

3) Back-up light switch circuit is through 2 outside terminals of switch. Continuity should exist between 2 terminals only when transmission/transaxle is in reverse. No continuity should exist from either terminal to case.

4) To replace, unscrew switch from case (some fluid will escape). Move shift selector lever to Park, and then to Neutral position. Ensure that switch operating fingers are centered in switch opening in case. Install switch with NEW seal into case and tighten. Check transaxle fluid level.

OIL PAN GASKET IDENTIFICATION

NOTE: For oil pan gasket identification, see Fig. 2 or 3.

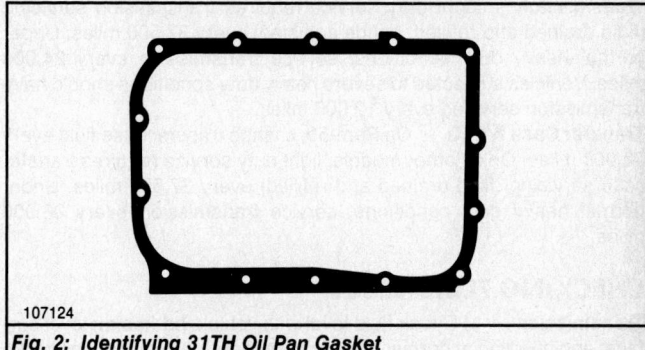

107124

Fig. 2: Identifying 31TH Oil Pan Gasket

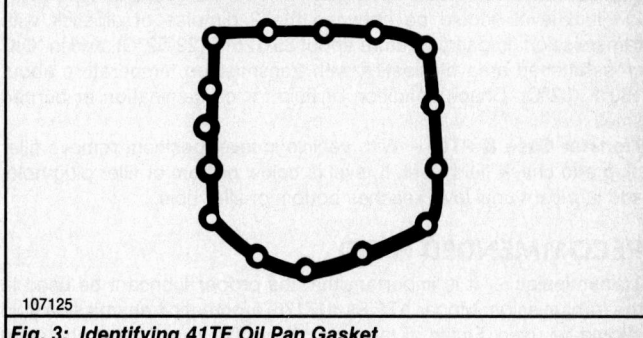

107125

Fig. 3: Identifying 41TE Oil Pan Gasket

AUTOMATIC TRANSMISSION SERVICING
Chrysler Corp. RWD Light Trucks & Vans

Dakota, Pickup, Ramcharger, Ram-50, Van

APPLICATIONS

TRANSMISSION APPLICATIONS

Model	Transmission
Dakota (AN)	
3.9L	42RH
5.2L	46RH
BR Series Pickup (1994)	
3.9L	42RH Or 32RH
5.2L	46RH Or 36RH
5.9L	
Gasoline (Except V10)	36RH Or 46RH
Gasoline (V10)	37RH Or 47RH
Diesel	37RH, 46RH or 47RH
D & W Series Pickup (1993)	
3.9L	42RH Or 32RH
5.2L	46RH Or 36RH
5.9L	
Gasoline	36RH Or 46RH
Diesel	37RH
Ramcharger	
5.2L	46RH Or 36RH
5.9L	46RH
Ram Van (AB)	
3.9L	42RH Or 32RH
5.2L	46RH Or 36RH
5.9L	46RH
Ram-50	
2WD	R4AC1
4WD	V4AC1

WARNING: Before removing engine/transmission assembly on compressed natural gas powered vehicles, see COMPRESSED NATURAL GAS SAFETY PRECAUTIONS in CAUTIONS & WARNINGS article in APPLICATIONS & IDENTIFICATION.

LUBRICATION

SERVICE INTERVALS

Transmission – Light duty service requires transmission servicing (fluid drained and refilled, bands adjusted) every 37,500 miles. Under normal heavy duty conditions, service transmission every 24,000 miles. Vehicles subjected to severe heavy duty conditions should have transmission serviced every 12,000 miles.

Transfer Case & PTO – On Ram-50, change transfer case fluid every 30,000 miles. On all other models, light duty service requires transfer case servicing (fluid drained and refilled) every 37,500 miles. Under normal heavy duty conditions, service transmission every 36,000 miles.

CHECKING FLUID LEVEL

Transmission – 1) Check fluid level with vehicle parked on level surface, engine idling at normal operating temperature and parking brake applied. Move selector lever through all gear ranges, ending in "N".
2) Fluid level should be between the 2 dimples of dipstick with transmission fluid temperature about 85-125°F (29-52°C), and in "OK" crosshatched area of dipstick with transmission temperature about 180°F (82°C). Check condition of fluid for contamination or burned smell.
Transfer Case & PTO – With vehicle in level position, remove filler plug and check fluid level. If level is below bottom of filler plug hole, add lubricant until level reaches bottom of filler hole.

RECOMMENDED FLUID

Transmission – It is important that the proper lubricant be used in the transmission. Mopar ATF Plus (7176) automatic transmission fluid should be used. Fluids of the type labeled Dexron-II should be used only if the recommended fluid is not available.
Transfer Case (NP205) – Engine oils labeled for API Service SF or SF/CC may be used in this transfer case. SAE viscosity grade should be SAE 30.

Transfer Case & PTO (NP231, NP241 & NV021) – Fluids of the type labeled Mopar ATF Plus (7176) or Dexron-II are recommended.
Transfer Case (Ram-50) – Use SAE 75W-85 gear oil with API GL-4 rating or higher.

FLUID CAPACITY

NOTE: Use capacities listed in table as a guide. Correct fluid level should always be determined by marks on dipstick. Capacities listed include torque converter.

REFILL CAPACITIES

Application	Qts. (L)
Transmission [1]	
32RH	8.6 (8.1)
36RH/37RH	8.4 (7.9)
37RH [2]	8.6 (8.1)
42RH	10.2 (9.6)
46RH	10.2 (9.9)
R4AC1 & V4AC1	[3] 10.2 (9.7)
PTO	
NV021	4.6 (2.2)
Transfer Case	
NP205	2.4 (2.2)
NP231	1.6 (1.5)
NP241	3.0 (2.8)
Ram-50	4.6 (2.2)

[1] – Includes torque converter.
[2] – Diesel.
[3] – Idle engine in Neutral, then add fluid to bring level between notches at "H" mark.

DRAINING & REFILLING

NOTE: Although manufacturer recommends changing only fluid, the oil filter/screen may also require replacement. If replacing oil filter/screen, note length and location of all bolts.

Transmission – 1) Loosen oil pan bolts. Tap lightly at one corner to break loose and allow fluid to drain. Remove pan. Install NEW filter on bottom of valve body and tighten retaining screws. Check oil pan. Ensure magnet (if used) is over boss in right front corner of pan. Install pan with NEW gasket.
2) Refill transmission with 4 qts. (3.8L) of fluid. Start engine and allow to run at idle for at least 2 minutes. With engine at curb side and parking brake applied, move shift selector lever through all ranges, ending in "N". Add fluid up to 2 dimples on dipstick. DO NOT overfill. Recheck fluid level when transmission reaches normal operating temperature.
Transfer Case & PTO – Raise vehicle. Position drain pan under transfer case. Remove drain and fill plugs, and drain lubricant completely. Install drain plug. Tighten plug to 40 ft. lbs. (54 N.m). Remove drain pan. Fill transfer case to bottom edge of fill plug opening with lubricant. Lower vehicle.

ADJUSTMENTS

KICKDOWN (FRONT) BAND

Ram-50 – 1) Locate kickdown band adjusting screw on left side of transmission case. Loosen lock nut, and back off nut 5 turns. Ensure adjusting screw turns freely in transmission case.
2) Using torque wrench, tighten adjusting screw to 72 INCH lbs. (8 N.m). Back off adjusting screw 2 7/8 turns. Hold adjusting screw in this position, and tighten lock nut to 30 ft. lbs. (41 N.m).
Except Ram-50 – 1) Locate kickdown band adjusting screw at left side of transmission case, near throttle lever shaft. See Fig. 1. Loosen adjusting screw lock nut and back off screw 5 turns. Ensure adjusting screw turns freely in case.
2) Using Wrench (C-3380-A) with Adapter (C-3705), tighten adjusting screw to 48 INCH lbs. (5 N.m). If adapter is not used, tighten adjusting screw to 72 INCH lbs. (8 N.m).
3) Back off front adjusting screw 2 1/2 turns. Hold adjusting screw in position and tighten lock nut to 35 ft. lbs. (47 N.m).

AUTOMATIC TRANSMISSION SERVICING
Chrysler Corp. RWD Light Trucks & Vans (Cont.)

2-7

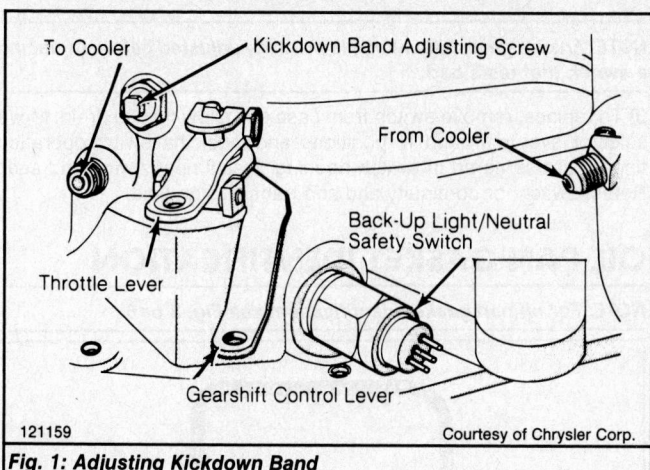

Fig. 1: Adjusting Kickdown Band

LOW-REVERSE (REAR) BAND

Ram-50 – 1) Raise vehicle, drain transmission and remove oil pan. Loosen adjusting screw lock nut, and back off nut 5 turns. Ensure adjusting screw turns freely in lever.

2) Using torque wrench, tighten band adjusting screw to 30 INCH lbs. (3.5 N.m). Back off adjusting screw 6 turns. Hold adjusting screw in this position, and tighten lock nut to 25 ft. lbs. (34 N.m).

3) Reinstall oil pan using NEW gasket. Tighten pan bolts to 150 INCH lbs. (17 N.m). Refill with specified transmission fluid.

Except Ram-50 – 1) Drain transmission and remove oil pan. Locate low-reverse band adjusting screw on rear servo lever. *See Fig. 2.* Loosen adjusting screw lock nut and back off screw about 5 turns. Ensure screw turns freely in lever. Using Wrench (C-3380A), tighten adjusting screw to 72 INCH lbs. (8 N.m).

2) Back off rear adjusting screw. See LOW-REVERSE BAND ADJUSTMENT table. Hold adjusting screw in position and tighten lock nut to 35 ft. lbs. (47 N.m). Clean oil pan, install NEW gasket with pan and fill transmission with fluid. Tighten pan bolts to 150 INCH lbs. (17 N.m).

LOW-REVERSE BAND ADJUSTMENT

Application	Back Off Screw
32RH	4 Turns
36RH/37RH	2 Turns
42RH	4 Turns
46RH	2 Turns

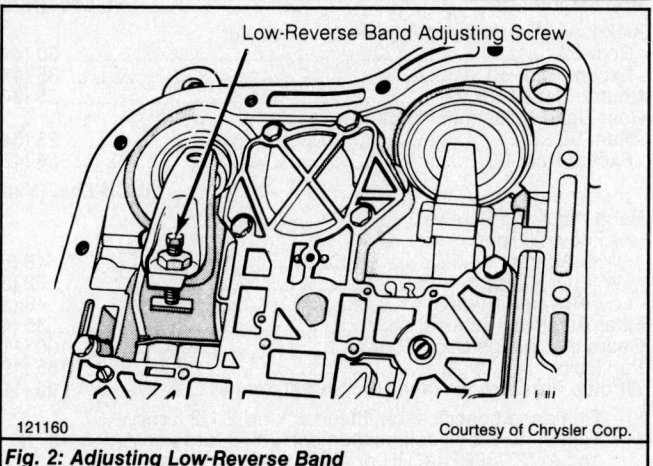

Fig. 2: Adjusting Low-Reverse Band

LINE PRESSURE

Ram-50 – 1) Incorrect throttle pressure setting will cause incorrect line pressure readings, even though line pressure adjustment is correct. Always inspect and correct throttle pressure adjustment before adjusting line pressure.

2) Adjustment, measured from valve body to inner edge of adjusting nut, is about 1 5/16". Adjustment can be changed to obtain correct line pressure.

3) Turn screw with an Allen wrench. One complete turn of adjusting screw changes closed throttle line pressure 1 2/3 psi. Turn adjusting screw counterclockwise to increase pressure or clockwise to decrease pressure.

THROTTLE PRESSURE

Ram-50 – 1) Throttle pressures cannot be accurately tested. If a malfunction exists, adjustment should be measured.

2) Insert Gauge Pin (C-3763) between throttle lever cam and kickdown valve. Push in on tool to compress kickdown valve against its spring.

3) As force is being exerted to compress spring, turn throttle lever screw with Allen wrench until head of screw touches throttle lever tang with gauge pin, and throttle valve bottoms.

THROTTLE PRESSURE CABLE

NOTE: A .180 (4.57 mm) diameter gauge Is required to check and adjust throttle pressure cable on diesel models. Use a drill bit of correct diameter or fabricate gauge from metal stock.

37RH Transmission (1993 Only) – 1) Start engine and let it warm to operating temperature. Adjust idle speed if necessary. Using gauge, check clearance between rear of cable actuating pin and end of slot in throttle pressure cable.

2) Clearance should be .180 (4.57 mm). If clearance is okay, cable adjustment is correct. If clearance is not as specified, proceed to next step.

3) Release cable lock pawl. Insert gauge between cable actuating pin and end of slot in cable. Slide cable forward or rearward to obtain specified clearance. Press cable lock pawl down until it snaps into locked position. Recheck clearance.

CAUTION: On Pickup and Ram-50, always adjust throttle control cable whenever idle is adjusted.

Ram-50 – 1) Ensure engine idle is adjusted correctly. Ensure throttle lever and throttle cable bracket are not bent. Pull lightly on inner throttle cable.

2) While in closed throttle position, measure gap between inner cable stopper and outer cable housing. Adjust cable as necessary to obtain a gap of .031-.059" (.79-1.50 mm).

3) While holding throttle in wide open position, pull on inner throttle cable. Adjust bellcrank as necessary to obtain a gap of 1.46-1.50" (37.08-38.10 mm) between inner cable stopper and outer cable.

4) With throttle fully closed, recheck gap between inner cable stopper and outer cable housing. Gap should be .031-.059" (.79-1.50 mm). While holding throttle in wide open position, pull on inner throttle cable. Check for a gap of 1.30-1.38" (33.02-35.05 mm).

Except Ram-50 & 37RH Transmission (1993) – 1) Start engine and let it warm to operating temperature. Adjust idle speed if necessary. Push and hold cable lock button to release cable. Pull cable housing toward rear of vehicle until fully retracted. Release cable lock button.

2) Raise and support vehicle. Rotate throttle valve lever toward front of vehicle. Cable housing should ratchet back through lock mechanism. Continue rotating throttle valve lever until ratcheting stops.

3) To check adjustment, observe throttle valve lever while a helper opens throttle lever on throttle body. Throttle valve lever should begin to move just as throttle lever comes off curb idle position. Readjust as necessary.

Except Ram-50 & 37RH Transmission (1994) – 1) Turn ignition off. Remove air cleaner. Remove cable froim throttle lever. Make sure transmission throttle lever is fully closed. Push and hold cable lock button to release cable. Center cable housing over throttle lever and install. Release cable lock button.

2-8

AUTOMATIC TRANSMISSION SERVICING
Chrysler Corp. RWD Light Trucks & Vans (Cont.)

GEARSHIFT LINKAGE

Ram-50 – Adjust shift cable at transaxle/transmission end of cable. Place shift lever in Neutral. Ensure shift lever and neutral safety switch are in Neutral position. If cable was replaced, ensure toothed washer is installed (if equipped). Turn adjuster at cable end so it fits into manual lever on transmission and no slack exists in cable.

Except Ram-50 – 1) With column shift lever in "P" position, loosen adjustable swivel lock screw. *See Fig. 3.* Ensure swivel is free to move on shift rod. Disassemble and clean components if necessary.

2) Move shift lever on transmission to full rear detent ("P") position and tighten swivel lock screw. When linkage is properly adjusted, detent positions for "N" and "D" will be within limits of shift lever gate stops and engine will start only in "P" or "N".

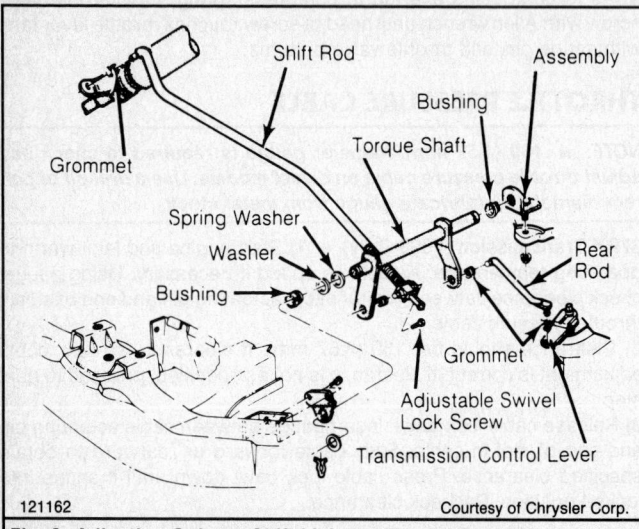

Fig. 3: Adjusting Column Shift Linkage (Except Ram-50)

NEUTRAL SAFETY SWITCH

NOTE: On Ram-50, neutral safety switch is part of transmission-mounted neutral safety/back-up light switch assembly, and is non-adjustable.

Except Ram-50 – 1) With transmission linkage properly adjusted, switch should allow starter operation in "P" and "N" only. To test switch, remove wire connector and test for continuity between center pin of switch and case. *See Fig. 4.* Continuity should exist only with transmission in "P" or "N".

2) Check for continuity between 2 outer pins. Continuity should exist with transmission in reverse only. There should be no continuity between either outside pin or transmission case.

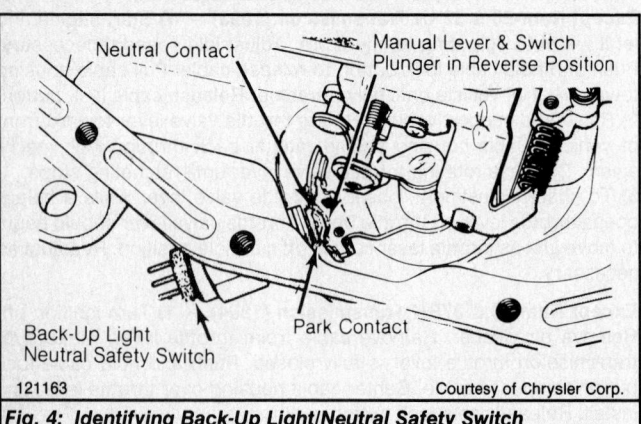

Fig. 4: Identifying Back-Up Light/Neutral Safety Switch

NOTE: Ensure gearshift linkage is properly adjusted before replacing a switch that tests bad.

3) To replace, remove switch from case and allow fluid to drain. Move selector lever to "P" and "N" positions, and check that switch operation fingers are centered in switch opening. Install new switch and seal. Retest switch for continuity and add transmission fluid.

OIL PAN GASKET IDENTIFICATION

NOTE: For oil pan gasket identification, see Fig. 5 or 6.

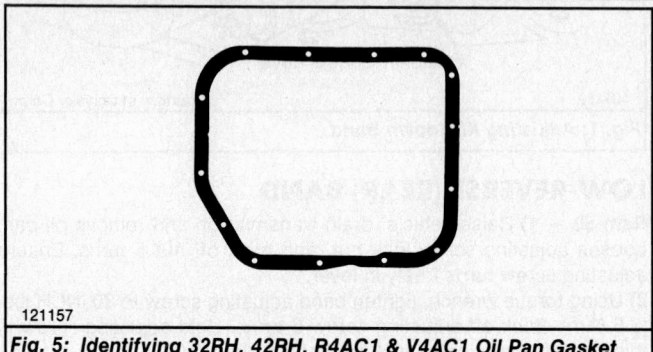

Fig. 5: Identifying 32RH, 42RH, R4AC1 & V4AC1 Oil Pan Gasket

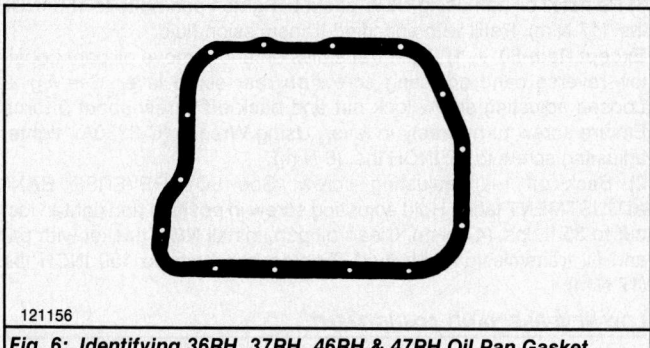

Fig. 6: Identifying 36RH, 37RH, 46RH & 47RH Oil Pan Gasket

TORQUE SPECIFICATIONS
TORQUE SPECIFICATIONS

Application	Ft. Lbs. (N.m)
Kickdown (Front) Band Adjustment Lock Nut	
Ram-50	30 (41)
Except Ram-50	35 (47)
Neutral Safety Switch	25 (34)
Rear Band Adjustment Lock Nut	
Ram-50	25 (34)
Except Ram-50	35 (47)

	INCH Lbs. (N.m)
Band Adjusting Screws [1]	
Kickdown (Front)	
With Adapter	48 (5)
Without Adapter	72 (8)
Low-Reverse (Rear) [2]	48 (5)
Filter Retaining Screws	35 (4)
Gearshift Linkage Lock Screw	100 (11)
Pan Bolts	165 (19)
Throttle Pressure Linkage Rod Swivel Screw	100 (11)

[1] – Tighten to specification; then back off 2 1/2 turns.
[2] – Tighten to specification; then back off 2 turns on A-518/46RH and A-727/36RH/37RH or 4 turns on all others.

Aspire, Capri, Continental, Cougar, Crown Victoria, Escort, Festiva, Grand Marquis, Mark VII, Mustang, Probe, Sable, Taurus, Tempo, Thunderbird, Topaz, Town Car, Tracer

APPLICATION

NOTE: For automatic transmission applications, see appropriate table in APPLICATIONS & IDENTIFICATION.

LUBRICATION

SERVICE INTERVALS

Check fluid level at every engine oil change. Fluid, filter change and band adjustments are not required under normal operation. If vehicle is operated under following conditions, replace transmission fluid and filter every 30 months or 30,000 miles:
- In hot weather with temperature greater than 90°F (32°C), carrying heavy loads and/or in hilly terrain.
- Towing a trailer or using a car top carrier.
- In police, taxi or delivery service.

CHECKING FLUID LEVEL

NOTE: On AXOD-E and AX4S transmission/transaxle, fluid level should only be checked when fluid is cold.

1) Transmission or transaxle must be at normal operating temperature with vehicle on level ground. Apply parking brake, and run engine at curb idle. Shift gear selector lever through all positions, ending in Park.
2) Fluid level should be in crosshatch area on dipstick if checked at operating temperature. If transmission is at room temperature, fluid level should be between 2 dimples on bottom of dipstick.
3) DO NOT overfill. Check condition of fluid for contamination and burned smell. Fully reseat dipstick.

RECOMMENDED FLUID

On Festiva, use Dexron-II. On all others, use Mercon (XT-2-QDX) ATF.

FLUID CAPACITIES

NOTE: Transmission fluid capacities in TRANSMISSION FLUID CAPACITIES table are approximate quantities. Correct fluid level should be determined using dipstick.

TRANSMISSION FLUID CAPACITIES

Application	¹ Qts. (L)
AOD (1993)	12.3 (11.6)
AOD-E & 4R70W	12.5 (11.8)
AXOD-E (1993)	12.8 (12.2)
ATX	5.6-6.0 (5.3-5.7)
A4LD (1993)	9.7 (9.2)
AX4S (1994)	12.3 (11.6)
CD4E (1994)	8.8 (8.3)
FLC	8.6 (8.1)
4EAT	
Capri	6.0 (5.7)
Escort & Tracer	6.7 (6.3)
Probe	9.3 (8.8)

¹ – Includes oil cooler (if equipped).

DRAINING & REFILLING

1) To drain torque converter on AOD transmission, remove lower engine dust cover. Rotate torque converter until drain plug is accessible. Remove plug and allow to drain.
2) On all models, loosen oil pan attaching bolts to drain fluid. Remove oil pan. If filter is to be replaced, reinstall using NEW gasket or "O" rings. Install NEW filter and gasket.

3) On all models, clean oil pan and install pan with NEW gasket. Tighten bolts to specification. See OIL PAN TIGHTENING SPECIFICATIONS table. Pour fresh fluid through filler tube. Check fluid level.

NOTE: Cooler and lines should be thoroughly flushed if transmission was removed for overhaul. Cooler Line Disconnector (T82L-9500-AH) is necessary to remove cooler lines.

ADJUSTMENTS

CAUTION: When battery is disconnected, vehicle computer and memory systems may lose memory data. Driveability problems may exist until computer systems have completed a relearn cycle. See COMPUTER RELEARN PROCEDURES article in GENERAL INFORMATION before disconnecting battery.

2-4 BAND

4EAT – Remove lower oil pan. Loosen 2-4 band lock nut and tighten piston stem to 105-130 INCH lbs. (12-15 N.m). Loosen piston stem 1 1/2 turns. Hold piston stem and tighten lock nut to 18-29 ft. lbs. (24-39 N.m). Install oil pan and refill transmission.

INTERMEDIATE & OVERDRIVE BANDS

A4LD – Remove and discard lock nut(s). Install new sealing nut(s) and tighten piston stem(s) to 105-130 INCH lbs. (12-15 N.m). Loosen piston stem(s) 2 turns. Hold piston stem and lighten lock nut to 18-29 ft. lbs. (25-39 N.m).
ATX (Aspire & Festiva) – Loosen intermediate band lock nut and tighten band adjusting stop to 105-130 INCH lbs. (12-15 N.m). Loosen band adjusting stop 3 turns. Apply Liquid Gasket (E1FZ-19562-A) to band adjusting stop. Hold band adjusting stop and tighten lock nut to 41-59 ft. lbs. (55-80 N.m).

THROTTLE VALVE CABLE/LINKAGE

AOD – 1) Apply parking brake. Set transmission selector in Neutral position. DO NOT set selector in Park. Remove air cleaner cover and inlet duct. Pry cable assembly from grommet on throttle body lever.
2) Using small screwdriver, push out White locking tab. Ensure plastic block slides freely on notched rod. While holding throttle lever firmly against idle stop, push grooved pin into grommet as far as it will go.
FLC (3.0L) – Remove throttle body linkage cover shield. Disengage throttle valve adjustment tab. Rotate throttle cam pulley 2-3 times to remove previous setting. Hold transaxle throttle valve lever fully toward dash panel using a long screwdriver, and secure adjustment tab.

SHIFT CABLE/LINKAGE

AOD, AOD-E, AXOD-E, AX4S, 4ALD & 4R70W – 1) Position transmission shift lever in Overdrive position. Hold shift lever against rear overdrive stop with a constant force of about 3 lbs. (1.4 kg). Loosen shift control cable retaining nut at transmission. Ensure transmission/transaxle manual lever is in Overdrive position. On AOD and 4ALD, overdrive is third detent from rearmost position. On AOD-E, AXOD-E, AX4S and 4R70W, overdrive is second detent from rearmost position.
2) Tighten shift control cable retaining nut to 10-18 ft. lbs. (13.5-25 N.m). Check transmission operation in each position. Ensure neutral start switch and back-up lights operate properly.
CD4E & 4EAT (Probe) – 1) Disconnect negative battery cable. Remove floor console. Shift gear shift lever to Park position. Remove position indicator mounting screws and position indicator. On 4EAT, slide lock cover back. *See Fig. 1.*
2) On all models, disconnect set button. Slide gear shift lever to adjust Park position. Connect set button. On 4EAT, slide lock cover to lock set button in place. On all models, install position indicator. Install floor console.
FLC – Position shift lever in Drive position. Loosen shift control cable retaining nut at transaxle. Ensure transaxle manual lever is in Drive position (second detent from rearmost position). Tighten retaining nut to 10-19 ft. lbs. (14-27 N.m). Check transaxle operation in all positions. Ensure neutral start switch and back-up lights operate.

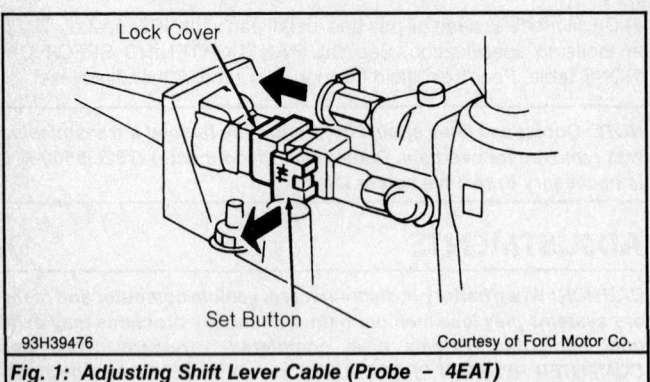

Fig. 1: Adjusting Shift Lever Cable (Probe – 4EAT)

4EAT (Capri) – **1)** Place shift lever in Neutral. Remove spring clip and pin attaching shift cable to transaxle shift lever. Rotate transaxle shift lever fully counterclockwise to Park position, then rotate transaxle shift lever clockwise 2 detents to Neutral.

2) While rotating lever, position it between ends of shift cable trunnion. If hole in transaxle shift lever aligns with hole in shift cable trunnion, shift cable is properly adjusted. If holes do not align, go to next step. If holes align, go to step **5)**.

3) Loosen lock nut and unscrew shift knob. Raise ashtray receptacle and disconnect wiring. Remove shift quadrant. Loosen adjuster nuts on shift cable. Position shifter lever in Park, and check position of detent spring roller. If spring roller is not centered in Park detent, loosen attaching screws and move detent spring to center spring roller.

4) Install shift quadrant. Place shift lever in Neutral. Thread adjuster nuts on shift cable until holes in transaxle shift lever and shift cable trunnion are aligned. See Fig. 2.

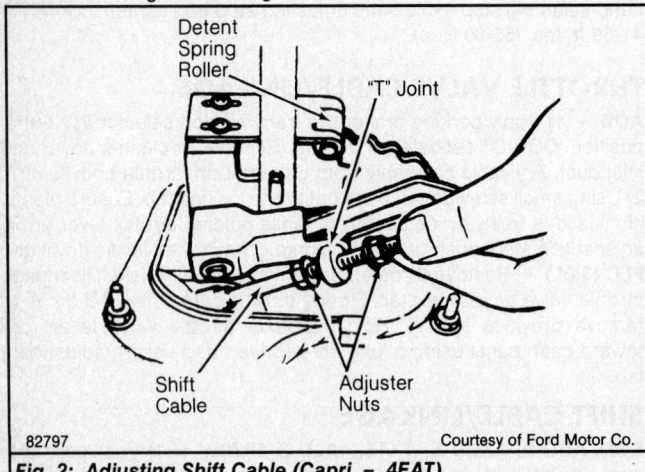

Fig. 2: Adjusting Shift Cable (Capri – 4EAT)

5) Tighten adjuster nuts to 71-97 INCH lbs. (8-11 N.m). Check alignment of holes in transaxle shift lever and shift cable trunnion to see if adjustment was disturbed while tightening adjuster nuts.

6) If adjustment was not disturbed, install transaxle shift lever-to-shift cable pin and retaining clip. With shift lever in Neutral, press shift interlock button and carefully pull shift lever rearward while assistant watches transaxle shift lever. When transaxle shift lever begins to move, note amount shift lever has moved.

7) When transaxle shift lever begins to move, note amount shift lever has moved. With shift lever in Neutral, press shift interlock button and carefully pull shift lever rearward. When shift lever begins to move, note amount shift lever has moved.

8) If forward and rearward movements of shift lever are not equal, turn adjuster nuts slightly forward and rearward until movements are the same. Tighten adjuster nuts to 71-97 INCH lbs. (8-11 N.m). Positon and install console. Install shift control knob.

4EAT (Escort & Tracer) – **1)** Disconnect negative battery cable to deactivate shift-lock system. Put shift lever in Park position. Remove shift lever knob-to-shift lever screw. Remove knob. Remove shift selector console.

2) Disconnect wiring connectors as needed. Remove position indicator. Disconnect shift lock servo connector. Loosen shift cable bracket mounting bolts. See Fig. 3. Push shift selector lever in Park position and hold it.

3) Tighten shift cable bracket mounting bolts. Lightly press shift selector push rod and make sure guide plate and guide pin clearances are correct when gear shift lever is in Park, Neutral and Overdrive. See Fig. 4. To install remaining components, reverse removal procedure.

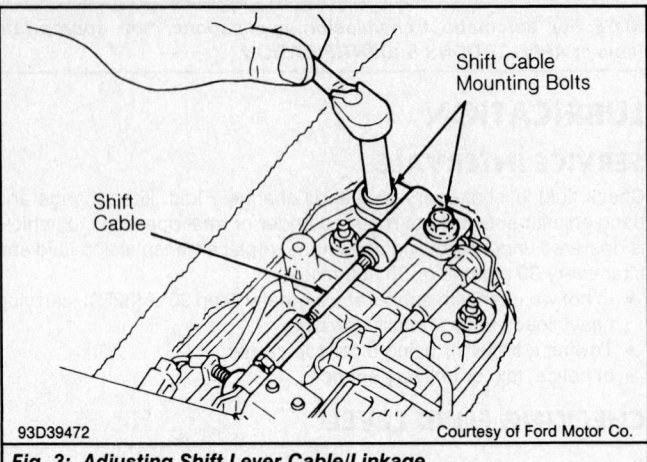

Fig. 3: Adjusting Shift Lever Cable/Linkage (Escort & Tracer – 4EAT)

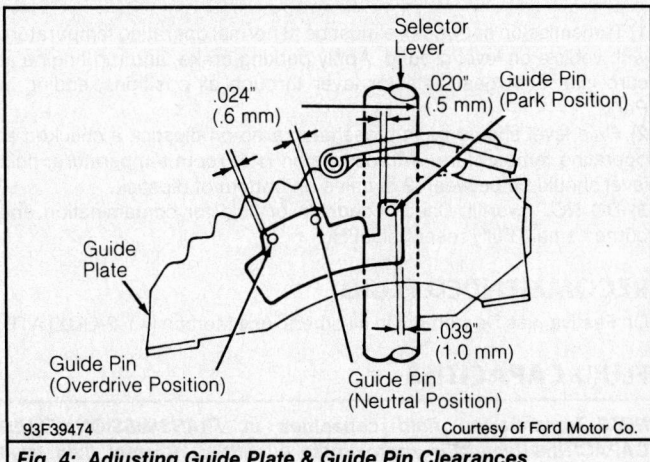

Fig. 4: Adjusting Guide Plate & Guide Pin Clearances (Escort & Tracer – 4EAT)

ATX (Aspire & Festiva) – **1)** Disconnect negative battery cable to deactivate shift-lock system. Put shift lever in Park position. Remove shift lever knob-to-shift lever screw. Remove knob. Remove shift selector console.

2) Loosen shift cable adjuster nuts until they reach and of cable threads. See Fig. 2. Place shift lever in Park. Tighten lower adjustment nut until it lightly touches "T" joint, then tighten upper adjustment nut to 80-97 INCH lbs. (9-11 N.m).

3) Lightly press selector push rod and make sure guide pin clearance is correct. See Fig. 5. Check guide pin clearance when shift lever is in Neutral and Drive. Readjust shift cable as necessary.

4) Install 4 shift quadrant attaching screws, shift lever knob, lock nut and shift console. Connect negative battery cable.

SHIFT-LOCK

ATX (Aspire & Festiva) – **1)** Put shift lever in Park position. Remove shift lever knob-to-shift lever screw. Remove knob. Remove shift selector console. Remove shift quadrant. Align holes in slider and shift quadrant. Install an alignment pin.

2) Install quadrant and remove alignment pin. Clearance between lock lever and emergency override lever. See Fig. 6. Install lock nut and shift lever knob. Tighten lock nut to 11-15 ft. lbs. (15-20 N.m). Install console.

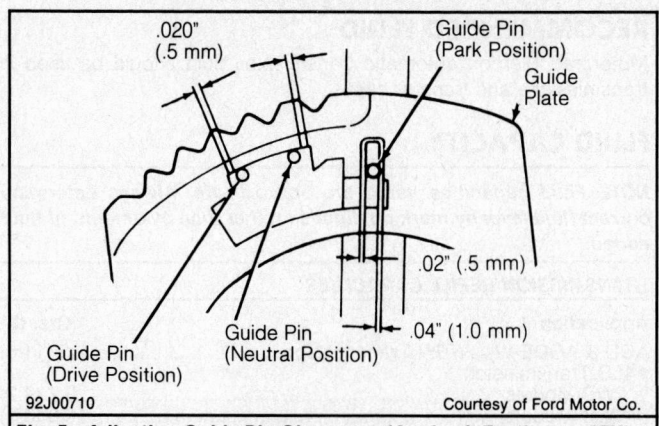

Fig. 5: Adjusting Guide Pin Clearance (Aspire & Festiva – ATX)

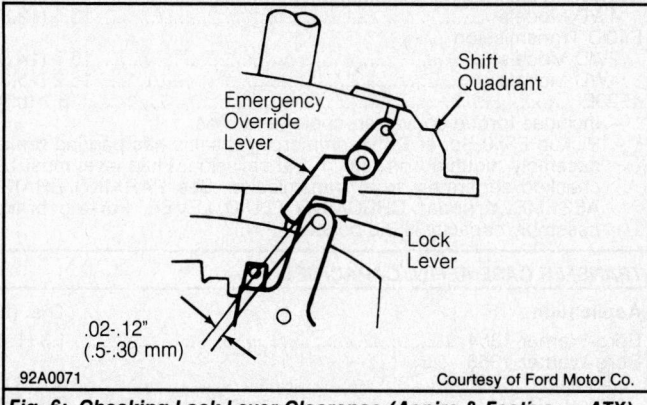

Fig. 6: Checking Lock Lever Clearance (Aspire & Festiva – ATX)

KICKDOWN CABLE

NOTE: Procedure for other models is not available from manufacturer.

4EAT (Capri) – 1) Connect a pressure gauge to line pressure port. Shift transaxle into Park. Start and warm up engine. Engine idle speed should be 800-900 RPM.
2) Turn locknuts on kickdown cable toward throttle connection until line pressure exceeds 60 psi (4.2 kg/cm²). Turn locknuts on kickdown cable away from throttle connection until line pressure is 54-60 psi (3.7-4.2 kg/cm²). Stop engine.
3) To install new cable, fully open throttle valve. Crimp pin with protector installed around kickdown cable. Remove protector and check inner cable for slack. Adjust as necessary.

MANUAL LEVER POSITION (MLP) SENSOR/SWITCH

AOD-E, AX4S, CD4E & 4R70W – Remove nut securing Manual Lever Position (MLP) sensor to manual lever. Turn manual lever to neutral position. Loosen bolts securing MLP sensor to transaxle. Using Adjuster (T92P-70010-AH), align MLP sensor slots. Tighten MLP sensor mounting bolts. Install manual lever retaining nut. Tighten nut to specification. See TORQUE SPECIFICATIONS. Test sensor operation.

4EAT (Escort & Tracer) – 1) Put shift selector lever in Neutral position. Remove nut holding manual shaft lever to manual shaft. Remove lever from manual shaft. Loosen MLP sensor mount bolts.
2) Insert a .079" (2.0 mm) pin in alignment holes. Tighten sensor mounting bolts to specification and remove alignment pin. See TORQUE SPECIFICATIONS. Install manual shaft lever onto manual shaft.

NOTE: Probe models equipped with 4EAT transaxle use MLP switch instead of MLP sensor.

4EAT (Probe) – 1) Disconnect negative battery cable. Remove shift cable from manual shaft. Disconnect MLP switch connector. Rotate manual shaft to align with alignment mark on top of MLP switch.
2) Loosen MLP sensor mounting bolts. Adjust MLP switch so that continuity is present between terminals "A" and "H", and between terminals "F" and "I". Tighten mounting bolts to specification. See TORQUE SPECIFICATIONS. *See Fig. 7.* Install shift cable and negative battery cable.

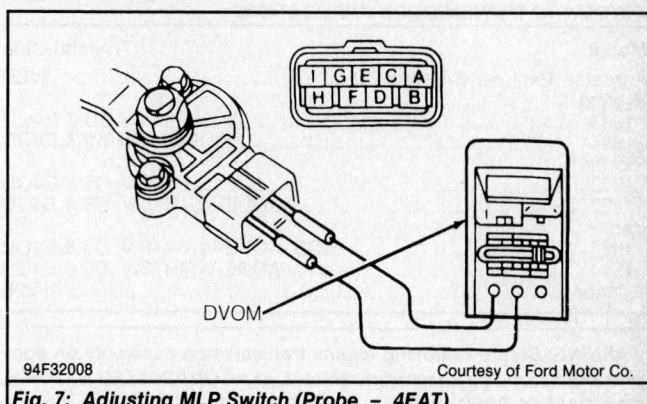

Fig. 7: Adjusting MLP Switch (Probe – 4EAT)

PARK/NEUTRAL POSITION (PNP) SWITCH

NOTE: On AOD, AOD-E and A4LD transmissions, PNP adjustment is not necessary. On 4EAT transaxle, see MANUAL LEVER POSITION (MLP) SENSOR/SWITCH under ADJUSTMENTS.

AXOD-E – 1) Remove steering column tilt release lever by removing retainer screw. Remove upper and lower steering column shrouds. Remove ignition lock cylinder. Put shift lever in Overdrive position.
2) Shift lever should be located firmly in Overdrive position. Adjust shift select switch with adjustment wheel on shift select cable. When adjusted properly, PRNDL indicator should completely cover overdrive letter. Calibration dots should not show Red.
3) Cycle shift lever through all positions, and ensure PRNDL indicator completely covers proper letter or number in each position. Install upper and lower shrouds. Install ignition lock cylinder and tilt release.
FLC – Loosen Park/Neutral Position (PNP) switch mounting bolts. Hold manual valve in neutral position. Insert .089" (2.3 mm) drill bit through PNP switch housing and internal actuator until bit seats against back of PNP switch. Tighten mounting bolts. See TORQUE SPECIFICATIONS.

TORQUE SPECIFICATIONS

TORQUE SPECIFICATIONS

Transmission	Ft. Lbs (N.m)
Drain Plug (ATX)	29-40 (39-54)
Manual Lever-To-MLP Sensor Nut	12-16 (16-22)

	INCH Lbs. (N.m)
Filter Screen	
AOD, AOD-E, AXOD-E & 4R70W	80-124 (8.9-14)
A4LD	71-97 (8-11)
FLC	80-108 (8.9-12)
4EAT	71-97 (8-11)
Manual Lever Position Sensor/Switch Bolts	
AOD-E, AX4S & 4R70W	84-108 (9-12)
CD4E & 4EAT	71-95 (8-11)
Park/Neutral Position Switch Bolts	84 (9)
Oil Pan	
AOD, AOD-E & 4R70W	71-124 (8-14)
AXOD-E & AX4S	124-144 (14-16)
ATX	43-69 (5-8)
CD4E	1
FLC	2
4EAT	71-88 (8-10)
Valve Body Cover (FLC)	84-108 (9-12)

1 – Tighten to 15-20 ft. lbs. (22-27 N.m)
2 – Tighten to 12-17 ft. lbs. (16-23 N.m)

Aerostar, Bronco, Explorer, "E" & "F" Series, Ranger, Villager

NOTE: Unless otherwise specified, references to Pickup include the F350 Super Duty commercial chassis.

APPLICATION

AUTOMATIC TRANSMISSION APPLICATIONS

Model	[1] Transmission
Aerostar, Explorer & Ranger	A4LD
Bronco	
1993	AOD & E4OD
1994	AODE-W/4R70W & E4OD
Pickup	
1993	AOD, C6 & E4OD
1994	AODE-W/4R70W, C6 & E4OD
Van	
1993	AOD, AODE-W/4R70W, C6 & E4OD
1994	AODE-W/4R70W, C6 & E4OD
Villager	4F20E

WARNING: Before removing engine/transmission assembly on compressed natural gas powered vehicles, see COMPRESSED NATURAL GAS SAFETY PRECAUTIONS in CAUTIONS & WARNINGS article in APPLICATIONS & IDENTIFICATION.

LUBRICATION

SERVICE INTERVALS

Transmission – Vehicles used in normal service do not require regularly scheduled maintenance. Fluid level should be checked whenever underhood maintenance is performed, or if leakage is detected. Clutch bands on A4LD and C-6 should be adjusted when quality of shifts deteriorates or otherwise indicates improper band adjustment. On vehicles used for fleet service or those operated under severe conditions (police, taxi or towing), regular transmission fluid changes are required every 30,000 miles.

Transfer Case – Under normal driving conditions, replace transfer case fluid every 60,000 miles. Under severe driving conditions, perform this service more frequently.

CHECKING FLUID LEVEL

NOTE: Pickup F350 Super Duty commercial chassis has a parking brake assembly mounted on rear of transmission. Parking brake assembly contains a separate reservoir; fluid level must be checked separately from transmission. See PARKING BRAKE ASSEMBLY under CHECKING FLUID LEVEL.

Transmission – **1)** Check fluid level with vehicle parked on level surface, engine and transmission at normal operating temperatures and engine idling. Apply parking brake and move transmission selector lever through all ranges, ending in "P".

WARNING: On 4WD models, ensure transfer case is in any gear range EXCEPT Neutral before checking transmission fluid level.

2) Fluid level should be between ADD and DON'T ADD marks on dipstick (in crosshatched area). Add fluid through filler tube as needed. DO NOT overfill.
Parking Brake Assembly (Pickup F350 Super Duty Commercial Chassis) – Check lubricant level at filler plug hole on side of parking brake assembly mounted on rear of transmission. Fluid level should be even with bottom of filler plug hole. Add lubricant as needed.
Transfer Case – Remove fill plug. If fluid drains out or is level with opening, reinstall drain plug. If not, fill until fluid is level with fill plug opening.

RECOMMENDED FLUID

Motorcraft Mercon automatic transmission fluid should be used in transmissions and transfer cases.

FLUID CAPACITY

NOTE: Fluid capacities listed are approximate. Always determine correct fluid level by mark on dipstick rather than by amount of fluid added.

TRANSMISSION REFILL CAPACITIES

Application [1]	Qts. (L)
AOD & AODE-W/4R70W Transmission	12.3 (11.6)
A4LD Transmission	
2WD Models	9.7 (9.2)
4WD Models	10.0 (9.5)
C-6 Transmission	
2WD Models	12.0 (11.4)
4WD Models	13.5 (12.8)
E4OD Transmission	
2WD Models	15.7 (14.8)
4WD Models	16.2 (15.3)
4F20E	8.7 (8.3)

[1] – Includes torque converter, cooler and lines.
[2] – Pickup F350 Super Duty commercial chassis has parking brake assembly mounted on rear of transmission. Fluid level must be checked separately from transmission. See PARKING BRAKE ASSEMBLY under CHECKING FLUID LEVEL. Parking brake assembly capacity is 3.8 ounces (.11L).

TRANSFER CASE REFILL CAPACITIES

Application	Qts. (L)
Borg-Warner 1354	1.3 (1.2)
Borg-Warner 1356	
With PTO	4.1 (3.8)
Without PTO	2.0 (1.9)
Dana TC-28	2.3 (2.2)

DRAINING & REFILLING

Transmission – **1)** Loosen oil pan bolts and tap pan to break gasket seal. Allow fluid to drain. Remove oil pan bolts and oil pan. Discard used filter and gasket. Install NEW filter and gasket. On all transmissions, clean pan and install with NEW gasket.

CAUTION: On AOD transmission, do not attempt to reuse oil filter after soaking filter in solvent. Filter material may disintegrate.

2) On all transmissions, add 3 qts. (2.8L) transmission fluid. Check fluid level. When filling a dry transmission and converter, refer to TRANSMISSION REFILL CAPACITIES table. Recheck fluid level when transmission is at normal operating temperature. DO NOT overfill.
Transfer Case – Remove drain plug from transfer case. Remove fill plug for easier draining. With fluid fully drained, reinstall drain plug. Fill transfer case to fill plug opening with Mercon ATF.

ADJUSTMENTS

INTERMEDIATE (FRONT) BAND & OVERDRIVE BAND

A4LD Transmission – **1)** Remove and discard lock nut. Install NEW lock nut. Tighten adjusting screw to 120 INCH lbs. (14 N.m). *See Fig. 1.*
2) Back off 2 turns for overdrive and intermediate bands. Hold adjusting screw in position and tighten NEW lock nut to 40 ft. lbs. (54 N.m).

NOTE: C-6 transmission does not have an overdrive band.

C-6 Transmission – **1)** Clean dirt from band adjusting screw area. Remove and discard band adjusting screw lock nut. Install NEW lock nut.
2) Tighten adjusting screw to 120 INCH lbs. (14 N.m). *See Fig. 2.* Back off screw 1 1/2 turns. Hold adjusting screw in position and tighten NEW lock nut to 40 ft. lbs. (54 N.m).

AUTOMATIC TRANSMISSION SERVICING
Ford Motor Co. Light Trucks & Vans (Cont.)

2-13

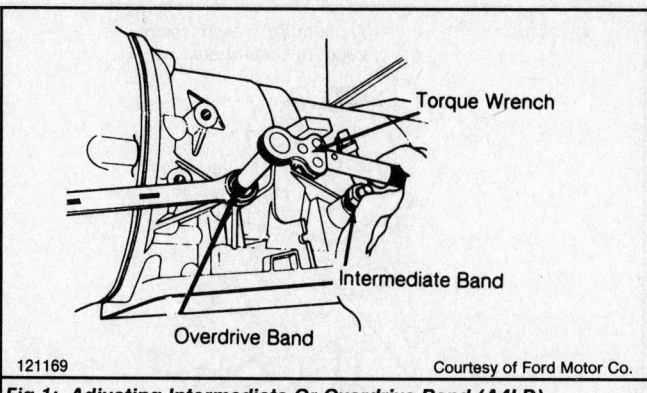

Fig 1: Adjusting Intermediate Or Overdrive Band (A4LD)

121169   Courtesy of Ford Motor Co.

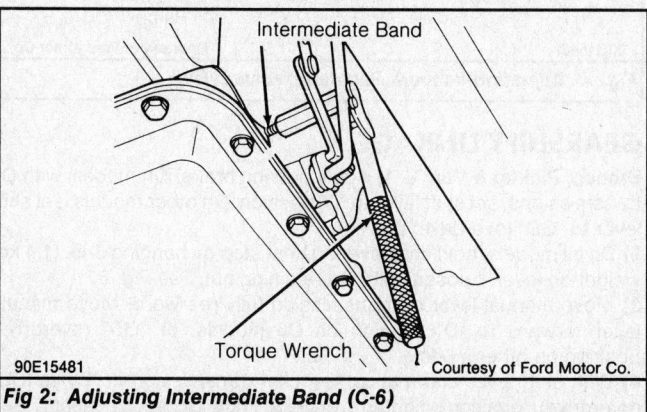

Fig 2: Adjusting Intermediate Band (C-6)

90E15481   Courtesy of Ford Motor Co.

NOTE: On 4F20E (Villager), the 2-4 band is adjusted during overhaul and does not require adjustment during normal service.

KICKDOWN CONTROL CABLE

NOTE: Kickdown control cable self-adjusts after installation by depressing accelerator pedal to floor. No adjustment is required, but cable must be locked in the adjusted position manually. Cable must be adjusted whenever removed or replaced.

Initial Adjustment (A4LD) – If cable has been replaced or removed, adjust kickdown cable. From under the hood, depress the "D"-shaped locking tab while pulling the cable conduit out from cable body. See Fig. 3. Adjust cable by depressing accelerator pedal to floor.

NOTE: If transmission kickdown is difficult to achieve at Wide Open Throttle (WOT), ensure aftermarket floor mats have not been installed or mispositioned behind accelerator pedal, thus restricting full pedal movement.

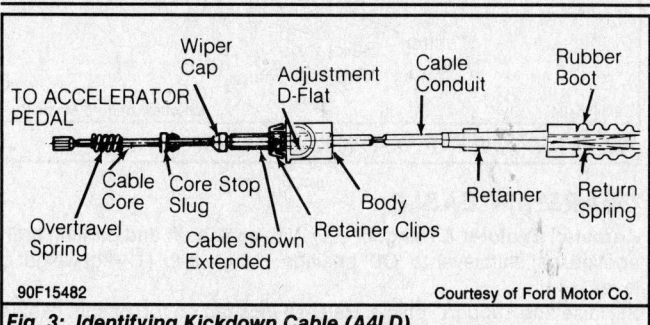

Fig. 3: Identifying Kickdown Cable (A4LD)

90F15482   Courtesy of Ford Motor Co.

THROTTLE VALVE (T.V.) CONTROL CABLE

NOTE: T.V. control cable is locked to proper length during initial assembly. Control cable may require adjustment if throttle body, control cable, or transmission is replaced.

Cable Adjustment With Engine Off – 1) Apply parking brake. Shift transmission to Neutral. DO NOT place transmission in Park. On F150/250 and Bronco models, remove cable linkage protective cover. On all models, ensure throttle lever is resting against idle stop. DO NOT adjust idle stop.
2) Ensure T.V. control cable is properly routed, free of sharp bends, and operates freely. Using small screwdriver, pry lock tab outward to release T.V. control cable at throttle body. See Fig. 4.

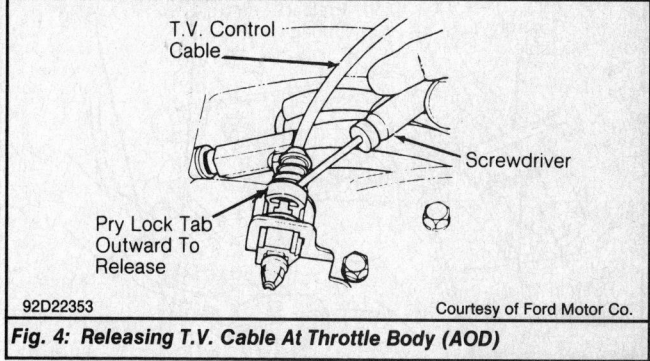

Fig. 4: Releasing T.V. Cable At Throttle Body (AOD)

92D22353   Courtesy of Ford Motor Co.

3) Install return spring on T.V. control lever at the transmission. Hook spring onto rear of transmission case. Ensure T.V. control lever is held in idle position (fully rearward toward rear of transmission).

NOTE: If necessary, use 2 return springs to retain T.V. control lever in position.

4) With T.V. cable lock tab released and return spring in place, rotate T.V. control lever at transmission about 20 degrees and return slowly. Push lock tab downward on T.V. control cable at throttle body until lock tab is flush. Remove return spring.
T.V. Pressure Check & Adjustment With Engine On – 1) Remove plug. Install Pressure Gauge (T86L-70002-A) in T.V. pressure tap on side of transmission case. See Fig. 5. Remove cover from T.V. control cable linkage.
2) Insert tapered end of T.V. Cable Control Pressure Gauge Adjuster (T86L-70332-A) between slug on end of cable and plastic fitting attached to throttle lever. See Fig. 6.
3) Push T.V. cable control pressure gauge adjuster inward as far as possible, forcing slug away from plastic fitting. Start and warm engine and transmission to normal operating temperature.

NOTE: Transmission fluid temperature must be 100-150°F (37-65°C) when checking T.V. pressure.

4) Apply parking brake. Place transmission in Neutral. DO NOT check T.V. control pressure with transmission in Park. With engine idling, T.V. control pressure should be 28-38 psi (1.97-2.67 kg/cm²).
5) If T.V. control pressure is not within specification, adjust T.V. control cable. To adjust T.V. control cable, pry up on T.V. control cable locking tab at throttle body. See Fig. 6.
6) The adjuster preload spring should cause adjusting slider to move away from throttle body, causing T.V. control pressure to increase. Push on adjusting slider from behind throttle body bracket until T.V. control pressure is 33 psi (2.3 kg/cm²). See Fig. 6.
7) While holding slider, push T.V. control cable locking tab downward as far as possible to lock slider into position. Remove T.V. cable control pressure gauge adjuster. Allow engine to return to idle.
8) With engine idling and transmission in Neutral, T.V. control pressure should be less than 5 psi (.3 kg/cm²), preferably near zero. If T.V. control pressure is not as specified, readjust. Remove pressure gauge. Install and tighten plug to specification. See TORQUE SPECIFICATIONS.

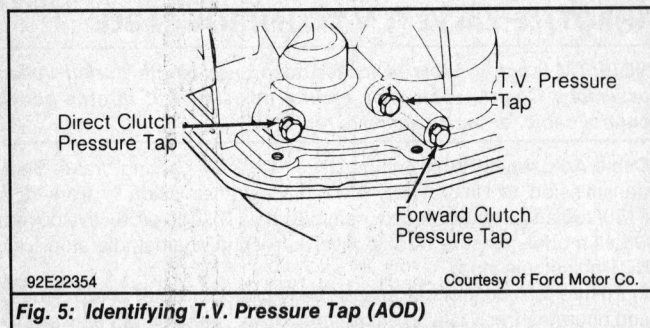

Fig. 5: Identifying T.V. Pressure Tap (AOD)

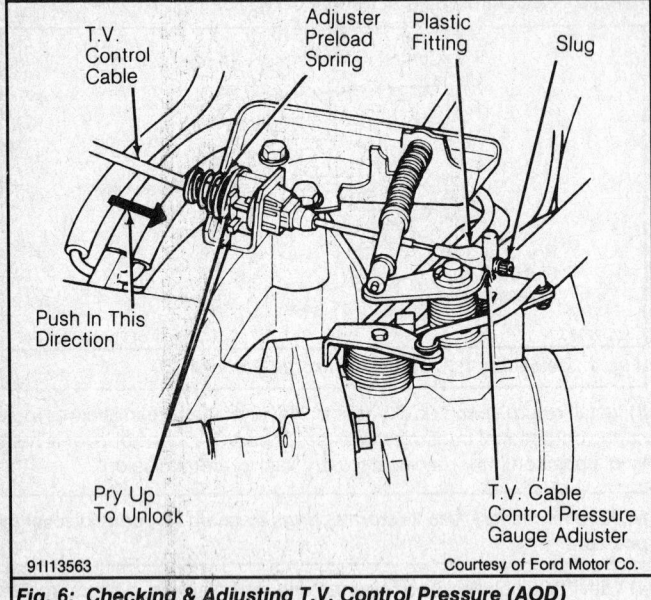

Fig. 6: Checking & Adjusting T.V. Control Pressure (AOD)

VACUUM REGULATOR VALVE (VRV)

Only 7.3L V8 diesel A/T vehicles have a VRV. VRV is mounted on the left side of fuel injection pump and provides transmission with vacuum signal to control shift points. Signal strength is determined by VRV.

Checking VRV Operation – 1) With engine off, disconnect the 2-port vacuum connector from VRV. Remove throttle cable from injection pump throttle lever (on right side of pump). Disconnect throttle return spring.

2) Attach one end of return spring over throttle lever ball stud. Install other end of spring over throttle cable support bracket. Insert .515 in. (13.0 mm) Gauge Block (T83T-7B200-AH) between pump boss and wide open throttle stop screw.

3) Spring will hold throttle lever against gauge block during vacuum check and VRV adjustment. Attach vacuum pump to VAC (upper) port of VRV, and attach vacuum gauge to TRANS (lower) port. Apply and maintain 20 in. Hg. Vacuum gauge should indicate 6-8 in. Hg. If reading is not as specified, adjust VRV.

Adjusting VRV – 1) Loosen 2 VRV adjustment screws. See Fig. 7. With vacuum pump, gauge, gauge block and return spring in position (as during checking procedure), maintain 20 in. Hg with pump. Rotate VRV until vacuum gauge reads 6.5-7.5 in. Hg. Tighten mounting screws.

2) If correct vacuum reading cannot be obtained by adjusting VRV, replace VRV. If correct reading is obtained, remove gauge block, and connect throttle return spring. Ensure pump lever returns to idle position. Apply 20 in. Hg with vacuum pump.

3) While maintaining vacuum, cycle throttle lever from idle to wide open throttle 5 times. Vacuum gauge must indicate a minimum of 13 in. Hg at idle position. If vacuum gauge reads less than 13 in. Hg, replace VRV. Remove vacuum pump and gauge and reconnect vacuum connector to VRV. Connect throttle cable.

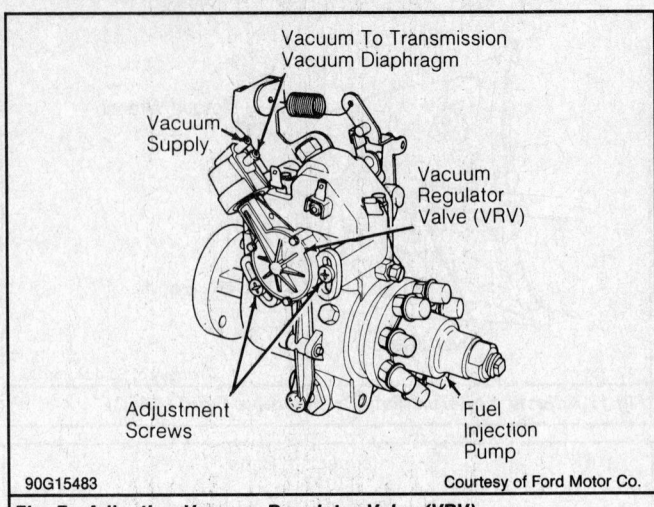

Fig. 7: Adjusting Vacuum Regulator Valve (VRV)

GEARSHIFT LINKAGE

Bronco, Pickup & Van – 1) Apply parking brake. On models with C6 transmissions, set shift lever to "D" position. On other models, set shift lever to "OD" (overdrive) position.

2) On all models, hold shift lever against stop by hanging 3-lb. (1.4 kg) weight on lever. Loosen shift rod retaining nut. See Fig. 8.

3) Move manual lever on transmission fully rearward. Move manual lever forward to "D" position on C6 models, or "OD" (overdrive) position on other models.

4) With shift lever and manual lever on transmission in "D" or "OD" (overdrive) position, tighten retaining nut to specification. See TORQUE SPECIFICATIONS. Remove weight from shift lever. Check for normal operation in all selected positions.

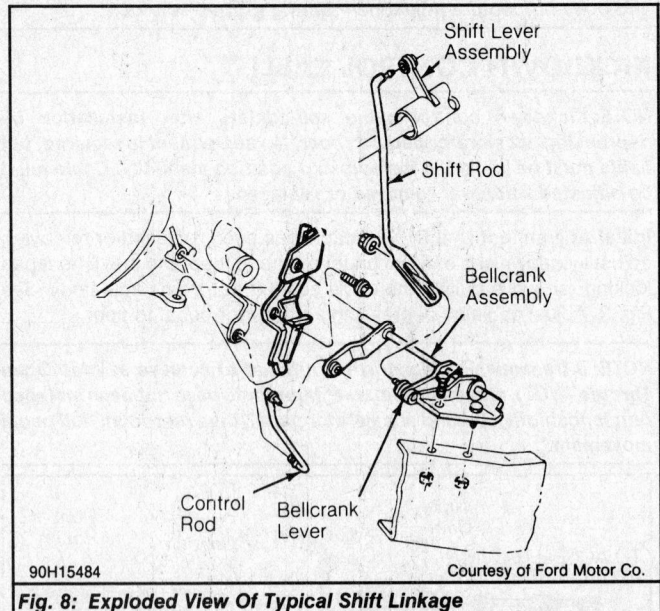

Fig. 8: Exploded View Of Typical Shift Linkage

GEARSHIFT CABLE

Aerostar, Explorer & Ranger – 1) With engine off and parking brake applied, set shift lever to "OD" position. Hang a 3-lb. (1.4 kg) weight on lever.

2) Raise and support vehicle. Release lock tab on top of shift cable at transmission bracket by pushing tangs downward. Disconnect shift cable from manual lever on transmission.

3) On Aerostar models, move manual lever all the way forward, then rearward 3 detent positions. On Explorer and Ranger models, move manual lever all the way rearward, then forward 3 detent positions.

AUTOMATIC TRANSMISSION SERVICING
Ford Motor Co. Light Trucks & Vans (Cont.)

2-15

4) On all models, reconnect shift cable at manual lever on transmission. Push lock tab downward. Ensure lock tab fully engages and gearshift cable is locked in place.

5) Ensure shift cable is properly secured to floor panels. Lower vehicle. If shift indicator does not align with "OD" position on instrument panel, rotate thumb screw near shift indicator until properly aligned. Remove weight from shift lever.

NOTE: If necessary, remove steering column covers to gain access to thumb screw for shift indicator adjustment. Ensure transmission operates in all gear ranges with correct transmission detent position.

Bronco, Pickup & Van – 1) Apply parking brake. On models with C6 transmissions, set shift lever to "D" position. On remaining models, set shift lever to "OD" (overdrive) position. Hang a 3-lb. (1.4 kg) weight on lever.

2) On all models, raise and support vehicle. Disconnect shift cable from manual lever on transmission. Pull downward on lock tab on shift cable at transmission bracket.

3) Move manual lever on transmission fully forward. Move manual lever backward 3 detent positions to "D" position on C6 models, or "OD" (overdrive) position on other models.

4) Reconnect shift cable to manual lever on transmission. Push lock tab upward. Lower vehicle.

5) If shift indicator does not align with "D" position on C6 models, or "OD" (overdrive) position on other models, rotate thumb screw near shift indicator until properly aligned. Remove weight from shift lever.

NOTE: If necessary, remove steering column covers to gain access to thumb screw for shift indicator adjustment. Ensure transmission operates in all gear ranges with correct transmission detent position.

Villager – Place gear selector in Park. Loosen shift cable nut. Remove slack from cable. Tighten shift cable nut. Check selector operation.

NEUTRAL SAFETY SWITCH

NOTE: AOD and A4LD switches are not adjustable. Use Neutral Start Switch Socket (T74P-77247-A) to replace switch. If any other socket is used, damage to switch may occur. Other transmissions use manual position lever sensor.

MANUAL LEVER POSITION SENSOR

AODE-W/4R70W – Install Gear Position Adjuster (T91P-70010-A) into slots in area of MLPS on left side of transmission. *See Fig. 9.* If slots on sensor do not align with slots on adjuster, loosen sensor mounting bolts and rotate sensor as required. Tighten mounting bolts to specification. See TORQUE SPECIFICATIONS.

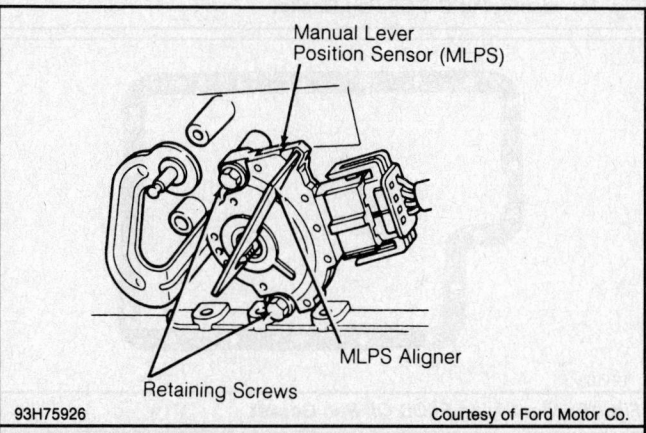

Fig. 9: *Adjusting Manual Lever Position Sensor (AODE-W/4R70W)*

C6 – 1) Ensure shift cable or linkage is properly adjusted. See GEARSHIFT CABLE or GEARSHIFT LINKAGE under ADJUSTMENTS. Apply parking brake. Set shift lever to Neutral position.

2) Loosen MLPS retaining screws. Install MLPS Aligner (T92P-70010-AH) in 3 slots on switch and actuator plate of MLPS. *See Fig. 10.*

CAUTION: Ensure each leg of MLPS aligner engages with each slot of MLPS.

3) Tighten MLPS retaining screws to specification. See TORQUE SPECIFICATIONS. Remove MLPS aligner.

4) Proper adjustment can be confirmed by ensuring etched line in actuator and housing are aligned when shift lever is in Neutral. Verify vehicle starts only in Park or Neutral, and back-up lights operate only in Reverse.

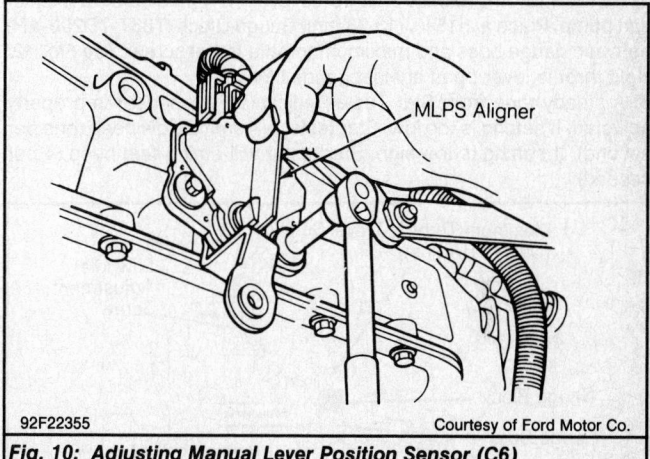

Fig. 10: *Adjusting Manual Lever Position Sensor (C6)*

E4OD – Remove shift linkage from transmission. Loosen MLPS retaining screws. Using MLPS Aligner (T89T-70010-J), align manual lever position sensor for Neutral gear. *See Fig. 11.* Tighten retaining bolts to specification. See TORQUE SPECIFICATIONS. Install shift linkage.

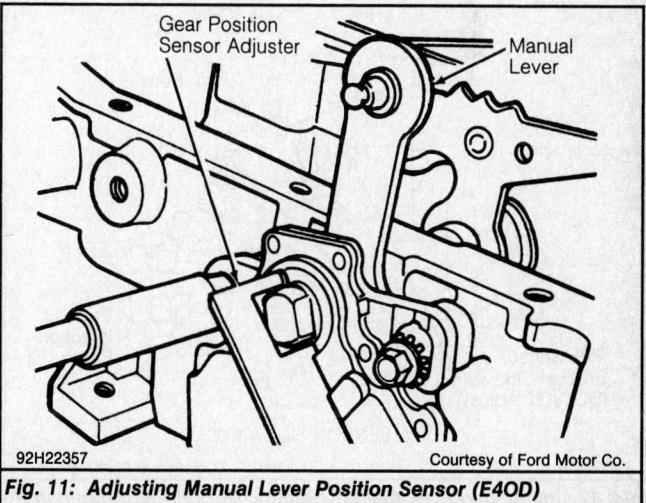

Fig. 11: *Adjusting Manual Lever Position Sensor (E4OD)*

4F20E – Place manual shift lever to Neutral. Install MLPS Adjuster (T92P-70010-CH) through manual lever and MLPS. If tool does not align with hole on sensor, loosen sensor mounting bolts and rotate sensor as required. Tighten mounting bolts to specification. See TORQUE SPECIFICATIONS.

2-16

AUTOMATIC TRANSMISSION SERVICING
Ford Motor Co. Light Trucks & Vans (Cont.)

FUEL INJECTION PUMP LEVER (FIPL) SENSOR (DIESEL ONLY)

NOTE: Checking and adjusting FIPL requires a Star tester.

Checking FIPL Operation – 1) Perform Key On Engine Off (KOEO) self-test. During self-test, hold throttle to floor (wide open throttle) until codes have been displayed. After last service code has been displayed, press Overdrive Cancel Switch (OCS) to initiate FIPL sensor adjustment mode.

NOTE: Star tester will remain in adjustment mode for 10 minutes. Steps 2) and 3) must be done during this time frame. If time limit is exceeded, procedure must be repeated starting at step 1).

2) Remove throttle cable from throttle lever on right side of fuel injection pump. Place a .515 in. (13.08 mm) Gauge Block (T83T-7B200-AH) between gauge boss and maximum throttle travel screw. *See Fig. 12.* Hold throttle lever open against gauge block.

3) A steady tone from Star Tester indicates FIPL sensor is properly adjusted. If setting is too low, Star tester will emit a slow beep (one per second). If setting is too high, Star tester will emit a fast beep (4 per second).

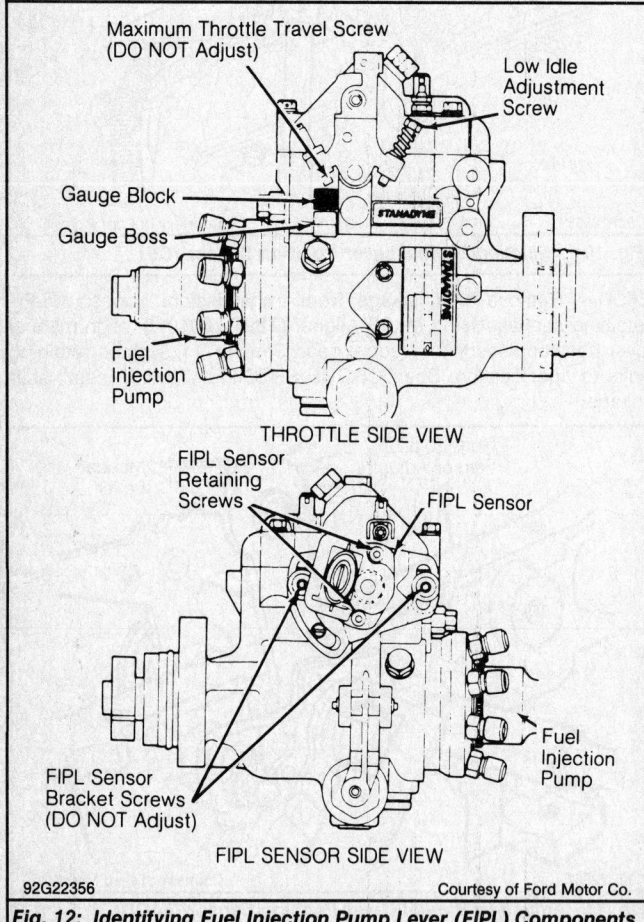

Fig. 12: *Identifying Fuel Injection Pump Lever (FIPL) Components*

Adjusting FIPL – 1) After checking FIPL sensor operation, loosen 2 FIPL sensor-to-mounting bracket screws. Rotate FIPL sensor until a steady tone is heard from Star tester. A constant tone indicates sensor is within range.

CAUTION: FIPL sensor bracket is permanently attached to injection pump with tamper-proof screws. Movement of bracket is NOT intended as means of adjustment.

2) If FIPL sensor cannot be adjusted to obtain a steady tone, replace sensor and repeat adjustment procedure. Remove gauge block. Attach throttle cable. Start engine. Check throttle and transmission shift operation.

CAUTION: DO NOT turn maximum throttle travel screw. This screw has been preset and should not be adjusted.

OIL PAN GASKET IDENTIFICATION

NOTE: For oil pan gasket identification, see Fig. 13, 14, 15, 16 or 17.

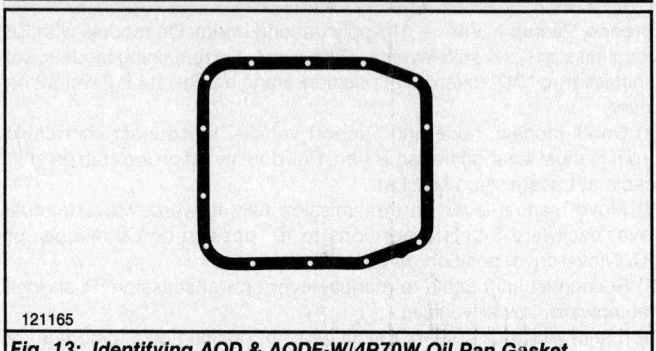

121165

Fig. 13: **Identifying AOD & AODE-W/4R70W Oil Pan Gasket**

121166

Fig. 14: **Identifying A4LD Oil Pan Gasket**

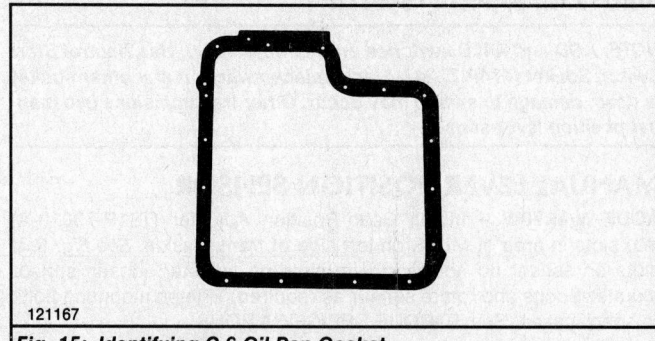

121167

Fig. 15: **Identifying C-6 Oil Pan Gasket**

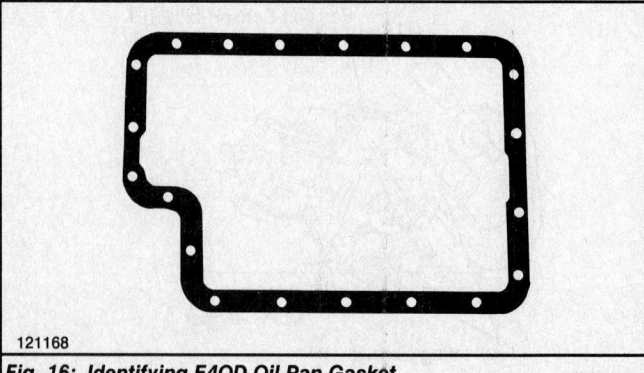

121168

Fig. 16: **Identifying E4OD Oil Pan Gasket**

AUTOMATIC TRANSMISSION SERVICING
Ford Motor Co. Light Trucks & Vans (Cont.)

2-17

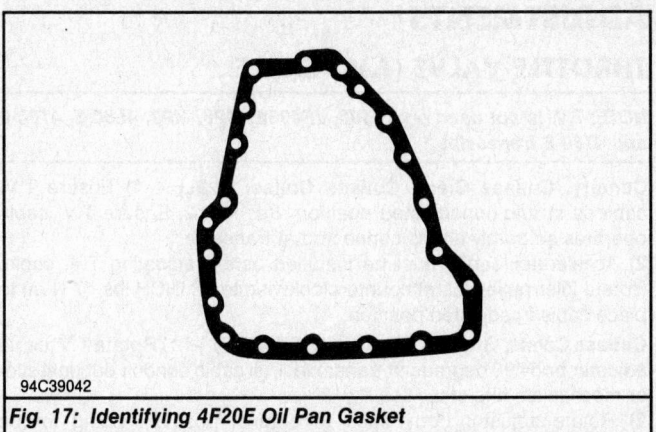

Fig. 17: Identifying 4F20E Oil Pan Gasket

TORQUE SPECIFICATIONS

TORQUE SPECIFICATIONS

Application	Ft. Lbs. (N.m)
Band Adjusting Screw Lock Nut	35-40 (47-54)
Oil Pan Bolt	10-11 (14-15)
Shift Rod-To-Bellcrank Assembly Nut	12-18 (16-24)
	INCH Lbs. (N.m)
Manual Lever Position Sensor Screw	
AODE-W/4R70W	55-75 (6.2-8.5)
C6	80-100 (9.0-11.2)
Neutral Safety Switch Bolt	96-132 (10.8-14.9)
Oil Filter/Screen Bolt	
AOD	80-120 (9.0-13.6)
A4LD	71-97 (8.0-10.9)
C6	40-55 (4.5-6.2)
T.V. Pressure Tap Plug	72-144 (8.1-16.2)

General Motors Passenger Cars

Achieva, Beretta, Bonneville, Brougham, Camaro, Caprice, Cavalier, Century, Corsica, Corvette, Custom Cruiser, Cutlass Calais, Cutlass Ciera, Cutlass Cruiser, Cutlass Supreme, DeVille, Eighty-Eight, Eldorado, Firebird, Fleetwood, Grand Am, Grand Prix, LeMans, LeSabre, Lumina, Metro, Ninety-Eight, Park Avenue, Prizm, Regal, Riviera, Roadmaster, Saturn, Seville, Skylark, Storm, Sunbird, Toronado

IDENTIFICATION

NOTE: For automatic transmission applications, see appropriate table in APPLICATIONS & IDENTIFICATION article.

LUBRICATION

SERVICE INTERVALS

Check fluid level at every oil change. Replace fluid and filter every 100,000 miles under normal operating conditions. Under continuous extreme operating conditions (trailer towing, heavy city traffic with ambient temperature over 90°F (32°C), or delivery service), replace fluid and filter every 15,000 miles.

CHECKING FLUID LEVEL

1) Warm transmission or transaxle to normal operating temperature by driving vehicle at least 15 miles. With engine at curb idle, move selector lever through all ranges, ending in Park.
2) Remove dipstick, wipe clean and reinsert fully. Remove again and inspect level. Fluid level should be between HOT marks on dipstick.

CAUTION: If vehicle has been driven for extended period at high speed, in city traffic in hot weather, or if vehicle has been pulling a trailer, fluid level cannot be checked accurately until ATF has cooled about 30 minutes.

RECOMMENDED FLUID

Use only Dexron-IIE fluid on all except Geo vehicles. Use Dexron-II on Geo vehicles.

FLUID CAPACITY

NOTE: Quantities listed are approximate. Correct fluid level should be determined by mark on dipstick, rather than by amount added.

TRANSMISSION REFILL CAPACITIES

Application	Fluid Change Qts. (L)	Overhaul Qts. (L)
4L60 & 4L60-E		
V6 Engine	5.0 (4.7)	8.4 (7.9)
V8 Engine	5.0 (4.7)	11.6 (11)

TRANSAXLE REFILL CAPACITIES

Application	Refill Qts. (L)	Total Qts. (L)
3T40		
"A" & "N"	4.0 (3.8)	6.0 (5.7)
"J" & "L"	4.0 (3.8)	7.0 (6.6)
4T60	6.6 (6.2)	10 (9.5)
4T60-E	6.0 (5.7)	11 (10.6)
4T80-E	11.0 (10.4)	15 (14.2)
A131L	2.6 (2.5)	[1]
A245E	3.7 (3.5)	[1]
KF400	4.4 (4.2)	6.9 (6.5)
JF403E	4.4 (4.2)	7.0 (6.6)
Metro 3-Spd.	1.6 (1.5)	5.2 (4.9)
MP6 & MP7	4.0 (3.5)	2.4 (7.0)

[1] – Information not available from manufacturer.

DRAINING & REFILLING

All Transmissions Except 4T80-E – 1) Raise and support vehicle. Remove drain plug (if equipped). Remove front and side oil pan bolts. Loosen rear pan bolts about 4 turns each. Carefully loosen pan. Allow fluid to drain.
2) Remove remaining bolts, oil pan, and gasket. Remove filter and "O" ring or seal. Clean pan and magnet with solvent. Dry with compressed air. Replace filter. Install NEW "O" ring or seal, lubricated with clean transmission fluid, onto filter.
3) Install pan with NEW gasket. Tighten bolts to specification. See OIL PAN TIGHTENING SPECIFICATIONS table. Add fresh fluid through filler tube. Apply parking brake. Set transmission range selector lever to Park position. Start engine. Check fluid level and add as required. DO NOT overfill.

4T80-E – 1) Raise vehicle. Remove transmission oil pan bolts. Pry oil pan loose and allow to drain. Remove oil pan.

2) Remove drain plug inside case. Allow fluid to drain from side cover. Remove left and right scavenger screens and multi-lip scavenger seals. Inspect scavenger screens for cuts, cracked housings and debris. Replace if damaged.

3) Install scavenger screens and NEW seals. Install oil pan using NEW gasket. Tighten oil pan bolts to specification (3 passes) in sequence. *See Fig. 1.* See TORQUE SPECIFICATIONS (OIL PAN BOLTS) table. Add required amount of fluid through filler tube.

6) Start engine with gear selector lever in Park and parking brake applied. Select each gear, ending in Park. Check fluid level with engine warm. Add fluid if necessary. DO NOT overfill.

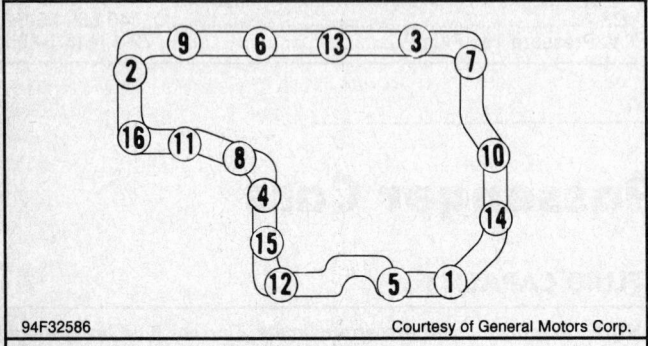

94F32586   Courtesy of General Motors Corp.

Fig. 1: 4T80-E Oil Pan Tightening Sequence

OIL PAN TIGHTENING SPECIFICATIONS

Application	INCH Lbs. (N.m)
Transmission	
4L60	180 (20)
4L60-E	
Except "Y" Body	144 (16)
"Y" Body	97 (11)
Transaxle	
3T40	96 (11)
4T60	112 (13)
4T60-E	150 (17)
4T80-E	
Initial	27 (3)
Intermediate	53 (6)
Final	106 (12)
A131L	44 (5.0)
A245E	44 (5.0)
KF400	62 (7.0)
JF403E	62 (7.0)
MP6 & MP7	88 (10)

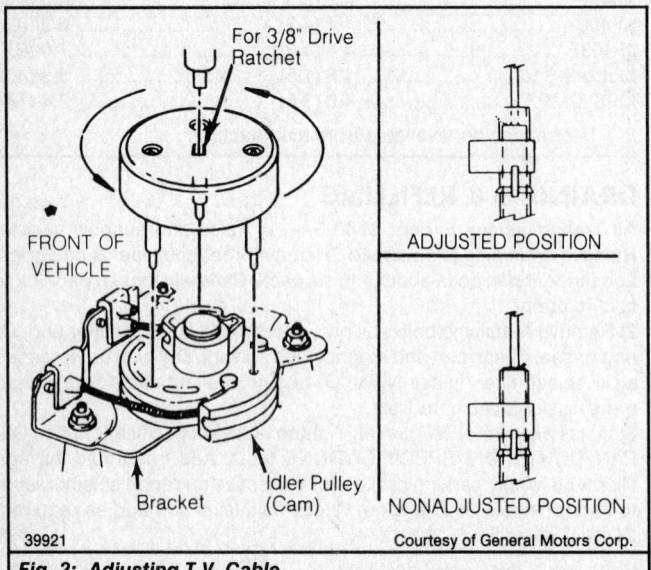

39921   Courtesy of General Motors Corp.

**Fig. 2: Adjusting T.V. Cable
Century, Cutlass Ciera, Cutlass Cruiser (2.2L)**

ADJUSTMENTS

THROTTLE VALVE (T.V.) CABLE

NOTE: T.V. is not used on KF400, JF403E, MP6, MP7, 4L60-E, 4T60-E and 4T80-E transaxles.

Century, Cutlass Ciera, Cutlass Cruiser (2.2L) – 1) Ensure T.V. cable is in full, nonadjusted position. *See Fig. 2.* Ensure T.V. cable operates smoothly and is connected at transaxle.

2) Accelerator cable must be installed before adjusting T.V. cable. Rotate idler pulley (cam) counterclockwise to 62 INCH lbs. (7 N.m) to place cable in adjusted position.

Cutlass Calais, Grand Am & Skylark (VIN "D") – 1) Rotate T.V. cable adjuster body 90 degrees at transaxle. Pull cable conduit out until slider mechanism hits stop. *See Fig. 3.*

2) Rotate adjuster body back to original position. Using torque wrench, tighten T.V. cable adjuster to 75 INCH lbs. (8.5 N.m).

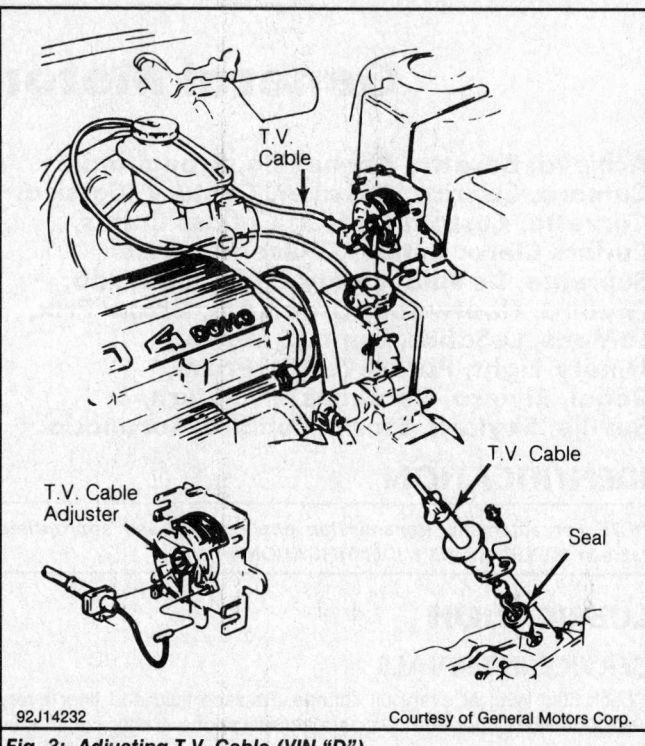

92J14232   Courtesy of General Motors Corp.

Fig. 3: Adjusting T.V. Cable (VIN "D")

Achieva (VIN "D" & "3") – Press and hold plastic adjuster button. Pull cable conduit out until slider mechanism hits stop. Release button. Using torque wrench, tighten T.V. cable adjuster to 120 INCH lbs. (14 N.m). Ensure cable moves freely. Recheck after engine is hot.

LeMans – 1) Remove air cleaner assembly. Release locking spring clip adjuster. Pull locking tab or remove locking spring clip to release cable adjuster spring tension.

2) Depress accelerator pedal until contact is made with kickdown switch (below accelerator pedal). In this position, throttle valve must be fully open. Adjust accelerator cable if necessary.

3) Position of throttle cable adjustment is correct when accelerator pedal is depressed beyond full wide open throttle position. Do not touch cable during adjustment. Lock cable adjustment with locking tab or spring clip.

Metro – 1) Ensure there is zero end play in accelerator cable. Warm engine to normal operating temperature. Remove T.V. cable adjustment cover. Measure clearance between T.V. cable boot and stop. *See Fig. 4.* If clearance is greater than .02" (.5 mm), go to next step.

2) Turn T.V. cable adjuster nuts "A" until clearance is .02" (.5 mm). If nuts "A" do not provide sufficient adjustment range, accelerator cable adjuster nuts "B" may also be used.

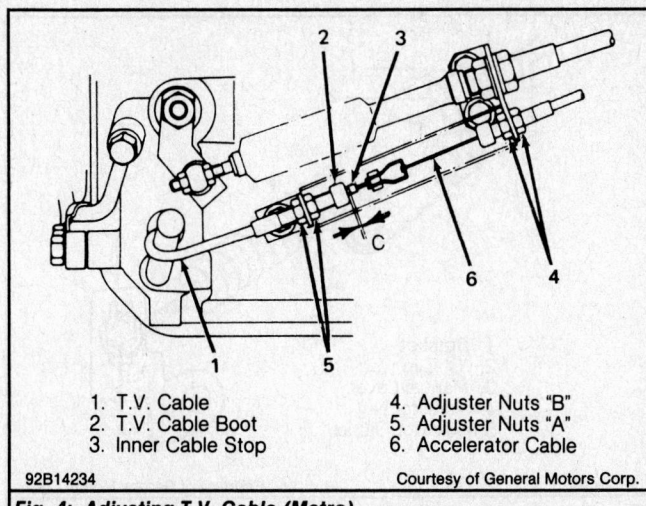

1. T.V. Cable
2. T.V. Cable Boot
3. Inner Cable Stop
4. Adjuster Nuts "B"
5. Adjuster Nuts "A"
6. Accelerator Cable

92B14234

Courtesy of General Motors Corp.

Fig. 4: Adjusting T.V. Cable (Metro)

Prizm – On A131L only, have assistant press accelerator pedal to floor and hold in position. On all models, loosen T.V. cable lock nut and adjuster nut. Rotate cable end so that distance between end of rubber boot and cable stop is 0-.04" (0-1 mm).

All Other Models – Adjuster is located at cable support bracket on engine. Engine must be off. Press and hold metal lock tab on adjuster. Move slider until it stops against fitting. Release tab. *See Fig. 5.* Rotate throttle lever to full travel position. Slider must ratchet toward lever when lever is in full travel position.

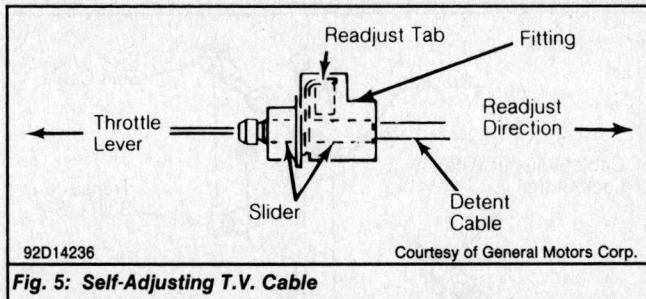

92D14236

Courtesy of General Motors Corp.

Fig. 5: Self-Adjusting T.V. Cable

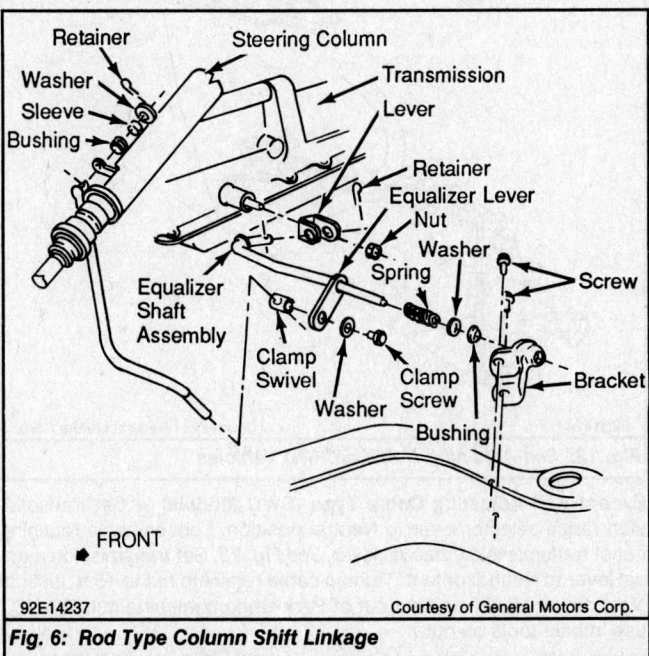

92E14237

Courtesy of General Motors Corp.

Fig. 6: Rod Type Column Shift Linkage

TRANSMISSION RANGE SELECTOR LINKAGE

Linkage should be adjusted so that engine cannot be started with transmission selector lever in any position except Park or Neutral. If linkage is improperly adjusted, an internal leak could occur, causing clutch and/or band failure. With selector lever in Park position, parking pawl should be engaged, and drive wheels should be locked. Pointer on indicator quadrant should align with range indicators in all ranges.

Column Shift (RWD Models) – **1)** Position transmission range selector lever in Neutral gate notch. Loosen swivel clamp screw. Set transmission manual lever to Neutral position. *See Fig. 6.*
2) Hold swivel clamp against equalizer lever. Tighten clamp screw, taking care not to apply tension to equalizer lever or selector rod. Ensure there is no tension on equalizer lever or selector rod. Tighten clamp screw to 21 ft. lbs. (28 N.m).

Camaro, Corvette & Firebird – Set transmission range selector lever to Neutral position. Raise and support vehicle. Loosen cable nut at transmission. *See Fig. 7.* Set transmission manual lever to Neutral position by moving it fully clockwise to Park detent, then back (counterclockwise) 2 detents to Neutral. Tighten cable nut to 15 ft. lbs. (20 N.m).

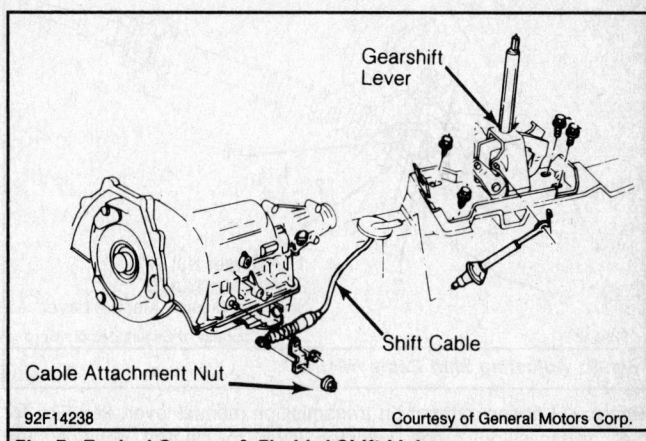

92F14238

Courtesy of General Motors Corp.

Fig. 7: Typical Camaro & Firebird Shift Linkage

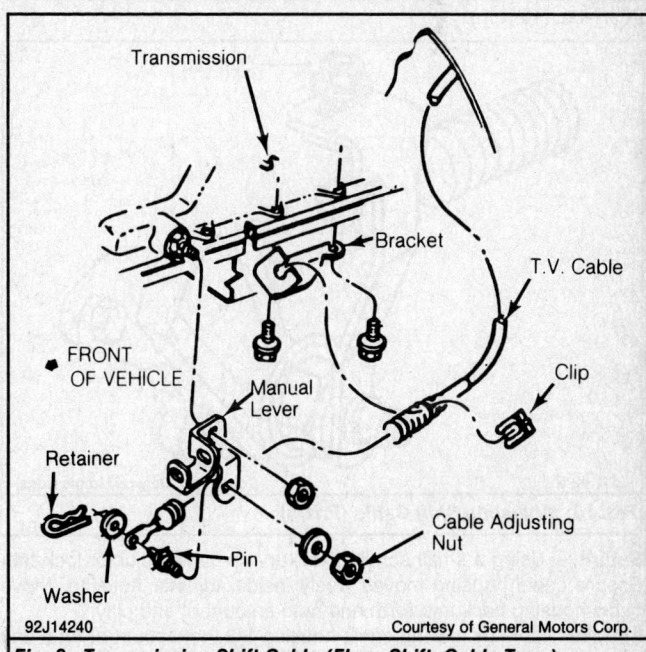

92J14240

Courtesy of General Motors Corp.

Fig. 8: Transmission Shift Cable (Floor Shift, Cable Type)

LeMans – 1) When adjusting selector lever actuation, ensure that lever on transaxle will catch in the "P", "R", "N", "D", "2" and "1" positions. If lever does not catch, adjust cable at selector lever.

2) Remove center console to gain access to gear selector lever assembly. Loosen cable adjustment lock nut at selector lever. Adjust cable as necessary and tighten lock nut. Check for proper engagement in all gear positions. Install center console.

All Other RWD Vehicles – 1) Set shift lever to Park position. Raise and support vehicle. Ensure transmission is fully engaged in Park by rotating propeller shaft until parking pawl engages.

2) Loosen adjusting nut on transmission manual lever to allow pin to slide freely. With transmission range selector lever and transmission manual lever both in Park, tighten adjusting nut. *See Fig. 8.*

Metro – Set transmission range selector lever to Neutral position. At transmission, loosen adjuster nuts "A" and "B". *See Fig. 9.* Ensure transmission manual lever is in Neutral position. Hand-tighten adjuster nut "A" until it contacts manual lever. Tighten adjuster nut "B". Check transmission for proper operation in all ranges.

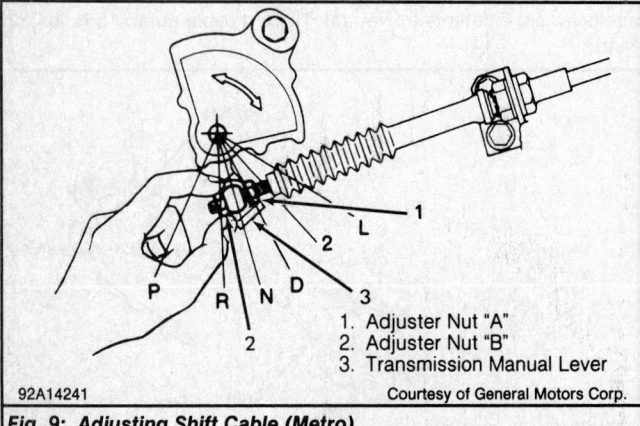

1. Adjuster Nut "A"
2. Adjuster Nut "B"
3. Transmission Manual Lever

92A14241   Courtesy of General Motors Corp.

Fig. 9: Adjusting Shift Cable (Metro)

Prizm – Loosen cap nut on transmission manual lever. *See Fig. 10.* Set transmission range selector lever to Neutral position. Set transmission manual lever to Neutral position. Tighten cap nut to 89 INCH lbs. (10 N.m).

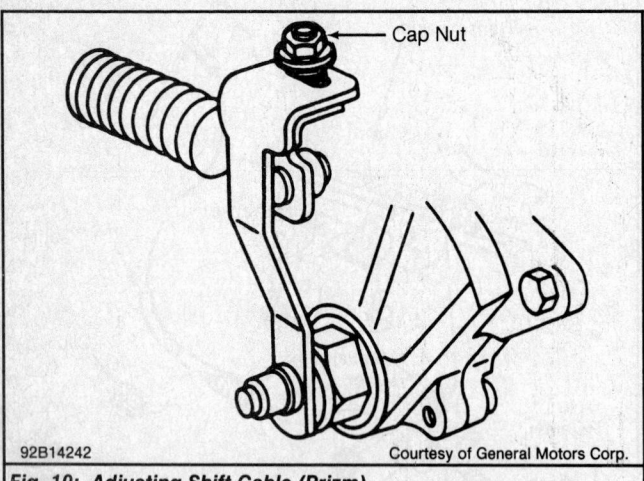

Cap Nut

92B14242   Courtesy of General Motors Corp.

Fig. 10: Adjusting Shift Cable (Prizm)

Saturn – Using a small screwdriver, pry up cable adjuster lock tab. Ensure cable housing moves freely inside adjuster housing. Move cable housing back and forth and note amount of end play.

2) Adjust cable by moving cable housing 1/2 the amount of total end play. Press lock tab down and ensure cable housing is secure. Check park/lock cable adjustment. See PARK/LOCK CONTROL CABLE.

Storm – Ensure ignition switch is in LOCK position. Set transmission range selector lever to Park position. At transmission, loosen range selector cable adjuster nut. *See Fig. 11.* Set transmission manual lever to Park (full clockwise) position. Tighten adjuster nut to 42 ft. lbs. (24 N.m).

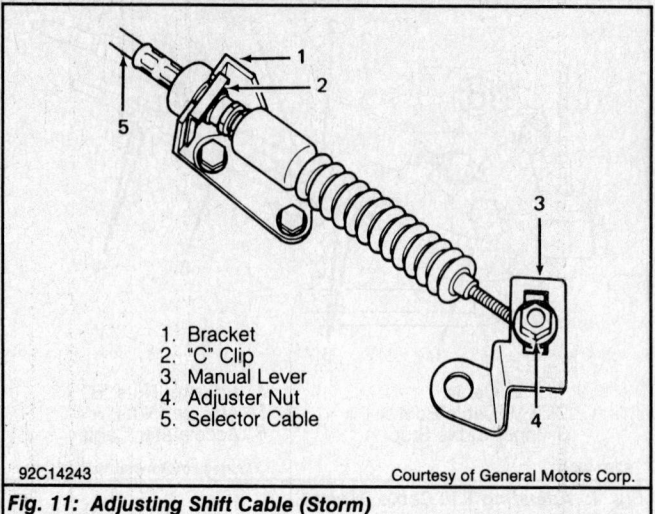

1. Bracket
2. "C" Clip
3. Manual Lever
4. Adjuster Nut
5. Selector Cable

92C14243   Courtesy of General Motors Corp.

Fig. 11: Adjusting Shift Cable (Storm)

Self-Adjusting Cable (FWD Models) – Ensure selector cable is self-adjusting type. *See Fig. 12.* If not, see EXCEPT SELF-ADJUSTING CABLE TYPE (FWD MODELS). Set transmission range selector lever to Neutral position. Lift lock button on cable adjuster at transaxle mounting bracket. Ensure transaxle manual lever is in Neutral detent. Press lock button.

NOTE: Self-adjusting shift cable is commonly used on "A", "C", "H", "L", "N", "W" and "Z" body styles.

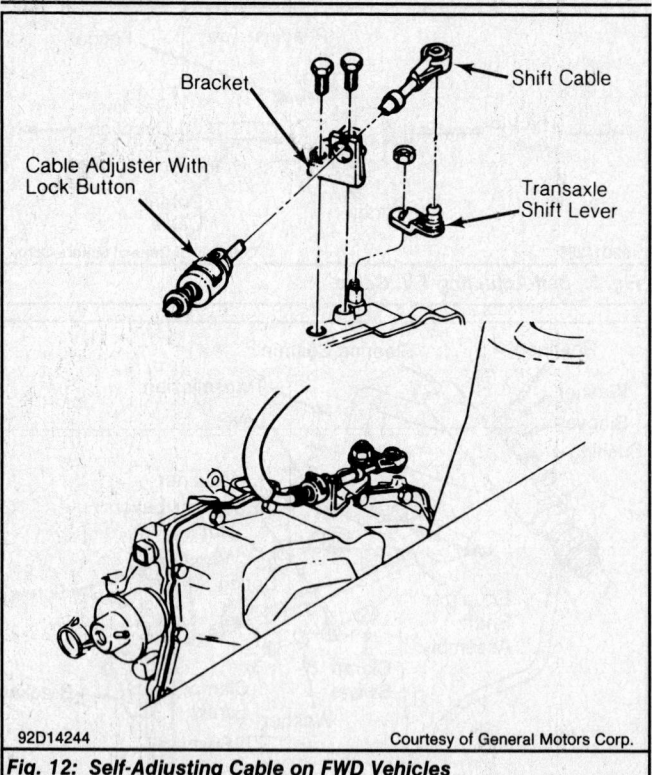

Bracket   Shift Cable

Cable Adjuster With Lock Button

Transaxle Shift Lever

92D14244   Courtesy of General Motors Corp.

Fig. 12: Self-Adjusting Cable on FWD Vehicles

Except Self-Adjusting Cable Type (FWD Models) – Set transmission range selector lever to Neutral position. Loosen cable retaining nut at transmission manual lever. *See Fig. 13.* Set transmission manual lever to Neutral detent. Tighten cable retaining nut to 15 ft. lbs. (20 N.m). Lever MUST be held out of Park when tightening nut. DO NOT use impact tools on nut.

NOTE: Lever must be held out of Park position when tightening nut.

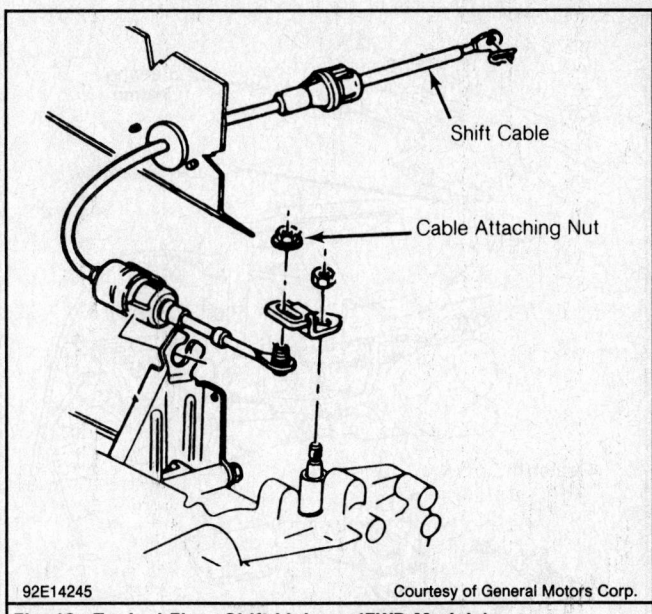

92E14245   Courtesy of General Motors Corp.

Fig. 13: Typical Floor Shift Linkage (FWD Models)

PARK/LOCK CONTROL CABLE

WARNING: When battery is disconnected, vehicle computer and memory systems may lose memory data. Driveability problems may exist until computer systems have completed a relearn cycle. See COMPUTER RELEARN PROCEDURES article in APPLICATIONS & IDENTIFICATION before disconnecting battery.

NOTE: Vehicles with column shift, do not use a park/lock control cable. On all vehicles, with transmission range selector lever in Park position and ignition switch in Lock position, ensure transmission range selector cannot be moved to any other position. Ignition key should be removable.

LeMans – 1) Remove center console assembly to gain access to gear selector assembly and park lock cable. Remove locking spring clip at cable adjuster. Remove return spring.
2) Pull locking pin to release tension. Push selector lever to "P" position until pin contacts catch. Ensure extra travel distance is present during operation. If travel distance cannot be obtained, check cable length for stretching and replace if necessary.

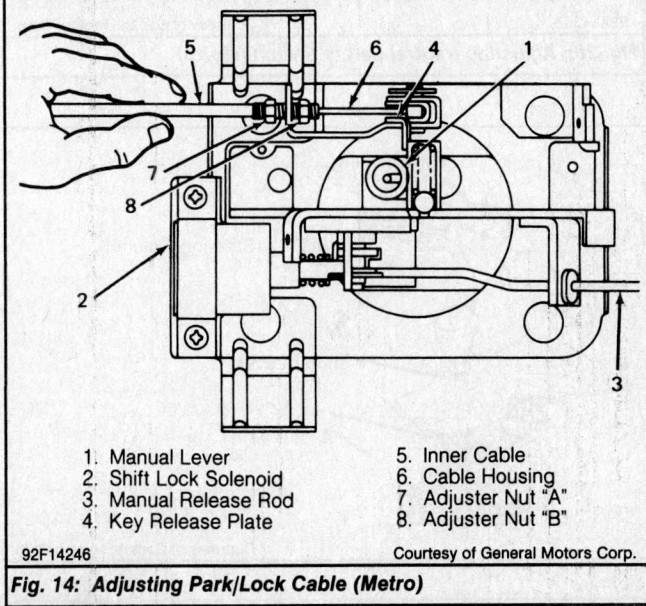

1. Manual Lever	5. Inner Cable
2. Shift Lock Solenoid	6. Cable Housing
3. Manual Release Rod	7. Adjuster Nut "A"
4. Key Release Plate	8. Adjuster Nut "B"

92F14246   Courtesy of General Motors Corp.

Fig. 14: Adjusting Park/Lock Cable (Metro)

Metro – 1) Remove console. Remove covers from transmission range selector lever. Set transmission range selector to Park position. Loosen interlock cable adjuster nuts "A" and "B". *See Fig. 14.*
2) Pull cable housing toward front of vehicle until there is slack in cable. Hand-tighten adjuster nuts "A" and "B" to hold cable in place. Tighten adjuster nuts "A" and "B".

Prizm – Remove console halves. Set transmission range selector to Park position. Set ignition switch to OFF position. Release Park/Lock cable lock. *See Fig. 15.* Adjust dimension "A" to .19" (4.8 mm). Engage cable lock.

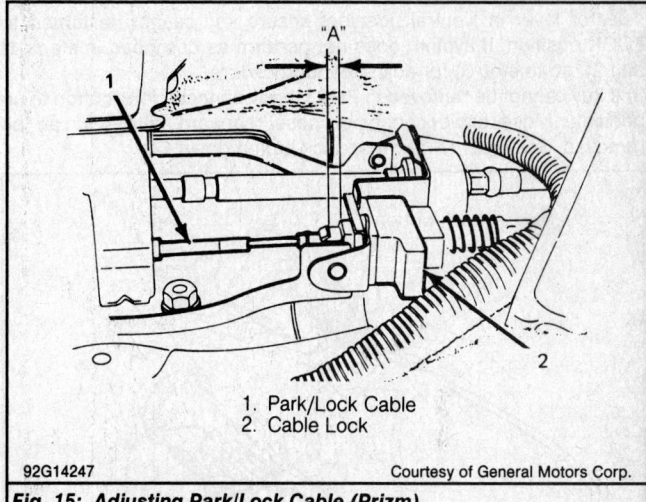

1. Park/Lock Cable
2. Cable Lock

92G14247   Courtesy of General Motors Corp.

Fig. 15: Adjusting Park/Lock Cable (Prizm)

Saturn – 1) Remove ashtray. Without touching brake pedal and with gear selector in Park, turn ignition switch on. Lift lock tab on cable end. Move adjustable end of cable against spring force until it is held by solenoid. Press lock tab on cable end.
2) With ignition off and shifter in Park position, attempt to shift lever out of Park. Lever should not move. Turn ignition on. Shift lever should be allowed out of Park.
3) Place shift lever in any position except Park and turn ignition off. Ignition key should not be removable. Attempt to place shift lever in Park. Lever should go into Park position and ignition key should be able to be removed. If park lock cable fails any test, readjust cable.

Storm – 1) Disconnect negative battery cable. Set ignition switch to LOCK position. Remove console. Set transmission range selector to Park position. Remove retaining clip from end of interlock cable.

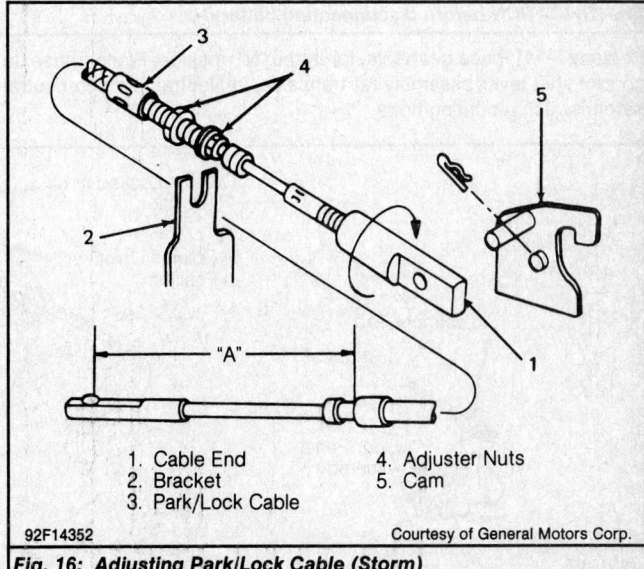

1. Cable End	4. Adjuster Nuts
2. Bracket	5. Cam
3. Park/Lock Cable	

92F14352   Courtesy of General Motors Corp.

Fig. 16: Adjusting Park/Lock Cable (Storm)

2) Disconnect cable from cam. Rotate cable end clockwise until it reaches end of threads, then counterclockwise 1/2 to one turn. Loosen adjuster nuts. Turn adjuster nuts as required until dimension "A" at ignition switch end of cable is 2.70" (68.5 mm). See Fig. 16.

3) Tighten adjuster nuts. Ensure dimension "A" has not changed. Install cable end and retaining clip.

All Other Floor Shift Models – **1)** Disconnect negative battery cable. With shift lever in Park position and ignition switch in Lock position, ensure transmission range selector cannot be moved to other gear positions. Ignition key should be removable.

2) With ignition switch in RUN position and transmission range selector lever in Neutral position, ensure key cannot be turned to LOCK position. If system does not perform as described in steps **1)** and **2)**, go to step **3)** for adjustment procedure.

3) If key cannot be removed in Park, snap connector lock button to up position. Move cable connector nose rearward until key can be removed. See Figs. 17-19. Snap lock button down.

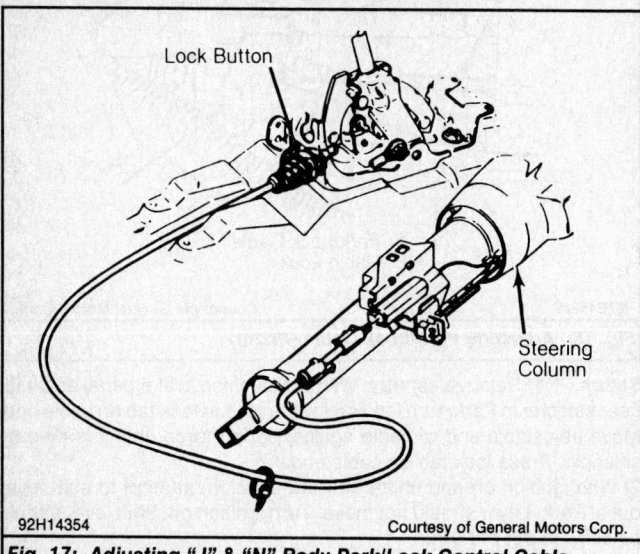

Fig. 17: Adjusting "J" & "N" Body Park/Lock Control Cable

NEUTRAL SAFETY SWITCH

WARNING: When battery is disconnected, vehicle computer and memory systems may lose memory data. Driveability problems may exist until computer systems have completed a relearn cycle. See COMPUTER RELEARN PROCEDURES article in APPLICATIONS & IDENTIFICATION before disconnecting battery.

LeMans – **1)** Place gear selector in the "N" position. Place transaxle control shift lever assembly (at transaxle) in Neutral. Loosen neutral safety switch mounting bolts.

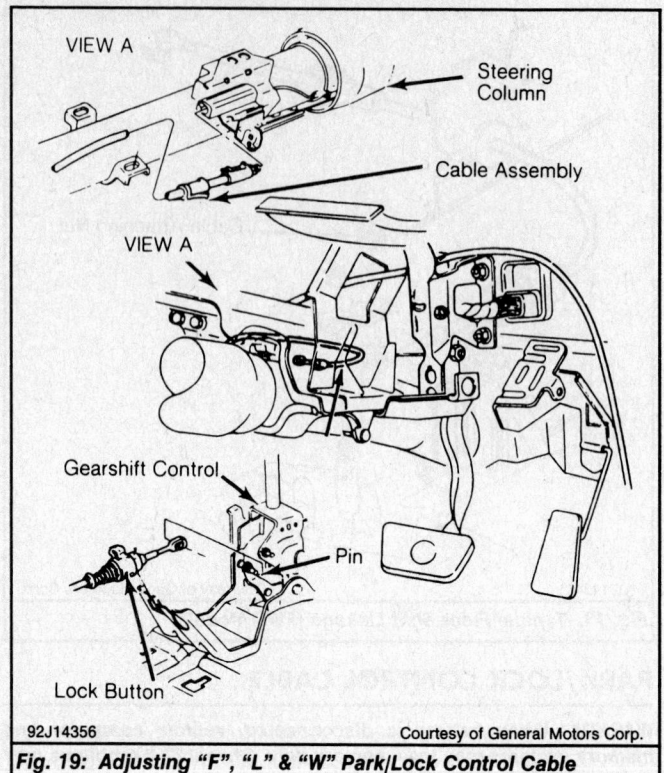

Fig. 19: Adjusting "F", "L" & "W" Park/Lock Control Cable

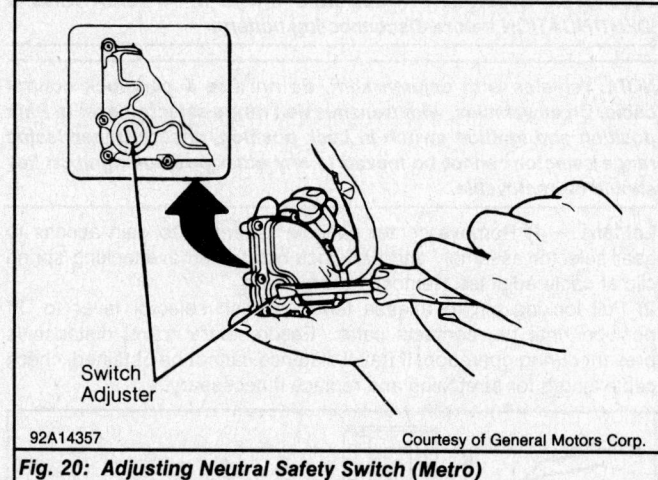

Fig. 20: Adjusting Neutral Safety Switch (Metro)

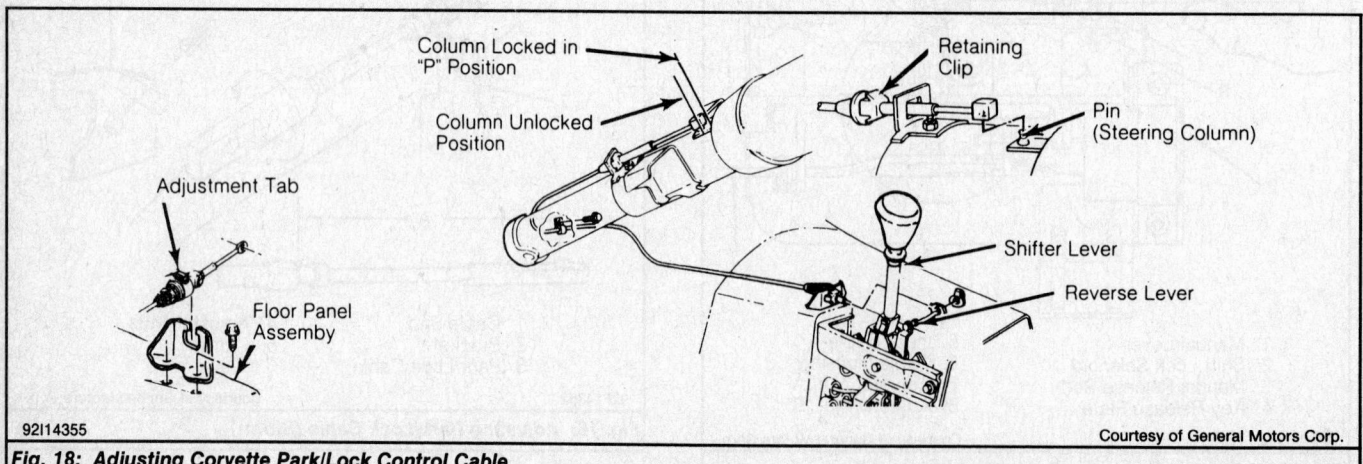

Fig. 18: Adjusting Corvette Park/Lock Control Cable

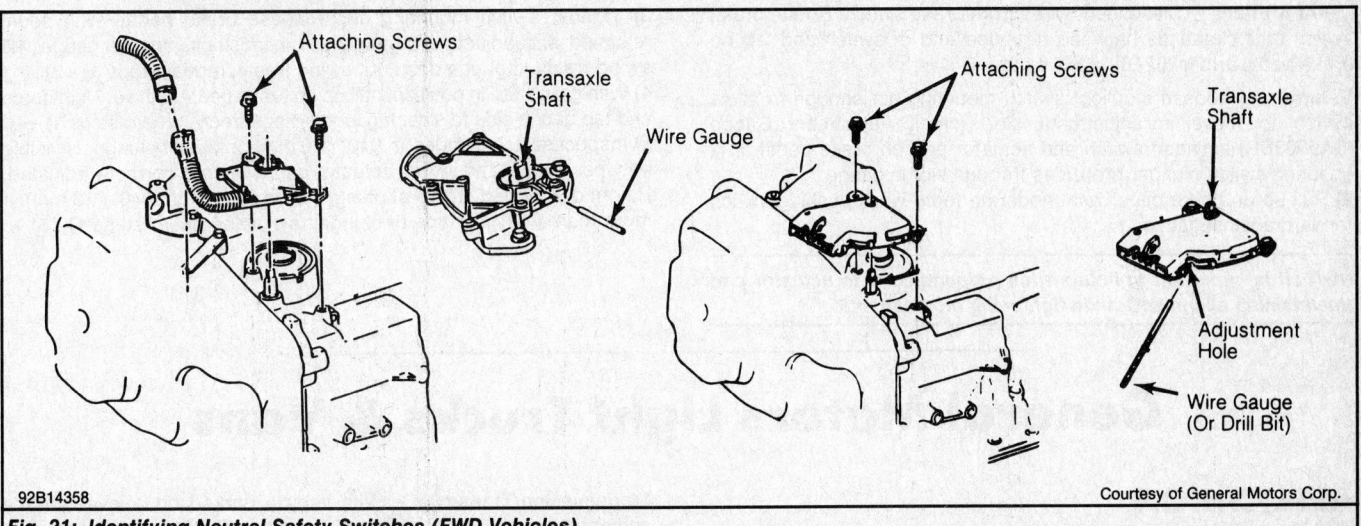

Fig. 21: Identifying Neutral Safety Switches (FWD Vehicles)

92B14358 Courtesy of General Motors Corp.

2) Rotate switch on shifter assembly to align service adjustment hole with carrier tang hole. Using a 3/32" drill bit, insert drill bit into adjustment hole to a depth of 3/8" and tighten mounting bolts to 22 ft. lbs. (30 N.m).

Metro – Neutral safety switch is located in area of manual lever at transaxle. Set transmission range selector to Neutral position. Remove neutral safety switch. Rotate adjuster as necessary until it clicks. See Fig. 20. Install neutral safety switch. Tighten mounting bolt to 17 ft. lbs. (23 N.m).

Prizm – Neutral safety switch is located in area of transmission manual lever. Raise and support vehicle. Loosen neutral safety switch mounting bolts. Rotate switch until line on switch aligns with line on manual lever. Tighten mounting bolts to 71 INCH lbs. (8 (N.m).

Saturn – Place shifter lever in Drive position. Using an ohmmeter, check for continuity across switch terminals. If continuity does not exist, loosen switch retaining bolts and rotate switch to obtain continuity. Tighten switch retaining bolts to 12 ft. lbs. (16 N.m) and recheck continuity.

Storm – Neutral safety switch is located in area of transmission manual lever. Set transmission range selector to Neutral position. Loosen switch mounting bolts. Insert rod through hole in transmission lever. Rotate switch until rod engages hole in switch. Tighten mounting bolts to 26 INCH lbs. (3 N.m).

All Other FWD Models – **1)** There are 2 different neutral safety/back-up light switch types in use on other FWD models. See Fig. 21. Disconnect negative battery cable. To adjust switch, set transmission range selector lever to Neutral position.
2) Ensure shift cable is adjusted correctly and transaxle shift lever is in Neutral position. Loosen switch retaining screws. Rotate switch on shifter assembly to align adjustment hole with carrier tang hole.
3) Insert a 3/32" wire gauge about 5/8" into switch holes. Tighten retaining screws. Remove wire gauge. New switches may have plastic pin installed in hole. Plastic pin is designed to shear off at first operation of shift lever.

Camaro, Corvette & Firebird – **1)** Disconnect negative battery cable. Remove floor console cover. Set transmission range selector lever to Neutral position. If old switch is to be readjusted, go to step **2)**. If new switch is to be installed, go to step **4)**.
2) Align tang on switch with tang slot on shift control. See Fig. 22. Loosen switch mounting nuts. Rotate switch to align service adjustment hole with carrier tang hole.
3) Insert a 3/32" wire gauge into adjustment hole in top of switch. Rotate switch until pin drops to depth of 19/32". Tighten mounting nuts. Vehicle should start in Park or Neutral only.
4) If new switch is being installed, insert switch tang into slot on shift control. Tighten mounting nuts.

5) If holes do not align with shift control, ensure transmission range selector lever is in Neutral position. DO NOT rotate switch; switch is pinned in Neutral position.

NOTE: If new switch has been rotated and pin broken during installation, use adjustment procedure in steps 2) and 3).

6) If holes align with shift control, move transmission range selector lever out of Neutral position to shear plastic pin.

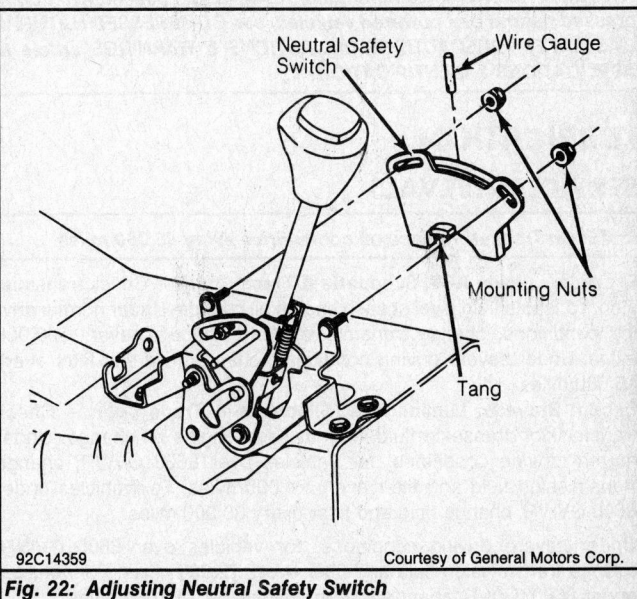

Fig. 22: Adjusting Neutral Safety Switch

92C14359 Courtesy of General Motors Corp.

All Other RWD Models – Column shift models use a mechanical interference-type neutral start system. A wedge-shaped finger, attached to the ignition switch actuator rod, blocks movement of switch to START position in all transmission range selector positions except Park or Neutral.

STOPLIGHT SWITCH

NOTE: Stoplight switch information for Storm is not available from the manufacturer.

Except Metro, Prizm & Saturn – Ensure torque converter clutch brake switch is adjusted to prevent vehicle from stalling at idle due to clutch remaining applied. Ensure brake pedal is fully released. Adjust switch until switch plunger just touches brake pedal lever.

Metro & Prizm – Disconnect wires from brake switch. Rotate brake switch until clearance between threaded end of switch and tab on brake pedal arm is .02-.09" (.5-2.4 mm).

Saturn – 1) Loosen stoplight switch mounting nut enough to allow switch to move in adjustment slot. Install Adjustment Gauge (SA9303BR) between switch and actuator pad on brake pedal arm, ensuring switch plunger protrudes through slot in gauge.
2) Pull up on brake pedal with moderate force while pushing switch forward against gauge.

NOTE: It is important to hold switch perpendicular to actuator pad (maintaining alignment) while tightening mounting nut.

3) Tighten switch mounting nut. Release brake pedal. With pedal released and adjustment gauge still in position, ensure gauge will swing freely. If gauge does not swing freely, repeat steps **1)** - **3)**.
4) With gauge still in position, pull up on brake pedal with very light force and tap gauge side to side. If gauge swings freely, repeat steps **1)** - **4)**.
5) Inspect switch plunger. If .040" (1.0 mm) or less of plunger is visible between switch and switch actuator pad, switch is correctly adjusted. Height of rounded crown of plunger is equivalent to .040" (1.0 mm). If more than .040" (1.0 mm) of plunger is visible, repeat steps **1)** - **5)**.

General Motors Light Trucks & Vans

APPLICATION

TRANSMISSION APPLICATION

Model	Transmission/Transaxle
Astro & Safari	Hydra-Matic 4L60-E
"C", "G" & "K" Series	Hydra-Matic 4L60-E & 4L80-E
Lumina APV, Silhouette & Trans Sport	Hydra-Matic 3T40 & 4T60-E
"P" & P/G Series	Hydra-Matic 4L60-E & 4L80-E
"S" & "T" Series	Hydra-Matic 4L60 & 4L60-E
Tracker	3L30

WARNING: Before removing engine/transmission assembly on compressed natural gas powered vehicles, see COMPRESSED NATURAL GAS SAFETY PRECAUTIONS in CAUTIONS & WARNINGS article in APPLICATIONS & IDENTIFICATION.

LUBRICATION

SERVICE INTERVALS

NOTE: On Tracker, replace oil cooler lines every 45,000 miles.

Bravada, Lumina APV, Silhouette & Trans Sport – Check transmission/transaxle fluid level at each engine oil change. Under normal driving conditions, change transmission fluid and filter every 100,000 miles. Under severe driving conditions, change fluid and filter every 15,000 miles.

Except Bravada, Lumina APV, Silhouette & Trans Sport – Check transmission/transaxle fluid level at each engine oil change. Under normal driving conditions, for vehicles over 8600 GVWR, change transmission fluid and filter every 24,000 miles. For vehicles under 8600 GVWR, change fluid and filter every 30,000 miles.

Under severe driving conditions, for vehicles over 8600 GVWR, change transmission fluid and filter every 12,000 miles. For vehicles under 8600 GVWR, change fluid and filter every 15,000 miles.

Transfer Case (Tracker) – Replace transfer case fluid at 7500 miles. Change fluid every 30,000 miles after first 7500 miles. Under severe driving conditions, change fluid every 15,000 miles after first 7500 miles.

Transfer Case (Except Tracker) – Check transfer case lubricant at every oil change or every 12 months. Under severe conditions check more frequently.

CHECKING FLUID LEVEL

NOTE: Transmission/transaxle must be at normal operating temperature (180-200 degrees) when checking fluid level. One pint of fluid will raise level from ADD 1 PT. OR .5L to FULL mark on dipstick with a transmission/transaxle at normal temperature. DO NOT overfill.

Transmission/Transaxle – With vehicle parked on a level surface and engine at idle, move selector lever through all positions, ending in Park. Remove dipstick, wipe clean and check fluid level. Fluid level should be between ADD 1 PT. and FULL marks on dipstick. If vehicle has been driven for extended period of time at high speed, in city traffic or pulling a trailer, an accurate fluid level cannot be immediately determined. Allow transmission/transaxle to cool for about 30 minutes after vehicle is parked, then check fluid level.

Transfer Case – Remove fill plug. Check oil level. If level is not up to fill plug opening, add lubricant as necessary.

RECOMMENDED FLUID

Transmissions/transaxles and transfer cases (except Tracker) use Dexron-IIE ATF. Tracker transfer case uses SAE 75W-90 or 80W-90 GL-4 gear oil.

FLUID CAPACITY

Transmission/Transaxle – The transmission/transaxle refill capacities given below are approximate. Correct fluid level should always be determined by marks on dipstick, rather than by amount of fluid added. DO NOT overfill transmission/transaxle.

TRANSMISSION/TRANSAXLE REFILL CAPACITIES

Application	Refill (Service) Qts. (L)	Dry Fill (Overhaul) Qts. (L)
3L30	3.7 (3.5)	5.1 (4.9)
3T40	4.0 (3.8)	7.0 (6.6)
4L60 & 4L60-E	5.0 (4.8)	11 (10.6)
4T60-E	6.0 (5.7)	7.1 (6.7)
4L80-E	5.0 (4.7)	11.5 (10.9)

TRANSFER CASE REFILL CAPACITIES

Application	Capacity
Models 231 & 233	2.2 Pts. (1.1L)
Model 241	5.2 Pts. (2.5L)
Models 4401 & 4472	2.9 Pts. (1.4L)
Model 4470	6.6 Pts. (3.1L)
Tracker	3.6 Pts. (1.7L)

DRAINING & REFILLING

Transmission/Transaxle – 1) Loosen transmission/transaxle oil pan bolts. Pry pan loose with a large screwdriver and allow fluid to drain. Remove oil pan, gasket and filter or filter screen. Replace paper element filter (if equipped).
2) Clean filter screen and pan with a solvent and blow dry with compressed air. Install oil pan with NEW gasket. Add fluid to proper mark on dipstick.

Transfer Case – Remove drain plug from transfer case. Remove fill plug for easier draining. With fluid drained, reinstall drain plug. Fill transfer case to fill plug opening with appropriate fluid.

ADJUSTMENTS

THROTTLE VALVE (T.V.) CABLE

NOTE: The Hydra-Matic 4L60-E, 4T60-E and 4L80-E are electronically controlled transmissions/transaxles and do not require adjustment.

3T40 & 4L60 – Depress metal lock tab on adjuster and hold. Move slider back through fitting away from throttle body lever until slider stops at fitting. *See Fig. 1.* Release lock tab and open throttle body lever to full throttle stop. This automatically adjusts slider to correct setting.

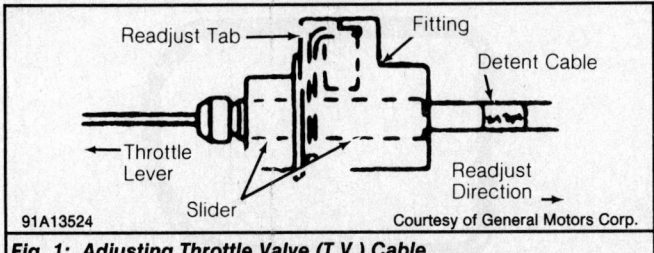

Fig. 1: *Adjusting Throttle Valve (T.V.) Cable*

Courtesy of General Motors Corp.

Tracker – 1) Set ignition switch to LOCK position. Have assistant press accelerator pedal to floor and hold in position. Loosen T.V. cable lock nut and adjuster nut. Ensure neither nut contacts bracket on throttle body. Pull T.V. cable casing away from throttle body until tight. *See Fig. 2.*
2) Thread T.V. cable lock nut along cable until clearance between lock nut and bracket is .04" (1.0 mm). Have assistant release accelerator pedal. Maintain .04" (1.0 mm) clearance between lock nut and bracket.
3) Rotate T.V. cable adjuster nut until it engages and fits inside bracket. Tighten T.V. cable lock nut.

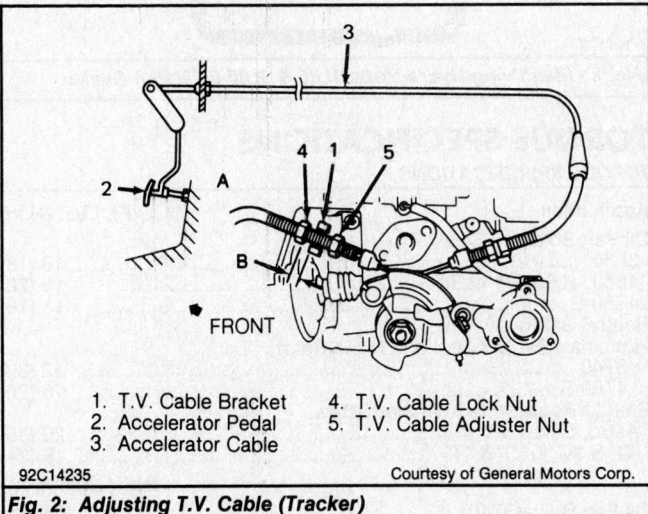

1. T.V. Cable Bracket   4. T.V. Cable Lock Nut
2. Accelerator Pedal   5. T.V. Cable Adjuster Nut
3. Accelerator Cable

92C14235   Courtesy of General Motors Corp.

Fig. 2: *Adjusting T.V. Cable (Tracker)*

SHIFT LINKAGE

Commercial Van – 1) Remove clevis pin retaining clip and clevis pin. Move shift lever arm at transmission fully forward and then pull back 2 detents to Neutral position.
2) Loosen jam nut and adjust cable end to align with shift lever arm at transmission. Tighten jam nut. Reinstall clevis pin and clip. Ensure engine starts in Park and Neutral only.
Lumina APV, Silhouette & Trans Sport – Place shift lever in Neutral. Neutral can be found by rotating transaxle select lever clockwise from Park to Reverse to Neutral. Place shift control lever in Neutral. Push tab on cable adjuster to adjust cable in cable mounting bracket.
Tracker – Set transmission range selector lever to Neutral position. At transmission, loosen selector cable adjuster nuts. *See Fig. 3.* Set transmission manual lever to Neutral position. Hand-tighten adjuster nut "A" until it contacts manual lever. Tighten adjuster nut "B" to 62 INCH lbs. (7 N.m). Check transmission for proper operation in all ranges.

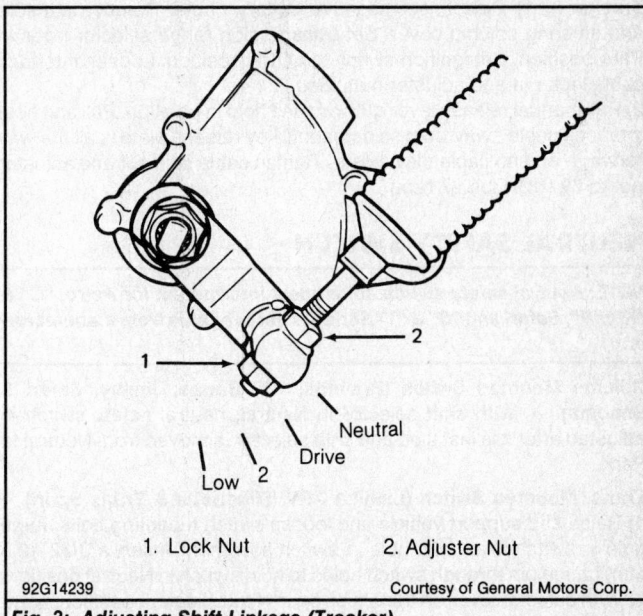

1. Lock Nut   2. Adjuster Nut

92G14239   Courtesy of General Motors Corp.

Fig. 3: *Adjusting Shift Linkage (Tracker)*

All Models Except Commercial Van, Lumina APV, Silhouette, Tracker & Trans Sport – 1) Ensure shift tube and lever are free in steering column. To adjust linkage, remove screw and spring washer from swivel. Turn transmission lever clockwise to stop, then counterclockwise 2 detents. This is Neutral position.
2) Place selector lever in Neutral. Locate proper position using mechanical stops, NOT indicator pointer. Hold swivel against shift lever. Install spring washer and screw and tighten finger tight. Avoid applying force in either direction (along shift rod or lever) while tightening screw to 20 ft. lbs. (27 N.m).

PARK/LOCK CONTROL CABLE

NOTE: Park/Lock Control Cable adjustment information for Astro, "C" & "K", "P", Safari and "S" & "T" Series is not available from manufacturer.

Lumina APV, Silhouette & Trans Sport) – 1) Lift cable lock button. Move shift lever to Park. Snap cable connector into shifter base. Ensure ignition key is in RUN position.
2) Snap cable housing into inhibitor. Turn key to LOCK position. Snap cable end onto park lock lever pin. Remove slack from cable connector. Snap cable connector lock button down.

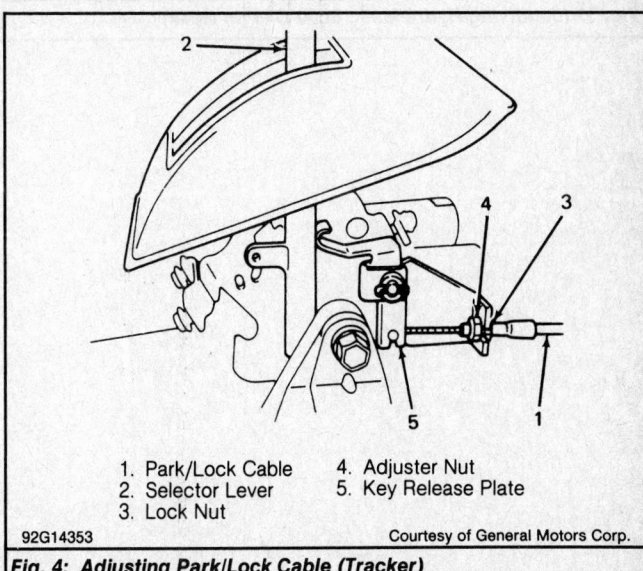

1. Park/Lock Cable   4. Adjuster Nut
2. Selector Lever   5. Key Release Plate
3. Lock Nut

92G14353   Courtesy of General Motors Corp.

Fig. 4: *Adjusting Park/Lock Cable (Tracker)*

Tracker – 1) Disconnect negative battery cable. Remove console and steering column cover. Set transmission range selector lever to Park position. Set ignition switch to LOCK position. Loosen interlock cable lock nut and adjuster nuts. See Fig. 4.

2) Pull manual release lever outward and hold in position. Pull and hold interlock cable away from selector until key release plate is all the way forward, and no cable play exists. Tighten cable lock nut and adjuster nut to 62 INCH lbs. (7 N.m).

NEUTRAL SAFETY SWITCH

NOTE: Neutral safety switch adjustment information for Astro, "C" & "K", "P", Safari and "S" & "T" Series is not available from manufacturer.

Column Mounted Switch (Bravada, "G" Series, Jimmy, Safari & Sonoma) – With shift selector in Neutral, neutral safety switch is adjusted after it is installed and shift selector is moved from Neutral to Park.

Trans. Mounted Switch (Lumina APV, Silhouette & Trans Sport) – 1) Raise and support vehicle and loosen switch mounting bolts. Align hole in switch lever with hole in switch assembly. Insert a 3/32" (2.5 mm) gauge pin through switch holes to hold switch in Neutral position.

2) With selector lever on transmission in Neutral detent position, tighten switch mounting bolts and remove gauge pin. Lower vehicle and check operation of switch.

Transmission Mounted Switch (Tracker) – 1) Set transmission range selector to Neutral position. Loosen switch mounting bolt. Unplug connectors from switch. Connect DVOM to terminals on 2-pin switch connector "C1".

2) Rotate switch counterclockwise as far as possible. Slowly rotate switch clockwise until it clicks, and meter indicates continuity. Tighten switch mounting bolt to 15 ft. lbs. (20 N.m). Reconnect wiring.

OIL PAN GASKET IDENTIFICATION

NOTE: For oil pan gasket identification, see Fig. 5, 6, 7 or 8.

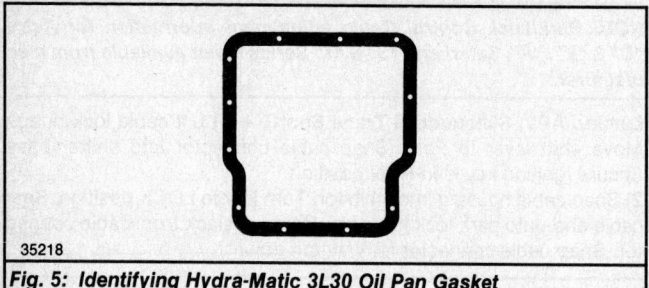

35218
Fig. 5: Identifying Hydra-Matic 3L30 Oil Pan Gasket

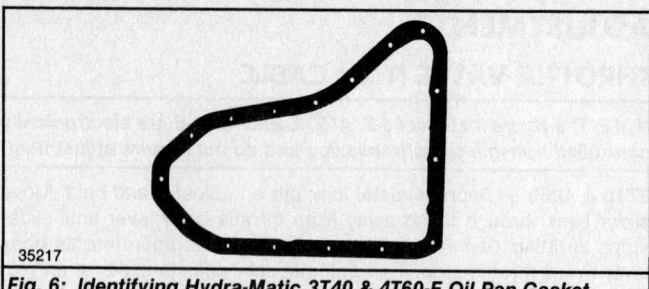

35217
Fig. 6: Identifying Hydra-Matic 3T40 & 4T60-E Oil Pan Gasket

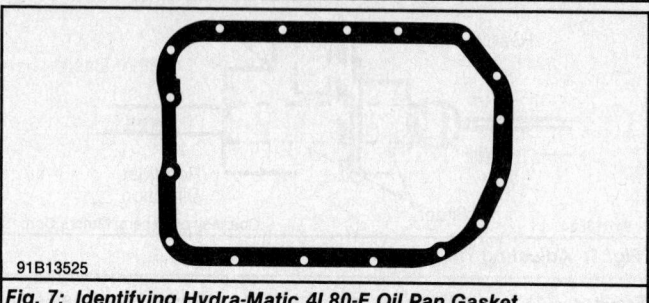

91B13525
Fig. 7: Identifying Hydra-Matic 4L80-E Oil Pan Gasket

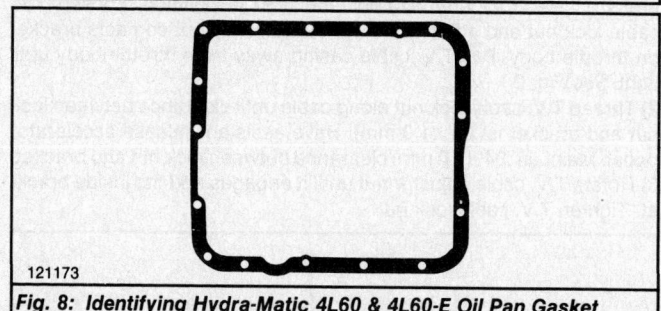

121173
Fig. 8: Identifying Hydra-Matic 4L60 & 4L60-E Oil Pan Gasket

TORQUE SPECIFICATIONS
TORQUE SPECIFICATIONS

Application	Ft. Lbs. (N.m)
Oil Pan Bolts	
3L30	10 (13)
4L60, 4L60-E & 4L80-E	15 (20)
4T60-E	13 (18)
Neutral Safety Switch	
Lumina APV, Silhouette & Trans Sport	
3T40	22 (30)
4T60-E	15 (20)
Shift Linkage Spring Washer Screw	
Astro, Safari & Van	26 (35)
"C" & "K", & "S" & "T"	18 (24)

	INCH Lbs. (N.m)
Oil Pan Bolts (3T40)	96 (11)

Cherokee, Grand Cherokee, Wrangler

IDENTIFICATION

JEEP AUTOMATIC TRANSMISSION APPLICATIONS

Model (Body Code)	Transmission
Cherokee (XJ)	
2.5L (1994)	30RH
4.0L	
1993	AW4
1994	32RH
Grand Cherokee (ZJ)	
4.0L	[1] AW4, 42RE Or 42RH
5.2L	46RH
Wrangler (YJ)	
2.5L (1994)	30RH
4.0L	32RH

[1] – Earlier models used the Aisin Warner 4 transmission. Some models may use the 42RE and some models may use the 42RH. The 42RE is used with 4.0L engine only.

LUBRICATION

SERVICE INTERVALS

Transmission – Check fluid level and condition at 7500 mile intervals. Change fluid, replace filter and adjust bands every 30,000 miles or 30 months.
Transfer Case – Check transfer case fluid every 7500 miles and replace fluid every 30,000 miles or 30 months.

CHECKING FLUID LEVEL

Transmission – Park vehicle on a level surface and apply parking brake. With engine idling at normal operating temperature, move transmission selector lever through all gears. On AW4 models, place select lever in Park. On all other models, place select lever in Neutral. Check fluid level. Fluid level should be between FULL and ADD ONE PINT mark on dipstick. Add fluid as needed. DO NOT overfill.
Transfer Case – Remove fill plug. Check oil level. If level is not at fill plug opening, add lubricant.

RECOMMENDED FLUID

All transmissions and transfer cases use Mopar ATF Plus fluid.

FLUID CAPACITY

NOTE: Transmission and transfer case capacities are approximate. Fluid level should always be determined by reading dipstick or checking fluid level hole, rather than amount of fluid added.

TRANSMISSION REFILL CAPACITIES

Application	Qts. (L)
Overhaul	8.5 (8.0)
Routine Fluid Change	4.3 (4.0)

TRANSFER CASE REFILL CAPACITIES [1]

Application	Qts. (L)
Model 231	1.5 (1.4)
Model 242	1.4 (1.5)
Model 249	1.5 (1.4)

[1] – Application of transfer case may vary due to transmission application. More than one transfer case may be available for each transmission. See TRANSFER CASE APPLICATIONS in APPLICATIONS & IDENTIFICATION.

DRAINING & REFILLING

Transmission – 1) Loosen oil pan bolts, tap pan to break it loose and allow fluid to drain. Remove pan and oil filter. Install NEW filter on bottom of valve body and tighten retaining screws to 35 INCH lbs (4.0 N.m). Install NEW "O" ring on fluid pick-up pipe (if needed). Clean oil pan and install with NEW gasket.

2) Refill transmission with fluid. Start engine and allow to run at curb idle for a few minutes. Ensure vehicle is on level surface. Allow engine to idle and apply parking brake. Move shift selector lever through all gear ranges. On AW4, place select lever in Park.
3) On all other models, place select lever in Neutral. Add fluid up to "ADD ONE PINT" mark on dipstick. Recheck fluid level when transmission reaches normal operating temperature. Fluid should be between "ADD ONE PINT" and "FULL" marks on dipstick. Transmission must NOT be overfilled.
Transfer Case – Remove drain plug from transfer case. Remove fill plug for easier draining. With fluid fully drained, reinstall drain plug. Fill transfer case to fill plug opening with Mopar ATF Plus (1767).

ADJUSTMENTS

NOTE: Bands on the AW4 (4-speed overdrive) transmission are not adjustable. If slippage occurs, bands must be replaced.

KICKDOWN (FRONT) BAND

30RH, 32RH, 42RE Or 42RH Transmissions – 1) Locate kickdown band adjusting screw on left side of case (near throttle lever shaft). *See Fig. 1.* Loosen adjusting screw lock nut and back off approximately 5 turns. Ensure adjusting screw turns freely in case.
2) Using Adapter (C-24063), tighten screw to 36 INCH lbs. (4 N.m). If adapter is not used, tighten screw to 72 INCH lbs. (8 N.m). Back off adjusting screw 2 1/2 turns. Hold adjusting screw in position and tighten lock nut to 35 ft. lbs. (48 N.m).

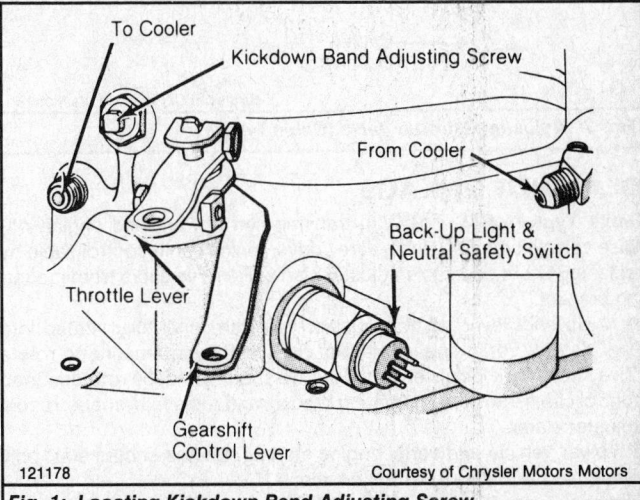

121178   Courtesy of Chrysler Motors Motors

Fig. 1: Locating Kickdown Band Adjusting Screw

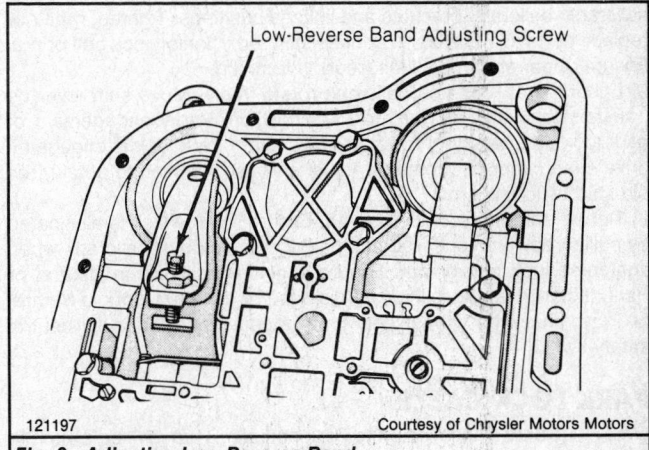

121197   Courtesy of Chrysler Motors Motors

Fig. 2: Adjusting Low-Reverse Band

LOW-REVERSE (REAR) BAND

30RH, 32RH, 42RE Or 42RH Transmissions – **1)** Raise vehicle, drain transmission fluid and remove oil pan. Locate adjusting screw on rear servo lever. *See Fig. 2.* Loosen adjusting screw lock nut and back off about 5-6 turns.

2) Tighten adjusting screw to 72 INCH lbs. (8 N.m) then back off adjusting screw 4 turns. Hold adjusting screw in position and tighten lock nut to 25 ft. lbs. (34 N.m). Install oil pan and fill transmission with fluid.

THROTTLE VALVE (T.V.) CABLE

Cable Type – With transmission in Park and ignition off, press cable release button. Push cable conduit back into cable adjuster as far as possible. Rotate throttle lever to wide open throttle position. Cable will ratchet to correct adjustment as throttle lever is rotated. *See Fig. 3.*

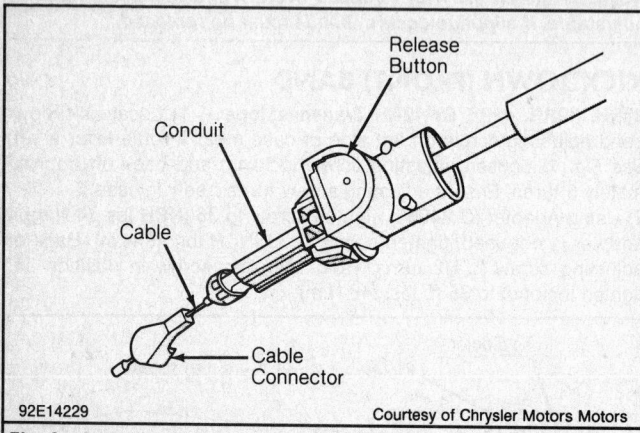

Fig. 3: Adjusting Throttle Valve (Cable Type)

GEARSHIFT LINKAGE

Cable Type (AW4) – **1)** With transmission in Park and engine off, raise vehicle on hoist. Using screwdriver, unlock shift control cable by releasing U-shaped cable adjuster clamp. Remove cable from mounting bracket.

2) Move shift lever on transmission rearward until fully seated into Park detent. Verify engagement of park lock by attempting to rotate drive shaft. Park lock is engaged if drive shaft cannot be rotated. Snap control cable into cable mounting bracket and replace U-shaped cable adjuster clamp.

3) Lower vehicle and verify engine starting. Engine should start only with shifter in Park or Neutral positions.

Linkage Type (Except AW4) – **1)** With transmission in Park and engine off, raise vehicle on hoist. Check condition of shift rods, bellcrank, bellcrank brackets and linkage bushings. Tighten, repair or replace parts as necessary. Loosen shift rod trunnion lock bolt or nut. Ensure upper shift rod slides freely in trunnion.

2) Ensure shift rods and bellcrank rotate freely. Move shift lever on transmission fully rearward to Park position. Verify engagement of park lock by attempting to rotate drive shaft. Park lock is engaged if drive shaft cannot be rotated. Adjust shift rod trunnion to obtain free pin fit in bellcrank arm.

3) Tighten trunnion lock bolt or nut. Ensure linkage lash is eliminated by pulling down on shift rod and pushing up on outer bellcrank when tightening lock bolt or nut. Ensure engine starts only in Neutral or Park. If starter engages in any drive gear, or does not work in Neutral or Park, check for proper shift linkage adjustment or faulty neutral safety switch.

PARK LOCK CABLE

AW4 – **1)** Shift transmission to Park position. Turn ignition switch to LOCK position. Remove outer console bezel to access cable adjustment. Pull cable lock button up to release cable. *See Fig. 4.* Pull cable forward and release.

2) Snap lock button into place. Verify adjustment by attempting to move shifter. Shifter should not move. Turn ignition on. Move shifter to Neutral. If ignition switch cannot be turned to LOCK position, adjustment is okay. Repeat this step with shifter in Drive.

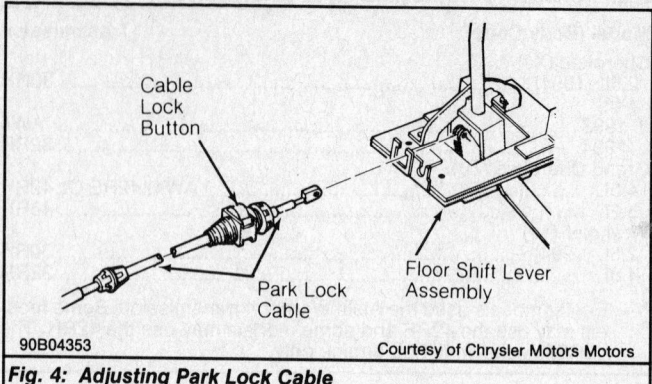

Fig. 4: Adjusting Park Lock Cable

NEUTRAL SAFETY SWITCH

AW4 – **1)** Disconnect shift linkage rod from shift lever on left side of transmission. Rotate shift lever on transmission fully rearward. Then rotate shift lever forward 2 shift positions to Neutral. Verify transmission is in Neutral position.

2) Rotate neutral safety switch to align neutral standard line with vertical groove on shift lever on transmission. Tighten switch adjusting bolt to 108 INCH lbs. (13 N.m). Bend at least 2 washer lock tabs over switch attaching nut. Connect linkage and electrical connector. Check switch operation.

3) If engine starts in shift positions other than Park and Neutral, test switch continuity. To test switch, remove wire connector. Using DVOM, check for continuity between proper terminals with transmission in indicated positions. *See Fig. 5.* If continuity is not present at each circuit, replace neutral safety switch. Install switch and NEW seal in case.

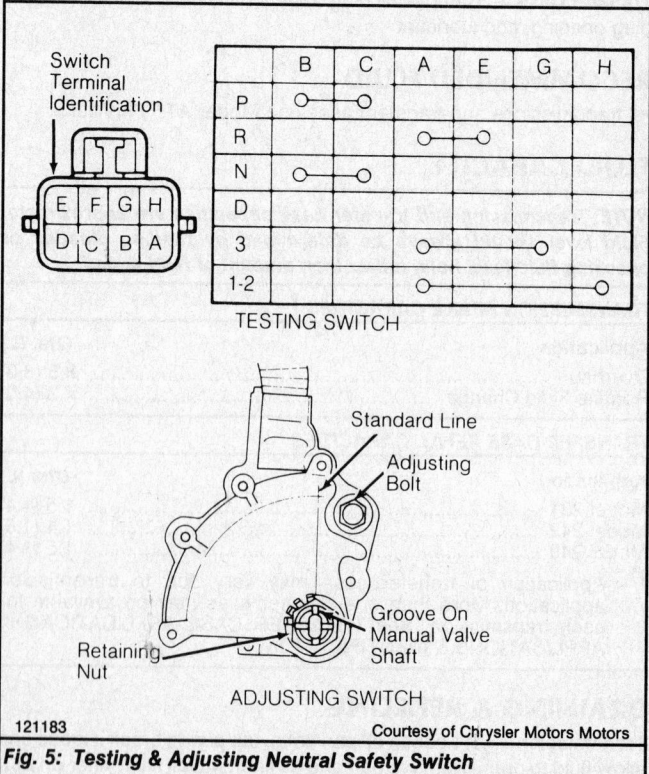

Fig. 5: Testing & Adjusting Neutral Safety Switch

30RH, 32RH, 42RE & 42RH – **1)** With transmission linkage properly adjusted, switch should allow starter operation in Park or Neutral only.

2) To test switch, remove wire harness and test for continuity between center pin of switch and transmission case. Continuity should only exist when transmission is in Park or Neutral.

3) Shift transmission into Reverse. Check for continuity between 2 outer switch terminals. Continuity should exist with transmission in Reverse only. With transmission in Reverse, check continuity between each outer switch terminal and transmission case. No continuity should exist between other terminals and transmission case.

4) To replace switch, disconnect wire connector and unscrew switch from case. Move selector lever to Park and Neutral positions and ensure switch operating fingers are centered in switch opening.

5) Install switch and NEW seal in case. Tighten switch to 24 ft. lbs. (33 N.m). Check fluid level and add as needed.

OIL PAN GASKET IDENTIFICATION

NOTE: For oil pan gasket identification, see Fig. 6, 7 or 8.

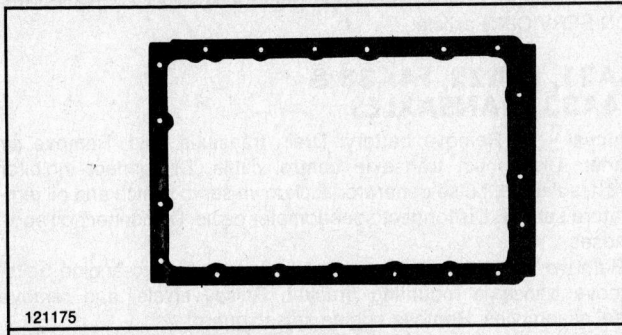

121175

Fig. 6: Identifying AW4 Oil Pan Gasket

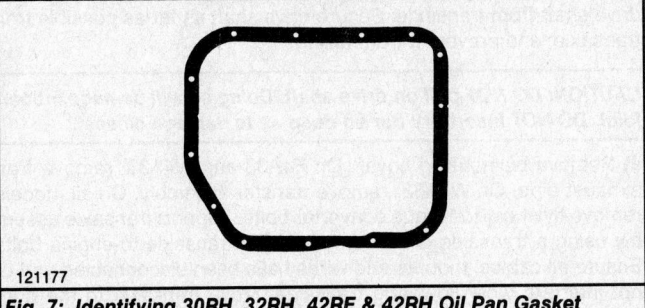

121177

Fig. 7: Identifying 30RH, 32RH, 42RE & 42RH Oil Pan Gasket

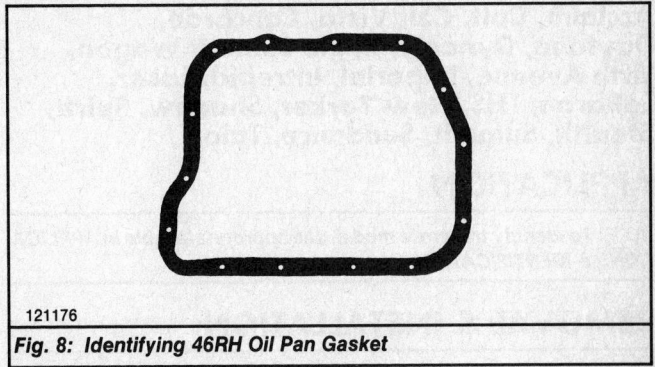

121176

Fig. 8: Identifying 46RH Oil Pan Gasket

TORQUE SPECIFICATIONS
TORQUE SPECIFICATIONS

Application	Ft. Lbs. (N.m)
Kickdown (Front) Band Lock Nut	30 (41)
Low-Reverse (Rear) Band Lock Nut	25 (34)
Neutral Safety Switch (30RH, 32RH, 46RE & 46RH)	25 (34)
Oil Pan Bolts	13 (18)
Transfer Case Fill Plug	20 (27)

	INCH Lbs. (N.m)
Filter	
AW4	84 (10)
30RH, 32RH, 46RE & 46RH	35 (4)
Kickdown (Front) Band	35 (4)
Low-Reverse (Rear) Band	[1] 72 (8)
Neutral Safety Switch (AW4)	
Retaining Nut	61 (7)
Adjusting Bolt	108 (13)

[1] – If adapter extension is used tighten to 50 INCH lbs. (5 N.m). See text for complete adjusting procedure.

AUTOMATIC TRANSMISSION REMOVAL
Chrysler Corp. Passenger Cars

Acclaim, Colt, Colt Vista, Concorde, Daytona, Dynasty, Eagle Summit Wagon, Fifth Avenue, Imperial, Intrepid, Laser, LeBaron, LHS, New Yorker, Shadow, Spirit, Stealth, Summit, Sundance, Talon

APPLICATION

NOTE: To identify transaxle model, see appropriate table in APPLICATIONS & IDENTIFICATION.

REMOVAL & INSTALLATION

WARNING: When battery is disconnected, vehicle computer and memory systems may lose memory data. Driveability problems may exist until computer systems have completed a relearn cycle. See COMPUTER RELEARN PROCEDURES article in APPLICATIONS & IDENTIFICATION before disconnecting battery.

30TH, 31TH & 41TE TRANSAXLE

Removal – 1) Disconnect negative battery cable. On vehicles using A-604/41TE transaxle, drain engine cooling system and remove coolant return extension pipe. On all models, disconnect throttle linkage and shift linkage from transaxle. Disconnect cooler line hoses and lock-up torque converter harness connector.

2) Attach engine support fixture to upper engine compartment, and support engine. Remove upper bellhousing bolts. Raise and support vehicle, and remove front wheels. Remove oil pan bolts, and drain transaxle. Reinstall oil pan.

3) Remove axle nut cotter pin, nut lock and spring washer. Remove axle nut. Remove speedometer pinion gear and cable assembly from transaxle. Remove ball joint-to-steering knuckle clamp bolt.

4) Remove clamp bolt securing ball joint stud to steering knuckle. Separate ball joint stud from steering knuckle by prying against knuckle leg and control arm. DO NOT damage ball joint or CV joint boots.

5) Separate outer CV joint splined shaft from hub by holding CV housing while pushing knuckle assembly away from shaft. Support CV joint housing assemblies out of way.

6) Remove left splash shield. Remove torque converter dust cover, and index mark torque converter to drive plate. Remove access plug in right splash shield to rotate engine crankshaft. Remove torque converter mounting bolts.

7) Disconnect neutral safety switch connector from neutral safety switch, and disconnect all other sensor connectors. Remove engine mount bracket from front crossmember, and remove front mount insulator through bolt.

8) Support transaxle with transmission jack. Remove left engine mount near transaxle differential cover. Remove starter mounting bolts and lower bellhousing bolts.

9) Pry transaxle away from and slightly lower than engine. Pry transaxle from engine at extension housing (if needed). Ensure all external connections are clear from transaxle, and lower unit from vehicle.

Installation – To install transaxle, reverse removal procedure. Check drive axle shaft lengths. See appropriate AXLE SHAFTS article in AXLE SHAFTS & TRANSFER CASES. Adjust throttle cable and shift linkage as necessary. Replace oil pan gasket, and fill transaxle with required amount of fluid. See appropriate AUTOMATIC TRANSMISSION SERVICING article.

42LE TRANSAXLE

Removal – 1) Disconnect battery. Remove engine air inlet tube. Disconnect crankshaft position sensor, located on right side of bell housing. Remove sensor. Disconnect transaxale harness connector, located on right shock tower.

2) Lift vehicle and remove front wheels. Remove strut-to-steering knuckle bolts on both sides of vehicle. Remove ABS wheel speed sensors (if equipped). Pry inner CV joints from transaxle. Pull axle shafts

outward enough to allow clearance for transaxle removal. Support axle shafts with wire. It is not necessary to remove axle shafts from vehicle.

3) Remove engine-to-transaxle bracket. Remove bellhousing cover. Mark flexplate and torque converter for installation reference. Remove torque converter bolts.

4) Unbolt starter and allow it to rest between engine and frame. Disconnect cooler lines from transaxle. Disconnect gear selector cable from transaxle. Unbolt exhaust pipe from manifolds. Remove exhaust from vehicle.

5) Secure transaxle to transmission jack. Raise jack slightly. Remove rear mount bolt. Remove rear crossmember bolts. Lower transaxle slightly to access bellhousing bolts. Remove bellhousing bolts.

6) Remove transaxle dipstick tube. Remove engine-to-transaxle bolts. Carefully lower transaxle.

Installation – To install transaxle, reverse removal procedure. Check drive axle shaft lengths. See appropriate AXLE SHAFTS article in AXLE SHAFTS & TRANSFER CASES. Adjust throttle cable and shift linkage as necessary. Replace oil pan gasket, and fill transaxle with required amount of fluid. See appropriate AUTOMATIC TRANSMISSION SERVICING article.

F3A21, F4A22, F4A33 & W4A33 TRANSAXLES

Removal – 1) Remove battery. Drain transaxle fluid. Remove air cleaner. Disconnect transaxle control cable. Disconnect inhibitor switch, solenoid, pulse generator, kickdown servo switch and oil temperature sensor. Disconnect speedometer cable. Disconnect oil cooler hoses.

2) Remove starter motor. Remove upper transaxle-to-engine bolts. Remove transaxle mounting bracket. Raise vehicle, and remove wheel assemblies. Remove engine splash guard.

3) Disconnect tie rod end from knuckle. Separate lower ball joint from knuckle. Insert pry bar between transaxle case and drive shaft. Pry drive shaft from transaxle. Secure drive shaft as far as possible from transaxle, and prevent it from falling.

CAUTION: DO NOT pull on drive shaft. Doing so will damage inboard joint. DO NOT insert pry bar so deep as to damage oil seal.

4) Remove bellhousing cover. On F4A33 and W4A33, remove front exhaust pipe. On W4A33, remove transfer assembly. On all models, remove flywheel-to-torque converter bolts. Support transaxle assembly using a transaxle jack. Remove lower transaxle-to-engine bolts. Ensure all cables, mounts and wires have been disconnected and do not interfere when lowering transaxle. Move transaxle to the right. Lower and remove from vehicle.

CAUTION: DO NOT damage oil seal lip or serrated part of drive shaft.

Installation – To install, reverse removal procedure. On turbocharged models, protect lower radiator hose. On all models, install drive shaft so inboard joint of drive shaft is straight and not bent relative to transaxle. Tighten starter bolts with wiring harness clip and ground cable. Replace drain plug gasket, and fill transaxle with required amount of fluid. See appropriate AUTOMATIC TRANSMISSION SERVICING article.

TORQUE SPECIFICATIONS
TORQUE SPECIFICATIONS (30TH, 31TH & 41TE)

Application	Ft. Lbs. (N.m)
Axle Nut	180 (244)
Bellhousing Bolts	70 (95)
Control Arm Pinch Bolts	70 (95)
Engine Mount Bolts	40 (54)
Oil Pan Bolts	14 (19)
Shift Linkage Bolts	20 (27)
Starter Mounting Bolts	40 (54)
Sway Bar Bolts	40 (54)
Torque Converter Bolts	55 (74)
Wheel Lug Nuts	95 (129)

TORQUE SPECIFICATIONS (42LE)

Application	Ft. Lbs. (N.m)
Bellhousing Bolts	65 (88)
Cooler Lines	13 (18)
Engine Mount Bolts	40 (54)
Differential Fill Plug	35 (47)
Exhaust Pipe Bracket Bolts	35 (47)
Rear Crossmember Bolts	30 (41)
Steering Knuckle Nuts	125 (170)
Starter Mounting Bolts	40 (54)
Torque Converter Bolts	55 (74)
Wheel Lug Nuts	85-115 (115-156)

TORQUE SPECIFICATIONS (F3A21, F4A22, F4A33 & W4A33)

Application	Ft. Lbs. (N.m)
Starter Bolts	20-25 (27-34)
Steering Knuckle Nuts	43-52 (60-72)
Tie Rod End Nuts	17-25 (24-34)
Torque Converter Bolts	54-57 (73-77)
Transaxle-To-Engine Bolts	22-35 (30-47)
Transfer Assembly	41-44 (55-60)

Chrysler Corp. Light Trucks & Vans

Caravan, Dakota, Pickup, Ramcharger, RWD & AWD Van, Town & Country, Ram-50, Voyager

REMOVAL & INSTALLATION

WARNING: When battery is disconnected, vehicle computer and memory systems may lose memory data. Driveability problems may exist until computer systems have completed a relearn cycle. See COMPUTER RELEARN PROCEDURES article in APPLICATIONS & IDENTIFICATION before disconnecting battery.

FWD MODELS

AWD Power Transfer Unit (PTU) – 1) Raise and support vehicle. Remove front wheel assemblies. Remove propeller shaft. Remove crossmember bridge attaching bolts. Remove power steering hose bracket attaching bolt. Using tie wraps, secure steering gear assembly to frame rails.

2) Disconnect ball joints from steering knuckles. Remove lower transaxle-to-crossmember strut bolt. Support crossmember with suitable transmission jack. Remove crossmember attaching bolts and remove crossmember from vehicle.

3) Remove right front drive axle. Remove PTU support bracket and strut assembly. Remove rear PTU brace attaching bolts. Remove speed sensor. Remove PTU remote vent from left engine mount. Remove 4 PTU mounting bolts and remove PTU. To install PTU, reverse removal procedure.

NOTE: Transaxle removal does not require engine removal.

CAUTION: Transaxle and torque converter must be removed as an assembly; otherwise, the torque converter drive plate, pump bushing or oil seal may be damaged. The drive plate will not support a load; therefore, none of the weight of the transaxle should be allowed to rest on the plate during removal.

Transaxle Removal – 1) Disconnect battery negative cable. Disconnect throttle linkage and shift linkage from transaxle. Remove upper and lower oil cooler hoses. Support engine using an engine support fixture. Remove bellhousing upper bolts.

2) Raise vehicle and remove front wheels. Remove wheel hub nut. Remove left splash shield. Remove speedometer adapter, cable and pinion as an assembly. Disconnect sway bar. Remove both lower ball joint-to-steering knuckle bolts.

3) Pry lower ball joint from steering knuckle. Remove both axle shafts. Remove access plug in right splash shield to rotate engine crankshaft. Remove dust cover, mark torque converter and drive plate, and remove torque converter mounting bolts.

4) Remove neutral safety switch connector. Remove engine mount bracket from front crossmember. Remove front mount insulator through bolt and bellhousing bolts. Position transmission jack under transaxle. Remove left engine mount. Remove starter and lower bellhousing bolts.

5) Attach a small "C" clamp to edge of bellhousing to hold torque converter in place during transaxle removal and installation. Slowly lower transaxle. It may be necessary to pry engine aside to provide for clearance.

Transaxle Installation – To install, reverse removal procedure. Adjust gearshift and throttle cables. Refill transaxle with ATF Plus 7176 automatic transmission fluid.

RWD MODELS

NOTE: For transfer case replacement procedures, see CHRYSLER MOTORS RWD LIGHT TRUCKS & VANS article in MANUAL TRANSMISSION REMOVAL section.

Removal – 1) On all models except Ram-50, remove transfer case from 4WD vehicles. Disconnect negative battery cable. Disconnect lower exhaust system as needed for removal clearance. Remove engine-to-transmission struts (if equipped). Disconnect cooler lines at transmission. Remove starter, cooler line bracket and converter access cover.

2) Loosen oil pan bolts. Tap pan to break loose and allow fluid to drain. Reinstall pan. Rotate crankshaft clockwise with socket on vibration damper bolt to gain access to converter-to-drive plate bolts. Remove bolts. Mark propeller shaft for reassembly reference and remove from vehicle.

NOTE: Crankshaft flange bolt circle, inner and outer circle of holes in drive plate and tapped holes in converter all have one hole offset so parts can only be installed in original position.

3) Disconnect wiring connector from back-up light/neutral safety switch. Disconnect gearshift rod and torque shaft assembly from transmission. Disconnect transmission throttle rod from lever. Remove linkage bellcrank assembly, if equipped. Remove oil filler tube. Disconnect speedometer cable.

4) Install an engine support fixture under rear of engine. Raise transmission with service jack to relieve load on supports. Remove bolts securing crossmember to transmission and frame, then remove crossmember. Remove all converter housing-to-engine attaching bolts.

5) Carefully work transmission and converter assembly rearward off engine block dowel pins, disengaging converter hub from end of crankshaft. Attach a small "C" clamp on edge of converter housing to hold converter in place while transmission is being removed. Lower transmission and remove from vehicle.

2-32

AUTOMATIC TRANSMISSION REMOVAL
Chrysler Corp. Light Trucks & Vans (Cont.)

Installation – **1)** Before installing converter, rotate front pump rotors with Aligner (C3756) until 2 small holes in tool handle are vertical. Slide torque converter over input and reaction shafts. Ensure converter hub slots are vertical and pump inner rotor lugs are fully engaged.

2) Test for full engagement by placing a straightedge across face of transmission case. Surface of converter front cover lug should be at least 1/2" to rear of straightedge when converter is fully engaged. Attach a small "C" clamp to edge of converter housing to hold converter in place while installing transmission.

3) Inspect converter flexplate for distortion or cracks and replace if necessary. Install flexplate and tighten bolts to 55 ft. lbs. (75 N.m).

4) Coat converter hub hole in crankshaft with multipurpose grease. Place transmission assembly on jack and position under vehicle. Ensure marks on converter and drive plate (made during removal) are aligned. Check converter bolts for proper length. See CONVERTER BOLT LENGTH table.

CONVERTER BOLT LENGTH

Converter Diameter & Configuration	In. (mm)
9 1/2" 3-Bolt	.46" (11.7)
9 1/2" & 10" 4-Bolt	.52" (13.2)
10 3/4" 4-Bolt	.44" (11.2)

5) Carefully move transmission assembly into position over dowels. Install all converter housing-to-engine retaining bolts. Tighten bolts to 30 ft. lbs. (41 N.m). Adjust shift and throttle linkages and fill transmission with fluid. On 4WD models, install transfer case.

TORQUE SPECIFICATIONS
TORQUE SPECIFICATIONS (FWD & AWD)

Application	Ft. Lbs. (N.m)
Flexplate-To-Crankshaft	70 (95)
Front Motor Mount	40 (54)
Left Motor Mount	40 (54)
Manual Cable-To-Transaxle Case	21 (28)
Starter-To-Transaxle Bellhousing	40 (54)
Transaxle-To-Cylinder Block	70 (95)
Torque Converter-To-Flexplate Bolts	40 (54)

	INCH Lbs. (N.m)
Bell Housing Cover	108 (12)
Lower Bell Housing Cover	108 (12)
Manual Control Lever	108 (12)
Throttle Cable-To-Transaxle Case	108 (12)
Throttle Lever-To-Transaxle Shaft	108 (12)
Speedometer-To-Extension	60 (7)

TORQUE SPECIFICATIONS (RWD & 4WD)

Application	Ft. Lbs. (N.m)
Converter Housing-To-Engine	30 (41)
Cooler Line Fitting	13 (18)
Oil Pan Bolts	12 (17)
Rear Mount Bolt	50 (68)
Torque Converter-To-Flexplate Bolts	
Ram-50	33-38 (45-52)
9 1/2" 3-Bolt	40 (54)
9 1/2" & 10" 4-Bolt	55 (74)
10 3/4" 4-Bolt	23 (31)
12 1/4" [1]	35 (47)
Transfer Case-To-Transmission	
Ram-50	22-30 (30-41)
All Others	40 (54)
Transmission-To-Engine Block Bolt	
Ram-50	
10 x 16-mm Bolt	22-30 (30-41)
10 x 50-mm Bolt	31-40 (42-54)
10 x 70-mm Bolt	31-40 (42-54)
All Others	30 (41)

[1] – Diesel models.

Ford Motor Co. Passenger Cars

Aspire, Capri, Continental, Cougar, Crown Victoria, Escort, Festiva, Grand Marquis, Mark VII, Mustang, Probe, Sable, Taurus, Tempo, Thunderbird, Topaz, Town Car, Tracer

APPLICATION
TRANSMISSION APPLICATIONS

Vehicle Model	Transmission Application
Aspire	ATX
Capri	4EAT
Continental	AXOD-E/AX4S
Cougar	
1993	AOD
1994	4R70W
Crown Victoria	AOD-E
Escort	4EAT
Festiva	ATX
Grand Marquis	AOD-E
Mark VIII	4R70W
Mustang	
2.3L (1993)	A4LD
3.8L (1994)	AOD-E
5.0L (1993)	AOD
5.0L (1994)	AOD-E

TRANSMISSION APPLICATIONS (Cont.)

Vehicle Model	Transmission Application
Probe	CD4E & 4EAT
Sable	AXOD-E/AX4S
Taurus	AXOD-E/AX4S
Tempo	[1] FLC/ATX
Thunderbird	
1993	AOD
1994	4R70W
Topaz	[1] FLC/ATX
Town Car	AOD-E
Tracer	4EAT

[1] – Manufacturer uses FLC in some publications, ATX in others.

REMOVAL & INSTALLATION

WARNING: When battery is disconnected, vehicle computer and memory systems may lose memory data. Driveability problems may exist until computer systems have completed a relearn cycle. See COMPUTER RELEARN PROCEDURES article in APPLICATIONS & IDENTIFICATION before disconnecting battery.

AOD, AOD-E & 4R70W TRANSMISSIONS

Removal – **1)** Raise and support vehicle. Remove torque converter access cover and adapter plate bolts from lower left side of torque converter housing. Drain transmission fluid (including torque converter). Mark torque converter-to-flexplate position for installation reference. Remove 4 torque converter-to-flexplate nuts. Turn crankshaft clockwise (as viewed from front) to access nuts.

2) Mark position of yokes, and remove propeller shaft. Install Seal Replacer (T74P-77052-A) in extension housing to prevent leakage. Disconnect and remove speedometer sensor from extension housing. Remove starter.

3) Remove rear mount-to-crossmember bolts and 2 crossmember-to-frame bolts. Remove 2 engine rear support-to-extension housing attaching bolts.

4) Disconnect throttle valve linkage rod or cable from transmission. On Cougar and Thunderbird, disconnect cable from bellcrank lever stud, and remove self-tapping bolt from bellhousing bracket.

5) On all models, disconnect manual rod from transmission manual lever. Remove 2 bellcrank bracket-to-torque converter housing bolts. Disconnect neutral safety switch wires.

6) Position jack under transmission, and raise it slightly. Remove engine support-to-crossmember bolts. Remove crossmember-to-frame bolts. Remove crossmember, insulator support and damper.

7) Remove any interfering exhaust system hardware. Lower jack slightly to access oil cooler lines. Using Cooler Line Disconnector (T86P-77265-AH), disconnect oil cooler lines from transmission. Plug openings.

8) Remove lower torque converter housing bolts. Remove transmission filler tube. Secure transmission to jack using a safety chain. Slide transmission to rear, and lower it from vehicle.

Installation – **1)** To install transmission, reverse removal procedure. Ensure torque converter is fully seated in pump. Lubricate torque converter pilot with chassis grease.

2) Align Orange balancing marks (if present) on torque converter and flexplate. Align torque converter drive studs and drain plug with holes in flexplate.

3) Adjust manual and downshift linkage. Fill transmission with required amount of ATF. See appropriate AUTOMATIC TRANSMISSION SERVICING article. If any shift rods are disassembled, install new plastic grommets.

ATX TRANSAXLE

Removal – **1)** Disconnect negative battery cable. Disconnect speedometer cable from transaxle. Disconnect transaxle electrical connectors located next to governor. Disconnect ground wire from transaxle.

2) Disconnect transaxle vacuum hose. Remove shift lever-to-manual shaft assembly nut. Remove shift cable from transaxle. Support engine using Engine Support Bar (D87L-6000-A). Raise and support vehicle remove front wheels. Drain transaxle fluid.

3) Remove left splash shield. Remove stabilizer mounting nuts and brackets. Remove left stabilizer body bracket. Remove lower control arm clamp bolts and nuts. Pull lower control arms downward, separating lower control arms from knuckle.

4) Remove cotter pin and nut and disconnect tie rod end from knuckle. Remove halfshafts and install Differential Plugs (T87C-7025-C) into halfshaft seals or between differential side gears. Disconnect oil cooler hoses. Remove crossmember and gusset plate-to-transaxle bolts.

5) Remove flywheel cover. Index mark torque converter and flexplate for reassembly reference. Remove torque converter bolts. Remove starter. Support transaxle with suitable transmission jack. Remove engine-to-transaxle bolts. Lower transaxle from vehicle.

Installation – To install, reverse removal procedure. Align reference marks on flexplate and torque converter. Fill transaxle with required amount of fluid. Adjust shift linkage. Check and adjust axle shaft positioning. See appropriate AXLE SHAFTS article in AXLE SHAFTS & TRANSFER CASES.

AXOD-E & AX4S TRANSAXLES

Removal – **1)** Turn off air suspension switch located in trunk (if equipped). Remove air cleaner assembly. Disconnect battery cables, and remove battery. Remove battery tray. Disconnect harness connectors from engine. Remove main wiring harness retaining bolt. Remove shift lever.

2) Remove through bolt from left motor mount strut. Secure wiring harness aside. Remove radiator sight shield. Remove upper transaxle-to-engine bolts. On Sable and Taurus, attach Engine Lifting Bracket (D81L-6001-D) to left rear of cylinder head. Lifting bracket should already be installed on right front of cylinder head.

3) On all models, attach Engine Support Bar (D87L-6000-A) across shock towers. Attach engine to support bar. Raise engine to take pressure off engine mounts. Turn off air suspension switch located in trunk (if equipped). Remove dipstick. Disconnect power steering pump pressure and return line retaining bracket.

4) Remove 4 torque converter housing bolts from top of transaxle. Raise vehicle on hoist. Remove front wheels. Separate left tie rod end from steering knuckle. Remove suspension height sensor. Disconnect brake line support brackets. Remove retaining bolts from stabilizer bar. Disconnect lower control arm assemblies. Remove steering gear retaining nuts.

5) Remove front exhaust pipe, converter assembly and mounting bracket. Remove 2 transaxle mount bolts. Remove 4 left engine support bolts, and remove support. Remove power steering gear-to-subframe retaining bolts, and tie gear assembly to rear of engine compartment. Remove all subframe-to-engine mount bolts. Support subframe. Remove remaining subframe-to-body bolts, and lower subframe.

6) Position transaxle jack under transaxle. Remove speedometer or vehicle speed sensor from transaxle. Remove transaxle-to-engine supports and transaxle mount. Remove starter and dust cover. Remove transaxle cooler line retaining clips. Disconnect transaxle cooler lines using Cooler Line Disconnector (T86P-77265-AH).

7) Remove 4 flexplate-to-torque converter nuts. Pull CV joints from transaxle using a slide hammer, CV Joint Puller (T86P-3514-A1) and Extension (T86P-3514-A2). Remove remaining transaxle-to-engine bolts. Separate transaxle from engine, and lower it out of vehicle.

CAUTION: DO NOT let puller contact speed sensor, or damage may result.

Installation – **1)** To install transaxle, reverse removal procedure. A NEW circlip must be installed on axle shaft before installation. Fill transaxle to correct level with ATF.

2) Check subframe alignment by installing a 3/4" (19 mm) pipe or alignment bar into subframe and body alignment holes. Alignment holes are located at front left subframe assembly.

3) Slightly tighten mount bolts. Repeat procedure for right subframe assembly. Check left alignment holes. After both sides are aligned, tighten subframe-to-body mount bolts. Check and adjust axle shaft positioning. See appropriate AXLE SHAFTS article in AXLE SHAFTS & TRANSFER CASES.

A4LD TRANSMISSION

Removal – **1)** Disconnect negative battery cable. Raise and support vehicle. Remove oil pan, and drain transmission fluid. Remove torque converter access cover and adapter plate bolts from torque converter housing.

CAUTION: DO NOT rotate crankshaft in a counterclockwise direction (as viewed from front).

---

2) Turn engine crankshaft clockwise (as viewed from front) to access torque converter nuts. Remove 4 torque converter-to-flexplate nuts.

3) Mark position of yokes, and remove propeller shaft. Install plug in extension housing to prevent leakage. Disconnect and remove speedometer sensor from extension housing (if equipped).

4) Remove starter. Disconnect neutral safety switch connector. Remove 2 engine rear support-to-extension housing attaching bolts. Disconnect vacuum line from transmission vacuum modulator.

5) Disconnect selector rod from transmission lever at transmission using Shift Linkage Grommet Remover (T84P-7341-A). Remove 2 bellcrank bracket-to-torque converter housing bolts.

6) Raise transmission using a transmission jack to provide clearance to remove crossmember. Remove rear mount from crossmember. Remove crossmember from side supports.

7) Disconnect any interfering exhaust system hardware. Lower transmission to access oil cooler lines. Using Cooler Line Disconnector (T86P-77265-AH), disconnect oil cooler line from fittings on transmission.

8) Disconnect speedometer cable from extension housing. Remove transmission filler tube-to-engine block bolt. Remove filler tube. Secure transmission to jack using a chain.

9) Remove transmission-to-engine bolts. Move transmission and torque converter assembly away from engine while lowering jack to clear underside of vehicle.

Installation – 1) To install, reverse removal procedure. Torque converter is properly installed when pilot hub is 7/16-9/16" from engine mating surface of housing.

2) Fill transmission with required amount of fluid. Adjust shift cable and throttle valve cable as needed. See appropriate AUTOMATIC TRANSMISSION SERVICING article.

FLC/ATX TRANSAXLE

Removal – 1) Disconnect negative battery cable. Remove air cleaner assembly. Disconnect wiring from Park/Neutral Position (PNP) switch. Disconnect throttle valve linkage (throttle cable on 3.0L) and manual lever cable at transaxle.

2) Cover up timing window in converter housing to prevent contamination. Remove bolts retaining air injection system hoses (if equipped). Position valve and hoses away from tubing and master cylinder. Remove ground strap above engine mount (if equipped).

3) Remove coil and bracket assembly. Remove the 2 upper transaxle-to-engine attaching bolts. Raise and support vehicle. Remove wheels.

4) Remove control arm-to-steering knuckle attaching bolt and nut (at both ball joints) and discard. A NEW bolt and nut must be used during transaxle installation. Using pry bar, carefully separate control arms from steering knuckles.

CAUTION: Use care not to damage ball joint boot. Pry bar must not contact control arm. DO NOT use hammer on ball joints.

5) Remove bolts attaching stabilizer bar brackets to frame. Remove stabilizer bar-to-control arm nut and washer. Discard bolts and washer. Manufacturer recommends using NEW hardware on installation.

6) Pull stabilizer bar out of control arms. Remove bolts attaching brake hose routing clips to suspension strut brackets. Disconnect tie rod ends from steering knuckles.

7) Pry right side drive axle shaft out of transaxle using Half-Shaft Remover (D83P-4026-A). See appropriate AXLE SHAFTS article in AXLE SHAFTS & TRANSFER CASES. Position shaft on transaxle housing.

NOTE: Due to FLC/ATX case configuration, RH half-shaft must be removed first.

8) Insert Differential Rotator (T81P-4026-A) into right side differential side gear. Drive left drive axle shaft from differential side gear. Pull drive axle shaft from transaxle and support out of way.

CAUTION: Do not let axle shaft hang unsupported. Damage to outboard CV joint may result.

9) Install Seal Plugs (T81P-1177-B) into differential seals to prevent spline misalignment. Remove starter. On throttle body equipped vehicles, remove 2 hose/bracket bolts on starter and one bolt attached to converter. Disconnect hoses.

10) Remove transaxle support bracket. Remove bellhousing dust cover. Remove flexplate-to-converter nuts. Position transmission jack under transaxle. Remove rear support bracket nuts. Remove nuts attaching left front insulator to body bracket. Remove bracket-to-body bolts and remove bracket.

11) Disconnect oil cooler lines at transaxle using Cooler Line Disconnector (T82L-9500-AH). Remove bolts attaching manual lever bracket

to transaxle case. Support engine. Position transmission jack under transaxle and remove 4 remaining transaxle-to-engine bolts.

12) Insert screwdriver between flexplate and converter. Carefully move transaxle and converter away from engine. When converter studs are clear of flexplate, lower transaxle about 3" and disconnect speedometer cable. Lower transaxle from vehicle.

NOTE: If left-front insulator contacts body before converter studs clear flexplate, remove left-front insulator.

Installation – 1) To install transaxle, reverse removal procedure. ALWAYS replace snap ring on CV joint stub shaft.

2) To install drive axle shafts, carefully align splines on shaft with differential splines. Push CV joint until snap ring is felt to seat in groove in side gear.

3) Attach lower ball joint to steering knuckle, taking care not to damage or cut ball joint boot. Install NEW pinch bolt and NEW nut. DO NOT tighten bolt, tighten NUT to specification. See appropriate TORQUE SPECIFICATIONS table. Fill transaxle with required amount of ATF. See appropriate AUTOMATIC TRANSMISSION SERVICING article.

4EAT TRANSAXLE

Removal (Capri) – 1) Disconnect and remove battery. Remove air cleaner assembly. Disconnect speedometer cable from transaxle. Remove shift cable retaining bolts. Disconnect kickdown cable from throttle body. Disconnect transaxle electrical connectors located next to governor.

2) Remove dipstick bracket. Remove starter upper retaining bolts. Remove upper intake manifold support retaining bolts. Remove heater by-pass tube bracket. Remove transaxle-to-engine upper mount bolts. Install Engine Support Bar (D88L-6000-A).

3) Raise and support vehicle. Remove front wheels. Drain transaxle fluid. Remove lower intake manifold support mount bolts. Remove starter. Separate ball joints from control arms. Remove left control arm retaining bolt. Loosen right control arm retaining bolt.

4) Remove frame brace-to-crossmember bolts. Remove front and rear transaxle mount-to-crossmember bolts. Remove crossmember braces and crossmember. Remove left drive axle. Disconnect right drive axle from transaxle. Install Differential Plugs (T88C-7025-AH).

5) Remove front and rear trans axle mounts. Lower vehicle. Lower engine/transaxle assembly using support bar. Raise vehicle. Remove torque converter cover plate. Index mark torque converter and flexplate for reassembly reference.

6) Remove torque converter bolts. Support transaxle with suitable transmission jack. Remove transaxle-to-engine lower bolts and remove transaxle.

Installation – To install, reverse removal procedure. Align reference marks on flexplate and torque converter. Fill transaxle with required amount of fluid. Adjust shift linkage. Check and adjust axle shaft positioning. See appropriate AXLE SHAFTS article in AXLE SHAFTS & TRANSFER CASES.

CD4E & 4EAT TRANSAXLE

Removal (Escort, Probe & Tracer) – 1) Remove battery and battery carrier. Disconnect wiring harness retaining clip from battery tray. Remove air cleaner assembly. Disconnect shift control cable. Disconnect speedometer cable. Disconnect transaxle electrical connectors, and separate harness from retaining clips. On CD4E transaxle, remove ignition coil and cruise control servo, and secure out of the way.

2) On all models, remove Manual Lever Position (MPL) sensor/switch harness brackets from transaxle. Disconnect ground cables from transaxle. Disconnect MPL sensor/switch harness connectors. On CD4E transaxle, remove MPL sensor. On all models, install Engine Support Fixture (D88L-6000-A). Disconnect kickdown cable at throttle cam. Disconnect transaxle cooler lines at transaxle. Remove upper transaxle mount.

3) Remove upper transaxle housing bolts. Disconnect oxygen sensor. Disconnect transaxle vent hose. Disconnect speed sensor harness connector at sensor. Raise vehicle on hoist, and remove wheels. Using a hammer and flat punch, straighten detent on axle retaining nut.

CAUTION: DO NOT damage threads on outer CV joint.

4) Remove nuts attaching axles to steering knuckles. Disconnect lower ball joints from steering knuckles. Disconnect axle shaft bearing support from back of engine. Disconnect axles from steering knuckles. Remove starter. Remove lower splash shields and torque converter inspection plate. Mark torque converter-to-flexplate position for installation reference.

5) Remove torque converter-to-flexplate nuts. Disconnect lower crossmember from vehicle chassis. Remove axle shafts from transaxle using a prybar inserted between axle shaft and transaxle case. Install 2 Transaxle Plugs (T88C-7025-AH) into differential side gears.

6) Remove pan and differential drain plug. Support transaxle using transaxle jack. Remove transaxle-to-engine lower bolts. Lower transaxle from vehicle.

Installation – To install, reverse removal procedure. Tighten transaxle-to-engine bolts to specification. See TORQUE SPECIFICATIONS. On CD4E transaxle, tighten transaxle-to-engine mounting bolts to correct specification. *See Fig. 1.* On all transaxles, align reference marks on torque converter and flexplate. Use new circlip on axle shaft inboard-stub shaft. Fill transaxle with required amount of fluid. See AUTOMATIC TRANSMISSION article. Adjust throttle valve cable and shift linkage. Check and adjust axle shaft positioning. See AXLE SHAFTS article under DRIVE AXLES.

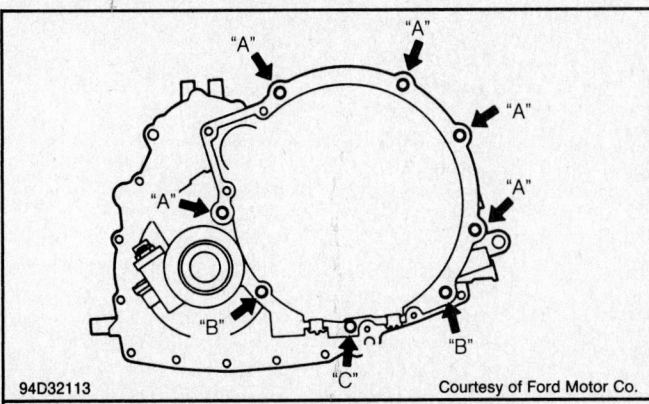

94D32113   Courtesy of Ford Motor Co.

Fig. 1: Identifying Transaxle-To-Engine Bolts (CD4E)

TORQUE SPECIFICATIONS

TORQUE SPECIFICATIONS (AOD, AOD-E & 4R70W)

Application	Ft. Lbs. (N.m)
Converter Drain Plug	
AOD	8-28 (11-38)
AOD-E & 4R70W	21-23 (28-31)
Crossmember-To-Side Support Bolt	70-100 (95-136)
Crossmember-To-Transmission	
AOD-E & 4R70W	64-81 (87-110)
Extension Housing Bolts	
AOD	16-20 (22-27)
AOD-E & 4R70W	18-22 (25-30)
Front Pump-To-Case	15-19 (20-26)
Torque Converter Access Cover Bolt	12-16 (16-22)
Torque Converter-To-Flexplate Nut	20-34 (27-46)
Transmission Oil Cooler Line	15-19 (20-26)
Transmission-To-Engine Bolt	40-50 (54-67)
Wheel Lug Nut	85-105 (115-142)

	INCH Lbs. (N.m)
Cover Plate-To-Valve Body	80-100 (9-11)
Oil Pan Bolt	107-144 (12-16)
Valve Body Bolt	80-100 (9-11)

TORQUE SPECIFICATIONS (ATX – ASPIRE & FESTIVA)

Application	Ft. Lbs. (N.m)
Crossmember Attaching Bolt	47-66 (64-89)
Engine-To-Transaxle Bolt	41-59 (55-80)
Front Engine Mount-To-Crossmember Nut	32-38 (43-52)
Gusset Plate-To-Transaxle Bolt	27-38 (36-52)
Left Stabilizer Body Bracket Nut/Bolt	40-45 (54-61)
Lower Control Arm Clamp Nut/Bolt	32-40 (43-54)
Manual Shift Lever Shaft Assembly Nut	35-57 (44-64)
Rear Engine Mount-To-Crossmember Nut	21-34 (28-46)
Stabilizer Bracket Mounting Nut	40-50 (54-68)
Tie Rod End-To-Knuckle Nut	26-30 (35-40)
Torque Converter Bolt	26-36 (35-49)

	INCH Lbs. (N.m)
Flywheel Cover Bolt	61-87 (7-10)
Line Pressure Plug	43-87 (5-10)

TORQUE SPECIFICATIONS (AXOD-E & AX4S)

Application	Ft. Lbs. (N.m)
Cooler Line Nut At Radiator	8-12 (11-16)
Cooler Line Push Connector At Transaxle	18-23 (24-31)
Lower Control Arm-To-Knuckle	40-53 (53-72)
Rod-To-Knuckle Nut	¹ 23-35 (31-47)
Stabilizer U-Clamp Bolt	23-29 (31-40)
Torque Converter-To-Flexplate Nut	23-39 (31-53)
Transaxle-To-Engine Bolt	41-50 (55-68)
Wheel Lug Nut	85-105 (115-142)

	INCH Lbs. (N.m)
Oil Pan Bolt	96-132 (11-15)

¹ – Tighten to minimum torque; then tighten to nearest cotter pin slot.

TORQUE SPECIFICATIONS (A4LD)

Application	Ft. Lbs. (N.m)
Access Cover Bolt	12-16 (16-22)
Crossmember-To-Frame Bolt	70-100 (95-136)
Engine Support-To-Crossmember Nut	50-70 (68-95)
Filler Tube Bolt	28-38 (38-52)
Propeller Shaft Nut	70-95 (95-129)
Starter Mounting Bolt	15-20 (20-27)
Torque Converter Access Cover Bolt	12-16 (16-22)
Torque Converter-To-Flexplate Nut	20-34 (27-46)
Transmission Cooling Line	18-23 (24-31)
Transmission-To-Engine Bolt	40-50 (55-67)
Wheel Lug Nut	85-105 (115-142)

	INCH Lbs. (N.m)
Oil Pan Bolt	72-120 (8-14)

TORQUE SPECIFICATIONS (CD4E)

Application	Ft. Lbs. (N.m)
Lower Control Arm Ball Joint Bolt & Nut	32-44 (43-59)
Torque Converter-To-Flexplate Nut	32-45 (43-61)
Transaxle-To-Engine Bolt	
"A"	66-86 (90-116)
"B"	28-38 (38-51)
"C"	14-18 (19-25)
Wheel Lug Nut	65-87 (88-118)

	INCH Lbs. (N.m)
Manual Lever Position Sensor Bolt	84 (10)
Oil Filler Tube Bolt	72 (8)
Oil Pan Bolt	72-97 (8-11)

TORQUE SPECIFICATIONS (FLC/ATX)

Application	Ft. Lbs. (N.m)
Axle Shaft Bolt	16-23 (21-32)
Ball Joint Nut-To-Steering Knuckle Bolt	40-54 (54-73)
Cooler Line Nut At Transaxle	18-22 (24-31)
Control Arm Pinch Bolt	40-54 (54-73)
Insulator Bracket-To-Frame Bolt	40-50 (54-68)
Insulator Mount-To-Transaxle Bolt	25-33 (34-45)
Insulator-To-Bracket Bolt	55-70 (75-95)
Oil Pan Bolt	12-17 (16-23)
Stabilizer-To-Control Arm Bolt	99-112 (134-153)
Starter Nuts	30-40 (41-54)
Tie Rod-To-Steering Knuckle Nut	[1] 27-32 (37-43)
Torque Converter-To-Flexplate Nut	23-39 (31-53)
Transaxle Support Bracket	45-64 (61-88)
Transaxle-To-Engine Bolt	
2.3L	25-33 (34-45)
3.0L	34-47 (46-64)
Wheel Lug Nut	85-105 (115-142)

	INCH Lbs. (N.m)
Cooler Line At Radiator	106-144 (11-16)
Cooler Line Push Connector At Transaxle	120-144 (14-16)

[1] – Tighten to minimum torque; then tighten to nearest cotter pin slot.

TORQUE SPECIFICATIONS (4EAT – CAPRI)

Application	Ft. Lbs. (N.m)
Center Mount	
Bolt	27-40 (37-54)
Nut	47-66 (64-90)
Crossmember	
Bolt	27-40 (37-54)
Nut	55-69 (75-94)
Drain Plug	29-43 (39-59)
Left Mount Nut	63-86 (85-117)
Left Mount-To-Bracket Bolt & Nut	49-69 (66-94)
Lower Control Arm	
Bolt	27-40 (37-54)
Nut	55-69 (75-94)
Lower Control Arm Ball Joint Bolt & Nut	32-40 (43-54)
Right Mount Bolt & Nut	63-86 (85-117)
Selector Cable Bolt	22-29 (30-39)
Stabilizer Link Nut	12-17 (16-23)
Starter Mounting Bolt	23-34 (31-46)
Throttle Cable Bracket Bolt	14-19 (19-26)
Tie Rod End Nut	22-33 (30-45)
Torque Converter Bolt	32-54 (43-61)
Transaxle-To-Engine Bracket Bolt	27-38 (37-52)
Transaxle-To-Mount Bolt	66-86 (90-117)
Wheel Lug Nut	65-87 (88-118)

	INCH Lbs. (N.m)
Oil Pan Bolt	72-97 (8-11)

TORQUE SPECIFICATIONS (4EAT – ESCORT, PROBE & TRACER)

Application	Ft. Lbs. (N.m)
Escort & Tracer	
Lower Crossmember-To-Chassis Nut	47-66 (64-89)
Lower Crossmember-To-Transaxle Nut	27-38 (37-52)
Tie Rod-To-Knuckle	31-42 (42-57)
Torque Converter-To-Flexplate Nut	25-36 (34-49)
Transaxle-To-Engine Bolt	41-59 (55-80)
Upper Transaxle Mount Nut	49-69 (66-94)
Wheel Lug Nut	65-87 (88-118)
Probe	
Left Mount Through-Bolt	63-86 (86-116)
Left Mount-To-Bracket Bolt & Nut	50-68 (67-93)
Lower Control Arm Ball Joint Bolt & Nut	32-44 (43-59)
Lower Transaxle Mount Bolt	50-68 (67-93)
Rear Transaxle Mount Bolt	50-68 (67-93)
Torque Converter-To-Flexplate Nut	32-45 (43-61)
Transaxle Lower Mount Bolt	50-68 (67-93)
Transaxle-To-Engine Bolt	50-73 (67-99)
Wheel Lug Nut	65-87 (88-118)

	INCH Lbs. (N.m)
Oil Pan Bolt	72-97 (8-11)

Ford Motor Co. Light Trucks & Vans

Aerostar, Bronco, Explorer, "E" & "F" Series, Ranger, Villager

APPLICATION

NOTE: For transmission application, see appropriate table in APPLICATIONS & IDENTIFICATION.

REMOVAL & INSTALLATION

WARNING: When battery is disconnected, vehicle computer and memory systems may lose memory data. Driveability problems may exist until computer systems have completed a relearn cycle. See COMPUTER RELEARN PROCEDURES article in APPLICATIONS & IDENTIFICATION before disconnecting battery.

A4LD TRANSMISSION

Removal (Aerostar, Explorer & Ranger) – **1)** Disconnect negative battery cable. Raise and support vehicle. Loosen oil pan bolts, allowing fluid to drain.

2) Remove torque converter access cover. Remove starter motor. Remove torque converter-to-drive plate retaining nuts. Rotate engine clockwise (viewed from front of engine) for access to retaining nuts.

CAUTION: On 2.3L, DO NOT rotate engine counterclockwise (viewed from front of engine) or engine damage may result.

3) Mark drive shaft and axle flange or yoke for reassembly reference. Remove drive shaft. Disconnect speedometer cable, vacuum hoses, electrical connections, and shift cable at transmission.

4) Disconnect kickdown cable from ball stud lever. Press tabs on kickdown cable, and disengage cable from bracket. Raise transmission slightly.

5) Remove transmission mount-to-crossmember nuts. Remove crossmember. Allow transmission to hang downward.

6) On Explorer and Ranger models, raise front of engine slightly. This must be done for access to upper transmission-to-cylinder block bolts.

7) On all models, disconnect oil cooler lines at transmission. Plug all oil cooler line openings. Remove lower transmission-to-cylinder block bolts. Remove transmission filler tube.

8) Secure transmission to floor jack with safety chain. Remove upper transmission-to-cylinder block bolts. Move transmission rearward and lower from vehicle.

Installation – 1) To install, reverse removal procedure. Ensure torque converter is fully seated. Align reference marks on drive shaft and axle flange. Tighten bolts and nuts to specification. See appropriate TORQUE SPECIFICATIONS table.

2) Fill transmission with Motorcraft Mercon ATF (XT-2-QDX). For fluid capacity and control cable adjustment, see appropriate TRANSMISSION SERVICING article.

AOD TRANSMISSION

Removal (Bronco, Pickup & Van) – 1) Disconnect negative battery cable. Raise and support vehicle. Loosen oil pan bolts, allowing fluid to drain.

2) Remove torque converter cover. Remove drain plug from torque converter (if equipped) and drain torque converter. Reinstall drain plug. Remove torque converter-to-drive plate nuts.

3) Mark drive shaft and axle flange or yoke for reassembly reference. Remove drive shaft. Remove starter motor. Disconnect speedometer cable, necessary electrical connections, and control cables at transmission.

4) On 4WD, remove transfer case. On all models, support transmission with floor jack. Remove transmission mount-to-crossmember nuts and crossmember-to-frame bolts. Remove transmission mount from transmission extension housing.

5) Remove crossmember and transmission mount. Disconnect oil cooler lines and filler tube from transmission. Plug all oil cooler line openings. Secure transmission to floor jack with safety chain.

6) Remove transmission-to-cylinder block bolts. Move transmission rearward and lower it from vehicle.

Installation – 1) To install, reverse removal procedure. Use NEW "O" ring on filler tube. Ensure torque converter is fully seated. Align reference marks on drive shaft and axle flange or yoke.

2) Tighten torque converter drain plug and all bolts/nuts to specification. See appropriate TORQUE SPECIFICATIONS table. Fill transmission with Motorcraft Mercon ATF (XT-2-QDX). For fluid capacity and control cable adjustment, see appropriate AUTOMATIC TRANSMISSION SERVICING article.

C-6 TRANSMISSION

Removal (Pickup & Van) – 1) Disconnect negative battery cable. Raise and support vehicle. On Van models, remove engine cover. Remove flexible hose from air cleaner heat tube (V8 models only). On all models, loosen oil pan bolts to drain fluid.

2) Remove torque converter cover. Remove drain plug from torque converter (if equipped) and drain torque converter. Reinstall drain plug. Remove torque converter-to-drive plate nuts.

3) Mark drive shaft and axle flange or yoke for reassembly reference. Remove drive shaft. Remove starter motor. Disconnect speedometer cable, electrical connections, and control cables or rods at transmission.

4) On Pickup 4WD, remove transfer case. On all models, support transmission with floor jack. Remove transmission mount-to-crossmember nuts and crossmember-to-frame bolts. Remove transmission mount from transmission extension housing.

5) Remove crossmember and transmission mount. Disconnect oil cooler lines and filler tube from transmission. Plug all oil cooler line openings. Secure transmission to floor jack with safety chain.

6) Remove transmission-to-cylinder block bolts. Move transmission rearward and lower from vehicle.

Installation – 1) To install, reverse removal procedure. Use NEW "O" ring on filler tube. Ensure torque converter is fully seated. Align reference marks on drive shaft and axle flange or yoke.

2) Tighten torque converter drain plug and all bolts/nuts to specification. See appropriate TORQUE SPECIFICATIONS table. Fill transmission with Motorcraft Mercon ATF (XT-2-QDX). For fluid capacity and control cable or linkage adjustment, see appropriate TRANSMISSION SERVICING article.

E4OD TRANSMISSION

Removal (Bronco, Pickup & Van) – 1) Disconnect negative battery cable. Raise and support vehicle. Remove dipstick. Place transmission in Neutral. Remove skid plate (if equipped). Mark drive shaft and axle flange or yoke for reassembly reference. Remove drive shaft(s).

2) On F350 Super Duty commercial chassis, disconnect speedometer cable from parking brake assembly. See Fig. 1. Loosen lock nut on parking brake cable at clevis.

3) Remove clevis pin, clevis, and lock nut from parking brake cable. Remove parking brake cable from bracket on parking brake assembly.

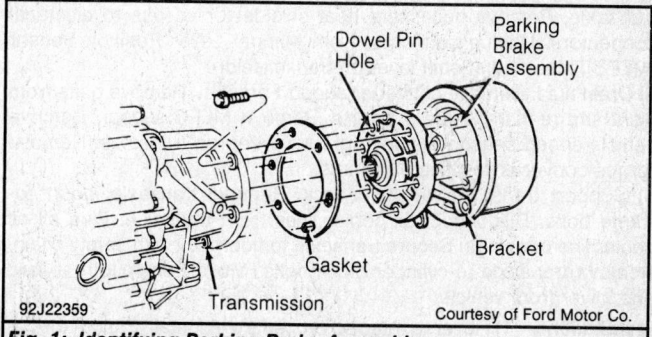

92J22359   Courtesy of Ford Motor Co.

Fig. 1: Identifying Parking Brake Assembly

4) On all models, disconnect control cables, shift linkage, and speedometer cable from transmission. On 4WD models, remove shift linkage from transfer case (manual shift models), or unplug connector at transfer case (models with electronic shift). Unplug 4WD switch connector from transfer case. Detach wiring harness from retainers on frame rail.

5) On all models, remove necessary heat shields for access to electrical connectors. Unplug connector from Manual Lever Position Sensor (MLPS), mounted at shift lever on transmission. Unplug connector from solenoid assembly on side of transmission.

CAUTION: Remove electrical connector from MLPS by squeezing tabs together and pulling connector from MLPS. Remove electrical connector from solenoid assembly by pushing inward on center tab. DO NOT pry on tab(s) with screwdriver.

---

6) Drain fluid. Remove torque converter cover. Remove starter motor. Remove torque converter-to-drive plate nuts. Support transmission with floor jack. Remove transmission mount-to-crossmember nuts and crossmember-to-frame bolts.

7) Remove crossmember. Disconnect oil cooler lines and filler tube from transmission. Plug all oil cooler line openings. Secure transmission to floor jack with safety chain. Remove transmission-to-cylinder block bolts. Move transmission rearward and lower from vehicle.

8) On F350 Super Duty commercial chassis, remove parking brake assembly, remove retaining bolts, parking brake assembly, and gasket if necessary. See Fig. 1.

CAUTION: Store parking brake assembly with breather assembly facing upward to prevent oil leakage onto brake shoes.

Installation – 1) Reverse removal procedure to install. Use NEW "O" ring on filler tube. Ensure torque converter is fully seated. Align reference marks on drive shaft and axle flange or yoke.

AUTOMATIC TRANSMISSION REMOVAL
Ford Motor Co. Light Trucks & Vans (Cont.)

2-38

2) On F350 Super Duty commercial chassis, use NEW gasket and retaining bolts when installing parking brake assembly. DO NOT reuse bolt. On all models, tighten all bolts/nuts to specification. See appropriate TORQUE SPECIFICATIONS table.

CAUTION: Pickup F350 Super Duty commercial chassis parking brake assembly contains a separate reservoir from transmission. Check lubricant level at filler plug hole on side of parking brake assembly. Fluid lever should be even with bottom of filler plug hole. Add Motorcraft Mercon ATF (XT-2-QDX) as needed.

---

3) Fill transmission with Motorcraft Mercon ATF (XT-2-QDX). For fluid capacity and control cable or linkage adjustment, see appropriate TRANSMISSION SERVICING article.

4F20E TRANSAXLE

Removal (Villager) – **1)** Disconnect negative battery cable. Remove starter motor. Remove dipstick. Remove upper transaxle mounting bolts. Raise and support vehicle. Mark axle shafts for reassembly reference. Remove axle shafts.

2) Disconnect control cables, shift linkage, and electrical cables from transaxle. Remove necessary heat shields for access to electrical connectors. Unplug connector from Manual Lever Position Sensor (MLPS), mounted at shift lever on transmission.

3) Drain fluid. Remove converter support bracket. Remove bolts from front and rear transaxle supports. Remove MLPS sensor. Remove vehicle speed sensor. Remove ground wires on transaxle. Remove torque converter-to-drive plate nuts.

4) Support transaxle with floor jack. Remove transaxle mount-to-frame bolts. Disconnect oil cooler lines from transaxle. Plug all oil cooler line openings. Secure transaxle to floor jack with safety chain. Remove transaxle-to-cylinder block bolts. Move transaxle rearward and lower from vehicle.

Installation – **1)** Reverse removal procedure to install. Ensure torque converter is fully seated. Align reference marks on axle shafts.

2) Tighten all bolts/nuts to specification. See appropriate TORQUE SPECIFICATIONS table. Fill transaxle with Motorcraft Mercon ATF (XT-2-QDX). For fluid capacity and control cable or linkage adjustment, see appropriate TRANSMISSION SERVICING article.

4R70W TRANSMISSION

Removal (Van) – **1)** Disconnect negative battery cable. Raise and support vehicle. Drain transmission fluid. Remove converter access cover. Remove converter nuts.

2) Mark rear drive shaft yoke and companion flange for reassembly reference. Disconnect drive shaft from companion flange. Slide drive shaft to rear to separate from transmission. Install plug into extension housing to prevent leaks.

3) Remove starter. Unplug connector at manual lever position sensor. Remove rear mount bolts and crossmember bolts. Remove rear support bolts. Raise transmission enough to remove rear mount from crossmember. Remove crossmember.

4) Lower transmission enough to disconnect oil cooler lines. Plug oil cooler line openings. Remove filler tube and dipstick. Secure transmission to jack. Remove converter housing bolts. Move transmission to rear and downward to remove it from vehicle.

Installation - **1)** Lubricate torque converter pilot with chassis grease. Install torque converter into transmission. Rotate torque converter to engage drive flats with pump gear.

2) Raise transmission into position. Torque converter will move freely with respect to flywheel when it is properly positioned. Install and

tighten housing bolts. See appropriate TORQUE SPECIFICATIONS table.

3) Reverse removal procedure to complete installation. Use NEW "O" ring on filler tube. Lubricate drive shaft yoke splines with grease. Align reference marks on drive shaft and axle flange.

4) Fill transmission with Motorcraft Mercon ATF (XT-2-QDX). For fluid capacity and control cable adjustment, see appropriate TRANSMISSION SERVICING article.

TORQUE SPECIFICATIONS

TORQUE SPECIFICATIONS

Application	Ft. Lbs. (N.m)
A4LD	
Crossmember-To-Frame Bolt	
2.9L & 3.0L	65-85 (88-115)
Crossmember-To-Frame Through Bolt	
4.0L	37-52 (51-71)
2.3L	65-85 (88-115) [1]
Oil Pan Bolt	
Torque Converter-To-Drive Plate Nut	20-34 (27-46)
Transmission Mount-To-Crossmember Nut	71-85 (96-115)
Transmission-To-Engine Bolt	
3.0L	33-44 (45-60)
All Others	28-38 (38-52)
AOD	
Crossmember-To-Frame Bolt	43-57 (58-77) [1]
Oil Pan Bolt	
Torque Converter-To-Drive Plate Nut	20-34 (27-46)
Transmission Mount-To-Crossmember Nut	60-80 (81-109)
Transmission Mount-To-Transmission Extension	
Housing Bolt	60-80 (81-109)
Transmission-To-Engine Bolt	40-50 (54-68)
C6	
Crossmember-To-Frame Bolt	40-60 (54-81)
Oil Pan Bolt	10-12 (14-16)
Torque Converter-To-Drive Plate Nut	20-30 (27-41)
Transmission Mount-To-Crossmember Nut	50-70 (68-95)
Transmission Mount-To-Transmission Extension	
Housing Bolt	60-80 (81-109)
Transmission-To-Engine Bolt	40-50 (54-68)
E4OD	
Crossmember-To-Frame Bolt	43-57 (58-77)
Oil Pan Bolt	10-12 (14-16)
Parking Brake Assembly Filler Plug	25-30 (34-41)
Parking Brake Assembly-To-Transmission Bolt [2]	25-43 (34-58)
Oil Pan Bolt	[3]
Torque Converter-To-Drive Plate Nut	20-30 (27-41)
Transmission Mount-To-Crossmember Nut	60-80 (81-109)
Transmission-To-Engine Bolt	40-50 (54-68)
4F20E	
Drain Plug	22-30 (29-41)
Front Transaxle Mount Nut	32-41 (43-55)
Front Transaxle Mount Through Bolt	57-72 (77-98)
Oil Pan Bolt	[1]
Rear Transaxle Mount Nut	32-41 (43-55)
Torque Converter-To-Drive Plate Nut	33-43 (44-59)
Transaxle-To-Engine Bolt	
Lower	22-30 (30-40)
Upper	29-36 (39-49)
4R70W	
Crossmember-To-Frame Bolt	70-100 (95-136)
Parking Brake Assembly Filler Plug	25-30 (34-41)
Parking Brake Assembly-To-Transmission Bolt [2]	25-43 (34-58)
Torque Converter-To-Drive Plate Nut	20-34 (27-46)
Transmission Mount-To-Crossmember Nut	64-81 (87-110)
Transmission-To-Engine Bolt	40-50 (54-68)

[1] – Tighten bolts to 97-115 INCH lbs. (11-13 N.m).
[2] – Always use NEW bolts. DO NOT reuse bolts.
[3] – Tighten bolts to 106-133 INCH lbs. (12-15 N.m).

"A","B","C","D","E","F","H","J"
"K","L","M","N","R","S","T"
"W","Y","Z" Bodies

APPLICATION

NOTE: For body code identification and model application, see GENERAL MOTORS BODY IDENTIFICATION CODES in APPLICATIONS & IDENTIFICATION section.

REMOVAL & INSTALLATION

WARNING: When battery is disconnected, vehicle computer and memory systems may lose memory data. Driveability problems may exist until computer systems have completed a relearn cycle. See COMPUTER RELEARN PROCEDURES in APPLICATIONS & IDENTIFICATION article before disconnecting battery.

3T40 TRANSAXLE

Removal ("A" Body) – **1)** Disconnect and shield negative battery cable. Remove air cleaner. Remove bolt securing transaxle throttle valve cable to transaxle. Remove shift cable and bracket from transaxle. Disconnect electrical connectors as necessary.

2) Disconnect oil cooler lines from transaxle. Plug ends of lines. Remove all transaxle-to-engine bolts except bolt nearest starter motor (leave this bolt loosely installed). Support engine from top. Raise and support vehicle on hoist. Remove left front wheel. Remove left engine splash shield. Remove pinch bolt from left ball joint. Disconnect ball joint from left control arm.

CAUTION: If steering intermediate shaft is not disconnected from steering gear stub shaft as described in next step, these components could be damaged, possibly resulting in loss of steering control.

3) Remove pinch bolt securing steering intermediate shaft to steering gear stub shaft. Remove stabilizer bar. Center-punch the 2 spot welds securing left crossmember to rear crossmember. Left crossmember is the 90-degree frame piece that acts as left frame and front crossmember. Drill out spot welds using 7/16" drill bit.

4) Remove bolt securing left end of steering rack to rear crossmember. Remove 4 bolts securing left crossmember to right frame. Using jack stand, support left crossmember from bottom. Remove 2 bolts securing left crossmember to body.

5) Remove 2 nuts securing left transaxle mount to left crossmember. Remove left crossmember and jack stand. Remove starter and torque converter shields. Remove 3 flexplate-to-converter bolts. Remove 2 transaxle extension bolts from engine-to-transaxle bracket.

6) Remove rear transaxle mount bracket assembly (it may be necessary to raise transaxle). Using transaxle jack, support transaxle from bottom. Remove 2 braces from right end of transaxle. Remove left drive axle. See appropriate AXLE SHAFTS article in AXLE SHAFTS & TRANSFER CASES.

7) Remove remaining transaxle-to-engine bolt near starter. Remove transaxle and right drive axle as an assembly.

Installation – To install, reverse removal procedure. Adjust T.V. cable and shift cable after installation. Refill transaxle to proper level with fluid. See appropriate AUTOMATIC TRANSMISSION SERVICING article.

Removal ("J", "L", "N" & "T" Bodies) – **1)** Disconnect negative battery cable. Remove air cleaner and T.V. cable from throttle lever and transaxle. Remove airflow meter and intake duct (if equipped). Remove shift linkage and wiring harness routing clips and straps.

2) Disconnect exhaust pipe from manifold on 4-cylinder engine and front exhaust manifold and pipe on V6 engine. Remove filler tube and install Engine Support Fixture (J-28467-A). Insert a 1/4 x 2" bolt in hole at front right motor mount to maintain driveline alignment ("N" Body only).

3) Remove nut securing wiring harness to transaxle. Disconnect all external wiring connectors from transaxle. Disconnect manual shift linkage and remove from bracket. Remove top 4 transaxle-to-engine bolts and upper left transaxle bracket and mount.

4) Remove rubber hose from transaxle to vent pipe. Raise and support vehicle and remove front wheels. Drain transaxle. Separate lower ball joints from control arms.

5) Install Axle Boot Protectors (J-34754). Disengage inner CV joints from differential and support axles with wire. See appropriate AXLE SHAFTS article in AXLE SHAFTS & TRANSFER CASES. Remove transaxle mounting strut. Remove left stabilizer bar pin bolt and left stabilizer bar clamp nuts attaching left stabilizer bar to frame. Remove left frame support assembly.

6) On models equipped with 2.0L, remove header pipe at exhaust manifold. On models equipped with 2.8L, 3.1L and 3.3L, remove header pipe and front exhaust manifold. On all models, disconnect speedometer cable and remove starter motor. Remove torque converter cover. Index mark torque converter to flexplate, and remove converter mounting bolts.

7) Disconnect oil cooler lines. Remove transaxle-to-engine support bracket. Secure transaxle jack under transaxle and remove remaining engine-to-transaxle bolts. Slide transaxle away from engine and right axle shaft. Lower transaxle from vehicle.

Installation – To install, reverse removal procedure. Guide right axle shaft into transaxle when raising transaxle to engine. Adjust T.V. and shift cables after installation. Refill transaxle to proper fluid level. See appropriate AUTOMATIC TRANSMISSION SERVICING article.

Removal ("W" Body) – **1)** Remove air cleaner assembly. Disconnect negative battery cable. Remove coolant reservoir. Disconnect shift cable and transaxle throttle valve cable from transaxle. Remove throttle cable bracket and brake booster hose (if equipped). Remove bolts securing torque struts to engine.

2) Remove left torque strut bracket. Disconnect fluid cooler lines from transaxle. Support engine from top using Engine Support Fixture (J-28467-A). Raise and support vehicle on hoist. Remove front wheels. Remove caliper/bracket assemblies and rotors. Remove both lower engine splash shields.

3) Remove axle assemblies. See appropriate AXLE SHAFTS article in AXLE SHAFTS & TRANSFER CASES. Separate tie rod ends from steering knuckles. Separate lower ball joints at control arms and steering knuckles. See BALL JOINT under REMOVAL & INSTALLATION in appropriate article in SUSPENSION. Remove rack and pinion heat shield.

4) Remove bolts holding main engine wiring harness to transaxle case. Wire rack and pinion to exhaust, and remove rack and pinion bolts from frame. Remove bolts holding power steering lines to frame. Remove engine and transaxle mounts from frame. Support frame with a jack stand at each end, and remove frame-to-body mount bolts.

5) Remove frame with both lower control arms and stabilizer shaft attached by working frame downward toward rear of vehicle. Remove flexplate cover and torque converter bolts. Remove starter bolts and support starter. Disconnect ground cable from transaxle. Remove fluid fill tube bolt and mount bracket.

6) Lower vehicle. Disconnect electrical connectors as necessary. Remove fluid fill tube. Lower left side of engine about 4 inches. Raise and support vehicle on hoist. Remove fuel line bracket from transaxle. Install transaxle jack. Remove transaxle-to-engine bolts. Remove transaxle.

Installation – **1)** To install, reverse removal procedure. Install frame insulators and spacers, if removed. Ensure insulators are completely seated against frame. Tighten nuts and bolts to specification. See TORQUE SPECIFICATIONS.

2) Align frame to body by inserting two 8" long pins in alignment holes on right side of frame. With aid of a helper, position frame and install (but DO NOT tighten) NEW body mount bolts. To maintain alignment, tighten right side, then left side body mount bolts. Adjust transaxle throttle valve cable and shift cables. See ADJUSTMENTS in appropriate AUTOMATIC TRANSMISSION article. Fill transaxle to proper fluid level.

4T60 & 4T60-E TRANSAXLE

Removal ("A" Body) – **1)** Disconnect and shield negative battery cable. Remove air cleaner. Disconnect electrical connectors as necessary. Remove shift cable and bracket from transaxle. Disconnect vacuum modulator hose from modulator. Remove 3 upper transaxle-to-engine bolts.

CAUTION: *If steering intermediate shaft is not disconnected from steering gear stub shaft as described in next step, these components could be damaged, possibly resulting in loss of steering control.*

2) Remove pinch bolt securing steering intermediate shaft to steering gear stub shaft. Support engine from top. Raise and support vehicle on hoist. Remove front wheels. Remove engine splash shields. Remove pinch bolts from ball joints. Disconnect ball joints from control arms.
3) Remove stabilizer bar. Center-punch the 2 spot welds securing left crossmember to rear crossmember. Left crossmember is the 90-degree frame piece that acts as left frame and front crossmember. Drill out spot welds using 7/16" drill bit.
4) Remove nuts from front and rear transaxle mounts. Remove bolts from power steering cooler line bracket. Remove bolts securing left crossmember to right frame. Using jack stand, support left crossmember from bottom. Loosen 2 right frame mounts and discard bolts.
5) Remove 2 left crossmember-to-body bolts. Remove left crossmember. Remove torque converter shields. Remove flexplate-to-converter bolts. Remove drive axles. See appropriate AXLE SHAFTS article in AXLE SHAFTS & TRANSFER CASES.
6) Remove transaxle support bracket bolts from transaxle. Disconnect transaxle cooler lines from transaxle. Using transaxle jack, support transaxle from bottom. Remove rear transaxle bolts from engine. Remove remaining transaxle-to-engine bolts. Remove transaxle.
Installation – To install, reverse removal procedure. Tighten nuts and bolts to specification. See TORQUE SPECIFICATIONS. Adjust transaxle throttle valve cable and gear shift linkage. See ADJUSTMENTS in appropriate AUTOMATIC TRANSMISSION article. Adjust front wheel toe-in, if necessary. Fill transaxle to proper fluid level.

CAUTION: *Before installing pinch bolt in hole at steering gear stub shaft, ensure shaft is seated. If shaft is not seated, components may separate, causing loss of steering control.*

Removal ("C", "E", "H", "K" & "W" Bodies) – 1) Disconnect negative battery cable. Remove air cleaner, air injection crossover pipe, air management valve and exhaust crossover pipe.
2) Disconnect T.V. cable at throttle body. Disconnect shift linkage and vacuum modulator line. Disconnect neutral safety switch, cruise control and vehicle speed sensor wiring. Remove 3 upper transaxle-to-engine mounting bolts.
3) Install Engine Support Fixture (J-28467-A) and raise engine to unload engine mounts. If equipped, remove driveline damper and engine mount. Raise and support vehicle. Remove front wheels.

NOTE: *Drive Axle Boot Protectors (J-34754) should be modified and installed on any drive axle prior to service on or near drive axle, or seal damage and possible joint failure can result.*

4) Disengage both lower ball joints from steering knuckle. Install Axle Boot Protectors (J-34754). Disengage right drive axle from transaxle only. DO NOT remove drive axle from hub and knuckle assembly. Remove left drive axle from both the transaxle and hub and knuckle assembly. See appropriate AXLE SHAFTS article in AXLE SHAFTS & TRANSFER CASES.
5) Remove stabilizer linkage at left side. Remove left splash shield, vacuum pump (if equipped), and disconnect all wiring and hoses. Remove transaxle-to-cradle bolts. Remove engine-to-left cradle assembly mounting bolts. Support left cradle assembly. Remove right and left cradle attaching bolts and remove left cradle assembly.

NOTE: *Whenever cradle assembly is removed or lowered from vehicle, rack and pinion steering assembly must be disconnected from cradle. To prevent damage to intermediate shaft, steering assembly must be supported so it does not hang by intermediate shaft.*

6) Disconnect oil cooler lines and remove dust cover. Index mark torque converter and flexplate. Remove torque converter-to-flexplate bolts. Support transaxle with transmission jack. Remove remaining transaxle mounting bolts and remove transaxle from vehicle.

NOTE: *Locate one bolt connecting transaxle-to-engine installed from opposite direction. On some models, a 3-FOOT socket extension placed through right wheelhousing will help remove this bolt.*

Installation – To install, reverse removal procedure. Guide right axle shaft into transaxle when raising transaxle to engine. Adjust T.V. and shift cables. Refill transaxle to proper fluid level. See appropriate AUTOMATIC TRANSMISSION SERVICING article.
Removal ("L" & "N" Bodies) – 1) Disconnect negative battery cable. Remove air intake duct. Disconnect shift linkage from transaxle. Disconnect vacuum modulator vacuum line at modulator. Disconnect electrical connectors from torque converter clutch, neutral safety switch and shift solenoid connector.
2) Support engine from top using Engine Support Fixture (J-28467-A). Remove 2 top transaxle-to-engine bolts and remaining upper transaxle-to-engine bolts. Disconnect rubber hose from transaxle-to-vent pipe. Raise and support vehicle on hoist.
3) Remove front wheels. Remove left splash shield. Remove both front ABS wheel speed sensors and harness from left side suspension support. Disconnect both ball joints from control arms. Disconnect left stabilizer shaft frame bushing clamp nuts and left stabilizer shaft frame bushing clamp.
4) Disconnect left suspension support assembly. Install Drive Axle Boot Protector (J-34754) on both boots. Remove drive axles. See appropriate AXLE SHAFTS article in AXLE SHAFTS & TRANSFER CASES. Remove left and right stabilizer links. Remove left suspension support and attaching bolts.
5) Disconnect vehicle speed sensor connector from transaxle. Remove torque converter cover. Mark torque converter in relation to flexplate for alignment during installation. Remove torque converter-to-flexplate bolts.
6) Disconnect fluid cooler lines from transaxle. Remove transaxle shift cable from lower cable bracket. Remove transaxle-to-engine brace bolts at transaxle. Support transaxle with jack. Remove remaining engine-to-transaxle bolts. Lower transaxle.
Installation – To install, reverse removal procedure. Tighten nuts and bolts to specification. See TORQUE SPECIFICATIONS. Adjust shift cable. See appropriate ADJUSTMENTS in AUTOMATIC TRANSMISSION article. Refill transaxle to proper fluid level.

4T80-E TRANSAXLE

Removal ("E" & "K" Bodies) – 1) Disconnect negative battery cable. Remove air cleaner assembly. Disconnect range control cable and bracket at transaxle. Disconnect manual shaft lever and transaxle range switch. Install Engine Support Fixture (J-28467-A).
2) Raise and support vehicle on hoist. Remove both front tires and wheels. Remove front wheel splash shields. Disconnect vacuum hoses and electrical connectors as necessary. Disconnect power steering pressure hose at steering gear. Install plugs into steering gear and pressure line to prevent fluid leakage or contamination.
3) Disconnect power steering return hose at auxiliary cooler. Install plugs into cooler and return hose to prevent fluid leakage or contamination. Rotate steering intermediate shaft allowing steering gear stub shaft clamp bolt access from left wheel opening. Remove clamp bolt and steering intermediate shaft from steering gear.

NOTE: *Failure to disconnect intermediate shaft from rack and pinion stub shaft can result in damage to steering gear and/or intermediate shaft and personal injury.*

CAUTION: *DO NOT rotate steering wheel or move position of steering gear once intermediate shaft is disconnected. This will reposition the inflatable restraint coil in the steering column. If the inflatable restraint coil becomes off centered, it may be damaged during vehicle operation.*

4) Disconnect both front suspension position sensors from lower control arms and position out of way. Disconnect both stabilizer links from steering knuckles. Disconnect both tie rod cotter pins and nuts. Separate both tie rods from steering knuckles.

5) Remove both drive axle nuts, and separate both drive axles from hubs. Remove both drive axles from transaxle. Remove A/C splash shield from frame. Disconnect ABS modulator from bracket and support. Remove engine oil pan-to-transaxle bracket.

6) Remove torque converter cover. Remove flywheel-to-converter bolts. Disconnect transaxle cooler pipes from transaxle. Remove left and right transaxle mount nuts and right engine mount nuts at frame. Support frame.

7) Remove 6 frame mount bolts. Lower frame and/or raise vehicle with steering gear attached. Remove left transaxle mount and bracket from transaxle. Remove engine-to-transaxle bracket. Install Transaxle Support Fixture (J-28664). Remove engine-to-transaxle bolts. Lower and remove transaxle.

Installation – To install, reverse removal procedure. Tighten nuts and bolts to specification. See TORQUE SPECIFICATIONS. Adjust shift cable. See ADJUSTMENTS in appropriate AUTOMATIC TRANSMISSION article. Refill transaxle to proper fluid level.

4L60 & 4L60-E TRANSMISSIONS

Removal ("B", "D", "F" & "Y" Bodies) – **1)** Disconnect negative battery cable and remove air cleaner. Disconnect T.V. cable at throttle body. Remove filler tube. Raise and support vehicle. Index mark and remove propeller shaft.

2) On Corvette models, remove complete exhaust system and driveline beam. On Corvette convertible, remove upper and lower body braces. On Camaro and Firebird models, remove torque arm from rear suspension. On Brougham, remove header pipe at exhaust manifold, catalytic converter, fuel line-to-transmission bracket and transmission-to-engine ground strap bolt.

3) On all models, remove floor reinforcement (if equipped). Disconnect speedometer cable. Remove shifter linkage and harness connectors. Remove flexplate cover. Index mark flexplate and torque converter. Remove torque converter-to-flexplate bolts.

4) Remove catalytic converter support bracket and remove crossmember. Lower transmission slightly, disconnect oil cooler lines and remove T.V. cable hold down bolt.

5) Support engine with a screw jack and block of wood. Support transmission with transmission jack. Remove transmission-to-engine bolts. Pull transmission back enough to install Torque Converter Holder (J-21366). Lower transmission and remove from vehicle.

Installation – To install transmission, reverse removal procedures. Observe index marks made during removal, and align marks to original positions. Adjust shift linkage and T.V. cable as necessary. Fill transmission to proper level with fluid. See appropriate AUTOMATIC TRANSMISSION SERVICING article.

GEO VEHICLES

Removal (Metro) – **1)** Disconnect air intake tubing from air cleaner. Disconnect battery cables. Remove battery and tray. Disconnect ground cable at transaxle. Disconnect electrical connections, speedometer cable and control cables from transaxle.

2) Remove starter motor. Raise and support vehicle. Drain transaxle fluid. Disconnect and plug oil cooler lines from transaxle. Disconnect exhaust pipe from exhaust manifold. Remove lower cover from torque converter housing.

3) Remove drive plate-to-torque converter bolts. Drive plate can be held by engaging a screwdriver into drive plate gear through notch provided at underside of transaxle case.

4) Left axle shaft must be removed and right axle shaft must be disengaged from differential. Remove left wheel. Remove staked area from left axle shaft nut at hub assembly. Remove nut and washer from left axle shaft.

5) Remove left ball joint-to-steering knuckle bolt. Separate ball joint from steering knuckle. Using 2 screwdrivers, pry axle shafts from transaxle case. Remove left axle shaft. Disconnect engine torque rod and bracket from transaxle.

6) Support transaxle with a jack. Disconnect transaxle mounts. Remove transaxle-to-engine bolts. Remove transaxle assembly.

Installation – **1)** To install transaxle, apply grease around cup at center of torque converter and reverse removal procedure.

2) Ensure torque converter is correctly installed. Distance from torque converter drive lugs to engine mating surface of transaxle housing should be at least .85" (21.4 mm).

3) When installing transaxle, guide right axle into differential side gear as transaxle is being raised. After inserting inner CV joints of right and left axles into differential side gears, push inner joints into side gears until snap rings on axle shafts engage with side gears.

4) Tighten all fasteners to specification. See TORQUE SPECIFICATIONS. Adjust all control cables. Fill and check fluid levels.

Removal (Prizm) – **1)** Support engine from above with Engine Support Fixture (J-28467-A). Disconnect battery cables. Remove battery and tray. Remove air cleaner assembly.

2) Disconnect throttle valve cable at throttle body. Disconnect ground cable at transaxle. Disconnect electrical connections, speedometer cable and control cables and brackets from transaxle.

3) Disconnect and plug oil cooler lines from transaxle. On left side of engine compartment, remove brace that connects upper part of transaxle to transaxle mount. Remove transaxle-to-mount through bolt. Remove 2 upper transaxle-to-engine bolts.

4) Raise and support vehicle. Drain transaxle fluid. Remove starter motor. Remove wheels. Remove lower splash shields. Remove nut and washer from ends of both axle shafts at hub assemblies.

5) Remove tie rod nuts from steering knuckles. Separate tie rods from steering knuckles. Remove lower ball joint-to-steering knuckle bolts. Separate lower control arms from steering knuckles.

6) Remove brake caliper and rotor from steering knuckle. Using brass hammer, tap on axle shaft until it is free of hub assembly. Using slide hammer and Shaft Puller (J-35762), pull axle shafts from transaxle.

7) Remove 3 center crossmember-to-radiator support bolts. Remove transaxle mount bolts. Remove center crossmember-to-main crossmember bolts.

8) Remove exhaust hanger bracket. Supporting main crossmember with jack, remove all bolts securing main crossmember and lower A-frame brackets to the body. Slowly lower main crossmember, being careful to support center crossmember.

9) Remove torque converter-to-drive plate bolts. Support transaxle with jack. Remove remaining transaxle-to-engine bolts. Remove remaining transaxle mounts and lower transaxle from vehicle. It may be necessary to lower engine slightly so transaxle can clear body.

Installation – **1)** To install, reverse removal procedure. Before installing, apply grease around cup at center of torque converter.

2) Ensure torque converter is correctly installed. Distance from torque converter drive lugs to engine mating surface of transaxle housing should be at least .9" (23 mm).

3) Tighten all fasteners to specification. See TORQUE SPECIFICATIONS. Adjust all control cables. Fill and check fluid levels.

Removal (Storm & Storm GSi) – **1)** Disconnect air intake tubing and air breather tube from air cleaner. Disconnect battery cables. Remove battery and tray. Disconnect electrical connections, speedometer cable and control cables from transaxle.

2) Disconnect and plug oil cooler lines from transaxle. Using Engine Support Fixture (J-28467-A), support engine. Remove 4 upper transaxle-to-cylinder block bolts. Raise and support vehicle. Remove lower engine covers.

3) Drain transaxle fluid. Remove front tire and wheel assemblies. Remove staked area from axle shaft nuts at hub assemblies. Remove nut from axle shafts. Remove tie rod nut from steering knuckles.

4) Separate tie rods from steering knuckles. Remove ball joint-to-lower control arm retaining nuts. Using brass hammer, tap on axle shaft until it is free of hub assembly. Using slide hammer and Shaft Puller (J-35762), pull axle shafts from transaxle.

5) Remove transaxle mount bolts. Disconnect exhaust pipe at exhaust manifold. Remove center crossmember. Slightly lower engine and transaxle assembly at engine support fixture.

6) Support transaxle with a jack. Disconnect transaxle mounts. Disconnect front mount bracket at engine. Remove drive plate cover.

Remove torque converter-to-drive plate bolts. Remove transaxle-to-engine bolts. Lower transaxle from engine.

Installation – To install, reverse removal procedure. Tighten all fasteners to specification. See TORQUE SPECIFICATIONS. DO NOT tighten transaxle mounting bolts until all bolts are installed. Adjust all control cables. Fill and check fluid levels.

SATURN VEHICLES

Removal & Installation – **1)** To disable air bag system, turn ignition off. Remove SIR fuse from fuse block. Remove Connector Position Assurance (CPA) clip from Yellow SIR connector at base of steering column. Disconnect Yellow connector. Wait 15 minutes before working on vehicle.

WARNING: DERM maintains back-up voltage for about 15 minutes after disabling air bag system. Wait at least 15 minutes after disabling air bag system before servicing, as accidental deployment may result in personal injury.

---

2) Disconnect negative battery cable. On SOHC models, remove 2 inlet air duct fasteners, disconnect air temperature sensor and remove inlet air duct. On DOHC models, remove 2 cross-car duct fasteners, disconnect air temperature sensor, and remove cross-car air duct. Loosen flex tube-to-air box clamp. Remove air box fasteners and remove air box.

3) Remove transaxle strut-to-cradle bracket fasteners. Disconnect all electrical connectors from transaxle. Remove vent tube retaining clip. Disconnect 2 ground terminals from top 2 converter housing bolts. Disengage O2S wire from converter housing.

4) Remove top 2 converter housing-to-engine bolts. Remove DIS coil pack and discard retaining bolts. Wire radiator to upper radiator support prior to removing cradle.

5) Install Engine Support Bar Assembly (SA9105E). Raise and support vehicle. Drain transaxle. Remove front wheel assemblies. Remove left and right splash shields. Remove front splash shield and fascia braces (if equipped).

6) Remove engine strut cradle bracket-to-cradle bolts. Remove transaxle mount-to-cradle nut. Separate lower ball joints from steering knuckles.

CAUTION: DO NOT damage ABS sensor ring while disengaging ball joints.

---

7) Remove front exhaust pipe. Remove engine-to-transaxle brackets. Support steering gear with wire and remove steering gear-to-cradle bolts. Disengage brake line from rear of cradle.

8) Remove torque converter cover. Remove torque converter-to-flywheel bolts. Support power train on power train support dolly. Remove 4 cradle-to-body bolts and lower cradle and power train assembly with power train support dolly.

9) Disconnect transaxle cooler lines and cap to prevent contamination. Support transaxle with jack. Using a pry bar, separate left and right drive axles from transaxle.

10) Remove 2 lower transaxle-to-engine bolts and separate transaxle from engine enough to reach shifter cable. Disconnect shifter cable from transaxle. To install, reverse removal procedure. Use NEW retaining bolts for DIS coil pack.

11) To activate air bag system, turn ignition off. Connect Yellow SIR connector and CPA clip at base of steering column. Install AIR BAG fuse. Turn ignition switch to RUN position. Observe AIR BAG indicator light. If light does not flash 7 times, and then go out, system is faulty.

TORQUE SPECIFICATIONS
TORQUE SPECIFICATIONS

Application	Ft. Lbs. (N.m)
"A" Body	
Flywheel-To-Converter Bolt	46 (62)
Frame Mount Bolt	40 (54)
Intermediate Shaft-To-Steering Gear Shaft Bolt	40 (54)
Shift Control Cable Bracket-To-Transaxle Bolt	18 (24)
Transaxle-To-Engine Bolt	55 (75)
Wheel Lug Nuts	100 (136)
"B", "D", "F" & "Y" Bodies	
Flywheel-To-Converter Bolt	46 (62)
Torque Arm-To Rear Differential Nut	98 (133)
Transmission Crossmember-To-Frame Bolt	25 (34)
Transmission-To-Engine Bolt	35 (47)
Transmission Mount-To-Transmission Bolt	35 (47)
Transmission Mount-To-Transmission Crossmember Nut	30 (41)
"C", "E", "H" & "K" Bodies (4T60-E Transaxle)	
Flywheel-To-Converter Bolt	46 (62)
Frame-To-Body Bolt	83 (113)
Shift Control Cable Bracket-To-Transaxle Bolt	18 (24)
Starter Mounting Bolt	32 (43)
Transaxle Brace-To-Engine Assembly Bolt	37 (50)
Transaxle-To-Engine Bolt	55 (75)
Transaxle Mount Bolt	38 (52)
Wheel Lug Nuts	100 (136)
"E" & "K" Bodies (4T80-E Transaxle)	
Flywheel-To-Converter Bolt	35 (47)
Flywheel-To-Cover Bolt	1
Frame-To-Body Bolt	74 (100)
Shift Control Cable Bracket-To-Transaxle Bolt	18 (24)
Starter Mounting Bolt	32 (43)
Transaxle Brace-To-Engine Assembly Bolt	35 (47)
Transaxle Mount Bolt	35 (47)
Transaxle-To-Engine Bolt	35 (47)
Wheel Lug Nuts	100 (136)
"J" Body	
Cooler Pipes	16 (22)
Flywheel-To-Converter Bolt	46 (62)
Lower Transaxle-To-Engine Bolt	55 (75)
Transaxle Brace Bolt	37 (50)
"L" Body	
Cooler Pipes	16 (22)
Flywheel-To-Converter Bolt	46 (62)
Frame-To-Body Bolt	37 (50)
Transaxle-To-Engine Bolt	55 (75)
"M" Body	
Axle Shaft Nut	129 (175)
Ball Joint Bolt	44 (60)
Torque Converter Bolt	14 (19)
Transaxle-To-Engine Bolt	40 (54)
Wheel Lug Nut	44 (60)
"N" & "T" Body	
Cooler Pipes	16 (22)
Flywheel-To-Converter Bolt	46 (62)
Starter Bolt	32 (43)
Transaxle-To-Engine Bolt	55 (75)
"R" Body	
Axle Shaft Nut	137 (186)
Ball Joint-To-Lower Control Arm Bolt	115 (156)
Center Crossmember Bolt	45 (61)
Front Transaxle Mount Bolt	45 (61)
Left Transaxle Through Bolt	64 (87)
Lower Control Arm Bolt	105 (142)
Rear Transaxle Mount	
Retaining Bolt	29 (39)
Through Bolt	64 (87)
Tie Rod End Nut	36 (49)
Torque Converter Bolt	31 (42)
Transaxle-To-Engine Bolt	31 (42)
Wheel Lug Nut	87 (118)

TORQUE SPECIFICATIONS (Cont.)

Application	Ft. Lbs. (N.m)
"S" Body	
Axle Shaft Nut	137 (186)
Ball Joint-To-Lower Control Arm Bolt	105 (142)
Brake Caliper Bolt	65 (88)
Center Crossmember-To-Radiator Support Bolt	45 (61)
Center Mount-To-Transaxle Bolt	45 (61)
Front Mount-To-Transaxle Bolt	13 (18)
Lower A-Frame Bracket-To-Body Bolt	94 (127)
Main Crossmember-To-Body Bolt	152 (206)
Tie Rod Nut	36 (49)
Torque Converter Bolt	31 (42)
Transaxle Mount Bolt	45 (61)
Transaxle-To-Engine Bolt	34 (46)
Upper Transaxle Mount Bracket Bolt	45 (61)
Upper Transaxle Mount Through Bolt	64 (87)
Wheel Lug Nut	76 (103)
"W" Body	
Cooler Pipes	16 (22)
Flywheel-To-Converter Bolt	44 (60)
Frame-To-Body Bolt	103 (140)
Transaxle-To-Engine Bolt	55 (75)
"Z" Body	
Converter Housing-To-Engine (Lower) Bolts	96 (130)
Converter Housing-To-Engine (Upper) Bolts	74 (100)
Cradle-To-Body Bolts	151 (205)
Engine-To-Transaxle Brackets	35 (48)
Exhaust Pipe-To-Catalytic Converter Bolts	33 (45)
Exhaust Pipe-To-Manifold Nuts	23 (31)
Lower Ball Joint Nut	55 (75)
Steering Gear-To-Cradle Nuts	40 (54)
Tie Rod End Nut	33 (45)
Transaxle Strut-To-Cradle Bracket Nuts	52 (70)
Transaxle Strut-To-Cradle Bracket-To-Cradle Bolts	52 (70)
Wheel Lug Nuts	103 (140)

General Motors Light Trucks & Vans

"C" & "K" Series, "G" Series, "J", "M" & "L" Series, "P" Series, "R" & "V" Series, "S" & "T" Series, "U" Series

APPLICATIONS

NOTE: For vehicle applications, see GENERAL MOTORS IDENTIFICATION CODES in APPLICATIONS & IDENTIFICATION.

REMOVAL & INSTALLATION

FWD VEHICLES

Removal & Installation – 1) Place transaxle gear selector in Park. Set parking brake and block drive wheels. Although fuel pressure drops to zero when ignition is turned off, loosen fuel filler cap to relieve tank pressure. To further minimize risk of fire and personal injury, cover surrounding areas with a shop rag while removing fuel lines.

WARNING: To avoid possible personal injury and fire danger, relieve fuel pressure as outlined in step 1).

2) Disconnect battery cables. Drain cooling system. Remove airflow tube from air cleaner and radiator core support. Disconnect wiring harness at ECM and pull through firewall. Separate engine wiring harness from body connectors and lay harness on engine.

3) Remove accelerator and throttle valve cables. Disconnect fuel lines and transaxle shift linkage. Disconnect radiator and heater hoses. Disconnect transaxle cooler lines at radiator.

4) Discharge A/C system using approved refrigerant recovery/recycling equipment. Remove A/C compressor and bracket. Disconnect A/C hose at rear of compressor. Cap disconnected hoses and compressor fittings. Remove upper engine strut. Raise and support vehicle.

5) Remove front wheels and stabilizer shaft. Disconnect tie rod ends at steering knuckle. Remove lower control arm ball joints from steering knuckles.

6) Remove drive axles from transaxle, and wire out of way. Remove intermediate steering shaft pinch bolt. Remove power steering lines from frame rail and disconnect as required for removal. Remove starter.

7) Remove torque converter cover. Remove converter-to-flexplate bolts. Separate exhaust pipe at rear manifold. Support engine/frame/transaxle assembly (with hydraulic table). Remove frame bolts. Lower engine/frame/transaxle assembly. Remove transaxle from engine and frame.

8) To install, reverse removal procedure. Tighten all nuts and bolts to specification. See TORQUE SPECIFICATIONS. Fill cooling system and charge A/C system. Check all systems for leaks.

RWD (EXCEPT "J" BODY) VEHICLES

Removal & Installation – 1) Disconnect negative battery cable. Remove air cleaner. Disconnect Throttle Valve (T.V.) cable from throttle linkage, if equipped. Raise and support vehicle. Drain transmission fluid. Disconnect shift linkage. Mark rear propeller shaft for installation reference and remove from vehicle. Mark front propeller shaft and remove from transfer case, if equipped.

2) Relieve fuel pressure, and remove fuel lines. Remove support bracket at catalytic converter. Support transmission with transmission jack. Remove transmission crossmember.

NOTE: DO NOT stretch or damage any cables, wires or other component when lowering transmission.

3) Lower transmission far enough to provide clearance for other components. Remove dipstick tube and seal. Cover opening in transmission. Remove speedometer harness and vacuum modulator line, if equipped. Remove electrical connectors from transmission. Remove cooler lines, and cap all openings.

4) Remove transfer case shifter and move it aside, if equipped. Remove transmission support braces. Note location of braces for installation. Remove converter housing cover. Mark flexplate and torque converter alignment. Remove flexplate-to-torque converter bolts.

NOTE: Support engine with jack or hoist before disconnecting transmission.

5) Remove transmission-to-engine bolts. Note location of any brackets or clips and move them aside. Slide transmission straight back, off locating pins, and install Converter Holding Strap (J-21366). Remove transmission from vehicle.

6) To install, reverse removal procedure. Torque converter must be against flexplate and rotate freely by hand. Ensure all reference marks align. Tighten all bolts to specification, and fill transmission with fluid.

RWD ("J" BODY – TRACKER) VEHICLES

Removal – 1) On 4-wheel drive models, remove transfer case shift lever knob. Remove console box. Remove clamp and small boot located on top of transfer case at shift lever opening.

2) Push downward on case cover (center area around shift lever) and rotate counterclockwise. Remove transfer case shift lever. Remove retaining screws, shift lever boot and bracket.

3) On all models, disconnect negative battery cable. Disconnect kickdown cable at throttle body. Remove fan shroud, transmission dipstick and distributor cap. Using Engine Support Fixture (J-28467-A), support engine.

4) Disconnect electrical connections, breather hose and control cables from transmission. Disconnect speedometer cable. Disconnect and plug oil cooler lines from transmission. It may be necessary to remove gearshift assembly.

5) Raise and support vehicle. On 4-wheel drive models, remove transfer case skid plate. On all models, place reference marks on drive shaft flange(s) and yokes for reassembly reference. Remove drive shaft(s).

6) Remove drive plate cover. Remove torque converter-to-drive plate bolts. Remove exhaust pipe bracket at catalytic converter and transmission. Support transmission with jack.

7) Remove crossmember located below transmission (and transfer case on 4-wheel drive). Remove remaining transmission-to-engine bolts. Move transmission (and transfer case on 4-wheel drive) away from engine, and remove from vehicle.

Installation – To install, reverse removal procedure. Tighten all fasteners to specification. See appropriate TORQUE SPECIFICATIONS table. Ensure reference marks are aligned on drive shaft flanges and yokes. Adjust all control cables. Fill and check fluid levels.

TORQUE SPECIFICATIONS

TORQUE SPECIFICATIONS (TRACKER)

Application	Ft. Lbs. (N.m)
Crossmember Bolt	63 (85)
Flexplate-To-Torque Converter Bolts	41 (55)
Transmission-To-Engine Bolts	62 (84)
Skid Plate Bolts	40 (54)

TORQUE SPECIFICATIONS (3T40)

Application	Ft. Lbs. (N.m)
Cooler Lines-To-Radiator	20 (27)
Cooler Lines-To-Transaxle	16 (22)
Crossmember-To-Frame Bolts	56 (76)
Dipstick Tube-To-Engine	14 (19)
Flexplate-To-Torque Converter Bolts	35 (47)
Transaxle Mounts Bolts	22 (30)
Transaxle Mount-To-Bracket Nut	35 (47)
Transaxle-To-Engine Bolts	55 (75)

	INCH Lbs. (N.m)
Converter Cover Housing	48 (5)
T.V. Cable	80 (9)

TORQUE SPECIFICATIONS (4T60 & 4T60-E)

Application	Ft. Lbs. (N.m)
Cooler Lines-To-Radiator	20 (27)
Cooler Pipe & Tube Nut	30 (41)
Crossmember-To-Frame Bolts	56 (76)
Flexplate-To-Torque Converter Bolts	46 (62)
Transaxle Mounts Bolts	52 (71)
Transaxle Mount-To-Bracket Nut	30 (41)
Transaxle-To-Engine Bolts	55 (75)

	INCH Lbs. (N.m)
Converter Cover Housing	62 (7)
T.V. Cable	80 (9)

TORQUE SPECIFICATIONS (4L60 & 4L60-E)

Application	Ft. Lbs. (N.m)
Cooler Lines-To-Transmission	18 (24)
Crossmember-To-Frame Bolts	56 (76)
Dipstick Tube-To-Engine	23 (31)
Flexplate-To-Torque Converter Bolts	46 (62)
Transmission-To-Engine Bolts	23 (31)

	INCH Lbs. (N.m)
T.V. Cable	80 (9)
Converter Housing Cover	88 (10)

TORQUE SPECIFICATIONS (4L80-E)

Application	Ft. Lbs. (N.m)
Cooler Lines-To-Transmission	28 (38)
Crossmember-To-Frame Bolts	56 (76)
Dipstick Tube-To-Engine	33 (45)
Flexplate-To-Torque Converter Bolts	33 (45)
Transmission-To-Engine Bolts	33 (45)

	INCH Lbs. (N.m)
Converter Housing Cover	62 (7)
Speed Sensor-To-Case	96 (11)

Cherokee, Grand Cherokee, Wrangler

IDENTIFICATION

TRANSMISSION APPLICATIONS

Model (Body Code)	Transmission
Cherokee (XJ)	
2.5L (1994)	30RH
4.0L	
1993	AW4
1994	32RH
Grand Cherokee (ZJ)	
4.0L	[1] AW4, 42RE Or 42RH
5.2L	46RH
Wrangler (YJ)	
2.5L (1994)	30RH
4.0L	32RH

[1] – Earlier models used the Aisin Warner 4 transmission. Some models may use the 42RE and some models may use the 42RH. The 42RE is used with 4.0L engine only.

REMOVAL & INSTALLATION

Removal (AW4) – 1) Raise vehicle. Drain fluid and remove upper half of transmission fill tube.

2) Disconnect cooler lines at transmission. Press fitting release tabs and pull cooler line and fitting out of case.

3) Support transmission/transfer case with jack. Disconnect or remove following: transmission and transfer case shift linkage; necessary exhaust components; speedometer cable; transmission wire harnesses; transfer case vacuum and wire harnesses.

4) Mark drive shafts for reassembly. Disconnect front and rear drive shaft at transfer case and wire to frame. Do not allow drive shafts to hang free. Remove rear crossmember. Disconnect necessary vacuum and fluid hoses and transmission throttle cable at engine.

5) Remove crankshaft position sensor. Remove starter. Remove converter-to-drive plate and converter housing-to-engine bolts.

6) Secure transmission (and transfer case assembly on 4WD models) to transmission jack with safety chains. Remove transmission/transfer case.

NOTE: Remove transfer case from transmission if transmission is to be overhauled.

Installation – 1) To install, reverse removal procedure. On 4WD models, connect transfer case shift linkage and vacuum hoses. Install NEW "O" ring seal on upper half of transmission fill tube. Connect upper and lower tube halves.

2) Tighten all bolts to specification. See TORQUE SPECIFICATIONS. Fill transmission with Mopar ATF Plus (7176) transmission fluid.

Removal (30RH, 32RH, 42RE, 42RH & 46RH) – 1) Disconnect fan shroud and transmission fill tube upper bracket. Raise vehicle. Remove converter inspection cover and fill tube. Remove starter.

2) Mark drive shafts for reassembly. Disconnect shafts at transfer case and wire to frame rails. DO NOT allow shafts to hang free, as damage to universal joints may result. Disconnect exhaust pipes from exhaust manifolds. Drain transfer case lubricant. Disconnect speedometer cable from transmission.

3) Disconnect all shift and throttle linkages and wiring from transmission and transfer case. Mark converter drive plate and converter for reassembly, and remove torque converter-to-drive plate bolts. Rotate crankshaft to gain access to bolts.

4) Support transmission/transfer case assembly. Remove bolts and rear transmission crossmember. Lower transmission enough to disconnect cooler lines at transmission. Remove transmission-to-engine retaining bolts and slowly slide transmission assembly away from engine.

5) Hold converter in position while lowering transmission assembly from vehicle. Separate transmission from transfer case.

Installation – To install, reverse removal procedure. DO NOT tighten exhaust pipe attaching bolts until crossmember has been installed and transmission jack has been removed. Ensure all index marks made at removal are aligned. Tighten all bolts to specification. See TORQUE SPECIFICATIONS. Fill transmission and transfer case with fluid.

TORQUE SPECIFICATIONS

TORQUE SPECIFICATIONS

Application	Ft. Lbs. (N.m)
AW4	
Cooler Line Nuts	13-16 (18-23)
Converter Housing Bolts	
10-mm	25 (34)
12-mm	42 (57)
Dust Cover	13-17 (18-23)
Filler Tube Bracket	37-47 (50-64)
Torque Converter-To-Drive Plate Bolts	22 (30)
Transfer Case-To-Transmission Bolts	22-30 (30-41)
Transmission-To-Engine Bolts	37-47 (50-64)
Transmission-To-Rear Mount Bolt	44-66 (60-81)
30RH, 32RH, 42RE, 42RH & 46RH	
Cooler Line Nuts	13 (18)
Drive Plate-To-Converter	22 (30)
Drive Plate-To-Crankshaft	55 (75)
Filler Tube	24 (33)
Transfer Case-To-Transmission Bolts	22-30 (30-41)
Transmission-To-Engine Bolts	30 (41)

Acclaim, Colt, Colt Vista, Daytona, Laser, LeBaron, Shadow, Spirit, Stealth, Summit, Sundance, Talon

APPLICATION

MANUAL TRANSAXLE APPLICATIONS

Model	Transaxle
Acclaim	
2.5L	A-523
3.0L	A-543
Colt & Summit	F5M21 & F5M22
Colt Vista & Summit Wagon	
FWD	
1.8L	F5M22
2.4L	F5M31
AWD	
1.8L	W5M31
2.4L	W5M33
Daytona & LeBaron Convertible/Coupe	
2.2L Turbo (Daytona)	A-568
2.5L TBI	A-523
3.0L	A-543
Laser & Talon	
FWD	
1.8L	F5M22
2.0L	F5M33
AWD	W5M33
Shadow & Sundance	
2.2L & 2.5L	A-523
3.0L	A-543
Spirit	
2.2L & 2.5L	A-523
3.0L	A-543
Stealth	
FWD	F5M33
AWD	
1993	W5MG1
1994	W6MG1

LUBRICATION

SERVICE INTERVALS

Check fluid level whenever other underhood services are performed. Under normal driving conditions, factory installed fluid will give satisfactory lubrication for the life of the vehicle. Under severe driving conditions, drain and refill at 15,000 mile intervals.

CHECKING FLUID LEVEL

1) Check lubricant level at filler plug hole on left side of transaxle (on rear end cover). Lubricant should be level with bottom of filler plug hole.
2) Fluid is drained by removing differential cover. Clean magnet. Use RTV sealant on differential cover.

RECOMMENDED FLUID

A-523, A-543 & A-568 – Use SAE 5W-30 engine oil.
All Others – Use SAE 75W-85/API GL-4 gear lube.
Transfer Case – Use SAE 80W-90/API GL-4 gear lube.

FLUID CAPACITY

TRANSAXLE REFILL CAPACITIES

Application	Pts. (L)
A-523, A-543 & A-568	4.2 (2.0)
F5M21 & F5M22	3.8 (1.8)
F5M31	2.4 (1.1)
F5M33	4.6 (2.2)
W5MG1, W5M31 & W6M33	5.0 (2.4)
W5M33	4.9 (2.3)

TRANSFER CASE REFILL CAPACITIES

Application	Pts. (L)
W5MG1, W5M31 & W5M33	1.3 (0.6)

ADJUSTMENTS

SELECT CABLE

NOTE: A-523, A-543 and A-568 models are not equipped with select cable.

Except A-523, A-543 & A-568 – **1)** Place transaxle side shift lever in Neutral. This will also place transaxle side select lever in Neutral.
2) Loosen select cable adjuster nuts (inside of vehicle). With select lever in Neutral, adjust select cable end until eye fits easily over select lever pin. Tighten adjuster nuts.

SHIFT CABLE

A-523, A-543 & A-568 – **1)** Place transaxle in Neutral position. Working over left front fender, remove lock pin from transaxle selector shaft housing. *See Fig. 1.*
2) Invert lock pin (long end down) and insert into same threaded hole while pushing selector shaft into selector housing. When hole in selector shaft aligns with lock pin, insert lock pin in housing. Selector shaft will be locked in 3-4/Neutral position.
3) Remove gearshift knob and boot. Loosen crossover adjustment screw. Shifter will move to centered position. Tighten crossover adjustment screw to 70 INCH lbs. (8 N.m). Ensure shifter does not move while tightening crossover adjustment screw. Install boot and gearshift knob.
4) Remove lock pin from selector shaft housing, and reinstall lock pin upside down (long end up) into selector shaft housing. Tighten lock pin to 70 INCH lbs. (8 N.m). Check for shift into 1st and Reverse. Check for lock-out function in Reverse.

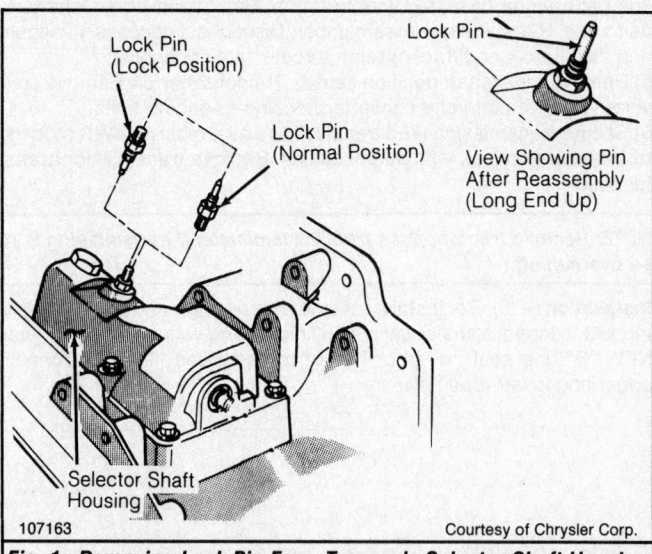

Lock Pin (Lock Position)

Lock Pin (Normal Position)

Lock Pin

View Showing Pin After Reassembly (Long End Up)

Selector Shaft Housing

107163　　　　　　　Courtesy of Chrysler Corp.

Fig. 1: Removing Lock Pin From Transaxle Selector Shaft Housing

F5M22, F5M33 & W5M33 – **1)** Place transaxle select lever in Neutral position. Disconnect shift cable from shifter lever. Place transaxle shifter lever in 4th gear position. Cable is properly adjusted if hole in cable end aligns with shifter lever pin.
2) If cable requires adjustment, turn threaded barrel on cable housing until alignment is correct. Connect cable and ensure shifter is equidistant between 3rd and 4th gear position stops when shifter is in Neutral position.
All Others – **1)** With transaxle select lever in Neutral, move gearshift lever into 4th gear. It may be necessary to depress clutch pedal.
2) Loosen shift cable adjuster nuts (inside of vehicle) and disconnect cable end from shift lever pin. Tilt gearshift lever into 4th gear position until it touches stopper. Hold lever in this position and adjust shift lever cable until it aligns with shift lever pin.
3) Move shift lever between 3rd, Neutral and 4th gear positions. Shift lever-to-stopper clearances should be equal on both sides of lever. If clearances are not equal, readjust shift cable. Road test vehicle to ensure proper adjustment and smooth shifting.

Caravan, Voyager
IDENTIFICATION

NOTE: Transaxle model A-523 is used on vehicles with 2.5L engine only.

LUBRICATION

SERVICE INTERVALS

Under normal operating conditions, factory installed fluid provides satisfactory lubrication for vehicle life. Fluid changes are not required unless contaminated with water.

Vehicle operation at high speeds with ambient temperature above 90°F (32°C) requires that transaxle fluid should be changed and drain plug magnet cleaned every 15,000 miles.

SHIFT & CLUTCH LINKAGE

If linkage squeaks, pivot hole in adjuster and adjusting positioner teeth requires lubrication. If high shift effort or mechanism rattle exists, control mechanism requires lubrication. Lubricate with multipurpose grease.

CHECKING FLUID LEVEL

Lubricant should be level with bottom of filler plug hole, located on side of transaxle. Add lubricant as needed.

RECOMMENDED FLUID

Use SAE 5W-30 (Grade SG or SG-CC) engine oil.

FLUID CAPACITY
TRANSMISSION REFILL CAPACITIES

Application	Qts. (L)
A-523 [1]	2.3 (2.2)

[1] – Refill until level with bottom of fill hole.

ADJUSTMENTS

SHIFT LINKAGE

1) Remove lock pin from selector shaft housing. See Fig. 1. Reverse lock pin and reinstall with long end toward housing while pushing selector shaft into housing. Selector shaft hole will align with lock pin and lock selector shaft in the 3-4 Neutral position.

2) Remove gearshift knob and boot. Loosen crossover cable adjusting screw and retighten to 70 INCH lbs. (8 N.m). Ensure crossover bellcrank DOES NOT move when tightening adjusting screw. See Fig. 1.

3) Reverse removal procedure for remaining components. Remove lock pin and reinstall with long end away from housing. Tighten lock pin to 70 INCH lbs. (8 N.m). Check shift movement into first and reverse gear. Check reverse lockout.

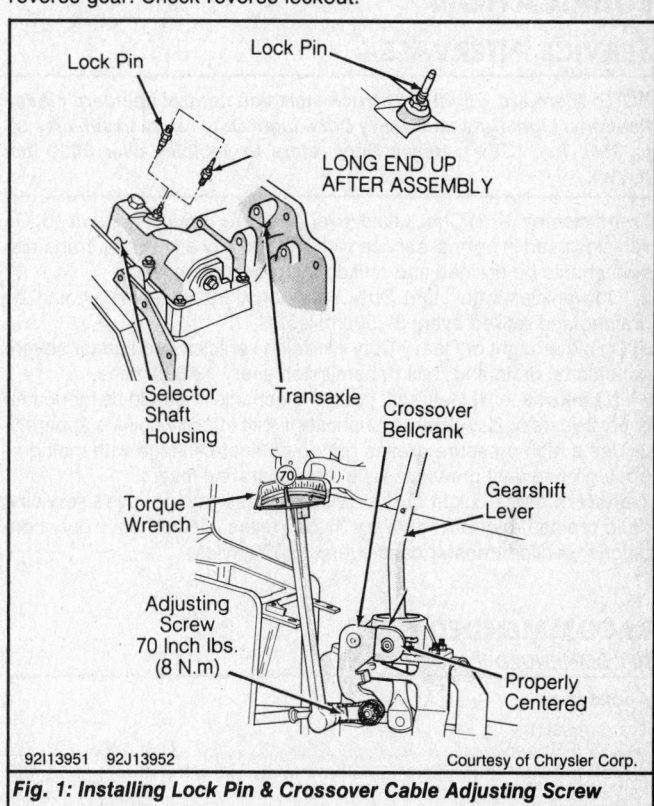

92I13951 92J13952 Courtesy of Chrysler Corp.

Fig. 1: Installing Lock Pin & Crossover Cable Adjusting Screw

Chrysler Corp. RWD Light Trucks & Vans

Dakota, Pickup, Ramcharger, Ram-50, Van
APPLICATION

TRANSMISSION APPLICATION

Application	Model Number
Transmission	
Dakota (AN)	AX15 & NV3500
D & W Series Pickup (AD)	[1] Getrag 360 & NV4500
BR Series Pickup	NV4500
Ramcharger	NV4500
Ram Van (AB)	AX15
Ram-50	
2WD	R5M21
4WD	
2.4L	V5M21
3.0L	V5MT1

[1] – Used on 1993 diesel only.

TRANSFER CASE APPLICATION

Application	Model Number
Transfer Case	
Dakota	NP231
Pickup	
1993	
W150	NP241
W250/350	NP205
1994	
BR1500	NP241
BR2500/3500	NP241 (HD) Or [1] NV021
Ramcharger	NP241

[1] – PTO unit used on 1994 2WD BR2500/3500 vehicles.

2-48

MANUAL TRANSMISSION SERVICING
Chrysler Corp. RWD Light Trucks & Vans (Cont.)

WARNING: Before removing engine/transmission assembly on compressed natural gas powered vehicles, see COMPRESSED NATURAL GAS SAFETY PRECAUTIONS in CAUTIONS & WARNINGS article in APPLICATIONS & IDENTIFICATION.

LUBRICATION

SERVICE INTERVALS

NOTE: There are 2 light duty truck emission control standard classifications: Light Duty and Heavy Duty. Light Duty refers to vehicles up to 8500 lbs. (GVW); Heavy Duty refers to vehicles over 8500 lbs. (GVW).

Transmission – **1)** Check fluid level whenever vehicle is serviced. On vehicles used in normal service with Heavy Duty emissions, transmission should be drained and refilled every 36,000 miles.
2) On vehicles with Light Duty emissions, transmission should be drained and refilled every 37,500 miles.
3) On either Light or Heavy Duty emission vehicles used under severe conditions, drain and refill transmission every 18,000 miles.
Shift Linkage – **1)** Gearshift control mechanism should be lubricated every 2 years or 22,500 miles. Lubricate if shift effort or noise is apparent.
2) Use a high pressure grease gun to lubricate linkage with multipurpose grease until grease is visible on operating levers.
Transfer Case – Light duty service requires transfer case servicing (fluid drained and refilled) every 37,500 miles. Under heavy duty conditions, service transfer case every 36,000 miles.

RECOMMENDED FLUID

CHECKING FLUID LEVEL

Transmission – With vehicle in level position, check lubricant level at filler plug hole on side of transmission. Lubricant should be level with bottom of filler plug hole. Add lubricant as needed to bring to correct level.
Transfer Case – With vehicle in level position, remove filler plug and check fluid level. If level is below bottom of filler plug hole, add sufficient lubricant to restore level to bottom of filler hole.

CAUTION: On transfer cases with PTO, if proper fill procedures are not followed, transfer case or PTO failure could result. Transfer cases with PTO's will have a fill plug labeled FOR PTO FILL ONLY on front of case.

FLUID CAPACITY

TRANSMISSION REFILL CAPACITIES

Application	Pts. (L)
Transmissions	
AX15 5-Speed	6.55 (3.1)
G360 5-Speed	7.0 (3.3)
NV3500 5-Speed	4.4 (2.0)
NV4500 5-Speed	8.0 (3.8)
R5M21	4.9 (2.3)
V5M21 & V5MT1	4.6 (2.2)
Transfer Cases	Qts. (L)
NP231	1.6 (1.5)
NP241	[1]
NP205	4.6 (2.2)
NV021	4.6 (2.2)
Ram-50	4.6 (2.2)

[1] – Fill to bottom of fill plug hole.

RECOMMENDED FLUIDS

Application	Fluid Specification
Transmissions	
AX15 5-Speed	SAE 75W-90 (API GL-5) Multipurpose Gear Oil
G360 5-Speed	SAE 5W-30 (API SG or SG-CD) Engine Oil
NV3500 5-Speed	MOPAR (4761526) only
NV4500 5-Speed	Castrol Syntorq SAE 75W-90 (API GL-4)
R5M21, V5M21 & V5MT1	SAE 75W-85 (API GL-4 Or Higher) Gear Oil
Transfer Cases	
NP205	SAE 30 (API SF or SF-CC) Engine Oil
NP231, NP241 & NV021	Mopar ATF Plus Type 7176 Or Dexron-II
Ram-50	SAE 75W-85 (API GL-4) Gear Oil

Ford Motor Co. Passenger Cars

Aspire, Capri, Escort, Festiva, Mustang, Probe, Sable, Taurus, Tempo, Thunderbird, Topaz, Tracer

IDENTIFICATION

NOTE: For manual transmission applications, see appropriate table in APPLICATIONS & IDENTIFICATION.

LUBRICATION

SERVICE INTERVALS

Check fluid level at 15-month or 15,000-mile intervals. Draining and refilling are not required except at time of overhaul or service.

CHECKING FLUID LEVEL

Capri, Escort, Festiva & Tracer – Ensure vehicle is level. To check fluid, remove retaining bolt and pry out speedometer driven gear assembly or vehicle speed sensor from transaxle. Wipe fluid from driven gear assembly and housing. Remove "O" ring from gear sleeve.

Reinsert driven gear assembly or vehicle speed sensor into transaxle, remove again and check fluid level. Level should be at the FULL mark on gear sleeve. *See Fig. 1 or 2.* Add fluid through driven gear hole as necessary. Check "O" ring and replace if necessary. Reinstall driven gear assembly.
All Others – Ensure vehicle is level. Check lubricant level at filler plug hole on side of transmission. Lubricant should be within 1/4" of filler hole bottom. Add lubricant as necessary to correct fluid level.

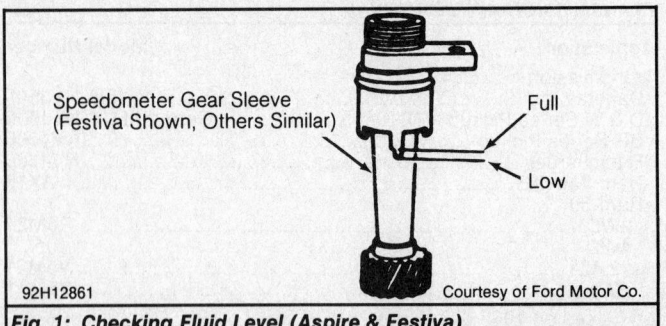

Speedometer Gear Sleeve
(Festiva Shown, Others Similar)

Full

Low

92H12861   Courtesy of Ford Motor Co.

Fig. 1: Checking Fluid Level (Aspire & Festiva)

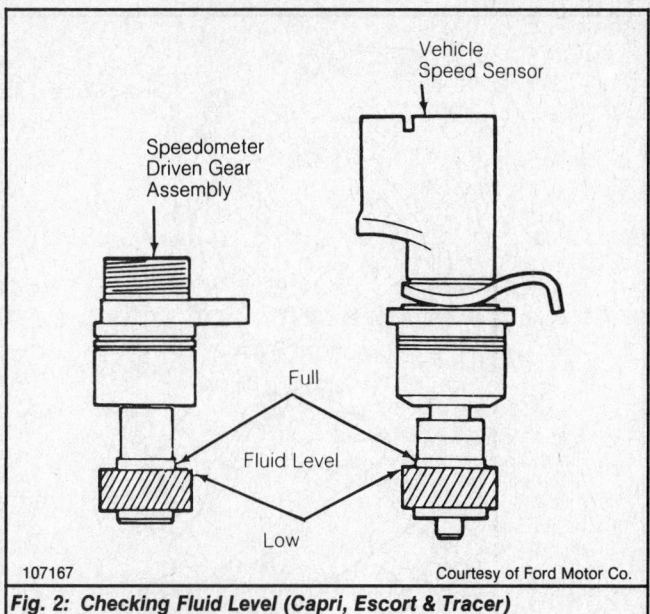

Fig. 2: Checking Fluid Level (Capri, Escort & Tracer)

RECOMMENDED FLUID

All Models Except Probe – Use Mercon.

Probe – Use 75W-90 Gear Oil.

FLUID CAPACITY

CAUTION: Drain and fill plugs for T50D are on right side of case. DO NOT remove reverse shift-lever pin (top hex bolt) on left side of case. Damage may result.

TRANSMISSION REFILL CAPACITIES

Application	Pts. (L)
Aspire & Festiva	2.6 (2.5)
Capri	3.4 (3.2)
Escort & Tracer	
1.8L	7.2 (3.4)
1.9L	5.6 (2.6)
Mustang	5.6 (2.6)
Probe	5.8 (2.7)
Taurus, Tempo & Topaz	6.1 (2.9)
Thunderbird	6.3 (3.0)

ADJUSTMENTS

SHIFT LINKAGE

NOTE: No in-service adjustments are necessary.

Ford Motor Co. Light Trucks & Vans

Aerostar, Bronco, Explorer, "F" Series, Ranger

APPLICATION

NOTE: For manual transaxle applications, see appropriate table in APPLICATIONS & IDENTIFICATION.

WARNING: Before removing engine/transmission assembly on compressed natural gas powered vehicles, see COMPRESSED NATURAL GAS SAFETY PRECAUTIONS in CAUTIONS & WARNINGS article in APPLICATIONS & IDENTIFICATION.

LUBRICATION

SERVICE INTERVALS

Transmission – Under normal driving conditions, replace transmission fluid every 60,000 miles. Under severe driving conditions, replace transmission fluid every 30,000 miles. Change fluid after vehicle operation in water.

Transfer Case – Under normal driving conditions, replace transfer case fluid every 60,000 miles. Under severe 4WD driving conditions, perform this service more frequently.

CHECKING FLUID LEVEL

Transmission – Check lubricant level at transmission filler plug hole. It should be level with bottom of filler hole. Add lubricant as needed.

Transfer Case – Remove filler plug. If fluid drains out or is level with opening, replace filler plug. If not, fill until fluid is level with filler plug opening.

CAUTION: On Warner 1356 transfer cases with PTO, additional fluid is required. If proper procedures are not followed, transfer case or PTO failure could result. Transfer cases with PTO's will have fill plug labeled FOR PTO FILL ONLY on front of case.

RECOMMENDED FLUID

Transmission – All transmissions use Mercon ATF (XT-2-QDX).

Parking Brake Assembly (Pickup F350 Super Duty Commercial Chassis) – Use Motorcraft Mercon (XT-2-QDX).

Transfer Case – Motorcraft Mercon (XT-2-QDX) should be used in transfer cases.

FLUID CAPACITY

NOTE: Capacities given are approximate. Correct fluid level should be determined by level at filler plug hole, rather than amount added.

TRANSMISSION REFILL CAPACITIES

Application	Pts. (L)
Borg-Warner T-18	7.0 (3.3)
Ford S5-42 ZF 5-Speed	7.0 (3.3)
Mazda M50D 5-Speed Overdrive	
Aerostar, Explorer & Ranger	5.6 (2.6)
Bronco & Pickup	7.6 (3.6)

TRANSFER CASE REFILL CAPACITIES

Application	Pts. (L)
Dana TC-28	4.5 (2.1)
Warner 1354	2.5 (1.2)
Warner 1356	4.0 (1.9)
Warner 1356 With PTO	8.1 (3.8)

MANUAL TRANSMISSION SERVICING
General Motors Passenger Cars

Achieva, Beretta, Camaro, Cavalier, Corsica, Corvette, Cutlass Calais, Cutlass Supreme, Firebird, Grand Am, Grand Prix, LeMans, Lumina, Metro, Prizm, Saturn, Storm, Sunbird

IDENTIFICATION
FWD MANUAL TRANSAXLE APPLICATION

Manufacturer/Model	Transaxle
Chevrolet	
Beretta	5-Spd. NVT550 Or 5-Spd. Isuzu 76-mm
Cavalier	5-Spd. NVT550 Or 5-Spd. Isuzu 76-mm
Corsica	5-Spd. NVT550 Or 5-Spd. Isuzu 76-mm
Lumina (1993)	5-Spd. Getrag 284
Geo	
Metro	5-Spd. Suzuki Transaxle
Prizm	5-Spd. Toyota
Storm	5-Spd. Isuzu 76-mm Transaxle
Oldsmobile	
Achieva	5-Spd. NVT550 Or 5-Spd. Isuzu 76-mm
Cutlass Calais	5-Spd. Muncie 5TM40 Or 5-Spd. Isuzu 76-mm
Pontiac	
Grand Am	5-Spd. NVT550 Or 5-Spd. Isuzu 76-mm
Grand Prix (1993)	5-Spd. Getrag 284
Grand Prix (1994)	5-Spd. NVT550 Or 5-Spd. Isuzu 76-mm
LeMans	4 & 5 Spd. F16 Transaxle
Saturn	
SOHC	MP2
DOHC	MP3

RWD MANUAL TRANSMISSION APPLICATION

Manufacturer/Model	Transmission
Chevrolet	
Camaro	5-Spd. Borg-Warner 77-mm, Or 6-Spd. Borg-Warner 85-mm
Corvette	6-Spd. ZF S6-40 95-mm
Pontiac	
Firebird	5-Spd. Borg-Warner 77-mm, Or 6-Spd. Borg-Warner 85-mm

LUBRICATION
SERVICE INTERVALS

Corvette – Change fluid in overdrive unit every 30,000 miles.
Metro – Under normal driving conditions, transaxle fluid does not need replacing. Under severe driving conditions, replace fluid every 12,000 miles or 12 months.
Prizm – Transaxle fluid only needs replacing when transaxle is overhauled.
Saturn – Change fluid at 6000 miles. After initial oil change, no regular service is required.
Storm – Replace transaxle fluid every 30,000 miles under normal driving conditions. Under severe driving conditions, change fluid every 15,000 miles.
All Others – Fluid replacement is not required, except at time of overhaul. Check fluid level at each engine oil change.

CHECKING FLUID LEVEL

CAUTION: On Camaro and Firebird, DO NOT remove reverse shift lever pin (largest hex-shaped bolt) on LEFT side of case. Removing this bolt may damage the transmission.

Camaro, Corvette, Firebird, Metro, Prizm & Storm – Check lubricant level at filler plug hole on right side of transmission. Lubricant should be level with bottom of filler plug hole. Add lubricant as necessary to bring to correct level.
All Others – Park vehicle on level surface. Check fluid level when fluid is COLD. Fluid should be at FULL mark on dipstick. *See Fig. 1.* Drain plug is below dipstick tube.

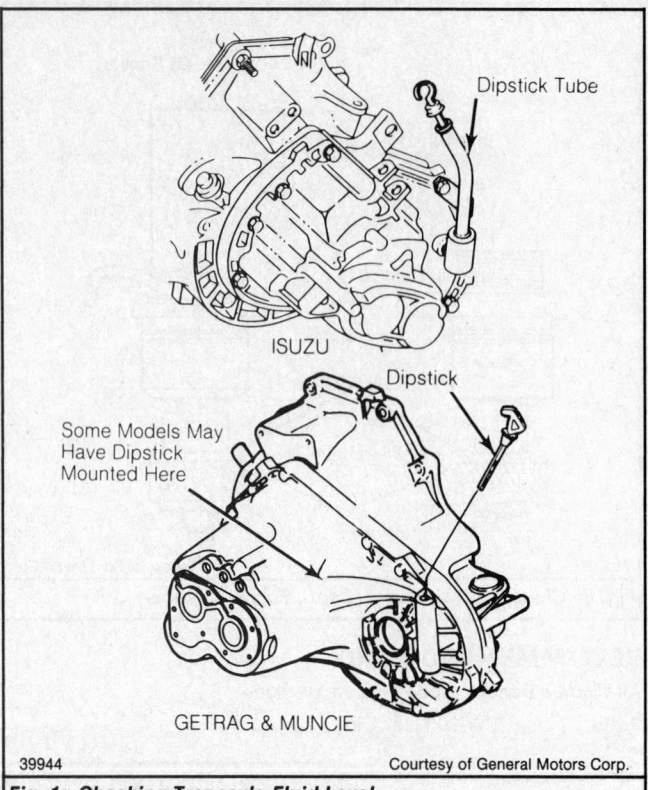

Fig. 1: Checking Transaxle Fluid Level

FLUID CAPACITY & RECOMMENDED FLUID
FLUID CAPACITIES

Application	[1] Qts. (L)
Camaro & Firebird	[2] 3.0 (2.8)
LeMans	2.2 (2.0)
Metro	2.5 (2.4)
Prizm	2.7 (2.6)
Saturn	2.6 (2.5)
Storm	2.0 (1.9)
All Others	[3] 2.0 (1.9)

[1] – Fluid capacities listed are approximate. Always use procedure specified under CHECKING FLUID LEVEL when filling transaxle/transmission.
[2] – Dexron-II.
[3] – In all vehicles except Corvette, use Synchromesh Transmission Fluid (GM 12345349). In Corvette, use SAE 5W-30 (GM 1052931).

ADJUSTMENTS
GEAR SHIFT LINKAGE (LEMANS ONLY)

WARNING: When battery is disconnected, vehicle computer and memory systems may lose memory data. Driveability problems may exist until computer systems have completed a relearn cycle. See COMPUTER RELEARN PROCEDURES article in APPLICATIONS & IDENTIFICATION before disconnecting battery.

LeMans – **1)** Disconnect negative battery cable. Position gearshift lever in Neutral. Loosen shift rod clamp bolt. *See Fig. 2.* Remove adjustment hole plug from shift lever cover. *See Fig. 3.*
2) Turn shift rod to the left until a 3/16" pin can be inserted in oil plug hole of intermediate shift lever. Remove boot from center console and pull it upward to expose shift control lever mechanism.
3) Position gearshift lever to the 1st/2nd shift plane while still in Neutral. Position lever against stop and align arrow with notch. *See Fig. 4.* Tighten shift rod clamp bolt to 10 ft. lbs. (14 N.m) and turn bolt an additional 90-180 degrees.

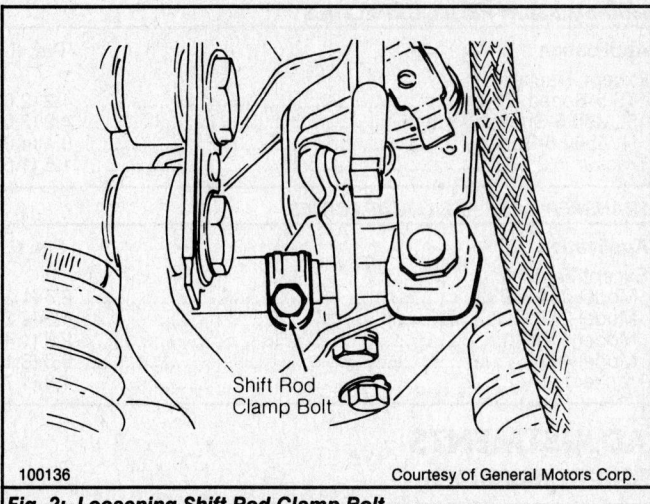

Fig. 2: Loosening Shift Rod Clamp Bolt

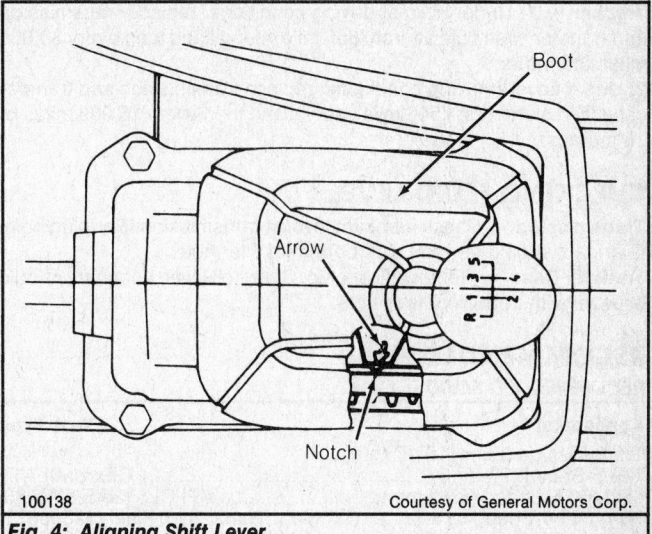

Fig. 4: Aligning Shift Lever

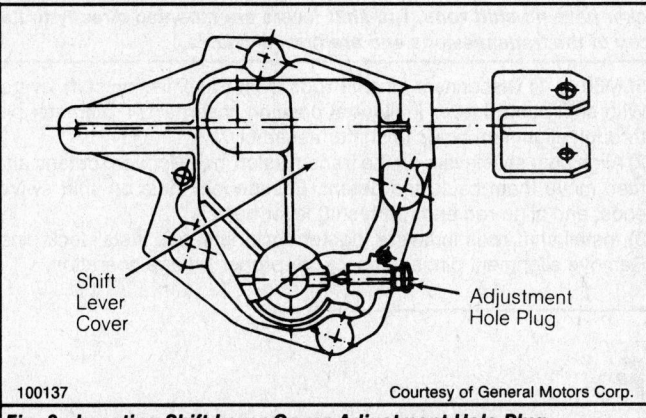

Fig. 3: Locating Shift Lever Cover Adjustment Hole Plug

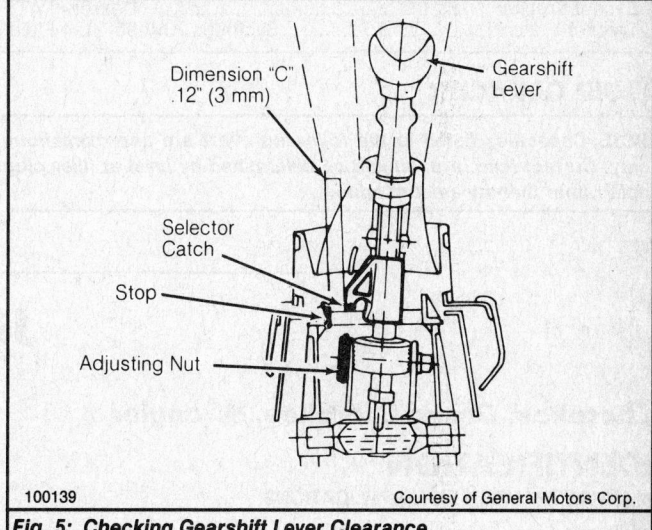

Fig. 5: Checking Gearshift Lever Clearance

4) Check clearance between selector catch and stop with shift lever in Neutral. Clearance is shown in dimension "C". See *Fig. 5*. If not, bend 2 locking tabs and turn adjusting nut until clearance is correct. Bend locking tabs down and remove gauge pin and install plug.
5) Check gearshift lever for proper adjustment. Readjust if necessary. Install boot, center console and connect negative battery cable.

General Motors Light Trucks & Vans

"C" & "K" Series, "J" Tracker, P" Series, "R" & "V" Series, "S" & "T" Series

NOTE: For body code identification and model application, see GENERAL MOTORS BODY IDENTIFICATION CODES in APPLICATIONS & IDENTIFICATION section.

NOTE: The following manual transmissions are used on 1993 and 1994 light trucks: 5LM60 5-Speed, NV4500 5-Speed, T5 5-Speed and Suzuki 5-Spd.

WARNING: Before removing engine/transmission assembly on compressed natural gas powered vehicles, see COMPRESSED NATURAL GAS SAFETY PRECAUTIONS in CAUTIONS & WARNINGS article in APPLICATIONS & IDENTIFICATION.

LUBRICATION

SERVICE INTERVALS

NOTE: There are 2 light truck emission control standard classifications: Light Duty and Heavy Duty. Light Duty refers to vehicles weighing up to 8500 lbs. (GVW); Heavy Duty refers to vehicles weighing over 8500 lbs. (GVW).

Transmission (Except Tracker) – On all Light Duty vehicles, check transmission fluid every 12 months or 7500 miles. On Heavy Duty vehicles, check fluid level every 12 months or 6000 miles. Periodic draining and refilling is not required.
Transfer Case (Except Tracker) – Check transfer case lubricant every oil change or 12 months. Under severe conditions, check it more frequently.

Tracker – 1) Under normal driving conditions, replace transmission and transfer case fluid at first 7500 mile interval and then every 30,000 miles thereafter.

2) Under severe driving conditions, replace transmission and transfer case fluid at the first 7500 mile interval and then every 15,000 miles or 15 months.

CHECKING FLUID LEVEL

Transmission – Check lubricant level at transmission filler plug hole. Lubricant should be level with bottom of filler hole.

Transfer Case – Remove filler plug. Check oil level. Lubricant should be level with bottom of filler hole.

RECOMMENDED FLUID
RECOMMENDED FLUID

Application	Fluid Type
Transmission (Except Tracker)	
T5 5-Speed (77-mm)	Dexron-II ATF
5LM60 5-Speed (85-mm)	API GL5 (SAE 80W-90)
NV4500 5-Speed	GM Man. Trans. Syn. Fluid (12345871)
Transmission (Tracker)	GM Man. Trans. Fluid (12345349)
Transfer Cases	
Except Tracker	Dexron-II ATF
Tracker	Synthetic 75W-90 GL-4 Fluid.

FLUID CAPACITY

NOTE: Capacities listed in the following chart are approximations only. Correct fluid level should be determined by level at filler plug hole rather than by amount added.

TRANSMISSION REFILL CAPACITIES

Application	Pts. (L)
Except Tracker	
T5 5-Speed (77-mm)	4.2 (2.0)
5LM60 5-Speed (85-mm)	4.2 (2.0)
NV4500 5-Speed	8.4 (4.0)
Tracker	1.6 (1.5)

TRANSFER CASE REFILL CAPACITIES

Application	Pts. (L)
Except Tracker	
Model 231 & 233	2.5 (1.2)
Model 241	4.6 (2.2)
Model 4401	2.9 (1.4)
Model 4470	6.6 (3.1)
Tracker	1.8 (1.7)

ADJUSTMENTS
SHIFT LINKAGE

NOTE: The NV4500, T5 transmissions and transmission used on Tracker have no shift rods. The shift levers are mounted directly to the top of the transmissions and are not adjustable.

5LM60 – 1) Disconnect all shift rods from transmission shift levers. With shift control lever in Neutral position, insert a 1/4" diameter pin through alignment holes in shifter assembly.

2) Align both shift levers on the transmission in the forward detent, and then move them back one detent. Loosen lock nuts on shift swivel ends, and align rod ends with shift lever holes.

3) Install shift rods in levers, tighten lock nuts, and install lock pins. Remove alignment pin, and check for proper linkage operation.

Jeep

Cherokee, Grand Cherokee, Wrangler

IDENTIFICATION
MANUAL TRANSMISSION APPLICATIONS

Model	Transmission
Cherokee, Grand Cherokee & Wrangler	
4-Cylinder	AX5 5-Speed
6-Cylinder	AX15 5-Speed

LUBRICATION

SERVICE INTERVALS

Transmission & Transfer Case – Transmission and transfer case fluid should be checked every 7500 miles or when serviced. Transmission and transfer case fluid should be changed every 30,000 miles or 30 month intervals.

CHECKING FLUID LEVEL

Transmission – Check lubricant level at transmission filler plug hole. Lubricant should be level with bottom of hole. Add lubricant as needed.

Transfer Case – Remove fill plug. Check oil level. Add lubricant if level is not up to fill plug opening.

RECOMMENDED FLUID

Transmission – Use SAE 75W-90 GL-5 gear lubricant.
Transfer Cases – Use Mopar ATF Plus (1767) or equivalent.

FLUID CAPACITY

NOTE: Capacities given are approximate. Correct fluid level should be determined by level at filler plug hole.

TRANSMISSION REFILL CAPACITIES

Application	Pts. (L)
2WD	
AX5 5-Speed	3.5 (3.3)
AX15 5-Speed	3.3 (3.2)
4WD	
AX5 5-Speed	3.7 (3.5)
AX15 5-Speed	3.3 (3.2)

TRANSFER CASE REFILL CAPACITIES

Application	Qts. (L)
Model 231	
Cherokee	1.0 (.95)
Wrangler	1.6 (1.5)
Model 242	1.4 (1.3)

ADJUSTMENTS
SHIFT LINKAGE

NOTE: All Jeep models use transmission shift linkage that does not require external adjustments.

TORQUE SPECIFICATIONS
TORQUE SPECIFICATIONS

	Application – Ft. Lbs. (N.m)
Drain & Fill Plugs	27 (37)

Acclaim, Colt, Colt Vista, Daytona, Laser, LeBaron, Shadow, Spirit, Stealth, Summit, Summit Wagon, Sundance, Talon

REMOVAL & INSTALLATION

WARNING: When battery is disconnected, vehicle computer and memory systems may lose memory data. Driveability problems may exist until computer systems have completed a relearn cycle. See COMPUTER RELEARN PROCEDURES in APPLICATIONS & IDENTIFICATION before disconnecting battery.

Acclaim, Daytona, LeBaron Convertible/Coupe, Shadow, Spirit, Sundance – 1) Disconnect negative battery cable. Disconnect speedometer cable and clutch cable. Disconnect back-up light harness and starter motor wiring. Remove starter motor.

2) Disconnect gearshift operating lever from selector shaft. Install lifting eye on battery ground strap bolt (on left side of engine), and support engine using engine support fixture. Remove screw retaining operating lever to transaxle.

3) Raise and support vehicle. Remove front wheel assemblies and left front splash shield. Drain transaxle oil. Remove left engine mount from transaxle. Remove anti-rotational link from crossmember bracket; DO NOT remove bracket from transaxle.

4) Remove left and right drive axle shafts, and support aside. Secure transaxle jack under transaxle, and remove transaxle-to-engine bolts. Ensure all cables, mounts and wires have been disconnected and do not interfere when lowering transaxle.

5) To install, reverse removal procedure. Install a NEW gearshift operating lever attaching bolt. Adjust clutch cable and refill transaxle. See appropriate MANUAL TRANSMISSION SERVICING article.

Colt, Colt Vista, Summit & Summit Wagon (2WD) – 1) Remove battery, battery tray and air cleaner assembly. Drain transaxle oil and clutch fluid (if equipped). On Colt and Summit, disconnect tension rod located above transaxle mounting bracket.

2) On all models, disconnect control cables, speedometer cable and electrical connections at transaxle. Remove clutch release cylinder with line connected.

3) Remove starter motor. Support transaxle. Remove upper transaxle-to-engine bolts and transaxle mounting bracket bolt. Loosen nuts and disconnect ball joint and tie rod ends from steering knuckles. DO NOT remove ball joint and tie rod end nuts.

4) Disengage axle shafts and support aside. See appropriate AXLE SHAFTS article in AXLE SHAFTS & TRANSFER CASES. DO NOT damage oil seal. Plug shaft openings in transaxle.

CAUTION: DO NOT pull on axle shafts during removal, or damage to shaft assembly will result.

5) Remove bellhousing cover. Support engine. Remove remaining transaxle-to-engine bolts. Remove transaxle assembly.

6) To install, reverse removal procedure. Refill all fluids to proper levels. Adjust all control cables, clutch pedal height and free play.

NOTE: For transaxle and clutch service on Colt Vista and Summit Wagon (4WD), manufacturer recommends removing engine and transaxle as a unit.

Colt Vista & Summit Wagon (4WD) – 1) Remove engine and transaxle as a unit. Remove propeller shaft. See COLT, COLT VISTA, SUMMIT & SUMMIT WAGON (2WD) transaxle removal under REMOVAL & INSTALLATION. After engine/transaxle assembly has been removed, remove vacuum tank assembly from transaxle case. Support transaxle and remove transaxle-to-engine bolts. Separate transaxle from engine.

2) Reverse removal procedure to install transaxle and engine assembly. Ensure reference mark aligns on propeller shaft.

3) Refill all fluids to proper levels. Adjust all control cables, clutch pedal height and free play.

Laser & Talon – 1) Remove clutch release cylinder and clutch hydraulic line bracket installation bolt. Secure cylinder at body side without disconnecting hydraulic line coupling.

2) Lift vehicle and remove undercover. Disconnect tie rod end from knuckle. Separate lower ball joint from knuckle. Insert pry bar between transaxle case and axle shaft. Pry axle shaft from transaxle. Secure drive shaft as far as possible from transaxle and prevent shaft from falling. On AWD models, remove propeller shaft.

CAUTION: DO NOT pull on axle shaft as damage to inboard joint will result. DO NOT insert pry bar too deep as damage to oil seal will result. On turbo models, ensure end of transaxle housing does not damage lower radiator hose.

3) Support transaxle assembly using a transaxle jack. Ensure all cables, mounts and wires have been disconnected and do not interfere when lowering transaxle. Move transaxle to right, lower it and remove it from vehicle.

4) To install, reverse removal procedure. On turbo models, protect lower radiator hose. On all models, install drive shaft so inboard joint of drive shaft is straight and not bent relative to transaxle. Tighten starter bolts with wiring harness clip and ground cable.

CAUTION: DO NOT damage oil seal lip or serrated part of drive shaft. Align serrations, and securely insert drive shaft into transaxle.

Stealth – 1) Remove left and right undercovers. On 4WD models, remove air cleaner cover, air hoses and vacuum pipe. On all models, remove air cleaner, intake hose, battery, battery tray and washer tank.

2) On Stealth SOHC, disconnect lower radiator hose and water inlet pipe. On all models, disconnect transaxle control cables and speedometer cable.

3) Remove clutch tube bracket and disconnect clutch release cylinder (including clutch damper assembly on 2WD models). Support transaxle assembly with jack and disconnect transaxle mount. Remove mount, bracket, plug and stoppers.

4) Remove transaxle assembly upper coupling bolts. Disconnect tie rod ends and lower arm ball joints. Remove right support member, starter cover (if equipped) and starter.

5) Remove left side bearing bracket mounting bolts and pry left drive shaft from transaxle. Wire left drive shaft and inner shaft assembly aside. Pry right drive shaft from transaxle and hang with wire.

6) Remove front and rear transaxle stays. Support transaxle assembly with a jack. Remove transaxle assembly lower coupling bolts and slowly lower transaxle.

7) To install, reverse removal procedure. When reconnecting water inlet pipe on Stealth SOHC, apply water to outer circumference of "O" ring and connect pipe. DO NOT allow engine oil to contaminate "O" ring.

8) Reverse removal procedure for remaining components. Refill all fluids to proper levels. See appropriate MANUAL TRANSMISSION SERVICING article. Adjust all control cables, clutch pedal height and free play.

TORQUE SPECIFICATIONS
TORQUE SPECIFICATIONS

Application	Ft. Lbs. (N.m.)
Transaxle-To-Engine Bolt	
Colt, Laser, Summit & Talon	
8-mm Bolt	[1]
10-mm Bolt	22-25 (30-34)
12-mm Bolt	32-39 (43-53)
Colt Vista & Summit Wagon	
2WD	32-39 (43-53)
4WD	
8-mm Bolt	22-25 (30-34)
10-mm Bolt	31-40 (42-54)
Stealth	
Upper Mounting Bolt	54 (73)
Lower Mounting Bolt	65 (88)
All Others	70 (95)
Transfer Case-To-Transaxle Bolt	
Stealth	64 (87)
All Others	40-43 (54-58)
	INCH Lbs. (N.m.)
Transaxle Cover-To-Case Bolts	108 (12)

[1] – Tighten to 84-108 INCH lbs. (9.5-12.2 N.m).

Caravan, Voyager

REMOVAL

WARNING: *When battery is disconnected, vehicle computer and memory systems may lose memory data. Driveability problems may exist until computer systems have completed a relearn cycle. See COMPUTER RELEARN PROCEDURES article in APPLICATIONS & IDENTIFICATION before disconnecting battery.*

1) Disconnect negative battery cable. Disconnect speed sensor harness connector and clutch cable. Disconnect back-up light harness and starter motor wiring. Remove starter motor.

2) Disconnect gearshift operating lever from selector shaft. Install lifting eye on battery ground strap bolt (on left side of engine), and support engine using engine support fixture. Remove screw retaining operating lever to transaxle.

3) Raise and support vehicle. Remove front wheel assemblies and left front splash shield. Drain transaxle oil. Remove left engine mount from transaxle. Remove anti-rotational link from crossmember bracket; DO NOT remove bracket from transaxle.

4) Remove left and right drive axle shafts, and support aside. Secure transaxle jack under transaxle, and remove transaxle-to-engine bolts.

Ensure all cables, mounts and wires have been disconnected and do not interfere when lowering transaxle.

INSTALLATION

To install, reverse removal procedure. Install a NEW gearshift operating lever attaching bolt. Adjust clutch cable and refill transaxle with fluid to proper lever. See appropriate MANUAL TRANSMISSION SERVICING article.

TORQUE SPECIFICATIONS

TORQUE SPECIFICATIONS

Application	Ft. Lbs. (N.m.)
Anti-Rotational Strut Ball Joint Clamp Bolt	70 (95)
Bracket-To-Stud Nut	17 (23)
Front Motor Mount Bolt	40 (54)
Left Motor Mount Bolt	40 (54)
Mount-To-Engine Block & Transaxle Case Bolt	70 (95)
Transaxle Case-To-Engine Block Bolts	70 (95)
	INCH Lbs. (N.m)
Transaxle Cover-To-Case Bolts	108 (12)

Chrysler Corp. RWD Light Trucks & Vans

Dakota, Pickup, Ramcharger, Ram-50, Van

IDENTIFICATION

NOTE: *For manual transmission applications, see appropriate table in APPLICATIONS & IDENTIFICATION.*

REMOVAL & INSTALLATION

WARNING: *When battery is disconnected, vehicle computer and memory systems may lose memory data. Driveability problems may exist until computer systems have completed a relearn cycle. See COMPUTER RELEARN PROCEDURES article in APPLICATIONS & IDENTIFICATION before disconnecting battery.*

TRANSFER CASE (EXCEPT RAM-50)

Removal – 1) Raise and support vehicle. Drain transfer case. Mark front and rear drive shaft yokes for installation reference. Disconnect drive shafts at transfer case and support to one side. Disconnect shift lever rod from shift rail link.

2) Secure transfer case to transmission jack. Remove transfer case-to-transmission adapter bolts and nuts. Move transfer case to rear. Lower from vehicle.

Installation – To install, reverse removal procedure. Tighten bolts. See TORQUE SPECIFICATIONS table. Fill transfer case with API Service SF or SF/CC SAEw30 (NP205) or Mopar ATF Plus type 7176 (all others).

TRANSMISSION

AX15 (Removal) – 1) Shift transmission lever to Neutral. Raise and support vehicle. Support transmission with jackstand, remove rear crossmember and lower transmission slightly. Press shift lever retainer downward and turn it counterclockwise to release shifter.

2) Drain transmission fluid. Mark propeller shaft and rear axle yokes for reassembly reference. Remove propeller shaft. Disconnect wires from distance sensor. Loosen sensor coupling and remove sensor from speedometer adapter. Remove speedometer adapter and pinion gear. Disconnect back-up light switch wires.

3) Install Engine Support (C-3487-A) over frame rails. Ensure ends of engine support are positioned against underside of oil pan flange. Raise engine slightly. Remove clutch slave cylinder and secure aside. Remove engine timing sensor and starter motor. Disconnect insulator from extension housing.

4) Remove clutch housing-to-engine bolts. Support transmission with transmission jack. Remove center crossmember. Remove transmission-to-clutch housing bolts. Slide transmission rearward and lower from vehicle.

AX15 (Installation) – To install, reverse removal procedure. Apply high-temperature grease to pilot bushing located in end of crankshaft. Fill transmission with appropriate fluid. See appropriate MANUAL TRANSMISSION SERVICING article.

Getrag 360 (Removal) – 1) Disconnect negative battery cable. Remove upper shift boot attaching screws and upper shift boot. Remove shift lever extension by unthreading it from shift lever stub shaft. Remove lower boot. Remove shift tower boot. Remove 2 shifter alignment bolts from side of shift tower. Remove snap ring securing stub shaft in tower. Remove stub shaft.

2) Raise and support vehicle. Mark propeller shaft and axle yokes for installation reference, and remove propeller shaft(s). Disconnect speed sensor connector. Support transmission. On 4WD vehicles, remove skid plates (if equipped), and transfer case crossmember.

3) Disconnect shift rods at transfer case. Support transfer case with transmission jack. Remove transfer case bolts. Move transfer case rearward, and disengage front input spline. Lower transfer case from vehicle.

4) On all vehicles, remove bolts attaching transmission rear mount to crossmember. Support transmission, and move jackstand underneath engine. Remove crossmember-to-frame braces and crossmember. Remove clutch slave cylinder shield. Remove slave cylinder, and secure aside. Disconnect back-up light switch connector.

5) Remove transmission-to-clutch housing bolts. Secure transmission to transmission jack. Slide transmission rearward and lower from vehicle.

Getrag 360 (Installation) – To install, reverse removal procedure. Apply high-temperature grease to pilot bushing located in end of crankshaft. Align propeller shaft reference marks made during removal.

MANUAL TRANSMISSION REMOVAL
Chrysler Corp. RWD Light Trucks & Vans (Cont.)

2-55

NV3500 & NV4500 (Removal) – 1) Disconnect negative battery cable. Shift transmission to Neutral. Disconnect shift boot and remove shifter lever from transmission stub lever. Raise and support vehicle. Remove skid plate (if equipped).

2) Index mark propeller shaft(s) for reassembly reference and remove shaft(s). Remove front exhaust pipe. Support engine with adjustable jackstand. Disconnect speed sensor harness connector, back-up light harness connector and speedometer cable (if equipped).

3) On 4WD models, remove transfer case. On all models, support transmission with transmission jack and remove rear crossmember. Disconnect transmission harness connectors. Remove clutch slave cylinder and secure aside. Remove transmission-to-clutch housing bolts. Slide transmission rearward and lower from vehicle.

NV3500 & NV4500 (Installation) – To install, reverse removal procedure. Apply high-temperature grease to pilot bushing located in end of crankshaft. Align reference marks made on propeller shaft(s) during removal.

R5M21 (Removal) – 1) Disconnect negative battery cable. Drain oil from transmission. Place gearshift in Neutral. Remove shift lever and assembly from inside vehicle. Disconnect exhaust pipe from exhaust manifold.

2) Disconnect speedometer cable and back-up light connector. Disconnect clutch cable from transmission. Remove bellhousing cover. Place reference mark on propeller shaft flange and remove propeller shaft.

3) Remove upper transmission-to-bellhousing bolts. Support transmission on jack. Raise transmission. Remove rear mount and crossmember. Remove remaining transmission mounting bolts. Note length and location of transmission bolts. Remove transmission. Ensure input shaft clears clutch assembly.

R5M21 (Installation) – To install, reverse removal procedure. Apply high-temperature grease to pilot bushing located in end of crankshaft. Align reference marks made on propeller shaft during removal.

V5M21 & V5MT1 (Removal) – 1) Remove negative battery cable. Drain transmission and/or transfer case oil. Remove transfer case protector and skid plates or undercovers. Mark propeller shafts and remove.

> **CAUTION: When removing gearshift assembly, position transmission shift lever in Neutral, and transfer case shift lever in 2WD/High Range position.**

2) Place transfer case shift lever in 2WD/High Range position. Place transmission in Neutral. Remove gearshift assembly. Disconnect front exhaust pipe and remove mounting bracket (if equipped). Remove seal guard on rear of transmission. Disconnect speedometer cable

and electrical connectors at transmission and transfer case. Disconnect ground cable.

3) Remove clutch release cylinder (with hose connected). Remove starter and cover (if equipped). Remove transmission stays and bellhousing cover. Support transmission/transfer case and engine with a jack. Remove transfer case mounting bracket. Remove insulator bolts and crossmember. Remove insulator from transmission if necessary.

4) Remove remaining transmission-to-engine bolts. Note length and location of transmission bolts. Pull transmission assembly rearward from engine until input shaft clears clutch assembly. Carefully lower assembly from vehicle.

V5M21 & V5MT1 (Installation) – To install, reverse removal procedure. Apply high-temperature grease to pilot bushing located in end of crankshaft. Align reference marks made on propeller shaft during removal. Fill transmission and transfer case with API GL-4 SAE75w-85.

TORQUE SPECIFICATIONS

TORQUE SPECIFICATIONS

Application	Ft. Lbs. (N.m)
Clutch Housing-To-Engine Bolt [1]	
AX15	50 (68)
NV3500 & NV4500	80 (108)
Ram-50	
8 X 25-mm Bolt	15-20 (20-27)
8 X 50-mm Bolt	15-20 (20-27)
10 X 40-mm Bolt	31-40 (43-55)
10 X 60-mm Bolt	16-23 (22-32)
10 X 65-mm Bolt	31-40 (43-55)
Crossmember-To-Frame Bolts	
Ram-50	40-54 (55-75)
All Others	35 (47)
Engine-To-Clutch Housing [2]	
AX15	50 (68)
Transfer Case-To-Transmission Bolts	
Ram-50	25 (35)
All Others	40 (50)
Transmission Case-To-Clutch Housing Bolts	50 (68)
Transmission-To-Insulator	33 (45)
	INCH Lbs. (N.m)
Clutch Slave Cylinder Nuts	200 (23)
Flywheel Cover Bolt	45 (5)
Propeller Shaft Clamp Bolts	
AX15	170 (19)

[1] – Bolts thread into engine from clutch housing side.
[2] – Bolts thread into clutch housing from engine side.

Ford Motor Co. Passenger Cars

Aspire, Capri, Escort, Festiva, Mustang, Probe, Taurus, Tempo, Thunderbird, Topaz, Tracer

REMOVAL & INSTALLATION

> **WARNING: When battery is disconnected, vehicle computer and memory systems may lose memory data. Driveability problems may exist until computer systems have completed a relearn cycle. See COMPUTER RELEARN PROCEDURES article in APPLICATIONS & IDENTIFICATION before disconnecting battery.**

FWD VEHICLES

Removal & Installation (Aspire) – 1) Remove engine splash shields. Disengage right and left side drive axle shafts from transaxle and support out of the way. See appropriate FWD AXLE SHAFTS article in AXLE SHAFTS & TRANSFER CASES.

2) Disconnect electrical connectors, clutch cable and speedometer cable. Remove starter. Remove 2 top bolts from clutch housing. Install Engine Support Bar (D88L-6000-A).

3) Remove shifter control rods and stbilizer bar. Remove lower support brackets between engine and clutch housing. Remove rear engine support and crossmember.

4) Place transmission jack under transaxle, ensuring it is secure. Remove remaining clutch housing bolts. Pull transaxle away from engine and lower from vehicle.

5) Lightly coat input shaft splines with Clutch Grease (C1AZ-19590-B). Install transaxle and remove transmission jack. Install crossmember and transaxle mount bolts. To complete installation, reverse removal procedure.

Removal & Installation (Capri & Festiva) – **1)** Disconnect negative battery cable. Disconnect back-up light switch and neutral switch. On Capri turbo and Festiva, loosen clutch cable adjuster nut and disengage cable from release lever. On Capri non-turbo, remove clutch slave cylinder. On all models, remove starter. Disconnect speedometer cable from transaxle.

2) Remove top transaxle-to-engine bolts. On Capri turbo, remove air intake by-pass valve mounting nut. On all models, install Engine Support Bar (D88L-6000-A). Raise vehicle. Remove bolt and nut retaining shift rod to input shift rail. Drain transaxle fluid. Remove front wheels.

3) Remove engine splash shields. Disengage right and left side drive axle shafts from transaxle and support out of the way. On Capri turbo, remove intermediate shaft and support bearing assembly. See appropriate AXLE SHAFTS article in AXLE SHAFTS & TRANSFER CASES. On all models, remove left and right transaxle mount through bolts.

4) Remove crossmember. Place transmission jack under transaxle, ensuring it is secure. Remove remaining flywheel housing bolts. Pull transaxle away from engine and lower from vehicle.

5) Lightly coat input shaft splines with Clutch Grease (C1AZ-19590-B). Install transaxle and remove transmission jack. Install crossmember and transaxle mount bolts. To complete installation, reverse removal procedure.

Removal & Installation (Escort & Tracer) – **1)** Remove battery and battery tray. Remove air cleaner outlet tube and engine air intake resonator. Disconnect speedometer cable from transaxle. Disconnect lower clutch slave cylinder tube from hydraulic clutch hose and cap hydraulic clutch hose.

2) Disconnect transaxle ground strap. Disconnect 3 transaxle wiring connectors located above transaxle. Remove electrical connector wiring bracket. Install engine support. Remove left transaxle support bracket nuts. Loosen insulator pivot nut and rotate bracket aside.

3) Remove left transaxle support bracket bolts and support bracket. Remove 2 upper engine-to-transaxle bolts. Raise and support vehicle. Remove front wheels. Remove front fender splash shields. Drain transaxle fluid. Install transaxle drain plug.

4) Remove front wheel axle shafts. See AXLE SHAFTS article in DRIVE AXLES. Install 2 Transaxle Plugs (T88C-7025-AH) between transaxle differential side gears.

NOTE: Failure to install Transaxle Plugs (T88C-7025-AH) may allow transaxle differential side gears to become mispositioned.

5) Remove intake manifold support. Remove starter motor. Remove gearshift stabilizer bar. Remove gearshift rod and clevis bolt and nut. Remove transmission gearshift rod and clevis from transaxle.

6) Remove engine and transmission splash shields. Remove rear engine support bracket, if necessary. Remove front transaxle support insulator and bracket. Ensure transaxle jack is secured to transaxle. Remove lower engine-to-transaxle bolts. Lower transaxle from vehicle.

7) To install, reverse removal procedure. Install NEW circlips on ends of axle shafts and NEW nut and bolt when attaching lower control arm ball joint to steering knuckle.

Removal & Installation (Probe) – **1)** Remove air cleaner assembly and air cleaner intake tube. Remove battery and battery tray. Remove transaxle ground straps. Disconnect vehicle speed sensor, park/neutral position switch and back-up light switch connectors. Remove clutch release (slave) cylinder, with hydraulic lines connected and position aside.

2) Install engine support. Remove 4 upper transaxle-to-engine bolts. Remove 2 upper starter motor bolts. Remove fuel filter (with fuel lines connected) and position aside. Remove 2 nuts and through bolt from left transaxle insulator. Raise and support vehicle. On 2.0L models, remove intake manifold support bracket. On all models, disconnect starter motor "S" and "B" terminal wires and remove starter motor. Drain transaxle fluid. Remove front wheels.

3) Remove and discard axle shaft attaching nuts. Remove splash shield. Remove lower crossmember. Remove bolt and nut from left lower control arm ball joints. Pry lower control arm down to separate from steering knuckle. Pull lower edge of spindle outward to separate from end of axle shaft. Using pry bar, separate left axle shaft from

transaxle. Install 2 Transaxle Plugs (T88C-7025-AH) between transaxle differential side gears.

NOTE: Failure to install Transaxle Plugs (T88C-7025-AH) may allow transaxle differential side gears to become mispositioned.

4) Remove opposite end of left axle shaft from steering knuckle and remove from vehicle. On ABS equipped models, remove clips from left wheel speed sensor and nuts from sensor harness mount.

5) On 2.5L models, disconnect left and right oxygen sensor connectors. Remove and discard 3 exhaust inlet pipe-to-exhaust manifold nuts from exhaust inlet pipes. Lower exhaust system to gain access to right axle shaft support bearing. Remove 3 right axle shaft support bearing bolts. On ABS equipped models, remove clips from right wheel speed sensor and nuts from sensor harness mount.

6) On all models, remove bolt and nut from right lower control arm ball joints. Pry lower control arm down to separate from steering knuckle. Pull lower edge of spindle outward to separate from end of axle shaft. Using pry bar, separate right axle shaft from transaxle. Install 2 Transaxle Plugs (T88C-7025-AH) between transaxle differential side gears.

7) Remove transaxle cradle. Disconnect transaxle shift linkage and stabilizer bar from transaxle. Remove transaxle mount-to-transaxle bolts. Position transaxle jack under transaxle and secure transaxle to jack. Remove rear transaxle mount. Remove lower transaxle-to-engine bolts. Separate from engine and lower transaxle out of vehicle.

8) To install, reverse removal procedure. Install NEW circlips on ends of axle shafts and NEW nut and bolt when attaching lower control arm ball joint to steering knuckle.

Removal & Installation (Taurus, Tempo 2.3L & Topaz 2.3L) – **1)** Disconnect negative battery cable. Wedge a wood block (about 7" long) between clutch pedal and floor to hold clutch pedal up beyond normal position. Pull clutch cable forward and disconnect from clutch release lever.

2) Remove clutch cable from rib on top of transaxle case. Install lifting eyes to engine block (if required). Remove 2 upper transaxle-to-engine bolts. Remove wiring bracket. Remove air cleaner assembly. Raise and support vehicle. Remove front wheels. Remove front stabilizer bar.

3) Remove nut and bolt securing lower control arm ball joint to steering knuckle assembly. Discard nut and bolt. Using large pry bar, pry lower control arm away from knuckle. Repeat procedure on other side. On Taurus, remove stabilizer and connecting rod end from steering knuckle. Disconnect oxygen sensor and power steering cooler. Remove catalytic converter and battery cable bracket. On all models, install 2 Transaxle Plugs (T81P-1177-B), one for each seal, to prevent lubricant from draining.

CAUTION: Use care to prevent oil seal damage when removing axle shaft.

4) Using Half-Shaft Remover (D83P-4026-A), pry left axle shaft from transaxle. If axle shaft cannot be pried from transaxle, insert Differential Rotator (T81P-4026-A) and tap joint out. Swing steering knuckle and axle shaft outward from transaxle. Secure axle shaft with wire in level position to prevent damage. Repeat procedure on other side.

5) Disconnect back-up light switch connector. Remove engine ground strap. Remove starter motor. Remove shift mechanism-to-shift shaft attaching nut and bolt. Disconnect mechanism from shift shaft. Remove shift mechanism stabilizer bar from transaxle and remove control selector indicator switch arm from shaft. Remove braces from front of bellhousing and remove speedometer cable. Remove 2 oil pan-to-clutch housing bolts.

6) Secure transaxle jack under transaxle and remove bolts attaching rear support mount to floorpan brace. Loosen nut on bottom of front support mount. Remove 2 nuts at left rear transaxle mount. Remove bolts at front transaxle mount. Lower transaxle until it clears rear mount. Support engine block under oil pan. Remove engine-to-transaxle bolts. Lower transaxle from vehicle.

7) To install, reverse removal procedure. Install NEW circlips on ends of axle shafts and NEW nut and bolt when attaching lower control arm ball joint to steering knuckle.

Removal & Installation (Tempo & Topaz – 3.0L) – 1) Disconnect negative battery cable. Prop clutch pedal to keep clutch pedal from moving toward floor when clutch cable is disconnected. Disconnect MAF sensor and intake temperature sensor connectors from air cleaner. Remove air cleaner assembly.

2) Remove 2 bolts holding coil bracket assembly to left rear of cylinder head and position coil bracket aside. Install engine lifting brackets on rear of left cylinder head. Disconnect back-up light switch. Disconnect clutch cable from clutch release lever.

3) Remove starter cable bracket. Remove 2 transaxle mount-to-engine bolts. Remove power steering line bracket-to-engine nuts. Remove top 4 transaxle-to-engine bolts. Disconnect speed sensor connector. Remove speedometer cables from speed sensor. DO NOT remove clip holding cable to speed sensor. Install engine support.

CAUTION: DO NOT loosen any engine mount bolts other than those specified, or damage to engine may occur due to excessive movement.

---

4) Loosen 2 T-50 Torx bolts attaching right engine mounts to right frame rail. Ensure steering column is in unlocked position. Raise and support vehicle. Remove front wheels. Remove and discard both lower ball joint pinch bolts. Slightly spread pinch joint and separate ball joint from steering knuckle. Use punch to remove bolts, if necessary. DO NOT damage ball joint seals.

5) Remove cotter pin and retaining nuts from tie rod end. Using Half-Shaft Remover (D83P-4026-A), pry left axle shaft from transaxle. Install Transaxle Plugs (T81P-1177-B) to prevent fluid loss. Remove both half-shafts. Remove bolt attaching shift lever linkage to transaxle shift rod and position linkage aside. Remove stabilizer rod-to-transaxle bolt and position stabilizer rod aside.

6) Disconnect neutral sensing switch connector. Remove starter cable bracket. Remove starter motor. Loosen 2 front engine-to-transaxle support bracket bolts. Remove 2 rear engine-to-transaxle bracket bolts. Remove 2 bracket-to-transaxle bolts.

7) Using T-50 Torx bit, remove accessory drive belt tensioner. Install Damper Tool (T93P-6316-A). Loosen, but DO NOT remove, 2 right engine mount retaining nuts. Remove lower bolt from left front transaxle mount. Loosen through-bolt and pivot transaxle mount aside. Remove nuts from rear transaxle mount.

CAUTION: DO NOT allow weight of engine to rest on crankshaft damper. Damage to crankshaft damper and crankshaft thrust bearings may occur.

---

8) Using engine support fixture, lower engine and transaxle assembly until crankshaft damper just contacts right frame rail. Secure transaxle jack under transaxle and install safety chains. Lower transaxle and remove 2 transaxle-to-engine bolts. Remove transaxle from vehicle.

9) To install, reverse removal procedure. Install NEW circlips on ends of axle shafts and NEW nut and bolt when attaching lower control arm ball joint to steering knuckle.

RWD VEHICLES

Removal & Installation (Thunderbird) – 1) Disconnect battery ground cable. Shift transmission into Neutral and remove shift knob. Remove console top cover, both shifter retaining bolts and shifter. Raise vehicle on hoist. Drain oil from transmission and remove body reinforcement in front of rear axle.

2) Disconnect rear exhaust assembly from resonator, and remove bolts retaining drive shaft to companion flange. Position axle stand under front of rear axle housing and remove front and rear retaining nuts and bolt plate. Pull vent tube from hole in sub-frame.

3) Lower front of axle housing with axle stand and slide drive shaft out of transmission above axle housing. Let drive shaft rest on the front drive shaft support and rear axle assembly.

CAUTION: Use care when positioning drive shaft so as not to nick, burr or contaminate drive shaft yoke or companion flange.

---

4) Remove catalytic converter assembly. Disconnect hydraulic clutch line and electrical connectors. Remove starter. Position transmission jack under transmission and remove crossmember. Remove bellhousing bolts and move transmission to rear until input shaft clears flywheel. Lower transmission from vehicle.

5) Install guide studs in engine block, and raise transmission until input shaft splines are aligned with clutch disk splines. Slide transmission forward on guide studs until it is positioned in the vehicle. Remove guide studs. Install bellhousing bolts.

NOTE: Reuse aluminum washers under attaching bolts to prevent galvanic corrosion.

---

6) Install crossmember. Remove transmission jack, connect electrical connectors and hydraulic oil line. Install starter and catalytic converter assembly. Slide drive shaft into transmission.

NOTE: Lubricate yoke splines with Lubricant (C1AZ-19590-BA).

---

7) Raise rear axle housing with axle stand, and install bushings and retaining nuts. Remove axle stand and position vent tube in hole of sub-frame. Align drive shaft yoke and companion flange and install retaining bolts.

8) Connect exhaust pipe muffler assembly to resonator and lower vehicle. Position shifter and install retaining bolts. Install console top cover and install shifter knob. Connect battery ground cable.

Removal & Installation (Mustang) – 1) On 5.0L engines, lift clutch pedal to disengage pawl from quadrant (located above pedal). Unhook clutch cable from quadrant and allow pedal to slowly swing rearward.

2) On all models, disconnect negative battery cable. Raise and support vehicle. Remove cable dust shield. Disconnect clutch cable from release fork and remove cable from bellhousing (if applicable). If hydraulically controlled, remove clutch release (slave) cylinder and support to one side.

3) Disconnect and remove starter. Remove rear engine plate-to-bellhousing bolts. Index mark rear propeller shaft flange to differential. Remove propeller shaft. Install transmission rear seal plug. Remove catalytic converter. Remove transmission mount nuts.

4) Support transmission with transmission jack. Remove crossmember and transmission mount. Lower transmission enough to expose 2 bolts securing shift handle to transmission shift tower. Disconnect shift handle. Disconnect wiring harnesses from transmission. Disconnect speedometer cable.

5) Remove transmission-to-bellhousing bolts and pull transmission rearward until input shaft clears bellhousing. Lower and remove transmission assembly. To install, reverse removal procedure.

TORQUE SPECIFICATIONS
TORQUE SPECIFICATIONS

Application	Ft. Lbs. (N.m)
Aspire	
Clutch Housing-To-Engine Bolts	14-19 (19-26)
Front Transaxle Mount Bolts	32-38 (43-52)
Rear Transaxle Support Bolts	14-19 (19-26)
Stabilizer Bolt	28-38 (38-52)
Transaxle-To-Engine Bolts	27-38 (37-52)
Capri & Festiva	
Crossmember Bolts (Capri)	
Large	47-66 (64-89)
Small	21-34 (28-46)
Engine Mount Stud Nut	50-70 (68-95)
Lower Ball Joint Pinch Bolt	32-40 (43-54)
Rear Mount-To-Transmission Bolt	50-70 (68-95)
Rear Transmission Mount-To-Body Bolt	25-35 (34-48)
Starter Motor-To-Mount Bolt	15-20 (20-27)
Wheel Lug Nut	65-87 (88-118)
Escort & Tracer	
Flywheel Bolts	
1.8L Engine	71-76 (96-103)
1.9L Engine	54-67 (73-91)
Pressure Plate Bolts	13-20 (18-27)
Transaxle-To-Engine Bolts	
Lower	27-38 (37-52)
Upper	47-66 (64-89)

TORQUE SPECIFICATIONS (Cont.)

Application	Ft. Lbs. (N.m)
Mustang	
Bellhousing Bolts	38-55 (52-75)
Probe	
Flywheel Bolts	
2.0L Engine	71-75 (97-102)
2.5L Engine	45-49 (61-67)
Pressure Plate Bolts	13-18 (18-26)
Transaxle Mount	
Left Nuts	32-44 (43-60)
Left Through Bolt	63-86 (85-117)
Rear Bolts	50-68 (68-92)
Taurus	
Bellhousing Bolts	34-46 (46-62)
Flywheel Bolts	51-58 (69-79)
Pressure Plate Bolts	24 (33)
Release Fork Bolt	30-40 (41-54)

TORQUE SPECIFICATIONS (Cont.)

Application	Ft. Lbs. (N.m)
Tempo & Topaz	
Bellhousing Bolts	
2.3L Engine	25-35 (34-47)
3.0L Engine	34-46 (46-62)
Flywheel Bolts	54-64 (73-87)
Pressure Plate Bolts	24 (33)
Release Fork Bolt	30-40 (41-54)
Transaxle Mounting Stud	38-41 (52-56)
Transaxle-To-Engine Bolts	34-46 (46-63)
Thunderbird	
Axle Housing Bolts	68-100 (92-136)
Bellhousing-To-Engine Bolt	28-38 (38-51)
Crossmember Bolts	35-50 (47-68)
Drive Shaft Companion Flange Bolts	79-95 (107-129)
Shifter Attaching Bolts	18-24 (24-33)

Ford Motor Co. Light Trucks & Vans

Aerostar, Bronco, Explorer, "F" Series, Ranger

REMOVAL & INSTALLATION

AEROSTAR, EXPLORER & RANGER (M50D 5-SPEED)

WARNING: When battery is disconnected, vehicle computer and memory systems may lose memory data. Driveability problems may exist until computer systems have completed a relearn cycle. See COMPUTER RELEARN PROCEDURES article in APPLICATIONS & IDENTIFICATION before disconnecting battery.

Removal – 1) Disconnect negative battery cable from battery. Shift transmission into Neutral.

2) Remove shift lever, ball and boot assembly. Raise vehicle on hoist. Scribe a mark on drive shaft and rear axle flange for installation reference.

3) Disconnect drive shaft at rear drive axle flange. Remove drive shaft. Cap transmission extension housing to prevent lubricant spillage. Disconnect starter cable and wires. Remove starter.

4) Disconnect clutch slave cylinder hydraulic line by pressing White retainer bushing with Disconnect Tool (T88T-70522-A) while pulling on line. Cap end of line to prevent fluid leakage.

5) Disconnect back-up light switch from sender on transmission. Remove speedometer cable from extension housing or transfer case (if equipped). Position jack under engine, protecting oil pan with wood block.

6) On 4WD models, remove transfer case. Remove transmission mount/damper-to-crossmember nuts/bolts. On all models, position transmission jack under transmission.

7) Place jack safety chain around transmission. Slightly raise transmission. Remove nuts and bolts retaining crossmember to frame. Remove crossmember.

8) Remove bellhousing-to-engine bolts. Slide transmission rearward to separate bellhousing from dowel pins on rear of engine block. Lower transmission from vehicle.

Installation – 1) Ensure mating surfaces and locating dowels are clean and free of burrs. Ensure transmission input shaft splines are clean. Place transmission on transmission jack and position under vehicle.

2) Raise transmission into position and start input shaft into clutch disc. Align splines on input shaft with splines on clutch disc. Move transmission forward until bellhousing seats on locating dowels.

3) Install bellhousing-to-engine block bolts. Tighten bolts to specification. See TORQUE SPECIFICATIONS. To complete installation, reverse removal procedure.

BRONCO & "F" SERIES (M50D 5-SPEED)

Removal (2WD) – 1) Shift transmission into Neutral. Remove shift lever retainer bolt and shift lever. Raise vehicle on hoist. Disconnect speedometer cable. Disconnect back-up light switch. Drain gear oil. Position transmission jack under transmission.

2) Disconnect drive shaft from extension housing and wire to one side. On models with 7.3L engine, disconnect clutch slave cylinder hydraulic line. On all others, remove clutch slave cylinder hydraulic line by pressing White retainer bushing with Disconnect Tool (T88T-70522-A) while pulling on line.

3) Remove transmission rear mount and lower retainer. Remove skid plate (if equipped). Remove catalytic converter heat shield. Remove 2 upper gusset-to-frame nuts from both sides. Remove transmission-to-support plate bolts on crossmember. Raise transmission with transmission jack.

4) Remove nut and bolt connecting support plate to crossmember. Remove support plate. Remove right gusset. Remove nuts and bolts holding crossmember to frame. Remove crossmember.

5) Remove transmission-to-engine block bolts. Move transmission rearward until input shaft clears flywheel. Lower transmission from vehicle.

Installation – 1) Ensure transmission input shaft splines are clean and free of rust. Place transmission on transmission jack. Install guide studs in engine block. Raise transmission until input shaft splines are aligned with clutch disc splines.

2) Slide transmission forward into position on guide studs. Remove guide studs and install bell housing-to-engine bolts. Tighten to specification. See TORQUE SPECIFICATIONS. To complete installation, reverse removal procedure.

Removal (4WD) – 1) Shift transmission into Neutral. Remove shift lever retainer bolt and shift lever.

2) Raise vehicle on hoist. Drain gear oil from transmission and transfer case. Disconnect front and rear drive shafts from transfer case.

3) Remove clutch slave cylinder hydraulic line by pressing White retainer bushing with Disconnect Tool (T88T-70522-A) while pulling on line. Disconnect back-up light switch. Disconnect speedometer cable from transfer case.

4) Remove skid plate (if equipped). Position transmission jack under transfer case. Remove transfer case-to-transmission bolts. Lower transfer case. Ensure transfer case shift lever clears opening in floor pan. Remove transmission rear mount and lower retainer.

5) Remove catalytic converter heat shield. Remove 2 upper gusset-to-frame nuts from both sides. Remove transmission-to-support plate bolts on crossmember. Raise transmission with transmission jack. Remove nut and bolt connecting support plate to crossmember.

MANUAL TRANSMISSION REMOVAL
Ford Motor Co. Light Trucks & Vans (Cont.)

2-59

6) Remove support plate. Remove right gusset. Remove crossmember-to-frame nuts and bolts. Remove crossmember. Remove bellhousing-to-engine block bolts. Move transmission rearward until input shaft clears flywheel. Lower transmission from vehicle.

Installation – 1) Ensure transmission input shaft splines are clean and free of rust. Place transmission on transmission jack. Install guide studs in engine block. Raise transmission until input shaft splines are aligned with clutch disc splines.

2) Slide transmission forward into position on guide studs. Remove guide studs and install bell housing-to-engine bolts. Tighten to specification. See TORQUE SPECIFICATIONS. To complete installation, reverse removal procedure.

BRONCO & "F" SERIES (ZF S5-42 5-SPEED)

Removal & Installation (2WD) – 1) Shift transmission into Neutral. Remove upper shift lever from lower shift lever.

2) Raise vehicle on hoist and position safety stands under vehicle. Disconnect speedometer cable. Disconnect back-up light switch. Drain oil. Position transmission jack under transmission.

3) Disconnect drive shaft and clutch linkage from transmission, and wire aside. On "F" Series Super Duty vehicles, remove transmission parking brake from transmission. Remove transmission rear insulator and lower retainer.

4) On all models, remove crossmember. Remove bolts that retain transmission to engine block. Move transmission to rear until input shaft clears clutch disc. Lower transmission from vehicle. To install transmission, reverse removal procedure.

Removal & Installation (4WD) – 1) Shift transmission into Neutral. Remove upper shift lever from lower shift lever. Raise vehicle on hoist. Drain transmission and transfer case.

2) Disconnect rear drive shaft from transfer case, and wire aside. Disconnect front drive shaft from transfer case, and wire aside. Disconnect back-up light switch. Remove speedometer cable from transfer case. Remove skid pan from beneath transfer case (if equipped).

3) Position transmission jack under transfer case. Remove 6 bolts holding transfer case to transmission and lower transfer case from vehicle. Ensure transfer case shift lever clears opening in floor pan.

4) Support transmission with transmission jack and secure with safety chain. Remove transmission rear insulator and lower retainer. Remove crossmember. Remove transmission-to-engine block bolts. Move transmission to rear until input shaft clears clutch disc and lower transmission from vehicle. To install transmission, reverse removal procedure.

BRONCO & "F" SERIES (T18 4-SPEED)

Removal & Installation (2WD) – 1) Remove upper gearshift lever, shift ball boot and vapor seal as an assembly. Remove inner isolator pad. Raise vehicle and position safety stands. Position transmission jack under transmission and disconnect speedometer cable (if equipped).

2) Disconnect back-up light switch located at rear of gear shift housing cover. Disconnect drive shaft and clutch linkage from transmission and wire aside.

3) Disconnect transmission mount and remove transmission crossmember. Remove transmission attaching bolts. Move transmission rearward until input shaft clears clutch housing and lower transmission. To install transmission, reverse removal procedures.

Removal & Installation (4WD) – 1) Remove 4 screws holding floor mat. Remove 2 bolts holding upper shift lever. Remove transmission shift lever, shift ball, boot and vapor seal as an assembly. Raise vehicle and position safety stands. Remove drain plug and drain transmission. Disconnect front and rear drive shafts, and wire aside.

2) Remove shift link and speedometer cable from transfer case. Remove transfer case drain plug and drain transfer case. Position transmission jack under transfer case, remove 6 bolts holding transfer case to transmission and lower transfer case from vehicle. Remove 8 bolts holding rear support bracket to transmission. Position transmission jack under transmission and remove rear support bracket.

3) Remove 4 bolts holding transmission to bellhousing. Remove transmission from vehicle. To install transmission and transfer case, reverse removal procedure. Ensure drain plugs are replaced and fluids are added.

TORQUE SPECIFICATIONS

TORQUE SPECIFICATIONS

Application	Ft. Lbs. (N.m)
Aerostar, Explorer & Ranger	
Bellhousing-To-Engine Bolt	28-38 (38-52)
Drive Shaft U-Bolt	10-15 (14-21)
Starter Bolt	15-20 (21-27)
Transfer Case-To-Extension Housing	
Aerostar (Spicer TC-28) [1]	23-35 (31-47)
Explorer & Ranger (Borg-Warner 1354)	25-35 (34-47)
Transmission Mount-To-Crossmember Nut	60-80 (81-109)
Transmission-To-Bellhousing Bolt	30-40 (41-54)
Crossmember-To-Right Frame Nut	110-140 (149-190)
Crossmember-To-Left Frame Nut	
Except Ranger 2.3L 4WD	110-140 (149-190)
Ranger 2.3L 4WD	75-95 (102-129)
Bronco, Pickup & Van	
Bellhousing-To-Engine Bolt	40-50 (54-68)
Front Drive Shaft-To-Front Output Yoke Nut	10-15 (14-21)
Starter Bolt	15-20 (21-27)
Transfer Case-To-Extension Housing	
Bronco & Pickup (Borg-Warner 1356)	25-43 (34-58)
F150/250 4WD (Borg-Warner 1345)	25-43 (34-58)
Transmission Mount-To-Crossmember Nut	60-80 (81-109)

General Motors Passenger Cars

Achieva, Beretta, Camaro, Cavalier, Corsica, Corvette, Cutlass Calais, Cutlass Supreme, Firebird, Grand Am, Grand Prix, LeMans, Lumina, Metro, Prizm, Saturn, Storm, Sunbird

REMOVAL & INSTALLATION

WARNING: When battery is disconnected, vehicle computer and memory systems may lose memory data. Driveability problems may exist until computer systems have completed a relearn cycle. See COMPUTER RELEARN PROCEDURES article in APPLICATIONS & IDENTIFICATION before disconnecting battery.

FWD VEHICLES

WARNING: On models equipped with air bags, read and carefully follow all WARNINGS and SERVICE PRECAUTIONS to avoid injury from accidental air bag deployment.

NOTE: For information on air bag DIAGNOSIS & TESTING or DISPOSAL PROCEDURES, see MITCHELL® AIR BAG SERVICE & REPAIR MANUAL, DOMESTIC & IMPORTED MODELS.

Removal (Achieva & Grand Am – NVT550 Transaxle) – 1) Disconnect negative battery cable. Install Engine Support Fixture (J-28467-A), Support Fixture Adapters (J-28467-90) and Support Adapter Leg (J-36462). Remove air cleaner assembly. Remove left instrument panel sound insulator. Remove actuator cylinder push rod from clutch pedal.

2) Disconnect clutch actuator cylinder and set aside. Remove power steering pump and brackets and set aside. Disconnect shift cables and levers from transaxle. Disconnect vehicle speed sensor electrical connector. Disconnect vacuum lines.

3) Remove shift cable bracket. Remove upper transaxle-to-engine bolts. Remove upper transaxle mount and through bolt. Raise and support vehicle. Remove left front tire. Remove left drive axle nut and left ball joint nut.

CAUTION: Modify Drive Axle Boot Protector (J-34754) and install on drive axle prior to any service procedures on or near drive axle. Failure to do so may result in boot damage and possible joint failure.

---

4) Remove left drive axle. Remove left stabilizer link nut. Drain transaxle. Remove left inner splash shield. Remove transaxle strut and strut bracket. Remove left suspension support attaching bolts and support. Remove heater hose bolt. Remove clutch housing cover. Remove lower transaxle mount and through bolt.

5) Disconnect back-up light switch electrical connector. Lower vehicle. Lower engine and transaxle assembly. Raise vehicle. Support transaxle case with transmission jack. Remove remaining transaxle-to-engine mounting bolts. Disconnect ground connections. Remove transaxle by carefully sliding away from engine and guiding intermediate shaft out of transaxle.

Removal (Beretta, Cavalier, Corsica, Cutlass Calais & Sunbird – NVT550 Transaxle) – **1)** Disconnect negative battery cable. Install Engine Support Fixture (J-28467-A), Support Fixture Adapters (J-28467-90) and Support Adapter Leg (J-36462). Remove air cleaner assembly. Remove left instrument panel sound insulator. Remove actuator cylinder push rod from clutch pedal.

2) Disconnect clutch actuator cylinder and set aside. Remove exhaust crossover pipe mounting nuts and remove exhaust crossover pipe. Disconnect shift cables and levers from transaxle. Remove upper transaxle-to-engine bolts. Remove upper transaxle mount and bracket.

3) Discharge air conditioning system (if equipped). Raise and support vehicle. Remove front tires. Remove right and left drive axle nuts and ball joint nuts.

CAUTION: Modify Drive Axle Boot Protector (J-34754) and install on drive axle prior to any service procedures on or near drive axle. Failure to do so may result in boot damage and possible joint failure.

---

4) Remove right and left drive axles. Remove right and left stabilizer link nuts. Remove stabilizer bar from right control arm. Using Ball Joint Separator (J-38892), separate right ball joint from steering knuckle. Remove rear engine mount through bolt. Remove intermediate shaft support bracket bolts. Separate intermediate shaft from transaxle and remove intermediate shaft.

5) Remove transaxle strut bracket. Remove left "U" bolt from stabilizer bar. Drain transaxle. Remove left inner splash shield. Remove left suspension support attaching bolts and support. Remove evaporator-to-accumulator line. Remove clutch housing cover. Remove shift linkage bracket. Disconnect vacuum lines.

6) Disconnect vehicle speed sensor electrical connector. Disconnect back-up light switch electrical connector. Lower vehicle. Lower engine and transaxle assembly. Raise vehicle. Support transaxle case with transmission jack. Remove remaining transaxle-to-engine mounting bolts. Disconnect ground connections. Remove transaxle by carefully sliding away from engine and guiding intermediate shaft out of transaxle.

Installation (NVT550 Transaxle) – **1)** Lubricate inner diameter of release bearing with grease.

CAUTION: Ensure clutch lever does not move toward flywheel until transaxle is mounted to engine, or damage to transaxle will occur.

---

2) To install, reverse removal procedure. Evacuate and charge A/C system (if discharged). Tighten all bolts and nuts to specification. See TORQUE SPECIFICATIONS.

Removal (Achieva, Beretta, Cavalier, Corsica, Cutlass Calais, Grand Am & Sunbird – Isuzu Transaxle) – **1)** Disconnect negative battery cable. Install Engine Support Fixture (J-28467-A), Support Fixture Adapters (J-28467-90) and Support Adapter Leg (J-36462). Remove left instrument panel sound insulator. Remove actuator cylinder push rod from clutch pedal.

2) Disconnect clutch actuator cylinder and set aside. Disconnect electrical connector at mount bracket. Remove upper transaxle mount and through bolt. Disconnect shift cables and retaining clamp from transaxle. Disconnect ground connections. Disconnect back-up light switch electrical connector.

3) Raise and support vehicle. Drain transaxle. Remove front tires. Remove left inner splash shield. Remove clutch housing cover. Disconnect vehicle speed sensor electrical connector.

CAUTION: Modify Drive Axle Boot Protector (J-34754) and install on drive axle prior to service procedures on or near drive axle. Failure to do so may result in boot damage and possible joint failure.

---

4) Remove right and left drive axle nuts and ball joint nuts. Remove drive axles. Remove right and left stabilizer link nuts. Remove left "U" bolt from stabilizer bar. Remove left suspension support attaching bolts and remove support. Remove lower transaxle mount and through bolt.

5) Lower vehicle. Lower engine and transaxle assembly. Raise vehicle. Support transaxle case with transmission jack. Remove transaxle-to-engine mounting bolts. Remove transaxle by carefully sliding away from engine and guiding intermediate shaft out of transaxle.

Installation (Isuzu Transaxle) – **1)** Pack inside diameter (I.D.) recess of release bearing with grease. Ensure bearing pads are located on fork ends and spring ends are in fork holes with spring completely seated in bearing groove.

CAUTION: Ensure clutch lever does not move toward flywheel until transaxle is mounted to engine, or damage to transaxle will occur.

---

2) To complete installation, reverse removal procedure. Evacuate and charge A/C system (if discharged). Tighten all bolts and nuts to specification. See TORQUE SPECIFICATIONS.

Removal & Installation (Cutlass Supreme, Grand Prix & Lumina) – **1)** Disconnect negative battery cable. Install Engine Support Fixture (J-28467-A), Support Fixture Adapters (J-28467-90) and Support Adapter Leg (J-36462). Remove air cleaner assembly. Remove sound insulator. Remove actuator cylinder push rod from clutch pedal. Remove exhaust crossover pipe mounting nuts and remove exhaust crossover pipe.

2) Remove shift cable-to-transaxle nut and retaining clamp. Using Hydraulic Line Separator (J-36221), disconnect clutch hydraulic line at quick connect fitting. Remove canister bracket mounting bolts. Remove actuator cylinder retaining nuts. Remove canister and actuator cylinder from transaxle.

3) Drain transaxle fluid. Remove transaxle vent hose. Remove upper transaxle-to-engine bolts. Raise and support vehicle. Remove front wheels. Disconnect back-up light switch electrical connector. Disconnect vehicle speed sensor electrical connector.

4) Remove power steering gear heat shield. Remove power steering cooler line screws and brackets. Remove intermediate shaft lower pinch bolt at steering gear. Remove intermediate shaft. Disconnect electrical connectors.

5) Using Tie Rod Puller/Ball Joint Remover (J-35917), separate tie rod ends from steering knuckles. Remove power steering gear mounting bolts and remove power steering gear. Remove right and left ball joints at steering knuckle.

6) Remove transaxle mount retaining bolts. Remove engine mount retaining nuts. Remove frame retaining bolts. Remove crossmember from body frame. Remove clutch housing cover screws and cover. Remove right and left drive axles from transaxle, and wire aside.

7) Remove left engine splash shield. Remove rear engine mount bracket brace bolts (if equipped). Lower vehicle. Lower engine. Raise vehicle. Support transaxle with transmission jack. Remove transaxle mounting studs. Remove transaxle assembly.

8) To install, reverse removal procedure. Tighten all bolts and nuts to specification. See TORQUE SPECIFICATIONS.

Removal & Installation (LeMans) – 1) Disconnect negative battery cable. Remove air cleaner. Disconnect clutch cable at release lever. Install Engine Support Fixture (J-28467-A), Support Fixture Adapters (J-28467-90) and Support Adapter Leg (J-36462).

2) Raise and support vehicle. Remove both front wheels and splash shields. Separate left and right ball joints from steering knuckles. Remove transaxle cover.

3) Using Axle Remover (J-36639) and Driver Handle (J-7079-2), remove axle shafts. Mark installation position of transaxle drive axle in gear cluster with paint.

4) Support transaxle with suitable transmission jack. Remove engine mounting and transaxle-to-engine bolts. Slide transaxle away from engine and lower transaxle from vehicle. To install, reverse removal procedure.

CAUTION: Support transaxle while out of vehicle in upright position ONLY.

Removal & Installation (Metro) – 1) Disconnect negative battery cable at battery and transaxle. Disconnect clutch cable from release lever. Disconnect wiring harness clamps and connectors.

2) Disconnect speedometer cable. Remove upper transaxle-to-engine bolts. Remove starter motor and starter motor retaining plate. Disconnect vacuum hoses.

3) Install engine support to prevent engine from lowering. Raise and support vehicle. Drain transaxle fluid. Disconnect gearshift control shaft bolt and nut. Disconnect control shaft from gearshift shaft.

4) Remove extension rod bolts and nuts with washers. Remove exhaust pipe front and rear flange nuts and bolts. Remove clutch housing lower plate. Remove left front wheel.

5) Disconnect left tie rod. Disconnect left ball joint by removing ball joint stud bolt. Disconnect drive axles from transaxle. Remove transaxle-to-engine nuts and bolts.

6) Support transaxle with jack. Remove rear engine mounting nuts. Remove nuts and bolts securing left transaxle mounting bracket. Remove left transaxle mounting bracket.

7) Lower engine and transaxle enough to remove rear engine mounting through bolt. Pull transaxle straight out toward left side and disconnect input shaft from clutch cover. Lower transaxle assembly.

8) To install, reverse removal procedure. Tighten all nuts and bolts to specification. See TORQUE SPECIFICATIONS. Fill transaxle with 75W GL-5 fluid.

Removal & Installation (Prizm) – 1) Install Engine Support Fixture (J-28467-A) to prevent engine from lowering. Remove battery, battery tray and air cleaner assembly. Disconnect back-up light switch electrical connector. Disconnect ground strap. Remove clutch slave cylinder. Disconnect shift control cables.

2) Remove left transaxle mount cover, brace and mount through bolt. Remove upper transaxle-to-engine bolts. Remove upper starter bolt. Disconnect speedometer cable. Raise and support vehicle.

3) Remove splash shields. Drain transaxle fluid. Disconnect starter electrical connections. Remove bottom starter bolt and remove starter. Disconnect drive axles from transaxle.

4) Remove front and center transaxle mount through bolt shields. Remove center crossmember-to-main crossmember bolts. Disconnect exhaust hanger from transaxle.

WARNING: Hold center crossmember when lowering main crossmember to prevent center crossmember from falling and causing injury.

---

5) Support main crossmember. Remove main crossmember-to-body bolts. Slowly lower main crossmember while holding center crossmember. Remove center crossmember. Remove lower control arm bracket-to-body bolts.

6) Remove front mount and bracket from transaxle. Remove center mount from transaxle. Remove flywheel inspection cover. Remove lower transaxle bracket-to-mount bolts. Lower vehicle.

7) Remove remaining transaxle bracket-to-mount bolts. Lower Engine Support Fixture (J-28467-A) to gain clearance for transaxle removal. Remove transaxle mount. Raise and support vehicle. Support transaxle. Remove front and rear lower transaxle-to-engine bolts. Remove transaxle.

8) Apply grease to release fork contact surfaces, release bearing and hub, and clutch disc splines. Use 75W-90 GL-5 gear lubricant. To complete installation, reverse removal procedure.

CAUTION: Disconnect clutch master cylinder push rod from clutch pedal before any service requiring actuator cylinder removal. If clutch pedal is depressed with actuator cylinder removed, permanent damage to actuator cylinder will result.

Removal & Installation (Saturn) – 1) Disable air bag system. See appropriate article in MITCHELL® AIR BAG SERVICE & REPAIR MANUAL, DOMESTIC & IMPORTED MODELS. Raise and support vehicle. Disconnect negative battery cable. On SOHC models, disconnect air temperature sensor and remove inlet air duct.

2) On DOHC models, remove cross-car air duct. Loosen clamp securing flex tube to air box. Remove air box. Disconnect battery terminals. Remove battery shield and battery. Remove bolt and nut securing transaxle strut to cradle bracket at front of transaxle. Loosen bolt at other end of strut and flip strut up out of way.

3) On all models, disconnect back-up light switch and vehicle speed sensor. Remove vent tube retaining clip. Disconnect 2 ground terminals from top 2 clutch housing bolts. Disengage O_2S wire from clutch housing.

4) Remove 2 upper bolts securing clutch housing to engine. Disconnect spark plug wires from coil towers. Disconnect electrical connectors at electronic ignition module. Remove and discard bolts securing electronic ignition module.

5) Carefully disconnect shift cables from shift arms and clutch housing. DO NOT damage boot. Ensure fluid level in clutch fluid reservoir is .35-.47" (9-12 mm) from top of reservoir (unless hydraulic system is being replaced). While pushing clutch actuator cylinder into clutch housing, rotate clutch actuator cylinder 1/4 turn counterclockwise. Remove clutch actuator cylinder from housing.

6) Remove 2 nuts securing clutch hydraulic damper to clutch housing. Wire actuator cylinder and damper to battery tray. DO NOT allow cylinder to hang free while removing transaxle. Wire radiator to upper radiator support to hold radiator in place when cradle is removed.

7) Install Engine Support Bar Assembly (SA9105E). Raise and support vehicle. Drain transaxle. Remove front wheels and inner splash shields. Remove braces securing lower fascia to cradle (if equipped). Remove front engine splash shield.

8) Near pulley end of engine, remove fasteners securing engine strut cradle bracket to cradle. Remove nut securing transaxle mount to cradle.

9) Remove front exhaust pipe. Support steering gear with safety wire. Remove fasteners securing steering gear to cradle. Near steering gear, remove push-pin securing brake tube to center of cradle. Remove bolts and bracket securing engine to transaxle, near right drive shaft output. Remove clutch housing dust cover.

CAUTION: On models with ABS, speed sensor ring on outer CV joint may be damaged if incorrect tool or procedure is used to separate lower ball joints. DO NOT use wedge-type ball joint separator, as seal may be damaged.

---

10) Separate lower ball joint from both steering knuckles. Carefully separate left axle shaft from transaxle, but do not pull out. Install Axle Seal Protector (SA91112T).

11) Place 2 pieces of 4 X 4 X 36" lumber on power train support dolly. Position dolly under cradle and power train assembly. Remove 4 bolts securing cradle to body. Partially lower cradle and power train assembly from vehicle.

NOTE: *There are 2 large spacing washers between cradle and body at 2 rear cradle attachments. Hold washers to cradle with wire or tape.*

12) Support transaxle with jack. Remove 2 lower bolts securing transaxle to engine. Separate transaxle from engine and lower transaxle. To install, reverse removal procedures. Use new bolts for DIS coil pack.

Removal & Installation (Storm) – **1)** Install Engine Support Fixture (J-28467-A) to prevent engine from lowering. Remove battery, battery tray and air cleaner assembly. Disconnect electrical connectors.

2) Disconnect engine ground cable. Disconnect ignition coil ground cable at engine. Disconnect ignition coil electrical connectors. Remove ignition coil assembly. Disconnect engine wiring harness clamp.

3) Disconnect speedometer cable, clutch cable and gearshift cables. Raise and support vehicle. Remove front tires. Remove splash shields. Disconnect ball joint from steering knuckle.

4) Disconnect drive axles from transaxle. Remove front exhaust pipe. Remove torque rod and bracket. Disconnect left transaxle mount.

5) Remove front transaxle mount through bolt. Remove center crossmember with rear transaxle mount. Remove engine stabilizer (stiffener). Remove flywheel dust cover from clutch housing. Support transaxle. Remove transaxle-to-engine bolts. Remove transaxle.

6) Apply grease to release fork contact surfaces, release bearing and hub, and clutch disc splines. Use 75W GL-5 Fluid (12345349). To complete installation, reverse removal procedure.

RWD VEHICLES

Removal & Installation (Camaro & Firebird) – **1)** Disconnect negative battery cable. Raise and support vehicle. Drain transmission. Mark position of propeller shaft to rear axle pinion yoke for installation reference. Remove propeller shaft retaining strap bolts and remove straps. Remove propeller shaft from transmission.

2) Support left side of rear axle with jack. Remove torque arm rear attaching bolts. Remove torque arm front outer bracket and torque arm. Disconnect vehicle speed sensor electrical connector. Disconnect back-up light switch electrical connector. Remove catalytic converter hanger. Support engine with transmission jack.

3) Remove transmission mount nuts at support. Remove support bolts and remove support. Lower transmission enough to access shift control assembly. Remove shift control assembly bolts and remove shift control assembly. Remove transmission-to-clutch housing bolts and remove transmission.

4) To install, reverse removal procedure. Tighten all bolts and nuts to specification. See TORQUE SPECIFICATIONS.

Removal & Installation (Corvette) – **1)** Disconnect negative battery cable. Remove 2 center air outlet-to-instrument panel attaching screws. Remove center air outlet. Pry up and remove shifter lever button. Remove set screw and shifter knob. Remove rear trim plate screws and screws under cup holder. Disconnect electrical connectors. Remove center console trim plate. Remove accessory trim plate screws and trim plate.

2) Raise and support vehicle. Mark position of parking brake cable through underbody braces (convertible) for installation reference. Remove underbody brace nuts and bolts and remove underbody braces (convertible). Remove front exhaust pipe flange-to-left catalytic converter rear flange bolts. Loosen clamp at right catalytic converter exhaust pipe connection.

3) Support exhaust system. Remove resonator assembly-to-front spring hanger assembly bolts. Remove resonator assembly-to-rear spring hanger assembly bolts. Remove muffler hanger nuts. Remove

exhaust system from vehicle. Remove front exhaust pipe hanger bracket from transmission.

4) Support transmission with transmission jack. Remove driveline support beam nuts, bolts and washers. Position driveline support out of way. Mark propeller shaft-to-pinion yoke for installation reference. Remove propeller shaft retainers. Disconnect rear universal joint. Tape bearing cups to trunnion to prevent loss of roller bearings. Slide slip yoke from transmission and remove propeller shaft.

5) Disconnect all electrical connections at transmission. Support engine and lower transmission. Remove transmission-to-clutch housing bolts. Remove transmission.

6) To install, reverse removal procedure. Tighten all bolts and nuts to specification. See TORQUE SPECIFICATIONS.

TORQUE SPECIFICATIONS
TORQUE SPECIFICATIONS

Application	Ft. Lbs. (N.m)
Actuator Cylinder & Heat Shield Bolts	
Camaro & Firebird	15 (20)
Actuator Cylinder Nuts	
Achieva, Beretta, Cavalier,	
Corsica, Grand Am & Sunbird	16 (22)
Corvette	19 (26)
Cutlass Supreme, Grand Prix & Lumina	18 (24)
Ball Stud	
Corvette	33 (45)
Ball Stud Locking Screw	
Corvette	20 (27)
Cutlass Supreme, Grand Prix & Lumina	28 (38)
LeMans	47 (65)
Clutch Housing-To-Engine Bolts	
Camaro & Firebird	
3.1L & 3.4L Engine	70 (95)
5.0L & 5.7L Engine	35 (47)
Corvette	37 (50)
Hydraulic Hose Fitting	
Corvette	13 (18)
Master Cylinder Nuts	
Achieva, Beretta, Cavalier,	
Corsica, Grand Am & Sunbird	16 (22)
Corvette	12 (16)
Transmission-To-Clutch Housing Bolts	
Camaro & Firebird	55 (75)
Corvette	37 (50)
Transaxle-To-Engine Bolts	
Achieva, Beretta, Cavalier, Corsica,	
Grand Am & Sunbird	
NVT550 Transaxle	71 (96)
Isuzu Transaxle	55 (75)
Cutlass Supreme, Grand Prix & Lumina	55 (75)
LeMans	55 (75)
Transaxle-To-Engine Nuts	
Achieva, Beretta, Cavalier, Corsica,	
Grand Am & Sunbird	41 (56)

	INCH Lbs. (N.m)
Anti-Rotation Screw	
Cutlass Supreme, Grand Prix & Lumina	18 (2)
Clutch Cover-To-Clutch Housing Bolts	
Camaro & Firebird	53 (6)
Corvette	80 (9)
Achieva, Beretta, Cavalier, Corsica, Cutlass Supreme,	
Grand Am, Grand Prix, Lumina & Sunbird	115 (13)
Clutch Fluid Reservoir Screws	
Camaro & Firebird	53 (6)
Master Cylinder Bolt	
Cutlass Supreme, Grand Prix & Lumina	18 (2)
Master Cylinder Nuts	
Camaro & Firebird	115 (13)
Transaxle-To-Engine Studs	
Achieva, Beretta, Cavalier, Corsica,	
Grand Am & Sunbird	106 (12)

Astro, Bravada, Commercial Van, Jimmy, Safari, Sierra, Sonoma, Suburban, Syclone, Typhoon, Van, Yukon, "C" & "K" Series (Blazer & Pickup), "J" (Tracker), "S" & "T" Series (Blazer & Pickup)

REMOVAL & INSTALLATION

WARNING: When battery is disconnected, vehicle computer and memory systems may lose memory data. Driveability problems may exist until computer systems have completed a relearn cycle. See COMPUTER RELEARN PROCEDURES article in APPLICATIONS & IDENTIFICATION before disconnecting battery.

ALL MODELS EXCEPT "J", "S" & "T" SERIES

Removal – 1) On "C" and "K" models, remove shift lever boot retainer bolts. Slide boot assembly upward on shift lever and remove lever. To remove shift lever, push down on collar and turn counterclockwise.

2) On all models, raise and support vehicle under frame. Drain fluid from transmission and transfer case, if equipped. Disconnect speedometer sensor, if equipped.

3) Remove shift controls from transmission (if not previously removed). Remove parking brake lever controls and electrical harness connectors from transmission as needed. Disconnect propeller shaft at transmission.

4) Remove transfer case (if equipped). Disconnect exhaust pipes from exhaust manifolds as needed. Remove clutch slave cylinder and lay aside. Remove any parts for clearance as needed. Remove frame crossmember and flywheel inspection plate.

5) On 4-speed transmission model, remove top 2 transmission-to-clutch housing bolts and install guide pins. Guide pins will support transmission and prevent damage to clutch disc.

6) On all models, remove all transmission-to-clutch housing attaching bolts. Slide transmission rearward until input shaft is clear of clutch hub. Remove assembly from vehicle and remove guide pins (if equipped).

NOTE: Support clutch release bearing and support assembly when removing transmission main drive gear from flywheel housing. This will prevent release bearing from falling out of flywheel housing.

Installation – 1) Ensure plugs located in rear of bellhousing below transmission mounting bolt holes are tight and not damaged. Note location before removal. Install new plugs if plugs are damaged.

2) Apply a light coat of high-temperature grease to main drive gear splines. Place transmission in high gear. To complete installation, reverse removal procedure. Tighten bolts to specification. See TORQUE SPECIFICATIONS.

"J" BODY (TRACKER)

Removal & Installation – 1) Disconnect negative battery cable. Disconnect gearshift and transfer case levers. Raise and support vehicle. Drain transfer case and transmission fluid.

2) Remove front and rear drive shafts. Remove transfer case skid plate. Disconnect speedometer cable. Disconnect catalytic converter-to-frame bracket bolts. Support transmission.

3) Remove transmission crossmember. Disconnect breather hose and all electrical connectors. Disconnect clutch cable. Remove starter. Remove flywheel inspection cover. Remove transmission-to-engine nuts and bolts. Lower transmission/transfer case assembly.

4) To install, reverse removal procedure. Tighten all nuts and bolts to specification. See TORQUE SPECIFICATIONS. Fill transmission and transfer case with 75W-90 GL-4 transmission fluid.

"S" & "T" SERIES (BLAZER & PICKUP)

Removal – 1) Disconnect negative battery cable. Remove shift lever boot and slide upward on shift lever. Shift transmission into neutral and remove shift lever bolts at transmission. Remove shift lever.

2) Remove parking brake cable for clearance. Raise vehicle and mark propeller shaft for reassembly reference. Remove propeller shaft. Remove skid plate, if equipped.

3) Remove transfer case, if equipped. Disconnect vehicle speed sensor and wiring harnesses as needed. On 4.3L models, purge fuel pressure and disconnect fuel lines at manifold. On all models, disconnect exhaust pipes at manifolds.

4) Remove slave cylinder from transmission. Support transmission and remove catalytic converter hanger and support braces. Remove necessary crossmembers.

5) Remove transmission-to-engine bolts. On 4.3L models, rotate transmission counterclockwise before pulling over clutch splines. On all models, remove transmission.

NOTE: DO NOT allow transmission to hang from clutch.

Installation – Apply a light coat of high-temperature grease to main drive gear splines. Place transmission in high gear. To complete installation, reverse removal procedure. Tighten bolts to specification. See TORQUE SPECIFICATIONS.

TORQUE SPECIFICATIONS

TORQUE SPECIFICATIONS

Application	Ft. Lbs. (N.m)
All Models Except "J", "S" & "T" Series	
Adapter-To-Transmission Bolt	24 (33)
Crossmember-To-Frame Bolt	55 (75)
Crossmember-To-Mount Bolt	40 (54)
Drain & Fill Plug	17 (23)
Inspection Cover	13 (18)
Mount-To-Transmission Bolt	
RPO M20	40 (54)
Except RPO M20	35 (47)
Speed Sensor (RPO M20)	32 (43)
Transfer Case-To-Extension Housing Bolts	45 (61)
Transmission-To-Clutch Housing Bolt	
RPO MG5	37 (50)
Except RPO MG5	74 (100)
"J" Body (Tracker)	
Crossmember Bolt	62 (84)
Drive Shaft Flange Bolt	37 (51)
Transfer Case Skid Plate	41 (55)
Transmission-To-Engine Bolt	62 (84)
"S" & "T" Series (Blazer & Tracker)	
Adapter-To-Transfer Case Bolt	24 (33)
Adapter-To-Transmission Bolt	24 (33)
Crossmember-To-Frame Bolt	25 (34)
Crossmember-To-Mount Bolt	25 (34)
Drain Plug	30 (41)
Fill Plug	17 (23)
Mount-To-Transmission Bolt	37 (50)
Shift Lever Nut	35 (47)
Transfer Case-To-Extension Housing Bolts	24 (33)
Transmission-To-Clutch Housing Bolt	55 (75)
	INCH Lbs. (N.m)
Speed Sensor Bolt (RPO MG5)	108 (12)

Cherokee, Grand Cherokee, Wrangler
REMOVAL & INSTALLATION

Removal & Installation (Cherokee, Grand Cherokee & Wrangler) –
1) Place transmission in 1st or 3rd gear (Neutral on Grand Cherokee). Raise and support vehicle. Remove skid plate (if equipped). Support engine with adjustable jackstand and remove rear crossmember.
2) Disconnect shift linkage, speedometer cable, transfer case vacuum lines (if equipped) and clutch hydraulic lines. Lower transmission/transfer case assembly no more than 3 inches to access shift lever. Unseat shift lever dust boot. Move boot upward to gain access to shift lever retainer.
3) Remove retainer and disengage shift lever from transmission. Mark front and rear drive shafts for installation reference. Remove front drive shaft (if equipped) and rear drive shaft. Remove engine timing sensor. Disconnect transmission and transfer case vent hose.

4) Disconnect clutch master cylinder line. Support transmission/transfer case assembly with transmission jack. Remove clutch housing brace. Remove clutch housing-to-engine bolts. Remove transmission/transfer case assembly. To install, reverse removal procedure. See TORQUE SPECIFICATIONS.

TORQUE SPECIFICATIONS
TORQUE SPECIFICATIONS

Application	Ft. Lbs. (N.m)
Clutch Housing-To-Engine	
Cherokee & Wrangler	28 (38)
Grand Cherokee	45 (60)
Clutch Housing-To-Transmission	27 (37)
Crossmember-To-Frame	30 (41)
Skid Plate	31 (42)
Transfer Case-To-Transmission	26 (35)
Transmission-To-Rear Support	33 (45)
U-Joint Bolt	14 (19)

AUTOMATIC TRANSMISSIONS

APPLICATION & LABOR TIMES

NOTE: Transmission may be referred to as AW4.

APPLICATION & LABOR TIMES

| Vehicle | Labor Times | | Trans. |
Application	[1] R & I	[2] Overhaul	Model
1993-94 Cherokee (4.0L)	3.4 [3]	7.5	AW4
1993 Grand Cherokee (4.0L)	3.4 [3]	7.5	AW4

[1] – Removal and installation of transmission from vehicle chassis.

[2] – Bench overhaul time for transmission only. DOES NOT include removal and installation.

[3] – Add .9 hour for 4WD models.

IDENTIFICATION

Transmission can be identified by identification plate attached on side of transmission case. *See Fig. 1.* Identification plate contains transmission model and serial numbers which may be required when ordering replacement components.

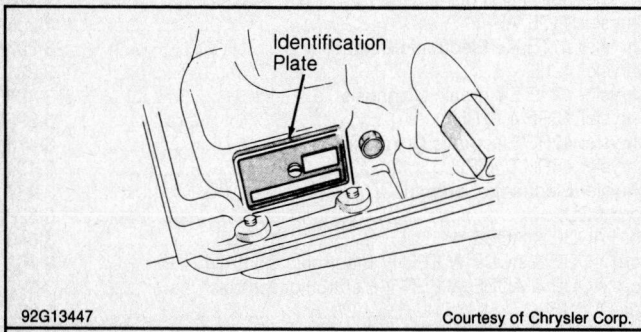

Identification Plate

92G13447   Courtesy of Chrysler Corp.

Fig. 1: Locating Transmission Identification Plate

DESCRIPTION & OPERATION

Transmission is a 4-speed overdrive electronically controlled automatic transmission. Transmission consists of lock-up torque converter, oil pump, 3 planetary gear sets, clutch and brake units, accumulator pistons, valve body and 3 valve body solenoids.

Valve body with solenoids and a Transmission Control Module (TCM) are used for controlling transmission operation. Valve body solenoids are controlled by the TCM. The No. 1 and 2 valve body solenoids are used for controlling transmission shifting. The No. 3 valve body solenoid is used for torque converter lock-up.

NOTE: Transmission Control Module (TCM) may also be referred to as Transmission Control Unit (TCU).

The TCM determines shift points and torque converter lock-up timing based on input signals received from various sensors and switches. The TCM contains a self-diagnostic system which stores a diagnostic trouble code if a transmission problem exists. Diagnostic trouble code can be retrieved to determine the transmission problem area. For information on transmission electronic controls, see AISIN WARNER 4 ELECTRONIC DIAGNOSIS article.

LUBRICATION & ADJUSTMENTS

NOTE: See appropriate AUTOMATIC TRANSMISSION SERVICING article in TRANSMISSION SERVICING.

TROUBLE SHOOTING

Transmission malfunctions may be caused by poor engine performance, improper adjustments or failure of hydraulic, mechanical or electronic components. Always begin by checking fluid level, fluid con-

dition and shift cable adjustment. Perform road test to determine if problem has been corrected. If problem still exists, several tests must be performed on transmission. See TESTING.

TRANSMISSION SYMPTOM DIAGNOSIS

Delayed 1-2, 2-3 Or 3-4 Upshift, Or Downshifts From 4-3 Or 3-2 And Shifts Back To "4" Or "3"
- Electronic controls faulty
- Valve body faulty
- Valve body solenoid faulty

Downshift Early Or Late During Coasting
- Electronic controls faulty
- Throttle cable faulty
- Transmission faulty
- Valve body faulty
- Valve body solenoid faulty

Drags Or Binds On 1-2, 2-3 Or 3-4 Upshift
- Shift cable improperly adjusted
- Transmission faulty
- Valve body faulty

Harsh Downshift
- Accumulator pistons faulty
- Throttle cable improperly adjusted
- Throttle cable or cam faulty
- Transmission faulty
- Valve body faulty

Harsh Engagement In All Gear Ranges
- Accumulator pistons faulty
- Throttle cable improperly adjusted
- Transmission faulty
- Valve body or primary regulator valve faulty

No Downshift When Coasting
- Electronic controls faulty
- Valve body faulty
- Valve body solenoid faulty

No Engine Braking In 1-2 Position
- Electronic controls faulty
- Transmission faulty
- Valve body faulty
- Valve body solenoid faulty

No Torque Converter Lock-Up In 2nd, 3rd Or Overdrive
- Electronic controls faulty
- Transmission faulty
- Valve body faulty
- Valve body solenoid faulty

No 4-3, 3-2 Or 2-1 Downshift
- Electronic controls faulty
- Valve body faulty
- Valve body solenoid faulty

Fluid Comes Out Of Filler Tube
- Breather vent in oil pump restricted
- Improper fluid level
- Oil cooler restricted

Shift Lever Position Incorrect
- Manual valve and lever faulty
- Shift cable improperly adjusted

Slips On 1-2, 2-3 Or 3-4 Upshift Or Slips/Shudders During Acceleration
- Shift cable improperly adjusted
- Throttle cable improperly adjusted
- Transmission faulty
- Valve body faulty
- Valve body solenoid faulty

Transmission Overheats & Fluid Is Discolored Or Smells Burnt
- Low fluid level
- Restricted oil cooler or lines
- Transmission faulty

Vehicle Will Not Hold In Park
- Parking rod, pawl and spring faulty
- Shift cable improperly adjusted

Vehicle Will Not Move In Any Forward Gear Or Reverse
- Oil screen restricted
- Parking rod and pawl faulty
- Shift cable improperly adjusted
- Torque converter drive plate broken
- Torque converter faulty
- Valve body or primary regulator valve faulty

ELECTRONIC TESTING

NOTE: For information on transmission electronic testing, see AISIN WARNER 4 ELECTRONIC DIAGNOSIS article.

TESTING

NOTE: Before performing transmission testing procedures, ensure preliminary inspection is performed. See PRELIMINARY INSPECTION under TESTING.

PRELIMINARY INSPECTION

1) Ensure shift cable and throttle cable are properly adjusted and no binding exists. If adjustment is required, see appropriate AUTOMATIC TRANSMISSION SERVICING article in TRANSMISSION SERVICING.

2) Check engine throttle operation. Fully depress accelerator and ensure throttle plate fully opens. Adjust cable or linkage if throttle plate does not fully open.

3) Ensure transmission fluid level is correct with transmission at normal operating temperature. If fluid is required, use Mopar Dexron-IIE/Mercon ATF.

4) Ensure engine will start with shift lever in Park or Neutral only. If engine starts in gear, adjust neutral safety switch. See NEUTRAL SAFETY SWITCH under REMOVAL & INSTALLATION.

5) Ensure Throttle Position Sensor (TPS) operates properly. See THROTTLE POSITION SENSOR (TPS) under TESTING in AISIN WARNER 4 ELECTRONIC DIAGNOSIS article.

ROAD TEST

NOTE: Perform road test to determine if problem is related to a mechanical or electrical component.

1) With ignition off, disconnect 32-pin electrical connector from Transmission Control Module (TCM). The TCM is located behind right side of instrument panel on Cherokee or above steering column or on top left side of instrument panel on Grand Cherokee. *See Fig. 2.*

2) Road test vehicle. Shift transmission into each gear. Transmission should operate as listed.
- Lock When In Park
- Back-Up When In Reverse
- Vehicle Should Not Move In Neutral
- Provide 1st Gear Only With Shift Lever In "1-2" Position
- Operate In 3rd Gear Only With Shift Lever In "3" Position
- Operate In 4th Gear (Overdrive Gear) In "D" Position

3) If transmission operates properly, proceed to step **5)**. If forward gears were difficult to distinguish (all feel the same), or vehicle would not back-up, see TROUBLE SHOOTING. DO NOT perform torque converter stall speed test or time lag test.

4) Continue road test. Manually downshift transmission from "D" to "3" and from "3" to "1-2" position. Manually upshift transmission through forward gears again.

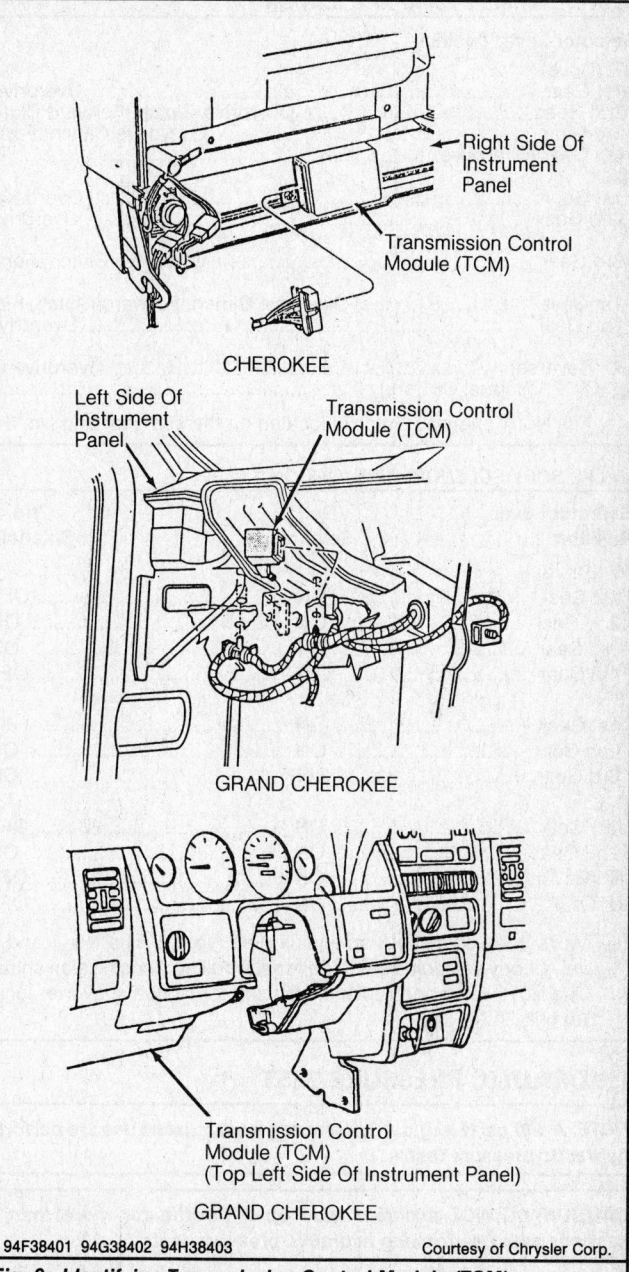

CHEROKEE

GRAND CHEROKEE

Transmission Control Module (TCM) (Top Left Side Of Instrument Panel)

GRAND CHEROKEE

94F38401 94G38402 94H38403   Courtesy of Chrysler Corp.

Fig. 2: Identifying Transmission Control Module (TCM)

CAUTION: DO NOT overspeed engine when performing downshifts. Release throttle and allow vehicle to slow down before downshifting.

5) If transmission operates properly, perform torque converter stall speed test, time lag test and hydraulic pressure test. If problem still exists, check electronic control system for stored diagnostic trouble codes. See AISIN WARNER 4 ELECTRONIC DIAGNOSIS article. Once road test is completed, reinstall electrical connector on TCM.

NOTE: For transmission gear component application, see CLUTCH, BRAKE & BAND APPLICATION table and VALVE BODY SOLENOID APPLICATION table.

CLUTCH, BRAKE & BAND APPLICATION

Selector Lever Position   [1] **Elements In Use**

"D" (Drive)
1st Gear .... Overdrive Clutch, Forward Clutch, Overdrive One-Way Clutch, No. 2 One-Way Clutch
2nd Gear .... Overdrive Clutch, Forward Clutch, Second Brake Clutch, Overdrive One-Way Clutch, No. 1 One-Way Clutch
3rd Gear .... Overdrive Clutch, Forward Clutch, Direct Clutch, Second Brake Clutch, Overdrive One-Way Clutch
4th Gear (Overdrive) .... Forward Clutch, Direct Clutch, Overdrive Brake Clutch, Second Brake Clutch
"3"
1st Gear .... Overdrive Clutch, Forward Clutch, Overdrive One-Way Clutch, No. 2 One-Way Clutch
2nd Gear .... Overdrive Clutch, Forward Clutch, Second Coast Brake Band, Second Brake Clutch, Overdrive One-Way Clutch, No. 1 One-Way Clutch
3rd Gear .... Overdrive Clutch, Forward Clutch, Direct Clutch, Second Brake Clutch, Overdrive One-Way Clutch
"1-2"
1st Gear .... Overdrive Clutch, Forward Clutch, First-Reverse Brake Clutch, Overdrive One-Way Clutch, No. 2 One-Way Clutch
2nd Gear .... Overdrive Clutch, Forward Clutch, Second Coast Brake Band, Second Brake Clutch, Overdrive One-Way Clutch, No. 1 One-Way Clutch
"R" (Reverse) .... Overdrive Clutch, Direct Clutch, First-Reverse Brake Clutch, Overdrive One-Way Clutch
"N" Or "P" (Neutral Or Park) .... Overdrive Clutch

[1] – The No. 1 one-way clutch is located on the sun gear and No. 2 one-way clutch is located on rear planetary gear.

VALVE BODY SOLENOID APPLICATION [1]

Selector Lever Position	No. 1 Solenoid	No. 2 Solenoid
"D" (Drive)		
1st Gear	ON	OFF
2nd Gear	ON	ON
3rd Gear	OFF	ON
4th Gear	OFF	OFF
"3"		
1st Gear	ON	OFF
2nd Gear	ON	ON
3rd Gear	OFF	ON
"1-2"		
1st Gear	ON	OFF
2nd Gear	ON	ON
"R" (Reverse)	ON	OFF
"N" Or "P"	ON	OFF

[1] – Valve body contains 3 solenoids. *See Fig. 52.* The No. 1 and 2 valve body solenoids are used for controlling transmission shifts. The No. 3 valve body solenoid is used for torque converter lockup only.

HYDRAULIC PRESSURE TEST

NOTE: A 300 psi (21 kg/cm²) pressure gauge must be used to perform hydraulic pressure test.

CAUTION: DO NOT maintain wide open throttle for more than 4 seconds when performing hydraulic pressure test.

1) Ensure fluid level and condition are okay. Install tachometer. Apply parking brake and block the wheels. Using Adapter (7554), connect pressure gauge to test port on side of transmission case. *See Fig. 3.*
2) Start engine and ensure engine idle speed is within specification. Refer to emission decal in engine compartment. Apply service brake. Allow engine to idle until transmission is at normal operating temperature.
3) Shift transmission into "D" (Drive) and note line pressure with engine idling. Line pressure should be 61-70 psi (4.3-4.9 kg/cm²).
4) Fully depress throttle to wide open throttle and note line pressure with transmission in "D" (Drive). Line pressure should be 173-209 psi (12.2-14.7 kg/cm²).
5) Shift transmission into Reverse and note line pressure with engine idling. Line pressure should be 75-90 psi (5.3-6.3 kg/cm²).
6) Fully depress throttle to wide open throttle and note line pressure with transmission in Reverse. Line pressure should be 213-263 psi (14.9-18.5 kg/cm²).
7) If line pressure is not within specification, adjust throttle cable and repeat hydraulic pressure test. See appropriate AUTOMATIC TRANSMISSION SERVICING article in TRANSMISSION SERVICING.

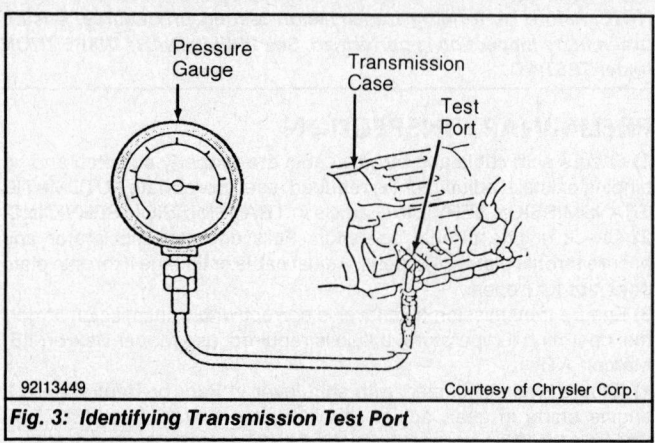

Fig. 3: Identifying Transmission Test Port

NOTE: Use the following symptoms for trouble shooting results of hydraulic pressure test.

Hydraulic Pressure Test Results – 1) If line pressure with transmission in "D" and Reverse is greater than specified, check for the following:
- Throttle cable loose, worn, binding or improperly adjusted.
- Throttle valve, downshift plug, throttle valve cam or primary regulator valve sticking, worn or damaged.

2) If line pressure with transmission in "D" and Reverse is less than specified, check for the following:
- Throttle cable loose, worn, binding or improperly adjusted.
- Throttle valve, downshift plug, throttle valve cam or primary regulator valve sticking, worn or damaged.
- Oil pump gears or pump body worn or damaged.
- Overdrive clutch worn or damaged.

3) If line pressure with transmission in "D" (Drive) only is less than specified, check for the following:
- Forward clutch worn or damaged.
- Fluid leakage in "D" (Drive) circuit.

4) If line pressure with transmission in Reverse only is less than specified, check for the following:
- Shift cable improperly adjusted.
- Fluid leakage in Reverse circuit.
- Direct clutch worn or damaged.
- First-reverse brake worn or damaged.

TORQUE CONVERTER STALL SPEED TEST

NOTE: Torque converter stall speed test checks holding ability of transmission clutches, brakes and torque converter stator clutch.

Torque Converter Stall Speed Test Procedure – 1) Ensure transmission fluid level is correct and transmission is at normal operating temperature.

2) Install tachometer. Apply parking brake and block wheels. Apply and hold service brake.

3) On Cherokee 4WD models, shift transfer case into 2H (2WD high position). On Grand Cherokee models with NP249 transfer case, shift transfer case into 4H (4WD high position) and with all other transfer cases, shift transfer case into 2H (2WD high position).

4) On all models, start engine. Shift transmission into "D" (Drive). Fully depress throttle to wide open throttle and note maximum engine RPM (torque converter stall speed). DO NOT maintain wide open throttle for more than 4 seconds. Torque converter stall speed should be 2100-2400 RPM in "D" (Drive).

5) Release throttle and shift transmission into Neutral. Allow transmission fluid to cool for 15-20 seconds.

6) Shift transmission into Reverse. Fully depress throttle to wide open throttle and note maximum engine RPM (torque converter stall speed). Torque converter stall speed should be 2100-2400 RPM in Reverse.

NOTE: Use the following symptoms for trouble shooting results of torque converter stall speed test.

Torque Converter Stall Speed Less Than Specified In Drive & Reverse – Check for improper engine performance or stator clutch in torque converter not holding if torque converter stall speed was 1500 RPM or less.

Torque Converter Stall Speed Greater Than Specified In Drive – Check for low line pressure. See HYDRAULIC PRESSURE TEST under TESTING. Check for slippage in forward clutch. Check for overdrive one-way clutch or No. 2 one-way clutch not holding. The No. 2 one-way clutch is located in rear planetary gear.

Torque Converter Stall Speed Greater Than Specified In Reverse – Check for low line pressure. See HYDRAULIC PRESSURE TEST under TESTING. Check for slippage in direct clutch or first-reverse brake. Check for overdrive one-way clutch not holding.

Torque Converter Stall Speed Greater Than Specified In Drive & Reverse – Check for low fluid level. Check for low line pressure. See HYDRAULIC PRESSURE TEST under TESTING. Check for overdrive one-way clutch not holding.

TIME LAG TEST

NOTE: Time lag test checks overdrive clutch, forward clutch, rear clutch and first-reverse brake. Condition is indicated by time required for component engagement with engine idling. Engagement time is measured in Drive and Reverse.

1) Ensure transmission fluid level is correct and transmission is at normal operating temperature. Apply parking brake. Ensure A/C is off.

2) On Cherokee 4WD models, shift transfer case into 2H (2WD high position). On Grand Cherokee models with NP249 transfer case, shift transfer case into 4H (4WD high position) and with all other transfer cases, shift transfer case into 2H (2WD high position).

3) On all models, start engine. Ensure engine idle speed is within specification. Refer to emission decal in engine compartment. Engine idle speed must be correct to ensure accurate test results.

4) Shift transmission into Neutral and set stop watch. During following test steps, start stop watch as soon as shift lever reaches "D" (Drive) and Reverse detents.

5) Shift transmission into "D" (Drive) and record time it takes for engagement. Repeat procedure at least 2 times. Reset stop watch and shift transmission to Neutral.

6) Shift transmission into Reverse and record time it takes for engagement. Repeat procedure at least 2 times.

7) Engagement time in "D" (Drive) should be a maximum of 1.2 seconds and Reverse should be a maximum of 1.5 seconds.

NOTE: Use the following symptoms for trouble shooting results of time lag test.

Time Lag Test Results – 1) If engagement time is longer than specified for "D" (Drive), check for improper shift cable adjustment, low line pressure or defective forward or overdrive clutches. To check line pressure, see HYDRAULIC PRESSURE TEST under TESTING.

2) If engagement time is longer than specified for Reverse, check for improper shift cable adjustment, low line pressure or defective first-reverse brake, direct clutch and overdrive clutch. To check line pressure, see HYDRAULIC PRESSURE TEST under TESTING.

TORQUE CONVERTER

CAUTION: Torque converter is a welded assembly and is not serviceable. If a stator clutch malfunction occurs or if torque converter becomes contaminated with foreign material, it MUST be replaced. It cannot be flushed or repaired.

NOTE: For torque converter stall speed test, see TORQUE CONVERTER STALL SPEED TEST under TESTING.

TORQUE CONVERTER STATOR CLUTCH TEST

1) Install Rotator (7547) into torque converter hub and engage with stator clutch. Install Stopper (7548) in torque converter hub so it engages with notch on torque converter hub and outer race of rotator. *See Fig. 4.*

2) Turn rotator clockwise. Stator clutch should rotate freely and smoothly. Less than 22 INCH lbs. (2.5 N.m) of torque should be required to rotate stator clutch.

3) Turn rotator counterclockwise. Ensure stator clutch locks. Replace torque converter if stator clutch is defective. Remove stopper and rotator.

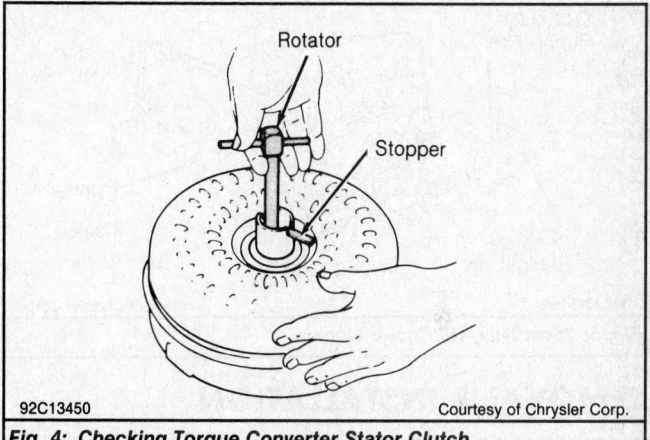

92C13450   Courtesy of Chrysler Corp.

Fig. 4: Checking Torque Converter Stator Clutch

ON-VEHICLE SERVICE

Following components can be serviced on the vehicle.
- Accumulator Pistons And Springs
- Adapter/Extension Housing Seal
- Manual Valve Shaft Seal
- Neutral Safety Switch
- Park Rod And Pawl
- Second Coast Brake Servo
- Speed Sensor
- Speed Sensor Rotor/Speedometer Drive Gear
- Valve Body
- Valve Body Solenoid

See appropriate component under REMOVAL & INSTALLATION.

OIL COOLER FLUSHING

CAUTION: Whenever transmission failure exists, oil cooler must be flushed and torque converter replaced. Some models may have an external oil cooler mounted in front of the radiator. This oil cooler must be flushed along with oil cooler mounted in the radiator.

NOTE: Manufacturer recommends using Mopar Dexron-IIE/Mercon ATF fluid.

1) Note oil cooler supply and return lines. *See Fig. 5.* Disconnect oil cooler lines at transmission. Using hand-held suction gun filled with mineral spirits, force mineral spirits into oil cooler return line until mineral spirits flows from oil cooler supply line. Replace radiator or external oil cooler if mineral spirits will not flow through oil cooler.

2) Continue flushing oil cooler until mineral spirits is clear and no sign of contamination exists. Once no contamination exists, apply compressed air on line from oil cooler in light applications until remaining mineral spirits is blown from oil cooler and oil cooler lines.

3) Pump at least one quart of ATF fluid through oil cooler to ensure oil cooler is free of mineral spirits. Reconnect oil cooler lines. Fill transmission to proper fluid level.

OIL COOLER FLOW CHECK

NOTE: Manufacturer recommends using Mopar Dexron-IIE/Mercon ATF fluid.

1) With transmission filled to proper fluid level, disconnect oil cooler return line from transmission. *See Fig. 5.* Place container under oil cooler return line.

2) Add one extra quart of ATF fluid to transmission. Apply parking brake. Start engine and allow to idle. Place gearshift in Neutral. Check fluid flow from oil cooler return line.

3) If fluid flow is intermittent or takes more than 20 seconds to obtain one quart, replace radiator or external oil cooler. Reconnect oil cooler return line. Fill transmission to proper fluid level with ATF.

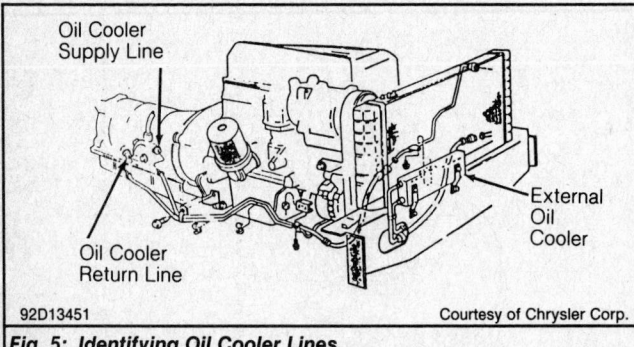

92D13451   Courtesy of Chrysler Corp.

Fig. 5: Identifying Oil Cooler Lines

REMOVAL & INSTALLATION

ACCUMULATOR PISTONS & SPRINGS

CAUTION: Ensure accumulator pistons and spring locations are marked for reassembly reference. Components must be installed in original location.

Removal – 1) Remove valve body. See VALVE BODY under REMOVAL & INSTALLATION. Note location of accumulator pistons. *See Fig. 6.*

2) Place shop towel over accumulator piston. Apply air pressure through small hole next to each accumulator piston to force accumulator piston from transmission case.

CAUTION: Use care not to apply excessive air pressure. Apply only enough air pressure to force accumulator piston from the bore.

3) Remove accumulator piston and spring. Note location of components for reassembly reference. *See Fig. 6.* Remove seal rings from accumulator pistons.

4) If removing small cushion spring from accumulator pistons, remove retainer clip and separate small cushion spring from inside of accumulator piston. *See Fig. 6.*

Installation – 1) Install small cushion spring and retainer clip in accumulator piston (if removed). Ensure retainer clip is fully seated in accumulator piston.

2) Install NEW seal rings on accumulator piston. Lubricate seal rings and accumulator piston bores with Mopar Dexron-IIE/Mercon ATF.

Install springs and accumulator pistons in original location. Install valve body. Fill transmission to proper fluid level with Mopar Dexron-IIE/Mercon ATF.

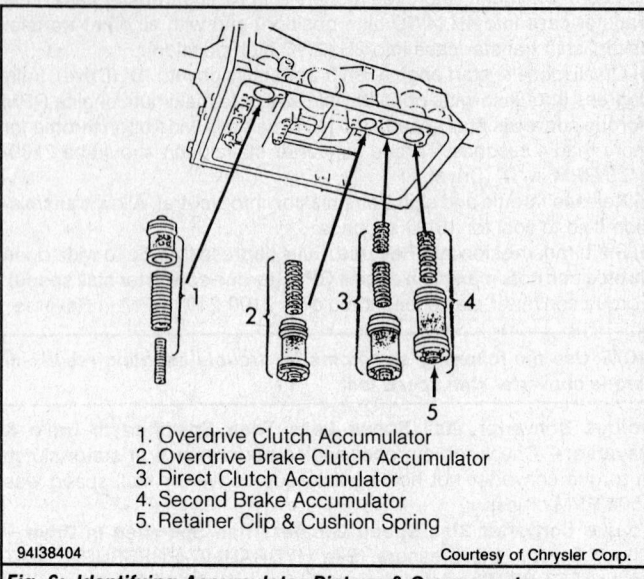

1. Overdrive Clutch Accumulator
2. Overdrive Brake Clutch Accumulator
3. Direct Clutch Accumulator
4. Second Brake Accumulator
5. Retainer Clip & Cushion Spring

94I38404   Courtesy of Chrysler Corp.

Fig. 6: Identifying Accumulator Pistons & Components

ADAPTER/EXTENSION HOUSING SEAL

Removal & Installation – 1) Raise and support vehicle. Remove necessary components for access to seal. Remove dust shield (if equipped). Remove seal from adapter or extension housing.

2) To install, reverse removal procedure. Install NEW seal using proper size seal installer. Fill transmission to proper fluid level with Mopar Dexron-IIE/Mercon ATF.

MANUAL VALVE SHAFT SEAL

Removal – 1) Remove neutral safety switch. See NEUTRAL SAFETY SWITCH under REMOVAL & INSTALLATION. Disconnect transmission shift lever. Remove valve body. See VALVE BODY under REMOVAL & INSTALLATION.

2) Remove park rod bracket bolts from transmission case. *See Fig. 9.* Remove park rod from shift sector located on manual valve shaft. *See Fig. 7.*

3) Using hammer and chisel, cut spacer sleeve and remove from manual valve shaft. Remove pin from manual valve shaft.

4) Remove manual valve shaft and shift sector from transmission case. Remove seals from transmission case.

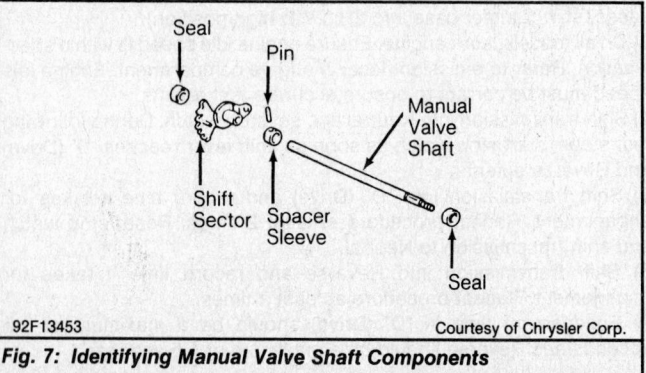

92F13453   Courtesy of Chrysler Corp.

Fig. 7: Identifying Manual Valve Shaft Components

Installation – 1) Coat NEW seals with petroleum jelly. Install seals in transmission case. Install NEW spacer sleeve on shift sector.

2) Lubricate manual valve shaft, shift sector and spacer sleeve with petroleum jelly. Install manual valve shaft in transmission case. Install shift sector and spacer sleeve on manual valve shaft. Align hole in spacer sleeve with notch in shift sector.

3) Install pin into shift sector and manual valve shaft. Stake spacer sleeve to shift sector and manual valve shaft.

CAUTION: Ensure spacer sleeve is staked to shift sector and manual valve shaft.

---

4) Install park rod on shift sector. Install park rod bracket. Install and tighten bolts to specification. See TORQUE SPECIFICATIONS. Install valve body. Fill transmission to proper fluid level with Mopar Dexron-IIE/Mercon ATF.

NEUTRAL SAFETY SWITCH

NOTE: For neutral safety switch testing, see AISIN WARNER 4 ELECTRONIC DIAGNOSIS article. Neutral safety switch may be referred to as Park/Neutral switch.

Removal – 1) Apply parking brake. Raise and support vehicle. Disconnect electrical connector at neutral safety switch. Pry lock washer tabs away from retaining nut. *See Fig. 8.*
2) Remove retaining nut, lock washer and adjusting bolt. *See Fig. 8.* Remove neutral safety switch from manual valve shaft.

Installation – 1) Disconnect shift control rod from transmission shift lever. Rotate transmission shift lever fully rearward and then forward 2 detent positions to Neutral position.
2) Install neutral safety switch on manual valve shaft. Install adjusting bolt. DO NOT tighten adjusting bolt at this time.
3) Install lock washer and retaining nut. Tighten retaining nut to specification. See TORQUE SPECIFICATIONS. DO NOT bend over lock washer tabs at this time.
4) Ensure transmission is still in Neutral. Rotate neutral safety switch and align neutral standard line with vertical groove on manual valve shaft. *See Fig. 8.*
5) Tighten adjusting bolt to specification. See TORQUE SPECIFICATIONS. Bend lock washer tabs over. Reconnect shift control rod and electrical connector. Ensure vehicle starts in Park and Neutral only.

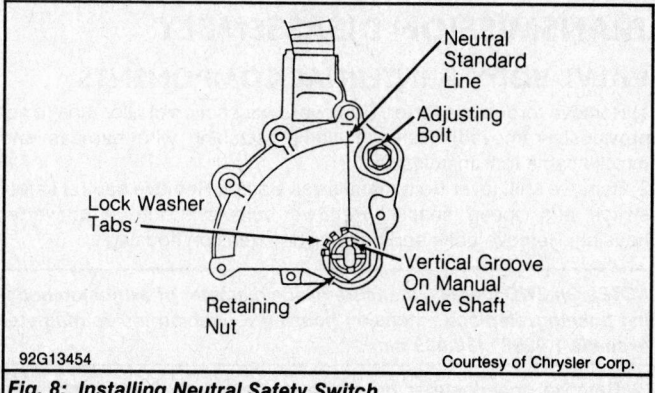

Fig. 8: Installing Neutral Safety Switch

PARK ROD & PAWL

Removal & Installation – 1) Remove valve body. See VALVE BODY under REMOVAL & INSTALLATION. Remove park rod bracket bolts from transmission case. *See Fig. 9.*
2) Disconnect park rod from shift sector on manual valve shaft. *See Fig. 7.* Remove park rod, spring, pin and pawl. *See Fig. 9.*
3) To install, reverse removal procedure. Ensure spring is positioned with long end toward inside of transmission case. Tighten park rod bracket bolts to specification. See TORQUE SPECIFICATIONS.

SECOND COAST BRAKE SERVO

Removal – 1) Remove valve body. See VALVE BODY under REMOVAL & INSTALLATION. Remove retaining snap ring for second coast brake servo from transmission case. *See Fig. 10.*
2) Apply air pressure to oil hole in transmission case and force cover and piston for second coast brake servo from transmission case. *See Fig. 10.* Disassemble second coast brake servo if necessary. *See Fig. 50.*

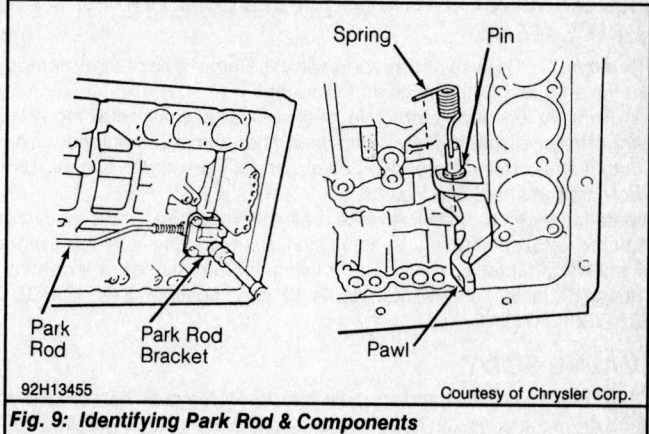

Fig. 9: Identifying Park Rod & Components

Installation – Install NEW piston seal ring on piston. Install NEW "O" rings on cover. Lubricate all components with Mopar Dexron-IIE/Mercon ATF and install. Depress cover and install snap ring. Install valve body. Fill transmission to proper fluid level with Mopar Dexron-IIE/Mercon ATF.

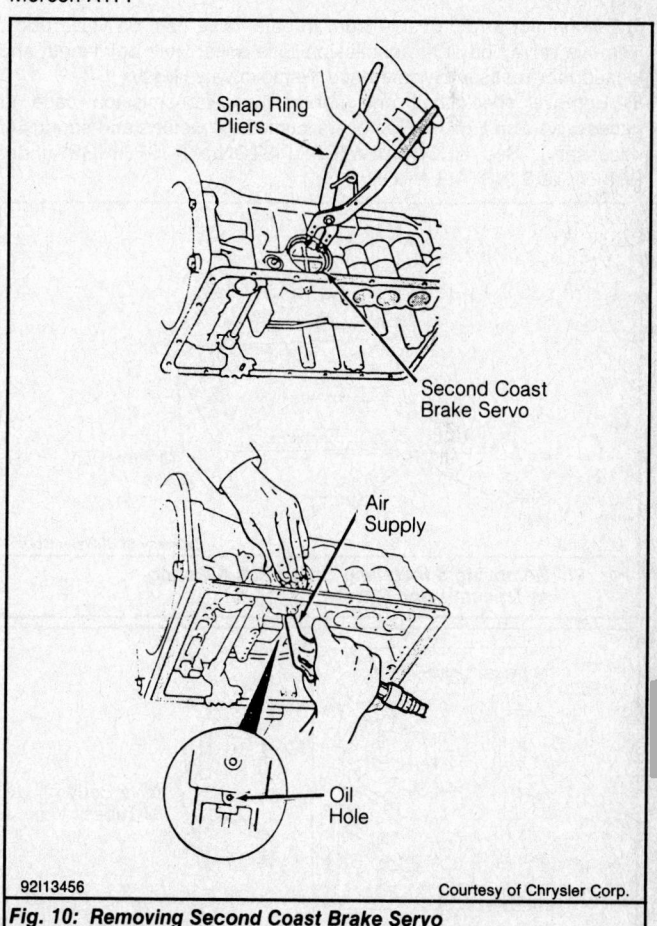

Fig. 10: Removing Second Coast Brake Servo

SPEED SENSOR

NOTE: For speed sensor testing, see AISIN WARNER 4 ELECTRONIC DIAGNOSIS article.

Removal & Installation – 1) Disconnect electrical connector at speed sensor located on adapter or extension housing. Remove bolt and speed sensor. Remove "O" ring from speed sensor.
2) To install, reverse removal procedure using NEW "O" ring. Tighten bolt to specification. See TORQUE SPECIFICATIONS.

SPEED SENSOR ROTOR/SPEEDOMETER DRIVE GEAR

Removal – **1)** Raise and support vehicle. Remove necessary components and adapter or extension housing.

2) Remove speedometer drive gear-to-output shaft retaining snap ring. Remove speedometer drive gear and spacer (if equipped) from output shaft. Using a wooden dowel, carefully pry speed sensor rotor from output shaft. *See Fig. 13.*

Installation – To install, reverse removal procedure. Apply a bead of Loctite 599 sealant on transmission case sealing surface before installing adapter or extension housing. Install adapter or extension housing. Install and tighten bolts to specification. See TORQUE SPECIFICATIONS.

VALVE BODY

Removal – **1)** Raise and support vehicle. Remove oil pan drain plug and drain transmission fluid. Remove bolts and oil pan. Remove bolts, oil screen and gasket.

2) Disconnect electrical connectors from valve body solenoids. Mark electrical connection location for reassembly reference.

3) Carefully pry valve body oil tubes from valve body and transmission case. Note location of valve body oil tubes for reassembly reference. *See Fig. 12.*

4) Disconnect throttle cable from throttle valve cam on valve body. Remove valve body-to-transmission case bolts. Note bolt length and location for reassembly reference. Remove valve body.

5) Remove check ball and spring from transmission case (if necessary). *See Fig. 11.* Remove accumulator pistons and springs (if necessary). See ACCUMULATOR PISTONS & SPRINGS under REMOVAL & INSTALLATION.

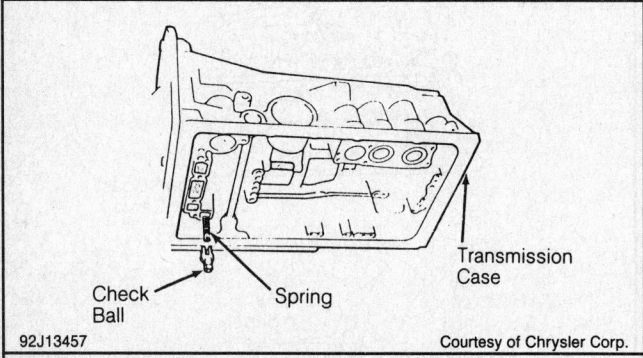

Check Ball — Spring — Transmission Case

92J13457   Courtesy of Chrysler Corp.
Fig. 11: Removing & Installing Check Ball & Spring In Transmission Case

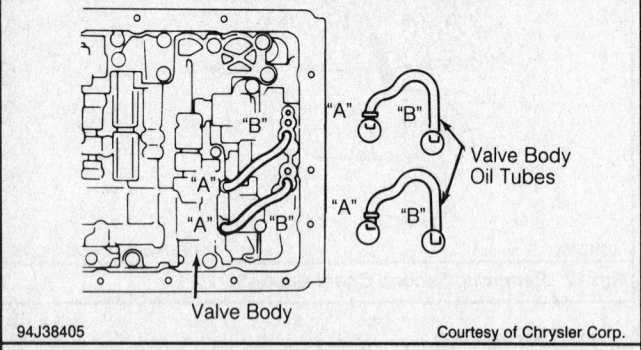

"A" "B" — "A" "B" — Valve Body Oil Tubes — "A" "B" — "A" "B" — Valve Body

94J38405   Courtesy of Chrysler Corp.
Fig. 12: Identifying Valve Body Oil Tubes

Installation – **1)** Install check ball and spring in transmission case (if removed). Install accumulator pistons and springs (if removed).

2) Connect throttle cable to throttle valve cam. Align manual valve with shift sector and position valve body on transmission case. Install valve body-to-transmission case bolts in original location and tighten to specification. See TORQUE SPECIFICATIONS.

3) Install valve body oil tubes in original location with proper end engaged in valve body. *See Fig. 12.*

4) Reconnect valve body solenoid electrical connectors. Ensure oil screen is clean. Using NEW gaskets, install oil screen. Install and tighten bolts to specification. See TORQUE SPECIFICATIONS.

5) Ensure magnet is installed in oil pan and does not interfere with valve body oil tubes. Apply 1/8" bead of Loctite 599 sealant on oil pan mounting flange. Install oil pan. Install and tighten bolts to specification. See TORQUE SPECIFICATIONS.

6) Install NEW gasket and oil pan drain plug. Tighten oil pan drain plug to specification. See TORQUE SPECIFICATIONS. Fill transmission to proper fluid level with Mopar Dexron-IIE/Mercon ATF.

VALVE BODY SOLENOID

NOTE: For testing of valve body solenoid, see AISIN WARNER 4 ELECTRONIC DIAGNOSIS article.

Removal – **1)** Raise and support vehicle. Remove oil pan drain plug and drain transmission fluid. Remove bolts and oil pan. Remove bolts, oil screen and gasket.

2) Disconnect electrical connector from valve body solenoid. Mark electrical connection location for reassembly reference if more than one valve body solenoid is being removed. Remove bolt, valve body solenoid and "O" ring.

CAUTION: DO NOT allow components to fall from valve body when removing valve body solenoid.

Installation – **1)** To install, reverse removal procedure using NEW "O" ring and NEW gaskets. Tighten valve body solenoid and oil screen bolts to specification. See TORQUE SPECIFICATIONS.

2) Apply 1/8" bead of Loctite 599 sealant on oil pan mounting flange. Install oil pan. Install and tighten bolts to specification. See TORQUE SPECIFICATIONS.

3) Install NEW gasket and oil pan drain plug. Tighten oil pan drain plug to specification. Fill transmission to proper fluid level with Mopar Dexron-IIE/Mercon ATF.

TRANSMISSION DISASSEMBLY

VALVE BODY & INTERNAL COMPONENTS

1) Remove torque converter. Remove lower section of filler tube (if not previously removed). Remove clamp attaching wire harness and throttle cable to transmission.

2) Remove shift lever from manual valve shaft. Remove neutral safety switch and speed sensor. Remove bolts and torque converter housing. Remove bolts and adapter or extension housing.

NOTE: On 2WD models, measure inside diameter of extension housing bushing. Replace extension housing if bushing inside diameter exceeds 1.4996" (38.089 mm).

3) Remove speedometer drive gear-to-output shaft retaining snap ring. Remove speedometer drive gear and spacer (if equipped) from output shaft. Using wooden dowel, pry speed sensor rotor from output shaft. *See Fig. 13.* Remove speed sensor rotor key from output shaft.

4) Mount transmission in holding fixture. Remove valve body, and check ball and spring. See VALVE BODY under REMOVAL & INSTALLATION. Remove accumulator pistons and springs. See ACCUMULATOR PISTONS & SPRINGS under REMOVAL & INSTALLATION.

5) Remove throttle cable from transmission case. Remove oil pump bolts. Using Puller (7536), remove oil pump from transmission case. *See Fig. 15.*

6) Note location of thrust bearings and races. *See Fig. 14.* Remove race from rear of oil pump. Remove overdrive planetary gear and overdrive clutch. *See Fig. 13.* Remove race from rear of overdrive planetary gear. Remove thrust bearing, race and overdrive planetary ring gear. *See Fig. 13.*

7) Overdrive brake piston stroke must be checked to see if proper clearance exists or if components must be replaced. Mount dial indicator on transmission case with Gauge (7546) contacting overdrive brake piston. *See Fig. 16.*

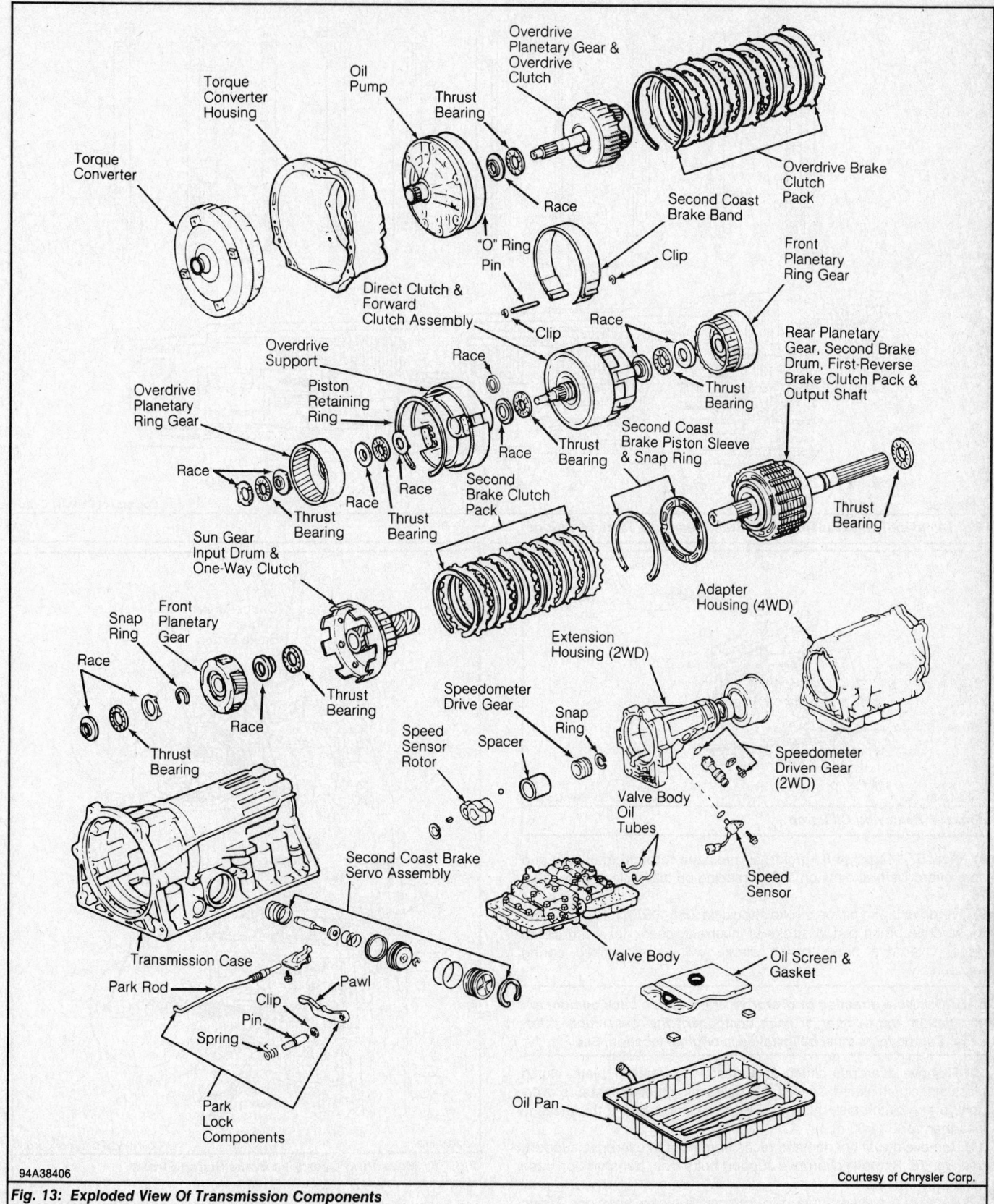

94A38406

Fig. 13: *Exploded View Of Transmission Components*

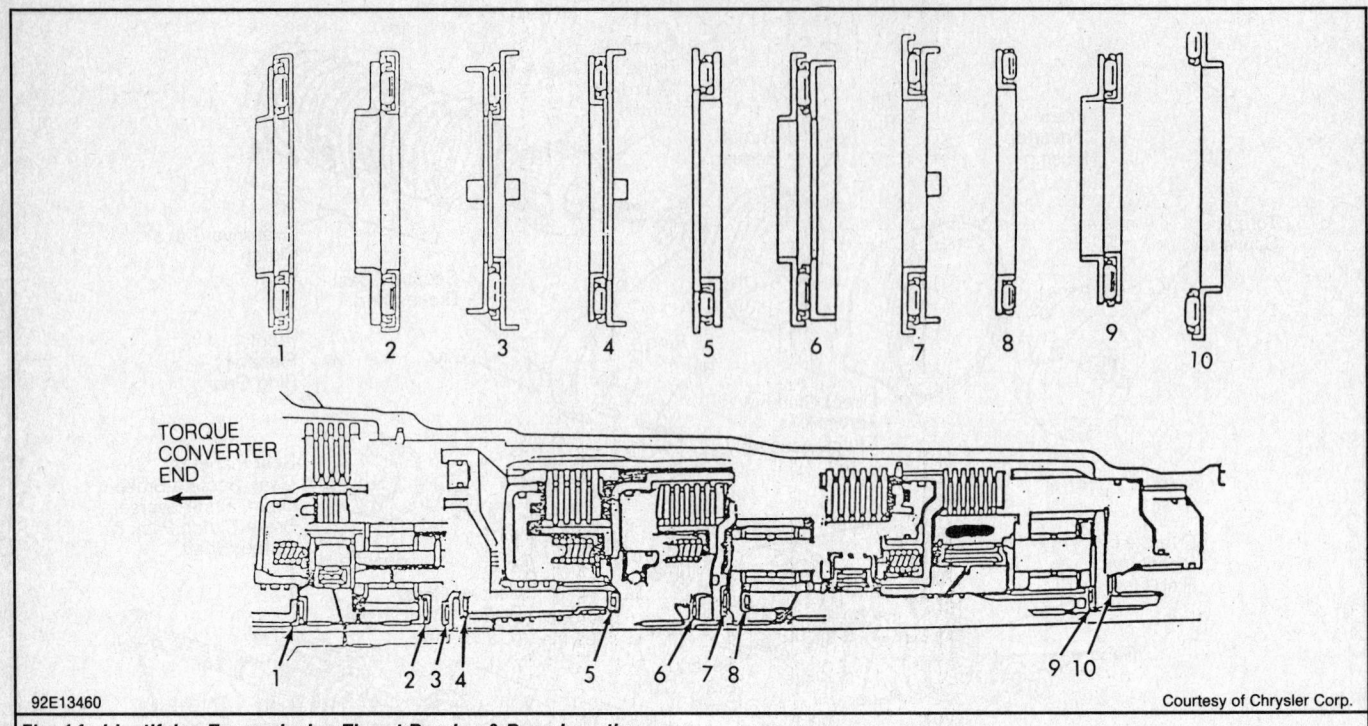

92E13460   Courtesy of Chrysler Corp.

Fig. 14: Identifying Transmission Thrust Bearing & Race Locations

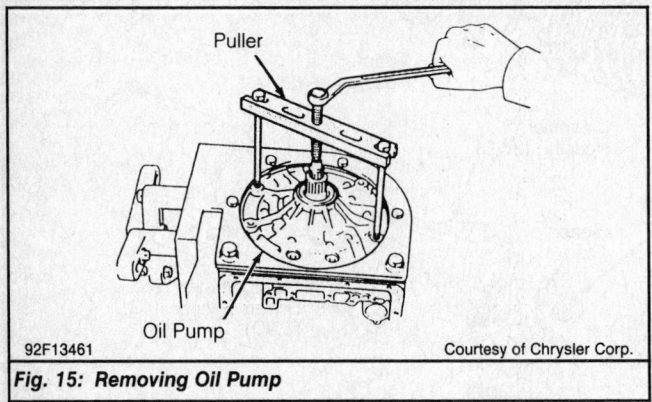

92F13461   Courtesy of Chrysler Corp.

Fig. 15: Removing Oil Pump

8) Apply 57-114 psi (4-8 kg/cm²) air pressure through feed hole and note overdrive brake piston stroke reading on dial indicator. *See Fig. 16.*

9) Overdrive brake piston stroke should be .055-.067" (1.40-1.70 mm). If overdrive brake piston stroke is incorrect, check for worn clutch discs. Overdrive brake piston stroke will be rechecked during reassembly.

CAUTION: Note direction of overdrive brake clutch pack component installation and number of each component for reassembly reference. Components must be installed in original location. See Fig. 17.

10) Remove overdrive clutch pack snap ring, retainer plate, clutch discs and clutch plates. *See Fig. 17.* Using micrometer, measure overdrive brake clutch disc thickness. Replace clutch disc if thickness is less than .072" (1.83 mm).

11) Remove thrust bearing and races from front of overdrive support. *See Fig. 13.* Remove overdrive support bolts from transmission case bolts. *See Fig. 18.*

12) Remove overdrive support-to-transmission case snap ring. Using puller, remove overdrive support. *See Fig. 18.* Remove race from hub on rear side of overdrive support.

13) Second coast brake piston stroke must be checked to see if proper clearance exists or if components must be replaced. Place reference mark on piston rod. *See Fig. 19.*

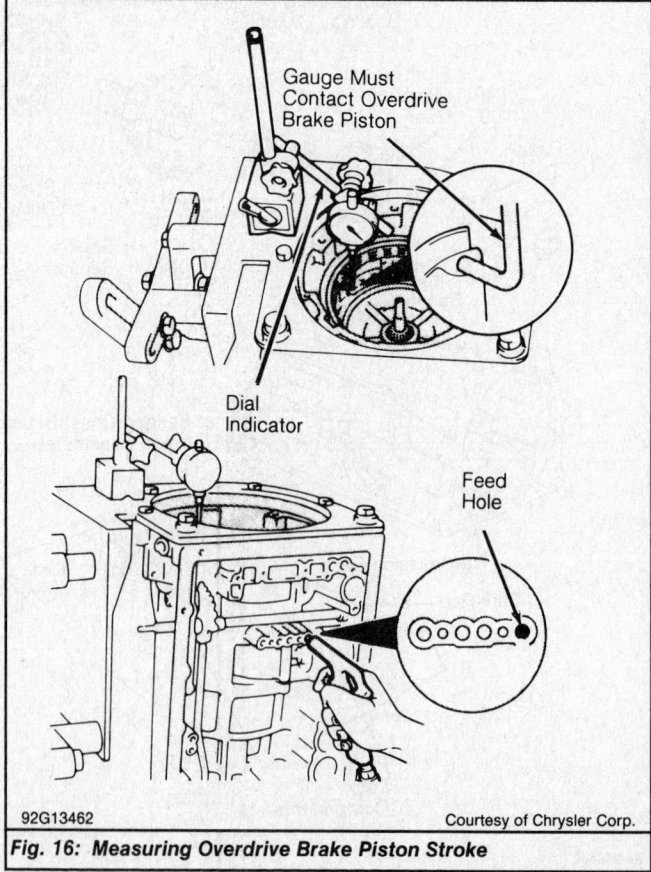

92G13462   Courtesy of Chrysler Corp.

Fig. 16: Measuring Overdrive Brake Piston Stroke

14) Apply 57-114 psi (4-8 kg/cm²) air pressure through piston feed hole. *See Fig. 19.* Using Gauge (7552), check second coast brake piston stroke. Second coast brake piston stroke should be .059-.118" (1.50-3.00 mm).

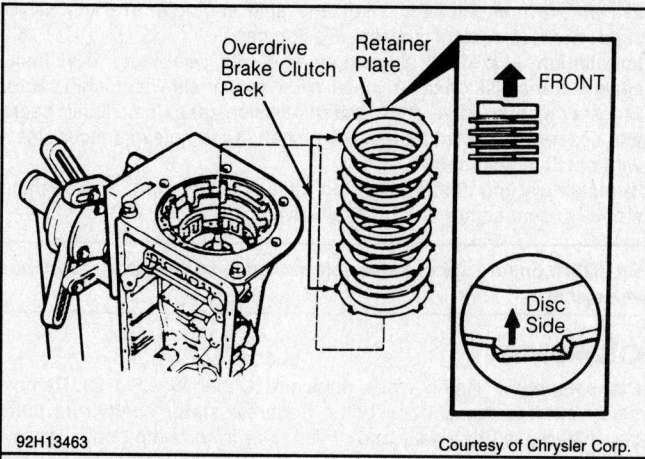

Fig. 17: Removing & Installing Overdrive Brake Clutch Pack

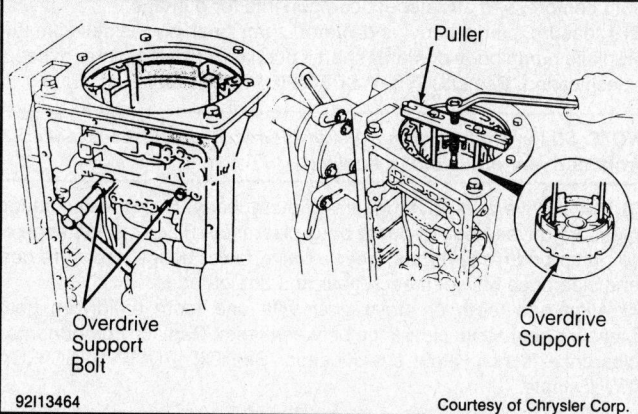

Fig. 18: Removing Overdrive Support

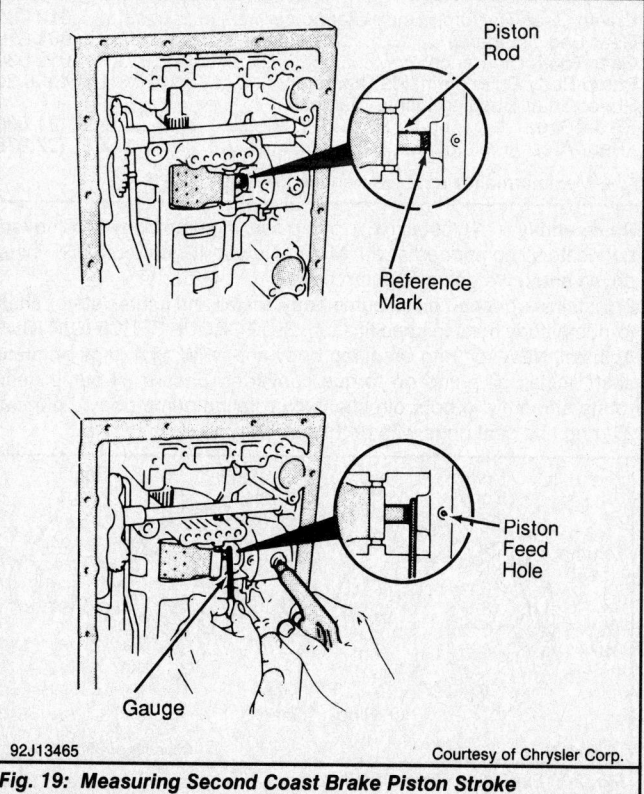

Fig. 19: Measuring Second Coast Brake Piston Stroke

15) If second coast brake piston is incorrect, install different length piston rod. Recheck second coast brake piston stroke. Replacement piston rods are available in lengths of 2.811" (71.40 mm) and 2.870" (72.90 mm). If second coast brake piston stroke is still incorrect, replace second coast brake band.

16) Remove second coast brake servo retaining snap ring from transmission case. See Fig. 10. Apply air pressure to oil hole in transmission case and force cover and piston for servo from transmission case. Disassemble second coast brake servo if necessary. See Fig. 50.

17) Remove direct clutch and forward clutch assembly. See Fig. 13. Remove thrust bearing and race from direct clutch hub. Remove clip, pin and second coast brake band.

18) Remove race and front planetary ring gear. See Fig. 13. Remove thrust bearing and race from rear of front planetary ring gear. Remove race from front of front planetary gear.

19) Relieve load on front planetary gear snap ring by positioning wooden blocks under output shaft. Allow output shaft to support transmission weight. Remove snap ring and front planetary gear. See Fig. 13.

20) Remove sun gear, input drum and one-way clutch as an assembly. See Fig. 13. Using feeler gauge, measure second brake clutch pack clearance. See Fig. 20. Second brake clutch pack clearance should be .024-.078" (.61-1.98 mm). Replace clutch discs if clearance is not within specification.

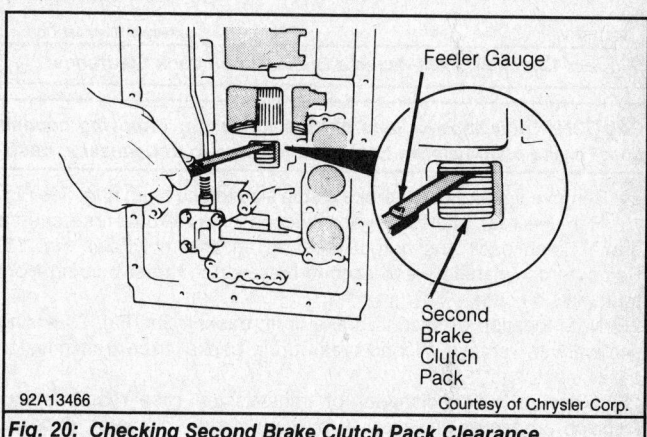

Fig. 20: Checking Second Brake Clutch Pack Clearance

CAUTION: *Note direction of second brake clutch pack component installation and number of each component for reassembly reference. Components must be installed in original location. See Fig. 21.*

21) Remove snap ring and second brake clutch pack. See Fig. 21. Using micrometer, measure second brake clutch disc thickness. Replace clutch disc if thickness is less than .072" (1.83 mm)

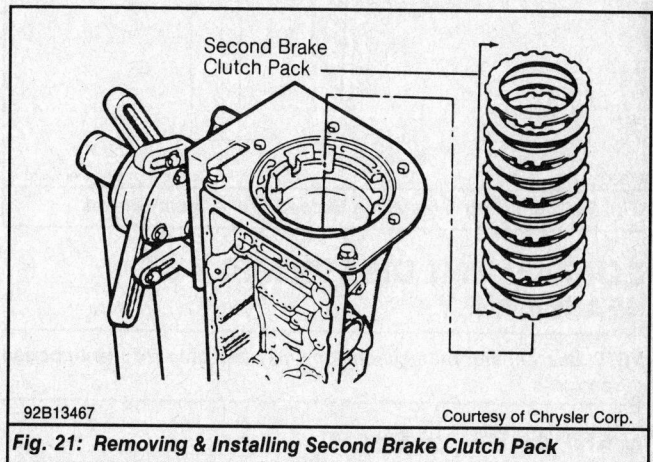

Fig. 21: Removing & Installing Second Brake Clutch Pack

22) Remove park rod bracket-to-transmission case bolts. *See Fig. 9.* Disconnect park rod from shift sector on manual valve shaft. Remove park rod and park rod bracket. Remove spring, pin and pawl.

23) Using feeler gauge, measure first-reverse brake clutch pack clearance. *See Fig. 22.* First-reverse clutch pack clearance should be .028-.047" (.71-1.19 mm). Replace clutch discs if clearance is not within specification.

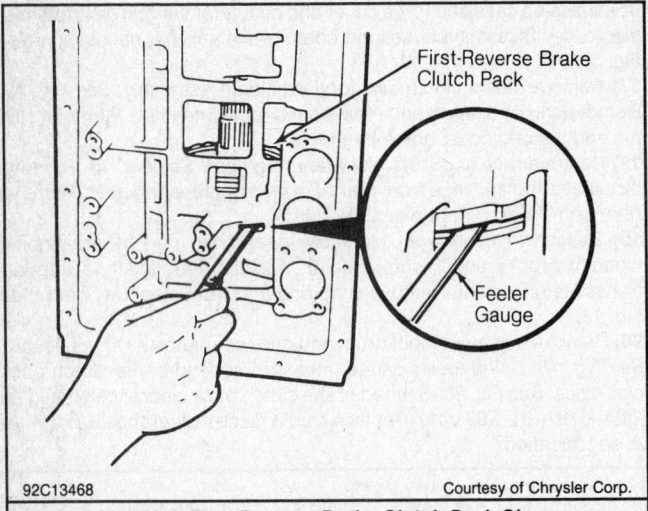

92C13468   Courtesy of Chrysler Corp.

Fig. 22: Checking First-Reverse Brake Clutch Pack Clearance

CAUTION: Apply tape on end of screwdriver for removing second coast brake piston sleeve to prevent damage to transmission case.

24) Remove second coast brake piston sleeve and snap ring. *See Fig. 13.* Remove rear planetary gear, second brake drum, first-reverse brake clutch pack and output shaft as an assembly. *See Fig. 13.* Remove rear planetary and second brake drum thrust bearing from transmission case.

25) Note location of second brake drum gasket. *See Fig. 23.* Using screwdriver, remove second brake drum gasket from transmission case.

26) Measure inside diameter of transmission case rear bushing. Replace transmission case if bushing inside diameter exceeds 1.5031" (38.179 mm), as bushing is not serviceable.

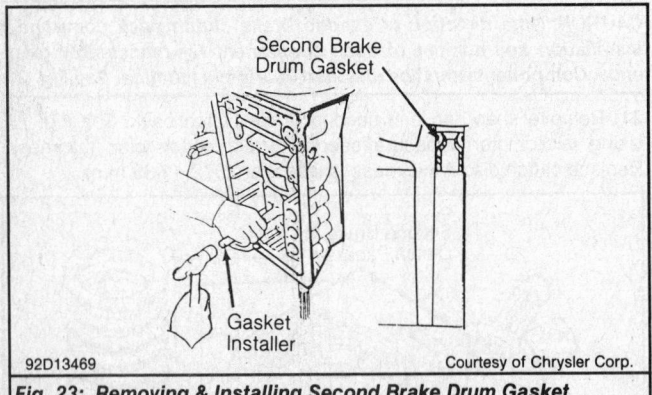

92D13469   Courtesy of Chrysler Corp.

Fig. 23: Removing & Installing Second Brake Drum Gasket

COMPONENT DISASSEMBLY & REASSEMBLY

NOTE: Bearing and race dimensions may be listed for identification purposes.

MANUAL VALVE SHAFT

Removal – 1) Using hammer and chisel, cut spacer sleeve and remove from manual valve shaft. Remove pin from manual valve shaft. *See Fig. 7.*

2) Remove manual valve shaft and shift sector from transmission case. Remove seals from transmission case.

Installation – 1) Coat all components with petroleum jelly. Install seals in transmission case. Install NEW spacer sleeve on shift sector.

2) Install manual valve shaft in transmission case. Install shift sector and spacer sleeve on manual valve shaft. Align hole in spacer sleeve with notch in shift sector.

3) Install pin into shift sector and manual valve shaft. Stake spacer sleeve to shift sector and manual valve shaft.

CAUTION: Ensure spacer sleeve is staked to shift sector and manual valve shaft.

OIL PUMP

Disassembly – Remove seal rings and "O" ring. *See Fig. 24.* Remove stator shaft-to-pump body bolts. Separate stator shaft from pump body. Remove drive gear and driven gear from pump body. Remove pump seal from pump body.

Cleaning & Inspection – 1) Clean components with solvent and dry with compressed air. Inspect components for damage.

2) Measure pump body and stator shaft bushing inside diameter. Replace pump body or stator shaft if bushing inside diameter exceeds specification. See OIL PUMP SPECIFICATIONS table.

NOTE: Stator shaft bushing inside diameter should be checked at front and rear areas of the bushing.

3) Install drive and driven gears in pump body. Using feeler gauge, measure driven gear-to-pump body clearance. Place straightedge on oil pump body, above both gears. Using feeler gauge, measure gear end clearance between each gear and straightedge.

4) Align one tooth on drive gear with one tooth on driven gear. Measure gear tooth clearance between teeth. Replace components if clearance is not within specification. See OIL PUMP SPECIFICATIONS table.

OIL PUMP SPECIFICATIONS [1]

Application	In. (mm)
Driven Gear-To-Pump Body Clearance	.012 (.30)
Gear End Clearance	.004 (.10)
Gear Tooth Clearance	.012 (.30)
Pump Body Bushing Inside Diameter	1.504 (38.20)
Stator Shaft Bushing Inside Diameter	
Front Area	.8496 (21.580)
Rear Area	1.0661 (27.079)

[1] – Maximum allowable clearances are listed.

Reassembly – 1) Install NEW pump seal in pump body (if removed). Lubricate all components with Mopar Dexron-IIE/Mercon ATF. Install driven and drive gears in pump body.

2) Install stator shaft on oil pump body. Install and tighten stator shaft-to-pump body bolts to specification. See TORQUE SPECIFICATIONS.

3) Install NEW "O" ring on pump body and NEW seal rings on stator shaft. install oil pump on torque converter. Ensure oil pump gears rotate smoothly in both directions by rotating pump body. Lubricate "O" ring and seal rings with petroleum jelly.

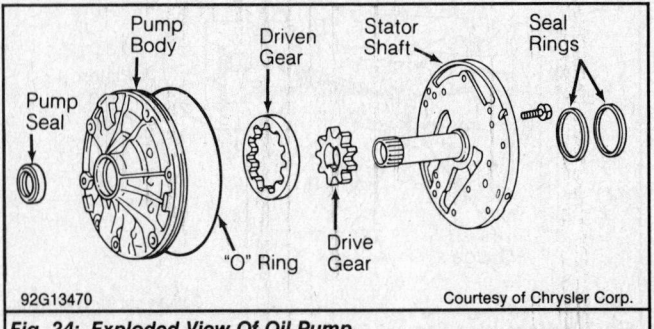

92G13470   Courtesy of Chrysler Corp.

Fig. 24: Exploded View Of Oil Pump

OVERDRIVE PLANETARY GEAR & OVERDRIVE CLUTCH

Disassembly – 1) Check operation of one-way clutch in clutch drum by holding clutch drum and rotating shaft on overdrive planetary gear clockwise and counterclockwise. *See Fig. 26.* Shaft should rotate freely clockwise but lock when rotated counterclockwise.

2) Remove clutch drum and components from planetary gear. Remove thrust bearing from clutch drum. *See Fig. 25.*

3) Measure overdrive clutch piston stroke by positioning oil pump and clutch drum on torque converter. Position dial indicator with stem resting on clutch piston. *See Fig. 27.*

4) Apply air pressure through feed hole in oil pump and note overdrive clutch piston stroke reading on dial indicator. *See Fig. 27.* Overdrive clutch piston stroke should be .073-.085" (1.85-2.16 mm).

5) If overdrive clutch piston stroke is not within specification, either clutch discs or retainer plate must be replaced. If clutch discs are okay, retainer plate must be replaced with different thickness retainer during reassembly.

CAUTION: Note direction of clutch pack component installation and number of each component for reassembly reference. Components must be installed in original location. See Fig. 25.

6) Remove snap ring, retainer plate, clutch discs and clutch plates. *See Fig. 25.* Using press and spring compressor, compress piston return springs. Remove snap ring. Remove spring compressor, retainer and piston return springs.

7) Position oil pump and clutch drum on torque converter. Hold overdrive clutch piston. Carefully apply air pressure through feed hole in oil pump to remove overdrive clutch piston from clutch drum.

8) Remove thrust bearing and race from planetary ring gear. *See Fig. 25.* Remove snap ring and separate ring gear hub from planetary ring gear.

9) Remove race from rear of overdrive planetary gear. Remove snap ring and retaining plate from overdrive planetary gear. *See Fig. 25.* Remove one-way clutch and one-way clutch outer race as an assembly from overdrive planetary gear. Separate one-way clutch from one-way clutch outer race. Remove thrust washer from overdrive planetary gear.

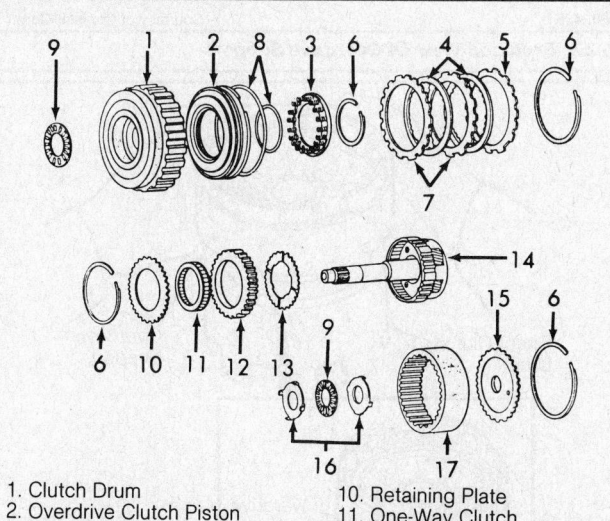

1. Clutch Drum
2. Overdrive Clutch Piston
3. Piston Return Springs & Retainer
4. Clutch Disc
5. Retainer Plate
6. Snap Ring
7. Clutch Plate
8. "O" Ring
9. Thrust Bearing
10. Retaining Plate
11. One-Way Clutch
12. One-Way Clutch Outer Race
13. Thrust Washer
14. Overdrive Planetary Gear
15. Ring Gear Hub
16. Race
17. Planetary Ring Gear

94B38407   Courtesy of Chrysler Corp.

Fig. 25: Exploded View Of Overdrive Planetary Gear & Clutch Components

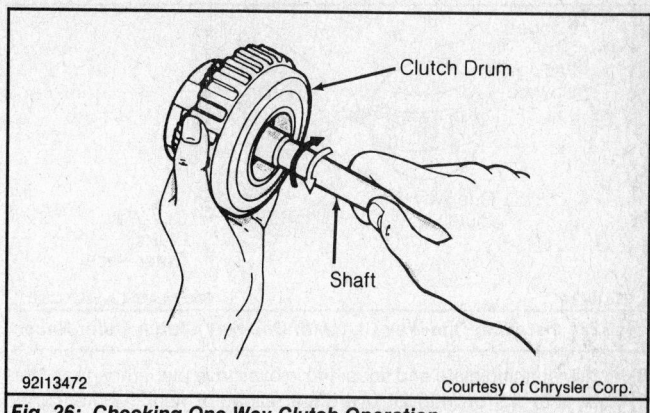

92I13472   Courtesy of Chrysler Corp.

Fig. 26: Checking One-Way Clutch Operation

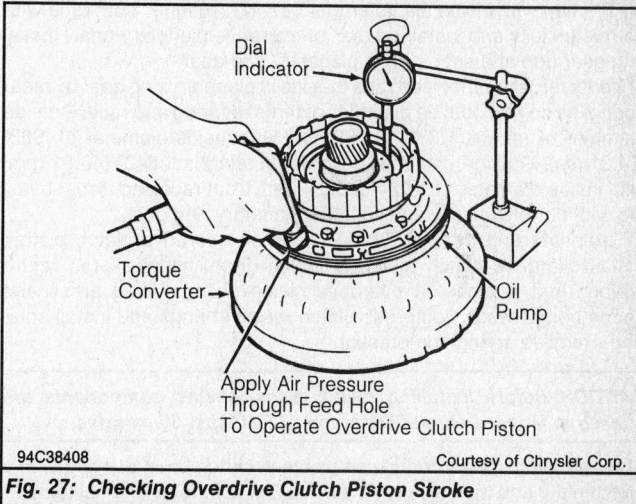

94C38408   Courtesy of Chrysler Corp.

Fig. 27: Checking Overdrive Clutch Piston Stroke

Cleaning & Inspection – 1) Clean metal components with solvent and dry with compressed air. Inspect components for damage. Using micrometer, measure clutch disc thickness. Replace clutch disc if thickness is less than .072" (1.83 mm).

2) Using caliper, measure free length of piston return springs with springs installed in retainer. Replace piston return springs if free length is not .661" (16.79 mm).

NOTE: Piston return spring free length also includes thickness of retainer.

3) Ensure check ball in overdrive clutch piston moves freely. Apply low air pressure against check ball in overdrive clutch piston. Air should not leak past check ball. Replace overdrive clutch piston if check ball is defective.

4) Measure inside diameter of clutch drum bushing. Replace clutch drum if bushing inside diameter exceeds 1.0673" (27.109 mm).

5) Measure inside diameter of bushing located on rear of overdrive planetary gear. Replace overdrive planetary gear if bushing inside diameter exceeds .4437" (11.270 mm).

Reassembly – 1) Install thrust washer in overdrive planetary gear with grooves facing toward shaft end of overdrive planetary gear.

CAUTION: Ensure grooves on thrust washer in overdrive planetary gear are facing toward shaft end of overdrive planetary gear.

2) Install one-way clutch in one-way clutch outer race with flanged side facing upward. *See Fig. 28.* Install one-way clutch assembly in overdrive planetary gear so that flanged side of one-way clutch is facing upward, toward shaft end of overdrive planetary gear.

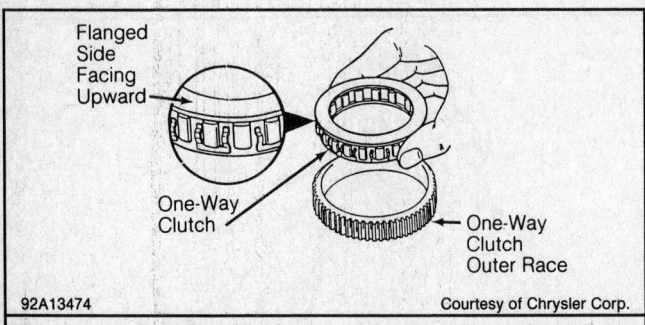

Fig. 28: Installing One-Way Clutch In One-Way Clutch Outer Race

92A13474   Courtesy of Chrysler Corp.

3) Install retaining plate and snap ring in overdrive planetary gear. Verify race that fits on rear of overdrive planetary gear by measuring inside and outside diameter of race. Race outside diameter is 1.646" (41.81 mm) with inside diameter of 1.067" (27.10 mm). Coat race with petroleum jelly and install on rear of overdrive planetary gear. Install ring gear hub and snap ring in planetary ring gear.

4) Verify thrust bearing and race that fits in planetary ring gear by measuring inside and outside diameter of thrust bearing and race. Outside diameter of race is 1.882" (47.80 mm) with inside diameter of .953" (24.21mm). Outside diameter of thrust bearing is 1.843" (46.81 mm) with inside diameter of 1.024" (26.01 mm). Coat race and thrust bearing with petroleum jelly and install in planetary ring gear.

5) Lubricate and install NEW "O" rings on overdrive clutch piston. Install overdrive clutch piston in clutch drum. Install piston return springs and retainer on overdrive clutch piston. Using press and spring compressor, compress piston return springs and install snap ring. Remove spring compressor.

CAUTION: Before installing clutch discs, ensure components are soaked in Mopar Dexron-IIE/Mercon ATF at least 30 minutes.

---

6) Install clutch discs and clutch plates in clutch drum starting with a clutch plate and then a clutch disc. See Fig. 25. Install original number of components. Install retainer plate with flat side toward clutch disc. Install snap ring.

CAUTION: Ensure retainer plate is installed with flat side toward clutch disc. Flanged side of retainer plate goes toward the snap ring.

---

7) Measure overdrive clutch piston stroke by positioning oil pump and clutch drum on torque converter. Position dial indicator with stem resting on clutch piston. See Fig. 27.

8) Apply air pressure through feed hole in oil pump and note overdrive clutch piston stroke reading on dial indicator. See Fig. 27. Overdrive clutch piston stroke should be .073-.085" (1.85-2.16 mm).

9) If overdrive clutch piston stroke is not within specification, install different thickness retainer plate. Retainer plate is available in various thickness. See OVERDRIVE CLUTCH RETAINER PLATE SPECIFICATIONS table.

OVERDRIVE CLUTCH RETAINER PLATE SPECIFICATIONS

Retainer Plate Identification Number	Thickness In. (mm)
16	.142 (3.61)
17	.138 (3.51)
18	.134 (3.40)
19	.130 (3 30)
20	.126 (3.20)
21	.122 (3.10)

10) Install thrust bearing in clutch drum with rollers facing away from clutch drum. Outside diameter of thrust bearing is 1.976" (50.19 mm) with inside diameter of 1.138" (28.91 mm).

11) Install clutch drum on overdrive planetary gear. Check operation of one-way clutch by holding clutch drum and rotating shaft on overdrive planetary gear clockwise and counterclockwise. See Fig. 26. Shaft should rotate freely clockwise but lock when rotated counterclockwise.

OVERDRIVE SUPPORT

Disassembly – 1) Check piston operation by placing overdrive support on direct clutch drum. See Fig. 30. Apply compressed air through overdrive support feed hole. Ensure piston moves smoothly and does not bind.

2) Remove overdrive support from direct clutch drum. Remove front race, thrust bearing, rear race, clutch drum thrust washer and race from overdrive support. See Fig. 29. Using press and spring compressor, compress piston return spring. Remove piston snap ring.

3) Place overdrive support on direct clutch drum. See Fig. 30. Apply compressed air through overdrive support feed hole and remove piston from overdrive support. Remove and discard seal rings and "O" rings.

Cleaning & Inspection – 1) Clean components with solvent and dry with compressed air. Inspect components for damage.

2) Using caliper, measure free length of piston return springs with springs installed in the retainer. Replace piston return springs if free length is not .678" (17.22 mm).

NOTE: Piston return spring free length also includes thickness of retainer.

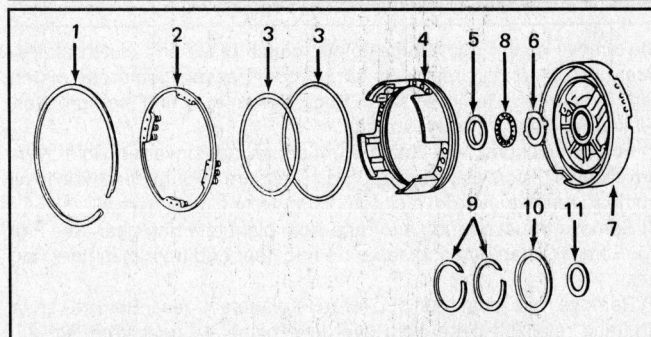

1. Piston Snap Ring
2. Piston Return Spring & Retainer
3. "O" Ring
4. Piston
5. Front Race
6. Rear Race
7. Overdrive Support
8. Thrust Bearing
9. Seal Ring
10. Clutch Drum Thrust Washer
11. Race

92B13475   Courtesy of Chrysler Corp.

Fig. 29: Exploded View Of Overdrive Support

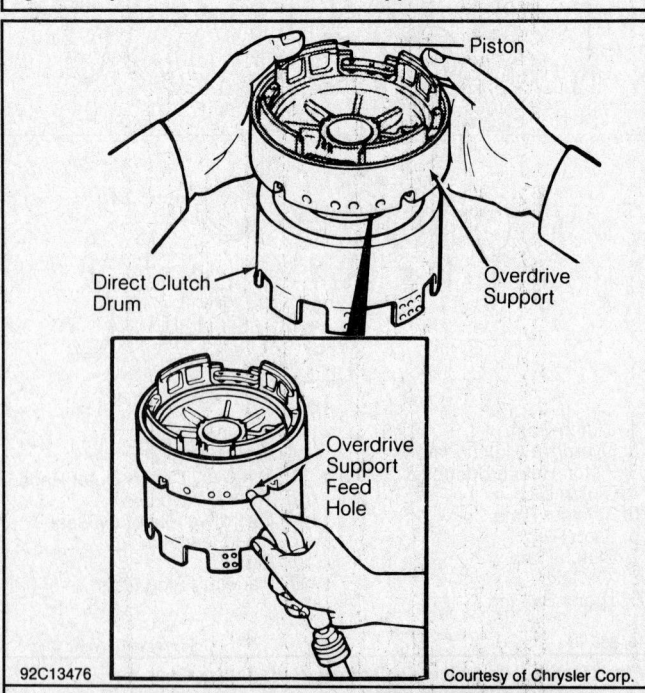

92C13476   Courtesy of Chrysler Corp.

Fig. 30: Checking Piston Operation & Removing Piston From Overdrive Support

Reassembly – 1) To reassemble, reverse disassembly procedure. Lubricate NEW seal rings and NEW "O" rings with Mopar Dexron-IIE/Mercon ATF before installing. Squeeze ends of seal ring together before installing on overdrive support. This aids in proper seating of seal rings.

2) Ensure tangs on rear race engage with slots on overdrive support. Thrust bearing must be installed with rollers facing upward (away from overdrive support).

3) Ensure piston moves smoothly by placing overdrive support on direct clutch drum and applying compressed air through overdrive support feed hole. Verify thrust bearing and race size identification for proper location by measuring inside and outside diameter. See OVERDRIVE SUPPORT BEARING & RACE IDENTIFICATION table.

OVERDRIVE SUPPORT BEARING & RACE IDENTIFICATION

Application	Outside Diameter In. (mm)	Inside Diameter In. (mm)
Front Race	1.882 (47.80)	1.209 (30.71)
Rear Race	1.882 (47.80)	1.350 (34.29)
Thrust Bearing	1.878 (47.70)	1.287 (32.69)

DIRECT CLUTCH

Disassembly – 1) Separate direct clutch drum from forward clutch. Remove thrust washer from center of direct clutch drum. *See Fig. 31.*

2) Direct clutch piston stroke must be checked. Position direct clutch drum on overdrive support. Mount dial indicator with stem resting on clutch piston. *See Fig. 32.*

3) Apply 57-114 psi (4-8 kg/cm²) air pressure through feed hole in overdrive support and note direct clutch piston stroke reading on dial indicator. Check direct clutch piston stroke at least twice.

4) Direct clutch piston stroke should be .054-.065" (1.37-1.65 mm). If direct clutch piston stroke is not within specification, either retainer or clutch discs must be replaced. If clutch discs are okay, retainer must be replaced with different thickness retainer during reassembly.

CAUTION: Note direction of clutch pack component installation and number of each component for reassembly reference. Components must be installed in original location. See Fig. 31.

---

5) Remove clutch pack snap ring, retainer, clutch discs and clutch plates. Using press and spring compressor, compress piston return springs. Remove piston return spring retaining snap ring. Remove spring compressor.

6) Remove piston return springs and retainer. Position direct clutch drum on overdrive support as when checking direct clutch piston stroke. Apply air pressure through feed hole in overdrive support and remove clutch piston. Remove "O" rings from clutch piston.

Cleaning & Inspection – 1) Clean metal components with solvent and dry with compressed air. Inspect components for damage. Using micrometer, measure clutch disc thickness. Replace clutch disc if thickness is less than .072" (1.83 mm).

2) Using caliper, measure free length of piston return springs with springs installed in retainer. Replace piston return springs if free length is not .839" (21.31 mm).

NOTE: Piston return spring free length also includes thickness of retainer.

---

3) Ensure check ball in clutch piston moves freely. Apply low air pressure against check ball in clutch piston. Air should not leak past check ball. Replace clutch piston if check ball is defective.

4) Measure inside diameter of direct clutch drum bushing. Replace direct clutch drum if the bushing inside diameter exceeds 2.1248" (53.970 mm).

Reassembly – 1) Lubricate NEW "O" rings with Mopar Dexron-IIE/Mercon ATF and install on clutch piston. Install clutch piston in direct clutch drum. Install piston return springs and retainer.

2) Using press and spring compressor, compress piston return springs. Install snap ring. Ensure ends of snap ring are not aligned with tab on retainer for piston return springs. Remove spring compressor.

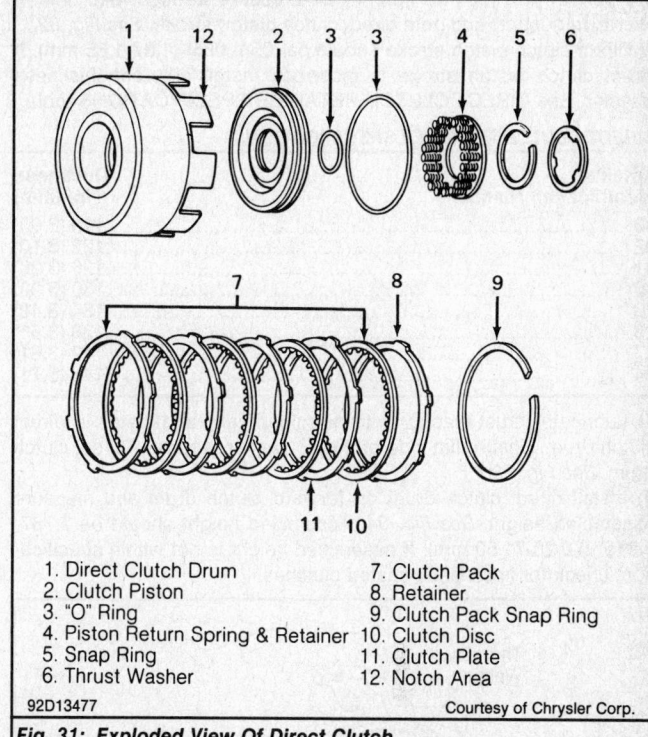

1. Direct Clutch Drum
2. Clutch Piston
3. "O" Ring
4. Piston Return Spring & Retainer
5. Snap Ring
6. Thrust Washer
7. Clutch Pack
8. Retainer
9. Clutch Pack Snap Ring
10. Clutch Disc
11. Clutch Plate
12. Notch Area

92D13477   Courtesy of Chrysler Corp.

Fig. 31: Exploded View Of Direct Clutch

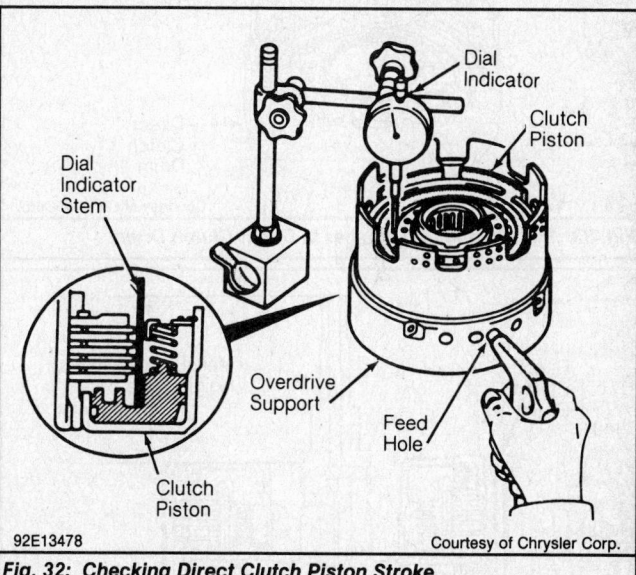

92E13478   Courtesy of Chrysler Corp.

Fig. 32: Checking Direct Clutch Piston Stroke

CAUTION: Before installing clutch discs, ensure components are soaked in Mopar Dexron-IIE/Mercon ATF at least 30 minutes.

---

3) Install clutch discs and clutch plates in direct clutch drum starting with a clutch plate and then a clutch disc. *See Fig. 31.* Install original number of components.

4) Install retainer with flat side toward clutch disc. Install clutch pack snap ring. Ensure ends of snap rings are not located in notch area in direct clutch drum. *See Fig. 31.*

CAUTION: Ensure retainer is installed with flat side toward clutch disc and flange side toward clutch pack snap ring. Ends of clutch pack snap ring must not be aligned with notch area in direct clutch drum.

---

5) Position direct clutch drum on overdrive support. Mount dial indicator with stem resting on clutch piston. *See Fig. 32.*

6) Apply 57-114 psi (4-8 kg/cm²) air pressure through feed hole in overdrive support and note direct clutch piston stroke. *See Fig. 32.*

7) Direct clutch piston stroke should be .054-.065" (1.37-1.65 mm). If direct clutch piston stroke is incorrect, install different thickness retainer. See DIRECT CLUTCH RETAINER SPECIFICATIONS table.

DIRECT CLUTCH RETAINER SPECIFICATIONS

Retainer Identification Number	Thickness In. (mm)
33	.118 (3.00)
32	.122 (3.10)
31	.126 (3.20)
30	.130 (3 30)
29	.134 (3.40)
28	.138 (3.51)
27	.142 (3.61)
34	.146 (3.71)

8) Lubricate thrust washer with petroleum jelly and install in direct clutch drum. Ensure flat side of thrust washer is toward direct clutch drum. *See Fig. 33.*

9) Install direct clutch drum on forward clutch drum and measure assembled height. *See Fig. 34.* Assembled height should be 2.767-2.815" (70.28-71.50 mm). If assembled height is not within specification, check for improperly seated clutches.

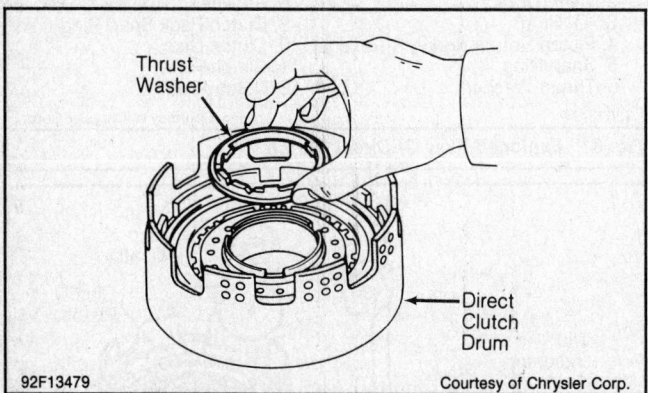

Fig. 33: *Installing Thrust Washer In Direct Clutch Drum*

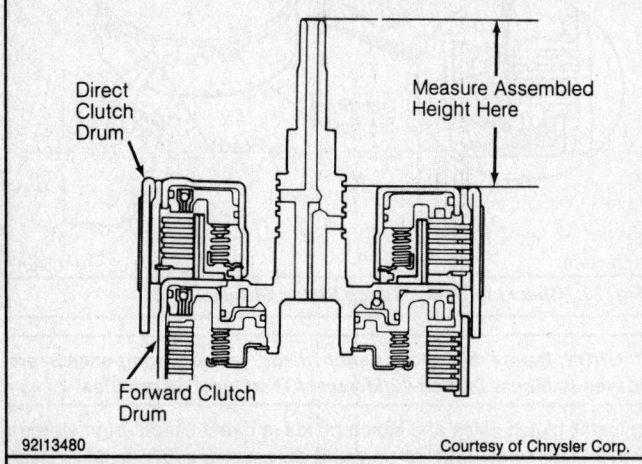

Fig. 34: *Measuring Direct Clutch & Forward Clutch Assembled Height*

FORWARD CLUTCH

Disassembly – 1) Remove thrust bearing and race from rear of forward clutch drum. *See Fig. 35.* Forward clutch piston stroke must be checked. Position overdrive support on wooden blocks.

2) Assemble forward clutch on overdrive support. Position dial indicator with stem resting on clutch piston. *See Fig. 36.* Apply compressed air into feed hole in overdrive support and note forward clutch piston stroke reading on dial indicator.

3) Forward clutch piston stroke should be .140-.147" (3.55-3.73 mm). Replace clutch discs if forward clutch piston stroke is not within specification.

CAUTION: Note direction of clutch pack component installation and number of each component for reassembly reference. Components must be installed in original location. Note direction of cushion plate installation for reassembly reference. See Fig. 35.

4) Remove forward clutch from overdrive support. Remove clutch pack snap ring, retainer, clutch pack and cushion plate. *See Fig. 35.*

5) Using press and spring compressor, compress piston return springs. Remove piston return spring retaining snap ring. Remove spring compressor.

6) Remove piston return springs and retainer. Assemble forward clutch on overdrive support. Apply compressed air through feed hole in overdrive support and remove clutch piston.

7) Remove "O" rings from clutch piston and rear of forward clutch drum. Remove seal rings and from shaft on forward clutch drum. Remove bearing and race from forward clutch drum. *See Fig. 35.*

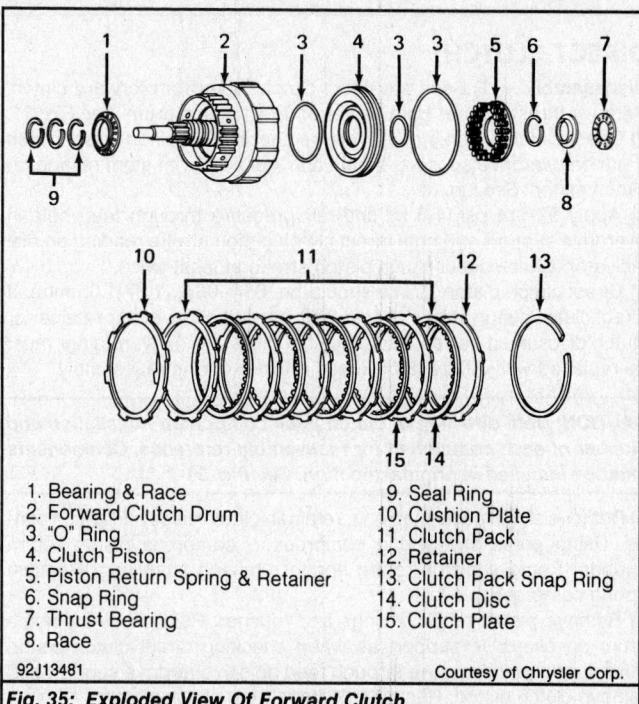

1. Bearing & Race
2. Forward Clutch Drum
3. "O" Ring
4. Clutch Piston
5. Piston Return Spring & Retainer
6. Snap Ring
7. Thrust Bearing
8. Race
9. Seal Ring
10. Cushion Plate
11. Clutch Pack
12. Retainer
13. Clutch Pack Snap Ring
14. Clutch Disc
15. Clutch Plate

Fig. 35: *Exploded View Of Forward Clutch*

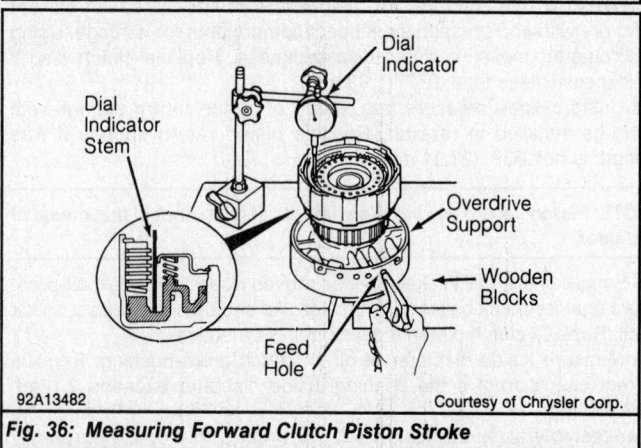

Fig. 36: *Measuring Forward Clutch Piston Stroke*

Cleaning & Inspection – 1) Clean metal components with solvent and dry with compressed air. Inspect components for damage. Using micrometer, measure clutch disc thickness. Replace clutch disc if thickness is less than .060" (1.52 mm).

2) Using caliper, measure free length of piston return springs with springs installed in retainer. Replace piston return springs if free length is not .767" (19.48 mm).

NOTE: Piston return spring free length also includes thickness of retainer.

3) Ensure check ball in clutch piston moves freely. Apply low air pressure against check ball in clutch piston. Air should not leak past check ball. Replace clutch piston if check ball is defective.

4) Measure inside diameter of forward clutch drum bushing. Replace forward clutch drum if bushing inside diameter exceeds .948" (24.08 mm).

Reassembly – 1) Lubricate bearing and race with petroleum jelly and install on front of forward clutch drum. Ensure flat side of race is against forward clutch drum and bearing rollers are upward, toward end of shaft on forward clutch drum.

2) Coat NEW seal rings with petroleum jelly. Squeeze ends of seal rings together so ends overlap. This tightens seal ring and aids in clutch installation. Install seal rings on shaft, using care not to over expand seal ring.

3) Lubricate NEW "O" rings with Mopar Dexron-IIE/Mercon ATF. Install "O" rings on clutch piston and hub of forward clutch drum. Install clutch piston in forward clutch drum. Install piston return springs and retainer.

4) Using press and spring compressor, compress piston return springs. Install snap ring. Ensure end of snap ring is not aligned with notches in forward clutch drum. Remove spring compressor. Install cushion plate in forward clutch drum with concave side of cushion plate facing downward (toward forward clutch drum).

CAUTION: Ensure cushion plate is installed with concave side facing downward (toward forward clutch drum).

CAUTION: Before installing clutch discs, ensure components are soaked in Mopar Dexron-IIE/Mercon ATF at least 30 minutes.

5) Install clutch discs and clutch plates in forward clutch drum starting with a clutch plate and then a clutch disc. *See Fig. 35.* Install original number of components.

6) Install retainer and clutch pack snap ring. Assemble forward clutch on overdrive support. Position dial indicator with stem resting on clutch piston. *See Fig. 36.*

7) Apply compressed air into feed hole in overdrive support and note forward clutch piston stroke reading on dial indicator. Forward clutch piston stroke should be .140-.147" (3.55-3.73 mm). Replace clutch discs or check for improperly assembled components if forward clutch piston stroke is not within specification.

8) Remove forward clutch from overdrive support. Verify thrust bearing and race size. Outer diameter of thrust bearing is 1.839" (46.71 mm) and outer diameter of race is 1.925" (48.90 mm). Inner diameter of thrust bearing and race is 1.024" (26.01 mm).

9) Lubricate thrust bearing and race with petroleum jelly. Install thrust bearing and race on rear of forward clutch drum. Ensure lip on race engages with forward clutch drum. Ensure bearing rollers are facing upward, away from shaft end of forward clutch drum.

10) Install forward clutch drum on direct clutch drum and measure assembled height. *See Fig. 34.* Assembled height should be 2.767-2.815" (70.28-71.50 mm). If assembled height is not within specification, check for improperly seated clutches.

FRONT PLANETARY GEAR

Disassembly – 1) Remove front planetary ring gear from front planetary gear. *See Fig. 37.* Remove front thrust bearing, front race and forward race from front planetary ring gear.

2) Remove thrust race from front planetary gear. *See Fig. 37.* Remove snap ring and front planetary from shaft (if necessary). Remove rear race and rear thrust bearing.

Cleaning & Inspection – Clean components with solvent and dry with compressed air. Inspect components for damage. Measure inside diameter of bushing in front planetary ring gear. Replace front planetary ring gear if bushing inside diameter exceeds .948" (24.08 mm).

Reassembly – 1) Verify thrust bearing and race identification by measuring inside and outside diameter. See FRONT PLANETARY GEAR BEARING & RACE SPECIFICATIONS table.

2) Lubricate all thrust bearings and races with petroleum jelly. Install rear race and rear thrust bearing in front planetary gear. Ensure flat side of rear race is against surface of front planetary gear surface.

3) Install thrust race on front side of front planetary gear. Ensure tabs on thrust race engage with holes in front planetary gear.

4) Install front race and front thrust bearing in rear of front planetary ring gear. Ensure flat side of front race is against surface of front planetary ring gear.

5) Install forward race on front planetary ring gear with lip of race is facing toward front planetary ring gear and smooth flat surface is facing away from front planetary ring gear. *See Fig. 37.*

FRONT PLANETARY GEAR BEARING & RACE SPECIFICATIONS

Application	Outside Diameter In. (mm)	Inside Diameter In. (mm)
Forward Race	1.850 (46.99)	1.043 (26.49)
Front Race	2.110 (53.59)	1.201 (30.51)
Front Thrust Bearing	1.878 (47.70)	1.283 (32.59)
Rear Race	1.874 (47.60)	1.327 (33.71)
Rear Thrust Bearing	1.878 (47.70)	1.398 (35.51)

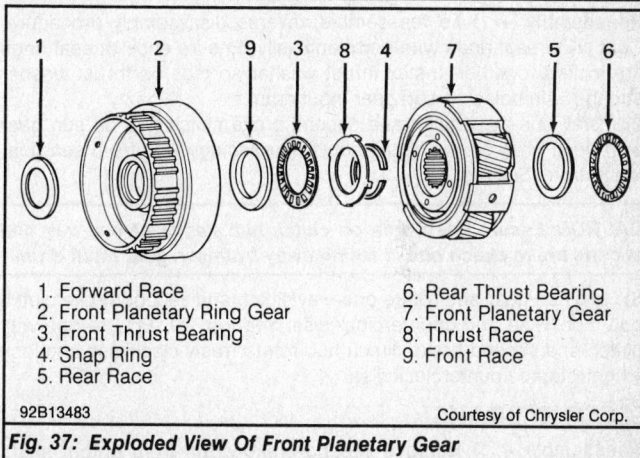

1. Forward Race
2. Front Planetary Ring Gear
3. Front Thrust Bearing
4. Snap Ring
5. Rear Race
6. Rear Thrust Bearing
7. Front Planetary Gear
8. Thrust Race
9. Front Race

92B13483   Courtesy of Chrysler Corp.

Fig. 37: Exploded View Of Front Planetary Gear

SUN GEAR & ONE-WAY CLUTCH

Disassembly – 1) Check one-way clutch operation by holding sun gear and rotating one-way clutch and second brake clutch hub clockwise and counterclockwise. *See Fig. 39.*

2) One-way clutch and second brake clutch hub should rotate freely clockwise and lock when rotated counterclockwise. Replace one-way clutch and second brake clutch hub if one-way clutch does not operate properly.

3) Remove one-way clutch and second brake clutch hub from sun gear input drum. Remove thrust washer from sun gear input drum. *See Fig. 38.* Remove seal rings from sun gear.

4) Support sun gear on wooden block with opening of sun gear input drum facing downward. Remove snap ring from sun gear. Separate sun gear input drum from sun gear.

Cleaning & Inspection – Clean components with solvent and dry with compressed air. Measure inside diameter of sun gear bushings. Replace sun gear if bushing inside diameter exceeds 1.0661" (27.079 mm).

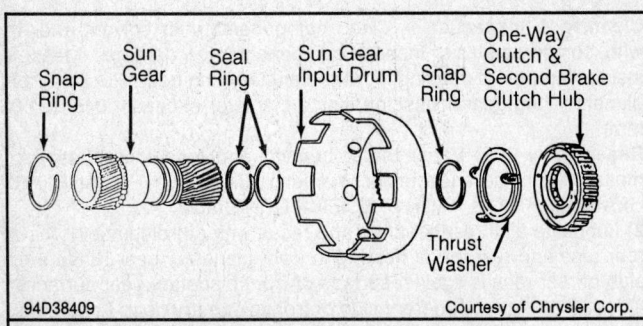

94D38409   Courtesy of Chrysler Corp.

Fig. 38: Exploded View Of Sun Gear & One-Way Clutch

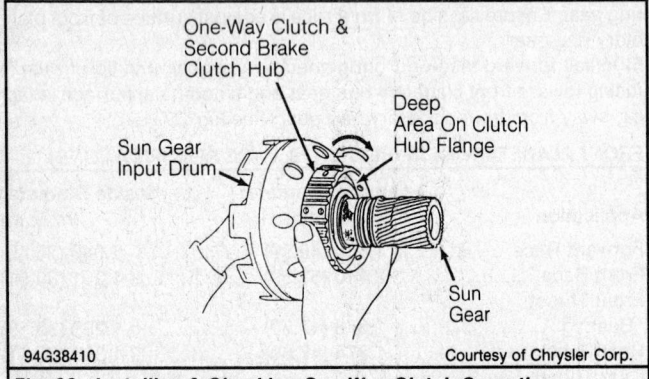

94G38410   Courtesy of Chrysler Corp.

Fig. 39: Installing & Checking One-Way Clutch Operation

Reassembly – 1) To reassemble, reverse disassembly procedure. Coat NEW seal rings with petroleum jelly. Ensure ends of seal rings are locked together. Install thrust washer so tabs on thrust washer engage with holes on sun gear input drum.

2) Install one-way clutch and second brake clutch hub on sun gear with deep area on the clutch hub flange facing away from sun gear input drum. See Fig. 39.

CAUTION: Ensure deep area on clutch hub flange of one-way and second brake clutch hub is facing away from sun gear input drum.

3) Hold sun gear and rotate one-way clutch and second brake clutch hub clockwise and counterclockwise. See Fig. 39. Ensure one-way clutch and second brake clutch hub rotate freely clockwise and lock when rotated counterclockwise.

SECOND BRAKE

Disassembly – 1) Remove second brake drum from output shaft assembly. See Fig. 40. Remove thrust washer from second brake drum.

2) Using press and spring compressor, compress piston return springs. Remove snap ring. Remove spring compressor. Remove spring retainer and piston return springs. See Fig. 40.

3) Remove second brake piston and piston sleeve from second brake drum by applying compressed air to feed hole on second brake drum. See Fig. 41. Remove "O" rings from second brake piston.

Cleaning & Inspection – Clean components with solvent and dry with compressed air. Using caliper, measure free length of piston return springs with springs installed in spring retainer. Replace piston return springs if free length is not .632" (16.05 mm).

NOTE: Piston return spring free length also includes thickness of spring retainer.

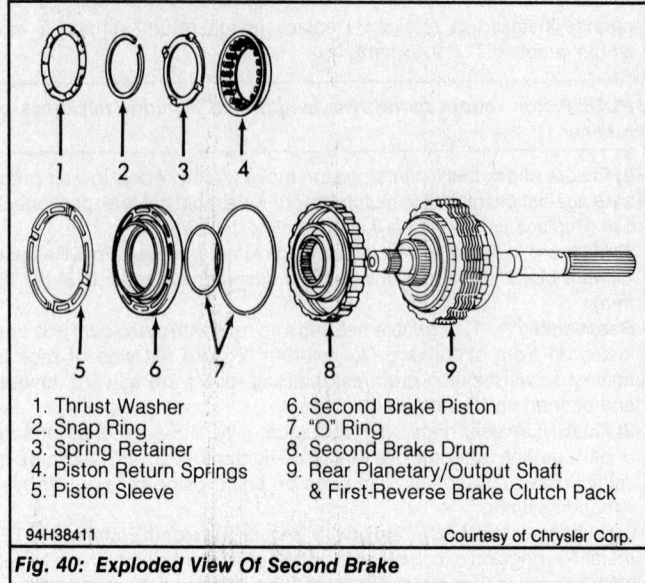

1. Thrust Washer
2. Snap Ring
3. Spring Retainer
4. Piston Return Springs
5. Piston Sleeve
6. Second Brake Piston
7. "O" Ring
8. Second Brake Drum
9. Rear Planetary/Output Shaft & First-Reverse Brake Clutch Pack

94H38411   Courtesy of Chrysler Corp.

Fig. 40: Exploded View Of Second Brake

Reassembly – 1) Lubricate NEW "O" rings with petroleum jelly. Install "O" rings on second brake piston. Install second brake piston and piston sleeve in second brake drum.

2) Install piston return springs and spring retainer on second brake piston. Using press and spring compressor, compress piston return springs. Install snap ring.

3) Remove spring compressor. Apply compressed air to feed hole on second brake drum which was used for removing second brake piston. See Fig. 41. Ensure second brake piston operates smoothly.

4) Coat thrust washer with petroleum jelly. Install thrust washer on second brake drum. Ensure notches on thrust washer engage with tabs on spring retainer.

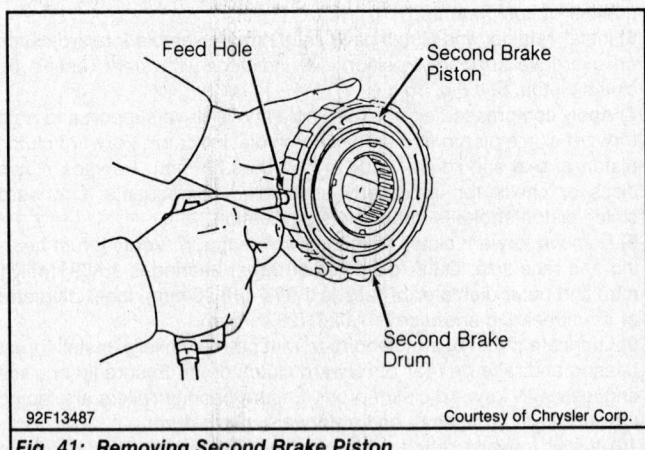

92F13487   Courtesy of Chrysler Corp.

Fig. 41: Removing Second Brake Piston

REAR PLANETARY, NO. 2 ONE-WAY CLUTCH & OUTPUT SHAFT

CAUTION: Note direction of low-reverse clutch pack component installation and number of each component for reassembly reference. Components must be installed in original location. See Fig. 42.

Disassembly – 1) Remove output shaft from rear planetary gear assembly. *See Fig. 42.* Remove seal ring from output shaft. Remove first-reverse brake clutch pack from rear planetary gear.

2) Remove rear planetary gear from planetary ring gear. *See Fig. 42.* The No. 2 one-way clutch operation should be checked by holding rear planetary gear and rotating one-way clutch inner race in both directions. *See Fig. 43.*

3) One-way clutch inner race should rotate freely counterclockwise and lock when rotated clockwise. Replace one-way clutch if improper operation exists.

4) Remove one-way clutch inner race from rear planetary gear. Remove snap ring and No. 2 one-way clutch from rear planetary gear. *See Fig. 42.*

5) Remove front and rear thrust washers from rear planetary gear. Remove thrust bearing and races from planetary ring gear. Remove snap ring and separate ring gear hub from planetary ring gear.

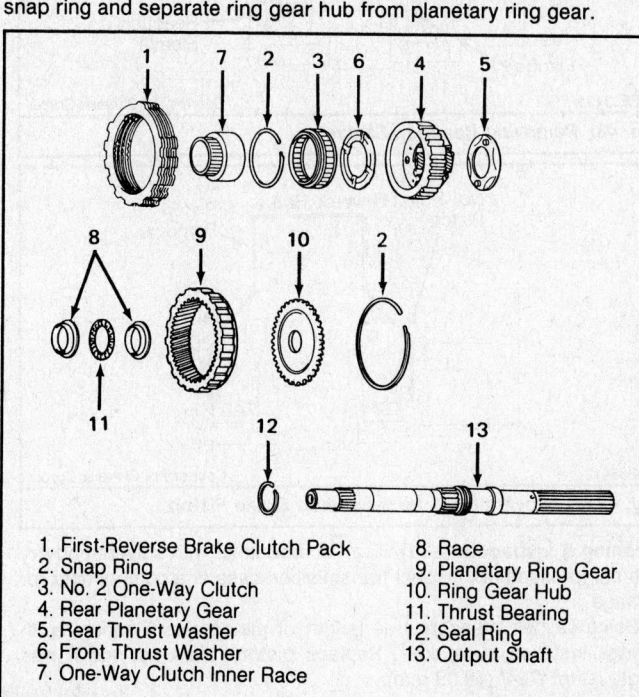

1. First-Reverse Brake Clutch Pack
2. Snap Ring
3. No. 2 One-Way Clutch
4. Rear Planetary Gear
5. Rear Thrust Washer
6. Front Thrust Washer
7. One-Way Clutch Inner Race
8. Race
9. Planetary Ring Gear
10. Ring Gear Hub
11. Thrust Bearing
12. Seal Ring
13. Output Shaft

92G13488   Courtesy of Chrysler Corp.

Fig. 42: Exploded View Of Rear Planetary, No. 2 One-Way Clutch & Output Shaft

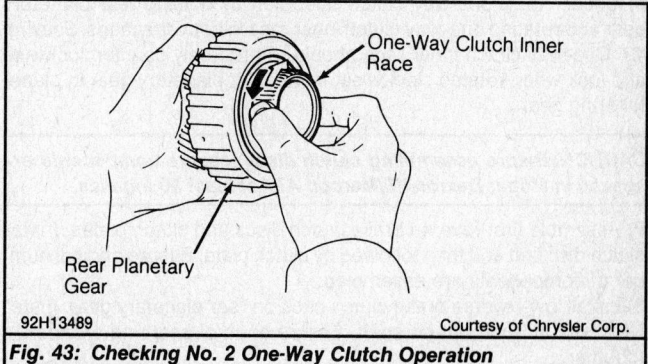

92H13489   Courtesy of Chrysler Corp.

Fig. 43: Checking No. 2 One-Way Clutch Operation

Cleaning & Inspection – 1) Clean metal components with solvent and dry with compressed air. Inspect components for damage.

2) Using micrometer, measure thickness of first-reverse brake clutch discs. Replace clutch disc if thickness is less than .059" (1.50 mm).

Reassembly – 1) Verify planetary ring gear thrust bearing and race identification by measuring inside and outside diameter. See PLANETARY RING GEAR BEARING & RACE SPECIFICATIONS table.

PLANETARY RING GEAR BEARING & RACE SPECIFICATIONS [1]

Application	Outside Diameter In. (mm)	Inside Diameter In. (mm)
Inner Race	1.764 (44.81)	1.087 (27.61)
Outer Race	1.764 (44.81)	1.134 (28.80)
Thrust Bearing	1.760 (44.70)	1.185 (30.10)

[1] – Inner race is race closest to planetary ring gear. Outer race is race that fits on outside of thrust bearing, away from planetary ring gear.

2) Install ring gear hub and snap ring in planetary ring gear. Lubricate thrust washer, thrust bearing and races with petroleum jelly. Install races and thrust bearing in rear planetary gear.

CAUTION: Ensure races are installed in rear planetary gear with flat side downward (toward rear planetary gear). The raised side should go away from planetary ring gear. See Fig. 42.

3) Install front and rear thrust washers on rear planetary gear. Ensure tabs on thrust washers engage with slots in rear planetary gear.

4) Install No. 2 one-way clutch in rear planetary gear with flanged side away from rear planetary gear. *See Fig. 44.*

CAUTION: Ensure flanged side of No. 2 one-way clutch is facing away from rear planetary gear. See Fig. 44.

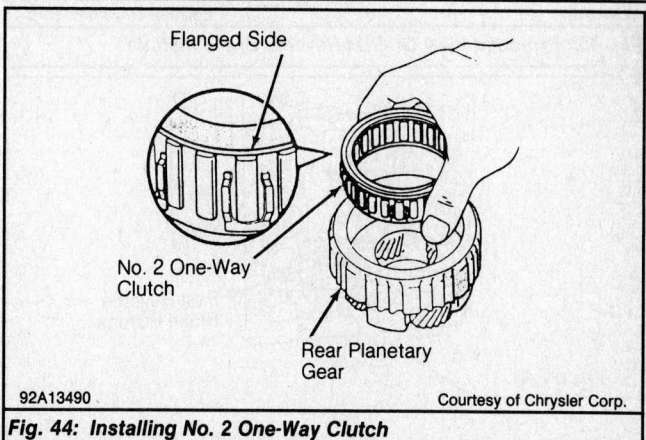

92A13490   Courtesy of Chrysler Corp.

Fig. 44: Installing No. 2 One-Way Clutch

5) Install No. 2 one-way clutch retaining snap ring and one-way clutch inner race. Rotate one-way clutch inner race counterclockwise to aid in installation.

6) Check No. 2 one-way clutch operation by holding rear planetary gear and rotating one-way clutch inner race in both directions. *See Fig. 43.* One-way clutch inner race should rotate freely counterclockwise and lock when rotated clockwise. Install rear planetary gear in planetary ring gear.

CAUTION: Before assembling clutch discs, ensure components are soaked in Mopar Dexron-IIE/Mercon ATF at least 30 minutes.

---

7) Assemble first-reverse brake clutch discs and clutch plates. Install clutch disc first and then followed by clutch plate. Ensure original number of components are assembled.

8) Install low-reverse brake clutch pack on rear planetary gear. Install NEW seal ring on output shaft. Ensure ends of seal ring are locked together.

FIRST-REVERSE BRAKE PISTONS

Disassembly – 1) Remove bearing and race assembly from transmission case. *See Fig. 45.* Apply low air pressure to transmission case port and check for smooth operation of No. 1 and 2 first-reverse brake pistons. *See Fig. 46.*

2) If pistons do not operate smoothly, transmission or piston may require replacement. Using Spring Compressor (7539), compress piston return springs. *See Fig. 47.* Remove snap ring. Remove spring compressor, piston return springs and retainer.

3) Apply air pressure to passage in transmission case used to check first-reverse brake piston operation and remove No. 2 first-reverse brake piston. *See Fig. 46.*

4) Using Reaction Sleeve Remover (7542), remove reaction sleeve by inserting flanges on reaction sleeve remover under reaction sleeve and lifting upward. *See Fig. 48.*

5) Using Piston Remover (7543), remove No. 1 first-reverse brake piston by inserting flanges on piston remover under first-reverse brake piston and lifting upward. *See Fig. 49.*

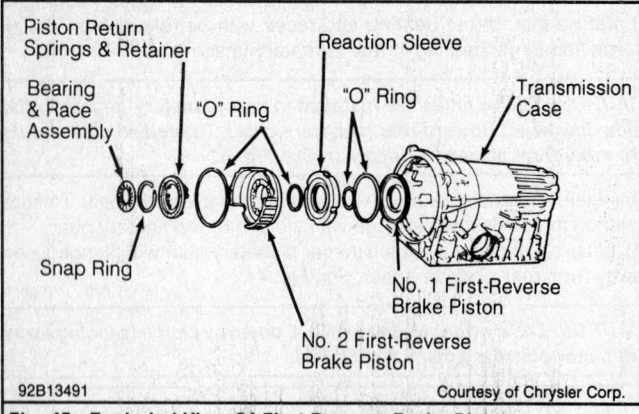

92B13491   Courtesy of Chrysler Corp.

Fig. 45: Exploded View Of First-Reverse Brake Pistons

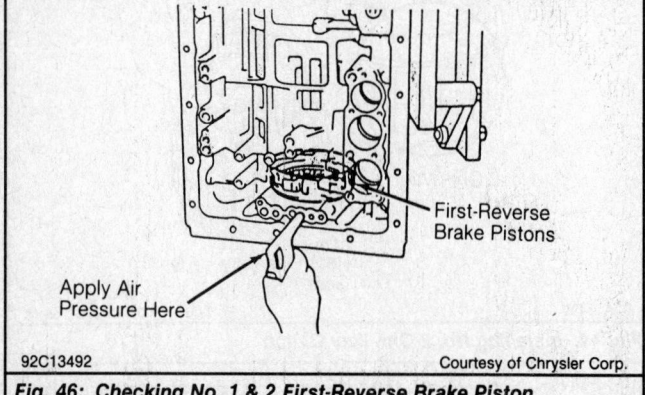

92C13492   Courtesy of Chrysler Corp.

Fig. 46: Checking No. 1 & 2 First-Reverse Brake Piston Piston Operation

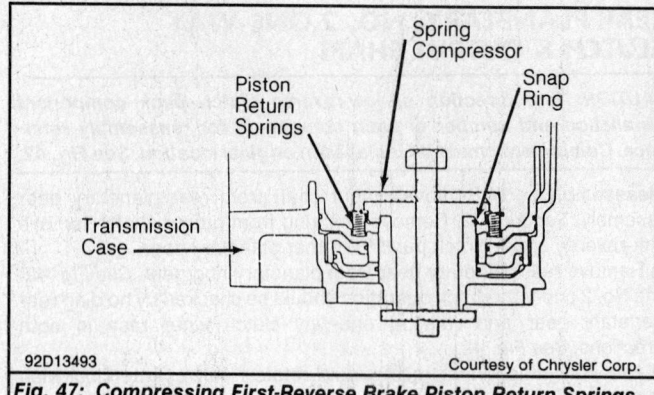

92D13493   Courtesy of Chrysler Corp.

Fig. 47: Compressing First-Reverse Brake Piston Return Springs

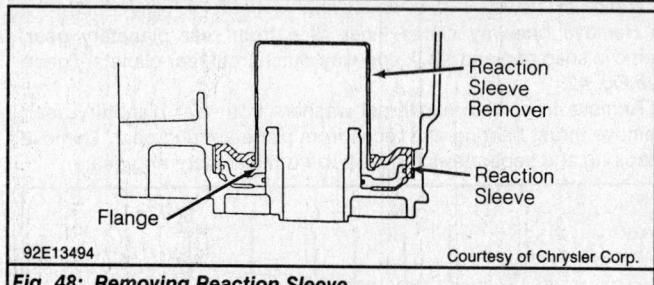

92E13494   Courtesy of Chrysler Corp.

Fig. 48: Removing Reaction Sleeve

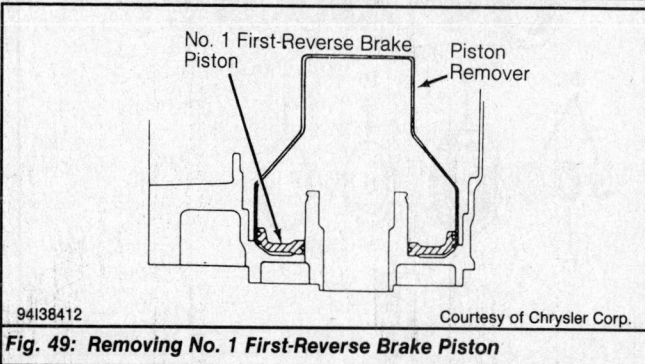

94I38412   Courtesy of Chrysler Corp.

Fig. 49: Removing No. 1 First-Reverse Brake Piston

Cleaning & Inspection – 1) Clean components with solvent and dry with compressed air. Inspect transmission case and components for damage.

2) Using caliper, measure free length of piston return springs with springs installed in retainer. Replace piston return springs if free length is not .724" (18.39 mm).

NOTE: Piston return spring free length also includes thickness of retainer.

Reassembly – 1) Lubricate NEW "O" rings with petroleum jelly. Install "O" rings on reaction sleeve and No. 1 and 2 first-reverse brake pistons.

2) Assemble No. 1 first-reverse brake piston on reaction sleeve. Install No. 1 first-reverse brake piston and reaction sleeve on No. 2 first-reverse brake piston.

3) Align piston assembly with slots in transmission case. Using hand pressure, install piston assembly in transmission case. Install piston return springs and retainer.

4) Using spring compressor, compress piston return springs and install snap ring. Ensure ends of snap ring are not aligned with tangs on retainer for piston return springs. Remove spring compressor.

5) Apply low air pressure on transmission case and check for smooth operation of No. 1 and 2 first-reverse brake pistons. *See Fig. 46.*

6) Verify bearing and race assembly identification by measuring inside and outside diameter. Bearing and race assembly outside diameter is 2.272" (57.71 mm) with inside diameter of 1.543" (39.19 mm). Coat bearing and race assembly with petroleum jelly and install.

ACCUMULATOR PISTONS & SPRINGS

Removal – 1) With valve body removed, note location of accumulator pistons. *See Fig. 6.*

2) Place shop towel over accumulator piston. Apply air pressure through small hole next to each accumulator piston to force accumulator piston from transmission case.

CAUTION: Use care not to apply excessive air pressure. Apply only enough air pressure to force accumulator piston from the bore.

3) Remove accumulator piston and spring. Note location of components for reassembly reference. *See Fig. 6.* Remove seal rings from accumulator pistons. If removing small cushion spring from accumulator pistons, remove retainer clip and separate small cushion spring from accumulator piston. *See Fig. 6.*

Installation – 1) Install small cushion spring and retainer clip in accumulator piston (if removed). Ensure retainer clip is fully seated in accumulator piston.

2) Install NEW seal rings on accumulator piston. Lubricate seal rings and accumulator piston bores with Mopar Dexron-IIE/Mercon ATF. Install springs and accumulator pistons in original location. Install valve body.

SECOND COAST BRAKE SERVO

Disassembly – 1) With valve body removed, remove retaining snap ring for second coast brake servo from transmission case. *See Fig. 10.*

2) Apply air pressure to oil hole in transmission case and force cover and piston for servo from transmission case. Disassemble second coast brake servo. *See Fig. 50.*

Reassembly – To reassemble, reverse disassembly procedure. Install NEW piston seal rings on piston. Install NEW "O" rings on cover. Lubricate all components with Mopar Dexron-IIE/Mercon ATF and install. Ensure piston rod properly engages with second coast brake band. Install and depress cover. Install snap ring.

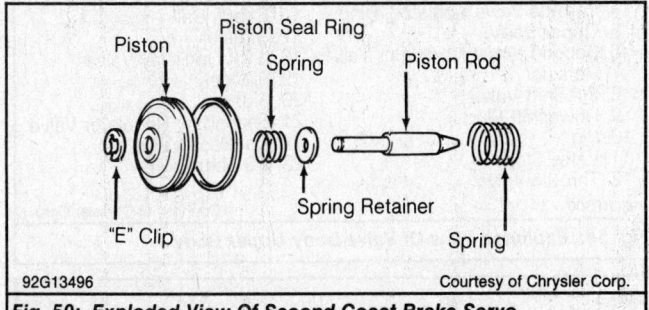

92G13496   Courtesy of Chrysler Corp.

Fig. 50: Exploded View Of Second Coast Brake Servo

PARK ROD & PAWL

Disassembly – Remove park rod bracket bolts from transmission case. *See Fig. 9.* Disconnect park rod from shift sector on manual valve shaft. *See Fig. 7.* Remove park rod, spring, pin and pawl.

Reassembly – To reassemble, reverse disassembly procedure. Ensure spring is positioned with long end toward inside of transmission case. Tighten park rod bracket bolts to specification. See TORQUE SPECIFICATIONS.

VALVE BODY

CAUTION: Place valve body components in order and mark spring locations for reassembly reference when disassembling valve body. DO NOT use force to remove components from valve body. Valve body assembly consists of upper body, lower body and separator plate. See Fig. 51.

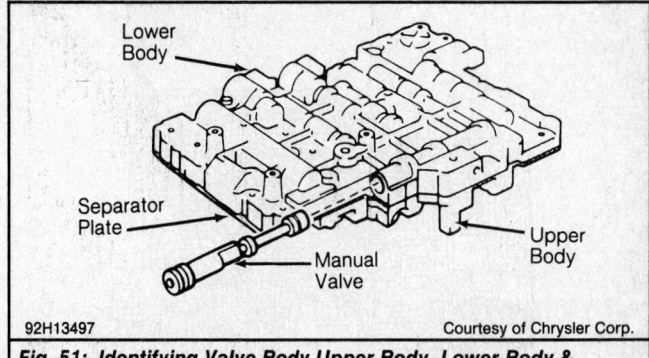

92H13497   Courtesy of Chrysler Corp.

Fig. 51: Identifying Valve Body Upper Body, Lower Body & Separator Plate

Disassembly – 1) Remove bolts and detent spring for manual valve. Detent spring contains 2 sections. Note location of detent spring components for reassembly reference.

2) Remove manual valve from lower body. *See Fig. 51.* Position valve body with upper body facing upward. Remove upper body-to-lower body bolts. Note bolt length and location for reassembly reference. Remove upper body, separator plate and gaskets (if equipped) from lower body.

CAUTION: Use care when separating upper body from lower body as not to allow components to fall from upper or lower body.

3) To disassemble lower body, remove check valve and spring, and pressure relief valve and spring. Remove strainers, check ball and seat. *See Fig. 52.*

CAUTION: Note length and location of strainers for reassembly reference.

4) Remove No. 1, 2 and 3 solenoids and "O" rings. Note location of retainers and clip for pressure reducing plug. *See Fig. 53.* Remove retainer, plug, spring and 1-2 shift valve. *See Fig. 52.*

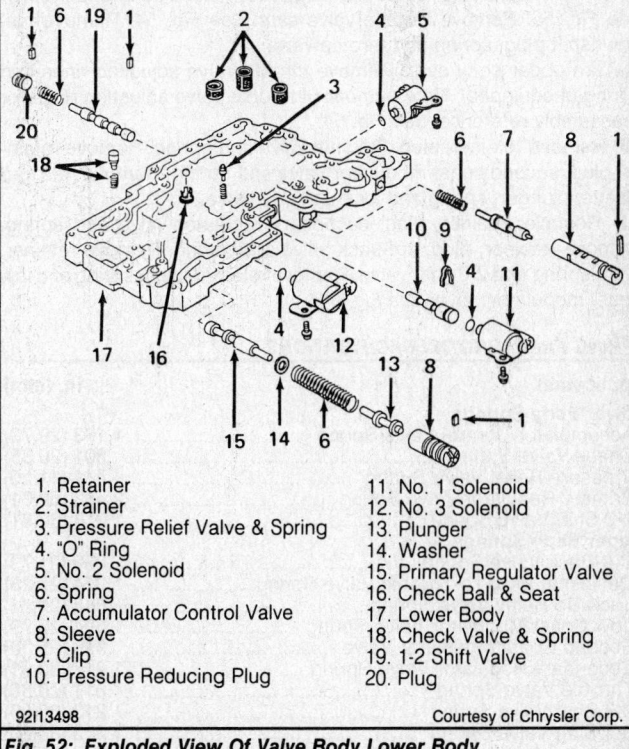

1. Retainer	11. No. 1 Solenoid
2. Strainer	12. No. 3 Solenoid
3. Pressure Relief Valve & Spring	13. Plunger
4. "O" Ring	14. Washer
5. No. 2 Solenoid	15. Primary Regulator Valve
6. Spring	16. Check Ball & Seat
7. Accumulator Control Valve	17. Lower Body
8. Sleeve	18. Check Valve & Spring
9. Clip	19. 1-2 Shift Valve
10. Pressure Reducing Plug	20. Plug

92I13498   Courtesy of Chrysler Corp.

Fig. 52: Exploded View Of Valve Body Lower Body

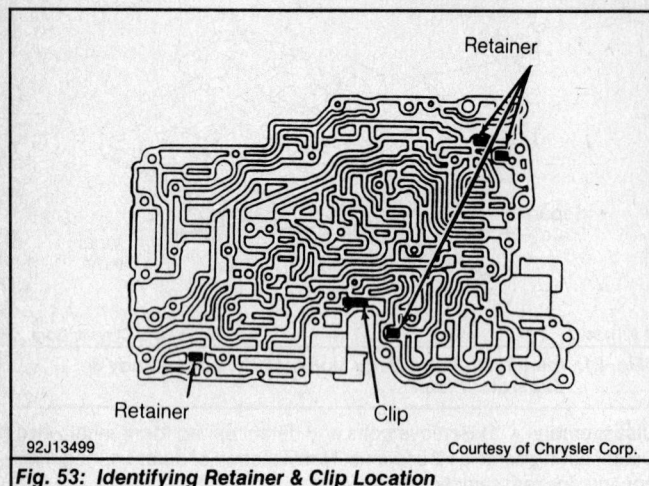

92J13499   Courtesy of Chrysler Corp.

Fig. 53: Identifying Retainer & Clip Location

CAUTION: Primary regulator valve, plunger and sleeve are under spring pressure. Spring must be compressed before removing retainer. Spring is compressed by pushing sleeve inward (toward lower body). Note position of sleeve before removing retainer.

5) Push sleeve for primary regulator valve inward. Using magnet, remove retainer. Slowly release pressure on sleeve. Remove sleeve with plunger, spring, washer and primary regulator valve. See Fig. 52.

CAUTION: Use care not to scratch sealing surface on lower body when removing clip or pressure reducing plug.

6) Remove plunger from sleeve. Remove clip for pressure reducing plug. See Figs. 52 and 53. Remove pressure reducing plug. Remove retainer, sleeve, accumulator control valve and spring. See Fig. 52.

7) To disassemble upper body, remove gaskets and separator plate. Note location of strainer and check balls. See Fig. 55. Remove strainer and check balls.

8) Remove valve stop located on separator plate side of upper body. See Fig. 56. Remove throttle valve cam. See Fig. 54. Remove pin, downshift plug, spring and throttle valve.

9) Turn upper body over. Remove throttle valve adjusting rings and spring (if equipped). Note number of throttle valve adjusting rings for reassembly reference. See Fig. 54.

10) Remove retainer, plug, 3-4 shift valve and spring. Remove retainer, plug, second coast modulator valve and spring. Remove retainer, sleeve, plunger, spring and lock-up relay valve.

11) Remove retainer, plug, secondary regulator valve and spring. Remove retainer, plug, cut-back valve and spring. Remove retainer, plug, spring and 2-3 shift valve. Remove retainer, plug, spring and low coast modulator valve. See Fig. 54.

SPRING FREE LENGTH SPECIFICATIONS

Application	In. (mm)
Lower Body Springs	
Accumulator Control Valve Spring	1.173 (29.79)
Check Valve Spring	.801 (20.35)
Pressure Relief Valve Spring	.441 (11.20)
Primary Regulator Valve Spring	2.453 (62.31)
1-2 Shift Valve Spring	1.213 (30.81)
Upper Body Springs	
Cut-Back Valve Spring	.858 (21.79)
Downshift Plug-To-Throttle Valve Spring	1.074 (27.28)
Lock-Up Relay Valve Spring	.843 (21.41)
Low Coast Modulator Valve Spring	1.094 (27.79)
Second Coast Modulator Valve	.996 (25.30)
Secondary Regulator Valve Spring	1.217 (30.91)
Throttle Valve Spring	.811 (20.60)
2-3 Shift Valve Spring	1.213 (30.80)
3-4 Shift Valve Spring	1.213 (30.80)

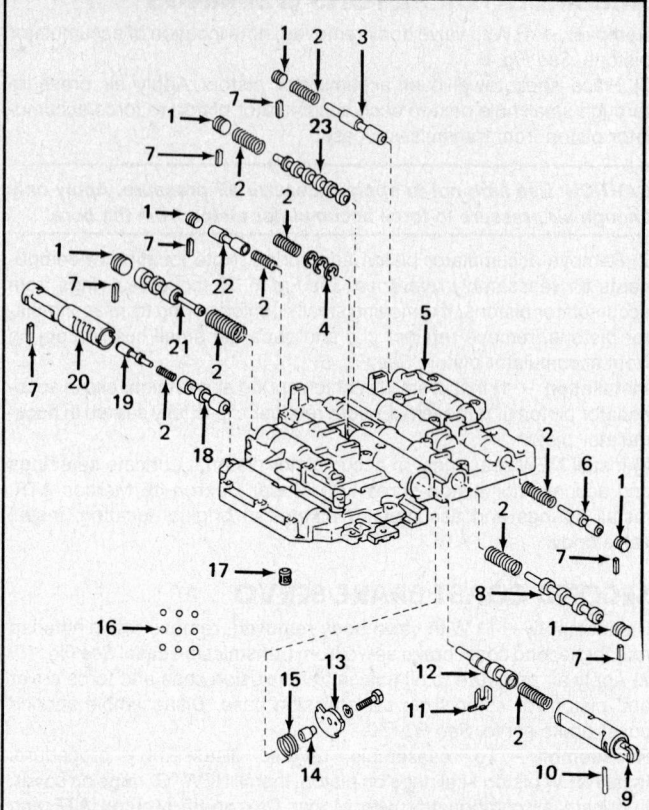

1. Plug
2. Spring
3. Low Coast Modulator Valve
4. Throttle Valve Adjusting Ring
5. Upper Body
6. Second Coast Modulator Valve
7. Retainer
8. 3-4 Shift Valve
9. Downshift Plug
10. Pin
11. Valve Stop
12. Throttle Valve
13. Throttle Valve Cam
14. Pin
15. Throttle Valve Cam Spring
16. Check Ball
17. Strainer
18. Lock-Up Relay Valve
19. Plunger
20. Sleeve
21. Secondary Regulator Valve
22. Cut-Back Valve
23. 2-3 Shift Valve

92C13500   Courtesy of Chrysler Corp.

Fig. 54: Exploded View Of Valve Body Upper Body

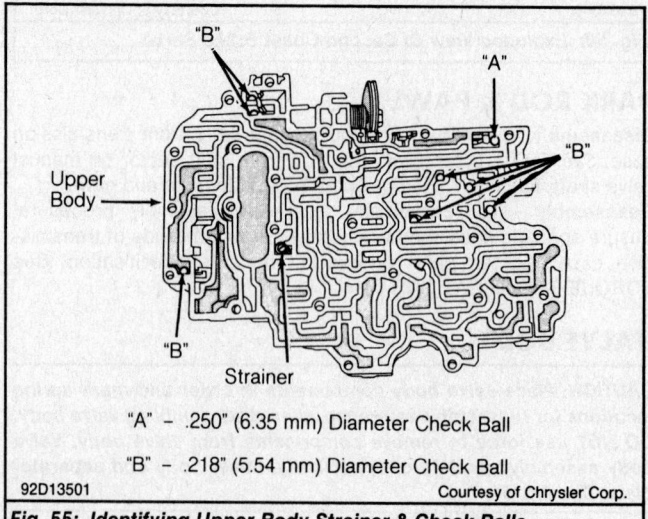

"A" – .250" (6.35 mm) Diameter Check Ball

"B" – .218" (5.54 mm) Diameter Check Ball

92D13501   Courtesy of Chrysler Corp.

Fig. 55: Identifying Upper Body Strainer & Check Balls

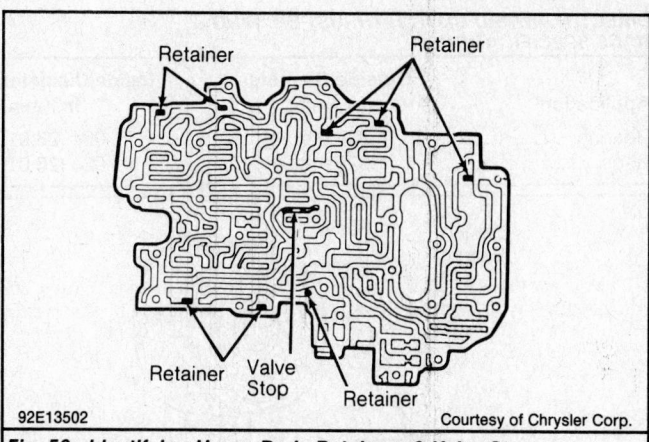

Fig. 56: Identifying Upper Body Retainers & Valve Stop

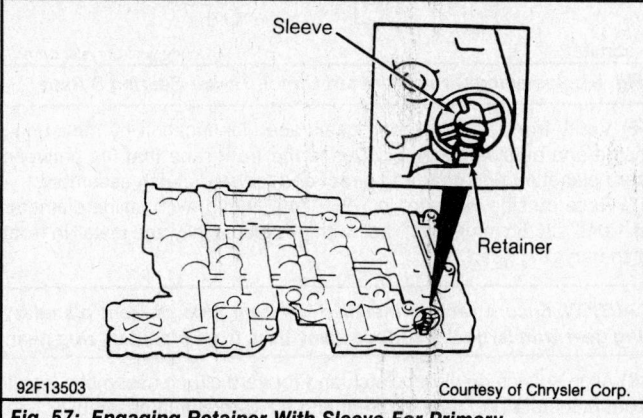

Fig. 57: Engaging Retainer With Sleeve For Primary Regulator Valve

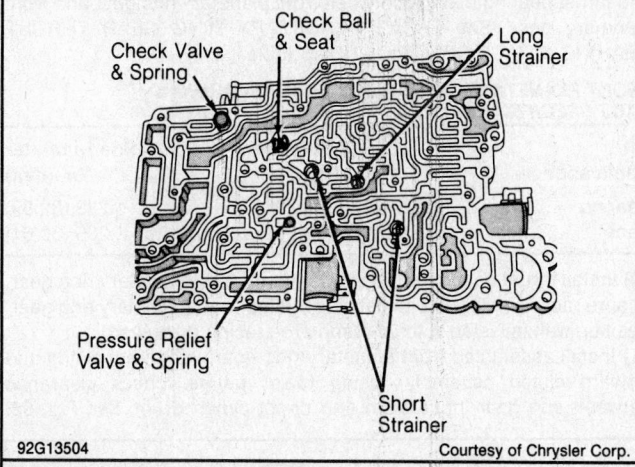

Fig. 58: Identifying Lower Body Strainer Locations

Cleaning & Inspection – **1)** Clean components with solvent and dry with compressed air. Inspect components for damage. Ensure all components slide freely in the bore of the body. Ensure strainers are not torn or damaged.

2) Inspect springs for distortion. Ensure spring free length is correct. See SPRING FREE LENGTH SPECIFICATIONS table. Replace damaged or defective components.

Reassembly – **1)** Lubricate all components and bores with Mopar Dexron-IIE/Mercon ATF. To reassemble upper body, reverse disassembly procedure. Ensure original number of throttle valve adjusting rings are installed (if equipped).

2) Ensure all retainers and valve stop are properly installed. See Fig. 56. Ensure end of throttle valve cam spring is engaged with hole in throttle valve cam and with slot in upper body. Tighten throttle valve cam bolt to specification. See TORQUE SPECIFICATIONS.

3) To reassemble lower body, reverse disassembly procedure. When installing retainer into sleeve for primary regulator valve, ensure retainer engages lugs on sleeve. See Fig. 57.

4) Install NEW "O" rings on solenoids. Tighten solenoid bolts to specification. See TORQUE SPECIFICATIONS. Ensure proper length strainer is installed in lower body. See Fig. 58.

CAUTION: Two different length strainers are used in lower body. Ensure proper length strainer is installed in specified location. See Fig. 58.

5) When reassembling upper and lower bodies, ensure check balls are installed in upper body. See Fig. 55. Install gasket on upper body (if equipped).

6) Install separator plate on upper body and gasket (if equipped). Ensure all openings in separator plate align with gasket (if equipped) and upper body.

7) Install remaining gasket (if equipped) on separator plate. Install lower body on upper body.

8) Install proper length upper body-to-lower body bolts in specified location. See Fig. 59. Tighten bolts to specification. See TORQUE SPECIFICATIONS.

9) Install manual valve. Install detent spring for manual valve and bolt. Ensure both pieces of detent spring are installed. Tighten bolt to specification.

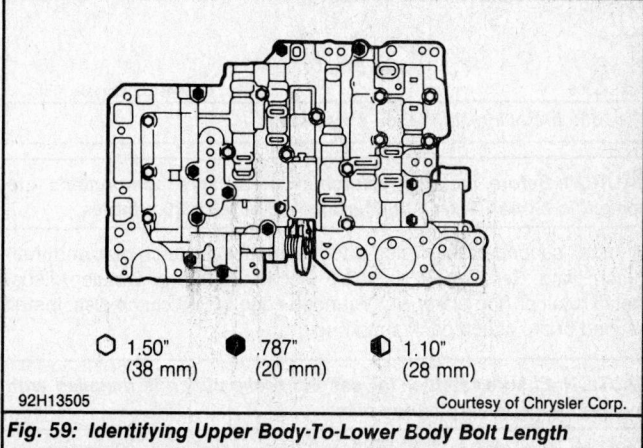

⬡ 1.50"	⬢ .787"	⬡ 1.10"
(38 mm)	(20 mm)	(28 mm)

Fig. 59: Identifying Upper Body-To-Lower Body Bolt Length

TRANSMISSION REASSEMBLY
VALVE BODY & INTERNAL COMPONENTS

NOTE: Lubricate all components with Mopar Dexron-IIE/Mercon ATF. Apply petroleum jelly on "O" rings and seal rings. Use petroleum jelly to hold thrust washers in position. Ensure thrust washers are installed in correct direction and location. See Fig. 14.

1) Locate thrust bearing that fits at output shaft end of transmission case. This is the No. 10 thrust bearing. See Fig. 14. Thrust bearing and race outside diameter is 2.272" (57.71 mm) with inside diameter of 1.543" (39.19 mm).

2) Install No. 10 thrust bearing in transmission case with race facing downward and rollers facing upward (toward oil pump). See Fig. 14. Align teeth of second brake drum and clutch pack. Align rear planetary gear, second brake drum and output shaft assembly teeth with slots in transmission case.

3) Install rear planetary gear, second brake drum and output shaft assembly. Install retaining snap ring in transmission case with chamfered side toward the oil pump.

CAUTION: Ensure snap ring is installed with chamfered side toward the oil pump.

4) Using feeler gauge, check first-reverse brake clutch pack clearance. *See Fig. 22.* Clutch pack clearance should be .028-.047" (.71-1.19 mm).

5) If first-reverse clutch pack clearance is not within specification, check for incorrect assembly of rear planetary gear, thrust bearing or improperly seated snap ring.

6) Install second coast brake piston sleeve with large area toward oil pump. *See Fig. 13.* Using Gasket Installer (7544), install NEW second brake drum gasket. *See Fig. 23.*

7) Install pawl, spring, pin, park rod, and park rod bracket. Install and tighten park rod bracket bolts to specification. See TORQUE SPECIFICATIONS. Position shift sector in Park position and ensure pawl engages ring gear on rear planetary gear.

8) Install No. 1 one-way clutch with short flange side upward (toward front of transmission case). *See Fig. 60.*

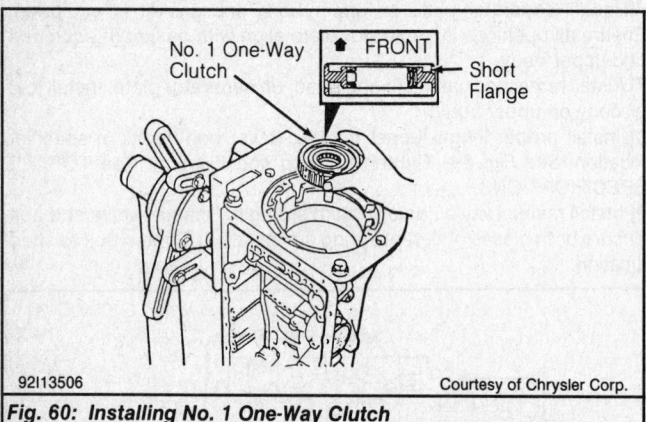

92I13506   Courtesy of Chrysler Corp.

Fig. 60: Installing No. 1 One-Way Clutch

CAUTION: Before installing clutch discs, ensure components are soaked in Mopar Dexron-IIE/Mercon ATF at least 30 minutes.

9) Install second brake clutch pack starting with clutch disc and then clutch plate. *See Fig. 21.* Install 5 clutch plates and 5 clutch discs. Install retainer (top plate) with rounded edge facing clutch disc. Install second brake clutch pack snap ring.

CAUTION: Ensure retainer for second brake clutch is installed with rounded edge toward clutch disc.

10) Using feeler gauge, measure second brake clutch pack clearance. *See Fig. 20.* Second brake clutch pack clearance should be .024-.078" (.61-1.98 mm). If second brake clutch pack clearance is not within specification, check for improper assembly of clutch pack.

11) Install sun gear and input drum. Ensure tabs on thrust washer are engaged with slots in input drum.

12) Install thrust bearing, race and front planetary gear on sun gear. Support output shaft on wooden block. Install snap ring to retain front planetary gear on output shaft.

13) Install race on front planetary gear with tabs on race toward front planetary gear. *See Fig. 13.* Race outside diameter is 1.882" (47.80 mm) with inside diameter of 1.350" (34.29 mm). Install second coast brake band, pin and clips.

14) Verify thrust bearing and race that fits in direct clutch and forward clutch by measuring inside and outside diameter. See DIRECT/FORWARD CLUTCH THRUST BEARING & RACE SPECIFICATIONS table. Coat thrust bearing and race with petroleum jelly.

15) Install thrust bearing and race in direct clutch and forward clutch with flat area of race away from clutch assembly. *See Fig. 61.*

DIRECT/FORWARD CLUTCH THRUST BEARING & RACE SPECIFICATIONS

Application	Outside Diameter In. (mm)	Inside Diameter In. (mm)
Bearing	1.839 (46.71)	1.024 (26.01)
Race	1.925 (48.90)	1.024 (26.01)

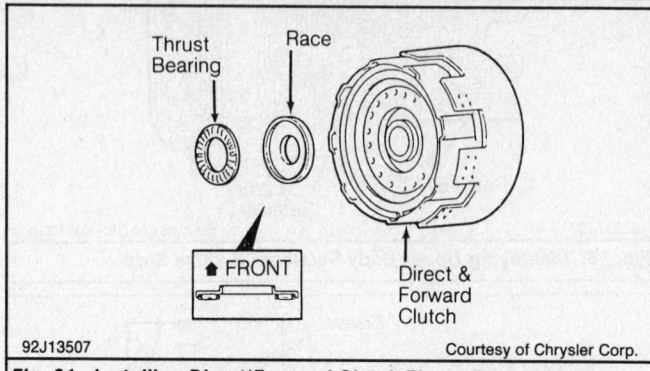

92J13507   Courtesy of Chrysler Corp.

Fig. 61: Installing Direct/Forward Clutch Thrust Bearing & Race

16) Verify front planetary ring gear race identification by measuring inside and outside diameter. This is the front race that fits between front planetary ring gear and direct and forward clutch assembly.

17) Race outside diameter is 1.850" (46.99 mm) with inside diameter of 1.045" (26.55 mm). Coat race with petroleum jelly and install in front planetary ring gear.

CAUTION: Ensure race is installed on front side of front planetary ring gear with large flat surface away from front planetary ring gear.

18) Align splines on direct clutch and forward clutch assembly. Install front planetary ring gear in direct and forward clutch assembly.

19) Verify front planetary ring gear thrust bearing and race identification by measuring inside and outside diameter. This is the rear race and thrust bearing that fits between front planetary ring gear and front planetary gear. See FRONT PLANETARY RING GEAR THRUST BEARING & RACE SPECIFICATIONS table.

FRONT PLANETARY RING GEAR THRUST BEARING & RACE SPECIFICATIONS

Application	Outside Diameter In. (mm)	Inside Diameter In. (mm)
Bearing	1.878 (47.70)	1.283 (32.59)
Race	2.110 (53.59)	1.205 (30.61)

20) Install thrust bearing and race on rear of front planetary ring gear. Ensure race is installed with flat side against front planetary ring gear. Position transmission with oil pump area facing downward.

21) Install assembled front planetary ring gear with direct clutch and forward clutch assembly. Using feeler gauge, check clearance between sun gear input drum and direct clutch drum. *See Fig. 62.*

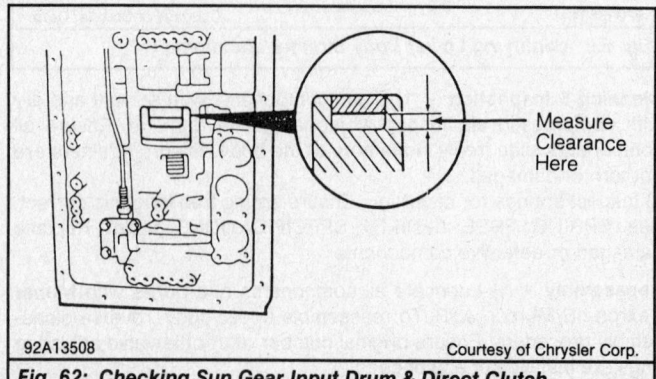

92A13508   Courtesy of Chrysler Corp.

Fig. 62: Checking Sun Gear Input Drum & Direct Clutch Drum Clearance

Clearance should be .386-.465" (9.80-11.81 mm). If clearance is not within specification, front planetary ring gear with direct clutch and forward clutch assembly is not fully seated.

22) Verify clutch shaft thrust bearing and race identification by measuring inside and outside diameter. This is the thrust bearing and race that fits on clutch shaft of direct clutch and forward clutch assembly. Thrust bearing and race outside diameter is 1.882" (47.8 mm) with inside diameter of 1.301" (33.0 mm). Install thrust bearing and race on clutch shaft.

23) Assemble second coast brake servo components. *See Fig. 50.* Install NEW seal rings on piston. Install NEW "O" rings on cover. Lubricate all components with Mopar Dexron-IIE/Mercon ATF and install. Depress cover. Install snap ring.

24) Check second brake piston stroke. Place reference mark on piston rod. *See Fig. 19.* Apply 57-114 psi (4-8 kg/cm²) air pressure through piston feed hole and check piston stroke with Gauge (7552). Piston stroke should be .059-.118" (1.50-3.00 mm).

25) If piston stroke is incorrect, check for improperly seated components. If components are seated okay, install different length piston rod and recheck piston stroke. Piston rod is available in 2 different lengths, 2.811" (71.39 mm) and 2.870" (72.90 mm).

26) Verify race that fits on rear of overdrive support by measuring inside and outside diameter. Race outside diameter is 2.004" (50.90 mm) with inside diameter of 1.426" (36.22 mm). Install race on rear of overdrive support.

27) Using 2 guide studs, install overdrive support. Install overdrive support retaining snap ring with chamfered side toward the oil pump, ensuring ends of snap ring must be centered within .940" (23.88 mm) of transmission case opening. *See Fig. 63.*

CAUTION: Ensure overdrive support retaining snap ring is installed with chamfered side toward oil pump. Ends of snap ring must be centered within .940" (23.88 mm) of transmission case opening. See Fig. 63.

---

28) Install and tighten overdrive support bolts to specification. See TORQUE SPECIFICATIONS. Using dial indicator, check output shaft end play. Output shaft end play should be .011-.034" (.28-.86 mm). If output shaft end play is incorrect, check for improperly assembled components.

CAUTION: Before installing clutch discs, ensure components are soaked in Mopar Dexron-IIE/Mercon ATF at least 30 minutes.

---

29) Install overdrive brake clutch pack starting with thickest clutch plate first. Ensure rounded edges of clutch plate faces upward. *See Fig. 17.* Install a clutch disc, and then a clutch plate.

30) Install retainer plate with flat side toward clutch disc. *See Fig. 17.* Install overdrive brake clutch pack retaining snap ring in transmission case. Mount dial indicator on transmission case with Gauge (7546) contacting overdrive brake piston. *See Fig. 16.*

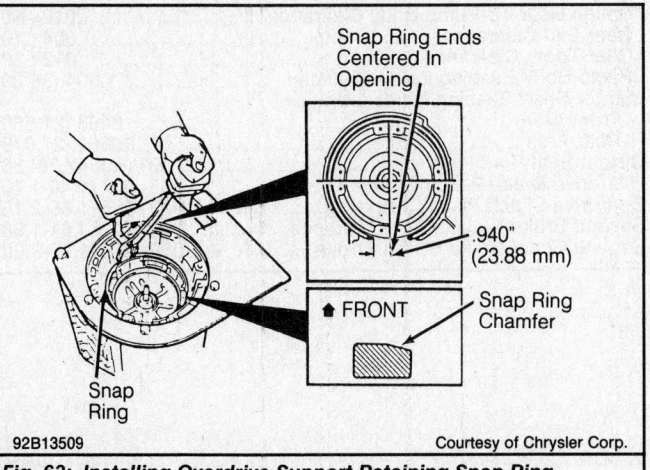

92B13509   Courtesy of Chrysler Corp.

Fig. 63: Installing Overdrive Support Retaining Snap Ring

31) Apply 57-114 psi (4-8 kg/cm²) air pressure through feed hole and note overdrive brake piston stroke reading on dial indicator. *See Fig. 16.* Overdrive brake piston stroke should be .055-.070" (1.40-1.78 mm).

32) If overdrive brake piston stroke is not within specification, check for improperly assembled components. Remove dial indicator, gauge, snap ring and overdrive clutch pack. Keep components in order for reassembly reference.

33) Verify identification of thrust bearing and races that fit on front of overdrive support by measuring inside and outside diameter. See OVERDRIVE SUPPORT THRUST BEARING & RACE SPECIFICATIONS table. Install lower race, thrust bearing and upper race on front of overdrive support.

CAUTION: Ensure tabs on lower race faces toward overdrive support. Flat surface on upper race must be facing upward (toward oil pump).

OVERDRIVE SUPPORT THRUST BEARING & RACE SPECIFICATIONS

Application	Outside Diameter In. (mm)	Inside Diameter In. (mm)
Bearing	1.878 (47.70)	1.287 (32.69)
Lower Race	1.882 (47.80)	1.350 (34.29)
Upper Race	1.882 (47.80)	1.209 (30.71)

34) Install overdrive planetary ring gear in overdrive support. Verify identification of thrust bearing and race that fit on front of overdrive planetary ring gear by measuring inside and outside diameter. See OVERDRIVE PLANETARY RING GEAR THRUST BEARING & RACE SPECIFICATIONS table.

OVERDRIVE PLANETARY RING GEAR THRUST BEARING & RACE SPECIFICATIONS

Application	Outside Diameter In. (mm)	Inside Diameter In. (mm)
Bearing	1.844 (46.84)	1.024 (26.01)
Race	1.882 (47.80)	.953 (24.21)

35) Install race and thrust bearing on front of overdrive planetary ring gear. Ensure tabs on race engage with slots on overdrive planetary ring gear.

36) Install race on rear of overdrive planetary gear and overdrive clutch. *See Fig. 13.* Race outside diameter is 1.646" (41.81 mm) with inside diameter of 1.067" (27.10 mm). Ensure tabs on race engage with slots on overdrive planetary gear and overdrive clutch.

37) Install overdrive planetary gear and overdrive clutch in transmission case. Verify size of thrust bearing and race that fits on input shaft of overdrive planetary gear and overdrive clutch. *See Fig. 13.*

38) Thrust bearing and race outside diameter is 1.976" (50.19 mm) with inside diameter of 1.138" (28.91 mm). Install thrust bearing and race on input shaft of overdrive planetary gear and overdrive clutch. Ensure flat side of race is against overdrive planetary gear.

39) Install overdrive brake clutch pack starting with thickest clutch plate first. Ensure rounded edges of clutch plate faces upward. *See Fig. 17.* Install clutch disc and then clutch plate. Install 4 clutch discs and 3 clutch plates.

40) Install retainer plate with flat side toward clutch disc. *See Fig. 17.* Install overdrive brake clutch pack retaining snap ring in transmission case.

41) Verify identification of race that fits on rear of oil pump by measuring inside and outside diameter. Race outside diameter is 1.858" (47.19 mm) with inside diameter of 1.106" (28.09 mm). Install race on rear of oil pump.

42) Ensure seal rings are installed on stator shaft on rear of oil pump. Lubricate NEW "O" ring with petroleum jelly and install on oil pump body. Align oil pump with transmission case bolt holes and install.

CAUTION: DO NOT use force to seat oil pump, as seal rings on stator shaft may be damaged.

---

43) Install and tighten oil pump-to-transmission case bolts to specification. See TORQUE SPECIFICATIONS. Ensure input shaft rotates smoothly and does not bind.

44) Lubricate NEW "O" ring with petroleum jelly and install on throttle cable adapter. Install throttle cable in transmission case. Apply air pressure to feed passages on transmission case to check clutch and brake application. *See Fig. 64.*

45) Listen for clutch and brake application when air is applied. Repair assembly if clutch or brake application cannot be heard.

NOTE: It is necessary to block overdrive clutch accumulator piston hole No. 8 in order to check direct clutch operation.

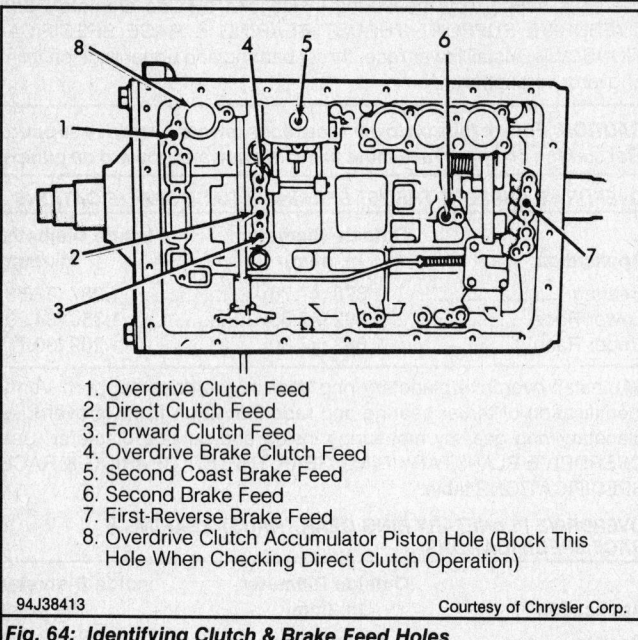

1. Overdrive Clutch Feed
2. Direct Clutch Feed
3. Forward Clutch Feed
4. Overdrive Brake Clutch Feed
5. Second Coast Brake Feed
6. Second Brake Feed
7. First-Reverse Brake Feed
8. Overdrive Clutch Accumulator Piston Hole (Block This Hole When Checking Direct Clutch Operation)

94J38413   Courtesy of Chrysler Corp.

Fig. 64: Identifying Clutch & Brake Feed Holes

46) Install NEW "O" rings on accumulator pistons and lubricate with petroleum jelly. Install accumulator pistons and springs. *See Fig. 6.* Install NEW check ball and spring. *See Fig. 11.*

47) Connect throttle cable to throttle valve cam. Align manual valve with shift sector and position valve body on transmission case. Install detent spring. Install valve body-to-transmission case bolts in original location and tighten to specification. See TORQUE SPECIFICATIONS.

48) Install valve body oil tubes in original location with proper end engaged in valve body. *See Fig. 12.*

49) Connect valve body solenoid electrical connections. Ensure oil screen is clean. Using NEW gaskets, install oil screen. Install and tighten bolts to specification.

50) Ensure magnet is installed in oil pan and does not interfere with valve body oil tubes. Apply 1/8" bead of Loctite 599 sealant on oil pan mounting flange and install oil pan. Install and tighten bolts to specification.

51) Install key, speed sensor rotor, spacer and speedometer drive gear on output shaft. Install snap ring. Apply bead of Loctite 599 sealant on adapter or extension housing-to-transmission case sealing surface.

52) Install adapter or extension housing. Install and tighten bolts to specification. Install speed sensor. Install and tighten bolt to specification. See TORQUE SPECIFICATIONS.

53) Install torque converter housing. Install and tighten bolts to specification. Install shift lever on manual valve shift. DO NOT install retaining nut at this time.

54) Move shift lever all the way rearward and then forward 2 detent positions to Neutral position. Install neutral safety switch on manual valve shaft. Install adjusting bolt, but DO NOT tighten at this time.

55) Install lock washer and retaining nut. Tighten retaining nut to specification. See TORQUE SPECIFICATIONS. DO NOT bend over tabs on lock washer at this time.

56) Ensure transmission is still in Neutral. Rotate neutral safety switch and align neutral standard line with vertical groove on manual valve shaft. *See Fig. 8.*

57) Tighten adjusting bolt to specification. Bend lock washer tabs over. Install retaining clamp for wire harness and throttle cable.

58) Install torque converter. To verify torque converter is fully seated, place straightedge across front of torque converter housing. Measure distance between edge of straightedge and torque converter-to-flexplate mounting pad.

59) Distance should be .650" (16.51 mm) if torque converter is fully seated. Install lower half of transmission filler tube.

CAUTION: If transmission failure existed, flush oil cooler and check oil cooler flow. See OIL COOLER FLUSHING and OIL COOLER FLOW CHECK under ON-VEHICLE SERVICE.

TORQUE SPECIFICATIONS
TORQUE SPECIFICATIONS

Application	Ft. Lbs. (N.m)
Adapter/Extension Housing Bolt	25 (34)
Oil Pan Drain Plug	15 (20)
Oil Pump-To-Transmission Case Bolt	16 (22)
Overdrive Support Bolt	19 (26)
Shift Lever-To-Manual Valve Shaft Nut	12 (16)
Torque Converter Housing Bolt	
10-mm Bolt	25 (34)
12-mm Bolt	42 (57)

	INCH Lbs. (N.m)
Detent Spring Bolt	84 (9.5)
Neutral Safety Switch Adjusting Bolt	108 (12.2)
Neutral Safety Switch Retaining Nut	61 (6.9)
Oil Pan Bolt	65 (7.3)
Oil Screen Bolt	84 (9.5)
Park Rod Bracket Bolt	84 (9.5)
Speed Sensor Bolt	65 (7.3)
Stator Shaft-To-Pump Body Bolt	84 (9.5)
Throttle Valve Cam Bolt	84 (9.5)
Valve Body Solenoid Bolt	84 (9.5)
Valve Body-To-Transmission Case Bolt	84 (9.5)
Valve Body Upper Body-To-Lower Body Bolt	56 (6.3)

TRANSMISSION SPECIFICATIONS
TRANSMISSION SPECIFICATIONS

Application	In. (mm)
Direct Clutch & Forward Clutch	
Assembled Height	2.767-2.815 (70.28-71.50)
Direct Clutch Piston Stroke	.054-.065 (1.37-1.65)
First-Reverse Brake Clutch	
Pack Clearance	.028-.047 (.71-1.19)
Forward Clutch Piston Stroke	.140-.147 (3.55-3.73)
Oil Pump Clearances	
Driven Gear-To-Pump Body Clearance	.012 (.30)
Gear End Clearance	.004 (.10)
Gear Tooth Clearance	.012 (.30)
Pump Body Bushing Inside Diameter	1.504 (38.20)
Stator Shaft Bushing Inside Diameter	
Front Area	.8496 (21.580)
Rear Area	1.0661 (27.079)
Output Shaft End Play	.011-.034 (.28-.86)
Overdrive Brake Piston Stroke	.055-.067 (1.40-1.70)
Overdrive Clutch Piston Stroke	.073-.085 (1.85-2.16)
Second Brake Clutch Pack Clearance	.024-.078 (.61-1.98)
Second Coast Brake Piston Stroke	.059-.118 (1.50-3.00)

APPLICATION

NOTE: Transmission may also be referred to as AW-4.

APPLICATION

Model	Trans.
1993-94 Cherokee [1]	AW-4
1993 Grand Cherokee	AW-4

[1] – Used on models with 4.0L engine.

NOTE: Vehicle body code may be required when diagnosing or repairing transmission, as body code may be used instead of vehicle model name. See BODY CODE DESIGNATION table.

BODY CODE DESIGNATION

Vehicle Model	Body Code
Cherokee	XJ
Grand Cherokee	ZJ

DESCRIPTION

The electronic control system for the AW-4 transmission controls transmission shift points and torque converter lock-up. Electronic control system consists of Transmission Control Module (TCM), valve body solenoids, throttle position sensor, speed sensor, neutral safety switch and brake switch.

NOTE: Transmission Control Module (TCM) may be referred to as Transmission Control Unit (TCU). Neutral safety switch may be referred to as park/neutral safety switch or gear select switch.

OPERATION

TRANSMISSION CONTROL MODULE (TCM)

The TCM determines shift points and torque converter lock-up based on input signals received from throttle position sensor, neutral safety switch, speed sensor and brake switch. The TCM controls transmission shift points and torque converter lock-up by operating electric solenoids mounted on the valve body.

The TCM contains a self-diagnostic system used for determining an electronic component failure. The TCM self-diagnostic system will store a diagnostic trouble code in the TCM memory if certain electronic problems exist. If electronic problem goes away, diagnostic trouble code will be erased from TCM memory after ignition has been cycled approximately 75 times.

NOTE: Diagnostic trouble code may be referred to as fault code.

Diagnostic trouble codes can be retrieved using a Diagnostic Readout Box-II (DRB-II). After repairing an electrical system problem, stored diagnostic trouble code must be cleared from TCM memory.

The TCM is located behind right side of instrument panel on Cherokee or above steering column or on top left side of instrument panel on Grand Cherokee. See Fig. 1.

VALVE BODY SOLENOIDS

Valve body solenoids, mounted on the valve body, are output devices controlled by signals received from the TCM. See Fig. 2. The No. 1 and 2 valve body solenoids control transmission shifts while the No. 3 valve body solenoid is used for torque converter lock-up.

When No. 1 and 2 valve body solenoids are energized, solenoid plunger moves from seat. This opens the drain port and releases line pressure. When either valve body solenoid is de-energized, plunger closes the drain port.

The No. 3 valve body solenoid operates in reverse. When No. 3 valve body solenoid is de-energized, solenoid plunger moves away from seat. This opens the drain port and releases line pressure. When No. 3 valve body solenoid is energized, the plunger closes the drain port.

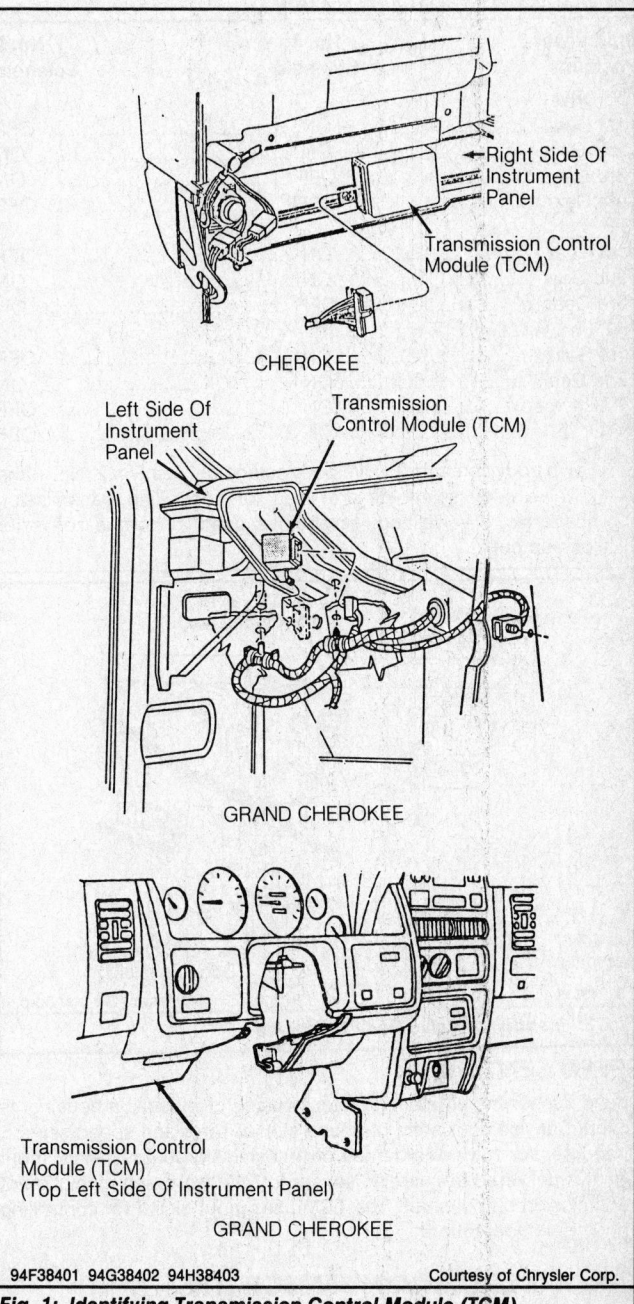

CHEROKEE

GRAND CHEROKEE

Transmission Control Module (TCM)
(Top Left Side Of Instrument Panel)

GRAND CHEROKEE

94F38401 94G38402 94H38403   Courtesy of Chrysler Corp.

Fig. 1: Identifying Transmission Control Module (TCM)

NOTE: For valve body solenoid usage, see VALVE BODY SOLENOID APPLICATION table.

BRAKE SWITCH

Brake switch is an input device mounted above the brake pedal. When brake pedal is operated, brake switch delivers an input signal to the TCM. The TCM uses input signal for controlling No. 3 valve body solenoid for torque converter lock-up.

NEUTRAL SAFETY SWITCH

NOTE: Neutral safety switch may be referred to as park/neutral safety switch or gear select switch.

Neutral safety switch is an input device mounted on the transmission manual valve shaft. Neutral safety switch delivers an input signal to TCM, indicating transmission manual valve gear position.

VALVE BODY SOLENOID APPLICATION [1]

Shift Lever Position	No. 1 Solenoid	No. 2 Solenoid
"D" (Drive)		
1st Gear	ON	OFF
2nd Gear	ON	ON
3rd Gear	OFF	ON
4th Gear	OFF	OFF
"3"		
1st Gear	ON	OFF
2nd Gear	ON	ON
3rd Gear	OFF	ON
"1-2"		
1st Gear	ON	OFF
2nd Gear	ON	ON
"R" (Reverse)	ON	OFF
"N" Or "P"	ON	OFF

[1] – Valve body contains 3 valve body solenoids. *See Fig. 2.* No. 1 and 2 valve body solenoids are used for controlling transmission shifts. No. 3 valve body solenoid is used for torque converter lock-up only.

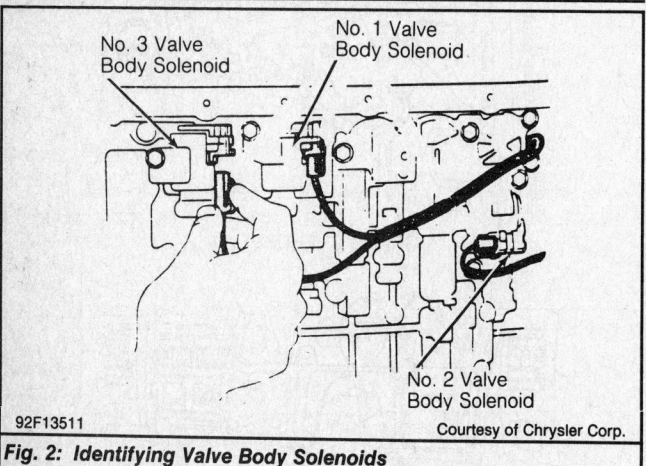

Fig. 2: Identifying Valve Body Solenoids

SPEED SENSOR

Speed sensor, mounted in adapter housing or extension housing, is an input device consisting of speed sensor rotor and speed sensor. Speed sensor rotor is mounted on transmission output shaft. Input signal is delivered from speed sensor to TCM with each revolution of transmission output shaft. The TCM uses input signal for controlling transmission operation.

THROTTLE POSITION SENSOR (TPS)

The TPS, mounted on throttle body, determines throttle position and delivers an input signal to TCM. The TCM uses input signal for controlling transmission upshifts and torque converter lock-up.

SELF-DIAGNOSTIC SYSTEM

DIAGNOSTIC PROCEDURE

When performing vehicle diagnosis:
- Ensure transmission fluid level is correct and fluid is neither contaminated nor aerated.
- Ensure shift cable is properly adjusted. See appropriate AUTOMATIC TRANSMISSION SERVICING article in TRANSMISSION SERVICING.
- Ensure battery is fully charged.
- Perform visual inspection, ensuring all electrical connections at transmission, TCM, throttle position sensor, neutral safety switch, speed sensor and brake switch are clean and properly installed.
- Perform TEST 1A – VERIFICATION OF COMPLAINT under TROUBLE SHOOTING CHARTS.

- Repair diagnostic trouble codes in order displayed.
- Always perform TEST 2A – VERIFICATION TEST after repair is completed. See TEST 2A – VERIFICATION TEST under TROUBLE SHOOTING CHARTS.

RETRIEVING DIAGNOSTIC TROUBLE CODES

NOTE: Manufacturer recommends using Chrysler's Diagnostic Readout Box-II (DRB-II) with proper cartridge for system diagnosis. Other after-market scan tools may be used for system diagnosis. The following procedure is for DRB-II scan tool usage. Use manufacturer's instruction for operating the DRB-II scan tool. When retrieving diagnostic trouble codes using DRB-II, you must first enter AW4 MENU and then retrieve diagnostic trouble codes.

NOTE: Ensure TEST 1A – VERIFICATION OF COMPLAINT is performed when trouble shooting the vehicle. This test checks for diagnostic trouble codes with vehicle stationary and during road test. See TEST 1A – VERIFICATION OF COMPLAINT under TROUBLE SHOOTING CHARTS.

NOTE: The DRB-II scan tool can be used in several different modes using manufacturer's instructions to activate system components and perform several tests on transmission. See DRB-II OPERATING MODES.

Entering AW4 MENU – 1) Ensure ignition is off. Connect DRB-II to 6-pin transmission diagnostic connector. *See Fig. 3.* Transmission diagnostic connector is located on driver's side of instrument panel, above accelerator pedal.

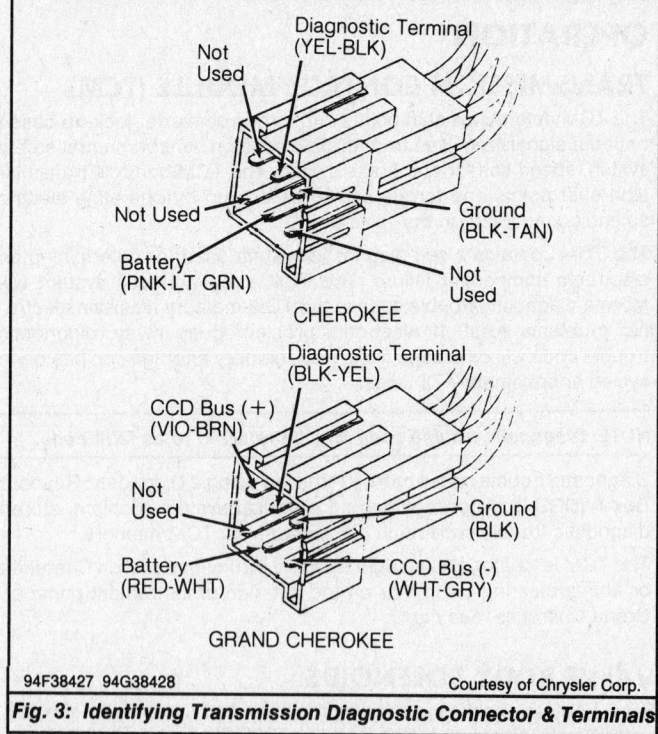

Fig. 3: Identifying Transmission Diagnostic Connector & Terminals

2) Turn ignition on. Copyright date and diagnostic program will be briefly displayed. If DRB-II displays an error message, proceed to DRB-II PROBLEMS & ERROR MESSAGES. The following are possible error messages that may appear.
- CARTRIDGE ERROR
- HIGH BATTERY
- KEYPAD TEST FAILURE
- LOW BATTERY
- RAM TEST FAILURE

3) If no error messages appear, display will read as follows after a few seconds: 1) VEHICLES TESTED, 2) HOW TO USE, 3) CONFIGURE and 4) SELECT SYSTEM.

4) Select 4) SELECT SYSTEM to enter diagnostic system. Once in SELECT SYSTEM, select 2) TRANSMISSION to enter transmission. Display will read 1) EATX and 2) AW4.

5) Select 2) AW4. After a few seconds display will change to read AW4, VERSION 01. After a few seconds, display will read AW4 MENU, 1) SYSTEM TEST and 2) READ FAULTS. If DOWN ARROW is depressed 3 times, display will read as follows: 3) STATE DISPLAY, 4) ACTUATOR TESTS and 5) ADJUSTMENTS.

NOTE: The ACTUATOR TESTS and ADJUSTMENTS cannot be used when diagnosing the AW-4 transmission.

Retrieving Diagnostic Trouble Codes – **1)** Select 2) READ FAULTS from AW4 MENU. If no diagnostic trouble code exists, display will read as follows: AW4 FAULTS, NO FAULTS DETECTED.

2) If diagnostic trouble code exists, the following message will be displayed: 1 OF 3 FAULTS. This number will vary depending on number of diagnostic trouble codes stored in the TCM memory.

3) Diagnostic trouble code and message will be displayed. Press DOWN ARROW key to display next diagnostic trouble code. To identify diagnostic trouble code, see DIAGNOSTIC TROUBLE CODE IDENTIFICATION table.

NOTE: See TROUBLE SHOOTING CHARTS to diagnose faults indicated by trouble codes.

NOTE: Valve body solenoid diagnostic trouble code 700 may appear in a FAULT PRESENT or FAULT STORED status. Status will be displayed along with diagnostic trouble code. Diagnostic trouble code must be diagnosed depending on the status. See TEST 1A – VERIFICATION OF THE COMPLAINT under TROUBLE SHOOTING CHARTS.

DIAGNOSTIC TROUBLE CODE IDENTIFICATION

Trouble Code	Problem Area
700 [1]	Valve Body Solenoid
702	Speed Sensor
703	[2] Gear Select Switch
705	Throttle Position Sensor
706	Brake Switch
707	Wrong TCM Or TCU

[1] – Trouble code may apply to individual valve body solenoids. Valve body solenoid may be referred to as S1 for No. 1, S2 for No. 2 and S3 for No. 3.

[2] – Gear select switch is the same as neutral safety switch.

CLEARING DIAGNOSTIC TROUBLE CODES

1) Once all diagnostic trouble codes have been obtained, diagnostic trouble code(s) can be erased from TCM memory by disconnecting electrical connector from TCM for at least 15 seconds.

CAUTION: DO NOT disconnect battery, as data stored in other vehicle control modules will be lost.

2) The TCM is located behind right side of instrument panel on Cherokee or above steering column or on top left side of instrument panel on Grand Cherokee. See Fig. 1.

DRB-II OPERATING MODES

NOTE: The DRB-II can be operated in several different modes to perform various tests. Except for voltmeter/ohmmeter and HOW TO USE modes, all other operating modes are selected from AW4 MENU. See ENTERING AW4 MENU under RETRIEVING DIAGNOSTIC TROUBLE CODES.

VOLTMETER/OHMMETER MODE

To access voltmeter/ohmmeter mode, connect Red volt-ohmmeter test lead to Red port at top right corner of DRB-II. There are 2 different ports on top of DRB-II; ensure test lead is connected to proper port. Access voltmeter or ohmmeter mode using manufacturer's instructions.

NOTE: The DRB-II is grounded through transmission diagnostic connector and only one test lead is required. When diagnosing transmission, an external volt-ohmmeter may sometimes be required.

HOW TO USE MODE

1) This mode gives instructions on DRB-II usage. To enter this mode, see steps 1) through 4) of ENTERING AW4 MENU under RETRIEVING DIAGNOSTIC TROUBLE CODES. Select 2) HOW TO USE.

2) A series of screens will be displayed explaining DRB-II key usage for system diagnosing.

SYSTEM TEST MODE

NOTE: SYSTEM TEST mode consists of a stationary test and a road test. The SYSTEM TEST mode must be selected from AW4 MENU. See ENTERING AW4 MENU under RETRIEVING DIAGNOSTIC TROUBLE CODES.

1) Stationary test monitors transmission system data, current valve body solenoid failures, switch failures, correct TCM application, calibration and operation. Road test checks all valve body solenoids and speed sensor.

2) Technician will be instructed to place shift lever in each gear position, starting by shifting into 1-2 position. Once transmission is in Park, brake pedal must be depressed to check brake switch.

3) After brake switch is checked, technician will be instructed to slowly depress throttle. DRB-II will display 7 asterisks (*******) corresponding to throttle position. While depressing accelerator, Throttle Position Sensor (TPS) sweeps through entire range of positions required by the TCM.

4) A corresponding asterisk will be cleared from DRB-II display as each throttle position is sensed by TCM. Several attempts may be required to clear all asterisks from the display, depending on how fast accelerator is depressed.

5) After throttle position is checked, technician will be instructed to drive the vehicle. The DRB-II will indicate if a requested action is seen by the TCM. If technician is requested to perform a particular operation and TCM does not acknowledge the action, press ENTER key to continue testing.

6) The TCM will instruct technician to accelerate vehicle at light throttle to ensure transmission shifts through all gears, indicating proper valve body solenoid operation.

7) During road test, ensure vehicle can be accelerated slowly and evenly to allow transmission to enter all gear ranges without downshifting or braking. If a failure is sensed, a diagnostic trouble code will be displayed on DRB-II.

NOTE: If TCM senses a failure, control logic activates a specified valve body solenoid to obtain a certain gear depending on failure. Because transmission diagnostic trouble codes are displayed one at a time, multiple diagnostic trouble codes must be identified by retesting transmission.

STATE DISPLAY MODE

NOTE: STATE DISPLAY mode must be selected from AW4 MENU. See ENTERING AW4 MENU under RETRIEVING DIAGNOSTIC TROUBLE CODES. Select 3) STATE DISPLAY on DRB-II.

Module Information – When selecting module information option, the TCM version will be indicated by a 2-digit number. Information can be used to verify proper TCM application.

Sensor – 1) When selecting sensor option, TPS and RPM indications will be shown. The TPS indicator will display a 7 segment bar graph, indicating TPS position and throttle plate angle.

2) A properly operating TPS should indicate 7 segments through full throttle travel. The RPM indicator will display transmission output shaft revolutions per minute.

Brake Switch Or Input/Output – Display indicates brake switch status, indicating whether brake pedal is applied or released. Display also indicates shift lever position, whether a valve body solenoid is on or off and present transmission operating gear.

DRB-II PROBLEMS & ERROR MESSAGES

CARTRIDGE ERROR

1) If CARTRIDGE ERROR message is displayed, disconnect DRB-II from transmission diagnostic connector. DO NOT touch keys on DRB-II keypad. Reconnect DRB-II to transmission diagnostic connector and note display.

2) If CARTRIDGE ERROR message is displayed, replace DRB-II cartridge and proceed with diagnostics. If KEYPAD TEST FAILURE message is displayed, replace DRB-II and proceed with diagnostics.

HIGH BATTERY

If HIGH BATTERY message is displayed, use external voltmeter to check battery voltage at battery terminals. If battery voltage is 11.7-13.0 volts, replace DRB-II. If battery voltage is not 11.7-13.0 volts, check charging system.

KEYPAD TEST FAILURE

1) If KEYPAD TEST FAILURE message is displayed, disconnect DRB-II from transmission diagnostic connector. DO NOT touch keys on DRB-II keypad. Reconnect DRB-II to transmission diagnostic connector and note display.

2) If KEYPAD TEST FAILURE message is not displayed, proceed with diagnostics. If KEYPAD TEST FAILURE message is displayed, replace DRB-II and proceed with diagnostics.

LOW BATTERY

If LOW BATTERY message is displayed, use external voltmeter to check battery voltage at battery terminals. If battery voltage is 11.7-13.0 volts, replace DRB-II. If battery voltage is not 11.7-13.0 volts, check charging system.

RAM TEST FAILURE

1) If RAM TEST FAILURE message is displayed, disconnect DRB-II from transmission diagnostic connector. DO NOT touch keys on DRB-II keypad. Reconnect DRB-II to transmission diagnostic connector and note display.

2) If RAM TEST FAILURE message is not displayed, proceed with diagnostics. If RAM TEST FAILURE message is displayed, replace DRB-II and proceed with diagnostics. If KEYPAD TEST FAILURE message is displayed, replace DRB-II and proceed with diagnostics.

TESTING

BRAKE SWITCH

Brake switch is mounted above brake pedal. When brake pedal is operated, brake switch delivers an input signal to TCM. The TCM uses input signal for controlling No. 3 valve body solenoid for torque converter lock-up. No other information is available from manufacturer.

NOTE: For proper brake switch adjustment, see BRAKE SWITCH under REMOVAL & INSTALLATION.

NEUTRAL SAFETY SWITCH

NOTE: Neutral safety switch may be referred to as park/neutral or gear select switch. For proper neutral safety switch adjustment, see NEUTRAL SAFETY SWITCH under REMOVAL & INSTALLATION.

Disconnect electrical connector. Note terminal identification. *See Fig. 4.* Using ohmmeter, check continuity between specified terminals in relation to shift lever position. See NEUTRAL SAFETY SWITCH CONTINUITY SPECIFICATIONS table. Replace neutral safety switch if continuity is not as specified.

NEUTRAL SAFETY SWITCH CONTINUITY SPECIFICATIONS

Shift Lever Position	Continuity Between Terminals
Park	"B" & "C"
Reverse	"A" & "E"
Neutral	"B" & "C"
Drive	[1]
3	"A" & "G"
1-2	"A" & "H"

[1] – No continuity should exist between any terminals.

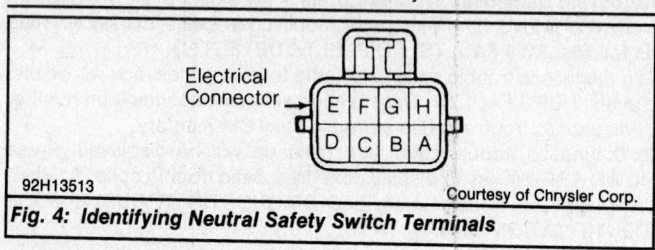

Electrical Connector →

92H13513   Courtesy of Chrysler Corp.

Fig. 4: Identifying Neutral Safety Switch Terminals

SPEED SENSOR

1) Disconnect electrical connector at speed sensor located on adapter housing or extension housing. Connect ohmmeter leads between speed sensor electrical terminals.

2) Rotate transmission output shaft and note ohmmeter reading. Ohmmeter needle should fluctuate to indicate speed sensor operation. Replace speed sensor if no reading is obtained.

THROTTLE POSITION SENSOR (TPS)

NOTE: Digital voltmeter must be used to check TPS.

1) Note location of TPS electrical connector. *See Fig. 5.* Turn ignition on. Using digital voltmeter, check output voltage at center terminal with throttle plate closed (idle position) and wide open (full throttle).

2) With throttle plate closed (idle position), output voltage should be greater than 200 millivolts. With throttle plate wide open (full throttle), output voltage should be less than 4.8 volts.

3) Ensure output voltage gradually increases as throttle plate is moved from closed to wide open throttle. If no voltage exists, check for defective wiring circuits or connections. Replace TPS if defective.

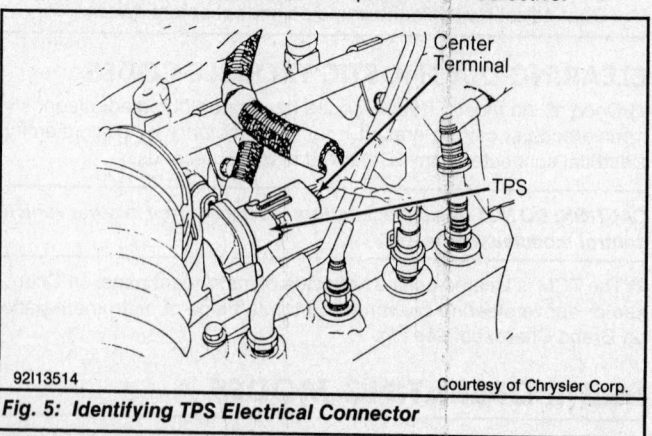

Center Terminal

TPS

92I13514   Courtesy of Chrysler Corp.

Fig. 5: Identifying TPS Electrical Connector

VALVE BODY SOLENOID

With oil pan removed, disconnect electrical connector from valve body solenoid. Using ohmmeter, check resistance between valve body solenoid electrical terminal and solenoid mounting bracket. Replace valve body solenoid if resistance is not 11-15 ohms.

REMOVAL & INSTALLATION

BRAKE SWITCH

Removal – Remove lower steering column cover or trim panels for access to brake switch (if necessary). Disconnect brake switch electrical connector. Thread brake switch from retainer and remove.

Installation – **1)** Install brake switch in retainer. Reconnect brake switch electrical connector.

2) To check brake switch adjustment, slightly depress brake pedal and note operation of brake switch plunger. Brake switch plunger should fully extend when brake pedal free play is taken up and brake application begins.

3) Clearance between brake switch plunger and brake pedal should be approximately 1/8". If clearance is not within specification, pull brake pedal rearward as far as possible.

4) Brake pedal should contact brake switch plunger, pushing brake switch backward in retainer to provide proper adjustment. Ensure brake lights operate.

5) Recheck clearance between brake switch plunger and brake pedal with brake pedal depressed and free play taken up. Reinstall lower steering column cover or trim panels.

NEUTRAL SAFETY SWITCH

NOTE: Neutral safety switch may be referred to as park/neutral or gear select switch.

Removal – **1)** Apply parking brake. Raise and support vehicle. Disconnect electrical connector at neutral safety switch. Pry lock washer tabs away from retaining nut. *See Fig. 6.*

2) Remove retaining nut, lock washer and adjusting bolt. *See Fig. 6.* Remove neutral safety switch from manual valve shaft.

Installation – **1)** Disconnect shift control rod from transmission shift lever. Rotate transmission shift lever fully rearward and then forward 2 detents to Neutral position.

2) Install neutral safety switch on manual valve shaft. Install adjusting bolt but DO NOT tighten at this time.

3) Install lock washer and retaining nut. Tighten retaining nut to specification. See TORQUE SPECIFICATIONS. DO NOT bend over lock washer tabs at this time.

4) Ensure transmission is still in Neutral. Rotate neutral safety switch and align neutral standard line with vertical groove on manual valve shaft. *See Fig. 6.*

5) Tighten adjusting bolt to specification. See TORQUE SPECIFICATIONS. Bend lock washer tabs over. Reconnect shift control rod and electrical connector. Ensure vehicle starts in Park and Neutral only.

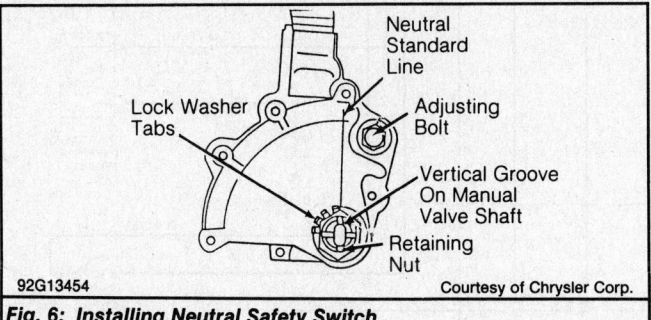

Fig. 6: Installing Neutral Safety Switch

SPEED SENSOR

Removal & Installation – **1)** Disconnect electrical connector at speed sensor located on adapter housing or extension housing. Remove bolt and speed sensor. Remove "O" ring from speed sensor.

2) To install, reverse removal procedure using NEW "O" ring. Tighten bolt to specification. See TORQUE SPECIFICATIONS.

THROTTLE POSITION SENSOR (TPS)

Removal & Installation – **1)** Note location of TPS electrical connector. *See Fig. 5.* Disconnect electrical connector. Remove screws and TPS.

2) To install, reverse removal procedure. Ensure throttle shaft on throttle body engages socket tangs on TPS. *See Fig. 7.* Tighten screws. Manually operate throttle and ensure no binding exists. Reinstall electrical connector.

NOTE: TPS must be installed so it can be rotated a few degrees. If TPS cannot be rotated, reinstall TPS with end of throttle shaft on other side of TPS socket tangs.

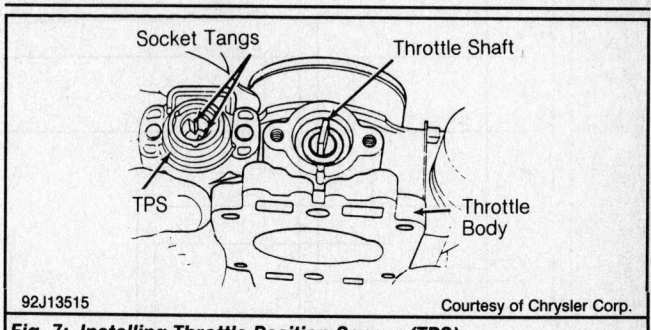

Fig. 7: Installing Throttle Position Sensor (TPS)

TRANSMISSION CONTROL MODULE (TCM)

Removal & Installation (Cherokee) – Ensure ignition is off. Disconnect electrical connector from TCM, located behind right side of instrument panel. *See Fig. 1.* Remove fastener and TCM from instrument panel. To install, reverse removal procedure.

Removal & Installation (Grand Cherokee) – Ensure ignition is off. Disconnect electrical connector from TCM, located above steering column or on top left side of instrument panel. *See Fig. 1.* TCM contains 32-pin connector. Remove fasteners and TCM. To install, reverse removal procedure.

VALVE BODY SOLENOID

Removal – **1)** Raise and support vehicle. Remove drain plug and drain transmission fluid. Remove bolts and oil pan. Remove bolts, oil screen and gasket.

2) Disconnect electrical connectors from valve body solenoid. Mark electrical connector location for reassembly reference if more than one valve body solenoid is being removed. Remove bolt, valve body solenoid and "O" ring.

CAUTION: DO NOT allow components to fall from valve body when removing valve body solenoid.

Installation – **1)** To install, reverse removal procedure using NEW "O" ring and NEW gaskets. Tighten valve body solenoid bolt and oil screen bolt to specification. See TORQUE SPECIFICATIONS.

2) Ensure magnet is installed in oil pan and does not interfere with valve body oil tubes. Apply 1/8" bead of Loctite 599 sealant on oil pan mounting flange. Install oil pan. Install and tighten bolts to specification. See TORQUE SPECIFICATIONS.

3) Install NEW gasket and drain plug. Tighten drain plug to specification. See TORQUE SPECIFICATIONS. Fill transmission to proper fluid level with Mopar Dexron-IIE/Mercon ATF.

TORQUE SPECIFICATIONS
TORQUE SPECIFICATIONS

Application	Ft. Lbs. (N.m)
Drain Plug	15 (20)

	INCH Lbs. (N.m)
Neutral Safety Switch Adjusting Bolt	108 (12.2)
Neutral Safety Switch Retaining Nut	61 (6.9)
Oil Pan Bolt	65 (7.3)
Oil Screen Bolt	84 (9.5)
Speed Sensor Bolt	65 (7.3)
Valve Body Solenoid Bolt	84 (9.5)

WIRING DIAGRAMS

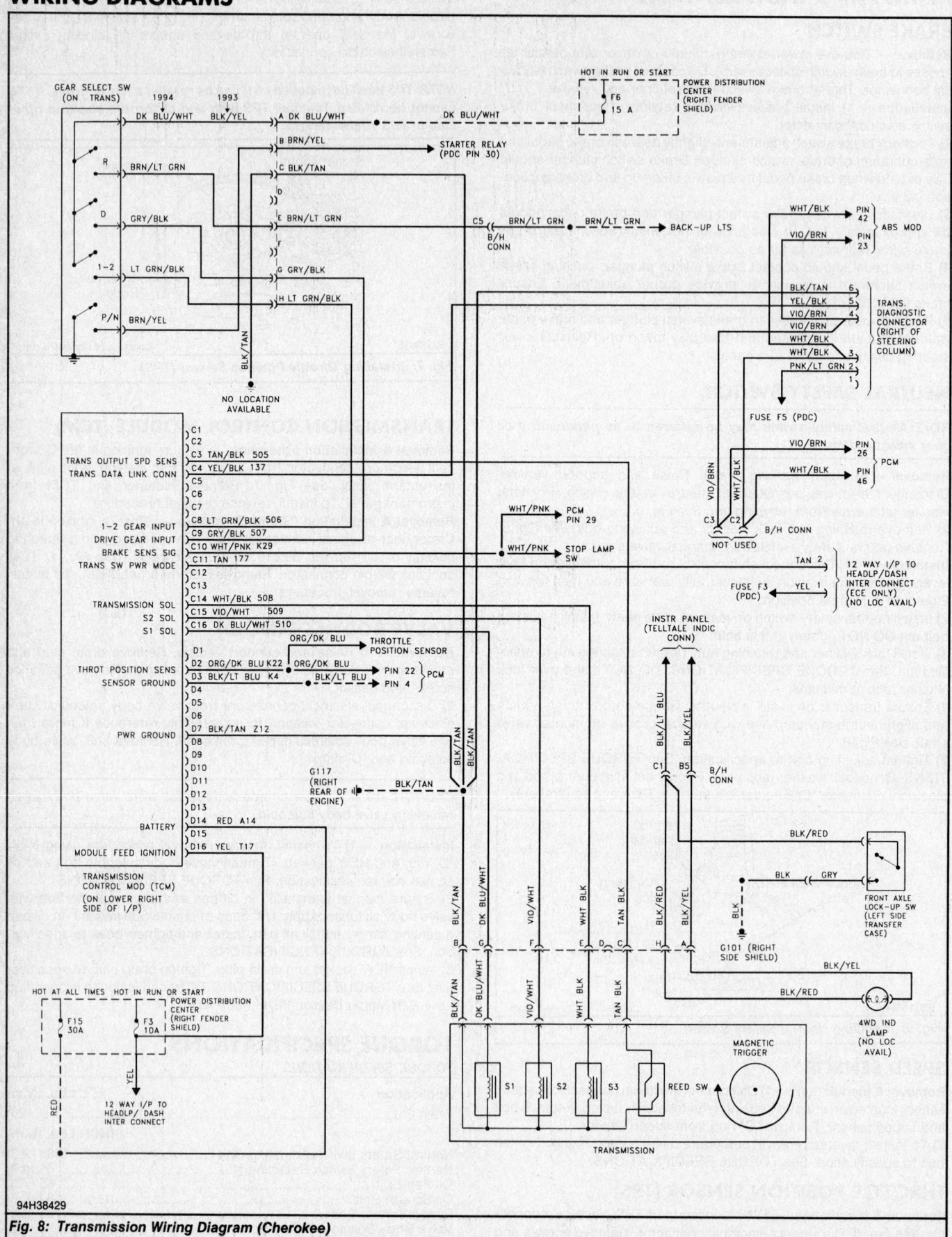

Fig. 8: *Transmission Wiring Diagram (Cherokee)*

94H38429

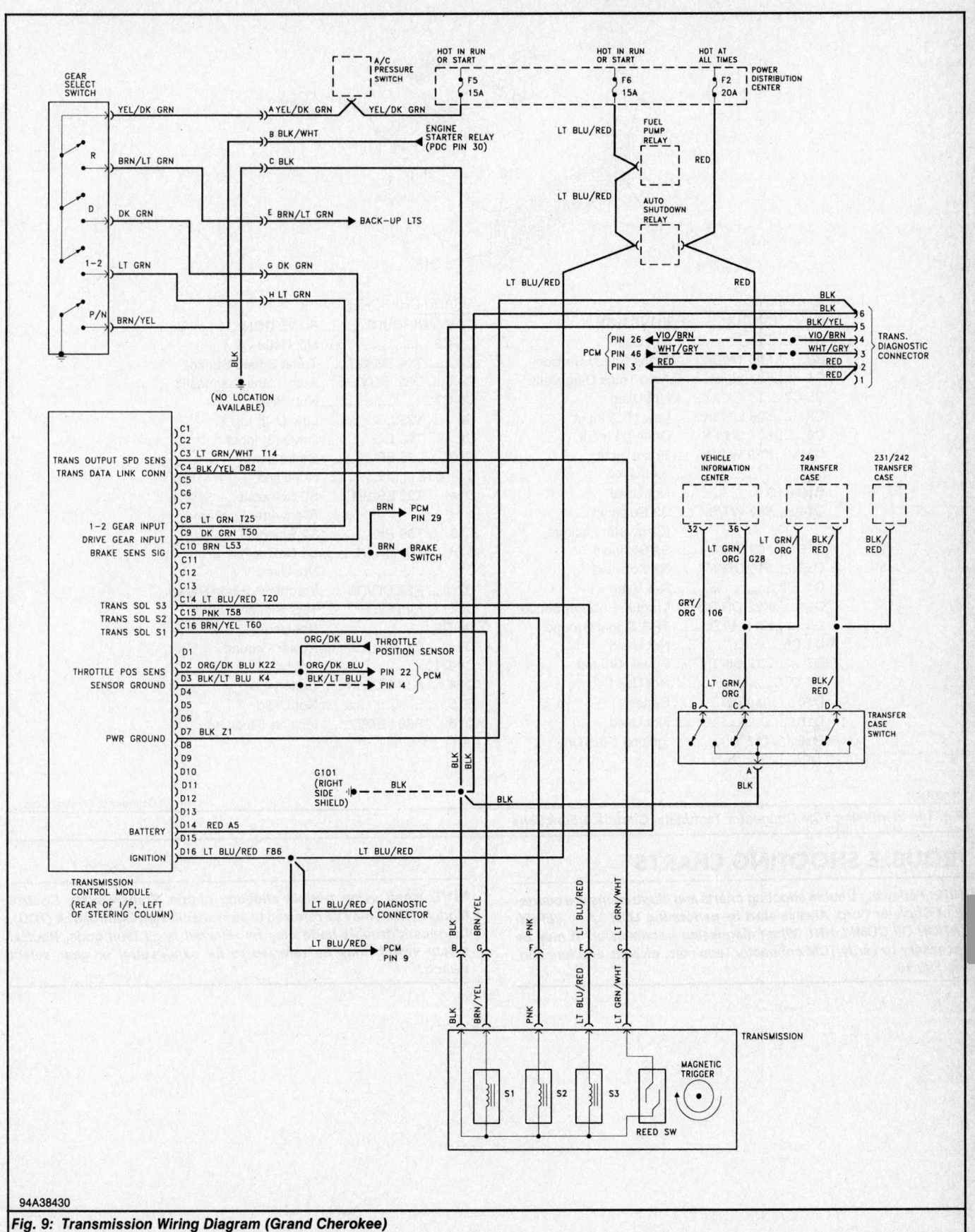

Fig. 9: Transmission Wiring Diagram (Grand Cherokee)

94A38430

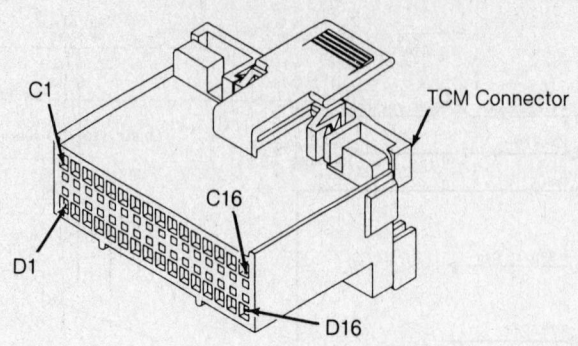

CHEROKEE

CAV ... CIRCUIT .... FUNCTION
C1-C2 .... Not Used
C3 .... 505 TN/BK ...... Trans Speed Sensor
C4 .... 137 YL/BK .... Auto Trans Diagnostic
C5-C7 .... Not Used
C8 .... 506 LG/BK .... Low (1-2) Input
C9 .... 507 GY/BK .... Drive (3) Input
C10 ..... K29 WT/PK ..... Brake Input
C11 .... Not Used
C12-C13 .... Not Used
C14 ..... 508 WT/BK ...... S3 Solenoid
(Converter Lockup)
C15 ..... 509 VT/WT ...... S2 Solenoid
C16 ..... 510 DB/WT ...... S1 Solenoid
D1 .... Not Used
D2 .... K22 OR/DB ..... Throttle Position Sensor
D3 .... K4 BK/LB .... TPS Signal Ground
D4-D6 .... Not Used
D7 .... Z12 BK/TN .... Power Ground
D8-D13 .... Not Used
D14 ..... A14 RD .... Battery
D15 .... Not Used
D16 ..... T17 YL .... Ignition (Run/On)

GRAND CHEROKEE

CAV ... CIRCUIT .... FUNCTION
C1-C2 .... Not Used
C3 ...... T14 LG/WT ..... Trans Speed Sensor
C4 ...... D82 BK/YL ...... Auto Trans Diagnostic
C5-C7 .... Not Used
C8 ...... T25 LG .... Low (1-2) Input
C9 ...... T50 DG .... Drive (3) Input
C10 .... L53 BR .... Brake Input
C11-C13 .... Not Used
C14 .... T20 LB/BR ...... S3 Solenoid
(Converter Lockup)
C15 .... T59 PK .... S2 Solenoid
C16 .... T60 BR/YL ...... S1 Solenoid
D1 .... Not Used
D2 ...... K22 OR/DB ..... Throttle Position Sensor
D3 ...... K4 BK/LB .... TPS Signal Ground
D4-D6 .... Not Used
D7 ...... Z1 BK............. Power Ground
D8-D13 .... Not Used
D14 .... A14 RD/WT ..... Battery
D15 .... Not Used
D16 .... F86 LB/RD ...... Ignition (Run/On)

94B38431

Courtesy of Chrysler Corp.

Fig. 10: Identifying TCM Connector Terminals, Circuits & Functions

TROUBLE SHOOTING CHARTS

NOTE: Following trouble shooting charts and illustrations are courtesy of Chrysler Corp. Always start by performing TEST 1A – VERIFICATION OF COMPLAINT. When diagnosing transmission, it may be necessary to verify TCM connector terminals, circuits and function, see Fig. 10.

NOTE: When using trouble shooting charts, Transmission Control Module (TCM) may be referred to as Transmission Control Unit (TCU). Diagnostic trouble code may be referred to as fault code. Neutral safety switch may be referred to as park/neutral or gear select switch.

TEST 2A
VERIFICATION TEST

Perform TEST 1A before proceeding.

This test verifies the correct operation of the AW4 transmission. It must be performed after finding no faults using the DRBII, and after a vehicle repair has been made.

1. Ignition key off.

2. Hold the MODE key and press the ATM key on the DRBII at the same time to restart the DRBII.

3. Ignition key on.

4. Reconnect all previously disconnected connectors.

5. Verify that the AW4 transmission control unit is properly mounted.

6. Make sure the transmission fluid is at the proper level. Check the fluid with the transmission temperature hot, the vehicle on level ground, and the gear selector in neutral.

7. If any repairs have been made, test the vehicle as instructed in TEST 1A, and read faults using the DRBII. If there are any fault messages present, repeat **TEST 1A**.

92C13592

TEST 1A
VERIFICATION OF THE COMPLAINT

1. Begin your testing of the transmission with a thorough visual inspection.

2. Connect the DRBII to the transmission diagnostic connector, See RETRIEVING FAULT CODES under SELF-DIAGNOSTIC SYSTEM for diagnostic connector location.

   CAUTION: If the vehicle is in 3rd or OD position and feels like it is stuck in 3rd or jumping from 2-1 or 3-1, perform TEST 10A (intermittent speed sensor test).

3. With the DRBII, perform the SYSTEM TEST. See SYSTEM TEST MODE under DRB-II OPERATING MODES.

4. The DRBII will instruct you to do some actions during the System Test. The DRBII will then look for the action to happen and automatically go to the next test function. If you perform the required action and the DRBII does not move to the next function, press ENTER. The DRBII will continue the testing.

5. When the DRBII states "DRIVE VEHICLE", the vehicle must be driven at a speed above 4 miles per hour to ensure accurate testing of the vehicle speed sensor. Afterwards, the DRBII will display any fault codes that may be present.

6. When the system test is complete, if there are any fault codes present, the DRBII will automatically display the code(s).

7. There are two types of faults for the transmission solenoids. They are displayed as "FAULT STORED" and "FAULT PRESENT". Note that the tests are different in the chart below.

8. Perform the tests shown below in response to the indicated fault codes. **NOTE:** Start with the most recent code.

CODE MESSAGES

NO FAULT CODES	Perform TEST 2A
CODE 700, SOLENOID #1, FAULT PRESENT	Perform TEST 4A
CODE 700, SOLENOID #1, FAULT STORED	Perform TEST 3A
CODE 700, SOLENOID #2, FAULT PRESENT	Perform TEST 4B
CODE 700, SOLENOID #2, FAULT STORED	Perform TEST 3A
CODE 700, SOLENOID #3, FAULT PRESENT	Perform TEST 4C
CODE 700, SOLENOID #3, FAULT STORED	Perform TEST 3A
CODE 702, SPEED SENSOR FAULT	Perform TEST 5A
CODE 703, GEAR SELECT FAULT	Perform TEST 6A
CODE 705, THROTTLE POSITION SENSOR FAULT	Perform TEST 7A
CODE 706, BRAKE SWITCH FAULT	Perform TEST 8A
CODE 708, WRONG TCU	Perform TEST 9A

92C13591

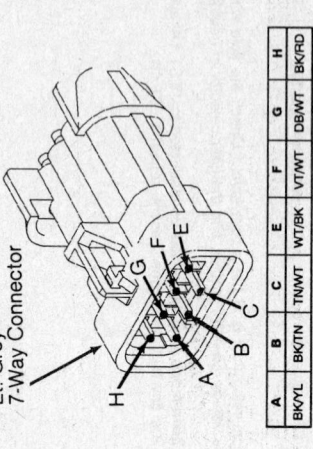

Transmission Lt. Grey 7-Way Connector

Transmission Black 8-Way Connector

Gear Select Switch

XJ BODY

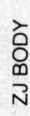

Transmission Lt. Grey 7-Way Connector

G F E

H A B C

ZJ BODY

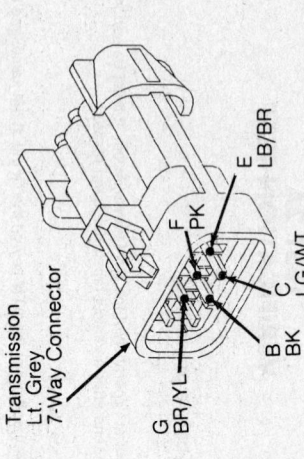

Transmission Lt. Grey 7-Way Connector

E LB/BR

F PK

C LG/WT

B BK

G BR/YL

A	B	C	E	F	G	H
BK/YL	BK/TN	TN/WT	WT/BK	VT/WT	DB/WT	BK/RD

TEST 3A
STORED DIAGNOSTIC TROUBLE CODES TEST

Perform TEST 1A before proceeding.

1. At this point, the Visual Inspection has been performed, a "FAULT STORED" code has been found, and the vehicle has been test driven. The fault code is not "FAULT PRESENT", so it cannot be considered a CURRENT or HARD fault.

2. All the solenoid circuits are in the same harness, and a common ground wire is used for these solenoids. Use the figure to identify the harness and connector to inspect.
If all three solenoid faults are present, repair the   BK or   BK/TN common ground wire for an open.

3. Carefully inspect the entire suspected circuit. Pay particular attention to connectors, corrosion, accident damage, and improper or missing parts.

4. If any problems are found, make the appropriate repair. Then perform TEST 1A using the DRBII.

5. Erase fault codes.

6. If no problems are found, perform the SYSTEM TEST using the DRBII. Re-check for fault codes; if there are no fault codes, perform TEST 2A. If the fault code returns, perform TEST 1A.

92E13593 92F13594 92G13595 92H13596

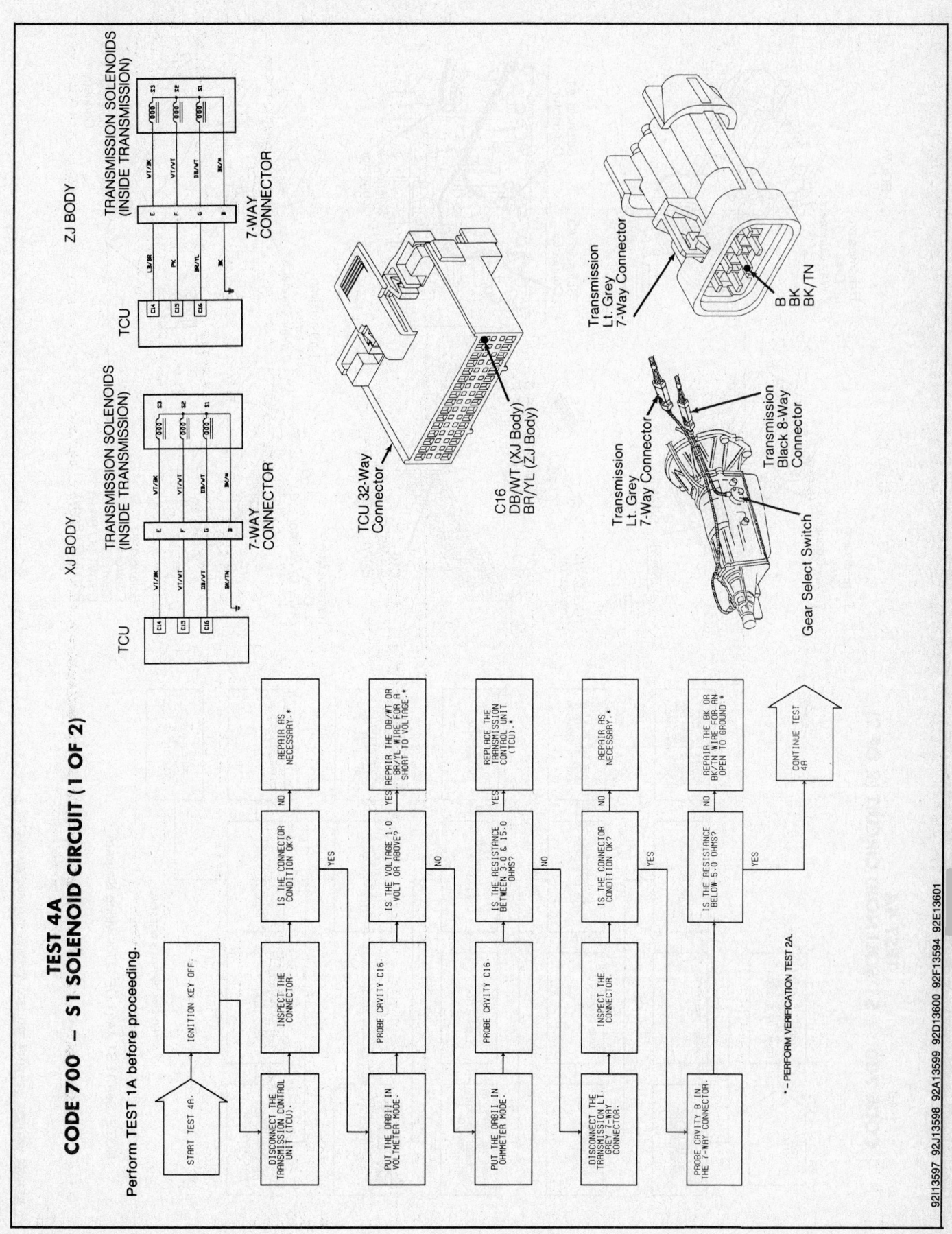

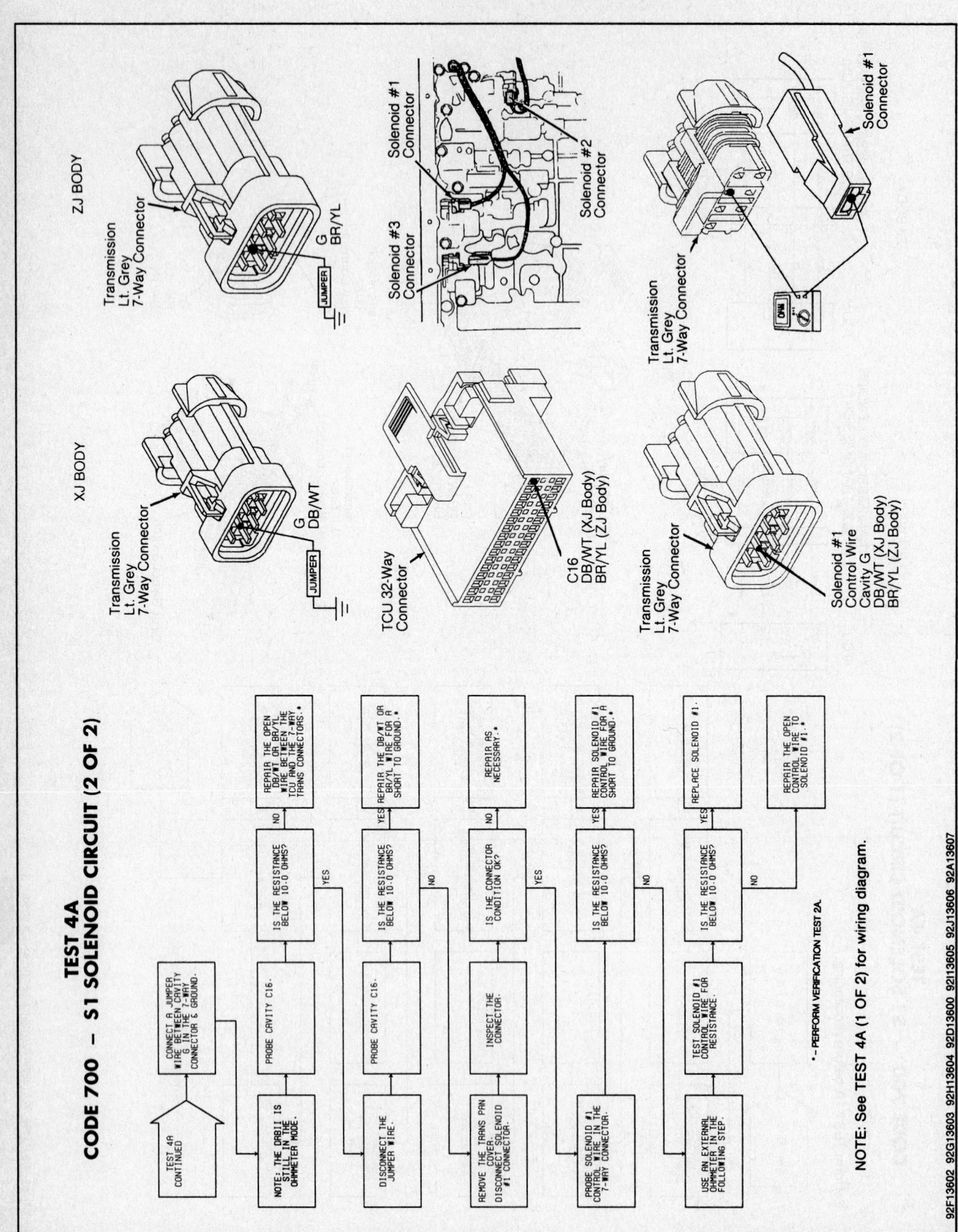

TEST 4A
CODE 700 – S1 SOLENOID CIRCUIT (2 OF 2)

ZJ BODY

Transmission
Lt. Grey
7-Way Connector

G
BR/YL

JUMPER

Solenoid #1
Connector

Solenoid #3
Connector

Solenoid #2
Connector

Solenoid #1
Connector

Transmission
Lt. Grey
7-Way Connector

XJ BODY

Transmission
Lt. Grey
7-Way Connector

G
DB/WT

JUMPER

TCU 32-Way
Connector

C16
DB/WT (XJ Body)
BR/YL (ZJ Body)

Transmission
Lt. Grey
7-Way Connector

Solenoid #1
Control Wire
Cavity G
DB/WT (XJ Body)
BR/YL (ZJ Body)

TEST 4A
CONTINUED

CONNECT A JUMPER
WIRE BETWEEN CAVITY
G IN THE 7-WAY
CONNECTOR & GROUND.

NOTE: THE DRBII IS
STILL IN THE
OHMMETER MODE.

PROBE CAVITY C16.

IS THE RESISTANCE
BELOW 10.0 OHMS?

NO → REPAIR THE OPEN
DB/WT OR BR/YL
WIRE BETWEEN THE
TCU AND THE 7-WAY
TRANS CONNECTORS. *

YES

DISCONNECT THE
JUMPER WIRE.

PROBE CAVITY C16.

IS THE RESISTANCE
BELOW 10.0 OHMS?

YES → REPAIR THE DB/WT OR
BR/YL WIRE FOR A
SHORT TO GROUND. *

NO

REMOVE THE TRANS PAN
COVER.
DISCONNECT SOLENOID
#1 CONNECTOR.

INSPECT THE
CONNECTOR.

IS THE CONNECTOR
CONDITION OK?

NO → REPAIR AS
NECESSARY. *

YES

PROBE SOLENOID #1
CONTROL WIRE IN THE
7-WAY CONNECTOR.

IS THE RESISTANCE
BELOW 10.0 OHMS?

YES → REPAIR SOLENOID #1
CONTROL WIRE FOR A
SHORT TO GROUND. *

NO

USE AN EXTERNAL
OHMMETER IN THE
FOLLOWING STEP.

TEST SOLENOID #1
CONTROL WIRE FOR
RESISTANCE.

IS THE RESISTANCE
BELOW 10.0 OHMS?

YES → REPLACE SOLENOID #1.

NO → REPAIR THE OPEN
CONTROL WIRE TO
SOLENOID #1. *

* – PERFORM VERIFICATION TEST 2A.

NOTE: See TEST 4A (1 OF 2) for wiring diagram.

92F13602 92G13603 92H13604 92D13600 92H13605 92J13606 92A13607

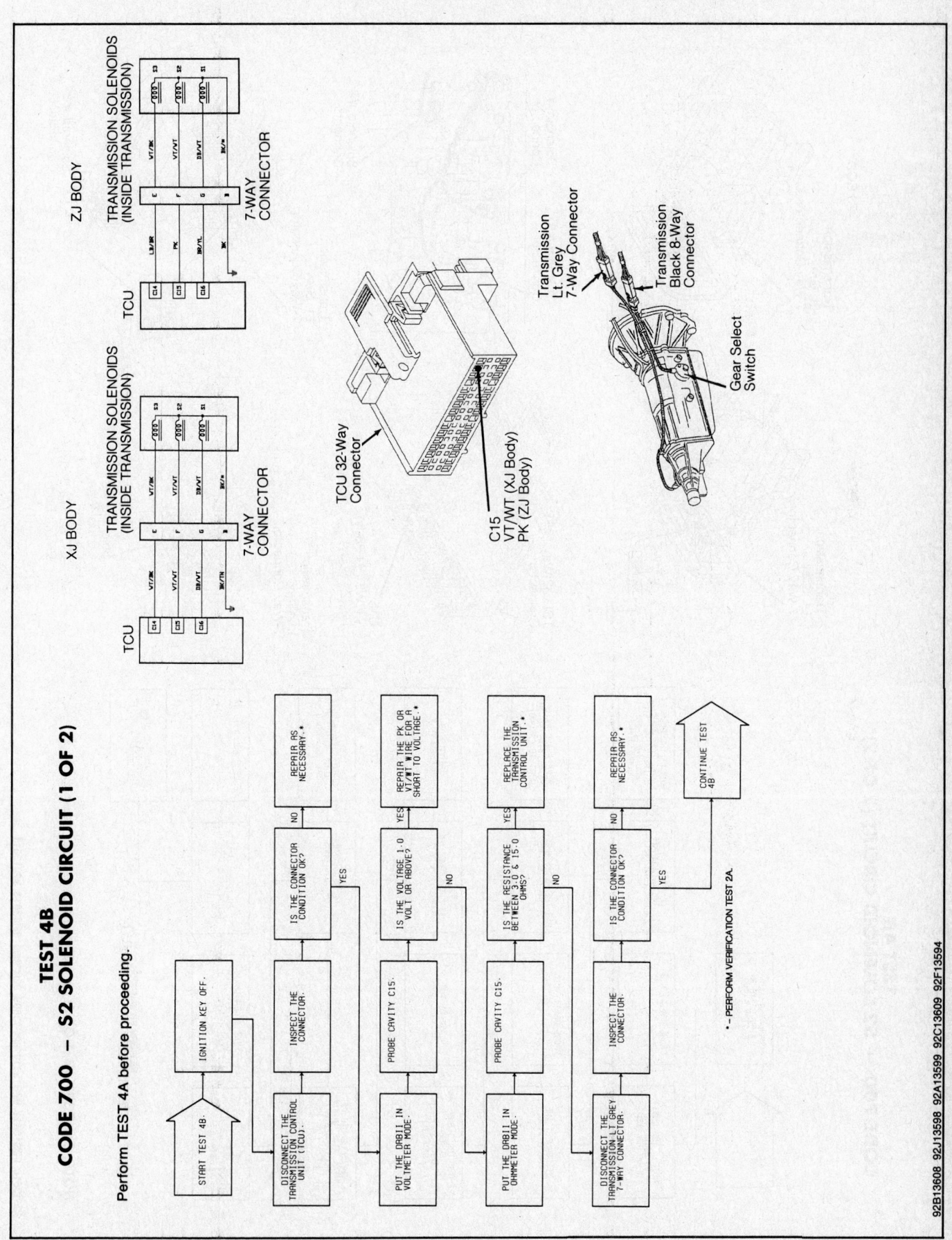

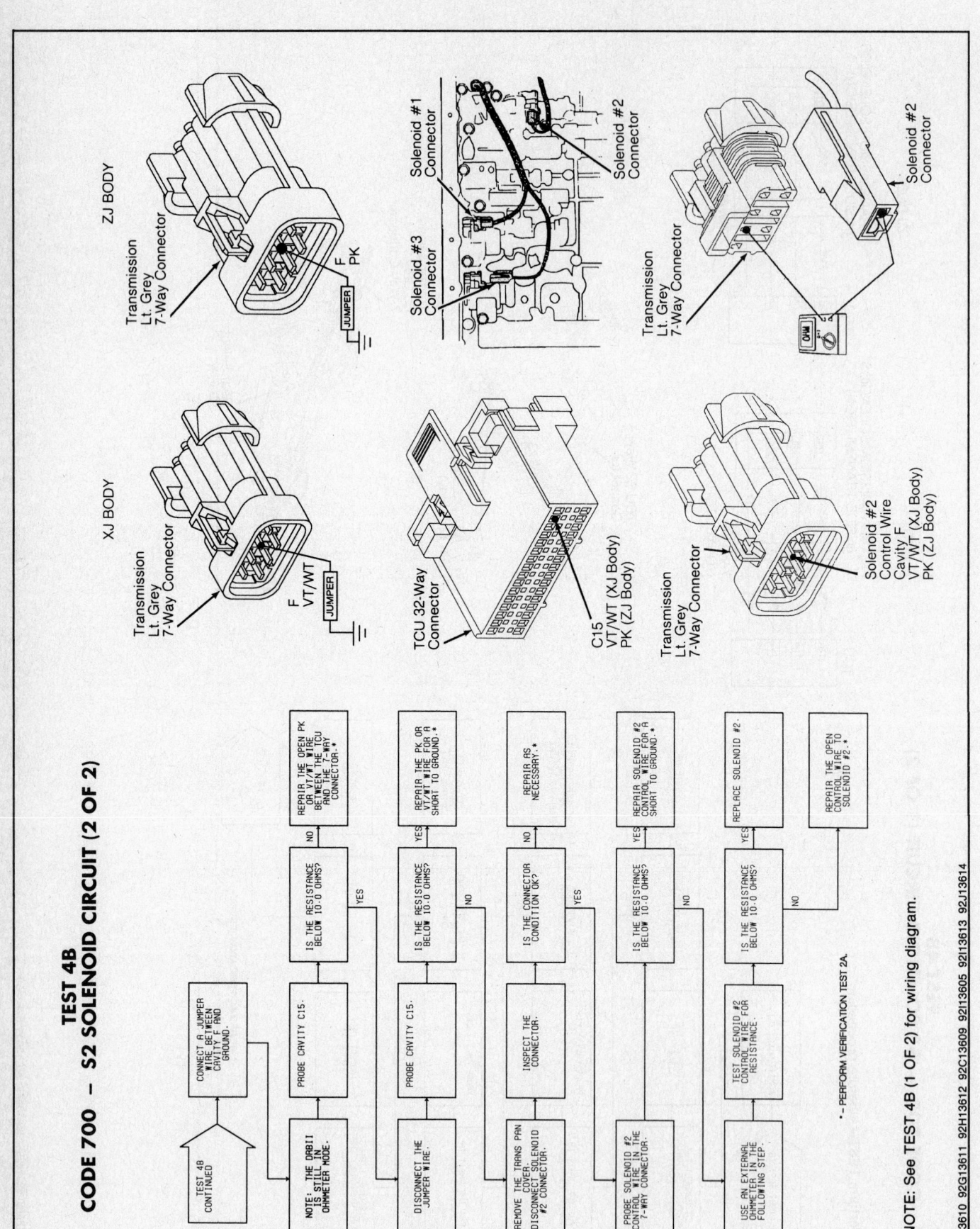

TEST 4B
CODE 700 – S2 SOLENOID CIRCUIT (2 OF 2)

NOTE: See TEST 4B (1 OF 2) for wiring diagram.

92F13610 92G13611 92H13612 92C13609 92I13605 92I13613 92J13614

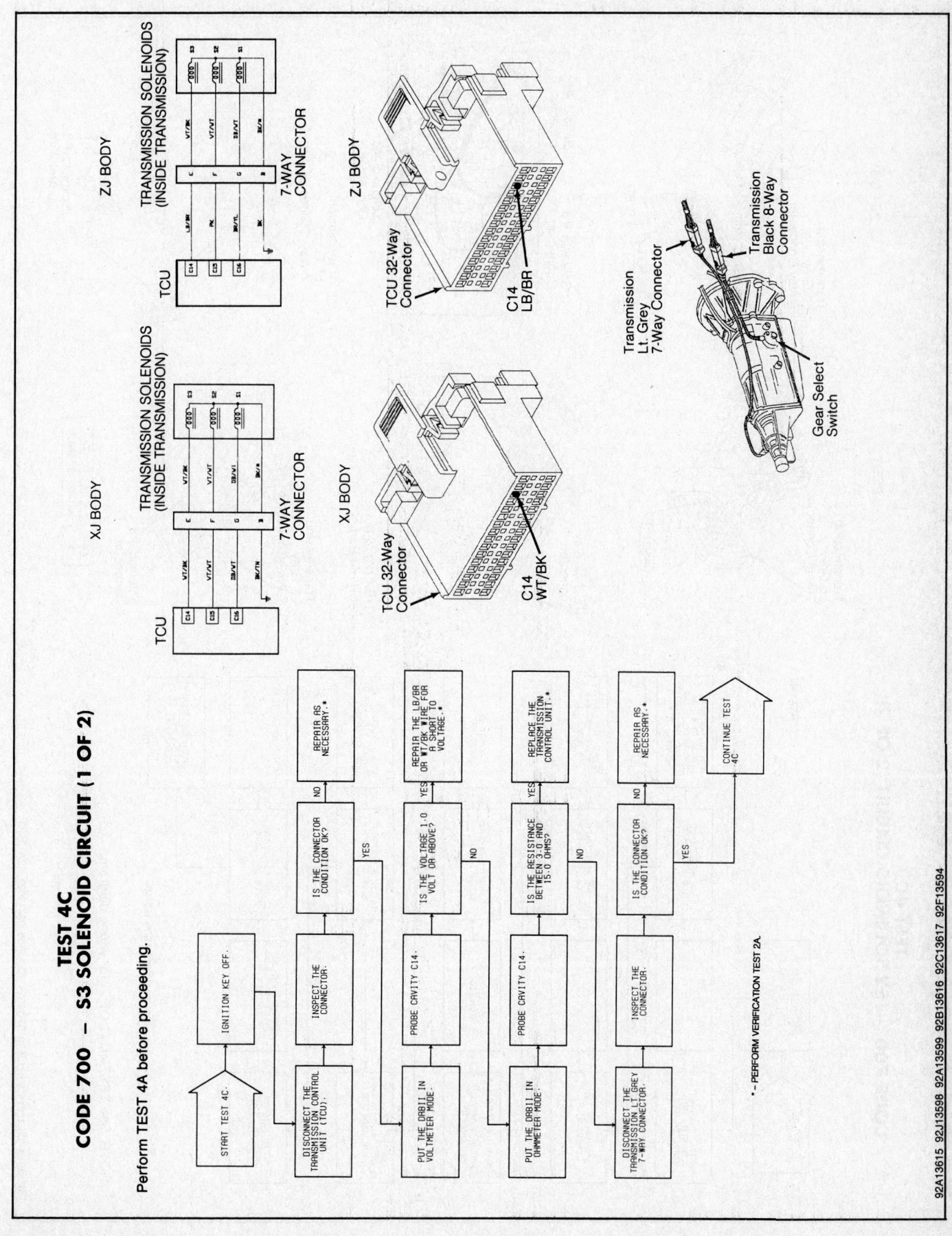

TEST 4C

CODE 700 – S3 SOLENOID CIRCUIT (1 OF 2)

Perform TEST 4A before proceeding.

92A13615 92J13598 92A13599 92B13616 92C13617 92F13594

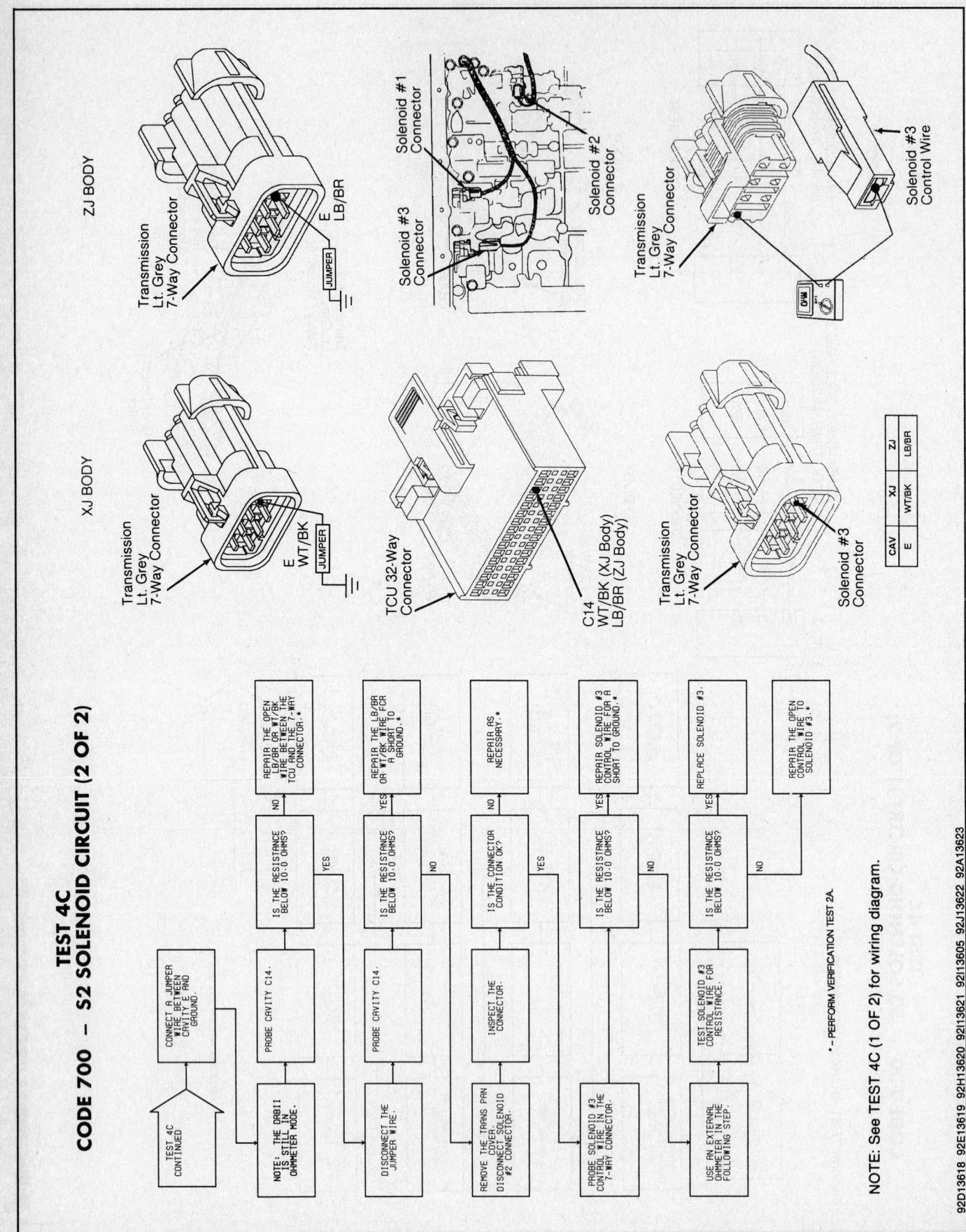

NOTE: See TEST 4C (1 OF 2) for wiring diagram.

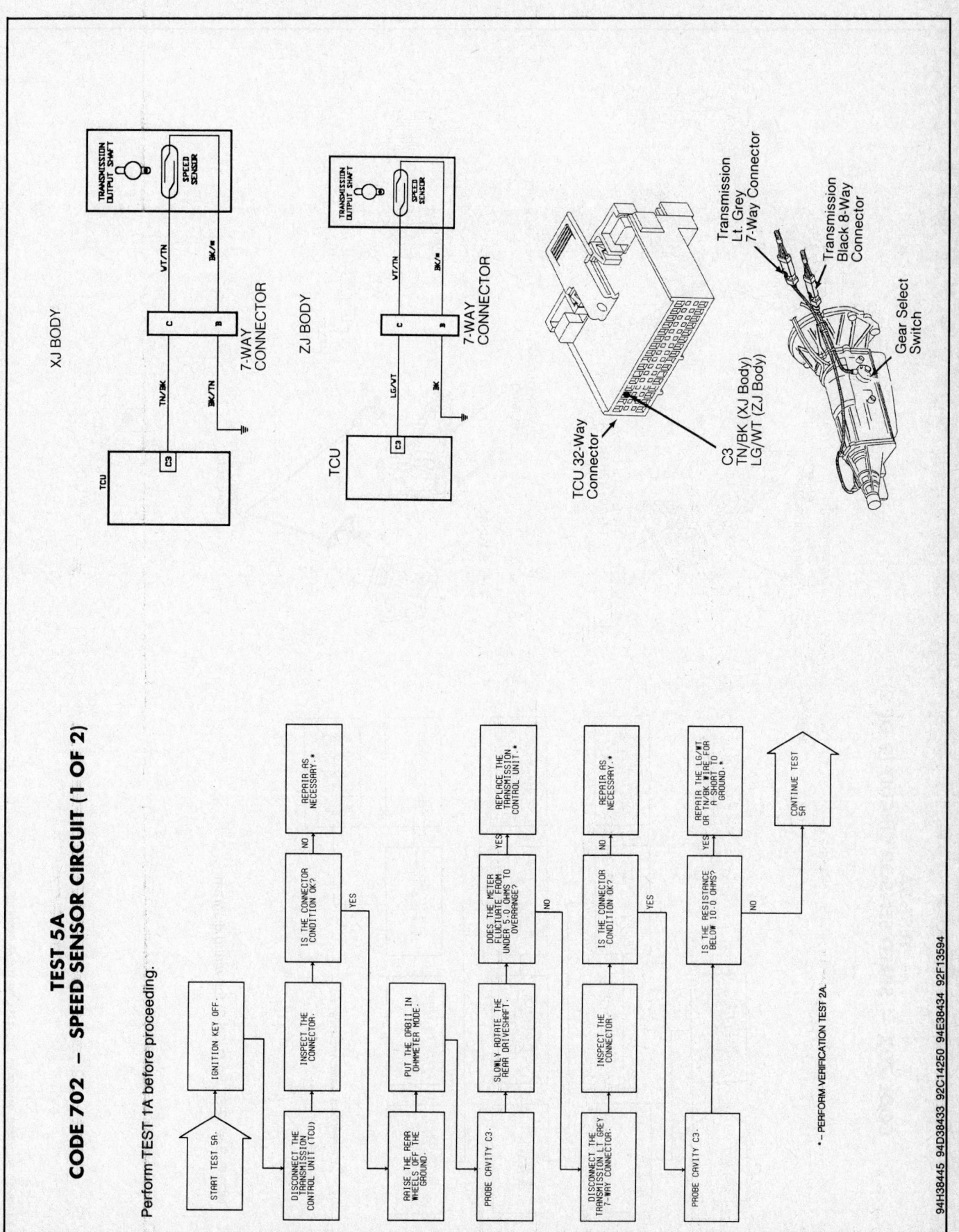

TEST 5A
CODE 702 – SPEED SENSOR CIRCUIT (1 OF 2)

Perform TEST 1A before proceeding.

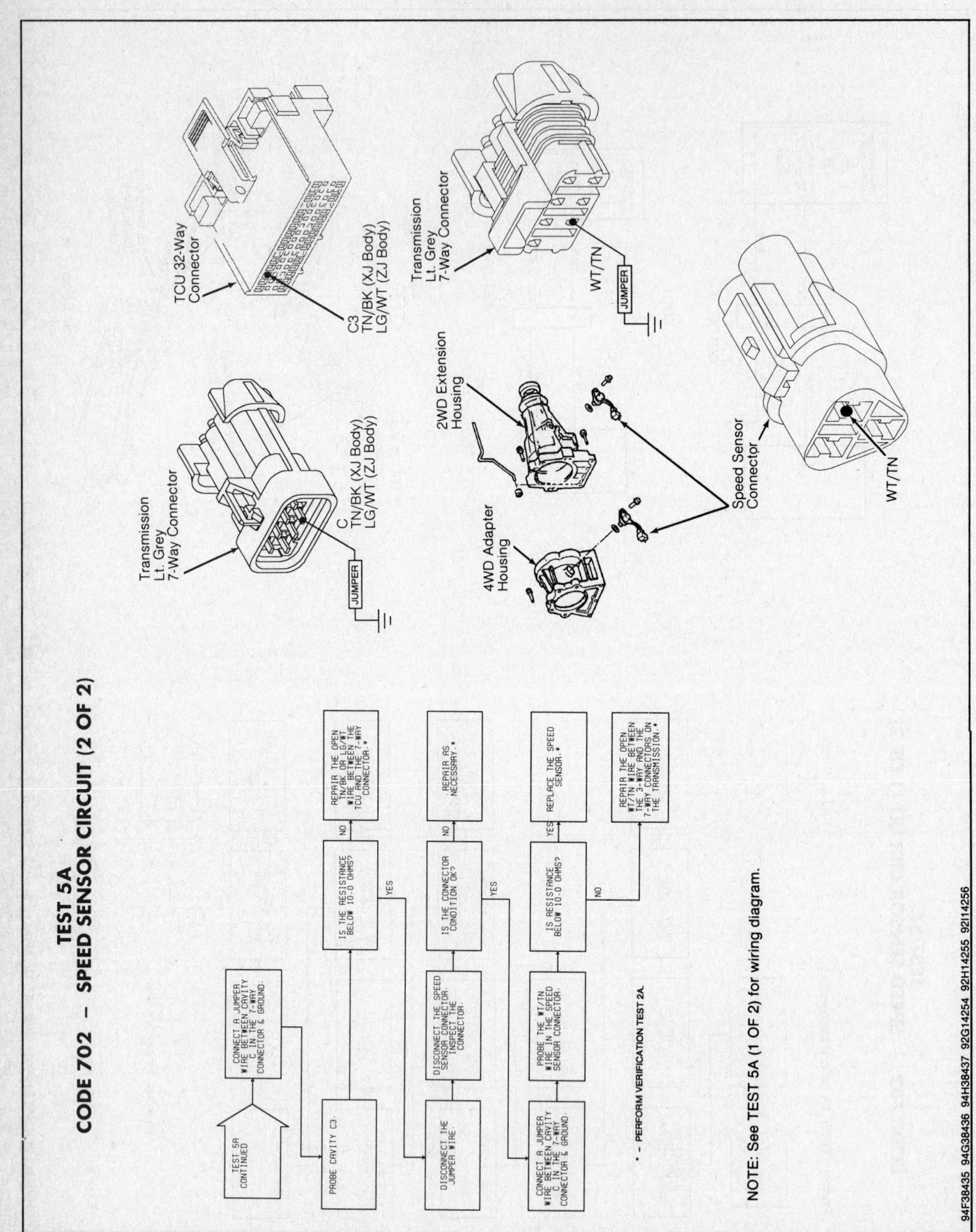

TCU 32-Way Connector

C3
TN/BK (XJ Body)
LG/WT (ZJ Body)

Transmission
Lt. Grey
7-Way Connector

WT/TN

JUMPER

2WD Extension Housing

4WD Adapter Housing

Speed Sensor Connector

WT/TN

Transmission
Lt. Grey
7-Way Connector

C
TN/BK (XJ Body)
LG/WT (ZJ Body)

JUMPER

TEST 5A
CODE 702 – SPEED SENSOR CIRCUIT (2 OF 2)

TEST 5A CONTINUED

PROBE CAVITY C3.

CONNECT A JUMPER WIRE BETWEEN CAVITY C IN THE 7-WAY CONNECTOR & GROUND.

IS THE RESISTANCE BELOW 10.0 OHMS?

— NO → REPAIR THE OPEN TN/BK OR LG/WT WIRE BETWEEN THE TCU AND THE 7-WAY CONNECTOR.*

— YES ↓

DISCONNECT THE JUMPER WIRE.

DISCONNECT THE SPEED SENSOR CONNECTOR. INSPECT THE CONNECTOR.

IS THE CONNECTOR CONDITION OK?

— NO → REPAIR AS NECESSARY.*

— YES ↓

CONNECT A JUMPER WIRE BETWEEN CAVITY C IN THE 7-WAY CONNECTOR & GROUND.

PROBE THE WT/TN WIRE IN THE SPEED SENSOR CONNECTOR.

IS RESISTANCE BELOW 10.0 OHMS?

— YES → REPLACE THE SPEED SENSOR.*

— NO → REPAIR THE OPEN WT/TN WIRE BETWEEN THE 3-WAY AND THE 7-WAY CONNECTOR ON THE TRANSMISSION.*

* — PERFORM VERIFICATION TEST 2A.

NOTE: See TEST 5A (1 OF 2) for wiring diagram.

94F38435 94G38436 94H38437 92G14254 92H14255 92I14256

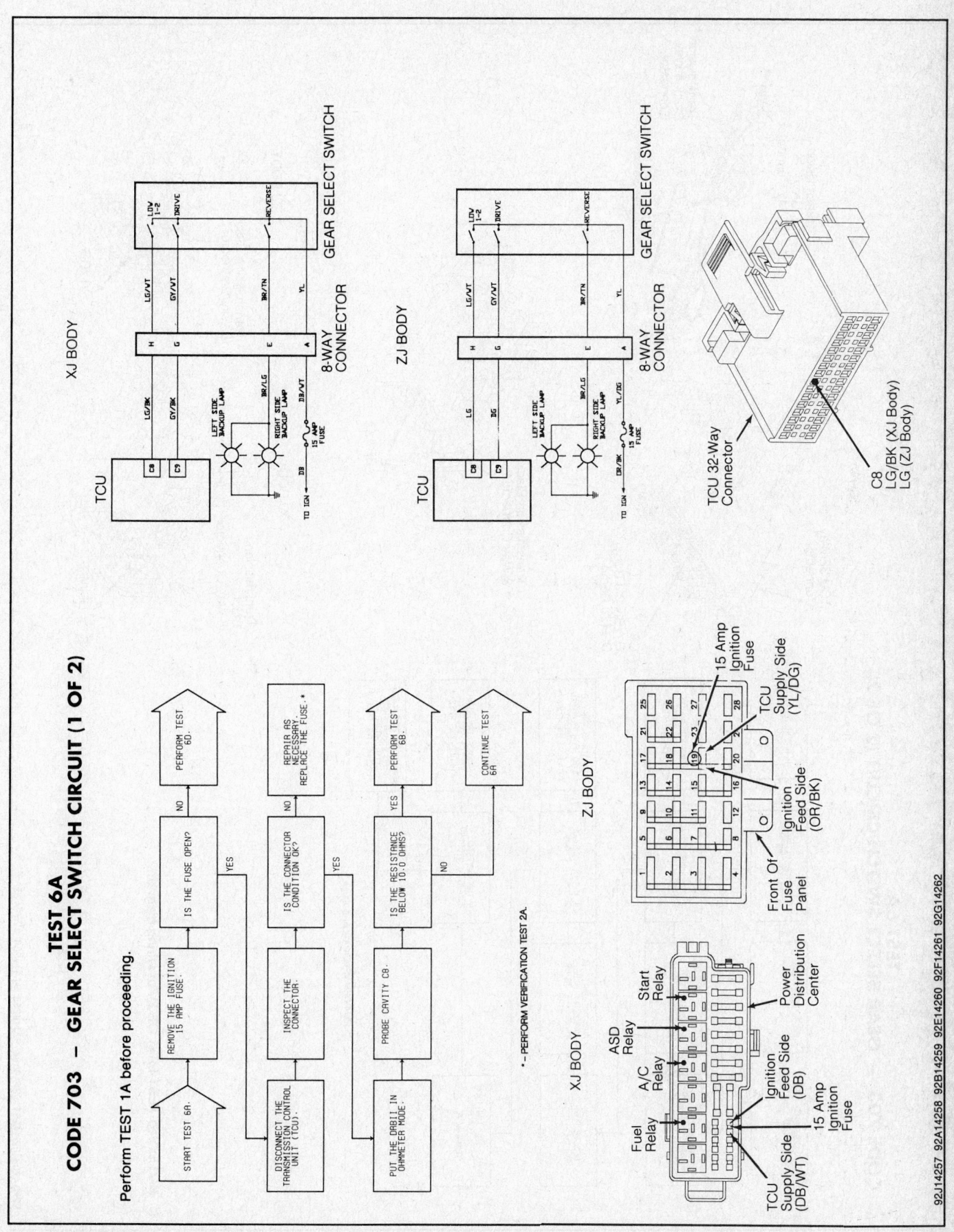

TEST 6A
CODE 703 — GEAR SELECT SWITCH CIRCUIT (1 OF 2)

Perform TEST 1A before proceeding.

92J14257 92A14258 92B14259 92E14260 92F14261 92G14262

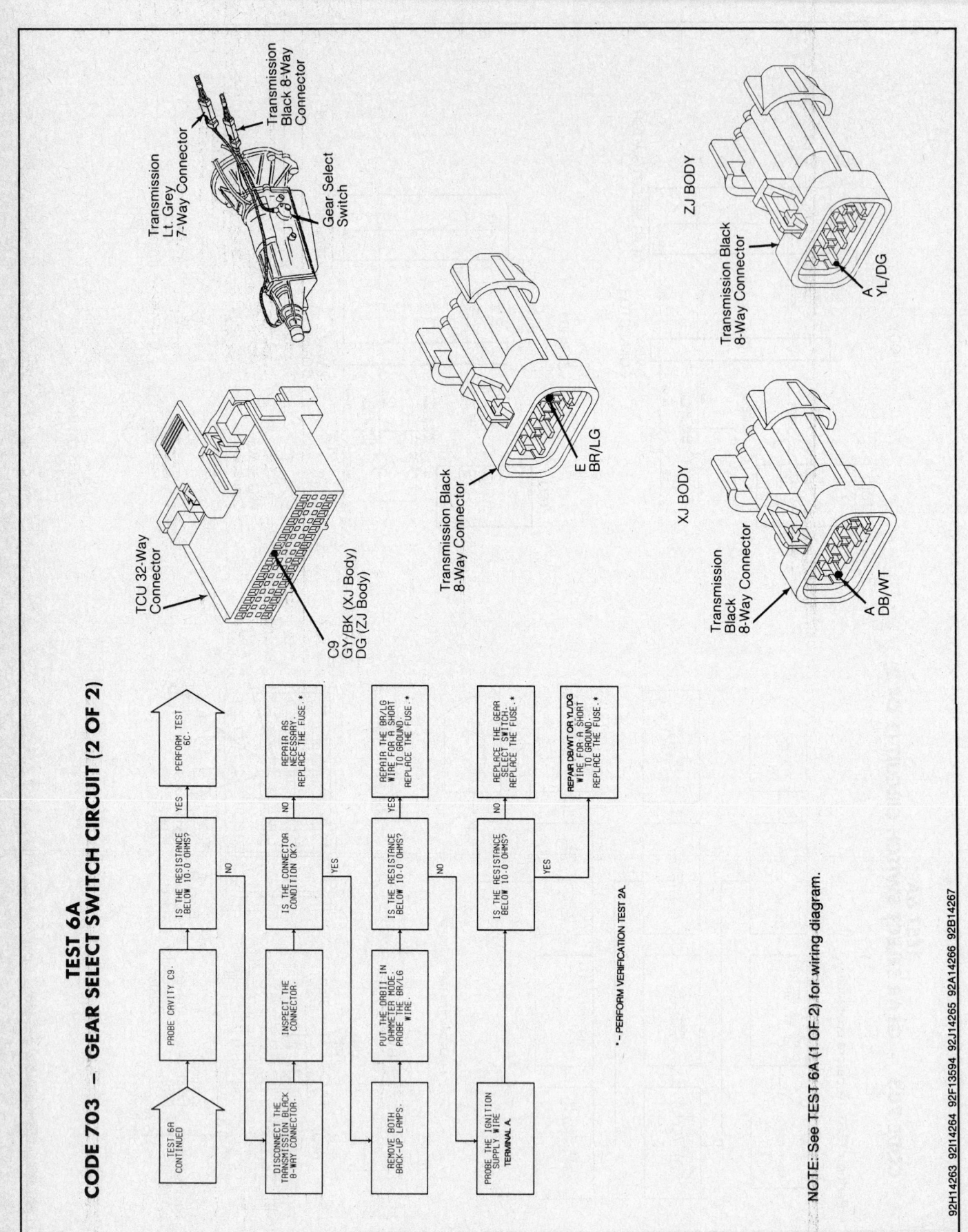

TEST 6A

CODE 703 — GEAR SELECT SWITCH CIRCUIT (2 OF 2)

Transmission Lt. Grey 7-Way Connector

Transmission Black 8-Way Connector

Gear Select Switch

TCU 32-Way Connector

C9
GY/BK (XJ Body)
DG (ZJ Body)

Transmission Black 8-Way Connector

E
BR/LG

ZJ BODY

Transmission Black 8-Way Connector

A
YL/DG

XJ BODY

Transmission Black 8-Way Connector

A
DB/WT

TEST 6A CONTINUED

PROBE CAVITY C9.

IS THE RESISTANCE BELOW 10.0 OHMS?

YES — PERFORM TEST 6C.

NO

DISCONNECT THE TRANSMISSION BLACK 8-WAY CONNECTOR.

INSPECT THE CONNECTOR.

IS THE CONNECTOR CONDITION OK?

NO — REPAIR AS NECESSARY. REPLACE THE FUSE. *

YES

REMOVE BOTH BACK-UP LAMPS.

PUT THE DVOB1 IN OHMMETER MODE. PROBE THE BR/LG WIRE.

IS THE RESISTANCE BELOW 10.0 OHMS?

YES — REPAIR THE BR/LG WIRE FOR A SHORT TO GROUND. REPLACE THE FUSE. *

NO

PROBE THE IGNITION SUPPLY WIRE TERMINAL A.

IS THE RESISTANCE BELOW 10.0 OHMS?

NO — REPLACE THE GEAR SELECT SWITCH. REPLACE THE FUSE. *

YES — REPAIR DB/WT OR YL/DG WIRE FOR A SHORT TO GROUND. REPLACE THE FUSE. *

* — PERFORM VERIFICATION TEST 2A.

NOTE: See TEST 6A (1 OF 2) for wiring diagram.

92H14263 92I14264 92F13594 92J14265 92A14266 92B14267

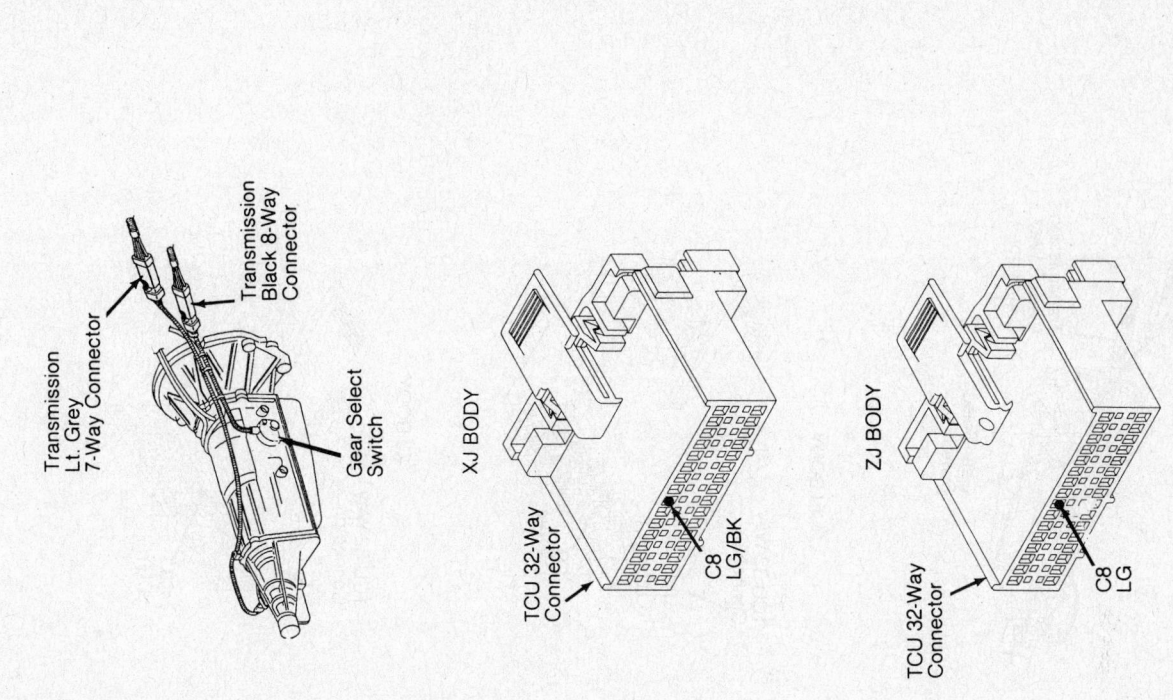

Transmission Lt. Grey 7-Way Connector

Transmission Black 8-Way Connector

Gear Select Switch

XJ BODY

TCU 32-Way Connector

C8 LG/BK

ZJ BODY

TCU 32-Way Connector

C8 LG

TEST 6B
CODE 703 — GEAR SELECT SWITCH CIRCUIT

Perform TEST 6A before proceeding.

START TEST 6B.

INSPECT THE CONNECTOR.

DISCONNECT THE TRANSMISSION BLACK 8-WAY CONNECTOR

NOTE: THE DRBII IS STILL IN THE OHMMETER MODE.

PROBE CAVITY C8.

IS THE CONNECTOR CONDITION OK?

NO → REPAIR AS NECESSARY. REPLACE THE FUSE. *

YES

IS THE RESISTANCE BELOW 10.0 OHMS?

NO → REPLACE THE GEAR SELECT SWITCH ASSEMBLY. REPLACE THE FUSE. *

YES → REPAIR THE LG OR LG/BK WIRE FOR A SHORT TO GROUND BETWEEN THE TCU & BLACK 8-WAY CONN.

REPLACE THE FUSE. *

* - PERFORM VERIFICATION TEST 2A.

NOTE: See TEST 6A (1 OF 2) for wiring diagram.

92C14268 92F13594 92D14269 92G14270

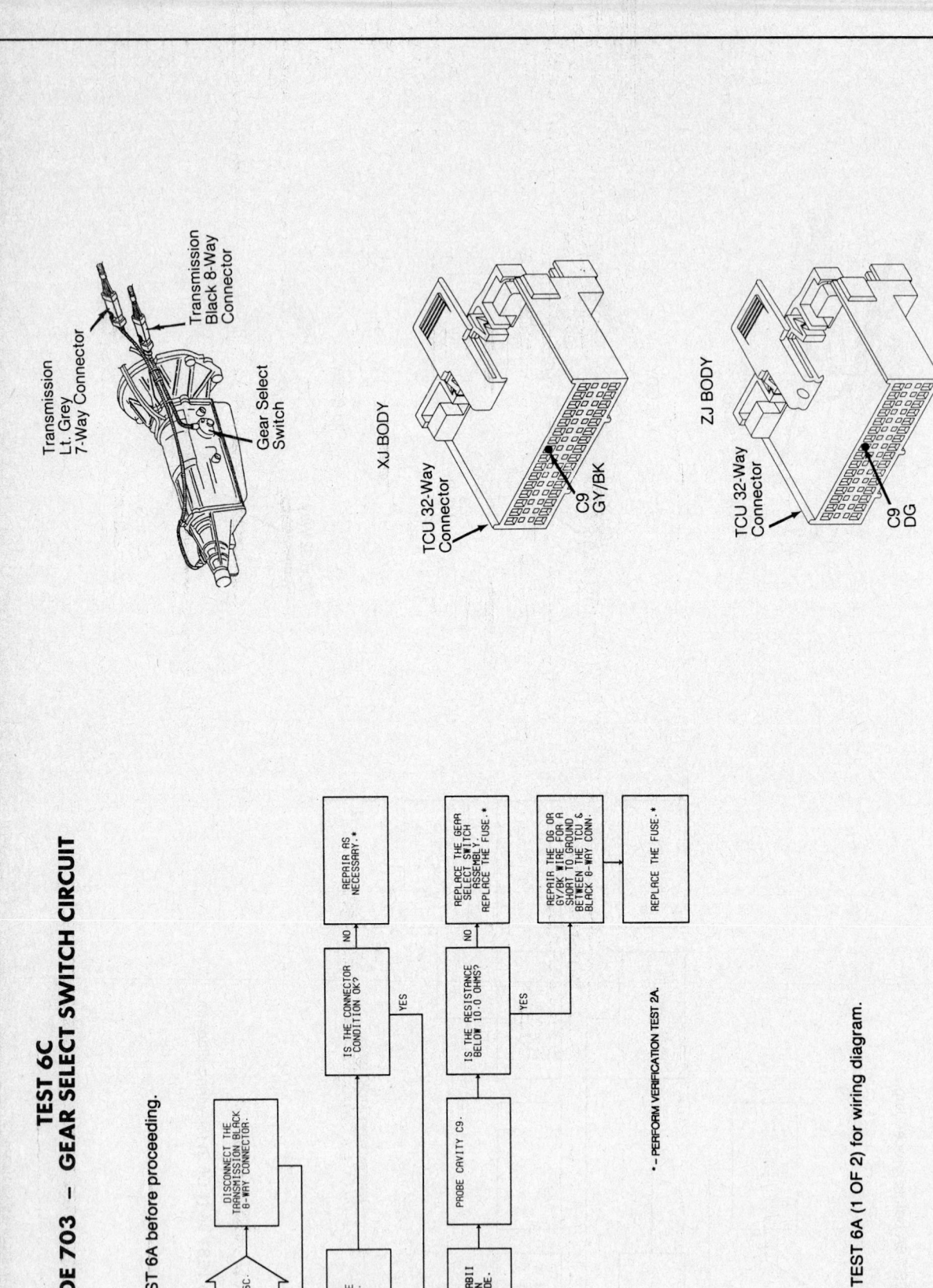

TEST 6C
CODE 703 – GEAR SELECT SWITCH CIRCUIT

Perform TEST 6A before proceeding.

Transmission Lt. Grey 7-Way Connector

Transmission Black 8-Way Connector

Gear Select Switch

XJ BODY

TCU 32-Way Connector

C9 GY/BK

ZJ BODY

TCU 32-Way Connector

C9 DG

START TEST 6C.

DISCONNECT THE TRANSMISSION BLACK 8-WAY CONNECTOR.

INSPECT THE CONNECTOR.

IS THE CONNECTOR CONDITION OK?

NO → REPAIR AS NECESSARY. *

YES ↓

NOTE: THE DRBII IS STILL IN OHMMETER MODE.

PROBE CAVITY C9.

IS THE RESISTANCE BELOW 10.0 OHMS?

NO → REPLACE THE GEAR SELECT SWITCH ASSEMBLY. REPLACE THE FUSE: *

YES ↓

REPAIR THE DG OR GY/BK WIRE FOR A SHORT TO GROUND BETWEEN THE TCU & BLACK 8-WAY CONN.

REPLACE THE FUSE: *

* – PERFORM VERIFICATION TEST 2A.

NOTE: See TEST 6A (1 OF 2) for wiring diagram.

92H14271 92F13594 92I14272 92J14273

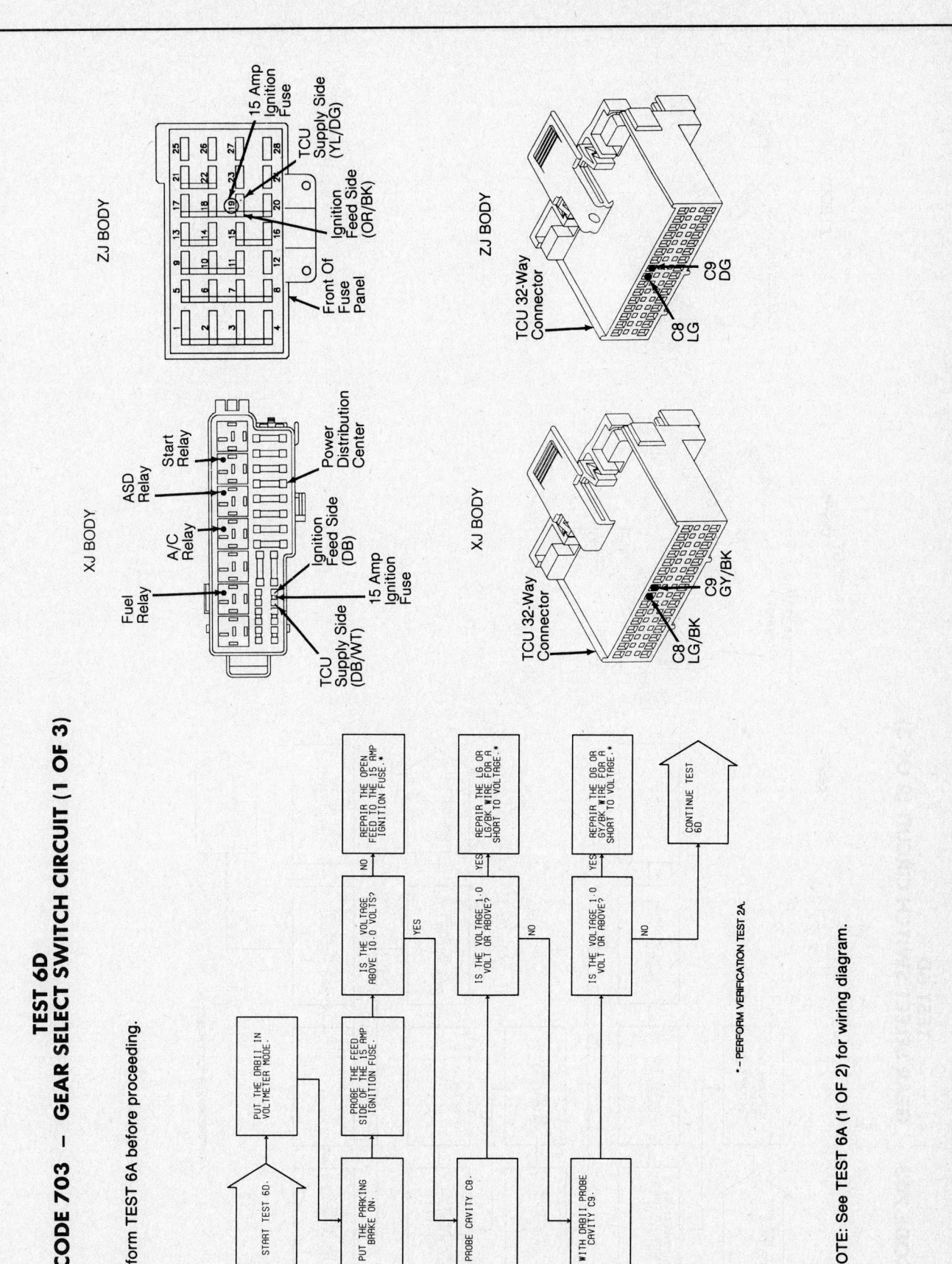

NOTE: See TEST 6A (1 OF 2) for wiring diagram.

92A14274 92E14260 92F14261 92B14275 92C14276

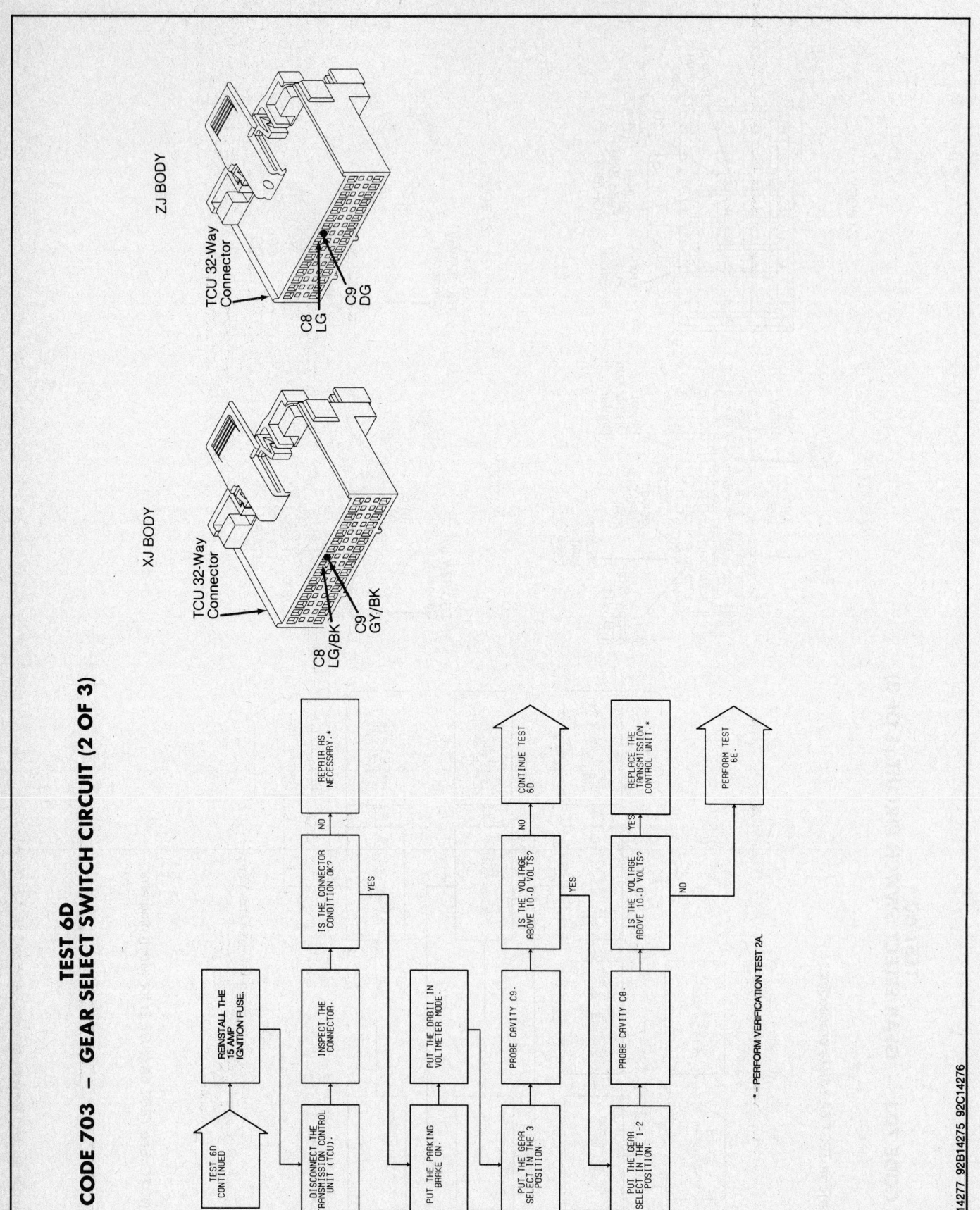

ZJ BODY

TCU 32-Way Connector

C8 LG

C9 DG

XJ BODY

TCU 32-Way Connector

C8 LG/BK

C9 GY/BK

TEST 6D
CODE 703 — GEAR SELECT SWITCH CIRCUIT (2 OF 3)

TEST 6D CONTINUED

DISCONNECT THE TRANSMISSION CONTROL UNIT (TCU).

REINSTALL THE 15 AMP IGNITION FUSE.

INSPECT THE CONNECTOR.

IS THE CONNECTOR CONDITION OK?

NO → REPAIR AS NECESSARY.*

YES →

PUT THE PARKING BRAKE ON.

PUT THE DRB1I IN VOLTMETER MODE.

PUT THE GEAR SELECT IN THE 3 POSITION.

PROBE CAVITY C9.

IS THE VOLTAGE ABOVE 10.0 VOLTS?

NO → CONTINUE TEST 6D

YES →

PUT THE GEAR SELECT IN THE 1-2 POSITION.

PROBE CAVITY C8.

IS THE VOLTAGE ABOVE 10.0 VOLTS?

YES → REPLACE THE TRANSMISSION CONTROL UNIT.*

NO → PERFORM TEST 6E.

* — PERFORM VERIFICATION TEST 2A.

92D14277 92B14275 92C14276

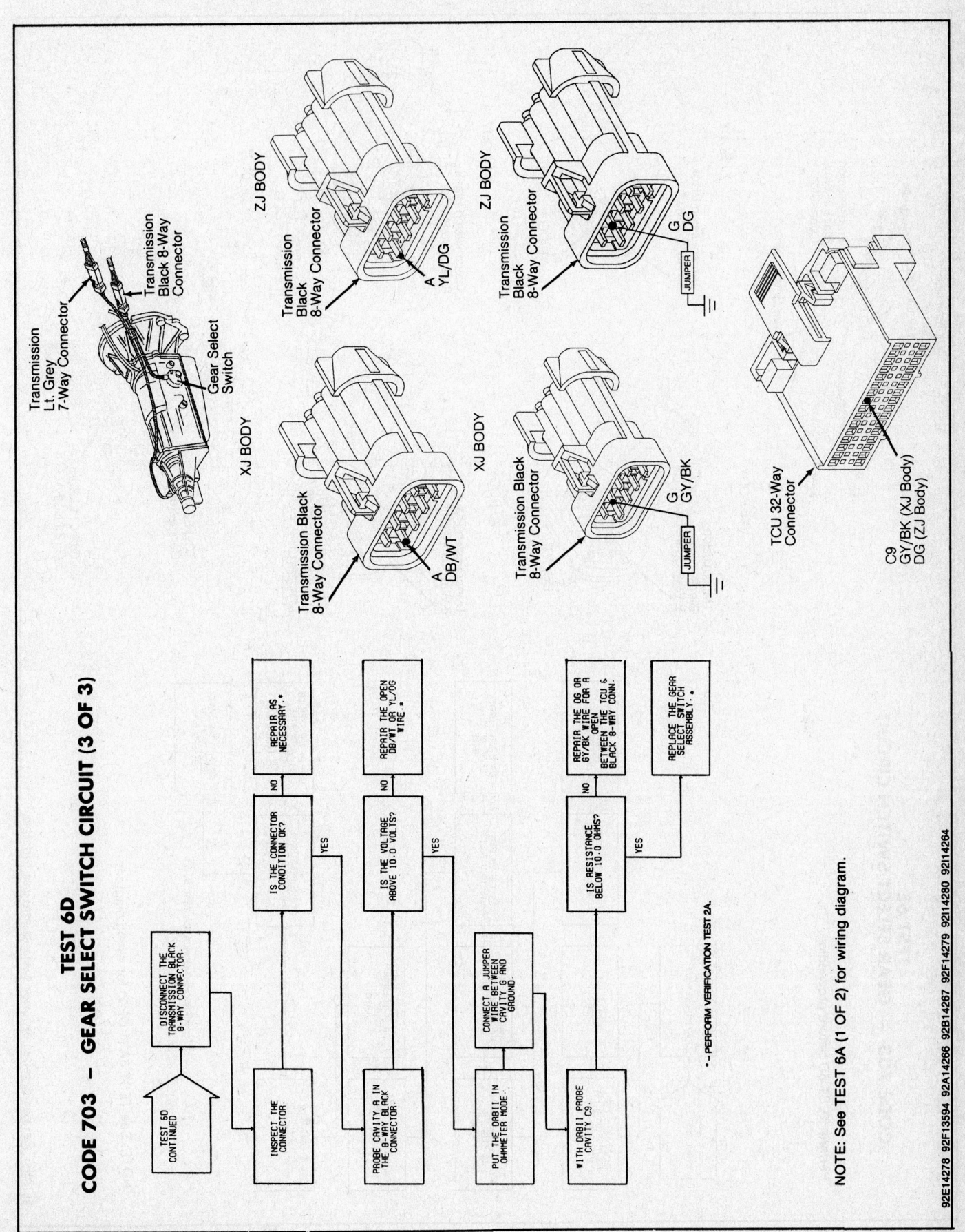

NOTE: See TEST 6A (1 OF 2) for wiring diagram.

92E14278 92F13594 92A14266 92B14267 92F14279 92I14280 92I14264

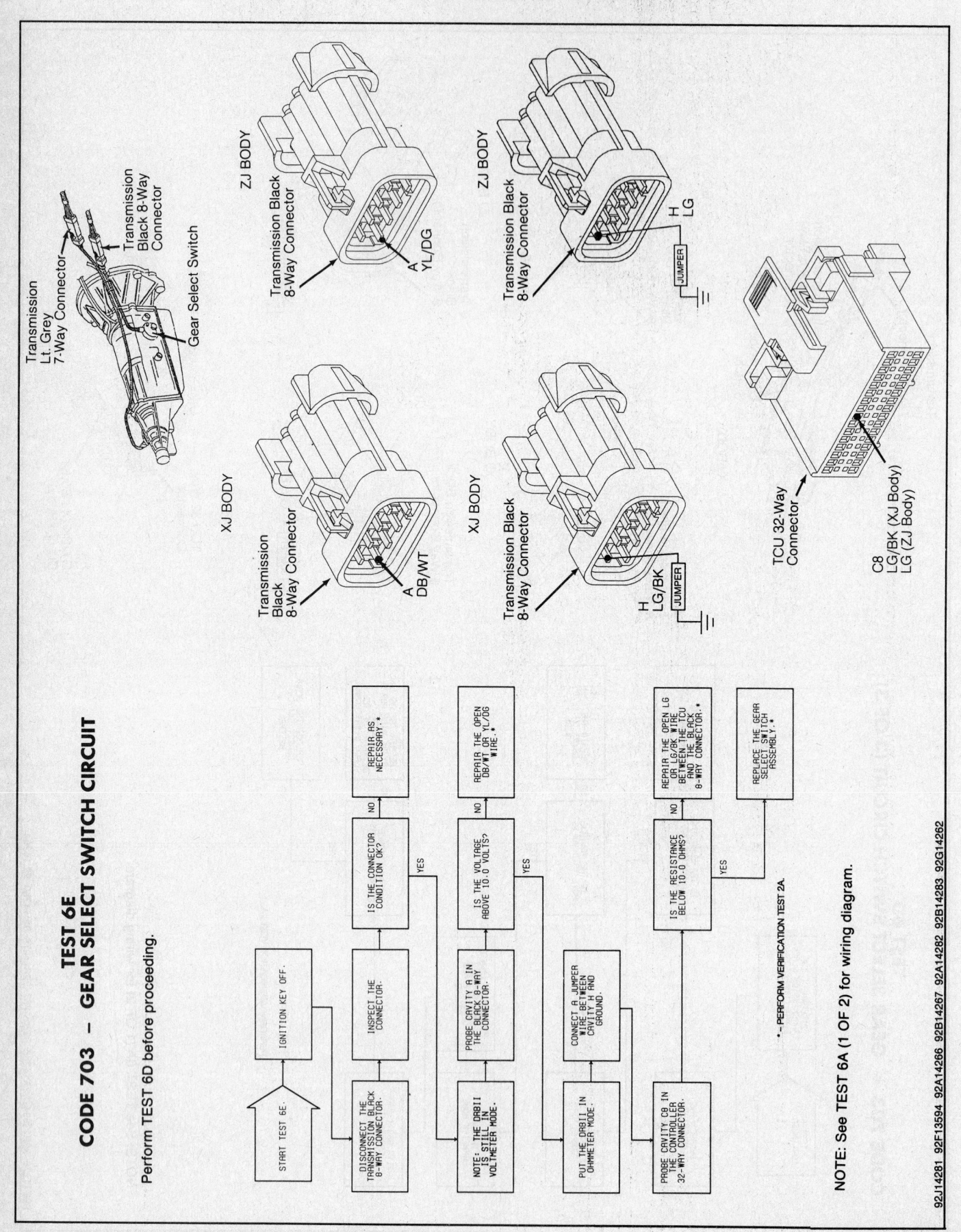

TEST 6E
CODE 703 – GEAR SELECT SWITCH CIRCUIT

Perform TEST 6D before proceeding.

START TEST 6E.

IGNITION KEY OFF.

DISCONNECT THE TRANSMISSION BLACK 8-WAY CONNECTOR.

INSPECT THE CONNECTOR.

IS THE CONNECTOR CONDITION OK?

NO → REPAIR AS NECESSARY.*

NOTE: THE DRBII IS STILL IN VOLTMETER MODE.

PROBE CAVITY A IN THE BLACK 8-WAY CONNECTOR.

IS THE VOLTAGE ABOVE 10.0 VOLTS?

NO → REPAIR THE OPEN DB/WT OR YL/DG WIRE.*

PUT THE DRBII IN OHMMETER MODE.

CONNECT A JUMPER WIRE BETWEEN CAVITY H AND GROUND.

PROBE CAVITY C8 IN THE CONTROLLER 32-WAY CONNECTOR.

IS THE RESISTANCE BELOW 10.0 OHMS?

NO → REPAIR THE OPEN LG OR LG/BK WIRE BETWEEN THE TCU AND THE BLACK 8-WAY CONNECTOR.*

YES → REPLACE THE GEAR SELECT SWITCH ASSEMBLY.*

* – PERFORM VERIFICATION TEST 2A.

NOTE: See TEST 6A (1 OF 2) for wiring diagram.

Transmission Lt. Grey 7-Way Connector

Transmission Black 8-Way Connector

Gear Select Switch

ZJ BODY

Transmission Black 8-Way Connector

A YL/DG

ZJ BODY

Transmission Black 8-Way Connector

H LG

JUMPER

XJ BODY

Transmission Black 8-Way Connector

A DB/WT

XJ BODY

Transmission Black 8-Way Connector

H LG/BK

JUMPER

TCU 32-Way Connector

C8
LG/BK (XJ Body)
LG (ZJ Body)

92J14281 92F13594 92A14266 92B14267 92A14282 92B14283 92G14262

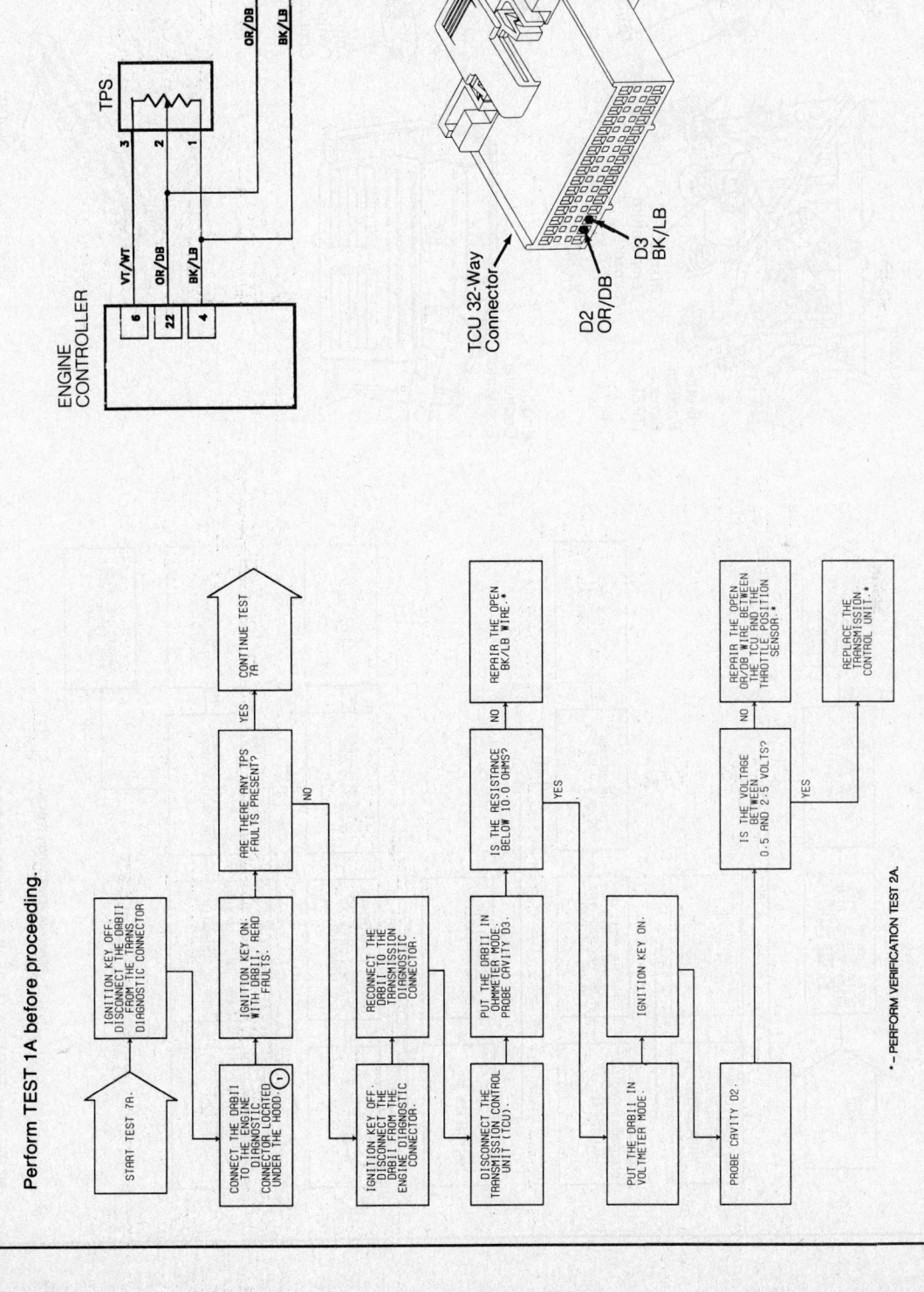

TEST 7A

CODE 705 – THROTTLE POSITION SENSOR CIRCUIT (1 OF 2)

Perform TEST 1A before proceeding.

① - On XJ models, engine diagnostic connector is located at left side of engine compartment, near engine controller. On ZJ models, engine diagnostic connector is located at right corner of engine compartment, near engine controller behind coolant reservoir. On all models, engine diagnostic connector is a 6-terminal connector.

* - PERFORM VERIFICATION TEST 2A.

9413B438 92D14285 92E14286

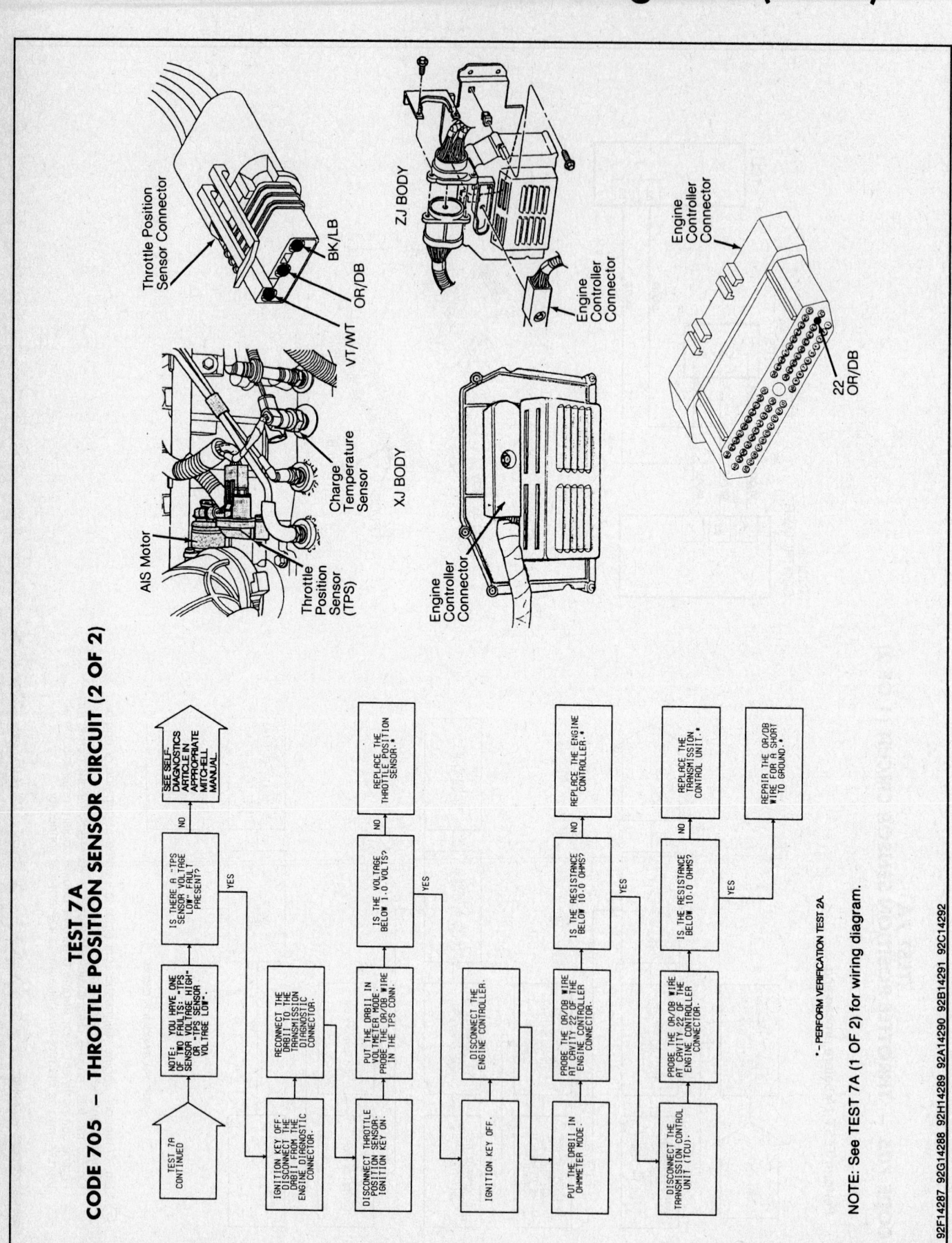

TEST 7A

CODE 705 – THROTTLE POSITION SENSOR CIRCUIT (2 OF 2)

Throttle Position Sensor Connector

BK/LB
OR/DB
VT/WT

ZJ BODY

Engine Controller Connector

AIS Motor

Throttle Position Sensor (TPS)

Charge Temperature Sensor

XJ BODY

Engine Controller Connector

Engine Controller Connector

22 OR/DB

TEST 7A CONTINUED

NOTE: YOU HAVE ONE OF TWO FAULTS: "TPS SENSOR VOLTAGE HIGH" OR "TPS SENSOR VOLTAGE LOW".

IS THERE A "TPS SENSOR VOLTAGE LOW" FAULT PRESENT?

NO → SEE SELF-DIAGNOSTICS ARTICLE IN APPROPRIATE MITCHELL MANUAL.

YES

IGNITION KEY OFF. DISCONNECT THE DRBII FROM THE ENGINE DIAGNOSTIC CONNECTOR.

RECONNECT THE DRBII TO THE TRANSMISSION DIAGNOSTIC CONNECTOR.

DISCONNECT THROTTLE POSITION SENSOR. IGNITION KEY ON.

PUT THE DRBII IN VOLTMETER MODE. PROBE THE OR/DB WIRE IN THE TPS CONN.

IS THE VOLTAGE BELOW 1.0 VOLTS?

NO → REPLACE THE THROTTLE POSITION SENSOR. *

YES

IGNITION KEY OFF.

DISCONNECT THE ENGINE CONTROLLER.

PUT THE DRBII IN OHMMETER MODE.

PROBE THE OR/DB WIRE AT CAVITY 22 OF THE ENGINE CONTROLLER CONNECTOR.

IS THE RESISTANCE BELOW 10.0 OHMS?

NO → REPLACE THE ENGINE CONTROLLER. *

YES

DISCONNECT THE TRANSMISSION CONTROL UNIT (TCU).

PROBE THE OR/DB WIRE AT CAVITY 22 OF THE ENGINE CONTROLLER CONNECTOR.

IS THE RESISTANCE BELOW 10.0 OHMS?

NO → REPLACE THE TRANSMISSION CONTROL UNIT. *

YES → REPAIR THE OR/DB WIRE FOR A SHORT TO GROUND. *

* - PERFORM VERIFICATION TEST 2A.

NOTE: See TEST 7A (1 OF 2) for wiring diagram.

92F14287 92G14288 92H14289 92A14290 92B14291 92C14292

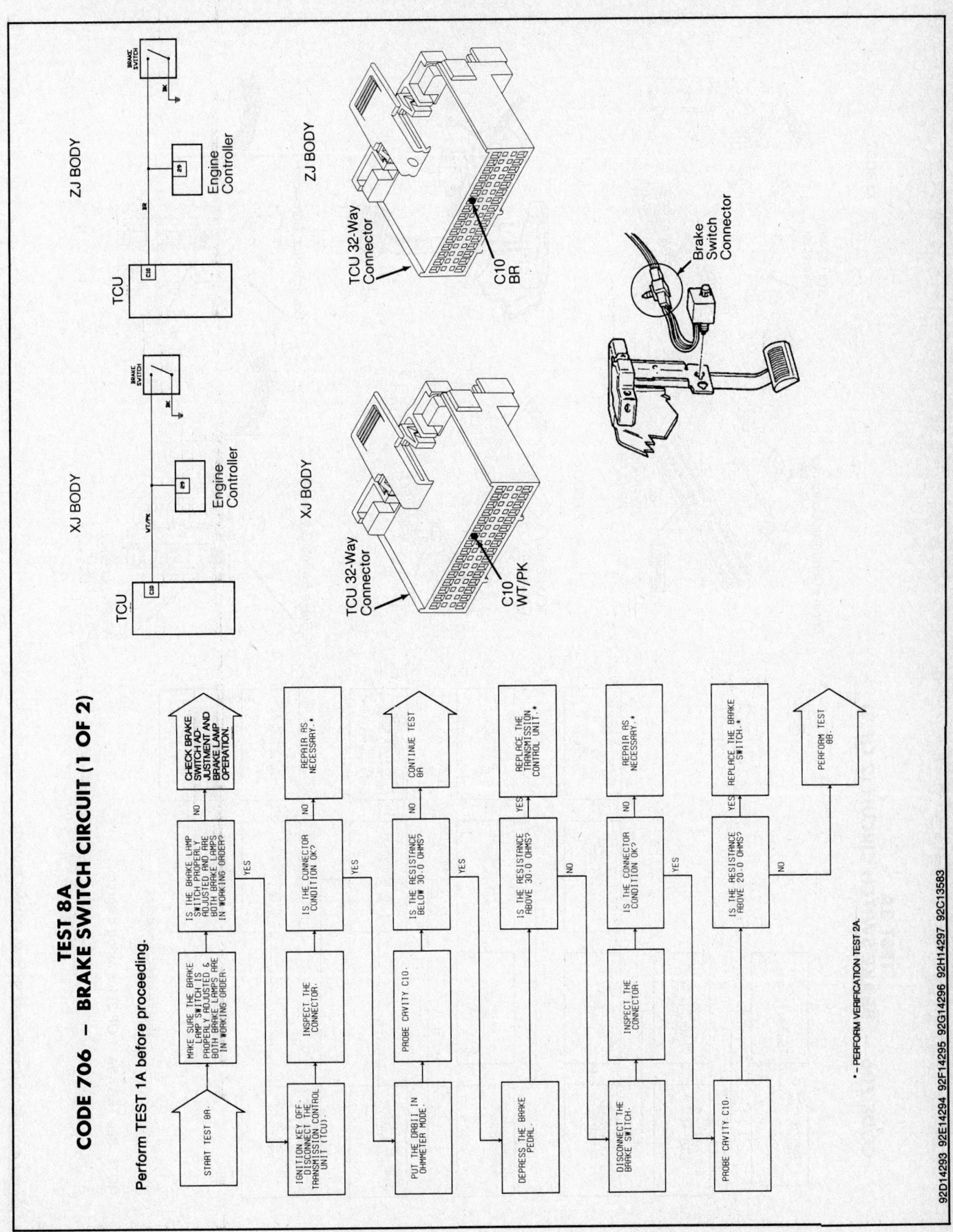

TEST 8A
CODE 706 – BRAKE SWITCH CIRCUIT (1 OF 2)

Perform TEST 1A before proceeding.

92D14293 92E14294 92F14295 92G14296 92H14297 92C13583

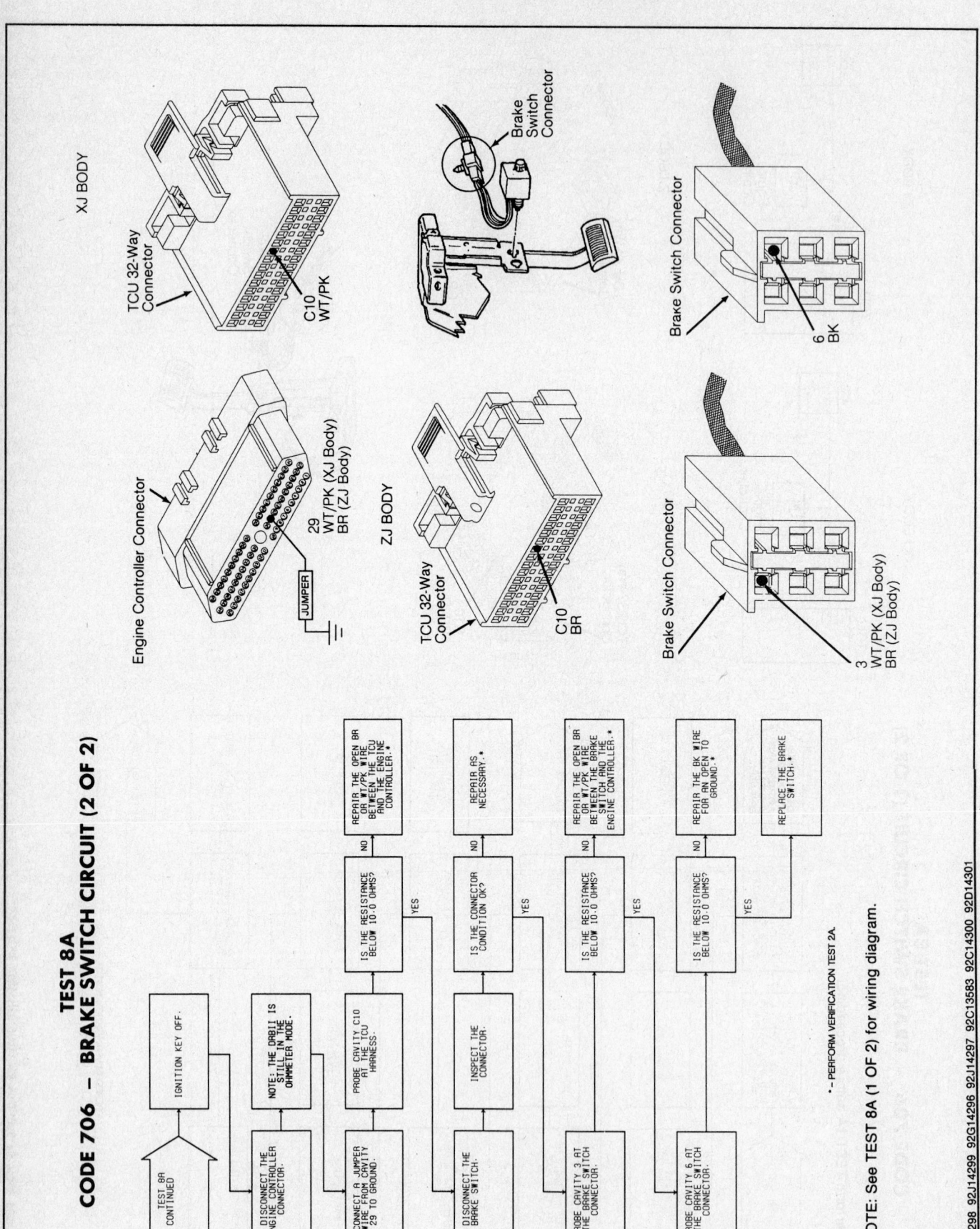

TEST 8A
CODE 706 – BRAKE SWITCH CIRCUIT (2 OF 2)

NOTE: See TEST 8A (1 OF 2) for wiring diagram.

92I14298 92J14299 92G14296 92J14297 92C13583 92C14300 92D14301

TEST 9A
WRONG TCU

Perform TEST 1A before proceeding.

The DRBII has determined that the wrong transmission control unit (TCU) has been installed in the vehicle. There are two transmission control units available for the Jeep AW4 transmission. One is for the four-cylinder 2.5L engine and the other is for the six-cylinder 4.0L engine.

1. Using the DRBII, read MODULE INFO. See HELP 1 for assistance.

2. Determine what TCU should be in the vehicle.

   2.5   Engine = 02
   4.0   Engine = 01

3. If the wrong transmission control unit is installed, the vehicle shift points will be slightly different (the 2.5L engine transmission control unit has higher shift points.)

   * – The AW-4 is used only with 4.0L.
     In earlier years, it was used with 2.5L.

94.J38439

TEST 8B
CODE 706 – BRAKE SWITCH CIRCUIT

Perform TEST 8A before proceeding.

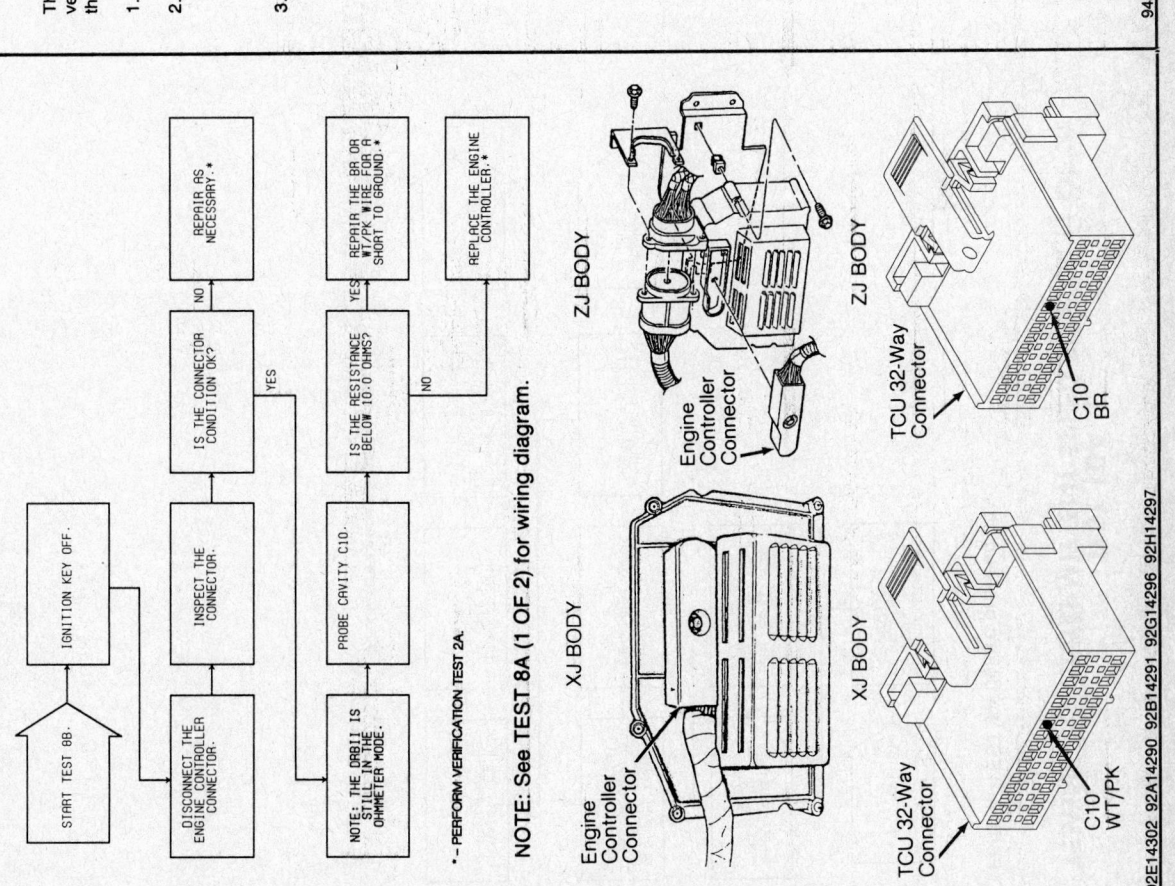

NOTE: See TEST 8A (1 OF 2) for wiring diagram.

92E14302 92A14290 92B14291 92G14296 92H14297

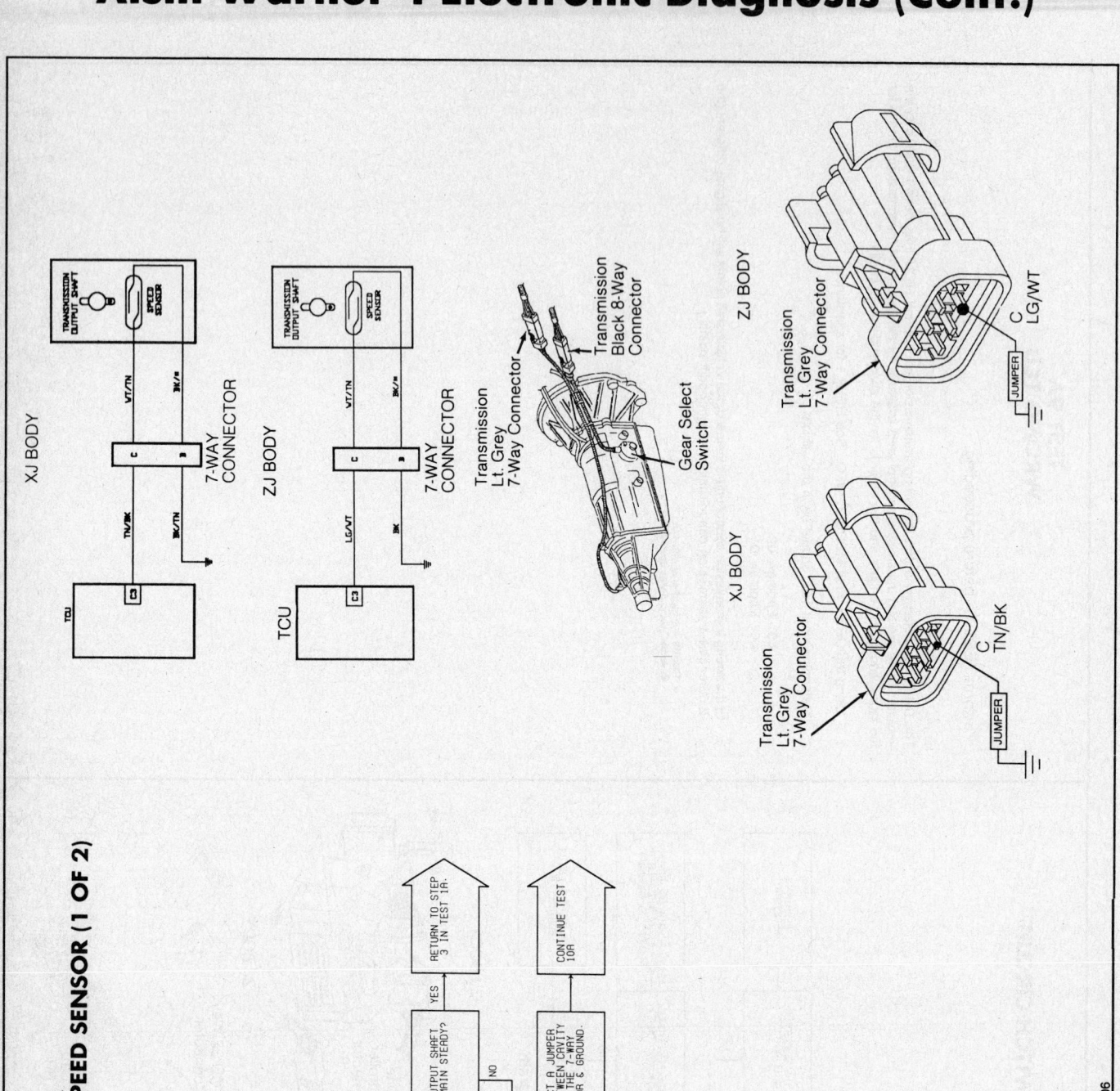

TEST 10A

TESTING FOR INTERMITTENT SPEED SENSOR (1 OF 2)

Perform TEST 1A before proceeding.

START TEST 10A

SHIFT TRANSFER CASE (IF APPLICABLE) TO THE 2 WHEEL DRIVE POSITION.

RAISE VEHICLE REAR WHEELS OFF THE GROUND.

START ENGINE, PLACE GEAR SELECT IN OD POSITION, LET WHEELS ROTATE AT IDLE.

WITH DRBII MONITOR RPM WHILE WIGGLING C3 WIRE BETWEEN TCU AND SPEED SENSOR.

TURN ENGINE OFF.

DID OUTPUT SHAFT RPM REMAIN STEADY?

YES → RETURN TO STEP 3 IN TEST 1A.

NO

DISCONNECT THE TCU 32-WAY CONNECTOR.

DISCONNECT TRANS. LT. GREY 7-WAY CONNECTOR.

CONNECT A JUMPER WIRE BETWEEN CAVITY C OF THE 7-WAY CONNECTOR & GROUND.

CONTINUE TEST 10A

* - PERFORM VERIFICATION TEST 2A.

92G14304 94C38440 92C14250 92F13594 94D38441 92I14306

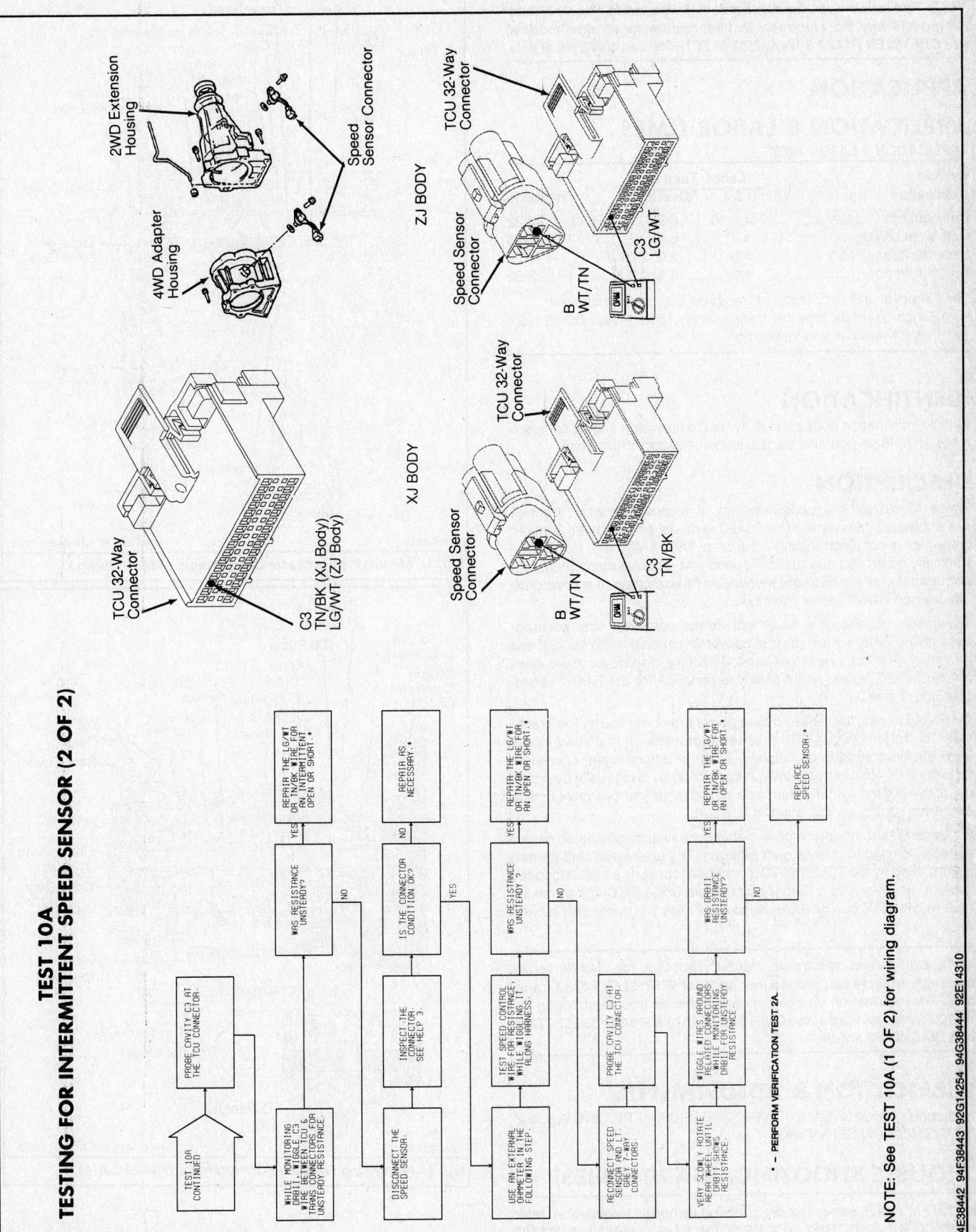

TEST 10A

TESTING FOR INTERMITTENT SPEED SENSOR (2 OF 2)

2WD Extension Housing

4WD Adapter Housing

Speed Sensor Connector

TCU 32-Way Connector

ZJ BODY

Speed Sensor Connector

C3 LG/WT

B WT/TN

TCU 32-Way Connector

C3 TN/BK (XJ Body) LG/WT (ZJ Body)

XJ BODY

TCU 32-Way Connector

Speed Sensor Connector

C3 TN/BK

B WT/TN

TEST 10A CONTINUED

WHILE MONITORING DRB11, WIGGLE C3 WIRE BETWEEN TCU & TRANS CONNECTORS FOR UNSTEADY RESISTANCE.

PROBE CAVITY C3 AT THE TCU CONNECTOR.

WAS RESISTANCE UNSTEADY? — YES → REPAIR THE LG/WT OR TN/BK WIRE FOR INTERMITTENT OPEN OR SHORT.*

NO

DISCONNECT THE SPEED SENSOR.

INSPECT THE CONNECTOR. SEE HELP 3.

IS THE CONNECTOR CONDITION OK? — NO → REPAIR AS NECESSARY.*

YES

USE AN EXTERNAL OHMMETER IN THE FOLLOWING STEP.

TEST SPEED CONTROL WIRE FOR RESISTANCE, WHILE WIGGLING IT ALONG HARNESS.

WAS RESISTANCE UNSTEADY? — YES → REPAIR THE LG/WT OR TN/BK WIRE FOR AN OPEN OR SHORT.*

NO

RECONNECT SPEED AND LT GREY 7-WAY CONNECTORS.

PROBE CAVITY C3 AT THE TCU CONNECTOR.

WIGGLE WIRES AROUND RELATED CONNECTORS WHILE MONITORING DRB11 FOR UNSTEADY RESISTANCE.

WAS DRB11 RESISTANCE UNSTEADY? — YES → REPAIR THE LG/WT OR TN/BK WIRE FOR AN OPEN OR SHORT.*

NO

VERY SLOWLY ROTATE REAR WHEEL UNTIL DRB11 SHOWS RESISTANCE.

REPLACE SPEED SENSOR.*

* – PERFORM VERIFICATION TEST 2A.

NOTE: See TEST 10A (1 OF 2) for wiring diagram.

94E38442 94F38443 92G14254 94G38444 92E14310

NOTE: *This article contains electronic test information for Colt/Summit models only. For electronic test information for all other models, see CHRYSLER F4A33 & W4A32/33 ELECTRONIC DIAGNOSIS article.*

APPLICATION

APPLICATION & LABOR TIMES

APPLICATION & LABOR TIMES

Vehicle Application	Labor Times		Transaxle
	[1] R & I	[2] Overhaul	
Colt/Summit	4.6	8.9	F3A21 & F4A22
Colt Vista (2WD)	4.6	8.9	F4A22/23
Laser & Talon (2WD)	4.6	8.9	F4A22
Summit Wagon	4.6	8.9	F4A22/23

[1] – Removal and installation of transaxle from vehicle chassis.
[2] – Bench overhaul time for transaxle and differential. DOES NOT include removal and installation.

IDENTIFICATION

Vehicle information code plate is riveted to firewall in engine compartment area. Plate contains transaxle identification information.

DESCRIPTION

These Mitsubishi transaxles consist of torque converter, transfer assembly and differential. The F3A20 series is an automatic 3-speed unit which is not electronically controlled. The F4A20 series is an electronically controlled automatic 4-speed unit. Internal components for both transaxles are basically identical, with exception of an overdrive 4th gear on F4A20 series transaxle.

Transaxles consist of a 3-element torque converter with governor assembly (F3A20 series), torque converter clutch (F4A20 series), one planetary gear set, one brake band, 3 multiple-disc clutch assemblies for the F3A20 series, and 4 clutch assemblies for the F4A20 series. *See Figs. 1 and 2.*

On F4A40 series, transaxle shifting points are controlled by the Transaxle Control Unit (TCU). TCU receives information from various inputs and controls solenoids on the valve body for different gear operation. Overdrive or 4th gear operation is controlled by a manually operated overdrive control switch. Transaxle will not shift into overdrive unless overdrive control switch is in ON position.

On Laser/Talon models, a power/economy switch, located on center console, is used to change shift patterns. The pre-stored shift pattern is controlled by the TCU. The TCU controller contains a self-diagnostic system, which stores a Diagnostic Trouble Code (DTC) if a transaxle fault exists. DTC can be retrieved to determine the transaxle problem area.

NOTE: *Component electronic trouble shooting for F4A20 series transaxle is same test procedures used for CHRYSLER F4A33 transaxle. For information on component electronic trouble shooting for F4A20 series transaxle, see CHRYSLER F4A33 & W4A32/33 ELECTRONIC DIAGNOSIS article.*

LUBRICATION & ADJUSTMENTS

See appropriate AUTOMATIC TRANSMISSION SERVICING article in TRANSMISSION SERVICING.

TROUBLE SHOOTING (F3A20 SERIES)

NOTE: *For F4A20 series trouble shooting symptom information, refer to TROUBLE SHOOTING in CHRYSLER F4A33, W4A32 & W4A33 overhaul article.*

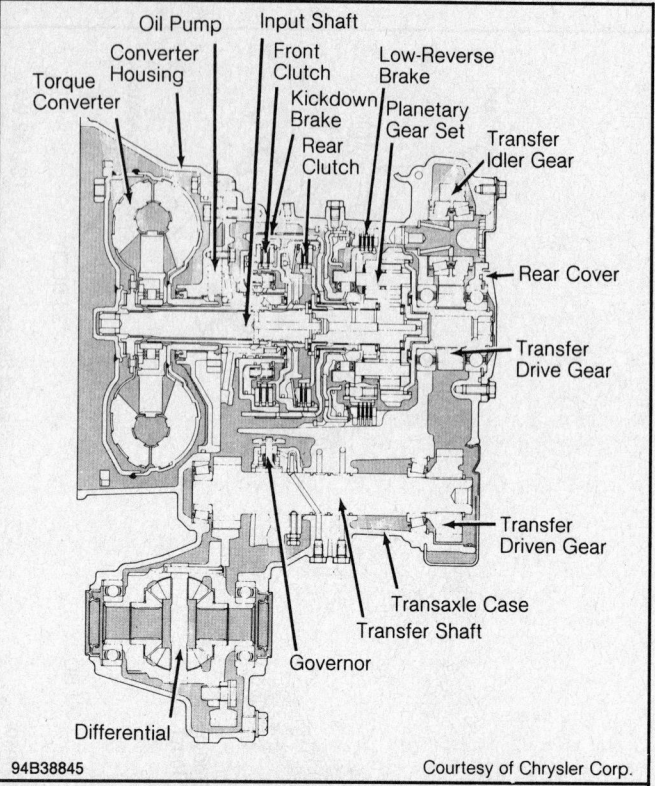

94B38845   Courtesy of Chrysler Corp.

Fig. 1: Identifying Transaxle Components (F3A20 Series)

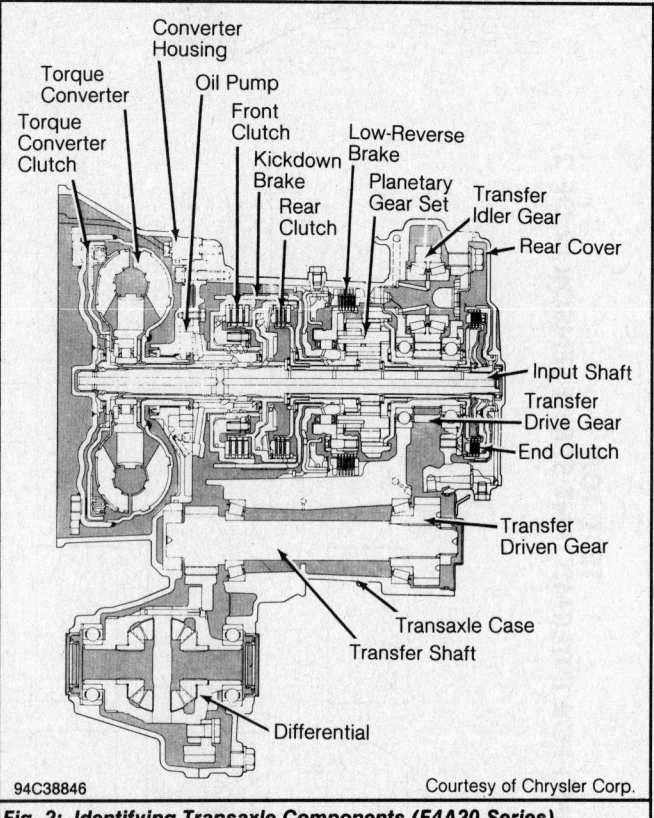

94C38846   Courtesy of Chrysler Corp.

Fig. 2: Identifying Transaxle Components (F4A20 Series)

SYMPTOM DIAGNOSIS

No Forward Or Reverse – Manual linkage misadjusted, improper fluid level or line pressure, clogged oil filter, incorrect valve body installation, regulator valve, line pressure relief valve or torque converter control valve malfunction.

No Movement In "D" Or "2" – Front clutch malfunction.

No Forward Gears – Rear clutch or N-D accumulator valve malfunction.

Engine Stalls When Shifting From "N" To "D" Or "R" – Insufficient engine performance, incorrect valve body installation, sticking valve body check ball, regulator valve, torque converter clutch valve or N-D accumulator valve malfunction.

Slips In Drive – Low fluid level or line pressure, faulty one-way clutch or valve body, or worn rear clutch.

Slips In Reverse – Low fluid level or line pressure, faulty low-reverse brake circuit, front clutch or valve body.

Poor Acceleration In 2nd & 3rd – Low fluid level or line pressure, torque converter malfunction, faulty rear clutch, kickdown band or valve body, incorrect valve body installation, or misadjusted kickdown servo.

Engine Braking Ineffective In "L" – Faulty low-reverse brake or valve body.

Stall RPM Too Low – Insufficient engine performance or torque converter failure.

Stall RPM Too High In "R" Or "D" – Low fluid lever or line pressure, faulty one-way clutch, front clutch, rear clutch or valve body.

Vehicle Creeps In "N" – Front or rear clutch malfunction.

Park Will Not Engage – Manual linkage misadjusted or parking mechanism failure.

Incorrect Shift Points – Low fluid level, low line pressure, faulty valve body, front clutch or kickdown band, misadjusted kickdown servo or governor failure.

No Downshift From Any Gear – Throttle valve, 1-2 shift valve, 2-3 shift valve or 2-3 control valve malfunction, faulty governor assembly.

No 1-2 Upshift – Low fluid level or line pressure, clogged oil filter, faulty kickdown band or kickdown servo misadjusted, faulty governor assembly or valve body.

No 2-3 Upshift – Low fluid level or line pressure, clogged oil filter, faulty kickdown band or kickdown servo misadjusted, faulty front clutch, governor assembly or valve body.

Excessive Shift Shock On 1-2 Or 2-3 Upshift – Throttle cable misadjusted, faulty valve body, governor assembly or front clutch, faulty kickdown band or kickdown servo misadjusted.

Excessive Shift Shock On 2-1 Or 3-2 Downshift – Faulty kickdown band or kickdown servo misadjusted, faulty governor assembly or valve body.

Engine Flares On 1-2 Or 2-3 Upshift – Low line pressure, low fluid level, clogged oil filter, torque converter malfunction, faulty governor assembly, rear clutch or valve body, incorrect valve body installation, faulty kickdown band or kickdown servo misadjusted.

Whining Noise From Converter Housing – Oil pump failure.

Rattling Noise From Converter Housing – Cracked flexplate or loose torque converter-to-flexplate bolt.

ELECTRONIC TESTING

NOTE: This article contains electronic test information for Colt/Summit models only. For electronic test information for all other models, or for component electronic trouble shooting of F4A20 series transaxle, see CHRYSLER F4A33 & W4A32/33 ELECTRONIC DIAGNOSIS article.

SELF-DIAGNOSTIC SYSTEM (COLT/SUMMIT – F4A20 SERIES ONLY)

DIAGNOSTIC PROCEDURE

When performing vehicle diagnosis, the following procedures must be followed:

- Ensure the transaxle fluid level is correct and not contaminated or aerated.
- Ensure shift cable is properly adjusted by ensuring vehicle starts in only Park or Neutral. If adjustment is required, see appropriate AUTOMATIC TRANSMISSION SERVICING article in TRANSMISSION SERVICING.
- Ensure all electrical connections at transaxle, TCU, throttle position sensor, inhibitor switch and accelerator switch are clean and properly installed.

RETRIEVING TROUBLE CODES

NOTE: Diagnostic trouble codes may also be retrieved using scan tester.

1) Locate diagnostic connector below left side of instrument panel. *See Fig. 3.* On 1993 models, install voltmeter between ground terminal and TCU diagnostic connector. On 1994 models, install voltmeter between ground terminal No. 4 or 5, and TCU diagnostic terminal No. 6. *See Fig. 3.*

2) On both models, turn ignition on. Note fluctuations of voltmeter needle to indicate the trouble code. The first fluctuations indicates first digit of trouble code. Following fluctuations indicates the second digit of trouble code. Record trouble codes in the order they are displayed.

3) If transaxle is not in fail-safe mode, a maximum of 10 trouble codes can be stored. If number of stored trouble codes exceeds 10, previously stored trouble codes will be erased beginning with the oldest trouble code.

4) If transaxle is in fail-safe mode and transaxle remains in 2nd or 3rd gear, a special fail-safe trouble code will be stored. Only 3 fail-safe trouble codes can be stored.

5) When in fail-safe mode with transaxle locked in 2nd or 3rd gear, fail-safe mode will be cancelled when ignition is turned off. Transaxle will no longer be locked in 2nd or 3rd gear, but fail-safe trouble code will be stored in TCU memory. To identify trouble code and items to be checked or adjusted, see DTC IDENTIFICATION.

CLEARING TROUBLE CODES

Trouble codes can be cleared from TCU memory by disconnecting negative battery cable for more than 10 seconds. Ensure trouble codes are cleared after performing repairs.

WARNING: When battery is disconnected, vehicle computer and memory systems may lose memory data. Driveability problems may exist until computer systems have completed a relearn cycle. See COMPUTER RELEARN PROCEDURES in APPLICATIONS & IDENTIFICATION section before disconnecting battery.

ADJUSTMENTS (COLT/SUMMIT – F4A20 SERIES ONLY)

NOTE: For component adjustment procedures for all other models, see ADJUSTMENTS in CHRYSLER F4A33 & W4A32/33 ELECTRONIC DIAGNOSIS article.

THROTTLE POSITION SENSOR (TPS)

1) Disconnect TPS electrical connector. Connect ohmmeter between terminal No. 1 (ground) and terminal No. 2 (idle switch) on TPS. *See Fig. 4.* Check continuity with throttle valve fully closed. Continuity should exist.

2) Check continuity with throttle valve fully open. Continuity should not exist. If continuity does not exist with throttle valve in fully closed position, loosen TPS screws and turn component counterclockwise until continuity exists.

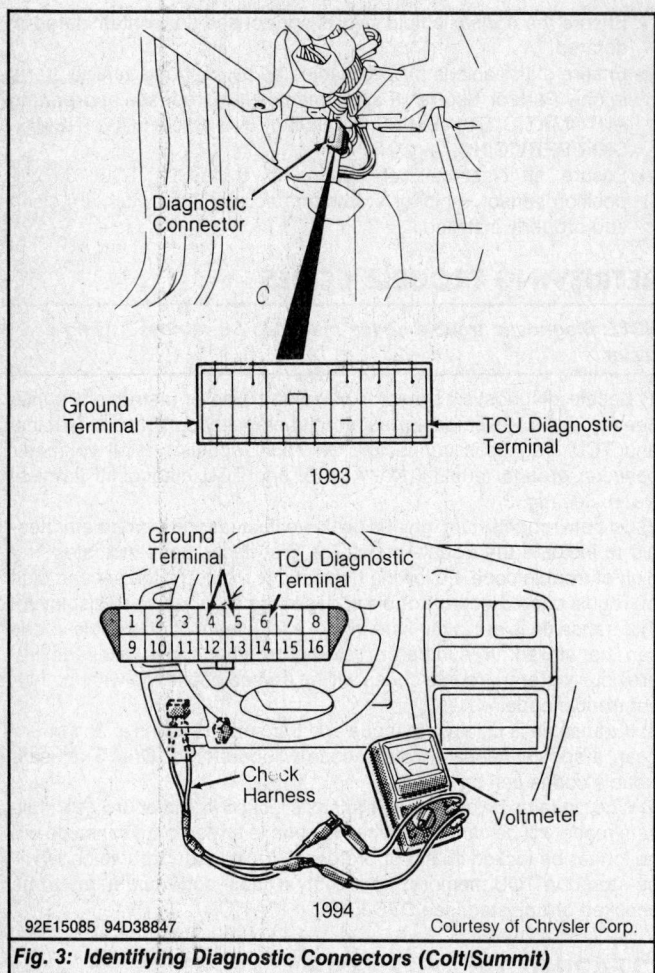

Diagnostic Connector

Ground Terminal

TCU Diagnostic Terminal

1993

Ground Terminal

TCU Diagnostic Terminal

Check Harness

Voltmeter

1994

92E15085 94D38847   Courtesy of Chrysler Corp.

Fig. 3: Identifying Diagnostic Connectors (Colt/Summit)

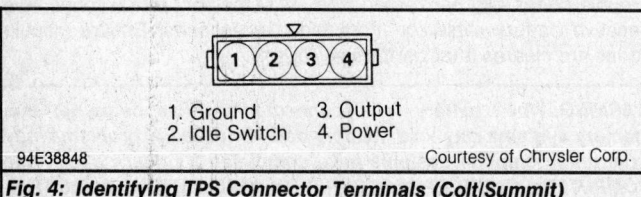

1. Ground   3. Output
2. Idle Switch   4. Power

94E38848   Courtesy of Chrysler Corp.

Fig. 4: Identifying TPS Connector Terminals (Colt/Summit)

ELECTRICAL COMPONENT TESTS (COLT/SUMMIT – F4A20 SERIES ONLY)

NOTE: For component testing procedures for all other models, see TESTING in CHRYSLER F4A33 & W4A32/33 ELECTRONIC DIAGNOSIS article.

OVERDRIVE CONTROL SWITCH

Disconnect electrical connector from overdrive control switch. Using ohmmeter, check continuity between specified wire terminals at switch connector. See OVERDRIVE CONTROL SWITCH CONTINUITY SPECIFICATIONS table. Replace overdrive control switch if defective.

OVERDRIVE CONTROL SWITCH CONTINUITY SPECIFICATIONS

Application & Switch Position	Continuity Between [1] Terminals
Colt/Summit	
ON	1 & 2
OFF	1 & 3

[1] – For wire color identification, see WIRING DIAGRAM.

VEHICLE SPEED SENSOR

NOTE: It may be necessary to remove instrument cluster for access to vehicle speed sensor.

Connect circuit tester between terminal No. 43 of connector "A" and terminal No. 12 of connector "B" on rear of instrument cluster. See Fig. 5. Rotate speedometer shaft and ensure circuit tester indicates an on/off pattern. Replace components if vehicle speed sensor does not operate correctly.

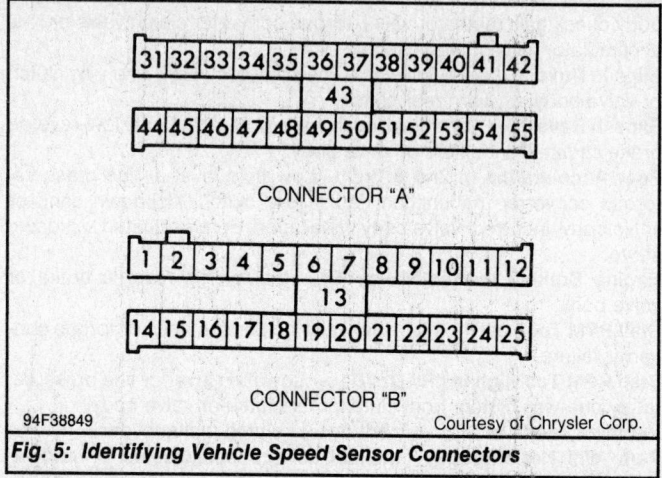

CONNECTOR "A"

CONNECTOR "B"

94F38849   Courtesy of Chrysler Corp.

Fig. 5: Identifying Vehicle Speed Sensor Connectors

TRANSAXLE TESTS

NOTE: A road test can be performed to check transaxle shift points. Pressure test can be performed to check operation of transaxle internal components. Torque converter stall speed test can be performed to check torque converter operation.

ROAD TEST

NOTE: Perform road test to ensure transaxle shift points are at specified speeds. See Figs. 6-9. Broken lines in shift point charts indicate downshifts, and solid lines indicate upshifts.

1) Ensure shift cable is properly adjusted, and fluid level and condition are okay. Add fluid and adjust shift cable if necessary. Road test vehicle, and check if shift points are at specified speeds. See Figs. 6-9.
2) If shift points are not as specified, check for stored trouble codes (F4A20 series). See DTC IDENTIFICATION table for Colt/Summit. For all other models, see CHRYSLER F4A33 & W4A32/33 ELECTRONIC DIAGNOSIS article.
3) For both series transaxles, if slippage occurs, determine which components are applied in each gear. See CLUTCH, BRAKE & BAND APPLICATION CHART. Perform hydraulic pressure test to check transaxle internal components. See HYDRAULIC PRESSURE TEST under TESTING.

CLUTCH, BRAKE & BAND APPLICATION CHART

Selector Lever Position	Elements In Use
"D" (Drive)	
1st Gear	Rear Clutch & One-Way Clutch
2nd Gear	Rear Clutch & Kickdown Band
3rd Gear	Front Clutch, Rear Clutch & [1] End Clutch
4th Gear [1]	End Clutch & Kickdown Band
"2" (Second)	
1st Gear	Rear Clutch & One-Way Clutch
2nd Gear	Rear Clutch & Kickdown Band
"1" (Low)	
1st Gear	Rear Clutch & Low-Reverse Brake
"R" (Reverse)	Front Clutch & Low-Reverse Brake
"N" Or "P" (Neutral Or Park)	All Clutches, Brakes & Bands Released Or Ineffective

[1] – F4A20 series only.

DTC IDENTIFICATION

DTC IDENTIFICATION (COLT/SUMMIT)

DTC Number	Probable Cause	Fail-Safe Mode	[1] Items To Check
11	High TPS Output	No	Check TPS Operation, Adjustment & Connector,
12	Low TPS Output	No	Check TPS Operation, Adjustment & Connector,
13	Defective Or Improperly Adjusted TPS	No	Check TPS Operation & Adjustment
14	Improperly Adjusted TPS	No	Check TPS Adjustment
15	Open Oil Temperature Sensor Circuit (Low Temperature Side)	No	Check Oil Temperature Sensor & Connector
21	Open Kickdown Servo Switch Circuit	No	Check Kickdown Servo Switch & Connector
22	Shorted Kickdown Servo Switch Circuit	No	Check Kickdown Servo Switch & Connector
23	Open Ignition Pulse Signal Circuit	No	Check For Open Circuit To Pin No. 46 At TCU
31	Open Pulse Generator "A" Circuit	No	Check Pulse Generator, Check Vehicle Speed Sensor
32	Open Pulse Generator "B" Circuit	No	Check Pulse Generator, Check Vehicle Speed Sensor
41	Open Shift Control Solenoid Valve "A" Circuit	No	Check Shift Control Solenoid Valve & Connector
42	Shorted Shift Control Solenoid Valve "A" Circuit	No	Check Shift Control Solenoid Valve & Connector
43	Open Shift Control Solenoid Valve "B" Circuit	No	Check Shift Control Solenoid Valve & Connector
44	Shorted Shift Control Solenoid Valve "B" Circuit	No	Check Shift Control Solenoid Valve & Connector
45	Open Pressure Control Solenoid Valve Circuit	No	Check Pressure Control Solenoid Valve & Connector
46	Shorted Pressure Control Solenoid Valve Circuit	No	Check Pressure Control Solenoid Valve & Connector
47	Open Torque Converter Clutch (TCC) Solenoid Valve Circuit	No	Check TCC Solenoid Valve & Connector
48	Shorted Torque Converter Clutch (TCC) Solenoid Valve Circuit	No	Check TCC Solenoid Valve & Connector
49	Defective TCC System	No	Check TCC Hydraulic Circuit, Check TCC Solenoid Valve, Defective TCU
51	Incorrect Or No Upshift From 1st Gear	No	Check Pulse Generators "A" & "B" Or Connectors, End Clutch Or Rear Clutch Slipping
52	Incorrect Or No Upshift From 2nd Gear	No	Check Pulse Generators "A" & "B" Or Connectors, Rear Clutch Slipping, Kickdown Band Slipping
53	Incorrect Or No Upshift From 3rd Gear	No	Check Pulse Generators "A" & "B" Or Connectors, Front Or Rear Clutch Slipping
54	Incorrect Or No Upshift From 4th Gear	No	Check Pulse Generators "A" & "B" Or Connectors, End Clutch Slipping, Kickdown Band Slipping
59	Abnormal Vibration	No	Check Pulse Generator "A" Or Connector, Replace ATF
81	Open Pulse Generator "A" Circuit	Yes	See DTC No. 31
82	Open Pulse Generator "B" Circuit	Yes	See DTC No. 32
83	Open Or Shorted Shift Control Solenoid Valve "A" Circuit	Yes	See DTC No. 41 & 42
84	Open Or Shorted Shift Control Solenoid Valve "B"	Yes	See DTC No. 43 & 44
85	Open Or Shorted Pressure Control Solenoid Valve	Yes	See DTC No. 45 & 46
86	Incorrect Or No Upshift	Yes	See DTC No. 51, 52, 53 & 54

[1] – To check items listed, see ELECTRONIC TROUBLE SHOOTING or TESTING in CHRYSLER F4A33 & W4A32/33 ELECTRONIC DIAGNOSIS article. For adjustment of all components except Colt/Summit TPS, see ADJUSTMENTS in CHRYSLER F4A33 & W4A32/33 ELECTRONIC DIAGNOSIS article.

HYDRAULIC PRESSURE TESTS

NOTE: In the following test procedures, an additional person may be necessary to activate the transaxle throttle control cable. Before performing pressure tests ensure fluid level and condition are acceptable.

1) Ensure transaxle is at normal operating temperature and fluid level is correct. Raise and support vehicle so drive wheels rotate freely. Install tachometer, and position so driver can view it.
2) Note locations of hydraulic pressure taps on side of transaxle case and near oil pan. *See Figs. 10 and 11.* Remove plug, and install adapter and pressure gauge to each pressure tap.

CAUTION: A 400-psi (28 kg/cm²) pressure gauge is required for checking certain pressures. See Figs. 12 and 13 to determine when this gauge should be used in accordance with hydraulic pressure specification.

3) Measure hydraulic pressure at various specified engine RPM and transaxle gears. *See Figs. 12 and 13.* Ensure pressure is within specification. If proper line pressure cannot be obtained, check for proper adjustment. See LINE PRESSURE under ADJUSTMENTS.
4) If proper line pressure cannot be obtained, check for probable defective components. See LINE PRESSURE TEST RESULTS. Remove pressure gauge. Install and tighten plug to specification. See TORQUE SPECIFICATIONS.

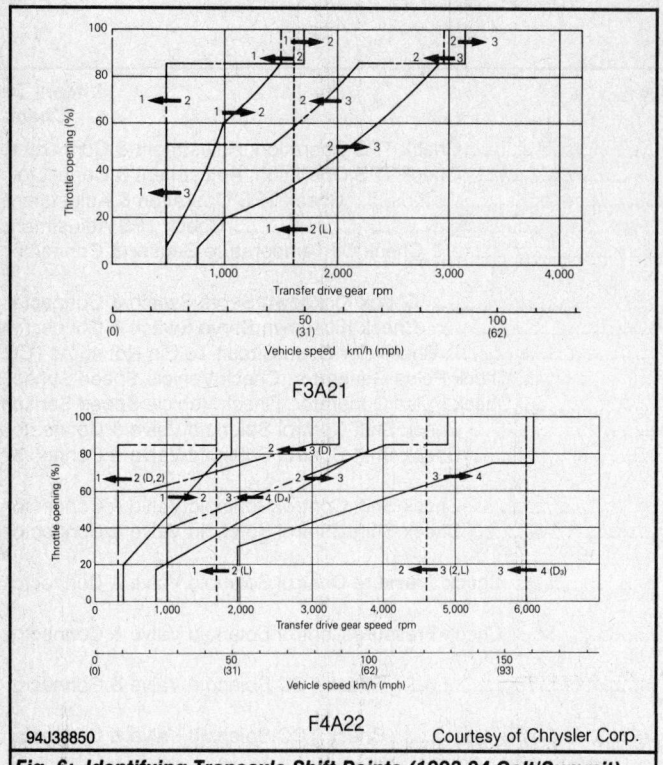

F3A21

F4A22

94J38850   Courtesy of Chrysler Corp.

Fig. 6: Identifying Transaxle Shift Points (1993-94 Colt/Summit)

LINE PRESSURE TEST RESULTS

F3A20 Series – 1) Low pressure in "D", "L" and "2" positions but correct pressure in "R" position indicates rear clutch circuit or 1-2 accumulator seal ring leakage.

2) Low pressure in "D" and "R" positions but correct pressure in "L" position indicates front clutch circuit leakage.

3) Low pressure in "D" and "L" positions but correct pressure in "2" position indicates low-reverse circuit leakage.

4) Low line pressure in all positions indicates faulty oil pump, loose valve body bolts, clogged filter or stuck pressure regulator valve.

F4A20 Series – 1) If line pressures are all low or high, probable causes are: clogged oil filter, incorrect pressure regulator adjustment, sticking pressure regulator valve, incorrect oil pump discharge pressure or fluid pressure leakage at valve body.

2) Incorrect reducing pressure reading indicates incorrect line pressure, reducing pressure filter clogging, reducing valve sticking or fluid pressure leakage at valve body.

3) Incorrect kickdown brake pressure reading indicates fluid pressure leakage at kickdown servo or valve body malfunction.

4) Incorrect front clutch pressure reading indicates fluid pressure leakage at kickdown servo or valve body, malfunction of valve body or fluid pressure leakage at front clutch piston or retainer.

5) Incorrect end clutch pressure reading indicates fluid leakage at end clutch piston, fluid pressure leakage at valve body or valve body malfunction.

6) Incorrect low-reverse brake pressure reading indicates fluid pressure leakage between valve body and transaxle case at "O" ring, valve body malfunction or fluid pressure leakage at low-reverse brake piston or retainer.

7) Incorrect torque converter pressure indicates clogging or leaking of oil cooler or lines, torque converter failure, leaking seal ring at input shaft or binding Torque Converter Clutch Solenoid Valve (TCCSV) or torque converter control valve.

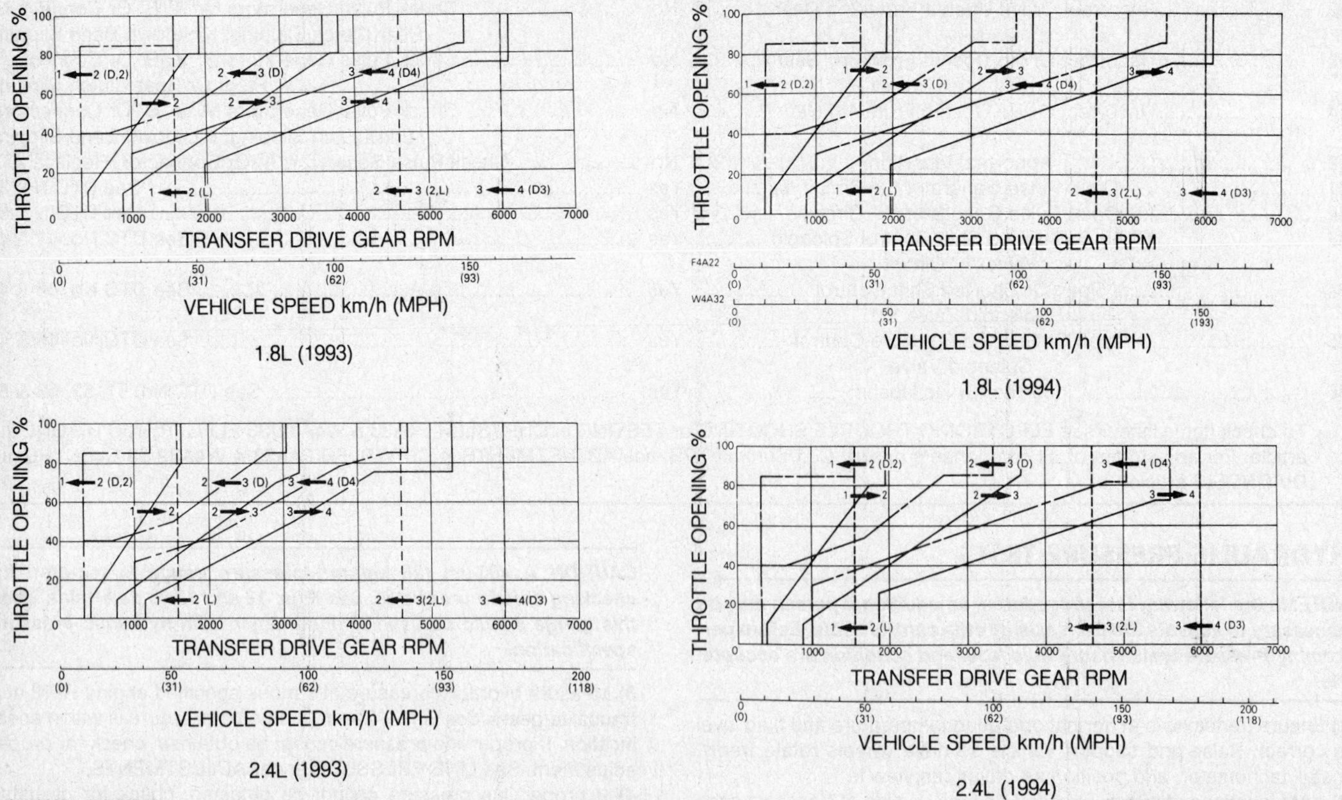

1.8L (1993)

1.8L (1994)

2.4L (1993)

2.4L (1994)

94A38851 94B38852   Courtesy of Chrysler Corp.

Fig. 7: Identifying Transaxle Shift Points (Colt Vista & Summit Wagon)

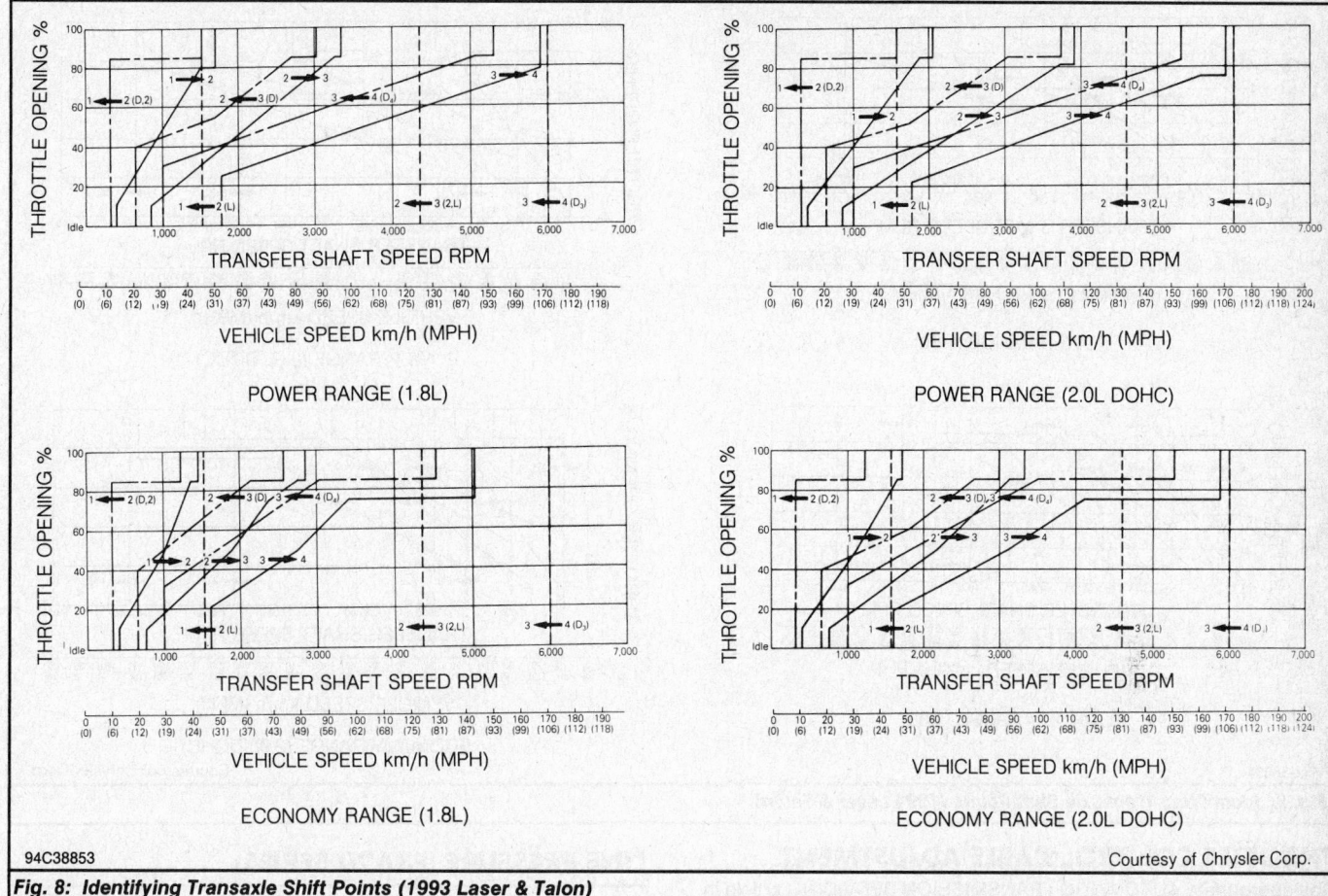

94C38853

Courtesy of Chrysler Corp.

Fig. 8: Identifying Transaxle Shift Points (1993 Laser & Talon)

GOVERNOR PRESSURE TEST (F3A20 SERIES)

1) Perform this test only if transaxle shifts at incorrect vehicle speeds when throttle control cable is properly adjusted. Connect oil pressure gauge to governor pressure test port. *See Fig. 10.*

2) Operate transaxle in "D" position to read pressures. Compare pressures to vehicle speeds and refer to GOVERNOR PRESSURE SPECIFICATIONS table.

3) If governor pressures are incorrect at given vehicle speeds, governor valve is probably sticking or filter in governor body is clogged. Governor pressure should respond smoothly to changes in vehicle speed and should return to 0-2.8 psi (0-20 kPa) when vehicle is stopped.

GOVERNOR PRESSURE SPECIFICATIONS (F3A20 SERIES)

Governor Pressure psi (kPa)	Vehicle Speed MPH
14 (100)	14
43 (300)	35-39
71 (500)	50-54

TORQUE CONVERTER STALL SPEED TEST

CAUTION: DO NOT allow anyone to stand in front of or behind vehicle while performing stall speed test. Always block both rear wheels and apply parking and service brakes fully.

Stall Speed Test Procedure – 1) Check transaxle fluid level. Fluid should be at normal operating temperature of 160-180°F (70-80°C). Engine coolant should also be at normal operating temperature of 180-190°F (60-90°C).

2) Block both rear wheels. Install engine tachometer to be seen from driver's seat. Apply parking and service brakes fully. Start engine and move gear selector to "D" position.

3) With brakes fully applied, depress accelerator pedal fully to read maximum engine RPM. See STALL SPEED SPECIFICATIONS table.

NOTE: DO NOT hold wide open throttle for longer than 5 seconds at a time. If more than one stall speed test is required, operate engine at approximately 1000 RPM in neutral for 2 minutes to cool transaxle fluid.

4) Move gear selector to "R" position and repeat stall speed test procedure. See STALL SPEED SPECIFICATIONS table.

Stall Speed Test Results – 1) If stall speed is above specification in "D" position, rear clutch or one-way clutch is slipping. HYDRAULIC PRESSURE TESTS can be performed to isolate problem.

2) If stall speed is above specification in "R" position, front clutch or low-reverse brake is slipping. HYDRAULIC PRESSURE TESTS can be performed to isolate problem.

3) If stall speed is below specification in "R" and "D" positions, insufficient engine performance or faulty torque converter are probable causes.

STALL SPEED SPECIFICATIONS

Transaxle Model	Stall Speed RPM
F3A20 Series	1000-2200
F4A20 Series	1800-2800

ON-VEHICLE SERVICE

INHIBITOR SWITCH & CONTROL CABLE ADJUSTMENTS

See appropriate AUTOMATIC TRANSMISSION SERVICING article in TRANSMISSION SERVICING.

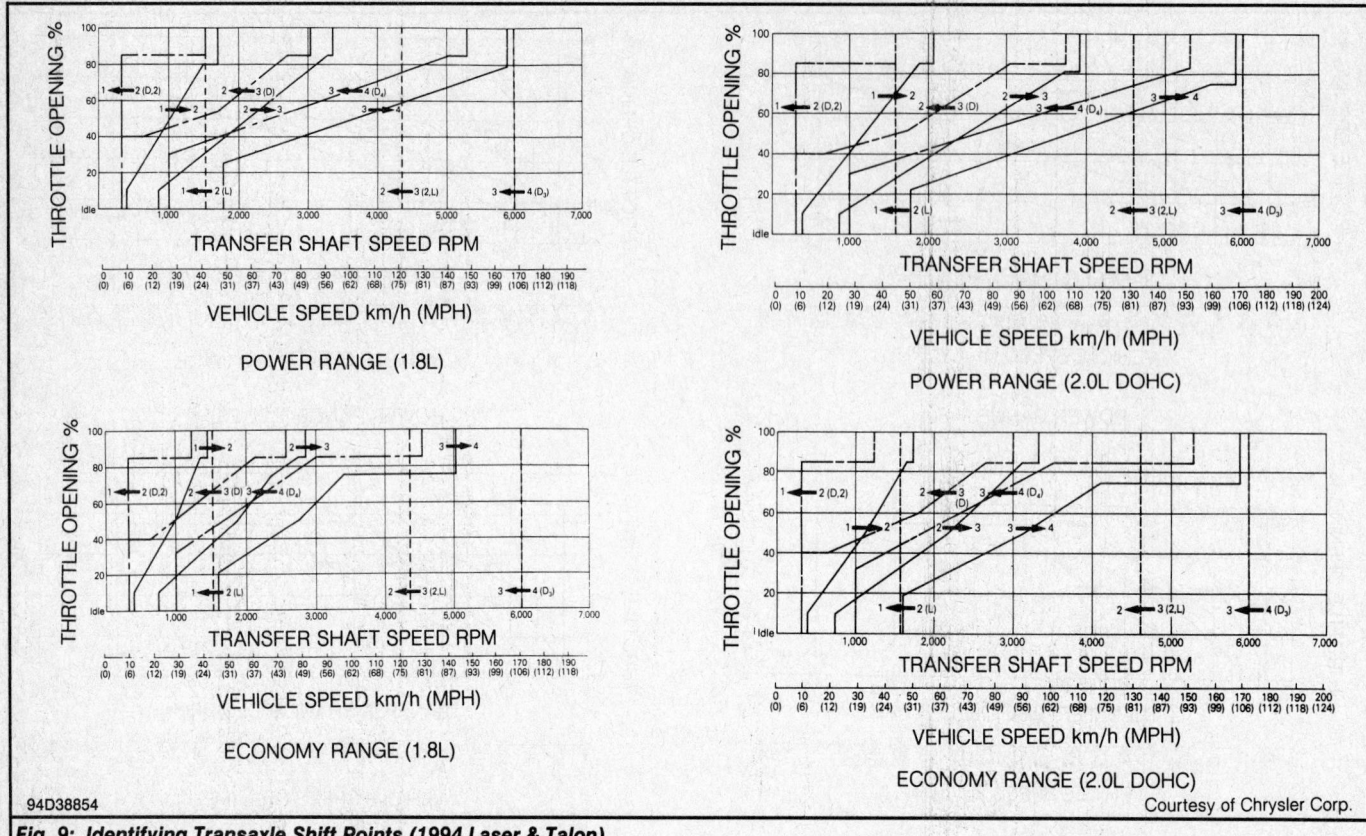

Fig. 9: Identifying Transaxle Shift Points (1994 Laser & Talon)

THROTTLE CONTROL CABLE ADJUSTMENT

See appropriate AUTOMATIC TRANSMISSION SERVICING article in TRANSMISSION SERVICING.

ADJUSTMENTS

KICKDOWN SERVO ADJUSTMENT (F4A20 SERIES)

1) Thoroughly clean area around kickdown servo switch. Remove snap ring. Remove kickdown servo switch. Using kickdown servo wrench and wrench adapter, secure kickdown servo piston from turning. See Fig. 14.

CAUTION: DO NOT press piston inward while engaging wrench in piston. Tighten wrench adapter by hand.

2) Loosen lock nut back to "V" groove in adjusting rod. See Fig. 15. Thread inner half of Kickdown Servo Socket Wrench Set (MD998916) onto adjusting rod, and tighten it until it contacts lock nut. See Fig. 16. Place outer half of wrench set onto lock nut. Tighten inner and outer halves together using open end wrenches.

3) Remove outer half of wrench set. Using a torque wrench, tighten inner half of wrench set to 89 INCH lbs. (10 N.m). See Fig. 17. Back off wrench and repeat tightening to specified torque. Back off wrench once again then tighten to 44 INCH lbs (5 N.m). When specified torque is reached, back off wrench 2-2 1/4 turns.

4) Unlock inner half of wrench set from kickdown servo lock nut. Tighten lock nut by hand until it contacts kickdown servo piston. Tighten servo lock nut to 18-23 Ft. Lbs. (25-32 N.m).

NOTE: Ensure adjusting rod DOES NOT turn while tightening lock nut.

LINE PRESSURE (F3A20 SERIES)

NOTE: Since valve body must be removed for adjustment, check line pressure before attempting to adjust line pressure. For line pressure adjustment procedures for F4A20 series transaxle, see CHRYSLER F4A33, W4A32 & W4A33 overhaul article.

1) Remove valve body. See VALVE BODY under REMOVAL & INSTALLATION. Note location of line pressure adjusting screw. See Fig. 37.

2) To adjust line pressure, rotate line pressure adjusting screw at regulator valve. Rotate line pressure adjusting screw clockwise to decrease line pressure and counterclockwise to increase line pressure.

3) Rotating line pressure adjusting screw one revolution will change line pressure approximately 5.4 psi (3.8 kPa). The standard adjusting value for line pressure is not available from manufacturer. For hydraulic pressure specifications, See Fig. 12. Reinstall valve body. Fill transaxle with Mopar ATF Plus-Type 7176, and check line pressure.

REMOVAL & INSTALLATION

For transaxle removal procedure, see appropriate AUTOMATIC TRANSMISSION REMOVAL article in TRANSMISSION SERVICING.

TORQUE CONVERTER

Torque converter is a sealed unit and cannot be disassembled for service. Replace unit if damaged or contaminated. For stall speed test, see TORQUE CONVERTER STALL SPEED TEST under TRANSAXLE TESTING.

TRANSAXLE DISASSEMBLY

F3A20 Series – 1) Prior to disassembling unit, plug all openings and thoroughly clean exterior. Remove torque converter and position transaxle with oil pan down.

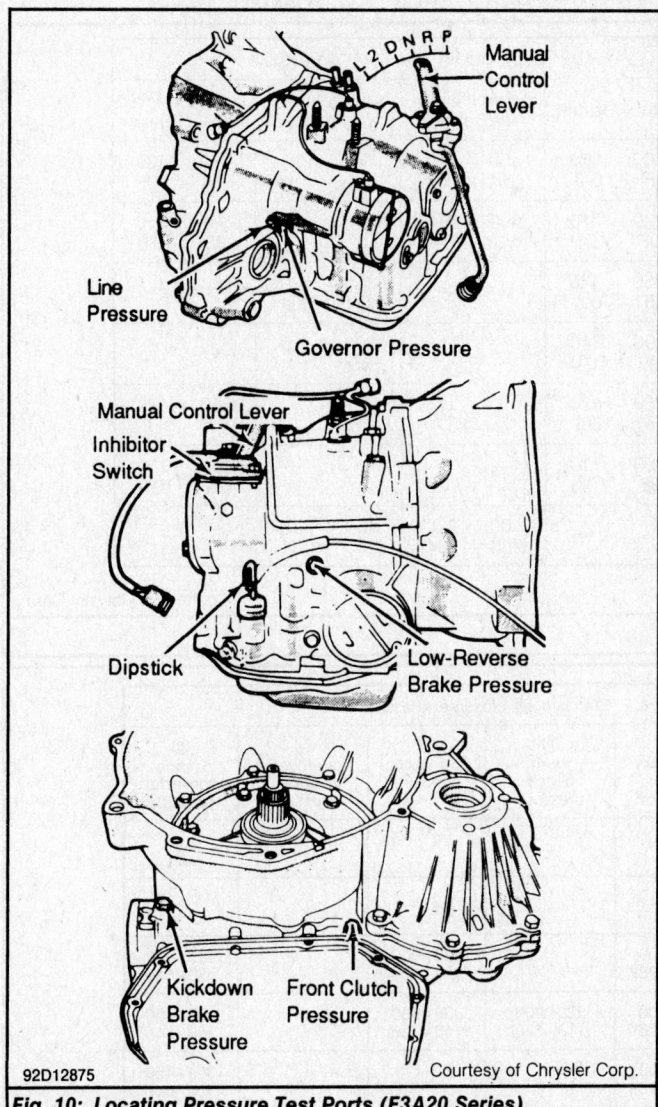

Fig. 10: Locating Pressure Test Ports (F3A20 Series)

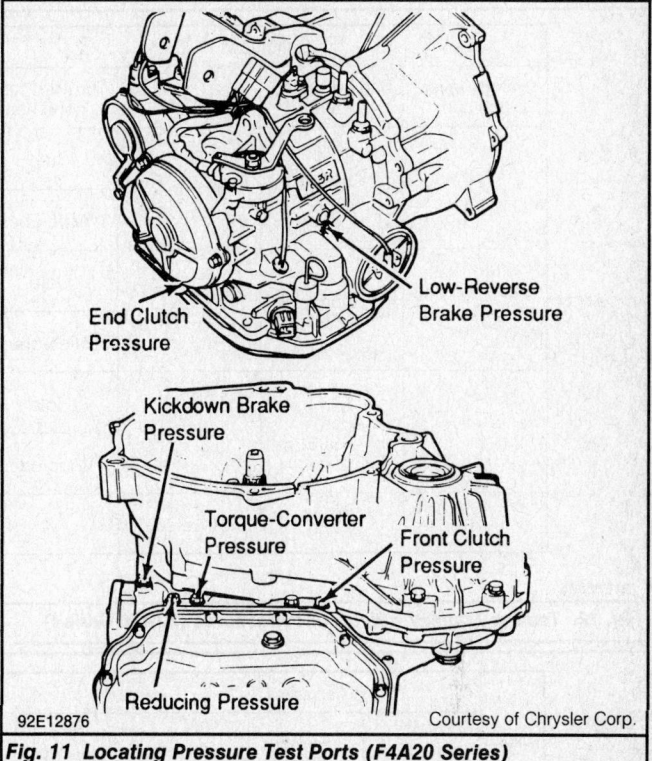

Fig. 11 Locating Pressure Test Ports (F4A20 Series)

2) Measure input shaft end play before disassembling transaxle. This will indicate when a thrust washer change is required (except when major parts are replaced). Record dial indicator reading for later use.
3) Remove transfer shaft cover and measure transfer shaft end play. Record dial indicator reading for use when reassembling transaxle. Remove inhibitor switch. Remove oil pan, gasket and filter. *See Fig. 19.* Remove solenoid valve connector and valve body assembly after throttle cable has been disconnected. Remove both accumulator pistons and springs.
4) Remove converter housing, oil pump assembly and thrust washer. *See Fig. 18.* Remove differential assembly with spacer. Remove input shaft with front and rear clutch assemblies as a unit.
5) Remove thrust bearing and clutch hub. Remove thrust washer and bearing. Remove kickdown drum and band. Remove kickdown servo snap ring, piston, spring and anchor rod. Remove snap ring and center support. Remove reverse and forward sun gears. Remove planetary gear set. *See Fig. 18.*
6) Remove wave spring, return spring, pressure plate, brake discs, brake plates and reaction plate. Note direction of return spring for reassembly reference. Remove transfer idler gear shaft lock plate and bolt. Remove transfer idler gear shaft using wrench adapter. Remove transfer idler gear bearing inner races (2) and spacer. *See Fig. 19.*
7) Remove output flange bearing retainer and "O" ring. Remove snap ring from outer race of bearing. Remove internal gear, output flange, transfer drive gear and bearing as an assembly.

8) Remove snap ring at rear end of transfer shaft. Using brass drift on rear end of transfer shaft, drive shaft toward engine mounting surface. Transfer driven gear will come off. Remove snap ring, then tapered roller bearing inner and outer races (if necessary). Remove sprag rod support then manual control shaft, steel ball and spring.
F4A20 Series – 1) Prior to disassembly, plug all openings and thoroughly clean exterior of transaxle. Remove torque converter and measure input shaft end play. This will indicate when a thrust washer change is required (except when major parts are replaced). Record dial indicator reading for later use.
2) Remove pulse generators "A" and "B" and inhibitor switch. Remove kickdown servo switch. Remove oil pan, gasket and filter. Remove oil temperature sensor. *See Fig. 19.*
3) Remove solenoid valve connector and valve body. Remove end clutch cover and end clutch assembly. Remove end clutch hub, thrust bearing and end clutch shaft.
4) Remove converter housing, oil pump assembly and thrust washer. Remove differential assembly and spacer. Remove input shaft with front and rear clutch assemblies. Remove thrust bearing and clutch hub. Remove thrust race and bearing. Remove kickdown drum and band. *See Fig. 18.*
5) Remove kickdown servo retainer, piston and spring. Remove anchor rod. Remove snap ring and center support. Remove reverse and forward sun gears. Remove planetary carrier assembly and thrust bearing. Remove wave spring, return spring, pressure plate, brake discs, brake plates and reaction plate. *See Fig. 18.* Note direction of return spring for reassembly reference. Remove end bearing retainer. Use impact driver if necessary.
6) Remove idler gear shaft lock bolt and plate. Remove transfer idler shaft with wrench adapter. Pull out transfer idler shaft and remove transfer idler gear bearing inner races (2) and spacer.
7) Remove snap ring from end bearing. Remove internal gear, output flange, transfer drive gear and bearing as an assembly from case. Remove transfer shaft cover.
8) Remove transfer shaft LEFT-HAND threaded lock nut. Remove transfer shaft with a press. Remove transfer shaft bearing using a bearing splitter. Remove set screw and manual control shaft with sprag rod support.

Conditions				Standard oil pressure kPa (psi)			
Select lever position	Engine speed (rpm)	Shift position	Throttle cable condition	Line pressure	Front clutch pressure	Low-reverse brake pressure	Kickdown brake pressure
D	Approx. 2,500	3rd gear	Idle	360 – 420 (51 – 60)	360 – 420 (51 – 60)	–	360 – 420 (51 – 60)
			Wide-open	690 – 710 (98 – 101)	690 – 710 (98 – 101)	–	690 – 710 (98 – 101)
L	Approx. 2,500	1st gear	Idle	360 – 420 (51 – 60)	–	360 – 420 (51 – 60)	–
			Wide-open	690 – 710 (98 – 101)	–	690 – 710 (98 – 101)	–
2	Approx. 2,500	2nd gear	Idle	360 – 420 (51 – 60)			360 – 420 (51 – 60)
			Wide-open	690 – 710 (98 – 101)			690 – 710 (98 – 101)
R	Approx. 2,500	Reverse	–	–	1,400 – 2,000 (200 – 284)	1,400 – 2,000 (200 – 284)	

94E38855   Courtesy of Chrysler Corp.

Fig. 12: Testing Transaxle Hydraulic Pressures (F3A20 Series)

No.	Conditions			Standard oil pressure kPa (psi)					
	Select lever position	Engine speed rpm	Shift position	① Reducing pressure	② Kickdown brake pressure	③ Front clutch pressure	④ End clutch pressure	⑤ Low-reverse brake pressure	⑥ Torque-converter pressure
1	N	Idling	Neutral	360–490 (51–70)	–	–	–	–	☆
2	D	Idling	2nd gear	360–490 (51–70)	100–210 (14–30)	–	–	–	☆
3	D (SW-ON)	Approx. 2,500	4th gear	360–490 (51–70)	830–900 (118–128)	–	830–900 (118–128)	–	350–450 (50–64)
4	D (SW-OFF)	Approx. 2,500	3rd gear	360–490 (51–70)	830–900 (118–128)	830–900 (118–128)	830–900 (118–128)	–	350–450 (50–64)
5	2	Approx. 2,500	2nd gear	360–490 (51–70)	830–900 (118–128)	–	–	–	350–450 (50–64)
6	L	Approx. 1,000	1st gear	360–490 (51–70)		–	–	300–420 (43–60)	☆
7	R	Approx. 2,500	Reverse	360–490 (51–70)	–	1,640–2,240 (233–319)		1,640–2,240 (233–319)	350–450 (50–64)
		Approx. 1,000				1.000 (142) or more		1.000 (142) or more	

NOTE
– must be 10 kPa (1.4 psi) or less.
SW-ON: Switch ON the overdrive control switch
SW-OFF: Switch OFF the overdrive control switch
☆: Hydraulic pressure is generated, but not the standard value.

94F38856   Courtesy of Chrysler Corp.

Fig. 13: Testing Transaxle Hydraulic Pressures (F4A20 Series)

COMPONENT DISASSEMBLY & REASSEMBLY

OIL PUMP

Disassembly – 1) Remove "O" ring from oil pump housing. Place reassembly reference mark on oil pump housing and reaction shaft support. Remove 5 retaining bolts and reaction shaft support from housing. Place reassembly reference marks on drive and driven gears.
2) Remove oil pump drive and driven gears from housing. See Fig. 20. Remove check ball from housing. Remove snap ring and oil seal from oil pump drive gear. Remove 2 seal rings from reaction shaft support.

Inspection – 1) Using a straightedge, check oil pump gear side clearance. Clearance should be .001-0.002" (.03-.05 mm). If clearance is not within specification, replace oil pump as an assembly.
2) Check reaction shaft support surface in contact with oil pump gear for evidence of interference and replace oil pump assembly if necessary.
Reassembly – 1) Fit oil seal and snap ring to oil pump drive gear. After immersing drive and driven gears in ATF, install gears in pump housing. Align reference marks made during disassembly.
2) Install check ball in pump housing. See Fig. 21. Install 2 seal rings to reaction shaft support. Install NEW "O" ring to pump housing, and lubricate with ATF.

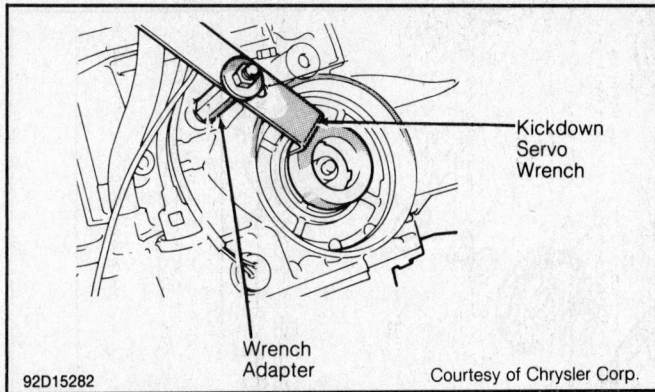

92D15282   Courtesy of Chrysler Corp.

Fig. 14: Installing Kickdown Servo Wrench

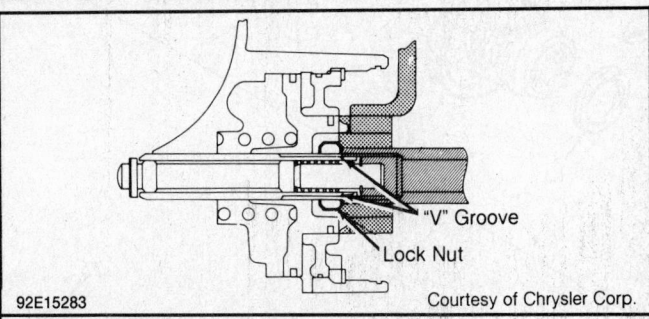

92E15283   Courtesy of Chrysler Corp.

Fig. 15: Sectional View Of Kickdown Servo Adjustment Mechanism

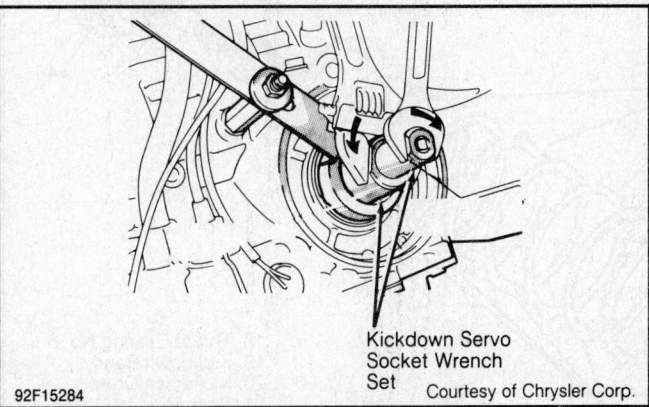

92F15284   Courtesy of Chrysler Corp.

Fig. 16: Locking Servo Wrench To Adjusting Rod

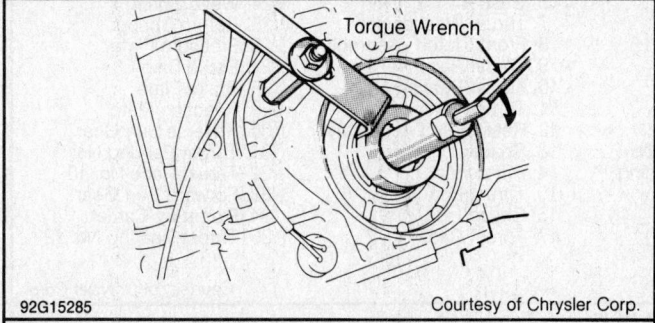

92G15285   Courtesy of Chrysler Corp.

Fig. 17: Adjusting Kickdown Servo

3) Install reaction shaft support to oil pump housing and tighten 5 bolts finger tight. Using guide pin and support band, align reaction shaft support with oil pump housing. See Fig. 22. Install oil pump bolts. Tighten bolts to specification. See TORQUE SPECIFICATIONS. Ensure oil pump gears turn freely.

FRONT CLUTCH

Disassembly – 1) Remove snap ring from clutch retainer. Remove clutch reaction plates and clutch discs. Note number of plates and discs removed.

NOTE: *If clutch reaction plates and clutch discs are to be reused, DO NOT change the installation order or direction. Soak NEW clutch discs in ATF for 2 hours prior to installation.*

---

2) Compress return spring and remove snap ring, retainer and return spring. Remove piston from retainer and "D" rings from piston and retainer.

Reassembly – 1) Install "D" rings in piston and retainer with round side out. Apply ATF to outside surface of "D" rings and install piston in front clutch retainer by pushing with hand. Install return spring and spring retainer. See Fig. 23. Compress return spring and install snap ring.

2) Apply ATF and install clutch reaction plates and clutch discs. See Fig. 23. Install snap ring. Using a feeler gauge, check clearance between snap ring and clutch reaction plate. Clearance should be .028-.035" (.71-.89 mm). If clearance is not as specified, replace snap ring. Selective snap rings are available in thicknesses of .063-.118" (1.6-3.0 mm), in increments of .004" (.10 mm).

REAR CLUTCH

Disassembly – 1) Remove snap ring and thrust race. Remove input shaft from rear clutch retainer. Remove snap ring from rear clutch retainer.

2) Remove clutch reaction plate, clutch plates, clutch discs and clutch pressure plate from retainer. Note number of plates and discs removed. See Fig. 24. Compress return spring and remove wave spring. Remove spring and piston. Remove "D" rings from piston.

NOTE: *If clutch reaction plates and clutch discs are to be reused, DO NOT change the installation order or direction. Soak NEW clutch discs in ATF for 2 hours prior to installation.*

Reassembly – 1) Install "D" rings in clutch piston. Apply ATF to outside surfaces of "D" rings and install piston in clutch retainer by pushing with hand.

2) Install return spring on piston. Compress return spring and install wave spring. Install clutch pressure plate, clutch discs, clutch plates and clutch reaction plate in rear clutch retainer. See Fig. 24. Apply ATF to plates and NEW discs and install snap ring.

3) Using a feeler gauge, check clearance between snap ring and clutch reaction plate with spring compressed. Clearance should be .016-.024" (.40-.60 mm). If clearance is not as specified, replace snap ring. Selective snap rings are available in thicknesses of .063-.118" (1.6-3.0 mm), in increments of .004" (.10 mm).

4) Insert input shaft with one oil groove aligned with reference mark or oil hole on rear clutch retainer. See Fig. 25. Install thrust race, snap ring and 3 seal rings on input shaft.

END CLUTCH (F4A20 SERIES ONLY)

Disassembly – Remove snap ring, washer and return spring. Remove large snap ring, clutch reaction plate, clutch discs and clutch plates. Note number of plates and discs removed. Remove clutch piston. Use compressed air if necessary. Remove seal ring from clutch retainer and 2 "D" rings from clutch piston.

NOTE: *If clutch reaction plates and clutch discs are to be reused, DO NOT change the installation order or direction. Soak NEW clutch discs in ATF for 2 hours prior to installation.*

Reassembly – 1) Install "D" rings in piston. Apply ATF to outer surfaces of "D" rings, and install clutch piston in end clutch retainer by pushing by hand.

2) Install return spring, washer and NEW snap ring. See Fig. 26. Install clutch plates, clutch discs and reaction plate in end clutch retainer. Install snap ring.

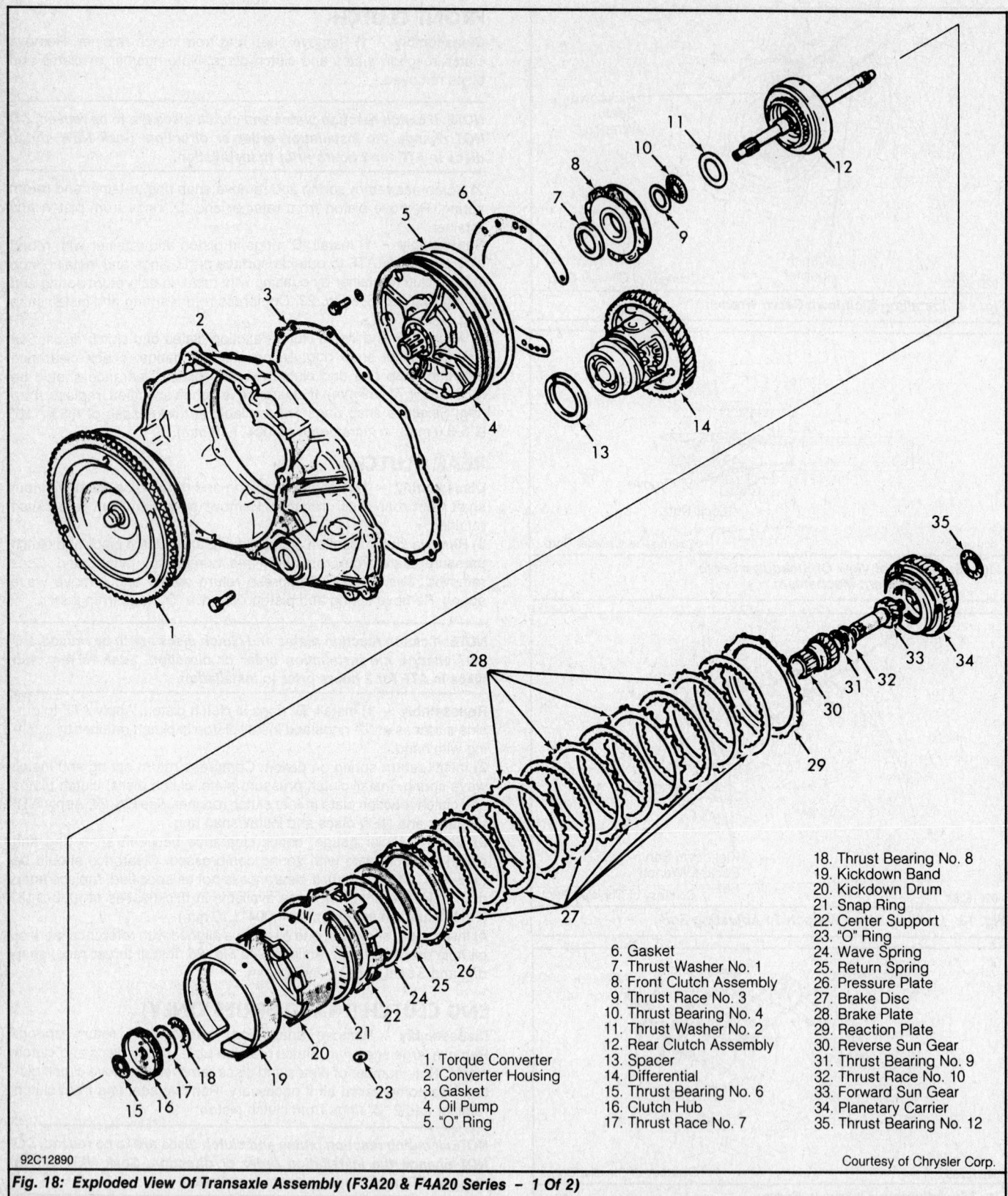

18. Thrust Bearing No. 8
19. Kickdown Band
20. Kickdown Drum
21. Snap Ring
22. Center Support
23. "O" Ring
24. Wave Spring
25. Return Spring
26. Pressure Plate
27. Brake Disc
28. Brake Plate
29. Reaction Plate
30. Reverse Sun Gear
31. Thrust Bearing No. 9
32. Thrust Race No. 10
33. Forward Sun Gear
34. Planetary Carrier
35. Thrust Bearing No. 12

6. Gasket
7. Thrust Washer No. 1
8. Front Clutch Assembly
9. Thrust Race No. 3
10. Thrust Bearing No. 4
11. Thrust Washer No. 1
12. Rear Clutch Assembly
13. Spacer
14. Differential
15. Thrust Bearing No. 6
16. Clutch Hub
17. Thrust Race No. 7

1. Torque Converter
2. Converter Housing
3. Gasket
4. Oil Pump
5. "O" Ring

92C12890

Courtesy of Chrysler Corp.

Fig. 18: Exploded View Of Transaxle Assembly (F3A20 & F4A20 Series – 1 Of 2)

3) Using a feeler gauge, check clearance between snap ring and clutch reaction plate while compressed. Clearance should be .016-.026" (.40-.65 mm) for F4A22 transaxle, or .024-.033" (.60-.85 mm) for F4A23 transaxle. If clearance is not as specified, replace snap ring. Selective snap rings are available in thicknesses of .041-.081" (1.05-2.05 mm) in increments of .010" (.25 mm).

LOW & REVERSE BRAKE

Disassembly & Reassembly – Remove piston using compressed air. Remove "D" ring from piston. Fit NEW "D" ring in piston and apply ATF. Press piston in center support by hand.

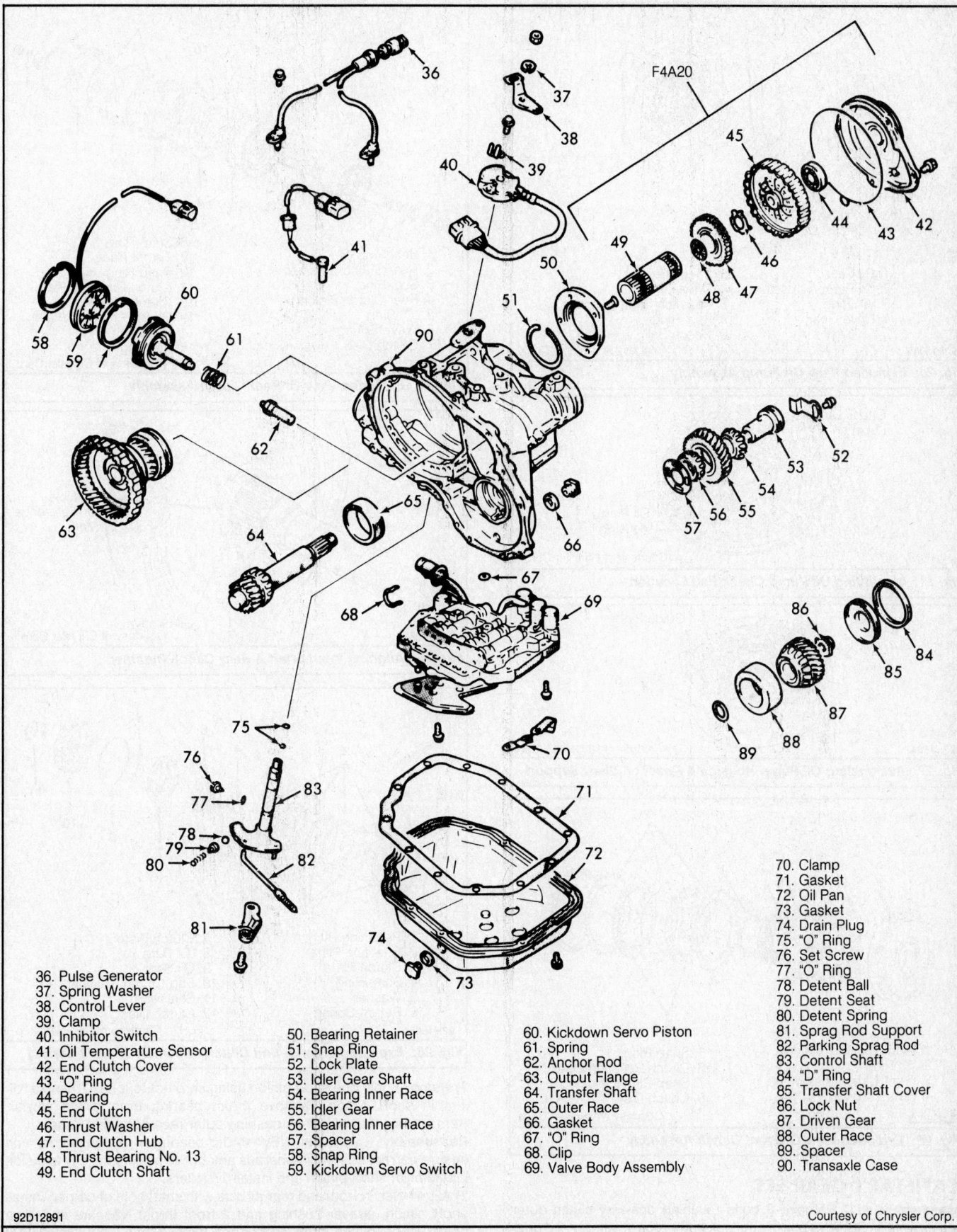

36. Pulse Generator
37. Spring Washer
38. Control Lever
39. Clamp
40. Inhibitor Switch
41. Oil Temperature Sensor
42. End Clutch Cover
43. "O" Ring
44. Bearing
45. End Clutch
46. Thrust Washer
47. End Clutch Hub
48. Thrust Bearing No. 13
49. End Clutch Shaft

50. Bearing Retainer
51. Snap Ring
52. Lock Plate
53. Idler Gear Shaft
54. Bearing Inner Race
55. Idler Gear
56. Bearing Inner Race
57. Spacer
58. Snap Ring
59. Kickdown Servo Switch

60. Kickdown Servo Piston
61. Spring
62. Anchor Rod
63. Output Flange
64. Transfer Shaft
65. Outer Race
66. Gasket
67. "O" Ring
68. Clip
69. Valve Body Assembly

70. Clamp
71. Gasket
72. Oil Pan
73. Gasket
74. Drain Plug
75. "O" Ring
76. Set Screw
77. "O" Ring
78. Detent Ball
79. Detent Seat
80. Detent Spring
81. Sprag Rod Support
82. Parking Sprag Rod
83. Control Shaft
84. "D" Ring
85. Transfer Shaft Cover
86. Lock Nut
87. Driven Gear
88. Outer Race
89. Spacer
90. Transaxle Case

92D12891

Courtesy of Chrysler Corp.

Fig. 19: Exploded View Of Transaxle Assembly (F3A20 & F4A20 Series – 2 Of 2)

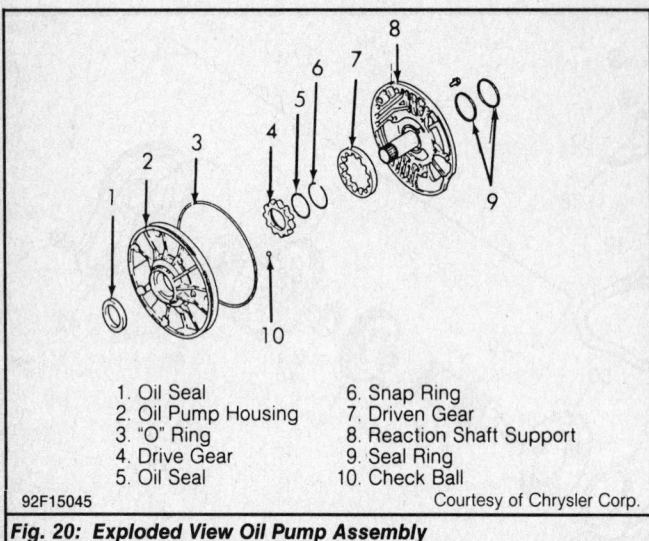

1. Oil Seal
2. Oil Pump Housing
3. "O" Ring
4. Drive Gear
5. Oil Seal
6. Snap Ring
7. Driven Gear
8. Reaction Shaft Support
9. Seal Ring
10. Check Ball

92F15045   Courtesy of Chrysler Corp.

Fig. 20: Exploded View Oil Pump Assembly

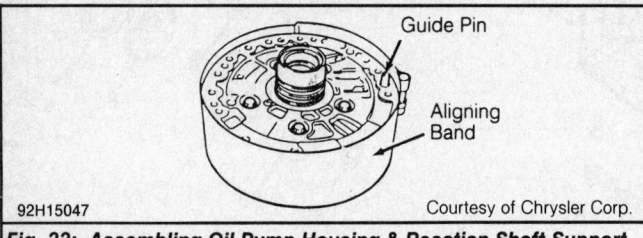

92G15046   Courtesy of Chrysler Corp.

Fig. 21: Identifying Oil Pump Check Ball Location

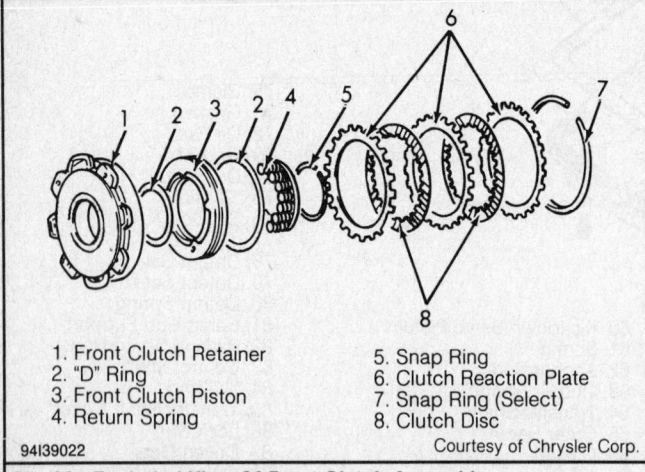

92H15047   Courtesy of Chrysler Corp.

Fig. 22: Assembling Oil Pump Housing & Reaction Shaft Support

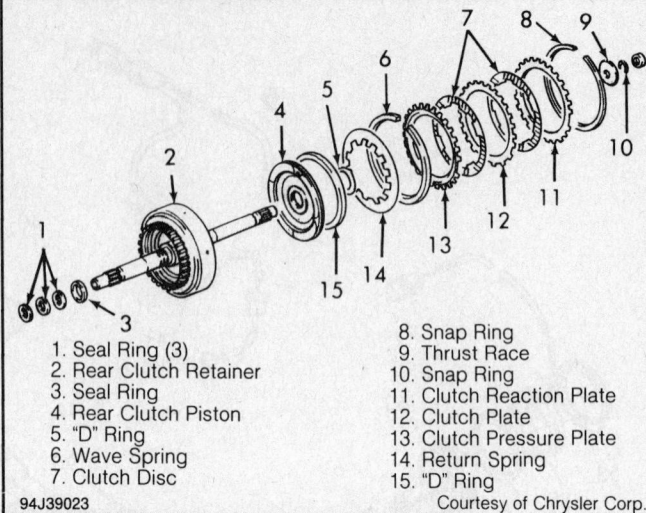

1. Seal Ring (3)
2. Rear Clutch Retainer
3. Seal Ring
4. Rear Clutch Piston
5. "D" Ring
6. Wave Spring
7. Clutch Disc
8. Snap Ring
9. Thrust Race
10. Snap Ring
11. Clutch Reaction Plate
12. Clutch Plate
13. Clutch Pressure Plate
14. Return Spring
15. "D" Ring

94J39023   Courtesy of Chrysler Corp.

Fig. 24: Exploded View Of Rear Clutch Assembly

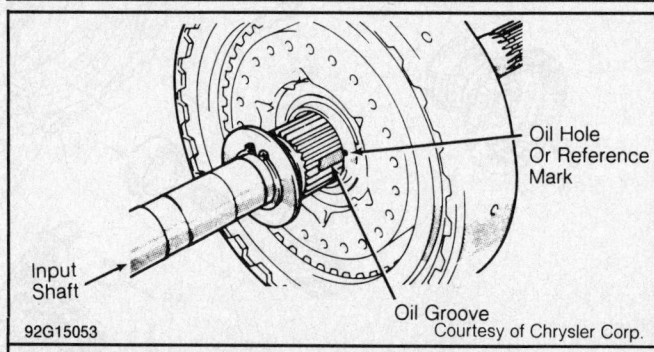

92G15053   Courtesy of Chrysler Corp.

Fig. 25: Aligning Input Shaft & Rear Clutch Retainer

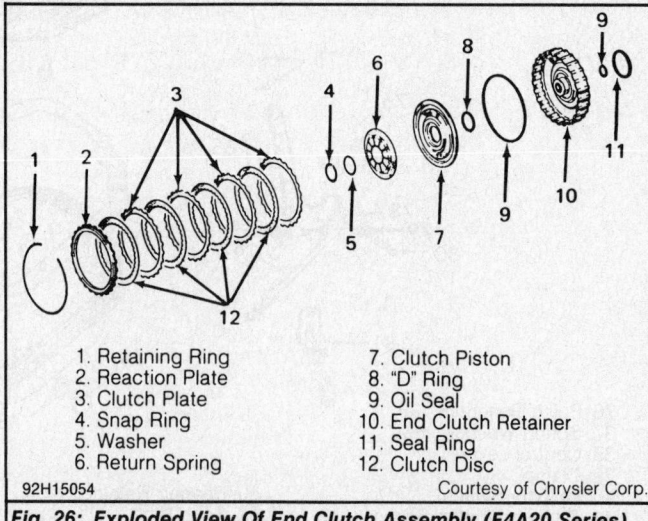

1. Retaining Ring
2. Reaction Plate
3. Clutch Plate
4. Snap Ring
5. Washer
6. Return Spring
7. Clutch Piston
8. "D" Ring
9. Oil Seal
10. End Clutch Retainer
11. Seal Ring
12. Clutch Disc

92H15054   Courtesy of Chrysler Corp.

Fig. 26: Exploded View Of End Clutch Assembly (F4A20 Series)

Fig. 23 image:

1. Front Clutch Retainer
2. "D" Ring
3. Front Clutch Piston
4. Return Spring
5. Snap Ring
6. Clutch Reaction Plate
7. Snap Ring (Select)
8. Clutch Disc

94I39022   Courtesy of Chrysler Corp.

Fig. 23: Exploded View Of Front Clutch Assembly

PLANETARY GEAR SET

Disassembly – 1) Remove 3 bolts retaining one-way clutch outer race assembly. Remove one-way clutch outer race assembly and one-way clutch end plate. Remove short pinion shaft, spacer bushing and front thrust washers. See Fig. 27.

2) Remove only one short pinion using care not to lose 17 needle rollers in short pinion. Remove thrust bearing from pinion carrier. Remove one-way clutch by pushing outer race out using fingers.

Reassembly – 1) Install NEW thrust bearing in pinion carrier and ensure correct fit. Apply generous amount of petroleum jelly to inside diameter of short pinion and install 17 rollers.

2) Align holes in front and rear thrusts with shaft hole of carrier. Install short pinion, spacer bushing and 2 front thrust washers and align holes. Insert pinion shaft. Install end plate in one-way clutch outer race. Push one-way clutch in outer race. Ensure one-way clutch is installed in proper direction. See Fig. 28.

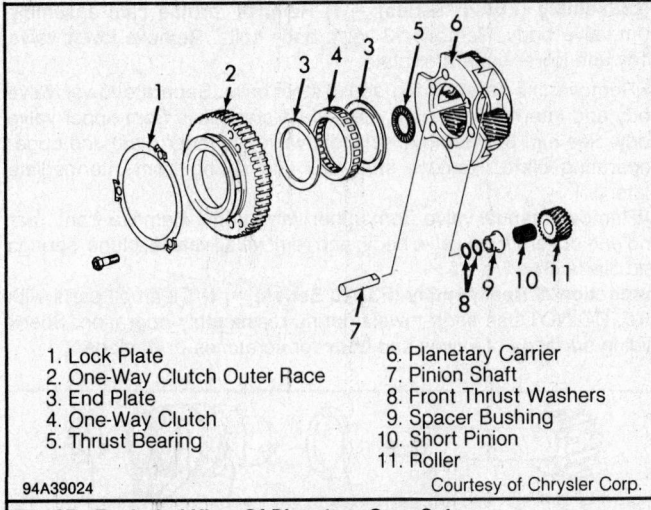

1. Lock Plate
2. One-Way Clutch Outer Race
3. End Plate
4. One-Way Clutch
5. Thrust Bearing
6. Planetary Carrier
7. Pinion Shaft
8. Front Thrust Washers
9. Spacer Bushing
10. Short Pinion
11. Roller

94A39024
Courtesy of Chrysler Corp.

Fig. 27: Exploded View Of Planetary Gear Set

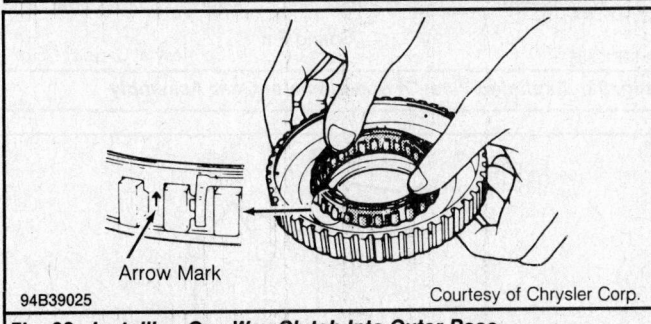

Arrow Mark

94B39025
Courtesy of Chrysler Corp.

Fig. 28: Installing One-Way Clutch Into Outer Race

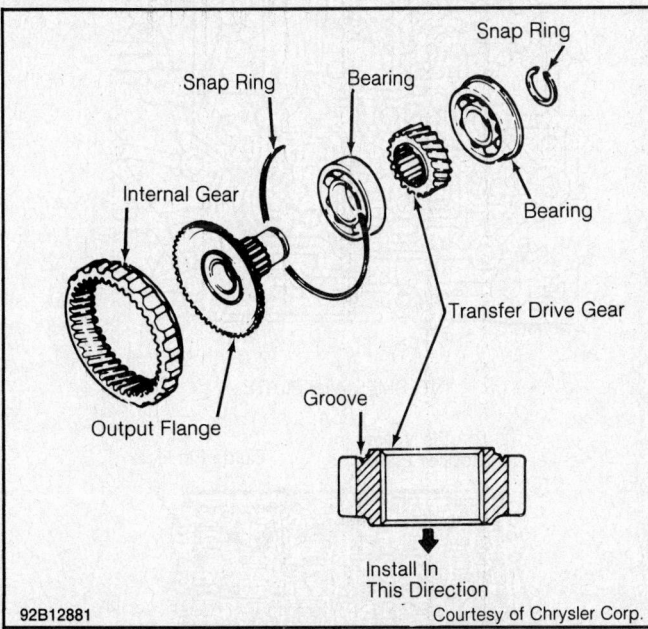

Snap Ring

Snap Ring

Bearing

Internal Gear

Bearing

Transfer Drive Gear

Output Flange

Groove

Install In
This Direction

92B12881
Courtesy of Chrysler Corp.

Fig. 29: Exploded View Of Internal & Transfer Gear

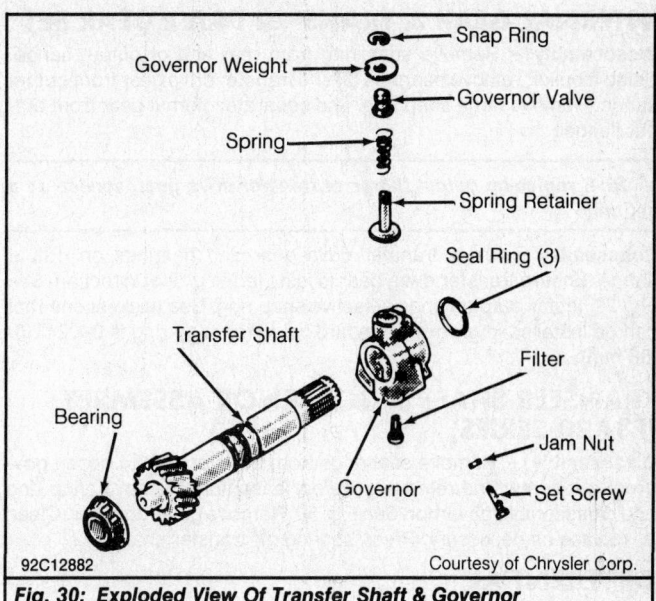

Snap Ring

Governor Weight

Governor Valve

Spring

Spring Retainer

Seal Ring (3)

Transfer Shaft

Filter

Bearing

Jam Nut

Governor

Set Screw

92C12882
Courtesy of Chrysler Corp.

Fig. 30: Exploded View Of Transfer Shaft & Governor (F3A20 Series)

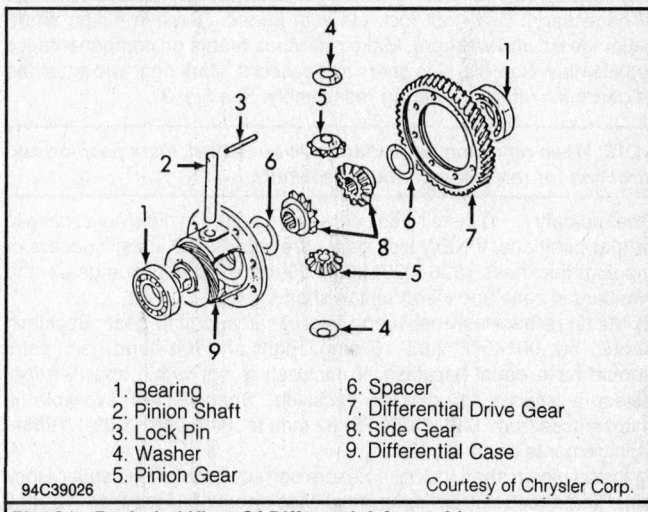

1. Bearing
2. Pinion Shaft
3. Lock Pin
4. Washer
5. Pinion Gear
6. Spacer
7. Differential Drive Gear
8. Side Gear
9. Differential Case

94C39026
Courtesy of Chrysler Corp.

Fig. 31: Exploded View Of Differential Assembly

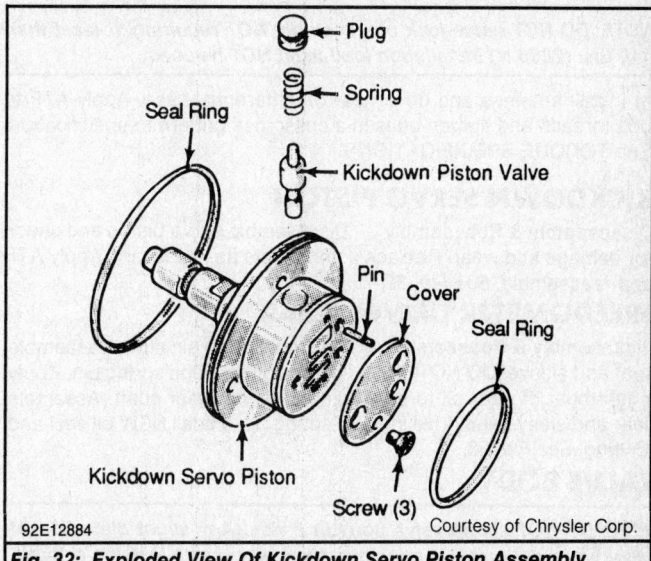

Plug

Spring

Kickdown Piston Valve

Seal Ring

Pin

Cover

Seal Ring

Kickdown Servo Piston

Screw (3)

92E12884
Courtesy of Chrysler Corp.

Fig. 32: Exploded View Of Kickdown Servo Piston Assembly

3) Apply petroleum jelly and install one-way clutch end plate. Install one-way clutch assembly to carrier and align bolt holes. Tighten bolts to specification. See TORQUE SPECIFICATIONS.

Reassembly – 1) Install bearing on transfer shaft. Install governor valve, spring, spring retainer and governor weight in governor body, then install snap ring.

2) Install governor filter. Assemble governor assembly with transfer shaft. Tighten set screw and jam nut to specification. See TORQUE SPECIFICATIONS.

INTERNAL GEAR & TRANSFER DRIVE GEAR SET

Disassembly – Remove snap ring from rear end of output flange. Using a puller, remove bearings (2) and transfer drive gear from output flange. Remove large snap ring, and separate internal gear from output flange.

NOTE: If replacing output flange or transfer drive gear, service as a set only.

Reassembly – Press transfer drive gear and bearings on output flange. Ensure transfer drive gear is installed in proper direction. *See Fig. 29.* Install output flange selective snap ring. Use thickest one that can be installed in groove. Standard value for snap ring is 0-.024" (0-.06 mm).

TRANSFER SHAFT & GOVERNOR ASSEMBLY (F3A20 SERIES)

Disassembly – Remove seal rings from transfer shaft. Loosen governor set screw and remove governor assembly. Remove snap ring and disassemble governor. *See Fig. 30.* Remove governor filter. Clean or replace as necessary. Press bearing off transfer shaft.

DIFFERENTIAL

Disassembly – Remove drive gear and bolts from differential case. Inspect bearings for wear or damage. Using puller, remove bearings (if necessary). Drive out lock pin with punch. Remove pinion shaft, pinion gears and washers. Make reference marks on components for reassembly. Remove side gears and spacers. Mark right and left sides of gears for reference during reassembly. *See Fig. 31.*

NOTE: When removing parts that are to be reused, mark position and direction for reference during reassembly.

Reassembly – **1)** Install side gears and spacers in differential case in proper positions. If NEW side gears are being used install spacers of medium thickness, .036-.039" (.93-1.00 mm). Install pinion gears and washers in case and insert pinion shaft.
2) Measure backlash between pinion gear and side gear. Backlash should be .001-.006" (.03-.15 mm). Right and left hand gear pairs should have equal backlash. If backlash is not within specification, select a spacer for correct backlash. Spacers are available in thicknesses from .030-.032" (.75-.82 mm) to .043-.046" (1.09-1.16mm) in increments of .004" (.10 mm).
3) Install pinion shaft lock pin. Ensure correct installation depth of lock pin. Pin projection from differential case should be less than .12" (3.0 mm).

NOTE: DO NOT reuse lock pin. Lock pin NOT requiring at least than 440 lbs. (2000 N) installation load must NOT be used.

4) Install bearings and drive gear on differential case. Apply ATF to bolt threads and tighten bolts in a crisscross pattern to specification. See TORQUE SPECIFICATIONS.

KICKDOWN SERVO PISTON

Disassembly & Reassembly – Disassemble servo piston and check for damage and wear. Replace components as necessary. Apply ATF and reassemble. *See Fig. 32.*

SPEEDOMETER DRIVEN GEAR

Disassembly & Reassembly – Drive out spring pin and disassemble gear and sleeve. DO NOT reuse "O" ring, oil seal and spring pin. Apply a light coat of gear oil to speedometer driven gear shaft. Assemble gear and sleeve and drive in NEW spring pin. Install NEW oil seal and "O" ring. *See Fig. 33.*

VALVE BODY

NOTE: DO NOT clamp valve body in a vise. Any slight distortion of valve body will result in sticking valves, excessive leakage or both. Clean all parts with ATF. DO NOT use shop towels during reassembly operation.

Disassembly (F3A20 Series) – **1)** Remove throttle cam assembly from valve body. Remove 13 valve body bolts. Remove lower valve body and lower separator plate.
2) Remove line relief spring and 3 steel balls. Separate lower valve body and intermediate plate. Remove 4 steel balls from upper valve body. *See Fig. 34.* Remove solenoid valve, stiffener plate and upper separating plate. Remove steel ball and spring from intermediate plate.
3) Remove manual valve from upper valve body. Remove front, rear and end covers from valve body, and remove all valves, plugs, springs and filters. *See Fig. 35.*

Inspection & Reassembly (F3A20 Series) – **1)** Clean all parts with ATF. DO NOT use shop towels during reassembly operation. Check sliding surfaces of valves and body for scratches or damage.

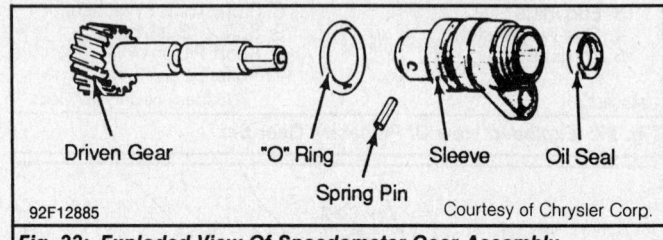

Fig. 33: Exploded View Of Speedometer Gear Assembly

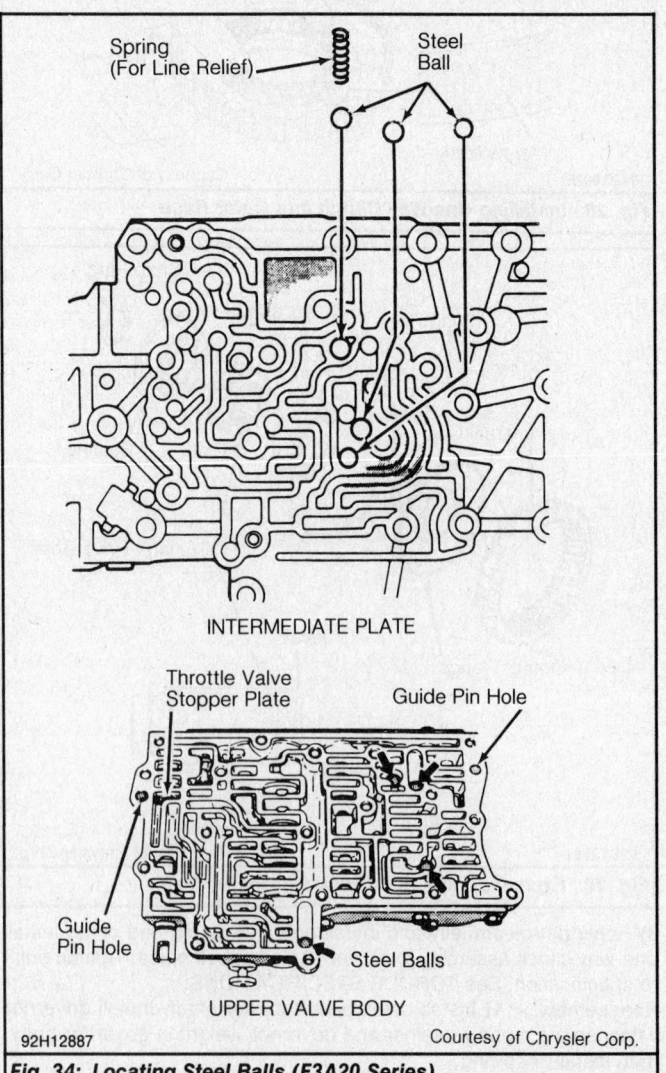

Fig. 34: Locating Steel Balls (F3A20 Series)

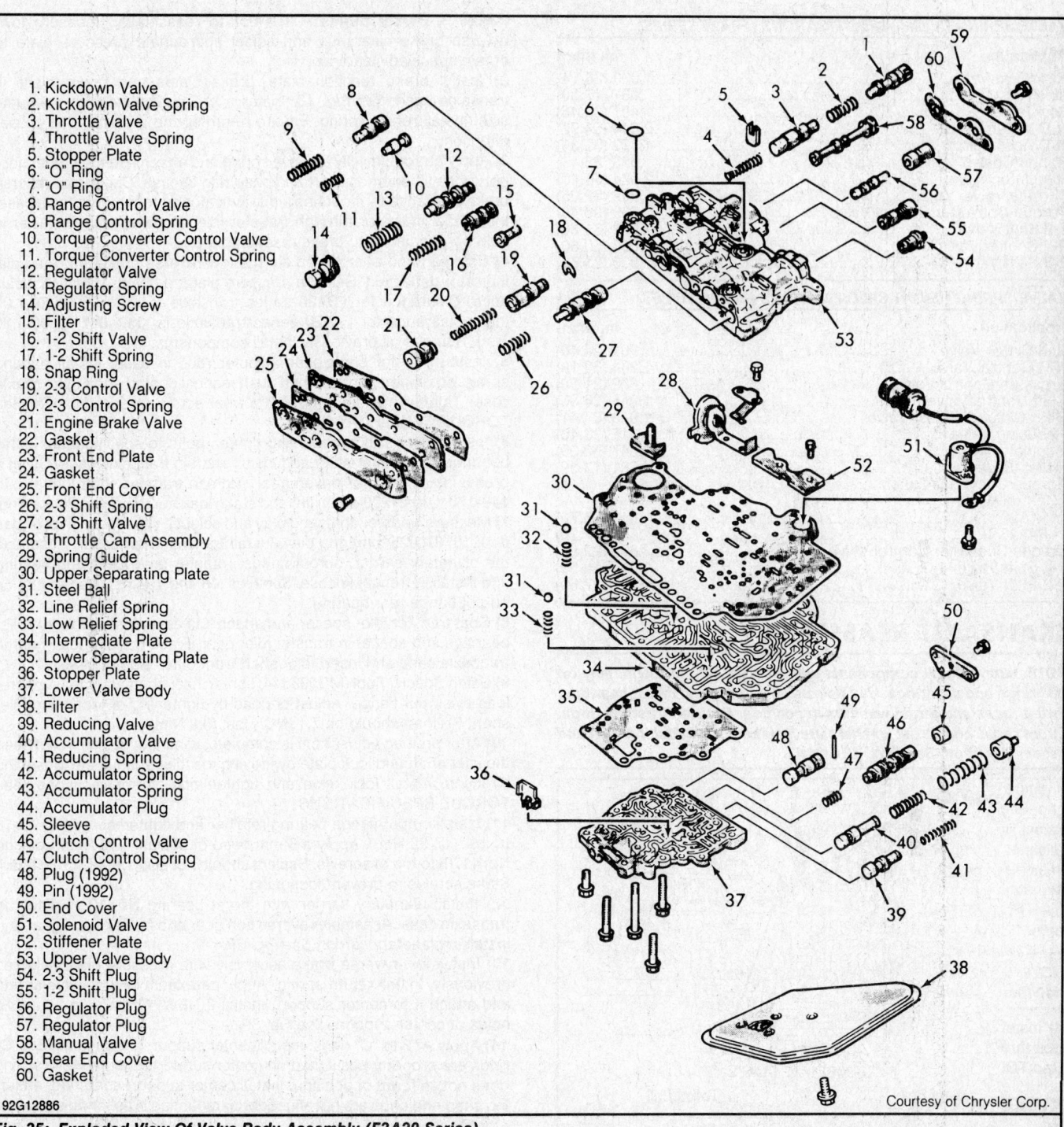

1. Kickdown Valve
2. Kickdown Valve Spring
3. Throttle Valve
4. Throttle Valve Spring
5. Stopper Plate
6. "O" Ring
7. "O" Ring
8. Range Control Valve
9. Range Control Spring
10. Torque Converter Control Valve
11. Torque Converter Control Spring
12. Regulator Valve
13. Regulator Spring
14. Adjusting Screw
15. Filter
16. 1-2 Shift Valve
17. 1-2 Shift Spring
18. Snap Ring
19. 2-3 Control Valve
20. 2-3 Control Spring
21. Engine Brake Valve
22. Gasket
23. Front End Plate
24. Gasket
25. Front End Cover
26. 2-3 Shift Spring
27. 2-3 Shift Valve
28. Throttle Cam Assembly
29. Spring Guide
30. Upper Separating Plate
31. Steel Ball
32. Line Relief Spring
33. Low Relief Spring
34. Intermediate Plate
35. Lower Separating Plate
36. Stopper Plate
37. Lower Valve Body
38. Filter
39. Reducing Valve
40. Accumulator Valve
41. Reducing Spring
42. Accumulator Spring
43. Accumulator Spring
44. Accumulator Plug
45. Sleeve
46. Clutch Control Valve
47. Clutch Control Spring
48. Plug (1992)
49. Pin (1992)
50. End Cover
51. Solenoid Valve
52. Stiffener Plate
53. Upper Valve Body
54. 2-3 Shift Plug
55. 1-2 Shift Plug
56. Regulator Plug
57. Regulator Plug
58. Manual Valve
59. Rear End Cover
60. Gasket

92G12886

Courtesy of Chrysler Corp.

Fig. 35: Exploded View Of Valve Body Assembly (F3A20 Series)

2) Check valve springs for deformation or damage. Measure valve spring height. See VALVE SPRING HEIGHT SPECIFICATIONS (F3A20 SERIES) table. Replace as necessary. Lubricate with ATF and install valves, springs and plugs. See Fig. 35.

3) Tighten all valve body bolts to specification. See TORQUE SPECIFICATIONS. When assembling upper and lower bodies use guide pins at locations shown in Fig. 34. Ensure steel balls are properly positioned. See Fig. 34.

Disassembly (F4A20 Series) – 1) Remove solenoid valves and manual valve. Remove valve stopper and clamp. Remove 13 bolts and remove lower valve body.

2) Remove separator plate from intermediate plate. Remove relief spring, 2 steel balls and oil filter from intermediate plate. See Fig. 36. Remove 8 bolts, and remove intermediate plate and upper separating plate.

3) Remove 3 steel balls, Teflon ball and 2 stopper plates from upper valve body. See Fig. 36. Remove valves, springs and plugs as shown in Fig. 37.

Inspection & Reassembly (F4A20 Series) – 1) Clean all parts with ATF. DO NOT use shop towels during reassembly operation. Check sliding surfaces of oil valves and valve body for scratches or damage. Check valve springs for deformation or damage.

2) Measure valve spring height. See VALVE SPRING HEIGHT SPECIFICATIONS (F4A20 SERIES) table. Replace as necessary. Lubricate with ATF and install valves, springs and plugs. See Fig. 37.

VALVE SPRING HEIGHT SPECIFICATIONS (F3A20 SERIES)

Application	In. (mm)
Kickdown Valve	1.029 (26.14)
Line Relief	.681 (17.30)
Low Relief	.491 (12.46)
N-D Accumulator	2.044 (51.92)
N-D Accumulator Plug	1.472 (37.39)
Range Control Valve	.923 (23.44)
Regulator Valve	2.024 (51.40)
Throttle Valve	1.262 (32.05)
Torque Converter Control Valve	1.039 (26.40)
1-2 Shift Valve	1.232 (31.30)
2-3 Control Valve	2.000 (50.80)
2-3 Shift Valve	.933 (23.71)

VALVE SPRING HEIGHT SPECIFICATIONS (F4A20 SERIES)

Application	In. (mm)
End Clutch Valve	.961 (24.40)
N-R Control Valve	1.264 (32.10)
Pressure Control Valve	.839 (21.30)
Shift Control Valve	1.055 (26.80)
Rear Clutch Exhaust Valve	1.079 (27.41)
Reducing Valve	1.315 (33.40)
Regulator Valve	2.047 (52.00)
Relief Valve	.681 (17.30)
Torque Converter Clutch Control Valve	
F4A22	.618 (15.70)
F4A23	.559 (14.20)
Torque Converter Control Valve	.890 (22.60)
1-2 Shift Valve	1.047 (26.60)
2-3 Shift Valve	1.083 (27.50)

TRANSAXLE REASSEMBLY

NOTE: Lubricate all components with ATF. Apply petroleum jelly on "O" rings and seal rings. Use petroleum jelly to hold thrust bearings, thrust races and thrust washers in position. Ensure thrust bearings, thrust races and thrust washers are installed in original location and proper direction. See Figs. 42 and 43.

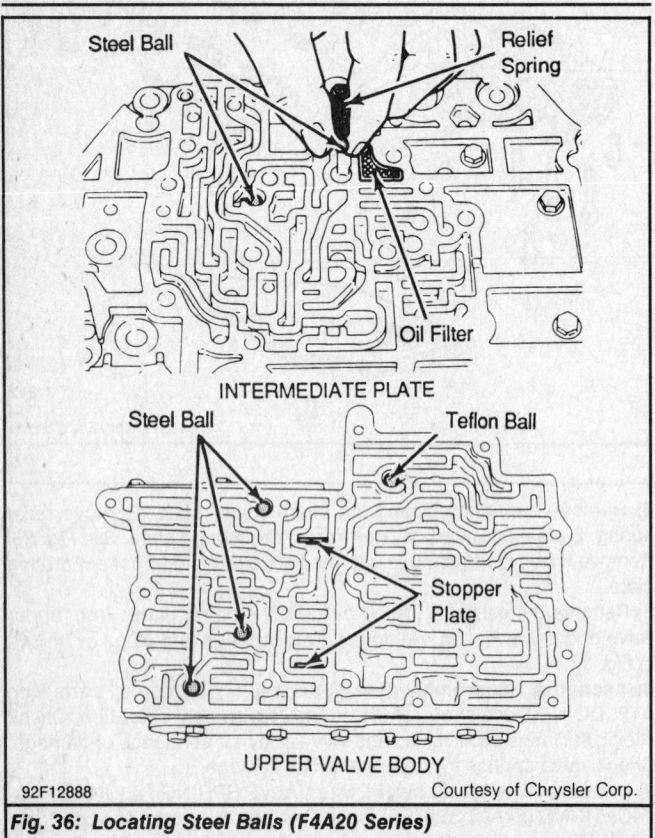

INTERMEDIATE PLATE

UPPER VALVE BODY

92F12888   Courtesy of Chrysler Corp.

Fig. 36: Locating Steel Balls (F4A20 Series)

F3A20 & F4A20 Series – 1) Prior to reassembly, measure low-reverse brake clearance and select appropriate pressure plate to obtain specified clearance.

2) Install brake reaction plate, brake plates and brake discs in transaxle case. *See Fig. 18.* Install a pressure plate with adequate size. Install return spring. Ensure return spring is installed in proper direction.

3) Apply petroleum jelly to wave spring and attach it to the center support. Install center support and snap ring in case. Check low-reverse brake clearance by mounting a dial indicator on rear of transaxle case. Install dial indicator through transfer idler shaft hole so its feeler is held perpendicular to brake reaction plate.

4) Using a hand pump, feed air into low-reverse brake and read dial indicator deflection. Select a pressure plate to obtain specified clearance. Clearance for F3A20 series transaxle is .032-.039" (.80-1.00 mm). Clearance for F4A20 series transaxle is .039-.047" (1.00-1.20 mm). Remove all previously install components.

5) Install transfer shaft bearing outer race in case. Install parking sprag rod on detent plate, then push manual control shaft in transaxle case. Tighten manual control shaft set screw to specification. See TORQUE SPECIFICATIONS.

6) Install sprag rod support and tighten bolts to specification. Install bearings on transfer shaft and install shaft in transaxle case. Using a press, install transfer driven gear. Tighten transfer shaft lock nut to 148-170 ft. lbs. (200-230 N.m) and stake lock nut to prevent loosening.

7) Measure transfer shaft end play and select a spacer which provides 0-.0010" (0-.025 mm) end play. Install transfer shaft cover. Assemble the planetary carrier, output flange, transfer drive gear and bearing and install in transaxle case. *See Figs. 18 and 19.* Install snap ring on output flange rear bearing.

8) Coat transfer idler spacer and attach it to case. Install 2 taper roller bearings and spacer in transfer idler gear. Place transfer idler gear in transaxle case and insert idler shaft from outer side of case.

9) Using Special Tool (MD998344) tighten idler shaft and measure preload at output flange. Adjust preload by tightening or loosening idler shaft. Preload should be 7.1 INCH lbs. (0.8 N.m).

10) After preload adjustment is complete, eliminate backlash between the idler shaft and lock plate by moving the idler shaft in the loosening direction. Install lock plate and tighten bolt to specifications. See TORQUE SPECIFICATIONS.

11) Install output flange bearing retainer and tighten screws to 13-16 ft. lbs. (17-22 N.m). Apply a 5 mm bead of sealant (3M Stud Locking No. 4176) to top of screws. Sealant should not stick out of screw head. Stake screws to prevent loosening.

12) Install planetary carrier with thrust bearing No. 12 in place, in transaxle case. Assemble reverse sun gear and forward sun gear and install in planetary carrier. *See Fig. 38.*

13) Install low-reverse brake assembly with pressure plate selected previously. Install return spring. Apply petroleum jelly to wave spring and attach it to center support. Install 2 NEW "O" rings to hydraulic holes of center support. *See Fig. 39.*

14) Apply ATF to "O" rings. Install center support ensuring 2 NEW "O" rings are properly positioned on center support. Ensure wave spring does not shift out of position. Install center support snap ring, ensuring snap ring ends are not aligned with mounting hole for pulse generator "A".

15) Install kickdown band anchor rod. Install NEW seal ring (large diameter) and "D" ring (small diameter) to kickdown servo piston. Install NEW "O" ring in groove around sleeve. Assembly kickdown servo spring, piston and sleeve in transaxle case. Install kickdown servo assembly and snap ring. Install kickdown band and attach ends to anchor rod and servo piston rod.

16) Install kickdown drum and position band on drum. Apply petroleum jelly to thrust bearing No. 8 and attach it to kickdown drum. Apply petroleum jelly to thrust race No. 7 and attach it to rear clutch hub.

17) Install clutch hub to sun gear splines and attach thrust bearing No. 6 to outer side of clutch hub. Install thrust washer No. 2 and thrust bearing No. 4 on rear clutch assembly. Assemble front and rear clutch assemblies and install in transaxle case. Install differential assembly.

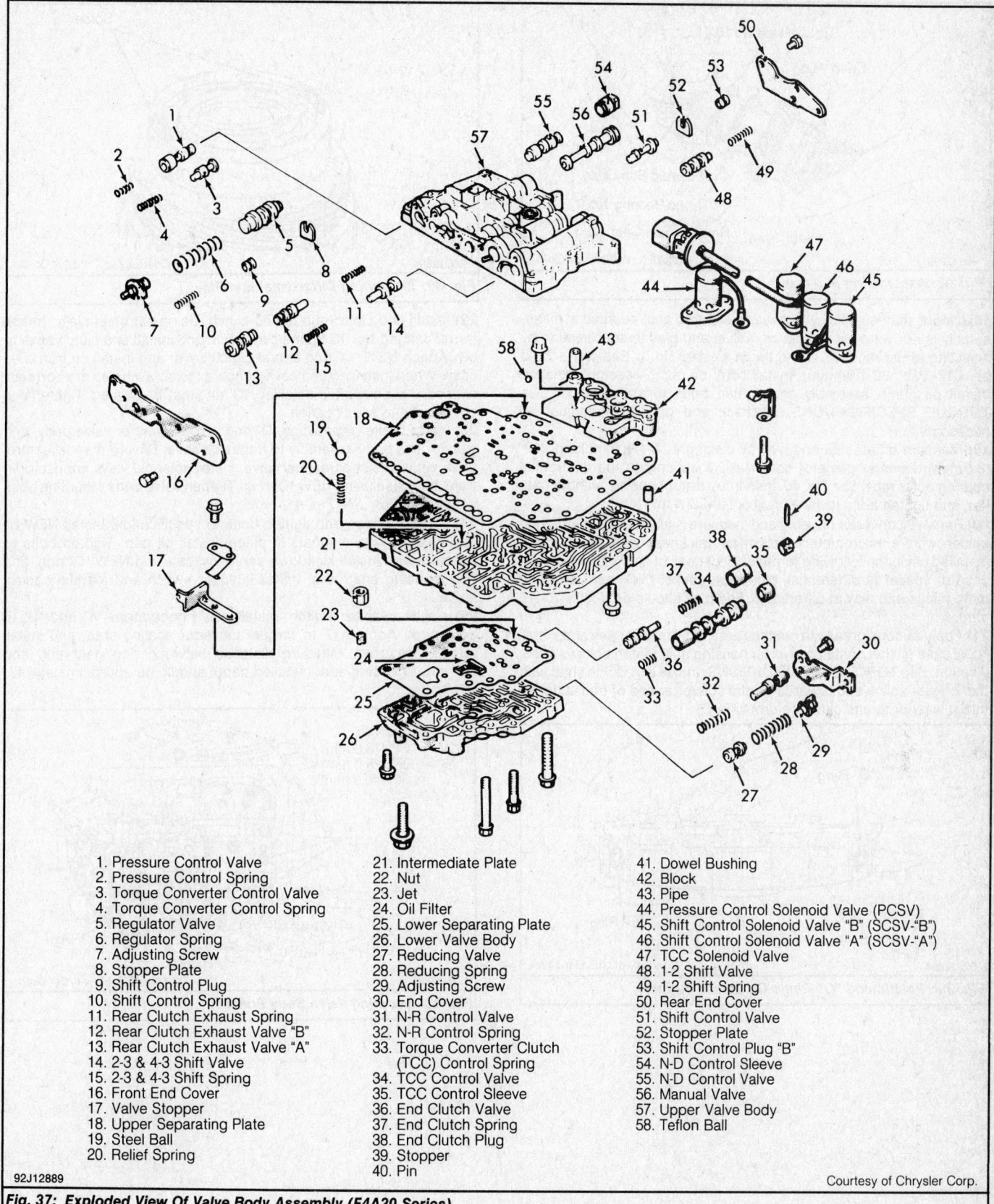

1. Pressure Control Valve
2. Pressure Control Spring
3. Torque Converter Control Valve
4. Torque Converter Control Spring
5. Regulator Valve
6. Regulator Spring
7. Adjusting Screw
8. Stopper Plate
9. Shift Control Plug
10. Shift Control Spring
11. Rear Clutch Exhaust Spring
12. Rear Clutch Exhaust Valve "B"
13. Rear Clutch Exhaust Valve "A"
14. 2-3 & 4-3 Shift Valve
15. 2-3 & 4-3 Shift Spring
16. Front End Cover
17. Valve Stopper
18. Upper Separating Plate
19. Steel Ball
20. Relief Spring

21. Intermediate Plate
22. Nut
23. Jet
24. Oil Filter
25. Lower Separating Plate
26. Lower Valve Body
27. Reducing Valve
28. Reducing Spring
29. Adjusting Screw
30. End Cover
31. N-R Control Valve
32. N-R Control Spring
33. Torque Converter Clutch (TCC) Control Spring
34. TCC Control Valve
35. TCC Control Sleeve
36. End Clutch Valve
37. End Clutch Spring
38. End Clutch Plug
39. Stopper
40. Pin

41. Dowel Bushing
42. Block
43. Pipe
44. Pressure Control Solenoid Valve (PCSV)
45. Shift Control Solenoid Valve "B" (SCSV-"B")
46. Shift Control Solenoid Valve "A" (SCSV-"A")
47. TCC Solenoid Valve
48. 1-2 Shift Valve
49. 1-2 Shift Spring
50. Rear End Cover
51. Shift Control Valve
52. Stopper Plate
53. Shift Control Plug "B"
54. N-D Control Sleeve
55. N-D Control Valve
56. Manual Valve
57. Upper Valve Body
58. Teflon Ball

92J12889

Courtesy of Chrysler Corp.

Fig. 37: Exploded View Of Valve Body Assembly (F4A20 Series)

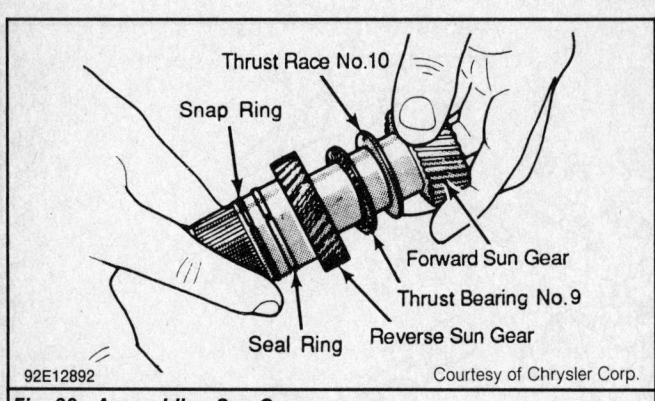

Fig. 38: Assembling Sun Gears

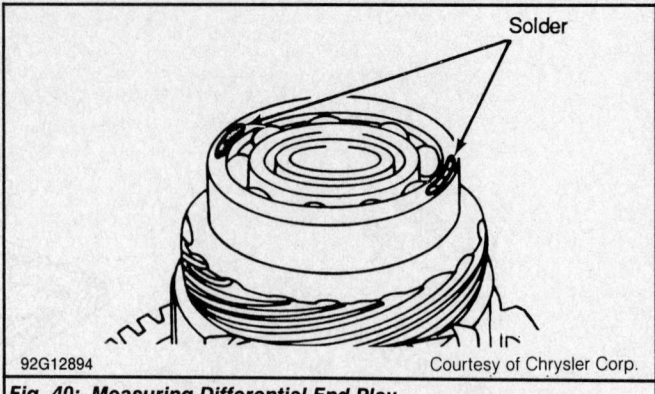

Fig. 40: Measuring Differential End Play

18) If input shaft end play which was measured and recorded at disassembly is not within specification, adjust end play to specification by selecting thrust race No. 3 and thrust washer No. 1. End play should be .012-.039"(.30-1.00 mm). Install NEW oil pump assembly gasket. Install oil pump assembly and tighten bolts to specification. See TORQUE SPECIFICATIONS. Recheck end play and readjust as necessary.

19) Measure differential end play by placing a .4" (10 mm) long, .12" (3.0 mm) diameter piece of solder at 2 locations on the differential bearing outer race. See Fig. 40. Install converter housing, without gasket, and tighten bolts to 14-17 ft. lbs. (19-23 N.m).

20) Remove converter housing and measure thickness of the crushed solder with a micrometer. Determine thickness of spacer to be installed using the following formula: Thickness of solder equals thickness of spacer at differential, plus case gasket thickness .015" (.38 mm), minus end play at differential. End play should be 0-.006" (0-.15 mm).

21) Apply silicone grease to hatched area of transaxle case and install NEW case gasket. Install converter housing and tighten bolts to specification. See TORQUE SPECIFICATIONS. Install end clutch shaft with the longest spline end towards torque converter end of transaxle. Fit thrust washer to end clutch return spring.

22) Install end clutch hub to end clutch. Using petroleum jelly, attach thrust bearing No. 13 to end clutch hub and install end clutch assembly. Attach NEW "O" ring to end clutch cover and install on transaxle case. When installing end cover, ensure the screw holes are correctly aligned. If aligned after installing, "O" ring may be twisted. Tighten end cover bolts to specification.

23) Install brake oil passage "O" ring at top center of valve body, and install valve body assembly to transaxle case. Ensure manual control shaft pin is in slot of manual valve. Install solenoid valve connector in transaxle case using NEW "O" ring. Tighten valve body mounting bolts to specification. See Fig. 41.

24) Install oil filter, and tighten bolts to specification. Install NEW oil pan gasket. With magnets in place, install oil pan. Tighten bolts to specification. Install kickdown servo switch using NEW "D" ring, and secure using snap ring. Install inhibitor switch and manual control lever.

25) Adjust inhibitor switch. Install pulse generators "A" and "B" (if equipped). Apply ATF to torque converter sealing area, and install torque converter. Measure distance between ring gear end and converter housing end. Installed depth should be approximately .47" (12.0 mm).

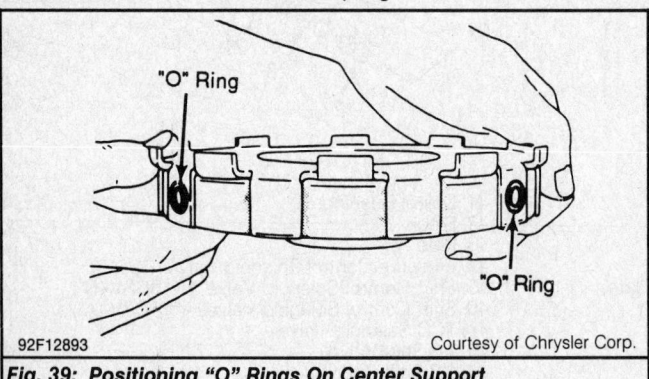

Fig. 39: Positioning "O" Rings On Center Support

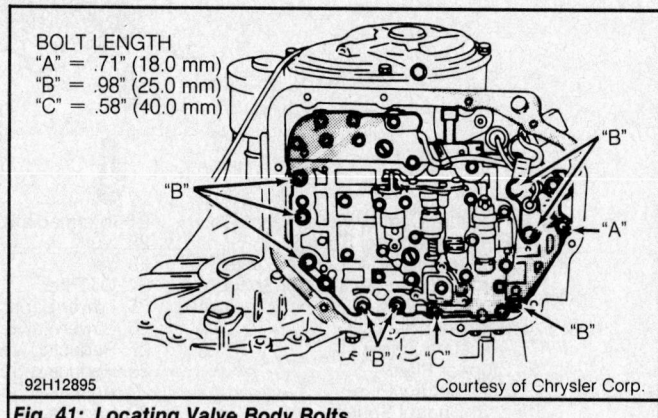

Fig. 41: Locating Valve Body Bolts

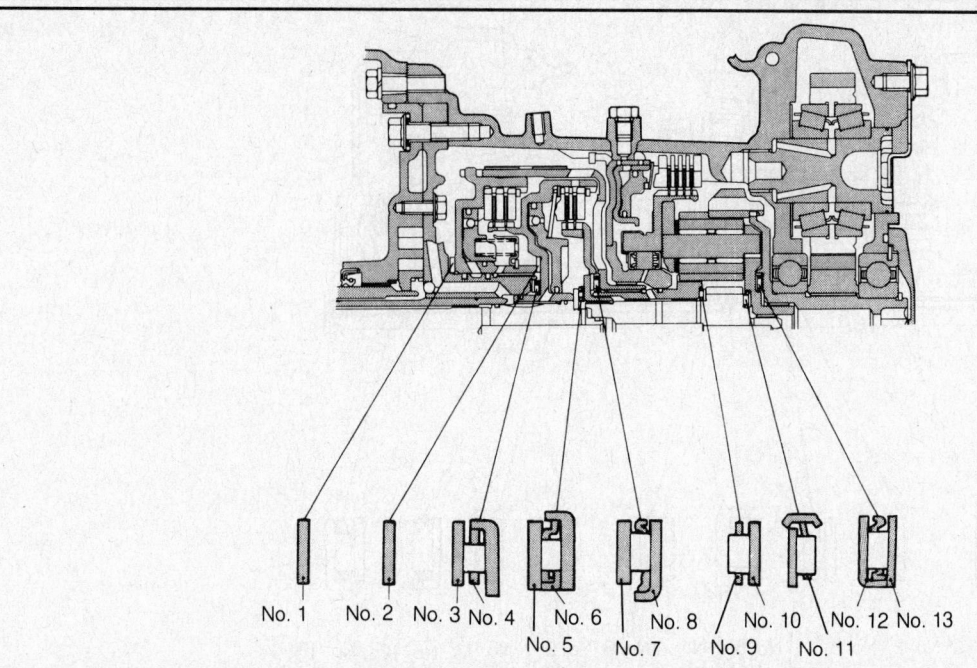

IDENTIFICATION OF THRUST BEARINGS, THRUST RACES & THRUST WASHERS

mm (in.)

O.D.	I.D.	Thickness	Part No.	Identification marking	O.D.	I.D.	Thickness	Part No.	Identification marking
70 (2.756)	55.7 (2.193)	1.4 (.055)	*1	#1	48.1 (1.906)	34.4 (1.354)	–	MD707271	#4
70 (2.756)	55.7 (2.193)	1.8 (.071)	*2		40 (1.575)	21 (.827)	2.4 (.094)	MD722552	#5
70 (2.756)	55.7 (2.193)	2.2 (.087)	*3		42.6 (1.677)	28 (1.102)	–	MD720753	#6
70 (2.756)	55.7 (2.193)	2.6 (.102)	*4		54 (2.126)	38.7 (1.524)	1.6 (.063)	MD704936	#7
70 (2.756)	55.7 (2.193)	1.8 (.071)	MD707290	#2	52 (2.047)	36.4 (1.433)	–	MD720010	#8
48.9 (1.925)	37 (1.457)	1.0 (.039)	MD997854 (incl. *1)		41 (1.614)	28 (1.102)	–	MD728763	#9
48.9 (1.925)	37 (1.457)	1.2 (.047)	MD997847 (incl. *1)		39 (1.535)	28 (1.102)	1.2 (.047)	MD728764	#10
48.9 (1.925)	37 (1.457)	1.4 (.055)	MD997848 (incl. *2)		38 (1.496)	22.2 (.874)	–	MD727787	#11
48.9 (1.925)	37 (1.457)	1.6 (.063)	MD997849 (incl. *2)	#3	52 (2.047)	36.4 (1.433)	–	MD720010	#12
48.9 (1.925)	37 (1.457)	1.8 (.071)	MD997850 (incl. *3)		54 (2.126)	38.7 (1.524)	0.8 (.031)	MD704935	#13
48.9 (1.925)	37 (1.457)	2.0 (.079)	MD997851 (incl. *3)						
48.9 (1.925)	37 (1.457)	2.2 (.087)	MD997852 (incl. *4)						
48.9 (1.925)	37 (1.457)	2.4 (.094)	MD997853 (incl. *4)						

94D39027

Courtesy of Chrysler Corp.

Fig. 42: Identifying Thrust Bearing, Thrust Race & Thrust Washer Locations (F3A20 Series)

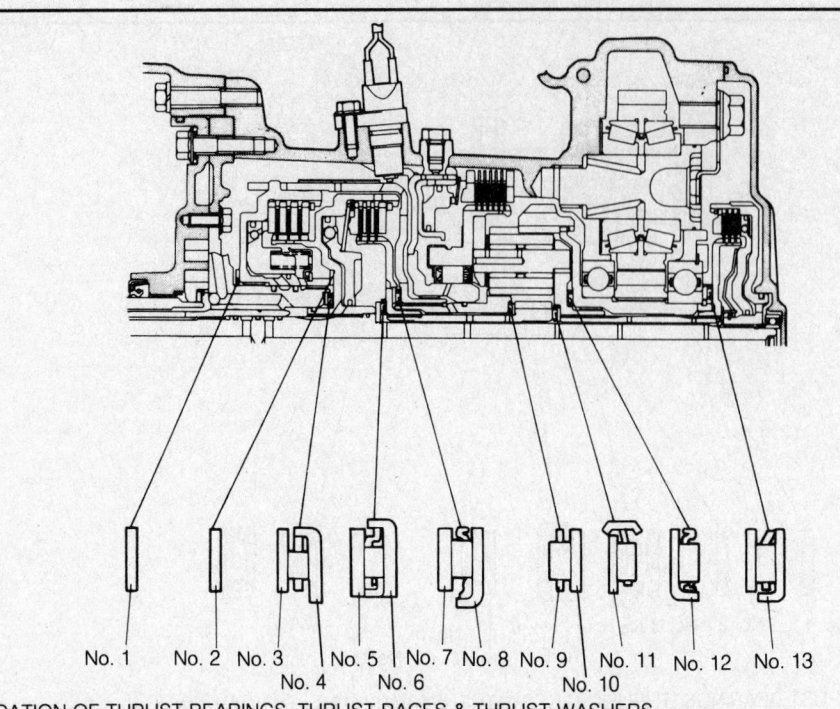

No. 1   No. 2   No. 3   No. 5   No. 7 No. 8 No. 9   No. 11   No. 12   No. 13
                     No. 4   No. 6   No. 10

IDENTIFICATION OF THRUST BEARINGS, THRUST RACES & THRUST WASHERS   Unit: mm (in.)

Outer diameter	Inner diameter	Thickness	Part No.	Code No.	Outer diameter	Inner diameter	Thickness	Part No.	Code No.
70 (2.756)	55.7 (2.193)	1.4 (.055)	*1		48.1 (1.906)	34.4 (1.354)	—	MD707271	#4
70 (2.756)	55.7 (2.193)	1.8 (.071)	*2		40 (1.575)	21 (.827)	2.4 (.094)	MD722552	#5
70 (2.756)	55.7 (2.193)	2.2 (.087)	*3	#1	42.6 (1.677)	28 (1.102)	—	MD720753	#6
70 (2.756)	55.7 (2.193)	2.6 (.102)	*4		54 (2.126)	38.7 (1.524)	1.6 (.063)	MD704936	#7
70 (2.756)	55.7 (2.193)	1.8 (.071)	MD707290	#2	52 (2.047)	36.4 (1.433)	—	MD720010	#8
48.9 (1.925)	37 (1.457)	1.0 (.039)	MD997854 (incl *1)		41 (1.614)	28 (1.102)	—	MD728763	#9
48.9 (1.925)	37 (1.457)	1.2 (.047)	MD997847 (incl *1)		39 (1.535)	28 (1.102)	1.2 (.047)	MD728764	#10
48.9 (1.925)	37 (1.457)	1.4 (.055)	MD997848 (incl *2)		38 (1.496)	22.2 (.874)	—	MD727787	#11
48.9 (1.925)	37 (1.457)	1.6 (.063)	MD997849 (incl *2)		52 (2.047)	36.4 (1.433)	—	MD720010	#12
48.9 (1.925)	37 (1.457)	1.8 (.071)	MD997850 (incl *3)	#3	58 (2.283)	44 (1.732)	—	MD724206	#13
48.9 (1.925)	37 (1.457)	2.0 (.079)	MD997851 (incl *3)						
48.9 (1.925)	37 (1.457)	2.2 (.087)	MD997852 (incl *4)						
48.9 (1.925)	37 (1.457)	2.4 (.094)	MD997853 (incl *4)						

94E39028   Courtesy of Chrysler Corp.

Fig. 43: Identifying Thrust Bearing, Thrust Race & Thrust Washer Locations (F4A20 Series)

AUTOMATIC TRANSMISSIONS
Chrysler F3A20 & F4A20 Series (Cont.)

TORQUE SPECIFICATIONS

TORQUE SPECIFICATIONS

Application	Ft. Lbs. (N.m)
Bearing Retainer Bolt	13-16 (17-22)
Converter Housing Bolt	14-17 (19-23)
Differential Drive Gear Bolt	96-103 (130-140)
Drive Plate-To-Converter Bolt	34-39 (46-53)
Idler Shaft Lock Plate Bolt	35-43 (47-58)
Manual Control Lever Nut	13-16 (17-22)
Oil Pump Bolt	11-15 (15-20)
Planetary Carrier-To-One-Way Clutch	26-33 (35-45)
Sprag Rod Support Bolt	15-20 (20-27)
Transfer Shaft Lock Nut	148-170 (200-230)
	INCH Lbs. (N.m)
End Clutch Cover Bolt	53-71 (6-8)
Governor Set Screw	71-89 (8-10)
Inhibitor Switch Bolt	89-106 (10-12)
Manual Control Lever Set Screw	71-89 (8-10)
Oil Filter Bolt	44-62 (5-7)
Oil Pan Bolt	89-106 (10-12)
Pulse Generator Bolt	89-106 (10-12)
Reaction Shaft Support-To-Oil Pump Housing Bolt	89-106 (10-12)
Valve Body Bolt	35-53 (4-6)
Valve Body-To-Case Bolt	89-106 (10-12)

TRANSAXLE SPECIFICATIONS

TRANSAXLE SPECIFICATIONS

Application	In. (mm)
Clearances	
End Clutch	.024-.031 (.60-.85)
Front Clutch	
F3A20 Series	.016-.023 (.40-.60)
F4A20 Series	1.028-.035 (.70-.90)
Low-Reverse Brake	
F3A20 Series	.032-.039 (.08-1.00)
F4A20 Series	.039-.047 (1.00-1.20)
Rear Clutch	.016-.023 (.40-.60)
Oil Pump	.001-.002 (.03-.05)
Differential Backlash	.001-.006 (.03-.15)
End Play	
Differential Case	0-0.006 (0-0.15)
Input Shaft	.012-.039 (0.30-1.00)
Output Flange Bearing	0-.002 (0-.06)
Transfer Shaft	0-0.0010 (0-0.025)

WIRING DIAGRAM

***NOTE:** For Colt Vista, Laser, Summit Wagon and Talon wiring diagrams, see WIRING DIAGRAMS in CHRYSLER F4A33 & W4A32/33 ELECTRONIC DIAGNOSIS article.*

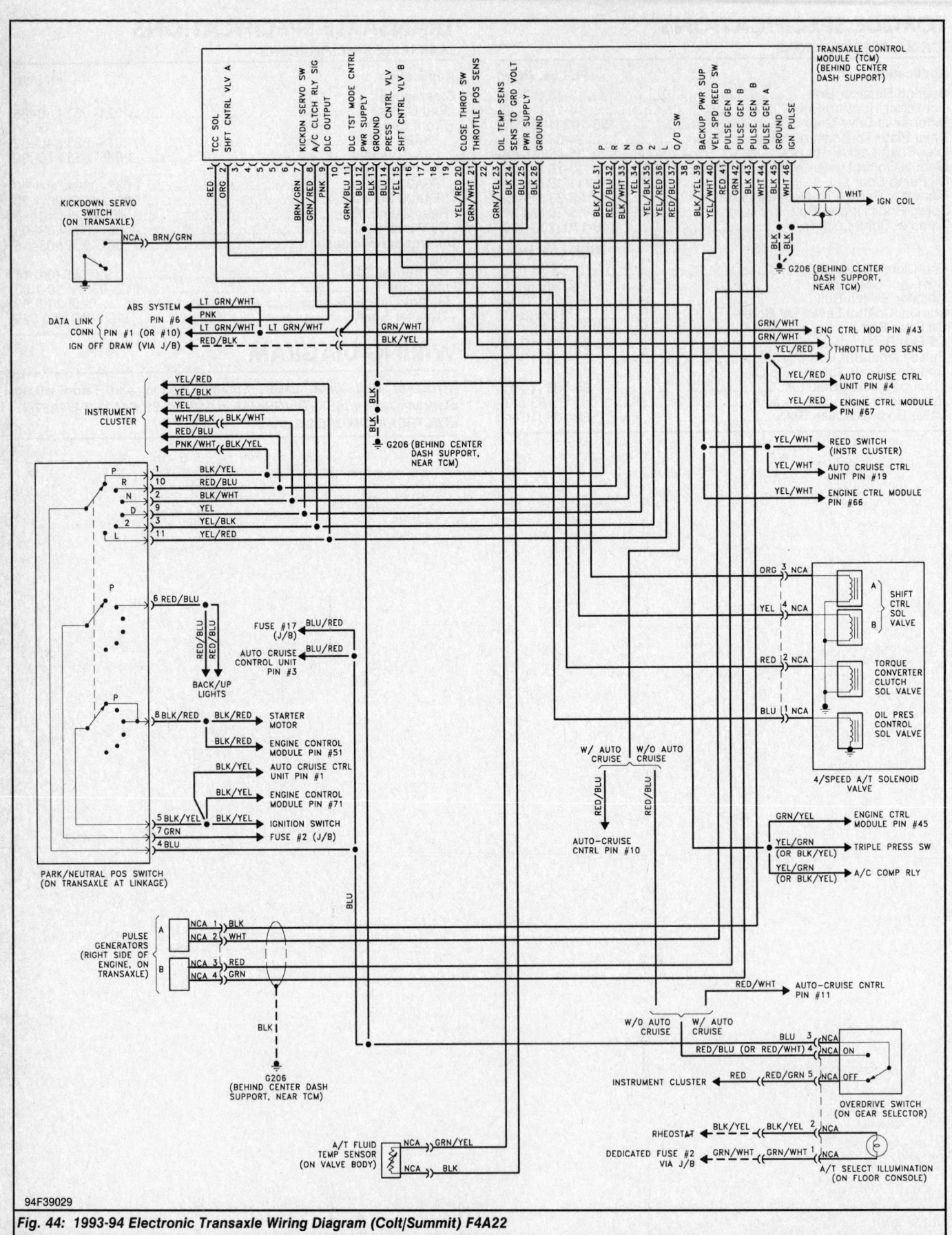

94F39029

Fig. 44: 1993-94 Electronic Transaxle Wiring Diagram (Colt/Summit) F4A22

APPLICATION & LABOR TIMES

APPLICATION & LABOR TIMES

Vehicle Application	Labor Times [1] R & I	[2] Overhaul	Transaxle
Colt Vista	7.4	8.9	W4A32
Laser & Talon (2.0L Turbo)			
2WD	4.6	8.9	F4A33
AWD	7.4	8.9	W4A33
Stealth	4.6	8.9	F4A33
Summit Wagon	7.4	8.9	W4A32

[1] – Removal and installation of transaxle from vehicle chassis.

[2] – Bench overhaul time for transaxle and differential. DOES NOT include removal and installation.

IDENTIFICATION

Transaxle model can be identified on metal tag attached to center of firewall. For parts replacement, identification is stamped on transaxle case on top of transaxle converter housing.

DESCRIPTION

Transaxle is a electronically controlled 4-speed automatic. Transaxle uses hydraulically operated clutches controlled by the Transaxle Control Unit (TCU). Transaxle consists of clutches, low-reverse brake, kickdown band, planetary gear sets and transfer case (W4A32 and W4A33). *See Figs. 1 and 2.*

The TCU receives information from various inputs and controls solenoids on the valve body for different gear operation. Overdrive or 4th gear operation is controlled by a manually operated overdrive control switch. Transaxle will not shift into overdrive unless overdrive control switch is in ON position.

On all models except Colt Vista and Summit Wagon, a power/economy switch, located on center console, is used to change shift patterns. The pre-stored shift pattern is controlled by the TCU. The TCU controller contains a self-diagnostic system, which stores a fault code if a transaxle fault exists. Fault code can be retrieved to determine the transaxle problem area. For information on electronic transaxle components, see CHRYSLER F4A33 & W4A32/33 ELECTRONIC DIAGNOSIS article.

LUBRICATION

See appropriate AUTOMATIC TRANSMISSION SERVICING article in TRANSMISSION SERVICING.

TROUBLE SHOOTING

SYMPTOM DIAGNOSIS

Transaxle malfunctions may be caused by poor engine performance, improper adjustments or failure of hydraulic, mechanical or electronic components. Always begin by checking fluid level, fluid condition and shift cable adjustment. Perform road test to determine if problem has been corrected. If problem still exists, several tests must be performed on transaxle. See TESTING.

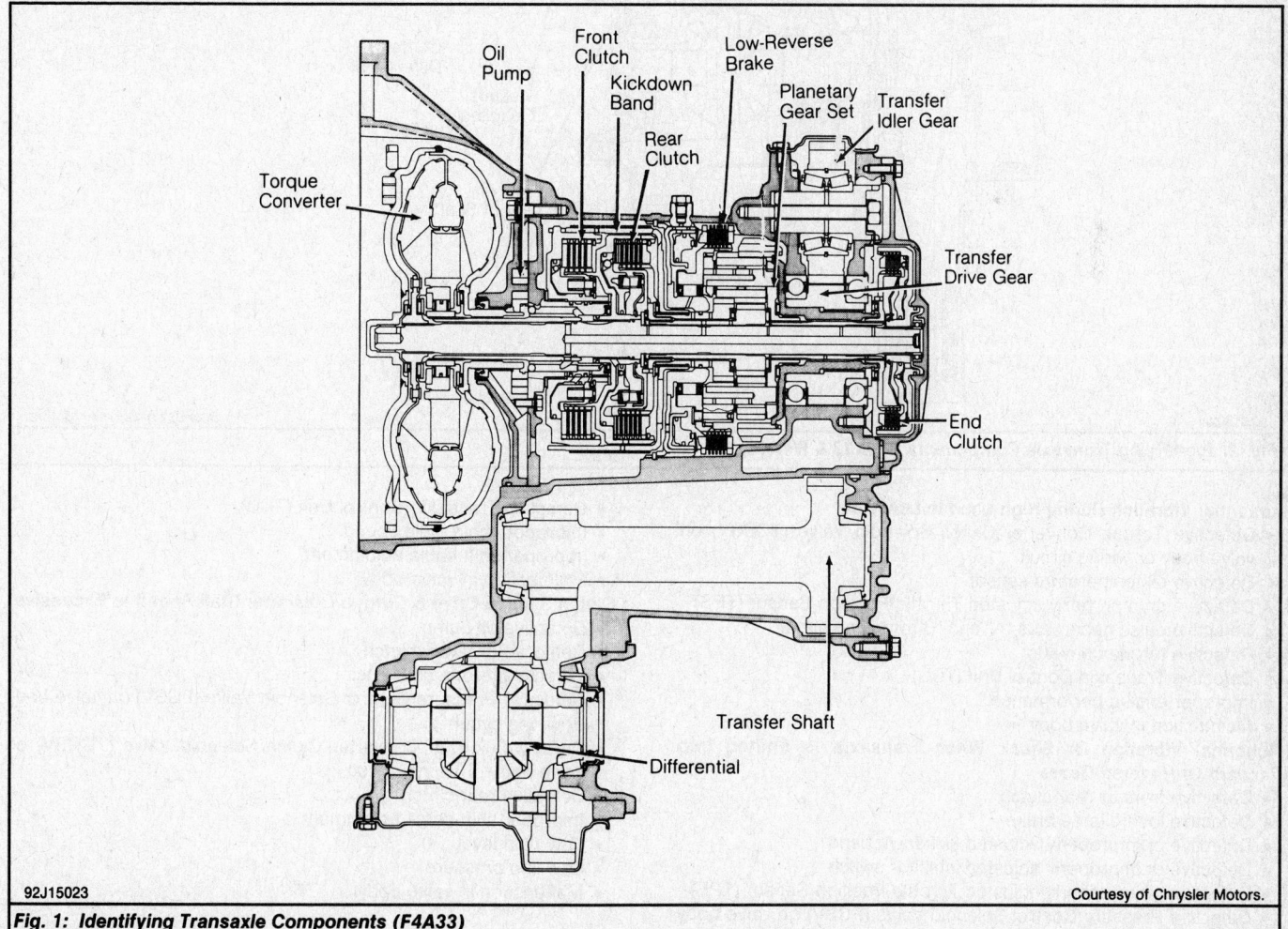

92J15023

Courtesy of Chrysler Motors.

Fig. 1: Identifying Transaxle Components (F4A33)

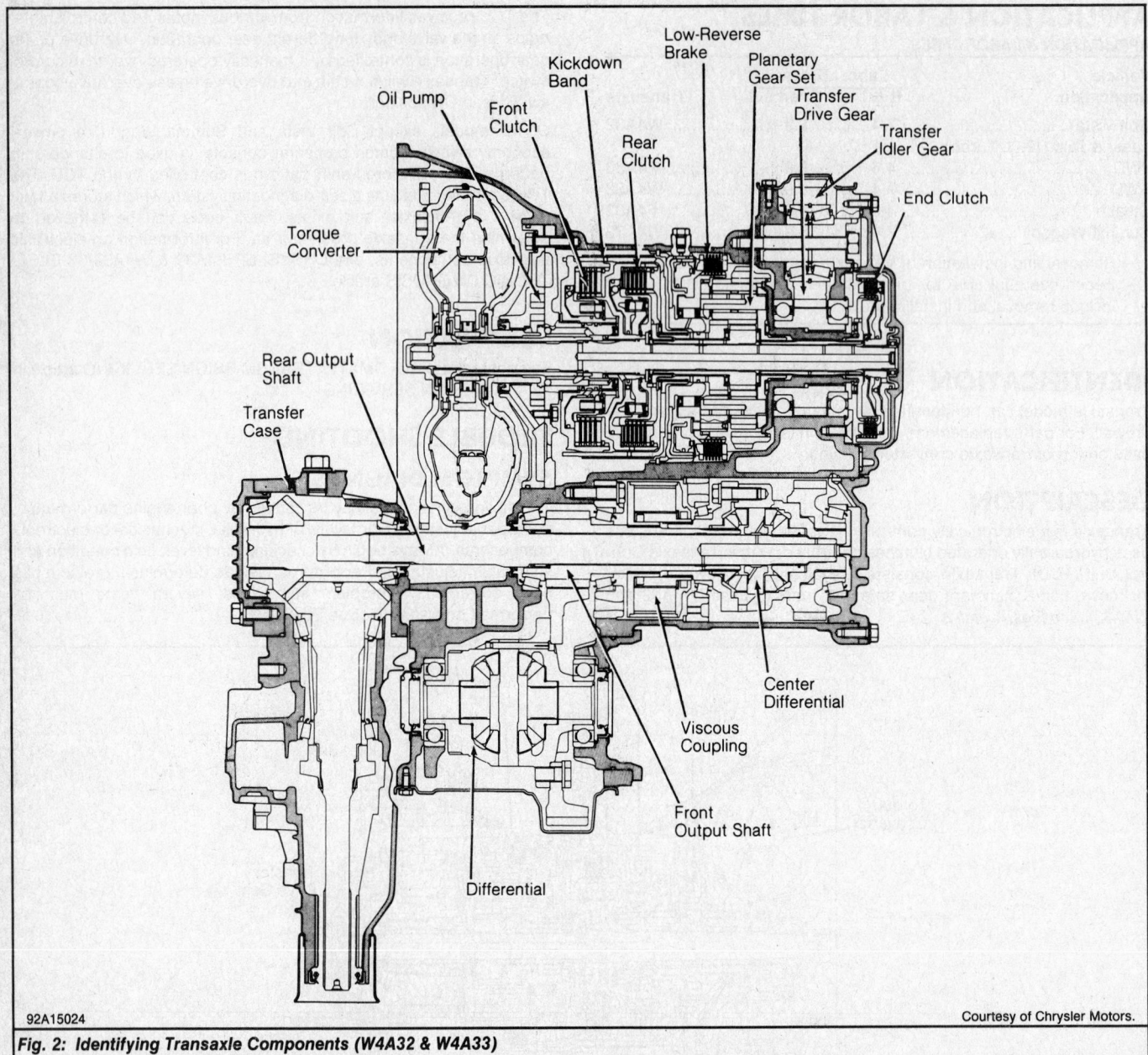

92A15024   Courtesy of Chrysler Motors.

Fig. 2: Identifying Transaxle Components (W4A32 & W4A33)

Abnormal Vibration During High Load In Low Gear
- Defective Torque Converter Clutch Solenoid Valve (TCCSV) on valve body or wiring circuit
- Defective oil temperature sensor
- Defective or improperly adjusted Throttle Position Sensor (TPS)
- Defective pulse generators "A" and "B" or wiring circuit
- Defective torque converter
- Defective Transaxle Control Unit (TCU)
- Improper engine performance
- Malfunction in valve body

Abnormal Vibration Or Shock When Transaxle Is Shifted Into Forward Or Reverse Gears
- Defective front or rear clutch
- Defective low-reverse brake
- Defective or improperly adjusted kickdown band
- Defective or improperly adjusted inhibitor switch
- Defective or improperly adjusted Throttle Position Sensor (TPS)
- Defective Pressure Control Solenoid Valve (PCSV) on valve body or wiring circuit

- Defective Transaxle Control Unit (TCU)
- Improper engine idle speed
- Improper shift cable adjustment
- Malfunction in valve body

Clutch Slips In Drive & Torque Converter Stall Speed Is Excessive
- Defective oil pump
- Defective one-way clutch
- Defective torque converter
- Defective Pressure Control Solenoid Valve (PCSV) on valve body or wiring circuit
- Defective Torque Converter Clutch Solenoid Valve (TCCSV) on valve body or wiring circuit
- Defective rear clutch
- Improper shift cable adjustment
- Low fluid level
- Low line pressure
- Malfunction in valve body

Clutch Slips In Reverse & Torque Converter Stall Speed Is Excessive
- Defective front clutch or retainer
- Defective low-reverse brake
- Defective torque converter
- Defective oil pump
- Defective Pressure Control Solenoid Valve (PCSV) on valve body or wiring circuit
- Improper shift cable adjustment
- Low fluid level
- Low line pressure
- Malfunction in valve body
- "O" Ring for low-reverse brake circuit not installed between valve body and transaxle case

Torque Converter Clutch Inoperative
- Defective Torque Converter Clutch Solenoid Valve (TCCSV) on valve body or wiring circuit
- Defective oil temperature sensor
- Defective or improperly adjusted Throttle Position Sensor (TPS)
- Defective pulse generators "A" and "B" or wiring circuit
- Defective torque converter
- Defective Transaxle Control Unit (TCU)
- Malfunction in ignition signal system
- Malfunction in valve body

Engine Stalls When Shifted From Neutral To Drive Or Reverse
- Defective Torque Converter Clutch Solenoid Valve (TCCSV) on valve body or wiring circuit
- Improper engine idle speed or performance
- Defective torque converter
- Malfunction in valve body

Engine Starts, Or Vehicle Moves Between Neutral & Reverse Or Neutral & Drive
- Defective or improperly adjusted inhibitor switch
- Improper shift cable adjustment
- Malfunction in valve body

Excessive Creeping Or Idling Vibration
- Defective or improperly adjusted accelerator switch
- Defective Transaxle Control Unit (TCU)
- Improper engine idle speed

Excessive Vibration During All Upshifts
- Defective front clutch
- Defective or improperly adjusted Throttle Position Sensor (TPS)
- Defective pulse generator "A" or wiring circuit
- Defective Transaxle Control Unit (TCU)
- Improper engine performance
- Malfunction in ignition signal system
- Malfunction in valve body

Excessive Vibration During D-2 Downshift
- Defective low-reverse brake
- Defective kickdown band or piston
- Defective kickdown servo switch
- Defective or improperly adjusted Throttle Position Sensor (TPS)
- Defective pulse generator "A" or wiring circuit
- Defective Transaxle Control Unit (TCU)
- Improper engine performance
- Malfunction in ignition signal system
- Malfunction in valve body

Excessive Vibration During 1-2 Or 3-4 Upshift
- Defective end clutch
- Defective kickdown band or piston
- Defective kickdown servo switch
- Defective or improperly adjusted Throttle Position Sensor (TPS)
- Defective pulse generator "A" or wiring circuit
- Defective Transaxle Control Unit (TCU)
- Improper engine performance
- Improper kickdown servo adjustment
- Malfunction in ignition signal system
- Malfunction in valve body

Excessive Vibration During 2-3 Or 4-3 Shift
- Defective front clutch
- Defective or improperly adjusted Throttle Position Sensor (TPS)
- Defective pulse generator "A" or wiring circuit
- Defective Transaxle Control Unit (TCU)
- Improper engine performance
- Malfunction in ignition signal system
- Malfunction in valve body

Excessive Vibration When Cold
- Improper engine performance
- Malfunction in valve body

Overdrive Control Switch Will Not Operate
- Defective overdrive control switch or wiring circuit
- Defective Transaxle Control Unit (TCU)

Sudden Engine RPM Increase During Upshift
- Low fluid level
- Defective end clutch
- Defective oil pump
- Defective front clutch or retainer
- Defective kickdown band
- Defective or improperly adjusted Throttle Position Sensor (TPS)
- Defective Pressure Control Solenoid Valve (PCSV) on valve body or wiring circuit
- Defective pulse generator "A" or wiring circuit
- Defective Transaxle Control Unit (TCU)
- Improper kickdown servo adjustment
- Low line pressure
- Malfunction in ignition signal system
- Malfunction in valve body

Sudden Engine RPM Increase During 3-2 Shift With Excessive Vibration
- Defective front clutch retainer
- Defective kickdown band
- Defective kickdown servo switch
- Defective oil pump
- Defective or improperly adjusted Throttle Position Sensor (TPS)
- Defective Pressure Control Solenoid Valve (PCSV) on valve body
- Defective pulse generator "A" or wiring circuit
- Defective Transaxle Control Unit (TCU)
- Improper kickdown servo adjustment
- Low fluid level
- Low line pressure
- Malfunction in ignition signal system
- Malfunction in valve body

Torque Converter Stall Speed Is Low
- Defective torque converter
- Improper engine performance

Transaxle Remains In 3rd Gear
- Defective contacts at ignition switch
- Defective Torque Converter Clutch Solenoid Valve (TCCSV) on valve body or wiring circuit
- Defective end clutch
- Defective front clutch retainer
- Defective front or rear clutch
- Defective kickdown band
- Defective kickdown servo switch
- Defective low-reverse brake
- Defective or improperly adjusted inhibitor switch
- Defective Pressure Control Solenoid Valve (PCSV) on valve body or wiring circuit
- Defective pulse generator "B" or wiring circuit
- Defective Shift Control Solenoid Valve (SCSV) "A" or "B" on valve body or wiring circuit
- Defective Transaxle Control Unit (TCU)
- Improper shift cable adjustment
- Low fluid level
- Low line pressure
- Malfunction in valve body
- "O" Ring for low-reverse brake circuit not installed between valve body and transaxle case

Transaxle Shifts But Not Within Specified Range
- Defective connection at ignition switch
- Defective or improperly adjusted Throttle Position Sensor (TPS)
- Defective pulse generator "B" or wiring circuit
- Defective Transaxle Control Unit (TCU)
- Malfunction in valve body

Transaxle Starts Off From 2nd Gear
- Defective or improperly adjusted accelerator switch
- Defective or improperly adjusted inhibitor switch
- Defective Transaxle Control Unit (TCU)
- Defective torque converter
- Improper engine performance
- Improper shift cable adjustment
- Malfunction in valve body

Transaxle Will Not Upshift From 2nd To 3rd Gear
- Defective front clutch or retainer
- Defective Pressure Control Solenoid Valve (PCSV) on valve body or wiring circuit
- Defective Transaxle Control Unit (TCU)
- Defective or improperly adjusted inhibitor switch
- Defective torque converter
- Malfunction in valve body

Transaxle Will Not Upshift Into 4th Gear
- Defective end clutch
- Defective front clutch retainer
- Defective or improperly adjusted inhibitor switch
- Defective overdrive control switch
- Defective Transaxle Control Unit (TCU)
- Improper shift cable adjustment
- Malfunction in valve body

Vehicle Moves In Park Or Neutral
- Defective or improperly adjusted inhibitor switch
- Defective parking mechanism
- Defective rear clutch
- Improper shift cable adjustment
- Malfunction in valve body

Vehicle Will Not Hold In Park
- Defective parking mechanism
- Improper shift cable adjustment

Vehicle Will Not Move Forward
- Defective oil pump
- Defective one-way clutch
- Defective Pressure Control Solenoid Valve (PCSV) on valve body or wiring circuit
- Defective rear clutch
- Defective torque converter
- Improper shift cable adjustment
- Low fluid level
- Low line pressure
- Malfunction in valve body

Vehicle Will Not Move Forward Or Backward
- Defective low-reverse brake
- Defective oil pump
- Defective Pressure Control Solenoid Valve (PCSV) on valve body or wiring circuit
- Defective torque converter
- Defective torque converter drive plate
- Improper shift cable adjustment
- Low fluid level
- Low line pressure
- Malfunction in valve body

Vehicle Will Not Move In Reverse
- Defective front clutch or retainer
- Defective low-reverse brake
- Defective oil pump
- Defective Pressure Control Solenoid Valve (PCSV) on valve body or wiring circuit
- Defective pulse generator "B" or wiring circuit
- Defective torque converter

- Improper shift cable adjustment
- Low fluid level
- Low line pressure
- Malfunction in valve body
- "O" Ring for low-reverse brake circuit not installed between valve body and transaxle case

ELECTRONIC TESTING

NOTE: For electronic component testing, see CHRYSLER F4A33 & W4A32/33 ELECTRONIC DIAGNOSIS article.

TESTING

NOTE: A road test can be performed to check transaxle shift points. Pressure test can be performed to check operation of transaxle internal components. Torque converter stall speed test can be performed to check torque converter operation.

ROAD TEST

NOTE: Perform road test to ensure transaxle shift points are at specified speeds. See Figs. 3-6. Broken lines in shift point charts indicate downshifts, and solid lines indicate upshifts.

1) Ensure shift cable is properly adjusted, and fluid level and condition are okay. Add fluid and adjust shift cable if necessary. Road test vehicle, and check if shift points are at specified speeds. *See Figs. 3-6.*
2) If shift points are not as specified, check for stored fault codes. See CHRYSLER F4A33 & W4A32/33 ELECTRONIC DIAGNOSIS article. If slippage occurs, determine which components are applied in each gear. See CLUTCH, BRAKE & BAND APPLICATION CHART table. Perform hydraulic pressure test to check transaxle internal components. See HYDRAULIC PRESSURE TEST under TESTING.

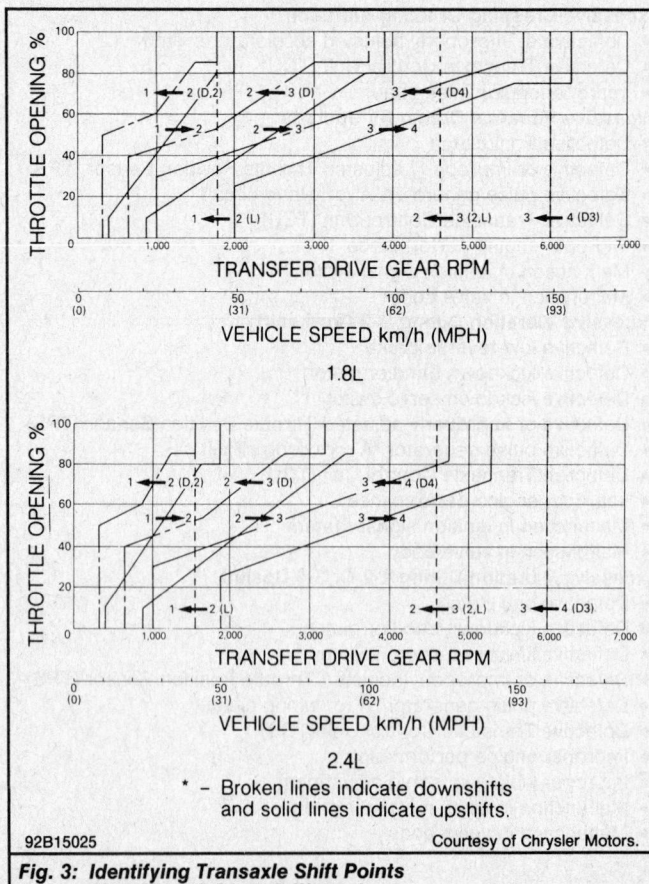

92B15025   Courtesy of Chrysler Motors.

Fig. 3: Identifying Transaxle Shift Points (Colt Vista & Summit Wagon)

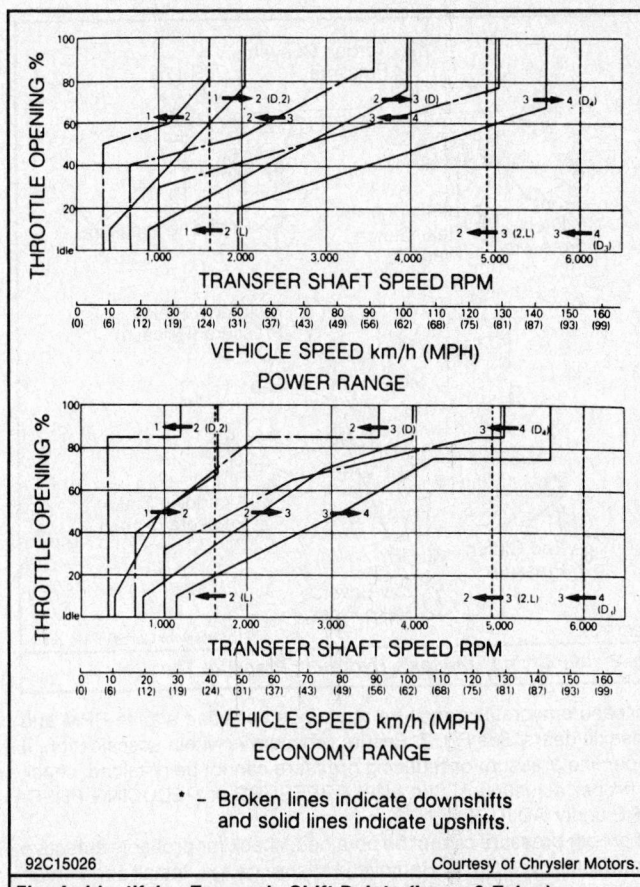

Fig. 4: Identifying Transaxle Shift Points (Laser & Talon)

* – Broken lines indicate downshifts and solid lines indicate upshifts.

92C15026   Courtesy of Chrysler Motors.

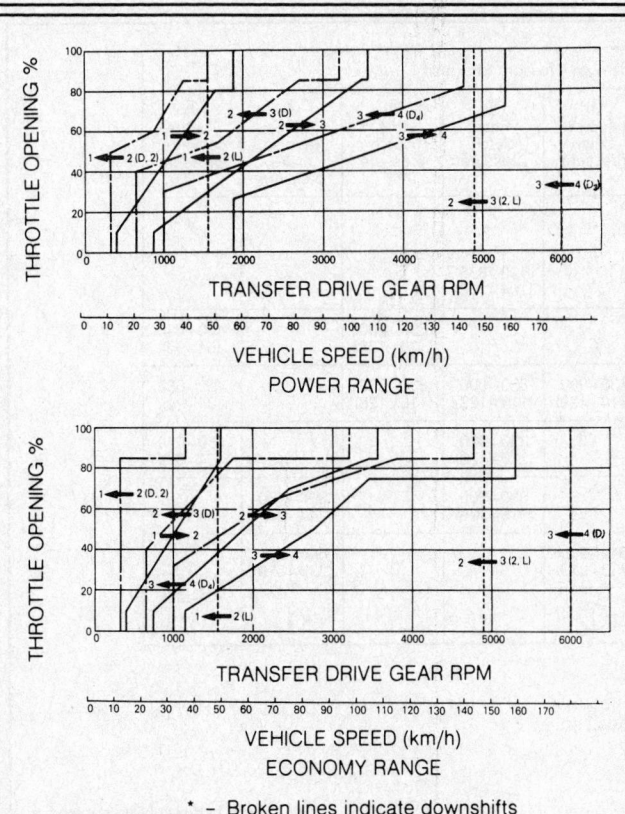

* – Broken lines indicate downshifts and solid lines indicate upshifts.

92D15027   Courtesy of Chrysler Motors.

Fig. 5: Identifying Transaxle Shift Points (Stealth SOHC)

CLUTCH, BRAKE & BAND APPLICATION CHART

Selector Lever Position	Elements In Use
"D" (Drive)	
1st Gear	Rear Clutch & One-Way Clutch
2nd Gear	Rear Clutch & Kickdown Band
3rd Gear	Front Clutch, Rear Clutch & End Clutch
4th Gear	End Clutch & Kickdown Band
"2" (Second)	
1st Gear	Rear Clutch & One-Way Clutch
2nd Gear	Rear Clutch & Kickdown Band
"1" (Low)	
1st Gear	Rear Clutch & Low-Reverse Brake
"R" (Reverse)	Front Clutch & Low-Reverse Brake
"N" Or "P" (Neutral Or Park)	All Clutches, Brakes & Bands Released Or Ineffective

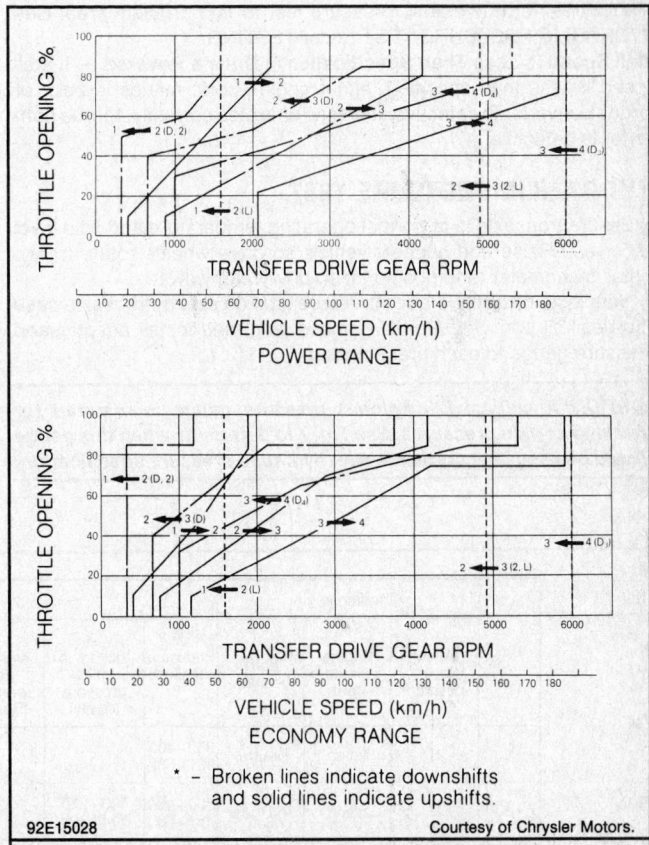

* – Broken lines indicate downshifts and solid lines indicate upshifts.

92E15028   Courtesy of Chrysler Motors.

Fig. 6: Identifying Transaxle Shift Points (Stealth DOHC)

TORQUE CONVERTER STALL SPEED TEST

Stall Speed Test Procedure – 1) Install tachometer. Ensure transaxle fluid level is correct. Start engine, and operate it until transaxle fluid is at normal operating temperature. Ensure engine operating temperature is approximately 180-190°F (80-90°C).

2) Block rear wheels. Apply parking and service brakes. Place transaxle in Drive, and open throttle to wide open position. Note maximum engine RPM. This is torque converter stall speed. Repeat procedure with transaxle in Reverse.

CAUTION: DO NOT open throttle to wide open position for more than 5 seconds, or transaxle damage may occur. If performing more than one torque converter stall speed test, operate engine at 1000 RPM in Neutral for at least 2 minutes to cool transaxle fluid before performing next stall speed test.

3) Stall speed should be within specification. See STALL SPEED SPECIFICATIONS table. Once stall speed is obtained, place transaxle in Neutral. Operate engine, allowing transaxle to cool. Stop engine and place transaxle in Park. Remove tachometer.

STALL SPEED SPECIFICATIONS

Application	Stall Speed Engine RPM
Colt Vista & Summit Wagon	1800-2800
Laser & Talon	1800-3200
Stealth	
DOHC	2200-3200
SOHC	1800-2800

NOTE: *Use the following symptoms for trouble shooting results of stall speed tests.*

Stall Speed Exceeds Specification – If stall speed exceeds specification in Drive, rear clutch or one-way clutch is slipping. If stall speed exceeds specification in Reverse, front clutch or low-reverse brake is slipping. Perform hydraulic pressure test to find problem area. See HYDRAULIC PRESSURE TEST under TESTING.

Stall Speed Is Less Than Specification In Drive & Reverse – If stall speed is less than specified, either engine performance is poor or torque converter is defective. If engine operates correctly, torque converter is defective.

HYDRAULIC PRESSURE TEST

1) Ensure transaxle is at normal operating temperature and fluid level is correct. Raise and support vehicle so drive wheels rotate freely. Install tachometer, and position it so driver can view it.
2) Note locations of hydraulic pressure taps on side of transaxle case and near oil pan. *See Fig. 8.* Remove plug, and install adapter and pressure gauge to each pressure tap.

CAUTION: *A 400-psi (28 kg/cm²) pressure gauge is required for checking certain pressures. See Fig. 7 to determine when this gauge should be used in accordance with hydraulic pressure specification.*

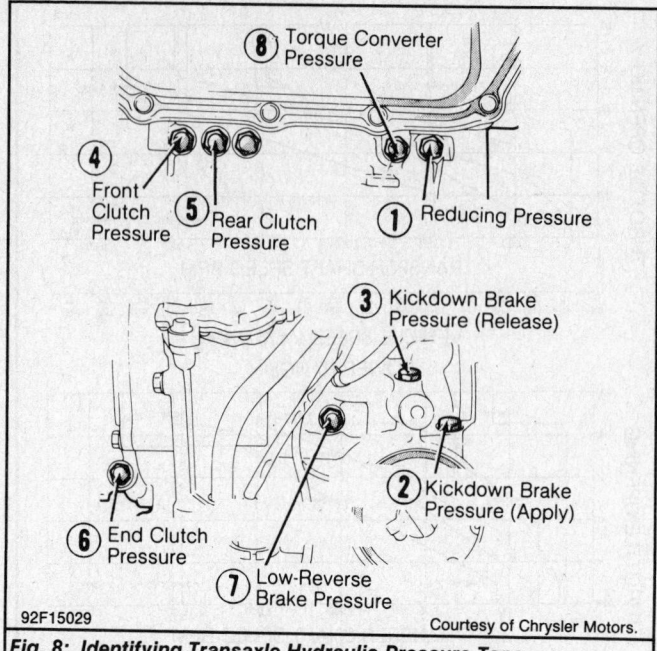

Fig. 8: *Identifying Transaxle Hydraulic Pressure Taps*

3) Measure hydraulic pressure at various specified engine RPM and transaxle gears. *See Fig. 7.* Ensure pressure is within specification. If proper line pressure or reducing pressure cannot be obtained, check for proper adjustment. See LINE PRESSURE or REDUCING PRESSURE under ADJUSTMENTS.
4) If proper pressure cannot be obtained, check for probable defective components. *See Fig. 9.* Remove pressure gauge. Install and tighten plug to specification. See TORQUE SPECIFICATIONS.

No.	Select lever position	Engine speed rpm	Shift position	① Reducing pressure	② Kickdown brake pressure (Apply)	③ Kickdown brake pressure (Release)	④ Front clutch pressure	⑤ Rear clutch pressure	⑥ End clutch pressure	⑦ Low-reverse brake pressure	⑧ Torque-converter pressure
							Standard oil pressure kPa (psi)				
1	N	Idling	Neutral	360–480 (51–68)	–	–	–	–	–	–	*
2	D	idling	2nd gear	360–480 (51–68)	100–210 (14–30)	–	–	730–830 (104–118)	–	–	*
3	D (SW-ON)	Approx. 2,500	4th gear	360–480 (51–68)	830–900 (118–128)	–	–	–	830–900 (118–128)	–	450–650 (64–92)
4	D (SW-OFF)	Approx. 2,500	3rd gear	360–480 (51–68)	830–900 (118–128)	830–900 (118–128)	830–900 (118–128)	830–900 (118–128)	830–900 (118–128)	–	450–650 (64–92)
5	2	Approx. 2,500	2nd gear	360–480 (51–68)	830–900 (118–128)	–	–	830–900 (118–128)	–	–	450–650 (64–92)
6	L	Approx. 1,000	1st gear	360–480 (51–68)	–	–	–	830–900 (118–128)	–	300–450 (43–64)	*
7	R	Approx. 2,500	Reverse	360–480 (51–68)	–	1,640–2,240 (233–319)	1,640–2,240 (233–319)			1,640–2,240 (233–319)	450–650 (64–92)
	R	Approx. 1,000	Reverse			①	①			①	

NOTE
– Must be 10 kPa (1.4 psi) or less.
SW-ON – This indicates overdrive control switch must be in ON position.
SW-OFF – This indicates overdrive control switch must be in OFF position.
* – Hydraulic pressure is generated, but no standard value exists.
① – On all models, pressure should be 1000 kPa (142 psi) or more.

92I15030

Courtesy of Chrysler Motors.

Fig. 7: *Testing Transaxle Hydraulic Pressures*

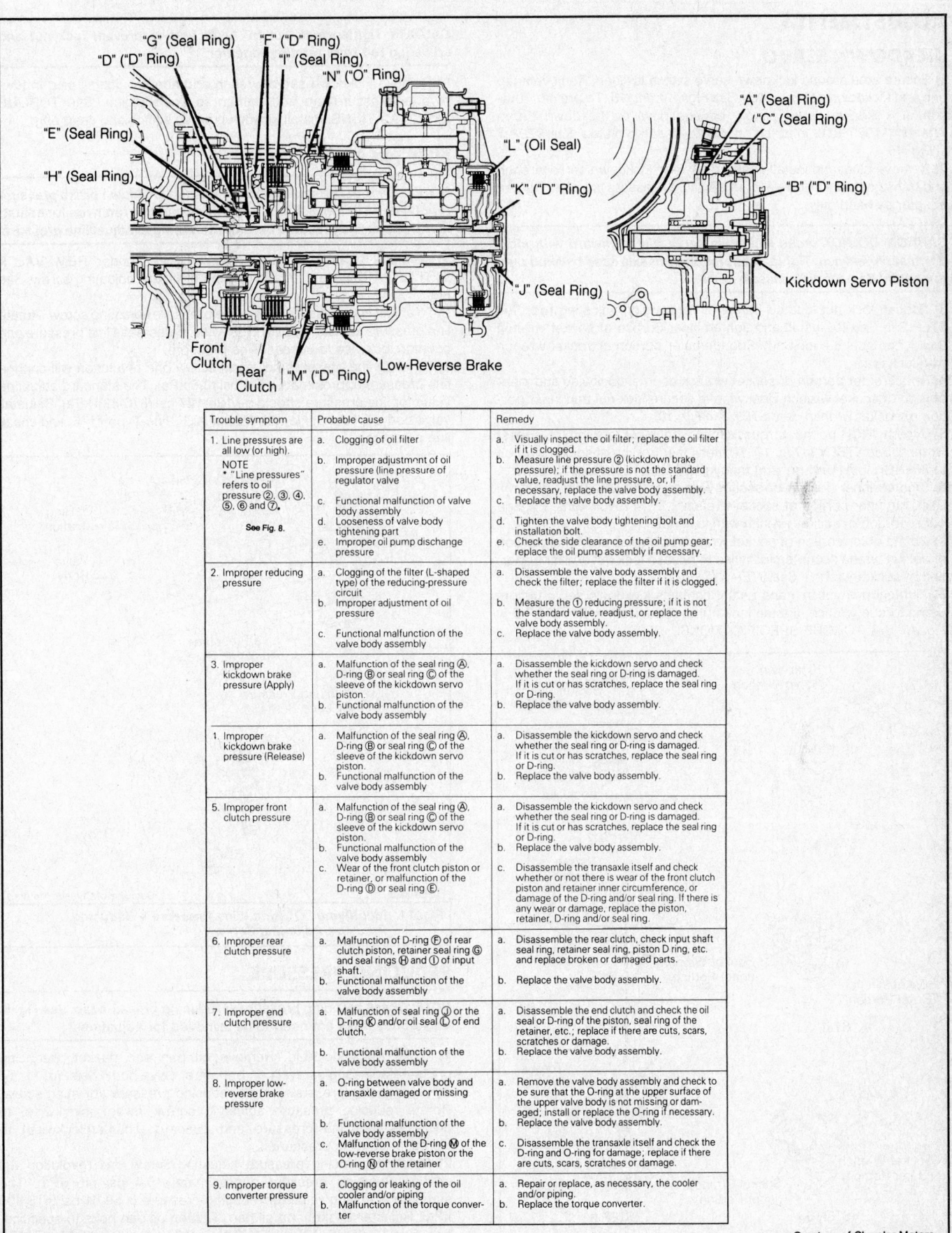

Trouble symptom	Probable cause	Remedy
1. Line pressures are all low (or high). NOTE • "Line pressures" refers to oil pressure ②, ③, ④, ⑤, ⑥ and ⑦. See Fig. 8.	a. Clogging of oil filter b. Improper adjustment of oil pressure (line pressure of regulator valve c. Functional malfunction of valve body assembly d. Looseness of valve body tightening part e. Improper oil pump discharge pressure	a. Visually inspect the oil filter; replace the oil filter if it is clogged. b. Measure line pressure ② (kickdown brake pressure); if the pressure is not the standard value, readjust the line pressure or, if necessary, replace the valve body assembly. c. Replace the valve body assembly. d. Tighten the valve body tightening bolt and installation bolt. e. Check the side clearance of the oil pump gear; replace the oil pump assembly if necessary.
2. Improper reducing pressure	a. Clogging of the filter (L-shaped type) of the reducing-pressure circuit b. Improper adjustment of oil pressure c. Functional malfunction of the valve body assembly	a. Disassemble the valve body assembly and check the filter; replace the filter if it is clogged. b. Measure the ① reducing pressure; if it is not the standard value, readjust, or replace the valve body assembly. c. Replace the valve body assembly.
3. Improper kickdown brake pressure (Apply)	a. Malfunction of the seal ring Ⓐ, D-ring Ⓑ or seal ring Ⓒ of the sleeve of the kickdown servo piston. b. Functional malfunction of the valve body assembly	a. Disassemble the kickdown servo and check whether the seal ring or D-ring is damaged. If it is cut or has scratches, replace the seal ring or D-ring. b. Replace the valve body assembly.
1. Improper kickdown brake pressure (Release)	a. Malfunction of the seal ring Ⓐ, D-ring Ⓑ or seal ring Ⓒ of the sleeve of the kickdown servo piston. b. Functional malfunction of the valve body assembly	a. Disassemble the kickdown servo and check whether the seal ring or D-ring is damaged. If it is cut or has scratches, replace the seal ring or D-ring. b. Replace the valve body assembly.
5. Improper front clutch pressure	a. Malfunction of the seal ring Ⓐ, D-ring Ⓑ or seal ring Ⓒ of the sleeve of the kickdown servo piston. b. Functional malfunction of the valve body assembly c. Wear of the front clutch piston or retainer, or malfunction of the D-ring Ⓓ or seal ring Ⓔ.	a. Disassemble the kickdown servo and check whether the seal ring or D-ring is damaged. If it is cut or has scratches, replace the seal ring or D-ring. b. Replace the valve body assembly. c. Disassemble the transaxle itself and check whether or not there is wear of the front clutch piston and retainer inner circumference, or damage of the D-ring and/or seal ring. If there is any wear or damage, replace the piston, retainer, D-ring and/or seal ring.
6. Improper rear clutch pressure	a. Malfunction of D-ring Ⓕ of rear clutch piston, retainer seal ring Ⓖ and seal rings Ⓗ and Ⓘ of input shaft. b. Functional malfunction of the valve body assembly	a. Disassemble the rear clutch, check input shaft seal ring, retainer seal ring, piston D ring, etc. and replace broken or damaged parts. b. Replace the valve body assembly.
7. Improper end clutch pressure	a. Malfunction of seal ring Ⓙ or the D-ring Ⓚ and/or oil seal Ⓛ of end clutch. b. Functional malfunction of the valve body assembly	a. Disassemble the end clutch and check the oil seal or D-ring of the piston, seal ring of the retainer, etc.; replace if there are cuts, scars, scratches or damage. b. Replace the valve body assembly.
8. Improper low-reverse brake pressure	a. O-ring between valve body and transaxle damaged or missing b. Functional malfunction of the valve body assembly c. Malfunction of the D-ring Ⓜ of the low-reverse brake piston or the O-ring Ⓝ of the retainer	a. Remove the valve body assembly and check to be sure that the O-ring at the upper surface of the upper valve body is not missing or damaged; install or replace the O-ring if necessary. b. Replace the valve body assembly. c. Disassemble the transaxle itself and check the D-ring and O-ring for damage; replace if there are cuts, scars, scratches or damage.
9. Improper torque converter pressure	a. Clogging or leaking of the oil cooler and/or piping b. Malfunction of the torque converter	a. Repair or replace, as necessary, the cooler and/or piping. b. Replace the torque converter.

92J15031 92F15078

Fig. 9: Analyzing Hydraulic Pressure Test Results

ADJUSTMENTS

KICKDOWN SERVO

1) Ensure area around kickdown servo switch is clean. Remove snap ring and kickdown servo switch. *See Figs. 14 and 15.* To prevent rotation of kickdown servo piston, engage pawl of Kickdown Servo Wrench (MD998918) in notch on kickdown servo piston. *See STEP 1 in Fig. 10.*

2) Remove plug, and install adapter between kickdown servo wrench and transaxle case in low-reverse hydraulic pressure tap port. Tighten adapter by hand only.

CAUTION: DO NOT press kickdown servo piston inward with kickdown servo wrench. Tighten adapter on transaxle case by hand only to prevent damage to transaxle case.

---

3) Loosen lock nut located before "V" groove on adjusting rod. *See STEP 2 in Fig. 10.* Install and tighten inner portion of socket wrench until it contacts the lock nut. Engage outer portion of socket wrench with lock nut.

4) Rotate outer portion of socket wrench counterclockwise and inner portion of socket wrench clockwise to secure lock nut and inner portion of socket wrench. *See STEP 3 in Fig. 10.*

5) Attach INCH-pound torque wrench on inner portion of socket wrench. *See STEP 4 in Fig. 10.* Tighten inner portion of socket wrench to 86 INCH lbs. (10 N.m), and then loosen lock nut at least 2 turns.

6) Tighten inner portion of socket wrench to 43 INCH lbs. (5 N.m). Back off inner portion of socket wrench 2-2 1/4 revolutions. Engage outer portion of socket wrench with lock nut.

7) Rotate outer portion of socket wrench clockwise and inner portion of socket wrench counterclockwise to release lock nut and inner portion of socket wrench. *See STEP 5 in Fig. 10.*

8) Tighten lock nut by hand until it contacts kickdown servo piston. Using torque wrench, tighten lock nut to specification. *See STEP 6 in Fig. 10.* See TORQUE SPECIFICATIONS.

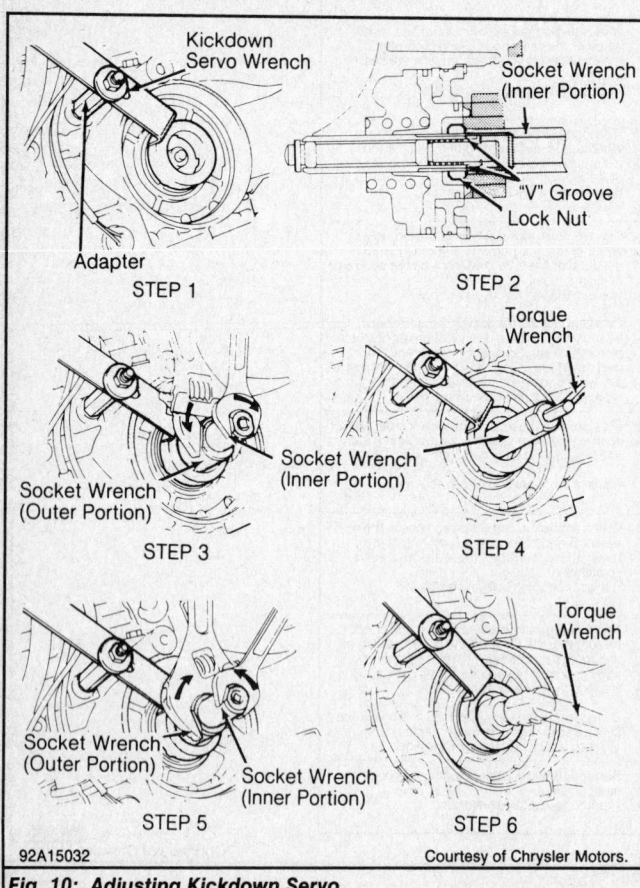

92A15032   Courtesy of Chrysler Motors.

Fig. 10: Adjusting Kickdown Servo

CAUTION: Tighten lock nut by hand first to prevent lock nut and adjusting rod from rotating together.

---

9) Remove kickdown servo wrench and adapter. Install plug in low-reverse pressure tap and tighten to specification. See TORQUE SPECIFICATIONS. Install kickdown servo switch and snap ring.

LINE PRESSURE

NOTE: Line pressure should be checked at kickdown brake pressure (apply) tap. See Fig. 8. Since valve body must be removed for adjustment, check line pressure before attempting to adjust line pressure.

1) Remove valve body. See VALVE BODY under REMOVAL & INSTALLATION. Note location of line pressure adjusting screw. *See Fig. 11.*

2) To adjust line pressure, rotate line pressure adjusting screw. Rotate line pressure adjusting screw clockwise to decrease line pressure and counterclockwise to increase line pressure.

3) Rotating line pressure adjusting screw one revolution will change line pressure approximately 5.4 psi (3.8 kPa). The standard adjusting value for line pressure should be 124-127 psi (870-890 kPa). Reinstall valve body. Fill transaxle with Mopar ATF Plus-Type 7176, and check line pressure.

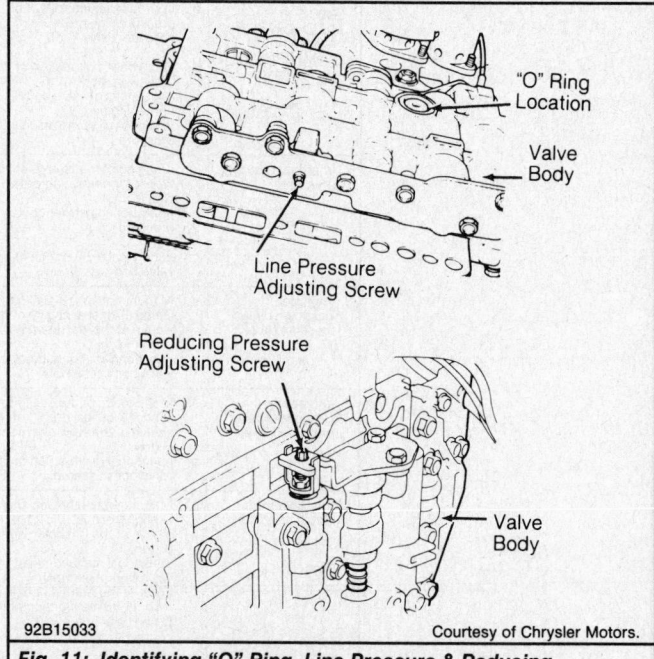

92B15033   Courtesy of Chrysler Motors.

Fig. 11: Identifying "O" Ring, Line Pressure & Reducing Pressure Adjusting Screw

REDUCING PRESSURE

NOTE: Check reducing pressure at reducing pressure tap. See Fig. 8. Valve body does not need to be removed for adjustment.

1) Drain transaxle fluid. Remove oil pan and gasket. Reducing pressure adjusting screw is on bottom of valve body. *See Fig. 11.* To adjust reducing pressure, rotate reducing pressure adjusting screw. Rotate reducing pressure adjusting screw inward (clockwise) to decrease reducing pressure and outward (counterclockwise) to increase reducing pressure.

2) Rotating reducing pressure adjusting screw one revolution will change reducing pressure approximately 6.4 psi (45 kPa). The standard adjusting value for reducing pressure is 59-61 psi (415-435 kPa). Reinstall gasket and oil pan. Tighten oil pan bolts to specification. See TORQUE SPECIFICATIONS. Fill transaxle with Mopar ATF Plus-Type 7176, and check reducing pressure.

TORQUE CONVERTER

CAUTION: Torque converter is a welded assembly and is not serviceable. If a malfunction occurs or torque converter becomes contaminated with foreign material, it MUST be replaced. Torque converter cannot be flushed or repaired.

NOTE: For torque converter stall speed test, see TORQUE CONVERTER STALL SPEED TEST under TESTING.

ON-VEHICLE SERVICE

Valve body can be serviced on vehicle. See VALVE BODY under REMOVAL & INSTALLATION.

REMOVAL & INSTALLATION

AXLE SHAFTS

See appropriate AXLE SHAFTS article in AXLE SHAFTS & TRANSFER CASES.

TRANSFER CASE

AWD – See appropriate TRANSFER CASE article in AXLE SHAFTS & TRANSFER CASES.

TRANSAXLE ASSEMBLY

See appropriate AUTOMATIC TRANSMISSION REMOVAL article in TRANSMISSION SERVICING.

VALVE BODY

Removal – Raise and support vehicle. Drain transaxle fluid. Remove retaining bolts, oil pan, gasket, oil filter and oil temperature sensor. Press solenoid valve wiring harness grommet and connector into transaxle case. Remove valve body bolts. Note bolt length and location for reassembly reference. See Fig. 12. Remove valve body.

CAUTION: DO NOT allow manual valve to fall from valve body during removal. Ensure "O" ring, located between valve body and transaxle case, is removed. See Fig. 11.

Installation – **1)** Always install NEW "O" ring between valve body and transaxle case and on solenoid valve wiring harness. Ensure "O" ring is seated on top of valve body. See Fig. 11.
2) Install valve body. Ensure detent plate pin engages groove on manual valve. Install retaining bolts, ensuring proper length bolt is installed in designated area. See Fig. 12. Tighten valve body bolts to specification. See TORQUE SPECIFICATIONS. Install oil temperature sensor and solenoid valve wiring harness.

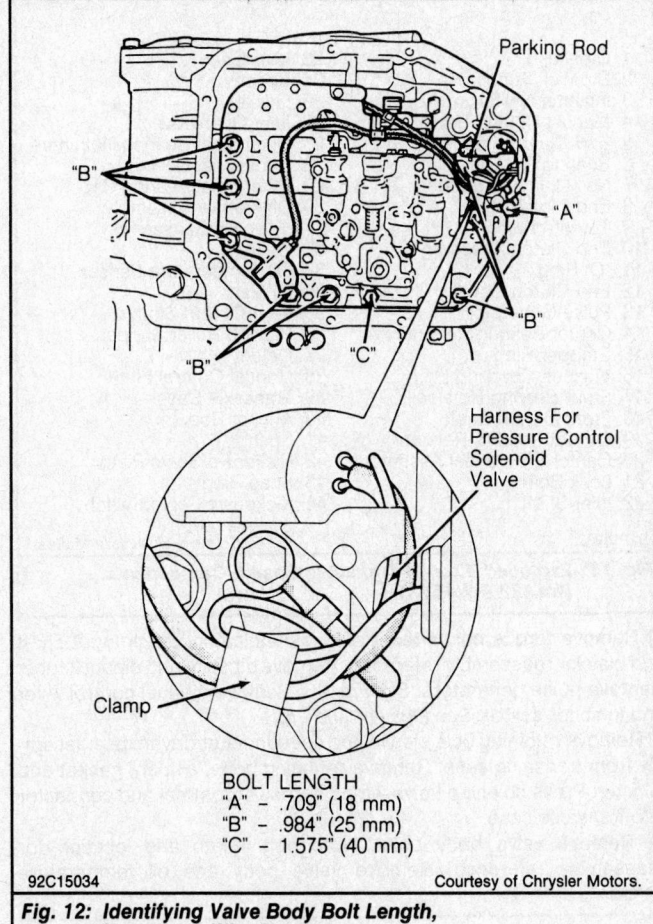

BOLT LENGTH
"A" – .709" (18 mm)
"B" – .984" (25 mm)
"C" – 1.575" (40 mm)

92C15034   Courtesy of Chrysler Motors.

Fig. 12: Identifying Valve Body Bolt Length, Location & Wire Routing

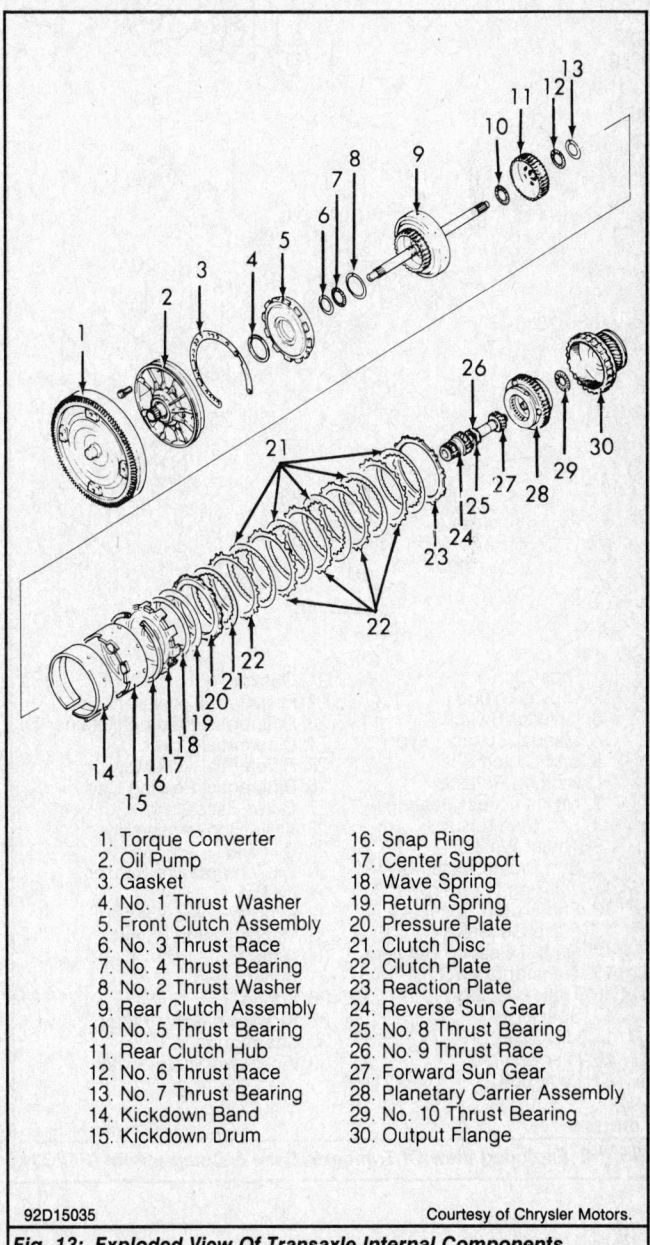

1. Torque Converter	16. Snap Ring
2. Oil Pump	17. Center Support
3. Gasket	18. Wave Spring
4. No. 1 Thrust Washer	19. Return Spring
5. Front Clutch Assembly	20. Pressure Plate
6. No. 3 Thrust Race	21. Clutch Disc
7. No. 4 Thrust Bearing	22. Clutch Plate
8. No. 2 Thrust Washer	23. Reaction Plate
9. Rear Clutch Assembly	24. Reverse Sun Gear
10. No. 5 Thrust Bearing	25. No. 8 Thrust Bearing
11. Rear Clutch Hub	26. No. 9 Thrust Race
12. No. 6 Thrust Race	27. Forward Sun Gear
13. No. 7 Thrust Bearing	28. Planetary Carrier Assembly
14. Kickdown Band	29. No. 10 Thrust Bearing
15. Kickdown Drum	30. Output Flange

92D15035   Courtesy of Chrysler Motors.

Fig. 13: Exploded View Of Transaxle Internal Components

CAUTION: *Position wiring so it does not contact detent plate. Ensure park rod is properly retained in the clamps. See Fig. 12.*

3) Install oil filter, magnet, gasket and oil pan. Tighten bolts to specification. See TORQUE SPECIFICATIONS. Fill transaxle with Mopar ATF Plus-Type 7176.

TRANSAXLE DISASSEMBLY
VALVE BODY & COMPONENTS

CAUTION: *Note locations of all thrust bearings, thrust races and thrust washers for reassembly reference. See Fig. 13.*

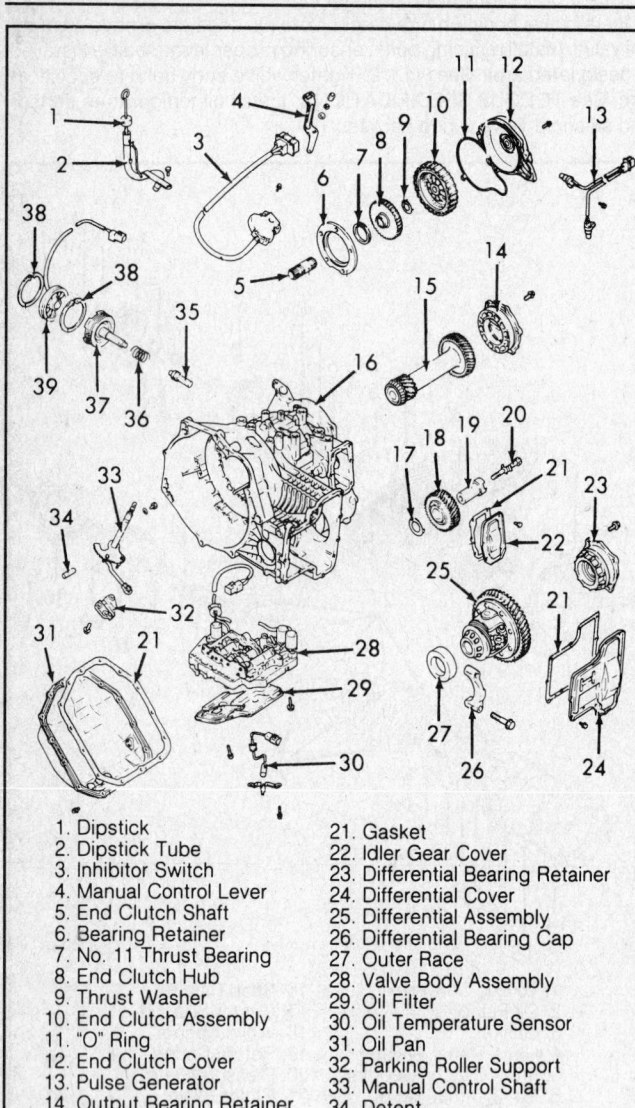

1. Dipstick	21. Gasket
2. Dipstick Tube	22. Idler Gear Cover
3. Inhibitor Switch	23. Differential Bearing Retainer
4. Manual Control Lever	24. Differential Cover
5. End Clutch Shaft	25. Differential Assembly
6. Bearing Retainer	26. Differential Bearing Cap
7. No. 11 Thrust Bearing	27. Outer Race
8. End Clutch Hub	28. Valve Body Assembly
9. Thrust Washer	29. Oil Filter
10. End Clutch Assembly	30. Oil Temperature Sensor
11. "O" Ring	31. Oil Pan
12. End Clutch Cover	32. Parking Roller Support
13. Pulse Generator	33. Manual Control Shaft
14. Output Bearing Retainer	34. Detent
15. Transfer Shaft	35. Anchor Rod
16. Transaxle Case	36. Spring
17. Spacer	37. Kickdown Servo Piston
18. Idler Gear	38. Snap Ring
19. Idler Shaft	39. Kickdown Servo Switch
20. Lock Bolt	

92E15036   Courtesy of Chrysler Motors.

Fig. 14: Exploded View Of Transaxle Case & Components (F4A33)

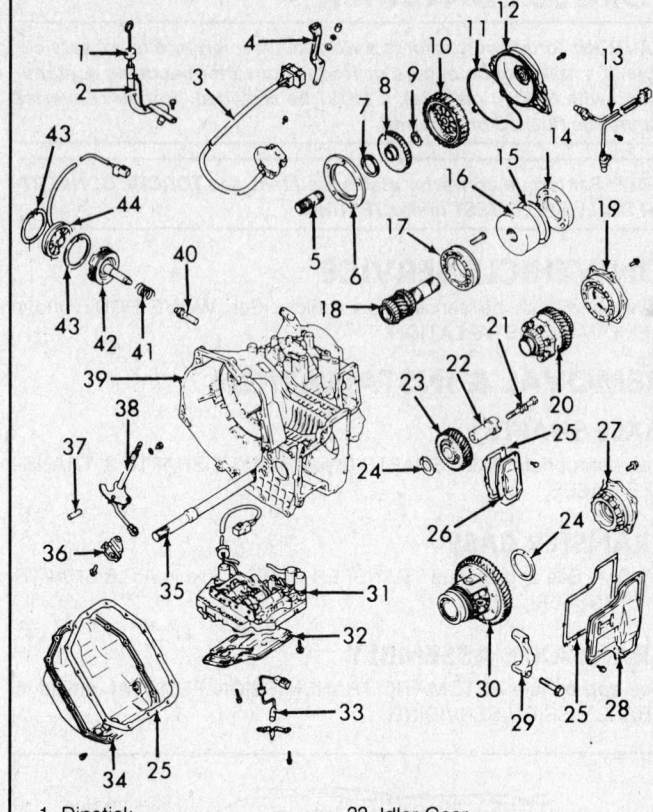

1. Dipstick	23. Idler Gear
2. Dipstick Tube	24. Spacer
3. Inhibitor Switch	25. Gasket
4. Manual Control Lever	26. Idler Gear Cover
5. End Clutch Shaft	27. Differential Bearing Retainer
6. Bearing Retainer	28. Differential Cover
7. No. 11 Thrust Bearing	29. Differential Bearing Cap
8. End Clutch Hub	30. Differential Assembly
9. Thrust Washer	31. Valve Body Assembly
10. End Clutch Assembly	32. Oil Filter
11. "O" Ring	33. Oil Temperature Sensor
12. End Clutch Cover	34. Oil Pan
13. Pulse Generator	35. Rear Output Shaft
14. Center Bearing Retainer	36. Parking Roller Support
15. Stopper Ring	37. Detent
16. Viscous Coupling Unit	38. Manual Control Shaft
17. Front Bearing Retainer	39. Transaxle Case
18. Front Output Shaft	40. Anchor Rod
19. Output Bearing Retainer	41. Spring
20. Center Differential Assembly	42. Kickdown Servo Piston
21. Lock Bolt	43. Snap Ring
22. Idler Shaft	44. Kickdown Servo Switch

92F15037   Courtesy of Chrysler Motors.

Fig. 15: Exploded View Of Transaxle Case & Components (W4A32 & W4A33)

1) Remove torque converter. Using dial indicator, check input shaft end play for reassembly reference. Remove dipstick and dipstick tube. Remove pulse generators. *See Fig. 16.* Remove manual control lever and inhibitor switch. *See Figs. 14 and 15.*

2) Remove retaining bolt, sleeve and speedometer driven gear assembly from transaxle case. Remove retaining bolts, oil pan, gasket and oil filter. Press solenoid valve wiring harness grommet and connector into transaxle case.

3) Remove valve body bolts. Note bolt length and location for reassembly reference. Remove valve body and oil temperature sensor.

CAUTION: *DO NOT allow manual valve to fall from valve body during removal. Ensure "O" ring, located between valve body and transaxle case, is removed. See Fig. 11.*

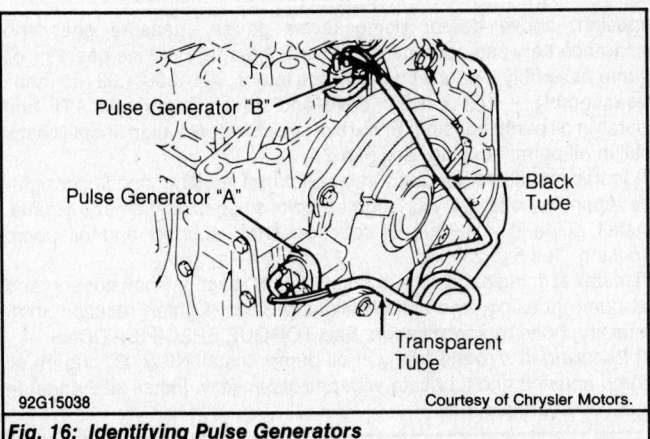

Fig. 16: Identifying Pulse Generators

4) Remove parking roller support, located on bottom of transaxle case, above valve body area. *See Figs. 14 and 15.* Remove manual control shaft retaining set screw, located near top of manual control shaft area, on transaxle case. Remove manual control shaft and detent. *See Figs. 14 and 15.*

5) Remove retaining bolts, differential cover, gasket and differential bearing cap. Remove retaining bolts and differential bearing retainer. *See Figs. 14 and 15.*

6) Remove differential assembly. Remove end clutch cover, "O" ring, end clutch assembly and thrust washer. Remove end clutch hub and No. 11 thrust bearing. *See Figs. 14 and 15.* Remove end clutch shaft.

7) Remove retaining bolts, idler gear cover and gasket. Bend lock tabs, and remove lock bolt for idler shaft. *See Figs. 14 and 15.* Using appropriate puller, pull idler shaft from transaxle case.

8) Remove idler gear and spacer. Remove oil pump retaining bolts. Install puller into threaded holes on oil pump. Pull oil pump and gasket from transaxle case.

9) Remove No.1 thrust washer and No. 3 thrust race from rear of oil pump. *See Fig. 13.* Holding input shaft, remove front and rear clutch assembly. Remove No. 10 thrust bearing.

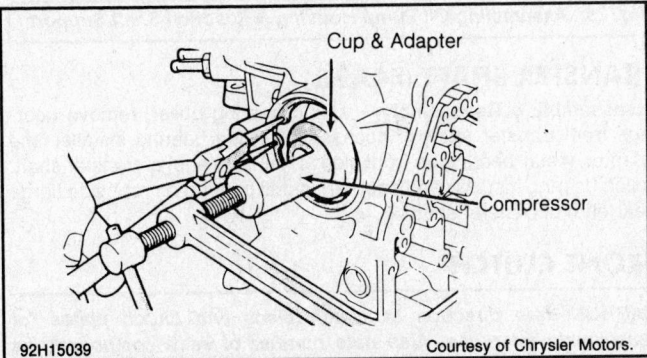

Fig. 17: Compressing Kickdown Servo Piston

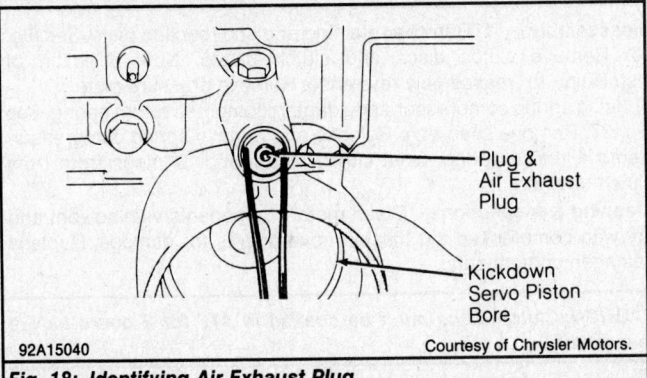

Fig. 18: Identifying Air Exhaust Plug

10) Remove rear clutch hub, No. 6 thrust race and No. 7 thrust bearing. Remove kickdown drum and kickdown band. Remove snap ring and kickdown servo switch. *See Figs. 14 and 15.*

11) Using cup, adapter and compressor, depress kickdown servo piston. *See Fig. 17.* Remove snap ring. Remove compressor, adapter, cup, kickdown servo piston and anchor rod.

12) Remove plug and air exhaust plug. *See Fig. 18.* Remove snap ring from inside transaxle case, located above center support. Secure handle on center support, and remove center support. *See Fig. 19.*

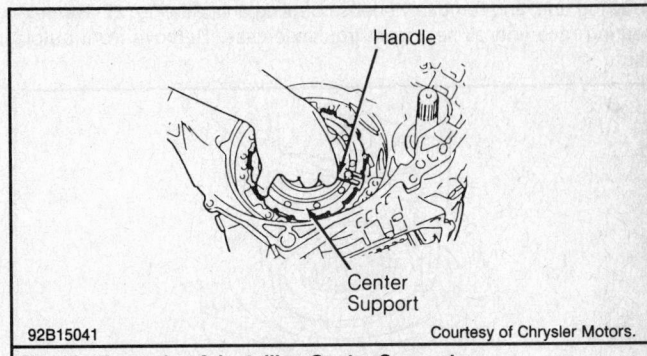

Fig. 19: Removing & Installing Center Support

13) Remove reverse sun gear, forward sun gear and planetary carrier assembly. *See Fig. 13.* Remove wave spring, return spring, pressure plate, clutch plates and clutch discs.

CAUTION: Note number of components and sequence of clutch plates and clutch discs installation for reassembly reference.

14) Remove retaining bolts and bearing retainer. Bearing retainer is located on transaxle case, near end clutch hub area. *See Figs. 14 and 15.*

15) Remove snap ring and output flange. *See Fig. 13.* Remove retaining bolts and output bearing retainer and outer bearing race. *See Figs. 14 and 15.* On F4A33 models, remove transfer shaft. *See Fig. 14.* Remove bearing race and oil seal from transaxle case.

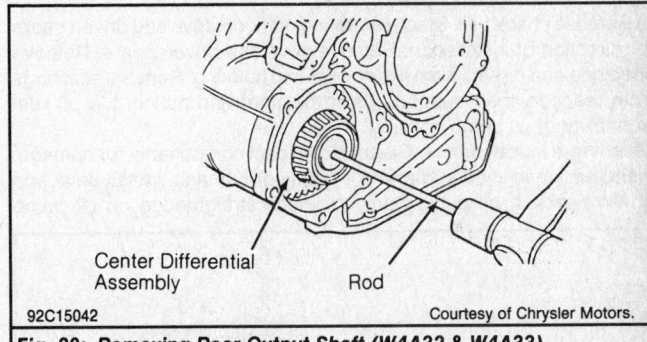

Fig. 20: Removing Rear Output Shaft (W4A32 & W4A33)

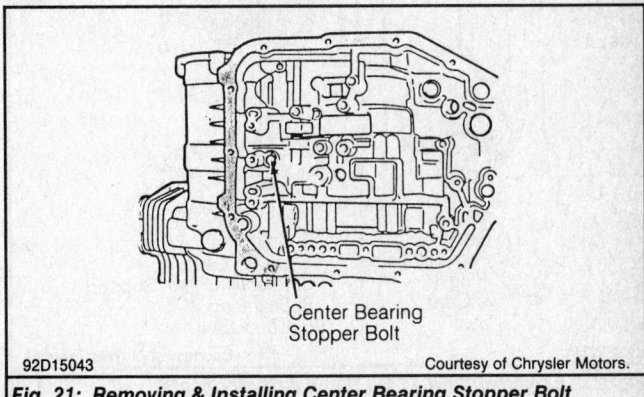

Fig. 21: Removing & Installing Center Bearing Stopper Bolt

16) On W4A32 and W4A33 models, insert a .31" (8 mm) diameter rod, 7.87" (199.9 mm) long, through hole in center differential assembly. See Fig. 20. Tap on rod to remove rear output shaft.

17) Thread puller into hole in end of center differential assembly. Remove center differential assembly. Install bolt in threaded areas on center bearing retainer. Hold bolts, and remove center bearing retainer from transaxle case. See Fig. 15.

18) Remove center bearing stopper bolt. See Fig. 21. Remove stopper ring. See Fig. 15. Place bearing puller across groove in viscous coupling unit, and remove viscous coupling unit. See Fig. 22. Remove bearing race and oil seal from transaxle case. Remove front output shaft.

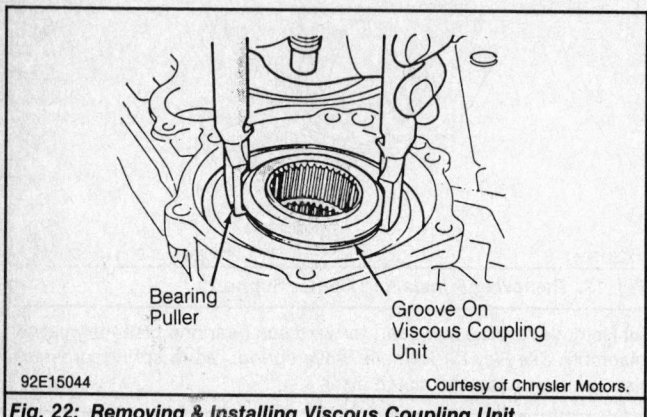

92E15044   Courtesy of Chrysler Motors.

Fig. 22: Removing & Installing Viscous Coupling Unit

COMPONENT DISASSEMBLY & REASSEMBLY

OIL PUMP

Disassembly – 1) Remove "O" ring from outer diameter of oil pump housing. Place reference mark on oil pump housing and reaction shaft support. Remove retaining bolts, and separate reaction shaft support from oil pump housing. See Fig. 23.

2) Remove check ball. Place reference mark on drive and driven gears for direction of installation. Remove drive and driven gears. Remove snap ring and oil seal from inside oil pump housing. Remove seal rings from reaction shaft support. Using hammer and punch, tap oil seal from front of oil pump housing.

Cleaning & Inspection – Clean and inspect components for damage. Inspect all machined surfaces for pitting or damage. Install drive and driven gears in oil pump housing. Place straightedge on oil pump

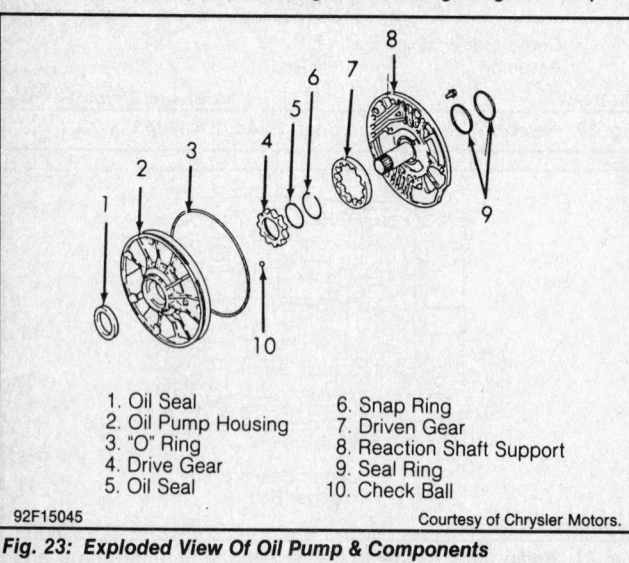

1. Oil Seal
2. Oil Pump Housing
3. "O" Ring
4. Drive Gear
5. Oil Seal
6. Snap Ring
7. Driven Gear
8. Reaction Shaft Support
9. Seal Ring
10. Check Ball

92F15045   Courtesy of Chrysler Motors.

Fig. 23: Exploded View Of Oil Pump & Components

housing, above gears. Using feeler gauge, measure gear end clearance between each gear and straightedge. Replace gears or oil pump assembly if gear end clearance is not .001-.002" (.03-.05 mm).

Reassembly – 1) Lubricate drive and driven gears with ATF and install in oil pump housing. Ensure reference marks align. Install check ball in oil pump housing. See Fig. 24.

2) Install reaction shaft support on oil pump housing, and finger tighten retaining bolts. DO NOT tighten bolts to specification at this time. Install guide pin in hole of reaction shaft support and oil pump housing. See Fig. 25.

3) Install aligning band on outer diameter of reaction shaft support and oil pump housing, and tighten aligning band. Tighten reaction shaft retaining bolts to specification. See TORQUE SPECIFICATIONS.

4) Ensure gears rotate freely in oil pump. Install NEW "O" ring on oil pump housing and lubricate with petroleum jelly. Install seal rings on reaction shaft support.

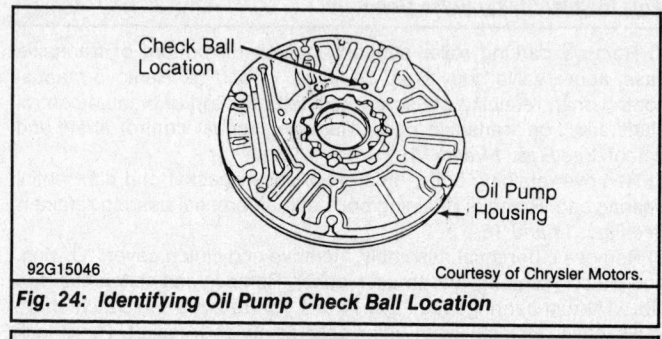

92G15046   Courtesy of Chrysler Motors.

Fig. 24: Identifying Oil Pump Check Ball Location

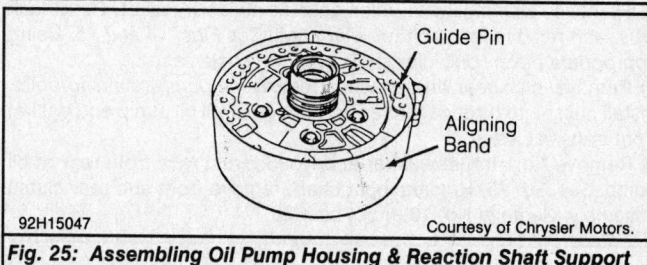

92H15047   Courtesy of Chrysler Motors.

Fig. 25: Assembling Oil Pump Housing & Reaction Shaft Support

TRANSFER SHAFT (F4A33)

Disassembly & Reassembly – Using bearing puller, remove bearings from transfer shaft (if necessary). Using bearing installer and adapter, install bearing on front side (small gear end) of transfer shaft. Using bearing installer and adapter, install bearing on rear side (large gear end) of transfer shaft.

FRONT CLUTCH

CAUTION: Note direction of clutch discs and clutch plates for reassembly reference. Also note number of each component, as some models may contain different number of clutch components. Components must be installed in correct sequence.

Disassembly – 1) Remove retaining ring and reaction plate. See Fig. 26. Remove clutch discs and clutch plates. Note direction of installation for reassembly reference. Remove pressure plate.

2) Using spring compressor and adapter, compress return spring. See Fig. 27. Remove snap ring. Release and remove spring compressor. Remove return spring, front clutch piston and "D" rings from front clutch retainer.

Cleaning & Inspection – Clean metal components with solvent and dry with compressed air. Inspect components for damage. Replace damaged components.

CAUTION: Clutch discs must be soaked in ATF for 2 hours before reassembly.

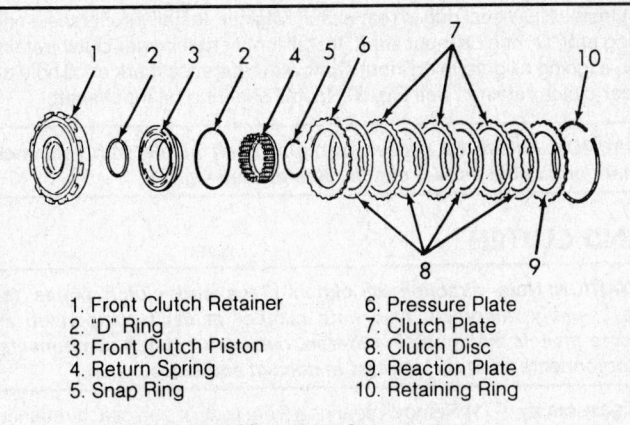

1. Front Clutch Retainer
2. "D" Ring
3. Front Clutch Piston
4. Return Spring
5. Snap Ring
6. Pressure Plate
7. Clutch Plate
8. Clutch Disc
9. Reaction Plate
10. Retaining Ring

NOTE: W4A32 contains 3 clutch disc
and 2 clutch plates.

92I15048   Courtesy of Chrysler Motors.

**Fig. 26: Exploded View Of Front Clutch
(F4A33 & W4A33 Shown; W4A32 Is Similar)**

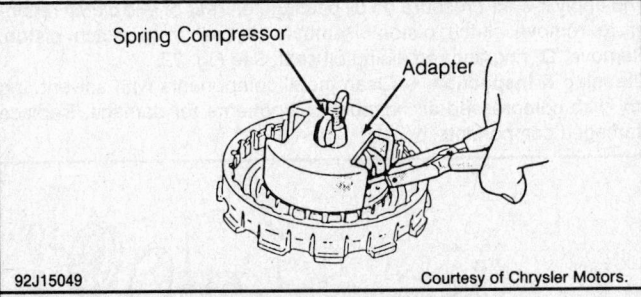

92J15049   Courtesy of Chrysler Motors.

**Fig. 27: Compressing Clutch Piston Return Spring
(Front Clutch Application Shown; Rear Clutch Is Similar)**

FRONT & REAR CLUTCH RETAINING RING IDENTIFICATION

Ring Thickness In. (mm)	Identification Mark	Part Number
F4A33 & W4A33		
.051 (1.3) [1]	None	MD731747
.055 (1.4) [1]	Blue	MD731748
.059 (1.5)	Brown	MD731749
.063 (1.6)	None	MD731750
.067 (1.7)	Blue	MD731751
.071 (1.8)	Brown	MD731752
.075 (1.9)	None	MD731753
.079 (2.0)	Blue	MD731754
.083 (2.1)	Brown	MD731755
.087 (2.2)	None	MD731756
.091 (2.3)	Blue	MD731757
.094 (2.4)	Brown	MD731758
W4A32		
.063 (1.6)	None	MD955630
.067 (1.7)	Brown	MD730930
.071 (1.8)	Blue	MD955631
.075 (1.9)	None	MD730931
.079 (2.0)	Brown	MD955632
.083 (2.1)	Blue	MD730932
.087 (2.2)	None	MD955633
.091 (2.3)	Brown	MD730933
.094 (2.4)	Blue	MD955634
.098 (2.5)	None	MD730934
.102 (2.6)	Brown	MD955635
.106 (2.7)	Blue	MD730935
.110 (2.8)	None	MD955636
.114 (2.9)	Brown	MD730936
.118 (3.0)	Blue	MD955637

[1] - Retaining ring applies to rear clutch application only.

Reassembly – 1) Install NEW "D" rings. Install front clutch piston and return spring in front clutch retainer. Using spring compressor and adapter, compress return spring and install snap ring. Install pressure plate, clutch discs, clutch plates and reaction plate.

CAUTION: Align missing tooth area on pressure plate, clutch plates and reaction plate before installing. See Fig. 28. This aids in cooling of clutch plates. Ensure pressure plate, clutch plates and reaction plate are installed with beveled side toward front clutch retainer. See Fig. 29.

2) Install retaining ring. To check front clutch clearance, hold entire circumference of reaction plate downward. Using feeler gauge, measure clearance between retaining ring and reaction plate.
3) Front clutch clearance should be .028-.035" (.71-.89 mm) on W4A32 models and .032-.039" (.81-.99 mm) on all others. If front clutch clearance is not within specification, select different thickness retaining ring to obtain correct clearance. See FRONT & REAR CLUTCH RETAINING RING IDENTIFICATION table.

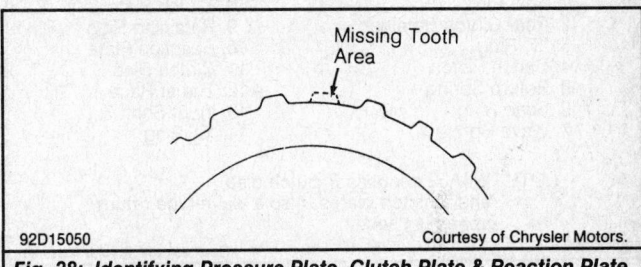

92D15050   Courtesy of Chrysler Motors.

Fig. 28: Identifying Pressure Plate, Clutch Plate & Reaction Plate Missing Tooth Area

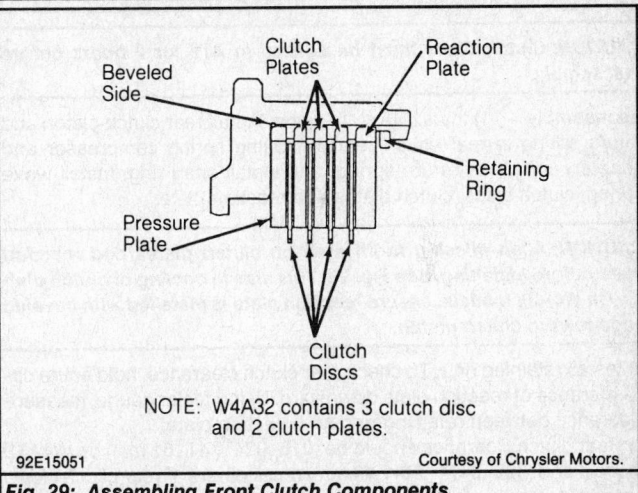

NOTE: W4A32 contains 3 clutch disc
and 2 clutch plates.

92E15051   Courtesy of Chrysler Motors.

Fig. 29: Assembling Front Clutch Components

REAR CLUTCH

CAUTION: Note direction of clutch discs and clutch plates for reassembly reference. Also note number of each component, as some models may contain different number of clutch components. Components must be installed in correct sequence.

Disassembly – 1) Note number of seal rings used on front of input shaft near rear clutch retainer. Some models may use more seal rings on input shaft. Remove seal ring from front of input shaft. *See Fig. 30.*
2) Remove input shaft. Remove "O" rings, snap ring and thrust race from input shaft. Remove seal ring from center of rear clutch retainer. *See Fig. 30.*
3) Remove retaining ring and reaction plate. *See Fig. 30.* Remove clutch discs and clutch plates. Note direction of installation for reassembly reference.
4) Remove wave spring. Using spring compressor and adapter, compress return spring. *See Fig. 27.* Remove snap ring. Release and

remove spring compressor. Remove return spring, rear clutch piston and "D" rings from rear clutch retainer.

Cleaning & Inspection – Clean metal components with solvent and dry with compressed air. Inspect components for damage. Replace damaged components.

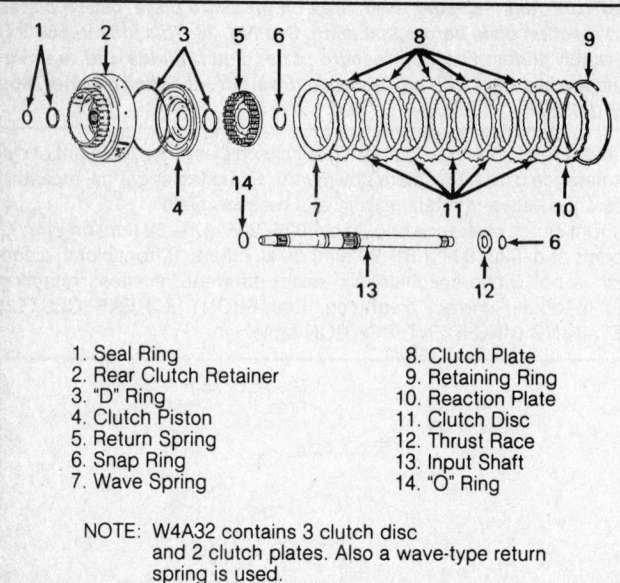

1. Seal Ring
2. Rear Clutch Retainer
3. "D" Ring
4. Clutch Piston
5. Return Spring
6. Snap Ring
7. Wave Spring
8. Clutch Plate
9. Retaining Ring
10. Reaction Plate
11. Clutch Disc
12. Thrust Race
13. Input Shaft
14. "O" Ring

NOTE: W4A32 contains 3 clutch disc and 2 clutch plates. Also a wave-type return spring is used.

92F15052   Courtesy of Chrysler Motors.

Fig. 30: Exploded View Of Rear Clutch (F4A33 & W4A33 Shown; W4A32 Is Similar)

CAUTION: Clutch discs must be soaked in ATF for 2 hours before reassembly.

Reassembly – **1)** Install NEW "D" rings. Install rear clutch piston and return spring in rear clutch retainer. Using spring compressor and adapter, compress return spring, and install snap ring. Install wave spring, clutch discs, clutch plates and reaction plate.

CAUTION: Align missing tooth area on clutch plates and reaction plate before installing. See Fig. 28. This aids in cooling of clutch plates. On W4A32 models, ensure reaction plate is installed with beveled edge toward clutch piston.

2) Install retaining ring. To check rear clutch clearance, hold entire circumference of reaction plate downward. Using feeler gauge, measure clearance between retaining ring and reaction plate.
3) Rear clutch clearance should be .016-.024" (.41-.61 mm) on W4A32 models and .039-.047" (.99-1.19 mm) on all others. If rear clutch clearance is not within specification, select different thickness retaining ring to obtain correct clearance. See FRONT & REAR CLUTCH RETAINING RING IDENTIFICATION table.

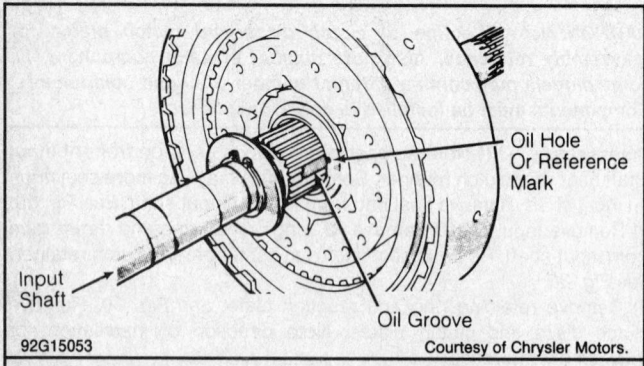

Oil Hole
Or Reference
Mark

Input
Shaft

Oil Groove

92G15053   Courtesy of Chrysler Motors.

Fig. 31: Aligning Input Shaft & Rear Clutch Retainer

---

4) Install NEW seal ring in rear clutch retainer. Install thrust race, snap ring and "O" ring on input shaft. Install input shaft in rear clutch retainer, aligning oil groove on input shaft with reference mark or oil hole on rear clutch retainer. *See Fig. 31.* Install seal ring on input shaft.

CAUTION: Ensure oil groove on input shaft aligns with reference mark or oil hole on rear clutch retainer. See Fig. 31.

END CLUTCH

CAUTION: Note direction of clutch discs and clutch plates for reassembly reference. Also note number of each component, as some models may contain different number of clutch components. Components must be installed in correct sequence.

Disassembly – **1)** Remove seal ring from rear of end clutch retainer. Remove retaining ring, reaction plate, clutch discs and clutch plates. Note direction of installation for reassembly reference. *See Fig. 32.* Remove snap ring, washer and return spring.
2) Remove clutch piston from end clutch retainer. If necessary, place end clutch retainer on workbench with clutch piston facing downward, and apply low air pressure on oil passage on rear of end clutch retainer to remove clutch piston. Remove oil seal from clutch piston. Remove "D" ring and remaining oil seal. *See Fig. 32.*

Cleaning & Inspection – Clean metal components with solvent and dry with compressed air. Inspect components for damage. Replace damaged components.

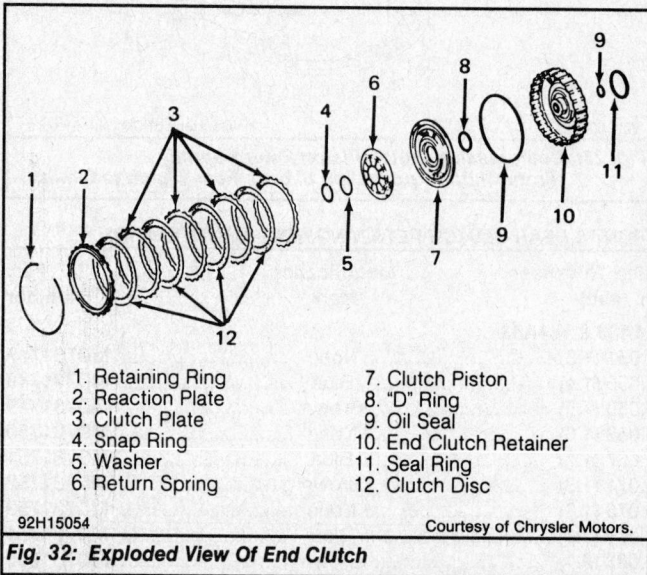

1. Retaining Ring
2. Reaction Plate
3. Clutch Plate
4. Snap Ring
5. Washer
6. Return Spring
7. Clutch Piston
8. "D" Ring
9. Oil Seal
10. End Clutch Retainer
11. Seal Ring
12. Clutch Disc

92H15054   Courtesy of Chrysler Motors.

Fig. 32: Exploded View Of End Clutch

CAUTION: Clutch discs must be soaked in ATF for 2 hours before reassembly.

Reassembly – **1)** Install NEW oil seals and "D" ring. Install clutch piston in end clutch retainer. Install return spring and washer. Install snap ring on end clutch retainer. Using snap ring installer, press snap ring onto end clutch retainer until it seats in groove. Ensure snap ring is fully seated.
2) Install clutch discs, clutch plates and reaction plate. *See Fig. 32.* Install retaining ring. To check end clutch clearance, hold entire circumference of reaction plate downward. Using feeler gauge, measure clearance between retaining ring and reaction plate.
3) End clutch clearance should be .024-.033" (.61-.84 mm). If end clutch clearance is not within specification, select different thickness retaining ring to obtain correct clearance. See END CLUTCH RETAINING RING IDENTIFICATION table. Install seal ring on rear of end clutch retainer.

END CLUTCH RETAINING RING IDENTIFICATION

Ring Thickness In. (mm)	Identification Mark	Part Number
.041 (1.04)	White	MD715800
.051 (1.30)	Yellow	MD715801
.061 (1.55)	None	MD715802
.071 (1.80)	Green	MD715803
.081 (2.05)	Pink	[1]

[1] – Part number is MD715804 (Laser and Talon) or MD720849 (all others).

PLANETARY CARRIER ASSEMBLY

Disassembly – Remove thrust bearing. *See Fig. 33.* Position stopper plate on one-way clutch outer race so it does not contact rivet. Using punch and hammer, drive out rivet. *See Fig. 34.* Remove waved washer, one-way clutch outer race and end plate. *See Fig. 33.* Remove one-way clutch and end plate from planetary carrier.

Cleaning & Inspection – Clean components with solvent and dry with compressed air. Inspect components for damage. Replace damaged components.

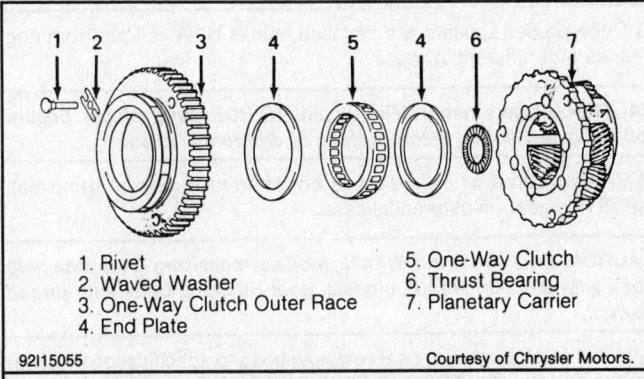

1. Rivet
2. Waved Washer
3. One-Way Clutch Outer Race
4. End Plate
5. One-Way Clutch
6. Thrust Bearing
7. Planetary Carrier

92I15055

Courtesy of Chrysler Motors.

Fig. 33: Exploded View Of Planetary Carrier Assembly

Position Stopper Plate To Clear Rivet

Punch

Stopper Plate

Rivet

Rivet

REMOVAL

Rivet

Waved Washer

Punch

Rivet

INSTALLATION

92J15056

Courtesy of Chrysler Motors.

Fig. 34: Removing & Installing Planetary Carrier Assembly Rivet

Reassembly – 1) Install end plate on one-way clutch outer race. Install one-way clutch so flange side is upward (away from one-way clutch outer race). *See Fig. 35.*

2) Install end plate. Install one-way clutch outer race on planetary carrier. Install waved washer on NEW rivet. Ensure concave side of wave washer faces away from rivet head. *See Fig. 34.*

CAUTION: DO NOT use old rivet. Always install NEW rivet.

3) Install waved washer and rivet in planetary carrier. Using press and punch with 60 degree angle tip, stake rivet. Apply 2425-2866 lbs. of pressure on press when staking rivet. Install thrust bearing.

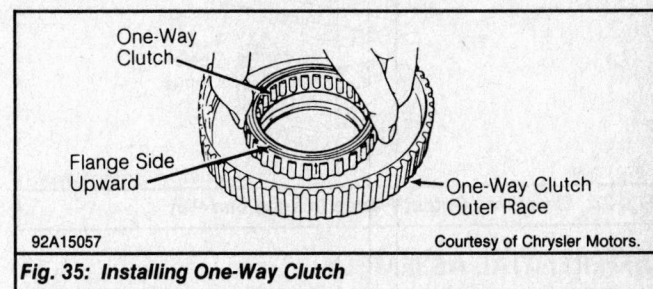

One-Way Clutch

Flange Side Upward

One-Way Clutch Outer Race

92A15057

Courtesy of Chrysler Motors.

Fig. 35: Installing One-Way Clutch

OUTPUT FLANGE & TRANSFER DRIVE GEAR

Disassembly – 1) Remove snap ring and stopper plate from end of transfer drive gear. *See Fig. 36.* Place bearing remover between output flange and bearing. Using press, remove bearings and transfer drive gear as a unit from output flange.

2) Using press and bearing remover, remove bearings from transfer drive gear (if necessary). Remove snap ring and output flange from annulus gear. *See Fig. 36.*

Cleaning & Inspection – Clean components with solvent and dry with compressed air. Inspect components for damage. Replace damaged components.

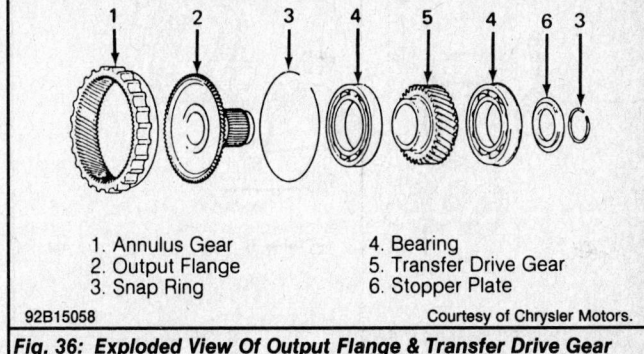

1. Annulus Gear
2. Output Flange
3. Snap Ring
4. Bearing
5. Transfer Drive Gear
6. Stopper Plate

92B15058

Courtesy of Chrysler Motors.

Fig. 36: Exploded View Of Output Flange & Transfer Drive Gear

Reassembly – 1) Install output flange and snap ring in annulus gear. *See Fig. 36.* Press NEW bearings on transfer drive gear. Using adapter, bearing installer and press, install transfer drive gear and bearings on output flange.

OUTPUT FLANGE BEARING SNAP RING IDENTIFICATION

Ring Thickness In. (mm)	Identification Mark	Part Number
.069 (1.75)	Brown	MD733314
.072 (1.82)	None	MD722538
.074 (1.88)	Blue	MD721014
.076 (1.93)	Brown	MD721015
.079 (2.00)	None	MD721016
.081 (2.06)	Blue	MD721017
.083 (2.11)	Brown	MD722539
.086 (2.18)	None	MD733315

2) Install stopper plate. Using feeler gauge, measure output flange bearing end play between groove on output flange and stopper plate surface. *See Fig. 37.*

3) Output flange end play should be 0-.0035" (0-.089 mm). If output flange bearing end play is not within specification, select different thickness snap ring to obtain correct clearance. See OUTPUT FLANGE BEARING SNAP RING IDENTIFICATION table. Install snap ring.

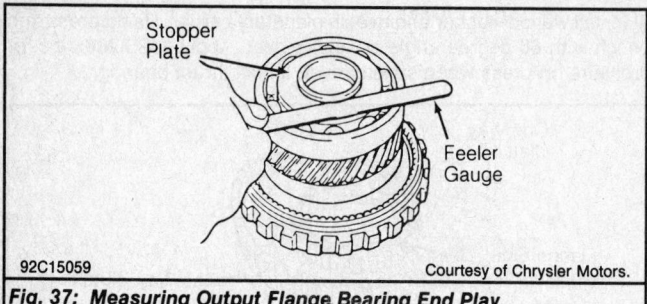

92C15059   Courtesy of Chrysler Motors.

Fig. 37: Measuring Output Flange Bearing End Play

DIFFERENTIAL ASSEMBLY

Disassembly – 1) Remove retaining bolts and ring gear. Remove tapered or ball bearings from differential case if replacement is required. *See Fig. 38.*

2) Using hammer and punch, drive roll pin toward ring gear side of differential case. Remove pinion shaft, pinion gears, thrust washers, side gears and spacers from differential case.

Cleaning & Inspection – Clean components with solvent and dry with compressed air. Inspect components for damage. Replace damaged components.

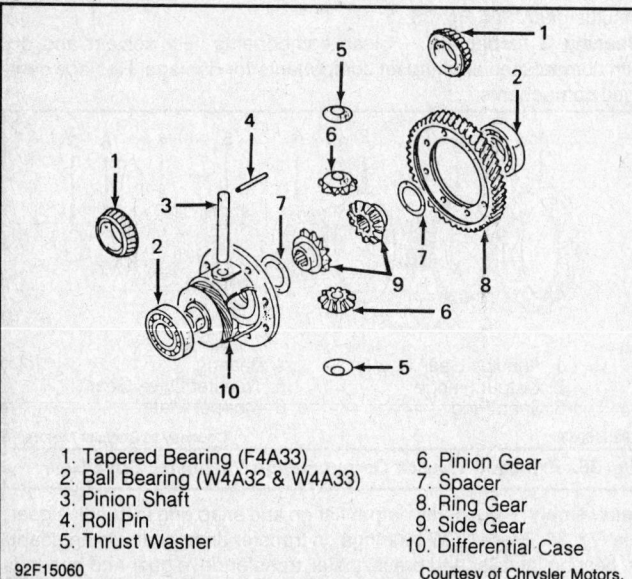

1. Tapered Bearing (F4A33)	6. Pinion Gear
2. Ball Bearing (W4A32 & W4A33)	7. Spacer
3. Pinion Shaft	8. Ring Gear
4. Roll Pin	9. Side Gear
5. Thrust Washer	10. Differential Case

92F15060   Courtesy of Chrysler Motors.

Fig. 38: Exploded View Of Differential Assembly

Reassembly – 1) Place spacer on side gear. Install side gear in differential case. Install thrust washers on pinion gears. Place pinion gears in differential case.

2) Rotate side gears and pinion gears until they align with pinion shaft opening. Install pinion shaft. Position dial indicator so stem rests against side gear. *See Fig. 39.* Rotate pinion gear, and note side gear-to-pinion gear backlash. Check backlash on both side gears.

3) Side gear-to-pinion gear backlash should be .0010-.0059" (.025-.150 mm). If side gear-to-pinion gear backlash is not within specification, select different thickness side gear spacer. See SIDE GEAR SPACER IDENTIFICATION table.

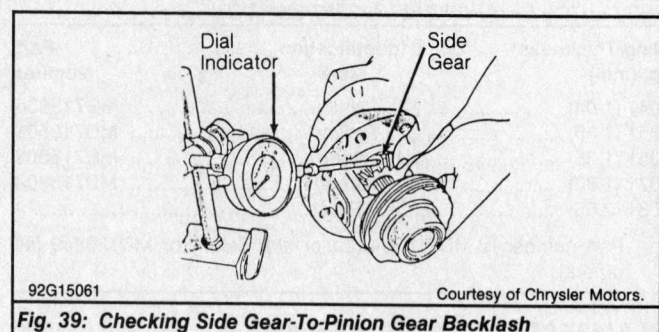

92G15061   Courtesy of Chrysler Motors.

Fig. 39: Checking Side Gear-To-Pinion Gear Backlash

SIDE GEAR SPACER IDENTIFICATION

Spacer Thickness In. (mm)	Part Number
.0295-.0323 (.749-.820)	MD722986
.0327-.0362 (.830-.919)	MD722985
.0366-.0394 (.930-1.001)	MD722984
.0398-.0425 (1.011-1.080)	MD722983
.0429-.0457 (1.090-1.161)	MD722982

4) Once proper spacers are installed, install NEW roll pin from ring gear side of differential case.

CAUTION: Always install NEW roll pin. DO NOT reuse roll pin. Ensure roll pin is positioned below surface of differential case.

5) Press tapered or ball bearings on differential case (if removed). Install ring gear on differential case.

CAUTION: On F4A33 and W4A33 models, coat ring gear retaining bolts with ATF. On W4A32 models, coat retaining bolts with thread sealant.

6) Install and tighten ring gear retaining bolts to specification in a crisscross pattern. See TORQUE SPECIFICATIONS.

CAUTION: Ensure ring gear retaining bolts are tightened to specification in a crisscross pattern to prevent damage to ring gear and differential case.

KICKDOWN SERVO

Disassembly & Reassembly – Remove "O" ring, kickdown servo, "D" ring and seal ring. *See Fig. 40.* Remove lock nut. Separate servo rod from kickdown servo piston. To reassemble, reverse disassembly procedure using NEW "O" ring, seal ring and "D" ring. Tighten lock nut to specification. See TORQUE SPECIFICATIONS.

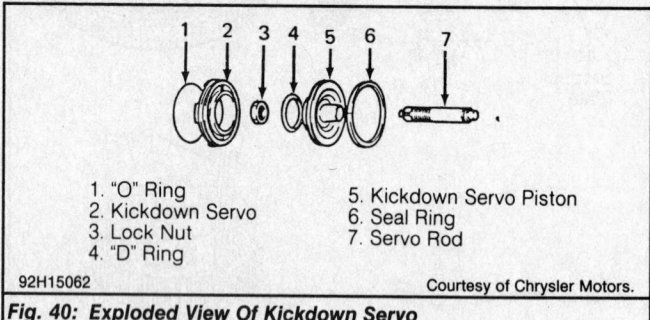

1. "O" Ring	5. Kickdown Servo Piston
2. Kickdown Servo	6. Seal Ring
3. Lock Nut	7. Servo Rod
4. "D" Ring	

92H15062   Courtesy of Chrysler Motors.

Fig. 40: Exploded View Of Kickdown Servo

LOW-REVERSE BRAKE

Disassembly & Reassembly – Remove low-reverse brake piston from center support. *See Fig. 41.* Remove "D" rings from low-reverse brake piston. To reassemble, reverse disassembly procedure using NEW "D" rings.

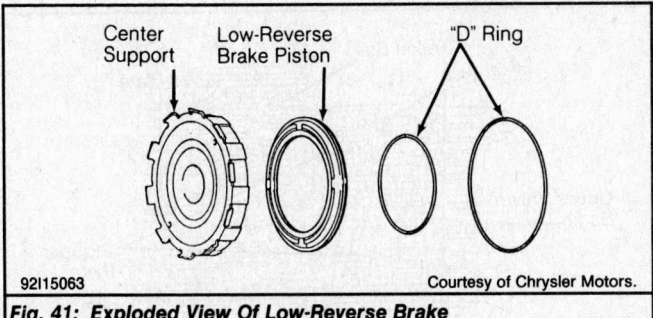

Fig. 41: Exploded View Of Low-Reverse Brake

Courtesy of Chrysler Motors.

92I15063

CENTER DIFFERENTIAL ASSEMBLY (W4A32 & W4A33)

Disassembly – 1) Install bearing remover between transfer driven gear and differential case. *See Fig. 42.* Using press, press differential case from transfer driven gear. Tapered bearing is removed along with transfer driven gear.

2) Using press and bearing remover, remove tapered bearings from transfer driven gear, and differential case if replacement is required. Remove retaining bolts. Separate differential flange from differential case. *See Fig. 42.* Remove spacers, front and rear side gears, pinion shaft, pinion gears, thrust washers and clip from differential case.

Cleaning & Inspection – Clean components with solvent and dry with compressed air. Inspect components for damage. Replace damaged components.

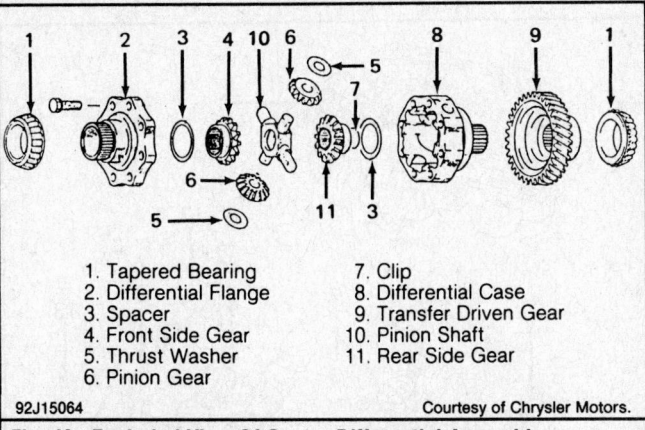

1. Tapered Bearing
2. Differential Flange
3. Spacer
4. Front Side Gear
5. Thrust Washer
6. Pinion Gear
7. Clip
8. Differential Case
9. Transfer Driven Gear
10. Pinion Shaft
11. Rear Side Gear

92J15064   Courtesy of Chrysler Motors.

Fig. 42: Exploded View Of Center Differential Assembly (W4A32 & W4A33)

Reassembly – 1) Install spacer, rear side gear, pinion gears, thrust washer and pinion shaft in differential case. *See Fig. 42.* Different thickness spacer for rear side gear may be required to obtain smooth and even rotation of pinion gears.

2) To check rear side gear for proper thickness spacer, press downward on pinion shaft, and rotate pinion gears. *See Fig. 43.* Pinion gears should rotate smoothly and evenly without binding if proper thickness spacer is installed.

3) If pinion gears do not rotate smoothly and evenly, remove components, and install proper thickness spacer on rear side gear. See CENTER DIFFERENTIAL SIDE GEAR SPACER SELECTION table.

4) Reinstall rear side gear, clip, pinion gears, thrust washer and pinion shaft in differential case. Install front side gear, spacer, differential flange and retaining bolts.

5) Tighten retaining bolts to specification in a crisscross pattern. See TORQUE SPECIFICATIONS. To check front side gear for proper thickness spacer, insert front output shaft into front side gear and, rotate front side gear. *See Fig. 43.*

6) Front side gear should rotate smoothly and evenly without binding if proper thickness spacer is installed. If front side gear does not rotate smoothly and evenly, install proper thickness spacer. See CENTER DIFFERENTIAL SIDE GEAR SPACER SELECTION table.

CENTER DIFFERENTIAL SIDE GEAR SPACER SELECTION

Spacer Thickness In. (mm)	Identification Mark	Part Number
Front Side Gear		
.0209-.0236 (.531-.599)	28	MD727928
.0284-.0299 (.721-.759)	30	MD727930
.0335-.0362 (.851-.919)	32	MD727932
.0398-.0425 (1.011-1.080)	34	MD727934
.0461-.0489 (1.171-1.242)	41	MD727941
Rear Side Gear		
.0232-.0260 (.589-.660)	73	MD724973
.0295-.0323 (.749-.820)	46	MD724946
.0366-.0394 (.930-1.001)	81	MD724981
.0429-.0457 (1.090-1.161)	43	MD724943
.0492-.0520 (1.249-1.321)	72	MD724972

7) Once proper spacers are installed, remove differential flange retaining bolts. Apply thread sealant to bolt threads. Install retaining bolts and tighten in a crisscross pattern to specification. See TORQUE SPECIFICATIONS.

8) Using press, bearing installer and adapter, press tapered bearing on differential flange (if removed). Using press, bearing installer and adapter, press tapered bearing on transfer driven gear (if removed). Press transfer driven gear on differential case.

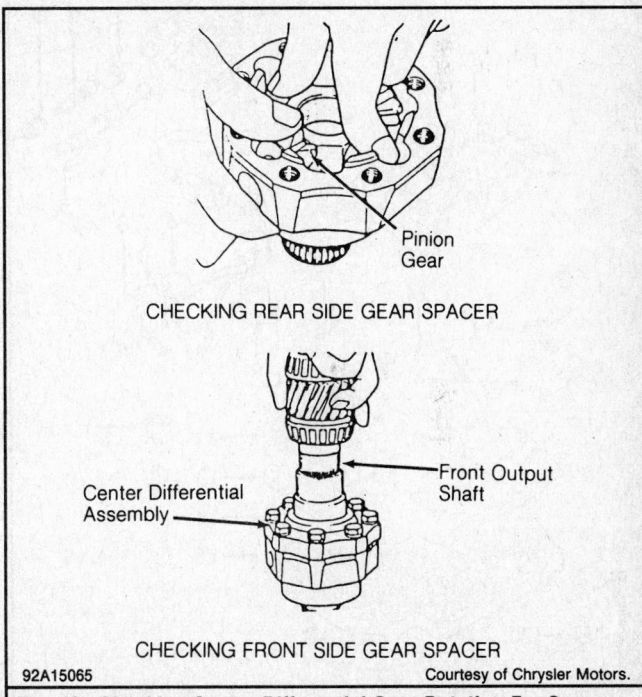

CHECKING REAR SIDE GEAR SPACER

CHECKING FRONT SIDE GEAR SPACER

92A15065   Courtesy of Chrysler Motors.

Fig. 43: Checking Center Differential Gear Rotation For Spacer Selection

FRONT OUTPUT SHAFT (W4A32 & W4A33)

Disassembly & Reassembly – Using press and bearing remover, remove tapered bearings from output shaft if replacement is required. To reassemble, using press, bearing installer and adapters, install tapered bearing on long end of front output shaft. Use bearing installer and adapter to install tapered bearing on short end of front output shaft.

VALVE BODY

CAUTION: When disassembling valve body, place valve body components in order, and mark spring locations for reassembly reference. DO NOT use force to remove components from valve body. Valve body assembly consists of upper and lower valve bodies and intermediate plate. See Fig. 44.

Disassembly – 1) Remove manual valve, all solenoid valves, clip and valve stopper. *See Fig. 44.* Remove N-D control valve and N-D control sleeve.

2) Separate lower valve body and lower separator plate from intermediate plate. Remove nut and jet. *See Fig. 44.* Remove relief spring, steel balls and oil filter from intermediate plate. *See Fig. 45.* Separate upper valve body from intermediate plate. Note location of steel balls, Teflon ball and N-D plate. *See Fig. 45.*

3) Remove steel balls, Teflon ball and N-D plate from upper valve body. Remove block and upper separator plate. Remove remaining components from upper and lower valve bodies. *See Figs. 46 and 47.*

Cleaning & Inspection – 1) Clean components with solvent and dry with compressed air. DO NOT use shop towels to dry components. Ensure all components slide freely in housing bores, and bores are not scored. Inspect machined surfaces for nicks, burrs or distortion.

2) Inspect valve and plugs for burrs or scratches. Ensure all fluid passages are open. Inspect transfer plate and separator plates for distortion. Inspect steel balls, Teflon ball and seats for damage.

Reassembly – 1) Lubricate all components and fluid passages with ATF. Install upper and lower valve body components in original location. *See Figs. 46 and 47.* To verify proper valve body spring application, see VALVE BODY SPRING SPECIFICATIONS table.

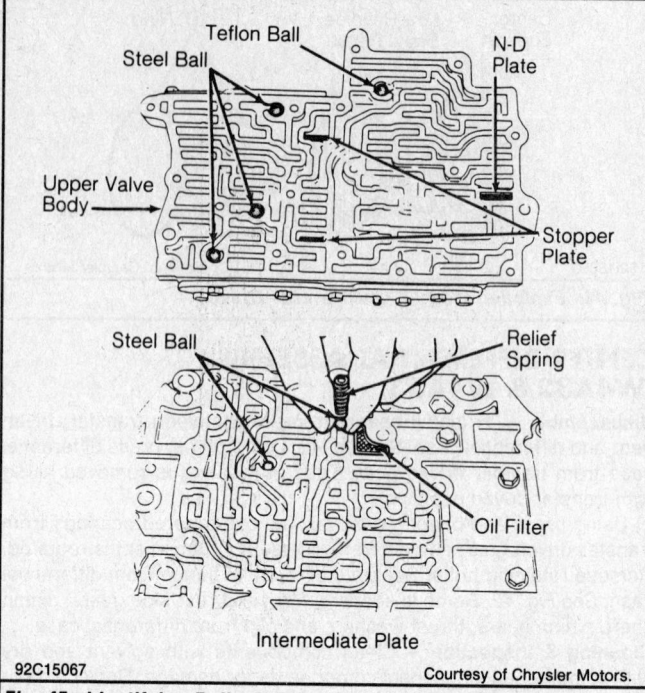

92C15067   Courtesy of Chrysler Motors.

Fig. 45: Identifying Balls, N-D Plate, Oil Filter & Relief Spring

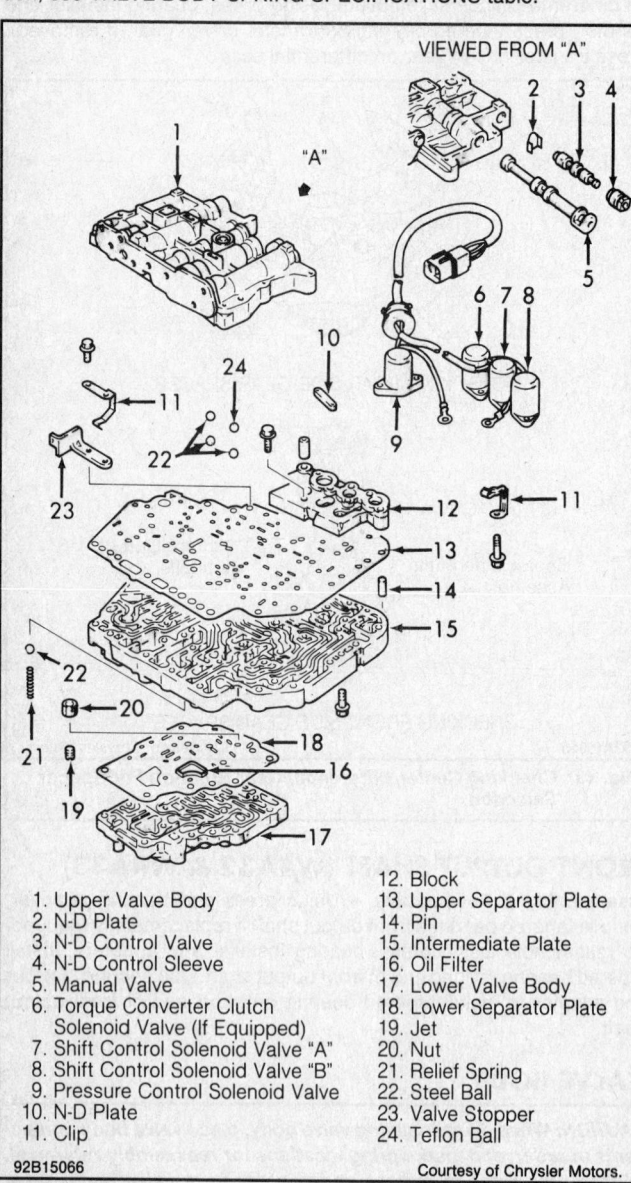

1. Upper Valve Body	12. Block
2. N-D Plate	13. Upper Separator Plate
3. N-D Control Valve	14. Pin
4. N-D Control Sleeve	15. Intermediate Plate
5. Manual Valve	16. Oil Filter
6. Torque Converter Clutch	17. Lower Valve Body
Solenoid Valve (If Equipped)	18. Lower Separator Plate
7. Shift Control Solenoid Valve "A"	19. Jet
8. Shift Control Solenoid Valve "B"	20. Nut
9. Pressure Control Solenoid Valve	21. Relief Spring
10. N-D Plate	22. Steel Ball
11. Clip	23. Valve Stopper
	24. Teflon Ball

92B15066   Courtesy of Chrysler Motors.

Fig. 44: Identifying Valve Bodies & Intermediate Plate

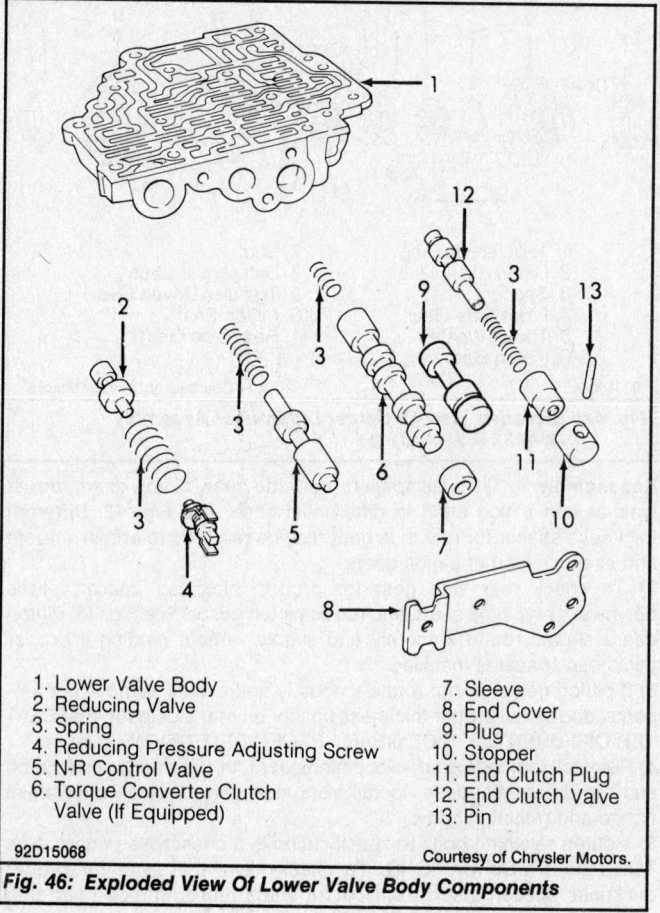

1. Lower Valve Body	7. Sleeve
2. Reducing Valve	8. End Cover
3. Spring	9. Plug
4. Reducing Pressure Adjusting Screw	10. Stopper
5. N-R Control Valve	11. End Clutch Plug
6. Torque Converter Clutch	12. End Clutch Valve
Valve (If Equipped)	13. Pin

92D15068   Courtesy of Chrysler Motors.

Fig. 46: Exploded View Of Lower Valve Body Components

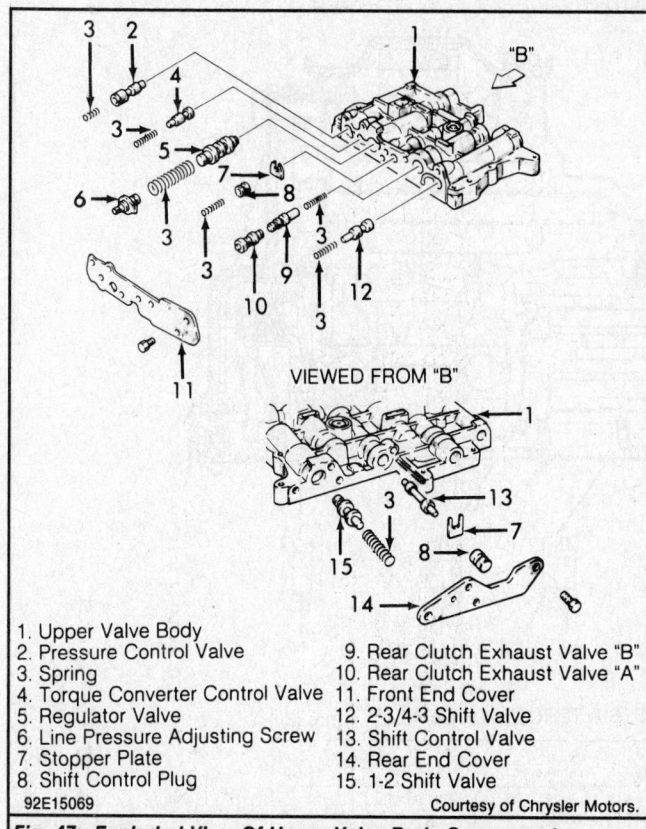

Fig. 47: **Exploded View Of Upper Valve Body Components**

1. Upper Valve Body
2. Pressure Control Valve
3. Spring
4. Torque Converter Control Valve
5. Regulator Valve
6. Line Pressure Adjusting Screw
7. Stopper Plate
8. Shift Control Plug
9. Rear Clutch Exhaust Valve "B"
10. Rear Clutch Exhaust Valve "A"
11. Front End Cover
12. 2-3/4-3 Shift Valve
13. Shift Control Valve
14. Rear End Cover
15. 1-2 Shift Valve

VIEWED FROM "B"

92E15069   Courtesy of Chrysler Motors.

2) Install upper separator plate and block on intermediate plate. *See Fig. 44.* Install steel balls, Teflon ball and N-D plate in upper valve body. *See Fig. 45.* Install guide pins in upper valve body. *See Fig. 48.* Install intermediate plate and upper separator plate on upper valve body.

3) Install valve body bolts to retain upper valve body on intermediate plate. Tighten bolts to specification. See TORQUE SPECIFICATIONS. Remove guide pins.

VALVE BODY SPRING SPECIFICATIONS

	Outside Diameter	Length
Application	In. (mm)	In. (mm)
End Clutch Valve Spring	.260 (6.60)	.961 (24.41)
Line Relief Spring	.276 (7.01)	.681 (17.30)
N-R Control Valve Spring	.370 (9.40)	1.335 (33.90)
Pressure Control Valve Spring	.299 (7.59)	.839 (21.31)
Rear Clutch Exhaust Valve Spring	.268 (6.81)	1.079 (27.41)
Reducing Valve Spring	.350 (8.89)	1.161 (29.49)
Regulator Valve Spring	.590 (14.99)	2.050 (52.07)
Shift Control Valve Spring	.224 (5.69)	1.055 (26.80)
Torque Converter Clutch Valve Spring	.244 (6.20)	.559 (14.20)
Torque Converter Control Valve Spring	.354 (8.99)	.890 (22.61)
1-2 Shift Valve Spring	.299 (7.59)	1.047 (26.59)
2-3 Shift Valve Spring	.276 (7.01)	1.083 (27.51)

4) Install steel balls, relief spring and oil filter in intermediate plate. *See Fig. 45.* Install guide pins in intermediate plate. *See Fig. 48.* Install lower separator plate on intermediate plate.

5) Install lower valve body on intermediate plate. Install valve body bolts to retain lower valve body on intermediate plate. Tighten bolts to specification. *See* TORQUE SPECIFICATIONS. Remove guide pins.

6) To reassemble remaining components, reverse disassembly procedure. Ensure all solenoids valves are installed in proper location. *See Fig. 44.* Solenoid valves can be identified by wire color. See SOLENOID VALVE IDENTIFICATION table.

SOLENOID VALVE IDENTIFICATION

Solenoid	Wire Color
Pressure Control Solenoid Valve	Blue
Shift Control Solenoid Valve "A"	Orange
Shift Control Solenoid Valve "B"	Yellow
Torque Converter Clutch Solenoid Valve	Red/Black

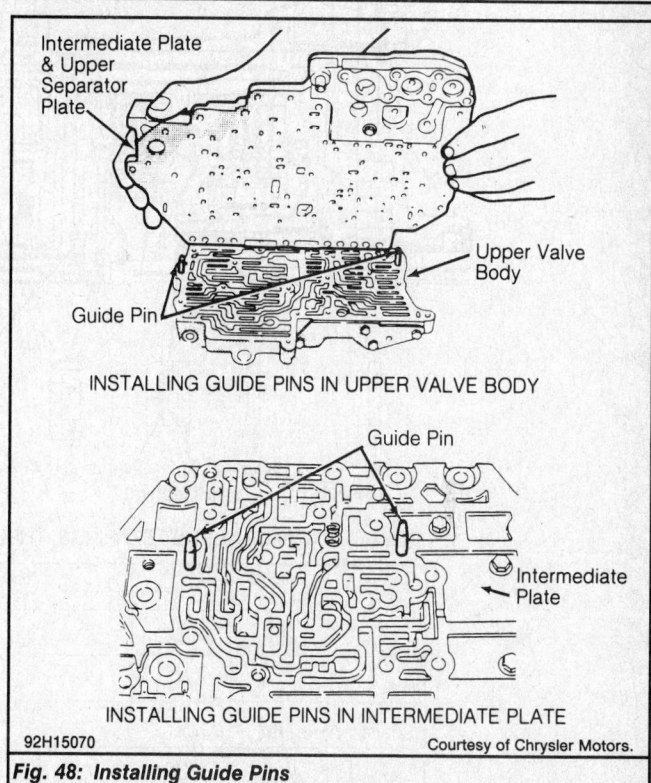

INSTALLING GUIDE PINS IN UPPER VALVE BODY

INSTALLING GUIDE PINS IN INTERMEDIATE PLATE

92H15070   Courtesy of Chrysler Motors.

Fig. 48: **Installing Guide Pins**

TRANSAXLE REASSEMBLY

VALVE BODY & INTERNAL COMPONENTS

NOTE: Lubricate all components with ATF. Apply petroleum jelly on "O" rings and seal rings. Use petroleum jelly to hold thrust bearings, thrust races and thrust washers in position. Ensure thrust bearings, thrust races and thrust washers are installed in original location and proper direction. See Fig. 49.

1) Using appropriate oil seal installer, install NEW drive shaft oil seals. On W4A32 and W4A33 models, align drive shaft oil seal with transaxle case positioning boss. Ensure drive shaft oil seal flange pieces are toward top of transaxle when installed.

2) On all models, use handle and bearing race installer to install bearing race in transaxle case. On F4A33 models, proceed to step **9)**.

3) On W4A32 and W4A33 models, use oil seal installer to install rear output shaft oil seal. Install front output shaft. Place a piece of solder, .06" (1.5 mm) diameter by .40" (10.1 mm) long, on each side of front bearing retainer. *See Fig. 50.* Install outer race.

4) Install front bearing retainer. Install and tighten front bearing retainer bolts to specification. See TORQUE SPECIFICATIONS. Remove retaining bolts and front bearing retainer.

5) Remove outer race from front bearing retainer. Remove solder, and measure thickness of solder. Using measurement of solder, determine proper thickness spacer so front output shaft bearing preload will be .002-.005" (.05-.13 mm). See FRONT OUTPUT SHAFT BEARING SPACER IDENTIFICATION table.

NOTE: If solder does not flatten, it may be necessary to use a larger diameter solder.

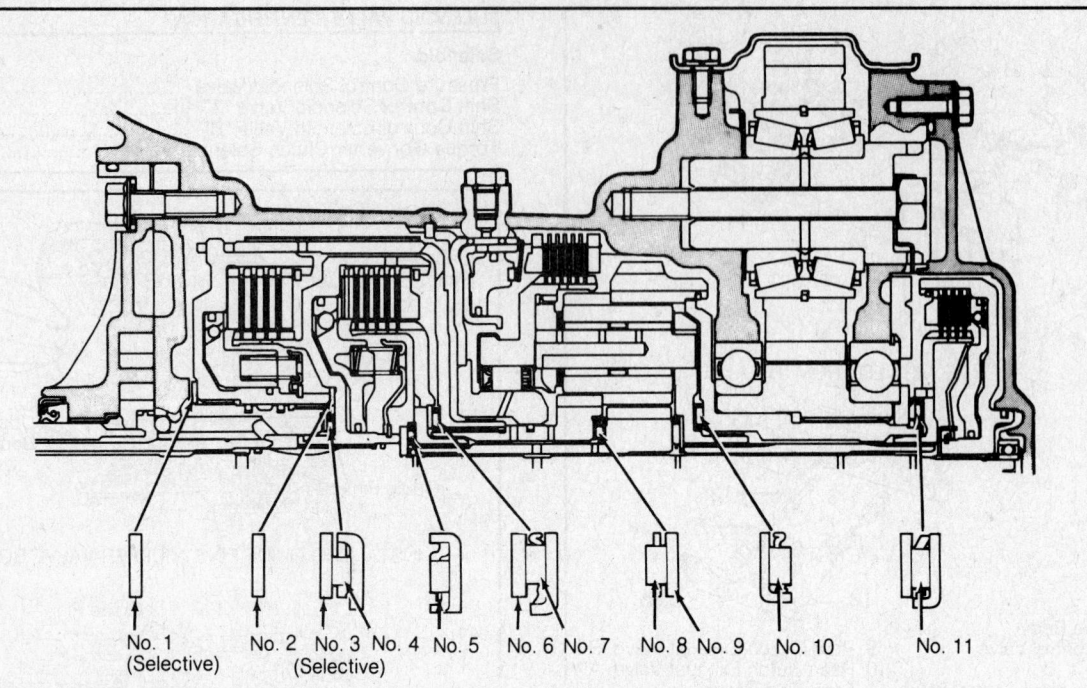

No. 1 (Selective)   No. 2   No. 3   No. 4   No. 5   No. 6   No. 7   No. 8   No. 9   No. 10   No. 11
          (Selective)

IDENTIFICATION OF THRUST BEARINGS, THRUST RACES & THRUST WASHERS   mm (in.)

Outer diameter	Inner diameter	Thickness	Part No.	Code No.	Outer diameter	Inner diameter	Thickness	Part No.	Code No.
70 (2.76)	55.7 (2.193)	1.4 (.055)	*1	#1	48.1 (1.906)	34.4 (1.354)	–	MD707271	#4
70 (2.76)	55.7 (2.193)	1.8 (.071)	*2		42.6 (1.677)	28 (1.10)	–	MD720753	#5
70 (2.76)	55.7 (2.193)	2.2 (.087)	*3		54 (2.13)	38.7 (1.524)	1.6 (.063)	MD704936	#6
70 (2.76)	55.7 (2.193)	2.6 (.102)	*4		52 (2.05)	36.4 (1.433)	–	MD720010	#7
66 (2.60)	54 (23)	1.8 (.071)	MD731212	#2	45 (1.77)	28 (1.10)	–	MD735062	#8
48.9 (1.925)	37 (1.46)	1.0 (.039)	MD997854 (incl. *1)	#3	46 (1.81)	31 (1.22)	0.8 (.031)	MD735063	#9
48.9 (1.925)	37 (1.46)	1.2 (.047)	MD997847 (incl. *1)		52 (2.05)	36.4 (1.433)	–	MD720010	#10
48.9 (1.925)	37 (1.46)	1.4 (.055)	MD997848 (incl. *2)		58 (2.29)	44 (1.73)	–	MD724206	#11
48.9 (1.925)	37 (1.46)	1.6 (.063)	MD997849 (incl. *2)						
48.9 (1.925)	37 (1.46)	1.8 (.071)	MD997850 (incl. *3)						
48.9 (1.925)	37 (1.46)	2.0 (.079)	MD997851 (incl. *3)						
48.9 (1.925)	37 (1.46)	2.2 (.087)	MD997852 (incl. *4)						
48.9 (1.925)	37 (1.46)	2.4 (.094)	MD997853 (incl. *4)						

92I15071   Courtesy of Chrysler Motors.

Fig. 49: Identifying Thrust Bearing, Thrust Race & Thrust Washer Locations

6) Install proper spacer and outer race in front bearing retainer. Install front bearing retainer. Apply thread sealant to front bearing retainer bolts. Install and tighten front bearing retainer bolts to specification.

CAUTION: Ensure thread sealant is applied to front bearing retainer bolts.

7) Using bearing puller installed in grooves, install viscous coupling unit. *See Fig. 22.* Install stopper ring. *See Fig. 15.* Using handle and bearing race installer, install bearing race in center bearing retainer. Install center bearing stopper bolt. *See Fig. 21.* Tighten center bearing stopper bolt to specification.

8) Install center bearing retainer in transaxle case so shoulder on center bearing stopper bolt engages notch on center bearing retainer. *See Fig. 51.* Thread puller into hole in end of center differential assembly and install center differential assembly.

CAUTION: Ensure shoulder on center bearing stopper bolt engages notch on center bearing retainer. See Fig. 51.

9) On F4A33 models, install transfer shaft in transaxle case. On all models, place a piece of solder, .06" (1.5 mm) diameter by .40" (10.1 mm) long, on each side of output bearing retainer. *See Fig. 50.* Install outer race.

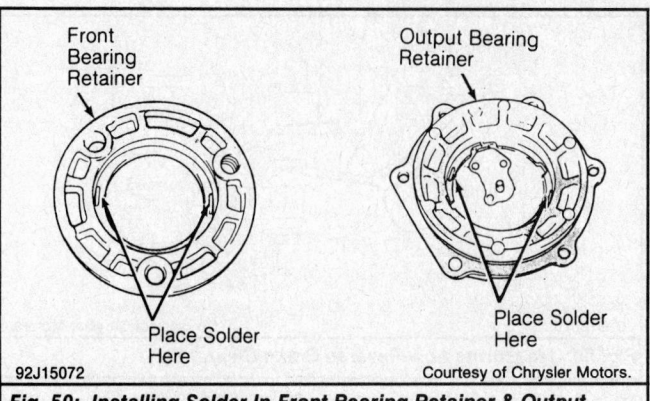

Front Bearing Retainer

Output Bearing Retainer

Place Solder Here

Place Solder Here

92J15072

Courtesy of Chrysler Motors.

Fig. 50: Installing Solder In Front Bearing Retainer & Output Bearing Retainer

FRONT OUTPUT SHAFT BEARING SPACER IDENTIFICATION

Spacer Thickness In. (mm)	Identification Mark	Part Number
.0457 (1.160)	16	MD736929
.0469 (1.191)	19	MD736751
.0480 (1.220)	22	MD736931
.0492 (1.250)	25	MD726166
.0504 (1.280)	28	MD718517
.0516 (1.310)	31	MD718518
.0528 (1.341)	34	MD718519
.0539 (1.369)	37	MD718520
.0551 (1.400)	40	MD718521
.0563 (1.430)	43	MD718522
.0575 (1.461)	46	MD718523
.0587 (1.491)	49	MD718524
.0598 (1.519)	52	MD718525
.0610 (1.549)	55	MD718526
.0622 (1.580)	58	MD718527
.0634 (1.610)	61	MD718528
.0646 (1.641)	64	MD718529
.0657 (1.669)	67	MD718530
.0669 (1.690)	70	MD718531
.0681 (1.730)	73	MD721959
.0693 (1.760)	76	MD721960

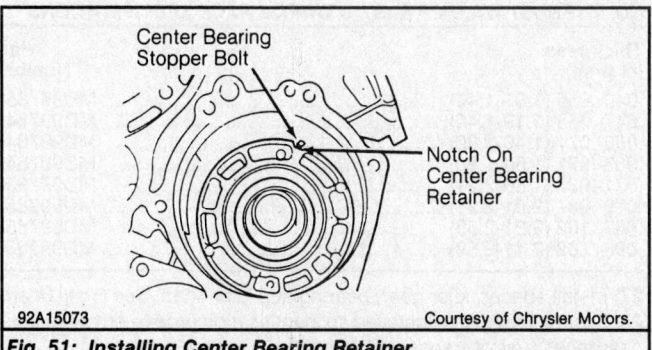

Center Bearing Stopper Bolt

Notch On Center Bearing Retainer

92A15073

Courtesy of Chrysler Motors.

Fig. 51: Installing Center Bearing Retainer

10) Install output bearing retainer without "O" ring. Install and tighten output bearing retainer bolts to specification. See TORQUE SPECIFICATIONS. Remove retaining bolts and output bearing retainer.

11) Remove outer race from output bearing retainer. Remove solder and measure thickness of solder. Using measurement of solder, determine proper thickness spacer so transfer shaft or center differential bearing preload will be .003-.005" (.07-.13 mm). See TRANSFER SHAFT OR CENTER DIFFERENTIAL BEARING SPACER IDENTIFICATION table.

NOTE: If solder does not flatten, it may be necessary to use a larger diameter solder.

TRANSFER SHAFT OR CENTER DIFFERENTIAL BEARING SPACER IDENTIFICATION

Spacer Thickness In. (mm)	Identification Mark	Part Number
.0244 (.620)	62	MD737444
.0256 (.650)	65	MD737445
.0268 (.681)	68	MD737446
.0280 (.711)	71	MD737447
.0291 (.739)	74	MD728802
.0303 (.770)	77	MD728803
.0315 (.800)	80	MD728804
.0327 (.831)	83	MD728805
.0339 (.861)	86	MD728806
.0350 (.889)	89	MD728807
.0362 (.919)	92	MD728808
.0374 (.950)	95	MD728809
.0386 (.980)	98	MD728810
.0398 (1.010)	01	MD728811
.0409 (1.039)	04	MD728812
.0421 (1.069)	07	MD728813
.0433 (1.100)	10	MD728814
.0445 (1.130)	13	MD728815
.0457 (1.161)	16	MD728816
.0469 (1.191)	19	MD728817
.0480 (1.220)	22	MD728818
.0492 (1.250)	25	MD728819
.0504 (1.280)	28	MD728820
.0516 (1.311)	31	MD728821

12) Install proper spacer and outer race in output bearing retainer. Install NEW "O" ring on output bearing retainer. Lubricate "O" ring with ATF.

13) Install output bearing retainer. Install and tighten output bearing retainer bolts to specification. See TORQUE SPECIFICATIONS. Install output flange in transaxle case. Install snap ring in bearing outer circumference.

14) Install bearing retainer and NEW retaining bolts. Tighten retaining bolts to specification. Stake heads of bearing retainer bolts against bearing retainer.

CAUTION: Always install NEW retaining bolts for bearing retainer. Ensure retaining bolts are staked against bearing retainer.

15) Coat No. 10 thrust bearing with petroleum jelly and install on rear of planetary carrier assembly. *See Fig. 13.* Install planetary carrier assembly in transaxle case.

16) Assemble forward sun gear, No. 9 thrust race, No. 8 thrust bearing and reverse sun gear. *See Fig. 52.* Install forward and reverse sun gear assembly in planetary carrier assembly.

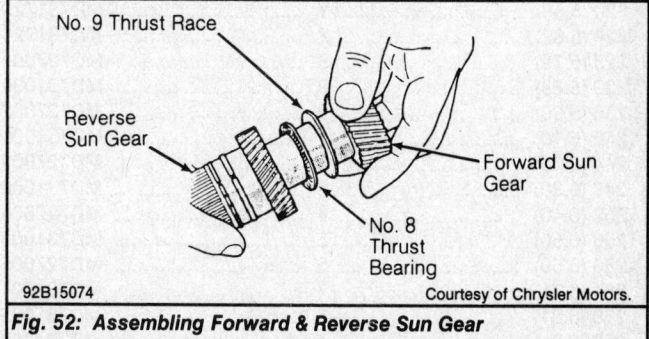

No. 9 Thrust Race

Reverse Sun Gear

Forward Sun Gear

No. 8 Thrust Bearing

92B15074

Courtesy of Chrysler Motors.

Fig. 52: Assembling Forward & Reverse Sun Gear

17) Ensure clutch discs have been soaked in ATF for at least 2 hours. Install reaction plate, clutch discs, clutch plates and pressure plate in transaxle case. *See Fig. 13.* Install return spring with raised side away from pressure plate. *See Fig. 53.*

CAUTION: Clutch discs must be soaked in ATF for 2 hours before installing. Ensure return spring is installed with raised side away from pressure plate. See Fig. 53.

18) Coat wave spring with petroleum jelly and install on center support. Using handle, install center support and 2 "O" rings in transaxle case.

CAUTION: Ensure center support aligns with oil hole and wave spring is aligned.

19) Install snap ring to retain center support in transaxle case. Using feeler gauge, measure low-reverse brake clearance. *See Fig. 54.* Low-reverse brake clearance should be .039-.047" (.99-1.19 mm).
20) If low-reverse brake clearance is not within specification, select different thickness pressure plate to obtain correct clearance. See PRESSURE PLATE IDENTIFICATION table.

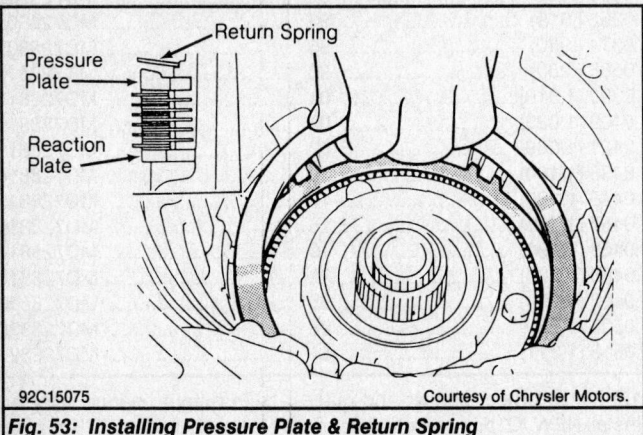

Fig. 53: Installing Pressure Plate & Return Spring

92C15075   Courtesy of Chrysler Motors.

PRESSURE PLATE IDENTIFICATION

Plate Thickness In. (mm)	Identification Mark	Part Number
F4A33 & W4A33		
.232 (5.89)	A	MD731736
.236 (5.99)	0	MD731737
.240 (6.10)	1	MD731738
.244 (6.20)	2	MD731739
.248 (6.30)	3	MD731740
.252 (6.40)	4	MD731588
.256 (6.50)	5	MD731741
.260 (6.60)	6	MD731742
.264 (6.71)	7	MD731743
.268 (6.81)	8	MD731744
.272 (6.91)	9	MD731745
W4A32		
.220 (5.59)	Y	MD731720
.224 (5.69)	Z	MD731721
.228 (5.79)	8	MD727801
.232 (5.89)	9	MD731000
.236 (5.99)	0	MD727802
.240 (6.10)	1	MD731001
.244 (6.20)	2	MD727803
.248 (6.30)	3	MD731002
.252 (6.40)	4	MD727804
.256 (6.50)	5	MD731003
.260 (6.60)	6	MD727805
.264 (6.71)	7	MD731004
.268 (6.81)	X	MD731005
.272 (6.91)	A	MD734766
.276 (7.01)	B	MD734767

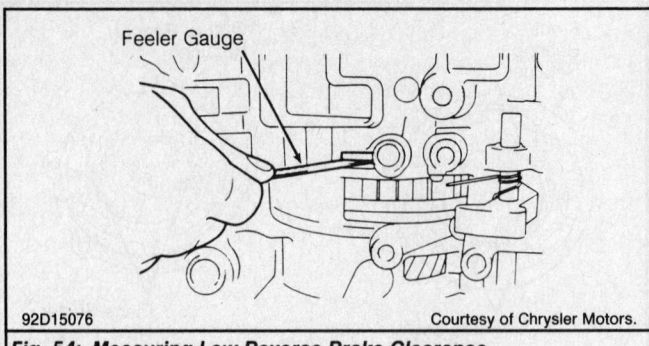

Fig. 54: Measuring Low-Reverse Brake Clearance

92D15076   Courtesy of Chrysler Motors.

21) Install air exhaust plug and plug. *See Fig. 18.* Tighten plug to specification. See TORQUE SPECIFICATIONS. Install anchor rod, spring and kickdown servo piston.

CAUTION: Ensure ends of seal rings on kickdown servo piston DO NOT align with oil supply passages in kickdown servo bore on transaxle case.

22) Using cup, adapter and compressor, depress kickdown servo piston. *See Fig. 17.* Install snap ring. Remove cup, adapter and compressor. Install kickdown band with arrow on kickdown band pointing toward oil pump end of transaxle.
23) Install No. 4 thrust bearing and No. 2 thrust washer on rear clutch assembly. *See Fig. 13.* Assemble front and rear clutch assembly. Install No. 5 thrust bearing in rear clutch hub. *See Fig. 13.* Install rear clutch hub in rear clutch. Install No. 6 thrust race on end of rear clutch hub.
24) Install No. 7 thrust bearing in kickdown drum. *See Fig. 13.* Install front and rear clutch assembly in kickdown drum. Install front and rear clutch assembly with kickdown drum in transaxle case.
25) Coat No. 1 thrust washer and No. 3 thrust race with petroleum jelly and install on rear of oil pump. *See Fig. 13.* Install NEW gasket and install oil pump in transaxle case. Install and tighten oil pump retaining bolts to specification. See TORQUE SPECIFICATIONS.
26) Using dial indicator, check input shaft end play. Input shaft end play should be .012-.039" (.30-.99 mm). If input shaft end play is not within specification, replace No. 1 thrust washer and No. 3 thrust race as a set to obtain correct end play. See NO. 1 THRUST WASHER & NO. 3 THRUST RACE SPECIFICATIONS table.

NO. 1 THRUST WASHER & NO. 3 THRUST RACE SPECIFICATIONS

Thickness In. (mm)	Part Number
.040-.055 (1.01-1.40)	MD997854
.047-.055 (1.19-1.40)	MD997847
.055-.071 (1.40-1.80)	MD997848
.063-.071 (1.60-1.80)	MD997849
.071-.087 (1.80-2.21)	MD997850
.079-.087 (2.01-2.21)	MD997851
.087-.102 (2.21-2.59)	MD997852
.095-1.02 (2.41-2.59)	MD997853

27) Install spacer, idler gear, bearing and idler shaft. *See Figs. 14 and 15.* Ensure idle gear is installed so identification groove on end of idler gear faces rear of transaxle (away from oil pump).
28) Install NEW lock plate on lock bolt for idler gear shaft. Install lock bolt and tighten to specification. Bend lock tabs over on lock plate.
29) Install NEW idler gear cover gasket. Install idler gear cover and retaining bolts. Tighten retaining bolts to specification. See TORQUE SPECIFICATIONS. Install end clutch shaft with long splined area toward transaxle.
30) Install thrust washer on end clutch assembly. Install end clutch hub in end clutch assembly. *See Figs. 14 and 15.* Coat No. 11 thrust bearing with petroleum jelly and install on end clutch hub.
31) Install end clutch assembly. Install NEW "O" ring and end clutch cover. Install and tighten end clutch cover retaining bolts to specification. See TORQUE SPECIFICATIONS.

32) On W4A32 and W4A33 models, install bearing outer race on differential assembly. Place a piece of solder, .06" (1.5 mm) diameter by .40" (10.1 mm) long, on each side of bearing outer race. *See Fig. 55.*

33) On F4A33 models, place a piece of solder, .06" (1.5 mm) diameter by .40" (10.1 mm) long, on each side of differential bearing retainer. *See Fig. 55.* Install outer race.

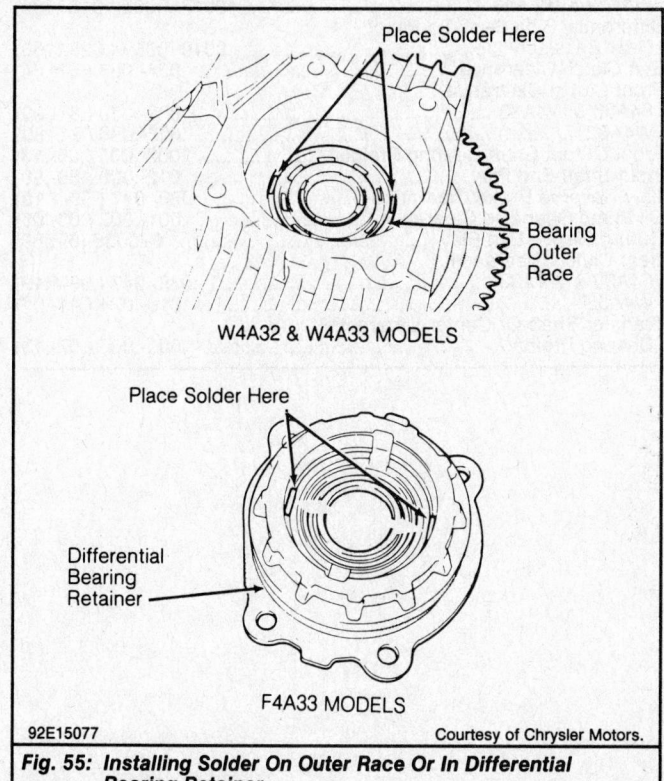

Place Solder Here

Bearing Outer Race

W4A32 & W4A33 MODELS

Place Solder Here

Differential Bearing Retainer

F4A33 MODELS

92E15077   Courtesy of Chrysler Motors.

Fig. 55: Installing Solder On Outer Race Or In Differential Bearing Retainer

34) On all models, install differential bearing retainer without "O" ring. Install and tighten differential bearing retainer bolts to specification. See TORQUE SPECIFICATIONS. Remove retaining bolts and differential bearing retainer.

35) On F4A33 models, remove outer race from differential bearing retainer. On all models, remove solder and measure thickness of the solder. Using measurement of solder, determine proper thickness spacer so differential assembly end play and preload are within specification. See DIFFERENTIAL ASSEMBLY END PLAY & PRELOAD SPECIFICATIONS and DIFFERENTIAL ASSEMBLY SPACER IDENTIFICATION tables.

NOTE: If solder does not flatten, it may be necessary to use a larger diameter solder.

---

36) Install proper spacer. Install NEW "O" ring on differential bearing retainer. Lubricate "O" ring with ATF. Install differential bearing retainer. Install and tighten differential bearing retainer bolts to specification. See TORQUE SPECIFICATIONS.

37) Install differential bearing cap. Position "S" mark on bearing cap at short bolt location and "L" mark at long bolt location. Install and tighten retaining bolts to specification.

38) Install NEW gasket and differential cover. Install and tighten retaining bolts to specification. Install detent in transaxle case. Detent fits in opening in transaxle case, near manual control shaft.

39) Install NEW "O" ring on manual control shaft and lubricate with ATF. Install manual control shaft. Install manual control shaft retaining set screw, located near top of manual control shaft area on transaxle case. Tighten set screw to specification.

40) Install parking roller support and retaining bolts. Tighten retaining bolts to specification. Install oil temperature sensor in transaxle case.

DIFFERENTIAL ASSEMBLY END PLAY & PRELOAD SPECIFICATIONS

Application	In. (mm)
F4A33	.0030-.0053 (.076-.135)
W4A32 & W4A33	.0018-.0065 (.046-.165)

DIFFERENTIAL ASSEMBLY SPACER IDENTIFICATION

Spacer Thickness In. (mm)	Identification Mark	Part Number
F4A33		
Laser & Talon		
.0327 (.831)	83	MD720937
.0339 (.861)	86	MD720938
.0350 (.889)	89	MD720939
.0362 (.919)	92	MD720940
.0374 (.950)	95	MD720941
.0386 (.980)	98	MD720942
.0409 (1.039)	04	MD720944
.0421 (1.069)	07	MD720945
.0445 (1.130)	D	MD700270
.0457 (1.161)	K	MD710455
.0480 (1.219)	G	MD700271
.0492 (1.250)	M	MD710457
.0516 (1.311)	E	MD706574
.0528 (1.341)	O	MD710459
.0539 (1.369)	P	MD710460
Stealth		
.0280 (.711)	71	MD754446
.0291 (.741)	74	MD754447
.0303 (.771)	77	MD754448
.0315 (.801)	80	MD754449
.0327 (.831)	83	MD740846
.0339 (.861)	86	MD740847
.0350 (.889)	89	MD740848
.0362 (.919)	92	MD740849
.0374 (.950)	95	MD740850
.0386 (.980)	98	MD740851
.0398 (1.011)	01	MD740852
.0409 (1.039)	04	MD740853
.0421 (1.069)	07	MD740854
.0433 (1.100)	10	MD740855
.0445 (1.130)	13	MD740856
.0457 (1.161)	16	MD740857
.0469 (1.191)	19	MD740858
.0480 (1.219)	22	MD740859
.0492 (1.250)	25	MD740860
.0504 (1.280)	28	MD740861
.0516 (1.311)	31	MD740862
.0528 (1.341)	34	MD740863
.0539 (1.369)	37	MD740864
W4A32 & W4A33		
.0398 (1.011)	01	MD720943
.0433 (1.100)	J	MD710454
.0469 (1.191)	L	MD710456
.0504 (1.280)	N	MD710458

41) Install NEW "O" ring on solenoid valve wiring harness and in groove on top of valve body. *See Fig. 11.* Install solenoid valve wiring harness connector from inside transaxle case, and install grommet.

42) Install valve body. Ensure detent plate pin engages with groove on manual valve. Install retaining bolts, ensuring proper length bolt is installed in designated area. *See Fig. 12.* Tighten valve body bolts to specification. See TORQUE SPECIFICATIONS.

CAUTION: Position wiring so it does not contact detent plate. Ensure parking rod is properly retained in clamps. See Fig. 12.

---

43) Install oil filter, magnet, gasket, oil pan, inhibitor switch, manual control lever and speedometer gear assembly. Tighten bolts to specification.

44) Note color of tubes on pulse generators. Install pulse generators in proper location according to color of tubes. See Fig. 16. Tighten bolts to specification.

CAUTION: Ensure pulse generators are installed in correct location. See Fig. 16.

---

45) Install dipstick tube and dipstick. Adjust kickdown servo. See KICKDOWN SERVO under ADJUSTMENTS. Install kickdown servo switch and snap ring.

46) On W4A32 and W4A33 models, coat seal for rear output shaft with ATF. Install rear output shaft. Using soft-faced hammer, lightly tap on rear output shaft to ensure shaft is fully seated. On all models, coat hub on torque converter with ATF and install torque converter. Ensure torque converter is fully seated.

CAUTION: If transaxle failure existed, ensure oil cooler is flushed.

TORQUE SPECIFICATIONS
TORQUE SPECIFICATIONS

Application	Ft. Lbs. (N.m)
Air Exhaust Plug	22-25 (30-34)
Bearing Retainer Bolt	13-14 (18-19)
Differential Bearing Cap Bolt	43-58 (58-79)
Differential Bearing Retainer Bolt	22-28 (30-38)
Differential Flange-To-Differential Case Bolt	51-57 (69-77)
Front Bearing Retainer Bolt	32-39 (43-53)
Idler Gear Lock Bolt	22-32 (30-43)
Kickdown Servo Lock Nut	18-23 (24-31)
Manual Control Lever Bolt	12-15 (16-20)
Oil Pump-To-Transaxle Case Bolt	14-16 (19-22)
Output Bearing Retainer Bolt	15-19 (20-26)
Parking Roller Support Bolt	15-19 (20-26)
Ring Gear Bolt	94-101 (127-137)

	INCH Lbs. (N.m)
Center Bearing Stopper Bolt	36-48 (4.1-5.4)
Differential Cover Bolt	89-102 (10.1-11.5)
End Clutch Cover Bolt	89-102 (10.1-11.5)
Hydraulic Pressure Tap Plug	36-48 (4.1-5.4)
Idler Gear Cover Bolt	89-102 (10.1-11.5)
Inhibitor Switch Bolt	89-102 (10.1-11.5)
Manual Control Shaft Set Screw	72-84 (8.1-9.5)
Oil Filter Bolt	48-60 (5.4-6.8)
Oil Pan Bolt	89-102 (10.1-11.5)
Pulse Generator Bolt	89-102 (10.1-11.5)
Reaction Shaft Support Bolt	84-108 (9.5-12.2)
Speedometer Gear Assembly Bolt	36-48 (4.1-5.4)
Valve Body Bolt	
Valve Body-To-Transaxle Case Bolt	89-102 (10.1-11.5)
Upper & Lower Valve Body Bolt	36-48 (4.1-5.4)

TRANSAXLE SPECIFICATIONS
TRANSAXLE SPECIFICATIONS

Application	In. (mm)
Differential Assembly End Play & Preload	
F4A33	.0030-.0053 (.076-.135)
W4A32 & W4A33	.0018-.0065 (.046-.165)
Differential Side Gear-To-Pinion	
Gear Backlash	.0010-.0059 (.025-.150)
End Clutch Clearance	.024-.033 (.61-.84)
Front Clutch Clearance	
F4A33 & W4A33	.032-.039 (.81-.99)
W4A32	.028-.035 (.71-.89)
Front Output Shaft Bearing Preload	.002-.005 (.05-.13)
Input Shaft End Play	.012-.039 (.30-.99)
Low-Reverse Brake Clearance	.039-.047 (.99-1.19)
Oil Pump Gear End Clearance	.001-.002 (.03-.05)
Output Flange End Play	0-.0035 (0-.089)
Rear Clutch Clearance	
F4A33 & W4A33	.039-.047 (.99-1.19)
W4A32	.016-.024 (.41-.61)
Transfer Shaft Or Center Differential	
Bearing Preload	.003-.005 (.07-.13)

APPLICATION

TRANSAXLE APPLICATIONS

Model	Transaxle
Colt Vista & Summit Wagon	
AWD	W4A32
Laser & Talon	
2.0L Turbo	
2WD	F4A33
AWD	W4A33
Stealth	F4A33

DESCRIPTION

The transaxle electronic control system controls transaxle shift points and torque converter clutch control for torque converter lock-up. Transaxle uses hydraulically operated clutches controlled by the Transaxle Control Unit (TCU). Overdrive or 4th gear operation is controlled by a manually operated overdrive control switch. Transaxle will not shift into overdrive unless overdrive control switch is in the ON position.

OPERATION

TRANSAXLE CONTROL UNIT (TCU)

The TCU receives information from various input devices and controls various output devices for different gear operation. The TCU is located behind instrument panel, near center of console, and contains a 42-pin connector. See Fig. 1, 2 or 3.

On all models except Colt Vista and Summit Wagon, a POWER/ECONOMY switch, located on center of console, is used to change shift patterns. The pre-set shift patterns are controlled by the TCU.

The TCU controller contains a self-diagnostic system which stores a Diagnostic Trouble Code (DTC) if a transaxle fault exists. Trouble code can be retrieved to determine transaxle problem area. See SELF-DIAGNOSTIC SYSTEM. The TCU contains a fail-safe mode. If certain trouble codes are set, transaxle will enter the fail-safe mode. When in fail-safe mode, transaxle will remain in 2nd or 3rd gear with no upshifts or downshifts. Transaxle will also function in Park, Neutral and Reverse when in fail-safe mode.

Transaxle controller works in conjunction with the engine controller for receiving information for transaxle control. See ENGINE CONTROLLER LOCATION table.

ENGINE CONTROLLER LOCATION

Application	Location
Colt Vista & Summit Wagon	Right Side Of Instrument Panel, Near Kick Panel
Laser, Stealth & Talon	Located Below Instrument Panel, Near Center Console

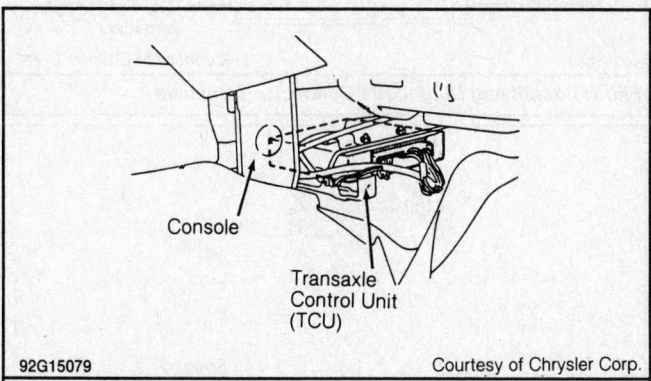

92G15079   Courtesy of Chrysler Corp.

Fig. 1: Identifying TCU Location (Colt Vista & Summit Wagon)

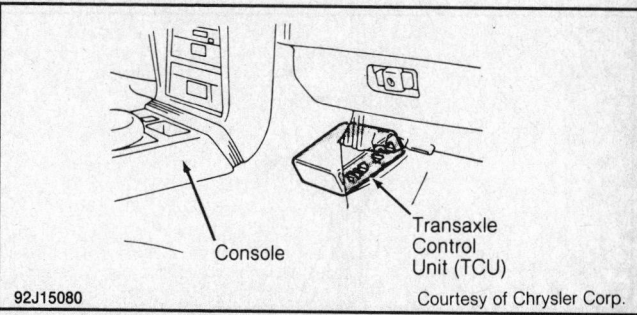

92J15080   Courtesy of Chrysler Corp.

Fig. 2: Identifying TCU Location (Laser & Talon)

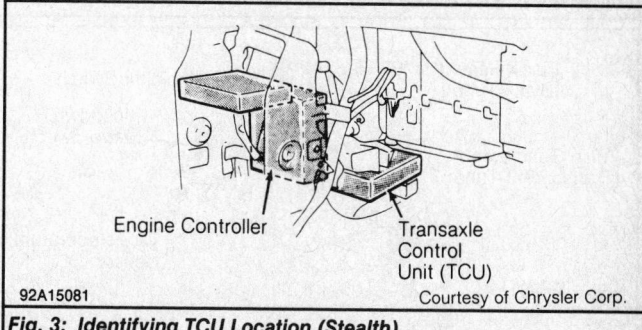

92A15081   Courtesy of Chrysler Corp.

Fig. 3: Identifying TCU Location (Stealth)

INPUT DEVICES

Accelerator Pedal Switch – Accelerator pedal switch is located near accelerator pedal. See Fig. 4. Accelerator pedal switch delivers an input signal to TCU to indicate position of accelerator pedal.

Inhibitor Switch – Inhibitor switch is an input device mounted on the transaxle manual control shaft. See Fig. 5. Inhibitor switch delivers an input signal to TCU, indicating transaxle manual valve gear position.

Kickdown Servo Switch – Kickdown servo switch is an input device mounted on the side of transaxle case. See Fig. 5. Kickdown servo switch delivers an input signal to the TCU to indicate kickdown servo operation.

Oil Temperature Sensor – Oil temperature sensor is an input device mounted inside the transaxle case. See Fig. 5. Oil temperature delivers an input signal to the TCU to indicate the fluid temperature.

NOTE: Oil temperature sensor may also be referred to as fluid temperature sensor. It may be necessary to identify wire color to oil temperature sensor for proper identification. See appropriate wiring diagram under WIRING DIAGRAMS.

Overdrive Control Switch – Overdrive control switch, located on gear selector lever, delivers an input signal to the TCU. Transaxle will not shift into overdrive unless overdrive control switch is in the ON position.

POWER/ECONOMY Switch (Except Colt Vista & Summit Wagon) – The POWER/ECONOMY switch, located on center of console, delivers an input signal to the TCU. The TCU uses this signal to change shift patterns.

Pulse Generators – Pulse generators are mounted on transaxle case. Pulse generator "A" is the lower pulse generator and "B" is the upper pulse generator. See Fig. 5. Pulse generators indicate shaft speed and delivers input signal to the TCU for transaxle control.

Throttle Position Sensor (TPS) – The TPS, mounted on the throttle body, determines throttle position and inputs a signal to the TCU. The TCU uses signal to control transaxle upshifts.

Vehicle Speed Sensor – Vehicle speed sensor inputs signal to the TCU to indicate vehicle speed. Vehicle speed sensor is mounted on rear of instrument cluster.

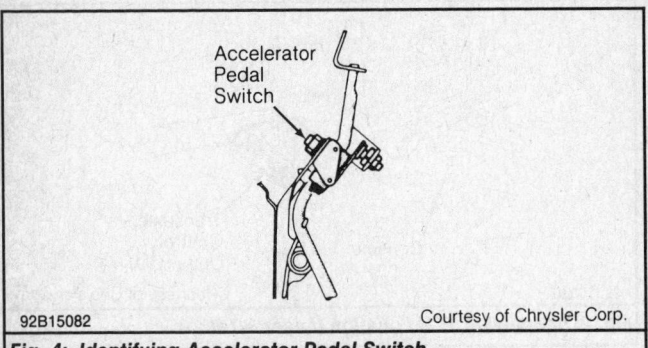

92B15082   Courtesy of Chrysler Corp.

Fig. 4: Identifying Accelerator Pedal Switch

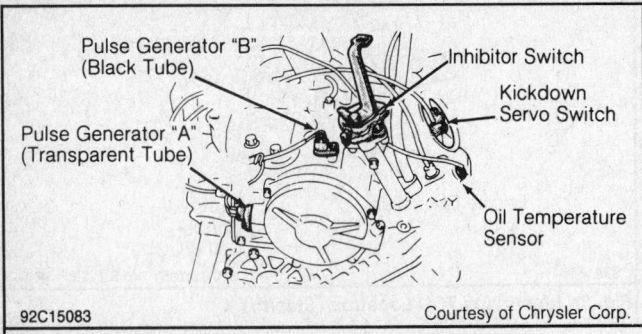

92C15083   Courtesy of Chrysler Corp.

Fig. 5: Identifying Inhibitor Switch, Oil Temperature Sensor, Kickdown Servo Switch & Pulse Generators

OUTPUT DEVICES

NOTE: For solenoid valve wire color identification, see WIRING DIAGRAMS.

Pressure Control Solenoid Valve (PCSV) – The PCSV is located on the valve body. *See Fig. 6.* The TCU operates the PCSV for controlling transaxle shifts.

Shift Control Solenoid Valve (SCSV) – The SCSV "A" or "B" are located on the valve body. *See Fig. 6.* The TCU operates the SCSV for controlling transaxle shifts.

Torque Converter Clutch Solenoid Valve (TCCSV) – The TCCSV is located on the valve body. *See Fig. 6.* The TCU operates the TCCSV for torque converter clutch control of torque converter lock-up.

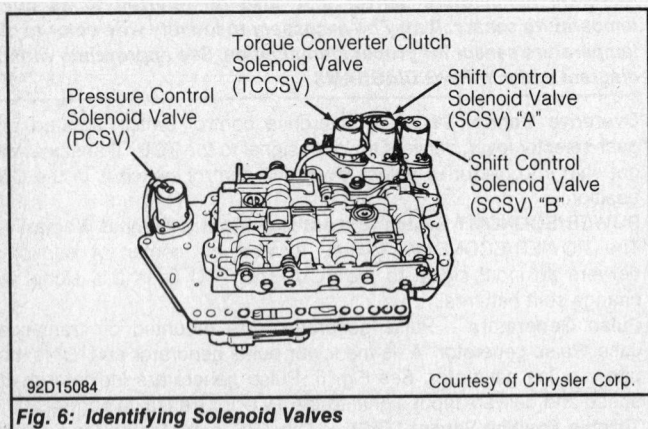

92D15084   Courtesy of Chrysler Corp.

Fig. 6: Identifying Solenoid Valves

SELF-DIAGNOSTIC SYSTEM

DIAGNOSTIC PROCEDURE

When performing vehicle diagnosis, the following procedures must be followed:
- Ensure transaxle fluid level is correct and not contaminated or aerated.

- Ensure shift cable is properly adjusted by ensuring vehicle starts in only Park or Neutral. If adjustment is required, see appropriate AUTOMATIC TRANSMISSION SERVICING article in TRANSMISSION SERVICING.
- Ensure all electrical connections at transaxle, TCU, throttle position sensor, inhibitor switch and accelerator switch are clean and properly installed.

RETRIEVING TROUBLE CODES

1) Locate diagnostic connector below left side of instrument panel. *See Fig. 7.* Install voltmeter between ground terminal and TCU diagnostic terminal.

NOTE: Diagnostic connector may also be referred to as CHECK CONNECTOR.

2) Turn ignition on. Note fluctuations of voltmeter needle to indicate the trouble code. The first fluctuation indicates first trouble code digit. Following fluctuations indicate the second trouble code digit. *See Fig. 8.* Record trouble codes in the order they are displayed.

3) If transaxle is not in fail-safe mode, a maximum of 10 trouble codes can be stored. If number of stored trouble codes exceeds 10, previously stored trouble codes will be erased beginning with the oldest trouble code.

4) If transaxle is in fail-safe mode and transaxle remains in 2nd or 3rd gear, a special fail-safe trouble code will be stored. Only 3 fail-safe trouble codes can be stored.

5) When in fail-safe mode with transaxle locked in 2nd or 3rd gear, fail-safe mode will be cancelled when ignition is turned off. Transaxle will no longer be locked in 2nd or 3rd gear, but fail-safe trouble code will be stored in TCU memory.

6) To identify trouble code and items to be checked or adjusted, see DTC IDENTIFICATION. To check electrical system components, see ELECTRONIC TROUBLE SHOOTING.

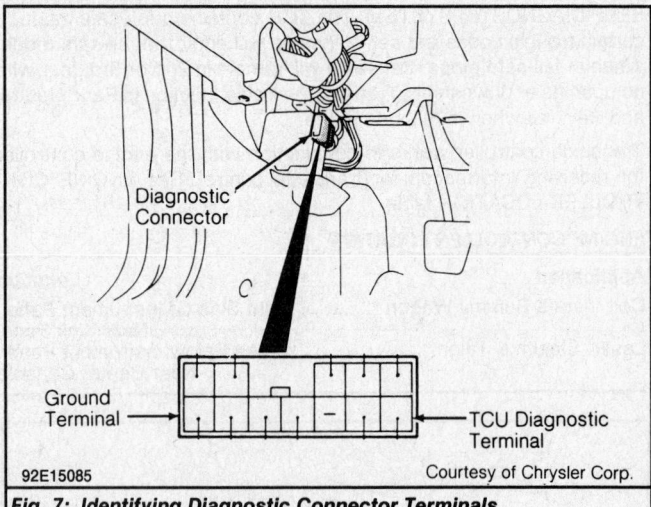

92E15085   Courtesy of Chrysler Corp.

Fig. 7: Identifying Diagnostic Connector Terminals

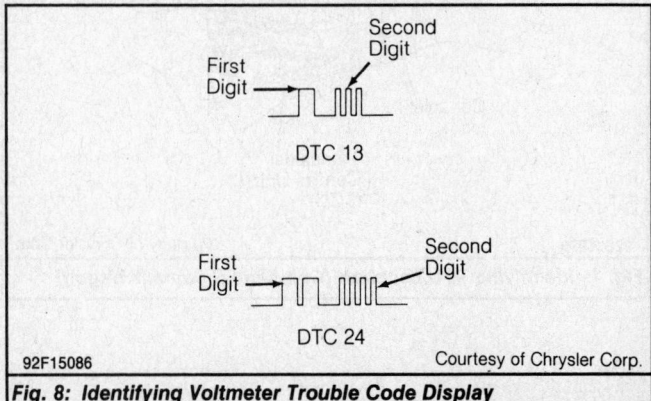

92F15086   Courtesy of Chrysler Corp.

Fig. 8: Identifying Voltmeter Trouble Code Display

DTC IDENTIFICATION

DIAGNOSTIC TROUBLE CODE (DTC) IDENTIFICATION

DTC Number	Probable Cause	Fail-Safe Mode	[1] Items To Check
11	High TPS Output	No	Check TPS Operation, Adjustment & Connector, Check Accelerator Switch, Check For DTC No. 24
12	Low TPS Output	No	Check TPS Operation, Adjustment & Connector, Check Accelerator Switch, Check For DTC No. 24
13	Defective Or Improperly Adjusted TPS	No	Check TPS Operation & Adjustment
14	Improperly Adjusted TPS	No	Check TPS Adjustment
15	Open Oil Temperature Sensor Circuit (Low Temperature Side)	No	Check Oil Temperature Sensor & Connector
21	Open Kickdown Servo Switch Circuit	No	Check Kickdown Servo Switch & Connector
22	Shorted Kickdown Servo Switch Circuit	No	Check Kickdown Servo Switch & Connector
23	Open Ignition Pulse Signal Circuit	No	Check For Open Circuit To Pins No. 46 Or 63 At TCU
24	Improperly Adjusted Accelerator Switch Or Open Circuit	No	Check Accelerator Switch Adjustment & Connector
31	Open Pulse Generator "A" Circuit	No	Check Pulse Generator, Check Vehicle Speed Sensor
32	Open Pulse Generator "B" Circuit	No	Check Pulse Generator, Check Vehicle Speed Sensor
41	Open Shift Control Solenoid Valve "A" Circuit	No	Check Shift Control Solenoid Valve & Connector
42	Shorted Shift Control Solenoid Valve "A" Circuit	No	Check Shift Control Solenoid Valve & Connector
43	Open Shift Control Solenoid Valve "B" Circuit	No	Check Shift Control Solenoid Valve & Connector
44	Shorted Shift Control Solenoid Valve "B" Circuit	No	Check Shift Control Solenoid Valve & Connector
45	Open Pressure Control Solenoid Valve Circuit	No	Check Pressure Control Solenoid Valve & Connector
46	Shorted Pressure Control Solenoid Valve Circuit	No	Check Pressure Control Solenoid Valve & Connector
47	Open Torque Converter Clutch (TCC) Solenoid Valve Circuit	No	Check TCC Solenoid Valve & Connector
48	Shorted Torque Converter Clutch (TCC) Solenoid Valve Circuit	No	Check TCC Solenoid Valve & Connector
49	Defective TCC System	No	Check TCC Hydraulic Circuit, Check TCC Solenoid Valve, Defective TCU
51	Incorrect Or No Upshift From 1st Gear	No	Check Pulse Generators "A" & "B" Or Connectors, Rear Clutch Slipping
52	Incorrect Or No Upshift From 2nd Gear	No	Check Pulse Generators "A" & "B" Or Connectors, Rear Clutch Slipping, Kickdown Band Slipping
53	Incorrect Or No Upshift From 3rd Gear	No	Check Pulse Generators "A" & "B" Or Connectors, Front Or Rear Clutch Slipping
54	Incorrect Or No Upshift From 4th Gear	No	Check Pulse Generators "A" & "B" Or Connectors, End Clutch Slipping, Kickdown Band Slipping
59	Abnormal Vibration	No	Check Pulse Generator "A" Or Connector, Replace ATF
61 [2]	Shorted Torque Reduction Request Signal Line Or Open Torque Converter Reduction Execution Signal Line	No	[3] [4] Check Torque Reduction Request Or Execution Signal Line
62 [2]	Open Circuit On Torque Reduction Request Signal Line	No	[3] Check Torque Reduction Request Signal Line
63 [2]	Shorted Circuit On Torque Reduction Execution Signal Line	No	[4] Check Torque Reduction Execution Signal Line
81	Open Pulse Generator "A" Circuit	Yes	See DTC No. 31
82	Open Pulse Generator "B" Circuit	Yes	See DTC No. 32
83	Open Or Shorted Shift Control Solenoid Valve "A" Circuit	Yes	See DTC No. 41 & 42
84	Open Or Shorted Shift Control Solenoid Valve "B"	Yes	See DTC No. 43 & 44
85	Open Or Shorted Pressure Control Solenoid Valve	Yes	See DTC No. 45 & 46
86	Incorrect Or No Upshift	Yes	See DTC No. 51, 52, 53 & 54

[1] – To check items listed, see ELECTRONIC TROUBLE SHOOTING or TESTING. For adjustment of components, see ADJUSTMENTS.

[2] – Applies to Stealth DOHC models only.

[3] – Torque reduction request signal circuit goes between TCU terminal No. 18 (White/Blue wire) and engine controller terminal No. 116 (White/Blue wire).

[4] – Torque reduction execution signal circuit goes between TCU terminal No. 17 (Blue/White wire) and engine controller terminal No. 7 (Blue/White wire).

CLEARING TROUBLE CODES

Trouble codes can be cleared from TCU memory by disconnecting negative battery cable for more than 10 seconds. Ensure trouble codes are cleared after performing repairs.

WARNING: When battery is disconnected, vehicle computer and memory systems may lose memory data. Driveability problems may exist until computer systems have completed a relearn cycle. See COMPUTER RELEARN PROCEDURES in APPLICATIONS & IDENTIFICATION section before disconnecting battery.

ELECTRONIC TROUBLE SHOOTING

ELECTRONIC SYSTEM COMPONENTS

Different electronic system components can be checked when performing electronic trouble shooting. *See Figs. 9-12.* For component, figure and step reference, see COMPONENT TESTING & FIGURE REFERENCE table.

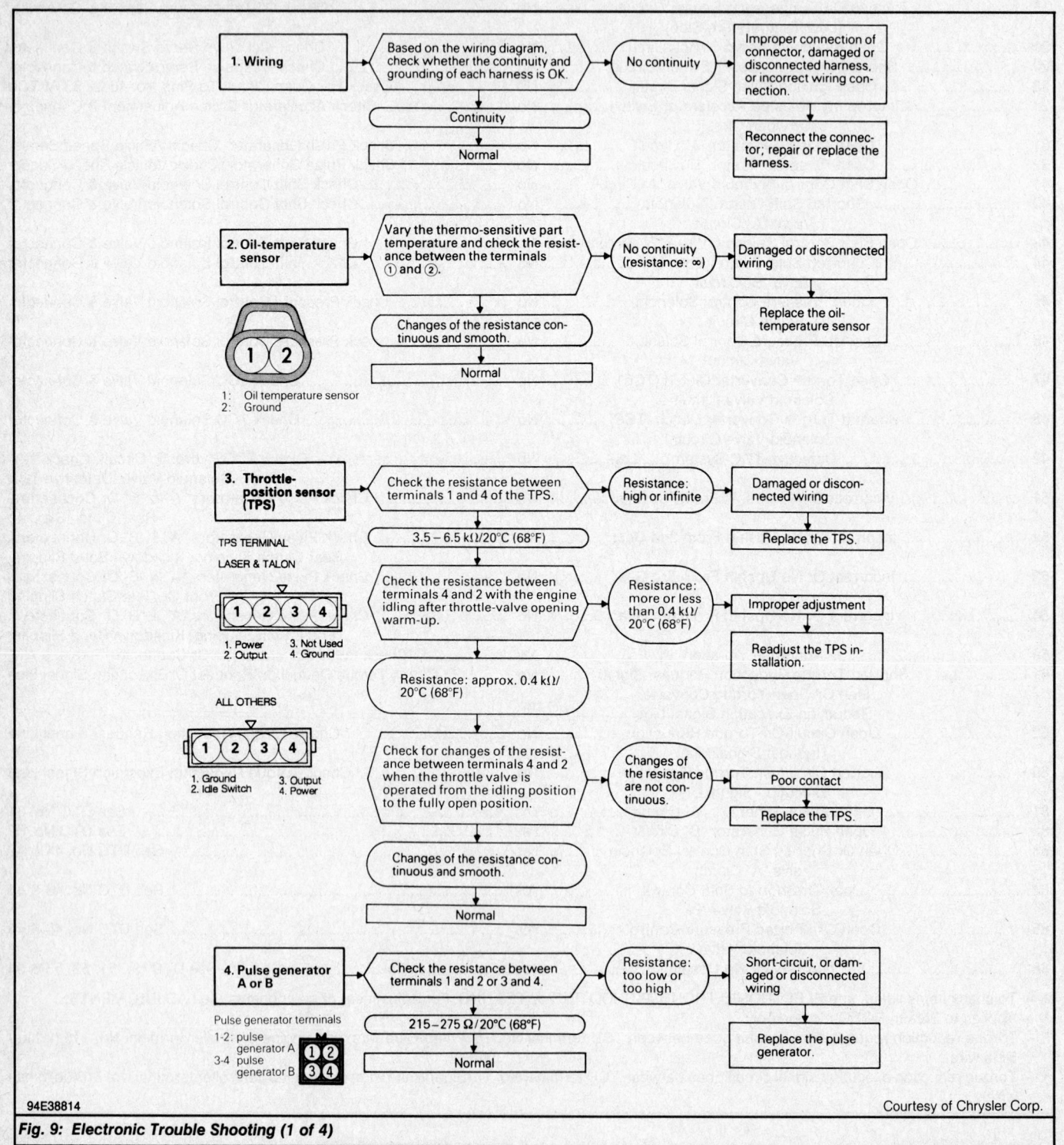

94E38814   Courtesy of Chrysler Corp.

Fig. 9: Electronic Trouble Shooting (1 of 4)

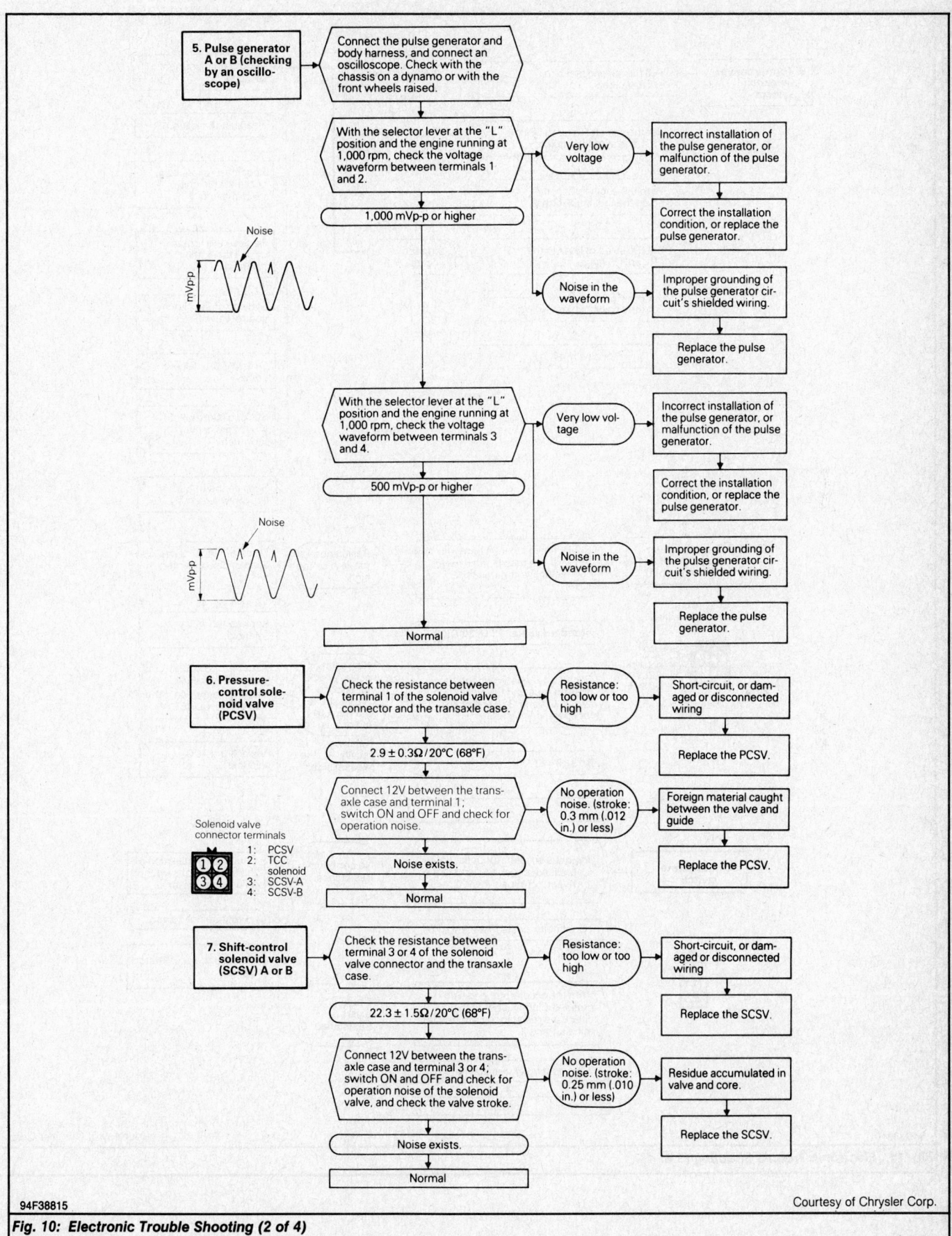

94F38815

Courtesy of Chrysler Corp.

Fig. 10: Electronic Trouble Shooting (2 of 4)

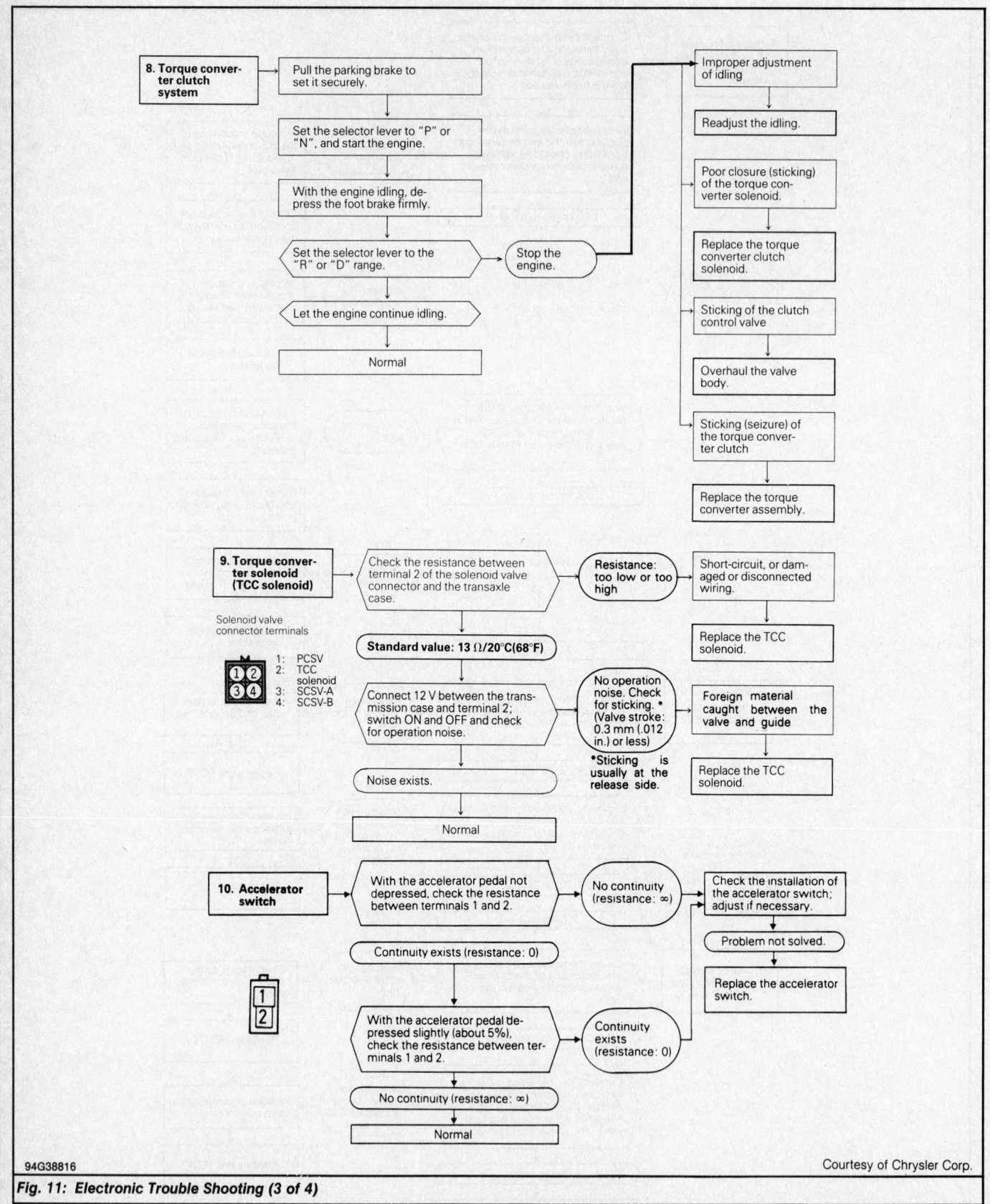

8. Torque converter clutch system
- Pull the parking brake to set it securely.
- Set the selector lever to "P" or "N", and start the engine.
- With the engine idling, depress the foot brake firmly.
- Set the selector lever to the "R" or "D" range.
- Let the engine continue idling.
- Normal

→ Stop the engine.

- Improper adjustment of idling → Readjust the idling.
- Poor closure (sticking) of the torque converter solenoid → Replace the torque converter clutch solenoid.
- Sticking of the clutch control valve → Overhaul the valve body.
- Sticking (seizure) of the torque converter clutch → Replace the torque converter assembly.

9. Torque converter solenoid (TCC solenoid)

Solenoid valve connector terminals
1: PCSV
2: TCC solenoid
3: SCSV-A
4: SCSV-B

- Check the resistance between terminal 2 of the solenoid valve connector and the transaxle case.
  - Resistance: too low or too high → Short-circuit, or damaged or disconnected wiring. → Replace the TCC solenoid.
- Standard value: 13 Ω/20°C(68°F)
- Connect 12 V between the transmission case and terminal 2; switch ON and OFF and check for operation noise.
  - No operation noise. Check for sticking. * (Valve stroke: 0.3 mm (.012 in.) or less) *Sticking is usually at the release side. → Foreign material caught between the valve and guide → Replace the TCC solenoid.
- Noise exists.
- Normal

10. Accelerator switch
1
2
- With the accelerator pedal not depressed, check the resistance between terminals 1 and 2.
  - No continuity (resistance: ∞) → Check the installation of the accelerator switch; adjust if necessary. → Problem not solved. → Replace the accelerator switch.
- Continuity exists (resistance: 0)
- With the accelerator pedal depressed slightly (about 5%), check the resistance between terminals 1 and 2.
  - Continuity exists (resistance: 0)
- No continuity (resistance: ∞)
- Normal

94G38816

Fig. 11: Electronic Trouble Shooting (3 of 4)

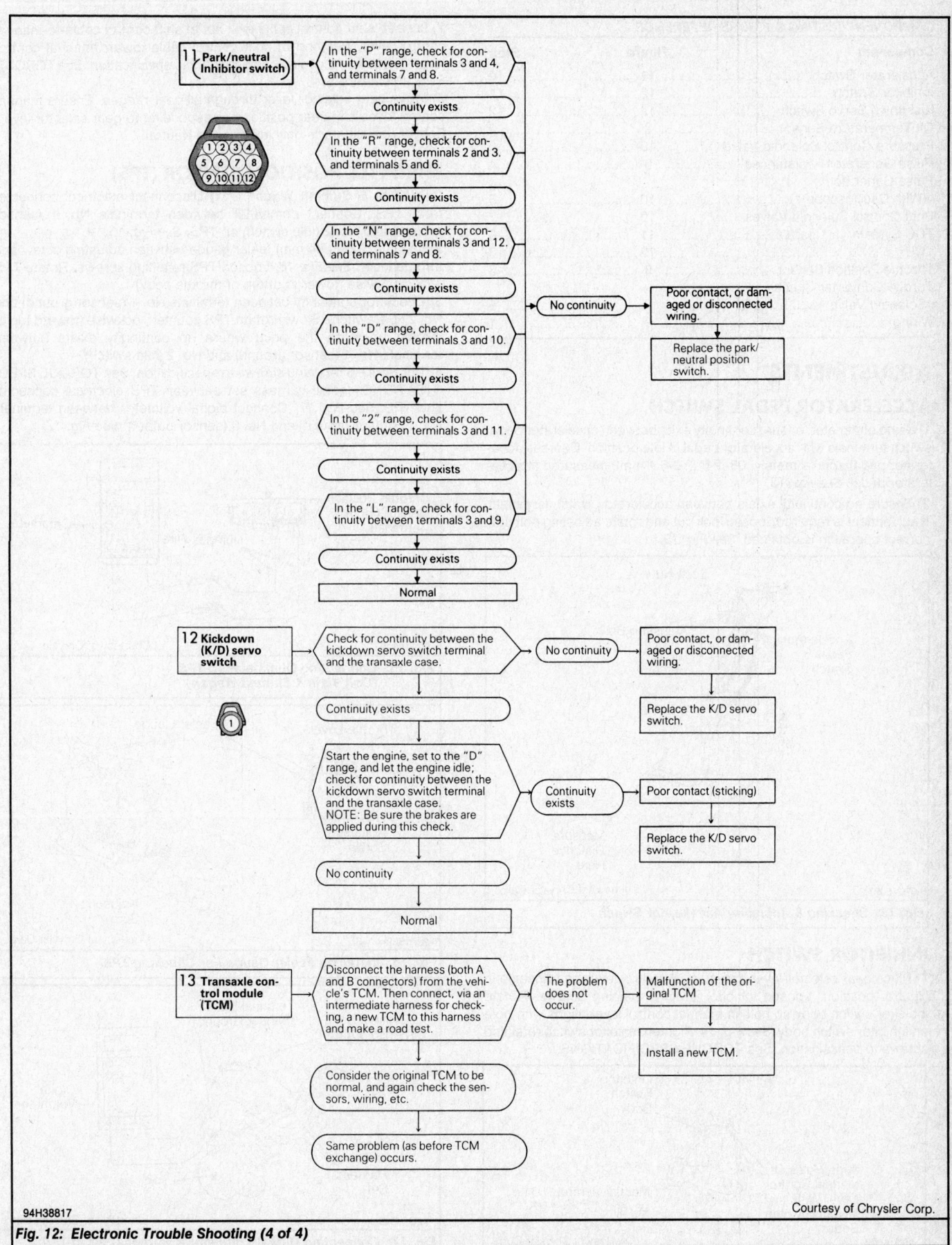

94H38817

Fig. 12: Electronic Trouble Shooting (4 of 4)

COMPONENT TESTING & FIGURE REFERENCE

Component	Figure	Step
Accelerator Switch	11	10
Inhibitor Switch	12	11
Kickdown Servo Switch	12	12
Oil Temperature Sensor	9	2
Pressure Control Solenoid Valve	10	6
Pulse Generator Resistances	9	4
Pulse Generator (With Oscilloscope)	10	5
Shift Control Solenoid Valves	10	7
TCC System	11	8
TCU	12	13
Throttle Position Sensor	9	3
Torque Converter Clutch Solenoid Valve	11	9
Wiring	9	1

ADJUSTMENTS

ACCELERATOR PEDAL SWITCH

1) Using ohmmeter, ensure continuity exits between accelerator pedal switch terminals with accelerator pedal in idle position. Depress accelerator pedal approximately .08-.24" (2.0-6.1 mm), measured at accelerator pedal. *See Fig. 13.*

2) Ensure no continuity exists between accelerator switch terminals. If adjustment is required, loosen lock nut and rotate adjusting bolt until correct operation is obtained. *See Fig. 13.*

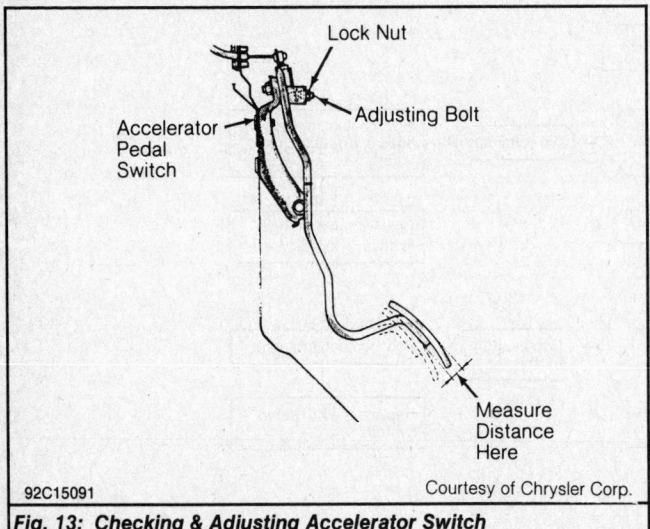

92C15091   Courtesy of Chrysler Corp.

Fig. 13: Checking & Adjusting Accelerator Switch

INHIBITOR SWITCH

1) Place gear selector lever and manual control lever on transaxle in Neutral position. Loosen inhibitor switch retaining screws. Rotate inhibitor switch body so hole in manual control lever aligns with hole on inhibitor switch body. *See Fig. 14.* Tighten inhibitor switch retaining screws to specification. See TORQUE SPECIFICATIONS.

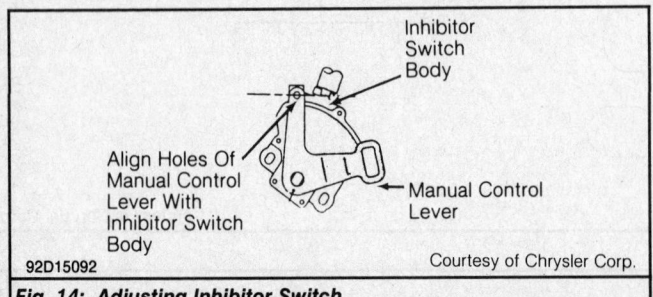

92D15092   Courtesy of Chrysler Corp.

Fig. 14: Adjusting Inhibitor Switch

2) Loosen shift control cable lock nut at shift control cable-to-manual control lever. Pull end of shift control cable toward manual control lever. Tighten shift control cable lock nut to specification. See TORQUE SPECIFICATIONS.

3) Move gear selector lever through all gear ranges. Ensure manual control lever is in gear position corresponding to gear selector lever. Ensure vehicle starts only in Park and Neutral.

THROTTLE POSITION SENSOR (TPS)

Colt Vista & Summit Wagon – 1) Disconnect electrical connector from TPS. Connect ohmmeter between terminals No. 1 (sensor ground) and No. 2 (idle switch) on TPS. *See Fig. 15.*

2) Install a .025" (.64 mm) feeler gauge between adjusting screw and throttle lever. *See Fig. 16.* Loosen TPS retaining screws. Rotate TPS fully clockwise (toward bottom of throttle body).

3) Check for continuity between terminals No. 1 (sensor ground) and No. 2 (idle switch). Slowly rotate TPS counterclockwise (toward top of throttle body) to the point where no continuity exists between terminals No. 1 (sensor ground) and No. 2 (idle switch).

4) Tighten TPS retaining screws to specification. See TORQUE SPECIFICATIONS. Install harness set between TPS electrical connector and TPS. *See Fig. 17.* Connect digital voltmeter between terminals No. 1 (sensor ground) and No. 3 (sensor output). *See Fig. 17.*

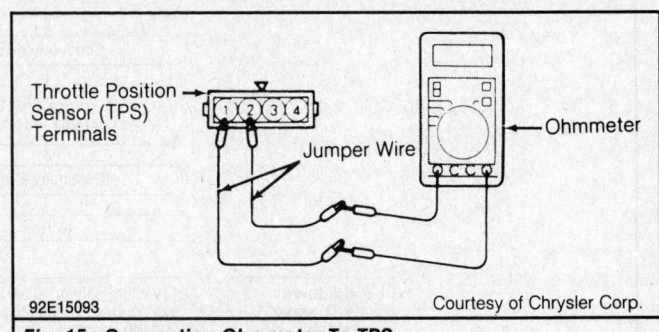

92E15093   Courtesy of Chrysler Corp.

Fig. 15: Connecting Ohmmeter To TPS (Colt Vista & Summit Wagon)

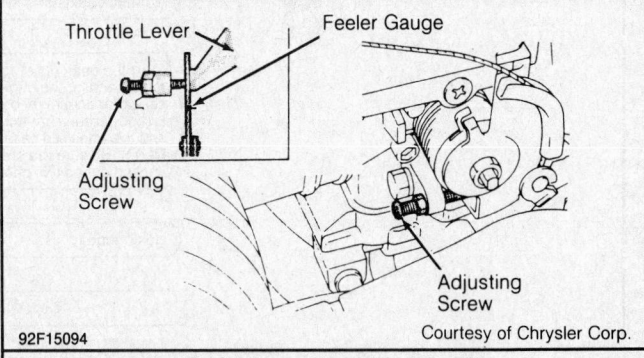

92F15094   Courtesy of Chrysler Corp.

Fig. 16: Installing Feeler Gauge For Checking TPS

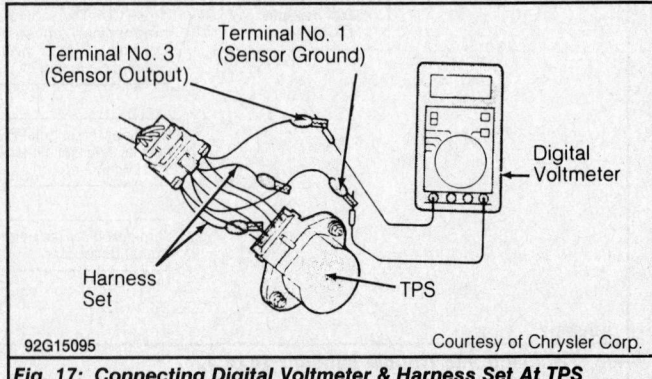

92G15095   Courtesy of Chrysler Corp.

Fig. 17: Connecting Digital Voltmeter & Harness Set At TPS

5) Turn ignition on. DO NOT start engine. Note TPS output voltage on digital voltmeter. The TPS output voltage should be .4-1 volt. If TPS output voltage is not within specification, check TPS and related wiring. *See Fig. 9 (step 3).* Turn ignition off. Remove harness set and feeler gauge. Reinstall TPS electrical connector.

Laser & Talon – 1) Disconnect electrical connector from TPS. Install harness set between TPS electrical connector and TPS. *See Fig. 17.* Connect digital voltmeter between terminals No. 2 (sensor output) and No. 4 (sensor ground). *See Fig. 18.*

2) Turn ignition on and note TPS output voltage. DO NOT start engine. The TPS output voltage should be .48-.52 volt. If TPS output voltage is not within specification, loosen TPS retaining screws. Rotate TPS to obtain correct output voltage. Rotating TPS clockwise increases output voltage, and counterclockwise decreases output voltage.

3) Once correct output voltage is obtained, tighten TPS retaining screws to specification. See TORQUE SPECIFICATIONS. Turn ignition off. Disconnect digital voltmeter. Connect electrical connector to TPS.

Stealth – 1) Disconnect electrical connector from TPS. Connect ohmmeter between terminals No. 3 (idle switch) and No. 4 (sensor ground) on TPS. *See Fig. 18.*

2) Install a .025" (.64 mm) feeler gauge between adjusting screw and throttle lever. *See Fig. 16.* Loosen TPS retaining screws. Rotate TPS fully counterclockwise (toward bottom of throttle body).

3) Check for continuity between terminals No. 3 (idle switch) and No. 4 (sensor ground). Slowly rotate TPS clockwise (toward top of throttle body) to the point where no continuity exists between terminals No. 3 (idle switch) and No. 4 (sensor ground).

4) Tighten TPS position sensor retaining screws to specification. See TORQUE SPECIFICATIONS. Install harness set between TPS electrical connector and TPS. *See Fig. 17.* Connect digital voltmeter between terminals No. 2 (sensor output) and No. 4 (sensor ground). *See Fig. 18.*

5) Turn ignition on and note TPS output voltage. DO NOT start engine. The TPS output voltage should be .4-1.0 volt. If TPS output voltage is not within specification, check TPS and related wiring. *See Fig. 9, Step 3).* Turn ignition off. Remove feeler gauge and digital voltmeter.

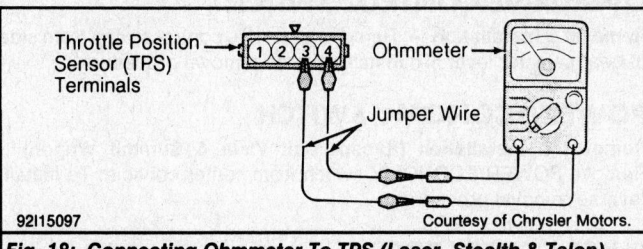

92I15097　Courtesy of Chrysler Motors.

Fig. 18: Connecting Ohmmeter To TPS (Laser, Stealth & Talon)

TESTING

NOTE: Different components can be tested. See Figs. 9-12. For component, figure and step reference, see COMPONENT TESTING & FIGURE REFERENCE table.

COMPONENT TESTING & FIGURE REFERENCE

Component	Figure	Step
Accelerator Switch	11	10
Inhibitor Switch	12	11
Kickdown Servo Switch	12	12
Oil Temperature Sensor	9	2
Pressure Control Solenoid Valve	10	6
Pulse Generator Resistances	9	4
Pulse Generator (With Oscilloscope)	10	5
Shift Control Solenoid Valves	10	7
TCC System	11	8
TCU	12	13
Throttle Position Sensor	9	3
Torque Converter Clutch Solenoid Valve	11	9
Wiring	9	1

OVERDRIVE CONTROL SWITCH

Disconnect electrical connector from overdrive control switch. Using ohmmeter, check continuity between specified wire terminals at switch connector. See OVERDRIVE CONTROL SWITCH CONTINUITY SPECIFICATIONS table. Replace overdrive control switch if defective.

OVERDRIVE CONTROL SWITCH CONTINUITY SPECIFICATIONS

Application & Switch Position	Continuity [1] Between Terminals
Colt Vista & Summit Wagon	
ON	1 & 2
OFF	1 & 3
Laser & Talon	
ON	1 & 2
OFF	1 & 3
Stealth	
ON	5 & 6
OFF	4 & 6

[1] – For terminal location and wire colors, see WIRING DIAGRAMS.

POWER/ECONOMY SWITCH

NOTE: The POWER/ECONOMY switch is not used on Colt Vista and Summit Wagon models.

Disconnect electrical connector from POWER/ECONOMY switch. Using ohmmeter, check continuity between specified wire terminals at switch connector. See POWER/ECONOMY SWITCH CONTINUITY SPECIFICATIONS table. Replace POWER/ECONOMY switch if defective.

POWER/ECONOMY SWITCH CONTINUITY SPECIFICATIONS

Application & Switch Position	Continuity [1] Between Terminals
Laser & Talon	
ON (Power Mode)	1 & 2
OFF (Economy Mode)	2 & 3
Stealth	
ON (Power Mode)	1 & 2
OFF (Economy Mode)	2 & 3

[1] – For terminal location and wire colors, see WIRING DIAGRAMS.

VEHICLE SPEED SENSOR

NOTE: It may be necessary to remove instrument cluster for access to vehicle speed sensor.

Colt Vista & Summit Wagon – Connect circuit tester between ground terminal and vehicle speed sensor on instrument cluster. *See Fig. 19.* Rotate speedometer shaft and ensure circuit tester indicates an on/off pattern. Replace components if vehicle speed sensor does not operate correctly.

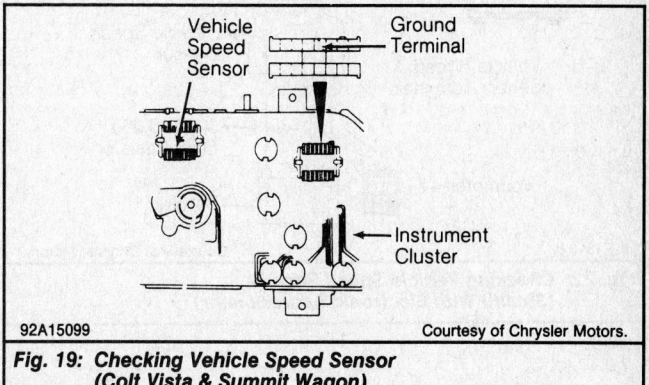

92A15099　Courtesy of Chrysler Motors.

Fig. 19: Checking Vehicle Speed Sensor (Colt Vista & Summit Wagon)

Laser & Talon – 1) Connect circuit tester between terminals on rear of instrument cluster. *See Fig. 20.*

CAUTION: Ensure circuit tester uses a measurement current of 4 milli-amps or less.

2) Rotate speedometer shaft and ensure circuit tester indicates an on/off pattern. Replace components if vehicle speed sensor does not operate correctly.

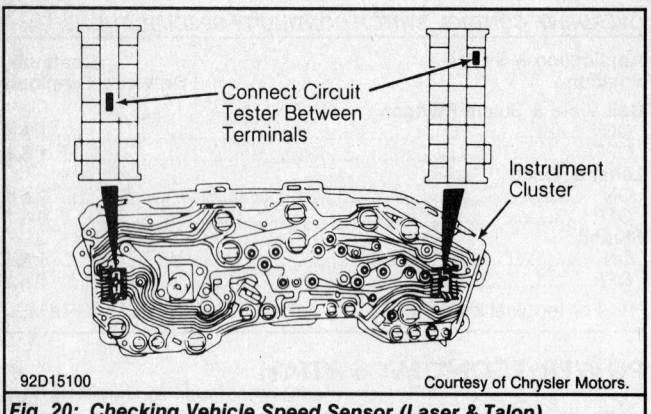

92D15100   Courtesy of Chrysler Motors.

Fig. 20: Checking Vehicle Speed Sensor (Laser & Talon)

Stealth (Mechanical Speedometer) – Connect circuit tester between terminals on rear of instrument cluster. See Fig. 21. Rotate speedometer shaft and ensure circuit tester indicates an on/off pattern. Replace components if vehicle speed sensor does not operate correctly.

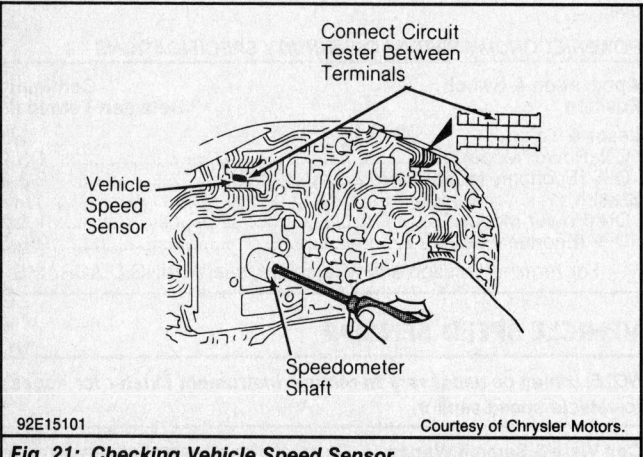

92E15101   Courtesy of Chrysler Motors.

Fig. 21: Checking Vehicle Speed Sensor (Stealth With Mechanical Speedometer)

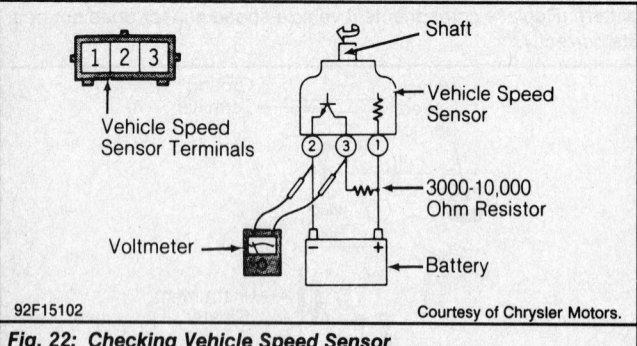

92F15102   Courtesy of Chrysler Motors.

Fig. 22: Checking Vehicle Speed Sensor (Stealth With Electronic Speedometer)

Stealth (Electronic Speedometer) – **1)** Remove vehicle speed sensor from rear of instrument cluster. Connect a 3000-10,000 ohm resistor and 12-volt battery to vehicle speed sensor. See Fig. 22.
2) Using voltmeter, check for voltage reading at terminals No. 2 and 3 while rotating the shaft. See Fig. 22. In one shaft revolution, there should be 4 voltage readings. Replace vehicle speed sensor if defective.

REMOVAL & INSTALLATION

ACCELERATOR PEDAL SWITCH

Removal & Installation – Disconnect electrical connector. Remove retaining nut and accelerator pedal switch. To install, reverse removal procedure. Adjust accelerator pedal switch. See ACCELERATOR PEDAL SWITCH under ADJUSTMENTS.

INHIBITOR SWITCH

Removal & Installation – **1)** Disconnect shift control cable. Remove retaining bolt and manual control lever. Remove retaining screws and inhibitor switch.
2) To install, reverse removal procedure. DO NOT tighten inhibitor switch retaining screws at this time. Tighten manual control lever retaining bolt to specification. See TORQUE SPECIFICATIONS. Adjust inhibitor switch. See INHIBITOR SWITCH under ADJUSTMENTS.

KICKDOWN SERVO SWITCH

Removal & Installation – Disconnect electrical connector. Remove snap ring and kickdown servo switch. To install, reverse removal procedure.

OIL TEMPERATURE SENSOR

Removal & Installation – Oil temperature sensor is mounted inside transaxle case. See Fig. 5.

OVERDRIVE CONTROL SWITCH

Removal & Installation – Remove overdrive control switch from side of gear selector lever. To install, reverse removal procedure.

POWER/ECONOMY SWITCH

Removal & Installation (Except Colt Vista & Summit Wagon) – Remove POWER/ECONOMY switch from center console. To install, reverse removal procedure.

PULSE GENERATORS

Removal & Installation – **1)** Note location of pulse generators "A" and "B" for reassembly reference. Pulse generator "A" has a transparent tube and "B" contains a Black tube. See Fig. 5.
2) Remove retaining bolt and pulse generator. To install, reverse removal procedure. Tighten retaining bolt to specification. See TORQUE SPECIFICATIONS.

THROTTLE POSITION SENSOR (TPS)

Removal & Installation – Disconnect electrical connector from TPS. Remove retaining screws and TPS. To install, reverse removal procedure. DO NOT tighten retaining screws. Ensure TPS engages with tang areas on throttle body. Adjust TPS. See THROTTLE POSITION SENSOR (TPS) under ADJUSTMENTS.

TRANSAXLE CONTROL UNIT (TCU)

Removal & Installation – The TCU is located behind instrument panel, near center of console and contains a 42-pin connector. See Fig. 1, 2 or 3.

VALVE BODY SOLENOIDS

NOTE: Valve body solenoids consist of torque converter clutch control, pressure control and shift control solenoid valves.

Removal & Installation – 1) Drain transaxle fluid. Remove retaining bolts, oil pan, magnet and gasket. Note location of solenoid valve. *See Fig. 6.* Disconnect necessary electrical connector. Remove retaining bolt and solenoid valve.

2) To install, reverse removal procedure. Ensure solenoid valve is installed in proper location. *See Fig. 6.* Solenoid valves can be identified by the wire color. For wire color identification, see WIRING DIAGRAMS. Fill transaxle with Mopar ATF Plus (7176).

VEHICLE SPEED SENSOR

Removal & Installation – Vehicle speed sensor is located on rear of instrument cluster.

TORQUE SPECIFICATIONS
TORQUE SPECIFICATIONS

Application	Ft. Lbs. (N.m)
Manual Control Lever Bolt	13-15 (18-20)
	INCH Lbs. (N.m)
Inhibitor Switch Bolt	89-102 (10.1-11.5)
Oil Filter Bolt	48-60 (5.4-6.8)
Oil Pan Bolt	48-60 (5.4-6.8)
Pulse Generator Bolt	89-102 (10.1-11.5)
Shift Control Cable Lock Nut	108 (12.2)
TPS Retaining Screw	17 (1.9)

WIRING DIAGRAMS

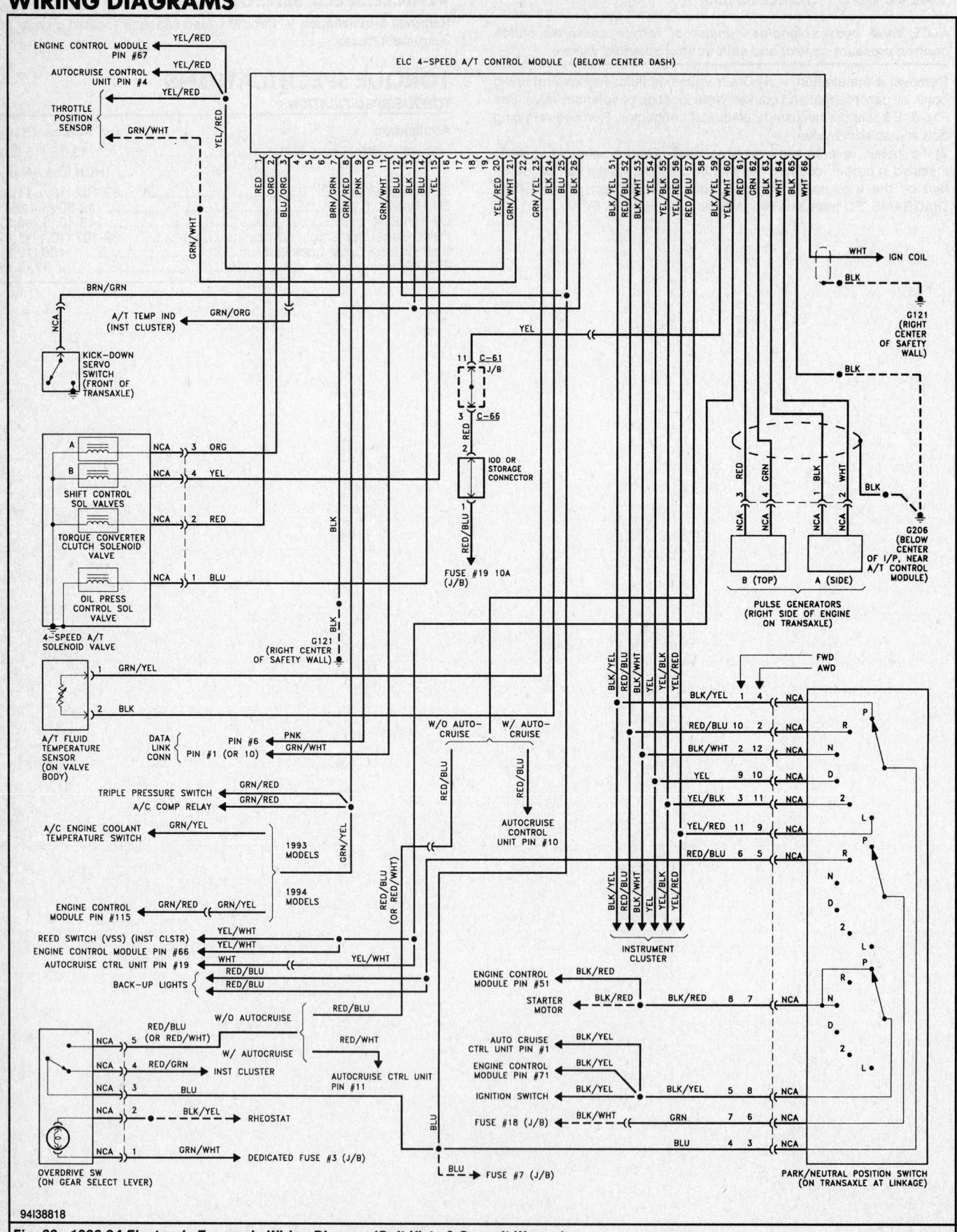

Fig. 23: 1993-94 Electronic Transaxle Wiring Diagram (Colt Vista & Summit Wagon)

94I38818

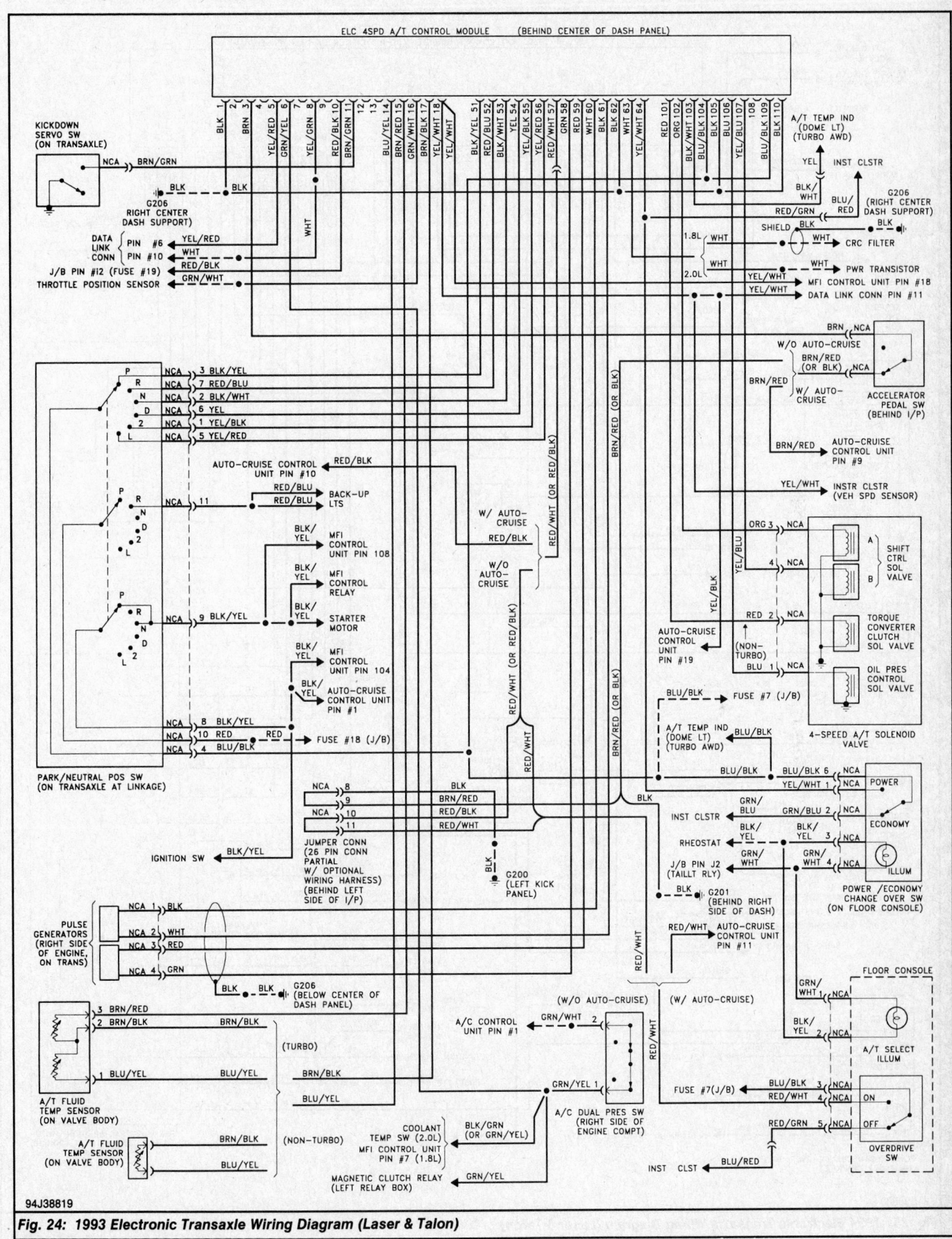

Fig. 24: 1993 Electronic Transaxle Wiring Diagram (Laser & Talon)

94J38819

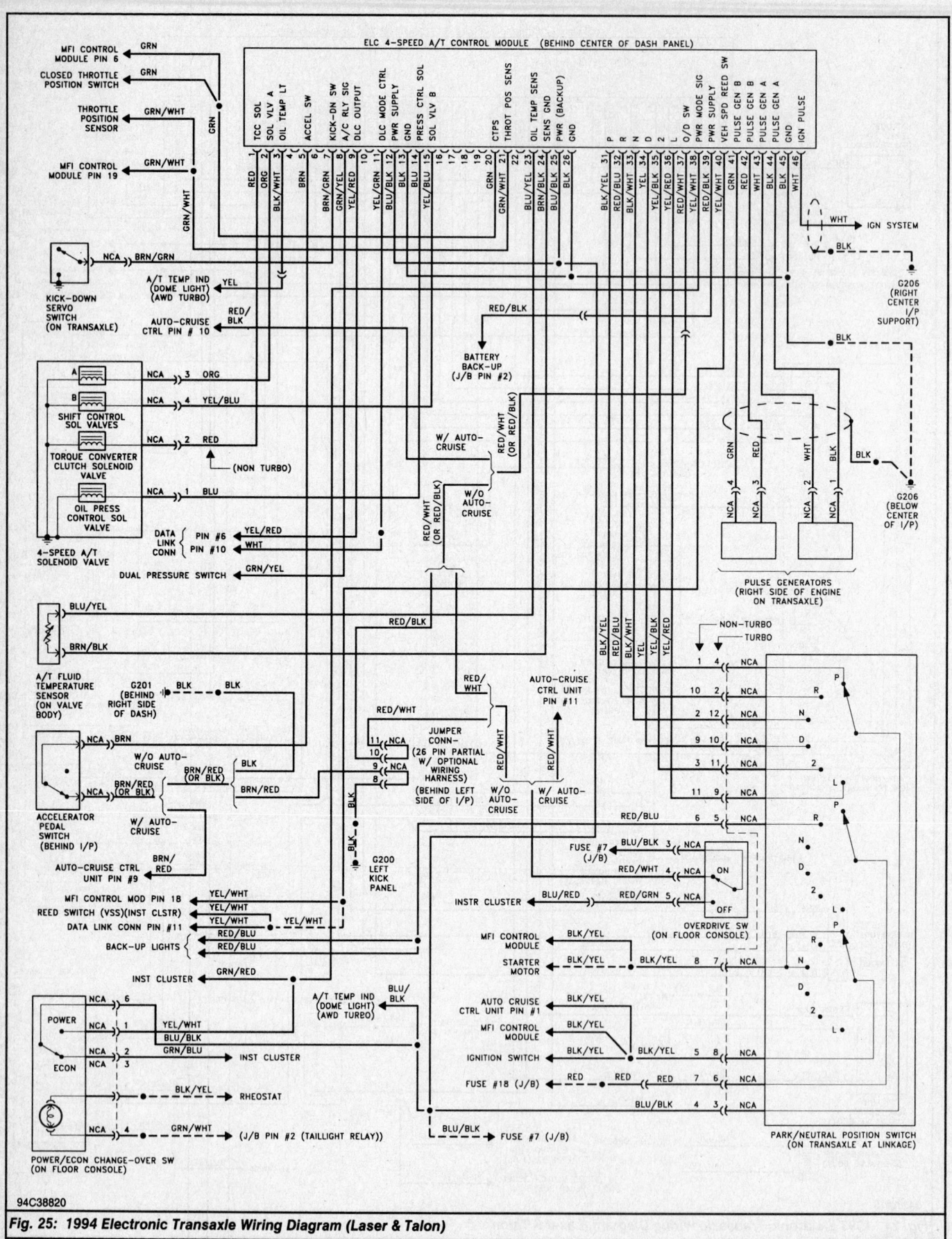

Fig. 25: 1994 Electronic Transaxle Wiring Diagram (Laser & Talon)

94C38820

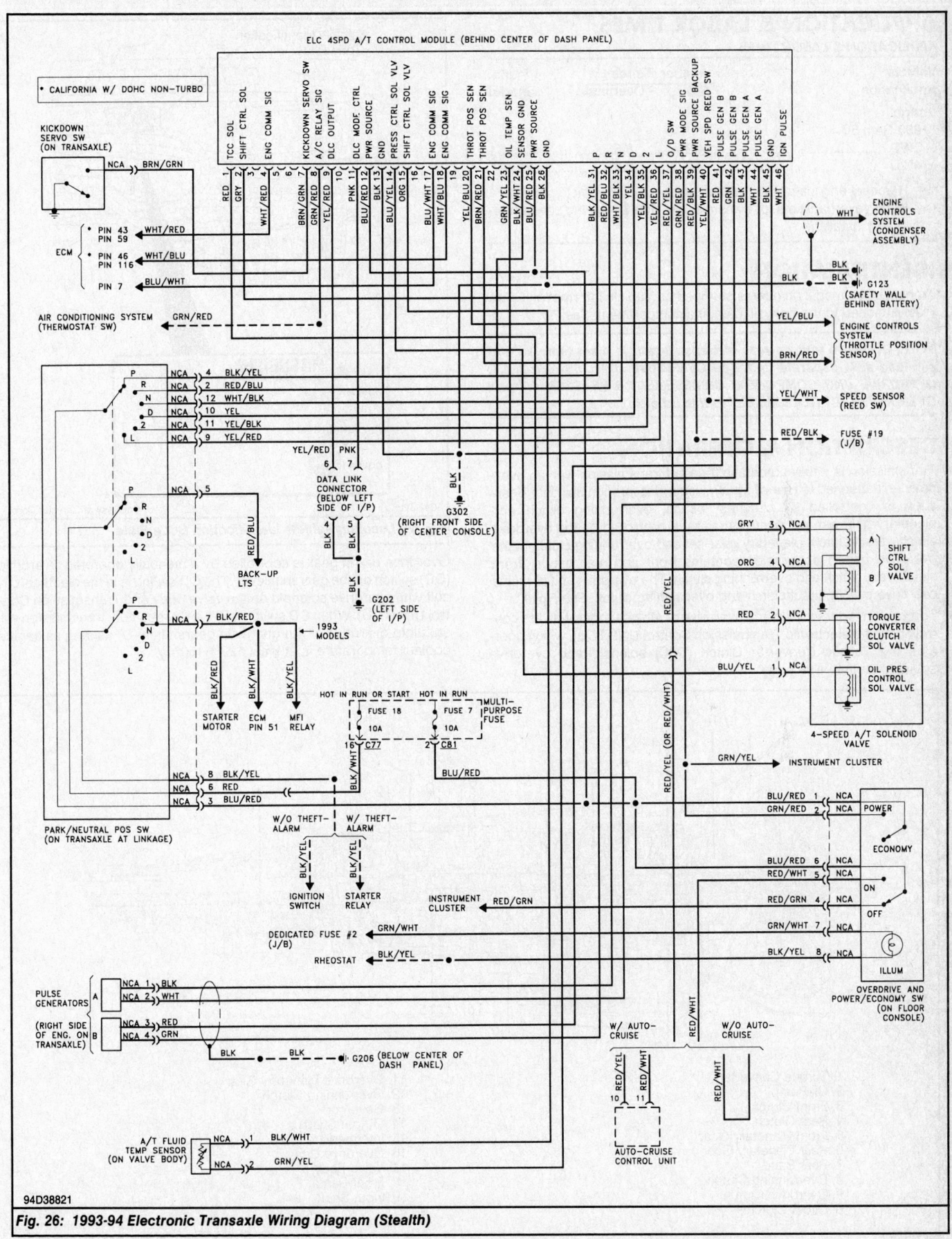

Fig. 26: 1993-94 Electronic Transaxle Wiring Diagram (Stealth)

94D38821

AUTOMATIC TRANSMISSIONS
Chrysler R4AC1 & V4AC1

APPLICATION & LABOR TIMES

APPLICATION & LABOR TIMES

Vehicle Application	Labor Times		Trans. Model
	¹ R & I	² Overhaul	
Dodge			
1993 Ram 50			
2WD	4.2	8.5	R4AC1
4WD	7.2	8.5	V4AC1

¹ – Removal and installation of transmission from vehicle chassis.
² – Bench overhaul time for transmission. DOES NOT include removal and installation.

IDENTIFICATION

Transmission model number is stamped on Vehicle Information Code Plate attached to the firewall in engine compartment. *See Fig. 2.*

NOTE: Overdrive unit on rear of transmission is disassembled and serviced as a separate unit. See OVERDRIVE UNIT DISASSEMBLY, OVERDRIVE UNIT COMPONENT DISASSEMBLY & REASSEMBLY and OVERDRIVE UNIT REASSEMBLY in this article.

DESCRIPTION & OPERATION

Transmission is a fully automatic 3-speed transmission with an overdrive unit attached to rear of transmission. 1st through 3rd gear operation is controlled by clutches, bands, overrunning clutch and planetary gear set. 4th gear operation is controlled by the overdrive clutch, direct clutch, planetary gear set and overrunning clutch in the overdrive unit. Transmission contains front and rear bands, front clutch, rear clutch and overrunning clutch. The overdrive unit contains overdrive clutch, direct clutch and overrunning clutch. *See Fig. 1.*

Torque converter lock-up and overdrive or 4th gear operation are controlled by the electronic Transmission Control Unit (TCU), which operates the Torque Converter Clutch (TCC) solenoid and overdrive solenoid on the valve body.

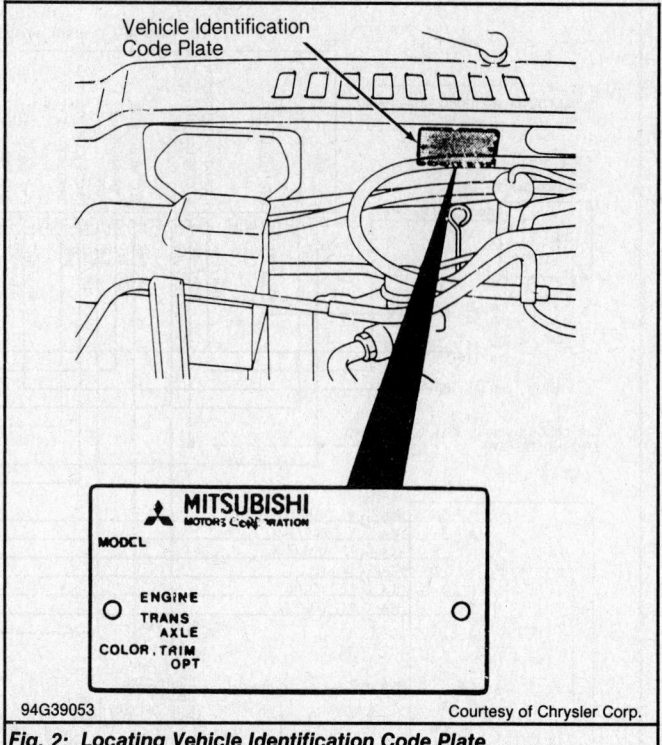

94G39053   Courtesy of Chrysler Corp.

Fig. 2: Locating Vehicle Identification Code Plate

Overdrive or 4th gear is controlled by a manually operated Overdrive (OD) switch on the gearshift lever. The OD switch is in the electrical circuit with overdrive solenoid on the valve body and Transmission Control Unit (TCU). When OD switch is in the ON position, transmission will shift into overdrive or 4th gear with gearshift in "D" as long as engine coolant temperature is at least 122°F (50°C).

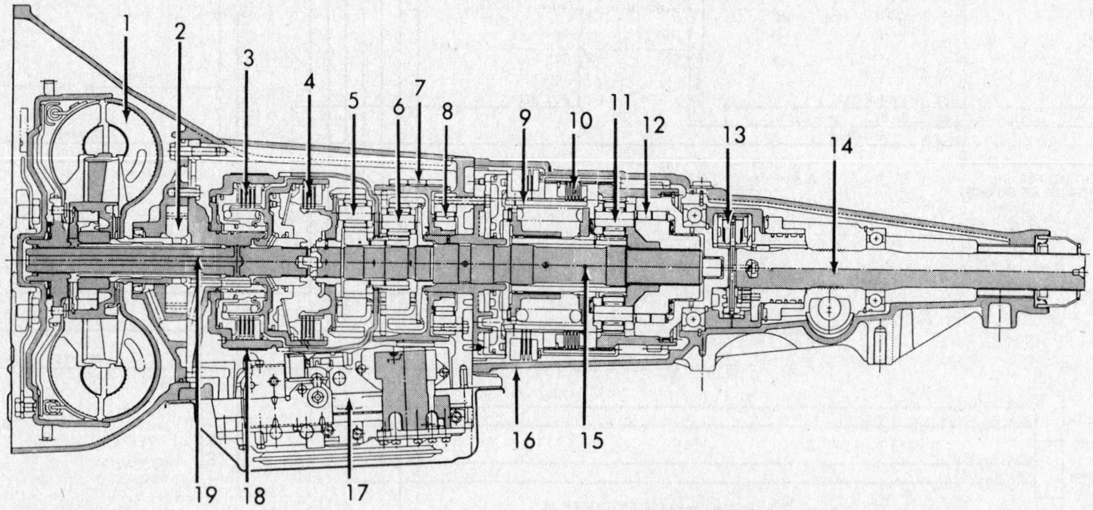

1. Torque Converter
2. Oil Pump
3. Front Clutch
4. Rear Clutch
5. Front Planetary Gear
6. Rear Planetary Gear
7. Rear Band
8. Overrunning Clutch
9. Overdrive Clutch
10. Direct Clutch
11. Overdrive Planetary Gear
12. Overrunning Clutch
13. Governor
14. Output Shaft
15. Intermediate Shaft
16. Overdrive Unit
17. Valve Body
18. Front Band
19. Input Shaft

94H39054   Courtesy of Chrysler Corp.

Fig. 1: Identifying Transmission Component Locations

When OD switch is in the OFF position, transmission will not upshift into overdrive or 4th gear. The OD OFF light on gearshift indicator will illuminate when overdrive switch is in the OFF position.

On 4WD models, a transmission oil temperature switch is mounted in the front oil cooler line, near the transmission case. Transmission oil temperature switch will illuminate the transmission oil temperature warning light on instrument panel if transmission oil temperature exceeds specification.

LUBRICATION & ADJUSTMENTS

NOTE: See appropriate AUTOMATIC TRANSMISSION SERVICING article in TRANSMISSION SERVICING.

NOTE: Manufacturer recommends using Mopar ATF Plus Type 7176 fluid in this transmission. This fluid should also be used during transmission assembly.

TROUBLE SHOOTING

Transmission malfunctions may be caused by poor engine performance, improper adjustments or failure of hydraulic, mechanical or electronic components. Always begin by checking fluid level, fluid condition, shift linkage or cable and throttle valve linkage adjustment. Perform road test to determine if problem has been corrected. If problem still exists, several tests must be performed on transmission. See TESTING in this article.

TRANSMISSION SYMPTOM DIAGNOSIS

Buzzing Noise
- Aerated fluid
- Damaged reaction shaft support seal rings
- Defective overrunning clutch
- Faulty oil pump
- Low fluid level
- Valve body malfunction or leakage

Delayed Engagement From Neutral To Drive Or Reverse
- Damaged clutch, band or servo
- Damaged oil pump components
- Damaged or worn reaction shaft seal rings
- Damaged reaction shaft support seal rings
- Engine idle speed too low
- Improper rear band adjustment
- Incorrect shift linkage or cable adjustment
- Low fluid level
- Restricted filter assembly

Delayed Upshifts
- Damaged reaction shaft support seal rings
- Defective front band or servo
- Defective governor
- Improper front band adjustment
- Incorrect throttle valve linkage adjustment

Drags Or Locks Up
- Defective band, band linkage or servo
- Defective planetary or overrunning clutch
- Dragging clutch
- Improper band adjustment

Fluid Blows Out Filler Tube
- Aerated fluid
- High fluid level
- Restricted breather vent in oil pump
- Restricted filter assembly

Growling, Grating Or Scraping Noise
- Defective intermediate shaft bearing or bushing
- Defective planetary or overrunning clutch
- Improper band adjustment

Harsh Engagement From Neutral To Drive Or Reverse
- Damaged clutch, band or planetary components
- Defective torque converter lock-up
- Engine idle speed too high
- Incorrect hydraulic pressure
- Valve body malfunction or leakage

Harsh Upshift
- Improper front band adjustment
- Incorrect hydraulic pressure
- Incorrect throttle valve linkage adjustment

Harsh 1-2, 2-3 And 3-2 Shifts
- Torque Converter Clutch (TCC) solenoid not venting

No Forward Gear In Any Position
- Defective overrunning clutch or planetary gear
- Incorrect shift linkage or cable adjustment
- Input shaft seal rings worn or damaged
- Low fluid level
- Rear clutch defective
- Valve body malfunction or leakage

No Kickdown Or Normal Downshift
- Damaged reaction shaft support seal rings
- Defective front servo, band or linkage
- Defective governor
- Improper front band adjustment
- Improper hydraulic pressure
- Improper throttle valve linkage adjustment
- Incorrect shift linkage or cable adjustment
- Valve body malfunction or clutch malfunction
- Valve body malfunction or leakage

Runaway Upshift
- Aerated fluid
- Damaged reaction shaft support seal rings
- Defective front band, servo or linkage
- Defective front clutch
- Improper front band adjustment
- Improper throttle valve linkage adjustment
- Low fluid level
- Low hydraulic pressure
- Restricted filter assembly
- Valve body malfunction or leakage

Shifts Erratic
- Aerated fluid
- Damaged reaction shaft support seal rings
- Defective clutch or servo
- Defective governor
- Defective oil pump
- Governor support seal rings broken or worn
- Improper fluid level
- Improper front band adjustment
- Improper throttle valve linkage adjustment or binding components
- Incorrect shift linkage or cable adjustment
- Low hydraulic pressure
- Restricted filter assembly
- Valve body malfunction or leakage

Slips In All Forward Gears
- Aerated fluid
- Damaged or worn accumulator components
- Defective clutch or servo
- Defective oil pump
- Defective overrunning clutch
- Improper throttle valve linkage adjustment or binding components
- Incorrect shift linkage or cable adjustment
- Low fluid level
- Low hydraulic pressure
- Restricted filter assembly
- Valve body malfunction or leakage

Slips In All Gears
- Aerated fluid
- Defective clutch or servo
- Defective oil pump
- Incorrect shift linkage or cable adjustment
- Low fluid level
- Low hydraulic pressure
- Restricted filter assembly
- Valve body malfunction or leakage

Slips In Reverse Only
- Aerated fluid
- Binding band linkage
- Damaged reaction shaft support seal rings
- Defective front clutch, rear servo or rear band
- Improper rear band adjustment
- Incorrect shift linkage or cable adjustment
- Low fluid level
- Low hydraulic pressure
- Valve body malfunction or leakage

Slips In Reverse Or Manual Low
- Improper rear band adjustment

Transmission Overheats
- Improper band adjustment
- Improper clutch clearance
- Low fluid level
- Restricted oil cooler
- Switch valve in valve body sticking

Vehicle Moves In Neutral
- Clutch dragging
- Incorrect shift linkage or cable adjustment
- Torque converter lock-up clutch dragging
- Valve body malfunction or leakage

Vehicle Will Not Move In Any Gear
- Defective oil pump
- Incorrect shift linkage or cable adjustment
- Internal transmission component failure
- Low fluid level
- Low hydraulic pressure
- Restricted filter assembly
- Valve body malfunction or leakage

Vibration When Engine RPM Is Increased
- Defective torque converter (out of balance)

Will Not Upshift
- Damaged reaction shaft support seal rings
- Defective clutch or servo
- Defective governor
- Defective oil pump, seal rings or valve body
- Improper front band adjustment
- Improper throttle valve linkage adjustment
- Incorrect shift linkage or cable adjustment
- Low hydraulic pressure

OVERDRIVE UNIT SYMPTOM DIAGNOSIS

Delayed 3-4 Upshift
- Defective throttle position sensor
- Incorrect overdrive piston thrust plate

No Reverse Or Slips In Reverse
- Defective direct clutch components
- Incorrect overdrive piston thrust plate

No 3-4 Upshift
- Defective overdrive solenoid or wiring circuit
- Defective overdrive switch, wiring circuit or fuse
- Defective Transmission Control Unit (TCU)
- Incorrect overdrive piston thrust plate
- Low hydraulic pressure
- Overdrive piston seals damaged
- Overdrive switch in OFF position
- Valve body malfunction or leakage

No 4-3 Downshift
- Defective Transmission Control Unit (TCU)
- Defective wiring or connections
- Torque Converter Clutch (TCC) solenoid not venting
- Valve body malfunction or leakage

No 4-3 Downshift With Overdrive Switch In OFF Position
- Defective overdrive switch or wiring
- Defective Transmission Control Unit (TCU)
- Torque Converter Clutch (TCC) solenoid not venting

Noisy Operation
- Defective output shaft bearings
- Defective overrunning clutch
- Planetary gears worn or damaged
- Planetary thrust bearing defective

Runaway 3-4 Upshift
- Defective overrunning clutch

3-4 Upshift Occurs Before Completing 2-3 Upshift
- Defective Transmission Control Unit (TCU)
- Defective overdrive solenoid wiring connections or faulty wiring
- Overdrive solenoid faulty
- Valve body malfunction

TORQUE CONVERTER CLUTCH SYMPTOM DIAGNOSIS

Lock-Up Drags In Low Or 2nd Gear
- Valve body malfunction

Lock-Up Stays Engaged At Too Low Speed In 4th Gear
- Defective oil pump
- Defective Transmission Control Unit (TCU)
- Sticking governor
- Stuck Torque Converter Clutch (TCC) solenoid
- Valve body malfunction

Lock-Up Will Not Disengage
- Sticking governor
- Valve body malfunction

Loud Chatter During Lock-Up When Transmission Is Cold
- Defective torque converter

No Lock-Up Operation
- Defective input shaft seal rings
- Defective governor
- Defective oil pump
- Defective torque converter
- Defective Torque Converter Clutch (TCC) solenoid or wiring
- Defective Transmission Control Unit (TCU)
- Valve body malfunction

Shudder After Lock-Up Engagement
- Defective oil pump
- Defective torque converter
- Improper throttle valve linkage adjustment
- Improperly tuned engine
- Restricted oil cooler or lines
- Valve body malfunction

Vibration After Lock-Up Engagement
- Defective torque converter
- Improper throttle valve linkage adjustment
- Improperly tuned engine

Vibration Or Shudder During Lock-Up
- Defective oil pump
- Defective torque converter
- Improperly tuned engine
- Valve body malfunction

TESTING

ROAD TEST

1) Ensure shift linkage/cable and throttle valve linkage are properly adjusted. See appropriate AUTOMATIC TRANSMISSION SERVICING article in TRANSMISSION SERVICING. Ensure fluid level and condition are okay. Add ATF and adjust control cables or linkages (if necessary).

CLUTCH & BAND APPLICATION [1]

Gearshift Position   **Elements In Use**

"D" (Drive)
1st Gear .... Rear Clutch, Transmission Overrunning Clutch, Overdrive Unit Direct & Overrunning Clutch
2nd Gear .... Front Band, Rear Clutch, Overdrive Unit Direct & Overrunning Clutch
3rd Gear .... Front Clutch, Rear Clutch, Overdrive Unit Direct & Overrunning Clutch
4th Gear .... Front Clutch, Rear Clutch & Overdrive Unit Overdrive Clutch
"2" (Second)
1st Gear .... Rear Clutch, Transmission Overrunning Clutch, Overdrive Unit Direct & Overrunning Clutch
2nd Gear .... Front Band, Rear Clutch, Overdrive Unit Direct & Overrunning Clutch
"1" (Low)
1st Gear .... Rear Clutch, Rear Band, Transmission Overrunning Clutch, Overdrive Unit Direct & Overrunning Clutch
"R" (Reverse) .... Front Clutch, Rear Band & Overdrive Unit Direct Clutch
"N" Or "P" (Neutral Or Park) .... All Clutches & Bands Released Or Ineffective

[1] – Transmission contains front and rear bands, front clutch, rear clutch and overrunning clutch. The overdrive unit contains overdrive clutch, direct clutch and overrunning clutch. Torque converter lock-up exists in 3rd and 4th gears only.

2) Ensure all electrical connections on transmission and overdrive switch are okay. Turn Overdrive (OD) switch to the ON position. Road test vehicle and operate transmission in each gear position. Observe engine performance during road test. A poorly tuned engine will not allow an accurate analysis of transmission operation.

3) Check for slippage and shift variations. Note if shifts are harsh, spongy, delayed or early. Slipping in any gear usually indicates clutch, band, or overrunning clutch problems. A slipping clutch or band in a particular gear can usually be identified by noting transmission operation in other gearshift positions and comparing internal components used. See CLUTCH & BAND APPLICATION table.

4) Problem area may be detected by determining which components are applied. By selecting another gear that does not use these clutches, the clutch that is slipping can be determined. See CLUTCH & BAND APPLICATION table.

5) Process of elimination can be used to detect slipping units and confirm proper operation of good units. Although road test analysis can usually diagnose slipping units, the actual malfunction, however, usually cannot be decided.

6) Practically any condition can be caused by leaking hydraulic circuits or sticking valves. Transmission failure may be determined by performing hydraulic pressure test along with clutch and servo air pressure test.

TORQUE CONVERTER STALL SPEED TEST

Torque Converter Stall Speed Test Procedure – 1) Install tachometer. Ensure transmission fluid level is correct. Start and operate engine until transmission fluid is at normal operating temperature.

CAUTION: DO NOT open throttle to wide open position for more than 5 seconds or transmission may be damaged. If performing more than one torque converter stall speed test, operate engine at 1000 RPM with transmission in Neutral for at least 20 seconds to cool transmission fluid before performing next torque converter stall speed test.

2) Block front wheels. Apply parking and service brakes. Place transmission in Drive. Open throttle to wide open position for no more than 5 seconds and note engine RPM and then release throttle. This is the torque converter stall speed.

3) Torque converter stall speed should be 2000-2300 RPM on 2.4L and 2300-2600 RPM on 3.0L. Once torque converter stall speed is obtained, place transmission in Neutral. Operate engine for 20 seconds, allowing transmission to cool. Stop engine. Place transmission in Park. Remove tachometer.

NOTE: Use following symptoms to trouble shoot results of torque converter stall speed test.

Torque Converter Stall Speed Exceeds Specification – If torque converter stall speed exceeds specification by more than 200 RPM, transmission clutch is slipping.

Torque Converter Stall Speed Less Than Specification – 1) If torque converter stall speed is less than specification with properly tuned engine, torque converter overrunning clutch may be slipping.

2) If torque converter overrunning clutch is slipping, torque converter stall speed will be 250-350 RPM less than the specification. Vehicle will operate properly at highway speeds, but will have poor low-speed acceleration.

Torque Converter Stall Speed Is Within Specification – If torque converter stall speed is within specification, but abnormal throttle opening is required to maintain highway speeds, torque converter overrunning clutch is seized. Torque converter must be replaced.

Noise When Performing Torque Converter Stall Speed Test – Whining noise caused by fluid flow is normal. A loud metallic sound indicates torque converter is damaged. To ensure sound is coming from torque converter, raise vehicle on hoist. Operate vehicle with transmission in Drive and then Neutral at light throttle. Ensure noise is coming from torque converter. Replace torque converter if defective.

HYDRAULIC PRESSURE TEST

Hydraulic Pressure Test Preparation – 1) Ensure fluid level and condition are okay. Install tachometer. Raise vehicle on hoist, allowing wheels to rotate freely.

2) Disconnect throttle valve and shift cables or linkages from manual throttle valve lever and manual selector lever on the transmission.

CAUTION: A 100 psi (7 kg/cm²) pressure gauge is required for checking all applications except rear servo. A 300 psi (21 kg/cm²) pressure gauge is required for checking pressure at rear servo and overdrive clutch.

Pressure Test With Transmission In "L" (1st Gear) – 1) Remove pressure port plugs and install pressure gauge in line pressure port and rear servo apply port. See Fig. 3. Start and operate engine at 1000 RPM.

2) Move manual selector lever on transmission fully forward to the gearshift "L" position. Read pressure on both pressure gauges as throttle valve lever on transmission is moved from fully forward position to fully rearward position.

3) Line pressure should be 54-60 psi (3.7-4.2 kg/cm²) with throttle valve lever fully forward and gradually increase to 90-96 psi (6.3-6.7 kg/cm²) as throttle valve lever is moved rearward. Rear servo pressure should be within 3 psi (.2 kg/cm²) of line pressure.

4) If line pressure is not within specification, adjust line pressure. See LINE PRESSURE under HYDRAULIC PRESSURE ADJUSTMENTS. If proper line pressure still cannot be obtained, check for defective components and hydraulic circuit.

5) This tests oil pump output, pressure regulation, condition of rear clutch and servo hydraulic circuits. Remove pressure gauges. Install and tighten pressure port plugs to specification. See TORQUE SPECIFICATIONS.

Pressure Test With Transmission In "2" (2nd Gear) – 1) Remove pressure port plug and install pressure gauge in line pressure port. See Fig. 3.

2) Install pressure gauge and tee into rear oil cooler line fitting for reading the lubrication pressure. Start and operate engine at 1000 RPM.

3) Move manual selector lever on transmission to fully forward position and then rearward one position to gearshift "2" position. Read pressure on both pressure gauges as throttle valve lever on transmission is moved from fully forward position to fully rearward position.

4) Line pressure should be 54-60 psi (3.7-4.2 kg/cm²) with throttle valve lever fully forward and gradually increase to 90-96 psi (6.3-6.7 kg/cm²) as throttle valve lever is moved rearward.

5) Lubrication pressure should be 5-15 psi (.4-1.1 kg/cm²) with throttle valve lever fully forward and gradually increase to 10-30 psi (.7-2.1 kg/cm²) as throttle valve lever is moved fully rearward.

6) If line pressure is not within specification, adjust line pressure. See LINE PRESSURE under HYDRAULIC PRESSURE ADJUSTMENTS. If proper line pressure still cannot be obtained, check for defective components and hydraulic circuit.

7) This tests oil pump output, pressure regulation, condition of rear clutch and lubrication hydraulic circuit. Remove pressure gauges. Install and tighten pressure port plug to specification. See TORQUE SPECIFICATIONS.

Pressure Test With Transmission In "D" (Drive Gear) – 1) Remove pressure port plugs and install pressure gauge in line pressure port and front servo release port. *See Fig. 3.* Start and operate engine at 1600 RPM.

2) Move manual selector lever on transmission to fully forward position and then rearward 2 positions to gearshift "D" position. Read pressure on both pressure gauges as throttle valve lever on transmission is moved from fully forward position to fully rearward position.

3) Line pressure should be 54-60 psi (3.7-4.2 kg/cm²) with throttle valve lever fully forward and gradually increase as throttle valve lever is moved rearward. Front servo release is pressurized only in direct gear and pressure should be within 3 psi (.2 kg/cm²) of line pressure up to the downshift point.

4) If line pressure is not within specification, adjust line pressure. See LINE PRESSURE under HYDRAULIC PRESSURE ADJUSTMENTS. If proper line pressure still cannot be obtained, check for defective components and hydraulic circuit.

5) This tests oil pump output, pressure regulation and condition of front clutch, rear clutch and torque converter clutch hydraulic circuits. Remove pressure gauges. Install and tighten pressure port plugs to specification. See TORQUE SPECIFICATIONS.

Pressure Test With Transmission In "R" (Reverse Gear) – 1) Remove pressure port plug and install 300 psi (21 kg/cm²) pressure gauge in rear servo apply port. *See Fig. 3.* Start and operate engine at 1600 RPM.

2) Move manual selector lever on transmission to fully forward position and then rearward 4 positions to gearshift "R" position. Read pressure on pressure gauge as throttle valve lever on transmission is moved from fully forward position to fully rearward position.

3) Pressure should be 145-175 psi (10.2-12.3 kg/cm²) with throttle valve lever fully forward and gradually increase to 230-280 psi (16.1-19.7 kg/cm²) with throttle valve lever fully rearward. This tests oil pump output, pressure regulation, front clutch and rear servo hydraulic circuits.

4) Move manual selector lever to the gearshift "D" position. Ensure rear servo apply pressure decreases to zero. This tests for leakage into rear servo due to transmission case problems which can cause rear band failure.

5) Remove pressure gauge. Install and tighten pressure port plug to specification. See TORQUE SPECIFICATIONS.

Transmission Governor Pressure – 1) Reconnect throttle valve and shift cables or linkages on manual selector lever and throttle valve lever on transmission (if removed). Remove pressure port plug and install pressure gauge in governor pressure port. *See Fig. 3.*

2) Lower vehicle, leaving wheels approximately 12" from floor. Start engine and allow to idle. Place gearshift in "D" (Drive). Note pressure gauge reading with engine idling.

3) Pressure should be 0-1.5 psi (0-.1 kg/cm²) with wheels not rotating. If pressure exceeds specification, governor valve or weights are stuck open.

4) If pressure is correct, slowly increase engine speed, noting governor pressure in relation to vehicle speed. Governor pressure should increase smoothly with the vehicle speed.

5) Governor pressure should rise smoothly and then drop back to 0-1.5 psi (0-.1 kg/cm²) when wheels stop rotating. High pressure with the wheels stopped will prevent transmission from downshifting.

6) This tests governor operation in relation to engine and vehicle speed. Repair governor if it does not operate properly. Remove pressure gauge. Install and tighten pressure port plug to specification. See TORQUE SPECIFICATIONS.

Hydraulic Pressure Test Result Indications – 1) If proper line pressure is obtained in any pressure test, oil pump and pressure regulator are working properly.

2) If line pressure is low in "D", "L" and "2", but is correct in "R", this indicates leakage in rear clutch circuit.

3) If line pressure is low in "D" and "R", but is correct in "1" and "2", this indicates leakage in front clutch circuit.

4) If line pressure is low in "R" and "L", but is correct in "2", this indicates leakage in rear servo circuit.

5) If line pressure is not within specification, adjust line pressure. See LINE PRESSURE under HYDRAULIC PRESSURE ADJUSTMENTS. If proper line pressure still cannot be obtained, check for defective components and hydraulic circuit. Low line pressure in all positions indicates a defective oil pump, restricted filter or stuck pressure regulator valve.

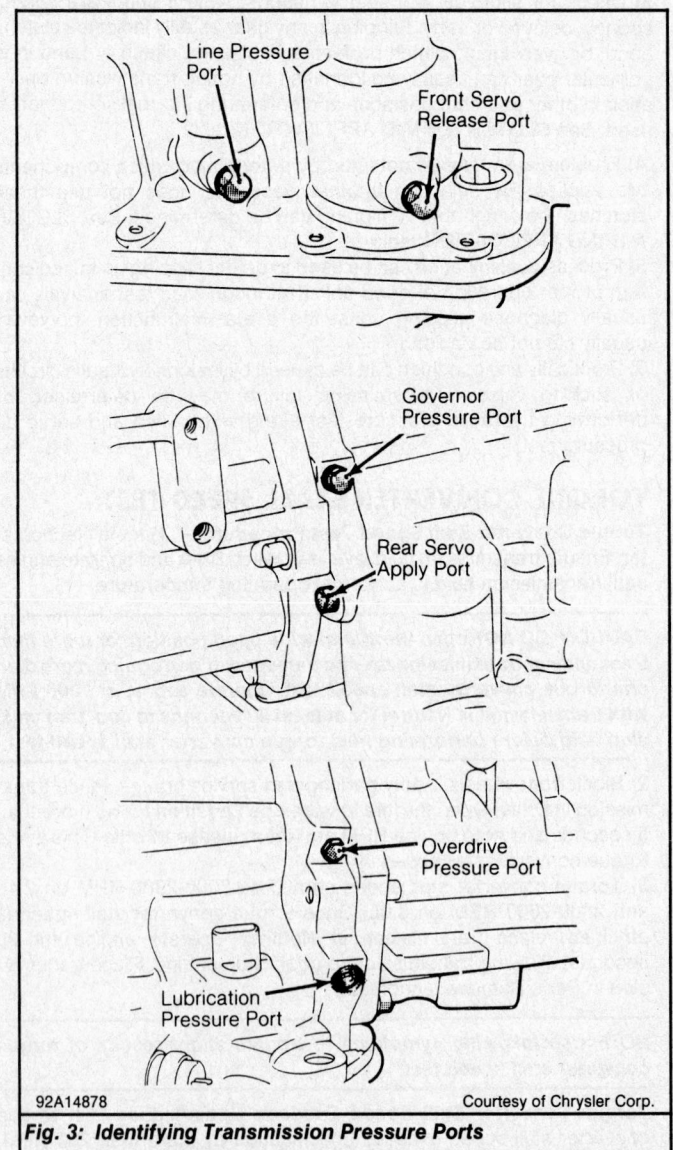

Line Pressure Port

Front Servo Release Port

Governor Pressure Port

Rear Servo Apply Port

Overdrive Pressure Port

Lubrication Pressure Port

92A14878   Courtesy of Chrysler Corp.

Fig. 3: Identifying Transmission Pressure Ports

CLUTCH & SERVO AIR PRESSURE TEST

NOTE: Inoperative clutches, servos and bands can be located by applying 30 psi (2.1 kg/cm²) air pressure to appropriate passages in transmission case.

Test Preparation – Remove valve body. See VALVE BODY under REMOVAL & INSTALLATION.

CAUTION: Ensure air supply is free of all dirt and moisture.

Front Clutch – Apply air pressure to front clutch apply passage and listen for a dull thud, indicating front clutch operation. *See Fig. 4.* Maintain air pressure on front clutch apply passage for a few seconds and inspect system for excessive oil leakage.

Rear Clutch – **1)** Apply air pressure to rear clutch apply passage and listen for a dull thud, indicating rear clutch operation. *See Fig. 4.*

2) If dull thud cannot be heard in clutches, place finger tips on clutch housing and apply air pressure again. Movement of piston should be felt as clutch is applied. Maintain air pressure on rear clutch apply passage for a few seconds and inspect system for excessive oil leakage.

Front Servo – Apply air pressure to front servo apply passage. *See Fig. 4.* Front band should tighten, indicating front servo operation. Release air pressure. Ensure spring tension on servo piston releases front band.

Rear Servo – Apply air pressure to rear servo apply passage. *See Fig. 4.* Rear band should tighten, indicating rear servo operation. Release air pressure. Ensure spring tension on servo piston releases rear band.

Overdrive Clutch – Apply air pressure to overdrive clutch apply passage and listen for dull thud, which indicates overdrive clutch is operating. *See Fig. 4.*

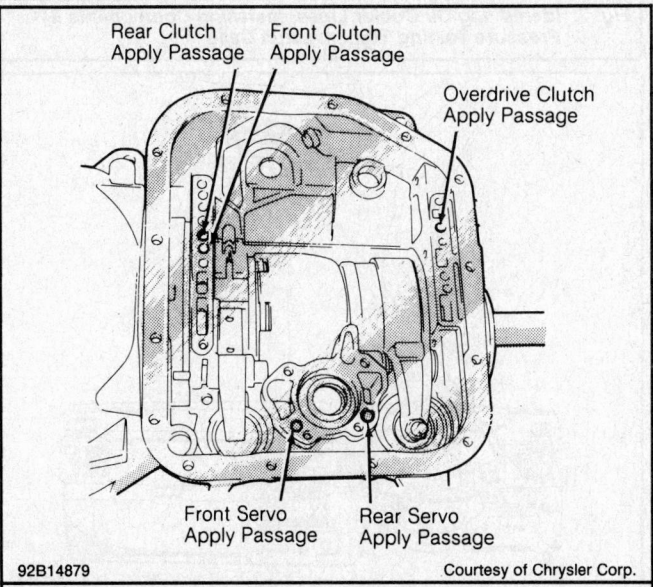

Fig. 4: Identifying Air Pressure Test Passages

TORQUE CONVERTER FLUID LEAKAGE TEST

NOTE: Fluid around torque converter may originate from engine oil or transmission. Ensure transmission fluid level is correct. Fluid leakage at torque converter may result if fluid level is too high. Transmission can be checked for leaks using the following method.

1) Remove torque converter dust shield. Clean inside area of torque converter housing using solvent and compressed air. Ensure area is clean and dry.

2) Fabricate leakage test probe using 1/32" sheet metal, 5 1/2" (140 mm) long and 1 1/2" (38 mm) wide. *See Fig. 5.* Install leakage test probe on torque converter dust shield bolt so leakage test probe is near torque converter. Ensure torque converter does not contact leakage test probe.

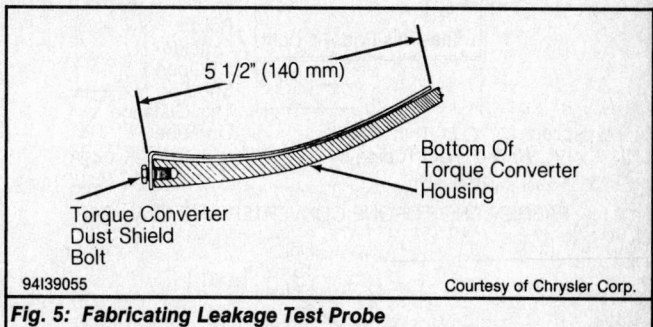

Fig. 5: Fabricating Leakage Test Probe

3) Apply parking brake. Start engine. Place transmission in Neutral. Operate engine at 2500 RPM for 2 minutes. Stop engine. Remove leakage test probe.

4) If upper surface of leakage test probe is dry, torque converter is not leaking. If upper surface of leakage test probe is wet with ATF, torque converter is leaking. If area below leakage test probe is wet with ATF, fluid is coming from around torque converter area.

5) Check following for possible causes of fluid leaks at torque converter areas.

- Defective Oil Pump Housing "O" Ring Or Oil Pump Housing
- Front Band Pin Access Plug
- Mispositioned Or Worn Bushing
- Oil Pump Seal
- Oil Pump-To-Transmission Case Bolts
- Oil Pump Vent

6) If torque converter is leaking, check for defective welds on outside diameter of torque converter and torque converter hub. Torque converter hub is welded on inside and is not visible. Replace torque converter if a leak exists. DO NOT attempt to repair torque converter.

TRANSMISSION CASE PRESSURE TEST

NOTE: Transmission case, gaskets and oil pump housing can be checked for leaks using the following method. Transmission must be removed to perform transmission case pressure test.

1) Remove torque converter from transmission. Fabricate torque converter hub seal cup, retaining strap and vent plug retainer. *See Fig. 6.* Retaining strap specifications are approximate. Measure hole positions on torque converter housing before drilling.

CAUTION: Ensure torque converter hub seal cup surface is smooth to prevent damage to seal in oil pump.

2) Install torque converter hub seal cup, vent plug retainer and retaining strap. *See Fig. 7.* Install shipping plug in rear output shaft opening. Install and secure plugs in remaining transmission openings except oil cooler return line.

3) Attach air pump to oil cooler return line. *See Fig. 7.* Ensure cap is installed on oil cooler supply line fitting. Using pressure regulator, apply 8-10 psi (.5-.7 kg/cm²) of air pressure to transmission case.

CAUTION: DO NOT apply more than 10 psi (.7 kg/cm²) of air pressure to transmission case.

4) Coat oil pump and front of transmission case with soapy water solution. Check for bubbles, indicating a leak in seals, "O" rings, gaskets or transmission case. Release air pressure. Remove test equipment. Replace defective components.

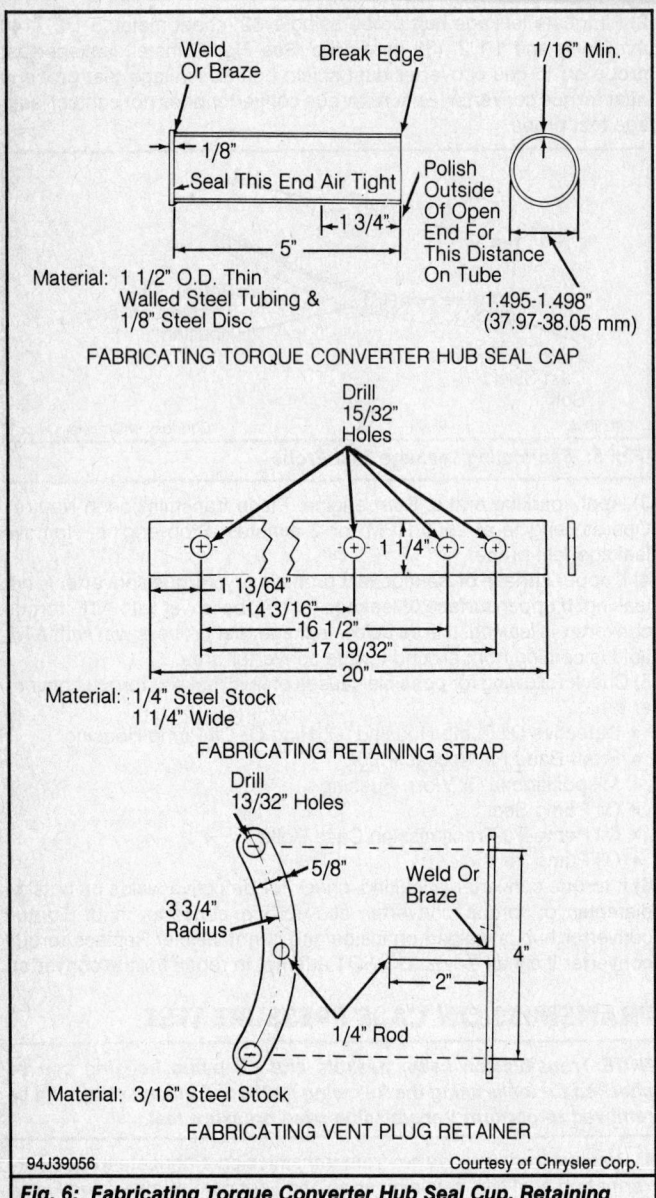

Fig. 6: Fabricating Torque Converter Hub Seal Cup, Retaining Strap & Vent Plug Retainer

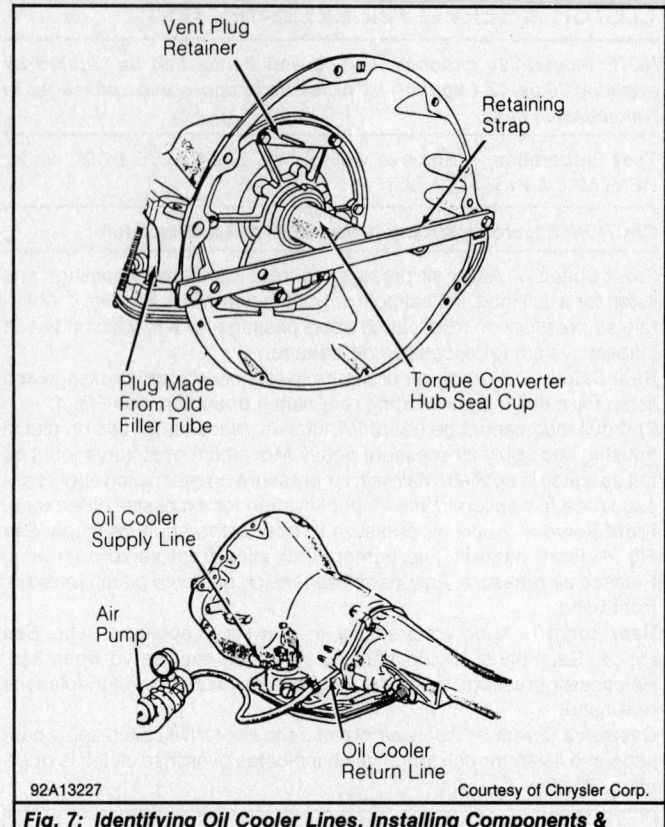

Fig. 7: Identifying Oil Cooler Lines, Installing Components & Pressure Testing Transmission Case

ELECTRICAL COMPONENT TESTING

OVERDRIVE RELAY

Overdrive relay is located below driver's side of instrument panel, in relay box. *See Fig. 8.* Testing information not available from manufacturer. It may be necessary to use wiring diagram for relay and circuit testing. See WIRING DIAGRAMS. Overdrive relay may also be referred to as the overdrive off relay.

OVERDRIVE (OD) SWITCH

1) Disconnect OD switch electrical connector and note terminal identification. *See Fig. 9.*
2) Using ohmmeter, check that continuity exists between terminals No. 1 and 3 with OD switch in the OFF position. Check that continuity exists between terminals No. 1 and 2 with OD switch in the ON position. Replace OD switch if defective.

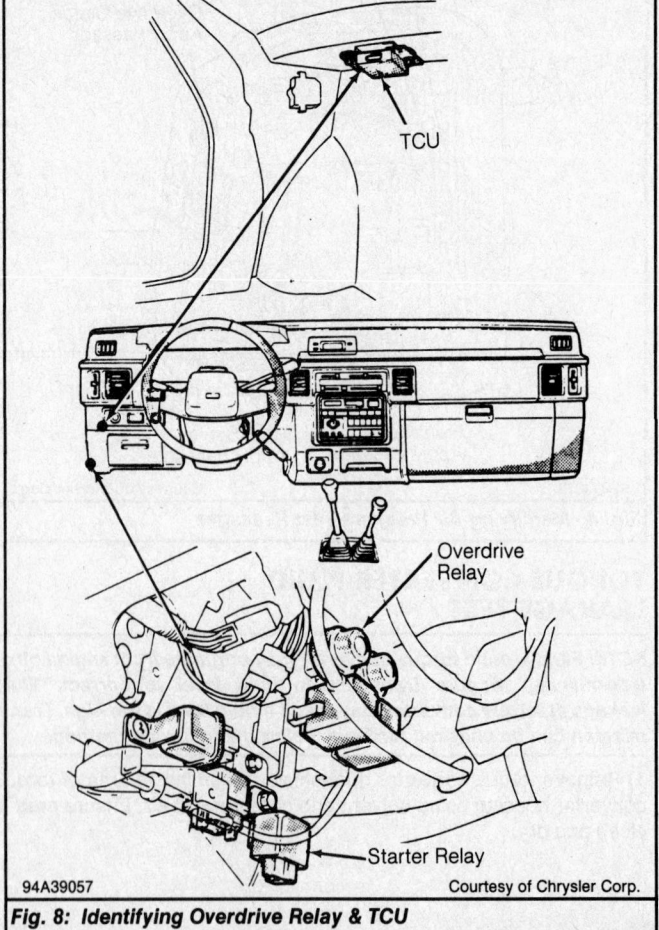

Fig. 8: Identifying Overdrive Relay & TCU

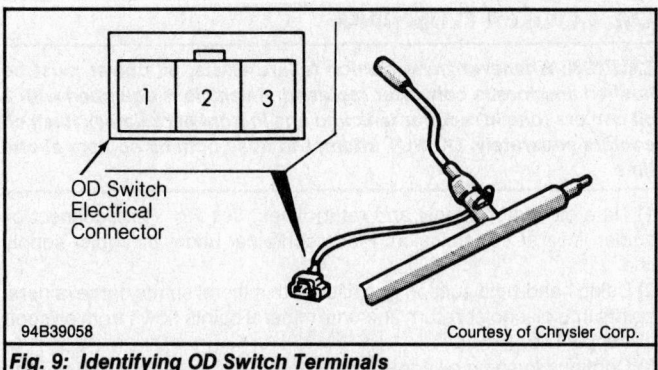

94B39058   Courtesy of Chrysler Corp.

Fig. 9: Identifying OD Switch Terminals

OVERDRIVE & TCC SOLENOID

1) Manufacturer list testing procedure with solenoid assembly removed from valve body. Remove solenoid assembly from valve body.
2) Shake solenoid assembly to ensure plunger moves freely in the solenoid. Replace solenoid if plunger fails to move freely. Check orifice in the nozzle on each solenoid for dirt or foreign material. Clean orifice as necessary.
3) To test solenoid operation, hold solenoid with nozzle pointing upward. Apply battery voltage between designated terminals of solenoid valve connector, ensuring plunger on solenoid moves up and down when voltage is applied and then released. *See Fig. 10.* Replace solenoid if defective. For testing of overdrive and TCC solenoid wiring circuits, see WIRING DIAGRAMS.

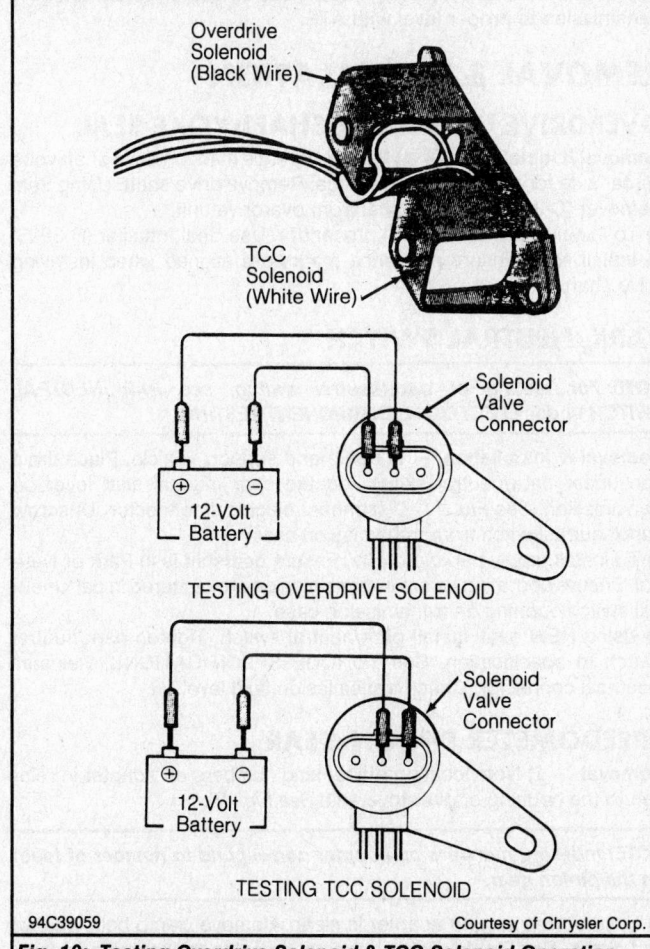

94C39059   Courtesy of Chrysler Corp.

Fig. 10: Testing Overdrive Solenoid & TCC Solenoid Operation

PARK/NEUTRAL SWITCH

NOTE: The start side of park/neutral start switch circuit is the center terminal of the park/neutral switch. Center terminal provides a ground circuit for starter solenoid when gearshift is in Park or Neutral. Back-up light side of park/neutral switch is the 2 outside terminals of park/neutral switch. These terminals complete the circuit for back-up lights when gearshift is in Reverse.

1) Disconnect electrical connector from park/neutral switch. To check start side of park/neutral switch, using ohmmeter, check for continuity between center terminal of park/neutral switch and transmission case.
2) Continuity should exist with gearshift in Park or Neutral. If continuity does not exist, check shift linkage or cable adjustment. See appropriate AUTOMATIC TRANSMISSION SERVICING article in TRANSMISSION SERVICING. Replace park/neutral switch if continuity does not exist and shift linkage or cable is properly adjusted.
3) To check back-up light side, using ohmmeter, check for continuity between the 2 outer terminals of park/neutral switch with gearshift in Reverse. Replace park/neutral switch if continuity does not exist.
4) Ensure no continuity exists between either outer terminal and transmission case. Replace park/neutral switch if continuity exists between outer terminal and transmission case.

TRANSMISSION CONTROL UNIT (TCU)

The TCU is located below driver's side of instrument panel and contains a 10-pin connector. *See Fig. 8.* Testing information not available from manufacturer. It may be necessary to use wiring diagram for testing wiring circuits to the TCU. See WIRING DIAGRAMS.

TRANSMISSION OIL TEMP. SWITCH

4WD Only – Transmission oil temperature switch is mounted in oil cooler supply line, near the transmission case. *See Fig. 11.* Transmission oil temperature switch will illuminate the transmission oil temperature warning light on instrument panel if transmission oil temperature becomes excessive. Testing information not available from manufacturer.

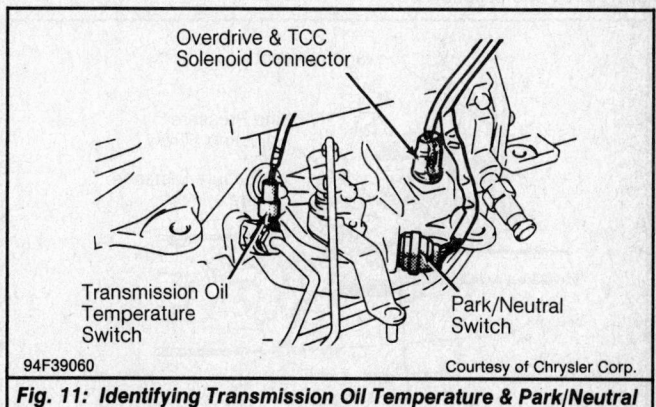

94F39060   Courtesy of Chrysler Corp.

Fig. 11: Identifying Transmission Oil Temperature & Park/Neutral Switch

HYDRAULIC PRESSURE ADJUSTMENTS

CAUTION: Line pressure and throttle pressure each affect shift quality. Throttle pressure must be adjusted before line pressure. Valve body may require removal for adjustments. See VALVE BODY under REMOVAL & INSTALLATION.

THROTTLE PRESSURE

1) Insert Gauge Pin (C-3763) between cam on throttle lever and kickdown valve. *See Fig. 12.*
2) Push inward on gauge pin and compress kickdown valve against spring until kickdown valve bottoms in valve body. Ensure spring is fully compressed and kickdown valve is bottomed in valve body.

3) Maintain pressure against kickdown valve and spring. Rotate throttle pressure adjusting screw until head of adjusting screw contacts tang on throttle lever. Ensure throttle lever cam contacts gauge pin. Remove gauge pin.

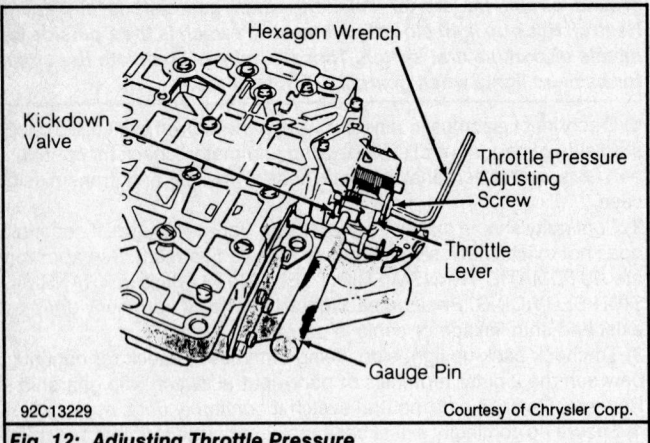

92C13229   Courtesy of Chrysler Corp.

Fig. 12: Adjusting Throttle Pressure

LINE PRESSURE

CAUTION: Throttle pressure must be adjusted before adjusting line pressure.

1) Measure distance from valve body to inner edge of line pressure adjusting screw. *See Fig. 13.* Rotate line pressure adjusting screw so distance is approximately 1 5/16".

NOTE: Due to manufacturing tolerances, adjustment can be varied to obtain specified line pressure.

2) Rotating line pressure adjusting screw one revolution will change line pressure approximately 1 2/3 psi. Rotating line pressure adjusting screw counterclockwise increases line pressure and clockwise decreases line pressure.

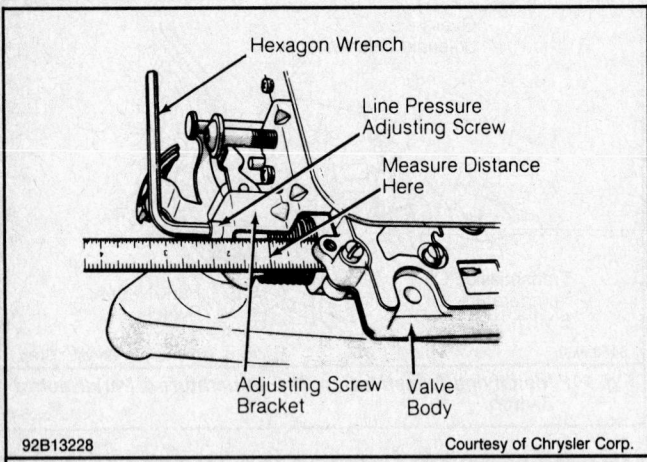

92B13228   Courtesy of Chrysler Corp.

Fig. 13: Identifying Adjusting Screw Bracket & Adjusting Line Pressure

ON-VEHICLE SERVICE

Following components can be serviced on the vehicle.
- Overdrive Unit Drive Shaft Yoke Seal
- Park/Neutral Switch
- Speedometer Pinion Gear
- Valve Body

See appropriate component under REMOVAL & INSTALLATION.

OIL COOLER FLUSHING

CAUTION: Whenever transmission failure exists, oil cooler must be flushed and torque converter replaced. If vehicle is equipped with 2 oil coolers (one in radiator tank and one in front of radiator), flush oil coolers separately. DO NOT attempt to flush both oil coolers at one time.

1) Note oil cooler supply and return lines. *See Fig. 7.* Disconnect oil cooler lines at transmission. Place container under oil cooler supply line.

2) Using hand-held suction gun filled with mineral spirits, force mineral spirits into oil cooler return line until mineral spirits flows from oil cooler supply line.

3) Continue flushing oil cooler until mineral spirits is clear and no sign of contamination exists. Once contamination is removed, apply compressed air on line from oil cooler in light applications until remaining mineral spirits is blown from oil cooler and oil cooler lines.

4) Pump at least one quart of Mopar ATF Plus Type 7176 fluid through oil cooler to ensure oil cooler is free of mineral spirits. Replace oil cooler if fluid does not flow freely through oil cooler.

OIL COOLER FLOW CHECK

1) With transmission filled to proper fluid level, disconnect oil cooler return line from transmission. *See Fig. 7.* Place container under oil cooler return line.

2) Add one extra quart of ATF to transmission. Apply parking brake. Start engine and allow to idle. Place gearshift in Neutral. Check fluid flow from oil cooler return line.

3) If fluid flow is intermittent or takes more than 20 seconds to obtain one quart, replace oil cooler. Reconnect oil cooler return line. Fill transmission to proper level with ATF.

REMOVAL & INSTALLATION

OVERDRIVE UNIT DRIVE SHAFT YOKE SEAL

Removal & Installation – 1) Place reference mark on drive shaft yoke at rear axle for reassembly reference. Remove drive shaft. Using Seal Remover (C-3985), remove seal from overdrive unit.

2) To install, reverse removal procedure. Use Seal Installer (C-3995) to install seal. Ensure reference marks are aligned when installing drive shaft.

PARK/NEUTRAL SWITCH

NOTE: For testing of park/neutral switch, see PARK/NEUTRAL SWITCH under ELECTRICAL COMPONENT TESTING.

Removal & Installation – 1) Raise and support vehicle. Place drain pan under park/neutral switch located near manual shift lever on transmission. *See Fig. 11.* Disconnect electrical connector. Unscrew park/neutral switch from transmission case.

2) To install, apply parking brake. Ensure gearshift is in Park or Neutral. Ensure operating levers in transmission are centered in park/neutral switch opening on transmission case.

3) Using NEW seal, install park/neutral switch. Tighten park/neutral switch to specification. See TORQUE SPECIFICATIONS. Reinstall electrical connector. Check transmission fluid level.

SPEEDOMETER PINION GEAR

Removal – 1) Note location of indexing numbers on adapter in relation to the housing of overdrive unit. *See Fig. 15.*

NOTE: Indexing numbers on adapter correspond to number of teeth on the pinion gear.

2) Ensure area around adapter is clean. Remove clamp bolt, washer and clamp. *See Fig. 14.* With speedometer cable connected on adapter, remove adapter, "O" ring and pinion gear from housing of overdrive unit. *See Fig. 14.*

3) Disconnect speedometer cable from adapter. Check for signs of ATF leakage around speedometer cable area on the adapter. If ATF leakage exists, oil seal is leaking and should be replaced. Remove oil seal from adapter (if necessary).

Installation – 1) If installing NEW oil seal in adapter, start oil seal in adapter by hand. Using Oil Seal Installer (C-4004), press oil seal in adapter until it bottoms.

2) Ensure housing is clean. Install NEW "O" ring on adapter (if necessary). Lubricate "O" ring on adapter, oil seal and pinion gear teeth with ATF. Count number of teeth on the pinion gear. Ensure number of teeth on pinion gear are within range of indexing numbers listed on the adapter. *See Fig. 15.*

3) Install pinion gear, "O" ring and adapter in the housing of overdrive unit. Rotate adapter until proper indexing number in relation to number of pinion gear teeth is at 6 o'clock position. *See Fig. 15.*

4) Ensure adapter is seated in the housing of overdrive unit. Install clamp so tangs on clamp engage with slots on adapter. Install washer and clamp bolt. Tighten clamp bolt to specification. See TORQUE SPECIFICATIONS. Install speedometer cable. Fill transmission with ATF.

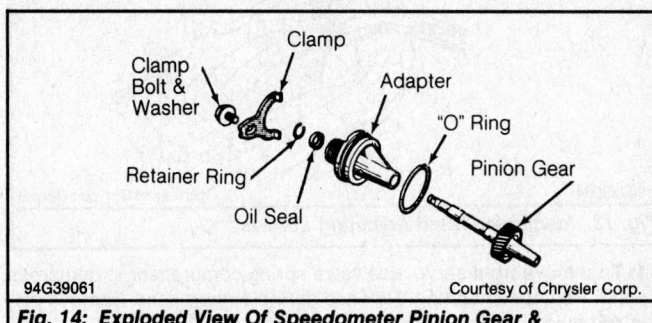

Clamp
Clamp Bolt & Washer
Adapter
"O" Ring
Retainer Ring
Oil Seal
Pinion Gear
94G39061
Courtesy of Chrysler Corp.

Fig. 14: *Exploded View Of Speedometer Pinion Gear & Components*

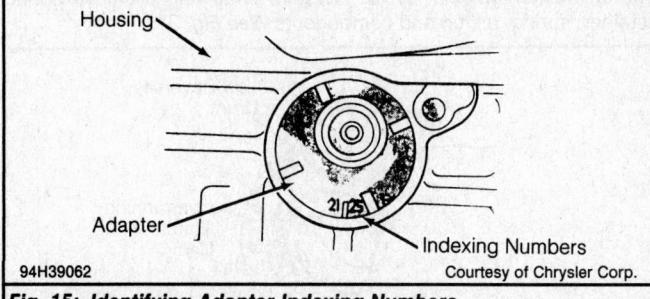

Housing
Adapter
Indexing Numbers
94H39062
Courtesy of Chrysler Corp.

Fig. 15: *Identifying Adapter Indexing Numbers*

TRANSMISSION

See appropriate AUTOMATIC TRANSMISSION REMOVAL article in TRANSMISSION SERVICING.

VALVE BODY

Removal – 1) Raise and support vehicle. Remove bolts, oil pan and gasket. Remove throttle valve and manual shift levers from transmission. Remove park/neutral switch. See PARK/NEUTRAL SWITCH under REMOVAL & INSTALLATION.

2) Remove bolts and filter assembly. Keep bolts with filter assembly for installation reference. Disconnect necessary solenoid electrical connectors from solenoid connector in transmission case.

3) Remove valve body-to-transmission case bolts. Note bolt length and location for installation reference. Lower valve body enough to remove spring above accumulator.

4) Lower valve body and rotate it away from transmission case. Use care not to damage solenoids on valve body. Pull park rod from parking sprag. Remove valve body.

Installation – 1) Ensure park/neutral switch is removed before installing valve body. Install NEW seal rings on accumulator. Lubricate seal rings, manual shift lever seal and accumulator and bore with petroleum jelly.

2) Install accumulator in transmission case. Place manual shift lever on valve body in low gear position so ball on park rod can be installed in parking sprag. Using screwdriver, push parking sprag to engage with park gear. This allows knob on park rod to move past parking sprag when installing valve body. Rotate output shaft to ensure parking sprag is engaged.

CAUTION: Ensure park rod enters parking sprag, as park rod may enter cavity in the case and not enter parking sprag. Park rod will be damaged if it is not engaged with parking sprag.

3) Install spring between accumulator and valve body. Install valve body, working park rod past parking sprag. Ensure spring for accumulator remains in place.

CAUTION: Alternately tighten valve body-to-transmission case bolts to prevent damage to valve body. DO NOT overtighten bolts or transmission and valve body may be damaged.

4) Install valve body-to-transmission case bolts in original location finger tight only. DO NOT tighten bolts at this time. Using NEW seal, install park/neutral switch. Tighten park/neutral switch to specification. See TORQUE SPECIFICATIONS. Tighten valve body-to-transmission case bolts evenly to specification.

5) Install NEW filter assembly. Install and tighten bolts to specification. Reconnect all necessary electrical connections.

6) Ensure throttle valve shaft seal is in place, then install flat washer and throttle valve lever and manual shift lever. Ensure throttle valve lever and manual shift levers rotate smoothly.

7) Using NEW gasket, install oil pan. Install and tighten bolts to specification. Fill transmission with ATF. Ensure shift linkage/cable and throttle valve linkage are properly adjusted. See appropriate AUTOMATIC TRANSMISSION SERVICING article in TRANSMISSION SERVICING.

TORQUE CONVERTER

CAUTION: Torque converter is a welded assembly and is not serviceable. If a malfunction occurs or if torque converter becomes contaminated with foreign material, it MUST be replaced. Torque converter cannot be flushed or repaired.

NOTE: For torque converter fluid leak test and torque converter stall speed test, see TESTING in this article.

TRANSMISSION DISASSEMBLY

NOTE: For overdrive unit disassembly, see OVERDRIVE UNIT DISASSEMBLY in this article.

VALVE BODY & COMPONENTS

CAUTION: Note location of all thrust washer and thrust plate locations for reassembly reference.

1) Prior to transmission disassembly, remove torque converter. Using dial indicator, check input shaft end play for reassembly reference. Input shaft end play should be .011-.080" (.28-2.03 mm). Different thickness thrust washer must be installed on end of intermediate shaft if input shaft end play is not within specification.

2) Remove bolts, oil pan and gasket. Loosen clamps and remove throttle valve and manual shift levers from transmission. Remove park/neutral switch and seal. Remove bolts and filter assembly. Keep bolts with filter assembly for reassembly reference.

3) Disconnect solenoid electrical connectors from solenoid connector in transmission case. Disconnect park rod from valve body. Remove valve body-to-transmission case bolts. Note bolt length and location for reassembly reference. Remove valve body, accumulator and spring.

4) Remove park rod from overdrive unit case. Remove overdrive unit-to-transmission bolts. Remove overdrive unit. *See Fig. 16.* If overdrive unit does not require servicing, install Alignment Shaft (C-6227-2) in overrunning clutch and planetary gear splines on overdrive unit, ensuring alignment shaft is fully seated. *See Fig. 17.* This maintains proper alignment of all components in overdrive unit.

5) Remove intermediate shaft selective spacer and overdrive piston thrust plate from intermediate shaft. *See Fig. 15.* Remove overdrive piston from overdrive piston retainer.

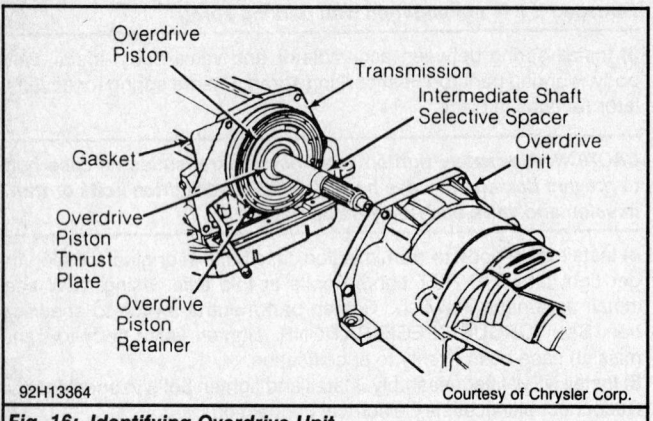

92H13364   Courtesy of Chrysler Corp.

Fig. 16: Identifying Overdrive Unit

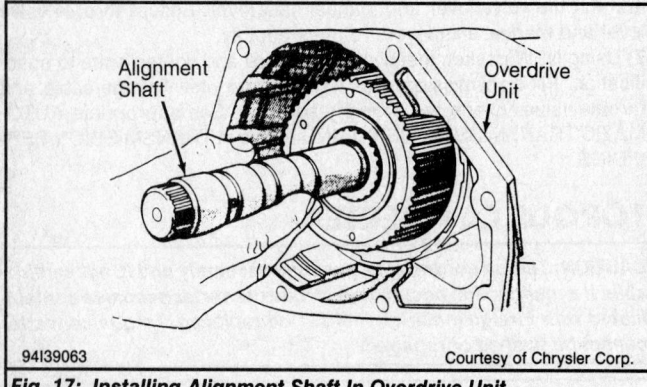

94I39063   Courtesy of Chrysler Corp.

Fig. 17: Installing Alignment Shaft In Overdrive Unit

6) Loosen lock nut on front band adjusting screw. *See Fig. 18.* Tighten front band adjusting screw until front band is tight. This prevents clutch components from coming out when oil pump is removed.

7) Remove oil pump bolts. Install slide hammers on opposite sides of oil pump. Pull oil pump from transmission case. Remove oil pump gasket.

8) Loosen front band adjusting screw. Remove strut located between front band and lever on transmission case. Slide front band out of transmission case.

9) Grasp input shaft, hold clutch units together, and remove front and rear clutch as an assembly. Use care not to lose thrust washer located between input shaft and intermediate shaft.

10) While supporting intermediate shaft and driving shell, carefully slide planetary gear train assembly out of transmission case. Use care not to damage machined surfaces on intermediate shaft during removal.

11) Remove low-reverse drum-to-overdrive piston retainer snap ring and spacer from inside of transmission case. Remove overdrive piston retainer and gasket from rear of transmission case.

12) Loosen overrunning clutch cam-to-transmission case bolts, located on rear of transmission case. Using soft faced hammer, tap on bolts until overrunning clutch cam is free from transmission case.

13) Remove bolts from overrunning clutch cam. Loosen lock nut and rear band adjusting screw. *See Fig. 18.* Remove rear band, low-reverse drum and overrunning clutch assembly with overrunning clutch cam. *See Fig. 19.*

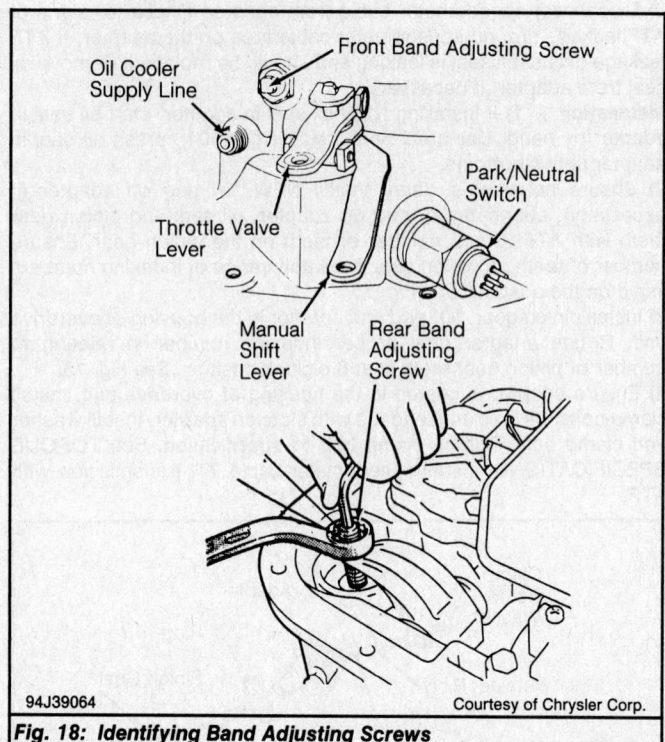

94J39064   Courtesy of Chrysler Corp.

Fig. 18: Identifying Band Adjusting Screws

14) To remove front servo, use valve spring compressor to compress spring. Remove snap ring. Release spring compressor. Remove piston rod guide, servo spring and piston. *See Fig. 30.*

15) To remove rear servo, use valve spring compressor to compress spring retainer on rear servo. Remove snap ring. Remove spring retainer, spring, piston and components. *See Fig. 31.*

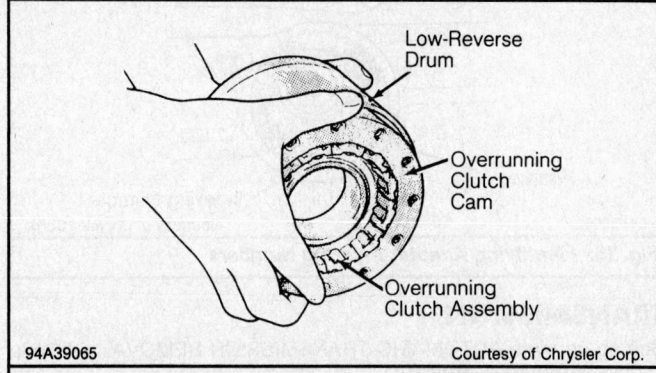

94A39065   Courtesy of Chrysler Corp.

Fig. 19: Identifying Low-Reverse Drum, Overrunning Clutch Assembly & Overrunning Clutch Cam

TRANSMISSION COMPONENT DISASSEMBLY & REASSEMBLY

NOTE: Manufacturer recommends using Mopar ATF Plus Type 7176 fluid in this transmission. This fluid should also be used during transmission assembly.

OIL PUMP & REACTION SHAFT SUPPORT

Disassembly – 1) Place reference mark on pump housing and reaction shaft support. Remove reaction shaft support bolts. Separate reaction shaft support from pump housing. *See Fig. 20.* Remove "O" ring from outer diameter of pump housing.

2) Remove oil seal from pump housing (if necessary). Remove seal rings and No. 1 thrust washer from reaction shaft support. Remove No. 1 thrust washer from reaction shaft support.

3) Note direction of inner and outer gear installation for reassembly reference. Remove inner and outer gears from pump housing.

NOTE: Manufacturer recommends replacing bushing in pump housing and reaction shaft support during any transmission overhaul.

4) To remove pump housing bushing, place pump housing on flat surface with gear cavity facing downward. Using press or hammer and bushing remover, remove bushing.

5) To remove bushing from reaction shaft support, use Cup (SP-3633), Nut (SP-1191) and Bushing Remover (SP-5324). *See Fig. 21.*

6) Hold cup against reaction shaft. By hand, thread bushing remover into bushing as far as possible. Using wrench, thread bushing remover an additional 3-4 turns into bushing. Tighten nut and remove bushing.

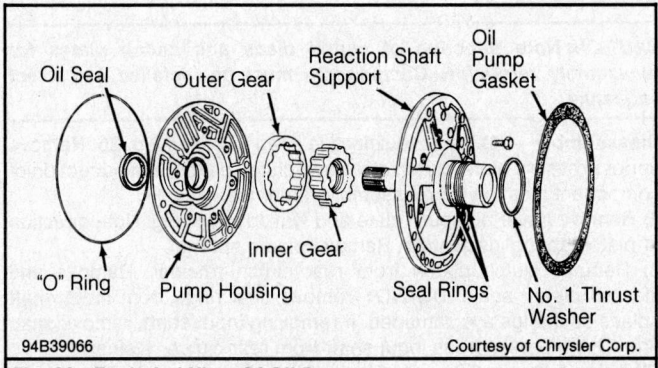

94B39066   Courtesy of Chrysler Corp.

Fig. 20: Exploded View Of Oil Pump

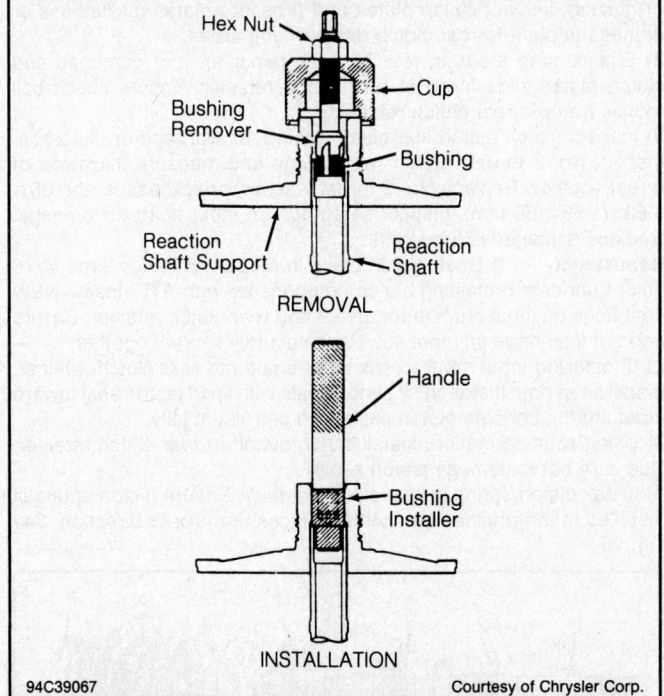

94C39067   Courtesy of Chrysler Corp.

Fig. 21: Removing & Installing Reaction Shaft Support Bushing

Cleaning & Inspection – 1) Clean and inspect components for damage. Inspect all machined surfaces for pitting or damage.

2) Inspect seal rings on reaction shaft support for wear or broken locks. Ensure seal rings rotate freely in grooves on reaction shaft support. Replace seal rings as required.

3) Inspect No. 1 thrust washer for wear and for proper thickness. No. 1 thrust washer thickness should be .061-.063" (1.55-1.60 mm). Replace No. 1 washer (if necessary).

4) Install inner and outer gears in pump housing. Using feeler gauge, measure outer gear-to-pump housing clearance.

5) Place straightedge on pump housing, above both inner and outer gears. Using feeler gauge, measure gear end clearance between each gear and straightedge.

6) Align one tooth on outer gear with one tooth on inner gear. Measure gear tooth clearance between the teeth on the gears. Replace components if clearance is not within specification. See OIL PUMP SPECIFICATIONS table.

OIL PUMP SPECIFICATIONS

Application	In. (mm)
Gear End Clearance	.0004-.0025 (.010-.064)
Gear Tooth Clearance	.0045-.0095 (.114-.241)
Outer Gear-To-Pump Housing Clearance	.0035-.0075 (.089-.190)

Reassembly – 1) To install NEW pump housing bushing, place pump housing on flat surface with gear cavity facing upward. Place bushing on bushing installer and start into pump housing.

2) Tap bushing in pump housing until bushing installer bottoms. Ensure bushing is installed evenly and does not bind in oil pump housing. Using blunt punch, stake bushing in 2 places. *See Fig. 22.* Using knife, clean burrs from stake areas.

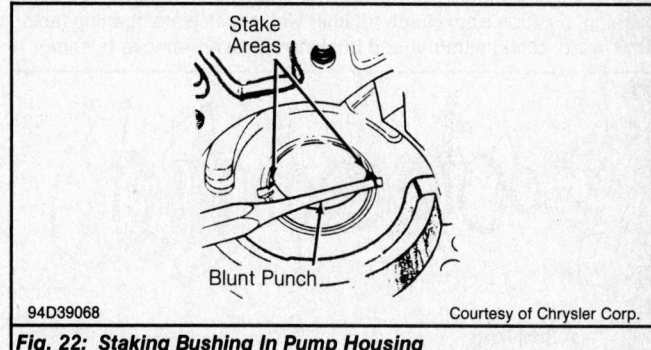

94D39068   Courtesy of Chrysler Corp.

Fig. 22: Staking Bushing In Pump Housing

3) To install NEW bushing in reaction shaft support, ensure reaction shaft support is clean and free of burrs. Place reaction shaft support on clean surface with bushing area facing upward.

4) Use Handle (C-4171) and Bushing Installer (SP-5325). *See Fig. 21.* Place bushing on bushing installer and start into reaction shaft support. Tap bushing into reaction shaft support until bushing installer bottoms. Clean reaction shaft support.

5) To reassemble oil pump, install reaction shaft support in Compressor Band (C-3759) with gear cavity facing upward. *See Fig. 23.* Install pilot studs on each side of reaction shaft support.

6) Install inner and outer gears in reaction shaft support. Lower pump housing onto pilot studs. Install Aligner (C-3756) through pump housing and into the inner gear. Rotate aligner to center inner and outer gears in the pump housing.

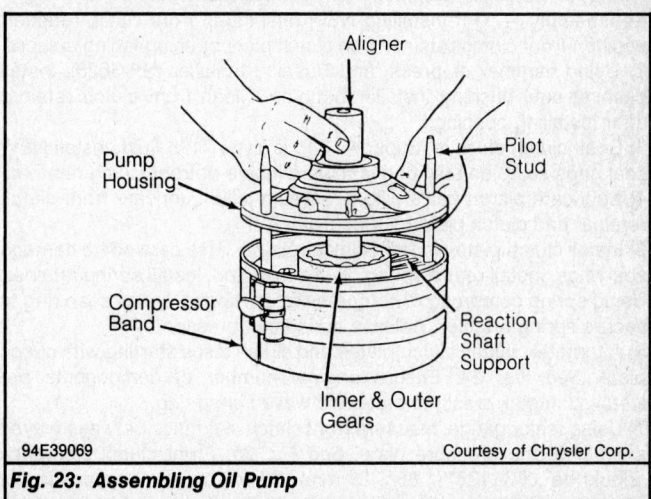

94E39069   Courtesy of Chrysler Corp.

Fig. 23: Assembling Oil Pump

7) With pump housing firmly against reaction shaft support, tighten compressor band. Invert oil pump assembly. Install and tighten reaction shaft support bolts to specification. See TORQUE SPECIFICATIONS.

8) Remove aligner, compressor band and pilot studs. Install NEW oil seal in pump housing with lip on oil seal facing inward (toward oil pump).

FRONT CLUTCH

CAUTION: Note direction of clutch discs and clutch plates for reassembly reference. Components must be installed in correct sequence.

Disassembly – 1) Remove waved snap ring, pressure plate, clutch discs and clutch plates. *See Fig. 24.*

2) Using spring compressor, compress return spring. Remove snap ring. Release spring compressor. Remove spring compressor and spring retainer.

3) Remove return spring and clutch piston from front clutch retainer. Remove and discard seal rings.

4) Inspect bushing in front clutch retainer for damage. If replacing bushing, position front clutch retainer with clutch plate opening facing downward. Using hammer and bushing remover, remove bushing.

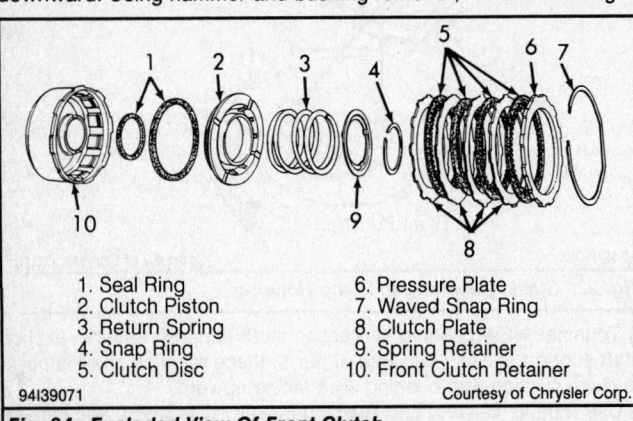

1. Seal Ring
2. Clutch Piston
3. Return Spring
4. Snap Ring
5. Clutch Disc
6. Pressure Plate
7. Waved Snap Ring
8. Clutch Plate
9. Spring Retainer
10. Front Clutch Retainer

94I39071   Courtesy of Chrysler Corp.

Fig. 24: Exploded View Of Front Clutch

Cleaning & Inspection – 1) Clean all metal components with solvent and dry with compressed air. Inspect clutch discs for flatness, flaking or glazing. Inspect clutch plates and pressure plate for flatness or damage at plate-to-front clutch retainer tang areas.

2) Ensure tang areas in front clutch retainer are not damaged and clutch plates slide freely in front clutch retainer. Ensure check ball, located in bottom of front clutch retainer, moves freely.

3) Inspect all sealing surfaces for burrs or scratches. Inspect return spring for distortion. Replace damaged components.

Reassembly – 1) If installing NEW bushing in front clutch retainer, position front clutch retainer with clutch plate opening facing upward.

2) Using hammer or press, and Bushing Installer (SP-3626), install bushing until bushing installer bottoms. Clean front clutch retainer after installing bushing.

3) Soak clutch discs in Mopar ATF Plus Type 7176 fluid. Install NEW seal rings so lip on seal ring is toward inside of front clutch retainer.

4) Lubricate piston seals with petroleum jelly. Lubricate front clutch retainer and clutch piston surface with ATF.

5) Install clutch piston in front clutch retainer. Use care not to damage seal rings. Install return spring on clutch piston. Install spring retainer. Using spring compressor, compress return spring. Install snap ring to secure spring retainer. Release spring compressor.

6) Alternately install clutch plates and clutch discs starting with clutch plate. *See Fig. 24.* Ensure original number of components are installed. Install pressure plate and waved snap ring.

7) Using feeler gauge, measure front clutch clearance between waved snap ring and pressure plate. *See Fig. 25.* Front clutch clearance should be .073-.128" (1.85-3.25 mm). If front clutch clearance is not within specification, check for defective or improperly assembled components.

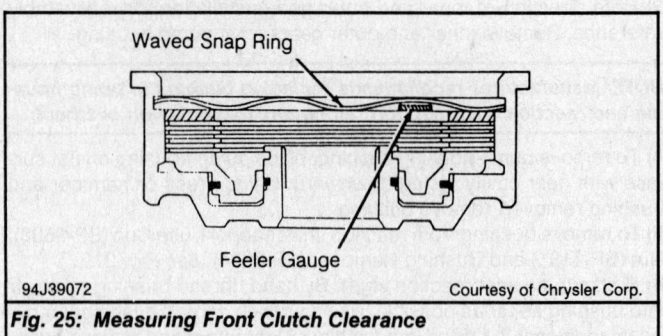

Waved Snap Ring

Feeler Gauge

94J39072   Courtesy of Chrysler Corp.

Fig. 25: Measuring Front Clutch Clearance

REAR CLUTCH

CAUTION: Note direction of clutch discs and clutch plates for reassembly reference. Components must be installed in correct sequence.

Disassembly – 1) Remove selective snap ring. *See Fig. 26.* Remove upper pressure plate, clutch discs and clutch plates. Note direction of component location for reassembly reference.

2) Remove lower pressure plate and waved snap ring. Note direction of piston spring installation. Remove piston spring.

3) Remove clutch piston from rear clutch retainer. Remove and discard piston seals. DO NOT remove seal rings from input shaft unless seal rings are damaged. If removing input shaft, remove snap ring. Using press, press input shaft from rear clutch retainer.

Cleaning & Inspection – 1) Clean all metal components with solvent and dry with compressed air. Inspect clutch discs for flatness, flaking or glazing. Inspect clutch plates and pressure plates for flatness or damage at plate-to-rear clutch retainer tang areas.

2) Ensure tang areas in rear clutch retainer are not damaged and clutch plates slide freely in rear clutch retainer. Ensure check ball moves freely in rear clutch retainer.

3) Inspect clutch piston and piston spring for warpage or distortion. Inspect No. 2 thrust washer for damage and measure thickness of thrust washer. Replace No. 2 thrust washer if thickness is not .061-.063" (1.55-1.60 mm). Inspect seal rings on input shaft for damage. Replace damaged components.

Reassembly – 1) Soak clutch discs in Mopar ATF Plus Type 7176 fluid. Lubricate remaining clutch components with ATF. Install NEW seal rings on input shaft (if removed) and rear clutch retainer. Ensure ends of seal rings on input shaft and securely locked together.

2) If installing input shaft, press input shaft into rear clutch retainer. Install snap ring. Install NEW piston seals with lip of piston seal toward input shaft. Lubricate piston seals with petroleum jelly.

3) Using twisting motion, install clutch piston in rear clutch retainer. Use care not to damage piston seals.

4) Install piston spring in rear clutch retainer. Ensure piston spring is installed in the original direction and faces the proper direction. *See Fig. 26.*

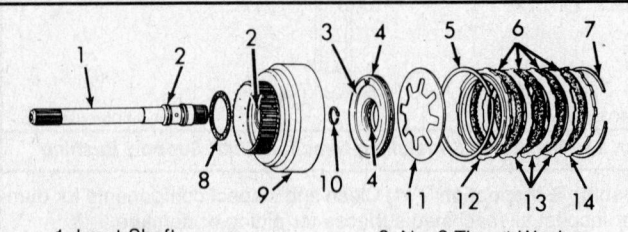

1. Input Shaft
2. Seal Ring
3. Clutch Piston
4. Piston Seal
5. Waved Snap Ring
6. Clutch Disc
7. Selective Snap Ring
8. No. 2 Thrust Washer
9. Rear Clutch Retainer
10. Snap Ring
11. Piston Spring
12. Lower Pressure Plate
13. Clutch Plate
14. Upper Pressure Plate

94A39073   Courtesy of Chrysler Corp.

Fig. 26: Exploded View Of Rear Clutch

5) Install waved snap ring in rear clutch retainer. Ensure waved snap ring is fully seated. Install lower pressure plate so raised area is toward the piston spring and flat side is toward the clutch disc.

6) Alternately install original number of clutch discs and clutch plates starting with a clutch disc. *See Fig. 26.* Install upper pressure plate and selective snap ring.

7) Using feeler gauge, measure rear clutch clearance between selective snap ring and upper pressure plate while pressing upper pressure plate downward. Rear clutch clearance should be .025-.048" (.64-1.22 mm).

8) If rear clutch clearance is not within specification, install different thickness selective snap ring. Selective snap ring is available in thicknesses of .060" (1.52 mm), .076" (1.93 mm) and .098" (2.49 mm). Apply petroleum jelly on No. 2 thrust washer and install over input shaft.

PLANETARY GEAR TRAIN

Disassembly – 1) Remove No. 3 thrust washer from front end of intermediate shaft. Remove select fit snap ring from end of intermediate shaft.

2) Remove front planetary gear and front annulus gear from intermediate shaft. Remove snap ring and thrust washer from hub on front planetary gear. Slide front annulus gear and front annulus gear support from front planetary gear.

3) Remove thrust washer from both sides of front planetary gear. *See Fig. 27.* Remove snap ring and separate front annulus gear support from front annulus gear (if necessary).

4) Slide sun gear with driving shell and rear planetary gear assembly from intermediate shaft. Separate sun gear and driving shell from rear planetary gear assembly.

5) If removing sun gear from driving shell, remove snap ring and thrust plate from rear side of driving shell. Remove sun gear and thrust plate from driving shell. Remove spacer from sun gear.

6) Remove thrust washer from front side of rear planetary gear. Remove rear planetary gear from rear annulus gear. Rear annulus gear fits on outside of rear planetary gear.

7) Remove thrust washer from rear side of rear planetary gear. Remove snap ring and separate rear annulus gear support from rear annulus gear (if necessary).

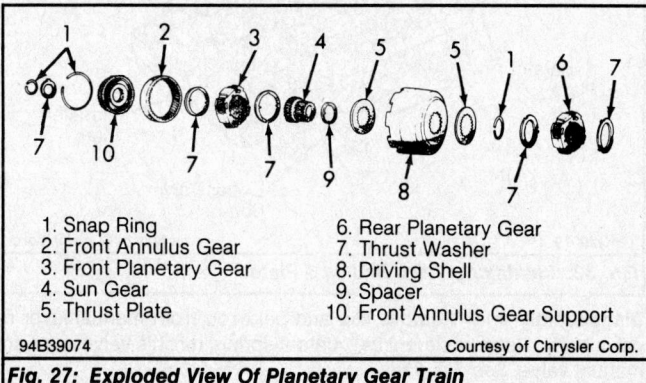

1. Snap Ring
2. Front Annulus Gear
3. Front Planetary Gear
4. Sun Gear
5. Thrust Plate
6. Rear Planetary Gear
7. Thrust Washer
8. Driving Shell
9. Spacer
10. Front Annulus Gear Support

94B39074   Courtesy of Chrysler Corp.

Fig. 27: Exploded View Of Planetary Gear Train

Cleaning & Inspection – 1) Clean all components with solvent and dry with compressed air. Inspect for damaged components. Inspect sun gear bushings for scoring or wear. Replace sun gear if bushings are damaged or worn.

2) Inspect planetary gears for defective pinion gears, pins, washers or carrier. Inspect intermediate shaft for damage at bushing/bearing surfaces and splined areas. Replace damaged components.

3) Measure thickness of thrust plates for sun gear. Replace thrust plates if thickness is not .050-.052" (1.27-1.32 mm).

4) Measure thickness of thrust washers for front and rear planetary gear. Replace thrust washers if thickness is not .048-.050" (1.22-1.27 mm).

5) Measure thickness of thrust washer that fits on front side of front annulus gear support. Replace thrust washer if thickness is not .121-.125" (3.07-3.18 mm).

NOTE: Manufacturer recommends using Mopar ATF Plus Type 7176 fluid in this transmission. This fluid should also be used during transmission assembly.

Reassembly – 1) Lubricate intermediate shaft and planetary gear train components with ATF. Use petroleum jelly to retain thrust washers and thrust plates in position.

2) Install rear annulus gear support in rear annulus gear (if removed) and install snap ring. Install thrust washer on rear side of rear planetary gear.

3) Install rear planetary gear in rear annulus gear. Install thrust washer on front side of rear planetary gear. Install intermediate shaft into rear annulus gear support and rear planetary gear.

4) If installing sun gear in driving shell, install spacer and thrust plate on sun gear. Install sun gear in driving shell. Install thrust plate and snap ring.

5) Install sun gear with driving shell on intermediate shaft. Ensure teeth on sun gear engage with pinion gears on rear planetary gear. Install front annulus gear support in front annulus gear (if removed) and install snap ring.

6) Install thrust washer on front side of front planetary gear. Install front planetary gear in front annulus gear. Install thrust washer and snap ring on front side of front planetary gear.

7) Install thrust washer on rear side of front planetary gear. Install front annulus gear and front planetary gear on intermediate shaft. Ensure front planetary gear fully engages with sun gear and assembly is fully seated on intermediate shaft.

8) Position planetary gear train in upright position. Ensure snap ring groove on end of intermediate shaft is fully visible. Install select fit snap ring on end of intermediate shaft. Position planetary gear train assembly with gear opening of driving shell facing workbench.

9) Place wooden block between end of intermediate shaft and workbench to support intermediate shaft. This moves planetary gear train components forward so planetary gear train end play can be checked.

10) Using feeler gauge, measure planetary gear train end play between shoulder on intermediate shaft and end of rear annulus gear. *See Fig. 28.*

11) Planetary gear train end play should be .005-.048" (.13-1.22 mm). If planetary gear train end play is not within specification, install different thickness select fit snap. Select fit snap ring is available in thicknesses of .040" (1.02 mm), 062" (1.57 mm) and .082" (2.08 mm).

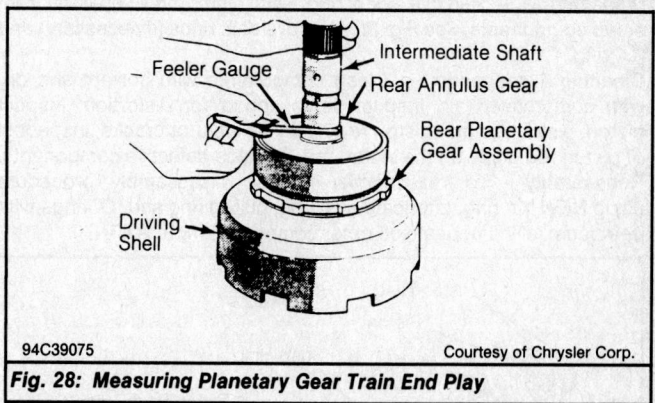

94C39075   Courtesy of Chrysler Corp.

Fig. 28: Measuring Planetary Gear Train End Play

OVERRUNNING CLUTCH

CAUTION: Ensure overrunning clutch components are properly installed, or inoperative transmission or transmission failure may result.

Disassembly – 1) Before disassembling overrunning clutch, check operation by holding low-reverse drum and rotating the overrunning clutch cam. Overrunning clutch cam should rotate freely clockwise and lock when rotated counterclockwise. *See Fig. 29.*

2) Note direction of springs, rollers and retainer installation in low-reverse drum. Disassemble overrunning clutch assembly. *See Fig. 29.*

Cleaning & Inspection – 1) Clean components with solvent and dry with compressed air. Inspect rollers for flat spots or chipped edges. **2)** Inspect roller contacting surfaces in overrunning clutch cam and inner race on low-reverse drum for wear. Inspect springs for distortion.

Reassembly – To reassemble, reverse disassembly procedure. When fully assembled, check operation by holding low-reverse drum and rotating overrunning clutch cam. Overrunning clutch cam should rotate freely clockwise and lock when rotated counterclockwise. *See Fig. 29.*

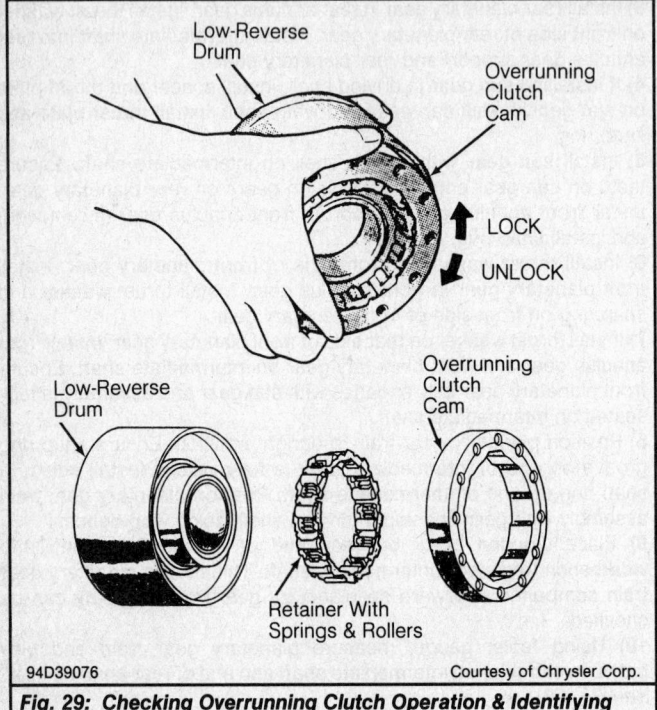

Fig. 29: Checking Overrunning Clutch Operation & Identifying Overrunning Clutch Components

FRONT SERVO

Disassembly – Remove snap ring from piston and separate front servo components. *See Fig. 30.* Remove seal rings (if necessary) and "O" ring.

Cleaning & Inspection – Clean components with solvent and dry with compressed air. Inspect servo spring for distortion. Inspect piston, piston rod and piston rod guide for wear or cracks. Inspect fit of piston rod guide on the piston rod. Replace defective components.

Reassembly – To reassemble, reverse disassembly procedure using NEW "O" ring. Lubricate seal ring, piston ring and "O" rings with petroleum jelly. Lubricate all other components with ATF.

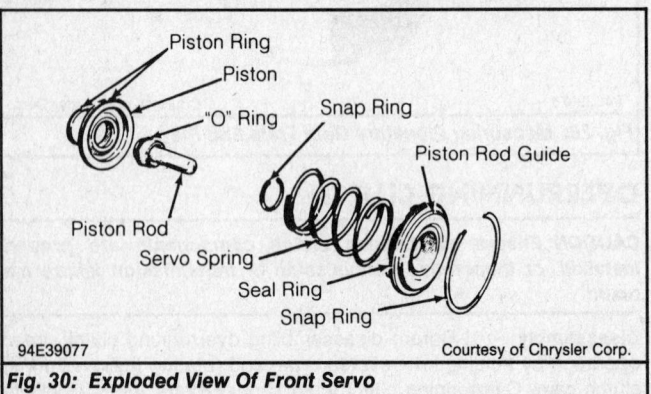

Fig. 30: Exploded View Of Front Servo

REAR SERVO

Disassembly – Remove snap ring from piston and separate rear servo components. *See Fig. 31.*

Cleaning & Inspection – Clean components with solvent and dry with compressed air. Inspect spring and plug spring for distortion. Inspect piston and piston plug for wear or cracks. Ensure piston plug slides freely in the bore on the piston. Replace defective components.

Reassembly – To reassemble, reverse disassembly procedure. Lubricate seal ring with petroleum jelly. Lubricate all other components with ATF.

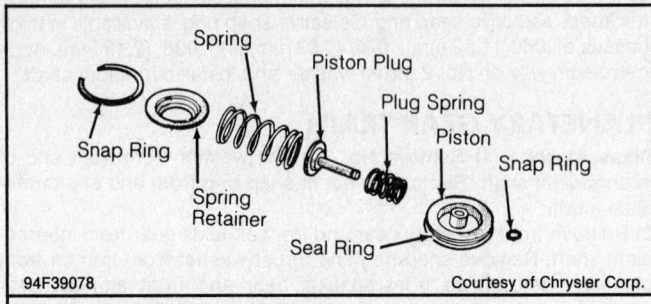

Fig. 31: Exploded View Of Rear Servo

VALVE BODY

CAUTION: When disassembling valve body, place valve body components in order and mark spring locations for reassembly reference. DO NOT use force to remove components from valve body. Valve body components are not interchangeable. Valve body consists of upper valve body, lower valve body, transfer plate and separator plates. See Fig. 32.

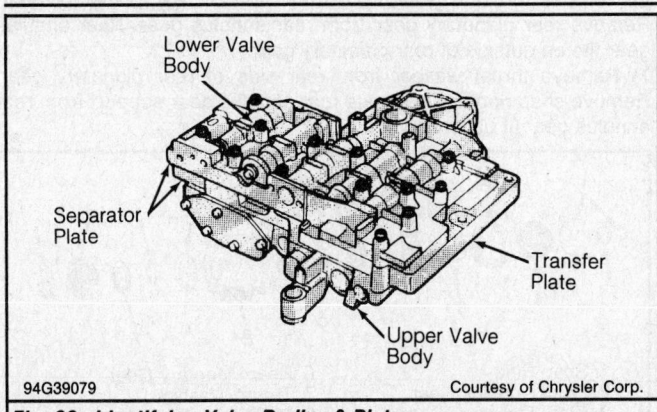

Fig. 32: Identifying Valve Bodies & Plates

Disassembly – 1) Remove clip and park rod from manual lever on valve body. Remove detent ball, detent spring, throttle valve lever and manual valve. *See Fig. 33.*

2) Remove solenoid connector retaining screw. Hold adjusting screw bracket against valve body and remove screws. *See Fig. 34.*

CAUTION: DO NOT disturb throttle pressure adjusting screw or line pressure adjusting screw locations in adjusting screw bracket.

3) Remove adjusting screw bracket with line pressure adjusting screw, line pressure regulator spring (large spring) and switch valve spring (small spring). *See Fig. 34.*

4) Remove line pressure regulator valve, switch valve, kickdown detent, kickdown valve, throttle valve spring and throttle valve from upper valve body. *See Fig. 34.*

5) Remove 3-4 accumulator housing, plug, lock-up valve spring and 3-4 shift valve spring from lower valve body. *See Fig. 35.* Remove lock-up valve and 3-4 shift valve from lower valve body.

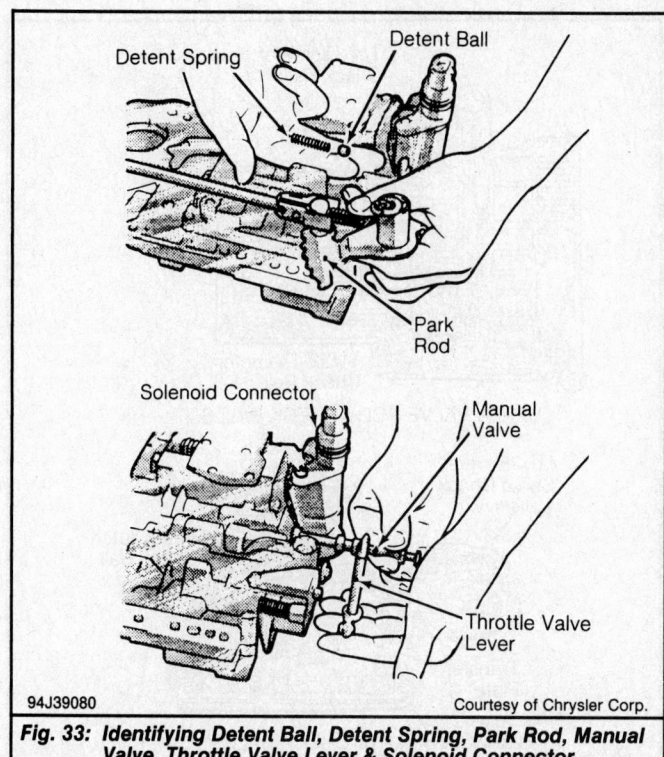

Fig. 33: Identifying Detent Ball, Detent Spring, Park Rod, Manual Valve, Throttle Valve Lever & Solenoid Connector

94J39080   Courtesy of Chrysler Corp.

6) Remove cover, 3-4 accumulator piston and 3-4 accumulator spring from 3-4 accumulator housing. Note routing of solenoid wiring. Remove solenoid assembly, gasket and case connector from lower valve body.

7) Position valve body so lower valve body is facing upward with upper valve body on the bottom. See Fig. 32.

8) Remove valve body bolts attaching lower valve body to the upper valve body. Remove lower valve body and separator plate from transfer plate. Remove lower valve body from separator plate.

9) Remove spring retainer and then lock-up timing valve spring and lock-up timing valve from lower valve body. See Fig. 35.

NOTE: Lock-up timing valve may be referred to as torque converter clutch timing valve.

10) Remove "E" clip for 3-4 shuttle valve from lower valve body. See Fig. 35. Remove end cover plate, 3-4 timing valve, 3-4 timing valve spring, 3-4 shuttle valve and 3-4 shuttle valve spring from lower valve body. Invert upper valve body so transfer plate is facing upward.

CAUTION: Ensure upper valve body is positioned with transfer plate facing upward. This prevents check balls from falling from upper valve body.

11) Remove transfer plate from upper valve body. Note location of check balls in upper valve body. See Fig. 36. Remove check balls from upper valve body.

12) Remove end plate, sleeve, regulator valve line pressure plug, regulator valve throttle pressure plug and regulator valve throttle pressure plug spring from upper valve body. See Fig. 34.

13) Remove end plate, 2-3 shift valve spring, 2-3 shift valve, 1-2 shift valve spring, 1-2 shift valve, 1-2 shift control valve spring and 1-2 shift control valve from upper valve body. See Fig. 34.

14) Remove "E" clip, shuttle valve secondary spring, spring guides and upper cover from upper valve body. Remove governor plug end plate, shuttle valve throttle plug, shuttle valve primary spring and shuttle valve from upper valve body.

15) Remove 1-2 shift valve governor plug and 2-3 shift valve governor plug from upper valve body. Position transfer plate with separator plate facing upward. This prevents check balls from falling from transfer plate.

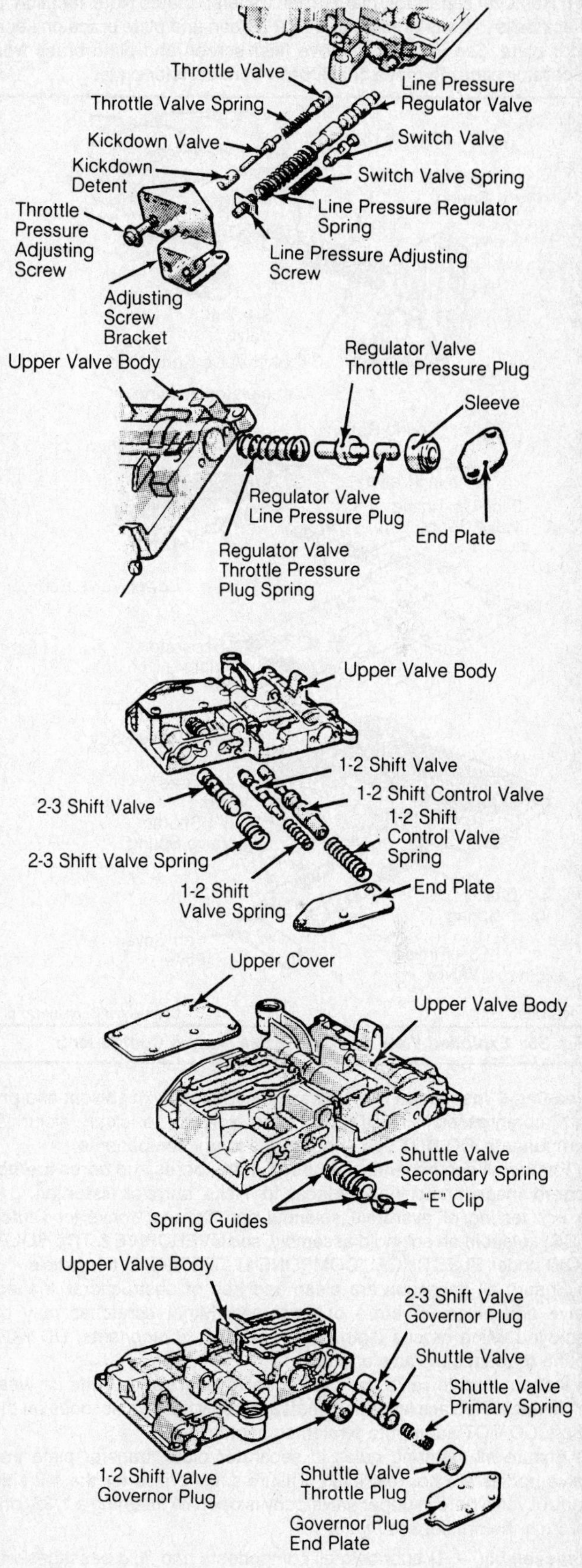

94A39081   Courtesy of Chrysler Corp.

Fig. 34: Exploded View Of Upper Valve Body & Components

16) Remove separator plate from transfer plate. Note location of check balls in transfer plate and filter screen and plate brace on separator plate. *See Fig. 36.* Remove filter screen and plate brace from separator plate. Remove check balls from transfer plate.

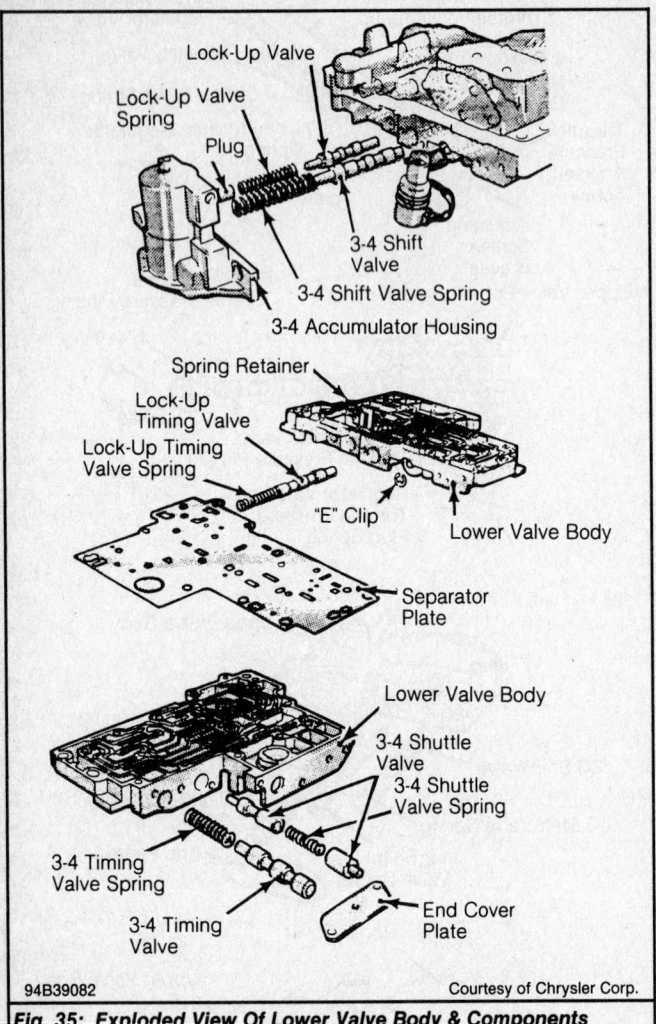

Fig. 35: **Exploded View Of Lower Valve Body & Components**

94B39082   Courtesy of Chrysler Corp.

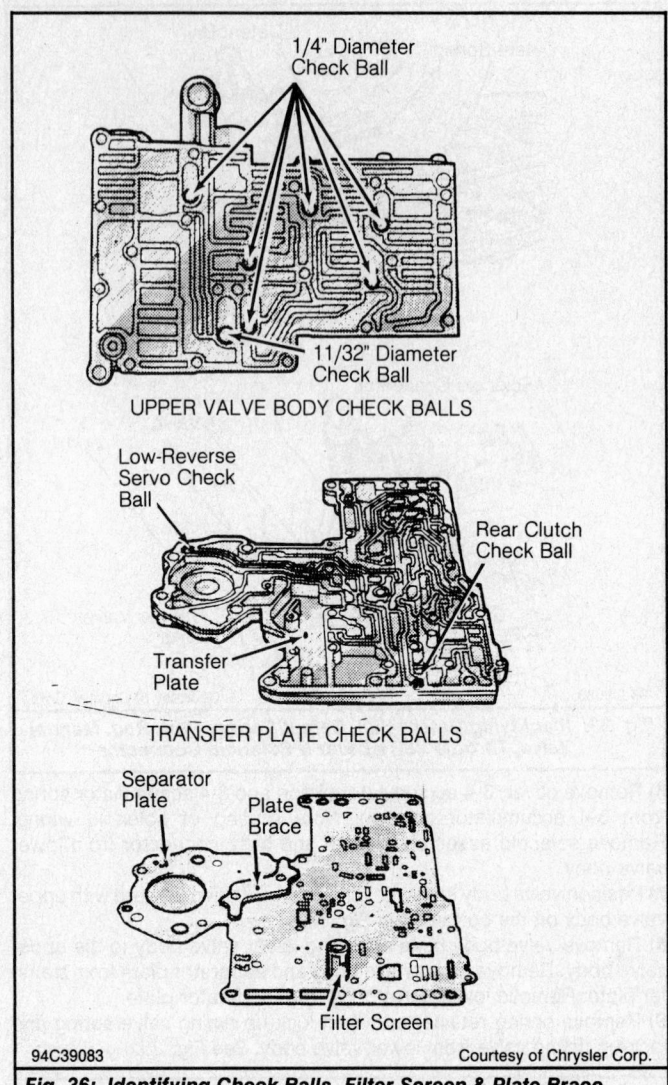

94C39083   Courtesy of Chrysler Corp.

Fig. 36: **Identifying Check Balls, Filter Screen & Plate Brace Locations**

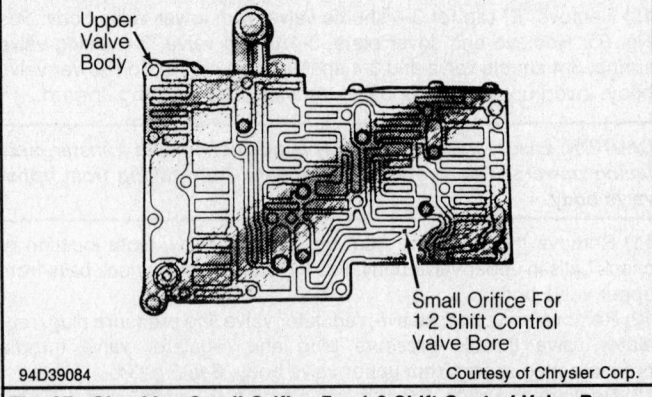

94D39084   Courtesy of Chrysler Corp.

Fig. 37: **Checking Small Orifice For 1-2 Shift Control Valve Bore**

Cleaning & Inspection – 1) Clean components with solvent and dry with compressed air. DO NOT use solvent to clean electrical components. DO NOT use shop towels to dry components.

2) Ensure all components slide freely in the bores and bores are not scored. Inspect machined surfaces for nicks, burrs or distortion.

3) For testing of overdrive solenoid and Torque Converter Clutch (TCC) solenoid on solenoid assembly, see OVERDRIVE & TCC SOLE-NOID under ELECTRICAL COMPONENT TESTING in this article.

4) Ensure all passages are clean and free of obstructions. Inspect valve and plugs for burrs or scratches. Minor scratches may be removed using crocus cloth. When sanding components, DO NOT round off edges of valve or plug.

5) Inspect throttle valve and manual valve levers and shafts for wear or damage. Replace lever and shaft assembly if a lever is loose on the shaft. DO NOT attempt to straighten bent levers.

6) Ensure all metering holes in separator plate, transfer plate and valve bodies are not restricted. Ensure small orifice for the 1-2 shift control valve bore in upper valve body is open by inserting a 1/32" drill through the orifice. *See Fig. 37.*

Reassembly – 1) Lubricate all components and fluid passages with ATF. Install all components in original locations.

2) Ensure all check balls and filter screen are installed in proper locations. *See Fig. 36.* Use NEW gasket when installing solenoid assembly. Tighten valve body bolts evenly to specification. See TORQUE SPECIFICATIONS.

CAUTION: *If line pressure or throttle pressure adjusting screws were moved from original setting, they must be readjusted. See HYDRAULIC PRESSURE ADJUSTMENTS in this article.*

TRANSMISSION REASSEMBLY

VALVE BODY & COMPONENTS

NOTE: Lubricate all components with Mopar ATF Plus Type 7176 fluid. Use petroleum jelly to hold thrust washers, thrust plates and gaskets in position. Ensure thrust washer and thrust plates are installed in original location.

1) Install front and rear servo assemblies in transmission case. Using valve spring compressor, compress springs and install snap ring to retain servo assembly.

2) If installing lever for rear band, install NEW "O" rings on the pin. Install lever and pin in transmission case. Install rear band, link and strut. *See Fig 38.* Ensure rear band adjusting screw is loose.

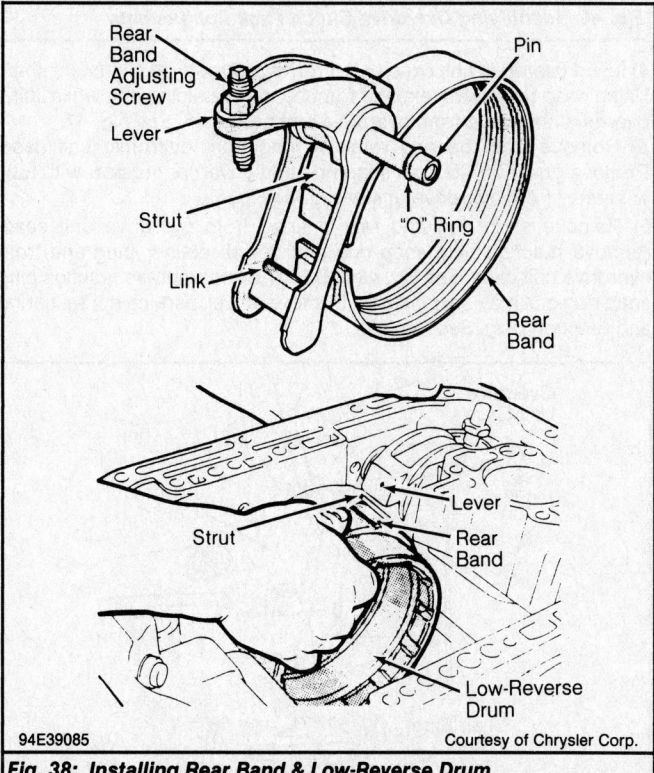

94E39085   Courtesy of Chrysler Corp.

Fig. 38: *Installing Rear Band & Low-Reverse Drum*

3) Install overrunning clutch assembly with low-reverse drum. Ensure non-threaded hole on overrunning clutch cam is positioned at the 7 o'clock position when viewed from rear of transmission case. This will position the non-threaded hole near the oil pan mounting surface.

4) Install and tighten overrunning clutch cam-to-transmission case bolts to specification. See TORQUE SPECIFICATIONS.

5) Install NEW gasket for overdrive piston retainer on rear of transmission case. Use petroleum jelly to hold gasket in place. Ensure governor tube supply holes on gasket align with holes on transmission case.

6) Install overdrive piston retainer so governor tube supply holes align with holes on transmission case. Install and tighten bolts to specification.

7) Install spacer and low-reverse drum-to-overdrive piston retainer snap ring. Ensure claws on the spacer are facing toward oil pump area on transmission case.

CAUTION: Ensure low-reverse drum rotates freely in proper direction and locks when rotated in the opposite direction. See Fig. 29. Check for improper overrunning clutch component installation if low-reverse drum will not rotate correctly.

8) Install NEW seal on overdrive piston and lubricate with petroleum jelly. Install overdrive piston in overdrive piston retainer. If necessary, use feeler gauge to guide seal on overdrive piston into overdrive pis-

ton retainer. Ensure guide pin on rear of overdrive piston engages with hole on overdrive piston retainer.

9) Install intermediate shaft and planetary gear train. Ensure rear planetary engages in slots on low-reverse drum. Use care not to damage sealing surfaces on intermediate shaft during installation.

10) If input shaft end play was not .011-.080" (.28-2.03 mm) during disassembly, install different thickness thrust washer on end of intermediate shaft. Thrust washer is available in thicknesses of .052" (1.32 mm), .068" (1.73 mm) and .083" (2.11 mm).

11) Coat thrust washer with petroleum jelly and install on end of intermediate shaft. Coat No. 2 thrust washer with petroleum jelly and install on input shaft. *See Fig. 26.*

12) Align teeth on front clutch discs. Install front clutch on rear clutch. Ensure front clutch is fully seated on rear clutch by rotating front clutch back and forth.

13) Position transmission case with oil pump opening facing upward. Using small screwdriver, align teeth on rear clutch discs. Install front and rear clutch assemblies. Rotate assembly back and forth until rear clutch discs fully engage with front annulus gear. Ensure front clutch drive lugs are fully engaged in slots in driving shell.

14) Install front band over front clutch assembly. Install strut and front band adjusting screw. Tighten front band adjusting screw enough to hold strut in place.

15) Install No. 1 thrust washer on rear of reaction shaft support. *See Fig. 20.* Ensure NEW "O" ring is installed on outer diameter of pump housing of oil pump. Coat "O" ring with petroleum jelly.

NOTE: If oil pump was difficult to remove from transmission case, it may be necessary to use a heat light to heat the oil pump area on transmission case prior to installing oil pump.

16) Ensure seal rings are installed on input shaft and rear of reaction shaft support. Install pilot studs in 2 oil pump bolt holes, opposite of each other in transmission case. Install oil pump gasket.

17) Install oil pump. Remove pilot studs. Install and tighten oil pump bolts in a diagonal pattern to specification.

CAUTION: Ensure input shaft and intermediate shaft rotate without binding. If binding exists, check for improperly assembled components.

18) To adjust rear band, tighten rear band adjusting screw to 30 INCH lbs. (3.4 N.m). Back off rear band adjusting screw 6 turns. Tighten lock nut on rear band adjusting to specification.

19) To adjust front band, tighten front band adjusting screw to 72 INCH lbs. (8.1 N.m). Back off front band adjusting screw 2 7/8 turns. Tighten lock nut on front band adjusting screw lock nut to specification.

CAUTION: Before installing intermediate shaft selective spacer and overdrive piston thrust bearing, ensure proper procedure is used to determine thickness of these components. See DETERMINING INTERMEDIATE SHAFT SELECTIVE SPACER & OVERDRIVE PISTON THRUST PLATE under OVERDRIVE UNIT ADJUSTMENTS.

20) Determine proper thickness intermediate shaft selective spacer and overdrive piston thrust bearing. See DETERMINING INTERMEDIATE SHAFT SELECTIVE SPACER & OVERDRIVE PISTON THRUST PLATE under OVERDRIVE UNIT ADJUSTMENTS.

21) Install intermediate shaft selective spacer on intermediate shaft. *See Fig. 16.* Install overdrive piston thrust plate in center of overdrive piston. *See Fig. 16.* Use petroleum jelly to hold overdrive piston thrust plate in position.

22) Install overdrive piston thrust bearing in direct clutch hub on overdrive unit with shoulder away from direct clutch hub. Use petroleum jelly to hold overdrive piston thrust bearing in position.

CAUTION: Ensure shoulder on overdrive piston thrust bearing faces away from direct clutch hub.

23) Using Alignment Shaft (C-6227-2), align splines of planetary gear assembly and overrunning clutch in overdrive unit. *See Fig. 17.* Ensure alignment shaft is fully seated.

24) Overdrive unit clutch splines must be aligned to aid in installation on intermediate shaft. Once splines are aligned, carefully remove alignment shaft.

CAUTION: Ensure intermediate shaft selective spacer on intermediate shaft, overdrive piston thrust plate and overdrive piston thrust bearing are installed.

---

25) Install overdrive unit on transmission case. Ensure governor tubes are seated in supply holes on overdrive piston retainer. DO NOT tilt overdrive unit during installation or components may rotate out of alignment.

26) Install and tighten overdrive unit-to-transmission case bolts to specification in a crisscross pattern. Using dial indicator, recheck input shaft end play. Input shaft end play should be .011-.080" (.28-2.03 mm).

27) Install valve body. See VALVE BODY under ON-VEHICLE SERVICE. Install torque converter.

28) To ensure torque converter is fully seated, use straightedge and measuring scale to measure torque converter installed depth. Measure distance from face of transmission case to surface on bolt hole lug on torque converter. *See Fig. 39.* Distance should be at least 1/2" if torque converter is fully seated.

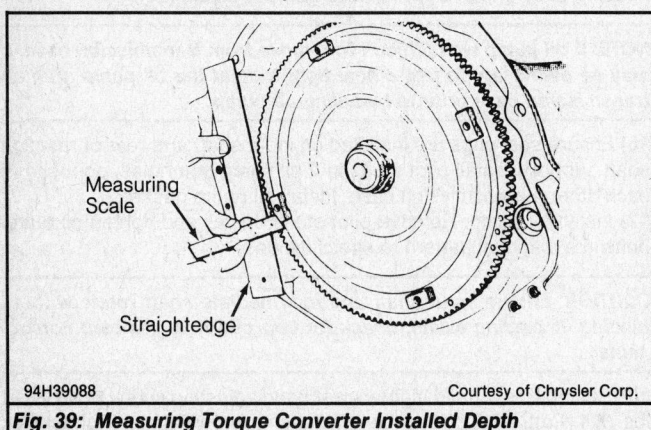

94H39088   Courtesy of Chrysler Corp.

Fig. 39: *Measuring Torque Converter Installed Depth*

CAUTION: If transmission failure existed, flush oil cooler and check oil cooler flow. See OIL COOLER FLUSHING and OIL COOLER FLOW CHECK under ON-VEHICLE SERVICE.

OVERDRIVE UNIT DISASSEMBLY

OVERDRIVE UNIT

1) Remove wire-type snap ring and overdrive clutch pack components from overdrive unit case. *See Fig. 40.* Note direction of clutch discs and clutch plates in overdrive clutch pack for reassembly reference. Components must be installed in correct sequence.

2) Remove waved snap ring and flat snap ring. Both snap rings are installed in same groove in overdrive unit case.

3) Remove access cover from top of overdrive unit case for access to front bearing retaining ring. *See Fig. 41.* Install Alignment Shaft (C-6227-2) into overdrive unit to hold components in proper alignment. *See Fig. 17.*

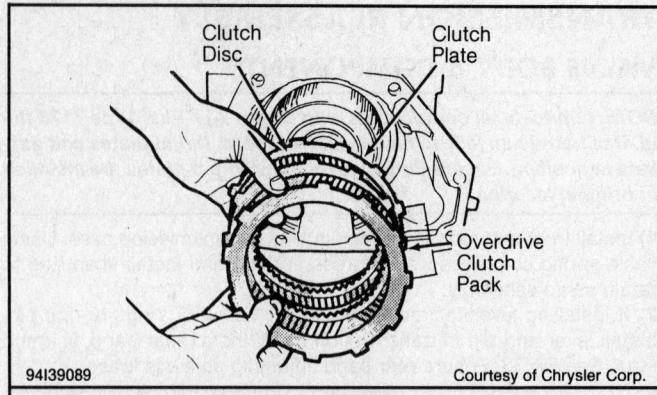

94I39089   Courtesy of Chrysler Corp.

Fig. 40: *Identifying Overdrive Clutch Pack Components*

4) Invert overdrive unit case so overdrive unit rests on alignment shaft. Using snap ring pliers, expand front bearing retaining ring while lifting overdrive unit case from overdrive unit gear train. *See Fig. 41.*

5) Remove front bearing retaining ring from overdrive unit case. Remove governor support snap ring and governor support with tube assembly from overdrive unit case. *See Fig. 42.*

6) Remove snap ring and rear bearing from overdrive unit case. Remove reaction plug snap ring and dowel retainer plug and from overdrive unit case. *See Fig. 43.* DO NOT overcompress reaction plug snap ring or it may be damaged. Remove dowel, parking sprag, spring and reaction plug. *See Fig. 43.*

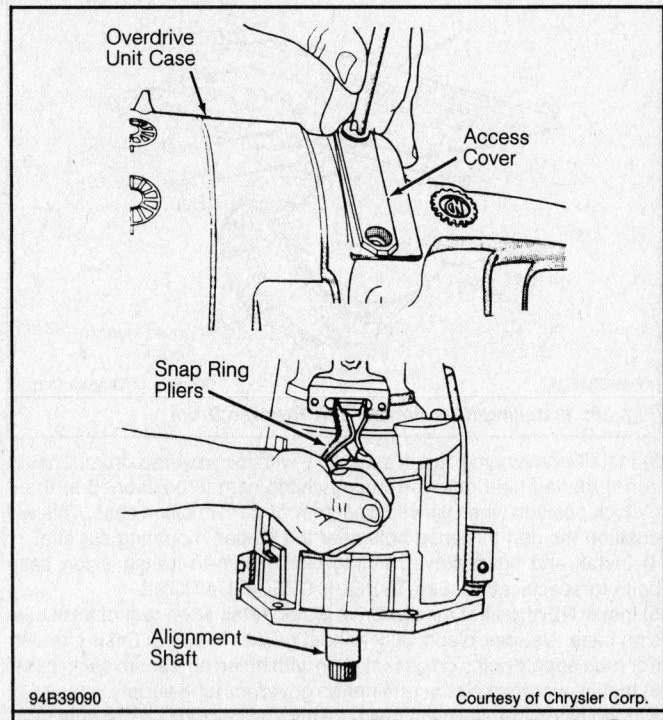

94B39090   Courtesy of Chrysler Corp.

Fig. 41: *Removing Access Cover & Releasing Front Bearing From Retaining Ring*

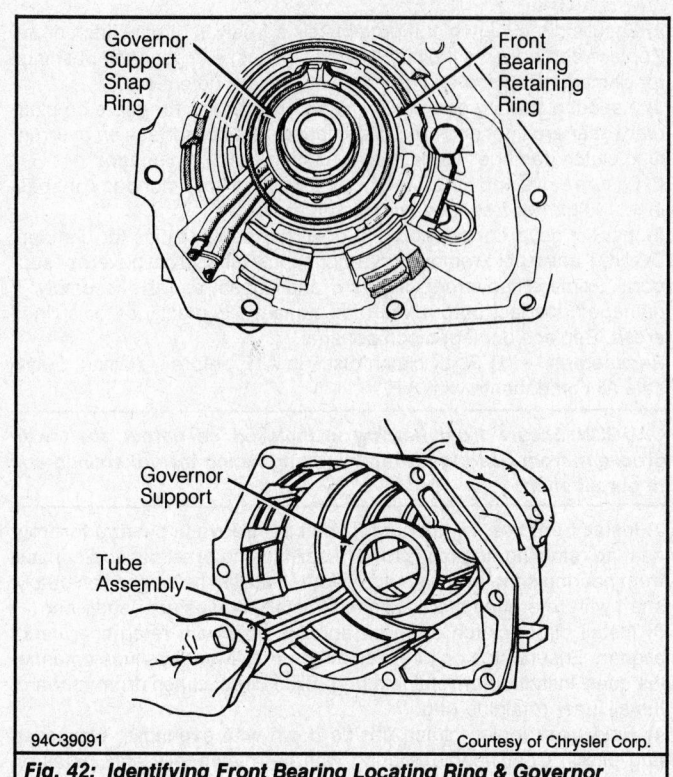

Fig. 42: Identifying Front Bearing Locating Ring & Governor Support

OVERDRIVE UNIT COMPONENT DISASSEMBLY & REASSEMBLY

OVERDRIVE UNIT GEAR TRAIN

Disassembly – 1) Remove clip from valve shaft on governor. Remove valve shaft and valve from governor body.

2) Remove governor snap ring from output shaft. Remove governor drive and governor body as an assembly. Remove key for governor from output shaft. Remove front bearing snap ring and front bearing from output shaft (if necessary).

3) Place overdrive unit gear train in press. Support assembly with press plates placed under flange on output shaft.

4) Position Spring Compressor (6227-1) on direct clutch hub. *See Fig. 44.*

CAUTION: Ensure proper equipment is used when compressing direct clutch hub spring, as direct clutch spring is under extreme pressure. Ensure ram on press has a minimum travel of approximately 3".

5) Slowly compress direct clutch spring. Remove load retaining snap ring for direct clutch pack from outer edge of direct clutch drum. Remove snap ring from outside of sun gear. *See Fig. 44.* Slowly release press. Remove spring compressor.

CAUTION: Note direction of clutch discs and clutch plates in direct clutch pack for reassembly reference. Components must be installed in correct sequence.

6) Remove direct clutch hub with direct clutch pack components from direct clutch drum, noting location of components for reassembly reference. *See Fig. 45.*

7) Remove direct clutch spring, sun gear, needle bearing and planetary gear from direct clutch hub. Insert expanding-type snap ring pliers into splines on overrunning clutch.

8) Expand snap ring pliers against splines. Rotate overrunning clutch counterclockwise and remove overrunning clutch assembly with needle bearing from direct clutch drum. *See Fig. 46.*

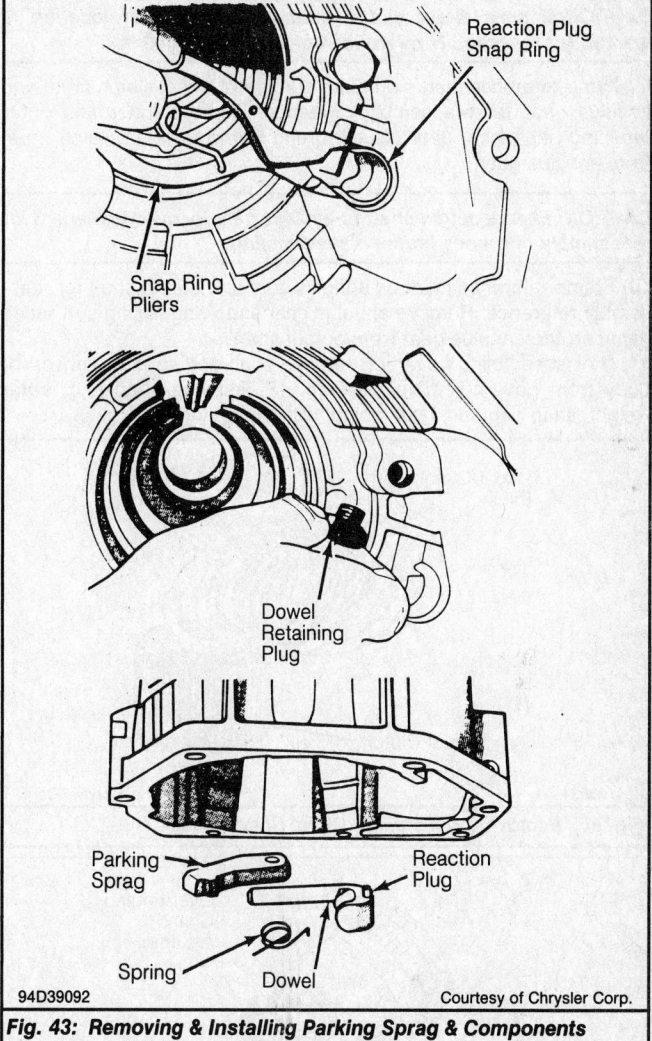

Fig. 43: Removing & Installing Parking Sprag & Components

Fig. 44: Removing & Installing Direct Clutch Hub & Direct Clutch Spring

CAUTION: Ensure direct clutch drum-to-annulus gear location is marked for reassembly reference before disassembling.

9) Stamp reference marks on outer surface of direct clutch drum and annulus gear for reassembly reference. Remove inner and outer retaining rings from direct clutch drum. Remove direct clutch drum from annulus gear.

CAUTION: Ensure output shaft-to-annulus gear location is marked for reassembly reference before disassembling.

10) Stamp reference mark on annulus gear and output shaft for reassembly reference. Remove annulus gear snap ring. Using soft-faced hammer, tap annulus gear from output shaft.
11) If disassembling governor, remove bolts and separate governor body from governor drive. *See Fig. 47.* Remove snap ring, outer weight, snap ring and inner weight with the spring.

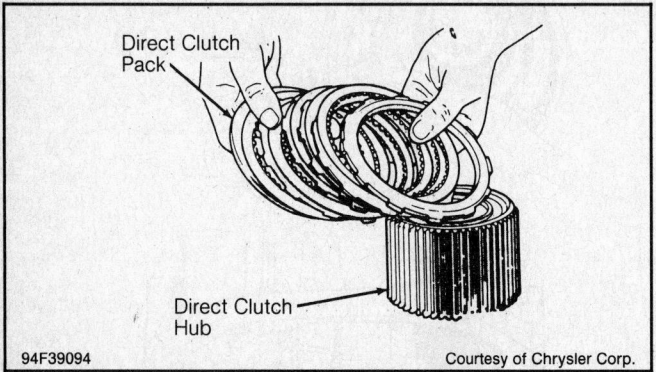

94F39094   Courtesy of Chrysler Corp.
Fig. 45: Removing & Installing Direct Clutch Pack

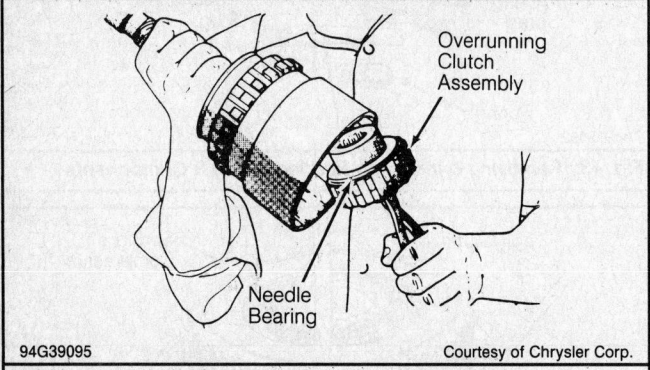

94G39095   Courtesy of Chrysler Corp.
Fig. 46: Removing & Installing Overrunning Clutch Assembly

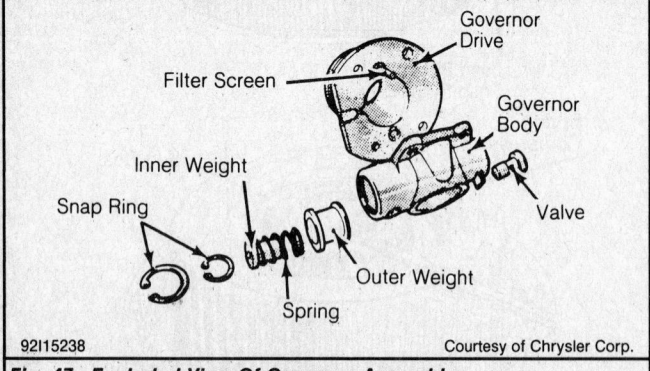

92I15238   Courtesy of Chrysler Corp.
Fig. 47: Exploded View Of Governor Assembly

Cleaning & Inspection – 1) Clean all metal components with solvent. Dry all components except bearings with compressed air. Inspect clutch discs for flatness, flaking or glazing. Inspect all clutch plates for flatness or damage at lug area.

2) Ensure direct clutch components slide freely in direct clutch drum. Replace components if binding exists. Inspect sun gear and bushings for damage. Replace sun gear if bushings are defective.
3) Inspect planetary gear for damage. Ensure pins for gears on planetary gear are tight and are not damaged. Inspect surface on overrunning clutch damage. Replace overrunning clutch if damaged.
4) Ensure valve and outer weight slide freely in governor body. Inspect inner weight for free movement in outer weight.
5) Inspect governor support and governor supply tubes for damage. DO NOT attempt to remove governor supply tubes from governor support. Replace governor support and tubes as an assembly if damaged. Inspect output shaft for damaged in machined or splined areas. Replace damaged components.
Reassembly – 1) Soak clutch discs in ATF before installing. Lubricate all components with ATF.

CAUTION: Ensure front bearing is installed on output shaft with groove in front bearing for retaining ring facing toward splined end of output shaft.

2) Install front bearing on output shaft so groove in bearing for front bearing retaining ring faces toward splined end of output shaft. Install front bearing snap ring on output shaft. Install annulus gear on output shaft with reference marks aligned. Install annulus gear snap ring.
3) Install direct clutch drum on annulus gear with reference marks aligned. Ensure lugs on direct clutch drum fully engage lugs on annulus gear. Install outer retaining ring. Slide direct clutch drum forward. Install inner retaining ring.
4) Hold overrunning clutch upside down with expanding-type snap ring pliers. Coat needle bearing with petroleum jelly and install on overrunning clutch. Ensure needle bearing is fully seated on overrunning clutch.
5) Hold output shaft assembly upside down. Using an upward, counterclockwise twisting motion, install overrunning clutch in direct clutch drum.
6) Carefully set planetary carrier assembly into annulus gear and align splines using alignment shaft. Ensure planetary gear is fully seated.
7) Install needle bearing over alignment shaft. Remove alignment shaft. Install sun gear, direct clutch spring and direct clutch hub. Reinstall alignment shaft.

CAUTION: Ensure direct clutch components are installed in original location and original number of components are installed.

8) Install direct clutch pack in direct clutch drum. Install spring compressor on top of direct clutch hub. Slightly compress direct clutch spring and install direct clutch pack in direct clutch drum as direct clutch spring is compressed.
9) Once direct clutch pack is in direct clutch drum, install load retaining snap ring in direct clutch drum and snap ring on the sun gear. Ensure snap rings are fully seated.
10) Release press. Remove spring compressor. Ensure alignment shaft is fully seated. If alignment shaft becomes unseated, it may be necessary to disassemble overdrive unit gear train and realign splines. Remove overdrive unit gear train assembly from press.

OVERDRIVE UNIT REASSEMBLY

OVERDRIVE UNIT

1) Install front bearing on output shaft (if not previously installed). Ensure groove in front bearing for front retaining ring faces toward splined end of output shaft. Install snap ring on output shaft.
2) Install key for governor in output shaft. Ensure seal rings are installed on governor drive. Install filter screen and governor body on governor drive. Ensure oil passage in governor drive aligns with oil passage in governor body. Install and tighten governor body-to-governor drive bolts finger tight.
3) Install governor body on output shaft. Install governor snap ring on output shaft. Tighten governor body-to-governor drive bolts to specification. See TORQUE SPECIFICATIONS.

4) Install inner weight, spring and outer weight in governor body. Install snap rings. Align valve shaft holes in governor body and output shaft. Install valve, valve shaft and clips.

5) Install dowel, parking sprag and spring in overdrive unit case. Ensure end of spring is hooked on parking sprag.

6) Install and tighten dowel retaining plug. Install reaction plug in overdrive unit case. Install reaction plug snap ring. DO NOT over compress snap ring when installing.

7) Install rear bearing and snap ring in overdrive unit case. Ensure snap ring groove on rear bearing is toward front of overdrive unit case. Install governor support and tube assembly in overdrive unit case. Install governor support snap ring.

8) Install front bearing retaining ring in overdrive unit case. Ensure ends of front bearing retaining ring face the access cover opening in overdrive unit case.

9) Place overdrive unit gear train in vertical position. Install overdrive unit case over the overdrive unit gear train. Using snap ring pliers, expand front bearing retaining ring through access hole cover.

10) Slide overdrive unit case downward until front bearing retaining ring engages locating groove on outside of front bearing. Release front bearing retaining ring.

11) Install gasket and access cover on overdrive unit case. Install flat snap ring and then waved snap ring in overdrive unit case. Both snap rings fit in same groove. Ensure both snap rings are fully seated.

12) Install overdrive clutch pack. *See Fig. 40.* Ensure thickest clutch plate is installed last. Install wire-type snap ring.

CAUTION: When installing overdrive clutch pack, ensure thickest clutch plate is installed last, nearest wire-type snap ring.

---

13) Proper thickness intermediate shaft selective spacer and overdrive piston thrust plate must be determined before installing overdrive unit. See DETERMINING INTERMEDIATE SHAFT SELECTIVE SPACER & OVERDRIVE PISTON THRUST PLATE under OVERDRIVE UNIT ADJUSTMENTS.

OVERDRIVE UNIT ADJUSTMENTS

DETERMINING INTERMEDIATE SHAFT SELECTIVE SPACER & OVERDRIVE PISTON THRUST PLATE

1) To determine intermediate shaft selective spacer, output shaft end play is checked. Place overdrive unit in vertical position. Install Adapter (6312) through sun gear, planetary gear and into pilot bushing in output shaft. *See Fig. 48.* Ensure adapter bottoms against shoulder on planetary gear.

2) Install Bar (6311) across surface of overdrive unit case. Position dial caliper on bar. Extend dial caliper downward through bar until it contacts adapter. Note reading on dial caliper. This is the output shaft end play.

3) Using output shaft end play reading, determine proper intermediate shaft selective spacer thickness. See INTERMEDIATE SHAFT SELECTIVE SPACER SELECTION table. Remove dial caliper, bar and adapter. Retain intermediate shaft selective spacer for overdrive unit installation.

INTERMEDIATE SHAFT SELECTIVE SPACER SELECTION

Output Shaft End Play [1] In. (mm)	Shaft Spacer Thickness In. (mm)
.7336-.7505 (18.633-19.063)	.158-.159 (4.01-4.04)
.7506-.7675 (19.065-19.494)	.175-.176 (4.44-4.47)
.7676-.7855 (19.497-19.951)	.193-.194 (4.90-4.93)
.7856-.8011 (19.954-20.348)	.211-.212 (5.35-5.38)

[1] – Measurement taken with Adapter (6312) installed through sun gear, planetary gear and into pilot bushing in output shaft.

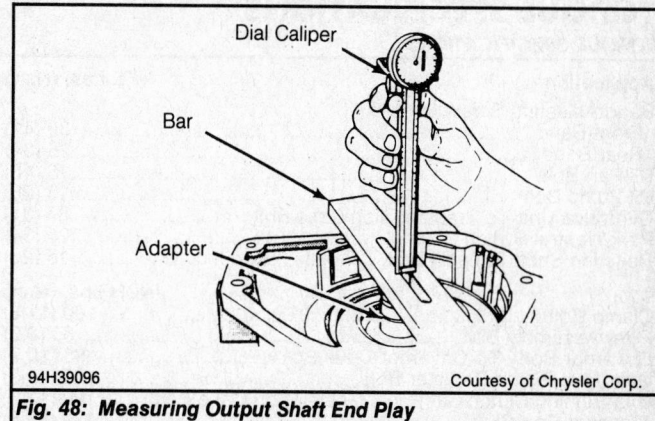

94H39096 — Courtesy of Chrysler Corp.

Fig. 48: Measuring Output Shaft End Play

4) To determine overdrive piston thrust plate thickness, install Bar (6311) across surface of overdrive unit case. Position dial caliper on bar.

5) Extend dial caliper through the bar and measure distance to surface of direct clutch hub thrust bearing seat in 4 places 90 degrees apart. *See Fig. 49.*

6) Determine average distance by adding 4 measurements together and dividing by 4. Using average distance, determine proper overdrive piston thrust plate thickness. See OVERDRIVE PISTON THRUST PLATE SELECTION table. Remove dial caliper and bar. Retain overdrive piston thrust plate for overdrive unit installation.

CAUTION: Ensure intermediate shaft selective spacer and overdrive piston thrust plate and overdrive piston thrust bearing are installed before installing overdrive unit on transmission.

OVERDRIVE PISTON THRUST PLATE SELECTION

Hub Thrust Bearing Seat Average Distance In. (mm)	Overdrive Piston Thrust Plate Thickness In. (mm)
1.7500-1.7649 (44.450-44.828)	.108-.110 (2.74-2.79)
1.7650-1.7799 (44.831-45.209)	.123-.125 (3.12-3.18)
1.7800-1.7949 (45.212-45.590)	.138-.140 (3.50-3.56)
1.7950-1.8099 (45.593-45.971)	.153-.155 (3.89-3.94)
1.8100-1.8249 (45.974-46.352)	.168-.170 (4.27-4.31)
1.8250-1.8399 (46.355-46.733)	.183-.185 (4.65-4.70)
1.8400-1.8549 (46.736-47.114)	.198-.200 (5.03-5.08)
1.8550-1.8699 (47.117-47.495)	.213-.215 (5.41-5.46)
1.8700-1.8849 (47.498-47.876)	.228-.230 (5.79-5.84)
1.8850-1.8999 (47.879-48.257)	.243-.245 (6.17-6.22)

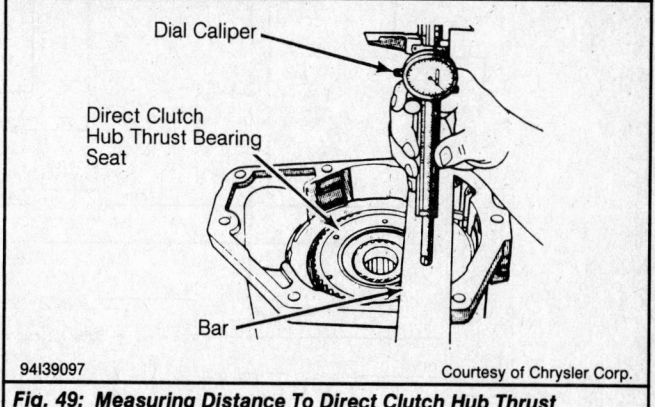

94I39097 — Courtesy of Chrysler Corp.

Fig. 49: Measuring Distance To Direct Clutch Hub Thrust Bearing Seat

TORQUE SPECIFICATIONS

TORQUE SPECIFICATIONS

Application	Ft. Lbs. (N.m)
Band Adjusting Screw Lock Nut	
Front Band	30 (41)
Rear Band	25 (34)
Oil Pan Bolt	13 (18)
Oil Pump Bolt	15 (20)
Overdrive Unit-To-Transmission Case Bolt	25 (34)
Park/Neutral Switch	25 (34)
Reaction Shaft Support Bolt	15 (20)

	INCH Lbs. (N.m)
Clamp Bolt	100 (11.3)
Filter Assembly Bolt	35 (4.0)
Governor Body-To-Governor Drive Bolt	95 (10.7)
Overdrive Piston Retainer Bolt	100 (11.3)
Overrunning Clutch Cam-To-Transmission Case Bolt	100 (11.3)
Pressure Port Plug	120 (13.6)
Valve Body Bolt	35 (4.0)
Valve Body-To-Transmission Case Bolt	105 (11.9)

TRANSMISSION SPECIFICATIONS

TRANSMISSION SPECIFICATIONS

Application	In. (mm)
Clutch Clearances	
Front Clutch	.073-.128 (1.85-3.25)
Rear Clutch	.025-.048 (.64-1.22)
Input Shaft End Play	.011-.080 (.28-2.03)
Oil Pump Clearances	
Gear End Clearance	.0004-.0025 (.010-.064)
Gear Tooth Clearance	.0045-.0095 (.114-.241)
Outer Gear-To-Pump	
Housing Clearance	.0035-.0075 (.089-.190)
Planetary Gear Train End Play	.005-.048 (.13-1.22)

WIRING DIAGRAMS

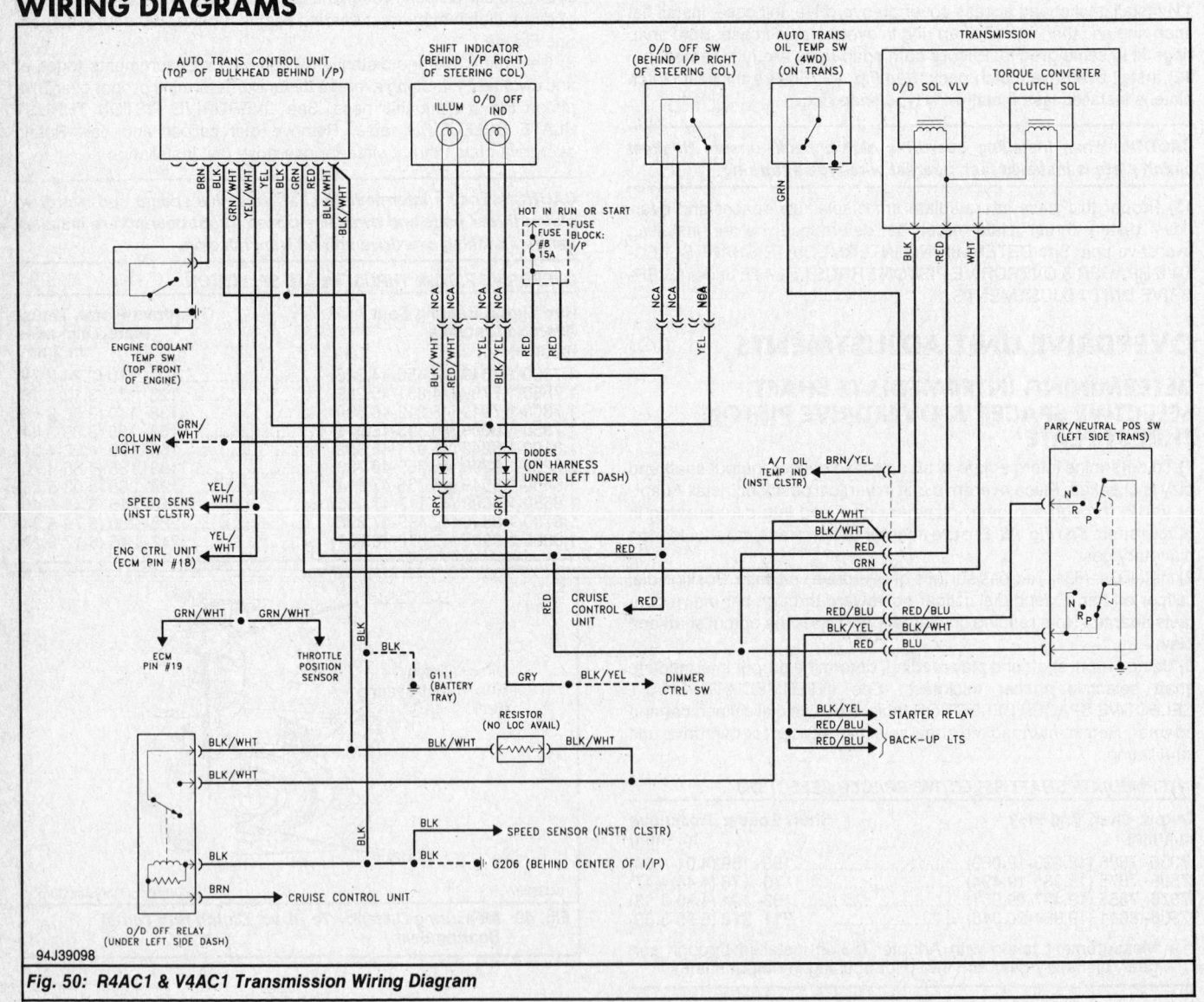

94J39098

Fig. 50: R4AC1 & V4AC1 Transmission Wiring Diagram

APPLICATION & LABOR TIMES

APPLICATION & LABOR TIMES

Vehicle Application	Labor Times [1] R & I	[2] Overhaul	Trans. Model
Dodge			
1993-94 Pickup (3.9L)	[3] 3.8	7.5	32RH
1993-94 Ram Van (3.9L)	3.1	7.5	32RH
Jeep			
1993 Wrangler (4.0L)	4.8	7.5	32RH
1994 Cherokee			
2.5L	[4] 3.9	7.5	30RH
4.0L	[4] 3.9	7.5	32RH
1994 Wrangler			
2.5L	4.8	7.5	30RH
4.0L	4.8	7.5	32RH

[1] – Removal and installation of transmission from vehicle chassis.
[2] – Bench overhaul time for transmission. DOES NOT include removal and installation.
[3] – Add 1.8 hrs. for 4WD.
[4] – Add .7 hr. for 4WD.

IDENTIFICATION

Transmission identification numbers are stamped on left side of transmission case, near oil pan flange. *See Fig. 1.* Identification numbers may be required when ordering replacement components.

NOTE: Selective sized snap rings and thrust washers may be needed to set and adjust clearances. For sizes and availability, refer to manufacturers parts department and reference transmission model and identification number.

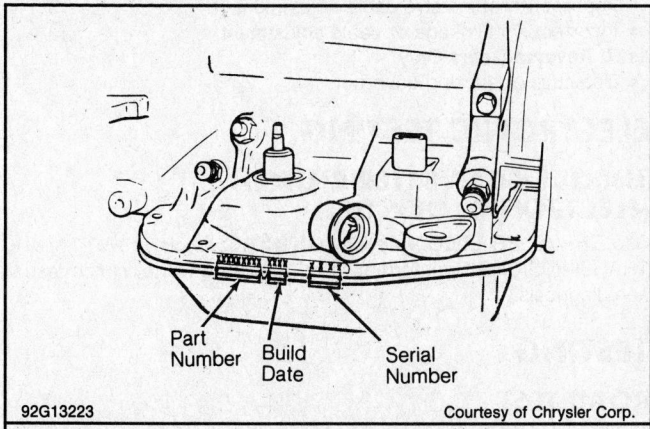

Part Number Build Date Serial Number

92G13223   Courtesy of Chrysler Corp.

Fig. 1: Locating Transmission Identification Numbers

DESCRIPTION

Transmission is a fully automatic 3-speed transmission with 1st through 3rd gears provided by clutches, bands, overrunning clutch and planetary gear sets. *See Fig. 2.*

On Jeep Cherokee 4WD models and Wrangler, an adapter housing is bolted to rear of transmission in place of extension housing. The transfer case is bolted to the adapter housing.

LUBRICATION & ADJUSTMENTS

NOTE: See appropriate AUTOMATIC TRANSMISSION SERVICING article in TRANSMISSION SERVICING.

NOTE: Manufacturer recommends Mopar ATF Plus Type 7176 fluid for use in this transmission. This ATF should also be used for lubrication during assembly.

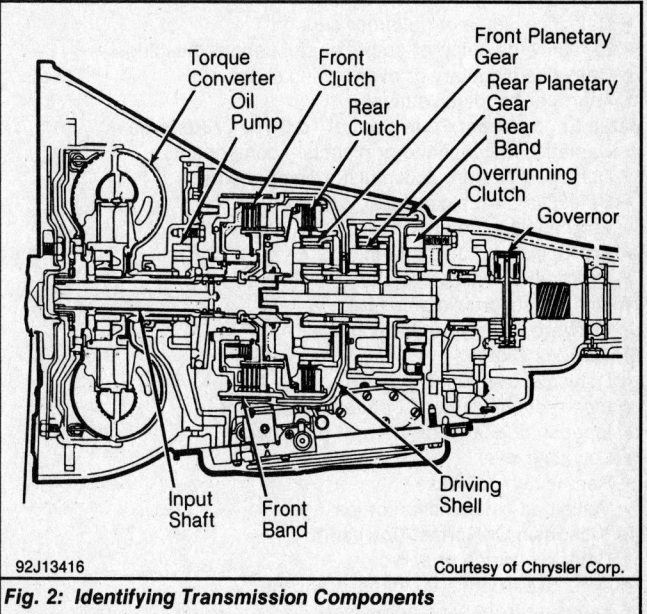

Torque Converter Oil Pump Front Clutch Rear Clutch Front Planetary Gear Rear Planetary Gear Rear Band Overrunning Clutch Governor

Input Shaft Front Band Driving Shell

92J13416   Courtesy of Chrysler Corp.

Fig. 2: Identifying Transmission Components

TROUBLE SHOOTING

Transmission malfunctions may be caused by poor engine performance, improper adjustments or failure of hydraulic, mechanical or electronic components. Always begin by checking fluid level, fluid condition, shift linkage or cable adjustment and throttle valve cable adjustment. Perform road test to determine if problem has been corrected. If problem still exists, several tests must be performed on transmission. See TESTING in this article.

TRANSMISSION SYMPTOM DIAGNOSIS

NOTE: The shift from Neutral to Reverse is normally quite firm, as rear servo pressure can approach 300 psi (21 kg/cm²). DO NOT confuse a firm engagement with a harsh engagement.

Buzzing Noise
- Aerated fluid
- Defective overrunning clutch
- Low fluid level
- Valve body malfunction or leakage

Delayed Engagement From Neutral To Drive Or Reverse
- Damaged clutch, band or servo
- Damaged oil pump components
- Damaged or worn reaction shaft seal rings
- Defective governor
- Engine idle speed too low
- Improper rear band adjustment
- Incorrect shift linkage or cable adjustment
- Low fluid level
- Low hydraulic pressure
- Restricted filter assembly

Drags Or Locks Up
- Defective band, band linkage or servo
- Defective planetary or overrunning clutch
- Dragging clutch
- Improper band adjustment

Fluid Blows Out Filler Tube
- Aerated fluid
- Defective rear servo
- High fluid level
- Oil cooler or lines restricted
- Restricted breather vent in oil pump
- Restricted filter assembly
- Valve in valve body sticking

Growling, Grating Or Scraping Noise
- Defective clutch or governor support
- Defective oil pump or output shaft bearings/bushings
- Defective planetary or overrunning clutch
- Improper band adjustment

Harsh Engagement From Neutral To Drive Or Reverse
- Damaged clutch, band or planetary components
- Damaged or worn accumulator components
- Defective torque converter lock-up
- Engine idle speed too high
- Improper band adjustment
- Improper throttle valve cable adjustment
- Incorrect hydraulic pressure

No Forward Gear In Any Position (Reverse Is Okay)
- Defective overrunning clutch
- Incorrect shift linkage or cable adjustment
- Input shaft seal rings worn or damaged
- Low fluid level
- Rear clutch defective
- Valve body malfunction or leakage

No Kickdown Or Normal Downshift
- Defective clutch or servo
- Defective front servo, band or linkage
- Improper front band adjustment
- Improper hydraulic pressure
- Improper throttle valve cable adjustment
- Incorrect shift linkage or cable adjustment

No Low Gear (Moves In 2nd & 3rd Gears Only)
- Front band linkage binding
- Front servo binding in bore
- Governor partially stuck open
- Improper throttle valve cable adjustment
- Incorrect shift linkage or cable adjustment
- Valve body malfunction or leakage

No Reverse
- Improper rear band adjustment
- Incorrect shift linkage or cable adjustment
- Rear servo or front clutch malfunction
- Valve body malfunction or leakage

Shifts Delayed Or Erratic
- Aerated fluid
- Defective clutch or servo
- Governor support seal rings broken or worn
- Improper fluid level
- Improper front band adjustment causing harsh 1-2 shift
- Improper throttle valve cable adjustment or binding components
- Incorrect shift linkage or cable adjustment
- Restricted filter assembly

Slips In All Forward Gears
- Aerated fluid
- Damaged or worn accumulator components
- Defective clutch or servo
- Defective overrunning clutch
- Improper throttle valve cable adjustment or binding components
- Incorrect shift linkage or cable adjustment
- Low fluid level
- Low hydraulic pressure

Slips In Low Gear In Drive But Not In Low Gear (1 Position)
- Defective overrunning clutch

Slips In Reverse Only
- Aerated fluid
- Binding band linkage
- Defective front clutch, rear servo or rear band
- Improper rear band adjustment
- Incorrect shift linkage or cable adjustment
- Low fluid level
- Low hydraulic pressure

Sluggish Acceleration Or Excessive Throttle To Maintain Speed
- Defective torque converter clutch
- Improper throttle valve cable adjustment
- Incorrect shift linkage or cable adjustment
- Poor engine performance
- Slipping clutches

Transmission Overheats
- Improper band adjustment
- Improper clutch clearance
- Low fluid level
- Restricted oil cooler
- Switch valve in valve body sticking

Vehicle Moves In Neutral
- Clutch dragging
- Incorrect shift linkage or cable adjustment
- Torque converter lock-up clutch dragging
- Valve body malfunction or leakage

Vehicle Moves In 2nd Or 3rd Gear & Abruptly Downshifts To Low
- Governor sticking
- Valve body malfunction or leakage

Vehicle Will Not Move In Any Gear
- Defective oil pump
- Incorrect shift linkage or cable adjustment
- Internal transmission component failure
- Low fluid level
- Valve body malfunction or leakage

Will Not Upshift From Low Gear
- Defective clutch or servo
- Defective oil pump, seal rings or valve body
- Governor stuck closed
- Improper front band adjustment
- Improper throttle valve cable adjustment
- Incorrect shift linkage or cable adjustment

1st & Reverse Gears Only
- Defective or sticking governor

ELECTRONIC TESTING

TORQUE CONVERTER CLUTCH (ELECTRONIC LOCK-UP)

See CHRYSLER ELECTRONIC CONTROLS article in AUTOMATIC TRANSMISSIONS for information on torque converter clutch testing and diagnosis.

TESTING

ROAD TEST

1) Ensure shift linkage/cable and throttle valve cable are properly adjusted. See appropriate AUTOMATIC TRANSMISSION SERVICING article in TRANSMISSION SERVICING. Ensure fluid level and condition are okay. Add ATF and adjust control cables or linkages (if necessary).

2) Road test vehicle, operating transmission in each gear position. Observe engine performance during road test. A poorly tuned engine will not allow an accurate analysis of transmission operation.

3) Check for slippage and shift variations. Note if shifts are harsh, spongy, delayed or early.

4) Slipping or flare-up in any gear usually indicates clutch, band, or overrunning clutch problems. A slipping clutch or band in a particular gear can usually be identified by noting transmission operation in other gearshift positions and comparing which internal units are applied in those positions. See CLUTCH & BAND APPLICATION table.

CLUTCH & BAND APPLICATION

Gearshift Position	Elements In Use
"D" (Drive)	
1st Gear	Rear Clutch & Overrunning Clutch
2nd Gear	Front Band & Rear Clutch
3rd Gear	Front Clutch & Rear Clutch
"2" (Second)	
1st Gear	Rear Clutch & Overrunning Clutch
2nd Gear	Front Band & Rear Clutch
"1" (Low)	
1st Gear	Rear Clutch, Rear Band & Overrunning Clutch
"R" (Reverse)	Front Clutch & Rear Band
"N" Or "P" (Neutral Or Park)	All Clutches & Bands Released Or Ineffective

5) Problem area may be detected by determining which components are applied. By selecting another gear that does not use these components, the defective component can be determined. See CLUTCH & BAND APPLICATION table.

6) Process of elimination can be used to detect any unit which slips and to confirm proper operation of good units. Road test analysis can usually diagnose slipping units. Actual malfunction usually cannot be decided.

7) Practically any condition can be caused by leaking hydraulic circuits or sticking valves. Transmission failure may be determined by performing hydraulic pressure test along with clutch and servo air pressure test.

TORQUE CONVERTER STALL SPEED TEST

Test Procedure – 1) Install tachometer. Ensure transmission fluid level is correct. Start and operate engine until transmission fluid is at normal operating temperature.

CAUTION: DO NOT open throttle to wide open position for more than 5 seconds or transmission may be damaged. If performing more than one torque converter stall speed test, operate engine at 1000 RPM with transmission in Neutral for at least 20 seconds to cool transmission fluid before performing next torque converter stall speed test.

2) Block front wheels. Apply parking and service brakes. Place transmission in Drive. Open throttle to wide open position for no more than 5 seconds and note engine RPM and then release throttle. This is the torque converter stall speed.

3) Torque converter stall speed should be 1800-2100 RPM on all models except Cherokee and Wrangler. On Cherokee and Wrangler, torque converter stall speed should be 1700-2000 RPM.

4) Once torque converter stall speed is obtained, place transmission in Neutral. Operate engine for 20 seconds, allowing transmission to cool. Stop engine. Place transmission in Park. Remove tachometer.

NOTE: Use following symptoms to trouble shoot results of torque converter stall speed test.

Stall Speed Exceeds Specification – If torque converter stall speed exceeds specification by more than 200 RPM, transmission clutch is slipping.

Stall Speed Less Than Specification – 1) If torque converter stall speed is less than specification with properly tuned engine, torque converter overrunning clutch may be slipping.

2) If torque converter overrunning clutch is slipping, torque converter stall speed will be 250-300 RPM less than the specification. Vehicle will operate properly at highway speeds, but will have poor low-speed acceleration.

Stall Speed Is Within Specification – If torque converter stall speed is within specification, but abnormal throttle opening is required to maintain highway speeds, torque converter overrunning clutch is seized. Torque converter must be replaced.

Noise When Performing Torque Converter Stall Speed Test – Whining noise caused by fluid flow is normal. A loud metallic sound indicates torque converter is damaged. To ensure sound is coming from torque converter, raise vehicle on hoist. Operate vehicle with transmission in Drive and then Neutral at light throttle. Ensure noise is coming from torque converter. Replace torque converter if defective.

HYDRAULIC PRESSURE TEST

Test Preparation – 1) Ensure fluid level and condition are okay. Install tachometer. Raise vehicle on hoist, allowing wheels to rotate freely.

2) Disconnect throttle valve and shift cables or linkages from manual selector lever and throttle valve lever on the transmission.

CAUTION: A 100 psi (7 kg/cm²) pressure gauge is required for checking all applications except rear servo. A 300 psi (21 kg/cm²) pressure gauge is required for checking pressure at rear servo.

Pressure Test With Transmission In "1" (1st Gear) – 1) Remove pressure tap plugs and install pressure gauge in accumulator and rear servo pressure taps. See Fig. 3. Start and operate engine at 1000 RPM.

2) Move manual selector lever on transmission fully forward to the gearshift "1" position. Read pressure on both pressure gauges as throttle valve lever on transmission is moved from fully forward position to fully rearward position.

3) Line pressure at accumulator pressure tap should be 54-60 psi (3.7-4.2 kg/cm²) with throttle valve lever fully forward and gradually increase to 90-96 psi (6.3-6.7 kg/cm²) as throttle valve lever is moved rearward. Rear servo pressure should be within 3 psi (.2 kg/cm²) of line pressure.

4) If line pressure is not within specification, adjust line pressure. See LINE PRESSURE under HYDRAULIC PRESSURE ADJUSTMENTS. If proper line pressure still cannot be obtained, check for defective components and hydraulic circuit.

5) This tests oil pump output, pressure regulation, condition of rear clutch and servo hydraulic circuits. Remove pressure gauges. Install and tighten pressure tap plugs to specification. See TORQUE SPECIFICATIONS.

Pressure Test With Transmission In "2" (2nd Gear) – 1) Remove pressure tap plug and install pressure gauge in accumulator pressure tap. See Fig. 3. Start and operate engine at 1000 RPM.

2) Move manual selector lever on transmission to fully forward position and then rearward one position to gearshift "2" position. Read pressure on pressure gauge as throttle valve lever on transmission is moved from fully forward position to fully rearward position.

3) Line pressure at accumulator pressure tap should be 54-60 psi (3.7-4.2 kg/cm²) with throttle valve lever fully forward and gradually increase to 90-96 psi (6.3-6.7 kg/cm²) as throttle valve lever is moved rearward.

4) If line pressure is not within specification, adjust line pressure. See LINE PRESSURE under HYDRAULIC PRESSURE ADJUSTMENTS. If proper line pressure still cannot be obtained, check for defective components and hydraulic circuit.

5) This tests oil pump output and pressure regulation. Remove pressure gauge. Install and tighten pressure tap plug to specification. See TORQUE SPECIFICATIONS.

Pressure Test With Transmission In "D" (Drive Gear) – 1) Remove pressure tap plugs and install pressure gauge in accumulator and front servo pressure taps. See Fig. 3. Start and operate engine at 1600 RPM.

2) Move manual selector lever on transmission to fully forward position and then rearward 2 positions to gearshift "D" position. Read pressure on both pressure gauges as throttle valve lever on transmission is moved from fully forward position to fully rearward position.

3) Line pressure at accumulator pressure tap should be 54-60 psi (3.7-4.2 kg/cm²) with throttle valve lever fully forward and gradually increase as throttle valve lever is moved rearward. Front servo is pressurized only in gearshift "D" position and pressure should be within 3 psi (.2 kg/cm²) of line pressure up to the downshift point.

4) If line pressure is not within specification, adjust line pressure. See LINE PRESSURE under HYDRAULIC PRESSURE ADJUSTMENTS. If proper line pressure still cannot be obtained, check for defective components and hydraulic circuit.

5) This tests oil pump output, pressure regulation and condition of clutch hydraulic circuits. Remove pressure gauges. Install and tighten pressure tap plugs to specification. See TORQUE SPECIFICATIONS.

Pressure Test With Transmission In "R" (Reverse Gear) – 1) Remove pressure tap plug and install 300 psi (21 kg/cm²) pressure gauge in rear servo pressure tap. *See Fig. 3.* Start and operate engine at 1600 RPM.

2) Move manual selector lever on transmission to fully forward position and then rearward 4 positions to gearshift "R" position. Read pressure on pressure gauge as throttle valve lever on transmission is moved from fully forward position to fully rearward position.

3) Pressure should be 145-175 psi (10.2-12.3 kg/cm²) with throttle valve lever fully forward and gradually increase to 230-280 psi (16.1-19.7 kg/cm²) with throttle valve lever fully rearward.

4) This tests oil pump output, pressure regulation, front clutch and rear servo hydraulic circuits. Remove pressure gauge. Install and tighten pressure tap plug to specification. See TORQUE SPECIFICATIONS.

NOTE: Transmission governor pressure is usually checked if shift speeds are incorrect or transmission will not upshift or downshift.

Transmission Governor Pressure – 1) Reconnect throttle valve and shift cables or linkages on manual selector lever and throttle valve lever on transmission (if removed). Remove pressure tap plug and install pressure gauge in governor pressure tap. *See Fig. 3.*

NOTE: Governor pressure tap is located in different area if adapter housing is used. See Fig. 3.

2) Lower vehicle, leaving wheels approximately 12" from floor. Start engine and allow to idle. Place gearshift in "D" (Drive). Note pressure gauge reading with engine idling.

3) Pressure should be 0-1.5 psi (0-.1 kg/cm²) with wheels not rotating. If pressure exceeds specification, governor valve or weights are stuck open.

4) If pressure is correct, slowly increase engine speed, noting governor pressure in relation to vehicle speed. Governor pressure should increase approximately 1 psi (.07 kg/cm²) for every MPH. Governor pressure should rise smoothly and then drop back to 0-1.5 psi (0-.1 kg/cm²) when wheels stop rotating.

5) This tests governor operation in relation to engine and vehicle speed. Repair governor if it does not operate properly. Remove pressure gauge. Install and tighten pressure tap plug to specification. See TORQUE SPECIFICATIONS.

Hydraulic Pressure Test Result Indications – 1) If proper line pressure is obtained in any pressure test, oil pump and pressure regulator are working properly.

2) If line pressure is low in "D", "1" and "2", but is correct in "R", this indicates leakage in rear clutch circuit.

3) If line pressure is low in "D" (3rd gear) and "R", but is correct in "1" and "2", this indicates leakage in front clutch circuit.

4) If line pressure is low in "R" and "1", but is correct in "2", this indicates leakage in rear servo circuit. If front servo pressure is low in "2", this indicates leakage in front servo circuit.

5) High governor pressure at idle indicates governor valve is stuck open. Low governor pressure at all vehicle speeds indicates governor valve is stuck closed.

6) If line pressure is not within specification, adjust line pressure. See LINE PRESSURE under HYDRAULIC PRESSURE ADJUSTMENTS. If proper line pressure still cannot be obtained, check for defective components and hydraulic circuit. Low line pressure in all positions indicates a defective oil pump, restricted filter or stuck pressure regulator valve.

CLUTCH & SERVO AIR PRESSURE TEST

NOTE: Inoperative clutches, servos and bands can be located by applying air pressure to appropriate passages in transmission case.

Test Preparation – Remove valve body. See VALVE BODY under REMOVAL & INSTALLATION.

CAUTION: Ensure air supply is free of all dirt and moisture.

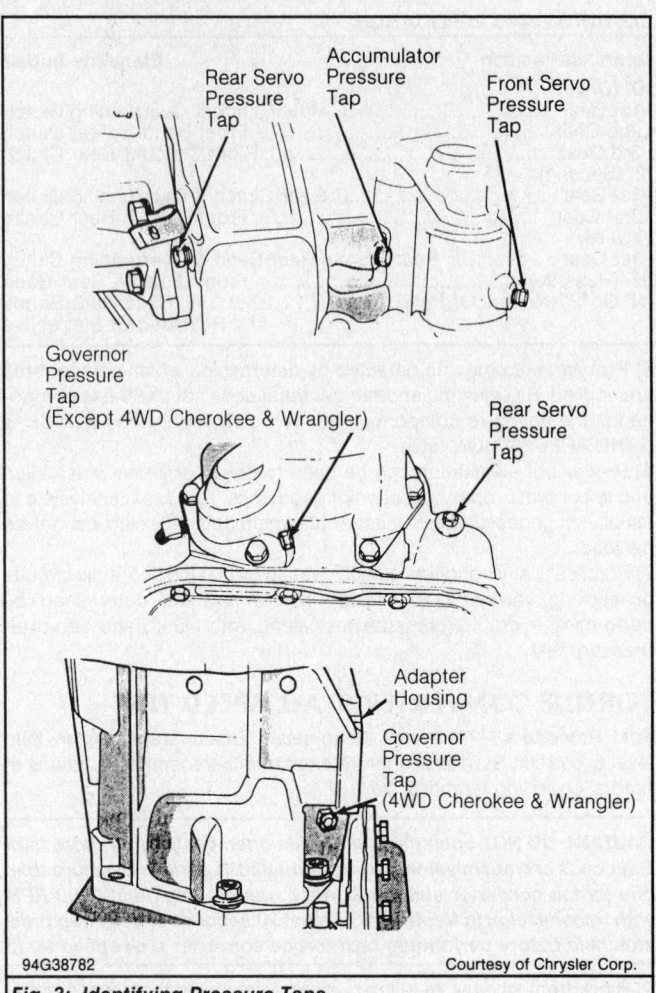

Fig. 3: Identifying Pressure Taps

94G38782   Courtesy of Chrysler Corp.

92I13225   Courtesy of Chrysler Corp.

Fig. 4: Identifying Air Pressure Test Passages

Front Clutch – Place finger on front clutch housing. Apply air pressure to front clutch apply passage. *See Fig. 4.* Piston movement will be felt and a soft thump will be heard when front clutch is applied.
Rear Clutch – Place finger on rear clutch housing. Apply air pressure to rear clutch apply passage. *See Fig. 4.* Piston movement will be felt and a soft thump will be heard when rear clutch is applied.

Front Servo – Apply air pressure to front servo apply passage. *See Fig. 4.* Front band should tighten, indicating front servo operation. Release air pressure. Ensure spring tension on servo piston releases front band.

Rear Servo – Apply air pressure to rear servo apply passage. *See Fig. 4.* Rear band should tighten, indicating rear servo operation. Release air pressure. Ensure spring tension on servo piston releases rear band.

TORQUE CONVERTER FLUID LEAKAGE TEST

NOTE: Fluid around torque converter may originate from engine oil or transmission. Ensure transmission fluid level is correct. Fluid leakage at torque converter may result if fluid level is too high. Transmission can be checked for leaks using the following method.

1) Remove torque converter dust shield. Clean inside area of torque converter housing using solvent and compressed air. Ensure area is clean and dry.

2) Fabricate leakage test probe using 1/32" sheet metal, 5 1/2" (140 mm) long and 1 1/2" (38 mm) wide. *See Fig. 5.* Install leakage test probe on torque converter dust shield bolt so leakage test probe is near torque converter. Ensure torque converter does not contact leakage test probe.

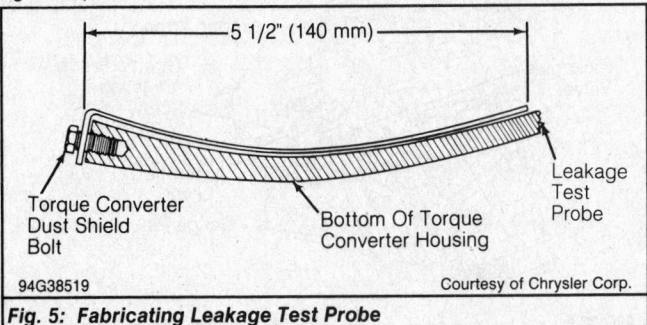

94G38519   Courtesy of Chrysler Corp.

Fig. 5: Fabricating Leakage Test Probe

3) Apply parking brake. Start engine. Place transmission in Neutral. Operate engine at 2500 RPM for 2 minutes. Stop engine. Remove leakage test probe.

4) If upper surface of leakage test probe is dry, torque converter is not leaking. If upper surface of leakage test probe is wet with ATF, torque converter is leaking. If area below leakage test probe is wet with ATF, fluid is coming from around torque converter area.

5) Check following for possible causes of fluid leaks at torque converter areas.

- Defective Oil Pump Housing "O" Ring Or Oil Pump Housing
- Front Band Pin Access Plug
- Mispositioned Or Worn Bushing
- Oil Pump Seal
- Oil Pump-To-Transmission Case Bolts
- Oil Pump Vent

6) If torque converter is leaking, check for defective welds on outside diameter of torque converter and torque converter hub. Torque converter hub is welded on inside and is not visible. Replace torque converter if a leak exists. DO NOT attempt to repair torque converter.

TRANSMISSION CASE PRESSURE TEST

NOTE: Transmission case, gaskets and oil pump housing can be checked for leaks using the following method. Transmission must be removed to perform transmission case pressure test.

1) Remove torque converter from transmission. Fabricate torque converter hub seal cup, retaining strap and vent plug retainer. *See Fig. 6.* Retaining strap specifications are approximate. Measure hole positions on torque converter housing before drilling.

CAUTION: Ensure torque converter hub seal cup surface is smooth to prevent damage to seal in oil pump.

2) Install torque converter hub seal cup, vent plug retainer and retaining strap. *See Fig. 7.* Install shipping plug in rear output shaft opening. Install and secure plugs in remaining transmission openings except oil cooler return line.

3) Attach air pump to oil cooler return line. *See Fig. 7.* Ensure cap is installed on oil cooler supply line fitting. Using pressure regulator, apply 8-10 psi (.5-.7 kg/cm²) of air pressure to transmission case.

CAUTION: DO NOT apply more than 10 psi (.7 kg/cm²) of air pressure to transmission case.

4) Coat oil pump and front of transmission case with soapy water solution. Check for bubbles, indicating a leak in seals, "O" rings, gaskets or transmission case. Release air pressure. Remove test equipment. Replace defective components.

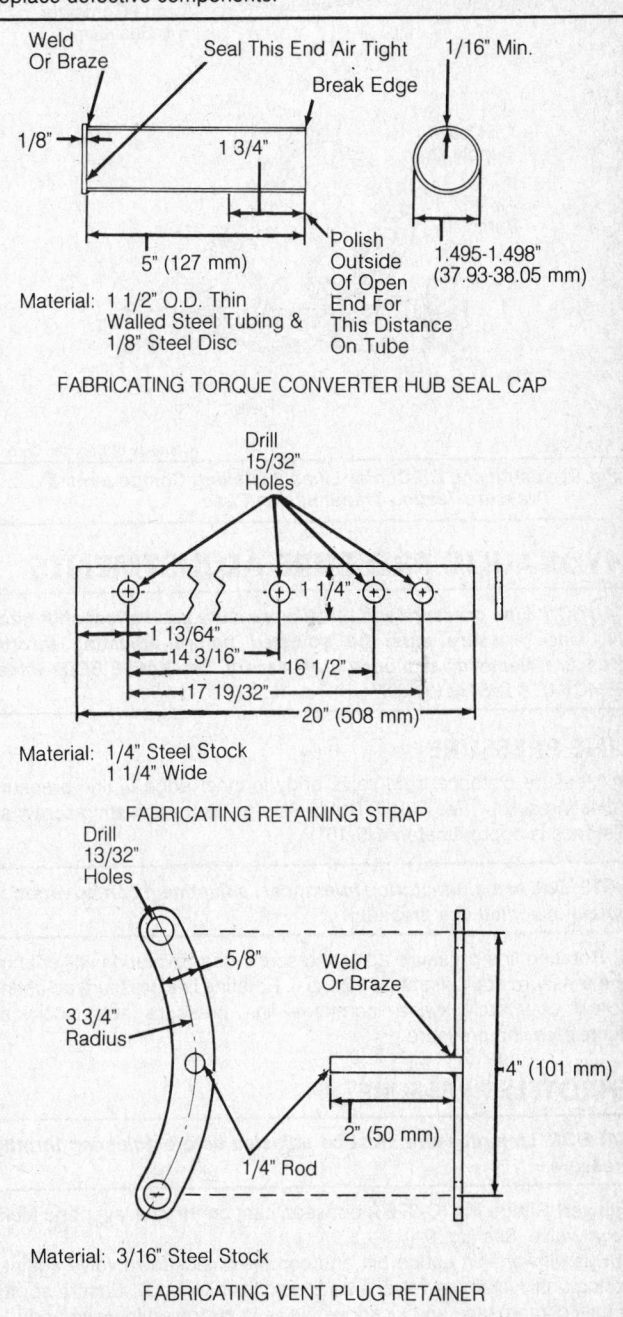

94J38520 94A38521 94B38522   Courtesy of Chrysler Corp.

Fig. 6: Fabricating Torque Converter Hub Seal Cup, Retaining Strap & Vent Plug Retainer

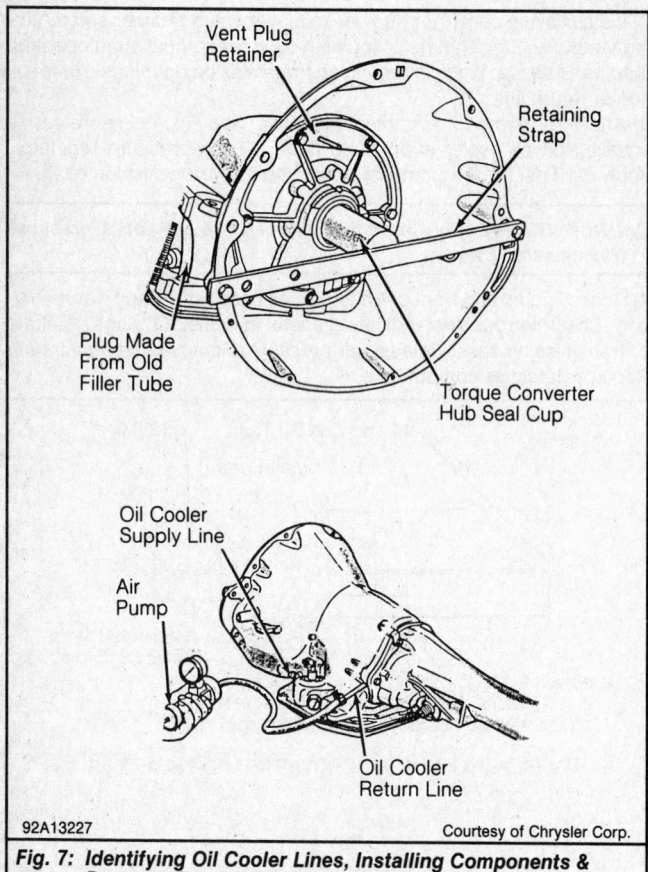

Fig. 7: Identifying Oil Cooler Lines, Installing Components & Pressure Testing Transmission Case

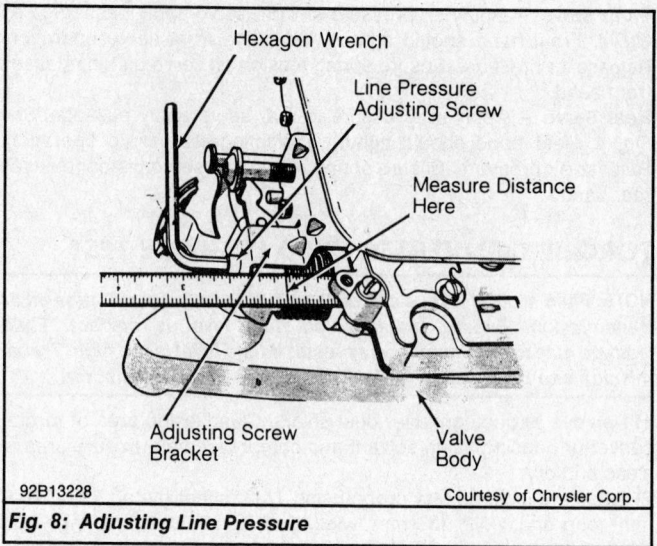

Fig. 8: Adjusting Line Pressure

Fig. 9: Adjusting Throttle Pressure

HYDRAULIC PRESSURE ADJUSTMENTS

CAUTION: Line pressure and throttle pressure each affect shift quality. Line pressure must be adjusted before adjusting throttle pressure. Remove valve body if necessary. See VALVE BODY under REMOVAL & INSTALLATION.

LINE PRESSURE

1) Measure distance from valve body to inner edge of line pressure adjusting screw. *See Fig. 8.* Rotate line pressure adjusting screw so distance is approximately 1 5/16".

NOTE: Due to manufacturing tolerances, adjustment can be varied to obtain specified line pressure.

2) Rotating line pressure adjusting screw one revolution will change line pressure approximately 1 2/3 psi. Rotating line pressure adjusting screw counterclockwise increases line pressure and clockwise decreases line pressure.

THROTTLE PRESSURE

CAUTION: Line pressure must be adjusted before adjusting throttle pressure.

1) Insert Gauge Pin (C-3763) between cam on throttle lever and kickdown valve. *See Fig. 9.*
2) Push inward on gauge pin and compress kickdown valve against spring until kickdown valve is bottomed in valve body. Ensure spring is fully compressed and kickdown valve is bottomed in valve body.
3) Maintain pressure against kickdown valve and spring. Rotate throttle pressure adjusting screw until head of adjusting screw contacts tang on throttle lever. Ensure throttle lever cam contacts gauge pin. Remove gauge pin.

ON-VEHICLE SERVICE

The following components can be serviced on the vehicle:
• Adapter Housing
• Extension Housing, Seal, Bushing & Output Shaft Rear Bearing
• Governor & Park Gear
• Park Lock Components
• Park/Neutral Switch
• Valve Body
• Vehicle Speed Sensor & Pinion Gear
See appropriate component under REMOVAL & INSTALLATION.

OIL COOLER FLUSHING

CAUTION: Whenever transmission failure exists, oil cooler must be flushed and torque converter replaced. If vehicle is equipped with 2 oil coolers (one in radiator tank and one in front of radiator), flush oil coolers separately. DO NOT attempt to flush both oil coolers at one time.

CAUTION: Some models may have a drainback relief valve installed in the oil cooler supply line next to the rubber hose at the radiator. See Fig. 42. If drainback relief valve is used, it must be removed before flushing the lines. Install NEW drainback relief valve once lines are flushed.

NOTE: On 1994 models, oil cooler lines are equipped with disconnect fittings. For disconnecting and installing procedures of oil cooler lines with disconnect fittings, see OIL COOLER LINE DISCONNECT FITTINGS under ON-VEHICLE SERVICE.

NOTE: Manufacturer recommends Mopar ATF Plus Type 7176 fluid for use in this transmission. This ATF should also be used for lubrication during assembly.

Flushing Procedure – 1) Note oil cooler supply and return lines. *See Fig. 7.* Disconnect oil cooler lines at transmission. Place container under oil cooler supply line.

2) Using hand-held suction gun filled with mineral spirits, force mineral spirits into oil cooler return line until mineral spirits flows from oil cooler supply line.

3) Continue flushing oil cooler until mineral spirits is clear and no sign of contamination exists. Once contamination is removed, apply compressed air on line from oil cooler in light applications until remaining mineral spirits is blown from oil cooler and oil cooler lines.

4) Pump at least one quart of ATF through oil cooler to ensure oil cooler is free of mineral spirits. Replace oil cooler if fluid does not flow freely through oil cooler.

OIL COOLER FLOW CHECK

1) With transmission filled to proper fluid level, disconnect oil cooler return line from transmission. *See Fig. 7.* Place container under oil cooler return line.

2) Add one extra quart of ATF to transmission. Apply parking brake. Start engine and allow to idle. Place gearshift in Neutral. Check fluid flow from oil cooler return line.

3) If fluid flow is intermittent or takes more than 20 seconds to obtain one quart, replace oil cooler. Reconnect oil cooler return line. Fill transmission to proper level with ATF.

OIL COOLER LINE DISCONNECT FITTINGS

NOTE: On 1994 models, there are 3 different types of disconnect fittings used. See Fig. 10. Release tool is required to disconnect oil cooler line. Release tool is attached to oil cooler line on Type 2 and 3 fittings. This release tool also can be used to disconnect Type 1 fittings.

Removal – 1) Ensure area around disconnect fitting and oil cooler line is clean. Slide release tool into disconnect fitting until it fully bottoms against flange on oil cooler line.

2) Push release tool inward and rotate to spread retaining clip and pull oil cooler line from disconnect fitting. *See Fig. 11.* Inspect disconnect fitting and oil cooler line for damage. Replace disconnect fitting as an assembly if damaged. Replace oil cooler line if swedge at hose or flange on line is damaged.

Installation – 1) If installing NEW disconnect fitting, apply Loctite 242 on disconnect fitting before installing. Ensure end of oil cooler line is clean. Insert oil cooler line into disconnect fitting.

CAUTION: After installing oil cooler line, pull outward on oil cooler line to ensure oil cooler line is locked in the disconnect fitting and retaining clip is fully seated.

2) Push oil cooler line inward until a snap or click is heard when retaining clip seats in oil cooler line. Pull outward on oil cooler line to ensure oil cooler line is locked in the disconnect fitting.

REMOVAL & INSTALLATION

ADAPTER HOUSING

Removal (Cherokee 4WD & Wrangler) – 1) Raise and support vehicle. Apply parking brake. Place reference marks on drive shaft yokes for reassembly reference. Remove drive shafts.

2) Place support stand under transmission torque converter housing. Remove rear crossmember. Disconnect parking brake cable and exhaust pipe support brackets (if necessary). Support transfer case with floor jack.

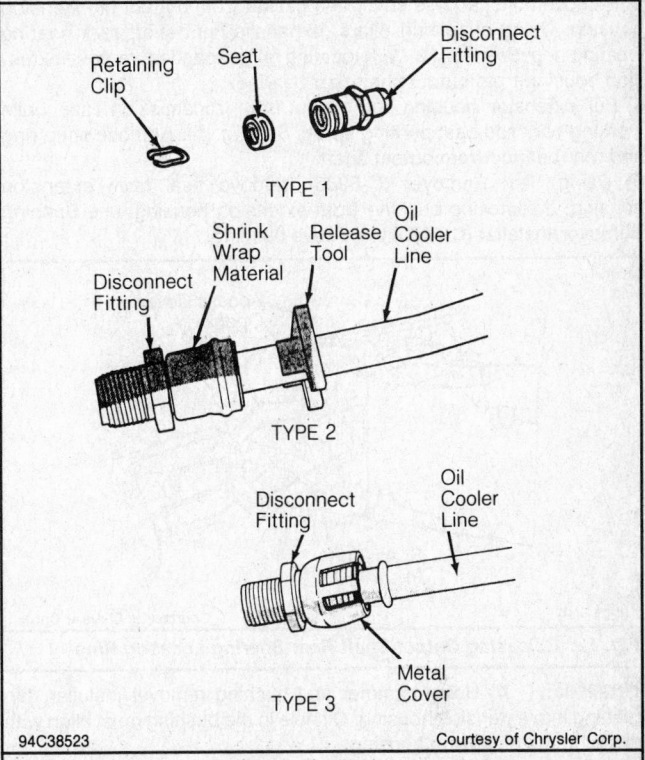

Fig. 10: Identifying Oil Cooler Line Disconnect Fittings

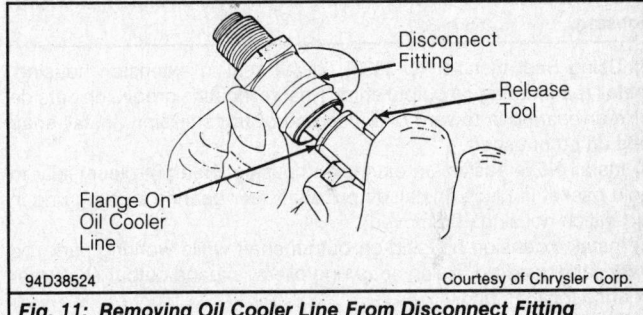

Fig. 11: Removing Oil Cooler Line From Disconnect Fitting (Type 2 Shown; Others Are Similar)

3) Disconnect linkages and electrical connections at transfer case. Remove transfer case-to-adapter housing bolts/nuts. Remove transfer case. Remove bolts, adapter housing and gasket from transmission.

Installation – To install, reverse removal procedure. Tighten bolts/nuts to specification. See TORQUE SPECIFICATIONS. Ensure reference marks are aligned on drive shaft yokes.

EXTENSION HOUSING, SEAL, BUSHING & OUTPUT SHAFT REAR BEARING

NOTE: On Jeep Cherokee 4WD and Wrangler models, an adapter housing is used in place of extension housing.

Removal (Cherokee 2WD, Pickup & Ram Van) – 1) Apply parking brake. Place transmission in "1" (Low gear). Raise and support vehicle.

2) Place reference marks on drive shaft yokes for reassembly reference. Remove drive shaft. Remove vehicle speed sensor and pinion gear. See VEHICLE SPEED SENSOR & PINION GEAR under REMOVAL & INSTALLATION.

3) Remove extension housing-to-rear mount bolts. Slightly raise transmission with floor jack. Remove rear crossmember. Remove extension housing-to-transmission case bolts.

4) Remove bolts, access cover and gasket from bottom of extension housing. Using snap ring pliers, expand output shaft rear bearing locating ring. *See Fig. 12.* With locating ring expanded, remove extension housing from output shaft rear bearing.

5) Pull extension housing and gasket from transmission case while working park rod past parking sprag. *See Fig. 14.* Remove snap ring and rear bearing from output shaft.

6) Using Seal Remover (C-3985), remove seal from extension housing. If removing bushing from extension housing, use Bushing Remover/Installer (C-4470) to remove bushing.

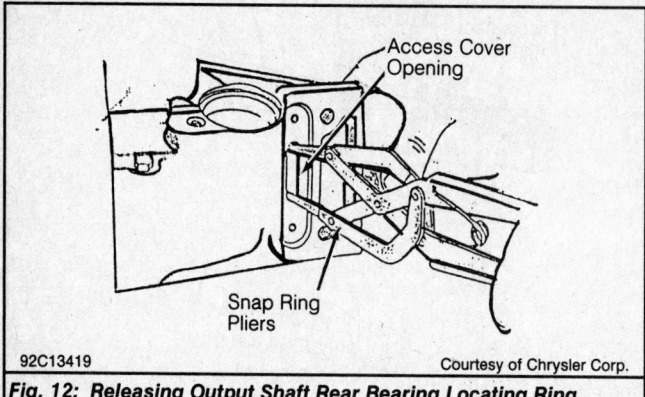

92C13419   Courtesy of Chrysler Corp.

Fig. 12: Releasing Output Shaft Rear Bearing Locating Ring

Installation – 1) Using hammer and bushing remover/installer, tap bushing into extension housing. Oil hole in the bushing must align with oil slot in the extension housing.

CAUTION: Ensure oil hole in bushing aligns with oil slot in extension housing.

---

2) Using Seal Installer (C-3995), install seal in extension housing. Install rear bearing on output shaft. Ensure locating groove on outside of rear bearing is toward oil pump end of transmission. Install snap ring on output shaft.

3) Install NEW gasket on extension housing. Use petroleum jelly to hold gasket in place. Install output shaft rear bearing locating ring in extension housing (if removed).

4) Install extension housing on output shaft while working park rod past parking sprag. Using snap ring pliers, expand output shaft rear bearing locating ring.

5) Work extension housing onto output shaft rear bearing and release locating ring. Ensure locating ring is fully seated in groove on the rear bearing.

6) Install and tighten extension housing-to-transmission case bolts to specification. See TORQUE SPECIFICATIONS.

7) Install gasket and access cover. Install and tighten bolts. Install rear crossmember. Install and tighten extension housing-to-rear mount bolts to specification.

8) To install remaining components, reverse removal procedure. Ensure reference marks are aligned on drive shaft yokes. Adjust transmission fluid level with Mopar ATF Plus-Type 7176 fluid.

GOVERNOR & PARK GEAR

CAUTION: Output shaft may contain an aluminum governor valve and a governor valve indexing area. Small end of governor valve must seat in governor valve indexing area. See Fig. 13. Aluminum governor valve cannot be used on earlier applications. Ensure original type governor components are installed. It may be necessary to use transmission identification number and to consult parts department if replacing any governor components. DO NOT interchange any governor components.

Removal – 1) On Cherokee 4WD and Wrangler models, remove adapter housing. See ADAPTER HOUSING under REMOVAL & INSTALLATION.

2) On all other models, remove extension housing and output shaft rear bearing. See EXTENSION HOUSING, SEAL, BUSHING & OUTPUT SHAFT REAR BEARING under REMOVAL & INSTALLATION.

3) On all models, remove snap ring from valve shaft. *See Fig. 13.* Remove governor valve and valve shaft from governor body. Remove governor body and park gear-to-output shaft snap ring.

NOTE: Some models may contain a thick snap ring, thrust washer and then a thin snap ring to retain the governor body and park gear on the output shaft.

---

4) Remove governor body and park gear from output shaft. Place reference mark on governor body and park gear for reassembly reference.

5) Remove governor body-to-park gear bolts. Separate governor body from park gear. Remove filter screen from governor body or park gear. Remove remaining components from governor body. *See Fig. 13.*

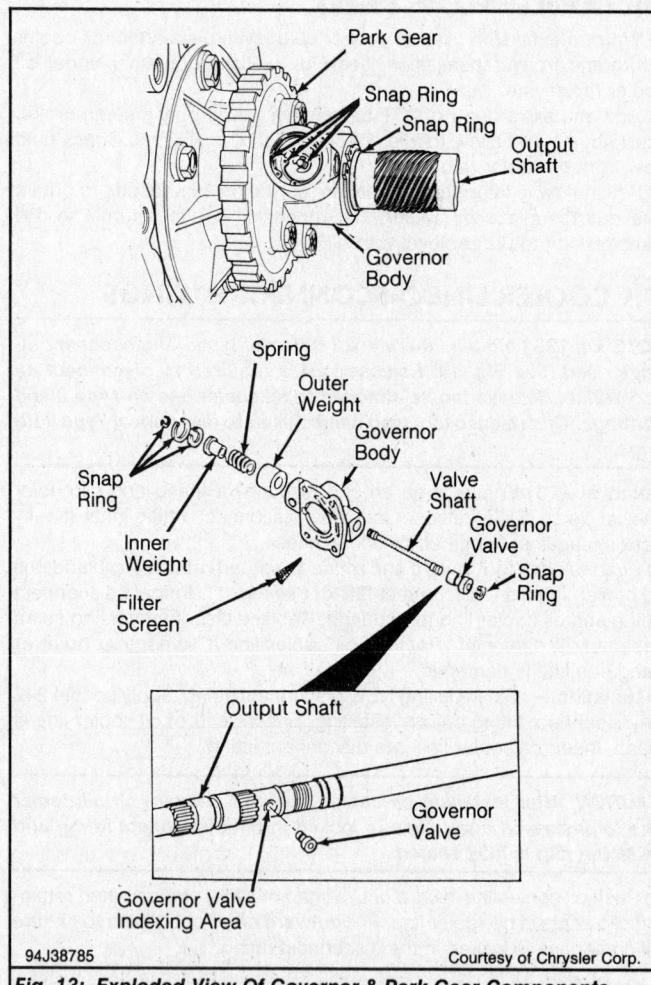

94J38785   Courtesy of Chrysler Corp.

Fig. 13: Exploded View Of Governor & Park Gear Components

Cleaning – 1) Clean components with solvent and dry with compressed air. Ensure inner and outer weights and governor valve slide freely in bore on governor body.

2) Inspect filter screen for damage. Replace damage components. Ensure original type governor components are installed. DO NOT interchange any governor components.

Installation – 1) Install filter screen in park gear. Install governor body on park gear so that oil passages in governor body and park gear are aligned. Ensure reference mark is aligned. Install governor body-to-park gear bolts finger tight. DO NOT tighten bolts at this time.

CAUTION: Ensure oil passages in governor body are aligned with those in park gear.

2) Install outer weight, spring, inner weight and snap ring in governor body. Install governor body and park gear on output shaft. Ensure valve shaft hole in governor body aligns with hole in output shaft.
3) Install snap ring on end of valve shaft (if removed). Install governor valve and valve shaft in governor body. Ensure valve shaft slides freely in the bore. Install snap ring on remaining end of valve shaft.
4) On models with only one snap ring on output shaft, install snap ring. Ensure snap ring fully seats in output shaft.
5) On models with a thick snap ring, thrust washer and then a thin snap ring, install thin snap ring on output shaft with flat side of snap ring toward the governor body. Ensure snap ring fully seats in output shaft.
6) Install thrust washer on output shaft. Install thick snap ring with flat side toward the governor body. Ensure snap ring fully seats in output shaft.
7) On all applications, tighten governor body-to-park gear bolts to specification. See TORQUE SPECIFICATIONS. To install remaining components, reverse removal procedure.

PARK LOCK COMPONENTS

Removal – 1) On Cherokee 4WD and Wrangler models, remove adapter housing. See ADAPTER HOUSING under REMOVAL & INSTALLATION.
2) On all other models, remove extension housing and output shaft rear bearing. See EXTENSION HOUSING, SEAL, BUSHING & OUTPUT SHAFT REAR BEARING under REMOVAL & INSTALLATION.
3) On all models, remove shaft, parking sprag and spring. *See Fig. 14.* Remove snap ring and reaction plug from adapter or extension housing. If removing park rod, valve body must be removed. See VALVE BODY under REMOVAL & INSTALLATION. Remove park rod.
Installation – To install, reverse removal procedure. Ensure square lug on parking sprag is positioned toward park gear. Parking sprag must be held away from park gear by the spring. If replacing park rod, ensure replacement rod is same length as the original park rod.

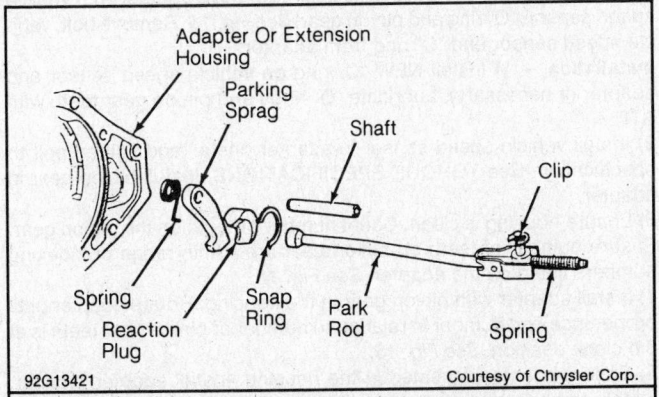

Fig. 14: **Exploded View Of Park Lock Components**

Labels: Adapter Or Extension Housing; Parking Sprag; Shaft; Clip; Spring; Reaction Plug; Snap Ring; Park Rod; Spring

92G13421 — *Courtesy of Chrysler Corp.*

PARK/NEUTRAL SWITCH

Removal & Installation – 1) Raise and support vehicle. Place drain pan under park/neutral switch located near manual shift lever on transmission. *See Fig. 17.* Disconnect electrical connector. Unscrew park/neutral switch from transmission case.
2) To install, apply parking brake. Ensure gearshift is in Park or Neutral. Ensure operating levers in transmission are centered in park/neutral switch opening on transmission case.
3) Using NEW seal, install park/neutral switch. Tighten park/neutral switch to specification. See TORQUE SPECIFICATIONS. Reinstall electrical connector. Adjust transmission fluid level with ATF.

TRANSMISSION

See appropriate AUTOMATIC TRANSMISSION REMOVAL article in TRANSMISSION SERVICING.

VALVE BODY

Removal – 1) Raise and support vehicle. Remove bolts, oil pan and gasket. Loosen clamps and remove throttle valve and manual shift levers from transmission.
2) Remove park/neutral switch. See PARK/NEUTRAL SWITCH under REMOVAL & INSTALLATION. Remove bolts and filter assembly.
3) Disconnect lock-up solenoid wire from case connector. Remove valve body-to-transmission case bolts. Note bolt length and location for reassembly reference.
4) Lower valve body enough to remove accumulator and spring. Rotate valve body downward and away from transmission case. Pull valve body forward and disengage park rod. Remove valve body.
Installation – 1) Ensure park/neutral switch is removed before installing valve body. Install NEW seal rings on accumulator. Lubricate seal rings, manual shift lever seal, accumulator, and bore with petroleum jelly.
2) Install accumulator in transmission case. Place manual shift lever on valve body in low gear position so ball on park rod can be installed in parking sprag. Using screwdriver, push parking sprag to engage with park gear. This allows knob on park rod to move past parking sprag when installing valve body. Rotate output shaft to ensure parking sprag is engaged.

CAUTION: Ensure park rod enters parking sprag, as park rod may enter cavity in the case and not enter parking sprag. Park rod will be damaged if it is not engaged with parking sprag.

3) Install spring between accumulator and valve body. Install valve body, working park rod past parking sprag. Ensure spring for accumulator remains in place.

CAUTION: Alternately tighten valve body-to-transmission case bolts to prevent damage to valve body. DO NOT overtighten bolts or transmission and valve body may be damaged.

4) Install valve body-to-transmission case bolts in original location finger tight only. DO NOT tighten bolts at this time. Using NEW seal, install park/neutral switch. Tighten park/neutral switch to specification. Tighten valve body-to-transmission case bolts evenly to specification. See TORQUE SPECIFICATIONS.
5) Install NEW filter assembly. Install and tighten bolts to specification. Reconnect all necessary electrical connections. Install throttle valve and manual shift levers. Ensure throttle valve lever and manual shift levers rotate smoothly.
6) Using NEW gasket, install oil pan. Install and tighten bolts to specification. Fill with ATF. Ensure shift linkage/cable and throttle valve cable are properly adjusted. See appropriate AUTOMATIC TRANSMISSION SERVICING article in TRANSMISSION SERVICING.

VEHICLE SPEED SENSOR & PINION GEAR

NOTE: On Cherokee 4WD and Wrangler models, vehicle speed sensor is mounted on the housing of the transfer case. On Cherokee 2WD, Pickup and Ram Van models, vehicle speed sensor is mounted on extension housing on transmission. On all models, note type of vehicle speed sensor and components used and determine proper service procedure. See Fig. 15.

Removal (Type 1 & 2) – 1) Raise and support vehicle. Disconnect electrical connector from vehicle speed sensor. *See Fig. 15.*
2) On Type 1 applications, remove vehicle speed sensor from adapter. On Type 2 applications, remove bolt and vehicle speed sensor from vehicle speed sensor adapter.
3) On all applications, check vehicle speed sensor mounting area on adapter for signs of ATF leakage. If ATF leakage exists, oil seal is leaking and should be replaced.
4) Remove bolt and adapter retainer. Note location of indexing numbers on adapter in relation to the housing. *See Fig. 16.*

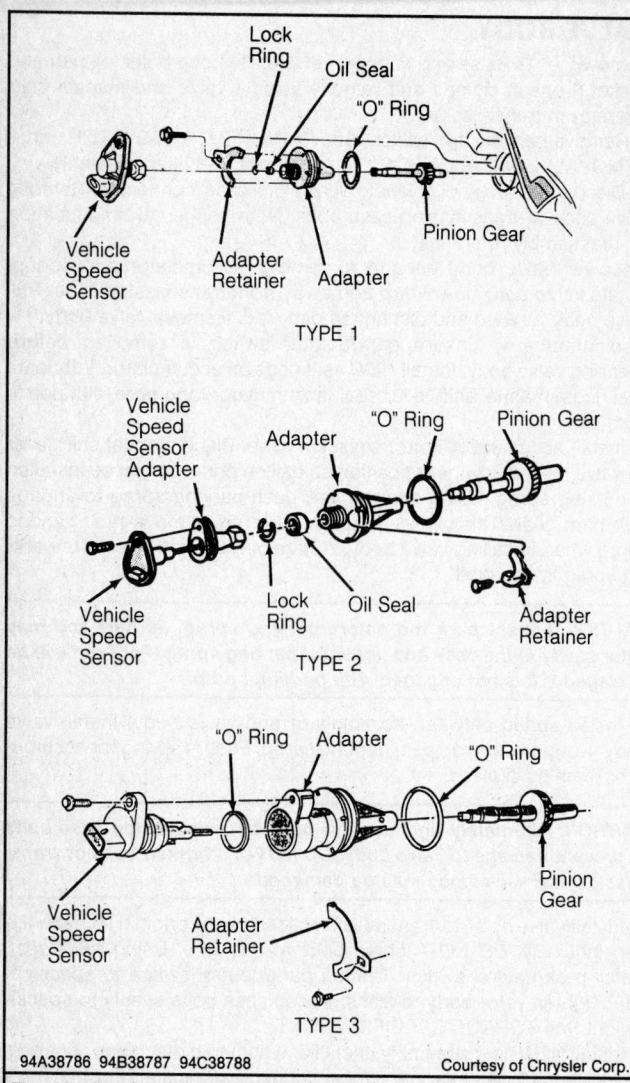

TYPE 1

TYPE 2

TYPE 3

94A38786 94B38787 94C38788

Courtesy of Chrysler Corp.

Fig. 15: Exploded View Of Vehicle Speed Sensor & Components

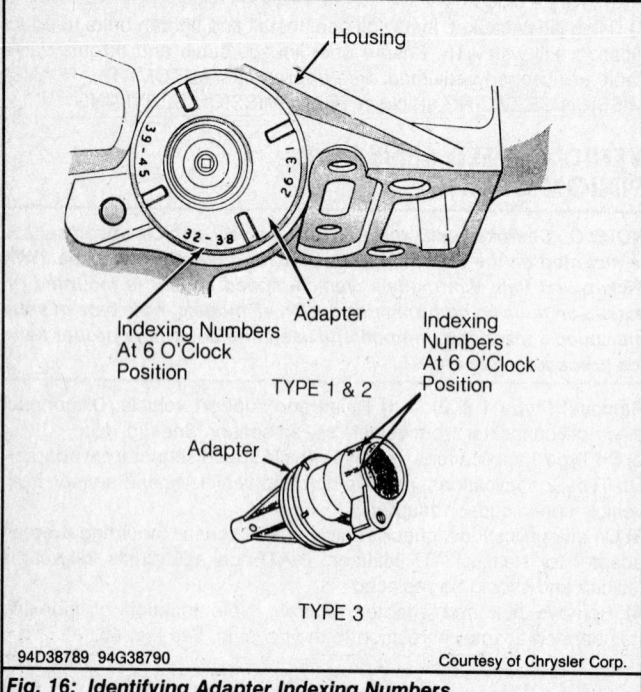

TYPE 1 & 2

TYPE 3

94D38789 94G38790

Courtesy of Chrysler Corp.

Fig. 16: Identifying Adapter Indexing Numbers

NOTE: Indexing numbers on adapter correspond to number of teeth on the pinion gear.

5) Ensure area around adapter is clean. Remove adapter, "O" ring and pinion gear. *See Fig. 15.* Remove oil seal from adapter (if necessary).
Installation – **1)** If installing NEW oil seal in adapter, start oil seal in adapter by hand. Using Oil Seal Installer (C-4004), press oil seal in adapter until it bottoms.
2) Ensure housing is clean. Install NEW "O" ring on adapter (if necessary). Lubricate "O" ring on adapter, oil seal and pinion gear teeth with ATF. Count number of teeth on the pinion gear. Ensure number of teeth on pinion gear are within range of indexing numbers listed on the adapter. *See Fig. 16.*
3) Install pinion gear, "O" ring and adapter in the housing. Rotate adapter until proper indexing number in relation to number of pinion gear teeth is at 6 o'clock position. *See Fig. 16.*
4) Ensure adapter is seated in the housing. Install adapter retainer. Install and tighten bolt to specification. See TORQUE SPECIFICATIONS.
5) On Type 1 applications, install vehicle speed sensor on adapter. Tighten nut to specification. See TORQUE SPECIFICATIONS.
6) On Type 2 applications, install vehicle speed sensor adapter on the adapter. Tighten vehicle speed sensor adapter nut to specification. See TORQUE SPECIFICATIONS.
7) Install vehicle speed sensor on vehicle speed sensor adapter. Install and tighten vehicle speed sensor bolt to specification. See TORQUE SPECIFICATIONS.
8) On all applications, install electrical connector on vehicle speed sensor. Adjust transmission fluid level with ATF.
Removal (Type 3) – **1)** Raise and support vehicle. Disconnect electrical connector from vehicle speed sensor. *See Fig. 15.*
2) Remove bolt and adapter retainer. Note location of indexing numbers on adapter in relation to the housing. *See Fig. 16.*

NOTE: Indexing numbers on adapter correspond to number of teeth on the pinion gear.

3) Ensure area around adapter is clean. Remove adapter with vehicle speed sensor, "O" ring and pinion gear. *See Fig. 15.* Remove bolt, vehicle speed sensor and "O" ring from adapter.
Installation – **1)** Install NEW "O" ring on vehicle speed sensor and adapter (if necessary). Lubricate "O" rings and pinion gear teeth with ATF.
2) Install vehicle speed sensor in adapter. Install and tighten bolt to specification. See TORQUE SPECIFICATIONS. Install pinion gear in adapter.
3) Ensure housing is clean. Count number of teeth on the pinion gear. Ensure number of teeth on pinion gear are within range of indexing numbers listed on the adapter. *See Fig. 16.*
4) Install adapter with pinion gear in the housing. Rotate adapter until proper indexing number in relation to number of pinion gear teeth is at 6 o'clock position. *See Fig. 16.*
5) Ensure adapter is seated in the housing. Install adapter retainer. Install and tighten bolt to specification. See TORQUE SPECIFICATIONS. Install electrical connector on vehicle speed sensor. Adjust transmission fluid level with ATF.

TORQUE CONVERTER

CAUTION: Torque converter is a welded assembly and is not service-able. If a malfunction occurs or if torque converter becomes contaminated with foreign material, it MUST be replaced. Torque converter cannot be flushed or repaired.

NOTE: For torque converter fluid leakage testing and torque converter stall speed test, see TESTING in this article.

TRANSMISSION DISASSEMBLY

VALVE BODY & COMPONENTS

CAUTION: Note all thrust washer and thrust plate locations for reassembly reference.

1) Remove torque converter. Loosen clamps and remove throttle valve and manual shift levers from transmission.

2) On Cherokee 4WD and Wrangler models, remove adapter housing-to-transmission case bolts. Remove adapter housing and gasket from rear of transmission case. Remove snap ring and rear bearing from output shaft (if equipped).

3) On Cherokee 2WD, Pickup and Ram Van models, remove bolts, access cover and gasket from bottom of extension housing. Using snap ring pliers, expand output shaft rear bearing locating ring. *See Fig. 12.* With locating ring expanded, remove extension housing from output shaft rear bearing.

4) Pull extension housing and gasket from transmission case while working park rod past parking sprag. *See Fig. 14.* Remove snap ring and rear bearing from output shaft.

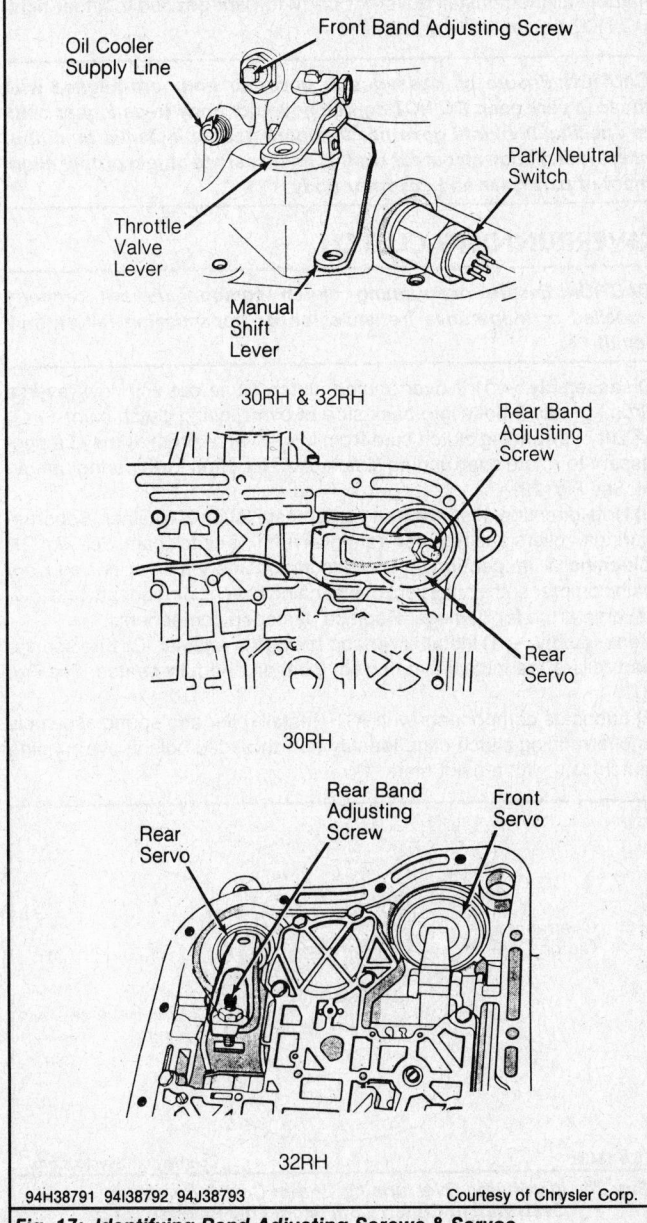

Fig. 17: Identifying Band Adjusting Screws & Servos

94H38791 94I38792 94J38793   Courtesy of Chrysler Corp.

5) On all models, remove bolts, oil pan and gasket. Remove park/neutral switch and seal. Remove bolts and filter assembly.

6) Disconnect lock-up solenoid wire from case connector. Remove valve body-to-transmission case bolts. Note bolt length and location for reassembly reference.

7) Lift valve body upward and guide park rod from transmission case. Remove valve body. Remove accumulator and spring.

8) Remove plug from front band pin access hole, located in front of transmission case, near top of oil pump. *See Fig. 18.* Loosen lock nut on front band adjusting screw approximately 5 revolutions. *See Fig. 17.*

9) Tighten front band adjusting screw until front band is tight. This prevents clutch components from coming out when oil pump is removed.

10) Remove oil pump bolts. Install slide hammers on opposite sides of oil pump. Pull oil pump from transmission case. Remove oil pump gasket.

11) Loosen front band adjusting screw until front band is loose. Squeeze front band together and remove front band strut, located between lever on transmission case and front band.

12) Remove front band pin through front band pin access hole. Remove lever for front band. Slide front band rearward onto driving shell.

13) Grasp input shaft, holding clutch units together, remove front and rear clutch as an assembly. *See Fig. 18.* Lift front clutch off of rear clutch assembly. Remove triangular shaped thrust washer from output shaft. This thrust washer may remain on hub of rear clutch. *See Fig. 28.*

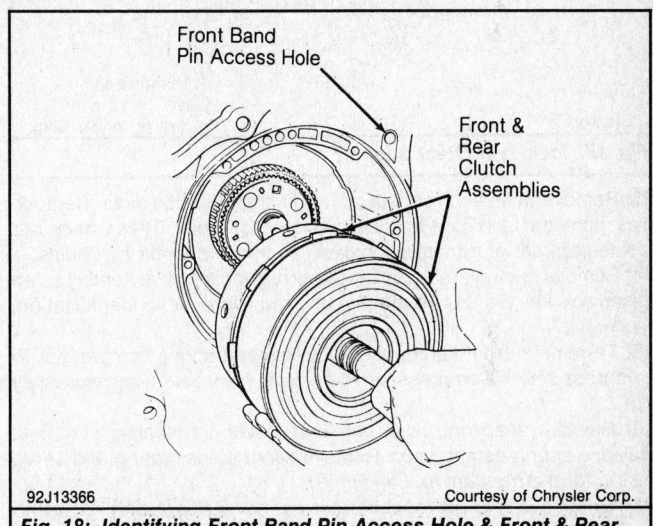

92J13366   Courtesy of Chrysler Corp.

Fig. 18: Identifying Front Band Pin Access Hole & Front & Rear Clutch Assemblies

14) Remove output shaft thrust plate from end of output shaft. *See Fig. 29.* Slide front band from driving shell and remove from transmission case.

15) Remove snap ring from valve shaft on the governor. *See Fig. 13.* Remove governor valve and valve shaft from governor body. Remove governor body and park gear-to-output shaft snap ring.

NOTE: Some models may contain a thick snap ring, thrust washer and then a thin snap ring to retain the governor body and park gear on the output shaft.

16) Remove governor body and park gear from output shaft. Place reference mark on governor body-to-park gear for reassembly reference.

17) Remove bolts and separate governor body from park gear (if necessary). Remove filter screen from governor body or park gear.

18) Remove output shaft and planetary gear train assembly from transmission case. Use care not to damage machined surfaces on output shaft during removal.

19) Loosen rear band adjusting screw 4-5 turns. *See Fig. 17.* Remove low-reverse drum-to-rear support snap ring from inside of transmission case. DO NOT remove low-reverse drum at this time.

20) On 30RH, remove pin for rear band from transmission case. Pin can be removed by inserting tip of snap ring pliers into opening of the pin. Expand snap ring pliers and pull pin from transmission case while using twisting motion.

21) On 32RH, remove rear band upper and lower pins from rear of transmission case. Pins can be removed by inserting tip of snap ring pliers into opening of the pin. Expand snap ring pliers and pull pins from case while using twisting motion.

CAUTION: Ensure rear support-to-transmission contains reference mark for reassembly reference.

22) On all models, remove rear band lever and strut. Place reference mark on rear support and transmission case for reassembly reference. *See Fig. 19.*

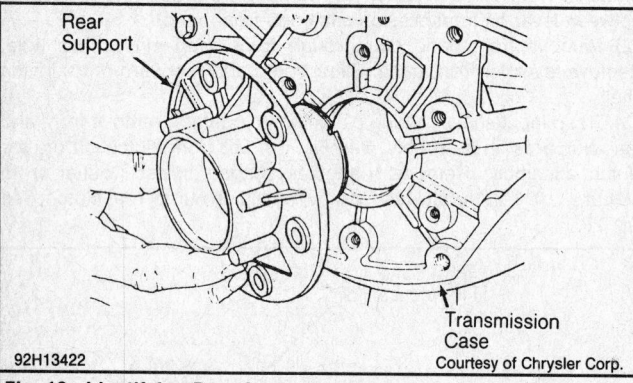

92H13422   Courtesy of Chrysler Corp.
Fig. 19: Identifying Rear Support

23) Remove bolts and rear support from transmission case. Remove overrunning clutch cam-to-transmission case bolts. These bolts are located on rear of transmission case, near rear support bolt holes.

24) Remove low-reverse drum and overrunning clutch assembly as an assembly. *See Fig. 20.* Remove rear band. Note servo identification. *See Fig. 17.*

25) To remove front servo, use "C" clamp and spring compressor to compress servo. Compress servo guide on front servo approximately 1/8".

26) Remove snap ring. Use care not to scratch sealing surfaces. Release spring compressor. Remove servo guide, spring and servo piston for the front servo. *See Fig. 31.*

27) To remove rear servo, compress spring retainer using "C" clamp and spring compressor. Compress spring retainer on rear servo approximately 1/16".

28) Remove snap ring. Use care not to scratch sealing surfaces. Release spring compressor. Remove spring retainer, spring and servo piston. *See Fig. 32.*

COMPONENT DISASSEMBLY & REASSEMBLY

NOTE: Manufacturer recommends Mopar ATF Plus Type 7176 fluid for use in this transmission. This ATF should also be used for lubrication during assembly.

GOVERNOR & PARK GEAR

CAUTION: Output shaft may contain an aluminum governor valve and a governor valve indexing area. Small end of governor valve must seat in governor valve indexing area. See Fig. 13. Aluminum governor valve cannot be used on earlier applications. Ensure original type governor components are installed. It may be necessary to use transmission identification number and to consult parts department if replacing any governor components. DO NOT interchange any governor components.

Disassembly – 1) With governor body and park gear removed from output shaft, place reference mark on governor body-to-park gear for reassembly reference.

2) Remove bolts and separate governor body from park gear. Remove filter screen from governor body or park gear. Remove remaining components from governor body. *See Fig. 13.*

Cleaning – 1) Clean components with solvent and dry with compressed air. Ensure inner and outer weights and governor valve slide freely in bore on governor body.

2) Inspect filter screen for damage. Replace damaged components. Ensure original type governor components are installed. DO NOT interchange any governor components.

3) Inspect gear teeth and seal rings on park gear for damage. The front seal ring (closest to park gear) is a hook-type ring. Ensure ends of seal ring are hooked together. Replace damaged components.

Reassembly – 1) Coat components with ATF. Install spring with inner and outer weights in governor body. DO NOT install valve shaft at this time.

2) Install NEW seal rings on park gear (if necessary). Install filter screen in park gear. Install governor body on park gear so that oil passages in governor body and park gear are aligned. Ensure reference mark is aligned. Install governor body-to-park gear bolts finger tight. DO NOT tighten bolts at this time.

CAUTION: Ensure oil passages in governor body are aligned with those in park gear. DO NOT tighten governor body-to-park gear bolts to specification until governor and park gear is installed on output shaft. Installation on output shaft is necessary to obtain proper alignment of park gear and governor body.

OVERRUNNING CLUTCH

CAUTION: Ensure overrunning clutch components are properly installed or inoperative transmission or transmission failure may result.

Disassembly – 1) If overrunning clutch came out with low-reverse drum, thread 2 bolts into back side of overrunning clutch cam.

2) Lift overrunning clutch cam from low-reverse drum. It may be necessary to rotate overrunning clutch cam back and forth during removal. *See Fig. 20.*

3) Note direction of springs and roller installation in retainer. Separate springs, rollers and retainer from overrunning clutch cam. *See Fig. 21.*

Cleaning & Inspection – Clean components with solvent and dry with compressed air. Inspect overrunning clutch components and low-reverse drum for damage. Replace damaged components.

Reassembly – 1) Install roller and springs in retainer. Ensure springs and rollers are installed in correct location and fully seated. *See Fig. 21.*

2) Lubricate components with ATF. Install roller and spring assembly in overrunning clutch cam. Identify non-threaded hole in overrunning clutch cam with a paint mark.

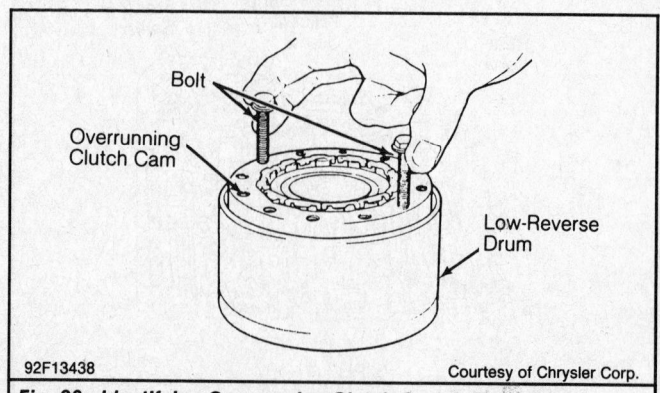

92F13438   Courtesy of Chrysler Corp.
Fig. 20: Identifying Overrunning Clutch Cam & Removing Overrunning Clutch Cam From Low-Reverse Drum

CAUTION: *Paint mark must be aligned with non-threaded hole on overrunning clutch cam. Paint mark is used for reassembly reference. Ensure countersunk holes in overrunning clutch cam are positioned so they will face rear of transmission when installed. See Figs. 21 and 40.*

3) Using twisting motion, install overrunning clutch cam and components on low-reverse drum. Operation of overrunning clutch will be checked when reassembling transmission.

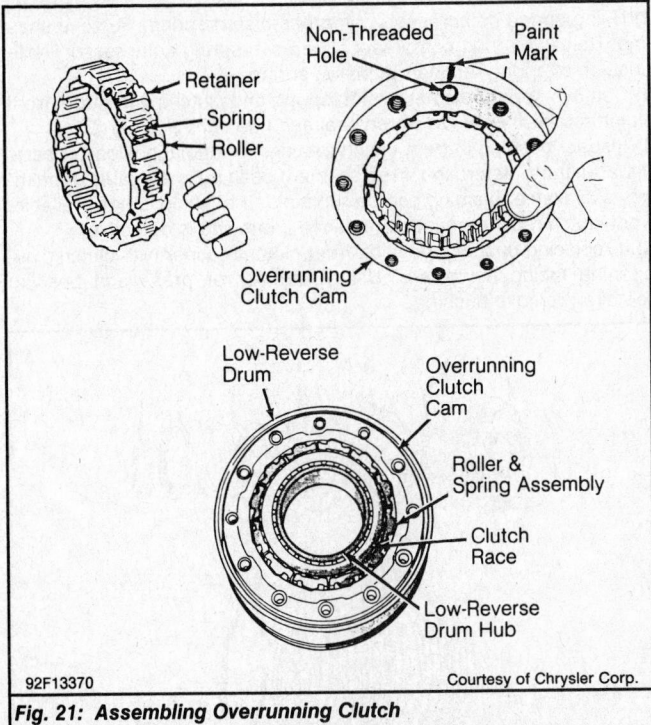

Fig. 21: Assembling Overrunning Clutch

OIL PUMP & REACTION SHAFT SUPPORT

NOTE: *Gears used in the oil pump on 1993-94 models are different than previous years. Drive lugs on the inner gear is different and is used with different type of hub on torque converter. If replacing gears, ensure proper type gear is installed.*

Disassembly – 1) Place reference mark on oil pump housing and reaction shaft support. Remove reaction shaft support bolts. Separate reaction shaft support from oil pump housing. *See Fig. 22.*
2) Remove seal ring from outer diameter of oil pump housing and reaction shaft support. Using hammer and punch, tap seal from oil pump housing.
3) Note direction of thrust washer installation on rear of reaction shaft support. Remove thrust washer from reaction shaft support.
4) Note direction of gear installation. Remove gears from oil pump housing.
5) Inspect bushing in oil pump housing and reaction shaft support for damage. If removing bushing from oil pump housing, place oil pump housing on flat surface with gear cavity facing downward. Using press or hammer and bushing remover, remove bushing.
6) If removing bushing from reaction shaft support, use Cup (SP-3633), Nut (SP-1191) and Bushing Remover (SP-5324). *See Fig. 23.*
7) Hold cup against reaction shaft. By hand, thread bushing remover into bushing as far as possible. Using wrench, thread bushing remover an additional 3-4 turns into bushing. Tighten nut and remove bushing.

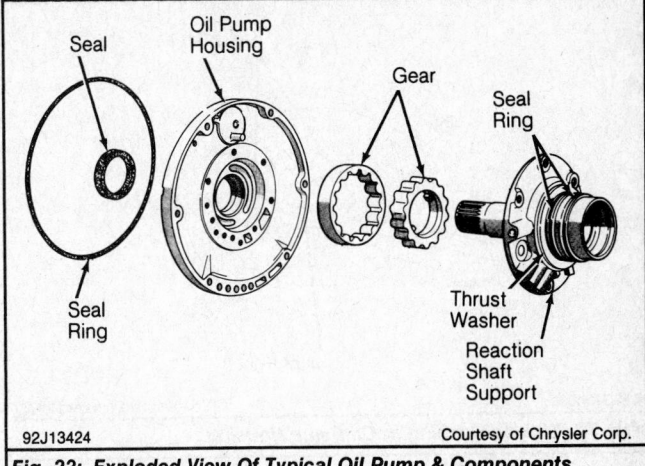

Fig. 22: Exploded View Of Typical Oil Pump & Components

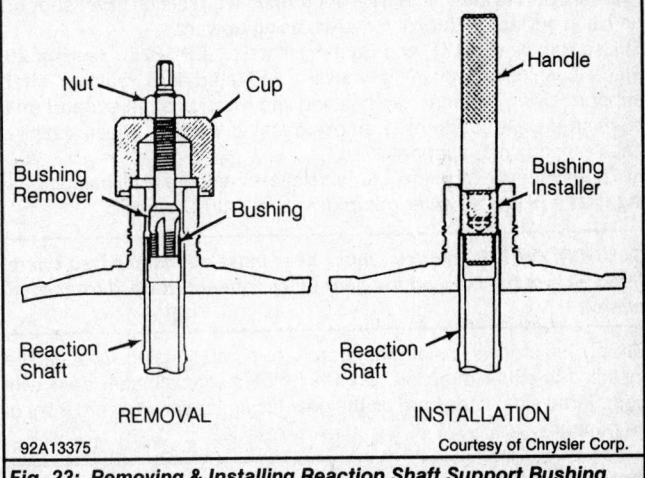

Fig. 23: Removing & Installing Reaction Shaft Support Bushing

Cleaning & Inspection – 1) Clean and inspect components for damage. Inspect all machined surfaces for pitting or damage.
2) Install both gears in oil pump housing. Using feeler gauge, measure outer gear-to-oil pump housing clearance.
3) Place straightedge on oil pump housing, above both gears. Using feeler gauge, measure gear end clearance between each gear and straightedge.
4) Align tooth on inner gear with tooth on outer gear. Using feeler gauge, measure gear tooth clearance between teeth. Replace components if clearance is not within specification. See OIL PUMP SPECIFICATIONS table.

OIL PUMP SPECIFICATIONS

Application	In. (mm)
Gear End Clearance	.0004-.0025 (.010-.063)
Gear Tooth Clearance	.0035-.0075 (.089-.190)
Outer Gear-To-Oil Pump Housing Clearance	.0035-.0075 (.089-.190)

Reassembly – 1) If installing NEW oil pump housing bushing, place oil pump housing on flat surface with gear cavity facing upward.
2) Place bushing on bushing installer and start into oil pump housing. Using hammer, tap bushing in oil pump housing until bushing is even with surface of oil pump housing bore. Ensure bushing is installed evenly and does not bind in oil pump housing.
3) Using blunt punch, stake bushing in 2 places. *See Fig. 24.* Using knife, clean burrs from stake areas.

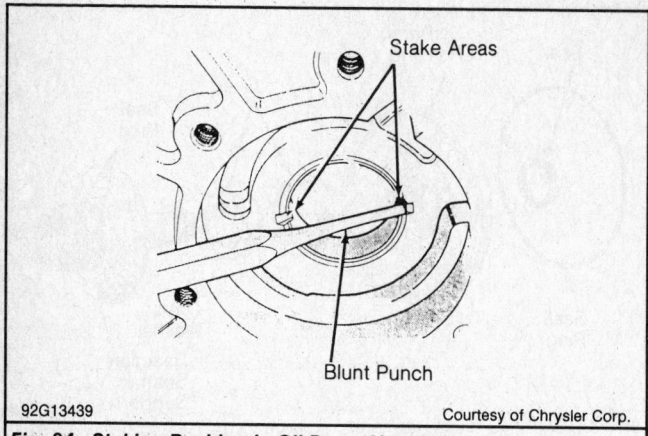

Fig. 24: Staking Bushing In Oil Pump Housing

92G13439   Courtesy of Chrysler Corp.

4) If installing NEW reaction shaft support bushing, ensure reaction shaft support is clean and free of burrs. Place reaction shaft support on clean surface with bushing area facing upward.

5) Use Handle (C-4171) and Bushing Installer (SP-5325). *See Fig. 23.* Place bushing on bushing installer and start into reaction shaft support. Using hammer, tap bushing into reaction shaft support until bushing installer bottoms. Remove bushing installer. Clean bushing and reaction shaft support.

6) To reassemble oil pump, lubricate gears and bore in oil pump housing with ATF. Install outer pump gear in oil pump housing.

CAUTION: On 1994 models, inner gear must be installed so chamfered side of the bore on the gear faces forward (toward front of oil pump).

7) On 1993 models, install inner gear in oil pump housing. Gear can be installed in either direction. On 1994 models, install inner gear with chamfered side of the bore on the gear facing forward (toward front of oil pump).

CAUTION: If thrust washer contains a chamfered edge on inside diameter of thrust washer, it must be installed on reaction shaft support with chamfered edge on inside diameter of thrust washer facing toward front of oil pump.

8) Install NEW thrust washer on rear of reaction shaft support. If thrust washer contains a chamfered edge on inside diameter of thrust washer, it must be installed on reaction shaft support with chamfered edge on inside diameter of thrust washer facing toward front of oil pump. Lubricate thrust washer with petroleum jelly.

CAUTION: DO NOT over expand or twist seal rings when installing on reaction shaft support. Ensure ends on seal rings are hooked together or otherwise seal rings will be damaged when installing oil pump.

9) If replacing seal rings on reaction shaft support, install NEW seal rings on reaction shaft support. Lubricate seal rings with petroleum jelly. Squeeze seal rings together until ends of seal rings hook together.

10) Install reaction shaft support on oil pump housing with reference mark aligned. Install reaction shaft support bolts finger tight. DO NOT tighten bolts at this time.

11) Install oil pump in transmission case with oil pump reversed so reaction shaft support bolts are facing outward (toward front of transmission).

12) Install 3 bolts to secure oil pump in transmission case. Tighten reaction shaft support bolts to specification. See TORQUE SPECIFICATIONS. Remove oil pump from transmission case.

13) Install NEW seal in oil pump housing with seal lip facing inward (toward oil pump). Install NEW seal ring on outer diameter of oil pump housing. Lubricate lip of seal and seal ring petroleum jelly.

FRONT CLUTCH

CAUTION: Note direction of clutch discs and clutch plates for reassembly reference. Note number of each component, as some models may contain different number of clutch components. Components must be installed in correct sequence.

Disassembly – 1) Remove waved snap ring, pressure plate, clutch discs and clutch plates. *See Fig. 25.* Note number of clutch discs and clutch plates for reassembly reference.

2) Using spring compressor, compress piston spring. Remove snap ring. Release spring compressor. Remove spring compressor. Note position of spring retainer on piston spring.

3) Remove spring retainer, piston spring and clutch piston from front clutch retainer. Remove piston seal and hub seal. *See Fig. 25.*

4) Inspect bushing in front clutch retainer for damage. Consult parts department to determine if replacement bushing is available. If bushing is available, bushing can be replaced. If bushing is not available, front clutch retainer must be replaced if bushing is defective.

5) If replacing bushing, position front clutch retainer with clutch plate opening facing downward. Using hammer or press and bushing remover, remove bushing.

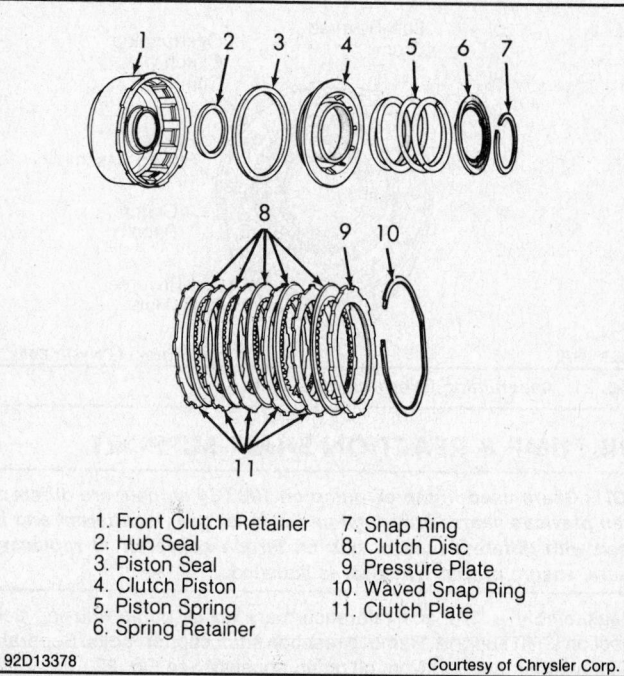

1. Front Clutch Retainer
2. Hub Seal
3. Piston Seal
4. Clutch Piston
5. Piston Spring
6. Spring Retainer
7. Snap Ring
8. Clutch Disc
9. Pressure Plate
10. Waved Snap Ring
11. Clutch Plate

92D13378   Courtesy of Chrysler Corp.

Fig. 25: Exploded View Of Typical Front Clutch

Cleaning & Inspection – 1) Clean all metal components with solvent and dry with compressed air. Inspect clutch discs for flatness, flaking or glazing. Inspect clutch plates and pressure plate for flatness or damage at plate-to-front clutch retainer tang areas.

2) Ensure tang areas in front clutch retainer are not damaged and clutch plates slide freely in front clutch retainer. Inspect all sealing surfaces for burrs or scratches. Ensure check ball located in bottom of front clutch retainer moves freely. Replace damaged components.

Reassembly – 1) If installing NEW bushing in front clutch retainer, position front clutch retainer with clutch plate opening facing upward.

2) Using hammer or press, handle and Bushing Installer (SP-3626), install bushing until bushing installer bottoms. Clean front clutch retainer after installing bushing.

3) Soak clutch discs in ATF. Install NEW piston and hub seals with lip of seal toward inside of front clutch retainer. Lubricate piston and hub seals with petroleum jelly.

CAUTION: Use twisting motion when installing clutch piston to prevent damage to piston and hub seals.

4) Lubricate front clutch retainer and clutch piston surface with ATF. Using twisting motion, install clutch piston in front clutch retainer.

5) Install piston spring on clutch piston. Install spring retainer. If spring retainer contains small tabs, ensure spring retainer is installed with small tabs facing upward, away from piston spring. See Fig. 26.

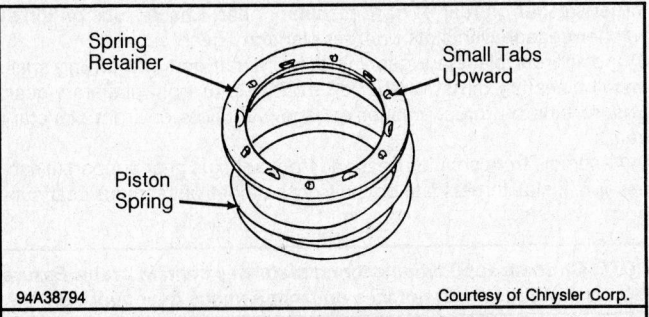

Fig. 26: **Installing Spring Retainer On Piston Spring**

6) Using spring compressor, compress piston spring. Install NEW snap ring to secure spring retainer. Release spring compressor.

7) Alternately install clutch plates and clutch discs starting with clutch plate. See Fig. 25. Ensure original number of components are installed. Install pressure plate and waved snap ring.

8) Using feeler gauge, measure front clutch clearance between waved snap ring and pressure plate. See Fig. 27.

9) Front clutch clearance should be .074-.125" (1.87-3.18 mm) on 3-disc clutches, .067-.134" (1.70-3.40 mm) on 4-disc clutches and .075-.152" (1.90-3.86 mm) on 5-disc clutches.

10) Front clutch clearance is not adjustable. If front clutch clearance is not within specification, check for defective or improperly assembled components.

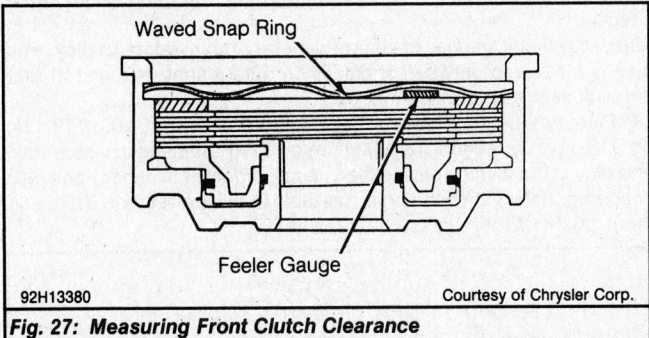

Fig. 27: **Measuring Front Clutch Clearance**

REAR CLUTCH

CAUTION: Note direction of clutch discs and clutch plates for reassembly reference. Note number of each component, as some models may contain different number of clutch components. Components must be installed in correct sequence.

Disassembly – **1)** Remove fiber thrust washer and selective snap ring. See Fig. 28. Remove top pressure plate, clutch discs and clutch plates. Note direction of components for reassembly reference.

2) Remove bottom pressure plate, waved snap ring and piston spring. Note direction of piston spring installation for reassembly reference.

3) Using rotating motion, remove clutch piston from rear clutch retainer. Remove and discard piston seals. If removing input shaft, remove snap ring. Using press, press input shaft from rear clutch retainer. Remove all seal rings from input shaft.

Cleaning & Inspection – **1)** Clean all metal components with solvent and dry with compressed air. Inspect clutch discs for flatness, flaking or glazing. Inspect clutch plates and pressure plates for flatness or damage at plate-to-rear clutch retainer tang areas.

2) Ensure tang areas in rear clutch retainer are not damaged and clutch plates slide freely in rear clutch retainer.

3) Inspect bushing in rear clutch retainer for damage. Ensure check balls move freely in clutch piston and rear clutch retainer. Inspect clutch piston and piston spring for warpage or distortion. Inspect thrust washers for damage. Replace damaged components.

Reassembly – **1)** Soak clutch discs in ATF. Install hub seal ring on rear clutch retainer. Ensure hub seal ring is fully seated and is not twisted.

2) Slightly squeeze together ends of Teflon seal ring for input shaft. This provides a better fit when seal ring is installed. Install NEW seal rings on input shaft.

CAUTION: Ensure ends of Teflon seal ring are properly engaged and ends of metal seal ring are locked together.

3) Lubricate input shaft seal rings and hub seal ring with petroleum jelly. If installing input shaft, lubricate splines of input shaft and rear clutch retainer with ATF.

4) Press input shaft into rear clutch retainer. Install snap ring. Install NEW piston seals with lip of piston seal toward inside of rear clutch retainer. Lubricate piston seals with petroleum jelly.

CAUTION: Use twisting motion when installing clutch piston to prevent damage to piston seals. Ensure piston spring is installed with concave side downward, toward clutch piston.

5) Lubricate rear clutch retainer and clutch piston surface with ATF. Using twisting motion, install clutch piston in rear clutch retainer. Install piston spring on clutch piston with concave side downward, toward clutch piston.

6) Install waved snap ring. Ensure waved snap ring is fully seated in groove of rear clutch retainer. Install bottom pressure plate with flat side toward the clutch pack.

7) Alternately install original number of clutch plates and clutch discs starting with clutch disc and alternating with a clutch plate. See Fig. 28. Install top pressure plate and selective snap ring.

8) Using feeler gauge, measure rear clutch clearance between selective snap ring and top pressure plate. Rear clutch clearance should be .025-.045" (.64-1.14 mm) on 30RH or .032-.055" (.81-1.40 mm) on 32RH.

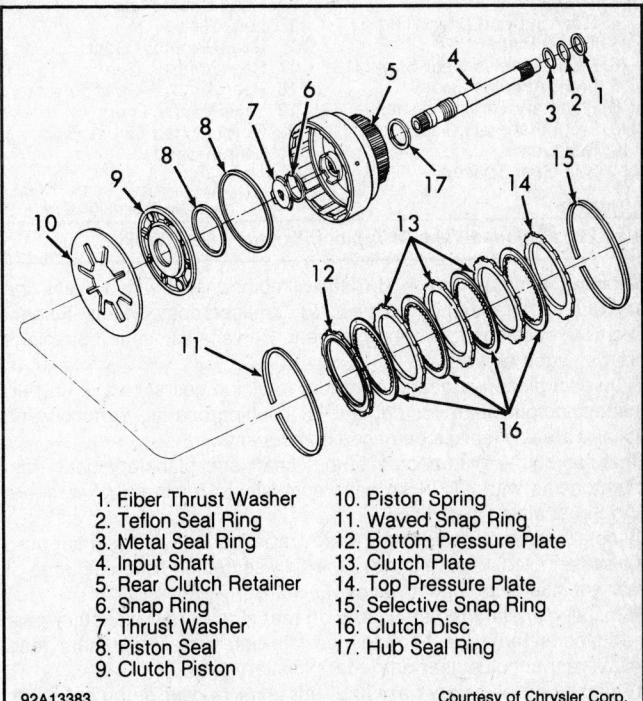

1. Fiber Thrust Washer	10. Piston Spring
2. Teflon Seal Ring	11. Waved Snap Ring
3. Metal Seal Ring	12. Bottom Pressure Plate
4. Input Shaft	13. Clutch Plate
5. Rear Clutch Retainer	14. Top Pressure Plate
6. Snap Ring	15. Selective Snap Ring
7. Thrust Washer	16. Clutch Disc
8. Piston Seal	17. Hub Seal Ring
9. Clutch Piston	

92A13383   Courtesy of Chrysler Corp.

Fig. 28: **Exploded View Of Rear Clutch**

9) If rear clutch clearance is not within specification, install different thickness selective snap ring. Selective snap ring is available in thicknesses of .060" (1.52 mm), .068" (1.73 mm), .076" (1.93 mm) and .098" (2.49 mm).

10) If proper rear clutch clearance cannot be obtained, clutch components may require replacement. Coat fiber thrust washer with petroleum jelly and install.

PLANETARY GEAR TRAIN

Disassembly – 1) Remove select fit snap ring, snap ring, thrust washer and output shaft thrust plate from front of output shaft. *See Fig. 29.* Remove front annulus gear and front annulus gear support. Remove planetary gear thrust washer and front planetary gear.

2) Remove planetary thrust washer located behind front planetary gear. Remove sun gear and driving shell. Remove lock ring. Separate sun gear with front and rear thrust plates from driving shell.

3) Remove planetary thrust washer from front of rear planetary gear. Remove rear planetary gear from rear annulus gear. Remove rear annulus gear from output shaft. Remove snap ring and separate front and rear annulus gears from annulus gear supports (if necessary).

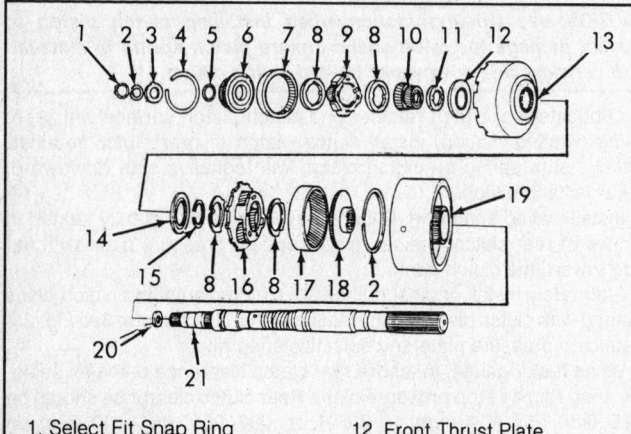

1. Select Fit Snap Ring
2. Snap Ring
3. Thrust Washer
4. Gear Support Snap Ring
5. Thrust Plate
6. Front Annulus Gear Support
7. Front Annulus Gear
8. Planetary Thrust Washer
9. Front Planetary Gear
10. Sun Gear
11. Sun Gear Spacer
12. Front Thrust Plate
13. Driving Shell
14. Rear Thrust Plate
15. Lock Ring
16. Rear Planetary Gear
17. Rear Annulus Gear
18. Rear Annulus Gear Support
19. Low-Reverse Drum
20. Output Shaft Thrust Plate
21. Output Shaft

94B38795   Courtesy of Chrysler Corp.

Fig. 29: Exploded View Of Typical Planetary Gear Train

Cleaning & Inspection – 1) Clean all components with solvent and dry with compressed air. Inspect for damaged components. Inspect sun gear bushings for scoring or wear. Replace sun gear if bushings are damaged or worn.

2) Inspect planetary gears for defective pinion gears, pins or carrier. Inspect output shaft for damage at bushing/bearing surfaces and splined areas. Replace damaged components.

Reassembly – 1) Lubricate output shaft and planetary gear train components with ATF. Use petroleum jelly to retain thrust washers and thrust plates in position.

2) Install rear annulus gear and snap ring in rear annulus gear support, if disassembled. Ensure snap ring is fully seated and shoulder area of rear annulus gear support faces rearward.

3) Install planetary thrust washer on rear side of rear planetary gear with tabs on thrust washer engaged with slots on rear planetary gear. Install rear annulus gear onto rear planetary gear.

4) Install rear planetary gear and rear annulus gear on output shaft. Ensure assembly is fully seated on output shaft. Install planetary thrust washer on front side of rear planetary gear.

5) Install sun gear spacer on sun gear. Install front thrust plate over sun gear and onto the sun gear spacer. Install sun gear in driving shell. Install rear thrust plate over sun gear and against driving shell.

6) Support sun gear on wooden block with opening of driving shell downward to aid in lock ring installation. Ensure rear thrust plate is seated on driving shell. Install lock ring on sun gear, ensuring lock ring is fully seated in groove on sun gear.

7) Install sun gear and driving shell on output shaft. Install planetary thrust washer on rear of front planetary gear. Ensure tabs on thrust washer engage with slots on front planetary gear.

8) Install front planetary gear on output shaft and into driving shell. Install planetary thrust washer on front side of front planetary gear. Ensure tabs on thrust washer engage with slots on front planetary gear.

9) Assemble front annulus gear and front annulus gear support (if necessary). Install thrust plate on the front side of front annulus gear support.

NOTE: On some applications, thrust plate may contain 2 tabs. Ensure tabs are engaged with notches on front annulus gear support.

---

10) Install front annulus gear support and front annulus gear on front planetary gear. Install thrust washer on front side of front annulus gear support with tab facing away from front annulus gear support.

CAUTION: Ensure flat side on thrust washer engages with flat side of front planetary gear. Thrust washer must be installed with tab facing away from front annulus gear support.

---

11) Install snap ring to retain front annulus gear. Install select fit snap ring on output shaft. Ensure snap rings are fully seated. Position planetary gear train assembly with opening of driving shell facing workbench.

12) Support output shaft with wooden block between end of output shaft and workbench. This is done so planetary gear train components will move forward and planetary gear train end play can be checked.

13) Using feeler gauge, measure planetary gear train end play. End play is measured between shoulder on output shaft and end of rear annulus gear support. *See Fig. 30.*

14) Planetary gear train end play should be .001-.047" (.03-1.19 mm) on 30RH or .005-.048" (.13-1.22 mm) on 32RH. If planetary gear train end play is not within specification, install different thickness select fit snap ring. Select fit snap ring is available in thicknesses of .040" (1.01 mm), .062" (1.57 mm) and .082" (2.08 mm).

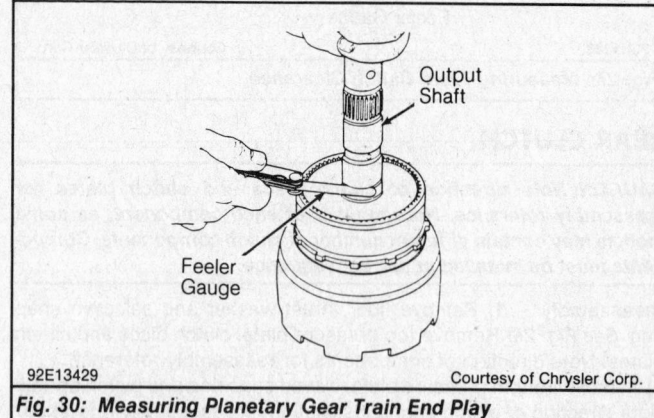

92E13429   Courtesy of Chrysler Corp.

Fig. 30: Measuring Planetary Gear Train End Play

FRONT SERVO

Disassembly – Remove snap ring from servo piston. Separate servo piston, servo rod, spring and servo guide. *See Fig. 31.* Remove and discard seal rings.

Cleaning & Inspection – Clean components with solvent and dry with compressed air. Inspect spring for distortion. Inspect servo piston, servo rod and servo guide for wear or cracks. Replace defective components. If servo piston or servo rod are damaged, both must be replaced as an assembly.

Reassembly – To reassemble, reverse disassembly procedure using NEW seal rings. Lubricate seal rings with petroleum jelly. Lubricate all other components with ATF.

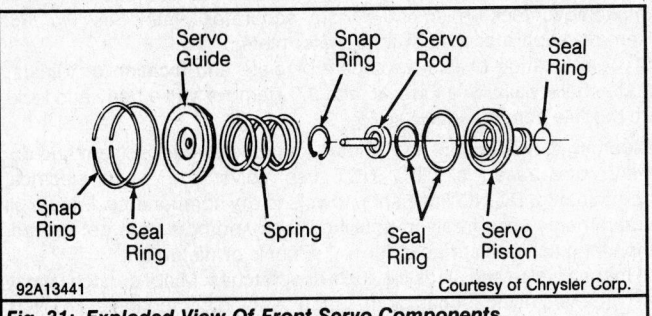

92A13441   Courtesy of Chrysler Corp.

Fig. 31: Exploded View Of Front Servo Components

REAR SERVO

Disassembly – **1)** Note direction of seal ring installation on servo piston. Remove seal ring from servo piston. Using small wooden block and vise, compress cushion spring enough to remove snap ring from end of piston plug. See Fig. 32.

2) Remove rear servo assembly from vise. Separate servo piston, springs, piston plug and spring retainer. See Fig. 32.

Cleaning & Inspection – Clean components with solvent and dry with compressed air. Inspect springs for distortion. Inspect servo piston and piston plug for wear or cracks. Replace defective components.

Reassembly – To reassemble, reverse disassembly procedure using NEW seal rings. Install seal ring on servo piston so lip area is toward servo bore in transmission case. Lubricate seal ring with petroleum jelly. Lubricate all other components with ATF.

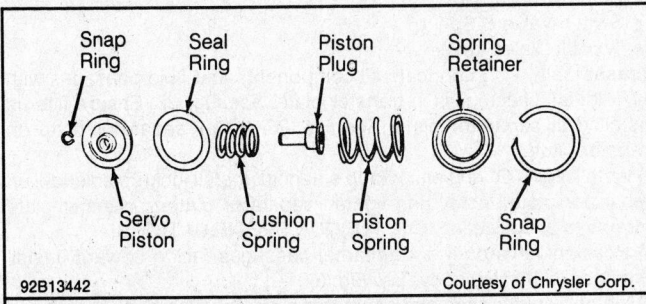

92B13442   Courtesy of Chrysler Corp.

Fig. 32: Exploded View Of Rear Servo Components

VALVE BODY

CAUTION: Place valve body components in order and mark spring locations for reassembly reference when disassembling valve body. DO NOT use force to remove components from valve body. Valve body assembly consists of valve body, transfer plate and separator plate. See Fig. 33.

NOTE: Lock-up module and lock-up solenoid may be referred to as converter clutch module, converter clutch solenoid or Torque Converter Clutch (TCC) solenoid.

Disassembly – **1)** Hold adjusting screw bracket against valve body and remove retaining screws. See Fig. 38.

2) Remove adjusting screw bracket with line pressure adjusting screw, pressure regulator spring (large spring) and switch valve spring (small spring).

CAUTION: DO NOT disturb throttle pressure or line pressure adjusting screw locations in adjusting screw bracket.

3) Depress detent ball. Install Detent Ball Retainer (6583) on detent ball and spring housing to secure detent ball and spring in the housing. See Fig. 34.

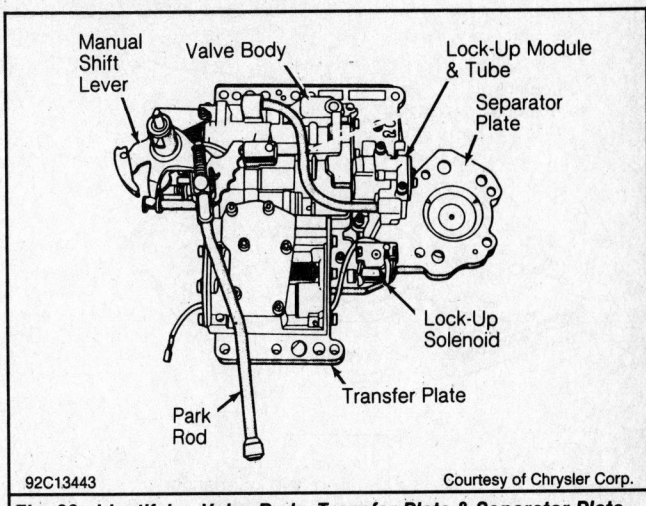

92C13443   Courtesy of Chrysler Corp.

Fig. 33: Identifying Valve Body, Transfer Plate & Separator Plate

4) Remove clip and washer from manual shift lever. Lift manual shift lever and park rod from throttle valve lever. See Fig. 35. Remove detent ball retainer. Remove detent ball and spring. Remove throttle valve lever.

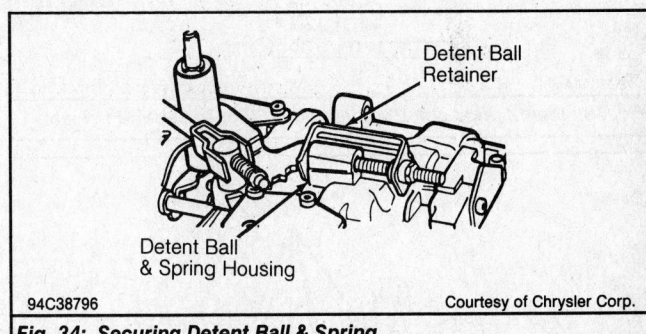

94C38796   Courtesy of Chrysler Corp.

Fig. 34: Securing Detent Ball & Spring

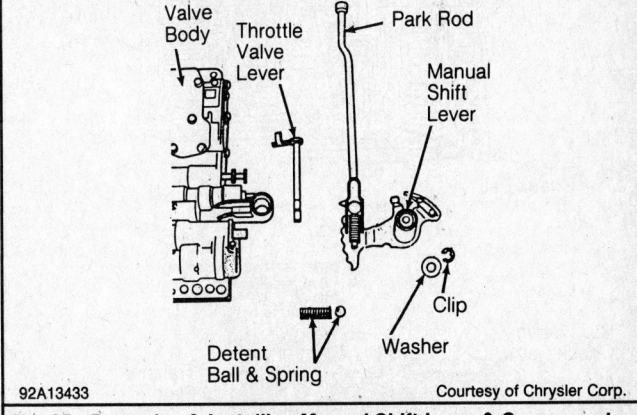

92A13433   Courtesy of Chrysler Corp.

Fig. 35: Removing & Installing Manual Shift Lever & Components

5) Remove clip and separate park rod from manual shift lever. Remove lock-up module-to-valve body bolts. Separate lock-up module and tube from valve body. See Fig. 33. Position valve body with transfer plate facing upward.

CAUTION: Ensure transfer plate is facing upward before removing transfer plate-to-valve body screws. This prevents check balls from falling from valve body.

6) Remove transfer plate-to-valve body screws. Remove transfer plate and separator plate from valve body. Note location of valve body check balls. See Fig. 37.

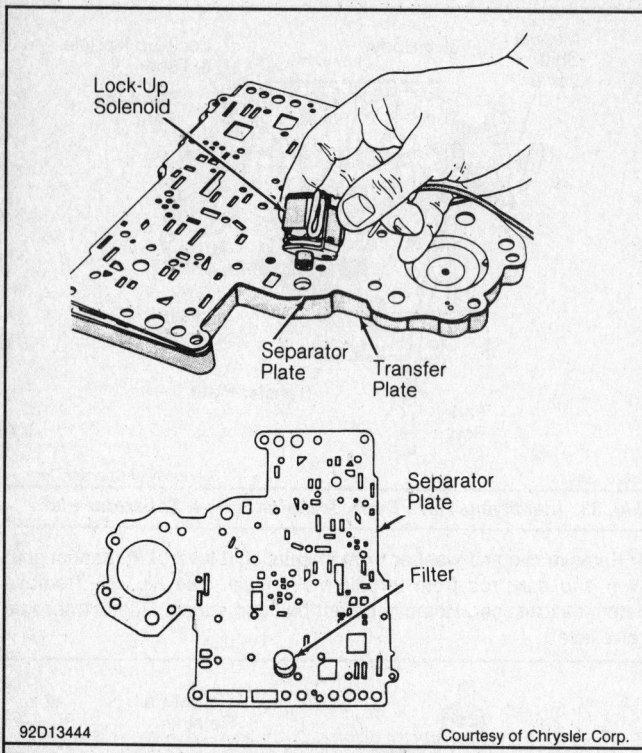

Fig. 36: Identifying Lock-Up Solenoid & Filter In Separator Plate

92D13444   Courtesy of Chrysler Corp.

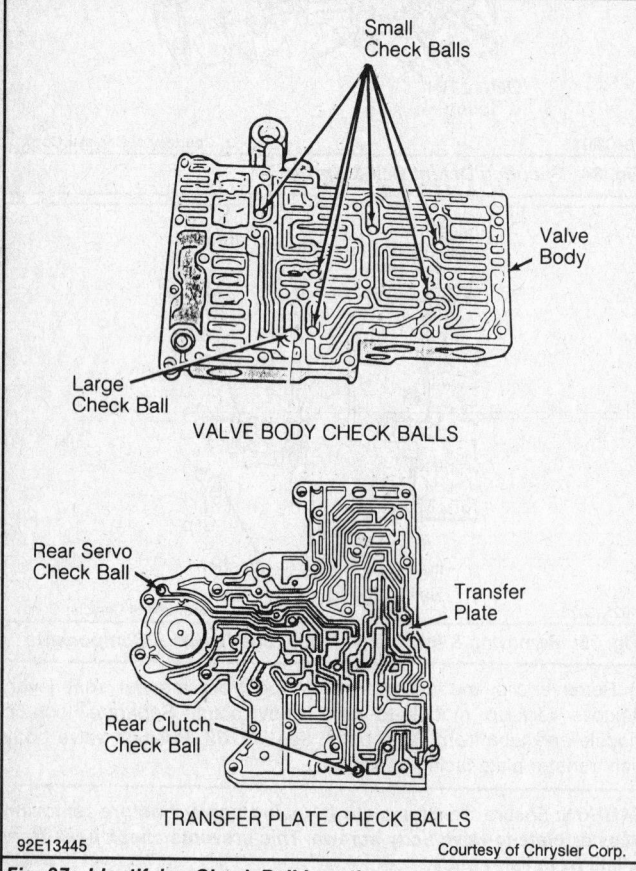

VALVE BODY CHECK BALLS

TRANSFER PLATE CHECK BALLS

92E13445   Courtesy of Chrysler Corp.

Fig. 37: Identifying Check Ball Locations

7) Position transfer plate with separator plate facing upward. This prevents check balls from falling from transfer plate. Remove separator plate-to-transfer plate screws.
8) Remove lock-up solenoid from separator plate. *See Fig. 36.* Remove separator plate from transfer plate.
9) Note location of filter in separator plate and location of transfer plate check balls. *See Figs. 36 and 37.* Remove valve body and lock-up module components. *See Fig. 38.*

Cleaning & Inspection – 1) Clean components with solvent and dry with compressed air. DO NOT use solvent to clean electrical components. DO NOT use shop towels to dry components. Ensure all components slide freely in housing bores and bores are not scored. Inspect machined surfaces for nicks, burrs or distortion.
2) Inspect valve and plugs for burrs or scratches. Minor scratches may be removed using crocus cloth. When sanding components, DO NOT round off edges of valve or plug.

CAUTION: Many of valve body components are made of aluminum and contain a special coating. DO NOT polish or sand aluminum components, as special coating will be removed. Use magnet to check if components are made of aluminum before polishing or sanding. Use care when polishing or sanding steel components, as not to round off the edges of component. Sharp edges may be maintained on the component.

---

3) Ensure all fluid passages are open. Inspect transfer plate and separator plates for distortion. Inspect check balls and seats for damage.
4) Valve body must be replaced if components are damaged. Only the following components can be serviced:
• Adjusting Screw Bracket
• Lock-Up Solenoid
• Manual Shift Lever, Seal & Detent Ball
• Park Rod And Clip
• Switch Valve & Spring
• Throttle Valve Lever

Reassembly – 1) Lubricate all components and fluid passages with ATF. Install check balls in transfer plate. *See Fig. 37.* Ensure filter is installed in separator plate. *See Fig. 36.* Install separator plate on transfer plate.
2) Install NEW "O" ring on lock-up solenoid. Install lock-up solenoid on separator plate. Install and tighten separator plate-to-transfer plate screws to specification. See TORQUE SPECIFICATIONS.
3) Position valve body with internal passages facing upward. Install check balls in valve body. *See Fig. 37.*
4) Install transfer plate and separator plate on valve body. Install and tighten transfer plate-to-valve body screws to specification in a diagonal pattern.
5) Install components in valve body. Ensure components are installed in original location. Tighten all end plate and cover screws to specification.

CAUTION: When installing shuttle valve, ensure clip fully engages groove on shuttle valve.

---

6) Install detent ball and spring in detent ball and spring housing and retain in position using detent ball retainer. Install spring on end of pressure regulator valve.
7) Install switch valve spring on tang at end of adjusting screw bracket. Install adjusting screw bracket. Ensure springs align with adjusting screw bracket.
8) Install upper screws (short screws) in adjusting screw bracket first and then install remaining lower screws. Tighten screws to specification. See TORQUE SPECIFICATIONS.
9) Install tube and lock-up module on valve body. Ensure tube engages with valve body and lock-up module. Install and tighten screws to specification.

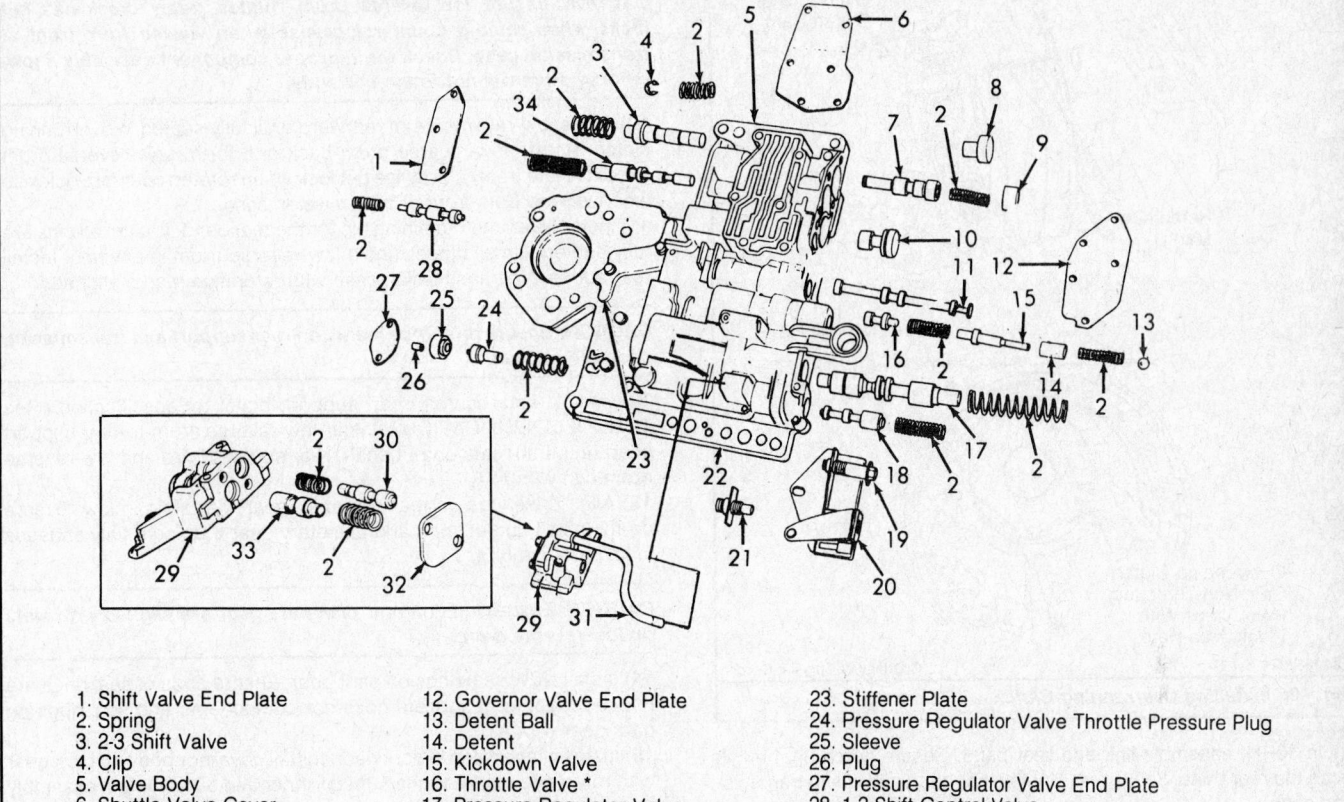

1. Shift Valve End Plate
2. Spring
3. 2-3 Shift Valve
4. Clip
5. Valve Body
6. Shuttle Valve Cover
7. Shuttle Valve
8. 2-3 Shift Valve Governor Plug
9. Shuttle Valve Plug *
10. 1-2 Shift Valve Governor Plug *
11. Manual Valve

12. Governor Valve End Plate
13. Detent Ball
14. Detent
15. Kickdown Valve
16. Throttle Valve *
17. Pressure Regulator Valve
18. Switch Valve
19. Throttle Pressure Adjusting Screw
20. Adjusting Screw Bracket
21. Line Pressure Adjusting Screw
22. Transfer Plate

23. Stiffener Plate
24. Pressure Regulator Valve Throttle Pressure Plug
25. Sleeve
26. Plug
27. Pressure Regulator Valve End Plate
28. 1-2 Shift Control Valve
29. Lock-Up Module
30. Fail-Safe Valve
31. Tube
32. Lock-Up Module End Plate
33. Lock-Up Valve
34. 1-2 Shift Valve *

* – Aluminum Component

92F13446

Courtesy of Chrysler Corp.

Fig. 38: Exploded View Of Valve Body Components

10) Install throttle valve lever in valve body. Install manual shift lever over throttle valve lever. Align manual shift lever with detent ball and manual valve. Hold throttle valve lever upward and press manual shift lever into the housing.

11) Install seal, washer and clip on manual shift lever. Remove detent ball retainer. Lubricate manual shift lever shaft with petroleum jelly. Ensure throttle valve lever is aligned with end of kickdown valve and manual shift lever arm is engaged with manual valve. *See Fig. 39.*

CAUTION: If line pressure or throttle pressure adjusting screws were moved from original setting, they must be readjusted. See HYDRAULIC PRESSURE ADJUSTMENTS.

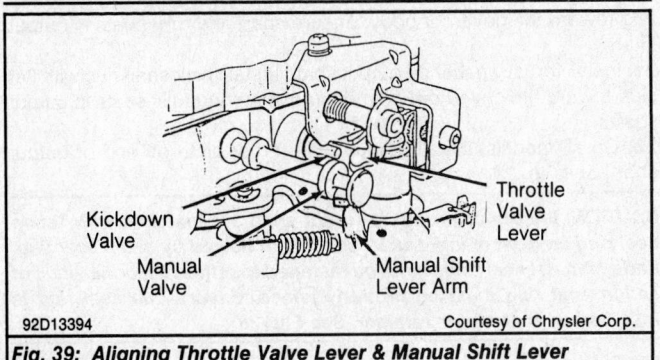

92D13394

Courtesy of Chrysler Corp.

Fig. 39: Aligning Throttle Valve Lever & Manual Shift Lever

TRANSMISSION REASSEMBLY

VALVE BODY & INTERNAL COMPONENTS

NOTE: Lubricate all components with Mopar ATF Plus Type 7176 fluid. Apply petroleum jelly on "O" rings and seal rings. Use petroleum jelly to hold thrust washers, thrust plates and gaskets in position. Ensure thrust washer and thrust plates are installed in original location.

1) Install NEW seal rings on front and rear servo pistons. Install front and rear servos and components in transmission case. Use twisting motion when installing servo pistons. Using "C" clamp, compress servo and install snap ring.

2) Ensure springs and rollers are installed in correct location and fully seated in overrunning clutch. *See Fig. 21.* Lubricate components with ATF. Identify non-threaded hole in overrunning clutch cam with a paint mark. Note countersunk holes in overrunning clutch cam. *See Fig. 21.*

CAUTION: Ensure overrunning clutch is installed with countersunk holes on overrunning clutch cam toward rear of transmission (rear support side) and reference marks are aligned.

3) Place reference mark on blank area at rear of transmission case for overrunning clutch installation. *See Fig. 40.* Install overrunning clutch cam with countersunk holes toward rear of transmission (rear support side) and reference marks aligned. Install and tighten bolts to specification. See TORQUE SPECIFICATIONS.

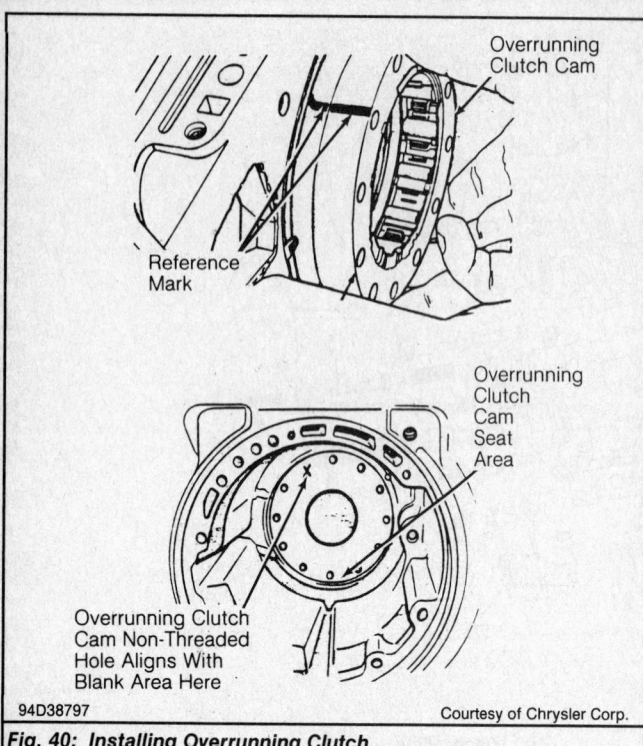

Fig. 40: Installing Overrunning Clutch

4) On 30RH, assemble link and rear band. Ensure notch on the link faces the rear band. See Fig. 41. Install rear band and link in transmission case.

5) Lubricate overrunning clutch race on rear of low-reverse drum with ATF. Install low-reverse drum through rear band. Tilt low-reverse drum and engage overrunning clutch race with rollers on overrunning clutch.

CAUTION: Ensure low-reverse drum rotates freely clockwise but locks when rotated counterclockwise when viewed from front of transmission case. Check for improper component assembly if low-reverse drum will not rotate correctly.

6) Press low-reverse drum rearward until fully seated in overrunning clutch. Rotate low-reverse drum back and forth. Low-reverse drum should rotate freely clockwise but lock when rotated counterclockwise when viewed from front of transmission case.

7) Install NEW "O" rings on pin for rear band. Install pin for rear band in transmission case. Ensure pin is fully seated in transmission case.

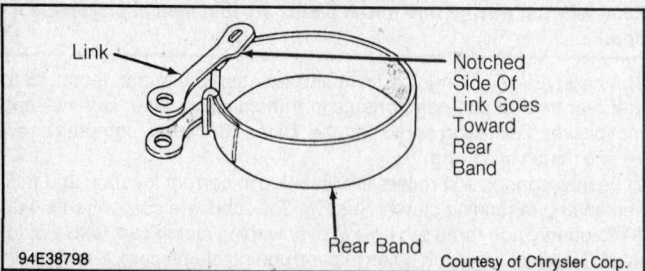

Fig. 41: Assembling Link & Rear Band (30RH)

8) On 32RH, install NEW "O" rings on pins for rear band. Install rear band reaction pin in rear of transmission. This is the pin near top of transmission, farthest distance away from oil pan surface. Install rear band so twin lugs on the band are seated against rear band reaction pin.

9) Lubricate overrunning clutch race on rear of low-reverse drum with ATF. Install low-reverse drum through rear band. Tilt low-reverse drum and engage overrunning clutch race with rollers on overrunning clutch.

CAUTION: Ensure low-reverse drum rotates freely clockwise but locks when rotated counterclockwise when viewed from front of transmission case. Check for improper component assembly if low-reverse drum will not rotate correctly.

10) Press low-reverse drum rearward until fully seated in overrunning clutch. Rotate low-reverse drum back and forth. Low-reverse drum should rotate freely clockwise but lock when rotated counterclockwise when viewed from front of transmission case.

11) Install lever and remaining pin for the rear band. Ensure all pins are fully seated. On all models, hold low-reverse drum in position. Install rear support in transmission case with reference marks aligned.

CAUTION: Ensure reference marks on rear support and transmission case are aligned.

12) Install and tighten rear support bolts to specification. See TORQUE SPECIFICATIONS. Install low-reverse drum-to-rear support snap ring. Lubricate output shaft, rear support bore and low-reverse drum hub with ATF.

13) Align drive lugs on rear planetary gear with slots in low-reverse drum. Install output shaft and planetary gear train so it fully engages in low-reverse drum.

CAUTION: Ensure lugs on rear planetary gear are aligned with slots on low-reverse drum.

14) Install NEW seal rings on park gear. Ensure ends of seal rings are hooked together. Lubricate governor components and seal rings on park gear with ATF.

15) Install filter screen in park gear. Install governor body on park gear with reference marks aligned. Install inner and outer weight assembly in governor body. Ensure snap ring retaining governor weights is fully seated.

CAUTION: Output shaft contains a governor valve indexing area. Small end of governor valve must seat in governor valve indexing area. See Fig. 13.

16) Rotate output shaft until governor valve indexing area is facing upward. Install governor body on output shaft. Align governor valve bore with governor valve indexing area of output shaft. See Fig. 13. Align valve shaft holes in governor body and output shaft.

17) Align splines on output shaft with hub of park gear. Push park gear into rear support. Ensure valve shaft holes in output shaft and governor body are aligned. Install and tighten governor body-to-park gear bolts to specification.

18) Install governor valve and valve shaft in governor body. Ensure valve shaft moves freely. Install snap ring on each end of valve shaft to hold assembly in governor body.

19) On models with only one snap ring on output shaft, install snap ring. Ensure snap ring fully seats in output shaft.

20) On models with a thick snap ring, thrust washer and then a thin snap ring, install thin snap ring on output shaft with flat side of snap ring toward the governor body. Ensure snap ring fully seats in output shaft.

21) Install thrust washer on output shaft. Install thick snap ring with flat side toward the governor body. Ensure snap ring fully seats in output shaft.

22) On all models, install output shaft thrust plate on end of output shaft. See Fig. 29.

CAUTION: Ensure seal rings on input shaft are installed with Teflon seal ring on front of input shaft and then followed by metal seal ring. Ends of metal seal rings must be fastened together. Diagonal ends of Teflon seal ring must be properly joined. Ensure hub seal ring is installed on rear clutch retainer. See Fig. 28.

23) Ensure fiber thrust washer is installed on front of rear clutch retainer. See Fig. 28. Align teeth on front clutch discs. Install front clutch on rear clutch. Ensure front clutch is fully seated on rear clutch by rotating front clutch back and forth.

24) Install thrust washer for output shaft in center of rear clutch retainer so groove in thrust washer faces toward output shaft. Thrust washer fits on inside of rear clutch retainer, near end of input shaft. *See Fig. 28.*

CAUTION: *Ensure thrust washer is installed in center of rear clutch retainer with groove in thrust washer toward output shaft.*

25) Using small screwdriver, align teeth on rear clutch discs. Position transmission case with oil pump opening facing upward.

26) Install front and rear clutch assemblies. Rotate assembly back and forth until rear clutch discs fully engage front annulus gear. Ensure lugs on front clutch fully engages with slots on driving shell.

27) Slide front band over front clutch retainer. Partially install pin for front band into transmission case. Install front band strut between front band and lever on transmission case. Install anchor between front band and transmission case. Finish installing pin for front band.

28) Tighten front band adjusting screw until front band is tight on front clutch retainer. Ensure front and rear clutch assemblies are fully seated. Apply thread sealant on plug for front band pin access hole. Install plug and tighten to specification. See TORQUE SPECIFICATIONS.

29) Ensure thrust washer and seal rings are installed on reaction shaft support and ends of seal rings are fastened together. If thrust washer contains a chamfered edge on inside diameter of thrust washer, it must be installed on reaction shaft support with chamfered edge on inside diameter of thrust washer facing toward front of oil pump.

30) Install pilot studs in 2 oil pump bolt holes, opposite of each other in transmission case. Install oil pump gasket. Lubricate reaction shaft seal rings and oil pump seal with ATF.

31) Install oil pump. Ensure oil pump is fully seated. Remove pilot studs. Install and tighten oil pump bolts in a diagonal pattern to specification.

CAUTION: *Ensure input shaft and output shaft rotate without binding. If binding exists, check for improperly assembled components.*

32) Attach dial indicator to transmission case with dial indicator stem seated against end of input shaft. Move input shaft inward and zero dial indicator. Pull input shaft outward and measure input shaft end play. Input shaft end play should be .022-.091" (.56-2.31 mm).

33) If input shaft end play is not within specification, change output shaft thrust washer/thrust plate or check for improperly assembled components.

34) Ensure park/neutral switch is removed before installing valve body. Using proper sized socket, install NEW seal for manual shift lever seal in transmission case.

35) Install NEW seal rings on accumulator. Lubricate seal rings, accumulator and bore with Mopar ATF Plus Type 7176 fluid. Install accumulator.

36) Install spring between accumulator and valve body. Ensure manual shift lever on valve body is in low position. This moves park rod fully rearward.

37) Install valve body. Install valve body-to-transmission case bolts in original location finger tight only. DO NOT tighten bolts at this time. Using NEW seal, install park/neutral switch. Tighten park/neutral switch to specification. See TORQUE SPECIFICATIONS.

CAUTION: *Alternate tightening valve body-to-transmission case bolts to prevent damage to valve body. DO NOT overtighten bolts or damage to valve body and transmission case may result.*

38) Tighten valve body-to-transmission case bolts evenly to specifications, starting at the center and working outward. Reconnect lock-up solenoid wire on the case connector.

39) Install NEW filter assembly. Install and tighten bolts to specification. Install throttle valve and manual shift levers. Ensure throttle valve and manual shift levers rotate smoothly.

40) Ensure lock nuts are backed off on front and rear band adjusting screws. *See Fig. 17.*

41) On 30RH, tighten front band adjusting screw to 72 INCH lbs. (8.1 N.m). Loosen front band adjusting screw 2 1/2 turns. Tighten lock nut on front band adjusting screw to specification.

42) Tighten rear band adjusting screw to 41 INCH lbs. (4.6 N.m). Loosen rear band adjusting screw 7 turns. Tighten lock nut on rear band adjusting screw to specification.

43) On 32RH, tighten front band adjusting screw to 72 INCH lbs. (8.1 N.m). Loosen front band adjusting screw 2 1/4 turns on 1994 Cherokee and Wrangler or 2 1/2 turns on all other models. On all models, tighten lock nut on front band adjusting screw to specification.

44) Tighten rear band adjusting screws to 72 INCH lbs. (8.1 N.m). Loosen rear band adjusting screw 4 turns. Tighten lock nut on rear band adjusting screw to specification.

45) On all transmissions, install magnet, NEW gasket and oil pan. Install and tighten bolts to specification.

46) On Cherokee 4WD and Wrangler models, install NEW gasket for adapter housing on rear of transmission case. Use petroleum jelly to hold gasket in place. Install adapter housing on transmission case. Ensure park rod engages parking sprag. Install and tighten bolts to specification.

47) On Cherokee 2WD, Pickup and Ram Van models, install NEW gasket for extension housing on transmission case. Use petroleum jelly to hold gasket in place.

48) Install rear bearing on output shaft. Ensure locating groove on outside of bearing is toward oil pump end of transmission. Install snap ring on output shaft.

49) Install output shaft rear bearing locating ring in extension housing (if removed). Install extension housing on output shaft while working park rod past parking sprag. Using snap ring pliers, expand output shaft rear bearing locating ring.

50) Install extension housing onto output shaft rear bearing and release locating ring. Ensure locating ring is fully seated in groove on output shaft rear bearing.

51) Install and tighten extension housing-to-transmission case bolts to specification. See TORQUE SPECIFICATIONS. Install gasket and access cover on extension housing. On all models, lubricate torque converter hub with Mopar ATF Plus Type 7176 fluid and install torque converter.

CAUTION: *If transmission failure existed, flush oil cooler and check oil cooler flow. See OIL COOLER FLUSHING and OIL COOLER FLOW CHECK under ON-VEHICLE SERVICE.*

TORQUE SPECIFICATIONS
TORQUE SPECIFICATIONS

Application	Ft. Lbs. (N.m)
Adapter Housing-To-Transmission Case Bolt	24 (33)
Band Adjusting Screw Lock Nut	25 (34)
Extension Housing-To-Rear Mount Bolt	50 (68)
Extension Housing-To-Transmission Case Bolt	32 (43)
Front Band Pin Access Hole Plug	13 (18)
Oil Pan Bolt	13 (18)
Oil Pump Bolt	15 (20)
Overrunning Clutch Cam-To-Transmission Case Bolt	13 (18)
Park/Neutral Switch	24 (33)
Reaction Shaft Support Bolt	15 (20)
Rear Support Bolt	13 (18)
Transfer Case-To-Adapter Housing Bolt/Nut	26 (35)
Vehicle Speed Sensor Adapter Nut (Type 2)	13 (18)
Vehicle Speed Sensor Nut (Type 1)	13 (18)

	INCH Lbs. (N.m)
Adapter Retainer Bolt	100 (11.3)
Adjusting Screw Bracket Screw	35 (4.0)
Filter Assembly Bolt	35 (4.0)
Governor Body-To-Park Gear Bolt	95 (10.7)
Governor Valve End Plate Screw	35 (4.0)
Lock-Up Module-To-Valve Body Screw	35 (4.0)
Pressure Regulator Valve End Plate Screw	35 (4.0)
Pressure Tap Plug	120 (13.6)
Separator Plate-To-Transfer Plate Screw	35 (4.0)
Shift Valve End Plate Screw	35 (4.0)
Shuttle Valve Cover Screw	35 (4.0)
Transfer Plate-To-Valve Body Screw	35 (4.0)
Valve Body-To-Transmission Case Bolt	105 (11.9)
Vehicle Speed Sensor Bolt (Type 2)	72 (8.1)
Vehicle Speed Sensor-To-Adapter Bolt (Type 3)	27 (3.1)

TRANSMISSION SPECIFICATIONS

TRANSMISSION SPECIFICATIONS

Application	In. (mm)
Clutch Clearances	
Front Clutch	
3-Disc Clutch	.074-.125 (1.87-3.18)
4-Disc Clutch	.067-.134 (1.70-3.40)
5-Disc Clutch	.075-.152 (1.90-3.86)
Rear Clutch	
30RH	.025-.045 (.64-1.14)
32RH	.032-.055 (.81-1.40)
Input Shaft End Play	.022-.091 (.56-2.31)
Oil Pump Clearances	
Gear End Clearance	.0004-.0025 (.010-.063)
Gear Tooth Clearance	.0035-.0075 (.089-.190)
Outer Gear-To-Oil Pump	
Housing Clearance	.0035-.0075 (.089-.190)
Planetary Gear Train End Play	
30RH	.001-.047 (.03-1.19)
32RH	.005-.048 (.13-1.22)

TECHNICAL SERVICE BULLETINS

UPSHIFTS TOO LOW OR CLOSE TOGETHER

Chrysler Corp. Service Bulletin 21-25-93 (September 3, 1993) –
Some 1992-93 Pickup and Ram Van with 42RH transmission may
have upshifts too low or close together. The 2-3 upshift will be very
close to the 1-2 upshift. To correct this condition, perform the following procedure.

1) Check for stored diagnostic trouble codes in the Powertrain Control
Module (PCM). See SELF-DIAGNOSTICS article in ENGINE PERFOR-
MANCE of appropriate MITCHELL® MANUAL.
2) Repair engine control system if a diagnostic trouble code exists and
recheck operation. If no diagnostic trouble codes exists or code has
been corrected and problem still exists, replace governor weights and
spring with components from Governor Weight Package (4617883).

DELAYED TRANSMISSION ENGAGEMENT

Chrysler Corp. Service Bulletin 21-08-94 (April 29, 1994) – Some
1990-94 Pickup, Ram Van, Cherokee and Wrangler models may experience a 2-8 second delay in transmission engagement when vehicle
is first started after vehicle has been parked for an extended period.
To correct this condition, perform the following procedure.

1) Check for stored diagnostic trouble codes in the Powertrain Control
Module (PCM). See SELF-DIAGNOSTICS article in ENGINE PERFOR-
MANCE of appropriate MITCHELL® MANUAL.
2) Repair engine control system if a diagnostic trouble code exists and
recheck operation. If no diagnostic trouble codes exists or code has
been corrected and problem still exists, Drainback Relief Valve
(4778670) must be installed.
3) Note location of oil cooler supply line on side of transmission. *See
Fig. 7.* Trace oil cooler supply line back to the radiator and identify this
line at the radiator. Ensure this is the oil cooler supply line.

CAUTION: *Drainback relief valve must be installed in oil cooler
supply line or transmission failure will exist if wrong line is selected.
Ensure oil cooler supply line is selected.*

4) Cut oil cooler supply line within 1/8" of the crimp on the hose. *See
Fig. 42.* Cut the hose and remove section of oil cooler supply line.

CAUTION: *Some vehicles may have a Black epoxy coating on the oil
cooler supply line. Ensure coating is removed before installing the
nut and sleeve from drainback relief valve on oil cooler supply line.*

5) Install nut and sleeve on metal portion of oil cooler supply line.
Install drainback relief valve on metal portion of oil cooler supply so
arrow on drainback relief valve is pointing toward the oil cooler.

CAUTION: *Ensure drainback relief valve is installed so arrow on
drainback relief valve is pointing toward the oil cooler. The arrow
indicates direction of the fluid flow.*

6) Install sleeve and nut on drainback relief valve. Tighten nut. Install
rubber portion of oil cooler supply line on drainback relief valve. Install
and tighten clamp to 10 INCH lbs. (1.1 N.m).
7) Note location of oil cooler return line on side of transmission. *See
Fig. 7.* Disconnect oil cooler return line from transmission. On 1994
models, oil cooler lines are equipped with a disconnect fitting. Use
proper procedure for disconnecting oil cooler line from disconnect fitting. See OIL COOLER LINE DISCONNECT FITTINGS under ON-
VEHICLE SERVICE in this article.

CAUTION: *Ensure flow from oil cooler return line is checked to
ensure drainback relief valve is installed in correct oil cooler line.*

8) Ensure transmission is full of fluid. Place container under oil cooler
return line. Start engine. Place gearshift in Neutral.
9) Ensure steady flow exists for oil cooler return line. If no fluid flow
exists, drainback relief valve has been installed in the wrong oil cooler
line. Remove and reinstall. If steady flow exists, shut engine off.
10) Reconnect oil cooler return line. On 1994 models, reconnect oil
cooler return line by pushing oil cooler line inward until a snap or click
is heard when retaining clip seats in oil cooler line. Pull outward on oil
cooler line to ensure oil cooler line is locked in the disconnect fitting.

CAUTION: *After installing oil cooler line, pull outward on oil cooler
line to ensure oil cooler line is locked in the disconnect fitting and
retaining clip is fully seated.*

11) On all models, fill transmission with Mopar ATF Plus Type 7176 fluid. Recheck all oil cooler lines for leaks.

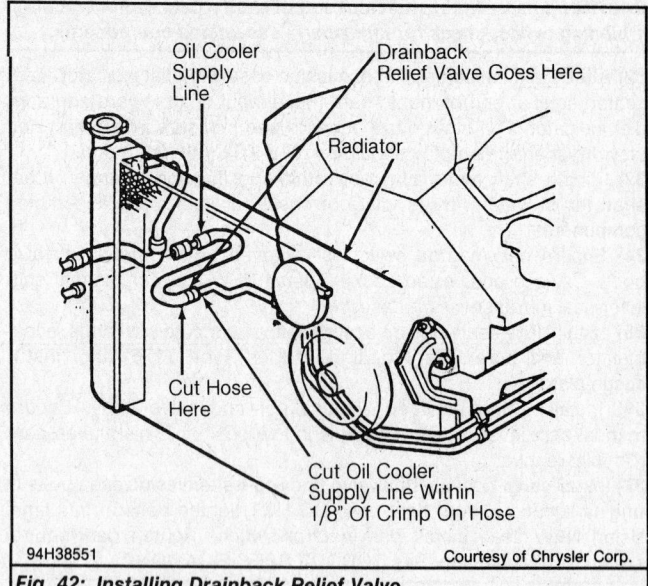

94H38551   Courtesy of Chrysler Corp.

Fig. 42: Installing Drainback Relief Valve

APPLICATION & LABOR TIMES

APPLICATION & LABOR TIMES

Vehicle Application	Labor Times [1] R & I	[2] Overhaul	Trans. Model
Chrysler			
Passenger Cars			
LeBaron			
1993 Coupe/Conv (2.5L) [4]	4.6	6.2	30TH
1993 Sedan (2.5L) [3] [4]	4.6	6.2	30TH
(3.0L) [4]	4.6	6.2	31TH
1994 Sedan (3.0L)	4.6	6.2	31TH
Dodge			
Passenger Cars			
1993 Daytona (2.5L) [3]	4.6	6.2	30TH
1993 Dynasty (2.5L)	4.6	6.2	30TH
1993-94 Shadow (2.2/2.5L) [3]	4.6	6.2	30TH
1993-94 Spirit (2.5L) [3]	4.6	6.2	30TH
(3.0L)	4.6	6.2	31TH
Vans			
1993-94 Caravan (2.5L)	4.6	6.2	30TH
1993-94 Caravan & Grand Caravan (3.0L)	4.6	6.2	31TH
Plymouth			
Passenger Cars			
1993-94 Acclaim (2.5L)	4.6	6.2	30TH
(3.0L)	4.6	6.2	31TH
1993-94 Sundance (2.2/2.5L) [3]	4.6	6.2	30TH
Vans			
1993-94 Voyager (2.5L)	4.6	6.2	30TH
1993-94 Voyager & Grand Voyager (3.0L)	4.6	6.2	31TH

[1] – Removal and installation of transaxle from vehicle chassis.

[2] – Bench overhaul time for transaxle and differential. DOES NOT include removal and installation.

[3] – With turbocharger, add .3 hr.

[4] – With Antilock Brake System (ABS), add .3 hr.

IDENTIFICATION

Transaxle contains identification numbers located on a pad just above oil pan. Identification numbers may be required when ordering replacement components.

DESCRIPTION & OPERATION

Automatic transaxle combines a torque converter, fully automatic 3-speed transaxle, final drive gearing and differential into a front wheel drive system. Transaxle consists of 2 multiple-disc clutches, overrunning clutch, 2 servos, hydraulic accumulator, 2 bands and 2 planetary gear sets to provide 3 forward gear ratios and one reverse gear.

A lock-up type torque converter is used. Torque converter lock-up is activated when Powertrain Control Module (PCM) provides voltage to Torque Converter Clutch (TCC) solenoid on the valve body.

Front and rear clutch pistons and both servo pistons are actuated hydraulically to engage the clutches and apply the bands. Clutch pistons are released by spring pressure when hydraulic pressure is released. On 2-3 upshifts, kickdown servo piston is released by spring tension and hydraulic pressure. Accumulator controls hydraulic pressure on apply side of kickdown servo during 1-2 upshift, cushioning kickdown band application.

LUBRICATION & ADJUSTMENTS

NOTE: See appropriate AUTOMATIC TRANSMISSION SERVICING article in TRANSMISSION SERVICING.

TROUBLE SHOOTING

Transaxle malfunctions may be caused by poor engine performance, improper adjustments or failure of hydraulic, mechanical or electronic components. Always begin by checking fluid level, fluid condition and shift linkage or cable adjustment. Perform road test to determine if problem has been corrected. If problem still exists, several tests must be performed on transaxle. See TESTING in this article.

TRANSAXLE

Buzzing Noise
- Aerated fluid
- Low fluid level
- Overrunning clutch inner race damaged
- Valve body malfunction or leakage

Delayed Engagement From Neutral To Drive
- Aerated fluid
- Defective oil pump
- Engine idle speed too low
- Hydraulic pressure too low
- Incorrect shift linkage or cable adjustment
- Low fluid level
- Restricted oil filter assembly
- Valve body malfunction or leakage
- Worn or broken input shaft seal rings
- Worn or faulty rear clutch

Delayed Engagement From Neutral To Reverse
- Aerated fluid
- Defective low-reverse servo, band or linkage malfunction
- Defective oil pump
- Engine idle speed too low
- Hydraulic pressure too low
- Improper low-reverse band adjustment
- Incorrect shift linkage or cable adjustment
- Low fluid level
- Restricted oil filter assembly
- Valve body malfunction or leakage
- Worn or broken input shaft seal rings
- Worn or broken reaction shaft support seal rings
- Worn or faulty front clutch

Delayed Upshift
- Governor malfunction
- Governor support seal rings broken or worn
- Incorrect throttle linkage adjustment
- Improper engine performance
- Improper kickdown band adjustment
- Kickdown servo, band or linkage malfunction
- Worn or broken reaction shaft support seal rings
- Worn or faulty front clutch

Drags Or Locks
- Kickdown band adjustment too tight
- Low-reverse band defective
- Overrunning clutch worn, broken or seized
- Planetary gear sets broken or seized

Grating, Scraping Or Growling Noise
- Bushings worn or damaged
- Improper kickdown band adjustment
- Low-reverse band defective
- Overrunning clutch worn, broken or seized
- Planetary gear sets broken or seized

Hard To Fill With Fluid, Fluid Blows Out Filler Tube
- Aerated fluid
- High fluid level
- Restricted oil filter assembly

Harsh Engagement From Neutral To Drive
- Engine idle speed too high
- Hydraulic pressure too high
- Improper engine performance
- Valve body malfunction or leakage
- Worn or faulty rear clutch

Harsh Engagement From Neutral To Reverse
- Defective low-reverse servo, band or linkage malfunction
- Engine idle speed too high
- Hydraulic pressure too high
- Improper engine performance
- Improper low-reverse band adjustment
- Worn or faulty rear clutch

Harsh Upshift
- Hydraulic pressure too high
- Hydraulic pressure too low
- Incorrect throttle linkage adjustment
- Improper engine performance
- Improper kickdown band adjustment

No Drive In Any Position
- Faulty oil pump
- Hydraulic pressure too low
- Low fluid level
- Planetary gear sets broken or seized
- Restricted oil filter assembly
- Valve body malfunction or leakage

No Kickdown Or Normal Downshift
- Governor malfunction
- Incorrect throttle linkage adjustment
- Kickdown servo, band or linkage malfunction
- Valve body malfunction or leakage

No Torque Converter Clutch Lock-Up
- Aerated fluid
- Faulty oil pump
- Hydraulic pressure too low
- Low fluid level
- Stuck switch valve
- Valve body malfunction or leakage
- Worn or broken input shaft seal rings

No Upshift
- Governor malfunction
- Governor support seal rings broken or worn
- Hydraulic pressure too low
- Improper engine performance
- Incorrect shift linkage or cable adjustment
- Incorrect throttle linkage adjustment
- Kickdown servo, band or linkage malfunction
- Low fluid level
- Valve body malfunction or leakage
- Worn or broken reaction shaft support seal rings
- Worn or faulty front clutch

Runaway Upshift
- Aerated fluid
- Hydraulic pressure too low
- Incorrect throttle linkage adjustment
- Kickdown servo, band or linkage malfunction
- Low fluid level
- Restricted oil filter assembly
- Valve body malfunction or leakage
- Worn or broken reaction shaft support seal rings
- Worn or faulty front clutch

Shifts Erratic
- Aerated fluid
- Faulty oil pump
- Governor malfunction
- Governor support seal rings broken or worn.
- Hydraulic pressure too low
- Improper engine performance
- Incorrect shift linkage or cable adjustment
- Incorrect throttle linkage adjustment
- Kickdown servo, band or linkage malfunction
- Low fluid level
- Restricted oil filter assembly
- Valve body malfunction or leakage
- Worn or broken governor support seal rings
- Worn or broken reaction shaft support seal rings
- Worn or faulty front clutch

Slips In All Positions
- Aerated fluid
- Faulty oil pump
- Hydraulic pressure too low
- Low fluid level
- Restricted oil filter assembly
- Valve body malfunction or leakage
- Worn or broken input shaft seal rings

Slips In Drive Positions
- Aerated fluid
- Faulty oil pump
- Hydraulic pressure too low
- Incorrect shift linkage or cable adjustment
- Incorrect throttle linkage adjustment
- Low fluid level
- Overrunning clutch not holding
- Overrunning clutch worn, broken or seized
- Restricted oil filter assembly
- Valve body malfunction or leakage
- Worn or broken input shaft seal rings
- Worn or faulty rear clutch

Slips In Reverse Only
- Aerated fluid
- Defective low-reverse servo, band or linkage malfunction
- Faulty oil pump
- Hydraulic pressure too low
- Improper low-reverse band adjustment
- Incorrect shift linkage or cable adjustment
- Low fluid level
- Valve body malfunction or leakage
- Worn or broken reaction shaft support seal rings
- Worn or faulty front clutch

Transaxle Overheats
- Engine idle speed too high
- Faulty cooling system
- Faulty oil pump
- Hydraulic pressure too low
- Incorrect shift linkage or cable adjustment
- Insufficient clutch clearance
- Kickdown band adjustment too tight
- Low fluid level
- Stuck switch valve

Vehicle Moves In Neutral
- Incorrect shift linkage or cable adjustment
- Insufficient clutch clearance
- Rear clutch dragging
- Valve body malfunction or leakage
- Worn or faulty rear clutch

Vehicle Will Not Move In All Forward Positions
- Hydraulic pressure too low
- Low fluid level
- Overrunning clutch not holding
- Overrunning clutch worn, broken or seized
- Planetary gear sets broken or seized
- Valve body malfunction or leakage
- Worn or broken inputs shaft seal ring
- Worn or faulty rear clutch

Vehicle Will Not Move In Reverse
- Hydraulic pressure too low
- Improper low-reverse band adjustment
- Incorrect shift linkage or cable adjustment
- Low-reverse servo, band or linkage malfunction
- Planetary gear sets broken or seized
- Valve body malfunction or leakage
- Worn or broken reaction shaft support seal rings
- Worn or faulty front clutch
- Worn or faulty rear clutch

3-2 Kickdown Runaway
- Aerated fluid
- Hydraulic pressure too low
- Improper kickdown band adjustment
- Incorrect throttle linkage adjustment
- Kickdown servo, band or linkage malfunction
- Low fluid level
- Valve body malfunction or leakage
- Worn or broken governor support seal rings
- Worn or faulty front clutch

ELECTRONIC TESTING

TORQUE CONVERTER CLUTCH ELECTRONIC LOCK-UP

See CHRYSLER ELECTRONIC CONTROLS article in AUTOMATIC TRANSMISSIONS for information on torque converter clutch testing and diagnosis.

TESTING

ROAD TEST

1) Ensure shift linkage or cable is properly adjusted, fluid level and condition are okay. Add fluid and adjust shift linkage or cable as needed.
2) Road test vehicle, operating transaxle in each gear position. Check for slipping and any variation in shifting.
3) If vehicle operates properly at highway speeds, but has poor acceleration, torque converter stator clutch may be slipping. If acceleration through all gears is normal, but high throttle opening is required to maintain highway speeds, torque converter stator clutch may be seized. Torque converter must be replaced if stator clutch is defective.
4) Slipping or flare-up in any gear usually indicates clutch, band, or overrunning clutch problems. The slipping clutch or band in a particular gear can usually be identified by noting transaxle operation in other shift lever positions and comparing which internal units are applied in those positions. See CLUTCH & BAND APPLICATION table.

CLUTCH & BAND APPLICATION

Shift Lever Position	¹ Elements In Use
"D" (Drive)	
1st Gear	Rear Clutch & Overrunning Clutch
2nd Gear	Rear Clutch & Kickdown Band
3rd Gear	Front Clutch, Rear Clutch & Torque Converter Clutch
"2" (Second)	
1st Gear	Rear Clutch & Overrunning Clutch
2nd Gear	Rear Clutch & Kickdown Band
"1" (Low)	
1st Gear	Rear Clutch & Low-Reverse Band
"R" (Reverse)	Front Clutch & Low-Reverse Band
"N" Or "P" (Neutral Or Park)	All Clutches & Bands Released Or Ineffective

¹ – Kickdown band is the front band and low-reverse band is the rear band.

5) Rear clutch is applied in "D" (1st gear) and Low gear. Also overrunning clutch is applied in "D" (1st gear) and low-reverse band is applied in Low gear. If transaxle slips in "D" (1st gear), but does not slip in Low gear, overrunning clutch is defective. If transaxle slips in any 2 forward gears, rear clutch is slipping.
6) If transaxle slips in "D" (3rd gear), either front or rear clutch are slipping. Select another gear which uses one of these clutches and determine which clutch is slipping. See CLUTCH & BAND APPLICATION table. If transaxle also slips in Reverse, front clutch is slipping. If transaxle does not slip in Reverse, rear clutch is slipping.
7) Process of elimination can be used to detect any unit which slips and to confirm proper operation of good units. However, although road test analysis can usually diagnose slipping units, the actual malfunction usually cannot be decided. Practically any condition can be caused by leaking hydraulic circuits or sticking valves. Hydraulic pressure tests should be performed on transaxle.

TORQUE CONVERTER STALL SPEED TEST

CAUTION: Manufacturer does not recommend performing torque converter stall speed test.

HYDRAULIC PRESSURE TEST

Pressure Test Preparation – **1)** Ensure fluid level and condition are okay. Add fluid (if necessary). Ensure transaxle fluid is at normal operating temperature of 150-200F° (66-93C°).
2) Install tachometer. Raise vehicle on hoist, allowing front wheels to rotate freely. Disconnect throttle and shift cable or linkage at transaxle so levers can be operated from below vehicle.

NOTE: A 150 psi (11 kg/cm²) pressure gauge is required for checking all clutches except reverse clutch. A 300 psi (21 kg/cm²) pressure gauge is required for checking reverse clutch.

Shift Lever In "1" (Low Gear) – **1)** Remove pressure tap plugs and install pressure gauges in line pressure tap and low-reverse pressure tap. *See Fig. 1.* Start engine and operate at 1000 RPM.
2) Move shift lever on transaxle fully rearward to shift lever "1" position. Read pressure on both gauges as Throttle Valve (T.V.) lever on transaxle is moved from fully clockwise position to fully counterclockwise position.
3) Line pressure should be 52-58 psi (3.6-4.1 kg/cm²) with T.V. lever fully clockwise and should gradually increase to 80-88 psi (5.6-6.2 kg/cm²) as T.V. lever is moved counterclockwise. Low-reverse pressure should be within 3 psi (.2 kg/cm²) of line pressure.
4) If line pressure is not within specification, adjust line pressure. See HYDRAULIC PRESSURE ADJUSTMENTS. If proper line pressure still cannot be obtained, check for defective components and hydraulic circuit.
5) This tests oil pump output, pressure regulation, condition of rear clutch and hydraulic circuits. Remove pressure gauges. Install and tighten pressure tap plugs to specification. See TORQUE SPECIFICATIONS.

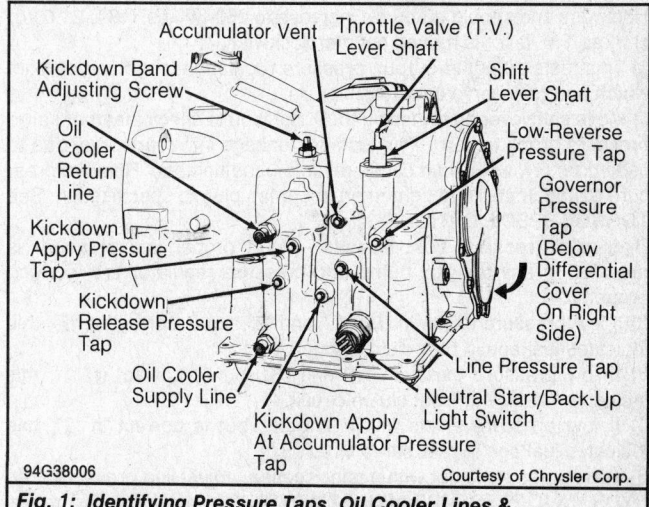

94G38006   Courtesy of Chrysler Corp.

Fig. 1: Identifying Pressure Taps, Oil Cooler Lines & Neutral Start/Back-Up Light Switch

Shift Lever In "2" (2nd Gear) – **1)** Remove pressure tap plug and install pressure gauge in line pressure tap. Install "T" connection and pressure gauge in oil cooler supply line fitting at transaxle so lubrication pressure can be read. *See Fig. 1.*
2) Start engine and operate at 1000 RPM. Move shift lever on transaxle one detent forward from fully rearward position to shift lever "2" position.
3) Read pressures on both gauges as Throttle Valve (T.V.) lever on transaxle is moved from fully clockwise position to fully counterclockwise position.
4) Line pressure should be 52-58 psi (3.6-4.1 kg/cm²) with T.V. lever fully clockwise and should gradually increase to 80-88 psi (5.6-6.2 kg/cm²) as T.V. lever is moved counterclockwise.

5) If line pressure is not within specification, adjust line pressure. See HYDRAULIC PRESSURE ADJUSTMENTS. If proper line pressure still cannot be obtained, check for defective components and hydraulic circuit.

6) Lubrication pressure should be 10-25 psi (.7-1.8 kg/cm²) with T.V. lever fully clockwise and 10-35 psi (.7-2.5 kg/cm²) with T.V. lever fully counterclockwise.

7) This tests oil pump output, pressure regulation, condition of rear clutch and hydraulic circuits. Remove pressure gauges. Install and tighten pressure tap plugs to specification. See TORQUE SPECIFICATIONS. Reconnect oil cooler line.

Shift Lever In "D" (Drive Gear) – 1) Remove pressure tap plugs and install pressure gauges in line pressure tap and kickdown release pressure taps. See Fig. 1. Start engine and operate at 1600 RPM.

2) Move shift lever on transaxle 2 detents forward from fully rearward position to shift lever "D" position. Read pressure on both gauges as Throttle Valve (T.V.) lever on transaxle is moved from fully clockwise position to fully counterclockwise position.

3) Line pressure should be 52-58 psi (3.6-4.1 kg/cm²) with T.V. lever fully clockwise and should gradually increase to 80-88 psi (5.6-6.2 kg/cm²) as T.V. lever is moved counterclockwise.

4) If line pressure is not within specification, adjust line pressure. See HYDRAULIC PRESSURE ADJUSTMENTS. If proper line pressure still cannot be obtained, check for defective components and hydraulic circuit.

5) Kickdown release is pressurized only in direct drive and should be within 3 psi (.2 kg/cm²) of line pressure up to kickdown point. This tests oil pump output, pressure regulation, condition of front and rear clutches and hydraulic circuits.

6) Remove pressure gauges. Install and tighten pressure tap plugs to specification. See TORQUE SPECIFICATIONS.

Shift Lever In "R" (Reverse Gear) – 1) Remove pressure tap plug and install 300 psi (21 kg/cm²) pressure gauge in low-reverse pressure tap. See Fig. 1. Start engine and operate at 1600 RPM.

2) Move shift lever on transaxle 4 detents forward from fully rearward position to shift lever "R" position. Low-reverse pressure should be 180-220 psi (12.6-15.4 kg/cm²) with Throttle Valve (T.V.) lever fully clockwise and should gradually increase to 260-300 psi (18.2-21.0 kg/cm²) as T.V. lever is moved counterclockwise.

3) This tests oil pump output, pressure regulation, condition of front clutch and rear servo hydraulic circuits.

4) Move shift lever on transaxle to "D" position to check that rear servo pressure drops to zero. This tests for leakage into rear servo, due to case porosity, which can cause reverse band damage. Remove pressure gauge. Install and tighten pressure tap plug to specification. See TORQUE SPECIFICATIONS.

Hydraulic Pressure Test Results – 1) If proper line pressure is obtained in any test, oil pump and pressure regulator are working properly.

2) If low pressure exists in "D", "1", and "2", but is correct in "R", this indicates leakage in rear clutch circuit.

3) If low pressure exists in "D" and "R", but is correct in "1", this indicates leakage in front clutch circuit.

4) If low pressure exists in "R" and "1", but is correct in "2", this indicates leakage in rear servo circuit.

5) If line pressure is not within specification, adjust line pressure. See HYDRAULIC PRESSURE ADJUSTMENTS. If proper line pressure still cannot be obtained, check for defective components and hydraulic circuit. Low line pressure in all positions indicates a defective oil pump, restricted oil filter assembly or stuck pressure regulator valve.

GOVERNOR PRESSURE TEST

NOTE: Governor pressure test should be performed only if transaxle shifts at wrong vehicle speeds with Throttle Valve (T.V.) cable properly adjusted.

1) Remove pressure tap plug and connect a 150 psi (10.5 kg/cm²) pressure gauge to governor pressure tap, located below differential cover on right side of transaxle case. See Figs. 1 and 2.

2) Road test vehicle and operate transaxle in 3rd gear while noting governor pressure. Governor pressure should respond smoothly with changes in vehicle speed and return to 0-3 psi (0-.2 kg/cm²) when vehicle is stopped.

3) Pressure greater than 3 psi (.2 kg/cm²) with vehicle stopped will prevent transaxle from downshifting. Remove pressure gauge. Install and tighten pressure tap plug to specification. See TORQUE SPECIFICATIONS.

THROTTLE PRESSURE TEST

1) No pressure tap is provided for testing throttle pressure. Incorrect throttle pressure should only be suspected if part throttle upshift speeds are either delayed or occur too early in relation to vehicle speed.

2) Engine run-away on either upshifts or downshifts can also be an indication of low throttle pressure setting or improper Throttle Valve (T.V) cable adjustment. Ensure T.V. cable is properly adjusted. See appropriate AUTOMATIC TRANSMISSIONS SERVICING article in TRANSMISSION SERVICING.

3) Throttle pressure can be adjusted if T.V. cable is properly adjusted. See THROTTLE PRESSURE under HYDRAULIC PRESSURE ADJUSTMENTS.

CLUTCH & SERVO AIR PRESSURE TEST

NOTE: Inoperative clutches, servos and bands can be located by applying air pressure to appropriate passages in transaxle case.

Test Preparation – Remove valve body. See VALVE BODY under REMOVAL & INSTALLATION.

CAUTION: Ensure air supply is free of all dirt and moisture. Using air pressure regulator, adjust air pressure to 30 psi (2.1 kg/cm²).

Front Clutch – Apply air pressure to front clutch apply passage. See Fig. 2. Listen for a dull thud sound to indicate front clutch operation. Maintain air pressure application for a few seconds and check system for excessive oil leaks. Release air pressure.

Rear Clutch – 1) Apply air pressure to rear clutch apply passage. See Fig. 2. Listen for a dull thud sound to indicate rear clutch operation. If dull thud sound is not heard, release air pressure.

2) Place finger tips on clutch housing and reapply air pressure. Movement of clutch piston must be felt if rear clutch is operating. Maintain air pressure application for a few seconds and check system for excessive oil leaks. Release air pressure.

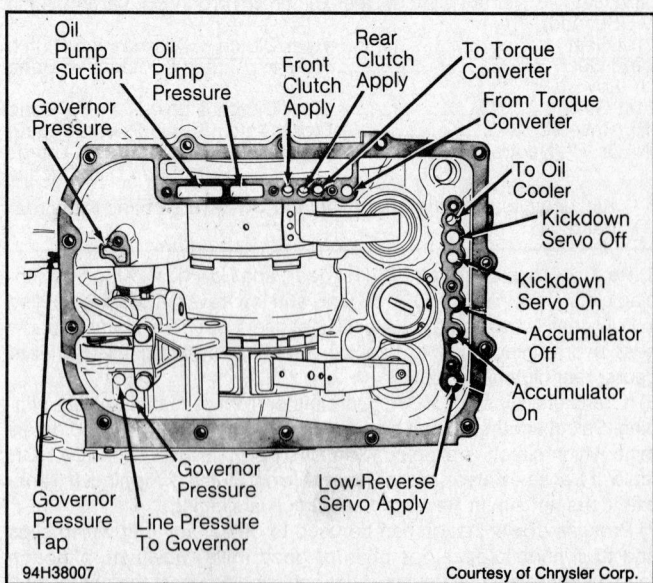

94H38007   Courtesy of Chrysler Corp.

Fig. 2: Identifying Governor Pressure Tap & Air Pressure Test Passages

Kickdown Servo (Front Band) – Apply air pressure to kickdown servo on passage. *See Fig. 2.* Front band should tighten, indicating kickdown servo operation. Release air pressure. Note that spring tension on servo piston releases the front band.

Low-Reverse Servo (Rear Band) – Apply air pressure to low-reverse servo apply passage. *See Fig. 2.* Rear band should tighten, indicating low-reverse servo operation. Release air pressure. Note that spring tension on servo piston releases the rear band.

NOTE: If clutches and servos operate properly, no upshift or erratic shift conditions indicates valve body is malfunctioning.

TORQUE CONVERTER FLUID LEAKAGE TEST

NOTE: Fluid around torque converter may originate from engine oil or the transaxle. Ensure transaxle fluid level is correct. Fluid leakage at torque converter may result if fluid level to high. Transaxle can be checked for leaks using the following method.

1) Remove torque converter housing dust shield. Clean inside area of torque converter housing using solvent and compressed air. Ensure area is clean and dry.
2) Fabricate leakage test probe using 1/32" sheet metal, 5" (127 mm) long and 1 1/2" (38.1 mm) wide. *See Fig. 3.* Operate engine until transaxle is at normal operating temperature. Shut engine off.
3) Install leakage test probe on torque converter housing dust shield bolt so leakage test probe is near torque converter. Ensure torque converter does not contact leakage test probe.

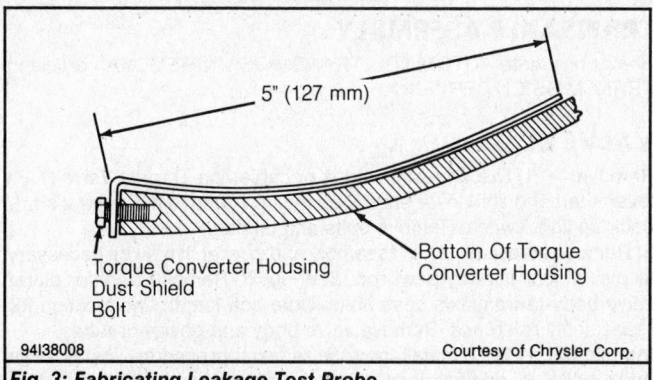

94I38008   Courtesy of Chrysler Corp.

Fig. 3: Fabricating Leakage Test Probe

4) Start engine. Place transaxle in Neutral. Operate engine at 2500 RPM for 2 minutes. Stop engine. Remove leakage test probe.
5) If upper surface of leakage test probe is dry, torque converter is not leaking. If upper surface of leakage test probe is wet with ATF, torque converter is leaking. If lower area below leakage test probe is wet with ATF, fluid is coming from around torque converter area.
6) Possible causes of fluid leaks at torque converter areas are:
- Torque converter hub seal
- Defective seal (check torque converter hub finish)
- Mispositioned or worn bushing
- Oil pump housing oil return hole restricted
- Defective oil pump housing "O" ring or oil pump housing
- Oil pump-to-transaxle case bolts

7) If torque converter is leaking, check for defective welds on outside diameter of torque converter and torque converter hub. Torque converter hub is welded on the inside and weld is not visible. Replace torque converter if a leak exists. DO NOT attempt to repair torque converter.

TRANSAXLE CASE PRESSURE TEST

NOTE: Transaxle case, gaskets and oil pump housing can be checked for leaks using following method. Transaxle must be removed to perform transaxle case pressure test.

1) Fabricate torque converter hub seal cup using thin wall tubing and a .125" (3.17 mm) steel disc. *See Fig. 4.* Fabricate torque converter hub seal cup retaining strap using 1/4" x 1 1/4" wide material. *See Fig. 5.*
2) Remove torque converter from transaxle. Plug dipstick tube and oil cooler supply (lower) line fitting. Using rotary motion, install torque converter hub seal cup over input shaft and through torque converter hub seal until cup bottoms against gear lugs of oil pump.
3) Install torque converter hub seal cup retaining strap using starter upper hole and opposite bracket hole. Attach air hose to oil cooler return (upper) line fitting on transaxle case.
4) Using pressure regulator, apply 8-10 psi (.5-.7 kg/cm²) of air pressure to transaxle case at oil cooler return line.

CAUTION: DO NOT apply more than 10 psi (.7 kg/cm²) of air pressure to transaxle case.

5) Coat oil pump and front of transaxle case with soapy water solution. Check for bubbles, indicating a leak in seals, "O" rings, gaskets or transaxle case. Release air pressure. Remove test equipment. Replace defective components.

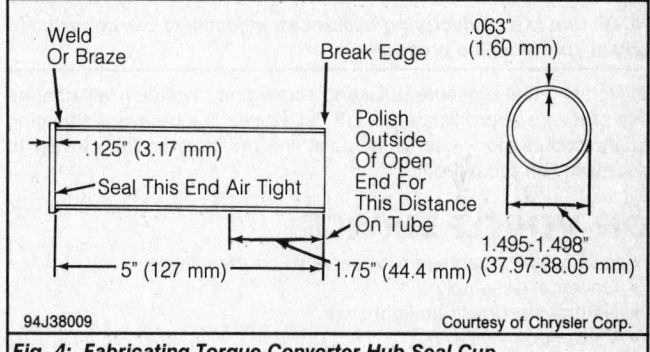

94J38009   Courtesy of Chrysler Corp.

Fig. 4: Fabricating Torque Converter Hub Seal Cup

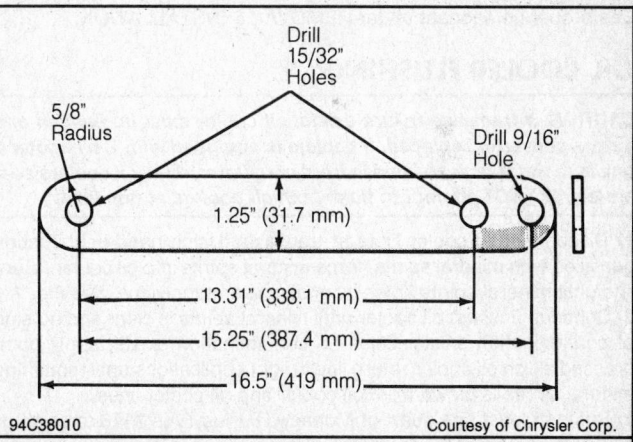

94C38010   Courtesy of Chrysler Corp.

Fig. 5: Fabricating Torque Converter Hub Seal Cup Retaining Strap

HYDRAULIC PRESSURE ADJUSTMENTS

CAUTION: Throttle pressure MUST NOT be adjusted until Throttle Valve (T.V.) cable adjustment has been checked and adjusted as needed. See appropriate AUTOMATIC TRANSMISSION SERVICING article in TRANSMISSION SERVICING. Incorrect throttle pressure setting will cause incorrect line pressure readings even though line pressure adjustment is correct. Always inspect and correct throttle pressure adjustment before adjusting line pressure.

THROTTLE PRESSURE

1) Remove valve body (if necessary). See VALVE BODY under REMOVAL & INSTALLATION. Insert gauge pin of Gauge (C-3763) between cam on throttle lever assembly and kickdown valve. *See Fig. 24.*

2) Push inward on gauge pin and compress kickdown valve against spring until kickdown valve is fully bottomed in valve body.

CAUTION: *Ensure spring is fully compressed and kickdown valve is bottomed in valve body.*

3) With spring fully compressed, using Adapter (C-4553), rotate throttle pressure adjusting screw until head of adjusting screw contacts tang on throttle valve lever assembly.
4) Ensure cam on throttle valve lever assembly contacts gauge pin and throttle valve is bottomed in valve body. Remove gauge pin.

LINE PRESSURE

CAUTION: *Always adjust throttle pressure before adjusting line pressure.*

1) Note location of line pressure adjusting screw. *See Fig. 25.* Rotate line pressure adjusting screw until distance between valve body and inner edge of adjusting screw is approximately 1 5/16".

NOTE: *Due to manufacturing tolerances, adjustment can be varied to obtain specified line pressure.*

2) Rotating line pressure adjusting screw one revolution will change line pressure approximately 1 2/3 psi. Rotate line pressure adjusting screw counterclockwise to increase line pressure and clockwise to decrease line pressure.

ON-VEHICLE SERVICE

Following components can be serviced on the vehicle:
- Governor assembly
- Neutral start/back-up light switch
- Valve body
- Vehicle speed sensor and pinion gear

See proper component under REMOVAL & INSTALLATION.

OIL COOLER FLUSHING

CAUTION: *If transaxle failure exists, oil cooler must be flushed and torque converter replaced. If vehicle is equipped with 2 oil coolers, one in radiator tank and one in front of radiator, flush oil coolers separately. DO NOT attempt to flush both oil coolers at one time.*

1) Disconnect oil cooler lines at transaxle. Using hand-held suction gun filled with mineral spirits, force mineral spirits into oil cooler return line until mineral spirits flows from oil cooler supply line. *See Fig. 1.*
2) Continue flushing oil cooler until mineral spirits is clear and no sign of contamination exists. Once no contamination exists, apply compressed air on oil cooler return line in light applications until remaining mineral spirits is blown from oil cooler and oil cooler lines.
3) Pump at least one quart of Mopar ATF Plus Type 7176 through oil cooler to ensure oil cooler is free of mineral spirits. Replace oil cooler if fluid does not flow freely through oil cooler.

OIL COOLER FLOW CHECK

1) With transaxle filled to proper fluid level, disconnect oil cooler return line from transaxle. *See Fig. 1.* Place container under oil cooler return line.

CAUTION: *DO NOT remove more than one quart of fluid, or transaxle may be damaged.*

2) Apply parking brake. Start engine and allow to idle. Place gearshift in Neutral. Check fluid flow from oil cooler return line. If fluid flow is intermittent or takes more than 20 seconds to obtain one quart, replace oil cooler. Reconnect oil cooler return line. Fill transaxle to proper fluid level with Mopar ATF Plus Type 7176.

REMOVAL & INSTALLATION

AXLE SHAFTS

See appropriate AXLE SHAFTS article in AXLE SHAFTS & TRANSFER CASES.

GOVERNOR ASSEMBLY

NOTE: *It is not necessary to remove transfer gear and governor support when servicing governor assembly.*

Removal & Installation – 1) Remove valve body. See VALVE BODY under REMOVAL & INSTALLATION. Remove governor assembly-to-governor support bolts. Remove governor assembly.
2) Ensure governor valves move freely in bores of governor assembly. To install, reverse removal procedure. Tighten bolts to specification. See TORQUE SPECIFICATIONS.

NEUTRAL START/BACK-UP LIGHT SWITCH

Removal & Installation – 1) Disconnect electrical connector from neutral start/back-up light switch, located on side of transaxle case. *See Fig. 1.*
2) Unscrew and remove neutral start/back-up light switch and seal from transaxle case. Some ATF may drain when switch is removed.
3) To install, reverse removal procedure using NEW seal. Tighten neutral start/back-up light switch to specification. See TORQUE SPECIFICATIONS. Fill transaxle to proper fluid level with Mopar ATF Plus Type 7176.

TRANSAXLE ASSEMBLY

See appropriate AUTOMATIC TRANSMISSION REMOVAL article in TRANSMISSION SERVICING.

VALVE BODY

Removal – 1) Disconnect linkages or cables on Throttle Valve (T.V.) lever shaft and shift lever shaft. *See Fig. 1.* Remove the neutral start/back-up light switch. Remove bolts and oil pan.
2) Remove screws, oil filter assembly and gasket. It may be necessary to disconnect parking pawl rod. *See Fig. 6.* Remove transfer plate/valve body-to-transaxle case bolts. Note bolt length and location for reassembly reference. Remove valve body and governor tubes.
Installation – 1) To install, reverse removal procedure. Install valve body bolts in original location and tighten to specification. See TORQUE SPECIFICATIONS.
2) Install NEW oil filter assembly and gasket. Tighten screws to specification. Apply RTV sealant on oil pan-to-transaxle surface and below head of oil pan bolts before installing. Tighten bolts to specification. See TORQUE SPECIFICATIONS. Fill transaxle to proper fluid level with Mopar ATF Plus Type 7176.

VEHICLE SPEED SENSOR & PINION GEAR

Removal – 1) Disconnect speedometer cable (if equipped) and electrical connector from vehicle speed sensor, located on extension housing of transaxle. Ensure weather seal remains on electrical connector.
2) Ensure area around vehicle speed sensor is clean. Remove bolt and vehicle speed sensor. Remove pinion gear from vehicle speed sensor.
Installation – To install, reverse removal procedure using NEW "O" ring on vehicle speed sensor. Tighten bolt to specification. See TORQUE SPECIFICATIONS.

TORQUE CONVERTER

CAUTION: *Torque converter is a welded assembly and is not serviceable. If a malfunction occurs or if torque converter becomes contaminated with foreign material, it MUST be replaced. It cannot be flushed or repaired.*

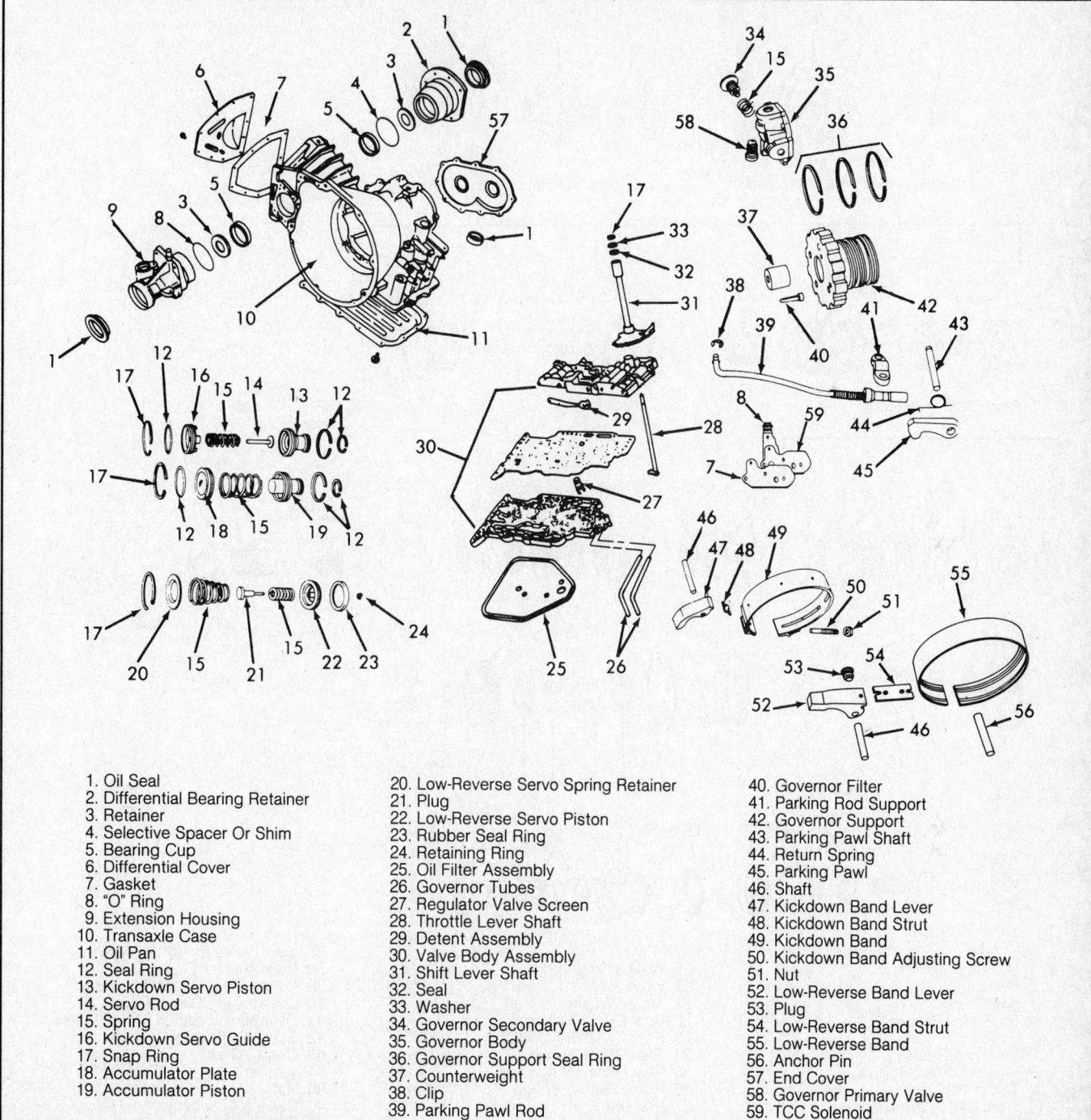

1. Oil Seal
2. Differential Bearing Retainer
3. Retainer
4. Selective Spacer Or Shim
5. Bearing Cup
6. Differential Cover
7. Gasket
8. "O" Ring
9. Extension Housing
10. Transaxle Case
11. Oil Pan
12. Seal Ring
13. Kickdown Servo Piston
14. Servo Rod
15. Spring
16. Kickdown Servo Guide
17. Snap Ring
18. Accumulator Plate
19. Accumulator Piston

20. Low-Reverse Servo Spring Retainer
21. Plug
22. Low-Reverse Servo Piston
23. Rubber Seal Ring
24. Retaining Ring
25. Oil Filter Assembly
26. Governor Tubes
27. Regulator Valve Screen
28. Throttle Lever Shaft
29. Detent Assembly
30. Valve Body Assembly
31. Shift Lever Shaft
32. Seal
33. Washer
34. Governor Secondary Valve
35. Governor Body
36. Governor Support Seal Ring
37. Counterweight
38. Clip
39. Parking Pawl Rod

40. Governor Filter
41. Parking Rod Support
42. Governor Support
43. Parking Pawl Shaft
44. Return Spring
45. Parking Pawl
46. Shaft
47. Kickdown Band Lever
48. Kickdown Band Strut
49. Kickdown Band
50. Kickdown Band Adjusting Screw
51. Nut
52. Low-Reverse Band Lever
53. Plug
54. Low-Reverse Band Strut
55. Low-Reverse Band
56. Anchor Pin
57. End Cover
58. Governor Primary Valve
59. TCC Solenoid

94D38011

Courtesy of Chrysler Corp.

Fig. 6: Exploded View Of Transaxle Case & Components

TRANSAXLE DISASSEMBLY

VALVE BODY & INTERNAL COMPONENTS

NOTE: Input shaft end play should be measured before transaxle disassembly. This indicates if thrust washer located between input and output shaft may need to be changed.

1) Remove torque converter. Attach dial indicator to transaxle case with dial indicator stem seated against end of input shaft.
2) Move input shaft inward and zero dial indicator. Pull input shaft outward and note reading. Input shaft end play should be .008-.060" (.20-1.52 mm). Record input shaft end play for reassembly reference.

3) Remove neutral start/back-up light switch. Remove bolts and oil pan. Remove screws, oil filter assembly and gasket. Remove clip and parking pawl rod. See Fig. 6. Remove transfer plate/valve body-to-transaxle case bolts. Note bolt length and location for reassembly reference. Remove valve body and governor tubes.
4) Loosen lock nut and tighten kickdown band adjusting screw before removing oil pump. See Fig. 1. Remove oil pump bolts. Install slide hammer pullers on opposite sides of oil pump. Remove oil pump, gasket and thrust washer from transaxle case.
5) Loosen kickdown band adjusting screw. Remove kickdown band and kickdown band strut. Remove front clutch assembly. Remove thrust washer located on oil pump end of input shaft. Remove input shaft, rear clutch retainer and rear clutch assembly. See Fig. 7.

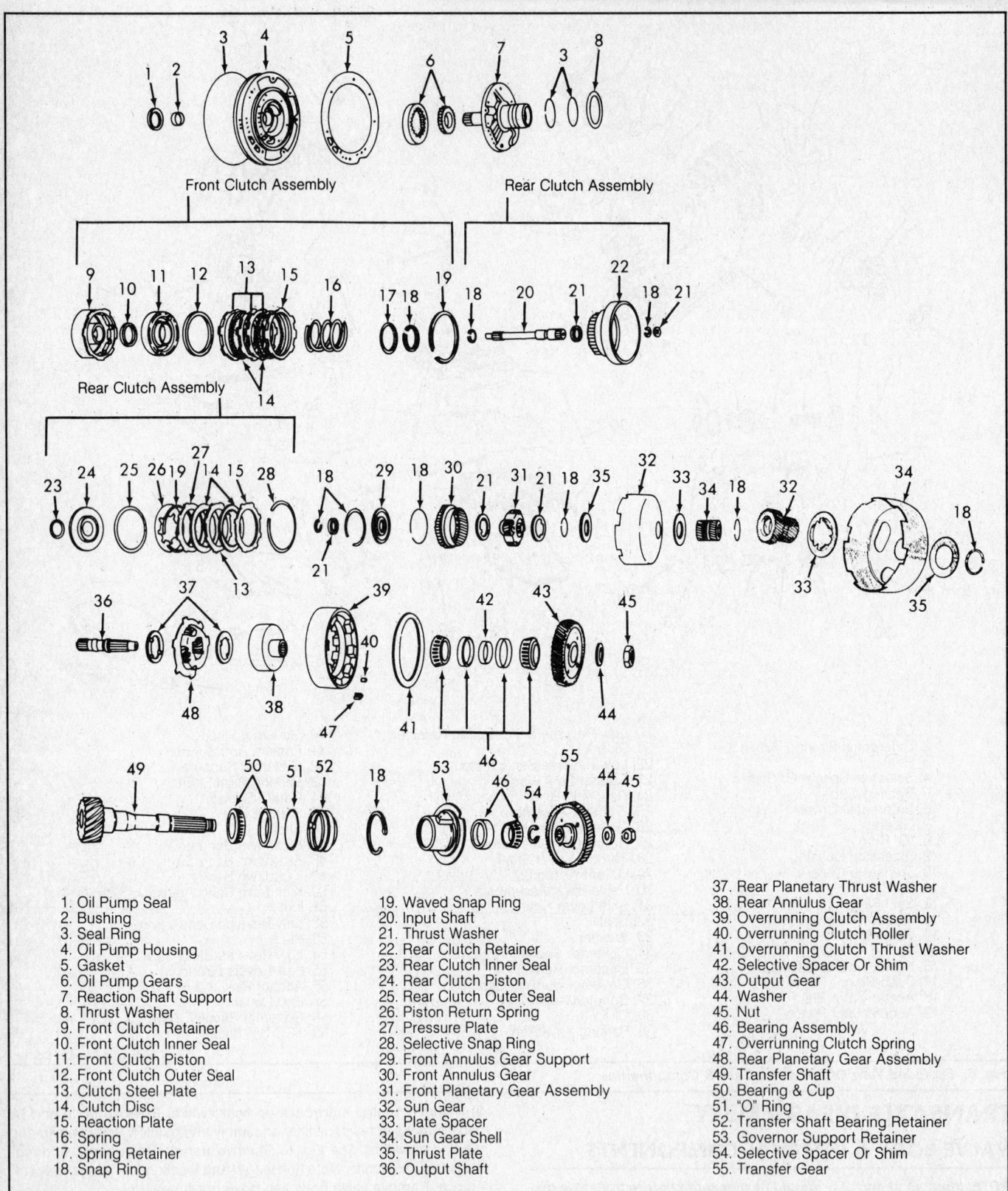

1. Oil Pump Seal
2. Bushing
3. Seal Ring
4. Oil Pump Housing
5. Gasket
6. Oil Pump Gears
7. Reaction Shaft Support
8. Thrust Washer
9. Front Clutch Retainer
10. Front Clutch Inner Seal
11. Front Clutch Piston
12. Front Clutch Outer Seal
13. Clutch Steel Plate
14. Clutch Disc
15. Reaction Plate
16. Spring
17. Spring Retainer
18. Snap Ring

19. Waved Snap Ring
20. Input Shaft
21. Thrust Washer
22. Rear Clutch Retainer
23. Rear Clutch Inner Seal
24. Rear Clutch Piston
25. Rear Clutch Outer Seal
26. Piston Return Spring
27. Pressure Plate
28. Selective Snap Ring
29. Front Annulus Gear Support
30. Front Annulus Gear
31. Front Planetary Gear Assembly
32. Sun Gear
33. Plate Spacer
34. Sun Gear Shell
35. Thrust Plate
36. Output Shaft

37. Rear Planetary Thrust Washer
38. Rear Annulus Gear
39. Overrunning Clutch Assembly
40. Overrunning Clutch Roller
41. Overrunning Clutch Thrust Washer
42. Selective Spacer Or Shim
43. Output Gear
44. Washer
45. Nut
46. Bearing Assembly
47. Overrunning Clutch Spring
48. Rear Planetary Gear Assembly
49. Transfer Shaft
50. Bearing & Cup
51. "O" Ring
52. Transfer Shaft Bearing Retainer
53. Governor Support Retainer
54. Selective Spacer Or Shim
55. Transfer Gear

94E38012

Courtesy of Chrysler Corp.

Fig. 7: Exploded View Of Transaxle Internal Components

6) Remove thrust washer located on end of output shaft. This is a selective fit thrust washer that fits between input and output shafts and controls input shaft end play.

7) Remove front planetary gear assembly retaining snap ring from output shaft. Remove front planetary gear assembly along with front annulus gear. Remove thrust washer located between front planetary gear assembly and sun gear. See Fig. 7.

8) Remove sun gear shell with sun gear. See Fig. 7. Remove rear planetary gear assembly and thrust washers. There are thrust washers on each side of rear planetary gear assembly.

9) Remove overrunning clutch assembly with 8 overrunning clutch rollers and 8 overrunning clutch springs. See Fig. 7. Loosen lock nut and low-reverse band adjusting screw. See Fig. 8.

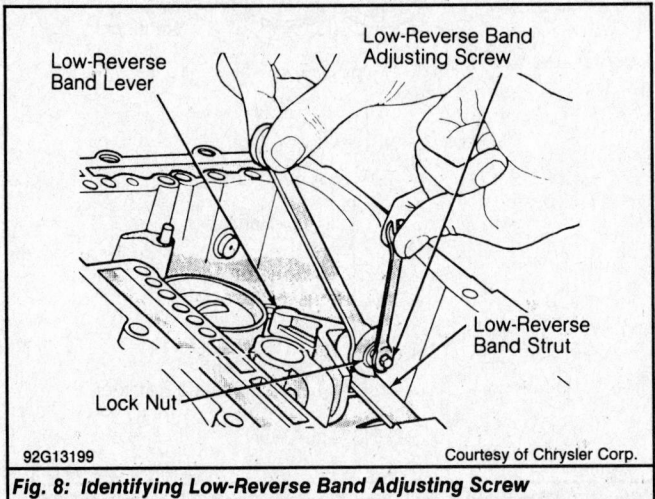

Fig. 8: Identifying Low-Reverse Band Adjusting Screw

10) Remove low-reverse band and low-reverse band strut. See Fig. 6. Remove overrunning clutch thrust washer. See Fig. 7. Remove bolts and end cover. Hold transfer gear. Remove nut and washer from end of transfer shaft.

11) Using puller, remove transfer gear and selective spacer or shim from transfer shaft. Remove governor support retainer. Remove anchor pin for low-reverse band, located at rear of transaxle, near transfer gear.

12) Slide governor support and governor assembly from transfer shaft. Remove transfer shaft bearing retaining snap ring from transaxle case. Using Puller (C-3752), Adapter (L-4437) and Transfer Shaft Remover/Installer (L-4512), remove transfer shaft bearing retainer and transfer shaft. See Fig. 9.

13) Remove bolts and parking rod support. See Fig. 6. Remove parking pawl shaft, parking pawl and return spring. Hold output gear. Remove nut and washer from output shaft.

14) Using puller, remove output gear and selective spacer or shim from output shaft. Remove output shaft and rear annulus gear from inside transaxle case. See Fig. 7.

15) If removing output shaft from rear annulus gear, support rear annulus gear in press. Ensure rear annulus gear is supported near center of the gear. Press output shaft from rear annulus gear.

16) If removing rear annulus gear bearing cup from transaxle case, use Bearing Cup Remover (L-4518). See Fig. 10.

NOTE: *Bearing cup remover used for rear annulus gear bearing cup removal can also be used to remove output shaft bearing cup from rear of transaxle case.*

17) Press bearing cup from governor support (if necessary). If removing bearing from transfer gear or output gear, use Bearing Remover (L-4406-1) and Adapter (L-4406-3 for transfer gear or L-4406-2 for output gear). See Fig. 11.

18) If removing bearing from transfer shaft, use Puller (C-293-A) and Adapter (C-293-52). See Fig. 12. If removing bearing cup from transfer shaft bearing retainer, use Bearing Cup Remover (L-4518). See Fig. 13. If removing bearing from rear annulus gear, use Puller (L-4406-1) and Adapter (L-4406-2). See Fig. 14.

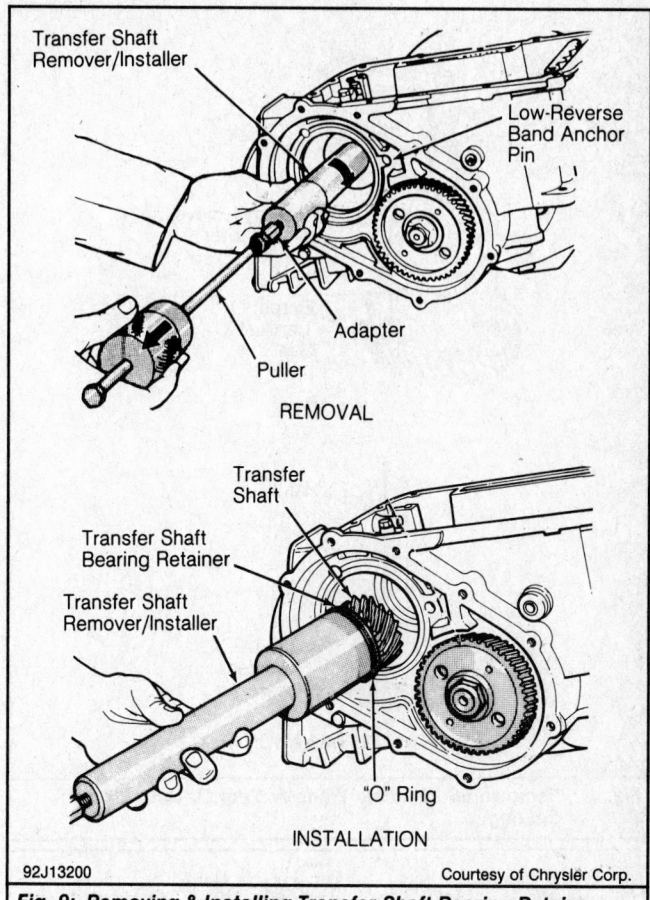

Fig. 9: Removing & Installing Transfer Shaft Bearing Retainer & Transfer Shaft

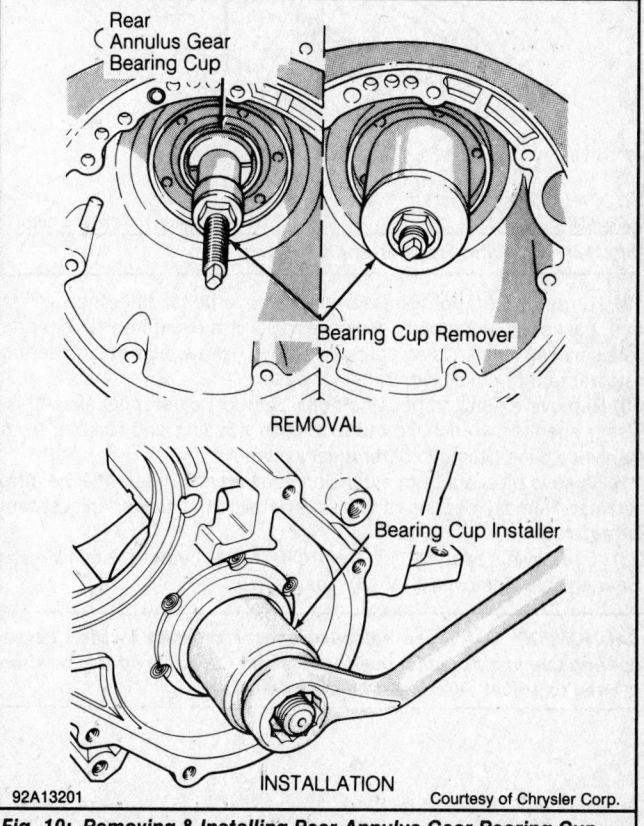

Fig. 10: Removing & Installing Rear Annulus Gear Bearing Cup

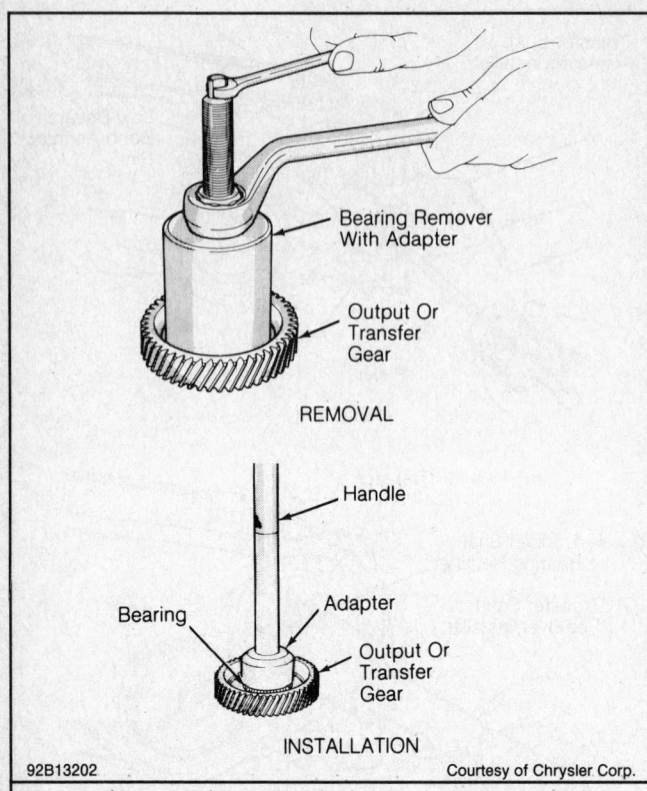

REMOVAL

INSTALLATION

92B13202   Courtesy of Chrysler Corp.

Fig. 11: Removing & Installing Transfer Gear Or Output Gear Bearing

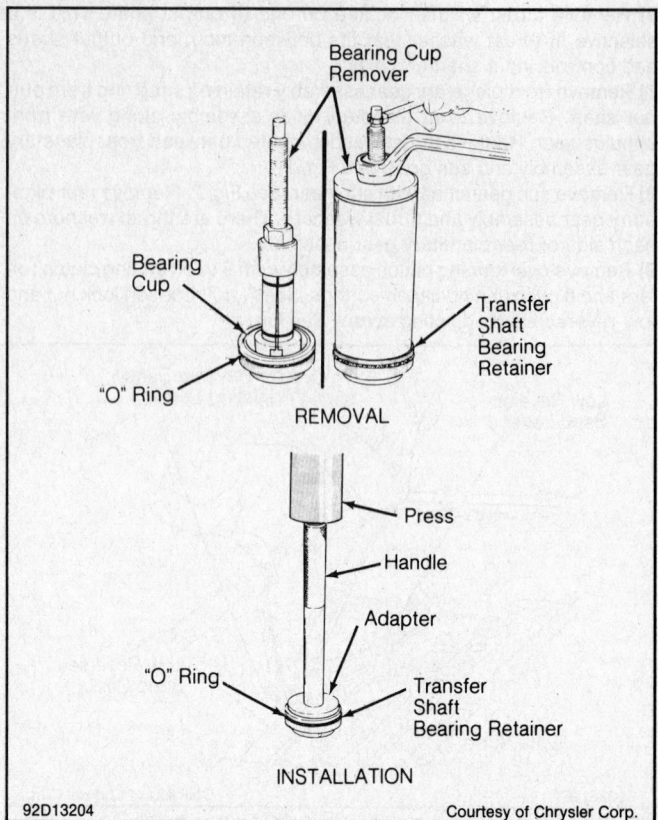

REMOVAL

INSTALLATION

92D13204   Courtesy of Chrysler Corp.

Fig. 13: Removing & Installing Transfer Shaft Bearing Retainer Bearing Cup

---

Transfer Shaft, Puller, Adapter, Vise diagram

92C13203   Courtesy of Chrysler Corp.

Fig. 12: Removing Transfer Shaft Bearing

19) To remove differential assembly, remove bolts, differential cover and gasket (if equipped). Remove bolts from differential bearing retainer. *See Fig. 6.* Using spanner wrench, rotate differential bearing retainer and remove from transaxle case.

20) Remove extension housing bolts. Support differential assembly. Using spanner wrench, rotate extension housing and remove from transaxle case. Remove differential assembly.

21) Remove oil seals from extension housing and differential bearing retainer. Remove bearing race from extension housing if replacement is required.

22) If removing bearing cup from differential bearing retainer, use Bearing Cup Remover (L-4518). *See Fig. 15.*

CAUTION: DO NOT loose selective spacer or shim located below bearing cup in differential bearing retainer. Selective spacer or shim is used to adjust differential bearing preload.

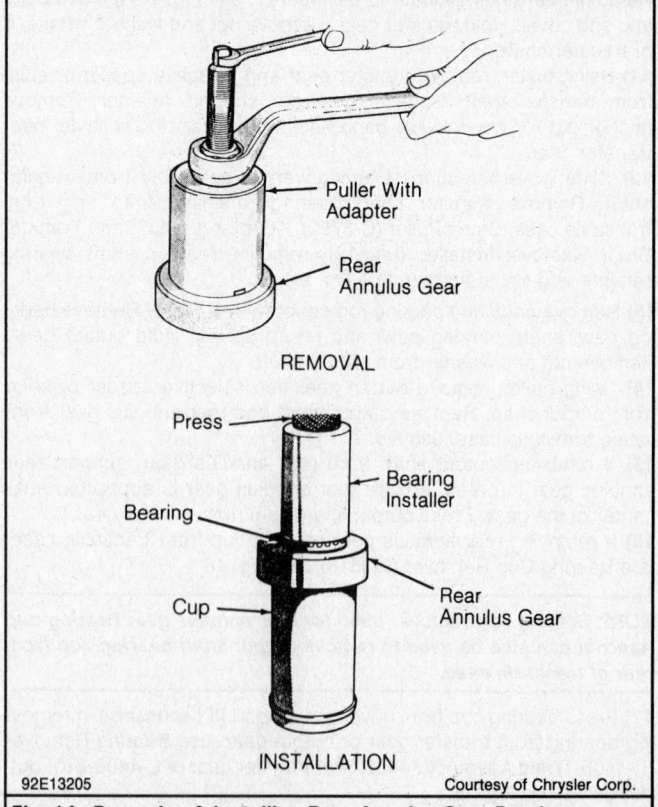

REMOVAL

INSTALLATION

92E13205   Courtesy of Chrysler Corp.

Fig. 14: Removing & Installing Rear Annulus Gear Bearing

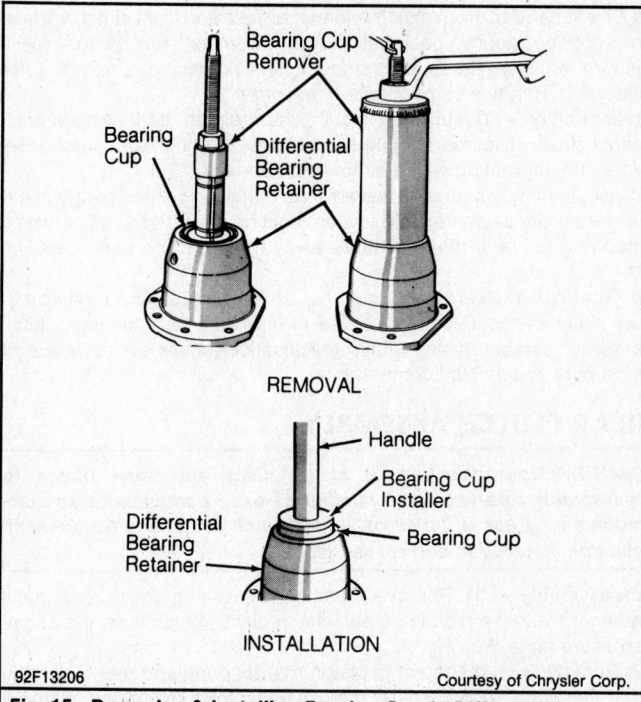

Fig. 15: **Removing & Installing Bearing Cup In Differential Bearing Retainer**

92F13206 — Courtesy of Chrysler Corp.

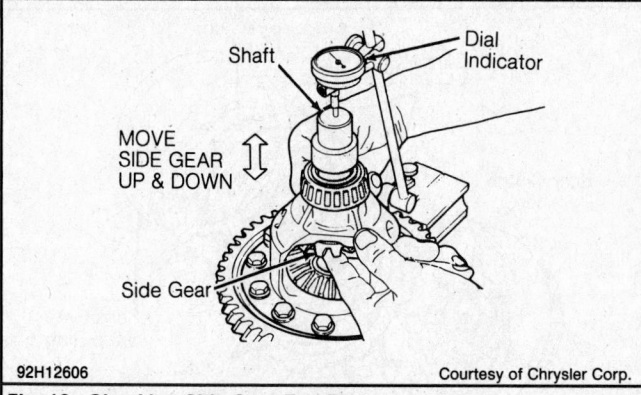

Fig. 16: **Checking Side Gear End Play**

92H12606 — Courtesy of Chrysler Corp.

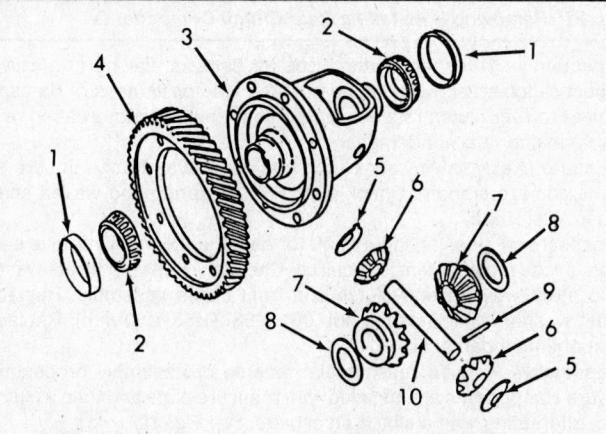

1. Bearing Cup
2. Side Bearing
3. Carrier
4. Ring Gear
5. Pinion Gear Thrust Washer
6. Pinion Gear
7. Side Gear
8. Side Gear Thrust Washer
9. Roll Pin
10. Pinion Gear Shaft

92G13207 — Courtesy of Chrysler Corp.

Fig. 17: **Exploded View Of Differential Assembly**

COMPONENT DISASSEMBLY & REASSEMBLY

DIFFERENTIAL ASSEMBLY

Disassembly – 1) Remove side bearings from carrier (if necessary). Remove bolts and ring gear.

2) Side gear end play should be checked before disassembling side gears to determine if different thickness side gear thrust washer is required.

3) Install Shaft (C-4996) in side gear. Install dial indicator. *See Fig. 16.* Move side gear upward and zero dial indicator. Move side gear downward and note side gear end play.

4) Side gear end play should be .001-.013" (.03-.33 mm). Repeat procedure on remaining side gear. If side gear end play is not within specification, 4 different thickness side gear thrust washers are available.

5) Using hammer and punch, remove roll pin from carrier. *See Fig. 17.* Remove pinion gear shaft. Rotate pinion gears and remove pinion gears and pinion gear thrust washers. Remove side gears and side gear thrust washers.

Reassembly – 1) To reassemble, reverse disassembly procedure. Recheck side gear end play once side gears and pinion gears are installed.

2) Install NEW ring gear bolts. DO NOT reuse ring gear bolts. Tighten ring gear bolts to specification. See TORQUE SPECIFICATIONS. Using press, install NEW side bearings (if removed).

ACCUMULATOR

Disassembly & Reassembly – Note location of accumulator. *See Fig. 18.* Remove snap ring, accumulator plate, spring and accumulator piston. *See Fig. 6.* Remove seal rings from accumulator piston (if necessary). To reassemble, reverse disassembly procedure using new seal rings.

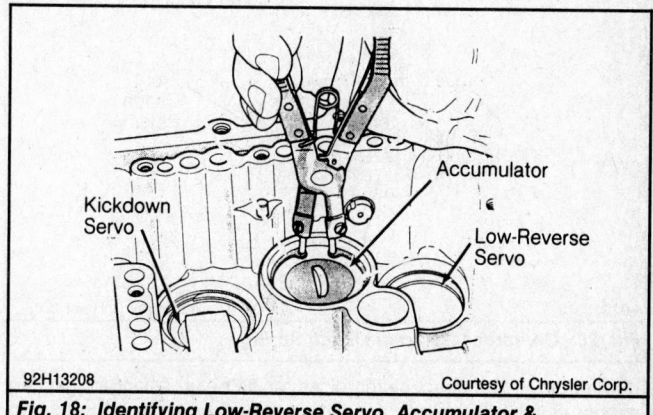

92H13208 — Courtesy of Chrysler Corp.

Fig. 18: **Identifying Low-Reverse Servo, Accumulator & Kickdown Servo**

KICKDOWN SERVO

Disassembly & Reassembly – 1) Note location of kickdown servo. *See Fig. 18.* Remove snap ring, kickdown servo guide, spring and kickdown servo piston. *See Fig. 6.*

2) Remove snap ring and separate servo rod from kickdown servo piston. Remove "O" rings from servo rod and kickdown servo guide. Remove seal rings from kickdown servo piston. To reassemble, reverse disassembly procedure using NEW "O" rings and NEW seal rings.

LOW-REVERSE SERVO

Disassembly & Reassembly – Note location of low-reverse servo. *See Fig. 18.* Remove snap ring, low-reverse servo spring retainer, spring and low-reverse servo piston. *See Fig. 6.* To reassemble, reverse disassembly procedure. Replace rubber seal ring on low-reverse servo piston (if necessary).

FRONT CLUTCH ASSEMBLY

CAUTION: Note direction of clutch discs and steel plates for reassembly reference and number of each components as some models may use a 3-disc or 4-disc clutch assembly. Components must be installed in correct sequence.

Disassembly – 1) Using screwdriver, remove waved snap and reaction plate. See Fig. 7. Remove clutch discs and clutch steel plates. See Fig. 19.

2) Using Spring Compressor (C-3575-A), compress spring and remove snap ring. See Fig. 20. Remove spring compressor. Remove spring retainer, spring and front clutch piston. See Fig. 7. Remove inner and outer seals (if necessary).

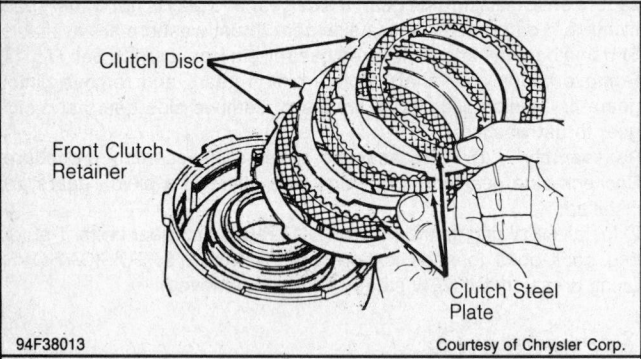

Clutch Disc

Front Clutch Retainer

Clutch Steel Plate

94F38013 — Courtesy of Chrysler Corp.
Fig. 19: Removing & Installing Front Clutch Components

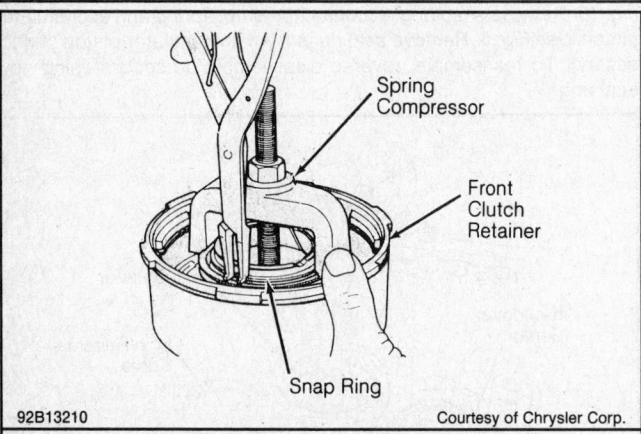

Spring Compressor

Front Clutch Retainer

Snap Ring

92B13210 — Courtesy of Chrysler Corp.
Fig. 20: Compressing Front Clutch Spring

Inspection – 1) Inspect clutch discs for flatness, flaking or glazing. Inspect clutch steel plates for flatness or damage at plate-to-front clutch retainer tang areas. Ensure tang areas in front clutch retainer are not damaged.

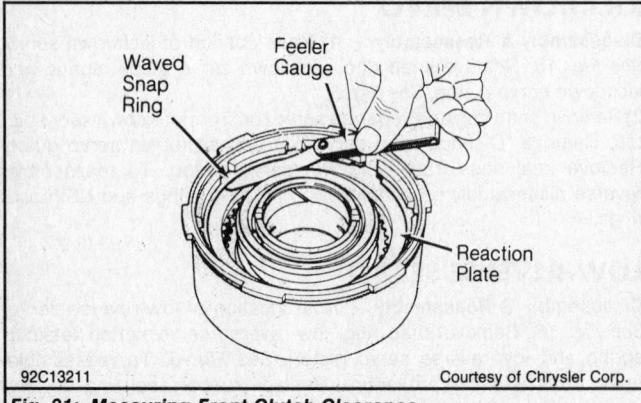

Waved Snap Ring

Feeler Gauge

Reaction Plate

92C13211 — Courtesy of Chrysler Corp.
Fig. 21: Measuring Front Clutch Clearance

2) Check band-to-front clutch retainer surface and front clutch surface for scoring. Ensure check ball in front clutch retainer moves freely. Ensure all seal areas are smooth. Check waved snap ring for distortion. Replace components if damaged.

Reassembly – 1) Reinstall front clutch piston and components. Install clutch discs and clutch steel plates, starting with clutch steel plate and alternating with a clutch disc. See Fig. 19.

2) Install reaction plate and waved snap ring. Using feeler gauge, measure front clutch clearance between reaction plate and edge of waved snap ring, at the farthest distance away from reaction plate. See Fig. 21.

3) Front clutch clearance should be .087-.133" (2.20-3.38 mm) on 3-disc clutches and .090-.146" (2.29-3.71 mm) on 4-disc clutches. Clutch is non-adjustable. If not within specification, check for defective or improperly assembled components.

REAR CLUTCH ASSEMBLY

CAUTION: Note direction of clutch discs and steel plates for reassembly reference and number of each components as some models may use a 3-disc or 4-disc clutch assembly. Components must be installed in correct sequence.

Disassembly – 1) Remove selective snap ring from rear clutch retainer. Remove reaction plate, clutch discs, clutch steel plates and pressure plate. See Fig. 22.

2) Remove waved snap ring, piston return spring and rear clutch piston. See Fig. 7. If necessary, remove seals from rear clutch piston. If removing input shaft, remove snap ring and press input shaft from rear clutch retainer.

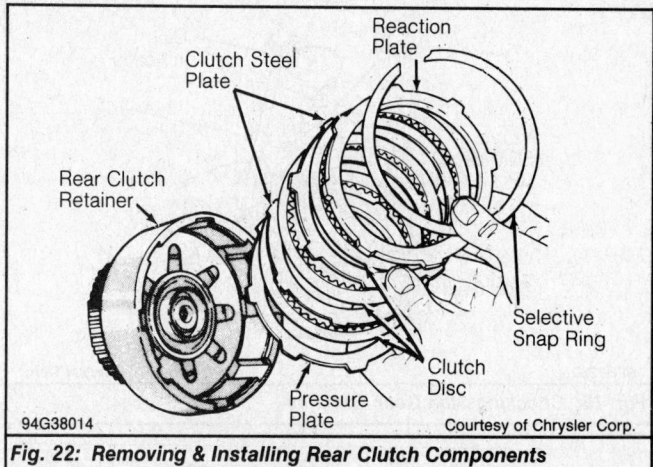

Reaction Plate

Clutch Steel Plate

Rear Clutch Retainer

Selective Snap Ring

Clutch Disc

Pressure Plate

94G38014 — Courtesy of Chrysler Corp.
Fig. 22: Removing & Installing Rear Clutch Components

Inspection – 1) Inspect clutch discs for flatness, flaking or glazing. Inspect clutch steel plates and pressure plate for flatness or damage at plate-to-rear clutch retainer tang areas. Ensure tang areas in rear clutch retainer are not damaged.

2) Ensure check ball in rear clutch retainer moves freely. Ensure all seal areas are smooth. Check piston return spring and waved snap ring for distortion.

3) Inspect seal rings on input shaft for damage. DO NOT remove seal rings unless replacement is required. Check thickness of thrust washer located between rear clutch and front clutch assembly. Replace thrust washer if thickness is not .061-.063" (1.55-1.60 mm). Replace components if damaged.

Reassembly – 1) To reassemble, reverse disassembly procedure. Ensure components are installed with pressure plate and then a clutch disc, alternating with a clutch steel plate. See Fig. 22.

2) Install reaction plate and selective snap ring. Using feeler gauge, measure rear clutch clearance between reaction plate and selective snap ring. See Fig. 23.

3) Rear clutch clearance should be .026-.043" (.66-1.09 mm), regardless of number of clutch discs used. If rear clutch clearance is not within specification, install different thickness selective snap ring to obtain correct clearance.

4) Selective snap ring is available in thickness of .048-.050" (1.22-1.27 mm), .060-.062" (1.52-1.57 mm), .068-.070" (1.73-1.78 mm), .074-.076" (1.88-1.93 mm) and .087-.089" (2.21-2.26 mm).

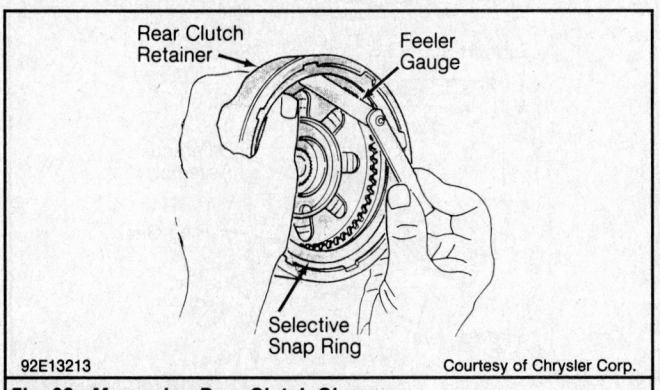

92E13213   Courtesy of Chrysler Corp.

Fig. 23: Measuring Rear Clutch Clearance

FRONT PLANETARY GEAR ASSEMBLY & FRONT ANNULUS GEAR

Disassembly & Reassembly – 1) Remove snap ring retaining front planetary gear assembly in front annulus gear. Remove thrust washer located below snap ring. Separate front annulus gear from front planetary gear assembly. *See Fig. 7.*

2) Remove snap ring and front annulus gear support from front annulus gear. To reassemble, reverse disassembly procedure.

OIL PUMP

Disassembly – Remove bolts and separate reaction shaft support from oil pump housing. *See Fig. 7.* Mark oil pump gear location for reassembly reference. Remove oil pump gears from pump housing.

Cleaning & Inspection – 1) Clean and inspect components for damage. Install both oil pump gears in oil pump housing. Using feeler gauge, measure outer gear-to-oil pump housing clearance.

2) Place straightedge on oil pump housing, above both oil pump gears. Using feeler gauge, measure gear side clearance between each oil pump gear and straightedge. Replace components if clearance is not within specification. See OIL PUMP SPECIFICATIONS table.

OIL PUMP SPECIFICATIONS

Measurement	In. (mm)
Gear Side Clearance	.0008-.0018 (.020-.046)
Outer Gear-To-Oil Pump Housing Clearance	.0018-.0056 (.046-.142)

Reassembly – To reassemble, reverse disassembly procedure. Ensure components are installed in original location. Tighten bolts to specification. See TORQUE SPECIFICATIONS.

VALVE BODY

CAUTION: For reassembly reference, place valve body components in order and mark spring locations when disassembling valve body. DO NOT use force to remove plugs or valves from valve body.

Disassembly – 1) Remove screw and detent assembly from valve body. Remove valve body screws. Remove separator plate and transfer plate from valve body.

CAUTION: DO NOT allow check balls to fall from valve body when removing separator plate and transfer plate. Note position of 8 check balls in valve body for reassembly reference. See Fig. 24.

2) Remove check balls from valve body. Remove snap ring, washer and seal from end of throttle lever shaft. *See Fig. 6.*

3) Slide shift lever shaft from throttle lever shaft. Remove throttle lever shaft from valve body. Remove manual valve from valve body. *See Fig. 25.*

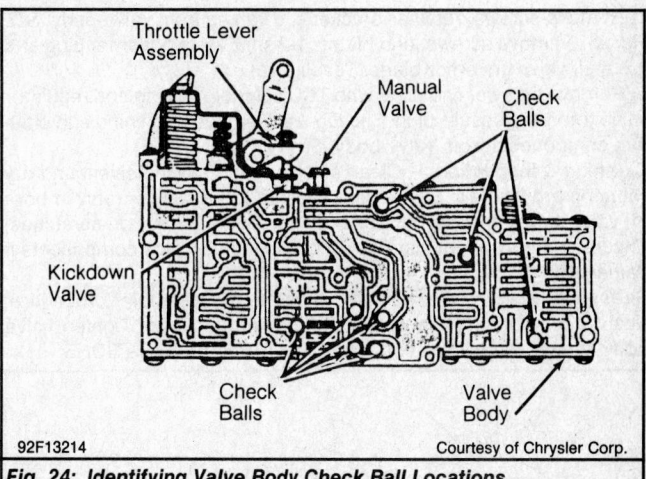

92F13214   Courtesy of Chrysler Corp.

Fig. 24: Identifying Valve Body Check Ball Locations

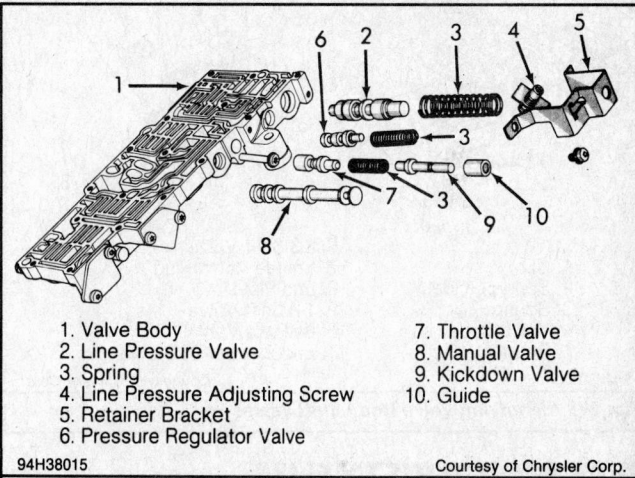

1. Valve Body
2. Line Pressure Valve
3. Spring
4. Line Pressure Adjusting Screw
5. Retainer Bracket
6. Pressure Regulator Valve
7. Throttle Valve
8. Manual Valve
9. Kickdown Valve
10. Guide

94H38015   Courtesy of Chrysler Corp.

Fig. 25: Identifying Valve Body Manual Valve & Components

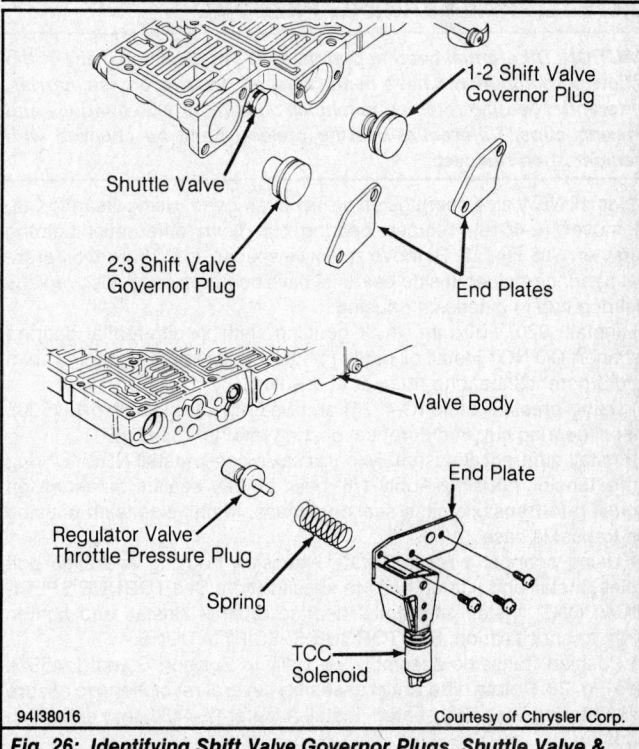

94I38016   Courtesy of Chrysler Corp.

Fig. 26: Identifying Shift Valve Governor Plugs, Shuttle Valve & Regulator Valve Throttle Pressure Plug

4) Remove screws, retainer bracket and valves from valve body. *See Fig. 25.* Remove screws, end plates, 1-2 shift valve governor plug and 2-3 shift valve governor plugs. *See Fig. 26.*

5) Remove screws, end plate with TCC solenoid, spring and regulator valve throttle pressure plug. *See Fig. 26.* Remove remaining end plate and components from valve body. *See Fig. 27.*

Cleaning & Inspection – Clean all components with solvent and dry with compressed air. Ensure all valves and plugs slide freely in bore of valve body. Inspect all surfaces for burrs, nicks or scratches. Ensure springs are not distorted or collapsed. Replace components if damaged.

Reassembly – To reassemble, reverse disassembly procedure. Ensure components are installed in original location. Tighten valve body screws to specification. See TORQUE SPECIFICATIONS.

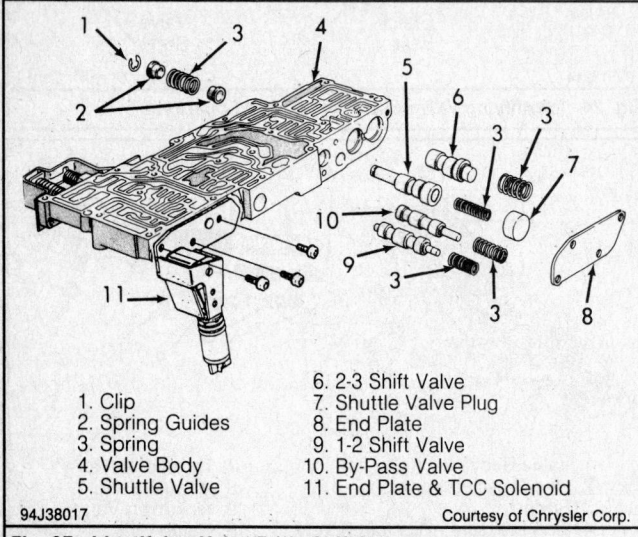

1. Clip
2. Spring Guides
3. Spring
4. Valve Body
5. Shuttle Valve
6. 2-3 Shift Valve
7. Shuttle Valve Plug
8. End Plate
9. 1-2 Shift Valve
10. By-Pass Valve
11. End Plate & TCC Solenoid

94J38017   Courtesy of Chrysler Corp.

Fig. 27: Identifying Valve Body Shift Valves

BEARING ADJUSTMENTS

DIFFERENTIAL BEARING PRELOAD

CAUTION: Differential bearing preload MUST be adjusted if any of the following components have been replaced: transaxle case, carrier, differential bearing retainer, extension housing or side bearings and bearing cups. Differential bearing preload must be checked with transfer shaft removed.

1) Install NEW side bearings on carrier if removed. Using Bearing Cup Remover (L-4518), remove bearing cup from differential bearing retainer. *See Fig. 15.* Remove selective spacer or shim from differential bearing retainer. If side bearings have been replaced, also replace bearing cup in extension housing.

2) Install .020" (.50 mm) thick gauging shim in differential bearing retainer. DO NOT install oil baffle (if equipped) between gauging shim and differential bearing retainer at this time.

3) Using press, Handle (C-4171) and Bearing Cup Installer (L-4520), install bearing cup in differential bearing retainer. *See Fig. 15.*

4) Install differential assembly in transaxle case. Install NEW "O" ring on extension housing. Apply 1/8" bead of RTV sealant on extension housing-to-transaxle case sealing surface. Install extension housing on transaxle case.

5) Using spanner wrench, rotate extension housing and align bolt holes. Install and tighten bolts to specification. See TORQUE SPECIFICATIONS. Install differential bearing retainer. Install and tighten bolts to specification. See TORQUE SPECIFICATIONS.

6) Position transaxle assembly vertically in Support Stand (L-4557). *See Fig. 28.* Rotate differential assembly several revolutions to ensure side bearings are fully seated. Install Adapter (L-4436) into extension housing.

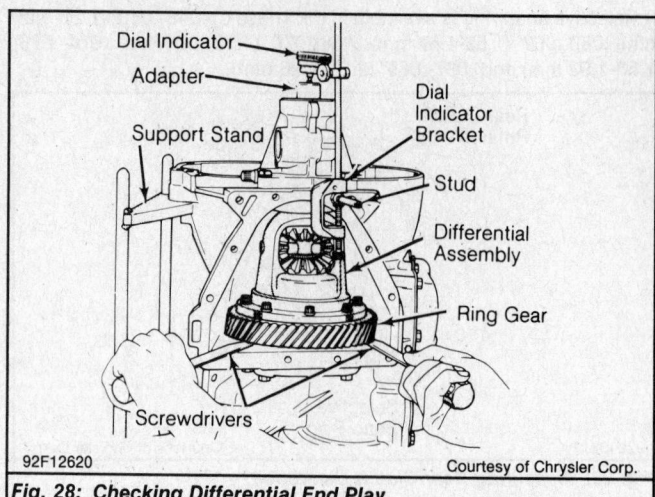

92F12620   Courtesy of Chrysler Corp.

Fig. 28: Checking Differential End Play

7) Install dial indicator with indicator stem resting on adapter and zero dial indicator. *See Fig. 28.* Using screwdrivers on each side of ring gear, pry ring gear upward and note differential end play reading on dial indicator.

CAUTION: DO NOT damage transaxle case or differential cover sealing surface when prying ring gear upward.

8) Using differential end play reading, determine selective spacer or shim to be required. *See Fig. 29.* Once proper selective spacer or shim is determined, remove bolts and differential bearing retainer.

End Play (with .50 mm gauging shim installed)		Required Shim Combination	Total Thickness	
mm	inch	mm	mm	inch
.0	.0	.50	.50	.020
.05	.002	.75	.75	.030
.10	.004	.80	.80	.032
.15	.006	.85	.85	.034
.20	.008	.90	.90	.035
.25	.010	.95	.95	.037
.30	.012	1.00	1.00	.039
.35	.014	1.05	1.05	.041
.40	.016	.50 + .60	1.10	.043
.45	.018	.50 + .65	1.15	.045
.50	.020	.50 + .70	1.20	.047
.55	.022	.50 + .75	1.25	.049
.60	.024	.50 + .80	1.30	.051
.65	.026	.50 + .85	1.35	.053
.70	.027	.50 + .90	1.40	.055
.75	.029	.50 + .95	1.45	.057
.80	.031	.50 + 1.00	1.50	.059
.85	.033	.50 + 1.05	1.55	.061
.90	.035	1.00 + .60	1.60	.063
.95	.037	1.00 + .65	1.65	.065
1.00	.039	1.00 + .70	1.70	.067
1.05	.041	1.00 + .75	1.75	.069
1.10	.043	1.00 + .80	1.80	.071
1.15	.045	1.00 + .85	1.85	.073
1.20	.047	1.00 + .90	1.90	.075
1.25	.049	1.00 + .95	1.95	.077
1.30	.051	1.00 + 1.00	2.00	.079
1.35	.053	1.00 + 1.05	2.05	.081
1.40	.055	1.05 + 1.05	2.10	.083

92G12621   Courtesy of Chrysler Corp.

Fig. 29: Determining Differential End Play Selective Spacer Or Shim

9) Using bearing cup remover, remove bearing cup from differential bearing retainer. Remove gauging shim. Install oil baffle (if equipped) and proper selective spacer or shim.

10) Using press, handle and bearing race installer, install bearing cup in differential bearing retainer. Apply 1/8" bead of RTV sealant on differential bearing retainer-to-transaxle case sealing surface. Install differential bearing retainer on transaxle case.

11) Using spanner wrench, rotate differential bearing retainer and align bolt holes. Install and tighten bolts to specification. See TORQUE SPECIFICATIONS.

12) Coat side bearings with oil. Using Adapter (L-4436-A) and INCH-lb. torque wrench, check differential rotating torque required to rotate differential assembly. *See Fig. 30.* Differential rotating torque should be 5-18 INCH lbs (.6-2.0 N.m).

13) If differential rotating torque exceeds specification, install a .002" (.05 mm) thinner selective spacer or shim in differential bearing retainer. If differential rotating torque is less than specified, install a .002" (.05 mm) thicker selective spacer or shim in differential bearing retainer. Recheck differential rotating torque.

14) If oil seal was removed from extension housing, install NEW oil seal in extension housing.

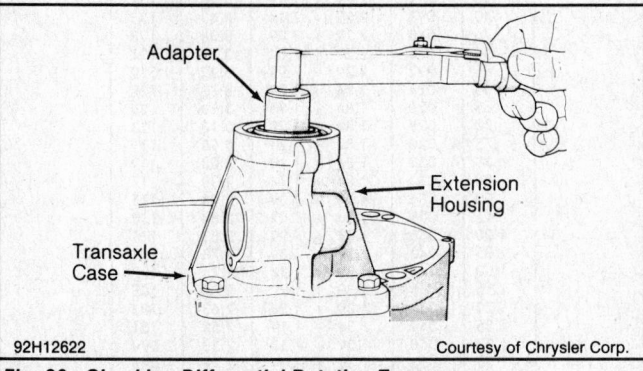

92H12622   Courtesy of Chrysler Corp.

Fig. 30: Checking Differential Rotating Torque

OUTPUT SHAFT BEARING PRELOAD

CAUTION: Output shaft bearing preload must be checked when transaxle case, output shaft, rear annulus gear, output gear, bearings or bearing cups are replaced. Output gear bearing preload must be checked with transfer gear removed from transfer shaft.

1) With output gear and selective spacers or shims removed, install .537" (13.65 mm) and .053" (1.34 mm) thick gauging shims on hub of rear annulus gear, using grease to hold gauging shims in place. *See Fig. 31.*

NOTE: The .537" (13.65 mm) gauging shim has a larger inside diameter and must be installed over output shaft first. The .053" (1.34 mm) gauging shim fits on the output shaft.

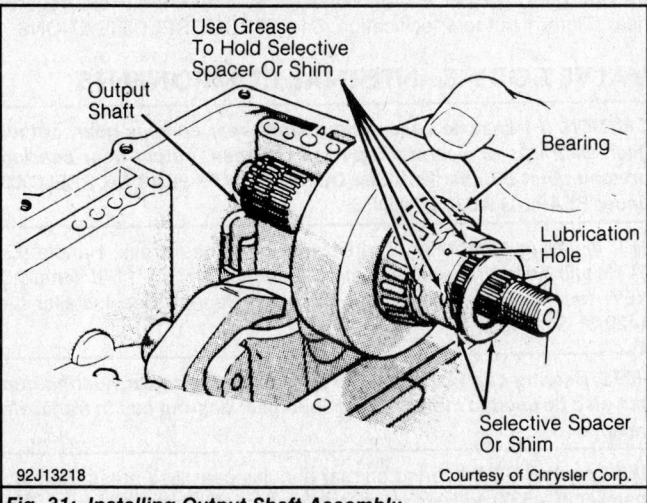

92J13218   Courtesy of Chrysler Corp.

Fig. 31: Installing Output Shaft Assembly

2) Install output shaft in transaxle case. Install output gear, washer and nut. Hold output gear and tighten nut to 200 ft. lbs. (271 N.m).

3) Attach Lever (L-4432) on output gear. *See Fig. 32.* Move output gear inward and outward while rotating back and forth to ensure bearings are seated. Mount steel ball in end of output shaft and retain in place with grease. Install Adapter (L-4438) and dial indicator with stem resting on steel ball. *See Fig. 32.*

4) Move output gear inward and zero dial indicator. Pull output gear outward and note output shaft end play. Using output shaft end play, determine proper selective shim or spacer. *See Fig. 33.*

NOTE: The .498" (12.65 mm), .518" (13.16 mm) and .537" (13.64 mm) selective shims or spacers are always installed first. These selective shims or spacers contain lubrication slots necessary for proper bearing lubrication.

5) Remove nut, washer and output gear. Remove gauging shims. Install correct selective spacers or shims. Hold shims in place with grease. Reinstall output shaft gear, washer and nut. Tighten nut to 200 ft. lbs. (271 N.m).

6) Using INCH lb. torque wrench, check output shaft rotating torque. Output shaft rotating torque should be 3-8 INCH lbs. (.3-.9 N.m).

7) If output shaft rotating torque exceeds specification, install a .002" (.05 mm) thicker selective spacer or shim. If output shaft rotating torque is less than specified, install a .002" (.05 mm) thinner selective spacer or shim. Recheck output shaft rotating torque.

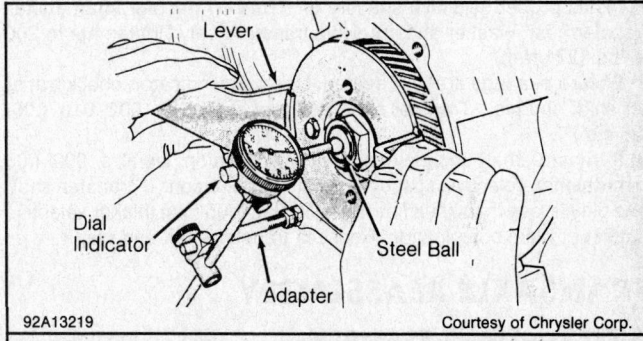

92A13219   Courtesy of Chrysler Corp.

Fig. 32: Checking Output Shaft Or Transfer Shaft End Play

End Play (with 13.65mm and 1.34mm gauging shims Installed)		Required Shim Combination	Total Thickness	
mm	inch		mm	inch
.0	.0	13.65 + 1.34	14.99	.590
.05	.002	13.65 + 1.24	14.89	.586
.10	.004	13.65 + 1.19	14.84	.584
.15	.006	13.65 + 1.14	14.79	.582
.20	.008	13.65 + 1.09	14.74	.580
.25	.010	13.65 + 1.04	14.69	.578
.30	.012	13.65 + .99	14.64	.576
.35	.014	13.65 + .94	14.59	.574
.40	.016	13.15 + 1.39	14.54	.572
.45	.018	13.15 + 1.34	14.49	.570
.50	.020	13.15 + 1.29	14.44	.568
.55	.022	13.15 + 1.24	14.39	.566
.60	.024	13.15 + 1.19	14.34	.564
.65	.026	13.15 + 1.14	14.29	.562
.70	.028	13.15 + 1.09	14.24	.560
.75	.030	13.15 + 1.04	14.19	.558
.80	.032	13.15 + .99	14.14	.556
.85	.034	13.15 + .94	14.09	.554
.90	.036	12.65 + 1.39	14.04	.552
.95	.038	12.65 + 1.34	13.99	.550
1.00	.040	12.65 + 1.29	13.94	.548
1.05	.042	12.65 + 1.24	13.89	.547
1.10	.044	12.65 + 1.19	13.84	.545
1.15	.046	12.65 + 1.14	13.79	.543
1.20	.048	12.65 + 1.09	13.74	.541
1.25	.049	12.65 + 1.04	13.69	.539
1.30	.051	12.65 + .99	13.64	.537
1.35	.053	12.65 + .94	13.59	.535
Average Conversion .05mm = .002"				

92D13220   Courtesy of Chrysler Corp.

Fig. 33: Determining Output Gear Selective Spacers Or Shims

TRANSFER SHAFT BEARING PRELOAD

CAUTION: Transfer shaft bearing preload must be checked when bearings, bearing cups, governor support, governor support retainer, transaxle case, transfer gear, transfer shaft or transfer shaft bearing retainer are replaced.

1) Using gear holder, hold transfer gear. Remove nut and washer from end of transfer shaft. Using puller, remove transfer gear and selective spacers or shims from transfer shaft.

2) Install a .090" (2.29 mm) and .055" (1.39 mm) thick gauging shims on transfer shaft behind governor support. Install transfer gear, washer and nut on transfer shaft. Hold transfer gear. Tighten nut to 200 ft. lbs. (271 N.m).

3) Attach Lever (L-4432) on transfer gear. See Fig. 32. Move transfer gear inward and outward while rotating back and forth to ensure bearings are seated. Mount steel ball in end of transfer gear and retain in place with grease. Install Adapter (L-4438) and dial indicator with stem resting on steel ball. See Fig. 32.

4) Move transfer gear inward and zero dial indicator. Pull transfer gear upward and note transfer shaft end play reading on dial indicator.

5) Using transfer shaft end play, determine proper selective spacers or shims. See Fig. 34.

6) Hold transfer gear. Remove nut and washer from end of transfer shaft. Using puller, remove transfer gear and gauging shims from transfer shaft.

7) Install proper selective spacers or shims on transfer shaft. Install transfer gear, washer and nut. Hold transfer gear. Tighten nut to 200 ft. lbs. (271 N.m).

8) Ensure bearings are fully seated. Using dial indicator, check transfer shaft end play. Transfer shaft end play should be .002-.010" (.05-.25 mm).

9) If transfer shaft end play exceeds specification, install a .002" (.05 mm) thinner selective spacer or shim combination. If transfer shaft end play is less than specified, install a .002" (.05 mm) thicker selective spacer or shim combination. Recheck transfer shaft end play.

TRANSAXLE REASSEMBLY

DIFFERENTIAL ASSEMBLY

CAUTION: Differential bearing preload MUST be adjusted if any of the following components have been replaced: transaxle case, carrier, differential bearing retainer, extension housing or side bearings and cups. See DIFFERENTIAL BEARING PRELOAD under BEARING ADJUSTMENTS. If no components are replaced, use original selective spacer or shim located behind bearing cup in differential bearing retainer.

1) Install differential assembly in transaxle case. Install NEW "O" ring on extension housing. Apply 1/8" bead of RTV sealant on extension housing-to-transaxle case sealing surface. Install extension housing on transaxle case.

2) Using spanner wrench, rotate extension housing and align bolt holes. Install and tighten bolts to specification. See TORQUE SPECIFICATIONS.

3) Apply 1/8" bead of RTV sealant on differential bearing retainer-to-transaxle case sealing surface. Install differential bearing retainer on transaxle case.

4) Using spanner wrench, rotate differential bearing retainer and align bolt holes. Install and tighten bolts to specification. See TORQUE SPECIFICATIONS.

5) Apply 1/8" bead of RTV sealant on differential cover-to-transaxle case sealing surface. Install differential cover. Install and tighten bolts to specification. See TORQUE SPECIFICATIONS. Install NEW oil seal in extension housing if necessary.

TRANSFER SHAFT & TRANSFER GEAR

CAUTION: If bearings, bearing cups, governor support, governor support retainer, transaxle case, transfer gear, transfer shaft or transfer shaft bearing retainer are replaced, transfer shaft bearing preload must be checked. See TRANSFER SHAFT BEARING PRELOAD under BEARING ADJUSTMENTS.

1) If installing NEW bearing cup in transfer shaft bearing retainer, use press, Handle (C-4171) and Bearing Cup Installer (L-4520). See Fig. 13.

End Play (with 2.29 mm and 1.39 mm gauging shims installed)		Required Shim Combination	Total Thickness	
mm	inch	mm	mm	inch
.0	.0	2.29 + 1.39	3.68	.145
.05	.002	2.29 + 1.39	3.68	.145
.10	.004	2.29 + 1.39	3.68	.145
.15	.006	2.29 + 1.39	3.68	.145
.20	.008	2.29 + 1.34	3.63	.143
.25	.010	2.29 + 1.29	3.58	.141
.30	.012	2.29 + 1.24	3.53	.139
.35	.014	2.29 + 1.19	3.48	.137
.40	.016	2.29 + 1.14	3.43	.135
.45	.018	2.29 + 1.09	3.38	.133
.50	.020	2.29 + 1.04	3.33	.131
.55	.022	2.29 + .99	3.28	.129
.60	.024	1.84 + 1.39	3.23	.127
.65	.026	1.84 + 1.34	3.18	.125
.70	.028	1.84 + 1.29	3.13	.123
.75	.030	1.84 + 1.24	3.08	.121
.80	.032	1.84 + 1.19	3.03	.119
.85	.034	1.84 + 1.14	2.98	.117
.90	.036	1.84 + 1.09	2.93	.115
.95	.038	1.84 + 1.04	2.88	.113
1.00	.040	1.84 + .99	2.83	.111
1.05	.042	1.39 + 1.39	2.78	.109
1.10	.044	1.39 + 1.34	2.73	.107
1.15	.046	1.39 + 1.29	2.68	.105
1.20	.048	1.39 + 1.24	2.63	.103
1.25	.049	1.39 + 1.19	2.58	.101
1.30	.050	1.39 + 1.14	2.53	.099
1.35	.052	1.39 + 1.09	2.48	.097
1.40	.055	1.39 + 1.04	2.43	.095
1.45	.057	1.39 + .99	2.38	.093
1.50	.059	.94 + 1.39	2.33	.091
1.55	.061	.94 + 1.34	2.28	.089
1.60	.063	.94 + 1.29	2.23	.087

92E13221　　　　　　　　　　　　　　　　Courtesy of Chrysler Corp.

Fig. 34: Determining Transfer Shaft Selective Spacers Or Shims

2) If installing NEW bearing on transfer gear, use press, Handle (C-4171) and Adapter (L-4410) to install bearing. See Fig. 11.

3) Install transfer shaft bearing retainer on transfer shaft. Install NEW "O" ring on transfer shaft bearing retainer. Using transfer shaft remover/installer, install transfer shaft. See Fig. 9.

4) Install transfer shaft retaining snap ring. Install governor support with governor assembly. Install low-reverse band anchor pin, located at rear of transaxle, near transfer gear. See Fig. 9.

5) Install governor support retainer. Install selective spacer or shim, transfer gear, washer and NEW nut on transfer shaft. Hold transfer gear. Tighten nut to specification. See TORQUE SPECIFICATIONS.

VALVE BODY & INTERNAL COMPONENTS

CAUTION: If transaxle case, output shaft, rear annulus gear, output gear, bearings or bearing cups are replaced, output gear bearing preload must be checked. See OUTPUT SHAFT BEARING PRELOAD under BEARING ADJUSTMENTS.

1) If installing NEW bearing on output gear, use press, Handle (C-4171) and Adapter (L-4408) to install bearing. See Fig. 11. If installing NEW rear annulus gear bearing cup, use Bearing Cup Installer (L-4429-3). See Fig. 10.

NOTE: Bearing cup installer used for rear annulus gear bearing cup can also be used to install output shaft gear bearing cup in transaxle case.

2) If installing NEW bearing on rear annulus gear, use press, Bearing Installer (C-4637) and cup from Adapter (L-4518) to install bearing. See Fig. 14.

3) Install output shaft assembly and selective spacers or shims using grease to retain selective spacers or shims in place. See Fig. 31. Install output gear, washer and NEW nut. Hold output gear. Tighten nut to specification. See TORQUE SPECIFICATIONS.

4) Install parking pawl, return spring and parking pawl shaft. Install parking rod support. Install and tighten bolts to specification. See TORQUE SPECIFICATIONS.

5) Apply 1/8" bead of RTV sealant on end cover and install. Install and tighten bolts to specification. See TORQUE SPECIFICATIONS.

6) Using Spacer (L-4440), install overrunning clutch rollers and overrunning clutch springs in overrunning clutch assembly. See Fig. 35.

CAUTION: Ensure 8 springs and 8 rollers are installed in overrunning clutch assembly with spring facing the proper direction. See Fig. 35.

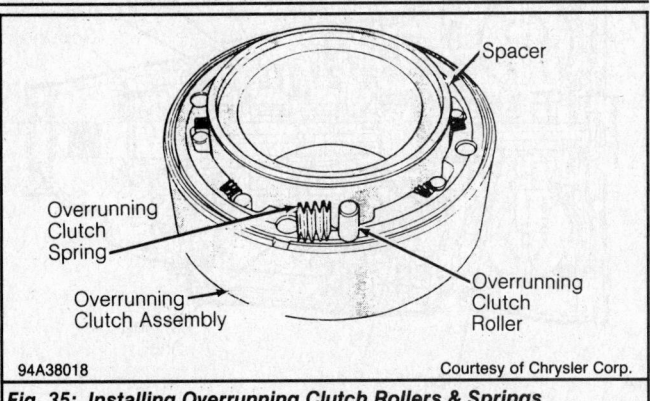

94A38018   Courtesy of Chrysler Corp.

Fig. 35: Installing Overrunning Clutch Rollers & Springs

---

7) Install overrunning clutch thrust washer in transaxle case and over rear annulus gear. Install low-reverse band and strut. Install overrunning clutch assembly.

8) Install thrust washer and rear planetary gear assembly in rear annulus gear. Install thrust washer on front of rear planetary gear assembly. Install sun gear shell with sun gear, thrust plate and plate spacer. See Fig. 7.

9) Install thrust washer and front planetary gear assembly with front annulus gear in sun gear shell. Install snap ring on output shaft to hold front planetary gear assembly in position.

10) Install thrust washer on end of output shaft. This is the selective thrust washer located between output shaft and input shaft and used for controlling input shaft end play.

11) Install rear clutch assembly. Install thrust washer over input shaft and on front of rear clutch retainer. Install front clutch assembly. Install kickdown band and strut. Ensure kickdown band adjusting screw is loose.

12) Install gasket for oil pump in transaxle case. Ensure all holes in gasket align with holes in transaxle case. Install thrust washer on rear of oil pump.

13) DO NOT install seal rings on oil pump at this time. Install oil pump. Install and tighten oil pump-to-transaxle case bolts to specification. See TORQUE SPECIFICATIONS.

14) Using dial indicator, check input shaft end play. Input shaft end play should be .008-.060" (.20-1.52 mm). If input shaft end play is not within specification, change selective thrust washer located between output shaft and input shaft. Selective thrust washer is available in following thickness: .077-.080" (1.96-2.03 mm), .085-.087" (2.16-2.21 mm) and .092-.095" (2.34-2.41 mm).

15) Once proper input shaft end play is obtained, remove oil pump. Install NEW seal rings on oil pump. Install oil pump. Install and tighten oil pump-to-transaxle case bolts to specification. See TORQUE SPECIFICATIONS. Ensure input shaft rotates smoothly.

16) Install NEW seal in oil pump (if removed). Install kickdown servo, accumulator and low-reverse servo components.

17) To adjust kickdown band (front band), ensure kickdown band adjusting screw located on top of transaxle is backed off at least 5 turns. See Fig. 1. Ensure adjusting screw rotates freely in transaxle case.

18) Using Wrench (C-3880-A) and Adapter (C-3705), tighten kickdown band adjusting screw to 47-50 INCH lbs. (5.3-5.6 N.m).

NOTE: When adjusting kickdown band, if adapter is not being used, tighten kickdown band adjusting screw to 72 INCH lbs. (8.1 N.m).

---

19) Back off kickdown band adjusting screw 2 1/2 turns. Tighten lock nut to 35 ft. lbs. (47 N.m).

20) To adjust low-reverse band (rear band), ensure low-reverse band adjusting screw located inside transaxle case is backed off at least 5 turns. See Fig. 8. Ensure adjusting screw rotates freely in transaxle case.

21) Using INCH lb. torque wrench, tighten low-reverse band adjusting screw to 41 INCH lbs. (4.6 N.m). Back off low-reverse band adjusting screw 3 1/2 turns. Tighten lock nut to 120 INCH lbs. (13.6 N.m).

22) Install valve body. See VALVE BODY under REMOVAL & INSTALLATION.

CAUTION: If transaxle failure existed, flush oil cooler and check oil cooler flow. See OIL COOLER FLUSHING and OIL COOLER FLOW CHECK under ON-VEHICLE SERVICE.

TORQUE SPECIFICATIONS
TORQUE SPECIFICATIONS

Application	Ft. Lbs. (N.m)
Differential Bearing Retainer Bolt	21 (29)
Differential Cover Bolt	14 (19)
End Cover Bolt	14 (19)
Extension Housing Bolt	21 (29)
Governor Counterweight Bolt	21 (29)
Kickdown Band Adjusting Screw Lock Nut	35 (47)
Neutral Start/Back-Up Light Switch	25 (34)
Oil Pan Bolt	14 (19)
Oil Pump-To-Transaxle Case Bolt	23 (31)
Parking Rod Support Bolt	21 (29)
Reaction Shaft Support Bolt	21 (29)
Ring Gear Bolt [1]	70 (95)
Transfer/Output Gear Bolt/Nut	200 (271)

Application	INCH Lbs. (N.m)
Governor Assembly-To-Governor Support Bolt	60 (6.8)
Low-Reverse Band Adjusting Screw Lock Nut	120 (13.6)
Oil Filter Assembly Screw	40 (4.5)
Pressure Tap Plug	45 (5.1)
Transfer Plate/Valve Body-To-Transaxle Case Bolt	105 (12)
Valve Body Screw	40 (4.5)
Vehicle Speed Sensor Bolt	60 (6.8)

[1] – Always use NEW bolts. DO NOT reuse old bolts.

TRANSAXLE SPECIFICATIONS
TRANSAXLE SPECIFICATIONS

Application	Specification
Clutch Clearances	
Front Clutch	
3-Disc Clutch	.087-.133" (2.21-3.38 mm)
4-Disc Clutch	.090-.146" (2.29-3.71 mm)
Rear Clutch	.026-.043" (.66-1.09 mm)
Differential Rotating Torque	5-18 INCH Lbs. (.6-2 N.m)
Differential Side Gear End Play	.001-.013" (.03-.33 mm)
Input Shaft End Play	.008-.060" (.20-1.52 mm)
Oil Pump Clearances	
Oil Pump Gear Side Clearance	.0008-.0018" (.020-.046 mm)
Outer Oil Pump Gear-To-Oil	
Pump Housing Clearance	.0018-.0056" (.046-.142 mm)
Output Shaft Rotating Torque	3-8 INCH Lbs. (.3-.9 N.m)
Transfer Shaft End Play	.002-.010" (.05-.25 mm)

AUTOMATIC TRANSMISSIONS
Chrysler 36RH & 37RH

APPLICATION & LABOR TIMES

APPLICATION & LABOR TIMES

Vehicle Application	Labor Times [1] R & I	[2] Overhaul	Trans. Model
Dodge			
1993 Pickup			
Gasoline (5.2L)	[3] 3.8	7.5	36RH
Diesel (5.9L)	[3] 3.8	7.5	37RH
1994 Pickup			
Gasoline (5.2L)	[3] 3.8	7.5	36RH
Gasoline (V10) &			
Diesel (5.9L)	[3] 3.8	7.5	37RH
1993-94 Ram Van			
Gasoline (5.2L)	3.1	7.5	36RH

[1] – Removal and installation of transmission from vehicle chassis.

[2] – Bench overhaul time for transmission. DOES NOT include removal and installation.

[3] – Add 1.8 hrs. for 4WD vehicles.

IDENTIFICATION

Transmission identification numbers are stamped on left side of transmission case, near oil pan flange. *See Fig. 1.* Identification numbers may be required when ordering replacement components. Transmission components may not be interchangeable and identification number is required to ensure proper component application.

NOTE: Selective sized snap rings and thrust washers may be needed to set and adjust clearances. For sizes and availability, refer to manufacturer's parts department, and reference transmission model and identification number.

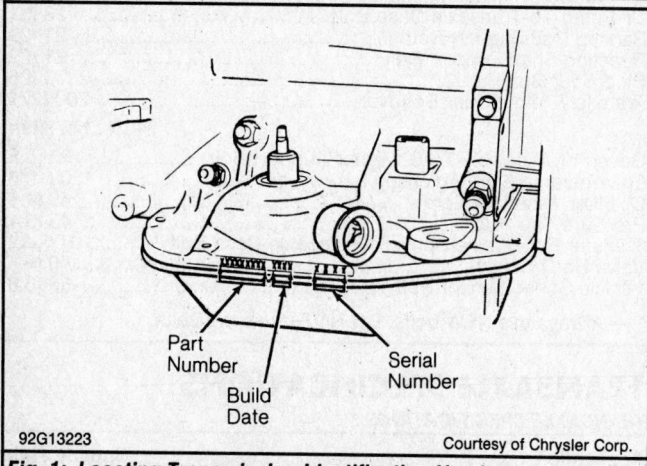

Fig. 1: Locating Transmission Identification Numbers

DESCRIPTION & OPERATION

Transmission is a fully automatic 3-speed transmission with 1st through 3rd gears provided by clutches, bands, overrunning clutch and planetary gear sets. *See Fig. 2.* The 37RH is a heavy duty version of the 36RH. The 37RH differs from the 36RH in that front and rear planetary gears contain more pinion gears and a different number of clutch pack components. Governor weights are also different.

LUBRICATION & ADJUSTMENTS

NOTE: See appropriate AUTOMATIC TRANSMISSION SERVICING article in TRANSMISSION SERVICING.

NOTE: Manufacturer recommends using Mopar ATF Plus Type 7176 fluid. This fluid should also be used during assembly.

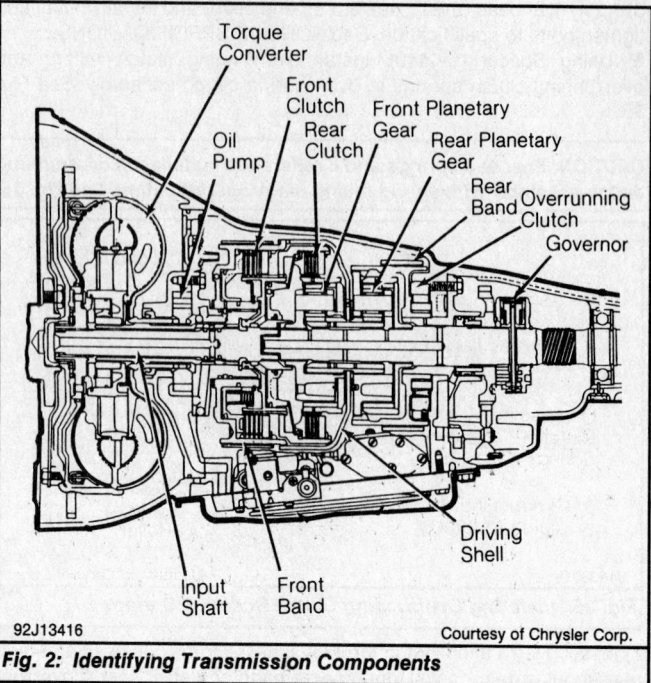

Fig. 2: Identifying Transmission Components

TROUBLE SHOOTING

Transmission malfunctions may be caused by poor engine performance, improper adjustments or failure of hydraulic, mechanical or electronic components. Always begin by checking fluid level, fluid condition, shift linkage or cable adjustment and throttle valve cable adjustment. Perform road test to determine if problem has been corrected. If problem still exists, several tests must be performed on transmission. See TESTING in this article.

TRANSMISSION SYMPTOM DIAGNOSIS

NOTE: The shift from Neutral to Reverse is normally quite firm, as rear servo pressure can approach 300 psi (21 kg/cm²). DO NOT confuse a firm engagement with a harsh engagement.

Buzzing Noise
- Aerated fluid
- Defective overrunning clutch
- Low fluid level
- Valve body malfunction or leakage

Delayed Engagement From Neutral To Drive Or Reverse
- Damaged clutch, band or servo
- Damaged oil pump components
- Damaged or worn reaction shaft seal rings
- Defective governor
- Engine idle speed too low
- Improper rear band adjustment
- Incorrect shift linkage or cable adjustment
- Low fluid level
- Low hydraulic pressure
- Restricted filter assembly

Drags Or Locks Up
- Defective band, band linkage or servo
- Defective planetary or overrunning clutch
- Dragging clutch
- Improper band adjustment

Fluid Blows Out Filler Tube
- Aerated fluid
- Defective rear servo
- High fluid level
- Oil cooler or lines restricted
- Restricted breather vent in oil pump
- Restricted filter assembly
- Valve in valve body sticking

Growling, Grating Or Scraping Noise
- Defective clutch or governor support
- Defective oil pump or output shaft bearings/bushings
- Defective planetary or overrunning clutch
- Improper band adjustment

Harsh Engagement From Neutral To Drive Or Reverse
- Damaged clutch, band or planetary components
- Damaged or worn accumulator components
- Defective torque converter lock-up
- Engine idle speed too high
- Improper band adjustment
- Improper throttle valve cable adjustment
- Incorrect hydraulic pressure

No Forward Gear In Any Position (Reverse Is Okay)
- Defective overrunning clutch
- Incorrect shift linkage or cable adjustment
- Input shaft seal rings worn or damaged
- Low fluid level
- Rear clutch defective
- Valve body malfunction or leakage

No Kickdown Or Normal Downshift
- Defective clutch or servo
- Defective front servo, band or linkage
- Improper front band adjustment
- Improper hydraulic pressure
- Improper throttle valve cable adjustment
- Incorrect shift linkage or cable adjustment

No Low Gear (Moves In 2nd & 3rd Gears Only)
- Front band linkage binding
- Front servo binding in bore
- Governor partially stuck open
- Improper throttle valve cable adjustment
- Incorrect shift linkage or cable adjustment
- Valve body malfunction or leakage

No Reverse
- Improper rear band adjustment
- Incorrect shift linkage or cable adjustment
- Rear servo or front clutch malfunction
- Valve body malfunction or leakage

Shifts Delayed Or Erratic
- Aerated fluid
- Defective clutch or servo
- Governor support seal rings broken or worn
- Improper fluid level
- Improper front band adjustment causing harsh 1-2 shift
- Improper throttle valve cable adjustment or binding components
- Incorrect shift linkage or cable adjustment
- Restricted filter assembly

Slips In All Forward Gears
- Aerated fluid
- Damaged or worn accumulator components
- Defective clutch or servo
- Defective overrunning clutch
- Improper throttle valve cable adjustment or binding components
- Incorrect shift linkage or cable adjustment
- Low fluid level
- Low hydraulic pressure

Slips In Low Gear In Drive But Not In Low Gear (1 Position)
- Defective overrunning clutch

Slips In Reverse Only
- Aerated fluid
- Binding band linkage
- Defective front clutch, rear servo or rear band
- Improper rear band adjustment
- Incorrect shift linkage or cable adjustment
- Low fluid level
- Low hydraulic pressure

Sluggish Acceleration Or Excessive Throttle To Maintain Speed
- Defective torque converter clutch
- Improper throttle valve cable adjustment
- Incorrect shift linkage or cable adjustment
- Poor engine performance
- Slipping clutches

Torque Converter Locks Up In 2nd And/Or 3rd Gear
- Defective lock-up solenoid, relay or wiring

Transmission Overheats
- Improper band adjustment
- Improper clutch clearance
- Low fluid level
- Restricted oil cooler
- Switch valve in valve body sticking

Vehicle Moves In Neutral
- Clutch dragging
- Incorrect shift linkage or cable adjustment
- Torque converter lock-up clutch dragging
- Valve body malfunction or leakage

Vehicle Moves In 2nd Or 3rd Gear & Abruptly Downshifts To Low
- Governor sticking
- Valve body malfunction or leakage

Vehicle Will Not Move In Any Gear
- Defective oil pump
- Incorrect shift linkage or cable adjustment
- Internal transmission component failure
- Low fluid level
- Valve body malfunction or leakage

Will Not Upshift From Low Gear
- Defective clutch or servo
- Defective oil pump, seal rings or valve body
- Governor stuck closed
- Improper front band adjustment
- Improper throttle valve cable adjustment
- Incorrect shift linkage or cable adjustment

1st & Reverse Gears Only
- Defective or sticking governor

TESTING

ROAD TEST

1) Ensure shift linkage/cable and throttle valve cable are properly adjusted. See appropriate AUTOMATIC TRANSMISSION SERVICING article in TRANSMISSION SERVICING. Ensure fluid level and condition are okay. Add ATF and adjust control cables or linkages (if necessary).

2) Road test vehicle, operating transmission in each gear position. Observe engine performance during road test. A poorly tuned engine will not allow an accurate analysis of transmission operation.

3) Check for slippage and shift variations. Note if shifts are harsh, spongy, delayed or early.

4) Slipping or flare-up in any gear usually indicates clutch, band, or overrunning clutch problems. A slipping clutch or band in a particular gear can usually be identified by noting transmission operation in other gearshift positions and comparing which internal units are applied in those positions. See CLUTCH & BAND APPLICATION table.

CLUTCH & BAND APPLICATION

Gearshift Position	Elements In Use
"D" (Drive)	
1st Gear	Rear Clutch & Overrunning Clutch
2nd Gear	Front Band & Rear Clutch
3rd Gear	Front Clutch & Rear Clutch
"2" (Second)	
1st Gear	Rear Clutch & Overrunning Clutch
2nd Gear	Front Band & Rear Clutch
"1" (Low)	
1st Gear	Rear Clutch, Rear Band & Overrunning Clutch
"R" (Reverse)	Front Clutch & Rear Band
"N" Or "P" (Neutral Or Park)	All Clutches & Bands Released Or Ineffective

5) Problem area may be detected by determining which components are applied. By selecting another gear that does not use these components, the defective component can be determined. See CLUTCH & BAND APPLICATION table.

6) Process of elimination can be used to detect any unit which slips and to confirm proper operation of good units. Road test analysis can usually diagnose slipping units. Actual malfunction usually cannot be decided.

7) Practically any condition can be caused by leaking hydraulic circuits or sticking valves. Transmission failure may be determined by performing hydraulic pressure test along with clutch and servo air pressure test.

TORQUE CONVERTER STALL SPEED TEST

Torque Converter Stall Speed Test Procedure – 1) Install tachometer. Ensure transmission fluid level is correct. Start and operate engine until transmission fluid is at normal operating temperature.

CAUTION: DO NOT open throttle to wide open position for more than 5 seconds or transmission may be damaged. If performing more than one torque converter stall speed test, operate engine at 1000 RPM with transmission in Neutral for at least 20 seconds to cool transmission fluid before performing next torque converter stall speed test.

2) Block front wheels. Apply parking and service brakes. Place transmission in Drive. Open throttle to wide open position for no more than 5 seconds and note engine RPM and then release throttle. This is the torque converter stall speed.

3) Torque converter stall speed should be 1800-2100 RPM on all models except 1993 Pickup and Ramcharger. On 1993 Pickup and Ramcharger, torque converter stall speed should be 1700-2000 RPM.

4) Once torque converter stall speed is obtained, place transmission in Neutral. Operate engine for 20 seconds, allowing transmission to cool. Stop engine. Place transmission in Park. Remove tachometer.

NOTE: Use following symptoms to trouble shoot results of torque converter stall speed test.

Torque Converter Stall Speed Exceeds Specification – If torque converter stall speed exceeds specification by more than 200 RPM, transmission clutch is slipping.

Torque Converter Stall Speed Less Than Specification – 1) If torque converter stall speed is less than specification with properly tuned engine, torque converter overrunning clutch may be slipping.

2) If torque converter overrunning clutch is slipping, torque converter stall speed will be 250-300 RPM less than the specification. Vehicle will operate properly at highway speeds, but will have poor low-speed acceleration.

Torque Converter Stall Speed Is Within Specification – If torque converter stall speed is within specification, but abnormal throttle opening is required to maintain highway speeds, torque converter overrunning clutch is seized. Torque converter must be replaced.

Noise When Performing Torque Converter Stall Speed Test – Whining noise caused by fluid flow is normal. A loud metallic sound indicates torque converter is damaged. To ensure sound is coming from torque converter, raise vehicle on hoist. Operate vehicle with transmission in Drive and then Neutral at light throttle. Ensure noise is coming from torque converter. Replace torque converter if defective.

HYDRAULIC PRESSURE TEST

Hydraulic Pressure Test Preparation – 1) Ensure fluid level and condition are okay. Install tachometer. Raise vehicle on hoist, allowing wheels to rotate freely.

2) Disconnect throttle valve and shift cables or linkages from throttle valve and manual selector lever on the transmission.

CAUTION: A 100 psi (7 kg/cm²) pressure gauge is required for checking all applications except rear servo. A 300 psi (21 kg/cm²) pressure gauge is required for checking pressure at rear servo.

Pressure Test With Transmission In "1" (1st Gear) – 1) Remove pressure tap plugs and install pressure gauge in accumulator and rear servo pressure taps. *See Fig. 3.* Start and operate engine at 1000 RPM.

2) Move manual selector lever on transmission fully forward to the gearshift "1" position. Read pressure on both pressure gauges as throttle valve lever on transmission is moved from fully forward position to fully rearward position.

3) Line pressure at accumulator pressure tap should be 54-60 psi (3.7-4.2 kg/cm²) with throttle valve lever fully forward and gradually increase to 90-96 psi (6.3-6.7 kg/cm²) as throttle valve lever is moved rearward. Rear servo pressure should be within 3 psi (.2 kg/cm²) of line pressure.

4) If line pressure is not within specification, adjust line pressure. See LINE PRESSURE under HYDRAULIC PRESSURE ADJUSTMENTS. If proper line pressure still cannot be obtained, check for defective components and hydraulic circuit.

5) This tests oil pump output, pressure regulation, condition of rear clutch and servo hydraulic circuits. Remove pressure gauges. Install and tighten pressure tap plugs to specification. See TORQUE SPECIFICATIONS.

Pressure Test With Transmission In "2" (2nd Gear) – 1) Remove pressure tap plug and install pressure gauge in accumulator pressure tap. *See Fig. 3.* Start and operate engine at 1000 RPM.

2) Move manual selector lever on transmission to fully forward position and then rearward one position to gearshift "2" position. Read pressure on pressure gauge as throttle valve lever on transmission is moved from fully forward position to fully rearward position.

3) Line pressure at accumulator pressure tap should be 54-60 psi (3.7-4.2 kg/cm²) with throttle valve lever fully forward and gradually increase to 90-96 psi (6.3-6.7 kg/cm²) as throttle valve lever is moved rearward.

4) If line pressure is not within specification, adjust line pressure. See LINE PRESSURE under HYDRAULIC PRESSURE ADJUSTMENTS. If proper line pressure still cannot be obtained, check for defective components and hydraulic circuit.

5) This tests oil pump output and pressure regulation. Remove pressure gauge. Install and tighten pressure tap plug to specification. See TORQUE SPECIFICATIONS.

Pressure Test With Transmission In "D" (Drive Gear) – 1) Remove pressure tap plugs and install pressure gauge in accumulator and front servo pressure taps. *See Fig. 3.* Start and operate engine at 1600 RPM.

2) Move manual selector lever on transmission to fully forward position and then rearward 2 positions to gearshift "D" position. Read pressure on both pressure gauges as throttle valve lever on transmission is moved from fully forward position to fully rearward position.

3) Line pressure at accumulator pressure tap should be 54-60 psi (3.7-4.2 kg/cm²) with throttle valve lever fully forward and gradually increase as throttle valve lever is moved rearward. Front servo is pressurized only in gearshift lever "D" position and pressure should be within 3 psi (.2 kg/cm²) of line pressure up to the downshift point.

4) If line pressure is not within specification, adjust line pressure. See LINE PRESSURE under HYDRAULIC PRESSURE ADJUSTMENTS. If proper line pressure still cannot be obtained, check for defective components and hydraulic circuit.

5) This tests oil pump output, pressure regulation and condition of clutch hydraulic circuits. Remove pressure gauges. Install and tighten pressure tap plugs to specification. See TORQUE SPECIFICATIONS.

Pressure Test With Transmission In "R" (Reverse Gear) – 1) Remove pressure tap plug and install 300 psi (21 kg/cm²) pressure gauge in rear servo pressure tap. See Fig. 3. Start and operate engine at 1600 RPM.

2) Move manual selector lever on transmission to fully forward position and then rearward 4 positions to gearshift "R" position. Read pressure on pressure gauge as throttle valve lever on transmission is moved from fully forward position to fully rearward position.

3) Pressure should be 145-175 psi (10.2-12.3 kg/cm²) with throttle valve lever fully forward and gradually increase to 230-280 psi (16.1-19.7 kg/cm²) with throttle valve lever fully rearward.

4) This tests oil pump output, pressure regulation, front clutch and rear servo hydraulic circuits. Remove pressure gauge. Install and tighten pressure tap plug to specification. See TORQUE SPECIFICATIONS.

NOTE: *Transmission governor pressure is usually checked if shift speeds are incorrect or transmission will not upshift or downshift.*

Transmission Governor Pressure – 1) Reconnect throttle valve and shift cables or linkages on manual selector lever and throttle valve lever on transmission (if removed). Remove pressure tap plug and install pressure gauge in governor pressure tap. See Fig. 3.

2) Lower vehicle, leaving wheels approximately 12" from floor. Start engine and allow to idle. Place gearshift in "D" (Drive). Note pressure gauge reading with engine idling.

3) Pressure should be 0-1.5 psi (0-.1 kg/cm²) with wheels not rotating. If pressure exceeds specification, governor valve or weights are stuck open.

4) If pressure is correct, slowly increase engine speed, noting governor pressure in relation to vehicle speed. Governor pressure should increase approximately 1 psi (.07 kg/cm²) for every MPH. Governor pressure should rise smoothly and then drop back to 0-1.5 psi (0-.1 kg/cm²) when wheels stop rotating.

5) This tests governor operation in relation to engine and vehicle speed. Repair governor if it does not operate properly. Remove pressure gauge. Install and tighten pressure tap plug to specification. See TORQUE SPECIFICATIONS.

Hydraulic Pressure Test Result Indications – 1) If proper line pressure is obtained in any pressure test, oil pump and pressure regulator are working properly.

2) If line pressure is low in "D", "1" and "2", but is correct in "R", this indicates leakage in rear clutch circuit.

3) If line pressure is low in "D" (3rd gear) and "R", but is correct in "1" and "2", this indicates leakage in front clutch circuit.

4) If line pressure is low in "R" and "1", but is correct in "2", this indicates leakage in rear servo circuit. If front servo pressure is low in "2", this indicates leakage in front servo circuit.

5) High governor pressure at idle indicates governor valve is stuck open. Low governor pressure at all vehicle speeds indicates governor valve is stuck closed.

6) If line pressure is not within specification, adjust line pressure. See LINE PRESSURE under HYDRAULIC PRESSURE ADJUSTMENTS. If proper line pressure still cannot be obtained, check for defective components and hydraulic circuit. Low line pressure in all positions indicates a defective oil pump, restricted filter or stuck pressure regulator valve.

CLUTCH & SERVO AIR PRESSURE TEST

NOTE: *Inoperative clutches, servos and bands can be located and tested by applying air pressure to appropriate passages in transmission case.*

Test Preparation – Remove valve body. See VALVE BODY under REMOVAL & INSTALLATION.

CAUTION: *Ensure air supply is free of all dirt and moisture.*

Front Clutch – Place finger on front clutch housing. Apply air pressure to front clutch apply passage. See Fig. 4. Piston movement will be felt and a soft thump will be heard when front clutch is applied.

Rear Clutch – Place finger on rear clutch housing. Apply air pressure to rear clutch apply passage. See Fig. 4. Piston movement will be felt and a soft thump will be heard when rear clutch is applied.

Front Servo – Apply air pressure to front servo apply passage. See Fig. 4. Front band should tighten, indicating front servo operation. Release air pressure and note that spring tension on servo piston releases the front band.

Rear Servo – Apply air pressure to rear servo apply passage. See Fig. 4. Rear band should tighten, indicating rear servo operation. Release air pressure and note that spring tension on servo piston releases the rear band.

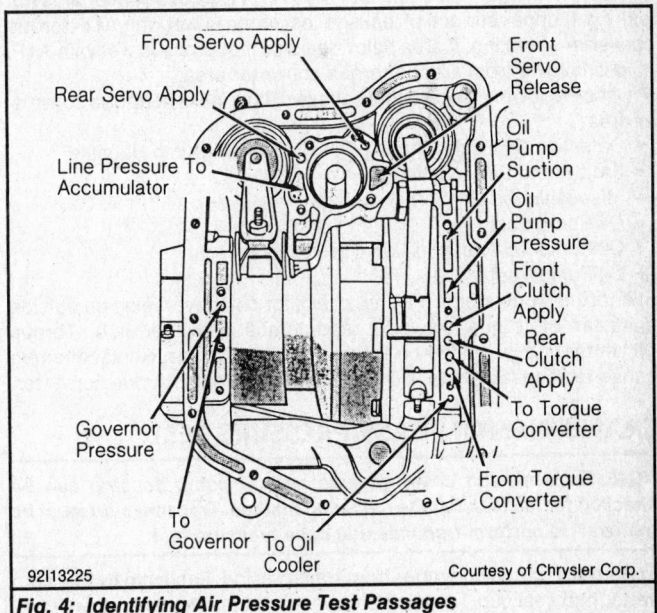

Fig. 4: **Identifying Air Pressure Test Passages**

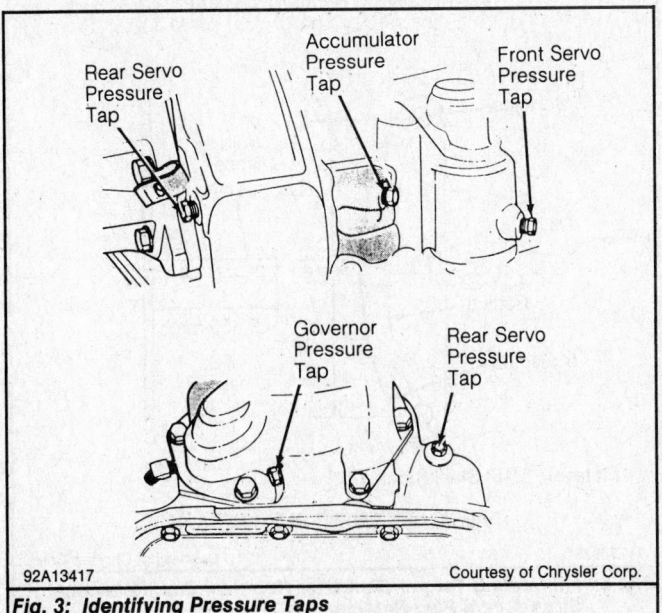

Fig. 3: **Identifying Pressure Taps**

TORQUE CONVERTER FLUID LEAKAGE TEST

NOTE: Fluid around torque converter may originate from engine oil or transmission. Ensure transmission fluid level is correct. Fluid leakage at torque converter may result if fluid level is too high. Transmission can be checked for leaks using the following method.

1) Remove torque converter dust shield. Clean inside area of torque converter housing using solvent and compressed air. Ensure area is clean and dry.

2) Fabricate leakage test probe using 1/32" sheet metal, 5 1/2" (140 mm) long and 1 1/2" (38 mm) wide. *See Fig. 5.* Install leakage test probe on torque converter dust shield bolt so leakage test probe is near torque converter. Ensure torque converter does not contact leakage test probe.

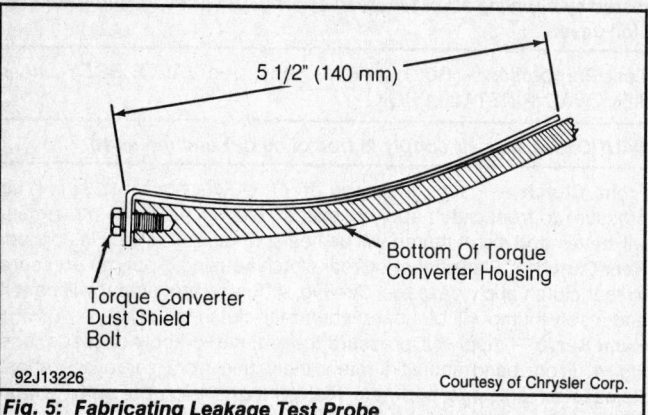

5 1/2" (140 mm)

Bottom Of Torque Converter Housing

Torque Converter Dust Shield Bolt

92J13226   Courtesy of Chrysler Corp.

Fig. 5: Fabricating Leakage Test Probe

3) Apply parking brake. Start engine. Place transmission in Neutral. Operate engine at 2500 RPM for 2 minutes. Stop engine. Remove leakage test probe.

4) If upper surface of leakage test probe is dry, torque converter is not leaking. If upper surface of leakage test probe is wet with ATF, torque converter is leaking. If area below leakage test probe is wet with ATF, fluid is coming from around torque converter area.

5) Check following for possible causes of fluid leaks at torque converter areas.

- Defective Oil Pump Housing "O" Ring Or Oil Pump Housing
- Front Band Pin Access Plug
- Mispositioned Or Worn Bushing
- Oil Pump Seal
- Oil Pump-To-Transmission Case Bolts
- Oil Pump Vent

6) If torque converter is leaking, check for defective welds on outside diameter of torque converter and torque converter hub. Torque converter hub is welded on inside and is not visible. Replace torque converter if a leak exists. DO NOT attempt to repair torque converter.

TRANSMISSION CASE PRESSURE TEST

NOTE: Transmission case, gaskets and oil pump housing can be checked for leaks using the following method. Transmission must be removed to perform transmission case pressure test.

1) Remove torque converter from transmission. Fabricate torque converter hub seal cup, retaining strap and vent plug retainer. *See Fig. 6.* Retaining strap specifications are approximate. Measure hole positions on torque converter housing before drilling.

CAUTION: Ensure torque converter hub seal cup surface is smooth to prevent damage to seal in oil pump.

2) Install torque converter hub seal cup, vent plug retainer and retaining strap. *See Fig. 7.* Install shipping plug in rear output shaft opening. Install and secure plugs in remaining transmission openings except oil cooler return line.

3) Attach air pump to oil cooler return line. *See Fig. 7.* Ensure cap is installed on oil cooler supply line fitting. Using pressure regulator, apply 8-10 psi (.5-.7 kg/cm²) of air pressure to transmission case.

CAUTION: DO NOT apply more than 10 psi (.7 kg/cm²) of air pressure to transmission case.

4) Coat oil pump and front of transmission case with soapy water solution. Check for bubbles, indicating a leak in seals, "O" rings, gaskets or transmission case. Release air pressure. Remove test equipment. Replace defective components.

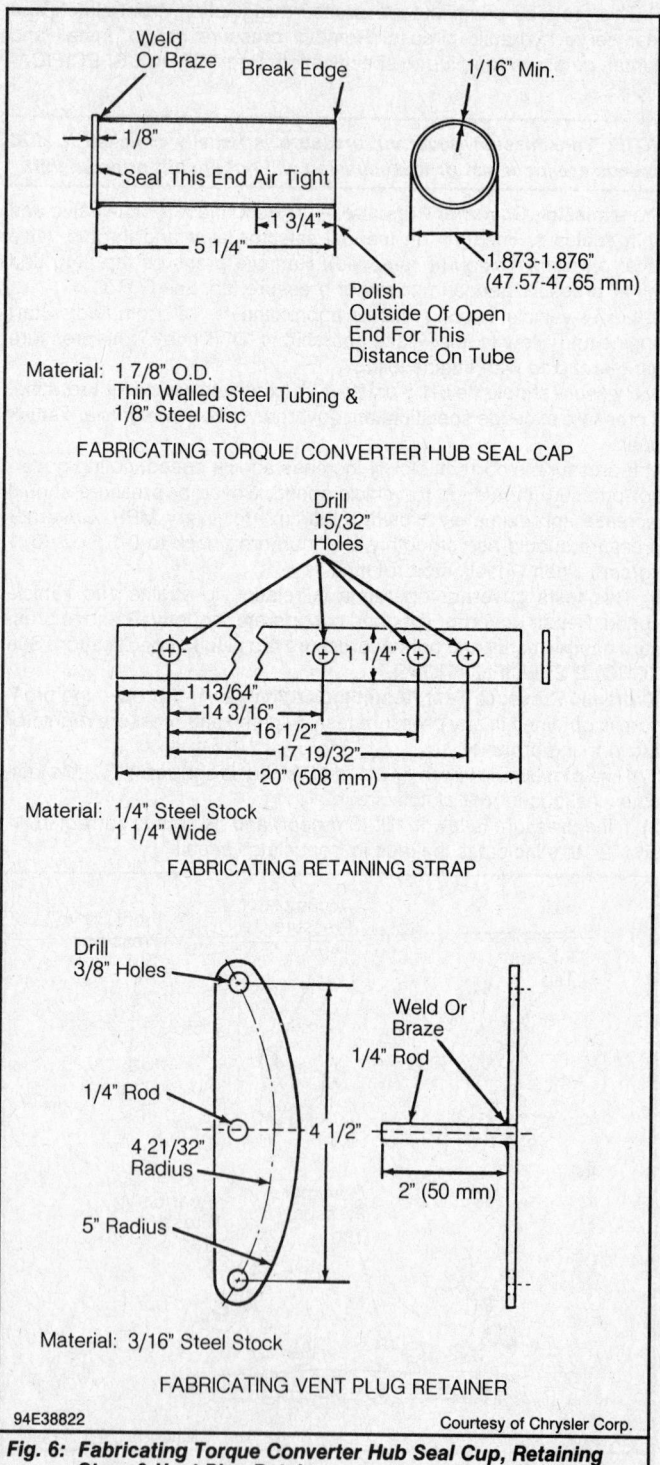

Weld Or Braze   Break Edge   1/16" Min.

1/8"

Seal This End Air Tight

1 3/4"

5 1/4"

1.873-1.876"
(47.57-47.65 mm)

Polish Outside Of Open End For This Distance On Tube

Material: 1 7/8" O.D. Thin Walled Steel Tubing & 1/8" Steel Disc

FABRICATING TORQUE CONVERTER HUB SEAL CAP

Drill 15/32" Holes

1 1/4"

1 13/64"
14 3/16"
16 1/2"
17 19/32"
20" (508 mm)

Material: 1/4" Steel Stock 1 1/4" Wide

FABRICATING RETAINING STRAP

Drill 3/8" Holes

Weld Or Braze

1/4" Rod

1/4" Rod

4 21/32" Radius

4 1/2"

2" (50 mm)

5" Radius

Material: 3/16" Steel Stock

FABRICATING VENT PLUG RETAINER

94E38822   Courtesy of Chrysler Corp.

Fig. 6: Fabricating Torque Converter Hub Seal Cup, Retaining Strap & Vent Plug Retainer

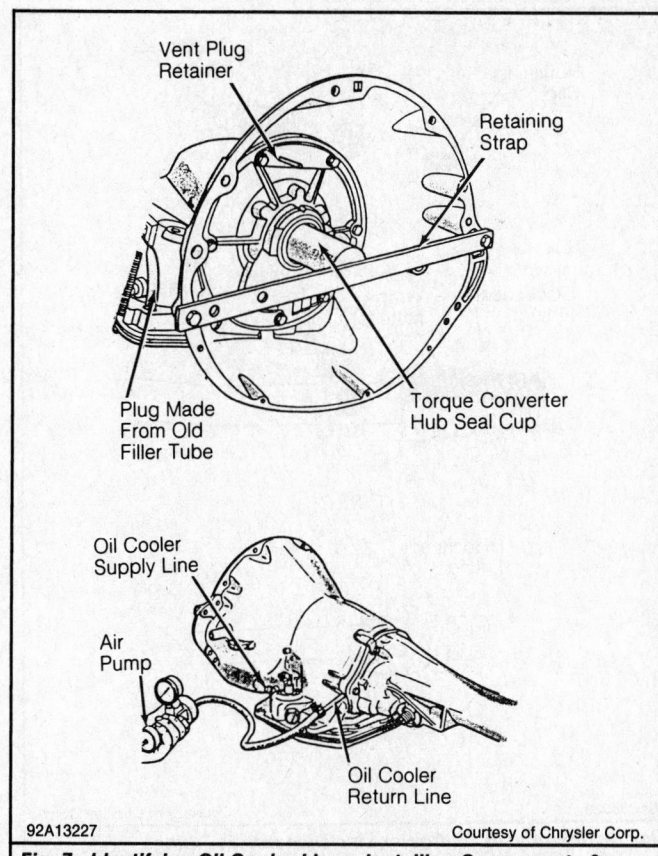

Fig. 7: Identifying Oil Cooler Lines, Installing Components & Pressure Testing Transmission Case

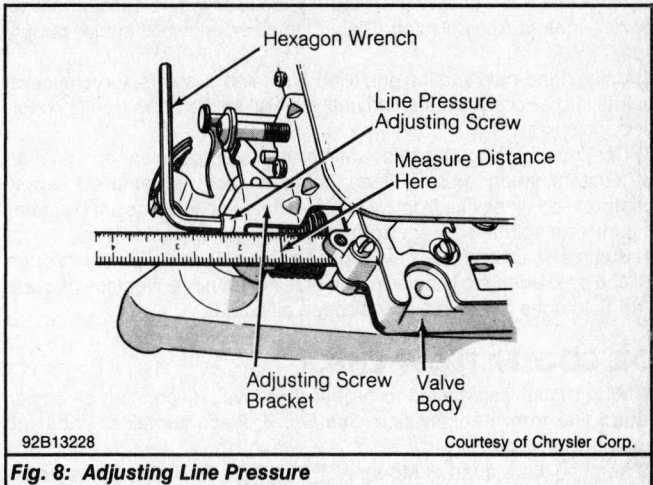

92B13228   Courtesy of Chrysler Corp.

Fig. 8: Adjusting Line Pressure

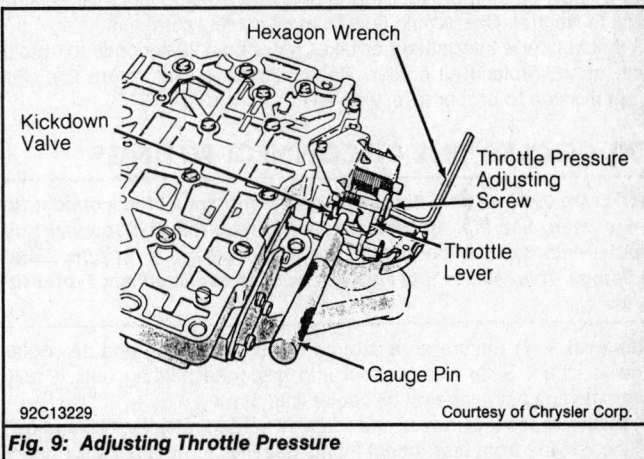

92C13229   Courtesy of Chrysler Corp.

Fig. 9: Adjusting Throttle Pressure

HYDRAULIC PRESSURE ADJUSTMENTS

CAUTION: Line pressure and throttle pressure each affect shift quality. Line pressure must be adjusted before adjusting throttle pressure. Remove valve body if necessary. See VALVE BODY under REMOVAL & INSTALLATION.

LINE PRESSURE

1) Measure distance from valve body to inner edge of line pressure adjusting screw. *See Fig. 8.* Rotate line pressure adjusting screw so distance is approximately 1 5/16".

NOTE: Due to manufacturing tolerances, adjustment can be varied to obtain specified line pressure.

2) Rotating line pressure adjusting screw one revolution will change line pressure approximately 1 2/3 psi. Rotating line pressure adjusting screw counterclockwise increases line pressure, and clockwise decreases line pressure.

THROTTLE PRESSURE

CAUTION: Line pressure must be adjusted before adjusting throttle pressure.

1) Insert Gauge Pin (C-3763) between cam on throttle lever and kickdown valve. *See Fig. 9.*
2) Push inward on gauge pin and compress kickdown valve against spring until kickdown valve is bottomed in valve body. Ensure spring is fully compressed and kickdown valve is bottomed in valve body.
3) Maintain pressure against kickdown valve and spring. Rotate throttle pressure adjusting screw until head of adjusting screw contacts tang on throttle lever. Ensure throttle lever cam contacts gauge pin. Remove gauge pin.

ON-VEHICLE SERVICE

The following components can be serviced on the vehicle.
* Extension Housing, Seal, Bushing & Output Shaft Rear Bearing
* Governor & Park Gear
* Park Lock Components
* Park/Neutral Switch
* Valve Body
* Vehicle Speed Sensor & Pinion Gear
See appropriate component under REMOVAL & INSTALLATION.

OIL COOLER FLUSHING

CAUTION: Whenever transmission failure exists, oil cooler must be flushed and torque converter replaced. If vehicle is equipped with 2 oil coolers (one in radiator tank and one in front of radiator), flush oil coolers separately. DO NOT attempt to flush both oil coolers at one time.

CAUTION: Some models may have a drainback relief valve installed in the oil cooler supply line next to the rubber hose at the radiator. See Fig. 41. If drainback relief valve is used, it must be removed before flushing the lines. Install NEW drainback relief valve once lines are flushed.

NOTE: On 1994 models, oil cooler lines are equipped with disconnect fittings. For disconnecting and installing procedures of oil cooler lines with disconnect fittings, see OIL COOLER LINE DISCONNECT FITTINGS under ON-VEHICLE SERVICE.

NOTE: Manufacturer recommends using Mopar ATF Plus Type 7176 fluid. This fluid should also be used during assembly.

1) Note oil cooler supply and return lines. *See Fig. 7.* Disconnect oil cooler lines at transmission. Place container under oil cooler supply line.

2) Using hand-held suction gun filled with mineral spirits, force mineral spirits into oil cooler return line until mineral spirits flows from oil cooler supply line.

3) Continue flushing oil cooler until mineral spirits is clear and no sign of contamination exists. Once contamination is removed, apply compressed air on line from oil cooler in light applications until remaining mineral spirits is blown from oil cooler and oil cooler lines.

4) Pump at least one quart of Mopar ATF Plus Type 7176 fluid through oil cooler to ensure oil cooler is free of mineral spirits. Replace oil cooler if fluid does not flow freely through oil cooler.

OIL COOLER FLOW CHECK

1) With transmission filled to proper fluid level, disconnect oil cooler return line from transmission. *See Fig. 7.* Place container under oil cooler return line.

2) Add one extra quart of Mopar ATF Plus Type 7176 fluid to transmission. Apply parking brake. Start engine and allow to idle. Place gearshift in Neutral. Check fluid flow from oil cooler return line.

3) If fluid flow is intermittent or takes more than 20 seconds to obtain one quart, replace oil cooler. Reconnect oil cooler return line. Fill transmission to proper level with ATF.

OIL COOLER LINE DISCONNECT FITTINGS

NOTE: On 1994 models, there are 3 different types of disconnect fittings used. See Fig. 10. Release tool is required to disconnect oil cooler line. Release tool is attached to oil cooler line on Type 2 and 3 fittings. This release tool also can be used to disconnect Type 1 fittings.

Removal – 1) Ensure area around disconnect fitting and oil cooler line is clean. Slide release tool into disconnect fitting until it fully bottoms against flange on oil cooler line.

2) Push release tool inward and rotate to spread retaining clip and pull oil cooler line from disconnect fitting. *See Fig. 11.* Inspect disconnect fitting and oil cooler line for damage. Replace disconnect fitting as an assembly if damaged. Replace oil cooler line if swedge at hose or flange on line is damaged.

Installation – 1) If installing NEW disconnect fitting, apply Loctite 242 on disconnect fitting before installing. Ensure end of oil cooler line is clean. Insert oil cooler line into disconnect fitting.

CAUTION: After installing oil cooler line, pull outward on oil cooler line to ensure oil cooler line is locked in the disconnect fitting and retaining clip is fully seated.

2) Push oil cooler line inward until a snap or click is heard when retaining clip seats in oil cooler line. Pull outward on oil cooler line to ensure oil cooler line is locked in the disconnect fitting.

REMOVAL & INSTALLATION

EXTENSION HOUSING, SEAL, BUSHING & OUTPUT SHAFT REAR BEARING

Removal – 1) Apply parking brake. Place transmission in "1" (Low gear). Raise and support vehicle.

2) Place reference marks on drive shaft yokes for reassembly reference. Remove drive shaft. Remove vehicle speed sensor and pinion gear. See VEHICLE SPEED SENSOR & PINION GEAR under REMOVAL & INSTALLATION.

3) Remove extension housing-to-rear mount bolts. Slightly raise transmission with floor jack. Remove rear crossmember. Remove extension housing-to-transmission case bolts.

4) Remove bolts, access cover and gasket from bottom of extension housing. Using snap ring pliers, expand output shaft rear bearing locating ring. *See Fig. 12.* With locating ring expanded, remove extension housing from output shaft rear bearing.

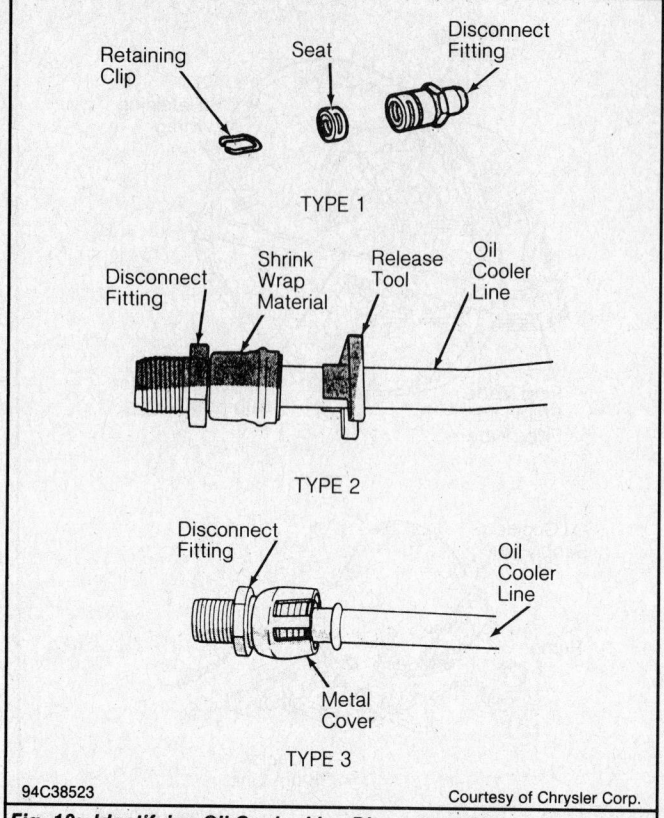

94C38523   Courtesy of Chrysler Corp.

Fig. 10: Identifying Oil Cooler Line Disconnect Fittings

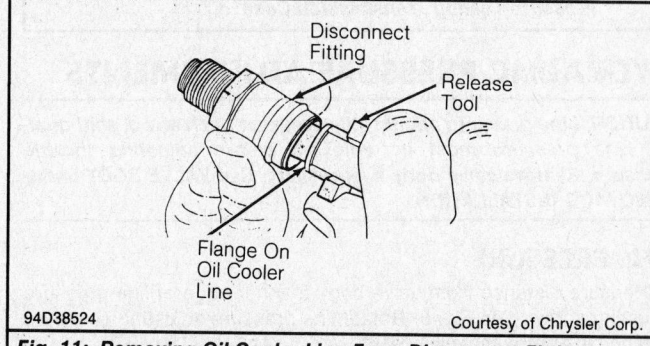

94D38524   Courtesy of Chrysler Corp.

Fig. 11: Removing Oil Cooler Line From Disconnect Fitting (Type 2 Shown; Others Are Similar)

5) Pull extension housing and gasket from transmission case while working park rod past parking sprag. *See Fig. 14.* Remove snap ring(s) and rear bearing from output shaft.

6) Using Seal Remover (C-3985), remove seal from extension housing. If removing bushing from extension housing, use Bushing Remover/Installer (C-4469) to remove bushing.

Installation – 1) Using hammer and bushing remover/installer, tap bushing into extension housing. Oil hole in the bushing must align with oil slot in the extension housing.

CAUTION: Ensure oil hole in bushing aligns with oil slot in extension housing.

2) Using Seal Installer (C-3972), install seal in extension housing. Install rear bearing on output shaft. Ensure locating groove on outside of rear bearing is toward oil pump end of transmission. Install snap ring(s) on output shaft.

3) Install NEW gasket on extension housing. Use petroleum jelly to hold gasket in place. Install output shaft rear bearing locating ring in extension housing (if removed).

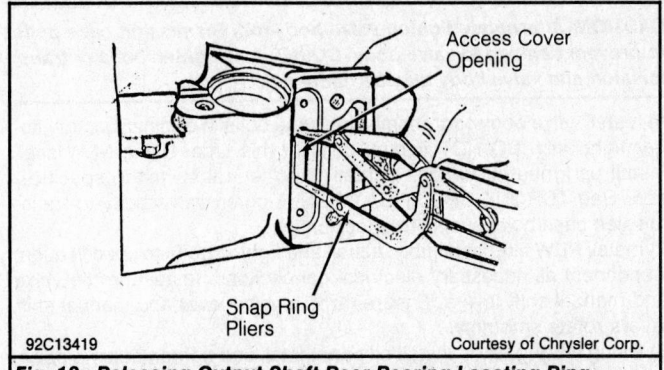

92C13419   Courtesy of Chrysler Corp.

Fig. 12: Releasing Output Shaft Rear Bearing Locating Ring

4) Install extension housing on output shaft while working park rod past parking sprag. Using snap ring pliers, expand output shaft rear bearing locating ring.

5) Work extension housing onto output shaft rear bearing and release locating ring. Ensure locating ring is fully seated in groove on the rear bearing.

6) Install and tighten extension housing-to-transmission case bolts to specification. See TORQUE SPECIFICATIONS.

7) Install gasket and access cover. Install and tighten bolts. Install rear crossmember. Install and tighten extension housing-to-rear mount bolts to specification.

8) To install remaining components, reverse removal procedure. Ensure reference marks are aligned on drive shaft yokes. Adjust transmission fluid level with ATF.

GOVERNOR & PARK GEAR

CAUTION: Output shaft may contain a governor valve indexing area. Small end of governor valve must seat in governor valve indexing area. See Fig. 13. On 37RH diesel applications, governor valve is made of alloyed brass and is not interchangeable with other applications. On all other models, governor valve is made of aluminum and is not interchangeable with previous models. On all models, ensure original type governor components are installed. It may be necessary to use transmission identification number and to consult parts department if replacing any governor components. DO NOT interchange any governor components.

Removal – **1)** Remove extension housing and output shaft rear bearing. See EXTENSION HOUSING, SEAL, BUSHING & OUTPUT SHAFT REAR BEARING under REMOVAL & INSTALLATION.

2) Remove snap ring from valve shaft. See Fig. 13. Remove governor valve and valve shaft from governor body. Remove governor body and park gear-to-output shaft snap ring.

3) Remove governor body and park gear from output shaft. Place reference mark on governor body and park gear for reassembly reference. Remove governor body-to-park gear bolts. Separate governor body from park gear. Remove filter screen from governor body or park gear. Remove remaining components from governor body. See Fig. 13.

Cleaning – **1)** Clean components with solvent and dry with compressed air. Ensure inner and outer weights and governor valve slide freely in bore on governor body.

2) Inspect filter screen for damage. Replace damage components. Ensure original type governor components are installed. DO NOT interchange any governor components.

Installation – **1)** Coat all components with ATF. Install filter screen in park gear. Install governor body on park gear so oil passages in governor body and park gear are aligned. Ensure reference mark is aligned. Install governor body-to-park gear bolts finger tight. DO NOT tighten bolts at this time.

CAUTION: Ensure oil passages in governor body are aligned with those in park gear.

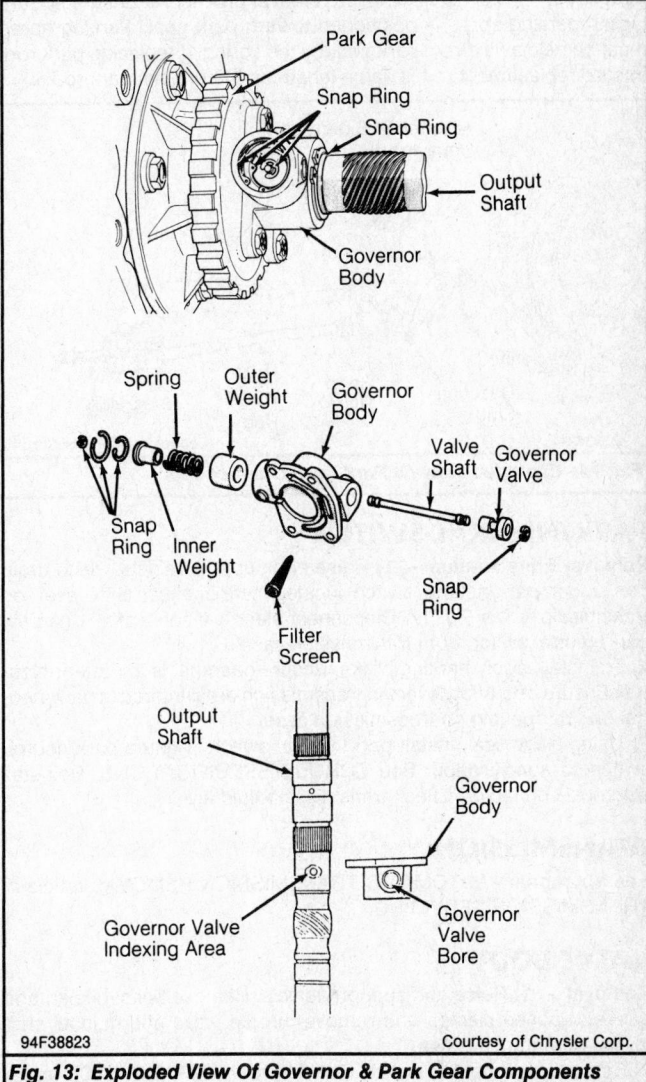

94F38823   Courtesy of Chrysler Corp.

Fig. 13: Exploded View Of Governor & Park Gear Components

2) Rotate output shaft until governor valve indexing area is facing upward. Install governor body and park gear on output shaft. Align governor valve bore with governor valve indexing area of output shaft. See Fig. 13. Align valve shaft holes in governor body and output shaft.

3) Align splines on output shaft with hub of park gear. Push park gear into rear support. Ensure valve shaft holes in output shaft and governor body are aligned.

4) Install governor body and park gear-to-output shaft snap ring. Tighten governor body-to-park gear bolts to specification. See TORQUE SPECIFICATIONS. Install outer weight, spring, inner weight and snap ring in governor body.

5) Ensure valve shaft hole in governor body aligns with hole in output shaft. Install snap ring on end of valve shaft (if removed). Install governor valve and valve shaft in governor body. Ensure valve shaft slides freely in the bore.

6) Install snap ring on remaining end of valve shaft. To install remaining components, reverse removal procedure.

PARK LOCK COMPONENTS

Removal – **1)** Remove extension housing and output shaft rear bearing. See EXTENSION HOUSING, SEAL, BUSHING & OUTPUT SHAFT REAR BEARING under REMOVAL & INSTALLATION.

2) Remove shaft, parking sprag and spring. See Fig. 14. Remove snap ring and reaction plug from extension housing. If removing park rod, valve body must be removed. See VALVE BODY under REMOVAL & INSTALLATION. Remove park rod.

Installation – To install, reverse removal procedure. Ensure square lug on parking sprag is positioned toward park gear. Parking sprag must be held away from park gear by the spring. If replacing park rod, ensure replacement rod is same length as the original park rod.

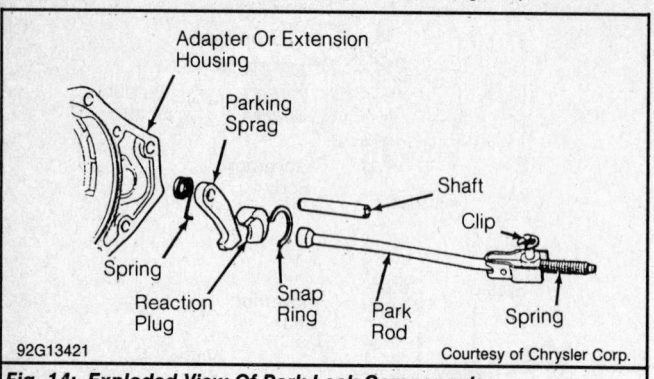

Adapter Or Extension
Housing

Parking
Sprag

Shaft

Clip

Spring

Reaction
Plug

Snap
Ring

Park
Rod

Spring

92G13421   Courtesy of Chrysler Corp.

Fig. 14: Exploded View Of Park Lock Components

PARK/NEUTRAL SWITCH

Removal & Installation – **1)** Raise and support vehicle. Place drain pan under park/neutral switch located near manual shift lever on transmission. See Fig. 17. Disconnect electrical connector. Unscrew park/neutral switch from transmission case.
2) To install, apply parking brake. Ensure gearshift is in Park or Neutral. Ensure operating levers in transmission are centered in park/neutral switch opening on transmission case.
3) Using NEW seal, install park/neutral switch. Tighten park/neutral switch to specification. See TORQUE SPECIFICATIONS. Reinstall electrical connector. Check transmission fluid level.

TRANSMISSION

See appropriate AUTOMATIC TRANSMISSION REMOVAL article in TRANSMISSION SERVICING.

VALVE BODY

Removal – **1)** Raise and support vehicle. Remove bolts, oil pan and gasket. Loosen clamps and remove throttle valve and manual shift levers from transmission.
2) Remove park/neutral switch. See PARK/NEUTRAL SWITCH under REMOVAL & INSTALLATION. Remove bolts and filter assembly.
3) Disconnect lock-up solenoid wire from case connector (if equipped). Remove valve body-to-transmission case bolts. Note bolt length and location for reassembly reference.
4) Lower valve body enough to remove accumulator and spring. Rotate valve body downward and away from transmission case. Pull valve body forward and disengage park rod. Remove valve body.
Installation – **1)** Ensure park/neutral switch is removed before installing valve body. Install NEW seal rings on accumulator. Lubricate seal rings, manual shift lever seal and accumulator and bore with petroleum jelly.
2) Install accumulator in transmission case. Place manual shift lever on valve body in low gear position so ball on park rod can be installed in parking sprag. Using screwdriver, push parking sprag to engage with park gear. This allows knob on park rod to move past parking sprag when installing valve body. Rotate output shaft to ensure parking sprag is engaged.

CAUTION: Ensure park rod enters parking sprag, as park rod may enter cavity in the case and not enter parking sprag. Park rod will be damaged if it is not engaged with parking sprag.

3) Install spring between accumulator and valve body. Install valve body, working park rod past parking sprag. Ensure spring for accumulator remains in place.

CAUTION: Alternately tighten valve body-to-transmission case bolts to prevent damage to valve body. DO NOT overtighten bolts or transmission and valve body may be damaged.

4) Install valve body-to-transmission case bolts in original location finger tight only. DO NOT tighten bolts at this time. Using NEW seal, install park/neutral switch. Tighten park/neutral switch to specification. See TORQUE SPECIFICATIONS. Tighten valve body-to-transmission case bolts evenly to specification.
5) Install NEW filter assembly. Install and tighten bolts to specification. Reconnect all necessary electrical connections. Install throttle valve and manual shift levers. Ensure throttle valve lever and manual shift levers rotate smoothly.
6) Using NEW gasket, install oil pan. Install and tighten bolts to specification. Fill with ATF. Ensure shift linkage/cable and throttle valve cable are properly adjusted. See appropriate AUTOMATIC TRANSMISSION SERVICING article in TRANSMISSION SERVICING.

VEHICLE SPEED SENSOR & PINION GEAR

Removal (1993 Models) – **1)** Raise and support vehicle. Disconnect electrical connector from vehicle speed sensor. See Fig. 15.
2) Remove vehicle speed sensor from adapter. Check vehicle speed sensor mounting area on adapter for signs of ATF leakage. If ATF leakage exists, oil seal is leaking and should be replaced.
3) Remove bolt and adapter retainer. Note location of indexing numbers on adapter in relation to the housing. See Fig. 16.

NOTE: Indexing numbers on adapter correspond to number of teeth on the pinion gear.

4) Ensure area around adapter is clean. Remove adapter, "O" ring and pinion gear. See Fig. 15. Remove oil seal from adapter (if necessary).
Installation – **1)** If installing NEW oil seal in adapter, start oil seal in adapter by hand. Using Oil Seal Installer (C-4004), press oil seal in adapter until it bottoms.
2) Ensure housing is clean. Install NEW "O" ring on adapter (if necessary). Lubricate "O" ring on adapter, oil seal and pinion gear teeth with ATF. Count number of teeth on the pinion gear. Ensure number of teeth on pinion gear are within range of indexing numbers listed on the adapter. See Fig. 16.
3) Install pinion gear, "O" ring and adapter in the housing. Rotate adapter until proper indexing number in relation to number of pinion gear teeth is at 6 o'clock position. See Fig. 16.
4) Ensure adapter is seated in the housing. Install adapter retainer. Install and tighten bolt to specification. See TORQUE SPECIFICATIONS.
5) Install vehicle speed sensor. Tighten nut to specification. Install electrical connector on vehicle speed sensor. Adjust transmission fluid level with ATF.
Removal (1994 Models) – **1)** Raise and support vehicle. Disconnect electrical connector from vehicle speed sensor. See Fig. 15.
2) Remove bolt and adapter retainer. Note location of indexing numbers on adapter in relation to the housing. See Fig. 16.

NOTE: Indexing numbers on adapter correspond to number of teeth on the pinion gear.

3) Ensure area around adapter is clean. Remove adapter with vehicle speed sensor, "O" ring and pinion gear. See Fig. 15. Remove bolt, vehicle speed sensor and "O" ring from adapter.
Installation – **1)** Install NEW "O" ring on vehicle speed sensor and adapter (if necessary). Lubricate "O" rings and pinion gear teeth with ATF.
2) Install vehicle speed sensor in adapter. Install and tighten bolt to specification. See TORQUE SPECIFICATIONS. Install pinion gear in adapter.
3) Ensure housing is clean. Count number of teeth on the pinion gear. Ensure number of teeth on pinion gear are within range of indexing numbers listed on the adapter. See Fig. 16.

4) Install adapter with pinion gear in the housing. Rotate adapter until proper indexing number in relation to number of pinion gear teeth is at 6 o'clock position. *See Fig. 16.*

5) Ensure adapter is seated in the housing. Install adapter retainer. Install and tighten bolt to specification. Install electrical connector on vehicle speed sensor. Adjust transmission fluid level with ATF.

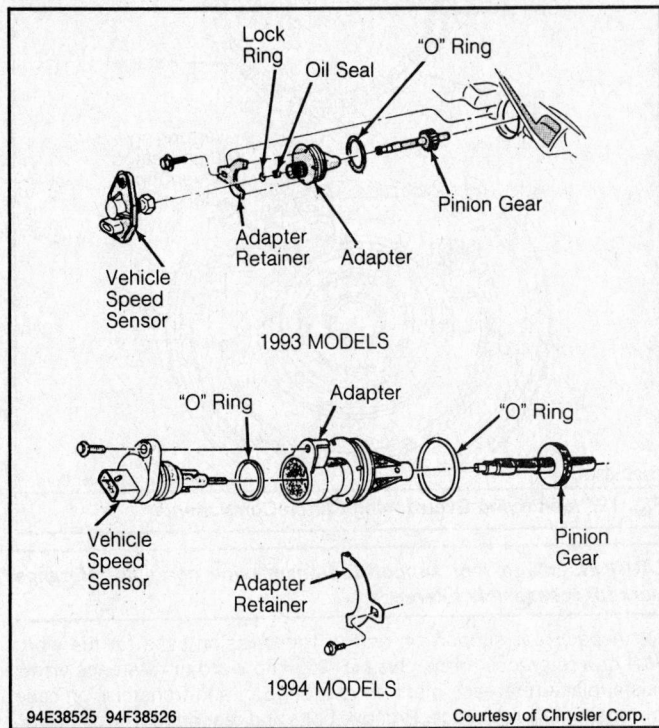

94E38525 94F38526   Courtesy of Chrysler Corp.

Fig. 15: Exploded View Of Vehicle Speed Sensor & Components

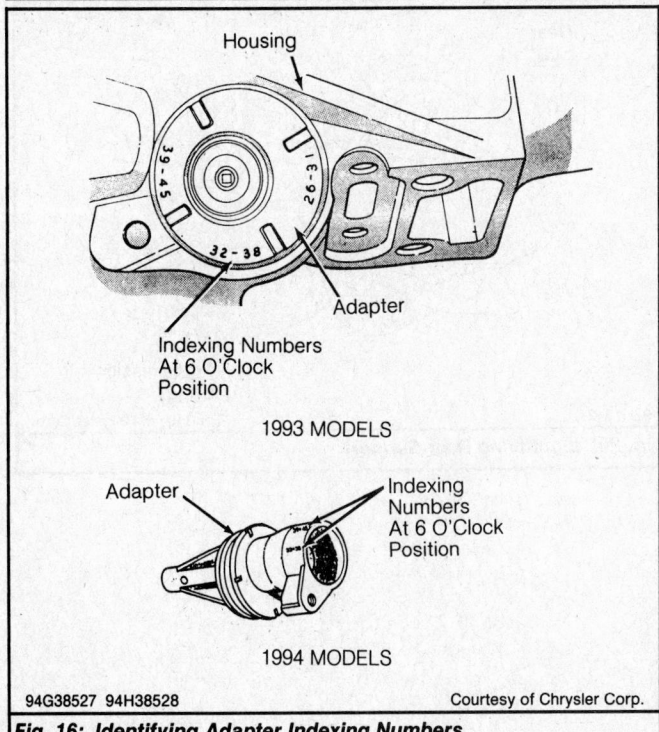

94G38527 94H38528   Courtesy of Chrysler Corp.

Fig. 16: Identifying Adapter Indexing Numbers

TORQUE CONVERTER

CAUTION: Torque converter is a welded assembly and is not serviceable. If a malfunction occurs or if torque converter becomes contaminated with foreign material, it MUST be replaced. It cannot be flushed or repaired.

NOTE: For torque converter fluid leakage testing and torque converter stall speed test, see TESTING.

TRANSMISSION DISASSEMBLY

VALVE BODY & COMPONENTS

CAUTION: Note all thrust washer and thrust plate locations for reassembly reference.

1) Remove torque converter. Loosen clamps and remove throttle valve and manual shift levers from transmission. Remove bolts, access cover and gasket from bottom of extension housing. Using snap ring pliers, expand output shaft rear bearing locating ring. *See Fig. 12.*

2) With locating ring expanded, remove extension housing from output shaft rear bearing. Pull extension housing and gasket from transmission case while working park rod past parking sprag. *See Fig. 14.*

3) Remove snap ring(s) and rear bearing from output shaft. Remove bolts, oil pan and gasket. Remove park/neutral switch. Remove bolts and filter assembly.

4) Remove valve body-to-transmission case bolts. Note bolt length and location for reassembly reference. Lift valve body upward and guide park rod from transmission case. Remove valve body, accumulator and spring. Note location of spring and accumulator for reassembly reference.

5) Remove plug from front band pin access hole, located in front of transmission case, near top of oil pump. *See Fig. 18.* Loosen lock nut on front band adjusting screw approximately 5 revolutions. *See Fig. 17.*

6) Tighten front band adjusting screw until front band is tight. This prevents clutch components from coming out when oil pump is removed.

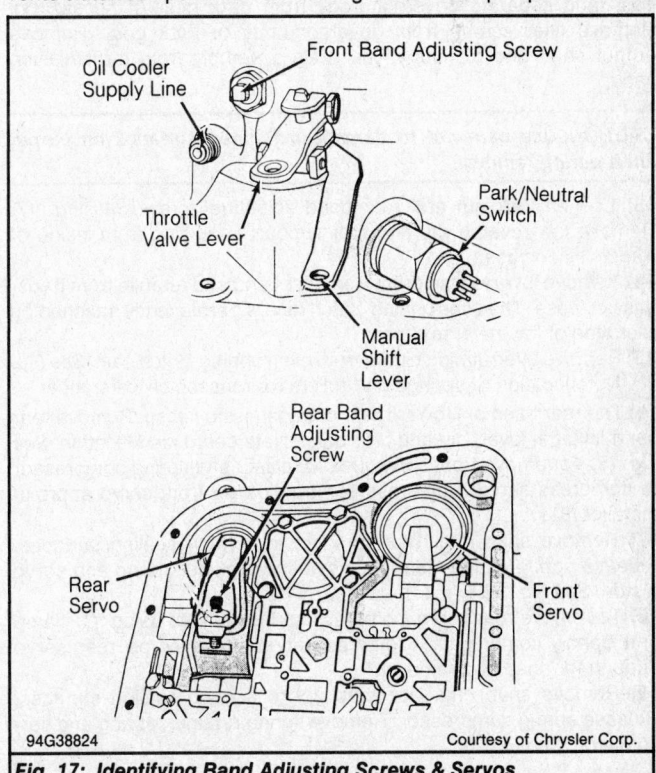

94G38824   Courtesy of Chrysler Corp.

Fig. 17: Identifying Band Adjusting Screws & Servos

7) Remove oil pump bolts. Install slide hammers on opposite sides of oil pump. Pull oil pump from transmission case. Remove oil pump gasket.

8) Loosen front band adjusting screw until front band is loose. Remove front band strut located between lever on transmission case and front band. Remove front band anchor, located between front band and transmission case.

9) Squeeze front band together and remove from transmission case. Remove front band pin through front band pin access hole. Remove lever for front band.

10) Grasp input shaft, holding clutch units together, remove front and rear clutch as an assembly. See Fig. 18. Remove triangular shaped thrust washer from output shaft. This thrust washer may remain on hub of rear clutch.

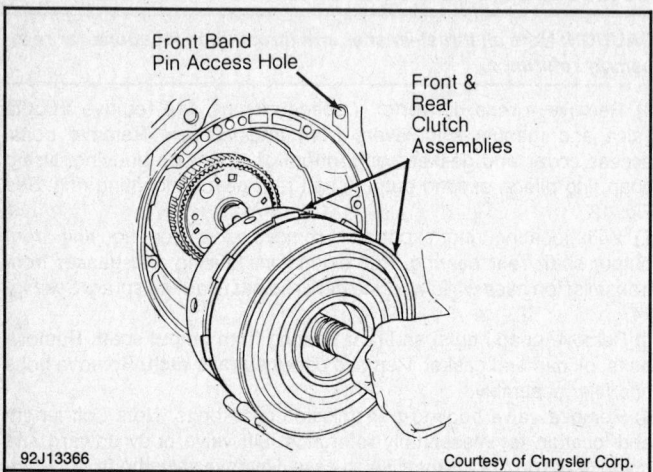

92J13366   Courtesy of Chrysler Corp.

Fig. 18: Identifying Front Band Pin Access Hole & Front & Rear Clutch Assemblies

11) Remove thrust plate from end of output shaft. See Fig. 31. Remove snap ring from valve shaft on the governor. See Fig. 13. Remove governor valve and valve shaft from governor body. Remove governor body and park gear-to-output shaft snap ring.

12) Remove governor body and park gear from output shaft. Remove bolts and separate governor body from park gear (if necessary). Remove filter screen from governor body or park gear. Remove output shaft and planetary gear train assembly from transmission case.

CAUTION: Use care not to damage machined surfaces on output shaft during removal.

13) Loosen lock nut and rear band adjusting screw. See Fig. 17. Remove low-reverse drum-to-rear support snap ring from inside of transmission case.

14) Remove low-reverse drum from rear band and remove from transmission case. The overrunning clutch race is permanently attached on rear side of low-reverse drum.

15) Remove overrunning clutch from overrunning clutch cam. See Fig. 19. Note location of springs and rollers for reassembly reference.

16) Tap rear band pin toward rear of transmission case. Remove rear band linkage, lever, pin and rear band. Note servo identification. See Fig. 17. To remove front servo, use "C" clamp and spring compressor to compress servo. Compress servo guide on front servo approximately 1/8".

17) Remove snap ring. Use care not to scratch sealing surfaces. Release spring compressor. Remove servo guide, spring and servo piston. See Fig. 33.

18) To remove rear servo, compress spring retainer using "C" clamp and spring compressor. Compress spring retainer on rear servo enough for snap ring removal.

19) Remove snap ring. Use care not to scratch sealing surfaces. Release spring compressor. Remove spring retainer, spring and servo piston. See Fig. 34.

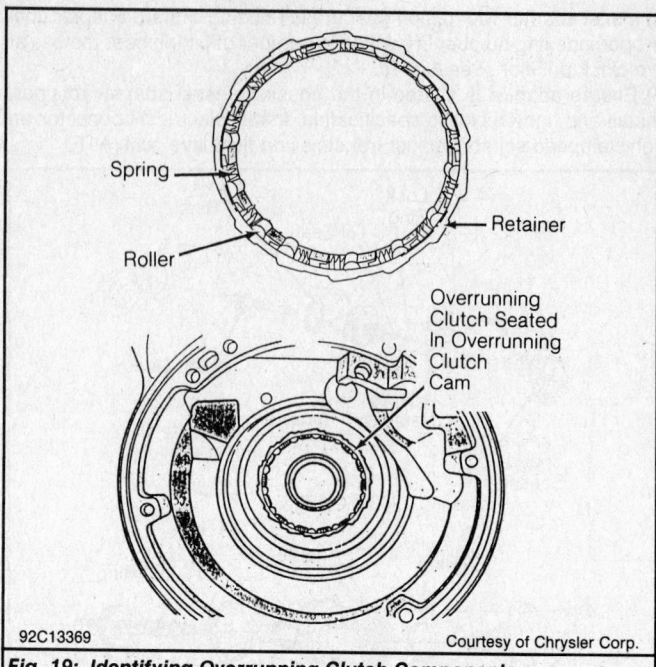

92C13369   Courtesy of Chrysler Corp.

Fig. 19: Identifying Overrunning Clutch Components

CAUTION: Ensure rear support-to-transmission contains reference mark for reassembly reference.

20) Inspect rear support on rear of transmission case for the word PAN or a reference arrow. See Fig. 20. If no word or reference arrow exists, place reference mark on rear support and transmission case for reassembly reference. Remove bolts and rear support from transmission case.

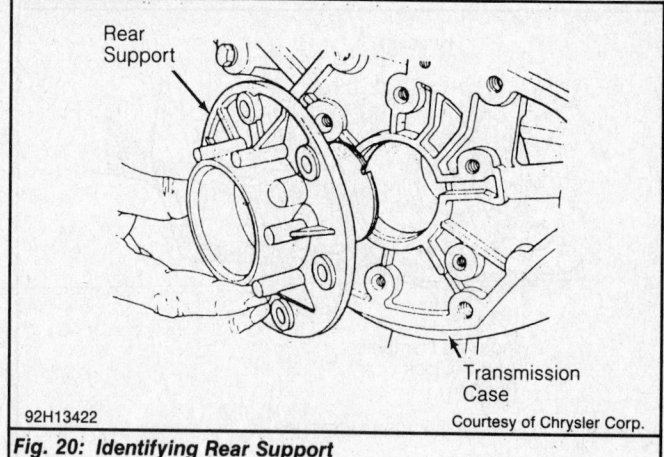

92H13422   Courtesy of Chrysler Corp.

Fig. 20: Identifying Rear Support

COMPONENT DISASSEMBLY & REASSEMBLY

GOVERNOR & PARK GEAR

CAUTION: Output shaft may contain a governor valve indexing area. Small end of governor valve must seat in governor valve indexing area. See Fig. 13. On 37RH diesel applications, governor valve is made of alloyed brass and is not interchangeable with other applications. On all other models, governor valve is made of aluminum and is not interchangeable with previous models. On all models, ensure original type governor components are installed. It may be necessary to use transmission identification number and to consult parts department if replacing any governor components. DO NOT interchange any governor components.

Disassembly – 1) Place reference mark on governor body and park gear for reassembly reference. Remove bolts and separate governor body from park gear.
2) Remove filter screen from governor body or park gear. Remove snap ring, inner and outer weights from governor body. Remove snap ring and separate inner and outer weights.
Cleaning & Inspection – 1) Clean components with solvent and dry with compressed air. Inspect components for damage. Ensure governor valve and weights slide freely in governor body.
2) Inspect gear teeth and seal rings on park gear for damage. The front seal ring (closest to park gear) is a hook-type ring. Ensure ends of seal ring are hooked together. Replace damaged components. DO NOT interchange any governor components.
Reassembly – 1) Coat components with ATF. Install spring with inner and outer weights in governor body. DO NOT install valve shaft at this time.

CAUTION: Ensure oil passages in governor body are aligned with those in park gear.

2) Install NEW seal rings on park gear (if necessary). Install filter screen in park gear. Install governor body on park gear so oil passages in governor body and park gear are aligned. Ensure reference mark is aligned.
3) Install governor body-to-park gear bolts finger tight only. DO NOT tighten bolts at this time. Governor body-to-park gear bolts will be tightened to specification when governor and park gear are installed on output shaft. Installation on output shaft is necessary to obtain proper alignment of park gear and governor body.

OVERRUNNING CLUTCH

CAUTION: Ensure overrunning clutch components are properly installed or inoperative transmission or transmission failure may result.

Disassembly – 1) If replacing overrunning clutch cam, remove set screw from overrunning clutch cam. *See Fig. 21.* Insert punch through rear support bolt holes in rear of transmission case.
2) Using hammer, tap overrunning clutch cam from transmission case. It may be necessary to alternate from hole-to-hole to prevent overrunning clutch cam from binding in transmission case.
Cleaning & Inspection – Clean components with solvent and dry with compressed air. Inspect overrunning clutch components and low-reverse drum for damage. Replace damaged components.
Reassembly – 1) Ensure overrunning clutch cam bore in transmission case is clean. Install rear support in transmission case. Ensure reference mark on rear support is aligned with that on transmission case.
2) Align and start overrunning clutch cam in transmission case. Ensure serrations on overrunning cam and transmission case are aligned. *See Fig. 22.* Narrow ends of cam ramps on overrunning clutch cam should face the left when viewed from front of transmission. *See Fig. 22.*

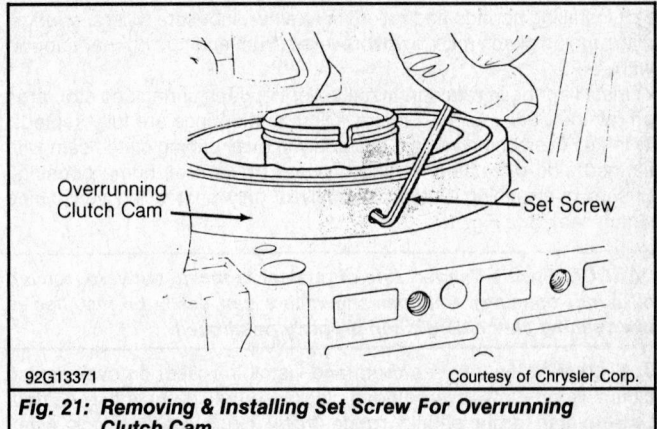

92G13371   Courtesy of Chrysler Corp.

Fig. 21: Removing & Installing Set Screw For Overrunning Clutch Cam

CAUTION: Ensure narrow ends of cam ramps on overrunning clutch are to the left when viewing overrunning clutch cam from front of transmission case. See Fig. 22.

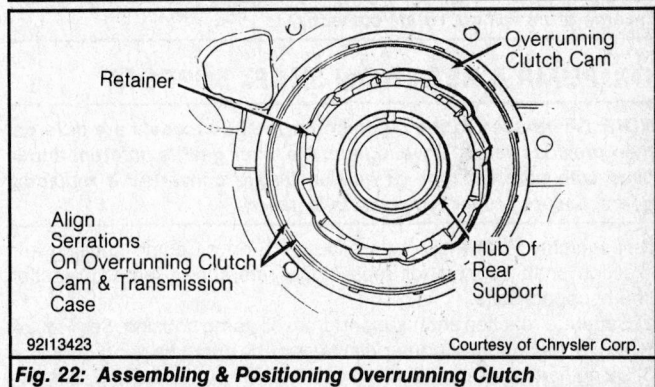

92I13423   Courtesy of Chrysler Corp.

Fig. 22: Assembling & Positioning Overrunning Clutch

3) Install Adapter (SP-5124) in output shaft bore of rear support. Install Puller Bolt (SP-3701) and Plate (SP-3583-A) on overrunning clutch cam. *See Fig. 23.* Ensure plate is seated squarely on overrunning clutch cam.
4) Install nut on puller bolt. *See Fig. 23.* Tighten nut and pull overrunning clutch cam into transmission case. Ensure overrunning clutch cam enters transmission case evenly and does not bind.
5) Install set screw in overrunning clutch cam. Tighten set screw to specification. See TORQUE SPECIFICATIONS. Remove nut, adapters, plate and puller bolt. Using blunt chisel, stake transmission case in 12 areas to retain overrunning clutch cam.

CAUTION: Ensure transmission case is staked in 12 areas to retain overrunning clutch cam.

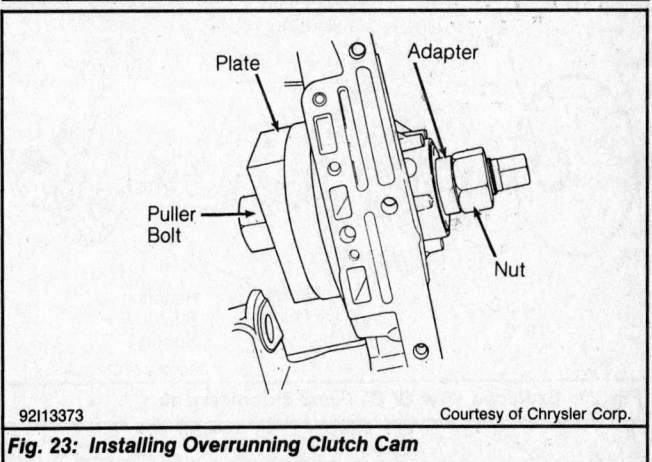

92I13373   Courtesy of Chrysler Corp.

Fig. 23: Installing Overrunning Clutch Cam

6) If installing springs and rollers in retainer, lubricate rollers, springs, overrunning clutch race on low-reverse drum and hub on rear support with ATF.

7) Install spring in retainer. Install roller between spring and stop area on retainer. *See Fig. 19.* Ensure rollers and springs are fully seated.

8) Install overrunning clutch assembly in overrunning clutch cam with flanged side of retainer facing outward (toward oil pump opening). Ensure overrunning clutch assembly is fully seated in overrunning clutch cam. *See Fig. 19.*

CAUTION: Ensure flanged side of retainer is facing outward (toward oil pump opening). Retainer and rollers can easily be installed in overrunning clutch cam when properly positioned.

9) Slightly tilt low-reverse drum and install in rollers on overrunning clutch. Rotate low-reverse drum clockwise until drum is fully seated. Low-reverse drum should rotate freely clockwise but lock when rotated counterclockwise when viewed from front of transmission.

CAUTION: Ensure low-reverse drum rotates freely clockwise but locks when rotated counterclockwise when viewed from front of transmission. Check for improper component assembly if low-reverse drum will not rotate correctly.

OIL PUMP & REACTION SHAFT SUPPORT

NOTE: Gears used in the oil pump on 1993-94 models are different than previous years. Drive lugs on the inner gear is different and is used with different type of hub on torque converter. If replacing gears, ensure proper type gear is installed.

Disassembly – 1) Place reference mark on oil pump housing and reaction shaft support for reassembly reference. Remove reaction shaft support bolts.

2) Separate reaction shaft support from oil pump housing. *See Fig. 24.* Remove seal ring from outer diameter of oil pump housing.

3) Using hammer and punch, tap seal from oil pump housing. Remove seal rings from reaction shaft support.

4) Note direction of thrust washer installation on rear of reaction shaft support. Remove thrust washer from reaction shaft support. Note direction of gear installation. Remove gears from oil pump housing.

5) Inspect bushing in oil pump housing and reaction shaft support for damage. If removing bushing from oil pump housing, place oil pump housing on flat surface with gear cavity facing downward.

6) Using press or hammer and bushing remover, remove bushing. If removing bushing from reaction shaft support, use Cup (SP-3633), Nut (SP-1191) and Bushing Remover (SP-5301). *See Fig. 25.*

7) Hold cup against reaction shaft. By hand, thread bushing remover into bushing as far as possible. Using wrench, thread bushing remover an additional 3-4 turns into bushing. Tighten nut and remove bushing.

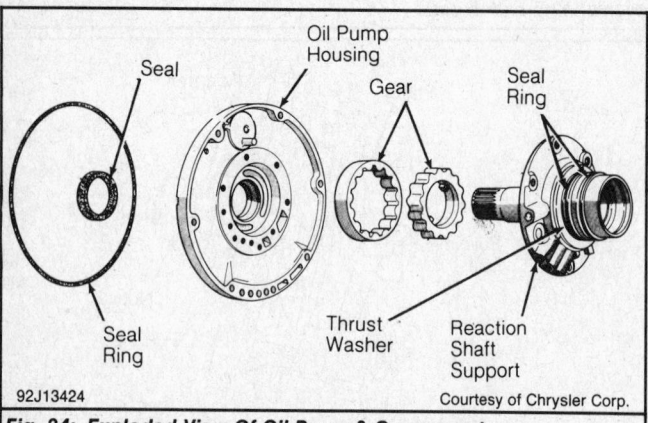

92J13424   Courtesy of Chrysler Corp.

Fig. 24: Exploded View Of Oil Pump & Components

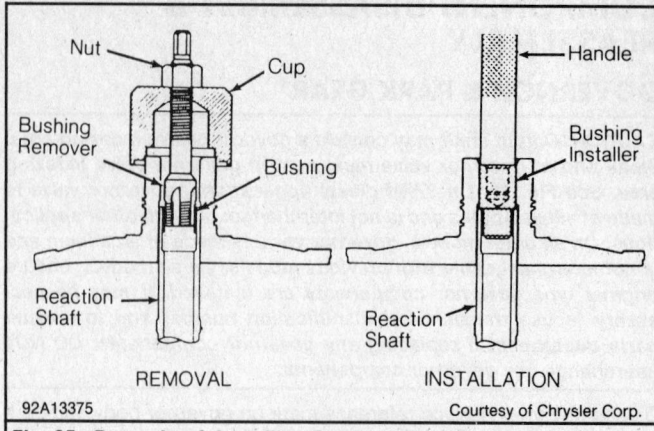

92A13375   Courtesy of Chrysler Corp.

Fig. 25: Removing & Installing Reaction Shaft Support Bushing

Cleaning & Inspection – 1) Clean and inspect components for damage. Inspect all machined surfaces for pitting or damage.

2) Install both gears in oil pump housing. Using feeler gauge, measure outer gear-to-oil pump housing clearance.

3) Place straightedge on oil pump housing, above both gears. Using feeler gauge, measure gear end clearance between each gear and straightedge.

4) Align tooth on inner gear with tooth on outer gear. Using feeler gauge, measure gear tooth clearance between teeth. Replace components if clearance is not within specification. See OIL PUMP SPECIFICATIONS table.

OIL PUMP SPECIFICATIONS

Application	In. (mm)
Gear End Clearance	.0010-.0025 (.025-.063)
Gear Tooth Clearance	.0035-.0075 (.089-.190)
Outer Gear-To-Oil Pump Housing Clearance	.0035-.0075 (.089-.190)

Reassembly – 1) If installing NEW oil pump housing bushing, place oil pump housing on flat surface with gear cavity facing upward.

2) Place bushing on bushing installer and start into oil pump housing. Tap bushing into oil pump housing until bushing installer bottoms. Ensure bushing is installed evenly and does not bind in oil pump housing. Using blunt punch, stake bushing in 2 places. *See Fig. 26.* Using knife, clean burrs from stake areas.

3) If installing NEW reaction shaft support bushing, ensure reaction shaft support is clean and free of burrs. Place reaction shaft support on clean surface with bushing area facing upward.

4) Use Handle (C-4171) and Bushing Installer (SP-5302). Place bushing on bushing installer and start into reaction shaft support. *See Fig. 25.* Tap bushing in reaction shaft support until bushing installer bottoms. Clean reaction shaft support.

5) To reassemble oil pump, lubricate gears with Mopar ATF Plus Type 7176 fluid. Install gears in oil pump housing.

CAUTION: If thrust washer contains a chamfered edge on inside diameter of thrust washer, it must be installed on reaction shaft support with chamfered edge on inside diameter of thrust washer facing toward front of oil pump.

6) Install NEW thrust washer on rear of reaction shaft support. If thrust washer contains a chamfered edge on inside diameter of thrust washer, it must be installed on reaction shaft support with chamfered edge on inside diameter of thrust washer facing toward front of oil pump. Lubricate thrust washer with petroleum jelly.

CAUTION: DO NOT over expand or twist seal rings when installing on reaction shaft support. Ensure ends on seal rings are hooked together or otherwise seal rings will be damaged when installing oil pump.

7) If replacing seal rings on reaction shaft support, install NEW seal rings on reaction shaft support. Lubricate seal rings with petroleum jelly. Squeeze seal rings together until ends of seal rings hook together.

8) Install reaction shaft support on oil pump housing. Install and tighten reaction shaft support bolts to specification. See TORQUE SPECIFICATIONS.

9) Install NEW seal in oil pump housing with seal lip facing inward (toward oil pump). Install NEW seal ring on outer diameter of oil pump housing. Lubricate lip of seal and seal ring with petroleum jelly.

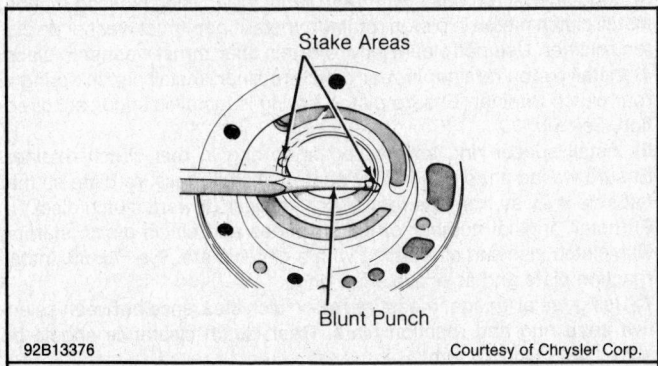

92B13376   Courtesy of Chrysler Corp.

Fig. 26: Staking Bushing In Oil Pump Housing

FRONT CLUTCH

CAUTION: Note direction of clutch discs and clutch plates for reassembly reference. Note number of each component, as some models may contain different number of clutch components. Components must be installed in correct sequence.

Disassembly – 1) Remove waved snap ring, pressure plate, clutch discs and clutch plates. Note number of clutch discs and plates for reassembly. *See Fig. 27.*

2) Using spring compressor, compress piston springs. Remove snap ring. Release spring compressor. Remove spring compressor and spring retainer.

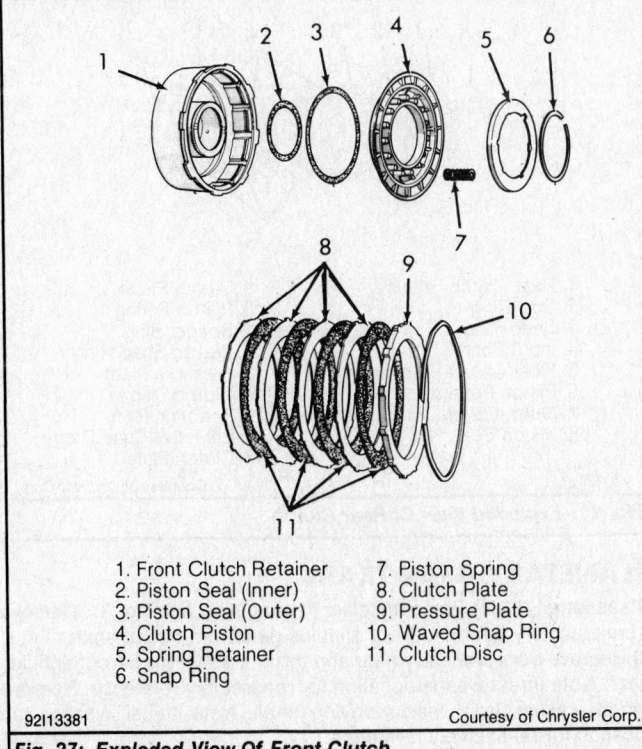

1. Front Clutch Retainer	7. Piston Spring
2. Piston Seal (Inner)	8. Clutch Plate
3. Piston Seal (Outer)	9. Pressure Plate
4. Clutch Piston	10. Waved Snap Ring
5. Spring Retainer	11. Clutch Disc
6. Snap Ring	

92I13381   Courtesy of Chrysler Corp.

Fig. 27: Exploded View Of Front Clutch

CAUTION: Note number of piston springs and location before removing, as the number of piston springs may vary.

3) Note number of piston springs and location for reassembly reference. Remove piston springs and clutch piston from front clutch retainer. Remove and discard piston seals.

4) Inspect bushing in front clutch retainer for damage. If replacing bushing, position front clutch retainer with clutch plate opening facing downward. Using hammer or press and bushing remover, remove bushing.

Cleaning & Inspection – 1) Clean all metal components with solvent and dry with compressed air. Inspect clutch discs for flatness, flaking or glazing. Inspect clutch plates and pressure plate for flatness or damage at plate-to-front clutch retainer tang areas.

2) Ensure tang areas in front clutch retainer are not damaged and clutch plates slide freely in front clutch retainer. Ensure check ball located in bottom of front clutch retainer moves freely.

3) Inspect all sealing surfaces for burrs or scratches. Inspect piston springs for distortion. Replace damaged components.

Reassembly – 1) If installing NEW bushing in front clutch retainer, position front clutch retainer with clutch plate opening facing upward.

2) Using hammer or press, handle and Bushing Installer (SP-5511), install bushing until bushing installer bottoms. Clean front clutch retainer after installing bushing.

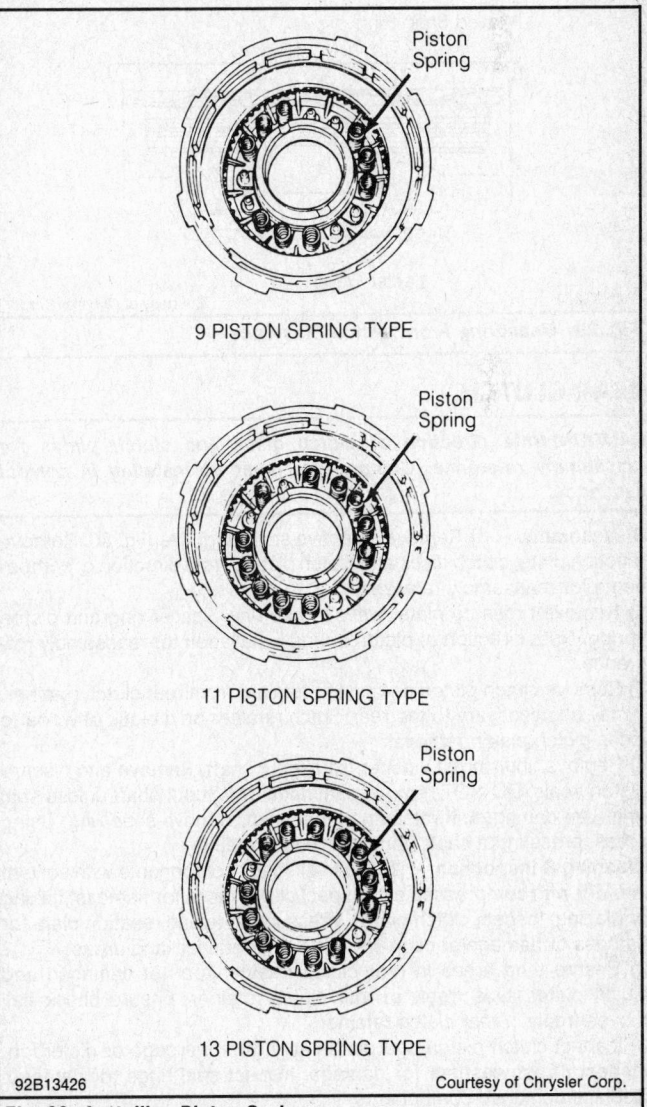

92B13426   Courtesy of Chrysler Corp.

Fig. 28: Installing Piston Springs

3) Soak clutch discs in Mopar ATF Plus Type 7176 fluid. Install NEW piston seals with lip of piston seal toward inside of front clutch retainer. Lubricate piston seals with petroleum jelly. Lubricate front clutch retainer and clutch piston surface with ATF.

CAUTION: Use twisting motion when installing clutch piston to prevent damage to piston seals.

---

4) Using twisting motion, install clutch piston in front clutch retainer. Install piston springs on clutch piston. Ensure piston springs are properly positioned in accordance with amount of piston springs used. *See Fig. 28.*

5) Install spring retainer. Using spring compressor, compress piston springs. Install NEW snap ring to secure spring retainer. Release spring compressor.

6) Install clutch plates and clutch discs, starting with a clutch plate and alternating with a clutch disc. *See Fig. 27.* Ensure original number of components are installed. Install pressure plate and waved snap ring.

7) Using feeler gauge, measure front clutch clearance between pressure plate and waved snap ring. *See Fig. 29.*

8) Front clutch clearance should be .070-.129" (1.78-3.28 mm) on 3-disc clutches or .082-.151" (2.08-3.84 mm) on 4-disc clutches. Front clutch clearance is non-adjustable. If front clutch clearance is not within specification, check for defective or improperly assembled components.

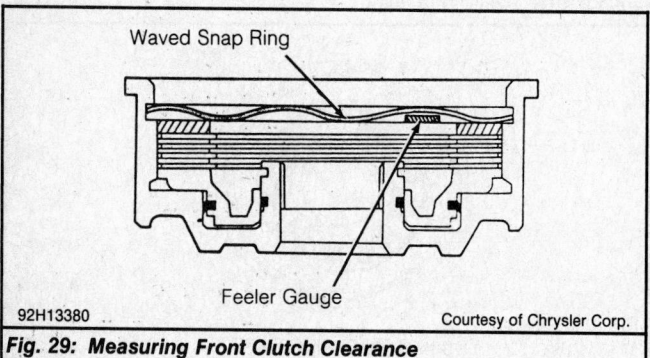

Fig. 29: Measuring Front Clutch Clearance

REAR CLUTCH

CAUTION: Note direction of clutch discs and clutch plates for reassembly reference. Components must be installed in correct sequence.

Disassembly – 1) Remove selective snap ring. *See Fig. 30.* Remove reaction plate, clutch discs and clutch plates. Note direction of components for reassembly reference.

2) Remove pressure plate, waved snap ring, spacer ring and piston spring. Note direction of piston spring installation for reassembly reference.

3) Remove clutch piston and piston retainer from rear clutch retainer. It may be necessary to tap rear clutch retainer on a block of wood to aid in clutch piston removal.

4) Remove fiber thrust washer from input shaft. Remove and discard piston seals. DO NOT remove seal rings from input shaft unless seal rings are damaged. If removing input shaft, remove snap ring. Using press, press input shaft from rear clutch retainer.

Cleaning & Inspection – 1) Clean all metal components with solvent and dry with compressed air. Inspect clutch discs for flatness, flaking or glazing. Inspect clutch plates, pressure plate and reaction plate for flatness or damage at plate-to-rear clutch retainer tang areas.

2) Ensure tang areas in rear clutch retainer are not damaged and clutch plates slide freely in rear clutch retainer. Ensure check ball moves freely in rear clutch retainer.

3) Inspect clutch piston and piston spring for warpage or distortion. Inspect thrust washers for damage. Inspect seal rings for damage. Replace damaged components.

Reassembly – 1) Soak clutch discs in Mopar ATF Plus Type 7176 fluid. Lubricate remaining clutch components with ATF. Install NEW seal rings on input shaft (if removed) and piston retainer.

2) If installing input shaft, press input shaft into rear clutch retainer. Install snap ring. Install NEW piston seals on clutch piston with lip of piston seal toward input shaft.

CAUTION: Use twisting motion when installing clutch piston to prevent damage to piston seals.

---

3) Lubricate piston seals with petroleum jelly. Using twisting motion, install clutch piston in piston retainer. Install fiber thrust washer on piston retainer. Use petroleum jelly to retain fiber thrust washer in place.

4) Install piston retainer in rear clutch retainer. Install piston spring in rear clutch retainer. Ensure piston spring is installed in correct direction. *See Fig. 30.*

5) Install spacer ring and waved snap ring in rear clutch retainer. Ensure waved snap ring is fully seated. Install pressure plate so that flat side is away from the rear clutch retainer (toward clutch disc).

6) Install original number of clutch plates and clutch discs, starting with clutch disc and alternating with a clutch plate. *See Fig. 30.* Install reaction plate and selective snap ring.

7) Using feeler gauge, measure rear clutch clearance between selective snap ring and reaction plate. Rear clutch clearance should be .025-.045" (.64-1.14 mm).

8) If rear clutch clearance is not within specification, install different thickness selective snap ring. Selective snap ring is available in thicknesses of .060" (1.52 mm), .074" (1.88 mm), .088" (2.23 mm) and .106" (2.69 mm). If proper rear clutch clearance cannot be obtained, clutch components may require replacement.

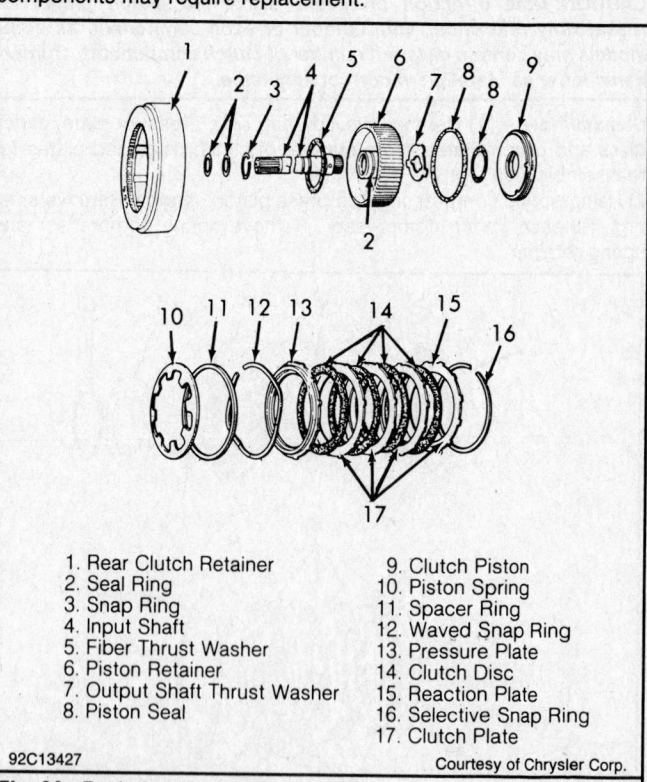

1. Rear Clutch Retainer	9. Clutch Piston
2. Seal Ring	10. Piston Spring
3. Snap Ring	11. Spacer Ring
4. Input Shaft	12. Waved Snap Ring
5. Fiber Thrust Washer	13. Pressure Plate
6. Piston Retainer	14. Clutch Disc
7. Output Shaft Thrust Washer	15. Reaction Plate
8. Piston Seal	16. Selective Snap Ring
	17. Clutch Plate

Fig. 30: Exploded View Of Rear Clutch

PLANETARY GEAR TRAIN

Disassembly – 1) Remove select fit snap ring. *See Fig. 31.* Remove front planetary gear and front annulus gear from output shaft.

2) Remove front planetary gear and thrust washer from front annulus gear. Note thrust washer location for reassembly reference. Remove thrust washer from inside driving shell. Note thrust washer tab location for reassembly reference.

3) Remove sun gear and driving shell. Remove thrust washer from front side of rear planetary gear. Remove rear planetary gear from rear annulus gear. Remove thrust plate and rear annulus gear from output shaft. *See Fig. 31.*

4) If removing sun gear from driving shell, remove snap ring from sun gear. Remove sun gear and thrust plate.

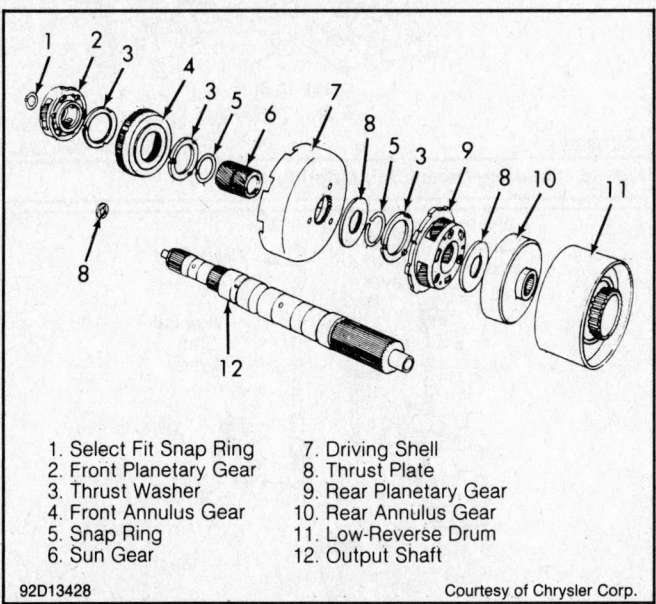

1. Select Fit Snap Ring
2. Front Planetary Gear
3. Thrust Washer
4. Front Annulus Gear
5. Snap Ring
6. Sun Gear
7. Driving Shell
8. Thrust Plate
9. Rear Planetary Gear
10. Rear Annulus Gear
11. Low-Reverse Drum
12. Output Shaft

92D13428   Courtesy of Chrysler Corp.

Fig. 31: Exploded View Of Planetary Gear Train

Cleaning & Inspection – 1) Clean all components with solvent and dry with compressed air. Inspect for damaged components. Inspect sun gear bushings for scoring or wear. Replace sun gear if bushings are damaged or worn.

2) Inspect planetary gears for defective pinion gears, pins, washers or carrier. Pinion gears, pins and washers can be replaced if defective. If carrier is damaged, entire planetary gear assembly must be replaced.

3) Inspect output shaft for damage at bushing/bearing surfaces and splined areas. Replace damaged components.

Reassembly – 1) Lubricate output shaft and planetary gear train components with ATF. Use petroleum jelly to retain thrust washers and thrust plates in position.

2) If installing sun gear in driving shell, install front snap ring on sun gear. Install sun gear in driving shell. Install thrust plate and snap ring. Install rear annulus gear on output shaft.

3) Install thrust plate in rear annulus gear. Ensure thrust plate is seated on output shaft splines and against rear annulus gear. Install rear planetary gear in rear annulus gear.

4) Install thrust washer on front side of rear planetary gear. Ensure tabs on thrust washer engage with slots on rear planetary gear. Install driving shell and sun gear on output shaft. Ensure thrust washer remains in position on rear planetary gear.

5) Install thrust washer on front side of driving shell. Ensure tabs on thrust washer engage with slots on driving shell. Install thrust washer on front planetary gear. Ensure tabs on thrust washer engage with slots on front planetary gear.

6) Install front annulus gear on front planetary gear. Ensure gears are fully seated. Install front annulus gear and front planetary gear on output shaft. Ensure front planetary gear fully engages with sun gear and assembly is fully seated on output shaft.

7) Position planetary gear train in upright position. Ensure snap ring groove on end of output shaft is fully visible. Install select fit snap ring. Position gear train assembly with opening of driving shell facing workbench.

8) Support output shaft with wooden block between end of output shaft and workbench. This is done so planetary gear train components will move forward so planetary gear train end play can be checked.

9) Using feeler gauge, measure planetary gear train end play between shoulder on output shaft and end of rear annulus gear. *See Fig. 32.*

10) Planetary gear train end play should be .006-.048" (.15-1.22 mm). If planetary gear train end play is not within specification, install different thickness select fit snap ring. Select fit snap ring is available in thicknesses of .048" (1.22 mm), .055" (1.40 mm) and .062" (1.57 mm).

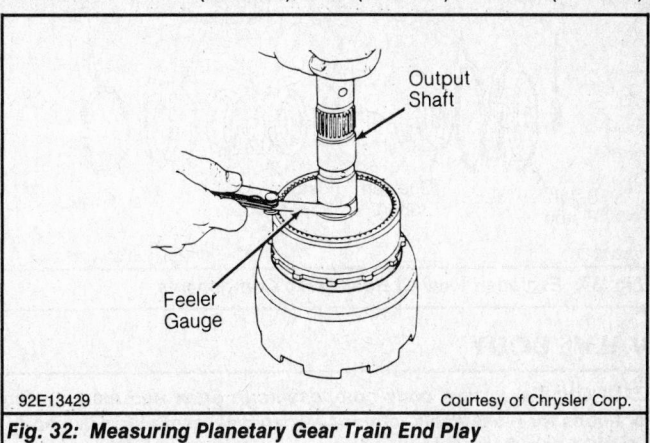

92E13429   Courtesy of Chrysler Corp.

Fig. 32: Measuring Planetary Gear Train End Play

FRONT SERVO

Disassembly – 1) Note direction of seal ring installation on servo piston and servo guide. Remove seal ring from servo guide. Remove snap ring from servo rod. *See Fig. 33.*

2) Separate servo rod, springs and washer from servo piston. Remove and discard seal rings and "O" rings.

Cleaning & Inspection – Clean components with solvent and dry with compressed air. Inspect springs for distortion. Inspect servo piston, servo rod and servo guide for wear or cracks. Replace defective components.

Reassembly – To reassemble, reverse disassembly procedure using NEW seal rings and "O" rings. Ensure seal rings are installed in original direction. Lubricate seal rings and "O" rings with petroleum jelly. Lubricate all other components with ATF.

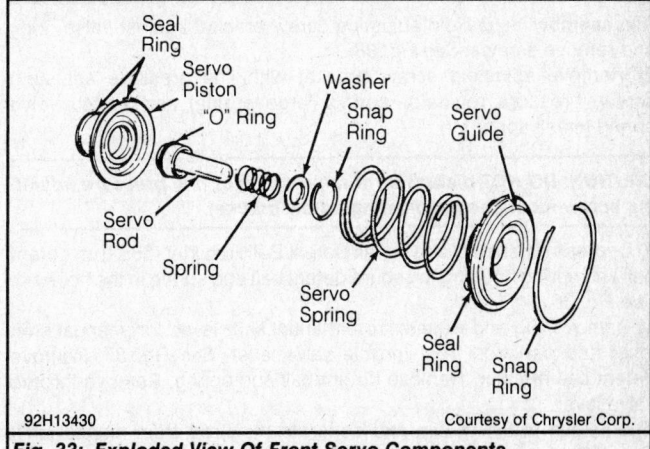

92H13430   Courtesy of Chrysler Corp.

Fig. 33: Exploded View Of Front Servo Components

REAR SERVO

Disassembly – Note direction of seal ring installation on servo piston. Remove seal ring from servo piston. Remove snap ring from end of piston plug. *See Fig. 34.* Separate servo piston and spring from piston plug.

Cleaning & Inspection – Clean components with solvent and dry with compressed air. Inspect springs for distortion. Inspect servo piston and piston plug for wear or cracks. Replace defective components.

Reassembly – To reassemble, reverse disassembly procedure using NEW seal ring. Ensure seal ring is installed on servo piston in original direction. Lubricate seal ring with petroleum jelly. Lubricate all other components with ATF.

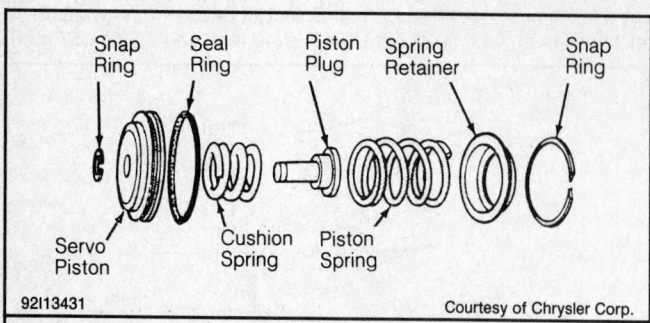

Fig. 34: Exploded View Of Rear Servo Components

VALVE BODY

CAUTION: Place valve body components in order and mark spring locations for reassembly reference when disassembling valve body. DO NOT use force to remove components from valve body. Valve body assembly consists of valve body, transfer plate and separator plate. See Fig. 35.

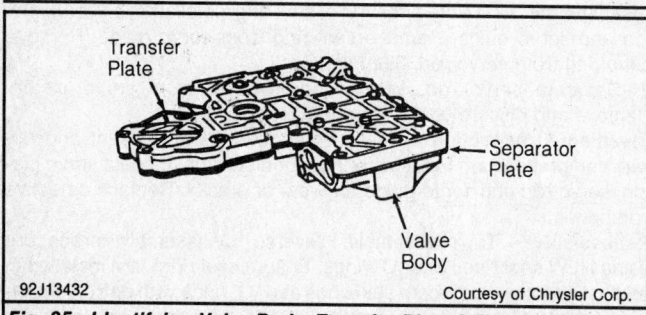

Fig. 35: Identifying Valve Body, Transfer Plate & Separator Plate

Disassembly – 1) Hold adjusting screw bracket against valve body and remove screws. See Fig. 38.
2) Remove adjusting screw bracket with line pressure adjusting screw, pressure regulator spring (large spring) and switch valve spring (small spring).

CAUTION: DO NOT disturb throttle pressure or line pressure adjusting screw locations in adjusting screw bracket.

3) Depress detent ball and install Detent Ball Retainer (6583) on detent ball and spring housing to secure detent ball and spring in the housing. See Fig. 36.
4) Remove clip and washer from manual shift lever. Lift manual shift lever and park rod from throttle valve lever. See Fig. 37. Remove detent ball retainer. Remove detent ball and spring. Remove throttle valve lever.
5) Remove retaining clip and separate park rod from manual shift lever. Remove components and stiffener plate from valve body. Ensure components are placed in order for reassembly reference. See Fig. 38. Position valve body with transfer plate facing upward.

CAUTION: Ensure transfer plate is facing upward before removing transfer plate-to-valve body screws. This prevents check balls from falling from valve body.

6) Remove transfer plate-to-valve body screws. Remove transfer plate from valve body. Note location of valve body check balls. See Fig. 39.
7) Position transfer plate with separator plate facing upward. This prevents check ball from falling from transfer plate. Remove separator plate-to-transfer plate screws.

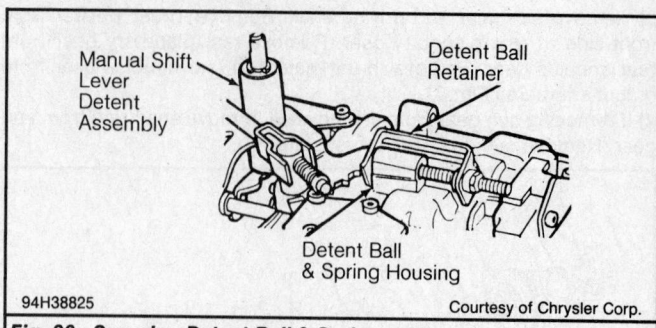

Fig. 36: Securing Detent Ball & Spring

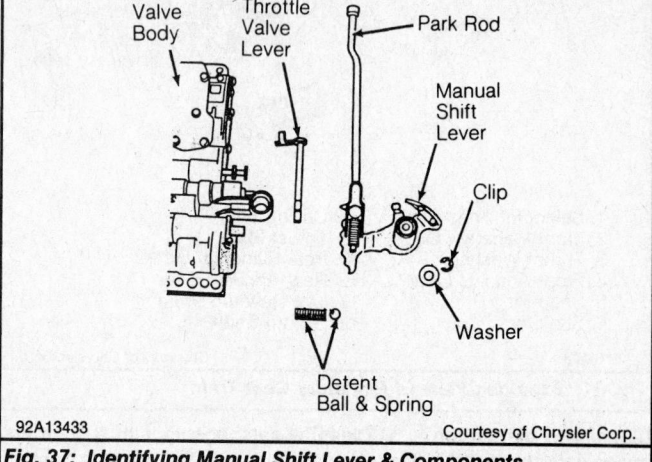

Fig. 37: Identifying Manual Shift Lever & Components

8) Remove separator plate from transfer plate. Note location of filter in separator plate and check ball in transfer plate. See Fig. 39.
Cleaning & Inspection – 1) Clean components with solvent and dry with compressed air. DO NOT use shop towels to dry components. Ensure all components slide freely in housing bores and bores are not scored. Inspect machined surfaces for nicks, burrs or distortion.
2) Inspect valve and plugs for burrs or scratches. Minor scratches may be removed using crocus cloth. When sanding components, DO NOT round off the edges of valve or plug.

CAUTION: Many of valve body components are made of aluminum and contain a special coating. DO NOT polish or sand aluminum components, as special coating will be removed. Use magnet to check if components are made of aluminum before polishing or sanding. Use care when polishing or sanding components not to round off the edges of component.

3) Ensure all fluid passages are open. Inspect transfer plate and separator plates for distortion. Inspect check balls and seats for damage.
4) Valve body must be replaced if components are damaged. Only the following components can be serviced.
• Adjusting Screw Bracket
• Manual Shift Lever, Seal And Detent Ball
• Park Rod And Clip
• Switch Valve And Spring
• Throttle Valve Lever
Reassembly – 1) Lubricate all components and fluid passages with ATF. Install check ball in transfer plate. See Fig. 39. Ensure filter is installed in separator plate. Install separator plate and stiffener plate on transfer plate.

CAUTION: With separator plate installed on transfer plate, ensure check ball in transfer plate is visible through orifice hole in separator plate. See Fig. 39.

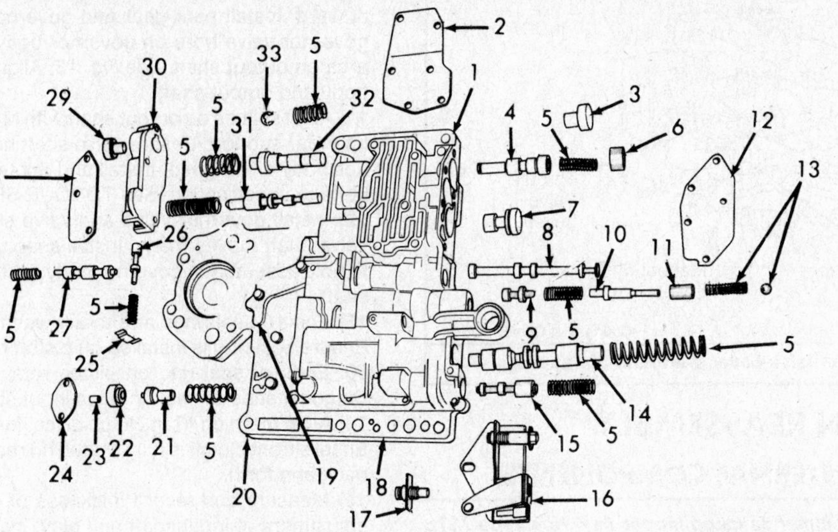

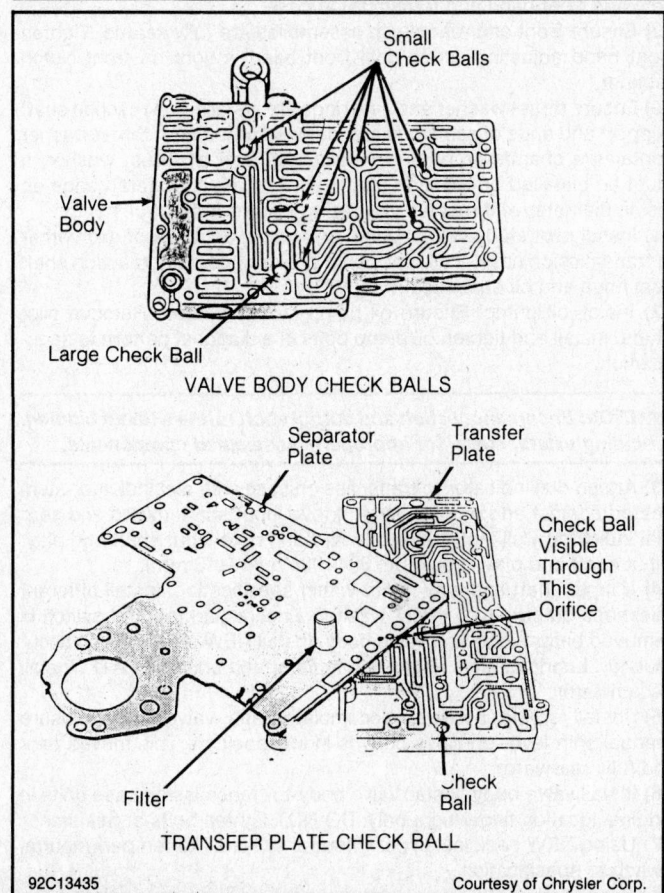

1. Valve Body
2. Shuttle Valve End Plate
3. 2-3 Shift Valve Governor Plug
4. Shuttle Valve
5. Spring
6. Shuttle Valve Plug *
7. 1-2 Shift Valve Governor Plug *
8. Manual Valve
9. Throttle Valve *
10. Kickdown Valve
11. Detent
12. Governor Valve End Plate
13. Detent Ball & Spring
14. Pressure Regulator Valve
15. Switch Valve
16. Adjusting Screw Bracket
17. Line Pressure Adjusting Screw
18. Transfer Plate
19. Stiffener Plate
20. Separator Plate
21. Regulator Valve Throttle Pressure Plug
22. Sleeve
23. Regulator Valve Pressure Plug
24. Regulator Valve End Plate
25. Retainer
26. Limit Valve
27. 1-2 Shift Control Valve
28. Shift Valve End Plate
29. Throttle Plug
30. 3-2 Downshift Housing
31. 1-2 Shift Valve *
32. 2-3 Shift Valve
33. Clip

* – Aluminum Component

94138826

Courtesy of Chrysler Corp.

Fig. 38: Exploded View Of Valve Body Components

VALVE BODY CHECK BALLS

TRANSFER PLATE CHECK BALL

92C13435

Courtesy of Chrysler Corp.

Fig. 39: Identifying Check Ball Locations

2) Install and tighten separator plate-to-transfer plate and stiffener plate screws to specification. See TORQUE SPECIFICATIONS. Position valve body with internal passages facing upward. Install check balls in valve body. See Fig. 39.

3) Install transfer plate on valve body. Install and tighten transfer plate-to-valve body screws to specification in a diagonal pattern.

4) Install components in valve body. Ensure components are installed in original location. Tighten all end plate screws to specification.

CAUTION: When installing shuttle valve, ensure clip fully engages groove on shuttle valve.

5) Install detent ball and spring in housing and retain in position using detent ball retainer. Install spring on end of pressure regulator valve.

6) Install switch valve spring on tang at end of adjusting screw bracket. Install adjusting screw bracket. Ensure springs align with adjusting screw bracket.

7) Install lower screw (long screw) in adjusting bracket first and then install remaining screws. Tighten screws to specification. Install throttle valve lever in valve body.

8) Install manual shift lever over throttle valve lever. Align manual shift lever with detent ball and manual valve. Hold throttle valve lever upward and press manual shift lever into the housing.

9) Install seal, washer and clip on manual shift lever. Remove detent ball retainer. Lubricate manual shift lever shaft with petroleum jelly.

10) Ensure throttle valve lever is aligned with end of kickdown valve and manual shift lever arm is engaged with manual valve. See Fig. 40.

CAUTION: If line pressure or throttle pressure adjusting screws were moved from original setting, they must be readjusted. See HYDRAULIC PRESSURE ADJUSTMENTS in this article.

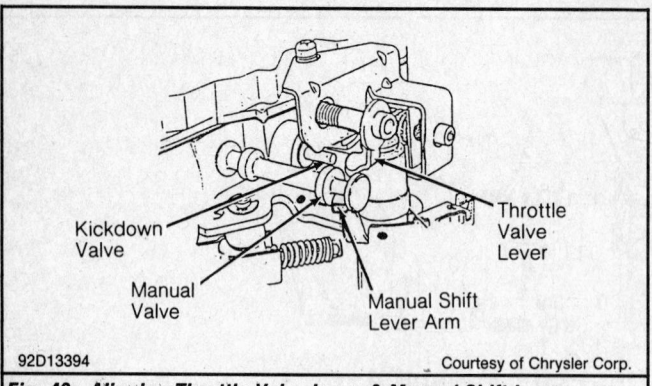

Kickdown Valve

Manual Valve

Throttle Valve Lever

Manual Shift Lever Arm

92D13394   Courtesy of Chrysler Corp.

Fig. 40: Aligning Throttle Valve Lever & Manual Shift Lever

TRANSMISSION REASSEMBLY

VALVE BODY & INTERNAL COMPONENTS

NOTE: Manufacturer recommends using Mopar ATF Plus Type 7176 fluid. This fluid should also be used during assembly. Apply petroleum jelly on "O" rings and seal rings. Use petroleum jelly to hold thrust washers, thrust plates and gaskets in position. Ensure thrust washer and thrust plates are installed in original location.

1) Install NEW seal rings on front and rear servo pistons. Lubricate rear servo bore with ATF. Install rear servo and components in transmission case. It may be necessary to use twisting motion when installing servo piston. Using "C" clamp and spring compressor, compress rear servo and install snap ring.

2) Install overrunning clutch components. See OVERRUNNING CLUTCH under TRANSMISSION COMPONENT DISASSEMBLY & REASSEMBLY. Install rear band and rear band linkage in transmission case. Ensure notched side of link faces away from rear band.

3) Slightly tilt low-reverse drum and install in rollers on overrunning clutch. Rotate low-reverse drum clockwise until drum is fully seated. Low-reverse drum should rotate freely clockwise but lock when rotated counterclockwise when viewed from front of transmission case.

CAUTION: Ensure low-reverse drum rotates freely clockwise but locks when rotated counterclockwise when viewed from front of transmission case. Check for improper component assembly if low-reverse drum will not rotate correctly.

4) Install low-reverse drum-to-rear support snap ring. Install NEW "O" rings on pin for rear band and partially install into transmission case and rear band linkage. Pin is located between rear support and transmission case.

5) Install lever, reaction lever and strut on rear band. Finish installing pin to retain rear band components.

6) Lubricate front servo bore with ATF. Install front servo and components in transmission case. It may be necessary to use small screwdriver to help seat seal ring in front servo bore while using twisting motion to install front servo piston.

7) Bottom front servo piston in bore and install spring. Using "C" clamp and spring compressor, compress servo guide and install snap ring.

8) Install lever for front band in transmission case. Install front band pin through front band pin access hole on front of transmission. See Fig. 18. Apply thread sealant on plug for front band pin access hole. Install and tighten plug to specification. See TORQUE SPECIFICATIONS.

9) Install output shaft and planetary gear train. Install thrust plate on end of output shaft. Install park gear on output shaft.

CAUTION: Output shaft contains a governor valve indexing area. Small end of governor valve must seat in governor valve indexing area. See Fig. 13.

10) Rotate output shaft until governor valve indexing area is facing upward. Install park gear and governor body on output shaft. Align governor valve bore on governor body with governor valve indexing area on output shaft. See Fig. 13. Align valve shaft holes in governor body and output shaft.

11) Align splines on output shaft with hub of park gear. Push park gear into rear support. Ensure valve shaft holes in output shaft and governor body are aligned. Install and tighten governor body-to-park gear bolts to specification. See TORQUE SPECIFICATIONS.

12) Install governor valve and valve shaft in governor body. Ensure valve shaft moves freely. Install snap ring on each end of valve shaft to hold assembly in governor body. Install thrust plate on end of output shaft.

13) Ensure seal rings and thrust washer are installed on input shaft. Ensure seal ring is installed on piston retainer on rear clutch. See Fig. 30. Ends of seal ring on piston retainer must be hooked together. Diagonal ends of seal rings on input shaft must be properly joined.

14) Align teeth on front clutch discs. Install front clutch on rear clutch. Ensure front clutch is fully seated on rear clutch by rotating front clutch back and forth.

15) Measure and record thickness of output shaft thrust washer for adjustment of input shaft end play. Install output shaft thrust washer in center of rear clutch with groove in thrust washer toward output shaft. See Fig. 30.

CAUTION: Ensure output shaft thrust washer is installed with groove in thrust washer toward output shaft.

16) Using small screwdriver, align teeth on rear clutch discs. Position transmission case with oil pump opening facing upward. Install front band onto driving shell.

17) Install front and rear clutch assemblies. Rotate assembly back and forth until rear clutch discs are fully seated on front annulus gear.

18) Slide front band over front clutch retainer. Install front band strut between front band and lever on transmission case. Install anchor between front band and transmission case.

19) Ensure front and rear clutch assemblies are fully seated. Tighten front band adjusting screw until front band is tight on front clutch retainer.

20) Ensure thrust washer and seal rings are installed on reaction shaft support and ends of seal rings are fastened together. If thrust washer contains a chamfered edge on inside diameter of thrust washer, it must be installed on reaction shaft support with chamfered edge on inside diameter of thrust washer facing toward front of oil pump.

21) Install pilot studs in 2 oil pump bolt holes, opposite of each other in transmission case. Install oil pump gasket. Lubricate reaction shaft seal rings and oil pump seal with ATF.

22) Install oil pump. Ensure oil pump is fully seated. Remove pilot studs. Install and tighten oil pump bolts in a diagonal pattern to specification.

CAUTION: Ensure input shaft and output shaft rotate without binding. If binding exists, check for improperly assembled components.

23) Attach dial indicator to transmission case with dial indicator stem seated against end of input shaft. Move input shaft inward and zero dial indicator. Pull input shaft outward and note input shaft end play. Input shaft end play should be .034-.084" (.86-2.13 mm).

24) If input shaft end play is not within specification, install different thickness output shaft thrust washer. Ensure park/neutral switch is removed before installing valve body. Install NEW seal rings on accumulator. Lubricate seal rings, accumulator and bore with ATF. Install accumulator.

25) Install spring between accumulator and valve body. Ensure manual shift lever on valve body is in low position. This moves park rod fully rearward.

26) Install valve body. Install valve body-to-transmission case bolts in original location finger tight only. DO NOT tighten bolts at this time.

27) Using NEW seal, install park/neutral switch. Tighten park/neutral switch to specification.

CAUTION: Alternately tighten valve body bolts to prevent damage to valve body. DO NOT overtighten bolts or damage to valve body and transmission case may result.

28) Tighten valve body bolts evenly to specification, starting at the center and working outward. Install NEW filter assembly. Install and tighten bolts to specification.

29) Install NEW seal for manual shift lever in transmission case. Install throttle and manual shift levers. Ensure throttle and manual shift levers rotate smoothly.

30) Ensure lock nuts are backed off 4-5 turns on front and rear band adjusting screws. *See Fig. 17.* Tighten front and rear band adjusting screws to 72 INCH lbs. (8.1 N.m).

31) Loosen front band adjusting screw 2 1/2 turns and rear band adjusting screw 2 turns. Tighten each lock nut to specification while holding band adjusting screw.

32) Install magnet over small protrusion area on oil pan. Using NEW gasket, install oil pan. Install and tighten bolts to specification.

33) Install rear bearing on output shaft. Ensure locating groove on outside of rear bearing is toward oil pump end of transmission. Install snap ring on output shaft.

34) Install NEW gasket on extension housing. Use petroleum jelly to hold gasket in place. Install output shaft rear bearing locating ring in extension housing (if removed).

35) Install extension housing on output shaft while working park rod past parking sprag. Using snap ring pliers, expand output shaft rear bearing locating ring.

36) Work extension housing onto output shaft rear bearing and release locating ring. Ensure locating ring is fully seated in groove on output shaft rear bearing.

37) Install and tighten extension housing-to-transmission case bolts to specification. Install gasket and access cover on extension housing. Lubricate torque converter hub with ATF. Install torque converter.

CAUTION: If transmission failure existed, flush oil cooler and check oil cooler flow. See OIL COOLER FLUSHING and OIL COOLER FLOW CHECK under ON-VEHICLE SERVICE.

TORQUE SPECIFICATIONS

TORQUE SPECIFICATIONS

Application	Ft. Lbs. (N.m)
Band Adjusting Screw Lock Nut	25 (34)
Extension Housing-To-Rear Mount Bolt	50 (68)
Extension Housing-To-Transmission Case Bolt	32 (43)
Front Band Pin Access Hole Plug	13 (18)
Park/Neutral Switch	25 (34)
Oil Pan Bolt	13 (18)
Oil Pump Bolt	15 (20)
Reaction Shaft Support Bolt	15 (20)
Rear Support Bolt	13 (18)
Vehicle Speed Sensor Nut (1993 Models)	13 (18)

	INCH Lbs. (N.m)
Adapter Retainer Bolt	100 (11.3)
Adjusting Screw Bracket Screw	35 (4.0)
Filter Assembly Bolt	35 (4.0)
Governor Body-To-Park Gear Bolt	95 (10.7)
Governor Valve End Plate Screw	35 (4.0)
Overrunning Clutch Cam Set Screw	40 (4.5)
Pressure Tap Plug	120 (13.6)
Regulator Valve Body End Plate Screw	35 (4.0)
Separator Plate-To-Transfer Plate Screw	35 (4.0)
Shift Valve End Plate Screw	35 (4.0)
Shuttle Valve End Plate Screw	35 (4.0)
Stiffener Plate Screw	35 (4.0)
Transfer Plate-To-Valve Body Screw	35 (4.0)
Valve Body-To-Transmission Case Bolt	100 (11.3)
Vehicle Speed Sensor-To-Adapter Bolt (1994 Models)	27 (3.1)

TRANSMISSION SPECIFICATIONS

TRANSMISSION SPECIFICATIONS

Application	In. (mm)
Clutch Clearances	
Front Clutch	
3-Disc Clutch	.070-.129 (1.78-3.28)
4-Disc Clutch	.082-.151 (2.08-3.84)
Rear Clutch	.025-.045 (.64-1.14)
Input Shaft End Play	.034-.084 (.86-2.13)
Oil Pump Clearances	
Gear End Clearance	.0010-.0025 (.025-.063)
Gear Tooth Clearance	.0035-.0075 (.089-.190)
Outer Gear-To-Oil Pump	
Housing Clearance	.0035-.0075 (.089-.190)
Planetary Gear Train End Play	.006-.048 (.15-1.22)

TECHNICAL SERVICE BULLETINS

UPSHIFT TOO LOW OR CLOSE TOGETHER

Chrysler Corp. Service Bulletin 21-25-93 (September 3, 1993) – Some 1992-93 Pickup and Ram Van with 36RH transmission may have upshifts too low or close together. The 2-3 upshift will be very close to the 1-2 upshift. To correct this condition, perform the following procedure.

1) Check for stored diagnostic trouble codes in the Powertrain Control Module (PCM). See SELF-DIAGNOSTICS article in ENGINE PERFORMANCE of appropriate MITCHELL® MANUAL.

2) Repair engine control system if a diagnostic trouble code exists and recheck operation. If no diagnostic trouble codes exists or code has been corrected and problem still exists, replace governor weights and spring with components from Governor Weight Package (4617882).

DELAYED TRANSMISSION ENGAGEMENT

NOTE: Service bulletin does not apply to models with V10 or diesel engines.

Chrysler Corp. Service Bulletin 21-08-94 (April 29, 1994) – Some 1990-94 Pickup and 1990-94 Ram Van models with a 36RH or 37RH transmission may experience a 2-8 second delay in transmission engagement when vehicle is first started after vehicle has been parked for an extended period. To correct this condition, perform the following procedure.

1) Check for stored diagnostic trouble codes in the Powertrain Control Module (PCM). See SELF-DIAGNOSTICS article in ENGINE PERFORMANCE of appropriate MITCHELL® MANUAL.

2) Repair engine control system if a diagnostic trouble code exists and recheck operation. If no diagnostic trouble codes exists or code has been corrected and problem still exists, Drainback Relief Valve (4778670) must be installed.

3) Note location of oil cooler supply line on side of transmission. *See Fig. 7.* Trace oil cooler supply line back to the radiator and identify this line at the radiator. Ensure this is the oil cooler supply line.

CAUTION: Drainback relief valve must be installed in oil cooler supply line or transmission failure will exist if wrong line is selected. Ensure oil cooler supply line is selected.

4) Cut oil cooler supply line within 1/8" of the crimp on the hose. *See Fig. 41.* Cut the hose and remove section of oil cooler supply line.

CAUTION: Some vehicles may have a Black epoxy coating on the oil cooler supply line. Ensure coating is removed before installing the nut and sleeve from drainback relief valve on oil cooler supply line.

5) Install nut and sleeve on metal portion of oil cooler supply line. Install drainback relief valve on metal portion of oil cooler supply so arrow on drainback relief valve is pointing toward the oil cooler.

CAUTION: Ensure drainback relief valve is installed so arrow on drainback relief valve is pointing toward the oil cooler. The arrow indicates direction of the fluid flow.

6) Install sleeve and nut on drainback relief valve. Tighten nut. Install rubber portion of oil cooler supply line on drainback relief valve. Install and tighten clamp to 10 INCH lbs. (1.1 N.m).

7) Note location of oil cooler return line on side of transmission. *See Fig. 7.* Disconnect oil cooler return line from transmission. On 1994 models, oil cooler lines are equipped with a disconnect fitting. Use proper procedure for disconnecting oil cooler line from disconnect fitting. See OIL COOLER LINE DISCONNECT FITTINGS under ON-VEHICLE SERVICE in this article.

CAUTION: Ensure flow from oil cooler return line is checked to ensure drainback relief valve is installed in correct oil cooler line.

---

8) Ensure transmission is full of fluid. Place container under oil cooler return line. Start engine. Place gearshift in Neutral.

9) Ensure steady flow exists for oil cooler return line. If no fluid flow exists, drainback relief valve has been installed in the wrong oil cooler line. Remove and reinstall. If steady flow exists, shut engine off.

10) Reconnect oil cooler return line. On 1994 models, reconnect oil cooler return line by pushing oil cooler line inward until a snap or click is heard when retaining clip seats in oil cooler line. Pull outward on oil cooler line to ensure oil cooler line is locked in the disconnect fitting.

CAUTION: After installing oil cooler line, pull outward on oil cooler line to ensure oil cooler line is locked in the disconnect fitting and retaining clip is fully seated.

---

11) On all models, fill transmission with Mopar ATF Plus Type 7176 fluid. Recheck all oil cooler lines for leaks.

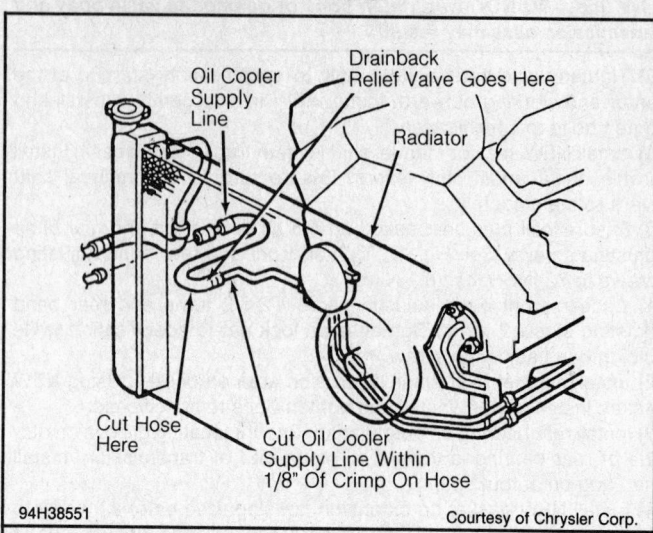

94H38551   Courtesy of Chrysler Corp.

Fig. 41: Installing Drainback Relief Valve

NOTE: The 41AE is used on All-Wheel Drive (AWD) FWD Van models. The 41AE internal components are the same as the 41TE, except 41AE contains power transfer unit (transfer case) attached to trans-axle case. Service procedures for 41TE also apply to 41AE unless designated.

APPLICATIONS & IDENTIFICATION

APPLICATION & LABOR TIMES

Vehicle Application	Labor Times [1] [2] R & I	[3] Overhaul	Trans. Model
Chrysler			
Passenger Cars			
1993 Fifth Ave (3.3/3.8L)	4.6	8.9	41TE
1993 Imperial (3.8L)	4.6	8.9	41TE
1993-94 LeBaron (3.0L)	4.6	8.9	41TE
1993 New Yorker (3.3L)	4.6	8.9	41TE
Vans			
1993-94 Town & Country			
2WD	4.6	8.9	41TE
AWD	6.1	8.9	41AE
Dodge			
Passenger Cars			
1993 Daytona (3.0L)	4.6	8.9	41TE
1993 Dynasty (3.0/3.3L)	4.6	8.9	41TE
1993-94 Shadow (3.0L)	4.6	8.9	41TE
1993-94 Spirit (3.0L)	4.6	8.9	41TE
Vans			
1993-94 Caravan			
2WD	4.6	8.9	41TE
AWD	6.1	8.9	41AE
1993-94 Grand Caravan			
2WD	4.6	8.9	41TE
AWD	6.1	8.9	41AE
Plymouth			
Passenger Cars			
1993-94 Acclaim (3.0L)	4.6	8.9	41TE
1993-94 Sundance (3.0L)	4.6	8.9	41TE
Vans			
1993-94 Voyager			
2WD	4.6	8.9	41TE
AWD	6.1	8.9	41AE
1993-94 Grand Voyager			
2WD	4.6	8.9	41TE
AWD	6.1	8.9	41AE

[1] – Removal and installation of transaxle from vehicle chassis.
[2] – If equipped with ABS, add .3 Hr.
[3] – Bench overhaul time for transaxle and differential. DOES NOT include removal and installation.

NOTE: Vehicle body code may be required when servicing or repairing transaxle, as references may be made to body code instead of model. See BODY CODE IDENTIFICATION table.

BODY CODE IDENTIFICATION

Model	Body Code
Acclaim, LeBaron Sedan & Spirit	AA
Caravan & Grand Caravan [1]	AS
Daytona	AG
Dynasty	AC
Fifth Avenue & Imperial	AY
LeBaron Convertible/Coupe	AJ
Shadow & Sundance	AP
Town & Country [1]	AS
New Yorker	AC
Voyager & Grand Voyager [1]	AS

[1] – Includes All-Wheel Drive (AWD) models.

CAUTION: If battery is disconnected or voltage supply to Transaxle Control Module (TCM) is interrupted, TCM will have to relearn shift characteristics. If TCM, transaxle internal components, solenoid assembly or torque converter are replaced, TCM will have to relearn shift characteristics. Perform shift quality quick-learn procedure. See SHIFT QUALITY QUICK-LEARN PROCEDURE.

CAUTION: If torque converter is replaced or Transaxle Control Module (TCM) is changed from one vehicle to another, proper procedure must be used to reset the break-in procedure in TCM for the Electronically Modulated Converter Clutch (EMCC) in torque converter to prevent shudder during clutch engagement for lock-up. Perform EMCC reset procedure. See ELECTRONICALLY MODULATED CONVERTER CLUTCH (EMCC) RESET PROCEDURE under TORQUE CONVERTER.

CAUTION: If Transaxle Control Module (TCM) is replaced or changed from one vehicle to another, proper procedure must be used to calibrate TCM for different equipment combinations to provide speedometer operation and correct readings. Failure to perform this procedure will result in no speedometer operation. See PINION FACTOR PROCEDURE.

NOTE: Transaxle control module may also be referred to as transmission control module.

IDENTIFICATION

Transaxle identification code is stamped on identification tag mounted near solenoid assembly. Identification code may be required when ordering replacement components.

DESCRIPTION

The 41TE/AE is an electronically-controlled 4-speed transaxle. Transaxle uses hydraulically operated clutches controlled by the Transaxle Control Module (TCM). Transaxle consists of 3 multiple-disc input clutches, 2 multiple-disc holding clutches, accumulators and 2 planetary gear sets to provide 4 forward speeds and a reverse gear. *See Fig. 1.*

The TCM receives information from various sensors and controls solenoid assembly through transaxle control relay. Solenoid assembly consists of 4 solenoids for controlling hydraulic pressure to 4 of the 5 transaxle clutches.

The TCM contains an adaptive memory which learns application and release rates of transaxle components for maximum shift efficiency. The TCM also learns the rate at which applied elements build pressure sufficient for a speed change.

OPERATION

When gearshift is in "OD" (overdrive) position, transaxle will shift through all 4 speeds with torque converter lock-up in overdrive. When gearshift is in "3" position, transaxle uses only 1st, 2nd and 3rd gears with 2nd-to-3rd gear shift delayed until vehicle speed is at least 40 MPH. When operating with gearshift in "3" position, torque converter lock-up occurs in 3rd gear for improved transaxle cooling. If engine coolant temperature becomes excessively warm, torque converter lock-up will occur in 2nd gear. When gearshift is in "L" position, engine braking is provided for descending grades.

NOTE: On 1994 AS bodies only, an overdrive lock-out switch is located on instrument panel. Overdrive lock-out switch can be used to prevent transaxle from shifting into overdrive.

Transaxle Control Module (TCM) contains a self-diagnostic system which stores a diagnostic trouble code if a transaxle problem exists. Diagnostic trouble code can be retrieved to determine the transaxle problem area. For information on electronic transaxle components, see CHRYSLER 41TE/AE ELECTRONIC DIAGNOSIS article.

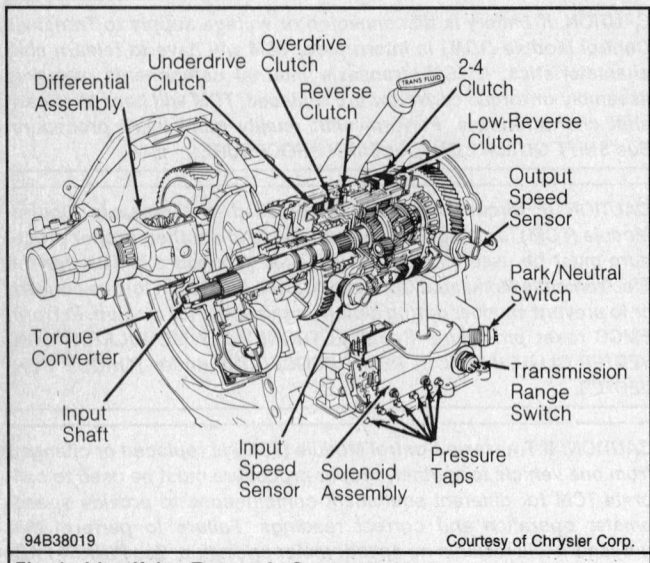

94B38019   Courtesy of Chrysler Corp.

Fig. 1: Identifying Transaxle Components

SHIFT QUALITY QUICK-LEARN PROCEDURE

NOTE: This procedure quickly optimizes shift quality. Procedure must be performed after disconnecting battery or loss of voltage supply to Transaxle Control Module (TCM), replacing TCM, transaxle internal components, solenoid assembly or torque converter. Chrysler's Diagnostic Readout Box (DRB) scan tool with proper cartridge must be used to perform shift quality quick-learn procedure.

NOTE: Following conditions must be met when performing shift quality quick-learn procedure: oil temperature must be greater than 60°F (16°C), brakes must be applied when indicated, engine speed greater than 500 RPM, throttle angle less than 3 degrees, gearshift must be moved only when indicated, gearshift must remain in overdrive as indicated until DRB indicates procedure is completed.

NOTE: If unused replacement TCM is installed on vehicle with engine at normal operating temperature, shift quality quick-learn procedure will cause TCM to indicate a cold oil temperature. Oil temperature must be monitored with DRB. If oil temperature is less than 60°F (16°C), allow engine to idle until oil temperature is greater than 60°F (16°C). If oil temperature is greater than 200°F (94°C), allow transaxle to cool until oil temperature is less than 200°F (94°C).

1) Connect DRB to data link connector, located near brake pedal at bottom of instrument panel. *See Fig. 2.* Using proper cartridge and DRB manufacture's instructions, move through program to enter 41TE/AE menu. Start vehicle. Select ADJUSTMENTS function.
2) Apply brakes. Select QUICK-LEARN function. Place gearshift in Neutral and then "OD" (overdrive) when indicated. Wait until TEST COMPLETE is indicated on DRB. Place gearshift in Park. Release brakes. Remove DRB.

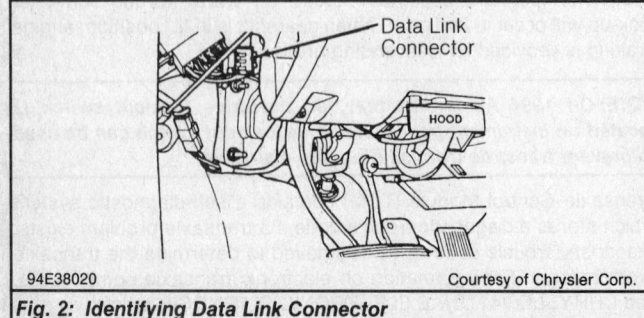

94E38020   Courtesy of Chrysler Corp.

Fig. 2: Identifying Data Link Connector

PINION FACTOR PROCEDURE

CAUTION: Pinion factor procedure must be performed if Transaxle Control Module (TCM) is replaced or changed from one vehicle to another. Procedure must be used to calibrate TCM for different equipment combinations to provide speedometer operation and correct readings. Failure to perform this procedure will result in no speedometer operation.

NOTE: It may be necessary to consult manufacturer to determine Final Drive Ration (FDR) number when performing pinion factor procedure.

1) Connect DRB to data link connector, located near brake pedal at bottom of instrument panel. *See Fig. 2.* Using proper cartridge and DRB manufacture's instructions, move through program to enter 41TE/AE menu. Select ADJUSTMENTS function.
2) Select PINION FACTOR function. Select appropriate Final Drive Ratio (FDR) number and then the tire size. Remove DRB. Road test vehicle and verify speedometer operation.

LUBRICATION & ADJUSTMENTS

NOTE: See appropriate AUTOMATIC TRANSMISSION SERVICING article in TRANSMISSION SERVICING.

TROUBLE SHOOTING

Transaxle malfunctions may be caused by poor engine performance, improper adjustments or failure of hydraulic, mechanical or electronic components. Always begin by checking fluid level, fluid condition and shift linkage or cable adjustment. Perform road test to determine if problem has been corrected. If problem still exists, several tests must be performed on transaxle. See TESTING in this article.

CAUTION: Before attempting any repair on electronic transaxles, ALWAYS check for diagnostic trouble codes. See CHRYSLER 41TE/AE ELECTRONIC DIAGNOSIS article.

SYMPTOMS

Buzzing Noise
- Aerated fluid
- Incorrect fluid level
- Valve body malfunction or leakage

Buzzing Noise During Transaxle Shifts
- Normal solenoid operation
- Solenoid assembly sound cover loose or missing

Delayed Engagement From Neutral To Drive
- Aerated fluid
- Damaged clutch seals
- Engine idle speed too low
- Faulty oil pump
- Hydraulic pressures too low
- Incorrect shift linkage or cable adjustment
- Low fluid level
- Oil filter restricted
- Valve body malfunction or leakage
- Worn or broken reaction shaft support seal rings
- Worn or damaged accumulator seal rings
- Worn or damaged input shaft seal rings
- Worn or faulty underdrive clutch

Delayed Engagement From Neutral To Reverse
- Aerated fluid
- Damaged clutch seals
- Engine idle speed too low
- Faulty oil pump
- Hydraulic pressures too low
- Incorrect shift linkage or cable adjustment
- Low fluid level

- Oil filter restricted
- Valve body malfunction or leakage
- Worn or broken reaction shaft support seal rings
- Worn or damaged accumulator seal rings
- Worn or damaged input shaft seal rings
- Worn or faulty reverse clutch

Grating, Scraping Or Growling Noise
- Axle shaft bushing worn or damaged
- Bearings worn or damaged
- Chipped or damaged gear teeth
- Defective planetary gear sets

Hard To Fill With Fluid Or Fluid Blows Out Filler Tube
- Aerated fluid
- High fluid level
- Oil filter restricted

Harsh Downshifts
- Aerated fluid
- Damaged clutch seals
- Engine idle speed too high
- Hydraulic pressures too high
- Improper engine performance
- Low fluid level
- Valve body malfunction or leakage
- Worn or broken reaction shaft support seal rings
- Worn or damaged accumulator seal rings
- Worn or faulty low-reverse clutch
- Worn or faulty underdrive clutch
- Worn or faulty 2-4 clutch

Harsh Engagement From Neutral To Drive
- Defective torque converter
- Engine idle too high
- Hydraulic pressures too high
- Improper engine performance
- Valve body malfunction or leakage
- Worn or damaged accumulator seal rings
- Worn or faulty low-reverse clutch
- Worn or faulty underdrive clutch

Harsh Engagement From Neutral To Reverse
- Engine idle too high
- Hydraulic pressures too high
- Improper engine performance
- Valve body malfunction or leakage
- Worn or damaged accumulator seal rings
- Worn or faulty low-reverse clutch
- Worn or faulty reverse clutch

Harsh Torque Converter Lock-Up
- Sticking lock-up piston in torque converter

Harsh Upshift
- Improper engine performance
- Incorrect hydraulic pressure
- Worn or faulty overdrive clutch
- Worn or faulty 2-4 clutch

High Shift Efforts
- Valve body malfunction or leakage
- Worn or damaged shift linkage or cable

No Torque Converter Lock-Up
- Aerated fluid
- Defective torque converter
- Engine coolant temperature low
- Faulty oil pump
- Hydraulic pressures too low
- Low fluid level
- Valve body malfunction or leakage
- Worn or damaged input shaft seal rings

No Upshift Into Overdrive
- Engine coolant temperature low
- Worn or faulty overdrive clutch

Poor Shift Quality
- Aerated fluid
- Hydraulic pressures too low

- Low fluid level
- Oil filter restricted
- Valve body malfunction or leakage
- Worn or broken reaction shaft support seal rings

Shifts Erratically
- Aerated fluid
- Faulty oil pump
- Hydraulic pressures too low
- Improper engine performance
- Incorrect shift linkage or cable adjustment
- Low fluid level
- Oil filter restricted
- Worn or broken reaction shaft support seal rings
- Worn or faulty low-reverse clutch
- Worn or faulty overdrive clutch
- Worn or faulty underdrive clutch
- Worn or faulty 2-4 clutch
- Valve body malfunction or leakage

Transaxle Overheats
- Aerated fluid
- Defective torque converter
- Engine idle speed too high
- Faulty engine cooling system
- Faulty oil pump
- Hydraulic pressures too low
- Incorrect fluid level
- Incorrect shift linkage or cable adjustment
- Insufficient clutch plate clearance

Vehicle Drags Or Locks
- Bearings worn or damaged
- Chipped or damaged gear teeth
- Defective planetary gear sets
- Worn or faulty low-reverse clutch
- Worn or faulty overdrive clutch
- Worn or faulty reverse clutch
- Worn or faulty underdrive clutch
- Worn or faulty 2-4 clutch

Vehicle Moves In Neutral
- Dragging clutch
- Incorrect shift linkage or cable adjustment
- Insufficient clutch plate clearance
- Valve body malfunction or leakage
- Worn or faulty overdrive clutch
- Worn or faulty reverse clutch
- Worn or faulty underdrive clutch

TESTING

SHIFT LINKAGE, PARK/NEUTRAL SWITCH & TRANSMISSION RANGE SWITCH

NOTE: Shift linkage or cable adjustment can be verified by determining if vehicle will start with gearshift in Park or Neutral positions. This indicates if Park/Neutral switch and transmission range switch are operating properly.

1) Normal operation of Park/Neutral switch and transmission range switch provides a quick check to confirm proper adjustment of shift linkage or cable.
2) Apply parking brake. Move gearshift into a forward gear. Move gearshift slowly into Park. Ensure vehicle starts with gearshift in Park.
3) Move gearshift to Neutral. Ensure vehicle starts with gearshift in Neutral. If vehicle does not start in both of these positions, shift linkage or cable must be adjusted. See appropriate AUTOMATIC TRANSMISSION SERVICING article in TRANSMISSION SERVICING.

ROAD TEST

1) Ensure shift linkage or cable is properly adjusted and fluid level and condition are okay. Add fluid and adjust shift linkage or cable as needed.

AUTOMATIC TRANSMISSIONS
Chrysler 41TE/AE (Cont.)

Gearshift Position	Park/Neutral Switch	Parking Sprag	CLUTCHES Underdrive	Overdrive	Reverse	2-4	Low-Reverse
P — PARK	X	X					X
R — REVERSE					X		X
N — NEUTRAL	X						X
OD — OVERDRIVE							
First			X				X
Second			X			X	
Direct			X	X			
Overdrive				X		X	
3 — DRIVE*							
First			X				X
Second			X			X	
Direct			X	X			
L — LOW*							
First			X				X
Second			X			X	
Direct			X	X			

* – Vehicle upshift and downshift speeds are increased when in these gearshift positions.

94F38021   Courtesy of Chrysler Corp.

Fig. 3: Clutch Application Chart

2) Road test vehicle, operating transaxle in each gear position. Check for slipping or any variation in shifting.

3) If vehicle operates properly at highway speeds but has poor acceleration, torque converter stator clutch may be slipping. If acceleration through all gears is normal, but high throttle opening is required to maintain highway speeds, torque converter stator clutch may be seized. Torque converter must be replaced if stator clutch is defective.

4) In most cases, the clutch that is slipping can be determined by noting transaxle operation in all gear positions and noting which clutches are applied. See Fig. 3.

5) Process of elimination can be used to detect any unit which slips and to confirm proper operation of good units. Although road test analysis can usually diagnose slipping units, the actual malfunction usually cannot be decided. Practically any condition can be caused by leaking hydraulic circuits or sticking valves.

NOTE: If torque converter is replaced or Transaxle Control Module (TCM) is changed from one vehicle to another, proper procedure must be used to reset the break-in procedure in TCM for the Electronically Modulated Converter Clutch (EMCC) in torque converter to prevent shudder during clutch engagement. Perform EMCC reset procedure. See ELECTRONICALLY MODULATED CONVERTER CLUTCH (EMCC) RESET PROCEDURE under TORQUE CONVERTER.

TORQUE CONVERTER STALL SPEED TEST

CAUTION: Manufacturer does not recommend performing torque converter stall speed test on 41TE/AE transaxle.

HYDRAULIC PRESSURE TESTS

Pressure Test Preparation – **1)** Ensure shift linkage or cable is properly adjusted, and that fluid level and condition are okay. Add fluid and adjust shift linkage or control cable as needed.

2) Ensure fluid is at normal operating temperature of 150-200°F (66-93°C). Install tachometer. Raise vehicle on hoist, allowing front wheels to rotate freely.

NOTE: A 150 psi (11 kg/cm²) pressure gauge is used for checking all clutches except reverse clutch. A 300 psi (21 kg/cm²) pressure gauge is used for checking reverse clutch.

Low-Reverse Clutch Pressure Test – **1)** Remove plug and install pressure gauge in low-reverse clutch pressure tap. See Fig. 4.

2) Place gearshift in "L" position. Allowing front wheels to rotate, accelerate until vehicle speed indicates 20 MPH.

3) Low-reverse clutch pressure should be 115-145 psi (8.0-10.1 kg/cm²). This pressure test checks oil pump output, pressure regulation and low-reverse clutch hydraulic circuit and shift schedule. Remove pressure gauge. Install and tighten pressure tap plug to specification. See TORQUE SPECIFICATIONS.

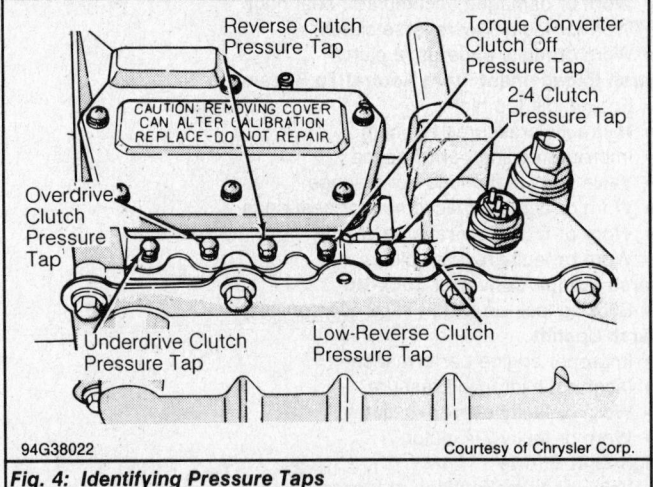

94G38022   Courtesy of Chrysler Corp.

Fig. 4: Identifying Pressure Taps

Underdrive Clutch Pressure Test – **1)** Remove plug and install pressure gauge in underdrive clutch pressure tap. See Fig. 4.

2) Place gearshift in "3" position. Allowing front wheels to rotate, accelerate until vehicle speed indicates 30 MPH.

3) Underdrive clutch pressure should be 110-145 psi (7.7-10.1 kg/cm²). This pressure test checks underdrive clutch hydraulic circuit and shift schedule. Remove pressure gauge. Install and tighten pressure tap plug to specification. See TORQUE SPECIFICATIONS.

Overdrive Clutch Pressure Test – **1)** Remove plug and install pressure gauge in overdrive clutch pressure tap. See Fig. 4.

2) Place gearshift in "OD" (overdrive) position. Allowing front wheels to rotate, accelerate until vehicle speed indicates 20 MPH.

3) Overdrive clutch pressure should be 74-95 psi (5.2-6.7 kg/cm²). Place gearshift in "3" position and increase vehicle speed to 30 MPH.

4) Transaxle should be in 2nd gear and overdrive clutch pressure should now be less than 5 psi (.35 kg/cm²). This pressure test checks overdrive clutch hydraulic circuit and shift schedule. Remove pressure gauge. Install and tighten pressure tap plug to specification. See TORQUE SPECIFICATIONS.

2-4 Clutch Pressure Test – 1) Remove plug and install pressure gauge in 2-4 clutch pressure tap. *See Fig. 4.*

2) Place gearshift in "OD" (overdrive) position. Allowing front wheels to rotate, accelerate until vehicle speed indicates 30 MPH.

3) The 2-4 clutch pressure should be 75-95 psi (5.3-6.7 kg/cm²). This pressure test checks 2-4 clutch hydraulic circuit. Remove pressure gauge. Install and tighten pressure tap plug to specification. See TORQUE SPECIFICATIONS.

Torque Converter Clutch Off Pressure Test – 1) Remove plug and install pressure gauge in torque converter clutch off pressure tap. *See Fig. 4.* Place gearshift in "OD" (overdrive) position.

2) Allowing front wheels to rotate, accelerate until vehicle speed indicates 50 MPH.

CAUTION: Ensure both front wheels are rotating at the same speed when performing torque converter clutch off pressure test.

---

3) Torque converter clutch off pressure should be less than 5 psi (.35 kg/cm²). This pressure test checks torque converter clutch hydraulic circuit. Remove pressure gauge. Install and tighten pressure tap plug to specification. See TORQUE SPECIFICATIONS.

Reverse Clutch Pressure Test – 1) Remove plug and install pressure gauge in reverse clutch pressure tap. *See Fig. 4.* Place gearshift in Reverse.

2) Apply brakes. Accelerate until engine speed is 1500 RPM and note reverse clutch pressure. Reverse clutch pressure should be 165-235 psi (11.6-16.5 kg/cm²). This pressure test checks reverse clutch hydraulic circuit.

3) Remove pressure gauge. Install and tighten pressure tap plug to specification. See TORQUE SPECIFICATIONS.

Pressure Test Result Indications – 1) If proper hydraulic pressure exists in any one pressure test, oil pump and pressure regulator valve are operating properly. Various clutch operating hydraulic pressures exist depending on gearshift position. *See Fig. 5.*

2) Low hydraulic pressure in any or all positions indicates a defective oil pump, restricted oil filter or stuck pressure regulator valve. If hydraulic pressure is not within specification, clutch hydraulic circuit is leaking.

3) If overdrive clutch hydraulic pressure exceeds 5 psi (.35 kg.cm²) in step **4)** of OVERDRIVE CLUTCH PRESSURE, a worn reaction shaft seal ring is indicated.

CLUTCH AIR PRESSURE TESTS

NOTE: Inoperative clutches can be located by applying air pressure to appropriate passages in transaxle case. Clutch assembly is defective if it does not operate correctly.

Test Preparation – Remove valve body. See VALVE BODY under REMOVAL & INSTALLATION. Install Adapter Plate (6056) on transaxle case. *See Fig. 6.*

CAUTION: Ensure air supply is free of all dirt and moisture. Using air pressure regulator, adjust air pressure to 30 psi (2.1 kg/cm²).

Overdrive Clutch – Apply air pressure to Overdrive clutch (OD) passage on adapter plate. *See Fig. 6.* Ensure overdrive clutch piston moves forward and returns to original position when air pressure is released.

Reverse Clutch – Apply air pressure to reverse clutch (REV) passage on adapter plate. *See Fig. 6.* Ensure Reverse clutch piston moves rearward and returns to original position when air pressure is released.

2-4 Clutch – Apply air pressure to feed hole located on 2-4 clutch retainer. Ensure 2-4 clutch piston moves rearward and returns to original position when air is released.

Low-Reverse Clutch – Apply air pressure to low-reverse clutch supply hole, located on rear of transaxle case, between the 2 bolt holes. Ensure low-reverse clutch piston moves forward and returns to original position when air is released.

Underdrive Clutch – 1) Apply air pressure to low-reverse and 2-4 clutches. Output shaft should now be locked. Wrap rubber hose around input shaft. Install clamp-on pliers on input shaft. Rotate input shaft.

2) Apply air pressure to Underdrive clutch (UD) passage on adapter plate. *See Fig. 6.* Input shaft should not rotate with hand torque. Release air pressure. Ensure input shaft now rotates.

ALL PRESSURE SPECIFICATIONS ARE PSI
(VEHICLE ON HOIST WITH WHEELS FREE TO ROTATE)

| Gearshift Position | Actual Gear | PRESSURE TAPS | | | | | |
		Underdrive Clutch	Overdrive Clutch	Reverse Clutch	Torque Converter Clutch Off	2-4 Clutch	Low-Reverse Clutch
PARK ① 0 mph	PARK	0-2	0-5	0-2	60-110	0-2	115-145
REVERSE ① 0 mph	REVERSE	0-2	0-7	165-235	50-100	0-2	165-235
NEUTRAL ① 0 mph	NEUTRAL	0-2	0-5	0-2	60-110	0-2	115-145
L ② 20 mph	FIRST	110-145	0-5	0-2	60-110	0-2	115-145
3 ② 30 mph	SECOND	110-145	0-5	0-2	60-110	115-145	0-2
3 ② 45 mph	DIRECT	75-95	75-95	0-2	60-90	0-2	0-2
OD ② 30 mph	OVERDRIVE	0-2	75-95	0-2	60-90	75-95	0-2
OD ② 50 mph	OVERDRIVE LOCKUP	0-2	75-95	0-2	0-5	75-95	0-2

¹ – Check with engine speed at 1500 RPM.
² – CAUTION: Both front wheels must rotate at the same speed.

94H38023

Courtesy of Chrysler Corp.

Fig. 5: Identifying Clutch Operating Pressures

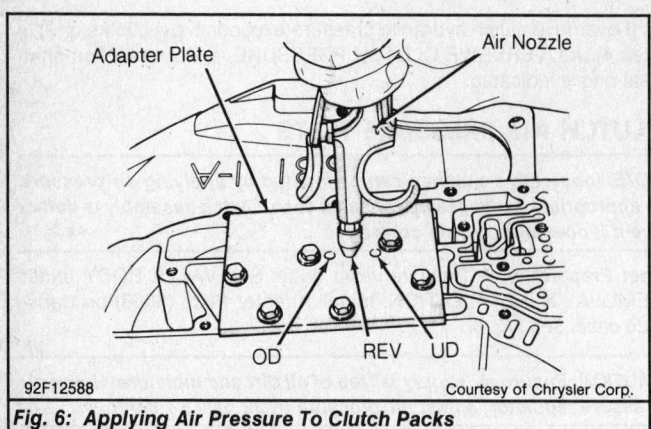

Fig. 6: Applying Air Pressure To Clutch Packs

TORQUE CONVERTER FLUID LEAKAGE TEST

NOTE: Fluid around torque converter may originate from engine oil or transaxle. Ensure transaxle fluid level is correct. Fluid leakage at torque converter may result if fluid level is too high. Transaxle can be checked for leaks using the following method.

1) Remove torque converter housing dust shield. Using solvent, clean inside area of torque converter housing. Dry with compressed air. Ensure area is clean and dry.

2) Fabricate leakage test probe using 1/32" sheet metal, 5" long and 1 1/2" wide. *See Fig. 7.* Operate engine until transaxle is at normal operating temperature. Install leakage test probe on torque converter dust shield bolt so leakage test probe is near torque converter. Ensure torque converter does not contact leakage test probe.

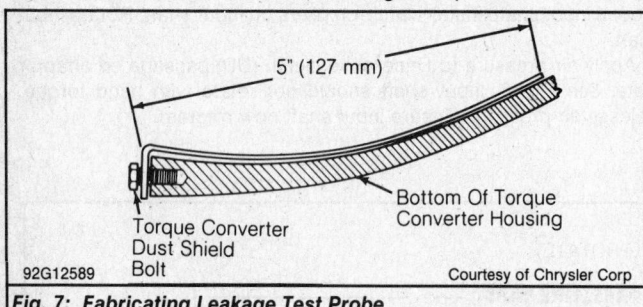

Fig. 7: Fabricating Leakage Test Probe

3) Start engine. Place gearshift in Neutral. Operate engine at 2500 RPM for 2 minutes. Stop engine. Remove leakage test probe.

4) If upper surface of leakage test probe is dry, torque converter is not leaking. If upper surface of leakage test probe is wet with ATF, torque converter is leaking. If lower area below leakage test probe is wet with ATF, fluid is coming from around torque converter area.

5) Possible causes of fluid leaks at torque converter areas are:
- Defective oil pump housing "O" ring or oil pump housing
- Defective seal (check torque converter hub finish)
- Mispositioned or worn bushing
- Oil pump-to-transaxle case bolts
- Restricted oil pump housing oil return hole
- Torque converter hub

6) If torque converter is leaking, check for defective welds on outside diameter of torque converter and torque converter hub. Torque converter hub is welded on the inside and weld is not visible. Replace torque converter if a leak exists. DO NOT attempt to repair torque converter.

CAUTION: If torque converter is replaced, a special torque converter break-in procedure must be performed to prevent shudder during clutch engagement. See ELECTRONICALLY MODULATED CONVERTER CLUTCH (EMCC) RESET PROCEDURE under TORQUE CONVERTER.

TRANSAXLE CASE PRESSURE TEST

NOTE: Transaxle case, gaskets and oil pump housing can be checked for leaks using the following method. Transaxle must be removed to perform transaxle case pressure test.

1) Fabricate a torque converter hub seal cup using thin wall tubing and a .125" (3.17 mm) steel disc. *See Fig. 8.* Fabricate torque converter hub seal cup retaining strap using a .25" (6.3 mm) thick and 1.25" (31.7 mm) wide material. *See Fig. 9.*

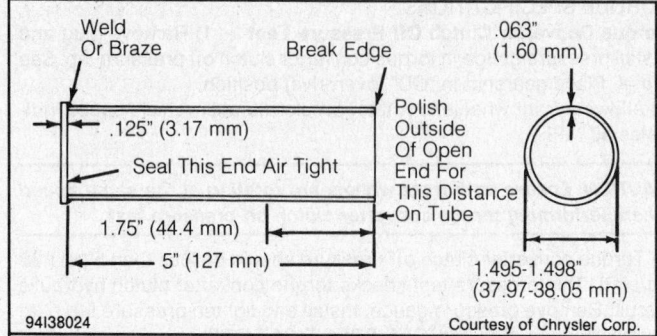

Fig. 8: Fabricating Torque Converter Hub Seal Cup

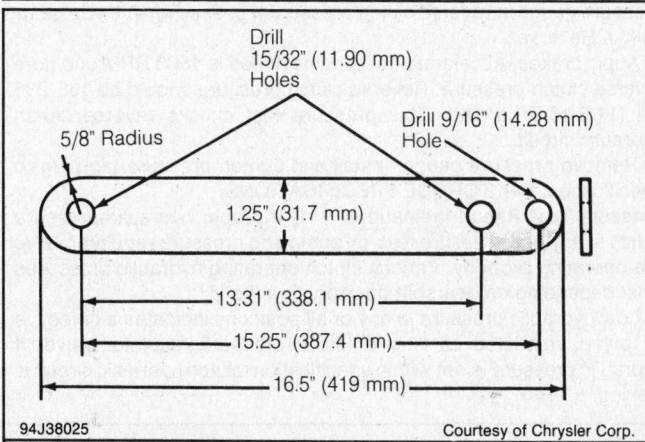

Fig. 9: Fabricating Torque Converter Hub Seal Cup Retaining Strap

2) Remove torque converter from transaxle. Plug dipstick tube and lower oil cooler line fitting. Remove vent from manual shaft and install a 1/8" pipe plug.

CAUTION: DO NOT allow manual shaft to rotate when installing pipe plug.

3) Using rotary motion, install torque converter hub seal cup over input shaft and through torque converter hub seal until cup bottoms against gear lugs of oil pump.

4) Install torque converter hub seal cup retaining strap using starter upper hole and opposite bracket hole. Attach hose from Nozzle (C-4080) to upper oil cooler line fitting on transaxle case.

5) Using pressure regulator, apply 8-10 psi (.5-.7 kg/cm²) of air pressure to transaxle case.

CAUTION: DO NOT apply more than 10 psi (.7 kg/cm²) of air pressure to transaxle case.

6) Coat oil pump and front of transaxle case with soapy water solution. Check for bubbles, indicating a leak in seals, "O" rings, gaskets or transaxle case. Release air pressure. Remove test equipment. Replace defective components.

ON-VEHICLE SERVICE

The following components can be serviced on the vehicle:
- Input speed sensor
- Output speed sensor
- Park/Neutral switch
- Solenoid assembly
- Transmission range switch
- Valve body

See appropriate component under REMOVAL & INSTALLATION.

OIL COOLER FLUSHING

CAUTION: Whenever transaxle failure exists, oil cooler must be flushed. Oil cooler by-pass valve in transaxle and torque converter must be replaced. Oil cooler by-pass valve is located in transaxle case, behind oil pump. See Fig. 15. If vehicle is equipped with 2 oil coolers (one in radiator tank and one in front of radiator), flush oil coolers separately. DO NOT attempt to flush both oil coolers at one time.

1) Disconnect oil cooler lines at transaxle. Using hand-held suction gun filled with mineral spirits, force mineral spirits into oil cooler return line until mineral spirits flows from oil cooler supply line. *See Fig. 10.*

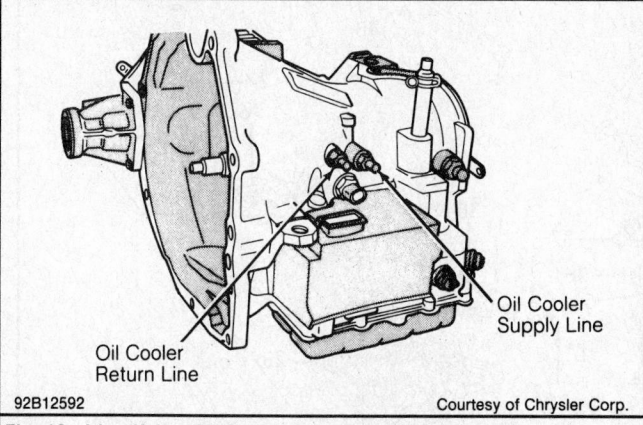

92B12592   Courtesy of Chrysler Corp.

Fig. 10: Identifying Oil Cooler Lines On Transaxle

2) Continue flushing oil cooler until mineral spirits is clear and no sign of contamination exists. Once no contamination exists, apply compressed air on oil cooler return line in light applications until remaining mineral spirits is blown from oil cooler and oil cooler lines.
3) Pump at least one quart of Mopar ATF Plus-Type 7176 through oil cooler to ensure oil cooler is free of solvent. Replace oil cooler if fluid does not flow freely from oil cooler.

OIL COOLER FLOW CHECK

1) With transaxle filled to proper fluid level, disconnect oil cooler return line at transaxle. *See Fig. 10.* Place container under oil cooler return line.

CAUTION: DO NOT obtain more than one quart of fluid or transaxle may be damaged.

2) Apply parking brake. Start engine and allow to idle. Place gearshift in Neutral. Check fluid flow from oil cooler return line.
3) If fluid flow is intermittent or it takes more than 20 seconds to obtain one quart of fluid, replace oil cooler. Reconnect oil cooler return line. Fill to proper fluid level with Mopar ATF Plus-Type 7176.

REMOVAL & INSTALLATION

NOTE: If battery is disconnected or voltage supply to Transaxle Control Module (TCM) is interrupted, TCM will have to relearn shift characteristics. Perform shift quality quick-learn procedure. See SHIFT QUALITY QUICK-LEARN PROCEDURE at beginning of article.

AXLE SHAFTS

See appropriate AXLE SHAFTS article in AXLE SHAFTS & TRANSFER CASES.

INPUT SPEED SENSOR

Removal & Installation – 1) Disconnect electrical connector from input speed sensor, located on side of transaxle case. *See Fig. 1.* Ensure weather seal remains on electrical connector. Remove input speed sensor from transaxle case.
2) To install, reverse removal procedure. Tighten input speed sensor to specification. See TORQUE SPECIFICATIONS. Reconnect electrical connector.

OUTPUT SPEED SENSOR

Removal & Installation – 1) Disconnect electrical connector from output speed sensor, located on side of transaxle case. *See Fig. 1.* Ensure weather seal remains on electrical connector. Remove output speed sensor from transaxle case.
2) To install, reverse removal procedure. Tighten output speed sensor to specification. See TORQUE SPECIFICATIONS. Reconnect electrical connector.

PARK/NEUTRAL SWITCH

Removal & Installation – 1) Disconnect electrical connector from park/neutral switch, located on transaxle case. *See Fig. 1.* Remove park/neutral switch and sealing washer.
2) To install, reverse removal procedure using NEW sealing washer. Ensure sealing washer is fully seated in transaxle case before tightening park/neutral switch to specification. See TORQUE SPECIFICATIONS. Reconnect electrical connector.

POWER TRANSFER UNIT (TRANSFER CASE)

All-Wheel Drive Models – See appropriate TRANSFER CASES article in AXLE SHAFTS & TRANSFER CASES.

SOLENOID ASSEMBLY

Removal & Installation – 1) Disconnect electrical connector from solenoid assembly. Remove input speed sensor. See INPUT SPEED SENSOR under REMOVAL & INSTALLATION. Remove solenoid assembly sound cover. *See Fig. 11.*
2) Remove bolts, solenoid assembly, solenoid assembly gaskets and solenoid plate. *See Fig. 11.*
3) To install, reverse removal procedure using NEW solenoid assembly gaskets. Install and tighten bolts to specification. See TORQUE SPECIFICATIONS. Reconnect electrical connector.

TRANSAXLE ASSEMBLY

See appropriate AUTOMATIC TRANSMISSION REMOVAL article in TRANSMISSION SERVICING.

TRANSMISSION RANGE SWITCH

Removal & Installation – 1) Disconnect electrical connector from transmission range switch, located on transaxle case. *See Fig. 1.* Remove transmission range switch and sealing washer.
2) To install, reverse removal procedure. Ensure sealing washer is fully seated in transaxle case before tightening transmission range switch to specification. See TORQUE SPECIFICATIONS. Reconnect electrical connector.

VALVE BODY

Removal – 1) Raise and support vehicle. Disconnect shift linkage or cable from shift lever on manual shaft assembly. Remove shift lever from manual shaft assembly.
2) Remove bolts, oil pan, oil filter and "O" ring. Remove the valve body/transfer plate-to-transaxle case bolts. Note bolt length and location for reassembly reference.

AUTOMATIC TRANSMISSIONS
Chrysler 41TE/AE (Cont.)

3) Move roller on parking sprag rod from parking sprag guide bracket. *See Fig. 11.* Lift valve body and manual shaft assembly from transaxle case.

Installation – 1) To install, reverse removal procedure. Ensure roller on parking sprag rod engages with parking sprag guide bracket. Install valve body/transfer plate-to-transaxle case bolts in original location. Tighten bolts to specification. See TORQUE SPECIFICATIONS.

2) Install NEW oil filter and NEW "O" ring. Apply RTV sealant on oil pan-to-transaxle surface and below head of oil pan bolts before installing. Install and tighten oil pan bolts to specification. See TORQUE SPECIFICATIONS.

3) Install shift lever on manual shaft assembly. Reconnect shift linkage or cable. Fill with Mopar ATF PLUS-Type 7176.

TORQUE CONVERTER

CAUTION: Torque converter is a welded assembly and is not serviceable. If a malfunction occurs or if torque converter becomes contaminated with foreign material, it MUST be replaced. It cannot be flushed or repaired. If torque converter is replaced, special torque converter break-in procedure must be performed to prevent shudder during clutch engagement for lock-up. See ELECTRONICALLY MODULATED CONVERTER CLUTCH (EMCC) RESET PROCEDURE under TORQUE CONVERTER.

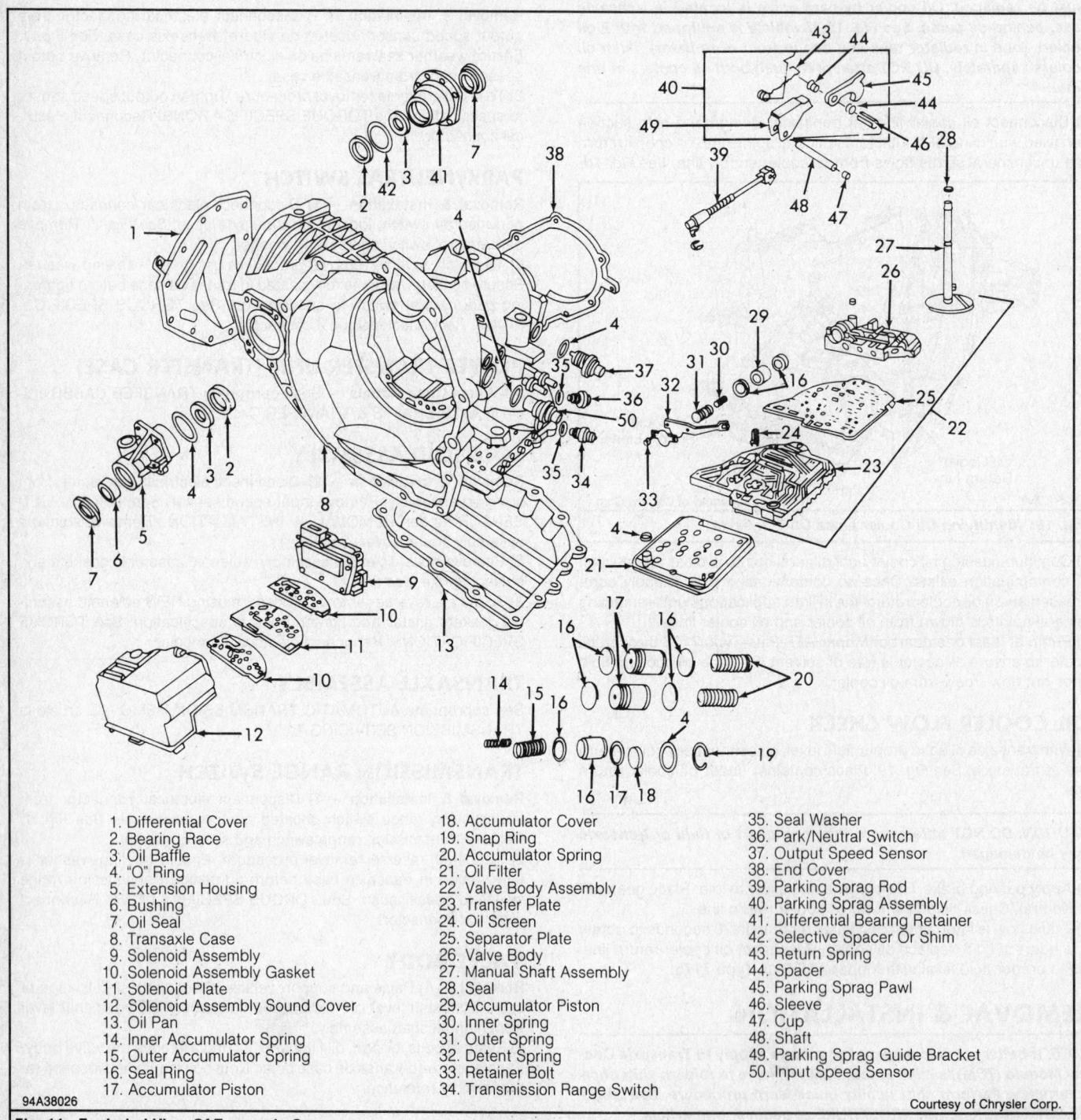

1. Differential Cover
2. Bearing Race
3. Oil Baffle
4. "O" Ring
5. Extension Housing
6. Bushing
7. Oil Seal
8. Transaxle Case
9. Solenoid Assembly
10. Solenoid Assembly Gasket
11. Solenoid Plate
12. Solenoid Assembly Sound Cover
13. Oil Pan
14. Inner Accumulator Spring
15. Outer Accumulator Spring
16. Seal Ring
17. Accumulator Piston

18. Accumulator Cover
19. Snap Ring
20. Accumulator Spring
21. Oil Filter
22. Valve Body Assembly
23. Transfer Plate
24. Oil Screen
25. Separator Plate
26. Valve Body
27. Manual Shaft Assembly
28. Seal
29. Accumulator Piston
30. Inner Spring
31. Outer Spring
32. Detent Spring
33. Retainer Bolt
34. Transmission Range Switch

35. Seal Washer
36. Park/Neutral Switch
37. Output Speed Sensor
38. End Cover
39. Parking Sprag Rod
40. Parking Sprag Assembly
41. Differential Bearing Retainer
42. Selective Spacer Or Shim
43. Return Spring
44. Spacer
45. Parking Sprag Pawl
46. Sleeve
47. Cup
48. Shaft
49. Parking Sprag Guide Bracket
50. Input Speed Sensor

94A38026

Courtesy of Chrysler Corp.

Fig. 11: Exploded View Of Transaxle Case

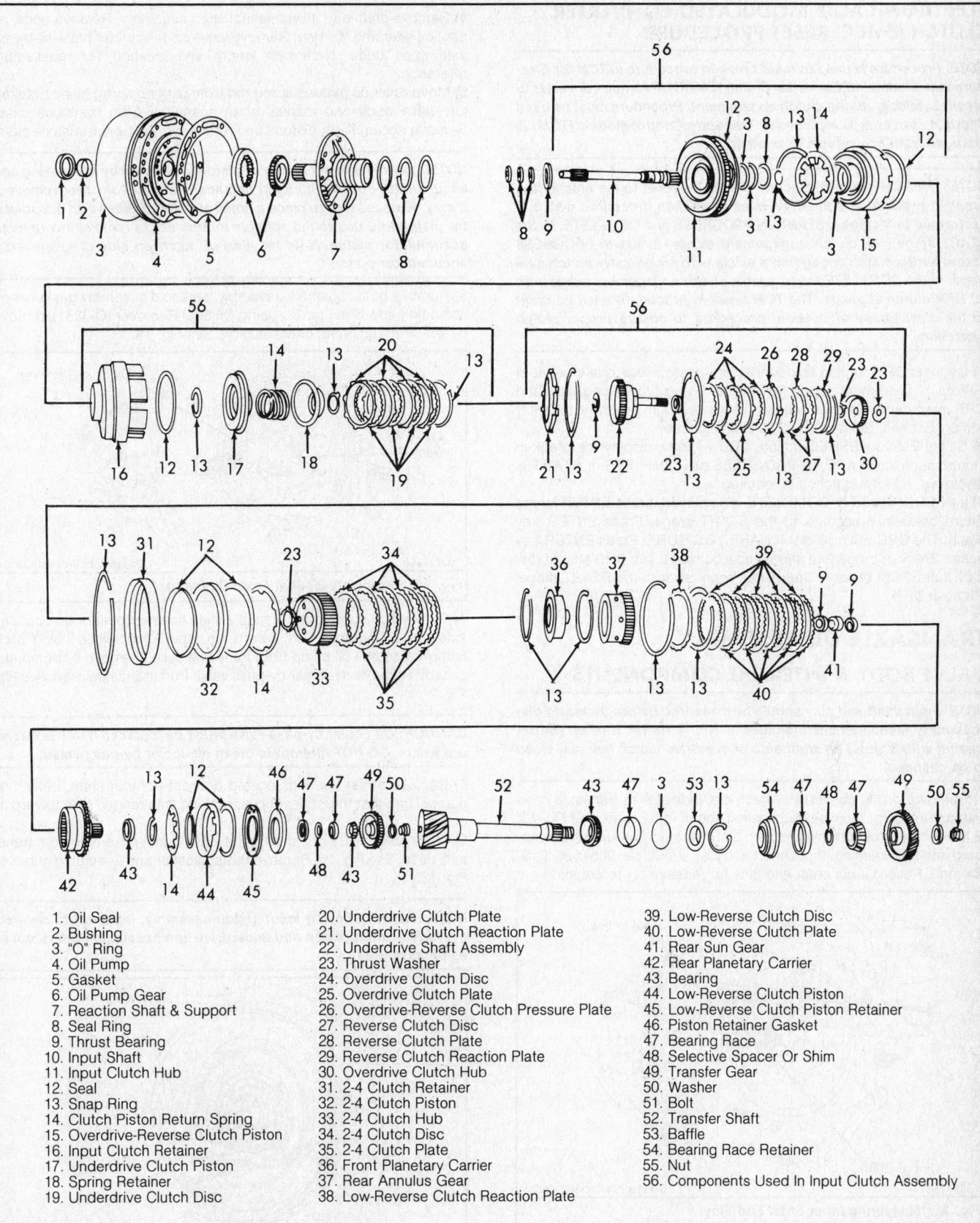

1. Oil Seal
2. Bushing
3. "O" Ring
4. Oil Pump
5. Gasket
6. Oil Pump Gear
7. Reaction Shaft & Support
8. Seal Ring
9. Thrust Bearing
10. Input Shaft
11. Input Clutch Hub
12. Seal
13. Snap Ring
14. Clutch Piston Return Spring
15. Overdrive-Reverse Clutch Piston
16. Input Clutch Retainer
17. Underdrive Clutch Piston
18. Spring Retainer
19. Underdrive Clutch Disc

20. Underdrive Clutch Plate
21. Underdrive Clutch Reaction Plate
22. Underdrive Shaft Assembly
23. Thrust Washer
24. Overdrive Clutch Disc
25. Overdrive Clutch Plate
26. Overdrive-Reverse Clutch Pressure Plate
27. Reverse Clutch Disc
28. Reverse Clutch Plate
29. Reverse Clutch Reaction Plate
30. Overdrive Clutch Hub
31. 2-4 Clutch Retainer
32. 2-4 Clutch Piston
33. 2-4 Clutch Hub
34. 2-4 Clutch Disc
35. 2-4 Clutch Plate
36. Front Planetary Carrier
37. Rear Annulus Gear
38. Low-Reverse Clutch Reaction Plate

39. Low-Reverse Clutch Disc
40. Low-Reverse Clutch Plate
41. Rear Sun Gear
42. Rear Planetary Carrier
43. Bearing
44. Low-Reverse Clutch Piston
45. Low-Reverse Clutch Piston Retainer
46. Piston Retainer Gasket
47. Bearing Race
48. Selective Spacer Or Shim
49. Transfer Gear
50. Washer
51. Bolt
52. Transfer Shaft
53. Baffle
54. Bearing Race Retainer
55. Nut
56. Components Used In Input Clutch Assembly

94B38027

Courtesy of Chrysler Corp.

Fig. 12: Exploded View Of Internal Transaxle Components

ELECTRONICALLY MODULATED CONVERTER CLUTCH (EMCC) RESET PROCEDURE

NOTE: Procedure is used to reset break-in procedure in TCM for Electronically Modulated Converter Clutch (EMCC) in torque converter to prevent shudder during clutch engagement. Procedure must be used if torque converter is replaced or Transaxle Control Module (TCM) is changed from one vehicle to another.

NOTE: The TCM break-in procedure must be reset to the start of the break-in procedure. The TCM's uses a break-in procedure which is performed in 3 stages, START, IN PROGRESS and COMPLETE. In the START stage, full clutch engagement exists. In the IN-PROGRESS stage, partial clutch engagement exists with progressive clutch slippage. In the COMPLETE stage, partial clutch engagement exists with 60 RPM clutch slippage. The TCM break-in procedure must be reset to the start phase of break-in procedure to ensure proper clutch operation.

1) Connect DRB to data link connector, located near brake pedal at bottom of instrument panel. See Fig. 2. Using proper cartridge and DRB manufacture's instructions, move through program to enter 41TE/AE menu. Select ADJUSTMENTS function.
2) Select EMCC RESET function. DRB will now display the break-in status, such as START, IN-PROGRESS or COMPLETE. If START is displayed, no further action is required.
3) If IN-PROGRESS or COMPLETE is displayed, press ENTER key to return brake-in procedure to the START stage. Press ENTER key again. The DRB will now display ARE YOU SURE. Press ENTER key again. Break-in procedure should now be reset. The DRB should display that ECCM break-in status has been reset to the START stage. Remove DRB.

TRANSAXLE DISASSEMBLY

VALVE BODY & INTERNAL COMPONENTS

NOTE: Input shaft end play should be measured before transaxle disassembly. Measurement indicates if No. 4 thrust washer (thrust washer with 3 slots) on shaft side of overdrive clutch hub may need to be changed.

1) Remove torque converter. Attach dial indicator to transaxle case with dial indicator stem seated against end of input shaft. See Fig. 13.
2) Move input shaft inward and zero dial indicator. Pull input shaft outward and note reading. Input shaft end play should be .005-.025" (.13-.64 mm). Record input shaft end play for reassembly reference.

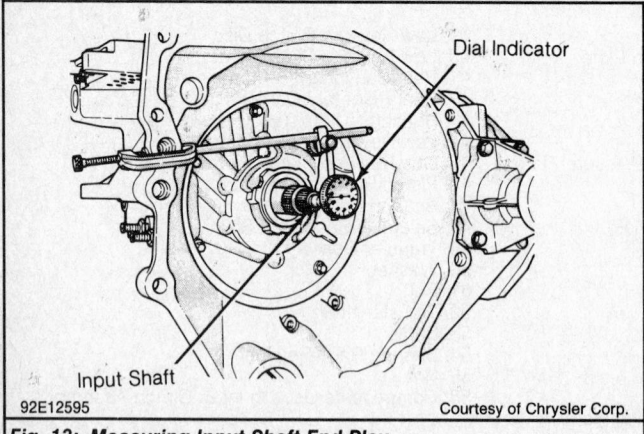

Courtesy of Chrysler Corp.

Fig. 13: Measuring Input Shaft End Play

3) Remove park/neutral switch, transmission range switch, input speed sensor and output speed sensor from transaxle case. See Fig. 1. Remove solenoid assembly sound cover. See Fig. 11.

4) Remove shift lever from manual shaft assembly. Remove bolts, oil pan, oil filter and "O" ring. Remove valve body/transfer plate-to-transaxle case bolts. Note bolt length and location for reassembly reference.
5) Move roller on parking sprag rod from parking sprag guide bracket. Lift valve body and manual shaft assembly from transaxle case. Remove accumulator pistons and return springs from transaxle case.

NOTE: Low-reverse accumulator piston is retained by a snap ring and accumulator cover. With snap ring and accumulator cover removed, it may be necessary to place a small amount of grease on accumulator piston and use round suitable instrument to remove low-reverse accumulator piston. Note location of notch on side of low-reverse accumulator piston.

6) Remove bolts, solenoid assembly, solenoid assembly gaskets and solenoid plate. See Fig. 11. Using Oil Seal Remover (C-3981), remove oil seal from oil pump (if necessary). See Fig. 14.

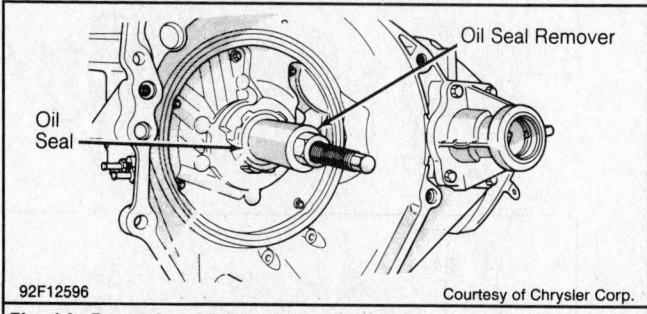

Courtesy of Chrysler Corp.

Fig. 14: Removing Oil Seal From Oil Pump

7) Remove oil pump bolts. Install 2 slide hammer pullers on opposite sides of oil pump. Push inward on input shaft while using slide hammers to pull oil pump from transaxle case. Remove oil pump and gasket. Remove oil cooler by-pass valve from transaxle case. See Fig. 15.

CAUTION: Oil cooler by-pass valve MUST be replaced if transaxle failure exists. DO NOT attempt to clean oil cooler by-pass valve.

8) Remove thrust bearing, located on front of input shaft, behind oil pump. Note that thrust bearing is installed with tanged side toward oil pump.
9) While pulling on input shaft, slide input clutch assembly from transaxle case. See Fig. 16. Remove thrust washer and 2-4 clutch hub. See Fig. 12.

NOTE: When removing input clutch assembly, input shaft, reverse-overdrive clutch piston and underdrive shaft assembly are removed as an assembly.

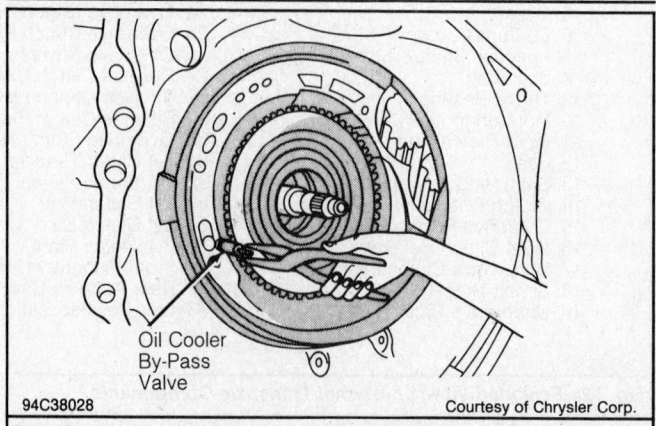

Courtesy of Chrysler Corp.

Fig. 15: Removing & Installing Oil Cooler By-Pass Valve

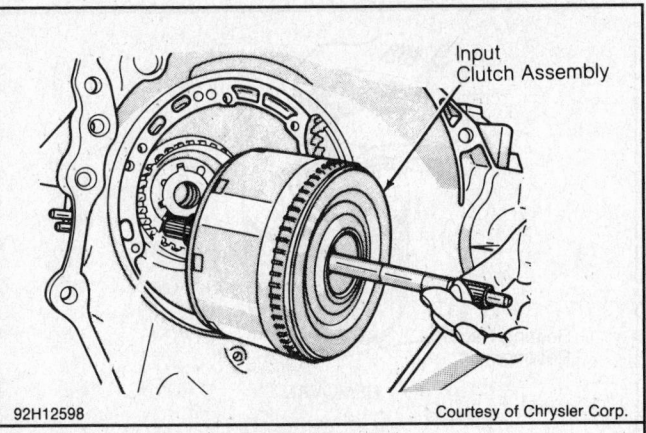

Fig. 16: *Removing Input Clutch Assembly*

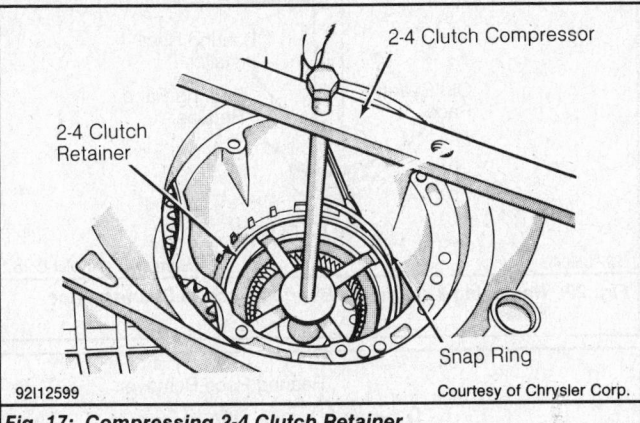

Fig. 17: *Compressing 2-4 Clutch Retainer*

10) Remove front planetary carrier and rear annulus gear by slightly rotating assembly. Remove rear sun gear and thrust bearing. *See Fig. 12.*

11) Install 2-4 Clutch Compressor (5058) on transaxle case. *See Fig. 17.* Compress 2-4 clutch retainer enough to remove snap ring from transaxle case. Note location of the ends of snap ring. Remove snap ring. Remove 2-4 clutch compressor.

CAUTION: *Ensure 2-4 clutch components are tagged for location. Note sequence of 2-4 clutch plates and clutch discs for reassembly reference.*

12) Remove 2-4 clutch retainer and clutch piston return spring. Remove and tag 2-4 clutch discs and clutch plates for reassembly reference. *See Fig. 12.*

13) Remove tapered snap ring, located above low-reverse clutch reaction plate in transaxle case. Note location of the ends of snap ring and that tapered side of snap ring is toward oil pump side of transaxle case.

CAUTION: *Ensure low-reverse clutch components are tagged for location. Note sequence of low-reverse clutch plates and clutch discs for reassembly reference.*

14) Remove low-reverse clutch reaction plate and one low-reverse clutch disc. Remove flat snap ring. Remove remaining low-reverse clutch discs and clutch plates. *See Fig. 12.*

15) Remove bolts and end cover. *See Fig. 11.* Using Gear Holder (6259), hold transfer gear. Remove nut and washer from end of transfer shaft. *See Fig. 12.* Using puller, remove transfer gear and selective spacer or shim from transfer shaft. Note that notch in top of bearing race retainer is aligned with notch in transaxle case. *See Fig. 18.* Remove bearing race retainer from transaxle case. *See Fig. 12.*

16) Remove transfer shaft bearing retaining snap ring from transaxle case. Using Transfer Shaft Remover/Installer (5049-A), remove transfer shaft. *See Fig. 18.* Remove bearing race, "O" ring and baffle from transfer shaft. *See Fig. 12.*

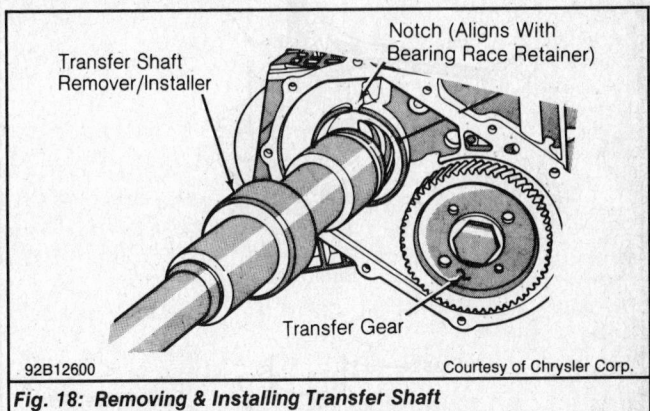

Fig. 18: *Removing & Installing Transfer Shaft*

17) Using transfer gear holder, hold remaining transfer gear. This transfer gear may be referred to as output gear. Remove bolt and washer from transfer gear. Note direction of coned area of washer for reassembly reference. Using puller, remove transfer gear and selective spacer or shim.

18) Remove rear planetary carrier from inside of transaxle case. *See Fig. 12.* Using Clutch Compressor (5059), Adapter (6057) and Rod (5058-3), slightly compress low-reverse clutch piston return spring. *See Fig. 19.*

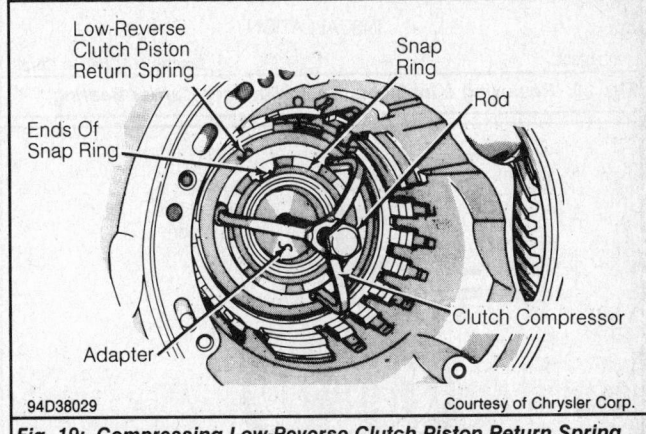

Fig. 19: *Compressing Low-Reverse Clutch Piston Return Spring*

19) Remove snap ring. Remove clutch compressor and components. Remove low-reverse clutch piston return spring. Remove parking sprag components from transaxle case.

20) Remove low-reverse clutch piston from transaxle case. Remove 3 screws, low-reverse clutch piston retainer and piston retainer gasket. *See Fig. 12.*

21) Tap bearing race for rear planetary carrier from transaxle case (if necessary). Using Bearing Race Remover (6062), pull transfer gear bearing race from transaxle case.

22) If removing bearing from rear planetary carrier, use Puller (5048), Jaws (5048-3) and Button (6055). *See Fig. 20.* If removing bearing from transfer gear, use Puller (5048), Jaws (5048-5) and Button (L-4539-2). *See Fig. 21.*

23) Using press, press bearing from transfer shaft (if necessary). If removing bearing race from bearing race retainer for transfer shaft, use Puller (6062) to remove bearing race. *See Fig. 22.*

24) To remove differential assembly, remove bolts and differential cover. Remove bolts from differential bearing retainer. *See Fig. 11.* Using spanner wrench, rotate differential bearing retainer and remove from transaxle case.

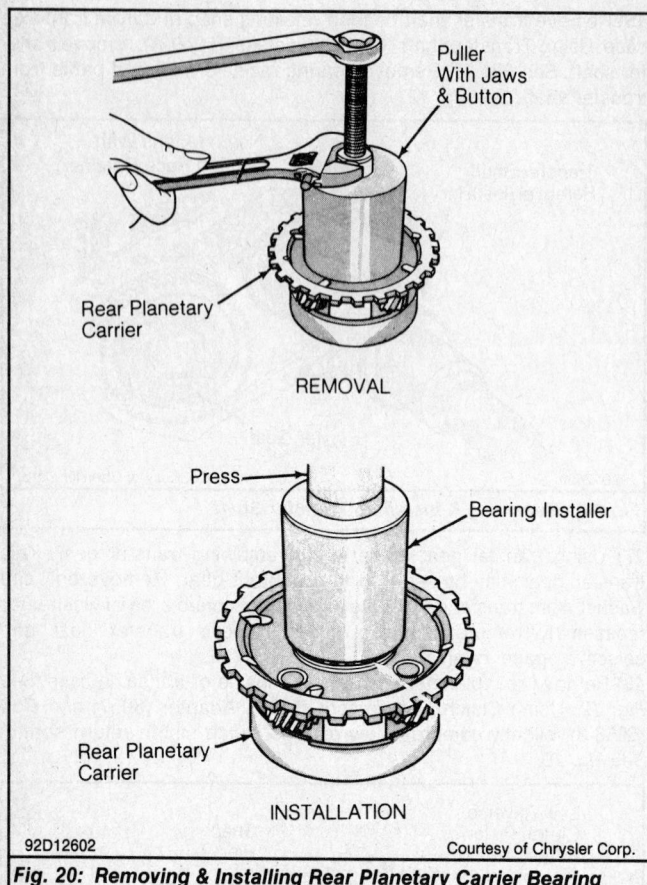

92D12602   Courtesy of Chrysler Corp.

Fig. 20: Removing & Installing Rear Planetary Carrier Bearing

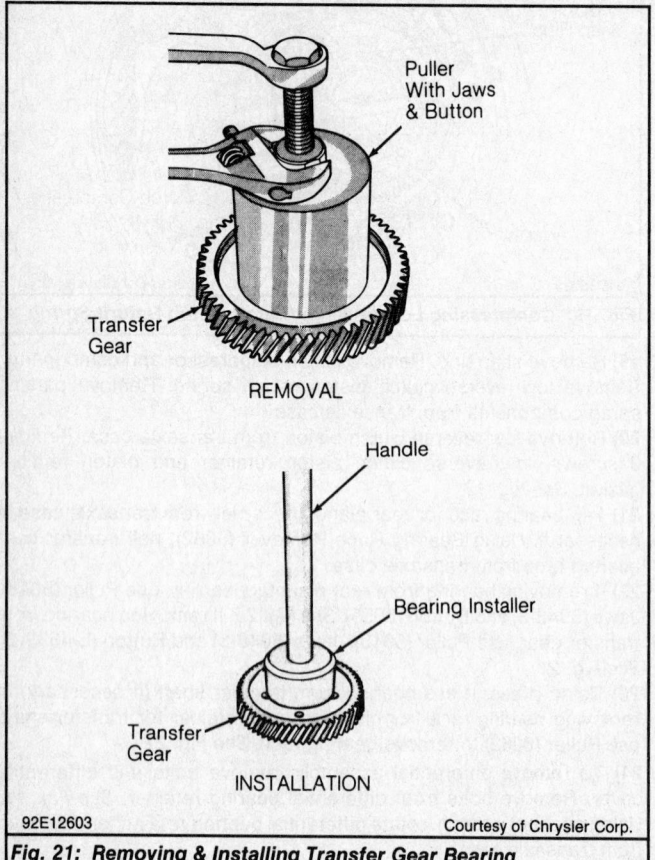

92E12603   Courtesy of Chrysler Corp.

Fig. 21: Removing & Installing Transfer Gear Bearing

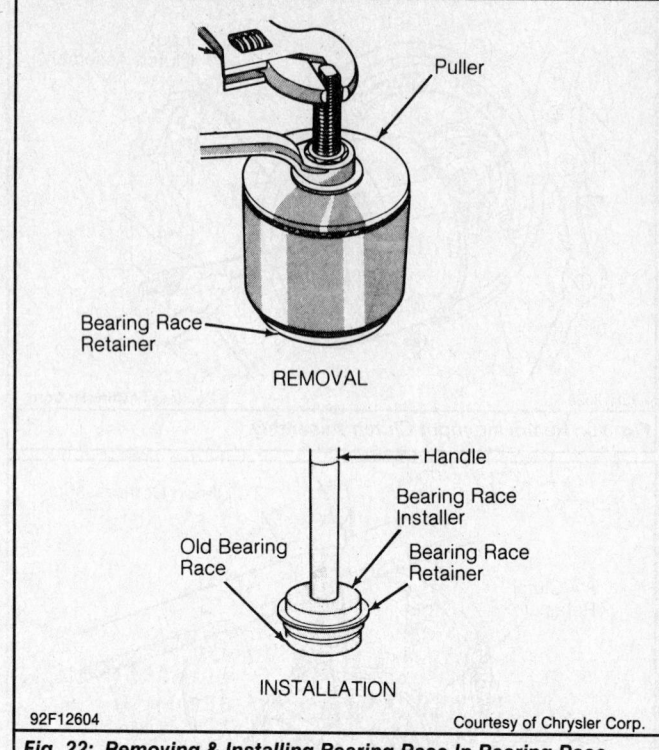

92F12604   Courtesy of Chrysler Corp.

Fig. 22: Removing & Installing Bearing Race In Bearing Race Retainer

92G12605   Courtesy of Chrysler Corp.

Fig. 23: Removing & Installing Bearing Race In Differential Bearing Retainer

NOTE: On All-Wheel Drive (AWD) drive models, extension housing is replaced with a transfer retainer plate.

25) Remove extension housing bolts. Support differential assembly. Using spanner wrench, rotate extension housing and remove from transaxle case. Remove differential assembly.

26) Remove oil seal from extension housing. Remove bearing race from extension housing if replacement is required.

27) Remove oil seal from differential bearing retainer. If removing bearing race from differential bearing retainer, use Bearing Race Remover (L-4518). *See Fig. 23.*

COMPONENT DISASSEMBLY & REASSEMBLY

DIFFERENTIAL ASSEMBLY

Disassembly – 1) Side gear end play should be checked before disassembling side gears to determine if different thickness thrust washer is required.

2) Install Shaft (C-4996) in side gear. Install dial indicator. *See Fig. 24.* Move side gear upward and zero dial indicator. Move side gear downward and note side gear end play.

3) Side gear end play should be .001-.013" (.03-.33 mm). Repeat procedure on remaining side gear. If side gear end play is not within specification, install different thickness side gear thrust washer. Side gear thrust washer is available in following thickness: .032" (.81 mm), .037" (.94 mm), .042" (1.06 mm) and .047" (1.19 mm).

4) Remove side bearings from carrier (if necessary). Remove bolts and ring gear. Using hammer and punch, remove roll pin from carrier. *See Fig. 25.*

5) Remove pinion gear shaft. Rotate pinion gears and remove pinion gears and thrust washers. Remove side gears and thrust washers.

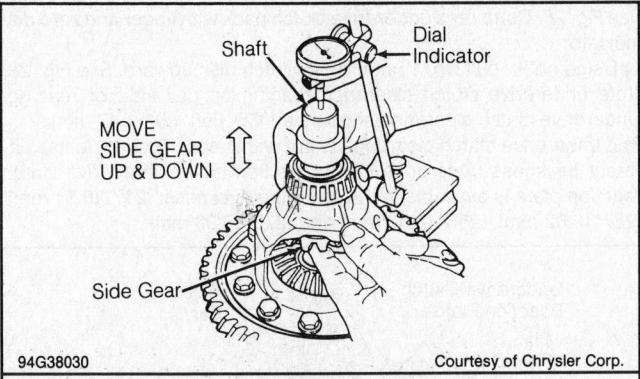

MOVE SIDE GEAR UP & DOWN

Shaft

Dial Indicator

Side Gear

94G38030   Courtesy of Chrysler Corp.

Fig. 24: Checking Side Gear End Play

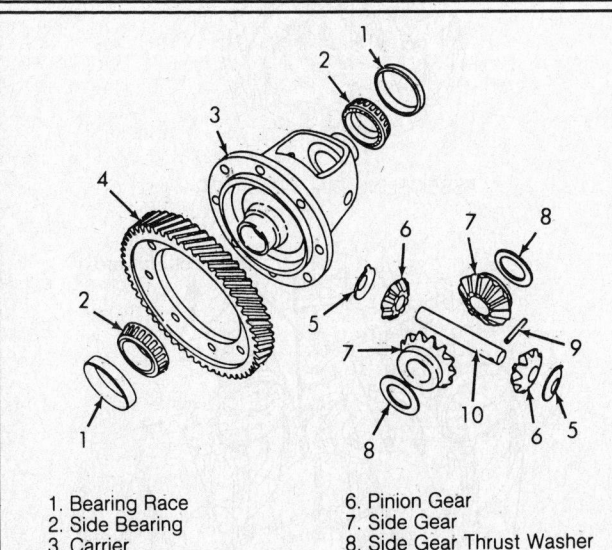

1. Bearing Race
2. Side Bearing
3. Carrier
4. Ring Gear
5. Pinion Gear Thrust Washer
6. Pinion Gear
7. Side Gear
8. Side Gear Thrust Washer
9. Roll Pin
10. Pinion Gear Shaft

92I12607   Courtesy of Chrysler Corp.

Fig. 25: Exploded View Of Differential Assembly

Reassembly – 1) To reassemble, reverse disassembly procedure. Recheck side gear end play once side gears and pinion gears are installed.

2) Install NEW ring gear bolts. DO NOT reuse ring gear bolts. Tighten ring gear bolts to specification. See TORQUE SPECIFICATIONS. Install NEW side bearings (if necessary).

INPUT CLUTCH ASSEMBLY

CAUTION: Ensure all clutch components are tagged for location. Note sequence of all clutch plates and clutch discs for reassembly reference. Note snap ring location and direction of installation for reassembly reference, as both flat and wave snap rings are used.

Disassembly – 1) Support input clutch assembly with input shaft pointing downward. Tap downward on reverse clutch reaction plate. *See Fig. 12.*

2) Remove snap ring located above reverse clutch reaction plate. Remove reverse clutch reaction plate, reverse clutch plates and clutch discs. Note sequence of reverse clutch plate and clutch discs for reassembly reference.

3) Remove snap ring located above overdrive-reverse clutch pressure plate. *See Fig. 12.* This is the flat snap ring located in the outside groove. Remove overdrive-reverse clutch pressure plate.

4) Remove overdrive clutch wave snap ring from outside groove. Remove overdrive hub with overdrive clutch plates and clutch discs. Remove thrust washers located on both sides of overdrive hub. *See Fig. 12.* Note sequence of overdrive clutch plates and clutch discs for reassembly reference.

5) Remove thrust washer and underdrive shaft assembly. *See Fig. 12.* Remove thrust bearing, located below underdrive shaft assembly.

6) Remove tapered snap ring and underdrive clutch reaction plate. *See Fig. 12.* Remove one underdrive clutch disc. Remove flat snap ring and remaining underdrive clutch plates and clutch discs. Note sequence of underdrive clutch plates and clutch discs for reassembly reference. *See Fig. 12.*

7) Using press and spring compressor, compress clutch piston return spring located above underdrive clutch piston.

CAUTION: Compress clutch piston return spring just enough to remove snap ring located above spring retainer for underdrive clutch piston. See Fig. 12.

8) Remove snap ring. Remove spring compressor. Remove spring retainer, clutch piston return spring and underdrive clutch piston. Remove input clutch hub-to-input clutch retainer snap ring. Snap ring is a tapered snap ring located inside input clutch retainer in groove of input clutch hub. Note direction of snap ring installation.

9) Using soft-faced hammer, tap input clutch hub from input clutch retainer. Separate input clutch retainer from overdrive-reverse clutch piston. *See Fig. 12.*

10) Using press and spring compressor, slightly compress clutch piston return spring on rear of overdrive-reverse clutch piston. Remove snap ring from rear of overdrive-reverse clutch piston.

11) Release press. Remove spring compressor and clutch piston return spring. Note direction of clutch piston return spring for reassembly reference.

12) Remove snap ring from end of input shaft. Using press and correctly sized socket, support input clutch hub and press input shaft from input clutch hub.

NOTE: Coat all NEW lip seals and "O" rings with petroleum jelly before installing. It may be necessary to use petroleum jelly to hold thrust washers and thrust bearings in place. Underdrive, overdrive and reverse clutch clearances must be checked before final assembly of input clutch assembly.

Reassembly – 1) Using press and suitable sized socket, support input clutch hub and press input shaft into input clutch hub. Install snap ring on input shaft. Install NEW lip seals and NEW "O" ring on input clutch hub.

2) Install clutch piston return spring on rear of overdrive-reverse clutch piston. Using press and spring compressor, slightly compress clutch piston return spring and install snap ring. Remove spring compressor.

3) Install overdrive-reverse clutch piston over input clutch retainer. Push downward on overdrive-reverse clutch piston until it fully seats on input clutch retainer.

4) Align splines and install input clutch hub and input shaft assembly on overdrive-reverse clutch piston. Push downward on input clutch hub until fully seated. Install input clutch hub retaining snap ring on inside of overdrive-reverse clutch piston.

CAUTION: Ensure input clutch hub retaining snap ring is installed with tapered side upward (away from torque converter end of input shaft).

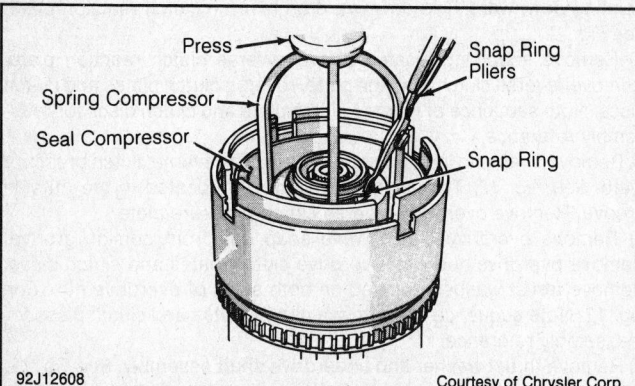

Fig. 26: **Installing Underdrive Clutch Piston & Clutch Piston Return Spring**

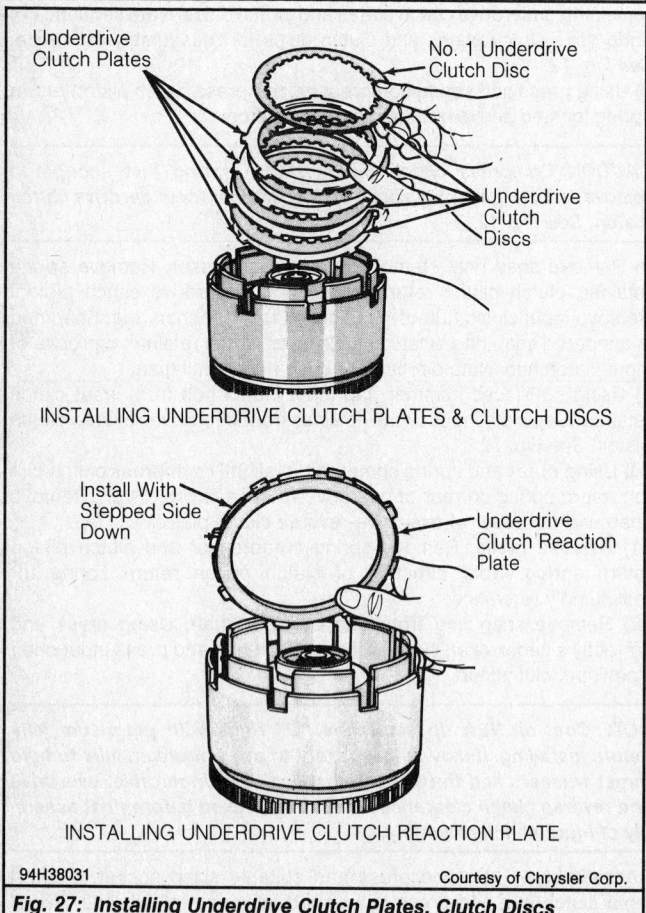

INSTALLING UNDERDRIVE CLUTCH PLATES & CLUTCH DISCS

INSTALLING UNDERDRIVE CLUTCH REACTION PLATE

Fig. 27: **Installing Underdrive Clutch Plates, Clutch Discs & Underdrive Clutch Reaction Plate**

5) Install underdrive clutch piston and Seal Compressor (5067). Install clutch piston return spring and spring retainer. Using press and Spring Compressor (5059A), compress clutch piston return spring. *See Fig. 26.* Install snap ring.

CAUTION: Compress clutch piston return spring just enough to install snap ring.

---

6) Release press. Remove spring compressor and seal compressor. Install underdrive clutch plates and clutch discs, starting with a clutch plate and alternating with a clutch disc. DO NOT install No. 1 underdrive clutch disc at this time. *See Fig. 27.*

7) Install underdrive clutch reaction plate flat snap ring in groove above underdrive clutch plates and clutch discs. Install No. 1 underdrive clutch disc. Install underdrive clutch reaction plate with stepped side down. *See Fig. 27.*

8) Install NEW tapered snap ring in groove to retain underdrive clutch reaction plate. DO NOT reuse old tapered snap ring. Check underdrive clutch clearance.

CAUTION: Use care when installing tapered snap ring to not scratch underdrive clutch reaction plate surface. Ensure snap ring is fully seated with ends of snap ring against solid area of input clutch retainer.

Checking Underdrive Clutch Clearance – 1) Assemble dial indicator and steel bar with dial indicator stem resting on underdrive clutch disc. *See Fig. 28.* Compress underdrive clutch pack with finger and zero dial indicator.

2) Using hook, pull No. 1 underdrive clutch disc upward. *See Fig. 28.* Note underdrive clutch clearance reading on dial indictor reading. Underdrive clutch clearance should be .036-.058" (.91-1.47 mm).

3) If underdrive clutch clearance is not within specification, install different thickness underdrive clutch reaction plate. Underdrive clutch reaction plate is available in the following thickness: .217" (5.51 mm), .237" (6.02 mm), .256" (6.50 mm) and .275" (6.99 mm).

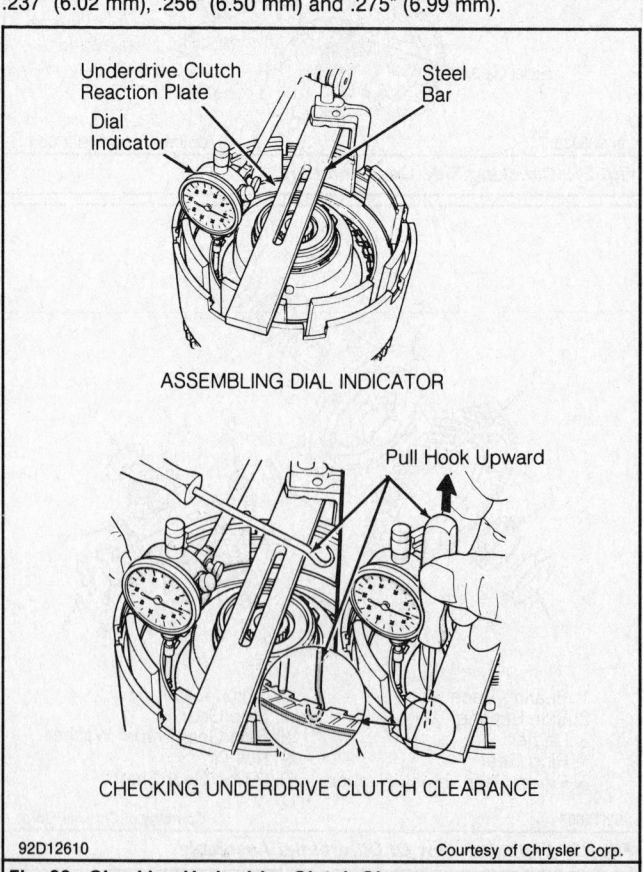

ASSEMBLING DIAL INDICATOR

CHECKING UNDERDRIVE CLUTCH CLEARANCE

Fig. 28: **Checking Underdrive Clutch Clearance**

Overdrive Clutch – 1) Install overdrive clutch plates and clutch discs. *See Fig. 29.* Install overdrive clutch wave snap ring in the outside groove. Install overdrive-reverse clutch pressure plate with stepped side down. *See Fig. 29.*

CAUTION: Compress overdrive-reverse clutch assembly just enough to install flat snap ring.

---

2) Using press and spring compressor, press overdrive-reverse clutch pressure plate downward until flat snap ring can be installed in outer groove. Install flat snap ring. Release press. Remove spring compressor. Check overdrive clutch clearance.

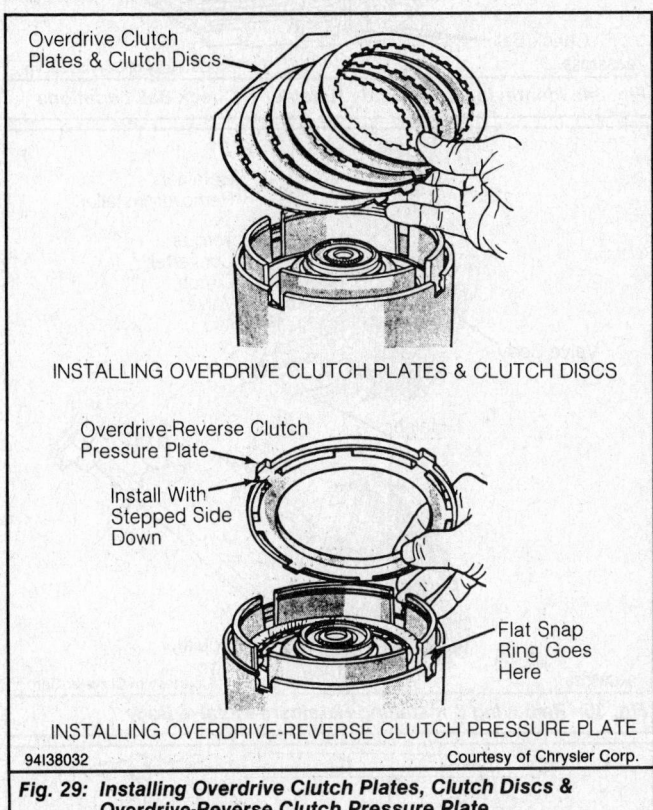

INSTALLING OVERDRIVE CLUTCH PLATES & CLUTCH DISCS

INSTALLING OVERDRIVE-REVERSE CLUTCH PRESSURE PLATE

94I38032   Courtesy of Chrysler Corp.

Fig. 29: Installing Overdrive Clutch Plates, Clutch Discs & Overdrive-Reverse Clutch Pressure Plate

Checking Overdrive Clutch Clearance – 1) Assemble dial indicator and steel bar with dial indicator stem resting on overdrive clutch disc. *See Fig. 30.* Compress overdrive clutch pack with finger and zero dial indicator.
2) Using hook, raise overdrive clutch disc. *See Fig. 30.* Note overdrive clutch clearance reading on dial indicator. Overdrive clutch clearance should be .042-.096" (1.07-2.44 mm). If overdrive clutch clearance is not within specification, check for improperly assembled overdrive clutch components.

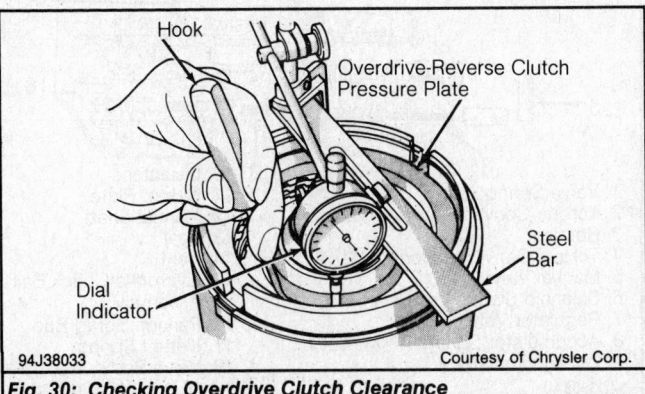

94J38033   Courtesy of Chrysler Corp.

Fig. 30: Checking Overdrive Clutch Clearance

Reverse Clutch – 1) Install reverse clutch plate and clutch discs. Install reverse clutch reaction plate with stepped side down. *See Fig. 31.*
2) Install snap ring in groove above reverse clutch reaction plate. Using screwdriver on each side of reverse clutch reaction plate, pry reaction plate upward to ensure snap ring is fully seated. Check reverse clutch clearance.

Checking Reverse Clutch Clearance – 1) Assemble dial indicator and steel bar with indicator stem resting on reverse clutch disc. *See Fig. 31.* Compress reverse clutch pack with finger and zero dial indicator.
2) Using hook, raise reverse clutch disc. *See Fig. 32.* Note reverse clutch clearance reading on dial indicator. Reverse clutch clearance should be .030-.049" (.76-1.24 mm).
3) If reverse clutch clearance is not within specification, snap ring can be changed to obtain correct clearance. Snap rings are available in the following thickness: .061" (1.55 mm), .071" (1.80 mm), .081" (2.06 mm) and .090" (2.29 mm).

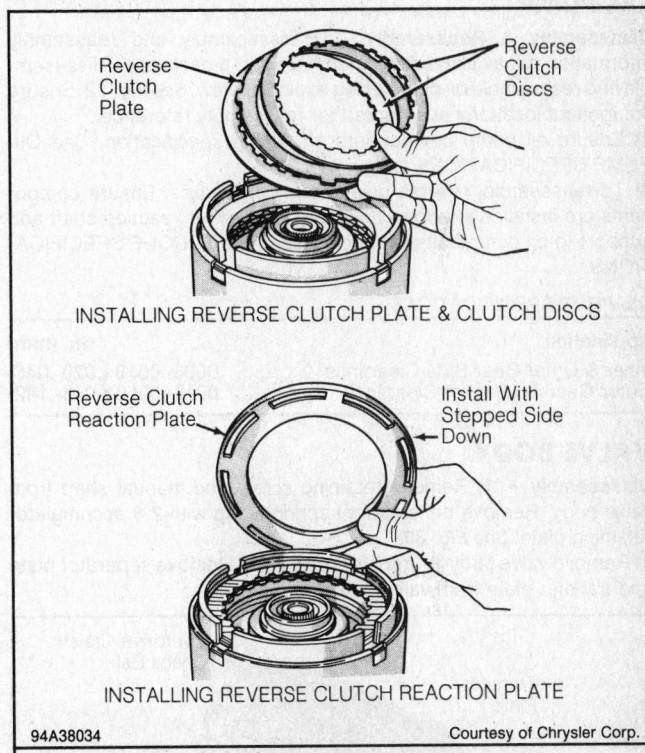

INSTALLING REVERSE CLUTCH PLATE & CLUTCH DISCS

INSTALLING REVERSE CLUTCH REACTION PLATE

94A38034   Courtesy of Chrysler Corp.

Fig. 31: Installing Reverse Clutch Discs, Clutch Plate & Reverse Clutch Reaction Plate

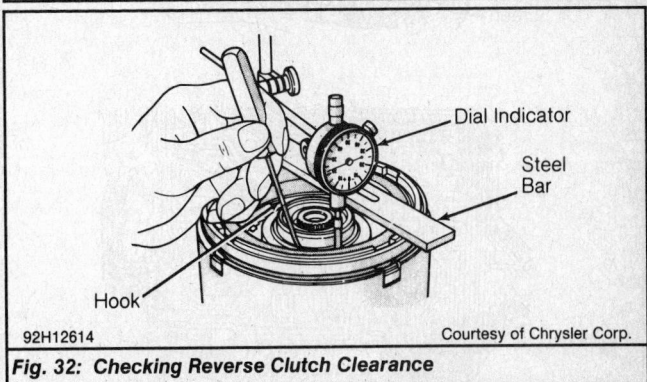

92H12614   Courtesy of Chrysler Corp.

Fig. 32: Checking Reverse Clutch Clearance

CAUTION: During final reassembly of input clutch assembly, reverse and overdrive clutch assemblies must be removed. Ensure clutch components are kept in order for reassembly reference.

Final Assembly Of Input Clutch Assembly – 1) Remove reverse and overdrive clutch assemblies. Install thrust bearing located below underdrive shaft assembly. *See Fig. 12.* Thrust bearing must be installed with 3 small tabs pointing upward (away from torque converter end of input shaft).

NOTE: It may be necessary to apply petroleum jelly to thrust bearing to hold it in position during reassembly of input clutch assembly.

2) Install underdrive shaft assembly. Install 5-tab thrust washer on shaft side of underdrive shaft assembly. *See Fig. 12.*
3) Install 3-tab thrust washer on back side (opposite shaft side) of overdrive clutch hub. *See Fig. 12.* Install overdrive clutch hub. Ensure tabs on all thrust washers remain fully engaged.
4) To complete final assembly, reinstall overdrive and reverse clutch components. Ensure all clutch components are installed in original location as when clutch clearances were checked.

OIL PUMP

Disassembly & Reassembly – 1) Disassembly and reassembly information not available from manufacturer. If necessary, disassemble and reassemble oil pump using exploded view. *See Fig. 12.* Ensure component locations are marked for reassembly reference.
2) Ensure oil pump components are within specification. See OIL PUMP SPECIFICATIONS table.
3) To reassemble, reverse disassembly procedure. Ensure components are installed in original location. Tighten the reaction shaft and support-to-oil pump bolts to specification. See TORQUE SPECIFICATIONS.

OIL PUMP SPECIFICATIONS

Application	In. (mm)
Inner & Outer Gear Side Clearance	.0008-.0018 (.020-.046)
Outer Gear-To-Pocket Clearance	.0018-.0056 (.046-.142)

VALVE BODY

Disassembly – 1) Remove retaining screw and manual shaft from valve body. Remove bolts, detent spring along with 2-4 accumulator retaining plate. *See Fig. 36.*
2) Remove valve body-to-transfer plate bolts. Remove separator plate and transfer plate from valve body.

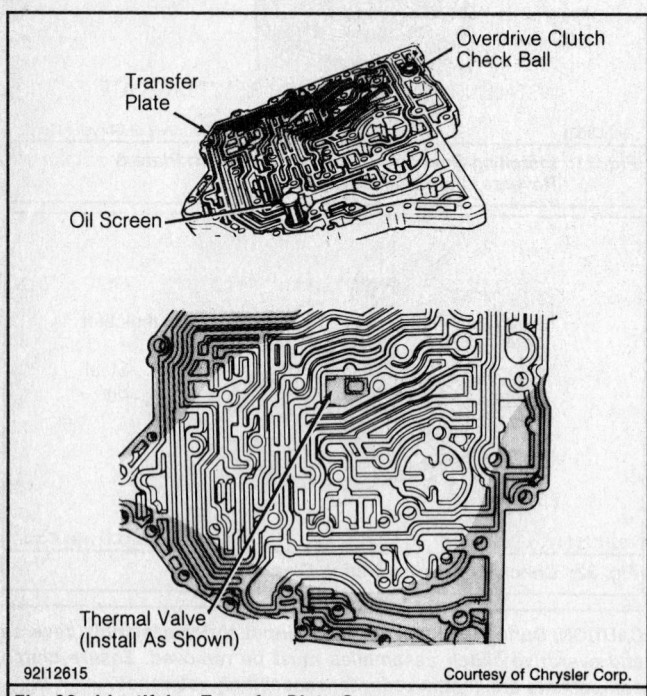

94B38035   Courtesy of Chrysler Corp.

Fig. 34: Identifying Valve Body Retainer & Check Ball Locations

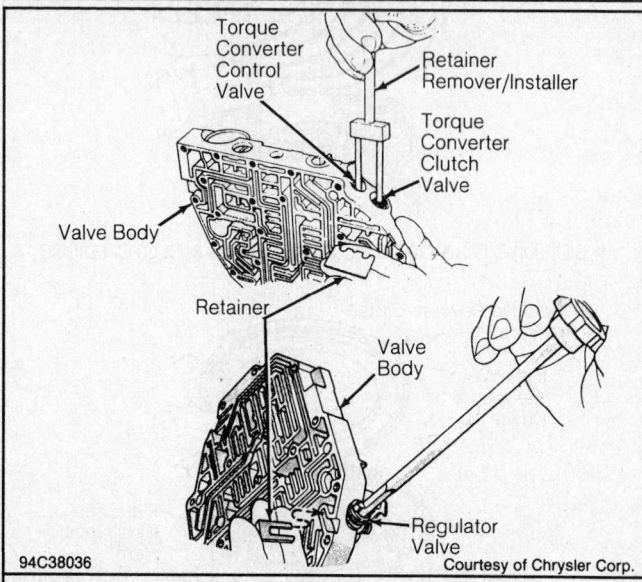

94C38036   Courtesy of Chrysler Corp.

Fig. 35: Removing & Installing Retainers In Valve Body

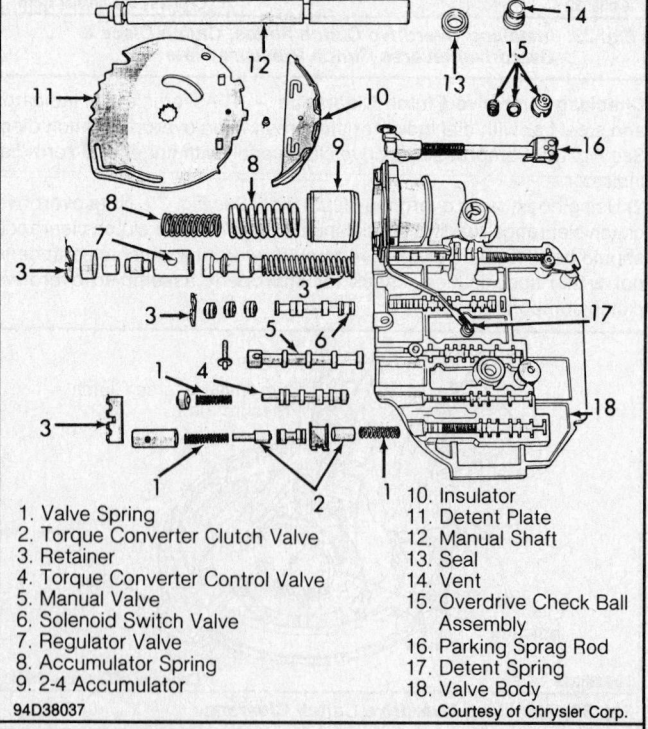

1. Valve Spring
2. Torque Converter Clutch Valve
3. Retainer
4. Torque Converter Control Valve
5. Manual Valve
6. Solenoid Switch Valve
7. Regulator Valve
8. Accumulator Spring
9. 2-4 Accumulator
10. Insulator
11. Detent Plate
12. Manual Shaft
13. Seal
14. Vent
15. Overdrive Check Ball Assembly
16. Parking Sprag Rod
17. Detent Spring
18. Valve Body

94D38037   Courtesy of Chrysler Corp.

Fig. 36: Exploded View Of Valve Body

92I12615   Courtesy of Chrysler Corp.

Fig. 33: Identifying Transfer Plate Components

CAUTION: Use care when removing separator plate and transfer plate from valve body. DO NOT allow check balls to fall from valve body. Use care when removing separator plate from transfer plate, as overdrive clutch check ball is located in transfer plate. See Fig. 33.

3) Remove separator plate from transfer plate, noting location of overdrive clutch check ball, oil screen and thermal valve. *See Fig. 33.* Remove oil screen and thermal valve from transfer plate.

4) Note location of check balls and retainers in valve body. *See Fig. 34.* Using Retainer Remover/Installer (6301), remove retainer for torque converter clutch valve and torque converter control valve. *See Fig. 35.*

5) Using Retainer Remover/Installer (6302), remove retainer for regulator valve. *See Fig. 35.* Remove valve body components. *See Fig. 36.*

Reassembly – To reassemble, reverse removal procedure. Ensure all components are installed in original location. Tighten valve body-to-transfer plate bolts to specification. See TORQUE SPECIFICATIONS.

BEARING ADJUSTMENTS

NOTE: Various gauging shims and selective spacers or shim applications are used for performing bearing preload adjustments. For application and available thickness, see Fig. 44.

DIFFERENTIAL BEARING PRELOAD

CAUTION: Differential bearing preload MUST be adjusted if any of the following components have been replaced: transaxle case, carrier, differential retainer, extension housing or side bearings and races. Differential bearing preload must be checked with transfer shaft removed.

1) Install NEW side bearings on carrier (if removed). Using Bearing Race Remover (L-4518), remove bearing race from differential bearing retainer. *See Fig. 23.* Remove selective spacer or shim from differential bearing retainer. If side bearings have been replaced, also replace bearing race in extension housing.

2) Install .020" (.50 mm) thick gauging shim in differential bearing retainer. DO NOT install oil baffle between gauging shim and differential bearing retainer at this time.

3) Using press, Handle (C-4171) and Bearing Race Installer (L-4520), install bearing race in differential bearing retainer. *See Fig. 23.*

4) Install differential assembly in transaxle case. Install NEW "O" ring on extension housing. Apply 1/8" bead of RTV sealant on extension housing-to-transaxle case sealing surface. Install extension housing on transaxle case.

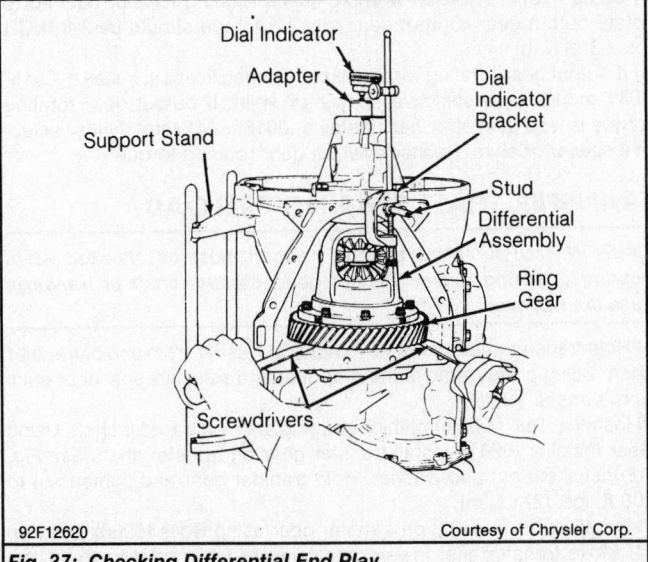

NOTE: On All-Wheel Drive (AWD) models, retainer plate is used in place of extension housing.

5) Using spanner wrench, rotate extension housing and align bolt holes. Install and tighten bolts to specification. See TORQUE SPECIFICATIONS. Install differential bearing retainer and tighten bolts to 21 ft. lbs. (29 N.m).

6) Position transaxle assembly vertically in Support Stand (L-4557). *See Fig. 37.* Rotate differential at least one full revolution to ensure side bearings are fully seated. Install Adapter (L-4436) into extension housing. *See Fig. 37.*

7) Install dial indicator with indicator stem resting on adapter and zero dial indicator. Using screwdrivers on each side of ring gear, pry ring gear upward and note differential end play reading on dial indicator. *See Fig. 37.*

CAUTION: DO NOT damage transaxle case or differential cover sealing surface when prying ring gear upward.

8) Using differential end play reading, determine selective spacer or shim thickness required. *See Fig. 38.* Once proper selective spacer or shim is determined, remove bolts and differential bearing retainer.

End Play (with .50 mm gauging shim installed)		Required Shim Combination			Total Thickness	
mm	inch	mm			mm	inch
.0	.0	.50			.50	.020
.05	.002	.75			.75	.030
.10	.004	.80			.80	.032
.15	.006	.85			.85	.034
.20	.008	.90			.90	.035
.25	.010	.95			.95	.037
.30	.012	1.00			1.00	.039
.35	.014	1.05			1.05	.041
.40	.016	.50	+	.60	1.10	.043
.45	.018	.50	+	.65	1.15	.045
.50	.020	.50	+	.70	1.20	.047
.55	.022	.50	+	.75	1.25	.049
.60	.024	.50	+	.80	1.30	.051
.65	.026	.50	+	.85	1.35	.053
.70	.027	.50	+	.90	1.40	.055
.75	.029	.50	+	.95	1.45	.057
.80	.031	.50	+	1.00	1.50	.059
.85	.033	.50	+	1.05	1.55	.061
.90	.035	1.00	+	.60	1.60	.063
.95	.037	1.00	+	.65	1.65	.065
1.00	.039	1.00	+	.70	1.70	.067
1.05	.041	1.00	+	.75	1.75	.069
1.10	.043	1.00	+	.80	1.80	.071
1.15	.045	1.00	+	.85	1.85	.073
1.20	.047	1.00	+	.90	1.90	.075
1.25	.049	1.00	+	.95	1.95	.077
1.30	.051	1.00	+	1.00	2.00	.079
1.35	.053	1.00	+	1.05	2.05	.081
1.40	.055	1.05	+	1.05	2.10	.083

92G12621   Courtesy of Chrysler Corp.

Fig. 38: Determining Differential End Play Selective Spacer Or Shim

9) Using bearing race remover, remove bearing race from differential bearing retainer. Remove .020" (.50 mm) gauging shim. Install oil baffle and proper selective spacer or shim.

10) Using press, install bearing race in differential bearing retainer. Apply 1/8" bead of RTV sealant on differential bearing retainer-to-transaxle case sealing surface. Install differential bearing retainer on transaxle case.

11) Using spanner wrench, rotate differential bearing retainer and align bolt holes. Install and tighten bolts to 21 ft. lbs. (29 N.m).

12) Coat side bearings with oil. Using Adapter (L-4436-A) and INCH-lb. torque wrench, check differential rotating torque required to rotate differential assembly. *See Fig. 39.* Differential rotating torque should be 5-18 INCH lbs (.6-2.0 N.m).

13) If differential rotating torque exceeds specification, install a .002" (.05 mm) thinner selective spacer or shim in differential bearing retainer. If differential rotating torque is less than specified, install a .002" (.05 mm) thicker selective spacer or shim in differential bearing retainer.

14) Recheck differential rotating torque. If oil seal was removed from extension housing, install NEW oil seal in extension housing.

92F12620   Courtesy of Chrysler Corp.

Fig. 37: Checking Differential End Play

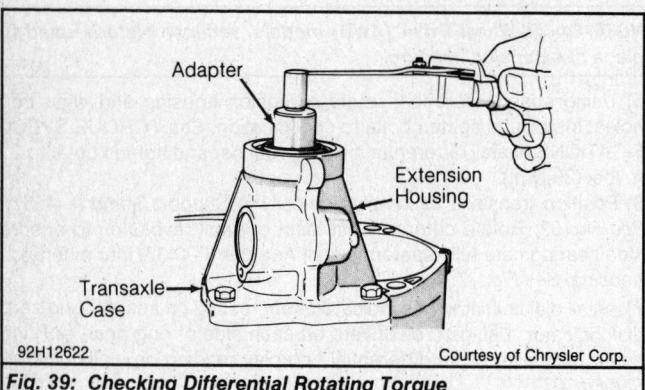

92H12622   Courtesy of Chrysler Corp.

Fig. 39: Checking Differential Rotating Torque

OUTPUT GEAR BEARING PRELOAD

CAUTION: Output gear is transfer gear located on rear planetary carrier in transaxle case. Output gear bearing preload must be checked when bearings, bearing races, output gear, rear planetary carrier or transaxle case are replaced. Output gear bearing preload must be checked with transfer gear removed from transfer shaft.

1) With output gear and selective spacer or shim removed, install a .177" (4.50 mm) thick gauging shim on rear planetary carrier. Use grease to hold gauging shim in place. Install output gear on rear planetary carrier using Gear Installer (6261) with stud. See Fig. 40.
2) Install bolt and washer. Using Gear Holder (6259), hold output gear. Tighten bolt to 200 ft. lbs. (271 N.m). Install Lever (L-4432) on output gear using Bolts (6260). See Fig. 41.
3) Move output gear inward and outward while rotating to ensure bearings are seated. Install dial indicator with indicator stem against output gear. See Fig. 41.
4) Move output gear inward and zero dial indicator. Pull output gear outward and note output gear end play reading on dial indicator. Using output gear end play, determine proper selective spacer or shim. See Fig. 42.

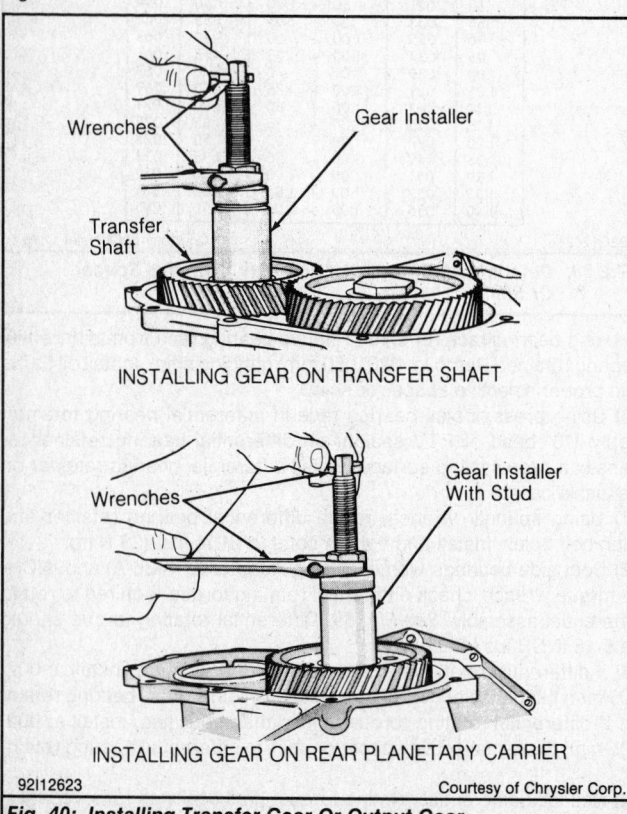

INSTALLING GEAR ON TRANSFER SHAFT

INSTALLING GEAR ON REAR PLANETARY CARRIER

92I12623   Courtesy of Chrysler Corp.

Fig. 40: Installing Transfer Gear Or Output Gear

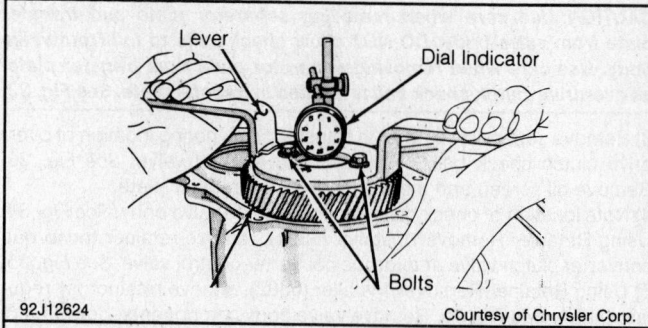

92J12624   Courtesy of Chrysler Corp.

Fig. 41: Checking Transfer Or Output Gear & Transfer Shaft End Play

End Play (with 4.50 mm gauging shim installed)		Required Shim	End Play (with 4.50 mm gauging shim installed)		Required Shim
mm	inch	mm	mm	inch	mm
.05	.002	4.42	.53	.021	3.94
.08	.003	4.38	.56	.022	3.90
.10	.004	4.38	.58	.023	3.90
.13	.005	4.34	.61	.024	3.86
.15	.006	4.30	.64	.025	3.82
.18	.007	4.30	.66	.026	3.82
.20	.008	4.26	.69	.027	3.78
.23	.009	4.22	.71	.028	3.74
.25	.010	4.22	.74	.029	3.74
.28	.011	4.18	.76	.030	3.70
.30	.012	4.14	.79	.031	3.66
.33	.013	4.14	.81	.032	3.66
.36	.014	4.10	.84	.033	3.62
.38	.015	4.10	.86	.034	3.62
.41	.016	4.06	.89	.035	3.58
.43	.017	4.02	.91	.036	3.54
.46	0.18	4.02	.94	.037	3.54
.48	.019	3.98	.97	.038	3.50
.51	.020	3.94			

Average Conversion .04 mm = .0016"

92A12625   Courtesy of Chrysler Corp.

Fig. 42: Determining Transfer Or Output Gear Selective Spacer Or Shim

5) Using gear holder, hold output gear. Remove bolt and washer. Using puller, remove output gear and gauging shim. Install proper selective spacer or shim using grease to hold in place.
6) Using gear installer and stud, install output gear. Install retaining bolt and washer. Using gear holder, hold output gear and tighten retaining bolt to 200 ft. lbs. (271 N.m).
7) Using INCH lb. torque wrench, check rotating torque required to rotate output gear. Output gear rotating torque should be 3-8 INCH lbs. (.3-.9 N.m).
8) If output gear rotating torque exceeds specification, install a .0016" (.041 mm) thicker selective spacer or shim. If output gear rotating torque is less than specified, install a .0016" (.041 mm) thinner selective spacer or shim. Recheck output gear rotating torque.

TRANSFER SHAFT BEARING PRELOAD

CAUTION: Transfer shaft bearing preload must be checked when bearings, bearing races, transfer gear, transfer shaft or transaxle case are replaced.

1) Hold transfer gear and remove nut and washer from end of transfer shaft. Using puller, remove transfer gear and selective spacer or shim from transfer shaft.
2) Install a .184" (4.66 mm) thick gauging shim on transfer shaft. Using Gear Installer (6261), install transfer gear on transfer shaft. See Fig. 40. Install old nut and washer. Hold transfer gear and tighten nut to 200 ft. lbs. (271 N.m).
3) Install Lever (L-4432) on transfer gear using Bolts (6260). See Fig. 41. Move transfer gear inward and outward while rotating to ensure bearings are seated.

End Play (with 4.66 mm gauging shim installed)		Required Shim	End Play (with 4.66 mm gauging shim installed)		Required Shim
mm	inch	mm	mm	inch	mm
.05	.002	4.66	.79	.031	3.90
.08	.003	4.62	.81	.032	3.90
.10	.004	4.58	.84	.033	3.86
.13	.005	4.58	.86	.034	3.82
.15	.006	4.54	.89	.035	3.82
.18	.007	4.50	.91	.036	3.78
.20	.008	4.50	.94	.037	3.74
.23	.009	4.46	.97	.038	3.74
.25	.010	4.46	.99	.039	3.70
.28	.011	4.42	1.02	.040	3.66
.30	.012	4.38	1.04	.041	3.66
.33	.013	4.38	1.07	.042	3.62
.36	.014	4.34	1.08	.043	3.62
.38	.015	4.30	1.12	.044	3.58
.41	.016	4.30	1.14	.045	3.54
.43	.017	4.26	1.17	.046	3.54
.46	.018	4.22	1.19	.047	3.50
.48	.019	4.22	1.22	.048	3.46
.50	.020	4.18	1.24	.049	3.46
.53	.021	4.18	1.27	.050	3.42
.56	.022	4.14	1.30	.051	3.38
.58	.023	4.10	1.32	.052	3.38
.61	.024	4.10	1.35	.053	3.34
.64	.025	4.06	1.37	.054	3.34
.66	.026	4.02	1.40	.055	3.30
.69	.027	4.02	1.42	.056	3.26
.71	.028	3.98	1.45	.057	3.26
.74	.029	3.94	1.47	.058	3.22
.76	.030	3.94			

92B12626   Courtesy of Chrysler Corp.

Fig. 43: Determining Transfer Shaft Selective Spacer Or Shim

Shim Thickness		Bearing Usage		
mm	inch	Output Gear	Transfer Shaft	Differ-ential
3.22	.127	X	X	—
3.26	.128	X	X	—
3.30	.130	X	X	—
3.34	.132	X	X	—
3.38	.133	X	X	—
3.42	.135	X	X	—
3.46	.136	X	X	—
3.50	.138	X	X	—
3.54	.139	X	X	—
3.58	.141	X	X	—
3.62	.143	X	X	—
3.66	.144	X	X	—
3.70	.146	X	X	—
3.74	.147	X	X	—
3.78	.149	X	X	—
3.82	.150	X	X	—
3.86	.152	X	X	—
3.90	.154	X	X	—
3.94	.155	X	X	—
3.98	.157	X	X	—
4.02	.158	X	X	—
4.06	.160	X	X	—
4.10	.161	X	X	—
4.14	.163	X	X	—
4.18	.165	X	X	—
4.22	.166	X	X	—
4.26	.168	X	X	—
4.30	.169	X	X	—
4.34	.171	X	X	—
4.38	.172	X	X	—
4.42	.174	X	X	—
4.46	.175	X	X	—
4.50	.177	X*	X	—
4.54	.178	X	X	—
4.58	.180	X	X	—
4.62	.182	X	X	—
4.66	.183	X	X*	—
0.50	.020	—	—	X*
0.55	.022	—	—	X
0.60	.024	—	—	X
0.65	.026	—	—	X
0.70	.027	—	—	X
0.75	.029	—	—	X
0.80	.031	—	—	X
0.85	.033	—	—	X
0.90	.035	—	—	X
0.95	.037	—	—	X
1.00	.039	—	—	X
1.05	.041	—	—	X

* – Also used as gauging shims.

94E38038   Courtesy of Chrysler Corp.

Fig. 44: Identifying Selective Spacer Or Shim Application

4) Install grease-coated steel ball in end of transfer shaft. Install dial indicator on transaxle case with stem resting on steel ball so transfer shaft end play can be checked.

5) Move transfer gear inward and zero dial indicator. Pull transfer gear outward and note transfer shaft end play reading on dial indicator.

6) Using transfer shaft end play, determine correct selective spacer or shim thickness. See Fig. 43.

7) Hold transfer gear. Remove nut and washer from end of transfer shaft. Using puller, remove transfer gear and gauging shim from transfer shaft.

8) Install correct selective spacer or shim on transfer shaft. Using gear installer, install transfer gear on transfer shaft. Install nut and washer. Using gear holder, hold transfer gear and tighten nut to 200 ft. lbs. (271 N.m).

9) Ensure bearings are fully seated. Using dial indicator, check transfer shaft end play. Transfer shaft end play should be .002-.004" (.05-.10 mm).

10) If transfer shaft end play exceeds specification, install a .0016" (.041 mm) thinner selective spacer or shim. If transfer shaft end play is less than specified, install a .0016" (.041 mm) thicker selective spacer or shim. Recheck transfer shaft end play.

TRANSAXLE REASSEMBLY

DIFFERENTIAL ASSEMBLY

CAUTION: Differential bearing preload MUST be adjusted if any of the following components have been replaced: transaxle case, carrier, differential retainer, extension housing or side bearings and races. See DIFFERENTIAL BEARING PRELOAD under BEARING ADJUSTMENTS. If no components are replaced, use original selective spacer or shim located behind bearing race in differential bearing retainer.

1) Install differential assembly in transaxle case. Install NEW "O" ring on extension housing. Apply 1/8" bead of RTV sealant on extension housing-to-transaxle case sealing surface. Install extension housing on transaxle case.

2) Using spanner wrench, rotate extension housing and align retaining bolt holes. Install and tighten bolts to specification. See TORQUE SPECIFICATIONS.

3) Apply 1/8" bead of RTV sealant on differential bearing retainer-to-transaxle case sealing surface. Install differential bearing retainer on transaxle case.

4) Using spanner wrench, rotate differential bearing retainer and align retaining bolt holes. Install and tighten bolts to specification. See TORQUE SPECIFICATIONS.

5) Apply 1/8" bead of RTV sealant on differential cover-to-transaxle case sealing surface. Install differential cover. Install and tighten bolts to specification. See TORQUE SPECIFICATIONS. Install NEW oil seal in extension housing (if removed).

TRANSFER SHAFT & TRANSFER GEAR

CAUTION: If transfer shaft, transfer gear, transaxle case or bearings are replaced, transfer shaft bearing preload must be checked. See TRANSFER SHAFT BEARING PRELOAD under BEARING ADJUSTMENTS.

1) Using transfer shaft remover/installer, install transfer shaft. Install bearing race, NEW "O" ring and baffle. Install transfer shaft bearing retaining snap ring in transaxle case.

2) Install bearing race retainer. Ensure notch in outer edge of bearing race retainer is aligned with notch in transaxle case. See Fig. 18. Install selective spacer or shim.

3) Using Gear Installer (6261), install transfer gear on transfer shaft. See Fig. 40. Install NEW nut and washer. Using gear holder, hold transfer gear and tighten nut to specification. See TORQUE SPECIFICATIONS.

VALVE BODY & INTERNAL COMPONENTS

CAUTION: If output gear, rear planetary carrier, transaxle case or bearings are replaced, output gear bearing preload must be checked. See OUTPUT GEAR BEARING PRELOAD under BEARING ADJUSTMENTS.

1) If installing NEW bearing on output gear, use press, Handle (C-4171) and Bearing Installer (5052) to install bearing. *See Fig. 21.* If installing NEW bearing on rear planetary carrier, use press and Bearing Installer (6053). *See Fig. 20.*

2) If installing NEW bearing races in transaxle case for rear planetary carrier and output gear, use Bearing Race Installer (5050) to install bearing races.

3) Install piston retainer gasket in transaxle case. Ensure holes in piston retainer gasket align with holes in transaxle case. Install low-reverse clutch piston retainer.

4) Install and tighten low-reverse clutch piston retainer screws to specification. See TORQUE SPECIFICATIONS. Install low-reverse clutch piston.

5) Ensure return spring is properly installed on parking sprag assembly. *See Fig. 45.* Install parking sprag assembly, pivot shaft, shaft and cup in transaxle.

CAUTION: Ensure sleeve at center of parking sprag assembly and parking sprag guide bracket contact rear of transaxle case.

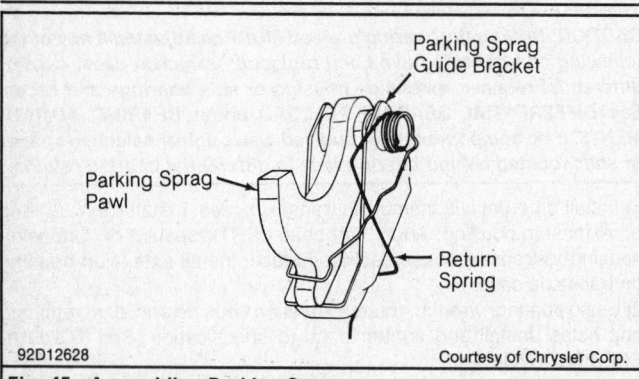

92D12628   Courtesy of Chrysler Corp.

Fig. 45: Assembling Parking Sprag

6) Install clutch piston return spring for low-reverse clutch piston in transaxle case. Using spring compressor and adapter, compress clutch assembly. Install snap ring. Ensure ends of snap ring are properly positioned. *See Fig. 19.*

7) Install rear planetary carrier in transaxle case. Install selective spacer or shim on rear planetary carrier. Install output gear using Gear Installer (6261) with stud. *See Fig. 40.* Output gear may also be referred to as transfer gear.

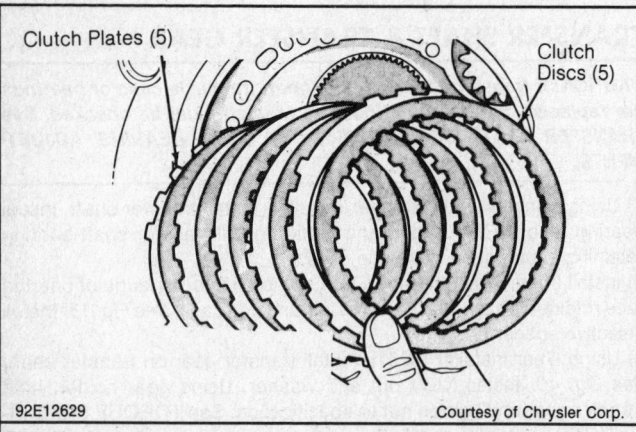

92E12629   Courtesy of Chrysler Corp.

Fig. 46: Installing Low-Reverse Clutch Plates & Clutch Discs

CAUTION: If output gear, rear planetary carrier, transaxle case or bearings are replaced, output gear bearing preload must be checked. See OUTPUT GEAR BEARING PRELOAD under BEARING ADJUSTMENTS.

8) Install NEW retaining bolt and washer. Using gear holder, hold output gear. Tighten retaining bolt to specification. See TORQUE SPECIFICATIONS.

9) Apply 1/8" bead of RTV sealant on end cover and install. Install and tighten end cover bolts to specification. See TORQUE SPECIFICATIONS. Install low-reverse clutch plates and clutch discs. *See Fig. 46.*

10) Install flat snap ring above top low-reverse clutch plate. Ensure ends of flat snap ring are positioned in proper area. *See Fig. 47.* Use care not to scratch clutch plate when installing flat snap ring.

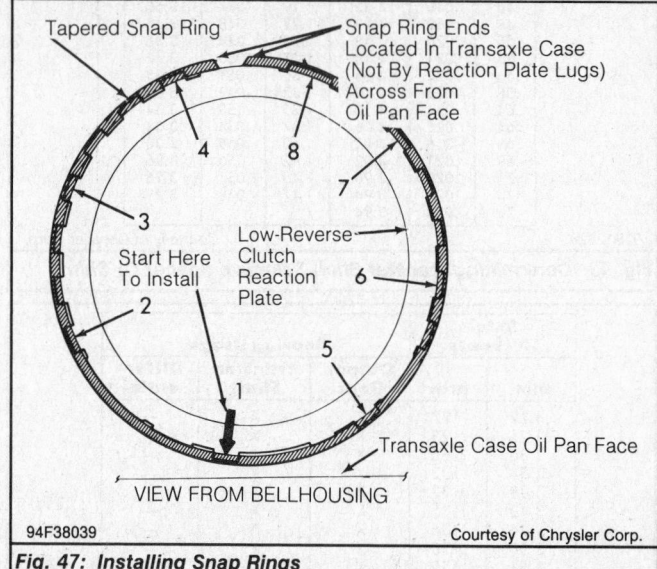

94F38039   Courtesy of Chrysler Corp.

Fig. 47: Installing Snap Rings

11) Install No. 1 low-reverse clutch disc. Install low-reverse clutch reaction plate. Install tapered snap ring above low-reverse clutch reaction plate with tapered side facing upward, toward oil pump. Ensure ends of tapered snap ring are positioned in proper area. *See Fig. 47.*

CAUTION: Low-reverse clutch clearance must be checked after installing clutch assembly.

12) To check low-reverse clutch clearance, assemble dial indicator and Dial Indicator Tip (6268) on transaxle case. *See Fig. 48.* Press low-reverse clutch pack downward and zero dial indicator. Using hook, pull No. 1 low-reverse clutch disc upward and note low-reverse clutch clearance on dial indicator.

13) Low-reverse clutch clearance should be .042-.065" (1.06-1.65 mm). If clearance is not within specification, install different thickness low-reverse clutch reaction plate. Low-reverse clutch reaction plate is available in the following thicknesses: .211" (5.36 mm), .221" (5.61 mm), .232" (5.89 mm), .242" (6.15 mm), .252" (6.40 mm), .262" (6.65 mm) and .273" (6.93 mm).

14) Install 2-4 clutch plates and clutch discs. *See Fig. 49.* Install 2-4 clutch piston return spring and 2-4 clutch retainer. Using spring compressor, compress 2-4 clutch assembly and install snap ring. *See Fig. 17.* Ensure ends of snap ring are positioned in proper area. *See Fig. 47.*

CAUTION: The 2-4 clutch clearance must be checked after installing clutch assembly.

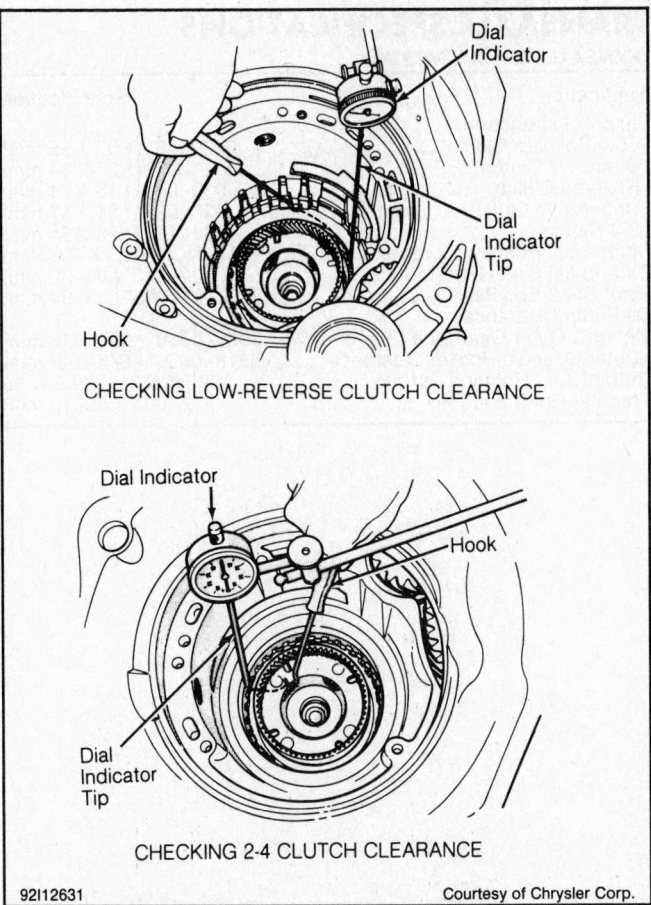

CHECKING LOW-REVERSE CLUTCH CLEARANCE

CHECKING 2-4 CLUTCH CLEARANCE

92I12631   Courtesy of Chrysler Corp.

Fig. 48: Checking Low-Reverse & 2-4 Clutch Clearances

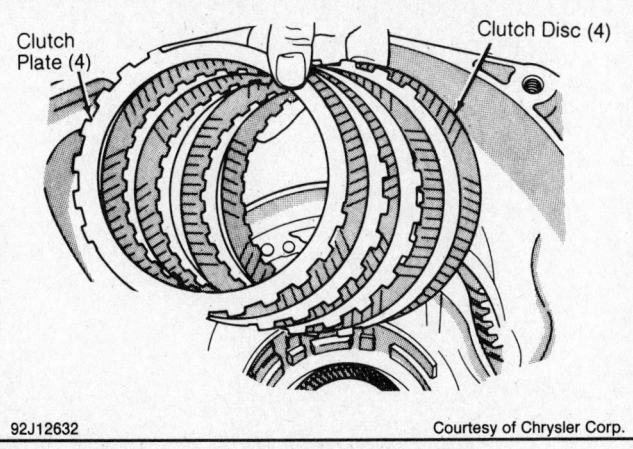

92J12632   Courtesy of Chrysler Corp.

Fig. 49: Installing 2-4 Clutch Plates & Clutch Discs

15) To check 2-4 clutch clearance, assemble dial indicator and Dial Indicator Tip (6268) on transaxle case. *See Fig. 48.* Press 2-4 clutch pack downward and zero dial indicator. Using hook, pull one 2/4 clutch disc upward and note 2-4 clutch clearance on dial indicator.
16) The 2-4 clutch clearance should be .030-.104" (.76-2.64 mm). If clearance is not within specification, check for improper installation of clutch components. There is no adjustment for 2-4 clutch clearance.
17) Install thrust bearing and rear sun gear. Install thrust bearing, rear annulus gear and front planetary carrier. *See Fig. 12.* Install 2-4 clutch hub and thrust washer. Thrust washer goes on oil pump end of transaxle case.

CAUTION: Correct thickness No. 4 thrust washer located on shaft end of overdrive clutch hub must be determined to maintain proper input shaft end play. See Fig. 50.

18) Apply petroleum jelly on overdrive clutch hub in 3 places. Install a .032-.040" (.81-1.02 mm) thick No. 4 thrust washer on overdrive clutch hub. *See Fig. 50.*
19) Install input clutch assembly. Ensure input clutch assembly is fully seated by looking through input speed sensor hole in transaxle case. If input clutch assembly is fully seated, input clutch retainer will be fully visible. *See Fig. 51.* If input clutch assembly is not fully seated, remove and check for improper installation.

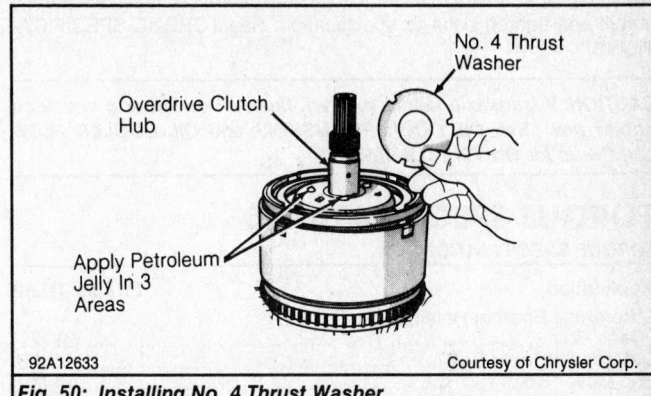

92A12633   Courtesy of Chrysler Corp.

Fig. 50: Installing No. 4 Thrust Washer

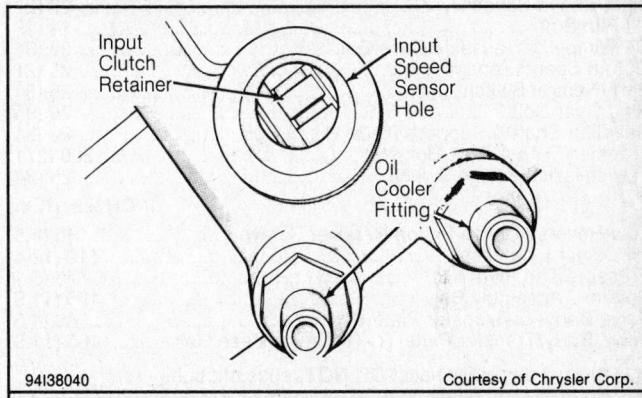

94I38040   Courtesy of Chrysler Corp.

Fig. 51: Checking Input Clutch Assembly Installation

20) Install gasket and oil pump. DO NOT install "O" ring on oil pump at this time. Install and tighten oil pump-to-transaxle case bolts to specification. See TORQUE SPECIFICATIONS.
21) Using dial indicator, check input shaft end play. Input shaft end play should be .005-.025" (.13-.64 mm). If input shaft end play is not within specification, change No. 4 thrust washer thickness to obtain correct input shaft end play.
22) For example, if input shaft end play is .055" (1.40 mm) with No. 4 thrust washer installed in step **18)**, select a thrust washer with thickness of .071-.074" (1.80-1.88 mm). Replace No. 4 washer with replacement thrust washer selection. This should change input shaft end play to .020" (.51 mm). The No. 4 thrust washer is available in thicknesses ranging from .032" (.81 mm) to .136" (3.45 mm). Consult manufacturers' parts department for available thrust washers.
23) Once proper input shaft end play is obtained, remove oil pump and gasket. Install NEW "O" ring on oil pump. Install oil cooler by-pass valve in transaxle case with "O" ring end toward rear (transfer gear end) of transaxle case. *See Fig. 15.*

CAUTION: If transaxle failure existed, DO NOT attempt to clean or reuse oil cooler by-pass valve. Replace oil cooler by-pass valve.

24) Install NEW gasket and oil pump. Tighten oil pump-to-transaxle case bolts to specification. See TORQUE SPECIFICATIONS. Ensure input shaft rotates smoothly.

25) Install accumulator pistons and springs using NEW seal rings. Install valve body. See VALVE BODY under REMOVAL & INSTALLATION.

26) Using NEW "O" rings, install and tighten input and output speed sensors to specification. See TORQUE SPECIFICATIONS.

27) Using NEW sealing washer, install park/neutral switch and transmission range switch. Ensure sealing washer is fully seated in transaxle case before tightening switch to specification. See TORQUE SPECIFICATIONS.

28) Using NEW solenoid assembly gaskets, install solenoid assembly. Install and tighten bolts to specification. See TORQUE SPECIFICATIONS.

CAUTION: If transaxle failure existed, flush oil cooler and check oil cooler flow. See OIL COOLER FLUSHING and OIL COOLER FLOW CHECK under ON-VEHICLE SERVICE.

TORQUE SPECIFICATIONS
TORQUE SPECIFICATIONS

Application	Ft. Lbs. (N.m)
Differential Bearing Retainer-To-Transaxle Case Bolt	21 (29)
Differential Cover Bolt	14 (19)
End Cover Bolt	14 (19)
Extension Housing-To-Transaxle Case Bolt	21 (29)
Input Speed Sensor	20 (27)
Oil Pan Bolt	14 (19)
Oil Pump-To-Transaxle Case Bolt	23 (31)
Output Speed Sensor	20 (27)
Park/Neutral Switch	25 (34)
Ring Gear Bolt [1]	70 (95)
Reaction Shaft & Support-To-Oil Pump Bolt	23 (31)
Transfer/Output Gear Bolt/Nut	200 (271)
Transmission Range Switch	25 (34)

	INCH lbs. (N.m)
Low-Reverse Clutch Piston Retainer Screw	40 (4.5)
Oil Cooler Line Fitting	110 (12.4)
Pressure Tap Plug	45 (5.1)
Solenoid Assembly Bolt	105 (11.9)
Valve Body-To-Transfer Plate Bolt	40 (4.5)
Valve Body/Transfer Plate-To-Transaxle Case Bolt	105 (11.9)

[1] – Always use NEW bolts. DO NOT reuse old bolts.

TRANSAXLE SPECIFICATIONS
TRANSAXLE SPECIFICATIONS

Application	Specification
Clutch Clearances	
Low-Reverse Clutch	.042-.065" (1.07-1.65 mm)
Overdrive Clutch	.042-.096" (1.07-2.44 mm)
Reverse Clutch	.030-.049" (.76-1.24 mm)
Underdrive Clutch	.036-.058" (.91-1.47 mm)
2-4 Clutch	.030-.104" (.76-2.64 mm)
Differential Rotating Torque	5-18 INCH lbs. (.6-2.0 N.m)
Differential Side Gear End Play	.001-.013" (.03-.33 mm)
Input Shaft End Play	.005-.025" (.13-.64 mm)
Oil Pump Clearances	
Inner & Outer Gear Side Clearance	.0008-.0018" (.020-.046 mm)
Outer Gear-To-Pocket Clearance	.0018-.0056" (.046-.142 mm)
Output Gear Rotating Torque	3-8 INCH lbs. (.3-.9 N.m)
Transfer Shaft End Play	.002-.004" (.05-.10 mm)

1993-94 APPLICATIONS

Model	Engine
Chrysler	
Passenger Cars	
1993 Fifth Avenue	3.3L & 3.8L
1993 Imperial	3.8L
1993 LeBaron Convertible/Coupe	3.0L
1994 LeBaron Convertible	3.0L
1993-94 LeBaron Sedan	3.0L
1993 New Yorker	3.3L
Vans	
1993 Town & Country [1]	3.3L
1994 Town & Country [1]	3.8L
Dodge	
Passenger Cars	
1993 Daytona	3.0L
1993 Dynasty	3.0L & 3.3L
1993-94 Shadow	3.0L
1993-94 Spirit	3.0L
Vans	
1993 Caravan [1]	3.0L & 3.3L
1994 Caravan	3.0L & 3.3L
1993 Grand Caravan [1]	3.0L & 3.3L
1994 Grand Caravan [1]	3.0L, 3.3L & 3.8L
Plymouth	
Passenger Cars	
1993-94 Acclaim	3.0L
1993-94 Sundance	3.0L
Vans	
1993 Voyager	[1] 3.0L & 3.3L
1994 Voyager	3.0L & 3.3L
1993 Grand Voyager [1]	3.0L & 3.3L
1994 Grand Voyager [1]	3.0L, 3.3L & 3.8L

[1] – Includes All-Wheel Drive (AWD) model.

NOTE: Vehicle body code may be required when diagnosing or repairing transaxle, as body code may be used instead of vehicle model name. See BODY CODE IDENTIFICATION table.

BODY CODE IDENTIFICATION

Model	Body Code
Acclaim, LeBaron Sedan & Spirit	AA
Caravan & Grand Caravan [1]	AS
Daytona	AG
Dynasty	AC
Fifth Avenue & Imperial	AY
LeBaron Convertible/Coupe	AJ
Shadow & Sundance	AP
Town & Country [1]	AS
New Yorker	AC
Voyager & Grand Voyager [1]	AS

[1] – Includes All-Wheel Drive (AWD) models.

DESCRIPTION

The 41TE/AE is an electronically controlled, 4-speed transaxle. Transaxle contains hydraulically operated clutches, which are controlled by the Transaxle Control Module (TCM). The TCM receives information from various inputs and uses this information to control solenoid assembly for proper transaxle operation.

NOTE: Transaxle Control Module (TCM) may also be referred to as the Transmission Control Module (TCM).

OPERATION

NOTE: If battery is disconnected or voltage supply to Transaxle Control Module (TCM) is lost, TCM will have to relearn shift characteristics. It may be necessary to perform shift quality quick-learn procedure so TCM can relearn shift characteristics. See SHIFT QUALITY QUICK-LEARN PROCEDURE in CHRYSLER 41TE/AE article.

CAUTION: If torque converter is replaced or Transaxle Control Module (TCM) is changed from one vehicle to another, proper procedure must be used to reset the break-in procedure in TCM for the Electronically Modulated Converter Clutch (EMCC) in torque converter to prevent shudder during torque converter clutch engagement for lock-up. Perform EMCC reset procedure. See ELECTRONICALLY MODULATED CONVERTER CLUTCH (EMCC) RESET PROCEDURE under TORQUE CONVERTER in CHRYSLER 41TE/AE article.

CAUTION: If Transaxle Control Module (TCM) is replaced or changed from one vehicle to another, proper procedure must be used to calibrate TCM for different equipment combinations to provide speedometer operation and correct readings. Failure to perform this procedure will result in no speedometer operation. See PINION FACTOR PROCEDURE in CHRYSLER 41TE/AE article.

TRANSAXLE CONTROL MODULE (TCM)

The TCM may receive signal data in 2 ways: directly from a sensor or component, or through a twisted-pair bus circuit, which connects all of the vehicle computer systems. This modulated bidirectional bus system is called Chrysler Collision Detection (CCD) bus and allows the various vehicle control modules to share signal data. *See Fig. 1.* If CCD bus failure exists, appropriate values are substituted by the TCM, allowing continued, but degraded operation.

Direct battery voltage is supplied to TCM. If TCM loses battery voltage, transaxle will enter limp-in mode. For additional information on limp-in mode, see LIMP-IN MODE under OPERATION. When TCM receives an ignition run signal from ignition switch, it performs a series of circuit and relay checks. If no problem is found, TCM provides voltage to transaxle control relay, causing contacts to close, supplying voltage to solenoid assembly.

NOTE: Transaxle control relay may also be referred to as "transmission control relay" or "trans. system relay".

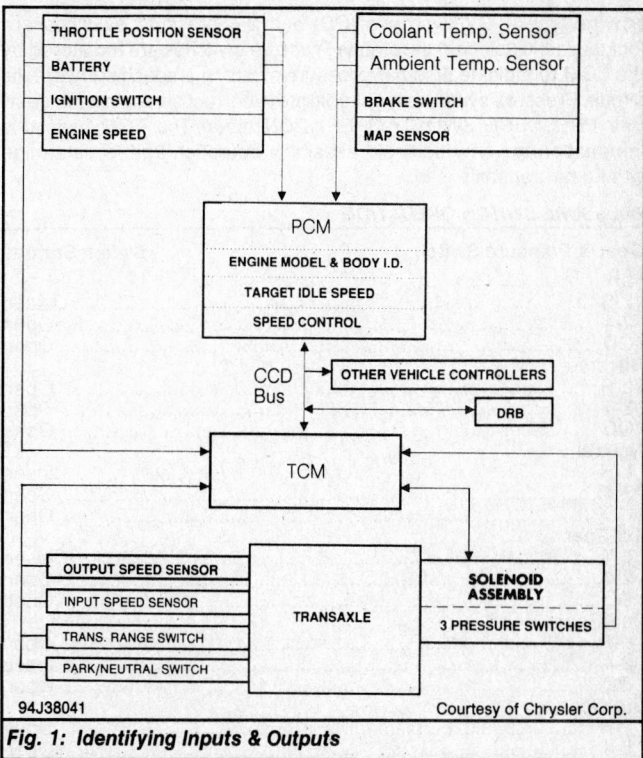

Fig. 1: Identifying Inputs & Outputs

The TCM contains a self-diagnostic system, which stores a diagnostic trouble code if transaxle failure exists. Diagnostic trouble code can be retrieved to identify transaxle problem areas. If malfunction goes away after diagnostic trouble code is stored in TCM memory, the TCM will erase diagnostic trouble code after ignition has been cycled at least 75 times.

The TCM contains an adaptive control method, which learns application and release rates of transaxle components for smooth operation. The TCM also learns the rate at which applied elements build pressure sufficient for a speed change.

LIMP-IN MODE

The TCM monitors transaxle for electrical or internal problems. If battery voltage is lost, or TCM senses a transaxle failure and diagnostic trouble code is set, the TCM de-energizes the transaxle control relay which then de-energizes the solenoid assembly. Transaxle then enters limp-in mode. In limp-in mode, only Park, Neutral, Reverse and 2nd gears function. Transaxle will not upshift or downshift. Vehicle can be operated, but performance will be reduced.

When ignition is turned off and the back on again, the TCM will reset for normal operation until it senses the failure again. Once failure is noted again, transaxle will enter limp-in mode.

NOTE: Transaxle will not enter limp-in mode when certain diagnostic trouble codes are set.

SOLENOID ASSEMBLY

NOTE: Solenoid assembly may be referred to as the solenoid pack. Transaxle control relay may be referred to as "transmission control relay" or "trans. system relay".

Solenoid assembly is controlled by the TCM. The TCM provides voltage to transaxle control relay, causing contacts to close, supplying voltage to solenoid assembly. Solenoid assembly, consisting of 4 electric solenoids, controls transaxle hydraulic circuits. The TCM completes the ground circuit, operating solenoid for proper hydraulic circuit control.

Low-reverse (L-R), overdrive (OD) and 2-4 pressure switches are located in the solenoid assembly. Pressure switches are monitored by the TCM to indicate whether pressure exists in a specified hydraulic circuit. Pressure switches must operate in correct status in each gear. See PRESSURE SWITCH OPERATION table. The TCM uses this information to verify solenoid assembly operation and to determine what gear transaxle is in.

PRESSURE SWITCH OPERATION

Gear & Pressure Switch	Switch Statues
Park	
L-R	Closed
2-4	Open
OD	Open
Reverse	
L-R	Open
2-4	Open
OD	Open
Neutral	
L-R	Closed
2-4	Open
OD	Open
1st Gear	
L-R	Closed
2-4	Open
OD	Open
2nd Gear	
L-R	Open
2-4	Closed
OD	Open
3rd Gear	
L-R	Open
2-4	Open
OD	Closed
4th Gear	
L-R	Open
2-4	Closed
OD	Closed

INPUT DEVICES

NOTE: Input devices supply information to Transaxle Control Module (TCM) or Powertrain Control Module (PCM) for transaxle control. Direct input devices provide input information to TCM and do not use CCD bus circuit. The CCD bus inputs use CCD bus circuit from PCM to TCM to supply information.

DIRECT INPUT DEVICES

Battery Supply Voltage – Battery supply voltage is sent, directly from battery by fuse or fusible link to Pin No. 56 of TCM.

Cranking Signal – Starter relay delivers a cranking signal to TCM to indicate engine is cranking.

Engine Speed Signal – The TCM uses a direct signal from distributor pick-up coil or crankshaft position sensor to determine engine RPM. The TCM uses the direct signal and compares it to the engine speed received from the Powertrain Control Module (PCM) by the CCD bus to confirm that direct engine speed signal is valid.

NOTE: The TCM uses a direct engine speed signal instead of using CCD bus signal to avoid any time delay that may occur when CCD bus circuit is used.

Ignition Signal – When ignition is turned to OFF, ON or START position, the TCM checks the incoming voltage. If voltage is less than specified or exceeds specified voltage, TCM will cause transaxle to enter limp-in mode to prevent damage to electrical components.

When ignition is turned on, TCM performs a series of circuit and relay checks. If no problem exists, TCM provides voltage to transaxle control relay, causing contacts to close, supplying voltage to solenoid assembly and pins No. 16 and 17 of TCM. Voltage supplied to pins No. 16 and 17 is referred to as switched battery voltage. If problem exists, TCM turns off power supply to transaxle control relay, which causes transaxle to enter limp-in mode.

Input Speed Sensor – Input speed sensor uses a magnetic pick-up coil to generate an AC voltage input signal when trigger teeth on input clutch assembly pass magnetic pick-up coil. The TCM uses input signal to determine input shaft speed.

Low-Reverse (L-R), Overdrive (OD) & 2-4 Pressure Switches – Pressure switches are located in solenoid assembly. Switches provide input information to TCM, indicating whether pressure exists in a specified hydraulic circuit. The TCM uses this information to verify solenoid assembly operation.

Overdrive Lock-Out Switch (1994 AS Bodies Only) – An overdrive lock-out switch is located on instrument panel. Overdrive lock-out switch delivers an input signal to TCM to prevent transaxle from shifting into overdrive.

Park/Neutral Position Switch & Transmission Range Switch – The TCM uses input signals from these switches to determine selected gear position. The TCM then selects gear and determines shift pattern. Switches are also used to activate starter relay and back-up lights and prevent starter engagement in any gear except Park or Neutral.

NOTE: If back-up lights are not working, perform TEST 38A under TROUBLE SHOOTING CHARTS.

Output Speed Sensor Signal – Output speed sensor uses a magnetic pick-up coil to generate an AC voltage input signal when trigger teeth on output shaft pass the magnetic pick-up coil. The TCM uses input signal to determine output shaft speed. The TCM compares output speed sensor signal against the input speed sensor signal to determine gear ratio and clutch slippage. Output speed sensor signal is also compared to throttle position sensor signal to determine transaxle shift points.

Output speed sensor signal is also used for determining vehicle speed. Vehicle speed signal is delivered from TCM to Powertrain Control Module (PCM). The PCM delivers vehicle speed signal on CCD bus for use by Body Control Module (BCM) if equipped and other vehicle control modules.

Throttle Position Sensor (TPS) – The TPS uses a 5-volt input voltage supplied by Powertrain Control Module (PCM). A common TPS return wire is connected to TCM and PCM. The TCM uses TPS reference signal to determine throttle position for controlling shift points, shift quality and torque converter clutch operation for lock-up.

CCD BUS INPUTS

NOTE: The following sensors or inputs deliver data to Powertrain Control Module (PCM), which then processes the data and sends signal on CCD bus circuit for use by other vehicle control modules.

Ambient Temperature Sensor – Ambient temperature sensor monitors intake air temperature. The PCM-supplied CCD bus signal is used by TCM to estimate transaxle fluid temperature. When TCM detects low temperatures, it adjusts transaxle operation to allow for slower response of the valves.

Brake Switch Input – Brake switch input signal is used by TCM to disengage torque converter clutch for lock-up when brakes are applied.

Coolant Temperature Sensor – Coolant temperature sensor indicates engine coolant temperature to the TCM. When engine coolant temperature is cold, TCM may delay upshifts slightly to improve driveability. The TCM prevents torque converter clutch for lock-up from engaging until engine reaches normal operating temperature. If engine coolant temperature becomes excessively warm, TCM engages torque converter clutch for lock-up to aid in engine cooling and prevent transaxle overheating.

Engine & Body ID – The Powertrain Control Module (PCM) transmits input information across CCD bus to the TCM for identifying engine size and body ID. The TCM uses input information for determining proper shift schedule.

Engine Speed Signal – The TCM uses a PCM-supplied CCD bus signal and compares it to the direct input signal to confirm that direct engine speed signal is valid.

Manifold Absolute Pressure (MAP) Sensor – The MAP sensor provides a PCM-supplied CCD bus signal to indicate engine load on input shaft and output torque load on output shaft. The TCM uses these input signals for modifying transaxle shifting and reduce 3-4 shift hunting on grades.

Target Idle Speed Signal – The TCM uses both direct engine idle speed input signal and calculated engine idle speed (target idle speed) from PCM-supplied CCD bus signal. Calculated engine idle speed is compared to actual engine idle speed to determine the learned Throttle Position Sensor (TPS) reading for closed throttle at idle.

Speed Control Switch – The TCM uses PCM-supplied CCD bus speed control switch signal from for controlling operation of torque converter clutch for lock-up and transaxle kickdown shifts.

OUTPUT DEVICES

NOTE: Output devices are devices or signals controlled by Transaxle Control Module (TCM) or Powertrain Control Module (PCM).

DIRECT OUTPUT DEVICES

NOTE: Direct output devices are devices that are controlled by Transaxle Control Module (TCM) or other control modules and do not use the CCD bus circuit.

Back-Up Light Relay — When Park/Neutral position switch is moved to Reverse gear position, the TCM selects Reverse gear and activates back-up light relay. Back-up light relay may also be referred to as back-up lamp relay.

Park/Neutral Signal – The Park/Neutral position switch on the transaxle provides an input signal to Powertrain Control Module (PCM), indicating when transaxle is in Park, Neutral or if a drive gear is selected. The PCM uses input signal for determining idle speed and ignition timing.

Solenoid Assembly – Solenoid assembly is controlled by the TCM. The TCM provides voltage to transaxle control relay, causing contacts to close, supplying voltage to solenoid assembly. Solenoid assembly controls transaxle hydraulic circuits. The TCM completes ground circuit, operating solenoid for proper hydraulic circuit control. Solenoid assembly may be referred to as solenoid pack.

Transaxle Control Relay – The TCM provides voltage to transaxle control relay, causing contacts to close, supplying voltage to solenoid assembly and pins No. 16 and 17 of TCM. Voltage supplied to pins No. 16 and 17 is referred to as switched battery voltage. The TCM uses pins No. 16 and 17 to monitor both the function of transaxle control relay and applied battery voltage.

Vehicle Speed Signal (VSS) – Output speed sensor signal is also used for determining vehicle speed and delivers signal to TCM. Vehicle speed signal is delivered from TCM to Powertrain Control Module (PCM). The PCM delivers vehicle speed signal across CCD bus for use by other vehicle control modules. The PCM uses vehicle speed signal and throttle position sensor input to determine when a deceleration condition exists.

CCD BUS OUTPUT SIGNALS

NOTE: The CCD bus output signals are controlled by CCD bus signal from PCM to the TCM.

CCD Bus Communications – The TCM outputs diagnostic data stream signals to the CCD bus circuit. These signals are received at data link connector by scan tools and diagnostic equipment.

SELF-DIAGNOSTIC SYSTEM

SYSTEM DIAGNOSIS

The Transaxle Control Module (TCM) monitors transaxle operation along with input and output information. If TCM self-diagnostic system senses a transaxle or electrical circuit failure, a diagnostic trouble code will be stored in TCM memory. If malfunction goes away after diagnostic trouble code is stored in TCM memory, TCM will erase diagnostic trouble code after ignition has been cycled at least 75 times. Diagnostic trouble codes are classified as either hard or intermittent codes.

Hard Code – Any diagnostic trouble code that returns within 3 ignition cycles is called a hard code. Hard code indicates that failure exists every time TCM checks the system.

Intermittent Code – An intermittent code is a diagnostic trouble code that occurs intermittently and is most likely caused by defective wiring or connections. Intermittent code indicates that failure does not exist every time TCM checks the system. Intermittent codes must be checked under conditions in which diagnostic trouble code would be set.

NOTE: A reset counter, located on Chrysler's Diagnostic Readout Box (DRB) scan tool, indicates number of engine starts since diagnostic trouble code was set. This aids in determining if diagnostic trouble code is a hard or intermittent code. If reset counter shows less than 3 engine starts, it indicates a hard code. If reset counter shows 3 or more engine starts, an intermittent code exists.

DIAGNOSTIC PROCEDURE

When performing vehicle diagnosis, ensure the following:
- Battery is fully charged.
- Transaxle fluid level is correct and not contaminated or aerated.
- Shift cable or linkage is properly adjusted.
- All electrical connections at transaxle switches/sensors, TCM, solenoid assembly, transaxle control relay and back-up light relays are clean and properly installed. *See Figs. 2-7.*
- Repair diagnostic trouble codes in the order displayed.
- Always perform VERIFICATION TEST after repair is completed. See TEST 40 under TROUBLE SHOOTING CHARTS.

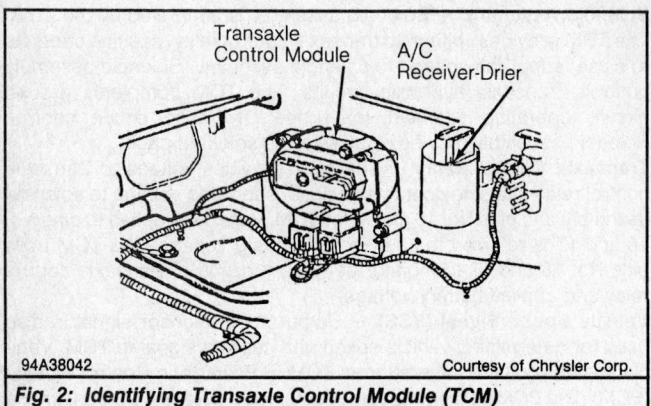

94A38042   Courtesy of Chrysler Corp.

Fig. 2: Identifying Transaxle Control Module (TCM) (AA, AC With 3.0L, AG, AJ & AP Bodies)

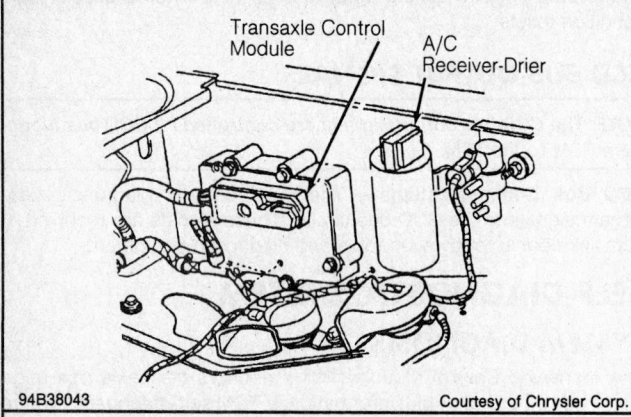

94B38043   Courtesy of Chrysler Corp.

Fig. 3: Identifying Transaxle Control Module (TCM) (AC & AY Bodies With 3.3L Or 3.8L)

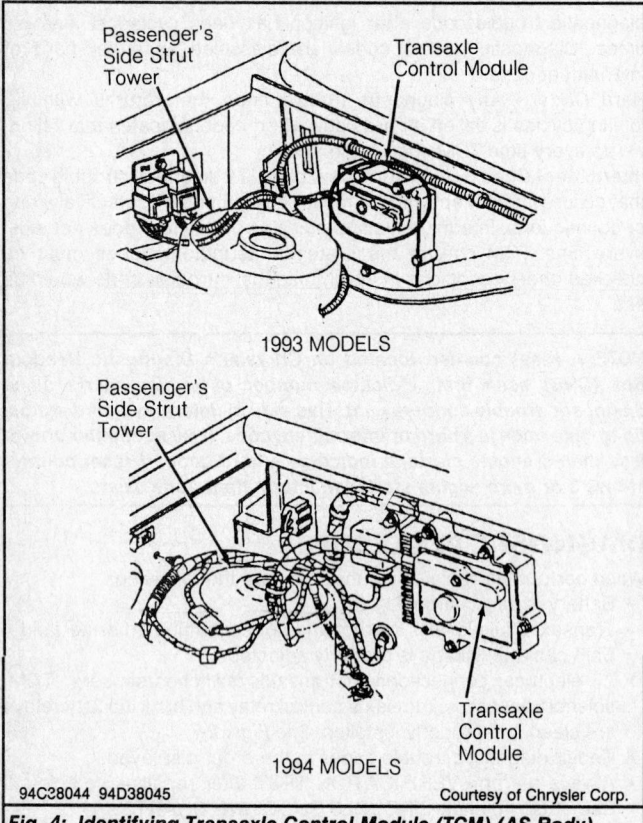

1993 MODELS

1994 MODELS

94C38044   94D38045   Courtesy of Chrysler Corp.

Fig. 4: Identifying Transaxle Control Module (TCM) (AS Body)

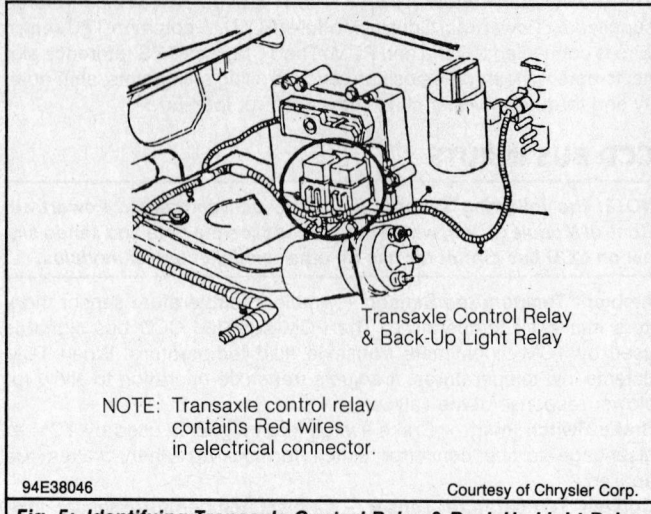

NOTE: Transaxle control relay contains Red wires in electrical connector.

94E38046   Courtesy of Chrysler Corp.

Fig. 5: Identifying Transaxle Control Relay & Back-Up Light Relay (AA, AG, AJ & AP Bodies)

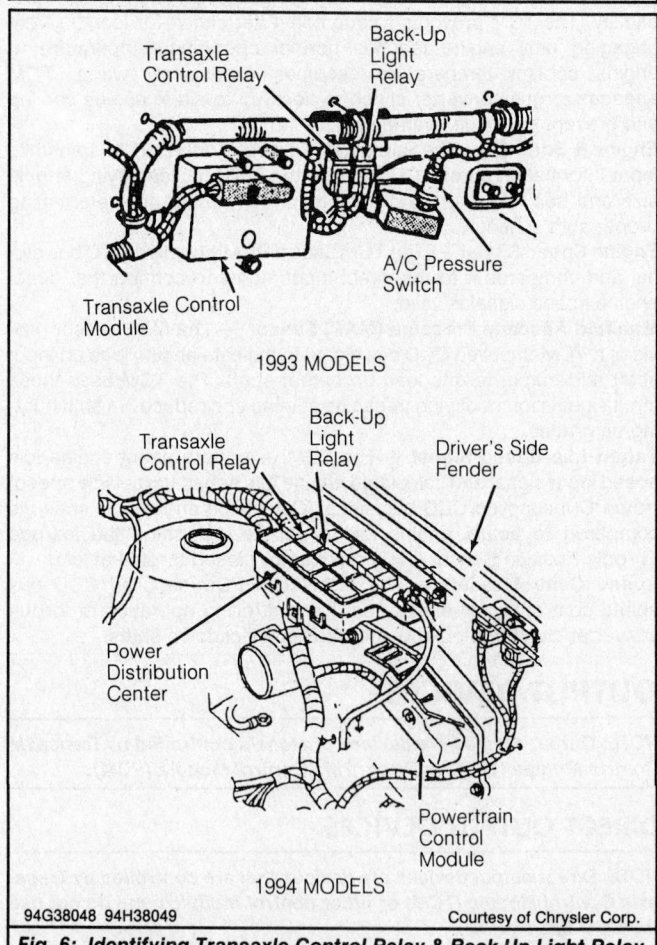

1993 MODELS

1994 MODELS

94G38048   94H38049   Courtesy of Chrysler Corp.

Fig. 6: Identifying Transaxle Control Relay & Back-Up Light Relay (AS Bodies)

NOTE: The DRB scan tool can be used in several different modes using manufacturer's instructions to activate system components and perform several tests on transaxle. Use following procedures if retrieving diagnostic trouble codes using DRB scan tool.

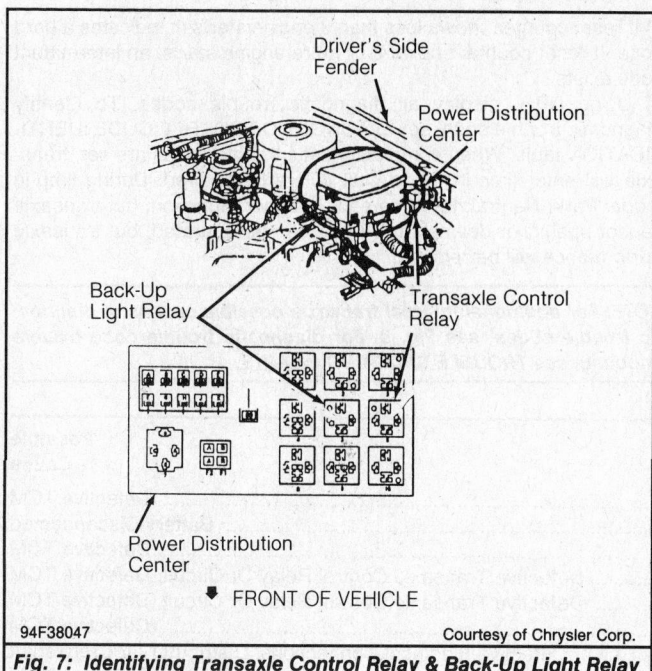

Fig. 7: Identifying Transaxle Control Relay & Back-Up Light Relay (AC & AY Bodies)

94F38047   Courtesy of Chrysler Corp.

RETRIEVING DIAGNOSTIC TROUBLE CODES

NOTE: Manufacturer recommends using Chrysler's Diagnostic Readout Box (DRB) scan tool with proper cartridge for system diagnosis. Other after-market scan tools may be used for system diagnosis. Following procedure is for DRB scan tool usage. Use manufacturer's instruction for operating the DRB scan tool.

1) Ensure ignition is off. Connect DRB to data link connector located under left side of instrument panel. See Fig. 9.
2) Enter diagnostics and perform CCD bus test. See TEST 1A – ENTERING DIAGNOSTICS & CCD BUS TEST under TROUBLE SHOOTING CHARTS.

NOTE: For additional internal transaxle possible causes of diagnostic trouble codes, see Fig. 8. For diagnostic trouble code trouble shooting, see TROUBLE SHOOTING CHARTS.

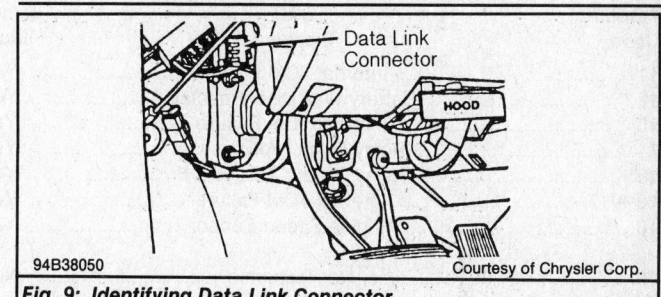

94B38050   Courtesy of Chrysler Corp.

Fig. 9: Identifying Data Link Connector

POSSIBLE CAUSE

Possible Cause	21	22	23	24	25	26	27	31	32	33	37	38	47	50	51	52	53	54	60	61	62
Low fluid level	X	X	X	X	X	X	X	X	X	X				X	X	X	X	X			
Aeroled fluid (high fluid level)	X	X	X	X	X	X	X	X	X	X											
Worn or damaged reaction shaft support seal rings	X													X	X	X	X	X			
Worn or damaged input shaft seal rings												X		X	X	X	X	X			
Worn pump	X	X	X	X	X	X	X	X	X	X				X	X	X	X	X			
Damaged or failed clutches:																					
UD clutch														X	X	X					
OD clutch	X						X								X	X					X
Reverse clutch														X							
2/4 clutch		X					X									X		X		X	
L/R clutch				X											X				X		
Damaged clutch seals	X	X	X	X	X	X	X							X	X	X	X	X	X	X	X
Worn or damaged accumulator seal rings	X	X	X	X	X	X	X							X	X	X	X	X	X	X	X
Plugged filter	X	X	X	X	X	X	X					X		X	X	X					
Stuck/sticky valves	X	X	X	X	X	X	X				X	X	X	X	X	X	X	X			
Solenoid switch valve											X		X								
Torque converter clutch switch valve												X									
Torque converter control valve												X									
Regulator valve	X	X	X	X	X	X	X							X	X	X	X	X			X
Valve body leakage	X	X	X	X	X	X	X	X	X	X			X	X	X	X	X	X			
Pressures too high	X	X	X	X	X	X	X					X		X	X	X	X	X			
Internal solenoid leak	X	X	X	X	X	X	X	X	X	X			X	X	X	X	X	X			
Torque converter clutch failure	X	X	X	X	X	X	X					X									
Faulty cooling system	X	X	X	X	X	X	X							X	X	X					
Planetary gear sets broken or seized														X	X	X	X	X	X	X	X

NOTE:
Code 36 is not stored alone. It is stored if a speed error (codes 50 through 58) is detected immediately after a shift. Look at the possible causes associated with the speed error code.

Code Number — Condition:

Code Number	Condition
21	OD clutch—pressure too low
22	2/4 clutch—pressure too low
23	2/4 clutch and OD clutch pressures too low
24	L/R clutch—pressure too low
25	L/R clutch and OD clutches pressures too low
26	L/R clutch and 2/4 clutches pressures too low
27	OD, 2/4, and L/R clutches pressures too low
31	OD clutch pressure switch response failure
32	2/4 pressure switch response failure
33	2/4 and O/D clutch pressure response failures
37	Solenoid switch valve stuck in the LO position
38	Partial torque converter clutch out of range
47	Solenoid switch valve stuck in the LR position
50	Speed ratio default in reverse
51	Speed ratio default in 1st
52	Speed ratio default in 2nd
53	Speed ratio default in 3rd
54	Speed ratio default in 4th
60	Inadequate LR element volume
61	Inadequate 2/4 element volume
62	Inadequate OD element volume

94C38051   Courtesy of Chrysler Corp.

Fig. 8: Identifying Internal Transaxle Possible Causes Of Diagnostic Trouble Codes

3) If an error message appears on DRB, proceed to DRB PROBLEMS & ERROR MESSAGES. The following are possible error messages that may appear.
- CARTRIDGE ERROR
- HIGH BATTERY
- KEYPAD TEST FAILURE
- LOW BATTERY
- RAM TEST FAILURE

4) If no error message appears, retrieve diagnostic trouble codes using DRB manufacturer's instructions. Note diagnostic trouble code display and reset counter display.

5) Reset counter indicates number of engine starts since trouble code was set. This helps determine if a hard or intermittent diagnostic trouble code exists.

6) If reset counter shows less than 3 engine starts, it indicates a hard code. If reset counter shows 3 or more engine starts, an intermittent code exists.

7) Using DRB, display all diagnostic trouble codes. To identify diagnostic trouble code, see DIAGNOSTIC TROUBLE CODE IDENTIFICATION table. When some diagnostic trouble codes are set, transaxle will enter limp-in mode until failure is repaired. During limp-in mode, Park, Neutral, Reverse and 2nd gears function, but transaxle cannot upshift or downshift. Vehicle can be operated, but transaxle performance will be reduced.

NOTE: For additional internal transaxle possible causes of diagnostic trouble codes, see Fig. 9. For diagnostic trouble code trouble shooting, see TROUBLE SHOOTING CHARTS.

DIAGNOSTIC TROUBLE CODE IDENTIFICATION (1 OF 2)

Trouble Code	DRB Display [1]	Limp-In Mode	Possible Cause
11	Internal TCM Failure	Yes	Defective TCM
12 [2]	Battery Was Disconnected	Yes	Battery Disconnected
13	Internal TCM Failure	Yes	Defective TCM
14	Relay Output Always On	Yes	Defective Transaxle Control Relay Or Circuit, Defective TCM
15	Relay Output Always Off	Yes	Defective Transaxle Control Relay Or Circuit, Defective TCM
16 & 17	Internal TCM Failure	Yes	Defective TCM
18	Engine Speed Sensor	Yes	Defective Electrical Connections, Distributor Or Crankshaft Position Sensor, Defective TCM
19	No Response	No [3]	Defective CCD Bus Circuit Between TCM & PCM, Defective TCM Or PCM
20	Switched Battery	Yes	Defective Transaxle Control Relay, Short To Battery Voltage On Transaxle Control Relay Circuit, Defective TCM
21	OD Pressure Switch Circuit	Yes	Improper Transaxle Fluid Level, Defective Pressure Switch Circuit, Defective Pressure Switch In Solenoid Assembly, Defective Transaxle Controller, Internal Transaxle Failure
22	2-4 Pressure Switch Circuit	Yes	Improper Transaxle Fluid Level, Defective Pressure Switch Circuit, Defective Pressure Switch In Solenoid Assembly, Defective Transaxle Controller, Internal Transaxle Failure
23	2-4/OD Pressure Switch Circuit	Yes	Improper Transaxle Fluid Level, Defective Pressure Switch Circuit, Defective Pressure Switch In Solenoid Assembly, Defective Transaxle Controller, Internal Transaxle Failure
24	LR Pressure Switch Circuit	Yes	Improper Transaxle Fluid Level, Defective Pressure Switch Circuit, Defective Pressure Switch In Solenoid Assembly, Defective Transaxle Controller, Internal Transaxle Failure
25	LR/OD Pressure Switch Circuit	Yes	Improper Transaxle Fluid Level, Defective Pressure Switch Circuit, Defective Pressure Switch In Solenoid Assembly, Defective Transaxle Controller, Internal Transaxle Failure
26	LR/2-4 Pressure Switch Circuit	Yes	Improper Transaxle Fluid Level, Defective Pressure Switch Circuit, Defective Pressure Switch In Solenoid Assembly, Defective Transaxle Controller, Internal Transaxle Failure
27	All Pressure Switch Circuits	Yes	Improper Transaxle Fluid Level, Defective Pressure Switch Circuit, Defective Pressure Switch In Solenoid Assembly, Defective Transaxle Controller, Internal Transaxle Failure
28	Check Shifter Signal	No [4]	Defective Park/Neutral Position Switch Or Circuit, Defective TCM Defective Transmission Range Switch Or Circuit, Defective Or Disconnected Back-Up Light Relay Open Or Shorted Starter Relay Ground Circuit
29	Throttle Position Signal	No [5]	Defective Throttle Position Sensor Or Circuit, Defective TCM Or PCM

[1] – When using DRB, display may show LR, OD or UD. The LR indicates low-reverse, OD indicates overdrive and UD indicates underdrive.

[2] – This is not a trouble code to indicate a transaxle problem. This trouble code is used for reference information only to indicate if battery was disconnected.

[3] – For a few minutes after engine is started, transaxle may have a delayed 3-4 upshift, early 4-3 downshift and no torque converter clutch operation for lock-up.

[4] – No limp-in mode is caused by this diagnostic trouble code. If incorrect gearshift lever signals are received, this may result in other diagnostic trouble codes which may cause a limp-in mode.

[5] – No limp-in mode is caused by this diagnostic trouble code. If diagnostic trouble code exists, there will be no torque converter clutch operation for lock-up, no 4th gear and a limited shift schedule.

DIAGNOSTIC TROUBLE CODE IDENTIFICATION (2 OF 2)

Trouble Code	DRB Display [1]	Limp-In Mode	Possible Cause
31	OD Hydraulic Pressure Switch	Yes	Improper Transaxle Fluid Level, Defective Solenoid Assembly, Internal Transaxle Failure
32	2-4 Hydraulic Pressure Switch	Yes	Improper Transaxle Fluid Level, Defective Solenoid Assembly, Internal Transaxle Failure
33	OD/2-4 Hydraulic Pressure Switch	Yes	Improper Transaxle Fluid Level, Defective Solenoid Assembly, Internal Transaxle Failure
35	Loss Of Prime	No	Low Transaxle Fluid Level, Defective Or Restricted Oil Filter, Missing Oil Filter "O" Ring, Defective Oil Cooler Line Fittings
36 [2]	Fault Immediately After Shift	Yes	Internal Transaxle Failure
37	Solenoid Switch Valve In LU Position	No [3]	Internal Transaxle Failure
38	Torque Converter Clutch Control	No [4]	Improper Transaxle Fluid Level, Internal Transaxle Failure
41	LR Solenoid Circuit	Yes	Defective Solenoid Assembly Or Circuit, Defective TCM
42	2-4 Solenoid Circuit	Yes	Defective Solenoid Assembly Or Circuit, Defective TCM
43	OD Solenoid Circuit	Yes	Defective Solenoid Assembly Or Circuit, Defective TCM
44	UD Solenoid Circuit	Yes	Defective Solenoid Assembly Or Circuit, Defective TCM
45	Internal TCM Failure	No	Defective TCM
46	UD Hydraulic Circuit	No	Internal Transaxle Failure
47	Solenoid Switch Valve In LR Position	Yes	Internal Transaxle Failure
50	Speed Error In Reverse	Yes	Defective Input Or Output Speed Sensor Or Circuit, Defective TCM, Internal Transaxle Failure
51	Speed Error In 1st	Yes	Defective Input Or Output Speed Sensor Or Circuit, Defective TCM, Internal Transaxle Failure
52	Speed Error In 2nd	Yes	Internal Transaxle Failure
53	Speed Error In 3rd	Yes	Internal Transaxle Failure
54	Speed Error In 4th	Yes	Internal Transaxle Failure
56	Input Speed Sensor	Yes	Defective Input Speed Sensor Or Circuit, Defective TCM
57	Output Speed Sensor Error	Yes	Defective Output Sensor Or Circuit, Defective TCM
58	Speed Sensor's Ground	Yes	Open In Output Speed Sensor Ground Circuit, Defective TCM
60 [5]	Inadequate LR Element Volume	No	Internal Transaxle Failure
61 [6]	Inadequate 2-4 Element Volume	No	Internal Transaxle Failure
62 [7]	Inadequate OD Element Volume	No	Internal Transaxle Failure

[1] – When using DRB, display may show LR, OD or UD. The LR indicates low-reverse, OD indicates overdrive and UD indicates underdrive.

[2] – Diagnostic trouble code will not be stored alone. Diagnostic trouble Code 36 is stored if a speed error code (Codes 50-58) is detected.

[3] – No limp-in mode is caused by this diagnostic trouble code. If diagnostic trouble code exists, there will be no 1st gear, as 2nd gear is substituted and no torque converter clutch operation for lock-up.

[4] – No limp-in mode is caused by this diagnostic trouble code. If diagnostic trouble code exists, there will be no torque converter clutch operation for lock-up.

[5] – Typical clutch volume for LR (low-reverse) clutch is 35-83.

[6] – Typical clutch volume for 2-4 clutch is 20-77.

[7] – Typical clutch volume for OD (overdrive) clutch is 75-150.

CLEARING DIAGNOSTIC TROUBLE CODES

After repairs have been performed, use DRB and manufacturer's instructions to clear or erase diagnostic trouble code from TCM memory.

NOTE: If malfunction goes away after diagnostic trouble code is stored in TCM memory, TCM will erase diagnostic trouble code after ignition has been cycled at least 75 times.

TESTING

For non-electrical testing and mechanical overhaul procedures, see CHRYSLER 41TE/AE article. For electronic component testing and diagnostic procedures, use a DRB scan tool to retrieve diagnostic trouble codes and diagnosis the system. See RETRIEVING DIAGNOSTIC TROUBLE CODES under SELF-DIAGNOSTIC SYSTEM.

DRB PROBLEMS & ERROR MESSAGES

CARTRIDGE ERROR

1) If CARTRIDGE ERROR message is displayed, disconnect DRB from data link connector. DO NOT touch keys on DRB keypad. Reconnect DRB to data link connector and note display.

2) If CARTRIDGE ERROR message is displayed, replace DRB cartridge, and proceed with diagnostics. If KEYPAD TEST FAILURE message is displayed, replace DRB and proceed with diagnostics.

HIGH BATTERY

If HIGH BATTERY message is displayed, use external voltmeter to check battery voltage at battery terminals. If battery voltage is 11.7-13.0 volts, replace DRB. If battery voltage is not 11.7-13.0 volts, check charging system.

KEYPAD TEST FAILURE

1) If KEYPAD TEST FAILURE message is displayed, disconnect DRB from data link connector. DO NOT touch keys on DRB keypad. Reconnect DRB to data link connector and note display.

2) If KEYPAD TEST FAILURE message is not displayed, proceed with diagnostics. If KEYPAD TEST FAILURE message is displayed, replace DRB and proceed with diagnostics.

LOW BATTERY

If LOW BATTERY message is displayed, use external voltmeter to check battery voltage at battery terminals. If battery voltage is 11.7-13.0 volts, replace DRB. If battery voltage is not 11.7-13.0 volts, check charging system.

RAM TEST FAILURE

1) If RAM TEST FAILURE message is displayed, disconnect DRB from data link connector. DO NOT touch keys on DRB keypad. Reconnect DRB to data link connector and note display.

2) If RAM TEST FAILURE message is not displayed, proceed with diagnostics. If RAM TEST FAILURE message is displayed, replace DRB and proceed with diagnostics. If KEYPAD TEST FAILURE message is displayed, replace DRB and proceed with diagnostics.

TROUBLE SHOOTING CHARTS

NOTE: The following trouble shooting charts and illustrations are courtesy of Chrysler Corp.

NOTE: When using trouble shooting charts, solenoid assembly may be referred to as the solenoid pack. Transaxle control module may be referred to as "transmission control module". Transaxle control relay may be referred to as "trans. control relay". It may be necessary to consult figs. 2-7 for component location when using trouble shooting charts.

NOTE: If back-up lights are not working, perform TEST 38A under TROUBLE SHOOTING CHARTS.

WIRING DIAGRAMS

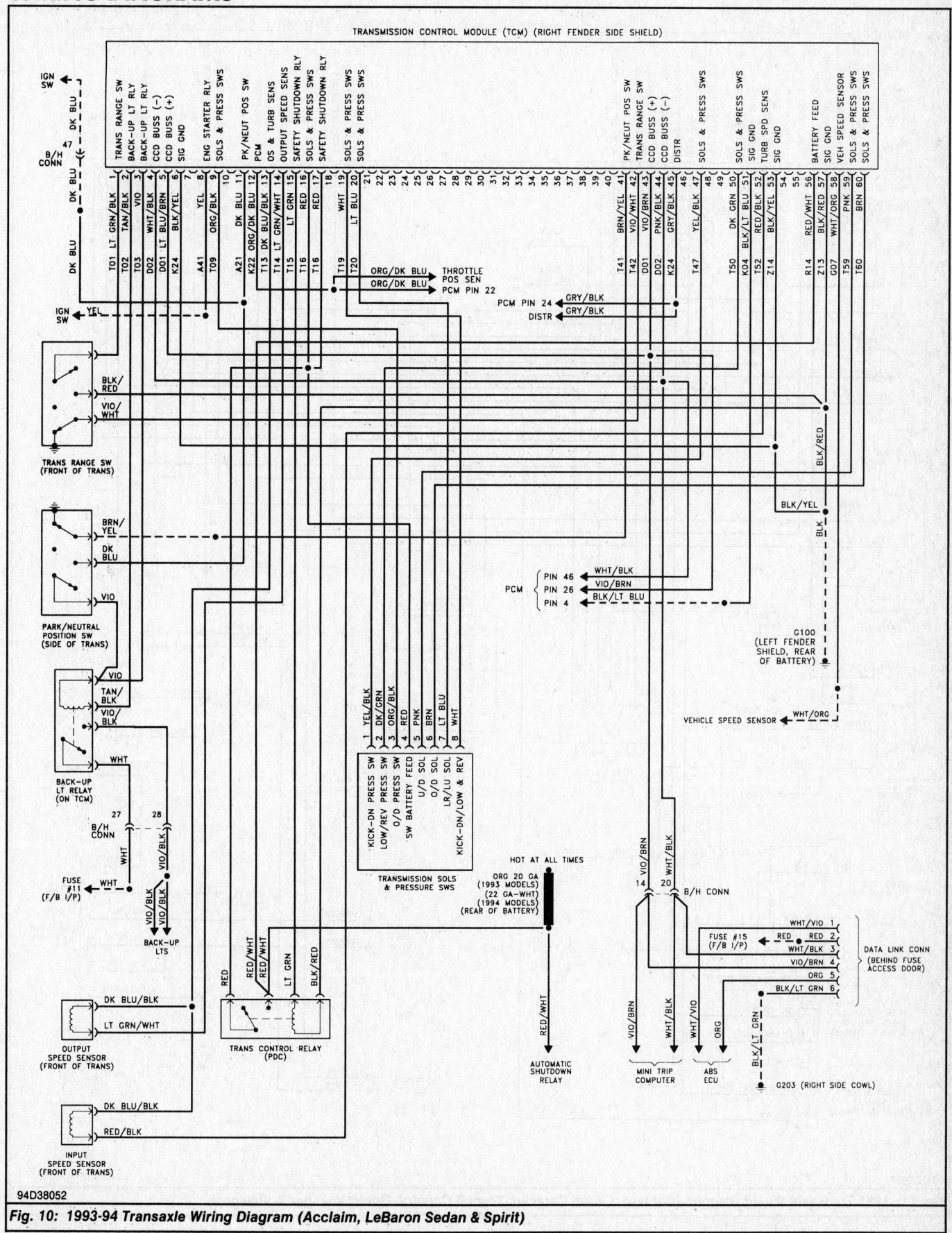

94D38052

Fig. 10: 1993-94 Transaxle Wiring Diagram (Acclaim, LeBaron Sedan & Spirit)

AUTOMATIC TRANSMISSIONS
Chrysler 41TE/AE Electronic Diagnosis (Cont.)

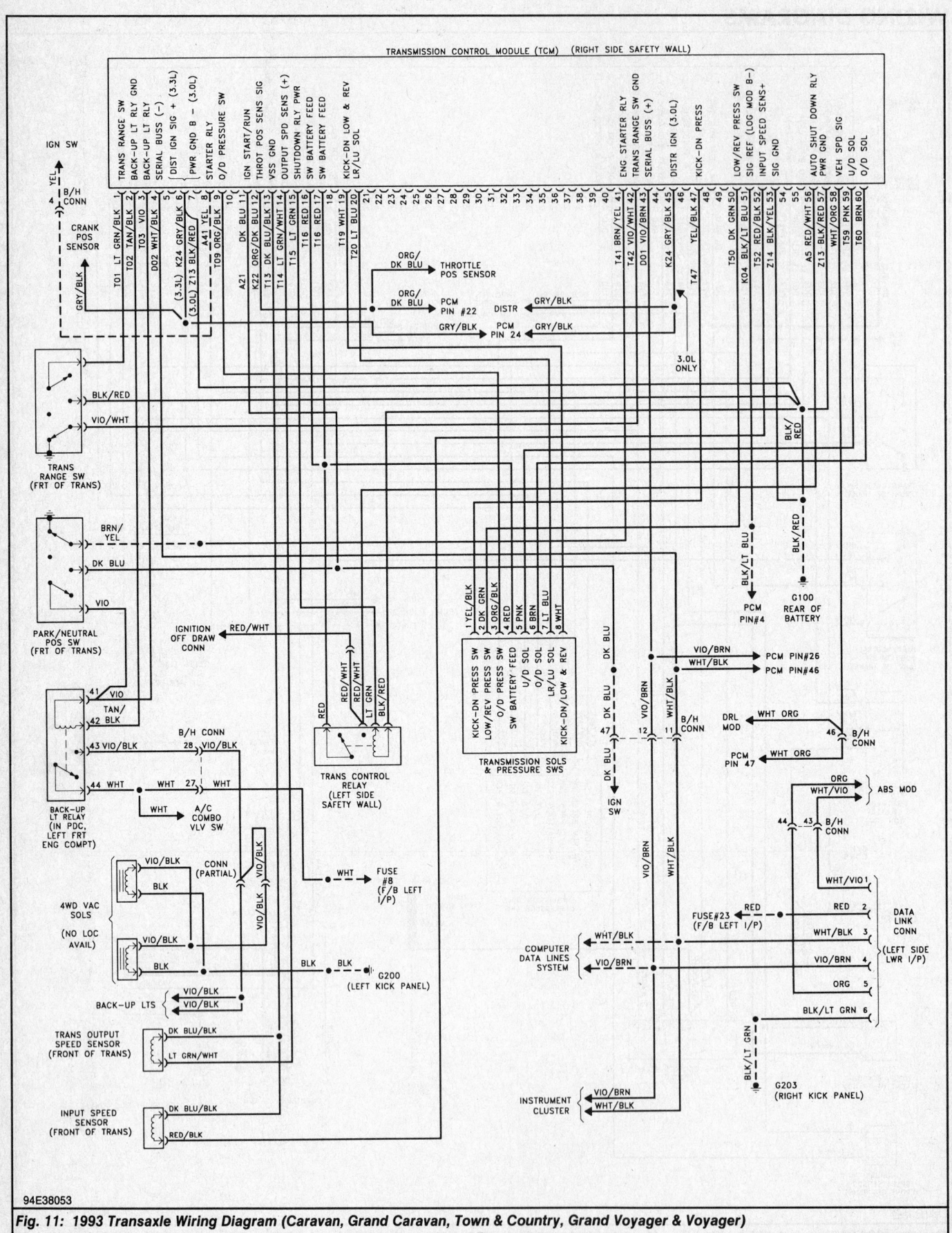

Fig. 11: 1993 Transaxle Wiring Diagram (Caravan, Grand Caravan, Town & Country, Grand Voyager & Voyager)

94E38053

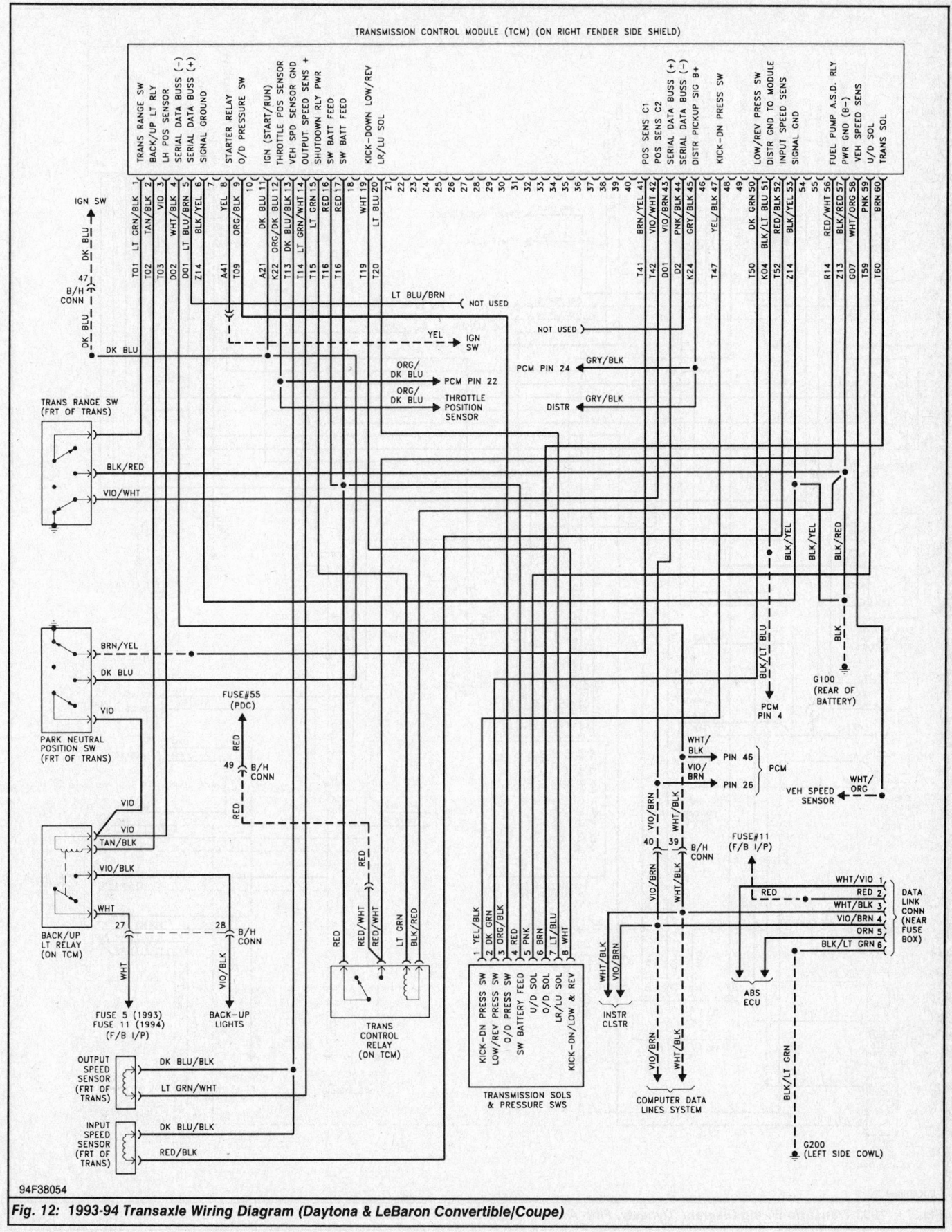

Fig. 12: 1993-94 Transaxle Wiring Diagram (Daytona & LeBaron Convertible/Coupe)

94F38054

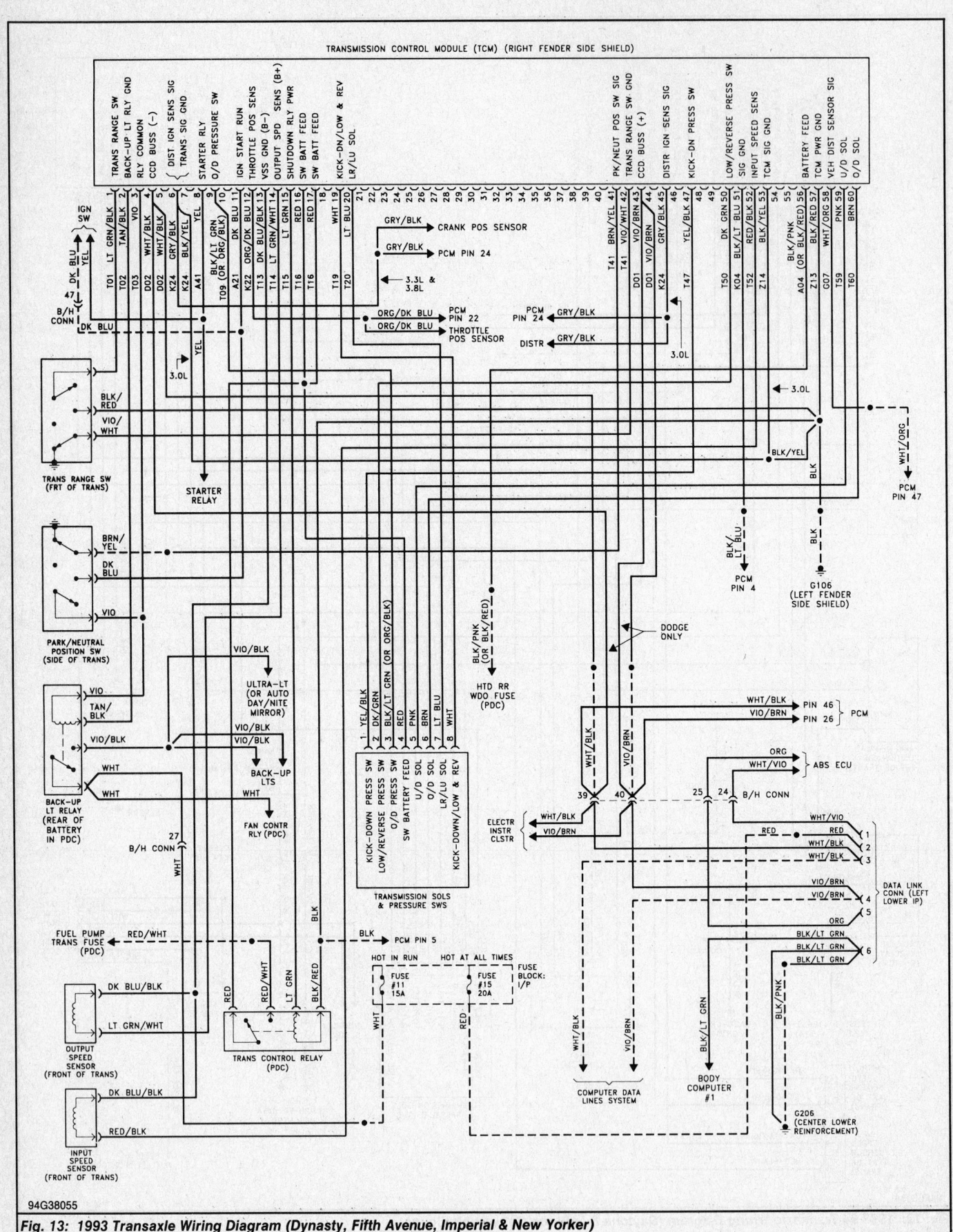

94G38055

Fig. 13: 1993 Transaxle Wiring Diagram (Dynasty, Fifth Avenue, Imperial & New Yorker)

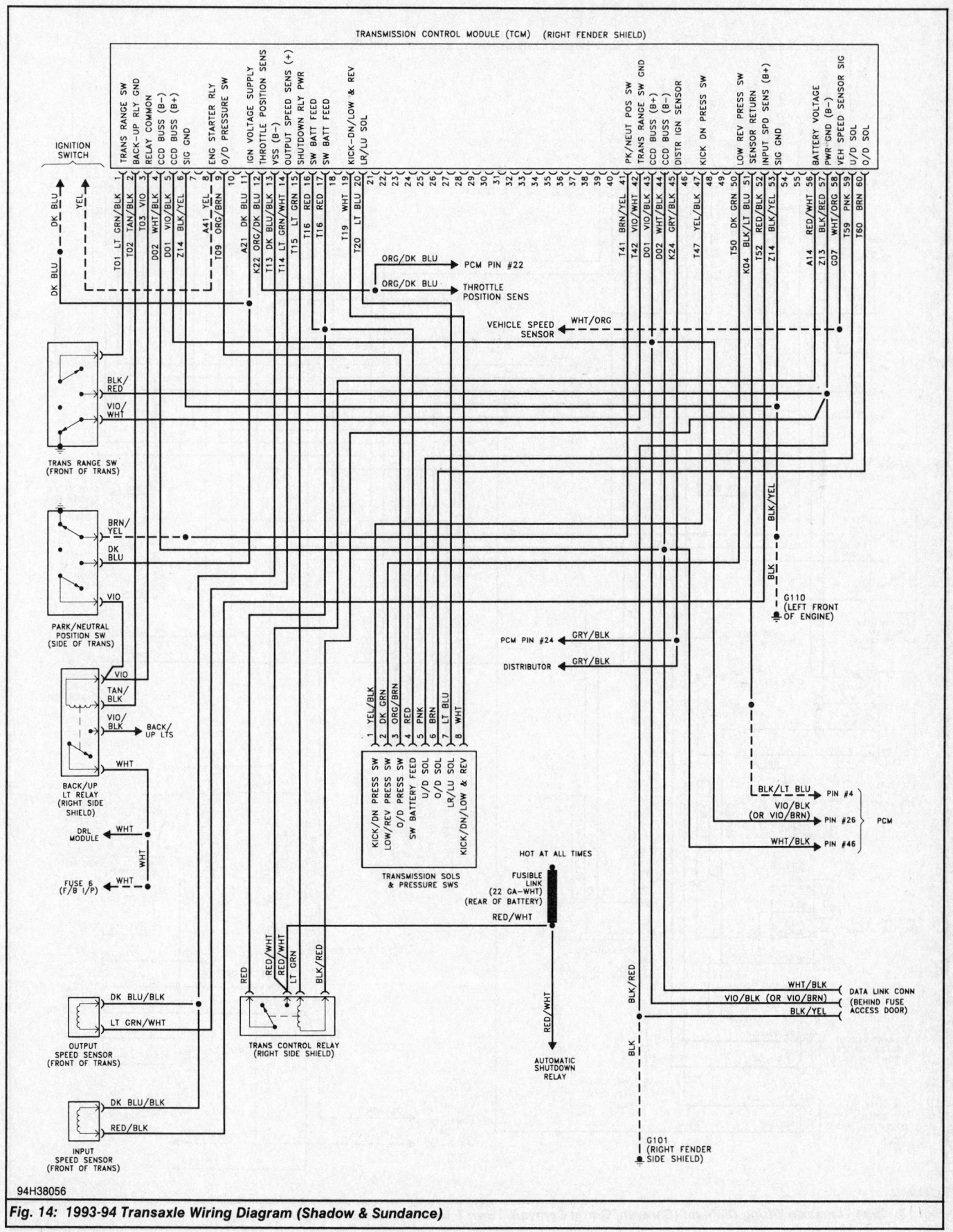

Fig. 14: 1993-94 Transaxle Wiring Diagram (Shadow & Sundance)

94H38056

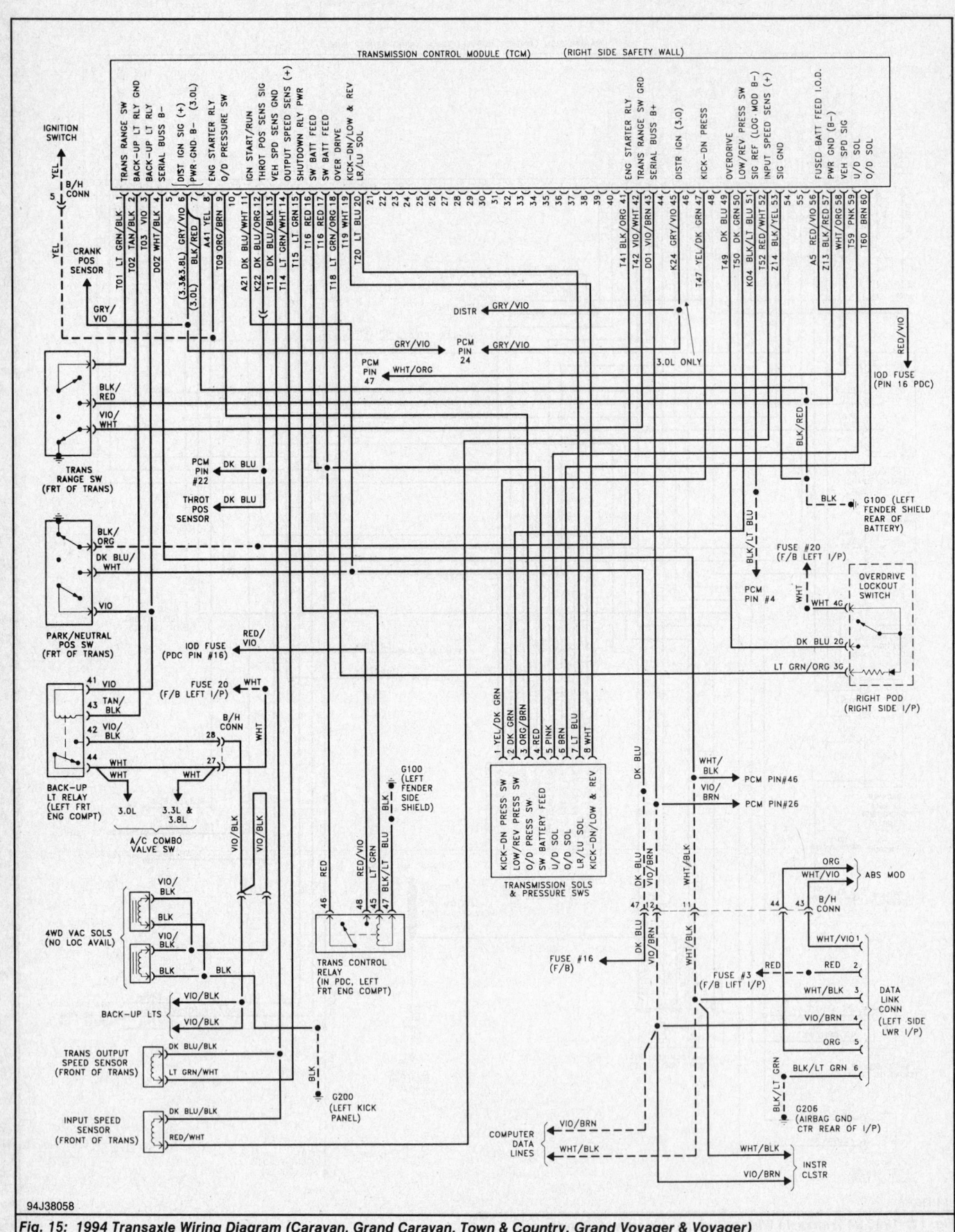

Fig. 15: 1994 Transaxle Wiring Diagram (Caravan, Grand Caravan, Town & Country, Grand Voyager & Voyager)

94J38058

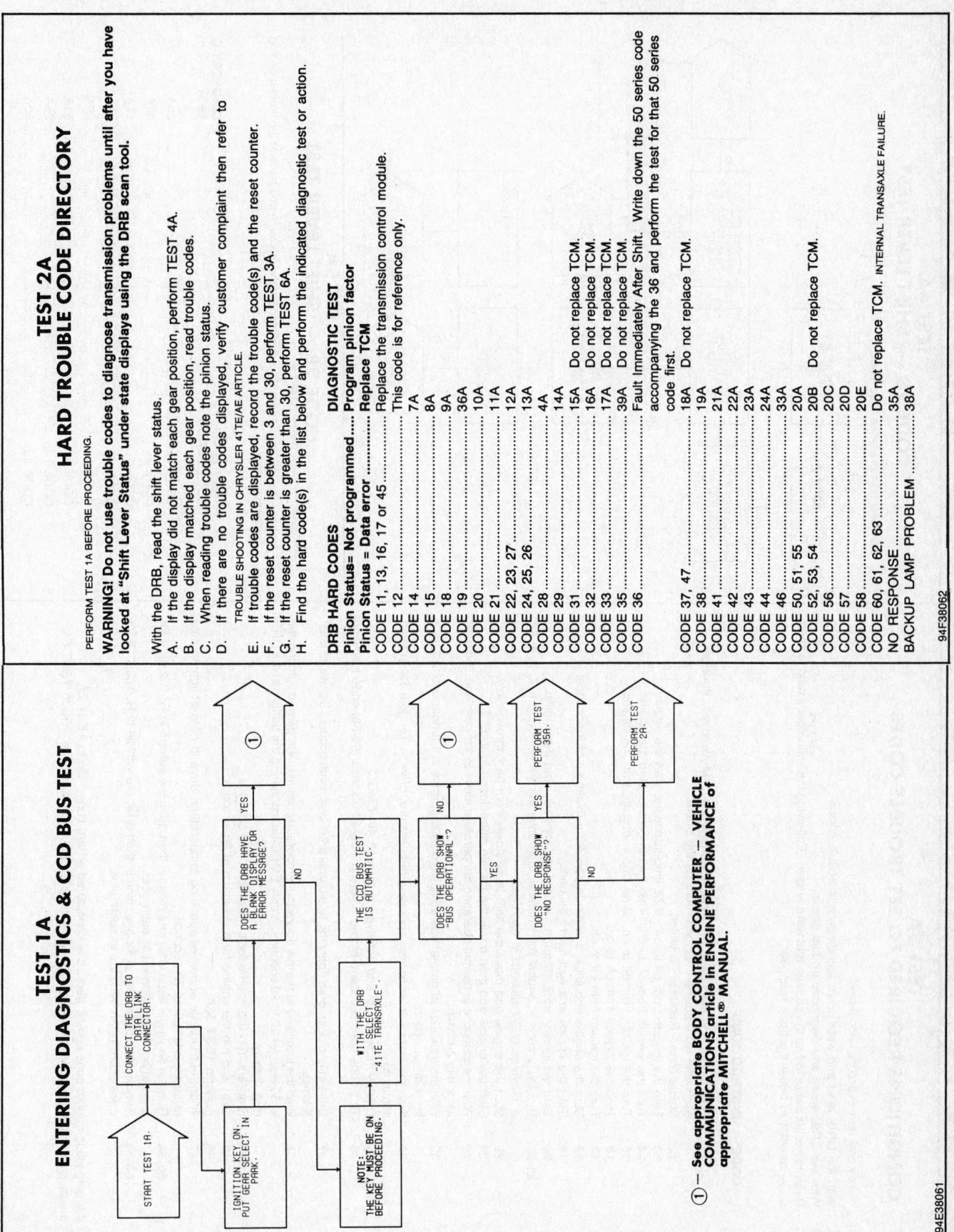

TEST 2A
HARD TROUBLE CODE DIRECTORY

PERFORM TEST 1A BEFORE PROCEEDING.

WARNING! Do not use trouble codes to diagnose transmission problems until after you have looked at "Shift Lever Status" under state displays using the DRB scan tool.

With the DRB, read the shift lever status.

A. If the display did not match each gear position, perform TEST 4A.
B. If the display matched each gear position, read trouble codes.
C. When reading trouble codes note the pinion status.
D. If there are no trouble codes displayed, verify customer complaint then refer to TROUBLE SHOOTING IN CHRYSLER 41TE/AE ARTICLE.
E. If trouble codes are displayed, record the trouble code(s) and the reset counter.
F. If the reset counter is between 3 and 30, perform TEST 3A.
G. If the reset counter is greater than 30, perform TEST 6A.
H. Find the hard code(s) in the list below and perform the indicated diagnostic test or action.

DRB HARD CODES — **DIAGNOSTIC TEST**

Pinion Status= Not programmed ..... Program pinion factor
Pinion Status = Data error .... Replace TCM

DRB HARD CODES	DIAGNOSTIC TEST
CODE 11, 13, 16, 17 or 45	Replace the transmission control module.
CODE 12	This code is for reference only.
CODE 14	7A
CODE 15	8A
CODE 18	9A
CODE 19	36A
CODE 20	10A
CODE 21	11A
CODE 22, 23, 27	12A
CODE 24, 25, 26	13A
CODE 28	4A
CODE 29	14A
CODE 31	15A — Do not replace TCM.
CODE 32	16A — Do not replace TCM.
CODE 33	17A — Do not replace TCM.
CODE 35	39A — Do not replace TCM.
CODE 36	Fault Immediately After Shift. Write down the 50 series code accompanying the 36 and perform the test for that 50 series code first.
CODE 37, 47	18A — Do not replace TCM.
CODE 38	19A
CODE 41	21A
CODE 42	22A
CODE 43	23A
CODE 44	24A
CODE 46	33A
CODE 50, 51, 55	20A
CODE 52, 53, 54	20B — Do not replace TCM.
CODE 56	20C
CODE 57	20D
CODE 58	20E
CODE 60, 61, 62, 63	Do not replace TCM. INTERNAL TRANSAXLE FAILURE.
NO RESPONSE	35A
BACKUP LAMP PROBLEM	38A

94F38062

TEST 1A
ENTERING DIAGNOSTICS & CCD BUS TEST

START TEST 1A.

CONNECT THE DRB TO DATA LINK CONNECTOR.

IGNITION KEY ON. PUT GEAR SELECT IN PARK.

DOES THE DRB HAVE A BLANK DISPLAY OR ERROR MESSAGE?
- YES → (1)
- NO ↓

NOTE: THE KEY MUST BE ON BEFORE PROCEEDING.

WITH THE DRB SELECT "41TE TRANSAXLE".

THE CCD BUS TEST IS AUTOMATIC.

DOES THE DRB SHOW "BUS OPERATIONAL"?
- NO → (1)
- YES ↓

DOES THE DRB SHOW "NO RESPONSE"?
- YES → PERFORM TEST 35A.
- NO → PERFORM TEST 2A.

(1) — See appropriate **BODY CONTROL COMPUTER — VEHICLE COMMUNICATIONS** article in **ENGINE PERFORMANCE** of appropriate **MITCHELL® MANUAL.**

94E38061

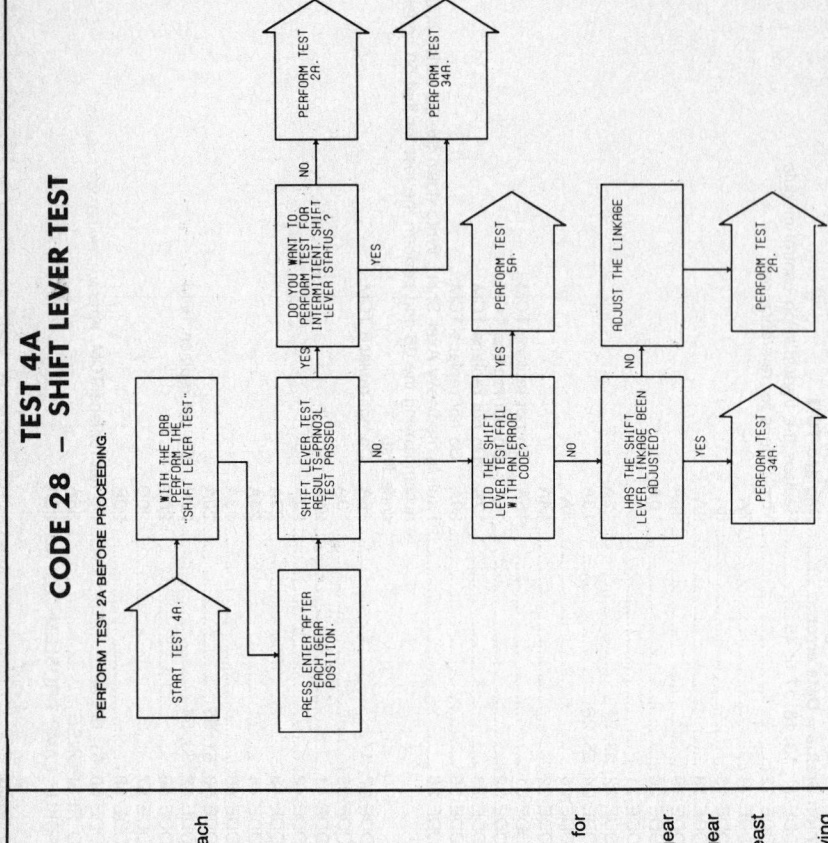

TEST 4A
CODE 28 – SHIFT LEVER TEST

PERFORM TEST 2A BEFORE PROCEEDING.

TEST 5A
CODE 28 – SHIFT LEVER TEST

PERFORM TEST 4A BEFORE PROCEEDING.

Match the shift lever "Error Code" with one of the following and perform the corresponding diagnostic test:

SHIFT LEVEL CODE ERROR	DIAGNOSTIC TEST
CODE 1	28A
CODE 2	30A
CODE 3	27A
CODE 4	29A
CODE 5	26A
CODE 6	31A
CODE 7	25A
CODE 8	32A

94H38064 94138065

TEST 3A
CONDITIONS REQUIRED TO SET TROUBLE CODES

PERFORM TEST 2A BEFORE PROCEEDING.

A. With the DRB, read and write down any diagnostic trouble codes.
B. With the DRB, erase any diagnostic trouble codes.
C. Refer to the list below to find the code(s) that were erased. Following the instructions next to each code, attempt to make the code reappear.

CODE	INSTRUCTIONS
11	Turn the ignition from off to on, then start the engine. Move slowly through each shift level position with your foot on the brake.
12	Status code. Requires no action.
13	Turn the ignition from off to on. If no limp-in occurs, start the engine.
14	Turn the ignition from off to on. If no limp-in occurs, start the engine.
15	Turn the ignition from off to on. If no limp-in occurs, start the engine.
16	Turn the ignition from off to on.
17	Turn the ignition from off to on.
18	Start the engine and allow it to run in park for a minimum of 3 seconds.
19	Start the engine and wait for 15 seconds.
20	Turn the ignition from off to on. If no code appears, start the engine.
21-27	Run the vehicle in neutral for 1 minute, then drive the vehicle in R, 1, 2, 3, 4, for a minimum of 30 seconds in each gear.
28	Start the engine and move the shift lever slowly from park through low.
29	Start the engine and then move the throttle from closed to W.O.T.
30	With the transaxle at normal operating temperature, drive in 1st gear and 2nd gear for a minute each.
32	With the transaxle at normal operating temperature, drive in 1st gear and 3rd gear for a minute each.
33	With the transaxle at normal operating temperature, drive in 1st gear for at least 1 minute.
35	Drive vehicle in OD and acheive 1st through 4th EMCC.
36	This code does not stand alone. There will be a 50 series (50-58) code following it.
37	Drive in 2nd gear, then apply the brake until a 2-1 downshift occurs. Do this at least 3 times.
38	With the transaxle at normal operating temperature, drive in 4th gear at light throttle at 50 mph for 17 to 20 seconds. Verify EMCC by monitoring the bottom of the DRB rpm display.
41-44	Start and run the engine for a minimum of 30 seconds.
45	Start and run the engine for a minimum of 20 seconds.
46	Perform TEST 33A.
47	With the transaxle at normal operating temperature, drive in gear at light throttle at 50 mph for about 20 seconds.
50-58	Run the engine in neutral for one minute, then drive the vehicle in R, 1, 2, 3, 4 for a minimum of 30 seconds in each gear.
60-63	Run the vehicle in neutral for one minute, then drive the vehicle in R, 1, 2, 3, 4 for a minimum of 30 seconds in each gear.

If the diagnostic trouble code comes back, it is considered a hard code. Go to TEST 2A.
If the diagnostic trouble code does not reappear, it may be an intermittent code. Go to TEST 6A.

94G38063

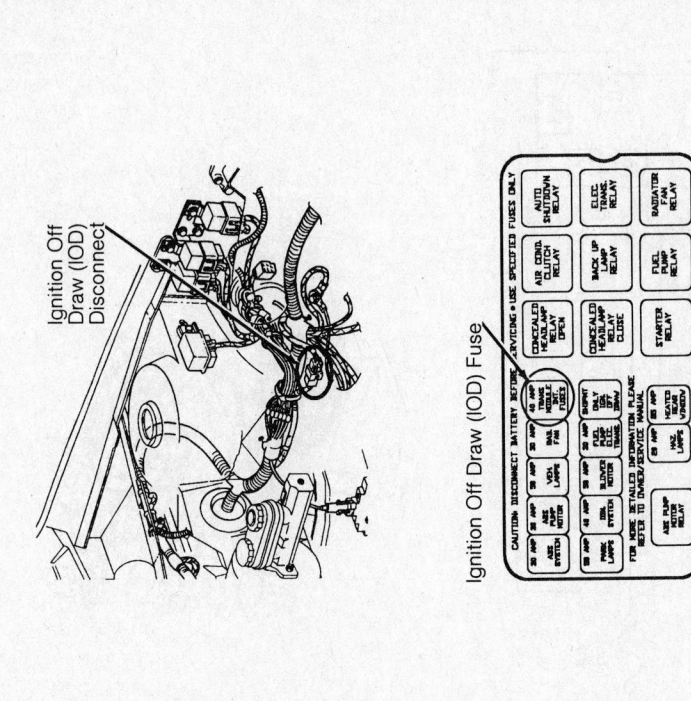

Ground

3.3L & 3.8L

3.0L

Grounds

Ignition Off Draw (IOD) Disconnect

Ignition Off Draw (IOD) Fuse

TEST 6A
TESTING FOR INTERMITTENT TROUBLE CODES

PERFORM TEST 2A BEFORE PROCEEDING.

1. Inspect the following for push-outs or flared connections:
   - engine ground connection
   - TCM ground pins 53 & 57
   - TCM battery feed pin 56
   - battery feed to TCM relay from I.O.D. connector
   - TCM feed pin 11

2. If the above connections are in good condition, find the applicable intermittent code in the following list. Carefully inspect the indicated terminals, cavities, or connectors for push-outs or damage.

INTERMITTENT CODE	60-WAY TERMINAL #	IN-LINE 8-WAY TERMINAL	OTHER
11, 13, 16, 17, 45	8, 11, 53, 54		Clear fault code. Requires no action.
12	56, 57, 58		TCM connector/relay
14	15, 16, 17		TCM connector/relay
15	15, 16, 17		
18	45		
19	4 and 43		PCM pins 26 and 46 (A-Body: pins 5 and 44)
20	16 and 17	3 and 4	TCM connector/relay
21	9	1 and 4	
22	47	1, 3, 4	
23	9 and 47	2 and 4	
24	50	2, 3, 4	
25	9 and 50	1, 2, 4	
26	47 and 50	1, 2, 3, 4	
27	7, 9, and 50		
28	1, 2, 3, 41, 42		Park/Neutral Position Switch connector/ switch; Transmission Range Switch connector; Throttle Position Sensor connector
29	12 and 51		
31, 32, 33			
37, 38, 47			
41	13, 14, 15		
42	16, 20, 57, 58	4 and 7	
43	16, 20, 57, 58	4 and 8	
44	16 and 60	4 and 6	
46	16 and 59	4 and 5	
36, 50 to 58	13, 14, 52		Input or Output Speed Sensor Connector(s)
60 to 62	13, 14, 15		Input or Output Speed Sensor Connector(s)

3. If steps 1 and 2 fail to turn up a defective condition, use the DRB to erase trouble codes and set the reset counter equal to zero (0). Road test the vehicle for proper transaxle operation.

4. IF TRANSAXLE STILL EXPERIENCES IMPROPER OPERATION, SEE TROUBLE SHOOTING IN CHRYSLER 41TE/AE ARTICLE.

94J38066 94A38067 94B38068 94C38069 94F38070

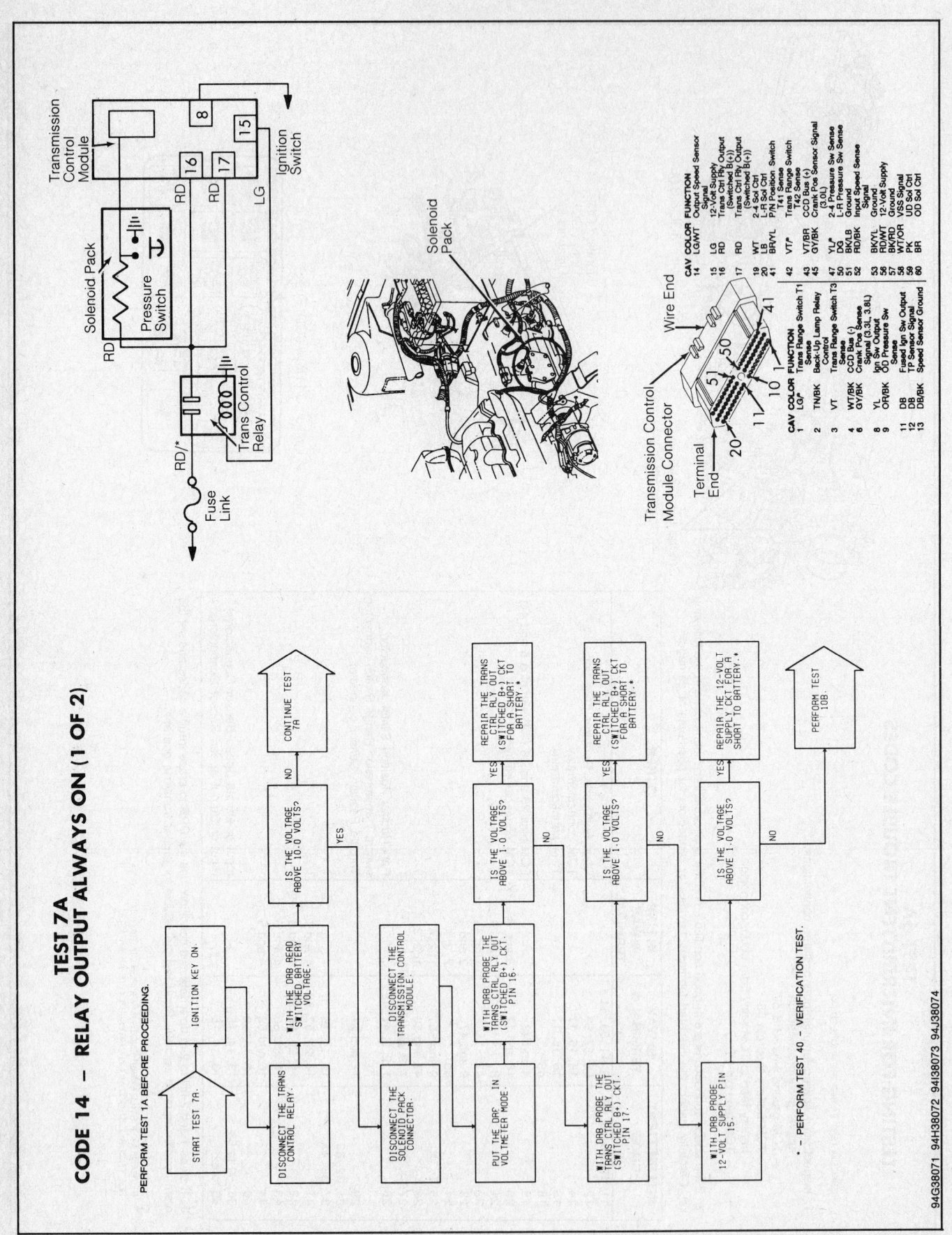

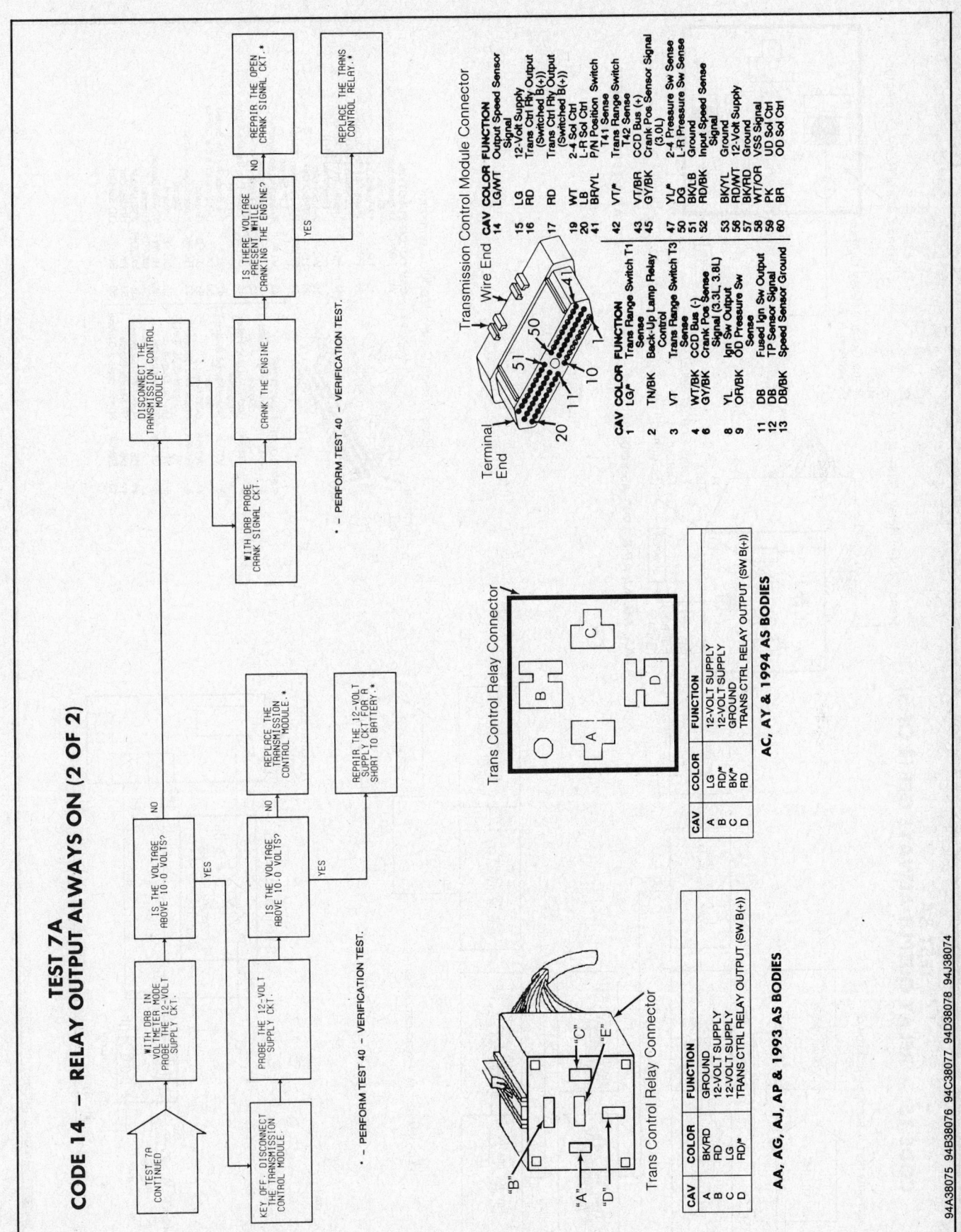

TEST 7A
CODE 14 – RELAY OUTPUT ALWAYS ON (2 OF 2)

Transmission Control Module Connector

Wire End CAV	COLOR	FUNCTION
14	LG/WT	Output Speed Sensor Signal
15	LG	12-Volt Supply
16	RD	Trans Ctrl Rly Output (Switched B(+))
17	RD	Trans Ctrl Rly Output (Switched B(+))
19	WT	2-4 Sol Ctrl
20	LB	L-R Sol Ctrl
41	BR/YL	P/N Position Switch
		T41 Sense
42	VT/*	Trans Range Switch T42 Sense
43	VT/BR	CCD Bus (+)
45	GY/BK	Crank Pos Sensor Signal (3.0L)
47	YL/*	2-4 Pressure Sw Sense
50	DG	L-R Pressure Sw Sense
51	BK/LB	Ground
52	RD/BK	Input Speed Sense Signal
53	BK/YL	Ground
56	RD/WT	12-Volt Supply
57	BK/RD	Ground
58	WT/OR	VSS Signal
59	PK	UD Sol Ctrl
60	BR	OD Sol Ctrl

CAV	COLOR	FUNCTION
1	LG/*	Trans Range Switch T1 Sense
2	TN/BK	Back-Up Lamp Relay Control
3	VT	Trans Range Switch T3 Sense
4	WT/BK	CCD Bus (-)
6	GY/BK	Crank Pos Sense Signal (3.3L, 3.8L)
8	YL	Ign Sw Output
9	OR/BK	OD Pressure Sw Sense
11	DB	Fused Ign Sw Output
12	DB	TP Sensor Signal
13	DB/BK	Speed Sensor Ground

Terminal End

Trans Control Relay Connector

CAV	COLOR	FUNCTION
A	LG	12-VOLT SUPPLY
B	RD/*	12-VOLT SUPPLY
C	BK/*	GROUND
D	RD	TRANS CTRL RELAY OUTPUT (SW B(+))

AC, AY & 1994 AS BODIES

Trans Control Relay Connector

CAV	COLOR	FUNCTION
A	BK/RD	GROUND
B	RD	12-VOLT SUPPLY
C	LG	12-VOLT SUPPLY
D	RD/*	TRANS CTRL RELAY OUTPUT (SW B(+))

AA, AG, AJ, AP & 1993 AS BODIES

* – PERFORM TEST 40 – VERIFICATION TEST.

94A38075 94B38076 94C38077 94D38078 94J38074

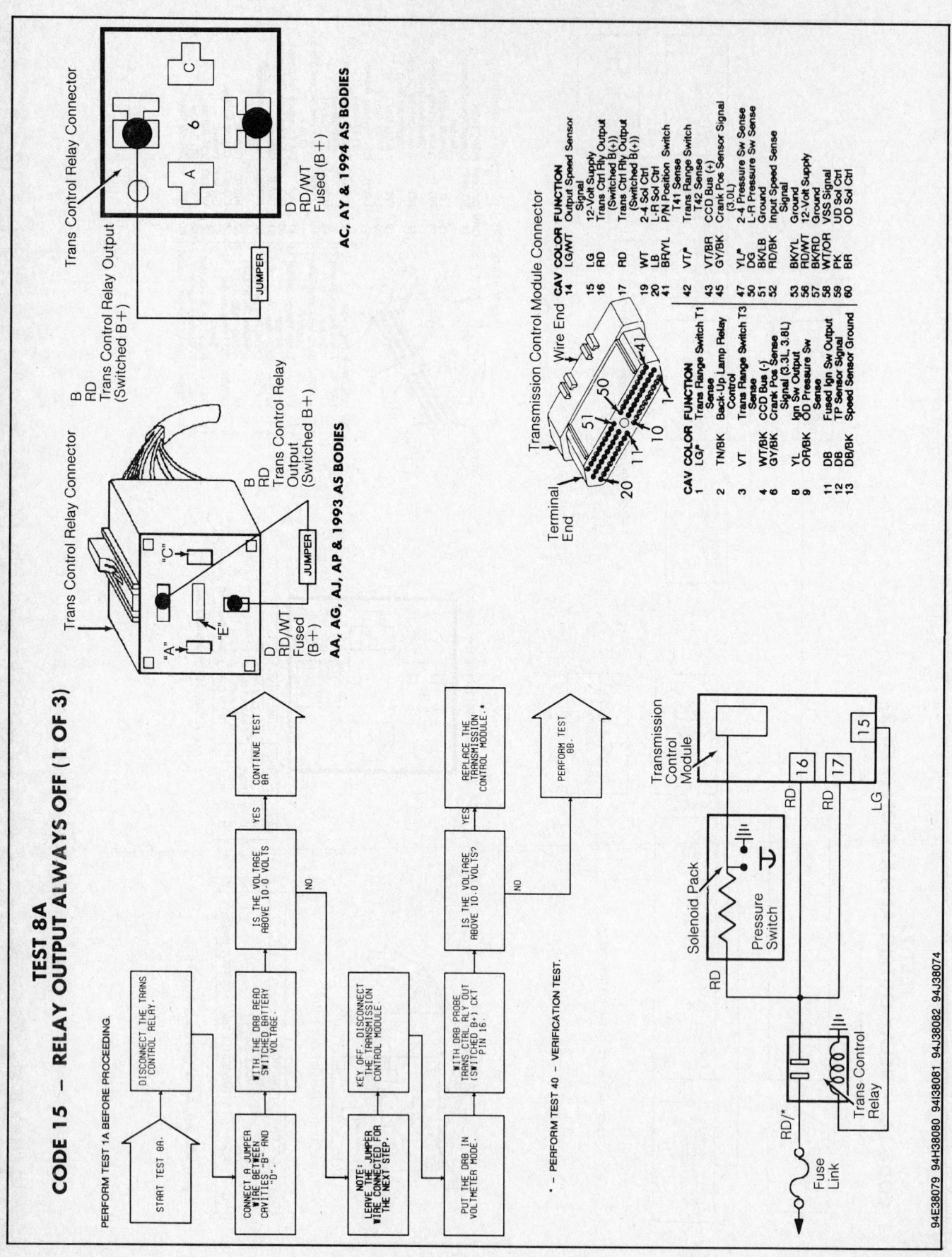

CODE 15 — RELAY OUTPUT ALWAYS OFF (1 OF 3)

TEST 8A

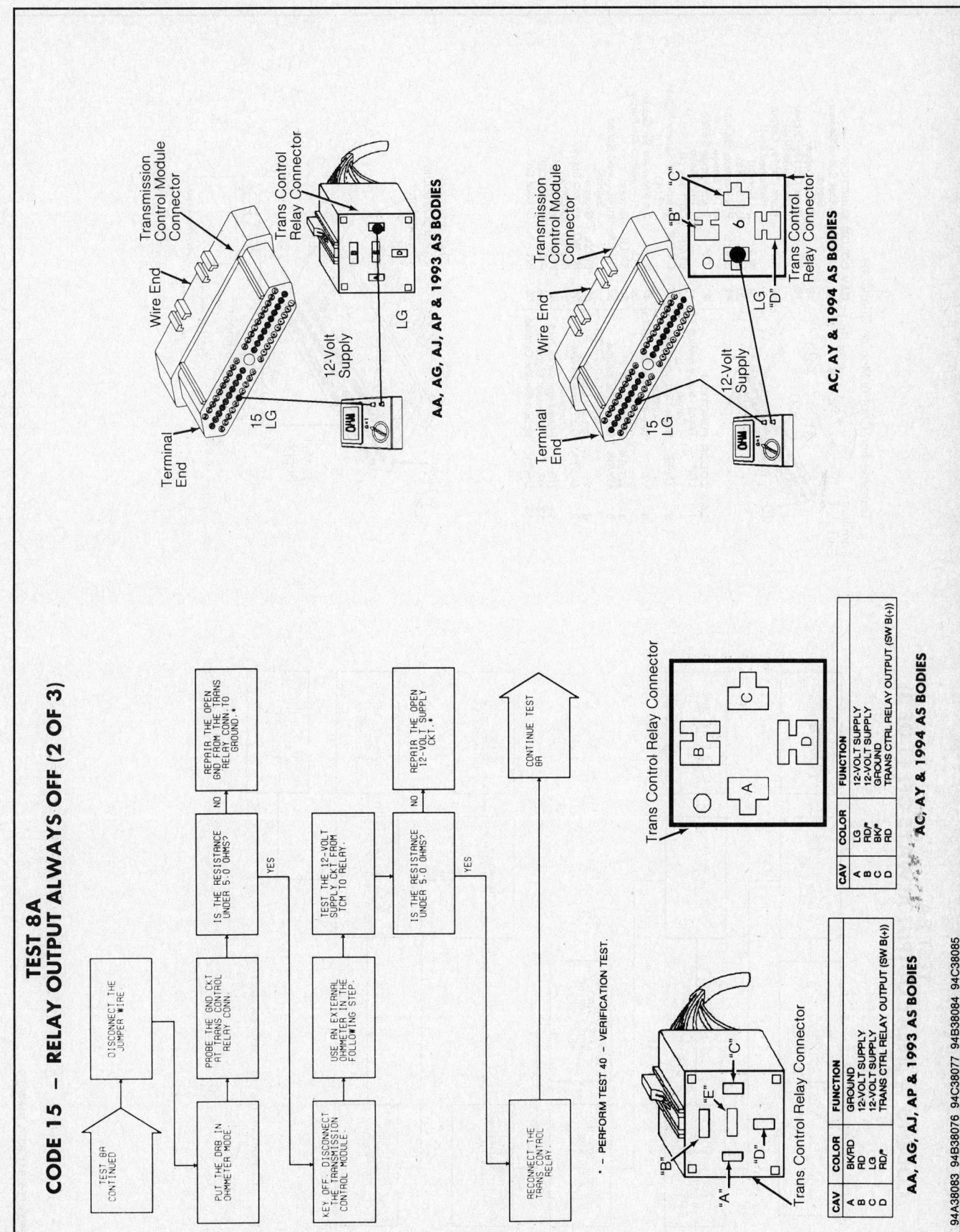

TEST 8A

CODE 15 — RELAY OUTPUT ALWAYS OFF (2 OF 3)

* — PERFORM TEST 4O — VERIFICATION TEST.

AA, AG, AJ, AP & 1993 AS BODIES

AC, AY & 1994 AS BODIES

94A38083 94B38076 94C38077 94B38084 94C38085

Trans Control Relay Connector

CAV	COLOR	FUNCTION
A	BK/RD	GROUND
B	RD	12-VOLT SUPPLY
C	LG	12-VOLT SUPPLY
D	RD/*	TRANS CTRL RELAY OUTPUT (SW B(+))

CAV	COLOR	FUNCTION
A	LG	12-VOLT SUPPLY
B	RD/*	12-VOLT SUPPLY
C	BK/*	GROUND
D	RD	TRANS CTRL RELAY OUTPUT (SW B(+))

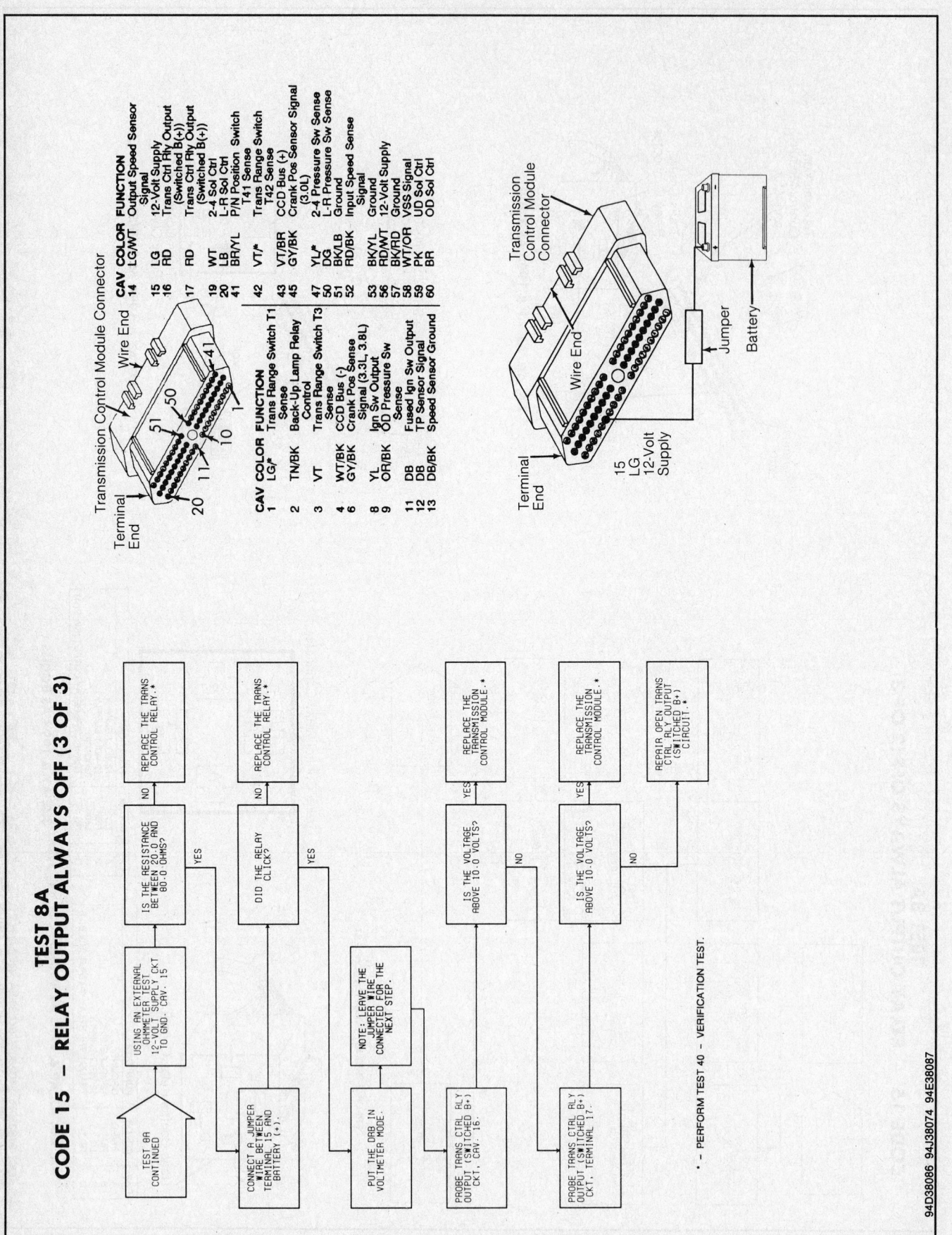

TEST 8A
CODE 15 – RELAY OUTPUT ALWAYS OFF (3 OF 3)

CAV	COLOR	FUNCTION
14	LG/WT	Output Speed Sensor Signal
15	LG	12-Volt Supply
16	RD	Trans Ctrl Rly Output (Switched B(+))
17	RD	Trans Ctrl Rly Output (Switched B(+))
19	WT	2-4 Sol Ctrl
20	LB	L-R Sol Ctrl
41	BR/YL	P/N Position Switch
42	VT/*	T41 Sense
		Trans Range Switch T42 Sense
43	VT/BR	CCD Bus (+)
45	GY/BK	Crank Pos Sensor Signal (3.0L)
47	YL/*	2-4 Pressure Sw Sense
50	DG	L-R Pressure Sw Sense
51	BK/LB	Input Speed Sense
52	RD/BK	Ground
53	BK/YL	Ground
56	RD/WT	12-Volt Supply
57	BK/RD	Ground
58	WT/OR	VSS Signal
59	PK	UD Sol Ctrl
60	BR	OD Sol Ctrl

CAV	COLOR	FUNCTION
1	LG/*	Trans Range Switch T1 Sense
2	TN/BK	Back-Up Lamp Relay Control
3	VT	Trans Range Switch T3 Sense
4	WT/BK	CCD Bus (-)
6	GY/BK	Crank Pos Sense Signal (3.3L, 3.8L)
8	YL	OD Pressure Sw Output
9	OR/BK	OD Pressure Sw Sense
11	DB	Fused Ign Sw Output
12	DB	TP Sensor Signal
13	DB/BK	Speed Sensor Ground

* – PERFORM TEST 40 – VERIFICATION TEST.

94D38086 94J38074 94E38087

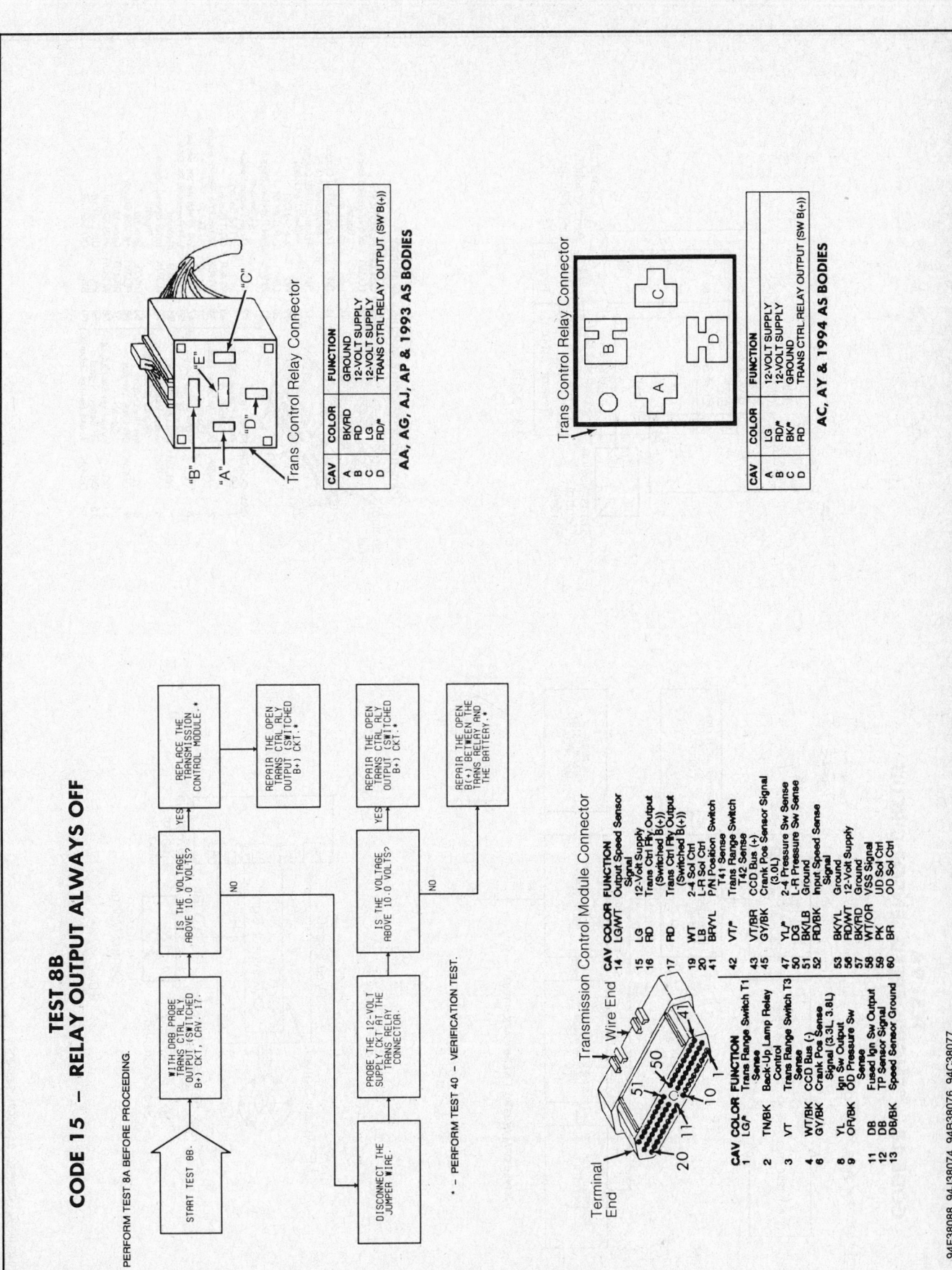

TEST 8B
CODE 15 – RELAY OUTPUT ALWAYS OFF

PERFORM TEST 8A BEFORE PROCEEDING.

* – PERFORM TEST 40 – VERIFICATION TEST.

Trans Control Relay Connector

CAV	COLOR	FUNCTION
A	BK/RD	GROUND
B	RD	12-VOLT SUPPLY
C	LG	12-VOLT SUPPLY
D	RD/*	TRANS CTRL RELAY OUTPUT (SW B(+))

AA, AG, AJ, AP & 1993 AS BODIES

Trans Control Relay Connector

CAV	COLOR	FUNCTION
A	LG	12-VOLT SUPPLY
B	RD/*	12-VOLT SUPPLY
C	BK/*	GROUND
D	RD	TRANS CTRL RELAY OUTPUT (SW B(+))

AC, AY & 1994 AS BODIES

Transmission Control Module Connector

CAV	COLOR	FUNCTION
14	LG/WT	Output Speed Sensor Signal
15	LG	12-Volt Supply
16	RD	Trans Ctrl Rly Output (Switched B(+))
17	RD	Trans Ctrl Rly Output (Switched B(+))
19	WT	2-4 Sol Ctrl
20	LB	L-R Sol Ctrl
41	BR/YL	P/N Position Switch
42	VT/*	T41 Sense
43	VT/BR	Trans Range Switch T42 Sense
45	GY/BK	CCD Bus (+)
47	YL/*	Crank Pos Sensor Signal (3.0L)
50	DG	2-4 Pressure Sw Sense
51	BK/LB	L-R Pressure Sw Sense
52	RD/BK	Input Speed Sense
53	BK/YL	Ground
56	RD/WT	12-Volt Supply
57	BK/RD	Ground
58	WT/OR	VSS Signal
59	PK	UD Sol Ctrl
60	BR	OD Sol Ctrl

Wire End

CAV	COLOR	FUNCTION
1	LG/*	Trans Range Switch T1 Sense
2	TN/BK	Back-Up Lamp Relay Control
3	VT	Trans Range Switch T3 Sense
4	WT/BK	CCD Bus (-)
6	GY/BK	Crank Pos Sense Signal (3.3L 3.8L)
8	YL	Ign Sw Output
9	OR/BK	OD Pressure Sw Sense
11	DB	Fused Ign Sw Output
12	DB	TP Sensor Signal
13	DB/BK	Speed Sensor Ground

Terminal End

94F38088   94J38074   94B38076   94C38077

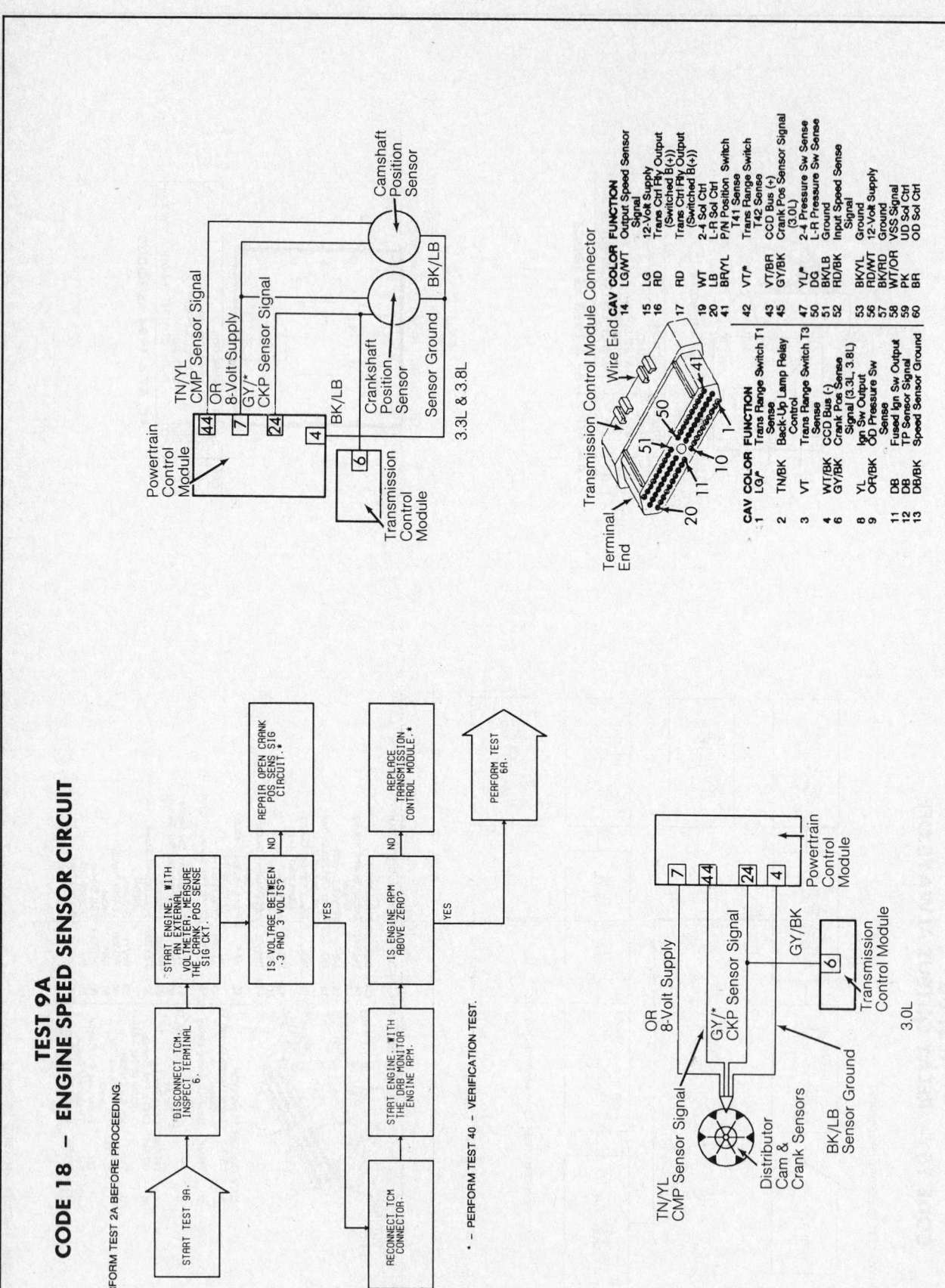

TEST 9A
CODE 18 – ENGINE SPEED SENSOR CIRCUIT

94G38089 94J38090 94A38091 94J38074

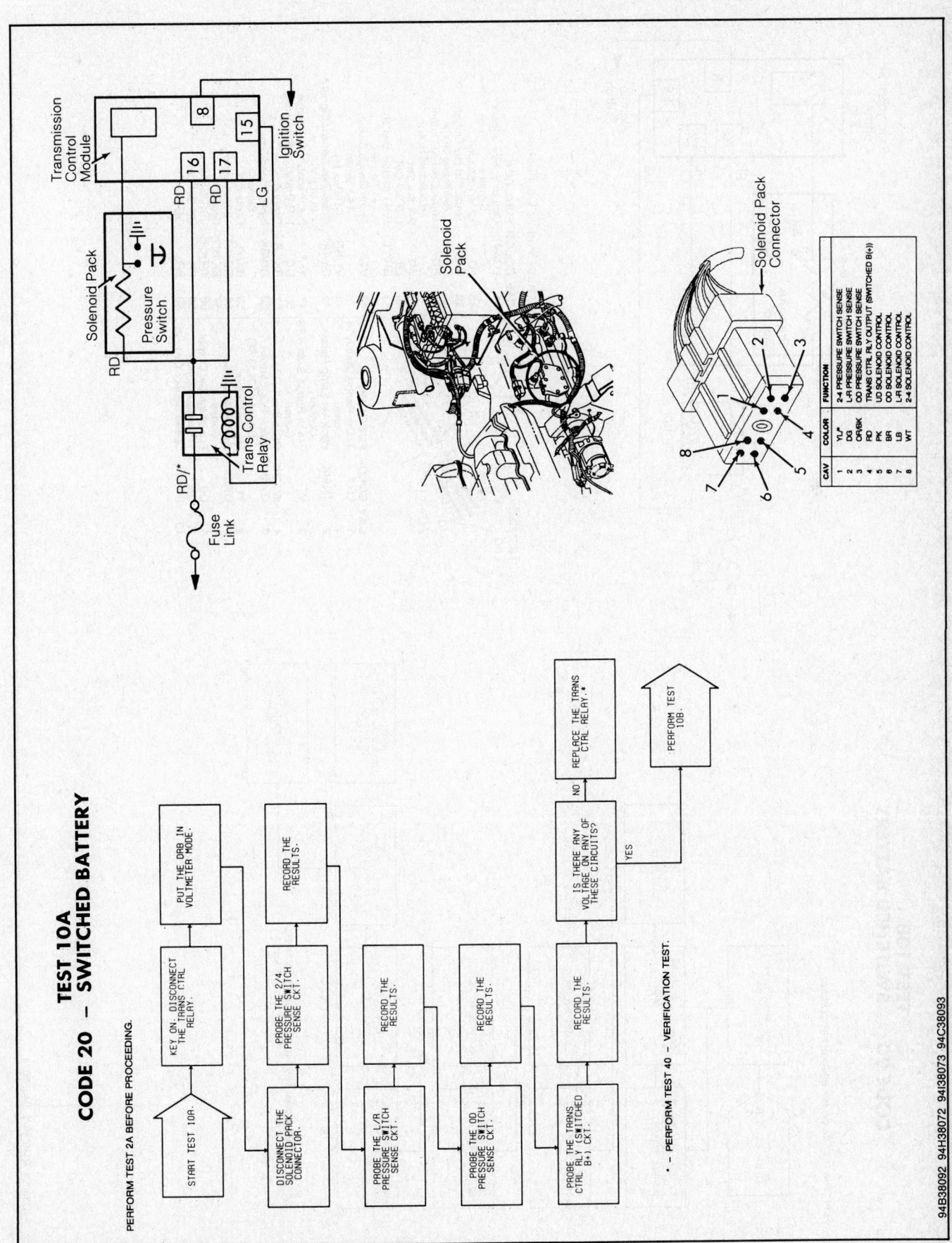

TEST 10A

CODE 20 - SWITCHED BATTERY

PERFORM TEST 2A BEFORE PROCEEDING.

START TEST 10A.

KEY ON. DISCONNECT THE TRANS CTRL RELAY.

PUT THE DRB IN VOLTMETER MODE.

DISCONNECT THE SOLENOID PACK CONNECTOR.

PROBE THE 2/4 PRESSURE SWITCH SENSE CKT.

RECORD THE RESULTS.

PROBE THE L/R PRESSURE SWITCH SENSE CKT.

RECORD THE RESULTS.

PROBE THE OD PRESSURE SWITCH SENSE CKT.

RECORD THE RESULTS.

PROBE THE TRANS CTRL RLY (SWITCHED B+) CKT.

RECORD THE RESULTS.

IS THERE ANY VOLTAGE ON ANY OF THESE CIRCUITS?

NO → REPLACE THE TRANS CTRL RELAY.*

YES → PERFORM TEST 10B.

* - PERFORM TEST 40 - VERIFICATION TEST.

94B38092 94H38072 94I38073 94C38093

CAV	COLOR	FUNCTION
1	YL*	2-4 PRESSURE SWITCH SENSE
2	DG	L-R PRESSURE SWITCH SENSE
3	OR&BK	OD PRESSURE SWITCH SENSE
4	RD	TRANS CTRL RLY OUTPUT (SWITCHED B(+))
5	PK	UD SOLENOID CONTROL
6	BR	OD SOLENOID CONTROL
7	LB	L-R SOLENOID CONTROL
8	WT	2-4 SOLENOID CONTROL

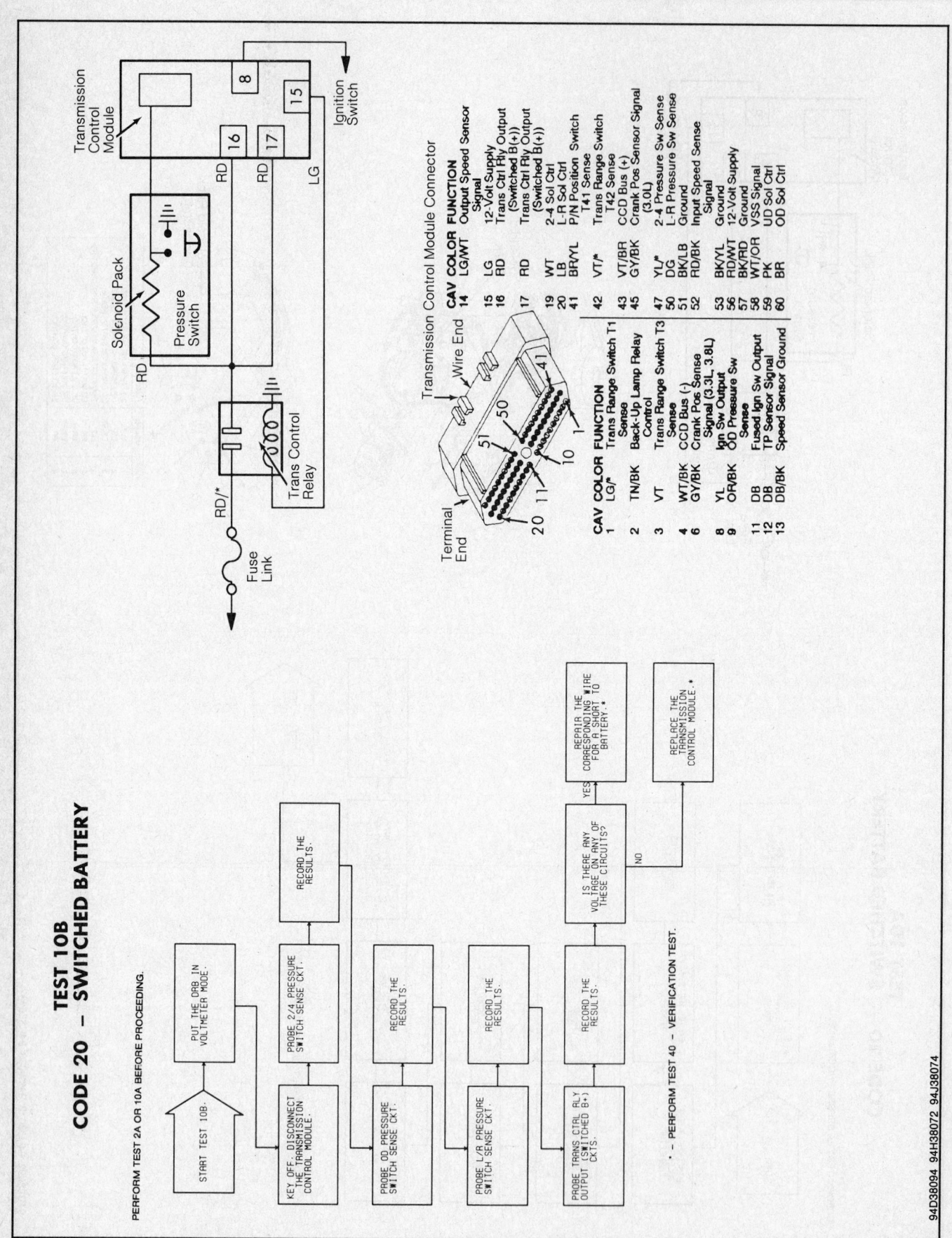

Transmission Control Module Connector

CAV	COLOR	FUNCTION
14	LG/WT	Output Speed Sensor Signal
15	LG	12-Volt Supply
16	RD	Trans Ctrl Rly Output (Switched B(+))
17	RD	Trans Ctrl Rly Output (Switched B(+))
19	WT	2-4 Sol Ctrl
20	LB	L-R Sol Ctrl
41	BR/YL	P/N Position Switch
42	VT*	Trans Range Switch T41 Sense
43	VT/BR	CCD Bus (+)
45	GY/BK	Crank Pos Sensor Signal (3.0L)
47	YL*	2-4 Pressure Sw Sense
50	DG	L-R Pressure Sw Sense
51	BK/LB	Ground
52	RD/BK	Input Speed Sensor Signal
53	BK/YL	Ground
56	RD/WT	12-Volt Supply
57	BK/RD	Ground
58	WT/OR	VSS Signal
59	PK	UD Sol Ctrl
60	BR	OD Sol Ctrl

CAV	COLOR	FUNCTION
1	LG/*	Trans Range Switch T1 Sense
2	TN/BK	Back-Up Lamp Relay Control
3	VT	Trans Range Switch T3 Sense
4	WT/BK	CCD Bus (-)
6	GY/BK	Crank Pos Sense Signal (3.3L, 3.8L)
8	YL	Ign Sw Output
9	OR/BK	OD Pressure Sw Sense
11	DB	Fused Ign Sw Output
12	DB	TP Sensor Signal
13	DB/BK	Speed Sensor Ground

Wire End

Terminal End

CODE 20 - TEST 10B
SWITCHED BATTERY

PERFORM TEST 2A OR 10A BEFORE PROCEEDING.

START TEST 10B.

PUT THE DRB IN VOLTMETER MODE.

KEY OFF, DISCONNECT THE TRANSMISSION CONTROL MODULE.

PROBE 2/4 PRESSURE SWITCH SENSE CKT.

RECORD THE RESULTS.

PROBE OD PRESSURE SWITCH SENSE CKT.

RECORD THE RESULTS.

PROBE L/R PRESSURE SWITCH SENSE CKT.

RECORD THE RESULTS.

PROBE TRANS CTRL RLY OUTPUT (SWITCHED B+) CKTS.

RECORD THE RESULTS.

IS THERE ANY VOLTAGE ON ANY OF THESE CIRCUITS?

YES → REPAIR THE CORRESPONDING WIRE FOR A SHORT TO BATTERY.*

NO → REPLACE THE TRANSMISSION CONTROL MODULE. *

* - PERFORM TEST 40 - VERIFICATION TEST.

Transmission Control Module

Ignition Switch

RD   RD   LG

8   15   16   17

Solenoid Pack

Pressure Switch

RD

RD/*

Trans Control Relay

Fuse Link

94D38094 94H38072 94J38074

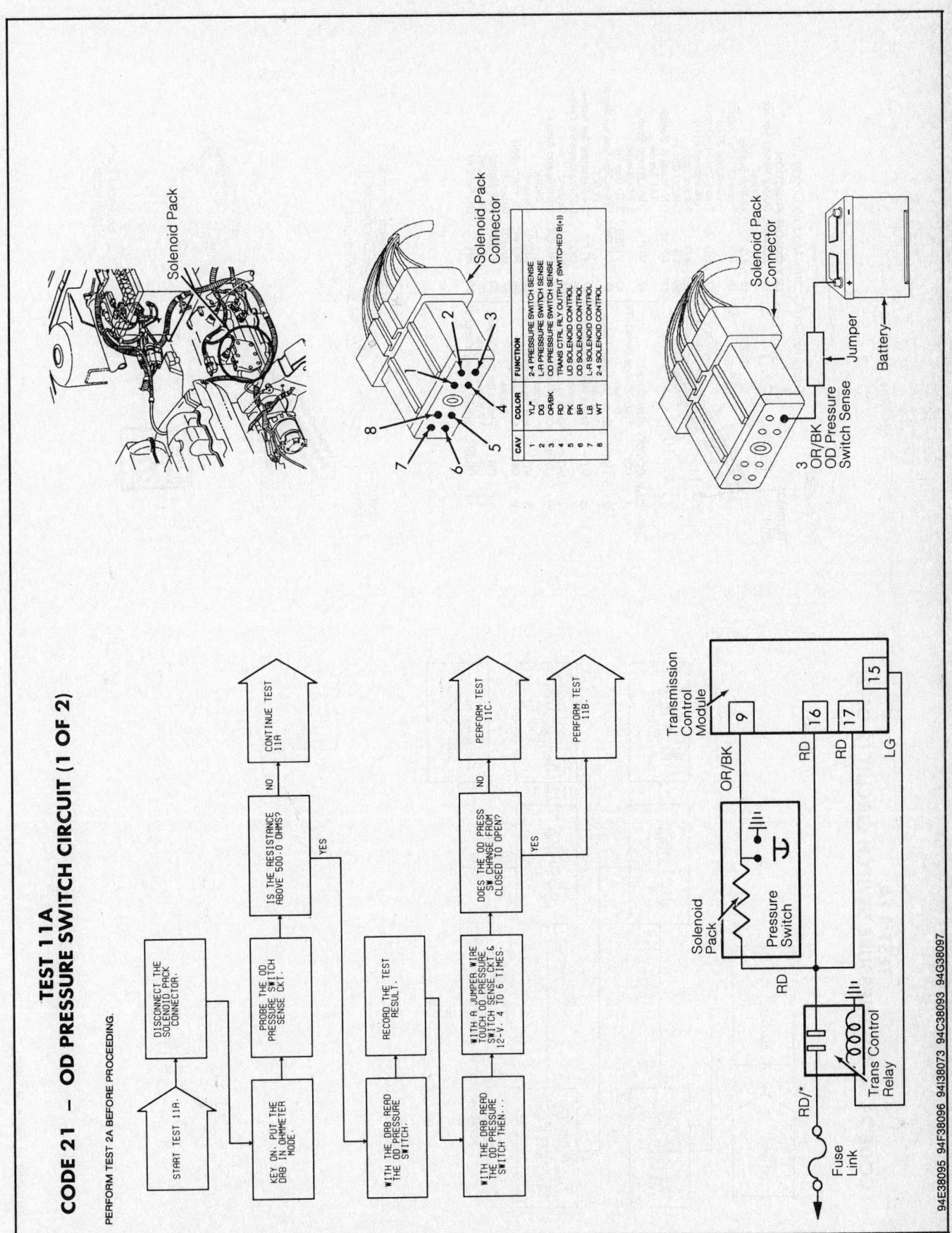

TEST 11A
CODE 21 — OD PRESSURE SWITCH CIRCUIT (1 OF 2)

PERFORM TEST 2A BEFORE PROCEEDING.

START TEST 11A.

DISCONNECT THE SOLENOID PACK CONNECTOR.

KEY ON. PUT THE DRB IN OHMMETER MODE.

PROBE THE OD PRESSURE SWITCH SENSE CKT.

IS THE RESISTANCE ABOVE 500.0 OHMS?

NO — CONTINUE TEST 11A

YES

RECORD THE TEST RESULT.

WITH THE DRB READ THE OD PRESSURE SWITCH.

WITH THE DRB READ THE OD PRESSURE SWITCH THEN...

WITH A JUMPER WIRE TOUCH OD PRESSURE SWITCH SENSE CKT & SWITCH SENSE. 12-V. 4 TO 6 TIMES.

DOES THE OD PRESS SW CHANGE FROM CLOSED TO OPEN?

NO — PERFORM TEST 11C.

YES

PERFORM TEST 11B.

Solenoid Pack

Solenoid Pack Connector

CAV	COLOR	FUNCTION
1	YL/*	2-4 PRESSURE SWITCH SENSE
2	OG	L-R PRESSURE SWITCH SENSE
3	OR/BK	OD PRESSURE SWITCH SENSE
4	RD	TRANS RLY OUTPUT (SWITCHED B(+))
5	PK	UD SOLENOID CONTROL
6	BR	OD SOLENOID CONTROL
7	LG	L-R SOLENOID CONTROL
8	WT	2-4 SOLENOID CONTROL

Solenoid Pack Connector

Jumper

Battery

3 OR/BK OD Pressure Switch Sense

Transmission Control Module

9   16   17   15

OR/BK   RD   RD   LG

Solenoid Pack

Pressure Switch

RD

RD/*

Fuse Link

Trans Control Relay

94E38095 94F38096 94138073 94C38093 94G38097

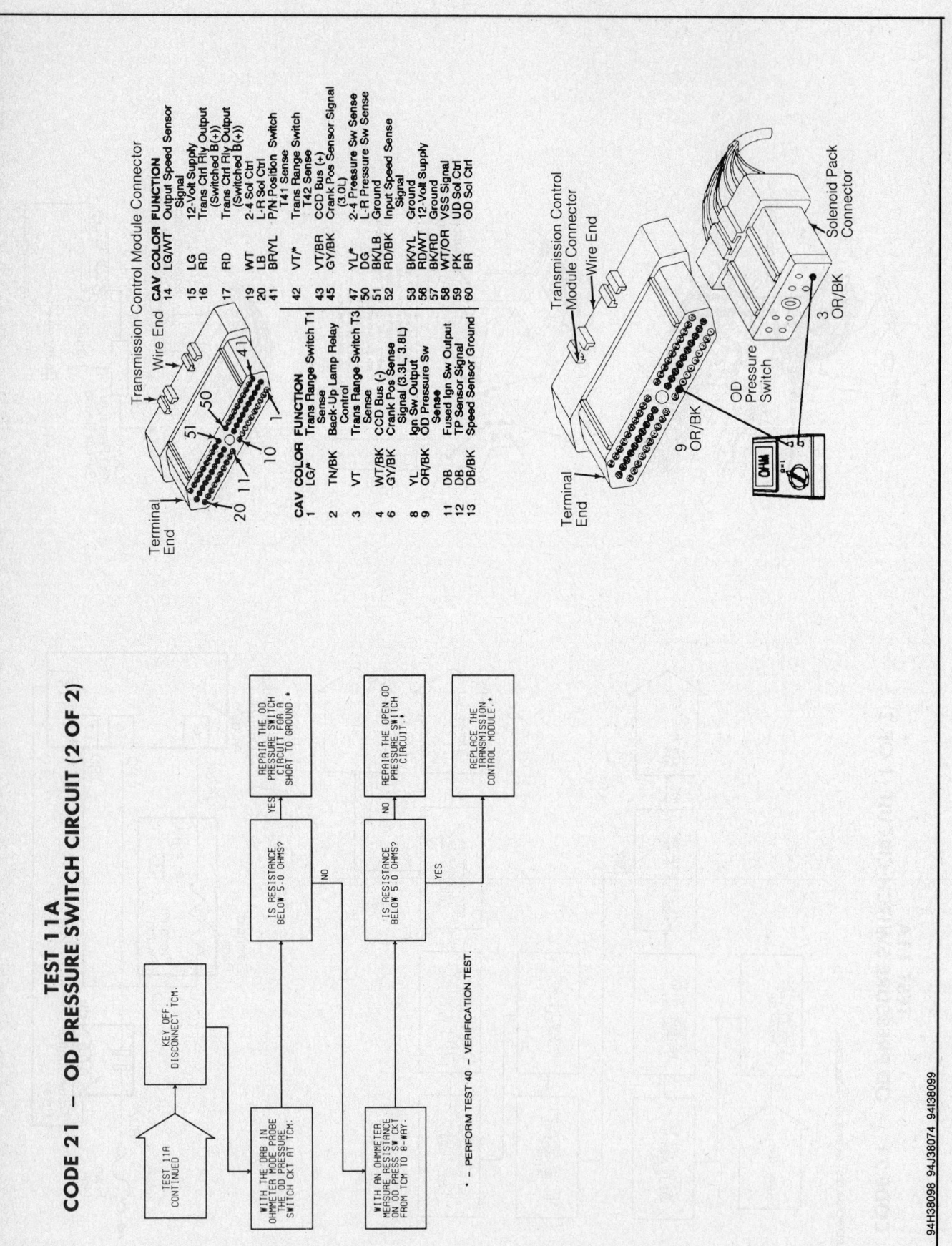

Transmission Control Module Connector

CAV	COLOR	FUNCTION
14	LG/WT	Output Speed Sensor Signal
15	LG	12-Volt Supply
16	RD	Trans Ctrl Rly Output (Switched B(+))
17	RD	Trans Ctrl Rly Output (Switched B(+))
19	WT	2-4 Sol Ctrl
20	LB	L-R Sol Ctrl
41	BR/YL	P/N Position Switch
42	VT/*	Trans Range Switch T41 Sense
43	VT/BR	Trans Range Switch T42 Sense
45	GY/BK	CCD Bus (+)
47	YL/*	Crank Pos Sensor Signal (3.0L)
50	DG	2-4 Pressure Sw Sense
51	BK/LB	L-R Pressure Sw Sense
52	RD/BK	Input Speed Sense Signal
53	BK/YL	Ground
56	RD/WT	Ground
57	BK/RD	12-Volt Supply
58	WT/OR	Ground
59	PK	VSS Signal
60	BR	UD Sol Ctrl
		OD Sol Ctrl

CAV	COLOR	FUNCTION
1	LG/*	Trans Range Switch T1 Sense
2	TN/BK	Back-Up Lamp Relay Control
3	VT	Trans Range Switch T3 Sense
4	WT/BK	CCD Bus (-)
6	GY/BK	Crank Pos Sense Signal (3.3L, 3.8L)
8	YL	Ign Sw Output
9	OR/BK	OD Pressure Sw Sense
11	DB	Fused Ign Sw Output
12	DB	TP Sensor Signal
13	DB/BK	Speed Sensor Ground

Transmission Control Module Connector — Wire End — Terminal End

Solenoid Pack Connector — 3 OR/BK

OD Pressure Switch — 9 OR/BK

OHM

TEST 11A
CODE 21 – OD PRESSURE SWITCH CIRCUIT (2 OF 2)

TEST 11A CONTINUED

↓

KEY OFF. DISCONNECT TCM.

↓

WITH THE DRB IN OHMETER MODE, PROBE THE OD PRESSURE SWITCH CKT AT TCM.

↓

IS RESISTANCE BELOW 5.0 OHMS?

— YES → REPAIR THE OD PRESSURE SWITCH CIRCUIT FOR A SHORT TO GROUND. *

— NO →

WITH AN OHMMETER MEASURE RESISTANCE ON OD PRESS SW CKT FROM TCM TO 8-WAY.

↓

IS RESISTANCE BELOW 5.0 OHMS?

— NO → REPAIR THE OPEN OD PRESSURE SWITCH CIRCUIT. *

— YES → REPLACE THE TRANSMISSION CONTROL MODULE. *

* – PERFORM TEST 40 – VERIFICATION TEST.

94H38098 94J38074 94J38099

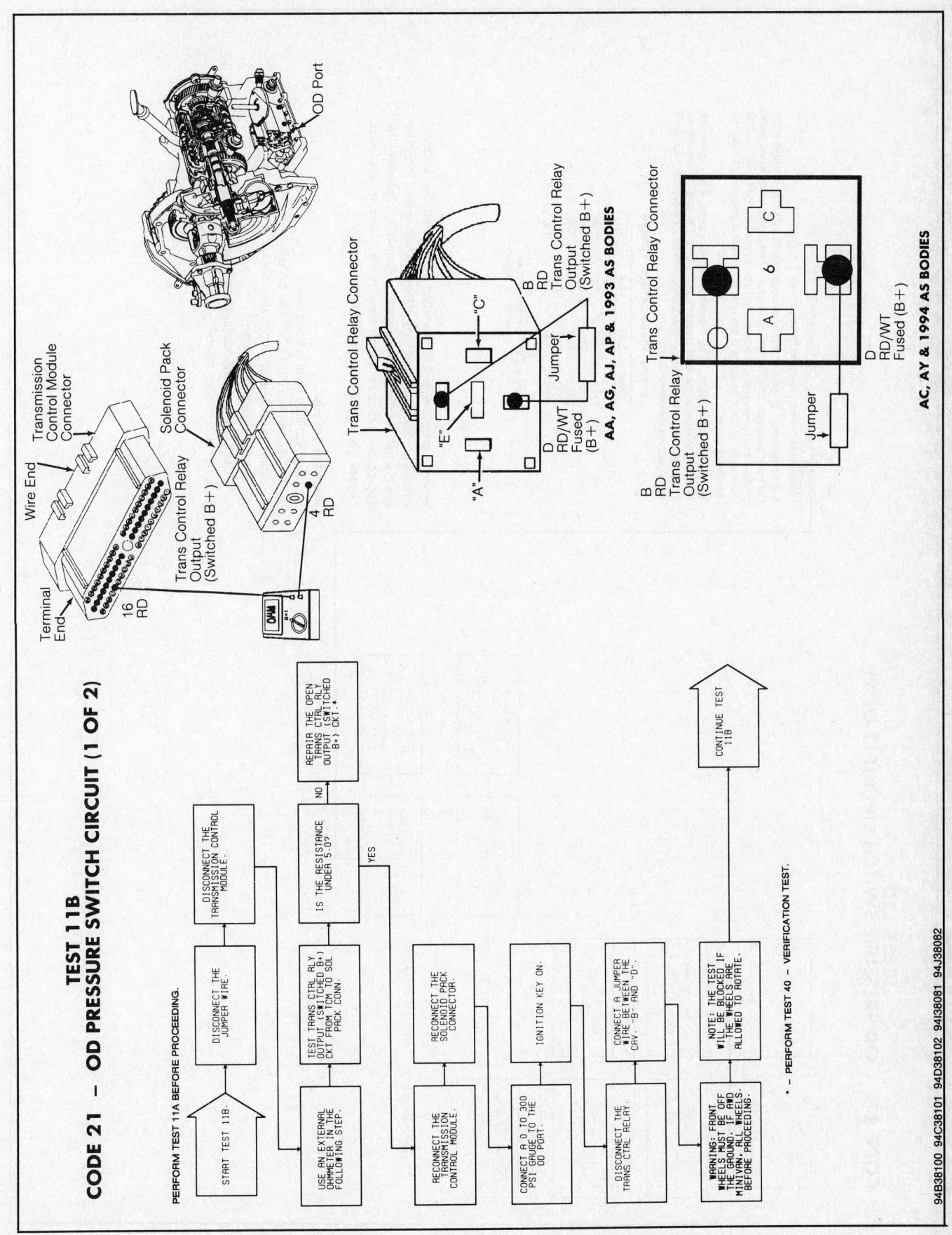

94B38100 94C38101 94D38102 94J38081 94J38082

Name of code: 21 - OD Pressure Switch Circuit

When monitored: Approximately every 1 second.

Set condition: Engine speed must be greater than 500 rpm; a shift must not be in progress; and there must be more than 2.0 seconds since start-up, no loss of prime test in progress, and a pressure switch mismatch. The code sets within 4 seconds if the pressure switch error count reaches maximum value.

Theory of operation: The transaxle system uses three pressure switches to monitor the fluid pressure in the L-R, 2-4, and OD elements. The pressure switches are continuously checked for the correct states in each gear as indicated below.

Normal Pressure Switch States

GEAR	L-R	2-4	OD
R	OP	OP	OP
N	CL	OP	OP
1ST	CL	OP	OP
2ND	OP	CL	OP
3RD	OP	OP	CL
4TH	OP	CL	CL

OP = switch is open
CL = switch is closed

When a pressure switch mismatch is detected, the solenoid circuits are tested for continuity. If that test fails, solenoid circuits are blamed for the pressure switch mismatch. Otherwise, the appropriate pressure switch code is set. This trouble code causes the transaxle to go into limp-in mode.

Possible causes:

> Low/high fluid level in transaxle
> Short/open in T09, T47 or T50 circuits
> Solenoid pack internal problem
> Internal transaxle problem
> TCM 60-way connector problem (cavities 9, 47, and 50)
> Internal controller failure

TEST 11B
CODE 21 – OD PRESSURE SWITCH CIRCUIT (2 OF 2)

```
      TEST 11B
      CONTINUED
          │
   START THE ENGINE.
          │
   PUT THE SHIFT
   LEVER IN OD.
          │
   STEP ON THE BRAKE
   SO THE WHEELS
   WON'T ROTATE.
          │
   WITH THE DRB
   ACTUATE THE OD
   SOLENOID.
          │
   READ THE PRESSURE
   GAUGE.
          │
   NOTE: IT MAY BE
   NECESSARY TO RAISE
   ENGINE RPM
   SLIGHTLY OFF IDLE.
          │
   DOES THE PRESSURE      YES    REPLACE THE
   FLUCTUATE FROM 0  ─────────► SOLENOID PACK. *
   TO 75-95 PSI?                (OD PRESSURE
          │ NO                   SWITCH FAILURE)
          ▼
   DOES THE PRESSURE      NO     REPLACE THE
   RISE ABOVE 5 PSI? ─────────► SOLENOID PACK. *
          │ YES                 (OD SOLENOID
          ▼                      FAILURE)
   * - PERFORM TEST 40 - VERIFICATION TEST.
```

* - PERFORM TEST 40 - VERIFICATION TEST.

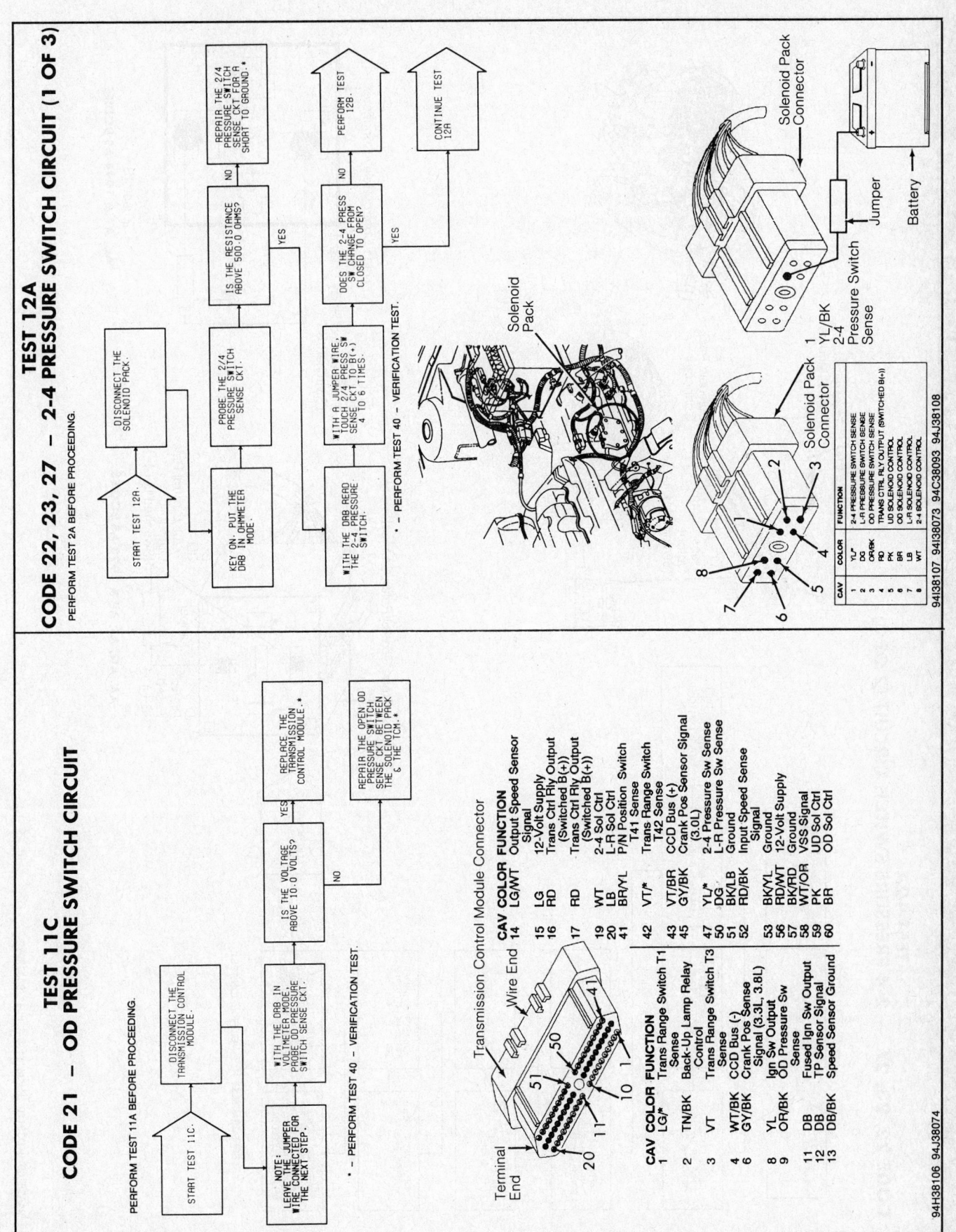

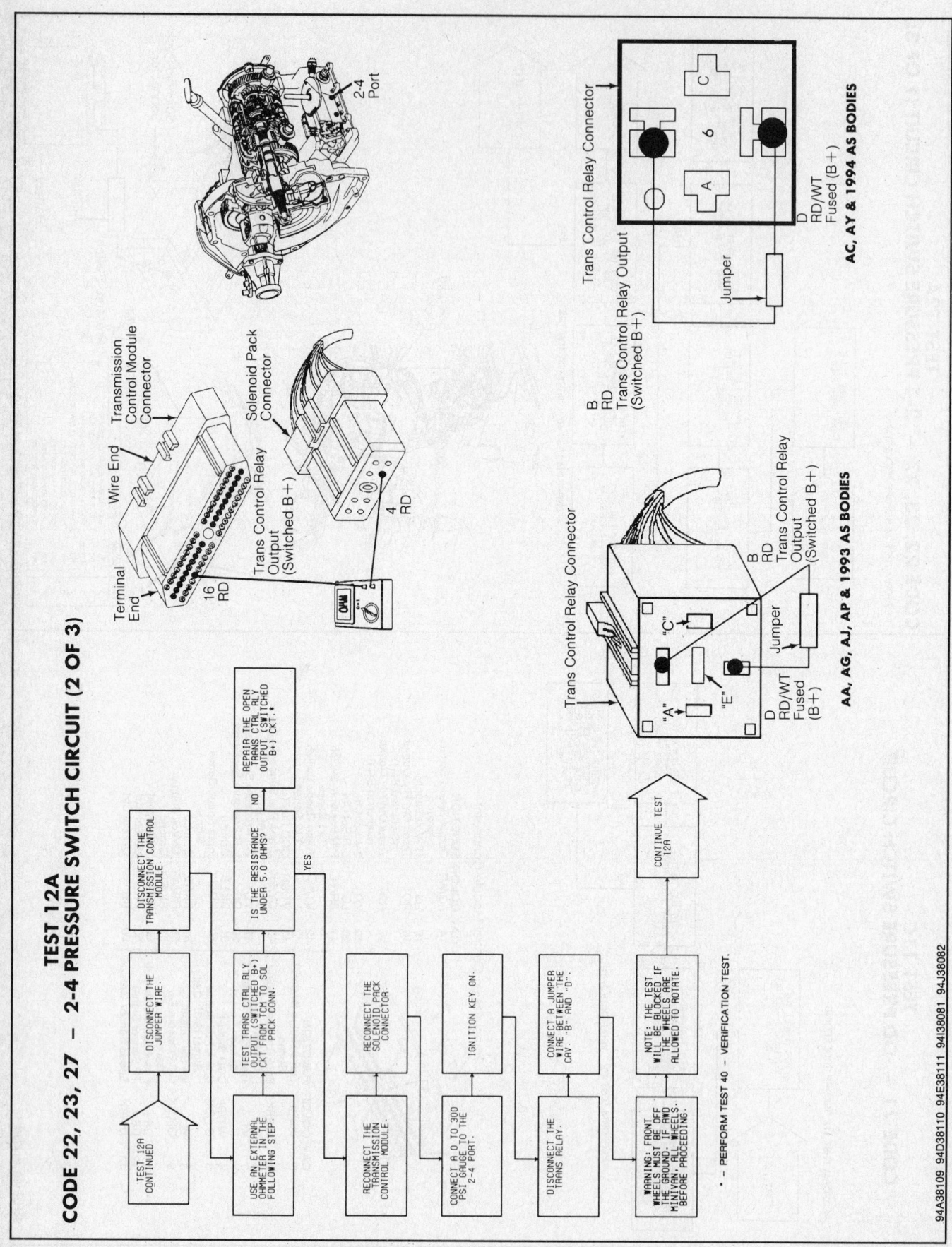

TEST 12A

CODE 22, 23, 27 – 2-4 PRESSURE SWITCH CIRCUIT (2 OF 3)

94A38109 94D38110 94E38111 94I38081 94J38082

When monitored: Approximately every 1 second.

Set condition: Engine speed must be greater than 500 rpm; a shift must not be in progress; and there must be more than 2.0 seconds since start-up, no loss of prime test in progress, and a pressure switch mismatch. The code sets within 4 seconds if the pressure switch error count reaches maximum value.

Theory of operation: The transaxle system uses three pressure switches to monitor the fluid pressure in the L-R, 2-4, and OD elements. The pressure switches are continuously checked for the correct states in each gear as indicated below.

Normal Pressure Switch States

GEAR	L-R	2-4	OD
R	OP	OP	OP
N	CL	OP	OP
1ST	CL	OP	OP
2ND	OP	CL	CL
3RD	OP	OP	CL
4TH	OP	CL	CL

OP = switch is open
CL = switch is closed

When a pressure switch mismatch is detected, the solenoid circuits are tested for continuity. If that test fails, solenoid circuits are blamed for the pressure switch mismatch. Otherwise, the appropriate pressure switch code is set. This trouble code causes the transaxle to go into limp-in mode.

Possible causes:

> Low/high fluid level in transaxle
> Short/open in T09, T47 or T50 circuits
> Solenoid pack internal problem
> Internal transaxle problem
> TCM 60-way connector problem (cavities 9, 47, and 50)
> Internal controller failure

TEST 12A
CODE 22, 23, 27 – 2-4 PRESSURE SWITCH CIRCUIT (3 OF 3)

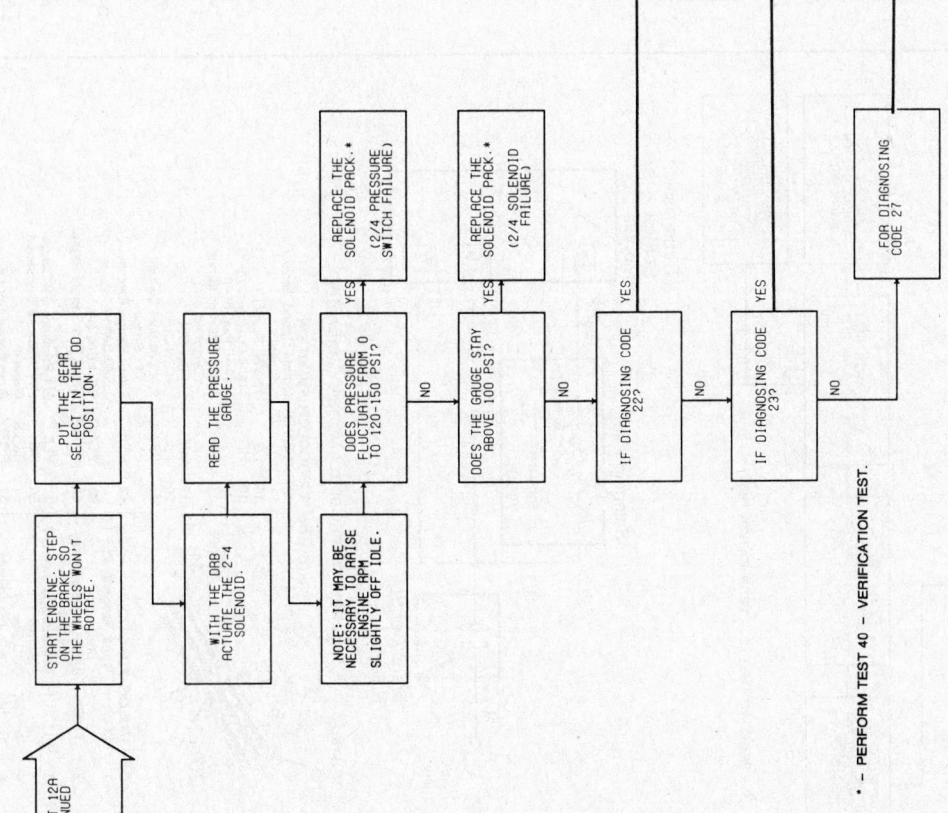

* – PERFORM TEST 40 – VERIFICATION TEST.

94F38112 94G38113 94H38114

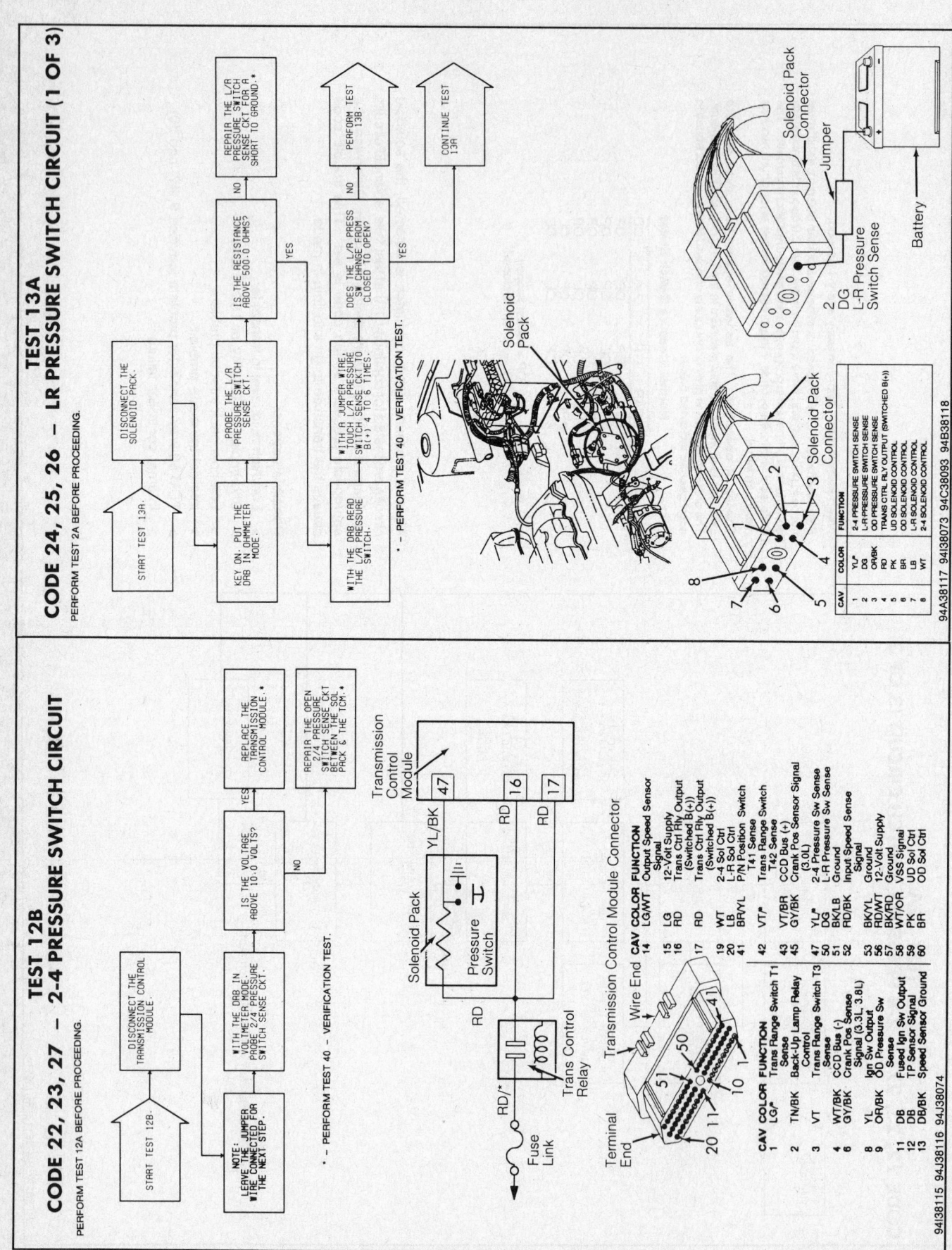

TEST 13A

CODE 24, 25, 26 — LR PRESSURE SWITCH CIRCUIT (1 OF 3)

PERFORM TEST 2A BEFORE PROCEEDING.

START TEST 13A.

DISCONNECT THE SOLENOID PACK.

KEY ON. PUT THE DRB IN OHMMETER MODE.

PROBE THE L/R PRESSURE SENSE CKT.

IS THE RESISTANCE ABOVE 500-0 OHMS? — NO → REPAIR THE L/R PRESSURE SENSE CKT FOR A SHORT TO GROUND.*

YES

WITH THE DRB READ THE L/R PRESSURE SWITCH.

WITH A JUMPER WIRE, TOUCH L/R PRESSURE SWITCH SENSE CKT TO B(+) 4 TO 6 TIMES.

DOES THE L/R PRESS SW CHANGE FROM CLOSED TO OPEN? — NO → PERFORM TEST 13B.

YES

CONTINUE TEST 13A

* - PERFORM TEST 40 - VERIFICATION TEST.

Solenoid Pack

Solenoid Pack Connector

Jumper

Battery

DG
L-R Pressure
Switch Sense

Solenoid Pack Connector

CAV	COLOR	FUNCTION
2	YL*	2-4 PRESSURE SWITCH SENSE
3	DG	L-R PRESSURE SWITCH SENSE
4	OR/BK	OD PRESSURE SWITCH SENSE
5	RD	TRANS CTRL RLY OUTPUT (SWITCHED B(+))
6	PK	UD SOLENOID CONTROL
7	BR	OD SOLENOID CONTROL
8	LB	L-R SOLENOID CONTROL
	WT	2-4 SOLENOID CONTROL

94A38117 94I38073 94C38093 94B38118

TEST 12B

CODE 22, 23, 27 — 2-4 PRESSURE SWITCH CIRCUIT

PERFORM TEST 12A BEFORE PROCEEDING.

START TEST 12B.

NOTE: LEAVE JUMPER WIRE CONNECTED FOR THE NEXT STEP.

DISCONNECT THE TRANSMISSION CONTROL MODULE.

WITH THE DRB IN VOLTMETER MODE, PROBE 2/4 PRESSURE SWITCH SENSE CKT.

IS THE VOLTAGE ABOVE 10.0 VOLTS? — YES → REPLACE THE TRANSMISSION CONTROL MODULE. *

NO

REPAIR THE OPEN 2/4 PRESSURE SWITCH SENSE CKT BETWEEN THE SOL PACK & THE TCM.*

* - PERFORM TEST 40 - VERIFICATION TEST.

Transmission Control Module

47 YL/BK
16 RD
17 RD

Solenoid Pack

Pressure Switch

RD

RD/*

Fuse Link

Trans Control Relay

Transmission Control Module Connector

Wire End

CAV	COLOR	FUNCTION
14	LG/WT	Output Speed Sensor Signal
15	LG	12-Volt Supply
16	RD	Trans Ctrl Rly Output (Switched B(+))
17	RD	Trans Ctrl Rly Output (Switched B(+))
19	WT	2-4 Sol Ctrl
20	LB	L-R Sol Ctrl
41	BR/YL	P/N Position Switch
42	VT*	Trans Range Switch T41 Sense
43	VT/BR	Trans Range Switch T42 Sense
45	GY/BK	CCD Bus (+)
47	YL*	Crank Pos Sensor Signal (3.0L)
50	DG	2-4 Pressure Sw Sense
51	RD/BK	L-R Pressure Sw Sense
52	RD/BK	Input Speed Sense
53	BK/YL	Ground
56	RD/WT	Ground
57	BK/RD	Ground
58	WT/OR	12-Volt Supply
59	PK	UD Sol Ctrl
60	BR	OD Sol Ctrl

Terminal End

Transmission Control Module Connector

CAV	COLOR	FUNCTION
1	LG*	Trans Range Switch T1 Sense
2	TN/BK	Back-Up Lamp Relay Control
3	VT	Trans Range Switch T3 Sense
4	WT/RD	CCD Bus (-)
6	GY/BK	Crank Pos Sense Signal (3.3L, 3.8L)
8	YL	Ign Sw Output
9	OR/BK	OD Pressure Sw Sense
11	DB	Fused Ign Sw Output
12	DB	TP Sensor Signal
13	DB/BK	Speed Sensor Ground

94I38115 94J38116 94J38074

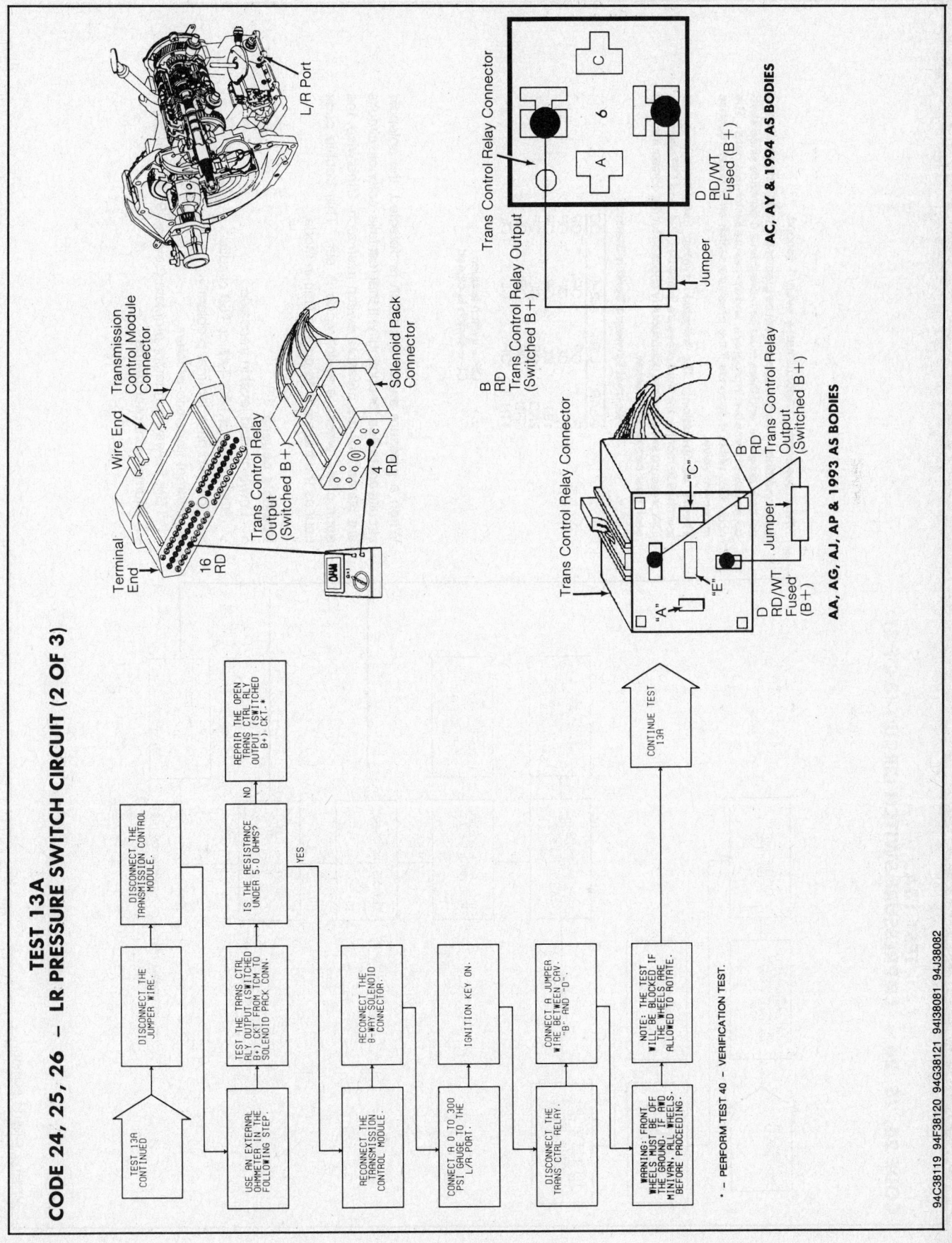

TEST 13A
CODE 24, 25, 26 — LR PRESSURE SWITCH CIRCUIT (2 OF 3)

L/R Port

Transmission Control Module Connector

Wire End

Terminal End

Solenoid Pack Connector

Trans Control Relay Output (Switched B+)

16 RD

4 RD

Trans Control Relay Connector

Trans Control Relay Output (Switched B+)

B RD
Trans Control Relay Output (Switched B+)

D RD/WT Fused (B+)

Jumper

AC, AY & 1994 AS BODIES

Trans Control Relay Connector

"C"

"A"

"E"

B RD
Trans Control Relay Output (Switched B+)

Jumper

D RD/WT Fused (B+)

AA, AG, AJ, AP & 1993 AS BODIES

TEST 13A CONTINUED

DISCONNECT THE JUMPER WIRE.

DISCONNECT THE TRANSMISSION CONTROL MODULE.

TEST THE TRANS CTRL RLY OUTPUT (SWITCHED B+) CKT FROM TCM TO SOLENOID PACK CONN.

IS THE RESISTANCE UNDER 5.0 OHMS?

NO → REPAIR THE OPEN TRANS CTRL RLY OUTPUT (SWITCHED B+) CKT.*

YES

USE AN EXTERNAL OHMMETER IN THE FOLLOWING STEP.

RECONNECT THE TRANSMISSION CONTROL MODULE.

RECONNECT THE 8-WAY SOLENOID CONNECTOR.

CONNECT A 0 TO 300 PSI GAUGE TO THE L/R PORT.

IGNITION KEY ON.

DISCONNECT THE TRANS CTRL RELAY.

CONNECT A JUMPER WIRE BETWEEN CAV. "B" AND "D".

WARNING: FRONT WHEELS MUST BE OFF THE GROUND. IF AWD MINIVAN, ALL WHEELS BEFORE PROCEEDING.

NOTE: THE TEST WILL BE BLOCKED IF THE WHEELS ARE ALLOWED TO ROTATE.

CONTINUE TEST 13A

* — PERFORM TEST 40 — VERIFICATION TEST.

94C38119 94F38120 94G38121 94I38061 94J38082

When monitored: Approximately every 1 second.

Set condition: Engine speed must be greater than 500 rpm; a shift must not be in progress; and there must be more than 2.0 seconds since start-up, no loss of prime test in progress, and a pressure switch mismatch. The code sets within 4 seconds if the pressure switch error count reaches maximum value.

Theory of operation: The transaxle system uses three pressure switches to monitor the fluid pressure in the L-R, 2-4, and OD elements. The pressure switches are continuously checked for the correct states in each gear as indicated below.

Normal Pressure Switch States

GEAR	L-R	2-4	OD
R	OP	OP	OP
N	CL	OP	OP
1ST	CL	OP	OP
2ND	OP	CL	OP
3RD	OP	OP	CL
4TH	CL	CL	CL

OP = switch is open
CL = switch is closed

When a pressure switch mismatch is detected, the solenoid circuits are tested for continuity. If that test fails, solenoid circuits are blamed for the pressure switch mismatch. Otherwise, the appropriate pressure switch code is set. This trouble code causes the transaxle to go into limp-in mode.

Possible causes:

> Low/high fluid level in transaxle
> Short/open in T09, T47 or T50 circuits
> Solenoid pack internal problem
> Internal transaxle problem
> TCM 60-way connector problem (cavities 9, 47, and 50)
> Internal controller failure

TEST 13A
CODE 24, 25, 26 - LR PRESSURE SWITCH CIRCUIT (3 OF 3)

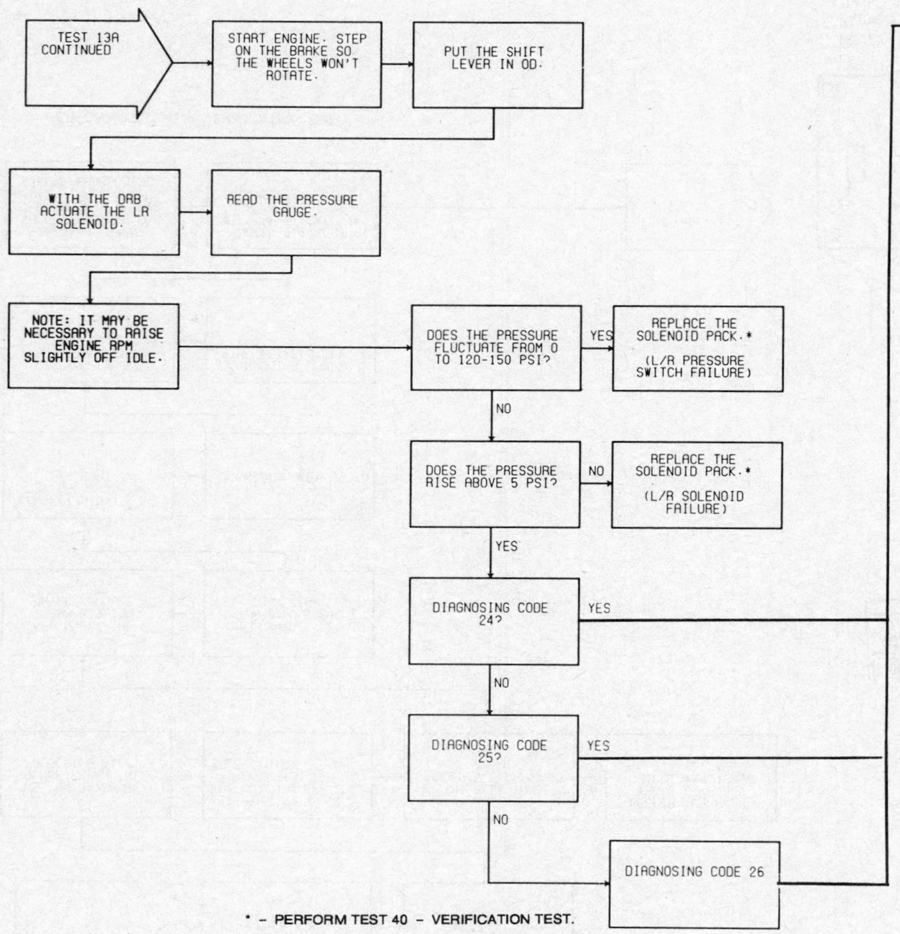

TEST 13A CONTINUED

START ENGINE. STEP ON THE BRAKE SO THE WHEELS WON'T ROTATE.

PUT THE SHIFT LEVER IN OD.

WITH THE DRB ACTUATE THE LR SOLENOID.

READ THE PRESSURE GAUGE.

NOTE: IT MAY BE NECESSARY TO RAISE ENGINE RPM SLIGHTLY OFF IDLE.

DOES THE PRESSURE FLUCTUATE FROM 0 TO 120-150 PSI?
— YES → REPLACE THE SOLENOID PACK.* (L/R PRESSURE SWITCH FAILURE)
— NO → DOES THE PRESSURE RISE ABOVE 5 PSI?
  — NO → REPLACE THE SOLENOID PACK.* (L/R SOLENOID FAILURE)
  — YES → DIAGNOSING CODE 24?
    — YES →
    — NO → DIAGNOSING CODE 25?
      — YES →
      — NO → DIAGNOSING CODE 26

* - PERFORM TEST 40 - VERIFICATION TEST.

94H38122 94J38123 94J38124

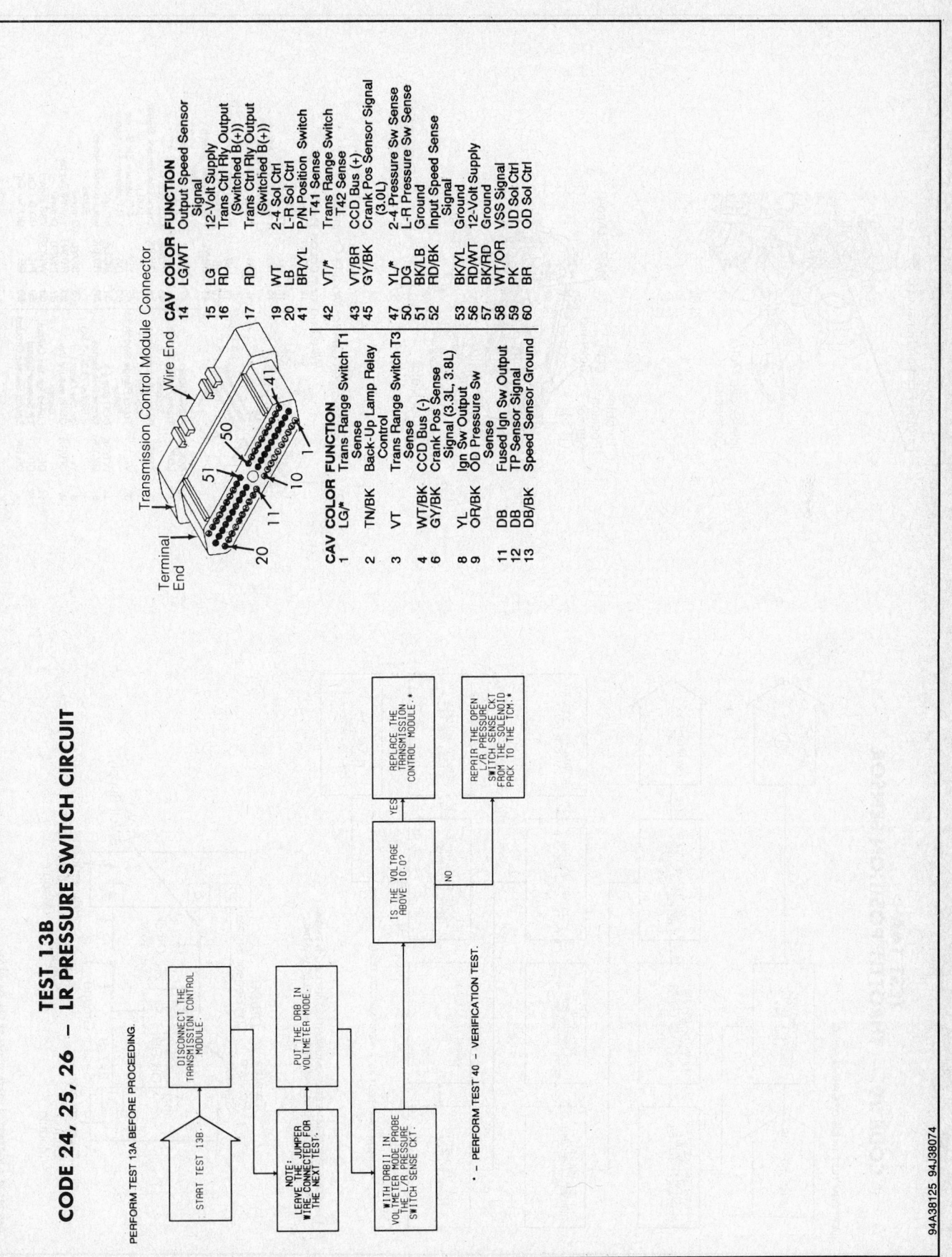

Transmission Control Module Connector

CAV	COLOR	FUNCTION
14	LG/WT	Output Speed Sensor Signal
15	LG	12-Volt Supply
16	RD	Trans Ctrl Rly Output (Switched B(+))
17	RD	Trans Ctrl Rly Output (Switched B(+))
19	WT	2-4 Sol Ctrl
20	LB	L-R Sol Ctrl
41	BR/YL	P/N Position Switch T41 Sense
42	VT/*	Trans Range Switch T42 Sense
43	VT/BR	CCD Bus (+)
45	GY/BK	Crank Pos Sensor Signal (3.0L)
47	YL/*	2-4 Pressure Sw Sense
50	DG	L-R Pressure Sw Sense
51	BK/LB	Ground
52	RD/BK	Input Speed Sense Signal
53	BK/YL	Ground
56	RD/WT	12-Volt Supply
57	BK/RD	Ground
58	WT/OR	VSS Signal
59	PK	UD Sol Ctrl
60	BR	OD Sol Ctrl

CAV	COLOR	FUNCTION
1	LG/*	Trans Range Switch T1 Sense
2	TN/BK	Back-Up Lamp Relay Control
3	VT	Trans Range Switch T3 Sense
4	WT/BK	CCD Bus (-)
6	GY/BK	Crank Pos Sense Signal (3.3L, 3.8L)
8	YL	Ign Sw Output
9	OR/BK	OD Pressure Sw Sense
11	DB	Fused Ign Sw Output
12	DB	TP Sensor Signal
13	DB/BK	Speed Sensor Ground

CODE 24, 25, 26 – TEST 13B
LR PRESSURE SWITCH CIRCUIT

PERFORM TEST 13A BEFORE PROCEEDING.

START TEST 13B.

DISCONNECT THE TRANSMISSION CONTROL MODULE.

NOTE: LEAVE THE JUMPER WIRE CONNECTED FOR THE NEXT TEST.

PUT THE DRB IN VOLTMETER MODE.

WITH DRB1 IN VOLTMETER MODE PROBE THE L/R PRESSURE SWITCH SENSE CKT.

IS THE VOLTAGE ABOVE 10.0?

YES → REPLACE THE TRANSMISSION CONTROL MODULE. *

NO → REPAIR THE OPEN L/R PRESSURE SWITCH SENSE CKT FROM THE SOLENOID PACK TO THE TCM. *

* – PERFORM TEST 40 – VERIFICATION TEST.

94A38125   94J38074

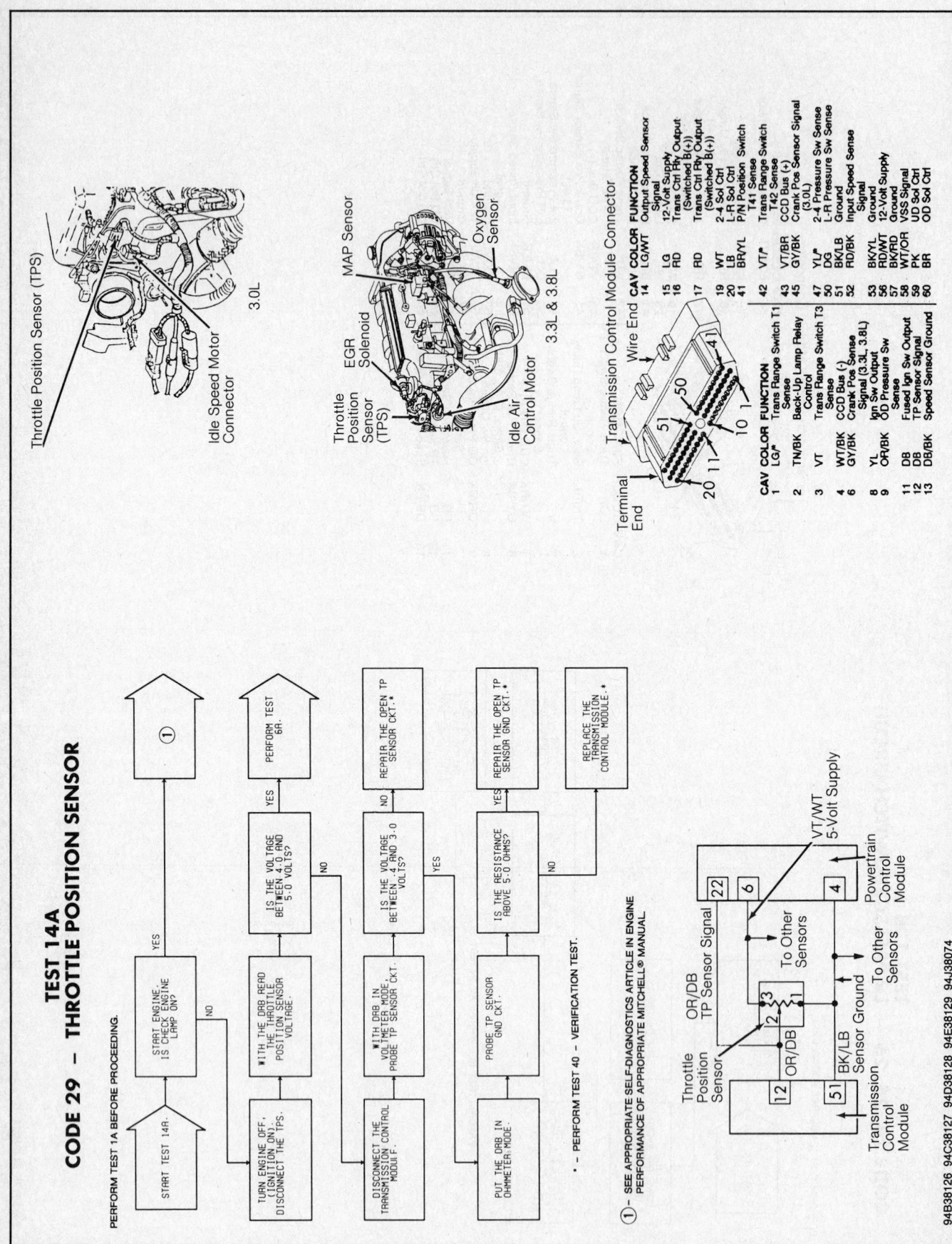

94B38126 94C38127 94D38128 94E38129 94J38074

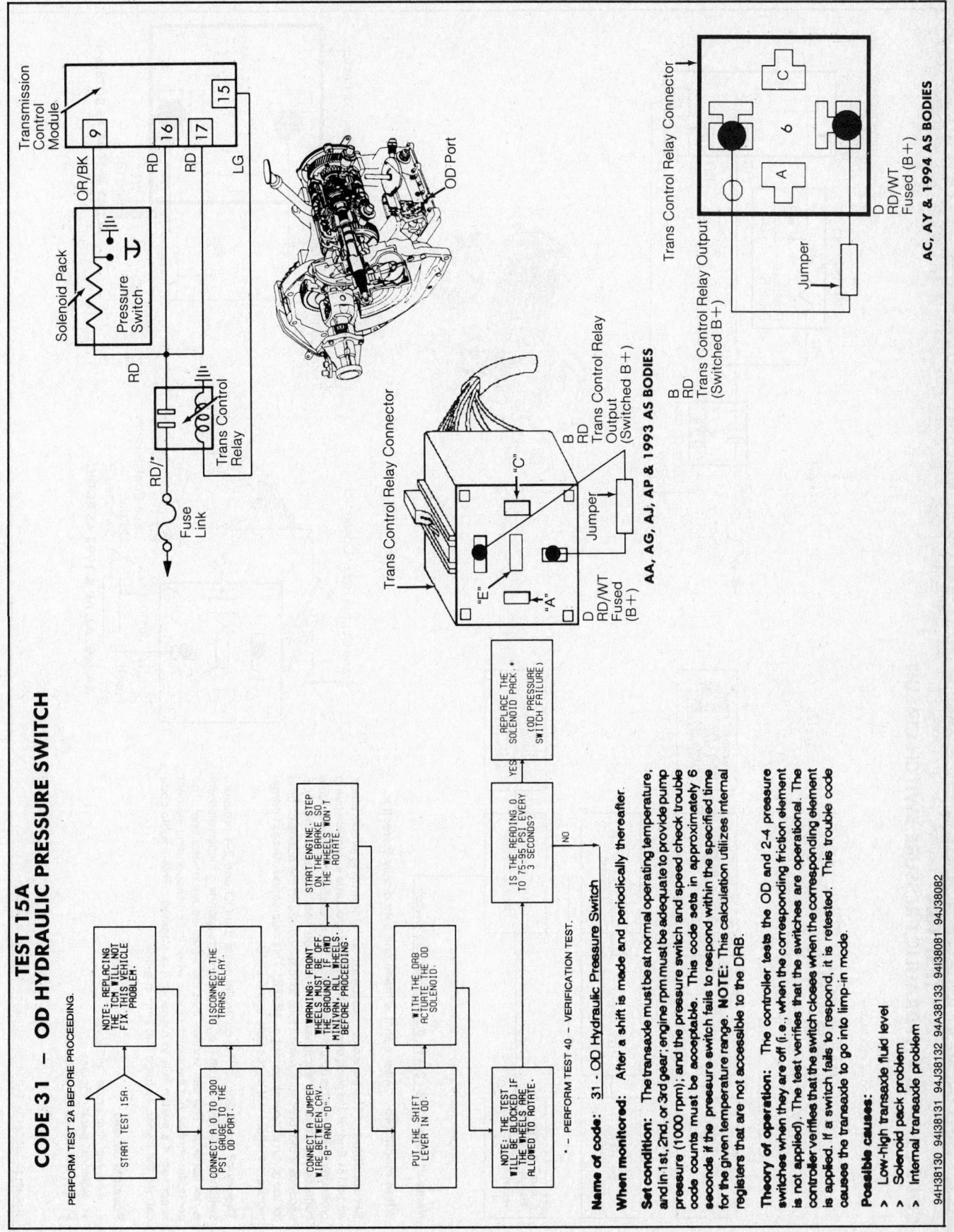

TEST 15A
CODE 31 – OD HYDRAULIC PRESSURE SWITCH

PERFORM TEST 2A BEFORE PROCEEDING.

START TEST 15A.

NOTE: REPLACING THE TCM WILL NOT FIX THIS VEHICLE PROBLEM.

CONNECT A 0 TO 300 PSI GAUGE TO THE OD PORT.

DISCONNECT THE TRANS RELAY.

CONNECT A JUMPER WIRE BETWEEN CAV. "B" AND "D".

WARNING: FRONT WHEELS MUST BE OFF THE GROUND. IF AWD MINIVAN, ALL WHEELS MUST BE OFF BEFORE PROCEEDING.

PUT THE SHIFT LEVER IN OD.

START ENGINE. STEP ON THE BRAKE SO THE WHEELS WON'T ROTATE.

NOTE: THE TEST WILL FAIL BELOW IF THE WHEELS ARE ALLOWED TO ROTATE.

WITH THE DRB ACTUATE THE OD SOLENOID.

IS THE READING 0 TO 75-95 PSI EVERY 3 SECONDS?

— YES → REPLACE THE SOLENOID PACK. * (OD PRESSURE SWITCH FAILURE)

— NO

* – PERFORM TEST 40 – VERIFICATION TEST.

Name of code: 31 – OD Hydraulic Pressure Switch

When monitored: After a shift is made and periodically thereafter.

Set condition: The transaxle must be at normal operating temperature, and in 1st, 2nd, or 3rd gear; engine rpm must be adequate to provide pump pressure (1000 rpm); and the pressure switch and speed sensor trouble code counts must be acceptable. This code sets in approximately 6 seconds if the pressure switch fails to respond within the specified time for the given temperature range. NOTE: This calculation utilizes internal registers that are not accessible to the DRB.

Theory of operation: The controller tests the OD and 2-4 pressure switches when they are off (i.e., when the corresponding friction element is not applied). The test verifies that the switches are operational. The controller verifies that the switch closes when the corresponding element is applied. If a switch fails to respond, it is retested. This trouble code causes the transaxle to go into limp-in mode.

Possible causes:
> Low-high transaxle fluid level
> Solenoid pack problem
> Internal transaxle problem

94H38130 94J38131 94J38132 94A38133 94J38081 94J38082

(Diagram labels)

Transmission Control Module

9 16 17 15

OR/BK RD RD LG

Solenoid Pack

Pressure Switch

RD

RD/*

Fuse Link

Trans Control Relay

OD Port

Trans Control Relay Connector

"C"

"E" "A"

B RD Trans Control Relay Output (Switched B+)

D RD/WT Fused (B+)

Jumper

AA, AG, AJ, AP & 1993 AS BODIES

Trans Control Relay Connector

C 6 A

B RD Trans Control Relay Output (Switched B+)

D RD/WT Fused (B+)

Jumper

AC, AY & 1994 AS BODIES

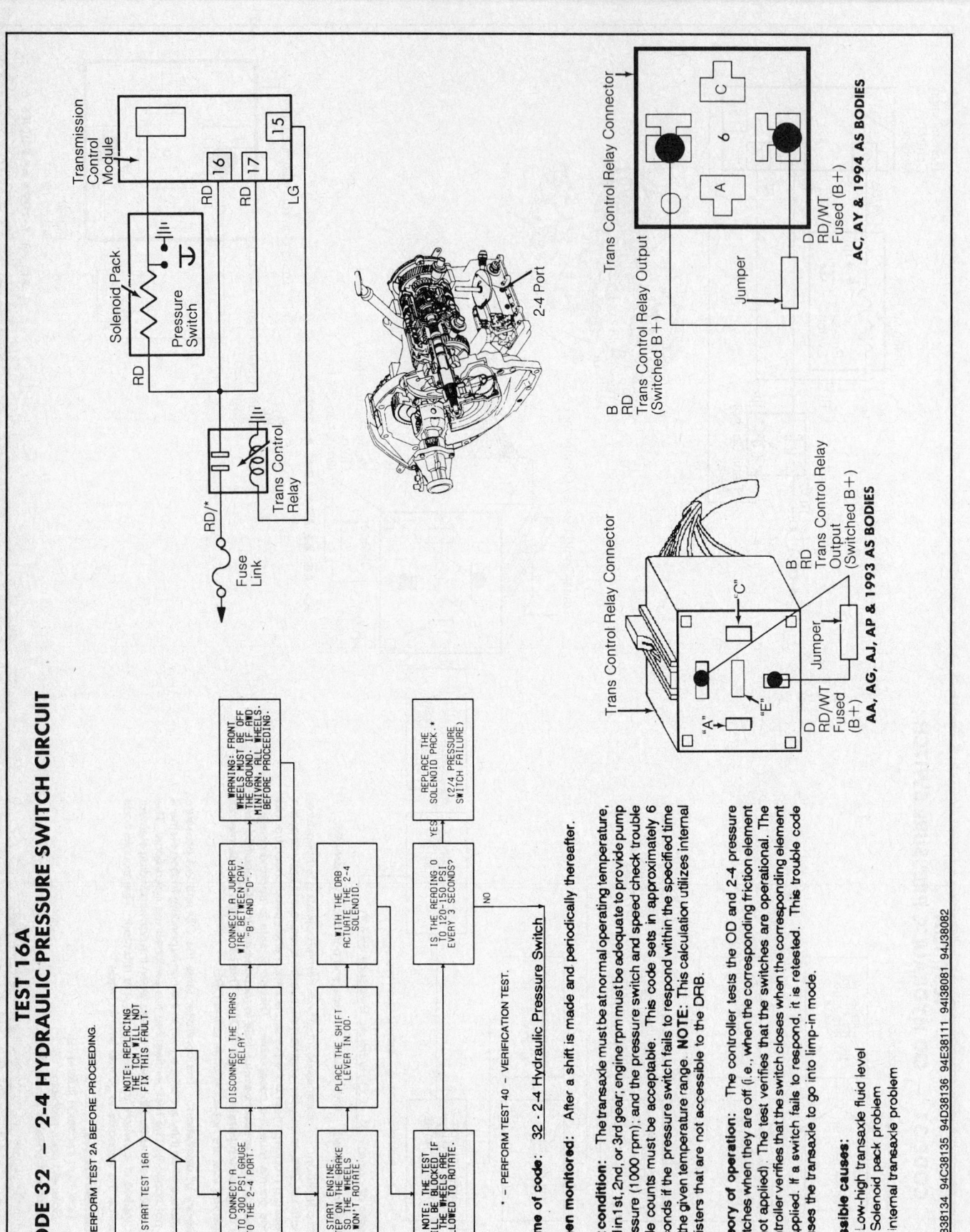

TEST 16A

CODE 32 – 2-4 HYDRAULIC PRESSURE SWITCH CIRCUIT

PERFORM TEST 2A BEFORE PROCEEDING.

START TEST 16A.

NOTE: REPLACING THE TCM WILL NOT FIX THIS FAULT.

CONNECT A 0 TO 300 PSI GAUGE TO THE 2-4 PORT.

DISCONNECT THE TRANS RELAY.

CONNECT A JUMPER WIRE BETWEEN CAV. "B" AND "D".

PLACE THE SHIFT LEVER IN OD.

START ENGINE - STEP ON THE BRAKE SO THE WHEELS WON'T ROTATE.

WARNING: FRONT WHEELS MUST BE OFF THE GROUND. WITH AN ALL WHEELS BEFORE PROCEEDING.

WITH THE DRB ACTUATE THE 2-4 SOLENOID.

NOTE: THE TEST WILL BE BLOCKED IF THE WHEELS ARE ALLOWED TO ROTATE.

IS THE READING 0 TO 120-150 PSI EVERY 3 SECONDS?

YES → REPLACE THE SOLENOID PACK. * (2/4 PRESSURE SWITCH FAILURE)

NO

* - PERFORM TEST 40 - VERIFICATION TEST.

Name of code: 32 - 2-4 Hydraulic Pressure Switch

When monitored: After a shift is made and periodically thereafter.

Set condition: The transaxle must be at normal operating temperature, and in 1st, 2nd, or 3rd gear; engine rpm must be adequate to provide pump pressure (1000 rpm); and the pressure switch and speed check trouble code counts must be acceptable. This code sets in approximately 6 seconds if the pressure switch fails to respond within the specified time for the given temperature range. NOTE: This calculation utilizes internal registers that are not accessible to the DRB.

Theory of operation: The controller tests the OD and 2-4 pressure switches when they are off (i.e., when the corresponding friction element is not applied). The test verifies that the switches are operational. The controller verifies that the switch closes when the corresponding element is applied. If a switch fails to respond, it is retested. This trouble code causes the transaxle to go into limp-in mode.

Possible causes:
> Low-high transaxle fluid level
> Solenoid pack problem
> Internal transaxle problem

94B38134 94C38135 94D38136 94E38111 94J38081 94J38082

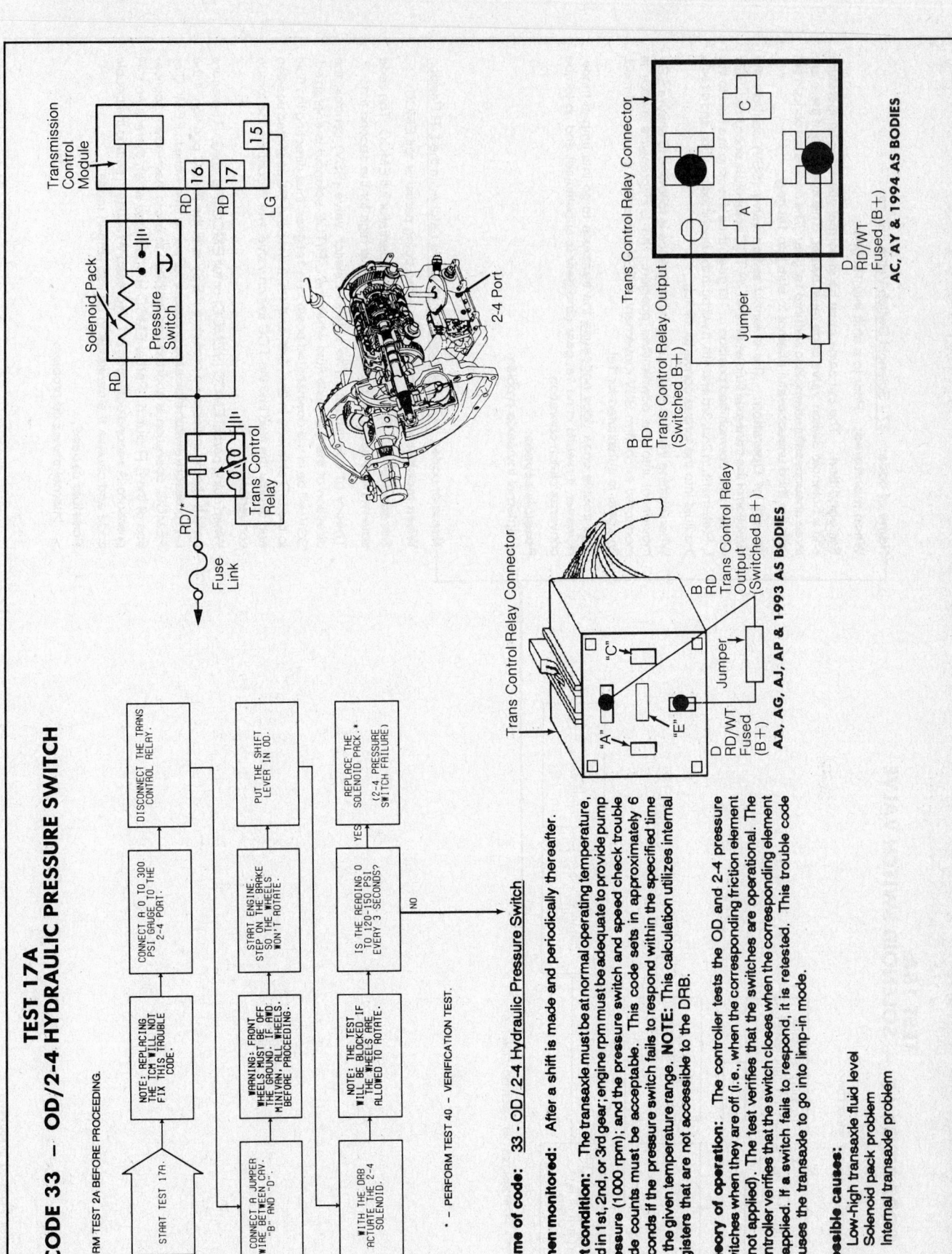

TEST 17A
CODE 33 – OD/2-4 HYDRAULIC PRESSURE SWITCH

PERFORM TEST 2A BEFORE PROCEEDING.

START TEST 17A.

NOTE: REPLACING THE TCM WILL NOT FIX THIS TROUBLE CODE.

CONNECT A 0 TO 300 PSI GAUGE TO THE 2-4 PORT.

DISCONNECT THE TRANS CONTROL RELAY.

CONNECT A JUMPER WIRE BETWEEN CAV. "B" AND "D".

WARNING: FRONT WHEELS MUST BE OFF THE GROUND. IF AND MINIVAN, ALL WHEELS. BEFORE PROCEEDING.

START ENGINE. STEP ON THE BRAKE SO THE WHEELS WON'T ROTATE.

PUT THE SHIFT LEVER IN OD.

WITH THE DRB ACTUATE THE 2-4 SOLENOID.

NOTE: THE TEST WILL BE BLOCKED IF THE WHEELS ARE ALLOWED TO ROTATE.

IS THE READING 0 TO 120-150 PSI EVERY 3 SECONDS?

NO →

YES → REPLACE THE SOLENOID PACK.* (2-4 PRESSURE SWITCH FAILURE)

* – PERFORM TEST 40 – VERIFICATION TEST.

Name of code: 33 - OD / 2-4 Hydraulic Pressure Switch

When monitored: After a shift is made and periodically thereafter.

Set condition: The transaxle must be at normal operating temperature, and in 1st, 2nd, or 3rd gear; engine rpm must be adequate to provide pump pressure (1000 rpm); and the pressure switch and speed check trouble code counts must be acceptable. This code sets in approximately 6 seconds if the pressure switch fails to respond within the specified time for the given temperature range. NOTE: This calculation utilizes internal registers that are not accessible to the DRB.

Theory of operation: The controller tests the OD and 2-4 pressure switches when they are off (i.e., when the corresponding friction element is not applied). The test verifies that the switches are operational. The controller verifies that the switch closes when the corresponding element is applied. If a switch fails to respond, it is retested. This trouble code causes the transaxle to go into limp-in mode.

Possible causes:
> Low-high transaxle fluid level
> Solenoid pack problem
> Internal transaxle problem

94E38137 94F38138 94D38136 94E38111 94I38081 94J38082

Transmission Control Module

15
16
17

RD
RD
LG

Solenoid Pack

Pressure Switch

RD

Trans Control Relay

RD/*

Fuse Link

2-4 Port

Trans Control Relay Connector

C
A
D
B

Trans Control Relay Connector

B RD Trans Control Relay Output (Switched B+)

D RD/WT Fused (B+)

Jumper

AC, AY & 1994 AS BODIES

Trans Control Relay Connector

"C"
"A"
"E"

B RD Trans Control Relay Output (Switched B+)

D RD/WT Fused (B+)

Jumper

AA, AG, AJ, AP & 1993 AS BODIES

Name of code: 37 - Solenoid Switch Valve Failure

When monitored: Prior to a shift into 1st gear.

Set condition: The transaxle must be at normal operating temperature and a Solenoid Switch Valve code must be set. This code sets if there are three unsuccessful attempts to shift into 1st gear. The code is set concurrent with the third unsuccessful attempt to shift into 1st gear.

Theory of Operation: The solenoid switch valve (SSV) controls the direction of the transaxle fluid when the L-R/TCC solenoid is energized. SSV will be in the downshifted position in 1st gear, thus directing the fluid to the L-R element. In 2nd, 3rd and 4th, it will be in the upshifted position and directs the fluid into the torque converter clutch.

When shifting into 1st gear, a special sequence is followed to ensure SSV movement into the downshifted position. The L-R pressure switch is monitored to confirm SSV movement. If SSV movement is not confirmed, 2nd gear is substituted for 1st.

This trouble code does not cause the transaxle to go into limp-in mode. However, it results in no 1st gear (2nd gear is substituted) and no torque converter clutch operation.

Possible causes:
> Internal transaxle problem

Name of code: 47 - Solenoid Switch Valve Latched in the L-R Position

When monitored: Continuously when doing partial or full EMCC.

Set condition: The transaxle must be in partial or full EMCC. The code sets within 3 seconds if the L-R pressure is high for the second time.

Theory of operation: The solenoid switch valve (SSV) controls the direction of the transaxle fluid when the L-R/TCC solenoid is energized. SSV will be in the downshifted position in 1st gear, thus directing the fluid to the L-R element. In 2nd, 3rd, and 4th, it will be in the upshifted position and directs the fluid into the TCC switch valve, which controls the torque converter.

When doing partial EMCC (PEMCC) or full EMCC (FL), the L-R pressure switch should indicate no pressure if SSV is in the EMCC position. If the L-R pressure switch indicates pressure for some time while in PEMCC or FEMCC, operation is aborted and inhibited to avoid inadvertent application of the L-R clutch. Partial EMCC is attempted when there is no L-R pressure. A second detection of L-R pressure results in setting the trouble code and causes the transaxle to go into limp-in mode.

Possible causes:
> Internal transaxle problem

TEST 18A
CODE 37 OR 47 - SOLENOID SWITCH VALVE

PERFORM TEST 2A BEFORE PROCEEDING.

START TEST 18A.

NOTE: REPLACING THE TCM WILL NOT FIX THIS VEHICLE TROUBLE CODE.

DRAIN THE TRANSAXLE.

REMOVE THE TRANSMISSION PAN.

INSPECT THE BOTTOM OF THE PAN FOR CLUTCH OR METAL DEBRIS.

DOES THE PAN CONTAIN EXCESS DEBRIS?

YES — REPAIR THE TRANSAXLE.*

NO

* - PERFORM TEST 40 - VERIFICATION TEST.

94G38139   94J38140   94A38141

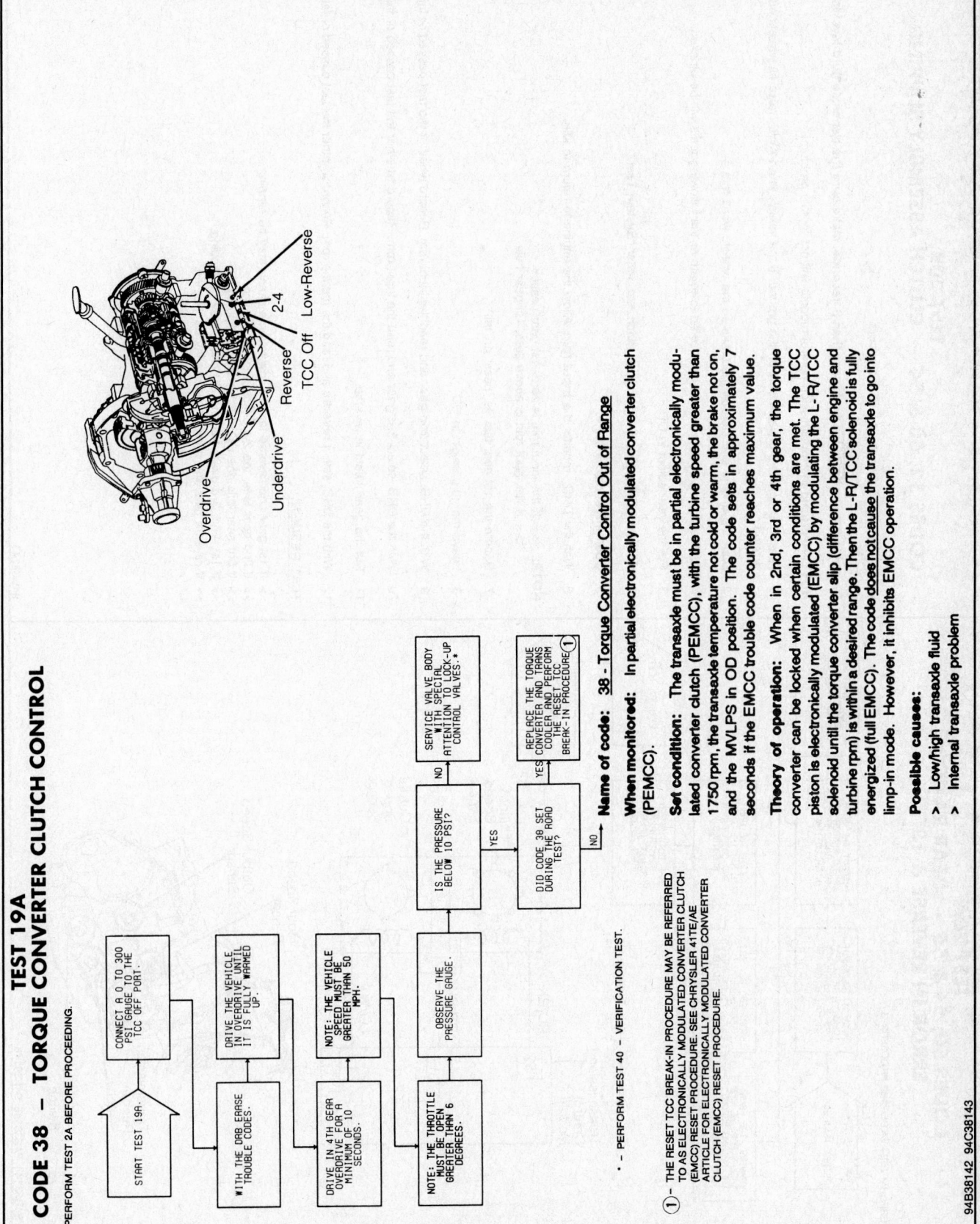

TEST 19A

CODE 38 — TORQUE CONVERTER CLUTCH CONTROL

PERFORM TEST 2A BEFORE PROCEEDING.

START TEST 19A.

→ CONNECT A 0 TO 300 PSI GAUGE TO THE TCC OFF PORT.

→ WITH THE DRB ERASE TROUBLE CODES.

→ DRIVE THE VEHICLE IN OVERDRIVE UNTIL IT IS FULLY WARMED UP.

→ DRIVE IN 4TH GEAR OVERDRIVE FOR A MINIMUM OF 10 SECONDS.

NOTE: THE VEHICLE SPEED MUST BE GREATER THAN 50 MPH.

→ NOTE: THE THROTTLE MUST BE OPEN GREATER THAN 6 DEGREES.

→ OBSERVE THE PRESSURE GAUGE.

→ IS THE PRESSURE BELOW 10 PSI?

NO → SERVICE VALVE BODY WITH SPECIAL ATTENTION TO LOCK-UP CONTROL VALVES.*

YES → DID CODE 38 SET DURING THE ROAD TEST?

YES → REPLACE THE TORQUE CONVERTER AND TRANS COOLER AND PERFORM THE RESET TCC BREAK-IN PROCEDURE ①

NO → * — PERFORM TEST 40 — VERIFICATION TEST.

* — PERFORM TEST 40 — VERIFICATION TEST.

① — THE RESET TCC BREAK-IN PROCEDURE MAY BE REFERRED TO AS ELECTRONICALLY MODULATED CONVERTER CLUTCH (EMCC) RESET PROCEDURE. SEE CHRYSLER 41TE/AE ARTICLE FOR ELECTRONICALLY MODULATED CONVERTER CLUTCH (EMCC) RESET PROCEDURE.

Name of code: <u>38 - Torque Converter Control Out of Range</u>

When monitored: In partial electronically modulated converter clutch (PEMCC).

Set condition: The transaxle must be in partial electronically modulated converter clutch (PEMCC), with the turbine speed greater than 1750 rpm, the transaxle temperature not cold or warm, the brake not on, and the MVLPS in OD position. The code sets in approximately 7 seconds if the EMCC trouble code counter reaches maximum value.

Theory of operation: When in 2nd, 3rd or 4th gear, the torque converter can be locked when certain conditions are met. The TCC piston is electronically modulated (EMCC) by modulating the L-R/TCC solenoid until the torque converter slip (difference between engine and turbine rpm) is within a desired range. Then the L-R/TCC solenoid is fully energized (full EMCC). The code does not cause the transaxle to go into limp-in mode. However, it inhibits EMCC operation.

Possible causes:
➤ Low/high transaxle fluid
➤ Internal transaxle problem

Overdrive
Underdrive
Reverse
2-4
TCC Off
Low-Reverse

94B38142 94C38143

TEST 20B
CODES 52, 53 & 54 – CLUTCH ASSEMBLY SLIPPING

PERFORM TEST 2A OR TEST 20A BEFORE PROCEEDING.

CAUTION!!!
Do not test any gear range for longer than 5 seconds. Make sure the transaxle fluid level is ok.

NOTE: Replacing the transmission control module will not fix this problem!

1. Raise the vehicle's drive wheels off the ground. If the vehicle is an AWD, raise all wheels off the ground.

2. Start the engine and step on the brake so the wheels won't rotate.

NOTE: The drive wheels must not be allowed to rotate or the following tests will be blocked.

3. Put the gear select in OD.

4. With the DRB, select the **1st gear** clutch test under "System Test."

5. Open the throttle to 30%.

6. With the DRB, monitor the **input rpm.** Allow the engine to return to idle.

NOTE: >> If the input rpm is zero, 1st gear passes.
>> If the input rpm is above zero, 1st gear fails.

7. Record the 1st gear test as "pass" or "fail".

8. Leave the gear select in OD.

9. With the DRB, select **2nd gear** and read the input rpm. Record whether the test passed or failed.

10. With the DRB, select **3rd gear** and read the input rpm. Record whether the test passed or failed.

11. Put the gear select in reverse.

12. With the DRB, select **reverse** and read the turbine rpm. Record whether the test passed or failed.

TEST RESULTS

>> If 1st gear and reverse fail, the low/reverse clutch may be slipping.
>> If 2nd gear fails, the 2-4 clutch may be slipping.
>> If 3rd gear fails, the OD clutch may be slipping.
>> If 1st, 2nd, 3rd gears fail, the UD clutch may be slipping.
>> If reverse fails, the reverse clutch may be slipping.

94G38147

TEST 20A
CODES 50, 51 & 55 – GEAR RATIO ERROR IN REVERSE & 1ST

PERFORM TEST 2A BEFORE PROCEEDING.

START TEST 20A.

INSPECT THE INPUT SPEED SENSOR FOR DAMAGE AND PROPER INSTALLATION.

INSPECT THE OUTPUT SPEED SENSOR FOR DAMAGE AND IMPROPER INSTALLATION.

BE SURE THAT BOTH SPEED SENSOR CONNECTORS ARE SECURELY FASTENED.

WARNING: THE FRONT WHEELS MUST BE OFF THE GROUND BEFORE PROCEEDING.

START ENGINE. PUT GEAR SELECT IN "D". ALLOW WHEELS TO ROTATE AT IDLE SPEED.

WITH THE DRB MONITOR THE INPUT AND OUTPUT RPM READINGS.

ARE BOTH SPEED SENSOR RPM READINGS GREATER THAN ZERO?

YES → PERFORM TEST 20B.

NO → PERFORM TEST 20C.

Input Speed Sensor

Output Speed Sensor

Transmission Control Module

52 — RD/BK
13 — DB/BK
14 — LG/WT

Input Speed Sensor

Output Speed Sensor

Transmission Range Switch

Park/Neutral Switch

94D38144 94E38145 94F38146

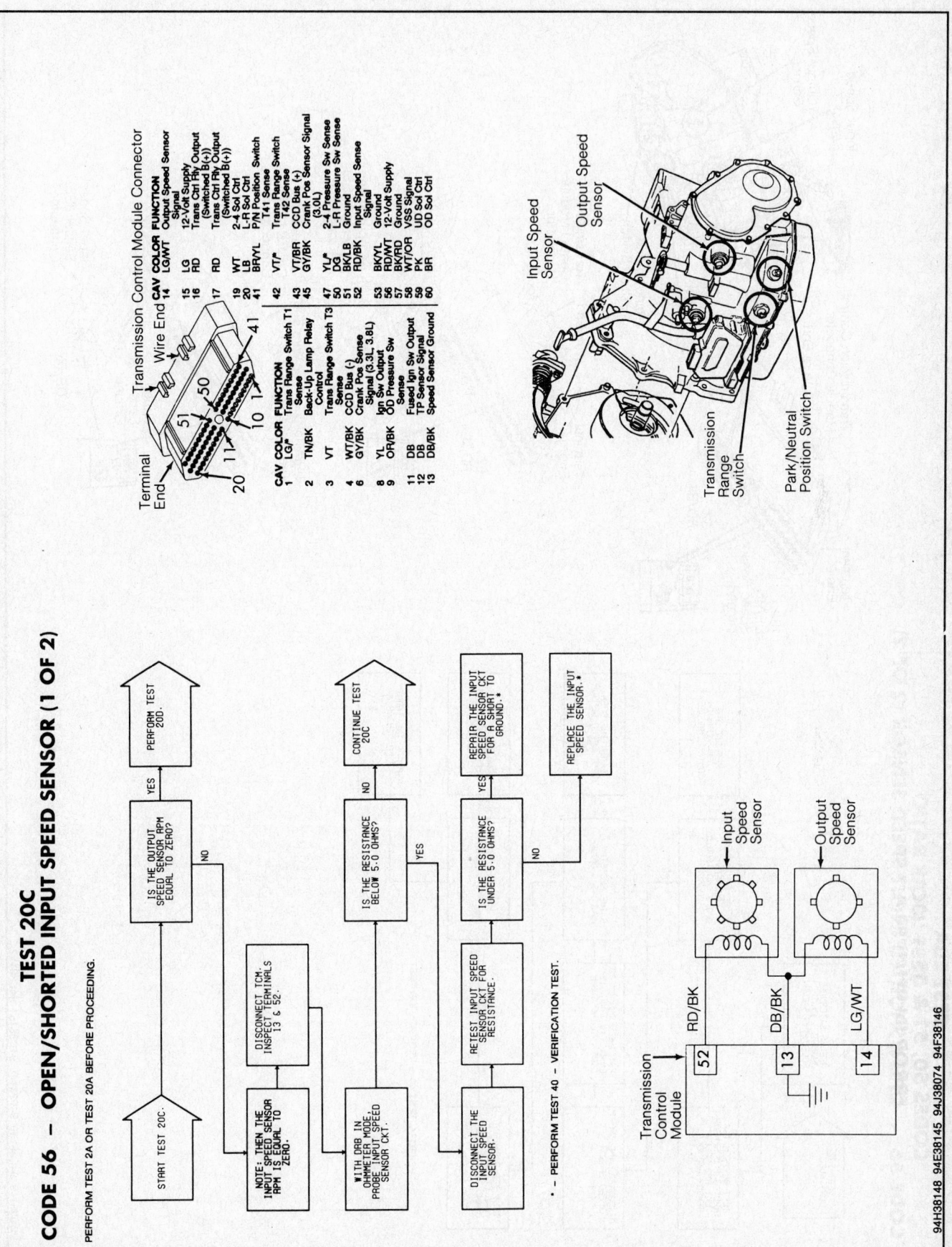

TEST 20C

CODE 56 – OPEN/SHORTED INPUT SPEED SENSOR (1 OF 2)

PERFORM TEST 2A OR TEST 20A BEFORE PROCEEDING.

94H38148 94E38145 94J38074 94F38146

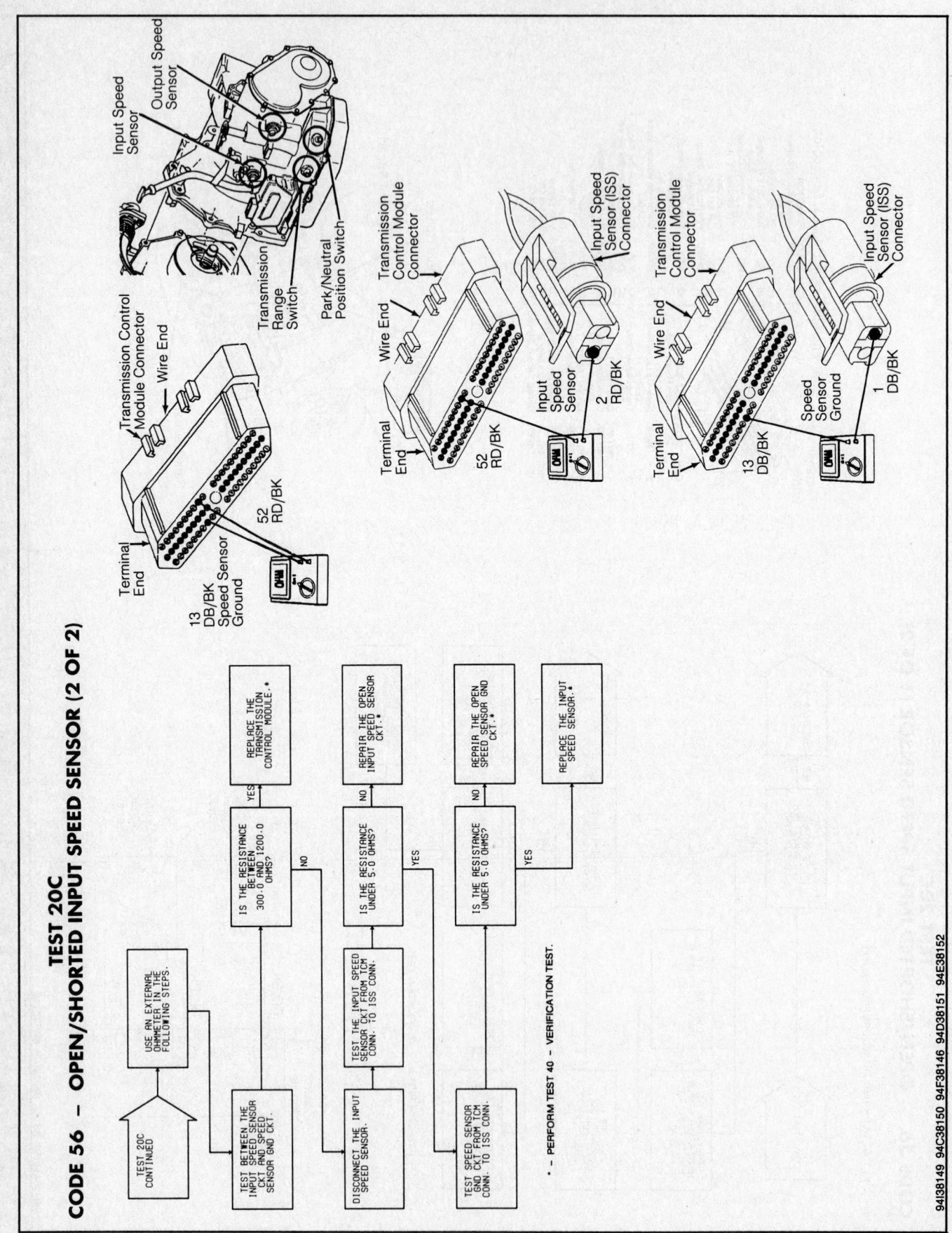

TEST 20C

CODE 56 – OPEN/SHORTED INPUT SPEED SENSOR (2 OF 2)

94I38149 94C38150 94F38146 94D38151 94E38152

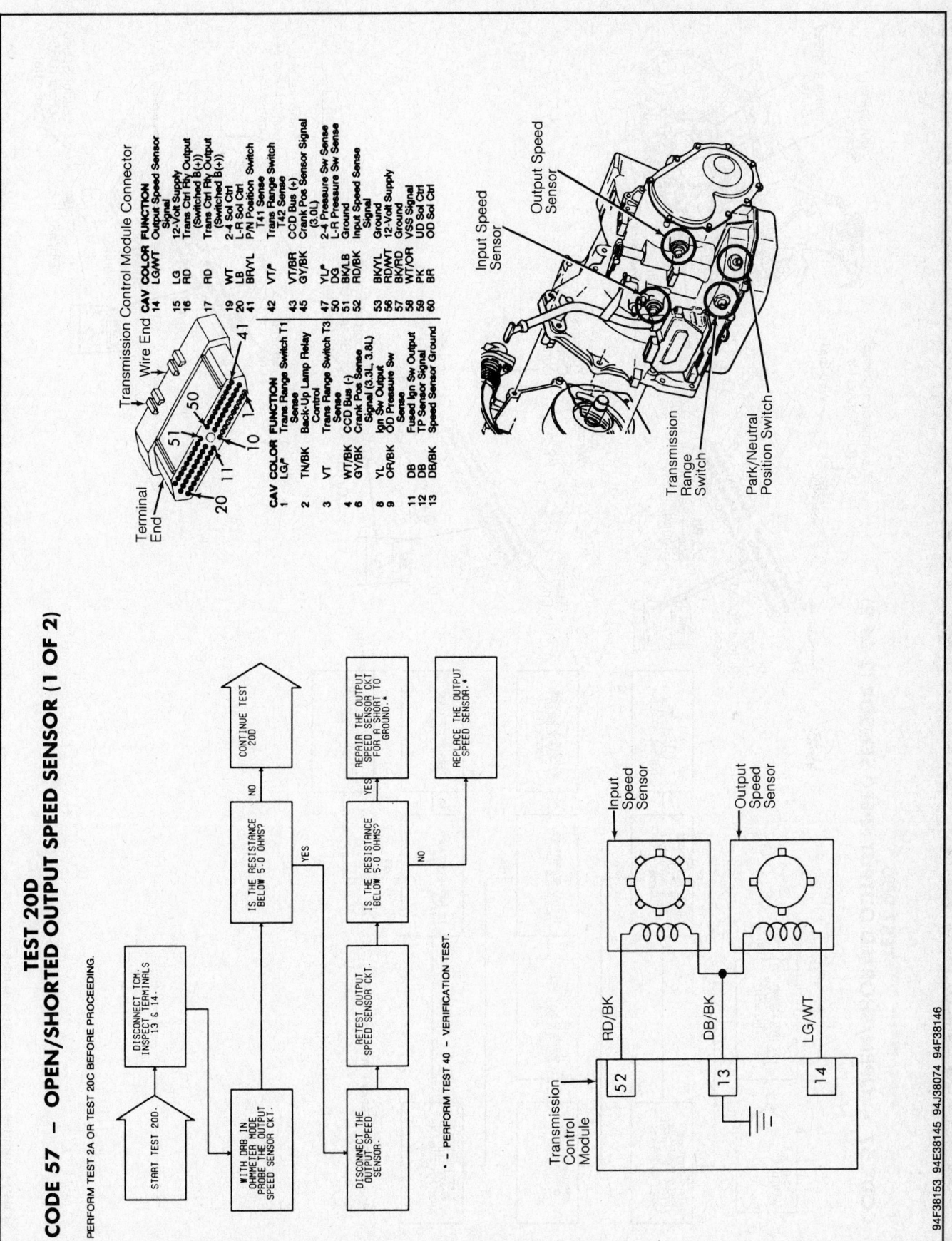

Transmission Control Module Connector

Wire End			
CAV	COLOR	FUNCTION	
14	LG/WT	Output Speed Sensor Signal	
15	LG	12-Volt Supply	
16	RD	Trans Ctrl Rly Output (Switched B(+))	
17	RD	Trans Ctrl Rly Output (Switched B(+))	
19	WT	2-4 Sol Ctrl	
20	LB	L-R Sol Ctrl	
41	BR/YL	P/N Position Switch	
42	VT/*	Trans Range Switch T41 Sense	
43	VT/BR	Trans Range Switch T42 Sense	
45	GY/BK	CCD Bus (+)	
47	YL/*	Crank Pos Sensor Signal (3.0L)	
50	DG	2-4 Pressure Sw Sense	
51	BK/LB	L-R Pressure Sw Sense	
52	RD/LB	Input Speed Sensor Signal	
53	BK/YL	Ground	
56	RD/WT	12-Volt Supply	
57	BK/RD	Ground	
58	WT/OR	VSS Signal	
59	PK	UD Sol Ctrl	
60	BR	OD Sol Ctrl	

CAV	COLOR	FUNCTION	
1	LG/*	Trans Range Switch T1 Sense	
2	TN/BK	Back-Up Lamp Relay Control	
3	VT	Trans Range Switch T3 Sense	
4	WT/BK	CCD Bus (-)	
6	GY/BK	Crank Pos Sense Signal (3.3L, 3.8L)	
8	YL	Ign Sw Output	
9	OR/BK	OD Pressure Sw Sense	
11	DB	Fused Ign Sw Output	
12	DB	TP Sensor Signal	
13	DB/BK	Speed Sensor Ground	

Terminal End

Input Speed Sensor

Output Speed Sensor

Transmission Range Switch

Park/Neutral Position Switch

TEST 20D
CODE 57 – OPEN/SHORTED OUTPUT SPEED SENSOR (1 OF 2)

PERFORM TEST 2A OR TEST 20C BEFORE PROCEEDING.

START TEST 20D.

↓

WITH DRB IN OHMMETER MODE PROBE THE OUTPUT SPEED SENSOR CKT.

↓

IS THE RESISTANCE BELOW 5.0 OHMS?

— NO → CONTINUE TEST 20D

— YES ↓

DISCONNECT THE OUTPUT SPEED SENSOR.

↓

RETEST OUTPUT SPEED SENSOR CKT.

↓

IS THE RESISTANCE BELOW 5.0 OHMS?

— YES → REPAIR THE OUTPUT SPEED SENSOR CKT FOR A SHORT TO GROUND. *

— NO → REPLACE THE OUTPUT SPEED SENSOR. *

* – PERFORM TEST 40 – VERIFICATION TEST.

DISCONNECT TCM. INSPECT TERMINALS 13 & 14.

Input Speed Sensor

Output Speed Sensor

RD/BK

DB/BK

LG/WT

52

13

14

Transmission Control Module

94F38153 94E38145 94E38145 94J38074 94F38146

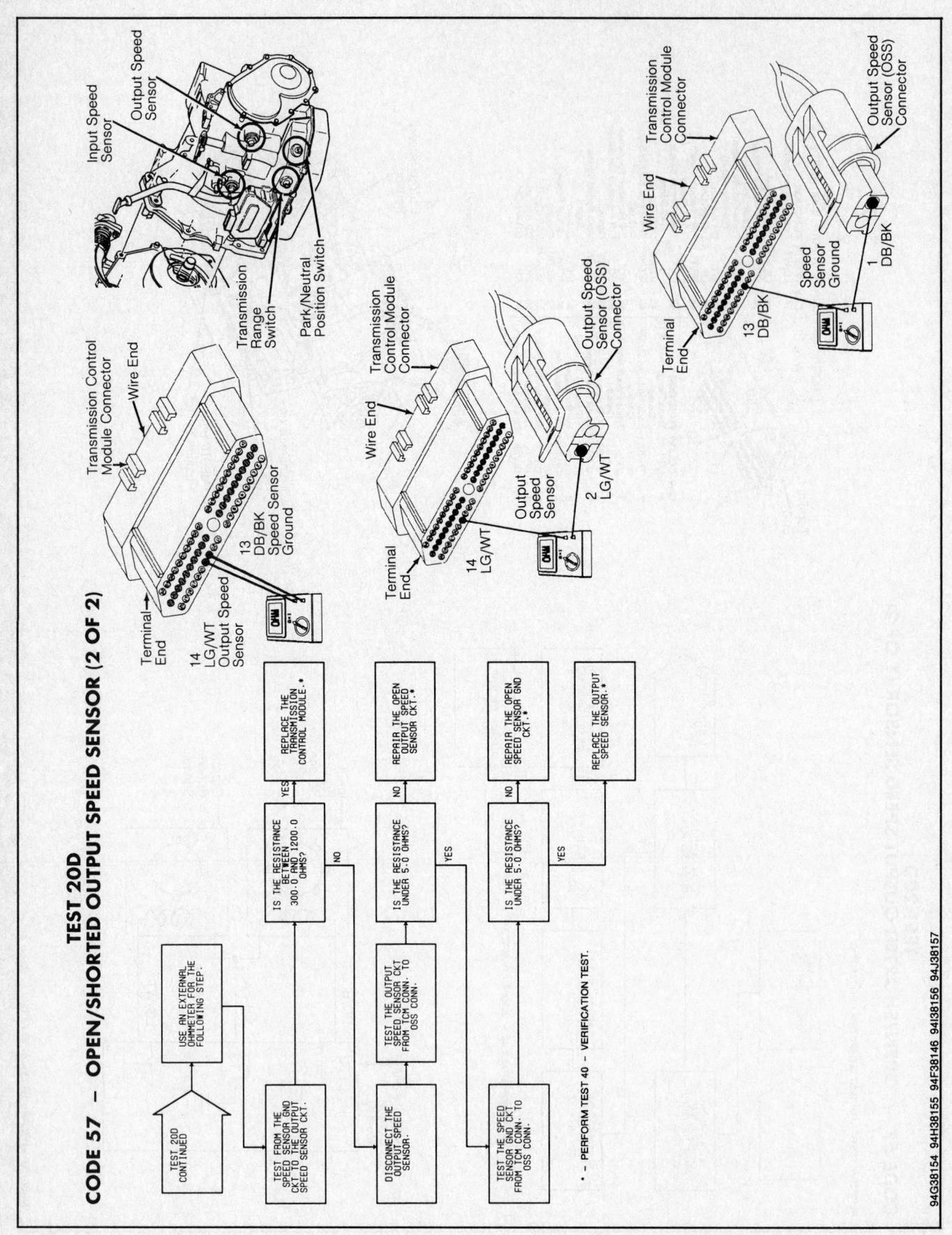

TEST 20D

CODE 57 – OPEN/SHORTED OUTPUT SPEED SENSOR (2 OF 2)

94G38154 94H38155 94F38146 94I38156 94J38157

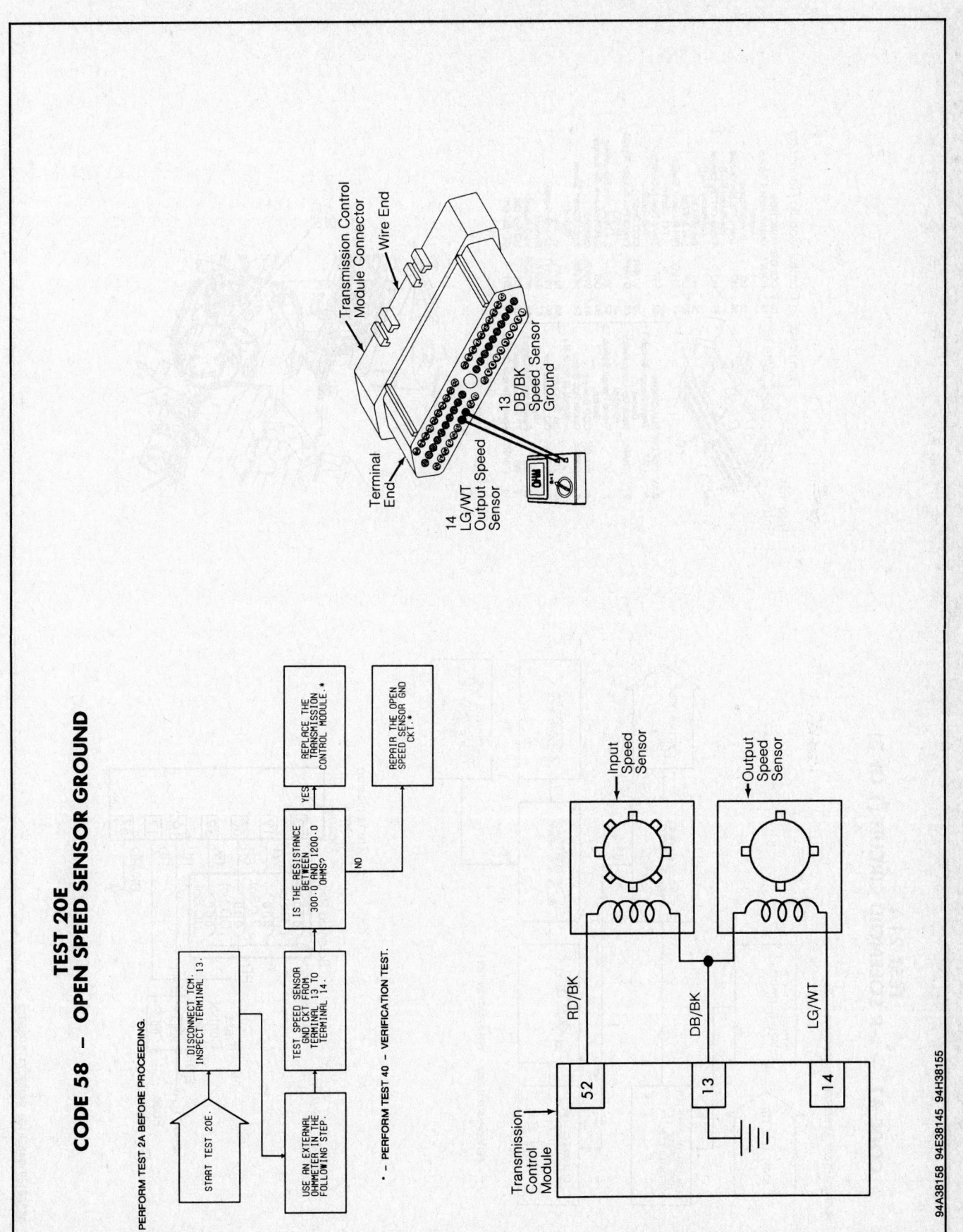

TEST 20E
CODE 58 – OPEN SPEED SENSOR GROUND

PERFORM TEST 2A BEFORE PROCEEDING.

START TEST 20E.

DISCONNECT TCM. INSPECT TERMINAL 13.

USE AN EXTERNAL OHMMETER IN THE FOLLOWING STEP.

TEST SPEED SENSOR GND CKT FROM TERMINAL 13 TO TERMINAL 14.

IS THE RESISTANCE BETWEEN 300.0 AND 1200.0 OHMS?

YES — REPLACE THE TRANSMISSION CONTROL MODULE. *

NO — REPAIR THE OPEN SPEED SENSOR GND CKT. *

* – PERFORM TEST 40 – VERIFICATION TEST.

Input Speed Sensor

Output Speed Sensor

RD/BK

DB/BK

LG/WT

Transmission Control Module

52

13

14

Transmission Control Module Connector

Wire End

13 DB/BK Speed Sensor Ground

Terminal End

14 LG/WT Output Speed Sensor

OHM

94A38158 94E38145 94H38155

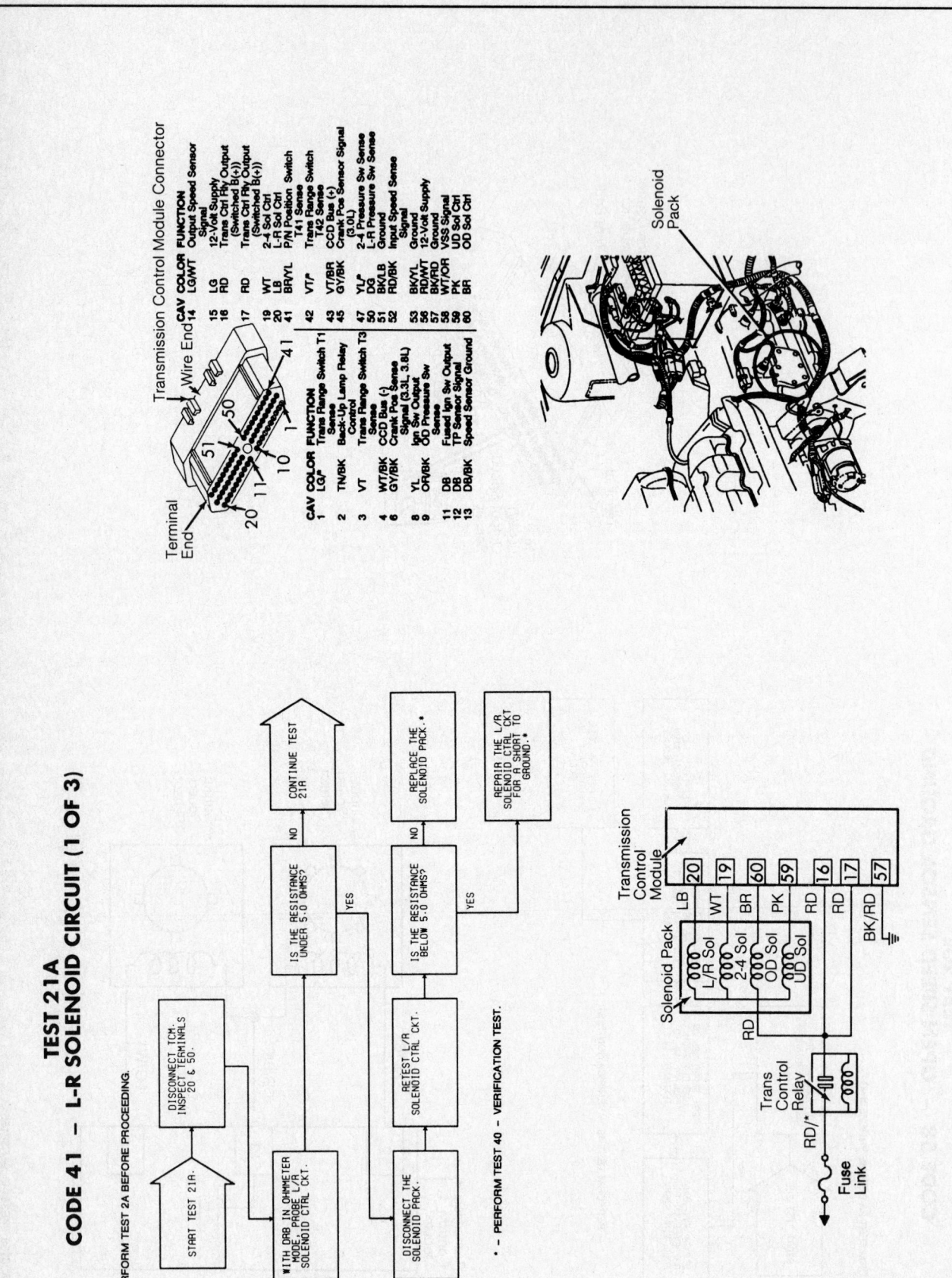

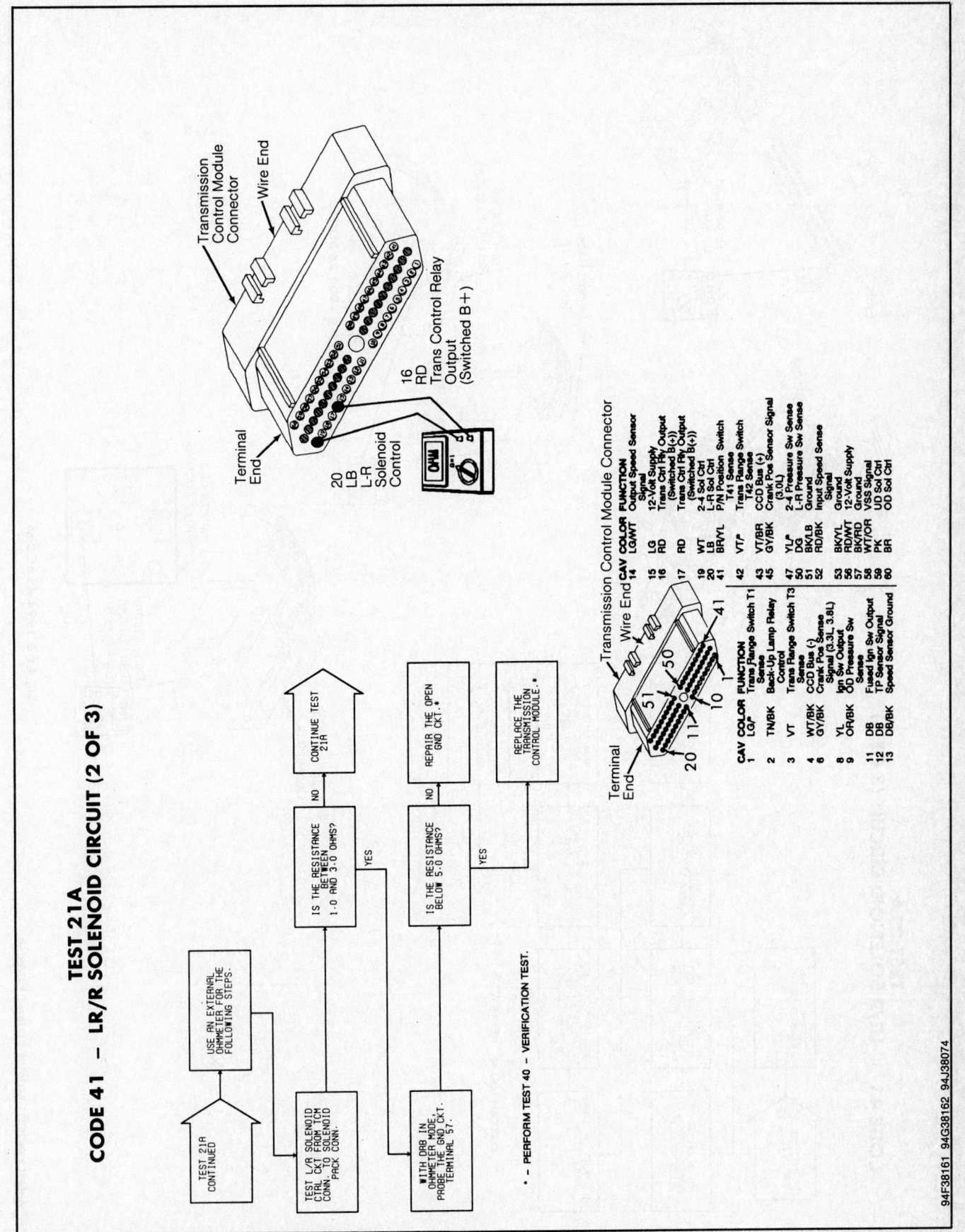

TEST 21A
CODE 41 – LR/R SOLENOID CIRCUIT (2 OF 3)

TEST 21A
CONTINUED

USE AN EXTERNAL OHMMETER FOR THE FOLLOWING STEPS.

TEST L/R SOLENOID CTRL CKT FROM TCM CONN. TO SOLENOID PACK CONN.

IS THE RESISTANCE BETWEEN 1.0 AND 3.0 OHMS?

NO → CONTINUE TEST 21A

YES

WITH DRB IN OHMMETER MODE, PROBE THE GND CKT. TERMINAL 57.

IS THE RESISTANCE BELOW 5.0 OHMS?

NO → REPAIR THE OPEN GND CKT. *

YES

REPLACE THE TRANSMISSION CONTROL MODULE. *

* – PERFORM TEST 40 – VERIFICATION TEST.

Transmission Control Module Connector

Wire End

16 RD Trans Control Relay Output (Switched B+)

Terminal End

20 LB L-R Solenoid Control

CAV	COLOR	FUNCTION
14	LG/WT	Output Speed Sensor Signal
15	LG	12-Volt Supply
16	RD	Trans Ctrl Rly Output (Switched B(+))
17	RD	Trans Ctrl Rly Output (Switched B(+))
19	WT	2-4 Sol Ctrl
20	LB	L-R Sol Ctrl
41	BR/YL	P/N Position Switch
42	VT*	Trans Range Switch T41 Sense
43	VT/BR	Trans Range Switch T42 Sense
45	GY/BK	CCD Bus (+)
47	YL*	Crank Pos Sensor Signal (3.0L)
50	DG	2-4 Pressure Sw Sense
51	BK/LB	L-R Pressure Sw Sense
52	RD/BK	Input Speed Sensor Signal
53	BK/YL	Ground
56	RD/WT	12-Volt Supply
57	BK/RD	Ground
58	WT/OR	VSS Signal
59	PK	TP Sensor Signal
60	BR	OD Sol Ctrl

Transmission Control Module Connector

Wire End

CAV	COLOR	FUNCTION
1	LG*	Trans Range Switch T1 Sense
2	TN/BK	Back-Up Lamp Relay Control
3	VT	Trans Range Switch T3 Sense
4	WT/BK	CCD Bus (-)
6	GY/BK	Crank Pos Sense Signal (3.3L, 3.8L)
8	YL	Crank Pos Sense
9	OR/BK	Ign Sw Output
10		OD Pressure Sw Sense
11	DB	Fused Ign Sw Output
12	DB	TP Sensor Signal
13	DB/BK	Speed Sensor Ground

Terminal End

94F38161 94G38162 94J38074

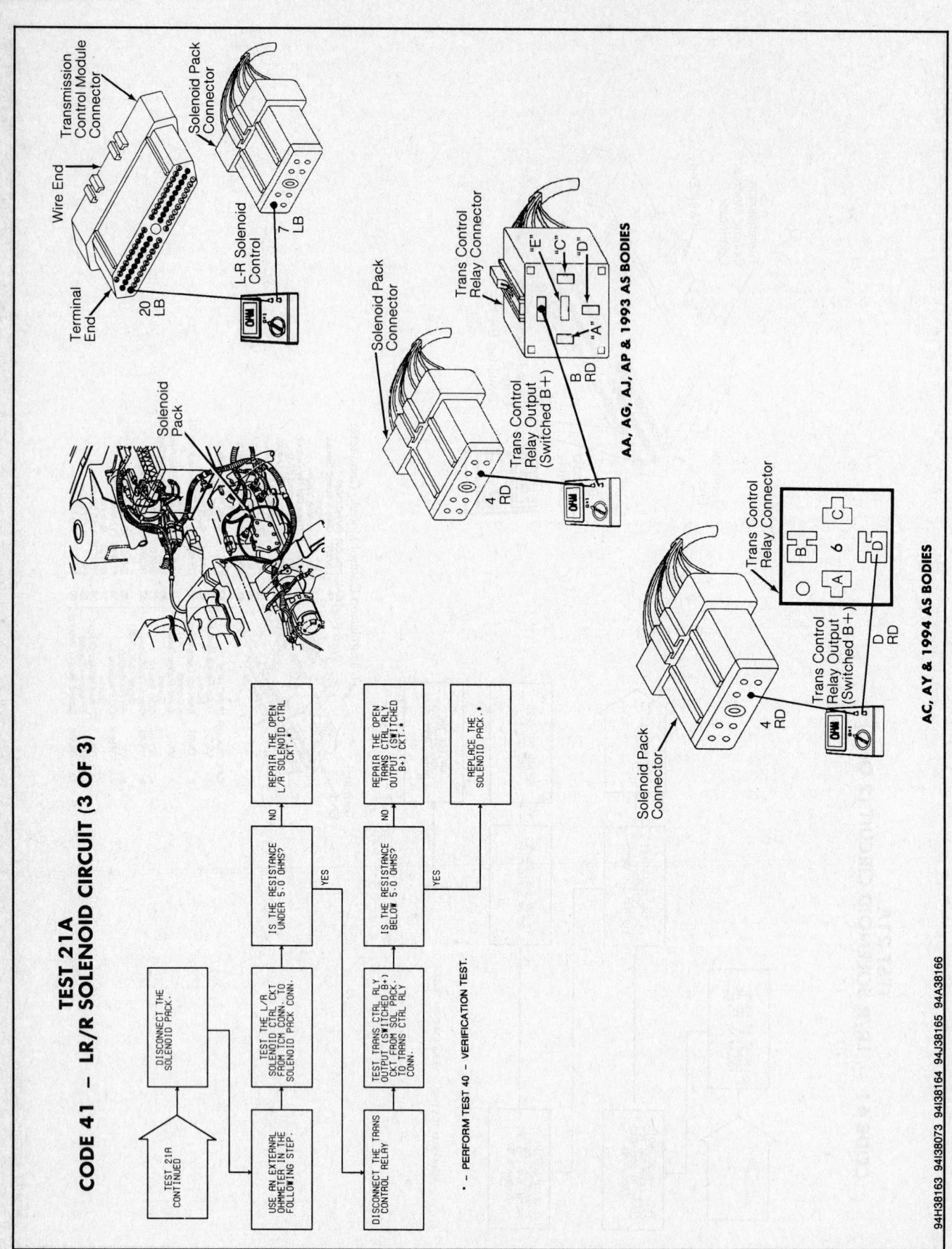

TEST 21A
CODE 41 — LR/R SOLENOID CIRCUIT (3 OF 3)

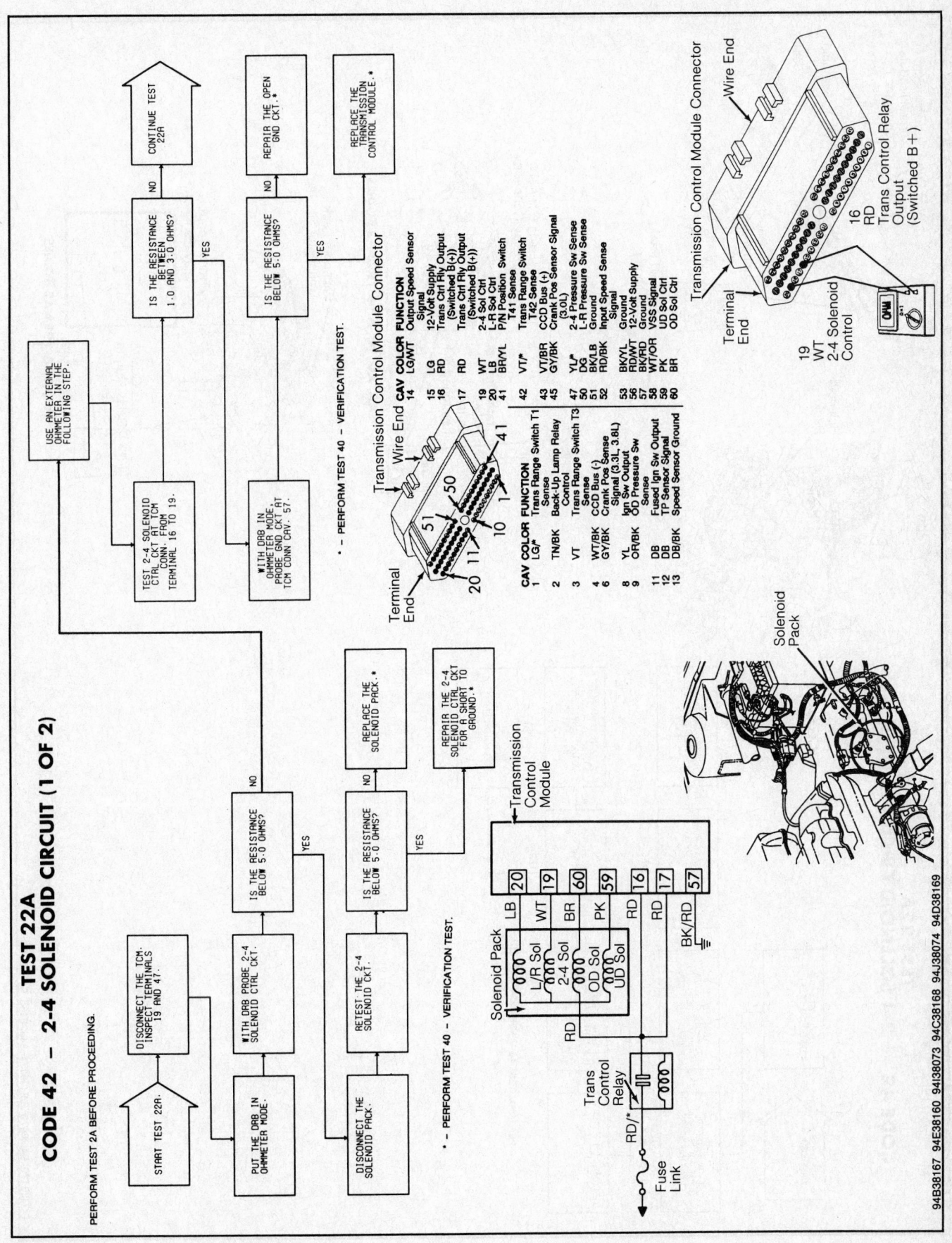

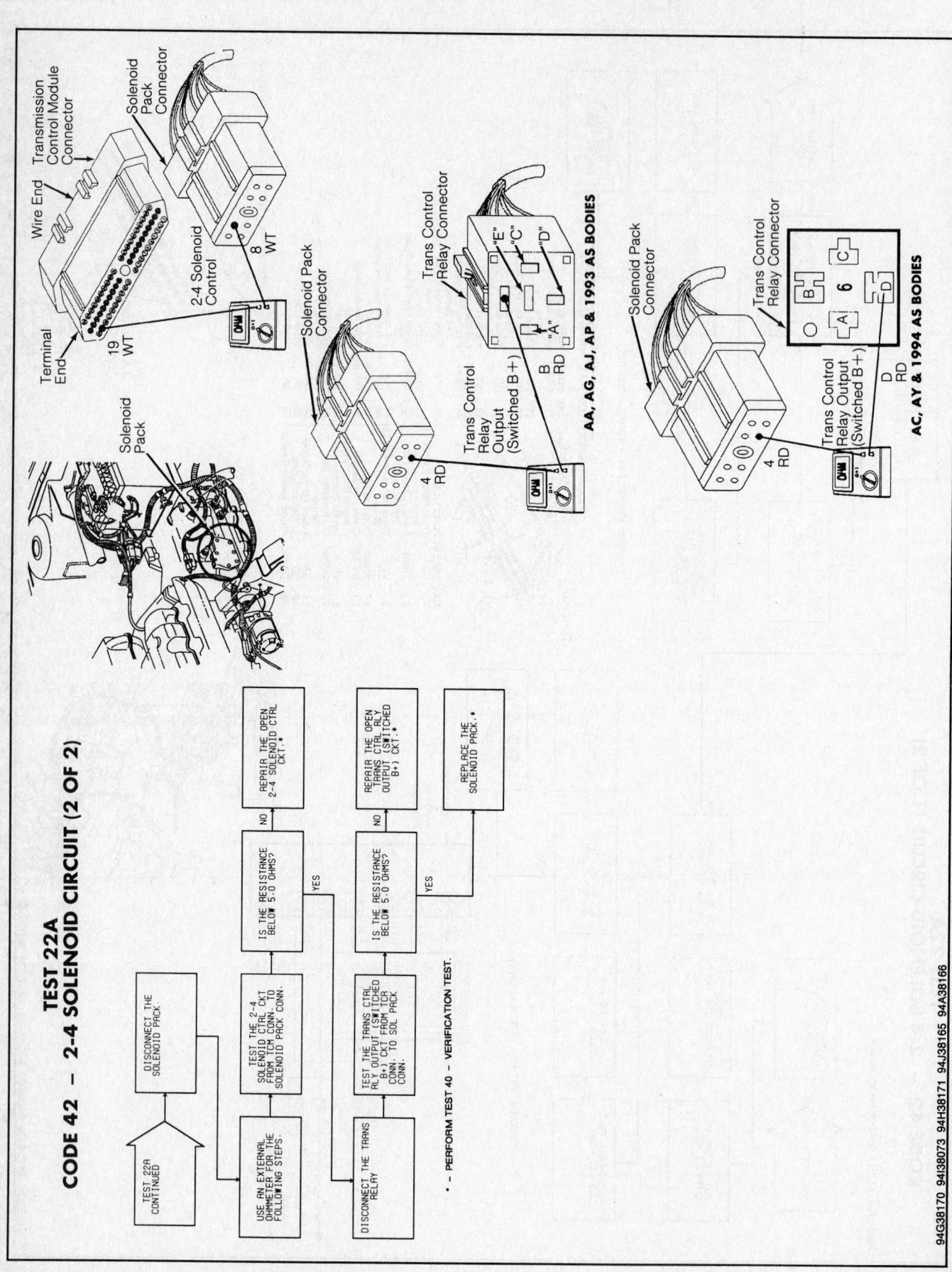

TEST 22A
CODE 42 – 2-4 SOLENOID CIRCUIT (2 OF 2)

TEST 22A CONTINUED

DISCONNECT THE SOLENOID PACK

USE AN EXTERNAL OHMMETER FOR THE FOLLOWING STEPS.

TEST THE 2-4 SOLENOID CTRL CKT FROM TCM CONN. TO SOLENOID PACK CONN.

IS THE RESISTANCE BELOW 5.0 OHMS? — NO → REPAIR THE OPEN 2-4 SOLENOID CTRL CKT.*

YES

DISCONNECT THE TRANS RELAY

TEST THE TRANS CTRL RLY OUTPUT (SWITCHED B+) CKT FROM TCR CONN. TO SOL PACK CONN.

IS THE RESISTANCE BELOW 5.0 OHMS? — NO → REPAIR THE OPEN TRANS CTRL RLY OUTPUT (SWITCHED B+) CKT.*

YES

REPLACE THE SOLENOID PACK.*

* – PERFORM TEST 40 – VERIFICATION TEST.

94G38170 94J38073 94H38171 94J38165 94A38166

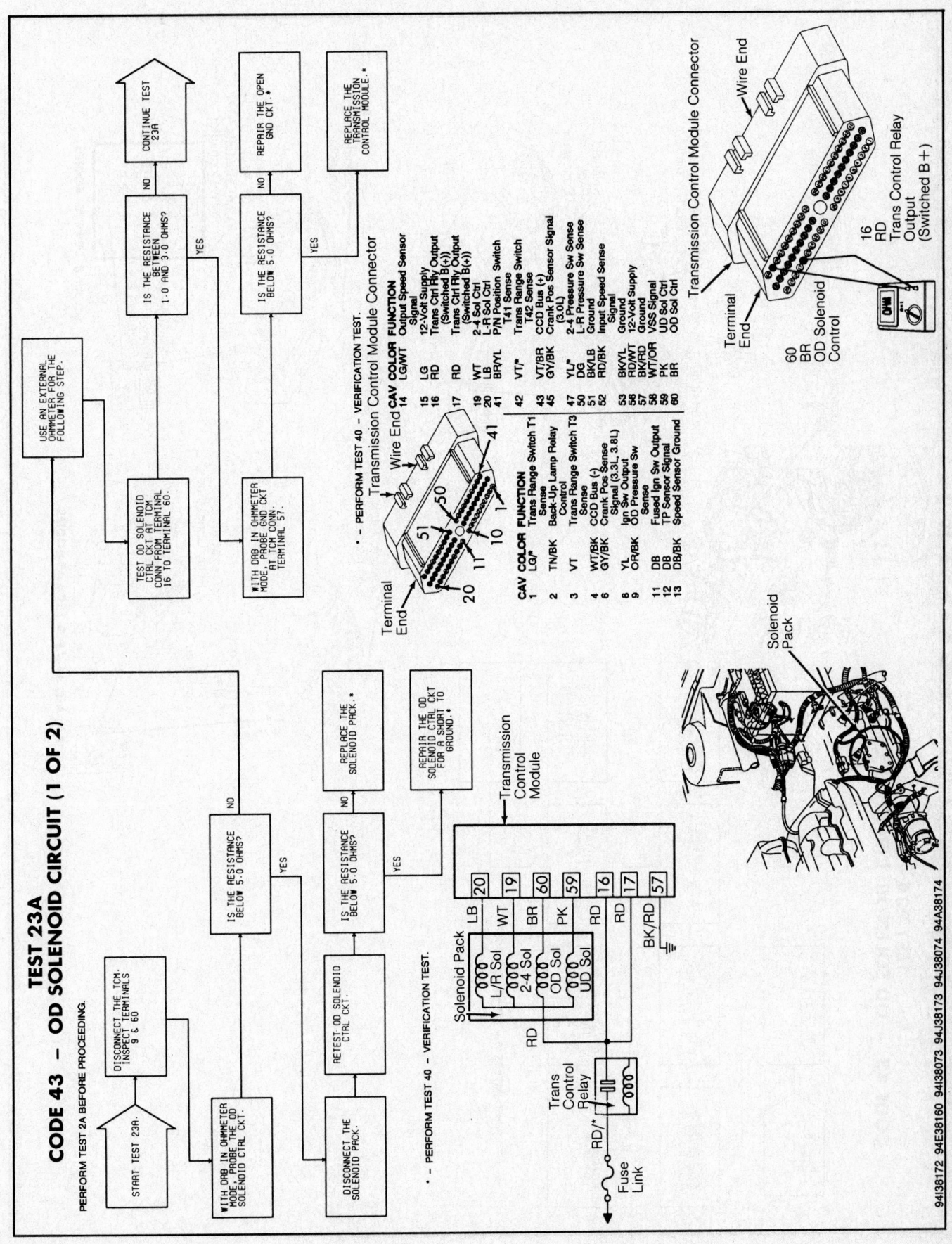

TEST 23A
CODE 43 – OD SOLENOID CIRCUIT (1 OF 2)

PERFORM TEST 2A BEFORE PROCEEDING.

94J38172 94E38160 94J38073 94J38173 94J38074 94A38174

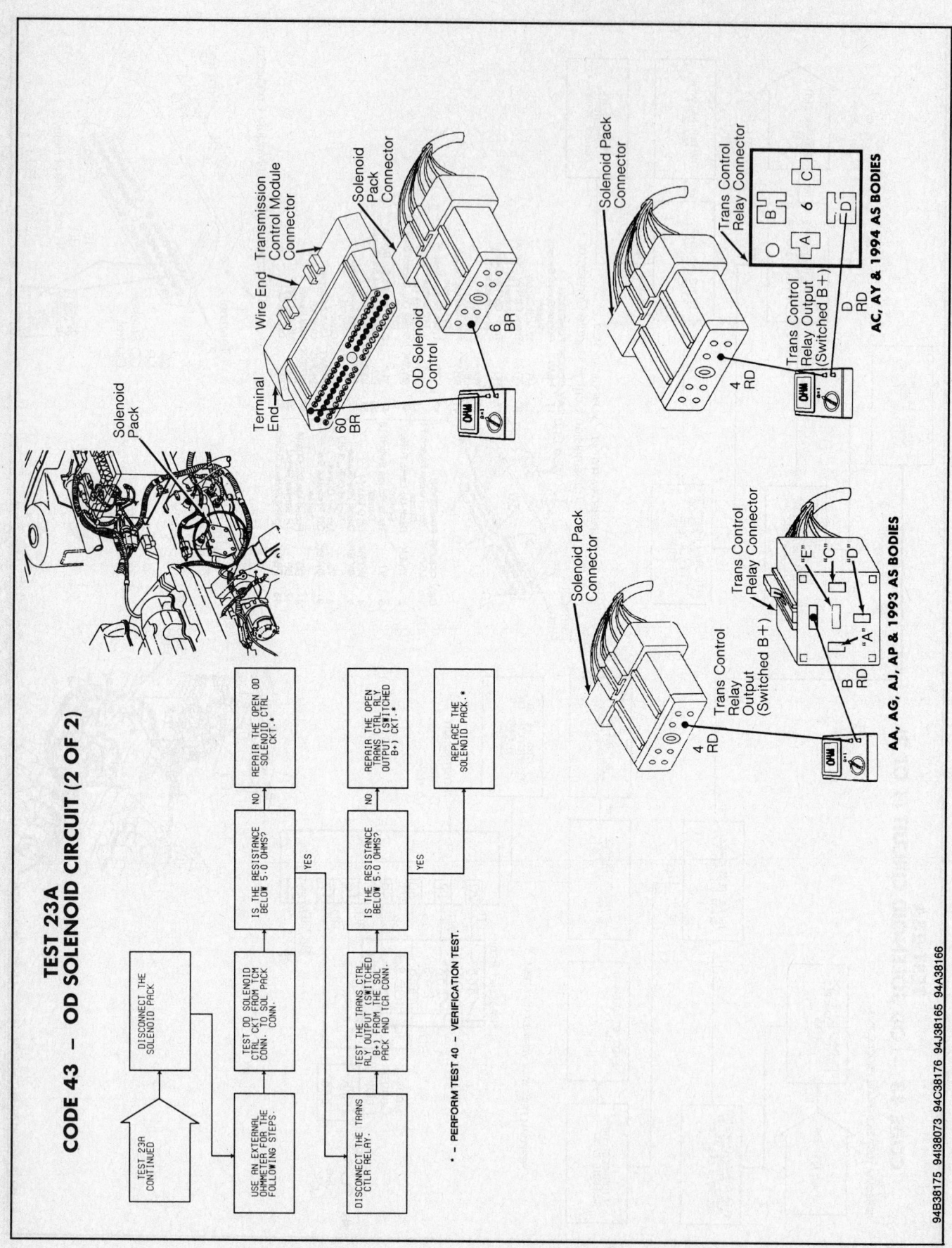

TEST 23A

CODE 43 – OD SOLENOID CIRCUIT (2 OF 2)

Solenoid Pack

Solenoid Pack Connector

Transmission Control Module Connector

Wire End

Terminal End

60 BR

OD Solenoid Control

6 BR

Solenoid Pack Connector

Trans Control Relay Connector

Trans Control Relay Output (Switched B+)

4 RD

AC, AY & 1994 AS BODIES

Solenoid Pack Connector

Trans Control Relay Connector

Trans Control Relay Output (Switched B+)

4 RD

AA, AG, AJ, AP & 1993 AS BODIES

TEST 23A CONTINUED

DISCONNECT THE SOLENOID PACK

USE AN EXTERNAL OHMMETER FOR THE FOLLOWING STEPS:

TEST OD SOLENOID CTRL CKT FROM TCM CONN. TO SOL PACK CONN.

IS THE RESISTANCE BELOW 5.0 OHMS?

NO → REPAIR THE OPEN OD SOLENOID CTRL CKT.*

YES ↓

DISCONNECT THE TRANS CTLR RELAY.

TEST THE TRANS CTRL RLY OUTPUT (SWITCHED B+) FROM THE SOL PACK AND TCR CONN.

IS THE RESISTANCE BELOW 5.0 OHMS?

NO → REPAIR THE OPEN TRANS CTRL RLY OUTPUT (SWITCHED B+) CKT.*

YES ↓

REPLACE THE SOLENOID PACK.*

* – PERFORM TEST 40 – VERIFICATION TEST.

94B38175 94I38073 94C38176 94J38165 94A38166

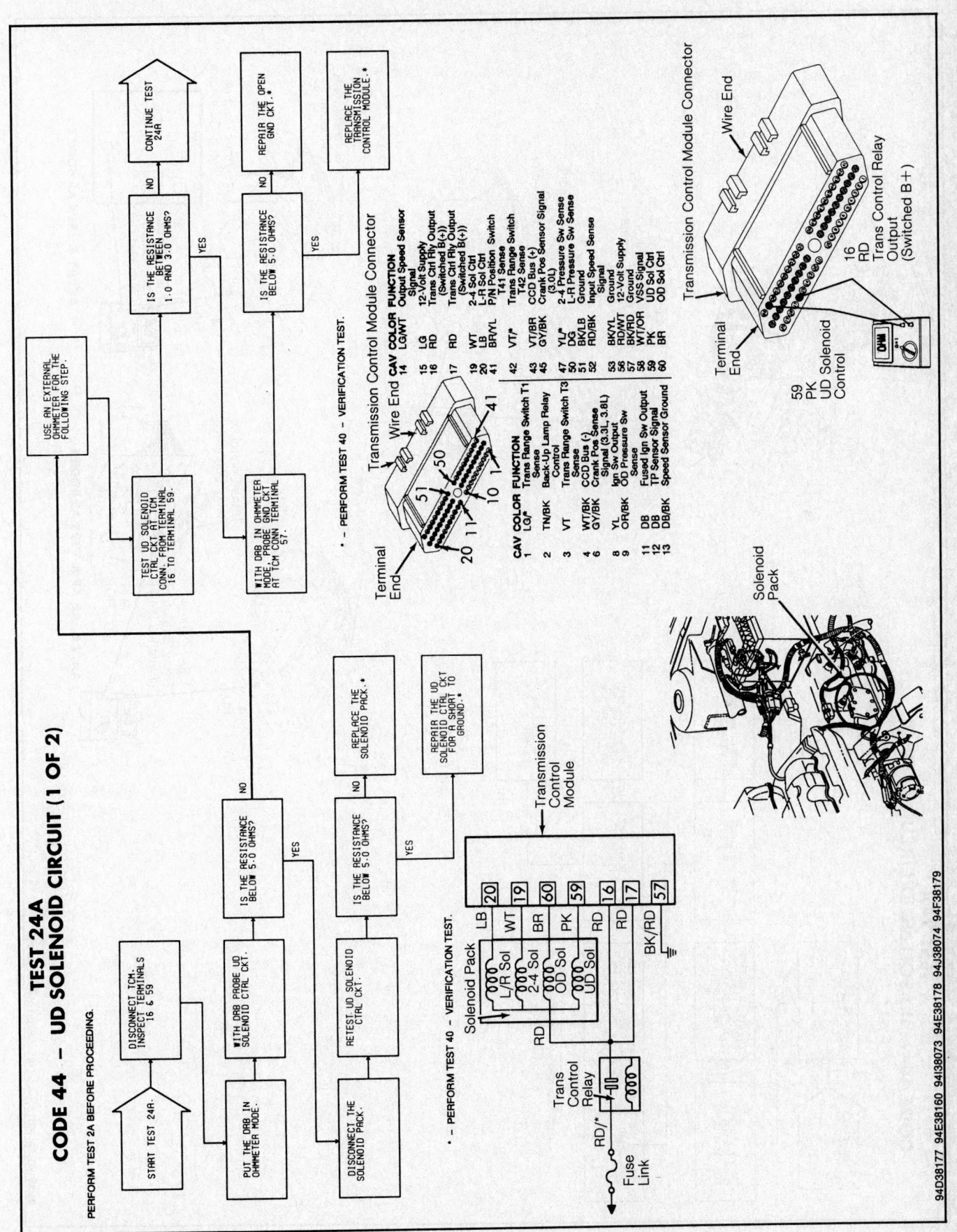

TEST 24A
CODE 44 — UD SOLENOID CIRCUIT (1 OF 2)

PERFORM TEST 2A BEFORE PROCEEDING.

START TEST 24A.

DISCONNECT TCM. INSPECT TERMINALS 16 & 59.

PUT THE DRB IN OHMMETER MODE.

WITH DRB PROBE UD SOLENOID CTRL CKT.

IS THE RESISTANCE BELOW 5.0 OHMS?

NO → RETEST UD SOLENOID CTRL CKT.

YES → DISCONNECT THE SOLENOID PACK.

IS THE RESISTANCE BELOW 5.0 OHMS?

NO → REPLACE THE SOLENOID PACK. *

YES → REPAIR THE UD SOLENOID CTRL CKT FOR A SHORT TO GROUND. *

USE AN EXTERNAL OHMMETER FOR THE FOLLOWING STEP.

TEST UD SOLENOID CTRL CKT. FROM TERMINAL 16 TO TERMINAL 59.

IS THE RESISTANCE BETWEEN 1.0 AND 3.0 OHMS?

NO → CONTINUE TEST 24A.

YES → WITH DRB IN OHMMETER MODE, PROBE GND CKT AT TCM CONN TERMINAL 57.

IS THE RESISTANCE BELOW 5.0 OHMS?

NO → REPAIR THE OPEN GND CKT. *

YES → REPLACE THE TRANSMISSION CONTROL MODULE. *

* — PERFORM TEST 40 — VERIFICATION TEST.

Transmission Control Module Connector

Wire End

CAV	COLOR	FUNCTION
14	LG/WT	Output Speed Sensor Signal
15	LG	12-Volt Output
16	RD	Trans Ctrl Rly Output (Switched B(+)
17	RD	Trans Ctrl Rly Output (Switched B(+)
19	WT	2-4 Sol Ctrl
20	LB	L-R Sol Ctrl
41	BR/VL	P/N Position Switch
42	VT/*	T41 Sense
43	VT/BR	Trans Range Switch T42 Sense
45	GY/BK	CCD Bus (+)
47	YL/*	Crank Pos Sensor Signal (3.0L)
50	DG	2-Pressure Sw Sense
51	BK/LB	L-R Pressure Sw Sense
52	RD/BK	Ground
53	BK/YL	Input Speed Sensor Signal
56	RD/WT	Ground
57	BK/RD	12-Volt Supply
58	WT/OR	Ground
59	PK	VSS Signal
60	BR	UD Sol Ctrl
		OD Sol Ctrl

Terminal End

CAV	COLOR	FUNCTION
1	LG/*	Trans Range Switch T1 Sense
2	TN/BK	Back-Up Lamp Relay Control
3	VT	Trans Range Switch T3 Sense
4	WT/BK	CCD Bus (-)
6	GY/BK	Crank Pos Sense Signal (3.3L, 3.8L)
8	YL	Ign Sw Output
9	OR/BK	OD Pressure Sw
11	DB	Fused Ign Sw Output
12	DB	TP Sensor Signal
13	DB/BK	Speed Sensor Ground

* — PERFORM TEST 40 — VERIFICATION TEST.

Transmission Control Module Connector

Wire End

16 RD — Trans Control Relay Output (Switched B+)

Terminal End

59 PK — UD Solenoid Control

Solenoid Pack

Transmission Control Module

Solenoid Pack

20	19	60	59	16	17	57
LB	WT	BR	PK	RD	RD	BK/RD

L/R Sol — 2-4 Sol — OD Sol — UD Sol

RD

Trans Control Relay

RD/*

Fuse Link

94D38177 94E38160 94J38073 94J38074 94E38178 94J38074 94F38179

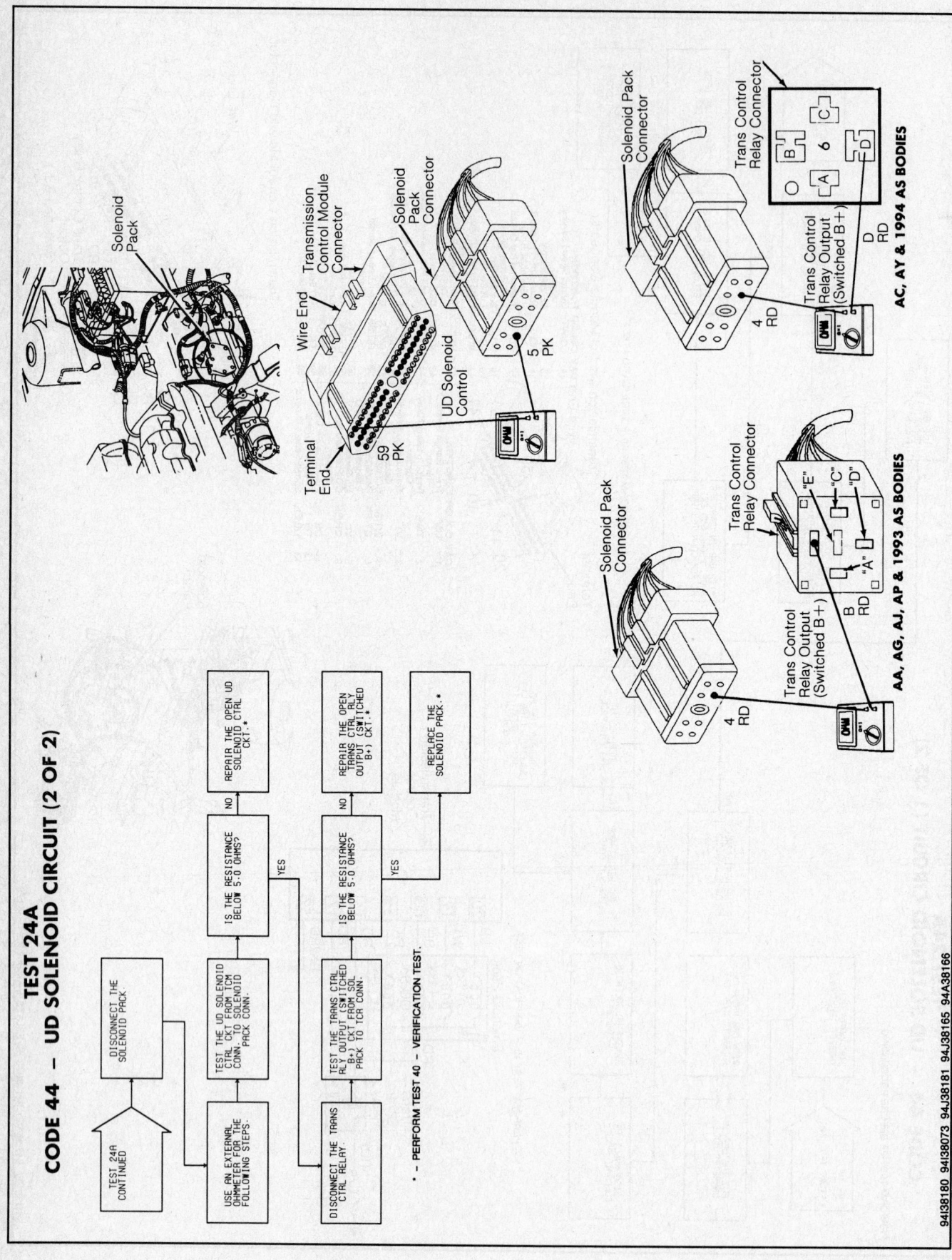

TEST 24A

CODE 44 – UD SOLENOID CIRCUIT (2 OF 2)

Solenoid Pack

Solenoid Pack Connector

Transmission Control Module Connector

Wire End

Terminal End

UD Solenoid Control

59 PK

5 PK

Solenoid Pack Connector

Trans Control Relay Connector

Trans Control Relay Output (Switched B+)

4 RD

D RD

AC, AY & 1994 AS BODIES

Solenoid Pack Connector

Trans Control Relay Connector

"E" "C" "D" "A"

Trans Control Relay Output (Switched B+)

B RD

4 RD

AA, AG, AJ, AP & 1993 AS BODIES

TEST 24A CONTINUED

DISCONNECT THE SOLENOID PACK

USE AN EXTERNAL OHMMETER FOR THE FOLLOWING STEPS.

TEST THE UD SOLENOID CTRL CKT FROM TCM CONN. TO SOLENOID PACK CONN.

IS THE RESISTANCE BELOW 5.0 OHMS?

NO → REPAIR THE OPEN UD SOLENOID CTRL CKT.*

YES

DISCONNECT THE TRANS CTRL RELAY.

TEST THE TRANS CTRL RLY OUTPUT (SWITCHED B+) CKT FROM SOL PACK TO TCR CONN.

IS THE RESISTANCE BELOW 5.0 OHMS?

NO → REPAIR THE OPEN TRANS CTRL RLY OUTPUT (SWITCHED B+) CKT.*

YES

REPLACE THE SOLENOID PACK.*

* – PERFORM TEST 40 – VERIFICATION TEST.

94J38180 94J38073 94J38181 94J38165 94J38166

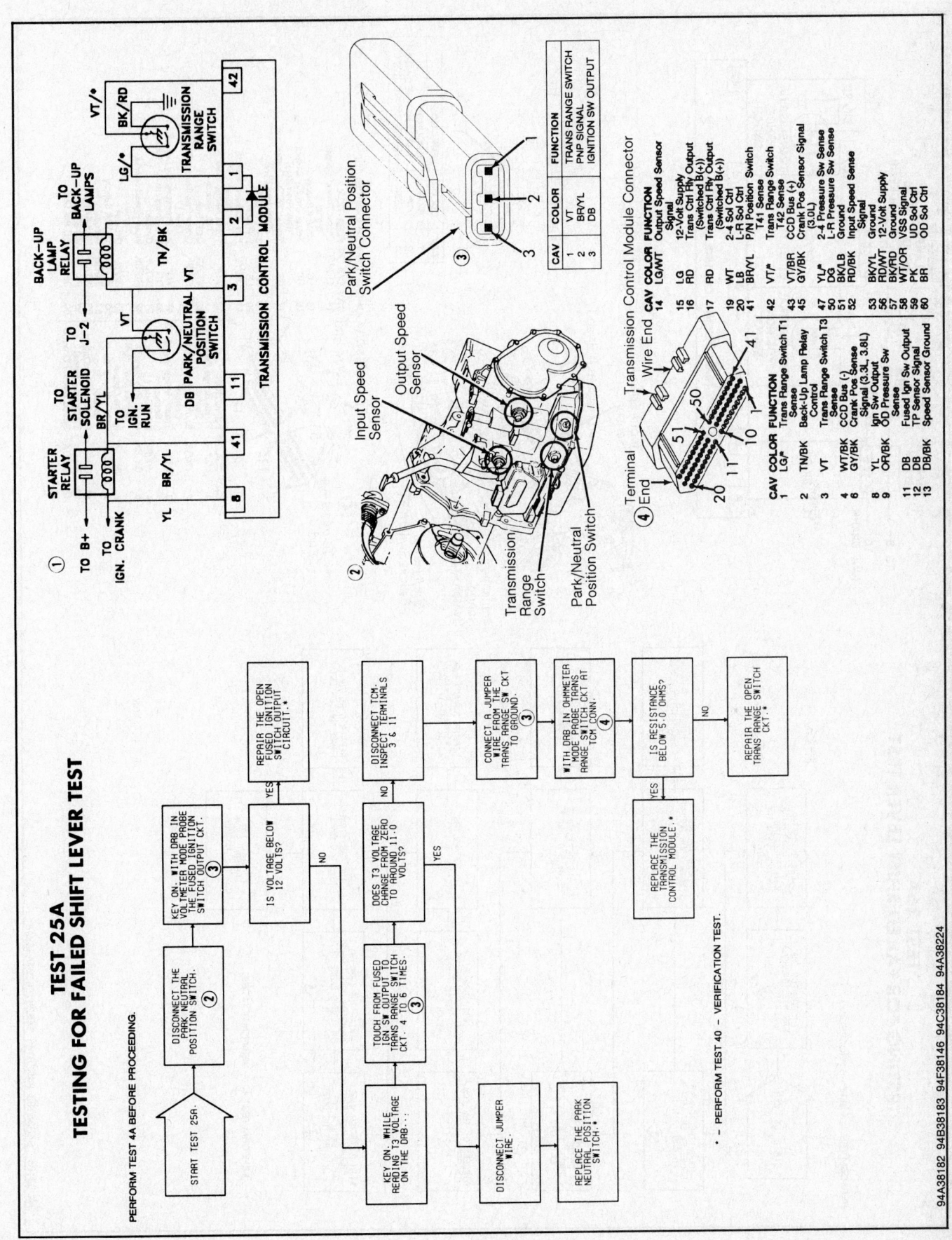

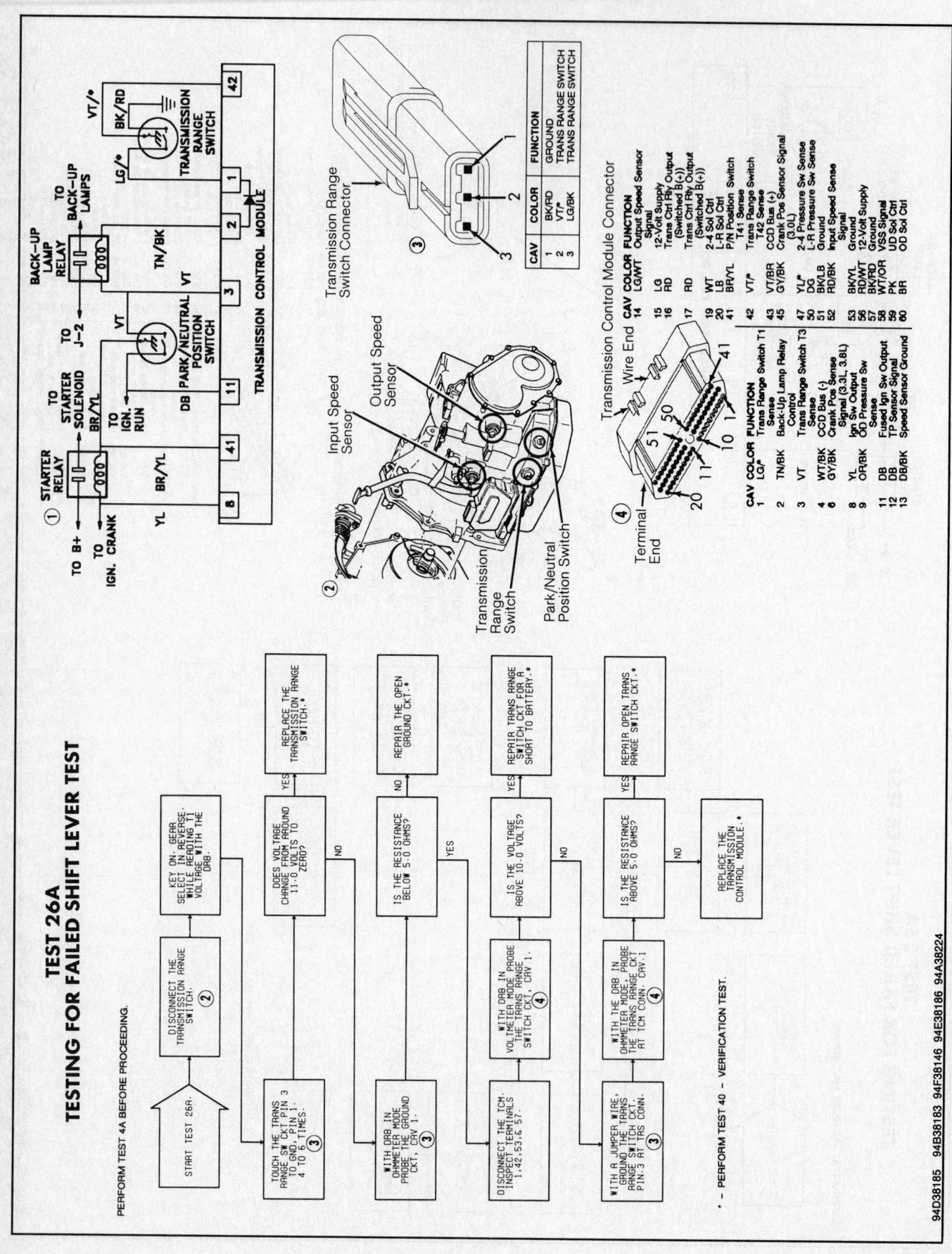

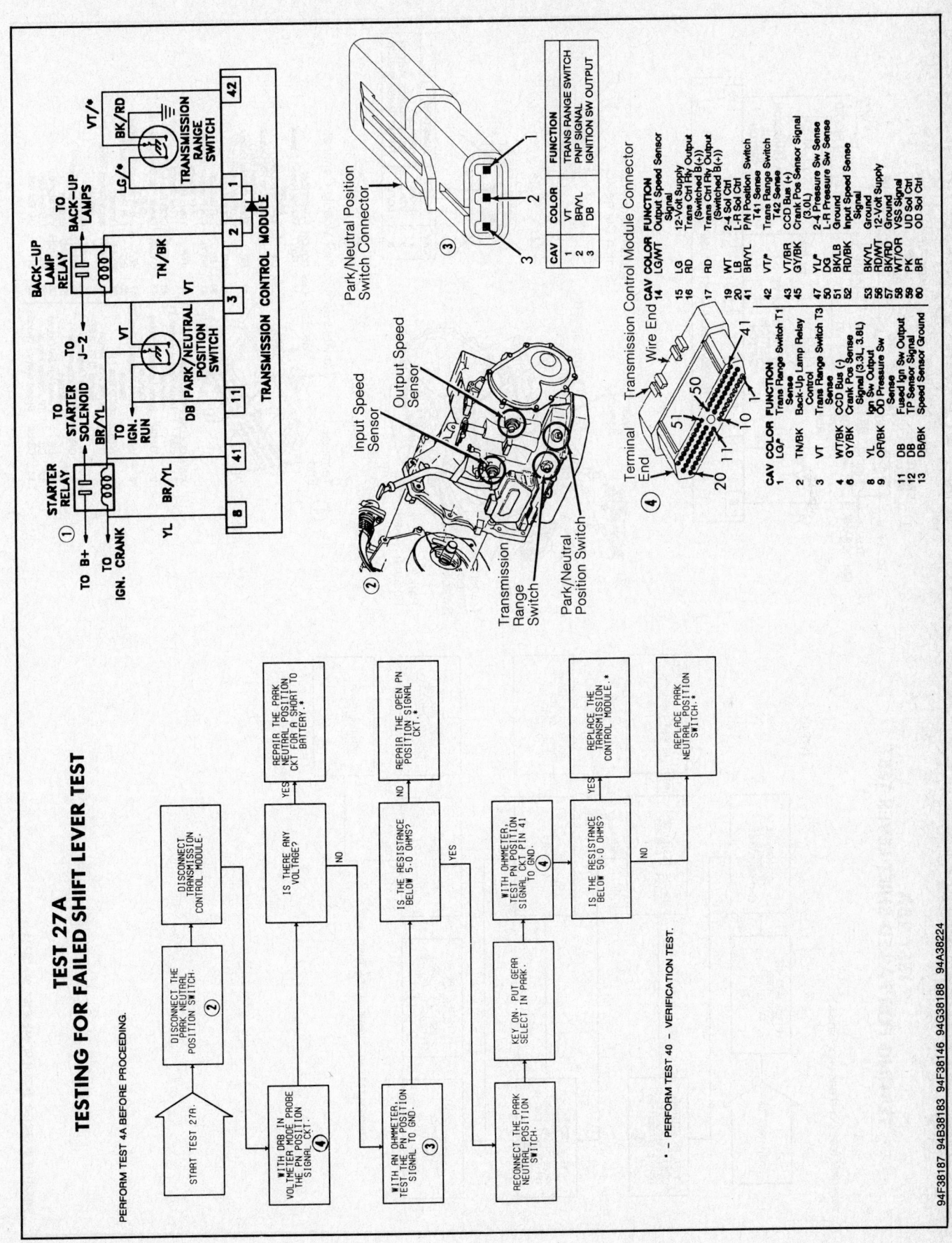

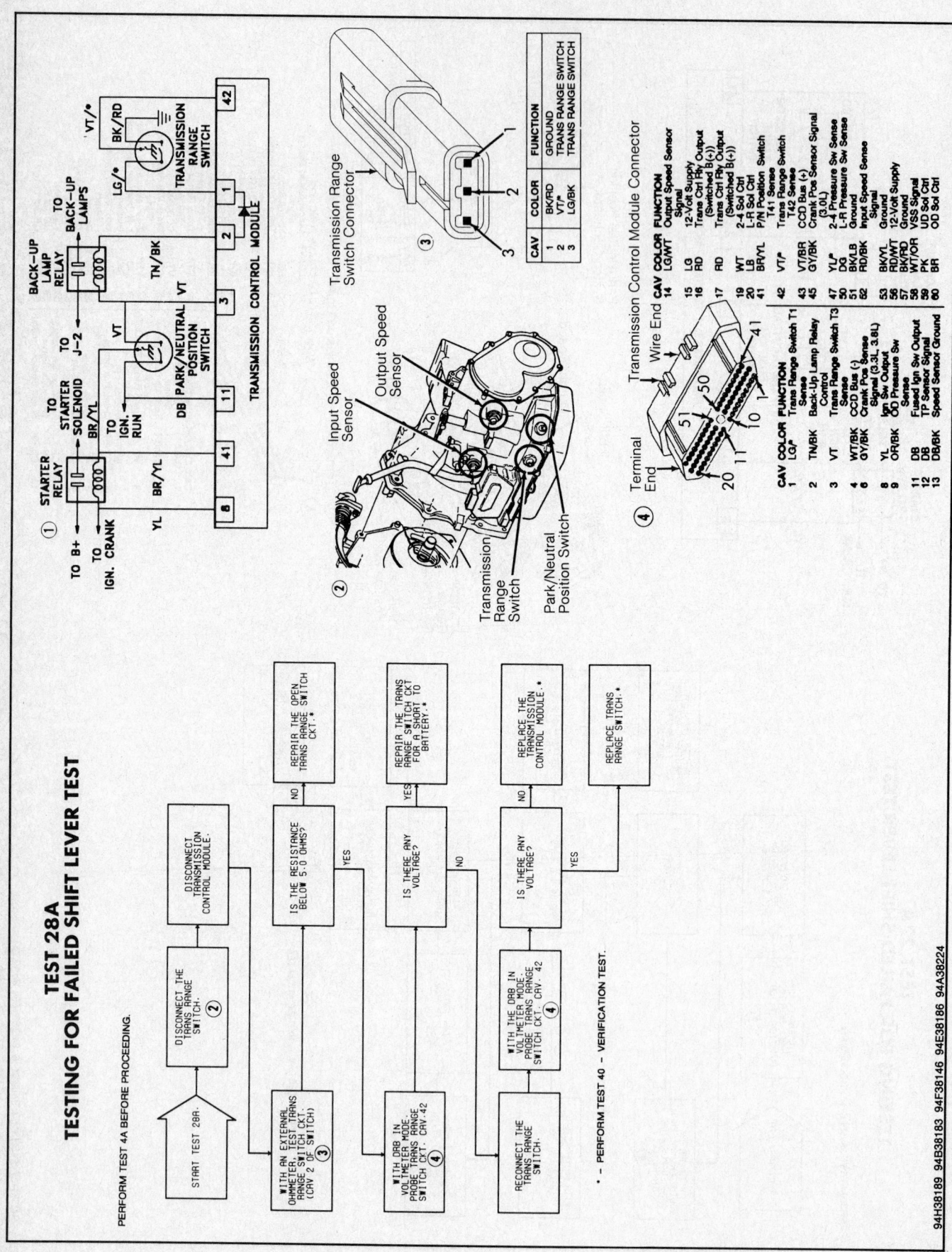

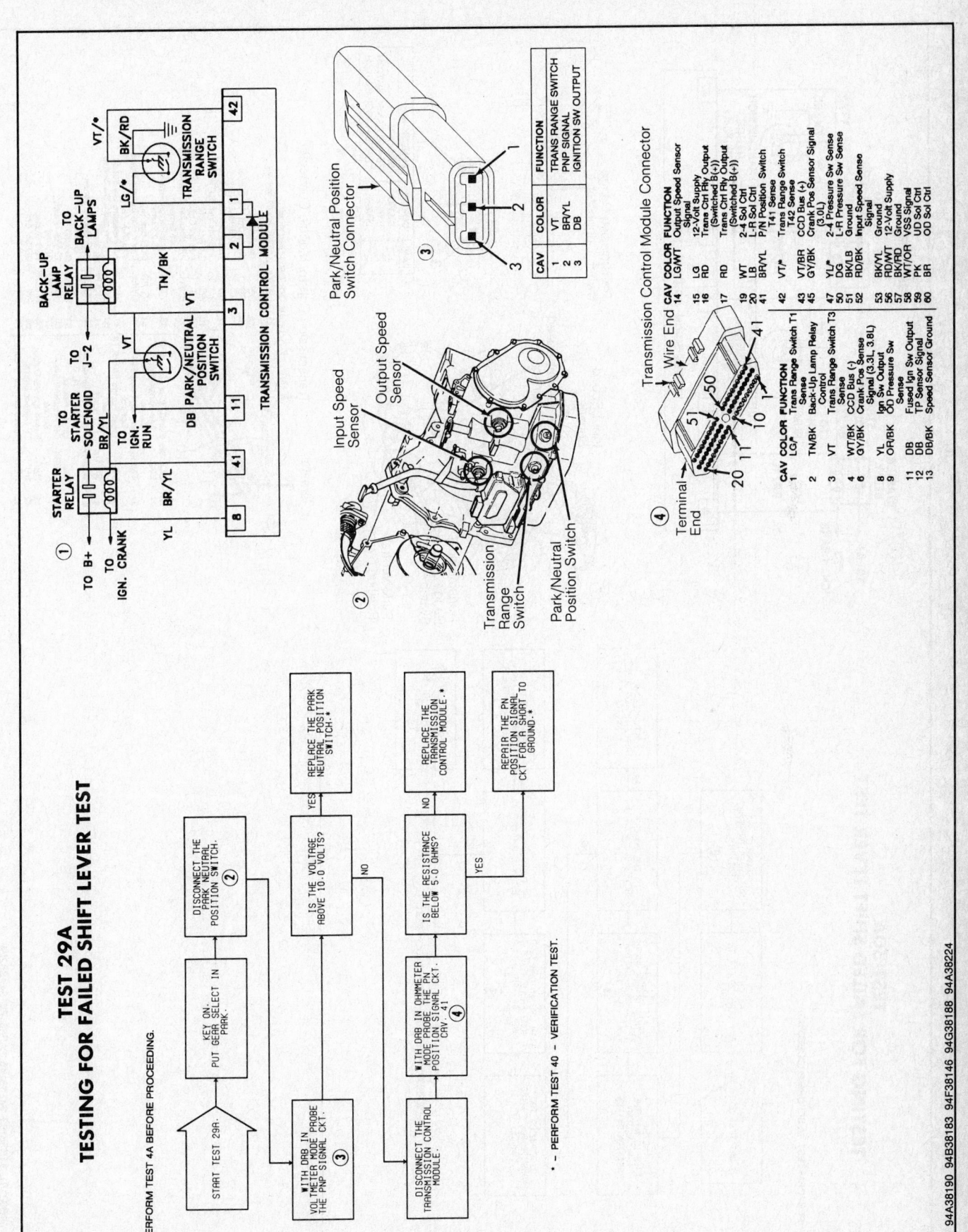

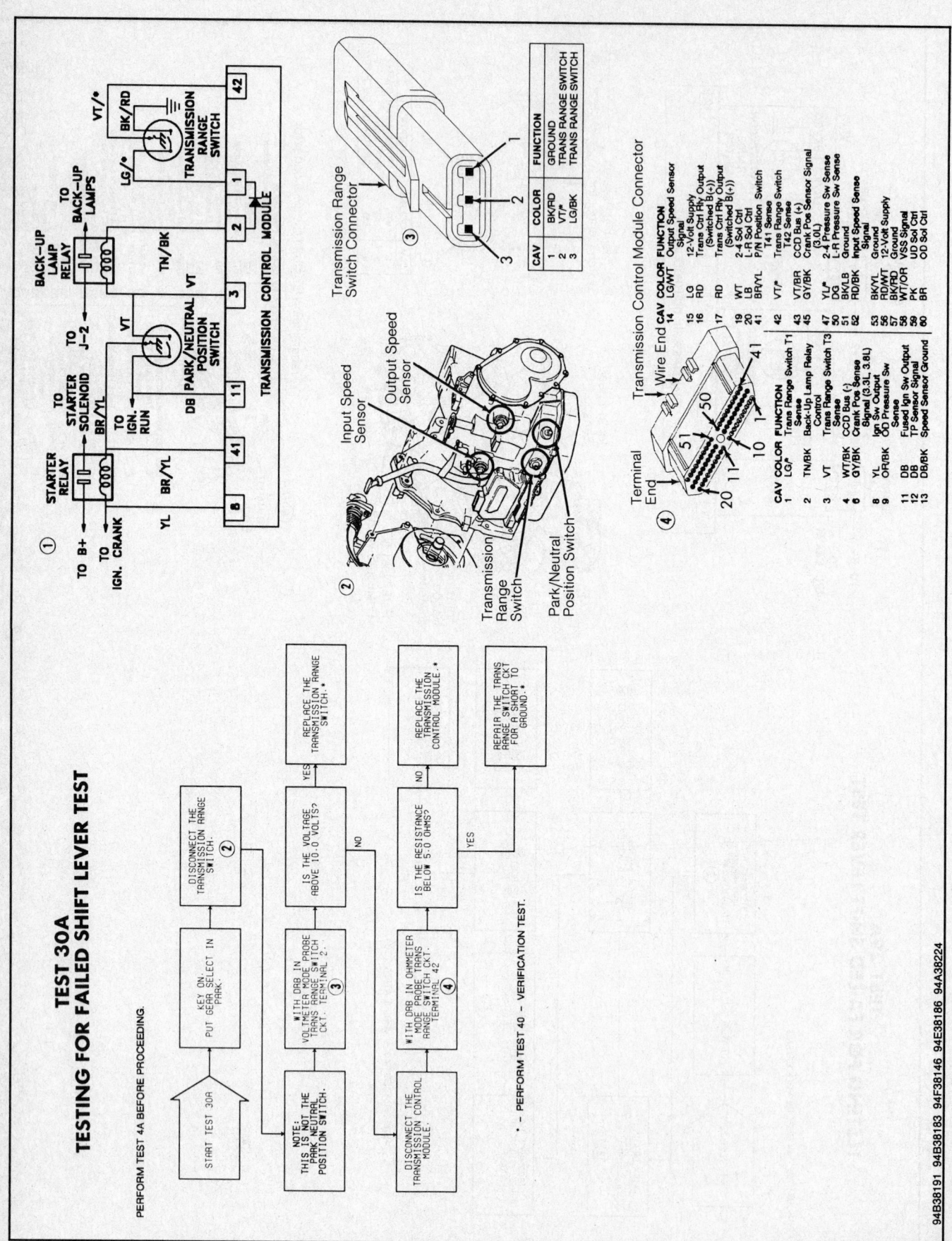

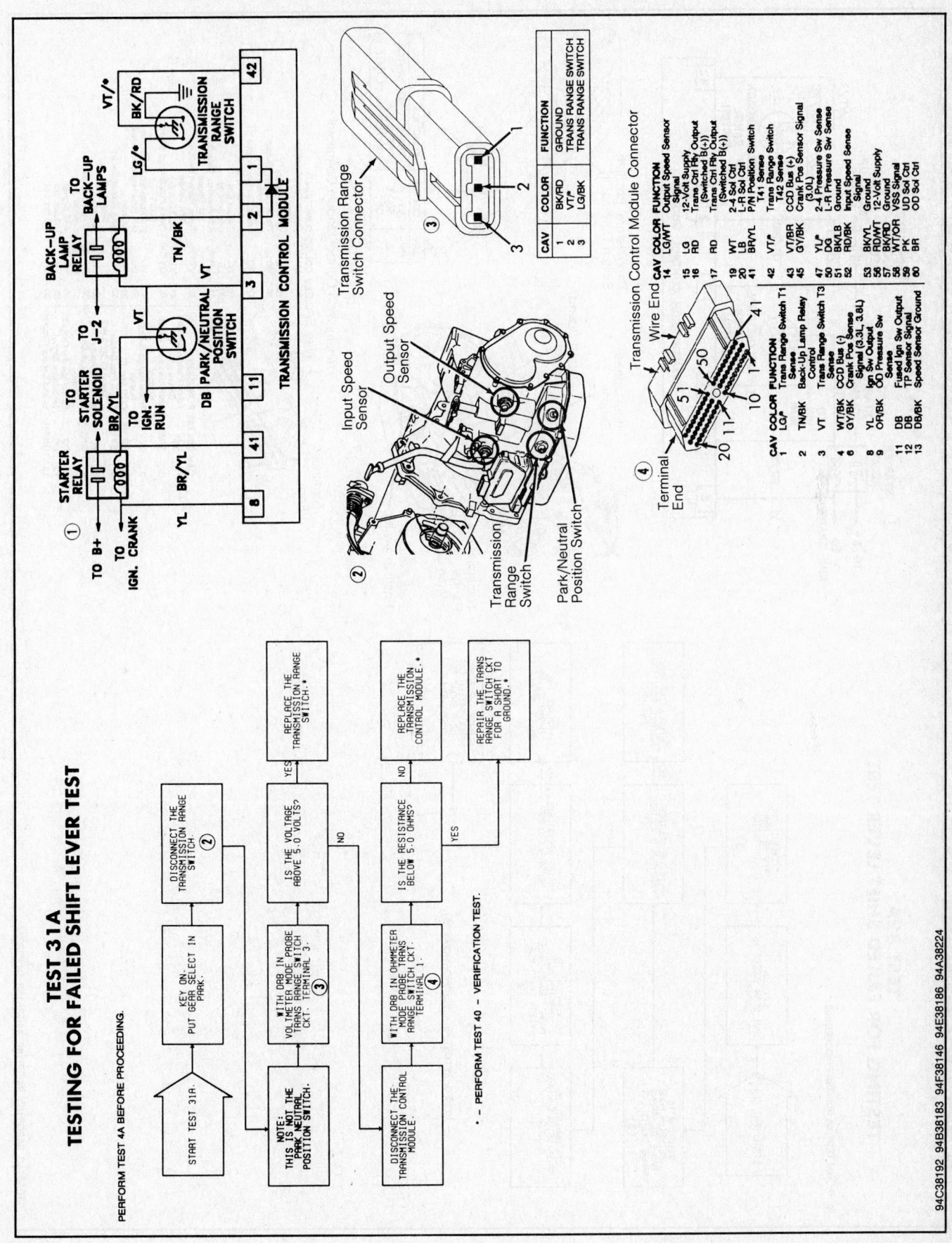

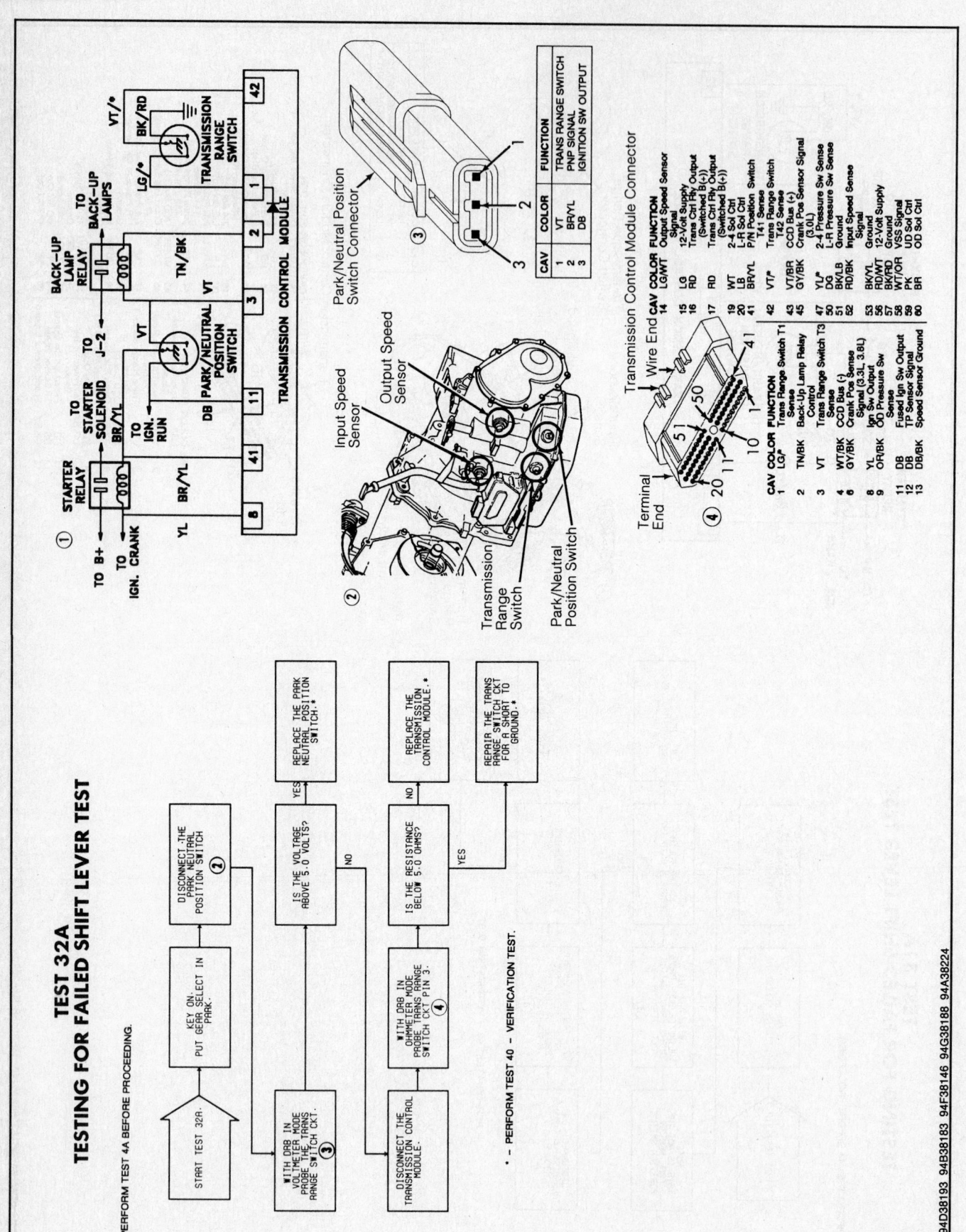

TEST 33A
CODE 46 - UD HYDRAULIC PRESSURE SWITCH CIRCUIT

Input Speed Sensor

Output Speed Sensor

Transmission Range Switch

Park/Neutral Position Switch

PERFORM TEST 2A BEFORE PROCEEDING.

START TEST 33A.

IGNITION KEY ON.

WITH THE DRB MONITOR CLUTCH VOLUME INDEX (CVI) VALUE.

RECORD EACH CLUTCH VOLUME.

ARE THE CLUTCH VOLUMES WITHIN RANGE? (1)
 NO → REFER TO (3)
 YES →

DISCONNECT THE TRANSMISSION CONTROL MODULE.

CONNECT THE TRANSMISSION CONTROL MODULE.

DISCONNECT THE INPUT SPEED SENSOR. (2)

CONNECT THE INPUT SPEED SENSOR.

DISCONNECT THE OUTPUT SPEED SENSOR (2)

CONNECT OUTPUT SPEED SENSOR.

ROAD TEST THE VEHICLE.

DID A CODE 46 SET DURING THE TEST?
 YES → REFER TO (3)
 NO → WERE ANY OTHER CODES SET?
   YES → PERFORM TEST 2A.
   NO → DID THE TRANSAXLE SHIFT OK DURING THE ROAD TEST?
     YES → RETURN VEHICLE TO OWNER.
     NO → SEE TROUBLE SHOOTING IN CHRYSLER 41TE/AE ARTICLE.

(1) In order for clutch volumes to be read, the ignition must be ON and the gear select in PARK.

CLUTCH VOLUMES

LR: 35 to 85   OD: 75 to 150
2-4: 20 to 77   UD: 24 to 70

Clutch volumes must fall between the above values to be considered functional.

(3) Name of code: 46 - UD Hydraulic Circuit Failure /3-4 Shift Abort

When monitored: Prior to the 3-4 shift.

Set condition: A 3-4 shift must be in progress, and the UDF flag must be set (temperature must not be cold). The code sets concurrent with the third consecutive 3-4 shift abort if the UDF counter is greater than three.

Theory of operation: The following table shows the clutches applied in each gear:

GEAR	UD	OD	REV.	2-4	L-R
PARK					X
REVERSE			X		X
NEUTRAL					X
1ST	X				X
2ND	X			X	
3RD	X	X			
4TH		X		X	

When shifting from third to fourth gear, a delayed speed change will indicate a problem in the UD hydraulic circuit. When this is detected, the 3-4 shift is aborted temporarily. The controller will attempt the 3-4 shift again. After three unsuccessful shift attempts, the trouble code is set. This code does not cause the transmission to go into limp-in.

Possible causes: Internal transmission failure.

94E38194 94F38195 94F38146 94G38196

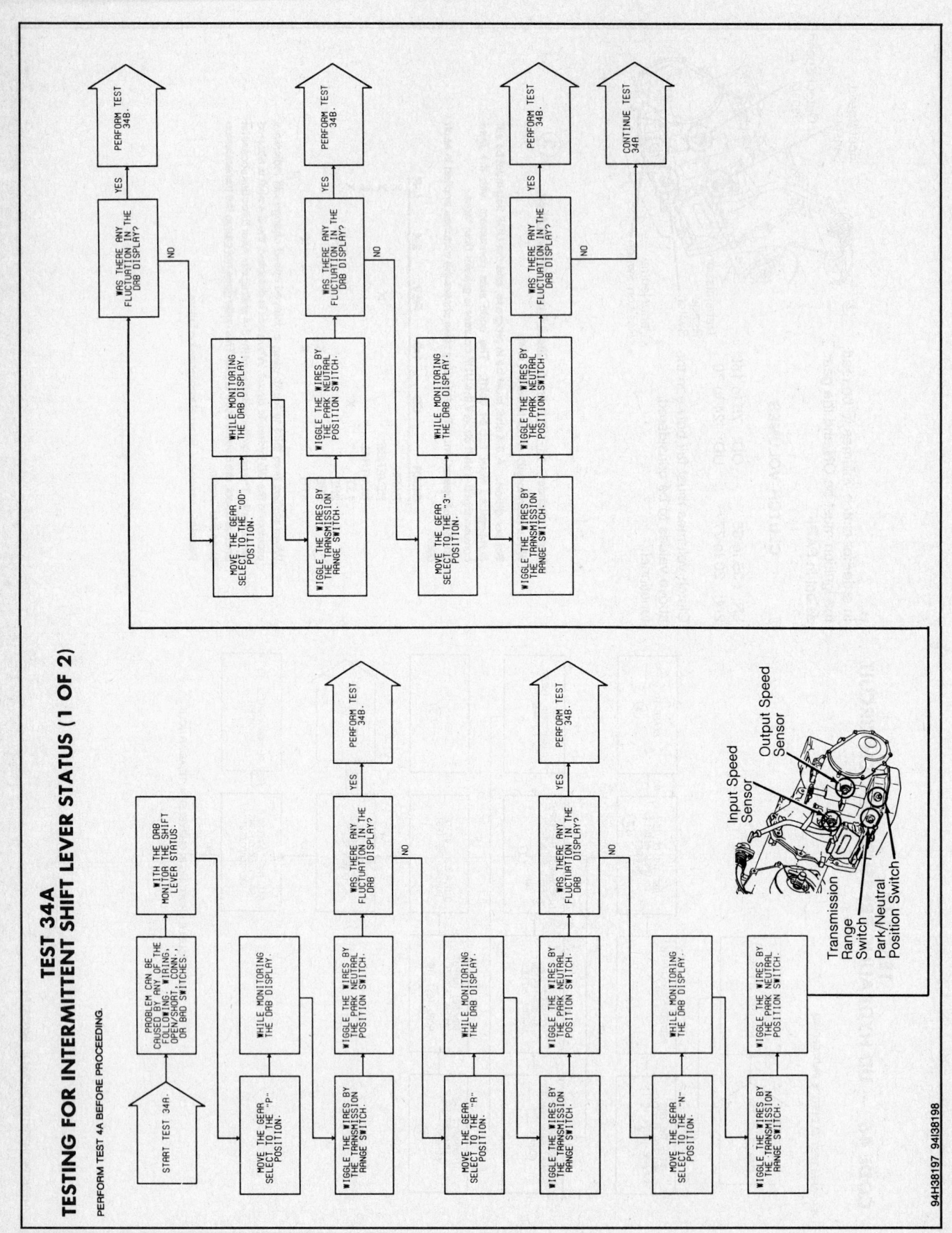

TEST 34A

TESTING FOR INTERMITTENT SHIFT LEVER STATUS (1 OF 2)

PERFORM TEST 4A BEFORE PROCEEDING.

94H38197   94I38198

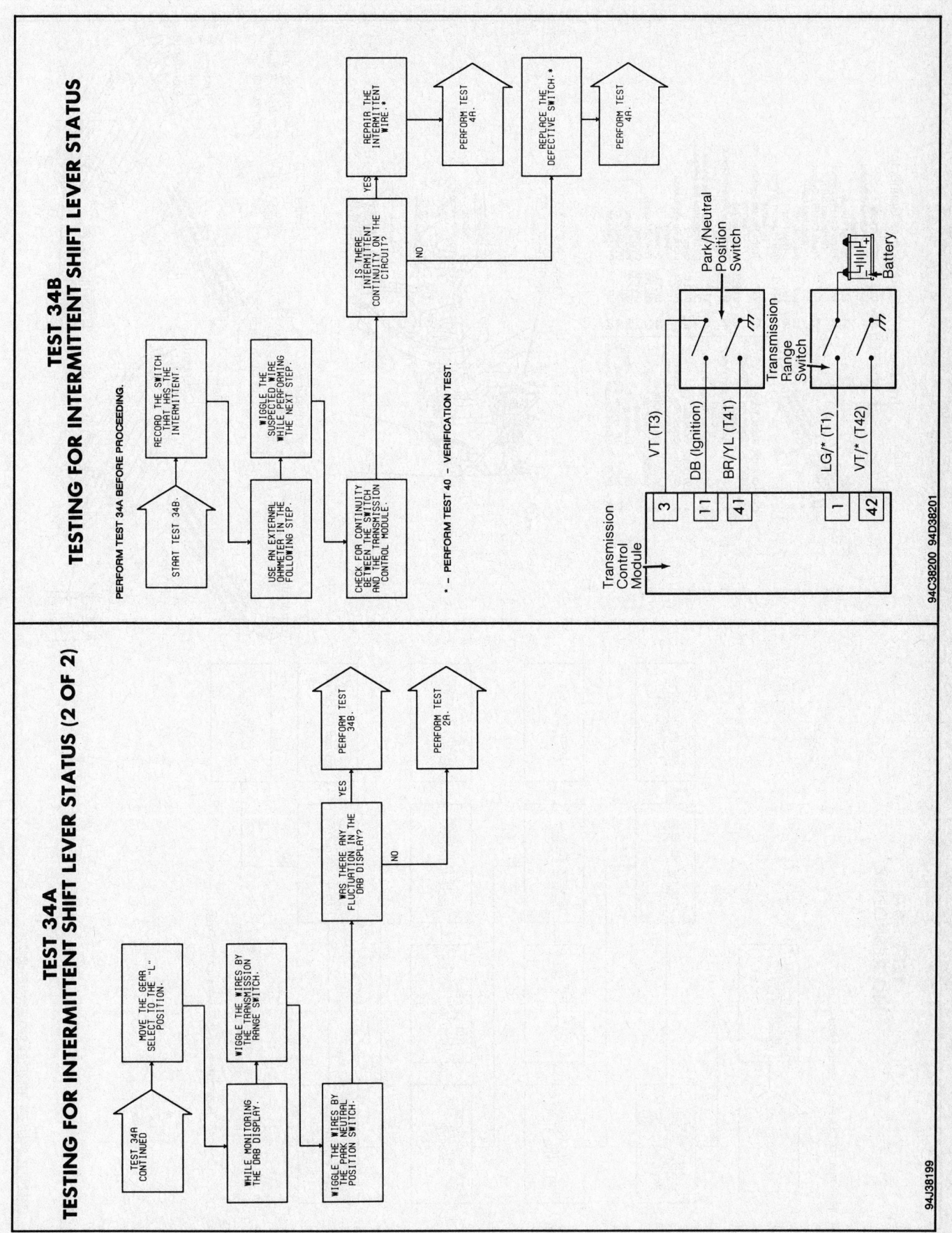

TEST 34B
TESTING FOR INTERMITTENT SHIFT LEVER STATUS

PERFORM TEST 34A BEFORE PROCEEDING.

START TEST 34B.

RECORD THE SWITCH THAT HAS THE INTERMITTENT.

USE AN EXTERNAL OHMMETER IN THE FOLLOWING STEP.

WIGGLE THE SUSPECTED WIRE WHILE PERFORMING THE NEXT STEP.

CHECK FOR CONTINUITY BETWEEN THE SWITCH AND THE TRANSMISSION CONTROL MODULE.

IS THERE INTERMITTENT CONTINUITY ON THE CIRCUIT?

YES → REPAIR THE INTERMITTENT WIRE. * → PERFORM TEST 4A.

NO → REPLACE THE DEFECTIVE SWITCH. * → PERFORM TEST 4A.

* - PERFORM TEST 40 - VERIFICATION TEST.

Transmission Control Module

3 — VT (T3) — Park/Neutral Position Switch
11 — DB (Ignition)
41 — BR/YL (T41)

Transmission Range Switch
1 — LG/* (T1)
42 — VT/* (T42) — Battery

94C38200 94D38201

TEST 34A
TESTING FOR INTERMITTENT SHIFT LEVER STATUS (2 OF 2)

TEST 34A CONTINUED

MOVE THE GEAR SELECT TO THE "L" POSITION.

WIGGLE THE WIRES BY THE TRANSMISSION RANGE SWITCH.

WHILE MONITORING THE DRB DISPLAY.

WIGGLE THE WIRES BY THE PARK NEUTRAL POSITION SWITCH.

WAS THERE ANY FLUCTUATION IN THE DRB DISPLAY?

YES → PERFORM TEST 34B.

NO → PERFORM TEST 2A.

94J38199

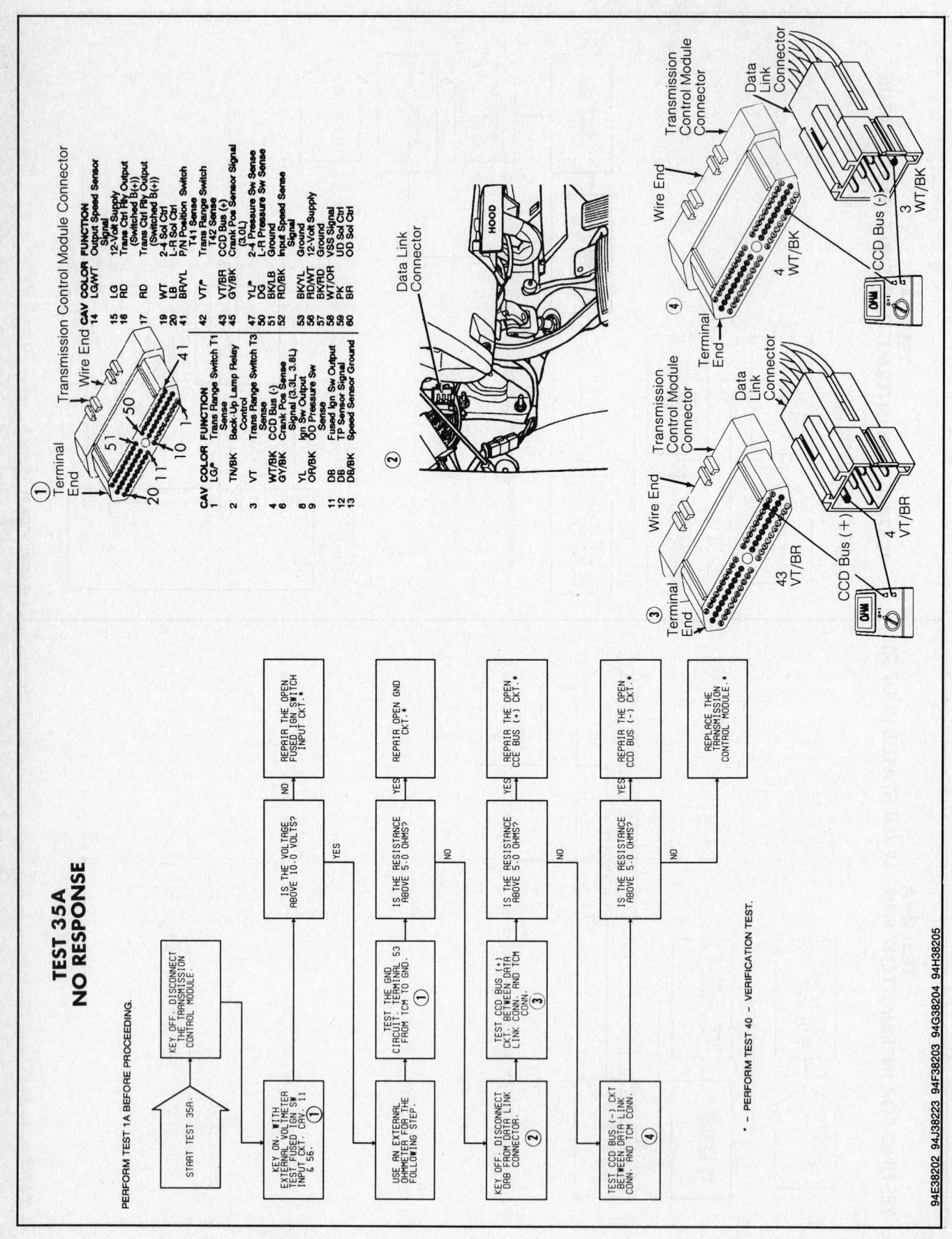

Transmission Control Module Connector

CAV	COLOR	FUNCTION
14	LG/WT	Output Speed Sensor Signal
15	LG	12-Volt Supply
16	RD	Trans Ctrl Rly Output (Switched B(+))
17	RD	Trans Ctrl Rly Output (Switched B(+))
19	WT	2-4 Sol Ctrl
20	LB	L-R Sol Ctrl
41	BR/YL	P/N Position Switch T41 Sense
42	VT*	Trans Range Switch T42 Sense
43	VT/BR	CCD Bus (+)
45	GY/BK	Crank Pos Sensor Signal (3.0L)
47	YL*	2-4 Pressure Sw Sense
50	DG	L-R Pressure Sw Sense
51	BK/LB	Ground
52	RD/BK	Input Speed Sense Signal
53	BK/YL	Input Speed Sense
56	RD/WT	Ground
57	BK/RD	12-Volt Supply
58	WT/OR	VSS Signal
59	PK	UD Sol Ctrl
60	BR	OD Sol Ctrl

CAV	COLOR	FUNCTION
1	LG*	Trans Range Switch T1 Sense
2	TN/BK	Back-Up Lamp Relay Control
3	VT	Trans Range Switch T3 Sense
4	WT/BK	CCD Bus (-)
6	GY/BK	Crank Pos Sense Signal (3.3L, 3.8L)
8	YL	Ign Sw Output
9	OR/BK	OD Pressure Sw Sense
11	DB	Fused Ign Sw Output
12	DB	TP Sensor Signal
13	DB/BK	Speed Sensor Ground

Terminal End ①

Wire End

Data Link Connector

HOOD

②

Transmission Control Module Connector

Wire End

Data Link Connector

Terminal End ④

WT/BK

4 WT/BK

CCD Bus (-)

3 WT/BK

Transmission Control Module Connector

Wire End

Data Link Connector

Terminal End ③

VT/BR

43 VT/BR

CCD Bus (+)

4 VT/BR

TEST 35A
NO RESPONSE

PERFORM TEST 1A BEFORE PROCEEDING.

START TEST 35A.

KEY OFF. DISCONNECT THE TRANSMISSION CONTROL MODULE.

KEY ON. WITH EXTERNAL VOLTMETER TEST FUSED IGN SW INPUT CKT. CAV. 11 & 56. ①

IS THE VOLTAGE ABOVE 10.0 VOLTS? — NO → REPAIR THE OPEN FUSED IGN SWITCH INPUT CKT.*

YES

USE AN EXTERNAL OHMMETER FOR THE FOLLOWING STEP.

TEST THE GND CIRCUIT. TERMINAL 53 FROM TCM TO GND. ①

IS THE RESISTANCE ABOVE 5.0 OHMS? — YES → REPAIR OPEN GND CKT.*

NO

KEY OFF. DISCONNECT DRB FROM DATA LINK CONNECTOR. ②

TEST CCD BUS (+) CKT. BETWEEN DATA LINK CONN. AND TCM CONN. ③

IS THE RESISTANCE ABOVE 5.0 OHMS? — YES → REPAIR THE OPEN CCE BUS (+) CKT.*

NO

TEST CCD BUS (-) CKT BETWEEN DATA LINK CONN. AND TCM CONN. ④

IS THE RESISTANCE ABOVE 5.0 OHMS? — YES → REPAIR THE OPEN CCD BUS (-) CKT.*

NO

IS THE RESISTANCE ABOVE 5.0 OHMS? — NO → REPLACE THE TRANSMISSION CONTROL MODULE.*

* - PERFORM TEST 40 - VERIFICATION TEST.

94E38202 94J38223 94F38203 94G38204 94H38205

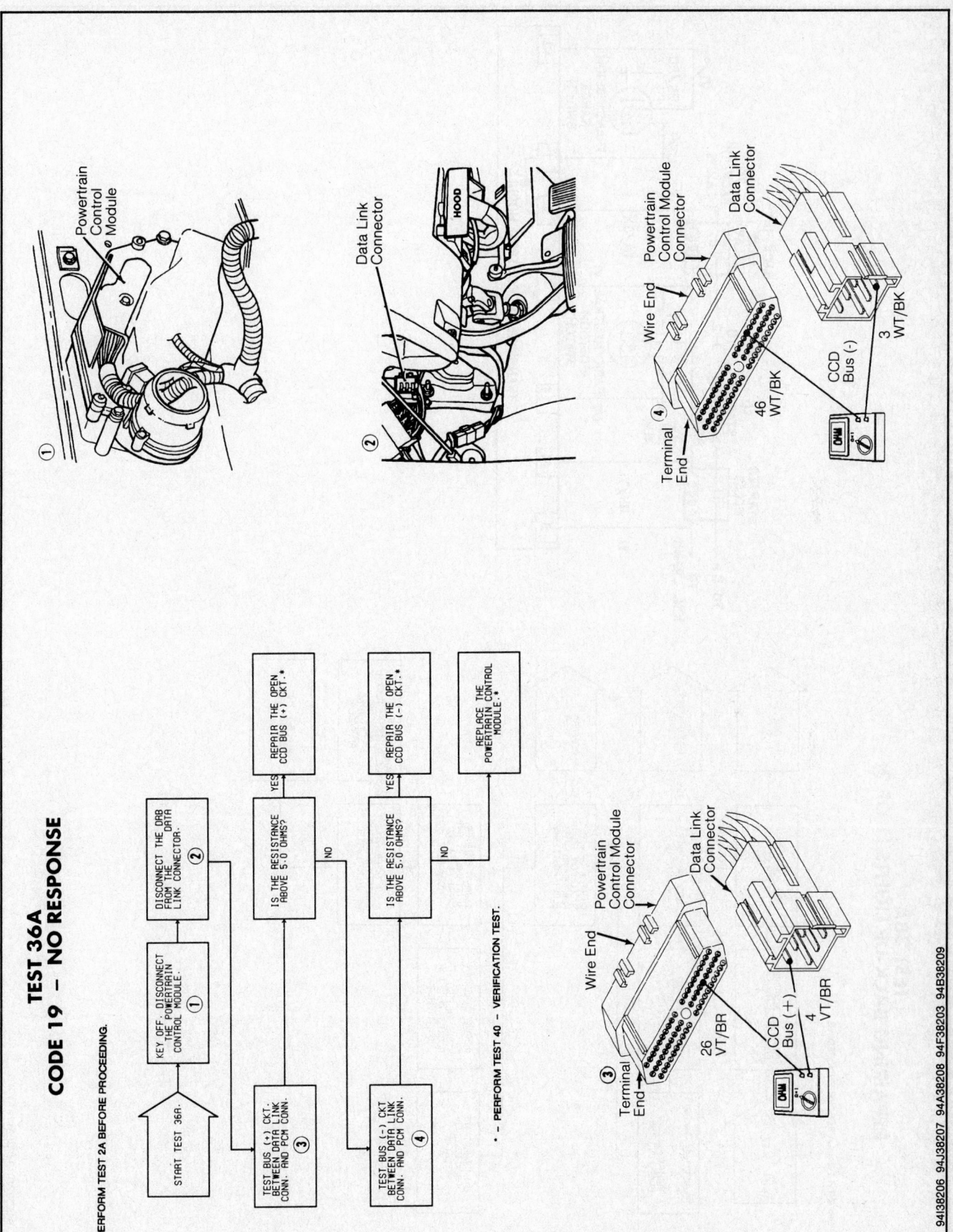

TEST 36A

CODE 19 – NO RESPONSE

PERFORM TEST 2A BEFORE PROCEEDING.

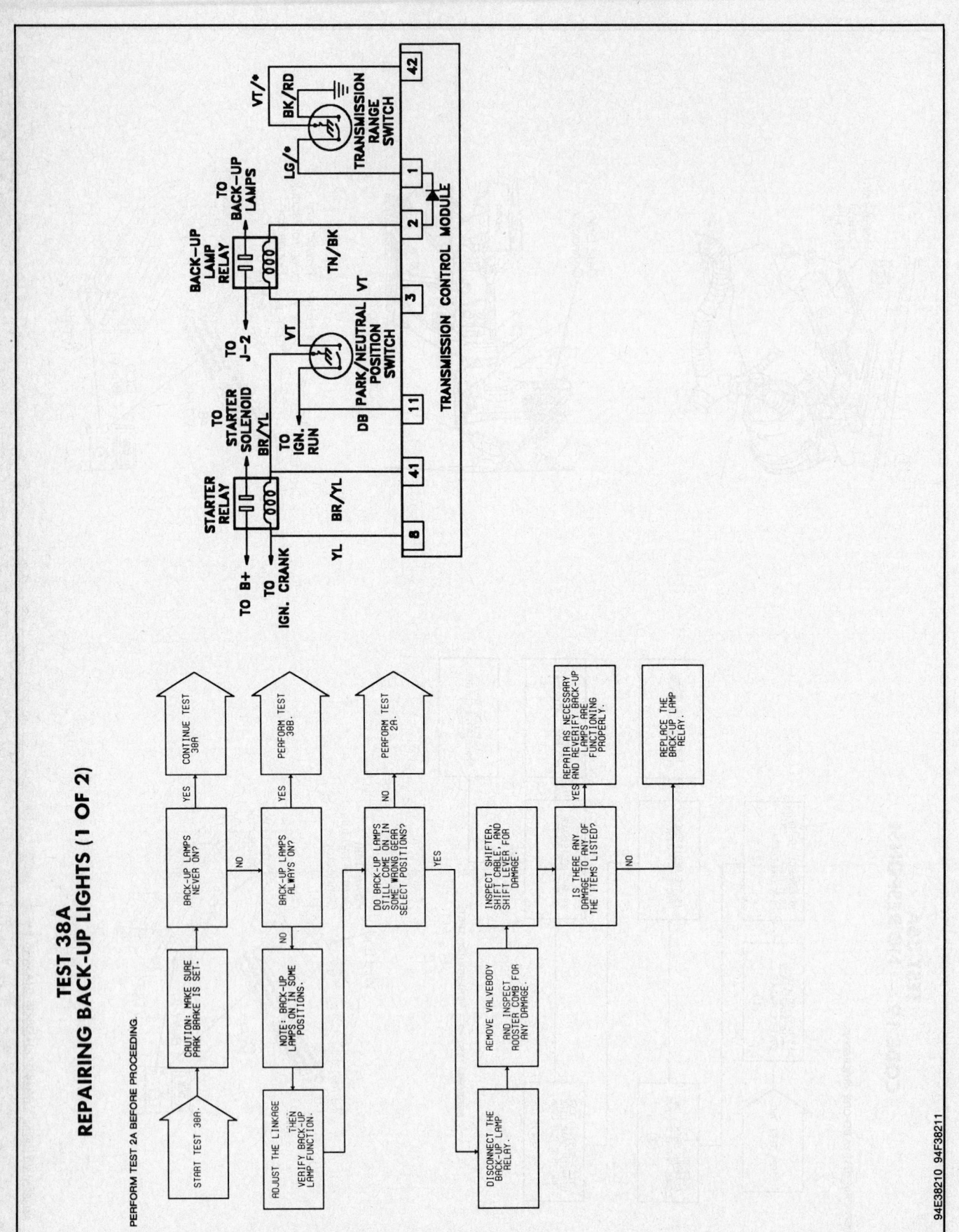

TEST 38A
REPAIRING BACK-UP LIGHTS (1 OF 2)

PERFORM TEST 2A BEFORE PROCEEDING.

94E38210 94F38211

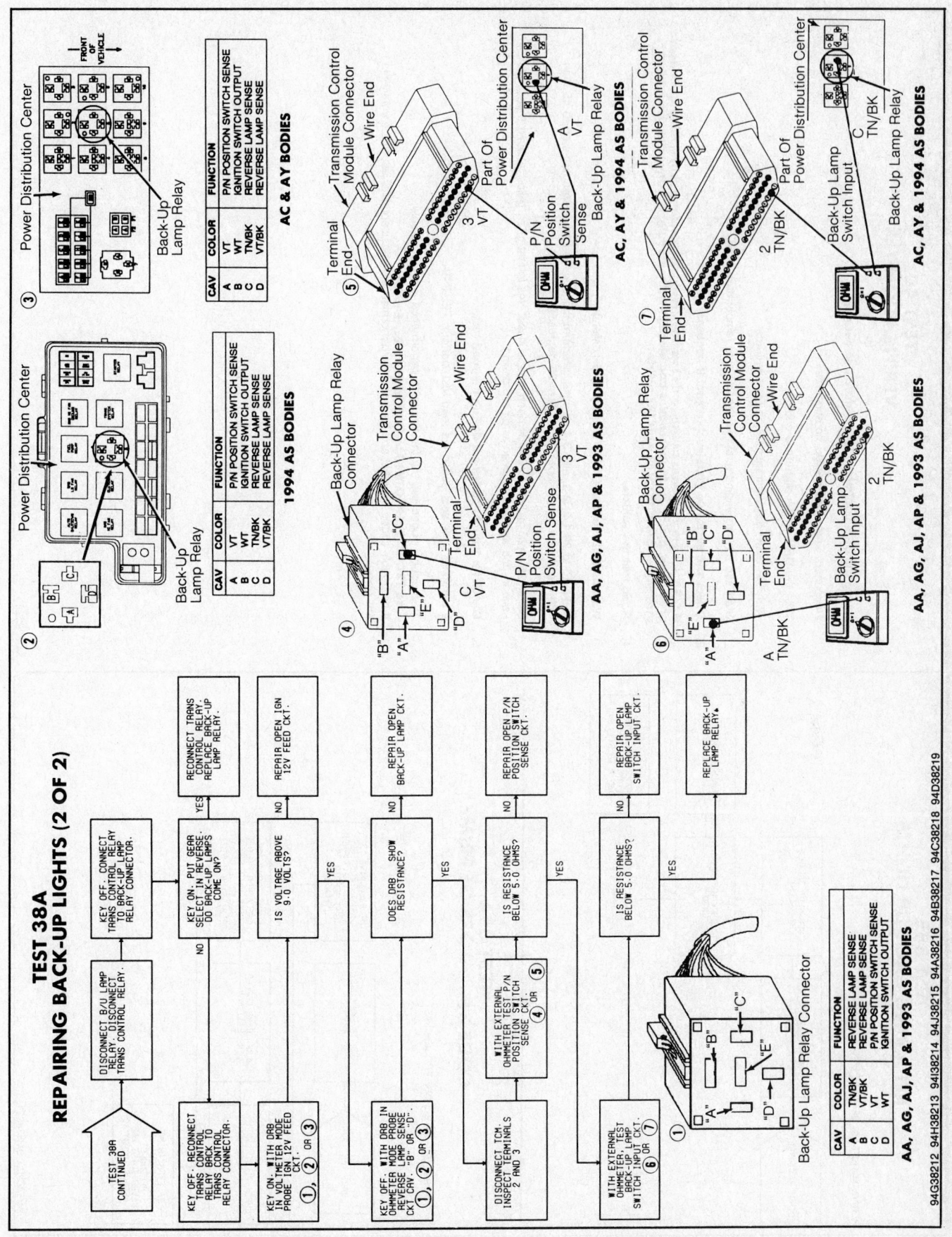

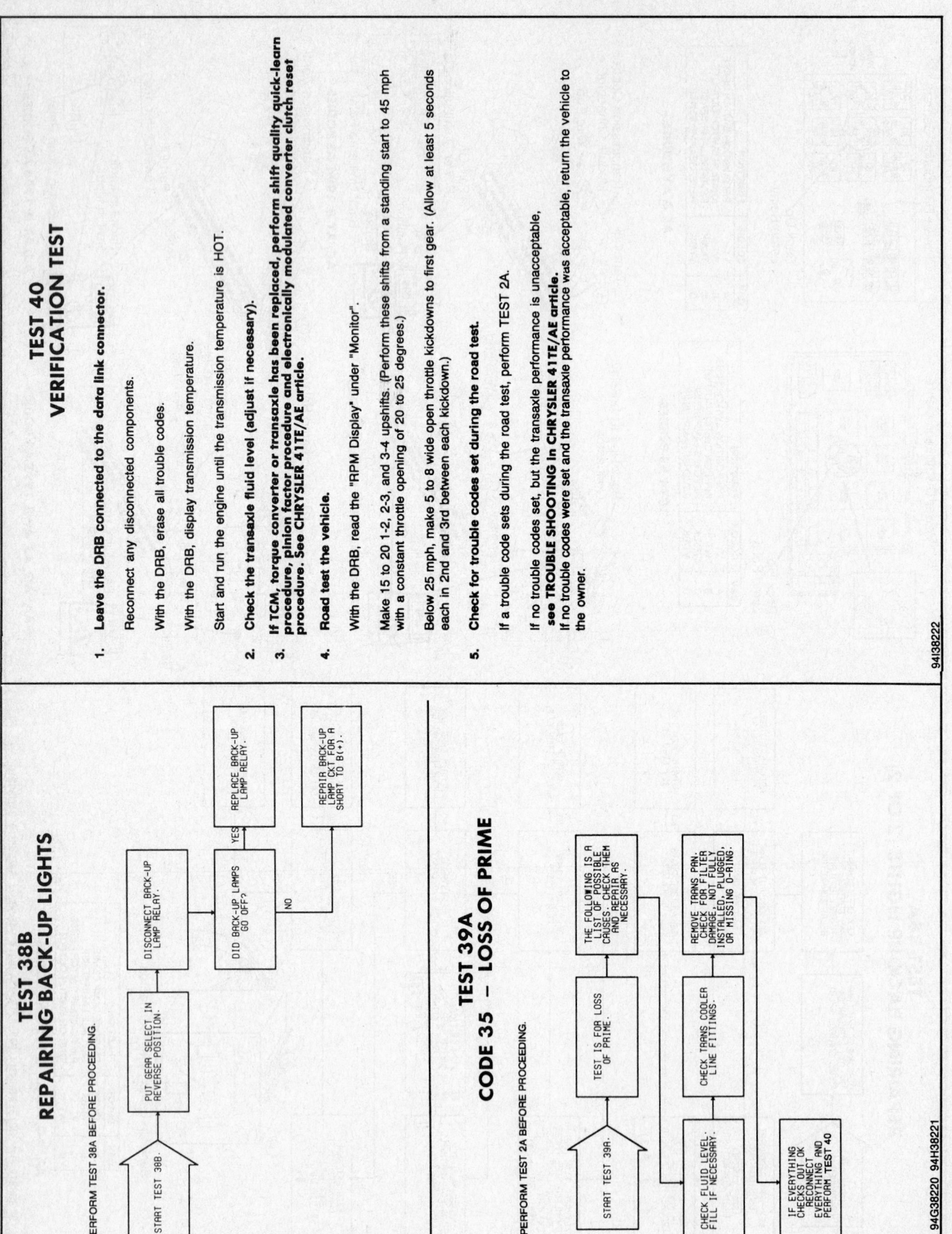

TEST 40
VERIFICATION TEST

1. **Leave the DRB connected to the data link connector.**

   Reconnect any disconnected components.

   With the DRB, erase all trouble codes.

   With the DRB, display transmission temperature.

   Start and run the engine until the transmission temperature is HOT.

2. **Check the transaxle fluid level (adjust if necessary).**

3. **If TCM, torque converter or transaxle has been replaced, perform shift quality quick-learn procedure, pinion factor procedure and electronically modulated converter clutch reset procedure. See CHRYSLER 41TE/AE article.**

4. **Road test the vehicle.**

   With the DRB, read the "RPM Display" under "Monitor".

   Make 15 to 20 1-2, 2-3, and 3-4 upshifts. (Perform these shifts from a standing start to 45 mph with a constant throttle opening of 20 to 25 degrees.)

   Below 25 mph, make 5 to 8 wide open throttle kickdowns to first gear. (Allow at least 5 seconds each in 2nd and 3rd between each kickdown.)

5. **Check for trouble codes set during the road test.**

   If a trouble code sets during the road test, perform TEST 2A.

   If no trouble codes set, but the transaxle performance is unacceptable, see TROUBLE SHOOTING in CHRYSLER 41TE/AE article.
   If no trouble codes were set and the transaxle performance was acceptable, return the vehicle to the owner.

94I38222

TEST 38B
REPAIRING BACK-UP LIGHTS

PERFORM TEST 38A BEFORE PROCEEDING.

START TEST 38B.

PUT GEAR SELECT IN REVERSE POSITION.

DISCONNECT BACK-UP LAMP RELAY.

DID BACK-UP LAMPS GO OFF?

YES → REPLACE BACK-UP LAMP RELAY.

NO → REPAIR BACK-UP LAMP CKT FOR A SHORT TO B(+).

TEST 39A
CODE 35 – LOSS OF PRIME

PERFORM TEST 2A BEFORE PROCEEDING.

START TEST 39A.

TEST IS FOR LOSS OF PRIME.

THE FOLLOWING IS A LIST OF POSSIBLE CAUSES. CHECK THEM AND REPAIR AS NECESSARY.

CHECK FLUID LEVEL. FILL IF NECESSARY.

CHECK TRANS COOLER LINE FITTINGS.

REMOVE TRANS PAN. CHECK FOR FILTER DAMAGE. NOT FULLY INSTALLED, PLUGGED, OR MISSING O-RING.

IF EVERYTHING CHECKS OUT OK RECONNECT EVERYTHING AND PERFORM TEST 40

94G38220 94H38221

APPLICATION & LABOR TIMES

APPLICATION & LABOR TIMES

Vehicle Application	Labor Times		Trans. Model
	[1] R & I	[2] Overhaul	
Chrysler			
1993-94 Concorde			
3.3L & 3.5L	5.6	8.9	42LE
1994 LHS & New			
Yorker 3.5L	5.6	8.9	42LE
Dodge			
1993-94 Intrepid			
3.3L & 3.5L	5.6	8.9	42LE
Eagle			
1993-94 Vision			
3.3L & 3.5L	5.6	8.9	42LE

[1] – Removal and installation of transaxle from vehicle chassis.
[2] – Bench overhaul time for transaxle and differential. DOES NOT include removal and installation.

CAUTION: If battery is disconnected or voltage supply to Transaxle Control Module (TCM) is interrupted, TCM will have to relearn shift characteristics. If TCM, transaxle internal components, solenoid assembly or torque converter are replaced, TCM will have to relearn shift characteristics. Perform shift quality quick-learn procedure. See SHIFT QUALITY QUICK-LEARN PROCEDURE.

CAUTION: If torque converter is replaced or Transaxle Control Module (TCM) is changed from one vehicle to another, proper procedure must be used to reset the break-in procedure in TCM for the Electronically Modulated Converter Clutch (EMCC) in torque converter to prevent shudder during clutch engagement. Perform EMCC reset procedure. See ELECTRONICALLY MODULATED CONVERTER CLUTCH (EMCC) RESET PROCEDURE under TORQUE CONVERTER.

IDENTIFICATION

Transaxle identification code is stamped on identification tag located on side of transaxle. *See Fig. 1.* Transaxle identification code may be required when ordering replacement components.

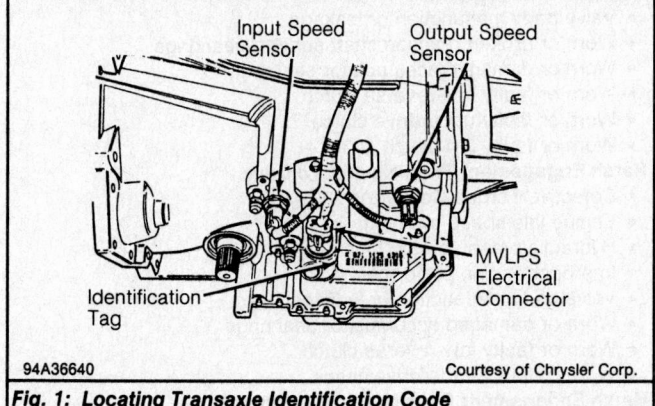

94A36640   Courtesy of Chrysler Corp.

Fig. 1: Locating Transaxle Identification Code

DESCRIPTION

The 42LE is a electronically controlled 4-speed transaxle. Transaxle uses hydraulically operated clutches controlled by the Transaxle Control Module (TCM). Transaxle consists of 3 multiple-disc input clutches, 2 multiple-disc holding clutches, 4 hydraulic accumulators and 2 planetary gear sets to provide 4 forward speeds and a reverse gear. *See Fig. 2.*

The TCM receives information from various sensors and in turn controls the solenoid assembly through the transaxle control relay. Solenoid assembly consists of 4 solenoids for controlling hydraulic pressure to 4 of the 5 transaxle clutches.

The TCM contains an adaptive memory which learns application and release rates of transaxle components for smooth operation. The TCM also learns the rate at which applied elements build pressure sufficient for a speed change. Adaptive control can adapt to altitude, temperature, engine output, etc.

NOTE: The TCM may also be referred to as transmission control module.

OPERATION

When "OD" (overdrive) gear position is selected, transaxle will shift through all 4 speeds with torque converter lock-up in 3rd gear and overdrive. When in "3" (3rd) gear position, transaxle uses only 1st, 2nd and 3rd (direct) gears with 2nd-to-3rd gear shift delayed until vehicle speed is at least 40 MPH. If operating in "3" (3rd) gear position or "L" (low) gear position, torque converter lock-up occurs in 3rd gear for improved transaxle cooling. If engine coolant temperature becomes excessively warm, torque converter will also lock-up in 2nd gear. The "L" (low) gear position provides engine braking when operating in descending grades.

The TCM contains a self-diagnostic system which stores a diagnostic trouble code if a transaxle failure exists. Diagnostic trouble code can be retrieved to determine the transaxle problem areas. For information on transaxle electronic components, see CHRYSLER 42LE ELECTRONIC DIAGNOSIS article.

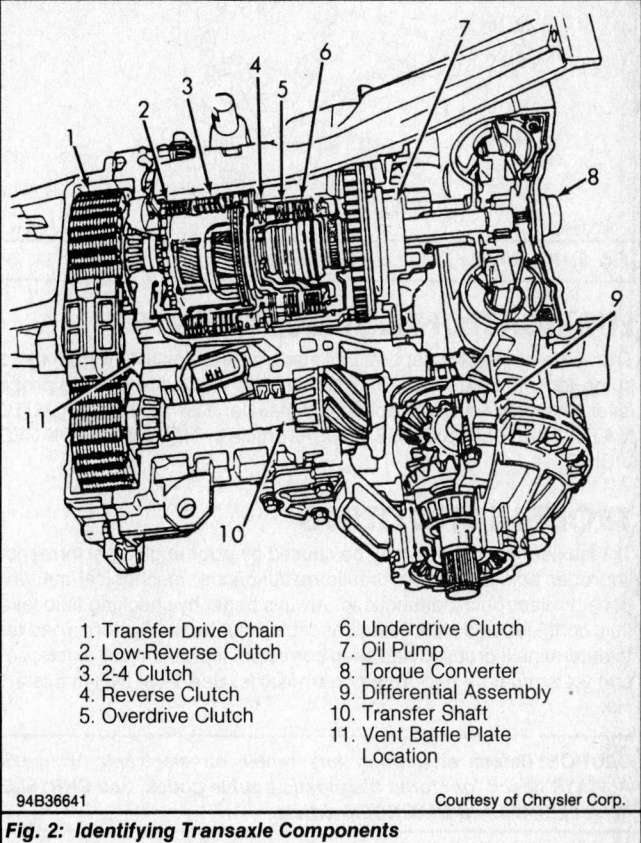

1. Transfer Drive Chain
2. Low-Reverse Clutch
3. 2-4 Clutch
4. Reverse Clutch
5. Overdrive Clutch
6. Underdrive Clutch
7. Oil Pump
8. Torque Converter
9. Differential Assembly
10. Transfer Shaft
11. Vent Baffle Plate Location

94B36641   Courtesy of Chrysler Corp.

Fig. 2: Identifying Transaxle Components

SHIFT QUALITY QUICK-LEARN PROCEDURE

NOTE: This procedure quickly optimizes shift quality. Procedure must be performed after disconnecting battery or loss of voltage supply to Transaxle Control Module (TCM), replacing TCM, transaxle internal components, solenoid assembly or torque converter. Chrysler's Diagnostic Readout Box (DRB) scan tool is used to perform shift quality quick-learn procedure.

NOTE: Following conditions must be met when performing shift quality quick-learn procedure: oil temperature must be greater than 60°F (16°C), brakes must be applied when indicated, engine speed greater than 500 RPM, throttle angle less than 3 degrees, gearshift lever must be moved only when indicated and remain in overdrive as indicated until DRB indicates procedure is completed.

NOTE: If new replacement TCM is installed on vehicle with engine at normal operating temperature, shift quality quick-learn procedure will cause TCM to indicate a cold oil temperature. Oil temperature must be monitored with DRB. If oil temperature is less than 60°F (16°C), allow engine to idle until oil temperature is greater than 60°F (16°C). If oil temperature is greater than 200°F (94°C), allow transaxle to cool until oil temperature is less than 200°F (94°C).

1) Connect DRB to Blue colored data link connector. *See Fig. 3.* Using proper cartridge and DRB manufacture's instructions, move through program to enter 42LE menu. Start vehicle. Select ADJUSTMENTS function.

2) Apply brakes. Select QUICK-LEARN function. Place shift lever in Neutral and then Overdrive when indicated. Wait until TEST COMPLETE is indicated on DRB. Place shift lever in Park. Release brakes. Remove DRB.

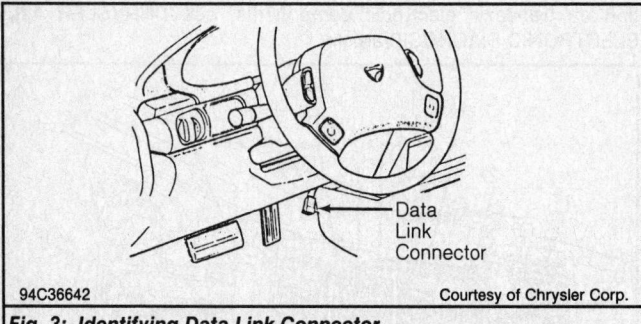

94C36642   Courtesy of Chrysler Corp.

Fig. 3: Identifying Data Link Connector

LUBRICATION & ADJUSTMENTS

Transaxle contains a separate oil sump for transaxle ATF from the oil sump for the differential. Ensure both fluid levels are filled to proper level when servicing or repairing transaxle. See appropriate AUTOMATIC TRANSMISSION SERVICING article in TRANSMISSION SERVICING.

TROUBLE SHOOTING

Transaxle malfunctions may be caused by poor engine performance, improper adjustments, hydraulic malfunctions, mechanical malfunctions or electronic malfunctions. Always begin by checking fluid level, fluid condition and shift linkage or cable adjustment. Perform road test to determine if problem has been corrected. If problem still exists, several tests must be performed on transaxle. See TESTING in this article.

CAUTION: Before attempting any repair on electronic transaxle, ALWAYS check for stored diagnostic trouble codes. See CHRYSLER 42LE ELECTRONIC DIAGNOSIS article.

TRANSAXLE SYMPTOM DIAGNOSIS

Buzzing Noise
- Aerated fluid
- Low fluid level
- Valve body malfunction or leakage

Buzzing Noise During Transaxle Shifts
- Normal solenoid operation
- Solenoid assembly sound cover loose or missing

Delayed Engagement From Neutral To Drive
- Aerated fluid
- Damaged clutch seals
- Engine idle speed too low
- Faulty oil pump
- Hydraulic pressures too low
- Incorrect shift linkage or cable adjustment
- Low fluid level
- Oil filter restricted
- Valve body malfunction or leakage
- Worn or broken reaction shaft support seal rings
- Worn or damaged accumulator seal rings
- Worn or damaged input shaft seal rings
- Worn or faulty underdrive clutch

Delayed Engagement From Neutral To Reverse
- Aerated fluid
- Damaged clutch seals
- Engine idle speed too low
- Faulty oil pump
- Hydraulic pressures too low
- Incorrect shift linkage or cable adjustment
- Low fluid level
- Oil filter restricted
- Valve body malfunction or leakage
- Worn or broken reaction shaft support seal rings
- Worn or damaged input shaft seal rings
- Worn or damaged accumulator seal rings
- Worn or faulty reverse clutch

Grating, Scraping Or Growling Noise
- Bearings worn or damaged
- Chipped or damaged gear teeth
- Defective drive plate
- Defective planetary gear sets
- Shaft bushing worn or damaged

Hard To Fill With Fluid Oil Or Fluid Blows Out Filler Tube
- Aerated fluid
- High fluid level
- Oil filter restricted

Harsh Downshifts
- Aerated fluid
- Damaged clutch seals
- Engine idle speed too high
- Hydraulic pressures too high
- Improper engine performance
- Low fluid level
- Valve body malfunction or leakage
- Worn or broken reaction shaft support seal rings
- Worn or damaged accumulator seal rings
- Worn or faulty low-reverse clutch
- Worn or faulty underdrive clutch
- Worn or faulty 2-4 clutch

Harsh Engagement From Neutral To Drive
- Defective Torque Converter
- Engine idle speed too high
- Hydraulic pressures too high
- Improper engine performance
- Valve body malfunction or leakage
- Worn or damaged accumulator seal rings
- Worn or faulty low-reverse clutch
- Worn or faulty underdrive clutch

Harsh Engagement From Neutral To Reverse
- Engine idle speed too high
- Hydraulic pressures too high
- Improper engine performance
- Valve body malfunction or leakage
- Worn or damaged accumulator seal rings
- Worn or faulty low-reverse clutch
- Worn or faulty reverse clutch

Harsh Lock-Up Shift
- Defective torque converter
- Sticking lock-up piston

Harsh Upshift
- Incorrect hydraulic pressure
- Improper engine performance
- Worn or faulty overdrive clutch

- Worn or faulty 2-4 clutch

High Shift Efforts
- Worn or damaged shift cable or linkage
- Valve body malfunction or leakage

No Torque Converter Lock-Up
- Aerated fluid
- Defective torque converter
- Engine coolant temperature low
- Faulty oil pump
- Hydraulic pressure too low
- Low fluid level
- Valve body malfunction or leakage
- Worn or damaged input shaft seal rings

No Upshift Into Overdrive
- Engine coolant temperature low
- Worn or faulty overdrive clutch

Poor Shift Quality
- Aerated fluid
- Hydraulic pressures too low
- Low fluid level
- Oil filter restricted
- Valve body malfunction or leakage
- Worn or broken reaction shaft support seal rings

Shifts Erratically
- Aerated fluid
- Faulty oil pump
- Hydraulic pressures too low
- Improper engine performance
- Incorrect shift linkage or cable adjustment
- Low fluid level
- Oil filter restricted
- Valve body malfunction or leakage
- Worn or broken reaction shaft support seal rings
- Worn or faulty low-reverse clutch
- Worn or faulty overdrive clutch
- Worn or faulty underdrive clutch
- Worn or faulty 2-4 clutch

Transaxle Overheats
- Aerated fluid
- Defective torque converter
- Engine idle speed too high
- Faulty engine cooling system
- Faulty oil pump
- Hydraulic pressure too low
- Improper fluid level
- Insufficient clutch plate clearance
- Incorrect shift linkage or cable adjustment

Vehicle Drags Or Locks
- Bearings worn or damaged
- Chipped or damaged gear teeth
- Defective planetary gear sets
- Worn or faulty low-reverse clutch
- Worn or faulty overdrive clutch
- Worn or faulty reverse clutch
- Worn or faulty underdrive clutch
- Worn or faulty 2-4 clutch

Vehicle Moves In Neutral
- Clutch(es) dragging
- Incorrect shift linkage or cable adjustment
- Insufficient clutch plate clearance
- Valve body malfunction or leakage
- Worn or faulty overdrive clutch
- Worn or faulty reverse clutch
- Worn or faulty underdrive clutch

TESTING

ROAD TEST

1) Ensure shift linkage, fluid level and condition are okay. Add fluid and adjust control cable as needed. Road test vehicle, operating transaxle in each gear position. Check for slipping and any variation in shifting.

2) If vehicle operates properly at highway speeds, but has poor acceleration, torque converter stator clutch may be slipping. If acceleration through all gears is normal, but high throttle opening is required to maintain highway speeds, torque converter stator clutch may be seized. Torque converter must be replaced if stator clutch is defective.

3) In most cases, the clutch that is slipping can be determined by noting transaxle operation in all gear positions and noting which clutches are applied in proper gear position. See Fig. 4.

4) Process of elimination can be used to detect any unit which slips and to confirm proper operation of good units. However, although road test analysis can usually diagnose slipping units, actual malfunction usually cannot be decided. Practically any condition can be caused by leaking hydraulic circuits or sticking valves.

NOTE: Clutch volume may be checked using DRB and manufacturer's instructions to determine if clutch is defective.

TORQUE CONVERTER STALL SPEED TEST

CAUTION: Manufacturer does not recommend performing torque converter stall speed test on 42LE transaxle.

HYDRAULIC PRESSURE TEST

Pressure Test Preparation – **1)** Ensure shift linkage or cable, transaxle fluid level and condition are okay. Add fluid and adjust shift control cable or linkage as needed.

2) Ensure transaxle fluid is at normal operating temperature of 150-200°F (66-93°C). Install tachometer. Raise vehicle on hoist, allowing front wheels to rotate freely.

NOTE: A 300 psi (21 kg/cm²) pressure gauge and Adapter (L-4559) are required for checking hydraulic pressures.

Low-Reverse Clutch Pressure Test – **1)** Remove pressure tap plug and install pressure gauge in low-reverse clutch pressure tap. See Fig. 5.

2) Place gearshift in "L" position. Allowing front wheels to rotate, accelerate until vehicle speed indicates 20 MPH.

3) Low-reverse clutch pressure should be 115-145 psi (8.0-10.1 kg/cm²). This pressure test checks oil pump output, pressure regulation and low-reverse clutch hydraulic circuit and shift schedule. Remove pressure gauge. Install and tighten pressure tap plug to specification. See TORQUE SPECIFICATIONS.

Underdrive Clutch Pressure Test – **1)** Remove pressure tap plug and install pressure gauge in underdrive clutch pressure tap. See Fig. 5.

2) Place gearshift in "3" position. Allowing front wheels to rotate, accelerate until vehicle speed indicates 30 MPH.

3) Underdrive clutch pressure should be 110-145 psi (7.7-10.1 kg/cm²). This pressure test checks underdrive clutch hydraulic circuit and shift schedule. Remove pressure gauge. Install and tighten pressure tap plug to specification. See TORQUE SPECIFICATIONS.

Overdrive Clutch Pressure Test – **1)** Remove pressure tap plug and install pressure gauge in overdrive clutch pressure tap. See Fig. 5.

2) Place gearshift in "OD" position. Allowing front wheels to rotate, accelerate until vehicle speed indicates 20 MPH.

3) Overdrive clutch pressure should be 74-95 psi (5.2-6.7 kg/cm²). Place gearshift in "3" position and increase vehicle speed to 30 MPH.

4) Overdrive clutch pressure should now be less than 5 psi (.35 kg/cm²). This pressure test checks overdrive clutch hydraulic circuit and shift schedule. Remove pressure gauge. Install and tighten pressure tap plug to specification. See TORQUE SPECIFICATIONS.

2-4 Clutch Pressure Test – **1)** Remove pressure tap plug and install pressure gauge in 2-4 clutch pressure tap. See Fig. 5.

2) Place gearshift in "OD" position. Allowing front wheels to rotate, accelerated until vehicle speed indicates 30 MPH.

3) The 2-4 clutch pressure should be 75-95 psi (5.3-6.7 kg/cm²). This pressure test checks 2-4 clutch hydraulic circuit. Remove pressure gauge. Install and tighten pressure tap plug to specification. See TORQUE SPECIFICATIONS.

Gearshift Position	MVLPS	Parking Sprag	CLUTCHES				
			Underdrive	Overdrive	Reverse	2-4	Low-Reverse
P — PARK	X	X					X
R — REVERSE					X		X
N — NEUTRAL	X						X
OD — OVERDRIVE							
First			X				X
Second			X			X	
Direct			X	X			
Overdrive				X		X	
③ — DRIVE*							
First			X				X
Second			X			X	
Direct			X	X			
L — LOW*							
First			X				X
Second			X			X	
Direct			X	X			

* – Vehicle upshift and downshift speeds are increased when in these gearshift positions.

NOTE: MVLPS is the manual valve lever position sensor.

94D36643

Courtesy of Chrysler Corp.

Fig. 4: Clutch Application Chart

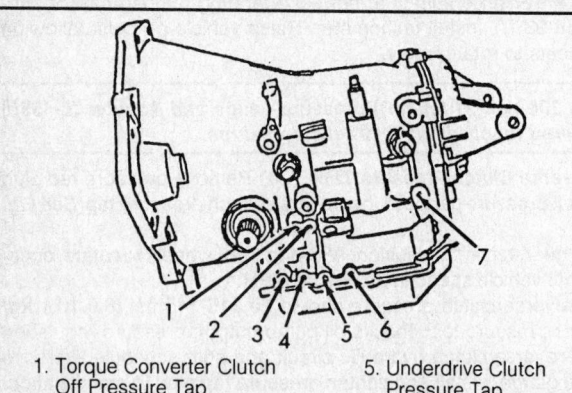

1. Torque Converter Clutch Off Pressure Tap
2. Reverse Clutch Pressure Tap
3. Overdrive Clutch Pressure Tap
4. Torque Converter Clutch On Pressure Tap
5. Underdrive Clutch Pressure Tap
6. 2-4 Clutch Pressure Tap
7. Low-Reverse Clutch Pressure Tap

94E36644

Courtesy of Chrysler Corp.

Fig. 5: Identifying Pressure Taps

Torque Converter Clutch Pressure Test – 1) Remove pressure tap plug and install pressure gauge in torque converter clutch off pressure tap. *See Fig. 5.*

2) Place gearshift in "OD" position. Allowing front wheels to rotate, accelerate until vehicle speed indicates 50 MPH.

CAUTION: Ensure both front wheels are rotating at the same speed.

3) Torque converter clutch off pressure should be less than 5 psi (.35 kg/cm²). Remove pressure gauge. Install and tighten pressure tap plug to specification. See TORQUE SPECIFICATIONS.

4) Remove pressure tap plug and install pressure gauge in torque converter clutch on pressure tap. *See Fig. 5.* Place gearshift in "OD" position.

5) Allowing front wheels to rotate, accelerate until vehicle speed indicates 50 MPH. Ensure torque converter clutch is applied.

NOTE: It may be necessary to use DRB scan tool to monitor engine RPM to verify when torque converter clutch is applied. If DRB usage is required, connect DRB to Blue data link connector. See Fig. 3. Use proper cartridge and DRB manufacture's instructions for monitoring torque converter clutch operation.

6) Torque converter clutch on pressure should be 60-90 psi (4.2-6.3 kg/cm²). This pressure test checks torque converter clutch hydraulic circuit. Remove pressure gauge. Install and tighten pressure tap plug to specification. See TORQUE SPECIFICATIONS.

Reverse Clutch Pressure Test – 1) Remove pressure tap plug and install pressure gauge in reverse clutch pressure tap. *See Fig. 5.* Place gearshift in Reverse.

2) Apply brakes. Accelerate until engine speed is 1500 RPM. Reverse clutch pressure should be 165-235 psi (11.6-16.5 kg/cm²). This pressure test checks reverse clutch hydraulic circuit. Remove pressure gauge. Install and tighten pressure tap plug to specification. See TORQUE SPECIFICATIONS.

Pressure Test Result Diagnosis – 1) If proper hydraulic pressure exists in any one pressure test, oil pump and pressure regulator valve are operating properly. Various clutch operating hydraulic pressures exist depending on gearshift position. *See Fig. 6.*

2) Low hydraulic pressure in all hydraulic pressure tests, indicates a defective oil pump, restricted oil filter or stuck pressure regulator valve. If hydraulic pressure is not within specification, clutch hydraulic circuit is leaking.

3) If overdrive clutch pressure exceeds 5 psi (.35 kg.cm²) in step **4)** of OVERDRIVE CLUTCH PRESSURE TEST, a worn reaction shaft seal ring is indicated.

CLUTCH AIR PRESSURE TEST

NOTE: Inoperative clutches can be located by applying air pressure to appropriate passages in transaxle case. Clutch assembly is defective if it does not operate correctly.

Test Preparation – Remove valve body. See VALVE BODY under REMOVAL & INSTALLATION. Install Adapter Plates (6599-1 and 6599-2) on transaxle case. *See Fig. 7.*

CAUTION: Ensure air supply is free of all dirt and moisture. Using air pressure regulator, adjust air pressure to 30 psi (2.1 kg/cm²).

Overdrive Clutch – Apply air pressure to Overdrive clutch (OD) passage on adapter plate. *See Fig. 7.* Ensure overdrive clutch push-pull piston moves forward and returns to original position when air pressure is released.

Reverse Clutch – Apply air pressure to Reverse clutch (REV) passage on adapter plate. *See Fig. 7.* Ensure reverse clutch push-pull piston moves rearward and returns to original position when air pressure is released.

ALL PRESSURE SPECIFICATIONS ARE PSI
(VEHICLE ON HOIST WITH WHEELS FREE TO ROTATE)

Gearshift Position		Actual Gear	PRESSURE TAPS					
			Underdrive Clutch	Overdrive Clutch	Reverse Clutch	Torque Converter Clutch Off	2-4 Clutch	Low-Reverse Clutch
PARK 0 mph	①	PARK	0-2	0-5	0-2	60-110	0-2	115-145
REVERSE 0 mph	①	REVERSE	0-2	0-7	165-235	50-100	0-2	165-235
NEUTRAL 0 mph	①	NEUTRAL	0-2	0-5	0-2	60-110	0-2	115-145
L 20 mph	②	FIRST	110-145	0-5	0-2	60-110	0-2	115-145
③ 30 mph	②	SECOND	110-145	0-5	0-2	60-110	115-145	0-2
③ 45 mph	②	DIRECT	75-95	75-95	0-2	60-90	0-2	0-2
OD 30 mph	②	OVERDRIVE	0-2	75-95	0-2	60-90	75-95	0-2
OD 50 mph	②	OVERDRIVE LOCKUP	0-2	75-95	0-2	0-5	75-95	0-2

¹ – Check with engine speed at 1500 RPM.
² – CAUTION: Both front wheels must rotate at the same speed.

94F36645

Courtesy of Chrysler Corp.

Fig. 6: Identifying Clutch Operating Hydraulic Pressures

2-4 Clutch – Apply air pressure to 2-4 clutch retainer hole. See Fig. 7. Ensure 2-4 clutch piston moves rearward and returns to original position when air is released.

Low-Reverse Clutch – Apply air pressure to Low-Reverse (LR) passage on adapter plate. See Fig. 7. Ensure low-reverse clutch piston moves forward and returns to original position when air is released.

Underdrive Clutch – 1) Apply air pressure to low-reverse (L-R) and 2-4 clutch retainer hole. The output shaft should now be locked. Wrap rubber hose around input shaft. Install clamp-on pliers on input shaft and rotate input shaft.

2) Apply air pressure to Underdrive clutch (UD) passage on adapter plate. Input shaft should not rotate with hand torque. Release air pressure and note that input shaft rotates.

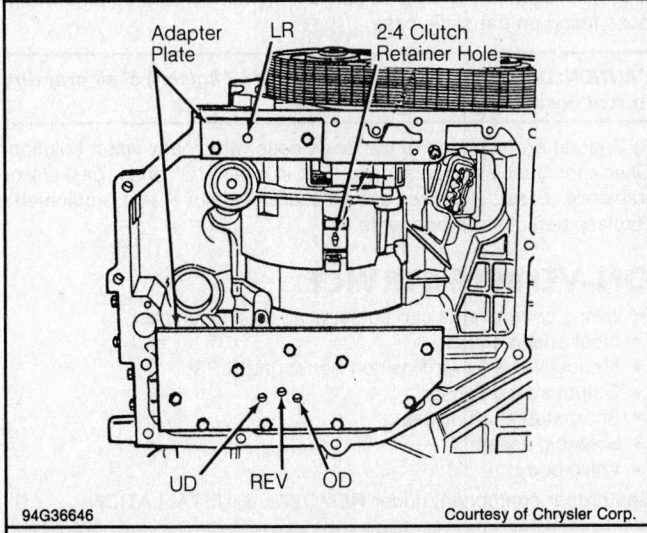

94G36646

Courtesy of Chrysler Corp.

Fig. 7: Applying Air Pressure To Clutch Packs

TORQUE CONVERTER FLUID LEAKAGE TEST

NOTE: Transaxle contains a separate oil sump for the differential. Transmission uses ATF and differential uses hypoid gear oil. Transaxle contains oil seals for each individual sump. A fluid leakage weep hole is located on side of transaxle case. See Fig. 8. Before performing torque converter fluid leakage test, check for fluid leakage at fluid leakage weep hole. If fluid leakage exists, note if fluid is ATF or differential gear oil. This indicates which oil seal is leaking and must be replaced.

NOTE: Fluid around torque converter may originate from engine oil or the transaxle. Ensure transaxle fluid level is correct. Fluid leakage at torque converter may result if fluid level is too high. Transaxle can be check for torque converter leaks using following method.

1) Remove torque converter dust shield. Using solvent and compressed air, clean inside area of torque converter housing. Ensure area is clean and dry.

2) Fabricate leakage test probe using 1/32" sheet metal, 6" (152 mm) long and 1 1/2" (38.1 mm) wide. See Fig. 9. Start and operate engine until transaxle is at normal operating temperature. Shut engine off.

3) Install leakage test probe using dust shield bolt so leakage test probe is near torque converter. Ensure leakage test probe does not contact torque converter.

4) Start engine. Place gearshift in Neutral. Operate engine at 2500 RPM for 2 minutes. Stop engine. Remove leakage test probe.

5) If upper surface of leakage test probe is dry, torque converter is not leaking. If upper surface of leakage test probe is wet with transaxle ATF fluid, torque converter is leaking. If lower area below leakage test probe is wet with transaxle ATF fluid, fluid is coming from the transaxle.

6) Possible causes of ATF fluid leaks at torque converter areas are:
- Torque converter hub
- Defective seal (check torque converter hub finish)
- Mispositioned or worn bushing
- Oil pump housing oil return hole restricted
- Defective oil pump housing or "O" ring
- Oil pump-to-transaxle case bolts

7) If torque converter is leaking, check for defective welds on outside diameter of torque converter and torque converter hub. Torque converter hub weld is welded on the inside and is not visible. Replace torque converter if a leak exists. DO NOT attempt to repair torque converter.

CAUTION: If torque converter is replaced, a special torque converter break-in procedure must be performed to prevent shudder during clutch engagement. See ELECTRONICALLY MODULATED CONVERTER CLUTCH (EMCC) RESET PROCEDURE under TORQUE CONVERTER.

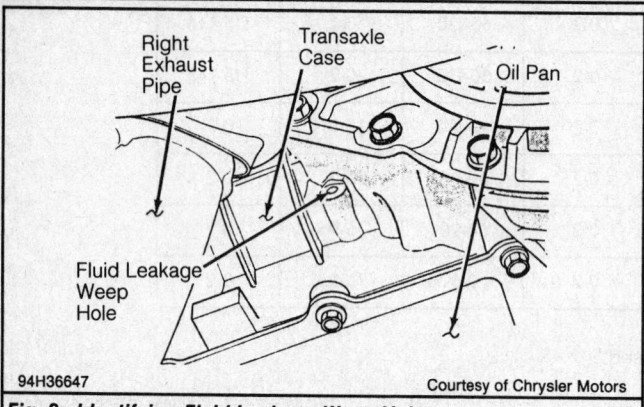

94H36647   Courtesy of Chrysler Motors

Fig. 8: Identifying Fluid Leakage Weep Hole

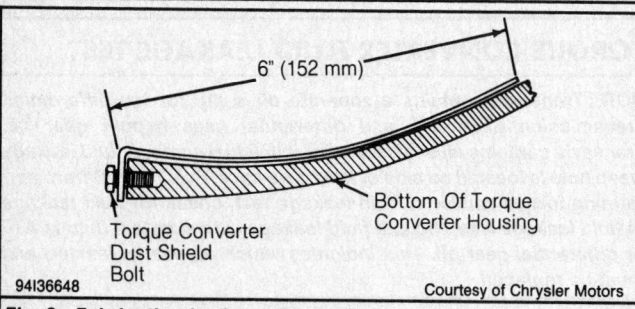

94I36648   Courtesy of Chrysler Motors

Fig. 9: Fabricating Leakage Test Probe

TRANSAXLE CASE PRESSURE TESTS

NOTE: Transaxle must be removed to perform pressure tests. Transaxle must be pressure tested for leaks in transaxle ATF sump and differential oil sump. Transaxle case, gaskets and oil pump housing can be checked for leaks using the transaxle ATF sump pressure test. Transaxle case, gaskets and seals for differential can be checked using differential oil sump pressure test.

Transaxle ATF Sump Pressure Test – 1) Fabricate a torque converter hub seal cup using 1.5" (38.1 mm) outside diameter thin wall tubing and a .125" (3.17 mm) steel disc. *See Fig. 10.* Fabricate torque converter hub seal cup retaining strap using a .25" (6.3 mm) thick and 1.25" (31.75 mm) wide material. *See Fig. 11.*

2) Remove torque converter from transaxle. Plug dipstick tube and plug oil cooler line fittings. Using rotary motion, install torque converter hub seal cup over input shaft and through torque converter hub seal until cup bottoms against gear lugs of the oil pump.

3) Install torque converter hub seal cup retaining strap using starter upper hole and opposite bracket hole. Remove vent hose for transaxle ATF sump from transaxle case.

4) Attach air hose to vent hose fitting for transaxle ATF sump on transaxle case. Using pressure regulator, apply 8-10 psi (.5-.7 kg/cm²) of air pressure to vent hose fitting on transaxle case.

CAUTION: DO NOT apply more than 10 psi (.7 kg/cm²) of air pressure to vent hose fitting on transaxle case.

5) Coat oil pump and front of transaxle case with soapy water solution. Check for bubbles, indicating a leak in seals, "O" rings, gaskets or transaxle case. Release air pressure. Remove test equipment. Replace defective components.

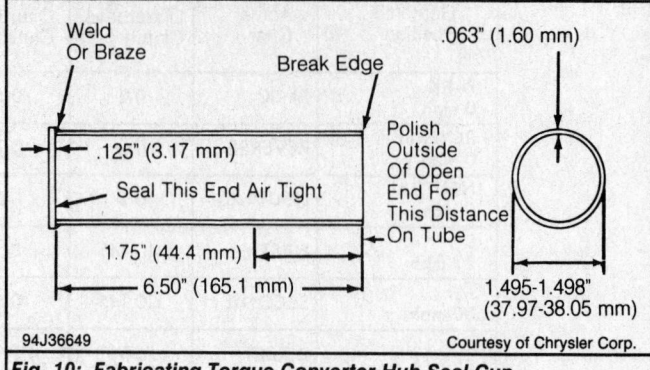

94J36649   Courtesy of Chrysler Corp.

Fig. 10: Fabricating Torque Converter Hub Seal Cup

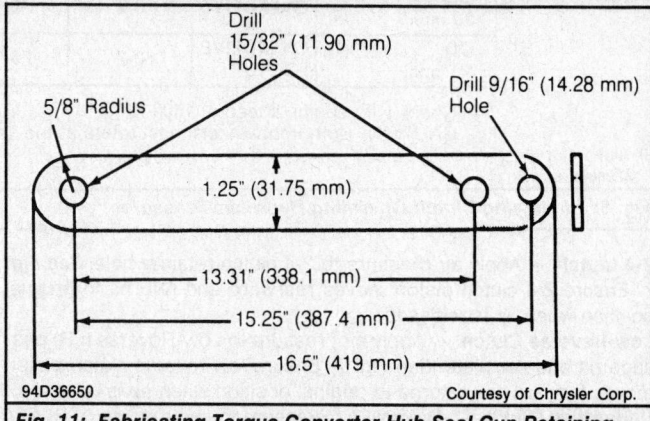

94D36650   Courtesy of Chrysler Corp.

Fig. 11: Fabricating Torque Converter Hub Seal Cup Retaining Strap

Differential Oil Sump Pressure Test – 1) Ensure short and long stub shafts are installed in transaxle. Remove vent hose for differential oil sump from transaxle case.

2) Attach air hose to vent hose fitting on transaxle case. Using pressure regulator, apply 8-10 psi (.5-.7 kg/cm²) of air pressure to vent hose fitting on transaxle case.

CAUTION: DO NOT apply more than 10 psi (.7 kg/cm²) of air pressure to vent hose fitting on transaxle case.

3) Coat differential area of transaxle case with soapy water solution. Check for bubbles, indicating a leak in seals, "O" rings, gaskets or transaxle case. Release air pressure. Remove test equipment. Replace defective components.

ON-VEHICLE SERVICE

Following components can be serviced on the vehicle:
- Input speed sensor
- Manual Valve Lever Position Sensor (MVLPS)
- Output speed sensor
- Short stub shaft oil seal
- Solenoid assembly
- Valve body

See proper component under REMOVAL & INSTALLATION.

NOTE: Manufacturer states that transfer drive chain and sprockets can be changed on the vehicle. See DIFFERENTIAL ASSEMBLY, TRANSFER SHAFT & COMPONENTS under TRANSAXLE DISASSEMBLY and TRANSAXLE REASSEMBLY.

OIL COOLER FLUSHING

CAUTION: Whenever transaxle failure exists, oil cooler(s) must be flushed and oil cooler by-pass valve in transaxle replaced. If vehicle is equipped with 2 oil coolers, one in radiator tank and one in front of radiator, flush oil coolers separately. DO NOT attempt to flush both oil coolers at one time. Oil cooler by-pass valve is located behind oil pump in transaxle case. See Fig. 19.

1) Disconnect oil cooler lines at transaxle. Using hand-held suction gun filled with mineral spirits, force mineral spirits into oil cooler return line until mineral spirits flows from oil cooler supply line. *See Fig. 12.*
2) Continue flushing oil cooler until mineral spirits is clear and no signs of contamination exists. Once no contamination exists, apply compressed air on oil cooler return line in light applications until remaining mineral spirits is blown from oil cooler and oil cooler lines.
3) Pump at least one quart of Mopar ATF Plus-Type 7176 though oil cooler to ensure oil cooler is free of mineral spirits. Replace oil cooler if fluid does not flow freely through oil cooler. Reinstall oil cooler lines. Fill to proper fluid level with Mopar ATF Plus-Type 7176.

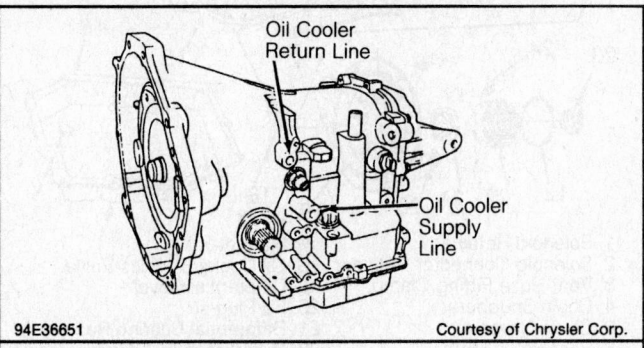

94E36651   Courtesy of Chrysler Corp.

Fig. 12: Identifying Oil Cooler Lines

OIL COOLER FLOW CHECK

1) With transaxle filled to proper fluid level, disconnect oil cooler return line at transaxle. *See Fig. 12.* Place container under oil cooler return line.

CAUTION: DO NOT obtain more than one quart of fluid or transaxle may be damaged.

2) Apply parking brake. Start engine and allow to idle. Place gearshift in Neutral. Check fluid flow from oil cooler return line.
3) If fluid flow is intermittent or it takes more than 20 seconds to obtain one quart of fluid, replace oil cooler. Reinstall oil cooler return line. Fill to proper fluid level with Mopar ATF Plus-Type 7176.

REMOVAL & INSTALLATION

CAUTION: If battery is disconnected or voltage supply to Transaxle Control Module (TCM) is lost, TCM will have to relearn shift characteristics. It may be necessary to perform shift quality quick-learn procedure so TCM can relearn shift characteristics. See SHIFT QUALITY QUICK-LEARN PROCEDURE at beginning of article.

AXLE SHAFTS

See appropriate AXLE SHAFTS article in AXLE SHAFTS & TRANSFER CASES.

INPUT SPEED SENSOR

Removal – 1) Disconnect electrical connector from input speed sensor, located on side of transaxle. *See Fig. 1.* Ensure weather seal for electrical connector remains on the electrical connector. Unscrew input speed sensor from transaxle case.
2) To install, reverse removal procedure using NEW "O" ring on input speed sensor. Tighten input speed sensor to specification. See TORQUE SPECIFICATIONS.

LONG STUB SHAFT OIL SEAL

NOTE: Following procedure can be used to change oil seal with transaxle removed and without having to reset ring gear backlash and differential bearing rotating torque. If any components except oil seals are replaced, following procedure cannot be used. Long stub shaft is left stub shaft when viewed from rear of transaxle. Short stub shaft is right stub shaft when viewed from rear of transaxle.

Removal – 1) Remove transaxle. See appropriate AUTOMATIC TRANSMISSION REMOVAL article in TRANSMISSION SERVICING. Remove snap ring retaining long stub shaft in transaxle case. Install Adapter (6669) on end of long stub shaft. Attach slide hammer on adapter. Using slide hammer, pull long stub shaft from transaxle case.
2) Place reference marks on transaxle case and inner bearing adjuster, located near input shaft for reassembly reference. *See Fig. 13.* Place reference marks on differential cover and outer bearing adjuster, located near short stub shaft on right side of transaxle for reassembly reference. *See Fig. 13.*
3) Remove bolt and lock bracket from outer bearing adjuster. *See Fig. 13.* Using Socket (6503), rotate outer bearing adjuster counterclockwise one full revolution.

NOTE: Check for corrosion on short stub shaft before removing differential cover. If corrosion exists, clean short stub shaft and use care not to damage oil seal when removing differential cover.

4) Remove bolts and differential cover. *See Fig. 14.* Remove differential assembly.

CAUTION: Note amount of revolutions that inner bearing adjuster is threaded into transaxle case when removing inner bearing adjuster. Inner bearing adjuster must be set at the exact position when reinstalled.

5) Remove bolt and bearing adjuster lock bracket from inner bearing adjuster. *See Fig. 13.* Using Socket (6502-B), unscrew inner bearing adjuster from transaxle case, noting amount of revolutions for reassembly reference. Press oil seal from inner bearing adjuster.
Installation – 1) Press NEW oil seal into inner bearing adjuster. Install NEW "O" ring on inner bearing adjuster. Lubricate threads on inner bearing adjuster and lip of oil seal with gear oil.
2) Screw inner bearing adjuster into transaxle case original number of revolutions and align reference marks. Install bearing adjuster lock bracket. Install and tighten bearing adjuster lock bracket bolt to specification. See TORQUE SPECIFICATIONS.
3) Install differential assembly. Install Seal Protector (6591) on short stub shaft. Lubricate seal protector and lip of oil seal in outer bearing adjuster with gear oil.
4) Apply sealant on differential cover-to-transaxle case contact areas. Install differential cover. Install and tighten differential cover bolts to specification. See TORQUE SPECIFICATIONS.
5) Tighten outer bearing adjuster 3/4 of a revolution. Rotate differential assembly several times in both directions to seat the bearings. Tighten outer bearing adjuster an additional 1/4 revolution until reference marks are aligned.
6) Install lock bracket on outer bearing adjuster. Install and tighten lock bracket bolt to specification. See TORQUE SPECIFICATIONS. Remove seal protector from short stub shaft.
7) Install NEW "C" clip and "O" ring on outer ends of long and short stub shafts. Install long stub shaft. Install snap ring retaining long stub shaft in transaxle case. Reinstall transaxle. Fill differential with 80W-90 API GL-5 gear oil. DO NOT use synthetic gear oil. Fill transaxle with Mopar ATF Plus-Type 7176.

SHORT STUB SHAFT OIL SEAL

NOTE: Following procedure can be used to change oil seal without removing transaxle from vehicle or having to reset ring gear backlash and differential bearing rotating torque. If any components except oil seals are replaced, following procedure cannot be used. Short stub shaft is right stub shaft when viewed from rear of transaxle.

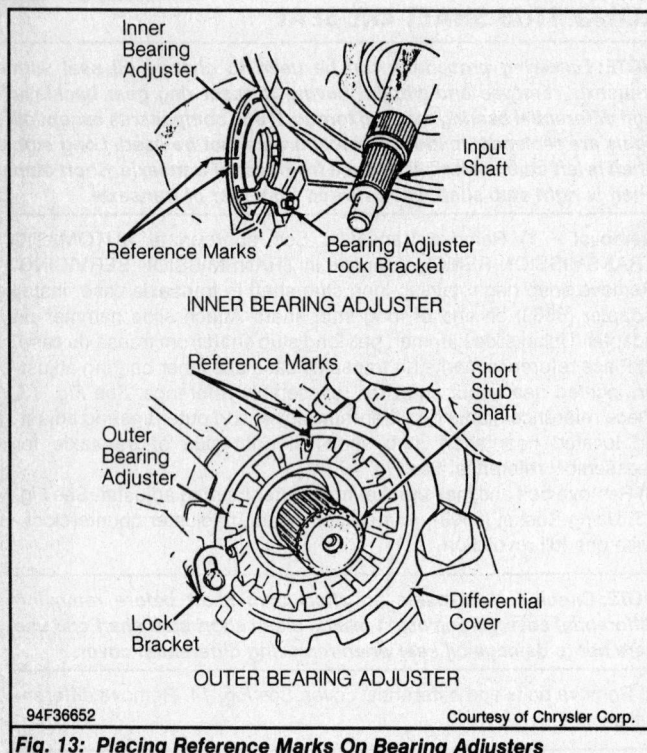

Fig. 13: Placing Reference Marks On Bearing Adjusters

Removal – 1) Raise and support vehicle. Remove passenger's side axle shaft. See appropriate AXLE SHAFTS article in AXLE SHAFTS & TRANSFER CASES.

2) Place reference marks on differential cover and outer bearing adjuster, located near short stub shaft on right side of transaxle for reassembly reference. *See Fig. 13.*

3) Remove bolt and lock bracket from outer bearing adjuster. *See Fig. 13.* Using Socket (6503), rotate outer bearing adjuster slightly counterclockwise.

4) Using torque wrench, measure amount of torque required to rotate outer bearing adjuster clockwise until reference marks are realigned. Note torque reading for reassembly reference.

5) Using socket, remove outer bearing adjuster from differential cover. Press oil seal from outer bearing adjuster.

Installation – 1) Press NEW oil seal into inner bearing adjuster. Check for corrosion on short stub shaft. If corrosion exists, wrap short stub shaft with wax paper before installing seal protector.

2) Install Seal Protector (6591) on short stub shaft. Lubricate seal protector and lip of oil seal with gear oil. Install NEW "O" ring on outer bearing adjuster. Lubricate threads on outer bearing adjuster with gear oil.

3) Screw outer bearing adjuster into transaxle case until torque reading is 120 INCH lbs. (13.6 N.m) less than that obtained in step **4)** during removal. Rotate differential assembly several times in both directions to seat the bearings.

4) Tighten outer bearing adjuster until reference marks are aligned. Install lock bracket on outer bearing adjuster. Install and tighten lock bracket bolt to specification. Remove seal protector and wax paper (if used) from short stub shaft.

5) Install NEW "C" clip and "O" ring on outer end of short stub shaft. Install axle shaft. Fill differential with 80W-90 API GL-5 gear oil. DO NOT use synthetic gear oil.

MANUAL VALVE LEVER POSITION SENSOR (MVLPS)

Removal & Installation – 1) Remove valve body. See VALVE BODY under REMOVAL & INSTALLATION. Remove manual valve lever-to-valve body retaining bolt. Slide MVLPS from manual valve lever. *See Fig. 15.*

2) To install, reverse removal procedure. Tighten manual valve lever-to-valve body bolt to specification. See TORQUE SPECIFICATIONS.

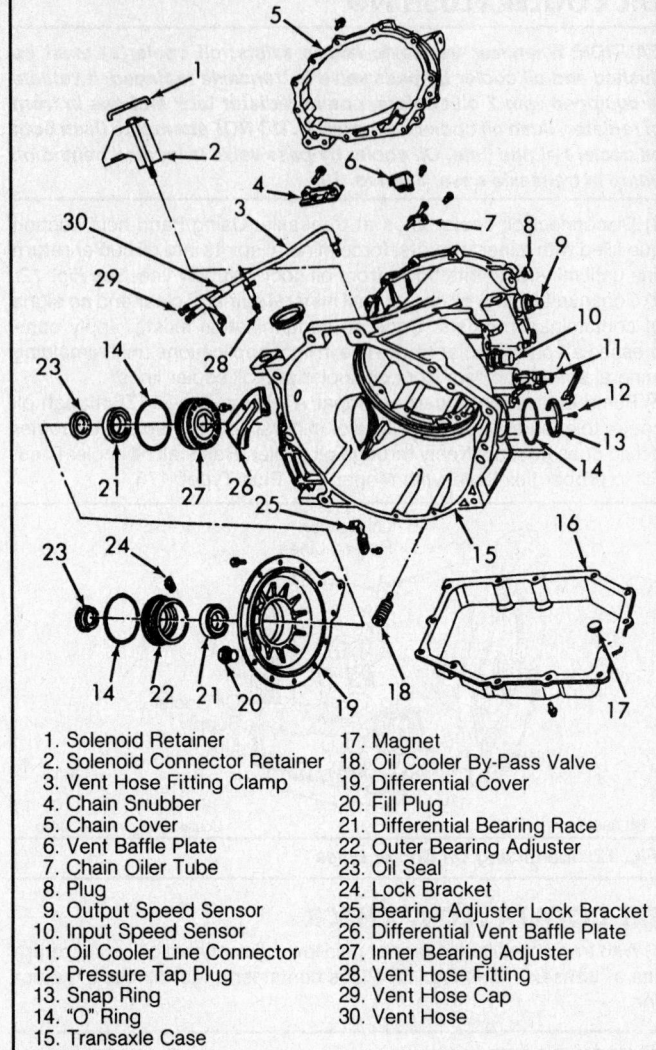

1. Solenoid Retainer	17. Magnet
2. Solenoid Connector Retainer	18. Oil Cooler By-Pass Valve
3. Vent Hose Fitting Clamp	19. Differential Cover
4. Chain Snubber	20. Fill Plug
5. Chain Cover	21. Differential Bearing Race
6. Vent Baffle Plate	22. Outer Bearing Adjuster
7. Chain Oiler Tube	23. Oil Seal
8. Plug	24. Lock Bracket
9. Output Speed Sensor	25. Bearing Adjuster Lock Bracket
10. Input Speed Sensor	26. Differential Vent Baffle Plate
11. Oil Cooler Line Connector	27. Inner Bearing Adjuster
12. Pressure Tap Plug	28. Vent Hose Fitting
13. Snap Ring	29. Vent Hose Cap
14. "O" Ring	30. Vent Hose
15. Transaxle Case	
16. Oil Pan	

94G36653   Courtesy of Chrysler Corp.

Fig. 14: Exploded View Of Transaxle Case & Components

OIL PUMP OIL SEAL

Removal & Installation – 1) Remove transaxle. See appropriate AUTOMATIC TRANSMISSION REMOVAL article in TRANSMISSION SERVICING. Remove torque converter. Using Oil Seal Remover (C-3981B), remove oil seal from oil pump. *See Fig. 16.*

2) To install, ensure oil seal seating surfaces in oil pump are clean. Using Oil Seal Installer (C-4193-A), install oil seal.

3) Apply light coat of Mopar ATF Plus-Type 7176 to hub on torque converter and seal lips on oil seal. Install torque converter. Ensure torque converter fully engages in oil pump.

CAUTION: If torque converter is replaced, proper procedure must be used to reset the break-in procedure in TCM for the Electronically Modulated Converter Clutch (EMCC) in torque converter to prevent shudder during clutch engagement. Perform EMCC reset procedure. See ELECTRONICALLY MODULATED CONVERTER CLUTCH (EMCC) RESET PROCEDURE under TORQUE CONVERTER.

OUTPUT SPEED SENSOR

Removal – 1) Disconnect electrical connector from output speed sensor, located on side of transaxle. *See Fig. 1.* Ensure weather seal for electrical connector remains on the electrical connector. Unscrew output speed sensor from transaxle case.

2) To install, reverse removal procedure using NEW "O" ring on output speed sensor. Tighten output speed sensor to specification. See TORQUE SPECIFICATIONS.

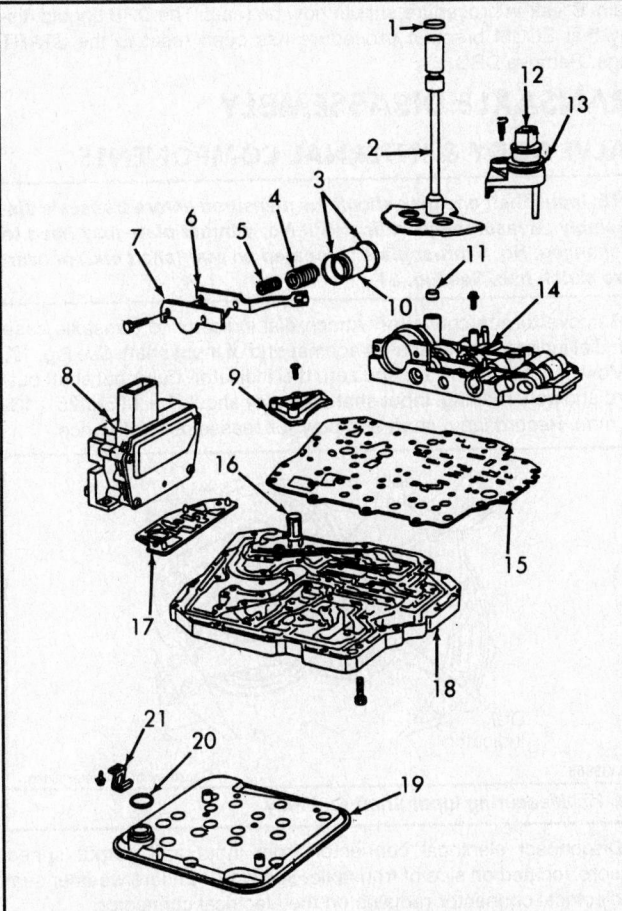

1. Oil Seal
2. Manual Valve Lever
3. Seal Ring
4. 2-4 Accumulator Outer Spring
5. 2-4 Accumulator Inner Spring
6. Detent Assembly
7. Accumulator Spring Retainer
8. Solenoid Assembly
9. Valve Body Plate Support
10. 2-4 Accumulator Piston
11. 2-4 Clutch Seal
12. Manual Valve Lever Position Sensor (MVLPS)
13. Seal
14. Valve Body
15. Separator Plate
16. Regulator Valve Screen
17. Screen
18. Transfer Plate
19. Oil Filter
20. "O" Ring
21. Oil Filter Retainer

94H36654   Courtesy of Chrysler Corp.

Fig. 15: Exploded View Of Valve Body Assembly & Components

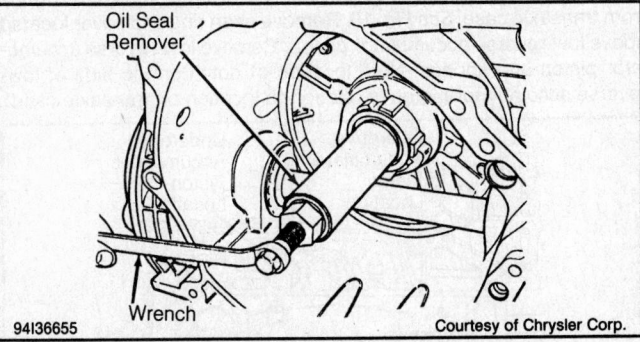

94I36655   Courtesy of Chrysler Corp.

Fig. 16: Removing Oil Pump Oil Seal

SOLENOID ASSEMBLY

Removal & Installation – 1) Remove valve body. See VALVE BODY under REMOVAL & INSTALLATION. Remove solenoid assembly-to-transfer plate bolts. Remove solenoid assembly and screen. See Fig. 15.

2) To install, reverse removal procedure. Tighten solenoid assembly-to-transfer plate bolts to specification. See TORQUE SPECIFICATIONS.

TRANSAXLE ASSEMBLY

See appropriate AUTOMATIC TRANSMISSION REMOVAL article in TRANSMISSION SERVICING.

TRANSFER SHAFT OIL SEALS

NOTE: Following procedure can be used to change oil seals with transaxle removed and without having to reset ring gear backlash and differential bearing rotating torque. If any components except oil seals are replaced, following procedure cannot be used, as special procedure must be used to reset the bearings. If components are replaced, see DIFFERENTIAL ASSEMBLY & TRANSFER SHAFT under TRANSAXLE REASSEMBLY.

Removal – 1) Remove transaxle. See appropriate AUTOMATIC TRANSMISSION REMOVAL article in TRANSMISSION SERVICING. Remove valve body. See VALVE BODY under REMOVAL & INSTALLATION.

2) Remove solenoid connector from transaxle case. Remove snap ring retaining long stub shaft in transaxle case. Long stub shaft is left stub shaft when viewed from rear of transaxle.

3) Install Adapter (6669) on end of long stub shaft. Attach slide hammer on adapter. Using slide hammer, pull long stub shaft from transaxle case.

4) Place reference marks on transaxle case and inner bearing adjuster, located near input shaft for reassembly reference. See Fig. 13. Place reference marks on differential cover and outer bearing adjuster, located near short stub shaft on right side of transaxle for reassembly reference. See Fig. 13.

5) Remove bolt and lock bracket from outer bearing adjuster. See Fig. 13. Using Socket (6503), rotate outer bearing adjuster counterclockwise one full revolution.

NOTE: Check for corrosion on short stub shaft before removing differential cover. If corrosion exists, clean short stub shaft and use care not to damage oil seal when removing differential cover.

6) Remove bolts and differential cover. See Fig. 14. Remove differential assembly.

CAUTION: Note amount of revolutions that inner bearing adjuster is threaded into transaxle case when removing inner bearing adjuster. Inner bearing adjuster must be set at the exact position when reinstalled.

7) Remove bolt and bearing adjuster lock bracket from inner bearing adjuster. See Fig. 13. Using Socket (6502-B), unscrew inner bearing adjuster from transaxle case, noting amount of revolutions for reassembly reference.

8) Remove transfer shaft and oil seals. See DIFFERENTIAL ASSEMBLY, TRANSFER SHAFT & COMPONENTS under TRANSAXLE DISASSEMBLY.

Installation – 1) Install transfer shaft and NEW oil seals using proper procedure. See DIFFERENTIAL ASSEMBLY & TRANSFER SHAFT under TRANSAXLE REASSEMBLY.

2) Install NEW "O" ring on inner bearing adjuster. Lubricate threads on inner bearing adjuster and lip of oil seal with gear oil.

3) Screw inner bearing adjuster into transaxle case original number of revolutions and align reference marks. Install bearing adjuster lock bracket. Install and tighten bearing adjuster lock bracket bolt to specification. See TORQUE SPECIFICATIONS.

4) Install differential assembly. Install Seal Protector (6591) on short stub shaft. Lubricate seal protector and lip of oil seal in outer bearing adjuster with gear oil.

5) Apply sealant on differential cover-to-transaxle case contact areas. Install differential cover. Install and tighten differential cover bolts to specification. See TORQUE SPECIFICATIONS.

6) Tighten outer bearing adjuster 3/4 of a revolution. Rotate differential assembly several times in both directions to seat the bearings. Tighten outer bearing adjuster an additional 1/4 revolution until reference marks are aligned.

7) Install lock bracket on outer bearing adjuster. Install and tighten lock bracket bolt to specification. Remove seal protector from short stub shaft.

8) Install long stub shaft. Install snap ring retaining long stub shaft in transaxle case. Install NEW "C" clip and "O" ring on outer ends of long and short stub shafts.

9) Reinstall solenoid connector, valve body and transaxle. Fill differential with 80W-90 API GL-5 gear oil. DO NOT use synthetic gear oil. Fill transaxle with Mopar ATF Plus-Type 7176.

VALVE BODY

Removal – 1) Raise and support vehicle. Disconnect Manual Valve Lever Position Sensor (MVLPS) electrical connector. *See Fig. 1.*
2) Disconnect shift cable from shift lever on transaxle. Rotate shift lever on transaxle fully clockwise. Remove shift lever from manual valve lever on transaxle. Remove bolts and oil pan.

CAUTION: Overdrive and underdrive accumulator pistons and springs may fall from transaxle case when removing valve body. Note location of components for reassembly reference. Components must be installed in original location. See Fig. 18.

---

3) Remove bolts, oil filter retainers, oil filter and "O" ring. *See Fig. 15.* Remove bolts and valve body with transfer plate from transaxle. If necessary to disassemble valve body assembly, see VALVE BODY under COMPONENT DISASSEMBLY & REASSEMBLY.
Installation – To install, reverse removal procedure using NEW "O" ring and NEW oil filter. Apply silicone sealant on oil pan before installing. Tighten all bolts to specification. See TORQUE SPECIFICATIONS. Fill to proper fluid level with Mopar ATF Plus-Type 7176.

TORQUE CONVERTER

CAUTION: Torque converter is a welded assembly and is not serviceable. If a malfunction occurs or if torque converter becomes contaminated with foreign material, it MUST be replaced. It cannot be flushed or repaired. If torque converter is replaced, special torque converter break-in procedure must be performed to prevent shudder during clutch engagement. See ELECTRONICALLY MODULATED CONVERTER CLUTCH (EMCC) RESET PROCEDURE under TORQUE CONVERTER.

ELECTRONICALLY MODULATED CONVERTER CLUTCH (EMCC) RESET PROCEDURE

NOTE: Procedure is used to reset the break-in procedure in TCM for Electronically Modulated Converter Clutch (EMCC) in torque converter to prevent shudder during clutch engagement. Procedure must be used if torque converter is replaced or Transaxle Control Module (TCM) is changed from one vehicle to another. Chrysler's Diagnostic Readout Box (DRB) scan tool is used to perform reset procedure.

NOTE: The TCM break-in procedure must be reset to the start of the break-in procedure. The TCM's uses a break-in procedure which is performed in 3 stages, START, IN PROGRESS and COMPLETE. In the START stage, full clutch engagement exists. In the IN-PROGRESS stage, partial clutch engagement exists with progressive clutch slippage. In the COMPLETE stage, partial clutch engagement exists with 60 RPM clutch slippage. The TCM break-in procedure must be reset to the start phase of break-in procedure to ensure proper clutch operation.

---

1) Connect DRB to Blue colored data link connector. *See Fig. 3.* Using proper cartridge and DRB manufacture's instructions, move through program to enter 42LE menu. Select ADJUSTMENTS function.
2) Select EMCC RESET function. DRB will now display the break-in stage, such as START, IN-PROGRESS or COMPLETE. If START is displayed, no further action is required.
3) If IN-PROGRESS or COMPLETE is displayed, press ENTER key to return brake-in procedure to the START stage. Press ENTER key again. The DRB will now display ARE YOU SURE. Press ENTER key

again. Break-in procedure should now be reset. The DRB should display that ECCM break-in procedure has been reset to the START stage. Remove DRB.

TRANSAXLE DISASSEMBLY
VALVE BODY & INTERNAL COMPONENTS

NOTE: Input shaft end play should be measured before transaxle disassembly. Measurement indicates if No. 4 thrust plate may need to be changed. No. 4 thrust plate is located on rear (shaft end) of overdrive clutch hub. See Fig. 31.

1) Remove torque converter. Attach dial indicator to transaxle case with dial indicator stem seated against end of input shaft. *See Fig. 17.*
2) Move input shaft inward and zero dial indicator. Pull input shaft outward and note reading. Input shaft end play should be .005-.025" (.13-.64 mm). Record input shaft end play for reassembly reference.

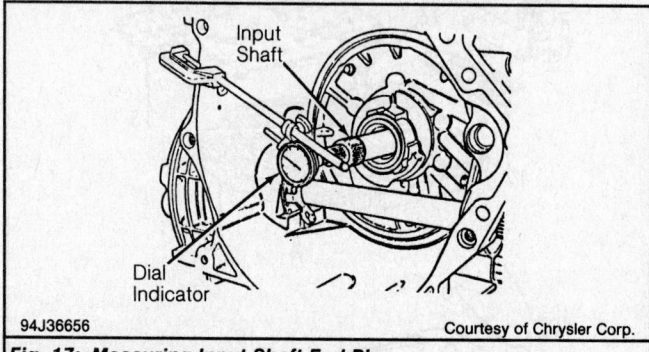

94J36656   Courtesy of Chrysler Corp.

Fig. 17: Measuring Input Shaft End Play

3) Disconnect electrical connector from input and output speed sensors, located on side of transaxle. *See Fig. 1.* Ensure weather seal for electrical connector remains on the electrical connector.
4) Unscrew input and output speed sensors from transaxle case. Disconnect Manual Valve Lever Position Sensor (MVLPS) electrical connector. *See Fig. 1.*
5) Rotate shift lever on transaxle fully clockwise. Remove shift lever from manual valve lever on transaxle. Remove bolts and oil pan. Remove bolts, oil filter retainers, oil filter and "O" ring. *See Fig. 15.* Remove bolts and valve body assembly.

CAUTION: Note location of all accumulators and springs for reassembly reference. Components must be installed in correct locations.

---

6) Remove overdrive and underdrive accumulator pistons and springs from transaxle case. *See Fig. 18.* Remove snap ring and cover located above low-reverse accumulator piston. Remove low-reverse accumulator piston and springs. Note location of notch on the side of low-reverse accumulator piston in relation to location on transaxle case.

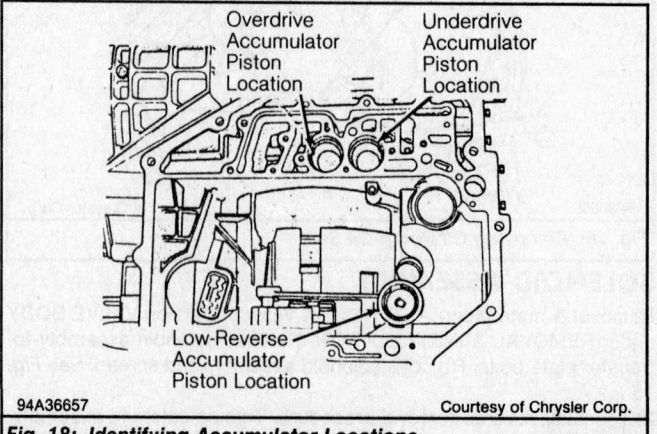

94A36657   Courtesy of Chrysler Corp.

Fig. 18: Identifying Accumulator Locations

7) Remove snap ring retaining long stub shaft in transaxle case. Long stub shaft is left stub shaft when viewed from rear of transaxle. Install Adapter (6669) on end of long stub shaft. Attach slide hammer on adapter. Using slide hammer, pull long stub shaft from transaxle case.

8) Remove oil pump bolts. Install 2 slide hammer pullers on opposite sides of oil pump. Push inward on input shaft while using slide hammer pullers to pull oil pump from transaxle case. Remove oil pump and gasket. Remove oil cooler by-pass valve. See Fig. 19.

9) Remove thrust bearing from front of input shaft. Remove input clutch assembly. See Fig. 20. Remove thrust washer, 2-4 clutch hub, rear annulus gear and thrust bearing. See Fig. 21. Remove sun gear and thrust bearing. See Fig. 21.

CAUTION: Oil cooler by-pass valve must be replaced if transaxle failure exists. DO NOT attempt to clean oil cooler by-pass valve.

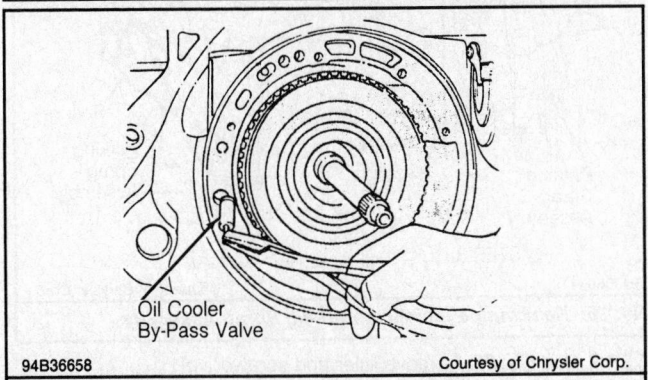

94B36658   Courtesy of Chrysler Corp.

Fig. 19: Removing & Installing Oil Cooler By-Pass Valve

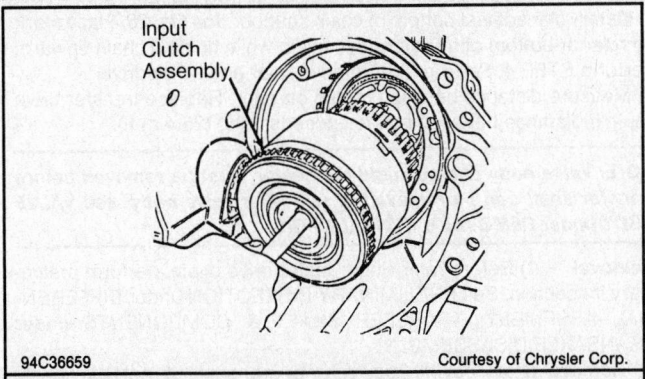

94C36659   Courtesy of Chrysler Corp.

Fig. 20: Removing Input Clutch Assembly

10) Using 2-4 Clutch Compressor (5058), compress 2-4 clutch piston retainer enough to remove snap ring. See Fig. 22. Remove snap ring. Remove 2-4 clutch compressor.

11) Remove 2-4 clutch piston retainer, 2-4 clutch piston and clutch piston return spring. See Fig. 21. Remove 2-4 clutch discs and clutch plates. See Fig. 21. Note direction of 4 clutch plates and 4 clutch discs installation for reassembly reference.

12) Remove snap ring and low-reverse clutch reaction plate. See Fig. 21. Note direction of snap ring installation. Snap ring is tapered and must be installed with tapered side toward the oil pump area.

13) Remove one low-reverse clutch disc and flat snap ring. Remove low-reverse clutch plates and clutch discs. See Fig. 21. Note direction of 5 clutch plates and 5 clutch discs installation for reassembly reference.

14) Remove transfer drive chain, output shaft sprocket and transfer shaft sprocket. See DIFFERENTIAL ASSEMBLY, TRANSFER SHAFT & COMPONENTS under TRANSAXLE DISASSEMBLY.

CAUTION: Failure to release staked areas on output shaft nut before removing output shaft nut will result in thread damage on output shaft.

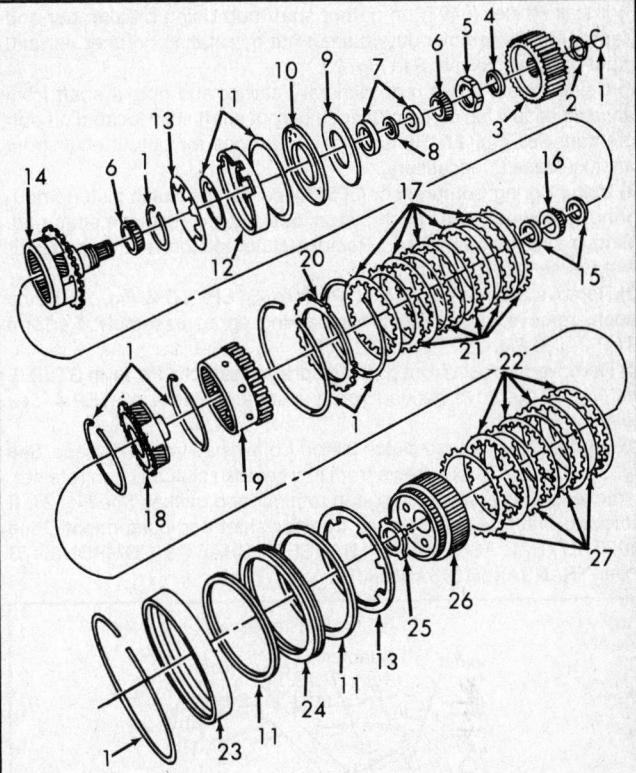

1. Snap Ring
2. Wave Washer
3. Output Shaft Sprocket
4. Output Sprocket Shim (Selective)
5. Output Shaft Nut
6. Bearing
7. Bearing Race
8. Output Shaft Shim (Selective)
9. Gasket
10. Low-Reverse Clutch Piston Retainer
11. Seal Ring
12. Low-Reverse Clutch Piston
13. Clutch Piston Return Spring
14. Rear Planetary Carrier & Output Shaft

15. Thrust Bearing
16. Sun Gear
17. Low-Reverse Clutch Disc
18. Front Planetary Carrier
19. Rear Annulus Gear
20. Low-Reverse Clutch Reaction Plate (Selective)
21. Low-Reverse Clutch Plate
22. 2-4 Clutch Disc
23. 2-4 Clutch Piston Retainer
24. 2-4 Clutch Piston
25. Thrust Washer
26. 2-4 Clutch Hub
27. 2-4 Clutch Plate

94F36660   Courtesy of Chrysler Corp.

Fig. 21: Exploded View Of Gear Train & Components

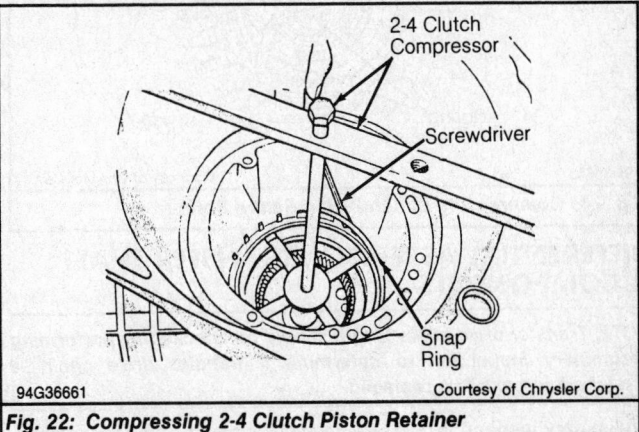

94G36661   Courtesy of Chrysler Corp.

Fig. 22: Compressing 2-4 Clutch Piston Retainer

15) Using die grinder, grind the 2 staked areas on shoulder of output shaft nut so staked area is thinner. Using hammer and chisel, release the 2 staked areas away from output shaft. Use care not to damage output shaft.

16) Install Holder (6497) on output shaft nut. Using breaker bar and Adapter (6498), remove output shaft nut by rotating breaker bar and output shaft clockwise. *See Fig. 23.*

17) Using press, press rear planetary carrier and output shaft from transaxle case. Use care not to lose output shaft shim located on output shaft. *See Fig. 21.* Remove bearing races for output shaft from transaxle case (if necessary).

18) Using Spring Compressor (5059A), compress clutch piston return spring for low-reverse clutch piston. *See Fig. 24.* Remove snap ring. Remove spring compressor. Remove clutch piston return spring for low-reverse clutch piston.

19) Remove parking sprag bolt. Perform STEP 1. *See Fig. 25.* Using punch, remove anchor shaft for parking sprag assembly. Perform STEP 2. *See Fig. 25.*

20) Remove pivot pin from parking sprag assembly. Perform STEP 3. *See Fig. 25.* Remove parking sprag assembly. Perform STEP 4. *See Fig. 25.*

21) Remove low-reverse clutch piston from inside transaxle case. *See Fig. 21.* Remove Torx screws from low-reverse clutch piston retainer. Remove low-reverse clutch piston retainer and gasket. *See Fig. 21.* If removing differential assembly, transfer shaft and components, see DIFFERENTIAL ASSEMBLY, TRANSFER SHAFT & COMPONENTS under TRANSAXLE DISASSEMBLY.

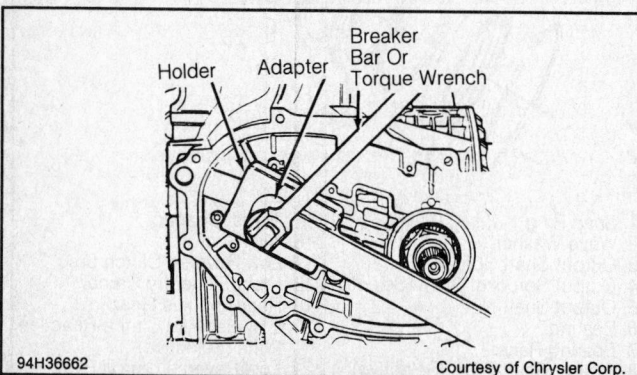

94H36662   Courtesy of Chrysler Corp.

Fig. 23: Removing Or Installing Output Shaft Nut (Transfer Shaft Nut Is Similar)

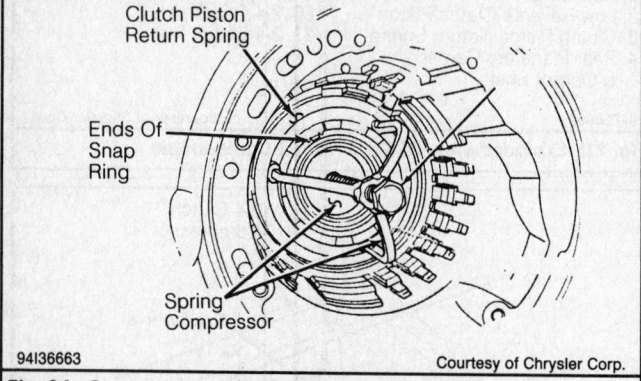

94I36663   Courtesy of Chrysler Corp.

Fig. 24: Compressing Clutch Piston Return Spring

DIFFERENTIAL ASSEMBLY, TRANSFER SHAFT & COMPONENTS

NOTE: Transfer drive chain length should be checked by performing preliminary inspection to determine if transfer drive chain is stretched and must be replaced.

Preliminary Inspection – 1) Remove chain cover from rear of transaxle. *See Fig. 14.* Insert screwdriver in hole above transfer drive chain. Pry transfer drive chain downward at center of chain. Perform STEP 1. *See Fig. 26.*

2) Install ruler against bottom of chain snubber. Place mark on ruler at bottom of transfer drive chain while holding chain downward. Perform

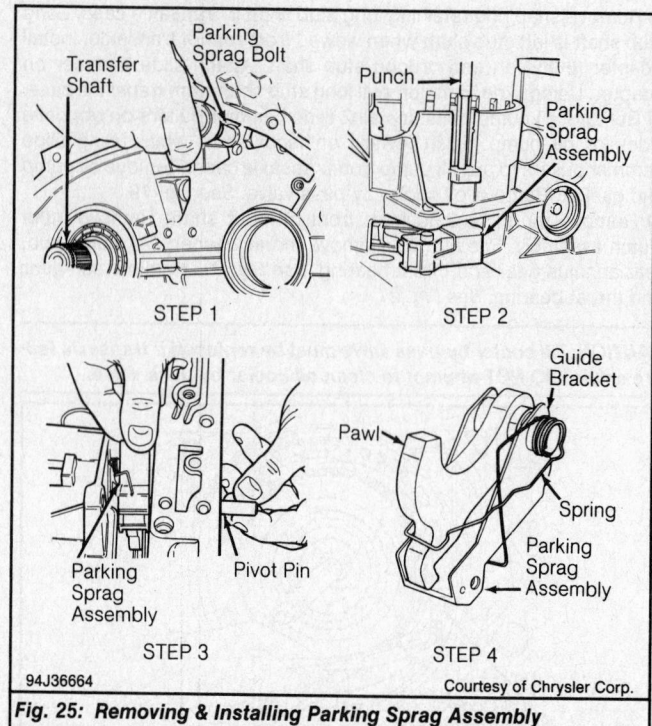

94J36664   Courtesy of Chrysler Corp.

Fig. 25: Removing & Installing Parking Sprag Assembly

STEP 2. *See Fig. 26.* Remove ruler and screwdriver.

3) Insert screwdriver in hole below transfer drive chain. Pry drive chain upward at center of chain. Perform STEP 3. *See Fig. 26.*

4) Install ruler against bottom of chain snubber. *See Fig. 26.* Place mark on ruler at bottom of transfer drive chain while holding chain upward. Perform STEP 4. *See Fig. 26.* Remove ruler and screwdriver.

5) Measure distance between marks on ruler. Replace transfer drive chain if distance between marks exceeds 1.00" (25.4 mm).

NOTE: Valve body and solenoid connector must be removed before transfer shaft can be removed. If removing valve body, see VALVE BODY under REMOVAL & INSTALLATION.

Removal – 1) Before removing transfer drive chain, perform preliminary inspection. See PRELIMINARY INSPECTION under DIFFERENTIAL ASSEMBLY, TRANSFER SHAFT & COMPONENTS under TRANSAXLE DISASSEMBLY.

2) Remove chain cover from rear of transaxle if not previously removed. *See Fig. 14.* Remove bolts, chain oiler and chain snubber. Remove snap ring and wave washer from end of output and transfer shafts.

CAUTION: Output shaft and transfer shaft sprockets are a slip fit on the shaft. Sprockets must be spread a small amount to release tension from transfer drive chain for removal and installation of sprockets to prevent component damage. DO NOT apply excessive force on sprockets when using chain spreader.

3) Install Chain Spreader (6550) between output shaft and transfer shaft sprockets. *See Fig. 27.* Rotate nuts on chain spreader to apply pressure against sprockets and release tension on sprockets from transfer drive chain.

4) Remove transfer drive chain with output shaft and transfer shaft sprockets as an assembly. Remove output sprocket shim from output shaft. *See Fig. 21.*

5) If long stub shaft is not removed, remove snap ring retaining long stub shaft in transaxle case. Long stub shaft is left stub shaft when viewed from rear of transaxle. Install Adapter (6669) on end of long stub shaft. Attach slide hammer on adapter. Using slide hammer, pull long stub shaft from transaxle case.

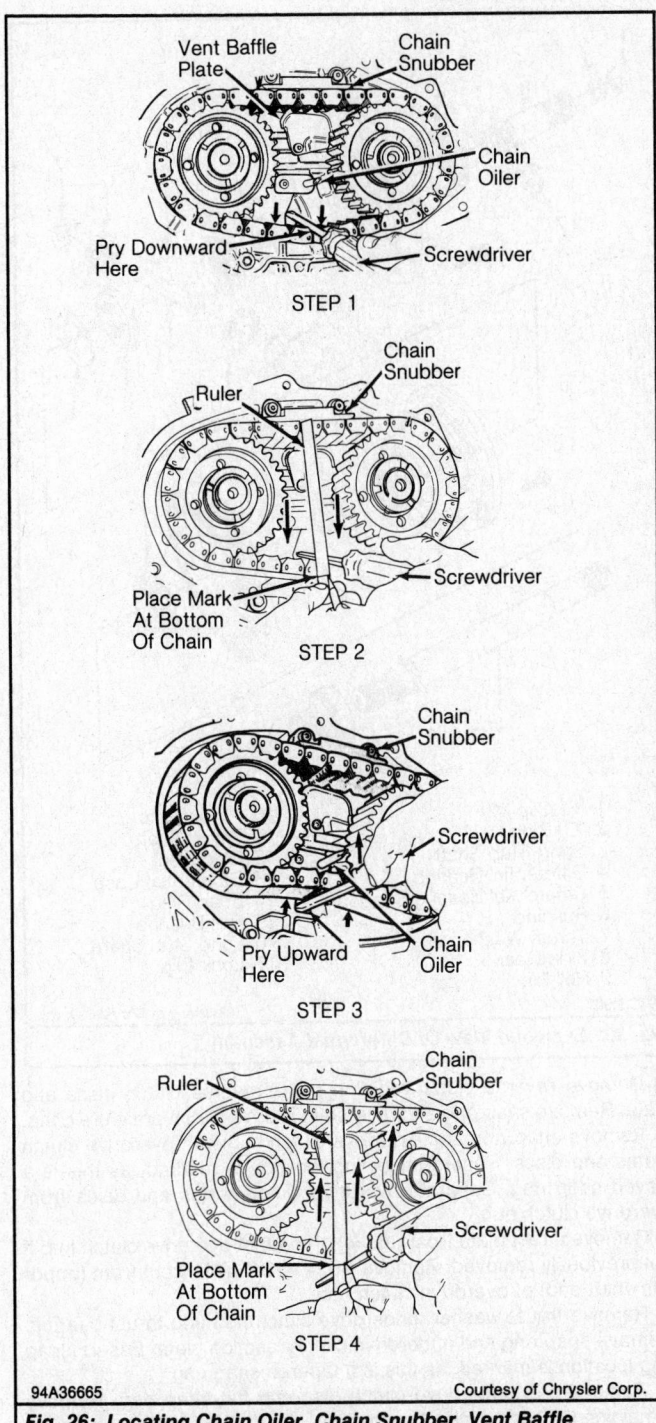

Fig. 26: Locating Chain Oiler, Chain Snubber, Vent Baffle Plate & Checking Transfer Drive Chain Length

94A36665   Courtesy of Chrysler Corp.

CAUTION: Reference marks must be placed on inner and outer bearing adjusters to ensure proper location during reassembly to maintain proper differential bearing torque. These marks will be used when no components are changed and original differential bearings and races are used.

6) Place reference marks on transaxle case and inner bearing adjuster, located near input shaft for reassembly reference. *See Fig. 13.* Place reference marks on differential cover and outer bearing adjuster, located near short stub shaft on right side of transaxle for reassembly reference. *See Fig. 13.*

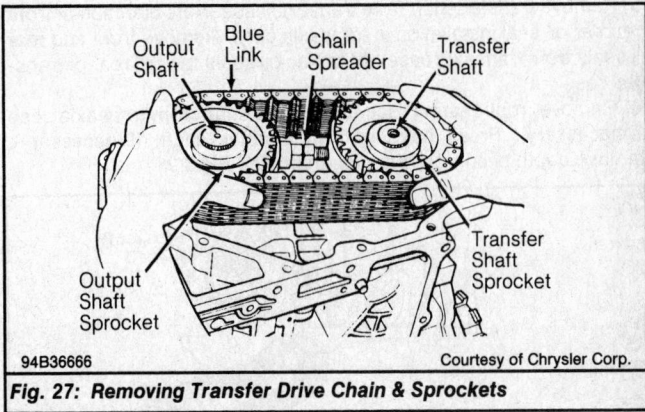

94B36666   Courtesy of Chrysler Corp.

Fig. 27: Removing Transfer Drive Chain & Sprockets

CAUTION: Note amount of revolutions that inner and outer bearing adjusters are threaded into transaxle case during removal. Bearing adjusters must be set at the exact position when reinstalled if original components are used.

7) Remove bolt and bearing adjuster lock bracket from inner bearing adjuster. *See Fig. 13.* Using Socket (6502-B), unscrew inner bearing adjuster from transaxle case, noting amount of revolutions for reassembly reference.
8) Remove bolt and lock bracket from outer bearing adjuster. *See Fig. 13.* Using Socket (6503), loosen outer bearing adjuster, noting amount of revolutions for reassembly reference.
9) Remove bolts and differential cover. *See Fig. 14.* Remove differential assembly. Remove differential vent baffle plate, located on inside of transaxle case, near bearing race opening for differential assembly. *See Fig. 14.*
10) Remove bolt and vent baffle plate. Vent baffle plate is located on rear of transaxle case, between output shaft and transfer shaft openings. *See Fig. 26.*

CAUTION: Failure to release staked areas on transfer shaft nut before removing nut will result in thread damage on transfer shaft.

11) Using die grinder, grind the 2 staked areas on shoulder of transfer shaft nut so staked area is thinner. Using hammer and chisel, release the 2 staked areas away from transfer shaft. Use care not to damage transfer shaft.
12) Install Holder (6497) on transfer shaft nut. Using breaker bar and Adapter (6498), remove transfer shaft nut by rotating breaker bar and transfer shaft clockwise. *See Fig. 23.*
13) Using press, press transfer shaft downward until rear bearing can be removed. Release press. Transfer shaft cannot be removed from transaxle case until bearing race for rear bearing is removed from transaxle housing.
14) Using Bearing Race Remover (6577), pull bearing race for rear bearing from transaxle case. *See Fig. 28.* Remove baffle plate (if equipped) from transfer shaft. *See Fig. 29.* Remove transfer shaft shim from transfer shaft. *See Fig. 29.*

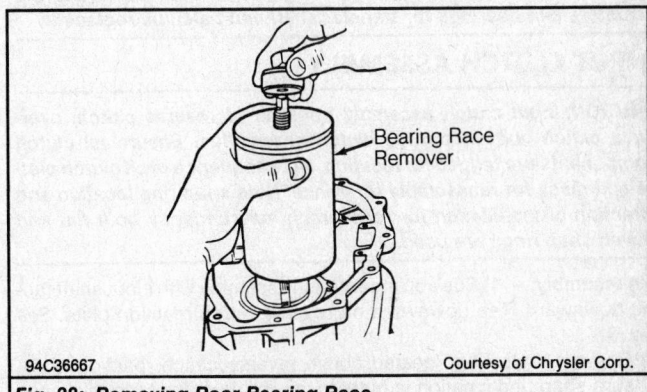

94C36667   Courtesy of Chrysler Corp.

Fig. 28: Removing Rear Bearing Race

15) Remove transfer shaft from transaxle case. Note direction of front and rear oil seal installation in transaxle case. Remove front and rear oil seals from transaxle case by tapping oil seals toward rear of transaxle case.

16) Remove front bearing race for transfer shaft from transaxle case (if necessary). Press bearing from transfer shaft (if necessary). Remove depth shim from transfer shaft. *See Fig. 29.*

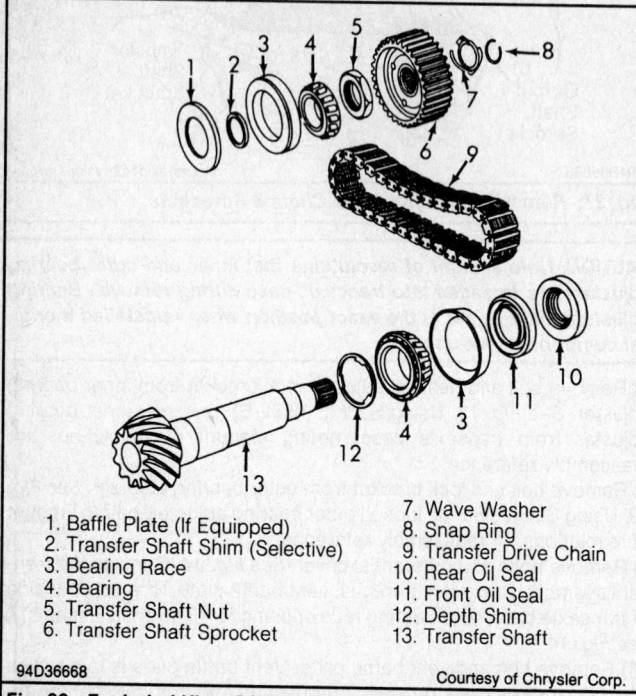

1. Baffle Plate (If Equipped)
2. Transfer Shaft Shim (Selective)
3. Bearing Race
4. Bearing
5. Transfer Shaft Nut
6. Transfer Shaft Sprocket
7. Wave Washer
8. Snap Ring
9. Transfer Drive Chain
10. Rear Oil Seal
11. Front Oil Seal
12. Depth Shim
13. Transfer Shaft

94D36668   Courtesy of Chrysler Corp.

Fig. 29: Exploded View Of Transfer Shaft & Components

COMPONENT DISASSEMBLY & REASSEMBLY
DIFFERENTIAL ASSEMBLY

Disassembly – 1) Remove ring gear bolts. Tap ring gear from differential case. Remove differential bearing support from differential case. *See Fig. 30.* Remove lock clip from end of short stub shaft. *See Fig. 30.* Remove short stub shaft from differential case.

2) Using hammer and punch, tap roll pin from differential case. Remove pinion shaft, side gears, pinion gears and thrust washers from differential case. *See Fig. 30.* Remove differential bearings from differential case and differential bearing support (if necessary).

Reassembly – To reassemble, reverse disassembly procedure using NEW roll pin and NEW ring gear bolts. Coat all components with 80W-90 API GL-5 gear oil before reassembly. Tighten ring gear bolts to specification. See TORQUE SPECIFICATIONS.

NOTE: If replacing differential bearings, inner and outer bearing adjusters and bearings for transfer shaft must also be replaced.

INPUT CLUTCH ASSEMBLY

CAUTION: Input clutch assembly consists of reverse clutch, overdrive clutch and underdrive clutch assemblies. Ensure all clutch components are tagged for location. Note sequence of all clutch plates and discs for reassembly reference. Note snap ring location and direction of installation for reassembly reference, as both flat and waved snap rings are used.

Disassembly – 1) Position input clutch assembly with input shaft facing downward. Tap downward on reverse clutch reaction plate. *See Fig. 31.*

2) Remove snap ring, located above reverse clutch reaction plate. Ensure snap ring location is marked, as this is a selective thickness snap ring.

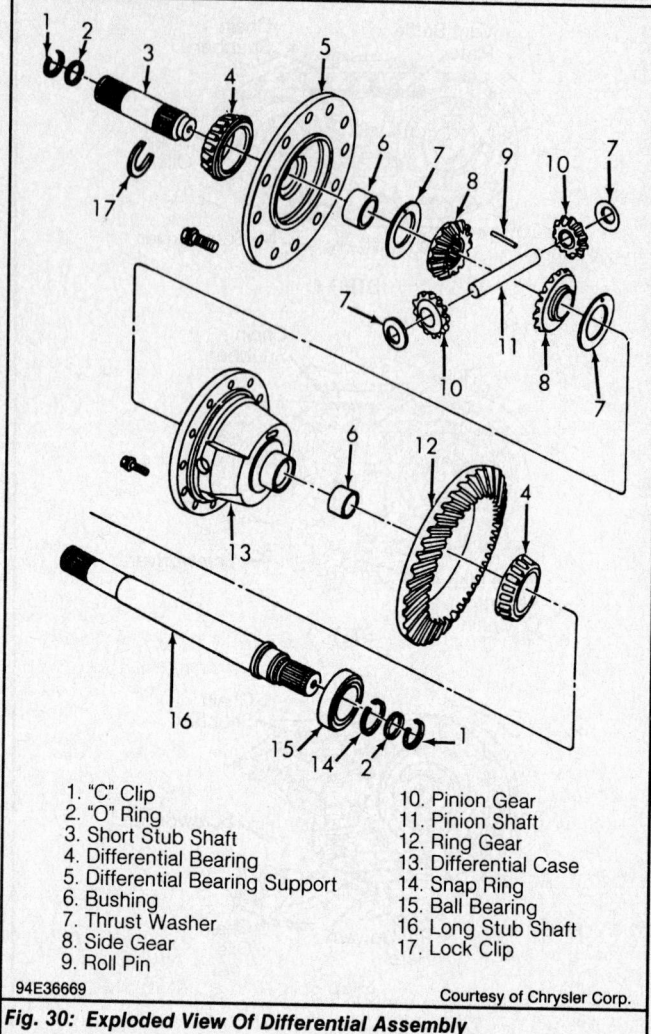

1. "C" Clip
2. "O" Ring
3. Short Stub Shaft
4. Differential Bearing
5. Differential Bearing Support
6. Bushing
7. Thrust Washer
8. Side Gear
9. Roll Pin
10. Pinion Gear
11. Pinion Shaft
12. Ring Gear
13. Differential Case
14. Snap Ring
15. Ball Bearing
16. Long Stub Shaft
17. Lock Clip

94E36669   Courtesy of Chrysler Corp.

Fig. 30: Exploded View Of Differential Assembly

3) Remove reverse clutch reaction plate, reverse clutch discs and plate. Remove snap ring and reverse-overdrive clutch pressure plate.

4) Remove snap ring and overdrive clutch hub with overdrive clutch plates and discs. Ensure snap ring location is marked, as this is a waved snap ring. Separate overdrive clutch plates and discs from overdrive clutch hub.

5) Remove thrust plate from rear (shaft end) of overdrive clutch hub if not previously removed. Remove No. 4 thrust plate from front (opposite shaft end) of overdrive clutch hub.

6) Remove thrust washer, underdrive clutch hub and thrust bearing. Remove snap ring and underdrive clutch reaction plate. Ensure snap ring location is marked, as this is a tapered snap ring.

7) Remove one underdrive clutch disc and flat snap ring. Remove remaining underdrive clutch plates and discs. Using press and spring compressor, compress spring retainer just enough for removal of snap ring, located above spring retainer. Remove snap ring.

8) Remove spring compressor. Remove snap ring, spring retainer, return spring and underdrive clutch piston. Remove tapered snap ring that retains input clutch hub on the input clutch retainer and reverse-overdrive clutch piston. Tapered snap ring is located at center of input clutch retainer.

9) Using soft-faced hammer, tap input clutch hub with input shaft from input clutch retainer and reverse-overdrive clutch piston. Pull input clutch retainer from reverse-overdrive clutch piston.

10) Using press, compress clutch piston return spring on rear of reverse-overdrive clutch piston just for snap ring removal. Remove snap ring.

11) Release press. Note direction of clutch piston return spring installation for reassembly reference. Remove clutch piston return spring. Remove all seal rings and "O" rings.

12) If removing input shaft from input clutch hub, remove snap ring from end of input shaft. Using press and socket, press input shaft from input clutch hub. Remove Teflon seal rings from end of input shaft.

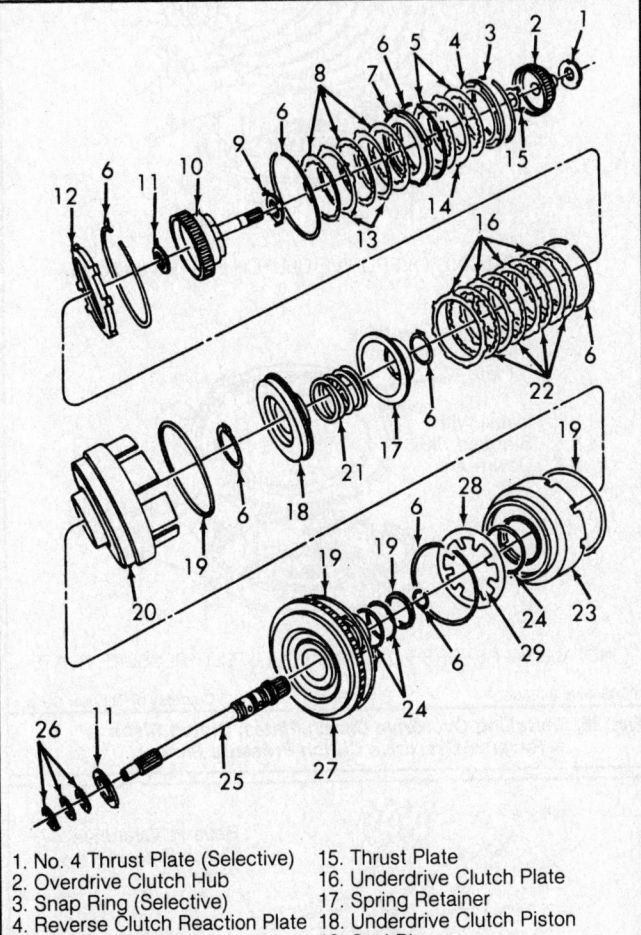

1. No. 4 Thrust Plate (Selective)
2. Overdrive Clutch Hub
3. Snap Ring (Selective)
4. Reverse Clutch Reaction Plate
5. Reverse Clutch Disc
6. Snap Ring
7. Reverse-Overdrive Clutch Pressure Plate
8. Overdrive Clutch Disc
9. Thrust Washer
10. Underdrive Clutch Hub
11. Thrust Bearing
12. Underdrive Clutch Reaction Plate (Selective)
13. Overdrive Clutch Plate
14. Reverse Clutch Plate
15. Thrust Plate
16. Underdrive Clutch Plate
17. Spring Retainer
18. Underdrive Clutch Piston
19. Seal Ring
20. Input Clutch Retainer
21. Return Spring
22. Underdrive Clutch Disc
23. Reverse-Overdrive Clutch Piston
24. "O" Ring
25. Input Shaft
26. Teflon Seal Ring
27. Input Clutch Hub
28. Clutch Piston Return Spring
29. Tang Areas

94H36670   Courtesy of Chrysler Corp.

Fig. 31: Exploded View Of Input Clutch Assembly

Reassembly – 1) Press input shaft into input clutch hub (if removed). Install snap ring on end on input shaft.
2) Install NEW seal rings and NEW "O" rings on proper components. See Fig. 31. Coat all seal rings and "O" rings with petroleum jelly. Install clutch piston return spring on rear of reverse-overdrive clutch piston with tang areas against reverse-overdrive clutch piston. See Fig. 31.
3) Using press, compress clutch piston return spring. Install snap ring. Release press. Install input clutch retainer on reverse-overdrive clutch piston.
4) Align splines on input clutch hub on the input clutch retainer. Install input clutch hub on input clutch and reverse-overdrive clutch piston. Install tapered snap ring.
5) Install underdrive clutch piston, return spring and spring retainer in input clutch retainer. Using press, Seal Compressor (5067) and Spring Compressor (5059A), compress spring retainer just enough for installation of snap ring. See Fig. 32. Install snap ring. Release press. Remove spring compressor and seal compressor.

6) Install 4 underdrive clutch discs and 4 underdrive clutch plates in proper sequence. See Fig. 33. Install flat snap ring in input clutch retainer. Install one underdrive clutch disc.
7) Install underdrive clutch reaction plate with stepped side downward. See Fig. 33. Install tapered snap ring above underdrive clutch reaction plate.

CAUTION: Use care when installing tapered snap ring to not scratch underdrive clutch reaction plate surface. Ensure snap ring is fully seated with ends of snap ring against solid area of input clutch retainer. Check underdrive clutch clearance.

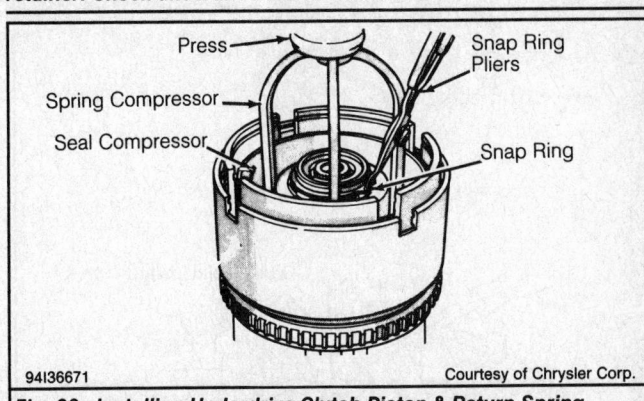

94I36671   Courtesy of Chrysler Corp.

Fig. 32: Installing Underdrive Clutch Piston & Return Spring

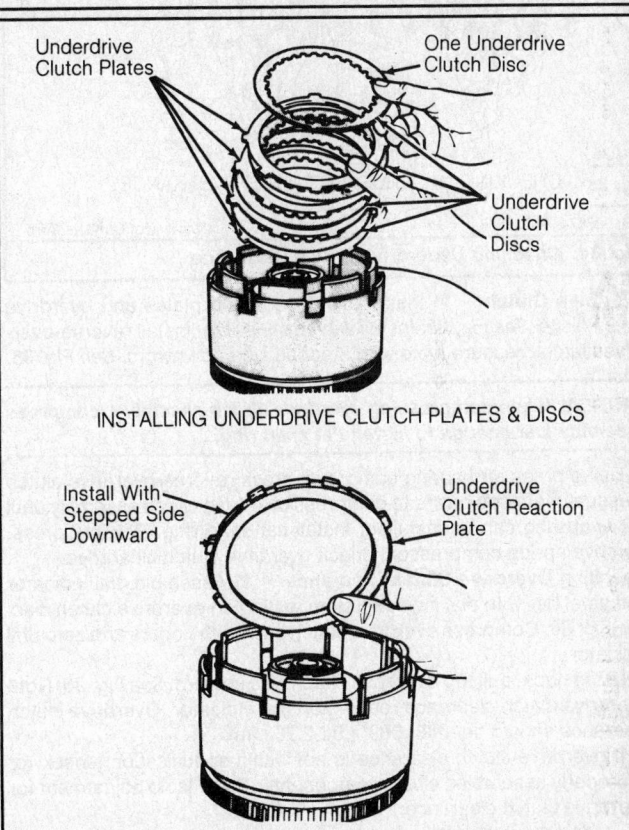

INSTALLING UNDERDRIVE CLUTCH PLATES & DISCS

INSTALLING UNDERDRIVE CLUTCH REACTION PLATE

94J36672 94A36673   Courtesy of Chrysler Corp.

Fig. 33: Installing Underdrive Clutch Plates, Clutch Discs & Clutch Reaction Plate

Checking Underdrive Clutch Clearance – 1) Assemble dial indicator and steel bar with dial indicator stem resting on the top underdrive clutch disc. See Fig. 34.
2) Using hook, pull top underdrive clutch disc upward. See Fig. 34. Note underdrive clutch clearance reading on dial indicator. Underdrive clutch clearance should be .036-.058" (.91-1.47 mm).

3) If underdrive clutch clearance is not within specification, install different thickness underdrive clutch reaction plate so proper clutch clearance is obtained. Underdrive clutch reaction plates are available in following thickness: .217" (5.52 mm), .237" (6.01 mm), .256" (6.50 mm) and .275" (6.99 mm).

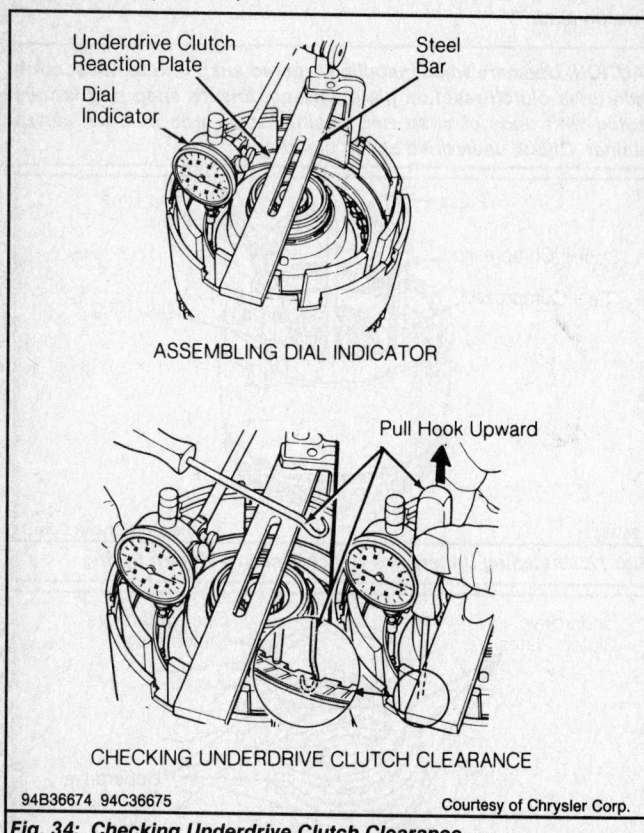

ASSEMBLING DIAL INDICATOR

CHECKING UNDERDRIVE CLUTCH CLEARANCE

94B36674 94C36675   Courtesy of Chrysler Corp.

Fig. 34: Checking Underdrive Clutch Clearance

Overdrive Clutch – 1) Install overdrive clutch plates and overdrive clutch discs. See Fig. 35. Install waved snap ring. Install reverse-overdrive clutch pressure plate with stepped side downward. See Fig. 35.

CAUTION: When compressing overdrive clutch assembly, compress assembly just enough to install flat snap ring.

---

2) Using press and spring compress, press reverse-overdrive clutch pressure plate downward to compress overdrive clutch assembly until flat snap ring can be installed. Install flat snap ring. Release press. Remove spring compressor. Check overdrive clutch clearance.

Checking Overdrive Clutch Clearance – 1) Assemble dial indicator and steel bar with dial indicator stem resting on overdrive clutch disc. See Fig. 36. Compress overdrive clutch pack with fingers and zero dial indicator.

2) Using hook, pull top overdrive clutch disc upward. See Fig. 36. Note overdrive clutch clearance reading on dial indicator. Overdrive clutch clearance should be .038-.089" (.96-2.26 mm).

3) If overdrive clutch clearance is not within specification, check for improperly assembled clutch components. There is no adjustment for overdrive clutch clearance.

Reverse Clutch – 1) Install reverse clutch plate and reverse clutch discs. See Fig. 37. Install reverse clutch reaction plate with flat side downward. See Fig. 37.

2) Install snap ring in groove above reverse clutch reaction plate. Using screwdriver on each side of reverse clutch reaction plate, pry reaction plate upward to ensure snap ring is fully seated for checking reverse clutch clearance.

Checking Reverse Clutch Clearance – 1) Assemble dial indicator and steel bar with dial indicator stem resting on reverse clutch disc. See Fig. 38. Compress reverse clutch pack with fingers and zero dial indicator.

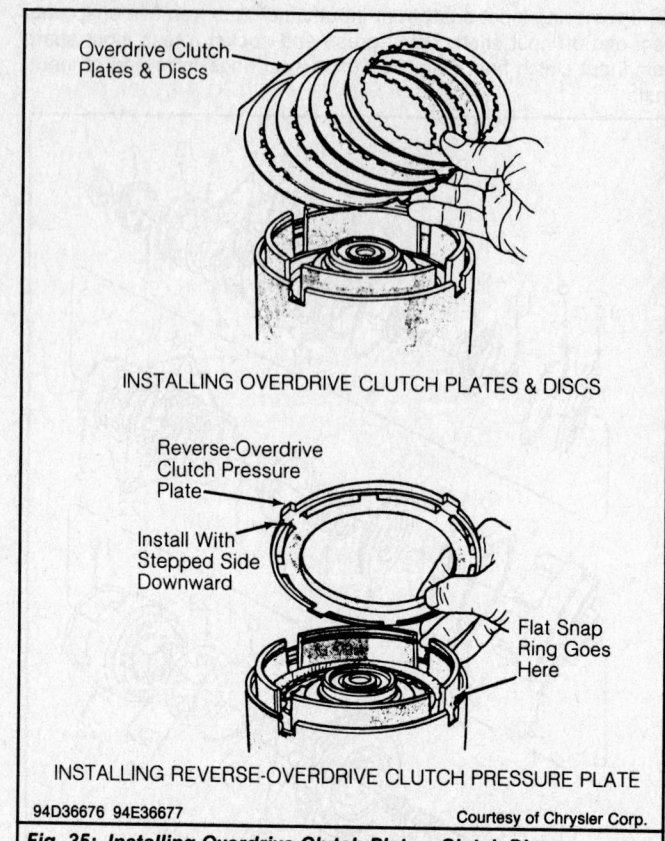

INSTALLING OVERDRIVE CLUTCH PLATES & DISCS

INSTALLING REVERSE-OVERDRIVE CLUTCH PRESSURE PLATE

94D36676 94E36677   Courtesy of Chrysler Corp.

Fig. 35: Installing Overdrive Clutch Plates, Clutch Discs & Reverse-Overdrive Clutch Pressure Plate

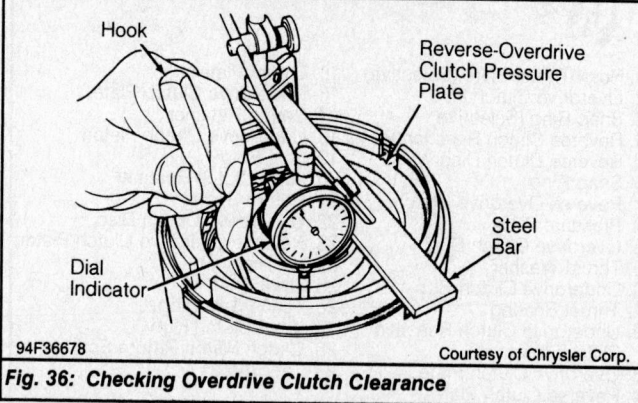

94F36678   Courtesy of Chrysler Corp.

Fig. 36: Checking Overdrive Clutch Clearance

2) Using hook, pull reverse clutch disc upward. See Fig. 38. Note reverse clutch clearance reading on dial indicator. Reverse clutch clearance should be .030-.049" (.76-1.24 mm).

3) If reverse clutch clearance is not within specification, install different thickness snap ring, located above reverse clutch reaction plate, so proper clutch clearance is obtained. Snap ring is available in following thicknesses: .061" (1.55 mm), .071" (1.80 mm), .081" (2.05 mm) and .090" (2.29 mm).

CAUTION: During final assembly of input clutch assembly, reverse and overdrive clutch assemblies must be removed. Ensure clutch components are kept in order for reassembly reference.

NOTE: It may be necessary to apply petroleum jelly to thrust bearings or thrust plates to hold them in position during reassembly of input clutch assembly.

Final Assembly Of Input Clutch Assembly – 1) Remove reverse and overdrive clutch assemblies. Install thrust bearing located below underdrive clutch hub. See Fig. 31. Thrust bearing must be installed

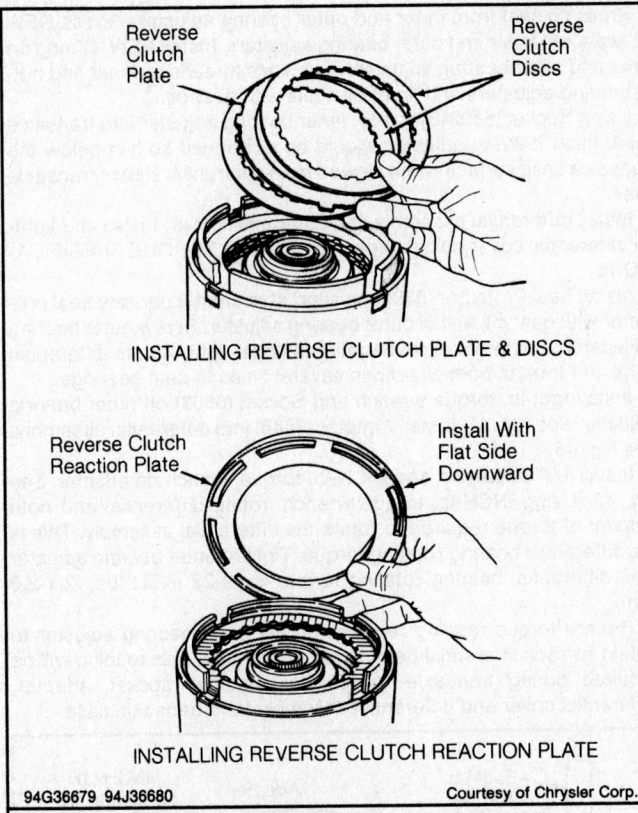

INSTALLING REVERSE CLUTCH PLATE & DISCS

INSTALLING REVERSE CLUTCH REACTION PLATE

94G36679 94J36680   Courtesy of Chrysler Corp.

Fig. 37: Installing Reverse Clutch Plate, Clutch Discs & Reverse Clutch Reaction Plate

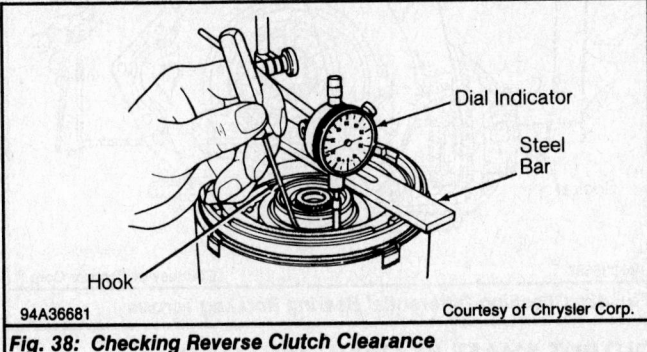

94A36681   Courtesy of Chrysler Corp.

Fig. 38: Checking Reverse Clutch Clearance

with 3 small tabs facing upward (away from torque converter end of input shaft).

2) Install underdrive clutch hub. Install 5-tab thrust washer on shaft end of underdrive clutch hub.

3) Install 3-tab thrust plate on front (opposite shaft end) of overdrive clutch hub. Install overdrive clutch hub on input clutch assembly. Ensure tabs on thrust plate remain fully engaged.

4) To complete final assembly, reinstall overdrive and reverse clutch components. Ensure all clutch components are installed in original location as when clutch clearances were checked. Install No. 4 thrust plate on overdrive clutch hub. See Fig. 31.

OIL PUMP

Disassembly & Reassembly – 1) Disassembly and reassembly information not available from manufacturer. If necessary, disassemble and reassemble oil pump using exploded view. See Fig. 39. Ensure component locations are marked for reassembly reference.

2) Ensure oil pump components are within specification. See OIL PUMP SPECIFICATIONS table.

3) To reassemble, reverse disassembly procedure. Ensure components are installed in original location. Use NEW oil seal, "O" ring and reaction shaft support seal rings. Tighten reaction shaft support-to-oil pump housing bolts to specification. See TORQUE SPECIFICATIONS.

OIL PUMP SPECIFICATIONS

Application	In. (mm)
Inner & Outer Gear Side Clearance	.0008-.0018 (.020-.046)
Outer Gear-To-Pocket Clearance	.0018-.0056 (.046-.142)

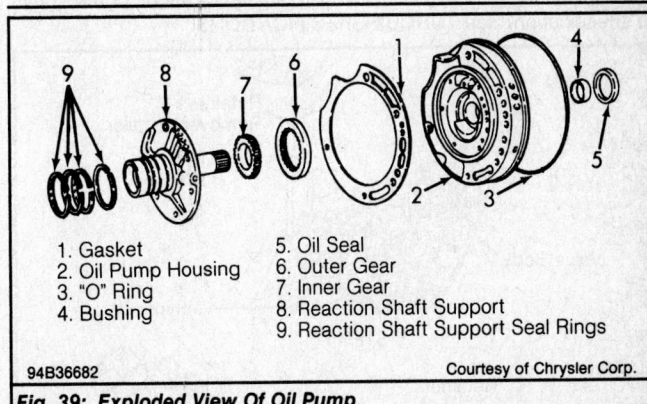

1. Gasket
2. Oil Pump Housing
3. "O" Ring
4. Bushing
5. Oil Seal
6. Outer Gear
7. Inner Gear
8. Reaction Shaft Support
9. Reaction Shaft Support Seal Rings

94B36682   Courtesy of Chrysler Corp.

Fig. 39: Exploded View Of Oil Pump

VALVE BODY

Disassembly – 1) Remove manual valve lever-to-valve body retaining bolt. Slide MVLPS from manual valve lever. See Fig. 15.

2) Remove solenoid assembly-to-transfer plate bolts. Remove solenoid assembly and screen. Remove bolts and valve body plate support.

CAUTION: Use care when separating transfer plate from valve body. DO NOT allow check balls to fall from valve body.

3) Separate transfer plate and separator plate from valve body, noting location of thermal valve and regulator valve screen in transfer plate. See Figs. 15 and 40.

4) Note location of check balls and retainers in valve body. See Fig. 40. Using Retainer Remover/Installer (6301), remove retainer for torque converter control valve and torque converter switch valve. Perform STEP 1. See Fig. 41.

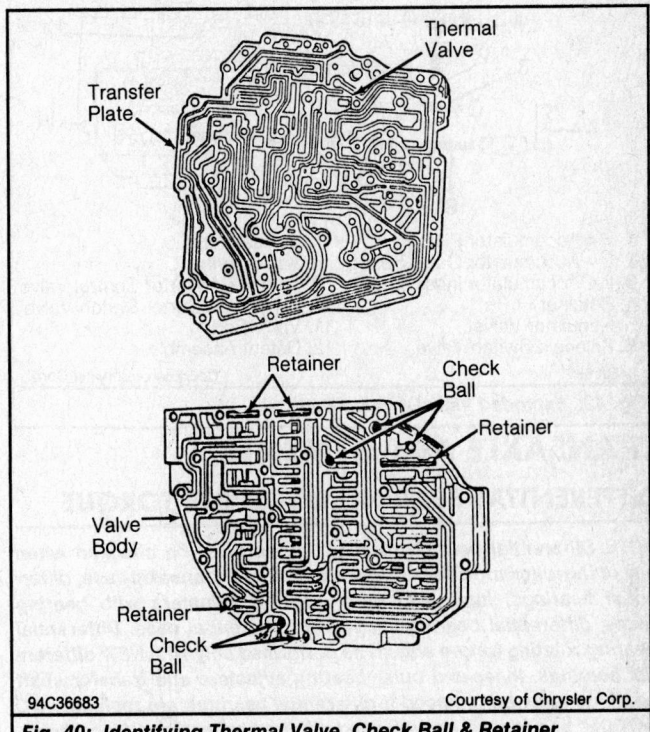

94C36683   Courtesy of Chrysler Corp.

Fig. 40: Identifying Thermal Valve, Check Ball & Retainer Locations

5) Using Retainer Remover/Installer (6302), remove retainer for regulator valve. Perform STEP 2. *See Fig. 41.* Remove valve body components. *See Fig. 42.*

Reassembly – To reassemble, reverse disassembly procedure. Ensure all components are installed in original location. Tighten bolts to specification. See TORQUE SPECIFICATIONS.

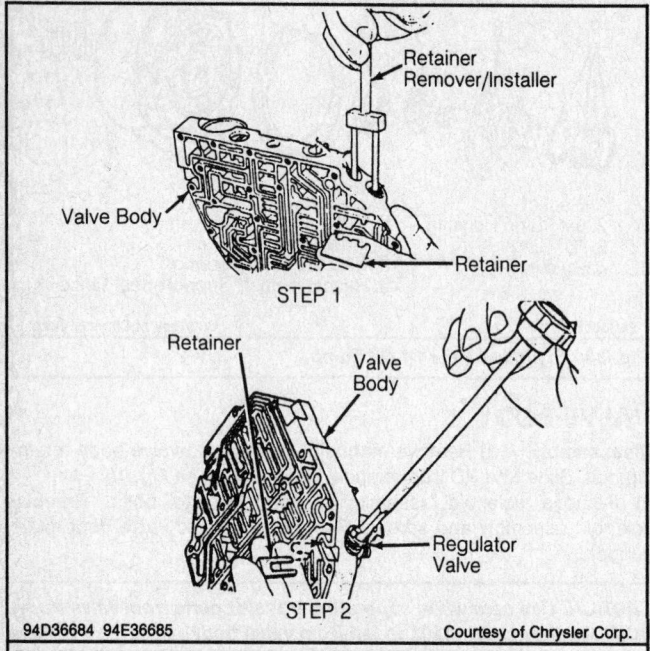

94D36684 94E36685   Courtesy of Chrysler Corp.

Fig. 41: Removing & Installing Retainers In Valve Body

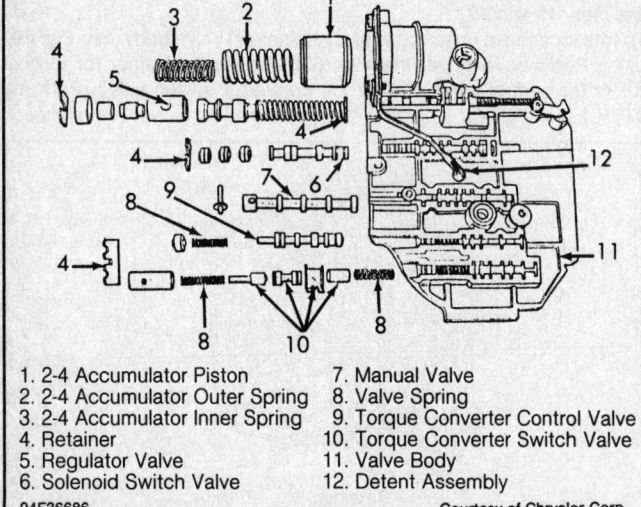

1. 2-4 Accumulator Piston
2. 2-4 Accumulator Outer Spring
3. 2-4 Accumulator Inner Spring
4. Retainer
5. Regulator Valve
6. Solenoid Switch Valve
7. Manual Valve
8. Valve Spring
9. Torque Converter Control Valve
10. Torque Converter Switch Valve
11. Valve Body
12. Detent Assembly

94F36686   Courtesy of Chrysler Corp.

Fig. 42: Exploded View Of Valve Body

TRANSAXLE ADJUSTMENTS

DIFFERENTIAL BEARING ROTATING TORQUE

NOTE: Differential bearing rotating torque must be checked when any of the following components are replaced: transaxle case, differential bearings, inner and outer bearing adjusters with bearing races, differential bearing support or differential case. Differential bearing rotating torque should be performed only with NEW differential bearings. Inner and outer bearing adjusters and transfer shaft bearings must be replaced if differential bearings are replaced. DO NOT use this procedure with used differential bearings. Manufacturer does not list differential bearing rotating torque with used differential bearings. Differential bearing torque must be checked with transfer shaft removed from transaxle case.

1) Press oil seal from inner and outer bearing adjusters. Press NEW oil seals into inner and outer bearing adjusters. Install NEW "O" ring on inner and outer bearing adjusters. Lubricate threads on inner and outer bearing adjusters and lip of oil seals with gear oil.

2) Using Socket (6502-B), screw inner bearing adjuster into transaxle case. Inner bearing adjuster should be positioned so it is below the transaxle case surface when viewed from differential side of transaxle case.

3) Install differential assembly and differential cover. Install and tighten differential cover bolts to specification. See TORQUE SPECIFICATIONS.

4) Install Seal Protector (6591) on short stub shaft. Lubricate seal protector with gear oil. Install outer bearing adjuster. Screw outer bearing adjuster into differential cover until it is finger tight. Rotate differential back and forth in both directions several times to seat bearings.

5) Install foot-lb. torque wrench and Socket (6503) on outer bearing adjuster. *See Fig. 43.* Install Adapter (6548) into differential assembly. *See Fig. 43.*

6) Install 1/4" extension and INCH-lb. torque wrench on adapter. *See Fig. 43.* Using INCH-lb. torque wrench, rotate differential and note amount of torque required to rotate the differential assembly. This is the differential bearing rotating torque. Tighten outer bearing adjuster until differential bearing rotating torque is 19-23 INCH lbs. (2.1-2.6 N.m).

7) Record torque reading required on the outer bearing adjuster to obtain correct differential bearing rotating torque. This reading will be required during transaxle reassembly. Remove socket, adapter, differential cover and differential assembly from transaxle case.

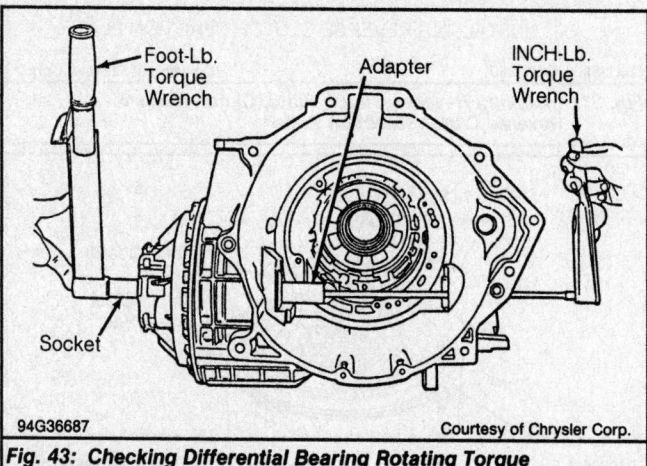

94G36687   Courtesy of Chrysler Corp.

Fig. 43: Checking Differential Bearing Rotating Torque

OUTPUT SHAFT BEARING PRELOAD

CAUTION: Output shaft bearing preload must be checked and/or adjusted if any of the following components are replaced: rear planetary carrier and output shaft, output shaft bearings or transaxle case. Output shaft bearing preload is determined by measuring output shaft rotating torque.

1) Install NEW bearing races for output shaft in transaxle case. Press NEW bearing on output shaft. Install NEW rear bearing for output shaft and Plate (6618-A) on rear of transaxle case. *See Fig. 44.* Slightly tighten retaining bolts on plate until bolt heads are below surface of the plate. DO NOT fully tighten bolts.

2) Place transaxle case in press so plate is supported. Ensure clearance exists so output shaft can extend through the plate when installed.

3) Original output shaft shim should be used as a starting point for adjusting bearing preload. If original output shaft shim is not available, use output shaft shim with thickness of .238-.239" (6.04-6.07 mm). This is the thickest shim available.

4) Apply small amount of petroleum jelly to original output shaft shim. Install output shaft shim on output shaft, just above the bearing. Install output shaft in transaxle case. Press output shaft into rear bearing and transaxle case.

5) Install NEW output shaft nut on output shaft. DO NOT reuse old output shaft nut. Install Holder (6497) on output shaft nut. Using torque wrench and Adapter (6498), tighten output shaft nut by torque wrench and output shaft counterclockwise. *See Fig. 23.* Tighten output shaft nut to specification. See TORQUE SPECIFICATIONS.

6) Using INCH-lb. torque wrench, measure output shaft rotating torque required to rotate output shaft to determine output shaft bearing preload. Output shaft rotating torque should be 1-8 INCH lbs. (.1-.9 N.m.).

7) If output shaft rotating torque exceeds specification, install thicker output shaft shim. If output shaft rotating torque is less than specified, install thinner output shaft shim. Output shaft shims are available in 15 thickness ranges of .203-.204" (5.16-5.18 mm) to .238-.239" (6.04-6.07 mm) in approximate .001" (.025 mm) increments.

8) Ensure no end play exists on output shaft. Once correct output shaft rotating torque is obtained, use press and Staking Adapter (6589) to stake output shaft nut against output shaft. Ensure staked area on output shaft nut is fully bottomed in groove area on output shaft. Remove transaxle case from press. Remove plate from rear of transaxle case.

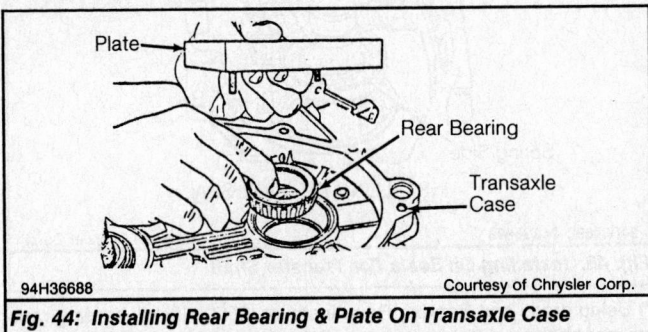

Fig. 44: Installing Rear Bearing & Plate On Transaxle Case

TRANSFER SHAFT DEPTH

NOTE: Transfer shaft depth must be checked if transfer shaft, bearings, bearing races, transaxle case or depth shim are replaced. Transfer shaft bearings must be replaced if differential bearings are replaced.

1) Using Bearing Race Installer (6494), install front (differential assembly side) bearing race for transfer shaft in transaxle case. Using feeler gauge, ensure no clearance exists between front bearing race and transaxle case. If clearance exists, fully seat front bearing race in transaxle case.

2) Screw Centering Block (6549-2) into inner bearing adjuster hole of transaxle case until it bottoms by using pegs on centering block. Perform STEP 1. *See Fig. 45 for STEPS 1 through 8.*

3) Install NEW front bearing and Gauge Disc (6549-3) in transaxle case. Perform STEP 2. Install Centering Disc (6494-2) and nut on gauge disc. Perform STEP 3. Hand-tighten nut until no play exists.

4) Install dial indicator in locating block. Screw extension rod into dial indicator. Perform STEP 4. Zero dial indicator by placing dial indicator assembly on Fixture (6549-6). Place fixture and dial indicator assembly on flat surface. Adjust dial indicator to zero. Perform STEP 5.

5) Slightly compress extension rod and insert dial indicator assembly on pin of centering block. Perform STEP 6.

6) Pivot dial indicator assembly back and forth on centering block to obtain the shortest distance (highest reading on dial indicator). Perform STEP 7. Record this reading.

7) Rotate gauge disc 1/3 revolution clockwise. Recheck dial indicator reading. Record this reading.

8) Rotate gauge disc 1/3 revolution clockwise. Recheck dial indicator reading. Record this reading. Take the average of all 3 readings. This is the transfer shaft measured depth. If reading varies by more than .002" (.05 mm), recheck gauge disc installation to ensure gauge disc is not cocked in transaxle case.

9) To determine thickness of depth shim, note the first digit of adjustment number on transfer shaft. *See Fig. 46.* Using first digit of adjustment, determine amount to be added or subtracted from transfer shaft measured depth obtained in step **8**). See ADJUSTMENT FACTOR table.

10) For example, if transfer shaft measured depth is .032" (.81 mm) and first digit of adjustment number is -1, the thickness of required depth shim is .033" (.84 mm).

11) If first digit of adjustment number is a minus (-) number, add this amount to transfer shaft measured depth reading obtained in step **8**). If first digit of adjustment number DOES NOT not contain a minus (-) number, subtract this amount from transfer shaft measured depth reading obtained in step **8**). Pinion head depth shims are available in 17 thicknesses of .0268-.0278" (.681-.707 mm) to .0438-.0448" (1.113-1.139 mm) in approximate .001 (.025 mm) increments.

ADJUSTMENT FACTOR

First Digit Of Adjustment Number	Amount Added Or Subtracted In. (mm)
0	0 (0)
1	-.001 (-.0250)
2	-.002 (-.0510)
3	-.003 (-.0760)
-1	+.001 (+.0250)
-2	+.002 (+.0510)
-3	+.003 (-.0760)

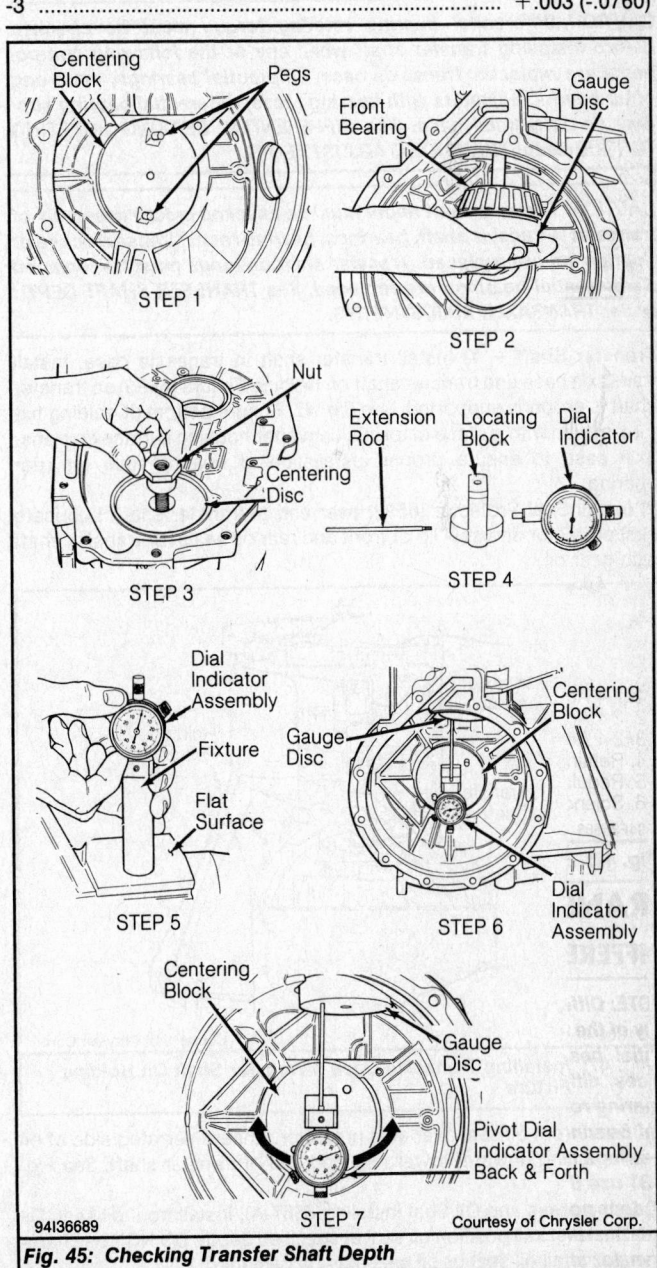

Fig. 45: Checking Transfer Shaft Depth

12) Remove dial indicator assembly, gauge disc, centering block and bearing from transaxle case. Install selected depth shim on transfer shaft. Press NEW bearing on transfer shaft.

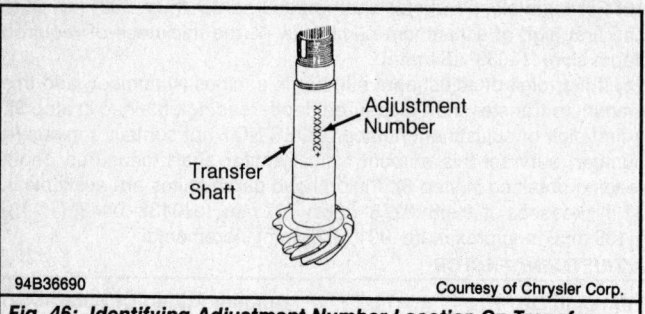

94B36690   Courtesy of Chrysler Corp.

Fig. 46: Identifying Adjustment Number Location On Transfer Shaft

TRANSAXLE REASSEMBLY

DIFFERENTIAL ASSEMBLY & TRANSFER SHAFT

CAUTION: Differential bearing rotating torque must be checked before installing transfer shaft when any of the following components are replaced: transaxle case, differential bearings, inner and outer bearing adjusters with bearing races, differential bearing support or differential case. See DIFFERENTIAL BEARING ROTATING TORQUE under TRANSAXLE ADJUSTMENTS.

CAUTION: Transfer shaft depth must be checked before assembly of transaxle if transfer shaft, bearings, bearing races, transaxle case or depth shim are replaced. Transfer shaft bearings must be replaced if differential bearings are replaced. See TRANSFER SHAFT DEPTH under TRANSAXLE ADJUSTMENTS.

Transfer Shaft – 1) Install transfer shaft in transaxle case. Install transaxle case and transfer shaft on Holding Fixture (6595) so transfer shaft is properly supported. *See Fig. 47.* Ensure bottom of holding fixture is even with surface of torque converter housing surface on transaxle case to ensure proper installation of bearing race for rear bearing.

2) Install Seal Protector (6592) over end of transfer shaft. Lubricate seal protector and seal lip of front and rear oil seals for transfer shaft with gear oil.

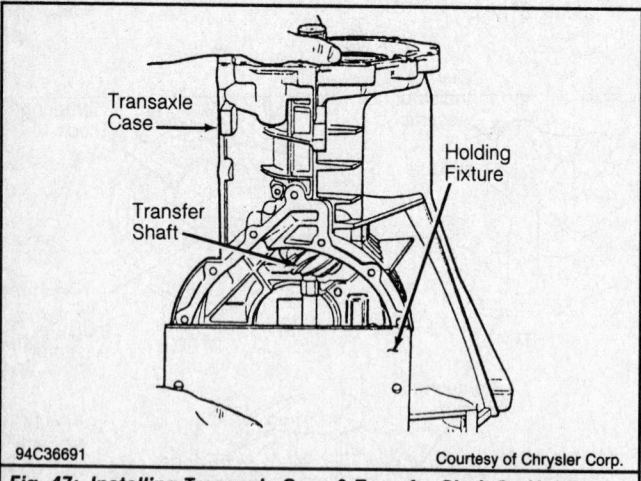

94C36691   Courtesy of Chrysler Corp.

Fig. 47: Installing Transaxle Case & Transfer Shaft On Holding Fixture

3) Install front oil seal over seal protector. Ensure serrated side of oil seal is facing upward, toward splined end of transfer shaft. *See Fig. 48.*

4) Using press and Oil Seal Installer (6567-A), install front oil seal. Oil seal installer will position oil seal at specified depth. DO NOT use hammer to install oil seal or oil seal may be damaged.

5) Install rear oil seal on seal protector. Ensure spring side of rear oil seal is facing upward, toward splined end of transfer shaft. *See Fig. 48.*

6) Using press and Oil Seal Installer (6567-A), install rear oil seal. Oil seal installer will position oil seal at specified depth. DO NOT use hammer to install oil seal or oil seal may be damaged.

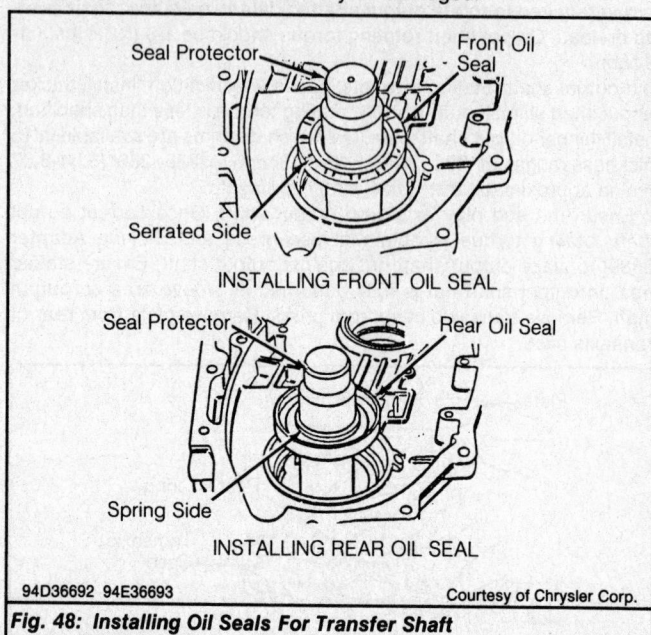

94D36692 94E36693   Courtesy of Chrysler Corp.

Fig. 48: Installing Oil Seals For Transfer Shaft

7) Using press and Bearing Race Installer (6560), install bearing race for rear bearing in transaxle case. Ensure bearing race is fully seated in transaxle case.

8) Using hammer and Baffle Plate Installer (6560), lightly tap NEW baffle plate (if equipped) into transaxle case. *See Fig. 29.*

9) Original transfer shaft shim should be used as a starting point for adjusting transfer shaft bearing preload. If original transfer shaft shim is not available, use transfer shaft shim with thickness of .184-.185" (4.67-4.69 mm). This is the thickest shim available.

10) Install transfer shim on transfer shaft. Press NEW rear bearing on transfer shaft. Remove transaxle case from holding fixture. Install NEW transfer shaft nut on transfer shaft. DO NOT reuse old transfer shaft nut.

11) Install Holder (6497) on transfer shaft nut. Using torque wrench and Adapter (6498), tighten transfer shaft nut by rotating torque wrench and transfer shaft counterclockwise. *See Fig. 23.* Tighten transfer shaft nut to specification. See TORQUE SPECIFICATIONS.

12) Using INCH-lb. torque wrench, measure transfer shaft rotating torque required to rotate the transfer shaft to determine transfer shaft bearing preload. Transfer shaft rotating torque should be 5-12 INCH lbs. (.6-1.4 N.m.).

13) If transfer shaft rotating torque exceeds specification, install thicker transfer shaft shim. If transfer shaft rotating torque is less than specified, install thinner transfer shaft shim. Transfer shaft rear shims are available in 39 thicknesses of .138-.140" (3.53-3.55 mm) to .184-.185" (4.67-4.69 mm) in approximate .001" (.025 mm) increments.

14) Ensure no end play exists on transfer shaft. Once correct transfer shaft rotating torque is obtained, use press and Staking Adapter (6589) to stake transfer shaft nut against output shaft.

CAUTION: DO NOT use hammer and staking adapter to stake the nut. If hammer is used, transfer shaft seals or bearings may be damaged.

15) Ensure staked area on transfer shaft nut is fully bottomed in groove area on transfer shaft. Apply sealant on back of vent baffle plate as indicated. *See Fig. 49.*

16) Install vent baffle plate on rear of transaxle case, near transfer shaft. *See Fig. 49.* Install and tighten vent baffle plate bolt to specification. See TORQUE SPECIFICATIONS.

NOTE: Transfer drive chain and sprockets cannot be installed at this time, as output shaft must first be installed.

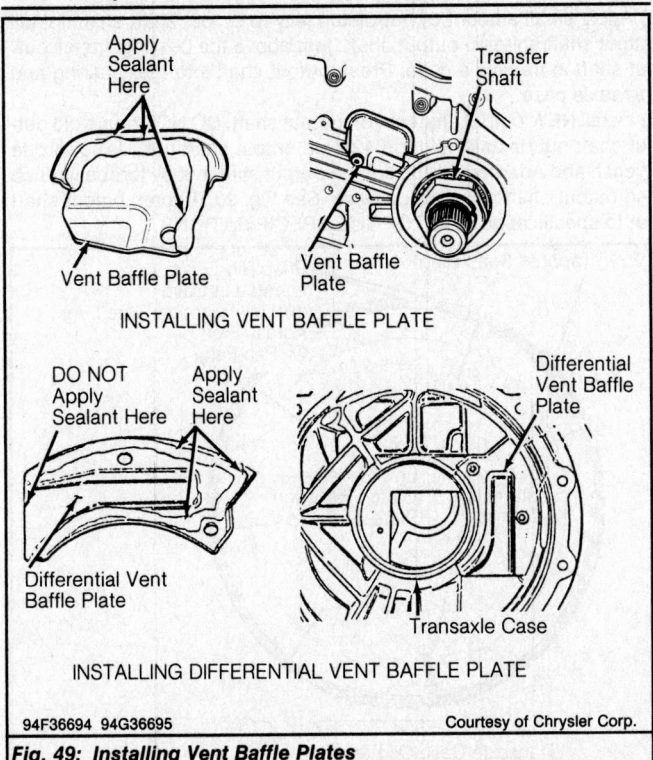

INSTALLING VENT BAFFLE PLATE

INSTALLING DIFFERENTIAL VENT BAFFLE PLATE

94F36694 94G36695   Courtesy of Chrysler Corp.

Fig. 49: Installing Vent Baffle Plates

NOTE: When installing differential assembly with NEW components and NEW bearings, it will be necessary to use torque reading obtained in step 7) under DIFFERENTIAL BEARING ROTATING TORQUE under TRANSAXLE ADJUSTMENTS. Inner and outer bearing adjusters must be replaced if differential bearings are replaced.

Differential Assembly With NEW Bearings & Components – 1) Apply sealant on back of differential vent baffle plate as indicated. See Fig. 49.

2) Install differential vent baffle plate on transaxle case. Install and tighten differential vent baffle plate bolts to specification. See TORQUE SPECIFICATIONS.

CAUTION: Inner and outer bearing adjusters must be replaced if differential bearings are replaced.

3) Install NEW "O" ring on inner bearing adjuster. Lubricate threads on inner bearing adjuster and lip of oil seal with gear oil.

4) Using Socket (6502-B), screw inner bearing adjuster into transaxle case original until surface of inner bearing adjuster is even with surface of differential side of transaxle case. Inner bearing adjuster must be at same position as when differential bearing rotating torque was checked.

5) Install differential assembly in transaxle case. Ensure ring gear backlash exists between ring gear and transfer shaft. Apply sealant on differential cover-to-transaxle case contact areas. Install differential cover. Install and tighten differential cover bolts to specification. See TORQUE SPECIFICATIONS.

6) Install Seal Protector (6591) on short stub shaft. Lubricate seal protector with gear oil. Install NEW "O" ring on outer bearing adjuster. Lubricate threads on outer bearing adjuster and lip of oil seal with gear oil.

7) Using Socket (6503), screw outer bearing adjuster into differential cover. Using torque wrench and socket, tighten outer bearing adjuster until the torque reading obtained in step 7) under DIFFERENTIAL BEARING ROTATING TORQUE under TRANSAXLE ADJUSTMENTS is obtained.

8) Rotate differential assembly back and forth several times to ensure bearings are seated. Retighten outer bearing adjuster until proper torque reading is obtained. Repeat this procedure until correct torque reading is maintained on outer bearing adjuster.

NOTE: When checking ring gear backlash it will be necessary to use torque reading obtained in step 7) under DIFFERENTIAL BEARING ROTATING TORQUE under TRANSAXLE ADJUSTMENTS using NEW bearings and races.

9) Remove inspection plug from inspection hole on top of transaxle case. Install dial indicator with stem of dial indicator against one tooth on ring gear. See Fig. 50.

10) Hold transfer shaft. Rotate differential assembly back and forth. Note ring gear backlash on dial indicator. Ring gear backlash should be .006-.009" (.15-.23 mm).

11) If excessive ring gear backlash exists, using Socket (6503), loosen outer bearing adjuster. Using Socket (6502-B), slightly rotate inner bearing adjuster so it moves away from ring gear.

12) Using torque wrench and socket, tighten outer bearing adjuster until torque reading obtained in step 7) under DIFFERENTIAL BEARING ROTATING TORQUE under TRANSAXLE ADJUSTMENTS is obtained. Recheck ring gear backlash.

13) If ring gear backlash is less than specified, using Socket (6503), slightly loosen outer bearing adjuster. Slightly rotate inner bearing adjuster so it moves toward the ring gear.

14) Using torque wrench and socket, tighten outer bearing adjuster until torque reading obtained in step 7) under DIFFERENTIAL BEARING ROTATING TORQUE under TRANSAXLE ADJUSTMENTS is obtained. Recheck ring gear backlash.

15) Once correct ring gear backlash is obtained, check ring gear backlash at 4 different areas on ring gear at 90 degrees apart. Ring gear backlash should be consistent and within specification.

16) Install bearing adjuster lock bracket on inner bearing adjuster. Install and tighten bearing adjuster lock bracket bolt to specification. See TORQUE SPECIFICATIONS.

17) Install lock bracket on outer bearing adjuster. Install and tighten lock bracket bolt to specification. See TORQUE SPECIFICATION. Use wooden block to tap NEW inspection plug into inspection hole on top of transaxle case.

NOTE: When installing differential assembly with all original components, inner and outer bearing adjusters must initially be placed at original location as during disassembly to proper bearing preload.

Differential Assembly With Original Bearings & Components – 1) Apply sealant on back of differential vent baffle plate as indicated. See Fig. 49.

2) Install differential vent baffle plate on transaxle case. Install and tighten differential vent baffle plate bolts to specification. See TORQUE SPECIFICATIONS.

3) Install NEW "O" ring on inner bearing adjuster. Lubricate threads on inner bearing adjuster and lip of oil seal with gear oil. Using Socket (6502-B), screw inner bearing adjuster into transaxle case original number of revolutions and align reference marks that were made during disassembly.

4) Install differential assembly in transaxle case. Ensure ring gear backlash exists between ring gear and transfer shaft. Apply sealant on differential cover-to-transaxle case contact areas. Install differential cover. Install and tighten differential cover bolts to specification. See TORQUE SPECIFICATIONS.

5) Install Seal Protector (6591) on short stub shaft. Lubricate seal protector with gear oil. Install NEW "O" ring on outer bearing adjuster. Lubricate threads on outer bearing adjuster and lip of oil seal with gear oil.

6) Using Socket (6503), screw outer bearing adjuster into differential cover original number of revolutions and align reference marks that were made during disassembly.

7) To check ring gear backlash, remove inspection plug from inspection hole on top of transaxle. Install dial indicator with stem of dial indicator against one tooth on ring gear. See Fig. 50.

8) Hold transfer shaft. Rotate differential assembly back and forth. Note ring gear backlash reading on dial indicator. Ring gear backlash should be .006-.009" (.15-.23 mm).

9) If excessive ring gear backlash exists, using Socket (6502-B), slightly rotate inner bearing adjuster so it moves away from ring gear. Note distance that inner bearing adjuster is moved, as outer bearing adjuster must be tightened the same amount to maintain proper preload on differential bearings.

10) Using Socket (6503), tighten outer bearing adjuster the same amount that inner bearing adjuster was moved. Recheck ring gear backlash.

11) If ring gear backlash is less than specified, using Socket (6503), slightly loosen outer bearing adjuster so it moves away from ring gear. Note distance that outer bearing adjuster is loosened, as inner bearing adjuster must be moved toward the ring gear the same amount to maintain proper preload on differential bearings.

12) Using Socket (6502-B), rotate inner bearing adjuster toward the ring gear the same amount that outer bearing adjuster was loosened. Recheck ring gear backlash.

13) Once correct ring gear backlash is obtained, check ring gear backlash at 4 different areas on ring gear at 90 degrees apart. Ring gear backlash should be consistent and within specification.

14) Install bearing adjuster lock bracket on inner bearing adjuster. Install and tighten bearing adjuster lock bracket bolt to specification. See TORQUE SPECIFICATIONS.

15) Install lock bracket on outer bearing adjuster. Install and tighten lock bracket bolt to specification. See TORQUE SPECIFICATION. Use wooden block to tap NEW inspection plug into inspection hole on top of transaxle case.

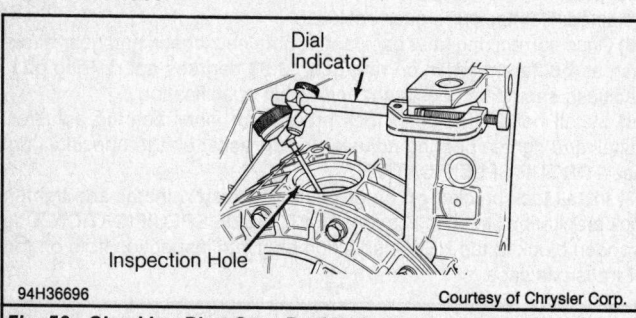

94H36696   Courtesy of Chrysler Corp.

Fig. 50: Checking Ring Gear Backlash

VALVE BODY & INTERNAL COMPONENTS

1) Using NEW gasket, install low-reverse clutch piston retainer in transaxle case. See Fig. 21. Ensure the 3 holes on gasket are aligned with 3 holes in transaxle case.

2) Install and tighten low-reverse clutch piston retainer Torx screws to specification. See TORQUE SPECIFICATIONS. Install low-reverse clutch piston inside transaxle case.

3) Ensure components and spring on parking sprag assembly are properly installed. Perform STEP 4. See Fig. 25. Install parking sprag assembly in transaxle case. Ensure guide bracket and sleeve on parking sprag assembly contacts rear of transaxle case.

4) Install pivot pin and anchor shaft. Install and tighten parking sprag bolt to specification. See TORQUE SPECIFICATIONS.

5) Install clutch piston return spring for low-reverse clutch in transaxle case. Using spring compressor, compress clutch piston return spring for low-reverse clutch. See Fig. 24. Install snap ring so ends of snap ring are properly positioned. See Fig. 24.

CAUTION: Output shaft bearing preload must be checked and/or adjusted if any of the following components are replaced: rear planetary carrier and output shaft, output shaft bearings or transaxle case. See OUTPUT SHAFT BEARING PRELOAD under TRANSAXLE ADJUSTMENTS.

6) Install rear bearing for output shaft and Plate (6618-A) on rear of transaxle case. See Fig. 44. Slightly tighten retaining bolts on plate until bolt heads are below surface of the plate. DO NOT fully tighten bolts.

7) Place transaxle case in press so plate is supported. Ensure clearance exists so output shaft can extend through the plate when installed.

8) Apply small amount of petroleum jelly to output shaft shim. Install output shaft shim on output shaft, just above the bearing. Install output shaft in transaxle case. Press output shaft into rear bearing and transaxle case.

9) Install NEW output shaft nut on output shaft. DO NOT reuse old output shaft nut. Install Holder (6497) on output shaft nut. Using torque wrench and Adapter (6498), tighten output shaft nut by torque wrench and output shaft counterclockwise. See Fig. 23. Tighten output shaft nut to specification. See TORQUE SPECIFICATIONS.

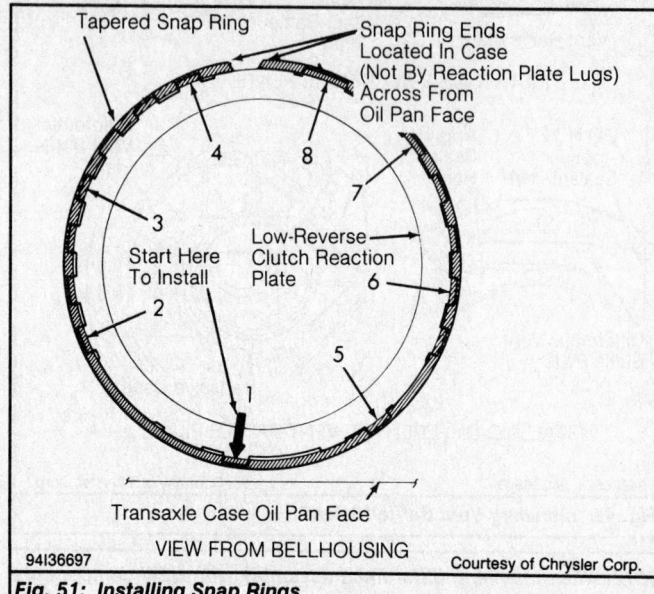

94I36697   Courtesy of Chrysler Corp.

Fig. 51: Installing Snap Rings

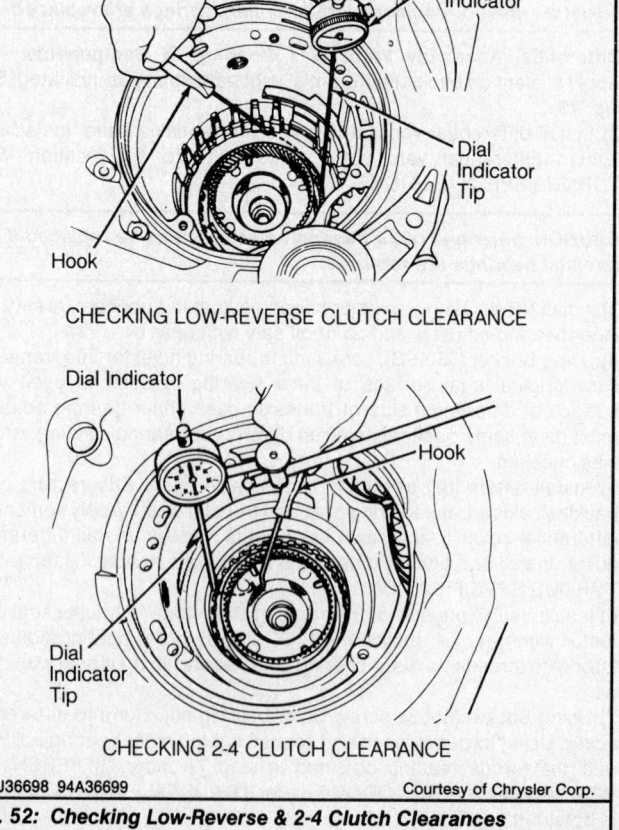

94J36698   94A36699   Courtesy of Chrysler Corp.

Fig. 52: Checking Low-Reverse & 2-4 Clutch Clearances

10) Ensure no end play exists on output shaft. Use press and Staking Adapter (6589) to stake output shaft nut against output shaft. Ensure staked area on output shaft nut is fully bottomed in groove area on output shaft. Remove transaxle case from press. Remove plate from rear of transaxle case.

11) Install transfer drive chain and sprockets. See TRANSFER DRIVE CHAIN & SPROCKETS under TRANSAXLE REASSEMBLY. Install 5 low-reverse clutch plates and 5 clutch discs, starting with a clutch plate and alternating with a clutch disc. *See Fig. 21.* Ensure components are in correct sequence.

12) Install flat snap ring and one low-reverse clutch plate. Ensure ends of snap ring are positioned in proper area. *See Fig. 51.*

13) Install low-reverse clutch reaction plate. *See Fig. 21.* Ensure flat side of low-reverse clutch reaction plate is facing upward (toward oil pump opening). Install tapered snap ring above lower clutch reaction plate. Ensure ends of tapered snap ring are in proper area. *See Fig. 51.*

CAUTION: Low-reverse clutch clearance must be checked after installing clutch assembly.

---

14) To check low-reverse clutch clearance, assemble dial indicator and Dial Indicator Tip (6268) on transaxle case. *See Fig. 52.* Press low-reverse clutch pack downward and zero dial indicator. Using hook, pull one low-reverse clutch disc upward and note low-reverse clutch clearance on dial indicator. Remove dial indicator.

15) Low-reverse clutch clearance should be .042-.065" (1.06-1.65 mm). If clearance is not within specification, different thickness low-reverse clutch reaction plate can be installed. Low-reverse clutch reaction plates are available in the following thickness:

- .211" (5.36 mm)
- .221" (5.61 mm)
- .232" (5.89 mm)
- .242" (6.15 mm)
- .252" (6.40 mm)
- .262" (6.65 mm)
- .273" (6.93 mm)

16) Install 2-4 clutch discs and clutch plates, starting with a clutch disc and alternating with a clutch plate. *See Fig. 21.* There should be 4 clutch discs and plates. Ensure components are in correct sequence.

17) Install clutch piston return spring, 2-4 clutch piston and 2-4 clutch piston retainer. *See Fig. 21.* Using 2-4 Clutch Compressor (5058), compress 2-4 clutch piston retainer. *See Fig. 22.* Install snap ring. Ensure ends of snap ring are positioned in proper area. *See Fig. 51.* Release 2-4 clutch compressor.

CAUTION: The 2-4 clutch clearance must be checked after installing clutch assembly.

---

18) To check 2-4 clutch clearance, assemble dial indicator and Dial Indicator Tip (6268) on transaxle case. *See Fig. 52.* Press 2-4 clutch pack downward and zero dial indicator. Using hook, pull one 2/4 clutch disc upward and note 2-4 clutch clearance on dial indicator.

19) The 2-4 clutch clearance should be .030-.104" (.76-2.64 mm). If clearance is not within specification, check for improper installation of clutch components. There is no adjustment for 2-4 clutch clearance. Remove dial indicator.

20) Apply small amount of petroleum jelly on thrust bearing and install on shaft side of sun gear. *See Fig. 21.* Ensure thrust bearing is flat against sun gear.

21) Install sun gear in rear planetary. Install thrust bearing on front of sun gear. Install rear annulus gear. *See Fig. 21.* It may be necessary to rotate rear annulus gear during installation. Install 2-4 clutch hub. Install thrust washer on front of 2-4 clutch hub.

CAUTION: Correct thickness No. 4 thrust plate located on rear (shaft end) of overdrive clutch hub must be determined to maintain proper input shaft end play. See Fig. 31.

---

22) Apply petroleum jelly on overdrive clutch hub in 3 places. Install a .037-.039" (.93-1.00 mm) thick No. 4 thrust plate on overdrive clutch hub. *See Fig. 31.*

23) Install input clutch assembly. *See Fig. 20.* Ensure input clutch assembly is fully seated by looking through input speed sensor hole in transaxle case. If input clutch assembly is fully seated, input clutch hub will be fully visible. *See Fig. 53.* If input clutch assembly is not fully seated, remove and check for improper installation.

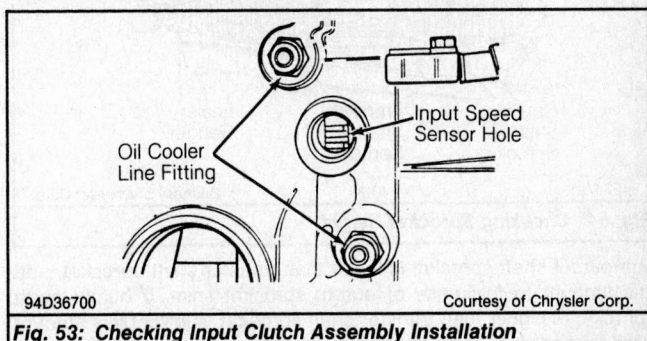

94D36700   Courtesy of Chrysler Corp.

Fig. 53: Checking Input Clutch Assembly Installation

24) Install gasket and oil pump. DO NOT install "O" ring on oil pump at this time. Install and tighten oil pump-to-transaxle case bolts to specification. See TORQUE SPECIFICATIONS.

25) Using dial indicator, check input shaft end play. Input shaft end play should be .005-.025" (.13-.64 mm). If input shaft end play is not within specification, change No. 4 thrust plate thickness to obtain correct input shaft end play.

26) For example, if input shaft end play is .055" (1.40 mm) with No. 4 thrust plate installed, select a No. 4 thrust plate with thickness of .071-.074" (1.80-1.88 mm). Install selected No. 4 thrust plate. This should change input shaft end play to .020" (.51 mm). The No. 4 thrust plate is available in thickness ranging from .037-.039" (.93-1.00 mm) to .132-.135" (3.35-3.42 mm).

27) Once proper input shaft end play is obtained, remove oil pump and gasket. Install NEW "O" ring on oil pump. Install oil cooler by-pass valve in transaxle case with "O" ring end toward rear of transaxle case. *See Fig. 19.*

CAUTION: If transaxle failure existed, DO NOT attempt to clean or reuse oil cooler by-pass valve. Replace oil cooler by-pass valve.

---

28) Install gasket and oil pump. Tighten oil pump-to-transaxle case bolts to specification. See TORQUE SPECIFICATIONS. Ensure input shaft rotates smoothly.

29) Using NEW seal rings, install overdrive and underdrive accumulator pistons and springs in transaxle case. *See Fig. 18.* Using NEW seal rings, install low-reverse accumulator piston and springs.

30) Install cover and snap ring above low-reverse accumulator piston. *See Fig. 18.* Install valve body. See VALVE BODY under REMOVAL & INSTALLATION.

CAUTION: If transaxle failure existed, flush oil cooler and check oil cooler flow. See OIL COOLER FLUSHING and OIL COOLER FLOW CHECK under ON-VEHICLE SERVICE.

TRANSFER DRIVE CHAIN & SPROCKETS

1) Sprocket height must be checked to ensure output shaft sprocket and transfer shaft sprockets are at the same height. Sprocket height must be within .015" (.38 mm) of each other.

2) Original output sprocket shim should be used as a starting point for checking output shaft sprocket height. If original output sprocket shim is not available, use output sprocket shim with thickness of .162-.170" (4.11-4.31 mm). This is the thickest shim available.

3) Install output sprocket shim on output shaft. Install output shaft sprocket on output shaft. Output shaft sprocket contains 32 teeth and transfer shaft sprocket contains 33 teeth.

4) Install transfer shaft sprocket on transfer shaft. Place straightedge on top of the highest sprocket so straightedge is positioned above the other sprocket. *See Fig. 54.* Using feeler gauge, measure height difference between the sprockets.

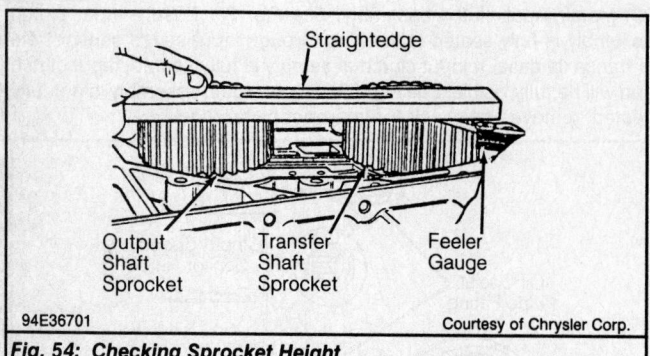

Fig. 54: Checking Sprocket Height

94E36701 — Courtesy of Chrysler Corp.

5) If output shaft sprocket is lower than transfer shaft sprocket, add this amount to thickness of output sprocket shim. If output shaft sprocket is higher than transfer shaft sprocket, subtract this amount from thickness of output sprocket shim. Output sprocket shims are available in 4 thicknesses of .104-.112" (2.64-2.84 mm) to .162-.170" (4.11-4.31 mm) in approximate .020" (.05 mm) increments.

6) Remove straightedge, output shaft sprocket and output sprocket shim. Install replacement output sprocket shim. Recheck sprocket height. Once correct sprocket height is obtained, remove output shaft and transfer shaft sprockets.

7) Install transfer drive chain on output shaft and transfer shaft sprockets with Blue link facing outward. See Fig. 27.

8) Install Chain Spreader (6550) between output shaft and transfer shaft sprockets. See Fig. 27. Rotate nuts on chain spreader to apply pressure against sprockets and drive chain.

9) Install transfer drive chain along with output shaft and transfer shaft sprockets on output shaft and transfer shaft. Ensure enough pressure exists on transfer drive chain, as not to damage splines on shafts when installing sprockets.

10) Remove chain spreader. Install wave washers and snap rings to retain sprockets on shafts. Remove chain spreader. Install original chain snubber. Tighten bolts to specification. See TORQUE SPECIFICATIONS.

CAUTION: Chain snubber clearance between chain snubber and transfer drive chain must be checked. Ensure clearance is checked.

11) To check chain snubber clearance, insert screwdriver in hole below transfer drive chain. Pry transfer drive chain upward to release slack in transfer drive chain. See Fig. 55.

12) Using feeler gauge, measure clearance between chain snubber and top of transfer drive chain. See Fig. 55. Clearance should be 0-.030" (0-.76 mm). If clearance is not within specification, different chain snubber must be installed.

13) Chain snubber are available in 3 different colors: Black, Green and Tan. Black colored chain snubber is the thinnest and provides the most clearance. Green colored chain snubber is the thickest and provides the least amount of clearance. Tan colored chain snubber is the standard chain snubber.

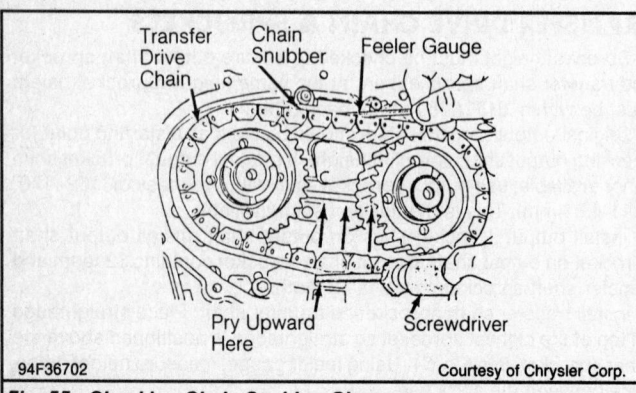

Fig. 55: Checking Chain Snubber Clearance

94F36702 — Courtesy of Chrysler Corp.

14) Install proper chain snubber to obtain correct clearance. Tighten bolts to specification. See TORQUE SPECIFICATIONS. Install chain oiler (if removed). See Fig. 26.

15) Apply sealant to chain cover. Install chain cover. Install and tighten chain cover bolts to specification. See TORQUE SPECIFICATIONS.

TORQUE SPECIFICATIONS
TORQUE SPECIFICATIONS

Application	Ft. Lbs. (N.m)
Chain Cover Bolt	21 (29)
Differential Cover Bolt	21 (29)
Input Speed Sensor	20 (27)
Oil Pan Bolt	14 (19)
Oil Pump-To-Transaxle Case Bolt	22 (30)
Output Shaft Nut	200 (271)
Output Speed Sensor	20 (27)
Reaction Shaft Support-To-Oil Pump Housing Bolt	21 (29)
Ring Gear Bolt [1]	70 (95)
Transfer Shaft Nut	200 (271)

Application	INCH Lbs. (N.m)
Bearing Adjuster Lock Bracket Bolt	40 (4.5)
Chain Snubber Bolt	40 (4.5)
Differential Vent Baffle Plate Bolt	40 (4.5)
Lock Bracket Bolt	40 (4.5)
Low Reverse Clutch Piston Retainer Torx Screw	40 (4.5)
Manual Valve Lever-To-Valve Body Bolt	40 (4.5)
Oil Filter Retainer Bolt	40 (4.5)
Parking Sprag Bolt	40 (4.5)
Pressure Tap Plug	45 (5.1)
Solenoid Assembly-To-Transfer Plate Bolt	50 (5.6)
Valve Body Plate Support Bolt	40 (4.5)
Valve Body-To-Transfer Plate Bolt	40 (4.5)
Valve Body/Transfer Plate-To-Transaxle Case Bolt	105 (11.9)
Vent Baffle Plate Bolt	40 (4.5)

[1] – Always use NEW bolts.

TRANSAXLE SPECIFICATIONS
TRANSAXLE SPECIFICATIONS

Application	Specification
Clutch Clearances	
Low-Reverse Clutch	.042-.065" (1.06-1.65 mm)
Overdrive Clutch	.038-.089" (.96-2.26 mm)
Reverse Clutch	.030-.049" (.76-1.24 mm)
Underdrive Clutch	.036-.058" (.91-1.47 mm)
2-4 Clutch	.030-.104" (.76-2.64 mm)
Differential Rotating Torque	
With NEW Bearings Only	19-23 INCH lbs. (2.1-2.6 N.m)
Input Shaft End Play	.005-.025" (.13-.64 mm)
Oil Pump Clearances	
Inner & Outer Gear Side Clearance	.0008-.0018 (.020-.046)
Outer Gear-To-Pocket Clearance	.0018-.0056 (.046-.142)
Output Shaft Rotating Torque	
For Bearing Preload	1-8 INCH lbs. (.1-.9 N.m)
Ring Gear Backlash	.006-.009" (.15-.23 mm)
Transfer Shaft Rotating Torque	
For Bearing Preload	5-12 INCH lbs. (.6-1.4 N.m)

TECHNICIAL SERVICE BULLETINS

WHISTLING NOISE

Chrysler Corp. Service Bulletin 21-01-93 (January 13, 1993) – Some 1993 42LE transaxles may experience a high pitched whistling noise. Condition may exist when gearshift is in Park, Neutral or "OD" position with engine idling after reaching normal operating temperature. Whistling noise is similar to a high pitched hydraulic noise or vacuum leak. For diagnosis of whistling noise, use the following procedure.

1) Place vehicle in quit area. Ensure engine and transaxle are at normal operating temperature. Apply parking brake. Place gearshift in "OD" position. With windows down, listen for high pitched whistle with engine idling.

2) If high pitched whistle exists, increase engine speed to 1200-1500 RPM. Note if high pitched whistle discontinues with engine speed at 1200-1500 RPM. Repeat procedure to ensure diagnosis.

3) If high pitched whistle continues with engine speed at 1200-1500 RPM, the problem is not within the transaxle. If high pitched whistle discontinues with engine speed at 1200-1500 RPM, replace regulator valve and separator plate on valve body.

4) Valve body must be removed for component servicing. See VALVE BODY under REMOVAL & INSTALLATION. Disassemble valve body and replace regulator valve and separator plate. See VALVE BODY under COMPONENT DISASSEMBLY & REASSEMBLY. Install Regulator Valve (4659081) and Separator Plate (4659083).

TRANSAXLE IN LIMP-IN MODE AND/OR ERRATIC TACHOMETER/SPEEDOMETER OPERATION

Chrysler Corp. Bulletin 21-35-93 (November 19, 1993) – Some 1994 LH models with 42LE transaxle may experience transaxle operating in limp-in mode and/or erratic tachometer operation. For diagnosis and repair of this problem, use the following procedure.

1) Inspect transaxle wiring harness clearance at rear of engine, near inner tie rod. There should be a minimum of 3/4" clearance between wiring harness and inner tie rod.

2) If a minimum of 3/4" clearance does not exist, inspect transaxle wiring harness for damaged wires. If damaged wires exist, replace transaxle wiring harness with Wiring Harness (4604900).

3) If a minimum of 3/4" clearance does not exist, replace bracket that secures transaxle wiring harness with Bracket (4604744). On 3.3L, bracket is located below EGR valve. On 3.5L, bracket is located to the left of EGR valve. On 3.5L, it will be necessary to remove right air duct for access to bracket.

4) On 3.3L, once bracket is installed, ensure transaxle wiring harness does not contact the EGR valve. On 3.5L, once bracket is installed, ensure transaxle wiring harness does not contact the EGR tube.

WIRING DIAGRAMS

For appropriate wiring diagram, see CHRYSLER 42LE ELECTRONIC DIAGNOSIS article.

AUTOMATIC TRANSMISSIONS
Chrysler 42LE Electronic Diagnosis

APPLICATIONS

CHRYSLER 42LE

Model	Engine
Chrysler	
1993-94 Concorde	3.3L & 3.5L
1994 LHS & New Yorker	3.5L
Dodge	
1993-94 Intrepid	3.3L & 3.5L
Eagle	
1993-94 Vision	3.3L & 3.5L

DESCRIPTION

The 42LE is an electronically controlled 4-speed transaxle. Transaxle contains hydraulically operated clutches, which are controlled by Transaxle Control Module (TCM). The TCM receives information from various inputs and uses this information to control solenoid assembly for proper transaxle operation.

NOTE: The TCM may also be referred to as transmission control module.

OPERATION

CAUTION: If battery is disconnected or voltage supply to Transaxle Control Module (TCM) is lost, TCM will have to relearn shift characteristics. Perform shift quality quick-learn procedure so TCM can relearn shift characteristics. See SHIFT QUALITY QUICK-LEARN PROCEDURE in CHRYSLER 42LE article.

TRANSAXLE CONTROL MODULE (TCM)

The TCM may receive signal data in 2 ways: directly from a sensor or component, or through a twisted-pair bus circuit, which connects all of the vehicle computer systems. This twisted-pair bus circuit is called Chrysler Collision Detection (CCD) bus and allows various vehicle control modules to share signal data. *See Fig. 1.* If CCD bus failure

exists, appropriate values are substituted by the TCM, allowing continued, but degraded transaxle operation.

If TCM loses battery voltage, transaxle will enter limp-in mode. For additional information on limp-in mode, see LIMP-IN MODE under OPERATION. When TCM receives an ignition run signal from ignition switch, it performs a series of circuit checks to ensure transaxle control relay and solenoid assembly are operating correctly. If no problem is found, TCM provides voltage to transaxle control relay, causing contacts to close, supplying voltage to solenoid assembly.

NOTE: Transaxle control relay may be referred to as transmission control relay.

The TCM contains a self-diagnostic system which stores a diagnostic trouble code if a transaxle failure exists. Diagnostic trouble codes can be retrieved to identify transaxle problem areas. If malfunction goes away after diagnostic trouble code is stored in TCM memory, the TCM will erase diagnostic trouble code after ignition has been cycled at least 75 times.

The TCM contains an adaptive memory which learns application and release rates of transaxle components for smooth operation. The TCM also learns the rate at which applied elements build pressure sufficient for a speed change.

LIMP-IN MODE

The TCM monitors transaxle for electrical or internal problems. If battery voltage is lost, or TCM senses a transaxle failure and diagnostic trouble code is set, the TCM de-energizes the transaxle control relay which then de-energizes the solenoid assembly. Transaxle then enters limp-in mode. In limp-in mode, only Park, Neutral, Reverse and 2nd gears function. Transaxle will not upshift or downshift. Vehicle can be operated, but performance will be reduced. When ignition is turned off and then back on again, the TCM will reset for normal operation until it senses the failure again. Once failure it noted again, transaxle will enter limp-in mode.

NOTE: Transaxle will not enter limp-in mode when certain diagnostic trouble codes are set.

SOLENOID ASSEMBLY

NOTE: Solenoid assembly may be referred to as the solenoid pack. Transaxle control relay may be referred to as transmission control relay.

Solenoid assembly is controlled by the TCM. The TCM provides voltage to transaxle control relay, causing contacts to close, supplying voltage to solenoid assembly. Solenoid assembly, consisting of 4 electric solenoids, controls transaxle hydraulic circuits. The TCM completes the ground circuit, operating solenoid for proper hydraulic circuit control.

Low-reverse (L-R), overdrive (OD) and 2-4 pressure switches are located in the solenoid assembly. Pressure switches are monitored by the TCM to indicate whether circuit hydraulic pressure exists. Pressure switches must operate in correct status in each gear. See PRESSURE SWITCH OPERATION table. The TCM uses this information to verify solenoid assembly operation and determining what gear transaxle is in.

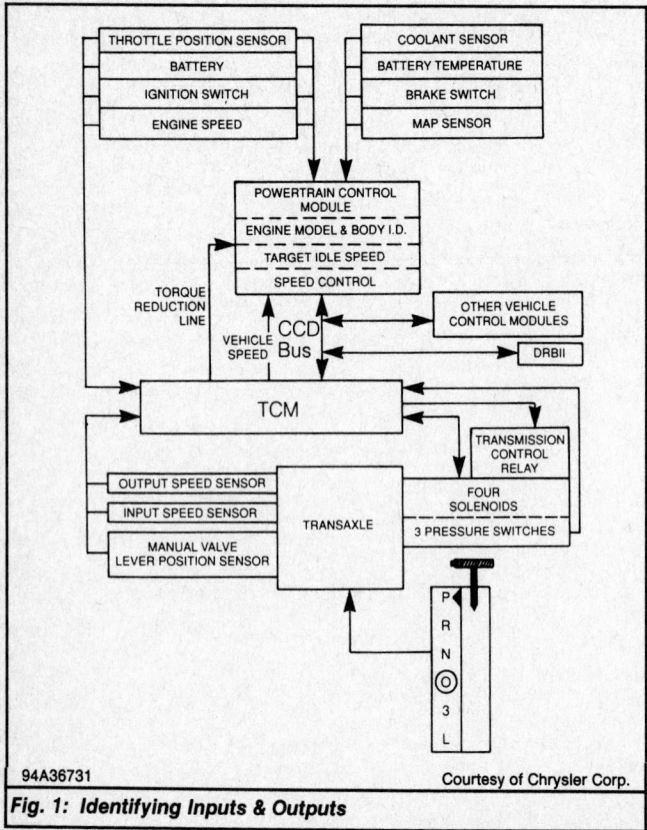

94A36731   Courtesy of Chrysler Corp.

Fig. 1: Identifying Inputs & Outputs

PRESSURE SWITCH OPERATION

Gear	Pressure Switch	Switch Statues
Park	L-R	Closed
	2-4	Open
	OD	Open
Reverse	L-R	Open
	2-4	Open
	OD	Open
Neutral	L-R	Closed
	2-4	Open
	OD	Open
1st Gear	L-R	Closed
	2-4	Open
	OD	Open
2nd Gear	L-R	Open
	2-4	Closed
	OD	Open
3rd Gear	L-R	Open
	2-4	Open
	OD	Closed
4th Gear	L-R	Open
	2-4	Closed
	OD	Closed

INPUT DEVICES

NOTE: Input devices supply information to Transaxle Control Module (TCM) or Powertrain Control Module (PCM) for transaxle control. Direct input devices provide input information to TCM and do not use CCD bus circuit. The CCD bus inputs use CCD bus circuit from PCM to TCM to supply information.

DIRECT INPUT DEVICES

Battery Supply Voltage – Battery supply voltage is sent directly from battery through 20-amp fuse in power distribution center to Pin No. 56 of TCM. Power distribution center is located near driver's side shock tower. *See Fig. 3.* The TCM is located in driver's side front corner of engine compartment. *See Fig. 2.*

Engine Cranking Signal – Ignition switch and starter relay deliver a cranking signal to TCM to indicate engine is cranking. Starter relay is located in power distribution center. Power distribution center is located near driver's side shock tower. *See Fig. 3.* The TCM is located in driver's side front corner of engine compartment. *See Fig. 2.*

Engine Speed Signal – The TCM uses a direct signal from crankshaft position sensor to determine engine RPM. The TCM uses the direct signal and compares it to engine speed received from Powertrain Control Module (PCM) by the CCD bus to confirm that direct engine speed signal is valid.

NOTE: Instead of using CCD bus signal, the TCM uses a direct engine speed signal from crankshaft position sensor. This avoids any time delay that may occur when CCD bus circuit is used.

Ignition Signal – When ignition is turned off, on or to the START position, the TCM checks the incoming voltage. If voltage is less than specified or exceeds specified voltage, TCM will cause transaxle to enter limp-in mode to prevent damage to electrical components.

When ignition is turned on, TCM performs a series of circuit and relay checks. If no problem exists, TCM provides voltage to transaxle control relay, causing contacts to close, supplying voltage to solenoid assembly and pins No. 16 and 17 of TCM. Voltage supplied to pins No. 16 and 17 is referred to as switched battery voltage. If problem exists, TCM turns off power supply to transaxle control relay, which causes transaxle to enter limp-in mode.

Input Speed Sensor – Input speed sensor uses a magnetic pick-up coil to generate an AC voltage input signal when trigger teeth on input clutch assembly pass magnetic pick-up coil. The TCM uses input signal to determine input shaft speed.

Low-Reverse (L-R), Overdrive (OD) & 2-4 Pressure Switches – Pressure switches are located in solenoid assembly. Switches provide input information to TCM, indicating whether hydraulic pressure exists on a certain hydraulic circuit. The TCM uses this information to verify solenoid assembly operation.

Manual Valve Lever Position Sensor (MVLPS) – The TCM uses input signals from MVLPS to determine selected gear position. The TCM then selects the gear and determines shift pattern. The MVLPS also activates starter relay and back-up lights and prevents starter engagement in any gear except Park or Neutral.

NOTE: The Manual Valve Lever Position Sensor (MVLPS) may also be referred to as Manual Valve Lever Position Switch (MVLPS).

NOTE: If back-up lights are not working, perform TEST 3A under TROUBLE SHOOTING CHARTS.

Output Speed Sensor Signal – Output speed sensor uses a magnetic pick-up coil to generate an AC voltage input signal when trigger teeth on output shaft pass the magnetic pick-up coil. The TCM uses input signal to determine output shaft speed. The TCM compares output speed sensor signal against the input speed sensor signal to determine gear ratio and clutch slippage. Output speed sensor signal is also compared to throttle position sensor signal to determine transaxle shift points.

Output speed sensor signal is also used for determining vehicle speed. Vehicle speed signal is delivered from TCM to Powertrain Control Module (PCM). The PCM delivers vehicle speed signal across CCD bus for use by Body Control Module (BCM) and other vehicle control modules.

NOTE: On 1994 models, vehicle speed signal is delivered to speed proportional steering module from the TCM. Speed proportional steering module uses vehicle speed signal for controlling steering assist while vehicle is stationary or at slow driving speed.

Throttle Position Sensor (TPS) – The TPS uses a 5-volt input voltage supplied by Powertrain Control Module (PCM). A common TPS return wire is connected to TCM and PCM. The TCM uses TPS reference signal to determine throttle position for controlling shift points, shift quality and torque converter clutch operation.

CCD BUS INPUTS

NOTE: The following sensors or inputs deliver data to Powertrain Control Module (PCM), which then processes the data and sends signal on CCD bus circuit for use by other vehicle control modules.

Battery Temperature – Battery temperature sensor is located in Powertrain Control Module (PCM). Battery temperature sensor signal is used for controlling charging system, engine and transaxle operation. This signal is also used by the TCM to estimate transaxle fluid temperature. When TCM estimates low temperatures, it adjusts transaxle operation to allow for slower response of the valves.

Brake Switch Input – Brake switch input signal is used by TCM to disengage torque converter clutch when brakes are applied.

Coolant Temperature Sensor – Coolant temperature sensor indicates engine coolant temperature to the TCM. When engine coolant temperature is cold, TCM may delay upshifts slightly to improve driveability. The TCM prevents torque converter clutch from engaging until engine reaches normal operating temperature. In any forward gear, if excessive coolant temperature exists, TCM engages torque converter clutch in 2nd, 3rd or 4th gears to aid in engine cooling and prevent transaxle overheating.

Engine & Body ID – The Powertrain Control Module (PCM) transmits input information across CCD bus to the TCM for identifying engine size and body ID. The TCM uses input information for determining proper shift schedule.

Engine Speed Signal – The TCM uses a PCM-supplied CCD bus signal and compares it to the direct input signal to confirm that direct engine speed signal is valid.

Manifold Absolute Pressure (MAP) Sensor – The MAP sensor provides a PCM-supplied CCD bus signal to indicate engine load on input shaft and output torque load on output shaft. The TCM uses these input signals for modifying transaxle shifting and reduce 3-4 shift hunting on grades.

Target Idle Speed Signal – The TCM uses both direct engine idle speed input signal and calculated engine idle speed (target idle speed) from PCM-supplied CCD bus signal. Calculated engine idle speed is compared to actual engine idle speed to determine the learned Throttle Position Sensor (TPS) reading for closed throttle at idle.

Torque Reduction Confirmation (3.5L Only) – The Powertrain Control Module (PCM) will deliver a confirmation signal to TCM on the CCD bus to indicate that a torque management request signal was received at the PCM. If confirmation signal is not received within specified time, a diagnostic trouble code will be set in the TCM memory.

Speed Control Switch – The TCM uses PCM-supplied CCD bus speed control switch signal for controlling torque converter clutch operation and transaxle kickdown shifts.

OUTPUT DEVICES

NOTE: *Output devices are devices or signals controlled by Transaxle Control Module (TCM) or Powertrain Control Module (PCM).*

DIRECT OUTPUT DEVICES

NOTE: *Direct output devices are devices that are controlled by Transaxle Control Module (TCM) or other modules and do not use the CCD bus circuit.*

Park/Neutral Signal – The Manual Valve Lever Position Sensor (MVLPS) on the transaxle provides an input signal to Powertrain Control Module (PCM), indicating when transaxle is in Park, Neutral or if a drive gear is selected. The PCM uses input signal for determining idle speed, fuel injector pulse width and ignition timing.

Solenoid Assembly – Solenoid assembly is controlled by the TCM. The TCM provides voltage to transaxle control relay, causing contacts to close, supplying voltage to solenoid assembly. Solenoid assembly controls transaxle hydraulic circuits. The TCM completes ground circuit, operating solenoid for proper hydraulic circuit control. Solenoid assembly may be referred to as solenoid pack.

Torque Management Signal (3.5L Only) – The TCM delivers an input signal to Powertrain Control Module (PCM) during high torque situations and high speed shifts. The PCM uses torque management input signal to shut off certain fuel injectors and to slightly retard ignition timing to reduce engine output torque.

Torque management signal is used to reduce torque applied to 2-4 and overdrive clutches. Torque management signal is a 9-volt supply to the PCM. Torque management request is reconized by PCM when TCM grounds the circuit.

Transaxle Control Relay – The TCM provides voltage to transaxle control relay, causing contacts to close, supplying voltage to solenoid assembly and pins No. 16 and 17 of TCM. Voltage supplied to pins No. 16 and 17 is referred to as switched battery voltage. The TCM uses pins No. 16 and 17 to monitor both the function of transaxle control relay and applied battery voltage.

Vehicle Speed Signal (VSS) – Output speed sensor signal is also used for determining vehicle speed and delivers signal to TCM. Vehicle speed signal is delivered from TCM to Powertrain Control Module (PCM). The PCM delivers vehicle speed signal across CCD bus for use by Body Control Module (BCM) and other vehicle control modules. The PCM uses vehicle speed signal and throttle position sensor input to determine when a deceleration condition exists.

NOTE: *On 1994 models, vehicle speed signal is delivered to speed proportional steering module from the TCM. Speed proportional steering module uses vehicle speed signal for controlling steering assist while vehicle is stationary or at slow driving speed.*

CCD BUS OUTPUT SIGNALS

NOTE: *The CCD bus output signals are controlled by CCD bus signal from PCM to the TCM.*

CCD Bus Communications – The TCM outputs diagnostic data stream signals to the CCD bus circuit. These signals are received at data link connector by scan tools and diagnostic equipment.

Gearshift Lever Position – The TCM supplies an output signal to Body Control Module (BCM) over CCD bus circuit to indicate gearshift lever position. The BCM uses this signal for controlling electronic gearshift position display on instrument panel.

Transaxle Gear Engagement (1994 3.3L Only) – The TCM supplies an output signal to PCM over CCD bus circuit to indicate when transaxle is in gear. The PCM uses this input signal for maintaining proper idle speed for smooth gear engagement.

SELF-DIAGNOSTIC SYSTEM

SYSTEM DIAGNOSIS

The Transaxle Control Module (TCM) monitors transaxle operation along with input and output information. If TCM self-diagnostic system senses a transaxle or electrical circuit failure, a diagnostic trouble code will be stored in TCM memory. If malfunction goes away after diagnostic trouble code is stored in TCM memory, TCM will erase diagnostic trouble code after ignition has been cycled at least 75 times. Diagnostic trouble codes are classified as either hard or intermittent codes.

Hard Code – Any diagnostic trouble code that returns within 3 ignition cycles is called a hard code. Hard code indicates that failure exists every time TCM checks the system.

Intermittent Code – A intermittent code is a diagnostic trouble code that occurs intermittently and is most likely caused by defective wiring or connections. Intermittent code indicates that failure does not exist every time TCM checks the system. Intermittent codes must be checked under conditions in which diagnostic trouble code would be set.

NOTE: *A reset counter, located on Chrysler's Diagnostic Readout Box (DRB) scan tool, indicates number of engine starts since diagnostic trouble code was set. This aids in determining if diagnostic trouble code is a hard or intermittent code. If reset counter shows less than 3 engine starts, it indicates a hard code. If reset counter shows 3 or more engine starts, an intermittent code exists.*

DIAGNOSTIC PROCEDURE

When performing vehicle diagnosis, the following must be done:
- Ensure battery is fully charged.
- Ensure transaxle fluid level is correct and not contaminated or aerated.
- Ensure shift cable or linkage is properly adjusted.
- Ensure all electrical connections at transaxle, TCM and transaxle control relay are clean and properly installed. *See Figs. 2 and 3.*
- Ensure transaxle wiring harness electrical connectors near right (passenger's side) shock tower are clean and properly installed. *See Fig. 4.*
- Repair diagnostic trouble codes in the order displayed.
- Always perform VERIFICATION TEST after repair is completed. See TEST 42B under TROUBLE SHOOTING CHARTS.

NOTE: *The DRB scan tool can be used in several different modes using manufacturer's instructions to activate system components and perform several tests on transaxle. Use following procedures if retrieving diagnostic trouble codes using DRB scan tool.*

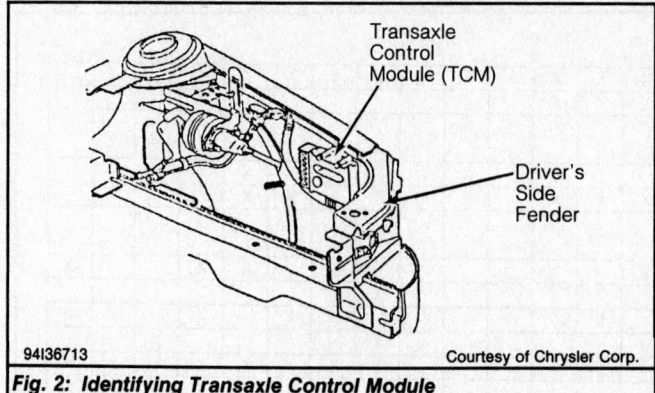

94I36713   Courtesy of Chrysler Corp.

Fig. 2: Identifying Transaxle Control Module

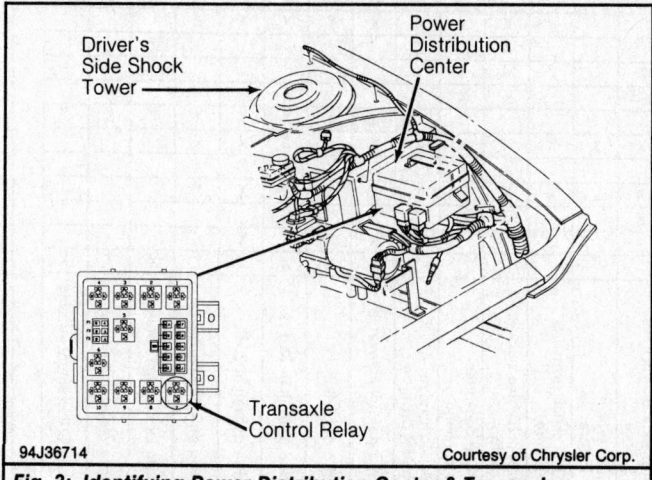

94J36714   Courtesy of Chrysler Corp.

Fig. 3: Identifying Power Distribution Center & Transaxle Control Relay

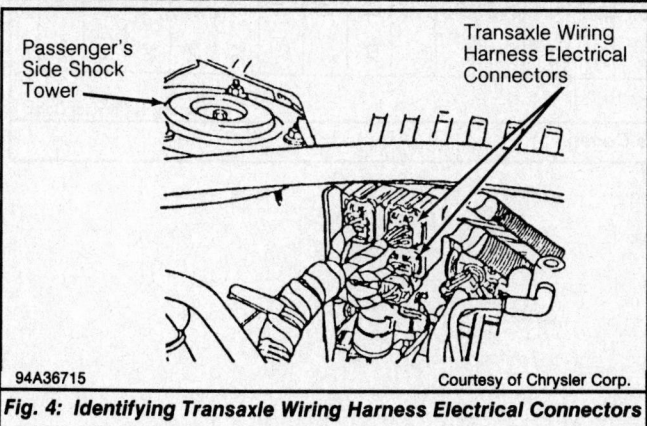

94A36715   Courtesy of Chrysler Corp.

Fig. 4: Identifying Transaxle Wiring Harness Electrical Connectors

RETRIEVING DIAGNOSTIC TROUBLE CODES

NOTE: Manufacturer recommends using Chrysler's Diagnostic Readout Box (DRB) scan tool with proper cartridge for system diagnosis. Other after-market scan tools may be used for system diagnosis. Following procedure is for DRB scan tool usage. Use manufacturer's instruction for operating the DRB scan tool.

1) Ensure ignition is off. Connect DRB to Blue colored data link connector located under left side of instrument panel. *See Fig. 5.*
2) Enter diagnostics and perform CCD bus test. See TEST 1A – ENTERING DIAGNOSTICS & CCD BUS TEST under TROUBLE SHOOTING CHARTS.
3) If an error message appears on DRB, proceed to DRB PROBLEMS & ERROR MESSAGES. The following are possible error messages that may appear.
- CARTRIDGE ERROR
- HIGH BATTERY
- KEYPAD TEST FAILURE
- LOW BATTERY
- RAM TEST FAILURE

4) If no error message appear, retrieve diagnostic trouble codes using DRB manufacturer's instructions. Note diagnostic trouble code display and reset counter display.
5) Reset counter indicates number of engine starts since trouble code was set. This helps determine if a hard or intermittent code exists.
6) If reset counter shows less than 3 engine starts, it indicates a hard code. If reset counter shows 3 or more engine starts, an intermittent code exists.
7) Using DRB, display all diagnostic trouble codes. To identify diagnostic trouble code, see DIAGNOSTIC TROUBLE CODE IDENTIFICATION chart. When some diagnostic trouble codes are set, transaxle will enter limp-in mode until failure is repaired. During limp-in mode, Park, Neutral, Reverse and 2nd gears function, but transaxle cannot upshift or downshift. Vehicle can be operated, but transaxle performance will be reduced.

NOTE: For additional internal transaxle possible causes of diagnostic trouble codes, see Fig. 6. For diagnostic trouble code trouble shooting, see TROUBLE SHOOTING CHARTS.

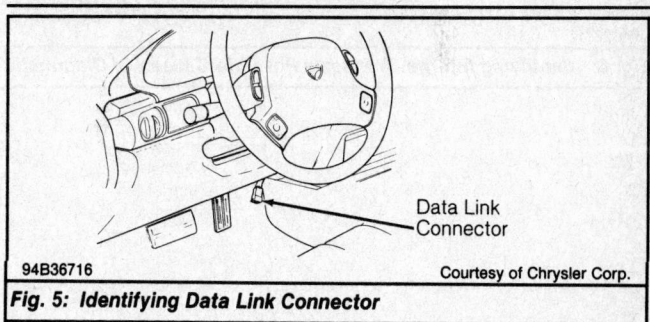

94B36716   Courtesy of Chrysler Corp.

Fig. 5: Identifying Data Link Connector

Possible Cause

Possible Cause	21	22	23	24	25	26	27	31	32	33	37	38	47	50	51	52	53	54	60	61	62
Low fluid level	X	X	X	X	X	X	X	X	X	X				X	X	X	X	X			
Aeroled fluid (high fluid level)	X	X	X	X	X	X	X	X	X	X											
Worn or damaged reaction shaft support seal rings	X													X	X	X	X	X			
Worn or damaged input shaft seal rings												X		X	X	X	X	X			
Worn pump	X	X	X	X	X	X	X	X	X	X		X		X	X	X	X	X			
Damaged or failed clutches:																					
UD clutch														X	X	X					
OD clutch	X								X								X	X			X
Reverse clutch														X							
2/4 clutch		X							X							X		X		X	
L/R clutch				X										X	X				X		
Damaged clutch seals	X	X	X	X	X	X	X							X	X	X	X	X	X	X	X
Worn or damaged accumulator seal rings	X	X	X	X	X	X	X							X	X	X	X	X	X	X	X
Plugged filter	X	X	X	X	X	X	X					X		X	X						
Stuck/sticky valves	X	X	X	X	X	X	X				X	X	X	X	X	X	X	X			
Solenoid switch valve											X		X								
Torque converter clutch switch valve												X									
Torque converter control valve												X									
Regulator valve	X	X	X	X	X	X	X							X	X	X	X	X	X	X	X
Valve body leakage	X	X	X	X	X	X	X	X	X	X			X	X	X	X	X	X			
Pressures too high	X	X	X	X	X	X	X						X	X	X	X	X	X			
Internal solenoid leak	X	X	X	X	X	X	X	X	X	X	X	X	X	X	X	X	X	X			
Torque converter clutch failure	X	X	X	X	X	X	X	X					X								
Faulty cooling system	X	X	X	X	X	X	X							X	X	X	X	X			
Planetary gear sets broken or seized														X	X	X	X	X	X	X	X

NOTE:
Code 36 is not stored alone. It is stored if a speed error (codes 50 through 58) is detected immediately after a shift. Look at the possible causes associated with the speed error code.

Condition / Trouble Code Number:

- 21 — OD clutch—pressure too low
- 22 — 2/4 clutch—pressure too low
- 23 — 2/4 clutch and OD clutch—pressures too low
- 24 — L/R clutch—pressure too low
- 25 — L/R clutch and OD clutches—pressures too low
- 26 — L/R clutch and 2/4 clutches—pressures too low
- 27 — OD, 2/4, and L/R clutches—pressures too low
- 31 — OD clutch pressure switch response failure
- 32 — 2/4 pressure switch response failure
- 33 — 2/4 and O/D clutch pressure response failures
- 37 — Solenoid switch valve stuck in the LO position
- 38 — Partial torque converter clutch out of range
- 47 — Solenoid switch valve stuck in the LR position
- 50 — Speed ratio default in reverse
- 51 — Speed ratio default in 1st
- 52 — Speed ratio default in 2nd
- 53 — Speed ratio default in 3rd
- 54 — Speed ratio default in 4th
- 60 — Inadequate LR element volume
- 61 — Inadequate 2/4 element volume
- 62 — Inadequate OD element volume

94C36717

Courtesy of Chrysler Corp.

Fig. 6: Identifying Internal Transaxle Possible Causes Of Diagnostic Trouble Codes

DIAGNOSTIC TROUBLE CODE IDENTIFICATION (1 OF 2)

Trouble Code	DRB Display [1]	Limp-In Mode	Possible Cause
11	Internal TCM Failure	Yes	Defective TCM
12 [2]	Battery Was Disconnected	Yes	Battery Disconnected
13	Internal TCM Failure	Yes	Defective TCM
14	Relay Output Always On	Yes	Defective Transaxle Control Relay Or Circuit, Defective TCM
15	Relay Output Always Off	Yes	2Defective Transaxle Control Relay Or Circuit, Defective TCM
16 & 17	Internal TCM Failure	Yes	Defective TCM
18	Engine Speed Sensor	Yes	Defective Electrical Connections, Crankshaft Position Sensor, Defective TCM
19	No Response	No [3]	Defective CCD Bus Circuit Between TCM & PCM, Defective TCM Or PCM
20	Switched Battery	Yes	Defective Transaxle Control Relay, Short To Battery Voltage On Transaxle Control Relay Circuit, Defective TCM
21	OD Pressure Switch Circuit	Yes	Improper Transaxle Fluid Level, Defective Pressure Switch Circuit, Defective Pressure Switch In Solenoid Assembly Defective Transaxle Controller, Internal Transaxle Failure
22	2-4 Pressure Switch Circuit	Yes	Improper Transaxle Fluid Level, Defective Pressure Switch Circuit, Defective Pressure Switch In Solenoid Assembly Defective Transaxle Controller, Internal Transaxle Failure
23	2-4/OD Pressure Switch Circuit	Yes	Improper Transaxle Fluid Level, Defective Pressure Switch Circuit, Defective Pressure Switch In Solenoid Assembly Defective Transaxle Controller, Internal Transaxle Failure
24	LR Pressure Switch Circuit	Yes	Improper Transaxle Fluid Level, Defective Pressure Switch Circuit, Defective Pressure Switch In Solenoid Assembly Defective Transaxle Controller, Internal Transaxle Failure
25	LR/OD Pressure Switch Circuit	Yes	Improper Transaxle Fluid Level, Defective Pressure Switch Circuit, Defective Pressure Switch In Solenoid Assembly Defective Transaxle Controller, Internal Transaxle Failure
26	LR/2-4 Pressure Switch Circuit	Yes	Improper Transaxle Fluid Level, Defective Pressure Switch Circuit, Defective Pressure Switch In Solenoid Assembly Defective Transaxle Controller, Internal Transaxle Failure
27	All Pressure Switch Circuits	Yes	Improper Transaxle Fluid Level, Defective Pressure Switch Circuit, Defective Pressure Switch In Solenoid Assembly Defective Transaxle Controller, Internal Transaxle Failure
28	Check Shifter Signal	No [4]	Defective MVLPS Or Circuit, Defective TCM
29	Throttle Position Signal	No [5]	Defective Throttle Position Sensor Or Circuit, Defective TCM Or PCM

[1] – When using DRB, display may show LR, OD or UD. The LR indicates low-reverse, OD indicates overdrive and UD indicates underdrive.

[2] – This is not a trouble code to indicate a transaxle problem. This trouble code is used for reference information only to indicate if battery was disconnected.

[3] – For a few minutes after engine is started, transaxle may have a delayed 3-4 upshift, early 4-3 downshift and no torque converter clutch operation.

[4] – No limp-in mode is caused by this diagnostic trouble code. If incorrect gearshift lever signals are received, this may result in other diagnostic trouble codes which may cause a limp-in mode.

[5] – No limp-in mode is caused by this diagnostic trouble code. If diagnostic trouble code exists, there will be no torque converter clutch operation, no 4th gear and a limited shift schedule.

DIAGNOSTIC TROUBLE CODE IDENTIFICATION (2 OF 2)

Trouble Code	DRB Display [1]	Limp-In Mode	Possible Cause
31	OD Hydraulic Pressure Switch	Yes	Improper Transaxle Fluid Level, Defective Solenoid Assembly, Internal Transaxle Failure
32	2-4 Hydraulic Pressure Switch	Yes	Improper Transaxle Fluid Level, Defective Solenoid Assembly, Internal Transaxle Failure
33	OD/2-4 Hydraulic Pressure Switch	Yes	Improper Transaxle Fluid Level, Defective Solenoid Assembly, Internal Transaxle Failure
35	Loss Of Prime	No	Low Transaxle Fluid Level, Defective Or Restricted Oil Filter, Missing Oil Filter "O" Ring, Defective Oil Cooler Line Fittings
36 [2]	Fault Immediately After Shift	Yes	Internal Transaxle Failure
37	Solenoid Switch Valve In LU Position	No [3]	Internal Transaxle Failure
38	Torque Converter Clutch Control	No [4]	Improper Transaxle Fluid Level, Internal Transaxle Failure
41	LR Solenoid Circuit	Yes	Defective Solenoid Assembly Or Circuit, Defective TCM
42	2-4 Solenoid Circuit	Yes	Defective Solenoid Assembly Or Circuit, Defective TCM
43	OD Solenoid Circuit	Yes	Defective Solenoid Assembly Or Circuit, Defective TCM
44	UD Solenoid Circuit	Yes	Defective Solenoid Assembly Or Circuit, Defective TCM
45	Internal TCM Failure	No	Defective TCM
46	UD Hydraulic Circuit	No	Internal Transaxle Failure
47	Solenoid Switch Valve In LR Position	Yes	Internal Transaxle Failure
48 [5]	Torque Management	No	CCD Bus Communication Problem
50	Speed Error In Reverse	Yes	Defective Input Or Output Speed Sensor Or Circuit, Defective TCM, Internal Transaxle Failure
51	Speed Error In 1st	Yes	Defective Input Or Output Speed Sensor Or Circuit, Defective TCM, Internal Transaxle Failure
52	Speed Error In 2nd	Yes	Internal Transaxle Failure
53	Speed Error In 3rd	Yes	Internal Transaxle Failure
54	Speed Error In 4th	Yes	Internal Transaxle Failure
56	Input Speed Sensor	Yes	Defective Input Speed Sensor Or Circuit, Defective TCM
57	Output Speed Sensor Error	Yes	Defective Output Sensor Or Circuit, Defective TCM
58	Speed Sensor's Ground	Yes	Open In Output Speed Sensor Ground Circuit, Defective TCM
60 [6]	Inadequate LR Element Volume	No	Internal Transaxle Failure
61 [7]	Inadequate 2-4 Element Volume	No	Internal Transaxle Failure
62 [8]	Inadequate OD Element Volume	No	Internal Transaxle Failure

[1] – When using DRB, display may show LR, OD or UD. The LR indicates low-reverse, OD indicates overdrive and UD indicates underdrive.

[2] – Diagnostic trouble code will not be stored alone. Diagnostic trouble Code 36 is stored if a speed error code (Codes 50-58) is detected.

[3] – No limp-in mode is caused by this diagnostic trouble code. If diagnostic trouble code exists, there will be no 1st gear, as 2nd gear is substituted and no torque converter clutch operation.

[4] – No limp-in mode is caused by this diagnostic trouble code. If diagnostic trouble code exists, there will be no torque converter clutch operation.

[5] – Applies to 3.5L models only.

[6] – Typical clutch volume for LR (low-reverse) clutch is 35-83.

[7] – Typical clutch volume for 2-4 clutch is 20-77.

[8] – Typical clutch volume for OD (overdrive) clutch is 75-150.

CLEARING DIAGNOSTIC TROUBLE CODES

After repairs have been performed, use DRB and manufacturer's instructions to clear or erase diagnostic trouble code from TCM memory.

NOTE: If malfunction goes away after diagnostic trouble code is stored in TCM memory, TCM will erase diagnostic trouble code after ignition has been cycled at least 75 times.

TESTING

For non-electrical testing and mechanical overhaul procedures, see CHRYSLER 42LE article. For electronic component testing and diagnostic procedures, use a DRB scan tool to retrieve diagnostic trouble codes and diagnosis the system. See RETRIEVING DIAGNOSTIC TROUBLE CODES under SELF-DIAGNOSTIC SYSTEM.

DRB PROBLEMS & ERROR MESSAGES

CARTRIDGE ERROR

1) If CARTRIDGE ERROR message is displayed, disconnect DRB from data link connector. DO NOT touch keys on DRB keypad. Reconnect DRB to data link connector and note display.
2) If CARTRIDGE ERROR message is displayed, replace DRB cartridge, and proceed with diagnostics. If KEYPAD TEST FAILURE message is displayed, replace DRB and proceed with diagnostics.

HIGH BATTERY

If HIGH BATTERY message is displayed, use external voltmeter to check battery voltage at battery terminals. If battery voltage is 11.7-13.0 volts, replace DRB. If battery voltage is not 11.7-13.0 volts, check charging system.

KEYPAD TEST FAILURE

1) If KEYPAD TEST FAILURE message is displayed, disconnect DRB from data link connector. DO NOT touch keys on DRB keypad. Reconnect DRB to data link connector and note display.
2) If KEYPAD TEST FAILURE message is not displayed, proceed with diagnostics. If KEYPAD TEST FAILURE message is displayed, replace DRB and proceed with diagnostics.

LOW BATTERY

If LOW BATTERY message is displayed, use external voltmeter to check battery voltage at battery terminals. If battery voltage is 11.7-13.0 volts, replace DRB. If battery voltage is not 11.7-13.0 volts, check charging system.

RAM TEST FAILURE

1) If RAM TEST FAILURE message is displayed, disconnect DRB from data link connector. DO NOT touch keys on DRB keypad. Reconnect DRB to data link connector and note display.
2) If RAM TEST FAILURE message is not displayed, proceed with diagnostics. If RAM TEST FAILURE message is displayed, replace DRB and proceed with diagnostics. If KEYPAD TEST FAILURE message is displayed, replace DRB and proceed with diagnostics.

TROUBLE SHOOTING CHARTS

NOTE: The following trouble shooting charts and illustrations are courtesy of Chrysler Corp.

NOTE: When using trouble shooting charts, solenoid assembly may be referred to as the solenoid pack. The manual lever position sensor may be referred to as manual lever position switch. Transaxle control module may be referred to as transmission control module.

NOTE: If back-up lights are not working, perform TEST 3A under TROUBLE SHOOTING CHARTS.

NOTE: On 1994 models, if steering system is operating incorrectly, problem may be caused by defective vehicle speed signal from TCM. Steering operation can be checked using DRB and performing SPD PROP STEER test. Before performing SPD PROP STEER test, ensure gearshift is in Park, apply brakes and start engine. The SPD PROP STEER test will cause speedometer to display 60 MPH and required steering effort will increase. Note effort required to turn steering during test with brakes applied. Release brake and note that steering effort decreases. Steering effort should be noticeably different. Repeat procedure to ensure correct steering effort. If steering operation is not correct, perform TEST 39A under TROUBLE SHOOTING CHARTS.

AUTOMATIC TRANSMISSIONS
Chrysler 42LE Electronic Diagnosis (Cont.)

WIRING DIAGRAMS

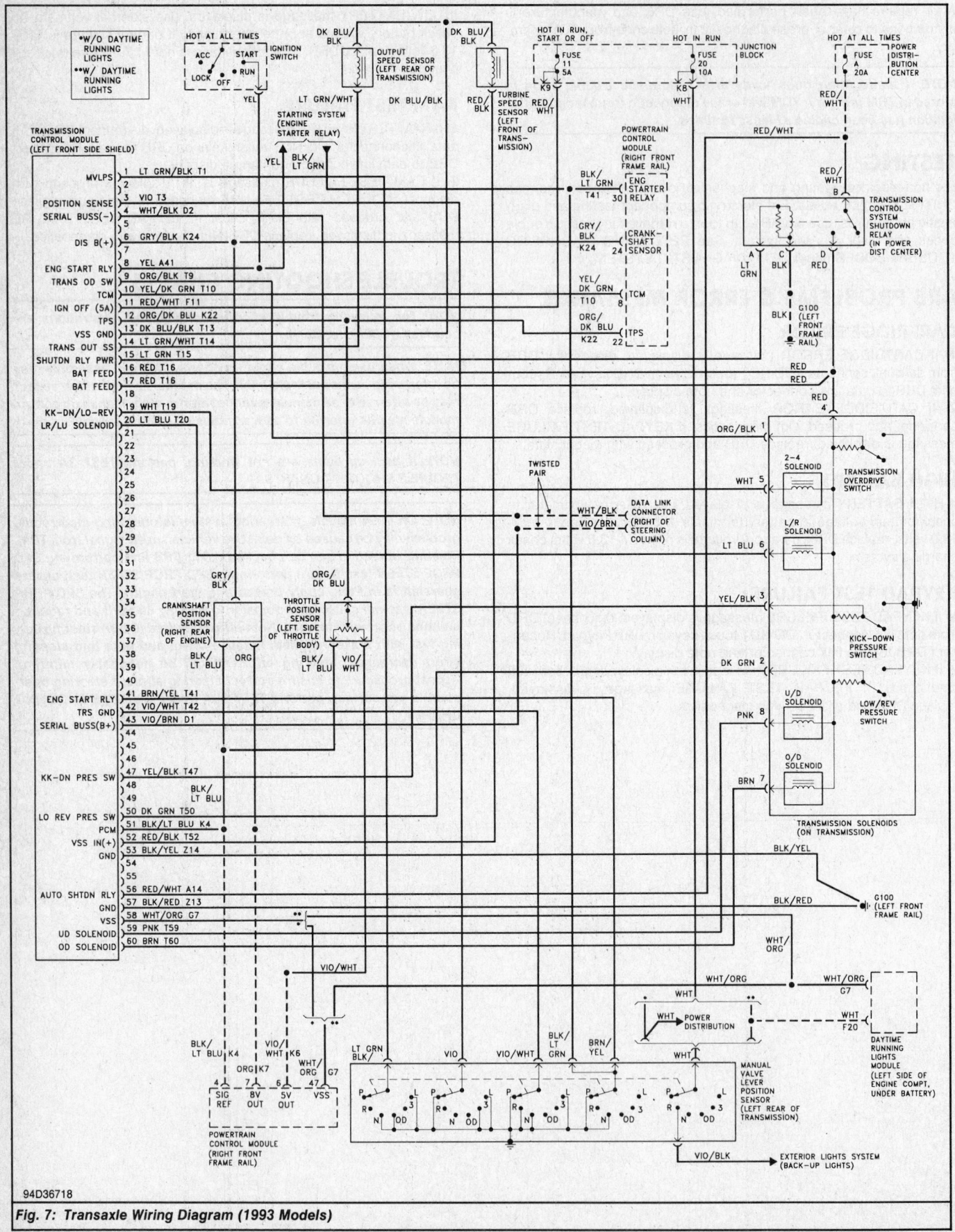

94D36718

Fig. 7: Transaxle Wiring Diagram (1993 Models)

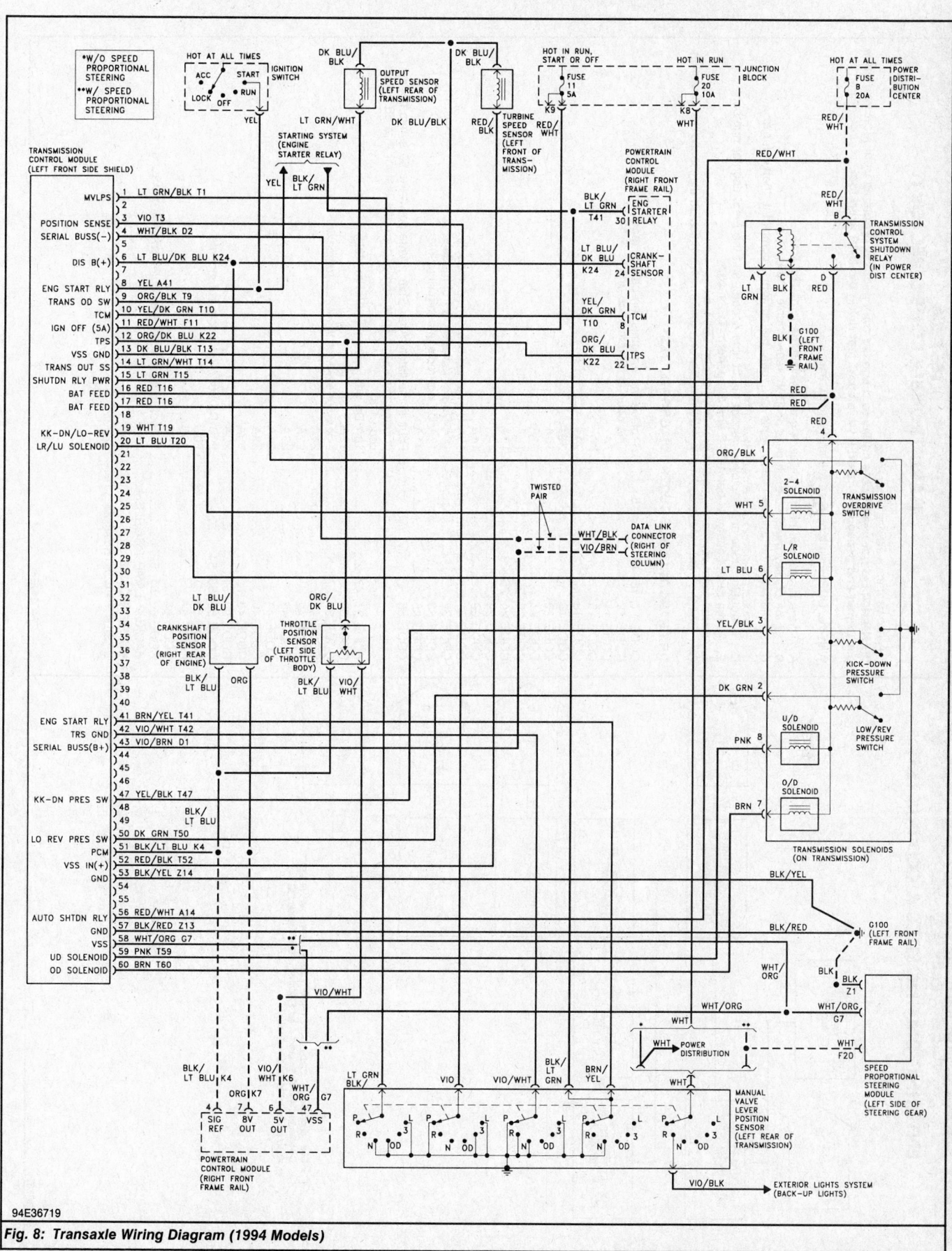

Fig. 8: Transaxle Wiring Diagram (1994 Models)

94E36719

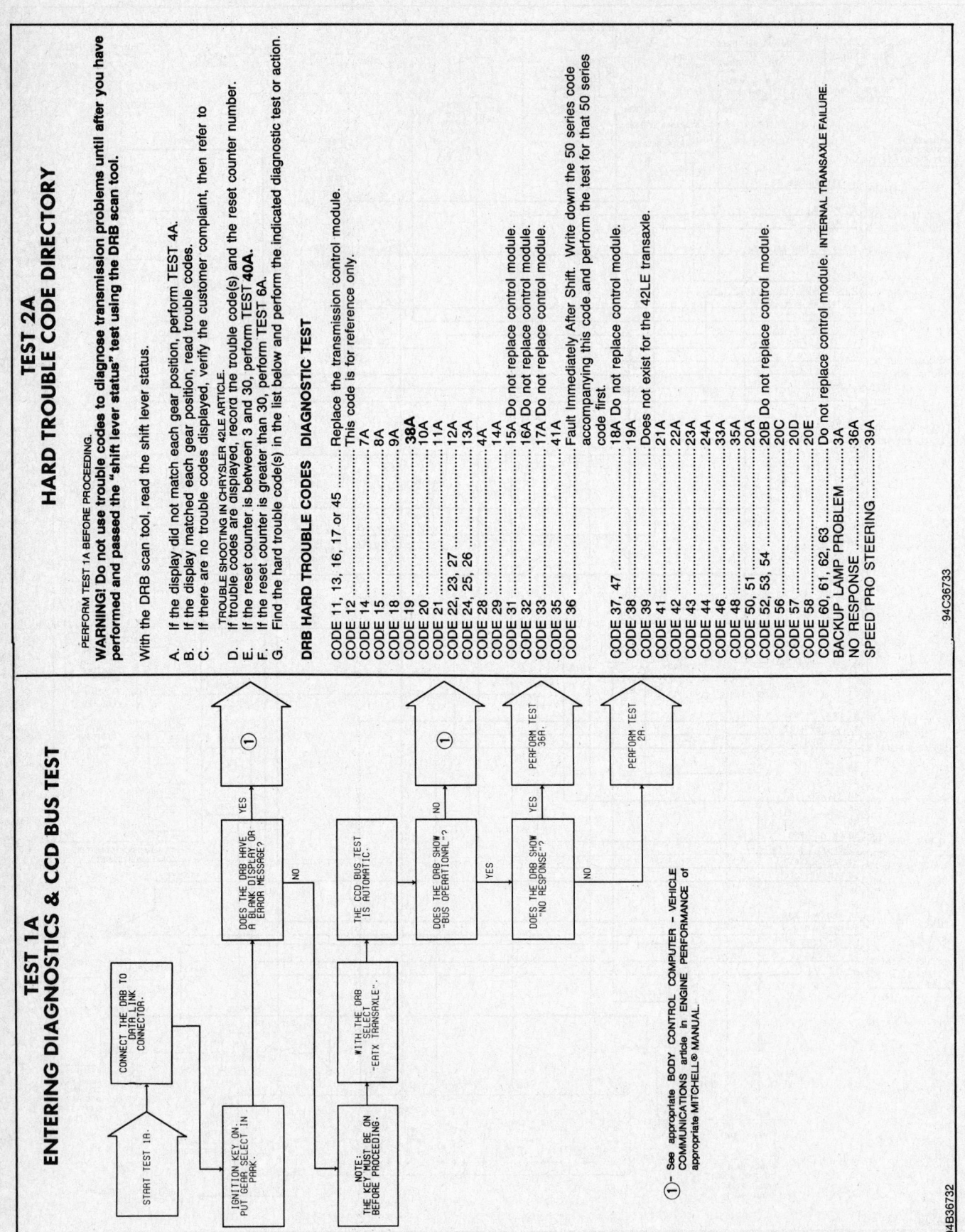

TEST 1A
ENTERING DIAGNOSTICS & CCD BUS TEST

START TEST 1A.

CONNECT THE DRB TO DATA LINK CONNECTOR.

IGNITION KEY ON. PUT GEAR SELECT IN PARK.

NOTE: THE KEY MUST BE ON BEFORE PROCEEDING.

WITH THE DRB SELECT "EATX TRANSAXLE".

DOES THE DRB HAVE A BLANK DISPLAY OR ERROR MESSAGE? — YES → ①
NO

THE CCD BUS TEST IS AUTOMATIC.

DOES THE DRB SHOW "BUS OPERATIONAL"? — NO → ①
YES

DOES THE DRB SHOW "NO RESPONSE"? — YES → PERFORM TEST 36A.
NO → PERFORM TEST 2A.

①- See appropriate BODY CONTROL COMPUTER – VEHICLE COMMUNICATIONS article in ENGINE PERFORMANCE of appropriate MITCHELL® MANUAL.

94B36732

TEST 2A
HARD TROUBLE CODE DIRECTORY

PERFORM TEST 1A BEFORE PROCEEDING.
WARNING! Do not use trouble codes to diagnose transmission problems until after you have performed and passed the "shift lever status" test using the DRB scan tool.

With the DRB scan tool, read the shift lever status.

A. If the display did not match each gear position, perform TEST 4A.
B. If the display matched each gear position, read trouble codes.
C. If there are no trouble codes displayed, verify the customer complaint, then refer to TROUBLE SHOOTING IN CHRYSLER 42LE ARTICLE.
D. If trouble codes are displayed, record the trouble code(s) and the reset counter number.
E. If the reset counter is between 3 and 30, perform TEST **40A**.
F. If the reset counter is greater than 30, perform TEST 6A.
G. Find the hard trouble code(s) in the list below and perform the indicated diagnostic test or action.

DRB HARD TROUBLE CODES   DIAGNOSTIC TEST

CODE 11, 13, 16, 17 or 45 .... Replace the transmission control module.
CODE 12 .... This code is for reference only.
CODE 14 .... 7A
CODE 15 .... 8A
CODE 18 .... 9A
CODE 19 .... **38A**
CODE 20 .... 10A
CODE 21 .... 11A
CODE 22, 23, 27 .... 12A
CODE 24, 25, 26 .... 13A
CODE 28 .... 4A
CODE 29 .... 14A
CODE 31 .... 15A Do not replace control module.
CODE 32 .... 16A Do not replace control module.
CODE 33 .... 17A Do not replace control module.
CODE 35 .... 41A
CODE 36 .... Fault Immediately After Shift. Write down the 50 series code accompanying this code and perform the test for that 50 series code first.
CODE 37, 47 .... 18A Do not replace control module.
CODE 38 .... 19A
CODE 39 .... Does not exist for the 42LE transaxle.
CODE 41 .... 21A
CODE 42 .... 22A
CODE 43 .... 23A
CODE 44 .... 24A
CODE 46 .... 33A
CODE 48 .... 35A
CODE 50, 51 .... 20A
CODE 52, 53, 54 .... 20B Do not replace control module.
CODE 56 .... 20C
CODE 57 .... 20D
CODE 58 .... 20E
CODE 60, 61, 62, 63 .... Do not replace control module.
BACKUP LAMP PROBLEM .... 3A INTERNAL TRANSAXLE FAILURE.
NO RESPONSE 36A
SPEED PRO STEERING 39A

94C36733

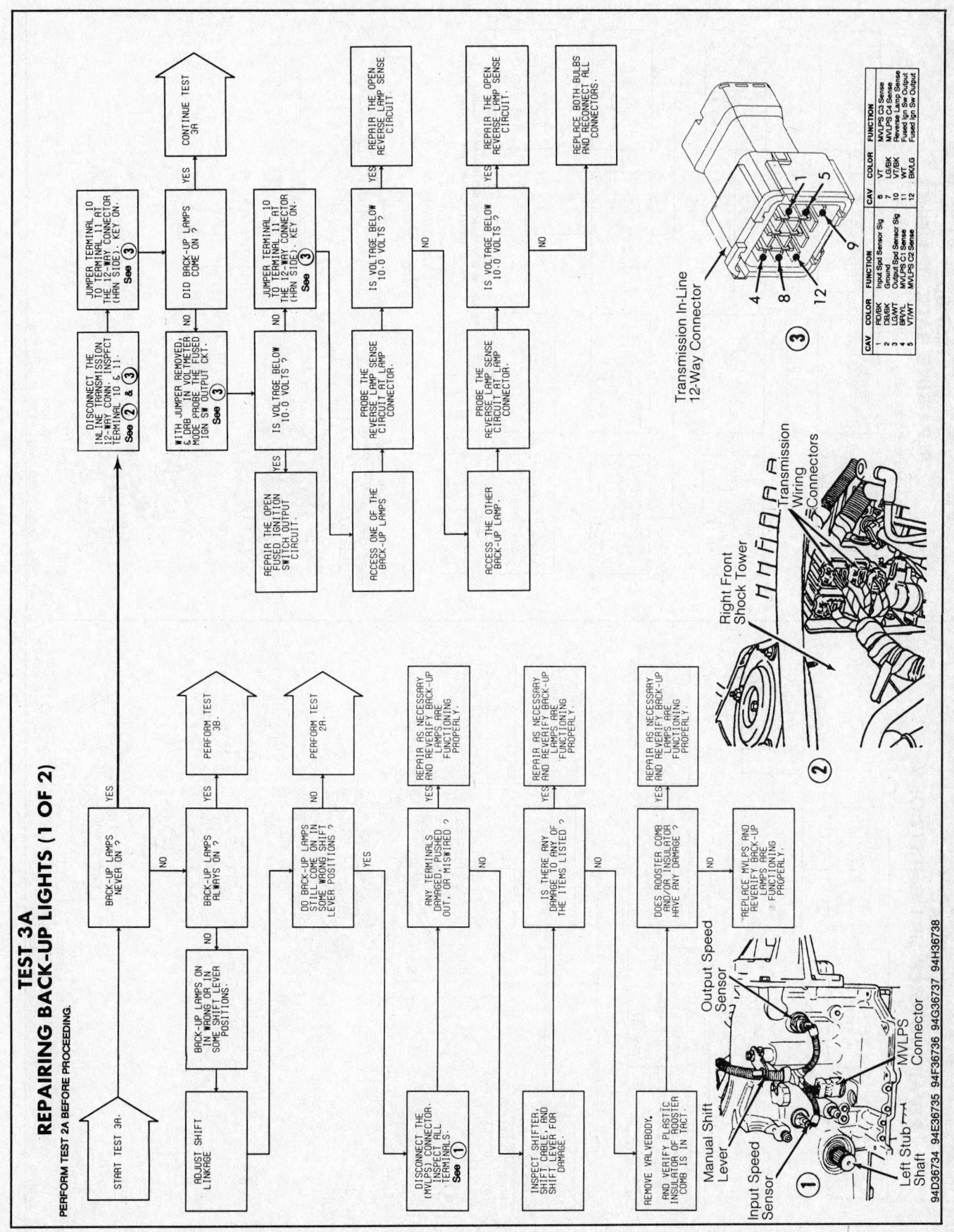

TEST 3A
REPAIRING BACK-UP LIGHTS (1 OF 2)

PERFORM TEST 2A BEFORE PROCEEDING.

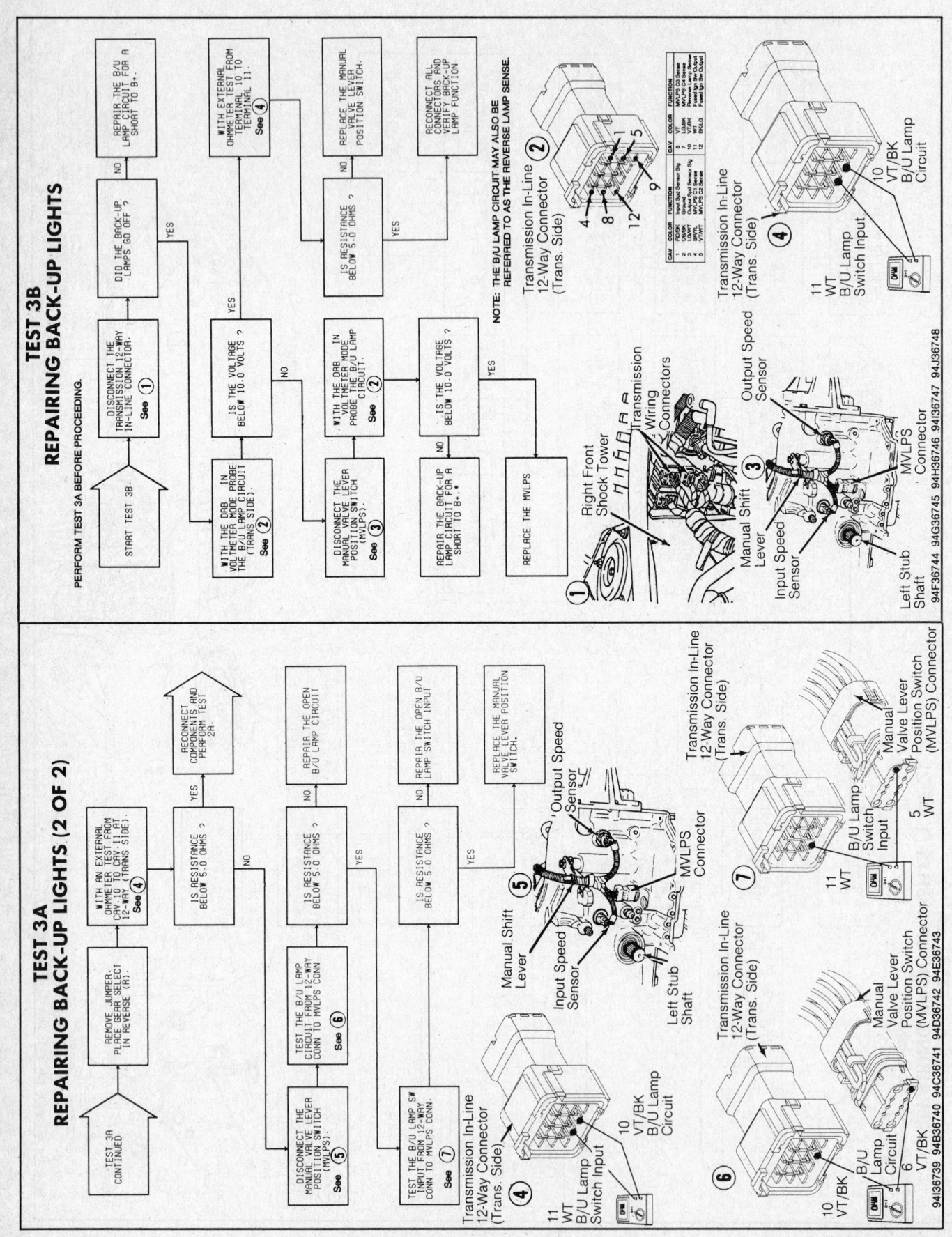

TEST 6A
TESTING FOR INTERMITTENT TROUBLE CODES

PERFORM TEST 2A BEFORE PROCEEDING.

1. Inspect the following for push-outs or flared connections:
   - >> engine ground connection
   - >> TCM ground pins 53 & 57
   - >> TCM battery feed pin 56
   - >> battery feed to TCM relay
   - >> TCM feed pin 11

2. If the above connections are in good condition, find the applicable intermittent code in the following list. Carefully inspect the indicated terminals, cavities, or connectors for push-outs or damage.

INTERMITTENT CODE	60-WAY TERMINAL #	IN-LINE 8-WAY TERMINAL	OTHER
11, 13, 16, 17, 45	8, 11, 53, 57		Clear trouble code. Requires no action.
12	56, 53, 57		TCM connector/relay
14	15, 16, 17		TCM connector/relay
15	15, 16, 17		
18	6		
19	4 and 43		PCM 60-way pin 26 and 46
20	16 and 17		TCM connector/relay
21	9	5 and 8	
22	47	2 and 5	
23	9 and 47	1, 2, 5, 6	
24	50	3 and 6	
25	9 and 50	4, 6, 7	
26	47 and 50	4, 5, 7	
27	9, 47 and 50	4, 5, 6, 7	
28	1, 3, 41, 42		
29	12 and 51		Manual Valve Lever Position Switch (MVLPS) connector
31, 32, 33			Throttle Position Sensor connector
37, 38, 47			
41	13, 14, 52	7 and 8	
42	16, 20, 53, 57	2 and 7	
43	16, 19, 53, 57	1 and 7	
44	16 and 60	3 and 7	
46	16 and 59		
48	10		
36, 50 to 58	13, 14, 52		PCM 60-way, pin 8
60 to 63	13, 14, 52		INPUT OR OUTPUT SPEED SENSOR

3. If steps 1 and 2 fail to turn up a defective condition, use the DRB to erase trouble codes and set the reset counter equal to zero (0). Road test the vehicle for proper transaxle operation.

4. IF TRANSAXLE STILL EXPERIENCES IMPROPER OPERATION, SEE TROUBLE SHOOTING IN CHRYSLER 42LE ARTICLE.

NOTE: ENGINE GROUND IS LOCATED ON DRIVER'S SIDE REAR OF CYLINDER BLOCK, NEAR CYLINDER HEAD. POWERTRAIN CONTROL MODULE (PCM) IS LOCATED ON PASSENGER'S SIDE FRONT CORNER OF ENGINE COMPARTMENT, BELOW AIR FILTER ASSEMBLY.

94F36751

TEST 4A
CODE 28 – FAILED SHIFT LEVER TEST

PERFORM TEST 2A BEFORE PROCEEDING.

START TEST 4A. → WITH THE DRB PERFORM SHIFT LEVER TEST. PRESS "ENTER" AFTER EACH GEAR SELECT POSITION. → SHIFT LEVER TEST RESULTS=PRNO3L TEST PASSED?

YES → DO YOU WANT TO PERFORM TEST FOR INTERMITTENT SHIFT LEVER STATUS? — YES → PERFORM TEST 2A. / NO → PERFORM TEST 34A.

NO → DID THE SHIFT LEVER TEST FAIL WITH AN ERROR CODE? — YES → PERFORM TEST 5A. / NO → HAS THE SHIFT LEVER LINKAGE BEEN ADJUSTED? — YES → PERFORM TEST 34A. / NO → ADJUST THE LINKAGE → PERFORM TEST 2A.

94A36749 94E36750

TEST 5A
CODE 28 – FAILED SHIFT LEVER TEST

PERFORM TEST 4A BEFORE PROCEEDING.

Match the shift lever "Error Code" with one of the following and perform the corresponding diagnostic test:

SHIFT LEVER ERROR CODE	DIAGNOSTIC TEST
CODE 1	26A
CODE 2	31A
CODE 3	25A
CODE 4	32A
CODE 5	28A
CODE 6	30A
CODE 7	27A
CODE 8	29A

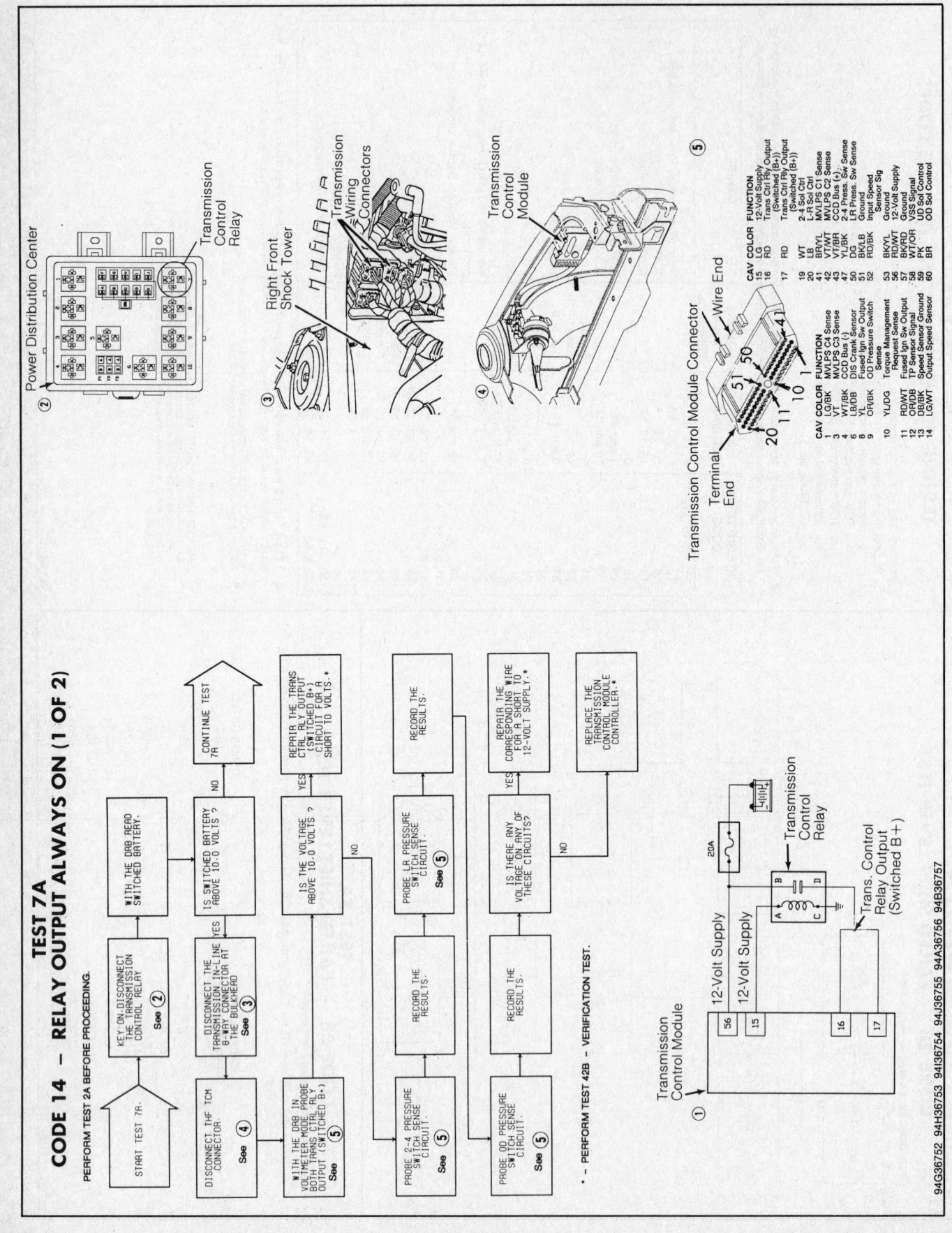

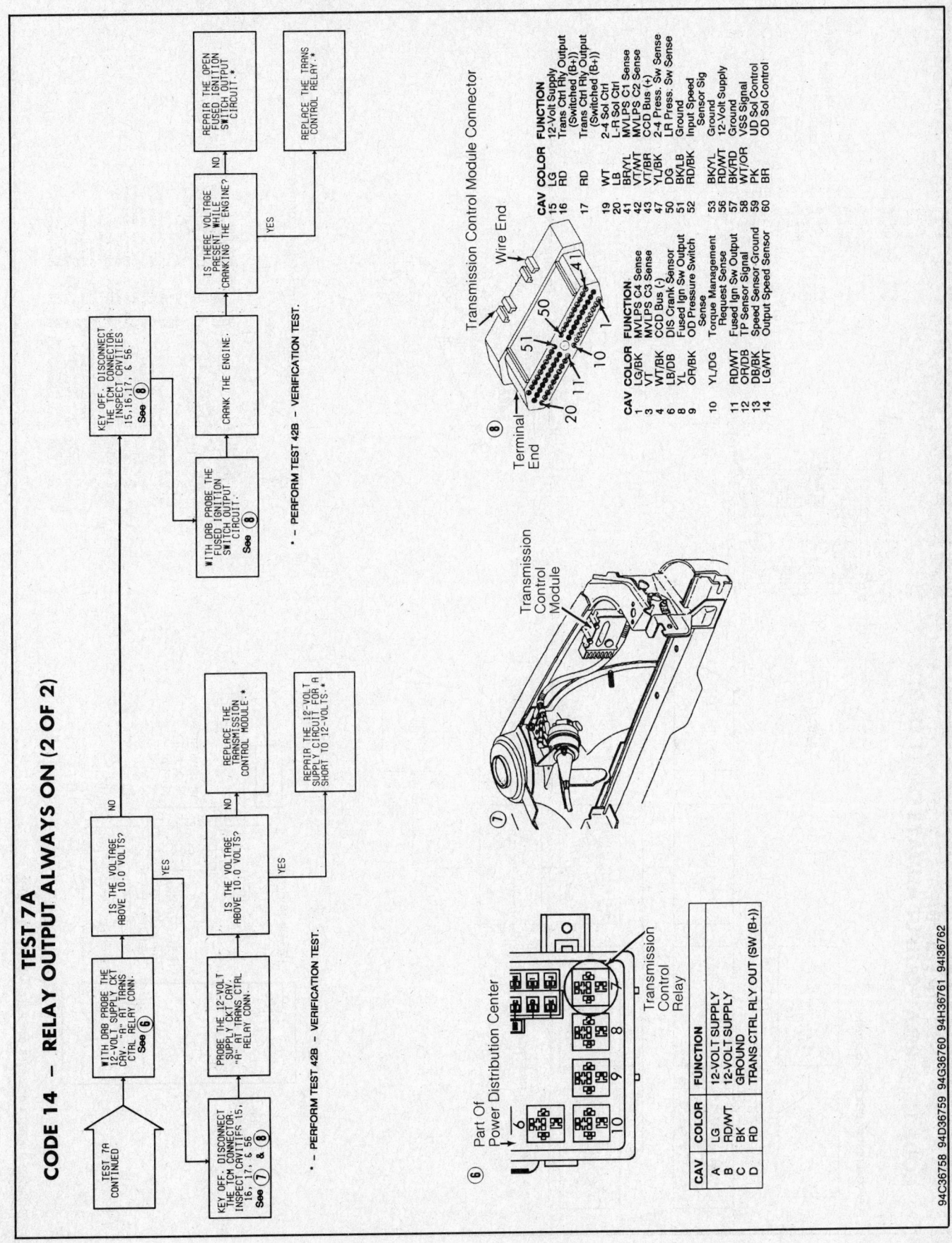

TEST 7A
CODE 14 — RELAY OUTPUT ALWAYS ON (2 OF 2)

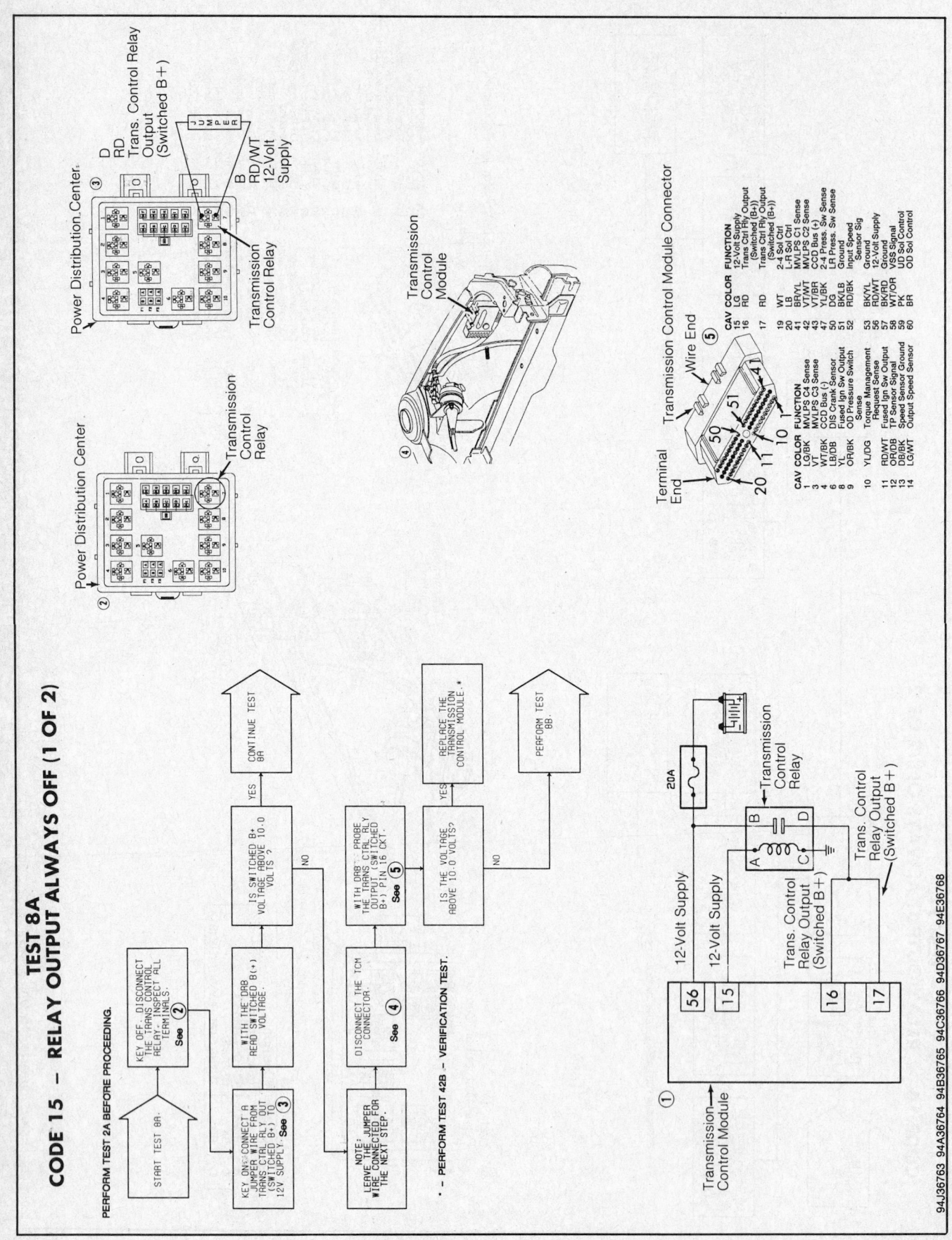

94J36763 94A36764 94B36765 94C36766 94D36767 94E36768

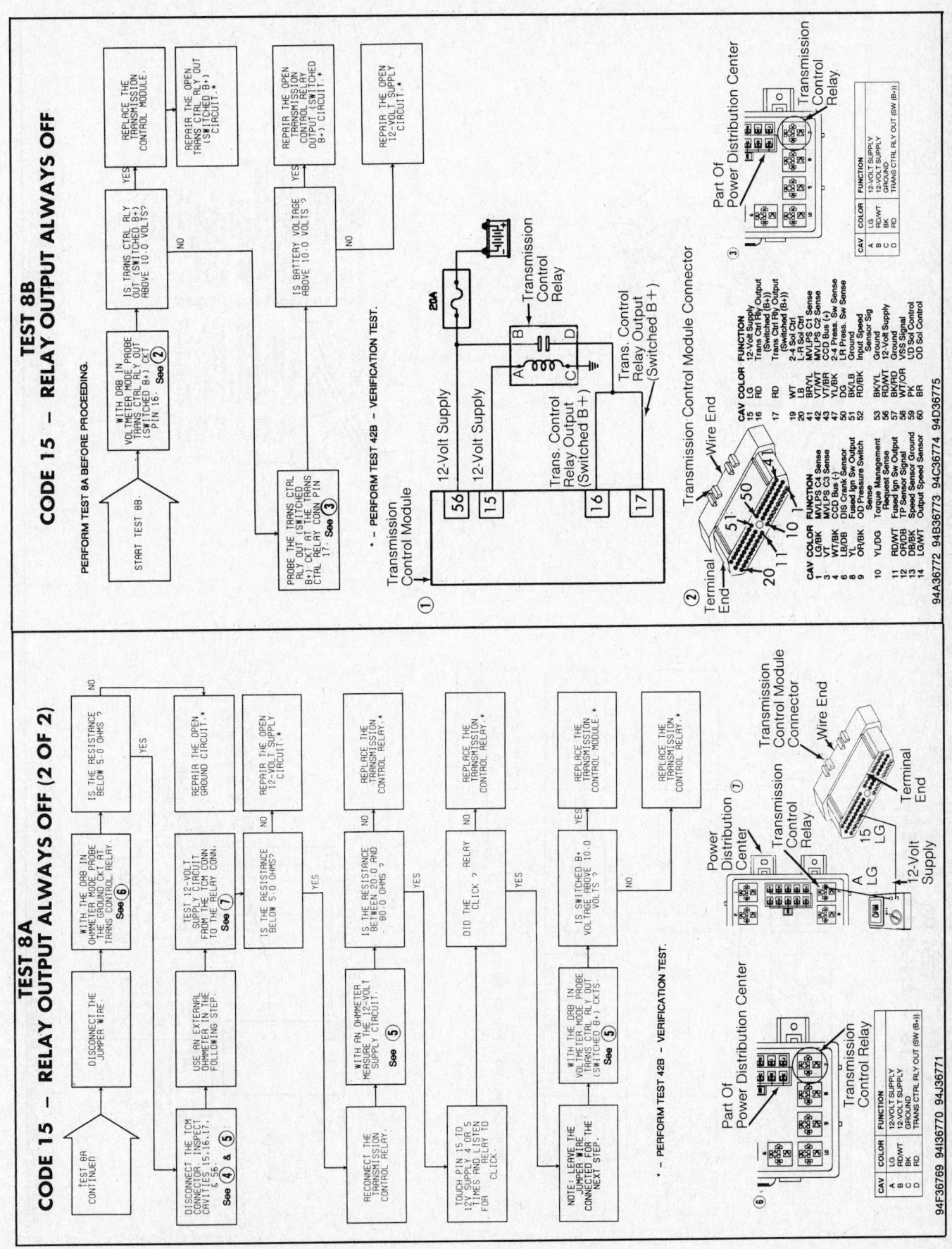

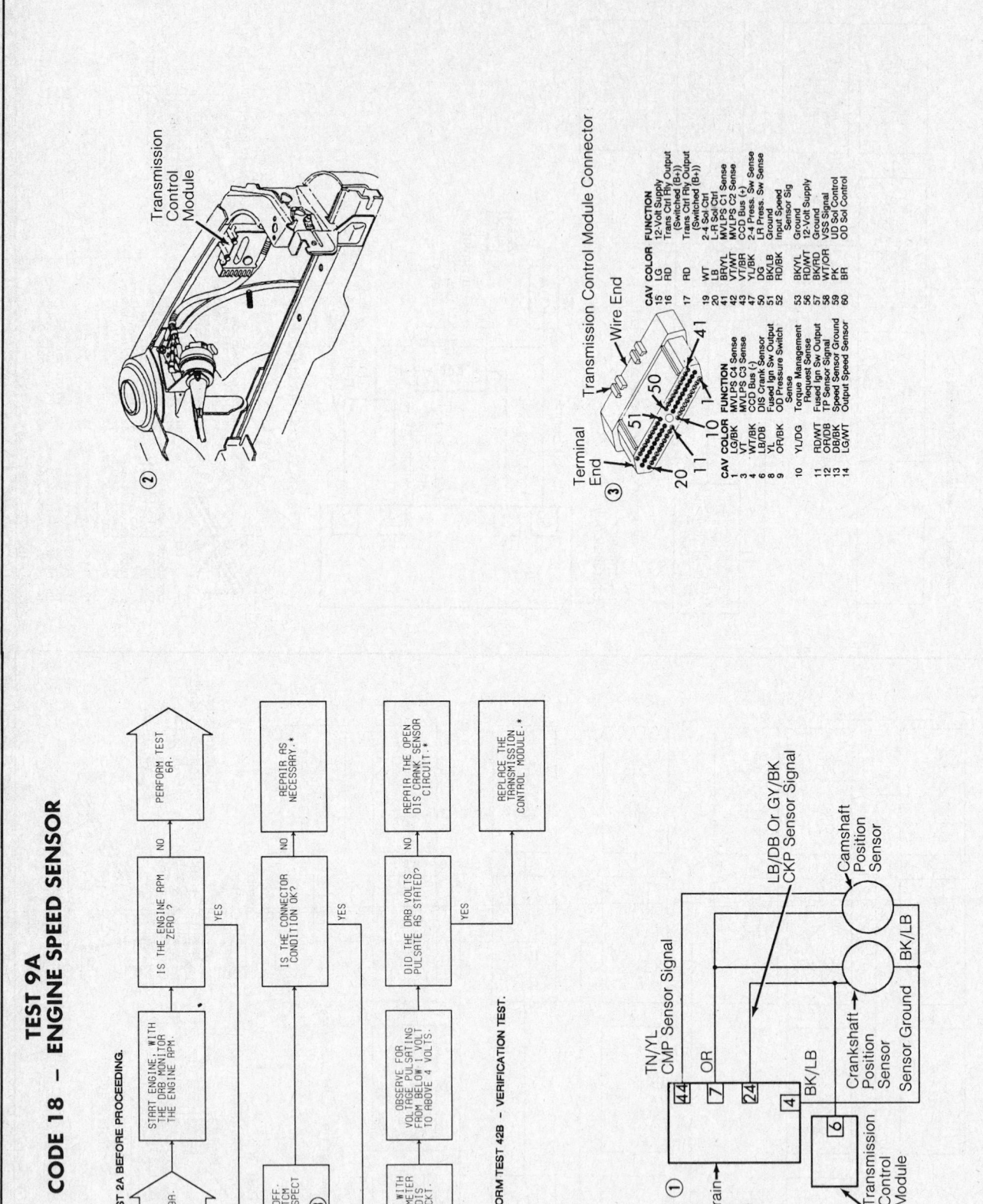

TEST 9A
CODE 18 – ENGINE SPEED SENSOR

94E36776 94F36777 94G36778 94H36779

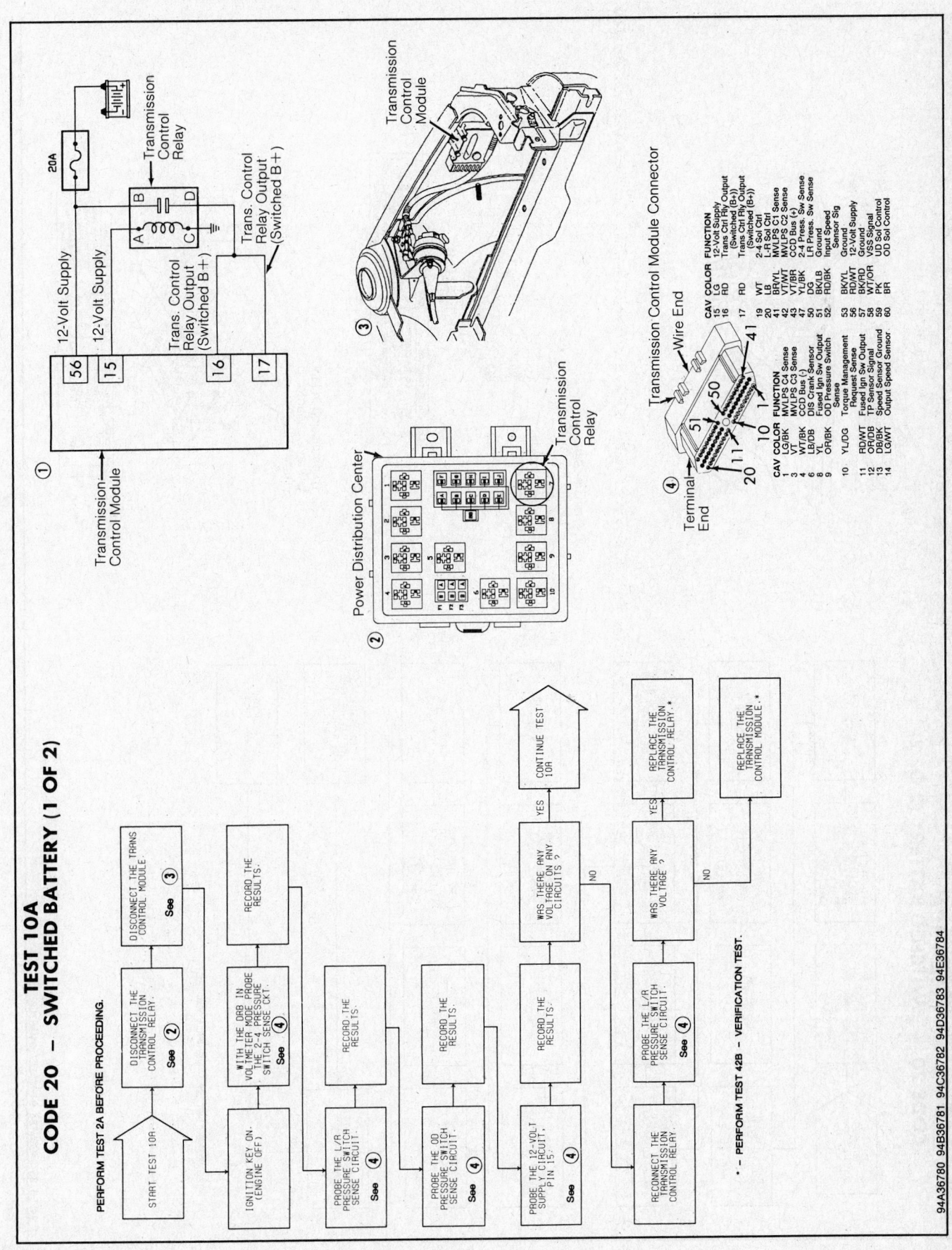

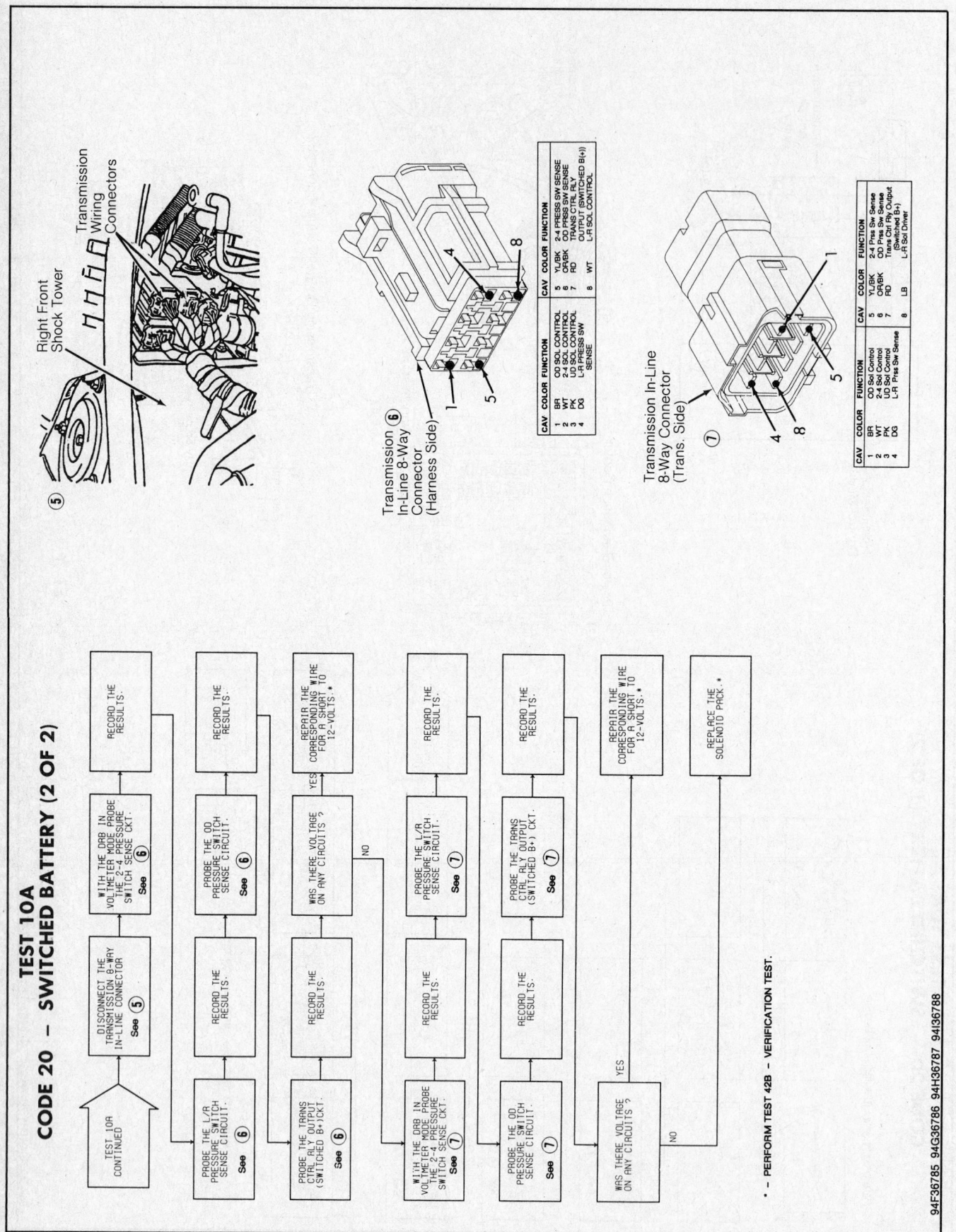

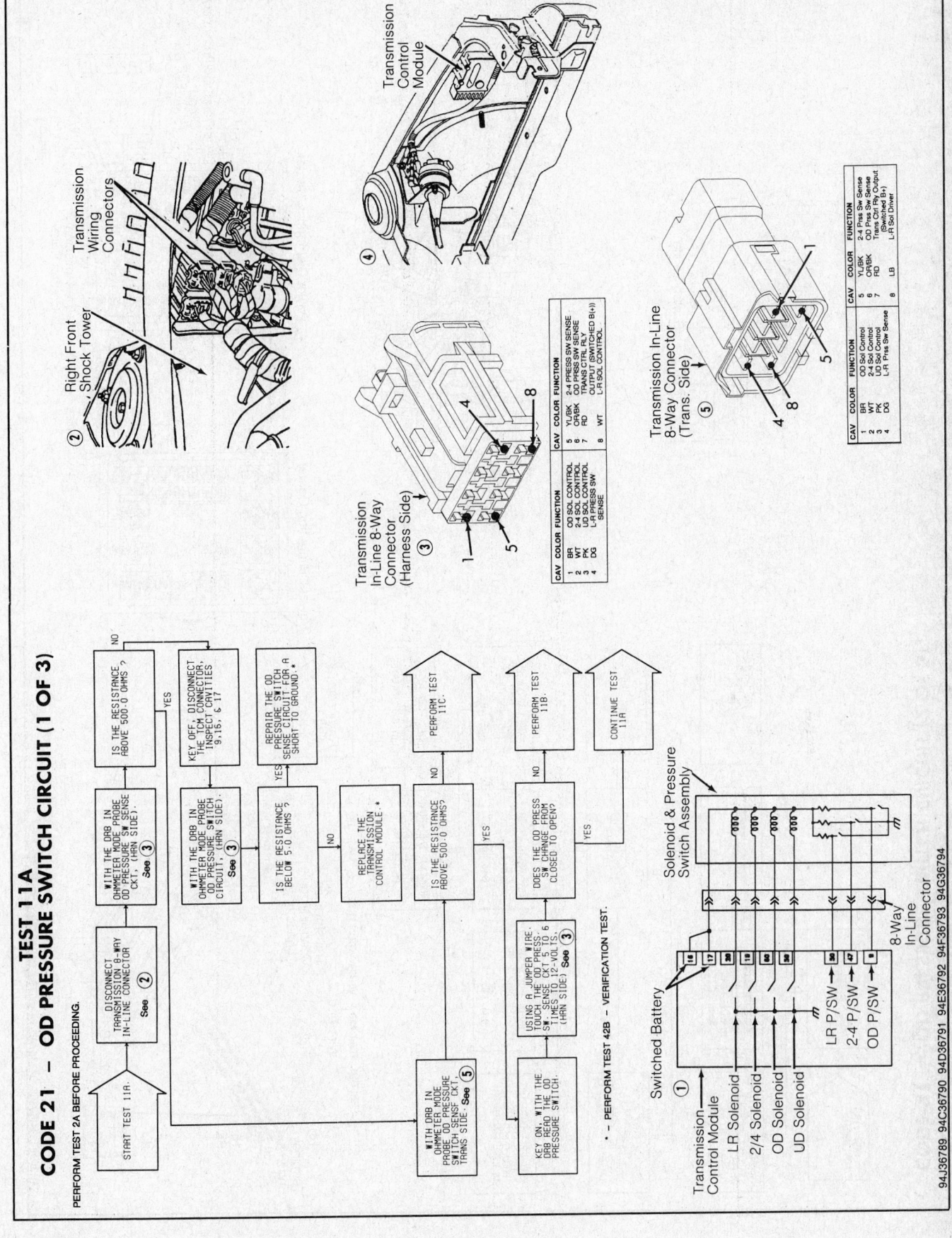

CODE 21 — OD PRESSURE SWITCH CIRCUIT (1 OF 3)

TEST 11A

94J36789 94C36790 94D36791 94E36792 94F36793 94G36794

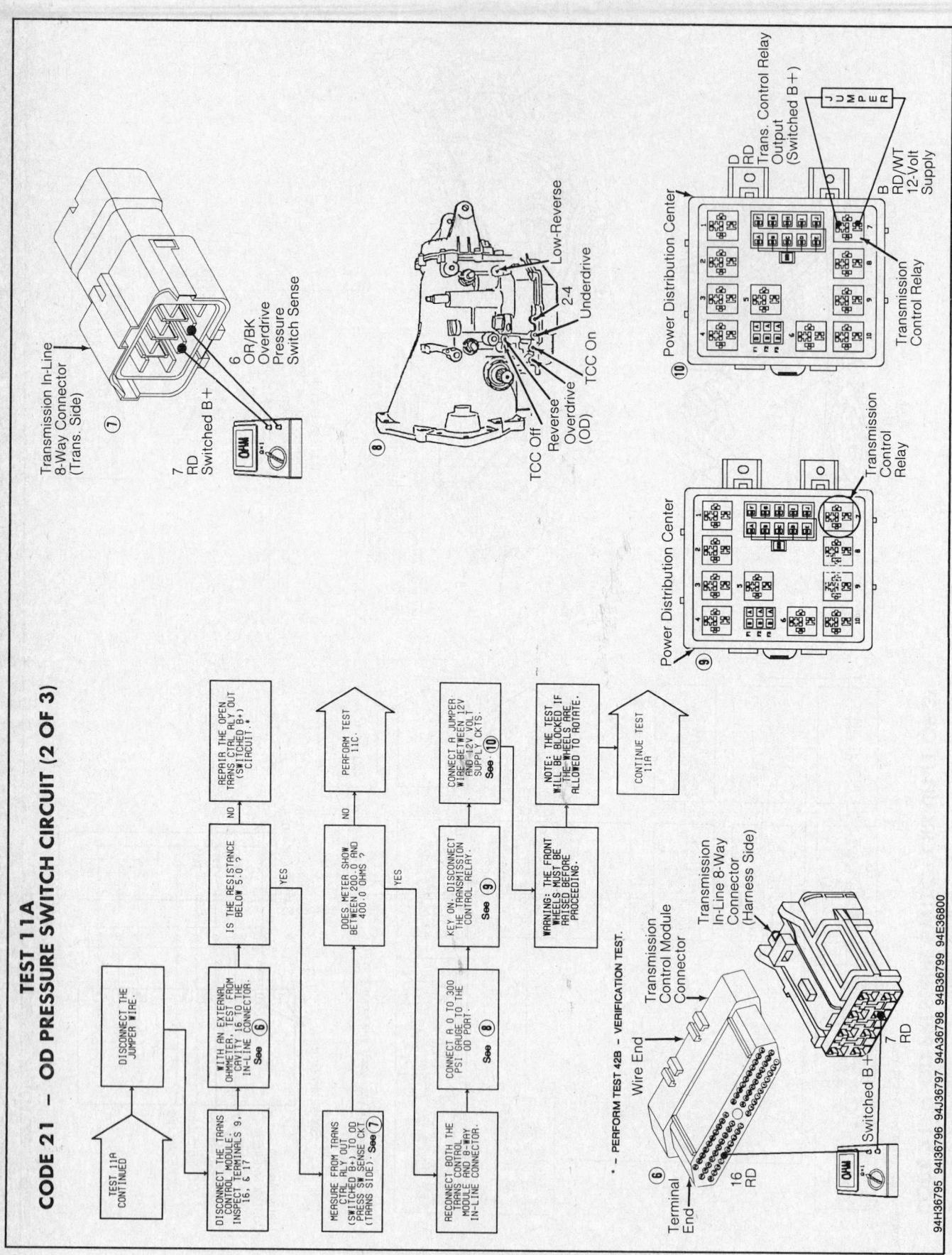

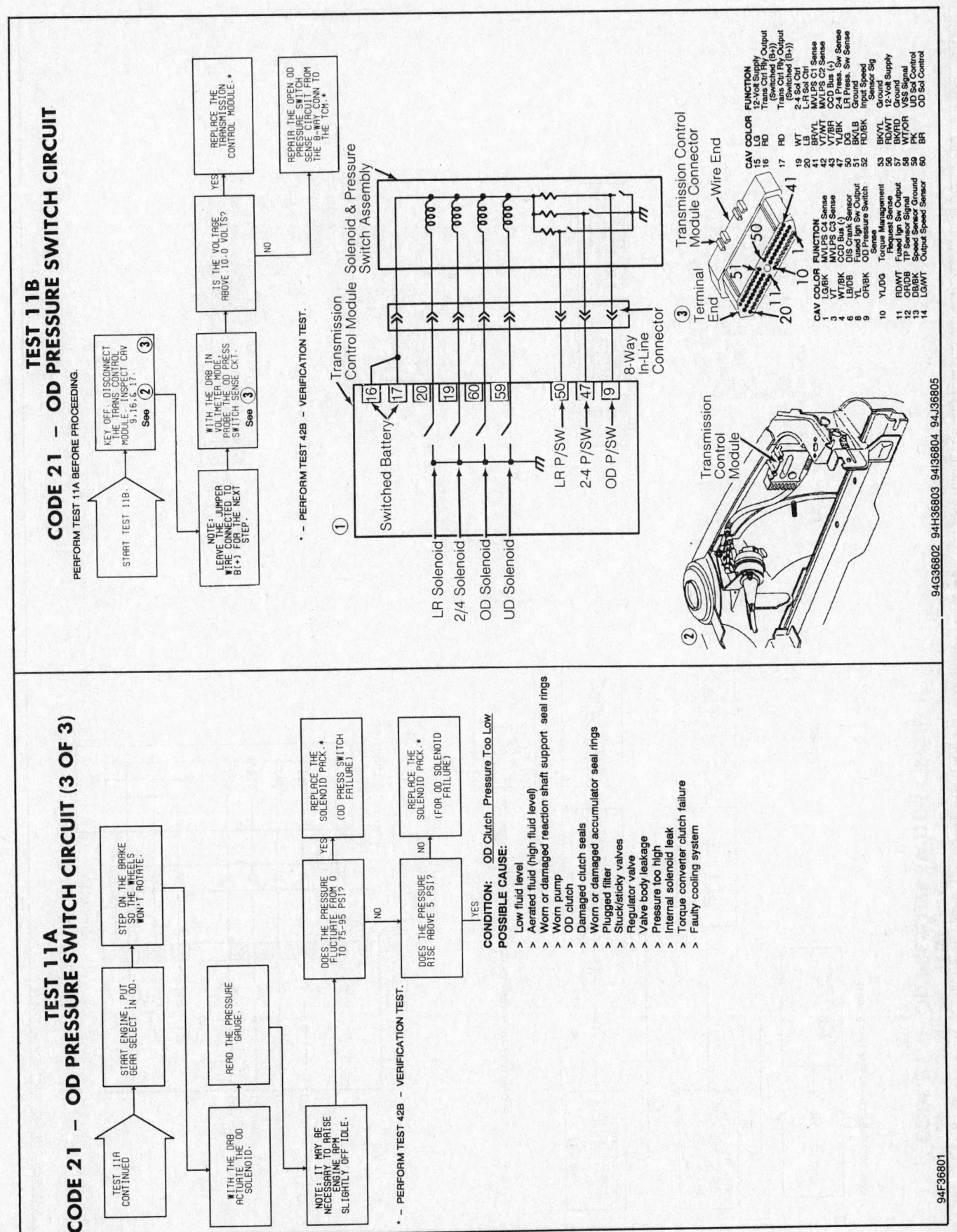

TEST 11B

CODE 21 – OD PRESSURE SWITCH CIRCUIT

PERFORM TEST 11A BEFORE PROCEEDING.

TEST 11A

CODE 21 – OD PRESSURE SWITCH CIRCUIT (3 OF 3)

CONDITION: OD Clutch Pressure Too Low

POSSIBLE CAUSE:

> Low fluid level
> Aerated fluid (high fluid level)
> Worn or damaged reaction shaft support seal rings
> Worn pump
> OD clutch
> Damaged clutch seals
> Worn or damaged accumulator seal rings
> Plugged filter
> Stuck/sticky valves
> Regulator valve
> Valve body leakage
> Pressure too high
> Internal solenoid leak
> Torque converter clutch failure
> Faulty cooling system

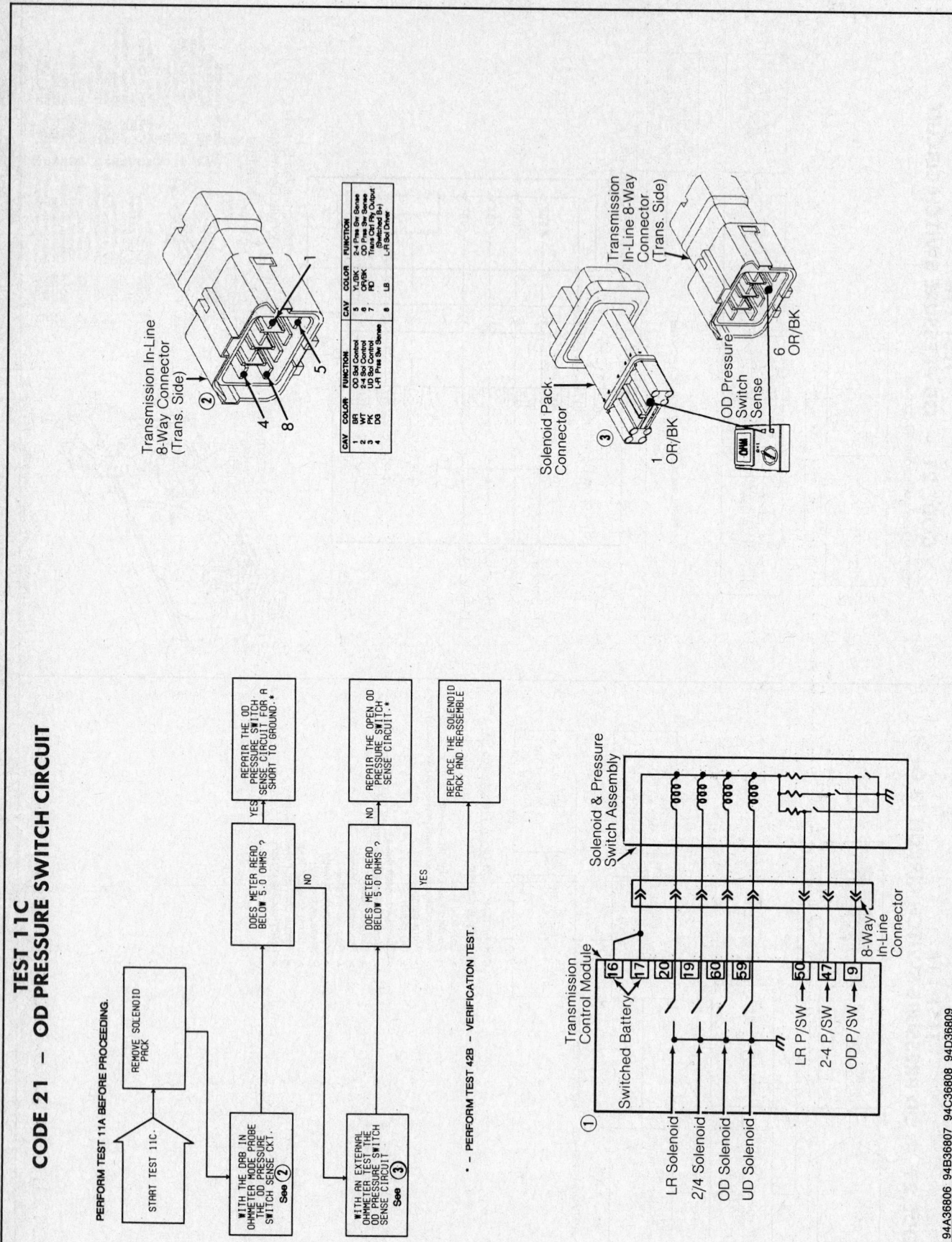

TEST 11C

CODE 21 – OD PRESSURE SWITCH CIRCUIT

94A36806 94B36807 94C36808 94D36809

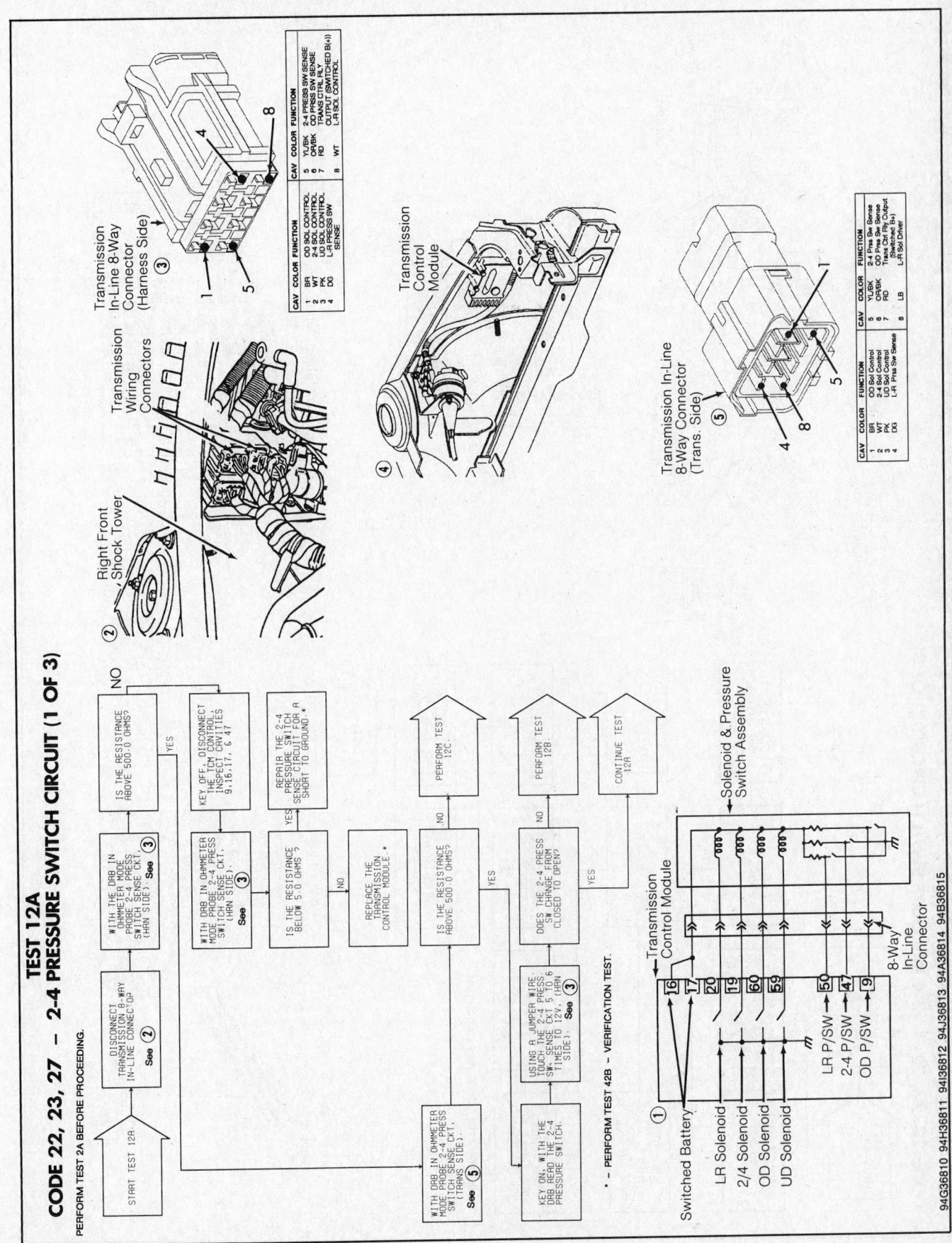

TEST 12A

CODE 22, 23, 27 — 2-4 PRESSURE SWITCH CIRCUIT (1 OF 3)

PERFORM TEST 2A BEFORE PROCEEDING.

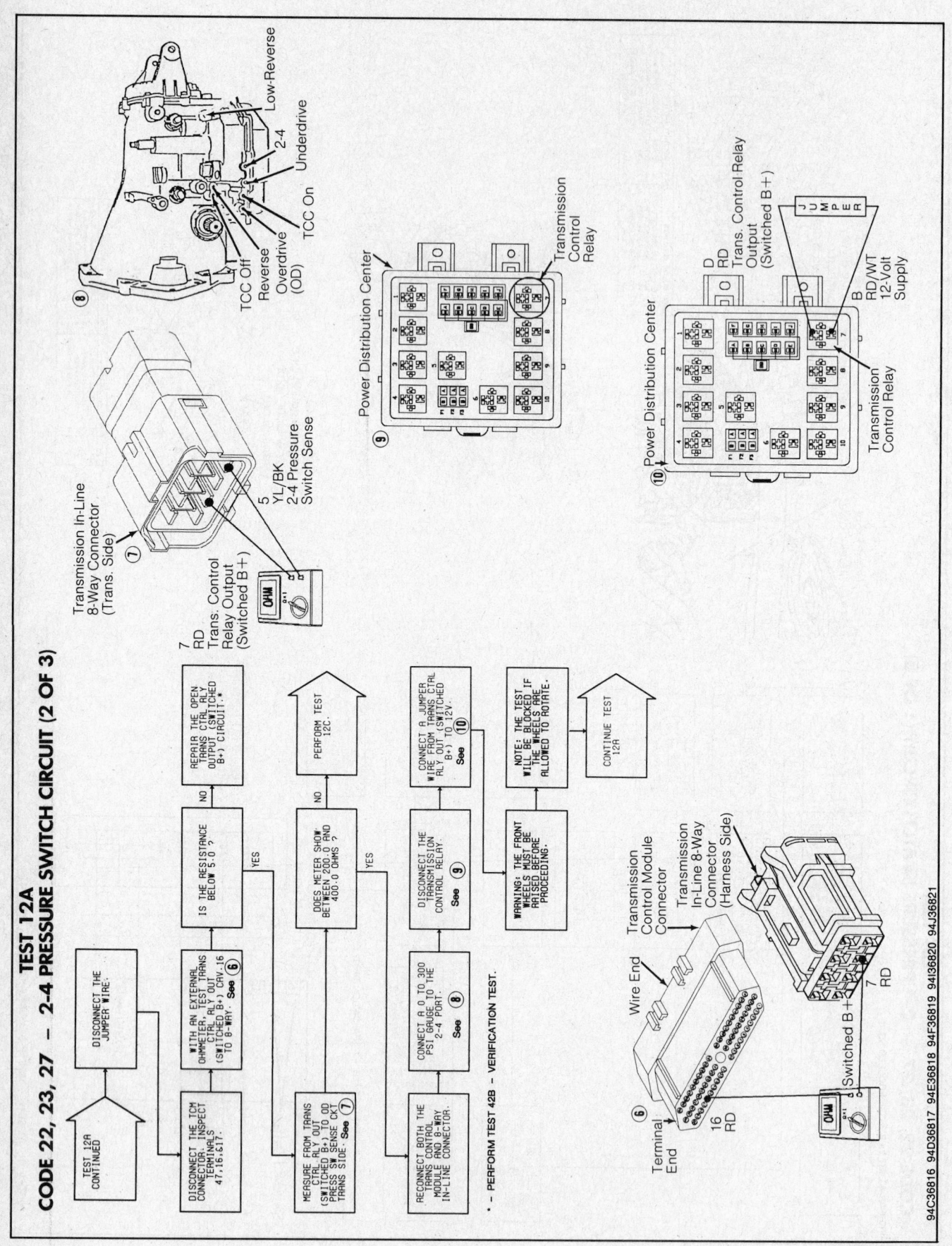

TEST 12A

CODE 22, 23, 27 – 2-4 PRESSURE SWITCH CIRCUIT (2 OF 3)

94C36816 94D36817 94E36818 94F36819 94I36820 94J36821

(11) Name of code: 22 - 2-4 Pressure Switch Circuit

When monitored: Approximately every 1 second.

Set condition: Engine speed must be greater than 500 rpm; a shift must not be in progress; and there must be more than 2.0 seconds since start-up, no loss of prime test in progress, and a pressure switch mismatch. The code sets within 4 seconds if the pressure switch error count reaches maximum value.

Theory of operation: The 42LE transaxle system uses three pressure switches to monitor the fluid pressure in the L-R, 2-4, and OD elements. The pressure switches are continuously checked for the correct states in each gear as indicated below.

Normal Pressure Switch States

GEAR	L-R	2-4	OD
R	OP	OP	OP
N	CL	OP	OP
1ST	CL	OP	OP
2ND	OP	CL	OP
3RD	OP	OP	CL
4TH	OP	CL	CL

OP = switch is open
CL = switch is closed

Trouble Code: 23

CONDITION: 2-4 Clutch and OD Clutch Pressures Too Low

(12) POSSIBLE CAUSE:

> Low fluid level
> Aerated fluid (high fluid level)
> Worn pump
> Damaged clutch seals
> Worn or damaged accumulator seal rings
> Plugged filter
> Stuck/sticky valves
> Regulator valve
> Valve body leakage
> Pressure too high
> Internal solenoid leak
> Torque converter clutch failure
> Faulty cooling system

(13) Name of code: 27 - All Pressure Switch Circuits

When monitored: Approximately every 1 second.

Set condition: Engine speed must be greater than 500 rpm; a shift must not be in progress; and there must be more than 2.0 seconds since start-up, no loss of prime test in progress, and a pressure switch mismatch. The code sets within 4 seconds if the pressure switch error count reaches maximum value.

Theory of operation: The 42LE transaxle system uses three pressure switches to monitor the fluid pressure in the L-R, 2-4, and OD elements. The pressure switches are continuously checked for the correct states in each gear as indicated below.

Normal Pressure Switch States

GEAR	L-R	2-4	OD
R	OP	OP	OP
N	CL	OP	OP
1ST	OP	CL	OP
2ND	OP	CL	OP
3RD	OP	OP	CL
4TH	OP	CL	CL

OP = switch is open
CL = switch is closed

TEST 12A
CODE 22, 23, 27 – 2-4 PRESSURE SWITCH CIRCUIT (3 OF 3)

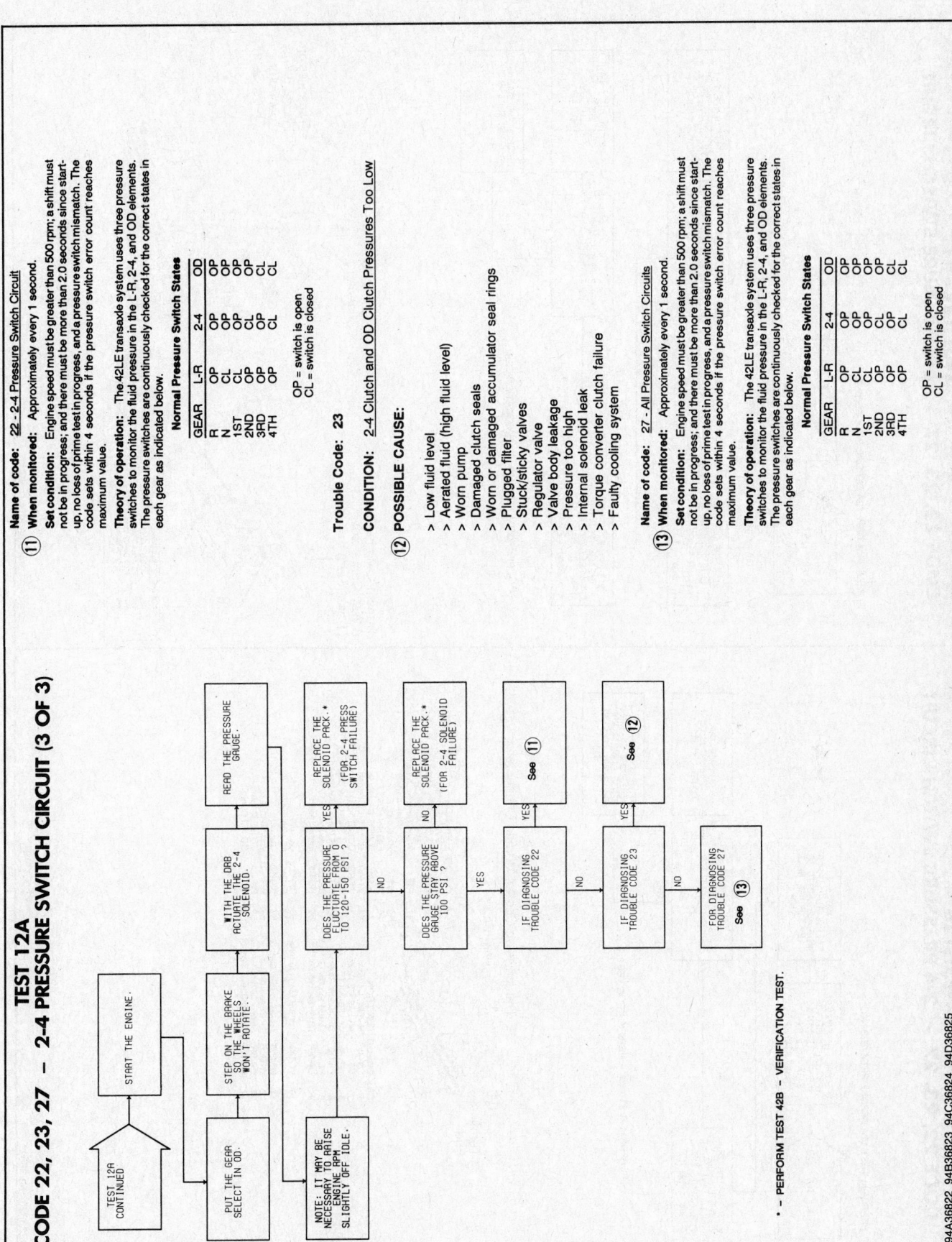

TEST 12A CONTINUED
→ START THE ENGINE.
→ PUT THE GEAR SELECT IN OD.
→ STEP ON THE BRAKE SO THE WHEELS WON'T ROTATE.
NOTE: IT MAY BE NECESSARY TO RAISE ENGINE RPM SLIGHTLY OFF IDLE.
→ WITH THE DRB ACTUATE THE 2-4 SOLENOID.
→ READ THE PRESSURE GAUGE.
→ DOES THE PRESSURE FLUCTUATE FROM 0 TO 120-150 PSI?
— YES → REPLACE THE SOLENOID PACK. * (FOR 2-4 PRESS SWITCH FAILURE)
— NO → DOES THE PRESSURE GAUGE STAY ABOVE 100 PSI?
— NO → REPLACE THE SOLENOID PACK. * (FOR 2-4 SOLENOID FAILURE)
— YES → IF DIAGNOSING TROUBLE CODE 22
— YES → See (11)
— NO → IF DIAGNOSING TROUBLE CODE 23
— YES → See (12)
— NO → FOR DIAGNOSING TROUBLE CODE 27 See (13)

* - PERFORM TEST 42B - VERIFICATION TEST.

94A36822 94B36823 94C36824 94D36825

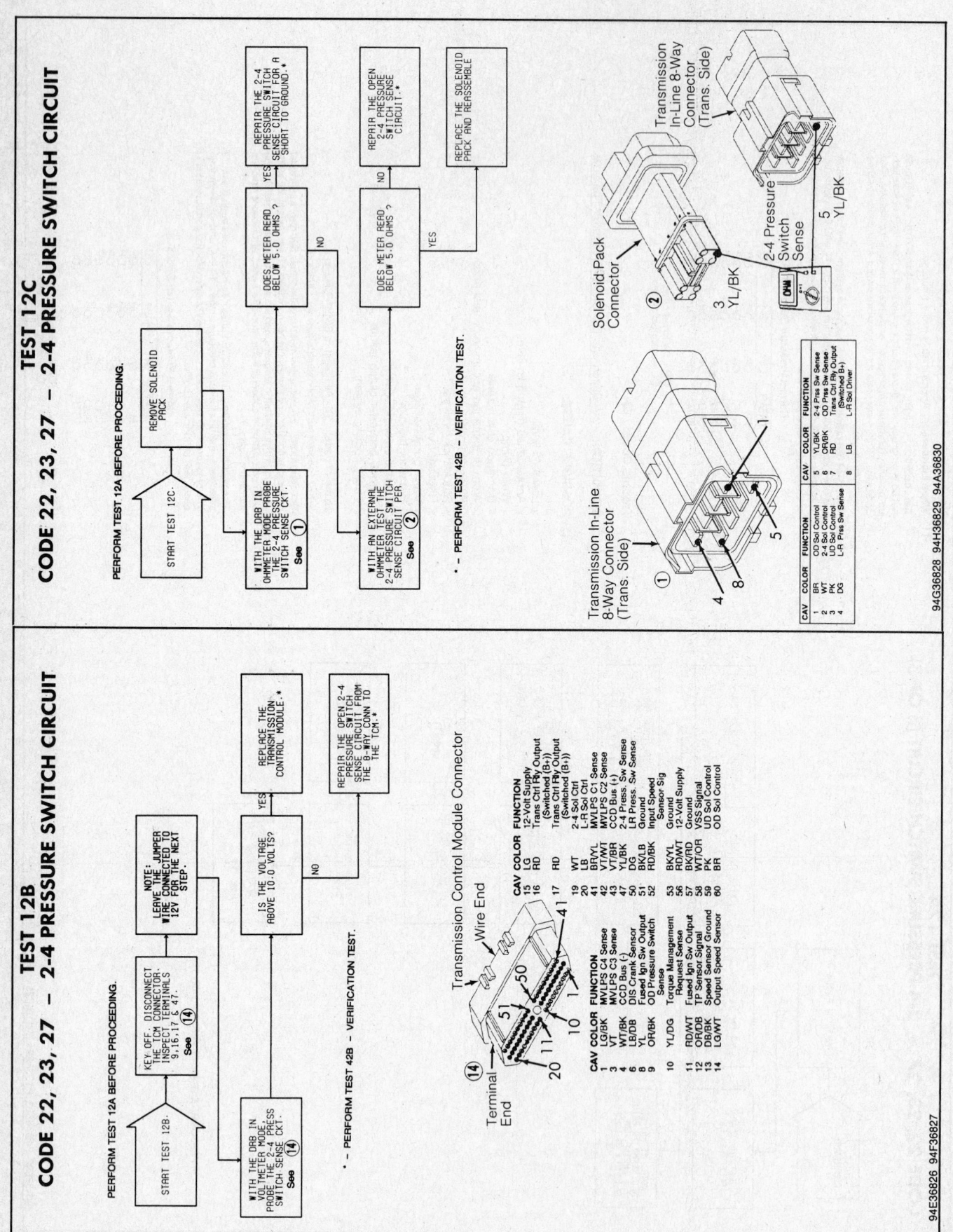

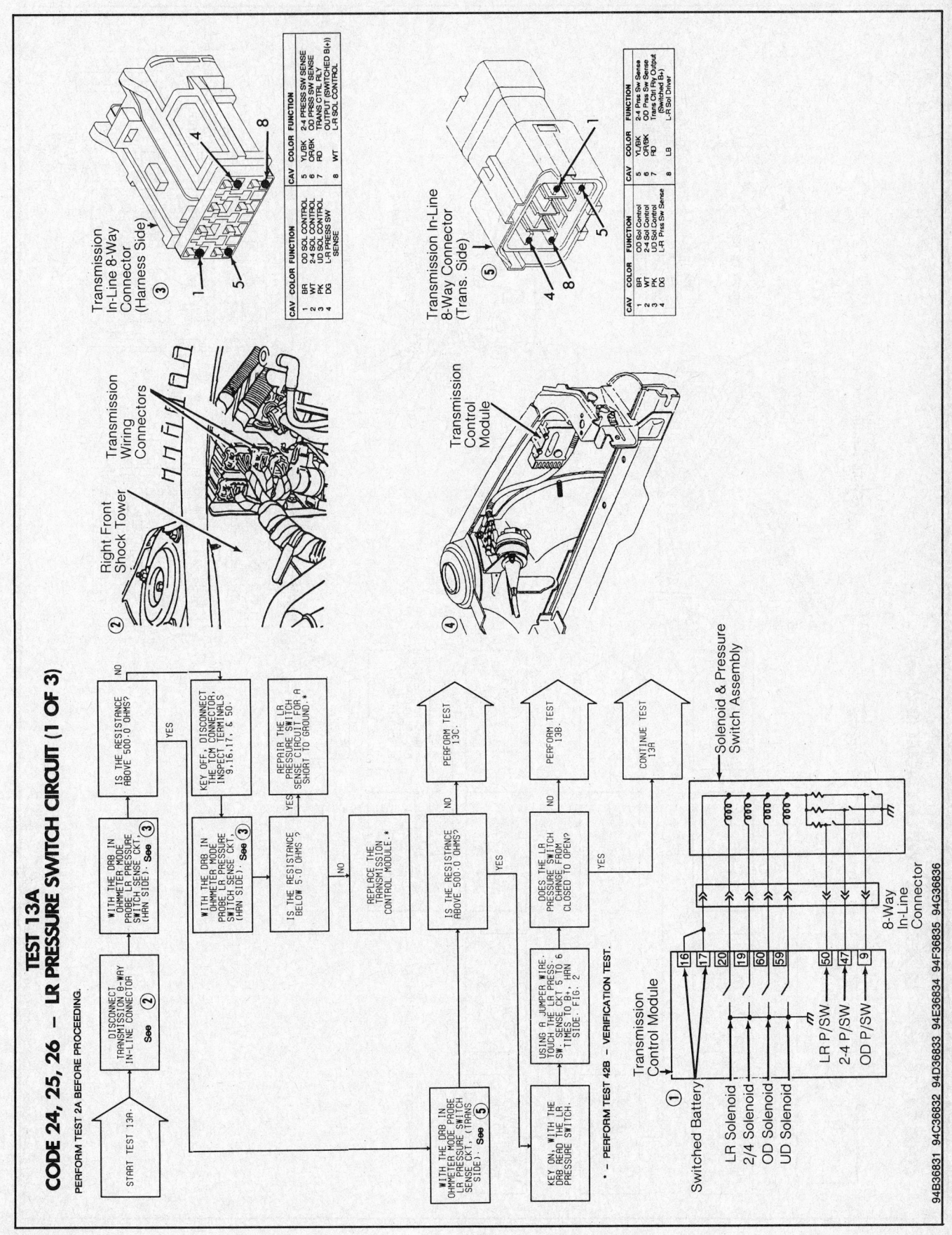

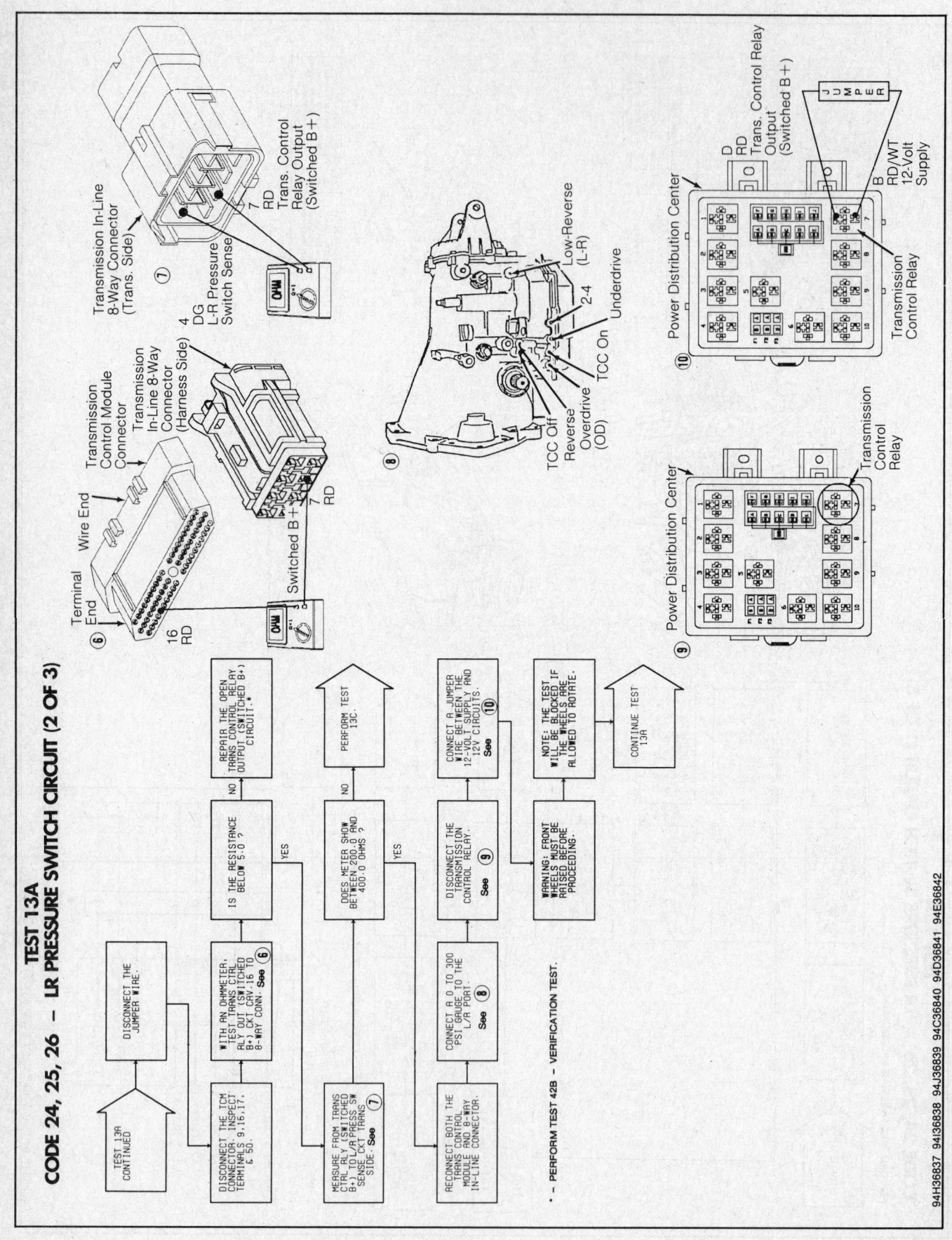

TEST 13A

CODE 24, 25, 26 – LR PRESSURE SWITCH CIRCUIT (2 OF 3)

94H36837 94J36838 94J36839 94C36840 94D36841 94E36842

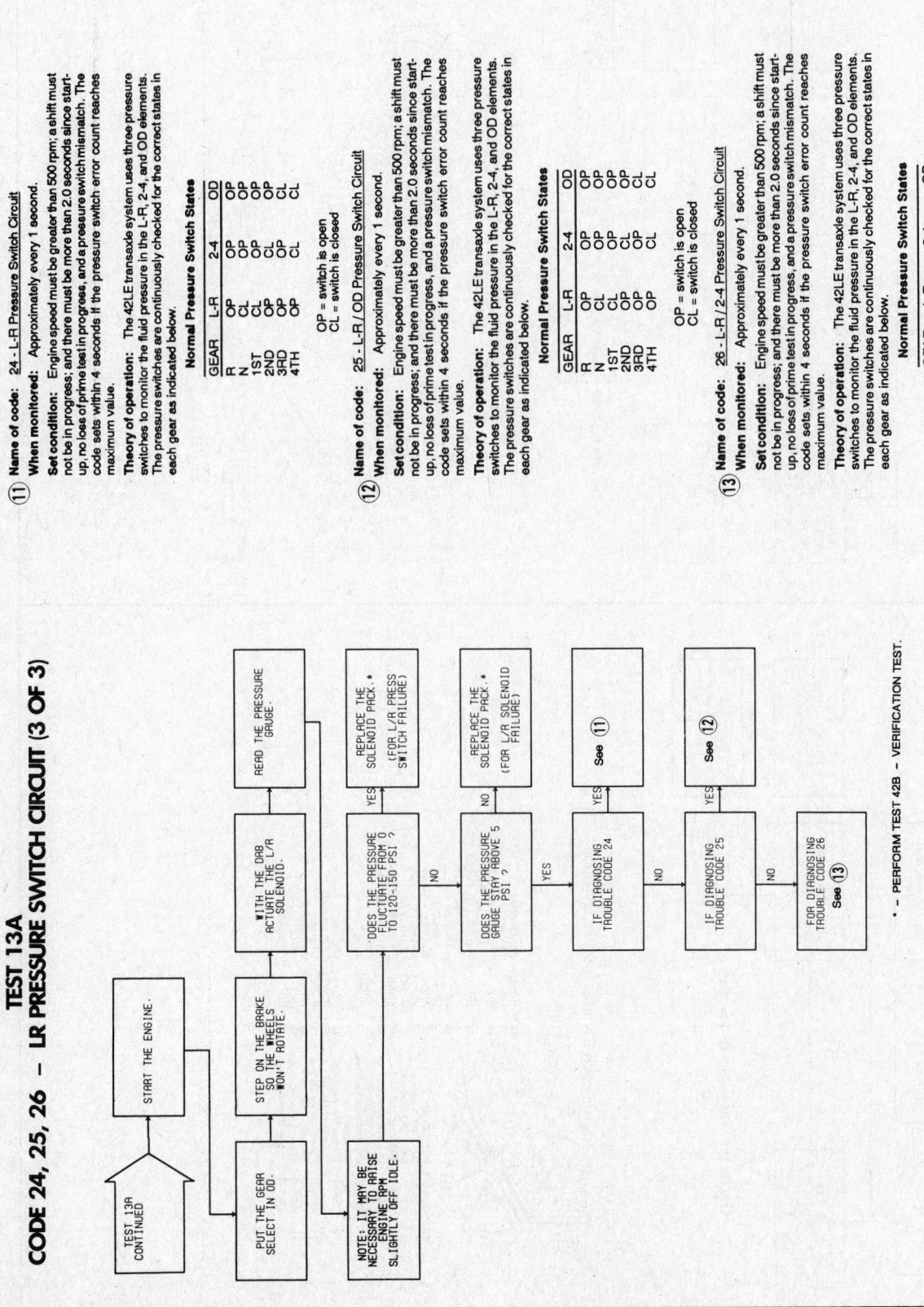

TEST 13A

CODE 24, 25, 26 — LR PRESSURE SWITCH CIRCUIT (3 OF 3)

⑪ **Name of code:** 24 - L-R Pressure Switch Circuit

When monitored: Approximately every 1 second.

Set condition: Engine speed must be greater than 500 rpm; a shift must not be in progress; and there must be more than 2.0 seconds since start-up, no loss of prime test in progress, and a pressure switch mismatch. The code sets within 4 seconds if the pressure switch error count reaches maximum value.

Theory of operation: The 42LE transaxle system uses three pressure switches to monitor the fluid pressure in the L-R, 2-4, and OD elements. The pressure switches are continuously checked for the correct states in each gear as indicated below.

Normal Pressure Switch States

GEAR	L-R	2-4	OD
R	OP	OP	OP
N	CL	OP	OP
1ST	CL	OP	OP
2ND	OP	CL	OP
3RD	OP	OP	CL
4TH	OP	CL	CL

OP = switch is open
CL = switch is closed

⑫ **Name of code:** 25 - L-R / OD Pressure Switch Circuit

When monitored: Approximately every 1 second.

Set condition: Engine speed must be greater than 500 rpm; a shift must not be in progress; and there must be more than 2.0 seconds since start-up, no loss of prime test in progress, and a pressure switch mismatch. The code sets within 4 seconds if the pressure switch error count reaches maximum value.

Theory of operation: The 42LE transaxle system uses three pressure switches to monitor the fluid pressure in the L-R, 2-4, and OD elements. The pressure switches are continuously checked for the correct states in each gear as indicated below.

Normal Pressure Switch States

GEAR	L-R	2-4	OD
R	OP	OP	OP
N	CL	OP	OP
1ST	CL	OP	OP
2ND	OP	CL	OP
3RD	OP	OP	CL
4TH	OP	CL	CL

OP = switch is open
CL = switch is closed

⑬ **Name of code:** 26 - L-R / 2-4 Pressure Switch Circuit

When monitored: Approximately every 1 second.

Set condition: Engine speed must be greater than 500 rpm; a shift must not be in progress; and there must be more than 2.0 seconds since start-up, no loss of prime test in progress, and a pressure switch mismatch. The code sets within 4 seconds if the pressure switch error count reaches maximum value.

Theory of operation: The 42LE transaxle system uses three pressure switches to monitor the fluid pressure in the L-R, 2-4, and OD elements. The pressure switches are continuously checked for the correct states in each gear as indicated below.

Normal Pressure Switch States

GEAR	L-R	2-4	OD
R	OP	OP	OP
N	CL	OP	OP
1ST	CL	OP	OP
2ND	OP	CL	OP
3RD	OP	OP	CL
4TH	OP	CL	CL

OP = switch is open
CL = switch is closed

94F36843 94G36844 94H36845 94J36846

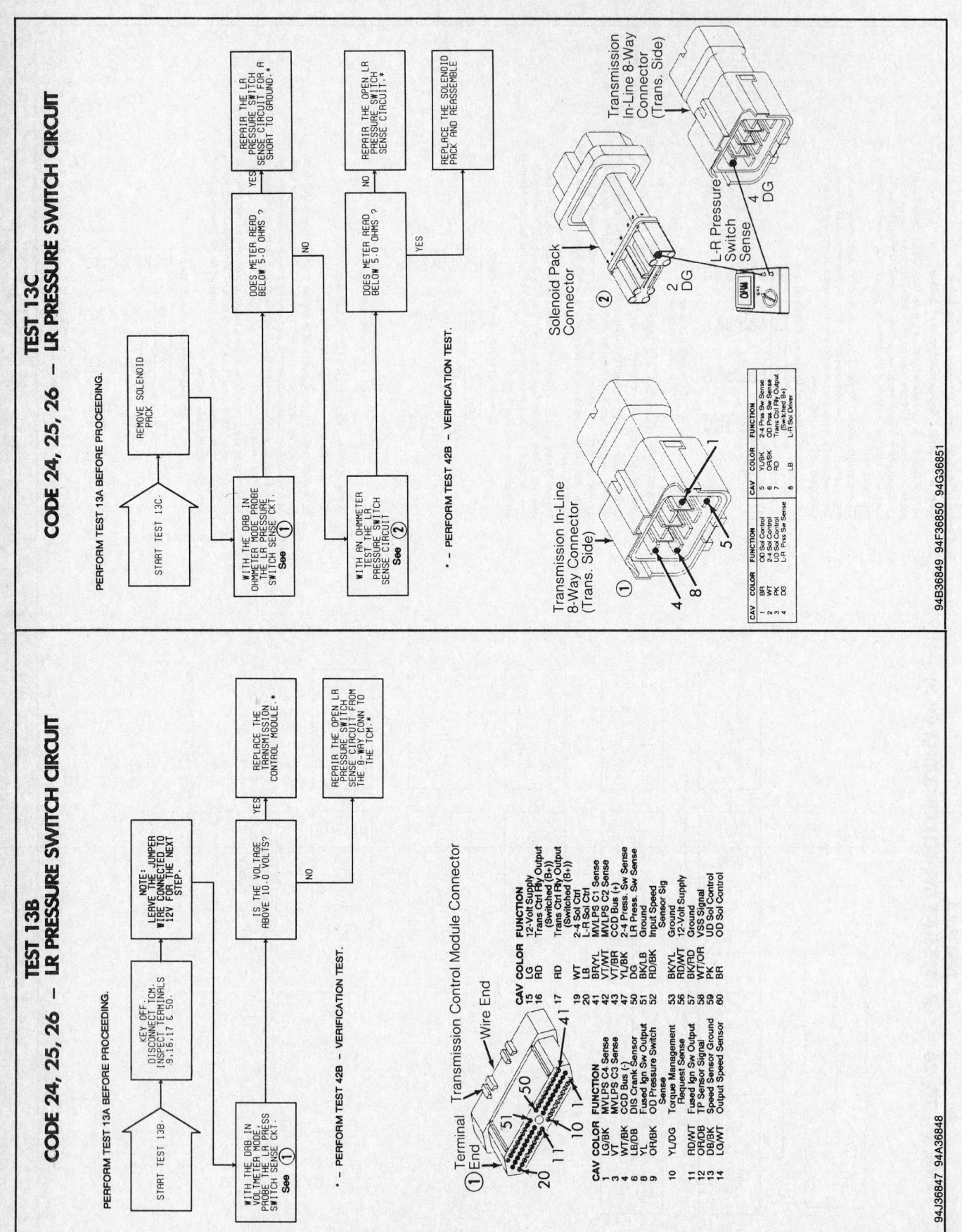

TEST 13C
CODE 24, 25, 26 – LR PRESSURE SWITCH CIRCUIT

PERFORM TEST 13A BEFORE PROCEEDING.

START TEST 13C.

REMOVE SOLENOID PACK

WITH THE DRB IN OHMMETER MODE PROBE THE LR PRESSURE SWITCH SENSE CKT. See ①

WITH AN OHMMETER TEST THE LR PRESSURE SWITCH SENSE CIRCUIT ② See ②

DOES METER READ BELOW 5.0 OHMS ?
YES → REPAIR THE LR PRESSURE SWITCH SENSE CIRCUIT FOR A SHORT TO GROUND. *
NO →

DOES METER READ BELOW 5.0 OHMS ?
NO → REPAIR THE OPEN LR PRESSURE SWITCH SENSE CIRCUIT. *
YES → REPLACE THE SOLENOID PACK AND REASSEMBLE.

* – PERFORM TEST 42B – VERIFICATION TEST.

Transmission In-Line 8-Way Connector (Trans. Side)

Solenoid Pack Connector ②

L-R Pressure Switch Sense 4 DG

2 DG

Transmission In-Line 8-Way Connector (Trans. Side) ①

4   8   5

CAV	COLOR	FUNCTION	CAV	COLOR	FUNCTION
1	BR	OD Sol Control	5	YL/BK	2-4 Prss Sw Sense
2	WT	2-4 Sol Control	6	OR/BK	OD Prss Sw Sense
3	PK	UD Sol Control	7	RD	Trans Ctrl Rly Output (Switched B+)
4	DG	L-R Prss Sw Sense	8	LB	L-R Sol Driver

94B36849 94F36850 94G36851

TEST 13B
CODE 24, 25, 26 – LR PRESSURE SWITCH CIRCUIT

PERFORM TEST 13A BEFORE PROCEEDING.

START TEST 13B.

KEY OFF. DISCONNECT TCM. INSPECT TERMINALS 9,16,17 & 50.

WITH THE DRB IN VOLTMETER MODE PROBE THE LR PRESS SWITCH SENSE CKT. See ①

NOTE: LEAVE THE JUMPER WIRE CONNECTED TO 12V FOR THE NEXT STEP.

IS THE VOLTAGE ABOVE 10.0 VOLTS?
YES → REPLACE THE TRANSMISSION CONTROL MODULE. *
NO → REPAIR THE OPEN LR PRESSURE SWITCH SENSE CIRCUIT FROM THE 8-WAY CONN TO THE TCM. *

* – PERFORM TEST 42B – VERIFICATION TEST.

Transmission Control Module Connector

Terminal End ① Wire End

41 50 51 10 1 11 20

CAV	COLOR	FUNCTION
1	LG/BK	MVLPS C4 Sense
3	VT	MVLPS C3 Sense
6	WT/BK	CCD Bus (-)
8	LB/DB	DIS Crank Sensor
9	YL	Fused Ign Sw Output
9	OR/BK	OD Pressure Switch
10	YL/DG	Torque Management Request Sense
11	RD/WT	Fused Ign Sw Output
12	OR/DB	TP Sensor Signal
13	DB/BK	Speed Sensor Ground
14	LG/WT	Output Speed Sensor

CAV	COLOR	FUNCTION
15	LG	12-Volt Supply
16	RD	Trans Ctrl Rly Output (Switched (B+))
17	RD	Trans Ctrl Rly Output (Switched (B+))
19	WT	2-4 Sol Ctrl
20	LB	L-R Sol Ctrl
41	BR/YL	MVLPS C1 Sense
42	VT/WT	MVLPS C2 Sense
43	VT/BR	CCD Bus (+)
47	YL/BK	2-4 Press. Sw Sense
50	DG	LR Press. Sw Sense
51	BK/LB	Input Speed Sensor Sig
52	RD/BK	Ground
53	BK/YL	Ground
56	RD/WT	12-Volt Supply
57	BK/RD	Ground
58	WT/OR	VSS Signal
59	YK	OD Sol Control
60	BR	OD Sol Control

94J36847 94A36848

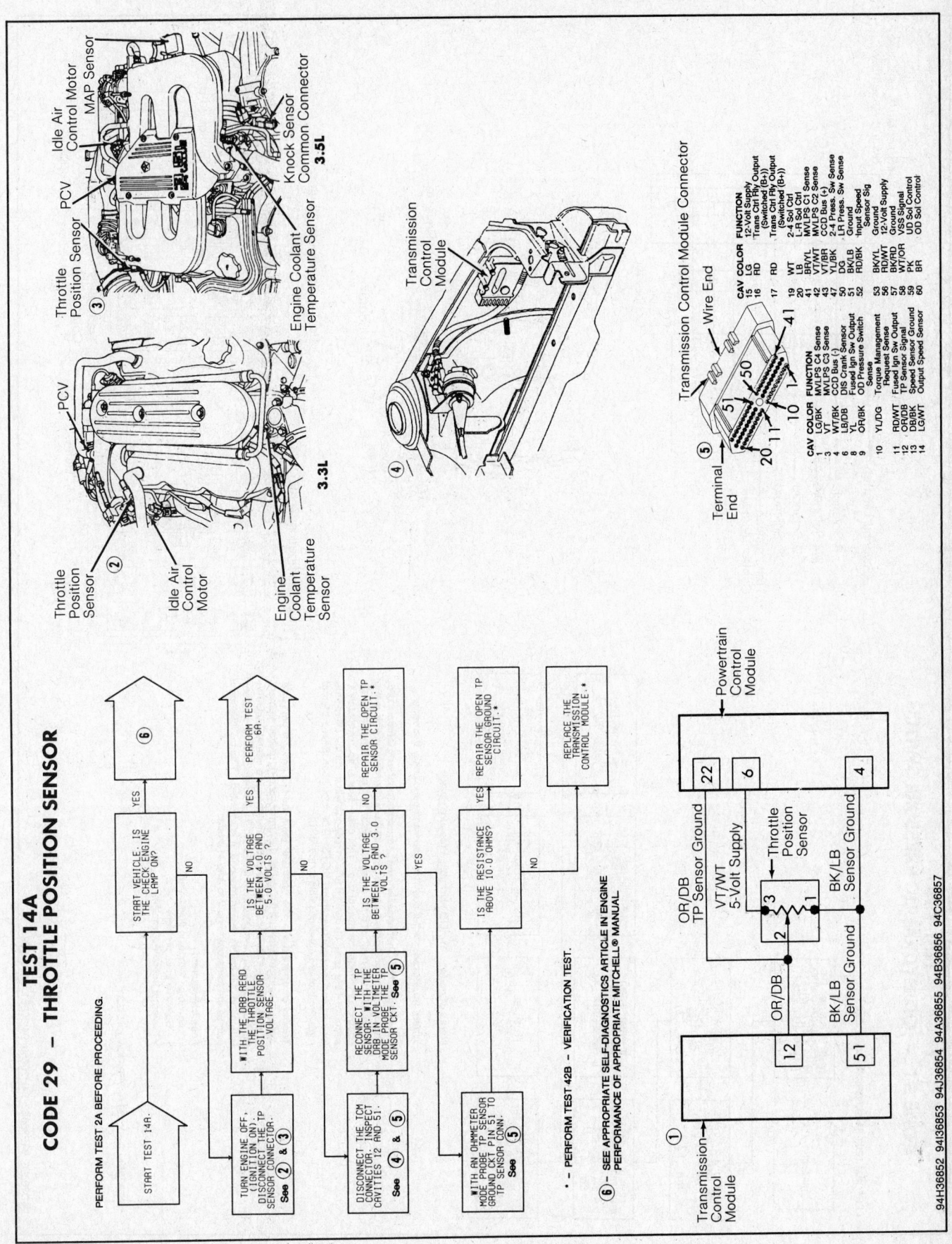

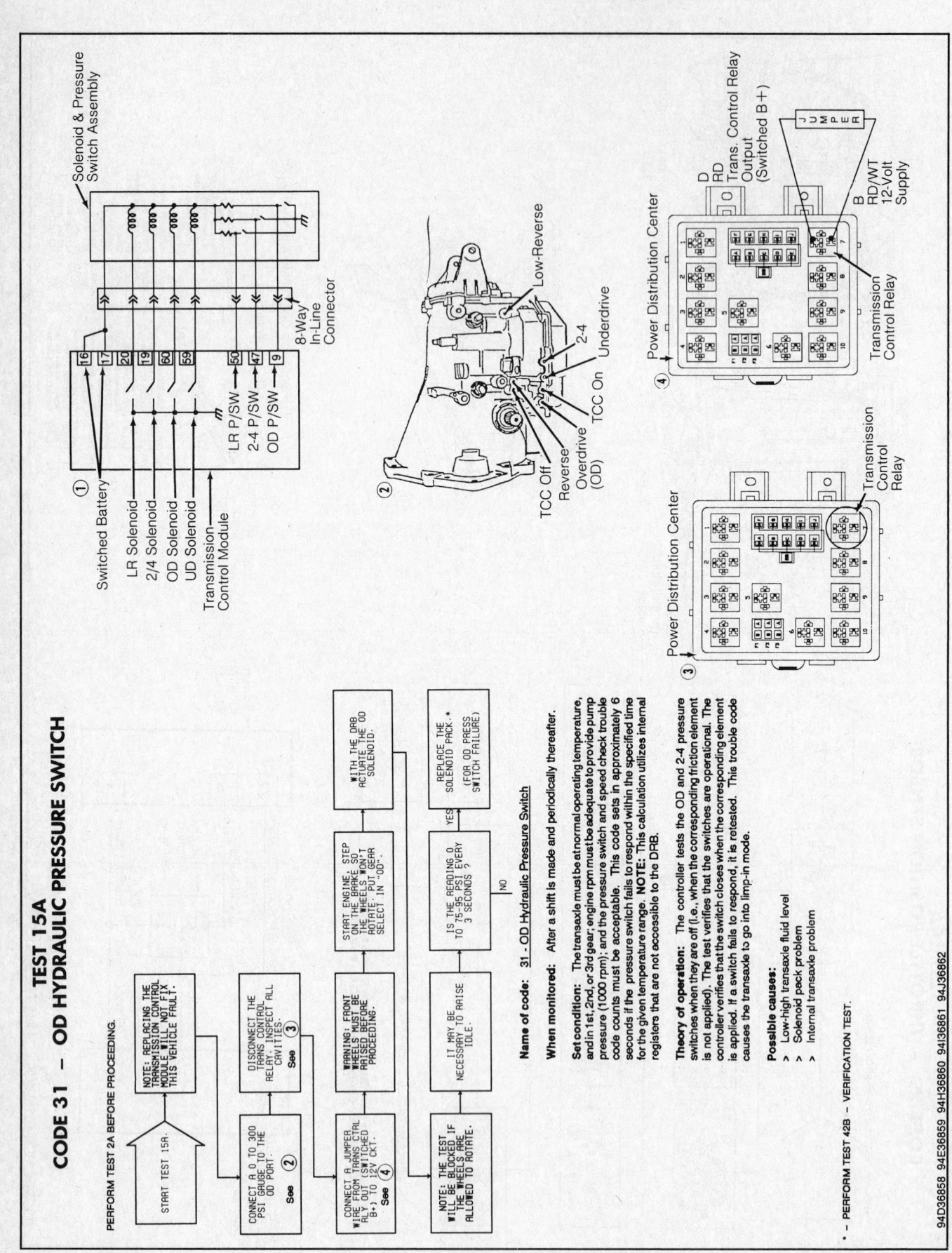

TEST 15A

CODE 31 — OD HYDRAULIC PRESSURE SWITCH

PERFORM TEST 2A BEFORE PROCEEDING.

START TEST 15A.

NOTE: REPLACING THE TRANSMISSION CONTROL MODULE WILL NOT FIX THIS VEHICLE FAULT.

CONNECT A 0 TO 300 PSI GAUGE TO THE OD PORT. See ②

DISCONNECT THE TRANS CONTROL RELAY. INSPECT ALL CAVITIES. See ③

CONNECT A JUMPER WIRE FROM TRANS CTRL RLY OUT (SWITCHED B+) TO 12V CKT. See ④

WARNING: FRONT WHEELS MUST BE RAISED BEFORE PROCEEDING.

START ENGINE, STEP ON THE BRAKE SO THE WHEELS WON'T ROTATE. PUT GEAR SELECT IN "OD".

WITH THE DRB ACTUATE THE OD SOLENOID.

NOTE: THE TEST WILL BE BLOCKED IF THE WHEELS ARE ALLOWED TO ROTATE.

IT MAY BE NECESSARY TO RAISE IDLE.

IS THE READING 0 TO 75-95 PSI EVERY 3 SECONDS ?

NO

YES

REPLACE THE SOLENOID PACK.*

(FOR OD PRESS SWITCH FAILURE)

Name of code: 31 - OD Hydraulic Pressure Switch

When monitored: After a shift is made and periodically thereafter.

Set condition: The transaxle must be at normal operating temperature, and in 1st, 2nd, or 3rd gear; engine rpm must be adequate to provide pump pressure (1000 rpm); and the pressure switch and speed check trouble code counts must be acceptable. This code sets in approximately 6 seconds if the pressure switch fails to respond within the specified time for the given temperature range. **NOTE:** This calculation utilizes internal registers that are not accessible to the DRB.

Theory of operation: The controller tests the OD and 2-4 pressure switches when they are off (i.e., when the corresponding friction element is not applied). The test verifies that the switches are operational. The controller verifies that the switch closes when the corresponding element is applied. If a switch fails to respond, it is retested. This trouble code causes the transaxle to go into limp-in mode.

Possible causes:
> Low-high transaxle fluid level
> Solenoid pack problem
> Internal transaxle problem

* - PERFORM TEST 42B — VERIFICATION TEST.

94D36858 94E36859 94H36860 94I36861 94J36862

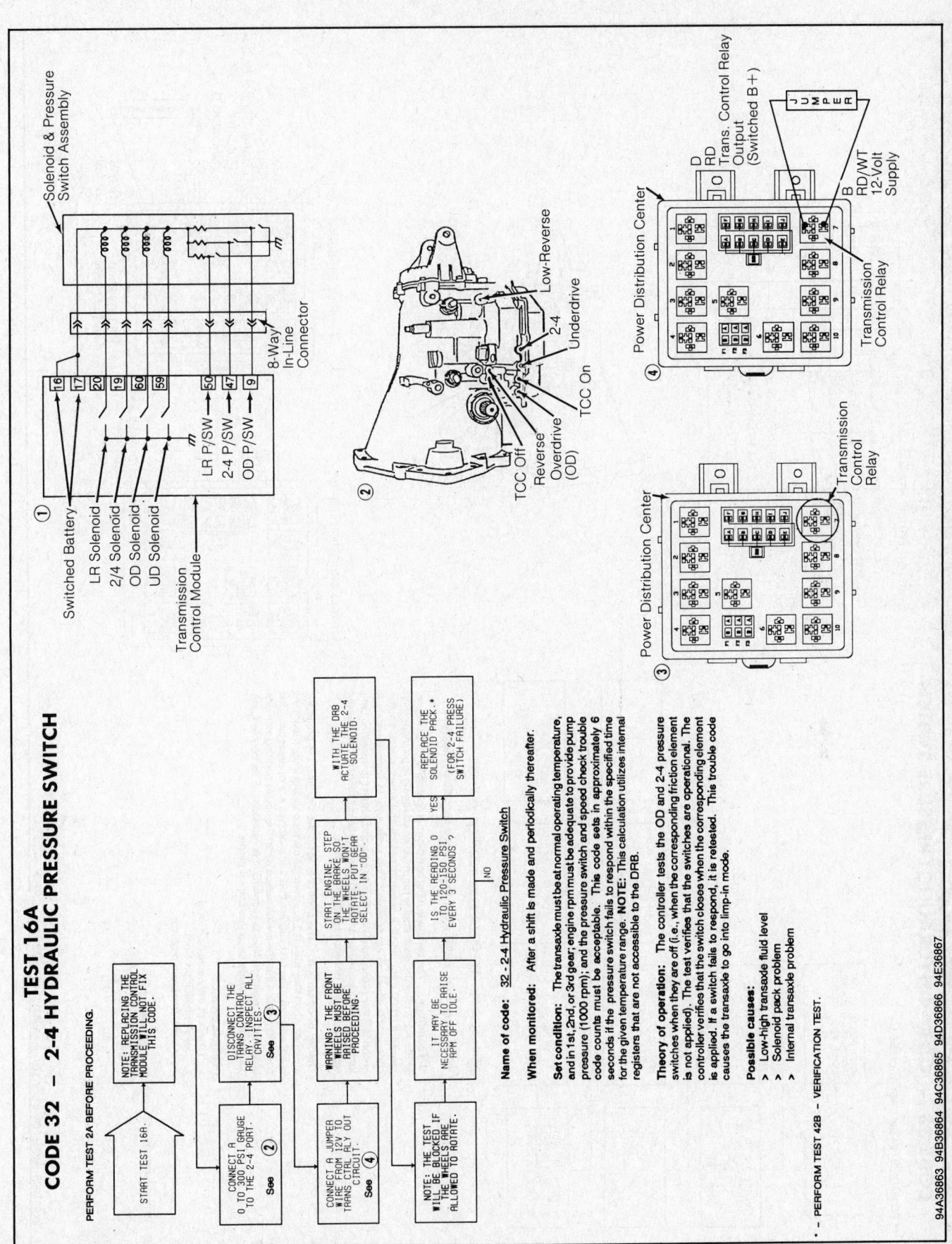

TEST 16A

CODE 32 – 2-4 HYDRAULIC PRESSURE SWITCH

PERFORM TEST 2A BEFORE PROCEEDING.

Name of code: 32 - 2-4 Hydraulic Pressure Switch

When monitored: After a shift is made and periodically thereafter.

Set condition: The transaxle must be at normal operating temperature, and in 1st, 2nd, or 3rd gear; engine rpm must be adequate to provide pump pressure (1000 rpm); and the pressure switch and speed check trouble code counts must be acceptable. This code sets in approximately 6 seconds if the pressure switch fails to respond within the specified time for the given temperature range. NOTE: This calculation utilizes internal registers that are not accessible to the DRB.

Theory of operation: The controller tests the OD and 2-4 pressure switches when they are off (i.e., when the corresponding friction element is not applied). The test verifies that the switches are operational. The controller verifies that the switch closes when the corresponding element is applied. If a switch fails to respond, it is retested. This trouble code causes the transaxle to go into limp-in mode.

Possible causes:
> Low-high transaxle fluid level
> Solenoid pack problem
> Internal transaxle problem

* - PERFORM TEST 42B - VERIFICATION TEST.

94A36863 94B36864 94C36865 94D36866 94E36867

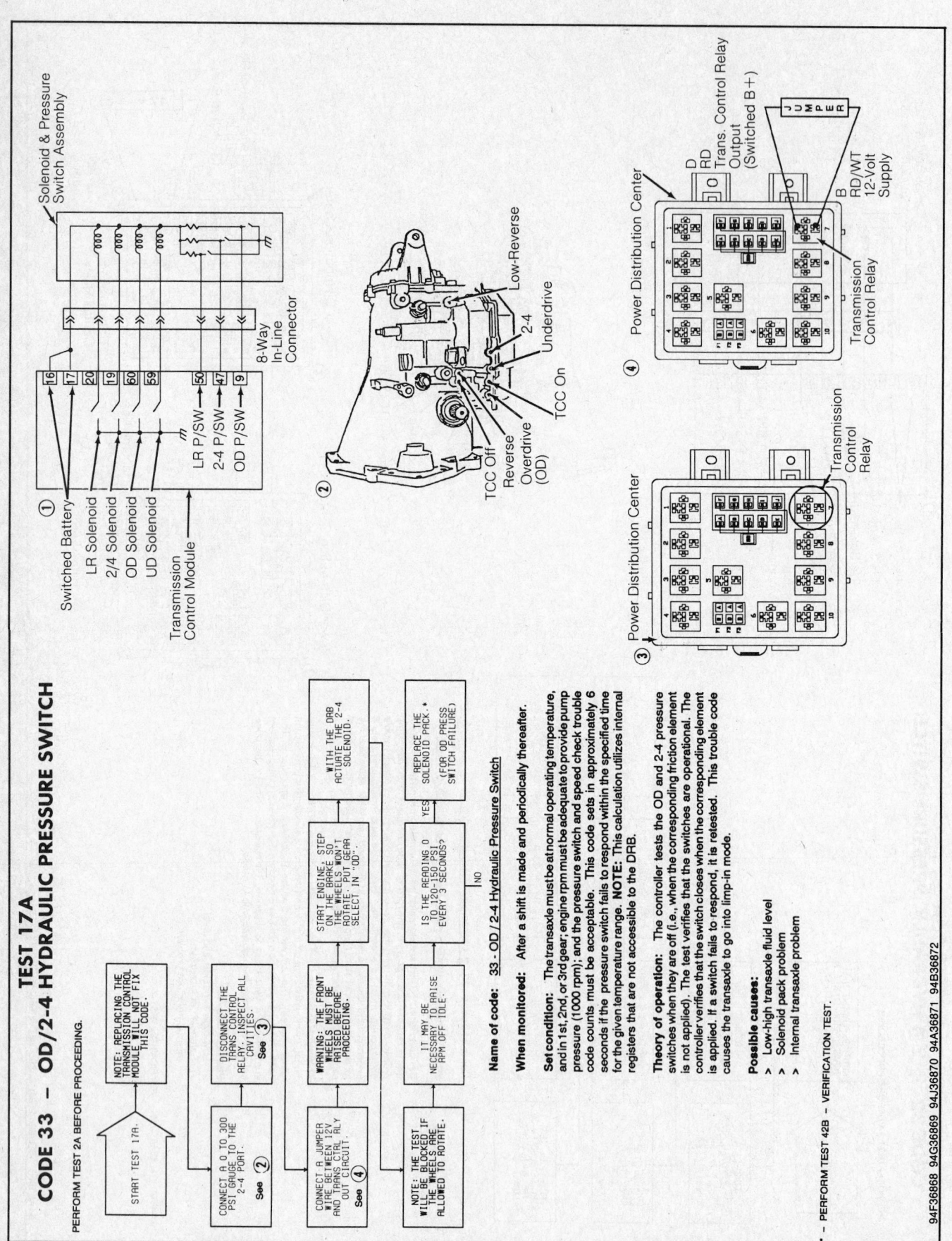

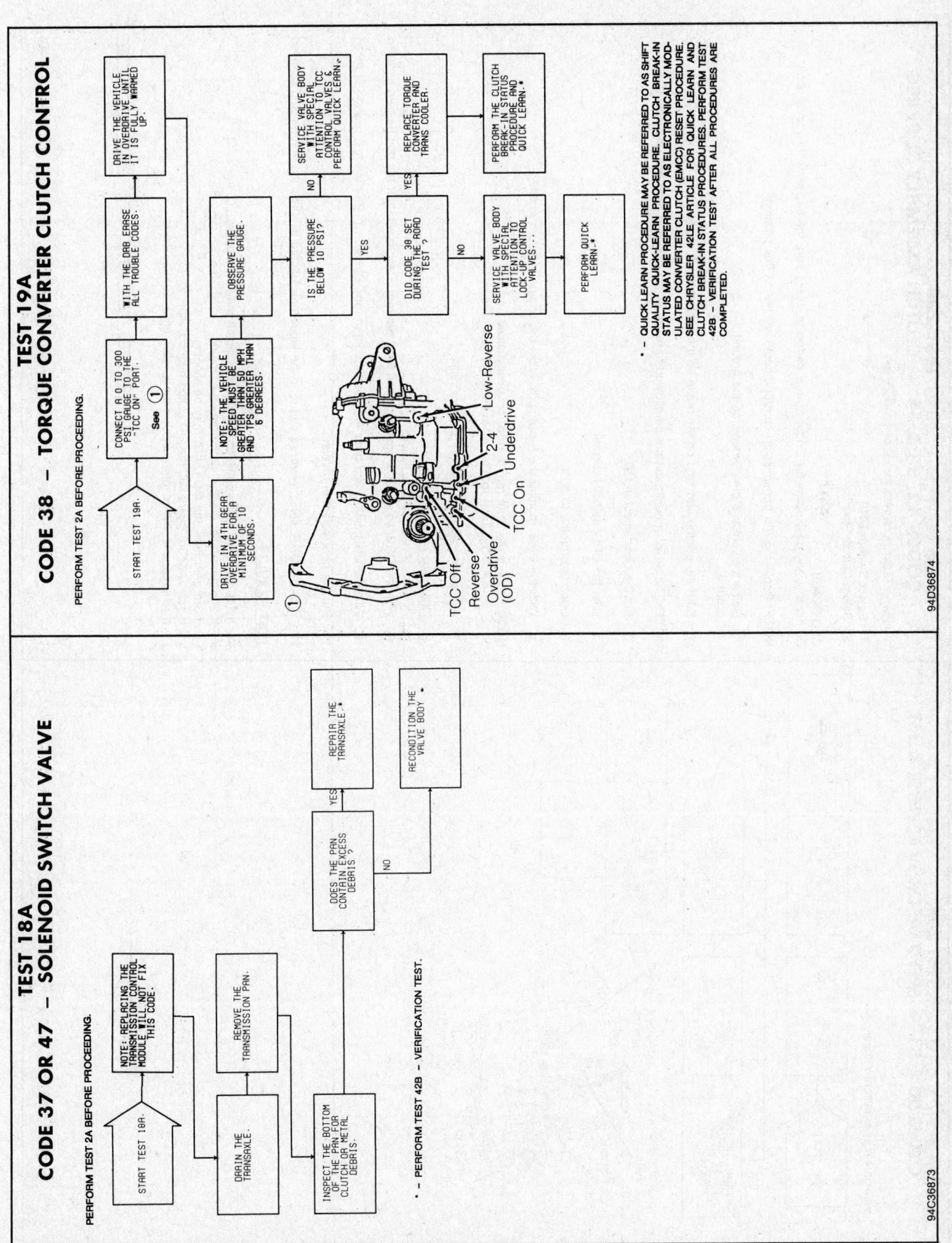

TEST 19A
CODE 38 – TORQUE CONVERTER CLUTCH CONTROL

PERFORM TEST 2A BEFORE PROCEEDING.

START TEST 19A.

DRIVE IN 4TH GEAR OVERDRIVE FOR A MINIMUM OF 10 SECONDS.

CONNECT A 0 TO 300 PSI GAUGE TO THE "TCC ON" PORT. See ①

WITH THE DRB ERASE ALL TROUBLE CODES.

DRIVE THE VEHICLE IN OVERDRIVE UNTIL IT IS FULLY WARMED UP.

NOTE: THE VEHICLE SPEED MUST BE GREATER THAN 50 MPH AND TPS GREATER THAN 6 DEGREES.

OBSERVE THE PRESSURE GAUGE.

IS THE PRESSURE BELOW 10 PSI?

NO → SERVICE VALVE BODY WITH SPECIAL ATTENTION TO TCC CONTROL VALVES & PERFORM QUICK LEARN.*

YES → DID CODE 38 SET DURING THE ROAD TEST ?

YES → REPLACE TORQUE CONVERTER AND TRANS COOLER.

→ PERFORM THE CLUTCH BREAK-IN STATUS PROCEDURE AND QUICK LEARN.*

NO → SERVICE VALVE BODY WITH SPECIAL ATTENTION TO LOCK-UP CONTROL VALVES.··· → PERFORM QUICK LEARN.*

① TCC Off
Reverse
Overdrive (OD)
TCC On
Underdrive
2-4
Low-Reverse

* – QUICK LEARN PROCEDURE MAY BE REFERRED TO AS SHIFT QUALITY QUICK-LEARN PROCEDURE. CLUTCH BREAK-IN STATUS MAY BE REFERRED TO AS ELECTRONICALLY MODULATED CONVERTER CLUTCH (EMCC) RESET PROCEDURE. SEE CHRYSLER 42LE ARTICLE FOR QUICK LEARN AND CLUTCH BREAK-IN STATUS PROCEDURES. PERFORM TEST 42B – VERIFICATION TEST AFTER ALL PROCEDURES ARE COMPLETED.

94D36874

TEST 18A
CODE 37 OR 47 – SOLENOID SWITCH VALVE

PERFORM TEST 2A BEFORE PROCEEDING.

START TEST 18A.

NOTE: REPLACING THE TRANSMISSION CONTROL MODULE WILL NOT FIX THIS CODE.

DRAIN THE TRANSAXLE.

REMOVE THE TRANSMISSION PAN.

INSPECT THE BOTTOM OF THE PAN FOR CLUTCH OR METAL DEBRIS.

DOES THE PAN CONTAIN EXCESS DEBRIS ?

YES → REPAIR THE TRANSAXLE.*

NO → RECONDITION THE VALVE BODY.*

* – PERFORM TEST 42B – VERIFICATION TEST.

94C36873

TEST 20B

CODES 52, 53 & 54 – CLUTCH ASSEMBLY SLIPPING

PERFORM TEST 2A OR TEST 20A BEFORE PROCEEDING.

1 - Select System DRB
2 - Select Clutch Test

CAUTION!!!
Do not test any gear range for longer than **5 seconds**. Make sure the transaxle fluid level is ok.

NOTE: Replacing the transmission control module will not fix this problem!

1. Raise the vehicle's drive wheels off the ground.

2. Start the engine and step on the brake so the wheels won't rotate.

NOTE: The drive wheels must not be allowed to rotate or the following tests will be blocked.

3. Put the gear select in OD.

4. With the DRB, select **1st gear.**

5. Open the throttle to 30%.

6. With the DRB, monitor the **input rpm.** Allow the engine to return to idle.

NOTE: >> If the input rpm is zero, 1st gear passes.
>> If the input rpm is above zero, 1st gear fails.

7. Record the 1st gear test as "pass" or "fail".

8. Leave the gear select in OD.

9. With the DRB, select **2nd gear** and read the input rpm. Record whether the test passed or failed.

10. With the DRB, select **3rd gear** and read the input rpm. Record whether the test passed or failed.

11. Put the gear select in reverse.

12. With the DRB, select **reverse** and read the input rpm. Record whether the test passed or failed.

TEST RESULTS

>> If 1st gear and reverse fail, the low/reverse clutch may be slipping.
>> If 2nd gear fails, the 2-4 clutch may be slipping.
>> If 3rd gear fails, the OD clutch may be slipping.
>> If 1st, 2nd, 3rd gears fail, the UD clutch may be slipping.
>> If reverse fails, the reverse clutch may be slipping.

94F36876

TEST 20A

CODES 50 & 51 – SPEED ERROR IN REVERSE & 1ST

PERFORM TEST 2A BEFORE PROCEEDING.

94E36875

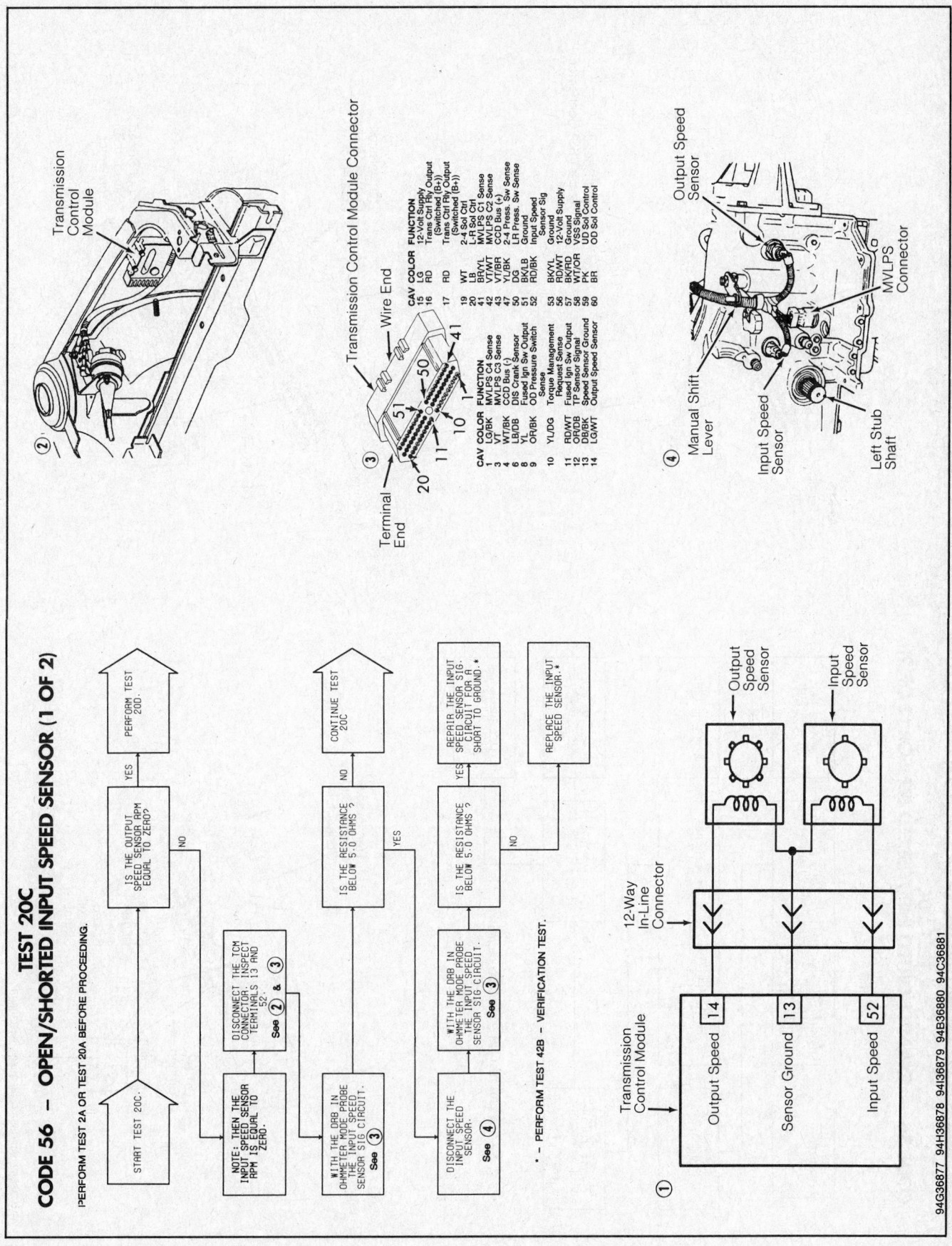

94G36877 94H36878 94I36879 94B36880 94C36881

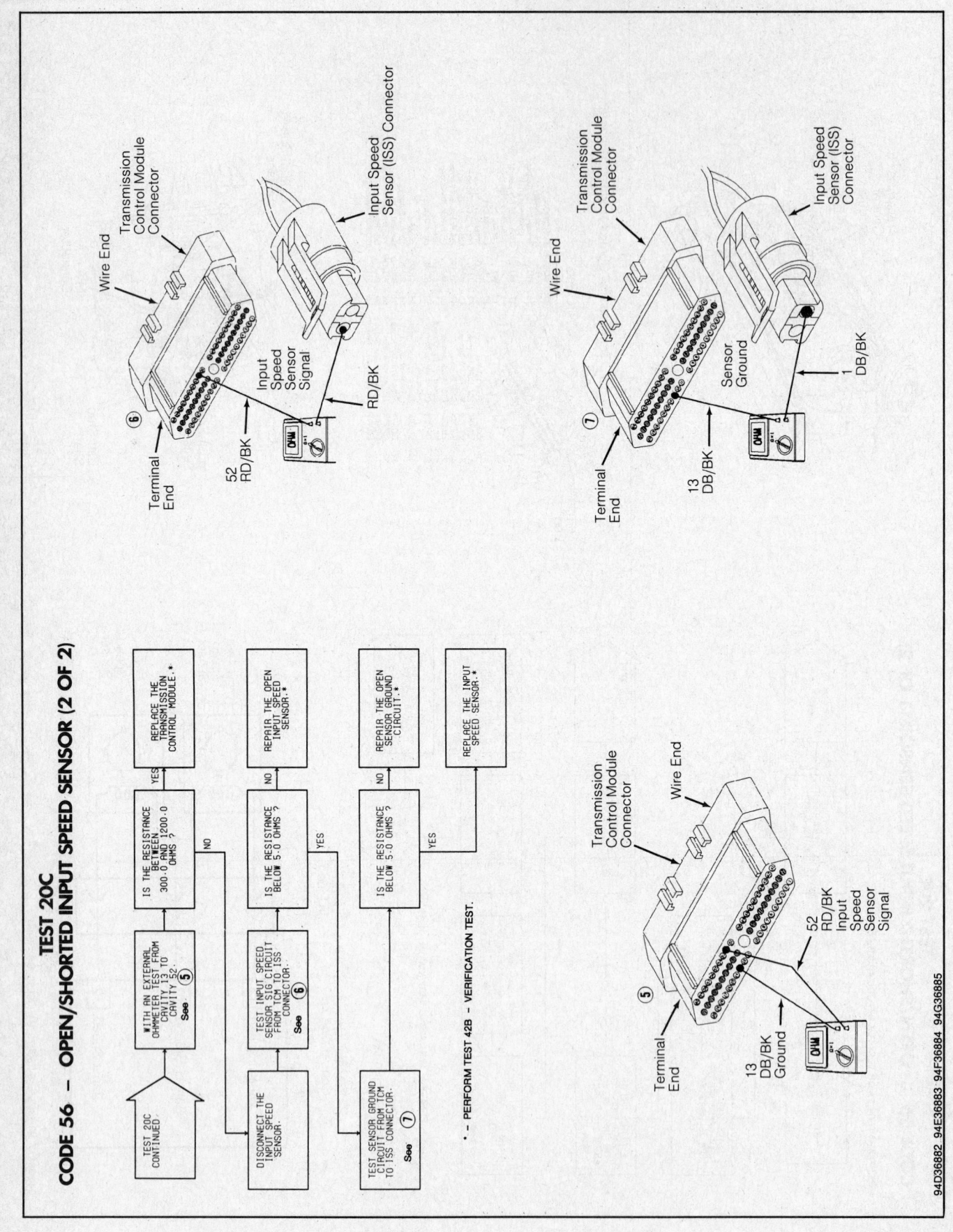

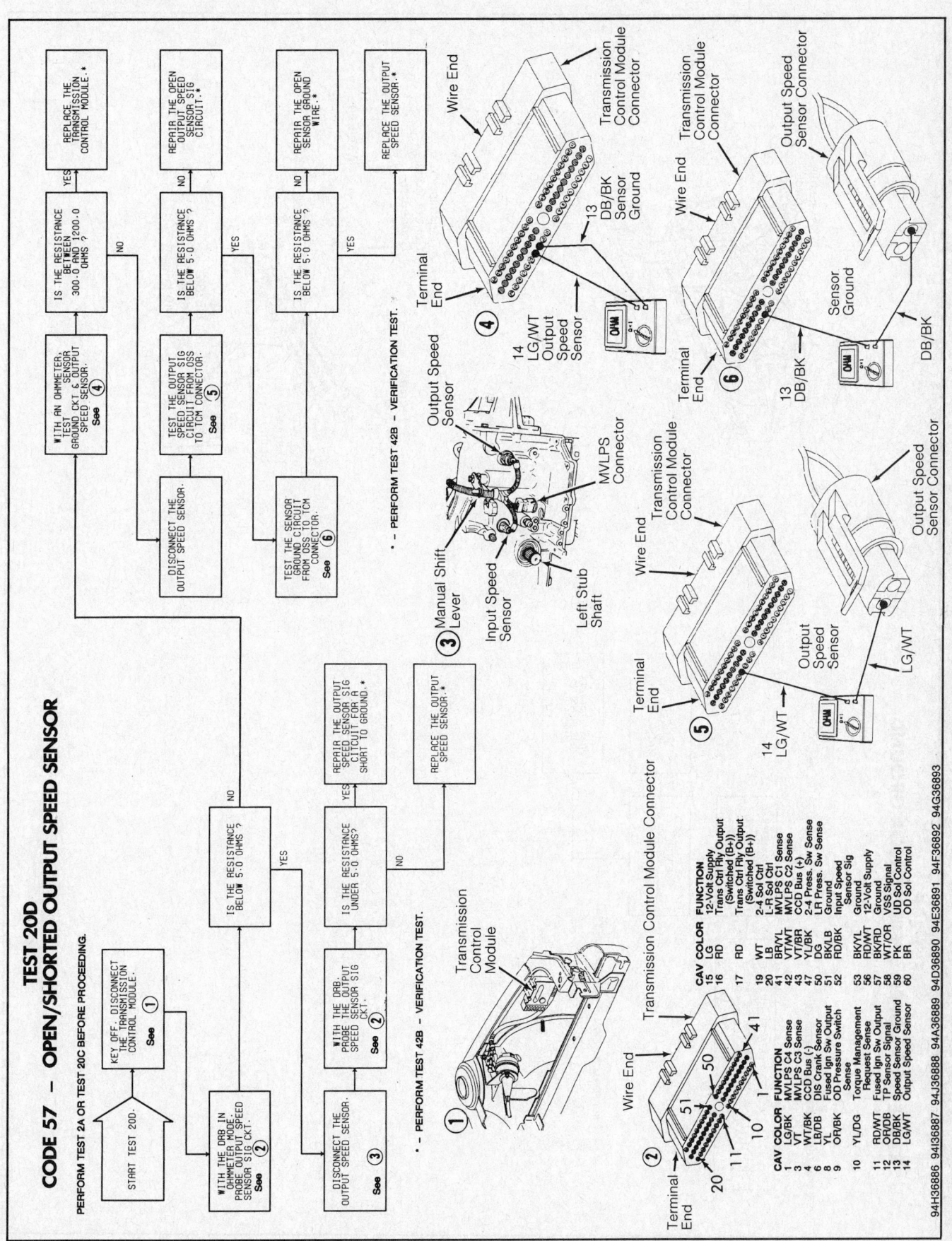

TEST 20D

CODE 57 – OPEN/SHORTED OUTPUT SPEED SENSOR

PERFORM TEST 2A OR TEST 20C BEFORE PROCEEDING.

94H36886   94I36887   94J36888   94A36889   94B36888   94C36890   94D36890   94E36891   94F36892   94G36893

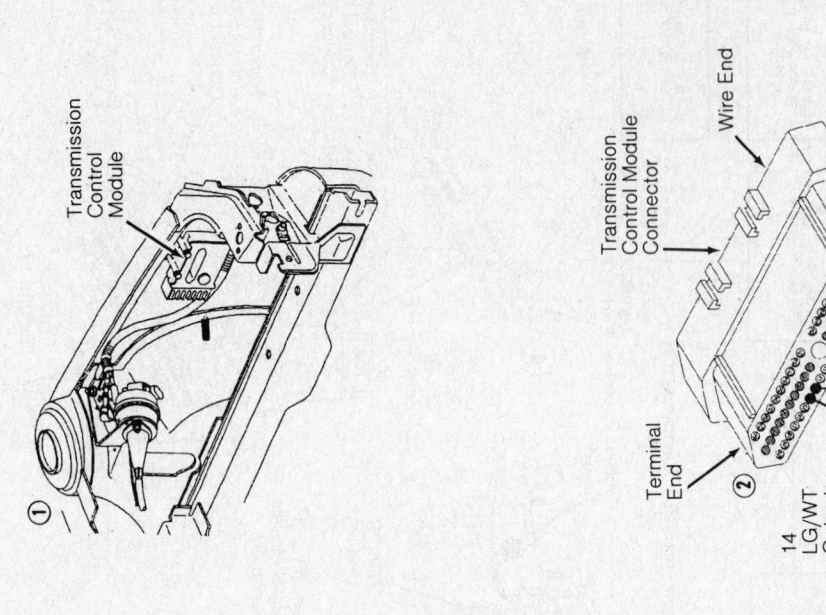

Transmission Control Module

①

Wire End

Transmission Control Module Connector

Terminal End

②

14 LG/WT Output Speed Sensor

13 DB/BK Sensor Ground

OHM

TEST 20E
CODE 58 – OPEN SPEED SENSOR GROUND

PERFORM TEST 2A BEFORE PROCEEDING.

START TEST 20E.

KEY OFF. DISCONNECT THE TRANSMISSION CONTROL MODULE CONNECTOR. See ①

WITH AN OHMMETER, TEST FROM CAVITY 13 TO CAVITY 14. See ②

IS THE RESISTANCE BETWEEN 300.0 AND 1200.0 OHMS ?

YES → REPLACE THE TRANSMISSION CONTROL MODULE. *

NO → REPAIR THE OPEN SENSOR GROUND CIRCUIT. *

* – PERFORM TEST 42B – VERIFICATION TEST.

94H36894 94J36895 94J36896

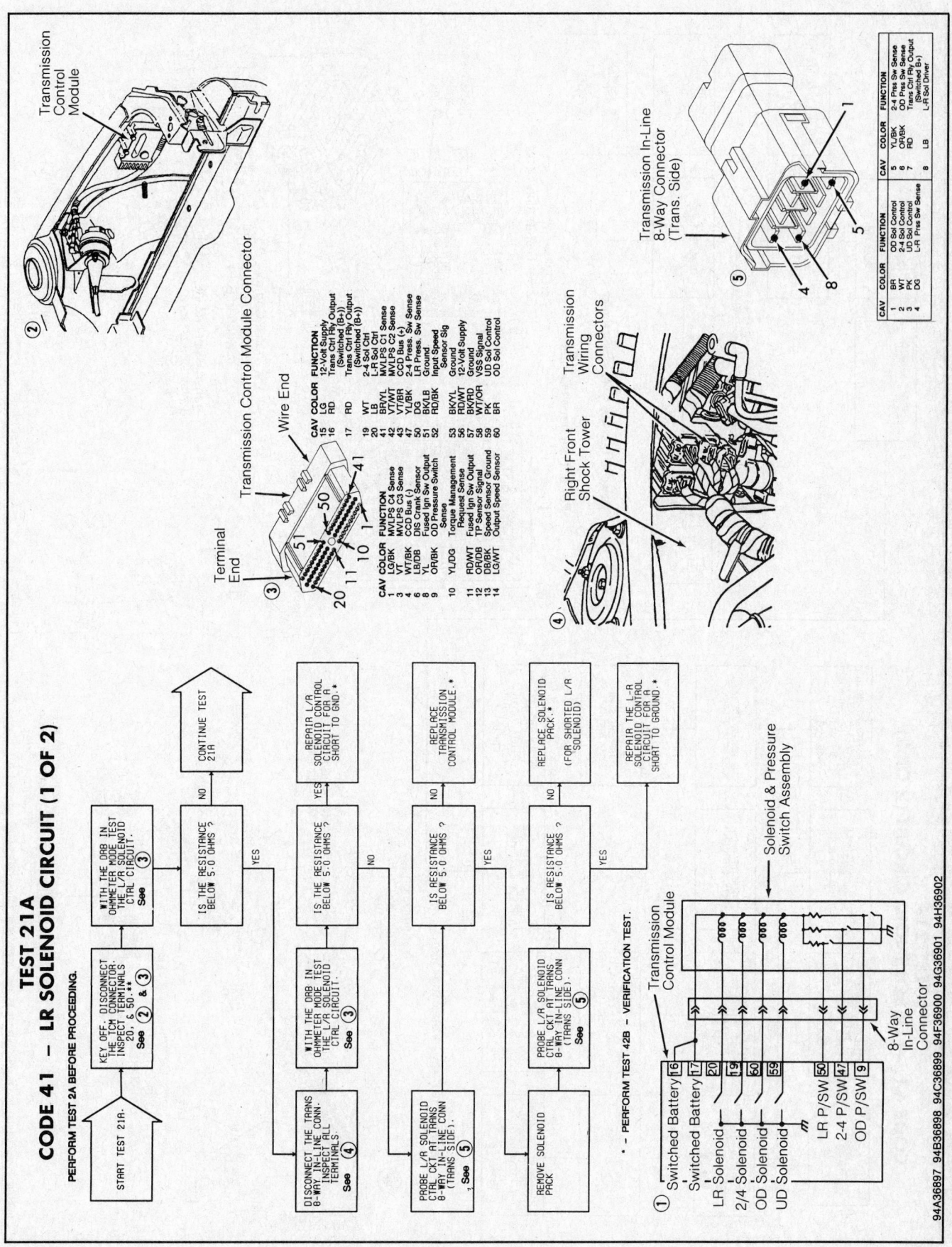

94A36897 94B36898 94C36899 94F36900 94G36901 94H36902

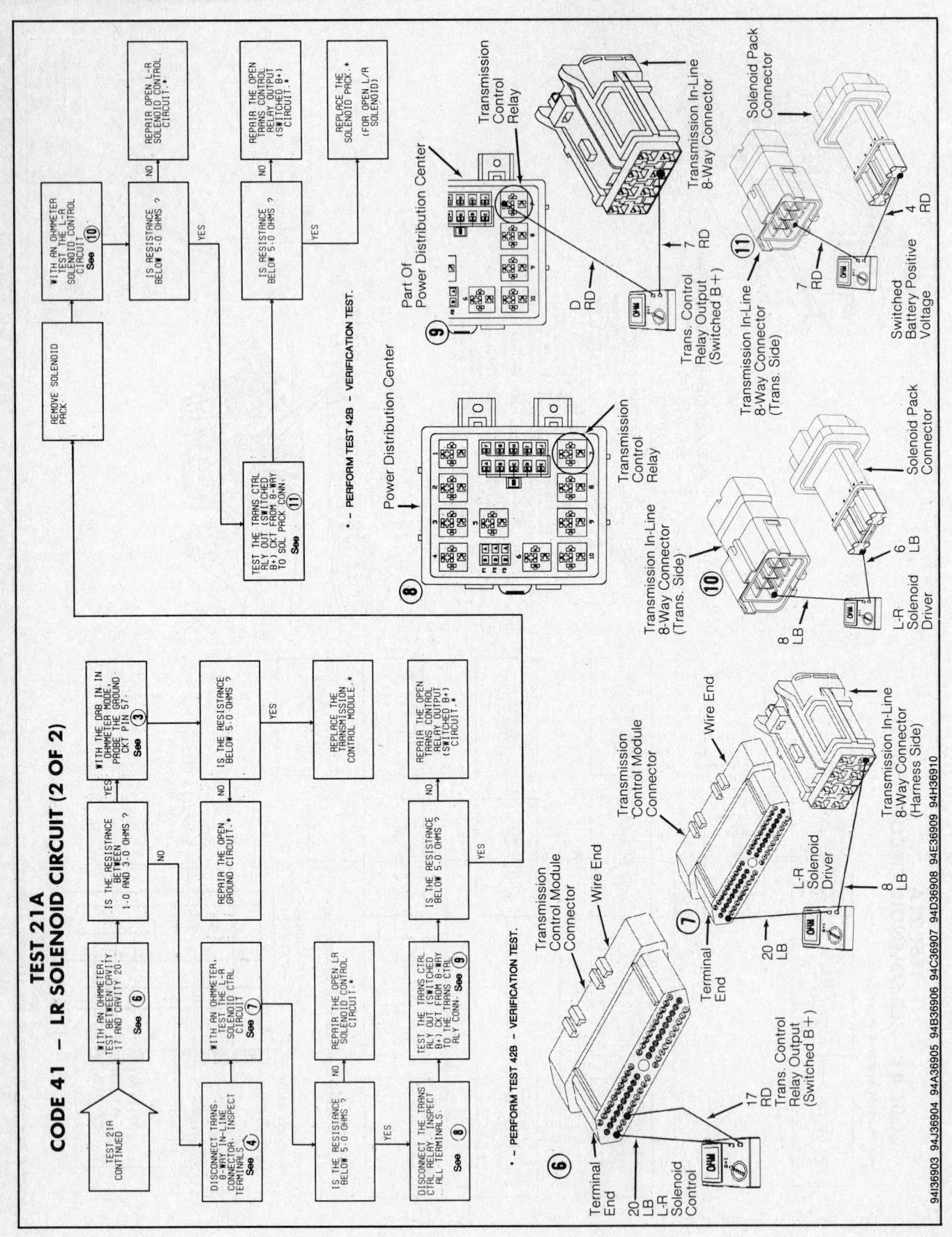

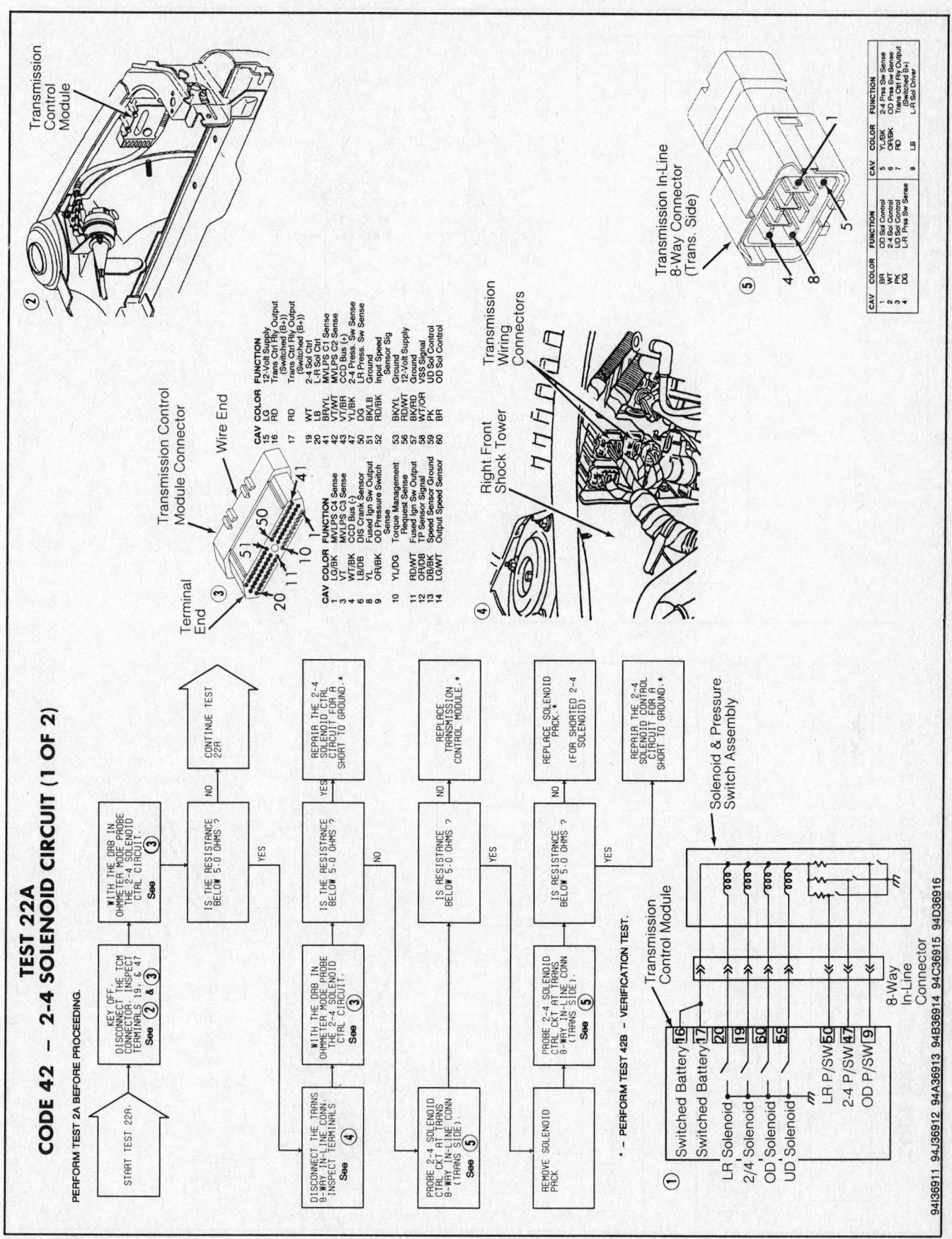

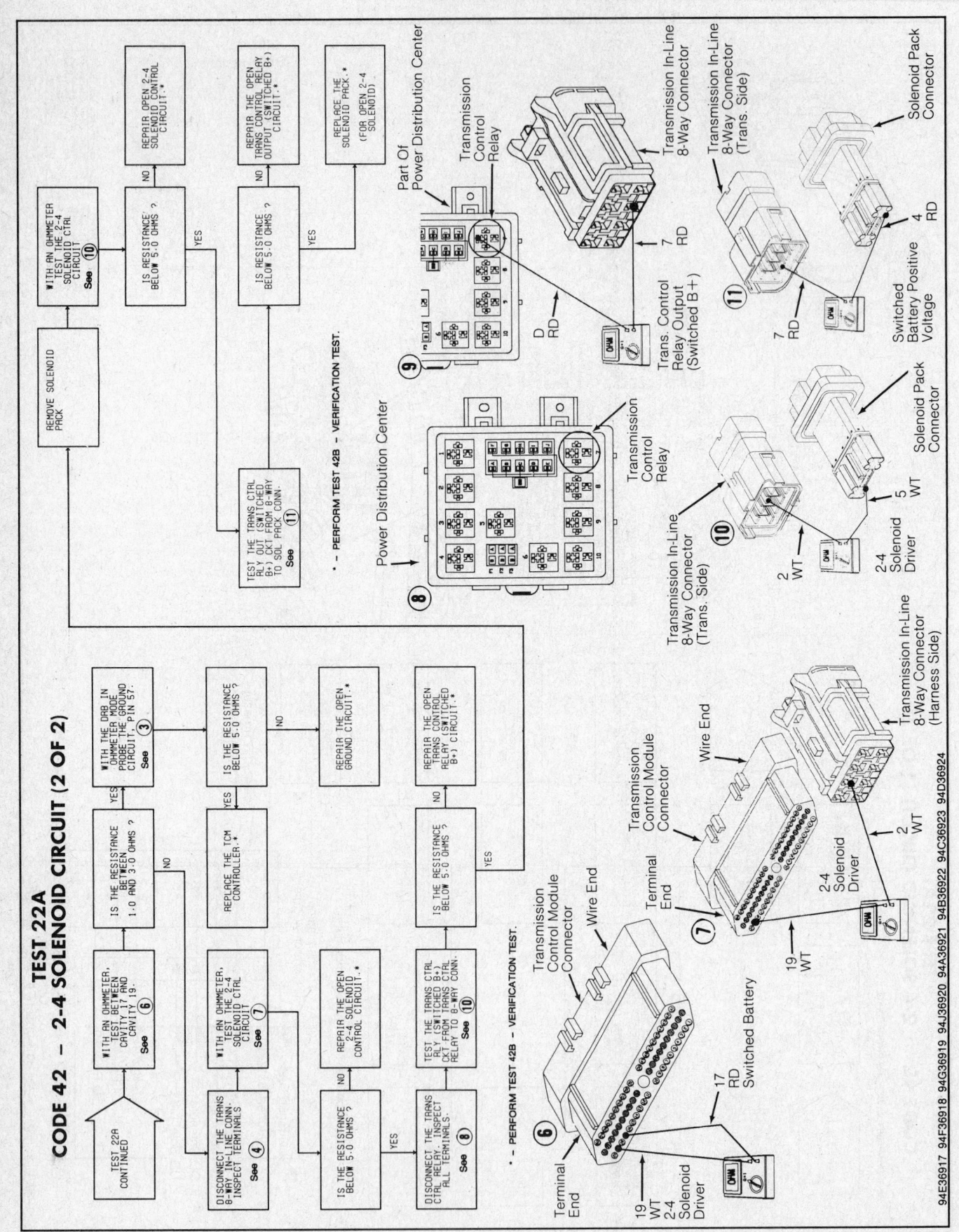

TEST 22A
CODE 42 – 2-4 SOLENOID CIRCUIT (2 OF 2)

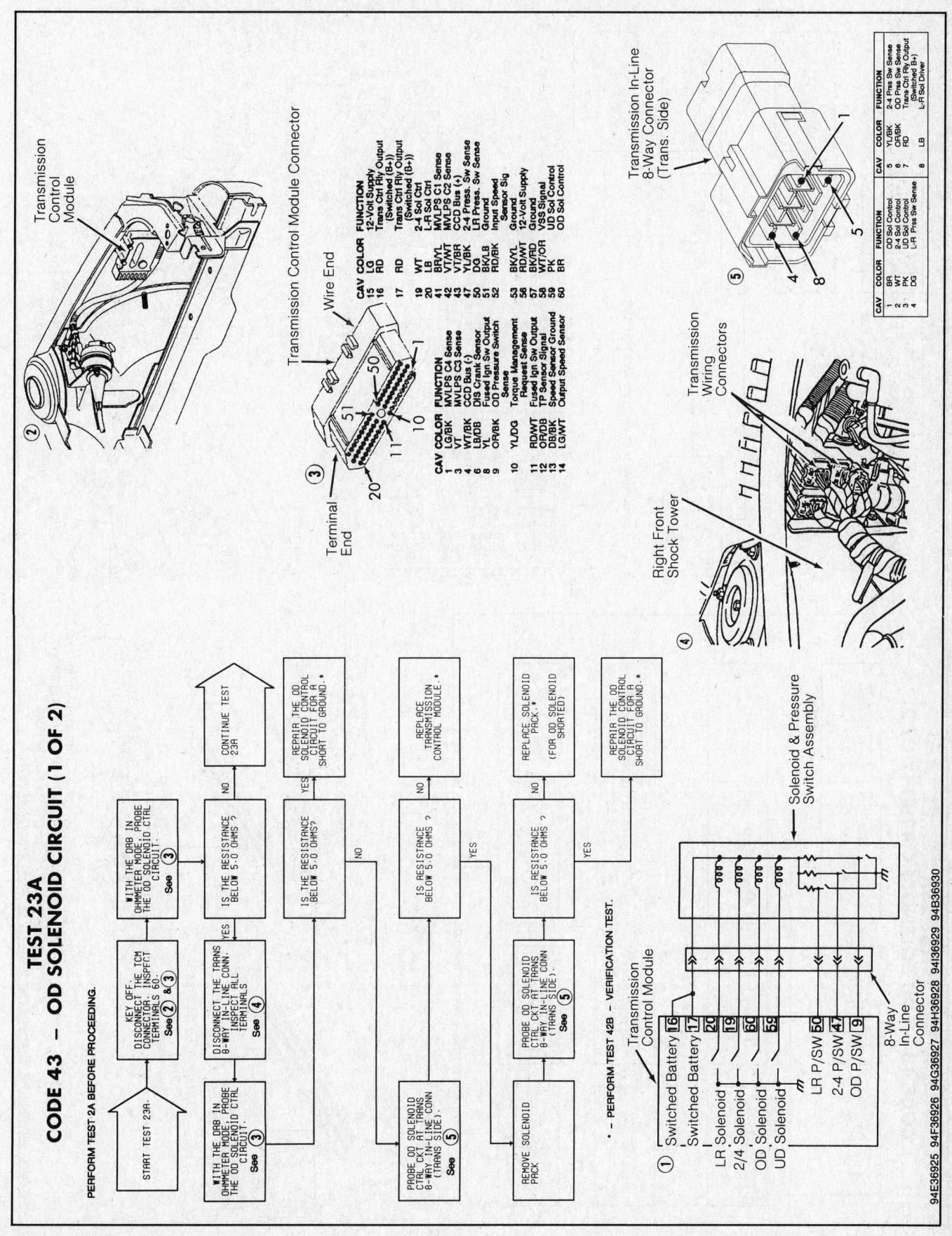

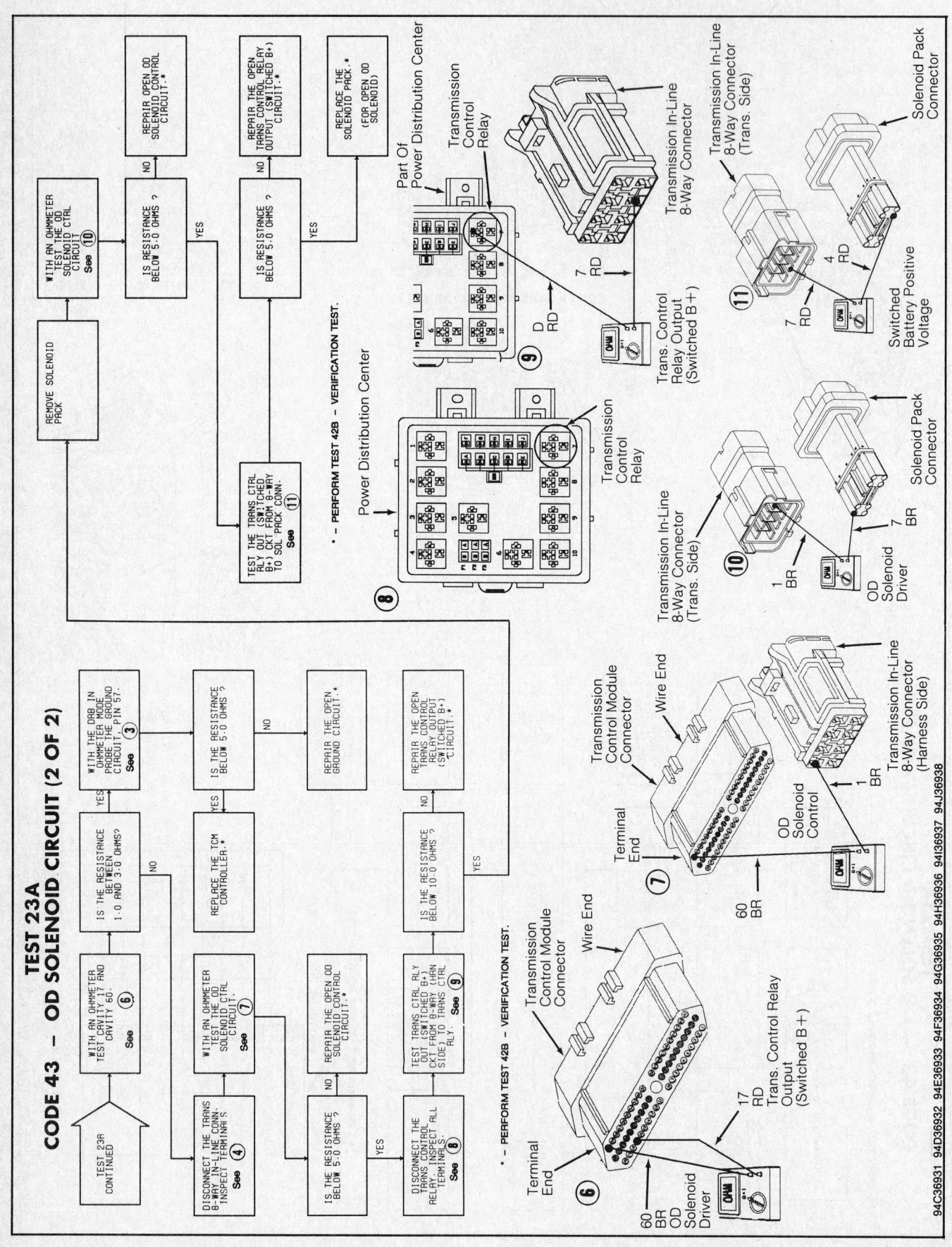

TEST 23A
CODE 43 — OD SOLENOID CIRCUIT (2 OF 2)

94C36931 94D36932 94E36933 94F36934 94G36935 94H36936 94I36937 94J36938

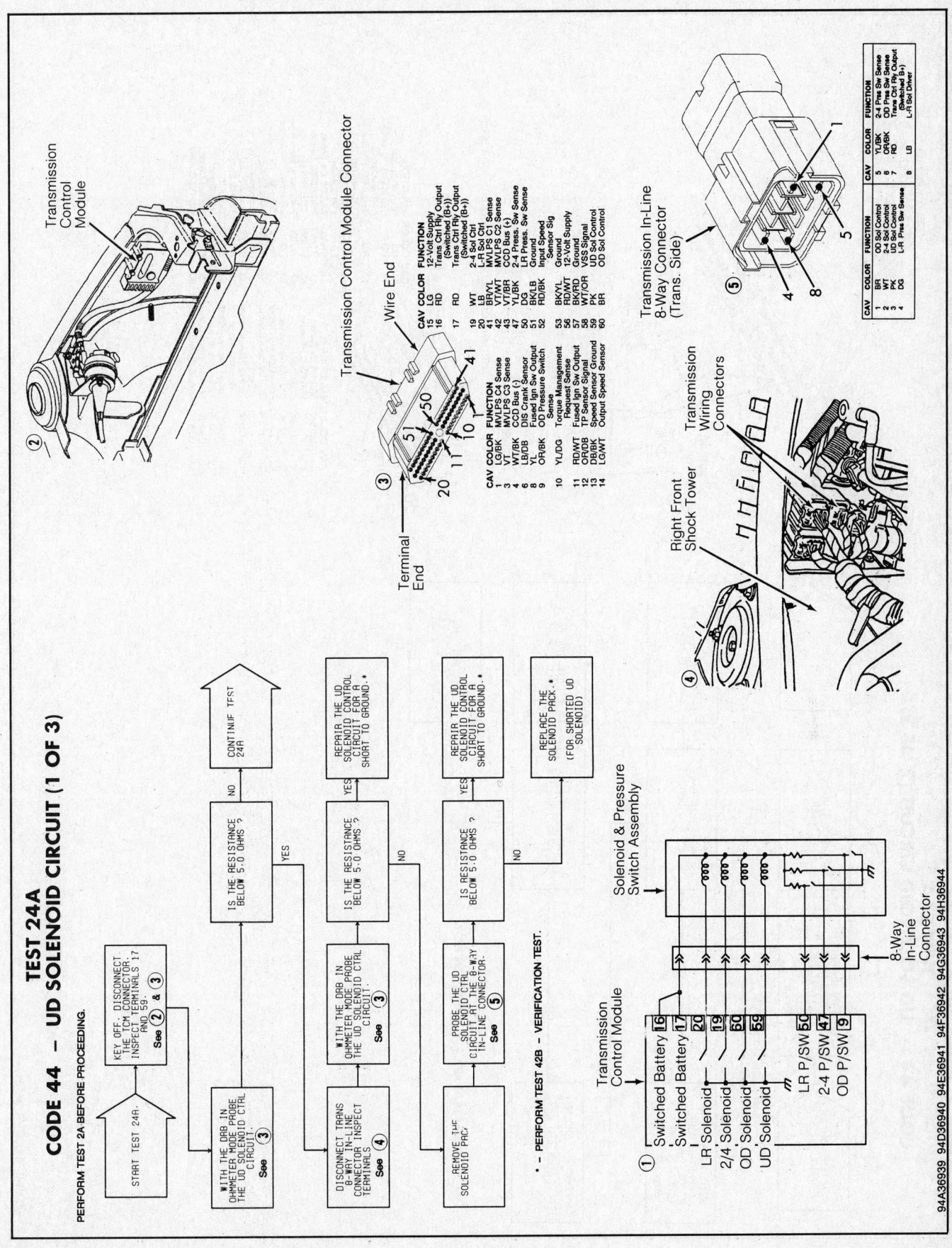

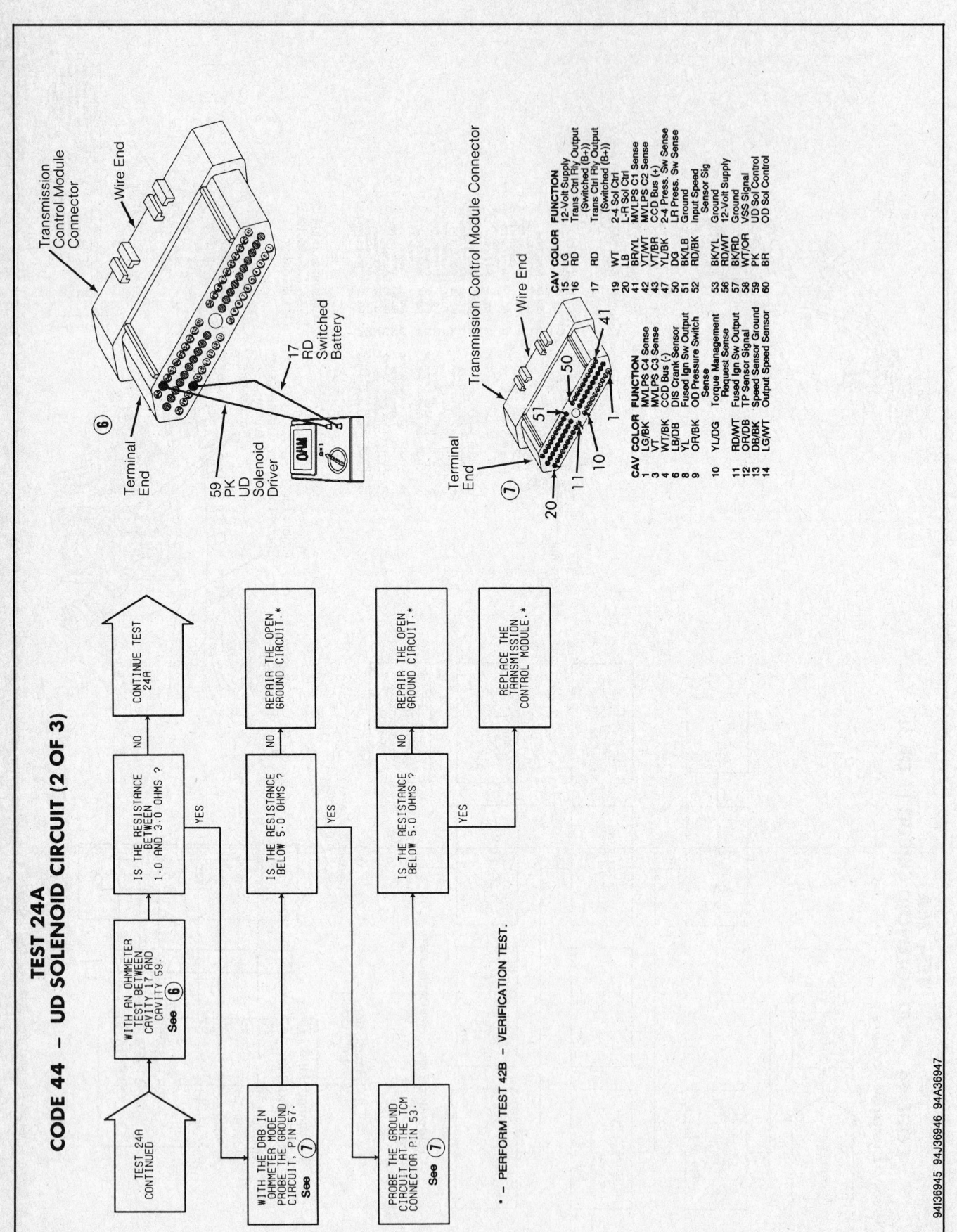

TEST 24A

CODE 44 – UD SOLENOID CIRCUIT (2 OF 3)

* – PERFORM TEST 42B – VERIFICATION TEST.

94J36945 94J36946 94A36947

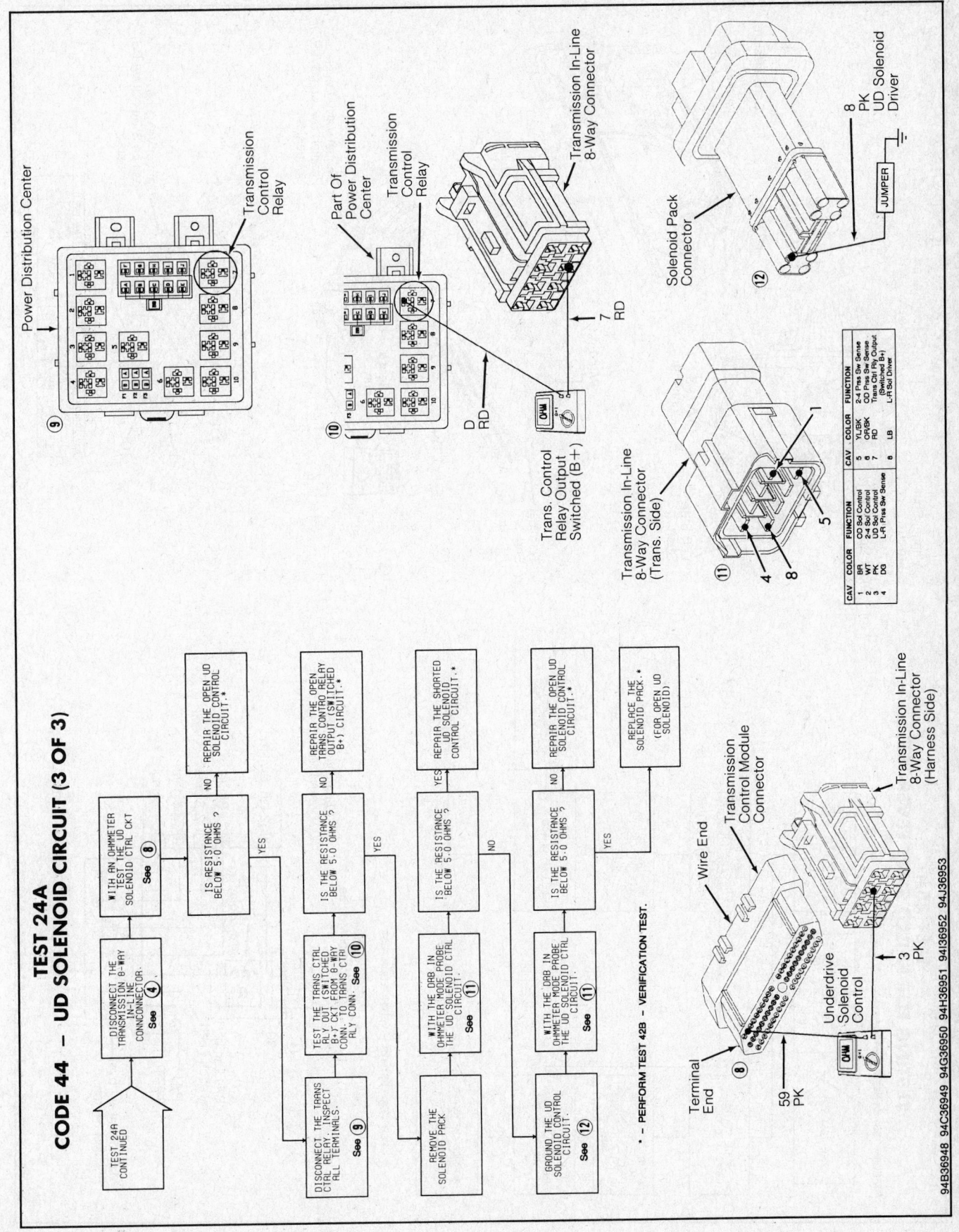

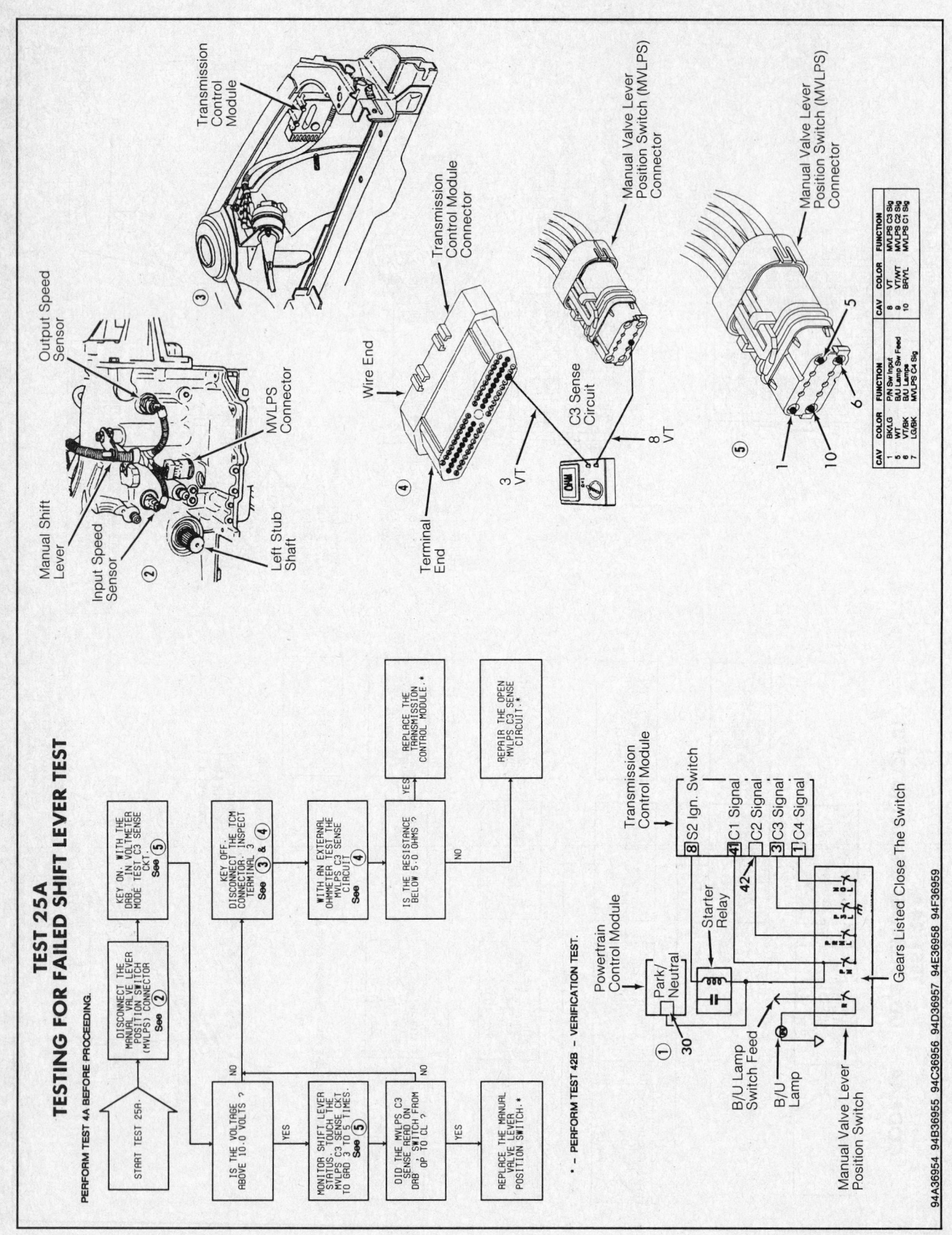

CAV	COLOR	FUNCTION
9	VT	MVLPS C3 Sig
8	VT/WT	MVLPS C2 Sig
10	BR/YL	MVLPS C1 Sig

CAV	COLOR	FUNCTION
1	BK/LG	P/N Sw Input
5	WT	B/U Lamp Sw Feed
6	VT/BK	B/U Lamps
7	LG/BK	MVLPS C4 Sig

94A36954 94B36955 94C36956 94D36957 94E36958 94F36959

TEST 25A
TESTING FOR FAILED SHIFT LEVER TEST

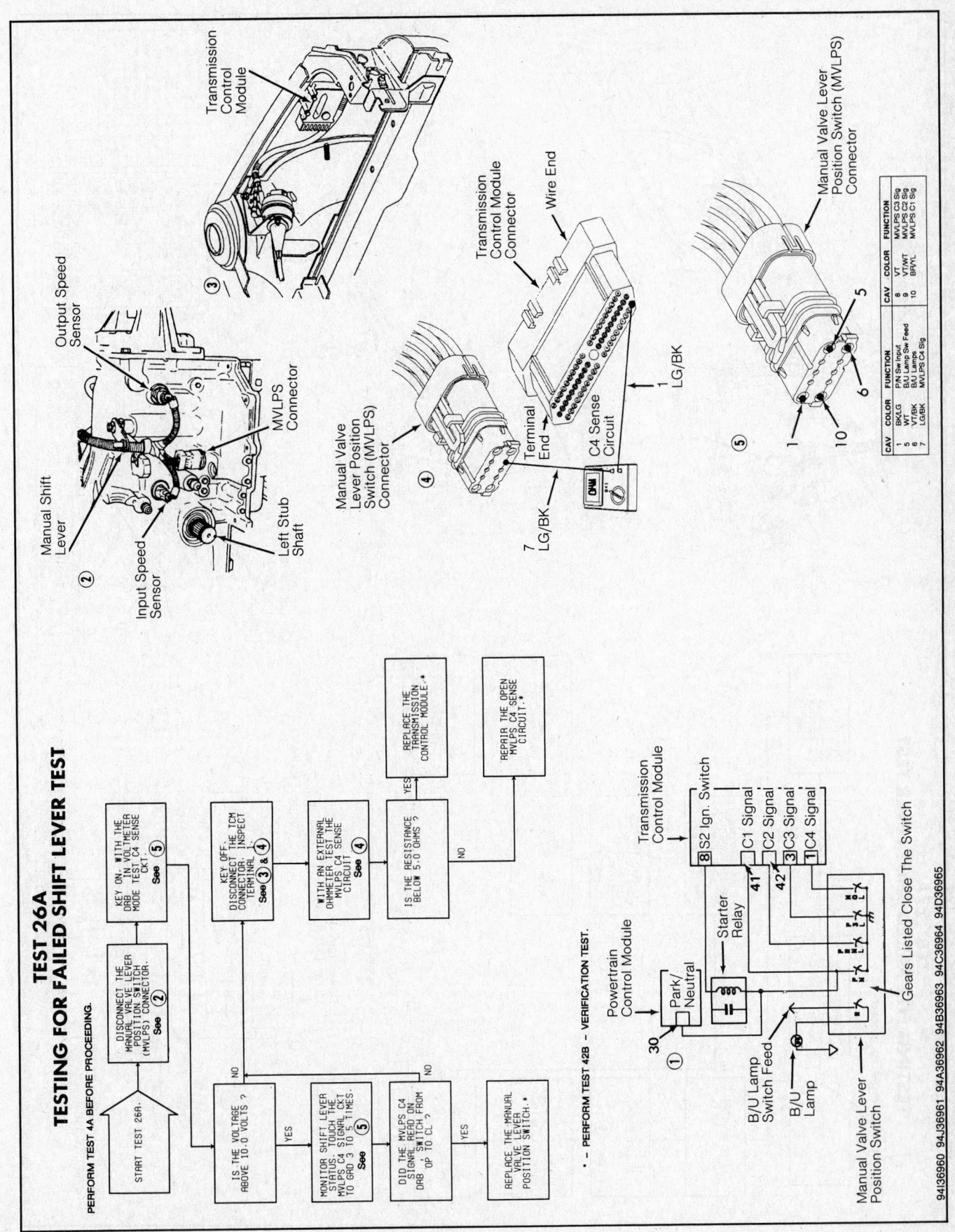

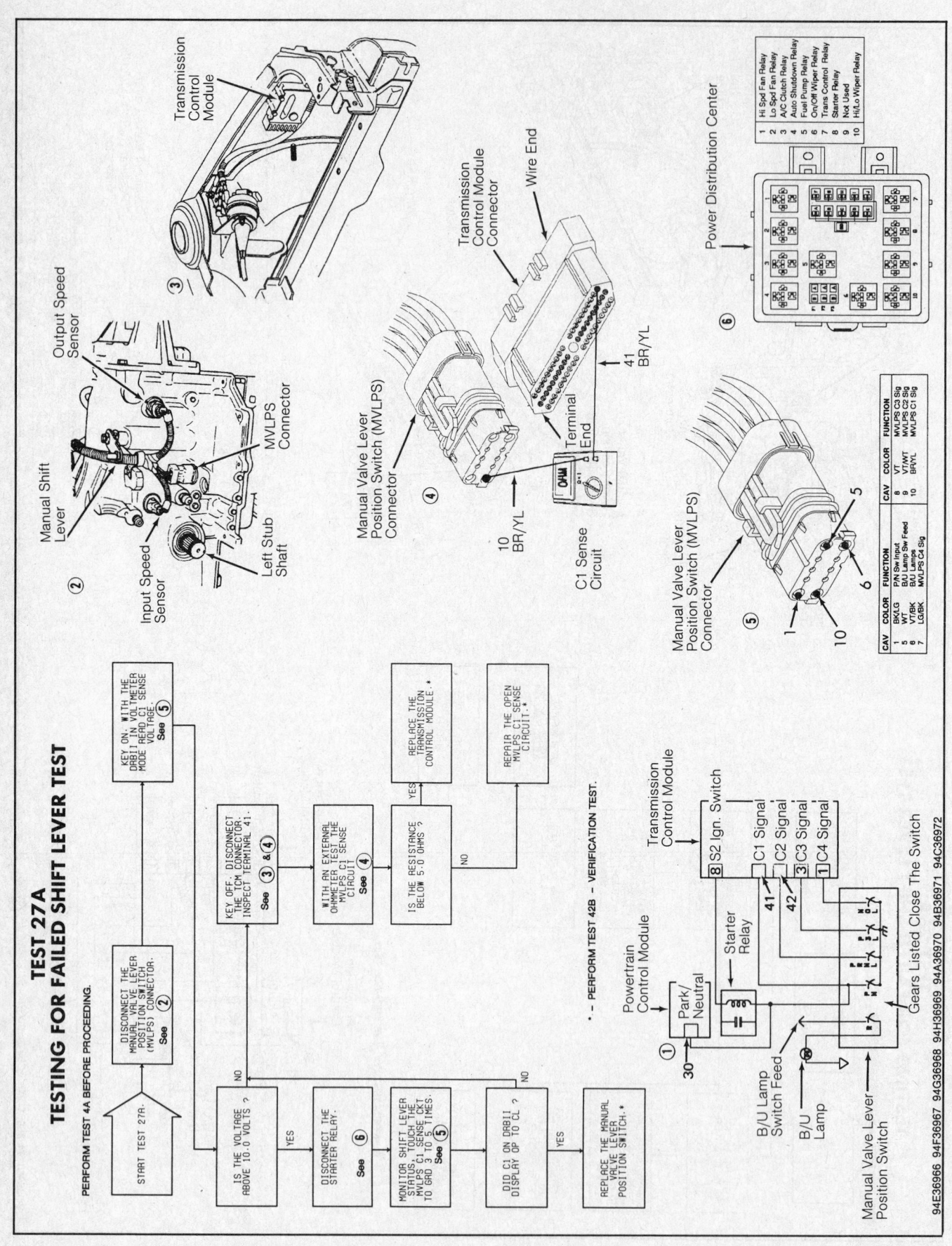

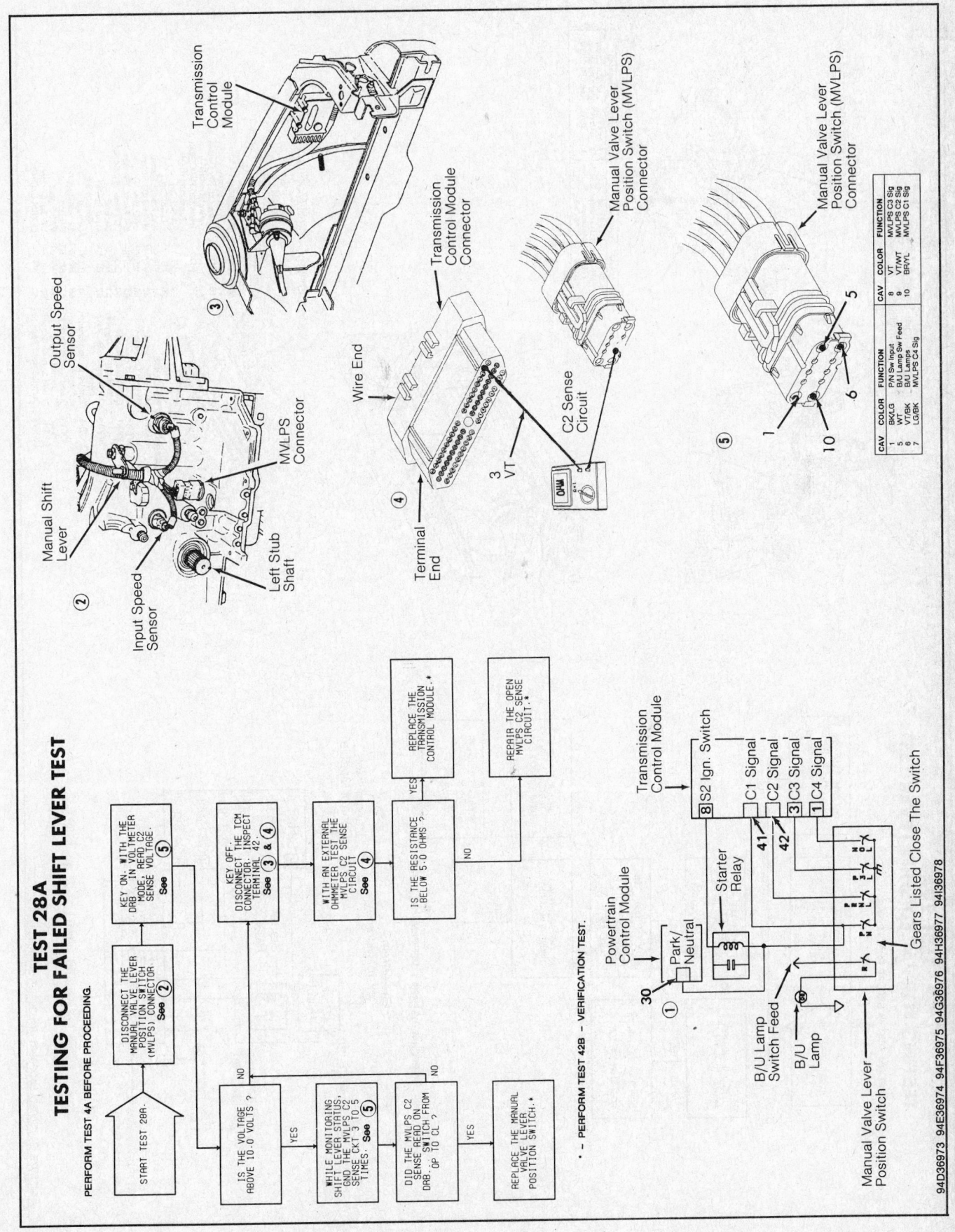

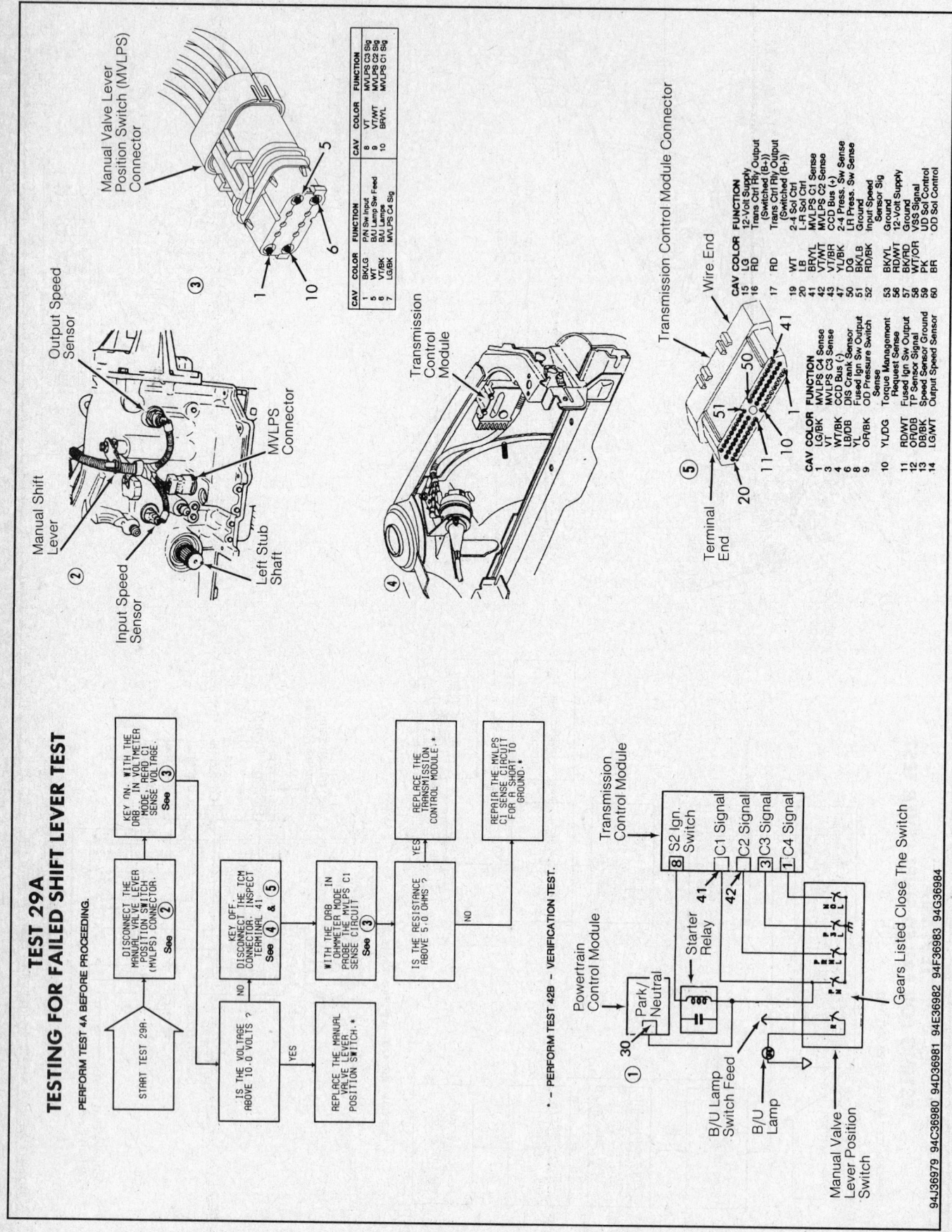

94J36979 94C36980 94D36981 94E36982 94F36983 94G36984

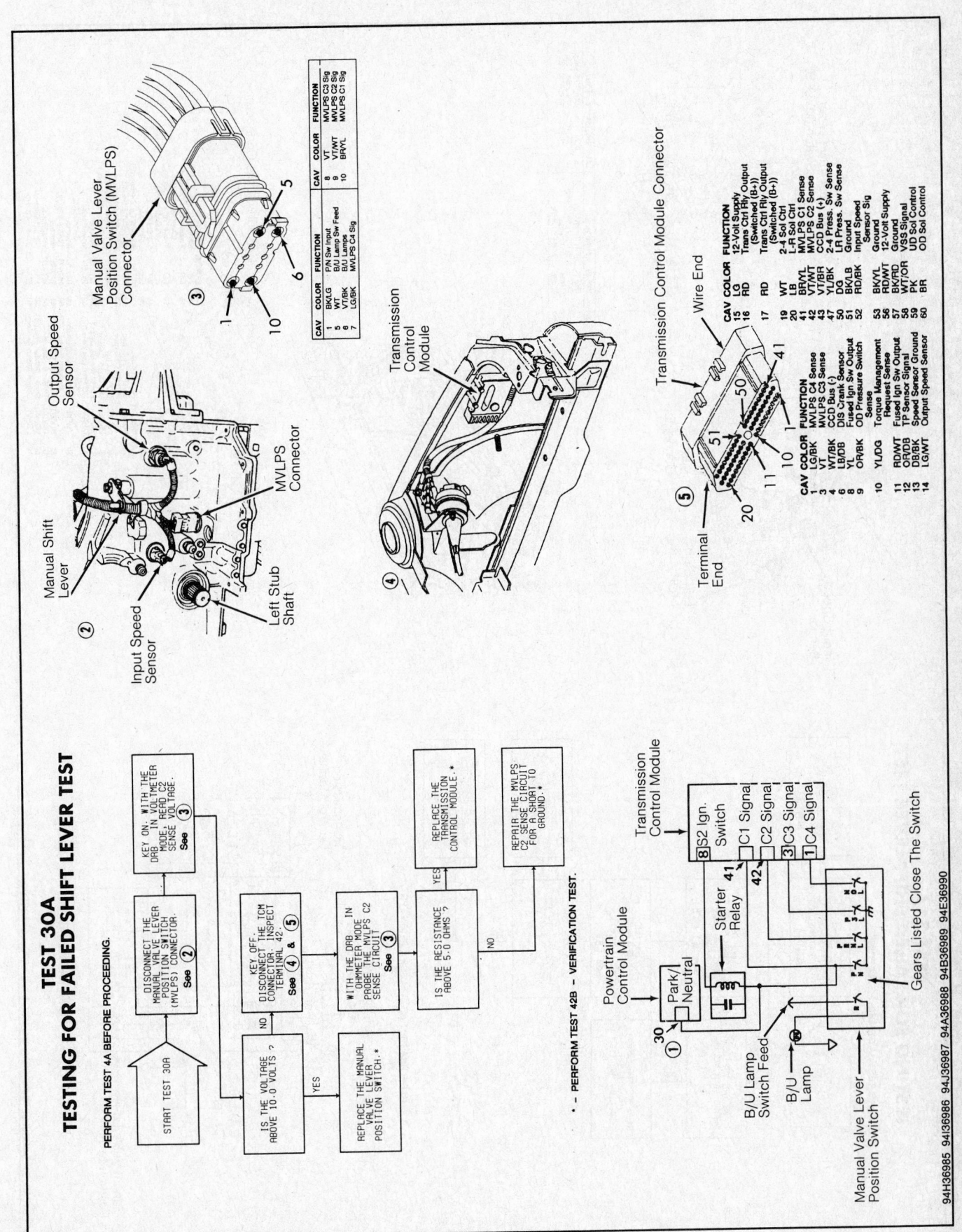

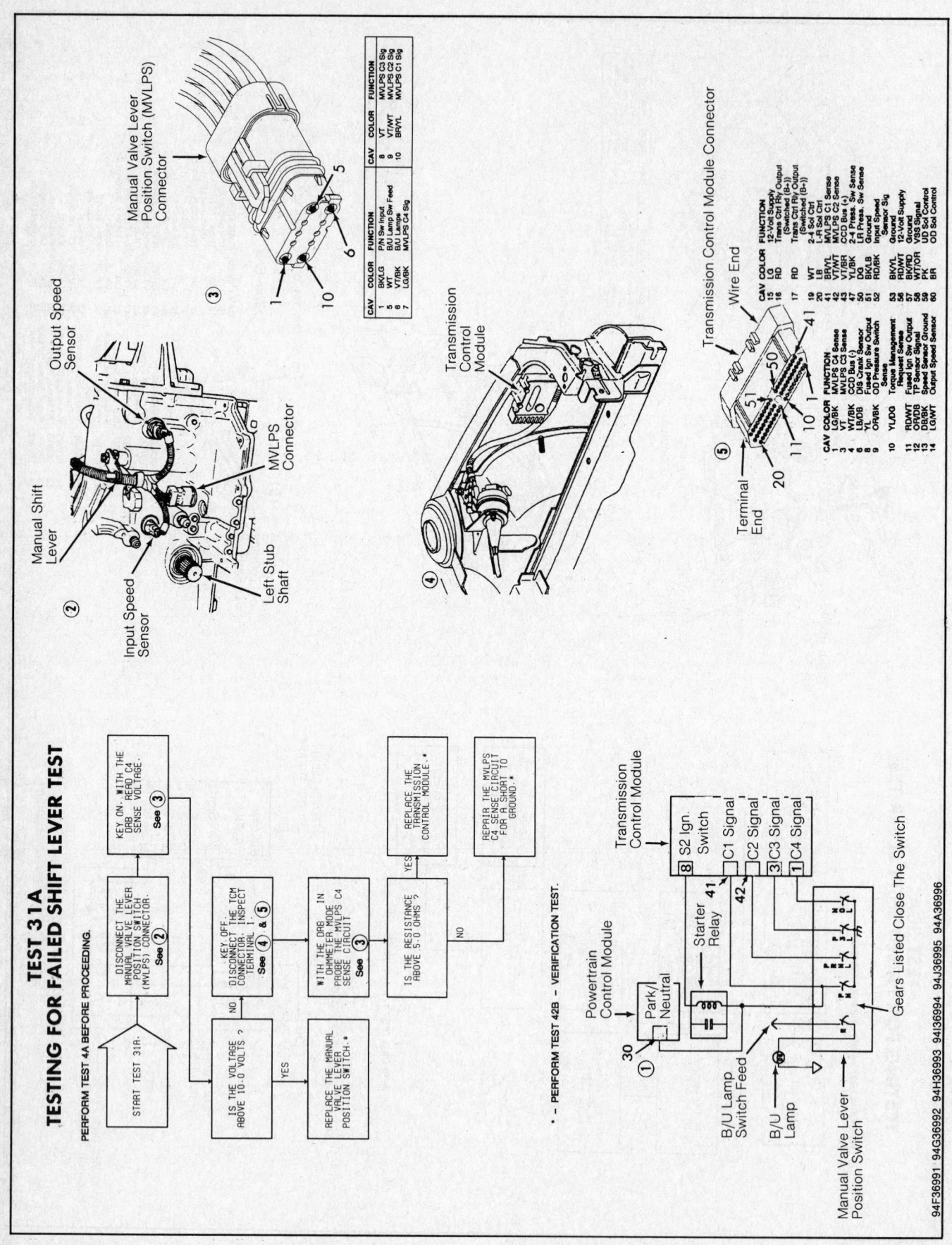

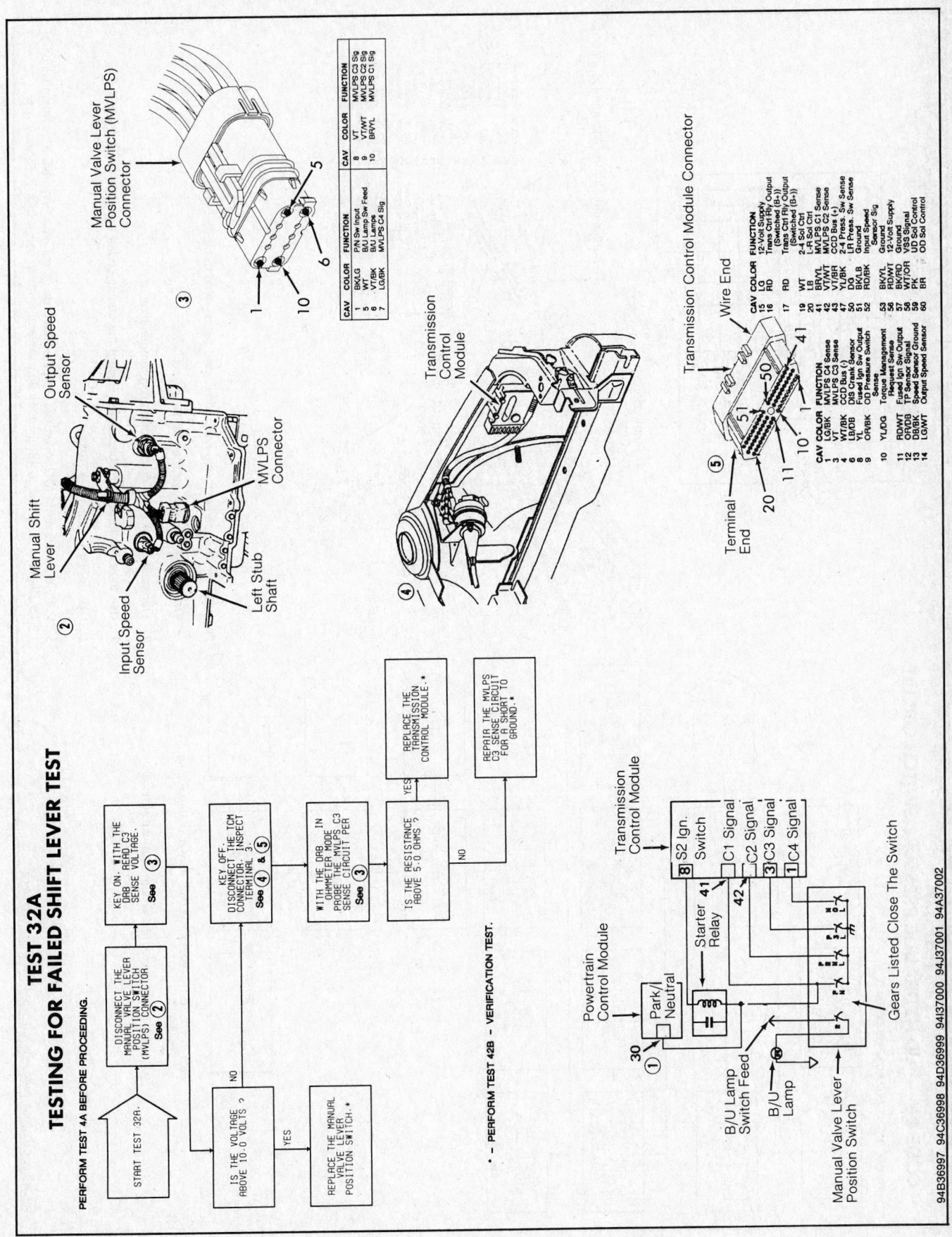

TEST 32A
TESTING FOR FAILED SHIFT LEVER TEST

PERFORM TEST 4A BEFORE PROCEEDING.

94B36997 94C36998 94D36999 94I37000 94J37001 94A37002

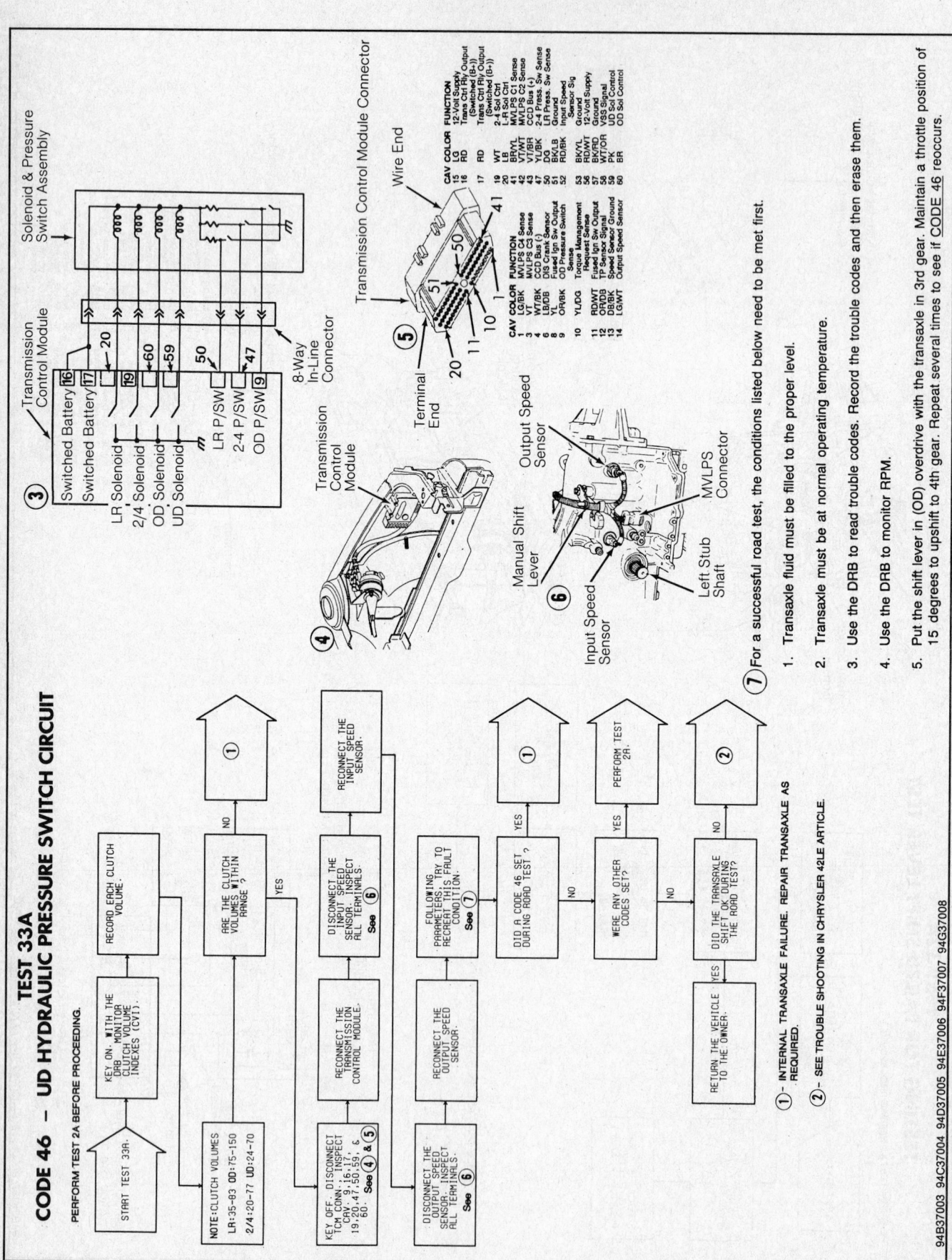

TEST 33A

CODE 46 — UD HYDRAULIC PRESSURE SWITCH CIRCUIT

94B37003 94C37004 94D37005 94E37006 94F37007 94G37008

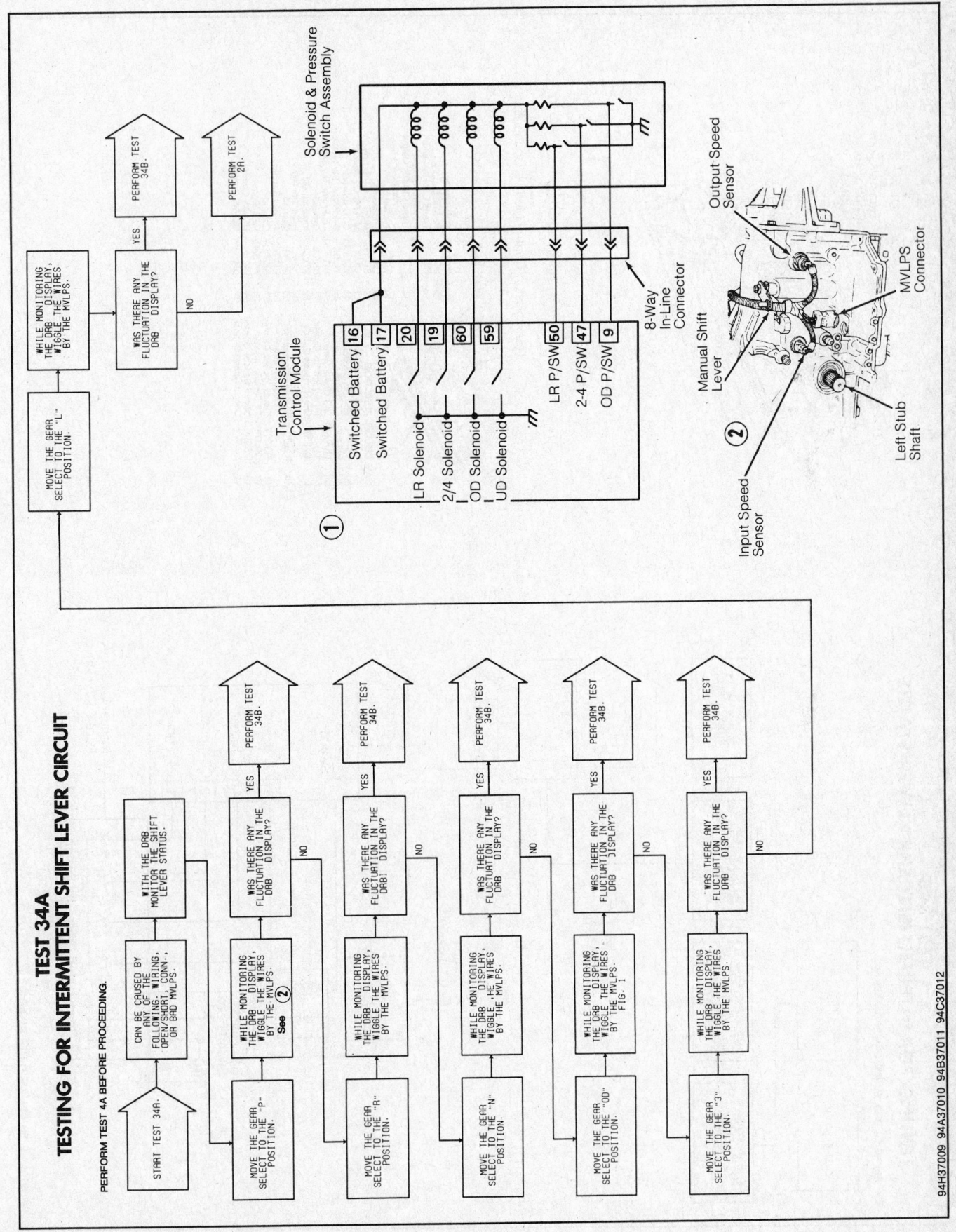

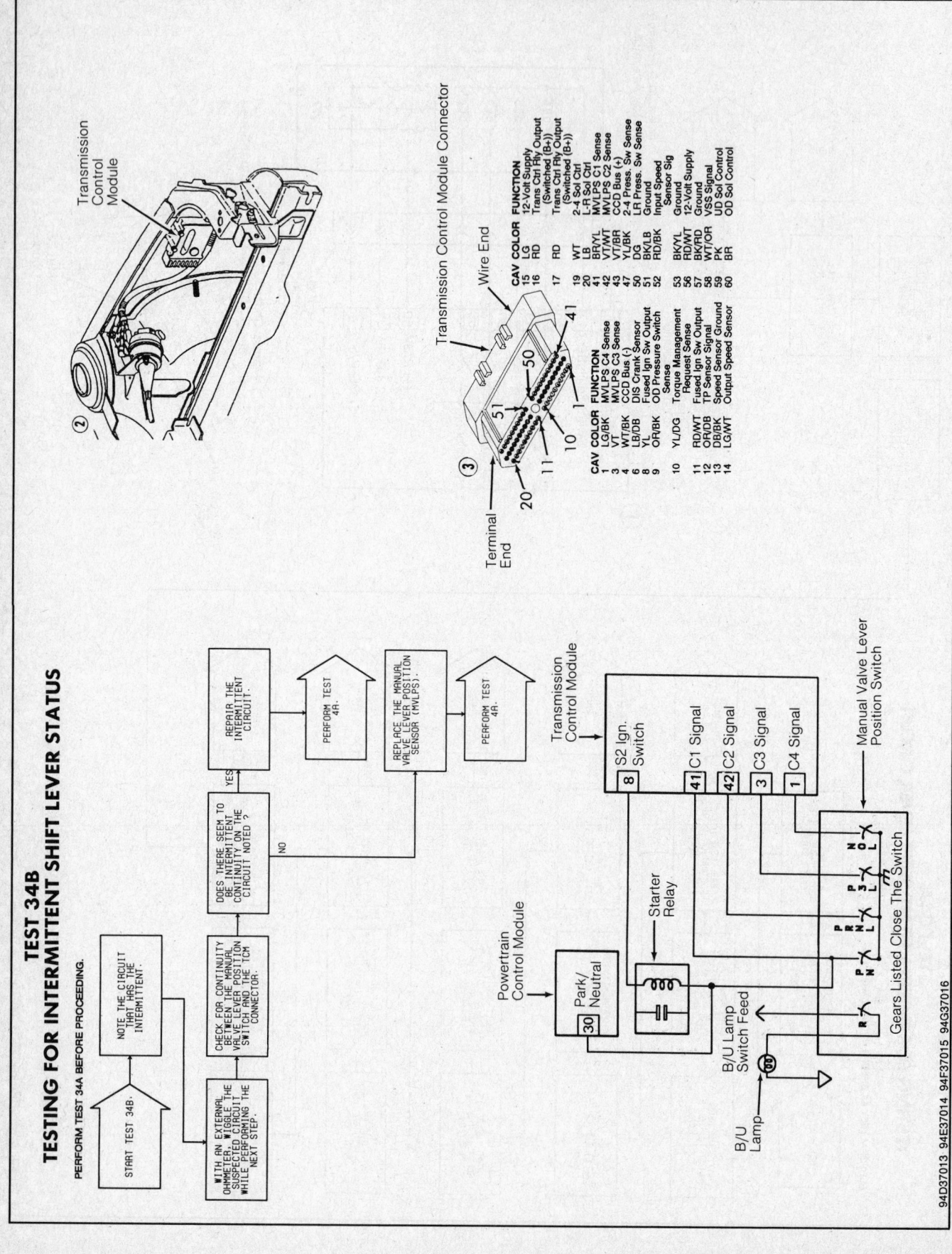

Transmission Control Module

Transmission Control Module Connector

Wire End

Terminal End

CAV	COLOR	FUNCTION
15	LG	12-Volt Supply
16	RD	Trans Ctrl Rly Output (Switched (B+))
17	RD	Trans Ctrl Rly Output (Switched (B+))
19	WT	2-4 Sol Ctrl
20	LB	L-R Sol Ctrl
41	BR/YL	MVLPS C1 Sense
42	VT/WT	MVLPS C2 Sense
43	YL/BK	CCD Bus (+)
47	VT/BK	2-4 Press. Sw Sense
50	DG	LR Press. Sw Sense
51	BK/LB	Input Speed Sensor Sig
52	RD/BK	Ground
53	BK/YL	Ground
56	RD/WT	12-Volt Supply
57	BK/RD	Ground
58	WT/OR	VSS Signal
59	PK	UD Sol Control
60	BR	OD Sol Control

CAV	COLOR	FUNCTION
1	LG/BK	MVLPS C4 Sense
3	VT	MVLPS C3 Sense
4	WT/BK	CCD Bus (-)
6	LB/DB	DIS Crank Sensor
8	YL	Fused Ign Sw Output
9	OR/BK	OD Pressure Switch Sense
10	YL/DG	Torque Management Request Sense
11	RD/WT	Fused Ign Sw Output
12	OR/DB	TP Sensor Signal
13	DB/BK	Speed Sensor Ground
14	LG/WT	Output Speed Sensor

TEST 34B
TESTING FOR INTERMITTENT SHIFT LEVER STATUS

PERFORM TEST 34A BEFORE PROCEEDING.

START TEST 34B.

WITH AN EXTERNAL OHMMETER, WIGGLE THE SUSPECTED CIRCUIT WHILE PERFORMING THE NEXT STEP.

NOTE THE CIRCUIT THAT HAS THE INTERMITTENT.

CHECK FOR CONTINUITY BETWEEN THE MANUAL VALVE LEVER POSITION SWITCH AND THE TCM CONNECTOR.

DOES THERE SEEM TO BE INTERMITTENT CONTINUITY ON THE CIRCUIT NOTED?

YES — REPAIR THE INTERMITTENT CIRCUIT. → PERFORM TEST 4R.

NO — REPLACE THE MANUAL VALVE LEVER POSITION SENSOR (MVLPS). → PERFORM TEST 4R.

Transmission Control Module

S2 Ign. Switch — 8
C1 Signal — 41
C2 Signal — 42
C3 Signal — 3
C4 Signal — 1

Manual Valve Lever Position Switch

Powertrain Control Module

Park/Neutral — 30

Starter Relay

B/U Lamp Switch Feed

B/U Lamp

Gears Listed Close The Switch

94D37013 94E37014 94F37015 94G37016

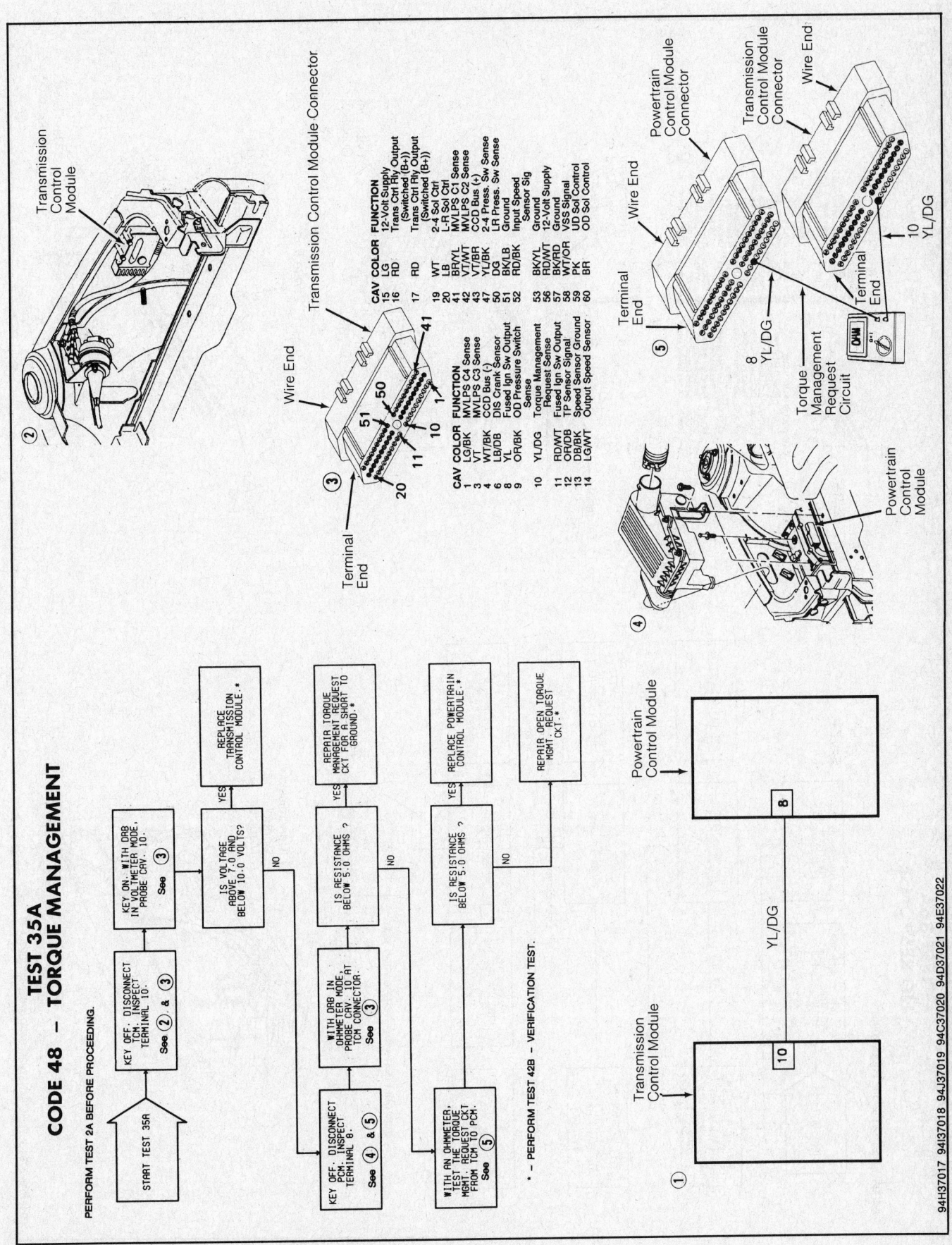

Transmission Control Module

Transmission Control Module Connector

Wire End

Terminal End

Transmission Control Module Connector

Powertrain Control Module Connector

Wire End

Terminal End

YL/DG

Terminal End

Wire End

Torque Management Request Circuit

8 YL/DG

10 YL/DG

Powertrain Control Module

CAV	COLOR	FUNCTION
15	LG	12-Volt Supply
16	RD	Trans Ctrl Rly Output (Switched (B+))
17	RD	Trans Ctrl Rly Output (Switched (B+))
19	WT	2-4 Sol Ctrl
20	LB	L-R Sol Ctrl
41	BF/YL	MVLPS C1 Sense
42	VT/WT	MVLPS C2 Sense
43	VT/BR	CCD Bus (+)
50	DG	LR Press. Sw Sense
51	BK/LB	Ground
52	RD/BK	Input Speed Sensor Sig
53	BK/YL	Ground
56	RD/WT	12-Volt Supply
57	BK/RD	Ground
58	WT/OR	VSS Signal
59	PK	UD Sol Control
60	BR	OD Sol Control

CAV	COLOR	FUNCTION
1	LG/BK	MVLPS C4 Sense
3	VT	MVLPS C3 Sense
4	WT/BK	CCD Bus (+)
6	LB/DB	DIS Crank Sensor
8	YL	Fused Ign Sw Output
9	OR/BK	OD Pressure Switch Sense
10	YL/DG	Torque Management Request Sense
11	RD/WT	Fused Ign Sw Output
12	OR/DB	TP Sensor Signal
13	DB/BK	Speed Sensor Ground
14	LG/WT	Output Speed Sensor

Powertrain Control Module

CODE 48 – TORQUE MANAGEMENT

TEST 35A

PERFORM TEST 2A BEFORE PROCEEDING.

START TEST 35A

KEY OFF. DISCONNECT TCM. INSPECT TERMINAL 10.
See ② & ③

KEY ON. WITH DRB IN VOLTMETER MODE, PROBE CRV. 10.
See ③

IS VOLTAGE ABOVE 7.0 AND BELOW 10.0 VOLTS?

YES → REPLACE TRANSMISSION CONTROL MODULE. *

NO ↓

KEY OFF. DISCONNECT PCM. INSPECT TERMINAL 8.
See ④ & ⑤

WITH DRB IN OHMMETER MODE, PROBE CRV. 10 AT TCM CONNECTOR.
See ③

IS RESISTANCE BELOW 5.0 OHMS ?

YES → REPAIR TORQUE MANAGEMENT REQUEST CKT FOR A SHORT TO GROUND. *

NO ↓

WITH AN OHMMETER, TEST TORQUE MGMT. REQUEST CKT FROM TCM TO PCM.
See ⑤

IS RESISTANCE BELOW 5.0 OHMS ?

YES → REPLACE POWERTRAIN CONTROL MODULE. *

NO ↓

REPAIR OPEN TORQUE MGMT. REQUEST CKT. *

* – PERFORM TEST 42B – VERIFICATION TEST.

Powertrain Control Module

8

YL/DG

Transmission Control Module

10

①

94H37017 94J37018 94J37019 94C37020 94D37021 94E37022

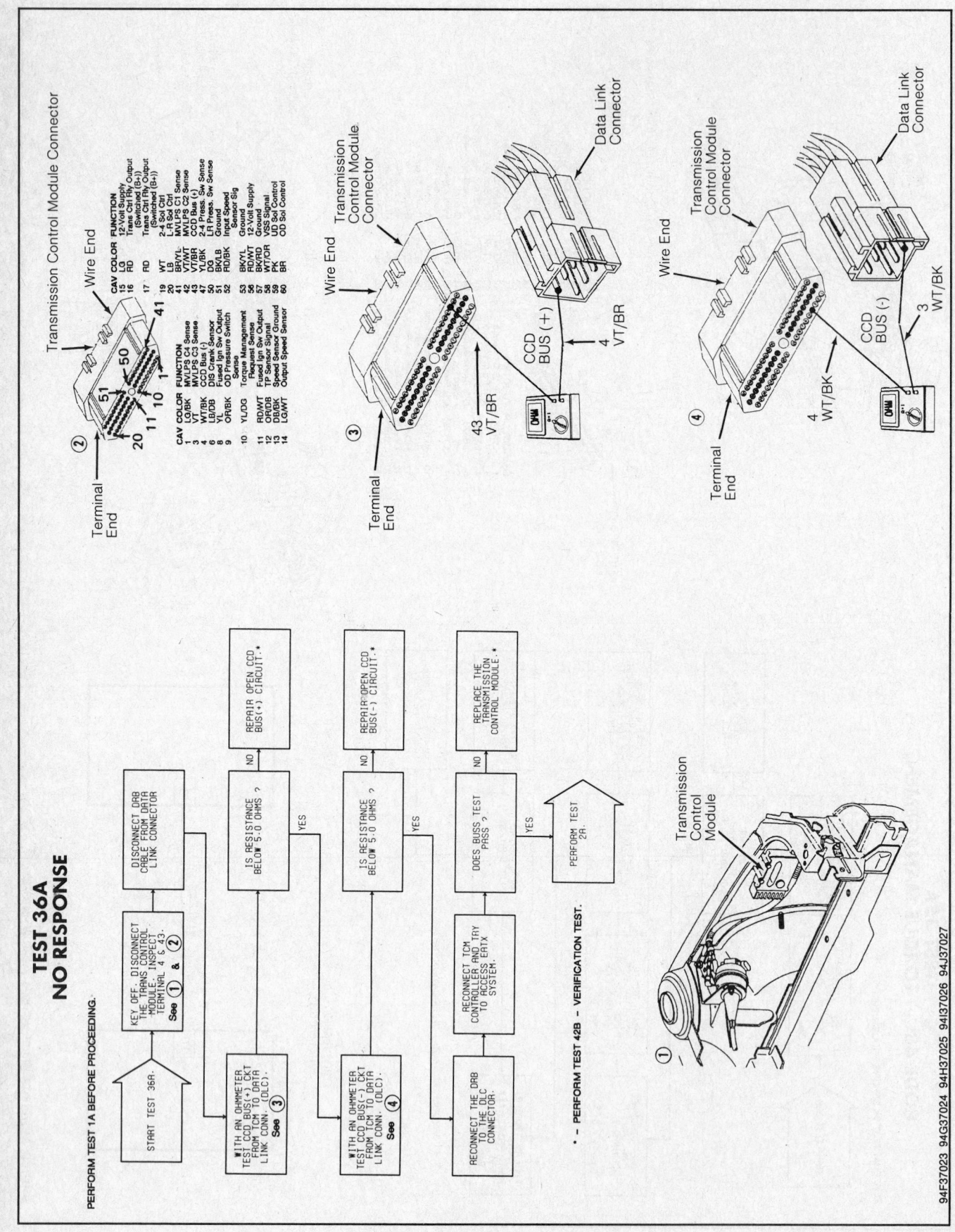

94F37023 94G37024 94H37025 94J37026 94J37027

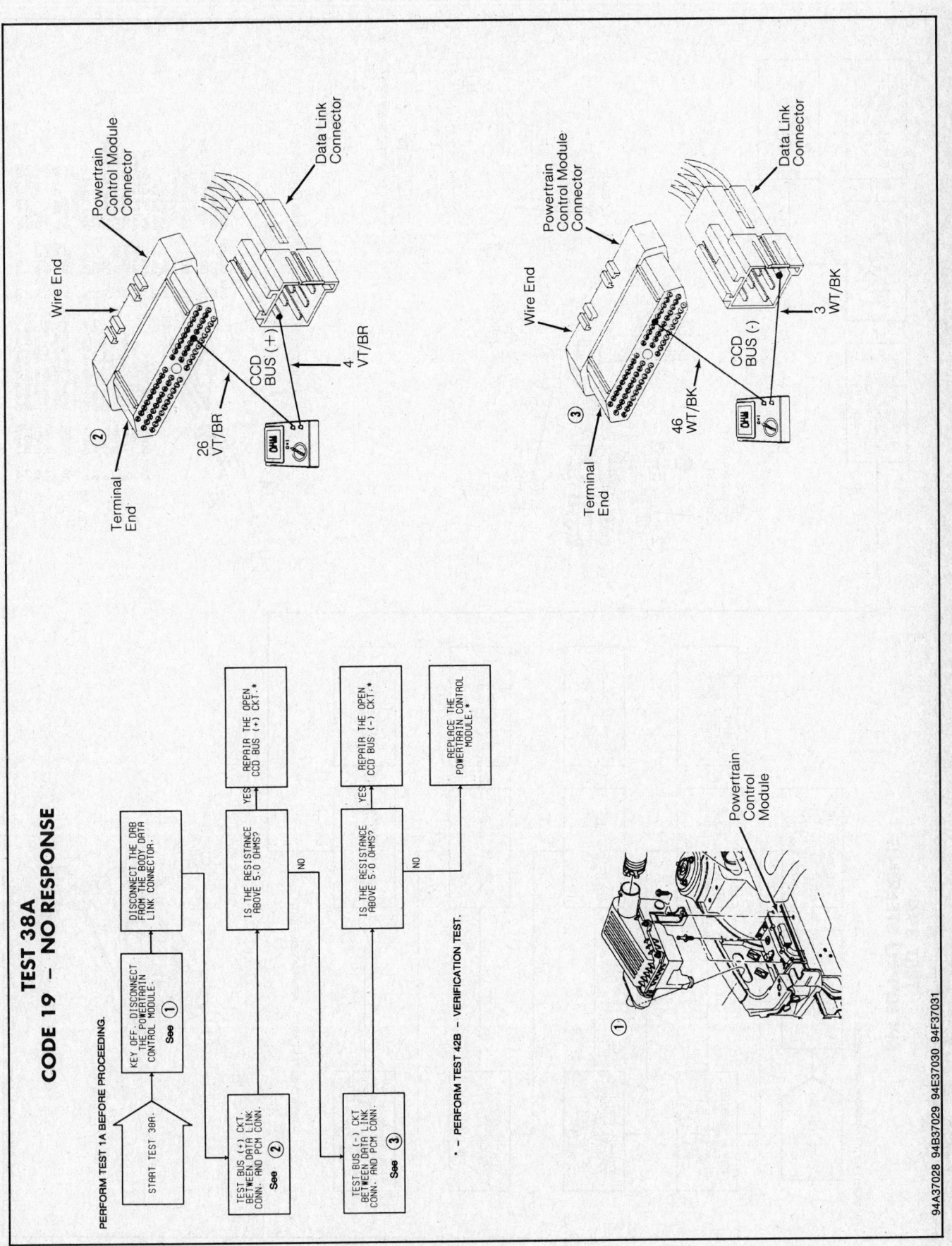

Powertrain Control Module Connector

Data Link Connector

Wire End

CCD BUS (+)

26 VT/BR

4 VT/BR

② Terminal End

Powertrain Control Module Connector

Data Link Connector

Wire End

3 WT/BK

CCD BUS (-)

46 WT/BK

③ Terminal End

Powertrain Control Module

①

TEST 38A
CODE 19 – NO RESPONSE

PERFORM TEST 1A BEFORE PROCEEDING.

START TEST 38A.

KEY OFF. DISCONNECT THE POWERTRAIN CONTROL MODULE. See ①

DISCONNECT THE DRB FROM THE BODY DATA LINK CONNECTOR.

TEST BUS (+) CKT. BETWEEN DATA LINK CONN. AND PCM CONN. See ②

IS THE RESISTANCE ABOVE 5.0 OHMS?

YES → REPAIR THE OPEN CCD BUS (+) CKT.*

NO

TEST BUS (-) CKT BETWEEN DATA LINK CONN. AND PCM CONN. See ③

IS THE RESISTANCE ABOVE 5.0 OHMS?

YES → REPAIR THE OPEN CCD BUS (-) CKT.*

NO

REPLACE THE POWERTRAIN CONTROL MODULE.*

* – PERFORM TEST 42B – VERIFICATION TEST.

94A37028 94B37029 94E37030 94F37031

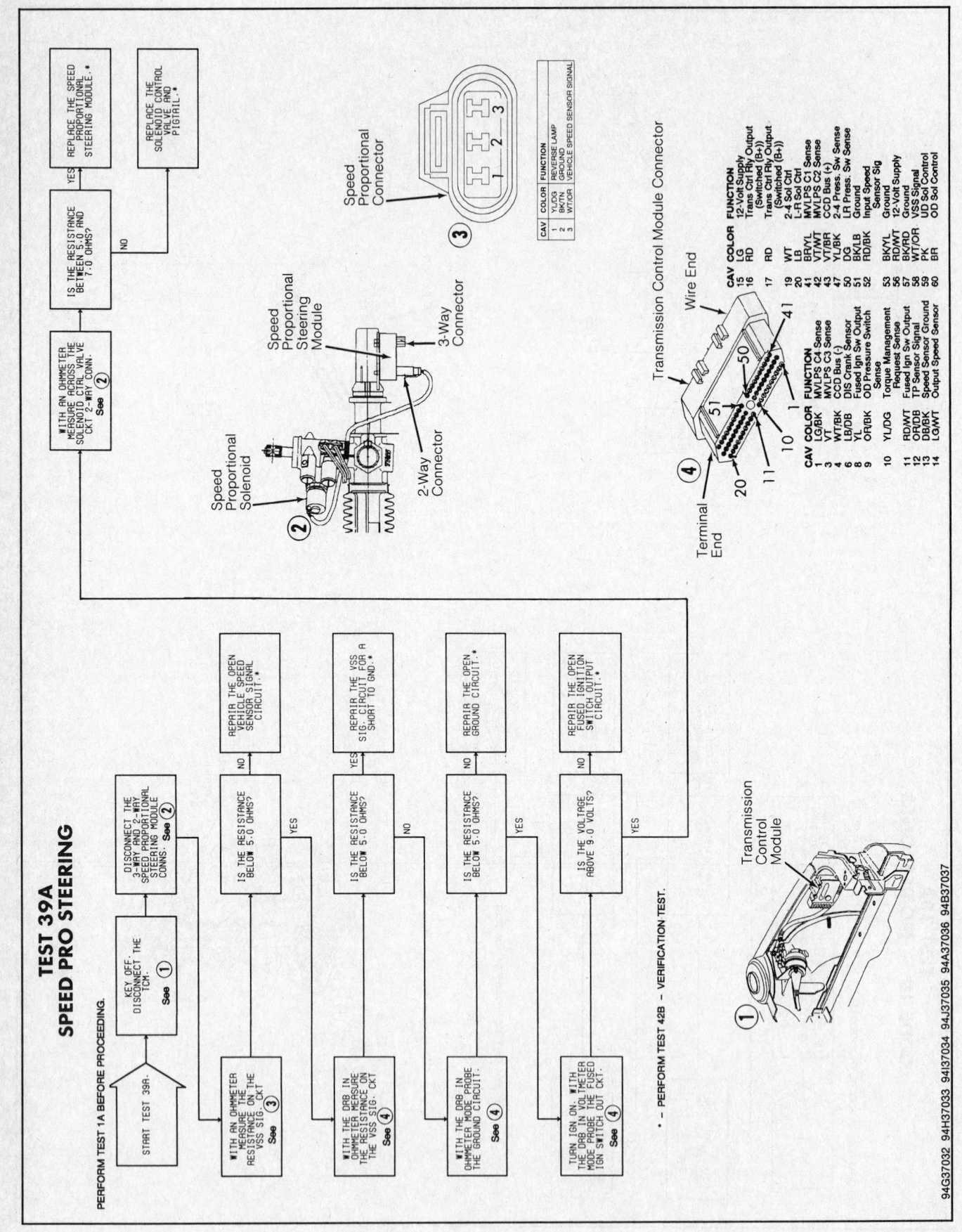

94G37032 94H37033 94I37034 94J37035 94A37036 94B37037

TEST 40A
TROUBLE CODE RESETTING CONDITIONS

PERFORM TEST 2A BEFORE PROCEEDING.

A. With the DRB, read any trouble codes.
B. With the DRB, erase any trouble codes.
C. Refer to the list below to find the code(s) that were erased. Following the instructions next to that code, attempt to make the code reappear on the DRB display.

CODE	INSTRUCTIONS
11	Turn the ignition from off to on, then start the engine. Move slowly through each shift lever position with your foot on the brake.
12	Status code. Requires no action.
13	Turn the ignition from off to on. If no limp-in occurs, start the engine.
14	Turn the ignition from off to on. If no limp-in occurs, start the engine.
15	Turn the ignition from off to on. If no limp-in occurs, start the engine.
16	Turn the ignition from off to on.
17	Turn the ignition from off to on.
18	Start the engine and allow it to run in PARK for a minimum of 3 seconds.
19	Start the engine and wait for 15 seconds.
20	Turn the ignition from off to on. If no code appears, start engine.
21-27	Run the vehicle in NEUTRAL for one minute, then drive the vehicle in R, 1, 2, 3, 4 for a minimum of 30 seconds in each gear.
28	Start the engine and move the shift lever slowly from PARK through LOW.
29	Start the engine, then move the throttle from closed to W.O.T.
31	With the transaxle at normal operating temperature, drive in 1ST GEAR and 2ND GEAR for a minute each.
32	With the transaxle at normal operating temperature, drive in 1ST GEAR and 3RD GEAR for a minute each.
33	With the transaxle at normal operating temperature, drive in 1ST GEAR for at least 1 minute.
36	This code does not stand alone. There will be a 50 series (50-58) code following it.
37	Drive in 2ND GEAR, then apply the brake until 2-1 downshift occurs. Do this at least 3 times 5 seconds apart.
38	With the transaxle at normal operating temperature, drive in 4TH GEAR at light throttle at 50 miles per hour for 17 to 20 seconds. Verify lockup by monitoring the bottom of the DRB rpm display.
41-44	Start and run the engine for a minimum of 30 seconds.
45	Start and run the engine for a minimum of 20 seconds.
46	Perform TEST 33A.
47	With the transaxle at normal operating temperature, drive in gear at light throttle at 50 miles per hour for about 20 seconds.
48	With the transaxle at normal operating temperature, drive in 1ST GEAR for at least 15 seconds.
50-58	Run the engine in NEUTRAL for one minute, then drive the vehicle in R, 1, 2, 3, 4 for a minimum of 30 seconds in each gear.
60-62	Run the engine in NEUTRAL for one minute, then drive the vehicle in R, 1, 2, 3, 4 for a minimum of 30 seconds in each gear.

D. If the trouble code comes back, it is considered a HARD code, go to TEST 2A.
E. If the trouble code does NOT reappear, it may be an INTERMITTENT code. Go to TEST 6A.

94C37038

TEST 42B
VERIFICATION TEST

1. **Leave the DRB connected to the data link connector.**

   Reconnect any disconnected components.

   With the DRB, erase all trouble codes.

   With the DRB, display transmission temperature.

   Start and run the engine until the transmission temperature is HOT.

2. **Check the transaxle fluid level (adjust if necessary).**

3. **If TCM, torque converter or transaxle has been replaced, perform shift quality quick-learn procedure and electronically modulated converter clutch (EMCC) reset procedure. See CHRYSLER 42LE article.**

4. **Road test the vehicle.**

   With the DRB, read the "RPM Display" under "Monitor".

   Make 15 to 20 1-2, 2-3, and 3-4 upshifts. (Perform these shifts from a standing start to 45 mph with a constant throttle opening of 20 to 25 degrees.)

   Below 25 mph, make 5 to 8 wide open throttle kickdowns to first gear. (Allow at least 5 seconds each in 2nd and 3rd between each kickdown.)

5. **Check for trouble codes set during the road test.**

   If a trouble code sets during the road test, perform TEST 2A.

   If no trouble codes set, but the transaxle performance is unacceptable, **see TROUBLE SHOOTING in CHRYSLER 42LE ARTICLE.**
   If no trouble codes were set and the transaxle performance was acceptable, return the vehicle back to the owner.

94G37040

TEST 41A
CODE 35 – LOSS OF PRIME

PERFORM TEST 1A BEFORE PROCEEDING.

START TEST 41A.

TEST IS FOR LOSS OF PRIME.

THE FOLLOWING IS A LIST OF POSSIBLE CAUSES. CHECK THEM AND REPAIR AS NECESSARY.

CHECK FLUID LEVEL. FILL IF NECESSARY.

CHECK TRANS COOLER LINE FITTINGS.

REMOVE TRANS PAN. CHECK FOR FILTER DAMAGE, NOT FULLY INSTALLED, PLUGGED OR MISSING O-RING.

IF EVERYTHING CHECKS OUT OK RECONNECT EVERYTHING AND PERFORM **TEST 42B**

94D37039

APPLICATION & LABOR TIMES

APPLICATION & LABOR TIMES

Vehicle Application	Labor Times [1] R & I	[2] Overhaul	Trans. Model
1993-94 Dodge			
Dakota (3.9L)	[3] 4.7	8.5	42RH
Pickup (3.9L)	[4] 4.7	8.5	42RH
Ram Van (3.9L)	4.7	8.5	42RH
1993 1/2-94 Jeep			
Grand Cherokee [5]	[6] 3.4	8.5	42RE

[1] – Removal and installation of transmission from vehicle chassis.

[2] – Bench overhaul time for transmission. DOES NOT include removal and installation.

[3] – Add 4.4 Hrs. for 4WD.

[4] – Add 2.1 Hrs. for 4WD.

[5] – Earlier models used the Aisin Warner 4 transmission. Some models may use the 42RE and some models may use the 42RH. The 42RE is used with 4.0L engine only.

[6] – Add .9 Hr. for 4WD.

IDENTIFICATION

Transmission identification numbers are stamped on left side of transmission case, near oil pan flange. *See Fig. 1.* Identification numbers may be required when ordering replacement components. Note that transmission components may not be interchangeable and identification number is required to ensure proper component application.

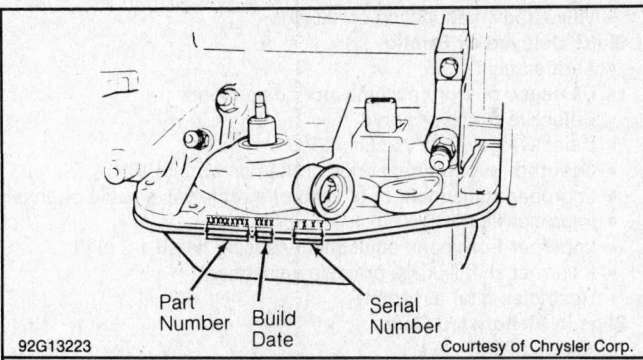

Part Number Build Date Serial Number

92G13223 Courtesy of Chrysler Corp.

Fig. 1: Locating Transmission Identification Numbers

NOTE: Selective sized snap rings and thrust washers may be needed to set and adjust clearances. For sizes and availability, refer to manufacturer's parts department, and reference transmission model and identification number.

NOTE: Overdrive unit on rear of transmission is disassembled and serviced as a separate unit. Overdrive unit on the 42RE is different than that used on the 42RH. See OVERDRIVE UNIT DISASSEMBLY, OVERDRIVE UNIT COMPONENT DISASSEMBLY & REASSEMBLY and OVERDRIVE UNIT REASSEMBLY in this article.

DESCRIPTION & OPERATION

Transmission is a fully automatic 3-speed transmission with an overdrive unit attached to rear of transmission. The 1st through 3rd gears are provided by clutches, bands, overrunning clutch and planetary gear set. The 4th gear is provided by overdrive clutch, direct clutch, planetary gear set and overrunning clutch in overdrive unit. Transmission contains front and rear bands, front clutch, rear clutch and overrunning clutch. The overdrive unit contains overdrive clutch, direct clutch and overrunning clutch. *See Fig. 2.*

On 42RH transmissions, overdrive or 4th gear operation is controlled by a manually operated overdrive switch on the instrument panel. Overdrive switch is in the electrical circuit with overdrive solenoid on the valve body and Powertrain Control Module (PCM). Transmission will not shift into overdrive if switch is not in the ON position. Torque converter lock-up is activated when the PCM provides voltage to lock-up solenoid located on the valve body.

On 42RE transmissions, governor pressure used for transmission shifting is developed and controlled electronically. Various sensors and Transmission Control Module (TCM) are used for controlling the governor pressure. Overdrive or 4th gear operation is controlled by a manually operated overdrive switch on the instrument panel. Overdrive switch supplies input signal to the TCM for controlling overdrive operation.

The TCM contains a self-diagnostic system which will store a Diagnostic Trouble Code (DTC) if a problem or failure exists in the electronic system or components. Diagnostic trouble code can be retrieved to determine the transmission problem area. For information on electronic transmission system and operation, see CHRYSLER 42RE ELECTRONIC DIAGNOSIS article.

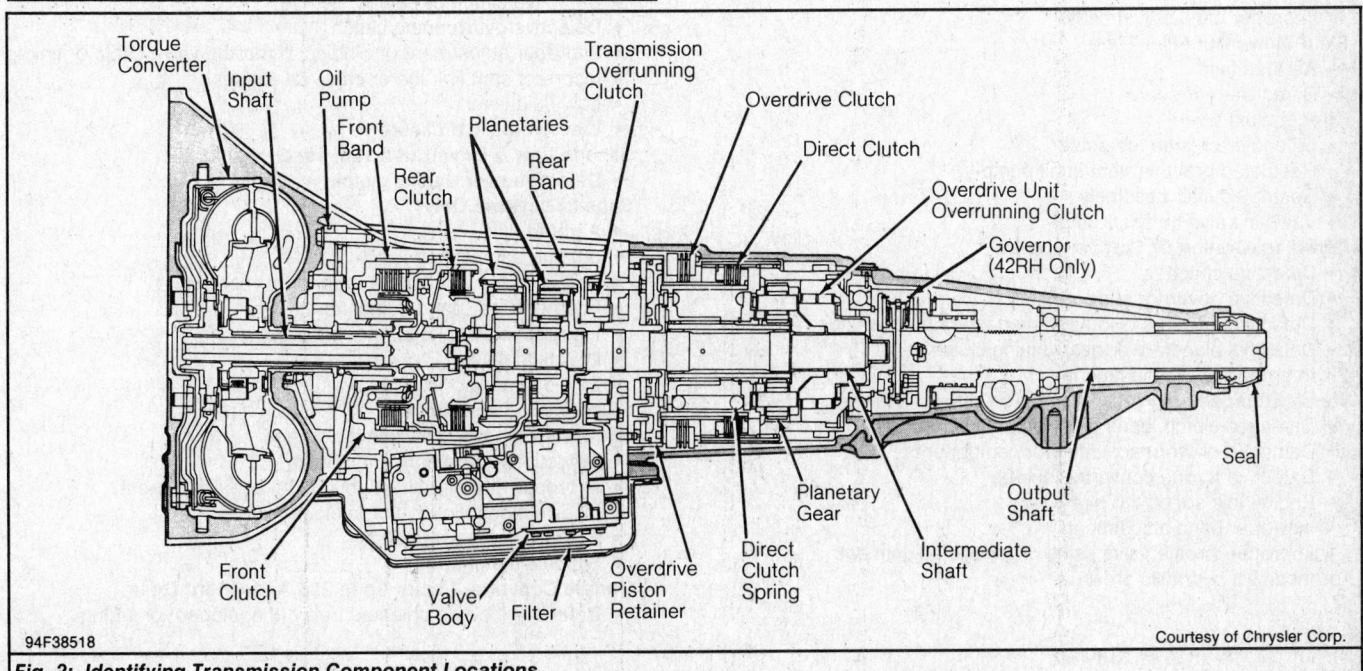

94F38518 Courtesy of Chrysler Corp.

Fig. 2: Identifying Transmission Component Locations

LUBRICATION & ADJUSTMENTS

NOTE: See appropriate AUTOMATIC TRANSMISSION SERVICING article in TRANSMISSION SERVICING.

TROUBLE SHOOTING

Transmission malfunctions may be caused by poor engine performance, improper adjustments or failure of hydraulic, mechanical or electronic components. On models with 42RE transmission, check for stored diagnostic trouble codes before trouble shooting or testing transmission. See CHRYSLER 42RE ELECTRONIC DIAGNOSIS article. On all transmissions, always begin by checking fluid level, fluid condition, shift or throttle valve linkage or cable adjustment. Perform road test to determine if problem has been corrected. If problem still exists, several tests must be performed on transmission. See TESTING in this article.

TRANSMISSION SYMPTOM DIAGNOSIS

NOTE: The shift from Neutral to Reverse is normally quite firm, as rear servo pressure can approach 300 psi (21 kg/cm²). DO NOT confuse a firm engagement with a harsh engagement.

Buzzing Noise
- Aerated fluid
- Defective overrunning clutch
- Low fluid level
- Valve body malfunction or leakage

Delayed Engagement From Neutral To Drive Or Reverse
- Damaged clutch, band or servo
- Damaged oil pump components
- Damaged or worn reaction shaft seal rings
- Defective governor (42RH)
- Defective governor solenoid or circuit (42RE)
- Engine idle speed too low
- Improper rear band adjustment
- Incorrect shift linkage or cable adjustment
- Low fluid level
- Low hydraulic pressure
- Restricted filter assembly

Drags Or Locks Up
- Defective band, band linkage or servo
- Defective planetary or overrunning clutch
- Dragging clutch
- Improper band adjustment

Fluid Blows Out Filler Tube
- Aerated fluid
- Defective rear servo
- High fluid level
- Oil cooler or lines restricted
- Restricted breather vent in oil pump
- Restricted filter assembly
- Valve in valve body sticking

Growling, Grating Or Scraping Noise
- Defective clutch
- Defective governor support (42RH)
- Defective oil pump or output shaft bearings/bushings
- Defective planetary or overrunning clutch
- Improper band adjustment

Harsh Engagement From Neutral To Drive Or Reverse
- Damaged clutch, band or planetary components
- Damaged or worn accumulator components
- Defective torque converter lock-up
- Engine idle speed too high
- Improper band adjustment
- Improper throttle valve cable or linkage adjustment
- Incorrect hydraulic pressure

No Drive Range In Any Position (Reverse Is Okay)
- Defective overrunning clutch
- Defective rear clutch
- Incorrect shift linkage or cable adjustment
- Input shaft seal rings worn or damaged
- Low fluid level
- Valve body malfunction or leakage

No Kickdown Or Normal Downshift
- Defective clutch or servo
- Defective front servo, band or linkage
- Defective governor (42RH)
- Defective governor circuit or TPS circuit (42RE)
- Improper front band adjustment
- Improper throttle valve cable or linkage adjustment
- Incorrect hydraulic pressure
- Incorrect shift linkage or cable adjustment

No Low Gear (Moves In 2nd & 3rd Gears Only)
- Defective governor circuit (42RE)
- Front band linkage binding
- Front servo binding in bore
- Governor partially stuck open (42RH)
- Improper throttle valve cable or linkage adjustment
- Incorrect shift linkage or cable adjustment
- Valve body malfunction or leakage

No Reverse
- Improper rear band adjustment
- Incorrect shift linkage or cable adjustment
- Direct clutch or front clutch malfunction
- Valve body malfunction or leakage

Shifts Delayed Or Erratic
- Aerated fluid
- Damaged or worn accumulator components
- Defective clutch or servo
- Defective governor circuit (42RE)
- Governor support seal rings broken or worn (42RH)
- Improper adjustment or binding of throttle valve cable or linkage
- Improper fluid level
- Improper front band adjustment causing harsh 1-2 shift
- Incorrect shift linkage or cable adjustment
- Restricted filter assembly

Slips In All Forward Gears
- Aerated fluid
- Damaged or worn accumulator components
- Defective clutch or servo
- Defective overrunning clutch
- Improper adjustment or binding of throttle valve cable or linkage
- Incorrect shift linkage or cable adjustment
- Low fluid level
- Low hydraulic pressure

Slips In Low & Drive But Not In 1st Gear
- Defective overrunning clutch

Slips In Reverse Only
- Aerated fluid
- Binding band linkage
- Defective front clutch, rear servo or rear band
- Improper rear band adjustment
- Incorrect shift linkage or cable adjustment
- Low fluid level
- Low hydraulic pressure

Sluggish Acceleration Or Excessive Throttle To Maintain Speed
- Defective torque converter clutch
- Improper throttle valve cable or linkage adjustment
- Incorrect shift linkage or cable adjustment
- Poor engine performance
- Slipping clutches

Torque Converter Locks Up In 2nd And/Or 3rd Gear
- Defective lock-up solenoid, relay (if equipped) or wiring

Transmission Overheats
- Improper band adjustment
- Improper clutch clearance
- Low fluid level
- Restricted oil cooler
- Switch valve in valve body sticking

Vehicle Moves In Neutral
- Clutch dragging
- Incorrect shift linkage or cable adjustment
- Valve body malfunction or leakage

Vehicle Moves In 2nd Or 3rd Gear & Abruptly Downshifts To Low
- Defective governor circuit (42RE)
- Governor sticking (42RH)
- Valve body malfunction or leakage

Vehicle Will Not Move In All Gears
- Defective oil pump
- Incorrect shift linkage or cable adjustment
- Internal transmission component failure
- Low fluid level
- Valve body malfunction or leakage

Will Not Upshift From Low Gear
- Defective clutch or servo
- Defective governor circuit (42RE)
- Defective oil pump, seal rings or valve body
- Governor stuck closed (42RH)
- Improper front band adjustment
- Improper throttle valve cable or linkage adjustment
- Incorrect shift linkage or cable adjustment

1st & Reverse Gears Only
- Defective governor circuit (42RE)
- Defective or sticking governor (42RH)

OVERDRIVE UNIT SYMPTOM DIAGNOSIS

Delayed 3-4 Upshift
- Defective overdrive clutch
- Defective overdrive solenoid or wiring
- Low fluid level
- Overdrive clutch bleed orifice restricted
- Overdrive piston thrust plate too thin
- Throttle position sensor defective

No Reverse Or Slips In Reverse
- Defective front clutch
- Direct clutch components
- Improper rear band adjustment
- Overdrive thrust bearing failure

No 3-4 Upshift
- Damaged neutral switch or wiring causing loss of park/neutral input to PCM (42RH)
- Defective engine coolant temp. sensor, transmission fluid temp. sensor (if equipped) or vehicle speed sensor (42RH)
- Defective overdrive solenoid or wiring circuit
- Defective overdrive switch, wiring circuit or fuse
- Defective Powertrain Control Module (42RH)
- Defective Transmission Control Module (42RE)
- Low hydraulic pressure
- Overdrive piston seals damaged or wrong spacer
- Overdrive solenoid supply orifice in valve body restricted
- Overdrive switch in OFF position

No 4-3 Downshift
- Defective engine coolant temp. sensor, transmission fluid temp. sensor (if equipped) or vehicle speed sensor (42RH)
- Defective Powertrain Control Module (42RH)
- Defective Transmission Control Module (42RE)
- Defective wiring or connections
- Defective 3-4 shift valve, shuttle valve, timing valve or accumulator
- Lock-up solenoid not venting
- Overdrive solenoid not venting
- Throttle position sensor faulty

No 4-3 Downshift With Overdrive Switch In OFF Position
- Defective overdrive solenoid wiring or connections
- Defective overdrive switch wiring
- Defective Powertrain Control Module (42RH)
- Defective Transmission Control Module (42RE)
- Overdrive solenoid or lock-up solenoid not venting

Noisy Operation In 4th Gear Only
- Defective output shaft bearings
- Overdrive clutch discs, plates or snap rings damaged
- Overdrive piston improperly installed or defective
- Overrunning clutch rollers worn
- Planetary gears worn or damaged
- Planetary thrust bearing improperly installed or defective

Slips In 4th Gear
- Defective overdrive clutch, overdrive clutch piston or seal
- Defective thrust bearing
- Defective 3-4 shift valve, timing valve or accumulator
- Low fluid level
- Overdrive piston retainer bleed orifice defective

3-4 Upshift Occurs Before Completing 2-3 Upshift
- Defective coolant temperature sensor or throttle position sensor
- Defective Powertrain Control Module (42RH)
- Defective Transmission Control Module (42RE)
- Loose overdrive solenoid wiring connections or faulty wiring
- Overdrive solenoid faulty
- Valve body malfunction

ELECTRONIC TESTING

TORQUE CONVERTER CLUTCH (ELECTRONIC LOCK-UP 42RH)

See CHRYSLER ELECTRONIC CONTROLS article in AUTOMATIC TRANSMISSIONS for information on torque converter clutch testing and diagnosis.

ELECTRONIC CONTROL SYSTEM (42RE)

See CHRYSLER 42RE ELECTRONIC DIAGNOSIS article.

TESTING

ROAD TEST

1) Ensure throttle valve and shift linkage or cable are properly adjusted. See appropriate AUTOMATIC TRANSMISSION SERVICING article in TRANSMISSION SERVICING. Ensure fluid level and condition are okay. Add ATF and adjust control cables or linkages (if necessary).

2) Ensure all electrical connections on transmission and overdrive switch are okay. Turn overdrive switch to the ON position. Road test vehicle and operate transmission in each gear position. Observe engine performance during road test. A poorly tuned engine will not allow an accurate analysis of transmission operation.

3) Check for slippage and shift variations. Note if shifts are harsh, spongy, delayed or early. Slipping in any gear usually indicates clutch, band, or overrunning clutch problems. A slipping clutch or band in a particular gear can usually be identified by noting transmission operation in other gearshift positions and comparing internal components used. See CLUTCH & BAND APPLICATION table.

4) Problem area may be detected by determining which components are applied. By selecting another gear that does not use these clutches, the clutch that is slipping can be determined. See CLUTCH & BAND APPLICATION table.

5) Process of elimination can be used to detect slipping units and confirm proper operation of good units. Although road test analysis can usually diagnose slipping units, the actual malfunction, however, usually cannot be decided.

6) Practically any condition can be caused by leaking hydraulic circuits or sticking valves. Transmission failure may be determined by performing hydraulic pressure test along with clutch and servo air pressure test.

CLUTCH & BAND APPLICATION [1]

Gearshift Position	Elements In Use
"D" (Drive)	
1st Gear	Rear Clutch, Transmission Overrunning Clutch, Overdrive Unit Direct & Overrunning Clutch
2nd Gear	Front Band, Rear Clutch, Overdrive Unit Direct & Overrunning Clutch
3rd Gear	Front Clutch, Rear Clutch, Overdrive Unit Direct & Overrunning Clutch
4th Gear	Front Clutch, Rear Clutch & Overdrive Unit Overdrive Clutch
"2" (Second)	
1st Gear	Rear Clutch, Transmission Overrunning Clutch, Overdrive Unit Direct & Overrunning Clutch
2nd Gear	Front Band, Rear Clutch, Overdrive Unit Direct & Overrunning Clutch
"1" (Low)	
1st Gear	Rear Clutch, Rear Band, Transmission Overrunning Clutch, Overdrive Unit Direct & Overrunning Clutch
"R" (Reverse)	Front Clutch, Rear Band & Overdrive Unit Direct Clutch
"N" Or "P" (Neutral Or Park)	All Clutches & Bands Released Or Ineffective

[1] – Transmission contains front and rear bands, front clutch, rear clutch and overrunning clutch. The overdrive unit contains overdrive clutch, direct clutch and overrunning clutch.

TORQUE CONVERTER STALL SPEED TEST

Test Procedure – 1) Install tachometer. Ensure transmission fluid level is correct. Start and operate engine until transmission fluid is at normal operating temperature.

CAUTION: DO NOT open throttle to wide open position for more than 5 seconds or transmission may be damaged. If performing more than one torque converter stall speed test, operate engine at 1000 RPM with transmission in Neutral for at least 20 seconds to cool transmission fluid before performing next torque converter stall speed test.

2) Block front wheels. Apply parking and service brakes. Place transmission in Drive. Open throttle to wide open position for no more than 5 seconds and note engine RPM, then release throttle. This is the torque converter stall speed.

3) Torque converter stall speed should be 1800-2100 RPM. Once torque converter stall speed is obtained, place transmission in Neutral. Operate engine for 20 seconds, allowing transmission to cool. Stop engine. Place transmission in Park. Remove tachometer.

NOTE: Use following symptoms to trouble shoot results of torque converter stall speed test.

Stall Speed Exceeds Specification – If torque converter stall speed exceeds specification by more than 200 RPM, transmission clutch is slipping.

Stall Speed Less Than Specification – 1) If torque converter stall speed is less than specification with properly tuned engine, torque converter overrunning clutch may be slipping.

2) If torque converter overrunning clutch is slipping, torque converter stall speed will be 250-300 RPM less than the specification. Vehicle will operate properly at highway speeds, but will have poor low-speed acceleration.

Stall Speed Is Within Specification – If torque converter stall speed is within specification, but abnormal throttle opening is required to maintain highway speeds, torque converter overrunning clutch is seized. Torque converter must be replaced.

Noise When Performing Torque Converter Stall Speed Test – Whining noise caused by fluid flow is normal. A loud metallic sound indicates torque converter is damaged. To ensure sound is coming from torque converter, raise vehicle on hoist. Operate vehicle with transmission in Drive and then Neutral at light throttle. Ensure noise is coming from torque converter. Replace torque converter if defective.

HYDRAULIC PRESSURE TEST

Test Preparation – 1) Ensure fluid level and condition are okay. Install tachometer. Raise vehicle on hoist, allowing wheels to rotate freely.

2) Disconnect throttle valve and shift cables or linkages from throttle valve and manual selector lever on the transmission.

CAUTION: A 100 psi (7 kg/cm²) pressure gauge is required for checking all applications except rear servo and overdrive clutch. A 300 psi (21 kg/cm²) pressure gauge is required for checking pressure at rear servo and overdrive clutch.

Pressure Test With Transmission In "1" (1st Gear) – 1) Remove pressure tap plugs and install pressure gauge in accumulator and rear servo pressure taps. *See Fig. 3.* Start and operate engine at 1000 RPM.

2) Move manual selector lever on transmission fully forward to the gearshift "1" position. Read pressure on both pressure gauges as throttle valve lever on transmission is moved from fully forward position to fully rearward position.

3) Line pressure at accumulator pressure tap should be 54-60 psi (3.7-4.2 kg/cm²) with throttle valve lever fully forward and gradually increase to 90-96 psi (6.3-6.7 kg/cm²) as throttle valve lever is moved rearward. Rear servo pressure should be within 3 psi (.2 kg/cm²) of line pressure.

4) If line pressure is not within specification, adjust line pressure. See LINE PRESSURE under HYDRAULIC PRESSURE ADJUSTMENTS. If proper line pressure still cannot be obtained, check for defective components and hydraulic circuit.

5) This tests oil pump output, pressure regulation, condition of rear clutch and servo hydraulic circuits. Remove pressure gauges. Install and tighten pressure tap plugs to specification. See TORQUE SPECIFICATIONS.

Pressure Test With Transmission In "2" (2nd Gear) – 1) Remove pressure tap plug and install pressure gauge in accumulator pressure tap. *See Fig. 3.* Start and operate engine at 1000 RPM.

2) Move manual selector lever on transmission to fully forward position and then rearward one position to gearshift "2" position. Read pressure on pressure gauge as throttle valve lever on transmission is moved from fully forward position to fully rearward position.

3) Line pressure at accumulator pressure tap should be 54-60 psi (3.7-4.2 kg/cm²) with throttle valve lever fully forward and gradually increase to 90-96 psi (6.3-6.7 kg/cm²) as throttle valve lever is moved rearward.

4) If line pressure is not within specification, adjust line pressure. See LINE PRESSURE under HYDRAULIC PRESSURE ADJUSTMENTS. If proper line pressure still cannot be obtained, check for defective components and hydraulic circuit.

5) This tests oil pump output and pressure regulation. Remove pressure gauge. Install and tighten pressure tap plug to specification. See TORQUE SPECIFICATIONS.

Pressure Test With Transmission In "D" (Drive Gear) – 1) Remove pressure tap plugs and install pressure gauge in accumulator and front servo pressure taps. *See Fig. 3.* Start and operate engine at 1600 RPM.

2) Move manual selector lever on transmission to fully forward position and then rearward 2 positions to gearshift "D" position. Read pressure on both pressure gauges as throttle valve lever on transmission is moved from fully forward position to fully rearward position.

3) Line pressure at accumulator pressure tap should be 54-60 psi (3.7-4.2 kg/cm²) with throttle valve lever fully forward and gradually increase as throttle valve lever is moved rearward. Front servo is pressurized only in gearshift lever "D" position and pressure should be within 3 psi (.2 kg/cm²) of line pressure up to the downshift point.

4) If line pressure is not within specification, adjust line pressure. See LINE PRESSURE under HYDRAULIC PRESSURE ADJUSTMENTS. If proper line pressure still cannot be obtained, check for defective components and hydraulic circuit.

5) This tests oil pump output, pressure regulation and condition of clutch hydraulic circuits. Remove pressure gauges. Install and tighten pressure tap plugs to specification. See TORQUE SPECIFICATIONS.

Pressure Test With Transmission In "R" (Reverse Gear) – 1) Remove pressure tap plug and install 300 psi (21 kg/cm²) pressure gauge in rear servo pressure tap. See Fig. 3. Start and operate engine at 1600 RPM.

2) Move manual selector lever on transmission to fully forward position and then rearward 4 positions to gearshift "R" position. Read pressure on pressure gauge as throttle valve lever on transmission is moved from fully forward position to fully rearward position.

3) Pressure should be 145-175 psi (10.2-12.3 kg/cm²) with throttle valve lever fully forward and gradually increase to 230-280 psi (16.1-19.7 kg/cm²) with throttle valve lever fully rearward.

4) This tests oil pump output, pressure regulation, front clutch and rear servo hydraulic circuits. Remove pressure gauge. Install and tighten pressure tap plug to specification. See TORQUE SPECIFICATIONS.

Pressure Test With Transmission In Overdrive (4th Gear) – 1) Reconnect throttle valve and shift cables or linkages on manual selector lever and throttle valve lever on transmission (if removed). Remove pressure tap plug and install 300 psi (21 kg/cm²) pressure gauge in overdrive clutch pressure tap. See Fig. 3.

2) Lower vehicle, leaving wheels approximately 12" from floor. Ensure overdrive switch is in the ON position. Start engine. Place gearshift in "D" (Drive). Gradually increase engine speed until a 3-4 shift occurs and note pressure gauge reading in 4th gear.

3) Pressure should be 68-72 psi (4.7-5.1 kg/cm²) at closed throttle and increase to 90-120 psi (6.3-8.4 kg/cm²) at 1/2 to 3/4 throttle. Pressure will increase to more than 130 psi (9.1 kg/cm²) at full throttle.

4) This tests line pressure at overdrive clutch in 4th gear. Remove pressure gauge. Install and tighten pressure tap plug to specification. See TORQUE SPECIFICATIONS.

NOTE: Transmission governor pressure is usually checked if shift speeds are incorrect or transmission will not upshift or downshift.

Transmission Governor Pressure – 1) Reconnect throttle valve and shift cables or linkages on manual selector lever and throttle valve lever on transmission (if removed). Remove pressure tap plug and install pressure gauge in governor pressure tap. See Fig. 3.

2) Lower vehicle, leaving wheels approximately 12" from floor. Start engine and allow to idle. Place gearshift in "D" (Drive). Note pressure gauge reading with engine idling.

3) Pressure should be 0-1.5 psi (0-.1 kg/cm²) with wheels not rotating. On 42RE, if pressure exceeds specification, a failure exists in the electronic governor system. Check for stored diagnostic trouble codes. See CHRYSLER 42RE ELECTRONIC DIAGNOSIS article. On 42RH, if pressure exceeds specification, governor valve or weights are stuck open.

4) On all models, if pressure is correct, slowly increase engine speed, noting governor pressure in relation to vehicle speed. Governor pressure should increase approximately 1 psi (.07 kg/cm²) for every MPH. Governor pressure should rise smoothly and then drop back to 0-1.5 psi (0-.1 kg/cm²) when wheels stop rotating.

5) This tests governor operation in relation to engine and vehicle speed. Repair governor (42RH) or governor circuit (42RE) if it does not operate properly. Remove pressure gauge. Install and tighten pressure tap plug to specification. See TORQUE SPECIFICATIONS.

Hydraulic Pressure Test Results – 1) If proper line pressure is obtained in any pressure test, oil pump and pressure regulator are working properly.

2) If line pressure is low in "D", "1" and "2", but is correct in "R", this indicates leakage in rear clutch circuit.

3) If line pressure is low in "D" (3rd gear) and "R", but is correct in "1" and "2", this indicates leakage in front clutch circuit.

4) If line pressure is low in "R" and "1", but is correct in "2", this indicates leakage in rear servo circuit. If front servo pressure is low in "2", this indicates leakage in front servo circuit.

5) If line pressure is low when in "D" (4th gear), this indicates overdrive clutch piston seal or check ball problem.

6) High governor pressure at idle indicates governor valve is stuck open on 42RH or defective governor solenoid valve on 42RE. Low governor pressure at all vehicle speeds indicates governor valve is stuck closed on 42RH or defective governor solenoid valve, TCM or governor pressure sensor on 42RE.

7) If line pressure is not within specification, adjust line pressure. See LINE PRESSURE under HYDRAULIC PRESSURE ADJUSTMENTS. If proper line pressure still cannot be obtained, check for defective components and hydraulic circuit. Low line pressure in all positions indicates a defective oil pump, restricted filter or stuck pressure regulator valve.

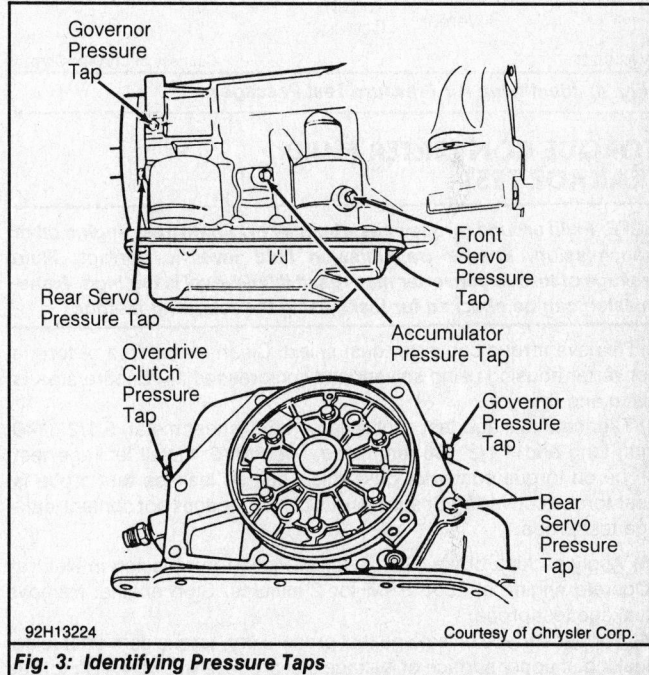

92H13224   Courtesy of Chrysler Corp.

Fig. 3: Identifying Pressure Taps

CLUTCH & SERVO AIR PRESSURE TEST

NOTE: Inoperative clutches, servos and bands can be located by applying air pressure to appropriate passages in transmission case.

Test Preparation – Remove valve body. See VALVE BODY under REMOVAL & INSTALLATION.

CAUTION: Ensure air supply is free of all dirt and moisture.

Front Clutch – Place finger on front clutch housing. Apply air pressure to front clutch apply passage. See Fig. 4. Piston movement will be felt and a soft thump will be heard when front clutch is applied.

Rear Clutch – Place finger on rear clutch housing. Apply air pressure to rear clutch apply passage. See Fig. 4. Piston movement will be felt and a soft thump will be heard when rear clutch is applied.

Front Servo – Apply air pressure to front servo apply passage. See Fig. 4. Front band should tighten, indicating front servo operation. Release air pressure. Ensure spring tension on servo piston releases front band.

Rear Servo – Apply air pressure to rear servo apply passage. See Fig. 4. Rear band should tighten, indicating rear servo operation. Release air pressure. Ensure spring tension on servo piston releases rear band.

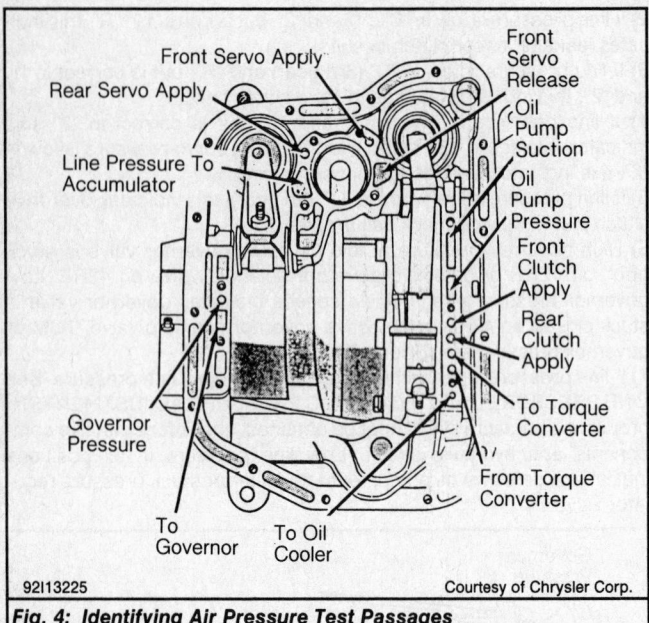

92I13225   Courtesy of Chrysler Corp.

Fig. 4: Identifying Air Pressure Test Passages

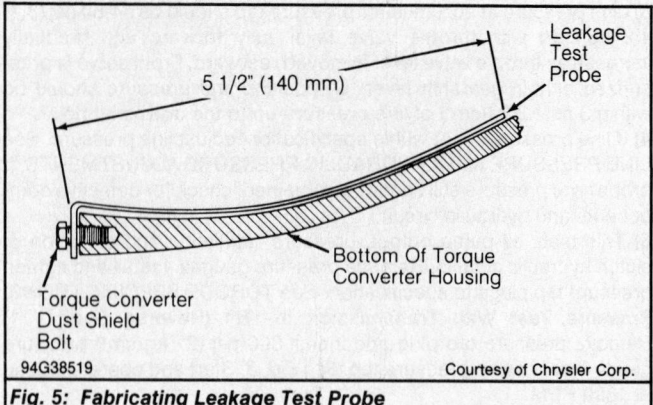

94G38519   Courtesy of Chrysler Corp.

Fig. 5: Fabricating Leakage Test Probe

TORQUE CONVERTER FLUID LEAKAGE TEST

NOTE: Fluid around torque converter may originate from engine oil or transmission. Ensure transmission fluid level is correct. Fluid leakage at torque converter may result if fluid level is too high. Transmission can be checked for leaks using the following method.

1) Remove torque converter dust shield. Clean inside area of torque converter housing using solvent and compressed air. Ensure area is clean and dry.

2) Fabricate leakage test probe using 1/32" sheet metal, 5 1/2" (140 mm) long and 1 1/2" (38 mm) wide. *See Fig. 5.* Install leakage test probe on torque converter dust shield bolt so leakage test probe is near torque converter. Ensure torque converter does not contact leakage test probe.

3) Apply parking brake. Start engine. Place transmission in Neutral. Operate engine at 2500 RPM for 2 minutes. Stop engine. Remove leakage test probe.

4) If upper surface of leakage test probe is dry, torque converter is not leaking. If upper surface of leakage test probe is wet with ATF, torque converter is leaking. If area below leakage test probe is wet with ATF, fluid is coming from around torque converter area.

5) Check following for possible causes of fluid leaks at torque converter areas:
- Defective oil pump housing "O" ring or oil pump housing
- Front band pin access plug
- Mispositioned or worn bushing
- Oil pump seal
- Oil pump-to-transmission case bolts
- Oil pump vent

6) If torque converter is leaking, check for defective welds on outside diameter of torque converter and torque converter hub. Torque converter hub is welded on inside and is not visible. Replace torque converter if a leak exists. DO NOT attempt to repair torque converter.

TRANSMISSION CASE PRESSURE TEST

NOTE: Transmission case, gaskets and oil pump housing can be checked for leaks using the following method. Transmission must be removed to perform transmission case pressure test.

1) Remove torque converter from transmission. Fabricate torque converter hub seal cup, retaining strap and vent plug retainer. *See Fig. 6.* Retaining strap specifications are approximate. Measure hole positions on torque converter housing before drilling.

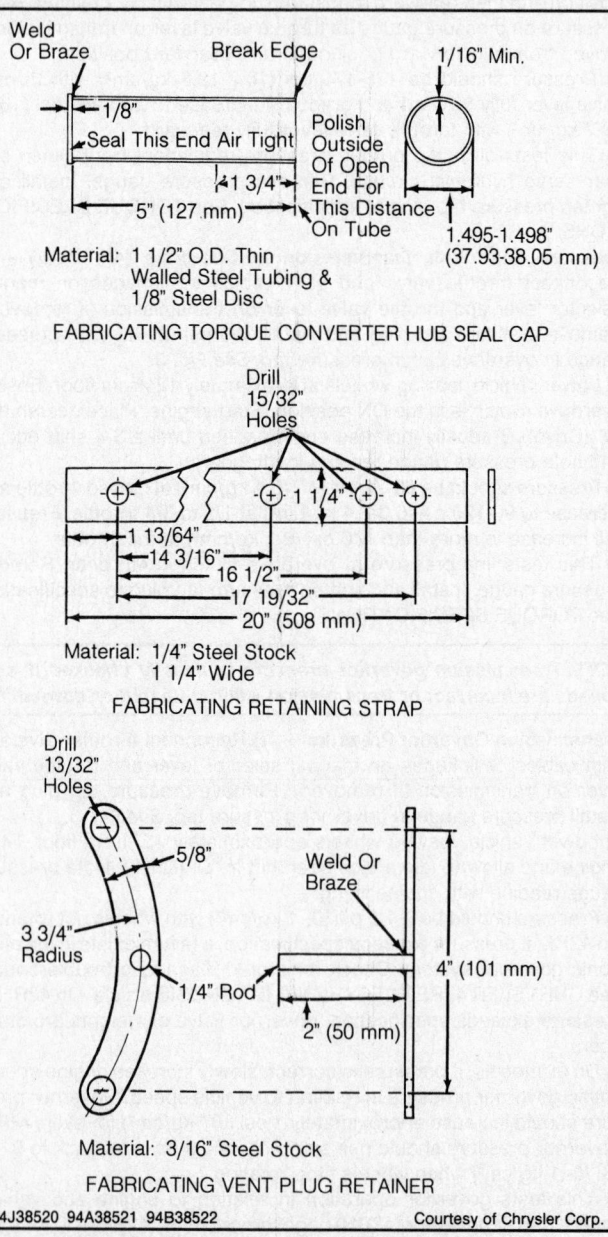

94J38520 94A38521 94B38522   Courtesy of Chrysler Corp.

Fig. 6: Fabricating Torque Converter Hub Seal Cup, Retaining Strap & Vent Plug Retainer

CAUTION: Ensure torque converter hub seal cup surface is smooth to prevent damage to seal in oil pump.

2) Install torque converter hub seal cup, vent plug retainer and retaining strap. *See Fig. 7.* Install shipping plug in rear output shaft opening. Install and secure plugs in remaining transmission openings except oil cooler return line.

3) Attach air pump to oil cooler return line. *See Fig. 7.* Ensure cap is installed on oil cooler supply line fitting. Using pressure regulator, apply 8-10 psi (.5-.7 kg/cm²) of air pressure to transmission case.

CAUTION: DO NOT apply more than 10 psi (.7 kg/cm²) of air pressure to transmission case.

4) Coat oil pump and front of transmission case with soapy water solution. Check for bubbles, indicating a leak in seals, "O" rings, gaskets or transmission case. Release air pressure. Remove test equipment. Replace defective components.

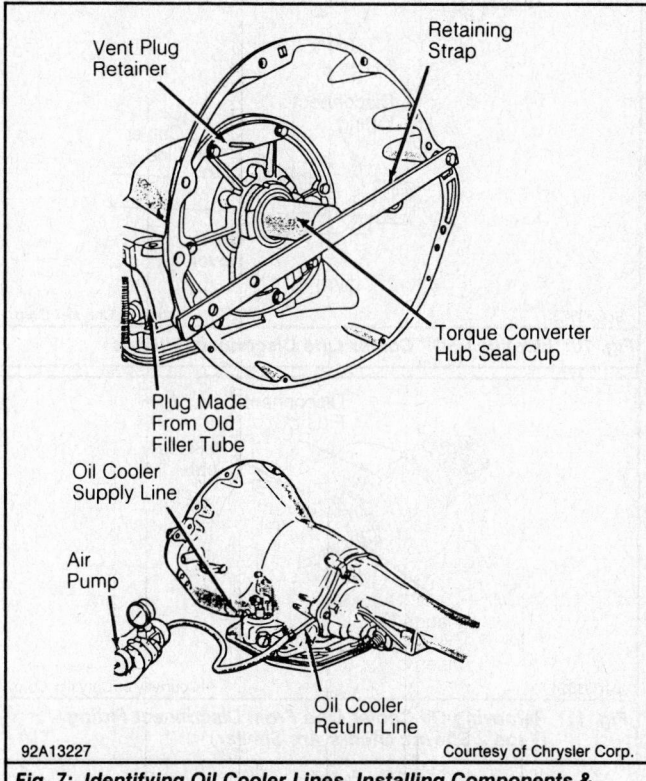

Fig. 7: Identifying Oil Cooler Lines, Installing Components & Pressure Testing Transmission Case

HYDRAULIC PRESSURE ADJUSTMENTS

CAUTION: Line pressure and throttle pressure each affect shift quality. Line pressure must be adjusted before adjusting throttle pressure. Valve body must be removed for adjustments. See VALVE BODY under REMOVAL & INSTALLATION.

LINE PRESSURE

1) Measure distance from valve body to inner edge of line pressure adjusting screw. *See Fig. 8.* Rotate line pressure adjusting screw so distance is approximately 1 5/16".

NOTE: Due to manufacturing tolerances, adjustment can be varied to obtain specified line pressure.

2) Rotating line pressure adjusting screw one revolution will change line pressure approximately 1 2/3 psi. Rotating line pressure adjusting screw counterclockwise increases line pressure and clockwise decreases line pressure.

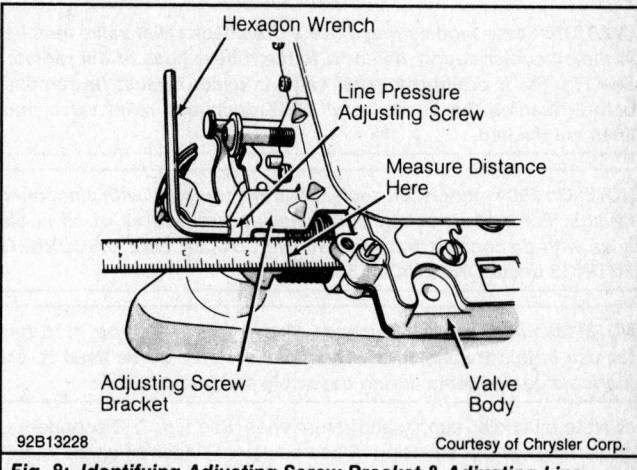

Fig. 8: Identifying Adjusting Screw Bracket & Adjusting Line Pressure

THROTTLE PRESSURE

CAUTION: Line pressure must be adjusted before adjusting throttle pressure.

1) Insert Gauge Pin (C-3763) between cam on throttle lever and kickdown valve. *See Fig. 9.*
2) Push inward on gauge pin and compress kickdown valve against spring until kickdown valve bottoms in valve body.

CAUTION: Ensure spring is fully compressed and kickdown valve is bottomed in valve body.

3) Maintain pressure against kickdown valve and spring. Rotate throttle pressure adjusting screw until head of adjusting screw contacts tang on throttle lever. Ensure throttle lever cam contacts gauge pin. Remove gauge pin.

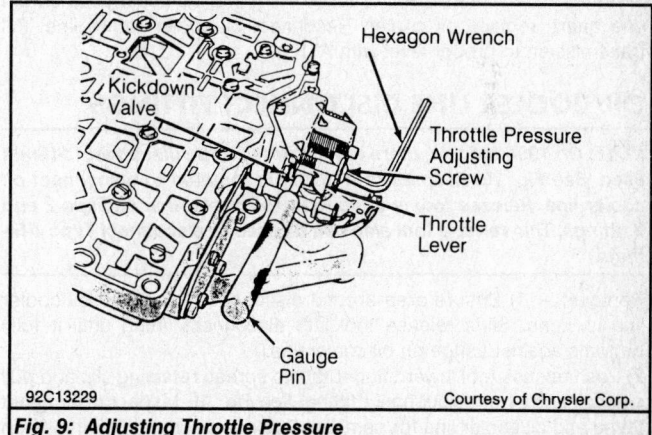

Fig. 9: Adjusting Throttle Pressure

ON-VEHICLE SERVICE

The following components can be serviced on vehicle:
- Park/Neutral Switch
- Valve Body
- Vehicle Speed Sensor & Pinion Gear

See appropriate component under REMOVAL & INSTALLATION.

OIL COOLER FLUSHING

CAUTION: Whenever transmission failure exists, oil cooler must be flushed and torque converter replaced. If vehicle is equipped with 2 oil coolers (one in radiator tank and one in front of radiator), flush oil coolers separately. DO NOT attempt to flush both oil coolers at one time.

CAUTION: *Some models may have a drainback relief valve installed in the oil cooler supply line next to the rubber hose at the radiator. See Fig. 54. If drainback relief valve is used, it must be removed before flushing the lines. Install NEW drainback relief valve once lines are flushed.*

NOTE: *On 1994 models, oil cooler lines are equipped with disconnect fittings. For disconnecting and installing procedures of oil cooler lines with disconnect fittings, see OIL COOLER LINE DISCONNECT FITTINGS under ON-VEHICLE SERVICE.*

NOTE: *Manufacturer recommends Mopar ATF Plus Type 7176 fluid for use in this transmission. This fluid should also be used to pre-lubricate components during assembly and installation.*

1) Note oil cooler supply and return lines. *See Fig. 7.* Disconnect oil cooler lines at transmission. Place container under oil cooler supply line.

2) Using hand-held suction gun filled with mineral spirits, force mineral spirits into oil cooler return line until mineral spirits flows from oil cooler supply line.

3) Continue flushing oil cooler until mineral spirits is clear and no sign of contamination exists. Once contamination is removed, apply compressed air on line from oil cooler in light applications until remaining mineral spirits is blown from oil cooler and oil cooler lines.

4) Pump at least one quart of ATF through oil cooler to ensure oil cooler is free of mineral spirits. Replace oil cooler if fluid does not flow freely through oil cooler.

OIL COOLER FLOW CHECK

1) With transmission filled to proper fluid level, disconnect oil cooler return line from transmission. *See Fig. 7.* Place container under oil cooler return line.

2) Add one extra quart of ATF to transmission. Apply parking brake. Start engine and allow to idle. Place gear selector in Neutral. Check fluid flow from oil cooler return line.

3) If fluid flow is intermittent or takes more than 20 seconds to obtain one quart, replace oil cooler. Reconnect oil cooler return line. Fill transmission to proper level with ATF.

OIL COOLER LINE DISCONNECT FITTINGS

NOTE: *On 1994 models, there are 3 different type disconnect fittings used. See Fig. 10. Release Tool (6762) is required to disconnect oil cooler line. Release tool is attached to oil cooler line on Type 2 and 3 fittings. This release tool also can be used to disconnect Type 1 fittings.*

Removal – 1) Ensure area around disconnect fitting and oil cooler line is clean. Slide release tool into disconnect fitting until it fully bottoms against flange on oil cooler line.

2) Push release tool inward and rotate to spread retaining clip and pull oil cooler line from disconnect fitting. *See Fig. 11.* Inspect disconnect fitting and oil cooler line for damage. Replace disconnect fitting as an assembly if damaged. Replace oil cooler line if swedge at hose or flange on line is damaged.

Installation – 1) If installing NEW disconnect fitting, apply Loctite 242 on disconnect fitting before installing. Ensure end of oil cooler line is clean. Insert oil cooler line into disconnect fitting.

CAUTION: *After installing oil cooler line, pull outward on oil cooler line to ensure oil cooler line is locked in the disconnect fitting and retaining clip is fully seated.*

2) Ensure oil cooler line is clean. Push oil cooler line inward until a snap or click is heard when retaining clip seats in oil cooler line. Pull outward on oil cooler line to ensure oil cooler line is locked in the disconnect fitting.

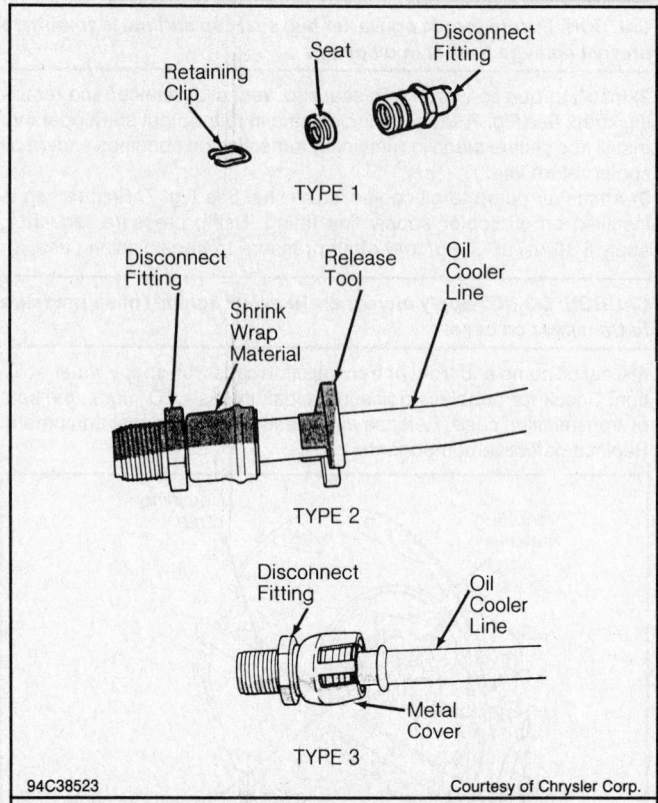

94C38523   Courtesy of Chrysler Corp.

Fig. 10: Identifying Oil Cooler Line Disconnect Fittings

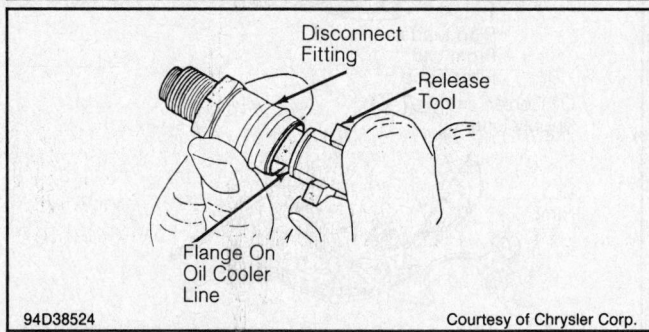

94D38524   Courtesy of Chrysler Corp.

Fig. 11: Removing Oil Cooler Line From Disconnect Fitting (Type 2 Shown; Others Are Similar)

REMOVAL & INSTALLATION

NOTE: *Manufacturer recommends Mopar ATF Plus Type 7176 fluid for use in this transmission. This fluid should also be used to pre-lubricate components during assembly and installation.*

PARK/NEUTRAL SWITCH

Removal & Installation – 1) Raise and support vehicle. Place drain pan under park/neutral switch located near manual shift lever on transmission. *See Fig. 17.* Disconnect electrical connector. Unscrew park/neutral switch from transmission case.

2) To install, apply parking brake. Ensure gearshift is in Park or Neutral. Ensure operating levers in transmission are centered in park/neutral switch opening on transmission case.

3) Using NEW seal, install park/neutral switch. Tighten park/neutral switch to specification. See TORQUE SPECIFICATIONS. Reinstall electrical connector. Adjust transmission fluid level with ATF.

TRANSMISSION

See appropriate AUTOMATIC TRANSMISSION REMOVAL article in TRANSMISSION SERVICING.

VALVE BODY

Removal – **1)** Raise and support vehicle. Remove bolts, oil pan and gasket. Remove throttle valve and manual shift levers from transmission. Remove park/neutral switch. See PARK/NEUTRAL SWITCH under REMOVAL & INSTALLATION.

2) Remove bolts and filter assembly. Keep bolts with filter assembly for installation reference. Disconnect necessary solenoid electrical connectors from solenoid connector in transmission case.

3) Remove valve body-to-transmission case bolts. Note bolt length and location for installation reference. Lower valve body enough to remove accumulator and springs. Note locations of springs for reassembly reference. Pull valve body forward and disengage park rod.

4) Push manual shift lever and solenoid connector from transmission case. Lower valve body and rotate it away from transmission case. Use care not to damage solenoids on valve body. Pull park rod from parking sprag. Remove valve body.

Installation – **1)** Ensure park/neutral switch is removed before installing valve body. Install NEW seal rings on accumulator and solenoid connector. Lubricate seal rings, manual shift lever seal and accumulator and bore with petroleum jelly.

2) Install inner spring and accumulator in transmission case. Place manual shift lever on valve body in low gear position so ball on park rod can be installed in parking sprag. Using screwdriver, push parking sprag to engage with park gear. This allows knob on park rod to move past parking sprag when installing valve body. Rotate output shaft to ensure parking sprag is engaged.

CAUTION: Ensure park rod enters parking sprag, as park rod may enter cavity in the case and not enter parking sprag. Park rod will be damaged if it is not engaged with parking sprag.

---

3) Install spring between accumulator and valve body. Install valve body, working park rod past parking sprag. Ensure accumulator spring remains in place.

CAUTION: Alternately tighten valve body-to-transmission case bolts to prevent damage to valve body. DO NOT overtighten bolts or transmission and valve body may be damaged.

---

4) Install valve body-to-transmission case bolts in original location finger tight only. DO NOT tighten bolts at this time. Using NEW seal, install park/neutral switch. Tighten park/neutral switch to specification. See TORQUE SPECIFICATIONS. Tighten valve body-to-transmission case bolts evenly to specification. See TORQUE SPECIFICATIONS.

5) Install NEW filter assembly. Install and tighten bolts to specification. See TORQUE SPECIFICATIONS. Reconnect all necessary electrical connections. Install throttle valve and manual shift levers. Ensure throttle valve lever and manual shift levers rotate smoothly.

6) Using NEW gasket, install oil pan. Install and tighten bolts to specification. See TORQUE SPECIFICATIONS. Fill transmission with ATF. Ensure shift linkage/cable and throttle valve cable/linkage are properly adjusted. See appropriate AUTOMATIC TRANSMISSION SERVICING article in TRANSMISSION SERVICING.

VEHICLE SPEED SENSOR & PINION GEAR

Removal (1993 Models) – **1)** Raise and support vehicle. Disconnect electrical connector from vehicle speed sensor. *See Fig. 12.*

2) Remove vehicle speed sensor from adapter. Check vehicle speed sensor mounting area on adapter for signs of ATF leakage. If ATF leakage exists, oil seal is leaking and should be replaced.

3) Remove bolt and adapter retainer. Note location of indexing numbers on adapter in relation to the housing. *See Fig. 13.*

NOTE: Indexing numbers on adapter correspond to number of teeth on the pinion gear.

---

4) Ensure area around adapter is clean. Remove adapter, "O" ring and pinion gear. *See Fig. 12.* Remove oil seal from adapter (if necessary).

Installation – **1)** If installing NEW oil seal in adapter, start oil seal in adapter by hand. Using Oil Seal Installer (C-4004), press oil seal in adapter until it bottoms.

2) Ensure housing is clean. Install NEW "O" ring on adapter (if necessary). Lubricate "O" ring on adapter, oil seal and pinion gear teeth with ATF. Count number of teeth on the pinion gear. Ensure number of teeth on pinion gear is within range of indexing numbers listed on the adapter. *See Fig. 13.*

3) Install pinion gear, "O" ring and adapter in the housing. Rotate adapter until proper indexing number in relation to number of pinion gear teeth is at 6 o'clock position. *See Fig. 13.*

4) Ensure adapter is seated in the housing. Install adapter retainer. Install and tighten bolt to specification. See TORQUE SPECIFICATIONS.

5) Install vehicle speed sensor. Tighten nut to specification. Install electrical connector on vehicle speed sensor. Adjust transmission fluid level with ATF.

Removal (1994 Models) – **1)** Raise and support vehicle. Disconnect electrical connector from vehicle speed sensor. *See Fig. 12.*

2) Remove bolt and adapter retainer. Note location of indexing numbers on adapter in relation to the housing. *See Fig. 13.*

NOTE: Indexing numbers on adapter correspond to number of teeth on the pinion gear.

---

3) Ensure area around adapter is clean. Remove adapter with vehicle speed sensor, "O" ring and pinion gear. *See Fig. 12.* Remove bolt, vehicle speed sensor and "O" ring from adapter.

Installation – **1)** Install NEW "O" ring on vehicle speed sensor and adapter (if necessary). Lubricate "O" rings and pinion gear teeth with ATF.

2) Install vehicle speed sensor in adapter. Install and tighten bolt to specification. See TORQUE SPECIFICATIONS. Install pinion gear in adapter.

3) Ensure housing is clean. Count number of teeth on the pinion gear. Ensure number of teeth on pinion gear is within range of indexing numbers listed on the adapter. *See Fig. 13.*

4) Install adapter with pinion gear in the housing. Rotate adapter until proper indexing number in relation to number of pinion gear teeth is at 6 o'clock position. *See Fig. 13.*

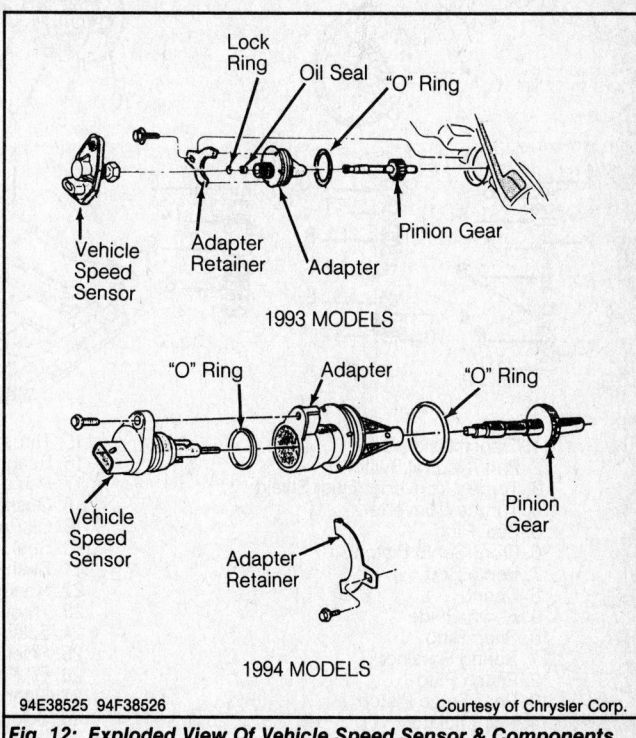

94E38525 94F38526   Courtesy of Chrysler Corp.

Fig. 12: Exploded View Of Vehicle Speed Sensor & Components

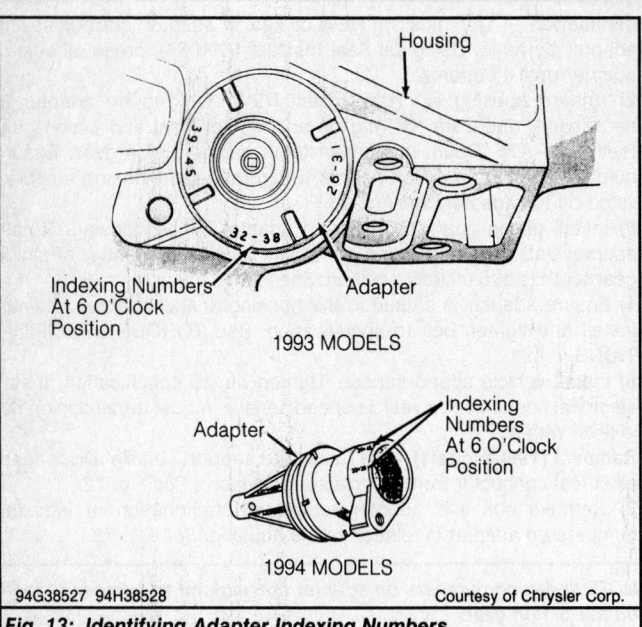

AUTOMATIC TRANSMISSIONS
Chrysler 42RE & 42RH (Cont.)

Housing
39-45
26-31
32-38
Indexing Numbers At 6 O'Clock Position
Adapter
1993 MODELS
Indexing Numbers At 6 O'Clock Position
Adapter
1994 MODELS
94G38527 94H38528
Courtesy of Chrysler Corp.

Fig. 13: Identifying Adapter Indexing Numbers

5) Ensure adapter is seated in the housing. Install adapter retainer. Install and tighten bolt to specification. See TORQUE SPECIFICATIONS. Install electrical connector on vehicle speed sensor. Adjust transmission fluid level with ATF.

TORQUE CONVERTER

CAUTION: Torque converter is a welded assembly and is not serviceable. If a malfunction occurs or if torque converter becomes contaminated with foreign material, it MUST be replaced. Torque converter cannot be flushed or repaired.

NOTE: For torque converter fluid leakage testing and torque converter stall speed test, see TESTING in this article.

TRANSMISSION DISASSEMBLY

NOTE: For overdrive unit disassembly, see OVERDRIVE UNIT DISASSEMBLY.

VALVE BODY & COMPONENTS

CAUTION: Note location of all thrust washer and thrust plate locations for reassembly reference.

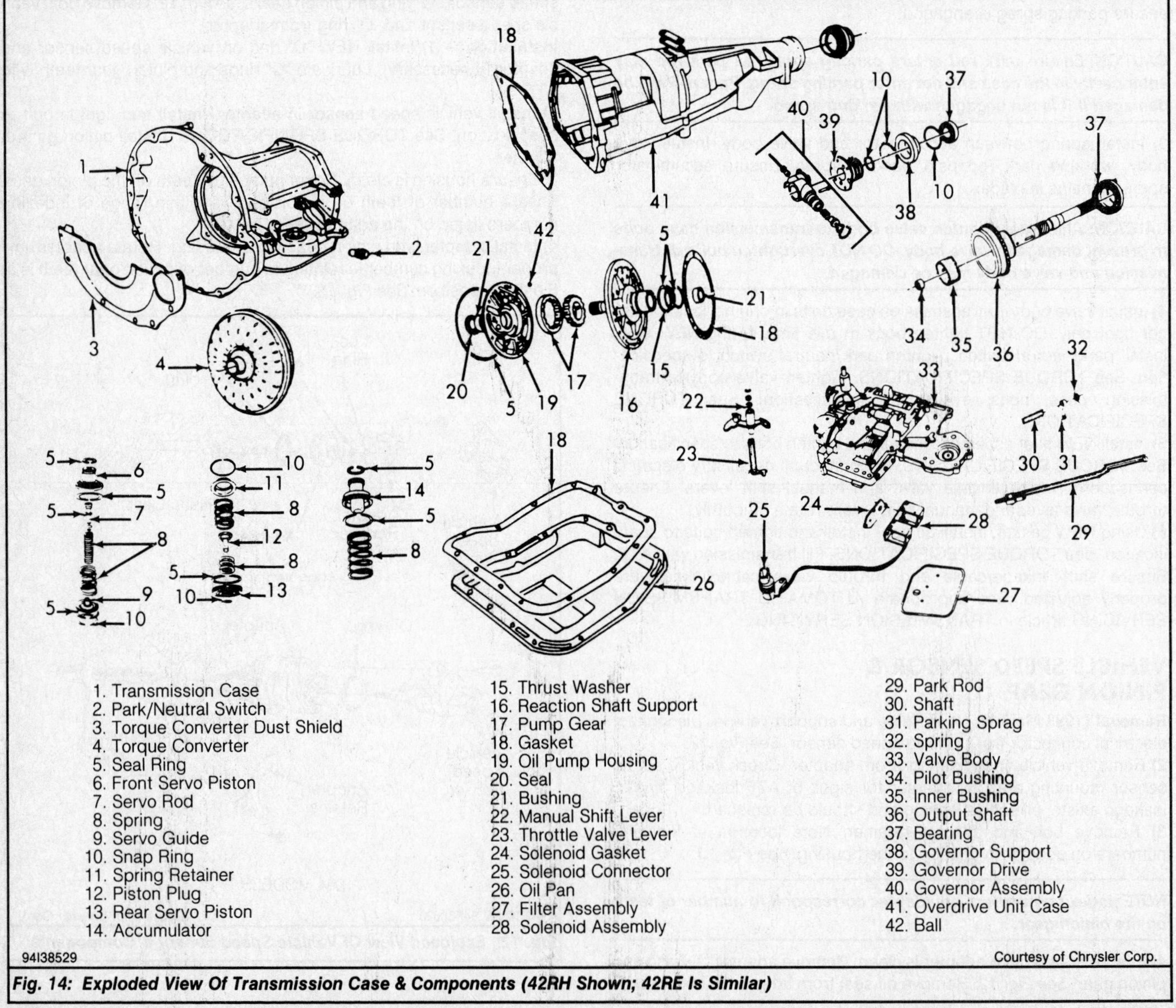

1. Transmission Case
2. Park/Neutral Switch
3. Torque Converter Dust Shield
4. Torque Converter
5. Seal Ring
6. Front Servo Piston
7. Servo Rod
8. Spring
9. Servo Guide
10. Snap Ring
11. Spring Retainer
12. Piston Plug
13. Rear Servo Piston
14. Accumulator
15. Thrust Washer
16. Reaction Shaft Support
17. Pump Gear
18. Gasket
19. Oil Pump Housing
20. Seal
21. Bushing
22. Manual Shift Lever
23. Throttle Valve Lever
24. Solenoid Gasket
25. Solenoid Connector
26. Oil Pan
27. Filter Assembly
28. Solenoid Assembly
29. Park Rod
30. Shaft
31. Parking Sprag
32. Spring
33. Valve Body
34. Pilot Bushing
35. Inner Bushing
36. Output Shaft
37. Bearing
38. Governor Support
39. Governor Drive
40. Governor Assembly
41. Overdrive Unit Case
42. Ball
94I38529
Courtesy of Chrysler Corp.

Fig. 14: Exploded View Of Transmission Case & Components (42RH Shown; 42RE Is Similar)

1) Remove torque converter. Loosen clamps and remove throttle valve and manual shift levers from transmission. On 42RH models, unscrew speed sensor from overdrive unit case. Place transmission in vertical position with overdrive unit facing upward.

CAUTION: If alignment shaft is not installed in overdrive unit, components may become out of alignment and overdrive unit must be disassembled to realign components.

2) On all models, remove overdrive unit-to-transmission case bolts. Remove overdrive unit. *See Fig. 15.* If overdrive unit does not require servicing, install Alignment Shaft (6227-2) in overrunning clutch and planetary gear splines on overdrive unit, ensuring alignment shaft is fully seated. *See Fig. 16.* This maintains proper alignment of all components in overdrive unit.

3) Remove intermediate shaft selective spacer and overdrive piston thrust plate from intermediate shaft. *See Fig. 15.* Remove overdrive piston from overdrive piston retainer.

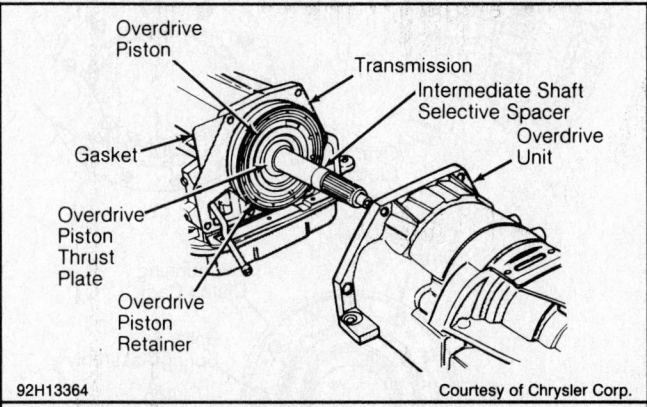

Fig. 15: Identifying Overdrive Unit

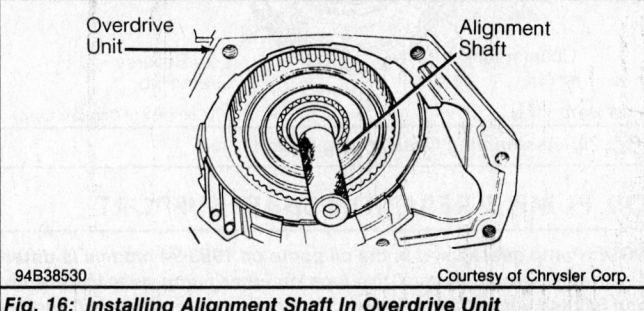

Fig. 16: Installing Alignment Shaft In Overdrive Unit

4) Remove bolts, oil pan and gasket. Remove park/neutral switch and seal. Remove bolts and filter assembly. Keep bolts with filter assembly for reassembly reference.

5) Remove park/neutral switch from transmission case. Remove valve body-to-transmission case bolts. Note bolt length and location for reassembly reference.

6) Lift valve body upward. Push manual shift lever and solenoid connector from transmission case. Guide park rod out of transmission case. Remove valve body. Remove accumulator and springs.

7) Remove plug from front band pin access hole located in front of transmission case, near top of oil pump. *See Fig. 18.* Loosen lock nut on front band adjusting screw approximately 5 revolutions. *See Fig. 17.* Tighten front band adjusting screw until front band is tight. This prevents clutch components from coming out when oil pump is removed.

8) Remove oil pump bolts. Install slide hammers on opposite sides of oil pump. Pull oil pump from transmission case. Remove oil pump gasket.

9) Loosen front band adjusting screw until front band is loose. Squeeze front band together. Remove front band strut located between lever on transmission case and front band.

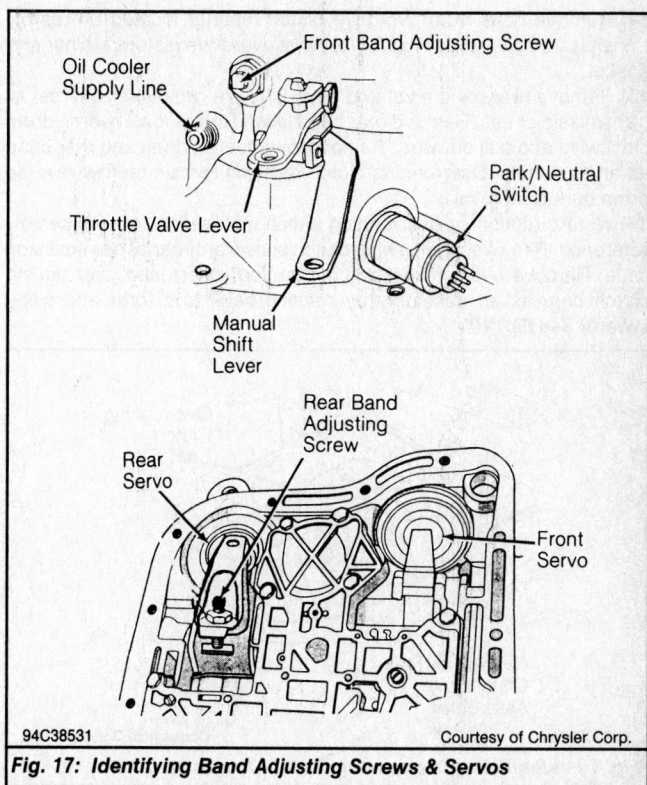

Fig. 17: Identifying Band Adjusting Screws & Servos

10) Remove front band pin through front band pin access hole. Remove lever for front band from transmission case. Slide front band rearward onto driving shell. Front band will be removed after front and rear clutch assemblies are removed.

11) Grasp input shaft, hold clutch units together. Remove front and rear clutch as an assembly. *See Fig. 18.* Remove triangular shaped thrust washer from intermediate shaft. This thrust washer may remain on hub of rear clutch.

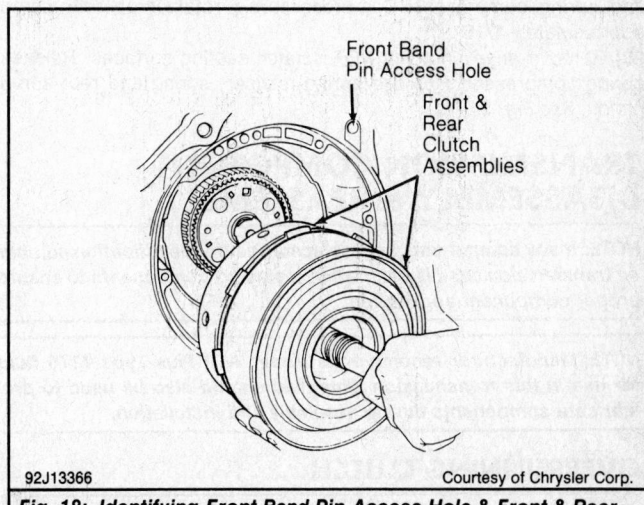

Fig. 18: Identifying Front Band Pin Access Hole & Front & Rear Clutch Assemblies

12) Remove intermediate shaft thrust plate from end of intermediate shaft. *See Fig. 27.* Remove front band. Remove intermediate shaft and planetary gear train assembly.

CAUTION: DO NOT damage machined surfaces on intermediate shaft during removal.

13) Loosen rear band adjusting screw. *See Fig. 17.* Remove low-reverse drum-to-overdrive piston retainer snap ring from inside of transmission case.

14) Remove bolts from overdrive piston retainer located on rear of transmission case. *See Fig. 15.* Remove overdrive piston retainer and gasket.

15) Remove rear band pivot and pins. Pins are removed from rear of transmission case. Remove rear band lever. Rotate low-reverse drum clockwise and pull outward. Remove low-reverse drum and rear band as an assembly. Overrunning clutch race will remain on low-reverse drum during removal.

16) Note direction of overrunning clutch installation for reassembly reference. Remove overrunning clutch bolts from rear of transmission case. Remove overrunning clutch cam and rollers and overrunning clutch cam as an assembly by rotating back and forth and tilting inward. *See Fig. 19.*

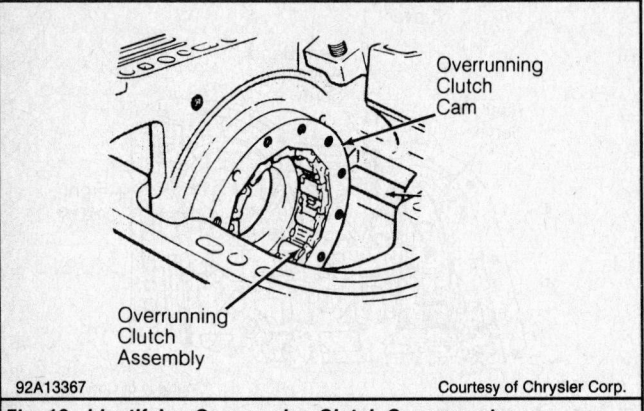

92A13367   Courtesy of Chrysler Corp.

Fig. 19: Identifying Overrunning Clutch Components

17) If removing servo components, note servo identification. *See Fig. 17.* To remove front servo, use "C" clamp and spring compressor to compress servo. Compress servo guide on front servo approximately 1/8".

18) Remove snap ring. DO NOT scratch sealing surfaces. Release spring compressor. Remove servo guide, spring and front servo piston. *See Fig. 14.*

19) To remove rear servo, compress spring retainer using "C" clamp and spring compressor. Compress spring retainer on rear servo approximately 1/16".

20) Remove snap ring. DO NOT scratch sealing surfaces. Release spring compressor. Remove spring retainer, spring and rear servo piston. *See Fig. 14.*

TRANSMISSION COMPONENT DISASSEMBLY & REASSEMBLY

NOTE: If any components are replaced, ensure identification number on transmission case is used when replacing components to ensure proper component application.

NOTE: Manufacturer recommends Mopar ATF Plus Type 7176 fluid for use in this transmission. This fluid should also be used to pre-lubricate components during assembly and installation.

OVERRUNNING CLUTCH

CAUTION: Ensure overrunning clutch components are properly installed, or inoperative transmission or transmission failure may result.

Disassembly – 1) If overrunning clutch assembly came out with low-reverse drum, thread 2 bolts into back side of overrunning clutch cam. Lift overrunning clutch assembly from low-reverse drum. It may be necessary to rotate overrunning clutch assembly back and forth during removal.

2) Note direction of springs and roller installation in retainer for reassembly reference. Separate springs, rollers and retainer from overrunning clutch cam.

Cleaning & Inspection – Clean components with solvent and dry with compressed air. Inspect overrunning clutch components and low-reverse drum for damage. Replace damaged components.

Reassembly – 1) Install roller and springs in retainer. Ensure springs and rollers are installed in correct location and fully seated. *See Fig. 20.*

2) Install roller and springs with retainer in overrunning clutch cam. Lubricate components with ATF. Identify non-threaded hole in overrunning clutch cam with a paint mark.

CAUTION: Paint mark must be in alignment with non-threaded hole on overrunning clutch cam. Paint mark is used for reassembly reference. Ensure countersunk holes in overrunning clutch cam face the rear of transmission when installed. See Figs. 20 and 37.

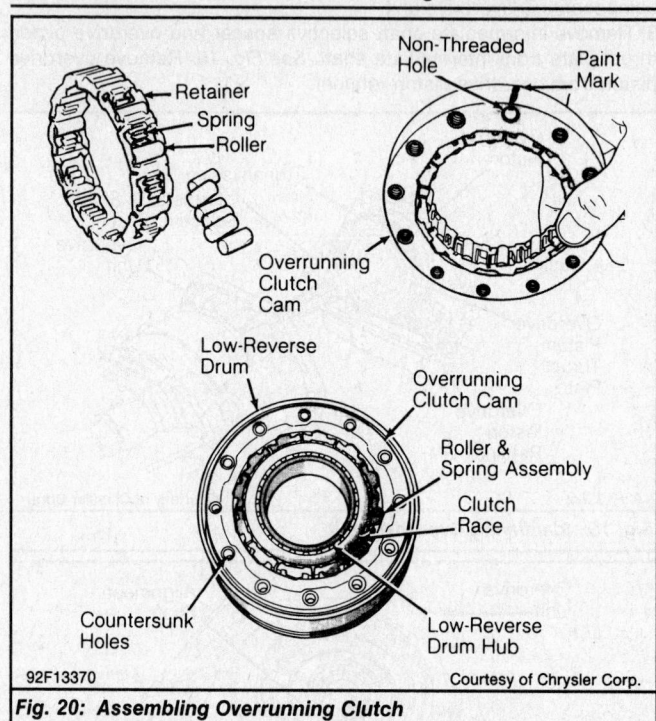

92F13370   Courtesy of Chrysler Corp.

Fig. 20: Assembling Overrunning Clutch

OIL PUMP & REACTION SHAFT SUPPORT

NOTE: Pump gears used in the oil pump on 1993-94 models is different than previous years. Drive lugs on inner pump gear is different and is used with different type of hub on torque converter. If replacing pump gears, ensure proper type gear is installed.

Disassembly – 1) Place reference mark on oil pump housing and reaction shaft support for reassembly reference. Remove reaction shaft support bolts. Separate reaction shaft support from oil pump housing. *See Fig. 14.* Remove seal ring from outer diameter of oil pump housing.

2) Using hammer and punch, tap seal from oil pump housing. Remove seal rings from reaction shaft support. Note direction of thrust washer installation on hub of reaction shaft support. Remove thrust washer from hub on reaction shaft support.

3) Note direction of pump gear installation. Remove pump gears from oil pump housing.

4) Inspect bushing in oil pump housing and reaction shaft support for damage. If removing bushing from oil pump housing, place oil pump housing on flat surface with pump gear cavity facing downward.

5) Using press or hammer and bushing remover, remove bushing. If removing bushing from reaction shaft support, use Cup (SP-3633), Nut (SP-1191) and Bushing Remover (SP-5324). *See Fig. 21.*

6) Hold cup against reaction shaft. By hand, thread bushing remover into bushing as far as possible. Using wrench, thread bushing remover an additional 3-4 turns into bushing. Tighten nut and remove bushing.

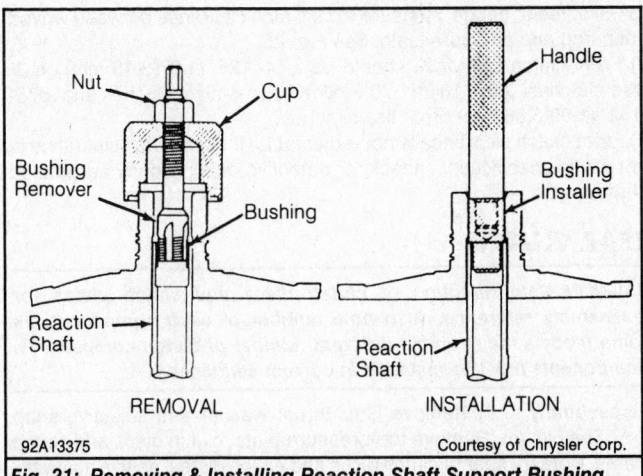

92A13375   Courtesy of Chrysler Corp.

Fig. 21: Removing & Installing Reaction Shaft Support Bushing

Cleaning & Inspection – 1) Clean and inspect components for damage. Inspect all machined surfaces for pitting or damage.
2) Install both pump gears in oil pump housing. Using feeler gauge, measure outer pump gear-to-oil pump housing clearance.
3) Place straightedge on oil pump housing, above both pump gears. Using feeler gauge, measure pump gear end clearance between each pump gear and straightedge.
4) Align one tooth on outer pump gear with one tooth on inner pump gear. Measure pump gear tooth clearance between the teeth on the pump gears. Replace components if clearance is not within specification. See OIL PUMP SPECIFICATIONS.

OIL PUMP SPECIFICATIONS

Application	In. (mm)
Outer Pump Gear-To-Oil Pump Housing Clearance	.0035-.0075 (.089-.190)
Pump Gear End Clearance	.0004-.0025 (.010-.063)
Pump Gear Tooth Clearance	.0035-.0075 (.089-.190)

Reassembly – 1) If installing NEW oil pump housing bushing, place oil pump housing on flat surface with pump gear cavity facing upward.
2) Place bushing on bushing installer and start into oil pump housing. Using hammer, tap bushing in oil pump housing until bushing is even with surface of oil pump housing bore. Ensure bushing is installed evenly and does not bind in oil pump housing.
3) Using blunt punch, stake bushing in 2 places. See Fig. 22. Using knife, clean burrs from stake areas.

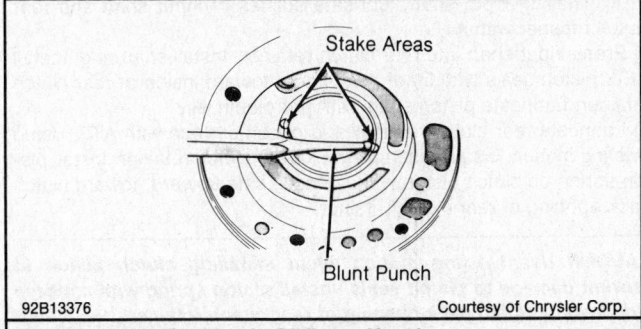

92B13376   Courtesy of Chrysler Corp.

Fig. 22: Staking Bushing In Oil Pump Housing

4) If installing NEW reaction shaft support bushing, ensure reaction shaft support is clean and free of burrs. Place reaction shaft support on clean surface with bushing area facing upward.
5) Use Handle (C-4171) and Bushing Installer (SP-5325). See Fig. 21. Place bushing on bushing installer and start into reaction shaft support. Using hammer, tap bushing into reaction shaft support until bushing installer bottoms. Remove bushing installer. Clean bushing and reaction shaft support.
6) To reassemble oil pump, lubricate pump gears and bore in oil pump housing with ATF. Install outer pump gear in oil pump housing.

CAUTION: On 1994 models, inner pump gear must be installed so chamfered side of the bore on the gear faces forward (toward front of oil pump).

7) On 1993 models, install inner pump gear in oil pump housing. Inner pump gear can be installed in either direction. On 1994 models, install inner pump gear with chamfered side of the bore on the gear facing forward (toward front of oil pump).

CAUTION: On 1994 models, thrust washer must be installed on reaction shaft support with chamfered edge on inside diameter of thrust washer facing toward front of oil pump.

8) On all models, install NEW thrust washer on rear of reaction shaft support. On 1993 models, thrust washer can be installed in either direction. On 1994 models, thrust washer must be installed with chamfered edge on inside diameter of thrust washer facing toward front of oil pump. On all models, lubricate thrust washer with petroleum jelly.

CAUTION: DO NOT over expand or twist seal rings when installing on reaction shaft support. Ensure ends on seal rings are hooked together or otherwise seal rings will be damaged when installing oil pump.

9) If replacing seal rings on reaction shaft support, install NEW seal rings on reaction shaft support. Lubricate seal rings with petroleum jelly. Squeeze seal rings together until ends of seal rings hook together.
10) Install reaction shaft support on oil pump housing with reference mark aligned. Install reaction shaft support bolts finger tight. DO NOT tighten bolts at this time.
11) Install oil pump in transmission case with oil pump reversed so reaction shaft support bolts are facing outward (toward front of transmission).
12) Install 3 bolts to secure oil pump in transmission case. Tighten reaction shaft support bolts to specification. See TORQUE SPECIFICATIONS. Remove oil pump from transmission case.
13) Install NEW seal in oil pump housing with seal lip facing inward (toward oil pump). Install NEW seal ring on outer diameter of oil pump housing. Lubricate lip of seal and seal ring with petroleum jelly.

FRONT CLUTCH

CAUTION: Note direction of clutch discs and clutch plates for reassembly reference. Also note number of each component, as some models may contain different number of clutch components. Components must be installed in correct sequence.

Disassembly – 1) Remove waved snap ring, pressure plate, clutch discs and clutch plates. Note number of clutch discs and clutch plates, as this may vary with application. See Fig. 23.
2) Using spring compressor, compress piston spring. Remove snap ring. Release spring compressor. Remove spring compressor. Note position of spring retainer on piston spring.
3) Remove spring retainer, piston spring and clutch piston from front clutch retainer. Remove piston seal and hub seal. See Fig. 23.
Cleaning & Inspection – 1) Clean all metal components with solvent and dry with compressed air. Inspect clutch discs for flatness, flaking or glazing. Inspect clutch plates and pressure plate for flatness or damage at plate-to-front clutch retainer tang areas.
2) Ensure tang areas in front clutch retainer are not damaged and clutch plates slide freely in front clutch retainer. Ensure check ball located in bottom of front clutch retainer moves freely.
3) Inspect all sealing surfaces for burrs or scratches. Replace damaged components. Inspect bushings in front clutch retainer. Replace front clutch retainer if bushings are damage.
Reassembly – 1) Soak clutch discs in ATF. Install NEW piston seal and NEW hub seal, with lip of seal toward inside of front clutch retainer. Lubricate piston seal and hub seal with petroleum jelly.

CAUTION: Use twisting motion when installing clutch piston to prevent damage to piston seal and hub seal.

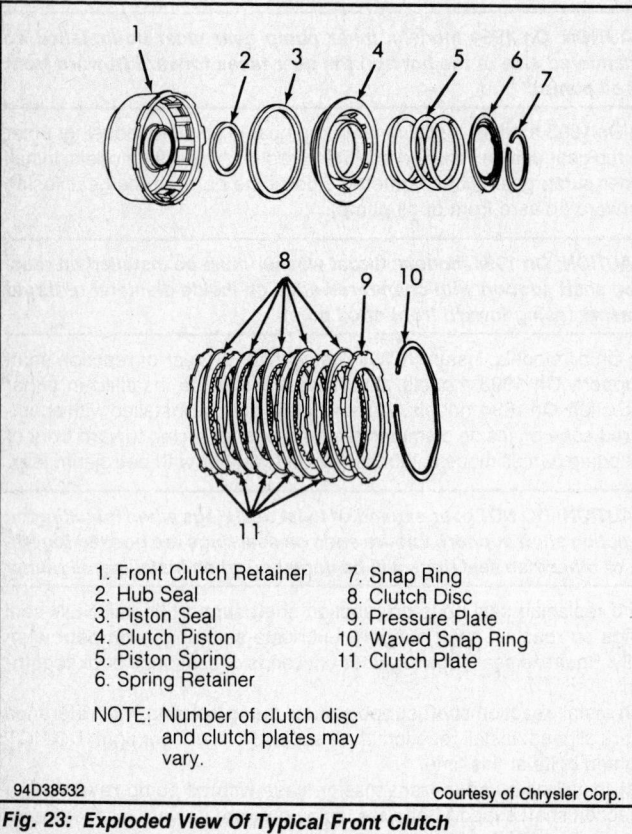

1. Front Clutch Retainer
2. Hub Seal
3. Piston Seal
4. Clutch Piston
5. Piston Spring
6. Spring Retainer
7. Snap Ring
8. Clutch Disc
9. Pressure Plate
10. Waved Snap Ring
11. Clutch Plate

NOTE: Number of clutch disc and clutch plates may vary.

94D38532   Courtesy of Chrysler Corp.

Fig. 23: Exploded View Of Typical Front Clutch

2) Lubricate front clutch retainer and clutch piston surface with ATF. Using twisting motion, install clutch piston in front clutch retainer.
3) Install piston spring and spring retainer on clutch piston. Ensure spring retainer is installed with small tabs away from piston spring. See Fig. 24.

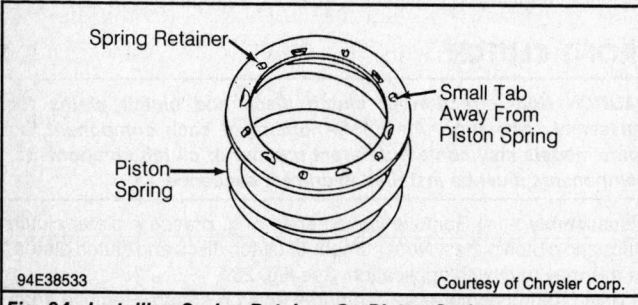

94E38533   Courtesy of Chrysler Corp.

Fig. 24: Installing Spring Retainer On Piston Spring

4) Using spring compressor, compress piston spring. Install NEW snap ring to secure spring retainer. Release spring compressor.
5) Alternately install clutch plates and clutch discs starting with clutch plate. See Fig. 23. Ensure original number of components are installed. Install pressure plate and waved snap ring.

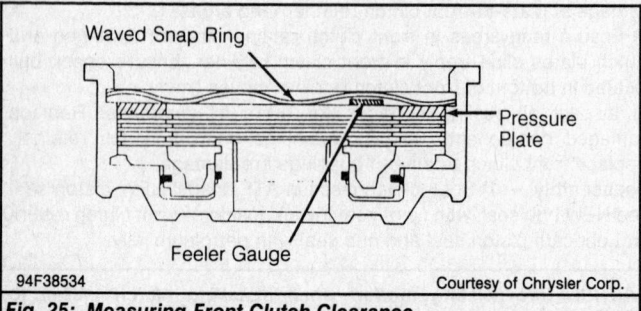

94F38534   Courtesy of Chrysler Corp.

Fig. 25: Measuring Front Clutch Clearance

6) Using feeler gauge, measure front clutch clearance between waved snap ring and pressure plate. See Fig. 25.
7) Front clutch clearance should be .074-.125" (1.87-3.18 mm) on 3-disc clutches, .067-.134" (1.70-3.40 mm) on 4-disc clutches and .075-.152" (1.90-3.86 mm) on 5-disc clutches.
8) Front clutch clearance is non-adjustable. If front clutch clearance is not within specification, check for defective or improperly assembled components.

REAR CLUTCH

CAUTION: Note direction of clutch discs and clutch plates for reassembly reference. Also note number of each component, as some models may contain different number of clutch components. Components must be installed in correct sequence.

Disassembly – 1) Remove fiber thrust washer and selective snap ring. See Fig. 26. Remove top pressure plate, clutch discs and clutch plates. Note number of clutch discs and clutch plates, as this may vary with application. See Fig. 26.
2) Remove bottom pressure plate, waved snap ring and piston spring. Using rotating motion, remove clutch piston. Remove and discard piston seals. If removing input shaft, remove snap ring. Using press, press input shaft from rear clutch retainer. Remove all seal rings from input shaft.
Cleaning & Inspection – 1) Clean all metal components with solvent and dry with compressed air. Inspect clutch discs for flatness, flaking or glazing. Inspect clutch plates and pressure plates for flatness or damage at plate-to-rear clutch retainer tang areas.
2) Ensure tang areas in rear clutch retainer are not damaged and clutch plates slide freely in rear clutch retainer. Ensure check ball moves freely in clutch piston.
3) Inspect bushing in rear clutch retainer for damage. Inspect clutch piston and piston spring for warpage or distortion. Inspect thrust washers for damage. Replace damaged components.
Reassembly – 1) Soak clutch discs in ATF. Install NEW hub seal ring on rear clutch retainer. Ensure hub seal ring is fully seated and is not twisted.
2) Slightly squeeze ends of input shaft Teflon seal ring together. This provides a better fit when seal ring is installed. Install NEW seal rings on input shaft so ends of Teflon seal ring are properly engaged and ends of metal seal ring are locked together.

CAUTION: Ensure ends of Teflon seal ring are properly engaged and ends of metal seal ring are locked together.

3) Lubricate input shaft seal rings and hub seal ring with petroleum jelly. If installing input shaft, lubricate splines of input shaft and rear clutch retainer with ATF.
4) Press input shaft into rear clutch retainer. Install snap ring. Install NEW piston seals with lip of piston seal toward inside of rear clutch retainer. Lubricate piston seals with petroleum jelly.
5) Lubricate rear clutch retainer and piston surface with ATF. Using twisting motion, install clutch piston in rear clutch retainer. Install piston spring on clutch piston with concave side upward, toward clutch pack opening of rear clutch retainer.

CAUTION: Use twisting motion when installing clutch piston to prevent damage to piston seals. Install piston spring with concave side toward clutch pack opening of rear clutch retainer.

6) Install waved snap ring. Ensure waved snap ring is fully seated in groove of rear clutch retainer. Install bottom pressure plate with flat side toward the clutch pack.
7) Alternately install original number of clutch plates and clutch discs starting with clutch disc. See Fig. 26. Install top pressure plate and selective snap ring.
8) Using feeler gauge, measure rear clutch clearance between selective snap ring and top pressure plate. Rear clutch clearance should be .032-.055" (.81-1.40 mm).

9) If rear clutch clearance is not within specification, install different thickness selective snap ring. Selective snap ring is available in thicknesses of .060" (1.52 mm), .076" (1.93 mm) and .098" (2.49 mm).

10) If proper rear clutch clearance cannot be obtained, clutch components may require replacement. Coat fiber thrust washer with petroleum jelly and install.

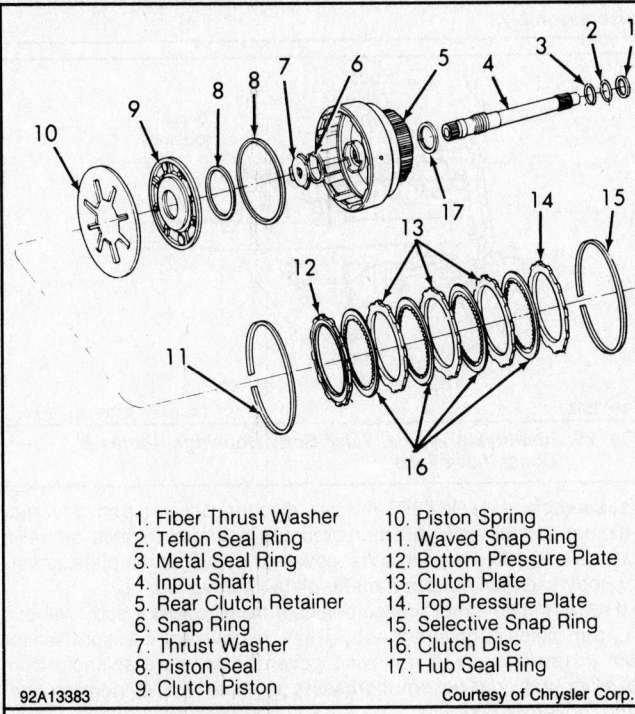

1. Fiber Thrust Washer
2. Teflon Seal Ring
3. Metal Seal Ring
4. Input Shaft
5. Rear Clutch Retainer
6. Snap Ring
7. Thrust Washer
8. Piston Seal
9. Clutch Piston
10. Piston Spring
11. Waved Snap Ring
12. Bottom Pressure Plate
13. Clutch Plate
14. Top Pressure Plate
15. Selective Snap Ring
16. Clutch Disc
17. Hub Seal Ring

92A13383

Courtesy of Chrysler Corp.

Fig. 26: Exploded View Of Rear Clutch

PLANETARY GEAR TRAIN

Disassembly – 1) Remove select fit snap ring, snap ring, thrust washer and thrust plate from front of intermediate shaft. *See Fig. 27.* Remove front annulus gear and front annulus gear support. Remove planetary thrust washer and front planetary gear.

2) Remove planetary thrust washer located behind front planetary gear. Remove sun gear and driving shell. Remove lock ring. Separate sun gear with front and rear thrust plates from driving shell.

NOTE: Check location of shoulder area on rear annulus gear support in relation to rear annulus gear before disassembling.

---

3) Remove planetary thrust washer from front of rear planetary gear. Remove rear planetary gear from rear annulus gear. Remove rear annulus gear from intermediate shaft. Remove snap ring. Separate front and rear annulus gears from annulus gear supports (if necessary).

Cleaning & Inspection – 1) Clean all components with solvent and dry with compressed air. Inspect for damaged components. Inspect sun gear bushings for scoring or wear. Replace sun gear if bushings are damaged or worn.

2) Inspect planetary gears for defective pinion gears, pins or carrier. Inspect intermediate shaft for damage at bushing/bearing surfaces and splined areas. Ensure intermediate shaft selective spacer fits properly in groove on intermediate shaft. Replace damaged components.

Reassembly – 1) Lubricate intermediate shaft and planetary gear train components with ATF. Use petroleum jelly to retain thrust washers and thrust plates in position.

2) Install rear annulus gear and snap ring in rear annulus gear support (if disassembled). Ensure snap ring is fully seated and shoulder area of rear annulus gear support faces rearward.

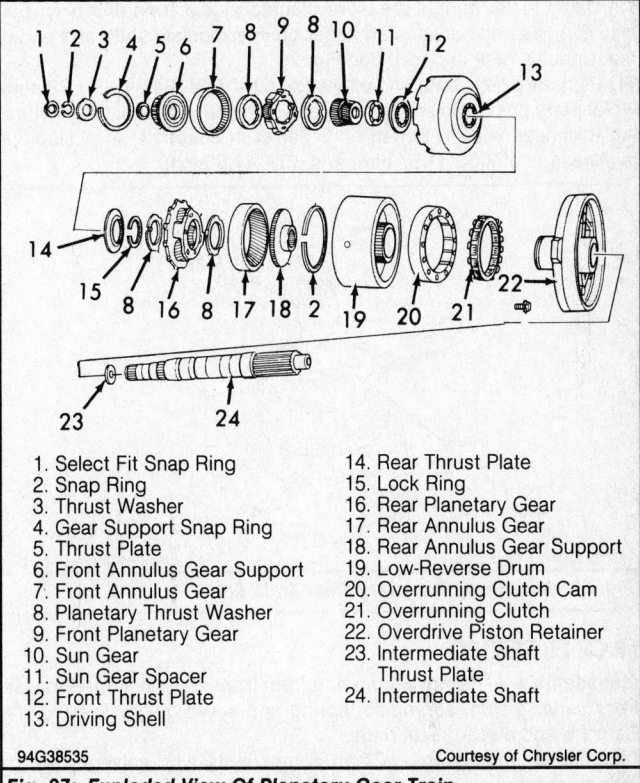

1. Select Fit Snap Ring
2. Snap Ring
3. Thrust Washer
4. Gear Support Snap Ring
5. Thrust Plate
6. Front Annulus Gear Support
7. Front Annulus Gear
8. Planetary Thrust Washer
9. Front Planetary Gear
10. Sun Gear
11. Sun Gear Spacer
12. Front Thrust Plate
13. Driving Shell
14. Rear Thrust Plate
15. Lock Ring
16. Rear Planetary Gear
17. Rear Annulus Gear
18. Rear Annulus Gear Support
19. Low-Reverse Drum
20. Overrunning Clutch Cam
21. Overrunning Clutch
22. Overdrive Piston Retainer
23. Intermediate Shaft Thrust Plate
24. Intermediate Shaft

94G38535

Courtesy of Chrysler Corp.

Fig. 27: Exploded View Of Planetary Gear Train

3) Install planetary thrust washer on rear side of rear planetary gear. Ensure tabs on planetary thrust washer engage with slots on rear planetary gear. Install rear annulus gear onto rear planetary gear.

4) Install rear planetary gear and rear annulus gear on intermediate shaft. Ensure assembly is fully seated on intermediate shaft. Install planetary thrust washer on front side of rear planetary gear.

5) Install sun gear spacer on sun gear (if removed). Install front thrust plate over sun gear and onto sun gear spacer. Install sun gear in driving shell. Install rear thrust plate over sun gear and against driving shell.

6) Support sun gear on wooden block. Ensure opening of driving shell is downward so lock ring can be installed. This aids in installation of lock ring. Ensure rear thrust plate is seated on driving shell. Install lock ring on sun gear, ensuring lock ring is fully seated in groove on sun gear.

7) Install sun gear and driving shell on intermediate shaft. Install planetary thrust washer on rear of front planetary gear. Ensure tabs on thrust washer engage with slots on front planetary gear.

8) Assemble front annulus gear and front annulus gear support (if necessary). Install thrust plate on front side of front annulus gear support. Install front planetary gear on intermediate shaft and into driving shell.

9) Install planetary thrust washer on front side of front planetary gear. Ensure tabs on thrust washer engage with slots on front planetary gear.

10) Install front annulus gear support and front annulus gear on front planetary gear. Install thrust washer on front side of front annulus gear support with tab away from front annulus gear support.

CAUTION: Ensure flat side on thrust washer engages with flat side of front planetary. Thrust washer must be installed with tab facing away from front annulus gear support.

---

11) Install snap ring to retain front annulus gear and select fit snap ring on intermediate shaft. Ensure snap rings are fully seated. Position gear train assembly with gear opening of driving shell facing workbench.

12) Place wooden block between end of intermediate shaft and workbench to support intermediate shaft. This moves planetary gear train components forward so planetary gear train end play can be checked.

13) Using feeler gauge, measure planetary gear train end play. End play is measured between shoulder on intermediate shaft and end of rear annulus gear support. See Fig. 28.

14) Planetary gear train end play should be .005-.048" (.13-1.22 mm). If planetary gear train end play is not within specification, install different thickness select fit snap ring. Select fit snap ring is available in thicknesses of .062" (1.57 mm) and .074" (1.88 mm).

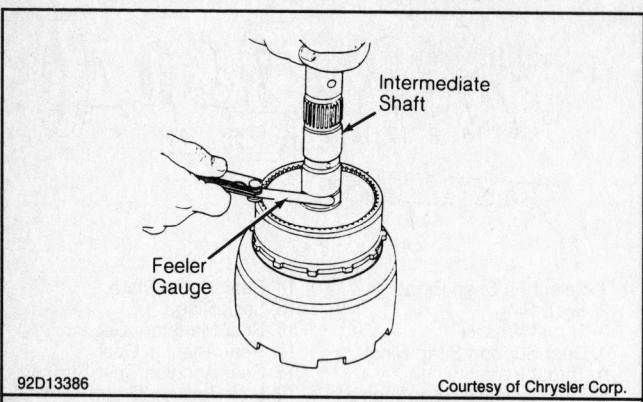

92D13386   Courtesy of Chrysler Corp.

Fig. 28: Measuring Planetary Gear Train End Play

FRONT SERVO

Disassembly – Remove snap ring from front servo piston. Separate front servo piston, servo rod, spring and servo guide. See Fig. 14. Remove and discard seal rings.

Cleaning & Inspection – Clean components with solvent and dry with compressed air. Inspect spring for distortion. Inspect front servo piston, servo rod and servo guide for wear or cracks. Replace defective components. If front servo piston or servo rod are damaged, both must be replaced as an assembly.

Reassembly – To reassemble, reverse disassembly procedure using NEW seal rings. Lubricate seal rings with petroleum jelly. Lubricate all other components with ATF.

REAR SERVO

Disassembly – 1) Note direction of seal ring installation on rear servo piston. Remove seal ring from rear servo piston. Using small wooden block and vise, compress spring enough to remove snap ring from end of piston plug. See Fig. 14.

2) Remove rear servo assembly from vise. Separate rear servo piston, springs, piston plug and spring retainer. See Fig. 14.

Cleaning & Inspection – Clean components with solvent and dry with compressed air. Inspect springs for distortion. Inspect rear servo piston and piston plug for wear or cracks. Replace defective components.

Reassembly – To reassemble, reverse disassembly procedure using NEW seal rings. Install seal ring so lip area is toward servo bore in transmission case. Lubricate seal ring with petroleum jelly. Lubricate all other components with ATF.

VALVE BODY

CAUTION: When disassembling valve body, place valve body components in order and mark spring locations for reassembly reference. DO NOT use force to remove components from valve body. Valve body components are not interchangeable. Valve body consists of upper housing, lower housing, transfer plate and separator plates. See Fig. 29.

CAUTION: On 1994 models, plastic check balls or steel check balls may be used in upper housing and transfer plate. Ensure original type of check ball is used. On all models, some valve bodies may contain the rear servo check ball and rear clutch check ball and some may not. Note original number of check balls during disassembly for reassembly reference. Some models may be equipped with a limit valve assembly.

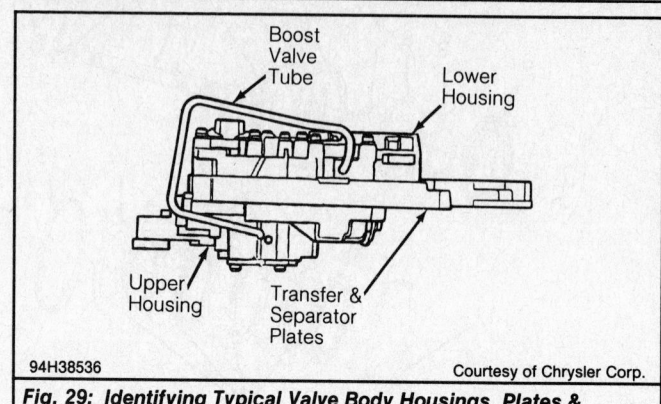

94H38536   Courtesy of Chrysler Corp.

Fig. 29: Identifying Typical Valve Body Housings, Plates & Boost Valve Tube

Disassembly – 1) On 42RE models, disconnect wires from governor pressure sensor and governor pressure solenoid located on valve body. See Fig. 30. Remove bolts, governor body retainer plate, governor body and gasket from transfer plate. See Fig. 30.

2) If removing governor pressure sensor from governor body, remove clip from inside of governor body. Remove governor pressure sensor from governor body. If removing governor pressure solenoid from governor body, pull governor pressure solenoid with "O" rings straight out of governor body.

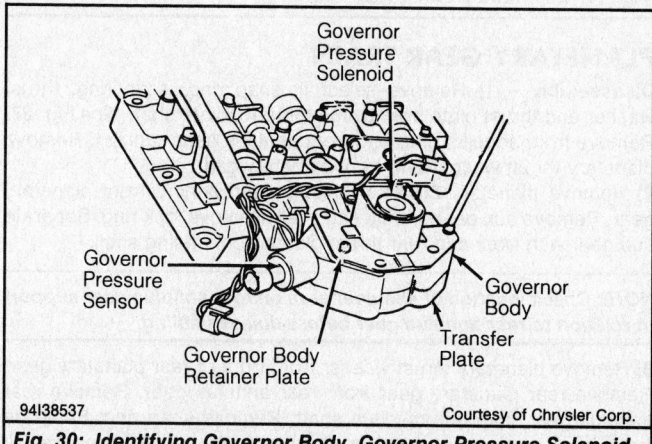

94I38537   Courtesy of Chrysler Corp.

Fig. 30: Identifying Governor Body, Governor Pressure Solenoid & Governor Pressure Sensor (42RE)

3) On all models, remove boost valve cover, retainer, boost valve spring, boost valve and boost valve plug (if equipped). See Fig. 31. Depress detent ball. Install Detent Ball Retainer (6583) on ball and spring housing to secure detent ball and spring in housing. See Fig. 32.

4) Remove clip and washer from throttle valve lever. Lift manual shift lever and park rod from throttle valve lever. See Fig. 14. Remove detent ball retainer. Remove detent ball and spring. Remove throttle valve lever.

5) Remove retaining clip. Separate park rod from manual shift lever. Hold adjusting screw bracket against valve body and remove screws. See Fig. 8.

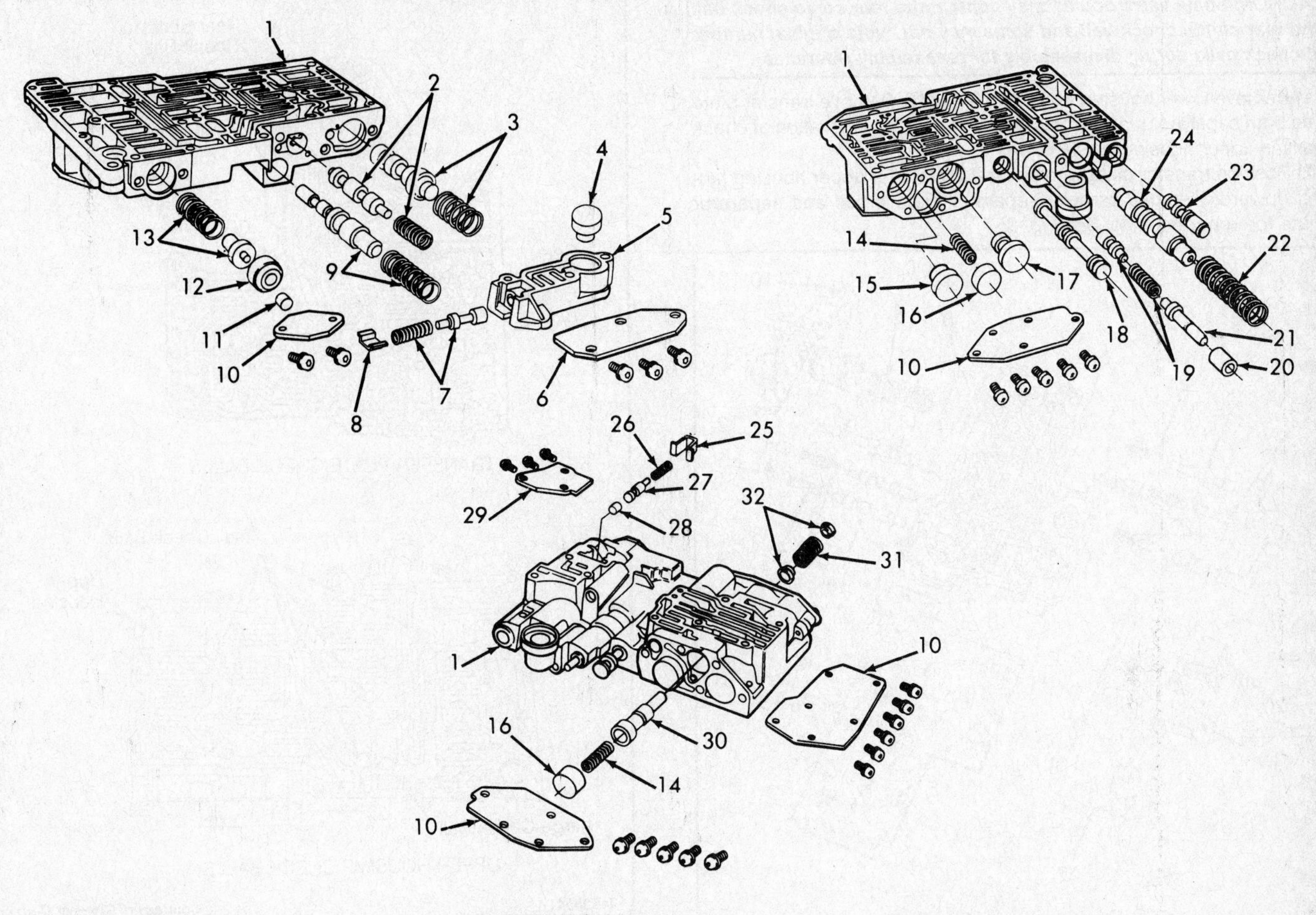

1. Upper Housing
2. 1-2 Shift Valve & Spring
3. 2-3 Shift Valve & Spring
4. 2-3 Throttle Plug (If Equipped)
5. Limit Valve Housing (If Equipped)
6. Limit Valve Cover (If Equipped)
7. Limit Valve & Spring (If Equipped)
8. Retainer (If Equipped)
9. 1-2 Shift Control Valve & Spring
10. Cover Plate
11. Line Pressure Plug
12. Plug Sleeve
13. Throttle Pressure Spring & Plug
14. Shuttle Valve Primary Spring
15. 2-3 Governor Plug
16. Throttle Plug
17. 1-2 Governor Plug
18. Manual Valve
19. Throttle Valve & Spring
20. Kickdown Detent
21. Kickdown Valve
22. Pressure Regulator Valve Spring
23. Switch Valve
24. Pressure Regulator Valve
25. Retainer (If Equipped)
26. Boost Valve Spring (If Equipped)
27. Boost Valve (If Equipped)
28. Boost Valve Plug (1994 Models If Equipped)
29. Boost Valve Cover (If Equipped)
30. Shuttle Valve
31. Shuttle Valve Secondary Spring
32. Clip

94J38538

Courtesy of Chrysler Corp.

Fig. 31: Exploded View Of Valve Body Upper Housing & Components

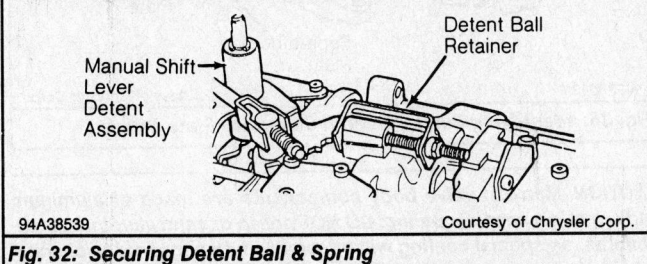

94A38539

Courtesy of Chrysler Corp.

Fig. 32: Securing Detent Ball & Spring

CAUTION: DO NOT disturb throttle pressure adjusting screw or line pressure adjusting screw locations in adjusting screw bracket.

6) Remove adjusting screw bracket with line pressure adjusting screw, pressure regulator valve spring (large spring) and switch valve spring (small spring).

7) Note routing of solenoid wiring. Remove solenoid assembly, gasket, 3-4 accumulator housing and case connector from lower housing. *See Fig. 33.* Case connector uses a shoulder-type screw and must be installed in original location.

CAUTION: Use care not to damage housings or tube when removing boost valve tube. Disengage boost valve tube from upper housing first and then from the lower housing. DO NOT pry boost valve tube from the housing

8) Remove spring, 3-4 shift valve, plug, spring and lock-up valve. *See Fig. 33.* Pull boost valve tube from upper housing first and then from the lower housing. *See Fig. 29.* It may be necessary to rotate boost valve tube back and forth when removing from lower housing.

9) Position valve body so lower housing faces upward, with upper housing on bottom. *See Fig. 29.*

CAUTION: Ensure lower housing faces upward before removing valve body screws. This prevents check balls from falling out of upper housing.

10) Note location of brace for the boost valve tube. Remove valve body screws attaching lower housing to the upper housing. Remove lower housing and separator plate from transfer plate.

CAUTION: *Some valve bodies may contain the rear servo check ball and rear clutch check ball and some may not. Note original number of check balls during disassembly for reassembly reference.*

11) Remove lower housing from transfer plate. Remove transfer plate and both separator plates from upper housing. Note location of check balls in upper housing. *See Fig. 34.*

12) Position transfer plate with separator plate for upper housing facing upward. Remove screws, separator plate brace and separator plate for upper housing. *See Fig. 35.*

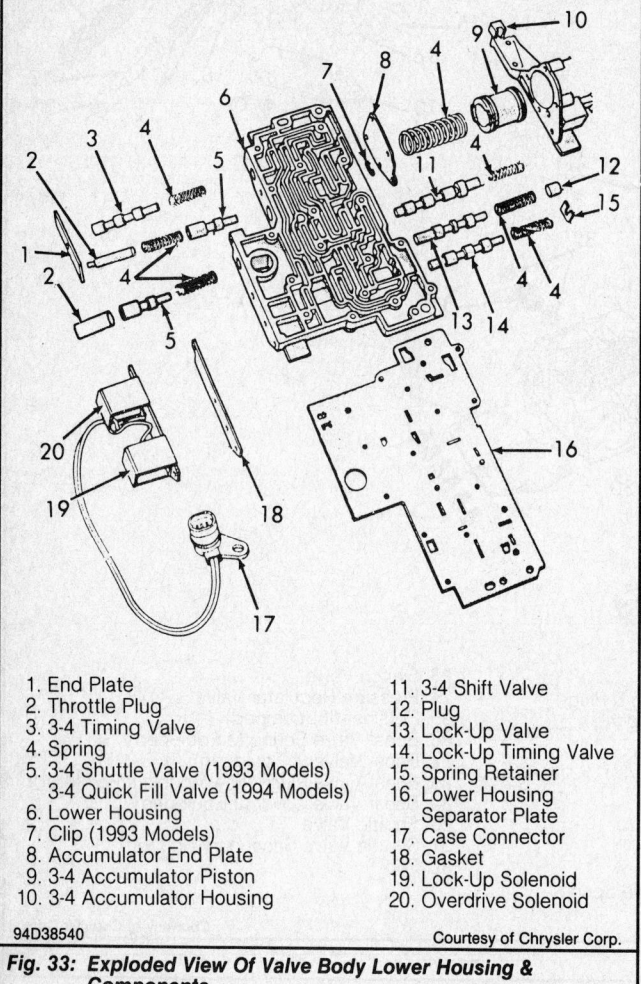

1. End Plate
2. Throttle Plug
3. 3-4 Timing Valve
4. Spring
5. 3-4 Shuttle Valve (1993 Models)
   3-4 Quick Fill Valve (1994 Models)
6. Lower Housing
7. Clip (1993 Models)
8. Accumulator End Plate
9. 3-4 Accumulator Piston
10. 3-4 Accumulator Housing
11. 3-4 Shift Valve
12. Plug
13. Lock-Up Valve
14. Lock-Up Timing Valve
15. Spring Retainer
16. Lower Housing
    Separator Plate
17. Case Connector
18. Gasket
19. Lock-Up Solenoid
20. Overdrive Solenoid

94D38540   Courtesy of Chrysler Corp.

Fig. 33: Exploded View Of Valve Body Lower Housing & Components

13) Remove separator plate for upper housing from transfer plate. Note location of filter screen in upper housing separator plate and check balls in transfer plate. *See Figs. 34 and 35.*

14) Remove components from upper and lower housings. Ensure components are placed in order for reassembly reference. *See Figs. 31 and 33.*

Cleaning & Inspection – 1) Clean components with solvent and dry with compressed air. DO NOT use solvent to clean electrical components. DO NOT use shop towels to dry components. Ensure all components slide freely in housing bores and bores are not scored. Inspect machined surfaces for nicks, burrs or distortion.

2) Inspect valve and plugs for burrs or scratches. Minor scratches may be removed using crocus cloth. When sanding components, DO NOT round off edges of valve or plug.

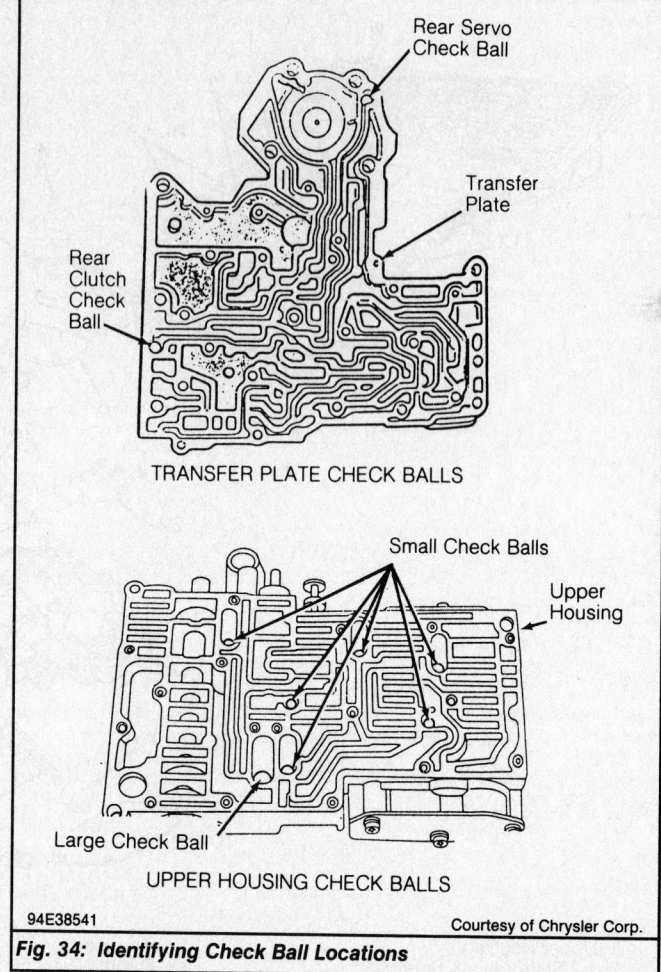

TRANSFER PLATE CHECK BALLS

UPPER HOUSING CHECK BALLS

94E38541   Courtesy of Chrysler Corp.

Fig. 34: Identifying Check Ball Locations

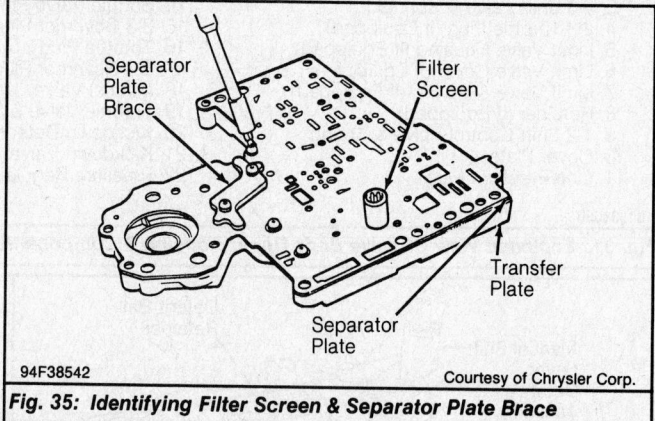

94F38542   Courtesy of Chrysler Corp.

Fig. 35: Identifying Filter Screen & Separator Plate Brace

CAUTION: *Many of valve body components are made of aluminum and contain a special coating. DO NOT polish or sand aluminum components, as special coating will be removed. Use magnet to check if components are made of aluminum before polishing or sanding. Use care when polishing or sanding components, as not to round off the edges of component. Sharp edges may be maintained on the component.*

3) Ensure all fluid passages are open. Inspect transfer plate and separator plates for distortion. Inspect check balls and seats for damage. Check flatness of mating surfaces on upper and lower housings.

4) On 42RE models, ensure vent ports in governor pressure solenoid are open and not blocked. DO NOT attempt to remove filter from governor pressure solenoid. The "O" rings on governor pressure solenoid and governor pressure sensor are the only parts of solenoid and valve that can be serviced.

CAUTION: On 42RE models, DO NOT rotate small screw located at the end of governor pressure solenoid for any reason or the solenoid calibration will be changed and solenoid will require replacement.

5) On all models, valve body must be replaced if components are damaged. Only the following components can be serviced.
- Adjusting Screw Bracket
- Governor Pressure Sensor (42RE)
- Governor Pressure Solenoid (42RE)
- Manual Shift Lever, Seal & Detent Ball
- Park Rod & Clip
- Solenoid Assembly
- Switch Valve & Spring
- Throttle Valve Lever & Seal

Reassembly – 1) Lubricate all components and fluid passages with ATF. Install components in lower housing. Ensure components are installed in original location. *See Fig. 33.* Tighten end plate screws to specification. See TORQUE SPECIFICATIONS.

2) Reassemble 3-4 accumulator using NEW seal rings on 3-4 accumulator piston. Install accumulator end plate.

CAUTION: On 1994 models, plastic check balls or steel check balls may be used in upper housing and transfer plate. Ensure original type of check ball is used in original location. On all models, some valve bodies may contain the rear servo check ball and rear clutch check ball and some may not. Install original number of check balls in original location.

3) Install rear clutch check ball and rear servo check ball in transfer plate. *See Fig. 34.* Ensure filter screen is installed in separator plate for upper housing. *See Fig. 35.*

4) Install separator plate for upper housing on transfer plate. Install separator plate brace. *See Fig. 35.* Install and tighten screws to specification. See TORQUE SPECIFICATIONS.

5) Install remaining screws securing separator plate for the upper housing to the transfer plate. Tighten screws to specification.

CAUTION: On 1994 models, plastic check balls may be used in upper housing and transfer plate. Ensure proper type check ball is used.

6) Install check balls in upper housing. *See Fig. 34.* Install transfer plate and separator plate for upper housing on the upper housing. Ensure filter screen is fully seated in recess area on upper housing.

7) Install separator plate for lower housing on transfer plate. Install lower housing on transfer plate and upper housing. Install and tighten valve body screws to specification, starting at the center and working outward.

8) Install components in upper housing. Ensure components are installed in original location. *See Fig. 31.* Install cover plates and limit valve cover. Install and tighten screws to specification.

CAUTION: When installing shuttle valve, ensure clip fully engages groove on shuttle valve.

9) Lubricate bores for boost valve tube in both housings and ends of boost valve tube with ATF. Install boost valve tube, by starting boost valve tube into lower housing first and then in the upper housing. Ensure boost valve tube is installed behind brace for boost valve tube and is fully seated in the housings.

10) Install 3-4 accumulator housing on lower housing. Ensure springs and lock-up valve plug are properly positioned before tightening 3-4 accumulator housing screws.

11) Install case connector on 3-4 accumulator housing. Ensure tab on case connector engages with groove on 3-4 accumulator housing. Install and tighten shouldered-type screw to retain case connector.

12) Using NEW gasket, install solenoid assembly. Install and tighten solenoid assembly screws to specification. See TORQUE SPECIFICATIONS. Ensure wiring for solenoid assembly is properly routed and clears and manual shift lever and park rod.

13) Install detent ball and spring in upper housing and retain in position using detent ball retainer. Install spring on end of line pressure regulator valve. Install switch valve spring on tang at end of adjusting screw bracket. Install adjusting screw bracket. Ensure springs align with adjusting screw bracket.

14) Install upper screw (short screw) in adjusting screw bracket first and then install lower screw (long screw). Tighten screws to specification. See TORQUE SPECIFICATIONS.

15) Install throttle valve lever in upper housing. Install manual shift lever over throttle valve lever. Align manual shift lever with detent ball and manual valve. Hold throttle valve lever upward and start manual shift lever into housing.

16) Install seal, washer and clip on manual shift lever. Remove detent ball retainer. Lubricate case connector "O" ring and manual shift lever shaft with petroleum jelly.

17) Ensure throttle valve lever aligns with end of kickdown valve and manual shift lever arm is engaged with manual valve. *See Fig. 36.*

CAUTION: If line pressure or throttle pressure adjusting screws were moved from original setting, they must be readjusted. See HYDRAULIC PRESSURE ADJUSTMENTS in this article.

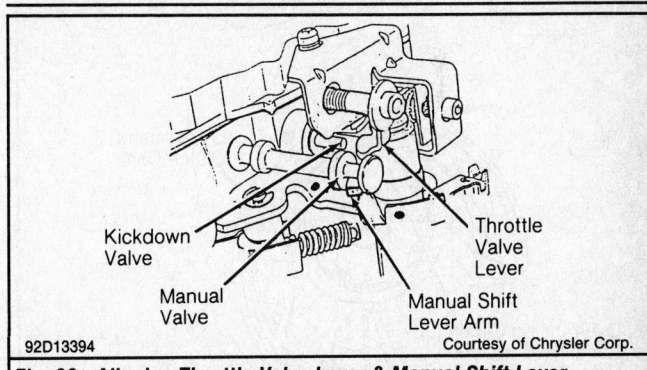

Kickdown Valve — Throttle Valve Lever — Manual Valve — Manual Shift Lever Arm

92D13394   Courtesy of Chrysler Corp.

Fig. 36: Aligning Throttle Valve Lever & Manual Shift Lever

18) Install boost valve and components. *See Fig. 31.* Install and tighten boost valve cover screws to specification. See TORQUE SPECIFICATIONS.

19) On 42RE models, install NEW "O" ring on governor pressure solenoid and governor pressure sensor. Lubricate "O" rings with ATF.

20) Install governor pressure sensor in governor body. Install clip on inside of governor body to retain governor pressure sensor. Install governor pressure solenoid in governor body until it snaps into the governor body.

21) Install NEW gasket for governor body on transfer plate. Install governor body retainer plate on governor body. Ensure electrical connector on governor pressure solenoid is in cutout area on governor body retainer plate.

22) Install and tighten governor body-to-transfer plate bolts to specifications. Install electrical connectors on governor pressure solenoid and governor pressure sensor.

TRANSMISSION REASSEMBLY

VALVE BODY & COMPONENTS

NOTE: Lubricate all components with Mopar ATF Plus Type 7176 fluid. Use petroleum jelly to hold thrust washers, thrust plates and gaskets in position. Ensure thrust washer and thrust plates are installed in original location.

1) Install NEW seal rings on front and rear servo pistons. Install front and rear servos and components in transmission case. It may be necessary to use twisting motion when installing servo pistons. Using "C" clamp and spring compressor, compress servo. Install snap ring. Remove "C" clamp and spring compressor.

2) Ensure springs and rollers are installed in correct location and fully seated in overrunning clutch. *See Fig. 20.* Lubricate components with ATF. Identify non-threaded hole in overrunning clutch cam with a paint mark. Note countersunk holes in overrunning clutch cam. *See Fig. 20.*
3) Place reference mark on blank area at rear of transmission case for overrunning clutch installation. *See Fig. 37.*
4) Install overrunning clutch cam with countersunk holes toward rear of transmission (overdrive piston side) and reference marks aligned. Install and tighten bolts to specification. See TORQUE SPECIFICATIONS.

CAUTION: Ensure overrunning clutch assembly is installed with countersunk holes toward rear of transmission (overdrive piston side) and reference marks aligned.

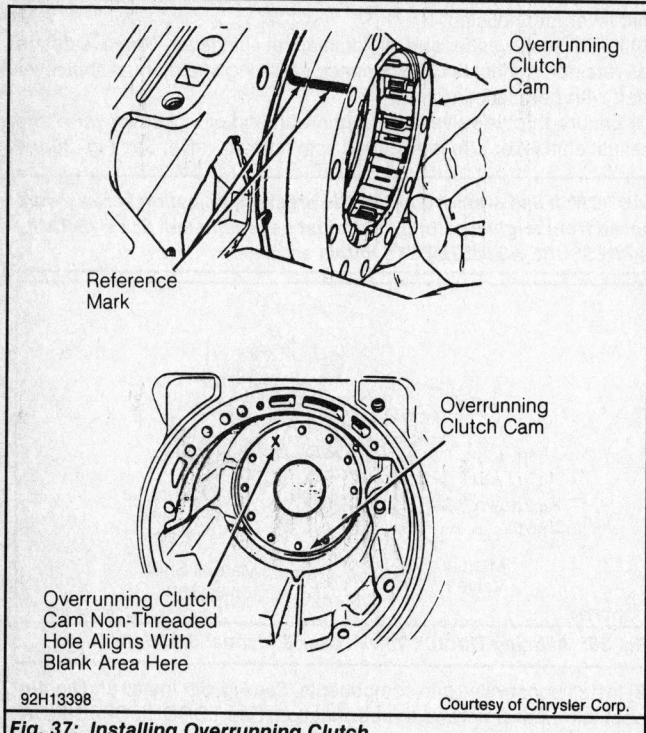

Overrunning Clutch Cam

Reference Mark

Overrunning Clutch Cam

Overrunning Clutch Cam Non-Threaded Hole Aligns With Blank Area Here

92H13398   Courtesy of Chrysler Corp.

Fig. 37: Installing Overrunning Clutch

5) Install NEW "O" rings on rear band reaction pin. Lubricate "O" rings with ATF. Install rear band reaction pin in rear of transmission. This is the pin near top of transmission, farthest from oil pan surface. Ensure rear band reaction pin is fully seated.
6) Install rear band so twin lugs on the rear band are seated against rear band reaction pin. Lubricate overrunning clutch race on rear of low-reverse drum with ATF.
7) Install low-reverse drum through rear band. Tilt low-reverse drum and engage overrunning clutch race with rollers on overrunning clutch. Press low-reverse drum rearward while rotating low-reverse drum clockwise until it fully seats in overrunning clutch. Rotate low-reverse drum back and forth. Low-reverse drum should rotate freely clockwise (viewed from front of transmission case), but lock when rotated counterclockwise.

CAUTION: Ensure low-reverse drum rotates freely clockwise (viewed from front of transmission case), but locks when rotated counterclockwise. Check for improper component assembly if low-reverse drum will not rotate correctly.

8) Install NEW gasket on rear of transmission case. Use petroleum jelly to hold gasket in place. Ensure governor tube supply holes on gasket align with holes on transmission case. *See Fig. 38.*
9) Install overdrive piston retainer so governor tube supply holes align with holes on transmission case. *See Fig. 38.* Install and tighten bolts to specification. See TORQUE SPECIFICATIONS.

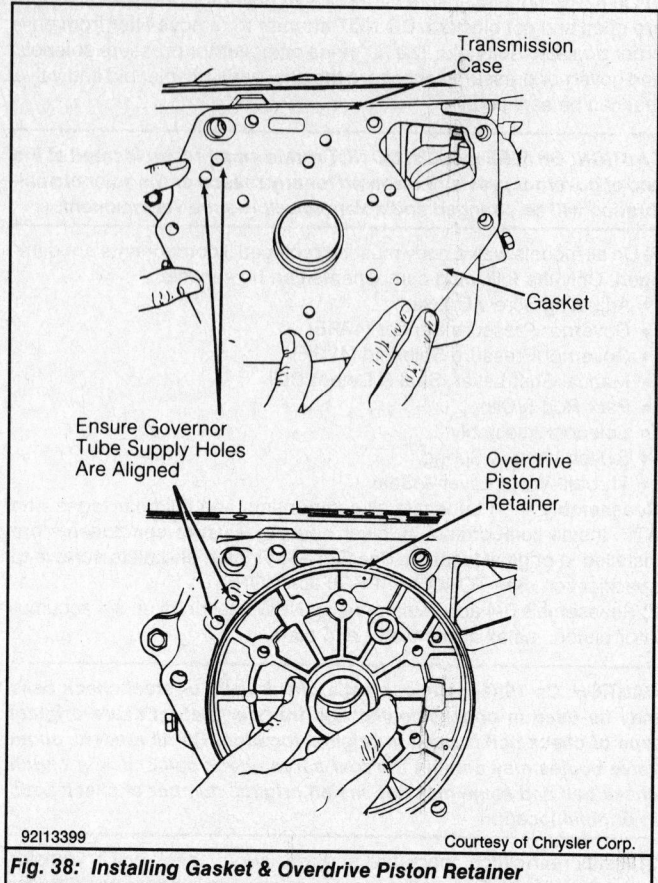

Transmission Case

Gasket

Ensure Governor Tube Supply Holes Are Aligned

Overdrive Piston Retainer

92I13399   Courtesy of Chrysler Corp.

Fig. 38: Installing Gasket & Overdrive Piston Retainer

10) Install low-reverse drum-to-overdrive piston retainer snap ring. Install rear band lever and remaining pin. Pin is located between overdrive piston retainer and transmission case.
11) Install intermediate shaft and planetary gear train. Install thrust plate on end of intermediate shaft.

CAUTION: Install input shaft seal rings with Teflon seal ring on front of input shaft followed by metal seal ring. Ensure hub seal ring is installed on rear clutch retainer. See Fig. 26. Ends of metal seal rings must be fastened together. Diagonal ends of Teflon seal ring must be properly joined.

12) Ensure fiber thrust washer is installed on front of rear clutch retainer. *See Fig. 26.* Align teeth on front clutch discs. Install front clutch on rear clutch. Ensure front clutch is fully seated on rear clutch by rotating front clutch back and forth.

CAUTION: Ensure thrust washer for intermediate shaft is installed with groove in thrust washer toward intermediate shaft.

13) Install thrust washer for intermediate shaft in center of rear clutch so groove in thrust washer is toward the intermediate shaft. Thrust washer fits on inside of rear clutch retainer, near end of input shaft. *See Fig. 26.* This is the washer used to control input shaft end play.
14) Using small screwdriver, align teeth on rear clutch discs. Position transmission case with oil pump opening facing upward. Install front and rear clutch assemblies. Rotate assembly back and forth until rear clutch discs fully engage with front annulus gear. Ensure lugs on front clutch retainer engages with slots in driving shell.

CAUTION: Ensure thrust washer in center of rear clutch and thrust plate on end of intermediate shaft do not move when installing front and rear clutch assemblies.

15) Install front band over front clutch retainer. Partially install front band pin through front band pin access hole on front of transmission.

See Fig. 18. Install front band strut, lever and front band adjusting screw.

16) Fully install front band pin. Tighten front band adjusting screw until front band is tight on front clutch retainer. Ensure front and rear clutch assemblies are fully seated.

17) Apply thread sealant on plug for front band pin access hole. Install and tighten plug to specification. See TORQUE SPECIFICATIONS.

CAUTION: On 1994 models, thrust washer must be installed on reaction shaft support with chamfered edge on inside diameter of thrust washer facing toward front of oil pump.

18) Ensure thrust washer and seal rings are installed on reaction shaft support and ends of seal rings are fastened together.

19) Install pilot stud in 2 oil pump bolt holes, opposite of each other in transmission case. Install oil pump gasket. Lubricate reaction shaft seal rings and oil pump seal with ATF.

20) Install oil pump. Remove pilot studs. Install and tighten oil pump bolts in a diagonal pattern to specification.

CAUTION: Ensure input shaft and intermediate shaft rotate without binding. If binding exists, check for improperly assembled components.

21) Install NEW seal on overdrive piston and lubricate with petroleum jelly. Install overdrive piston in overdrive piston retainer. If necessary, use feeler gauge to guide seal on overdrive piston into overdrive piston retainer.

CAUTION: Ensure 2 locating pins on transmission case side of overdrive piston engage with 2 holes on overdrive piston retainer.

CAUTION: Before installing intermediate shaft selective spacer and overdrive piston thrust bearing, ensure proper procedure is used to determine thickness of these components. See DETERMINING INTERMEDIATE SHAFT SELECTIVE SPACER & OVERDRIVE PISTON THRUST PLATE under OVERDRIVE UNIT ADJUSTMENTS.

22) Determine proper thickness intermediate shaft selective spacer and overdrive piston thrust bearing. See DETERMINING INTERMEDIATE SHAFT SELECTIVE SPACER & OVERDRIVE PISTON THRUST PLATE under OVERDRIVE UNIT ADJUSTMENTS.

23) Install intermediate shaft selective spacer on intermediate shaft. *See Fig. 15.* Install overdrive piston thrust plate in center of overdrive piston. *See Fig. 15.* Use petroleum jelly to hold thrust plate in position.

24) Install overdrive piston thrust bearing in direct clutch hub on overdrive unit with shoulder away from direct clutch hub. *See Fig. 39.* Use petroleum jelly to hold overdrive piston thrust bearing in position.

CAUTION: Ensure shoulder on overdrive piston thrust bearing faces away from direct clutch hub. Dark-colored surface of overdrive piston thrust bearing should be toward overdrive piston.

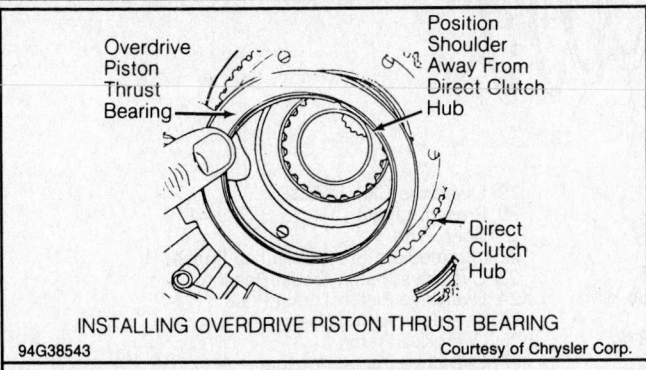

Overdrive Piston Thrust Bearing

Position Shoulder Away From Direct Clutch Hub

Direct Clutch Hub

INSTALLING OVERDRIVE PISTON THRUST BEARING

94G38543   Courtesy of Chrysler Corp.

Fig. 39: Installing Overdrive Piston Thrust Bearing

25) Apply small amount of petroleum jelly on end of intermediate shaft. Using Alignment Shaft (6227-2), align splines of planetary gear assembly and overrunning clutch in overdrive unit. *See Fig. 16.* Ensure alignment shaft is fully seated.

26) Overdrive unit clutch splines must be aligned to aid in installation on intermediate shaft. Once splines are aligned, carefully remove alignment shaft.

CAUTION: Ensure intermediate shaft selective spacer on intermediate shaft, overdrive piston thrust plate and overdrive piston thrust bearing are installed.

27) Install overdrive unit on transmission case. On 42RH models, ensure governor tubes are seated in supply holes on overdrive piston retainer. *See Fig. 38.* On all models, if overdrive unit will not fully seat, slightly rotate output shaft to align splines and ensure overdrive unit is fully seated.

28) Apply thread sealant on overdrive unit-to-transmission case bolts. Install and tighten bolts to specification. See TORQUE SPECIFICATIONS. Attach dial indicator to transmission case with dial indicator stem seated against end of input shaft.

29) Move input shaft inward and zero dial indicator. Pull input shaft outward and measure input shaft end play. Input shaft end play should be .022-.091" (.56-2.31 mm).

30) If input shaft end play is not within specification, install different thickness thrust washer for intermediate shaft located in center of rear clutch. Recheck input shaft end play.

31) Ensure lock nuts are backed off on front and rear band adjusting screws. *See Fig. 17.* Tighten front and rear band adjusting screws to 72 INCH lbs. (8.1 N.m).

32) Loosen front band adjusting screw 3 5/8 turns on 42RE models or 2 1/2 turns on 42RH models. On all models, loosen rear band adjusting screw 4 turns. Tighten each band adjusting screw lock nut to specification while holding band adjusting screw. See TORQUE SPECIFICATIONS.

33) Ensure park/neutral switch is removed before installing valve body. Install NEW seal rings on accumulator and solenoid connector. Lubricate seal rings, manual shift lever seal, accumulator and accumulator bore with petroleum jelly.

34) Install inner spring and accumulator in transmission case. Place manual shift lever on valve body in low gear position so ball on park rod can be installed in parking sprag.

35) Using screwdriver, push parking sprag to engage with park gear. This allows knob on park rod to move past parking sprag when installing valve body. Rotate output shaft to ensure parking sprag is engaged.

CAUTION: Ensure park rod enters parking sprag, as park rod may enter cavity in the case and not enter parking sprag. Park rod will be damaged if it is not engaged with parking sprag.

36) Install accumulator spring between accumulator and valve body. Install valve body, working park rod past parking sprag. Ensure accumulator spring remains in place.

CAUTION: Alternately tighten valve body bolts to prevent damage to valve body. DO NOT overtighten bolts or transmission and valve body may be damaged.

37) Install valve body-to-transmission case bolts in original location and tighten evenly to specification.

38) Install NEW filter assembly. Install and tighten bolts to specification. Reconnect all necessary electrical connections. Install throttle valve and manual shift levers. Ensure throttle and manual shift levers rotate smoothly.

39) Using NEW gasket, install oil pan. Install and tighten bolts to specification. Using NEW seal, install park/neutral switch. Tighten park/neutral switch to specification. See TORQUE SPECIFICATIONS.

CAUTION: If transmission failure existed, flush oil cooler and check oil cooler flow. See OIL COOLER FLUSHING and OIL COOLER FLOW CHECK under ON-VEHICLE SERVICE.

OVERDRIVE UNIT DISASSEMBLY

OVERDRIVE UNIT

Disassembly – **1)** Remove snap ring and overdrive clutch pack components from overdrive unit case. *See Figs. 40 and 41.* Note direction of clutch discs and clutch plates in overdrive clutch pack for reassembly reference. Components must be installed in correct sequence.

2) Remove waved snap ring and reaction plate snap ring. Both snap rings are installed in same groove in overdrive unit case.

3) Remove access cover from top of overdrive unit case for access to front bearing retaining ring. *See Fig. 42.* Using snap ring pliers, expand front bearing retaining ring while pushing output shaft forward to release front bearing from retaining ring. *See Fig. 42.*

4) Remove overdrive unit gear train from overdrive unit case. *See Fig. 43.* Remove bearing retaining ring from overdrive unit case. On 42RH, remove governor support snap ring from overdrive unit case. *See Fig. 44.*

5) Remove governor support with governor supply tube assembly from overdrive unit case. *See Fig. 44.* On all models, remove shaft retainer plug and snap ring for reaction plug from overdrive unit case. *See Fig. 44.* DO NOT over compress snap ring or it may be damaged.

6) Remove shaft, parking sprag, spring and reaction plug. *See Fig. 44.* On 42RH, remove rear bearing snap ring from overdrive unit case. If necessary, rotate snap ring until end of snap ring is adjacent to notch in case.

7) Remove rear bearing from overdrive unit case by tapping case on wooden block. Inspect bushings in overdrive unit case. Replace bushings if damaged.

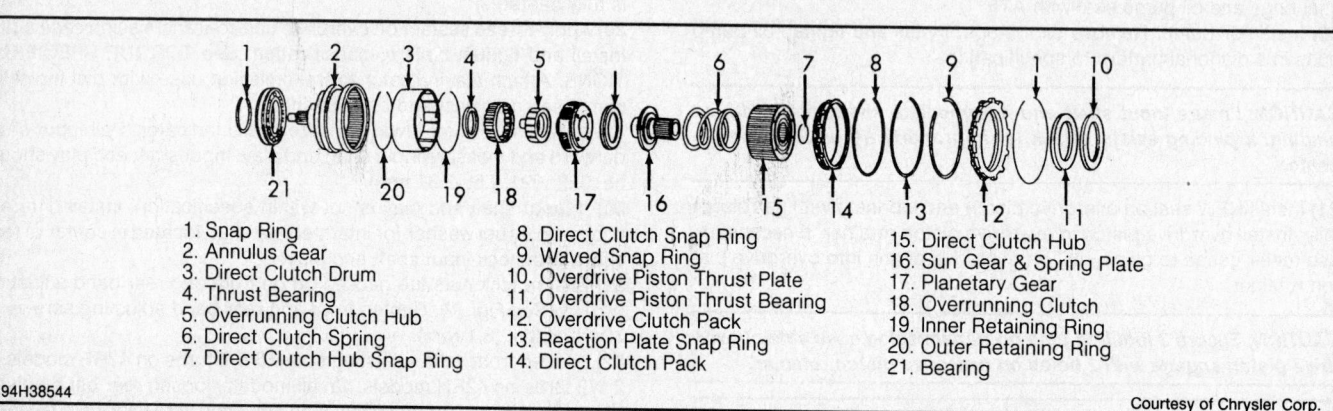

94H38544

1. Snap Ring
2. Annulus Gear
3. Direct Clutch Drum
4. Thrust Bearing
5. Overrunning Clutch Hub
6. Direct Clutch Spring
7. Direct Clutch Hub Snap Ring

8. Direct Clutch Snap Ring
9. Waved Snap Ring
10. Overdrive Piston Thrust Plate
11. Overdrive Piston Thrust Bearing
12. Overdrive Clutch Pack
13. Reaction Plate Snap Ring
14. Direct Clutch Pack

15. Direct Clutch Hub
16. Sun Gear & Spring Plate
17. Planetary Gear
18. Overrunning Clutch
19. Inner Retaining Ring
20. Outer Retaining Ring
21. Bearing

Courtesy of Chrysler Corp.

Fig. 40: Exploded View Of Overdrive Unit (42RE)

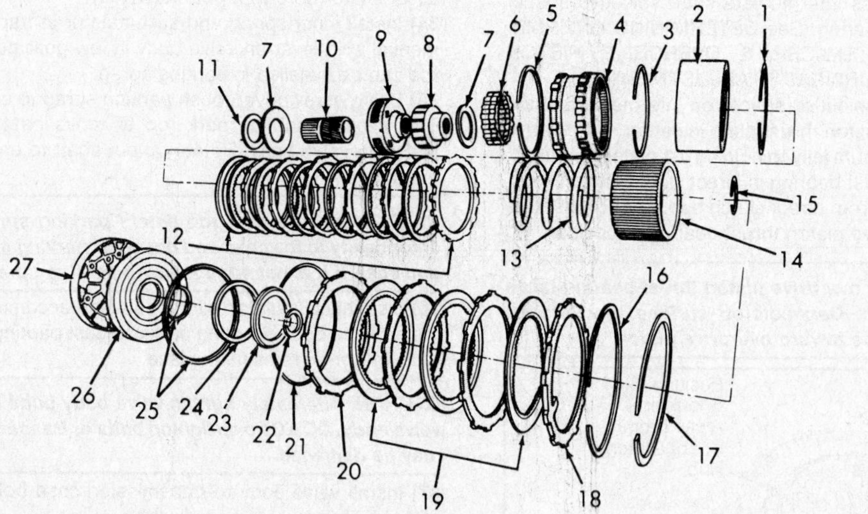

1. Inner Retaining Ring
2. Direct Clutch Drum
3. Outer Retaining Ring
4. Annulus Gear
5. Annulus Gear Snap Ring
6. Overrunning Clutch
7. Thrust Bearing
8. Overrunning Clutch Hub
9. Planetary Gear

10. Sun Gear
11. Spring Plate
12. Direct Clutch Pack
13. Direct Clutch Spring
14. Direct Clutch Hub
15. Direct Clutch Hub Snap Ring
16. Waved Snap Ring
17. Reaction Plate Snap Ring
18. Reaction Plate

19. Overdrive Clutch Pack
20. Pressure Plate
21. Snap Ring
22. Intermediate Shaft Selective Spacer
23. Overdrive Piston Thrust Bearing
24. Overdrive Piston Thrust Plate
25. Overdrive Piston Seals
26. Overdrive Piston
27. Overdrive Piston Retainer

92C13401

Courtesy of Chrysler Corp.

Fig. 41: Exploded View Of Overdrive Unit (42RH)

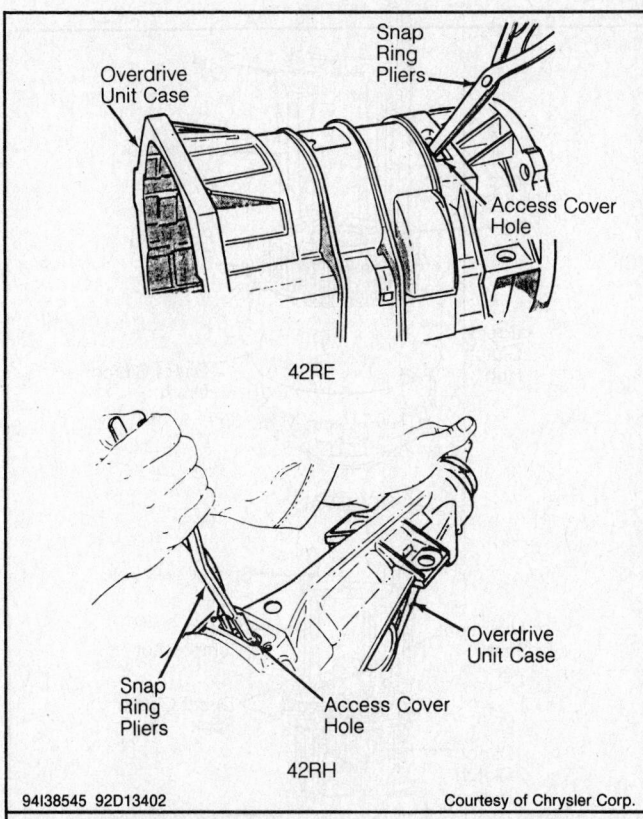

Fig. 42: Releasing & Installing Bearing From Retaining Ring

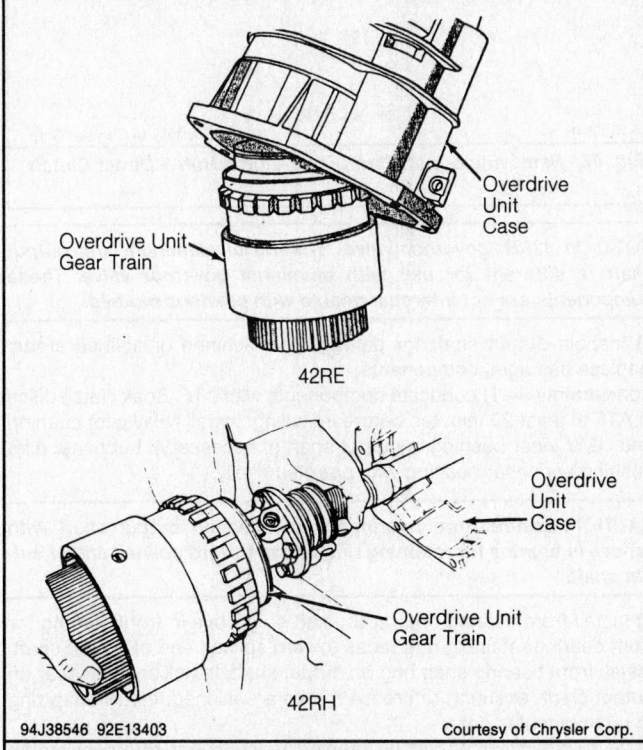

Fig. 43: Removing Overdrive Unit Gear Train

Fig. 44: Identifying Governor Support (42RH) & Parking Sprag Components

OVERDRIVE UNIT COMPONENT DISASSEMBLY & REASSEMBLY

OVERDRIVE UNIT GEAR TRAIN

Disassembly – 1) On 42RH, remove clip from valve shaft on governor. *See Fig. 45.* Remove valve shaft and governor valve. Note number of components in governor valve and direction of component installation for reassembly reference.

2) Remove governor snap ring from output shaft. Remove governor drive and governor body as an assembly. Remove key and front bearing snap ring from output shaft. Remove front bearing from output shaft.

3) On 42RE, remove snap ring and bearing from output shaft on annulus gear. On all models, place overdrive unit gear train in press and support assembly with press plates placed under flange on output shaft.

4) Position Spring Compressor (6227-1) on direct clutch hub. *See Fig. 46.* It may be necessary to install plate on top of spring compressor to provide extra press travel.

CAUTION: Ensure proper equipment is used when compressing direct clutch spring, as direct clutch spring is under excessive pressure. Ensure ram on press has a minimum travel of approximately 6".

5) Slowly compress direct clutch spring. Remove retaining ring for direct clutch pack from outer edge of direct clutch drum. Remove direct clutch hub snap ring, located at center of direct clutch hub. *See Fig. 46.* Slowly release press. Remove spring compressor.

CAUTION: Note direction of clutch discs and clutch plates in direct clutch pack for reassembly reference. Also note number of each component, as some models may contain different number of clutch components. Components must be installed in correct sequence.

6) Remove direct clutch pack components from direct clutch drum, noting location of components for reassembly reference. Remove direct clutch hub and direct clutch spring. Remove sun gear and spring plate. Remove thrust bearing and planetary gear. *See Fig. 40 and 41.*

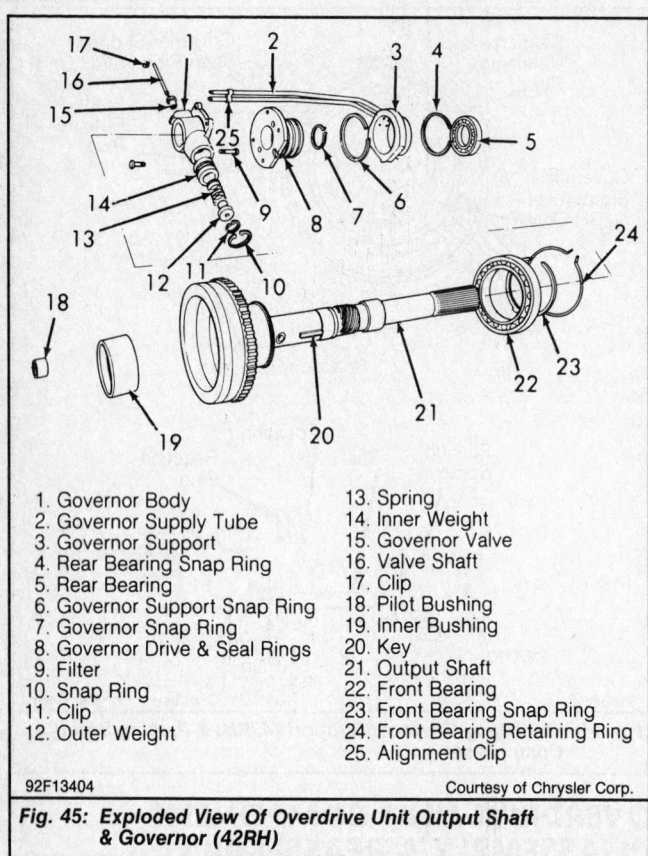

1. Governor Body
2. Governor Supply Tube
3. Governor Support
4. Rear Bearing Snap Ring
5. Rear Bearing
6. Governor Support Snap Ring
7. Governor Snap Ring
8. Governor Drive & Seal Rings
9. Filter
10. Snap Ring
11. Clip
12. Outer Weight
13. Spring
14. Inner Weight
15. Governor Valve
16. Valve Shaft
17. Clip
18. Pilot Bushing
19. Inner Bushing
20. Key
21. Output Shaft
22. Front Bearing
23. Front Bearing Snap Ring
24. Front Bearing Retaining Ring
25. Alignment Clip

92F13404   Courtesy of Chrysler Corp.

Fig. 45: Exploded View Of Overdrive Unit Output Shaft & Governor (42RH)

7) Insert expanding-type snap ring pliers into splines on overrunning clutch hub. Expand snap ring pliers against splines. Rotate overrunning clutch hub counterclockwise and remove overrunning clutch assembly from direct clutch drum.

CAUTION: Ensure direct clutch drum-to-annulus gear location is marked for reassembly reference before disassembling.

8) Remove thrust bearing from overrunning clutch hub. Remove overrunning clutch from overrunning clutch hub. *See Figs. 40 and 41.* Scribe alignment marks on outer surface of direct clutch drum and annulus gear for reassembly reference.

CAUTION: Ensure output shaft-to-annulus gear location is marked for reassembly reference before disassembling.

9) Remove inner and outer retaining rings from direct clutch drum. *See Figs 40 and 41.* Remove direct clutch drum from annulus gear. Scribe alignment marks on annulus gear and output shaft for reassembly reference. Remove snap ring for annulus gear. Using soft-faced hammer, tap annulus gear from output shaft.

Cleaning & Inspection – 1) Clean all metal components with solvent and dry all components except bearings with compressed air. Inspect clutch discs for flatness, flaking or glazing. Inspect all clutch plates, pressure plate and reaction plate for flatness or damage at lug area.
2) Ensure direct clutch components slide freely in direct clutch drum. Replace components if binding exists. Inspect sun gear and bushings for damage. Replace sun gear if bushings are defective.
3) Inspect planetary gear for damage. Ensure pins for gears on planetary gear are tight and are not damaged. Inspect surface on overrunning clutch hub or overrunning clutch for damage. Replace overrunning clutch as an assembly if damaged.
4) Inspect inner and pilot bushings for damage. On 42RH, ensure governor valve and weights slide freely in governor body. Inspect governor support and governor supply tubes for damage. DO NOT attempt to remove governor supply tubes from governor support. Replace governor support and tubes as an assembly if damaged.

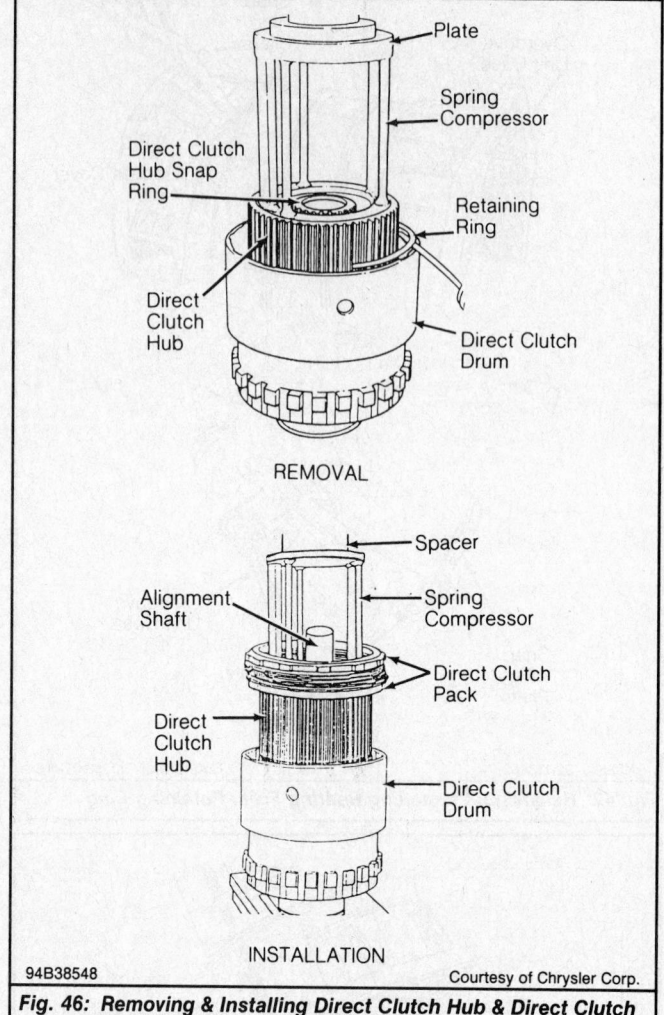

94B38548   Courtesy of Chrysler Corp.

Fig. 46: Removing & Installing Direct Clutch Hub & Direct Clutch Spring

NOTE: On 42RH, governor valve is made of aluminum and output shaft is different for use with aluminum governor valve. These components are not interchangeable with previous models.

5) Inspect output shaft for damage in machined or splined areas. Replace damaged components.
Reassembly – 1) Lubricate components with ATF. Soak clutch discs in ATF at least 20 minutes before installing. Install NEW pilot bushing and NEW inner bushing in output shaft (if necessary). Lubricate pilot bushing and inner bushing with petroleum jelly.

CAUTION: Ensure front bearing is installed on output shaft with groove in bearing for retaining ring facing toward splined end of output shaft.

2) Install front bearing on output shaft so groove in front bearing for front bearing retaining ring faces toward splined end of output shaft. Install front bearing snap ring on output shaft. Install annulus gear on output shaft, ensuring reference marks are aligned. Install snap ring to retain annulus gear.
3) Install direct clutch drum on annulus gear ensuring reference marks are aligned. Ensure lugs on direct clutch drum fully engage lugs on annulus gear. Install outer retaining ring.
4) Slide direct clutch drum forward. Install inner retaining ring. Install overrunning clutch on overrunning clutch hub. *See Fig. 47.* Shoulder on overrunning clutch should seat in small recess at edge of overrunning clutch hub.

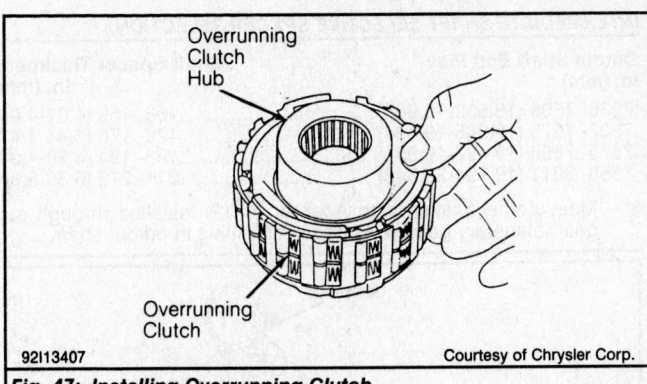

Fig. 47: *Installing Overrunning Clutch*

5) Coat thrust bearing with petroleum jelly and install on overrunning clutch hub. Ensure thrust bearing is fully seated on overrunning clutch hub.

6) Insert expanding-type snap ring pliers into splines on overrunning clutch hub. Expand snap ring pliers against splines. Rotate overrunning clutch hub counterclockwise and install overrunning clutch assembly in direct clutch drum.

7) Install planetary gear in annulus gear. Ensure planetary gear is fully seated. Install spring plate on sun gear with shoulder on spring plate toward front of sun gear (if removed). *See Fig. 48.* Install snap ring.

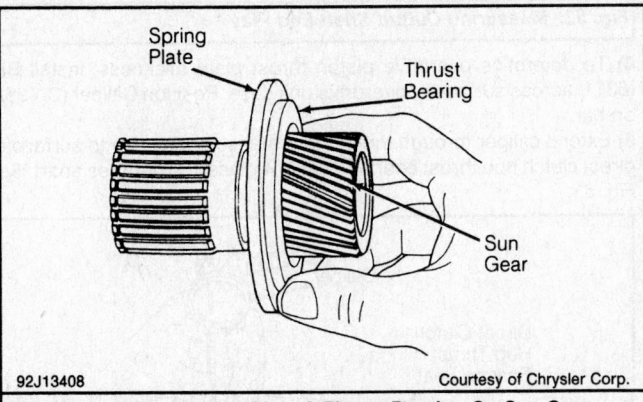

Fig. 48: *Installing Spring Plate & Thrust Bearing On Sun Gear*

8) Coat thrust bearing with petroleum jelly and install on sun gear. Ensure thrust bearing fully seats against spring plate.

9) Install sun gear, spring plate and thrust bearing in direct clutch drum. Install Alignment Shaft (6227-2) through sun gear to align splines of planetary gear and overrunning clutch hub. *See Fig. 49.* Ensure alignment shaft is fully seated.

CAUTION: Ensure direct clutch components are installed in original location and original number of components are installed.

10) Install direct clutch spring on spring plate in direct clutch hub. Ensure spring is properly seated. Assemble direct clutch pack. *See Fig. 50.*

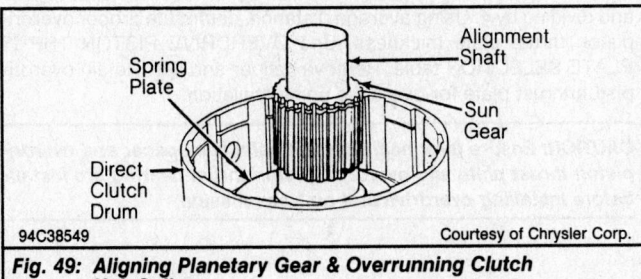

Fig. 49: *Aligning Planetary Gear & Overrunning Clutch Hub Splines*

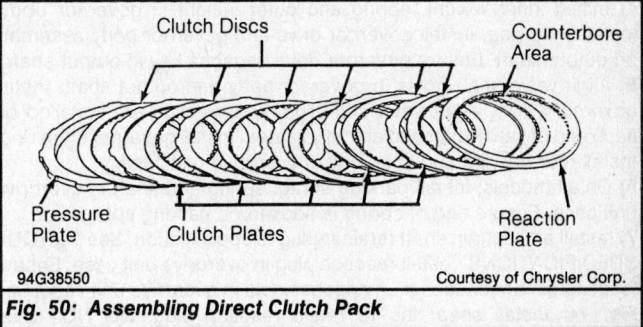

Fig. 50: *Assembling Direct Clutch Pack*

11) Install reaction plate on direct clutch hub. One side of reaction plate contains a counterbore area. *See Fig. 50.* Counterbore area should be installed so it fits over raised splines at rear of direct clutch hub. *See Fig. 51.*

CAUTION: With reaction plate installed, surface of reaction plate should be even with surface of direct clutch hub. Counterbore area on reaction plate should be against raised splines on direct clutch hub. See Fig. 51.

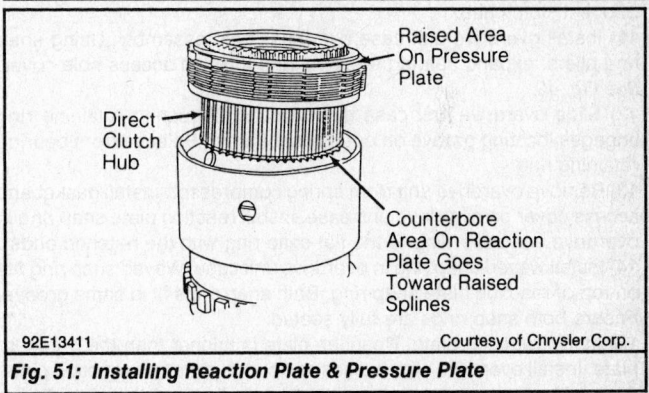

Fig. 51: *Installing Reaction Plate & Pressure Plate*

12) Alternately install clutch discs and clutch plates on reaction plate starting with clutch disc. *See Fig. 50.* Install pressure plate with raise area away from clutch pack. *See Fig. 51.*

13) Install direct clutch pack and direct clutch hub on direct clutch spring. Ensure direct clutch hub is started on the splines on the sun gear. Place overdrive unit gear train assembly in press.

14) Install spring compressor and spacer on top of direct clutch hub. *See Fig. 46.* Slide direct clutch pack upward and set it on edge of spring compressor.

15) Compress direct clutch spring so direct clutch hub snap ring and retaining ring for direct clutch pack grooves are visible. Install direct clutch pack in direct clutch drum. Install retaining ring for direct clutch pack and direct clutch hub snap ring. Ensure retaining ring and direct clutch hub snap ring are fully seated.

16) Release press. Remove spring compressor. Ensure alignment shaft is fully seated. If alignment shaft becomes unseated, it may be necessary to sassemble overdrive unit gear train and realign splines. Remove overdrive unit gear train assembly from press.

OVERDRIVE UNIT REASSEMBLY

OVERDRIVE UNIT

Reassembly – 1) Install front bearing on output shaft (if not previously installed). Ensure groove in bearing for retaining ring faces toward splined end of output shaft. Install front bearing snap ring on output shaft.

2) On 42RH, install key in output shaft for governor. Install NEW seal rings on governor drive. Ensure ends of seal rings are locked together.

3) Install governor body on governor drive. Ensure filter is properly seated in governor body. Tighten governor body-to-governor drive bolts to specification. See TORQUE SPECIFICATIONS.

4) Install inner weight, spring and outer weight in governor body. Install snap ring. Install governor drive and governor body assembly on output shaft. Ensure governor drive engages key in output shaft.

5) Align valve shaft holes in governor body and output shaft. Install governor valve, valve shaft and clips. Ensure clips are installed on each end of valve shaft and are fully seated. Install governor snap ring. Install rear bearing and snap ring in overdrive unit case.

6) On all models, install parking sprag, spring and shaft in overdrive unit case. Ensure end of spring is hooked on parking sprag.

7) Install and tighten shaft retainer plug to specification. See TORQUE SPECIFICATIONS. Install reaction plug in overdrive unit case. Ensure locating pin on reaction plug engages hole in overdrive unit case. *See Fig. 44.* Install snap ring to retain reaction plug. DO NOT over compress snap ring when installing.

8) On 42RH, install alignment clip on end of governor supply tube until clip contacts shoulder on each tube (if removed). *See Fig. 45.* Install governor support and governor supply tube assembly in overdrive unit case. Install governor support snap ring.

9) On all models, install bearing retaining ring in overdrive unit case. Ensure ends of bearing retaining ring face the access cover opening in overdrive unit case.

10) Place gear train in vertical position. Support assembly on Spring Compressor (6227-1) on workbench. Spring compressor fits in center of direct clutch hub.

11) Install overdrive unit case over gear train assembly. Using snap ring pliers, expand bearing retaining ring through access hole cover. *See Fig. 42.*

12) Slide overdrive unit case downward until bearing retaining ring engages locating groove on outside of bearing. Release front bearing retaining ring.

13) Remove overdrive unit from spring compressor. Install gasket and access cover on overdrive unit case. Install reaction plate snap ring in overdrive unit case. This is the flat snap ring with the notched ends.

14) Install waved snap ring in overdrive unit case. Waved snap ring fits on top of reaction plate snap ring. Both snap rings fit in same groove. Ensure both snap rings are fully seated.

15) Install reaction plate. Reaction plate is thinner than the pressure plate. Install overdrive clutch discs and clutch plates on reaction plate. Start with clutch disc followed with clutch disc and then alternating between clutch plates and clutch discs.

CAUTION: Ensure overdrive clutch pack components are installed in original location and original number of components are installed.

16) Install pressure plate and wire-type snap ring. Place overdrive unit in vertical position with access to direct clutch hub. Remove alignment shaft.

17) Proper thickness intermediate shaft selective spacer and overdrive piston thrust plate must be determined before installing overdrive unit. See DETERMINING INTERMEDIATE SHAFT SELECTIVE SPACER & OVERDRIVE PISTON THRUST PLATE under OVERDRIVE UNIT ADJUSTMENTS.

OVERDRIVE UNIT ADJUSTMENTS

DETERMINING INTERMEDIATE SHAFT SELECTIVE SPACER & OVERDRIVE PISTON THRUST PLATE

1) To determine intermediate shaft selective spacer, output shaft end play is checked. Place overdrive unit in vertical position. Install Adapter (6312) through sun gear, planetary gear and into pilot bushing in output shaft. *See Fig. 52.* Ensure adapter bottoms against shoulder on planetary gear.

2) Install Bar (6311) across surface of overdrive unit case. Position Caliper (C-4962) on bar. Extend caliper downward through bar until it contacts adapter. Note reading on caliper. This is the output shaft end play.

3) Using output shaft end play reading, determine proper intermediate shaft selective spacer thickness. See INTERMEDIATE SHAFT SELECTIVE SPACER SELECTION table. Remove adapter. Retain intermediate shaft selective spacer for overdrive unit installation.

INTERMEDIATE SHAFT SELECTIVE SPACER SELECTION

Output Shaft End Play [1] In. (mm)	Shaft Spacer Thickness In. (mm)
.7336-.7505 (18.633-19.063)	.158-.159 (4.01-4.04)
.7506-.7675 (19.065-19.494)	.175-.176 (4.44-4.47)
.7676-.7855 (19.497-19.951)	.193-.194 (4.90-4.93)
.7856-.8011 (19.954-20.348)	.211-.212 (5.35-5.38)

[1] – Measurement taken with Adapter (6312) installed through sun gear, planetary gear and into pilot bushing in output shaft.

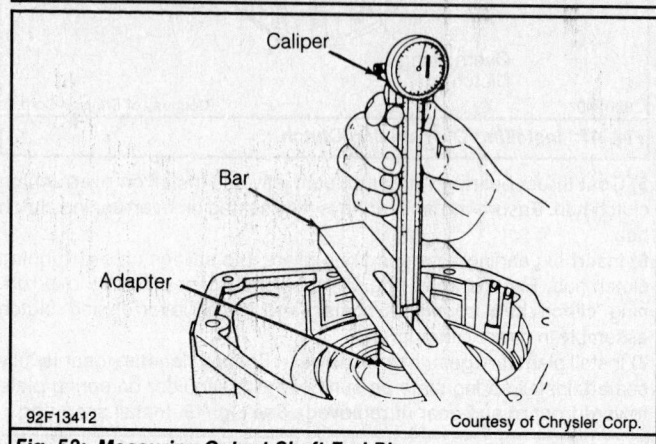

92F13412   Courtesy of Chrysler Corp.

Fig. 52: Measuring Output Shaft End Play

4) To determine overdrive piston thrust plate thickness, install Bar (6311) across surface of overdrive unit case. Position Caliper (C-4962) on bar.

5) Extend caliper through the bar and measure distance to surface of direct clutch hub thrust bearing seat in 4 places 90 degrees apart. *See Fig. 53.*

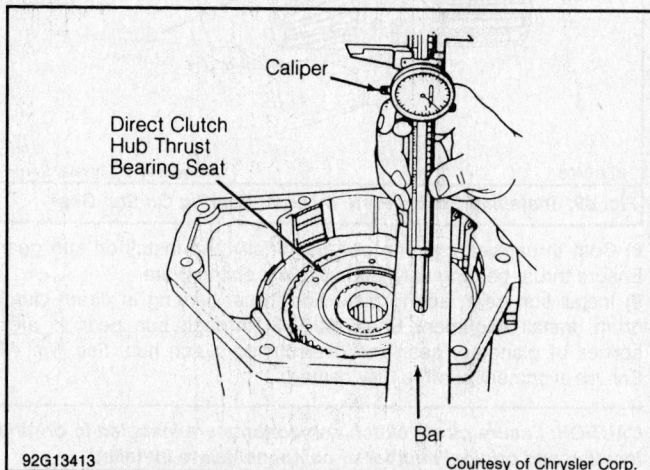

92G13413   Courtesy of Chrysler Corp.

Fig. 53: Measuring Distance To Direct Clutch Hub Thrust Bearing Seat

6) Determine average distance by adding 4 measurements together and dividing by 4. Using average distance, determine proper overdrive piston thrust plate thickness. See OVERDRIVE PISTON THRUST PLATE SELECTION table. Remove caliper and bar. Retain overdrive piston thrust plate for overdrive unit installation.

CAUTION: Ensure intermediate shaft selective spacer and overdrive piston thrust plate and overdrive piston thrust bearing are installed before installing overdrive unit on transmission.

OVERDRIVE PISTON THRUST PLATE SELECTION

Hub Thrust Bearing Seat Average Distance In. (mm)	Overdrive Piston Thrust Plate Thickness In. (mm)
1.7500-1.7649 (44.450-44.828)	.108-.110 (2.74-2.79)
1.7650-1.7799 (44.831-45.209)	.123-.125 (3.12-3.18)
1.7800-1.7949 (45.212-45.590)	.138-.140 (3.50-3.56)
1.7950-1.8099 (45.593-45.971)	.153-.155 (3.89-3.94)
1.8100-1.8249 (45.974-46.352)	.168-.170 (4.27-4.31)
1.8250-1.8399 (46.355-46.733)	.183-.185 (4.65-4.70)
1.8400-1.8549 (46.736-47.114)	.198-.200 (5.03-5.08)
1.8550-1.8699 (47.117-47.495)	.213-.215 (5.41-5.46)
1.8700-1.8849 (47.498-47.876)	.228-.230 (5.79-5.84)
1.8850-1.8999 (47.879-48.257)	.243-.245 (6.17-6.22)

TORQUE SPECIFICATIONS

TORQUE SPECIFICATIONS

Application	Ft. Lbs. (N.m)
Band Adjusting Screw Lock Nut	
Front Band	25 (34)
Rear Band	30 (41)
Front Band Pin Access Hole Plug	13 (18)
Oil Pan Bolt	13 (18)
Oil Pump Bolt	15 (20)
Overdrive Piston Retainer Bolt	13 (18)
Overdrive Unit-To-Transmission Case Bolt [1]	25 (34)
Overrunning Clutch Cam Bolt	13 (18)
Park/Neutral Switch	25 (34)
Reaction Shaft Support Bolt	15 (20)
Shaft Retainer Plug	20 (27)
Vehicle Speed Sensor Nut (1993 Models)	13 (18)
	INCH Lbs. (N.m)
Adapter Retainer Bolt	100 (11.3)
Adjusting Screw Bracket Screw	35 (4.0)
Boost Valve Cover Screw	35 (4.0)
Cover Plate Screw	35 (4.0)
End Plate Screw	35 (4.0)
Filter Assembly Bolt	35 (4.0)
Governor Body-To-Governor Drive Bolt	96 (10.8)
Governor Body-To-Transfer Plate Bolt	35 (4.0)
Governor End Plate Screw	35 (4.0)
Limit Valve Cover Screw	35 (4.0)
Pressure Tap Plug	120 (13.6)
Separator Plate Brace Screw	35 (4.0)
Separator Plate-To-Transfer Plate Screw	35 (4.0)
Solenoid Assembly Screw	72 (8.1)
Valve Body Screw	35 (4.0)
Valve Body-To-Transmission Case Bolt	100 (11.3)
Vehicle Speed Sensor-To-Adapter Bolt (1994 Models)	27 (3.1)

[1] – Apply thread sealant to bolt threads.

TRANSMISSION SPECIFICATIONS

TRANSMISSION SPECIFICATIONS

Application	In. (mm)
Clutch Clearances	
Front Clutch	
3-Disc Clutch	.074-.125 (1.87-3.18)
4-Disc Clutch	.067-.134 (1.70-3.40)
5-Disc Clutch	.075-.152 (1.90-3.86)
Rear Clutch	.032-.055 (.81-1.40)
Input Shaft End Play	.022-.091 (.56-2.31)
Oil Pump Clearances	
Outer Pump Gear-To-Oil Pump Housing Clearance	.0035-.0075 (.089-.190)
Pump Gear End Clearance	.0004-.0025 (.010-.063)
Pump Gear Tooth Clearance	.0035-.0075 (.089-.090)
Planetary Gear Train End Play	.005-.048 (.13-1.22)

SERVICE BULLETINS

UPSHIFT TOO LOW OR CLOSE TOGETHER

Chrysler Corp. Service Bulletin 21-25-93 (September 3, 1993) – Some 1992-93 Dakota, Pickup, Ram Van, and 1993 Grand Cherokee with 42RH transmission may have upshifts too low or close together.

The 2-3 upshift will be very close to the 1-2 upshift. To correct this condition, perform the following procedure:
1) Check for stored diagnostic trouble codes in the Powertrain Control Module (PCM). See SELF-DIAGNOSTICS article in ENGINE PERFORMANCE of appropriate MITCHELL® MANUAL.
2) Repair engine control system if a diagnostic trouble code exists and recheck operation. If no diagnostic trouble codes exists or code has been corrected and problem still exists, replace governor weights and spring with components from Governor Weight Package (4617883).

DELAYED TRANSMISSION ENGAGEMENT

Chrysler Corp. Service Bulletin 21-20-93 (October 22, 1993) – Some 1988-93 Dakota, Pickup, Ram Van and 1993 Grand Cherokee may exhibit a no drive or delayed transmission engagement condition. Customer complaint may state that vehicle does not move after shifting from Park into Drive or Reverse. The cause is a rough finish on the sides of park tooth on the annulus gear in the overdrive unit. Condition may exists only under conditions in which parking sprag is engaged in the annulus gear.

The transmission actually engages, but parking sprag is not released from the annulus gear. If throttle is opened slightly, it may appear that transmission is in Neutral. If throttle is opened rapidly, the engine acts as if transmission is in gear, but the brakes are applied. To correct this condition, perform the following procedure.
1) Before performing repairs, check for all causes of delayed engagement or no drive conditions, such as low transmission fluid level, improper shift linkage or cable adjustment, low line pressure, restricted filter assembly and broken oil pump drive.
2) If conditions are okay, replace annulus gear in overdrive unit with Annulus Gear (4746349) using NEW gaskets. Ensure proper thickness overdrive piston thrust plate is be determined before installing overdrive unit. See DETERMINING INTERMEDIATE SHAFT SELECTIVE SPACER & OVERDRIVE PISTON THRUST PLATE under OVERDRIVE UNIT ADJUSTMENTS. Fill transmission with Mopar ATF Plus Type 7176 fluid.

DELAYED TRANSMISSION ENGAGEMENT

Chrysler Corp. Service Bulletin 21-08-94 (April 29, 1994) – Some 1990-94 Dakota, Pickup and Ram Van, and 1993-94 Grand Cherokee may experience a 2-8 second delay in transmission engagement when vehicle is first started after vehicle has been parked for an extended period. To correct this condition, perform the following procedure.
1) Check for stored diagnostic trouble codes in the Powertrain Control Module (PCM). See SELF-DIAGNOSTICS article in ENGINE PERFORMANCE of appropriate MITCHELL® MANUAL.
2) Repair engine control system if a diagnostic trouble code exists and recheck operation. If no diagnostic trouble codes exists or code has been corrected and problem still exists, Drainback Relief Valve (4778670) must be installed.
3) Note location of oil cooler supply line on side of transmission. See Fig. 7. Trace oil cooler supply line back to the radiator and identify this line at the radiator. Ensure this is the oil cooler supply line.

CAUTION: Drainback relief valve must be installed in oil cooler supply line or transmission failure will exist if wrong line is selected. Ensure oil cooler supply line is selected.

4) Cut oil cooler supply line within 1/8" of the crimp on the hose. See Fig. 54. Cut the hose and remove section of oil cooler supply line.

CAUTION: Some vehicles may have a Black epoxy coating on the oil cooler supply line. Ensure coating is removed before installing the nut and sleeve from drainback relief valve on oil cooler supply line.

5) Install nut and sleeve on metal portion of oil cooler supply line. Install drainback relief valve on metal portion of oil cooler supply so arrow on drainback relief valve is pointing toward the oil cooler.

CAUTION: *Ensure drainback relief valve is installed so arrow on drainback relief valve is pointing toward the oil cooler. The arrow indicates direction of the fluid flow.*

6) Install sleeve and nut on drainback relief valve. Tighten nut. Install rubber portion of oil cooler supply line on drainback relief valve. Install and tighten clamp to 10 INCH lbs. (1.1 N.m).

7) Note location of oil cooler return line on side of transmission. *See Fig. 7.* Disconnect oil cooler return line from transmission. On 1994 models, oil cooler lines are equipped with a disconnect fitting. Use proper procedure for disconnecting oil cooler line from disconnect fitting. See OIL COOLER LINE DISCONNECT FITTINGS under ON-VEHICLE SERVICE in this article.

CAUTION: *Ensure flow from oil cooler return line is checked to ensure drainback relief valve is installed in correct oil cooler line.*

8) Ensure transmission is full of fluid. Place container under oil cooler return line. Start engine. Place gearshift in Neutral.

9) Ensure steady flow exists for oil cooler return line. If no fluid flow exists, drainback relief valve has been installed in the wrong oil cooler line. Remove and reinstall. If steady flow exists, shut engine off.

10) Reconnect oil cooler return line. On 1994 models, reconnect oil cooler return line by pushing oil cooler line inward until a snap or click is heard when retaining clip seats in oil cooler line. Pull outward on oil cooler line to ensure oil cooler line is locked in the disconnect fitting.

CAUTION: *After installing oil cooler line, pull outward on oil cooler line to ensure oil cooler line is locked in the disconnect fitting and retaining clip is fully seated.*

11) On all models, fill transmission with Mopar ATF Plus Type 7176 fluid. Recheck all oil cooler lines for leaks.

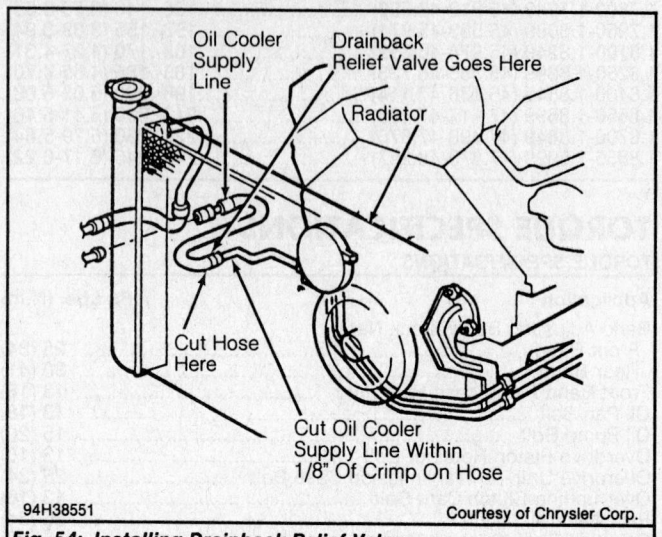

94H38551   Courtesy of Chrysler Corp.

Fig. 54: Installing Drainback Relief Valve

APPLICATION

Model	Trans.
1993 1/2-94 Grand Cherokee	42RE

DESCRIPTION

The 42RE transmission uses an electronic system for producing governor pressure which is used for controlling transmission shifting. Electronic control system consists of Transmission Control Module (TCM), governor pressure solenoid, governor pressure sensor, transmission fluid temperature sender, Overdrive (OD) switch, throttle position sensor and transmission shaft speed sensor.

NOTE: *Governor pressure sensor may be referred to as governor pressure transducer. Transmission fluid temperature sensor may be referred to as transmission fluid temperature sensor or transmission fluid temperature thermistor. Transmission shaft speed sensor may also be referred to as output shaft speed sensor or shaft speed sensor.*

Transmission shifting is controlled by throttle and governor pressure. Governor pressure is generated by electronic components. Transmission will not upshift into 4th gear if 3rd upshift is not complete, OD switch is in OFF position, throttle is at 3/4 to full throttle position, vehicle speed is too low for 3-4 upshift or transmission fluid temperature is less than 30°F (-1°C).

OPERATION

TRANSMISSION CONTROL MODULE (TCM)

The TCM controls Torque Converter Clutch (TCC) operation, overdrive clutch operation and the governor pressure solenoid. The TCM determines shift points and TCC operation based on input signals received from transmission fluid temperature sender, transmission shaft speed sensor, engine speed sensor, vehicle speed sensor and throttle position sensor.

There are 4 governor pressure curves programmed into the TCM. Governor pressure curves allow the TCM to adjust governor pressure for varying conditions. One governor pressure curve is used for operation when transmission fluid temperature is at or less than 30°F (1°C). The second governor pressure curve is used for operation when transmission fluid temperature is at or greater than 30°F (1°C) during normal city operation or highway driving. The third governor pressure curve is used for operation when wide open throttle operation exists. The fourth governor pressure curve is used for operation when transfer case in low range.

The TCM controls TCC operation by operating the lock-up solenoid located on the valve body. Lock-up solenoid may be referred to as the TCC solenoid. If OD switch is in the ON position, the TCC will lock-up once transmission is in 4th gear with vehicle speed greater than 45 MPH. If OD switch is in the OFF position, the TCC will lock-up once transmission is in 3rd gear with vehicle speed greater than 35 MPH at light throttle application. When OD switch is in the OFF position, the OD light on the instrument panel will be illuminated.

The TCM prevents TCC operation and overdrive operation when transmission fluid temperature is less than 30°F (-1°C). If transmission fluid temperature exceeds 260°F (126°C), the TCM will cause a 4-3 downshift and engage the TCC. The OD light will be illuminated when the downshift occurs. Transmission will not upshift until transmission fluid temperature decreases to approximately 230°F (110°F).

The TCM contains a self-diagnostic system used for determining an electronic component failure. The TCM self-diagnostic system will store a Diagnostic Trouble Code (DTC) in the TCM memory if certain electronic problems exist. If a diagnostic trouble code exists, transmission will enter limp-in mode. For additional information on limp-in mode, see LIMP-IN MODE under OPERATION.

Diagnostic trouble code can be retrieved using Chrysler's Diagnostic Readout Box (DRB) or by operating the OD light on the instrument panel. After repairing an electrical system problem, stored diagnostic trouble code must be cleared from TCM memory. The TCM is located on driver's side of instrument panel, adjacent to steering column and contains a 32-pin connector. See Fig. 1.

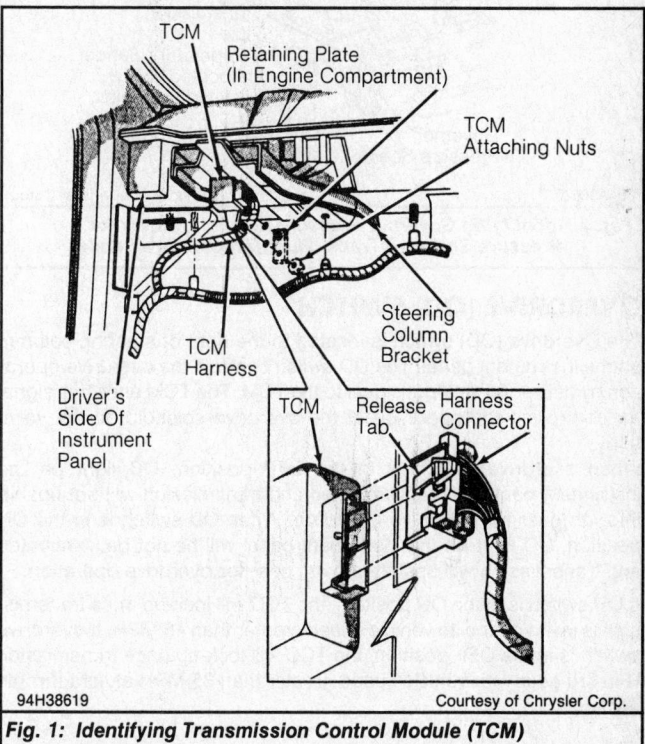

94H38619   Courtesy of Chrysler Corp.

Fig. 1: Identifying Transmission Control Module (TCM)

LIMP-IN MODE

The TCM monitors transmission for electrical or internal problems. If TCM senses a problem and diagnostic trouble code is set, the transmission enters limp-in mode. In limp-in mode, only Park, Neutral, Reverse and 3rd gears function. Transmission will not automatically upshift or downshift. Vehicle can be operated, but performance will be reduced. Transmission can be manually shifted by quickly downshifting to 1st to obtain 1st gear, then shifting to 2nd and then to 3rd. However, limp-in mode will not allow 4th gear or TCC operation.

GOVERNOR PRESSURE SENSOR

NOTE: *Governor pressure sensor may be referred to as governor pressure transducer.*

Governor pressure sensor delivers an output signal to the TCM indicating the output pressure of the governor pressure solenoid. The TCM uses this signal to control the governor pressure. Governor pressure solenoid is located on the valve body. See Fig. 2.

GOVERNOR PRESSURE SOLENOID

Governor pressure solenoid generates governor pressure required for transmission upshifts and downshifts. Governor pressure solenoid is located on the valve body. See Fig. 2. Inlet side of governor pressure solenoid is exposed to normal transmission line pressure and outlet side provides a passage to the governor circuit in the valve body. Governor pressure solenoid regulates the transmission line pressure to the governor circuit. Electrical supply voltage is supplied to governor pressure solenoid by the TCM. The TCM controls the ground circuit to governor pressure solenoid to provide solenoid operation.

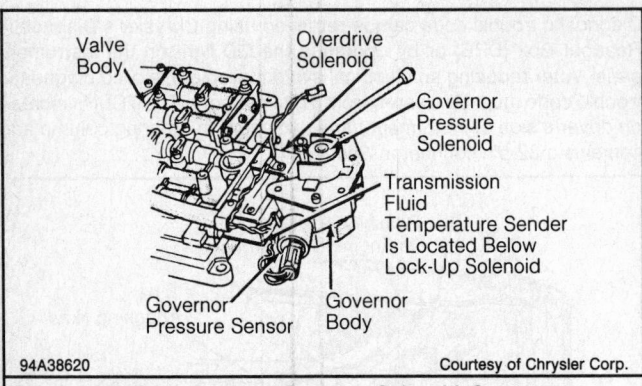

Fig. 2: Identifying Governor Pressure Solenoid, Governor Pressure Sensor & Trans. Fluid Temperature Sender

94A38620   Courtesy of Chrysler Corp.

OVERDRIVE (OD) SWITCH

The Overdrive (OD) switch is located to the right of steering column, on the instrument panel. The OD switch controls the overdrive operation by delivering an input signal to the TCM. The TCM uses this signal for controlling the operation of the overdrive solenoid on the valve body.

When overdrive switch is in the OFF position, OD light on the instrument panel will be illuminated and transmission will not upshift into 4th gear for overdrive operation. When OD switch is in the ON position, OD light on the instrument panel will be not be illuminated and transmission will upshift into 4th gear for overdrive operation.

If OD switch is in the ON position, the TCC will lock-up once transmission is in 4th gear with vehicle speed greater than 45 MPH. If overdrive switch is in the OFF position, the TCC will lock-up once transmission is in 3rd gear with vehicle speed greater than 35 MPH at light throttle application.

THROTTLE POSITION SENSOR (TPS)

The Throttle Position Sensor (TPS) delivers an input signal to the TCM and Powertrain Control Module (PCM) to indicate the throttle position. The TCM uses this input signal for controlling TCC operation, governor pressure and upshift into 4th gear for overdrive operation.

TRANSMISSION FLUID TEMPERATURE SENDER

NOTE: Transmission fluid temperature sensor may be referred to as transmission fluid temperature sensor or transmission fluid temperature thermistor.

Transmission fluid temperature sender delivers an input signal to the TCM to indicate the fluid temperature. The TCM uses this input signal for controlling the TCC, overdrive operation and governor pressure. Transmission fluid temperature sender is located below lock-up solenoid on the valve body and is immersed in transmission fluid at all times. *See Fig. 2.*

TRANSMISSION SHAFT SPEED SENSOR

NOTE: Transmission shaft speed sensor may also be referred to as output shaft speed sensor or shaft speed sensor.

Transmission shaft speed sensor is located on the case of overdrive unit attached to rear of transmission. *See Fig. 3.* Transmission shaft speed sensor is located above the lugs on the park gear in the overdrive unit. Transmission shaft speed sensor input signals are generated when lugs on the park gear rotate past the face of the transmission shaft speed sensor. Input signals are delivered to the TCM where the TCM uses this input signal for controlling transmission operation. The Vehicle Speed Sensor (VSS) also serves as a back-up to the transmission shaft speed sensor. The VSS signal is also shared with the Powertrain Control Module (PCM).

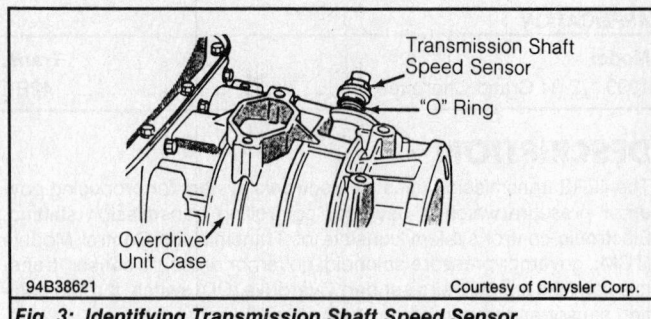

94B38621   Courtesy of Chrysler Corp.

Fig. 3: Identifying Transmission Shaft Speed Sensor

SELF-DIAGNOSTIC SYSTEM

DIAGNOSTIC PROCEDURE

When performing vehicle diagnosis:
- Ensure transmission fluid level is correct and fluid is neither contaminated nor aerated.
- Ensure shift cable is properly adjusted. See appropriate AUTOMATIC TRANSMISSION SERVICING article in TRANSMISSION SERVICING.
- Ensure battery is fully charged.
- Perform visual inspection, ensuring all electrical connections at transmission, TCM, throttle position sensor, transmission shaft speed sensor are clean and properly installed.
- Retrieve diagnostic trouble codes. See RETRIEVING DIAGNOSTIC TROUBLE CODES under SELF-DIAGNOSTIC SYSTEM.
- Repair diagnostic trouble codes in order displayed.
- Always perform TEST 3A – VERIFICATION TEST after repair is completed. See TEST 3A – VERIFICATION TEST under TROUBLE SHOOTING CHARTS.

RETRIEVING DIAGNOSTIC TROUBLE CODES

NOTE: Diagnostic trouble codes can be retrieved by using the OD light method or using Chrysler's Diagnostic Readout Box (DRB) scan tool method for system diagnosis.

OD Light Method – **1)** Turn ignition on, off, on, off and then on and remain in the on position. Immediately begin counting the number of flashes from the OD light on the instrument panel.
2) If OD light flashes 2 times, pauses, and then flashes one more time, a diagnostic trouble code No. 21 is indicated. If OD light flashes 2 times, pauses, and then flashes 6 more time, a diagnostic trouble code No. 26 is indicated.
3) Read all diagnostic trouble codes. Once all diagnostic trouble codes are displayed, a diagnostic trouble Code No. 55 will be displayed to indicate this is the end of the trouble code displays.
4) To identify diagnostic trouble code, see DIAGNOSTIC TROUBLE CODE IDENTIFICATION table. See TROUBLE SHOOTING CHARTS to diagnose faults indicated by trouble codes. It may be necessary to use DRB scan tool for trouble shooting diagnostic trouble codes.

NOTE: After-market scan tools may be used for system diagnosis. The following procedure is for DRB scan tool usage. Use manufacturer's instruction for operating the DRB scan tool.

Chrysler's Diagnostic Readout Box (DRB) Scan Tool Method – **1)** Ensure ignition is off. Connect DRB to 6-pin data link connector, located behind instrument panel on passenger's side of steering column. *See Fig. 4.*
2) Enter diagnostics. See TEST 1A – ENTERING DIAGNOSTICS under TROUBLE SHOOTING CHARTS. This will check operation of DRB and the system.
3) If a blank screen or an error message appears on DRB, proceed to DRB PROBLEMS & ERROR MESSAGES. The following are possible error messages that may appear.

- CARTRIDGE ERROR
- HIGH BATTERY
- KEYPAD TEST FAILURE
- LOW BATTERY
- RAM TEST FAILURE

NOTE: If NO RESPONSE is displayed, proceed to TEST 18A – NO RESPONSE in TROUBLE SHOOTING CHARTS for diagnosis of this problem.

4) If no error message appears, retrieve diagnostic trouble codes using DRB manufacturer's instructions. Note diagnostic trouble code. The DRB will display the diagnostic trouble code along with a message of ACTIVE or STORED. Note this message, as this will aid in the trouble shooting of the system. When more than one diagnostic trouble code is displayed, trouble shooting priority should be given to the ACTIVE trouble codes first.

5) There are 2 types of diagnostic trouble codes, ACTIVE or STORED. An ACTIVE diagnostic trouble code indicates that the problem exists every time the TCM checks the circuit or function.

6) A STORED diagnostic trouble code indicates that the problem does not exist every time the TCM checks the circuit or function. This is an intermittent problem usually caused by wiring or connector problems.

7) Using DRB, display all diagnostic trouble codes. To identify diagnostic trouble code, see DIAGNOSTIC TROUBLE CODE IDENTIFICATION table. When diagnostic trouble codes are set, transaxle will enter limp-in mode until failure is repaired. During limp-in mode, Park, Neutral, Reverse and 3rd gears function, but transmission cannot upshift or downshift. Vehicle can be operated, but transmission performance will be reduced.

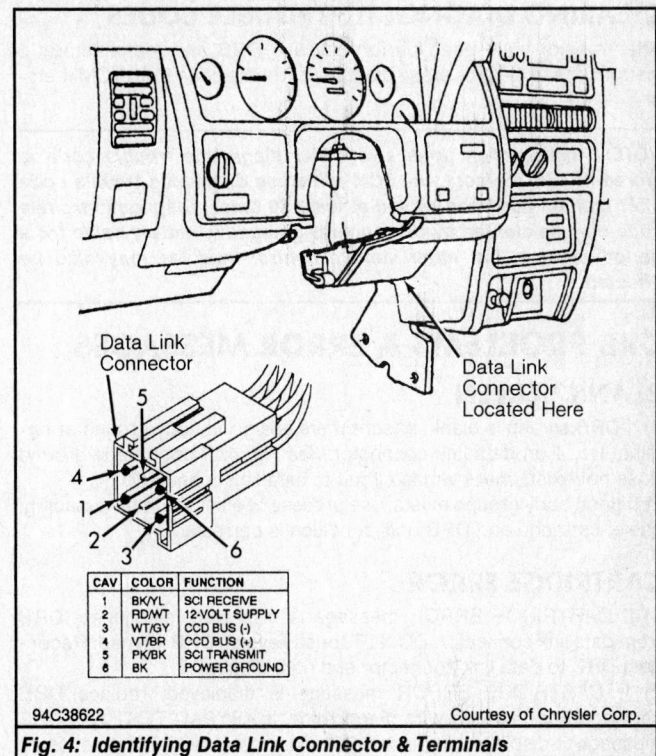

Data Link Connector

Data Link Connector Located Here

CAV	COLOR	FUNCTION
1	BK/YL	SCI RECEIVE
2	RD/WT	12-VOLT SUPPLY
3	WT/GY	CCD BUS (-)
4	VT/BR	CCD BUS (+)
5	PK/BK	SCI TRANSMIT
6	BK	POWER GROUND

94C38622
Courtesy of Chrysler Corp.

Fig. 4: Identifying Data Link Connector & Terminals

DIAGNOSTIC TROUBLE CODE IDENTIFICATION

Trouble Code	DRB Display	Limp-In Mode	Possible Cause
11	Engine RPM Input	Yes	Defective Engine RPM Circuit, Defective Engine RPM Signal From PCM, Defective TCM
12	Output Shaft Sensor Input	Yes	Defective Output Shaft Speed Sensor Or Circuit, Defective TCM
13	Vehicle Speed Input	Yes	Defective Vehicle Speed Sensor Or Circuit, Defective TCM
14	Governor Pressure Sensor Input	Yes	Defective Governor Pressure Sensor Or Circuit, Defective TCM
15	Throttle Position Sensor Input	Yes	Defective Throttle Position Sensor Or Circuit, Defective TCM
16	Transmission Fluid Temperature Input	Yes	Defective Trans. Fluid Temp. Sender Or Circuit, Defective TCM
17	Overdrive Switch Input	Yes	Defective Overdrive Switch Or Circuit, Defective TCM
18	System Voltage	Yes	No Input Voltage To Terminal C9 At TCM, Defective Ignition Fuse
19	Standby Voltage	Yes	Open Or Short In Wiring At Terminals C8, C9 Or D8 At TCM, Open Ignition Fuse Or Disconnected Wiring
21	Governor Pressure Solenoid Output	Yes	Defective Governor Pressure Solenoid Or Circuit, Defective TCM
22	3-4 Solenoid Output [1]	Yes	Defective 3-4 Solenoid Or Circuit, Defective TCM
23	Torque Converter TCC Output	Yes	Defective TCC Solenoid Or Circuit,e Fluid Level, Defective TCM
24	Overdrive Lamp Output	Yes	Defective OD Lamp Or Circuit Or OD Switch, Defective TCM
25	EEPROM Checksum	Yes	Defective TCM
26	Governor Pressure Sensor Offset Drift	Yes	Defective Governor Pressure Sensor Or Circuit, Defective TCM
55 [2]	End Of Code Display	No	No Components Or Circuits Are Defective

[1] – The 3-4 solenoid may be referred to as the overdrive solenoid.

[2] – Diagnostic trouble code No. 55 will be displayed when using OD light method to retrive diagnostic trouble codes. This diagnostic trouble code is displayed to indicate this is the end of the trouble code displays.

CLEARING DIAGNOSTIC TROUBLE CODES

After repairs have been performed, use DRB and manufacturer's instructions to clear or erase diagnostic trouble code from TCM memory.

NOTE: *If malfunction goes away after diagnostic trouble code is stored in TCM memory, the TCM will erase diagnostic trouble code after ignition has been cycled at least 50 times. Diagnostic trouble code may be cleared by disconnecting negative battery cable for a period of time, but other vehicle control modules may also be affected.*

DRB PROBLEMS & ERROR MESSAGES

BLANK SCREEN

1) If DRB screen is blank, ensure there is a good body ground at terminal No. 1 on data link connector. *See Fig. 4.* If good body ground does not exist, check wiring circuit to data link connector.
2) If good body ground exists, use process of elimination by replacing, cable, cartridge and DRB until condition is corrected.

CARTRIDGE ERROR

1) If CARTRIDGE ERROR message is displayed, disconnect DRB from data link connector. DO NOT touch keys on DRB keypad. Reconnect DRB to data link connector and note display.
2) If CARTRIDGE ERROR message is displayed, replace DRB cartridge and proceed with diagnostics. If KEYPAD TEST FAILURE message is displayed, replace DRB and proceed with diagnostics.

HIGH BATTERY

If HIGH BATTERY message is displayed, use external voltmeter to check battery voltage at battery terminals. If battery voltage is 11.7-13.0 volts, replace DRB. If battery voltage is not 11.7-13.0 volts, check charging system.

KEYPAD TEST FAILURE

1) If KEYPAD TEST FAILURE message is displayed, disconnect DRB from data link connector. DO NOT touch keys on DRB keypad. Reconnect DRB to data link connector and note display.
2) If KEYPAD TEST FAILURE message is not displayed, proceed with diagnostics. If KEYPAD TEST FAILURE message is displayed, replace DRB and proceed with diagnostics.

LOW BATTERY

If LOW BATTERY message is displayed, use external voltmeter to check battery voltage at battery terminals. If battery voltage is 11.7-13.0 volts, replace DRB. If battery voltage is not 11.7-13.0 volts, check charging system.

RAM TEST FAILURE

1) If RAM TEST FAILURE message is displayed, disconnect DRB from data link connector. DO NOT touch keys on DRB keypad. Reconnect DRB to data link connector and note display.
2) If RAM TEST FAILURE message is not displayed, proceed with diagnostics. If RAM TEST FAILURE message is displayed, replace DRB and proceed with diagnostics. If KEYPAD TEST FAILURE message is displayed, replace DRB and proceed with diagnostics.

TESTING

For non-electrical testing and mechanical overhaul procedures, see CHRYSLER 42RE & 42RH article. For diagnostic procedures, see DIAGNOSTIC PROCEDURE under SELF-DIAGNOSTIC SYSTEM

REMOVAL & INSTALLATION

GOVERNOR PRESSURE SOLENOID & GOVERNOR PRESSURE SENSOR

NOTE: *Governor pressure sensor may be referred to as governor pressure transducer.*

Removal & Installation – 1) Governor pressure solenoid and governor pressure sensor are mounted on the valve body. Manufacture lists procedure with valve body removed. For valve body removal and installation, see VALVE BODY under REMOVAL & INSTALLATION in CHRYSLER 42RE & 42RH article.
2) For governor pressure solenoid and governor pressure sensor removal and installation on valve body, see VALVE BODY under TRANSMISSION COMPONENT DISASSEMBLY & REASSEMBLY in CHRYSLER 42RE & 42RH article.

OVERDRIVE (OD) SWITCH

NOTE: *Overdrive (OD) switch is located to the right of steering column, on the instrument panel in the right switch pod. Entire right switch pod must be remove and replaced to service the OD switch.*

Removal – 1) Disconnect negative battery cable. Remove ash tray. Remove screw and the center cluster bezel. *See Fig. 5.* Remove the 2 screws retaining the dash pad located behind the center cluster bezel.
2) Pry defroster grill from the dash pad. Disconnect electrical connectors from auto headlight and solar sensors (if equipped). *See Fig. 5.* Remove defroster grille. Remove screws from defroster grill opening that retains dash pad to the instrument panel.
3) Remove dash pad screws from the instrument panel cluster, above the speedometer. Remove dash pad screws from inside of glove box.
4) Pull dash pad upward to disengage from clips at each end of dash pad. Remove lower cover from the steering column. Remove driver's side lower trim panel, located near the steering column. *See Fig. 5.*
5) Remove screws and knee blocker. Remove steering column-to-instrument panel nuts. Remove screws from both sides of switch pod bezel. *See Fig. 5.*
6) Pull switch pod bezel outward and disconnect electrical connectors from switch pods. Remove switch pod bezel. Remove screws and right switch pod with OD switch.
Installation – To install, reverse removal procedure. Tighten steering column retaining nuts to specification. See TORQUE SPECIFICATIONS. Reinstall negative battery cable.

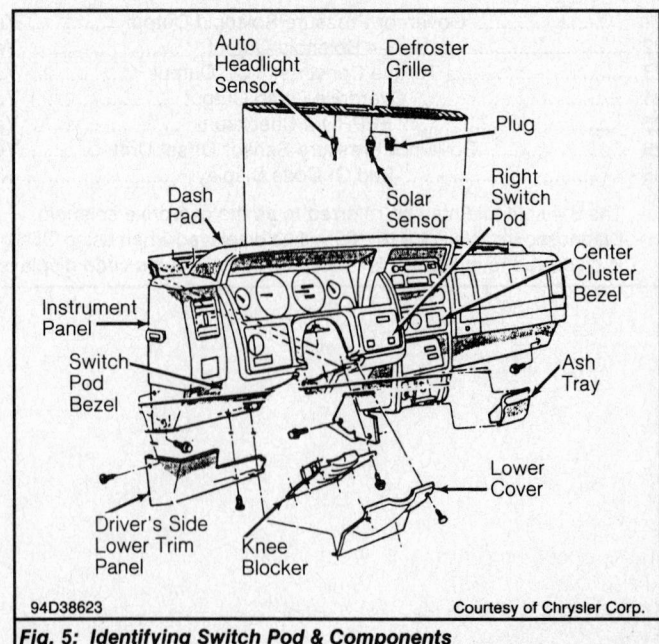

94D38623   Courtesy of Chrysler Corp.

Fig. 5: Identifying Switch Pod & Components

THROTTLE POSITION SENSOR (TPS)

Removal & Installation – 1) Disconnect electrical connector. Remove screws and TPS.

2) To install, reverse removal procedure. Ensure throttle shaft on throttle body engages socket tangs on TPS. *See Fig. 6.* Tighten screws. Manually operate throttle and ensure no binding exists. Reinstall electrical connector.

NOTE: TPS must be installed so it can be rotated a few degrees. If TPS cannot be rotated, reinstall TPS with end of throttle shaft on other side of socket tangs on TPS.

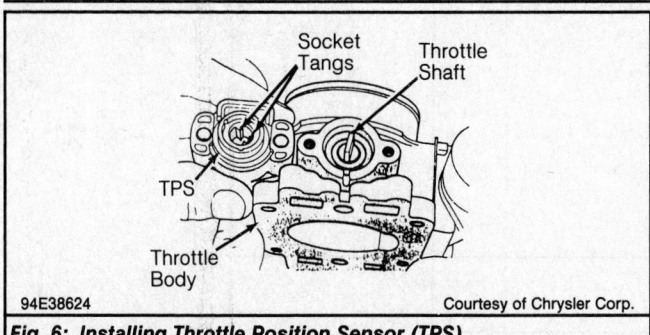

Fig. 6: Installing Throttle Position Sensor (TPS)

TRANSMISSION CONTROL MODULE (TCM)

Removal – 1) Disconnect negative battery cable. From engine compartment, remove TCM attaching nuts that secures retaining plate and the TCM to the bulkhead. *See Fig. 1.*

2) From below driver's side of instrument panel, lower TCM until harness connector is accessible. Lift release tab on harness connector upward. *See Fig. 1.* Disconnect harness connector from TCM.

Installation – To install, reverse removal procedure. Ensure harness connector is fully seated in the TCM. Install and tighten TCM attaching nuts to specification. See TORQUE SPECIFICATIONS. Reinstall negative battery cable.

TRANSMISSION FLUID TEMPERATURE SENDER

NOTE: Transmission fluid temperature sensor may be referred to as transmission fluid temperature sensor or transmission fluid temperature thermistor.

Removal & Installation – Transmission fluid temperature sender is located below lock-up solenoid on the valve body. *See Fig. 2.* Service procedures not available from manufacturer.

TRANSMISSION SHAFT SPEED SENSOR

NOTE: Transmission shaft speed sensor may also be referred to as output shaft speed sensor or shaft speed sensor.

Removal & Installation – 1) Disconnect electrical connector from transmission shaft speed sensor, located on the case of overdrive unit. *See Fig. 3.* Remove transmission shaft speed sensor with "O" ring.

2) To install, reverse removal procedure using NEW "O" ring. Tighten transmission shaft speed sensor to specification. See TORQUE SPECIFICATIONS.

TORQUE SPECIFICATIONS

TORQUE SPECIFICATIONS

Application	Ft. Lbs. (N.m)
TCM Attaching Nut	12 (16)
Transmission Shaft Speed Sensor	20 (27)
	INCH Lbs. (N.m)
Steering Column-To-Instrument Panel Nut	105 (11.9)

TROUBLE SHOOTING CHARTS

NOTE: Following trouble shooting charts and illustrations are courtesy of Chrysler Corp. Always start by performing TEST 1A – ENTERING DIAGNOSTICS.

NOTE: When using trouble shooting charts, transmission shaft speed sensor may also be referred to as output shaft speed sensor or shaft speed sensor.
Governor pressure sensor may be referred to as governor pressure transducer. Lock-up solenoid may be referred to as the TCC solenoid.

NOTE: When using trouble shooting charts, technician may be instructed to disconnect electrical connector from OD switch. This is the electrical connector at the right switch pod.

WIRING DIAGRAMS

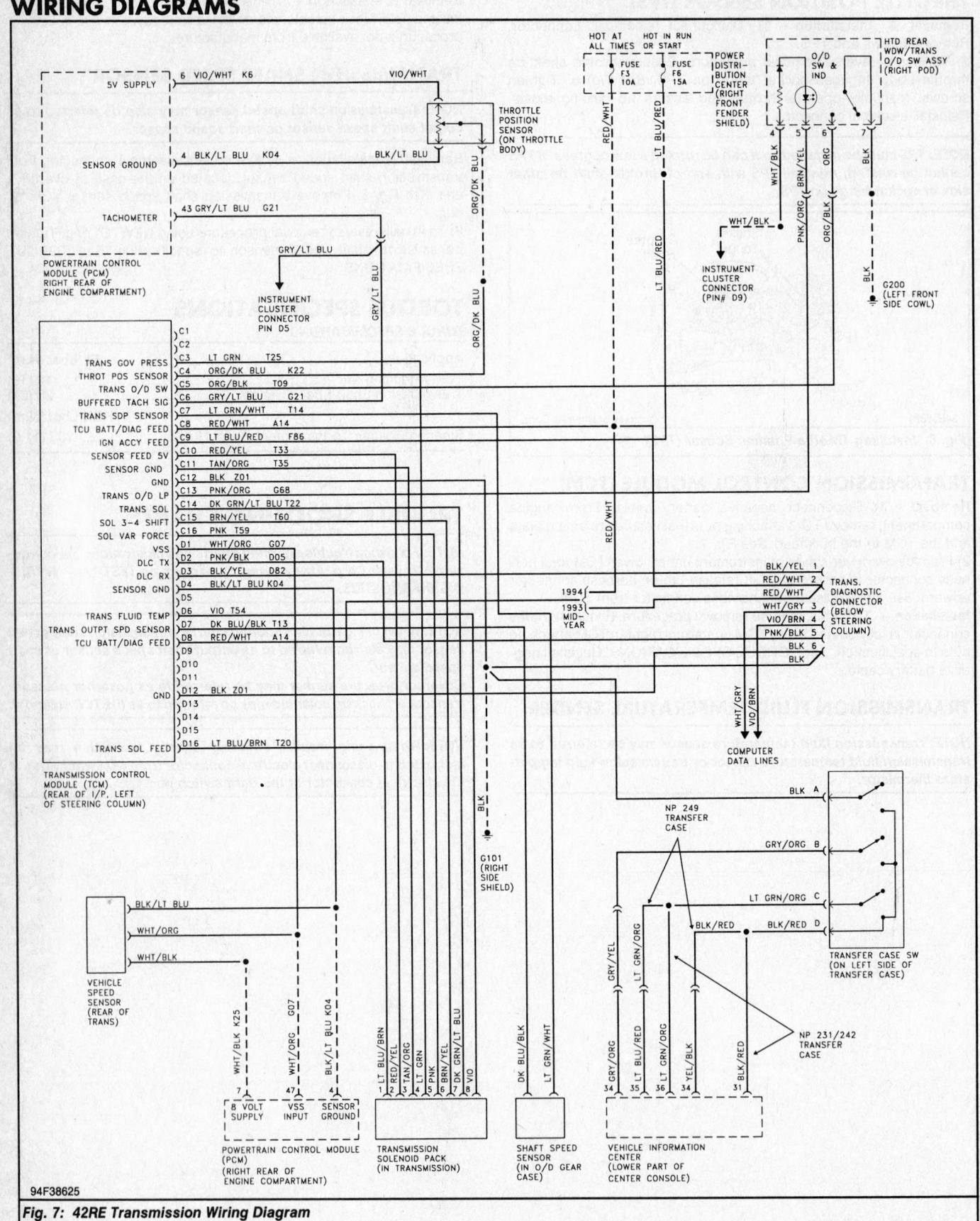

Fig. 7: 42RE Transmission Wiring Diagram

94F38625

TEST 2A
STORED DIAGNOSTIC TROUBLE CODES TEST

PERFORM TEST 1A BEFORE PROCEEDING.

1. Begin testing of the 42RE with a thorough inspection of component, connectors, and proper fluid levels.

2. With the DRB, read diagnostic trouble codes.

3. There are two types of codes for the transmission. They are displayed as "STORED" and "ACTIVE". Note that the tests are different in the chart below.

4. Perform the test shown below in response to the indicated code.

CODE	CODE MESSAGES	TEST ACTION
NO CODES		TEST 3A
CODE 11	Engine RPM Input	TEST 4A
CODE 12	Output Shaft Sensor Input	TEST 5A
CODE 13	Vehicle Speed Sensor	TEST 6A
CODE 14	Governor Pressure Sensor Input	TEST 7A
CODE 15	Throttle Position Sensor	TEST 8A
CODE 16	Trans Sump Temperature Input	TEST 9A
CODE 17	OD Off Switch Input	TEST 10A
CODE 18, 19	System/Standby Voltage	TEST 11A
CODE 21	Governor Pressure Solenoid	TEST 12A
CODE 22	3/4 Solenoid Output	TEST 13A
CODE 23	Torque Converter TCC Output	TEST 14A
CODE 24	OD Off Lamp Driver Output	TEST 15A
CODE 25	EEPROM Checksum	Replace TCM
CODE 26	Governor Pressure Sensor Offset Drift	TEST 16A
NO RESPONSE		TEST 18A
STORED CODES		TEST 19A

TEST 3A
VERIFICATION TEST

PERFORM TEST 1A BEFORE PROCEEDING.

This test verifies the correct operation of the 42RE Transmission. It must be performed after finding no codes using the DRB, and after any vehicle repair procedure.

1. Ignition key off.

2. Press the ATM key on the DRB until you reach the "SELECT SYSTEM" portion of the DRB.

3. Ignition key on.

4. Reconnect any previously disconnected components/connectors.

5. Verify that the 42RE TCM is properly mounted.

6. Check transmission fluid for proper level. Check the fluid with a hot trans on level ground and gear select in neutral.

7. If any repairs have been made, test the vehicle as instructed in TEST 1A, and read codes with the DRB. If any codes are present, repeat TEST 1A.

94H38627 94I38628

TEST 1A
ENTERING DIAGNOSTICS

① SEE DRB PROBLEMS & ERROR MESSAGES IN THIS ARTICLE.

② SEE BODY CONTROL COMPUTER VEHICLE COMMUNICATIONS ARTICLE IN ENGINE PERFORMANCE OF APPROPRIATE MITCHELL® MANUAL

94G38626

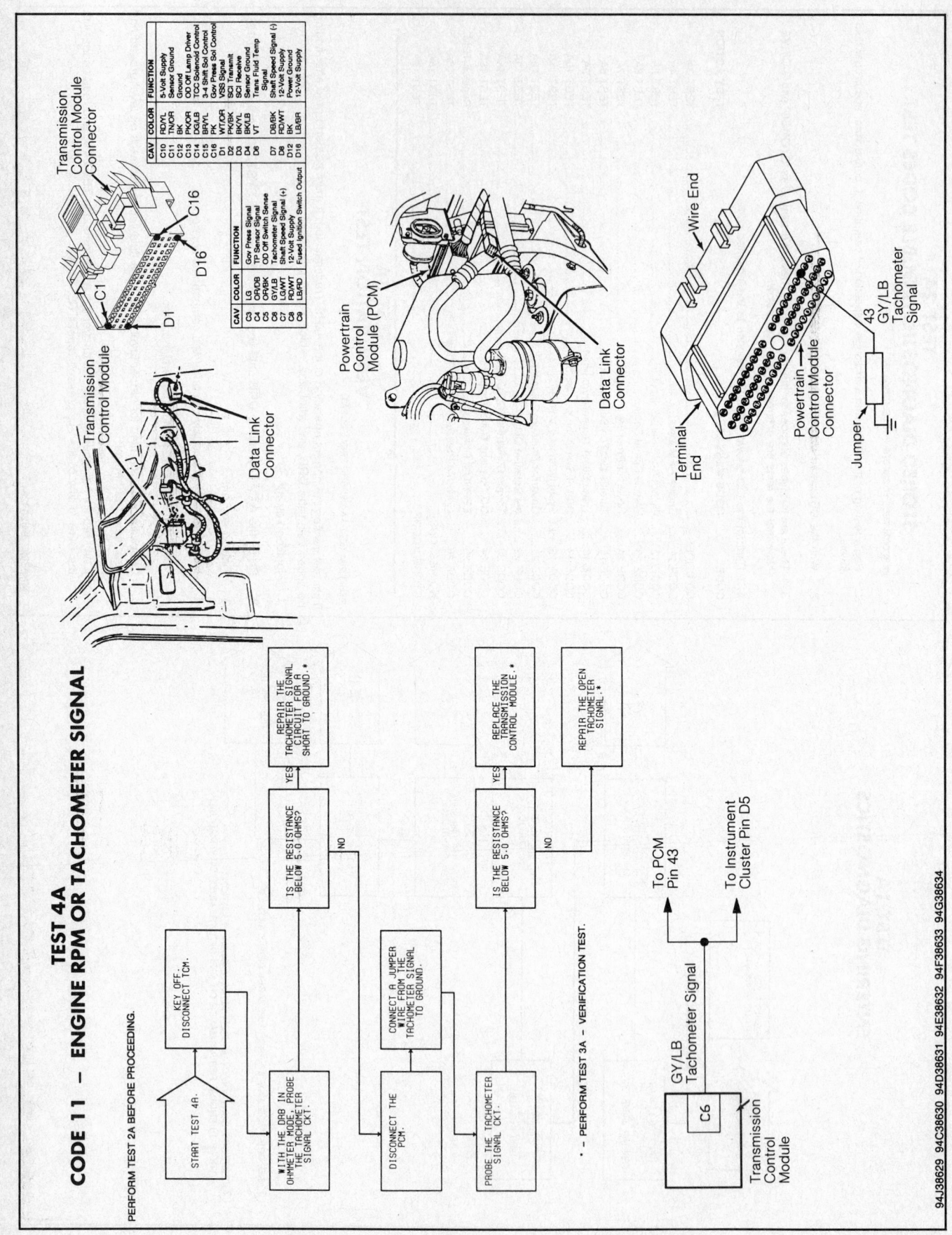

TEST 4A

CODE 11 – ENGINE RPM OR TACHOMETER SIGNAL

PERFORM TEST 2A BEFORE PROCEEDING.

Transmission Control Module Connector

CAV	COLOR	FUNCTION
C10	RD/YL	8-Volt Supply
C11	TN/OR	Sensor Ground
C12	BK	Ground
C13	PK/OR	OD Off Lamp Driver
C14	DG/LB	TCC Solenoid Control
C15	BR/YL	3-4 Shift Sol Control
C16	PK	Gov Press Sol Control
D1	WT/OR	VSS Signal
D2	PK/BK	SCI Transmit
D4	BK/YL	SCI Receive
D5	VT	Sensor Ground
D6		Trans Fluid Temp Signal
D7	DB/BK	Shaft Speed Signal (-)
D8	RD/WT	12-Volt Supply
D12	BK	Power Ground
D16	LB/BR	12-Volt Supply

CAV	COLOR	FUNCTION
C3	LG	Gov Press Signal
C4	OR/DB	TP Sensor Signal
C5	OR/BK	OD Off Switch Sense
C6	GY/LB	Tachometer Signal
C7	LG/WT	Shaft Speed Signal (+)
C8	RD/WT	12-Volt Supply
C8	LB/RD	Fused Ignition Switch Output

Transmission Control Module

Data Link Connector

Powertrain Control Module (PCM)

Data Link Connector

Wire End

43 GY/LB Tachometer Signal

Terminal End

Jumper

Powertrain Control Module Connector

START TEST 4A.

KEY OFF... DISCONNECT TCM.

WITH THE DRB IN OHMMETER MODE, PROBE THE TACHOMETER SIGNAL CKT.

IS THE RESISTANCE BELOW 5.0 OHMS?

— YES → REPAIR THE TACHOMETER SIGNAL CIRCUIT FOR A SHORT TO GROUND. *

— NO →

DISCONNECT THE PCM.

CONNECT A JUMPER WIRE FROM THE TACHOMETER SIGNAL TO GROUND.

PROBE THE TACHOMETER SIGNAL CKT.

IS THE RESISTANCE BELOW 5.0 OHMS?

— YES → REPLACE THE TRANSMISSION CONTROL MODULE. *

— NO → REPAIR THE OPEN TACHOMETER SIGNAL. *

* – PERFORM TEST 3A – VERIFICATION TEST.

GY/LB Tachometer Signal

C6

Transmission Control Module

To PCM Pin 43

To Instrument Cluster Pin D5

94J38629 94C38630 94D38631 94E38632 94F38633 94G38634

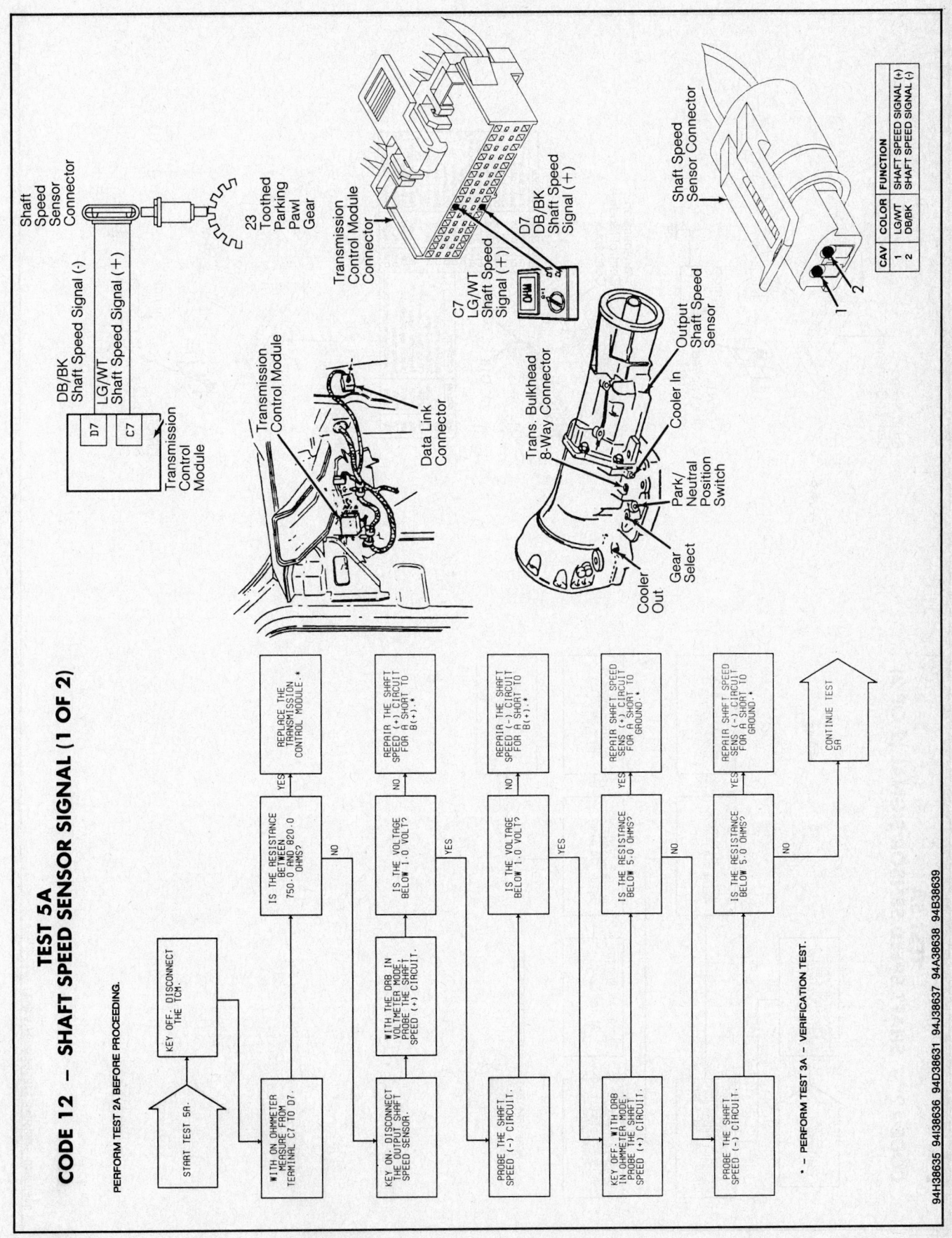

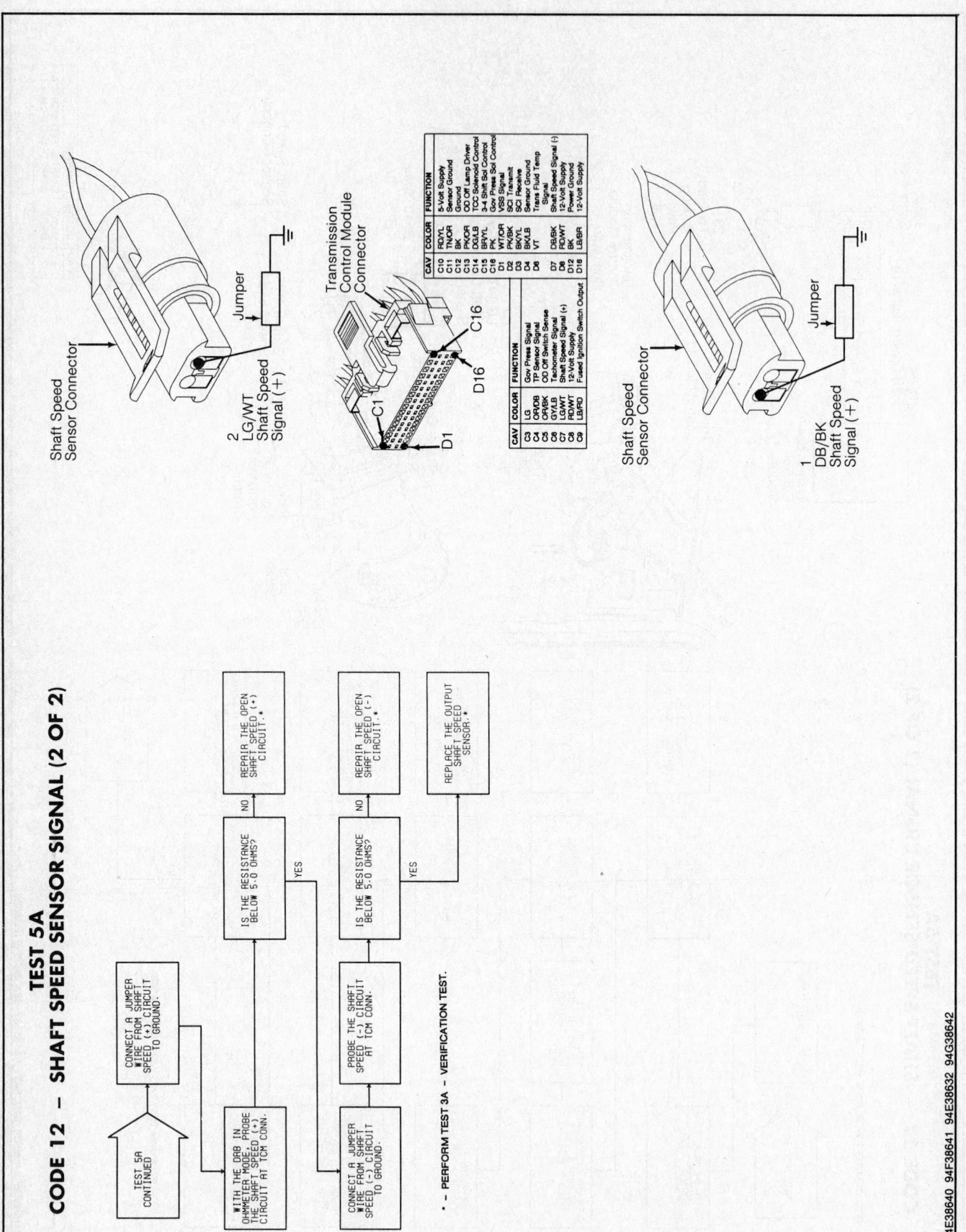

TEST 5A
CODE 12 – SHAFT SPEED SENSOR SIGNAL (2 OF 2)

Transmission Control Module Connector

CAV	COLOR	FUNCTION
C10	RD/YL	5-Volt Supply
C11	TN/OR	Sensor Ground
C12	BK	Ground
C13	PK/OR	OD Off Lamp Driver
C14	DG/LB	TCC Solenoid Control
C15	BR/YL	3-4 Shift Sol Control
C16	PK	Gov Press Sol Control
D1	WT/OR	VSS Signal
D2	PK/BK	SCI Transmit
D3	BK/YL	SCI Receive
D5	BK/LB	Sensor Ground
D6	VT	Trans Fluid Temp Signal
D7	DB/BK	Shaft Speed Signal (-)
D8	RD/WT	12-Volt Supply
D12	BK	Power Ground
D16	LB/BR	12-Volt Supply

CAV	COLOR	FUNCTION
C3	LG	Gov Press Signal
C5	OR/DB	TP Sensor Signal
C6	OR/BK	OD Off Switch Sense
C8	GY/LB	Tachometer Signal
C7	LG/WT	Shaft Speed Signal (+)
C8	RD/WT	12-Volt Supply
C9	LB/RD	Fused Ignition Switch Output

Shaft Speed Sensor Connector

Jumper

2 LG/WT Shaft Speed Signal (+)

Shaft Speed Sensor Connector

Jumper

1 DB/BK Shaft Speed Signal (+)

TEST 5A CONTINUED

WITH THE DRB IN OHMMETER MODE, PROBE THE SHAFT SPEED (+) CIRCUIT AT TCM CONN.

CONNECT A JUMPER WIRE FROM SHAFT SPEED (+) CIRCUIT TO GROUND.

IS THE RESISTANCE BELOW 5.0 OHMS?

NO → REPAIR THE OPEN SHAFT SPEED (+) CIRCUIT.*

YES

CONNECT A JUMPER WIRE FROM SHAFT SPEED (-) CIRCUIT TO GROUND.

PROBE THE SHAFT SPEED (-) CIRCUIT AT TCM CONN.

IS THE RESISTANCE BELOW 5.0 OHMS?

NO → REPAIR THE OPEN SHAFT SPEED (-) CIRCUIT.*

YES → REPLACE THE OUTPUT SHAFT SPEED SENSOR.*

* – PERFORM TEST 3A – VERIFICATION TEST.

94E38640 94F38641 94E38641 94E38632 94G38642

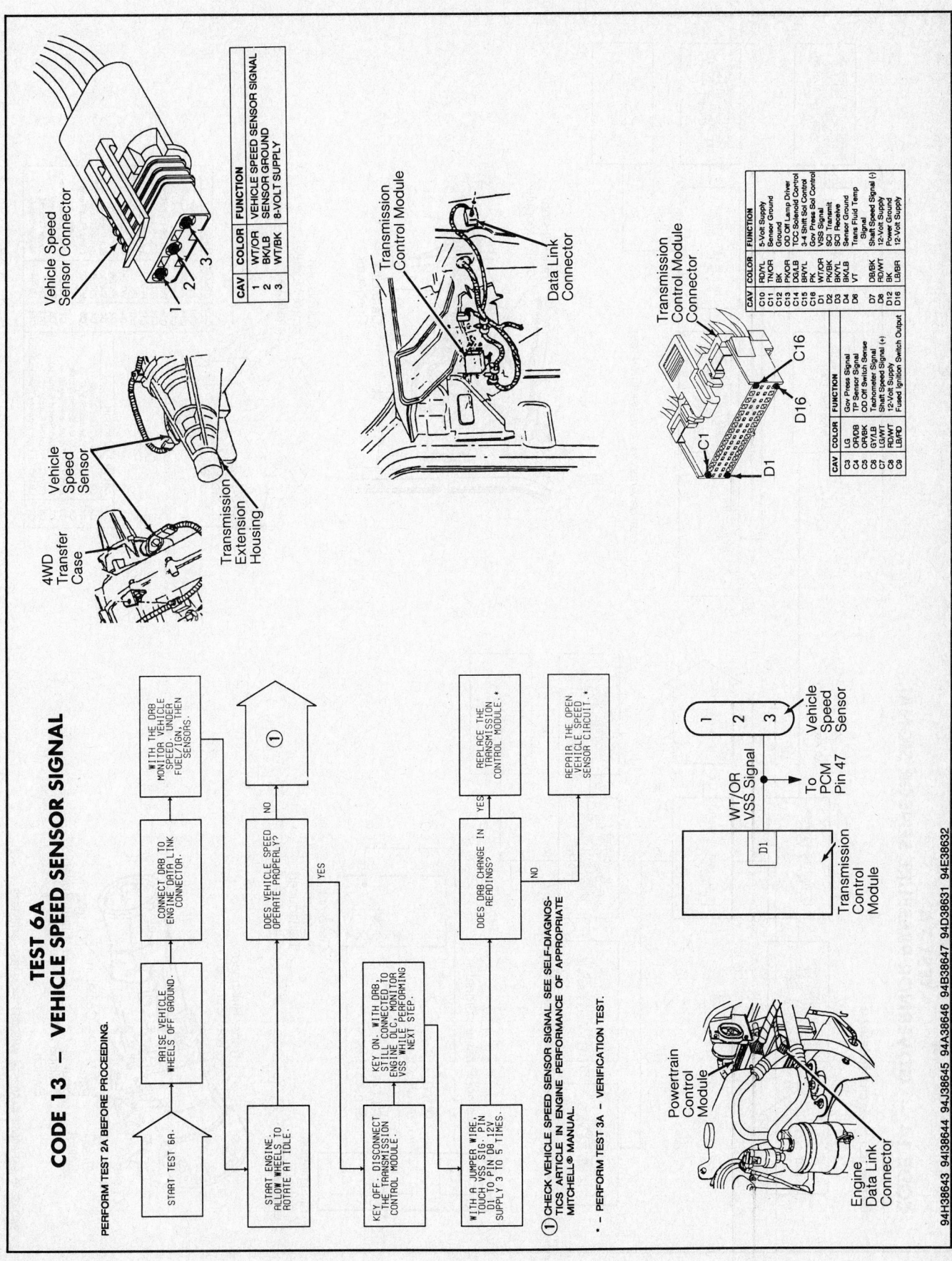

TEST 6A
CODE 13 – VEHICLE SPEED SENSOR SIGNAL

PERFORM TEST 2A BEFORE PROCEEDING.

① CHECK VEHICLE SPEED SENSOR SIGNAL. SEE SELF-DIAGNOSTICS ARTICLE IN ENGINE PERFORMANCE OF APPROPRIATE MITCHELL® MANUAL.

* – PERFORM TEST 3A – VERIFICATION TEST.

Vehicle Speed Sensor Connector

CAV	COLOR	FUNCTION
1	WT/OR	VEHICLE SPEED SENSOR SIGNAL
2	BK/LB	SENSOR GROUND
3	WT/BK	8-VOLT SUPPLY

4WD Transfer Case

Vehicle Speed Sensor

Transmission Extension Housing

Transmission Control Module

Data Link Connector

Transmission Control Module Connector

CAV	COLOR	FUNCTION
C10	RD/YL	5-Volt Supply
C11	TN/OR	Sensor Ground
C12	BK	Ground
C13	PK/OR	OD Off Lamp Driver
C14	DG/LB	TCC Solenoid Control
C15	BR/YL	3-4 Shift Sol Control
C16	PK	Gov Press Sol Control
D3	WT/OR	VSS Signal
D3	PK/BK	SCI Transmit
D3	BK/LB	SCI Receive
D6	VT	Sensor Ground
D7	DB/BK	Trans Fluid Temp Signal
D8	RD/WT	Shaft Speed Signal (-)
D12	BK	Power Ground
D16	LB/BR	12-Volt Supply

CAV	COLOR	FUNCTION
C3	LG	Gov Press Signal
C4	OR/DB	TP Sensor Signal
C5	OR/BK	OD Off Switch Sense
C7	GY/LB	Tachometer Signal
C7	LG/WT	Shaft Speed Signal (+)
C8	RD/WT	12-Volt Supply
C9	BK	12-Volt Supply
C16	LB/RD	Fused Ignition Switch Output

Powertrain Control Module

Engine Data Link Connector

To PCM Pin 47

WT/OR VSS Signal

Vehicle Speed Sensor

Transmission Control Module

94H38643 94I38644 94J38645 94A38646 94B38647 94D38631 94E38632

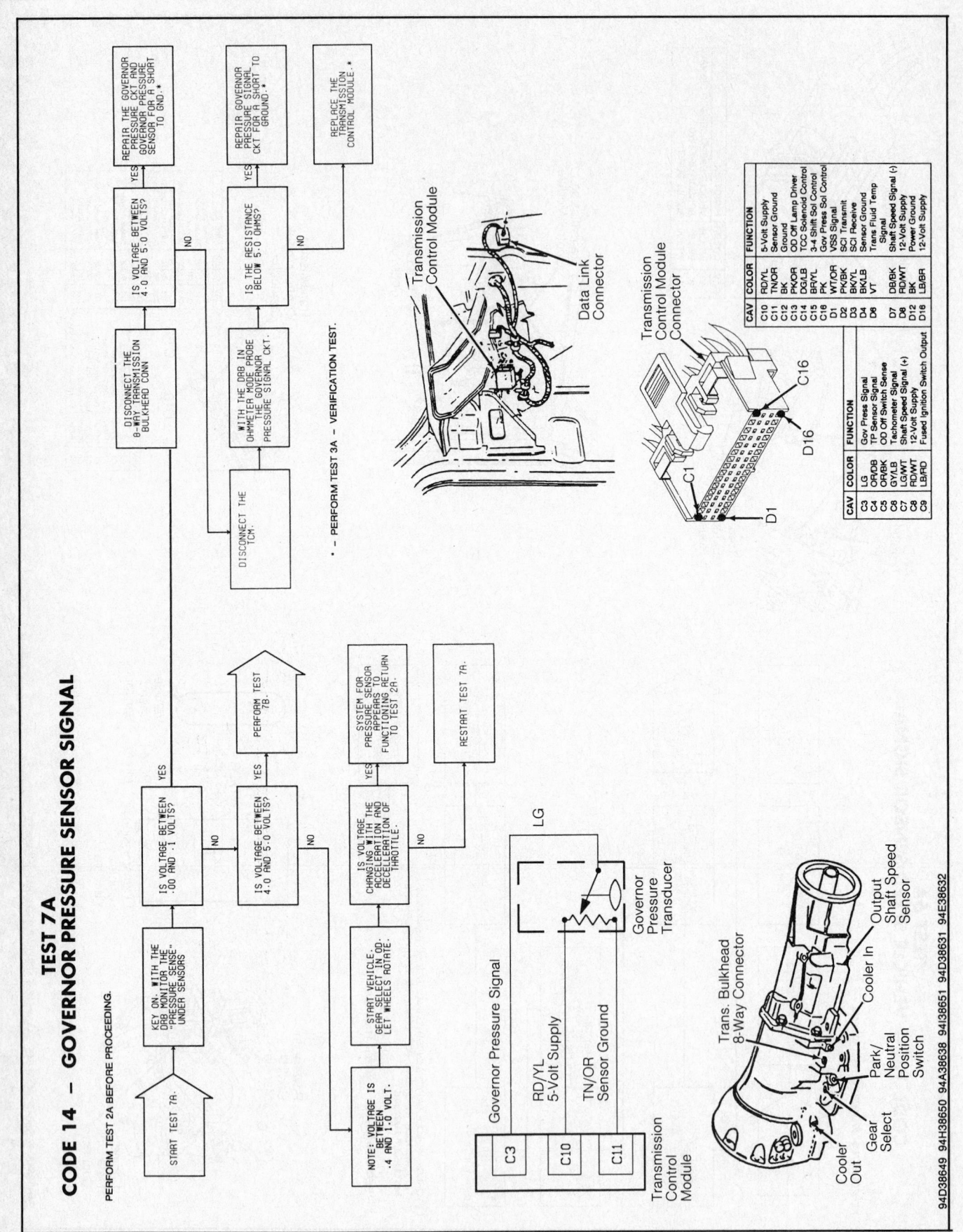

TEST 7A

CODE 14 – GOVERNOR PRESSURE SENSOR SIGNAL

PERFORM TEST 2A BEFORE PROCEEDING.

* – PERFORM TEST 3A – VERIFICATION TEST.

94D38649 94H38650 94A38650 94I38638 94I38651 94D38631 94E38632

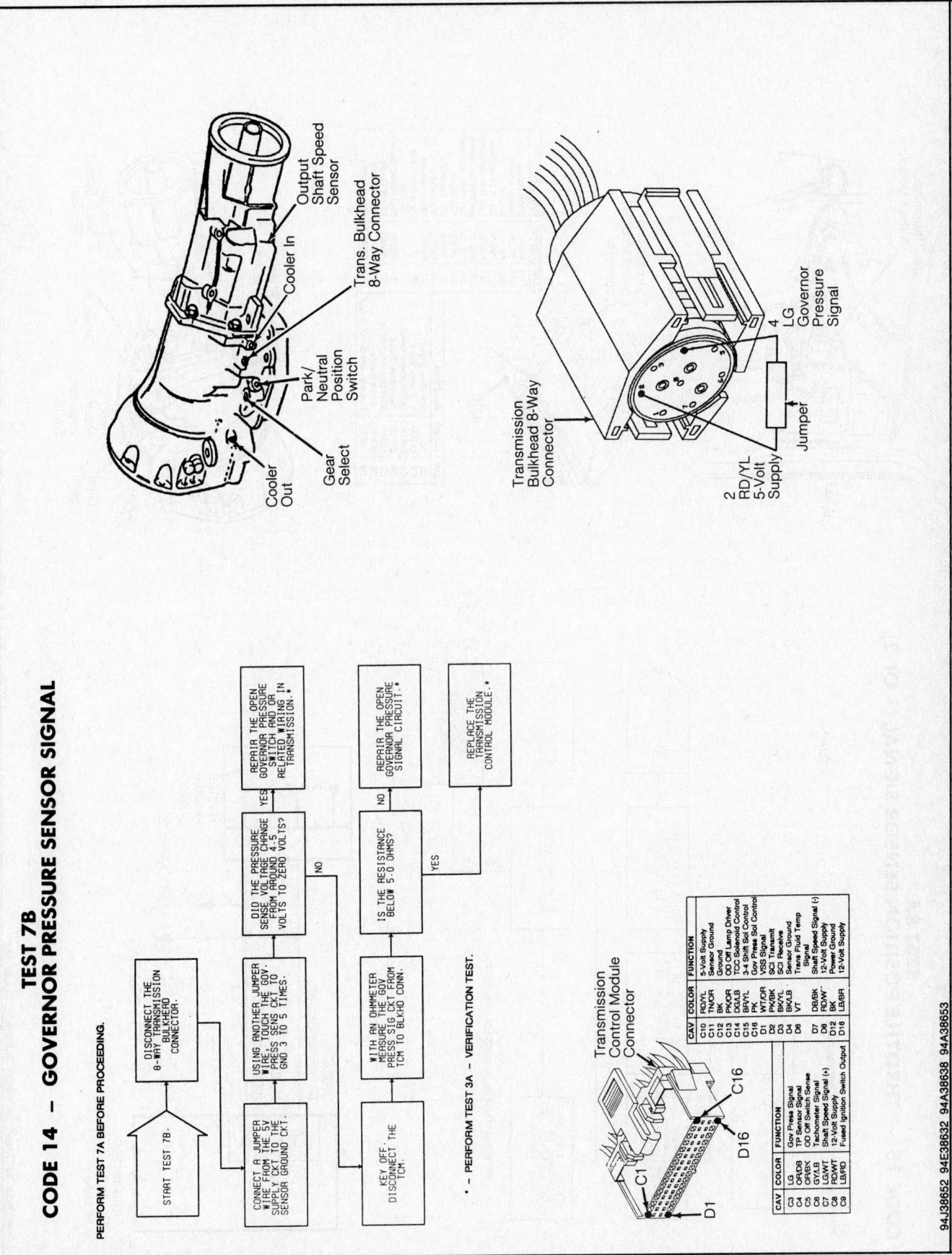

TEST 7B

CODE 14 – GOVERNOR PRESSURE SENSOR SIGNAL

PERFORM TEST 7A BEFORE PROCEEDING.

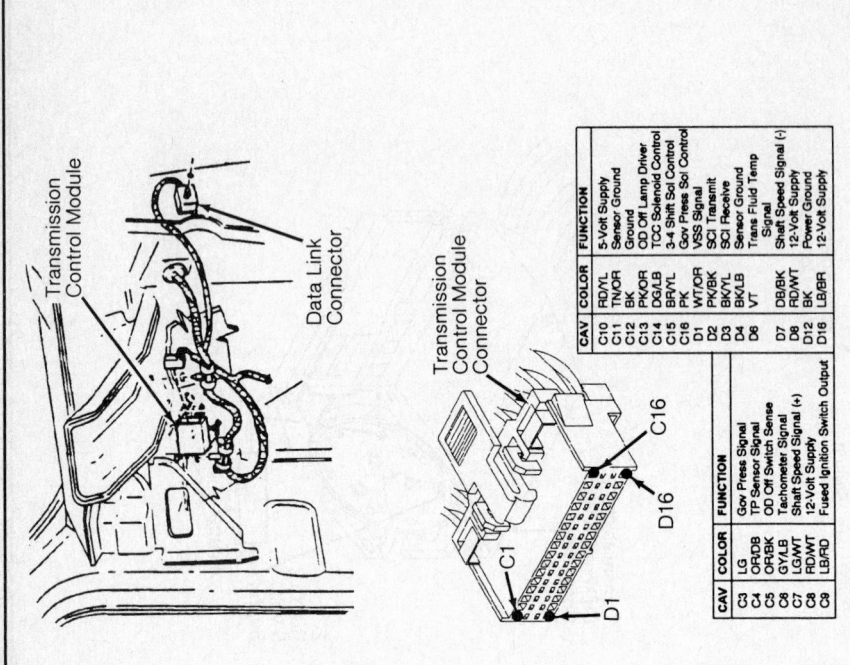

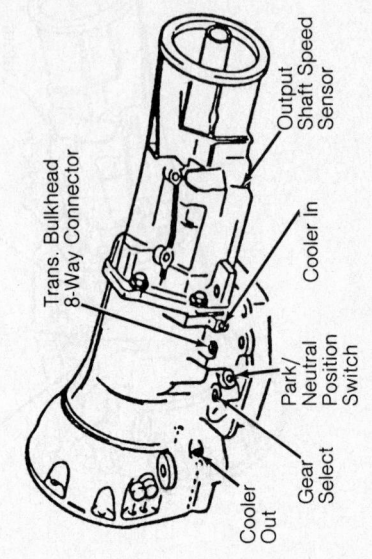

CAV	COLOR	FUNCTION
C10	RD/YL	5-Volt Supply
C11	TN/OR	Sensor Ground
C12	BK	Ground
C13	PK/OR	OD Off Lamp Driver
C14	DG/LB	TCC Solenoid Control
C15	BR/YL	3-4 Shift Sol Control
D1	PK	Gov Press Sol Control
D2	WT/OR	VSS Signal
D3	PK/BK	SCI Transmit
D4	BK/YL	SCI Receive
D5	VT	Sensor Ground
D6		Trans Fluid Temp Signal
D7	DB/BK	Shaft Speed Signal (+)
D8	RD/WT	12-Volt Supply
D12	BK	Power Ground
D16	LB/BR	12-Volt Supply

CAV	COLOR	FUNCTION
C3	LG	Gov Press Signal
C4	OR/DB	TP Sensor Signal
C5	OR/BK	OD Switch Sense
C6	GY/LB	Tachometer Signal
C7	LG/WT	Shaft Speed Signal (+)
C8	RD/WT	12-Volt Supply
C9	LB/RD	Fused Ignition Switch Output

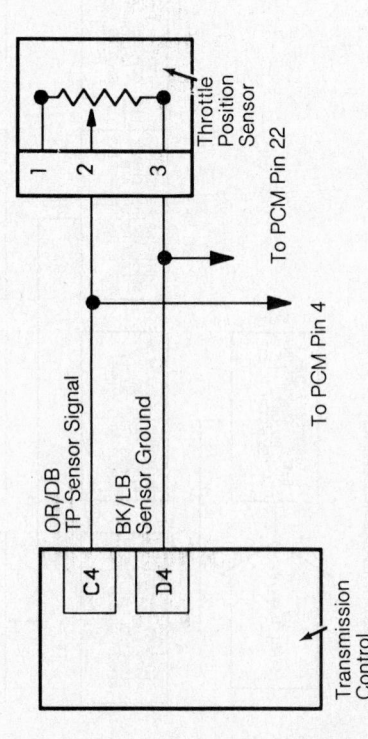

TEST 8A
CODE 15 – THROTTLE POSITION SENSOR SIGNAL (1 OF 2)

PERFORM TEST 2A BEFORE PROCEEDING.

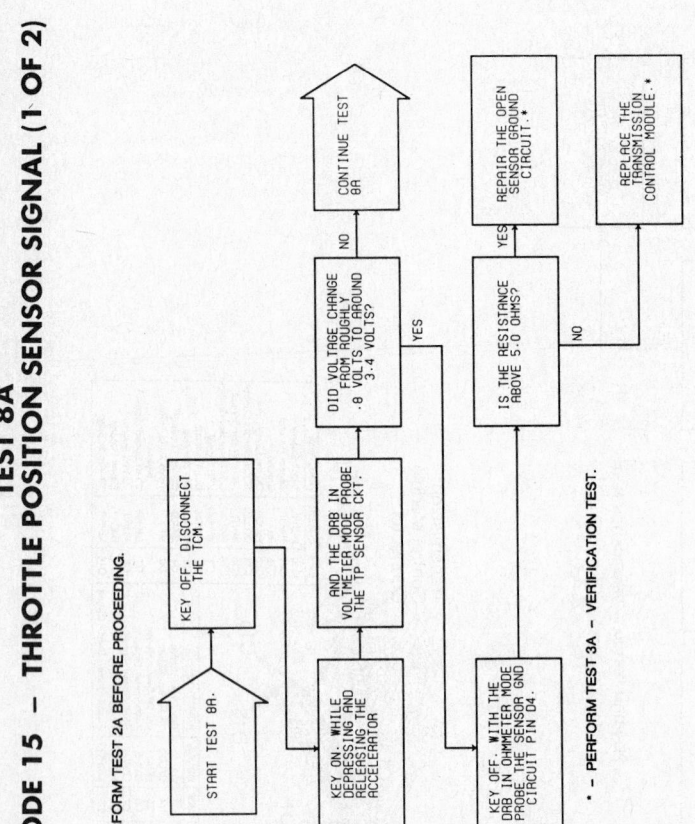

94B38654 94C38655 94D38631 94E38632 94A39638

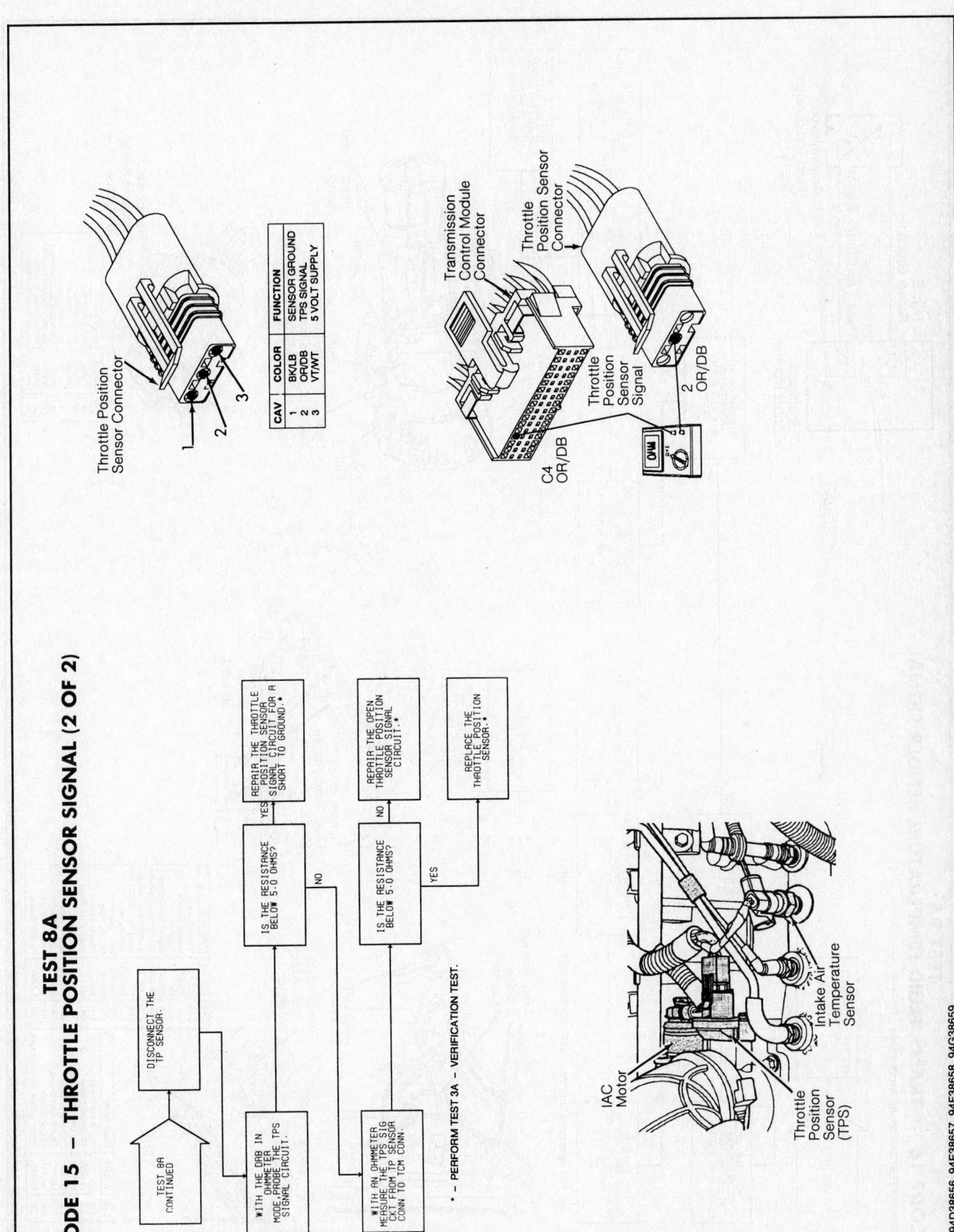

CODE 15 — THROTTLE POSITION SENSOR SIGNAL (2 OF 2)

TEST 8A

CAV	COLOR	FUNCTION
1	BK/LB	SENSOR GROUND
2	OR/DB	TPS SIGNAL
3	VT/WT	5 VOLT SUPPLY

Throttle Position Sensor Connector

Transmission Control Module Connector

Throttle Position Sensor Connector

Throttle Position Sensor Signal

C4 OR/DB

2 OR/DB

TEST 8A CONTINUED

DISCONNECT THE TP SENSOR.

WITH THE DRB IN OHMMETER MODE, PROBE THE TPS SIGNAL CIRCUIT.

IS THE RESISTANCE BELOW 5.0 OHMS?

YES → REPAIR THE THROTTLE POSITION SENSOR SIGNAL CIRCUIT FOR A SHORT TO GROUND. *

NO → WITH AN OHMMETER MEASURE THE TPS SIG CKT FROM TP SENSOR CONN TO TCM CONN.

IS THE RESISTANCE BELOW 5.0 OHMS?

NO → REPAIR THE OPEN THROTTLE POSITION SENSOR SIGNAL CIRCUIT. *

YES → REPLACE THE THROTTLE POSITION SENSOR. *

* — PERFORM TEST 3A — VERIFICATION TEST.

IAC Motor

Intake Air Temperature Sensor

Throttle Position Sensor (TPS)

94D38656 94E38657 94F38658 94G38659

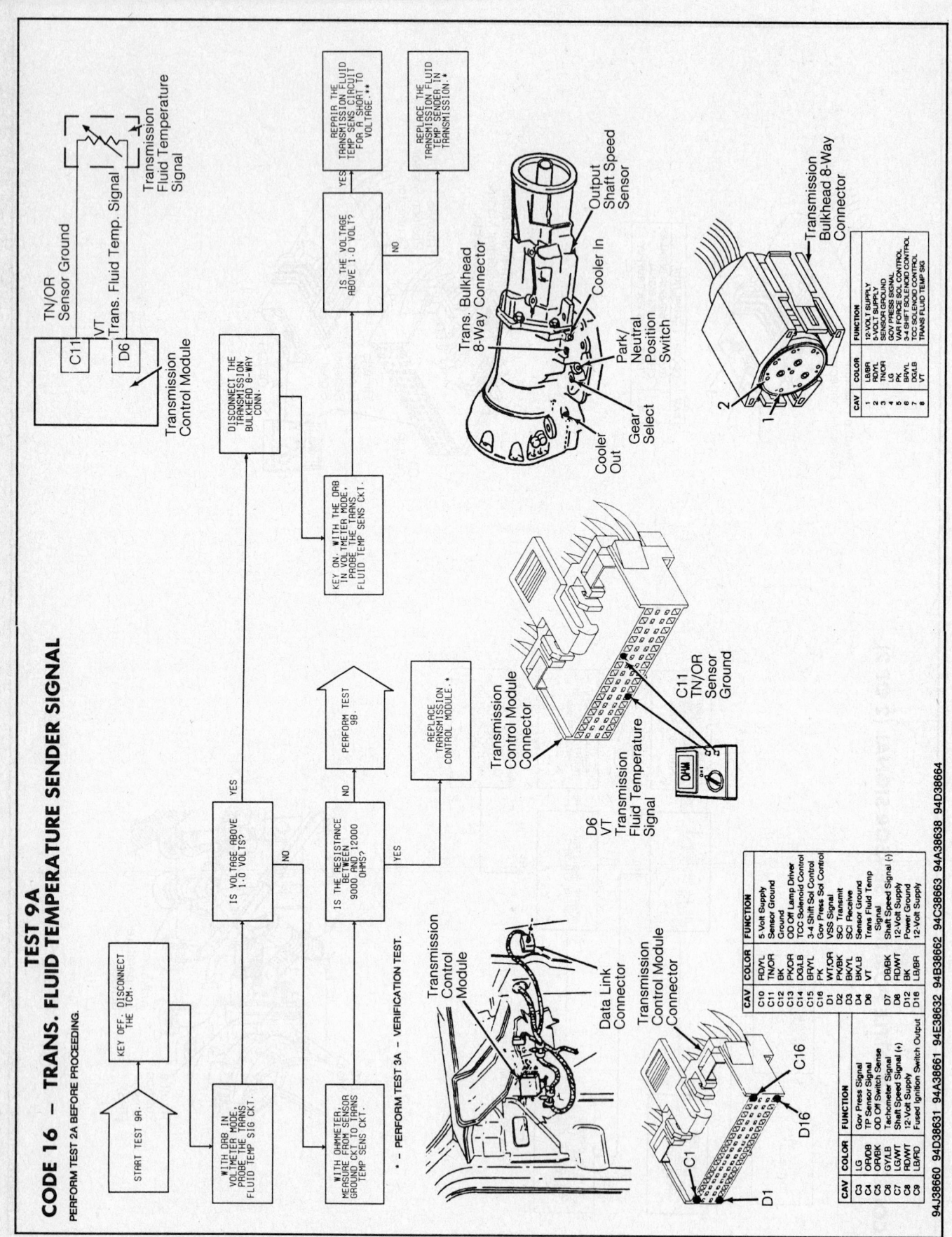

TEST 9A

CODE 16 — TRANS. FLUID TEMPERATURE SENDER SIGNAL

PERFORM TEST 2A BEFORE PROCEEDING.

START TEST 9A.

KEY OFF. DISCONNECT THE TCM.

WITH DRB IN VOLTMETER MODE. PROBE THE TRANS FLUID TEMP SIG CKT.

IS VOLTAGE ABOVE 1.0 VOLTS?

WITH OHMMETER, MEASURE FROM SENSOR GROUND CKT TO TRANS TEMP SENS CKT.

IS THE RESISTANCE BETWEEN 9000 AND 12000 OHMS?

PERFORM TEST 9B.

REPLACE TRANSMISSION CONTROL MODULE. *

DISCONNECT THE TRANSMISSION BULKHEAD 8-WAY CONN.

KEY ON. WITH THE DRB IN VOLTMETER MODE, PROBE THE TRANS FLUID TEMP SENS CKT.

IS THE VOLTAGE ABOVE 1.0 VOLT?

REPAIR THE TRANSMISSION FLUID TEMP SENS CIRCUIT FOR A SHORT TO VOLTAGE.**

REPLACE THE TRANSMISSION FLUID TEMP SENDER IN TRANSMISSION. *

* — PERFORM TEST 3A — VERIFICATION TEST.

** — PERFORM TEST 2A BEFORE PROCEEDING.

Transmission Control Module

TN/OR Sensor Ground

VT Trans. Fluid Temp. Signal

C11

D6

Transmission Fluid Temperature Signal

Trans. Fluid Temp. Signal

Transmission Fluid Temperature Signal

Output Shaft Speed Sensor

Cooler In

Trans. Bulkhead 8-Way Connector

Park/Neutral Position Switch

Gear Select

Cooler Out

Transmission Bulkhead 8-Way Connector

CAV	COLOR	FUNCTION
1	LB/BR	12-VOLT SUPPLY
2	RD/YL	5-VOLT SUPPLY
3	TN/OR	SENSOR GROUND
4	LG	GOV PRESS SIGNAL
5	PK	VAR FORCE SOL CONTROL
6	BR/YL	3-4 SHIFT SOLENOID CONTROL
7	DG/LB	TCC SOLENOID CONTROL
8	VT	TRANS FLUID TEMP SIG

Transmission Control Module Connector

C11 TN/OR Sensor Ground

D6 VT Transmission Fluid Temperature Signal

Transmission Control Module

Data Link Connector

Transmission Control Module Connector

CAV	COLOR	FUNCTION
C10	RD/YL	5 Volt Supply
C11	TN/OR	Sensor Ground
C12	BK	Ground
C13	PK/OR	OD Off Lamp Driver
C14	DG/LB	TCC Solenoid Control
C15	BR/YL	3-4 Shift Sol Control
C16	PK	Gov Press Sol Control
D1	WT/OR	VSS Signal
D2	PK/BK	SCI Transmit
D3	BK/YL	SCI Receive
D4	BK/LB	Sensor Ground
D6	VT	Trans Fluid Temp Signal
D7	DB/BK	Shaft Speed Signal (-)
D8	RD/WT	12-Volt Supply
D12	BK	Power Supply
D18	LB/BR	12-Volt Supply

CAV	COLOR	FUNCTION
C3	LG	Gov Press Signal
C4	OR/DB	TP Sensor Signal
C5	OR/BK	OD Off Switch Sense
C6	GY/LB	Tachometer Signal
C7	LG/WT	Shaft Speed Signal (+)
C8	RD/WT	12-Volt Supply
C9	LB/RD	Fused Ignition Switch Output

C16

D16

C1

D1

94J38660 94D38631 94A38661 94E38632 94B38662 94C38663 94A38638 94D38664

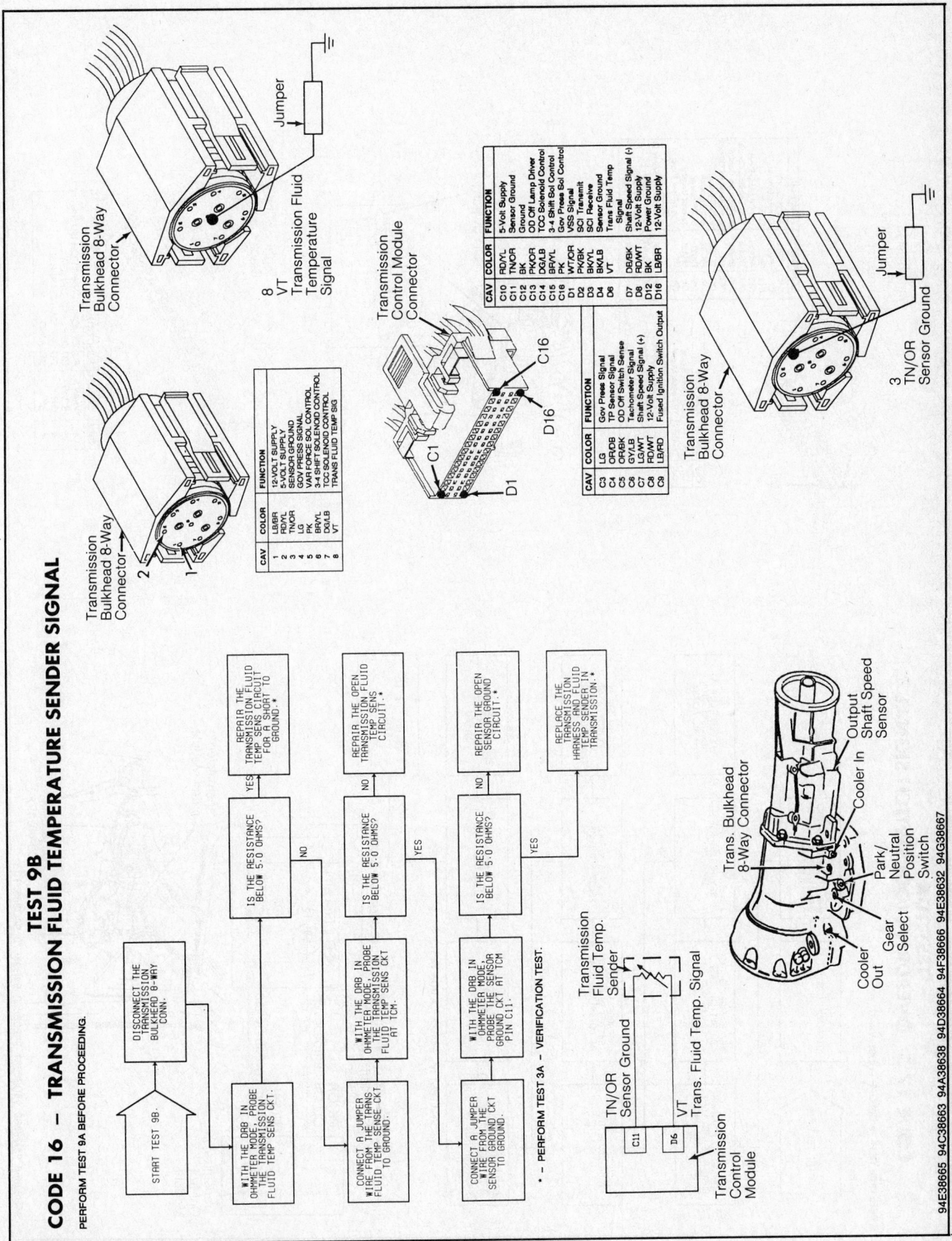

CODE 16 – TRANSMISSION FLUID TEMPERATURE SENDER SIGNAL

TEST 9B

PERFORM TEST 9A BEFORE PROCEEDING.

94E38665 94C38663 94A38638 94D38664 94F38666 94E38632 94G38667

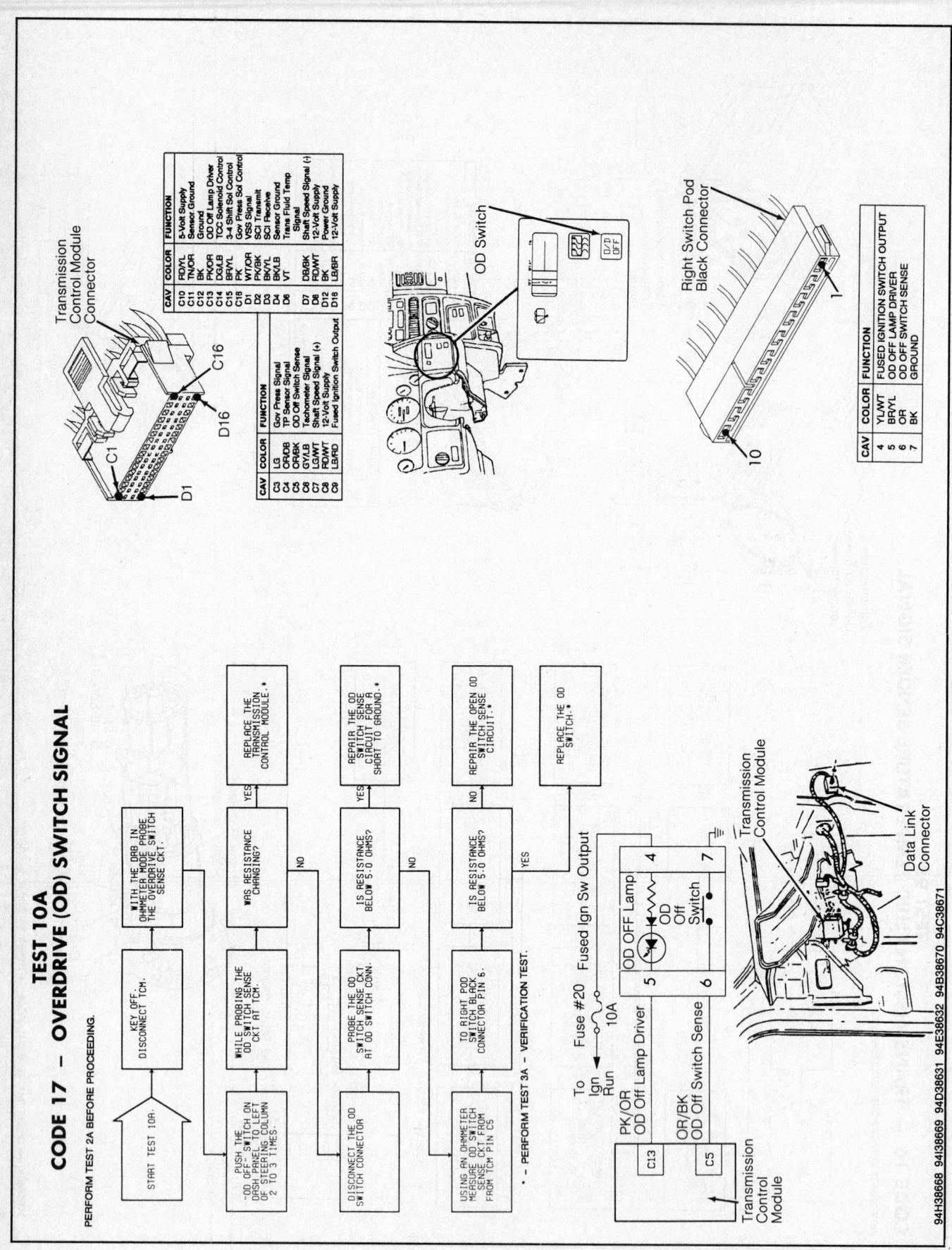

Transmission Control Module Connector

CAV	COLOR	FUNCTION
C10	RD/YL	5-Volt Supply
C11	TN/OR	Sensor Ground
C12	BK	Ground
C13	PK/OR	OD Off Lamp Driver
C14	DG/LB	TCC Solenoid Control
C15	BR/YL	3-4 Shift Sol Control
C16	PK	Gov Press Sol Control
D1	WT/OR	SCI Transmit
D2	PK/BK	SCI Receive
D3	BK/YL	Sensor Ground
D4	BK/LB	Trans Fluid Temp
D6	VT	Shaft Speed Signal (-) Signal
D7	DB/BK	Shaft Speed Signal (-)
D8	RD/WT	12-Volt Supply
D12	BK	Power Ground
D16	LB/BR	12-Volt Supply

CAV	COLOR	FUNCTION
C3	LG	Gov Press Signal
C4	OR/DB	TP Sensor Signal
C6	OR/BK	OD Off Switch Sense
C8	GY/LB	Tachometer Signal
C7	LG/WT	Shaft Speed Signal (+)
C8	RD/WT	12-Volt Supply
C9	LB/RD	Fused Ignition Switch Output

OD Switch

Right Switch Pod Black Connector

CAV	COLOR	FUNCTION
4	YL/WT	FUSED IGNITION SWITCH OUTPUT
5	BR/YL	OD OFF LAMP DRIVER
6	OR	OD OFF SWITCH SENSE
7	BK	GROUND

TEST 10A
CODE 17 – OVERDRIVE (OD) SWITCH SIGNAL

PERFORM TEST 2A BEFORE PROCEEDING.

START TEST 10A.

KEY OFF. DISCONNECT TCM.

PUSH THE "OD OFF" SWITCH ON DASH PANEL TO LEFT OF STEERING COLUMN 2 TO 3 TIMES.

WHILE PROBING THE OD SWITCH SENSE CKT AT TCM.

WITH THE DRB IN OHMMETER MODE PROBE THE OVERDRIVE SWITCH SENSE CKT.

WAS RESISTANCE CHANGING? — YES → REPLACE THE TRANSMISSION CONTROL MODULE. *

NO

DISCONNECT THE OD SWITCH CONNECTOR.

PROBE THE OD SWITCH SENSE CKT AT OD SWITCH CONN.

IS RESISTANCE BELOW 5.0 OHMS? — YES → REPAIR THE OD SWITCH SENSE CIRCUIT FOR A SHORT TO GROUND. *

NO

USING AN OHMMETER MEASURE OD SWITCH SENSE CKT FROM TCM PIN C5

TO RIGHT POD SWITCH BLACK CONNECTOR PIN 6.

IS RESISTANCE BELOW 5.0 OHMS? — NO → REPAIR THE OPEN OD SWITCH SENSE CIRCUIT. *

YES

REPLACE THE OD SWITCH. *

* – PERFORM TEST 3A – VERIFICATION TEST.

Fused Ign Sw Output

To Ign Run → Fuse #20 10A

Transmission Control Module

PK/OR C13	OD Off Lamp Driver
OR/BK C5	OD Off Switch Sense

OD OFF Lamp
OD Off Switch

Transmission Control Module

Data Link Connector

94H38668 94I38669 94D38631 94E38632 94B38670 94C38671

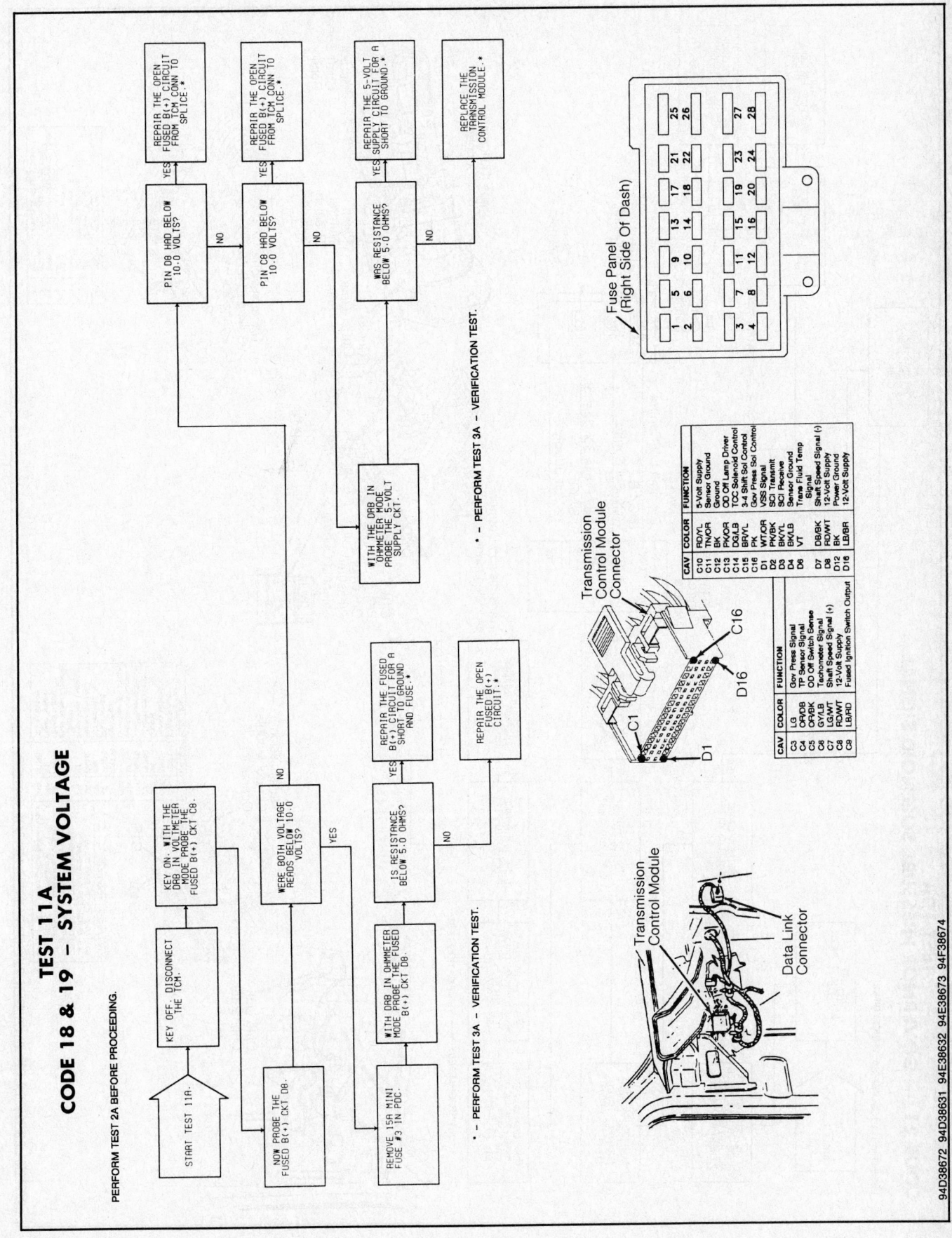

TEST 11A
CODE 18 & 19 – SYSTEM VOLTAGE

PERFORM TEST 2A BEFORE PROCEEDING.

START TEST 11A.

KEY OFF. DISCONNECT THE TCM.

KEY ON. WITH THE DRB IN VOLTMETER MODE PROBE THE FUSED B(+) CKT C8.

NOW PROBE THE FUSED B(+) CKT D8.

WERE BOTH VOLTAGE READS BELOW 10.0 VOLTS?

NO → PIN D8 HAD BELOW 10.0 VOLTS?
YES → REPAIR THE OPEN FUSED B(+) CIRCUIT FROM TCM CONN TO SPLICE.*

NO → PIN C8 HAD BELOW 10.0 VOLTS?
YES → REPAIR THE OPEN FUSED B(+) CIRCUIT FROM TCM CONN TO SPLICE.*

WAS RESISTANCE BELOW 5.0 OHMS?
YES → REPAIR THE 5-VOLT SUPPLY CIRCUIT FOR A SHORT TO GROUND.*
NO → REPLACE THE TRANSMISSION CONTROL MODULE.*

WITH THE DRB IN OHMMETER MODE PROBE THE 5-VOLT SUPPLY CKT.

* – PERFORM TEST 3A – VERIFICATION TEST.

YES → REMOVE 15A MINI FUSE #3 IN PDC.

WITH DRB IN OHMMETER MODE PROBE THE FUSED B(+) CKT D8.

IS RESISTANCE BELOW 5.0 OHMS?
YES → REPAIR THE FUSED B(+) CIRCUIT FOR A SHORT TO GROUND AND FUSE.*
NO → REPAIR THE OPEN FUSED B(+) CIRCUIT.*

* – PERFORM TEST 3A – VERIFICATION TEST.

Fuse Panel (Right Side Of Dash)

Transmission Control Module Connector

CAV	COLOR	FUNCTION
C10	RD/YL	5-Volt Supply
C11	TN/OR	Sensor Ground
C12	BK	Ground
C13	PK/OR	OD Off Lamp Driver
C14	DG/LB	TCC Solenoid Control
C15	BR/YL	3-4 Shift Sol Control
C16	PK	Gov Press Sol Control
D1	WT/OR	VSS Signal
D2	PK/BK	SCI Transmit
D3	BK/YL	SCI Receive
D4	BK/LB	Sensor Ground
D6	VT	Trans Fluid Temp Signal
D7	DB/BK	Shaft Speed Signal (-)
D8	RD/WT	12-Volt Supply
D12		Power Ground
D16	LB/BR	12-Volt Supply

CAV	COLOR	FUNCTION
C3	LG	Gov Press Signal
C4	OR/DB	TP Sensor Signal
C5	GY/BK	OD Off Switch Sense
C6	GY/LB	Tachometer Signal
C7	LG/WT	Shaft Speed Signal (+)
C8	RD/WT	12-Volt Supply
C9	LB/RD	Fused Ignition Switch Output

Transmission Control Module

Data Link Connector

94D38672 94D38631 94E38632 94E38673 94F38674

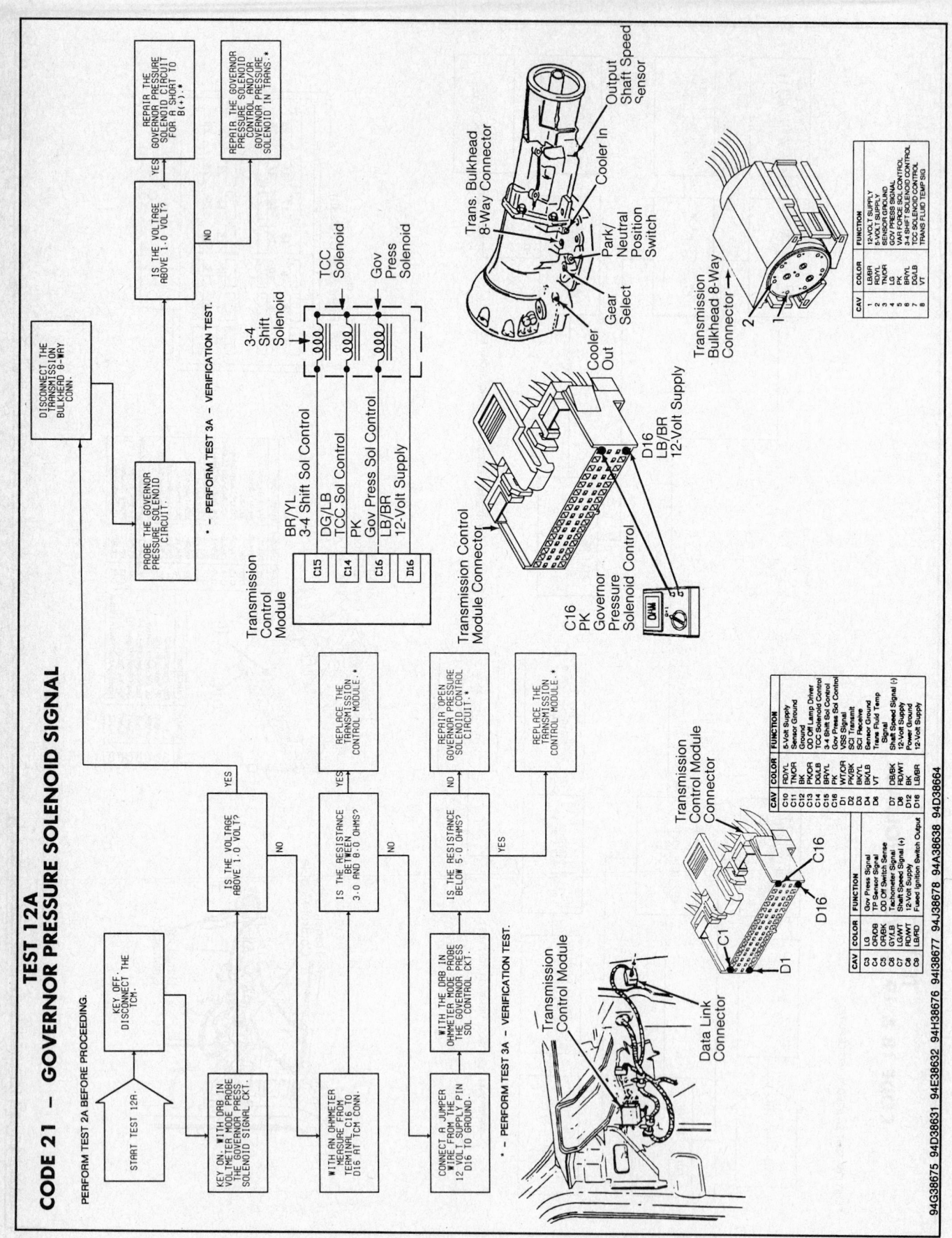

CODE 21 – GOVERNOR PRESSURE SOLENOID SIGNAL

TEST 12A

PERFORM TEST 2A BEFORE PROCEEDING.

START TEST 12A.

KEY OFF. DISCONNECT THE TCM.

KEY ON. WITH DRB IN VOLTMETER MODE PROBE THE GOVERNOR PRESS SOLENOID SIGNAL CKT.

IS THE VOLTAGE ABOVE 1.0 VOLT?

WITH AN OHMMETER MEASURE FROM TERMINAL C16 TO D16 AT TCM CONN.

IS THE RESISTANCE BETWEEN 3.0 AND 8.0 OHMS?

REPLACE THE TRANSMISSION CONTROL MODULE. *

CONNECT A JUMPER WIRE FROM THE 12 VOLT SUPPLY PIN D16 TO GROUND.

WITH THE DRB IN OHMMETER MODE PROBE THE GOVERNOR PRESS SOL CONTROL CKT.

IS THE RESISTANCE BELOW 5.0 OHMS?

REPAIR OPEN GOVERNOR PRESSURE SOLENOID CONTROL CIRCUIT. *

REPLACE THE TRANSMISSION CONTROL MODULE. *

* – PERFORM TEST 3A – VERIFICATION TEST.

DISCONNECT THE TRANSMISSION BULKHEAD 8-WAY CONN.

PROBE THE GOVERNOR PRESSURE SOLENOID CIRCUIT.

IS THE VOLTAGE ABOVE 1.0 VOLT?

REPAIR THE GOVERNOR PRESSURE SOLENOID CIRCUIT FOR A SHORT TO B(+). *

REPAIR THE GOVERNOR PRESSURE SOLENOID CONTROL AND/OR GOVERNOR PRESSURE SOLENOID IN TRANS. *

* – PERFORM TEST 3A – VERIFICATION TEST.

Transmission Control Module

3-4 Shift Sol Control BR/YL C15
TCC Sol Control DG/LB C14
Gov Press Sol Control PK C16
12-Volt Supply LB/BR D16

3-4 Shift Solenoid
TCC Solenoid
Gov Press Solenoid

Transmission Control Module Connector

C16 PK Governor Pressure Solenoid Control

D16 LB/BR 12-Volt Supply

Cooler Out

Trans. Bulkhead 8-Way Connector

Cooler In

Output Shaft Speed Sensor

Park/Neutral Position Switch

Gear Select

Transmission Bulkhead 8-Way Connector

CAV	COLOR	FUNCTION
1	LB/BR	12-VOLT SUPPLY
2	RD/YL	5-VOLT SUPPLY
3	TN/OR	SENSOR GROUND
4	LG	GOV PRESS SIGNAL
5	PK	VAR FORCE SOL CONTROL
6	BR/YL	3-4 SHIFT SOLENOID CONTROL
7	DG/LB	TCC SOLENOID CONTROL
8	VT	TRANS FLUID TEMP SIG

Transmission Control Module Connector

CAV	COLOR	FUNCTION
C10	RD/YL	5-Volt Supply
C11	TN/OR	Sensor Ground
C13	BK	Ground
C12	PK/OR	OD Off Lamp Driver
C14	DG/LB	TCC Solenoid Control
C15	BR/YL	3-4 Shift Sol Control
C16	PK	Gov Press Sol Control
D1	WT/OR	VSS Signal
D4	PK/BK	SCI Transmit
D3	BR/YL	SCI Receive
D5	BK/LB	Sensor Ground
D6	VT	Trans Fluid Temp
D7	DB/BK	Shaft Speed Signal (-)
D8	RD/WT	Shaft Speed Signal (+)
D12	BK	Power Ground
D16	LB/BR	12-Volt Supply

Transmission Control Module

CAV	COLOR	FUNCTION
C3	LG	Gov Press Signal
C4	OR/DB	TP Sensor Signal
C5	OR/BK	OD Off Switch Sense
C7	LG/WT	Tachometer Signal
C8	RD/WT	Shaft Speed Signal (+)
C9	BK	12-Volt Supply
C6	LB/RD	Fused Ignition Switch Output

Data Link Connector

Transmission Control Module

C16
D16
C1
D1

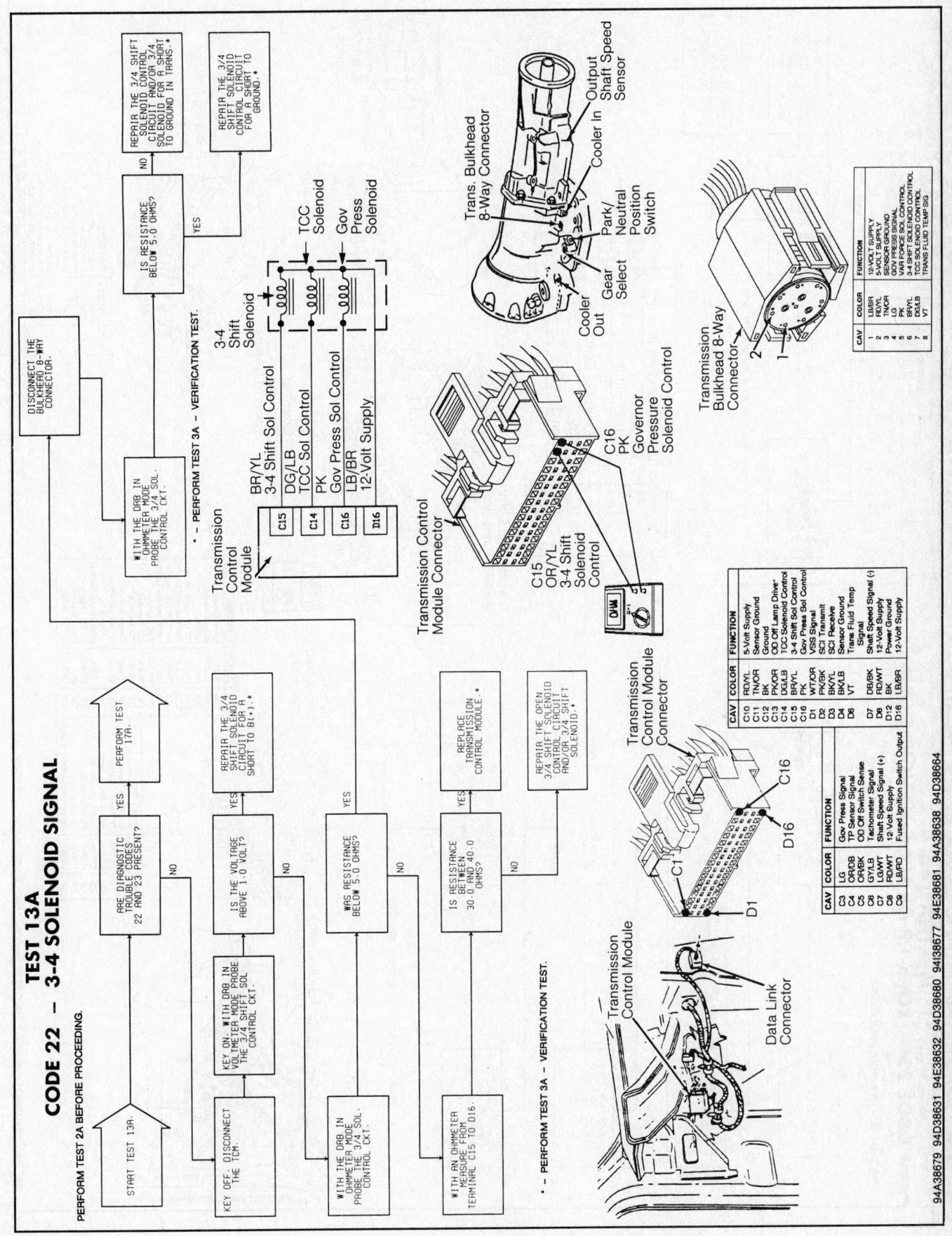

CODE 22 – 3-4 SOLENOID SIGNAL

TEST 13A

PERFORM TEST 2A BEFORE PROCEEDING.

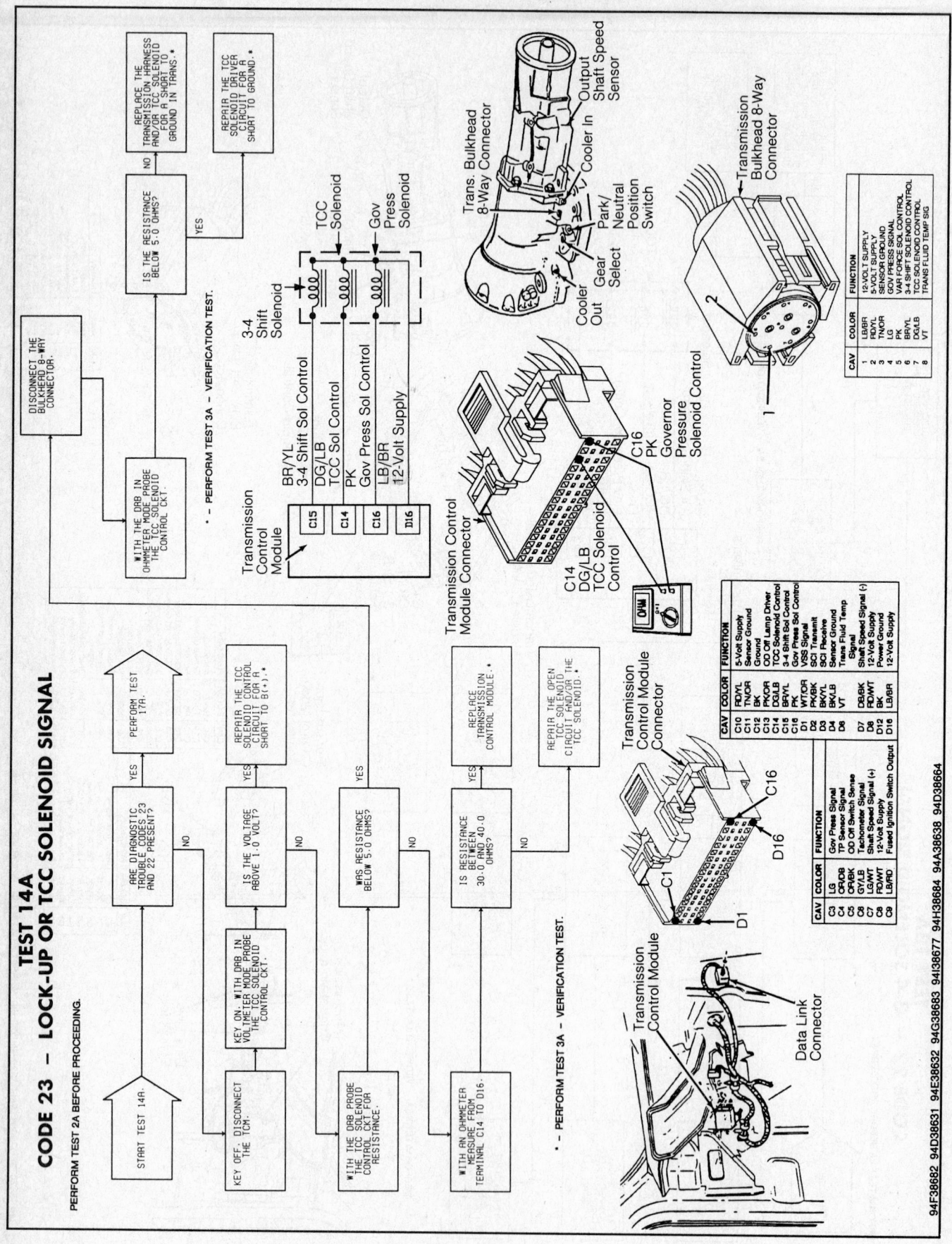

TEST 14A

CODE 23 – LOCK-UP OR TCC SOLENOID SIGNAL

PERFORM TEST 2A BEFORE PROCEEDING.

START TEST 14A.

KEY OFF. DISCONNECT THE TCM.

ARE DIAGNOSTIC TROUBLE CODES 23 AND 22 PRESENT?

YES → PERFORM TEST 17A.

NO ↓

KEY ON. WITH DRB IN VOLTMETER MODE PROBE THE TCC SOLENOID CONTROL CKT.

IS THE VOLTAGE ABOVE 1.0 VOLTS?

YES → REPAIR THE TCC SOLENOID CONTROL CIRCUIT FOR A SHORT TO B(+).*

NO ↓

WITH THE DRB PROBE THE TCC SOLENOID CONTROL CKT FOR RESISTANCE.

WAS RESISTANCE BELOW 5.0 OHMS?

YES → REPLACE TRANSMISSION CONTROL MODULE.*

NO ↓

WITH AN OHMMETER MEASURE FROM TERMINAL C14 TO D16.

IS RESISTANCE BETWEEN 30.0 AND 40.0 OHMS?

YES → REPAIR THE OPEN TCC SOLENOID CIRCUIT AND/OR THE TCC SOLENOID.*

NO

*– PERFORM TEST 3A – VERIFICATION TEST.

DISCONNECT THE BULKHEAD 8-WAY CONNECTOR.

WITH THE DRB IN OHMMETER MODE PROBE THE TCC SOLENOID CONTROL CKT.

IS THE RESISTANCE BELOW 5.0 OHMS?

NO → REPLACE THE TRANSMISSION HARNESS AND/OR TCC SOLENOID FOR A SHORT TO GROUND IN TRANS.*

YES → REPAIR THE TCC SOLENOID DRIVER CIRCUIT FOR A SHORT TO GROUND.*

*– PERFORM TEST 3A – VERIFICATION TEST.

3-4 Shift Solenoid

TCC Solenoid

Gov Press Solenoid

Transmission Control Module

C15	BR/YL	3-4 Shift Sol Control
C14	DG/LB	TCC Sol Control
C16	PK	Gov Press Sol Control
D16	LB/BR	12-Volt Supply

Output Shaft Speed Sensor

Cooler In

Trans. Bulkhead 8-Way Connector

Park/Neutral Position Switch

Cooler Out

Gear Select

Transmission Bulkhead 8-Way Connector

CAV	COLOR	FUNCTION
1	LB/BR	12-VOLT SUPPLY
2	RD/YL	5-VOLT SUPPLY
3	TN/OR	SENSOR GROUND
4	LG	GOV PRESS SIGNAL
5	PK	VAR FORCE SOL CONTROL
6	BR/YL	3-4 SHIFT SOLENOID CONTROL
7	DG/LB	TCC SOLENOID CONTROL
8	VT	TRANS FLUID TEMP SIG

Governor Pressure Solenoid Control

C16 PK

Transmission Control Module Connector

C14 DG/LB TCC Solenoid Control

CAV	COLOR	FUNCTION
C10	RD/YL	5-Volt Supply
C11	TN/OR	Sensor Ground
C12	BK	Ground
C13	PK/OR	OD Off Lamp Driver
C14	DG/LB	TCC Solenoid Control
C15	BR/YL	3-4 Shift Sol Control
C16	PK	Gov Press Sol Control
D1	WT/OR	OSS Signal
D4	PK/BK	SCI Transmit
D5	RD/YL	SCI Receive
D6	BK/LB	Sensor Ground
D7	VT	Trans Fluid Temp
D8	DB/BK	Shaft Speed Signal (–)
D12	RD/WT	12-Volt Supply
D16	BK	Power Ground
D16	LB/BR	12-Volt Supply

Transmission Control Module Connector

C16

D16

C1

D1

CAV	COLOR	FUNCTION
C4	LG	Gov Press Signal
C5	OR/DB	TP Sense Signal
C6	OR/BK	OD Off Switch Sense
C7	GY/LB	Tachometer Signal
C8	LG/WT	Shaft Speed Signal (+)
C8	RD/WT	12-Volt Supply
C9	LB/RD	Fused Ignition Switch Output

Transmission Control Module

Data Link Connector

94F38682 94D38631 94E38632 94G38683 94I38677 94H38684 94A38638 94D38664

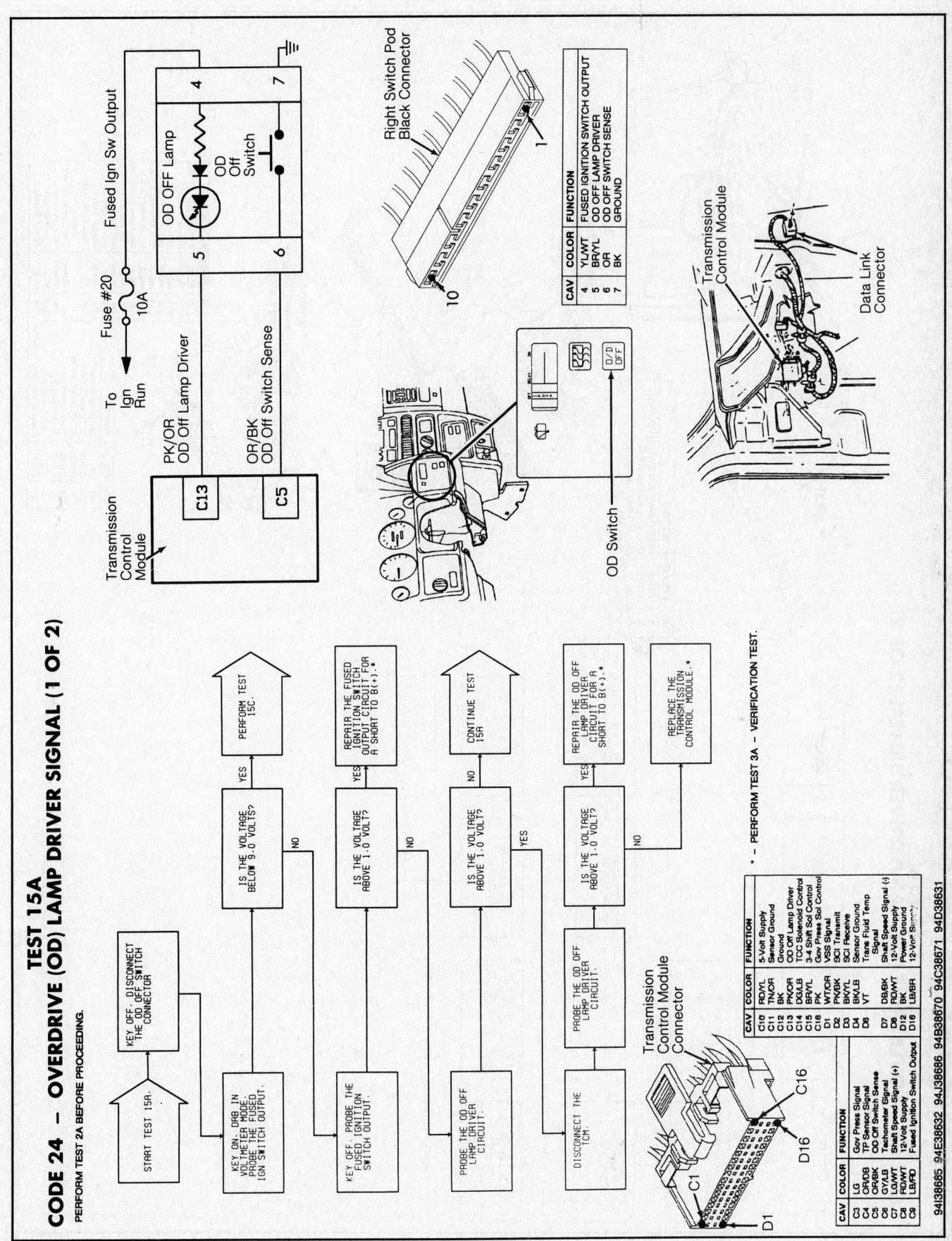

CODE 24 — OVERDRIVE (OD) LAMP DRIVER SIGNAL (1 OF 2)

TEST 15A

PERFORM TEST 2A BEFORE PROCEEDING.

Right Switch Pod Black Connector

CAV	COLOR	FUNCTION
4	YL/WT	FUSED IGNITION SWITCH OUTPUT
5	BR/YL	OD OFF LAMP DRIVER
6	OR	OD OFF SWITCH SENSE
7	BK	GROUND

Transmission Control Module

Data Link Connector

OD Switch

Transmission Control Module Connector

CAV	COLOR	FUNCTION
C10	RD/YL	5-Volt Supply
C11	TN/OR	Sensor Ground
C12	PK	Ground
C13	PK/OR	OD Off Lamp Driver
C14	DG/LB	TCC Solenoid Control
C15	BR/YL	3-4 Shift Sol Control
C16	PK	Gov Press Sol Control
D1	WT/OR	VSS Signal
D2	PK/BK	SCI Transmit
D3	BK/YL	SCI Receive
D4	BK/LB	Sensor Ground
D6	VT	Trans Fluid Temp
D7	DB/BK	Shaft Speed Signal (-)
D8	RD/WT	12-Volt Supply
D12	BK	Power Ground
D16	LB/BR	12-Volt Supply

94B38670 94C38671 94D38631
94I38685 94E38632 94J38686 94B38686

CAV	COLOR	FUNCTION
C3	LG	Gov Press Signal
C4	OR/DB	TP Sensor Signal
C5	OR/BK	OD Off Switch Sense
C6	GY/LB	Tachometer Signal
C7	LG/WT	Shaft Speed Signal (+)
C8	RD/WT	12-Volt Supply
C9	LB/RD	Fused Ignition Switch Output

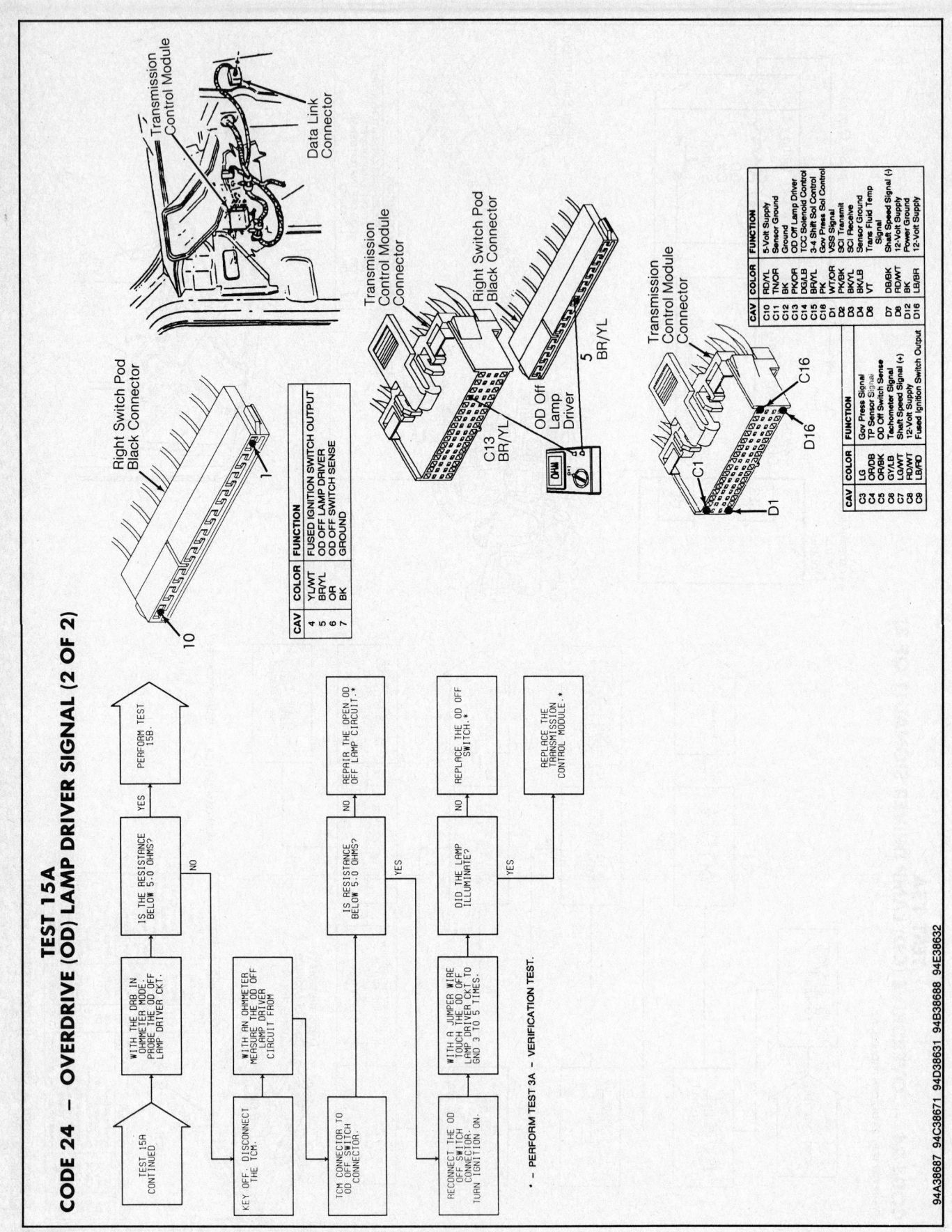

CODE 24 — OVERDRIVE (OD) LAMP DRIVER SIGNAL (2 OF 2)

TEST 15A

CAV	COLOR	FUNCTION
4	YL/WT	FUSED IGNITION SWITCH OUTPUT
5	BR/YL	OD OFF LAMP DRIVER
6	OR	OD OFF SWITCH SENSE
7	BK	GROUND

CAV	COLOR	FUNCTION
C10	RD/YL	5-Volt Supply
C11	TN/OR	Sensor Ground
C12	BK	Ground
C13	PK/OR	OD Off Lamp Driver
C14	DG/LB	TCC Solenoid Control
C15	BR/YL	3-4 Shift Sol Control
C16	PK	Gov Press Sol Control
D1	WT/OR	VSS Signal
D2	PK/BK	SCI Transmit
D3	BK/YL	SCI Receive
D4	BK/LB	Sensor Ground
D6	VT	Trans Fluid Temp Signal
D7	DB/BK	Shaft Speed Signal (+)
D8	RD/WT	12-Volt Supply
D12	BK	Power Ground
D16	LB/BR	12-Volt Supply

CAV	COLOR	FUNCTION
C3	LG	Gov Press Signal
C4	OR/DB	TP Sensor Signal
C5	OR/BK	OD Off Switch Sense
C7	GY/LB	Tachometer Signal
C8	LG/WT	Shaft Speed Signal (+)
C9	RD/WT	12-Volt Supply
C9	LB/RD	Fused Ignition Switch Output

* – PERFORM TEST 3A – VERIFICATION TEST.
* – PERFORM TEST 15B.

TEST 15A CONTINUED

WITH THE DRB IN OHMMETER MODE. PROBE THE OD OFF LAMP DRIVER CKT.

IS THE RESISTANCE BELOW 5.0 OHMS?

YES — PERFORM TEST 15B.

NO

KEY OFF. DISCONNECT THE TCM.

TCM CONNECTOR TO OD OFF SWITCH CONNECTOR.

WITH AN OHMMETER MEASURE THE OD OFF LAMP DRIVER CIRCUIT FROM

IS RESISTANCE BELOW 5.0 OHMS?

NO — REPAIR THE OPEN OD OFF LAMP CIRCUIT.*

YES

RECONNECT THE OD OFF SWITCH CONNECTOR. TURN IGNITION ON.

WITH A JUMPER WIRE TOUCH THE OD OFF LAMP DRIVER CKT TO GND 3 TO 5 TIMES.

DID THE LAMP ILLUMINATE?

NO — REPLACE THE OD OFF SWITCH.*

YES

REPLACE THE TRANSMISSION CONTROL MODULE.*

94A38687 94C38671 94D38631 94B38688 94E38632

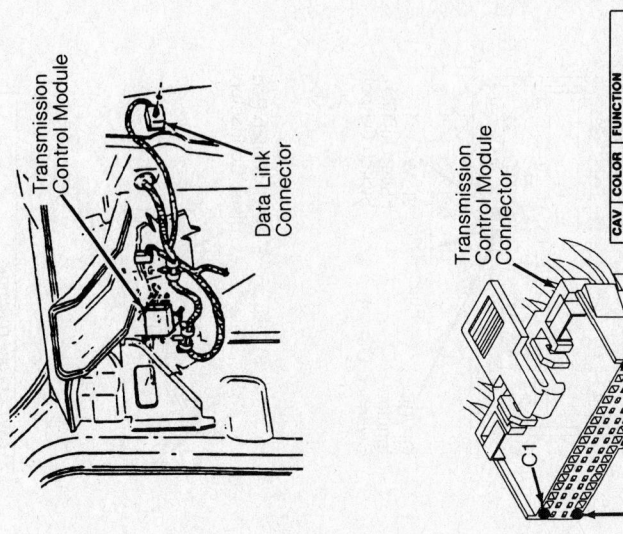

Transmission Control Module

Data Link Connector

Transmission Control Module Connector

CAV	COLOR	FUNCTION
C10	RD/YL	5-Volt Supply
C11	TN/OR	Sensor Ground
C12	BK	Ground
C13	PK/OR	OD Off Lamp Driver
C14	DG/LB	TCC Solenoid Control
C15	BR/YL	3-4 Shift Sol Control
C16	PK	Gov Press Sol Control
D1	WT/OR	VSS Signal
D2	PK/BK	SCI Transmit
D3	BK/YL	SCI Receive
D4	BK/LB	Sensor Ground
D6	VT	Trans Fluid Temp Signal
D7	DB/BK	Shaft Speed Signal (-)
D8	RD/WT	12-Volt Supply
D12	BK	Power Ground
D16	LB/BR	12-Volt Supply

CAV	COLOR	FUNCTION
C3	LG	Gov Press Signal
C4	OR/DB	TP Sensor Signal
C5	OR/BK	OD Off Switch Sense
C6	GY/LB	Tachometer Signal
C7	LG/WT	Shaft Speed Signal (+)
C8	RD/WT	12-Volt Supply
C9	LB/RD	Fused Ignition Switch Output

C16

D16

C1

D1

TEST 15B
CODE 24 – OVERDRIVE (OD) LAMP DRIVER SIGNAL

PERFORM TEST 15A BEFORE PROCEEDING.

START TEST 15B.

DISCONNECT THE TCM.

PROBE THE OD OFF LAMP DRIVER CIRCUIT.

IS THE RESISTANCE BELOW 5.0 OHMS?

YES → REPAIR THE OD OFF LAMP DRIVER CIRCUIT FOR A SHORT TO GROUND. *

NO → REPLACE THE TRANSMISSION CONTROL MODULE. *

* – PERFORM TEST 3A – VERIFICATION TEST.

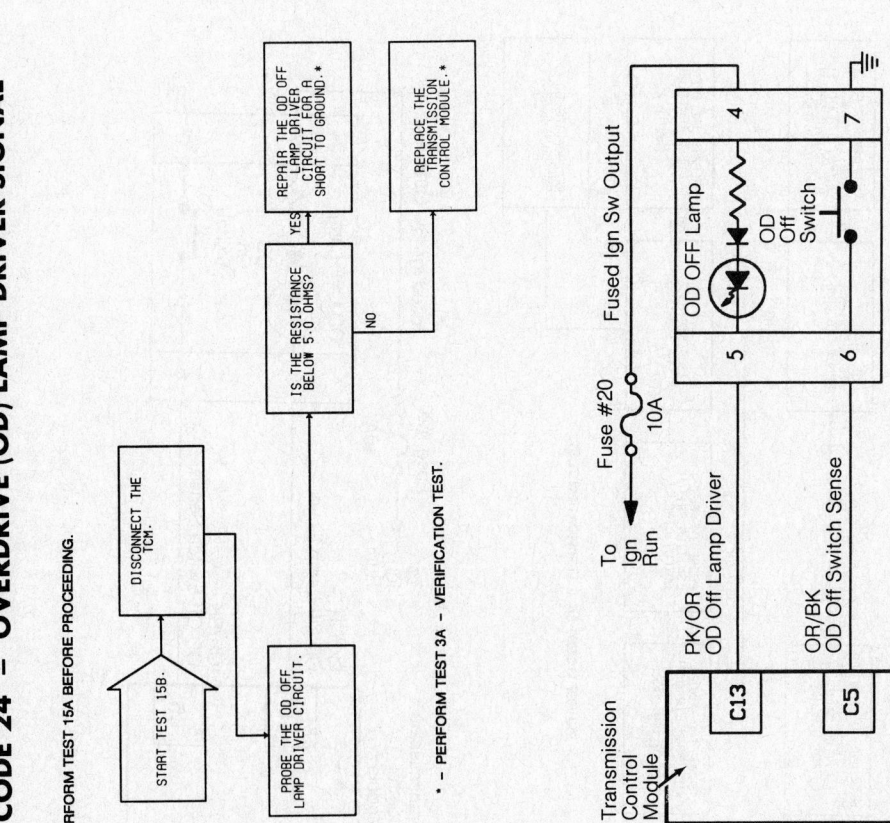

Fused Ign Sw Output

OD OFF Lamp

OD Off Switch

4

5

6

7

To Ign Run

Fuse #20 10A

PK/OR OD Off Lamp Driver

OR/BK OD Off Switch Sense

C13

C5

Transmission Control Module

94C38689 94J3686 94D38631 94E38632

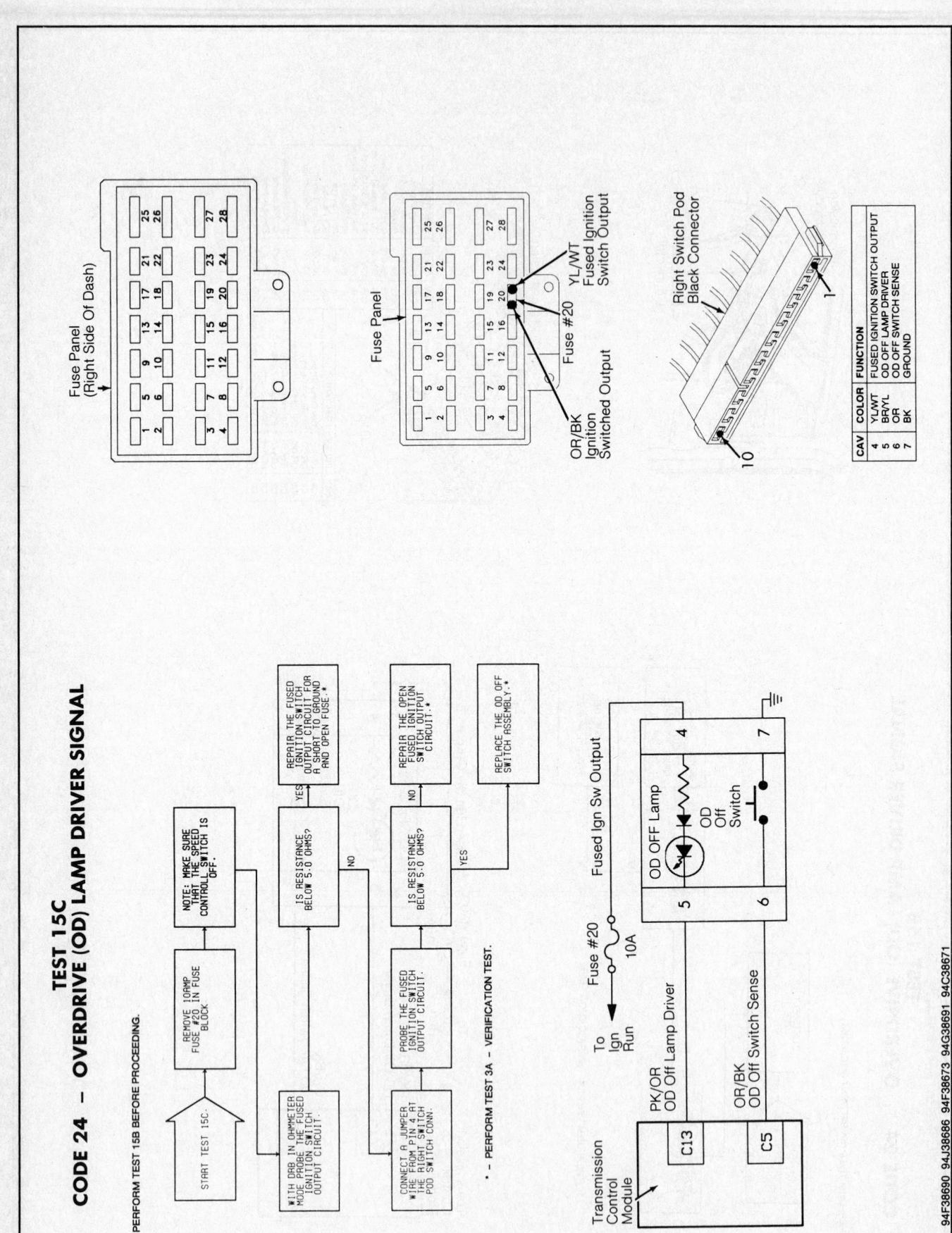

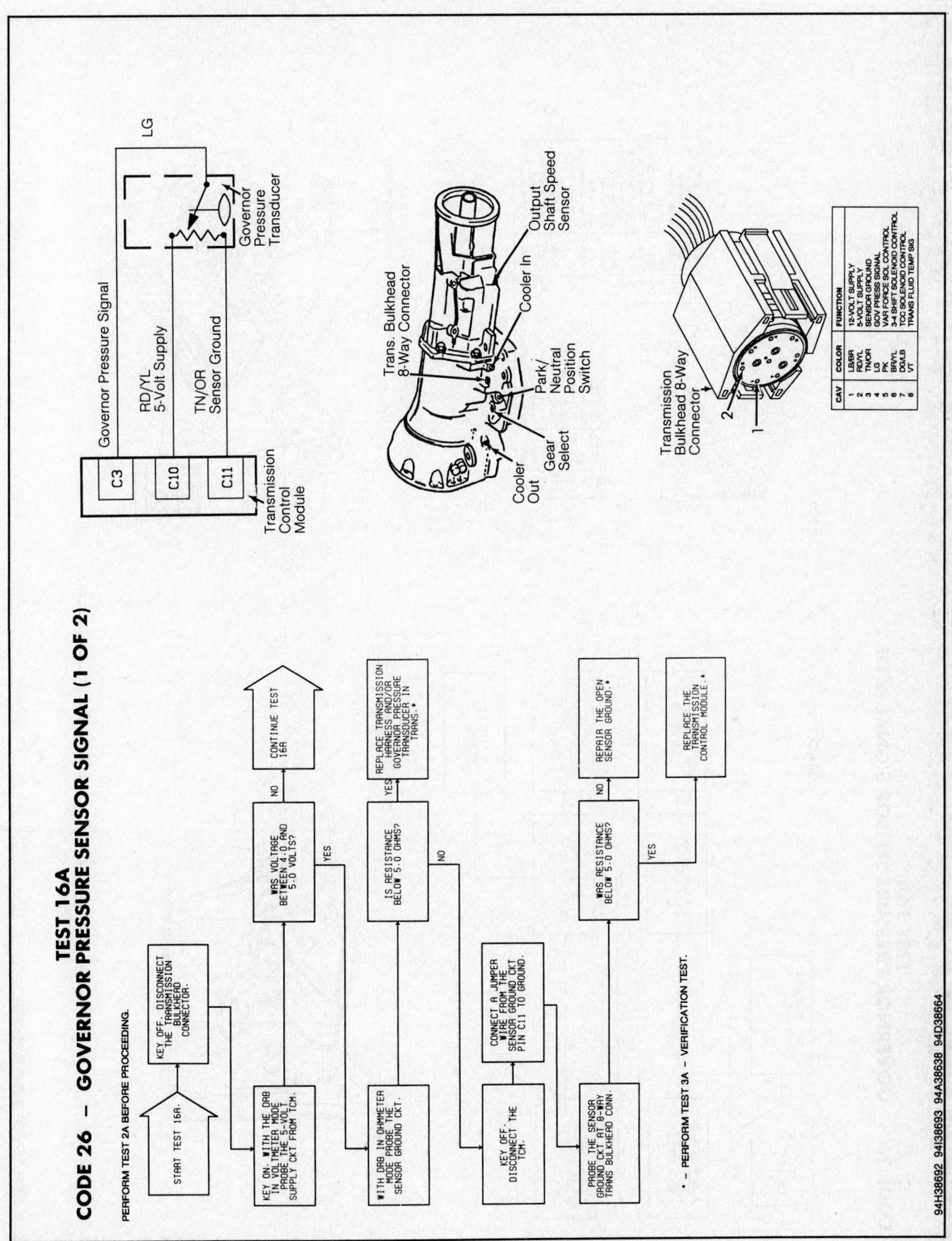

TEST 16A

CODE 26 – GOVERNOR PRESSURE SENSOR SIGNAL (1 OF 2)

PERFORM TEST 2A BEFORE PROCEEDING.

START TEST 16A.

KEY OFF. DISCONNECT THE TRANSMISSION BULKHEAD CONNECTOR.

KEY ON. WITH THE DRB IN VOLTMETER MODE PROBE THE 5-VOLT SUPPLY CKT FROM TCM.

WAS VOLTAGE BETWEEN 4.0 AND 5.0 VOLTS?

NO → CONTINUE TEST 16A

YES →

WITH DRB IN OHMMETER MODE PROBE THE SENSOR GROUND CKT.

IS RESISTANCE BELOW 5.0 OHMS?

YES → REPLACE TRANSMISSION GOVERNOR PRESSURE TRANSDUCER IN TRANS. *

NO →

KEY OFF. DISCONNECT THE TCM.

CONNECT A JUMPER WIRE FROM THE SENSOR GROUND CKT PIN C11 TO GROUND.

PROBE THE SENSOR GROUND CKT AT 8-WAY TRANS BULKHEAD CONN.

WAS RESISTANCE BELOW 5.0 OHMS?

NO → REPAIR THE OPEN SENSOR GROUND. *

YES → REPLACE THE TRANSMISSION CONTROL MODULE. *

* - PERFORM TEST 3A – VERIFICATION TEST.

Governor Pressure Signal

RD/YL 5-Volt Supply

TN/OR Sensor Ground

LG

Governor Pressure Transducer

C3 C10 C11

Transmission Control Module

Output Shaft Speed Sensor

Cooler In

Trans. Bulkhead 8-Way Connector

Park/Neutral Position Switch

Gear Select

Cooler Out

Transmission Bulkhead 8-Way Connector

2 1

CAV	COLOR	FUNCTION
1	LB/BR	12-VOLT SUPPLY
2	RD/YL	5-VOLT SUPPLY
3	TN/OR	SENSOR GROUND
4	LG	GOV PRESS SIGNAL
5	PK	VAR FORCE SOL CONTROL
6	BR/YL	3-4 SHIFT SOLENOID CONTROL
7	BK/LB	TCC SOLENOID CONTROL
8	VT	TRANS FLUID TEMP SIG

94H38692 94I38693 94A38638 94D38664

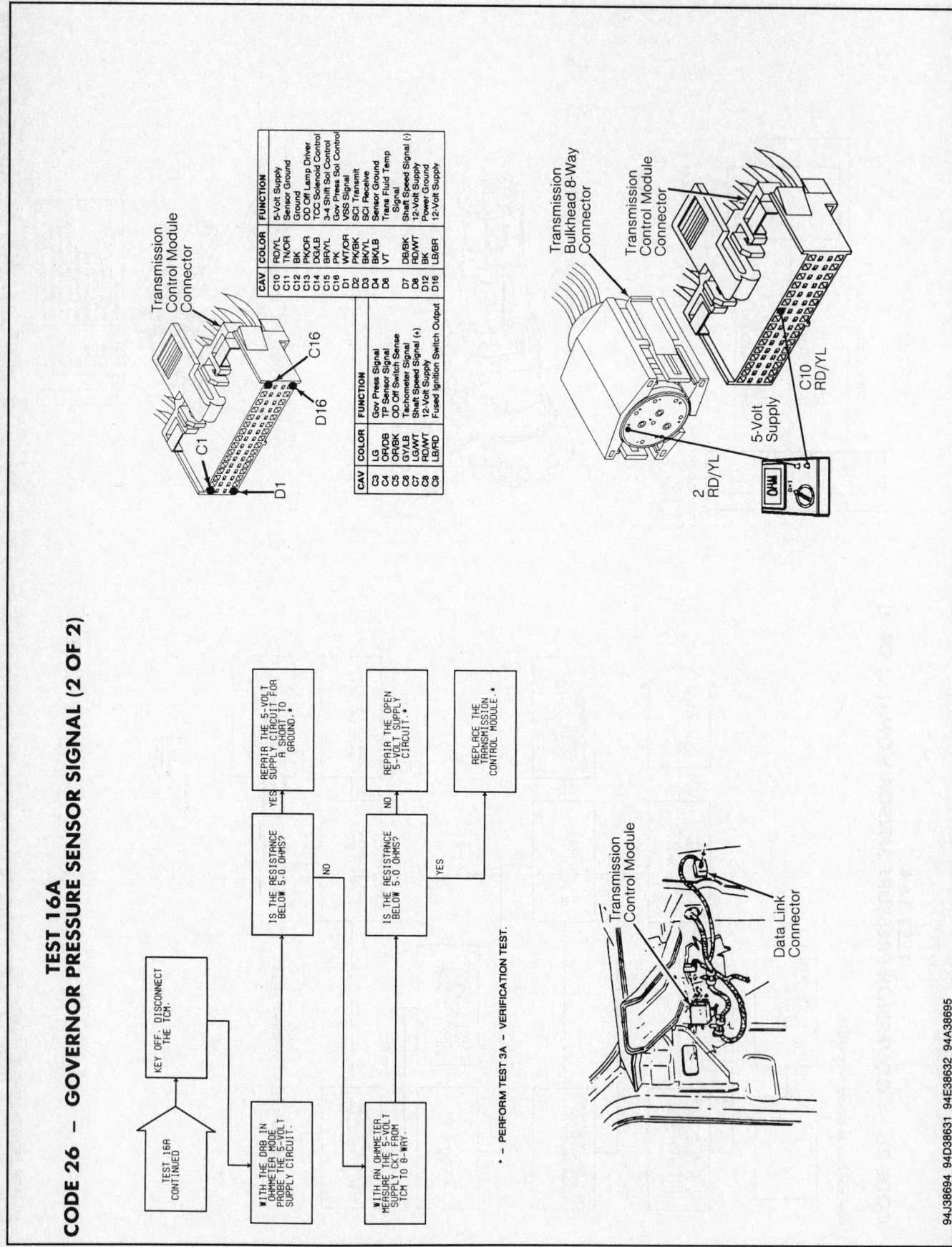

CODE 26 – GOVERNOR PRESSURE SENSOR SIGNAL (2 OF 2)

TEST 16A

Transmission Control Module Connector

CAV	COLOR	FUNCTION
C10	RD/YL	5-Volt Supply
C11	TN/OR	Sensor Ground
C12	BK	Ground
C13	PK/OR	OD Off Lamp Driver
C14	DG/LB	TCC Solenoid Control
C15	BR/YL	3-4 Shift Sol Control
C16	PK	Gov Press Sol Control
D1	WT/OR	VSS Signal
D2	PK/BK	SCI Transmit
D3	BK/YL	SCI Receive
D4	BK/LB	Sensor Ground
D6	VT	Trans Fluid Temp Signal
D7	DB/BK	Shaft Speed Signal (-)
D8	RD/WT	12-Volt Supply
D12	BK	Power Ground
D16	LB/BR	12-Volt Supply

CAV	COLOR	FUNCTION
C3	LG	Gov Press Signal
C4	OR/DB	TP Sensor Signal
C5	OR/BK	OD Off Switch Sense
C8	GY/LB	Tachometer Signal
C7	LG/WT	Shaft Speed Signal (+)
C8	RD/WT	12-Volt Supply
C9	LB/RD	Fused Ignition Switch Output

Transmission Bulkhead 8-Way Connector

Transmission Control Module Connector

C10 RD/YL

5-Volt Supply

2 RD/YL

Transmission Control Module

Data Link Connector

TEST 16A CONTINUED

KEY OFF. DISCONNECT THE TCM.

WITH THE DRB IN OHMMETER MODE PROBE THE 5-VOLT SUPPLY CIRCUIT.

IS THE RESISTANCE BELOW 5.0 OHMS?

YES → REPAIR THE 5-VOLT SUPPLY CIRCUIT FOR A SHORT TO GROUND. *

NO →

WITH AN OHMMETER MEASURE THE 5-VOLT SUPPLY CKT FROM TCM TO 8-WAY.

IS THE RESISTANCE BELOW 5.0 OHMS?

NO → REPAIR THE OPEN 5-VOLT SUPPLY CIRCUIT. *

YES → REPLACE THE TRANSMISSION CONTROL MODULE. *

* – PERFORM TEST 3A – VERIFICATION TEST.

94J38694 94D38631 94E38632 94A38695

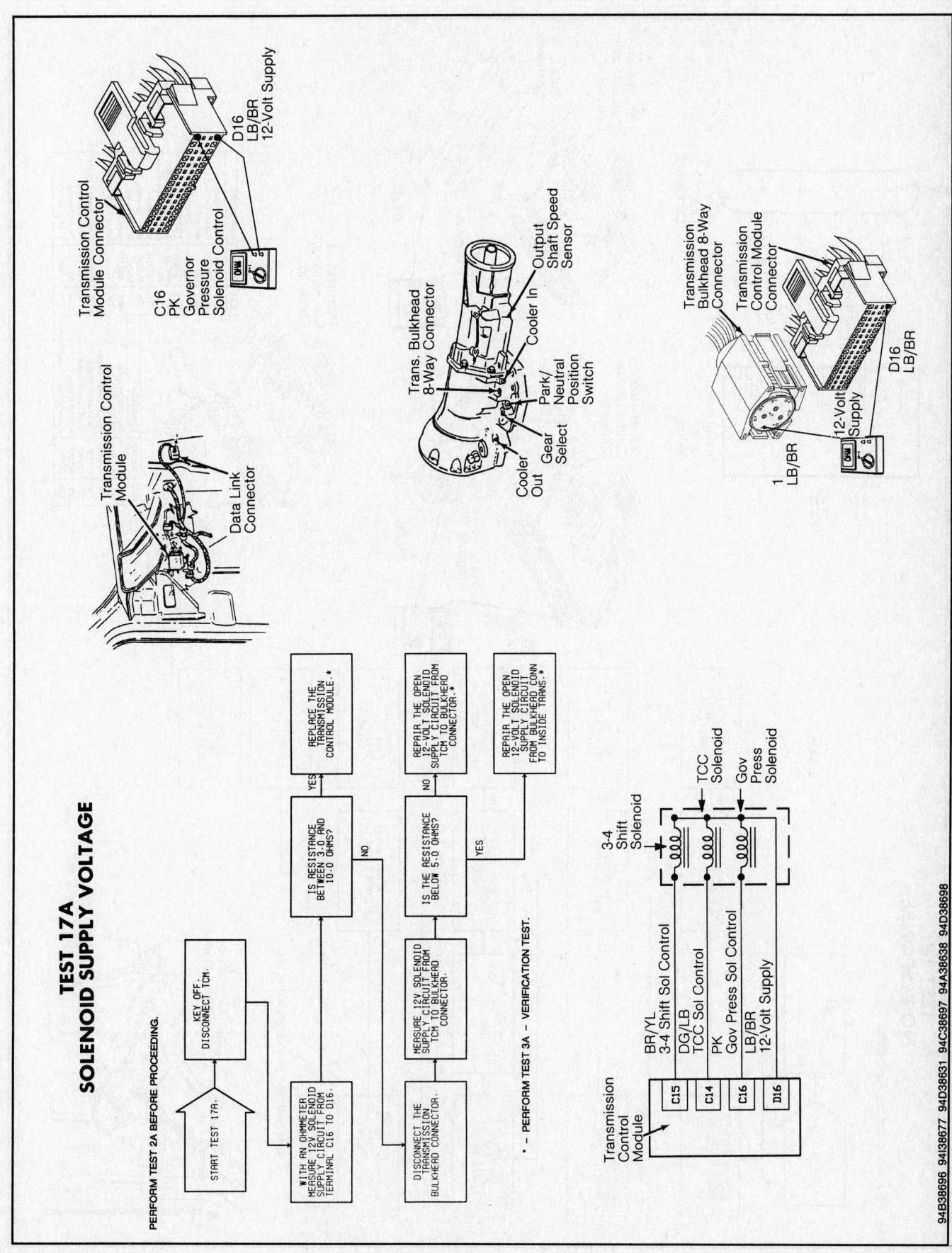

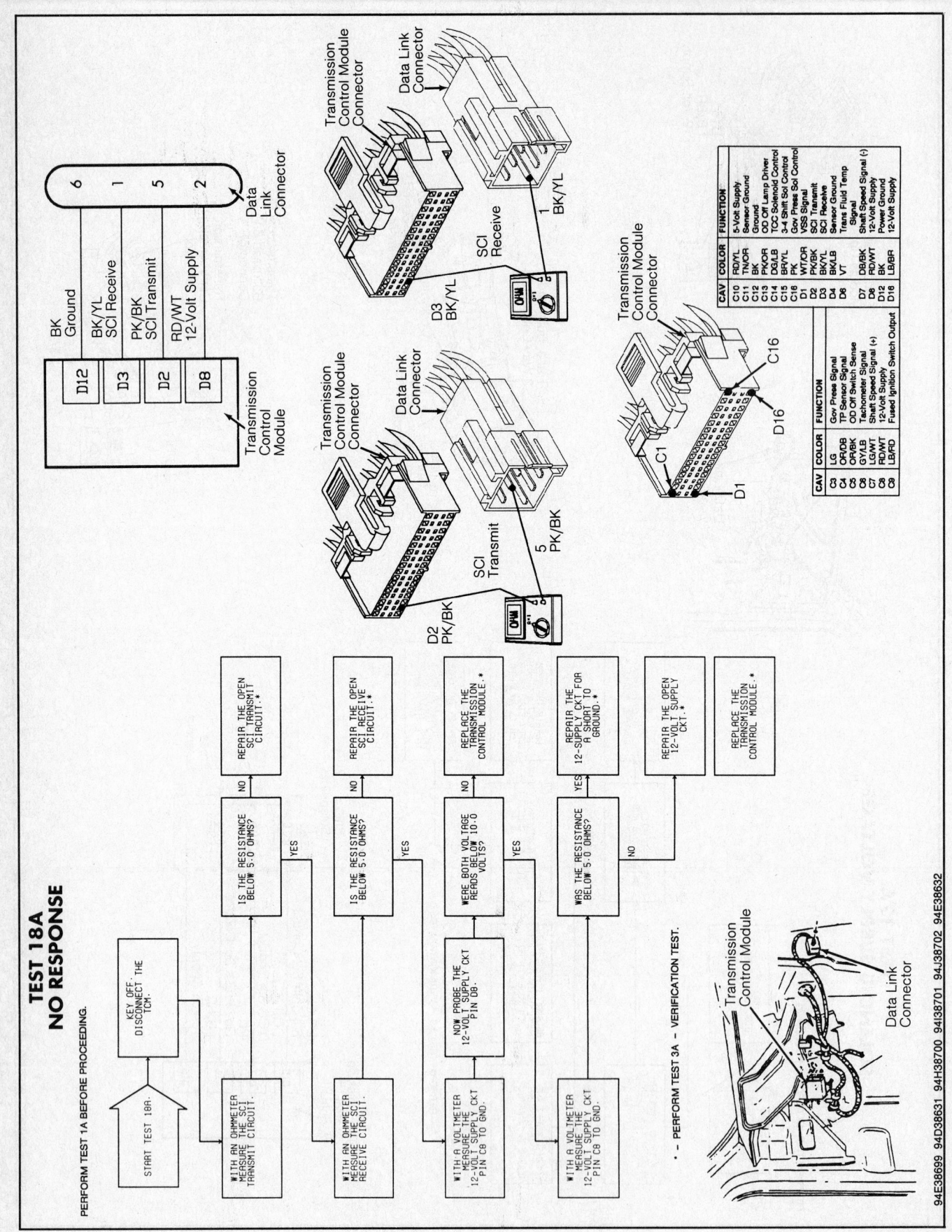

TEST 18A
NO RESPONSE

PERFORM TEST 1A BEFORE PROCEEDING.

START TEST 18A.

KEY OFF. DISCONNECT THE TCM.

WITH AN OHMMETER MEASURE THE SCI TRANSMIT CIRCUIT.

IS THE RESISTANCE BELOW 5.0 OHMS? — NO → REPAIR THE OPEN SCI TRANSMIT CIRCUIT.*

YES

WITH AN OHMMETER MEASURE THE SCI RECEIVE CIRCUIT.

IS THE RESISTANCE BELOW 5.0 OHMS? — NO → REPAIR THE OPEN SCI RECEIVE CIRCUIT.*

YES

WITH A VOLTMETER MEASURE THE 12-VOLT SUPPLY CKT PIN C8 TO GND.

NOW PROBE THE 12-VOLT SUPPLY CKT PIN D8.

WERE BOTH VOLTAGE READS BELOW 10.0 VOLTS? — NO → REPLACE THE TRANSMISSION CONTROL MODULE.*

YES

WITH A VOLTMETER MEASURE THE 12-VOLT SUPPLY CKT PIN C8 TO GND.

WAS THE RESISTANCE BELOW 5.0 OHMS? — YES → REPAIR THE 12-SUPPLY CKT FOR A SHORT TO GROUND.*

NO

REPAIR THE OPEN 12-VOLT SUPPLY CKT.*

REPLACE THE TRANSMISSION CONTROL MODULE.*

* - PERFORM TEST 3A - VERIFICATION TEST.

94E38699 94D38631 94H38700 94J38701 94J38702 94E38632

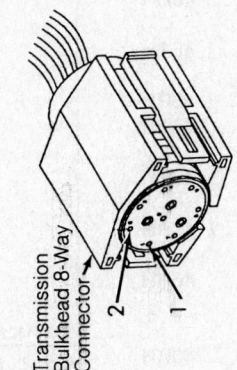

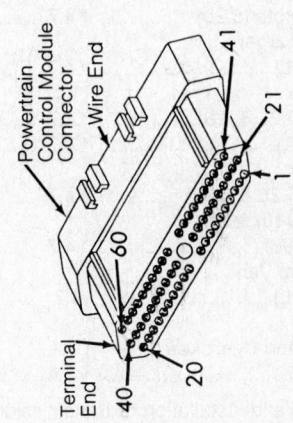

TEST 19A
STORED DIAGNOSTIC TROUBLE CODES

PERFORM TEST 2A BEFORE PROCEEDING.

This test verifies that connectors, terminals, and circuits are intact and are fully representative for the vehicle operation. This will verify the above criteria unique to the specific connector that is stored.

Perform the following tasks without disconnecting the actual connector from the component if possible. If you must disconnect any connector, make sure when you reconnect it, that it is secured properly. Misconnected connectors may cause transmission problems.

Perform the verification according to the "STORED CODE".

CODE	TCM 32-WAY CONN.	BULKHEAD 8-WAY	OTHER
CODE 11	C6	NA	PCM, Terminal 43
CODE 12	C7, D7	NA	Output shaft connector
CODE 13	D1	NA	Vehicle speed sensor, PCM Terminal 47
CODE 14	C3, C11	3, 4	NA
CODE 15	C4, D4, C10	2	TPS, PCM terminals 4, 6 & 22
CODE 16	C11, D6	3, 8	NA
CODE 17	C5	NA	OD off switch
CODE 18	C10	2, 3	NA
CODE 19	C10	2, 3	NA
CODE 21	C16	1, 5	NA
CODE 22	C15, D16	1, 6	NA
CODE 23	C14, D16	1, 7	NA
CODE 24	C13	NA	OD off switch
CODE 25			Replace TCM
CODE 26	C10	2	NA

94A38703 94B38704 94C38705 94D38706

AUTOMATIC TRANSMISSIONS
Chrysler 46RH & 47RH

APPLICATION & LABOR TIMES

APPLICATION & LABOR TIMES

Vehicle Application	Labor Times [1] R & I	[2] Overhaul	Trans. Model
Dodge			
1993-94 Dakota (5.2L)	[3] 4.7	8.5	46RH
1993 Ramcharger (5.2L & 5.9L)	[4] 4.7	8.5	46RH
1993 Pickup			
Gasoline (5.2L & 5.9L)	[4] 4.7	8.5	46RH
Diesel (5.9L)	[4] 4.7	8.5	[5] 46RH
1994 Pickup			
Gasoline (5.2L & 5.9L)	[4] 4.7	8.5	46RH
Gasoline (V10) & Diesel (5.9L)	[4] 4.7	8.5	47RH
1993-94 Ram Van (5.2L & 5.9L)	4.7	8.5	46RH
Jeep			
1993-94 Grand Cherokee (5.2L)	[6] 3.4	8.5	46RH

[1] – Removal and installation of transmission from vehicle chassis.
[2] – Bench overhaul time for transmission. DOES NOT include removal and installation.
[3] – Add 4.4 hrs. with 4WD.
[4] – Add 2.1 hrs. with 4WD.
[5] – Diesel models use a 46RH heavy-duty model.
[6] – Add .9 hr. with 4WD.

IDENTIFICATION

Transmission identification numbers are stamped on left side of transmission case, near oil pan flange. *See Fig. 2.* Identification numbers may be required when ordering replacement components. Note that transmission components may not be interchangeable and identification number is required to ensure proper component application.

NOTE: Selective sized snap rings and thrust washers may be needed to set and adjust clearances. For sizes and availability, refer to manufacturer's parts department, and reference transmission model and identification number.

NOTE: Overdrive unit on rear of transmission is disassembled and serviced as a separate unit. See OVERDRIVE UNIT DISASSEMBLY, OVERDRIVE UNIT COMPONENT DISASSEMBLY & REASSEMBLY and OVERDRIVE UNIT REASSEMBLY in this article.

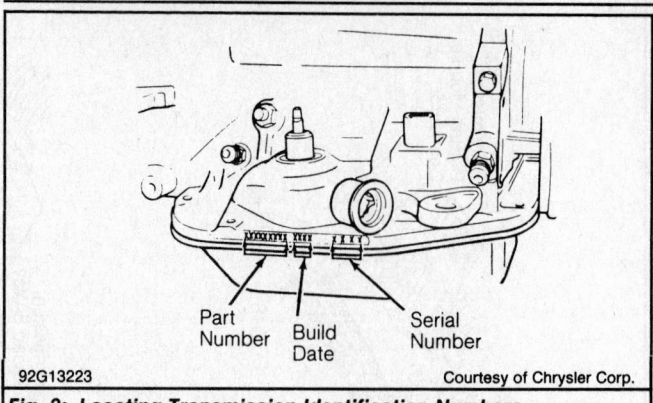

Fig. 2: Locating Transmission Identification Numbers

Courtesy of Chrysler Corp.

DESCRIPTION & OPERATION

Transmission is a fully automatic 3-speed transmission with an overdrive unit attached to rear of transmission. The 1st through 3rd gears are provided by clutches, bands, overrunning clutch and planetary gear set. The overdrive or 4th gear is provided by overdrive clutch, direct clutch, planetary gears and overrunning clutch in overdrive unit. Transmission contains front and rear bands, front clutch, rear clutch and overrunning clutch. The overdrive unit contains overdrive clutch, direct clutch and overrunning clutch. *See Fig. 1.*

Overdrive or 4th gear operation is controlled by a manually operated overdrive switch on the instrument panel. Overdrive switch is in the electrical circuit with overdrive solenoid on the valve body and Powertrain Control Module (PCM). Transmission will not shift into overdrive if switch is not in the ON position. Torque converter lock-up is activated when the PCM provides voltage to lock-up solenoid located on the valve body.

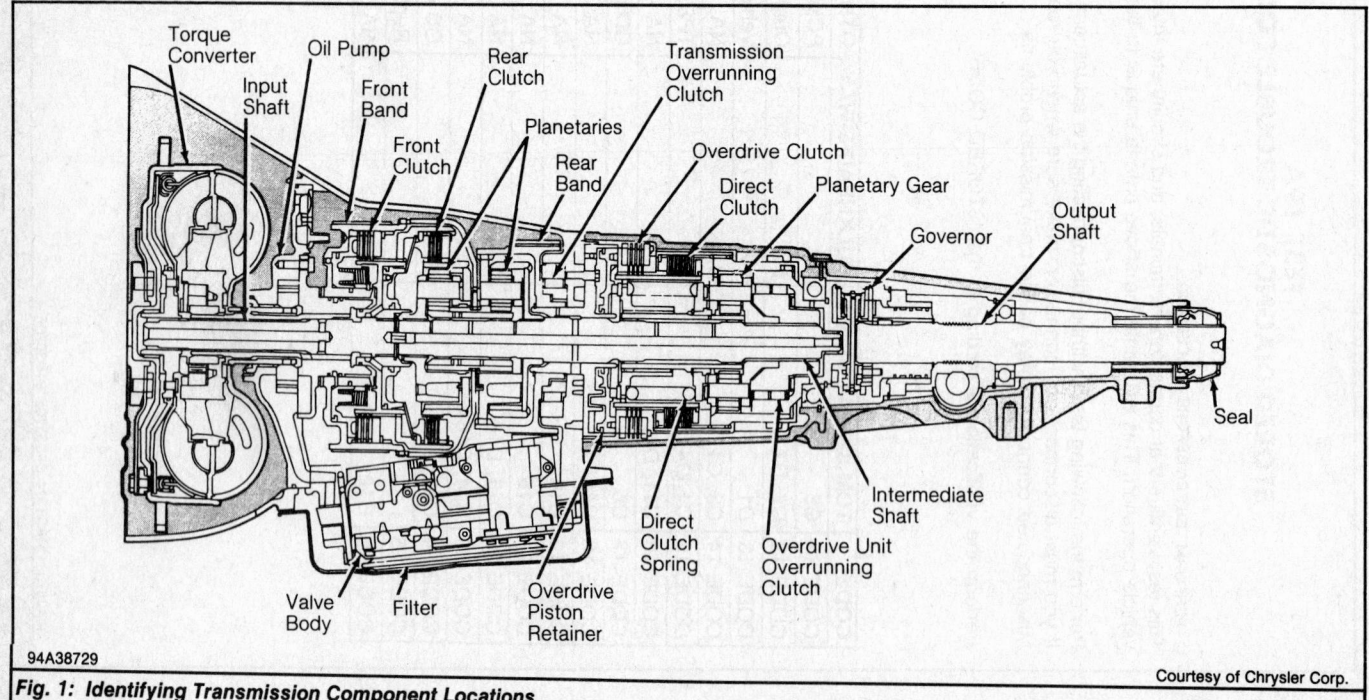

Fig. 1: Identifying Transmission Component Locations

Courtesy of Chrysler Corp.

On 1993 Pickup applications with diesel engine, overdrive or 4th gear operation is also controlled by engine coolant temperature and transmission fluid temperature switches. Engine coolant temperature switch prevents transmission from shifting into overdrive or 4th gear when engine coolant temperature is less than 65°F (18°C). Transmission fluid temperature switch will either downshift transmission to 3rd gear or prevent a 3-4 upshift when transmission fluid temperature exceeds 270-275°F (132-135°C). Transmission fluid temperature switch is located in oil cooler outlet line, near the transmission case.

On 1994 Pickup applications with diesel engine and gasoline models with special auxiliary transmission oil cooler, overdrive or 4th gear operation and torque converter lock-up are controlled by transmission fluid temperature sensor. Transmission fluid temperature sensor is located in oil cooler outlet line, near the transmission case. Transmission fluid temperature sensor monitors transmission fluid temperature and is in the circuit with the overdrive and lock-up solenoids on the valve body and the Powertrain Control Module (PCM).

Transmission fluid temperature sensor prevents overdrive or 4th gear operation when transmission fluid temperature is less than 60°F (15°C). Transmission fluid temperature sensor prevents torque converter lock-up operation when transmission fluid temperature is less than 70°F (21°C). Transmission fluid temperature sensor will either downshift transmission to 3rd gear or prevent a 3-4 upshift when transmission fluid temperature exceeds 270-275°F (132-135°C).

LUBRICATION & ADJUSTMENTS

NOTE: See appropriate AUTOMATIC TRANSMISSION SERVICING article in TRANSMISSION SERVICING.

TROUBLE SHOOTING

Transmission malfunctions may be caused by poor engine performance, improper adjustments or failure of hydraulic, mechanical or electronic components. Always begin by checking fluid level, fluid condition, shift linkage or cable adjustment and throttle valve cable adjustment. Perform road test to determine if problem has been corrected. If problem still exists, several tests must be performed on transmission. See TESTING in this article.

TRANSMISSION SYMPTOM DIAGNOSIS

NOTE: The shift from Neutral to Reverse is normally quite firm, as rear servo pressure can approach 300 psi (21 kg/cm²). DO NOT confuse a firm engagement with a harsh engagement.

Buzzing Noise
- Aerated fluid
- Defective overrunning clutch
- Low fluid level
- Valve body malfunction or leakage

Delayed Engagement From Neutral To Drive Or Reverse
- Damaged clutch, band or servo
- Damaged oil pump components
- Damaged or worn reaction shaft seal rings
- Defective governor
- Engine idle speed too low
- Improper rear band adjustment
- Incorrect shift linkage or cable adjustment
- Low fluid level
- Low hydraulic pressure
- Restricted filter assembly

Drags Or Locks Up
- Defective band, band linkage or servo
- Defective planetary or overrunning clutch
- Dragging clutch
- Improper band adjustment

Fluid Blows Out Filler Tube
- Aerated fluid
- Defective rear servo
- High fluid level
- Oil cooler or lines restricted
- Restricted breather vent in oil pump
- Restricted filter assembly
- Valve in valve body sticking

Growling, Grating Or Scraping Noise
- Defective clutch or governor support
- Defective oil pump or output shaft bearings/bushings
- Defective planetary or overrunning clutch
- Improper band adjustment

Harsh Engagement From Neutral To Drive Or Reverse
- Damaged clutch, band or planetary components
- Damaged or worn accumulator components
- Defective torque converter lock-up
- Engine idle speed too high
- Improper band adjustment
- Improper throttle valve cable adjustment
- Incorrect hydraulic pressure

No Forward Gear In Any Position (Reverse Is Okay)
- Defective overrunning clutch
- Incorrect shift linkage or cable adjustment
- Input shaft seal rings worn or damaged
- Low fluid level
- Rear clutch defective
- Valve body malfunction or leakage

No Kickdown Or Normal Downshift
- Defective clutch or servo
- Defective front servo, band or linkage
- Improper front band adjustment
- Improper hydraulic pressure
- Improper throttle valve cable adjustment
- Incorrect shift linkage or cable adjustment

No Low Gear (Moves In 2nd & 3rd Gears Only)
- Front band linkage binding
- Front servo binding in bore
- Governor partially stuck open
- Improper throttle valve cable adjustment
- Incorrect shift linkage or cable adjustment
- Valve body malfunction or leakage

No Reverse
- Improper rear band adjustment
- Incorrect shift linkage or cable adjustment
- Rear servo or front clutch malfunction
- Valve body malfunction or leakage

Shifts Delayed Or Erratic
- Aerated fluid
- Defective clutch or servo
- Governor support seal rings broken or worn
- Improper fluid level
- Improper front band adjustment causing harsh 1-2 shift
- Improper throttle valve cable adjustment or binding components
- Incorrect shift linkage or cable adjustment
- Restricted filter assembly

Slips In All Forward Gears
- Aerated fluid
- Damaged or worn accumulator components
- Defective clutch or servo
- Defective overrunning clutch
- Improper throttle valve cable adjustment or binding components
- Incorrect shift linkage or cable adjustment
- Low fluid level
- Low hydraulic pressure

Slips In Low Gear In Drive But Not In Low Gear (1 Position)
- Defective overrunning clutch

Slips In Reverse Only
- Aerated fluid
- Binding band linkage
- Defective front clutch, rear servo or rear band
- Improper rear band adjustment
- Incorrect shift linkage or cable adjustment
- Low fluid level
- Low hydraulic pressure

Sluggish Acceleration Or
Excessive Throttle To Maintain Speed
- Defective torque converter clutch
- Improper throttle valve cable adjustment
- Incorrect shift linkage or cable adjustment
- Poor engine performance
- Slipping clutches

Torque Converter Locks Up In 2nd And/Or 3rd Gear
- Defective lock-up solenoid, relay or wiring

Transmission Overheats
- Improper band adjustment
- Improper clutch clearance
- Low fluid level
- Restricted oil cooler
- Switch valve in valve body sticking

Vehicle Moves In Neutral
- Clutch dragging
- Incorrect shift linkage or cable adjustment
- Torque converter lock-up clutch dragging
- Valve body malfunction or leakage

Vehicle Moves In 2nd Or 3rd Gear &
Abruptly Downshifts To Low
- Governor sticking
- Valve body malfunction or leakage

Vehicle Will Not Move In Any Gear
- Defective oil pump
- Incorrect shift linkage or cable adjustment
- Internal transmission component failure
- Low fluid level
- Valve body malfunction or leakage

Will Not Upshift From Low Gear
- Defective clutch or servo
- Defective oil pump, seal rings or valve body
- Governor stuck closed
- Improper front band adjustment
- Improper throttle valve cable adjustment
- Incorrect shift linkage or cable adjustment

1st & Reverse Gears Only
- Defective or sticking governor

OVERDRIVE UNIT SYMPTOM DIAGNOSIS

Delayed 3-4 Upshift
- Defective overdrive clutch
- Defective overdrive solenoid or wiring
- Low fluid level
- Overdrive clutch bleed orifice restricted
- Overdrive piston thrust plate too thin
- Throttle position sensor defective

No Reverse Or Slips In Reverse
- Defective front clutch
- Direct clutch components
- Improper rear band adjustment
- Overdrive thrust bearing failure

No 1-2 Or 2-3 Upshift (Has Low & Reverse)
- Defective or loose governor

No 3-4 Upshift
- Damaged park/neutral switch or wiring causing loss of park/neutral input to PCM
- Defective engine coolant temp. sensor, transmission fluid temp. sensor or switches (if equipped) or vehicle speed sensor
- Defective overdrive solenoid or wiring circuit
- Defective overdrive switch, wiring circuit or fuse
- Defective Powertrain Control Module (PCM)
- Low hydraulic pressure
- Overdrive piston seals damaged or wrong spacer
- Overdrive solenoid supply orifice in valve body restricted
- Overdrive switch in OFF position

No 4-3 Downshift
- Defective engine coolant temp. sensor, transmission fluid temp. sensor or switches (if equipped) or vehicle speed sensor
- Defective Powertrain Control Module (PCM)
- Defective wiring or connections
- Defective 3-4 shift valve, shuttle valve, timing valve or accumulator
- Lock-up solenoid not venting
- Overdrive solenoid not venting
- Throttle position sensor faulty

No 4-3 Downshift With Overdrive Switch In OFF Position
- Defective overdrive solenoid wiring or connections
- Defective overdrive switch wiring
- Defective Powertrain Control Module
- Overdrive or lock-up solenoid not venting

Noisy Operation In 4th Gear Only
- Defective output shaft bearings
- Overdrive clutch discs, plates or snap rings damaged
- Overdrive piston improperly installed or defective
- Overrunning clutch rollers worn
- Planetary gears worn or damaged
- Planetary thrust bearing improperly installed or defective

Slips In 4th Gear
- Defective overdrive clutch, overdrive clutch piston or seal
- Defective thrust bearing
- Defective 3-4 shift valve, timing valve or accumulator
- Low fluid level
- Overdrive piston retainer bleed orifice defective

3-4 Upshift Occurs Before Completing 2-3 Upshift
- Defective coolant temperature sensor or throttle position sensor
- Defective Powertrain Control Module (PCM)
- Loose overdrive solenoid wiring connections or faulty wiring
- Overdrive solenoid faulty
- Valve body malfunction

ELECTRONIC TESTING

TORQUE CONVERTER CLUTCH
(ELECTRONIC LOCK-UP)

See CHRYSLER ELECTRONIC CONTROLS article in AUTOMATIC TRANSMISSIONS for information on torque converter clutch testing and diagnosis.

TESTING

ROAD TEST

1) Ensure shift linkage/cable and throttle valve cable are properly adjusted. See appropriate AUTOMATIC TRANSMISSION SERVICING article in TRANSMISSION SERVICING. Ensure fluid level and condition are okay. Add Mopar ATF Plus Type 7176 fluid and adjust control cables or linkages (if necessary).

2) Ensure all electrical connections on transmission and overdrive switch are okay. Turn overdrive switch to the ON position. Road test vehicle and operate transmission in each gear position. Observe engine performance during road test. A poorly tuned engine will not allow an accurate analysis of transmission operation.

CLUTCH & BAND APPLICATION [1]

Gearshift Position	Elements In Use
"D" (Drive)	
1st Gear	Rear Clutch, Transmission Overrunning Clutch, Overdrive Unit Direct & Overrunning Clutch
2nd Gear	Front Band, Rear Clutch, Overdrive Unit Direct & Overrunning Clutch
3rd Gear	Front Clutch, Rear Clutch, Overdrive Unit Direct & Overrunning Clutch
4th Gear	Front Clutch, Rear Clutch & Overdrive Unit Overdrive Clutch
"2" (Second)	
1st Gear	Rear Clutch, Transmission Overrunning Clutch, Overdrive Unit Direct & Overrunning Clutch
2nd Gear	Front Band, Rear Clutch, Overdrive Unit Direct & Overrunning Clutch
"1" (Low)	
1st Gear	Rear Clutch, Rear Band, Transmission Overrunning Clutch, Overdrive Unit Direct & Overrunning Clutch
"R" (Reverse)	Front Clutch, Rear Band & Overdrive Unit Direct Clutch
"N" Or "P" (Neutral Or Park)	All Clutches & Bands Released Or Ineffective

[1] – Transmission contains front and rear bands, front clutch, rear clutch and overrunning clutch. The overdrive unit contains overdrive clutch, direct clutch and overrunning clutch.

3) Check for slippage and shift variations. Note if shifts are harsh, spongy, delayed or early. Slipping in any gear usually indicates clutch, band, or overrunning clutch problems. A slipping clutch or band in a particular gear can usually be identified by noting transmission operation in other gearshift positions and comparing internal components used. See CLUTCH & BAND APPLICATION table.

4) Problem area may be detected by determining which components are applied. By selecting another gear that does not use these clutches, the clutch that is slipping can be determined. See CLUTCH & BAND APPLICATION table.

5) Process of elimination can be used to detect slipping units and confirm proper operation of good units. Although road test analysis can usually diagnose slipping units, the actual malfunction, however, usually cannot be decided.

6) Practically any condition can be caused by leaking hydraulic circuits or sticking valves. Transmission failure may be determined by performing hydraulic pressure test along with clutch and servo air pressure test.

TORQUE CONVERTER STALL SPEED TEST

Torque Converter Stall Speed Test Procedure – **1)** Install tachometer. Ensure transmission fluid level is correct. Start and operate engine until transmission fluid is at normal operating temperature.

CAUTION: DO NOT open throttle to wide open position for more than 5 seconds or transmission may be damaged. If performing more than one torque converter stall speed test, operate engine at 1000 RPM with transmission in Neutral for at least 20 seconds to cool transmission fluid before performing next torque converter stall speed test.

2) Block front wheels. Apply parking and service brakes. Place transmission in Drive. Open throttle to wide open position for no more than 5 seconds and note engine RPM and then release throttle. This is the torque converter stall speed.

3) Torque converter stall speed should be 1800-2100 RPM on all models except 1993 Pickup and Ramcharger. On 1993 Pickup and Ramcharger, torque converter stall speed should be 1700-2000 RPM. Once torque converter stall speed is obtained, place transmission in Neutral. Operate engine for 20 seconds, allowing transmission to cool. Stop engine. Place transmission in Park. Remove tachometer.

NOTE: Use following symptoms to trouble shoot results of torque converter stall speed test.

Torque Converter Stall Speed Exceeds Specification – If torque converter stall speed exceeds specification by more than 200 RPM, transmission clutch is slipping.

Torque Converter Stall Speed Less Than Specification – **1)** If torque converter stall speed is less than specification with properly tuned engine, torque converter overrunning clutch may be slipping.

2) If torque converter overrunning clutch is slipping, torque converter stall speed will be 250-300 RPM less than the specification. Vehicle will operate properly at highway speeds, but will have poor low-speed acceleration.

Torque Converter Stall Speed Is Within Specification – If torque converter stall speed is within specification, but abnormal throttle opening is required to maintain highway speeds, torque converter overrunning clutch is seized. Torque converter must be replaced.

Noise When Performing Torque Converter Stall Speed Test – Whining noise caused by fluid flow is normal. A loud metallic sound indicates torque converter is damaged. To ensure sound is coming from torque converter, raise vehicle on hoist. Operate vehicle with transmission in Drive and then Neutral at light throttle. Ensure noise is coming from torque converter. Replace torque converter if defective.

HYDRAULIC PRESSURE TEST

Hydraulic Pressure Test Preparation – **1)** Ensure fluid level and condition are okay. Install tachometer. Raise vehicle on hoist, allowing wheels to rotate freely.

2) Disconnect throttle valve and shift cables or linkages from throttle valve and manual selector lever on the transmission.

CAUTION: A 100 psi (7 kg/cm²) pressure gauge is required for checking all applications except rear servo and overdrive clutch. A 300 psi (21 kg/cm²) pressure gauge is required for checking pressure at rear servo and overdrive clutch.

Pressure Test With Transmission In "1" (1st Gear) – **1)** Remove pressure tap plugs and install pressure gauge in accumulator and rear servo pressure taps. See Fig. 3. Start and operate engine at 1000 RPM.

2) Move manual selector lever on transmission fully forward to the gearshift "1" position. Read pressure on both pressure gauges as throttle valve lever on transmission is moved from fully forward position to fully rearward position.

3) Line pressure at accumulator pressure tap should be 54-60 psi (3.7-4.2 kg/cm²) with throttle valve lever fully forward and gradually increase to 90-96 psi (6.3-6.7 kg/cm²) as throttle valve lever is moved rearward. Rear servo pressure should be within 3 psi (.2 kg/cm²) of line pressure.

4) If line pressure is not within specification, adjust line pressure. See LINE PRESSURE under HYDRAULIC PRESSURE ADJUSTMENTS. If proper line pressure still cannot be obtained, check for defective components and hydraulic circuit.

5) This tests oil pump output, pressure regulation, condition of rear clutch and servo hydraulic circuits. Remove pressure gauges. Install and tighten pressure tap plugs to specification. See TORQUE SPECIFICATIONS.

Pressure Test With Transmission In "2" (2nd Gear) – **1)** Remove pressure tap plug and install pressure gauge in accumulator pressure tap. See Fig. 3. Start and operate engine at 1000 RPM.

2) Move manual selector lever on transmission to fully forward position and then rearward one position to gearshift "2" position. Read pressure on pressure gauge as throttle valve lever on transmission is moved from fully forward position to fully rearward position.

3) Line pressure at accumulator pressure tap should be 54-60 psi (3.7-4.2 kg/cm²) with throttle valve lever fully forward and gradually increase to 90-96 psi (6.3-6.7 kg/cm²) as throttle valve lever is moved rearward.

4) If line pressure is not within specification, adjust line pressure. See LINE PRESSURE under HYDRAULIC PRESSURE ADJUSTMENTS. If proper line pressure still cannot be obtained, check for defective components and hydraulic circuit.

5) This tests oil pump output and pressure regulation. Remove pressure gauge. Install and tighten pressure tap plug to specification. See TORQUE SPECIFICATIONS.

Pressure Test With Transmission In "D" (Drive Gear) – **1)** Remove pressure tap plugs and install pressure gauge in accumulator and front servo pressure taps. See Fig. 3. Start and operate engine at 1600 RPM.

2) Move manual selector lever on transmission to fully forward position and then rearward 2 positions to gearshift "D" position. Read pressure on both pressure gauges as throttle valve lever on transmission is moved from fully forward position to fully rearward position.

3) Line pressure at accumulator pressure tap should be 54-60 psi (3.7-4.2 kg/cm²) with throttle valve lever fully forward and gradually increase as throttle valve lever is moved rearward. Front servo is pressurized only in gearshift lever "D" position and pressure should be within 3 psi (.2 kg/cm²) of line pressure up to the downshift point.

4) If line pressure is not within specification, adjust line pressure. See LINE PRESSURE under HYDRAULIC PRESSURE ADJUSTMENTS. If proper line pressure still cannot be obtained, check for defective components and hydraulic circuit.

5) This tests oil pump output, pressure regulation and condition of clutch hydraulic circuits. Remove pressure gauges. Install and tighten pressure tap plugs to specification. See TORQUE SPECIFICATIONS.

Pressure Test With Transmission In "R" (Reverse Gear) – **1)** Remove pressure tap plug and install 300 psi (21 kg/cm²) pressure gauge in rear servo pressure tap. See Fig. 3. Start and operate engine at 1600 RPM.

2) Move manual selector lever on transmission to fully forward position and then rearward 4 positions to gearshift "R" position. Read pressure on pressure gauge as throttle valve lever on transmission is moved from fully forward position to fully rearward position.

3) Pressure should be 145-175 psi (10.2-12.3 kg/cm²) with throttle valve lever fully forward and gradually increase to 230-280 psi (16.1-19.7 kg/cm²) with throttle valve lever fully rearward.

4) This tests oil pump output, pressure regulation, front clutch and rear servo hydraulic circuits. Remove pressure gauge. Install and tighten pressure tap plug to specification. See TORQUE SPECIFICATIONS.

Pressure Test With Transmission In Overdrive (4th Gear) – **1)** Reconnect throttle valve and shift cables or linkages on manual selector lever and throttle valve lever on transmission (if removed). Remove pressure tap plug and install 300 psi (21 kg/cm²) pressure gauge in overdrive clutch pressure tap. See Fig. 3.

2) Lower vehicle, leaving wheels approximately 12" from floor. Ensure overdrive switch is in the ON position. Start engine. Place gearshift in "D" (Drive). Gradually increase engine speed until a 3-4 shift occurs and note pressure gauge reading in 4th gear.

3) Pressure should be 68-72 psi (4.7-5.1 kg/cm²) at closed throttle and increase to 90-120 psi (6.3-8.4 kg/cm²) at 1/2 to 3/4 throttle. Pressure will increase to more than 130 psi (9.1 kg/cm²) at full throttle.

4) This tests line pressure at overdrive clutch in 4th gear. Remove pressure gauge. Install and tighten pressure tap plug to specification. See TORQUE SPECIFICATIONS.

NOTE: *Transmission governor pressure is usually checked if shift speeds are incorrect or transmission will not upshift or downshift.*

Transmission Governor Pressure – **1)** Reconnect throttle valve and shift cables or linkages on manual selector lever and throttle valve lever on transmission (if removed). Remove pressure tap plug and install pressure gauge in governor pressure tap. See Fig. 3.

2) Lower vehicle, leaving wheels approximately 12" from floor. Start engine and allow to idle. Place gearshift in "D" (Drive). Note pressure gauge reading with engine idling.

3) Pressure should be 0-1.5 psi (0-.1 kg/cm²) with wheels not rotating. If pressure exceeds specification, governor valve or weights are stuck open.

4) If pressure is correct, slowly increase engine speed, noting governor pressure in relation to vehicle speed. Governor pressure should increase approximately 1 psi (.07 kg/cm²) for every MPH. Governor pressure should rise smoothly and then drop back to 0-1.5 psi (0-.1 kg/cm²) when wheels stop rotating.

5) This tests governor operation in relation to engine and vehicle speed. Repair governor if it does not operate properly. Remove pressure gauge. Install and tighten pressure tap plug to specification. See TORQUE SPECIFICATIONS.

Hydraulic Pressure Test Result Indications – **1)** If proper line pressure is obtained in any pressure test, oil pump and pressure regulator are working properly.

2) If line pressure is low in "D", "1" and "2", but is correct in "R", this indicates leakage in rear clutch circuit.

3) If line pressure is low in "D" (3rd gear) and "R", but is correct in "1" and "2", this indicates leakage in front clutch circuit.

4) If line pressure is low in "R" and "1", but is correct in "2", this indicates leakage in rear servo circuit. If front servo pressure is low in "2", this indicates leakage in front servo circuit.

5) If line pressure is low when in "D" (4th gear), this indicates overdrive clutch piston seal or check ball problem.

6) High governor pressure at idle indicates governor valve is stuck open. Low governor pressure at all vehicle speeds indicates governor valve is stuck closed.

7) If line pressure is not within specification, adjust line pressure. See LINE PRESSURE under HYDRAULIC PRESSURE ADJUSTMENTS. If proper line pressure still cannot be obtained, check for defective components and hydraulic circuit. Low line pressure in all positions indicates a defective oil pump, restricted filter or stuck pressure regulator valve.

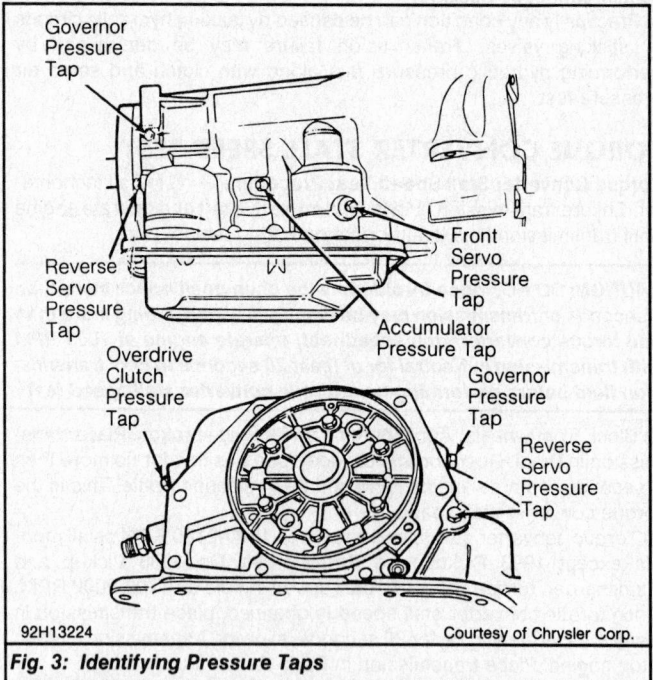

92H13224   Courtesy of Chrysler Corp.

Fig. 3: Identifying Pressure Taps

CLUTCH & SERVO AIR PRESSURE TEST

NOTE: *Inoperative clutches, servos and bands can be located by applying air pressure to appropriate passages in transmission case.*

Test Preparation – Remove valve body. See VALVE BODY under REMOVAL & INSTALLATION.

CAUTION: *Ensure air supply is free of all dirt and moisture.*

Front Clutch – Place finger on front clutch housing. Apply air pressure to front clutch apply passage. See Fig. 4. Piston movement will be felt and a soft thump will be heard when front clutch is applied.

Rear Clutch – Place finger on rear clutch housing. Apply air pressure to rear clutch apply passage. *See Fig. 4.* Piston movement will be felt and a soft thump will be heard when rear clutch is applied.

Front Servo – Apply air pressure to front servo apply passage. *See Fig. 4.* Front band should tighten, indicating front servo operation. Release air pressure. Ensure spring tension on servo piston releases front band.

Rear Servo – Apply air pressure to rear servo apply passage. *See Fig. 4.* Rear band should tighten, indicating rear servo operation. Release air pressure. Ensure spring tension on servo piston releases rear band.

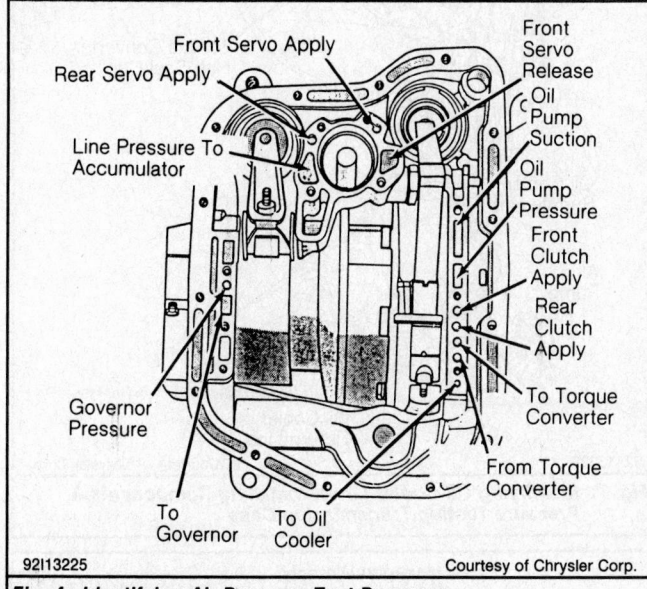

92I13225   Courtesy of Chrysler Corp.

Fig. 4: Identifying Air Pressure Test Passages

TORQUE CONVERTER FLUID LEAKAGE TEST

NOTE: Fluid around torque converter may originate from engine oil or transmission. Ensure transmission fluid level is correct. Fluid leakage at torque converter may result if fluid level is too high. Transmission can be checked for leaks using the following method.

1) Remove torque converter dust shield. Clean inside area of torque converter housing using solvent and compressed air. Ensure area is clean and dry.

2) Fabricate leakage test probe using 1/32" sheet metal, 5 1/2" (140 mm) long and 1 1/2" (38 mm) wide. *See Fig. 5.* Install leakage test probe on torque converter dust shield bolt so leakage test probe is near torque converter. Ensure torque converter does not contact leakage test probe.

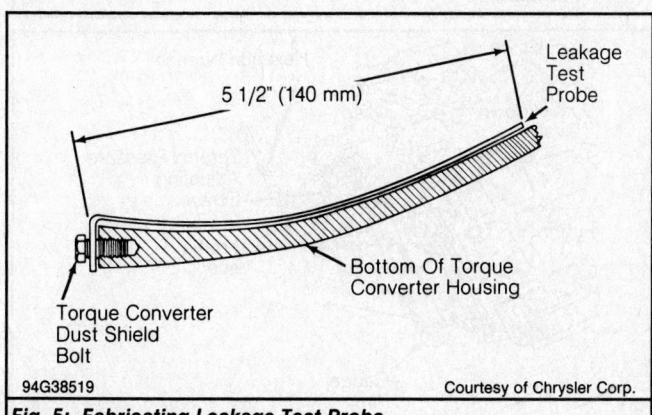

94G38519   Courtesy of Chrysler Corp.

Fig. 5: Fabricating Leakage Test Probe

3) Apply parking brake. Start engine. Place transmission in Neutral. Operate engine at 2500 RPM for 2 minutes. Stop engine. Remove leakage test probe.

4) If upper surface of leakage test probe is dry, torque converter is not leaking. If upper surface of leakage test probe is wet with ATF, torque converter is leaking. If area below leakage test probe is wet with ATF, fluid is coming from around torque converter area.

5) Check following for possible causes of fluid leaks at torque converter areas:
- Defective oil pump housing "O" ring or oil pump housing
- Front band pin access plug
- Mispositioned or worn bushing
- Oil pump seal
- Oil pump-to-transmission case bolts
- Oil pump vent

6) If torque converter is leaking, check for defective welds on outside diameter of torque converter and torque converter hub. Torque converter hub is welded on inside and is not visible. Replace torque converter if a leak exists. DO NOT attempt to repair torque converter.

TRANSMISSION CASE PRESSURE TEST

NOTE: Transmission case, gaskets and oil pump housing can be checked for leaks using the following method. Transmission must be removed to perform transmission case pressure test.

1) Remove torque converter from transmission. Fabricate torque converter hub seal cup, retaining strap and vent plug retainer. *See Fig. 6.* Retaining strap specifications are approximate. Measure hole positions on torque converter housing before drilling.

CAUTION: Ensure torque converter hub seal cup surface is smooth to prevent damage to seal in oil pump.

2) Install torque converter hub seal cup, vent plug retainer and retaining strap. *See Fig. 7.* Install shipping plug in rear output shaft opening. Install and secure plugs in remaining transmission openings except oil cooler return line.

3) Attach air pump to oil cooler return line. *See Fig. 7.* Ensure cap is installed on oil cooler supply line fitting. Using pressure regulator, apply 8-10 psi (.5-.7 kg/cm²) of air pressure to transmission case.

CAUTION: DO NOT apply more than 10 psi (.7 kg/cm²) of air pressure to transmission case.

4) Coat oil pump and front of transmission case with soapy water solution. Check for bubbles, indicating a leak in seals, "O" rings, gaskets or transmission case. Release air pressure. Remove test equipment. Replace defective components.

HYDRAULIC PRESSURE ADJUSTMENTS

CAUTION: Line pressure and throttle pressure each affect shift quality. Line pressure must be adjusted before adjusting throttle pressure. Valve body must be removed for adjustments. See VALVE BODY under REMOVAL & INSTALLATION.

LINE PRESSURE

1) Measure distance from valve body to inner edge of line pressure adjusting screw. *See Fig. 8.* Rotate line pressure adjusting screw so distance is approximately 1 5/16".

NOTE: Due to manufacturing tolerances, adjustment can be varied to obtain specified line pressure.

2) Rotating line pressure adjusting screw one revolution will change line pressure approximately 1 2/3 psi. Rotating line pressure adjusting screw counterclockwise increases line pressure and clockwise decreases line pressure.

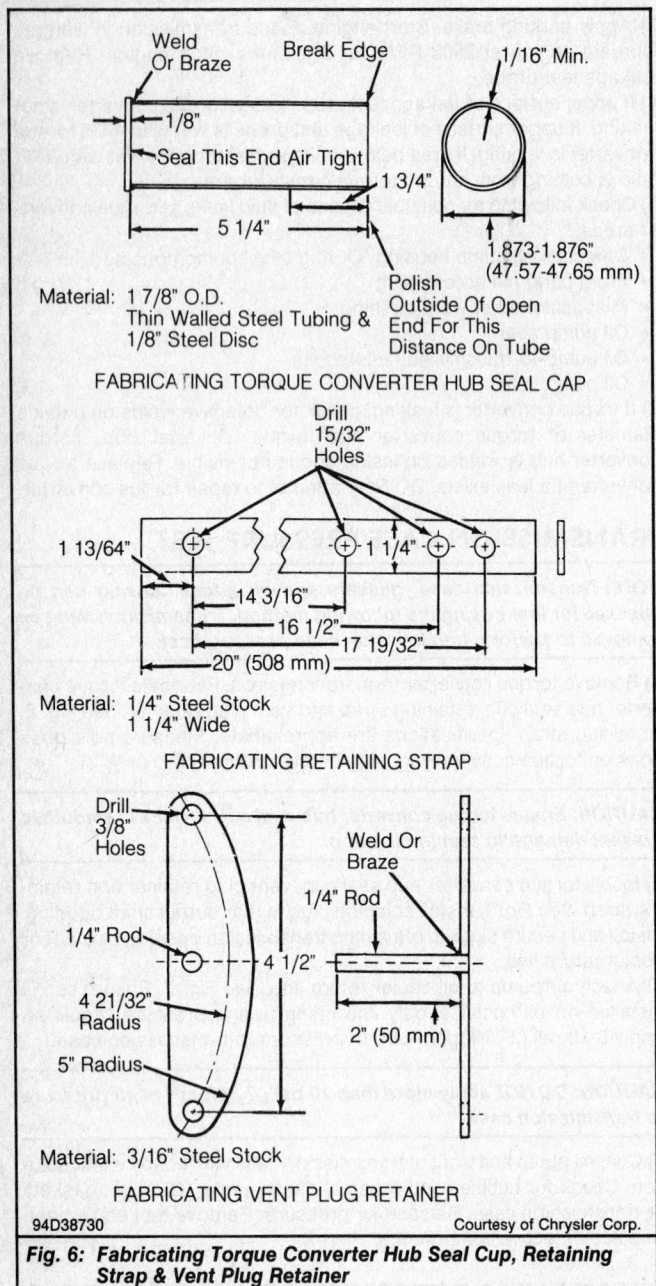

Fig. 6: Fabricating Torque Converter Hub Seal Cup, Retaining Strap & Vent Plug Retainer

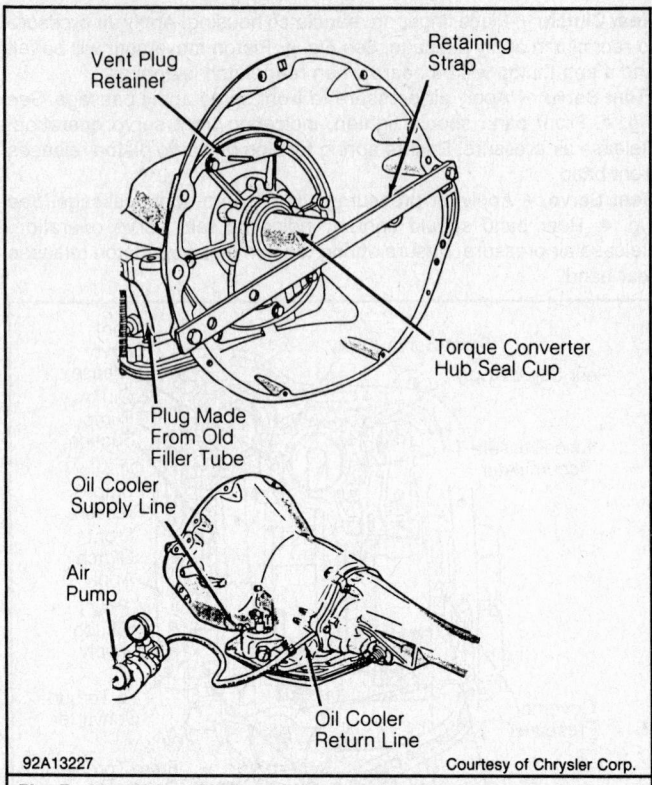

Fig. 7: Identifying Oil Cooler Lines, Installing Components & Pressure Testing Transmission Case

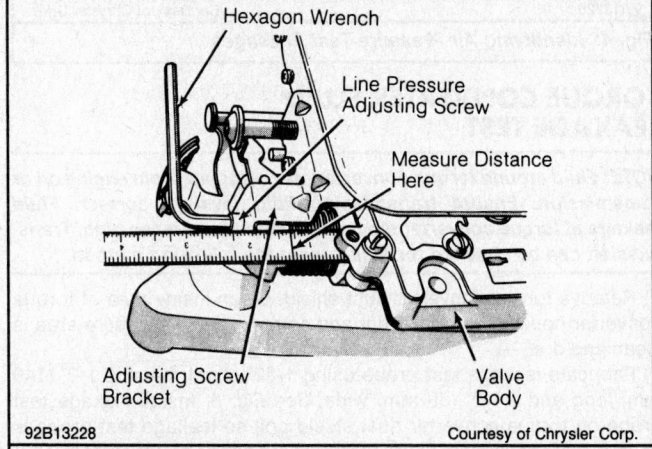

Fig. 8: Identifying Adjusting Screw Bracket & Adjusting Line Pressure

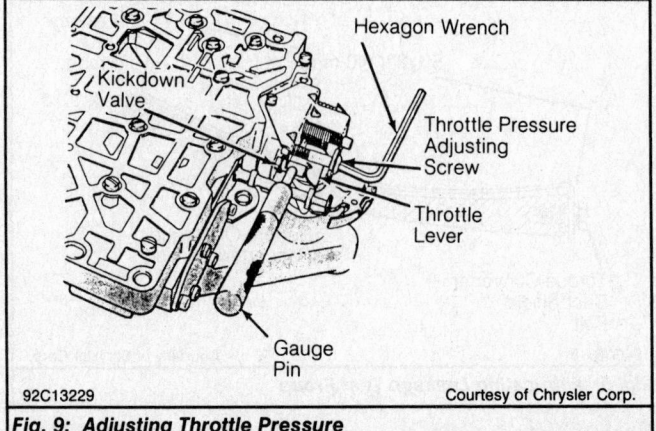

Fig. 9: Adjusting Throttle Pressure

THROTTLE PRESSURE

CAUTION: Line pressure must be adjusted before adjusting throttle pressure.

1) Insert Gauge Pin (C-3763) between cam on throttle lever and kickdown valve. *See Fig. 9.*
2) Push inward on gauge pin and compress kickdown valve against spring until kickdown valve bottoms in valve body.

CAUTION: Ensure spring is fully compressed and kickdown valve is bottomed in valve body.

3) Maintain pressure against kickdown valve and spring. Rotate throttle pressure adjusting screw until head of adjusting screw contacts tang on throttle lever. Ensure throttle lever cam contacts gauge pin. Remove gauge pin.

ON-VEHICLE SERVICE

Following components can be serviced on vehicle.
- Park/Neutral Switch
- Valve Body
- Vehicle Speed Sensor & Pinion Gear

See appropriate component under REMOVAL & INSTALLATION.

OIL COOLER FLUSHING

CAUTION: Whenever transmission failure exists, oil cooler must be flushed and torque converter replaced. If vehicle is equipped with 2 oil coolers (one in radiator tank and one in front of radiator), flush oil coolers separately. DO NOT attempt to flush both oil coolers at one time.

NOTE: On 1994 models, oil cooler lines are equipped with disconnect fittings. For disconnecting and installing procedures of oil cooler lines with disconnect fittings, see OIL COOLER LINE DISCONNECT FITTINGS under ON-VEHICLE SERVICE.

CAUTION: Some models may have a drainback relief valve installed in the oil cooler supply line next to the rubber hose at the radiator. See Fig. 55. If drainback relief valve is used, it must be removed before flushing the lines. Install NEW drainback relief valve once lines are flushed.

1) Note oil cooler supply and return lines. *See Fig. 7.* Disconnect oil cooler lines at transmission. Place container under oil cooler supply line.

2) Using hand-held suction gun filled with mineral spirits, force mineral spirits into oil cooler return line until mineral spirits flows from oil cooler supply line.

3) Continue flushing oil cooler until mineral spirits is clear and no sign of contamination exists. Once contamination is removed, apply compressed air on line from oil cooler in light applications until remaining mineral spirits is blown from oil cooler and oil cooler lines.

4) Pump at least one quart of Mopar ATF Plus Type 7176 fluid through oil cooler to ensure oil cooler is free of mineral spirits. Replace oil cooler if fluid does not flow freely through oil cooler.

OIL COOLER FLOW CHECK

1) With transmission filled to proper fluid level, disconnect oil cooler return line from transmission. *See Fig. 7.* Place container under oil cooler return line.

2) Add one extra quart of Mopar ATF Plus Type 7176 fluid to transmission. Apply parking brake. Start engine and allow to idle. Place gearshift in Neutral. Check fluid flow from oil cooler return line.

3) If fluid flow is intermittent or takes more than 20 seconds to obtain one quart, replace oil cooler. Reconnect oil cooler return line. Fill transmission to proper level.

OIL COOLER LINE DISCONNECT FITTINGS

NOTE: On 1994 models, there are 3 different types of disconnect fittings used. See Fig. 10. Release tool is required to disconnect oil cooler line. Release tool is attached to oil cooler line on Type 2 and 3 fittings. This release tool also can be used to disconnect Type 1 fittings.

Removal – 1) Ensure area around disconnect fitting and oil cooler line is clean. Slide release tool into disconnect fitting until it fully bottoms against flange on oil cooler line.

2) Push release tool inward and rotate to spread retaining clip and pull oil cooler line from disconnect fitting. *See Fig. 11.* Inspect disconnect fitting and oil cooler line for damage. Replace disconnect fitting as an assembly if damaged. Replace oil cooler line if swedge at hose or flange on line is damaged.

Installation – 1) If installing NEW disconnect fitting, apply Loctite 242 on disconnect fitting before installing. Ensure end of oil cooler line is clean. Insert oil cooler line into disconnect fitting.

CAUTION: After installing oil cooler line, pull outward on oil cooler line to ensure oil cooler line is locked in the disconnect fitting and retaining clip is fully seated.

2) Ensure oil cooler line is clean. Push oil cooler line inward until a snap or click is heard when retaining clip seats in oil cooler line. Pull outward on oil cooler line to ensure oil cooler line is locked in the disconnect fitting.

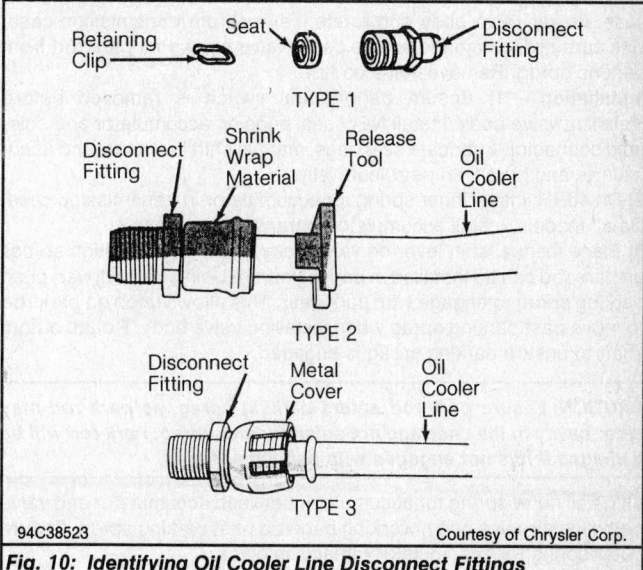

94C38523   Courtesy of Chrysler Corp.

Fig. 10: Identifying Oil Cooler Line Disconnect Fittings

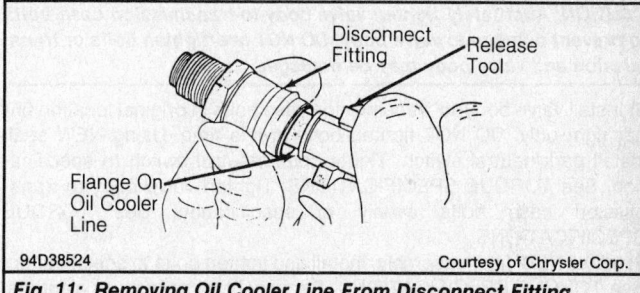

94D38524   Courtesy of Chrysler Corp.

Fig. 11: Removing Oil Cooler Line From Disconnect Fitting (Type 2 Shown; Others Are Similar)

REMOVAL & INSTALLATION

PARK/NEUTRAL SWITCH

Removal & Installation – 1) Raise and support vehicle. Place drain pan under park/neutral switch located near manual shift lever on transmission. *See Fig. 17.* Disconnect electrical connector. Unscrew park/neutral switch from transmission case.

2) To install, apply parking brake. Ensure gearshift is in Park or Neutral. Ensure operating levers in transmission are centered in park/neutral switch opening on transmission case.

3) Using NEW seal, install park/neutral switch. Tighten park/neutral switch to specification. See TORQUE SPECIFICATIONS. Reinstall electrical connector. Adjust transmission fluid level with Mopar ATF Plus Type 7176 fluid.

TRANSMISSION

See appropriate AUTOMATIC TRANSMISSION REMOVAL article in TRANSMISSION SERVICING.

VALVE BODY

Removal – 1) Raise and support vehicle. Remove bolts, oil pan and gasket. Remove throttle valve and manual shift levers from transmission. Remove park/neutral switch. See PARK/NEUTRAL SWITCH under REMOVAL & INSTALLATION.

2) Remove bolts and filter assembly. Keep bolts with filter assembly for installation reference. Disconnect necessary solenoid electrical connectors from solenoid connector in transmission case.

3) Remove valve body-to-transmission case bolts. Note bolt length and location for installation reference. Lower valve body enough to remove accumulator and springs. Note location of springs for reassembly reference. The 46RH uses 2 springs and 47RH uses only one spring. Pull valve body forward and disengage park rod.

4) Push manual shift lever and solenoid connector from transmission case. Lower valve body and rotate it away from transmission case. Use care not to damage solenoids on valve body. Pull park rod from parking sprag. Remove valve body.

Installation – 1) Ensure park/neutral switch is removed before installing valve body. Install NEW seal rings on accumulator and solenoid connector. Lubricate seal rings, manual shift lever seal and accumulator and bore with petroleum jelly.

2) On 46RH, install inner spring for accumulator in transmission case. On all models, install accumulator in transmission case.

3) Place manual shift lever on valve body in low gear position so ball on park rod can be installed in parking sprag. Using screwdriver, push parking sprag to engage with park gear. This allows knob on park rod to move past parking sprag when installing valve body. Rotate output shaft to ensure parking sprag is engaged.

CAUTION: Ensure park rod enters parking sprag, as park rod may enter cavity in the case and not enter parking sprag. Park rod will be damaged if it is not engaged with parking sprag.

4) Install outer spring for accumulator between accumulator and valve body. Install valve body, working park rod past parking sprag. Ensure outer spring for accumulator remains in place.

CAUTION: Alternately tighten valve body-to-transmission case bolts to prevent damage to valve body. DO NOT overtighten bolts or transmission and valve body may be damaged.

5) Install valve body-to-transmission case bolts in original location finger tight only. DO NOT tighten bolts at this time. Using NEW seal, install park/neutral switch. Tighten park/neutral switch to specification. See TORQUE SPECIFICATIONS. Tighten valve body-to-transmission case bolts evenly to specification. See TORQUE SPECIFICATIONS.

6) Install NEW filter assembly. Install and tighten bolts to specification. See TORQUE SPECIFICATIONS. Reconnect all necessary electrical connections. Install throttle valve and manual shift levers. Ensure throttle valve lever and manual shift levers rotate smoothly.

7) Using NEW gasket, install oil pan. Install and tighten bolts to specification. See TORQUE SPECIFICATIONS. Fill transmission with Mopar ATF Plus Type 7176 fluid. Ensure shift linkage/cable and throttle valve cable are properly adjusted. See appropriate AUTOMATIC TRANSMISSION SERVICING article in TRANSMISSION SERVICING.

VEHICLE SPEED SENSOR & PINION GEAR

Removal (1993 Models) – 1) Raise and support vehicle. Disconnect electrical connector from vehicle speed sensor. *See Fig. 12.*

2) Remove vehicle speed sensor from adapter. Check vehicle speed sensor mounting area on adapter for signs of ATF leakage. If ATF leakage exists, oil seal is leaking and should be replaced.

3) Remove bolt and adapter retainer. Note location of indexing numbers on adapter in relation to the housing. *See Fig. 13.*

NOTE: Indexing numbers on adapter correspond to number of teeth on the pinion gear.

4) Ensure area around adapter is clean. Remove adapter, "O" ring and pinion gear. *See Fig. 12.* Remove oil seal from adapter (if necessary).

Installation – 1) If installing NEW oil seal in adapter, start oil seal in adapter by hand. Using Oil Seal Installer (C-4004), press oil seal in adapter until it bottoms.

2) Ensure housing is clean. Install NEW "O" ring on adapter (if necessary). Lubricate "O" ring on adapter, oil seal and pinion gear teeth with Mopar ATF Plus Type 7176 fluid. Count number of teeth on the pinion gear. Ensure number of teeth on pinion gear are within range of indexing numbers listed on the adapter. *See Fig. 13.*

3) Install pinion gear, "O" ring and adapter in the housing. Rotate adapter until proper indexing number in relation to number of pinion gear teeth is at 6 o'clock position. *See Fig. 13.*

4) Ensure adapter is seated in the housing. Install adapter retainer. Install and tighten bolt to specification. See TORQUE SPECIFICATIONS.

5) Install vehicle speed sensor. Tighten nut to specification. See TORQUE SPECIFICATIONS. Install electrical connector on vehicle speed sensor. Adjust transmission fluid level with Mopar ATF Plus Type 7176 fluid.

Removal (1994 Models) – 1) Raise and support vehicle. Disconnect electrical connector from vehicle speed sensor. *See Fig. 12.*

2) Remove bolt and adapter retainer. Note location of indexing numbers on adapter in relation to the housing. *See Fig. 13.*

NOTE: Indexing numbers on adapter correspond to number of teeth on the pinion gear.

3) Ensure area around adapter is clean. Remove adapter with vehicle speed sensor, "O" ring and pinion gear. *See Fig. 12.* Remove bolt, vehicle speed sensor and "O" ring from adapter.

Installation – 1) Install NEW "O" ring on vehicle speed sensor and adapter (if necessary). Lubricate "O" rings and pinion gear teeth with Mopar ATF Plus Type 7176 fluid.

2) Install vehicle speed sensor in adapter. Install and tighten bolt to specification. See TORQUE SPECIFICATIONS. Install pinion gear in adapter.

3) Ensure housing is clean. Count number of teeth on the pinion gear. Ensure number of teeth on pinion gear are within range of indexing numbers listed on the adapter. *See Fig. 13.*

4) Install adapter with pinion gear in the housing. Rotate adapter until proper indexing number in relation to number of pinion gear teeth is at 6 o'clock position. *See Fig. 13.*

5) Ensure adapter is seated in the housing. Install adapter retainer. Install and tighten bolt to specification. See TORQUE SPECIFICATIONS. Install electrical connector on vehicle speed sensor. Adjust transmission fluid level with Mopar ATF Plus Type 7176 fluid.

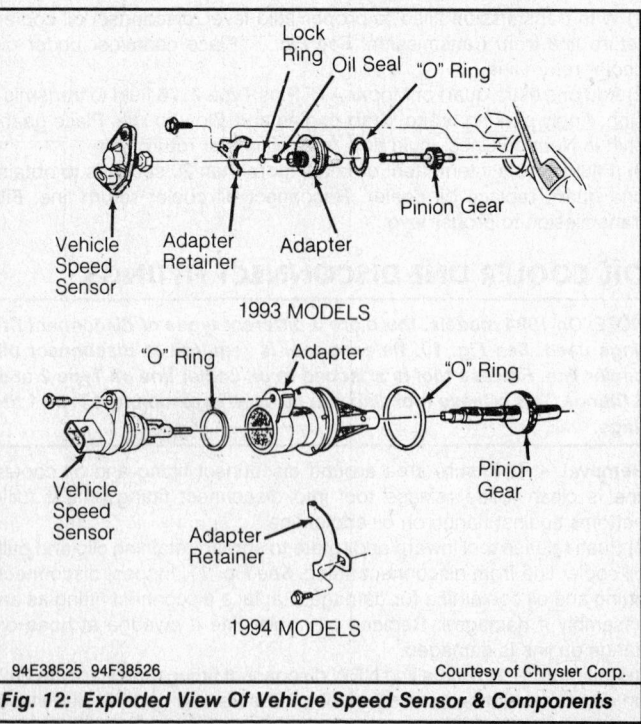

94E38525 94F38526   Courtesy of Chrysler Corp.

Fig. 12: Exploded View Of Vehicle Speed Sensor & Components

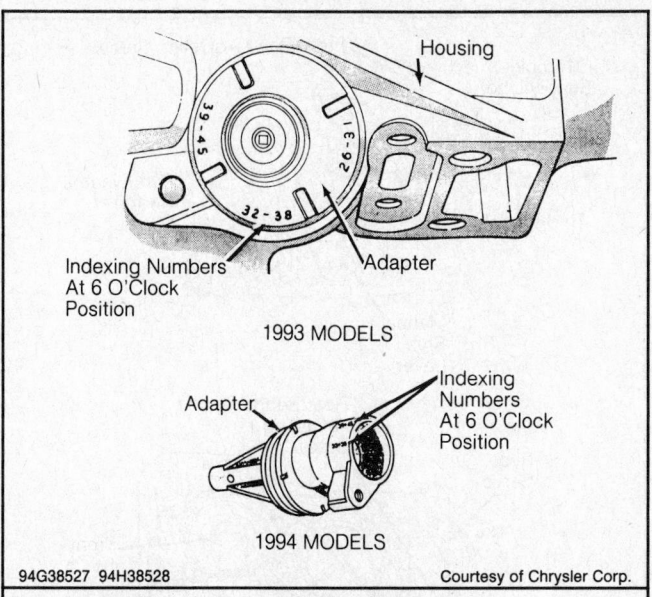

Indexing Numbers
At 6 O'Clock
Position

Housing

Adapter

1993 MODELS

Adapter

Indexing
Numbers
At 6 O'Clock
Position

1994 MODELS

94G38527 94H38528

Courtesy of Chrysler Corp.

Fig. 13: Identifying Adapter Indexing Numbers

TORQUE CONVERTER

CAUTION: Torque converter is a welded assembly and is not service-able. If a malfunction occurs or if torque converter becomes contaminated with foreign material, it MUST be replaced. Torque converter cannot be flushed or repaired.

NOTE: For torque converter fluid leakage testing and torque converter stall speed test, see TESTING in this article.

TRANSMISSION DISASSEMBLY

NOTE: For overdrive unit disassembly, see OVERDRIVE UNIT DISASSEMBLY in this article.

VALVE BODY & COMPONENTS

CAUTION: Note location of all thrust washer and thrust plate locations for reassembly reference.

1) Remove torque converter. Loosen clamps and remove throttle valve and manual shift levers from transmission.

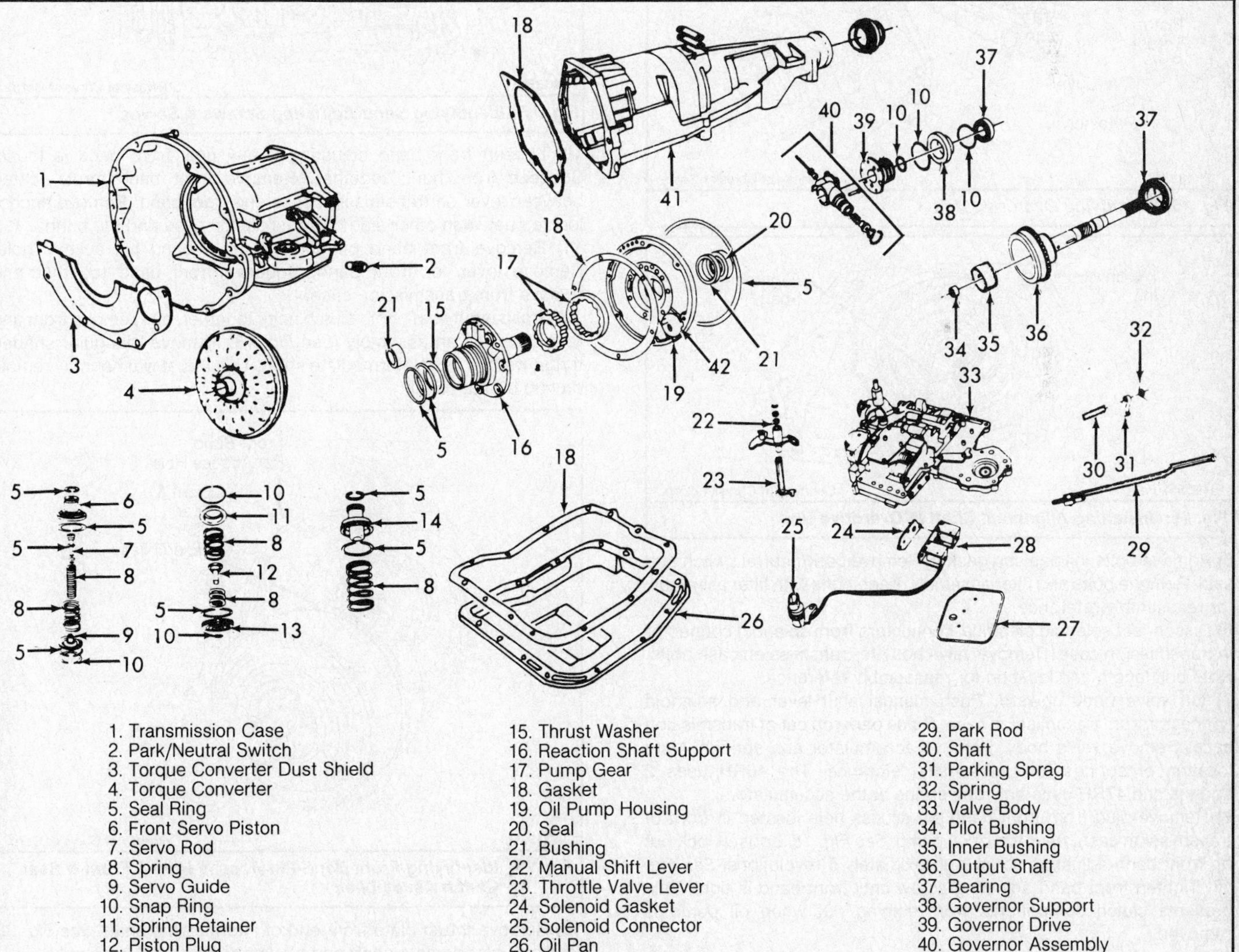

1. Transmission Case
2. Park/Neutral Switch
3. Torque Converter Dust Shield
4. Torque Converter
5. Seal Ring
6. Front Servo Piston
7. Servo Rod
8. Spring
9. Servo Guide
10. Snap Ring
11. Spring Retainer
12. Piston Plug
13. Rear Servo Piston
14. Accumulator

15. Thrust Washer
16. Reaction Shaft Support
17. Pump Gear
18. Gasket
19. Oil Pump Housing
20. Seal
21. Bushing
22. Manual Shift Lever
23. Throttle Valve Lever
24. Solenoid Gasket
25. Solenoid Connector
26. Oil Pan
27. Filter Assembly
28. Solenoid Assembly

29. Park Rod
30. Shaft
31. Parking Sprag
32. Spring
33. Valve Body
34. Pilot Bushing
35. Inner Bushing
36. Output Shaft
37. Bearing
38. Governor Support
39. Governor Drive
40. Governor Assembly
41. Overdrive Unit Case
42. Pump Vent

94E38731

Courtesy of Chrysler Corp.

Fig. 14: Exploded View Of Typical Transmission Case & Components

CAUTION: *If alignment shaft is not installed in overdrive unit, components may become out of alignment and overdrive unit must be disassembled to realign components.*

2) Remove overdrive unit-to-transmission bolts. Remove overdrive unit. *See Fig. 15.* If overdrive unit does not require servicing, install Alignment Shaft (6227-2) in overrunning clutch and planetary gear splines on overdrive unit, ensuring alignment shaft is fully seated. *See Fig. 16.* This maintains proper alignment of all components in overdrive unit.

3) Remove intermediate shaft selective spacer and overdrive piston thrust plate from intermediate shaft. *See Fig. 15.* Remove overdrive piston from overdrive piston retainer.

4) Inspect that check ball on front side of overdrive piston is secure in the overdrive piston and is not loose. Replace overdrive piston if check ball is loose.

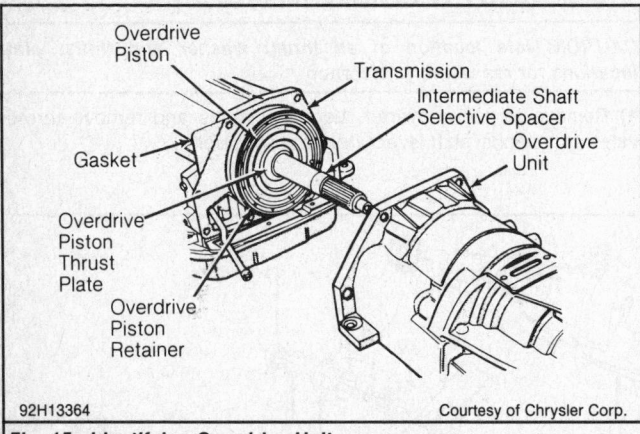

92H13364   Courtesy of Chrysler Corp.

Fig. 15: Identifying Overdrive Unit

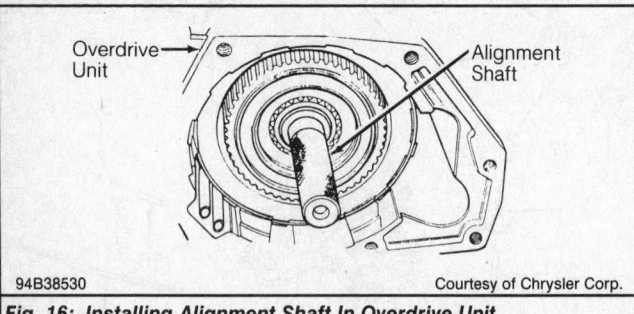

94B38530   Courtesy of Chrysler Corp.

Fig. 16: Installing Alignment Shaft In Overdrive Unit

5) Remove bolts, oil pan and gasket. Remove park/neutral switch and seal. Remove bolts and filter assembly. Keep bolts with filter assembly for reassembly reference.

6) Disconnect solenoid electrical connectors from solenoid connector in transmission case. Remove valve body-to-transmission case bolts. Note bolt length and location for reassembly reference.

7) Lift valve body upward. Push manual shift lever and solenoid connector from transmission case. Guide park rod out of transmission case. Remove valve body. Remove accumulator and springs. Note location of springs for reassembly reference. The 46RH uses 2 springs and 47RH uses only one spring at the accumulator.

8) Remove plug from front band pin access hole located in front of transmission case, near top of oil pump. *See Fig. 18.* Loosen lock nut on front band adjusting screw approximately 5 revolutions. *See Fig. 17.* Tighten front band adjusting screw until front band is tight. This prevents clutch components from coming out when oil pump is removed.

9) Remove oil pump bolts. Install slide hammers on opposite sides of oil pump. Pull oil pump from transmission case. Remove oil pump gasket.

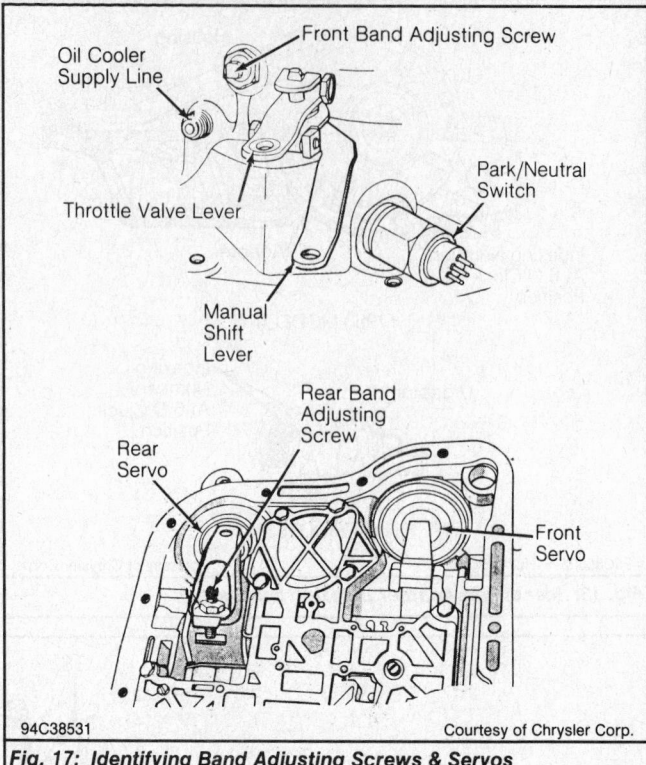

94C38531   Courtesy of Chrysler Corp.

Fig. 17: Identifying Band Adjusting Screws & Servos

10) Loosen front band adjusting screw until front band is loose. Squeeze front band together. Remove front band strut located between lever on transmission case and front band. Remove anchor located between other side of transmission case and the band.

11) Remove front band pin through front band pin access hole. Remove lever for front band. Squeeze front band together and remove from transmission case.

12) Grasp input shaft, hold clutch units together, and remove front and rear clutch as an assembly. *See Fig. 18.* Remove triangular shaped thrust washer from intermediate shaft. This thrust washer may remain on hub of rear clutch.

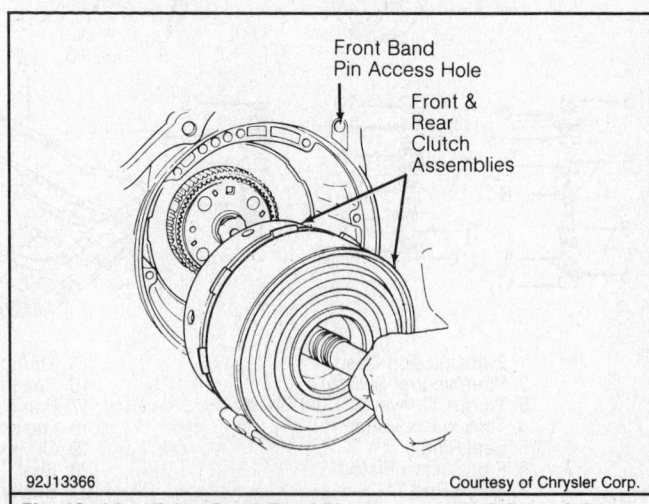

92J13366   Courtesy of Chrysler Corp.

Fig. 18: Identifying Front Band Pin Access Hole & Front & Rear Clutch Assemblies

13) Remove thrust plate from end of intermediate shaft. *See Fig. 30.* Remove intermediate shaft and planetary gear train assembly.

CAUTION: *DO NOT damage machined surfaces on intermediate shaft during removal.*

14) On 46RH, loosen rear band adjusting screw 3-4 turns. *See Fig. 17.* Remove low-reverse drum-to-overdrive piston retainer snap ring from inside of transmission case.

15) Remove low-reverse drum from rear band and remove from transmission case. Tap pin for rear band toward rear of transmission case. Remove rear band linkage, lever, pin and rear band.

16) On 47RH, low-reverse drum and rear band are removed as an assembly. Loosen rear band adjusting screw 4-5 turns. *See Fig. 17.* Using Allen wrench, push pivot pin for rear band out of rear of transmission case. Perform STEP 1. *See Fig. 19.*

17) Using small punch, push rear band reaction pin out of rear of transmission case. Perform STEP 2. *See Fig. 19.*

18) Remove low-reverse drum-to-overdrive piston retainer snap ring from inside of transmission case. Remove low-reverse drum and rear band from transmission case as a unit. Remove rear band from low-reverse drum.

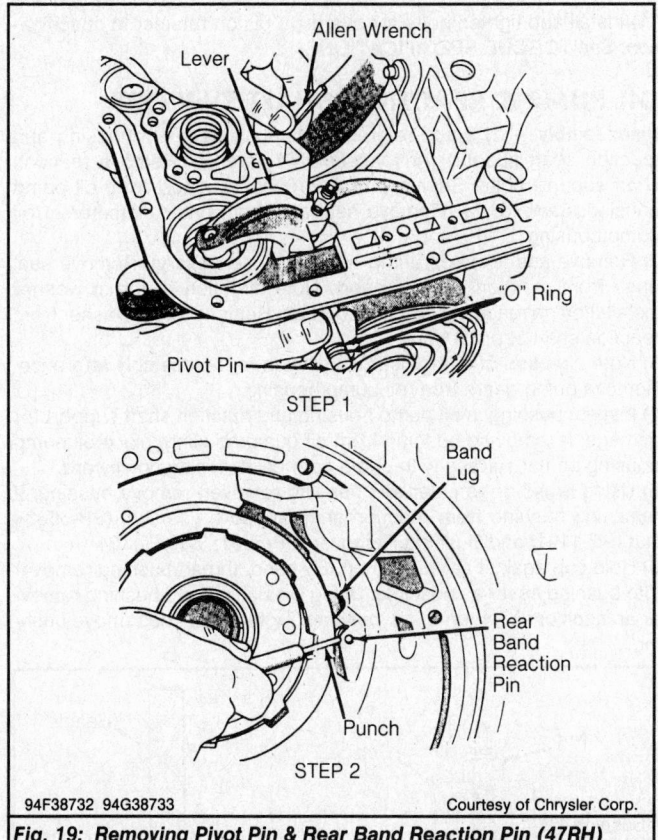

Fig. 19: Removing Pivot Pin & Rear Band Reaction Pin (47RH)

19) On all models, overrunning clutch race will remain on low-reverse drum during removal. This race is a permanent fit, DO NOT attempt to remove overrunning clutch race from low-reverse drum.

20) Remove overrunning clutch from overrunning clutch cam. *See Fig. 20.* Overrunning clutch can be removed without removing springs and rollers from the retainer. Note location of springs and rollers for reassembly reference.

21) If removing servo components, note servo identification. *See Fig. 17.* To remove front servo, use "C" clamp and spring compressor to compress servo. Compress servo guide on front servo approximately 1/8".

22) Remove snap ring. DO NOT scratch sealing surfaces. Release spring compressor. Remove servo guide, spring and front servo piston. *See Fig. 14.*

23) To remove rear servo, compress spring retainer on rear servo approximately 1/16". Remove snap ring. DO NOT scratch sealing surfaces. Remove spring retainer, spring and rear servo piston. *See Fig. 14.*

24) Remove bolts, overdrive piston retainer and gasket from rear of transmission case. *See Fig. 15.*

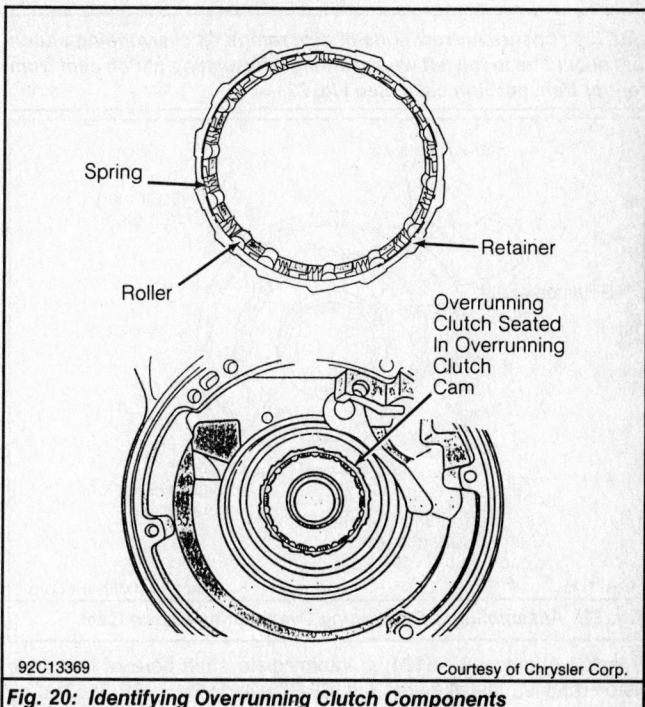

Fig. 20: Identifying Overrunning Clutch Components

TRANSMISSION COMPONENT DISASSEMBLY & REASSEMBLY

OVERRUNNING CLUTCH

CAUTION: Ensure overrunning clutch components are properly installed, or inoperative transmission or transmission failure may result.

Disassembly – 1) If replacing overrunning clutch cam, remove set screw from overrunning clutch cam. *See Fig. 21.* Insert punch through overdrive piston retainer bolt holes in rear of transmission case.

2) Using hammer, tap overrunning clutch cam from transmission case. It may be necessary to alternate from hole to hole to prevent overrunning clutch cam from binding in transmission case.

Fig. 21: Removing & Installing Set Screw For Overrunning Clutch Cam

Cleaning & Inspection – Clean components with solvent and dry with compressed air. Inspect overrunning clutch components and low-reverse drum for damage. Replace damaged components.

Reassembly – 1) Ensure overrunning clutch cam bore in transmission case is clean. Install overdrive piston retainer in transmission case.

2) Align and start overrunning clutch cam in transmission case. Ensure serrations on overrunning cam and transmission case are aligned. *See Fig. 22.*

CAUTION: Ensure narrow ends of cam ramps on overrunning clutch cam should be to the left when viewing overrunning clutch cam from front of transmission case. See Fig. 22.

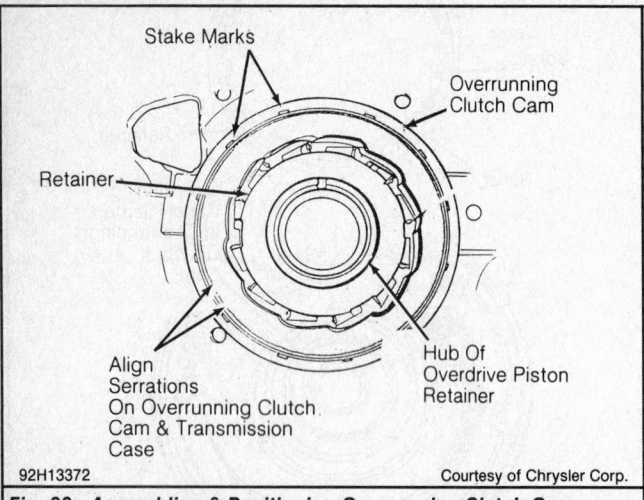

92H13372   Courtesy of Chrysler Corp.

Fig. 22: Assembling & Positioning Overrunning Clutch Cam

3) Install Adapter (SP-5124) in intermediate shaft bore of overdrive piston retainer. Install Puller Bolt (SP-3701) and Plate (SP-3583-A) on overrunning clutch cam. *See Fig. 23.* Ensure plate is seated squarely on overrunning clutch cam.

4) Install Adapter (SP-5124) and nut on puller bolt. *See Fig. 23.* Tighten nut and pull overrunning clutch cam into transmission case.

CAUTION: Ensure overrunning clutch cam enters transmission case evenly and does not bind.

5) Install set screw in overrunning clutch cam. Tighten set screw to specification. See TORQUE SPECIFICATIONS.

6) Remove nut, adapters, plate and puller bolt. Using blunt chisel, stake transmission case in 12 areas to retain overrunning clutch cam. Ensure transmission case is clean after performing staking procedure.

CAUTION: Ensure transmission case is staked in 12 areas to retain overrunning clutch cam.

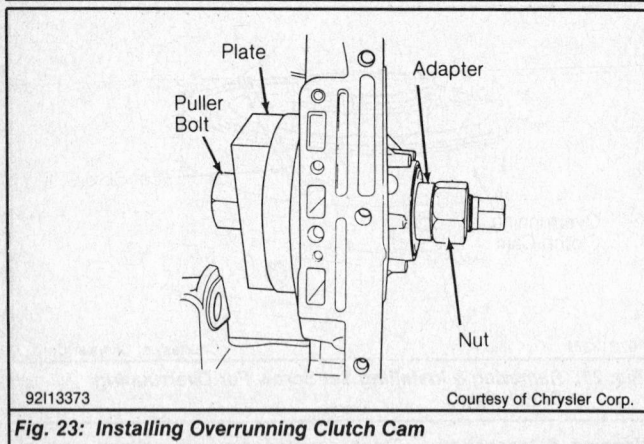

92I13373   Courtesy of Chrysler Corp.

Fig. 23: Installing Overrunning Clutch Cam

7) If installing springs and rollers in overdrive clutch, lubricate overdrive piston retainer hub, clutch race, overdrive clutch cam and rollers with Mopar ATF Plus Type 7176 fluid.

8) Install spring in retainer. Install roller between spring and stop area on retainer. Ensure spring and roller are fully seated in the retainer.

CAUTION: Ensure flanged side of retainer is facing outward. Retainer and rollers can easily be installed in overrunning clutch cam when properly positioned.

9) Install overrunning clutch assembly in overrunning clutch cam, with flanged side of retainer facing outward. Ensure clutch assembly is fully seated in overrunning clutch cam. *See Fig. 20.*

10) Slightly tilt low-reverse drum and install in rollers on overrunning clutch. Rotate low-reverse drum clockwise until low-reverse drum is fully seated.

CAUTION: Ensure low-reverse drum rotates freely clockwise (viewed from front of transmission), but locks when rotated counterclockwise. Check for improper component assembly if low-reverse drum will not rotate correctly.

11) Install and tighten bolts for overdrive piston retainer to specification. See TORQUE SPECIFICATIONS.

OIL PUMP & REACTION SHAFT SUPPORT

Disassembly – 1) Place reference mark on oil pump housing and reaction shaft support for reassembly reference. Remove reaction shaft support bolts. Separate reaction shaft support from oil pump housing. *See Fig. 14.* Remove seal ring from outer diameter of oil pump housing.

2) Remove seal from oil pump housing (if necessary). Remove seal rings from reaction shaft support. Note direction of thrust washer installation on reaction shaft support hub. Remove thrust washer from reaction shaft support hub.

3) Note direction of pump gear installation for reassembly reference. Remove pump gears from oil pump housing.

4) Inspect bushing in oil pump housing and reaction shaft support for damage. If removing bushing from oil pump housing, place oil pump housing on flat surface with pump gear cavity facing downward.

5) Using press or hammer and bushing remover, remove bushing. If removing bushing from reaction shaft support, use Cup (SP-3633), Nut (SP-1191) and Bushing Remover (SP-5301). *See Fig. 24.*

6) Hold cup against reaction shaft. By hand, thread bushing remover into bushing as far as possible. Using wrench, thread bushing remover an additional 3-4 turns into bushing. Tighten nut and remove bushing.

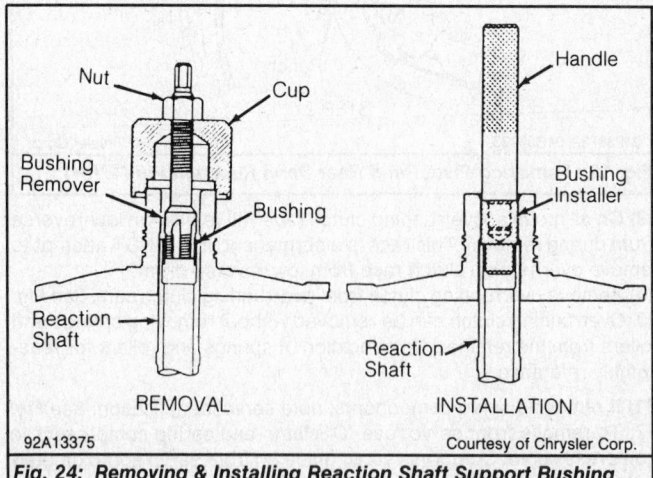

92A13375   Courtesy of Chrysler Corp.

Fig. 24: Removing & Installing Reaction Shaft Support Bushing

Cleaning & Inspection – 1) Clean and inspect components for damage. Inspect all machined surfaces for pitting or damage.

2) Ensure pump vent is not cracked and is secure in oil pump housing. *See Fig. 14.* Replace oil pump housing if pump vent is loose or cracked.

3) Install both pump gears in oil pump housing. Using feeler gauge, measure outer pump gear-to-oil pump housing clearance.

4) Place straightedge on oil pump housing, above both pump gears. Using feeler gauge, measure pump gear end clearance between each pump gear and straightedge.

5) Align one tooth on outer pump gear with one tooth on inner pump gear. Measure pump gear tooth clearance between the teeth on the pump gears. Replace components if clearance is not within specification. See OIL PUMP SPECIFICATIONS table.

OIL PUMP SPECIFICATIONS

Application	In. (mm)
Outer Pump Gear-To-Oil Pump	
Housing Clearance	.0035-.0075 (.089-.190)
Pump Gear End Clearance	.0035-.0075 (.089-.190)
Pump Gear Tooth Clearance	.0035-.0075 (.089-.190)

Reassembly – 1) If installing NEW oil pump housing bushing, place oil pump housing on flat surface with pump gear cavity facing upward.
2) Place bushing on bushing installer and start into oil pump housing. Tap bushing in oil pump housing until bushing installer bottoms. Ensure bushing is installed evenly and does not bind in oil pump housing. Using blunt punch, stake bushing in 2 places. *See Fig. 25.* Using knife, clean burrs from stake areas.

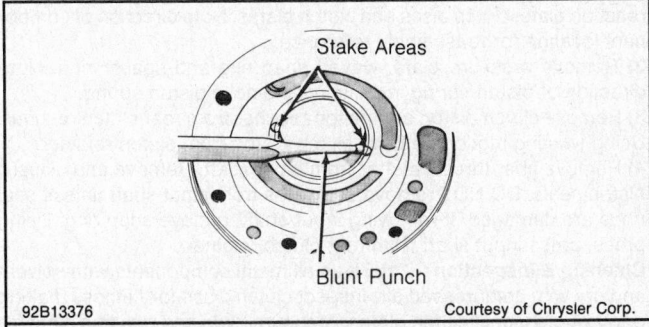

92B13376   Courtesy of Chrysler Corp.

Fig. 25: Staking Bushing In Oil Pump Housing

3) If installing NEW reaction shaft support bushing, ensure reaction shaft support is clean and free of burrs. Place reaction shaft support on clean surface with bushing area facing upward.
4) Use Handle (C-4171) and Bushing Installer (SP-5302). *See Fig. 24.* Place bushing on bushing installer and start into reaction shaft support. Tap bushing into reaction shaft support until bushing installer bottoms. Clean reaction shaft support.
5) To reassemble oil pump, lubricate pump gears with Mopar ATF Plus Type 7176 fluid. Install pump gears in oil pump housing. Ensure pump gears are installed in original direction of installation.

CAUTION: On 1994 models, thrust washer must be installed on reaction shaft support with chamfered edge on inside diameter of thrust washer facing toward front of oil pump.

6) Install thrust washer on rear of reaction shaft support. On 1993 models, thrust washer can be installed in either direction. On 1994 models, thrust washer must be installed with chamfered edge on inside diameter of thrust washer facing toward front of oil pump. On all models, lubricate thrust washer with petroleum jelly.

CAUTION: DO NOT over expand or twist seal rings when installing on reaction shaft support. Ensure ends on seal rings are hooked together or otherwise seal rings will be damaged when installing oil pump.

7) If replacing seal rings on reaction shaft support, install NEW seal rings on reaction shaft support. Lubricate seal rings with petroleum jelly. Squeeze seal rings together until ends of seal rings hook together.
8) Install reaction shaft support on oil pump housing with reference mark aligned. Install and tighten reaction shaft support bolts to specification. See TORQUE SPECIFICATIONS.
9) Install NEW seal in oil pump housing with seal lip facing inward (toward oil pump). Install NEW seal ring on outer diameter of oil pump housing. Lubricate lip of seal and seal ring with petroleum jelly.

FRONT CLUTCH

CAUTION: Note direction of clutch discs and clutch plates for reassembly reference. Also note number of each component, as some models may contain different number of clutch components. Components must be installed in correct sequence.

Disassembly – 1) Remove waved snap ring, pressure plate, clutch discs and clutch plates. *See Fig. 26.* Note number of clutch discs and plates, as some models may contain different number of clutch components.
2) Using spring compressor, compress piston springs. Remove snap ring. Release spring compressor. Remove spring compressor and spring retainer.

CAUTION: Note number of piston springs and location for reassembly reference.

3) Remove piston springs and clutch piston from front clutch retainer. Remove and discard piston seals.
4) Inspect bushing in front clutch retainer for damage. If replacing bushing, position front clutch retainer with clutch plate opening facing downward. Using hammer and bushing remover, remove bushing.

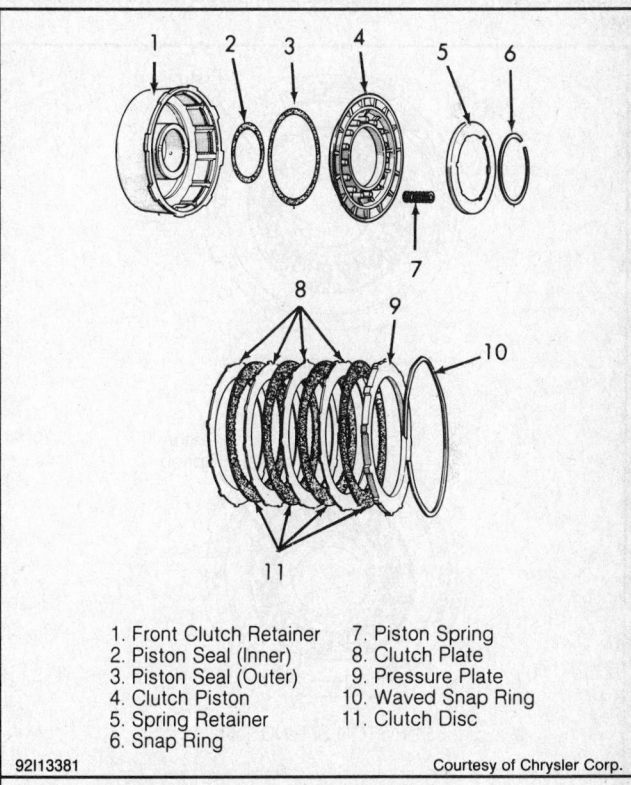

1. Front Clutch Retainer	7. Piston Spring
2. Piston Seal (Inner)	8. Clutch Plate
3. Piston Seal (Outer)	9. Pressure Plate
4. Clutch Piston	10. Waved Snap Ring
5. Spring Retainer	11. Clutch Disc
6. Snap Ring	

92I13381   Courtesy of Chrysler Corp.

Fig. 26: Exploded View Of Typical Front Clutch (47RH Shown; 46RH Is Similar)

Cleaning & Inspection – 1) Clean all metal components with solvent and dry with compressed air. Inspect clutch discs for flatness, flaking or glazing. Inspect clutch plates and pressure plate for flatness or damage at plate-to-front clutch retainer tang areas.
2) Ensure tang areas in front clutch retainer are not damaged and clutch plates slide freely in front clutch retainer. Ensure check ball, located in bottom of front clutch retainer, moves freely. Ensure check ball in the clutch piston is securely staked in place and does not move.
3) Inspect all sealing surfaces for burrs or scratches. Inspect piston springs for distortion. Replace damaged components.
Reassembly – 1) If installing NEW bushing in front clutch retainer, position front clutch retainer with clutch plate opening facing upward.
2) Using hammer or press, and Bushing Installer (SP-5511), install bushing until bushing installer bottoms. Clean front clutch retainer after installing bushing.

3) Soak clutch discs in Mopar ATF Plus Type 7176 fluid. Install NEW piston seals so lip on piston seal is toward inside of front clutch retainer.

4) Lubricate piston seals with petroleum jelly. Lubricate front clutch retainer and clutch piston surface with ATF.

CAUTION: Use twisting motion when installing clutch piston to prevent damage to piston seals.

---

5) Using twisting motion, install clutch piston in front clutch retainer. Install piston springs on clutch piston in proper location depending upon number of piston springs. *See Fig. 27.*

6) Install spring retainer. Using spring compressor, compress piston springs. Install snap ring to secure spring retainer. Release spring compressor.

7) Alternately install clutch plates and clutch discs starting with clutch plate. *See Fig. 26.* Ensure original number of components are installed. Install pressure plate and waved snap ring.

8) Using feeler gauge, measure front clutch clearance between waved snap ring and pressure plate. *See Fig. 28.* Front clutch clearance should be .070-.129" (1.78-3.28 mm) on 3-disc clutches and .082-.151" (2.08-3.84 mm) on 4-disc clutches. If front clutch clearance is not within specification, check for defective or improperly assembled components.

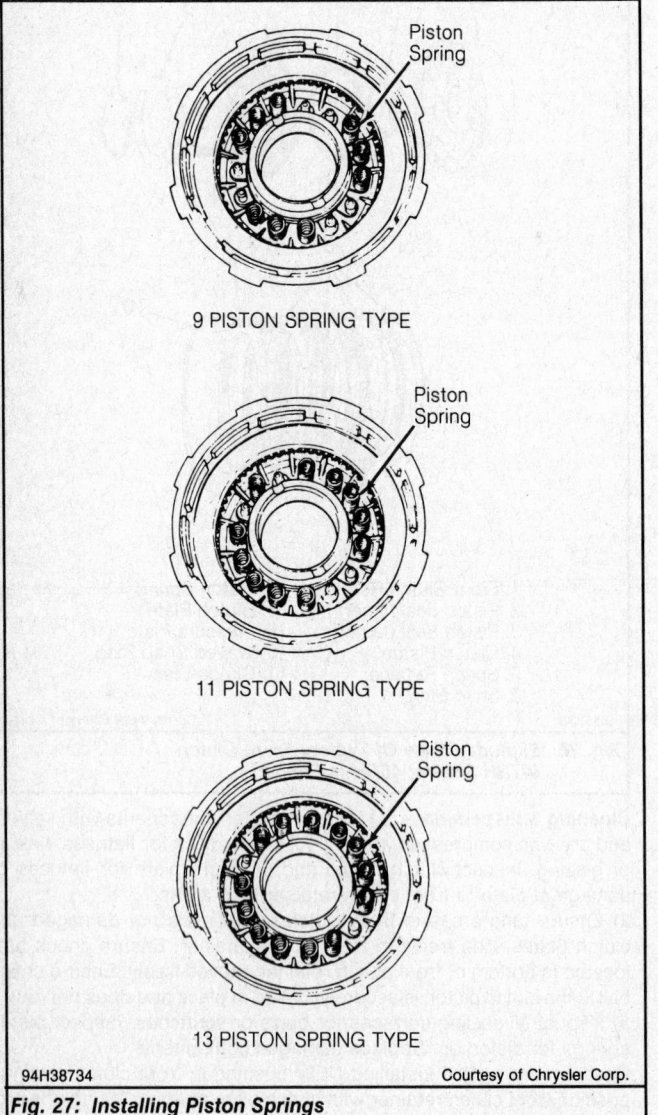

9 PISTON SPRING TYPE

11 PISTON SPRING TYPE

13 PISTON SPRING TYPE

94H38734   Courtesy of Chrysler Corp.

Fig. 27: Installing Piston Springs

Waved Snap Ring

Feeler Gauge

92H13380   Courtesy of Chrysler Corp.

Fig. 28: Measuring Front Clutch Clearance

REAR CLUTCH

CAUTION: Note direction of clutch discs and clutch plates for reassembly reference. Also note number of each component, as some models may contain different number of clutch components. Components must be installed in correct sequence.

Disassembly – 1) Remove selective snap ring. *See Fig. 29.* Remove reaction plate, clutch discs and clutch plates. Note direction of component location for reassembly reference.

2) Remove pressure plate, waved snap ring and spacer ring. Note direction of piston spring installation. Remove piston spring.

3) Remove clutch piston and piston retainer from rear clutch retainer. Using twisting motion, remove clutch piston from piston retainer.

4) Remove fiber thrust washer from input shaft. Remove and discard piston seals. DO NOT remove seal rings from input shaft unless seal rings are damaged. If removing input shaft, remove snap ring. Using press, press input shaft from rear clutch retainer.

Cleaning & Inspection – 1) Clean all metal components with solvent and dry with compressed air. Inspect clutch discs for flatness, flaking or glazing. Inspect clutch plates, pressure plate and reaction plate for flatness or damage at plate-to-rear clutch retainer tang areas.

2) Ensure tang areas in rear clutch retainer are not damaged, and clutch plates slide freely in rear clutch retainer.

3) Ensure check ball moves freely in rear clutch retainer. Inspect clutch piston and piston spring for warpage or distortion. Inspect thrust washers for damage. Inspect seal rings for damage. Replace damaged components.

Reassembly – 1) Soak clutch discs in Mopar ATF Plus Type 7176 fluid. Lubricate remaining clutch components with Mopar ATF Plus Type 7176 fluid. Install NEW seal rings on input shaft (if removed) and piston retainer. Ensure ends of seal rings on input shaft and securely locked together.

2) If installing input shaft, press input shaft into rear clutch retainer. Install snap ring. Install NEW piston seals with lip of seal toward input shaft. Lubricate piston seals with petroleum jelly.

CAUTION: Use twisting motion when installing clutch piston to prevent damage to piston seals.

---

3) Using twisting motion, install clutch piston in piston retainer. Install piston retainer in rear clutch retainer.

4) Install piston spring in rear clutch retainer so convex side is facing toward the clutch piston. *See Fig. 29.* Install spacer ring and waved snap ring in rear clutch retainer. Ensure waved snap ring is fully seated. Install pressure plate.

5) Alternately install original number of clutch plates and clutch discs starting with clutch disc. *See Fig. 29.* Install reaction plate and selective snap ring.

6) Using feeler gauge, measure rear clutch clearance between selective snap ring and reaction plate. Rear clutch clearance should be .025-.045" (.64-1.14 mm).

7) If rear clutch clearance is not within specification, clutch components or selective snap ring may have to be changed. Install fiber thrust washer on piston retainer. Use petroleum jelly to retain fiber thrust washer in place.

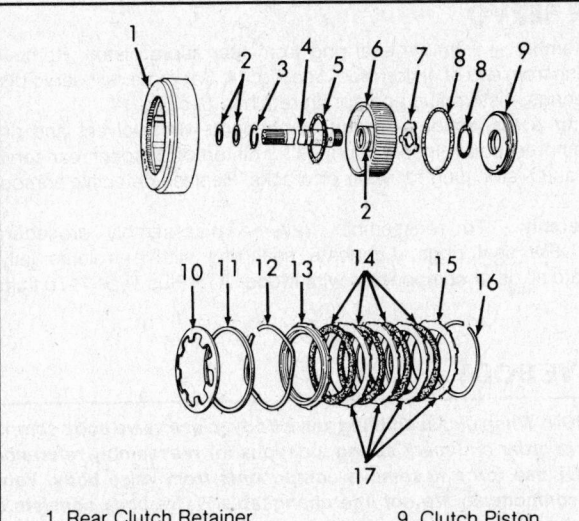

1. Rear Clutch Retainer
2. Seal Ring
3. Snap Ring
4. Input Shaft
5. Fiber Thrust Washer
6. Piston Retainer
7. Intermediate Shaft Thrust Washer
8. Piston Seal
9. Clutch Piston
10. Piston Spring
11. Spacer Ring
12. Waved Snap Ring
13. Pressure Plate
14. Clutch Disc
15. Reaction Plate
16. Selective Snap Ring
17. Clutch Plate

92B13384   Courtesy of Chrysler Corp.

Fig. 29: Exploded View Of Rear Clutch

PLANETARY GEAR TRAIN

Disassembly – 1) Remove select fit snap ring. See Fig. 30. Remove front planetary gear and front annulus gear from intermediate shaft.

2) Remove front planetary gear and thrust washer from front annulus gear. Note thrust washer location for reassembly reference. Remove thrust washer from inside driving shell. Note thrust washer tab location for reassembly reference.

3) Remove sun gear and driving shell. Remove thrust washer from rear planetary gear. Remove rear planetary gear and rear annulus gear from intermediate shaft. Remove thrust plate from rear annulus gear. See Fig. 30.

4) If removing sun gear from driving shell, remove snap ring from sun gear. Remove sun gear and thrust plate.

Cleaning & Inspection – 1) Clean all components with solvent and dry with compressed air. Inspect for damaged components. Inspect sun gear bushings for scoring or wear. Replace sun gear if bushings are damaged or worn.

2) Inspect planetary gears for defective pinion gears, pins, washers or carrier. Pinion gears, pins and washers can be replaced if defective. If carrier is damaged, entire rear planetary gear assembly must be replaced.

3) Inspect intermediate shaft for damage at bushing/bearing surfaces and splined areas. Replace damaged components.

Reassembly – 1) Lubricate intermediate shaft and planetary gear train components with Mopar ATF Plus Type 7176 fluid. Use petroleum jelly to retain thrust washers and thrust plates in position.

2) If installing sun gear in driving shell, install front snap ring on sun gear. Install sun gear in driving shell. Install thrust plate and snap ring. Install rear annulus gear on intermediate shaft.

3) Install thrust plate in rear annulus gear. Ensure thrust plate is seated on intermediate shaft splines and against rear annulus gear. Install rear planetary gear in rear annulus gear. Ensure rear planetary gear is fully seated in rear annulus gear.

4) Install thrust washer on front side of rear planetary gear. Ensure tabs on thrust washer engage with slots on rear planetary gear. Install driving shell and sun gear on intermediate shaft. Ensure thrust washer remains in position on rear planetary gear.

5) Install thrust washer on front side of driving shell. Ensure tabs on thrust washer engage with slots on driving shell. Install thrust washer on front planetary gear. Ensure tabs on thrust washer engage with slots on front planetary gear.

6) Install front annulus gear on front planetary gear. Ensure gears are fully seated. Install front annulus gear and front planetary gear on intermediate shaft. Ensure front planetary gear fully engages with sun gear and assembly is fully seated on intermediate shaft.

7) Position planetary gear train in upright position. Ensure snap ring groove on end of intermediate shaft is fully visible. Install snap ring. Position gear train assembly with gear opening of driving shell facing workbench.

8) Place wooden block between end of intermediate shaft and workbench to support intermediate shaft. This moves planetary gear train components forward so planetary gear train end play can be checked.

9) Using feeler gauge, measure planetary gear train end play. End play is measured between shoulder on intermediate shaft and end of rear annulus gear. See Fig. 31.

10) Planetary gear train end play should be .006-.048" (.15-1.22 mm). If planetary gear train end play is not within specification, install different thickness select fit snap ring. Select fit snap ring is available in thicknesses of .055-.059" (1.39-1.50 mm) and .062-.066" (1.57-1.68 mm).

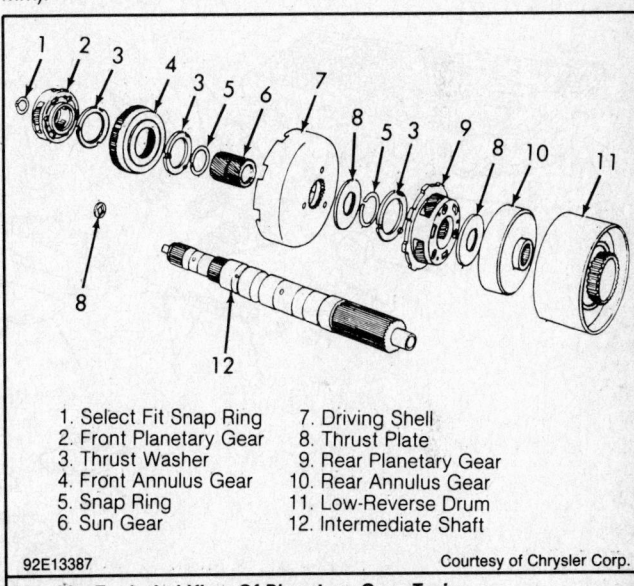

1. Select Fit Snap Ring
2. Front Planetary Gear
3. Thrust Washer
4. Front Annulus Gear
5. Snap Ring
6. Sun Gear
7. Driving Shell
8. Thrust Plate
9. Rear Planetary Gear
10. Rear Annulus Gear
11. Low-Reverse Drum
12. Intermediate Shaft

92E13387   Courtesy of Chrysler Corp.

Fig. 30: Exploded View Of Planetary Gear Train

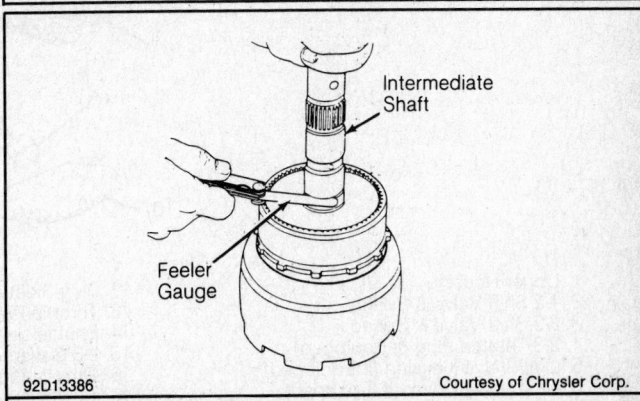

92D13386   Courtesy of Chrysler Corp.

Fig. 31: Measuring Planetary Gear Train End Play

FRONT SERVO

Disassembly – Remove snap ring from front servo piston. Remove front servo piston, servo rod, spring and servo guide. See Fig. 14. Remove and discard seal rings and "O" rings.

Cleaning & Inspection – Clean components with solvent and dry with compressed air. Inspect spring for distortion. Inspect front servo piston, servo rod and servo guide for wear or cracks. Replace defective components. If front servo piston or servo rod are damaged, both must be replaced as an assembly.

Reassembly – To reassemble, reverse disassembly procedure using NEW seal rings and NEW "O" rings. Lubricate seal rings and "O" rings with petroleum jelly. Lubricate all other components with Mopar ATF Plus Type 7176 fluid.

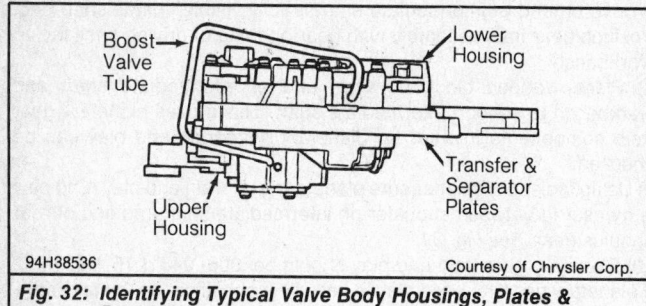

94H38536   Courtesy of Chrysler Corp.

Fig. 32: Identifying Typical Valve Body Housings, Plates & Boost Valve Tube

REAR SERVO

Disassembly – Remove seal ring from rear servo piston. Remove snap ring from end of piston plug. See Fig. 14. Separate rear servo piston, springs, piston plug and spring retainer. See Fig. 14.

Cleaning & Inspection – Clean components with solvent and dry with compressed air. Inspect springs for distortion. Inspect rear servo piston and piston plug for wear or cracks. Replace defective components.

Reassembly – To reassemble, reverse disassembly procedure using NEW seal rings. Lubricate seal ring with petroleum jelly. Lubricate all other components with Mopar ATF Plus Type 7176 fluid.

VALVE BODY

CAUTION: When disassembling valve body, place valve body components in order and mark spring locations for reassembly reference. DO NOT use force to remove components from valve body. Valve body components are not interchangeable. Valve body consists of upper housing, lower housing, transfer plate and separator plates. See Fig. 32.

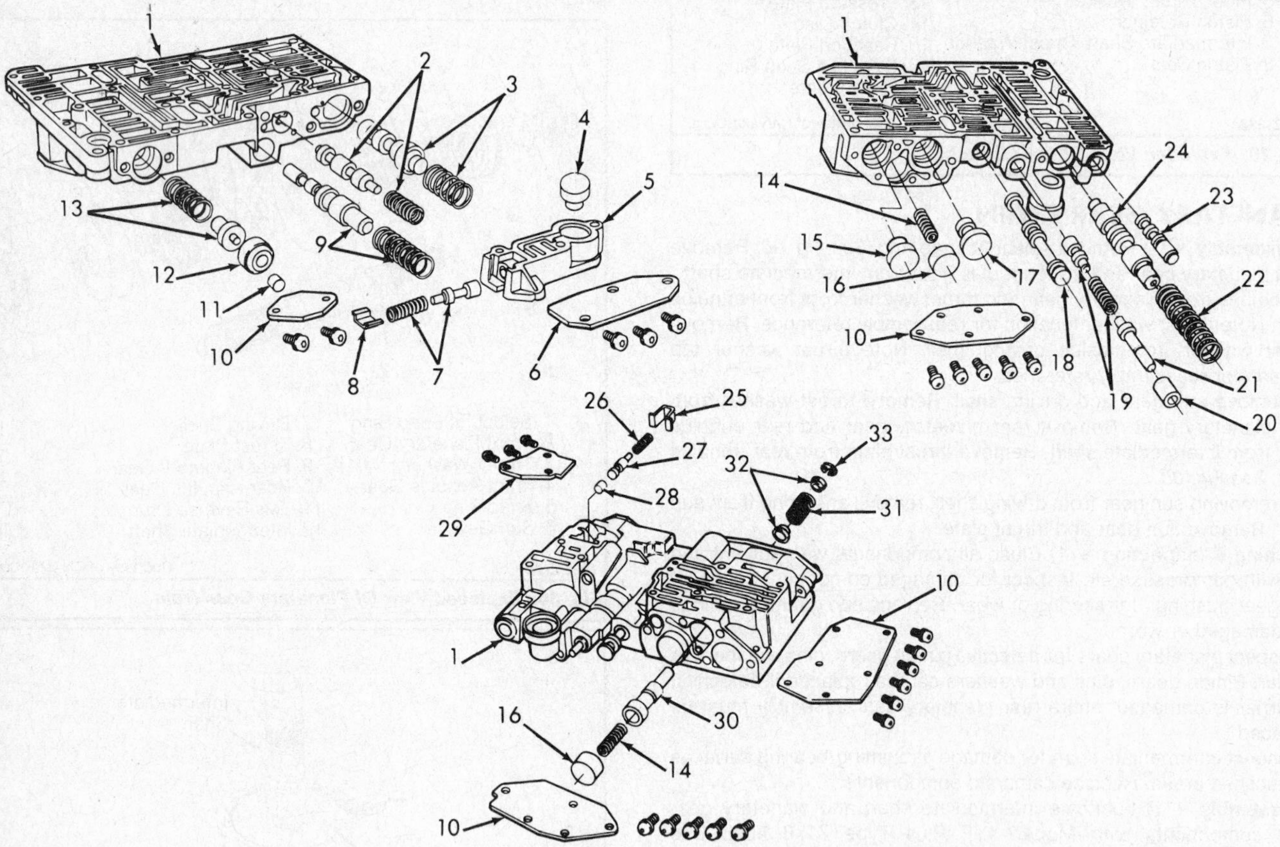

1. Upper Housing
2. 1-2 Shift Valve & Spring
3. 2-3 Shift Valve & Spring
4. 2-3 Throttle Plug (If Equipped)
5. Limit Valve Housing (If Equipped)
6. Limit Valve Cover (If Equipped)
7. Limit Valve & Spring (If Equipped)
8. Retainer (If Equipped)
9. 1-2 Shift Control Valve & Spring
10. Cover Plate
11. Line Pressure Plug
12. Plug Sleeve
13. Throttle Pressure Spring & Plug
14. Shuttle Valve Primary Spring
15. 2-3 Governor Plug
16. Throttle Plug
17. 1-2 Governor Plug
18. Manual Valve
19. Throttle Valve & Spring
20. Kickdown Detent
21. Kickdown Valve
22. Pressure Regulator Valve Spring
23. Switch Valve
24. Pressure Regulator Valve
25. Retainer (If Equipped)
26. Boost Valve Spring (If Equipped)
27. Boost Valve (If Equipped)
28. Boost Valve Plug (If Equipped)
29. Boost Valve Cover (If Equipped)
30. Shuttle Valve
31. Shuttle Valve Secondary Spring
32. Spring Guide
33. Clip

94J38538   Courtesy of Chrysler Corp.

Fig. 33: Exploded View Of Valve Body Upper Housing & Components

CAUTION: On some models, plastic check balls or steel check balls may be used in upper housing and transfer plate. Ensure original type of check ball is used. On all models, some valve bodies may contain the rear servo check ball and rear clutch check ball and some may not. Note original number of check balls during disassembly for reassembly reference. Some models may be equipped with a limit valve assembly.

Disassembly – 1) Remove boost valve cover, retainer, boost valve spring, boost valve and boost valve plug (if equipped). *See Fig. 33.*
2) Depress detent ball. Install Detent Ball Retainer (6583) on ball and spring housing to secure detent ball and spring in housing. *See Fig. 34.*
3) Remove clip and washer (if equipped) from throttle valve lever. Lift manual shift lever and park rod from throttle valve lever. *See Fig. 14.* Remove detent ball retainer. Remove detent ball and spring. Remove throttle valve lever.
4) Remove retaining clip. Separate park rod from manual shift lever. Hold adjusting screw bracket against valve body and remove screws. *See Fig. 8.*

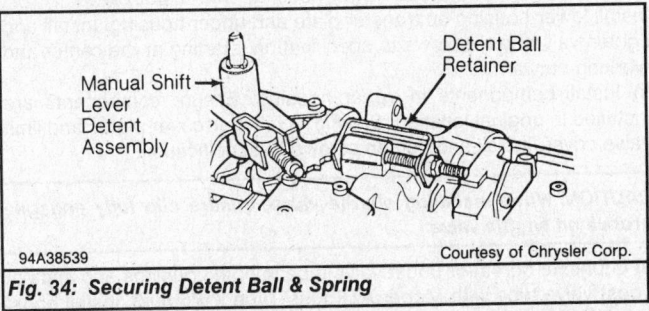

Manual Shift Lever Detent Assembly

Detent Ball Retainer

94A38539

Courtesy of Chrysler Corp.

Fig. 34: Securing Detent Ball & Spring

CAUTION: DO NOT disturb throttle pressure adjusting screw or line pressure adjusting screw locations in adjusting screw bracket.

5) Remove adjusting screw bracket, line pressure adjusting screw, pressure regulator valve spring (large spring) and switch valve spring (small spring).
6) Note routing of solenoid wiring. Remove solenoid assembly, gasket, 3-4 accumulator housing and case connector from lower housing. *See Fig. 35.* Case connector uses a shoulder-type screw and must be installed in original location.

CAUTION: Use care not to damage housings or tube when removing boost valve tube. Disengage boost valve tube from upper housing first and then from the lower housing. DO NOT pry boost valve tube from the housing

7) Remove spring, 3-4 shift valve, plug, spring and lock-up valve. *See Fig. 35.* Pull boost valve tube from upper housing first and then from the lower housing. *See Fig. 32.* It may be necessary to rotate boost valve tube back and forth when removing from lower housing.
8) Position valve body so lower housing faces upward, with upper housing on bottom. *See Fig. 32.*

CAUTION: Ensure lower housing faces upward before removing valve body screws. This prevents check balls from falling out of upper housing.

9) Note location of brace for the boost valve tube. Remove valve body screws attaching lower housing to the upper housing. Remove lower housing and separator plate from transfer plate.
10) Remove lower housing from transfer plate. Remove transfer plate and both separator plates from upper housing. Note location of check balls in upper housing. *See Fig. 36.*

CAUTION: Some valve bodies may contain the rear servo check ball and rear clutch check ball and some may not. Note original number of check balls during disassembly for reassembly reference.

11) Position transfer plate with separator plate for upper housing facing upward. Remove screws, separator plate brace and separator plate for upper housing. *See Fig. 37.*

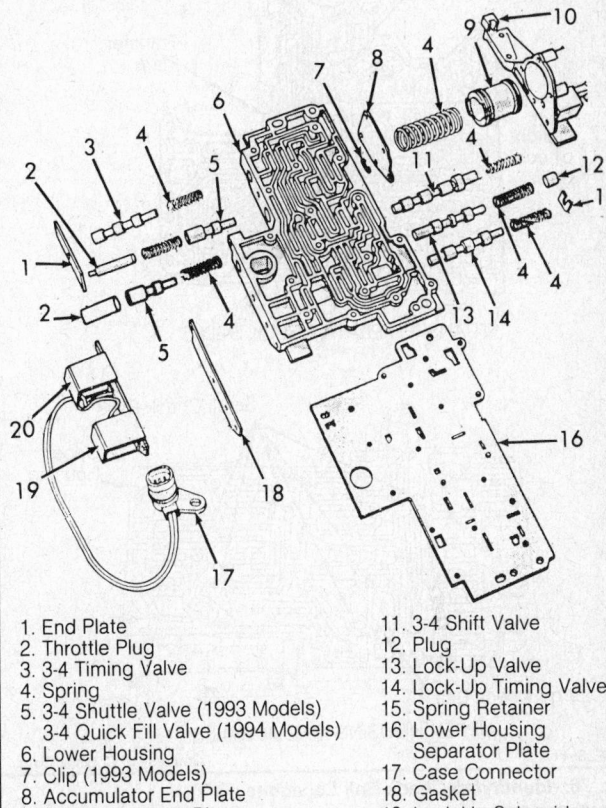

1. End Plate
2. Throttle Plug
3. 3-4 Timing Valve
4. Spring
5. 3-4 Shuttle Valve (1993 Models)
   3-4 Quick Fill Valve (1994 Models)
6. Lower Housing
7. Clip (1993 Models)
8. Accumulator End Plate
9. 3-4 Accumulator Piston
10. 3-4 Accumulator Housing
11. 3-4 Shift Valve
12. Plug
13. Lock-Up Valve
14. Lock-Up Timing Valve
15. Spring Retainer
16. Lower Housing Separator Plate
17. Case Connector
18. Gasket
19. Lock-Up Solenoid
20. Overdrive Solenoid

94D38540

Courtesy of Chrysler Corp.

Fig. 35: Exploded View Of Valve Body Lower Housing & Components

12) Remove separator plate for upper housing from transfer plate. Note location of filter screen in upper housing separator plate and check balls in transfer plate. *See Figs. 36 and 37.*

CAUTION: On some models, plastic check balls or steel check balls may be used in upper housing and transfer plate. Note location and type of check ball for reassembly reference.

13) Remove components from upper and lower housings. Ensure components are placed in order for reassembly reference. *See Figs. 33 and 35.*
Cleaning & Inspection – 1) Clean components with solvent and dry with compressed air. DO NOT use solvent to clean electrical components. DO NOT use shop towels to dry components. Ensure all components slide freely in housing bores and bores are not scored. Inspect machined surfaces for nicks, burrs or distortion.
2) Inspect valve and plugs for burrs or scratches. Minor scratches may be removed using crocus cloth. When sanding components, DO NOT round off edges of valve or plug.

CAUTION: Many valve body components are made of aluminum and contain a special coating. DO NOT polish or sand aluminum components, as special coating will be removed. Use magnet to check if components are made of aluminum before polishing or sanding. Use care when polishing or sanding components, DO NOT round off edges of component.

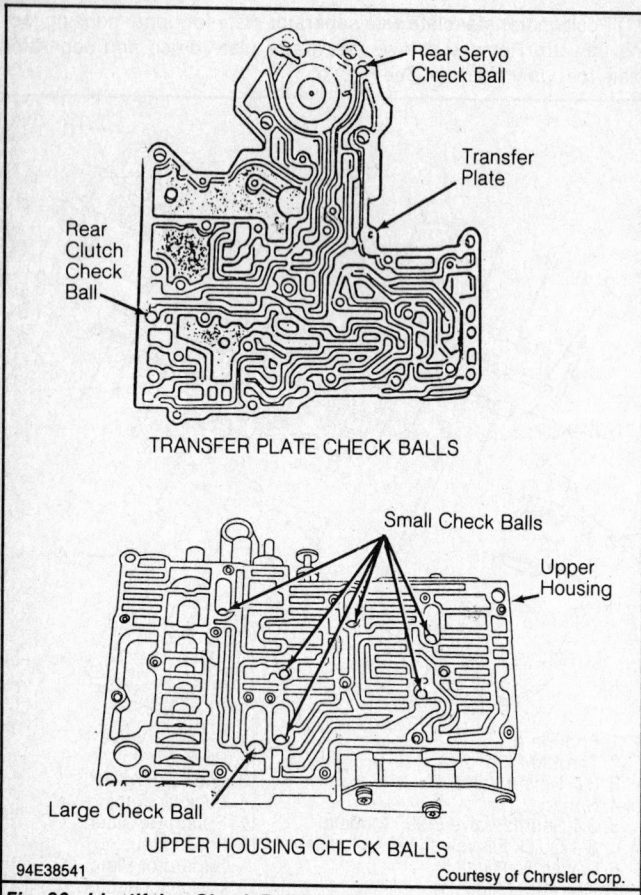

TRANSFER PLATE CHECK BALLS

UPPER HOUSING CHECK BALLS

94E38541   Courtesy of Chrysler Corp.

Fig. 36: Identifying Check Ball Locations

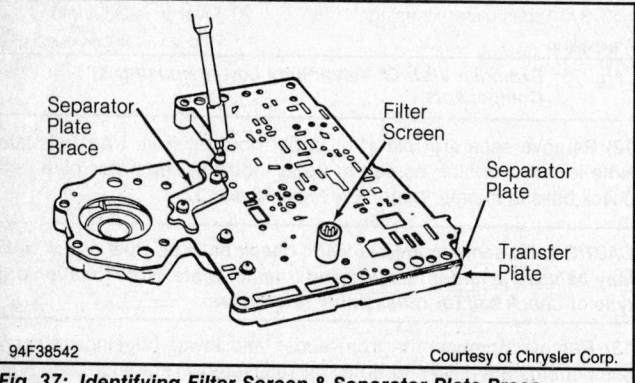

94F38542   Courtesy of Chrysler Corp.

Fig. 37: Identifying Filter Screen & Separator Plate Brace

3) Ensure all fluid passages are open. Inspect transfer plate and separator plates for distortion. Inspect check balls and seats for damage. Check flatness of mating surfaces on upper and lower housings.

4) Replace valve body if components are damaged. Only the following components can be serviced.

- Adjusting Screw Bracket
- Detent Ball & Spring
- Manual Shift Lever, Seal & Detent Ball
- Park Rod & Clip
- Solenoid Assembly
- Switch Valve & Spring
- Throttle Valve Lever & Seal

Reassembly – 1) Lubricate all components and fluid passages with Mopar ATF Plus Type 7176 fluid. Install components in lower housing. Ensure components are installed in original location. See Fig. 35. Tighten end plate screws to specification. See TORQUE SPECIFICATIONS.

2) Reassemble 3-4 accumulator using NEW seal rings on 3-4 accumulator piston. Install accumulator end plate.

CAUTION: On some models, plastic check balls or steel check balls may be used in upper housing and transfer plate. Ensure original type of check ball is used in original location. Some valve bodies may contain the rear servo check ball and rear clutch check ball and some may not. Install original number of check balls in original locations.

---

3) Install check balls in transfer plate. See Fig. 36. Ensure filter screen is installed in separator plate for upper housing. See Fig. 37.

4) Install separator plate for upper housing on transfer plate. Install separator plate brace. See Fig. 37. Install and tighten screws to specification.

5) Install remaining screws securing separator plate for the upper housing to the transfer plate. Tighten screws to specification.

6) Install check balls in upper housing. See Fig. 36. Install transfer plate and separator plate for upper housing on the upper housing. Ensure filter screen is fully seated in recess area on upper housing.

7) Install separator plate for lower housing on transfer plate. Install lower housing on transfer plate and upper housing. Install and tighten valve body screws to specification, starting at the center and working outward.

8) Install components in upper housing. Ensure components are installed in original location. See Fig. 33. Install cover plates and limit valve cover. Install and tighten screws to specification.

CAUTION: When installing shuttle valve, ensure clip fully engages groove on shuttle valve.

---

9) Lubricate bores for boost valve tube in both housings and ends of boost valve tube with Mopar ATF Plus Type 7176 fluid. Install boost valve tube, by starting boost valve tube into lower housing first and then in the upper housing. Ensure boost valve tube is installed behind brace for boost valve tube and is fully seated in the housings.

10) Install 3-4 accumulator housing on lower housing. Ensure springs and lock-up valve plug are properly positioned before tightening 3-4 accumulator housing screws.

11) Install case connector on 3-4 accumulator housing. Ensure tab on case connector engages with groove on 3-4 accumulator housing. Install and tighten shouldered-type screw to retain case connector.

12) Using NEW gasket, install solenoid assembly. Install and tighten solenoid assembly screws to specification. See TORQUE SPECIFICATIONS. Ensure wiring for solenoid assembly is properly routed and clears manual shift lever and park rod.

13) Install detent ball and spring in upper housing and retain in position using detent ball retainer. Install spring on end of line pressure regulator valve. Install switch valve spring on tang at end of adjusting screw bracket. Install adjusting screw bracket. Ensure springs align with adjusting screw bracket.

14) Install upper screw (short screw) in adjusting screw bracket first and then install lower screw (long screw). Tighten screws to specification. See TORQUE SPECIFICATIONS.

15) Install throttle valve lever in upper housing. Install manual shift lever over throttle valve lever. Align manual shift lever with detent ball and manual valve. Hold throttle valve lever upward and start manual shift lever into housing.

16) Install seal, washer and clip on manual shift lever. Remove detent ball retainer. Lubricate case connector "O" ring and manual shift lever shaft with petroleum jelly.

17) Ensure throttle valve lever aligns with end of kickdown valve and manual shift lever arm is engaged with manual valve. See Fig. 38.

CAUTION: If line pressure or throttle pressure adjusting screws were moved from original setting, they must be readjusted. See HYDRAULIC PRESSURE ADJUSTMENTS in this article.

---

18) Install boost valve and components. See Fig. 33. Install and tighten boost valve cover screws to specification. See TORQUE SPECIFICATIONS.

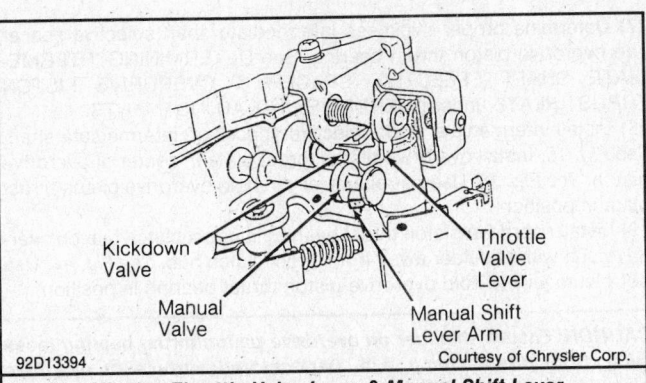

Kickdown Valve

Manual Valve

Throttle Valve Lever

Manual Shift Lever Arm

92D13394   Courtesy of Chrysler Corp.

Fig. 38: Aligning Throttle Valve Lever & Manual Shift Lever

TRANSMISSION REASSEMBLY

NOTE: Lubricate all components with Mopar ATF Plus Type 7176 fluid. Use petroleum jelly to hold thrust washers, thrust plates and gaskets in position. Ensure thrust washer and thrust plates are installed in original location.

1) Install NEW seal rings on front and rear servo pistons. Lubricate front and rear servo bores in transmission case with ATF. Using twisting motion, install rear servo piston in transmission case. It may be necessary to slightly tilt rear servo piston during installation.

2) Install spring and spring retainer on rear servo piston. Ensure spring is fully seated on rear servo piston. Compress spring and install snap ring.

3) Using twisting motion, install front servo piston in transmission case. It may be necessary to rock front servo piston back and forth during installation to ease front servo piston past snap ring groove.

4) Bottom front servo piston in bore on transmission case. Install spring on front servo piston. Compress spring and install snap ring.

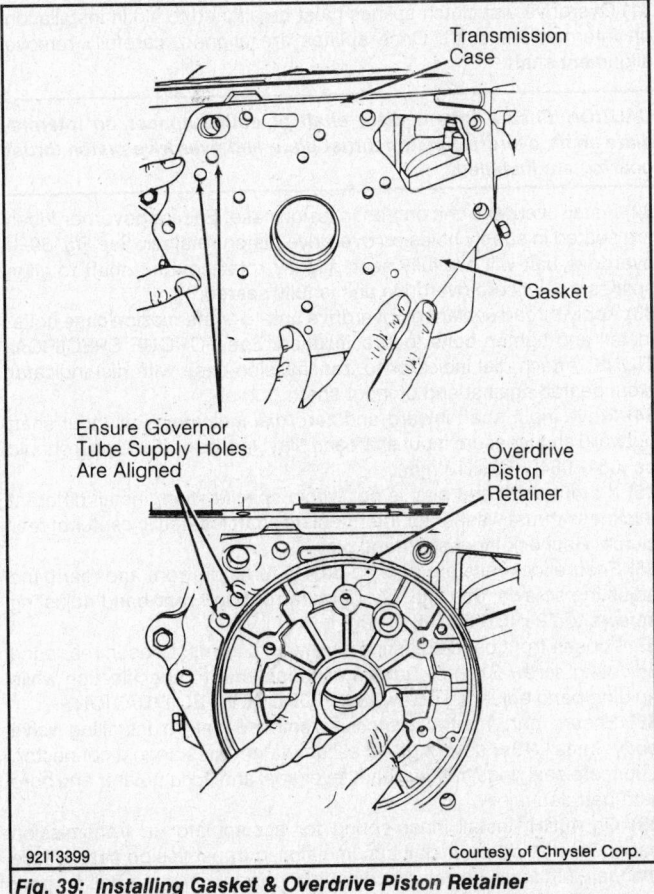

Transmission Case

Gasket

Ensure Governor Tube Supply Holes Are Aligned

Overdrive Piston Retainer

92I13399   Courtesy of Chrysler Corp.

Fig. 39: Installing Gasket & Overdrive Piston Retainer

5) Install NEW gasket on rear of transmission case. Use petroleum jelly to hold gasket in place. Ensure governor tube supply holes on gasket align with holes on transmission case. See Fig. 39.

6) Install overdrive piston retainer so governor tube supply holes align with holes on transmission case. See Fig. 39. Install and tighten bolts to specification. See TORQUE SPECIFICATIONS.

7) Install overrunning clutch components. See OVERRUNNING CLUTCH under TRANSMISSION COMPONENT DISASSEMBLY & REASSEMBLY.

8) On 46RH, install rear band and rear band linkage in transmission case. Ensure notched side of link faces away from rear band.

9) Slightly tilt low-reverse drum and install in rollers on overrunning clutch. Rotate low-reverse drum clockwise until low-reverse drum is fully seated. Low-reverse drum should rotate freely clockwise (viewed from front of transmission case), but lock when rotated counterclockwise.

CAUTION: Ensure low-reverse drum rotates freely clockwise (viewed from front of transmission case), but locks when rotated counterclockwise. Check for improper one-way clutch component assembly if low-reverse drum will not rotate correctly.

10) Install low-reverse drum-to-overdrive retainer snap ring. Install NEW "O" rings on reaction pin for rear band. Lubricate "O" rings with ATF. Partially install reaction pin for rear band in rear of transmission case. This is the pin near top of transmission case, farthest from oil pan surface. Ensure reaction pin is fully seated.

11) Install adjusting lever, reaction lever and strut on rear band. Finish installing reaction pin to retain rear band components. Install remaining pin for rear band. Pin is located between overdrive piston retainer and transmission case. Tighten rear band adjusting screw enough to hold components in place.

12) On 47RH, install rear band on low-reverse drum. See Fig. 40. Ensure rear band is installed in correct direction on low-reverse drum in relation to shoulder on low-reverse drum.

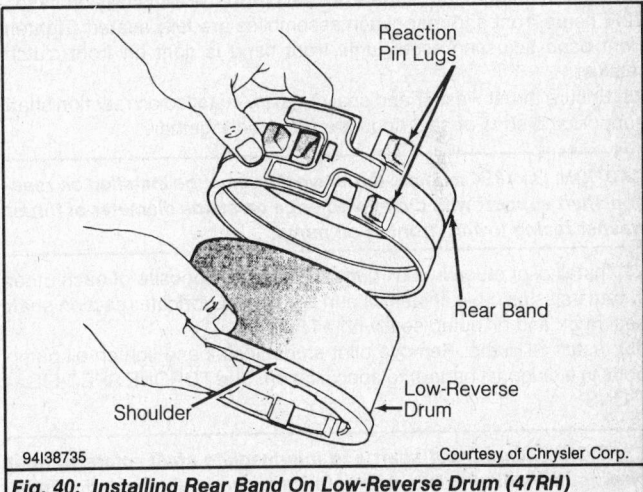

Reaction Pin Lugs

Rear Band

Low-Reverse Drum

Shoulder

94I38735   Courtesy of Chrysler Corp.

Fig. 40: Installing Rear Band On Low-Reverse Drum (47RH)

13) Slightly tilt low-reverse drum and install in rollers on overrunning clutch. Rotate low-reverse drum clockwise until low-reverse drum is fully seated. Low-reverse drum should rotate freely clockwise (viewed from front of transmission case), but lock when rotated counterclockwise.

CAUTION: Ensure low-reverse drum rotates freely clockwise (viewed from front of transmission case), but locks when rotated counterclockwise. Check for improper one-way clutch component assembly if low-reverse drum will not rotate correctly.

14) Install low-reverse drum-to-overdrive retainer snap ring. Install rear band reaction pin. This is the pin near top of transmission case, farthest from oil pan surface. Ensure reaction pin is fully seated.

15) Rotate rear band until reaction pin lugs on rear band contact the rear band reaction pin. Install NEW "O" rings on pivot pin for rear band. Lubricate "O" rings with ATF.

16) Install lever and pivot pin. Pivot pin is located between overdrive piston retainer and transmission case. Tighten rear band adjusting screw enough to hold components in place.

17) On all models, install lever for front band in transmission case and over servo guide. Install front band pin through front band pin access hole on front of transmission. See Fig. 18. Apply thread sealant on plug for front band pin access hole. Install plug and tighten to specification. See TORQUE SPECIFICATIONS.

18) Install intermediate shaft and planetary gear train. Install thrust plate on end of intermediate shaft.

CAUTION: *Ensure seal rings are installed on input shaft. Ensure seal rings and fiber thrust washer are installed on front of piston retainer. See Fig. 29. Ends of seal ring on front of piston retainer must be fastened together. Diagonal ends of seal rings on input shaft must be properly joined.*

---

19) Align teeth on front clutch discs. Install front clutch on rear clutch. Ensure front clutch is fully seated on rear clutch by rotating front clutch back and forth. Install intermediate shaft thrust washer in center of rear clutch so groove in thrust washer is toward intermediate shaft. See Fig. 29.

CAUTION: *Ensure intermediate shaft thrust washer is installed with groove in thrust washer toward intermediate shaft.*

---

20) Position transmission case with oil pump opening facing upward. Using small screwdriver, align teeth on rear clutch discs. Install front and rear clutch assemblies. Rotate assembly back and forth until rear clutch discs fully engage with front annulus gear.

21) Install front band over front clutch retainer. Install front band strut between front band and lever on transmission case. Install anchor between the other side of the front band and the transmission case.

22) Ensure front and rear clutch assemblies are fully seated. Tighten front band adjusting screw until front band is tight on front clutch retainer.

23) Ensure thrust washer and seal rings are installed on reaction shaft support and ends of seal rings are fastened together.

CAUTION: *On 1994 models, thrust washer must be installed on reaction shaft support with chamfered edge on inside diameter of thrust washer facing toward front of oil pump.*

---

24) Install pilot studs in 2 oil pump bolt holes, opposite of each other in transmission case. Install oil pump gasket. Lubricate reaction shaft seal rings and oil pump seal with ATF.

25) Install oil pump. Remove pilot studs. Install and tighten oil pump bolts in a diagonal pattern to specification. See TORQUE SPECIFICATIONS.

CAUTION: *Ensure input shaft and intermediate shaft rotate without binding. If binding exists, check for improperly assembled components.*

---

26) Install NEW seal on overdrive piston and lubricate with Mopar Door Ease. Install overdrive piston in overdrive piston retainer. If necessary, use feeler gauge to guide seal on overdrive piston into overdrive piston retainer.

CAUTION: *Ensure 2 locating pins on transmission case side of overdrive piston engage with 2 holes on overdrive piston retainer.*

CAUTION: *Before installing intermediate shaft selective spacer and overdrive piston thrust bearing, ensure proper procedure is used to determine thickness of these components. See DETERMINING INTERMEDIATE SHAFT SELECTIVE SPACER & OVERDRIVE PISTON THRUST PLATE under OVERDRIVE UNIT ADJUSTMENTS.*

---

27) Determine proper thickness intermediate shaft selective spacer and overdrive piston thrust bearing. See DETERMINING INTERMEDIATE SHAFT SELECTIVE SPACER & OVERDRIVE PISTON THRUST PLATE under OVERDRIVE UNIT ADJUSTMENTS.

28) Install intermediate shaft selective spacer on intermediate shaft. See Fig. 15. Install overdrive piston thrust plate in center of overdrive piston. See Fig. 15. Use petroleum jelly to hold overdrive piston thrust plate in position.

29) Install overdrive piston thrust bearing in direct clutch hub on overdrive unit with shoulder away from direct clutch hub. See Fig. 41. Use petroleum jelly to hold overdrive piston thrust bearing in position.

CAUTION: *Ensure shoulder on overdrive piston thrust bearing faces away from direct clutch hub. Dark-colored surface of overdrive piston thrust bearing should be toward overdrive piston.*

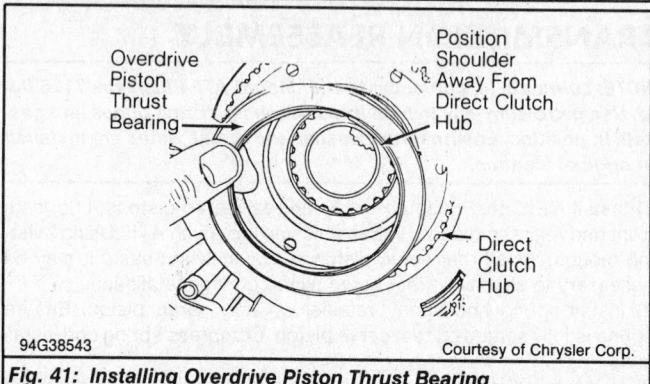

Fig. 41: **Installing Overdrive Piston Thrust Bearing**

30) Apply small amount of petroleum jelly on end of intermediate shaft. Using Alignment Shaft (6227-2), align splines of planetary gear assembly and overrunning clutch in overdrive unit. See Fig. 16. Ensure alignment shaft is fully seated.

31) Overdrive unit clutch splines must be aligned to aid in installation on intermediate shaft. Once splines are aligned, carefully remove alignment shaft.

CAUTION: *Ensure intermediate shaft selective spacer on intermediate shaft, overdrive piston thrust plate and overdrive piston thrust bearing are installed.*

---

32) Install overdrive unit on transmission case. Ensure governor tubes are seated in supply holes on overdrive piston retainer. See Fig. 39. If overdrive unit will not fully seat, slightly rotate output shaft to align splines and ensure overdrive unit is fully seated.

33) Apply thread sealant on overdrive unit-to-transmission case bolts. Install and tighten bolts to specification. See TORQUE SPECIFICATIONS. Attach dial indicator to transmission case with dial indicator stem seated against end of input shaft.

34) Move input shaft inward and zero dial indicator. Pull input shaft outward and measure input shaft end play. Input shaft end play should be .034-.084" (.86-2.13 mm).

35) If input shaft end play is not within specification, install different thickness thrust washer for intermediate shaft located in center of rear clutch. Recheck input shaft end play.

36) Ensure lock nuts are backed off 4-5 turns on front and rear band adjusting screws. See Fig. 17. Tighten front and rear band adjusting screws to 72 INCH lbs. (8.1 N.m).

37) Loosen front band adjusting screw 2 1/2 turns. Loosen rear band adjusting screw 2 turns. Tighten each lock nut to specification while holding band adjusting screw. See TORQUE SPECIFICATIONS.

38) Ensure park/neutral switch is removed before installing valve body. Install NEW seal rings on accumulator and solenoid connector. Lubricate seal rings, manual shift lever seal and accumulator and bore with petroleum jelly.

39) On 46RH, install inner spring for accumulator in transmission case. On all models, install accumulator in transmission case. Place manual shift lever on valve body in low gear position so ball on park rod can be installed in parking sprag.

40) Using screwdriver, push parking sprag to engage with park gear. This allows knob on park rod to move past parking sprag when installing valve body. Rotate output shaft to ensure parking sprag is engaged.

CAUTION: Ensure park rod enters parking sprag, as park rod may enter cavity in the case and not enter parking sprag. Park rod will be damaged if it is not engaged with parking sprag.

41) Install outer spring between accumulator and valve body. Install valve body, working park rod past parking sprag. Ensure accumulator spring remains in place.

CAUTION: Alternate tightening valve body-to-transmission case bolts to prevent damage to valve body. DO NOT overtighten bolts or transmission and valve body may be damaged.

42) Install valve body-to-transmission case bolts in original location and tighten evenly to specification. See TORQUE SPECIFICATIONS.
43) Install NEW filter assembly. Install and tighten bolts to specification. Reconnect all necessary electrical connections. Install throttle valve and manual shift levers. Ensure throttle valve and manual shift levers rotate smoothly.
44) Install magnet in the small protrusion area at the corner of the oil pan. Using NEW gasket, install oil pan. Install and tighten bolts to specification. Using NEW seal, install park/neutral switch. Tighten park/neutral switch to specification.

CAUTION: If transmission failure existed, flush oil cooler and check oil cooler flow. See OIL COOLER FLUSHING and OIL COOLER FLOW CHECK under ON-VEHICLE SERVICE.

OVERDRIVE UNIT DISASSEMBLY

OVERDRIVE UNIT

Disassembly – 1) Remove snap ring and overdrive clutch pack components from overdrive unit case. See Fig. 42. Note direction of clutch discs and clutch plates in overdrive clutch for reassembly reference. Components must be installed in correct sequence.

CAUTION: Note direction of clutch discs and clutch plates in overdrive clutch pack for reassembly reference. Also note number of each components, as some models may contain different number of clutch components.

2) Remove waved snap ring and reaction plate snap ring. Both snap rings are installed in same groove in overdrive unit case.
3) Remove access cover from top of overdrive unit case for access to front bearing retaining ring. See Fig. 43. Using snap ring pliers, expand front bearing retaining ring while pushing output shaft forward to release bearing from retaining ring. See Fig. 43.

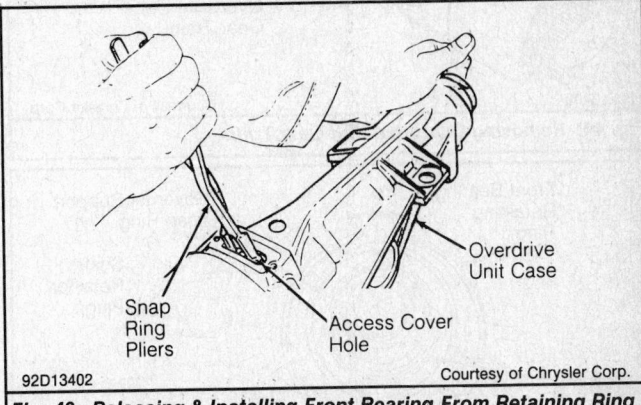

92D13402   Courtesy of Chrysler Corp.

Fig. 43: Releasing & Installing Front Bearing From Retaining Ring

4) Remove overdrive unit gear train from overdrive unit case. See Fig. 44. Remove front bearing retaining ring and governor support snap ring from overdrive unit case. See Fig. 45.
5) Remove governor support with governor supply tube assembly from overdrive unit case. See Figs. 45 and 46. Remove shaft retainer plug and snap ring for reaction plug from overdrive unit case. See Fig. 45. DO NOT overcompress snap ring or it may be damaged.
6) Remove shaft, parking sprag, spring and reaction plug. See Fig. 45. Remove rear bearing snap ring from overdrive unit case. If necessary, rotate snap ring until end of snap ring is adjacent to notch in case.

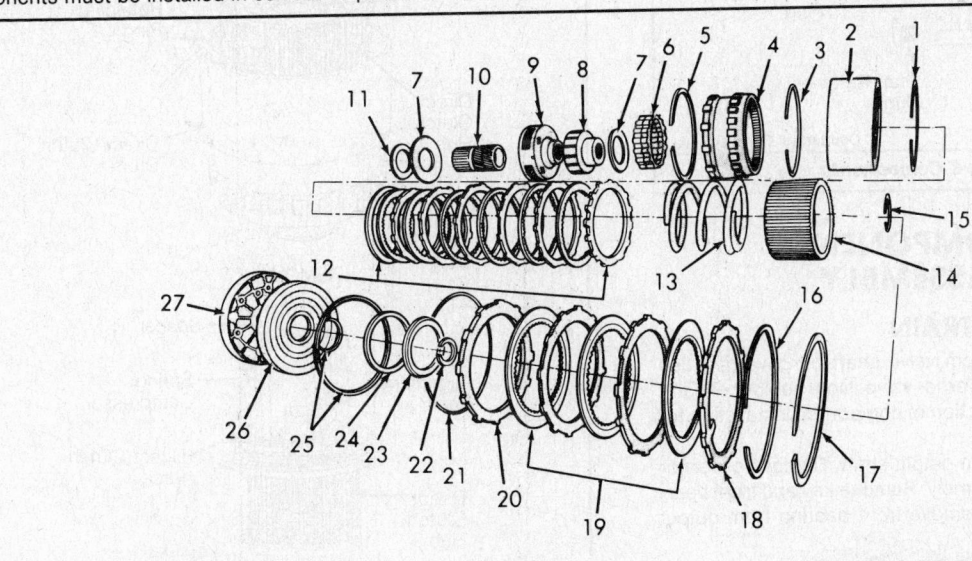

1. Inner Retaining Ring	10. Sun Gear
2. Direct Clutch Drum	11. Spring Plate
3. Outer Retaining Ring	12. Direct Clutch Pack
4. Annulus Gear	13. Direct Clutch Spring
5. Annulus Gear Snap Ring	14. Direct Clutch Hub
6. Overrunning Clutch	15. Direct Clutch Hub Snap Ring
7. Thrust Bearing	16. Waved Snap Ring
8. Overrunning Clutch Hub	17. Reaction Plate Snap Ring
9. Planetary Gear	18. Reaction Plate

19. Overdrive Clutch Pack	
20. Pressure Plate	
21. Snap Ring	
22. Intermediate Shaft Selective Spacer	
23. Overdrive Piston Thrust Bearing	
24. Overdrive Piston Thrust Plate	
25. Overdrive Piston Seals	
26. Overdrive Piston	
27. Overdrive Piston Retainer	

Courtesy of Chrysler Corp.

92C13401

Fig. 42: Exploded View Of Typical Overdrive Unit

7) Remove rear bearing from overdrive unit case by tapping case on wooden block. Inspect bushings in overdrive unit case. Replace bushings if damaged.

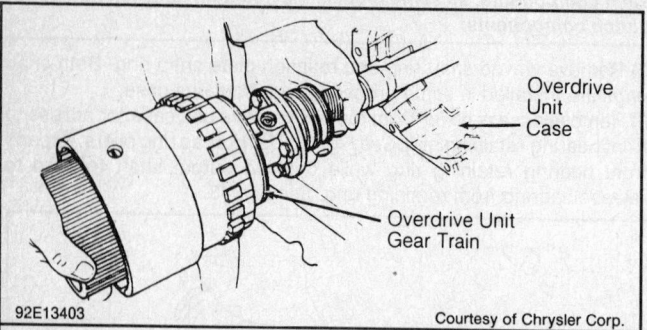

Fig. 44: *Removing Overdrive Unit Gear Train*

Courtesy of Chrysler Corp.

92E13403

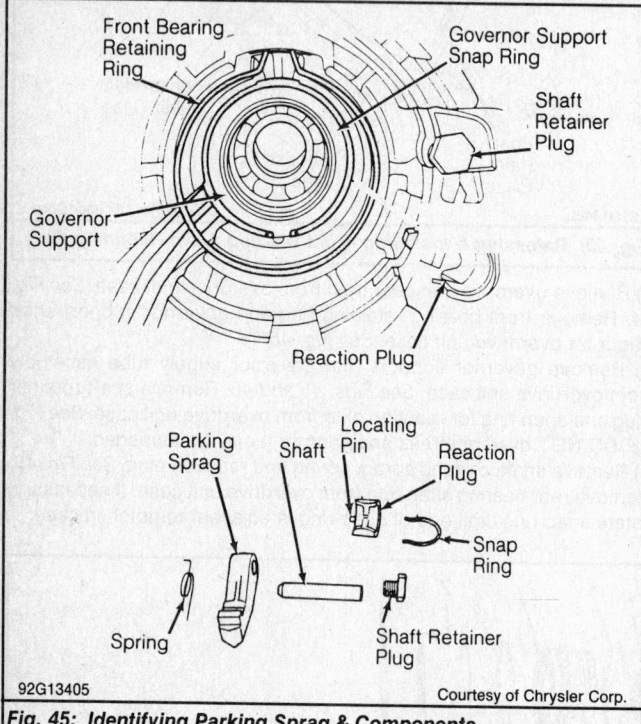

Fig. 45: *Identifying Parking Sprag & Components*

Courtesy of Chrysler Corp.

92G13405

OVERDRIVE UNIT COMPONENT DISASSEMBLY & REASSEMBLY

OVERDRIVE UNIT GEAR TRAIN

Disassembly – 1) Remove clip from valve shaft on governor. *See Fig. 46.* Remove valve shaft and governor valve. Note number of components in governor valve and direction of component installation for reassembly reference.

2) Remove governor snap ring from output shaft. Remove governor drive and governor body as an assembly. Remove key and front bearing snap ring from output shaft. Remove front bearing from output shaft.

3) Place overdrive unit gear train in press. Support assembly with press plates placed under flange on output shaft.

4) Position Spring Compressor (6227-1) on direct clutch hub. *See Fig. 47.* It may be necessary to install plate on top of spring compressor to provide extra press travel.

CAUTION: *Ensure proper equipment is used when compressing direct clutch spring, as direct clutch spring is under excessive pressure. Ensure ram on press has a minimum travel of approximately 6".*

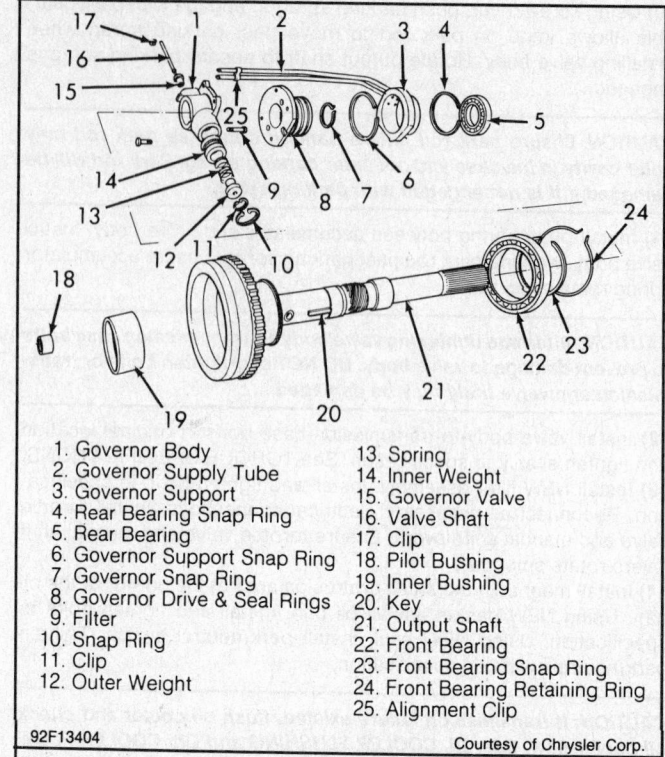

1. Governor Body
2. Governor Supply Tube
3. Governor Support
4. Rear Bearing Snap Ring
5. Rear Bearing
6. Governor Support Snap Ring
7. Governor Snap Ring
8. Governor Drive & Seal Rings
9. Filter
10. Snap Ring
11. Clip
12. Outer Weight
13. Spring
14. Inner Weight
15. Governor Valve
16. Valve Shaft
17. Clip
18. Pilot Bushing
19. Inner Bushing
20. Key
21. Output Shaft
22. Front Bearing
23. Front Bearing Snap Ring
24. Front Bearing Retaining Ring
25. Alignment Clip

Courtesy of Chrysler Corp.

92F13404

Fig. 46: *Exploded View Of Overdrive Unit Output Shaft & Governor*

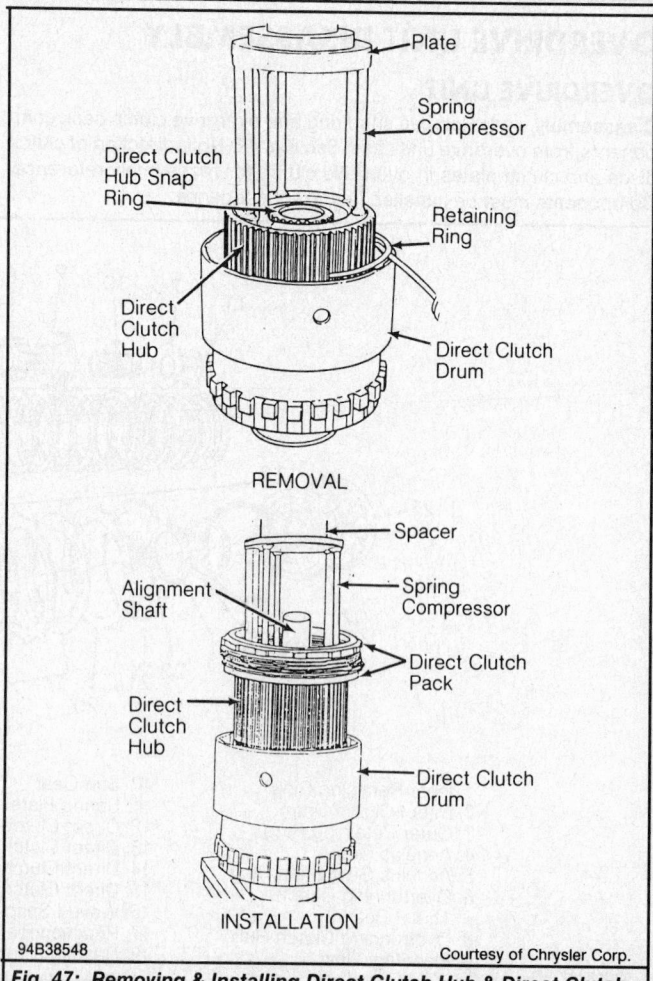

Courtesy of Chrysler Corp.

94B38548

Fig. 47: *Removing & Installing Direct Clutch Hub & Direct Clutch Spring*

5) Slowly compress direct clutch spring. Remove retaining ring for direct clutch pack from outer edge of direct clutch drum. Remove direct clutch hub snap ring, located at center of direct clutch hub. See Fig. 47. Slowly release press. Remove spring compressor.

CAUTION: Note direction of clutch discs and clutch plates in direct clutch pack for reassembly reference. Also note number of each component, as some models may contain different number of clutch components. Components must be installed in correct sequence.

6) Remove direct clutch pack components from direct clutch drum, noting location of components for reassembly reference. Remove direct clutch hub and direct clutch spring. Remove sun gear and spring plate. Remove thrust bearing and planetary gear. See Fig. 42.

7) Insert expanding-type snap ring pliers into splines on overrunning clutch hub. Expand snap ring pliers against splines. Rotate overrunning clutch hub counterclockwise and remove overrunning clutch assembly from direct clutch drum.

CAUTION: Ensure direct clutch drum-to-annulus gear location is marked for reassembly reference before disassembling.

8) Remove thrust bearing from overrunning clutch hub. Remove overrunning clutch from overrunning clutch hub. See Figs. 42. Scribe alignment marks on outer surface of direct clutch drum and annulus gear for reassembly reference.

9) Remove inner and outer retaining rings from direct clutch drum. See Fig 42. Remove direct clutch drum from annulus gear.

CAUTION: Ensure output shaft-to-annulus gear location is marked for reassembly reference before disassembling.

10) Scribe alignment marks on annulus gear and output shaft for reassembly reference. Remove annulus gear snap ring. Using soft-faced hammer, tap annulus gear from output shaft.

Cleaning & Inspection – 1) Clean all metal components with solvent and dry with compressed air. Inspect clutch discs for flatness, flaking or glazing. Inspect all clutch plates, pressure plate and reaction plate for flatness or damage at lug area.

2) Ensure direct clutch components slide freely in direct clutch drum. Replace components if binding exists. Inspect sun gear and bushings for damage. Replace sun gear if bushings are defective.

3) Inspect planetary gear for damage. Ensure pins for gears on planetary gear are tight and are not damaged. Inspect surface on overrunning clutch hub or overrunning clutch for damage. Replace overrunning clutch as an assembly if damaged.

4) Inspect inner and pilot bushings for damage. Ensure governor valve and weights slide freely in governor body. Inspect governor support and governor supply tubes for damage. DO NOT attempt to remove governor supply tubes from governor support. Replace governor support and tubes as an assembly if damaged.

NOTE: Governor valve is made of aluminum and output shaft is different for use with aluminum governor valve. These components are not interchangeable with previous models. Always install the original type governor components.

5) Inspect output shaft for damaged in machined or splined areas. Replace damaged components.

Reassembly – 1) Lubricate components with Mopar ATF Plus Type 7176 fluid. Soak clutch discs in ATF at least 20 minutes before installing. Install NEW pilot bushing and NEW inner bushing in output shaft (if necessary). Lubricate pilot bushing and inner bushing with petroleum jelly.

CAUTION: Ensure front bearing is installed on output shaft with groove in front bearing for retaining ring facing toward splined end of output shaft.

2) Install front bearing on output shaft so groove in front bearing for front bearing retaining ring faces toward splined end of output shaft.

Install front bearing snap ring on output shaft. Install annulus gear on output shaft, ensuring reference marks are aligned. Install annulus gear snap ring.

3) Install direct clutch drum on annulus gear ensuring reference marks are aligned. Ensure lugs on direct clutch drum fully engage lugs on annulus gear. Install outer retaining ring.

4) Slide direct clutch drum forward. Install inner retaining ring. Install overrunning clutch on overrunning clutch hub. See Fig. 48. Shoulder on overrunning clutch should seat in small recess at edge of overrunning clutch hub.

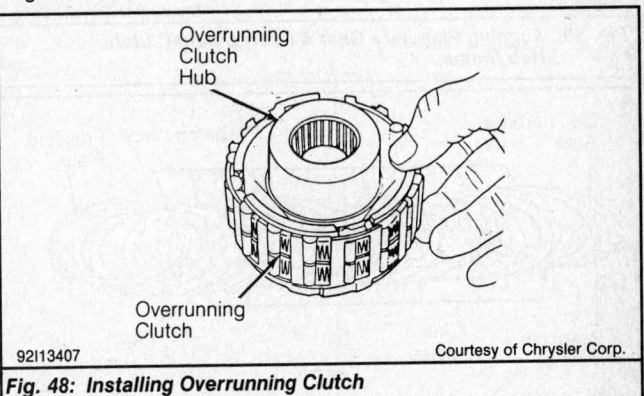

92I13407　　　　　　　　　　Courtesy of Chrysler Corp.

Fig. 48: Installing Overrunning Clutch

5) Coat thrust bearing with petroleum jelly and install on overrunning clutch hub. Ensure thrust bearing is fully seated on overrunning clutch hub.

6) Insert expanding-type snap ring pliers into splines on overrunning clutch hub. Expand snap ring pliers against splines. Rotate overrunning clutch hub counterclockwise and install overrunning clutch assembly in direct clutch drum.

7) Install planetary gear in annulus gear. Ensure planetary gear is fully seated. Install spring plate on sun gear with shoulder on spring plate toward front of sun gear (if removed). See Fig. 49. Install snap ring.

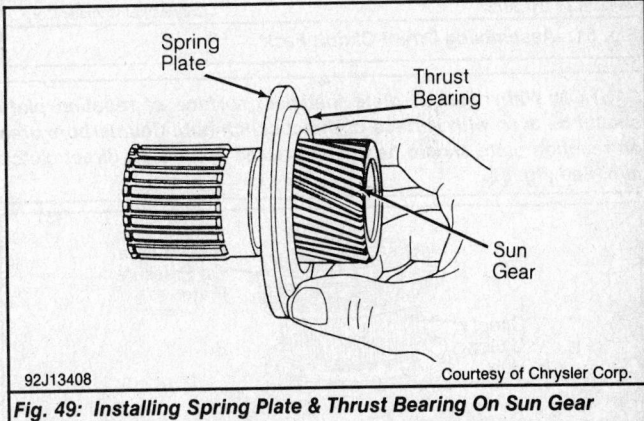

92J13408　　　　　　　　　　Courtesy of Chrysler Corp.

Fig. 49: Installing Spring Plate & Thrust Bearing On Sun Gear

8) Coat thrust bearing with petroleum jelly and install on sun gear. Ensure thrust bearing fully seats against spring plate.

9) Install sun gear, spring plate and thrust bearing in direct clutch drum. Install Alignment Shaft (6227-2) through sun gear to align splines of planetary gear and overrunning clutch hub. See Fig. 50. Ensure alignment shaft is fully seated.

CAUTION: Ensure direct clutch components are installed in original location and original number of components are installed.

10) Install direct clutch spring on spring plate in direct clutch hub. Ensure spring is properly seated. Assemble direct clutch pack. See Fig. 51.

11) Install reaction plate on direct clutch hub. One side of reaction plate contains a counterbore area. See Fig. 51. Counterbore area should be installed so it fits over raised splines at rear of direct clutch hub. See Fig. 52.

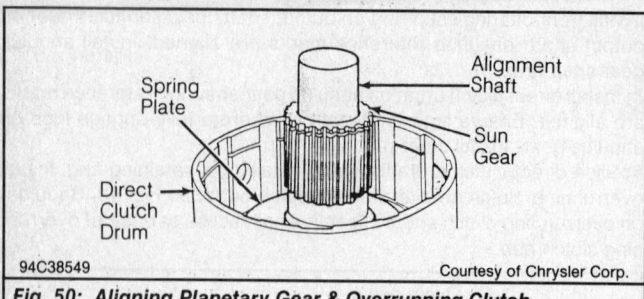

94C38549   Courtesy of Chrysler Corp.

Fig. 50: Aligning Planetary Gear & Overrunning Clutch Hub Splines

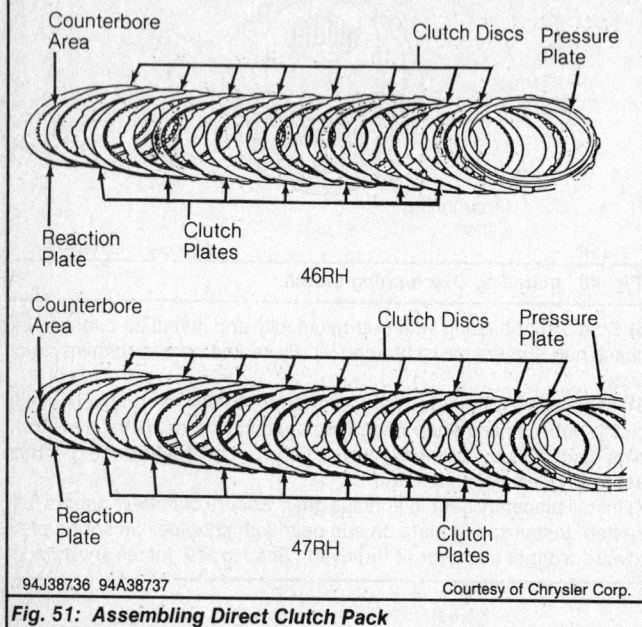

94J38736 94A38737   Courtesy of Chrysler Corp.

Fig. 51: Assembling Direct Clutch Pack

CAUTION: With reaction plate installed, surface of reaction plate should be even with surface of direct clutch hub. Counterbore area on reaction plate should be against raised splines on direct clutch hub. See Fig. 52.

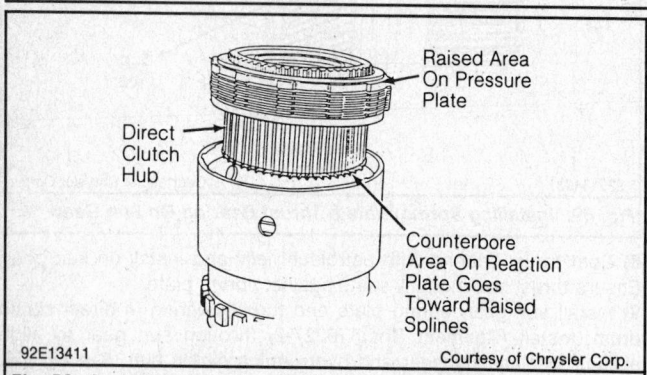

92E13411   Courtesy of Chrysler Corp.

Fig. 52: Installing Reaction Plate & Pressure Plate

12) Alternately install clutch discs and clutch plates on reaction plate starting with clutch disc. See Fig. 51. Install pressure plate with raise area away from clutch pack. See Fig. 52.

13) Install direct clutch pack and direct clutch hub on direct clutch spring. Ensure direct clutch hub is started on the splines on the sun gear. Place overdrive unit gear train assembly in press.

14) Install spring compressor and spacer on top of direct clutch hub. See Fig. 47. Slide direct clutch pack upward and set it on edge of spring compressor.

15) Compress direct clutch spring so direct clutch hub snap ring and retaining ring for direct clutch pack are visible. Install direct clutch pack in direct clutch drum. Install retaining ring for direct clutch pack ring and direct clutch hub snap ring.

CAUTION: Ensure retaining ring for direct clutch pack and direct clutch hub snap ring are fully seated.

---

16) Release press. Remove spring compressor. Ensure alignment shaft is fully seated. If alignment shaft becomes unseated, it may be necessary to disassemble overdrive unit gear train and realign splines. Remove overdrive unit gear train assembly from press.

OVERDRIVE UNIT

Reassembly – 1) Install front bearing on output shaft (if not previously installed). Ensure groove in front bearing for front bearing retaining ring faces toward splined end of output shaft. Install snap ring on output shaft.

2) Install key in output shaft for governor. Install NEW seal rings on governor drive. Ensure ends of seal rings are locked together.

3) Install governor body on governor drive. Ensure filter is properly seated in governor body. Tighten governor body-to-governor drive bolts to specification. See TORQUE SPECIFICATIONS.

4) Install inner weight, spring and outer weight in governor body. Install snap ring. Install governor drive and governor body assembly on output shaft. Ensure governor drive engages key in output shaft.

5) Align valve shaft holes in governor body and output shaft. Install governor valve, valve shaft and clips. Ensure clips are installed on each end of valve shaft and are fully seated. Install governor snap ring. Install rear bearing and snap ring in overdrive unit case.

6) Install parking sprag, spring and shaft in overdrive unit case. Ensure end of spring is hooked on parking sprag.

7) Install and tighten shaft retainer plug to specification. See TORQUE SPECIFICATIONS. Install reaction plug in overdrive unit case. Ensure locating pin on reaction plug engages hole in overdrive unit case. See Fig. 45. Install snap ring to retain reaction plug. DO NOT over compress snap ring when installing.

8) Install alignment clip on end of governor supply tube until clip contacts shoulder on each tube (if removed). See Fig. 46. Install governor support and governor supply tube assembly in overdrive unit case. Install governor support snap ring.

9) Install front bearing retaining ring in overdrive unit case. Ensure ends of front bearing retaining ring face the access cover opening in overdrive unit case.

10) Place gear train in vertical position. Support assembly on Spring Compressor (6227-1) on workbench. Spring compressor fits in center of direct clutch hub.

11) Install overdrive unit case over gear train assembly. Using snap ring pliers, expand front bearing retaining ring through access hole cover. See Fig. 43.

12) Slide overdrive unit case downward until front bearing retaining ring engages locating groove on outside of front bearing. Release front bearing retaining ring.

13) Remove overdrive unit from spring compressor. Install gasket and access cover on overdrive unit case. Install reaction plate snap ring in overdrive unit case. This is the flat snap ring with the notched ends.

14) Install waved snap ring in overdrive unit case. Waved snap ring fits on top of reaction plate snap ring. Both snap rings fit in same groove. Ensure both snap rings are fully seated.

15) Install reaction plate for overdrive clutch pack. Reaction plate is thinner than the pressure plate. Install overdrive clutch discs and clutch plates on reaction plate. Start with clutch disc followed with clutch plate and then alternating between clutch plates and clutch discs.

CAUTION: Ensure overdrive clutch components are installed in original location, and original number of components are installed. On 46RH, there should be 4 clutch discs and 3 clutch plates. On 47RH, there should be 5 clutch discs and 4 clutch plates.

16) Install pressure plate and snap ring. Place overdrive unit in vertical position with access to direct clutch hub. Remove alignment shaft.

17) Proper thickness intermediate shaft selective spacer and overdrive piston thrust plate must be determined before installing overdrive unit. See DETERMINING INTERMEDIATE SHAFT SELECTIVE SPACER & OVERDRIVE PISTON THRUST PLATE under OVERDRIVE UNIT ADJUSTMENTS.

OVERDRIVE UNIT ADJUSTMENTS

DETERMINING INTERMEDIATE SHAFT SELECTIVE SPACER & OVERDRIVE PISTON THRUST PLATE

1) To determine intermediate shaft selective spacer, output shaft end play is checked. Place overdrive unit in vertical position. Install Adapter (6312) through sun gear, planetary gear and into pilot bushing in output shaft. *See Fig. 53.* Ensure adapter bottoms against shoulder on planetary gear.

2) Install Bar (6311) across surface of overdrive unit case. Position Caliper (C-4962) on bar. Extend caliper downward through bar until it contacts adapter. Note reading on caliper. This is the output shaft end play.

3) Using output shaft end play reading, determine proper intermediate shaft selective spacer thickness. See INTERMEDIATE SHAFT SELECTIVE SPACER SELECTION table. Remove adapter. Retain intermediate shaft selective spacer for overdrive unit installation.

INTERMEDIATE SHAFT SELECTIVE SPACER SELECTION

Output Shaft End Play [1] In. (mm)	Shaft Spacer Thickness In. (mm)
.7336-.7505 (18.633-19.063)	.158-.159 (4.01-4.04)
.7506-.7675 (19.065-19.494)	.175-.176 (4.44-4.47)
.7676-.7855 (19.497-19.951)	.193-.194 (4.90-4.93)
.7856-.8011 (19.954-20.348)	.211-.212 (5.35-5.38)

[1] – Measurement taken with Adapter (6312) installed through sun gear, planetary gear and into pilot bushing in output shaft.

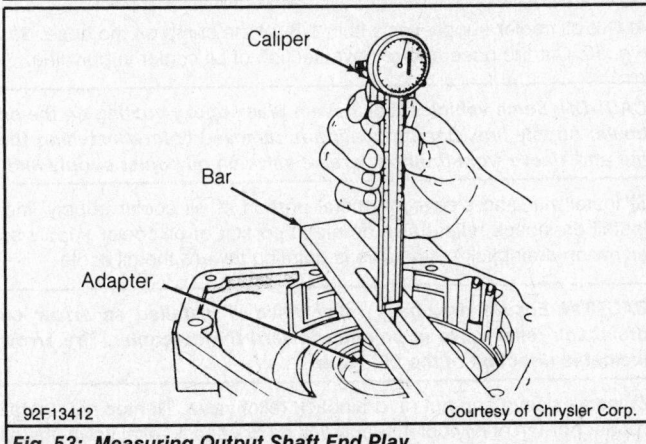

```
92F13412                          Courtesy of Chrysler Corp.
```

Fig. 53: Measuring Output Shaft End Play

4) To determine overdrive piston thrust plate thickness, install Bar (6311) across surface of overdrive unit case. Position Caliper (C-4962) on bar.

5) Extend caliper through the bar and measure distance to surface of direct clutch hub thrust bearing seat in 4 places 90 degrees apart. *See Fig. 54.*

6) Determine average distance by adding 4 measurements together and dividing by 4. Using average distance, determine proper overdrive piston thrust plate thickness. See OVERDRIVE PISTON THRUST PLATE SELECTION table. Remove caliper and bar. Retain overdrive piston thrust plate for overdrive unit installation.

CAUTION: Ensure intermediate shaft selective spacer and overdrive piston thrust plate and overdrive piston thrust bearing are installed before installing overdrive unit on transmission.

OVERDRIVE PISTON THRUST PLATE SELECTION

Hub Thrust Bearing Seat Average Distance In. (mm)	Overdrive Piston Thrust Plate Thickness In. (mm)
1.7500-1.7649 (44.450-44.828)	.108-.110 (2.74-2.79)
1.7650-1.7799 (44.831-45.209)	.123-.125 (3.12-3.18)
1.7800-1.7949 (45.212-45.590)	.138-.140 (3.50-3.56)
1.7950-1.8099 (45.593-45.971)	.153-.155 (3.89-3.94)
1.8100-1.8249 (45.974-46.352)	.168-.170 (4.27-4.31)
1.8250-1.8399 (46.355-46.733)	.183-.185 (4.65-4.70)
1.8400-1.8549 (46.736-47.114)	.198-.200 (5.03-5.08)
1.8550-1.8699 (47.117-47.495)	.213-.215 (5.41-5.46)
1.8700-1.8849 (47.498-47.876)	.228-.230 (5.79-5.84)
1.8850-1.8999 (47.879-48.257)	.243-.245 (6.17-6.22)

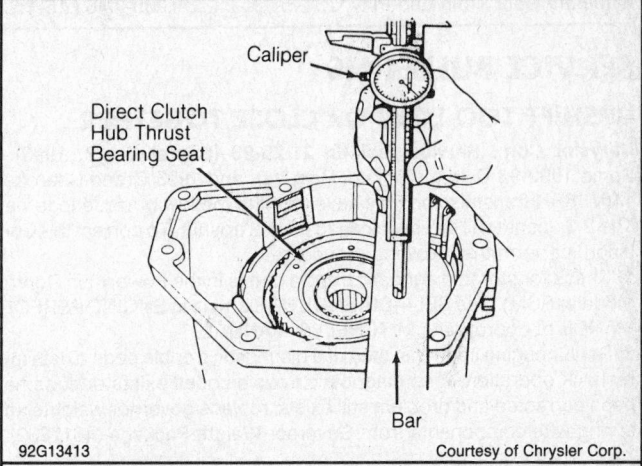

```
92G13413                          Courtesy of Chrysler Corp.
```

Fig. 54: Measuring Distance To Direct Clutch Hub Thrust Bearing Seat

TORQUE SPECIFICATIONS

TORQUE SPECIFICATIONS

Application	Ft. Lbs. (N.m)
Band Adjusting Screw Lock Nut	
Front Band	25 (34)
Rear Band	30 (41)
Front Band Pin Access Hole Plug	13 (18)
Park/Neutral Switch	25 (34)
Oil Pan Bolt	13 (18)
Oil Pump Bolt	15 (20)
Overdrive Piston Retainer Bolt	13 (18)
Overdrive Unit-To-Transmission Case Bolt [1]	25 (34)
Reaction Shaft Support Bolt	15 (20)
Shaft Retainer Plug	20 (27)
Vehicle Speed Sensor Nut (1993 Models)	13 (18)

	INCH Lbs. (N.m)
Adapter Retainer Bolt	100 (11.3)
Adjusting Screw Bracket Screw	35 (4.0)
Boost Valve Cover Screw	35 (4.0)
Cover Plate Screw	35 (4.0)
End Plate Screw	35 (4.0)
Filter Assembly Bolt	35 (4.0)
Governor Body-To-Governor Drive Bolt	96 (10.8)
Limit Valve Cover Screw	35 (4.0)
Overrunning Clutch Cam Set Screw	40 (4.5)
Pressure Tap Plug	120 (13.6)
Separator Plate Brace Screw	35 (4.0)
Separator Plate-To-Transfer Plate Screw	35 (4.0)
Solenoid Assembly Screw	72 (8.1)
Valve Body Screw	35 (4.0)
Valve Body-To-Transmission Case Bolt	100 (11.3)
Vehicle Speed Sensor-To-Adapter Bolt (1994 Models)	27 (3.1)

[1] – Apply thread sealant to bolt threads.

TRANSMISSION SPECIFICATIONS

TRANSMISSION SPECIFICATIONS

Application	In. (mm)
Clutch Clearances	
Front Clutch	
3-Disc Clutch	.070-.129 (1.78-3.28)
4-Disc Clutch	.082-.151 (2.08-3.84)
Rear Clutch	.025-.045 (.64-1.14)
Input Shaft End Play	.034-.084 (.86-2.13)
Oil Pump Clearances	
Outer Pump Gear-To-Oil Pump	
Housing Clearance	.0035-.0075 (.089-.190)
Pump Gear End Clearance	.0035-.0075 (.089-.190)
Pump Gear Tooth Clearance	.0035-.0075 (.089-.190)
Planetary Gear Train End Play	.006-.048 (.15-1.22)

SERVICE BULLETINS

UPSHIFT TOO LOW OR CLOSE TOGETHER

Chrysler Corp. Service Bulletin 21-25-93 (September 3, 1993) – Some 1992-93 Dakota, Pickup, Ram Van and 1993 Grand Cherokee With 46RH transmission may have upshifts too low or close together. The 2-3 upshift will be very close to the 1-2 upshift. To correct this condition, perform the following procedure.

1) Check for stored diagnostic trouble codes in the Powertrain Control Module (PCM). See SELF-DIAGNOSTICS article in ENGINE PERFORMANCE of appropriate MITCHELL® MANUAL.

2) Repair engine control system if a diagnostic trouble code exists and recheck operation. If no diagnostic trouble codes exists or code has been corrected and problem still exists, replace governor weights and spring with components from Governor Weight Package (4617882).

DELAYED TRANSMISSION ENGAGEMENT

Chrysler Corp. Service Bulletin 21-20-93 (October 22, 1993) –Some 1988-93 Dakota, Pickup, Ram Van and 1993 Grand Cherokee may exhibit a no drive or delayed transmission engagement condition. Customer complaint may state that vehicle does not move after shifting from Park into Drive or Reverse. The cause is a rough finish on the sides of park tooth on the annulus gear in the overdrive unit. Condition may exists only under conditions in which parking sprag is engaged in the annulus gear.

The transmission actually engages, but parking sprag is not released from the annulus gear. If throttle is opened slightly, it may appear that transmission is in Neutral. If throttle is opened rapidly, the engine acts as if transmission is in gear, but the brakes are applied. To correct this condition, perform the following procedure.

1) Before performing repairs, check for all causes of delayed engagement or no drive conditions, such as low transmission fluid level, improper shift linkage or cable adjustment, low line pressure, restricted filter assembly and broken oil pump drive.

2) If conditions are okay, replace annulus gear in overdrive unit with Annulus Gear (4746349 for gasoline models or 4746348 for diesel models) using NEW gaskets. Ensure proper thickness overdrive piston thrust plate is be determined before installing overdrive unit. See DETERMINING INTERMEDIATE SHAFT SELECTIVE SPACER & OVERDRIVE PISTON THRUST PLATE under OVERDRIVE UNIT ADJUSTMENTS. Fill transmission with Mopar ATF Plus Type 7176 fluid.

IMPROPER UPSHIFTS

Chrysler Corp. Service Bulletin 21-23-93 (September 3, 1993) – Some 1992-93 Pickup With Cummins Diesel may have improper upshifts. On 1992 models, transmission may not 3-4 upshift at 50-60 MPH or on late 1992 production and 1993 models, transmission may have a deep throttle 2-4 upshift. To correct this condition, perform the following procedure.

1) Check for stored diagnostic trouble codes in the Powertrain Control Module (PCM). See SELF-DIAGNOSTICS article in ENGINE PERFORMANCE of appropriate MITCHELL® MANUAL.

2) Repair engine control system if a diagnostic trouble code exists and recheck operation. If no diagnostic trouble codes exists or code has been corrected and problem still exists, replace Powertrain Control Module (PCM) with PCM (4746568) and Authorization Modification Label (4275086). Type required information on authorization modification label and attach near the vehicle emissions control information sticker attached to the hood.

DELAYED TRANSMISSION ENGAGEMENT

Chrysler Corp. Service Bulletin 21-08-94 (April 29, 1994) – Some 1990-94 Dakota, Pickup and Ram Van, and 1993-94 Grand Cherokee may experience a 2-8 second delay in transmission engagement when vehicle is first started after vehicle has been parked for an extended period.

NOTE: This service bulletin does not apply to Pickup with V10 gasoline engine or Cummins Diesel models.

To correct this condition, perform the following procedure.

1) Check for stored diagnostic trouble codes in the Powertrain Control Module (PCM). See SELF-DIAGNOSTICS article in ENGINE PERFORMANCE of appropriate MITCHELL® MANUAL.

2) Repair engine control system if a diagnostic trouble code exists and recheck operation. If no diagnostic trouble codes exists or code has been corrected and problem still exists, Drainback Relief Valve (4778670) must be installed.

3) Note location of oil cooler supply line on side of transmission. *See Fig. 7.* Trace oil cooler supply line back to the radiator and identify this line at the radiator. Ensure this is the oil cooler supply line.

CAUTION: Drainback relief valve must be installed in oil cooler supply line or transmission failure will exist if wrong line is selected. Ensure oil cooler supply line is selected.

---

4) Cut oil cooler supply line within 1/8" of the crimp on the hose. *See Fig. 55.* Cut the hose and remove section of oil cooler supply line.

CAUTION: Some vehicles may have a Black epoxy coating on the oil cooler supply line. Ensure coating is removed before installing the nut and sleeve from drainback relief valve on oil cooler supply line.

---

5) Install nut and sleeve on metal portion of oil cooler supply line. Install drainback relief valve on metal portion of oil cooler supply so arrow on drainback relief valve is pointing toward the oil cooler.

CAUTION: Ensure drainback relief valve is installed so arrow on drainback relief valve is pointing toward the oil cooler. The arrow indicates direction of the fluid flow.

---

6) Install sleeve and nut on drainback relief valve. Tighten nut. Install rubber portion of oil cooler supply line on drainback relief valve. Install and tighten clamp to 10 INCH lbs. (1.1 N.m).

7) Note location of oil cooler return line on side of transmission. *See Fig. 7.* Disconnect oil cooler return line from transmission. On 1994 models, oil cooler lines are equipped with a disconnect fitting. Use proper procedure for disconnecting oil cooler line from disconnect fitting. See OIL COOLER LINE DISCONNECT FITTINGS under ON-VEHICLE SERVICE in this article.

CAUTION: Ensure flow from oil cooler return line is checked to ensure drainback relief valve is installed in correct oil cooler line.

8) Ensure transmission is full of fluid. Place container under oil cooler return line. Start engine. Place gearshift in Neutral.

9) Ensure steady flow exists for oil cooler return line. If no fluid flow exists, drainback relief valve has been installed in the wrong oil cooler line. Remove and reinstall. If steady flow exists, shut engine off.

10) Reconnect oil cooler return line. On 1994 models, reconnect oil cooler return line by pushing oil cooler line inward until a snap or click is heard when retaining clip seats in oil cooler line. Pull outward on oil cooler line to ensure oil cooler line is locked in the disconnect fitting.

CAUTION: After installing oil cooler line, pull outward on oil cooler line to ensure oil cooler line is locked in the disconnect fitting and retaining clip is fully seated.

11) On all models, fill transmission with Mopar ATF Plus Type 7176 fluid. Recheck all oil cooler lines for leaks.

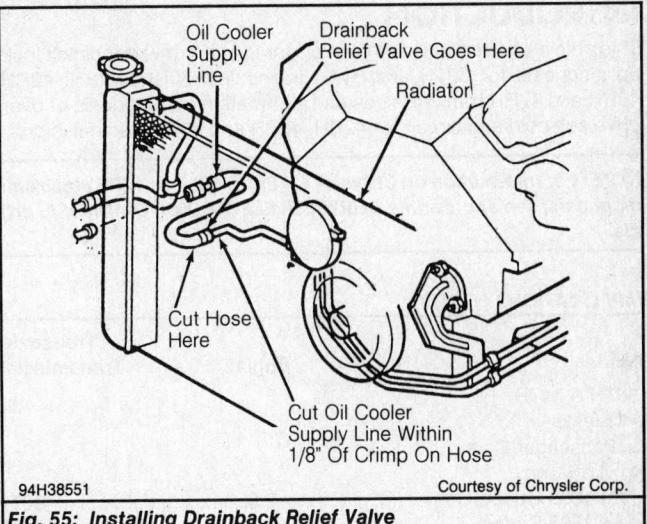

Fig. 55: Installing Drainback Relief Valve

AUTOMATIC TRANSMISSIONS
Chrysler Electronic Controls

INTRODUCTION

This article covers electronic controls for torque converter clutch lock-up diagnosis for 30TH and 31TH transaxles, 30RH, 32RH, 42RH, 46RH and 47RH transmissions and information for diagnosis of over-drive solenoid and circuit for 42RH, 46RH and 47RH transmissions.

NOTE: For information on Chrysler 41TE/AE, 42LE or 42RE electronic diagnosis, see appropriate CHRYSLER ELECTRONIC DIAGNOSIS article.

APPLICATIONS (1 OF 2)

Model	Engine	Transaxle/ Transmission
30TH & 31TH		
Chrysler		
Passenger Cars		
LeBaron		
1993 Coupe/Conv	2.5L	30TH
1993 Sedan	2.5L	30TH
	3.0L	31TH
1994 Sedan	3.0L	31TH
Dodge		
Passenger Cars		
1993 Daytona	2.5L	30TH
1993 Dynasty	2.5L	30TH
1993-94 Shadow	2.2L & 2.5L	30TH
1993-94 Spirit	2.5L	30TH
	3.0L	31TH
FWD Vans		
1993-94 Caravan	2.5L	30TH
1993-94 Caravan &		
Grand Caravan	3.0L	31TH
Plymouth		
Passenger Cars		
1993-94 Acclaim	2.5L	30TH
	3.0L	31TH
1993-94 Sundance	2.2L & 2.5L	30TH
FWD Vans		
1993-94 Voyager	2.5L	30TH
1993-94 Voyager &		
Grand Voyager	3.0L	31TH
30RH & 32RH		
Dodge		
1993-94 Pickup &		
Ram Van	3.9L	32RH
Jeep		
1993 Wrangler	4.0L	32RH
1994 Cherokee &		
Wrangler	2.5L	30RH
1994 Cherokee &		
Wrangler	4.0L	32RH
42RH		
Dodge		
1993-94 Dakota, Pickup		
& Ram Van	3.9L	42RH
Jeep		
1993-94 Grand		
Cherokee [1]	4.0L	42RH

[1] – Some models may use the 42RH and some models may use the 42RE transmission. For 42RE transmissions, see CHRYSLER 42RE & 42RH article. Information for diagnosis of TCC solenoid and overdrive solenoid on 42RH is not available.

APPLICATIONS (2 OF 2)

Model	Engine	Transaxle/ Transmission
46RH & 47RH		
Dodge		
1993-94 Dakota	5.2L	46RH
1993 Ramcharger	5.2L & 5.9L	46RH
1993 Pickup		
Gasoline	5.2L & 5.9L	46RH
Diesel	5.9L	[1] 46RH
1994 Pickup		
Gasoline	5.2L & 5.9L	46RH
Gasoline	8.0L (V10)	47RH
Diesel	5.9L	47RH
1993-94 Ram Van	5.2L & 5.9L	46RH
Jeep		
1993-94 Grand		
Cherokee	5.2L	46RH

[1] – Diesel applications use a heavy duty version of the 46RH.

NOTE: Vehicle body code may be required when diagnosing or repairing torque converter clutch lock-up or overdrive solenoid, as body code may be used instead of vehicle model name. See BODY CODE DESIGNATION table.

BODY CODE DESIGNATION

Body Designation	Model
Passenger Cars	
AA Body	Acclaim, LeBaron Sedan & Spirit
AC Body	Dynasty
AG Body	Daytona
AJ Body	LeBaron Coupe/Convertible
AP Body	Shadow & Sundance
Pickups & Vans	
AB Body	Ram Van
AD Body	1993 Pickup & Ramcharger
AN Body	Dakota
AS Body	[1] Caravan & Voyager
BR Body	1994 Pickup
XJ Body	Cherokee
YJ Body	Wrangler
ZJ Body	Grand Cherokee

[1] – Includes the Grand Caravan and Grand Voyager.

DESCRIPTION & OPERATION

TORQUE CONVERTER CLUTCH LOCK-UP

30TH & 31TH – Torque converter clutch lock-up is activated only in Drive and is controlled by Powertrain Control Module (PCM). See PCM LOCATION table for mounting location. The Torque Converter Clutch (TCC) solenoid, located on the valve body, receives battery voltage when ignition is turned on.

NOTE: The TCC solenoid may be referred to as the lock-up solenoid, lock/unlock solenoid or Electronic Modulated Converter Clutch (EMCC) solenoid.

The PCM controls the TCC solenoid ground circuit for torque converter clutch lock-up operation. Torque converter clutch lock-up depends on input signals to the PCM provided by input signals from various sensors.

Torque converter clutch lock-up is monitored by the PCM. The PCM self-diagnostic system stores a diagnostic trouble code in the memory in event of a malfunction. Diagnostic trouble code can be retrieved for torque converter clutch lock-up diagnosis. For more information on self-diagnostic system, see SELF-DIAGNOSTIC SYSTEM in this article.

PCM LOCATION [1]

Model	Location
Cherokee	Driver's Side Front Corner Of Engine Compartment
Dakota	Passenger's Side Of Engine Compartment, Above Fender Panel
Grand Cherokee	Passenger's Side Rear Corner Of Engine Compartment On Firewall, Near Coolant Level Bottle
Pickup	
1993 Models	Driver's Side Front Corner Of Engine Compartment
1994 Models	Passenger's Side Rear Corner Of Engine Compartment On Firewall
Ramcharger	Driver's Side Front Corner Of Engine Compartment
Ram Van	Center Of Firewall Above Engine, Near Wiper Motor
Wrangler	Driver's Side Rear Corner Of Engine Compartment On Firewall
All Others	Driver's Side Front Corner Of Engine Compartment

[1] – The PCM contains a 60-pin connector.

30RH & 32RH – Torque converter clutch lock-up is activated only in Drive and is controlled by Powertrain Control Module (PCM). The PCM controls the Torque Converter Clutch (TCC) solenoid through the Torque Converter Clutch (TCC) relay (if equipped). See PCM LOCATION table for mounting location.

The TCC relay is located on left fender near hood hinge on Pickup and Ramcharger or on firewall on Ram Van. See Figs. 1 and 2. The TCC relay is located in power distribution center in the engine compartment on Cherokee or on the firewall near the battery on Wrangler. See Fig. 3 and 4.

NOTE: The TCC solenoid may be referred to as the lock-up solenoid, lock/unlock solenoid or Electronic Modulated Converter Clutch (EMCC) solenoid.

The PCM controls the TCC relay ground circuit which provides power to the TCC solenoid for torque converter clutch lock-up operation. When TCC solenoid is energized, fluid flows into the lock-up module on the valve body, which then applies the torque converter clutch. Torque converter clutch lock-up depends on input signals to the PCM provided by various sensors.

Torque converter clutch lock-up is monitored by the PCM. The PCM self-diagnostic system stores a diagnostic trouble code in the memory in event of a malfunction. Diagnostic trouble code can be retrieved for torque converter clutch lock-up diagnosis. For more information on self-diagnostic system, see SELF-DIAGNOSTIC SYSTEM in this article.

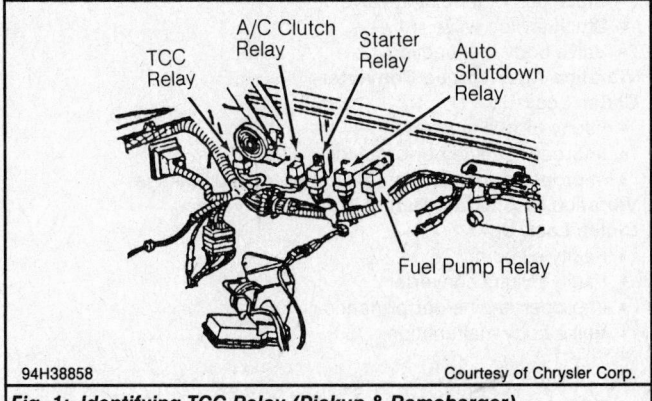

94H38858   Courtesy of Chrysler Corp.

Fig. 1: Identifying TCC Relay (Pickup & Ramcharger)

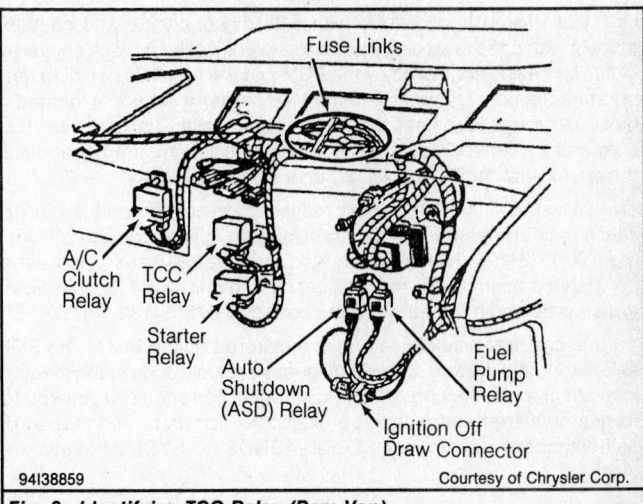

94I38859   Courtesy of Chrysler Corp.

Fig. 2: Identifying TCC Relay (Ram Van)

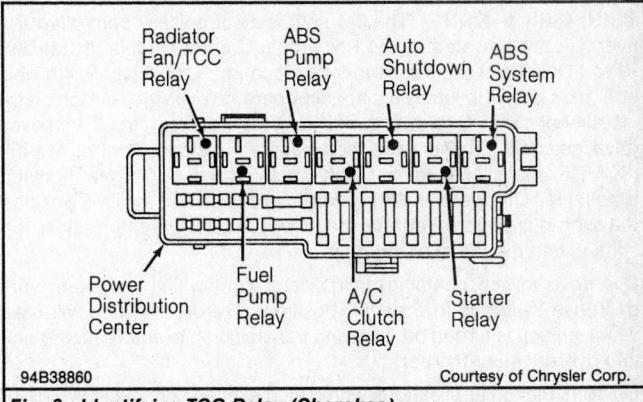

94B38860   Courtesy of Chrysler Corp.

Fig. 3: Identifying TCC Relay (Cherokee)

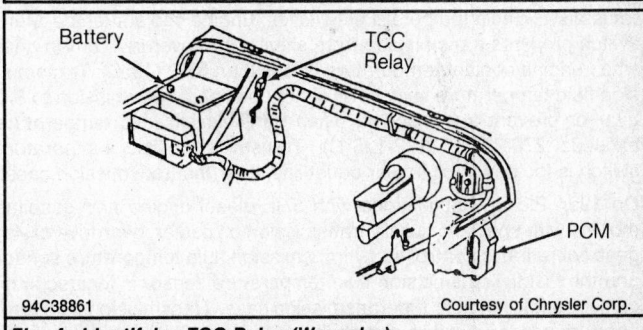

94C38861   Courtesy of Chrysler Corp.

Fig. 4: Identifying TCC Relay (Wrangler)

42RH, 46RH & 47RH – Torque converter clutch lock-up is activated only in Drive and is controlled by Powertrain Control Module (PCM). See PCM LOCATION table for mounting location. The Torque Converter Clutch (TCC) solenoid, located on the valve body, receives battery voltage when ignition is turned on. The TCC solenoid and overdrive solenoid share a 3-wire electrical connector at the transmission.

NOTE: The TCC solenoid may be referred to as the lock-up solenoid, lock/unlock solenoid or Electronic Modulated Converter Clutch (EMCC) solenoid.

The PCM controls the TCC solenoid ground circuit for torque converter clutch lock-up operation when transmission is in overdrive or 4th gear. The valve body lock-up timing valve releases torque converter clutch lock-up before the 4-3 downshift occurs. Torque converter clutch lock-up depends on input signals to the PCM provided by various sensors.

On 1994 Pickup applications with 5.9L diesel engine and gasoline models with special auxiliary transmission oil cooler, torque converter clutch lock-up is controlled by the PCM and the transmission fluid temperature sensor. Transmission fluid temperature sensor is located in oil cooler outlet line, near the transmission case. Transmission fluid temperature sensor monitors transmission fluid temperature and is in the circuit with the TCC solenoid on the valve body and the PCM.

Transmission fluid temperature sensor prevents torque converter clutch lock-up operation when transmission fluid temperature is less than 70°F (21°C). Transmission fluid temperature sensor will either downshift transmission to 3rd gear or prevent a 3-4 upshift when transmission fluid temperature exceeds 270-275°F (132-135°C).

Torque converter clutch lock-up is monitored by the PCM. The PCM self-diagnostic system stores a diagnostic trouble code in the memory in event of a malfunction. Diagnostic trouble code can be retrieved for torque converter clutch lock-up diagnosis. For more information on self-diagnostic system, see SELF-DIAGNOSTIC SYSTEM in this article.

OVERDRIVE UNIT OPERATION

42RH, 46RH & 47RH – The 3-4 shift is electronically controlled and hydraulically activated by the Powertrain Control Module (PCM). See PCM LOCATION table for mounting location. Overdrive or 4th gear operation is controlled by a manually operated overdrive switch on the instrument panel. Overdrive switch is in the electrical circuit with overdrive solenoid on the valve body and Powertrain Control Module (PCM). Transmission will not shift into overdrive or 4th gear if switch is not in the ON position. When overdrive switch is in the OFF position, the overdrive switch overrides the PCM, preventing transmission from shifting into overdrive or 4th gear.

Overdrive switch contains an indicator light which activates when overdrive switch is in the OFF position. Overdrive switch will reset when ignition is turned off, allowing transmission to automatically shift into overdrive or 4th gear.

On 1993 Pickup applications with 5.9L diesel engine, overdrive or 4th gear operation is also controlled by engine coolant temperature and transmission fluid temperature switches. Engine coolant temperature switch prevents transmission from shifting into overdrive or 4th gear when engine coolant temperature is less than 65°F (18°C). Transmission fluid temperature switch will either downshift transmission to 3rd gear or prevent a 3-4 upshift when transmission fluid temperature exceeds 270-275°F (132-135°C). Transmission fluid temperature switch is located in oil cooler outlet line, near the transmission case.

On 1994 Pickup applications with 5.9L diesel engine and gasoline models with special auxiliary transmission oil cooler, overdrive or 4th gear operation is controlled by transmission fluid temperature sensor and the PCM. Transmission fluid temperature sensor is located in oil cooler outlet line, near the transmission case. Transmission fluid temperature sensor monitors transmission fluid temperature and is in the circuit with the overdrive solenoid on the valve body and the PCM.

Transmission fluid temperature sensor prevents overdrive or 4th gear operation when transmission fluid temperature is less than 60°F (15°C). Transmission fluid temperature sensor will either downshift transmission to 3rd gear or prevent a 3-4 upshift when transmission fluid temperature exceeds 270-275°F (132-135°C).

On all models, the PCM controls overdrive solenoid, located on the valve body, using input signals from various sensors. Overdrive solenoid operation is monitored by the PCM. The PCM self-diagnostic system stores a diagnostic trouble code in the memory in event of a malfunction. Diagnostic trouble code can be retrieved for overdrive solenoid diagnosis. For more information on self-diagnostic system, see SELF-DIAGNOSTIC SYSTEM in this article.

TROUBLE SHOOTING

NOTE: The following are possible causes for designated problem. Some possible causes may not apply to all applications.

TORQUE CONVERTER CLUTCH LOCK-UP SYMPTOM DIAGNOSIS

Loud Chatter During Torque Converter Clutch Lock-Up When Cold
- Defective torque converter clutch
- Faulty torque converter
- Leaking turbine hub seal

No Torque Converter Clutch Lock-Up
- Defective TCC relay or wiring connections
- Defective TCC solenoid or wiring connections
- Failed torque converter clutch
- Faulty input shaft or seal ring
- Faulty oil pump
- Faulty torque converter
- Leaking turbine hub seal
- Sticking governor valve
- Stuck converter clutch valve
- Stuck switch valve
- Valve body malfunction

Shudder After Torque Converter Clutch Lock-Up
- Defective torque converter clutch
- Faulty oil pump
- Faulty torque converter
- Improper engine performance
- Improperly adjusted throttle valve cable or linkage
- Restricted oil cooler
- Valve body malfunction

Torque Converter Clutch Locks Up Or Drags In Low Or 2nd Gear
- Faulty oil pump
- Stuck switch valve
- Valve body malfunction

Torque Converter Clutch Stays Engaged At Low Speeds In Drive
- Defective TCC relay
- Sticking governor valve
- Stuck converter clutch valve
- Stuck switch valve
- Stuck TCC solenoid
- Valve body malfunction

Torque Converter Clutch Will Not Disengage
- Shorted wiring or electrical components
- Sticking governor valve
- Stuck converter clutch valve
- Stuck switch valve
- Valve body malfunction

Vibration After Torque Converter Clutch Lock-Up
- Faulty torque converter
- Improper engine performance
- Improperly adjusted throttle valve cable or linkage

Vibration Or Shudder During Torque Converter Clutch Lock-Up
- Faulty oil pump
- Faulty torque converter
- Improper engine performance
- Valve body malfunction

OVERDRIVE UNIT SYMPTOM DIAGNOSIS

Delayed 3-4 Upshift
- Defective overdrive clutch
- Defective overdrive solenoid or wiring
- Low fluid level
- Overdrive clutch bleed orifice restricted
- Overdrive piston thrust plate too thin
- Throttle position sensor defective

No Reverse Or Slips In Reverse
- Defective front clutch
- Direct clutch components
- Improper rear band adjustment
- Overdrive thrust bearing failure

No 1-2 Or 2-3 Upshift (Has Low & Reverse)
- Defective or loose governor

No 3-4 Upshift
- Damaged park/neutral switch or wiring causing loss of park/neutral input to PCM
- Defective engine coolant or transmission fluid temperature sensor or switches (if equipped) or vehicle speed sensor
- Defective overdrive solenoid or wiring circuit
- Defective overdrive switch, wiring circuit or fuse
- Defective Powertrain Control Module (PCM)
- Low hydraulic pressure
- Overdrive piston seals damaged or wrong spacer
- Overdrive solenoid supply orifice in valve body restricted
- Overdrive switch in OFF position

No 4-3 Downshift
- Defective engine coolant or transmission fluid temperature sensor or switches (if equipped) or vehicle speed sensor
- Defective Powertrain Control Module (PCM)
- Defective wiring or connections
- Defective 3-4 shift valve, shuttle valve, timing valve or accumulator
- Overdrive solenoid not venting
- TCC solenoid not venting
- Throttle position sensor faulty

No 4-3 Downshift With Overdrive Switch In OFF Position
- Defective overdrive solenoid wiring or connections
- Defective overdrive switch wiring
- Defective Powertrain Control Module
- Overdrive or TCC solenoid not venting

Noisy Operation In 4th Gear Only
- Defective output shaft bearings
- Overdrive clutch discs, clutch plates or snap rings damaged
- Overdrive piston improperly installed or defective
- Overrunning clutch rollers worn
- Planetary gears worn or damaged
- Planetary thrust bearing improperly installed or defective

Slips In 4th Gear
- Low fluid level
- Defective overdrive clutch, overdrive clutch piston or seal
- Defective thrust bearing
- Defective 3-4 shift valve, timing valve or accumulator
- Overdrive piston retainer bleed orifice defective

3-4 Upshift Occurs Before Completing 2-3 Upshift
- Defective coolant temperature sensor or throttle position sensor
- Defective Powertrain Control Module (PCM)
- Loose overdrive solenoid wiring connections or faulty wiring
- Overdrive solenoid faulty
- Valve body malfunction

SELF-DIAGNOSTIC SYSTEM

SYSTEM DIAGNOSIS

The Powertrain Control Module (PCM) monitors transaxle/transmission operation along with input and output information. If PCM self-diagnostic system senses a problem in torque converter clutch lock-up solenoid or overdrive solenoid electrical circuit, a diagnostic trouble code will be stored in the PCM memory. Diagnostic trouble codes are classified as either hard or intermittent trouble code.

Hard Trouble Code – Any trouble code that returns is called a hard trouble code. Hard trouble code indicates that failure exists every time the PCM checks the system.

Intermittent Trouble Code – Intermittent trouble occurs occasionally and are most likely caused by defective wiring or connections. Intermittent trouble codes must be checked under conditions in which trouble code would be set.

NOTE: A reset counter, located below the diagnostic trouble code message on Chrysler's Diagnostic Readout Box (DRB) scan tool, indicates number of engine starts since diagnostic trouble code was set or erased. This helps determine if diagnostic trouble code is a hard or intermittent trouble code.

DIAGNOSTIC PROCEDURE

When performing vehicle diagnosis, the following must be done:
- Ensure transmission/transaxle fluid level is correct and not contaminated or aerated.
- Ensure throttle valve and shift linkage or cable are properly adjusted. See appropriate TRANSMISSION SERVICING article in TRANSMISSION SERVICING.
- Ensure battery is fully charged.
- Ensure all electrical connections at transaxle/transmission, PCM and all sensors and switches on the engine are clean and properly installed.
- Retrieve diagnostic trouble codes. See RETRIEVING DIAGNOSTIC TROUBLE CODES under SELF-DIAGNOSTIC SYSTEM.
- Repair diagnostic trouble codes in the order displayed.
- Always perform appropriate verification test after repair is completed. See VERIFICATION TEST under TROUBLE SHOOTING CHARTS at end of article.

NOTE: The DRB scan tool may be used in several different modes using manufacturer's instructions to activate system components and perform several tests on transmission.

NOTE: On Pickup with 5.9L diesel, if no diagnostic trouble code exists for the overdrive solenoid, but problem exists, perform TEST NF-2A on 1993 models or TEST NTC-2A on 1994 models. Tests are listed under TROUBLE SHOOTING CHARTS at end of article.

RETRIEVING DIAGNOSTIC TROUBLE CODES

NOTE: Manufacturer recommends using Chrysler's Diagnostic Readout Box (DRB) scan tool with proper cartridge for system diagnosis. Other after-market scan tools may be used for system diagnosis. Following procedure is for DRB scan tool usage. Use manufacturer's instruction for operating the DRB scan tool.

1) Ensure engine will start. If engine fails to start, see appropriate SELF-DIAGNOSTICS article in ENGINE PERFORMANCE of appropriate MITCHELL® manual for diagnostic procedure.
2) If engine starts, turn ignition off. Connect DRB to data link connector. *See Figs. 5-16.* Turn ignition on.
3) If a blank message screen or an error message appears on DRB, proceed to DRB PROBLEMS & ERROR MESSAGES. The following are possible error messages that may appear.
- CARTRIDGE ERROR
- HIGH BATTERY
- KEYPAD TEST FAILURE
- LOW BATTERY
- NO RESPONSE
- RAM TEST FAILURE
4) If no error message appears, retrieve diagnostic trouble codes using DRB manufacturer's instructions. Note diagnostic trouble code display and reset counter display.
5) Reset counter indicates number of engine starts since trouble code was set. This helps determine if a hard or intermittent diagnostic trouble code exists.

6) If reset counter shows less than 3 engine starts, it indicates a hard code. If reset counter shows 3 or more engine starts, an intermittent code exists.

7) Using DRB, display all diagnostic trouble codes. To identify diagnostic trouble code, see DIAGNOSTIC TROUBLE CODE IDENTIFICATION table.

NOTE: Only diagnostic trouble codes applying to TCC solenoid, overdrive solenoid and transmission temperature sensor diagnosis are listed. If other diagnostic trouble codes are displayed, see appropriate SELF-DIAGNOSTICS article in ENGINE PERFORMANCE of appropriate MITCHELL® manual. For diagnostic trouble code trouble shooting, use proper trouble shooting chart according to engine size and diagnostic trouble code. See TROUBLE SHOOTING CHARTS at end of article.

NOTE: On Pickup with 5.9L diesel, if no diagnostic trouble code exists for the overdrive solenoid, but problem exists, perform TEST NF-2A on 1993 models or TEST NTC-2A on 1994 models. Tests are listed under TROUBLE SHOOTING CHARTS at end of article.

DIAGNOSTIC TROUBLE CODE IDENTIFICATION

DRB Display	Possible Cause
Torque Converter Clutch Solenoid Circuit [1]	Defective Solenoid, Wiring Or Circuit
Trans. Overdrive Solenoid Circuit [2]	Defective Solenoid, Wiring Or Circuit
Trans. Temp. Sensor Voltage Too Low [3]	Defective Sensor, Wiring Or Circuit
Trans. Temp. Sensor Voltage Too High [3]	Defective Sensor, Wiring Or Circuit

[1] – Diagnostic trouble code does not apply to 1993 5.9L Diesel applications.

[2] – Applies to 42RH, 46RH and 47RH transmissions only.

[3] – Applies to 1994 3.9L, 5.2L, 5.9L Gasoline, 5.9L Diesel and 8.0L (V10) models with transmission fluid temperature sensor located in oil cooler outlet line, near the transmission case.

CLEARING DIAGNOSTIC TROUBLE CODES

After repairs have been performed, use DRB and manufacturer's instructions to clear or erase diagnostic trouble code from PCM memory.

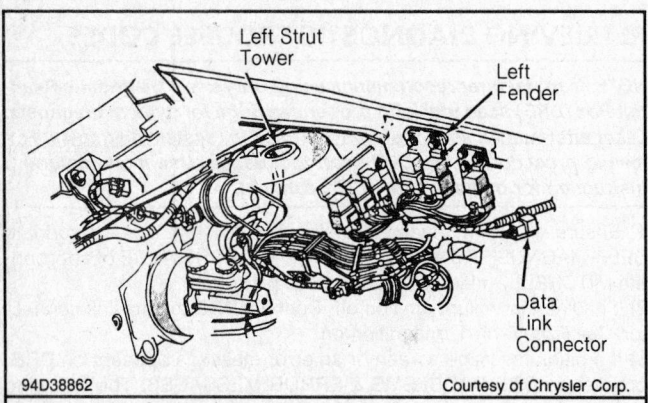

94D38862   Courtesy of Chrysler Corp.

Fig. 5: Identifying Data Link Connector (Acclaim, LeBaron Sedan & Spirit)

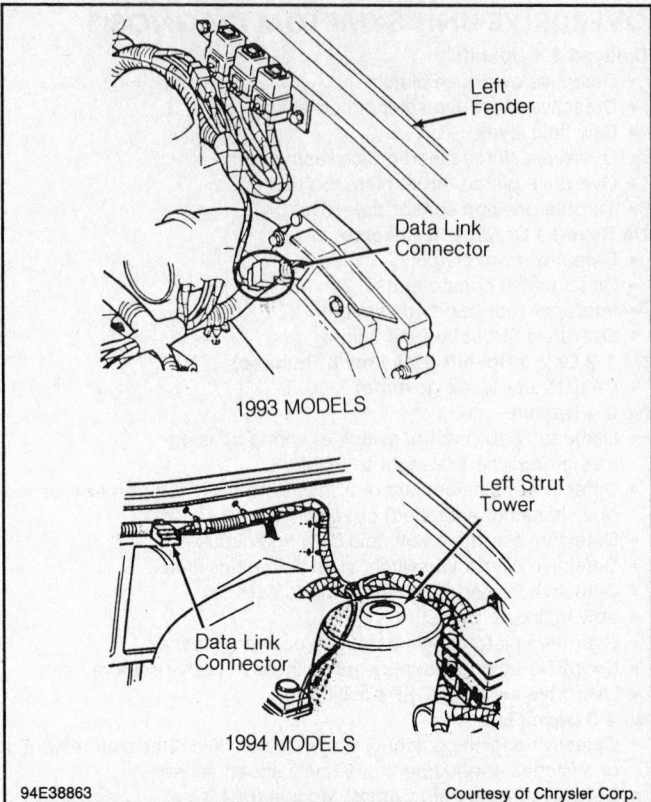

94E38863   Courtesy of Chrysler Corp.

Fig. 6: Identifying Data Link Connector (Caravan, Grand Caravan, Voyager & Grand Voyager)

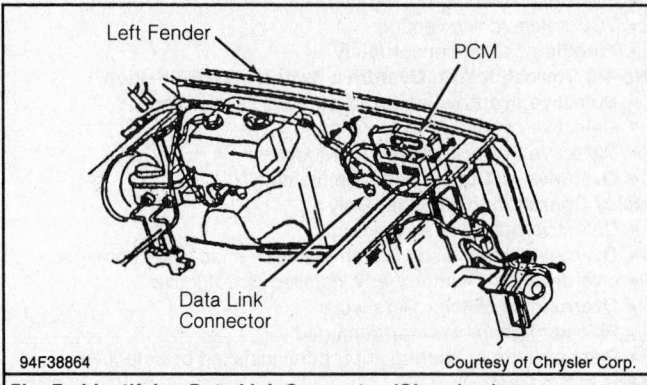

94F38864   Courtesy of Chrysler Corp.

Fig. 7: Identifying Data Link Connector (Cherokee)

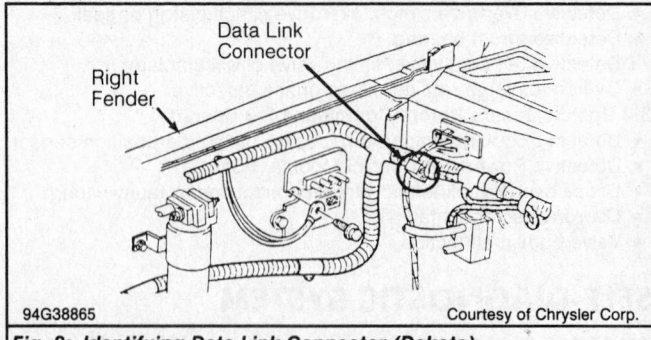

94G38865   Courtesy of Chrysler Corp.

Fig. 8: Identifying Data Link Connector (Dakota)

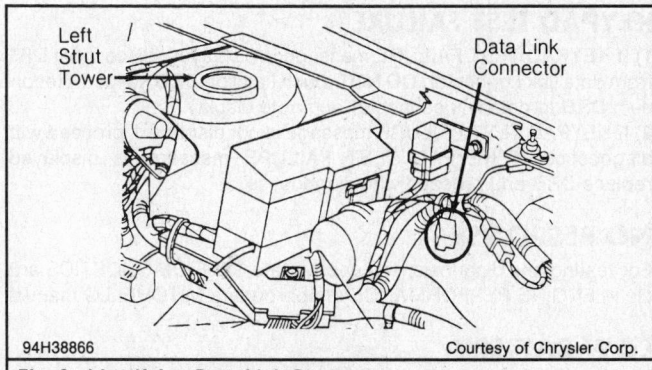

94H38866   Courtesy of Chrysler Corp.

Fig. 9: Identifying Data Link Connector (Daytona & LeBaron Coupe/Convertible)

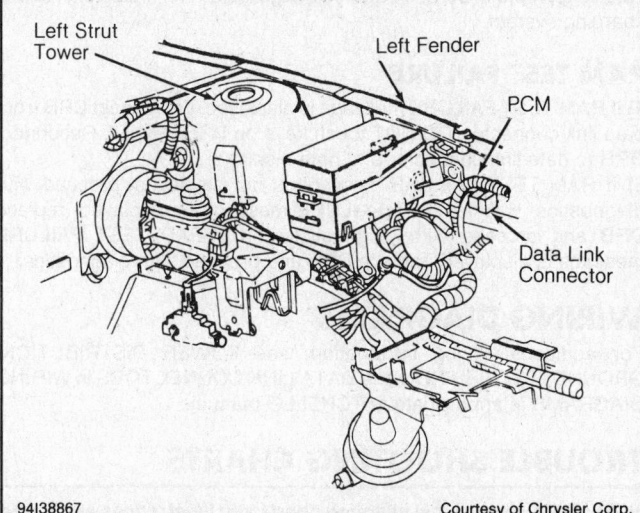

94I38867   Courtesy of Chrysler Corp.

Fig. 10: Identifying Data Link Connector (Dynasty)

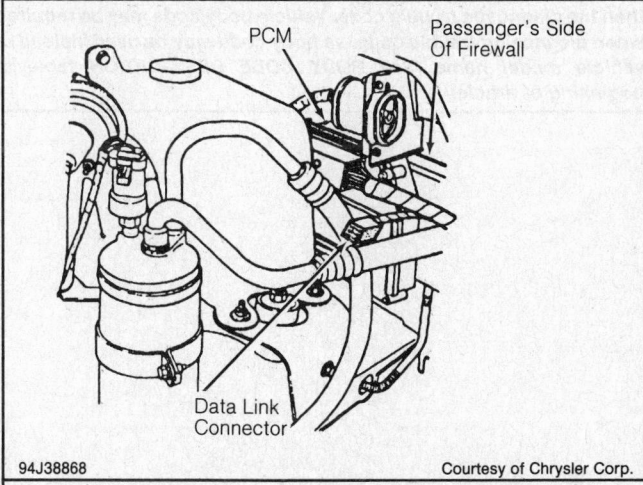

94J38868   Courtesy of Chrysler Corp.

Fig. 11: Identifying Data Link Connector (Grand Cherokee)

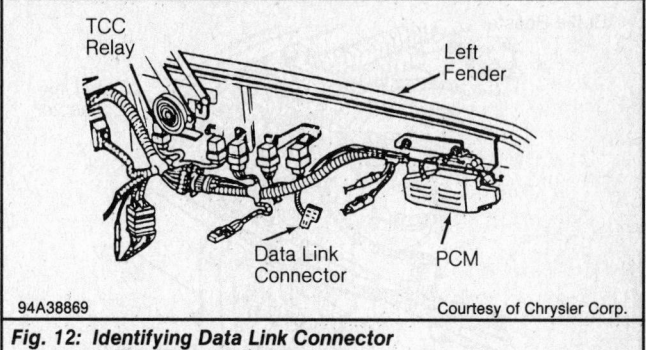

94A38869   Courtesy of Chrysler Corp.

Fig. 12: Identifying Data Link Connector (1993 Pickup & Ramcharger)

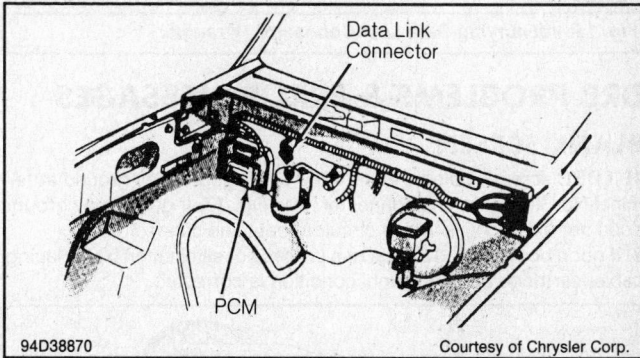

94D38870   Courtesy of Chrysler Corp.

Fig. 13: Identifying Data Link Connector (1994 Pickup)

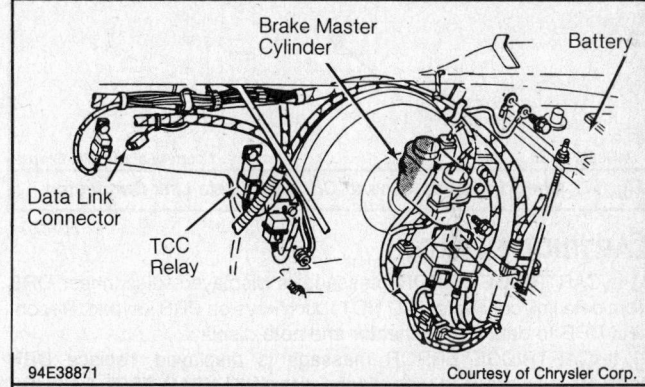

94E38871   Courtesy of Chrysler Corp.

Fig. 14: Identifying Data Link Connector (Ram Van)

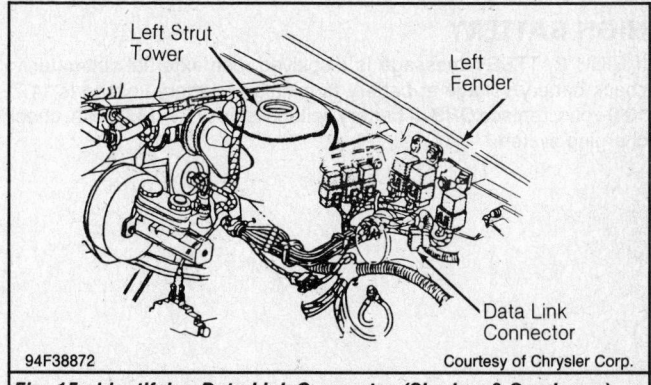

94F38872   Courtesy of Chrysler Corp.

Fig. 15: Identifying Data Link Connector (Shadow & Sundance)

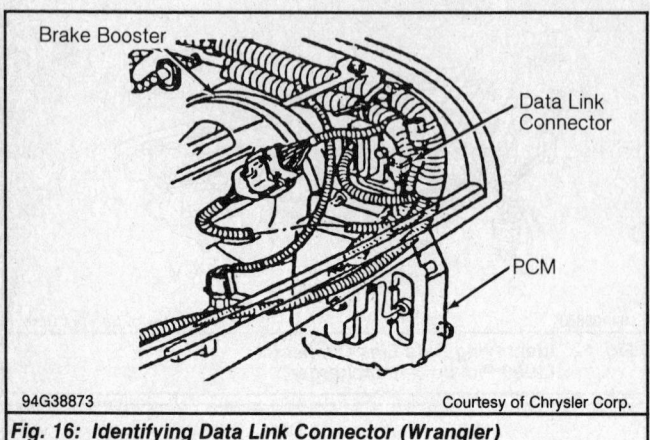

94G38873   Courtesy of Chrysler Corp.

Fig. 16: Identifying Data Link Connector (Wrangler)

DRB PROBLEMS & ERROR MESSAGES

BLANK SCREEN

1) If DRB screen is blank, ensure there is a good body ground at terminal No. 1 on data link connector. See Fig. 17. If good body ground does not exist, check wiring circuit to data link connector.
2) If good body ground exists, use process of elimination by replacing, cable, cartridge and DRB until condition is corrected.

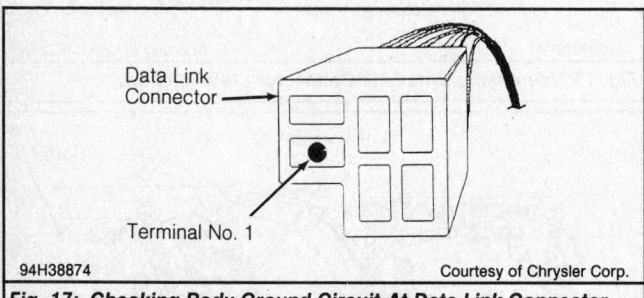

94H38874   Courtesy of Chrysler Corp.

Fig. 17: Checking Body Ground Circuit At Data Link Connector

CARTRIDGE ERROR

1) If CARTRIDGE ERROR message is displayed, disconnect DRB from data link connector. DO NOT touch keys on DRB keypad. Reconnect DRB to data link connector and note display.
2) If CARTRIDGE ERROR message is displayed, replace DRB cartridge and proceed with diagnostics. If KEYPAD TEST FAILURE message is displayed, replace DRB and proceed with diagnostics.

HIGH BATTERY

If HIGH BATTERY message is displayed, use external voltmeter to check battery voltage at battery terminals. If battery voltage is 11.7-13.0 volts, replace DRB. If battery voltage is not 11.7-13.0 volts, check charging system.

KEYPAD TEST FAILURE

1) If KEYPAD TEST FAILURE message is displayed, disconnect DRB from data link connector. DO NOT touch keys on DRB keypad. Reconnect DRB to data link connector and note display.
2) If KEYPAD TEST FAILURE message is not displayed, proceed with diagnostics. If KEYPAD TEST FAILURE message is displayed, replace DRB and proceed with diagnostics.

NO RESPONSE

For testing and diagnosis, see appropriate SELF-DIAGNOSTICS article in ENGINE PERFORMANCE of appropriate MITCHELL® manual.

LOW BATTERY

If LOW BATTERY message is displayed, use external voltmeter to check battery voltage at battery terminals. If battery voltage is 11.7-13.0 volts, replace DRB. If battery voltage is not 11.7-13.0 volts, check charging system.

RAM TEST FAILURE

1) If RAM TEST FAILURE message is displayed, disconnect DRB from data link connector. DO NOT touch keys on DRB keypad. Reconnect DRB to data link connector and note display.
2) If RAM TEST FAILURE message is not displayed, proceed with diagnostics. If RAM TEST FAILURE message is displayed, replace DRB and proceed with diagnostics. If KEYPAD TEST FAILURE message is displayed, replace DRB and proceed with diagnostics.

WIRING DIAGRAMS

For additional wiring information, see POWER DISTRIBUTION, GROUND DISTRIBUTION and DATA LINK CONNECTORS in WIRING DIAGRAMS in appropriate MITCHELL® manual.

TROUBLE SHOOTING CHARTS

NOTE: Following trouble shooting charts and illustrations are courtesy of Chrysler Corp. Trouble shooting charts are arranged in accordance with engine application and model application (if required) and then the diagnostic trouble code. Vehicle body code may be required when diagnosing trouble code, as body code may be used instead of vehicle model name. See BODY CODE DESIGNATION table at beginning of article.

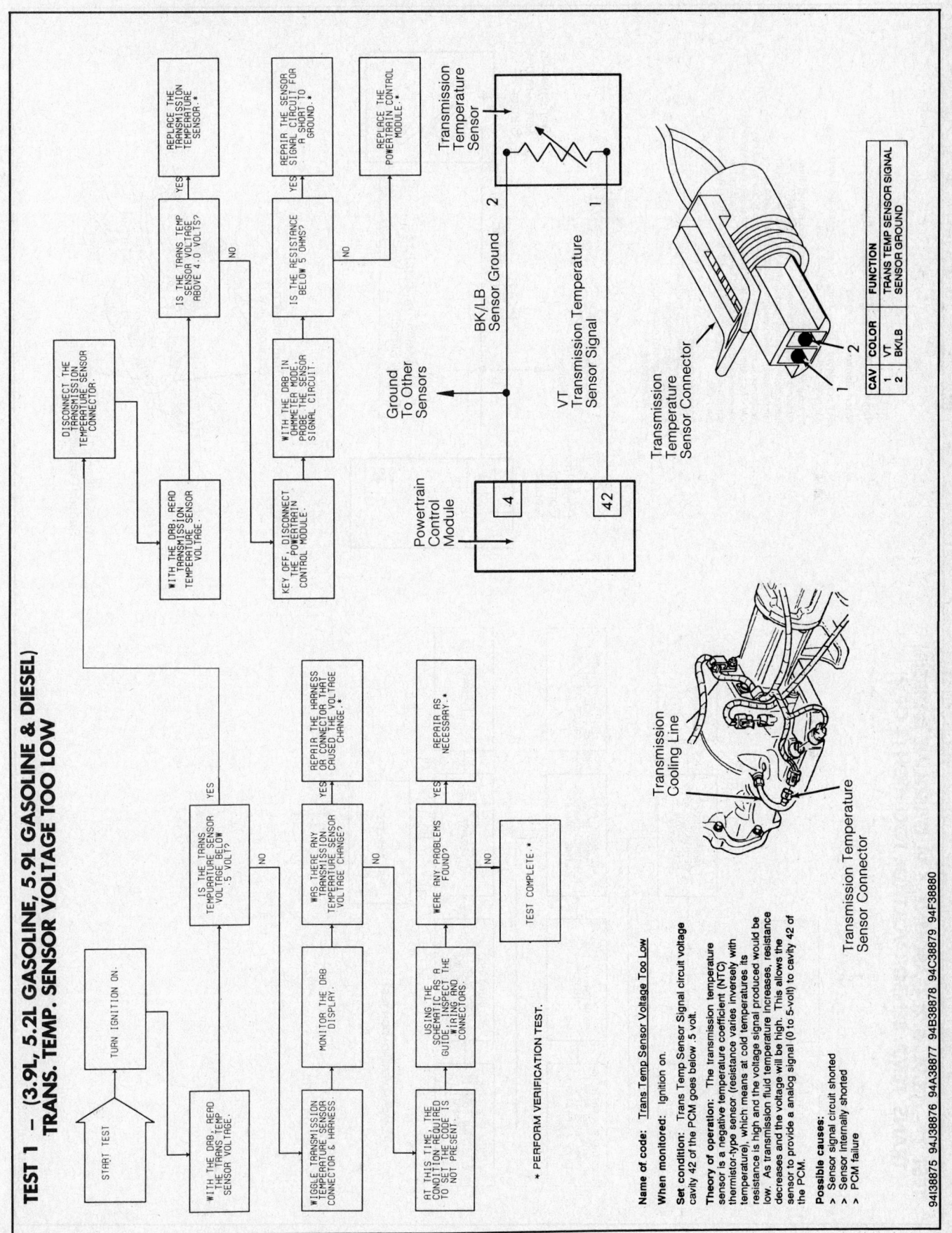

**TEST 1 – (3.9L, 5.2L GASOLINE, 5.9L GASOLINE & DIESEL)
TRANS. TEMP. SENSOR VOLTAGE TOO LOW**

Name of code: Trans Temp Sensor Voltage Too Low

When monitored: Ignition on.

Set condition: Trans Temp Sensor Signal circuit voltage cavity 42 of the PCM goes below .5 volt.

Theory of operation: The transmission temperature sensor is a negative temperature coefficient (NTC) thermistor-type sensor (resistance varies inversely with temperature), which means at cold temperatures its resistance is high and the voltage signal produced would be low. As transmission fluid temperature increases, resistance decreases and the voltage will be high. This allows the sensor to provide an analog signal (0 to 5-volt) to cavity 42 of the PCM.

Possible causes:
> Sensor signal circuit shorted
> Sensor internally shorted
> PCM failure

94138875 94J38876 94A38877 94B38878 94C38879 94F38880

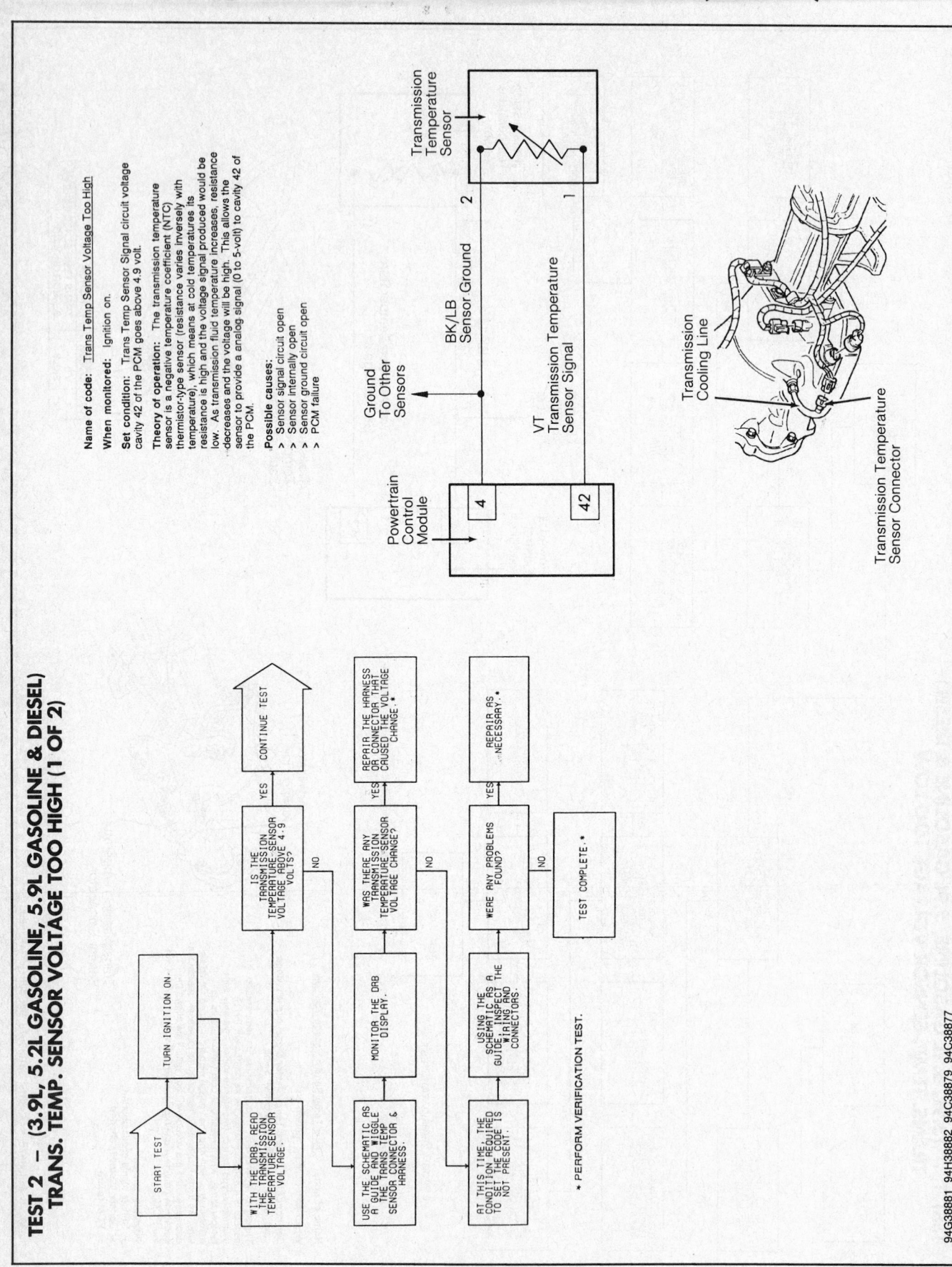

Name of code: Trans Temp Sensor Voltage Too High

When monitored: Ignition on.

Set condition: Trans Temp Sensor Signal circuit voltage cavity 42 of the PCM goes above 4.9 volt.

Theory of operation: The transmission temperature sensor is a negative temperature coefficient (NTC) thermistor-type sensor (resistance varies inversely with temperature), which means at cold temperatures its resistance is high and the voltage signal produced would be low. As transmission fluid temperature increases, resistance decreases and the voltage will be high. This allows the sensor to provide a analog signal (0 to 5-volt) to cavity 42 of the PCM.

Possible causes:
> Sensor signal circuit open
> Sensor internally open
> Sensor ground circuit open
> PCM failure

Transmission Temperature Sensor

2 BK/LB Sensor Ground

1 Transmission Temperature Sensor Signal

Ground To Other Sensors

VT Transmission Temperature Sensor Signal

Powertrain Control Module

4

42

Transmission Cooling Line

Transmission Temperature Sensor Connector

TEST 2 – (3.9L, 5.2L GASOLINE, 5.9L GASOLINE & DIESEL) TRANS. TEMP. SENSOR VOLTAGE TOO HIGH (1 OF 2)

START TEST

TURN IGNITION ON.

WITH THE DRB, READ THE TRANSMISSION TEMPERATURE SENSOR VOLTAGE.

IS THE TRANSMISSION TEMPERATURE SENSOR VOLTAGE ABOVE 4.9 VOLTS?

YES → CONTINUE TEST

NO

USE THE SCHEMATIC AS A GUIDE AND WIGGLE THE TRANS TEMP SENSOR CONNECTOR & HARNESS.

MONITOR THE DRB DISPLAY.

WAS THERE ANY TRANSMISSION TEMPERATURE SENSOR VOLTAGE CHANGE?

YES → REPAIR THE HARNESS OR CONNECTOR THAT CAUSED THE VOLTAGE CHANGE.*

NO

AT THIS TIME THE CONDITION REQUIRED TO SET THE CODE IS NOT PRESENT.

USING THE SCHEMATIC AS A GUIDE, INSPECT THE WIRING AND CONNECTORS.

WERE ANY PROBLEMS FOUND?

YES → REPAIR AS NECESSARY.*

NO

TEST COMPLETE.*

* PERFORM VERIFICATION TEST.

94G38881 94H38882 94C38879 94C38877

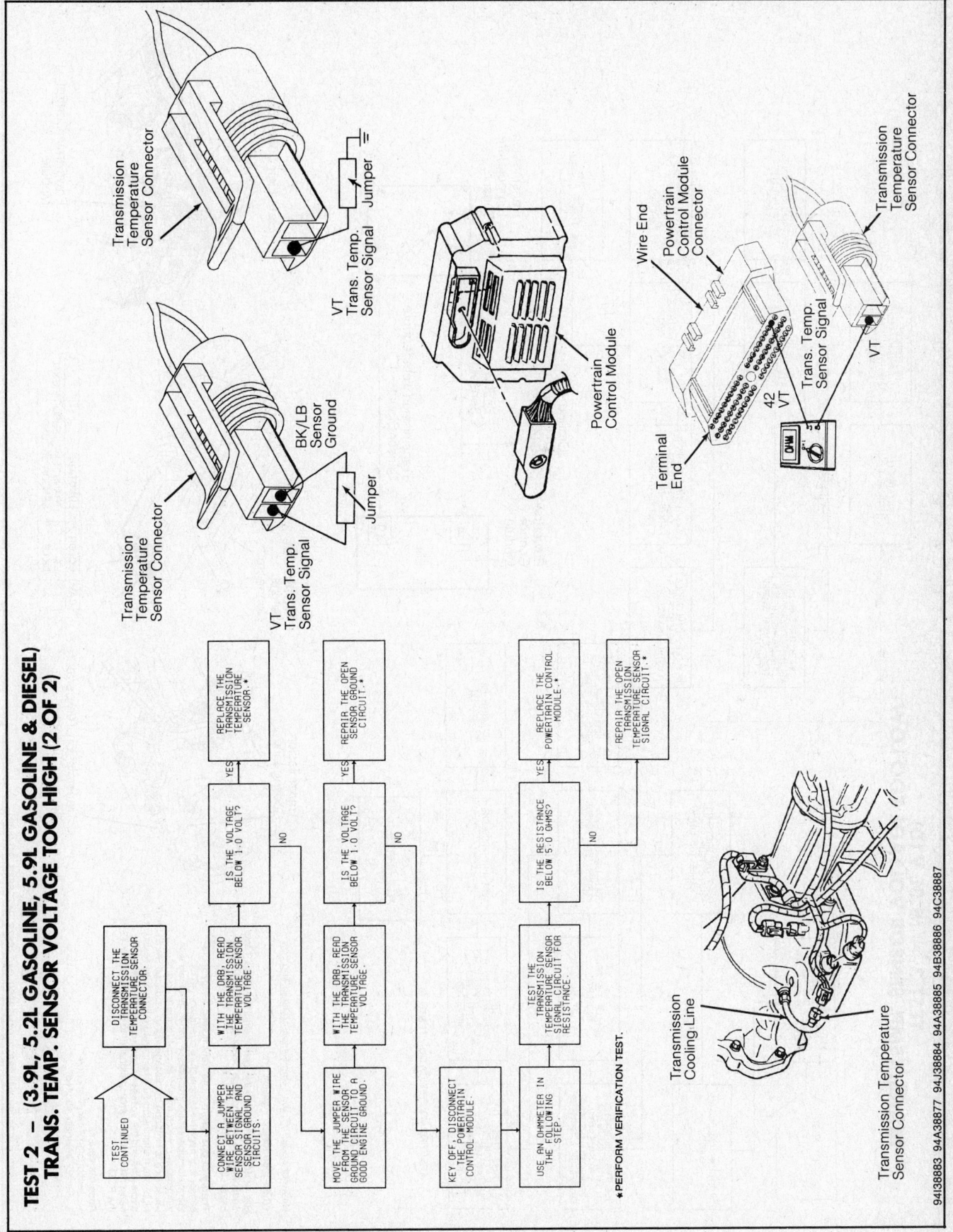

TEST 2 – (3.9L, 5.2L GASOLINE, 5.9L GASOLINE & DIESEL) TRANS. TEMP. SENSOR VOLTAGE TOO HIGH (2 OF 2)

Transmission Temperature Sensor Connector

VT Trans. Temp. Sensor Signal

Jumper

Transmission Temperature Sensor Connector

BK/LB Sensor Ground

Jumper

VT Trans. Temp. Sensor Signal

Powertrain Control Module

Wire End

Powertrain Control Module Connector

Terminal End

42 VT

Trans. Temp. Sensor Signal

VT

Transmission Temperature Sensor Connector

TEST CONTINUED

DISCONNECT THE TEMPERATURE SENSOR CONNECTOR.

CONNECT A JUMPER WIRE BETWEEN THE SENSOR SIGNAL AND SENSOR GROUND CIRCUITS.

WITH THE DRB, READ THE TRANSMISSION TEMPERATURE SENSOR VOLTAGE.

IS THE VOLTAGE BELOW 1.0 VOLT? — YES → REPLACE THE TRANSMISSION TEMPERATURE SENSOR.*

NO

MOVE THE JUMPER WIRE FROM THE SENSOR GROUND CIRCUIT TO A GOOD ENGINE GROUND.

WITH THE DRB, READ THE TRANSMISSION TEMPERATURE SENSOR VOLTAGE.

IS THE VOLTAGE BELOW 1.0 VOLT? — YES → REPAIR THE OPEN SENSOR GROUND CIRCUIT.*

NO

KEY OFF, DISCONNECT THE POWERTRAIN CONTROL MODULE.

USE AN OHMMETER IN THE FOLLOWING STEP.

TEST THE TRANSMISSION TEMPERATURE SENSOR SIGNAL CIRCUIT FOR RESISTANCE.

IS THE RESISTANCE BELOW 5.0 OHMS? — YES → REPLACE THE POWERTRAIN CONTROL MODULE.*

NO → REPAIR THE OPEN TRANSMISSION TEMPERATURE SENSOR SIGNAL CIRCUIT.*

*PERFORM VERIFICATION TEST.

Transmission Cooling Line

Transmission Temperature Sensor Connector

94I38883 94A38877 94J38884 94A38885 94B38886 94C38887

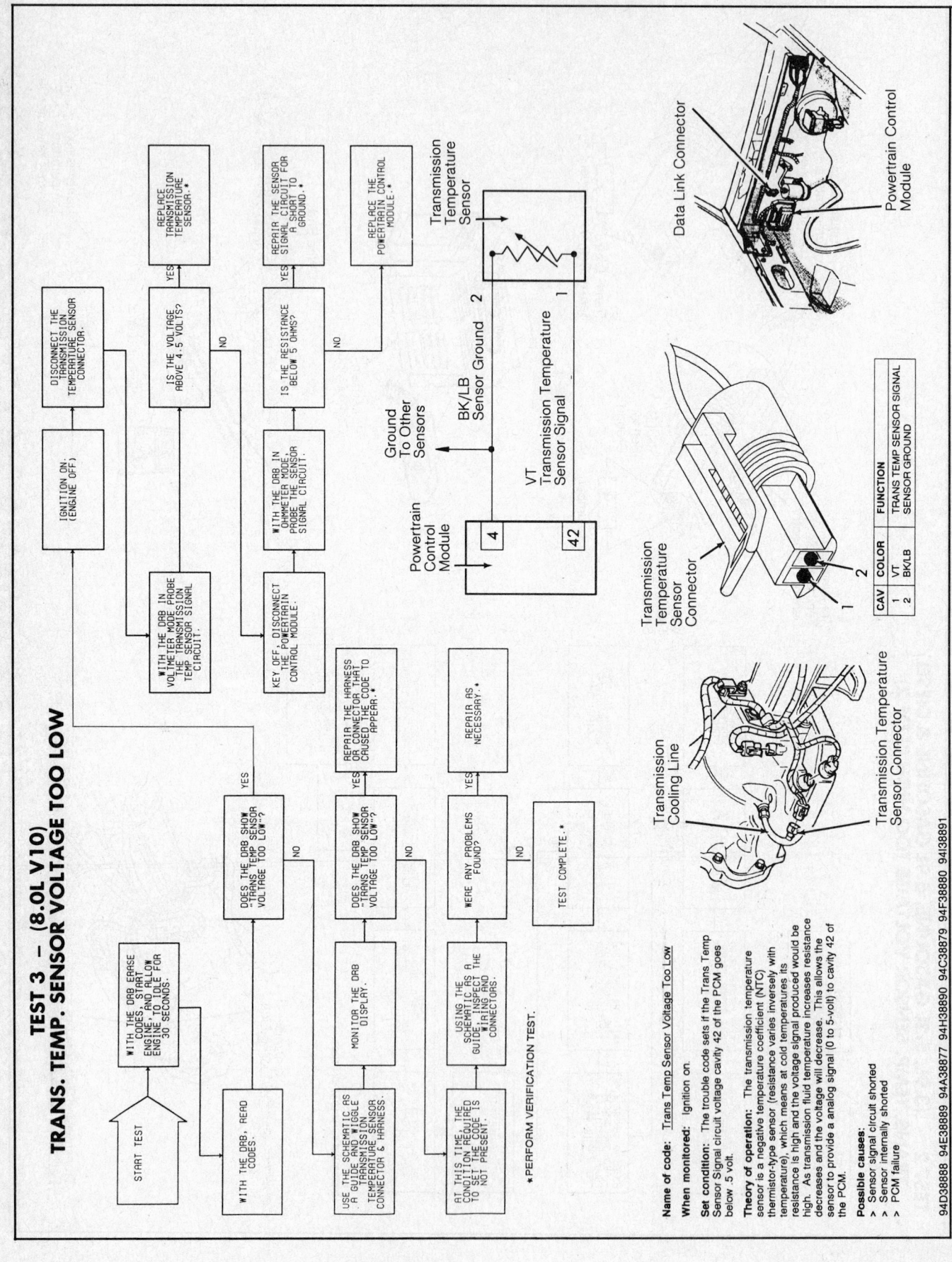

TEST 3 – (8.0L V10)
TRANS. TEMP. SENSOR VOLTAGE TOO LOW

START TEST

WITH THE DRB, READ CODES.

WITH THE DRB ERASE CODES, START ENGINE, AND ALLOW ENGINE TO IDLE FOR 30 SECONDS.

USE THE SCHEMATIC AS A GUIDE AND INSPECT THE TRANSMISSION TEMPERATURE SENSOR CONNECTOR & HARNESS.

DOES THE DRB SHOW "TRANS TEMP SENSOR VOLTAGE TOO LOW"?

YES → IGNITION ON. (ENGINE OFF)

DISCONNECT THE TRANSMISSION TEMPERATURE SENSOR CONNECTOR.

WITH THE DRB IN VOLTMETER MODE PROBE THE TRANSMISSION TEMP SENSOR SIGNAL CIRCUIT.

IS THE VOLTAGE ABOVE 4.5 VOLTS?

YES → REPLACE TRANSMISSION TEMPERATURE SENSOR.*

NO → KEY OFF DISCONNECT THE POWERTRAIN CONTROL MODULE.

WITH THE DRB IN OHMMETER MODE PROBE THE SENSOR SIGNAL CIRCUIT.

IS THE RESISTANCE BELOW 5 OHMS?

YES → REPAIR THE SENSOR SIGNAL CIRCUIT FOR A SHORT TO GROUND.*

NO → REPLACE THE POWERTRAIN CONTROL MODULE.*

MONITOR THE DRB DISPLAY.

DOES THE DRB SHOW "TRANS TEMP SENSOR VOLTAGE TOO LOW?

YES → REPAIR THE HARNESS OR CONNECTOR THAT CAUSED THE CODE TO APPEAR.*

NO → AT THIS TIME, THE CONDITION REQUIRED TO SET THE CODE IS NOT PRESENT.

USING THE GUIDE INSPECT THE WIRING AND CONNECTORS.

WERE ANY PROBLEMS FOUND?

YES → REPAIR AS NECESSARY.*

NO → TEST COMPLETE.*

*PERFORM VERIFICATION TEST.

Transmission Temperature Sensor

BK/LB Sensor Ground 2

VT Transmission Temperature Sensor Signal 1

Ground To Other Sensors

Powertrain Control Module 4

42

Data Link Connector

Powertrain Control Module

Transmission Temperature Sensor Connector

Transmission Cooling Line

Transmission Temperature Sensor Connector

CAV	COLOR	FUNCTION
1	VT	TRANS TEMP SENSOR SIGNAL
2	BK/LB	SENSOR GROUND

Name of code: Trans Temp Sensor Voltage Too Low

When monitored: Ignition on.

Set condition: The trouble code sets if the Trans Temp Sensor Signal circuit voltage cavity 42 of the PCM goes below .5 volt.

Theory of operation: The transmission temperature sensor is a negative temperature coefficient (NTC) thermistor-type sensor (resistance varies inversely with temperature), which means at cold temperatures its resistance is high and the voltage signal produced would be high. As transmission fluid temperature increases resistance decreases and the voltage will decrease. This allows the sensor to provide an analog signal (0 to 5-volt) to cavity 42 of the PCM.

Possible causes:
> Sensor signal circuit shorted
> Sensor internally shorted
> PCM failure

94D38888 94E38889 94A38877 94H38890 94C38879 94F38880 94J38891

Name of code: Trans Temp Sensor Voltage Too High

When monitored: Ignition on.

Set condition: The trouble code sets if the Trans Temp Sensor Signal circuit voltage cavity 42 of the PCM goes above 4.9 volt.

Theory of operation: The transmission temperature sensor is a negative temperature coefficient (NTC) thermistor-type sensor (resistance varies inversely with temperature), which means at cold temperatures its resistance is high and the voltage signal produced would be high. As transmission fluid temperature increases resistance decreases and the voltage will decrease. This allows the sensor to provide a analog signal (0 to 5-volt) to cavity 42 of the PCM.

Possible causes:
> Sensor signal circuit open
> Sensor internally open
> Sensor ground circuit open
> PCM failure

TRANS. TEMP. SENSOR VOLTAGE TOO HIGH (1 OF 2)
TEST 4 – (8.0L V10)

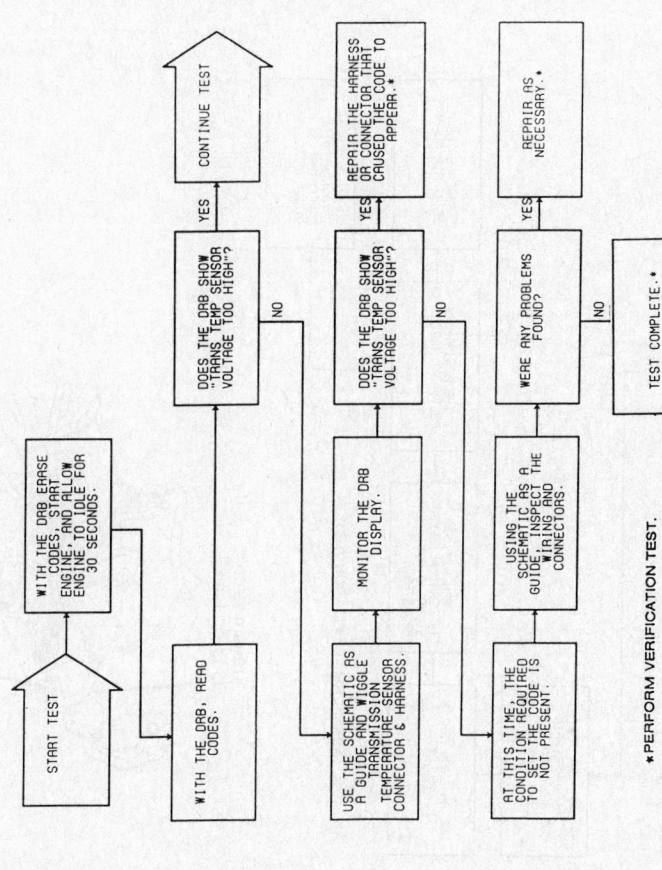

94J38892 94C38879 94A38893 NEW**

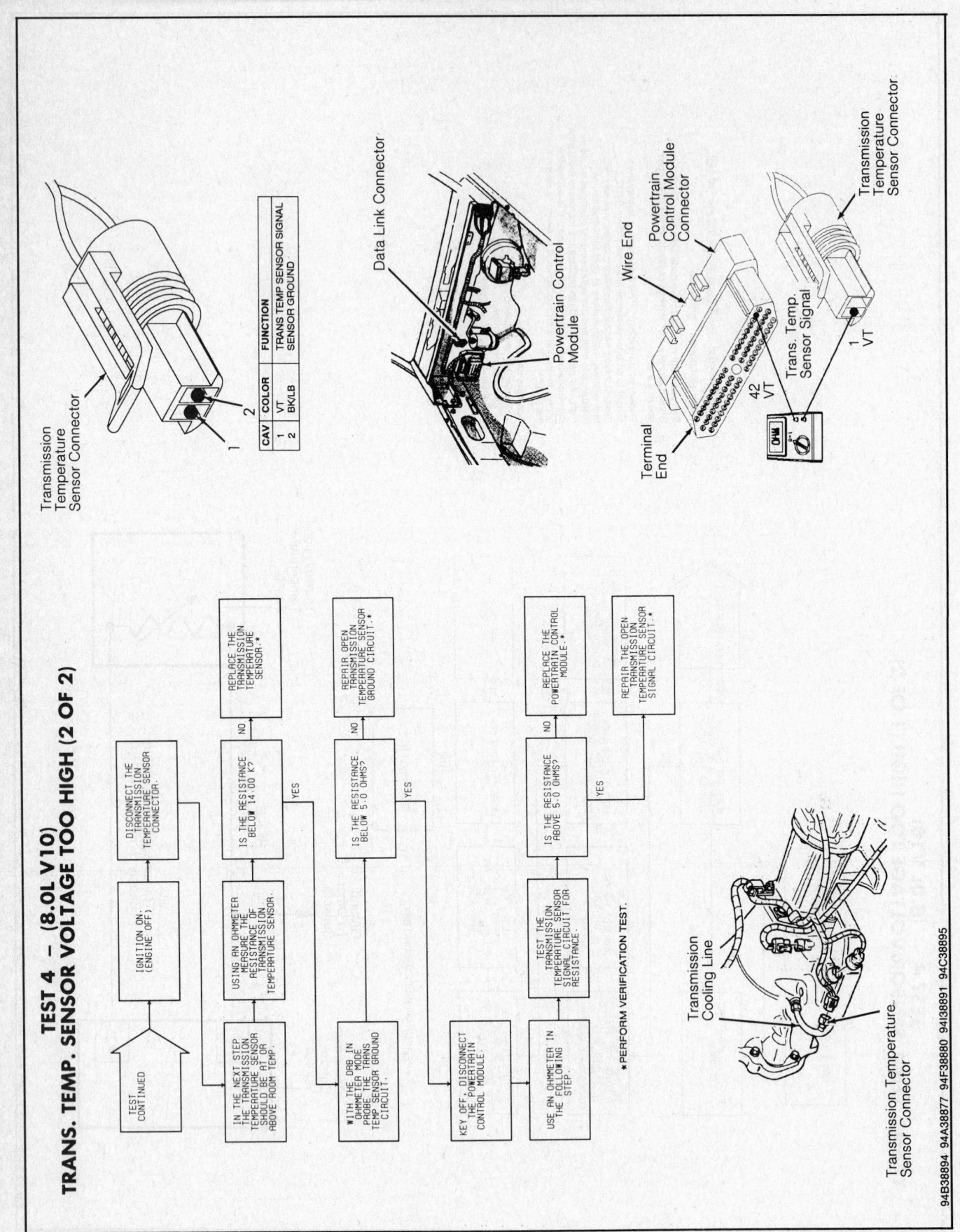

Transmission Temperature Sensor Connector

CAV	COLOR	FUNCTION
1	VT	TRANS TEMP SENSOR SIGNAL
2	BK/LB	SENSOR GROUND

Data Link Connector

Powertrain Control Module

Wire End

Powertrain Control Module Connector

Transmission Temperature Sensor Connector

Terminal End

Trans. Temp. Sensor Signal

42 VT

1 VT

TEST 4 — (8.0L V10)
TRANS. TEMP. SENSOR VOLTAGE TOO HIGH (2 OF 2)

TEST CONTINUED

IGNITION ON, (ENGINE OFF)

DISCONNECT THE TRANSMISSION TEMPERATURE SENSOR CONNECTOR.

IN THE NEXT STEP THE TRANSMISSION TEMPERATURE SENSOR SHOULD BE AT OR ABOVE ROOM TEMP.

USING AN OHMMETER MEASURE THE RESISTANCE OF TRANSMISSION TEMPERATURE SENSOR.

IS THE RESISTANCE BELOW 14.00 K? — NO → REPLACE THE TRANSMISSION TEMPERATURE SENSOR.*

YES

WITH THE DRB IN OHMMETER MODE PROBE THE TRANS TEMP SENSOR GROUND CIRCUIT.

IS THE RESISTANCE BELOW 5.0 OHMS? — NO → REPAIR OPEN TRANSMISSION TEMPERATURE SENSOR GROUND CIRCUIT.*

YES

KEY OFF, DISCONNECT THE POWERTRAIN CONTROL MODULE.

USE AN OHMMETER IN THE FOLLOWING STEP.

TEST THE TRANSMISSION TEMPERATURE SENSOR SIGNAL CIRCUIT FOR RESISTANCE.

IS THE RESISTANCE ABOVE 5.0 OHMS? — NO → REPLACE THE POWERTRAIN CONTROL MODULE.*

YES

REPAIR THE OPEN TRANSMISSION TEMPERATURE SENSOR SIGNAL CIRCUIT.*

*PERFORM VERIFICATION TEST.

Transmission Cooling Line

Transmission Temperature Sensor Connector

Transmission Temperature Sensor Connector

94B38894 94A38877 94F38880 94I38891 94C38895

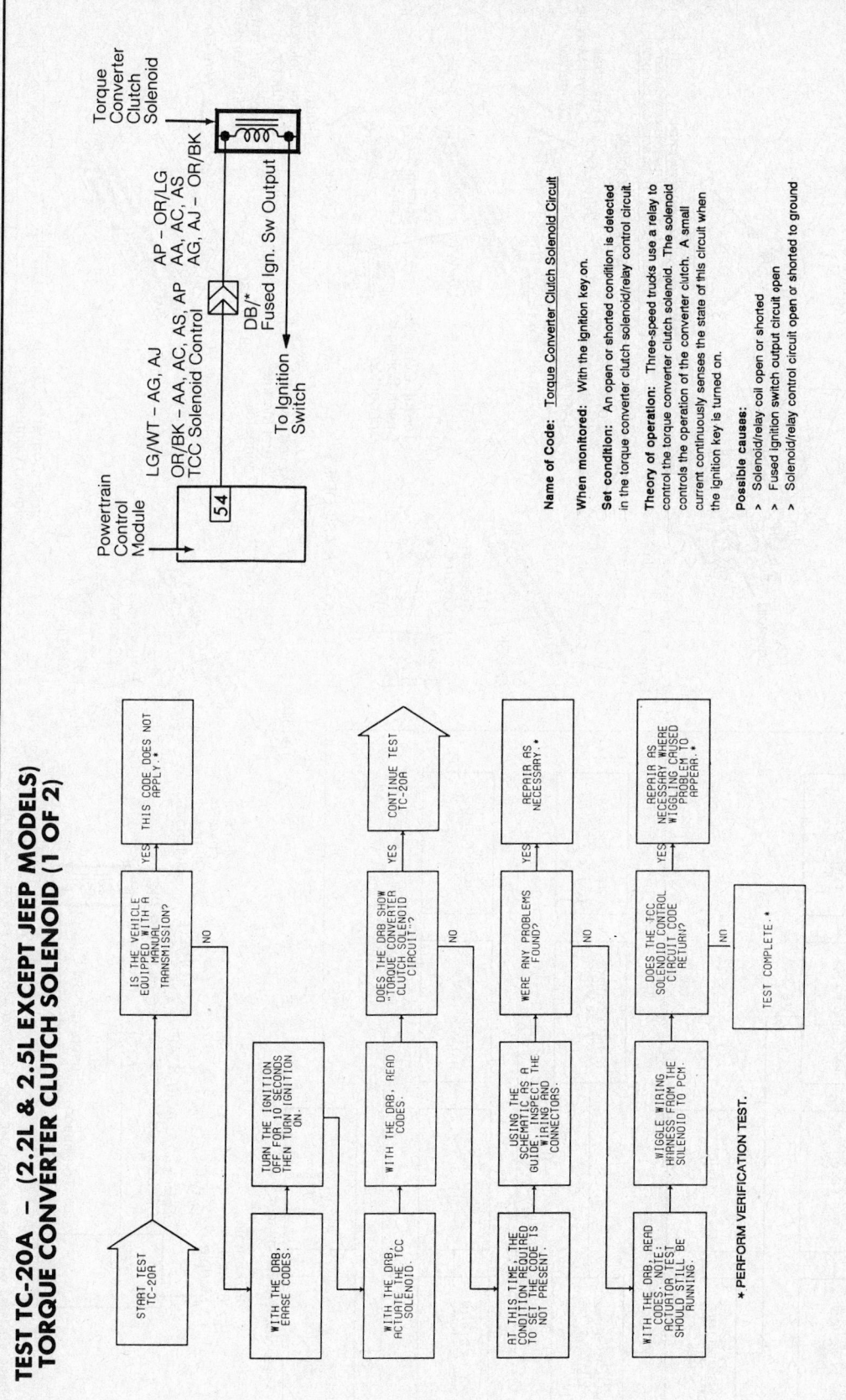

Name of Code: Torque Converter Clutch Solenoid Circuit

When monitored: With the ignition key on.

Set condition: An open or shorted condition is detected in the torque converter clutch solenoid/relay control circuit.

Theory of operation: Three-speed trucks use a relay to control the torque converter clutch solenoid. The solenoid controls the operation of the converter clutch. A small current continuously senses the state of this circuit when the ignition key is turned on.

Possible causes:
> Solenoid/relay coil open or shorted
> Fused ignition switch output circuit open
> Solenoid/relay control circuit open or shorted to ground

TEST TC-20A — (2.2L & 2.5L EXCEPT JEEP MODELS) TORQUE CONVERTER CLUTCH SOLENOID (1 OF 2)

94D38896 94E38897 94F38898

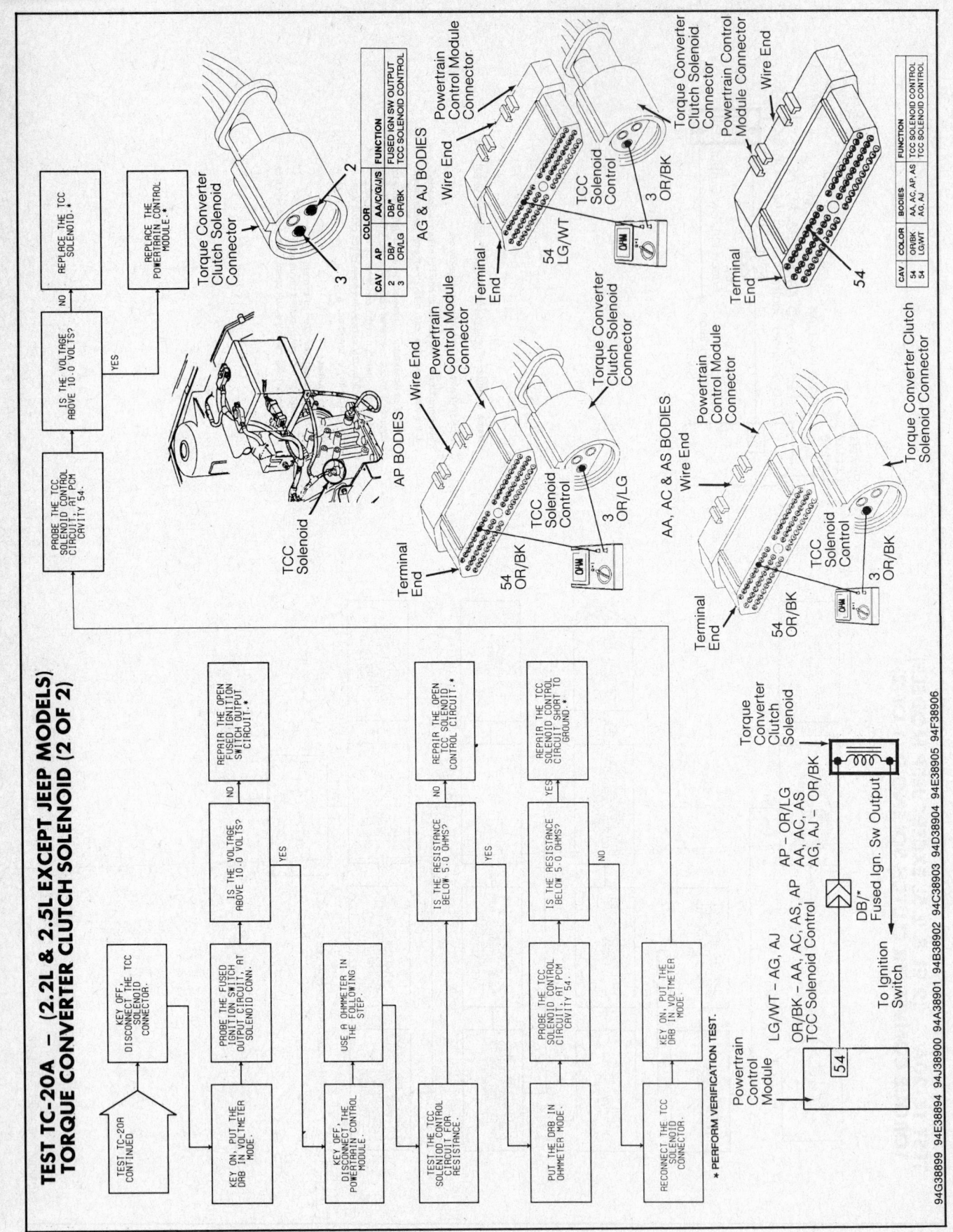

TEST TC-20A – (2.2L & 2.5L EXCEPT JEEP MODELS)
TORQUE CONVERTER CLUTCH SOLENOID (2 OF 2)

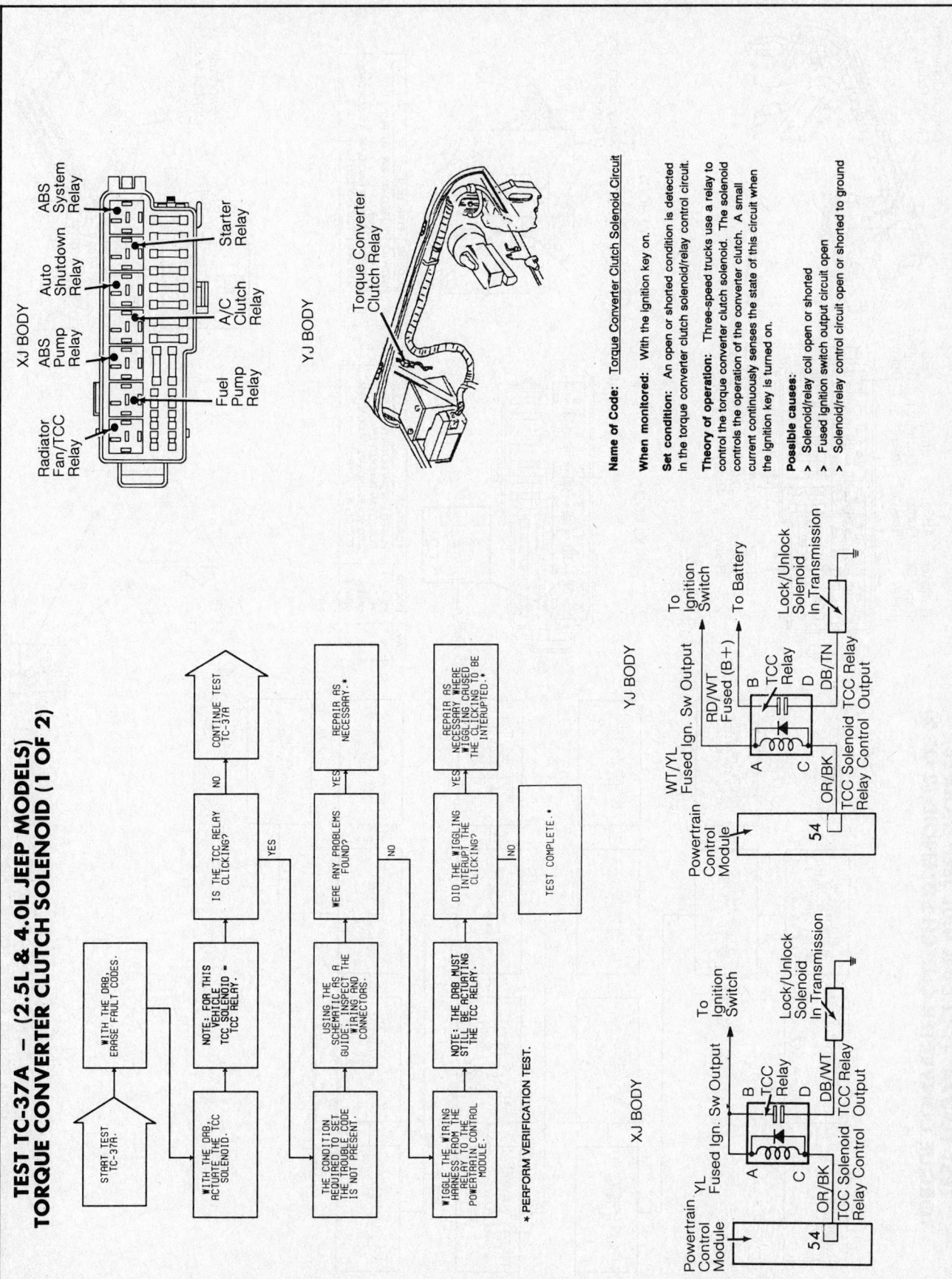

XJ BODY

ABS System Relay

Starter Relay

Auto Shutdown Relay

A/C Clutch Relay

ABS Pump Relay

Fuel Pump Relay

Radiator Fan/TCC Relay

YJ BODY

Torque Converter Clutch Relay

Name of Code: Torque Converter Clutch Solenoid Circuit

When monitored: With the ignition key on.

Set condition: An open or shorted condition is detected in the torque converter clutch solenoid/relay control circuit.

Theory of operation: Three-speed trucks use a relay to control the torque converter clutch solenoid. The solenoid controls the operation of the converter clutch. A small current continuously senses the state of this circuit when the ignition key is turned on.

Possible causes:
> Solenoid/relay coil open or shorted
> Fused ignition switch output circuit open
> Solenoid/relay control circuit open or shorted to ground

TEST TC-37A – (2.5L & 4.0L JEEP MODELS)
TORQUE CONVERTER CLUTCH SOLENOID (1 OF 2)

START TEST TC-37A.

→ WITH THE DRB, ERASE FAULT CODES.

→ WITH THE DRB, ACTUATE THE TCC SOLENOID.

→ NOTE: FOR THIS VEHICLE TCC SOLENOID = TCC RELAY.

→ IS THE TCC RELAY CLICKING?
— NO → CONTINUE TEST TC-37A.
— YES →

→ THE CONDITION REQUIRED TO SET THE TROUBLE CODE IS NOT PRESENT.

→ USING THE SCHEMATIC AS A GUIDE, INSPECT THE WIRING AND CONNECTORS.

→ WERE ANY PROBLEMS FOUND?
— YES → REPAIR AS NECESSARY. *
— NO →

→ WIGGLE THE WIRING HARNESS FROM THE RELAY TO THE POWERTRAIN CONTROL MODULE.

→ NOTE: THE DRB MUST BE ACTUATING THE TCC RELAY.

→ DID THE WIGGLING INTERRUPT THE CLICKING?
— YES → REPAIR AS NECESSARY WHERE THE WIGGLING CAUSED THE CLICKING TO BE INTERUPTED. *
— NO → TEST COMPLETE. *

* PERFORM VERIFICATION TEST.

YJ BODY

To Ignition Switch

To Battery

WT/YL Fused Ign. Sw Output

RD/WT Fused (B+)

TCC Relay

Lock/Unlock Solenoid In Transmission

A B C D

DB/TN

Powertrain Control Module

54

OR/BK

TCC Solenoid TCC Relay Relay Control Output

XJ BODY

To Ignition Switch

YL Fused Ign. Sw Output

TCC Relay

Lock/Unlock Solenoid In Transmission

A B C D

DB/WT

Powertrain Control Module

54

OR/BK

TCC Solenoid TCC Relay Relay Control Output

94G38907 94H38908 94J38909 94B38910 94C38911 94D38912

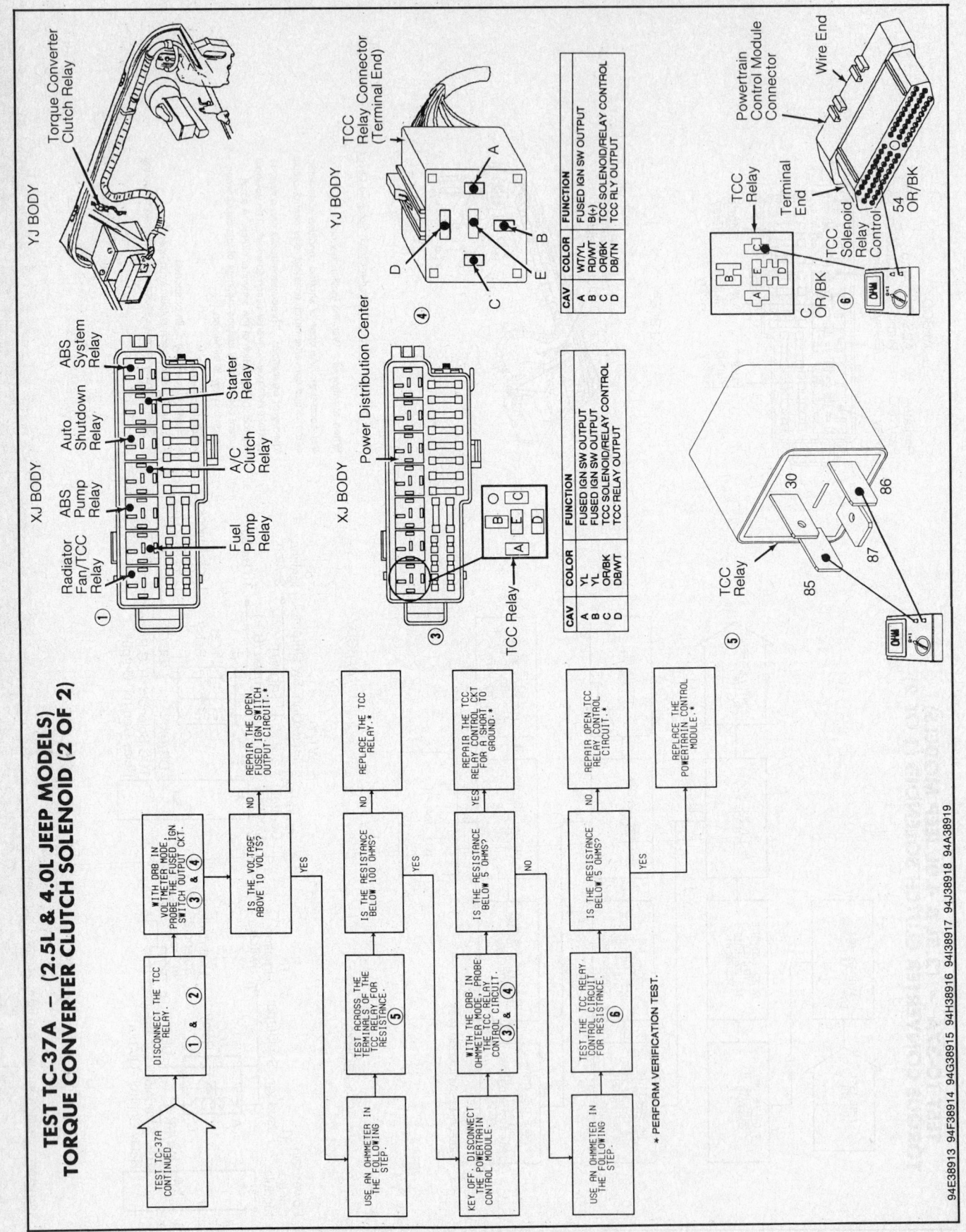

TEST TC-37A — (2.5L & 4.0L JEEP MODELS)
TORQUE CONVERTER CLUTCH SOLENOID (2 OF 2)

94E38913 94F38914 94G38915 94H38916 94J38917 94J38918 94A38919

Name of Code: Torque Converter Clutch Solenoid Circuit

When monitored: With the ignition key on.

Set condition: An open or shorted condition is detected in the torque converter clutch solenoid/relay control circuit.

Theory of operation: Three-speed trucks use a relay to control the torque converter clutch solenoid. The solenoid controls the operation of the converter clutch. A small current continuously senses the state of this circuit when the ignition key is turned on.

Possible causes:
> Solenoid/relay coil open or shorted
> Fused ignition switch output circuit open
> Solenoid/relay control circuit open or shorted to ground

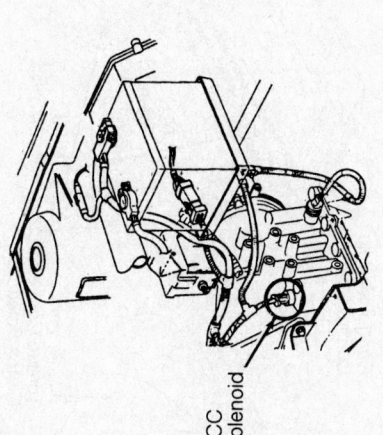

TCC Solenoid

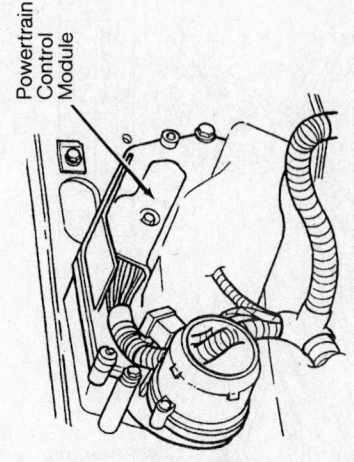

Powertrain Control Module

TEST TC-27A – (3.0L)
TORQUE CONVERTER CLUTCH SOLENOID (1 OF 2)

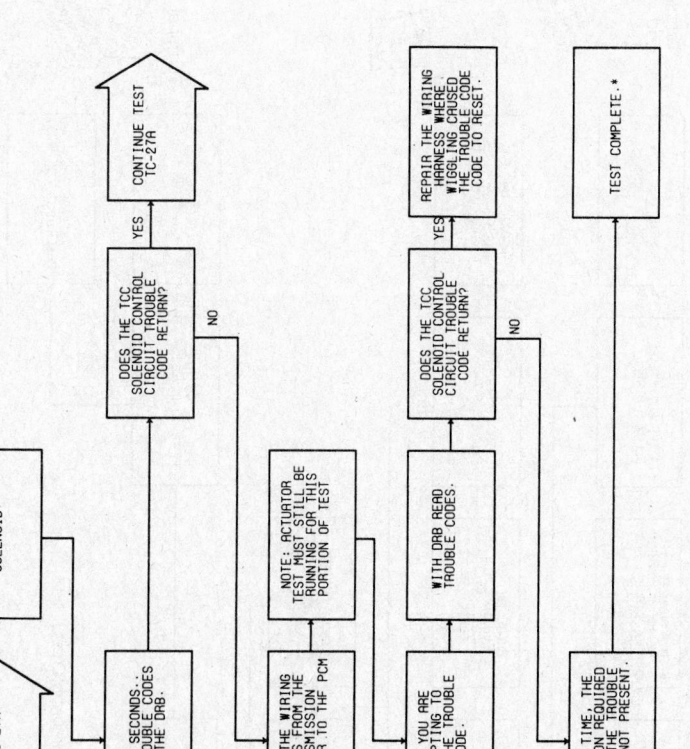

START TEST TC-27A.

WITH THE DRB, ACTUATE THE TCC SOLENOID.

WAIT 10 SECONDS. READ TROUBLE CODES WITH THE DRB.

DOES THE TCC SOLENOID CONTROL CIRCUIT TROUBLE CODE RETURN? — YES → CONTINUE TEST TC-27A

NO

WIGGLE THE WIRING HARNESS FROM THE TRANSMISSION CONNECTOR TO THE PCM

NOTE: ACTUATOR TEST MUST STILL BE RUNNING FOR THIS PORTION OF TEST

WITH DRB READ TROUBLE CODES.

NOTE: YOU ARE ATTEMPTING TO RESET THE TROUBLE CODE.

DOES THE TCC SOLENOID CONTROL CIRCUIT TROUBLE CODE RETURN? — YES → REPAIR THE WIRING HARNESS WHERE WIGGLING CAUSED THE TROUBLE CODE TO RESET.

NO

AT THIS TIME, THE CONDITION REQUIRED TO SET THE TROUBLE CODE IS NOT PRESENT.

TEST COMPLETE. *

* PERFORM VERIFICATION TEST.

Torque Converter Clutch Solenoid

AP – OR/LG
AA, AC, AS
AG, AJ – OR/BK

DB/*
Fused Ign. Sw Output

To Ignition Switch

Powertrain Control Module

LG/WT – AG, AJ
OR/BK – AA, AC, AS, AP
TCC Solenoid Control

54

94D38920 94E38897 94F38898 94A38901 94E38921

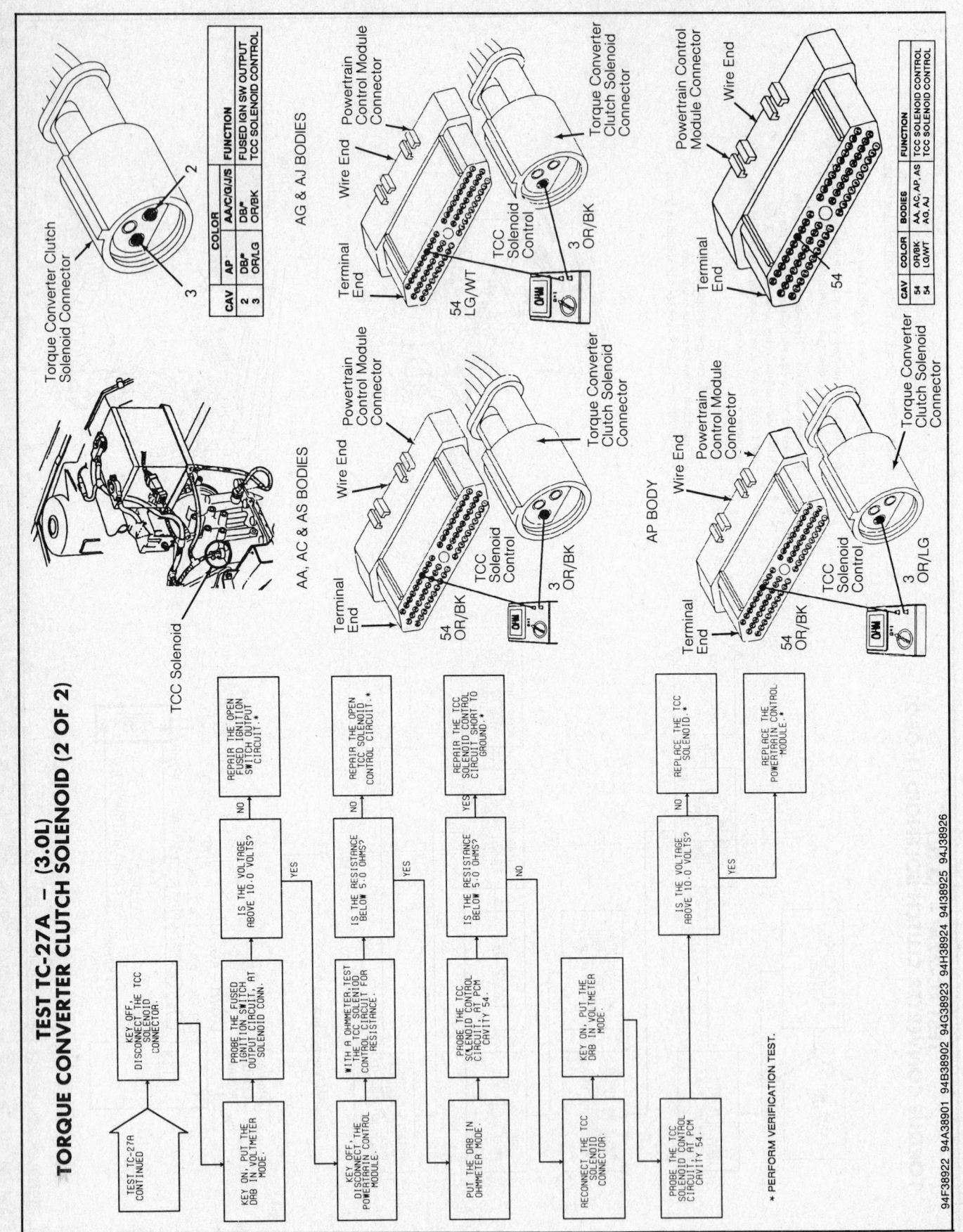

TEST TC-27A – (3.0L)
TORQUE CONVERTER CLUTCH SOLENOID (2 OF 2)

94F38922 94J38901 94B38902 94G38923 94H38924 94I38925 94J38926

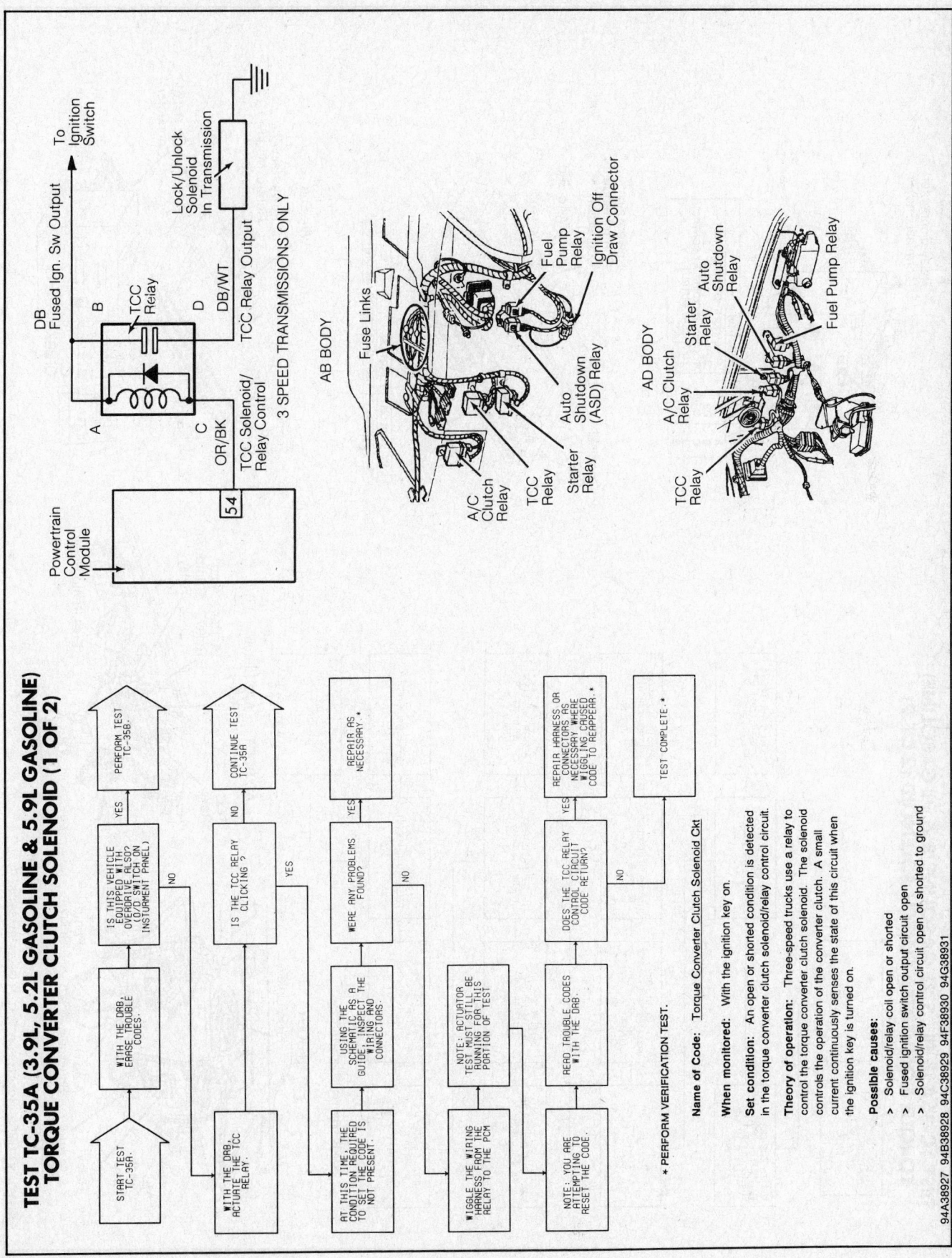

TEST TC-35A (3.9L, 5.2L GASOLINE & 5.9L GASOLINE)
TORQUE CONVERTER CLUTCH SOLENOID (1 OF 2)

* PERFORM VERIFICATION TEST.

Name of Code: Torque Converter Clutch Solenoid Ckt

When monitored: With the ignition key on.

Set condition: An open or shorted condition is detected in the torque converter clutch solenoid/relay control circuit.

Theory of operation: Three-speed trucks use a relay to control the torque converter clutch solenoid. The solenoid controls the operation of the converter clutch. A small current continuously senses the state of this circuit when the ignition key is turned on.

Possible causes:

> Solenoid/relay coil open or shorted
> Fused ignition switch output circuit open
> Solenoid/relay control circuit open or shorted to ground

94A38927 94B38928 94C38929 94F38930 94G38931

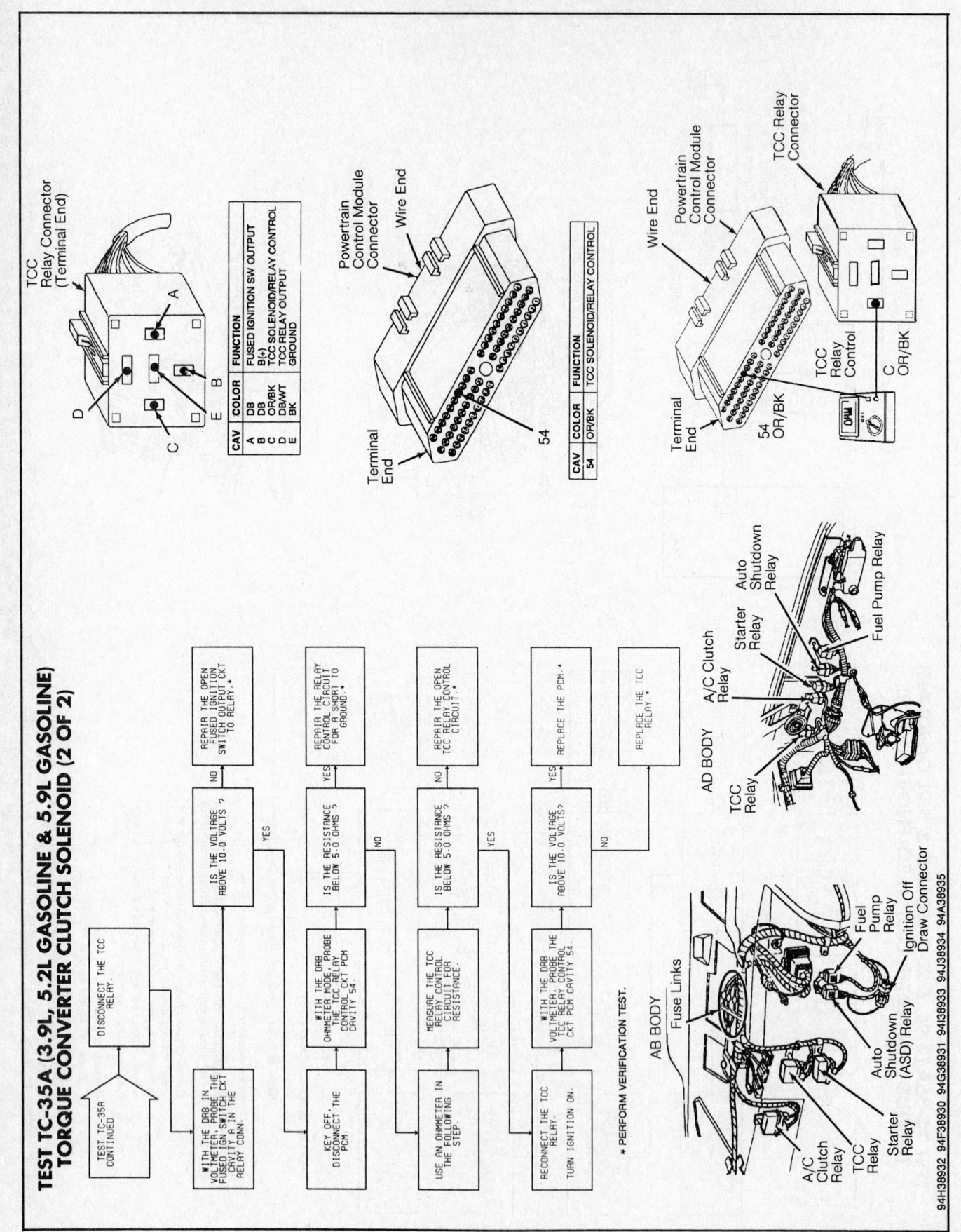

TCC Relay Connector (Terminal End)

CAV	COLOR	FUNCTION
A	DB	FUSED IGNITION SW OUTPUT
B	DB	B(+)
C	OR/BK	TCC SOLENOID/RELAY CONTROL
D	DB/WT	TCC RELAY OUTPUT
E	BK	GROUND

Powertrain Control Module Connector

Wire End

CAV	COLOR	FUNCTION
54	OR/BK	TCC SOLENOID/RELAY CONTROL

Terminal End

54

Powertrain Control Module Connector

TCC Relay Connector

Wire End

TCC Relay Control

C OR/BK

Terminal End

54 OR/BK

TEST TC-35A (3.9L, 5.2L GASOLINE & 5.9L GASOLINE) TORQUE CONVERTER CLUTCH SOLENOID (2 OF 2)

TEST TC-35A CONTINUED

DISCONNECT THE TCC RELAY.

WITH THE DRB IN VOLTMETER, PROBE THE FUSED IGN. SWITCH CKT CAVITY A IN THE TCC RELAY CONN.

IS THE VOLTAGE ABOVE 10.0 VOLTS? — NO → REPAIR THE OPEN FUSED IGNITION SWITCH OUTPUT CKT TO RELAY. *

YES

KEY OFF. DISCONNECT THE PCM.

WITH THE DRB IN OHMMETER MODE, PROBE THE TCC RELAY CONTROL CKT PCM CAVITY 54.

IS THE RESISTANCE BELOW 5.0 OHMS? — YES → REPAIR THE RELAY CONTROL CIRCUIT FOR SHORT TO GROUND. *

NO

USE AN OHMMETER IN THE FOLLOWING STEP.

MEASURE THE TCC RELAY CONTROL CIRCUIT FOR RESISTANCE.

IS THE RESISTANCE BELOW 5.0 OHMS? — NO → REPAIR THE OPEN TCC RELAY CONTROL CIRCUIT. *

YES

RECONNECT THE TCC RELAY. TURN IGNITION ON.

WITH THE DRB IN VOLTMETER, PROBE THE TCC RELAY CONTROL CKT PCM CAVITY 54.

IS THE VOLTAGE ABOVE 10.0 VOLTS? — YES → REPLACE THE PCM. *

NO

REPLACE THE TCC RELAY. *

* PERFORM VERIFICATION TEST.

AD BODY

Starter Relay

Auto Shutdown Relay

A/C Clutch Relay

Fuel Pump Relay

TCC Relay

AB BODY

Fuse Links

Fuel Pump Relay

Ignition Off Draw Connector

Auto Shutdown (ASD) Relay

A/C Clutch Relay

TCC Relay

Starter Relay

94H38932 94F38930 94G38931 94I38933 94.J38934 94A38935

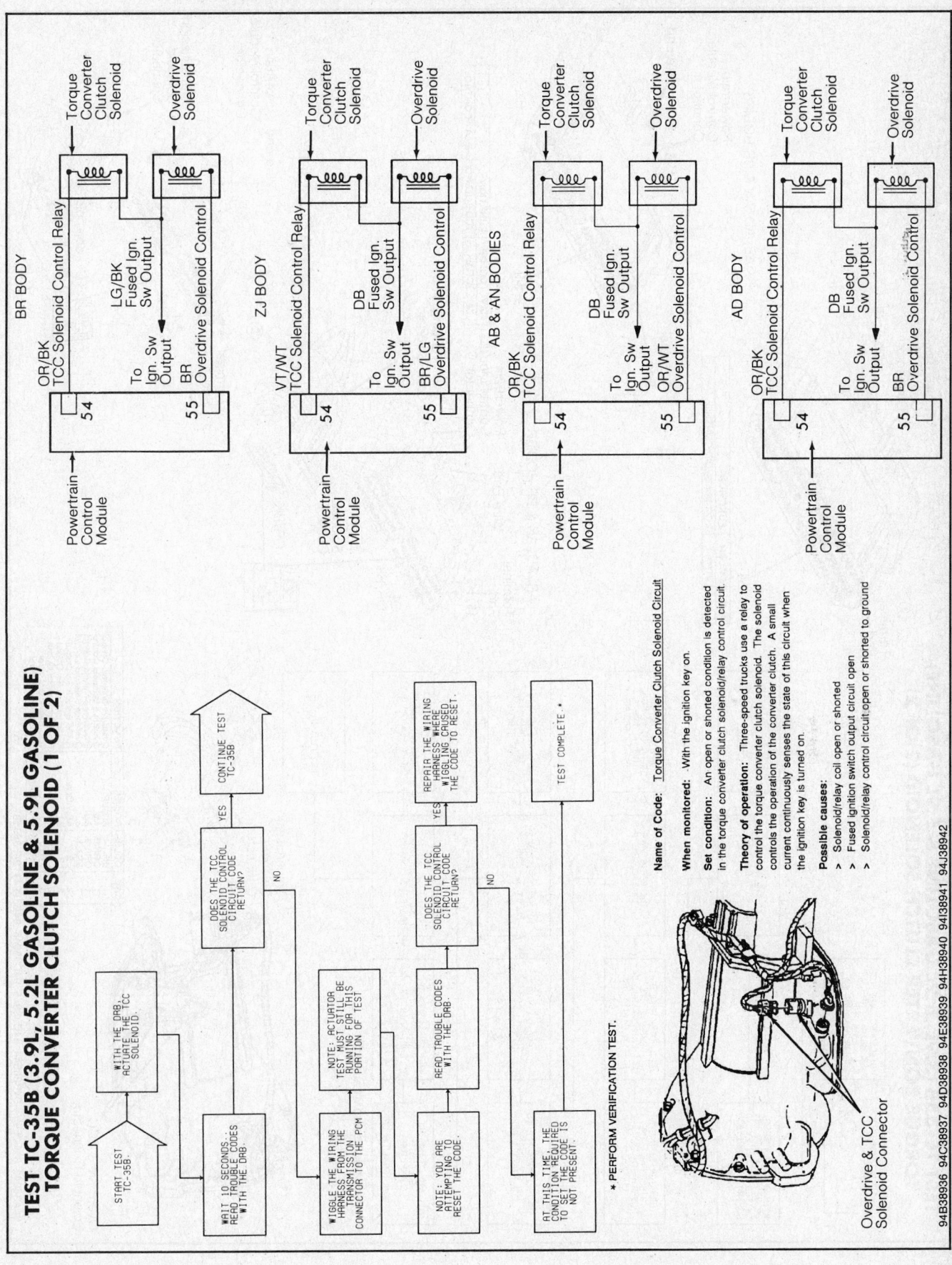

TEST TC-35B (3.9L, 5.2L GASOLINE & 5.9L GASOLINE) TORQUE CONVERTER CLUTCH SOLENOID (1 OF 2)

Name of Code: Torque Converter Clutch Solenoid Circuit

When monitored: With the ignition key on.

Set condition: An open or shorted condition is detected in the torque converter clutch solenoid/relay control circuit.

Theory of operation: Three-speed trucks use a relay to control the torque converter clutch solenoid. The solenoid controls the operation of the converter clutch. A small current continuously senses the state of this circuit when the ignition key is turned on.

Possible causes:
> Solenoid/relay coil open or shorted
> Fused ignition switch output circuit open
> Solenoid/relay control circuit open or shorted to ground

* PERFORM VERIFICATION TEST.

94B38936 94C38937 94D38938 94E38939 94H38940 94I38941 94J38942

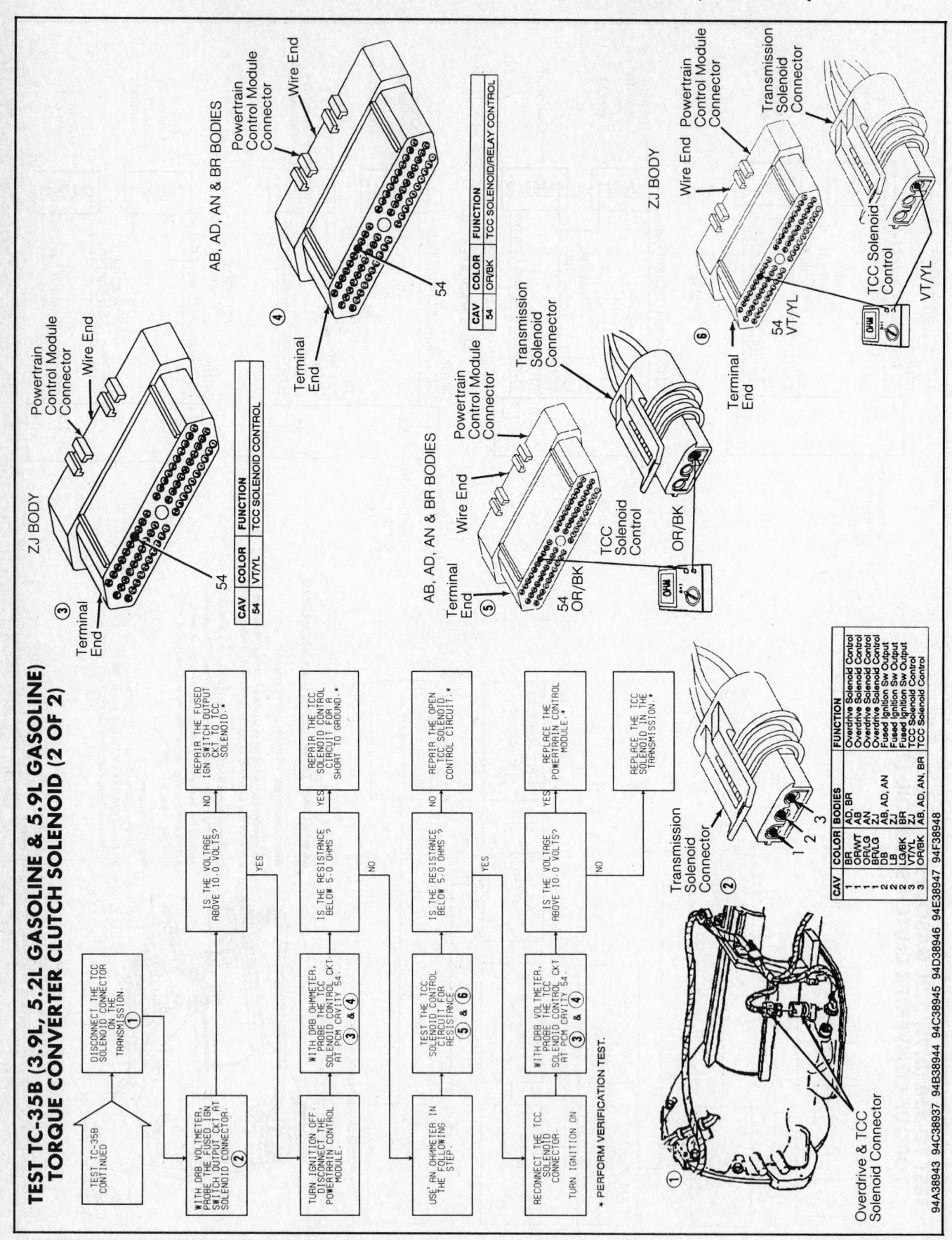

TEST TC-35B (3.9L, 5.2L GASOLINE & 5.9L GASOLINE)
TORQUE CONVERTER CLUTCH SOLENOID (2 OF 2)

③ ZJ BODY

Powertrain Control Module Connector

Wire End

Terminal End

54

CAV	COLOR	FUNCTION
54	VT/YL	TCC SOLENOID CONTROL

④ AB, AD, AN & BR BODIES

Powertrain Control Module Connector

Wire End

Terminal End

54

CAV	COLOR	FUNCTION
54	OR/BK	TCC SOLENOID/RELAY CONTROL

⑤ AB, AD, AN & BR BODIES

Powertrain Control Module Connector

Wire End

Transmission Solenoid Connector

Terminal End

TCC Solenoid Control

OR/BK

54 OR/BK

⑥ ZJ BODY

Wire End Powertrain Control Module Connector

Transmission Solenoid Connector

Terminal End

TCC Solenoid Control

54 VT/YL

VT/YL

② Transmission Solenoid Connector

1 2 3

CAV	COLOR	BODIES	FUNCTION
1	BR	AD, BR	Overdrive Solenoid Control
1	OR/WT	AB	Overdrive Solenoid Control
1	AN	AN	Overdrive Solenoid Control
1	BR/LG	ZJ	Overdrive Solenoid Control
2	DB	AB, AD, AN	Fused Ignition Sw Output
2	LB	ZJ	Fused Ignition Sw Output
3	LG/BK	BR	TCC Solenoid Control
3	VT/YL	ZJ	TCC Solenoid Control
3	OR/BK	AB, AD, AN, BR	TCC Solenoid Control

① Overdrive & TCC Solenoid Connector

TEST TC-35B CONTINUED

⟶ DISCONNECT THE TCC SOLENOID CONNECTOR ON THE TRANSMISSION. ①

WITH DRB VOLTMETER, PROBE THE FUSED IGN SWITCH OUTPUT CKT AT SOLENOID CONNECTOR. ②

IS THE VOLTAGE ABOVE 10.0 VOLTS?

NO → REPAIR THE FUSED IGN SWITCH OUTPUT CKT TO TCC SOLENOID.*

YES ↓

TURN IGNITION OFF. DISCONNECT THE POWERTRAIN CONTROL MODULE.

WITH DRB OHMMETER, PROBE THE TCC SOLENOID CONTROL CKT AT PCM CAVITY 54 ③ & ④

IS THE RESISTANCE BELOW 5.0 OHMS?

YES → REPAIR THE TCC SOLENOID CONTROL CIRCUIT FOR A SHORT TO GROUND.*

NO ↓

USE AN OHMMETER IN THE FOLLOWING STEP.

TEST THE TCC SOLENOID CONTROL CIRCUIT FOR RESISTANCE. ⑤ & ⑥

IS THE RESISTANCE BELOW 5.0 OHMS?

NO → REPAIR THE OPEN TCC SOLENOID CONTROL CIRCUIT.*

YES ↓

RECONNECT THE TCC SOLENOID CONNECTOR. TURN IGNITION ON.

WITH DRB VOLTMETER, PROBE THE TCC SOLENOID CONTROL CKT AT PCM CAVITY 54 ③ & ④

IS THE VOLTAGE ABOVE 10.0 VOLTS?

YES → REPLACE THE POWERTRAIN CONTROL MODULE.*

NO ↓

REPLACE THE TCC SOLENOID IN THE TRANSMISSION.*

* PERFORM VERIFICATION TEST.

94A38943 94C38937 94B38944 94C38945 94D38946 94E38947 94F38948

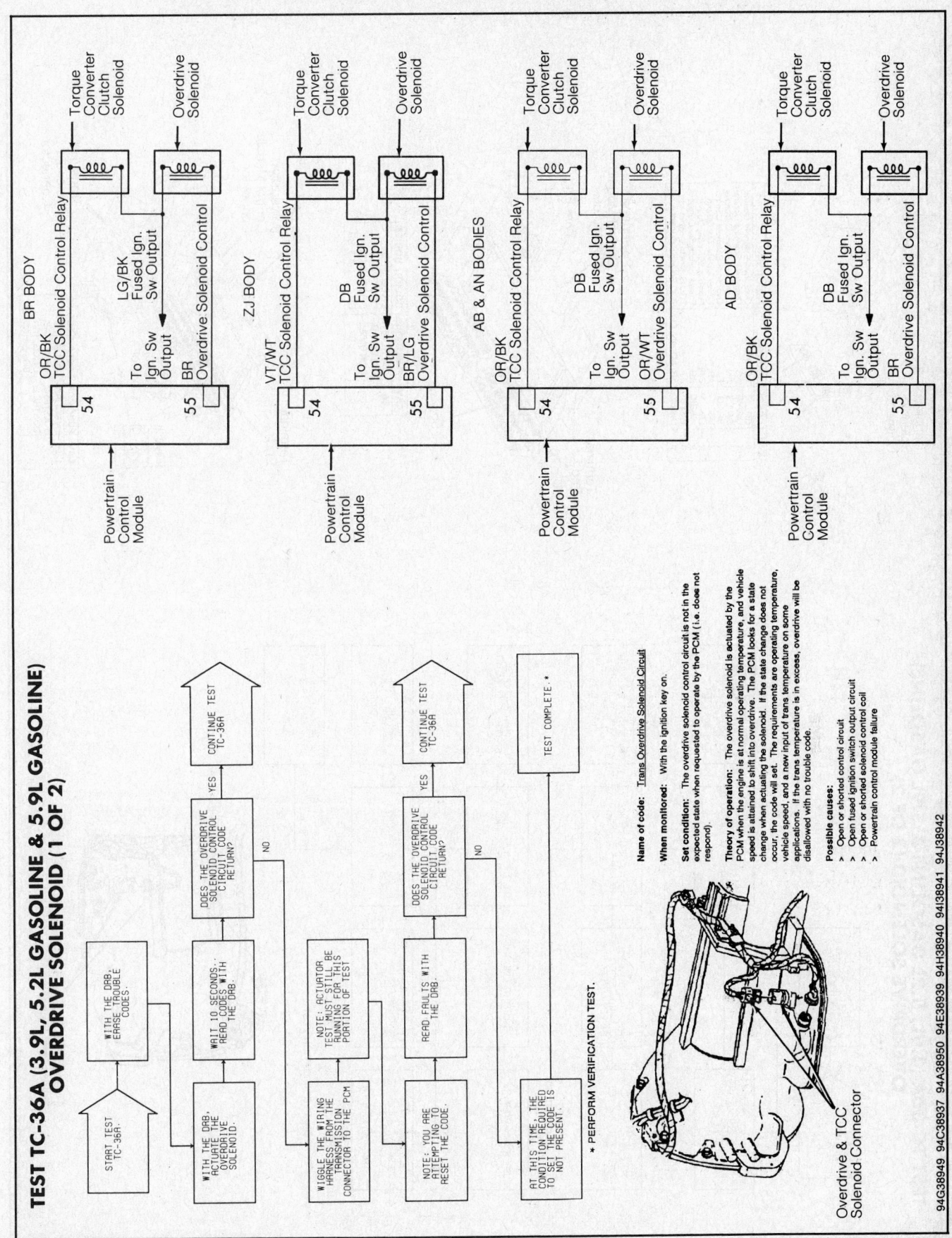

TEST TC-36A (3.9L, 5.2L GASOLINE & 5.9L GASOLINE) OVERDRIVE SOLENOID (1 OF 2)

BR BODY

Torque Converter Clutch Solenoid — Overdrive Solenoid

OR/BK TCC Solenoid Control Relay
LG/BK Fused Ign. Sw Output
To Ign. Sw Output
BR Overdrive Solenoid Control

54   55

Powertrain Control Module

ZJ BODY

Torque Converter Clutch Solenoid — Overdrive Solenoid

VT/WT TCC Solenoid Control Relay
DB Fused Ign. Sw Output
To Ign. Sw Output
BR/LG Overdrive Solenoid Control

54   55

Powertrain Control Module

AB & AN BODIES

Torque Converter Clutch Solenoid — Overdrive Solenoid

OR/BK TCC Solenoid Control Relay
DB Fused Ign. Sw Output
To Ign. Sw Output
OR/WT Overdrive Solenoid Control

54   55

Powertrain Control Module

AD BODY

Torque Converter Clutch Solenoid — Overdrive Solenoid

OR/BK TCC Solenoid Control Relay
DB Fused Ign. Sw Output
To Ign. Sw Output
BR Overdrive Solenoid Control

54   55

Powertrain Control Module

START TEST TC-36A.

WITH THE DRB, ERASE TROUBLE CODES.

WITH THE DRB, ACTUATE THE OVERDRIVE SOLENOID.

WAIT 10 SECONDS... READ CODE WITH THE DRB.

DOES THE OVERDRIVE SOLENOID CONTROL CIRCUIT CODE RETURN?

YES → CONTINUE TEST TC-36A

NO →

WIGGLE THE WIRING HARNESS FROM THE TRANSMISSION CONNECTOR TO THE PCM

NOTE: ACTUATOR TEST MUST STILL BE RUNNING FOR THIS PORTION OF TEST

READ FAULTS WITH THE DRB.

NOTE: YOU ARE ATTEMPTING TO RESET THE CODE.

DOES THE OVERDRIVE SOLENOID CONTROL CIRCUIT CODE RETURN?

YES → CONTINUE TEST TC-36A

NO →

AT THIS TIME, THE CONDITION REQUIRED TO SET THE CODE IS NOT PRESENT.

TEST COMPLETE. *

* PERFORM VERIFICATION TEST.

Name of code: Trans Overdrive Solenoid Circuit

When monitored: With the ignition key on.

Set condition: The overdrive solenoid control circuit is not in the expected state when requested to operate by the PCM (i.e. does not respond)

Theory of operation: The overdrive solenoid is actuated by the PCM when the engine is at normal operating temperature, and vehicle speed is attained to shift into overdrive. The PCM looks for a state change when actuating the solenoid. If the state change does not occur, the code will set. The requirements are operating temperature, vehicle speed, and a new input of trans temperature on some applications. If the trans temperature is in excess, overdrive will be disallowed with no trouble code.

Possible causes:
> Open or shorted control circuit
> Open fused ignition switch output circuit
> Open or shorted solenoid control coil
> Powertrain control module failure

Overdrive & TCC Solenoid Connector

94G38949 94C38937 94A38950 94E38939 94H38940 94I38941 94J38942

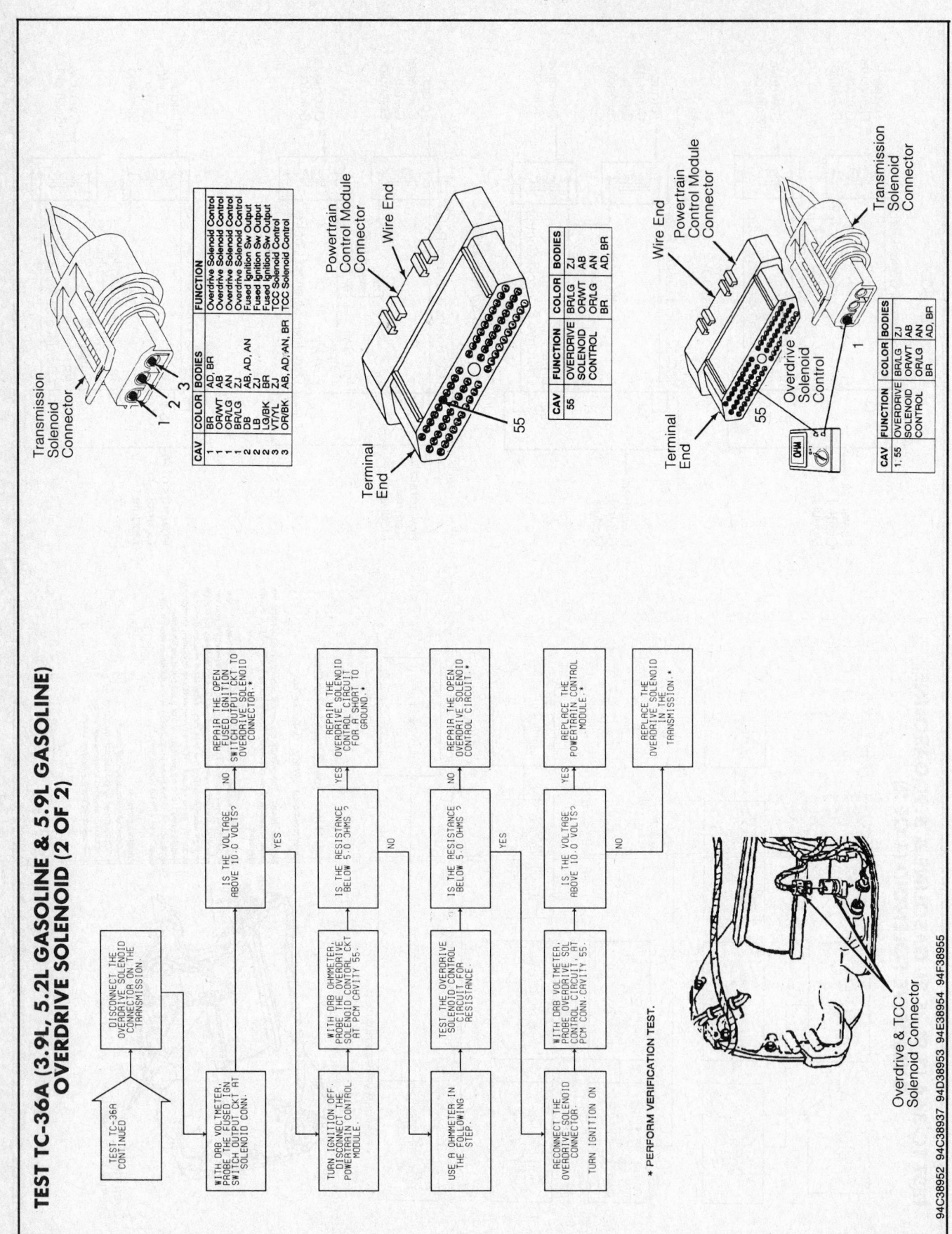

TEST TC-36A (3.9L, 5.2L GASOLINE & 5.9L GASOLINE) OVERDRIVE SOLENOID (2 OF 2)

94C38952 94C38937 94D38953 94E38954 94F38955

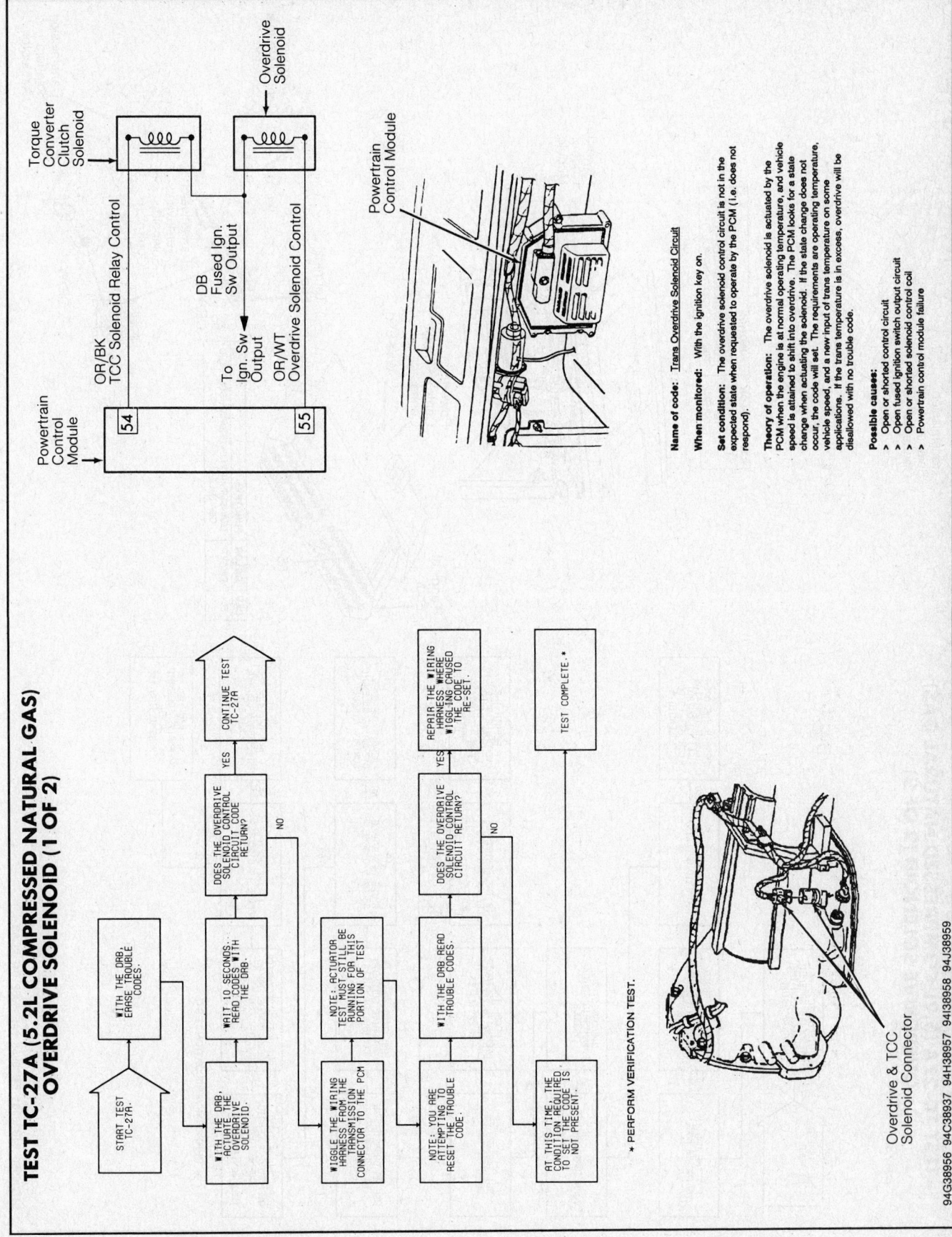

Name of code: Trans Overdrive Solenoid Circuit

When monitored: With the ignition key on.

Set condition: The overdrive solenoid control circuit is not in the expected state when requested to operate by the PCM (i.e. does not respond).

Theory of operation: The overdrive solenoid is actuated by the PCM when the engine is at normal operating temperature, and vehicle speed is attained to shift into overdrive. The PCM looks for a state change when actuating the solenoid. If the state change does not occur, the code will set. The requirements are operating temperature, vehicle speed, and a new input of trans temperature on some applications. If the trans temperature is in excess, overdrive will be disallowed with no trouble code.

Possible causes:
- Open or shorted control circuit
- Open fused ignition switch output circuit
- Open or shorted solenoid control coil
- Powertrain control module failure

TEST TC-27A (5.2L COMPRESSED NATURAL GAS) OVERDRIVE SOLENOID (1 OF 2)

* PERFORM VERIFICATION TEST.

94G38956 94C38937 94H38957 94I38958 94J38959

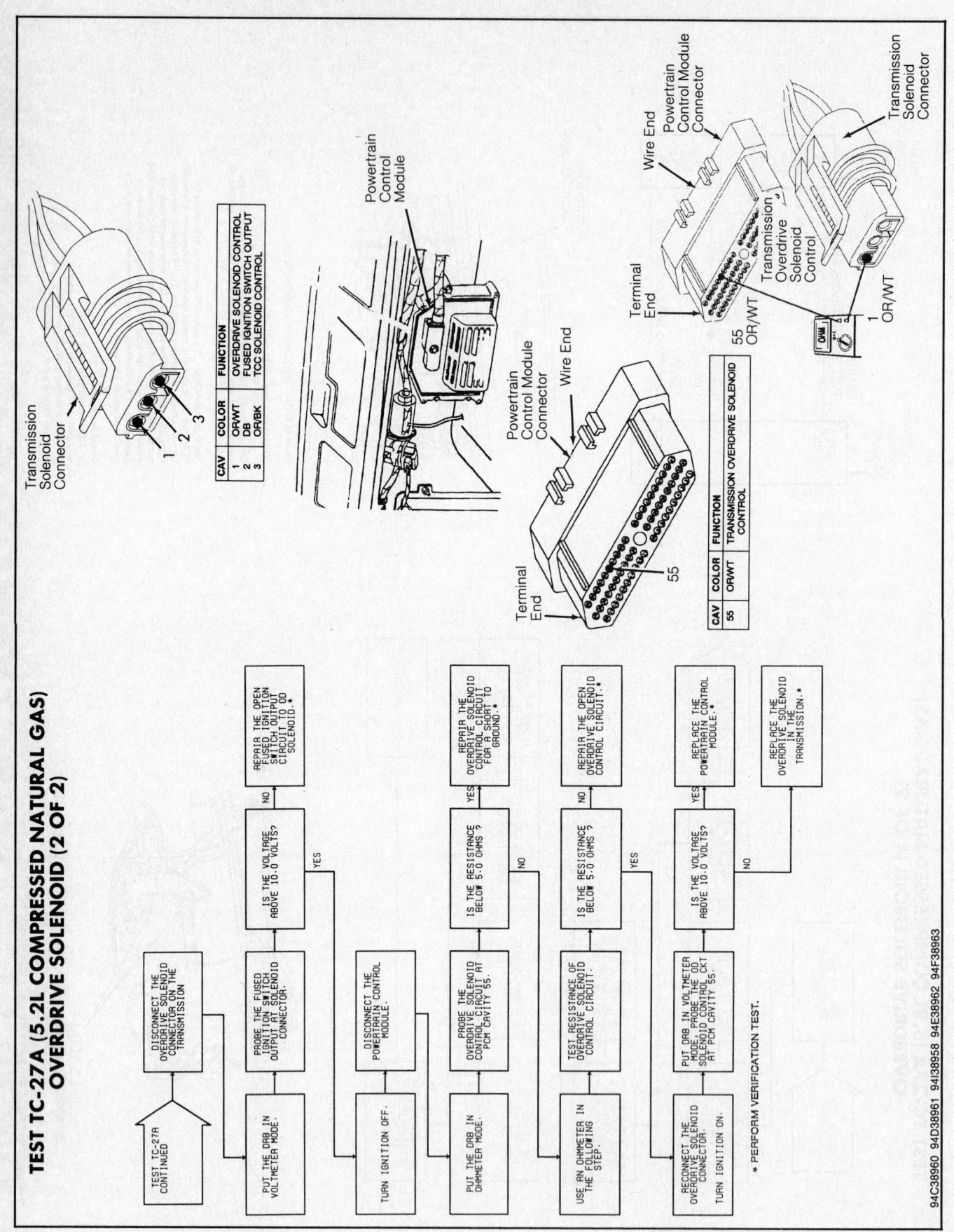

TEST TC-27A (5.2L COMPRESSED NATURAL GAS) OVERDRIVE SOLENOID (2 OF 2)

Transmission Solenoid Connector

CAV	COLOR	FUNCTION
1	OR/WT	OVERDRIVE SOLENOID CONTROL
2	DB	FUSED IGNITION SWITCH OUTPUT
3	OR/BK	TCC SOLENOID CONTROL

Powertrain Control Module

Wire End
Powertrain Control Module Connector
Transmission Solenoid Connector
Terminal End
Transmission Overdrive Solenoid Control
55 OR/WT
1 OR/WT

Powertrain Control Module Connector
Wire End
Terminal End

CAV	COLOR	FUNCTION
55	OR/WT	TRANSMISSION OVERDRIVE SOLENOID CONTROL

TEST TC-27A CONTINUED

DISCONNECT THE OVERDRIVE SOLENOID CONNECTOR ON THE TRANSMISSION

PUT THE DRB IN VOLTMETER MODE.

PROBE THE FUSED IGNITION SWITCH OUTPUT AT SOLENOID CONNECTOR.

IS THE VOLTAGE ABOVE 10.0 VOLTS?
NO → REPAIR THE OPEN FUSED IGNITION SWITCH OUTPUT CIRCUIT TO OD SOLENOID. *
YES →

TURN IGNITION OFF.

DISCONNECT THE POWERTRAIN CONTROL MODULE.

PUT THE DRB IN OHMMETER MODE.

PROBE THE OVERDRIVE SOLENOID CONTROL CIRCUIT AT PCM CAVITY 55.

IS THE RESISTANCE BELOW 5.0 OHMS?
YES → REPAIR THE OVERDRIVE SOLENOID CONTROL CIRCUIT FOR A SHORT TO GROUND. * *
NO →

USE AN OHMMETER IN THE FOLLOWING STEP.

TEST RESISTANCE OF OVERDRIVE SOLENOID CONTROL CIRCUIT.

IS THE RESISTANCE BELOW 5.0 OHMS?
NO → REPAIR THE OPEN OVERDRIVE SOLENOID CONTROL CIRCUIT. *
YES →

RECONNECT THE OVERDRIVE SOLENOID CONNECTOR. TURN IGNITION ON.

PUT DRB IN VOLTMETER MODE ON THE OD SOLENOID CONTROL CKT AT PCM CAVITY 55.

IS THE VOLTAGE ABOVE 10.0 VOLTS?
YES → REPLACE THE POWERTRAIN CONTROL MODULE. *
NO → REPLACE THE OVERDRIVE SOLENOID IN THE TRANSMISSION. *

* PERFORM VERIFICATION TEST.

94C38960 94D38961 94I38958 94E38962 94F38963

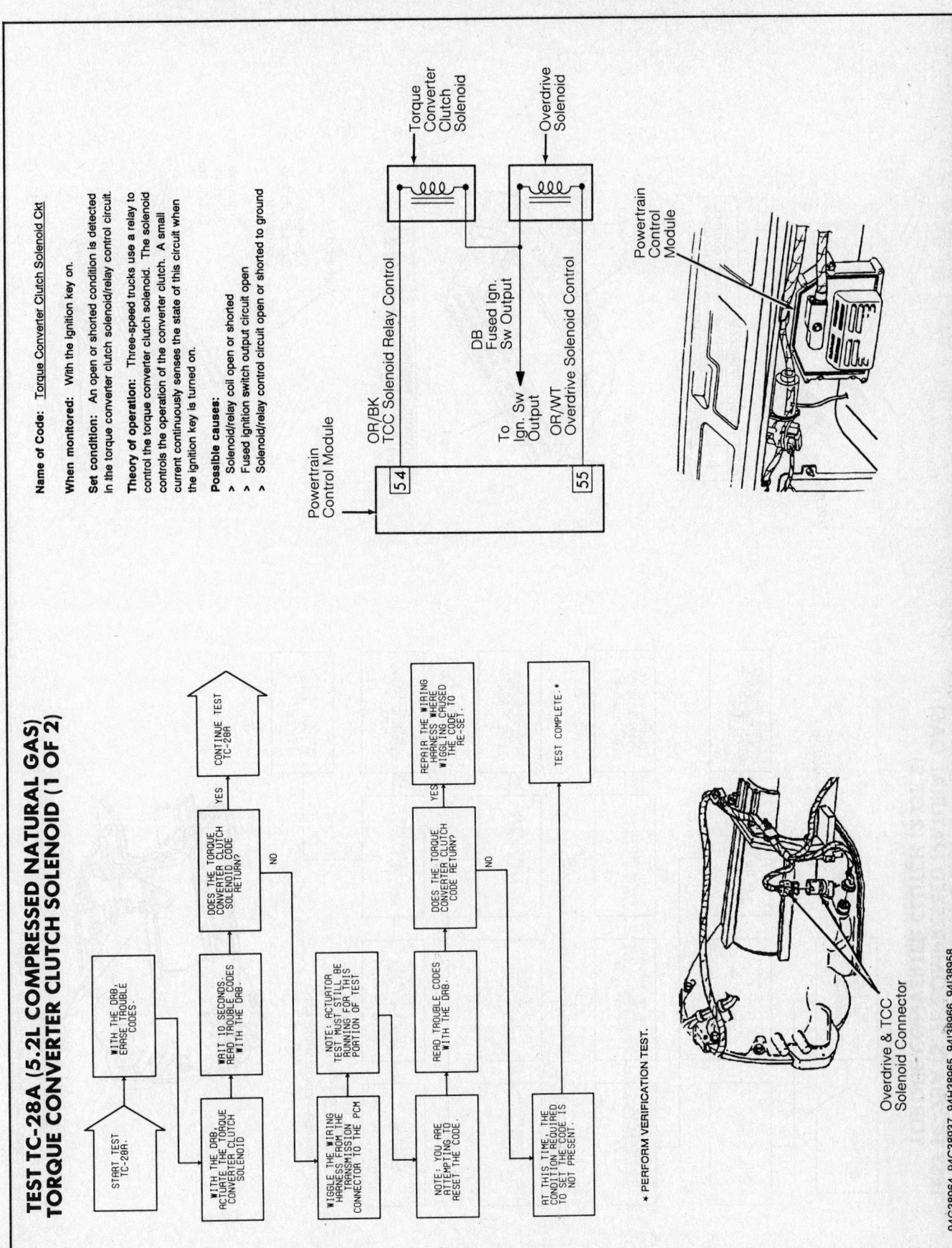

Name of Code: Torque Converter Clutch Solenoid Ckt

When monitored: With the ignition key on.

Set condition: An open or shorted condition is detected in the torque converter clutch solenoid/relay control circuit.

Theory of operation: Three-speed trucks use a relay to control the torque converter clutch solenoid. The solenoid controls the operation of the converter clutch. A small current continuously senses the state of this circuit when the ignition key is turned on.

Possible causes:
> Solenoid/relay coil open or shorted
> Fused ignition switch output circuit open
> Solenoid/relay control circuit open or shorted to ground

Torque Converter Clutch Solenoid

Overdrive Solenoid

Powertrain Control Module

OR/BK
TCC Solenoid Relay Control

DB
Fused Ign.
Sw Output

To
Ign. Sw
Output

OR/WT
Overdrive Solenoid Control

Powertrain Control Module

54

55

TEST TC-28A (5.2L COMPRESSED NATURAL GAS)
TORQUE CONVERTER CLUTCH SOLENOID (1 OF 2)

START TEST TC-28A.

WITH THE DRB, ERASE TROUBLE CODES.

WITH THE DRB, ACTUATE THE TORQUE CONVERTER CLUTCH SOLENOID

WAIT 10 SECONDS... READ TROUBLE CODES WITH THE DRB.

DOES THE TORQUE CONVERTER CLUTCH SOLENOID CODE RETURN?

YES → CONTINUE TEST TC-28A

NO

NOTE: ACTUATOR TEST MUST STILL BE RUNNING FOR THIS PORTION OF TEST.

WIGGLE THE WIRING HARNESS FROM THE TRANSMISSION CONNECTOR TO THE PCM

DOES THE TORQUE CONVERTER CLUTCH CODE RETURN?

YES → REPAIR THE WIRING HARNESS WHERE WIGGLING CAUSED THE CODE TO RE-SET.

NO

NOTE: YOU ARE ATTEMPTING TO RESET THE CODE.

READ TROUBLE CODES WITH THE DRB.

AT THIS TIME, THE CONDITION REQUIRED TO SET THE CODE IS NOT PRESENT.

TEST COMPLETE. *

* PERFORM VERIFICATION TEST.

Overdrive & TCC Solenoid Connector

94G38964 94C38937 94H38965 94138966 94138958

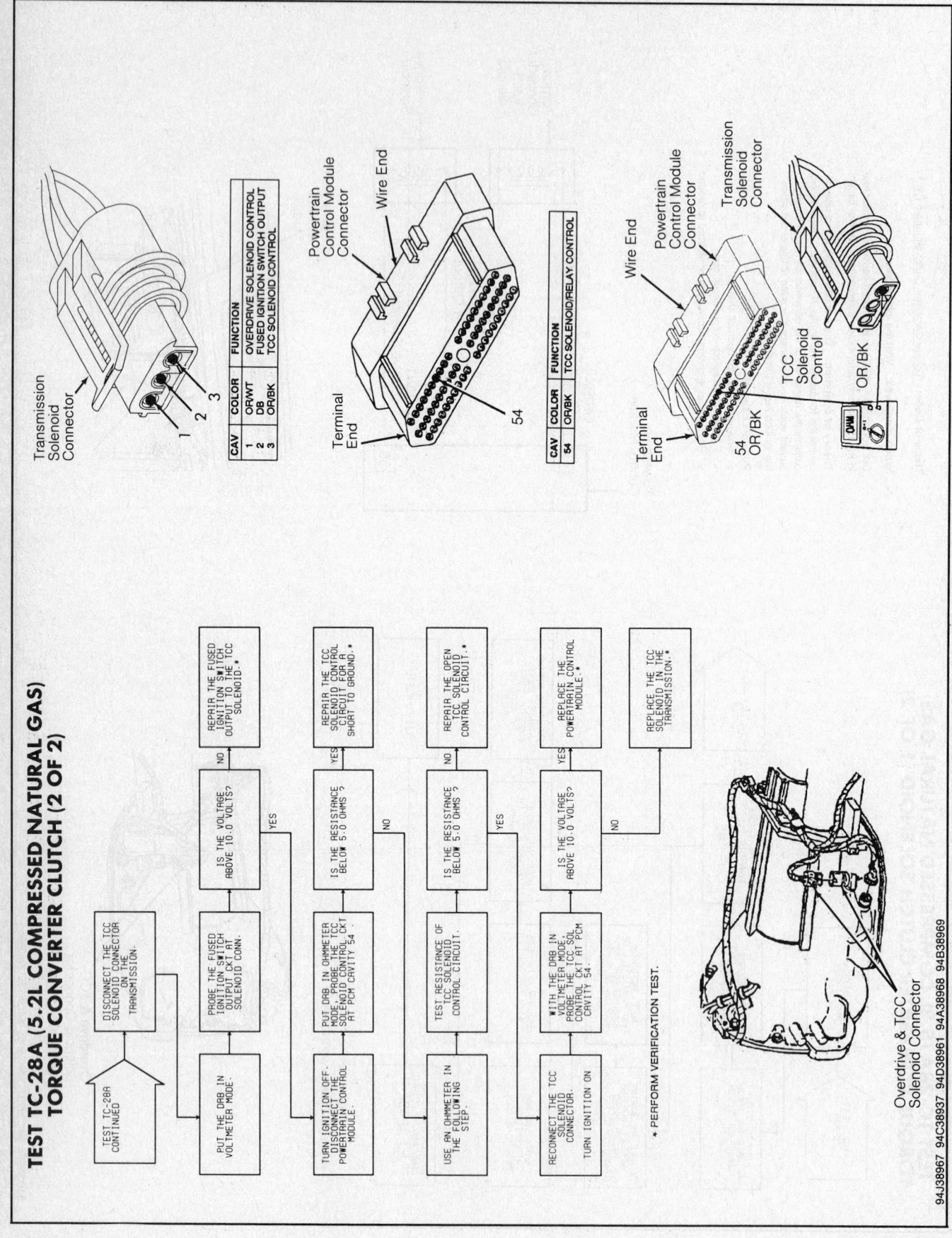

TEST TC-28A (5.2L COMPRESSED NATURAL GAS)
TORQUE CONVERTER CLUTCH (2 OF 2)

Transmission Solenoid Connector

CAV	COLOR	FUNCTION
1	OR/WT	OVERDRIVE SOLENOID CONTROL
2	DB	FUSED IGNITION SWITCH OUTPUT
3	OR/BK	TCC SOLENOID CONTROL

Powertrain Control Module Connector

Wire End

Terminal End

54

CAV	COLOR	FUNCTION
54	OR/BK	TCC SOLENOID/RELAY CONTROL

Wire End

Powertrain Control Module Connector

Transmission Solenoid Connector

TCC Solenoid Control

OR/BK

Terminal End

54 OR/BK

OHM

TEST TC-28A CONTINUED

DISCONNECT THE TCC SOLENOID CONNECTOR ON THE TRANSMISSION.

PUT THE DRB IN VOLTMETER MODE.

PROBE THE FUSED IGNITION SWITCH OUTPUT AT THE TCC SOLENOID CONN.

IS THE VOLTAGE ABOVE 10.0 VOLTS?

NO → REPAIR THE FUSED IGNITION SWITCH OUTPUT IN THE TCC SOLENOID.*

YES ↓

TURN IGNITION OFF- DISCONNECT THE POWERTRAIN CONTROL MODULE.

PUT DRB IN OHMMETER MODE, PROBE THE TCC SOLENOID CONTROL CKT AT PCM CAVITY 54.

IS THE RESISTANCE BELOW 5.0 OHMS?

YES → REPAIR THE TCC SOLENOID CONTROL CIRCUIT FOR A SHORT TO GROUND.*

NO ↓

USE AN OHMMETER IN THE FOLLOWING STEP.

TEST RESISTANCE OF TCC SOLENOID CONTROL CIRCUIT.

IS THE RESISTANCE BELOW 5.0 OHMS?

NO → REPAIR THE OPEN TCC SOLENOID CONTROL CIRCUIT.*

YES ↓

RECONNECT THE TCC SOLENOID CONNECTOR.

TURN IGNITION ON

WITH THE DRB IN VOLTMETER MODE, PROBE THE TCC SOL CONTROL CKT AT PCM CAVITY 54.

IS THE VOLTAGE ABOVE 10.0 VOLTS?

YES → REPLACE THE POWERTRAIN CONTROL MODULE.*

NO ↓

REPLACE THE TCC SOLENOID IN THE TRANSMISSION.*

* PERFORM VERIFICATION TEST.

Overdrive & TCC Solenoid Connector

94J38967 94C38937 94D38961 94A38968 94B38969

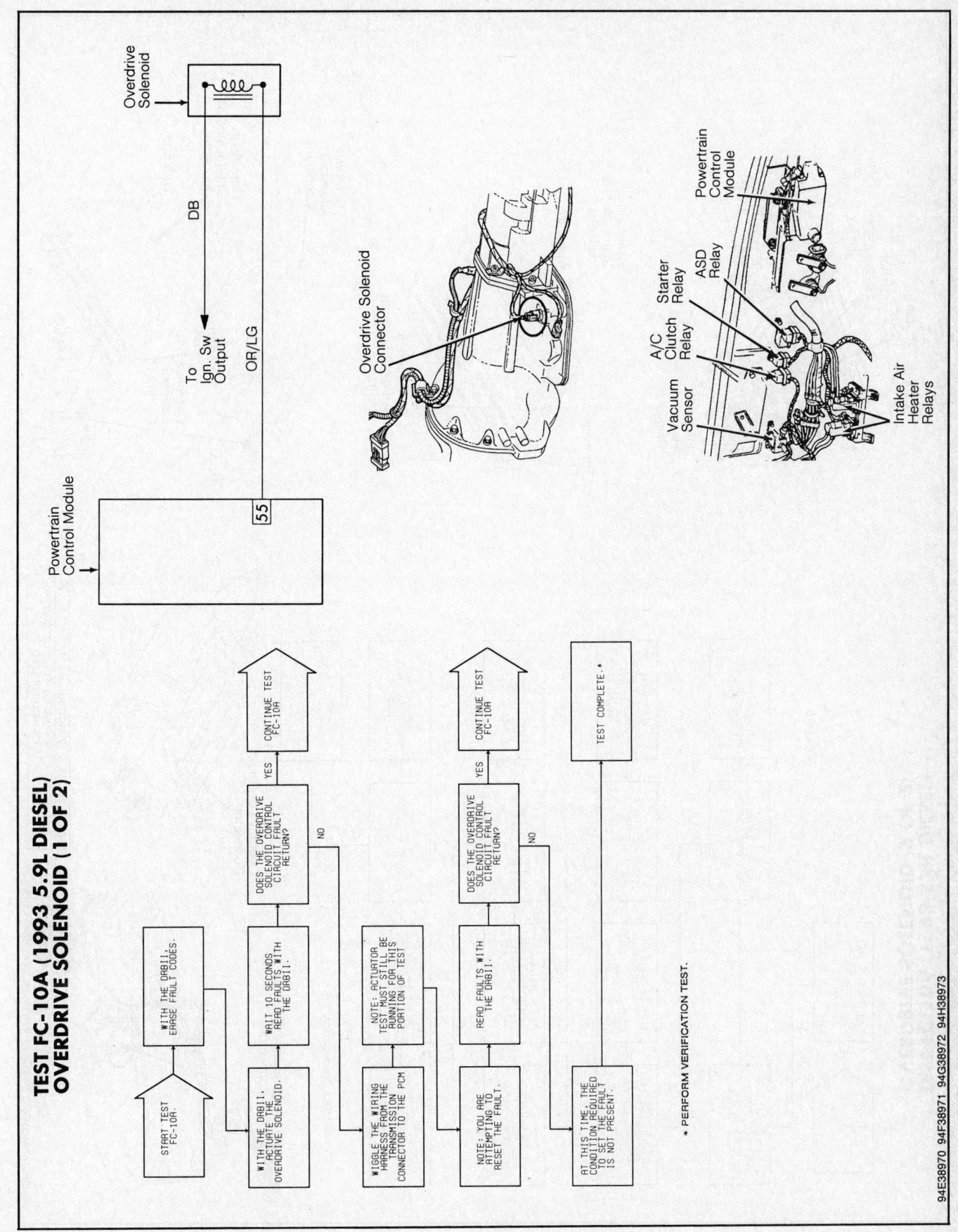

TEST FC-10A (1993 5.9L DIESEL) OVERDRIVE SOLENOID (1 OF 2)

Overdrive Solenoid

DB

To Ign. Sw Output

OR/LG

Overdrive Solenoid Connector

Vacuum Sensor

A/C Clutch Relay

Starter Relay

ASD Relay

Powertrain Control Module

Intake Air Heater Relays

Powertrain Control Module

55

START TEST FC-10A.

WITH THE DRBII, ERASE FAULT CODES.

WITH THE DRBII, ACTUATE THE OVERDRIVE SOLENOID.

WAIT 10 SECONDS READ FAULTS WITH THE DRBII.

DOES THE OVERDRIVE SOLENOID CONTROL CIRCUIT FAULT RETURN?

YES — CONTINUE TEST FC-10A.

NO

WIGGLE THE WIRING HARNESS FROM THE TRANSMISSION CONNECTOR TO THE PCM

NOTE: ACTUATOR TEST MUST STILL BE RUNNING FOR THIS PORTION OF TEST

NOTE: YOU ARE ATTEMPTING TO RESET THE FAULT.

READ FAULTS WITH THE DRBII.

DOES THE OVERDRIVE SOLENOID CONTROL CIRCUIT FAULT RETURN?

YES — CONTINUE TEST FC-10A

NO

AT THIS TIME, THE CONDITION REQUIRED TO SET THE FAULT IS NOT PRESENT.

TEST COMPLETE.*

* PERFORM VERIFICATION TEST.

94E38970 94F38971 94G38972 94H38973

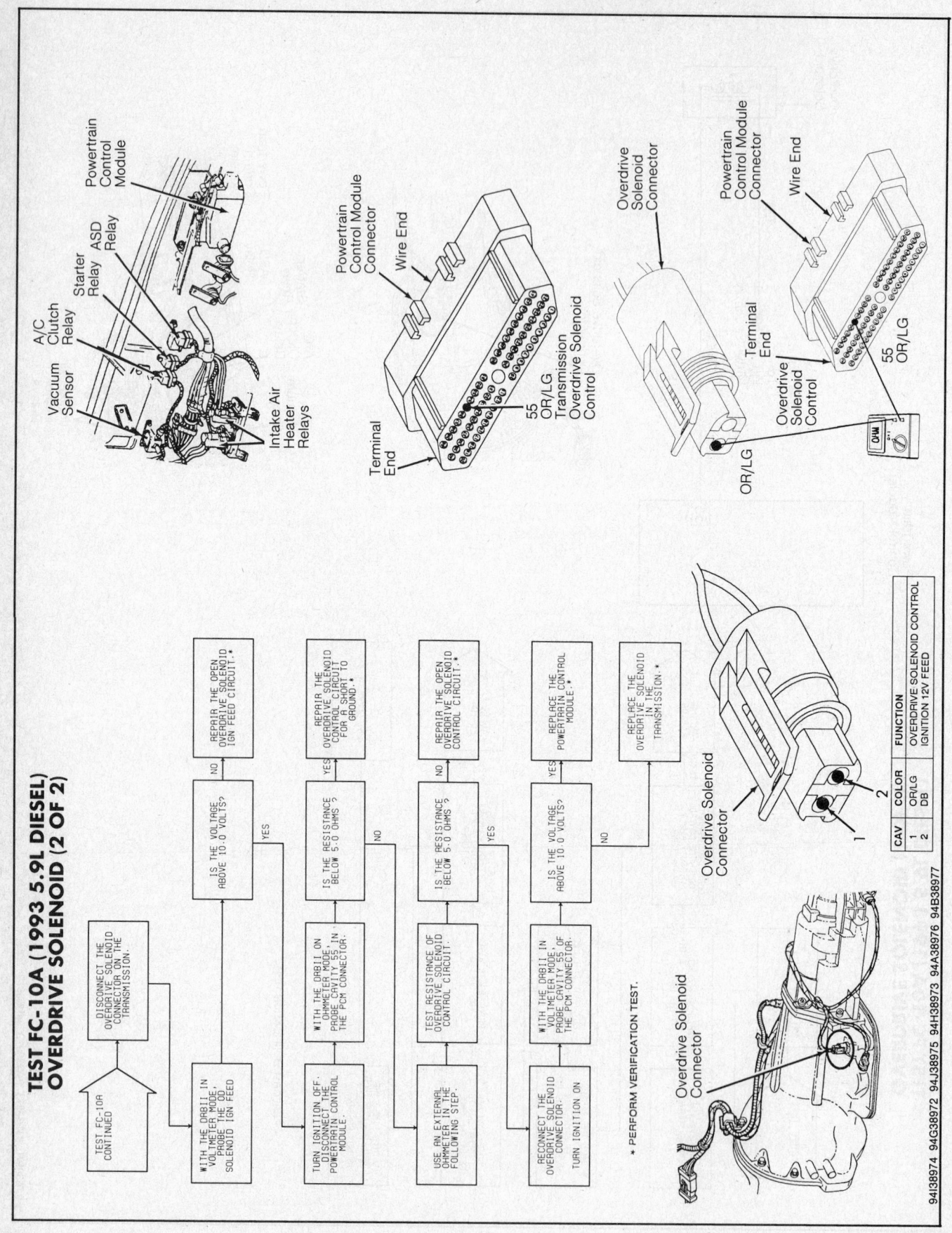

TEST FC-10A (1993 5.9L DIESEL) OVERDRIVE SOLENOID (2 OF 2)

CAV	COLOR	FUNCTION
1	OR/LG	OVERDRIVE SOLENOID CONTROL
2	DB	IGNITION 12V FEED

94J38974 94G38972 94J38975 94H38973 94A38976 94B38977

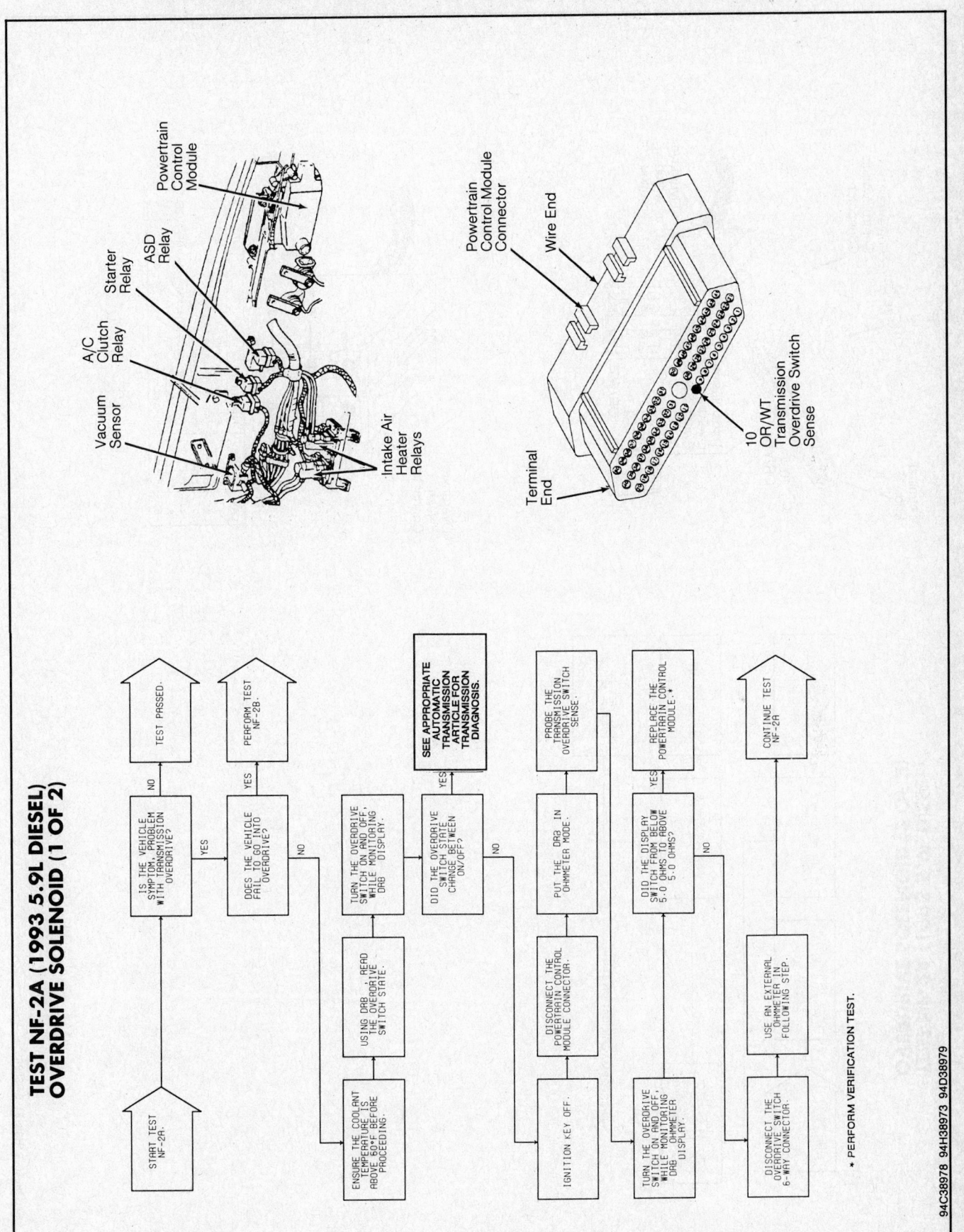

TEST NF-2A (1993 5.9L DIESEL) OVERDRIVE SOLENOID (1 OF 2)

Powertrain Control Module

ASD Relay

Starter Relay

A/C Clutch Relay

Vacuum Sensor

Intake Air Heater Relays

Powertrain Control Module Connector

Wire End

Terminal End

10 OR/WT Transmission Overdrive Switch Sense

START TEST NF-2A.

IS THE VEHICLE SYMPTOM, PROBLEM WITH TRANSMISSION OVERDRIVE?

NO → TEST PASSED.

YES

DOES THE VEHICLE FAIL TO GO INTO OVERDRIVE?

YES → PERFORM TEST NF-2B.

NO

ENSURE THE COOLANT TEMPERATURE IS ABOVE 60°F BEFORE PROCEEDING.

USING DRB, READ THE OVERDRIVE SWITCH STATE.

TURN THE OVERDRIVE SWITCH ON AND OFF, WHILE MONITORING DRB DISPLAY.

DID THE OVERDRIVE SWITCH STATE CHANGE BETWEEN ON/OFF?

YES → SEE APPROPRIATE AUTOMATIC TRANSMISSION ARTICLE FOR TRANSMISSION DIAGNOSIS.

NO

IGNITION KEY OFF.

DISCONNECT THE POWERTRAIN CONTROL MODULE CONNECTOR.

PUT THE DRB IN OHMMETER MODE.

PROBE THE TRANSMISSION OVERDRIVE SWITCH SENSE.

TURN THE OVERDRIVE SWITCH ON AND OFF, WHILE MONITORING DRB OHMMETER DISPLAY.

DID THE DISPLAY SWITCH FROM BELOW 5.0 OHMS TO ABOVE 5.0 OHMS?

YES → REPLACE THE POWERTRAIN CONTROL MODULE.*

NO

DISCONNECT THE OVERDRIVE SWITCH 6-WAY CONNECTOR.

USE AN EXTERNAL OHMMETER IN FOLLOWING STEP.

CONTINUE TEST NF-2A.

* PERFORM VERIFICATION TEST.

94C38978 94H38973 94D38979

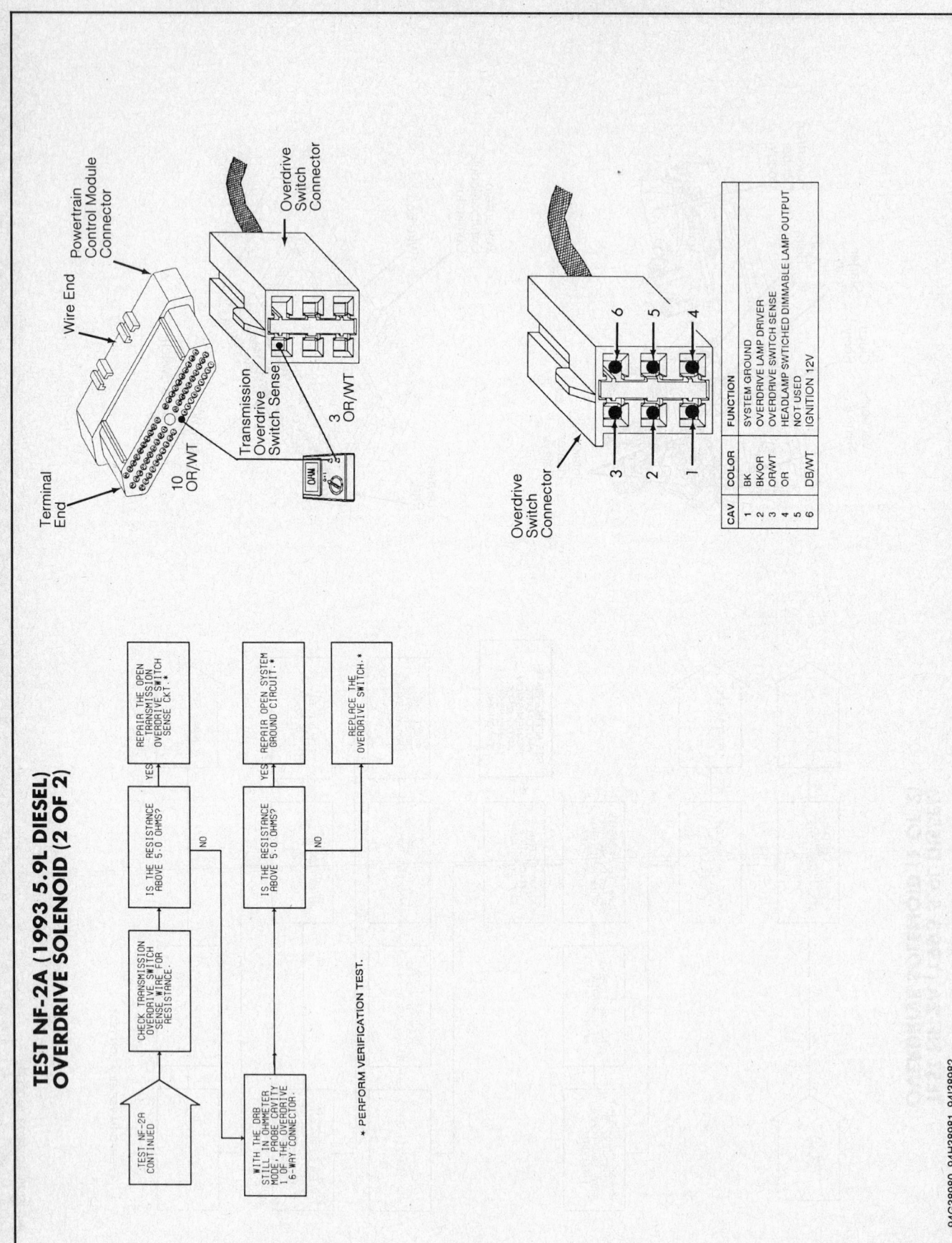

TEST NF-2A (1993 5.9L DIESEL) OVERDRIVE SOLENOID (2 OF 2)

Powertrain Control Module Connector

Overdrive Switch Connector

Wire End

Terminal End

Transmission Overdrive Switch Sense

10 OR/WT

3 OR/WT

OR/WT

Overdrive Switch Connector

CAV	COLOR	FUNCTION
1	BK	SYSTEM GROUND
2	BK/OR	OVERDRIVE LAMP DRIVER
3	OR/WT	OVERDRIVE SWITCH SENSE
4	OR	HEADLAMP SWITCHED DIMMABLE LAMP OUTPUT
5		NOT USED
6	DB/WT	IGNITION 12V

TEST NF-2A CONTINUED

CHECK TRANSMISSION OVERDRIVE SENSE WIRE FOR RESISTANCE.

IS THE RESISTANCE ABOVE 5.0 OHMS? — YES → REPAIR THE OPEN TRANSMISSION OVERDRIVE SWITCH SENSE CKT.*

NO

WITH THE DRB STILL IN OHMMETER MODE, PROBE CAVITY 1 OF THE OVERDRIVE 6-WAY CONNECTOR.

IS THE RESISTANCE ABOVE 5.0 OHMS? — YES → REPAIR OPEN SYSTEM GROUND CIRCUIT.*

NO

REPLACE THE OVERDRIVE SWITCH.*

* PERFORM VERIFICATION TEST.

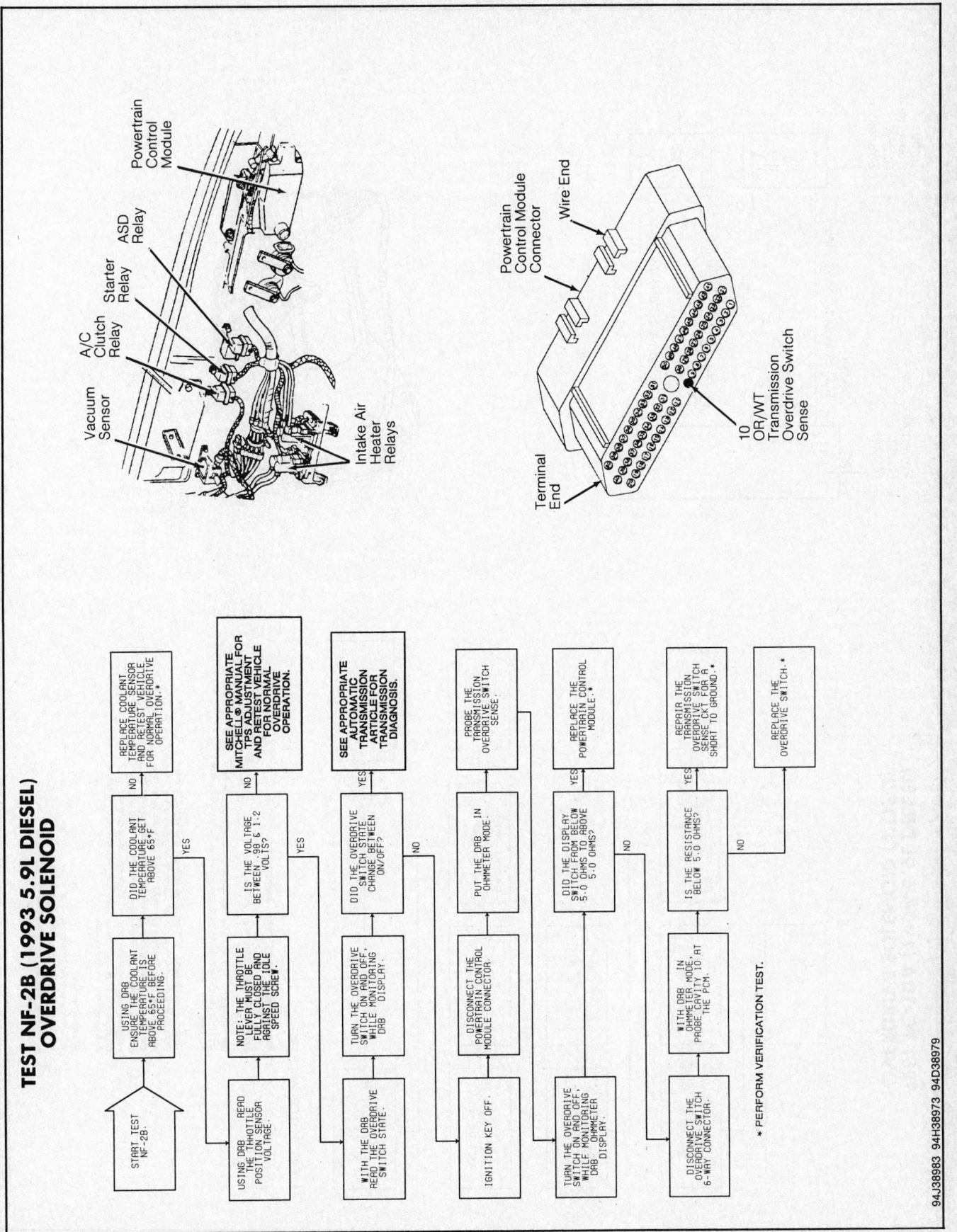

TEST NF-2B (1993 5.9L DIESEL) OVERDRIVE SOLENOID

Powertrain Control Module

ASD Relay

Starter Relay

A/C Clutch Relay

Vacuum Sensor

Intake Air Heater Relays

Powertrain Control Module Connector

Wire End

Terminal End

10 OR/WT Transmission Overdrive Switch Sense

START TEST NF-2B.

USING DRB ENSURE THE COOLANT TEMPERATURE IS ABOVE 65°F BEFORE PROCEEDING.

DID THE COOLANT TEMPERATURE GET ABOVE 65°F — NO → REPLACE COOLANT TEMPERATURE SENSOR AND RETEST VEHICLE FOR NORMAL OVERDRIVE OPERATION.*

YES

USING DRB READ THE THROTTLE POSITION SENSOR VOLTAGE.

NOTE: THE THROTTLE LEVER MUST BE FULLY CLOSED AND AGAINST THE IDLE SPEED SCREW.

IS THE VOLTAGE BETWEEN .98 & 1.2 VOLTS? — NO → SEE APPROPRIATE MITCHELL® MANUAL FOR TPS ADJUSTMENT AND RETEST VEHICLE FOR NORMAL OVERDRIVE OPERATION.

YES

WITH THE DRB READ THE OVERDRIVE SWITCH STATE.

TURN THE OVERDRIVE SWITCH ON AND OFF, WHILE MONITORING DRB DISPLAY.

DID THE OVERDRIVE SWITCH STATE CHANGE BETWEEN ON/OFF? — YES → SEE APPROPRIATE AUTOMATIC TRANSMISSION ARTICLE FOR TRANSMISSION DIAGNOSIS.

NO

IGNITION KEY OFF.

DISCONNECT THE POWERTRAIN CONTROL MODULE CONNECTOR.

PUT THE DRB IN OHMMETER MODE.

PROBE THE TRANSMISSION OVERDRIVE SWITCH SENSE.

TURN THE OVERDRIVE SWITCH ON AND OFF, WHILE MONITORING DRB DISPLAY.

DID THE DISPLAY SWITCH FROM BELOW 5.0 OHMS TO ABOVE 5.0 OHMS? — YES → REPLACE THE POWERTRAIN CONTROL MODULE.*

NO

DISCONNECT THE OVERDRIVE SWITCH 6-WAY CONNECTOR.

WITH DRB IN OHMMETER MODE PROBE CAVITY 10 AT THE PCM.

IS THE RESISTANCE BELOW 5.0 OHMS? — YES → REPAIR THE TRANSMISSION OVERDRIVE SWITCH SENSE CKT FOR A SHORT TO GROUND.*

NO

REPLACE THE OVERDRIVE SWITCH.*

* PERFORM VERIFICATION TEST.

94J38983 94H38973 94D38979

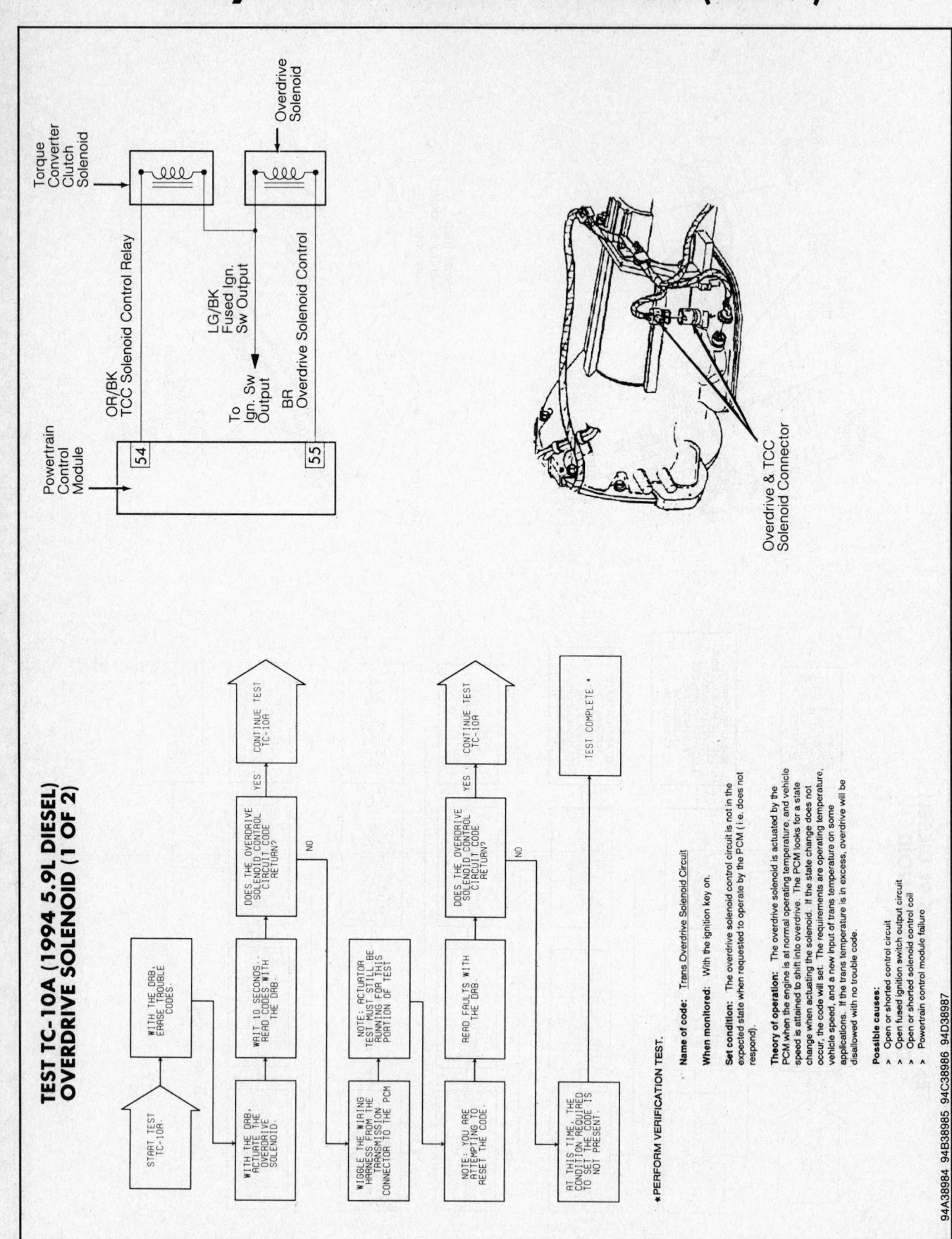

TEST TC-10A (1994 5.9L DIESEL)
OVERDRIVE SOLENOID (1 OF 2)

Torque Converter Clutch Solenoid

Overdrive Solenoid

Powertrain Control Module

OR/BK TCC Solenoid Control Relay

LG/BK Fused Ign. Sw Output

To Ign. Sw Output

BR Overdrive Solenoid Control

54

55

Overdrive & TCC Solenoid Connector

START TEST TC-10A.

WITH THE DRB, ERASE TROUBLE CODES.

WITH THE DRB, ACTUATE THE OVERDRIVE SOLENOID.

WAIT 10 SECONDS. READ CODES WITH THE DRB.

DOES THE OVERDRIVE SOLENOID CONTROL CIRCUIT CODE RETURN?

YES — CONTINUE TEST TC-10A

NO

WIGGLE THE WIRING HARNESS FROM THE TRANSMISSION CONNECTOR TO THE PCM.

NOTE: ACTUATOR TEST MUST STILL BE RUNNING FOR THIS PORTION OF TEST.

NOTE: YOU ARE ATTEMPTING TO RESET THE CODE.

READ FAULTS WITH THE DRB.

DOES THE OVERDRIVE SOLENOID CONTROL CIRCUIT CODE RETURN?

YES — CONTINUE TEST TC-10A

NO

AT THIS TIME, THE CONDITION REQUIRED TO SET THE CODE IS NOT PRESENT.

TEST COMPLETE. *

*PERFORM VERIFICATION TEST.

Name of code: Trans Overdrive Solenoid Circuit

When monitored: With the ignition key on.

Set condition: The overdrive solenoid control circuit is not in the expected state when requested to operate by the PCM (i.e. does not respond).

Theory of operation: The overdrive solenoid is actuated by the PCM when the engine is at normal operating temperature, and vehicle speed is attained to shift into overdrive. The PCM looks for a state change when actuating the solenoid. If the state change does not occur, the code will set. The requirements are operating temperature, vehicle speed, and a new input of trans temperature on some applications. If the trans temperature is in excess, overdrive will be disallowed with no trouble code.

Possible causes:
> Open or shorted control circuit
> Open fused ignition switch output circuit
> Open or shorted solenoid control coil
> Powertrain control module failure

94A38984 94B38985 94C38986 94D38987

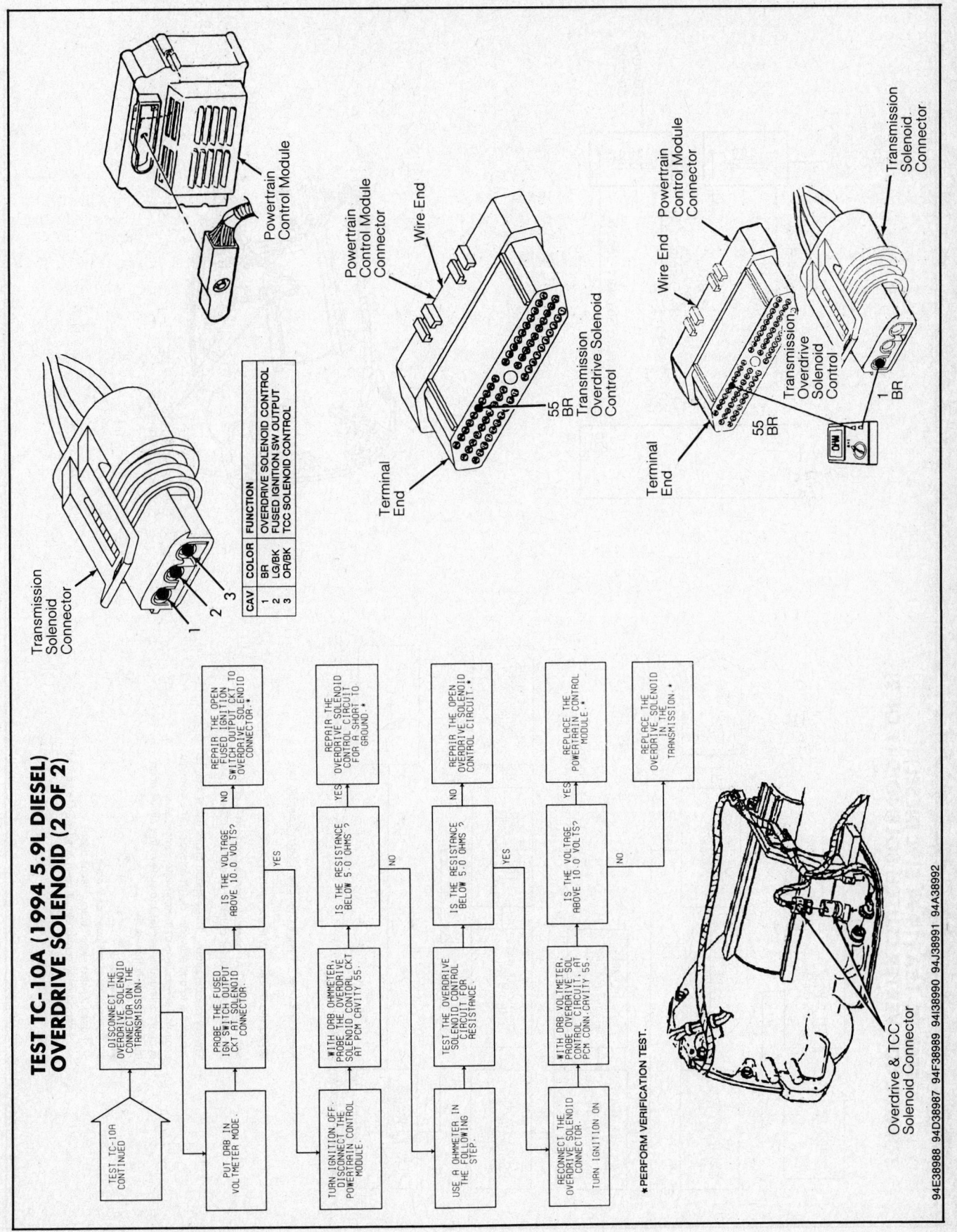

TEST TC-10A (1994 5.9L DIESEL)
OVERDRIVE SOLENOID (2 OF 2)

Powertrain Control Module

Transmission Solenoid Connector

Powertrain Control Module Connector

Wire End

Terminal End

55 BR Transmission Overdrive Solenoid Control

Powertrain Control Module Connector

Wire End

Transmission Solenoid Connector

55 BR

Terminal End

Transmission Overdrive Solenoid Control

1 BR

CAV	COLOR	FUNCTION
1	BR	OVERDRIVE SOLENOID CONTROL
2	LG/BK	FUSED IGNITION SW OUTPUT
3	OR/BK	TCC SOLENOID CONTROL

Overdrive & TCC Solenoid Connector

TEST TC-10A CONTINUED

DISCONNECT THE OVERDRIVE SOLENOID CONNECTOR ON THE TRANSMISSION.

PUT DRB IN VOLTMETER MODE.

PROBE THE FUSED IGN SWITCH OUTPUT CKT AT OVERDRIVE SOLENOID CONNECTOR.

IS THE VOLTAGE ABOVE 10.0 VOLTS? — NO — REPAIR THE OPEN FUSED IGNITION SWITCH OUTPUT CKT TO OVERDRIVE SOLENOID CONNECTOR.*

YES

TURN IGNITION OFF. DISCONNECT THE POWERTRAIN CONTROL MODULE.

WITH DRB OHMMETER, PROBE THE OVERDRIVE SOLENOID CONTROL CKT AT PCM CAVITY 55.

IS THE RESISTANCE BELOW 5.0 OHMS? — YES — REPAIR THE OVERDRIVE SOLENOID CONTROL CIRCUIT FOR A SHORT TO GROUND.*

NO

USE A OHMMETER IN THE FOLLOWING STEP.

TEST THE OVERDRIVE SOLENOID CONTROL CIRCUIT FOR RESISTANCE.

IS THE RESISTANCE BELOW 5.0 OHMS? — NO — REPAIR THE OPEN OVERDRIVE SOLENOID CONTROL CIRCUIT.*

YES

RECONNECT THE OVERDRIVE SOLENOID CONNECTOR.

TURN IGNITION ON

WITH DRB VOLTMETER, PROBE OVERDRIVE SOL CONTROL CIRCUIT AT PCM CONN. CAVITY 55.

IS THE VOLTAGE ABOVE 10.0 VOLTS? — YES — REPLACE THE POWERTRAIN CONTROL MODULE.*

NO

REPLACE THE OVERDRIVE SOLENOID IN THE TRANSMISSION.*

*PERFORM VERIFICATION TEST.

94E38988 94D38987 94C38989 94B38990 94J38991 94A38992

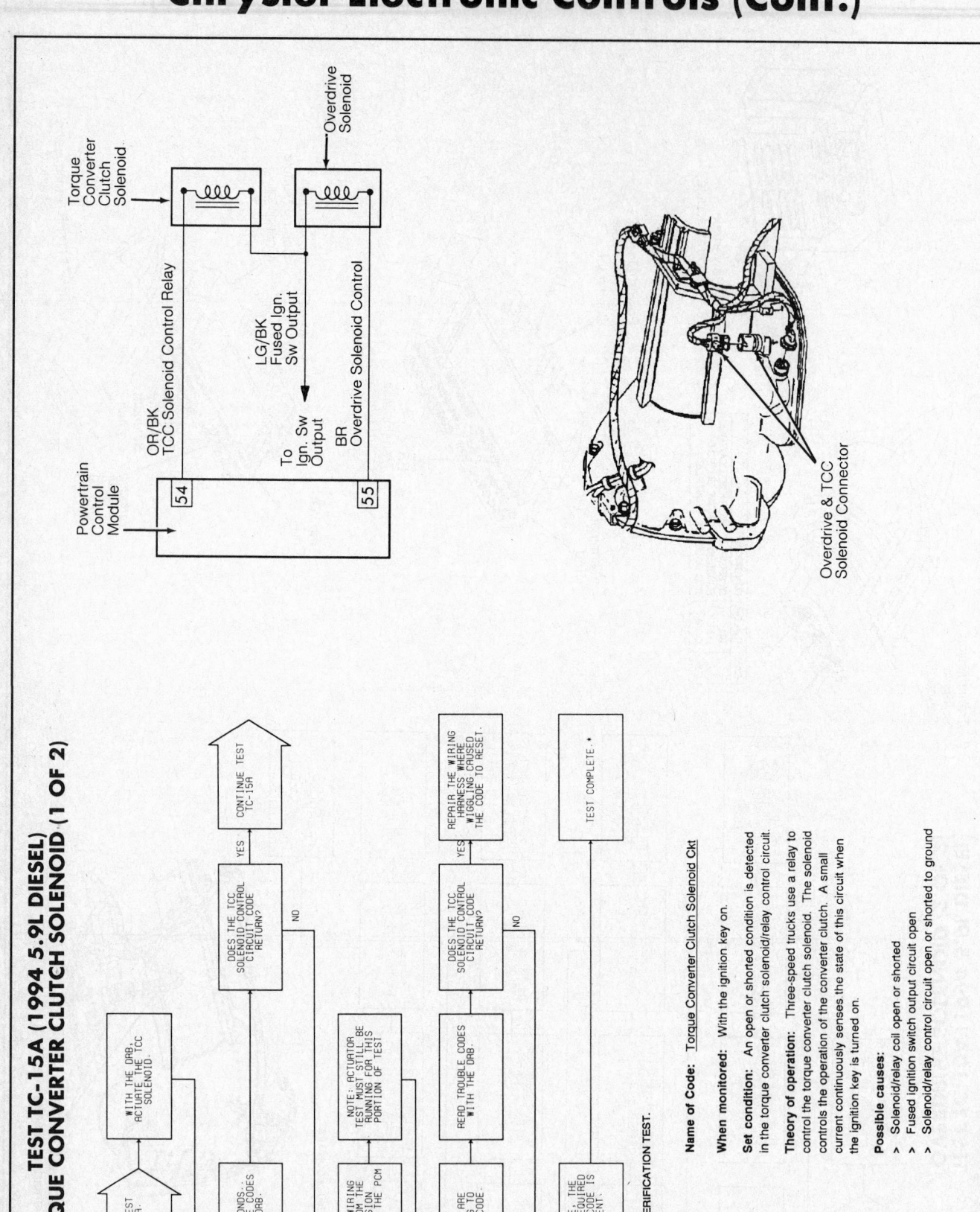

TEST TC-15A (1994 5.9L DIESEL)
TORQUE CONVERTER CLUTCH SOLENOID (1 OF 2)

Name of Code: Torque Converter Clutch Solenoid Ckt

When monitored: With the ignition key on.

Set condition: An open or shorted condition is detected in the torque converter clutch solenoid/relay control circuit.

Theory of operation: Three-speed trucks use a relay to control the torque converter clutch solenoid. The solenoid controls the operation of the converter clutch. A small current continuously senses the state of this circuit when the ignition key is turned on.

Possible causes:
> Solenoid/relay coil open or shorted
> Fused ignition switch output circuit open
> Solenoid/relay control circuit open or shorted to ground

94B38993 94C38994 94C38986 94D38987

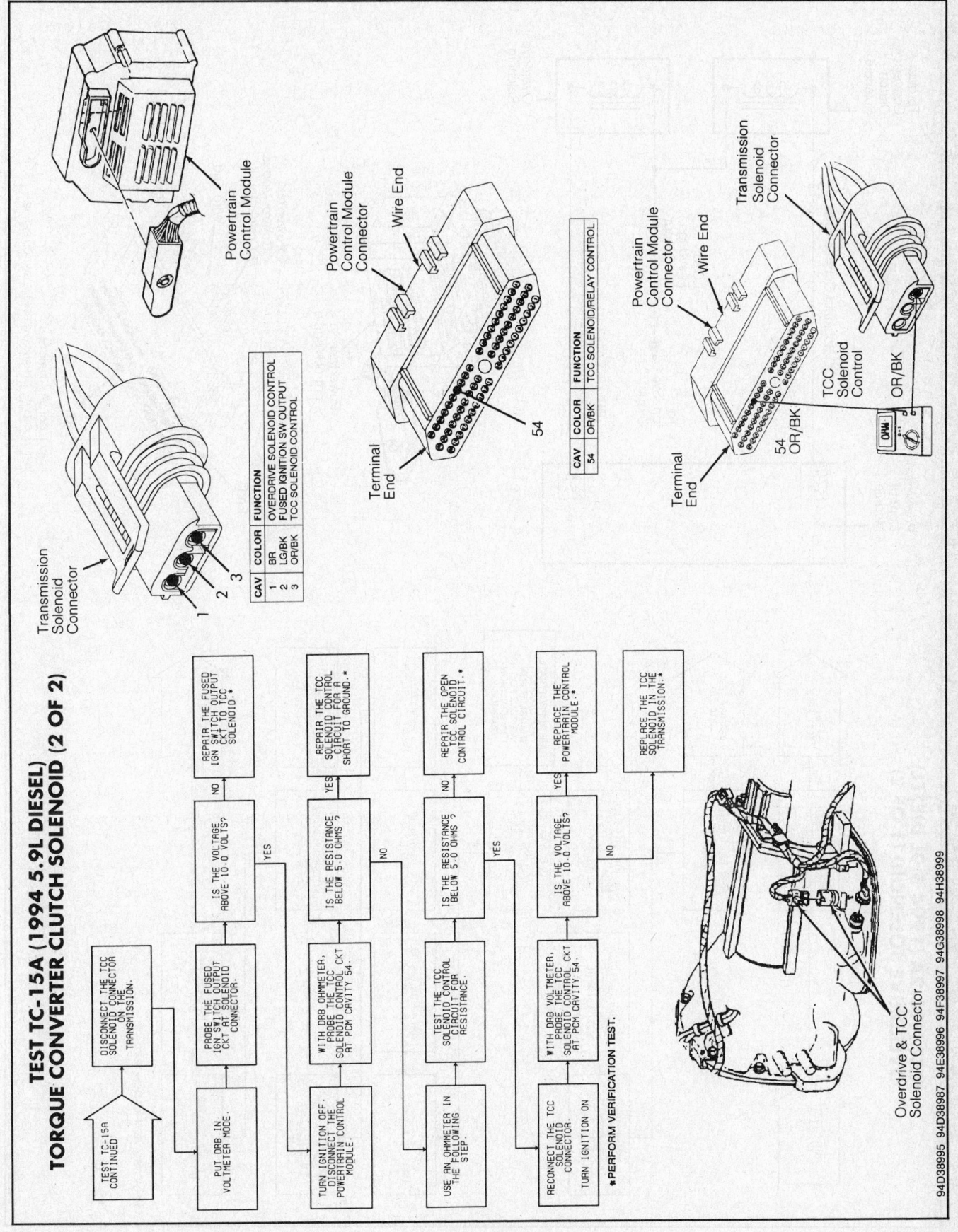

TEST TC-15A (1994 5.9L DIESEL)
TORQUE CONVERTER CLUTCH SOLENOID (2 OF 2)

Powertrain Control Module

Transmission Solenoid Connector

CAV	COLOR	FUNCTION
1	BR	OVERDRIVE SOLENOID CONTROL
2	LG/BK	FUSED IGNITION SW OUTPUT
3	OR/BK	TCC SOLENOID CONTROL

Powertrain Control Module Connector

Wire End

Terminal End

54

CAV	COLOR	FUNCTION
54	OR/BK	TCC SOLENOID/RELAY CONTROL

Powertrain Control Module Connector

Wire End

Transmission Solenoid Connector

TCC Solenoid Control

OR/BK

Terminal End

54 OR/BK

TEST TC-15A CONTINUED

DISCONNECT THE TCC SOLENOID CONNECTOR ON THE TRANSMISSION.

PUT DRB IN VOLTMETER MODE.

PROBE THE FUSED IGN SWITCH OUTPUT CKT AT SOLENOID CONNECTOR.

IS THE VOLTAGE ABOVE 10.0 VOLTS?

NO → REPAIR THE FUSED IGN SWITCH OUTPUT CKT AT SOLENOID.*

YES

TURN IGNITION OFF. DISCONNECT THE POWERTRAIN CONTROL MODULE.

WITH DRB OHMMETER, PROBE THE TCC SOLENOID CONTROL CKT AT PCM CAVITY 54.

IS THE RESISTANCE BELOW 5.0 OHMS?

YES → REPAIR THE TCC SOLENOID CONTROL CIRCUIT FOR A SHORT TO GROUND.*

NO

USE AN OHMMETER IN THE FOLLOWING STEP.

TEST THE TCC SOLENOID CONTROL CIRCUIT FOR RESISTANCE.

IS THE RESISTANCE BELOW 5.0 OHMS?

NO → REPAIR THE OPEN TCC SOLENOID CONTROL CIRCUIT.*

YES

RECONNECT THE TCC SOLENOID CONNECTOR. TURN IGNITION ON.

WITH DRB VOLTMETER, PROBE THE TCC SOLENOID CONTROL CKT AT PCM CAVITY 54.

IS THE VOLTAGE ABOVE 10.0 VOLTS?

YES → REPLACE THE POWERTRAIN CONTROL MODULE.*

NO → REPLACE THE TCC SOLENOID IN THE TRANSMISSION.*

*PERFORM VERIFICATION TEST.

Overdrive & TCC Solenoid Connector

94D38995 94D38887 94E38996 94F38997 94G38998 94H38999

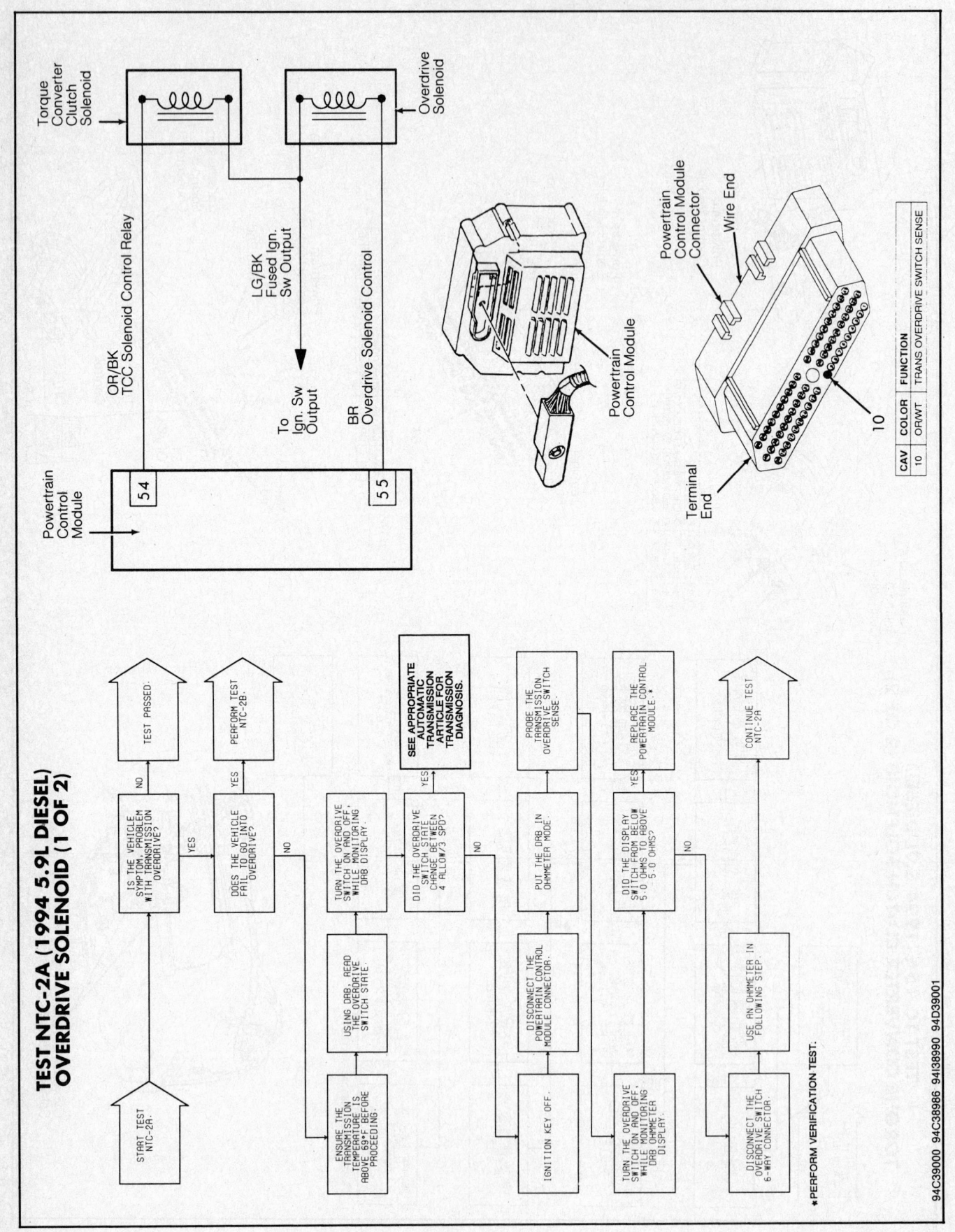

94C39000 94C38986 94I38990 94D39001

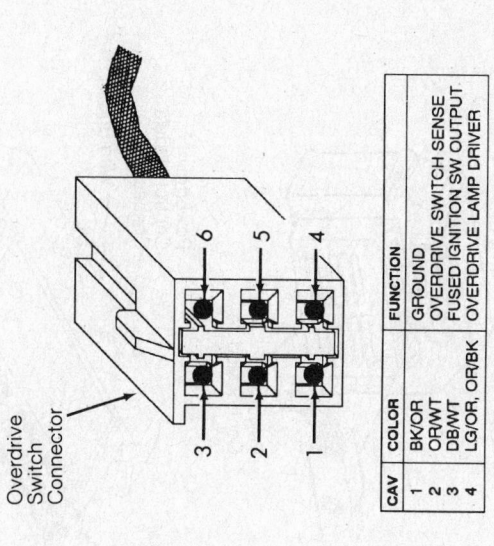

Overdrive Switch Connector

CAV	COLOR	FUNCTION
1	BK/OR	GROUND
2	OR/WT	OVERDRIVE SWITCH SENSE
3	DB/WT	FUSED IGNITION SW OUTPUT
4	LG/OR, OR/BK	OVERDRIVE LAMP DRIVER

TEST NTC-2A (1994 5.9L DIESEL) OVERDRIVE SOLENOID (2 OF 2)

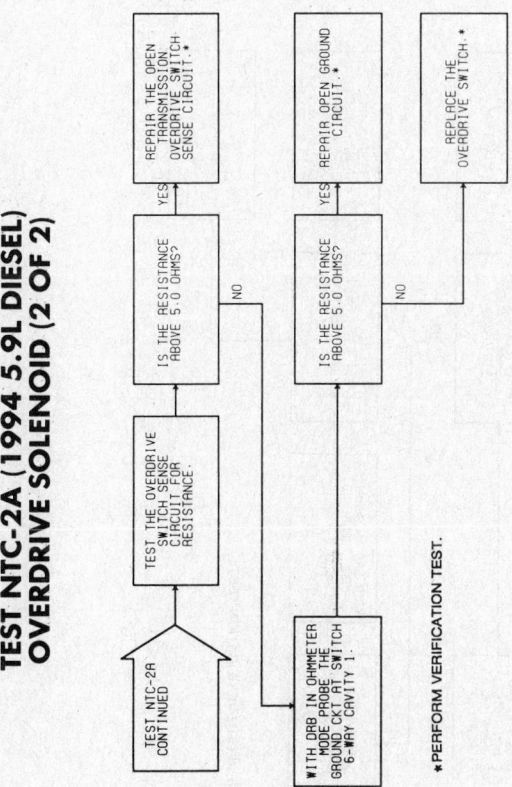

TEST NTC-2A CONTINUED

TEST THE OVERDRIVE SWITCH SENSE CIRCUIT FOR RESISTANCE.

IS THE RESISTANCE ABOVE 5.0 OHMS? — YES → REPAIR THE OPEN TRANSMISSION OVERDRIVE SWITCH SENSE CIRCUIT. *

NO

WITH DRB IN OHMMETER MODE PROBE THE GROUND CKT AT SWITCH 6-WAY CAVITY 1.

IS THE RESISTANCE ABOVE 5.0 OHMS? — YES → REPAIR OPEN GROUND CIRCUIT. *

NO

REPLACE THE OVERDRIVE SWITCH. *

* PERFORM VERIFICATION TEST.

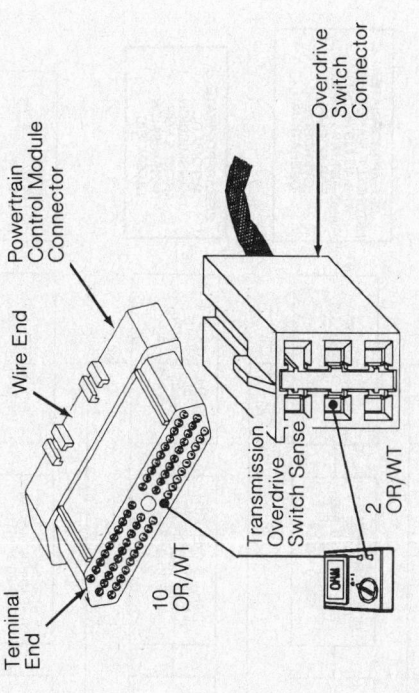

Powertrain Control Module Connector

Overdrive Switch Connector

Wire End

Terminal End

Transmission Overdrive Switch Sense

10 OR/WT

2 OR/WT

94E39002 94F39003 94G39004

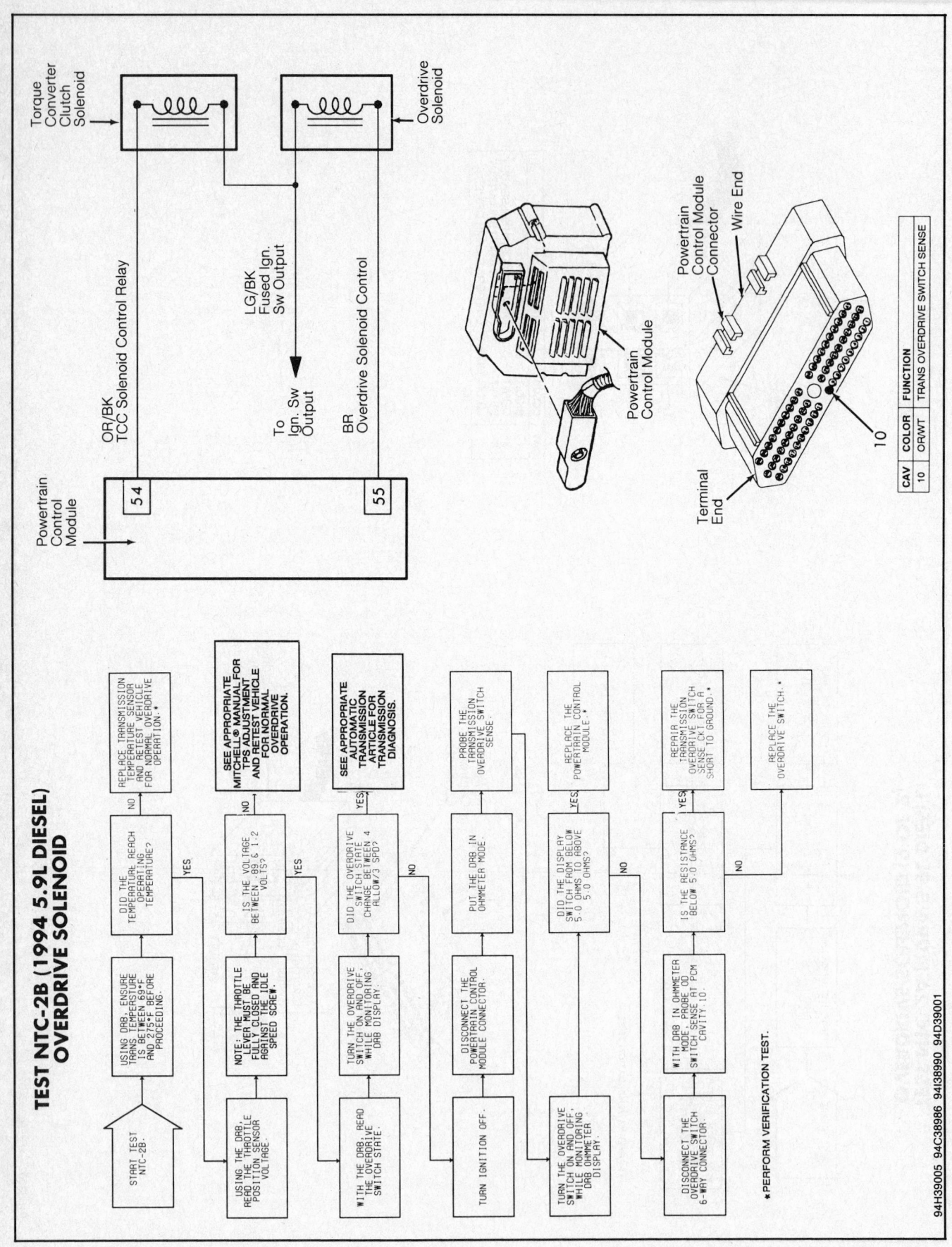

TEST NTC-2B (1994 5.9L DIESEL) OVERDRIVE SOLENOID

CAV	COLOR	FUNCTION
10	OR/WT	TRANS OVERDRIVE SWITCH SENSE

94H39005 94C38986 94I38990 94D39001

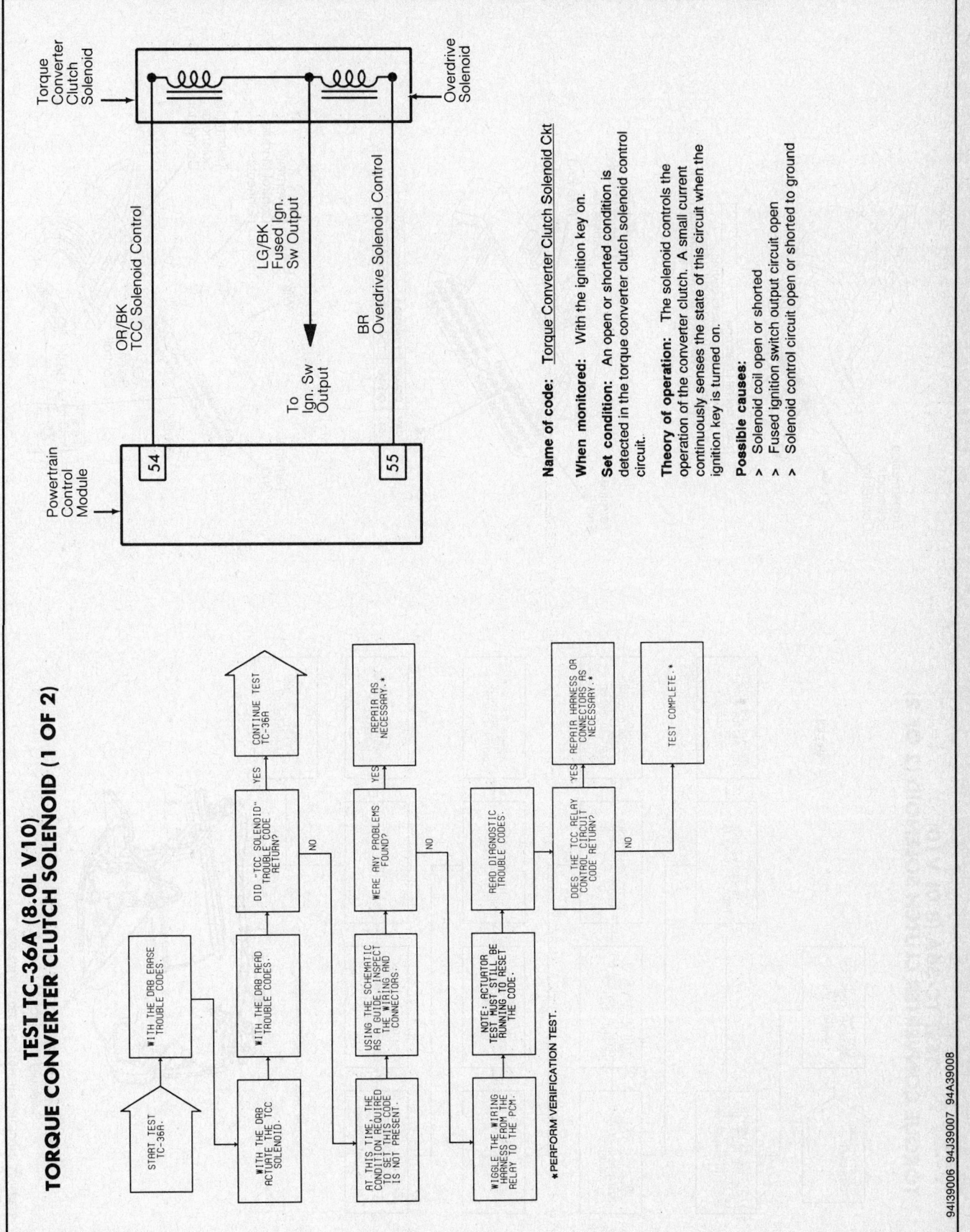

Name of code: Torque Converter Clutch Solenoid Ckt

When monitored: With the ignition key on.

Set condition: An open or shorted condition is detected in the torque converter clutch solenoid control circuit.

Theory of operation: The solenoid controls the operation of the converter clutch. A small current continuously senses the state of this circuit when the ignition key is turned on.

Possible causes:
> Solenoid coil open or shorted
> Fused ignition switch output circuit open
> Solenoid control circuit open or shorted to ground

TEST TC-36A (8.0L V10)
TORQUE CONVERTER CLUTCH SOLENOID (1 OF 2)

94J39006   94J39007   94A39008

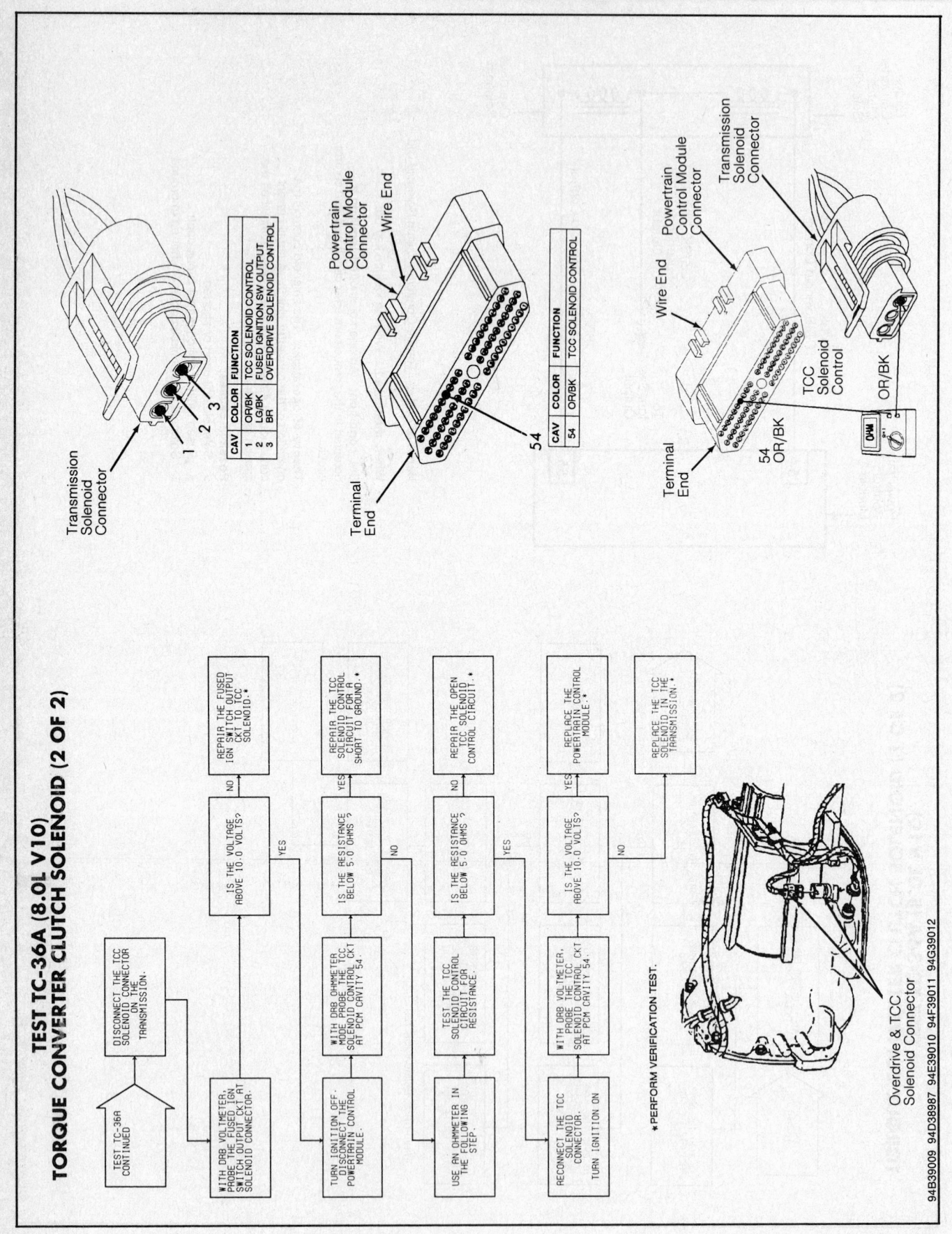

Transmission Solenoid Connector

CAV	COLOR	FUNCTION
1	OR/BK	TCC SOLENOID CONTROL
2	LG/BK	FUSED IGNITION SW OUTPUT
3	BR	OVERDRIVE SOLENOID CONTROL

Powertrain Control Module Connector

Wire End

Terminal End

CAV	COLOR	FUNCTION
54	OR/BK	TCC SOLENOID CONTROL

54

Powertrain Control Module Connector

Transmission Solenoid Connector

Wire End

Terminal End

54 OR/BK

TCC Solenoid Control

OR/BK

OHM

TEST TC-36A (8.0L V10)
TORQUE CONVERTER CLUTCH SOLENOID (2 OF 2)

TEST TC-36A CONTINUED

DISCONNECT THE TCC SOLENOID CONNECTOR ON THE TRANSMISSION.

WITH DRB VOLTMETER, PROBE THE FUSED IGN SWITCH OUTPUT CKT AT SOLENOID CONNECTOR.

IS THE VOLTAGE ABOVE 10.0 VOLTS?

NO → REPAIR THE FUSED IGN SWITCH OUTPUT CKT TO TCC SOLENOID.*

YES

TURN IGNITION OFF. DISCONNECT THE POWERTRAIN CONTROL MODULE.

WITH DRB OHMMETER, PROBE FROM THE TCC SOLENOID CONTROL CKT AT PCM CAVITY 54.

IS THE RESISTANCE BELOW 5.0 OHMS?

YES → REPAIR THE TCC SOLENOID CONTROL CIRCUIT FOR A SHORT TO GROUND.*

NO

USE AN OHMMETER IN THE FOLLOWING STEP.

TEST THE TCC SOLENOID CONTROL CIRCUIT FOR RESISTANCE.

IS THE RESISTANCE BELOW 5.0 OHMS?

NO → REPAIR THE OPEN TCC SOLENOID CONTROL CIRCUIT.*

YES

RECONNECT THE TCC SOLENOID CONNECTOR.

TURN IGNITION ON.

WITH DRB VOLTMETER, PROBE THE TCC SOLENOID CONTROL CKT AT PCM CAVITY 54.

IS THE VOLTAGE ABOVE 10.0 VOLTS?

YES → REPLACE THE POWERTRAIN CONTROL MODULE.*

NO → REPLACE THE TCC SOLENOID IN THE TRANSMISSION.*

*PERFORM VERIFICATION TEST.

Overdrive & TCC Solenoid Connector

94B39009 94D38987 94E39010 94E39010 94F39011 94G39012

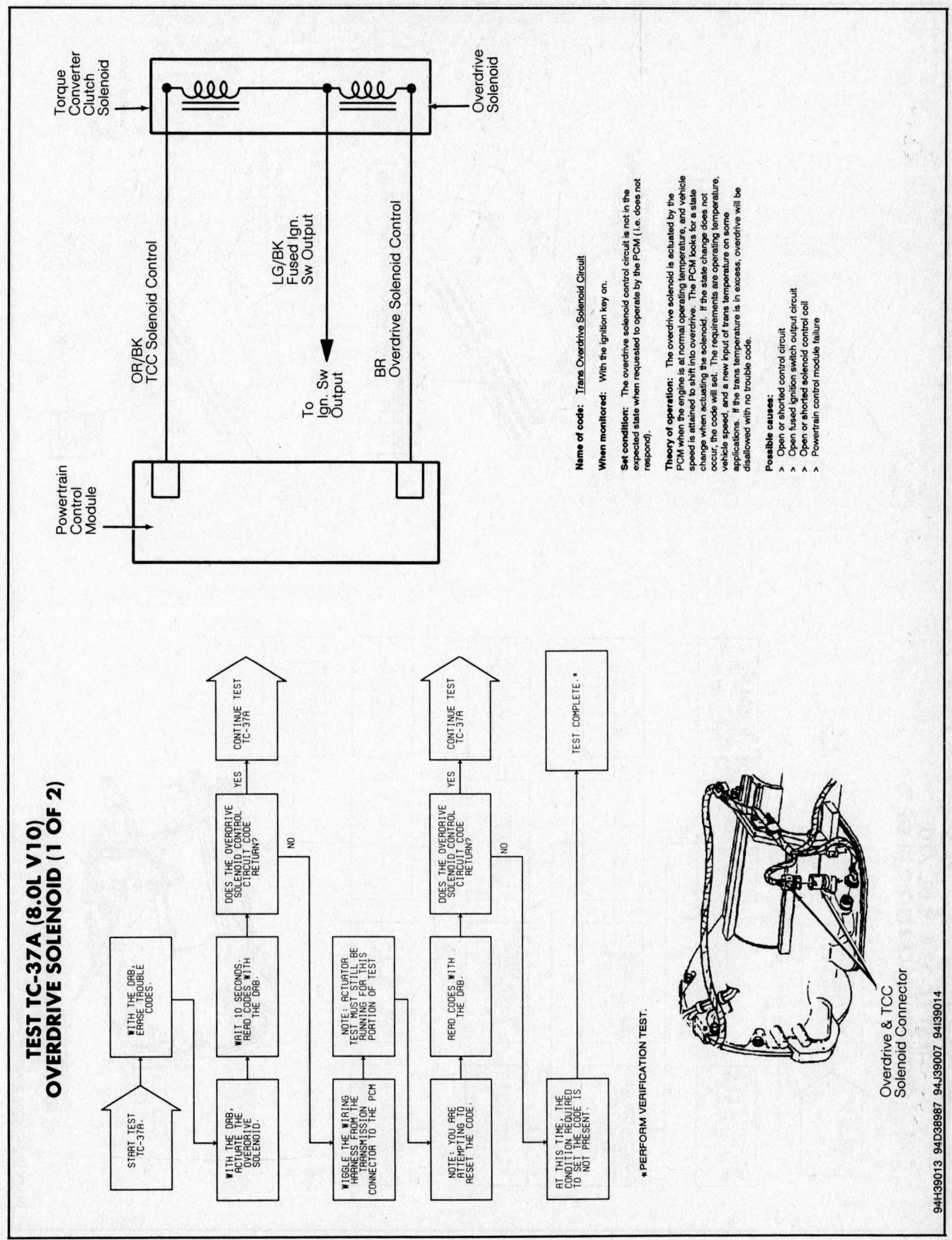

TEST TC-37A (8.0L V10)
OVERDRIVE SOLENOID (1 OF 2)

Torque Converter Clutch Solenoid

Overdrive Solenoid

OR/BK TCC Solenoid Control

LG/BK Fused Ign. Sw Output

To Ign. Sw Output

BR Overdrive Solenoid Control

Powertrain Control Module

Name of code: Trans Overdrive Solenoid Circuit

When monitored: With the ignition key on.

Set condition: The overdrive solenoid control circuit is not in the expected state when requested to operate by the PCM (i.e. does not respond).

Theory of operation: The overdrive solenoid is actuated by the PCM when the engine is at normal operating temperature, and vehicle speed is attained to shift into overdrive. The PCM looks for a state change when actuating the solenoid. If the state change does not occur, the code will set. The requirements are operating temperature, vehicle speed, and a new input of trans temperature on some applications. If the trans temperature is in excess, overdrive will be disallowed with no trouble code.

Possible causes:
> Open or shorted control circuit
> Open fused ignition switch output circuit
> Open or shorted solenoid control coil
> Powertrain control module failure

START TEST TC-37A.

WITH THE DRB, ERASE TROUBLE CODES.

WITH THE DRB, ACTUATE THE OVERDRIVE SOLENOID.

WAIT 10 SECONDS. READ CODES WITH THE DRB.

DOES THE OVERDRIVE SOLENOID CONTROL CIRCUIT CODE RETURN?

YES → CONTINUE TEST TC-37A

NO

NOTE: ACTUATOR TEST MUST STILL BE RUNNING FOR THIS PORTION OF TEST

WIGGLE THE WIRING HARNESS FROM THE TRANSMISSION CONNECTOR TO THE PCM

READ CODES WITH THE DRB.

DOES THE OVERDRIVE SOLENOID CONTROL CIRCUIT CODE RETURN?

YES → CONTINUE TEST TC-37A

NO

NOTE: YOU ARE ATTEMPTING TO RESET THE CODE.

AT THIS TIME, THE CONDITION REQUIRED TO SET THE CODE IS NOT PRESENT.

TEST COMPLETE: *

* PERFORM VERIFICATION TEST.

Overdrive & TCC Solenoid Connector

94H39013 94D38987 94J39007 94J39014

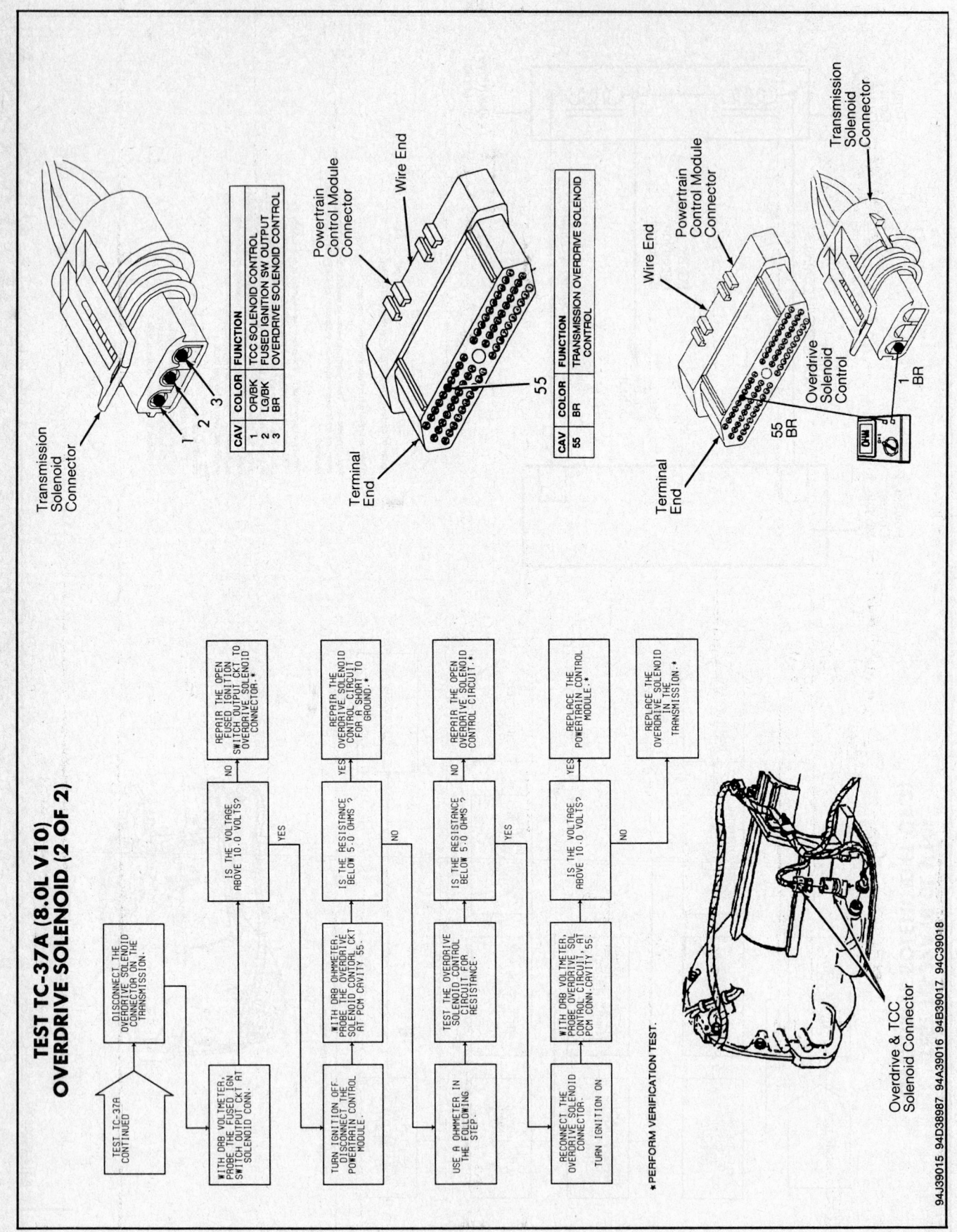

Transmission Solenoid Connector

CAV	COLOR	FUNCTION
1	OR/BK	TCC SOLENOID CONTROL
2	LG/BK	FUSED IGNITION SW OUTPUT
3	BR	OVERDRIVE SOLENOID CONTROL

Powertrain Control Module Connector

Wire End

Terminal End

55

CAV	COLOR	FUNCTION
55	BR	TRANSMISSION OVERDRIVE SOLENOID CONTROL

Powertrain Control Module Connector

Wire End

Transmission Solenoid Connector

Overdrive Solenoid Control

1 BR

Terminal End

55 BR

TEST TC-37A (8.0L V10)
OVERDRIVE SOLENOID (2 OF 2)

TEST TC-37A CONTINUED

DISCONNECT THE OVERDRIVE SOLENOID CONNECTOR ON THE TRANSMISSION.

WITH DRB VOLTMETER, PROBE THE FUSED IGN. SWITCH OUTPUT CKT AT SOLENOID CONN.

IS THE VOLTAGE ABOVE 10.0 VOLTS?
— NO → REPAIR THE OPEN FUSED IGNITION SWITCH OUTPUT CKT TO OVERDRIVE SOLENOID CONNECTOR.*
— YES →

TURN IGNITION OFF. DISCONNECT THE POWERTRAIN CONTROL MODULE.

WITH DRB OHMMETER, PROBE THE OVERDRIVE SOLENOID CONTROL CKT AT PCM CAVITY 55.

IS THE RESISTANCE BELOW 5.0 OHMS?
— YES → REPAIR THE OVERDRIVE SOLENOID CONTROL CIRCUIT FOR A SHORT TO GROUND.*
— NO →

USE A OHMMETER IN THE FOLLOWING STEP.

TEST THE OVERDRIVE SOLENOID CIRCUIT FOR RESISTANCE.

IS THE RESISTANCE BELOW 5.0 OHMS?
— NO → REPAIR THE OPEN OVERDRIVE SOLENOID CONTROL CIRCUIT.*
— YES →

RECONNECT THE OVERDRIVE SOLENOID CONNECTOR. TURN IGNITION ON.

WITH DRB VOLTMETER, PROBE OVERDRIVE SOL. CONTROL CIRCUIT AT PCM CONN. CAVITY 55.

IS THE VOLTAGE ABOVE 10.0 VOLTS?
— YES → REPLACE THE POWERTRAIN CONTROL MODULE.*
— NO → REPLACE THE OVERDRIVE SOLENOID IN THE TRANSMISSION.*

*PERFORM VERIFICATION TEST.

Overdrive & TCC Solenoid Connector

94J39015 94D38987 94A39016 94B39017 94C39018

VERIFICATION TEST

Inspect the vehicle to ensure that all engine components are connected. Reassemble and reconnect components as necessary.

If this verification procedure is being performed subsequent to a NO TROUBLE CODE, do the following:

1. Check to see if the initial symptom still exists.

2. If the initial or another symptom exists, the repair is not complete. Check all pertinent Technical Service Bulletins.

If this verification procedure is being performed subsequent to a TROUBLE CODE test, do the following:

For previously read trouble codes that have not been dealt with, return to and follow the path specified by the other code. Otherwise, continue.

If the powertrain control module has not been changed:

> Connect the DRB to the   data link connector and erase trouble codes.

> With the DRB, reset all values in the adaptive memory.

> Disconnect the DRB.

Ensure no other trouble code remains by doing the following:

1. If the vehicle is equipped with air conditioning, turn on the air conditioning and blower.

2. Drive the vehicle for at least five minutes and at some point attain a speed of 40 mph. Ensure the transmission shifts through all gears. Upon completion of the road test, turn the engine off.

3. Start the engine. Allow the engine to idle for at least two minutes.

4. Turn the engine off.

5. Connect the DRB to the   data link connector, and with the DRB, read all trouble codes.

If the repaired code has reset, the repair is not complete. Check all pertinent Technical Service Bulletins.

If another trouble code has set, return to and follow the path specified by the other trouble code.

If there are no trouble codes, the repair is now complete.

94D39019

AUTOMATIC TRANSMISSIONS
Ford AOD

APPLICATION & LABOR TIMES

NOTE: The AOD transmission is used through 1993 only.

APPLICATION & LABOR TIMES

Vehicle Application	Labor Times		Engine Size
	¹ R & I	² Overhaul	
1993 Models Only			
Cougar & Thunderbird	6.4	6.4	3.8L SFI
Cougar & Thunderbird	6.4	6.4	5.0L HO
Mustang	4.6	6.4	5.0L HO
Thunderbird	6.4	6.4	3.8L SC
Bronco	5.5	6.4	5.0L SFI
F150			
2WD	3.8	6.4	5.0L SFI
4WD	5.5	6.4	5.0L SFI

¹ – Removal and installation of transmission from vehicle chassis.
² – Bench overhaul time for transmission. DOES NOT include removal and installation.

IDENTIFICATION

Automatic Overdrive Transmission (AOD) is identified by the code letter "T". The identification code letter is found on the lower line of Vehicle Certification Label under "TR". This label is attached to driver's side door lock post.

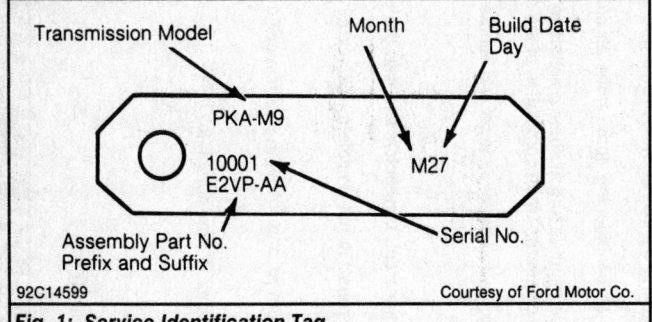

Transmission Model — Month — Build Date Day

PKA-M9

10001
E2VP-AA

M27

Assembly Part No. Prefix and Suffix

Serial No.

92C14599   Courtesy of Ford Motor Co.

Fig. 1: Service Identification Tag

The transmission model may be identified by a metal tag attached to transmission by the middle left hand extension housing retaining bolt. Top line of tag shows transmission model number and line shift code. Bottom line on tag shows the build date code. *See Fig. 1.*

DESCRIPTION

The AOD is a 4-speed, fully automatic transmission which combines automatic shifting with 2 fuel saving features: an overdrive gear ratio and mechanical lock-out split torque path in 3rd gear. AOD transmission differs from similar Ford C-6 automatic transmissions in that the planetary gear set operates in 4th gear. *See Fig. 2.*

LUBRICATION & ADJUSTMENTS

See appropriate AUTOMATIC TRANSMISSION SERVICING article in TRANSMISSION SERVICING.

TROUBLE SHOOTING

SYMPTOM DIAGNOSIS

NOTE: Always check fluid level and condition, and linkage adjustment prior to trouble shooting.

Slow Initial Engagement – Fluid level, linkage adjustment, improper clutch and band application, or low main control pressure.
Rough Initial Engagement – Fluid level, high idle speed, loose drive shaft, engine mounts, improper clutch or band application, or sticking valve body components.
Harsh Engagements (Warm Engine) – Fluid level, misadjusted T.V. linkage, sticking throttle valve, high idle, or improperly torqued valve body bolts.
Delayed Or No Forward Engagement, Reverse Ok – Fluid level, low main control pressure, forward clutch stator support seal rings leaking, forward clutch assembly burnt or damaged, forward clutch cylinder check ball leaking, valve body components sticking, improper torqued valve body bolts, plugged filter, or damaged/leaking pump.
Delayed Or No Reverse Engagement, Forward Ok – Fluid level, linkage adjustment, low main control pressure, reverse clutch stator support seal rings leaking or clutch assembly burnt, valve body components sticking, improperly torqued valve body bolts, reverse clutch piston check ball leaking or seal rings leaking, plugged filter, or damaged pump.

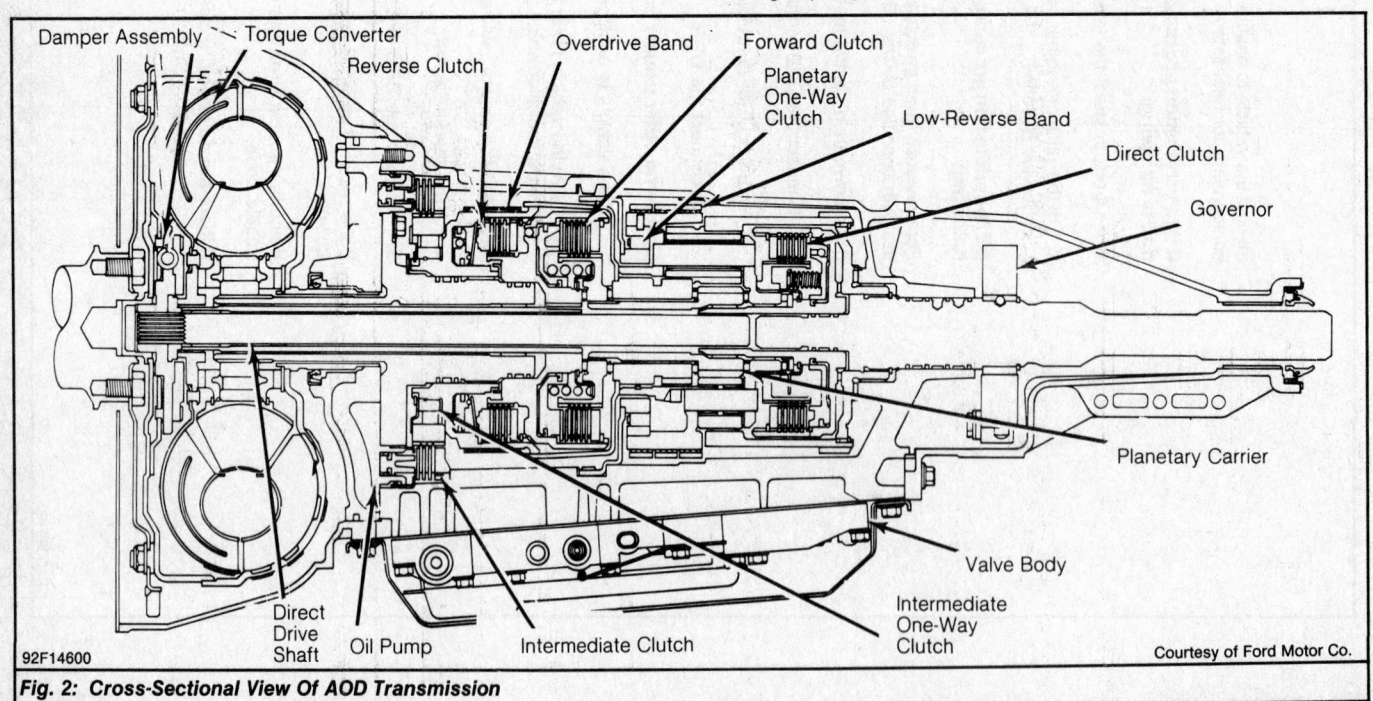

92F14600   Courtesy of Ford Motor Co.

Fig. 2: Cross-Sectional View Of AOD Transmission

Delayed Or No Reverse Engagement And/Or No Engine Braking In Manual Low – Fluid level, low reverse band burnt, planetary low one-way clutch damaged, low reverse servo piston seal leaking, or insufficient end play clearance.

No Engine Braking In Manual 2nd – Intermediate band improperly adjusted, overdrive servo leaking, intermediate one-way clutch damaged, or glazed intermediate band or drum.

Forward Engagement Slips, Shudders Or Chatters On Engagement – Fluid level, misadjusted linkage, low main control pressure, improperly torqued valve body bolts, sticking valve body components, leaking forward clutch piston check ball, cut or worn forward clutch piston seal, leaking forward clutch stator support seal rings, low one-way clutch damaged.

Reverse Engagement Slips, Shudders Or Chatters On Engagement – Fluid level, low main control pressure, low reverse servo leaking, low one-way clutch damaged, reverse clutch drum bushing damaged, reverse clutch piston seals defective or clutch assembly defective, reverse band improperly adjusted or damaged, or loose drive shaft or drive shaft components.

No Movement In Drive, Slips Or Chatters In 1st Gear ("D" Or "OD") – One-way roller clutch damaged or worn.

No Movement In Drive, Slips Or Chatters In 2nd Gear – Intermediate clutch, one-way roller clutch, Intermediate clutch piston bleed hole blocked, Improper band or clutch application, intermediate clutch incorrectly assembled, or sticking valve body components.

2nd Or 3rd Gear Starts ("D" Or "OD") – Improper band and/or clutch application, insufficient intermediate clutch pack clearance, valve body loose, sticking valve body components, or valve body cross-leaks.

Incorrect Shift Points – Fluid level, misadjusted T.V. linkage, incorrect speedometer gear, improper clutch or band application, damaged or worn governor, or sticking valve body components.

Upshifts Harsh Or Delayed, Or No Upshifts – Fluid level, misadjusted throttle linkage (high T.V.), sticking T.V. valve, sticking governor, high main control pressure, improperly torqued valve body bolts, or sticking valve body components.

Mushy, Early Upshifts – Fluid level, misadjusted throttle linkage (low T.V.), sticking T.V. valve, sticking governor, low main control pressure, improperly torqued valve body bolts, or sticking valve body components.

No 1-2 Upshift – Fluid level, misadjusted throttle linkage, low main control pressure to intermediate clutch, improperly torqued valve body bolts, sticking governor, or sticking valve body components.

Delayed/Harsh/Rough 1-2 Upshift – Fluid level, poor engine performance, misadjusted throttle linkage (high T.V.), sticking T.V. valve, sticking governor, improperly torqued valve body bolts, or sticking valve body components.

Mushy/Early/Soft/Slipping 1-2 Upshift – Fluid level, poor engine performance, misadjusted throttle linkage, sticking T.V. valve, low main control pressure, sticking governor, improperly torqued valve body bolts, burnt or worn intermediate clutch, or sticking valve body components.

No 2-3 Upshift – Fluid level, low main control pressure to direct clutch, improperly torqued valve body bolts, burnt or worn direct clutch, broken converter damper hub/weld, or sticking valve body components.

Delayed/Harsh 2-3 Upshift – Poor engine performance, misadjusted throttle linkage (high T.V.), plugged 2-3 accumulator piston passage, damaged/worn 2-3 accumulator and/or seals, improperly torqued valve body bolts, sticking valve body components (2-3 capacity modulator valve), or damaged T.V. cable.

Early/Mushy/Soft 2-3 Upshift – Misadjusted throttle linkage (low T.V.), improperly torqued valve body bolts, sticking valve body components, burnt/worn direct clutch assembly, or damaged T.V. cable.

No 3-4 Upshift – Misadjusted throttle linkage, improperly torqued valve body bolts, sticking valve body components, direct clutch circuit leakage, valve body gasket distortion, governor leakage, or case distortion at valve body mating surface.

Delayed/Harsh 3-4 Upshift – Poor engine performance, misadjusted T.V. cable, improperly torqued valve body bolts, or sticking valve body components.

Slipping 4th Gear (Flare) – Overdrive circuit leakage or blocked passage, lack of band application, mislocated overdrive band, converter damage, or direct drive shaft damage.

Erratic Shifts – Fluid level, misadjusted throttle linkage, sticking T.V. valve, sticking governor, improperly torqued valve body bolts, damaged output shaft collector body seal rings, or sticking valve body components.

1-3 Shift – Intermediate clutch burnt or damaged, damaged intermediate one-way roller clutch, improper clutch application, sticking valve body components, or sticking governor valve.

2-3 Shift Flare – Misadjusted shift linkage, improper clutch application, damaged or worn direct clutch, sticking valve body components, or damage converter.

Hunting 3-4, Or 4-3 Shift – Poor engine performance, or misadjusted shift linkage

3-1 Shift Shudder (Closed Throttle) – Incorrect idle speed, misadjusted shift linkage, improper clutch or band application, incorrect governor operation, or sticking valve body components.

Mushy Or Rough, 4-2 Or 3-1 Downshift (Kickdown) – Poor engine performance, poor application of intermediate friction and/or one-way roller clutch, or sticking valve body components.

No Forced Downshift (Kickdown) – Misadjusted throttle linkage, incorrect line pressure, sticking governor, or sticking valve body components.

Transmission Overheats – Fluid level, incorrect engine idle speed, incorrect clutch or band application, oil cooler restriction, seized converter one-way clutch, or sticking valve body components.

Clunk or Squawk During 1-2 Or 2-3 Shift – Intermediate clutch piston bleed hole blocked, incorrectly positioned anti-clunk spring, or broken converter damper spring.

Poor Acceleration – Poor engine performance, or seized converter one-way clutch.

Harsh Coasting Downshift Clunk – Incorrectly positioned anti-clunk spring, or misadjusted T.V. cable (high T.V.)

CLUTCH & BAND APPLICATION CHART

Selector Lever Position	Elements In Use
"OD" (Overdrive)	
1 Gear	Forward Clutch, Planetary One-Way Clutch
2 Gear	Intermediate Clutch, Forward Clutch & Intermediate One-Way Clutch
3 Gear	Forward Clutch, Intermediate Clutch & Direct Clutch
4 Gear	Overdrive Band, Intermediate Clutch & Direct Clutch
"D" (Drive)	
1 Gear	Forward Clutch, Planetary One-Way Clutch
2 Gear	Interedate Clutch, Forward Clutch & Intermediate One-Way Clutch
3 Gear	Forward Clutch, Intermediate Clutch & Direct Clutch
"2" (Downshift)	Forward Clutch, Intermediate Clutch, Intermediate One-Way Clutch & Overdrive Band
"1" (Low)	Forward Clutch, Planetary One-Way Clutch & Low Reverse Band
"R" (Reverse)	Reverse Clutch & Low Reverse Band

TESTING

ROAD TEST

1) Check minimum throttle upshifts in Overdrive. Transmission should start in 1st gear, shift to 2nd, then shift to 3rd, and finally shift to 4th gear at approximately the speeds shown in SHIFT SPEEDS SPECIFICATIONS (MPH) tables.

2) With transmission in 4th gear (Overdrive), completely depress accelerator pedal. Transmission should downshift to 3rd or 2nd gear, depending on vehicle speed. The AOD will not shift into Overdrive at wide open throttle, and will not make a 4th to 1st gear downshift. See SHIFT SPEEDS SPECIFICATIONS (MPH) tables.

3) Since closed throttle downshifts are extremely difficult to detect, it may be necessary to attach 0-100 psi (0-7.0 kg/cm²) pressure gauges to forward and direct clutch pressure taps in order to detect Overdrive to 3rd gear and 3rd to 2nd gear coast downshifts. *See Fig. 3.*

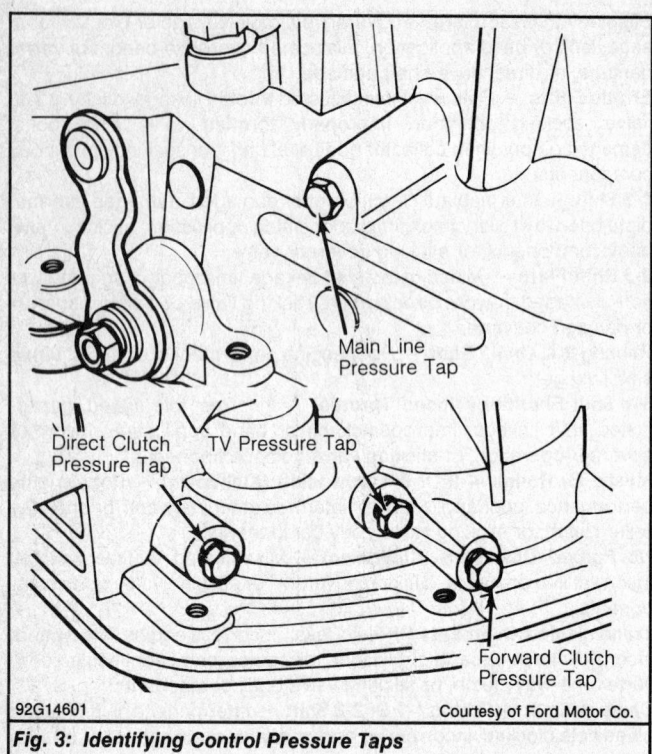

Fig. 3: Identifying Control Pressure Taps

Main Line Pressure Tap

Direct Clutch Pressure Tap

TV Pressure Tap

Forward Clutch Pressure Tap

92G14601

Courtesy of Ford Motor Co.

4) With gauges attached, a 4th to 3rd gear coast (closed throttle) downshift is detected by the application of the forward clutch. Pressure will increase from 0-60 psi (0-4.2 kg/cm²). The 3rd to 2nd gear downshift is detected by release of direct clutch pressure. Pressure will decrease from 60-0 psi (4.2-0 kg/cm²).

5) When selector lever is moved from either "OD" or "D" ranges to "1" position, transmission should downshift into 2nd gear if vehicle speed is above 25 MPH, and into 1st gear if speed is less than 25 MPH.

CONTROL PRESSURE TEST

NOTE: When testing line pressure, 2 readings must be taken: one at Idle position (zero T.V. opening) and the other at WOT (full T.V. opening).

1) Connect a 0-300 psi (0-21.1 kg/cm²) pressure gauge to main line pressure port tap on left side of transmission case just above control levers. *See Fig 3.* Gauge hose must be long enough to read gauge while operating engine.

2) Connect a 0-100 psi (0-7.0 kg/cm²) pressure gauge to T.V. pressure tap at right side of transmission case. *See Fig. 3.* Gauge hose must be long enough to read gauge while operating engine. Ensure T.V. linkage is properly adjusted.

CAUTION: Pressure gauges affect transmission shift quality. Do not accelerate or decelerate rapidly. Possible transmission failure could result.

3) With engine at normal operating temperature, apply parking and service brakes. Check line pressure and throttle pressure in all ranges. Pressure should be approximately as specified. See CONTROL PRESSURE SPECIFICATIONS table.

NOTE: Pressure test at idle position must be taken with engine at normal operating temperature. Pressure test at WOT position should be taken at full stall conditions. Run engine at a fast idle in "N" for 2 minutes to cool fluid between tests.

CONTROL PRESSURE SPECIFICATIONS [1]

Throttle Position	Line Pressure psi (kg/cm²)	T.V. Limit psi (kg/cm²)
Idle		
"R"	75-90 (5.3-6.3)	0
All Other Ranges	55-65 (3.9-4.6)	0
WOT Stall		
In "R"		
3.8L SC & All Trucks	250-300 (17.6-21.1)	79-91 (5.6-6.4)
All Others	250-290 (17.5-20.3)	79-91 (5.6-6.4)
All Other Ranges		
3.8L SC & All Trucks	176-204 (12.4-14.3)	79-91 (5.6-6.4)
All Others	180-215 (12.6-15.1)	79-91 (5.5-6.4)

[1] – With governor pressure at zero.

CONTROL PRESSURE TEST RESULTS

Low In "P" – Valve body loose, faulty main oil regulator valve sticking or low-reverse servo leakage.

Low In "R" – Reverse clutch or low-reverse servo leakage. Valve body loose.

Low In "N" – Loose valve body or main oil regulator valve sticking.

Low In O/D – Faulty forward clutch, Overdrive servo, main oil regulator valve or loose valve body.

Low In "D" – Forward clutch leakage. Overdrive servo leakage.

Low In "1st" – Leakage at forward clutch or low-reverse servo or overdrive servo.

Low At Idle In All Ranges – Low fluid level, restricted intake screen or filter, loose valve body bolts, pump leakage, case leakage, faulty valve body, excessively low engine idle, fluid too hot or main regulator valve sticking.

High At Idle In All Ranges – Check for T.V. linkage adjustment and condition and for faulty valve body.

Pressure Okay At Idle But Low At WOT – Internal leakage, pump leakage, restricted intake screen of filter, damaged or out of adjustment T.V. valve linkage. Also check for sticking T.V. or sticking T.V. limit valve in valve body.

Line Pressure And T.V. Pressure High – Replace valve body.

Line Pressure and T.V. Pressure Low – Check T.V. adjustment. If T.V. adjustment is okay, replace valve body.

DIRECT CLUTCH PRESSURE TEST

1) Attach accurate 0-300 psi (0-21.1 kg/cm²) pressure gauges to the forward and direct clutch pressure taps on right side of transmission. *See Fig. 3.* Gauge hose must be long enough to read gauge while road testing vehicle.

2) Drive vehicle. When pressure is applied to direct clutch, note difference between line pressure on forward clutch gauge and direct clutch gauge. If difference is less than 15 psi (1.1 kg/cm²), direct clutch circuit is good.

3) If difference is greater than 15 psi (1.1 kg/cm²), there could be a leak in direct clutch pressure circuit.

SHIFT SPEED SPECIFICATIONS (MPH)

NOTE: Shift speeds shown are approximate. All shift speeds may vary somewhat due to production tolerances and emission control equipment.

NOTE: To determine deceleration shift speeds, release throttle once transaxle has shifted into 4th gear (O/D). Manually downshift shift lever into next lower gear and record speed at which downshift occurs. Continue downshifting and recording vehicle speed until transaxle has downshifted into low gear.

3.8L COUGAR/THUNDERBIRD (3.27 AXLE RATIO) VEHICLE SHIFT SPEEDS

Operating Condition	Shift Speed MPH (km/h)
Closed Throttle	
1-2	10-14 (16-23)
2-3	17-21 (27-34)
3-4	35-45 (56-72)
4-3	40-31 (64-50)
3-2	26-19 (42-31)
2-1	13-9 (21-14)
Part Throttle (60 psi T.V.)	
1-2	17-27 (27-33)
2-3	29-42 (47-68)
3-4	43-61 (69-98)
4-3	49-35 (79-56)
3-2	33-17 (53-27)
2-1	15-12 (25-19)
Full Throttle (WOT)	
1-2	34-47 (54-76)
2-3	62-73 (100-117)
3-2	60-49 (97-79)
2-1	36-22 (58-35)

3.8L SC THUNDERBIRD (3.27 AXLE RATIO) VEHICLE SHIFT SPEEDS

Operating Condition	Shift Speed MPH (km/h)
Closed Throttle	
1-2	9-12 (14-19)
2-3	17-24 (27-39)
3-4	39-49 (63-79)
4-3	43-32 (69-51)
3-2	23-17 (37-27)
2-1	12-8 (19-13)
Part Throttle (60 psi T.V.)	
1-2	16-28 (25-45)
2-3	33-43 (53-69)
3-4	46-61 (74-98)
4-3	46-33 (74-53)
3-2	35-22 (56-35)
2-1	15-12 (24-19)
Full Throttle (WOT)	
1-2	33-47 (53-76)
2-3	63-72 (101-116)
3-2	61-53 (98-85)
2-1	39-26 (63-42)

5.0L COUGAR/THUNDERBIRD (3.08 AXLE RATIO) VEHICLE SHIFT SPEEDS

Operating Condition	Shift Speed MPH (km/h)
Closed Throttle	
1-2	10-13 (16-21)
2-3	16-26 (25-42)
3-4	35-45 (56-72)
4-3	41-24 (66-39)
3-2	27-18 (43-29)
2-1	15-11 (23-17)
Part Throttle (60 psi T.V.)	
1-2	19-30 (31-49)
2-3	38-47 (61-76)
3-4	46-61 (74-98)
4-3	53-31 (85-50)
3-2	42-23 (68-37)
2-1	18-13 (29-21)
Full Throttle (WOT)	
1-2	39-52 (63-83)
2-3	70-79 (112-127)
3-2	65-56 (97-90)
2-1	42-30 (68-48)

5.0L HO+ MUSTANG (3.27 AXLE RATIO) VEHICLE SHIFT SPEEDS

Operating Condition	Shift Speed MPH (km/h)
Closed Throttle	
1-2	8-10 (13-23)
2-3	17-25 (27-40)
3-4	34-44 (54-71)
4-3	38-30 (61-48)
3-2	23-16 (37-21)
2-1	9-6 (14-10)
Part Throttle (60 psi T.V.)	
1-2	16-20 (37-32)
2-3	35-46 (56-74)
3-4	41-57 (66-92)
4-3	40-28 (64-45)
3-2	38-27 (61-45)
2-1	14-12 (23-19)
Full Throttle (WOT)	
1-2	36-47 (58-76)
2-3	63-71 (101-114)
3-2	62-53 (100-85)
2-1	38-27 (61-43)

5.0L HO+ MUSTANG (2.73 AXLE RATIO) VEHICLE SHIFT SPEEDS

Operating Condition	Shift Speed MPH (km/h)
Closed Throttle	
1-2	8-13 (13-21)
2-3	21-28 (34-45)
3-4	34-47 (55-76)
4-3	40-25 (64-40)
3-2	21-16 (34-26)
2-1	13-9 (21-14)
Part Throttle (60 psi T.V.)	
1-2	18-36 (29-58)
2-3	38-50 (61-80)
3-4	44-64 (71-103)
4-3	45-25 (72-40)
3-2	41-27 (66-43)
2-1	18-16 (29-26)
Full Throttle (WOT)	
1-2	45-57 (72-92)
2-3	72-83 (116-134)
3-2	71-61 (114-98)
2-1	47-34 (76-55)

BRONCO & F-150 2WD (3.55 AXLE RATIO) VEHICLE SHIFT SPEEDS

Operating Condition	Shift Speed MPH (km/h)
Closed Throttle	
1-2	8-11 (13-18)
2-3	16-21 (26-34)
3-4	36-50 (54-80)
4-3	42-26 (68-42)
3-2	19-15 (31-24)
2-1	10-7 (16-11)
Part Throttle (60 psi T.V.)	
1-2	15-25 (24-41)
2-3	27-43 (43-69)
3-4	45-61 (72-98)
4-3	46-32 (79-56)
3-2	34-16 (55-26)
2-1	15-11 (24-19)
Full Throttle (WOT)	
1-2	28-47 (45-76)
2-3	56-74 (90-119)
3-2	62-46 (100-74)
2-1	38-21 (61-34)

BRONCO & F-150 4WD (4.10 AXLE RATIO) VEHICLE SHIFT SPEEDS

Operating Condition	Shift Speed MPH (km/h)
Closed Throttle	
1-2	8-11 (13-18)
2-3	16-20 (25-32)
3-4	39-49 (63-79)
4-3	43-32 (69-51)
3-2	17-14 (27-23)
2-1	10-7 (16-11)
Part Throttle (60 psi T.V.)	
1-2	16-25 (25-40)
2-3	31-42 (50-68)
3-4	43-59 (69-95)
4-3	46-31 (74-50)
3-2	35-23 (56-37)
2-1	15-12 (24-19)
Full Throttle (WOT)	
1-2	32-44 (51-71)
2-3	58-69 (93-111)
3-2	60-49 (97-79)
2-1	36-23 (58-37)

GOVERNOR CHECK

Accelerate vehicle quickly to 25 MPH and back off throttle completely. If governor is operating properly, transmission will shift to 3rd gear. If transmission does shift properly, see TROUBLE SHOOTING.

STALL SPEED TEST

Testing Precautions – When performing stall test, do not hold throttle open longer than 5 seconds. Allow a cooling period of 2 minutes with transmission in "N" and engine speed at 1000 RPM between each test. If engine speed exceeds maximum limits shown, release accelerator immediately, as this is an indication of clutch or band slippage.

Testing Procedure – Bring engine to normal operating temperature. Apply parking and service brakes. Stall test transmission in each driving range at WOT. Note maximum RPM obtained. Engine speed should be within limits. See STALL SPEED SPECIFICATIONS table. If maximum RPM obtained is not within specifications, see STALL SPEED TEST RESULTS.

STALL SPEED SPECIFICATIONS

Application	Engine	RPM
Cougar & Thunderbird	3.8L SFI	2172-2532
Thunderbird	3.8L SC SFI	2212-2572
Mustang	5.0L HO+ SFI	2154-2545
Cougar & Thunderbird	5.0L HO EFI	2105-2503
Bronco & "F" Series	5.0L EFI	2125-2477

STALL SPEED TEST RESULTS

High Stall Speeds Or Slip
- In "OD" or "D" position – Check planetary one-way clutch.
- In "OD", "D" and "1" position – Check forward clutch.
- In "R" position – Check reverse clutch and/or low-reverse band.
- In all ranges – Check T.V. control adjustment and perform control pressure test.

Low Stall Speeds
- Check engine tune-up.
- Check torque converter using bench test for stator one-way clutch slippage.

AIR PRESSURE TESTS

1) A "No Drive" condition can exist even with correct transmission fluid pressure, because of inoperative clutches or bands. The inoperative units can be located by substituting air pressure for fluid pressure to determine location of malfunction.

2) To make air pressure checks, drain transmission fluid. Remove oil pan and control valve body assembly. See VALVE BODY ASSEMBLY under ON-VEHICLE SERVICE. Install Adapter Plate (T82L-7006-A), with Adapter Plate Attaching Screws (T82P-7006-C) and control valve

body gasket in place of control valve body. Tighten attaching screws 80-100 INCH lbs. (9-11 N.m). With a rubber-tipped air nozzle, apply air pressure in indicated locations. *See Fig. 4.*

3) If servo or accumulator does not move when tested, clean and inspect servo or accumulator to locate cause. See appropriate component under ON-VEHICLE SERVICE. If during test 2 clutches apply or clutch fails to operate, check fluid passages in case and front pump for blockage or damage.

NOTE: Air pressure should be regulated between 40 psi (2.8 kg/cm²) and 90 psi (6.3 kg/cm²). Compressed air used for test should be filtered and dry to avoid contaminating transmission fluid.

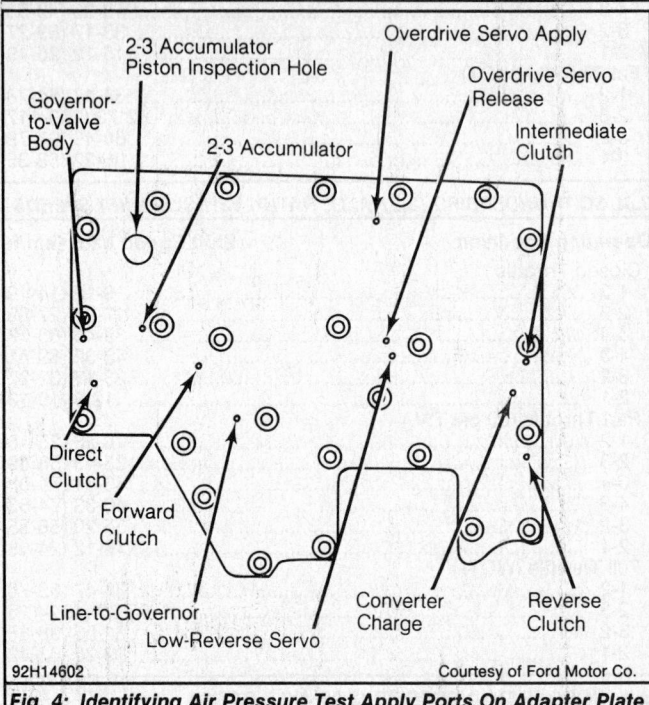

Fig. 4: Identifying Air Pressure Test Apply Ports On Adapter Plate

Reverse Clutch – Apply air pressure to reverse clutch passage. A dull thud can be heard when clutch piston is applied, or movement can be felt by placing fingertips on clutch drum.

Forward Clutch – Apply air pressure to forward clutch apply passage in adapter plate. A dull thud can be heard when clutch piston is applied, or movement can be felt by placing fingertips on input shell.

Intermediate Clutch – Apply air pressure to intermediate clutch apply passage in adapter plate. A dull thud can be heard or felt if clutch is operating properly.

Overdrive Servo – Apply air pressure to Overdrive servo apply passage. Operation of band is indicated by tightening of band around reverse clutch drum. A thud can be felt on servo cover when servo returns to release position as a result of spring force from release spring; band will then relax.

Low-Reverse Servo – Apply air pressure to low-reverse servo apply passage. A dull thud can be heard when low-reverse band tightens around planetary drum. Movement of ring gear should also be detected.

Direct Clutch – Apply air pressure to direct clutch passage in adapter plate. A dull thud can be heard or felt on drive shaft if clutch is operating properly.

2-3 Accumulator – Apply air pressure to 2-3 accumulator passage. Accumulator piston should unseat and can be detected by inserting a metal rod into 2-3 piston hole. When piston unseats, rod will move.

Governor – **1)** In order to check lines to governor passage and governor to valve body passage, drive shaft crossmember and extension housing must be removed. Apply air pressure to governor passage while holding finger near governor valve. Air should be felt exiting valve.

2) To air pressure check governor to valve body passage, governor must be removed. Apply air pressure to passage while holding finger over holes in output shaft. Air should be felt exiting one of the holes.

TORQUE CONVERTER

NOTE: Torque converter is a sealed unit and cannot be disassembled for service. Replace if found to be defective. The following tests will identify a defective converter.

FLUSHING CONVERTER

Whenever transmission has been disassembled to replace worn or damaged parts, or because valve body sticks due to foreign material, converter and oil cooler must be cleaned using a mechanically agitated cleaner (Rotunda 1400028). Under no conditions should converter or oil cooler be cleaned by hand agitation using solvent.

LEAK TEST

If torque converter welds indicate leakage, attach Torque Converter Leak Detector (Rotunda 7200004) to converter and follow detector kit instructions.

END PLAY CHECK

1) Insert Tester (T80L-7902-A) into converter pump drive hub until hub bottoms. Expand sleeve in turbine spline by tightening threaded inner post of tester until sleeve is securely locked into spline.
2) Attach a dial indicator to tool with button on indicator on converter pump drive hub. Zero dial face. Lift tool upward as far as tool will go and note indicator reading. *See Fig. 5.*
3) Reading is total end play of turbine and stator. If end play exceeds .050-.077" (1.27-1.95 mm), replace torque converter assembly.

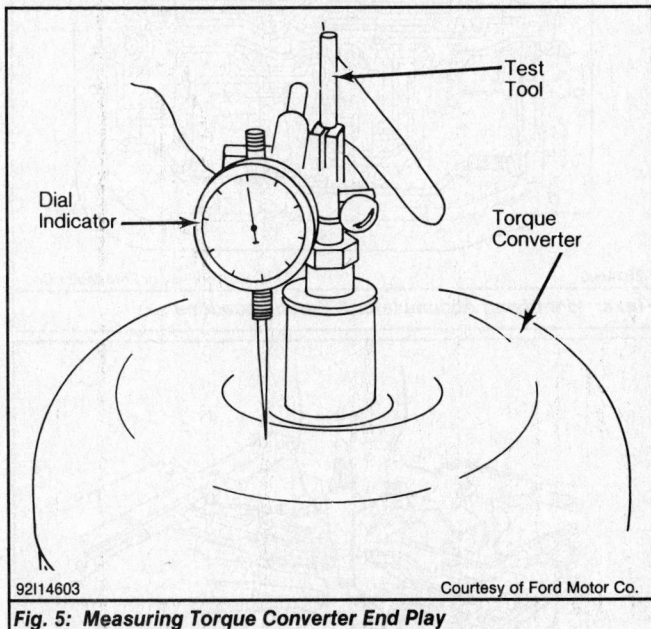

92I14603   Courtesy of Ford Motor Co.

Fig. 5: Measuring Torque Converter End Play

STATOR ONE-WAY CLUTCH CHECK

1) Insert one-way clutch Holding Wire (T77L-7902-R) into one of the grooves in stator thrust washer. Insert Torque Adapter (T76L-7902-C) into converter pump drive hub so as to engage one-way clutch inner race.
2) Attach a torque wrench to torque adapter. With clutch holding wire held stationary, turn torque wrench counterclockwise. *See Fig. 6.* The converter one-way clutch should lock-up and hold a 10 ft. lb. (14 N.m) force. One-way clutch should rotate freely in a clockwise direction.
3) Repeat lock-up test in at least 5 different locations around torque converter. If clutch fails to lock-up and hold, replace torque converter.

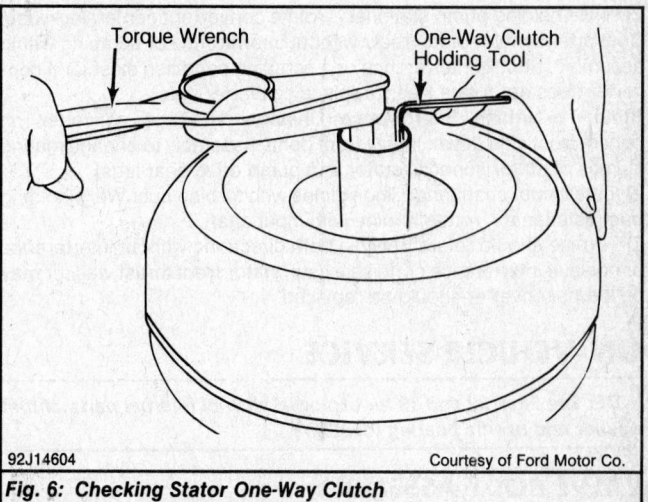

92J14604   Courtesy of Ford Motor Co.

Fig. 6: Checking Stator One-Way Clutch

DAMPER & HUB ASSEMBLY

1) Place torque converter in Holding Fixture (T83L-7902-A3). Place Turning Device (T83L-7902-A1) in converter. Ensure splines are engaged. Install Pilot Guide (T83L-7902-A2) over turning device and onto impeller hub.
2) Hold converter snug in holding fixture and rotate shaft clockwise and counterclockwise with 50 ft. lbs. (68 N.m), using a 3/4" socket and torque wrench. *See Fig. 7.* Shaft should not move more than 4 degrees. If shaft exceeds specification or grinding noise is heard, replace converter.

STATOR INTERFERENCE CHECK

Stator-To-Impeller Interference Check – 1) Position front pump assembly on bench with spline end of stator shaft pointing up. Mount converter on pump so splines of one-way clutch inner race engage splines of stator support and converter hub engages pump drive gear.

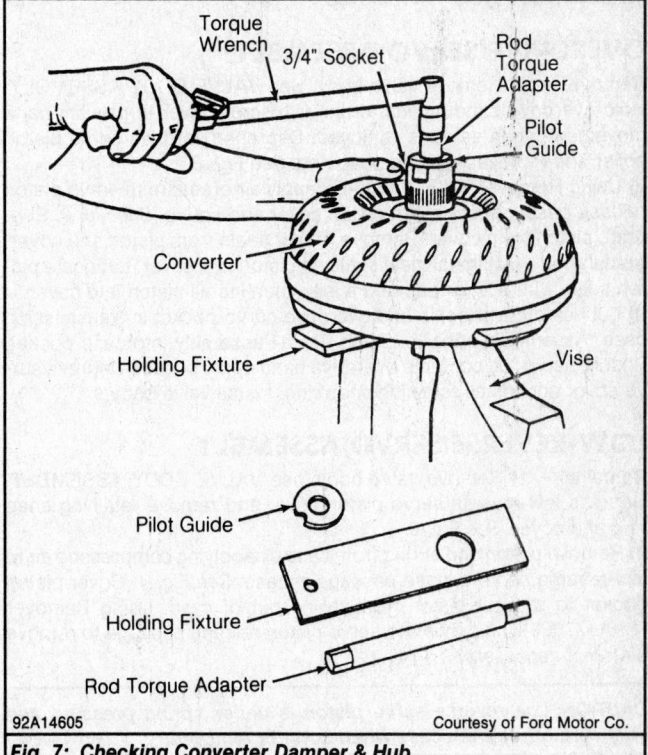

92A14605   Courtesy of Ford Motor Co.

Fig. 7: Checking Converter Damper & Hub

2) While holding pump stationary, rotate converter counterclockwise. Converter should rotate freely without interference or scraping within assembly. Should interference or a scraping condition exist, or if converter does not rotate freely, replace converter unit.

Stator-To-Turbine Interference Check – 1) Place converter on bench, front side down. Install front pump assembly to engage mating splines of stator support, stator and pump drive gear lugs.

2) Install input shaft, engaging splines with turbine hub. While holding pump stationary, rotate turbine with input shaft.

3) Turbine should rotate freely in both directions without interference or noise. If interference or noise exists, stator front thrust washer may be worn; converter should be replaced.

ON-VEHICLE SERVICE

NOTE: See Figs. 32 and 33 for exploded view of internal parts, thrust washer and needle bearing locations.

VALVE BODY ASSEMBLY

Removal – 1) Raise vehicle on hoist. Remove exhaust system, if necessary. Loosen oil pan retaining bolts and allow transmission fluid to drain. Remove oil pan and gasket. Discard gasket.

2) Remove 3 filter-to-valve body retaining bolts and remove filter, grommet and gasket. Remove detent spring retaining bolt and spring. Remove retaining bolts. Note positions and lengths of bolts for reassembly reference.

3) Remove valve body and gasket from transmission. For service or repair of valve body assembly, see VALVE BODY ASSEMBLY under COMPONENT DISASSEMBLY & REASSEMBLY.

Installation – 1) Using guide pins, position valve body (with new gasket) in case. Ensure inner manual lever and inner T.V. lever are engaged. Install and tighten valve body retaining bolts to specification. See TORQUE SPECIFICATIONS.

2) Install and tighten detent spring and retaining bolts. Remove guide pins and install 2 remaining valve body retaining bolts to specification. Load throttle lever torsion spring against separator plate. Install new filter and gasket. Install oil pan with new gasket and refill with fluid. Install exhaust system, if removed.

OVERDRIVE SERVO ASSEMBLY

Removal – 1) Remove valve body. See VALVE BODY ASSEMBLY. Hold overdrive band against drum with screwdriver to prevent band movement when servo is removed. Depress overdrive servo piston cover and remove retaining snap ring. *See Fig. 8.*

2) Using Remover (T80L-77030-B), apply air pressure to servo piston release passage to remove piston cover and spring. *See Fig. 9.* Separate piston from cover. Remove rubber seals from piston and cover.

Installation – 1) Install new seals on piston and cover. Lubricate piston seals with ATF or petroleum jelly, then install piston into cover.

2) Lubricate cover seals and overdrive servo pocket in transmission case. Assemble spring to piston. Install assembly into case pocket. Ensure servo rod contacts overdrive band apply pocket. Depress servo cover and install retaining snap ring. Install valve body.

LOW-REVERSE SERVO ASSEMBLY

Removal – 1) Remove valve body, see VALVE BODY ASSEMBLY. Depress low-reverse servo piston cover and remove retaining snap ring and cover. *See Fig. 8.*

2) Remove piston and spring from case by applying compressed air to low-reverse servo release passage in case. *See Fig. 4.* Cover piston pocket to prevent piston from falling out of case. Using Remover (T80L-77030-B), apply air to servo piston release passage to remove piston, if necessary.

CAUTION: Low-reverse servo piston is under spring pressure and may spring free from case when cover is removed.

Installation – To install, reverse removal procedure. Ensure servo piston is installed with same length rod as was removed.

2-3 ACCUMULATOR PISTON

Removal – Remove valve body. See VALVE BODY ASSEMBLY. Depress 2-3 accumulator piston cover. Remove retaining snap ring, cover, and spring. *See Fig. 8.* Remove accumulator piston. Remove accumulator seals from piston.

Installation – To install, reverse removal procedure. Prior to installation, lubricate piston seals and piston pocket in case.

EXTENSION HOUSING BUSHING & REAR OIL SEAL

Removal – 1) Raise vehicle on hoist. Mark drive shaft yoke and axle companion flange for reassembly reference. Disconnect drive shaft from transmission. Remove oil seal using Puller (T74P-77248-A).

2) Remove bushing using Puller (T77L-7697-A), taking care not to damage output shaft splines.

Installation – Install new bushing into extension housing using Driver (T80L-77034-A). Install new seal into housing using appropriate seal installer. Coat inside diameter of rubber portion of seal and yoke splines with lubricant. Install drive shaft.

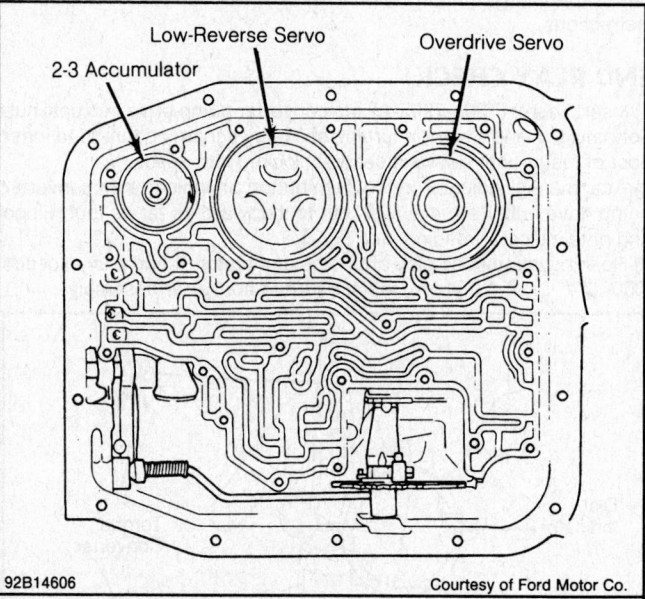

92B14606   Courtesy of Ford Motor Co.

Fig. 8: Identifying Accumulator & Servo Locations

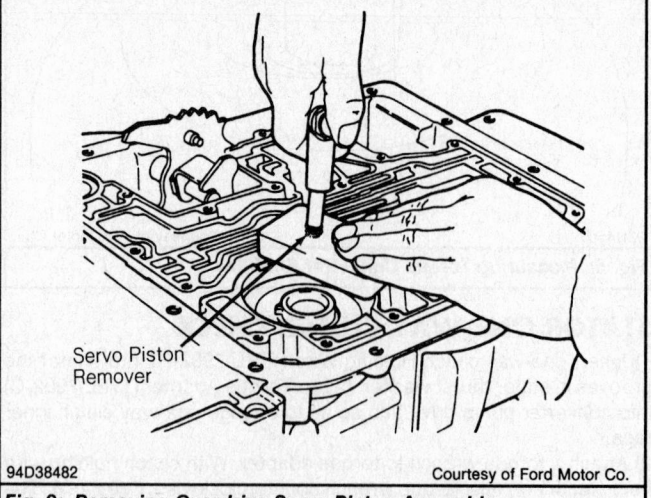

94D38482   Courtesy of Ford Motor Co.

Fig. 9: Removing Overdrive Servo Piston Assembly

EXTENSION HOUSING

Removal – 1) Raise and support vehicle. Remove exhaust system components as necessary for access. Disconnect parking brake cable from equalizer (if equipped). Mark drive shaft yoke and axle companion flange for reassembly reference. Remove drive shaft and disconnect speedometer cable from extension housing.

2) Remove engine rear support-to-extension housing retaining bolts. Raise transmission just enough to remove weight from rear support. Remove rear support-to-crossmember retaining bolt and remove rear support.

3) Lower transmission and remove extension housing retaining bolts. Slide housing off output shaft and allow fluid to drain. Remove and discard extension housing-to-case gasket.

Installation – 1) Clean mating surface on transmission and extension housing. Position new gasket on transmission. Slide extension housing into place.

2) Clean bolts and case holes for 2 bottom bolts and lower right hand corner bolt (as viewed from rear of extension housing). Coat bolts with Teflon tape and install. Install remaining bolts and tighten all to specification. See TORQUE SPECIFICATIONS. To complete installation, reverse removal procedure.

GOVERNOR ASSEMBLY

Removal – 1) Remove extension housing. See REMOVAL procedure under EXTENSION HOUSING. Remove governor-to-output shaft retaining snap ring. Using a mallet, tap governor assembly off output shaft.

2) Remove governor drive ball. Remove governor-to-counterweight retaining screws and lift governor from counterweight. For complete repair and servicing, see GOVERNOR ASSEMBLY under COMPONENT DISASSEMBLY & REASSEMBLY.

Installation – 1) Lubricate governor parts with clean transmission fluid. Ensure valve moves freely in bore. Position governor body on counterweight with cover facing toward front of vehicle. Install and tighten 2 retaining screws to specification. See TORQUE SPECIFICATIONS.

2) Position governor drive ball into pocket on output shaft. Align keyway in counterweight with drive ball and drive assembly onto output shaft with mallet. Install governor-to-output shaft retaining snap ring. To complete installation, reverse removal procedure.

INTERNAL & EXTERNAL SHIFT LINKAGE

NOTE: On some vehicles it may be necessary to loosen fan shroud and lower transmission to remove linkage.

Removal – 1) Raise vehicle on hoist. Disconnect any interfering exhaust system components. Apply penetrating oil to outer throttle lever retaining nut to prevent breaking inner throttle lever. *See Fig. 10.*

2) Hold outer throttle lever stationary and remove retaining nut and lock washer. Move lever and T.V. rod or cable out of way for clearance. Disconnect manual rod from manual lever at transmission.

3) Loosen oil pan retaining bolts and allow fluid to drain. Remove oil pan. Remove manual lever detent spring and roller assembly. Remove manual lever retaining pin carefully using a sharp narrow screwdriver. Note assembled position of T.V. lever torsion spring. Remove torsion spring.

4) Securely hold inner manual lever and use a 21 mm wrench to break manual lever attaching nut free. DO NOT allow tools to contact detents. Remove outer manual lever from case.

5) Remove inner throttle lever and shaft assembly. Remove inner manual lever and parking pawl rod assembly. Disconnect parking pawl rod from inner manual lever. Remove manual lever oil seal using a screwdriver.

Installation – 1) Install new manual lever oil seal into case using appropriate driver. With manual lever nut on inner throttle lever, slide inner throttle lever through inner manual lever. *See Fig. 11.*

2) Install outer manual lever in case ensuring lever is in proper position (either up or down). Install inner throttle lever and shaft into outer manual lever.

3) Tighten manual lever attaching nut to specification. See TORQUE SPECIFICATIONS. Ensure flats are aligned. Install T.V. lever torsion spring. Push manual lever into case. Ensure inner manual lever pin is engaged on manual valve detent slot and inner throttle lever is engaged on T.V. valve.

4) Neutral start switch plunger must also contact cam surface of inner manual lever. Install new manual lever retaining pin in case. Pin must be flush or below pan gasket surface. Install new throttle lever seal.

5) Install detent spring. Install throttle valve outer lever. DO NOT push inner lever past throttle valve, lock washer and nut. Tighten retaining nut to specification. See TORQUE SPECIFICATIONS.

6) Check Park function and operation of T.V. and manual levers. Connect shift linkage. Adjust linkage as necessary. See appropriate AUTOMATIC TRANSMISSION SERVICING article in TRANSMISSION SERVICING section.

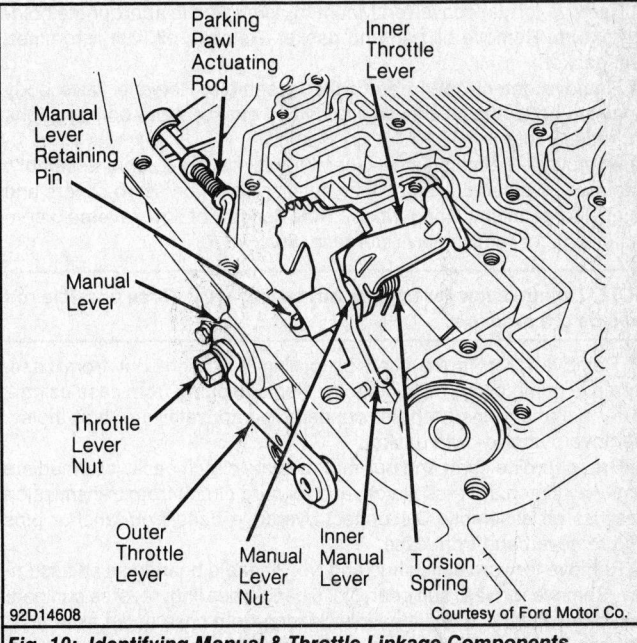

Fig. 10: Identifying Manual & Throttle Linkage Components

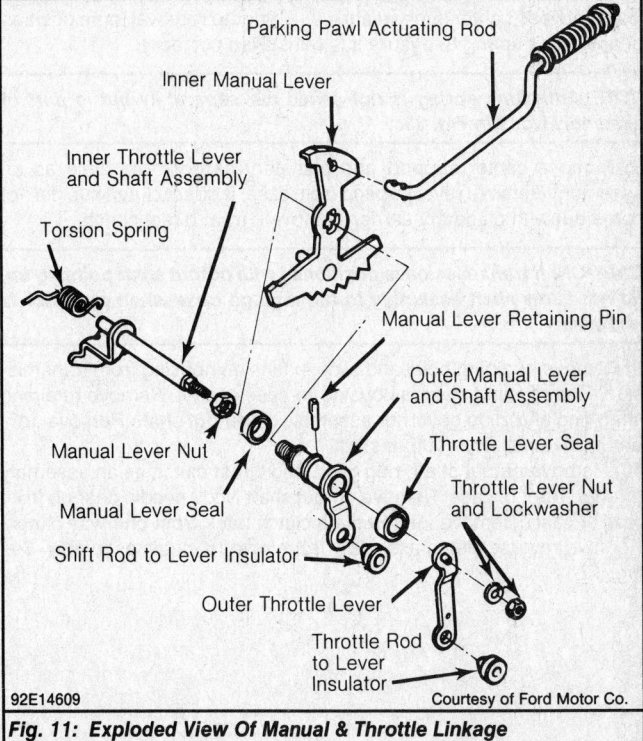

Fig. 11: Exploded View Of Manual & Throttle Linkage

NEUTRAL SAFETY SWITCH

See appropriate AUTOMATIC TRANSMISSION SERVICING article in TRANSMISSION SERVICING.

REMOVAL & INSTALLATION

TRANSMISSION

See appropriate AUTOMATIC TRANSMISSION REMOVAL article in TRANSMISSION SERVICING.

TRANSMISSION DISASSEMBLY

NOTE: See Figs. 32 and 33 for exploded view of internal parts, thrust washer and needle bearing locations.

1) Remove torque converter. Mount transmission in appropriate holding fixture. Remove oil pan and gasket. Remove oil filter, grommet, and gasket.
2) Remove detent spring and roller assembly. Remove valve body retaining bolts and lift off valve body and gasket. Note bolt positions for reassembly.
3) Remove 2-3 accumulator assembly, low-reverse servo assembly, and overdrive servo assembly by pushing down on servo covers and removing retaining snap rings. Note length of low-reverse servo piston rod for reassembly reference. See Fig. 8.

NOTE: Length of low-reverse piston rod may vary. Three possible rod lengths are available.

4) Remove direct drive shaft by pulling it straight out from case. Remove pump body retaining bolts. Remove pump from case using 2 slide hammers installed in opposite pump retaining bolt holes. Remove pump-to-case gasket.
5) Grasp turbine shaft and pull intermediate clutch pack, intermediate one-way clutch, reverse clutch, and forward clutch from transmission case as an assembly. Disconnect overdrive band from anchor pins and remove band from case.
6) Remove forward clutch hub and No. 3 needle bearing as an assembly. Remove forward sun gear, No. 5 needle bearing, reverse sun gear and drive shell, and No. 4 needle bearing from case as an assembly.
7) Note position of center support snap ring tangs for installation reference. Remove snap ring. Using a screwdriver, pry anti-clunk spring from between center support and case. Prior to removal, note position of anti-clunk spring to ensure it is reinstalled correctly.

NOTE: Anti-clunk spring is not called out separately but is part of assembly No. 9 in Fig. 33.

8) Remove center support and planetary carrier from case as an assembly. Remove reverse band from case. If direct clutch hub did not come out with planetary carrier, remove it from direct clutch.

CAUTION: If transmission is positioned with output shaft pointing up, do not allow shaft assembly to fall through case when governor is removed.

9) Remove retaining bolts and slide extension housing from transmission. Remove and discard housing-to-case gasket. Remove retaining snap ring and slide governor assembly off output shaft. Remove governor drive ball from output shaft.
10) Remove output shaft, ring gear, and direct clutch as an assembly through front of case. Remove output shaft No. 9 needle bearing from rear of case. Remove intermediate clutch pack from one-way clutch. Remove reverse clutch assembly from forward clutch assembly. See Fig. 12.

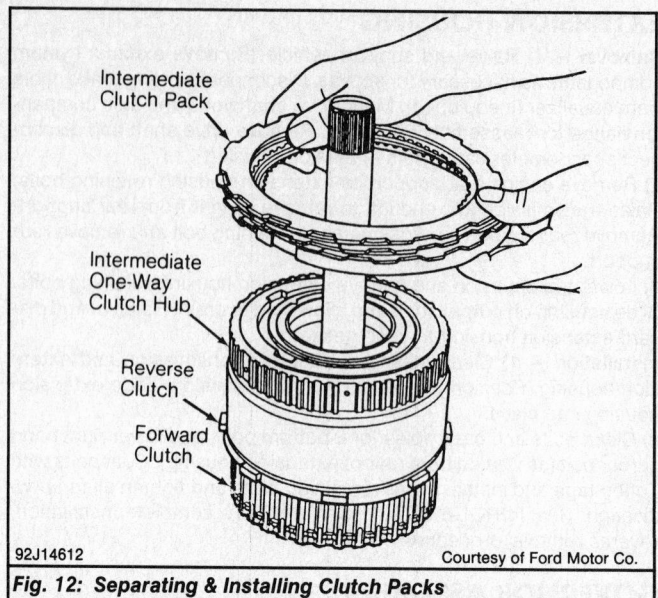

Fig. 12: Separating & Installing Clutch Packs

COMPONENT DISASSEMBLY & REASSEMBLY

NOTE: See Figs. 32 and 33 for exploded view of internal parts, thrust washer and needle bearing locations.

ACCUMULATOR & SERVOS

2-3 Accumulator – Install NEW seals on accumulator piston. Ensure diagonal cuts on seals are properly aligned. See Fig. 13.
Low-Reverse Servo – Inspect sealing edge on both servo cover and piston. Replace cover or piston, if necessary. Ensure servo piston rod length is same as the one removed. See Fig. 13.
Overdrive Servo – Separate piston from servo cover. Instal NEW seals on piston and cover. Lubricate and assemble piston to cover. See Fig. 13.

CENTER SUPPORT & PLANETARY ONE-WAY CLUTCH

NOTE: If a roller from planetary one-way clutch is lost or damaged, entire one-way clutch assembly must be replaced.

Disassembly – Remove center support from planetary carrier by lifting up on center support while rotating it counterclockwise. Carefully remove planetary one-way clutch from planetary assembly. See Fig. 14.
Reassembly – If necessary, assemble one-way clutch. See. Fig. 15. Lubricate clutch races and clutch assembly with petroleum jelly to aid in assembly. Install one-way clutch in planetary carrier. Install center support into one-way clutch by rotating center support counterclockwise.

DIRECT CLUTCH ASSEMBLY

Disassembly – 1) Remove No. 7 direct clutch hub inner needle bearing and bearing support. Using a screwdriver, remove clutch pack selective retaining snap ring and lift out clutch pack. See Fig. 16.
2) Using appropriate compressor, compress piston return springs and remove retaining snap ring. Remove tool and lift spring retainer assembly and piston from clutch drum.
3) If necessary, piston can be removed by applying compressed air to lubrication hole in clutch drum. Note position and direction of lip seals. Remove seals from drum and piston.

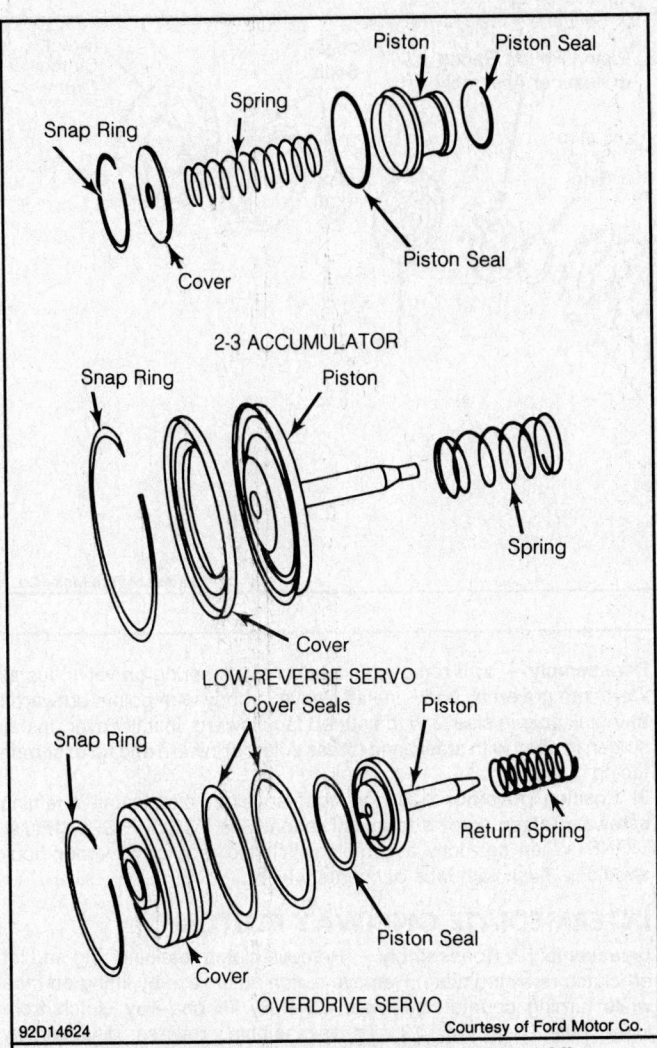

Fig. 13: Exploded View Of Accumulator & Servo Assemblies

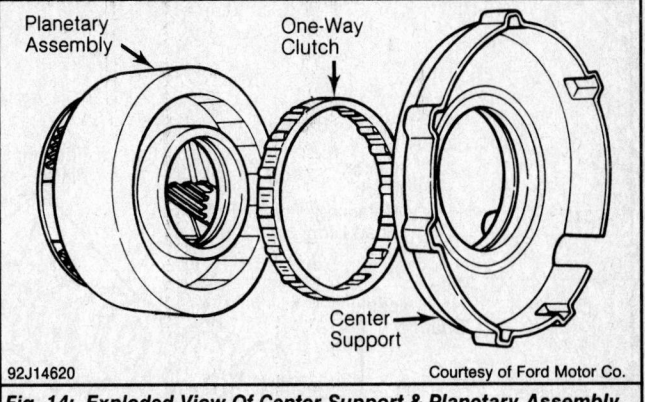

Fig. 14: Exploded View Of Center Support & Planetary Assembly

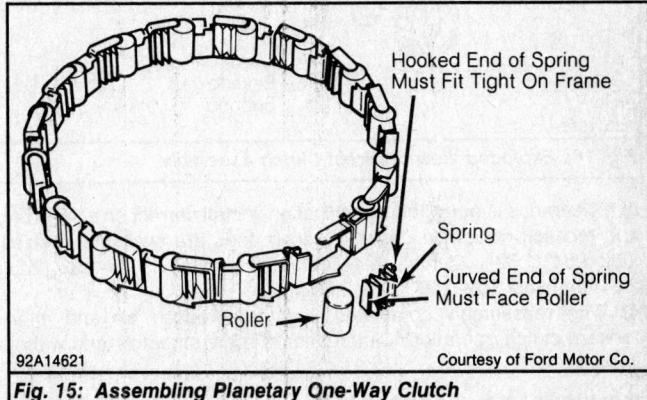

Fig. 15: Assembling Planetary One-Way Clutch

DIRECT CLUTCH PLATE USAGE & CLEARANCE

Engine Application	Steel Plates	Friction Plates	Clearance In. (mm)
3.8L SFI	5	5	.050-.073 (1.27-1.85)
3.8L SC & 5.0L HO	6	6	.060-.092 (1.53-2.34)
5.0 SFI	5	5	.050-.067 (1.27-1.70)

Inspection – 1) Check piston check ball for freedom of movement. Check for leakage by turning piston upside down (flat side up), allowing check ball to seat in piston.
2) Pour small quantity of solvent over check ball. If solvent drips past check ball, replace piston.
Reassembly – 1) Using Seal Protector (T80L-77234-A), install inner seal on clutch drum hub with sealing lip facing down into drum. Lubricate seals and seal protector with petroleum jelly prior to installation. Ensure inner seal is positioned in groove. Install outer seal on piston with lip pointing away from spring posts.
2) Coat piston seals, clutch drum sealing area, and piston inner seal area with petroleum jelly. Install piston into clutch drum using Seal Protector (T80L-77254-A) to prevent damaging seals.
3) Position piston spring and retainer assembly in clutch drum. Compress assembly and install retaining snap ring. Install clutch pack into drum. Install pressure plate on top of clutch pack. Install clutch pack selective retaining ring.
4) Using a feeler gauge, measure clearance between clutch pack retaining ring and pressure plate with pressure plate held down. See DIRECT CLUTCH PLATE USAGE & CLEARANCE table.
5) If clearance is not within specifications, install correct size snap ring and recheck clearance. Selective snap rings are available in sizes; .050-.054" (1.27-1.37 mm), .064-.068" (1.63-1.73 mm), .078-.082" (1.98-2.08 mm) and .092-.096" (2.34-2.44 mm).
6) To check clutch for proper operation, use compressed air at 30 psi (2.1 kg/cm²). Clutch should apply smoothly and without leakage.

FORWARD CLUTCH

Disassembly – 1) Lift clutch hub and No. 3 needle bearing from forward clutch assembly. Using a screwdriver, pry clutch pack selective retaining snap ring from drum. Remove clutch pack. See Fig. 17.
2) Using appropriate compressor, compress piston return spring and remove retaining snap ring. Lift out retainer and return spring.
3) Remove clutch piston from drum. Note position of inner and outer piston seals, then remove seals. Ensure check balls in piston move freely.
Reassembly – 1) Lubricate and install inner and outer seals on piston with seal lips facing into clutch drum. Lubricate piston seals and drum sealing area with petroleum jelly. Install piston into drum using Seal Protector (T80L-77140-A) to prevent damaging seals.
2) Position return spring and retainer on piston. Compress return spring and install retaining snap ring. Install clutch pack into clutch drum starting with waved plate. Install clutch pack retaining snap ring. Using a feeler gauge, measure clearance between retaining snap ring and pressure plate with pressure plate held down. See FORWARD CLUTCH PLATE USAGE & CLEARANCE table.

FORWARD CLUTCH PLATE USAGE & CLEARANCE

Engine Application	Steel Plates	Friction Plates	Clearance In. (mm)
3.8L SFI	4	4	.040-.075 (1.02-1.91)
3.8L SC	5	5	.050-.095 (1.27-2.41)
5.0L SFI & HO	5	5	.050-.089 (1.27-2.26)

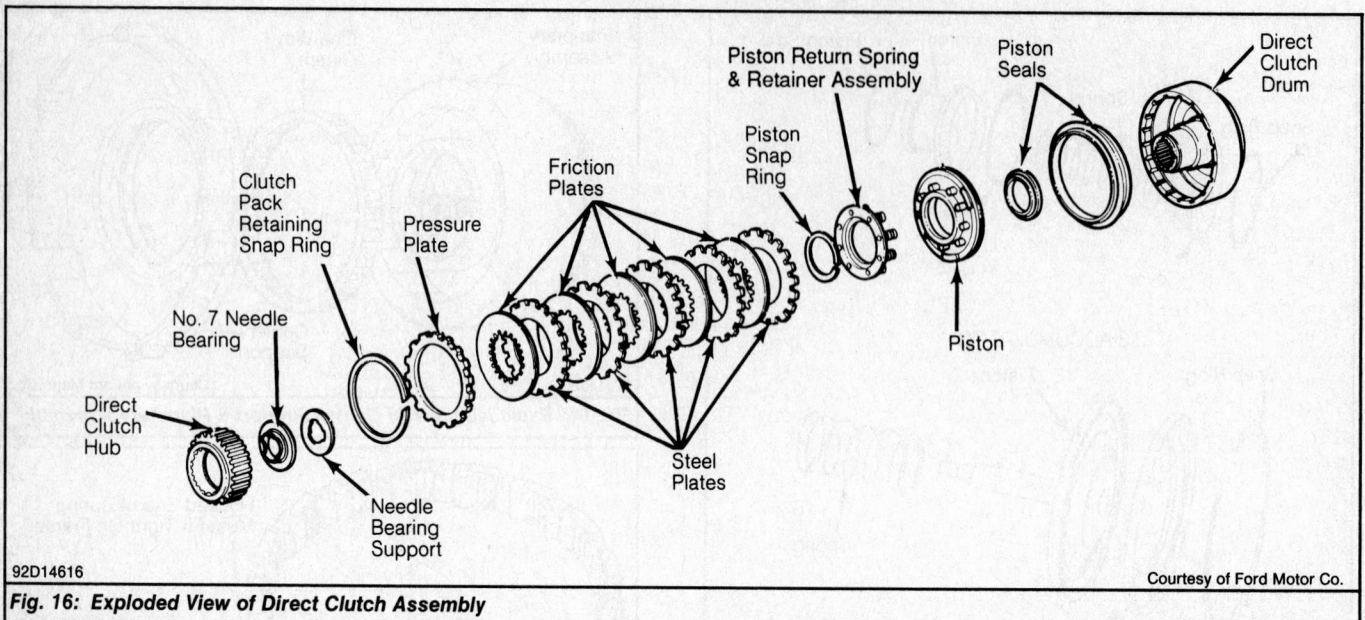

92D14616 Courtesy of Ford Motor Co.

Fig. 16: Exploded View of Direct Clutch Assembly

3) If clearance is not within specification, install correct size snap ring and recheck clearance. Selective snap rings are available in sizes; .060-.064" (1.52-1.73 mm), .074-.078" (1.88-1.98 mm), .088-.092" (2.24-2.34 mm) and .102-.106" (2.59-2.69 mm).

4) With reassembly completed, use compressed air and check forward clutch operation. Clutch should apply smoothly and without leakage.

GOVERNOR ASSEMBLY

Disassembly – Remove retaining screws and separate counterweight from governor body. Remove cover screws and cover. Remove plug, sleeve, and valve governor body. *See Fig. 18.* Remove governor screen.

NOTE: Handle all parts carefully to avoid damage. Lubricate parts with ATF before reassembly (petroleum jelly may be used on gaskets and thrust washers). Use all NEW gaskets and seals.

Reassembly – 1) If removed, install clip and spring on valve. Install valve into governor body. Install sleeve in body with points outward. **2)** Install plug in sleeve with knurled face inward. Install cover. Install screen in body with steel band (brass colored) inward and tip of screen facing outward.

3) Position governor body on counterweight and install retaining screws. Tighten screws to specification. See TORQUE SPECIFICATIONS. When correctly assembled, finished face of governor body should be flush with face of counterweight.

INTERMEDIATE ONE-WAY CLUTCH

Disassembly & Reassembly – Remove clutch retaining ring and lift off clutch retaining plate. Remove clutch outer race by lifting on race while turning counterclockwise. Carefully lift one-way clutch from inner race. *See Fig. 19.* To reassemble, reverse disassembly procedure.

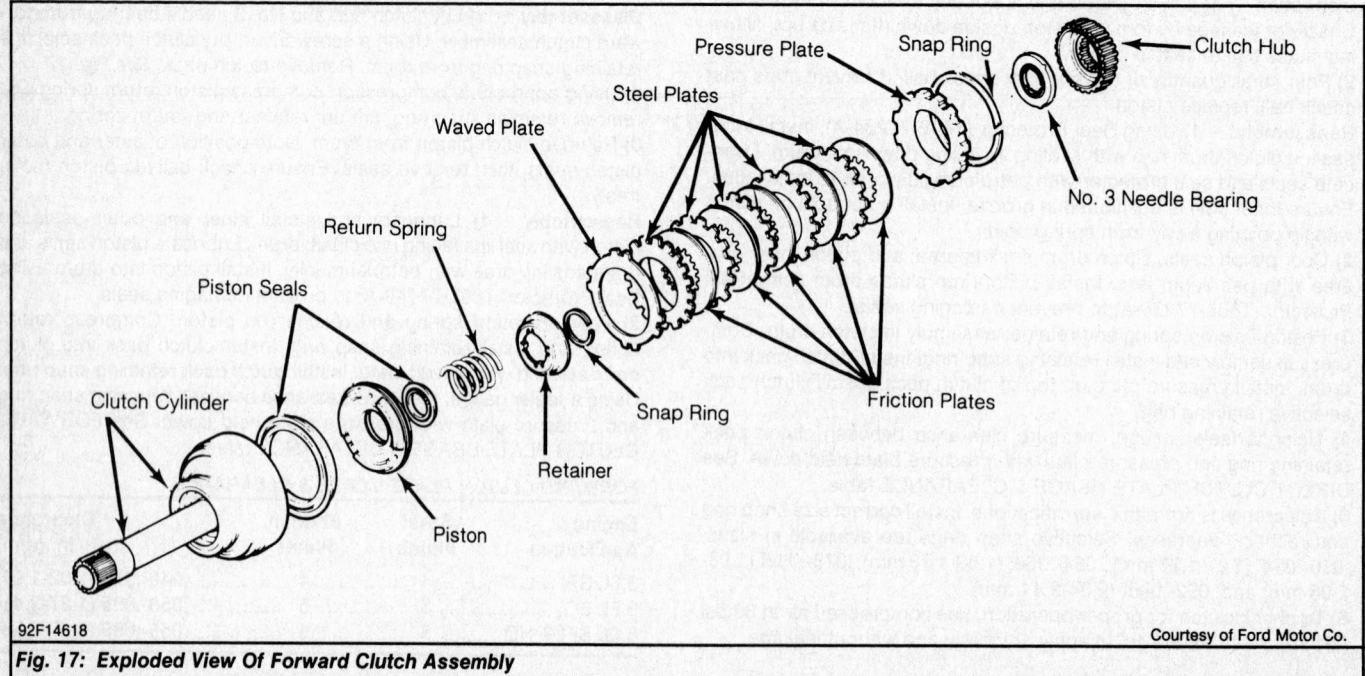

92F14618 Courtesy of Ford Motor Co.

Fig. 17: Exploded View Of Forward Clutch Assembly

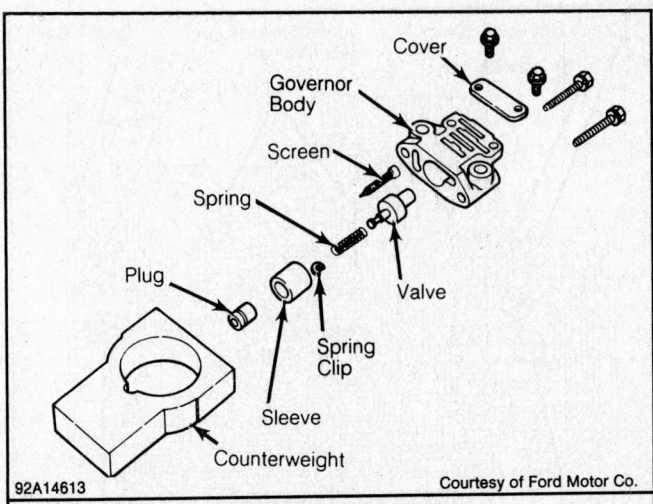

Fig. 18: Exploded View Of Governor Assembly

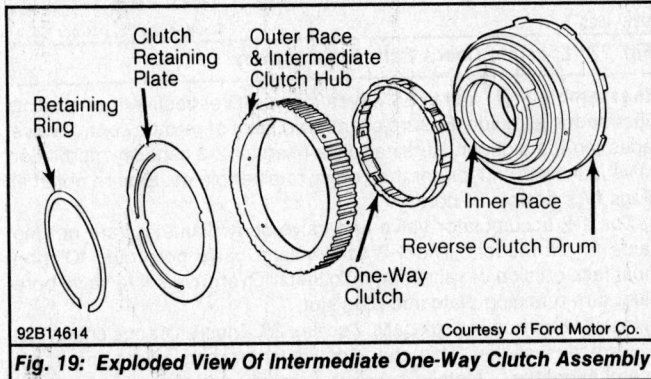

Fig. 19: Exploded View Of Intermediate One-Way Clutch Assembly

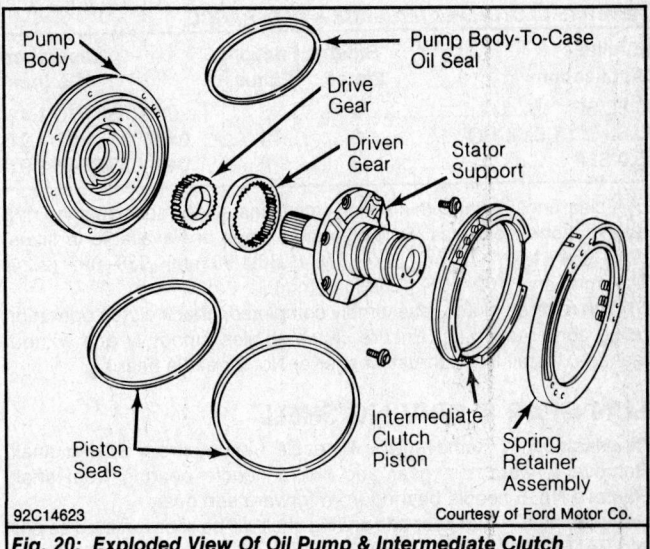

Fig. 20: Exploded View Of Oil Pump & Intermediate Clutch

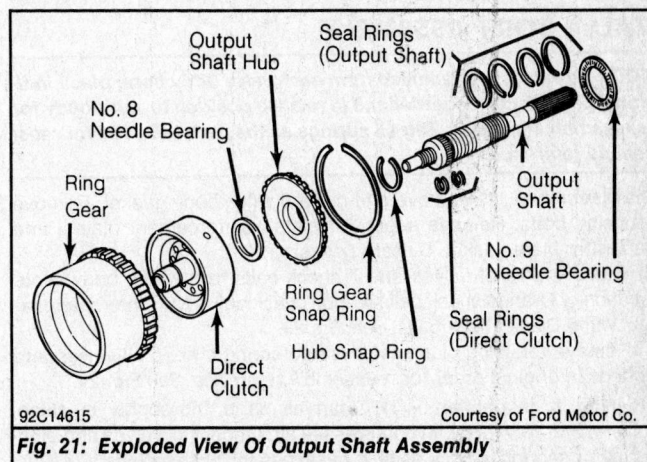

Fig. 21: Exploded View Of Output Shaft Assembly

NOTE: If a roller is damaged or lost, entire one-way clutch assembly must be replaced.

OIL PUMP & INTERMEDIATE CLUTCH PISTON

Disassembly – 1) Lift No. 1 thrust washer from stator support. Remove 4 seal rings from stator support. Remove pump body-to-case seal and discard. See Fig. 20.

2) Remove spring retainer assembly by carefully dislodging the tabs. Lift intermediate clutch piston from pump assembly. Remove retaining bolts and separate stator support from pump body. Remove drive and driven gears from pump body.

NOTE: Reverse clutch seal rings on stator support are larger than forward clutch seal rings.

Reassembly – 1) Install drive gear and driven gear into pump body with chamfer on both gears facing into pump body. Position stator support on pump body. Install and tighten retaining bolts to specification. See TORQUE SPECIFICATIONS. Install pump body-to-case seal around outer diameter of pump body.

2) Install NEW seals on intermediate clutch piston. Seal lips point away from spring posts. Coat piston seal and pump body sealing area with petroleum jelly. Use Seal Protector (T80L-77005-A) and install piston in pump body, ensuring piston bleed hole is located at 12 o'clock position (toward top of transmission case).

3) Snap spring retainer assembly into place on pump body using even pressure. Install seal rings on stator support. The 2 larger rings are installed closest to pump.

OUTPUT SHAFT ASSEMBLY

Disassembly & Reassembly – 1) Remove retaining ring and separate output hub assembly from ring gear. Remove direct clutch from ring gear and No. 8 needle bearing from rear of direct clutch.

2) Remove 4 output shaft seal rings and hub-to-shaft retaining ring. Separate hub from output shaft. Remove 2 direct clutch seal rings from end of output shaft. See Fig. 21. To reassemble, reverse disassembly procedure.

REVERSE CLUTCH

Disassembly – 1) Remove No. 2 needle bearing. Using a screwdriver, pry clutch pack retaining snap ring from clutch drum. Lift out clutch pack. See Fig. 22.

2) Compress return spring and remove waved snap ring. Remove return spring and thrust ring. Remove piston from drum. Remove seals from piston.

3) It may be necessary to apply compressed air to clutch drum lubrication hole to remove piston. Block remaining hole with finger.

Reassembly – 1) Prior to reassembly, ensure check ball in inner piston seal is free. Install NEW oil seal on piston. Coat seals and sealing surface in clutch drum with petroleum jelly.

2) Install piston into clutch drum using Inner and Outer Seal Protectors (T80L-77403-B and A) to prevent damaging seals. Seals used on reverse clutch piston are square cut; direction of installation is not important.

3) Install thrust ring and return spring. Compress return spring and install waved snap ring with points facing downward. Install apply plate into clutch drum with dished side facing piston. Install clutch pack and retaining snap ring.

4) Using a feeler gauge, measure clearance between clutch pack snap ring and pressure plate while pushing down on pressure plate. See REVERSE CLUTCH PLATE USAGE & CLEARANCE table.

REVERSE CLUTCH PLATE USAGE & CLEARANCE

Engine Application	Steel Plates	Friction Plates	Clearance In. (mm)
3.8L SFI	2	3	.030-.056 (.76-1.42)
3.8L SC & 5.0L HO	3	4	.040-.075 (1.02-1.91)
5.0 SFI	3	4	.040-.075 (1.02-1.91)

5) If clearance is not within specification, install correct size snap ring and recheck clearance. Selective snap rings are available in sizes; .060-.064" (1.52-1.73 mm), .074-.078" (1.88-1.98 mm), .088-.092" (2.24-2.34 mm) and .102-.106" (2.59-2.69 mm).

6) With reverse clutch reassembly completed, check clutch operation using compressed air. Ensure clutch applies smoothly and without leakage. Install No. 2 thrust washer or No. 2 needle bearing.

SUN GEAR & DRIVING SHELL

Disassembly – Remove No. 4 needle bearing from driving shell. Remove forward sun gear and No. 5 needle bearing from shell. Remove No. 5 needle bearing from forward sun gear.

Reassembly – Sun gear and driving shell will be reassembled as part of TRANSMISSION REASSEMBLY.

VALVE BODY ASSEMBLY

NOTE: As valves are removed from each valve body bore, place individual parts in correct order and in relative position to valve body for reassembly reference. Tag all springs as they are removed for reassembly reference.

Disassembly – 1) Remove and discard valve body gasket. Remove retaining bolts. Remove separator plate, reinforcement plates, and separator plate gasket. Discard gasket.

2) Remove 2 relief valves and 7 check balls from valve body. Note location of Orange check ball. Orange check ball is NOT interchangeable with 6 Black check balls. *See Fig. 23.*

3) Remove retaining plates, valves and springs. Keep all valves and springs in original order for reassembly reference. *See Fig. 24.*

Cleaning & Inspection – 1) Clean all parts thoroughly in clean solvent, and blow dry with compressed air. Inspect all valves and plug bores for scoring. Check all fluid passages for obstructions.

2) Inspect all mating surfaces, plugs, and valves for burrs and scoring. If necessary, use crocus cloth to polish valves and plugs.

3) Inspect all springs for distortion. Check all valves and plugs for free movement in their respective bores. Valves and plugs, when dry, must fall free of their own weight within their respective bores.

CAUTION: Avoid rounding off sharp edges of valves and plugs with crocus cloth. These edges perform a cleaning action.

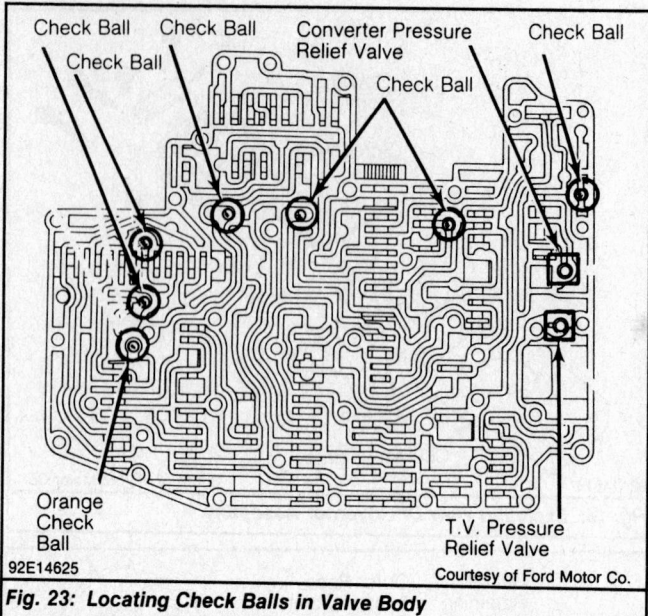

Fig. 23: Locating Check Balls in Valve Body

Reassembly – 1) Install all valves into their respective bores using illustrations as guide. Ensure chamfered stem of throttle control valve faces throttle plunger. Retainer plate used for 2-3 capacity modulator valve is thicker and longer than other retainer plates. Ensure notch in plugs face bottom of bore.

2) The 1-2 accumulator valve and valve body diameters are not the same for all models. The 1-2 accumulator valve bore plug "O" ring must face outside of valve body. To install Overdrive servo valve bore plug, turn retaining plate into plug slot.

3) Install valve body check balls. *See Fig. 23.* Ensure Orange check ball is correctly installed. This check ball is larger than others and is not interchangeable. Install pressure relief valves and springs. *See Fig. 25.*

4) Install Alignment Pins (T80L-77100-A) into holes. *See Fig. 26.* These 2 holes are smaller than other bolt holes to assure proper alignment of gasket and separator plate with valve body. These 2 holes also align valve body gasket and valve body assembly with case.

5) Using a NEW separator plate gasket, slide plate and gasket over alignment pins. Position 3 reinforcement plates and loosely install retaining bolts. *See Fig. 26.*

6) Loosely install detent spring guide bolt. Detent spring guide bolt is same length as short valve body-to-case retaining bolts. Starting at center (large) reinforcement plate and working outward, tighten retaining bolts to specification. See TORQUE SPECIFICATIONS. Remove alignment pins.

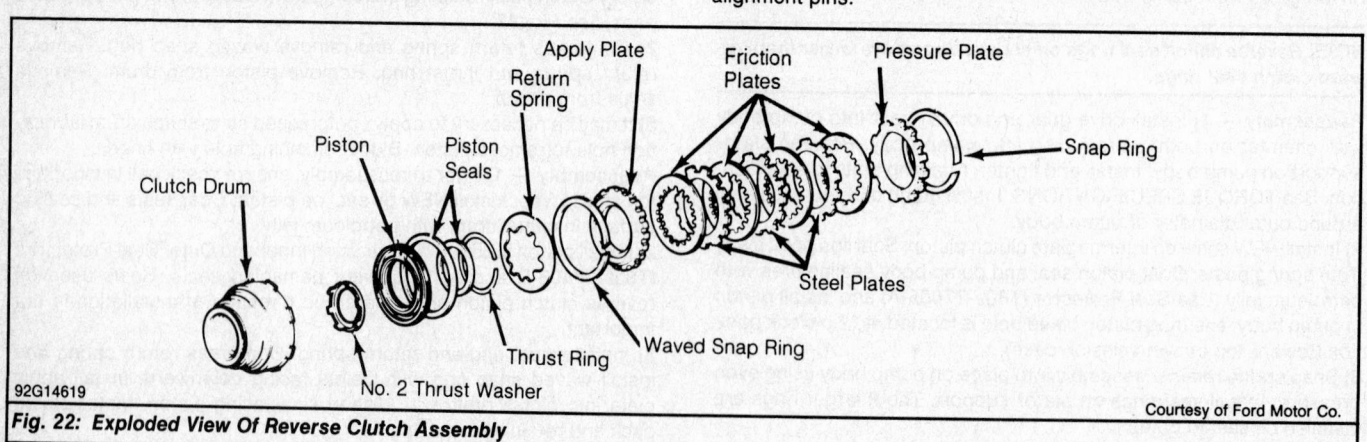

Fig. 22: Exploded View Of Reverse Clutch Assembly

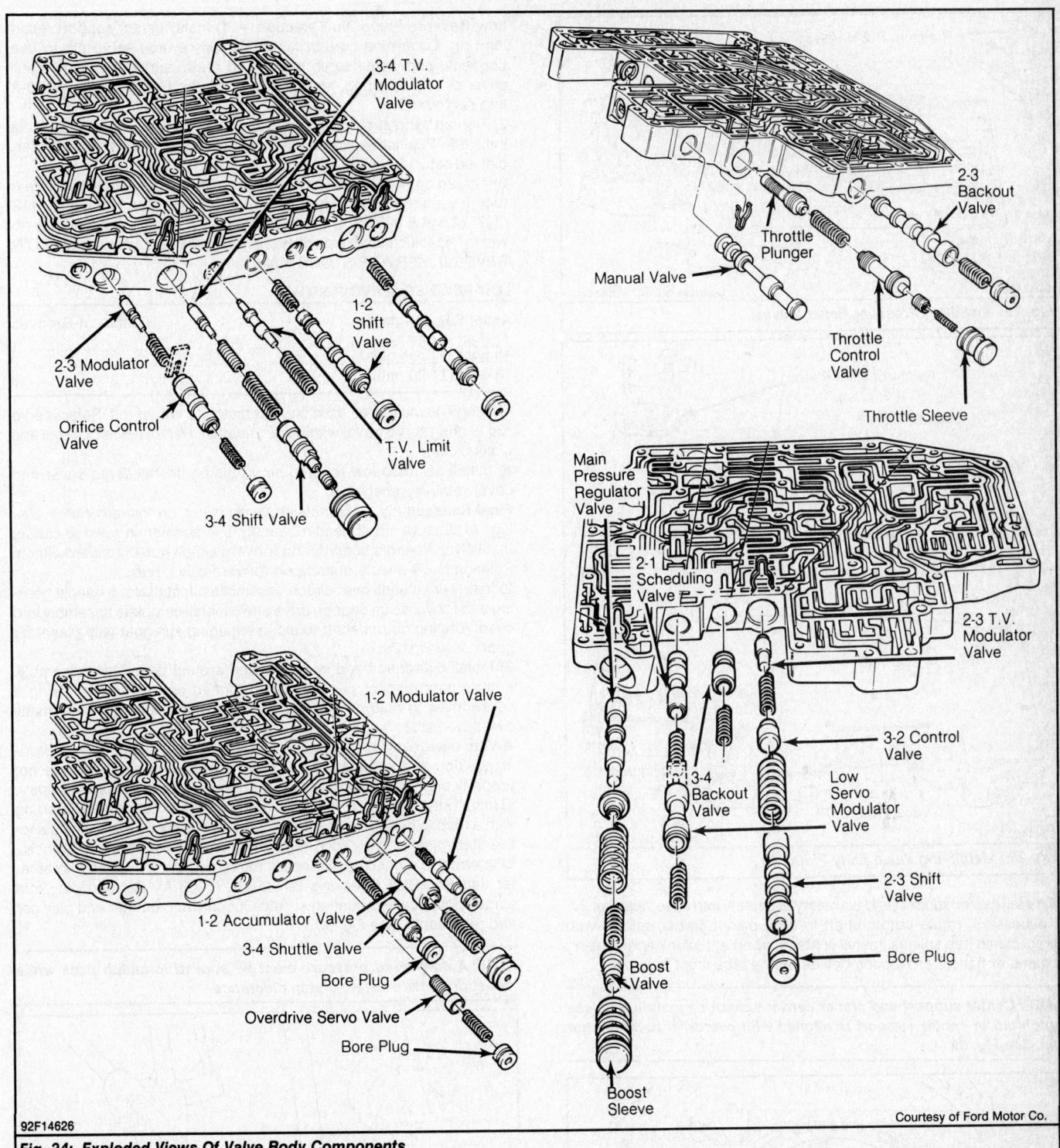

Fig. 24: Exploded Views Of Valve Body Components

92F14626

Courtesy of Ford Motor Co.

TRANSMISSION REASSEMBLY

NOTE: See Figs. 32 and 33 for exploded view of internal parts, thrust washer and needle bearing locations. Lubricate all parts with ATF. Use petroleum jelly on gaskets, thrust washers, and needle bearings to retain in place. Use NEW gaskets and seals.

Initial Reassembly – 1) Install No. 9 output shaft needle bearing in transmission case. Install bearing support, No. 7 needle bearing and direct clutch hub in direct clutch assembly. Assemble output shaft hub to output shaft and install retaining snap ring.

2) Place No. 8 needle bearing on rear of direct clutch drum. Slide output shaft into direct clutch drum. Attach output shaft hub to ring gear with retaining ring. Install output shaft, ring gear, and direct clutch assembly into transmission case.

3) Position governor drive ball in pocket on output shaft. Slide governor assembly onto output shaft with cover and attaching screws facing toward front of case. Ensure governor body is flush with counterweight. Install governor retaining snap ring.

4) Install low-reverse band into transmission case and ensure band is seated on anchor pins. When properly installed, center of band actuating rod seat can be seen through servo piston bore.

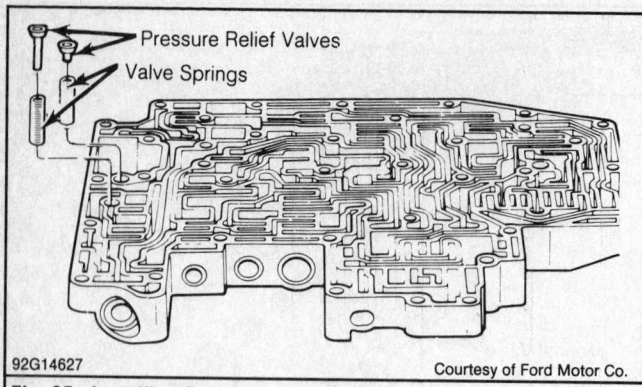

Fig. 25: Installing Pressure Relief Valves

Courtesy of Ford Motor Co.
92G14627

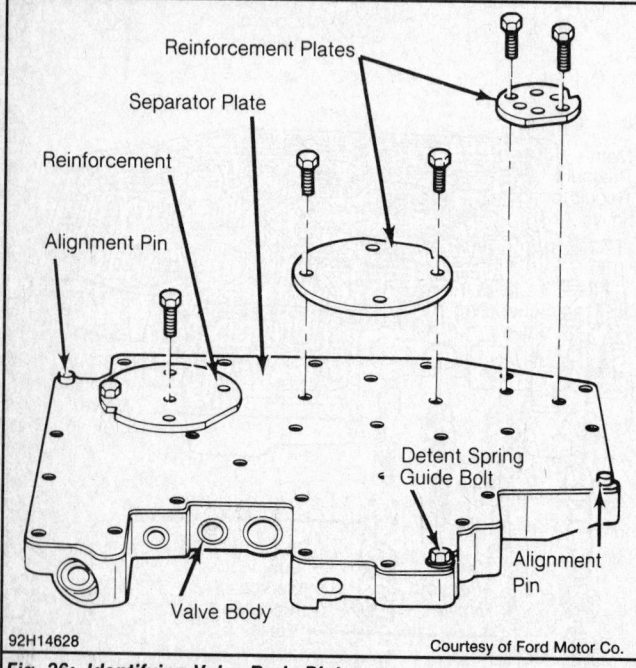

Fig. 26: Identifying Valve Body Plates

Courtesy of Ford Motor Co.
92H14628

5) Install center support and planetary assembly into case. See Fig. 27. If necessary, rotate output shaft to align planet carrier splines with direct clutch hub splines. Install center support anti-clunk spring using a hammer handle or wooden dowel. Spring tabs must face out.

NOTE: Center support and planet carrier cannot be installed unless notch cut in center support is aligned with overdrive band anchor pin. See Fig. 32.

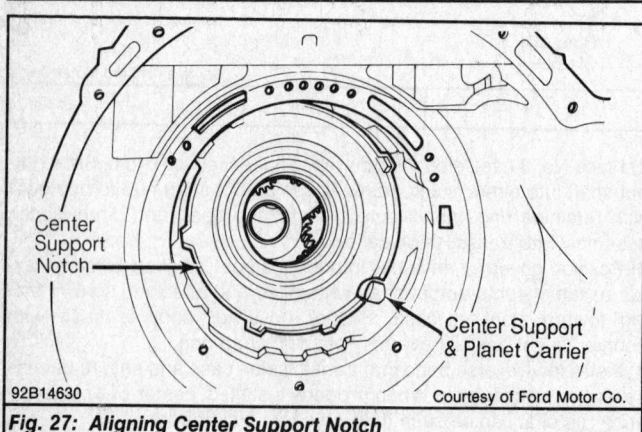

Fig. 27: Aligning Center Support Notch

Courtesy of Ford Motor Co.
92B14630

Low-Reverse Servo Pin Selection – **1)** Install center support retaining ring. Determine correct length of low-reverse servo pin to use. Lubricate and install servo piston and return spring. DO NOT install cover or retaining ring. Install Servo Selector Gauge (T80L-77030-A) into servo bore.

2) Tighten band apply bolt on tool to 50 INCH lbs. (5.6 N.m). Attach dial indicator. Position indicator stem on flat portion of servo piston. Zero dial indicator. See Fig. 28.

3) Thread bolt out of selector tool until piston stops against bottom of tool. Read amount of piston travel on dial indicator. If travel is .112-.237" (2.845-6.020 mm), correct servo pin is installed. If travel is not within specification, selective pistons are available. See LOW-REVERSE SERVO PISTONS table.

LOW-REVERSE SERVO PISTONS

Assembly Length	Number of Grooves
12.936" (74.57 mm)	1
12.989" (75.92 mm)	2
13.043" (77.29 mm)	3

4) Length is measured from base of piston to end of rod. Select servo rod to bring servo travel within specification. Remove selector tool and dial indicator.

5) Install selected low-reverse servo piston. Install servo cover and cover retaining snap ring.

Final Reassembly – **1)** Install reverse clutch on forward clutch. See Fig. 14. Ensure No. 2 needle bearing is in position in reverse clutch. Install No. 3 needle bearing and forward clutch hub in forward clutch. Position No. 4 needle bearing on forward clutch hub.

2) Install drive shell over clutch assemblies. Install No. 5 needle bearing and forward sun gear on drive shell. Install complete assembly into case, rotating output shaft to aid in engaging sun gear with planetary gears. See Fig. 29.

3) Install overdrive band into case and around drive shell assembly. Ensure band anchor is properly positioned on anchor pin. Using a screwdriver to hold overdrive band in position, lubricate and install overdrive servo.

4) With overdrive servo installed, inspect band and apply pin for proper position and engagement. If band anchor and apply pin are not properly engaged, remove servo and re-position band as necessary.

5) Install intermediate clutch pack pressure plate, clutch pack (starting with a friction plate and alternating steel and friction plates) and selective steel plate in this order. Measure intermediate clutch clearance.

6) Intermediate clutch clearance is measured using a depth micrometer and End Play Checking Bar (T80L-77003-A). Set end play tool across pump case mounting surface. Locate micrometer end play bar and read depth. See Fig. 30.

NOTE: A downward pressure must be applied to clutch pack while measuring intermediate clutch clearance.

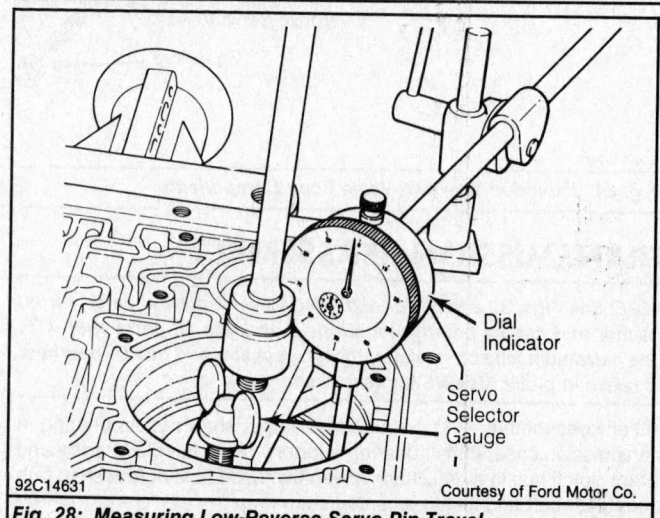

Fig. 28: Measuring Low-Reverse Servo Pin Travel

Courtesy of Ford Motor Co.
92C14631

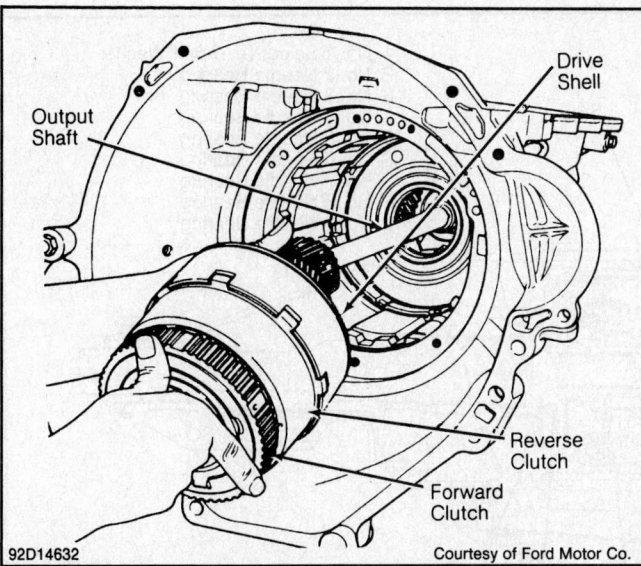

Fig. 29: *Installing Drive Shell & Clutch Assemblies*

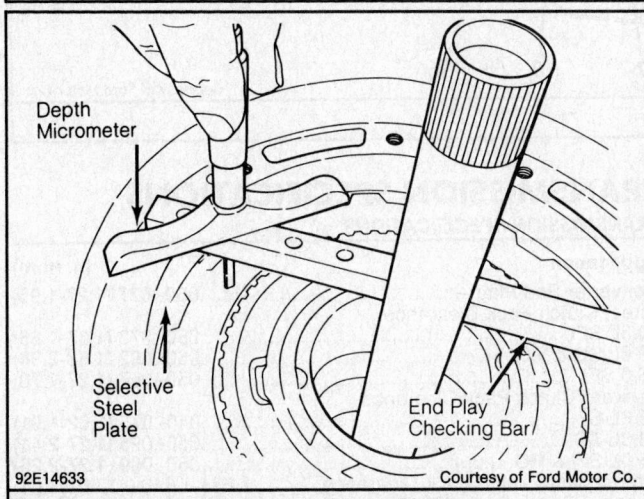

Fig. 30: *Measuring Intermediate Clutch Clearance*

7) Check depth again with micrometer 180 degrees opposite from previous measurement. Ensure depth at intermediate clutch selective steel plate is 1.634-1.636" (41.5-41.5 mm). Ensure average of the 2 measurements is within this range.

8) If intermediate clutch clearance (depth) is not within tolerance, select correct thickness steel separator plate. Selective plates are available in thicknesses of .067-.071" (1.70-1.80 mm), .077-.081" (1.95-2.05 mm), .087-.091" (2.20-2.31 mm) and .97-.101 (2.46-2.56 mm).

INTERMEDIATE CLUTCH PLATE USAGE

Application	Steel Plates	Friction Plates
All	3	3

9) Check transmission end play by locating depth micrometer on End Play Checking Bar (T80L-77003-A). Ensure depth is measured at reverse clutch drum thrust face. *See Fig. 31.* Standard end play is .004-.044" (.101-1.11 mm).

10) Check end play 180 degrees opposite end of reverse clutch drum thrust face to determine average depth. Thrust washer controlling transmission end play is located on stator support which is attached to back of pump housing.

11) Transmission end play can be adjusted using one of selective thrust washers available for service. After measuring depth, select required thrust washer. See END PLAY THRUST WASHER SELECTION table.

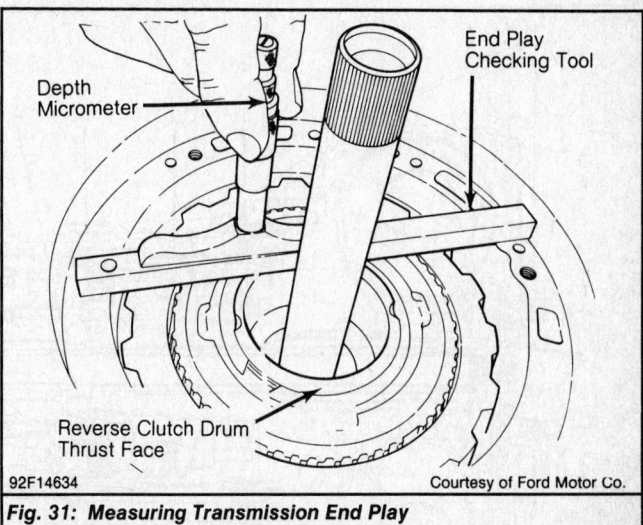

Fig. 31: *Measuring Transmission End Play*

END PLAY THRUST WASHER SELECTION

Measured Depth In. (mm)	Washer Thickness In. (mm)	Color Code
1.483-1.500 (37.67-38.10)	.050-.054 (1.27-1.37)	Green
1.501-1.517 (38.13-38.53)	.068-.072 (1.73-1.83)	Yellow
1.518-1.534 (38.56-38.96)	.085-.089 (2.16-2.26)	Natural
1.535-1.551 (38.99-39.40)	.102-.106 (2.59-2.69)	Red
1.552-1.568 (39.42-39.83)	.119-.123 (3.02-3.12)	Blue

12) Install selected transmission end play thrust washer on stator support. Use petroleum jelly to hold it in place. Install pump alignment dowel, made by cutting the head from a M8 x 1.25 bolt, into pump mounting bolt hole at 6 o'clock position.

13) Install new pump gasket into case. Install pump assembly into case using 2 slide hammers to lower pump into position. Remove alignment dowel. Coat all pump-to-case bolts with Loctite and install in case.

14) Alternately tighten bolts a few turns at a time to draw pump into case. Tighten bolts to specification. See TORQUE SPECIFICATIONS table. Install 2-3 accumulator assembly. Install 2 valve body Alignment Pins (T8OL-77100-A) into valve body.

15) Install valve body gasket and valve body assembly over pins. Ensure manual and throttle levers are properly positioned before installing valve body retaining bolts.

NOTE: Two different length valve body retaining bolts are used. Longer bolts are used at 4 front, 1 center and 3 rear locations.

16) Loosely install valve body retaining bolts. Starting at center and working outward, tighten bolts. Remove alignment pins and install bolts. Install detent spring and roller assembly and tighten bolts to specification. See TORQUE SPECIFICATIONS.

17) Position T.V. lever torsion spring against separator plate "V" notch. This spring pushes the throttle lever in direction of wide open throttle.

18) Install filter grommet, new filter gasket, and filter on valve body. Install filter attaching bolts and tighten. Position new pan gasket on case and install oil pan. Clean mating surface on transmission and extension housing. Position new gasket on transmission. Slide extension housing into place.

19) Clean bolts and case holes for 2 bottom bolts and lower right hand corner bolt (as viewed from rear of extension housing). Coat bolts with Teflon tape and install. Install remaining bolts and tighten to specification.

20) Slide direct drive shaft into turbine input shaft. Install torque converter. Ensure pump is fully seated.

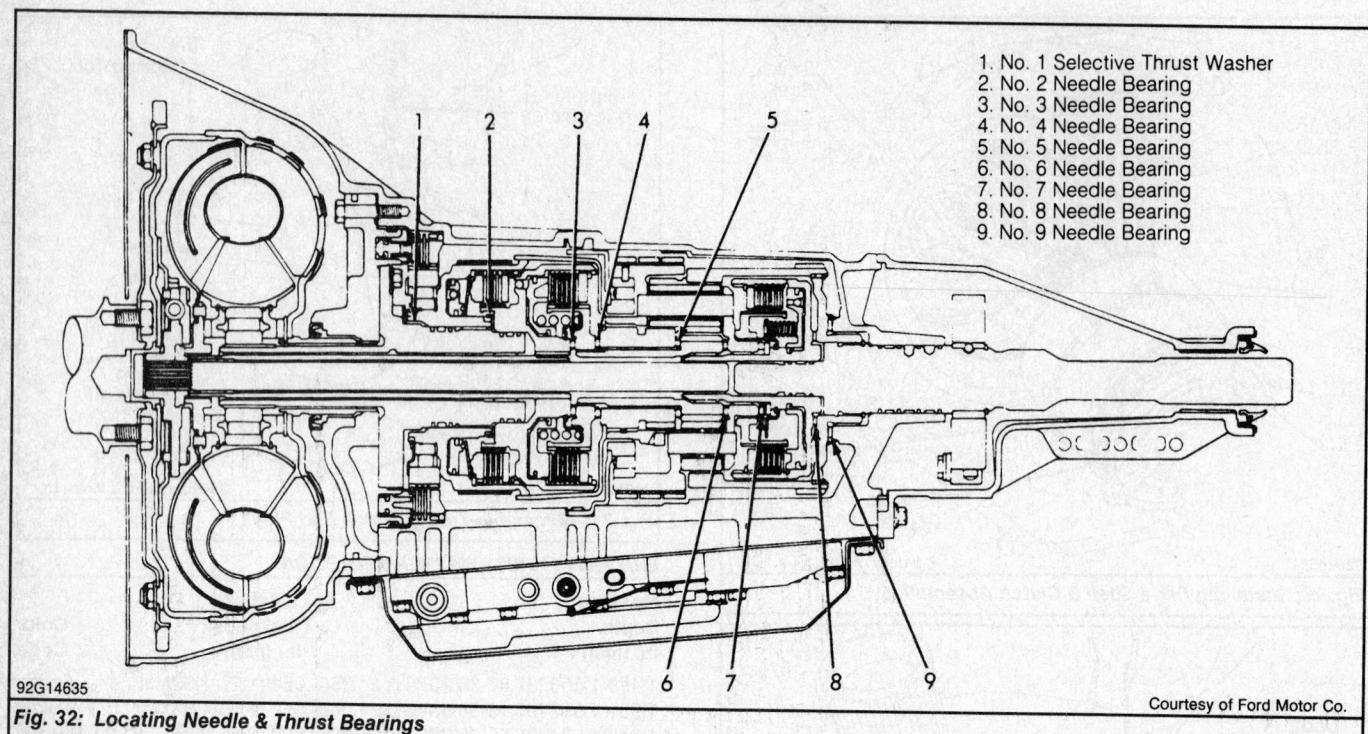

1. No. 1 Selective Thrust Washer
2. No. 2 Needle Bearing
3. No. 3 Needle Bearing
4. No. 4 Needle Bearing
5. No. 5 Needle Bearing
6. No. 6 Needle Bearing
7. No. 7 Needle Bearing
8. No. 8 Needle Bearing
9. No. 9 Needle Bearing

92G14635

Fig. 32: Locating Needle & Thrust Bearings

Courtesy of Ford Motor Co.

TORQUE SPECIFICATIONS
TORQUE SPECIFICATIONS

Application	Ft Lbs. (N.m)
Converter-To-Flywheel Bolt	20-34 (27-46)
Converter Housing Cover-To-Converter Housing	12-16 (16-22)
Converter Plug-To-Converter	8-28 (11-38)
Cooler Line-To-Case	18-23 (24-31)
Extension-To-Case Bolt	16-20 (22-27)
Inner Manual Lever-To-Shaft Nut	19-27 (26-37)
Outer Throttle Lever-To-Shaft Nut	12-16 (16-22)
Pump-To-Case Bolt	16-20 (22-27)
Stator Support-To-Pump Bolt	12-16 (16-22)
Stator Support-To-Pump Bolt	12-16 (16-22)
Transmission-To-Engine Bolt	40-50 (54-68)

Application	INCH lbs. (N.m)
Cover-To-Governor Body Bolt	20-30 (2.3-3.4)
Detent Spring Attaching Bolt	80-120 (9-14)
Filter-To-Valve Body	80-120 (9-14)
Governor Body-To-Counterweight Bolt	50-60 (6-7)
Neutral Start Switch-To-Case	95-130 (11-15)
Oil Pan-To-Case Bolt	72-120 (8-14)
Pressure Plug-To-Case	72-144 (8-16)
Reinforcing Plate-To-Valve Body Bolt	80-120 (9-14)
Separator Plate-To-Valve Body Bolt	80-100 (9-11)
Valve Body-To-Case Bolt	80-100 (9-11)

TRANSMISSION SPECIFICATIONS
TRANSMISSION SPECIFICATIONS

Application	In. (mm)
Converter End Play	.050-.077 (1.27-1.95)
Direct Clutch Pack Clearance	
3.8L SFI	.050-.073 (1.27-1.85)
3.8L SC & 5.0L HO	.060-.092 (1.53-2.34)
5.0 SFI	.050-.067 (1.27-1.70)
Forward Clutch Pack Clearance	
3.8L SFI	.040-.075 (1.02-1.91)
3.8L SC	.050-.095 (1.27-2.41)
5.0L SFI & HO	.050-.089 (1.27-2.26)
Intermediate Clutch Pack Clearance	1.634-1.646 (41.50-41.81)
Reverse Clutch Pack Clearance	
3.8L SFI	.030-.056 (.76-1.42)
3.8L SC & 5.0L HO	.040-.075 (1.02-1.91)
5.0 SFI	.040-.075 (1.02-1.91)

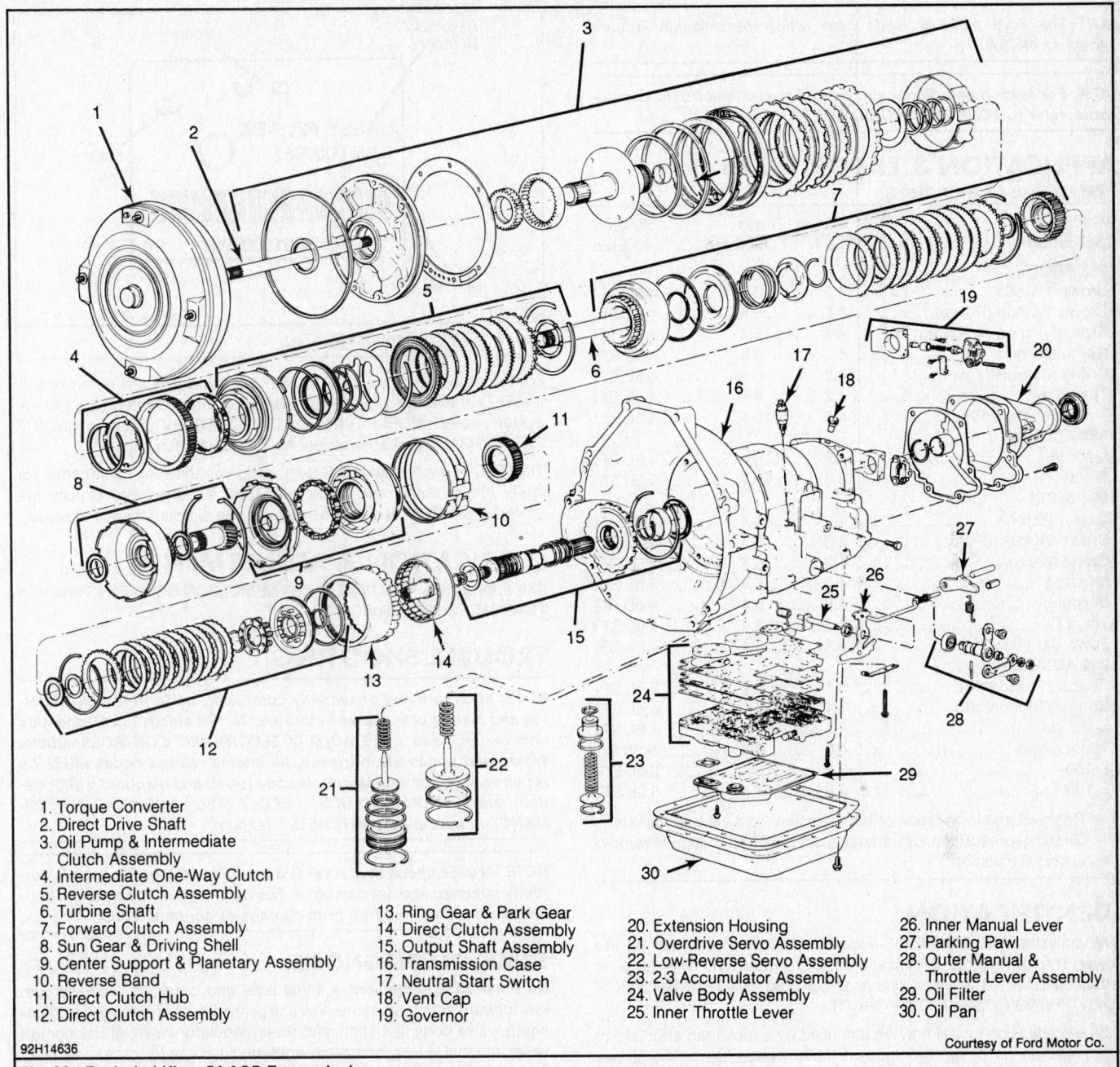

1. Torque Converter
2. Direct Drive Shaft
3. Oil Pump & Intermediate Clutch Assembly
4. Intermediate One-Way Clutch
5. Reverse Clutch Assembly
6. Turbine Shaft
7. Forward Clutch Assembly
8. Sun Gear & Driving Shell
9. Center Support & Planetary Assembly
10. Reverse Band
11. Direct Clutch Hub
12. Direct Clutch Assembly

13. Ring Gear & Park Gear
14. Direct Clutch Assembly
15. Output Shaft Assembly
16. Transmission Case
17. Neutral Start Switch
18. Vent Cap
19. Governor

20. Extension Housing
21. Overdrive Servo Assembly
22. Low-Reverse Servo Assembly
23. 2-3 Accumulator Assembly
24. Valve Body Assembly
25. Inner Throttle Lever

26. Inner Manual Lever
27. Parking Pawl
28. Outer Manual & Throttle Lever Assembly
29. Oil Filter
30. Oil Pan

92H14636

Courtesy of Ford Motor Co.

Fig. 33: Exploded View Of AOD Transmission

AUTOMATIC TRANSMISSIONS
Ford AODE & AODE-W

NOTE: The Ford AODE-W (wide gear ratio) transmission is also known as 4R70W.

NOTE: For testing and diagnostic procedures of electronic components, refer to AODE ELECTRONIC CONTROLS article.

APPLICATION & LABOR TIMES

APPLICATION & LABOR TIMES

Vehicle Application	Labor Times		Engine Size
	¹ R & I	² Overhaul	
1993 AODE			
Crown Victoria	4.2	6.4	4.6L SFI
Crown Victoria (Police)	4.2	6.4	4.6L SFI
Crown Victoria (Tow Pkg)	4.2	6.4	4.6L SFI
Grand Marquis	4.2	6.4	4.6L SFI
Grand Marquis (Tow Pkg)	4.2	6.4	4.6L SFI
Town Car	4.2	6.4	4.6L SFI
Town Car (Tow Pkg)	4.2	6.4	4.6L SFI
1993 AODE-W			
Mark VIII	4.6	6.4	4.6L SFI
E-150	3.8	6.4	5.0L SFI
1994 AODE			
Crown Victoria	4.2	6.4	4.6L SFI
Crown Victoria (Police)	4.2	6.4	4.6L SFI
Grand Marquis	4.2	6.4	4.6L SFI
Mustang	4.2	6.4	3.8L SFI
Mustang	4.6	6.4	5.0L HO
Town Car	4.2	6.4	4.6L SFI
Town Car (Tow Pkg)	4.2	6.4	4.6L SFI
1994 AODE-W			
Cougar/Thunderbird	6.4	6.4	3.8L SFI
Cougar/Thunderbird	6.4	6.4	4.6L SFI
Mark VIII	6.4	6.4	4.6L SFI
Thunderbird	4.6	6.4	3.8L SC
E-150	3.8	6.4	5.0L SFI
F-150	3.8	6.4	5.0L SFI

¹ – Removal and installation of transmission from vehicle chassis.

² – Bench overhaul time for transmission. DOES NOT include removal and installation.

IDENTIFICATION

Transmission AODE/AODE-W is identified by the code letter on the lower line of Vehicle Certification Label under TR. This label is attached to the left (driver's) side door lock post. See TRANSMISSION IDENTIFYING CODE LETTER CHART

The transmission model may be identified by a metal tag attached to transmission on passenger side of transmission case. Tag shows transmission model, assembly number, serial number and engine size. See Fig. 1.

TRANSMISSION IDENTIFYING CODE LETTER CHART

Application	Letter Identification
Cougar/Thunderbird	L
Crown Victoria, Grand Marquis Mustang & Town Car	P
Mark VIII	L
E, F Series	U

DESCRIPTION

AODE/AODE-W is a 4-speed, fully automatic transmission with electronic shift, converter clutch and line pressure controls. The AODE/AODE-W uses a double-pinion compound gearset to produce 4 forward speeds and reverse. The transmission uses 2 bands, 2 one-way roller clutches and 4 friction clutches to hold or drive the planetary gearset members. See Fig. 2.

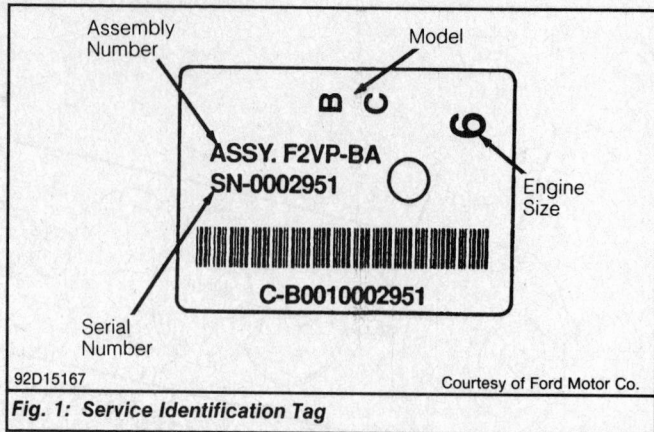

92D15167   Courtesy of Ford Motor Co.

Fig. 1: Service Identification Tag

Shift control solenoids provide gear selection and are controlled by the EEC-IV microprocessor. For additional information on the EEC-IV system, refer to SELF-DIAGNOSTICS – EEC-IV article in ENGINE PERFORMANCE of appropriate MITCHELL® manual.

The EEC-IV system has self-diagnostic capabilities. Fault codes for faulty engine and transmission sensors, switches and circuits are stored in the PCM and may be retrieved to aid diagnosis and repair.

LUBRICATION & ADJUSTMENTS

See appropriate AUTOMATIC TRANSMISSION SERVICING article in TRANSMISSION SERVICING.

TROUBLE SHOOTING

NOTE: After verifying driveability complaint, perform trouble shooting and testing procedures in this article. For electronic diagnostics and testing, see AODE/AODE-W ELECTRONIC CONTROLS article. When fault codes are retrieved, all engine related codes MUST be repaired first. For engine trouble code repair and diagnostic information, see SELF-DIAGNOSTICS – EEC-IV article in ENGINE PERFORMANCE in appropriate MITCHELL® manual.

NOTE: Always check fluid level and condition. Ensure linkage is correctly adjusted and not damaged. Ensure electronic component connectors are tight and free from damage or contamination.

SYMPTOM DIAGNOSIS

No Forward Engagement – Fluid level and condition, shift linkage, low forward clutch pressure, low line pressure, filter (plugged or damaged), valve body (3-4 shift valve, main regulator valve, orifice control valve, manual valve), incorrectly tightened valve body (cross-leaks), 2-3 accumulator, pump assembly, forward clutch assembly, low one-way clutch assembly (planetary) and output shaft.

No Reverse Engagement – Fluid level and condition, shift linkage, low reverse clutch pressure, low reverse band pressure, low line pressure, filter (plugged), valve body (No. 6 shuttle ball, manual valve, main regulator valve), 1-2 accumulator, incorrectly tightened valve body (cross-leaks), low reverse servo, pump assembly, reverse clutch assembly and low reverse band.

Harsh Reverse Engagement – Fluid level and condition, shift linkage, high line pressure, high Electronic Pressure Control (EPC) pressure, oil filter (plugged), valve body (No. 6 shuttle ball, No. 5 check ball, manual valve, main regulator valve), incorrectly tightened valve body (cross-leaks), low reverse servo, reverse clutch assembly and low reverse band.

Harsh Forward Engagement – Fluid level and condition, high forward clutch pressure, high line pressure, high Electronic Pressure Control (EPC) pressure, valve body (main regulator valve, 2-3 backout valve, 2-3 accumulator), incorrectly tightened valve body (cross-leaks), pump assembly and forward clutch assembly.

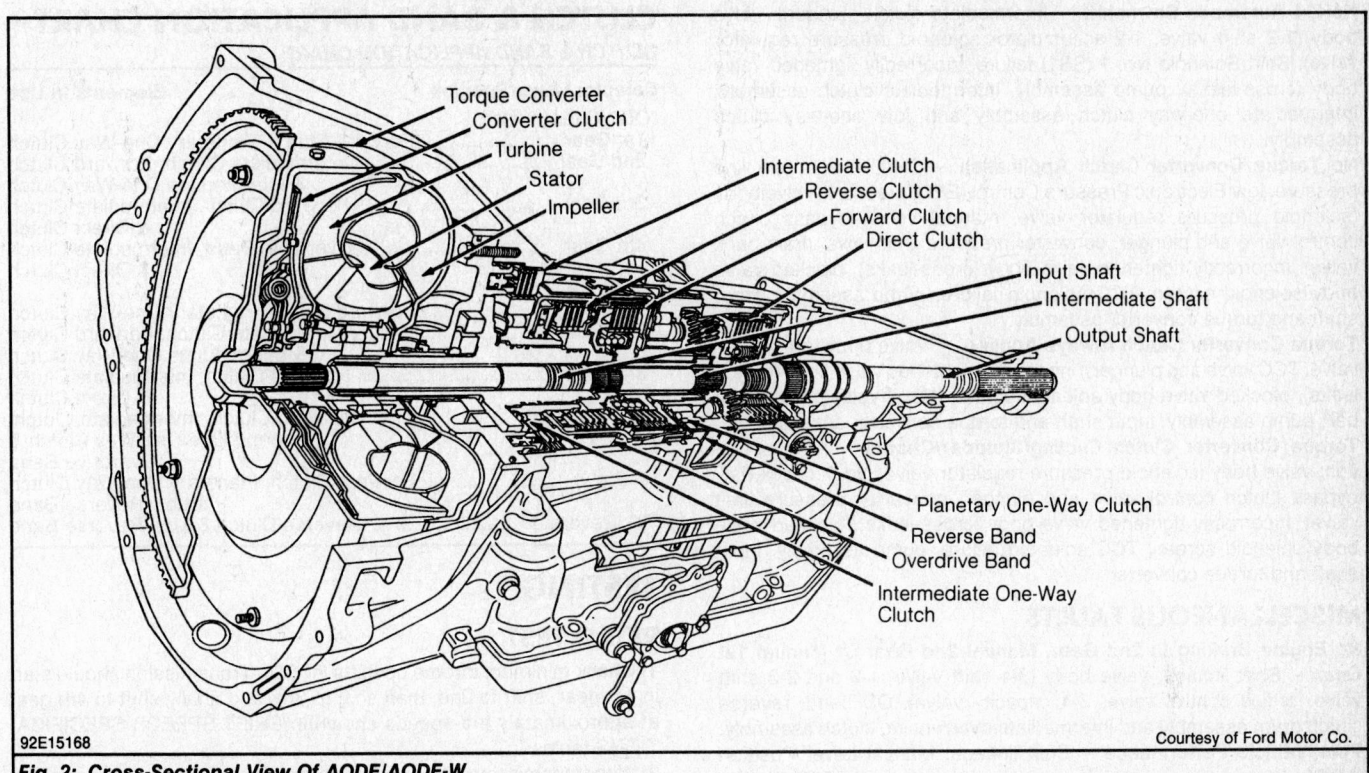

Torque Converter
Converter Clutch
Turbine
Stator
Impeller

Intermediate Clutch
Reverse Clutch
Forward Clutch
Direct Clutch

Input Shaft
Intermediate Shaft
Output Shaft

Planetary One-Way Clutch
Reverse Band
Overdrive Band
Intermediate One-Way Clutch

92E15168

Courtesy of Ford Motor Co.

Fig. 2: Cross-Sectional View Of AODE/AODE-W

Delayed/Soft Reverse Engagement – Fluid level and condition, shift linkage, low reverse clutch pressure, low reverse band pressure, low line pressure, filter (plugged), valve body (No. 6 shuttle ball, 1-2 accumulator, manual valve, main regulator valve), incorrectly tightened valve body (cross-leaks), low reverse servo, pump assembly, reverse clutch assembly and low reverse band.

Delayed/Soft Forward Engagement – Fluid level and condition, shift linkage, low forward clutch pressure, low line pressure, low Electronic Pressure Control (EPC) pressure, filter (plugged), valve body (3-4 shift valve, main regulator valve, orifice control valve), incorrectly tightened valve body (cross-leaks), 2-3 or 1-2 accumulator, pump assembly and forward clutch assembly.

Some Or All Shifts Missing – Fluid level and condition, shift linkage and Manual Lever Position (MLP) sensor.

Early/Late Shift Speeds – Incorrect tire size, incorrect axle ratio, fluid level and condition, line pressure, Electronic Pressure Control (EPC) pressure and valve body (EPC solenoid, miscellaneous components stuck, blocked solenoid screen).

Erratic/Hunting Shifting – Fluid level and condition, valve body (miscellaneous valves, accumulators-stuck), blocked valve body solenoid screen and Torque Converter Clutch (TCC).

Soft/Slipping Shift Feel – Fluid level and condition, low line pressure, Low Electronic Pressure Control (EPC) pressure, valve body (1-2 accumulator, 2-3 backout valve, main regulator valve, orifice control valve, overdrive servo regulator) and EPC solenoid (stuck).

Harsh Shift Feel – Fluid level and condition, high line pressure, high Electronic Pressure Control (EPC) pressure, valve body (1-2 accumulator, 2-3 backout valve, main regulator valve, orifice control valve, overdrive servo regulator) and EPC solenoid (stuck).

2nd Or 3rd Gear Starts In Drive (Or OD) – Shift linkage, Manual Lever Position (MLP) sensor, low reverse clutch pressure, low reverse band pressure, low line pressure and miscellaneous internal failures.

No Manual Low Gear – Shift linkage, Manual Lever Position (MLP) sensor, low reverse clutch pressure, low reverse band pressure, low line pressure, low Electronic Pressure Control (EPC) pressure, filter (plugged), valve body (No. 6 shuttle ball, manual valve, main regulator valve, low servo modulator valve), incorrectly tightened valve body (cross-leaks) and low reverse servo.

No Manual 2nd Gear – Shift linkage or cable, Manual Lever Position (MLP) sensor, valve body (orifice control valve, 3-4 shift valve, 1-2 and 2-3 shift valve, 3-4 capacity modulator valve) and incorrectly tightened valve body (cross-leaks).

No 1-2 Automatic Shift – Shift linkage, Manual Lever Position (MLP) sensor, intermediate clutch pressure, line pressure, valve body (1-2 shift valve, 1-2 accumulator valve), Shift Solenoid No. 1 (SS1) failure, damaged No. 8 check ball, incorrectly tightened valve body (cross-leaks), pump assembly, intermediate clutch assembly, intermediate one-way clutch assembly and low one-way clutch assembly.

No 2-3 Automatic Shift – Shift linkage, direct clutch pressure, valve body (2-3 shift valve, No. 1 or No. 3 check ball, solenoid pressure regulator valve, 2-3 backout valve, 2-3 modulator valve, orifice control valve), Shift Solenoid No. 2 (SS2) failure, output shaft seals, missing or leaking cup plug, 2-3 accumulator, blocked valve body solenoid screen, intermediate overrunning clutch assembly, direct clutch assembly and case (damaged output shaft seal area).

No 3-4 Automatic Shift – Shift linkage, Manual Lever Position (MLP) sensor, forward clutch pressure, direct clutch pressure, line pressure, valve body (3-4 shift valve, solenoid pressure regulator valve, OD servo regulator, 3-4 capacity modulator valve, 2-3 backout valve, orifice control valve, 1-2 and 2-3 shift valves), incorrectly tightened valve body (cross-leaks), Shift Solenoid No. 1 or 2 (SS1 or SS2) failure, OD servo cover, OD rod and piston cushion spring, No. 1, 2, 4 and/or 7 valve body check balls, blocked valve body solenoid screen, pump, OD Band and/or reverse clutch drum assembly, intermediate overrunning clutch assembly, forward clutch assembly and input shaft.

No 4-3 Automatic Downshift – Forward clutch pressure, line pressure, valve body (3-4 shift valve, solenoid pressure regulator valve, OD servo regulator, 3-4 capacity modulator valve, 2-3 backout valve, orifice control valve, 1-2 and 2-3 shift valves), incorrectly tightened valve body (cross-leaks), Shift Solenoid No. 1 (SS1) failure, OD servo, No. 1, 2, and/or 7 valve body check balls, blocked valve body solenoid screen, pump, OD Band and/or reverse clutch drum assembly, intermediate overrunning clutch assembly, forward clutch assembly and input shaft.

No 3-2 Automatic Downshift – Direct clutch pressure, valve body (2-3 shift valve, No. 1 or No. 3 check ball), Shift Solenoid No. 2 (SS2) failure, intermediate one-way clutch assembly and direct clutch assembly.

No 2-1 Automatic Downshift – Intermediate clutch pressure, valve body (1-2 shift valve, 1-2 accumulator solenoid pressure regulator valve), Shift Solenoid No. 1 (SS1) failure, incorrectly tightened valve body (cross-leaks), pump assembly, intermediate clutch assembly, intermediate one-way clutch assembly and low one-way clutch assembly.

No Torque Converter Clutch Application – Shift linkage, low line pressure, low Electronic Pressure Control (EPC) pressure, valve body (solenoid pressure regulator valve, manual valve, bypass clutch control valve and plunger, converter pressure limit valve, drain back valve), incorrectly tightened valve body (cross-leaks), blocked valve body solenoid screen, TCC solenoid failure, pump assembly, input shaft and torque converter assembly.

Torque Converter Clutch Always Applied – Valve body (drain back valve, TCC valve and plunger), incorrectly tightened valve body (cross-leaks), blocked valve body solenoid screen, No. 7 valve body check ball, pump assembly, input shaft and torque converter assembly.

Torque Converter Clutch Cycling/Shudder/Chatter – Fluid condition, valve body (solenoid pressure regulator valve, No. 7 check ball, bypass clutch control valve and plunger, converter pressure limit valve), incorrectly tightened valve body (cross-leaks), blocked valve body solenoid screen, TCC solenoid failure, pump assembly, input shaft and torque converter.

MISCELLANEOUS FAULTS

No Engine Braking In 2nd Gear, Manual 2nd Gear Or Manual 1st Gear – Shift linkage, valve body (3-4 shift valve, 1-2 and 2-3 shift valve, orifice control valve, 3-4 capacity valve), OD band, reverse clutch drum assembly and intermediate overrunning clutch assembly.

Poor Vehicle Performance – Shift linkage, Manual Lever Position (MLP) sensor, incorrect shift speed or engagement, TCC always applied and torque converter.

Transmission Overheating – Fluid level and condition, poor fluid flow (cooler lines, auxiliary oil cooler, engine performance, valve body (drain back valve, TCC control valve, converter limit valve) and torque converter.

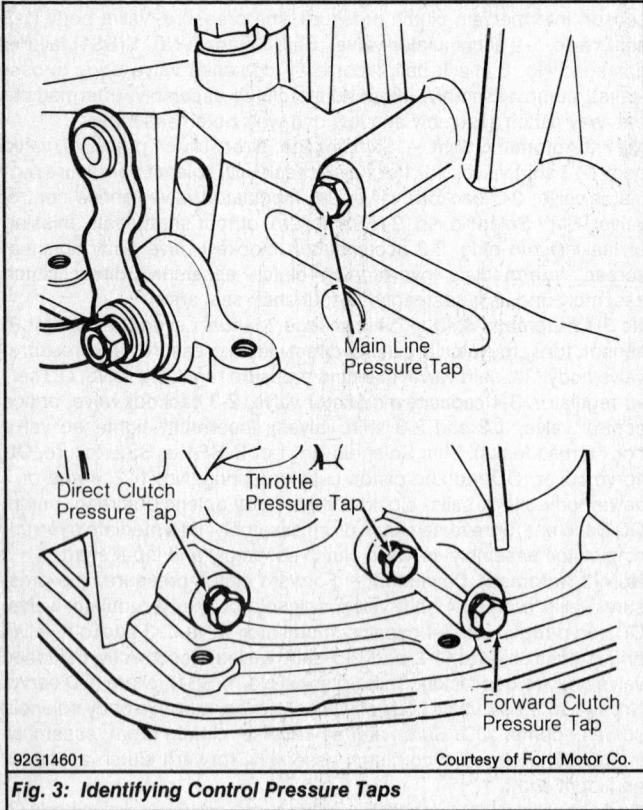

92G14601 Courtesy of Ford Motor Co.

Fig. 3: Identifying Control Pressure Taps

CLUTCH & BAND APPLICATION CHART

CLUTCH & BAND APPLICATION CHART

Selector Lever Position	Elements In Use
"OD" (Overdrive)	
1st Gear	Forward Clutch, Planetary One-Way Clutch
2nd Gear	Intermediate Clutch, Forward Clutch & Intermediate One-Way Clutch
3rd Gear	Forward Clutch, Intermediate Clutch & Direct Clutch
4th Gear	Overdrive Band, Intermediate Clutch & Direct Clutch
"D" (Drive)	
1st Gear	Forward Clutch, Planetary One-Way Clutch
2nd Gear	Interediate Clutch, Forward Clutch & Intermediate One-Way Clutch
3rd Gear	Forward Clutch, Intermediate Clutch & Direct Clutch
"2" (Downshift)	Forward Clutch, Intermediate Clutch, Intermediate One-Way Clutch & Overdrive Band
"1" (Low)	Forward Clutch, Planetary One-Way Clutch & Low Reverse Band
"R" (Reverse)	Reverse Clutch & Low Reverse Band

TESTING

ROAD TEST

1) Check minimum throttle upshifts in "OD". Transmission should start in 1st gear, shift to 2nd, then shift to 3rd, and finally shift to 4th gear at approximately the speeds shown in SHIFT SPEEDS SPECIFICATIONS tables.

2) With transmission in 4th gear (Overdrive), completely depress accelerator pedal. Transmission should downshift to 3rd or 2nd gear, depending on vehicle speed. The AODE/AODE-W will not make a 4th to 1st gear downshift. See SHIFT SPEEDS SPECIFICATIONS tables. The AODE/AODE-W will not shift into 4th gear at WOT.

3) Since closed throttle downshifts are extremely difficult to detect, it may be necessary to attach 0-100 psi (0-7.0 kg/cm²) pressure gauges to forward and direct clutch pressure taps in order to detect Overdrive to 3rd gear and 3rd to 2nd gear coast downshifts. See Fig. 3.

4) With gauges attached, a 4th to 3rd gear coast (closed throttle) downshift is detected by the application of the forward clutch. Pressure will increase from 0-60 psi (0-4.2 kg/cm²). The 3rd to 2nd gear downshift is detected by release of direct clutch pressure. Pressure will decrease from 60-0 psi (4.2-0 kg/cm²).

5) When selector lever is moved from either "OD" or "D" ranges to "1" position, transmission should downshift into 2nd gear if vehicle speed is above 25 MPH, and into 1st gear if speed is less than 25 MPH.

CONTROL PRESSURE TEST

NOTE: When testing line pressure, 2 readings must be taken: one at Idle position and the other at WOT.

1) Connect a 0-300 psi (0-21.1 kg/cm²) pressure gauge to main line pressure port tap on left side of transmission case just above control levers. See Fig 3. Gauge hose must be long enough to read gauge while operating engine.

2) Connect a 0-100 psi (0-7.0 kg/cm²) pressure gauge to throttle pressure tap at right side of transmission case. See Fig 3. Gauge hose must be long enough to read gauge while operating engine. Ensure shift linkage is properly adjusted.

CAUTION: Pressure gauges affect transmission shift quality. Do not accelerate or decelerate rapidly. Possible transmission failure could result.

3) With engine at normal operating temperature, apply parking and service brakes. Check line pressure and throttle pressure in all ranges. Pressure should be approximately as specified. See CONTROL PRESSURE SPECIFICATIONS table.

NOTE: Pressure test at idle position must be taken with engine at normal operating temperature. Pressure test at WOT position should be taken at full stall conditions. Run engine at a fast idle in "N" for 2 minutes to cool fluid between tests.

AODE CONTROL PRESSURE SPECIFICATIONS

Throttle Position	Line Pressure psi (kPa)	Throttle Pressure psi (kPa)
Idle		
Reverse Range		
Mustang	54-92 (372-634)	0-7 (0-48)
All Others	67-109 (462-752)	0-9 (0-62)
All Other Ranges		
Mustang	31-65 (214-448)	0-7 (0-48)
All Others	41-74 (283-510)	0-9 (0-62)
WOT@Stall		
Reverse Range		
Mustang	207-267 (1427-1841)	83-93 (572-641)
All Others	220-280 (1517-1931)	83-93 (572-641)
All Other Ranges		
Mustang	160-210 (1103-1448)	83-93 (572-641)
All Others	160-210 (1103-1448)	83-93 (572-641)

AODE-W CONTROL PRESSURE SPECIFICATIONS

Throttle Position	Line Pressure psi (kPa)	Throttle Pressure psi (kPa)
Idle		
Reverse Range		
Cougar/T-Bird [1]	60-104 (413-717)	3-13 (21-90)
Cougar/T-Bird [2]	54-92 (372-634)	0-7 (0-48)
Thunderbird SC	54-92 (372-634)	0-7 (0-48)
Mark VIII	54-92 (372-634)	0-7 (0-48)
E & F Series	54-96 (372-662)	0-9 (0-62)
All Other Ranges		
Cougar/T-Bird [1]	31-69 (214-476)	0-9 (0-62)
Cougar/T-Bird [2]	31-65 (214-448)	0-7 (0-48)
Thunderbird SC	31-65 (214-448)	0-7 (0-48)
Mark VIII	35-73 (241-503)	2-12 (13-83)
"E" & "F" Series	36-75 (248-448)	3-13 (21-90)
WOT@Stall		
Reverse Range		
All Models	207-267 (1427-1841)	83-93 (572-641)
All Other Ranges		
All Models	160-210 (1103-1448)	83-93 (572-641)

[1] – 3.8L engine.
[2] – 4.6L engine.

CONTROL PRESSURE TEST RESULTS

Low In "P" – Valve body loose, faulty main oil regulator valve sticking or low-reverse servo leakage.

Low In "R" – Reverse clutch or low-reverse servo leakage. Valve body loose.

Low In "N" – Loose valve body or main oil regulator valve sticking.

Low In O/D - Faulty forward clutch, Overdrive servo, main oil regulator valve or loose valve body.

Low In "D" – Forward clutch leakage. Overdrive servo leakage.

Low In "1st" – Leakage at forward clutch or low-reverse servo or overdrive servo.

Low At Idle In All Ranges – Low fluid level, restricted intake screen or filter, loose valve body bolts, pump leakage, case leakage, faulty valve body, excessively low engine idle, fluid too hot or main regulator valve sticking.

DIRECT CLUTCH PRESSURE TEST

NOTE: Shift quality is affected when test gauges are attached to transmission. DO NOT accelerate or decelerate rapidly during test. Transmission failure could result.

1) Attach pressure gauges capable of reading 300 psi (21.1 kg/cm²) to the forward clutch pressure tap and the direct clutch pressure tap. *See Fig. 3.* Mount gauges inside vehicle.

2) Drive vehicle. When pressure is applied to the direct clutch, note pressure difference between forward clutch pressure reading and direct clutch pressure reading.

3) If the difference is less than 15 psi (1.05 kg/cm²), direct clutch circuit is okay. If difference is greater than specification, there is a leak in direct clutch pressure circuit. Repair as necessary.

AODE SHIFT SPEED SPECIFICATIONS

NOTE: Shift speeds shown are approximate. All shift speeds may vary somewhat due to production tolerances and emission control equipment.

NOTE: To determine deceleration shift speeds, release throttle once transaxle has shifted into 4th gear (O/D). Manually downshift shift lever into next lower gear and record speed at which downshift occurs. Continue downshifting and recording vehicle speed until transaxle has downshifted into low gear.

3.8L MUSTANG (2.73 AXLE RATIO)

Operating Condition	Shift Speed MPH (km/h)
Closed Throttle	
1-2	11-14 (18-23)
2-3	19-22 (31-35)
3-4	38-44 (61-71)
4-3	27-25 (43-40)
3-2	16-14 (26-23)
2-1	9-7 (14-11)
Full Throttle (WOT)	
1-2	44-49 (71-79)
2-3	N/A
3-2	65 Max. (105 Max.)
2-1	35 Max. (56 Max.)

4.6L TOWN CAR (3.08 AXLE RATIO)

Operating Condition	Shift Speed MPH (km/h)
Closed Throttle	
1-2	9-12 (14-19)
2-3	13-17 (21-27)
3-4	33-38 (53-61)
4-3	33-31 (53-50)
3-2	14-12 (23-19)
2-1	9-7 (14-11)
Full Throttle (WOT)	
1-2	45-50 (72-80)
2-3	76-82 (122-132)
3-2	65 Max. (105 Max.)
2-1	38 Max. (61 Max.)

4.6L TOWN CAR (TOW PACKAGE – 3.55 AXLE RATIO)

Operating Condition	Shift Speed MPH (km/h)
Closed Throttle	
1-2	8-11 (13-18)
2-3	15-19 (24-31)
3-4	30-36 (48-58)
4-3	30-28 (48-45)
3-2	12-10 (19-16)
2-1	7-5 (11-8)
Full Throttle (WOT)	
1-2	42-47 (68-76)
2-3	68-74 (109-119)
3-2	60 Max. (97 Max.)
2-1	35 Max. (56 Max.)

4.6L CROWN VICTORIA/GRAND MARQUIS (3.08 AXLE RATIO)

Operating Condition	Shift Speed MPH (km/h)
Closed Throttle	
1-2	9-12 (14-19)
2-3	19-22 (31-35)
3-4	36-40 (58-64)
4-3	33-31 (53-51)
3-2	19-17 (31-27)
2-1	9-7 (14-11)
Full Throttle (WOT)	
1-2	46-51 (74-82)
2-3	78-84 (119-130)
3-2	65 Max. (105 Max.)
2-1	39 Max. (63 Max.)

4.6L CROWN VICTORIA/GRAND MARQUIS TOW PACKAGE (3.27 AXLE RATIO)

Operating Condition	Shift Speed MPH (km/h)
Closed Throttle	
1-2	8-11 (13-18)
2-3	18-21 (29-34)
3-4	35-38 (56-61)
4-3	34-32 (55-51)
3-2	18-16 (29-26)
2-1	8-6 (13-10)
Full Throttle (WOT)	
1-2	44-50 (71-80)
2-3	75-81 (120-130)
3-2	67-63 (92-102)
2-1	36-33 (58-53)

4.6L CROWN VICTORIA (POLICE – 3.27 AXLE RATIO)

Operating Condition	Shift Speed MPH (km/h)
Closed Throttle	
1-2	8-11 (13-18)
2-3	18-21 (29-34)
3-4	37-40 (59-64)
4-3	36-34 (48-51)
3-2	18-16 (29-28)
2-1	8-6 (13-10)
Full Throttle (WOT)	
1-2	43-49 (70-79)
2-3	75-81 (120-130)
3-2	70-66 (113-106)
2-1	38-35 (61-57)

5.0L MUSTANG (2.73 AXLE RATIO)

Operating Condition	Shift Speed MPH (km/h)
Closed Throttle	
1-2	12-15 (19-24)
2-3	23-26 (37-42)
3-4	41-45 (66-72)
4-3	28-26 (45-42)
3-2	17-15 (27-24)
2-1	9-7 (14-11)
Full Throttle (WOT)	
1-2	52-57 (84-92)
2-3	89-94 (143-151)
3-2	80 Max. (129 Max.)
2-1	45 Max. (72 Max.)

5.0L MUSTANG (3.27 AXLE RATIO)

Operating Condition	Shift Speed MPH (km/h)
Closed Throttle	
1-2	9-12 (14-19)
2-3	19-22 (31-35)
3-4	36-40 (58-64)
4-3	24-23 (39-37)
3-2	16-14 (26-23)
2-1	9-7 (14-11)
Full Throttle (WOT)	
1-2	39-44 (63-71)
2-3	74-79 (119-127)
3-2	68 Max. (109 Max.)
2-1	38 Max. (61 Max.)

AODE-W SHIFT SPEED SPECIFICATIONS

NOTE: Shift speeds shown are approximate. All shift speeds may vary somewhat due to production tolerances and emission control equipment.

NOTE: To determine deceleration shift speeds, release throttle once transaxle has shifted into 4th gear (O/D). Manually downshift shift lever into next lower gear and record speed at which downshift occurs. Continue downshifting and recording vehicle speed until transaxle has downshifted into low gear.

3.8L COUGAR/THUNDERBIRD (3.27 AXLE RATIO)

Operating Condition	Shift Speed MPH (km/h)
Closed Throttle	
1-2	8-14 (14-23)
2-3	18-23 (29-37)
3-4	28-36 (45-58)
4-3	32-28 (51-45)
3-2	16-12 (26-19)
2-1	10-6 (16-10)
Full Throttle (WOT)	
1-2	34-44 (55-71)
2-3	62-72 (100-116)
3-2	62-25 (100-40)
2-1	25-10 (40-16)

3.8L THUNDERBIRD SC (3.27 AXLE RATIO)

Operating Condition	Shift Speed MPH (km/h)
Closed Throttle	
1-2	7-10 (11-16)
2-3	16-20 (26-32)
3-4	31-34 (50-55)
4-3	32-30 (51-48)
3-2	18-16 (29-26)
2-1	9-7 (14-11)
Full Throttle (WOT)	
1-2	38-43 (61-69)
2-3	70-75 (113-121)
3-2	65 Max. (105 Max.)
2-1	27 Max. (43 Max.)

4.6L COUGAR/THUNDERBIRD (3.08 & 3.27 AXLE RATIO)

Operating Condition	Shift Speed MPH (km/h)
Closed Throttle	
1-2	10-13 (16-21)
2-3	19-23 (31-37)
3-4	32-37 (51-60)
4-3	33-29 (53-47)
3-2	19-18 (31-29)
2-1	12-9 (19-14)
Full Throttle (WOT)	
1-2	38-47 (61-76)
2-3	71-83 (114-134)
3-2	69-62 (111-100)
2-1	35-30 (56-48)

4.6L MARK VIII (3.07 AXLE RATIO)

Operating Condition	Shift Speed MPH (km/h)
Closed Throttle	
1-2	7-10 (11-16)
2-3	16-20 (26-32)
3-4	32-37 (51-59)
4-3	32-30 (51-48)
3-2	15-13 (24-21)
2-1	8-6 (13-10)
Full Throttle (WOT)	
1-2	50-55 (80-88)
2-3	94-100 (151-160)
3-2	76 Max. (122 Max.)
2-1	40 Max. (64 Max.)

5.0L E-150 (3.31 AXLE RATIO)

Operating Condition	Shift Speed MPH (km/h)
Closed Throttle	
1-2	8-12 (14-19)
2-3	16-22 (26-35)
3-4	35-40 (56-64)
4-3	35-29 (56-47)
3-2	16-12 (26-19)
2-1	9-5 (14-8)
Full Throttle (WOT)	
1-2	35-45 (56-73)
2-3	63-72 (103-116)
3-2	65-60 (105-97)
2-1	32-28 (51-45)

5.0L F-150 (2WD – 3.08, 3.31 & 3.55 AXLE RATIO)

Operating Condition	Shift Speed MPH (km/h)
Closed Throttle	
1-2	7-11 (11-18)
2-3	16-22 (26-35)
3-4	39-46 (62-74)
4-3	35-28 (56-45)
3-2	16-12 (26-19)
2-1	9-5 (15-8)
Full Throttle (WOT)	
1-2	36-43 (58-69)
2-3	69-76 (111-122)
3-2	65-59 (105-95)
2-1	34-28 (55-45)

5.0L F-150 (4WD – 3.31 & 3.55 AXLE RATIO)

Operating Condition	Shift Speed MPH (km/h)
Closed Throttle	
1-2	6-10 (10-16)
2-3	16-20 (26-32)
3-4	39-45 (64-72)
4-3	35-28 (56-45)
3-2	16-12 (26-19)
2-1	9-5 (14-8)
Full Throttle (WOT)	
1-2	36-40 (58-65)
2-3	65-75 (105-121)
3-2	65-58 (105-93)
2-1	33-28 (53-45)

STALL SPEED TEST

Testing Precautions – When performing stall test, do not hold throttle open longer than 5 seconds. Allow a cooling period of 2 minutes with transmission in "N" and engine speed at 1000 RPM between each test. If engine speed exceeds maximum limits shown, release accelerator immediately, as this is an indication of clutch or band slippage.

Testing Procedure – Bring engine to normal operating temperature. Apply parking and service brakes. Stall test transmission in each driving range at WOT. Note maximum RPM obtained. Engine speed should be within limits. See STALL SPEED SPECIFICATIONS table. If maximum RPM obtained is not within specifications, see STALL SPEED TEST RESULTS.

STALL SPEED SPECIFICATIONS

Application	Engine	RPM
AODE		
Crown Vic/Marquis	4.6L SFI	2326-2728
Crown Vic (Police)	4.6L SFI	2399-2811
Mustang	3.8L SC SFI	2189-2577
Mustang	5.0L HO SFI	2459-2904
Town Car	4.6L SFI	2326-2728
Town Car (Tow)	4.6L SFI	2397-2809
AODE-W		
Cougar & Thunderbird	3.8L SC SFI	2201-2579
Cougar & Thunderbird	4.6L SFI	1977-2337
Mark VIII	4.6L SFI	2343-2734
Thunderbird	3.8L SC SFI	1770-2086
E & F Series	5.0L EFI	2136-2488

STALL SPEED TEST RESULTS

High Stall Speeds Or Slip
- In "OD" or "D" position – Check planetary one-way clutch.
- In "OD", "D" and "1" position – Check forward clutch.
- In "R" position – Check reverse clutch and/or low-reverse band.

Low Stall Speeds
- Check engine tune-up.
- Check torque converter using bench test for stator one-way clutch slippage.

AIR PRESSURE TESTS

Test Procedures – **1)** A "No Drive" condition can exist even with correct transmission fluid pressure, because of inoperative clutches or bands. The inoperative units can be located by substituting air pressure for fluid pressure to determine location of malfunction.

2) Remove main control (valve body) assembly from transmission. See ON-VEHICLE SERVICE. Using attaching screws, install special adapter plate for AODE/AODE-W transmission and valve body gasket in place of valve body.

3) With a rubber-tipped air nozzle, apply air pressure into the appropriate locations specified in the following tests. *See Fig. 4.* If servo or accumulator does not move when air is applied, clean and inspect to locate cause. If during test 2 clutches apply or clutch fails to operate, check fluid passages in case and front pump for blockage or damage.

NOTE: Air pressure should be regulated between 40 psi (2.8 km/cm²) and 90 psi (6.3 km/cm²). Compressed air used for test should be filtered and dry to avoid contaminating transmission fluid.

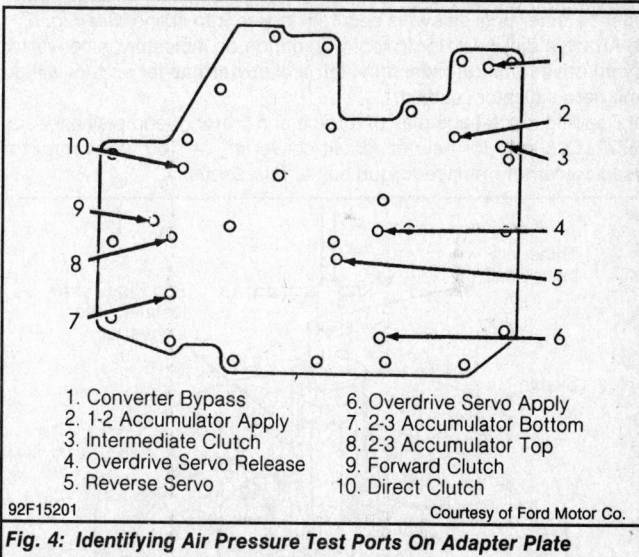

1. Converter Bypass
2. 1-2 Accumulator Apply
3. Intermediate Clutch
4. Overdrive Servo Release
5. Reverse Servo
6. Overdrive Servo Apply
7. 2-3 Accumulator Bottom
8. 2-3 Accumulator Top
9. Forward Clutch
10. Direct Clutch

92F15201   Courtesy of Ford Motor Co.

Fig. 4: Identifying Air Pressure Test Ports On Adapter Plate

Reverse Clutch – Apply air pressure to reverse clutch passage. A dull thud can be heard when clutch piston is applied, or movement can be felt by placing fingertips on clutch drum.

Forward Clutch – Apply air pressure to the forward clutch apply passage in the adapter plate. A dull thud can be heard when clutch piston is applied, or movement can be felt by placing fingertips on input shell.

Intermediate Clutch – Apply air pressure to intermediate clutch apply passage in the adapter plate. A dull thud can be heard or felt if clutch is operating properly.

Overdrive Servo – Apply air pressure to overdrive servo apply passage. Operation of the band is indicated by tightening of the band around reverse clutch drum. A thud can be felt on the servo cover when the servo returns to the release position as a result of spring force from the release spring. The band will then relax.

Low-Reverse Servo – Apply air pressure to low-reverse servo apply passage. A dull thud can be heard when the low-reverse band tightens around the planetary drum. Movement of the ring gear should also be detected.

Direct Clutch – Apply air pressure to direct clutch passage in the adapter plate. A dull thud can be heard or felt on the drive shaft if clutch is operating properly.

2-3 Accumulator – Apply air pressure to 2-3 accumulator passage. Accumulator piston should unseat and can be detected by inserting a metal rod into 2-3 piston hole. When piston unseats, rod will move.

TORQUE CONVERTER

NOTE: Torque converter is a sealed unit and cannot be disassembled for service. Replace if found to be defective. The following tests will identify a defective converter.

CONVERTER FLUSHING

Whenever transmission has been disassembled to replace worn or damaged parts or because valve body sticks due to foreign material, converter and oil cooler must be cleaned using a mechanically agitated Cleaner (Rotunda 1400028). Under no conditions should converter or oil cooler be cleaned by hand agitation using solvent.

LEAK TEST

If torque converter welds indicate leakage, attach Torque Converter Leak Detector (Rotunda 2100054) to converter and follow detector kit instructions.

END-PLAY CHECK

1) Insert Tester (T80L-7902-A) into converter pump drive hub until hub bottoms. Expand sleeve in turbine spline by tightening threaded inner post of tester until sleeve is securely locked into spline. *See Fig. 5.*

2) Attach a dial indicator to tool with button on indicator on converter pump drive hub. Zero dial face. Lift tool upward as far as tool will go and note indicator reading.

3) Reading is total end play of turbine and stator. If end play exceeds .077" (1.96 mm) for new or rebuilt converter, or .100" (2.54 mm) for used converter, replace torque converter assembly.

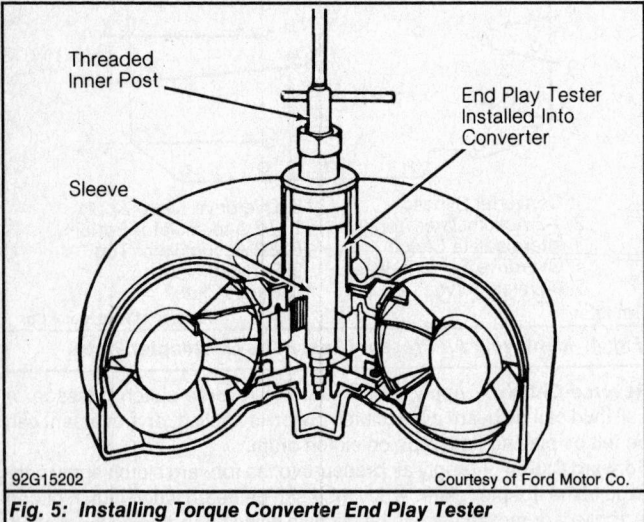

92G15202   Courtesy of Ford Motor Co.

Fig. 5: Installing Torque Converter End Play Tester

ONE-WAY CLUTCH CHECK

Insert fingers into torque converter. Attempt to spin the first splined segment. The segment should spin freely clockwise but not counterclockwise. One-way clutch should rotate freely in a clockwise direction only. If clutch fails to lock-up and hold as specified, replace torque converter.

STATOR INTERFERENCE CHECK

Stator-To-Impeller Interference Check – 1) Position stator support shaft on bench with spline end pointing up. Mount converter vertically onto shaft so support shaft splines engage one-way clutch splines. *See Fig. 6.*

2) While holding support shaft stationary, rotate converter counterclockwise. Converter should rotate freely without interference or scraping within assembly. Should interference or a scraping condition within converter exist or converter does not rotate freely, replace converter unit.

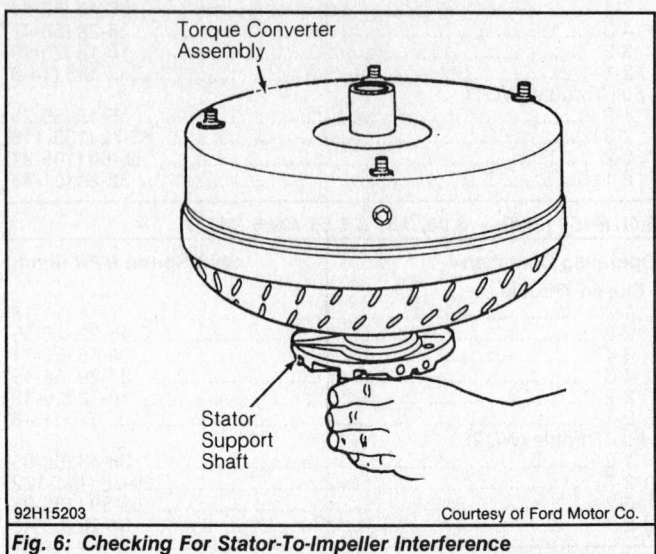

92H15203   Courtesy of Ford Motor Co.

Fig. 6: Checking For Stator-To-Impeller Interference

Stator-To-Turbine Interference Check – 1) Place converter on bench, front side down. Install stator support to engage mating splines of stator support shaft.

2) Install input shaft, engaging the splines with turbine hub. While holding stator shaft stationary, rotate turbine with input shaft.

3) Turbine should rotate freely in both directions without interference or noise. Torque required to turn shaft should not exceed 84 INCH lbs. (9.5 N.m) If interference or noise exists, stator front thrust washer may be worn and the converter should be replaced.

ON-VEHICLE SERVICE

VALVE BODY ASSEMBLY

Removal – 1) Raise and support vehicle. Remove exhaust system as necessary. Loosen oil pan retaining bolts and allow transmission fluid to drain. Remove oil pan and gasket. Discard gasket.

2) Remove transmission oil filter. Remove manual lever detent spring. Remove valve body bolts. Note position lengths of bolts for reassembly reference. Remove valve body and gasket from transmission.

Installation – 1) Using 2 alignment bolts as guides, position valve body (with new gasket) in case. Ensure check balls are in proper locations. Loosely install remaining valve body bolts. Install detent spring and roller.

2) Tighten valve body bolts to specification. See TORQUE SPECIFICATIONS. Install filter and grommet. Install pan gasket and oil pan. To complete installation, reverse removal procedure. Refill with fluid. Install exhaust system, if removed.

MANUAL LEVER POSITION (MLP) SENSOR

Removal – Raise and support vehicle. Disconnect linkage and electrical connector from sensor. Remove bolts and MLP from case.

Installation – 1) Install MLP onto transmission case and install bolts but do not tighten. Place manual lever in Neutral position (2 detent positions back from Park).

2) Insert Gear Position Sensor Adjuster (T71P-70010-A) into slots. *See Fig. 7.* Align the three slots on MLP with tabs on adjuster. Tighten bolts to specification. See TORQUE SPECIFICATIONS.

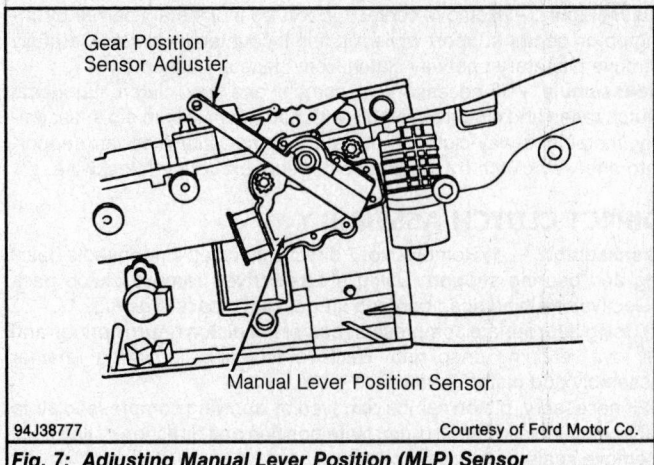

Courtesy of Ford Motor Co.

Fig. 7: Adjusting Manual Lever Position (MLP) Sensor

OVERDRIVE SERVO ASSEMBLY

Removal – Remove valve body, see VALVE BODY (MAIN CONTROL) ASSEMBLY. Locate overdrive servo. See Fig. 8. Using Servo Piston Remover/Replacer (T92P-70023-A), depress overdrive servo piston and remove retaining ring. See Fig. 9. Remove piston assembly and spring.

Installation – 1) Using ATF, lubricate overdrive servo pocket in transmission case. Assemble spring to piston. Install assembly into case pocket. Ensure servo rod contacts overdrive band apply pocket.
2) Using remover/replacer, depress piston and install retaining ring. See Fig. 9. Install valve body. To complete installation, reverse removal procedure.

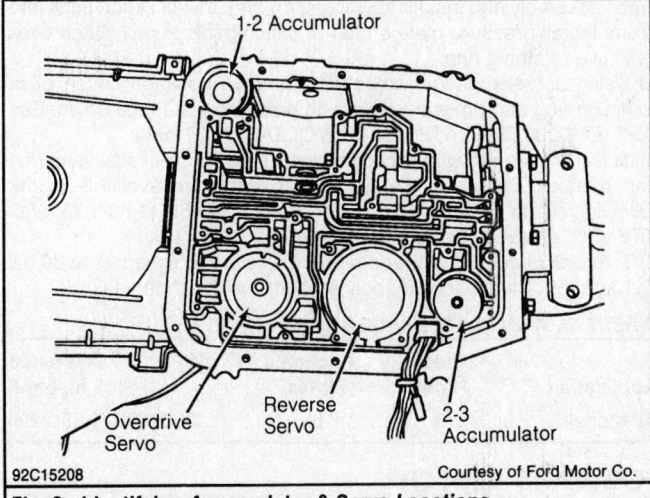

Courtesy of Ford Motor Co.

Fig. 8: Identifying Accumulator & Servo Locations

REVERSE SERVO ASSEMBLY

Removal – Remove valve body, see VALVE BODY (MAIN CONTROL) ASSEMBLY. Locate reverse servo. See Fig. 8. Using Remover/Replacer (T92P-70023-A), depress reverse servo piston cover and remove retaining snap ring and cover. Remove piston and spring from case.
Installation – To install, reverse removal procedure. Ensure servo piston is installed with the same length rod as was removed.

1-2 & 2-3 ACCUMULATOR PISTON

NOTE: Note location and number of springs during removal for reassembly reference.

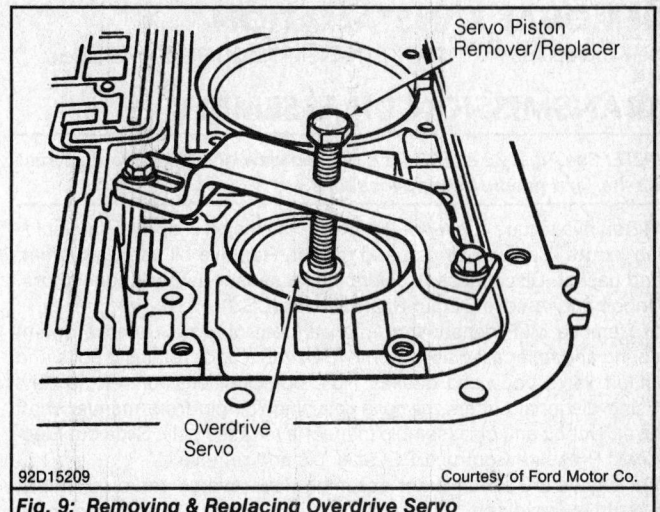

Courtesy of Ford Motor Co.

Fig. 9: Removing & Replacing Overdrive Servo

Removal – Remove valve body, see VALVE BODY (MAIN CONTROL) ASSEMBLY. Locate 1-2 or 2-3 accumulator. See Fig. 9. Using Remover/Replacer (T92P-70023-A), depress piston cover and remove retaining snap ring and cover or remove spring cover. Remove spring(s) and related components.
2) Remove accumulator piston (reverse snap ring pliers can be used, if necessary). Remove accumulator seals from piston.
Installation – To install, reverse removal procedure. Using ATF, lubricate piston seals and piston pocket in case prior to installation.

EXTENSION HOUSING BUSHING & REAR OIL SEAL

Removal – 1) Raise vehicle on hoist. Mark drive shaft yoke and axle companion flange for reassembly reference. Disconnect drive shaft from transmission. Remove oil seal using Puller (T74P-77248-A).
2) Remove bushing using Puller (T77L-7697-A), taking care not to damage output shaft splines.
Installation – Install new bushing into extension housing using Driver (T80L-77034-A). Install new seal into housing using appropriate seal installer. Coat inside diameter of rubber portion of seal and yoke splines with lubricant. Install drive shaft.

EXTENSION HOUSING

Removal – 1) Raise and support vehicle. Remove exhaust system components as necessary for access. Disconnect parking brake cable from equalizer (if equipped). Mark drive shaft yoke and axle companion flange for reassembly reference. Remove drive shaft and disconnect speedometer cable from extension housing.
2) Remove engine rear support-to-extension housing retaining bolts. Raise transmission just enough to remove weight from rear support. Remove rear support-to-crossmember retaining bolt and remove rear support.
3) Lower transmission and remove extension housing retaining bolts. Slide housing off output shaft and allow fluid to drain. Remove and discard extension housing-to-case gasket.
Installation – 1) Clean mating surface on transmission and extension housing. Position new gasket on transmission. Slide extension housing into place.
2) Clean bolts and case holes for 2 bottom bolts and lower right hand corner bolt (as viewed from rear of extension housing). Coat bolts with Teflon tape and install. Install remaining bolts and tighten all to specification. See TORQUE SPECIFICATIONS. To complete installation, reverse removal procedure.

REMOVAL & INSTALLATION

See appropriate AUTOMATIC TRANSMISSION REMOVAL article.

TRANSMISSION DISASSEMBLY

NOTE: See Figs. 22 and 23 for exploded view of internal parts, thrust washer and needle bearing locations.

1) Remove torque converter. Mount transmission in appropriate holding fixture. Remove oil pan and gasket. Remove oil filter, grommet, and gasket. Disconnect all solenoid and sensor harness connectors. Unbolt and remove Output Shaft Sensor (OSS).

2) Remove MLP sensor from manual control lever. Remove detent spring and roller assembly. Remove 24 valve body retaining bolts and lift off valve body and gasket. Note bolt positions for reassembly. Using diagonal cutters, remove retaining roll pin from manual shaft lever. Unbolt and disassemble manual lever assembly. Slide out Electronic Pressure Control (EPC) solenoid and remove.

3) Remove 2-3 accumulator assembly, low-reverse servo assembly, overdrive servo and 1-2 accumulator assembly by pushing down on servo covers and removing retaining snap rings. Note length of low-reverse servo piston rod for reassembly reference. *See Figs. 8 and 10.*

NOTE: Length of low-reverse piston rod may vary. Three possible rod lengths are available.

4) Remove oil screen. *See Fig. 10.* Remove retaining bolts and slide extension housing from transmission. Remove and discard housing-to-case gasket. Push transmission harness connector out through bottom of case.

NOTE: The output shaft may have shipping seal still attached. Remove and discard seal. Seal is not required for assembly.

5) Remove direct drive shaft by pulling it straight out from case. Remove pump body retaining bolts. Remove pump from case using 2 slide hammers installed in opposite pump retaining bolt holes. Remove pump-to-case gasket.

6) Grasp turbine shaft and pull intermediate clutch pack, intermediate one-way clutch, reverse clutch, and forward clutch from transmission case as an assembly. Disconnect overdrive band from anchor pins and remove band from case.

7) Remove forward clutch hub and No. 3 needle bearing as an assembly. Remove intermediate stub shaft. Rotate reverse clutch gear and shell to align indent with overdrive band anchor pin. Remove forward sun gear, No. 5 needle bearing, reverse sun gear and drive shell, and No. 4 needle bearing from case as an assembly.

8) Note position of center support snap ring tangs for installation reference. Remove snap ring. Using a screwdriver, pry anti-clunk spring from between center support and case. Prior to removal, note position of anti-clunk spring to ensure it is reinstalled correctly.

9) Remove center support and planetary carrier from case as an assembly. Remove reverse band from case. If direct clutch hub did not come out with planetary carrier, remove it from direct clutch.

10) Remove output shaft, ring gear, and direct clutch as an assembly through front of case. Remove output shaft No. 9 needle bearing from rear of case. Remove intermediate clutch pack from one-way clutch. Remove reverse clutch assembly from forward clutch assembly.

COMPONENT DISASSEMBLY & REASSEMBLY

NOTE: See Figs. 22 and 23 for exploded view of internal parts, thrust washer and needle bearing locations.

CENTER SUPPORT & PLANETARY ONE-WAY CLUTCH

NOTE: If a roller from planetary one-way clutch is lost or damaged, entire one-way clutch assembly must be replaced.

Disassembly – Remove center support from planetary carrier by lifting up on center support while rotating it counterclockwise. Carefully remove planetary one-way clutch from planetary assembly.

Reassembly – If necessary, assemble one-way clutch. Lubricate clutch races and clutch assembly with petroleum jelly to aid in assembly. Install one-way clutch in planetary carrier. Install center support into one-way clutch by rotating center support counterclockwise.

DIRECT CLUTCH ASSEMBLY

Disassembly – **1)** Remove No. 7 direct clutch hub inner needle bearing and bearing support. Using a screwdriver, remove clutch pack selective retaining snap ring and lift out clutch pack. *See Fig. 11.*

2) Using appropriate compressor, compress piston return springs and remove retaining snap ring. Remove tool and lift spring retainer assembly and piston from clutch drum.

3) If necessary, piston can be removed by applying compressed air to lubrication hole in clutch drum. Note position and direction of lip seals. Remove seals from drum and piston.

Inspection – **1)** Check piston check ball for freedom of movement. Check for leakage by turning piston upside down (flat side up), allowing check ball to seat in piston.

2) Pour small quantity of solvent over check ball. If solvent drips past check ball, replace piston.

Reassembly – **1)** Using Seal Protector (T80L-77234-A), install inner seal on clutch drum hub with sealing lip facing down into drum. Lubricate seals and seal protector with petroleum jelly prior to installation. Ensure inner seal is positioned in groove. Install outer seal on piston with lip pointing away from spring posts.

2) Coat piston seals, clutch drum sealing area, and piston inner seal area with petroleum jelly. Install piston into clutch drum using Seal Protector (T80L-77254-A) to prevent damaging seals.

3) Position piston spring and retainer assembly in clutch drum. Compress assembly and install retaining snap ring. Install clutch pack into drum. Install pressure plate on top of clutch pack. Install clutch pack selective retaining ring.

4) Using a feeler gauge, measure clearance between clutch pack retaining ring and pressure plate with pressure plate held down. See DIRECT CLUTCH PLATE USAGE & CLEARANCE table.

5) If clearance is not within specifications, install correct size snap ring and recheck clearance. Selective snap rings are available in the following sizes: .050-.054" (1.27-1.37 mm), .064-.068" (1.63-1.73 mm), .078-.082" (1.98-2.08 mm) and .092-.096" (2.34-2.44 mm).

6) To check clutch for proper operation, use compressed air at 30 psi (2.1 kg/cm²). Clutch should apply smoothly and without leakage.

DIRECT CLUTCH PLATE USAGE & CLEARANCE

Application	Steel Plates	Friction Plates	Clearance In. (mm)
All Models	6	6	.060-.092 (1.53-2.34)

FORWARD CLUTCH

Disassembly – **1)** Lift clutch hub and No. 3 needle bearing from forward clutch assembly. Using a screwdriver, pry clutch pack selective retaining snap ring from drum. Remove clutch pack. *See Fig. 12.*

2) Using appropriate compressor, compress piston return spring and remove retaining snap ring. Lift out retainer and return spring.

3) Remove clutch piston from drum. Note position of inner and outer piston seals, then remove seals. Ensure check balls in piston are move freely.

Reassembly – **1)** Lubricate and install inner and outer seals on piston with seal lips facing into clutch drum. Lubricate piston seals and drum sealing area with petroleum jelly. Install piston into drum using Seal Protector (T80L-77140-A) to prevent damaging seals.

2) Position return spring and retainer on piston. Compress return spring and install retaining snap ring. Install clutch pack into clutch drum starting with waved plate. Install clutch pack retaining snap ring. Using a feeler gauge, measure clearance between retaining snap ring and pressure plate with pressure plate held down. See FORWARD CLUTCH PLATE USAGE & CLEARANCE table.

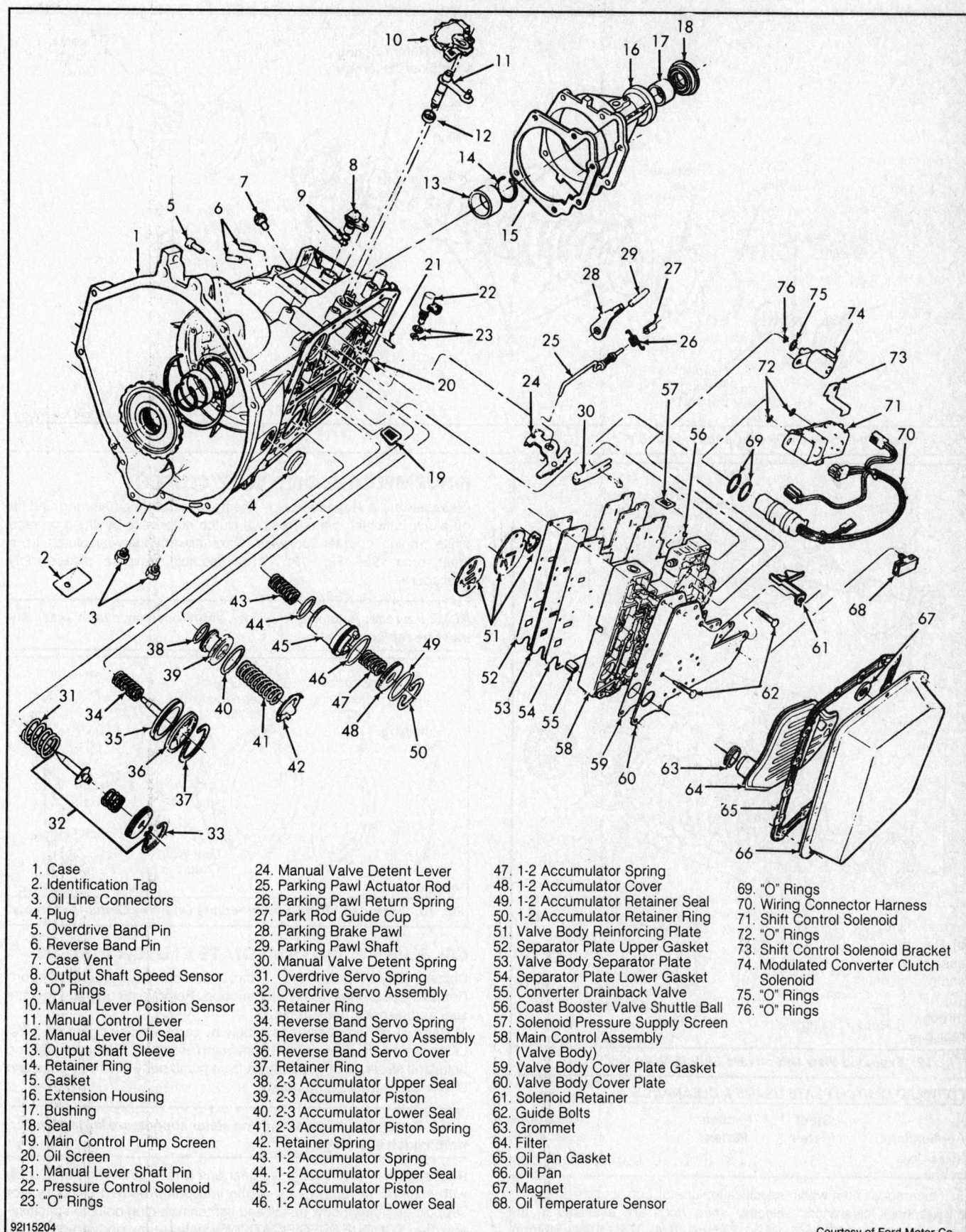

1. Case
2. Identification Tag
3. Oil Line Connectors
4. Plug
5. Overdrive Band Pin
6. Reverse Band Pin
7. Case Vent
8. Output Shaft Speed Sensor
9. "O" Rings
10. Manual Lever Position Sensor
11. Manual Control Lever
12. Manual Lever Oil Seal
13. Output Shaft Sleeve
14. Retainer Ring
15. Gasket
16. Extension Housing
17. Bushing
18. Seal
19. Main Control Pump Screen
20. Oil Screen
21. Manual Lever Shaft Pin
22. Pressure Control Solenoid
23. "O" Rings

24. Manual Valve Detent Lever
25. Parking Pawl Actuator Rod
26. Parking Pawl Return Spring
27. Park Rod Guide Cup
28. Parking Brake Pawl
29. Parking Pawl Shaft
30. Manual Valve Detent Spring
31. Overdrive Servo Spring
32. Overdrive Servo Assembly
33. Retainer Ring
34. Reverse Band Servo Spring
35. Reverse Band Servo Assembly
36. Reverse Band Servo Cover
37. Retainer Ring
38. 2-3 Accumulator Upper Seal
39. 2-3 Accumulator Piston
40. 2-3 Accumulator Lower Seal
41. 2-3 Accumulator Piston Spring
42. Retainer Spring
43. 1-2 Accumulator Spring
44. 1-2 Accumulator Upper Seal
45. 1-2 Accumulator Piston
46. 1-2 Accumulator Lower Seal

47. 1-2 Accumulator Spring
48. 1-2 Accumulator Cover
49. 1-2 Accumulator Retainer Seal
50. 1-2 Accumulator Retainer Ring
51. Valve Body Reinforcing Plate
52. Separator Plate Upper Gasket
53. Valve Body Separator Plate
54. Separator Plate Lower Gasket
55. Converter Drainback Valve
56. Coast Booster Valve Shuttle Ball
57. Solenoid Pressure Supply Screen
58. Main Control Assembly (Valve Body)
59. Valve Body Cover Plate Gasket
60. Valve Body Cover Plate
61. Solenoid Retainer
62. Guide Bolts
63. Grommet
64. Filter
65. Oil Pan Gasket
66. Oil Pan
67. Magnet
68. Oil Temperature Sensor

69. "O" Rings
70. Wiring Connector Harness
71. Shift Control Solenoid
72. "O" Rings
73. Shift Control Solenoid Bracket
74. Modulated Converter Clutch Solenoid
75. "O" Rings
76. "O" Rings

92I15204

Courtesy of Ford Motor Co.

Fig. 10: Exploded View Of AODE/AODE-W Valve Body, Servos, Accumulators & Case Components

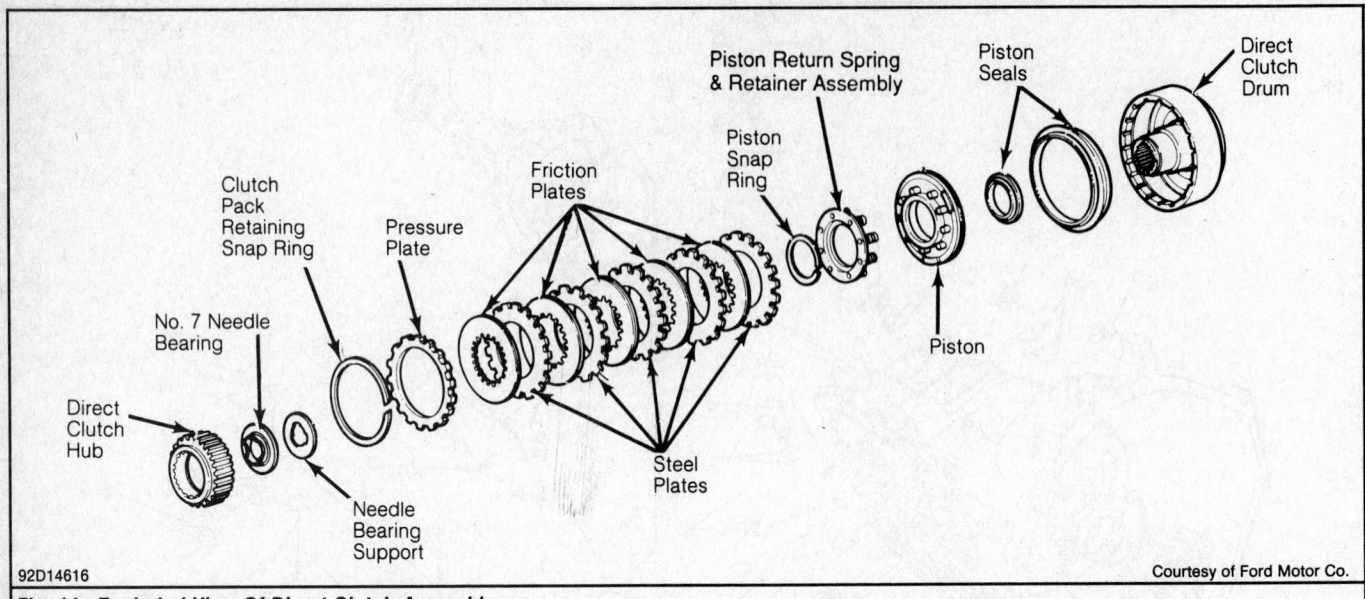

92D14616 · Courtesy of Ford Motor Co.

Fig. 11: Exploded View Of Direct Clutch Assembly

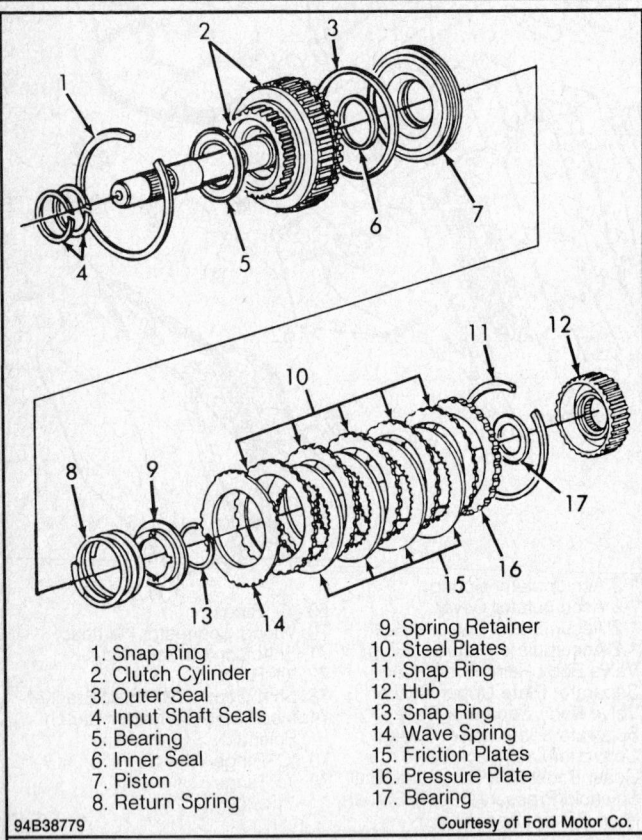

1. Snap Ring
2. Clutch Cylinder
3. Outer Seal
4. Input Shaft Seals
5. Bearing
6. Inner Seal
7. Piston
8. Return Spring
9. Spring Retainer
10. Steel Plates
11. Snap Ring
12. Hub
13. Snap Ring
14. Wave Spring
15. Friction Plates
16. Pressure Plate
17. Bearing

94B38779 · Courtesy of Ford Motor Co.

Fig. 12: Exploded View Of Forward Clutch Assembly

FORWARD CLUTCH PLATE USAGE & CLEARANCE

Application	Steel Plates	Friction Plates	Clearance In. (mm)
All Models	5	5	.050-.094 (1.27-2.38)

3) If clearance is not within specification, install correct size snap ring and recheck clearance. Selective snap rings are available in the following sizes: .060-.064" (1.52-1.73 mm), .074-.078" (1.88-1.98 mm), .086-.092" (2.23-2.34 mm) and .102-.106" (2.59-2.69 mm).

4) With reassembly completed, use compressed air and check forward clutch operation. Clutch should apply smoothly and without leakage.

INTERMEDIATE ONE-WAY CLUTCH

Disassembly & Reassembly – Remove clutch retaining ring and lift off clutch retaining plate. Remove clutch outer race by lifting on race while turning counterclockwise. Carefully lift one-way clutch from inner race. See Fig. 13. To reassemble, reverse disassembly procedure.

NOTE: If a roller is damaged or lost, entire one-way clutch assembly must be replaced.

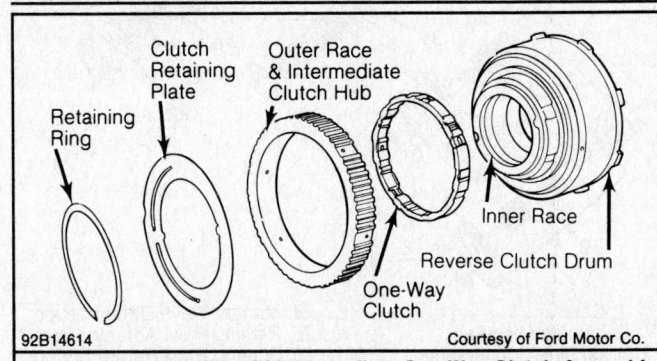

92B14614 · Courtesy of Ford Motor Co.

Fig. 13: Exploded View Of Intermediate One-Way Clutch Assembly

OIL PUMP & INTERMEDIATE CLUTCH PISTON

Disassembly – 1) Lift No. 1 thrust washer from stator support. Remove 4 seal rings from stator support. Remove pump body-to-case seal and discard. See Fig. 14.

2) Remove spring retainer assembly by carefully dislodging the tabs. Lift intermediate clutch piston from pump assembly. Remove retaining bolts and separate stator support from pump body. Remove drive and driven gears from pump body.

NOTE: Reverse clutch seal rings on stator support are larger than forward clutch seal rings.

Reassembly – 1) Install drive gear and driven gear into pump body with chamfer on both gears facing into pump body. Position stator support on pump body. Install and tighten retaining bolts to specification. See TORQUE SPECIFICATIONS. Install pump body-to-case seal around outer diameter of pump body.

2) Install NEW seals on intermediate clutch piston. Seal lips point away from spring posts. Coat piston seal and pump body sealing area with petroleum jelly. Use Seal Protector (T80L-77005-A) and install piston in pump body, ensuring piston bleed hole is located at 12 o'clock position (toward top of transmission case).

3) Snap spring retainer assembly into place on pump body using even pressure. Install seal rings on stator support. The 2 larger rings are installed closest to pump.

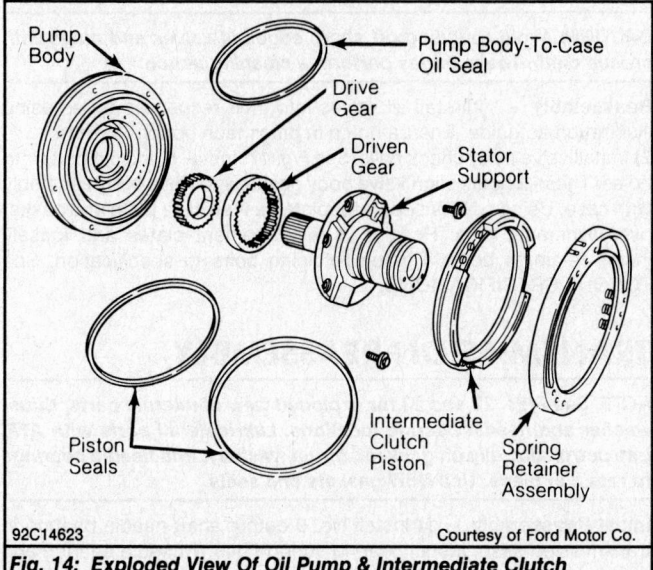

Fig. 14: **Exploded View Of Oil Pump & Intermediate Clutch**

92C14623   Courtesy of Ford Motor Co.

OUTPUT SHAFT ASSEMBLY

Disassembly & Reassembly – **1)** Remove retaining ring and separate output hub assembly from ring gear. Remove direct clutch from ring gear and No. 8 needle bearing from rear of direct clutch.

2) Remove 4 output shaft seal rings and hub-to-shaft retaining ring. Separate hub from output shaft. Remove 2 direct clutch seal rings from end of output shaft. *See Fig. 15.* To reassemble, reverse disassembly procedure.

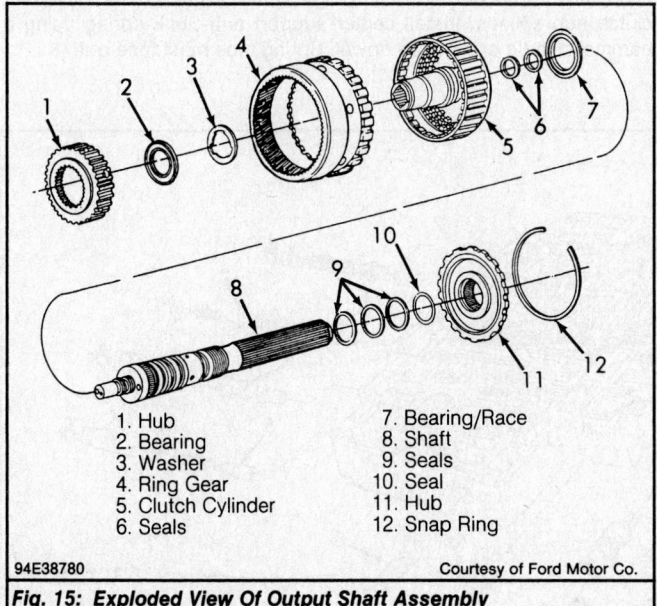

1. Hub
2. Bearing
3. Washer
4. Ring Gear
5. Clutch Cylinder
6. Seals
7. Bearing/Race
8. Shaft
9. Seals
10. Seal
11. Hub
12. Snap Ring

94E38780   Courtesy of Ford Motor Co.

Fig. 15: **Exploded View Of Output Shaft Assembly**

REVERSE CLUTCH

Disassembly – **1)** Remove No. 2 needle bearing. Using a screwdriver, pry clutch pack retaining snap ring from clutch drum. Lift out clutch pack. *See Fig. 16.*

2) Compress return spring and remove waved snap ring. Remove return spring and thrust ring. Remove piston from drum. Remove seals from piston.

3) It may be necessary to apply compressed air to clutch drum lubrication hole to remove piston. Block remaining hole with finger.

Reassembly – **1)** Prior to reassembly, ensure check ball in inner piston seal is free. Install NEW oil seal on piston. Coat seals and sealing surface in clutch drum with petroleum jelly.

2) Install piston into clutch drum using Inner and Outer Seal Protectors (T80L-77403-B and A) to prevent damaging seals. Seals used on reverse clutch piston are square cut; direction of installation is not important.

3) Install thrust ring and return spring. Compress return spring and install waved snap ring with points facing downward. Install apply plate into clutch drum with dished side facing piston. Install clutch pack and retaining snap ring.

4) Using a feeler gauge, measure clearance between clutch pack snap ring and pressure plate while pushing down on pressure plate. See REVERSE CLUTCH PLATE USAGE & CLEARANCE table.

REVERSE CLUTCH PLATE USAGE & CLEARANCE

Application	Steel Plates	Friction Plates	Clearance In. (mm)
All Models	3	4	.040-.060 (1.02-1.52)

5) If clearance is not within specification, install correct size snap ring and recheck clearance. Selective snap rings are available in sizes; .060-.064" (1.52-1.73 mm), .074-.078" (1.88-1.98 mm), .088-.092" (2.24-2.34 mm) and .102-.106" (2.59-2.69 mm).

6) With reverse clutch reassembly completed, check clutch operation using compressed air. Ensure clutch applies smoothly and without leakage. Install No. 2 thrust washer or No. 2 needle bearing.

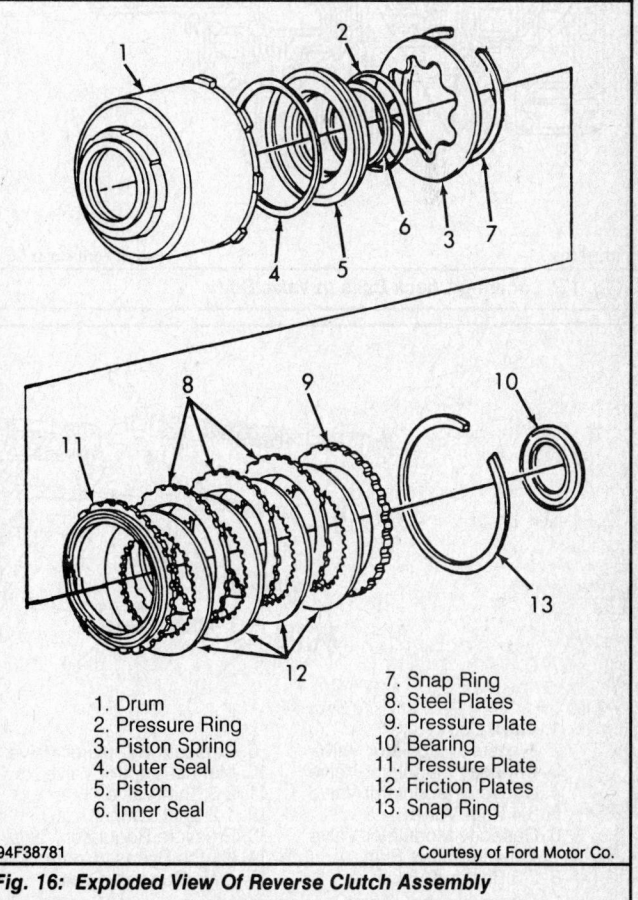

1. Drum
2. Pressure Ring
3. Piston Spring
4. Outer Seal
5. Piston
6. Inner Seal
7. Snap Ring
8. Steel Plates
9. Pressure Plate
10. Bearing
11. Pressure Plate
12. Friction Plates
13. Snap Ring

94F38781   Courtesy of Ford Motor Co.

Fig. 16: **Exploded View Of Reverse Clutch Assembly**

SUN GEAR & DRIVING SHELL

Disassembly – Remove No. 4 needle bearing from driving shell. Remove forward sun gear and No. 5 needle bearing from shell. Remove No. 5 needle bearing from forward sun gear.

Reassembly – Sun gear and driving shell will be reassembled as part of TRANSMISSION REASSEMBLY.

VALVE BODY ASSEMBLY

NOTE: As valves are removed from each valve body bore, place individual parts in correct order and in relative position to valve body for reassembly reference. Tag all springs as they are removed for reassembly reference.

Disassembly – **1)** Remove and discard valve body gasket. Remove retaining bolts. Remove separator plate, reinforcement plates, and separator plate gasket. Discard gasket.
2) Remove 8 check balls from valve body. *See Fig. 17.* Remove retaining plates, valves and springs. Keep all valves and springs in original order for reassembly reference. *See Fig. 18.*

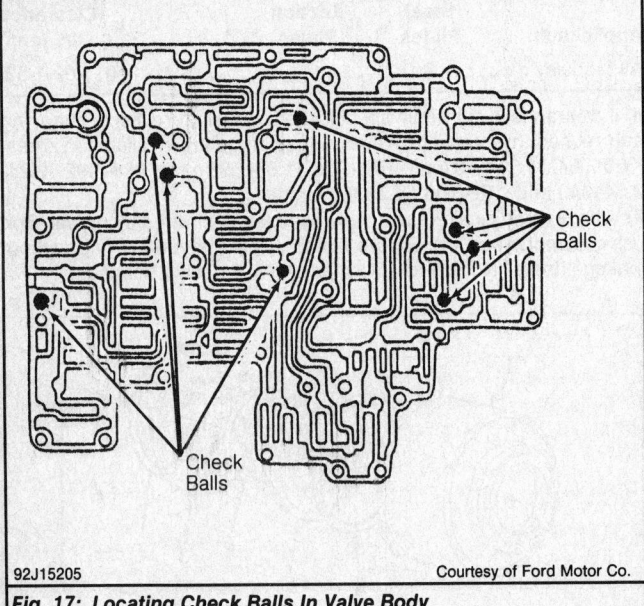

92J15205   Courtesy of Ford Motor Co.

Fig. 17: Locating Check Balls In Valve Body

Cleaning & Inspection – **1)** Clean all parts thoroughly in clean solvent, and blow dry with compressed air. Inspect all valves and plug bores for scoring. Check all fluid passages for obstructions.
2) Inspect all mating surfaces, plugs, and valves for burrs and scoring. If necessary, use crocus cloth to polish valves and plugs.
3) Inspect all springs for distortion. Check all valves and plugs for free movement in their respective bores. Valves and plugs, when dry, must fall free of their own weight within their respective bores.

CAUTION: Avoid rounding off sharp edges of valves and plugs with crocus cloth. These edges perform a cleaning action.

Reassembly – **1)** Install all valves into their respective bores using illustration as guide. Ensure notch in plugs face bottom of bore.
2) Install valve body check balls. *See Fig. 17.* Install guide pin bolts into holes. These 2 holes align valve body gasket and valve body assembly with case. Using a NEW separator plate gasket, slide plate and gasket over alignment pins. Position 3 reinforcement plates and loosely install retaining bolts. Tighten retaining bolts to specification. See TORQUE SPECIFICATIONS.

TRANSMISSION REASSEMBLY

NOTE: See Figs. 22 and 23 for exploded view of internal parts, thrust washer and needle bearing locations. Lubricate all parts with ATF. Use petroleum jelly on gaskets, thrust washers, and needle bearings to retain in place. Use NEW gaskets and seals.

Initial Reassembly – **1)** Install No. 9 output shaft needle bearing in transmission case. Install bearing support, No. 7 needle bearing and direct clutch hub in direct clutch assembly. Assemble output shaft hub to output shaft and install retaining snap ring.
2) Place No. 8 needle bearing on rear of direct clutch drum. Slide output shaft into direct clutch drum. Attach output shaft hub to ring gear with retaining ring. Install output shaft, ring gear, and direct clutch assembly into transmission case.
3) Install low-reverse band into transmission case and ensure band is seated on anchor pins. When properly installed, center of band actuating rod seat can be seen through servo piston bore.
4) Install center support and planetary assembly into case. If necessary, rotate output shaft to align planet carrier splines with direct clutch hub splines. Install center support anti-clunk spring using a hammer handle or wooden dowel. Spring tabs must face out.

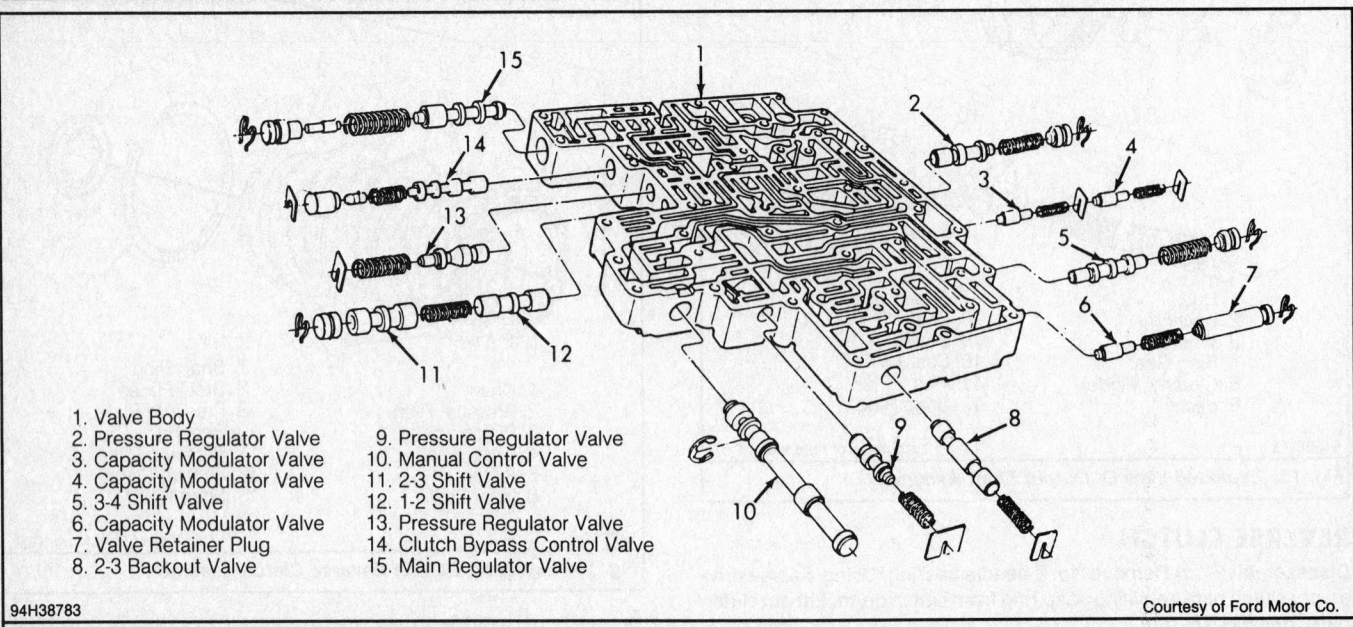

1. Valve Body
2. Pressure Regulator Valve
3. Capacity Modulator Valve
4. Capacity Modulator Valve
5. 3-4 Shift Valve
6. Capacity Modulator Valve
7. Valve Retainer Plug
8. 2-3 Backout Valve
9. Pressure Regulator Valve
10. Manual Control Valve
11. 2-3 Shift Valve
12. 1-2 Shift Valve
13. Pressure Regulator Valve
14. Clutch Bypass Control Valve
15. Main Regulator Valve

94H38783   Courtesy of Ford Motor Co.

Fig. 18: Exploded View Of Valve Body Components

NOTE: Center support and planet carrier cannot be installed unless notch cut in center support is aligned with overdrive band anchor pin.

Low-Reverse Servo Pin Selection – 1) Install center support retaining ring. Determine correct length of low-reverse servo pin to use. Lubricate and install servo piston and return spring. DO NOT install cover or retaining ring. Install Servo Selector Gauge (T80L-77030-A) into servo bore.

2) Tighten band apply bolt on tool to 50 INCH lbs. (5.6 N.m). Attach dial indicator. Position indicator stem on flat portion of servo piston. Zero dial indicator. *See Fig. 19.*

3) Thread bolt out of selector tool until piston stops against bottom of tool. Read amount of piston travel on dial indicator. If travel is .112-.237" (2.845-6.020 mm), correct servo pin is installed. If travel is not within specification, selective pistons are available. See LOW-REVERSE SERVO PISTONS table.

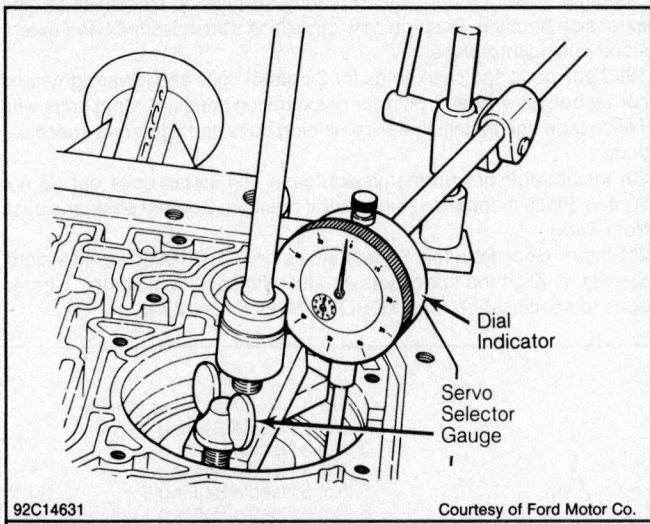

92C14631   Courtesy of Ford Motor Co.

Fig. 19: Measuring Low-Reverse Servo Pin Travel

LOW-REVERSE SERVO PISTONS

Assembly Length	Number Of Grooves
12.936" (74.57 mm)	1
12.989" (75.92 mm)	2
13.043" (77.29 mm)	3

4) Length is measured from base of piston to end of rod. Select servo rod to bring servo travel within specification. Remove selector tool and dial indicator.

5) Install selected low-reverse servo piston. Install servo cover and cover retaining snap ring.

Final Reassembly – 1) Install reverse clutch on forward clutch. Ensure No. 2 needle bearing is in position in reverse clutch. Install No. 3 needle bearing and forward clutch hub in forward clutch. Position No. 4 needle bearing on forward clutch hub.

2) Install drive shell over clutch assemblies. Install No. 5 needle bearing and forward sun gear on drive shell. Install complete assembly into case, rotating output shaft to aid in engaging sun gear with planetary gears.

3) Install overdrive band into case and around drive shell assembly. Ensure band anchor is properly positioned on anchor pin. Using a screwdriver to hold overdrive band in position, lubricate and install overdrive servo.

4) With overdrive servo installed, inspect band and apply pin for proper position and engagement. If band anchor and apply pin are not properly engaged, remove servo and re-position band as necessary.

5) Install intermediate clutch pack pressure plate, clutch pack (starting with a friction plate and alternating steel and friction plates) and selective steel plate in this order. Measure intermediate clutch clearance.

6) Intermediate clutch clearance is measured using a depth micrometer and End Play Checking Bar (T80L-77003-A). Set end play tool across pump case mounting surface. Locate micrometer end play bar and read depth. *See Fig. 20.*

NOTE: A downward pressure must be applied to clutch pack while measuring intermediate clutch clearance.

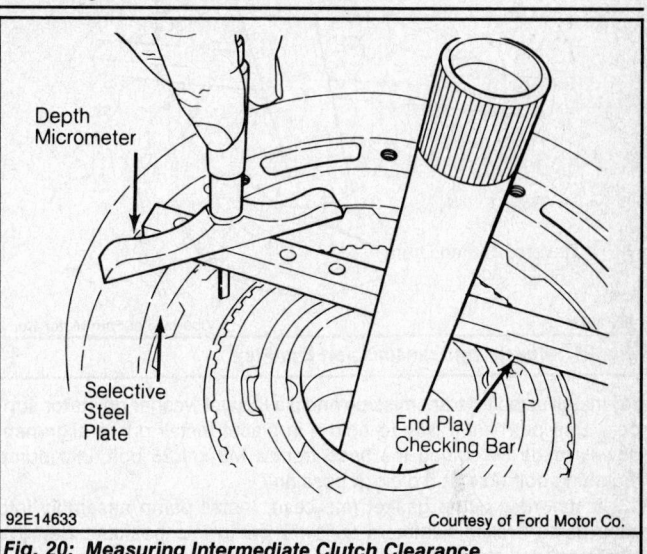

92E14633   Courtesy of Ford Motor Co.

Fig. 20: Measuring Intermediate Clutch Clearance

7) Check depth again with micrometer 180 degrees opposite from previous measurement. Ensure depth at intermediate clutch selective steel plate is 1.654-1.670" (42.0-42.4 mm). Ensure average of the 2 measurements is within this range.

8) If intermediate clutch clearance (depth) is not within tolerance, select correct thickness steel separator plate. Selective plates are available in the following thicknesses: .067-.071" (1.70-1.80 mm), .077-.081" (1.95-2.05 mm), .087-.091" (2.20-2.31 mm) and .97-.101 (2.46-2.56 mm).

INTERMEDIATE CLUTCH PLATE USAGE

Application	Steel Plates	Friction Plates
Cougar, Mark VIII, Thunderbird, E-150 & F-150	3	3
All Other Models	4	4

9) Check transmission end play by locating depth micrometer on End Play Checking Bar (T80L-77003-A). Ensure depth is measured at reverse clutch drum thrust face. *See Fig. 21.* Standard end play is .004-.044" (.101-1.11 mm).

10) Check end play 180 degrees opposite end of reverse clutch drum thrust face to determine average depth. Thrust washer controlling transmission end play is located on stator support which is attached to back of pump housing.

11) Transmission end play can be adjusted using one of selective thrust washers available for service. After measuring depth, select required thrust washer. See END PLAY THRUST WASHER SELECTION table.

END PLAY THRUST WASHER SELECTION

Measured Depth In. (mm)	Washer Thickness In. (mm)	Color Code
1.483-1.500 (37.67-38.10)	.050-.054 (1.27-1.37)	Green
1.501-1.517 (38.13-38.53)	.068-.072 (1.73-1.83)	Yellow
1.518-1.534 (38.56-38.96)	.085-.089 (2.16-2.26)	Natural
1.535-1.551 (38.99-39.40)	.102-.106 (2.59-2.69)	Red
1.552-1.568 (39.42-39.83)	.119-.123 (3.02-3.12)	Blue

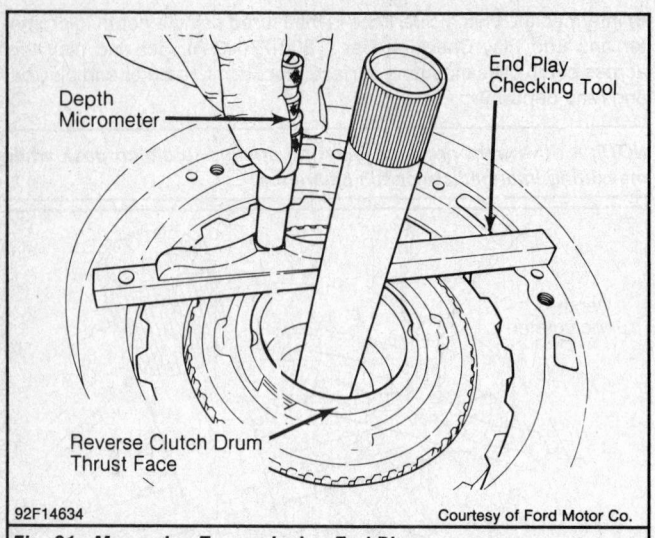

Fig. 21: Measuring Transmission End Play

92F14634   Courtesy of Ford Motor Co.

Depth Micrometer

End Play Checking Tool

Reverse Clutch Drum Thrust Face

12) Install selected transmission end play thrust washer on stator support. Use petroleum jelly to hold it in place. Install pump alignment dowel, made by cutting the head from a M8 x 1.25 bolt, into pump mounting bolt hole at 6 o'clock position.

13) Install new pump gasket into case. Install pump assembly into case using 2 slide hammers to lower pump into position. Remove alignment dowel. Coat all pump-to-case bolts with Loctite and install in case.

14) Alternately tighten bolts a few turns at a time to draw pump into case. Tighten bolts to specification. See TORQUE SPECIFICATIONS. Install 2-3 accumulator assembly. Install EPC solenoid.

15) Position manual valve detent lever and parking lever actuating rod into case. Parking lever actuating rod must be positioned over parking pawl. Slide manual control lever into case and position through detent. Install and tighten nut. Install manual lever shaft retaining roll pin. Install oil screen into case.

16) Install valve body gasket and valve body assembly using 2 alignment bolts as guide. Ensure manual and throttle levers are properly positioned before installing valve body retaining bolts.

17) Loosely install valve body retaining bolts. Starting at center and working outward, tighten bolts. Install EPC solenoid bracket. Install detent spring and roller assembly and tighten bolts to specification. See TORQUE SPECIFICATIONS.

18) Install filter grommet, new filter gasket, and filter on valve body. Install filter attaching bolts and tighten. Position new pan gasket on case and install oil pan. Clean mating surface on transmission and extension housing. Position new gasket on transmission. Slide extension housing into place.

19) Clean bolts and case holes for 2 bottom bolts and lower right hand corner bolt (as viewed from rear of extension housing). Coat bolts with Teflon tape and install. Install remaining bolts and tighten to specification.

20) Install MLP onto transmission case and install bolts but do not tighten. Place manual lever in Neutral position (2 detent positions back from Park).

21) Insert Gear Position Sensor Adjuster (T71P-70010-A) into slots. *See Fig. 7.* Align the three slots on MLP with tabs on adjuster. Tighten bolts to specification. See TORQUE SPECIFICATIONS.

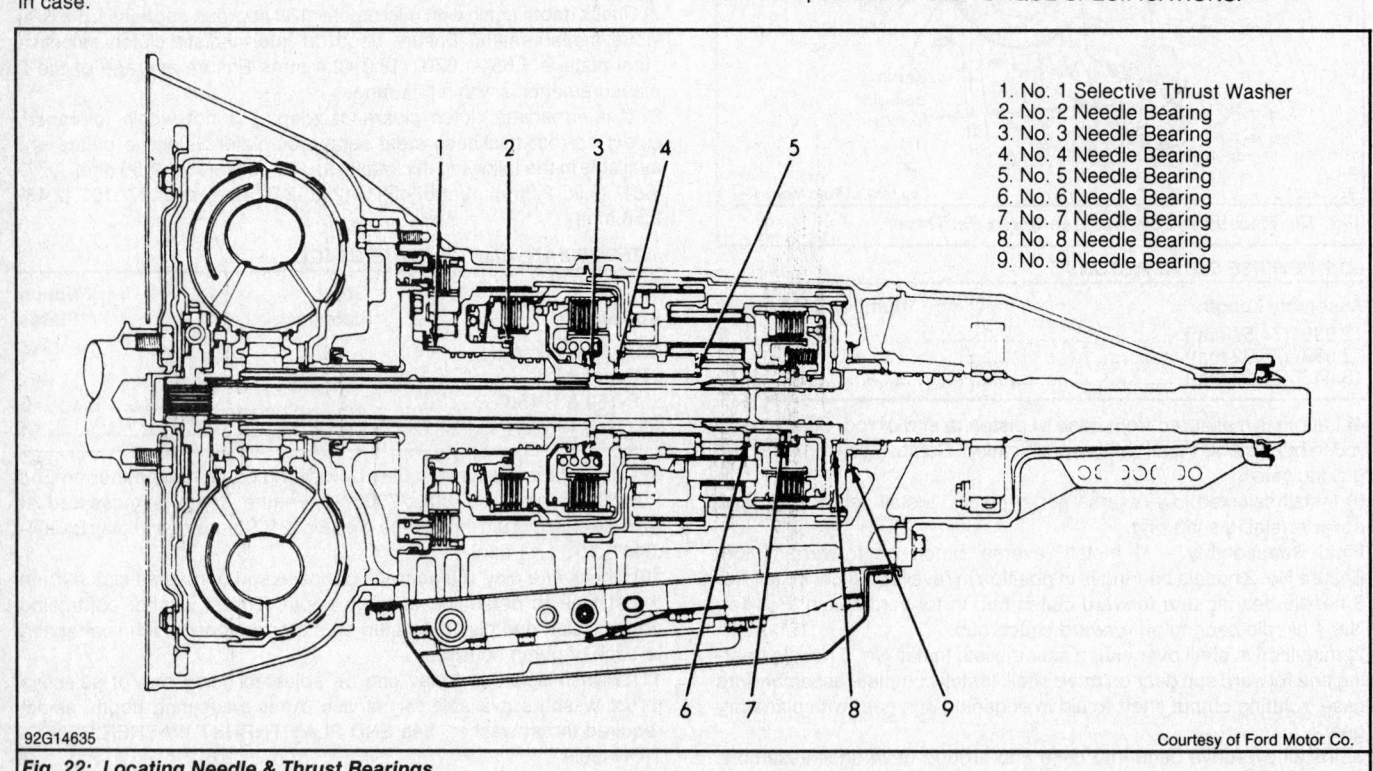

1. No. 1 Selective Thrust Washer
2. No. 2 Needle Bearing
3. No. 3 Needle Bearing
4. No. 4 Needle Bearing
5. No. 5 Needle Bearing
6. No. 6 Needle Bearing
7. No. 7 Needle Bearing
8. No. 8 Needle Bearing
9. No. 9 Needle Bearing

92G14635   Courtesy of Ford Motor Co.

Fig. 22: Locating Needle & Thrust Bearings

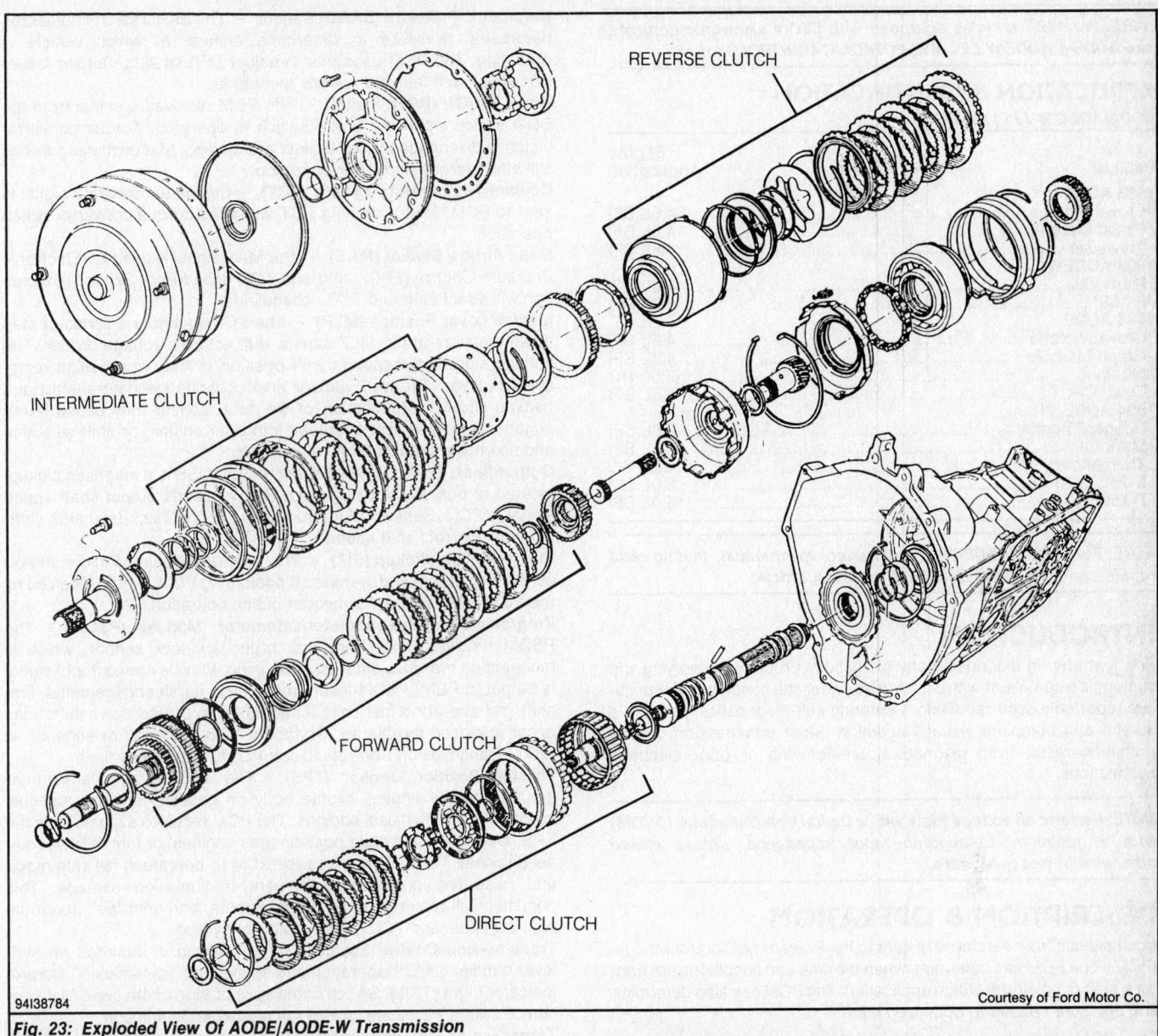

REVERSE CLUTCH

INTERMEDIATE CLUTCH

FORWARD CLUTCH

DIRECT CLUTCH

94138784

Courtesy of Ford Motor Co.

Fig. 23: Exploded View Of AODE/AODE-W Transmission

TORQUE SPECIFICATIONS

TORQUE SPECIFICATIONS

Application	Ft Lbs. (N.m)
Converter-To-Flywheel Bolt	20-34 (27-46)
Converter Housing Cover-To-Converter Housing	12-16 (16-22)
Converter Plug-To-Converter	8-28 (11-38)
Cooler Line-To-Case	18-23 (24-31)
Extension-To-Case Bolt	16-20 (22-27)
Inner Manual Lever-To-Shaft Nut	19-27 (26-37)
Outer Throttle Lever-To-Shaft Nut	12-16 (16-22)
Pump-To-Case Bolt	16-20 (22-27)
Stator Support-To-Pump Bolt	12-16 (16-22)
Stator Support-To-Pump Bolt	12-16 (16-22)
Transmission-To-Engine Bolt	40-50 (54-68)

Application	INCH lbs. (N.m)
Cover-To-Governor Body Bolt	20-30 (2.3-3.4)
Detent Spring Attaching Bolt	80-120 (9-14)
Filter-To-Valve Body	80-120 (9-14)
Governor Body-To-Counterweight Bolt	50-60 (6-7)
Neutral Start Switch-To-Case	95-130 (11-15)
Oil Pan-To-Case Bolt	72-120 (8-14)
Pressure Plug-To-Case	72-144 (8-16)
Reinforcing Plate-To-Valve Body Bolt	80-120 (9-14)
Separator Plate-To-Valve Body Bolt	80-100 (9-11)
Valve Body-To-Case Bolt	80-100 (9-11)

TRANSMISSION SPECIFICATIONS

TRANSMISSION SPECIFICATIONS

Application	In. (mm)
Converter End Play	.050-.077 (1.27-1.95)
Direct Clutch Pack Clearance	.060-.092 (1.53-2.34)
Forward Clutch Pack Clearance	.050-.094 (1.27-2.38)
Intermediate Clutch Pack Clearance	1.634-1.646 (41.50-41.81)
Reverse Clutch Pack Clearance	.040-.060 (1.02-1.52)

NOTE: For 1994 vehicles equipped with EEC-V electronic controls, see AODE & AODE-W EEC-V ELECTRONIC CONTROLS article.

APPLICATION & IDENTIFICATION
AODE/AODE-W APPLICATION

Vehicle	Engine Application
1993 AODE	
Crown Victoria	4.6L SFI
Grand Marquis	4.6L SFI
Town Car	4.6L SFI
1993 AODE-W	
Mark VIII	4.6L SFI
E-150	5.0L SFI
1994 AODE	
Crown Victoria	4.6L SFI
Grand Marquis	4.6L SFI
Mustang	5.0L HO
Town Car	4.6L SFI
1994 AODE-W	
Cougar/Thunderbird	3.8L SFI
Mark VIII	4.6L SFI
Thunderbird	3.8L SC
E-150	5.0L SFI
F-150	5.0L SFI

NOTE: For AODE/AODE-W transmission mechanical testing and repair, see Ford AODE & AODE-W overhaul article.

INTRODUCTION

The first step in diagnosing any driveability problem is verifying the customer's complaint with a test drive under the conditions the problem reportedly occurred. Before entering self-diagnostics, perform a careful and complete visual inspection. Most transmission control problems result from mechanical breakdowns or poor electrical connections.

NOTE: Perform all voltage tests with a Digital Volt-Ohmmeter (DVOM) with a minimum 10-megohm input impedance, unless stated otherwise in test procedure.

DESCRIPTION & OPERATION

Input signals from sensors are sent to the Powertrain Control Module (PCM). The PCM can determine when the time and conditions are right for a shift or converter clutch application. The PCM can also determine line pressure needed to optimize shift feel.

The PCM controls transmission operation through 4 electronic solenoids consisting of 3 On/Off solenoids for shifting and torque converter clutch control and one variable force solenoid for line pressure control. The PCM has built-in self-diagnosis, fail-safe code and warning code display for the main input sensors and solenoid valves.

NOTE: In addition to transmission fault codes, engine related fault codes may be output during QUICK TEST procedure. These fault codes pertain to engine performance and must be repaired first, as engine performance will greatly affect transmission operation. For information and testing procedures of engine related fault codes and components, see SELF-DIAGNOSTICS – EEC-IV article in ENGINE PERFORMANCE of appropriate MITCHELL® manual.

INPUT SENSORS

Air Conditioning Clutch (ACC) – On factory installed A/C system, PCM receives signal voltage from ACC switch indication that the air conditioning compressor clutch is engaged. The PCM uses the ACC switch signal to adjust line pressure to compensate for additional engine load. If the ACC switch fails with closed contacts, line pressure will be slightly low with air conditioning off. If the ACC switch fails with open contacts, line pressure will be slightly high with air conditioning on.

Barometric Pressure (BARO) Sensor – The BARO sensor measures barometric pressure to determine altitude at which vehicle is operating. The PCM uses this to adjust shift speeds. Sensor failure can affect shift feel and speeds at altitude.

Brake On/Off (BOO) Switch – The PCM receives a signal from the BOO switch when the brake switch is operated. Torque converter clutch is disengaged when brakes are applied. Malfunctioning switch will affect torque converter operation.

Coolant Temperature Sensor (ECT) – Engine temperature signal is sent to PCM. Malfunctioning ECT will affect torque converter clutch operation.

Mass Airflow Sensor (MAS) – The MAS signal is used for Electronic Pressure Control (EPC), shift and TCC scheduling. Sensor malfunction will affect shift and TCC scheduling.

Manual Lever Position (MLP) – The PCM monitors a series of step down resistors in the MLP sensor that act as a voltage divider. The voltage signal corresponds with position of the transmission range selector lever. The MLP sensor also contains the neutral/start and backup circuits. Malfunction of the MLP sensor may cause harsh engagements and firm shift feel. Improper shifting or shift selection and no engine cranking may also result.

Output Shaft Speed (OSS) Sensor – The OSS is a magnetic pickup, located at output shaft ring gear. Sensor sends output shaft speed signal to PCM. Sensor failure may cause no TCC lock-up, harsh shifting and incorrect shift speeds.

Profile Ignition Pickup (PIP) – The PIP sensor located in distributor, sends engine rpm and crankshaft position to PCM. Signal received by the PCM affects torque converter clutch operation.

Programmable Speedometer/Odometer Module (PSOM) – The PSOM receives input from rear brake anti-lock sensor, which is mounted on rear axle differential housing. Vehicle speed (mph) signal is output to PCM. PSOM failure may cause harsh engagements, firm shift feel and abnormal shift schedule. Unexpected downshifts may occur at closed throttle and abnormal TCC operation or engages at WOT. Transmission Control Indicator Light (TCIL) may flash.

Throttle Position Sensor (TPS) – The TPS is a potentiometer mounted to the engine throttle body on gasoline engines and fuel injection pump on diesel engines. The PCM receives a signal from the TPS relaying throttle plate position (gas engines) or fuel delivery (diesel engines). TPS failure will cause PCM to operate in fail safe mode and raise line pressure to prevent transmission damage. This condition will result in harsh engagements, firm shift feel, abnormal shift schedule and TCC not engaging or cycling.

Transmission Control Switch (TCS) – Switch is mounted on shift lever handle. On/Off operation is displayed by Transmission Control Indicator Light (TCIL). Switch controls operation of 4th gear. Malfunction of switch will cause lack of 4th gear disable function.

Transmission Oil Temperature (TOT) Sensor – The TOT sensor is located on the solenoid body assembly. The PCM monitors voltage across the TOT thermistor to determine transmission temperature. Depending on temperature, the PCM controls line pressure, shift scheduling and TCC operation. Malfunction of sensor will cause incorrect line pressure and possible lack of TCC operation.

Vehicle Speed Sensor (VSS) – The VSS is a magnetic pickup that sends vehicle speed signal to the PCM. Malfunction of sensor may cause harsh engagements of shifts. Lack of 4th gear, TCC lock-up, or engine braking in 2nd or 3rd gear may also be present.

OUTPUT DEVICES

Electronic Pressure Control (EPC) Solenoid – The EPC receives signal from the PCM to control line pressure and 2-3 backout valve function. If EPC fails in ON position, transmission is operated in failsafe mode. Minimum line pressure is present. If EPC fails in OFF position, line pressure at maximum pressure. Harsh engagements and shifts will result.

Shift Solenoid Assemblies – 1) Two ON/OFF solenoids are used for electronic shift scheduling. Solenoids used are Shift Solenoid No. 1 (SS1) and Shift Solenoid No. 2 (SS2). Solenoids control pressure to 3 shift valves and forward clutch control valve, located in valve body. See SOLENOID OPERATION CHART.

AUTOMATIC TRANSMISSIONS
AODE & AODE-W EEC-IV Electronic Controls (Cont.)

3-563

SOLENOID OPERATION CHART

Gear Position	SS1	SS2
"OD" (Overdrive) [1]		
Park	On	Off
Reverse	On	Off
Neutral	On	Off
1st Gear	On	Off
2nd Gear	Off	On
3rd Gear	Off	On
4th Gear	On	On
"D" Or "3" [2]		
1st Gear	On	Off
2nd Gear	Off	Off
3rd Gear	Off	On
Manual 2	Off	Off
Manual 1 [3]	On	Off
Manual 1	Off	Off

[1] – "OD" switch released.
[2] – "OD" switch depressed (OD cancelled).
[3] – Transmission is in 2nd gear until vehicle speed drops below calibrated speed.

2) When shift solenoid is "Always Off", failure could be due to PCM and/or vehicle wiring malfunction, and/or solenoid electrically stuck off, and/or hydraulically or mechanically stuck off. For shift symptoms, see Fig. 1.

3) When shift solenoid is "Always On", failure could be due to PCM and/or vehicle wiring malfunction, and/or solenoid electrically stuck off, and/or hydraulically or mechanically stuck off. For shift symptoms, see Fig. 2.

Torque Converter Clutch (TCC) Solenoid – The TCC receives signal from the PCM. The TCC controls application, modulation and release of torque converter clutch. If solenoid fails in ON position, vehicle engine will run rough (shudder) and engine stalls in Drive at low idle speeds (2nd, 3rd or 4th gear). If solenoid fails in OFF position, torque converter clutch will not engage.

SS-1 ALWAYS OFF:	Transmission Range Selector Lever Position		
	D	2	1
PCM Gear Commanded	Actual Gear Obtained		
1	2	2	2
2	2	2	2
3	3	2*	2*
4	3	2*	2*

*No Engine Braking

SS-2 ALWAYS OFF:	Transmission Range Selector Lever Position		
	D	2	1
PCM Gear Commanded	Actual Gear Obtained		
1	1	1	1
2	2	2	2
3	2	2	2
4	1	1	1

94D38805 94E38806   Courtesy of Ford Motor Co.

Fig. 1: Shift Solenoid Failure Charts (Always Off)

SS-1 ALWAYS ON:	Transmission Range Selector Lever Position		
	D	2	1
PCM Gear Commanded	Actual Gear Obtained		
1	1	1	1
2	1	1	1
3	4	2*	2*
4	4	2*	2*

*No Engine Braking

SS-2 ALWAYS ON:	Transmission Range Selector Lever Position		
	D	2	1
PCM Gear Commanded	Actual Gear Obtained		
1	4	2*	2*
2	3	2*	2*
3	3	2*	2*
4	4	2*	2*

*No Engine Braking

94F38807 94G38808   Courtesy of Ford Motor Co.

Fig. 2: Shift Solenoid Failure Charts (Always On)

PRELIMINARY INSPECTION

VISUAL INSPECTION

Visually inspect all electrical wiring, looking for chafed, stretched, cut or pinched wiring. Ensure electrical connectors fit tightly and are not corroded. Ensure vacuum hoses are properly routed and are not pinched or cut. Inspect air induction system for possible vacuum leaks. Check PCM, sensors and actuators for physical damage. Check engine coolant level. Check transmission fluid level and condition.

NOTE: In addition to transmission fault codes, engine-related fault codes may be output during QUICK TEST procedure. These fault codes pertain to engine performance and must be repaired first as engine performance will greatly affect transmission operation. For information and testing procedures of engine-related fault codes and components, see SELF-DIAGNOSTICS – EEC-IV article in ENGINE PERFORMANCE of appropriate MITCHELL® manual.

SELF-DIAGNOSTIC SYSTEM

DIAGNOSTIC FORMATS

QUICK TEST, CIRCUIT/PINPOINT TESTS are diagnostic formats used to test and service EEC-IV system. QUICK TEST allows technician to identify problems and retrieve service codes. CIRCUIT TESTS check engine circuits, sensors and actuators. PINPOINT TESTS check transmission circuits, sensors and actuators.

Before starting any circuit test, follow all steps under QUICK TEST to find correct circuit or pinpoint test. If vehicle passes QUICK TEST and no driveability symptoms or intermittent faults exist, EEC-IV system is okay.

DIAGNOSTIC TROUBLE CODES (DTC)

During QUICK TEST, 3 types of service codes are retrieved: Key On Engine Off (KOEO), Key On Engine Running (KOER) and Continuous Memory Codes. See QUICK TEST for self-test procedures. Codes may be cleared from PCM memory after they have been recorded or repaired. See CLEARING CODES.

3-564

AUTOMATIC TRANSMISSIONS
AODE & AODE-W EEC-IV Electronic Controls (Cont.)

KOEO & KOER Codes (Hard Faults) – These codes indicate faults are present at time of testing. A hard fault may cause CHECK ENGINE light or Malfunction Indicator Light (MIL) to glow and remain on until fault is repaired. If KOEO or KOER codes are retrieved during KOEO SELF-TEST or KOER SELF-TEST, use SERVICE CODE REFERENCE CHARTS to find correct testing and repair procedures.

Continuous Memory Codes (Soft Faults) – These codes indicate a fault that may or may not be present at time of testing. These codes are used to diagnose intermittent problems. Continuous Memory Codes are retrieved during KOEO SELF-TEST. Some codes may turn on MIL or CHECK ENGINE light. Corresponding soft trouble code will be retained in PCM memory. If fault does not reoccur within 40 warm-up cycles (80 cycles on some models), PCM will automatically clear code. Technician may clear service codes from memory. See CLEARING CODES. Intermittent faults may be caused by a sensor, connector or wiring-related problems.

CAUTION: Continuous Memory Codes should be recorded when retrieved during KOEO SELF-TEST. These codes may be used to identify intermittent problems that exist after all KOEO and KOER codes have been repaired and a Code 11 or 111 (pass code) has been obtained. Failure to follow this procedure may result in unnecessary testing. Some Continuous Memory Codes faults may not be valid after KOEO and KOER codes are repaired.

RETRIEVING CODES

Service codes are retrieved from EEC-IV system through self-test connector. Various methods and test equipment may be used to access these codes:

- Analog Volt-Ohmmeter (VOM)
- Scan Tester
- In-Dash Malfunction Indicator Light (MIL) Or CHECK ENGINE light
- STAR Series Tester

READING CODES

KOEO & KOER SELF-TEST Codes – PCM outputs codes one digit at a time. Record codes in order received. These codes indicate current faults in system and should be serviced in order of appearance. Use SERVICE CODE REFERENCE CHARTS to find correct CIRCUIT/PIN-POINT TEST.

If using analog VOM, pay careful attention to length of pauses in order to read codes correctly. A 1/2-second pause occurs between number of sweeps in a digit. A 2-second pause occurs between digits in a code. A 4-second pause occurs between each code. KOEO codes are separated from Continuous Memory codes by a 6-second delay, a 1/2-second sweep (separator) and another 6-second delay. See Fig. 3. If using MIL/CHECK ENGINE light, service codes are displayed as flashes.

Scan tester, if used, will count pulses and display them as a digital code. STAR Series Tester will add a zero (0) to single-digit Separator Code (10) and Dynamic Response Code (10). Dynamic Response Code is displayed in KOER SELF-TEST. See Fig. 3.

Engine Identification (ID) Codes – Engine ID codes are issued at beginning of KOER SELF-TEST. Codes are one-digit numbers represented by number of pulses displayed. See Fig. 3. Engine ID code is equal to one-half the number of engine cylinders. For example, 2 pulses would indicate that engine is a 4 cylinder. ID code is used to verify proper PCM is installed and that SELF-TEST has been entered.

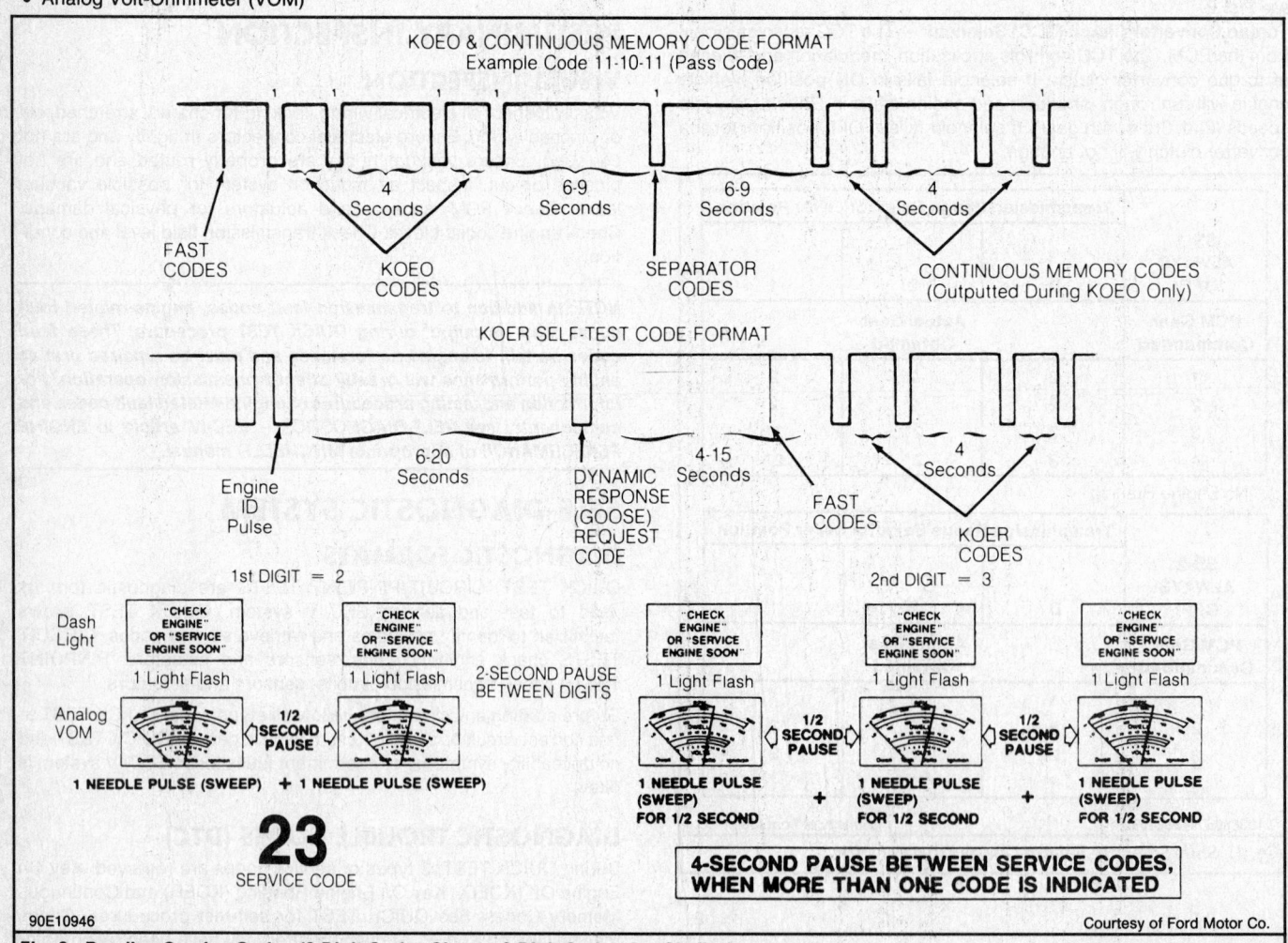

90E10946   Courtesy of Ford Motor Co.

Fig. 3: Reading Service Codes (2-Digit Codes Shown; 3-Digit Codes Are Similar)

AUTOMATIC TRANSMISSIONS
AODE & AODE-W EEC-IV Electronic Controls (Cont.)

3-565

Separator Pulse – Single 1/2-second separator pulse is issued 6-9 seconds after last KOEO code. Continuous Memory Codes (soft faults) are then displayed 6-9 seconds after 1/2-second separator pulse. Some digital test equipment may display separator code as "10" instead of "1".

Pass Codes – A Code 11 or 111 indicates no service codes were recorded in that portion of test; system passes that portion of test. If Code 11 or 111 is not retrieved in KOEO SELF-TEST, codes retrieved during KOER SELF-TEST may not be valid. Code 11 or 111 (pass code) must be obtained in KOEO SELF-TEST. A Code 11-1-11 or 111-1-111 output during KOEO SELF-TEST indicates no KOEO code or Continuous Memory Code was recorded.

Continuous Memory Codes – These codes result from information stored by PCM during continuous self-test monitoring. Codes are displayed after separator pulse code in KOEO SELF-TEST. Use these codes for diagnosis only when KOEO SELF-TEST and KOER SELF-TEST result in Code 11 or 111 (pass code) and all steps under QUICK TEST are successfully completed. A few codes are exceptions which may be checked after KOEO codes have been repaired. These codes indicate faults recorded within last 40 engine starts (80 engine starts on some models). Fault may or may not be currently present. See SERVICE CODE REFERENCE CHARTS.

Fast Codes – At start of KOEO SELF-TEST and after Wide Open Throttle (WOT) request in KOER SELF-TEST, PCM outputs short bursts of information, known as FAST CODES, which were used by manufacturer during assembly. With most equipment, these code bursts are not visible; an entire code sequence lasts less than 1/2 second. If this fluctuation is visible on test equipment, ignore it.

CLEARING CODES

To clear codes from PCM memory, start KOEO SELF-TEST under QUICK TEST. When service codes appear on test equipment or CHECK ENGINE light, disconnect jumper wire from Self-Test Input (STI) connector. If using STAR Series Tester, unlatch center button. This procedure erases Continuous Memory Codes from PCM memory. If problem has not been corrected or fault is still present, hard code will immediately be reset in PCM memory.

CAUTION: DO NOT disconnect vehicle battery to clear codes. This will erase stored operating information from Keep-Alive Memory (KAM). To clear KAM, disconnect negative battery terminal for at least 5 minutes.

WARNING: When battery is disconnected, vehicle computer and memory systems may lose memory data. Driveability problems may exist until computer systems have completed a relearn cycle. See COMPUTER RELEARN PROCEDURES in APPLICATIONS & IDENTIFICATION section before disconnecting battery.

QUICK TEST

Description – Following procedures are functional tests of EEC-IV system. These following 4 basic test steps must be carefully followed in sequence, otherwise misdiagnosis or replacement of non-faulty components may result:

- VISUAL CHECK
- EQUIPMENT HOOKUP.
- KOEO SELF-TEST.
- KOER SELF-TEST.

Diagnostic Aids – After each service or repair procedure has been completed, repeat QUICK TEST to ensure all EEC-IV systems work properly and service codes are no longer present.

VISUAL CHECK

Complete a basic inspection of engine compartment and all components before proceeding to self-diagnostic tests. Ensure vacuum hoses and EEC-IV wiring harnesses are properly connected.

EQUIPMENT HOOKUP

Apply parking brake, and place shift lever in "P" position. Block drive wheels. Turn off all electrical loads. Connect appropriate test equipment to vehicle as follows:

Analog Volt-Ohmmeter (VOM) – 1) Turn ignition switch to OFF position. Set VOM at 0-15V DC range. Connect positive lead of VOM to positive battery terminal.

2) Connect negative VOM lead to Self-Test Output (STO) terminal of self-test connector. *See Fig. 4.* Connect timing light, and go to KOEO SELF-TEST. Activate KOEO SELF-TEST by connecting jumper wire from Self-Test Input (STI) pigtail to signal return terminal of self-test connector with ignition on.

Scan Tester – Follow manufacturer instructions to hook up equipment and record service codes.

STAR Series Tester – Turn ignition switch to OFF position. Connect color-coded adapter cable leads to diagnostic tester. Connect 2 service connectors of adapter cable to vehicle self-test connector and STI pigtail connector. Connect timing light. Go to KOEO SELF-TEST.

CHECK ENGINE Light/Malfunction Indicator Light (MIL) – Turn ignition on. Connect a jumper wire between Self-Test Input (STI) pigtail and signal return (SIG RTN) terminal of Data Link Connector (DLC). *See Fig. 4.* Go to KOEO SELF-TEST.

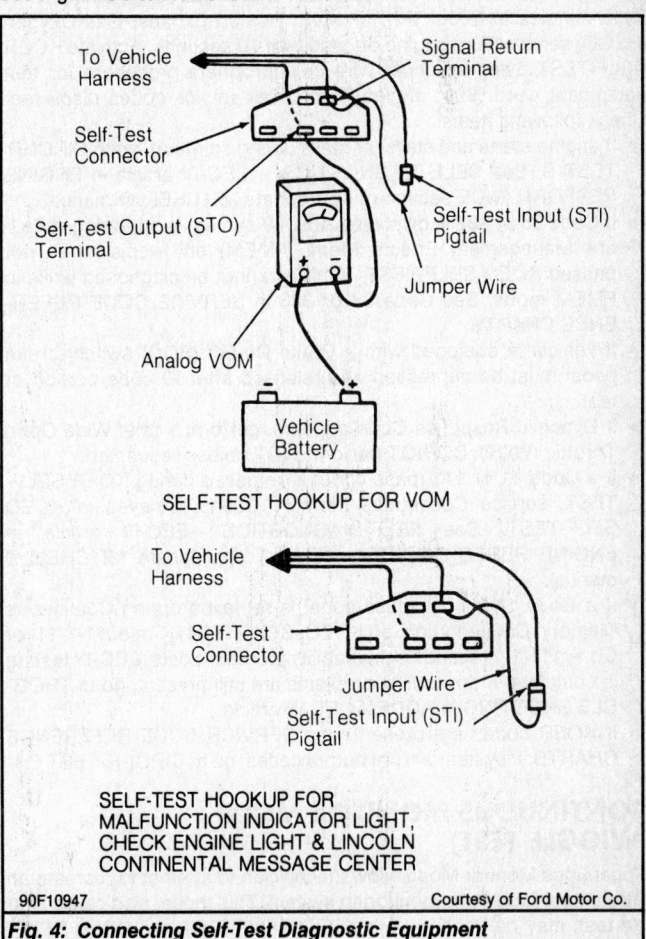

SELF-TEST HOOKUP FOR VOM

SELF-TEST HOOKUP FOR MALFUNCTION INDICATOR LIGHT, CHECK ENGINE LIGHT & LINCOLN CONTINENTAL MESSAGE CENTER

90F10947   Courtesy of Ford Motor Co.

Fig. 4: Connecting Self-Test Diagnostic Equipment

KOEO SELF-TEST

Ensure engine is at normal operating temperature. If engine does not start (or stalls after starting), continue KOEO SELF-TEST. DO NOT depress throttle on gasoline vehicles. Turn ignition off. Wait 10 seconds. Ensure test equipment is properly attached. Turn ignition on (engine off). Record all KOEO and Continuous Memory Codes.

If a Code 11 or 111 (pass code) is not retrieved in KOEO portion of test, service KOEO codes at this time. Service any engine codes recorded before servicing transmission codes (code Nos. 566 and

3-566

AUTOMATIC TRANSMISSIONS
AODE & AODE-W EEC-IV Electronic Controls (Cont.)

629). If PCM will not output codes, see SELF-DIAGNOSTICS – EEC-IV article in ENGINE PERFORMANCE section of appropriate MITCHELL® manual. If service codes are retrieved observe the following procedures:

- If CHECK ENGINE or SERVICE ENGINE SOON light is on, service codes in order retrieved.
- On vehicles equipped with DIS and EDIS ignition systems, see SYSTEM & COMPONENT TESTING article in ENGINE PERFORMANCE section of appropriate MITCHELL® manual if Continuous Memory Code 211, 212, 215, 216, 217, 232 or 238 is retrieved during KOEO SELF-TEST. Repair ignition system as necessary.
- If vehicle has a no-start condition, go to CIRCUIT TEST AA, AB or AC in SELF-DIAGNOSTICS – EEC-IV article in ENGINE PERFORMANCE section of appropriate MITCHELL® manual.

KOER SELF-TEST

Diagnostic Aids – DO NOT enter this test sequence until a Code 11 or 111 (pass code) has been retrieved in KOEO SELF-TEST. If system has not passed KOEO SELF-TEST, codes recorded in KOER SELF-TEST may not be valid.

Deactivate self-test by removing and reconnecting jumper wire or by procedure specified by test equipment in use. Start engine, and run it for 2 minutes at 2000 RPM to warm Heated Exhaust Gas Oxygen (HEGO) sensor. Turn engine off, and wait 10 seconds. Activate KOER SELF-TEST using a jumper wire or appropriate procedure for test equipment used. Start engine. Record all service codes displayed. Check following items:

- If engine starts and stalls (or stalls during self-test), go to CIRCUIT TEST S. See SELF-DIAGNOSTICS – EEC-IV article in ENGINE PERFORMANCE section of appropriate MITCHELL® manual.
- If Code 98 or 998 is displayed, EEC-IV system is operating in Failure Management Effects Mode (FMEM) and vehicle has not passed KOEO SELF-TEST. Vehicle cannot be diagnosed while in FMEM mode. See Code 98 or 998 in SERVICE CODE REFERENCE CHARTS.
- If vehicle is equipped with a Brake On-Off (BOO) switch, brake pedal must be depressed and released after ID code portion of test.
- If Dynamic Response Code appears, perform a brief Wide Open Throttle (WOT). DO NOT perform WOT unless requested.
- If a Code 11 or 111 (pass code) is retrieved during KOER SELF-TEST, service Continuous Memory Codes retrieved in KOEO SELF-TEST. See SELF-DIAGNOSTICS – EEC-IV article in ENGINE PERFORMANCE section of appropriate MITCHELL® manual.
- If a Code 11 or 111 (pass code) is retrieved during Continuous Memory Code portion of KOEO SELF-TEST (Code 11-1-11 or Code 111-1-111) and no driveability problem exists, EEC-IV testing is complete. If driveability problems are still present, go to TROUBLE SHOOTING in AODE/AODE-W article.
- If KOER codes are present, see SERVICE CODE REFERENCE CHARTS. If system will not output codes, go to CIRCUIT TEST QA.

CONTINUOUS MONITOR MODE (WIGGLE TEST)

Continuous Monitor Mode allows technician to attempt to recreate an intermittent fault while monitoring system. This mode, also called wiggle test, may be used in both KOEO SELF-TEST and KOER SELF-TEST. CIRCUIT/PINPOINT TESTS specify use of this procedure to identify intermittent faults in specific circuits or components.

KOEO Wiggle Test Procedure – Connect test equipment. *See Fig. 4.* Turn ignition on, and activate self-test using jumper lead or diagnostic tester. Wait 10 seconds, and then deactivate and reactivate self-test. Wiggle test mode is now activated. Tap, move and wiggle suspect sensor and/or harness area. If a fault is detected, a service code may be stored in memory and indicated at diagnostic tester or scan tester. Retrieve code, and perform appropriate test. See SERVICE CODE REFERENCE CHARTS.

KOER Wiggle Test Procedure – Connect test equipment. *See Fig. 4.* Turn ignition off, and wait 10 seconds. Start engine. Activate self-test using jumper lead or diagnostic tester. Wait 10 seconds, and then deactivate and reactivate self-test. DO NOT turn engine off. KOER wiggle test mode is now activated. Tap, move and wiggle suspect sensor and/or harness area. If a fault is detected, a service code may be stored in memory and indicated at diagnostic tester or scan tester. Retrieve code, and perform appropriate test. See SERVICE CODE REFERENCE CHARTS.

TRANSMISSION DRIVE CYCLE TEST

NOTE: The transmission drive cycle test must be followed exactly. Malfunctions have to occur 4 times consecutively for codes 617, 618 and 619 to be set and 5 times consecutively for continuous code 628.

1) Record and then erase Quick Test codes. Warm engine to normal operating temperature. Ensure transmission fluid level is correct. Shift transmission to overdrive (OD).
2) Accelerate from stop to 50 mph. Hold speed for at least 15 seconds (30 seconds above 4000 ft.). Press TCS and accelerate to 50 mph. Hold speed for at least 15 seconds (30 seconds above 4000 ft.). Hold speed and throttle position steady for at least 15 seconds. While maintaining speed with transmission in 4th gear, lightly depress brake pedal and release. Maintain speed for additional 5 seconds. Bring vehicle to stop for at least 20 seconds. Repeat steps 1) and 2) at least 5 times. Perform Quick Test and record continuous codes.

ADDITIONAL SYSTEM FUNCTIONS

Additional diagnostic system features are available to help diagnose driveability problems and service EEC-IV systems.

CHECK ENGINE Light & Malfunction Indicator Light (MIL) – CHECK DCL light, CHECK ENGINE light and MIL are intended to alert driver of certain malfunctions in EEC-IV system.

Light may also be used to retrieve service codes stored in PCM. When hooked up for KOEO SELF-TEST or KOER SELF-TEST, light will display all codes which turn on light during vehicle operation, not just Continuous Memory Codes.

If light comes on during vehicle operation, vehicle should be inspected as soon as possible. Immediately turning off engine is not necessary; vehicle can be driven with light on.

If light comes on and then goes off during vehicle operation, code causing light to glow will be stored in PCM memory as a Continuous Memory Code.

Light should come on when ignition is turned on and go out when engine is started. If hard fault codes are not present, PCM turns out light when it receives a Profile Ignition Pick-Up (PIP) signal. If light does not come on, see SYMPTOMS in TROUBLE SHOOTING – NO CODES article in ENGINE PERFORMANCE section of appropriate MITCHELL® manual.

Output State Check – Output State Check is used as an aid in servicing output actuators associated with EEC-IV system. It allows technicians to energize and de-energize most system output actuators on command. This mode is entered from KOEO SELF-TEST after all codes have been retrieved. Leave SELF-TEST activated, and depress throttle to initiate test sequence. Each time throttle is depressed and released, output actuators will change state (from on to off or off to on).

Failure Mode Effects Management (FMEM), Code 98 Or 998 – FMEM mode allows system operation when sensors fail or transmit signals that are out of normal operating range. During FMEM mode, PCM substitutes a mid-range signal for defective sensor while continuing to monitor sensor. If faulty sensor's signals return to normal operating range, PCM will use those signals. A Code 98 or 998 will be displayed when FMEM mode is in effect.

AUTOMATIC TRANSMISSIONS
AODE & AODE-W EEC-IV Electronic Controls (Cont.)

3-567

Hardware Limited Operational Strategy (HLOS) – If a number of system or sensor failures are present and PCM is not receiving enough information to operate, PCM will switch to HLOS mode. PCM will output fixed values to allow operation of vehicle. Driveability concerns will be present. PCM will not output service codes in this mode.

SUMMARY

If no service codes (or pass code 11-1-11 or 111-1-111) is present but driveability problem still exists, return to TROUBLE SHOOTING in AODE/AODE-W overhaul article.

SERVICE CODE REFERENCE CHARTS

NOTE: In addition to transmission fault codes, engine-related fault codes may be output during QUICK TEST procedure. These fault codes pertain to engine performance and must be repaired first as engine performance will greatly affect transmission operation. For information and testing procedures of engine-related fault codes and components, see SELF-DIAGNOSTICS – EEC-IV article in ENGINE PERFORMANCE of appropriate MITCHELL® manual.

CODE REFERENCE CHART

Fault Code	Code Definition	[1] Test
KOEO Codes		
No Code	N/A	QA1
111	Pass Code	N/A
112	IAT Indicates 254° F (125° C)	DA20
113	IAT Indicates -40° F (-40° C)	DA10
114	IAT Voltage High/Low	DA1
116	ECT Out Of Range	DA1
117	ECT Indicates 254° F (125° C)	DA20
118	ECT Indicates -40° F (-40° C)	DA10
121	TPS Voltage High/Low	DH2
122	TPS Malfunction	DH10
123	TPS Malfunction	DH3
158	MAF Sensor Malfunction	DC21
159	MAF Sensor Malfunction	DC1
519	PSP Open Circuit	FF1
522	MLP Open Circuit	D1
539	A/C Switch Failure	KM40
621	SS1 Solenoid Circuit Failure	A1
622	SS2 Solenoid Circuit Failure	A1
623	TCIL Circuit Failure	TB3
624	EPC Circuit Failure	E1
625	Open PCM Output Driver	E1
634	MLP Out Of Range	D1
636	TOT Out Of Range	B1
637	TOT Sensor Circuit Open	B1
638	TOT Sensor Circuit Grounded	B1
652	TCC Circuit Error	C1
654	MLP-No PARK Indication	A1
998	FMEM Failure	TC10

[1] – Circuit or Pinpoint test.

CODE REFERENCE CHART (Cont.)

Fault Code	Code Definition	[1] Test
Continuous Memory Codes		
No Code	N/A	QA1
111	Pass Code	N/A
112	IAT Indicates 254° F (125° C)	DA90
113	IAT Indicates -40° F (-40° C)	DA90
117	ECT Indicates 254° F (125° C)	DA90
118	ECT Indicates -40° F (-40° C)	DA90
121	TPS Voltage High/Low	G1
122	TPS Malfunction	DH94
123	TPS Malfunction	DH90
124	TPS Malfunction	G1
125	TPS Malfunction	G1
157	MAF Sensor Malfunction	DC10
158	MAF Sensor Malfunction	DC21
184	MAF Sensor Malfunction	G5
185	MAF Sensor Malfunction	G5
452	Insufficient VSS Input	DP1
536	BOO Switch Malfunction	FD90
617	1-2 Shift Error	A1
618	2-3 Shift Error	A1
619	3-4 Shift Error	A1
624	EPC Solenoid Circuit Failure	E1
625	Open PCM Circuit	E1
628	TCC Engagement Error	C1
634	MLP Sensor Voltage Error	D1
637	TOT Sensor Open Circuit	B1
638	TOT Sensor Grounded Circuit	B1
639	Insufficient Input From OSS	F1
652	TCC Circuit Failure	C1
654	MLP-No PARK Indication	D1
656	TCC Continuous Slip	C1
657	Transaxle Overtemp. Condition	B1
659	MLP-PARK Indication	D1
667	MLP-Low Circuit Voltage	D1
668	MLP-High Circuit Voltage	D1
675	MLP-Voltage Out Of Range	D1
KOER Codes		
No Code	N/A	QA1
111	Pass Code	N/A
114	IAT Voltage High/Low	DA1
116	ECT Out Of Range	DA1
121	TPS Voltage High/Low	DH1
159	MAF Sensor Malfunction	DC1
167	TPS Malfunction	DH20
521	No PSP Flucuation	FF5
536	BOO Switch Malfunction	FD1
539	A/C Switch Failure	KM40
632	TCS Not Cycled	TB2
636	TOT Sensor Voltage Error	B1
639	Insufficient Input From OSS	F1

[1] – Circuit or Pinpoint test.

CIRCUIT/PINPOINT TEST PROCEDURES

NOTE: A breakout box, connected to vehicle harness at PCM, is necessary to perform most circuit tests. References to Test Pin No. found in CIRCUIT/PINPOINT TEST steps refer to test terminals on manufacturer breakout box. Circuit diagrams at beginning of each test identify circuit and wire colors.

HOW TO USE CIRCUIT/PINPOINT TESTS

1) DO NOT perform any CIRCUIT/PINPOINT TEST unless specifically instructed by a QUICK TEST procedure. Follow each test step in order until fault is found. DO NOT replace any part unless directed to do so. When more than one code is retrieved, start with first code displayed.

AUTOMATIC TRANSMISSIONS
AODE & AODE-W EEC-IV Electronic Controls (Cont.)

3-568

2) CIRCUIT/PINPOINT TESTS ensure electrical circuits are okay before sensors or other components are replaced. Always test circuits for continuity between sensor and PCM. Test all circuits for short to power, opens or short to ground. Voltage Reference (VREF) and Voltage Power (VPWR) circuits should be tested with KOEO or as specified in CIRCUIT/PINPOINT TESTS.

3) DO NOT measure voltage or resistance at PCM. DO NOT connect any test light unless specified in testing procedure. All measurements are made by probing rear of connector. Isolate both ends of a circuit and turn ignition off when checking for shorts or continuity, unless instructed otherwise.

4) Disconnect solenoids and switches from harness before measuring continuity and resistance or applying voltage. After each repair, check all component connections and repeat QUICK TEST.

5) An open circuit is defined as a resistance reading of greater than 5 ohms. This specification tolerance may be too high for some items in EEC-IV system. If resistance approaches 5 ohms, always clean suspect connector and coat it with protective dielectric silicone grease. A short is defined as a resistance reading of less than 10 k/ohms to ground, unless stated otherwise in CIRCUIT/PINPOINT TEST.

Diagnostic Aids – Fuel-contaminated engine oil may set some codes and effect engine performance. If oil is suspect, remove PCV valve from valve cover and repeat QUICK TEST. If problem is corrected, change engine oil.

NOTE: In following tests, circuit diagrams and illustrations are courtesy of Ford Motor Co.

PINPOINT TESTS

NOTE: PINPOINT TESTS are diagnostic formats used to test and service EEC-IV system. PINPOINT TESTS check transmission circuits, sensors and actuators.

PINPOINT TEST A

SHIFT SOLENOID ELECTRICAL SYSTEM

1) AODE/AODE-W Electronic Diagnostics – Ensure transmission harness connector is in acceptable condition. Repair as necessary. Disconnect transmission harness connector. Connect Transmission Tester (007-0085A) or equivalent to transmission. Perform TRANSMISSION SOLENOID CYCLING AND DRIVE TEST. Perform KOEO test until Continuous Memory trouble code(s) have been displayed. See QUICK TEST. Depress throttle to WOT and release. If vehicle enters Output State, go to next step. If vehicle will not enter Output State, see SELF-DIAGNOSTICS – EEC-IV article in ENGINE PERFORMANCE of appropriate MITCHELL® manual.

2) Check Electrical Signal Operation – Disconnect transmission harness connector. Inspect condition of connector and repair as needed. Using DVOM (20-volt scale), connect positive lead to transmission harness connector VPWR terminal. See Fig. A1. Connect negative lead to suspect solenoid circuit. Depress and release throttle to cycle solenoid output. If voltage changes at least .5 volts, go to step **5)**. If voltage is unaffected, go to next step.

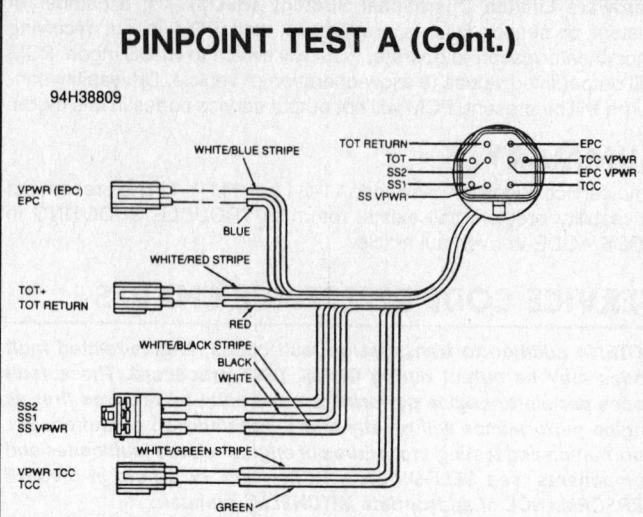

PINPOINT TEST A (Cont.)

94H38809

Fig. A1: Identifying Transmission Shift Solenoid Harness Connector

BREAKOUT BOX TEST PIN REFERENCE CHART

Component Circuit [1]	BOB Test Pin
EPC	38
EPC VPWR	37/57
SS1	51
SS2	52
SS VPWR	37/57
TCC	53
TCC VPWR	37/57
TOT Return	46
TOT	49

[1] – See Fig. A1.

3) Check Continuity Of Solenoid Signal & VPWR Harness Circuits – Ensure ignition is off. Disconnect PCM 60-pin connector, and inspect it for damaged pins, corrosion and loose wires. Repair as necessary. Install Breakout Box (007-00033), leaving PCM disconnected. Measure and record resistance between Breakout Box test pin No. 51 or 52 and corresponding transmission harness connector terminal. See Fig. A1. Measure and record resistance. Measure and record resistance between test pins No. 37 and 57 and transmission harness connector VPWR terminal. If any resistance is greater than 5 ohms, repair open circuit. Connect all components. Disconnect Breakout Box and repeat Quick Test. If resistance is 5 ohms or less, go to next step.

4) Check Solenoid Harness For Shorts To Power & Ground – Measure and record resistance between Breakout Box test pins No. 51 or 52 and test pins No. 37 and 57. Measure and record resistance between test pins No. 40, 46 and 60, and ground. If any resistance is less than 10 k/ohms, repair short circuit. Connect all components. Disconnect Breakout Box and repeat Quick Test. If resistance is 10 k/ohms or more, go to next step.

5) Solenoid Functional Test – Connect transmission Tester (007-00085). Perform solenoid function test. See tester instructions. If solenoid activates (LED green), go to next step. If solenoid does not activate, go to step **7)**.

6) Transmission Drive Test – Perform tester drive test. See tester instructions. If vehicle upshifts when operated with tester, go to TROUBLE SHOOTING in Ford AODE/AODE-W overhaul article. If vehicle does not upshift when operated by tester, go to next step.

7) Check Resistance Of Solenoid – Set tester Bench/Drive switch to Bench mode. Set Gear Selector switch to ohms check. Connect ohmmeter negative lead to SS1 jack and positive lead to VPWR jack on tester. Measure and record resistance. Connect ohmmeter negative lead to SS2 jack and positive lead to VPWR jack on tester. Measure and record resistance. Resistance for all solenoids should be 20-30 ohms. If resistance is within specification, go to next step. If resistance is not within specification, go to step **9)**.

8) Check Solenoid For Short To Ground – Check continuity between BAT(-) terminal and between SS1 and SS2. Check continuity between BAT(+) terminal and VPWR terminal. If continuity exists for any circuit, go to next step. If continuity does not exist, go to TROUBLE SHOOTING in Ford AODE/AODE-W overhaul article.

AUTOMATIC TRANSMISSIONS
AODE & AODE-W EEC-IV Electronic Controls (Cont.)

3-569

PINPOINT TEST A (Cont.)

9) AODE/AODE-W Internal Electronic Diagnostics – Drain transmission fluid. See TRANSMISSION SERVICING section. Remove transmission side pan. See OIL PUMP & VALVE BODY ASSEMBLY under ON-VEHICLE SERVICE in FORD AODE/AODE-W overhaul article. Inspect all internal harness connectors. Ensure all connectors are fully connected and not damaged. Repair as needed. Install all components in reverse order of disassembly. Fill transmission with fluid. Erase all trouble codes. See CLEARING CODES. Repeat QUICK TEST. If all connectors are okay, go to next step.

10) Check Internal Harness Continuity – Disconnect internal harness from solenoid assemblies. To test SS1, connect positive lead of ohmmeter to tester SS-1 jack and negative lead to SS1 White wire. Measure and record resistance. To test SS2, connect positive lead of ohmmeter to tester SS-2 jack and negative lead to SS2 Black wire. Measure and record resistance. Measure and record resistance.

To test SS1 and SS2 VPWR circuits, connect positive lead of ohmmeter to selected solenoid White/Black wire. Connect negative lead to corresponding VPWR tester terminal. Measure and record resistance. If all resistances measured are .5 ohms or less, go to next step. If any resistance measured is more than .5 ohms, replace internal harness. Go to step 12).

11) Check Internal Harness For Shorts To Ground – Using transmission tester, check continuity between each solenoid lead and BAT(-) terminal of tester. If continuity does not exist in any circuit, go to next step. If continuity exists in any circuit, replace internal harness. Go to Install all components in reverse order of disassembly. Fill transmission with fluid. Erase all trouble codes. See CLEARING CODES. Repeat QUICK TEST.

12) Check Resistance Of Solenoid – Using ohmmeter, check resistance between terminals of each solenoid. Resistance should be 20-30 ohms. If resistance is within specification, go to next step. If resistance measured for any solenoid is not within specification, replace solenoid assembly. Install all components in reverse order of disassembly. Fill transmission with fluid. Erase all trouble codes. See CLEARING CODES. Repeat QUICK TEST.

13) Check Solenoid For Short To Ground – Using ohmmeter, check continuity between each solenoid terminal and ground. If continuity exists, replace shift solenoid assembly. If continuity does not exist, go to TROUBLE SHOOTING in Ford AODE/AODE-W overhaul article. Install all components in reverse order of disassembly. Fill transmission with fluid. Erase all trouble codes. See CLEARING CODES. Repeat QUICK TEST.

PINPOINT TEST B

TOT ELECTRICAL SYSTEM

1) Visual Check – Check transmission harness connector. Inspect connector for damaged pins, corrosion and loose wires. Repair as necessary. Go to next step.

2) Check Electrical Signal Operation – Ensure ignition is off. Disconnect transmission connector. Using DVOM, connect positive lead to transmission harness connector TOT terminal and negative lead to SRTN terminal. See Fig. A1. Turn ignition on. If voltage is 4.75-5.25 volts, go to next step. If voltage is not within specification, see SELF-DIAGNOSTICS – EEC-IV article in ENGINE PERFORMANCE of appropriate MITCHELL® manual to diagnose NO VREF voltage.

3) Check Continuity Of TOT & Signal Return (SIG RTN) Circuits – Turn ignition off. Disconnect PCM 60-pin connector, and inspect it for damaged pins, corrosion and loose wires. Repair as necessary. Install Breakout Box (007-00033), leaving PCM disconnected. Measure and record resistance between Breakout Box test pin No. 49 and transmission harness connector TOT terminal. See Fig. A1. Measure and record resistance between test pin No. 46 and transmission harness connector SRTN terminal. If resistances measured are less than 5 ohms, go to next step. If resistances are more than 5 ohms, repair open circuit. Connect all components. Erase trouble codes. See CLEARING CODES. Repeat QUICK TEST.

4) Check TOT Circuit For Short To VPWR & Ground – Ensure ignition is off. Disconnect PCM 60-pin connector, and inspect it for damaged pins, corrosion and loose wires. Repair as necessary. Install Breakout Box (007-00033), leaving PCM disconnected. Measure and record resistance between Breakout Box test pin No. 49 and test pins No. 37 and 57. If resistance is less than 10 k/ohms, repair short circuit. Disconnect Breakout Box and repeat Quick Test. If resistance is 10 k/ohms or more, go to next step.

PINPOINT TEST B (Cont.)

NOTE: Code 637 is set if resistance measured exceeds 869 ohms (open circuit). Code 638 is set if resistance measured is below 597 ohms (short circuit).

5) Check Resistance Of TOT Sensor/Harness – Install Transmission Tester (007-00085). Set tester Bench/Drive switch to BENCH mode. Set Solenoid Select switch to OHMS CHECK. Connect ohmmeter lead to appropriate TOT jacks. Measure and record resistance. Resistance should be within specification. See TOT TEMPERATURE/RESISTANCE CHART. If resistance is within specification for specific temperature, either warm up transmission or allow transmission to cool to check resistance at different temperatures. If resistances measured remain within specification, go to next step. If resistances measured are not within specification, go to step 7).

TOT TEMPERATURE/RESISTANCE CHART

Temperature °F (°C)	Resistance-Ohms (K)
32-58 (0-20)	37-100
59-104 (21-40)	16-37
105-158 (41-70)	5-16
159-194 (71-90)	2.7-5
195-230 (91-110)	1.5-2.7
231-266 (111-130)	.8-1.5

6) Check TOT Sensor For Short To Ground – Check continuity between BAT (-) tester terminal and TOT terminals. If continuity exists, go to next step. If continuity does not exist, Erase all trouble codes. See CLEARING CODES. Repeat QUICK TEST. See FORD AODE/AODE-W overhaul article for non-electronic symptom diagnostics.

7) AODE/AODE-W Internal Electronic Diagnostics – Drain transmission fluid. See TRANSMISSION SERVICING section. Remove transmission side pan. See OIL PUMP & VALVE BODY ASSEMBLY under ON-VEHICLE SERVICE IN FORD AODE/AODE-W overhaul article. Inspect all internal harness connectors. Ensure all connectors are fully connected and not damaged. Repair as needed. Install all components in reverse order of disassembly. Fill transmission with fluid. Erase all trouble codes. See CLEARING CODES. Repeat QUICK TEST. If all connectors are okay, go to next step.

8) Check Internal Harness Continuity – Disconnect internal harness from TOT sensor. Connect positive lead of ohmmeter to tester TOT (+) jack and negative lead to TOT White/Red wire. Measure and record resistance. Connect positive lead of ohmmeter to tester TOT (-) jack and negative lead to TOT Red wire. If resistances measured are 5 ohms or less, go to next step. If any resistance measured is more than 5 ohms, replace internal harness. Go to step 10).

9) Check Internal Harness For Shorts To Ground – Using transmission tester, check continuity between each TOT sensor connector terminals and BAT(-) terminal of tester. If continuity does not exist in any circuit, go to next step. If continuity exists in any circuit, replace internal harness. Go to next step.

10) Check TOT Sensor Resistance – Using ohmmeter, check resistance between terminals TOT sensor. If resistance is within specification for specific temperature, go to next step. If resistances measured are not within specification, replace TOT sensor. Install all components in reverse order of disassembly. Fill transmission with fluid. Erase all trouble codes. See CLEARING CODES. Repeat QUICK TEST.

TOT TEMPERATURE/RESISTANCE CHART

Temperature °F (°C)	Resistance (k/ohms)
32-58 (0-20)	37-100
59-104 (21-40)	16-37
105-158 (41-70)	5-16
159-194 (71-90)	2.7-5
195-230 (91-110)	1.5-2.7
231-266 (111-130)	.8-1.5

11) Check Solenoid For Short To Ground – Using ohmmeter, check continuity between each TOT sensor terminal and ground. If continuity exists, replace faulty TOT sensor. If continuity does not exist, install all components in reverse order of disassembly. Fill transmission with fluid. Erase all trouble codes. See CLEARING CODES. Repeat QUICK TEST, see SELF-DIAGNOSTICS – EEC-IV article in ENGINE PERFORMANCE of appropriate MITCHELL® manual to diagnose vehicle harness or PCM malfunctions.

3-570

AUTOMATIC TRANSMISSIONS
AODE & AODE-W EEC-IV Electronic Controls (Cont.)

PINPOINT TEST C

TCC ELECTRICAL SYSTEM

NOTE: Transmission tester TCC terminals may be designated MCCC. Refer to tester instructions.

1) AODE/AODE-W Electronic Diagnostics – Ensure transmission harness connector is in acceptable condition. Repair as necessary. Disconnect transmission harness connector. Connect Transmission Tester (007-00085) or equivalent to transmission. Perform TRANSMISSION SOLENOID CYCLING AND DRIVE TEST. Perform KOEO test until Continuous Memory trouble code(s) have been displayed. See QUICK TEST. Depress throttle to WOT and release. If vehicle enters Output State, go to next step. If vehicle will not enter Output State, see SELF-DIAGNOSTICS – EEC-IV article in ENGINE PERFORMANCE of appropriate MITCHELL® manual.

2) Check Electrical Signal Operation – Disconnect transmission harness connector. Inspect condition of connector and repair as needed. Using DVOM (20-volt scale), connect positive lead to transmission harness connector VPWR terminal. See Fig. A1. Connect negative lead to TCC terminal. Depress and release throttle to cycle solenoid output. If voltage changes at least .5 volts, go to step 5). If voltage is unaffected, go to next step.

3) Check Continuity Of Solenoid Signal & VPWR Harness Circuits – Ensure ignition is off. Disconnect PCM 60-pin connector, and inspect it for damaged pins, corrosion and loose wires. Repair as necessary. Install Breakout Box (007-00033), leaving PCM disconnected. Measure and record resistance between Breakout Box test pin No. 53 and transmission harness connector TCC terminal. See Fig. A1. Measure and record resistance between test pins No. 37 and 57 and transmission harness connector VPWR terminal. If any resistance is greater than 5 ohms, repair open circuit. Connect all components. Disconnect Breakout Box and repeat Quick Test. If resistance is 5 ohms or less, go to step 5).

4) Check Solenoid Harness For Shorts To Power & Ground – Measure and record resistance between test pin No. 53 and test pins No. 37 and 57. Measure and record resistance between test pins No. 40, 46 and 60, and ground. If any resistance is less than 10 k/ohms, repair short circuit. Connect all components. Disconnect Breakout Box and repeat Quick Test. If resistance is 10 k/ohms or more, go to next step.

5) Solenoid Functional Test – Connect transmission Tester (007-00085). Perform solenoid voltage test. See tester instructions. If solenoid activates (LED green), go to next step. If solenoid does not activate, go to step 7).

6) transmission Drive Test – Perform tester drive test. See tester instructions. When transmission has shifted into 2nd gear, depress MCCC switch on tester. If engine rpm decreases when operated with tester, see SELF-DIAGNOSTICS – EEC-IV article in ENGINE PERFORMANCE of appropriate MITCHELL® manual to diagnose vehicle harness or PCM malfunctions. If engine rpm does not decrease when operated by tester, go to next step.

7) Check Resistance Of Solenoid – Set tester Bench/Drive switch to BENCH mode. Set Gear Selector switch to OHMS CHECK. Connect ohmmeter negative lead to MCCC jack and positive lead to MCCC VPWR jack on tester. Measure resistance. Resistance should be 1-3 ohms. If resistance is within specification, go to next step. If resistance is not within specification, go to step 9).

8) Check Solenoid For Short To Ground – Check continuity between BAT (-) tester terminal and MCCC terminals. If continuity exists, go to next step. If continuity does not exist, Erase all trouble codes. See CLEARING CODES. Repeat QUICK TEST. See TROUBLE SHOOTING in FORD AODE/AODE-W overhaul article for non-electronic symptom diagnostics.

9) AODE/AODE-W Internal Electronic Diagnostics – Drain transmission fluid. See TRANSMISSION SERVICING section. Remove transmission side pan. See OIL PUMP & VALVE BODY ASSEMBLY under ON-VEHICLE SERVICE in FORD AODE/AODE-W overhaul article. Inspect all internal harness connectors. Ensure all connectors are fully connected and not damaged. Repair as needed. Install all components in reverse order of disassembly. Fill transmission with fluid. Erase all trouble codes. See CLEARING CODES. Repeat QUICK TEST. If all connectors are okay, go to next step.

10) Check Internal Harness Continuity – Disconnect internal harness from TCC sensor. Connect positive lead of ohmmeter to tester MCCC jack and negative lead to TCC Green wire. Measure and record resistance. Connect positive lead of ohmmeter to tester VPWR jack and negative lead to TCC White/Green wire. If resistances measured are 5 ohms or less, go to next step. If any resistance measured is more than 5 ohms, replace internal harness. Go to step 12).

PINPOINT TEST C (Cont.)

11) Check Internal Harness For Shorts To Ground – Using transmission tester, check continuity between each TCC sensor connector terminals and BAT(-) terminal of tester. If continuity does not exist in either circuit, go to next step. If continuity exists in any circuit, replace internal harness. Go to next step.

12) Check TCC Solenoid Resistance – Using ohmmeter, check resistance between terminals TCC solenoid. If resistance is 1-3 ohms, go to next step. If resistance measured is not within specification, replace TCC solenoid assembly. Install all components in reverse order of disassembly. Fill transmission with fluid. Erase all trouble codes. See CLEARING CODES. Repeat QUICK TEST.

13) Check Solenoid For Short To Ground – Using ohmmeter, check continuity between each TCC solenoid terminal and ground. If continuity exists, replace faulty TCC solenoid. Install all components in reverse order of disassembly. Fill transmission with fluid. Erase all trouble codes. See CLEARING CODES. Repeat QUICK TEST. If continuity does not exist, install all components in reverse order of disassembly. Fill transmission with fluid. Erase all trouble codes. See CLEARING CODES. Repeat QUICK TEST. See TROUBLE SHOOTING in FORD AODE/AODE-W overhaul article for non-electronic symptom diagnostics.

PINPOINT TEST D

MLP Sensor

NOTE: Code 634 may be set if transmission is not in park or A/C is on when QUICK TEST is performed.

1) Preliminary Inspection – Disconnect MLP connector, and inspect it for damaged pins, corrosion and loose wires. Repair as necessary. Reconnect MLP connector. Ensure MLP sensor is correctly adjusted. See FORD AODE/AODE-W overhaul article. If sensor requires adjustment, clear trouble codes after adjustment. See CLEARING CODES. Repeat QUICK TEST. If sensor is correctly adjusted, go to next step.

2) Check Electrical Signal Operation – Ensure ignition is off. Disconnect MLP harness connector. Turn ignition on. Measure voltage between harness connector TOT terminal and SRTN terminal. See Fig. A1. If voltage is 4.75-5.25 volts, go to next step. If voltage is not within specification, see SELF-DIAGNOSTICS – EEC-IV article in ENGINE PERFORMANCE of appropriate MITCHELL® manual for NO VREF voltage.

3) Check Continuity Of MLP Sensor Harness Circuits – Turn ignition off. Disconnect PCM 60-pin connector, and inspect it for damaged pins, corrosion and loose wires. Repair as necessary. Install Breakout Box (007-00033), leaving PCM disconnected. Measure and record resistance between Breakout Box test pin terminal No. 46 and MLP harness connector terminal No. 359. See Fig. D1. Measure and record resistance between Breakout Box test pin terminal No. 30 and MLP harness connector terminal No. 199. If resistance is less than 5 ohms, go to next step. If resistance is more than 5 ohms, repair open circuit(s). Remove Breakout Box and connect all components. Erase all trouble codes. See CLEARING CODES. Repeat QUICK TEST.

94A38810

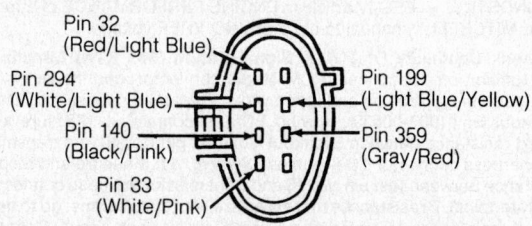

Pin 32 (Red/Light Blue)
Pin 294 (White/Light Blue)
Pin 140 (Black/Pink)
Pin 33 (White/Pink)
Pin 199 (Light Blue/Yellow)
Pin 359 (Gray/Red)

Fig. D1: Identifying transmission Harness Connector

4) Check MLP Circuit For Shorts To Power & Ground – Ensure MLP sensor harness connector is disconnected. Measure resistance between Breakout Box test pin No. 30 and test pins No. 37, 40, 46, 57 and 60. Measure resistance between Breakout Box test pin No. 30 and ground. If each measurement is more than 10 k/ohms, go to next step. If any measurement is less than 10 k/ohms, repair short circuit. Remove Breakout Box and connect all components. Erase all trouble codes. See CLEARING CODES. Repeat QUICK TEST.

AUTOMATIC TRANSMISSIONS
AODE & AODE-W EEC-IV Electronic Controls (Cont.)

3-571

PINPOINT TEST D (Cont.)

5) Operational Check Of MLP Sensor – Install MLP overlay on Transmission Tester (007-00085). Connect tester to MLP sensor. Check continuity and resistances in all positions. *See Fig. D1.* If MLP sensor does not operate within specification, replace sensor. Connect all components. Erase all trouble codes. See CLEARING CODES. Repeat QUICK TEST. If sensor operates within specification, connect all components. Erase all trouble codes. See CLEARING CODES. Repeat QUICK TEST. If code(s) 522, 634 or 659 are set, intermittent condition may be present. Attempt to duplicate malfunction by repeating previous steps.

94C38457

Transmission Range Selector Lever Position	Resistance (ohms)		Voltage**
	MIN	MAX	VOLTS
P	3770	4607	4.41
R	1304	1593	3.60
N	660	807	2.83
Ⓓ	361	442	2.09
2 / D	190	232	1.37
1	78	95	.68

** May vary ± 10% due to sensor and VREF variations.

Fig. D2: MLP Resistance Specification Chart

PINPOINT TEST E

EPC Solenoid

1) Check VPWR To Solenoid – Turn ignition off. Disconnect transmission harness connector. With KOEO, measure voltage between transmission harness connector EPC/TCC VPWR terminal and vehicle ground. *See Fig. A1.* If voltage is 10.5 volts or more, go to next step. If voltage is less than specification, repair open circuit. Connect all components. Erase all trouble codes. See CLEARING CODES. Repeat QUICK TEST.

2) Check Continuity Of Solenoid Signal & VPWR Harness Circuit – Turn ignition off, and wait 10 seconds. Disconnect PCM 60-pin connector, and inspect it for damaged pins, corrosion and loose wires. Repair as necessary. Install Breakout Box (007-00033), leaving PCM disconnected. Measure and record resistance between Breakout Box test pins No. 37 and 57, and transmission harness connector terminal EPC VPWR. *See Fig. A1.* Measure and record resistance between Breakout Box test pins No. 38, and transmission harness connector EPC terminal. If resistances measured are 5 ohms or less, go to next step. If resistances measured are more than 5 ohms, repair open circuit. Connect all components. Erase all trouble codes. See CLEARING CODES. Repeat QUICK TEST.

3) Check Harness For Short To Power Or Ground – Measure and record resistance between Breakout Box test pin No. 38 and test pins No. 37 and 57. Measure and record resistance between test pin No. 38 and test pins No. 40, 46 and 60. If any resistance measured is less than 10 k/ohms, repair short circuit. Disconnect Breakout Box and repeat Quick Test. If all resistances are 10 k/ohms or more, go to next step.

4) EPC Functional Test – Disconnect transmission harness connector. Connect transmission Tester (007-00085). Connect line pressure gauge. See FORD AODE/AODE-W overhaul article. Set Bench/Drive switch to DRIVE mode. Set Gear Selector switch to 1st gear position. Perform EPC function test. See tester instructions. Observe line pressure on gauge while depressing EPC switch (KOER). EPC solenoid should activate (LED green) and line pressure should drop when EPC switch is depressed. If solenoid operates correctly, replace PCM. Connect all components. Erase all trouble codes. See CLEARING CODES. Repeat QUICK TEST. If solenoid is not operating, go to next step.

5) Check Resistance Of Solenoid – Ensure tester power is off. Set Bench/Drive switch to BENCH mode. Connect ohmmeter negative lead to EPC jack. Connect positive lead to VPWR jack. If resistance is 2.48-5.66 ohms, go to next step. If resistance is not within specifications, go to step **7).**

6) Check Solenoid For Short To Ground – Check continuity between BAT(-) terminal of Transmission Tester and EPC jacks. If continuity exists, gp to next step. If continuity does not exist, see TROUBLE SHOOTING under FORD AODE/AODE-W overhaul article.

PINPOINT TEST E (Cont.)

7) AODE/AODE-W Internal Electronic Diagnostics – Drain transmission fluid. See TRANSMISSION SERVICING section. Remove transmission side pan. See OIL PUMP & VALVE BODY ASSEMBLY under ON-VEHICLE SERVICE IN FORD AODE/AODE-W overhaul article. Inspect all internal harness connectors. Ensure all connectors are fully connected and not damaged. Repair as needed. Install all components in reverse order of disassembly. Fill transmission with fluid. Erase all trouble codes. See CLEARING CODES. Repeat QUICK TEST. If all connectors are okay, go to next step.

8) Check Internal Harness Continuity – Disconnect internal harness from EPC solenoid assembly. Connect positive lead of ohmmeter to tester EPC jack and negative lead to EPC Blue wire. Measure and record resistance. Connect positive lead of ohmmeter to tester VPWR jack and negative lead to EPC White/Blue wire. If resistances measured are .5 ohms or less, go to next step. If any resistance measured is more than .5 ohms, replace internal harness. Go to step **10).**

9) Check Internal Harness For Shorts To Ground – Using transmission tester, check continuity between each EPC sensor connector terminals and BAT(-) terminal of tester. If continuity does not exist in either circuit, go to next step. If continuity exists in any circuit, replace internal harness. Go to next step.

10) Check EPC Solenoid Resistance – Using ohmmeter, check resistance between EPC solenoid terminals. Resistance should be 2.48-5.66 ohms. If resistance is within specification, go to next step. If resistance measured is not within specification, replace EPC solenoid. Install all components in reverse order of disassembly. Fill transmission with fluid. Erase all trouble codes. See CLEARING CODES. Repeat QUICK TEST.

11) Check Solenoid For Short To Ground – Using ohmmeter, check continuity between each EPC solenoid terminal and ground. If continuity exists, replace faulty EPC solenoid. Install all components in reverse order of disassembly. Fill transmission with fluid. Erase all trouble codes. See CLEARING CODES. Repeat QUICK TEST. If continuity does not exist, install all components in reverse order of disassembly. Fill transmission with fluid. Erase all trouble codes. See CLEARING CODES. Repeat QUICK TEST. See TROUBLE SHOOTING in FORD AODE/AODE-W overhaul article for non-electronic symptom diagnostics.

PINPOINT TEST F

Output Shaft Speed Sensor

1) Preliminary Inspection – Inspect condition of OSS harness and component connector. Repair as needed.

2) Check Continuity Of OSS Harness Circuit – Ensure ignition is off. Turn ignition off, and wait 10 seconds. Disconnect PCM 60-pin connector, and inspect it for damaged pins, corrosion and loose wires. Repair as necessary. Install Breakout Box (007-00033), leaving PCM disconnected. Disconnect OSS harness connector. Measure and record resistance between Breakout Box test pin No. 5 and OSS harness connector positive terminal. *See Fig. F1.* Measure and record resistance between Breakout Box test pin No. 46 and OSS harness connector negative terminal. If resistances measured are 5 ohms or less, go to next step. If resistances measured are more than 5 ohms, repair open circuit(s). Connect all components. Erase all trouble codes. See CLEARING CODES. Repeat QUICK TEST.

94B38811

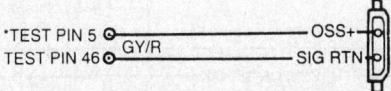

Fig. F1: Identifying OSS Harness Connector

3) Check OSS Circuit For Short To Power & Ground – Measure and record resistance between Breakout Box test pins No. 5 and 46, and test pins No. 37 and 57. Measure and record resistance between test pins No. 5, 37, 46 and 57, and test pins No. 40 and 60. If any resistance measured is less than 10 k/ohms, repair short circuit. Connect all components. Disconnect Breakout Box and repeat Quick Test. If resistance is 10 k/ohms or more, go to next step.

3-572

AUTOMATIC TRANSMISSIONS
AODE & AODE-W EEC-IV Electronic Controls (Cont.)

PINPOINT TEST F (Cont.)

4) OSS Functional Test – Ensure OSS harness connector is disconnected. Connect Transmission Tester (007-00085) to OSS component connector. Connect voltmeter leads to appropriate tester OSS jacks. Set voltmeter to 20 volt A/C scale. Perform drive cycle test. See TRANSMISSION DRIVE CYCLE TEST. If voltage increases with vehicle speed, replace PCM. Connect all components. Erase all trouble codes. See CLEARING CODES. Repeat QUICK TEST. If voltage does not increase with speed, go to next step.

5) Check Resistance Of OSS – Connect ohmmeter leads to appropriate Transmission Tester OSS jacks. If resistance is 450-750 ohms, go to next step. If resistance is not within specification, replace OSS. Connect all components. Erase all trouble codes. See CLEARING CODES. Perform drive cycle test. See TRANSMISSION DRIVE CYCLE TEST. Repeat QUICK TEST.

6) Check OSS For Short To Ground – Check for continuity between Transmission Tester OSS jacks and tester BAT(-) jack. If continuity does not exist, go to next step. If continuity exists, replace OSS. Connect all components. Erase all trouble codes. See CLEARING CODES. Perform drive cycle test. See TRANSMISSION DRIVE CYCLE TEST. Repeat QUICK TEST.

7) Check OSS Magnetism – Remove OSS from transmission. See FORD AODE/AODE-W overhaul article. Determine if OSS magnetically attracted to ferrous metal. If OSS acts like a magnet, go to next step. If OSS does not stick to ferrous metal surface, replace OSS. Connect all components. Erase all trouble codes. See CLEARING CODES. Perform drive cycle test. See TRANSMISSION DRIVE CYCLE TEST. Repeat QUICK TEST.

8) Check Output Shaft Ring Gear – With OSS removed, inspect condition of ring gear. Rotate driveshaft and ensure all 6 holes or indentations of ring gear are not damaged. Replace ring gear if damaged. See FORD AODE/AODE-W overhaul article. If ring gear is not damaged, replace OSS. Connect all components. Erase all trouble codes. See CLEARING CODES. Perform drive cycle test. See TRANSMISSION DRIVE CYCLE TEST. Repeat QUICK TEST.

CIRCUIT TESTS

NOTE: CIRCUIT TESTS are diagnostic formats used to test and service EEC-IV system. CIRCUIT TESTS check engine circuits, sensors and actuators.

CIRCUIT TEST CA

REFERENCE VOLTAGE

Diagnostic Aids – Perform this test when a check for VREF signal has failed in sensor input CIRCUIT TEST QA. SIG RTN is a dedicated ground used by most EEC-IV system sensors. VREF is a 5-volt reference voltage that is continuously output by PCM. This consistent voltage signal is used on all 3-wire sensors.

This circuit test is only intended to diagnose the following components and circuits:
- Powertrain Control Module (PCM).
- Vehicle wiring harness circuits (SIG RTN and VREF).

93E40422

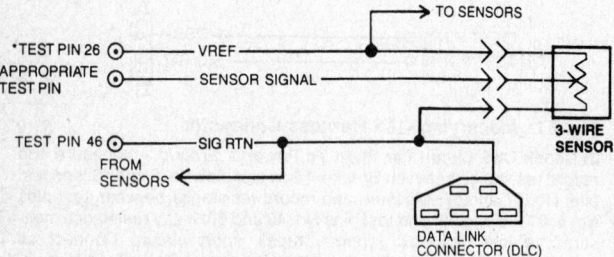

*TEST PINS LOCATED ON BREAKOUT BOX.
ALL HARNESS CONNECTORS VIEWED INTO MATING SURFACE.

Fig. CA1: Identifying Reference Voltage Circuits & Connector Terminals

CIRCUIT TEST CA (Cont.)

TEST PIN WIRE COLOR IDENTIFICATION

Terminal No.	Wire Color
No. 26 (VREF)	Brown/White
No. 46 (SIG RTN)	Gray/Red

1) Check Battery Power Circuit – Turn ignition off, and wait 10 seconds. Disconnect PCM 60-pin connector, and inspect it for damaged pins, corrosion and loose wires. Repair as necessary. Install Breakout Box (007-00033), leaving PCM connected. Turn ignition on. Measure and record voltage between breakout box test pin No. 37 and SIG RTN terminal of self-test connector. Measure and record voltage across battery terminals. If both readings are less than 10.5 volts or if they differ by more than 1.0 volt, reconnect sensor (if applicable). Go to CIRCUIT TEST XB for Mark VIII, CIRCUIT TEST X for Thunderbird SC or CIRCUIT TEST B for all other models under SELF-DIAGNOSTICS – EEC-IV article in ENGINE PERFORMANCE of appropriate MITCHELL® manual. If voltages are 10.5 volts or more and do not differ from one another by more than 1.0 volt, go to step **2)**.

2) Check VREF Voltage – With breakout box installed and PCM connected, set DVOM on 20-volt scale. Turn ignition on. Measure voltage between test pins No. 26 and 46 at breakout box. If voltage is 4-6 volts, go to step **3)**. If voltage is more than 6 volts, go to step **4)**. If voltage is less than 4 volts, go to step **5)**.

3) Check VREF & SIG RTN Circuit Continuity – Turn ignition off. Disconnect PCM. If directed here by a sensor test, ensure sensor is disconnected. Measure resistance between Breakout Box test pin No. 26 and VREF terminal at wiring harness connector of applicable sensor. Measure resistance between test pin No. 46 and SIG RTN circuit terminal at wiring harness connector of applicable sensor. If both readings are less than 5 ohms, VREF circuit is okay. If either reading is 5 ohms or more, repair open in VREF or SIG RTN circuit. Remove breakout box, and repeat QUICK TEST.

4) Check For Excess VREF Circuit Voltage – Turn ignition off. Ensure PCM is disconnected. With breakout box installed, disconnect scan tester or STAR tester (if applicable). Turn ignition on. Measure voltage between test pin No. 26 and battery ground. If voltage is less than 0.5 volt, replace PCM and repeat QUICK TEST. If voltage is 0.5 volt or more, repair short to battery power in wiring harness. Remove breakout box, reconnect components and repeat QUICK TEST. Replace PCM if fault still occurs.

5) Check For Shorted TPS – Turn ignition off. Connect PCM to breakout box. Disconnect Throttle Position Sensor (TPS) from wiring harness. Turn ignition on. Measure voltage between test pins No. 26 and 46 at breakout box. If voltage is 4 volts or more, replace TPS, remove breakout box and repeat QUICK TEST. If voltage is less than 4 volts on models with EVP, PFE or DPFE sensor, go to step **6)**. If voltage is less than 4 volts on all other models, go to step **7)**.

6) Check For Shorted EVP/PFE/DPFE Sensor – Turn ignition off, and wait 10 seconds. Disconnect EVP/PFE/DPFE sensor. Turn ignition on. Measure voltage between test pins No. 26 and 46. If voltage is 4 volts or more, replace EVP/PFE/DPFE sensor and repeat QUICK TEST. If voltage is less than 4 volts, reconnect EVP/PFE/DPFE sensor and go to step **8)**.

NOTE: A break in step numbering sequence occurs at this point. Procedure skips from step 6) to step 8). No test procedures have been omitted.

8) Check VREF Circuit For Short To Ground – Turn ignition off. Disconnect PCM. Disconnect TPS, MAP/BARO sensor and EVP/PFE/DPFE sensor. Measure resistance between test pin No. 26 and test pins No. 20, 40, 46 and 60. If any resistance is less than 1000 ohms, repair short to ground. Remove breakout box, and repeat QUICK TEST. If original problem still exists, replace PCM and repeat QUICK TEST. If readings are 1000 ohms or more, replace PCM and repeat QUICK TEST.

AUTOMATIC TRANSMISSIONS
AODE & AODE-W EEC-IV Electronic Controls (Cont.)

3-573

CIRCUIT TEST DA

TEMPERATURE SENSOR TEST (IAT & ECT)

Diagnostic Aids – Perform this test only when directed by QUICK TEST. Ambient air temperature must be at least 50°F (10°C) to receive valid input from IAT sensor. Engine coolant temperature must be greater than 50°F (10°C) to pass KOEO SELF-TEST and greater than 180°F (82°C) to pass KOER SELF-TEST. Voltage values in this test are based on a 5-volt VREF signal. Values may vary up to 15% due to sensor and VREF variations.

This circuit test is intended to diagnose the following components and circuits:
- Intake Air Temperature (IAT) sensor.
- Engine Coolant Temperature (ECT) sensor.
- Wiring harness circuits (IAT, ECT and SIG RTN).
- Powertrain Control Module (PCM).

To prevent replacing good components, ensure the following non-EEC areas or components are not cause of problem:
- Coolant level low.
- Cooling system, water pump or fan.
- Engine operating temperature.
- Engine oil level low.
- Thermostat.
- Air cleaner duct.
- Ambient temperature.

93J40427

*TEST PINS LOCATED ON BREAKOUT BOX.
ALL HARNESS CONNECTORS VIEWED INTO MATING SURFACE.

IAT SENSOR WIRING HARNESS CONNECTOR

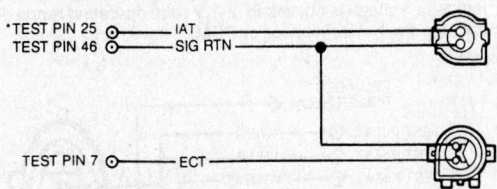

ECT SENSOR WIRING HARNESS CONNECTOR

On some applications, IAT sensor circuits may be reversed. Refer to appropriate table for correct identification.

Fig. DA1: Identifying Temperature Sensor Circuits & Connector Terminals

TEST PIN WIRE COLOR IDENTIFICATION

Application	Wire Color
No. 7 (ECT)	Light Green/Red
No. 25 (IAT)	Gray
No. 46 (SIG RTN)	Gray/Red

1) Code 116 Or 114: – Code 116 (ECT) or 114 (IAT) indicates corresponding sensor is out of self-test range. Correct range for measurement is .3-3.7 volts. Check for following possible causes:
- Low ambient temperature (less than 50°F).
- Low coolant level.
- Faulty harness connector.
- Faulty sensor.

Ensure upper radiator hose is hot and pressurized. Repeat QUICK TEST. If Code 114 or 116 is present, go to step **2)**. If none of these codes are present, service other codes as necessary.

2) Check VREF Circuit Voltage At TPS – Turn ignition off. Disconnect Throttle Position Sensor (TPS). With ignition on and engine off, measure voltage at TPS wiring harness connector between VREF and SIG RTN. See Fig. DA2. If voltage is 4-6 volts, reconnect TPS and go to step **3)**. If voltage is not 4-6 volts, go to CIRCUIT TEST CA.

3) Check Temperature Sensor Resistance – Turn ignition off. Disconnect suspect sensor. Measure resistance between sensor terminals. See ACT & ECT SENSOR SPECIFICATIONS table. If resistance is not within specification, replace suspected sensor and repeat QUICK TEST. If resistance is within specification, go to step **4)**.

CIRCUIT TEST DA (Cont.)

4) Check Temperature Sensor Resistance – Warm engine to normal operating temperature. Turn ignition off. Disconnect suspect sensor. Run engine at 2000 RPM for 2 minutes. Measure resistance between sensor terminals. See ACT & ECT SENSOR SPECIFICATIONS table. If resistance is within specification, replace PCM and repeat QUICK TEST. If sensor is not within specification, replace sensor and repeat QUICK TEST.

93A40428

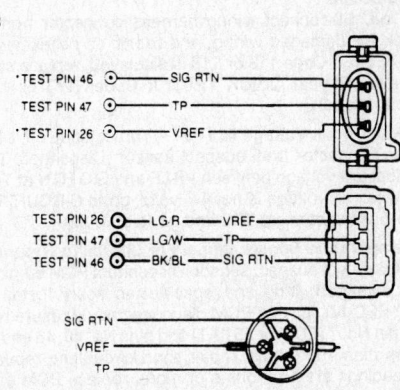

Fig. DA2: Identifying TPS Harness Connector Terminals

ACT & ECT SENSOR SPECIFICATIONS

Temperature °F (°C)	[1] Volts	[1] Ohms
50 (10)	3.51	58,750
68 (20)	3.07	27,300
86 (30)	2.60	24,270
104 (40)	2.13	16,150
122 (50)	1.70	10,970
140 (60)	1.33	7700
158 (70)	1.33	7700
176 (80)	0.78	3840
194 (90)	0.60	2800
212 (100)	0.46	2070

[1] – Values may vary by 15 percent.

NOTE: A break in step numbering sequence occurs at this point. Procedure skips from step 4) to step 10). No test procedures have been omitted.

10) Code 118 Or 113: Induce Opposite Code (Code 117 Or 112) –Code 118 (ECT) or 113 (IAT) indicate corresponding sensor signal is greater than self-test maximum. Maximum signal voltage for ECT and IAT sensor is 4.6 volts. Possible causes for excess voltage signals are:
- Open circuit in wiring harness (IAT or ECT).
- Faulty connection.
- Faulty sensor.
- Faulty PCM.

Turn ignition off. Disconnect suspect temperature sensor. Connect a jumper wire between SIG RTN terminal at sensor and SIG RTN terminal at sensor wiring harness connector. Repeat QUICK TEST. If Code 112 or 117 is displayed, replace suspect sensor and repeat QUICK TEST. If Code 112 or 117 is not displayed, remove jumper wire and go to next step.

11) Check Continuity Of Sensor Signal & SIG RTN Circuits – Turn ignition off. Ensure suspect temperature sensor is disconnected. Disconnect PCM 60-pin connector. Check for damaged wiring, and repair as necessary. Install Breakout Box (T83L-50-EEC-IV), leaving PCM disconnected. Measure resistance between test pin No. 7 (ECT sensor) or test pin No. 25 (IAT sensor) at breakout box and SIG RTN terminal at sensor wiring harness connector. Also measure resistance between test pin No. 46 and SIG RTN terminal at sensor wiring harness connector. If both readings are less than 5 ohms, replace PCM and repeat QUICK TEST. If either reading is 5 ohms or more, repair open circuit and repeat QUICK TEST.

NOTE: A break in step numbering sequence occurs at this point. Procedure skips from step 11) to step 20). No test procedures have been omitted.

3-574

AUTOMATIC TRANSMISSIONS
AODE & AODE-W EEC-IV Electronic Controls (Cont.)

CIRCUIT TEST DA (Cont.)

20) Code 117 or 112: Induce Opposite Code (118 or 113) – Code 117 (ECT) or 112 (IAT) indicates sensor signal is less than self-test minimum. Minimum signal for IAT and ECT sensor is 0.2 volt. Possible causes for this fault are:

- Circuit grounded in wiring harness.
- Faulty sensor.
- Faulty PCM.
- Faulty connection.

Turn ignition off. Disconnect wiring harness connector from suspect sensor. Check for damaged wiring, and repair as necessary. Repeat KOEO SELF-TEST. If Code 113 or 118 is displayed, replace sensor and connect harness. Repeat QUICK TEST. If Codes 113 or 118 is not displayed, go to step **21)**.

21) Check VREF Circuit Voltage At TPS – Turn ignition off. Disconnect wiring harness connector from suspect sensor. Disconnect TPS. Turn ignition on. Measure voltage between VREF and SIG RTN at TPS wiring harness connector. If voltage is not 4-6 volts, go to CIRCUIT TEST CA. If voltage is 4-6 volts, connect TPS and go to step **22)**.

22) Check Temperature Sensor Signal For Shorts To Ground – Turn ignition off. Disconnect suspect sensor. Disconnect PCM 60-pin connector. Check for damaged wiring, and repair as necessary. Install Breakout Box (T83L-50-EEC-IV), leaving PCM disconnected. Measure resistance between test pin No. 7 (ECT) or 25 (IAT) and pins No. 40, 46 and 60. If any reading is less than 10 k/ohms, repair short circuit and repeat QUICK TEST. If all readings are 10 k/ohms or more, replace PCM and repeat QUICK TEST.

NOTE: A break in step numbering sequence occurs at this point. Procedure skips from step 22) to step 90). No test procedures have been omitted.

90) Continuous Memory Code 118, 113, 117 Or 112: Check Sensor – A Continuous Memory Code 118 or 113 indicates sensor signal is greater than self-test maximum of 4.6 volts. Continuous Memory Code 117 or 112 indicates sensor signal is less than self-test minimum of 0.2 volt. Code is set during normal driving conditions. Possible causes for these faults are:

- Faulty sensor.
- Open or grounded circuit in harness.
- Faulty PCM.

SENSOR CODES

Sensor	Continuous Memory Code
IAT	113 Or 112
ECT	118 Or 117

Enter KOEO wiggle test mode. See CONTINUOUS MONITOR MODE (WIGGLE TEST) under QUICK TEST. Observe analog voltmeter or scan tester for indication of fault while tapping sensor lightly and wiggling sensor connector. If fault is indicated, disconnect and inspect connector and terminals. If connector and terminals are okay, replace sensor, clear continuous memory and repeat QUICK TEST. If fault is not indicated, go to step **91)**.

91) Check EEC-IV Wiring Harness – While in CONTINUOUS MONITOR MODE (WIGGLE TEST), observe analog voltmeter or scan tester while wiggling and bending wiring harness, a small section at a time, from sensor to cowl. Also check harness from cowl to PCM. If fault is indicated, isolate fault and repair as necessary. Clear continuous memory, and repeat QUICK TEST. If no fault is found, go to step **92)**.

92) Inspect PCM & Wiring Harness Connectors – Turn ignition off. Disconnect PCM 60-pin connector. Inspect both connector and connector terminals for damage. If connectors and terminals are damaged, repair as necessary and repeat QUICK TEST. If connectors and terminals are okay and fault cannot be duplicated at this time, see TROUBLE SHOOTING (EEC-IV) – NO CODES article in ENGINE PERFORMANCE in appropriate MITCHELL® manual.

NOTE: A break in step numbering sequence occurs at this point. Procedure skips from step 92) to step 100). No test procedures have been omitted.

100) Continuous Memory Code 338 – A Continuous Memory Code 338 indicates cooling system has not reached normal operating temperature. Possible causes for this fault are:

- Thermostat stuck open.
- Coolant outlet gasket leak.
- Water pump gasket leak.

Repair cooling system as necessary. Clear continuous memory, and repeat QUICK TEST.

CIRCUIT TEST DA (Cont.)

101) Continuous Memory Code 339 – A Continuous Memory Code 339 indicates cooling system has overheated. Possible causes for this fault are:

- Coolant level low.
- Thermostat stuck closed.
- Coolant system clogged.
- Water pump damaged or worn.
- Radiator cap damaged or worn.
- Cooling fan damaged or worn.

Repair cooling system as necessary. Clear continuous memory, and repeat QUICK TEST.

CIRCUIT TEST DC

MASS AIRFLOW (MAF) SENSOR

Diagnostic Aids – Perform this test when directed by QUICK TEST. This CIRCUIT TEST is intended to diagnose the following:

- MAF sensor.
- Wiring harness circuits (VPWR, PWR GND, MAF and MAF RTN).
- Powertrain Control Module (PCM).

To prevent replacement of good components, be aware the following non-EEC related areas may be cause of problem:

- Air cleaner element.
- Inlet air duct.
- Throttle body.

Code 159, retrieved during KOEO SELF-TEST, indicates voltage exceeded .7-volt test range. Code 159, retrieved during KOER SELF-TEST, indicates voltage is not within .2-1.5 volts operating range. Possible causes are faulty MAF sensor or PCM.

93F40431

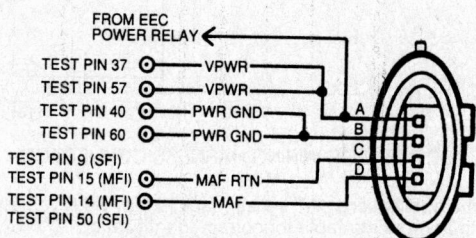

*TEST PINS LOCATED ON BREAKOUT BOX.
ALL HARNESS CONNECTORS VIEWED IN MATING SURFACE.

Fig. DC1: Identifying Mass Airflow (MAF) Sensor Circuits & Connector Terminals

TEST PIN WIRE COLOR IDENTIFICATION

Application	Wire Color
No. 9 Or 15 (MAF RTN)	Tan/Light Blue
No. 14 Or 50 (MAF)	Light Blue/Red
No. 37 & 57 (VPWR)	Red
No. 40 & 60 (PWR GND)	[1] Black/White

[1] – On Cougar and Thunderbird wire color is Black/Yellow.

MAF SIGNAL VOLTAGE [1]

Application	Volts
Idle	.6
20 MPH	1.1
40 MPH	1.7
60 MPH	2.1

[1] – MAF signal voltage is typical for normal operating temperature. Voltage signal may vary due to engine load and temperature.

AUTOMATIC TRANSMISSIONS
AODE & AODE-W EEC-IV Electronic Controls (Cont.)

3-575

CIRCUIT TEST DC (Cont.)

NOTE: Code 159 may be caused by use of a garage exhaust ventilation system. Ensure vehicle is vented to outside atmosphere before repeating QUICK TEST.

1) Code 159: Check VPWR Circuit Voltage – Code 159 indicates MAF sensor was out of range during KOEO or KOER SELF-TEST. Possible causes for this fault are:
- Air leak before or after MAF sensor.
- Faulty MAF sensor.
- Faulty IAC solenoid.
- Open or grounded wiring harness.
- Faulty PCM.

Repeat QUICK TEST. If Code 412 is present, go to CIRCUIT TEST KE, step 1), and/or if Code 411 is present, go to CIRCUIT TEST KE, step 15) under SELF-DIAGNOSTICS – EEC-IV article in ENGINE PERFORMANCE of appropriate MITCHELL® manual. If Code 411 or 412 is not present, go to step 2).

2) VPWR Circuit Voltage Check – Turn ignition off. Disconnect MAF sensor connector. Set DVOM on 20-volt scale. Turn ignition on. Measure voltage between VPWR terminal at MAF sensor wiring harness connector and negative battery terminal. If voltage is less than 10.5 volts, repair open in VPWR circuit and repeat QUICK TEST. If voltage is 10.5 volts or more, go to step 3).

3) Check MAF Sensor Ground – Turn ignition on. With MAF sensor disconnected, measure voltage between VPWR terminal and PWR GND terminal at MAF sensor connector. If voltage is less than 10.5 volts, repair open PWR GND circuit. Connect MAF sensor, and repeat QUICK TEST. If voltage is 10.5 volts or more, go to step 13).

NOTE: A break in step numbering sequence occurs at this point. Procedure skips from step 3) to step 10). No test procedures have been omitted.

10) Continuous Memory Code 157: Check For Intermittent Sensor Failure – Continuous Memory Code 157 indicates MAF signal was less than 0.4 volt sometime during last 80 warm-up cycles. Possible causes for this fault are:
- Open MAF circuit.
- MAF circuit shorted to ground.
- Faulty MAF sensor.
- MAF sensor disconnected.

Start engine and allow to idle for 5-10 minutes. Perform KOEO SELF-TEST. If Code 157 is present, go to step 13). If Code 157 is not present, go to next step.

11) Monitor MAF Circuit Under Simulated Road Shock – Turn ignition off. Disconnect and inspect 60-pin connector at PCM. Service if necessary. Install EEC-IV Breakout Box (T83L-50-EEC-IV), leaving PCM connected. Connect DVOM between MAF test pin and MAF RTN test pin. See appropriate table at beginning of this CIRCUIT TEST. DVOM should read about 0.4 volt. Start engine and allow to idle. Lightly tap on MAF sensor and wiggle wiring harness to simulate road conditions. If sudden change in DVOM reading occurs, fault is indicated. If fault is indicated, replace MAF sensor and repeat QUICK TEST. If no fault is indicated, leave DVOM connected and go to next step.

12) Check Wiring Harness For Open Or Short Circuit – Turn ignition on. Shake and bend small sections of wiring harness starting at MAF sensor and working toward dash panel. Shake and bend small sections of wiring harness starting at dash panel and working toward PCM. If fault is indicated, isolate and repair as necessary. If fault is not indicated, problem is intermittent and cannot be duplicated at this time.

13) Codes 157 Or 129: Check For Air Leak At MAF Sensor – Check for broken or loose air outlet tube clamps at throttle body and air cleaner assembly. Repair or replace as necessary. If no faults are found, go to next step.

14) Check Continuity Of MAF & VPWR Circuit – Turn ignition off. Disconnect MAF sensor and PCM wiring harness connector. Install EEC-IV Breakout Box (T83L-50-EEC-IV), leaving PCM disconnected. Measure resistance between MAF terminal of MAF sensor wiring harness connector and test pins No. 37 and 57. Measure resistance between MAF terminal of MAF sensor wiring harness connector and test pin No. 50 (Sequential Fuel Injected engines) or test pin No. 14 (except Sequential Fuel Injected engines). If resistance is more than 5 ohms, repair open circuit and repeat QUICK TEST. If resistance is 5 ohms or more, go to next step.

CIRCUIT TEST DC (Cont.)

15) Check MAF Signal For Short To Ground – Turn ignition off. Ensure MAF sensor and PCM wiring harness are disconnected. Measure resistance between test pin No. 50 and test pins No. 9, 40 and 60 (Sequential Fuel Injected engines) or between test pin No. 14 and test pins No. 15, 40 and 60 (except Sequential Fuel Injected engines). If resistance is less than 10 k/ohms, repair short circuit and repeat QUICK TEST. If resistance is 10 k/ohms or more, go to next step.

16) Check Power & Ground Circuit Continuity – Turn ignition off. Ensure MAP sensor and PCM wiring harness connector are disconnected. Measure resistance between PWR GND terminal at MAF sensor wiring harness connector and negative battery terminal. If resistance is 10 k/ohms or more, repair open PWR GND circuit and repeat QUICK TEST. If resistance is less than 10 k/ohms, go to next step.

17) Check Continuity Of MAF RTN Circuit – Ensure ignition is turned off. Measure resistance between MAF RTN terminal of MAF sensor wiring harness connector and test pin No. 9 (Sequential Fuel Injected engines) or test pin No. 15 (except Sequential Fuel Injected engines). If resistance is more than 5 ohms, repair open circuit and repeat QUICK TEST. If resistance is 5 ohms or more, go to next step.

18) Check MAF Circuit For Short To Ground – Turn ignition off. Ensure MAF sensor is disconnected. Connect PCM to breakout box. Measure resistance between test pin No. 50 and test pins No. 9, 40 and 60. If resistance is less than 10 k/ohms, replace PCM and repeat QUICK TEST. If resistance is 10 k/ohms or more, go to next step.

19) Check MAF Circuit Output – Turn ignition off. Connect MAF sensor wiring harness connector. Start engine. Measure resistance between test pin No. 50 and negative battery terminal. If voltage is .36-1.50 volts, go to next step. If voltage is not .36-1.50 volts, replace MAF sensor and repeat QUICK TEST.

20) Check MAF Circuit Output – With engine running, measure resistance between test pin No. 9 and test pin No. 50. If voltage is .36-1.50 volts, replace PCM and repeat QUICK TEST. If voltage is not .36-1.50 volts, replace MAF sensor and repeat QUICK TEST.

21) Code 158 – Turn ignition off. Disconnect MAF sensor wiring harness connector. Start engine, and allow it to idle for one minute. Turn ignition off. Repeat KOEO SELF-TEST. If Code 157 is present, replace MAF sensor and repeat QUICK TEST. If Code 157 is not present, go to step 22).

22) Check MAF Circuit For Short To VPWR – Turn ignition off. Disconnect PCM 60-pin connector, and inspect it for damaged or corroded terminals. Service if necessary. Measure resistance between MAF and VPWR terminals at MAF sensor wiring harness connector. If resistance is 10 k/ohms or more, replace PCM and repeat QUICK TEST. If resistance is less than 10 k/ohms, repair short circuit and repeat QUICK TEST.

CIRCUIT TEST DH

THROTTLE POSITION (TP) SENSOR

Diagnostic Aids – Perform this test only when directed by QUICK TEST. This test is intended to diagnose the following:
- TP sensor.
- Wiring harness circuits (TP, SIG RTN and VREF).
- Powertrain Control Module (PCM).

Normal range of throttle angle measurement for TP sensor is 0-85 degrees. To pass QUICK TEST procedure, range of throttle rotation (in degrees) must be within 3 percent of specification. See Fig. DH2.

To prevent replacement of good components, be aware the following non-EEC related areas may be at fault:
- Idle speed.
- Binding throttle shaft or linkage.
- Choke cam adjustment (if equipped).
- TP sensor not seated.

TEST PIN WIRE COLOR IDENTIFICATION

Application	Wire Color
No. 26 (VREF)	Light Green/Red
No. 46 (SIG RTN)	Black/Blue
No. 47 (TP)	Light Green/White

3-576

AUTOMATIC TRANSMISSIONS
AODE & AODE-W EEC-IV Electronic Controls (Cont.)

CIRCUIT TEST DH (Cont.)

93A40428

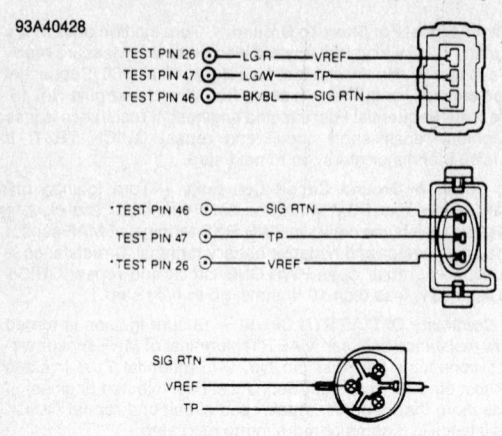

TEST PIN 26 — LG·R — VREF
TEST PIN 47 — LG/W — TP
TEST PIN 46 — BK/BL — SIG RTN

*TEST PIN 46 — SIG RTN
TEST PIN 47 — TP
*TEST PIN 26 — VREF

SIG RTN
VREF
TP

NOTE: EITHER TYPE MAY BE FITTED

Fig. DH1: Identifying TP Sensor Circuits & Connector Terminals

92G03822

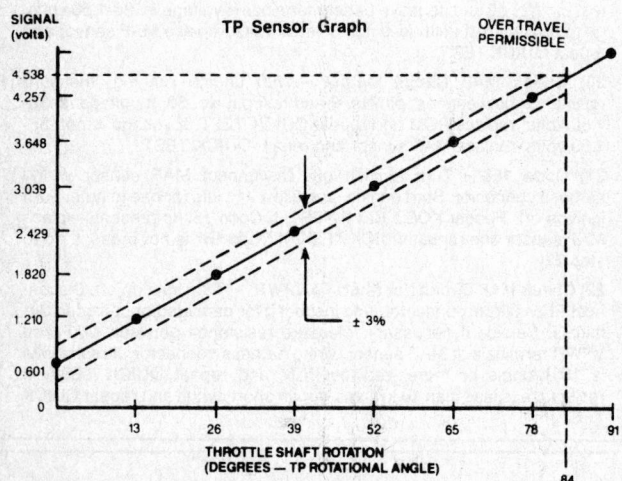

Fig. DH2: TP Sensor Specification Chart

1) KOER Code 121: Check For Other Codes – KOER Code 121 indicates TP sensor rotational setting may be out of self-test range. Possible causes for this fault are:
- Binding throttle linkage.
- TP sensor not seated correctly.
- Faulty TP sensor.
- Faulty Powertrain Control Module (PCM).

Perform KOER SELF-TEST. Check for Code 327. If either of these codes are present with Code 121, service Code 327 and repeat QUICK TEST. If these codes are not present, go to step **2)**.

2) Code 121: Check For Binding Throttle Plate – Inspect throttle body for binding. If throttle body is binding, check for binding throttle or cruise control linkage, vacuum line or harness interference, etc. Repair as necessary, and repeat QUICK TEST. If no mechanical problem is found, go to step **3)**.

3) Code 123: Attempt To Generate Code 122 – Code 123 indicates TP sensor signal is greater than self-test maximum value. Possible causes for this fault are:
- TP sensor not seated properly.
- Faulty TP sensor.
- Short circuit to power.
- Faulty PCM.

Turn ignition off. Disconnect TP sensor wiring harness connector. Inspect and repair connector pins if damaged. Repeat KOEO SELF-TEST. Ignore all other codes at this time. If Code 63/122 is not displayed, go to step **5)**. If Code 122 is displayed, go to step **4)**.

CIRCUIT TEST DH (Cont.)

4) Check VREF Circuit Voltage – Turn ignition on. Measure voltage between VREF and SIG RTN terminals at TP sensor wiring harness connector. If reading is 4-6 volts, replace TP sensor and repeat QUICK TEST. If reading is not 4-6 volts, reconnect sensor and go to CIRCUIT TEST CA.

5) Check TP Circuit For Short To Power – Turn ignition off. Leave TP sensor disconnected. Disconnect PCM 60-pin connector. Inspect it for damage and repair as necessary. Install EEC-IV Breakout Box (T83L-50-EEC-IV), leaving PCM disconnected. Measure resistance between test pin No. 47 and test pins No. 26 and 57. If either resistance is less than 10 k/ohms, repair short circuit in wiring harness and repeat QUICK TEST. If both resistances are 10 k/ohms or more, replace PCM and repeat QUICK TEST.

NOTE: A break in step numbering sequence occurs at this point. Procedure skips from step 5) to step 10). No test procedures have been omitted.

10) Code 122: Attempt To Generate Code 123 Or 121 – Code 122 indicates TP signal is less than minimum self-test value. See Fig. DH2. Possible causes for this fault are:
- TP sensor not seated correctly.
- Faulty TP sensor.
- Open circuit in wiring harness.
- Grounded circuit in wiring harness.
- Faulty PCM.

Turn ignition off, and wait 10 seconds. Disconnect TP sensor from harness. Install a jumper wire between VREF and TP terminals at TP sensor wiring harness connector. Perform KOEO SELF-TEST. If no codes are generated, remove jumper wire and go to step **13)**. If Codes 123 and 121 are not present, remove jumper wire and go to step **11)**. If either Code 123 or 121 is displayed, replace TP sensor and repeat QUICK TEST.

11) Check VREF Circuit Voltage – Turn ignition on. Measure voltage between VREF and SIG RTN terminals at TP sensor wiring harness connector. If voltage is not 4-6 volts, reconnect all components and go to CIRCUIT TEST CA. If voltage is 4-6 volts, go to step **12)**.

12) Check TP Sensor Circuit Continuity – Turn ignition off. Leave TP sensor disconnected. Disconnect PCM 60-pin connector. Inspect connector and repair if necessary. Install EEC-IV Breakout Box (T83L-50-EEC-IV), leaving PCM disconnected. Measure resistance between TP terminal at TP sensor wiring harness connector and test pin No. 47. If resistance is 5 ohms or more, repair open circuit and repeat QUICK TEST. If resistance is less than 5 ohms, go to step **13)**.

13) Check TP Circuit For Shorts To Ground – Turn ignition off. Leave TP sensor disconnected. Ensure both 4EAT module wiring harness connectors are disconnected (if applicable). Disconnect PCM 60-pin connector. Inspect wiring, and repair as necessary. With breakout box installed and PCM disconnected, measure resistance between test pin No. 47 and test pins No. 40, 46 and 60. If any reading is less than 10 k/ohms, repair short circuit and repeat QUICK TEST. If all readings are 10 k/ohms or more, replace PCM and repeat QUICK TEST.

NOTE: A break in step numbering sequence occurs at this point. Procedure skips from step 13) to step 20). No test procedures have been omitted.

20) Code 167: Repeat Dynamic Response Test – KOER Code 167 indicates TP sensor did not exceed 25% rotation during dynamic response portion of KOER SELF-TEST. A complete Wide Open Throttle (WOT) must be performed during dynamic response portion of test. Perform KOER SELF-TEST. Ensure WOT is completed during dynamic response portion of test. If Code 167 is still present, go to step **21)**. If code is not present, system is unable to duplicate Code 167 at this time. Service any other KOER codes. If no other service codes are present, testing is complete.

21) Check TP Sensor Movement During Dynamic Response Test – Turn ignition off. Disconnect PCM 60-pin connector. Inspect wiring, and repair as necessary. Install EEC-IV Breakout Box (T83L-50-EEC-IV), leaving PCM connected. Set DVOM on 20-volt scale. Connect DVOM between test pins No. 46 and 47 at breakout box. Perform KOER SELF-TEST and ensure proper WOT is completed during dynamic response test. If DVOM reading exceeds 3.5 volts during dynamic response test, replace PCM and repeat QUICK TEST. If reading does not exceed 3.5 volts, ensure TP sensor is correctly installed and adjusted. If TP sensor is correctly installed and adjusted, replace TP sensor. Repeat QUICK TEST.

AUTOMATIC TRANSMISSIONS
AODE & AODE-W EEC-IV Electronic Controls (Cont.)

3-577

CIRCUIT TEST DH (Cont.)

NOTE: A break in step numbering sequence occurs at this point. Procedure skips from step 21) to step 90). No test procedures have been omitted.

90) Continuous Memory Code 123 – This test monitors TP sensor under simulated road conditions. Enter wiggle test. See CONTINUOUS MONITOR MODE (WIGGLE TEST) under QUICK TEST. Connect DVOM or diagnostic tester to STO terminal of self-test connector. While slowly opening throttle to WOT, observe DVOM or diagnostic tester for indication of fault. Slowly bring throttle to closed position. Lightly tap TP sensor and wiggle harness connector. This test checks for open or short in TP sensor and wiring harness. If no fault is indicated, go to step **92)**. If fault is indicated, go to step **91)**.

91) Measure TP Circuit Voltage While Exercising TP Sensor – Turn ignition off, and wait 10 seconds. Disconnect PCM 60-pin connector. Inspect for damage and repair if necessary. Install EEC-IV Breakout Box (T83L-50-EEC-IV), leaving PCM connected. Stay in wiggle test (as in previous step). Connect DVOM between test pins No. 47 and 46. Set DVOM on 20-volt scale. With ignition on and engine off, observe DVOM and repeat step 90). If fault occurs at less than 4.25 volts, inspect TP sensor connectors and terminals. If connectors and terminals are okay, replace TP sensor, clear codes and repeat QUICK TEST. If fault does not occur at less than 4.25 volts, TP sensor over-travel may have caused Continuous Memory Code 123. TP sensor is okay. Go to step 92) to check wiring harness.

92) Check EEC-IV Wiring Harness – While in wiggle test, bend and shake small sections of EEC-IV harness from TP sensor wiring harness connector to firewall and from firewall to PCM while observing analog voltmeter or scan tester. If fault is indicated, isolate fault in wiring and repair as necessary. Clear codes, and repeat QUICK TEST. If no fault is indicated, go to step **93)**.

93) Check PCM & Harness Connectors – Turn ignition off, and wait 10 seconds. Disconnect PCM 60-pin connector from breakout box. Inspect connectors and terminals for damage, and repair as necessary. Clear codes from PCM memory, and repeat QUICK TEST. If connectors and terminals are okay, fault cannot be duplicated at this time. Continuous Memory Code 123 testing is complete.

94) Continuous Memory Code 122 – Enter wiggle test. See CONTINUOUS MONITOR MODE (WIGGLE TEST) under QUICK TEST. Connect DVOM or diagnostic tester to STO terminal of self-test connector. Observe DVOM or diagnostic tester for indication of fault while performing the following:
- Slowly open throttle to WOT.
- Slowly bring throttle to closed position.
- Lightly tap TP sensor and wiggle connector.

If fault is indicated, disconnect TP sensor. Inspect connectors and terminals. If connectors and terminals are okay, replace TP sensor. Clear codes from PCM memory, and repeat QUICK TEST. If no fault is indicated, go to next step.

95) Check EEC-IV Wiring Harness – Stay in wiggle test (as in previous step). Bend, wiggle and shake small sections of EEC-IV harness from TP sensor wiring harness connector to firewall and from firewall to PCM while observing analog voltmeter or scan tester. If fault is indicated, isolate fault in wiring and repair as necessary. Clear codes from PCM memory, and repeat QUICK TEST. If no fault is indicated, go to step **96)**.

96) Check PCM & Harness Connectors – Turn ignition off. Inspect PCM 60-pin connector and terminals for damage. Repair connector terminals if necessary. Clear codes from PCM memory, and repeat QUICK TEST. If connectors and terminals are okay, fault cannot be duplicated at this time. Continuous Memory Code 122 testing is complete.

CIRCUIT TEST DP

VEHICLE SPEED SENSOR (VSS)

Diagnostic Aids – Perform this test when directed by QUICK TEST. This CIRCUIT TEST is intended to diagnose:
- Vehicle Speed Sensor (VSS).
- VSS wiring harness circuits.
- Powertrain Control Module (PCM).

93I40525

Fig. DP1: Vehicle Speed Sensor Circuit

TEST PIN WIRE COLOR IDENTIFICATION

Application	Wire Color
All Except E-150 & F-150	
No. 3 (VSS +)	Gray/Black
No. 6 (VSS –)	[1] Pink/Orange
E-150 & F-150	
No. 3 (VSS +)	Dark Green/White
No. 6 (VSS –)	Pink/Orange

[1] – On Town Car wire color is Black/Light Blue.

Preliminary Instructions – Record and clear continuous memory codes. Warm engine to normal operating temperature. Place gear selector in Drive position. Accelerate hard to 35 MPH and coast down to a stop. Shut off engine. Perform KOEO SELF-TEST. Repeat step at least 2 more times. Go to step **1)**.

1) Continuous Memory Code 452 – Code 452 indicates PCM detected incorrect output from VSS sometime during vehicle operation. Possible causes for this code are:
- Faulty VSS.
- Open or shorted circuit.
- Faulty PCM.

Perform appropriate TRANSMISSION DRIVE CYCLE TEST. Ensure driveability complaint can be verified. If Code 452 is still present or driveability complaint can be verified, go to step **2)**. If code is not present or complaint cannot be verified, fault cannot be duplicated at this time. Clear codes, and see SYMPTOMS in TROUBLE SHOOTING (EEC-IV) – NO CODES article in appropriate MITCHELL® manual.

2) Check VSS Circuit Continuity – Turn ignition off. Disconnect VSS sensor. Remove PCM 60-pin connector. Inspect terminals, and repair if damaged. Install EEC-IV Breakout Box (T83L-50-EEC-IV). Measure resistance between VSS (+) terminal at VSS wiring harness connector and test pin No. 3 at breakout box. Measure resistance between VSS (–) terminal at VSS wiring harness connector and test pin No. 6 at breakout box. If any resistance reading is more than 5 ohms, service open circuit in VSS wiring harness and repeat step **1)**. If both resistance readings are 5 ohms or less, go to step **3)**.

3) Check VSS Circuits For Shorts To Power Or Ground – Turn ignition off. Ensure PCM and VSS are disconnected. Measure resistance between test pin No. 3 and test pins No. 6, 37 and 40 at breakout box. If all readings are greater than 500 ohms, go to step **4)**. If any reading is less than 500 ohms, repair shorts in VSS wiring harness and repeat step **1)**.

4) Check VSS Resistance – Turn ignition off, and wait 10 seconds. Disconnect VSS wiring harness connector. Measure resistance across VSS terminals. If reading is not 190-250 ohms, replace VSS and repeat step **1)**. If resistance is 190-250 ohms, replace PCM and repeat step **1)**.

3-578

AUTOMATIC TRANSMISSIONS
AODE & AODE-W EEC-IV Electronic Controls (Cont.)

CIRCUIT TEST FD

BRAKE ON-OFF (BOO) SWITCH

Diagnostic Aids – Perform this test when directed by QUICK TEST. This test is intended to diagnose a faulty BOO switch circuit or PCM. To prevent replacement of good components, be aware following non-EEC related areas may be at fault:
- Brakelight bulb.
- Brakelight switch or brakelight fuse.

93I40541

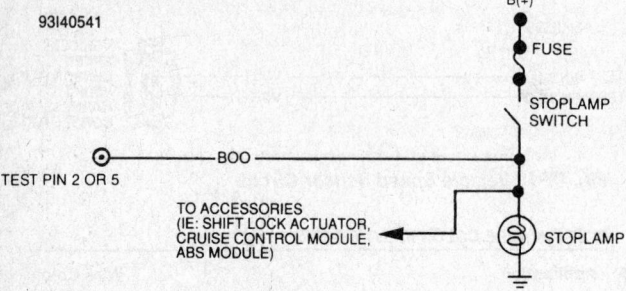

*TEST PINS LOCATED ON BREAKOUT BOX

Fig. FD1: BOO Switch Circuit

TEST PIN WIRE COLOR IDENTIFICATION

Application	Wire Color
No. 2 (BOO)	Light Green

1) Code 536: Verify Brake Pedal Was Depressed – Code 536 indicates that when brake pedal is applied during KOER SELF-TEST, BOO signal did not cycle high and low. Possible causes for this fault are:
- Brake pedal not applied during self-test.
- Brake pedal applied during entire self-test.
- Open brakelight circuit.
- Short to ground or power.
- Faulty Powertrain Control Module (PCM).

If brake was not applied during KOER SELF-TEST, repeat test. Depress and release brake pedal only once during test. If pedal was depressed, go to step **2)**.

2) Check Operation Of Brakelights – With ignition on, check operation of brakelights. If brakelights operate normally, go to step **3)**. If brakelights do not operate, go to step **4)**. If brakelights are always on, go to step **5)**.

3) Check For BOO Switch Circuit Cycling – Turn ignition off. Wait 10 seconds. Disconnect PCM 60-pin connector. Inspect terminals, and repair if damaged. Install EEC-IV Breakout Box (T83L-50-EEC-IV), leaving PCM disconnected. Measure voltage between BOO test pin (No. 2) and test pin No. 40 while applying and releasing brake. If voltage cycles, replace PCM and repeat QUICK TEST. If voltage does not cycle, repair open circuit in BOO switch circuit between PCM and BOO switch connection to brakelight circuit. Repeat QUICK TEST.

4) Check For Power To Brake Switch – Ensure related fuses and brakelight bulbs are in good condition. Turn ignition off. Disconnect brakelight switch (located on brake pedal). Measure voltage between BATT (+) input to brakelight switch and ground. If voltage is greater than 10 volts, check condition of brakelight switch. If brakelight switch is okay, repair open circuit between brakelight switch and brakelight ground. Repeat QUICK TEST. If voltage is less than 10 volts, repair open BATT (+) circuit to brakelight switch and repeat QUICK TEST.

5) Verify Brake Switch Is Not Always Closed – Turn ignition off. Disconnect brakelight switch (located on brake pedal). Turn ignition on. If brakelights are still on, go to step **6)**. If brakelights are not on, verify correct installation of brakelight switch. If installation is okay, replace brakelight switch and repeat QUICK TEST.

6) Check For Short To Power In PCM – Turn ignition off. Disconnect PCM. Turn ignition on. Check brakelights. If brakelights are on, go to step **7)**. If brakelights are not on, replace PCM and repeat QUICK TEST.

7) Check For Short To Power In Shift Lock Actuator – Turn ignition off. Ensure PCM and brakelight switch are disconnected. Disconnect shift lock actuator, cruise control module and ABS module (if equipped). Turn ignition on. If brakelights are still on, repair short to power in BOO or stoplight circuit and repeat QUICK TEST. If brakelights are not on, repair short circuit in shift lock actuator circuit, cruise control system circuit or ABS circuit. Repeat QUICK TEST.

CIRCUIT TEST FD (Cont.)

NOTE: A break in step numbering sequence occurs at this point. Procedure skips from step 7) to step 90). No test procedures have been omitted.

90) Code 536: Check For Proper Brakelight Switch Installation – Continuous memory Code 536 indicates a BOO circuit failure. If BOO input does not cycle after a predetermined number of transitions from 0 mph to a specific speed, the BOO input is assumed to be damaged and continuous memory Code 536 is set. Possible causes of failure are:
- Incorrect brakelight switch installation.
- Open brakelight/BOO circuit.
- Brakelight/BOO circuit short.
- Damaged switch or ground circuit.

If switch is correctly installed and in good condition, go to next step. If switch or harness is damaged, service as needed and clear continuous memory. Repeat QUICK TEST.

91) Inspect Brakelight Ground – Inspect brakelight ground connection and harness connector. Repair as needed. If connections are okay, go to next step.

92) Inspect Brakelight/BOO Circuits For Shorts – With KOEO and brake pedal released, perform wiggle test of brakelight/BOO circuit harness and connectors while observing brakelights. If brakelights illuminate, inspect and repair circuits as needed. If brakelights do not illuminate, go to next step.

93) Inspect Brakelight Circuit Continuity – With ignition off, depress brake pedal and hold. Perform wiggle test of brakelight circuits while observing brakelights. Lightly tap brakelight switch while observing brakelights. If brakelights intermittently go out, inspect and repair circuits as needed. If brakelights remain illuminated, go to next step.

94) Inspect BOO Circuit Continuity – With ignition off, ensure brake pedal is released. Disconnect PCM 60-pin connector. Inspect terminals, and repair if damaged. Install EEC-IV Breakout Box (T83L-50-EEC-IV), leaving PCM disconnected. Measure resistance between BOO test pin No. 2 and brakelight circuit at switch while performing wiggle test on harness and connector. If resistance intermittently increases above 5 ohms, inspect and repair open circuit. Repeat QUICK TEST. If resistance is within specification, go to next step for further diagnosis.

NOTE: A break in step numbering sequence occurs at this point. Procedure skips from step 94) to step 99). No test procedures have been omitted.

99) Road Test Vehicle – Purpose of this test is to identify faults by monitoring certain controlled parameters while trying to recreate a driveability or MIL symptom. To prepare for road test:
- Install fuel pressure gauge and if available, a MAP/BARO tester.
- Disconnect PCM 60-pin connector, install breakout box and reconnect PCM to breakout box.
- Connect "T" vacuum gauge into manifold vacuum line.
- Have DVOM, writing materials and appropriate schematics and pin voltage charts available.

With ignition on and negative lead of DVOM connected to negative battery terminal, ensure following signals are correct:
- POWERS: KAPWR (pin No. 1) is greater than 10.5 volts, VPWR (pins No. 37 and 57) is greater than 10.5 volts and VREF (pin No. 26) is 4-6 volts.
- GROUNDS: PWR GND (pins No. 40 and 60), SIG RTN (pin No. 46) and IGN GND (pin No. 16) are 0.0-0.5 volt.
- OPTIONAL GROUNDS: HO2S GND (pin No. 49), CSE GND (pin No. 20) and MAF RTN (pin No. 9 or 15) are 0.0-0.5 volt.

Diagnostic Aids – Test lights and DVOM are useful during diagnosis. For example: a testlight could be connected at brakelight switch between battery and ground and another testlight between switch bulb circuit and ground. Testlight to battery circuit should always be illuminated and other testlight should only illuminate when brakelight is depressed.

With DVOM connected between test pin No. 2 and 40 at Breakout Box, check voltage. If voltage is between 6-7 volts with brake pedal released, possible open circuit between PCM and brakelight ground could exist.

AUTOMATIC TRANSMISSIONS
AODE & AODE-W EEC-IV Electronic Controls (Cont.)

3-579

CIRCUIT TEST FF

POWER STEERING PRESSURE (PSP) SWITCH

Diagnostic Aids – The PSP switch, is a normally closed switch that opens as pressure in the power steering system increases.

Perform this test when instructed during QUICK TEST or if directed by other test procedures. Some vehicles may not have power steering, but PCM may be equipped with PSP switch software strategy. If a KOEO Code 519 is displayed, check if vehicle is equipped with power steering. If vehicle is not equipped with power steering, disregard Code 519. This test is only intended to diagnose:

- Power Steering Pressure (PSP) switch.
- PSP and SIG RTN wiring harness circuits.
- Powertrain Control Module (PCM).

To prevent replacement of good components, be aware the following non-EEC related areas may be at fault:

- Idle speed/throttle stop adjustment.
- Binding throttle shaft/linkage.
- Cruise control linkage.
- Power steering hydraulic system.

93F40548

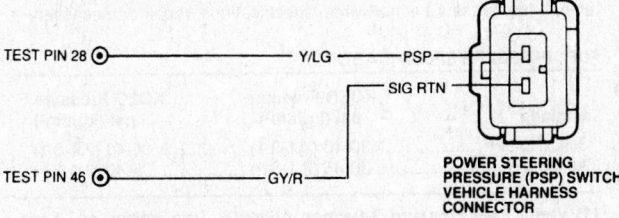

TEST PIN 28 — Y/LG — PSP
SIG RTN

TEST PIN 46 — GY/R

POWER STEERING PRESSURE (PSP) SWITCH VEHICLE HARNESS CONNECTOR

*TEST PINS LOCATED ON BREAKOUT BOX
ALL HARNESS CONNECTORS VIEWED IN MATING SURFACE

Fig. FF1: Power Steering Pressure (PSP) Switch Circuit

PSP SWITCH TEST PIN NUMBER IDENTIFICATION

Application	Test Pin No.
5.0L Truck (Non-California)	24
All Others	28

1) KOEO Code 519: Attempt To Eliminate Code – Code 519 indicates PSP switch circuit is open. Possible causes for this fault are:

- Damaged PSP switch.
- Open circuit in wiring harness.
- Faulty PCM.

Turn ignition off. Disconnect PSP switch. Install jumper wire between PSP terminal and SIG RTN terminal at wiring harness connector. Repeat KOEO SELF-TEST. If Code 519 is not displayed, replace PSP switch and repeat QUICK TEST. If Code 519 is displayed, remove jumper wire and go to next step.

2) Check Continuity Of PSP Circuits – Turn ignition off. Disconnect PCM 60-pin connector. Inspect connector for damaged pins, corrosion and loose wires. Repair as necessary. Install EEC-IV Breakout Box (T83L-50-EEC-IV), leaving PCM disconnected. Measure resistance between test pin No. 46 and SIG RTN terminal at PSP switch wiring harness connector. Also measure resistance between PSP test pin at breakout box and PSP terminal at switch wiring harness connector. If both readings are less than 5 ohms, replace PCM. Remove breakout box, reconnect all components, and repeat QUICK TEST. If readings are 5 ohms or more, repair open circuit. Remove breakout box, reconnect all components, and repeat QUICK TEST.

3) Check PSP Switch Operation – Turn ignition off. Connect tachometer, and start engine. Allow engine to idle in Park or Neutral. Disconnect PSP switch wiring harness connector. If RPM increases, replace PSP switch and recheck system. If RPM does not increase, go to next step.

4) Check PSP Switch Circuits For Shorts – Turn ignition off. Disconnect PSP switch wiring harness connector. Disconnect PCM 60-pin connector. Inspect connector for damaged pins, corrosion and loose wires. Repair as necessary. Install EEC-IV Breakout Box (T83L-50-EEC-IV), leaving PCM disconnected. Measure resistance between PSP test pin at breakout box and test pin No. 46 at breakout box. If resistance is 10 k/ohms or less, repair short in harness and recheck symptom. If resistance is more than 10 k/ohms, replace PCM and recheck symptom.

CIRCUIT TEST FF (Cont.)

5) KOER Code 521 – Disregard this code if vehicle does not have power steering. Code 521 indicates PSP switch did not change states due to open or closed switch. Possible causes for this fault are:

- Damaged PSP switch.
- Open or shorted circuit in wiring harness.
- Front wheels turned but not centered.
- Faulty PCM.

If steering wheel was turned 1/2 turn within 2 seconds after engine ID code and then returned to center, go to next step. If steering wheel was not turned, repeat QUICK TEST.

6) Check PCM Open Circuit Identifying Capabilities – Turn ignition off. Disconnect PSP switch. Perform KOEO SELF-TEST. If Code 519 is present, go to step **8)**. If Code 519 is not present, go to next step.

7) Check PSP Switch Circuits For Shorts – Turn ignition off. Disconnect PSP switch. Disconnect PCM 60-pin connector. Inspect connector for damaged pins, corrosion and loose wires. Repair as necessary. Install EEC-IV Breakout Box (T83L-50-EEC-IV), leaving PCM disconnected. Measure resistance between PSP test pin and test pin No. 46 at breakout box. If resistance is 10 k/ohms or less, repair short circuit. Remove breakout box, reconnect all components, and repeat QUICK TEST. If resistance is more than 10 k/ohms, replace PCM. Remove breakout box, reconnect all components, and repeat QUICK TEST.

8) Check PSP Switch Position Comparison – Turn ignition off. Connect PCM connector to breakout box. With PSP switch connected, turn ignition on. Measure and record resistance between PSP test pin and test pin No. 46 at breakout box. Start engine. Measure and record resistance between PSP test pin and test pin No. 46 at breakout box. If reading shows less than 10 ohms difference between key on engine off and key on engine running, go to next step. If reading is not as described, replace PSP switch and repeat QUICK TEST.

9) Check PSP Switch With Engine Running (Load & No Load) – Connect PSP switch. Start engine, and allow it to idle. On Taurus 3.0L SHO, ensure clutch is not depressed. On all models, measure resistance between PSP test pin and test pin No. 46 at breakout box. Turn steering wheel 1/2 turn and return to center position. If resistance changes from less than 10 ohms to infinity and then returns to 10 ohms or less (when steering wheel is centered), PSP switch system is okay. Testing is complete. If reading does not change as indicated, replace PSP switch. Repeat QUICK TEST.

CIRCUIT TEST G

MAF/TPS FUEL INJECTOR PULSE WIDTH TEST

Diagnostic Aids – Perform this test when instructed during QUICK TEST or if directed by other test procedures. To prevent replacement of good components, be aware the following non-EEC related areas may be at fault:

- Excessive blow-by.
- PCV malfunction.
- Vacuum leaks.
- Incorrect fuel pressure.
- Throttle binding.
- Improper fuel pressure.
- Idle air control solenoid.

This test is only intended to diagnose:

- MAP/BARO sensor.
- Throttle Position Sensor (TPS).
- Mass Airflow (MAF) sensor.
- Intake Air Temperature (IAT) sensor.
- Fuel injectors.

1) Check For Idle Air Codes – Code 121 indicates TPS is inconsistent with MAF value. Code 124 indicates TPS value is higher than expected. Code 125 indicates TPS value is lower than expected. Turn ignition on. Repeat KOEO SELF-TEST. If Code 411 or 412 is present, perform appropriate circuit test. See DIAGNOSTIC TROUBLE CODE REFERENCE CHARTS. If Code 411 or 412 is not present, go to next step.

2) Throttle Position (TP) Sensor: TP Sensor Integrity – Turn ignition off. Disconnect PCM 60-pin connector. Inspect connector for damaged pins, corrosion and loose wires. Repair as necessary. Install EEC-IV Breakout Box (T83L-50-EEC-IV). Connect PCM to breakout box. Connect DVOM to test pins No. 46 and 47 at breakout box. Turn ignition on. Slowly apply throttle to WOT, and release to closed position. Voltage should change smoothly from 0.4-4.5 volts. See CIRCUIT TEST DH for

3-580

AUTOMATIC TRANSMISSIONS
AODE & AODE-W EEC-IV Electronic Controls (Cont.)

CIRCUIT TEST G (Cont.)

schematics and specific engine values. If voltage change is incorrect or erratic, ensure TP sensor is properly installed. If TP sensor is properly installed, replace TP sensor. Remove breakout box, reconnect all components, and repeat QUICK TEST. If voltage is okay, go to step **8)** for Code 121 or next step for all other codes.

3) Check Idle – Ensure idle is correct. If idle is correct, go to next step. If idle is incorrect, see IDLE SPEED in ON-VEHICLE ADJUSTMENTS article.

4) Check Throttle Body – Ensure idle is correct. Check throttle and/or cruise control linkage for binding and rough operation. Inspect throttle body for sludge build-up. Check engine vacuum hoses. Refer to Vehicle Emission Control Information (VECI) decal for proper vacuum hose routing. Check for air leak between ISC solenoid and MAF sensor. If problems are found, repair as necessary. Remove breakout box, reconnect all components, and repeat QUICK TEST. If no problems are found, go to next step.

5) Check MAP/BARO Sensor Output – On vehicles without MAP/BARO go to next step. On vehicles with MAP/BARO, then continue with this test. With tester connected and engine running, measure sensor output voltage. If output voltage is within range for specified altitude, remove MAP/BARO tester and go to next step. See MAP SENSOR VOLTAGE OUTPUT table for specification. If output voltage is not within range, replace MAP/BARO sensor. Remove breakout box, reconnect all components, and repeat QUICK TEST.

Diagnostic Aids – If possible, measure several known good MAP/BARO sensors. Average voltage reading will be typical for location and day of testing. Also, refer to CIRCUIT TEST DF under SELF-DIAGNOSTICS – EEC-IV article in ENGINE PERFORMANCE of appropriate MITCHELL® manual for MAP/BARO sensor output check. See Fig. DF1 for connector terminal identification and MAP/BARO tester hookup.

MAP SENSOR VOLTAGE OUTPUT

Elevation (Feet)	Volts
0	1.55-1.63
1000	1.52-1.60
2000	1.49-1.57
3000	1.46-1.54
4000	1.43-1.51
5000	1.40-1.48
6000	1.37-1.45
7000	1.35-1.43

6) Check IAT Sensor – Ensure ambient temperature is more than 50°F (10°C) before performing this test. Also, check and repair any air leaks in front of IAT sensor. Turn ignition off. Connect breakout box to PCM. Set DVOM to 20-volt scale. Connect DVOM to test pins No. 25 and 46. Start engine, and let it idle. Observe voltage as engine warms up. See CIRCUIT TEST DA for voltage specifications. If voltage decreases smoothly and stabilizes when engine reaches operating conditions, system is operating properly at this time. Testing is complete. If voltage does not decrease smoothly and stabilize after engine reaches operating conditions, replace IAT sensor and repeat QUICK TEST.

7) Continuous Memory Code 184 & 185: Inspect MAF Sensor – Code 184 indicates MAF sensor signal is higher than expected. Code 185 indicates MAF sensor signal is lower than expected. Turn ignition off. Check for air leaks between Idle Air Control (IAC) solenoid and MAF sensor. Inspect MAF sensor for oil contamination caused by excessive blow-by or malfunctioning PCV. If problems are found, repair as necessary. Clear codes and repeat QUICK TEST. If no problems are found, go to step **10)**.

8) Check MAF Sensor Circuit Voltage – Turn ignition off. Disconnect PCM 60-pin connector. Inspect connector for damaged pins, corrosion and loose wires. Repair as necessary. Install EEC-IV Breakout Box (T83L-50-EEC-IV). Connect PCM to breakout box. Start engine, and warm it to normal operating temperature. Measure voltage between test pin No. 50 and test pin No. 40 or 60 at breakout box. If voltage is not within specification, replace MAF sensor. Remove breakout box, reconnect all components, and repeat QUICK TEST. See MAF SENSOR DATA table. If voltage is within acceptable range, system is operating normally at this time. Sometime during the last 80 warm-up cycles, MAF sensor signal was out of range.

CIRCUIT TEST G (Cont.)

MAF SENSOR DATA

Engine Condition	[1] Voltage
Idle	0.8
20 MPH	1.0
40 MPH	1.7
60 MPH	2.1

[1] – With engine at normal operating temperature.

9) Continuous Memory Code 186 & 187: Visual Vacuum Checks – Code 186 indicates pulse width is longer than expected (rich). Code 187 indicates pulse width is shorter than expected (lean). Inspect air cleaner and air inlet duct. Replace or repair an necessary. Check for unmetered air leaks between MAF sensor and IAC solenoid. Check all engine vacuum hoses for damage, blockage and improper routing. Repair as necessary, and repeat QUICK TEST. If all checks are okay, go to next step.

10) Check Fuel Pressure – Turn ignition off. Install fuel pressure gauge. Ensure vacuum hose is connected to fuel pressure regulator (if applicable). Start engine, and run it at idle. If fuel pressure is within specification, go to next step. See FUEL PRESSURE SPECIFICATIONS table. If fuel pressure is not within specifications, repair as necessary.

FUEL PRESSURE SPECIFICATIONS

Engine	KOER Pressure psi (kg/cm²)	KOEO Pressure psi (kg/cm²)
3.8L SC SFI	30-40 (2.1-3.1)	35-40 (2.4-3.1)
All Others	30-45 (2.1-3.2)	35-40 (2.4-3.1)

11) Verify Fuel Pressure Retention Ability – Turn ignition on. If fuel pressure remains at specification for 60 seconds, go to CIRCUIT TEST HB under SELF-DIAGNOSTICS – EEC-IV article in ENGINE PERFORMANCE of appropriate MITCHELL® manual. If fuel pressure does not remain at specification, repair fuel delivery system as necessary. For SFI equipped vehicles, go to next step.

12) Cylinder Balance Test – Perform KOER SELF-TEST. After last code, wait 5-10 seconds, and then goose throttle lightly (not wide open throttle). This will activate cylinder balance test. If Code 90 is present after test, go back to step **7)**. If Code 90 is not present after test, go to CIRCUIT TEST HB, step **5)** (Flex Fuel) under SELF-DIAGNOSTICS – EEC-IV article in ENGINE PERFORMANCE of appropriate MITCHELL® manual or CIRCUIT TEST H, step **4)** (except Flex Fuel).

CIRCUIT TEST KM

A/C DEMAND SWITCH

Diagnostic Aids – Perform this test when diagnosing a symptom. To prevent replacing good components, check the following non-EEC components and systems:
- Refrigerant charge.
- Low ambient temperature (less than 45°F).

40) Code 539: Check A/C Input – Code 539 indicates ACCS input to PCM was high during SELF-TEST. Turn ignition off. Disconnect 60-pin PCM connector. Inspect terminals, and repair if damaged. Install EEC-IV Breakout Box (T83L-50-EEC-IV), leaving PCM disconnected. Turn ignition on. Measure voltage between test pin No. 10 at breakout box and chassis ground. If voltage is 1.0 volt or more, repair short to power in A/C circuit and repeat QUICK TEST. If voltage is less than 1.0 volt, replace PCM and repeat QUICK TEST.

CIRCUIT TEST ML

SELF-TEST OUTPUT (STO) OR MALFUNCTION INDICATOR LIGHT (MIL)

Diagnostic Aids – The MIL is turned on when PCM detects a fault in EEC circuit(s). The light will remain on as long as fault remains in system.

Perform this test only when instructed by QUICK TEST or if directed by CIRCUIT TEST QA. This test does not include procedure for models with electronic instrument panel. To prevent replacing good components, be aware that fuse, bulb or bulb socket may be cause of problem. This test is only intended to diagnose:
- STO/MIL circuit.
- Faulty PCM.

AUTOMATIC TRANSMISSIONS
AODE & AODE-W EEC-IV Electronic Controls (Cont.)

3-581

CIRCUIT TEST ML (Cont.)

93H40433

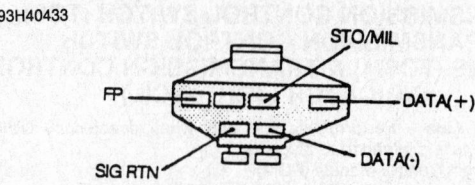

Fig. ML1: Identifying Data Link Connector (DLC) Terminals

TEST PIN WIRE COLOR IDENTIFICATION

Terminal No.	Wire Color
No. 17 (STO/MIL) .... [1] Pink/Light Green
No. 48 (STI) .... White/Pink
No. 18, Data(+) [2] .... Tan/Orange
No. 19, Data(-) [3] .... Pink/Light Blue

[1] – Wire color Tan/Red on Crown Victoria & Grand Marquis.
[2] – Test pin No. 28 on 5.0L "F" series.
[3] – Test pin No. 9 on 5.0L "F" series.

1) Malfunction Indicator Light (MIL) Always On – Service all KOEO and Continuous Memory Codes before proceeding with this test. Turn ignition off. Disconnect 60-pin PCM connector. Inspect terminals, and repair if damaged. Install EEC-IV Breakout Box (T83L-50-EEC-IV), leaving PCM disconnected. Measure resistance between test pins No. 17 and 40 at breakout box. If resistance is more than 5 ohms, replace PCM and repeat QUICK TEST. If reading is 5 ohms or less, repair short between test pin No. 17 and Diagnostic Link Connector (DLC) terminal No. 17 or MIL. Reconnect all components, and repeat QUICK TEST.

NOTE: A break in step numbering sequence occurs at this point. Procedure skips from step 1) to step 4). No test procedures have been omitted.

4) Malfunction Indicator Light (MIL) Does Not Light – Turn ignition on. Measure voltage between negative battery terminal and ground side of MIL fuse. If voltage is more than 10.5 volts, go to step 6). If voltage is 10.5 volts or less, go to step 5).

5) Check For Voltage At Fuse – Turn ignition on. Measure voltage from negative battery terminal to power side of MIL fuse. If voltage is more than 10.5 volts, replace fuse. Verify repair by turning ignition switch to RUN position. If voltage is 10.5 volts or less, repair open MIL/B+ circuit. Verify repair by turning ignition switch to RUN position.

6) Check Voltage At B+ Circuit – Turn ignition on. Measure voltage between B+ side of MIL bulb socket and negative battery terminal. If voltage is 10.5 volts or less, repair open in MIL circuit between fuse and bulb. Verify repair by turning ignition switch to RUN position. If voltage is more than 10.5 volts, go to step 7).

7) Check MIL Bulb Response To Grounding – Turn ignition off. Attach jumper wire between ground side of MIL bulb socket and chassis ground. Turn ignition on. If MIL light comes on, remove jumper wire, and go to step 8). If MIL light does not come on, remove jumper wire. Replace MIL bulb socket. Turn ignition on to verify correct MIL operation.

8) Check Continuity Of MIL Circuit – Turn ignition off. Disconnect 60-pin PCM connector. Inspect terminals, and repair if damaged. Install EEC-IV Breakout Box (T83L-50-EEC-IV), leaving PCM disconnected. Measure resistance between test pin No. 17 at breakout box and MIL wiring connector terminal. If resistance is less than 5 ohms, replace PCM. If resistance is 5 ohms or more, repair open MIL circuit. Turn ignition on to verify correct MIL operation.

NOTE: A break in step numbering sequence occurs at this point. Procedure skips from step 8) to step 10). No test procedures have been omitted.

10) MIL On Intermittently, Check For Intermittent Short From STO To Ground – MIL comes on when a fault code is present. Service all fault codes before proceeding. If no codes are output, proceed with this test. Enter KOEO wiggle test. See CONTINUOUS MONITOR MODE (WIGGLE TEST) under QUICK TEST. Check DVOM for indication of fault while performing wiggle test on harness in the following areas:
• From Diagnostic Link Connector (DLC) to dash panel.
• Dash panel to PCM.
• Dash panel to Malfunction Indicator Light (MIL).

CIRCUIT TEST ML (Cont.)

If a fault is indicated, repair short to ground and repeat QUICK TEST. If a fault is not indicated, fault cannot be duplicated at this time. Testing is complete.

NOTE: A break in step numbering sequence occurs at this point. Procedure skips from step 10) to step 15). No test procedures have been omitted.

15) MIL Flashes With Erratic Idle – Symptoms indicate STI is grounded and PCM is performing self-test without tester installed. Turn ignition off. Disconnect 60-pin PCM connector. Inspect terminals, and repair if damaged. Install EEC-IV Breakout Box (T83L-50-EEC-IV), leaving PCM disconnected. Measure resistance between STI connector and engine ground. If resistance is 10 k/ohms or less, repair short circuit. Reconnect PCM, and turn ignition on to verify correct MIL operation. If resistance is more than 10 k/ohms, MIL circuit is okay. Verify symptom, and test for other rough idle symptoms.

NOTE: A break in step numbering sequence occurs at this point. Procedure skips from step 15) to step 20). No test procedures have been omitted.

20) CHECK ENGINE Message Displayed – Perform KOEO SELF-TEST. If result is Code 111-10-111 (pass code), fault is in instrument cluster. If pass code is not displayed, service codes as necessary.

NOTE: A break in step numbering sequence occurs at this point. Procedure skips from step 20) to step 25). No test procedures have been omitted.

25) Continuous Memory Code 529 Or 533: CHECK ENGINE Or CHECK DLC Message Displayed – Codes 529 and 533 indicate circuit fault has occurred on Data Link Connector (DLC). These codes can occur alone or with another code. Fault will occur under following conditions:
• Code 529 indicates PCM or DLC circuit failure.
• Code 533 indicates DLC to electronic instrument cluster circuit failure.

If vehicle does not start, go to step 1). If vehicle starts, clear continuous memory codes. Wait 5 minutes, and repeat KOEO SELF-TEST. If result is pass code (Code 111-10-111), fault is in instrument cluster. If pass code is not displayed, service codes as necessary.

CIRCUIT TEST QA

NO CODES/CODES NOT LISTED

Diagnostic Aids – Aftermarket devices, such as alarm system, may cause SELF-TEST to abort if wiring is connected to certain EEC components. If a device is installed, disconnect it completely from EEC system. Before continuing with this circuit test, restore EEC circuits to original state and repeat QUICK TEST.

Perform this test when directed by QUICK TEST or other test procedures. This test is intended to diagnose:
• Powertrain Control Module (PCM).
• EEC power relay.
• Constant Control Relay Module (CCRM).
• Wiring harness circuits (HO2S, SIG RTN, STO, STI, VPWR and VREF).

93A40808

Fig. QA1: No Codes/Codes Not Listed Circuits

3-582

AUTOMATIC TRANSMISSIONS
AODE & AODE-W EEC-IV Electronic Controls (Cont.)

CIRCUIT TEST QA (Cont.)

TEST PIN WIRE COLOR IDENTIFICATION

Terminal No.	Wire Color
No. 17 (STO/MIL)	[1] Pink/Light Green
No. 37 & 57 (VPWR)	Red
No. 46 (SIG RTN)	Gray/Red
No. 48 (STI)	White/Pink

[1] – On Crown Victoria and Grand Marquis wire color is Tan/Red.

1) Check VREF Voltage At Data Link Connector (DLC) – Turn ignition off. Disconnect 60-pin PCM connector. Inspect terminals, and repair if damaged. Install EEC-IV Breakout Box (T83L-50-EEC-IV). Connect PCM to breakout box. Turn ignition on. Measure voltage between test pin No. 26 at breakout box and SIG RTN terminal at DLC. If reading is 4-6 volts, go to step **3)**. If reading is not 4-6 volts, go to step **2)**.

2) Check SIG RTN Circuit Continuity – Turn ignition off. Disconnect PCM from breakout box. Measure resistance between test pin No. 46 at breakout box and SIG RTN terminal at DLC. If reading is less than 5 ohms, go to CIRCUIT TEST CA. If resistance is 5 ohms or more, repair open circuit and repeat QUICK TEST.

3) Check STI Circuit Continuity – Turn ignition off. Disconnect PCM from breakout box. Measure resistance between test pin No. 48 at breakout box and Self-Test Input (STI) terminal at pigtail connector. If resistance is 5 ohms or more, repair open circuit and repeat QUICK TEST. If reading is less than 5 ohms, go to step **4)**.

4) Check STO Circuit Continuity – Leave ignition off and PCM disconnected. Measure resistance between test pin No. 17 at breakout box and STO terminal at DLC. If reading is less than 5 ohms, go to step **5)**. If resistance is 5 ohms or more, repair open circuit and repeat QUICK TEST.

5) Check HO2S Signal For Short To Power – Leave PCM disconnected. Turn ignition on. Measure voltage between test pin No. 40 or 60 and HO2S SIGNAL test pin No. 29 or 44 at breakout box. For HO2S circuit schematics, see SELF-DIAGNOSTICS – EEC-IV article in ENGINE PERFORMANCE of appropriate MITCHELL® manual. If voltage is more than 2 volts, go to step **6)**. If voltage is 2 volts or less, go to step **7)**.

6) Isolate Short To Harness Or HO2S Sensor – Turn ignition off. Leave PCM disconnected. Disconnect right/rear HO2S sensor connector. Turn ignition on. Measure voltage between HO2S SIGNAL test pin No. 29 or 44 and test pins No. 40 or 60 at breakout box. If any measurement is 2 volts or more, repair short to power in HO2S SIGNAL circuit, and repeat QUICK TEST. If voltage is less than 2 volts, replace right/rear HO2S sensor and repeat QUICK TEST.

7) Check STO Circuit For Short To Ground – Turn ignition off. Leave PCM disconnected. Measure resistance between STO at DLC and engine ground. If reading is more than 5 ohms, go to step **8)**. If resistance is 5 ohms or less, repair STO or MIL circuit for short to ground and repeat QUICK TEST.

8) Check If Power Relay Is Always On – Leave ignition off and PCM disconnected. Connect DVOM between test pin No. 37 or 57 and pin No. 40 or 60 at breakout box. Turn ignition on and then off. Wait 10 seconds. If voltage changes from 10.5 volts (or more) to less than 1.0 volt, go to step **10)**. If voltage does not change from 10.5 volts (or more) to less than 1.0 volt, go to step **9)**.

9) Check VPWR Circuit For Short To Power – Turn ignition off. Leave PCM disconnected. Disconnect EEC power relay or Constant Control Relay Module (CCRM). Connect DVOM to test pin No. 37 or 57 and test pin No. 40 or 60 at breakout box. If voltage is more than 1.0 volt, repair VPWR circuit short to power and repeat QUICK TEST. If voltage is 1.0 volt or less, replace EEC power relay or CCRM and repeat QUICK TEST.

10) Check Malfunction Indicator Light (MIL) Function – If MIL is always on, go to CIRCUIT TEST ML, step **1)**. If MIL is always off, go to CIRCUIT TEST ML, step **4)**. If MIL is working normally, replace PCM and repeat QUICK TEST.

CIRCUIT TEST TB

TRANSMISSION CONTROL SWITCH (TCS), TRANSMISSION CONTROL SWITCH, MODULE (TCSM) & TRANSMISSION CONTROL INDICATOR LIGHT (TCIL)

Diagnostic Aids – Perform this test only when directed by QUICK TEST. This test is intended to diagnose:
* Powertrain Control Module (PCM).
* Wiring harness circuits (TCIL, TCS and TCSM).

To prevent replacing good components, be aware the following non-EEC related areas may be at fault:
* Basic engine condition (valves, vacuum leaks, valve timing, etc.).
* Charging system.
* Transmission (fluid, friction elements and cooling).

TEST PIN NO. 41 (TCS) WIRE COLOR IDENTIFICATION

Application	Wire Color
All Models	Tan/Light Green

TEST PIN NO. 14 OR 55 (TCIL) WIRE COLOR IDENTIFICATION

Application	Wire Color
Cougar & Thunderbird 3.8L	Tan/Light Green
Thunderbird SC	Tan/White
All With 4.6L & 5.0L	Tan White

TEST PIN NO. 37 OR 57 (VPWR) WIRE COLOR IDENTIFICATION

Application	Wire Color
All Models	Red

NOTE: A break in step numbering sequence occurs at this point. Procedure starts at step 2). No test procedures have been omitted.

2) Code 632 Or 653 – Code 632 or 653 indicates that the TCS was not cycled between engine ID Code and WOT check during KOER SELF-TEST. Possible causes for this fault are:
* Faulty TCS or switch was not cycled during SELF-TEST.
* Shorted wiring harness.
* Faulty Powertrain Control Module (PCM).
* Open in wiring harness or fuse.

If TCS cycled during KOER SELF-TEST, go to step **4)**. If TCS did not cycle during KOER SELF-TEST, repeat KOER SELF-TEST while cycling TCS.

3) Code 623 or 631 – Code 623 or 631 indicates transmission control indicator light circuit fault during KOEO SELF-TEST. Possible causes for this fault are:
* Burned out bulb.
* Open or shorted wiring harness.

If TCS cycled during KOEO SELF-TEST, go to step **5)**. If TCS did not cycle during KOEO SELF-TEST, repeat KOER SELF-TEST while cycling TCS.

4) Check TCS Circuit – Turn ignition off. Disconnect 60-pin PCM connector. Inspect connector for damaged pins, corrosion and loose wires. Repair as necessary. Install EEC-IV Breakout Box (T83L-50-EEC-IV), leaving PCM disconnected. Turn ignition on. Measure voltage between test pin No. 41 and test pin No 40 or 60 while cycling TCS several times. If voltage cycles replace PCM. Remove breakout box, reconnect all components, and repeat QUICK TEST. If voltage does not cycle, go to next step if diagnosing a trouble code. Go to step **7)** if diagnosing a driveability symptom, or go to step **20)** if vehicle is a Mustang.

5) Check Circuits For Short To Ground – Turn ignition off. Leave PCM disconnected from breakout box. Disconnect TCS connector. Inspect connector for damage and repair as necessary. Measure resistance between test pin No. 41 and test pin 40 or 60. Also, measure resistance between test pin No. 55 (14 on 3.2L SHO) and test pin No. 40 or 60. If each reading is more than 10 k/ohms, go to next step for Code 623 or 631, or step **8)** for Code 632 or 653. If any reading is 10 k/ohms or less, repair short circuit. Repeat QUICK TEST. If code is still present, go to step **7)**.

6) Check Power Through TCIL Circuit – Turn ignition off. Leave PCM disconnected from breakout box. Measure voltage between test pin No. 55 (14 on 3.2L SHO) and test pin No. 40 or 60. If voltage is more than 10.5 volts, replace PCM. Remove breakout box, reconnect all components, and repeat QUICK TEST. If voltage is 10.5 volts or less, go to next step.

AUTOMATIC TRANSMISSIONS
AODE & AODE-W EEC-IV Electronic Controls (Cont.)

3-583

CIRCUIT TEST TB (Cont.)

7) Check Output Driver Voltage Signal – Leave PCM disconnected from breakout box. Turn ignition on. Measure voltage between test pin No. 55 (14 on 3.2L SHO) and test pin No. 40 or 60. If voltage is 2 volts or more, go to next step. If voltage is less than 2 volts, check bulb and fuse. Replace as necessary. If bulb and fuse are okay, repair open circuit. Remove breakout box, reconnect all components, and repeat QUICK TEST.

8) Check TCS & TCIL Circuits – Turn ignition off. Leave PCM disconnected from breakout box. Ensure TCS is disconnected. Measure resistance of Purple/Orange wire between KEY POWER terminal of fuse No. 1 at instrument panel fuse block and TCS wiring harness connector. Also, measure resistance between test pin No. 41 at breakout box and Purple/Orange wire at TCS wiring harness connector. If any reading is 5 ohms or more, repair open circuit. Remove breakout box, reconnect all components, and repeat QUICK TEST. If each reading is less than 5 ohms, go to next step.

9) Check For Short To Power – Turn ignition off. Leave PCM disconnected from breakout box. Ensure TCS is disconnected. Measure resistance between test pin No. 41 and test pin 37 or 57. Also, measure resistance between test pin No. 55 (14 on 3.2L SHO) and test pin No. 37 or 57. If each reading is more than 10 k/ohms, replace TCS switch. Remove breakout box, reconnect all components, and repeat QUICK TEST. If any reading is 10 k/ohms or less, repair short circuit. Remove breakout box, reconnect all components, and repeat QUICK TEST.

NOTE: A break in step numbering sequence occurs at this point. Procedure skips from step 9) to step 20). No test procedures have been omitted. Steps 20-27 are for Mustang only.

20) Check Transmission Control Switch Module (TCSM) – Turn ignition off. Leave PCM disconnected from breakout box. Remove TCSM to access wiring harness connector. TCSM is located behind right side of instrument panel. Turn ignition on. Measure voltage between Orange/Black wire and Black/White wire of TCSM connector while cycling Transmission Control Switch (TCS) several times. If voltage does not cycle, go to next step. If voltage cycles, repair open circuit between TCSM connector and PCM. If voltage cycles but Transmission Control Indicator Light (TCIL) does not turn off and on, go to step **25)**. If voltage does not cycle, go to next step.

21) Check TCSM Wiring – Turn ignition off. Leave PCM disconnected from breakout box. Leave TCSM connected. Turn ignition on. Measure voltage between Red/Light Green wire and ground. If voltage is more than 10.5 volts, go to next step. If voltage is 10.5 volts or less, repair open circuit between ignition switch and TCSM connector. Remove breakout box, reconnect all components, and repeat QUICK TEST.

22) Check TCSM Input From TCS – Ensure ignition is on and PCM is disconnected from breakout box. Measure voltage between Tan/White wire and Black/White wire of TCSM connector while cycling TCS several times. If voltage cycles, replace TCSM. Remove breakout box, reconnect all components, and repeat QUICK TEST. If voltage does not cycle, check TCS circuit. Repair as necessary.

23) Transmission Control Indicator Light (TCIL) Always On – Turn ignition on. Cycle Transmission Control Switch (TCS) and observe TCIL. If TCIL turns off and on, problem may be intermittent. Check all TCIL related wiring and repair as necessary. Recheck TCIL operation. If TCIL does not turn off and on, go to next step.

24) Check Transmission Control Switch Module (TCSM) For Short Circuit – Turn ignition off. Disconnect TCSM connector. TCSM is located behind right side of instrument panel. Turn ignition on. If TCIL is still on, repair short to ground in White/Light Green wire between TCIL and TCSM. Remove breakout box, reconnect all components, and repeat QUICK TEST. If TCIL is off, replace TCSM. Remove breakout box, reconnect all components, and repeat QUICK TEST.

25) Transmission Control Indicator Light (TCIL) Inoperative – Road test vehicle to ensure overdrive is functioning correctly. If overdrive is functioning correctly, repeat QUICK TEST. If Code 631 is present, return to step **3)**. If Code 631 is not present, go to next step.

26) Check Voltage At Fuse Panel – Turn ignition on. Remove and inspect fuse No. 18 at instrument panel fuse block. If fuse is blown, replace fuse and recheck TCIL operation. If fuse is okay, go to next step.

CIRCUIT TEST TB (Cont.)

27) Check Wiring To TCSM – Turn ignition off. Disconnect TCSM connector. TCSM is located behind right side of instrument panel. Connect one end of a jumper wire to ground and connector other end of jumper to White/Light Green wire at TCSM connector. Turn ignition on. If TCIL is on, problem may be intermittent. Check all TCIL related wiring and repair as necessary. Recheck TCIL operation. If TCIL light is off, check TCIL bulb. Replace bulb as necessary and recheck TCIL operation. If bulb is okay, repair open circuit between fuse block and TCSM connector. Recheck TCIL operation.

CIRCUIT TEST TC

TRANSMISSION SOLENOIDS

Diagnostic Aids – Perform this test only when directed by QUICK TEST. To prevent replacing good components, be aware the following non-EEC areas may be at fault:
- Engine condition (compression, cam timing, valves, etc.).
- Charging system or battery.
- Transmission linkage, internal components or cooling.

This test is not intended to diagnose transmission. This test is intended to diagnose:
- Wiring harness circuits TCC, EPC, SS1, SS2, SIG RTN, EPC PWR and VPWR.
- Faulty Powertrain Control Module (PCM).

CIRCUIT TEST TC ACRONYMS

Acronym	Definition
CCC	Converter Clutch Control
EPC	Electronic Pressure Control
MCCC	Modulated Converter Clutch Control
SS	Shift Solenoid
TCC	Torque Converter Clutch

AODE/AODE-W SERVICE CODE IDENTIFICATION

Application	PCM Pin No.	KOEO Code
EPC	38	624, 625
SS1	51	621
SS2	52	622
TCC	53	652

NOTE: A break in step numbering sequence occurs at this point. Procedure skips to step 10). No test procedures have been omitted.

10) Check VPWR To Solenoid – Ensure ignition is off. Disconnect transmission harness connector. With KOEO, measure voltage between VPWR, EPC PWR circuit at transmission harness connector and ground. If voltage is more than 10.5 volts, go to next step. If voltage is not within specification, repair open circuit in harness. Connect all components and repeat QUICK TEST.

11) Check Solenoid Signal & VPWR Circuit Continuity – Turn ignition off. Disconnect 60-pin PCM connector. Inspect terminals, and repair if damaged. Install EEC-IV Breakout Box (T83L-50-EEC-IV), leaving PCM disconnected. Measure resistance between VPWR/EPC PWR terminal at transmission wiring harness connector breakout box test pins No. 37 and 57. Measure resistance between test pin No. 38 at breakout box and EPC terminal at transmission wiring harness connector. If resistance is 5 ohms or more, repair open circuit and repeat QUICK TEST. If resistance is less than 5 ohms, go to step **12)**.

12) Check Circuit For Short To Power Or Ground – Leave ignition off and PCM disconnected. Leave transmission wiring harness connector disconnected. Measure and record resistance between test pins No. 37 and 57 and suspect solenoid test pin at breakout box. Measure and record resistance between test pins No. 40, 46 and 60 and suspect solenoid test pin at breakout box. If either resistance is less than 10 k/ohms, repair short circuit and repeat QUICK TEST. If all resistances are 10 k/ohms or more, check solenoids. If solenoids are okay, replace PCM and repeat QUICK TEST.

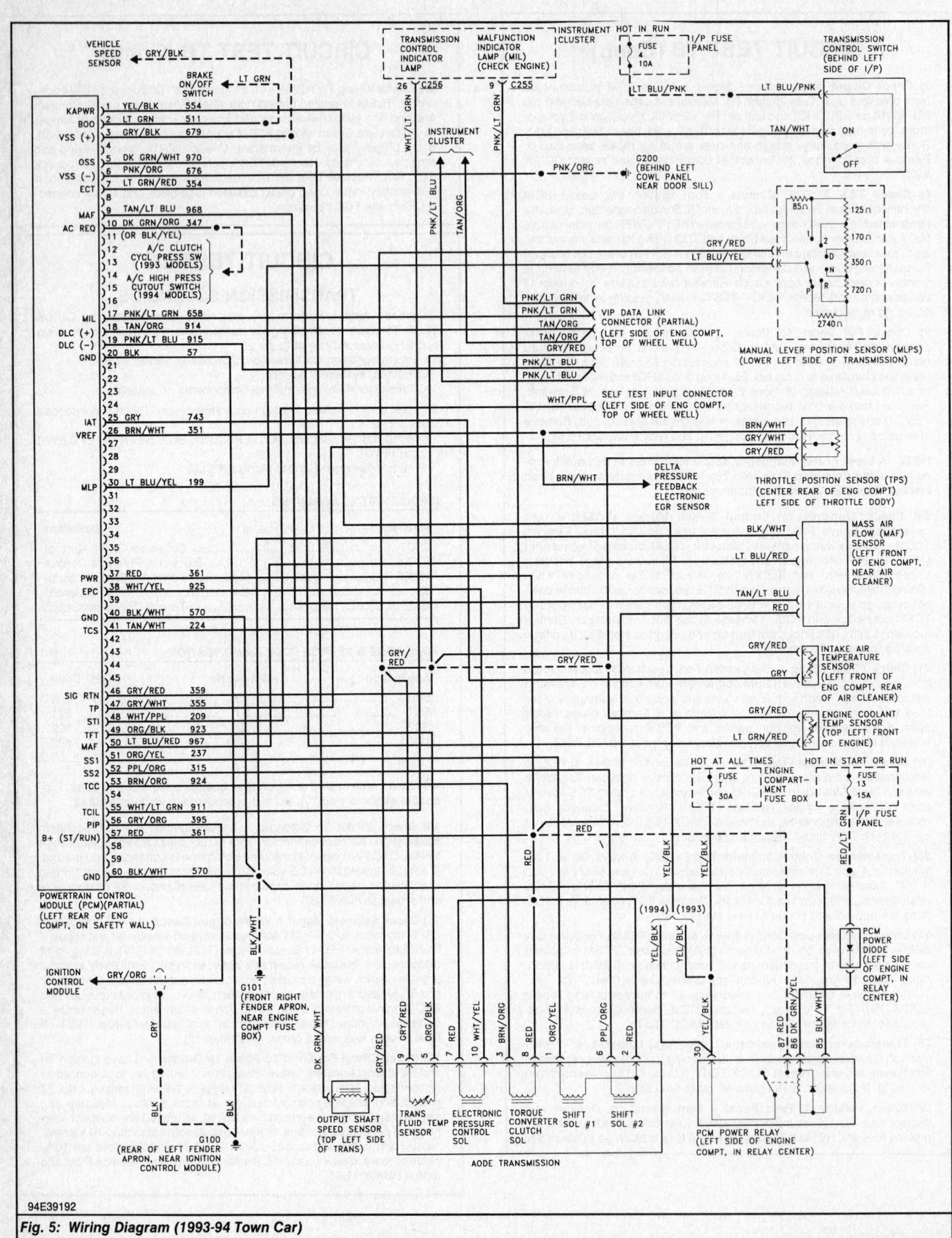

Fig. 5: *Wiring Diagram (1993-94 Town Car)*

94E39192

AUTOMATIC TRANSMISSIONS
AODE & AODE-W EEC-IV Electronic Controls (Cont.)

3-585

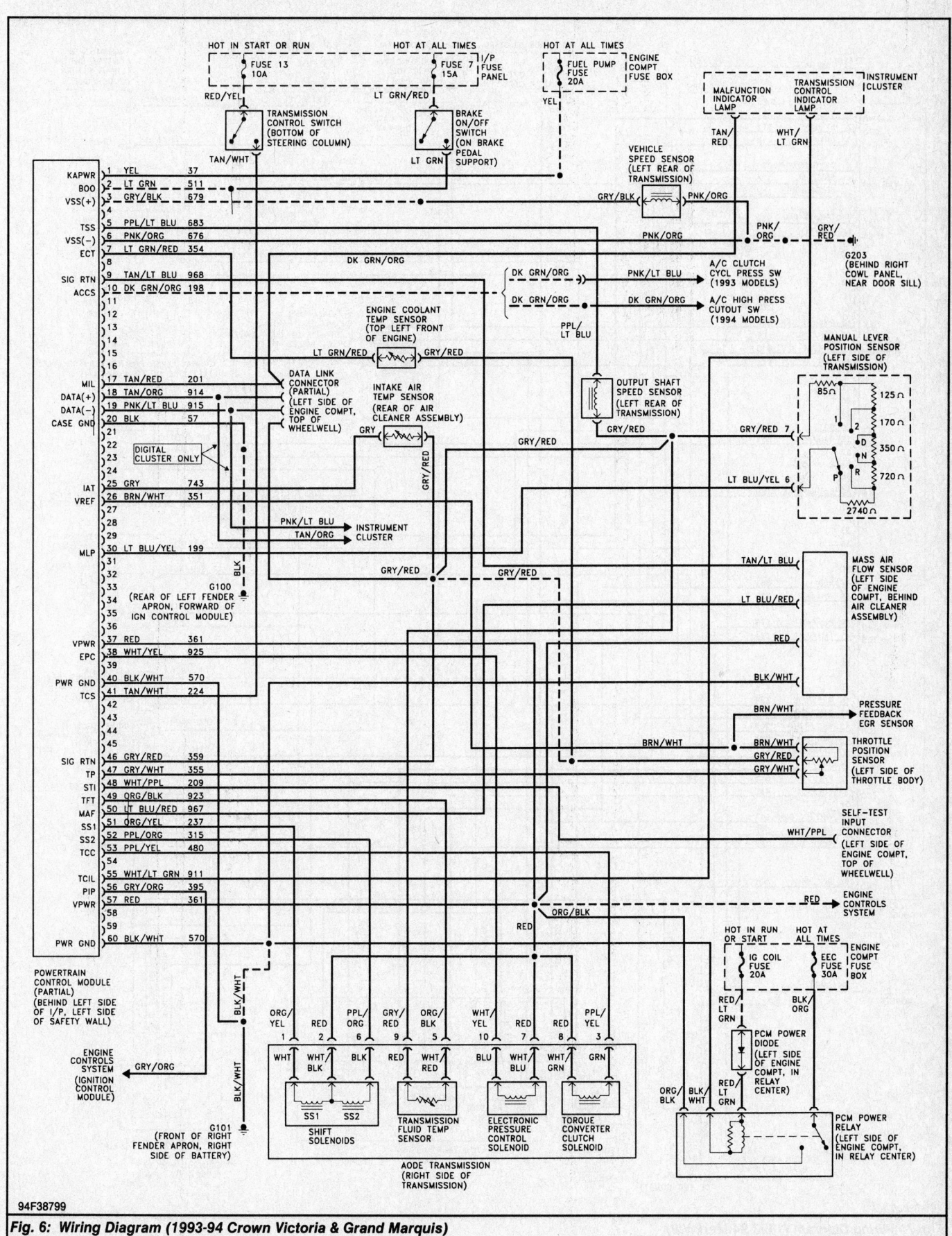

Fig. 6: Wiring Diagram (1993-94 Crown Victoria & Grand Marquis)

94F38799

3-586

AUTOMATIC TRANSMISSIONS
AODE & AODE-W EEC-IV Electronic Controls (Cont.)

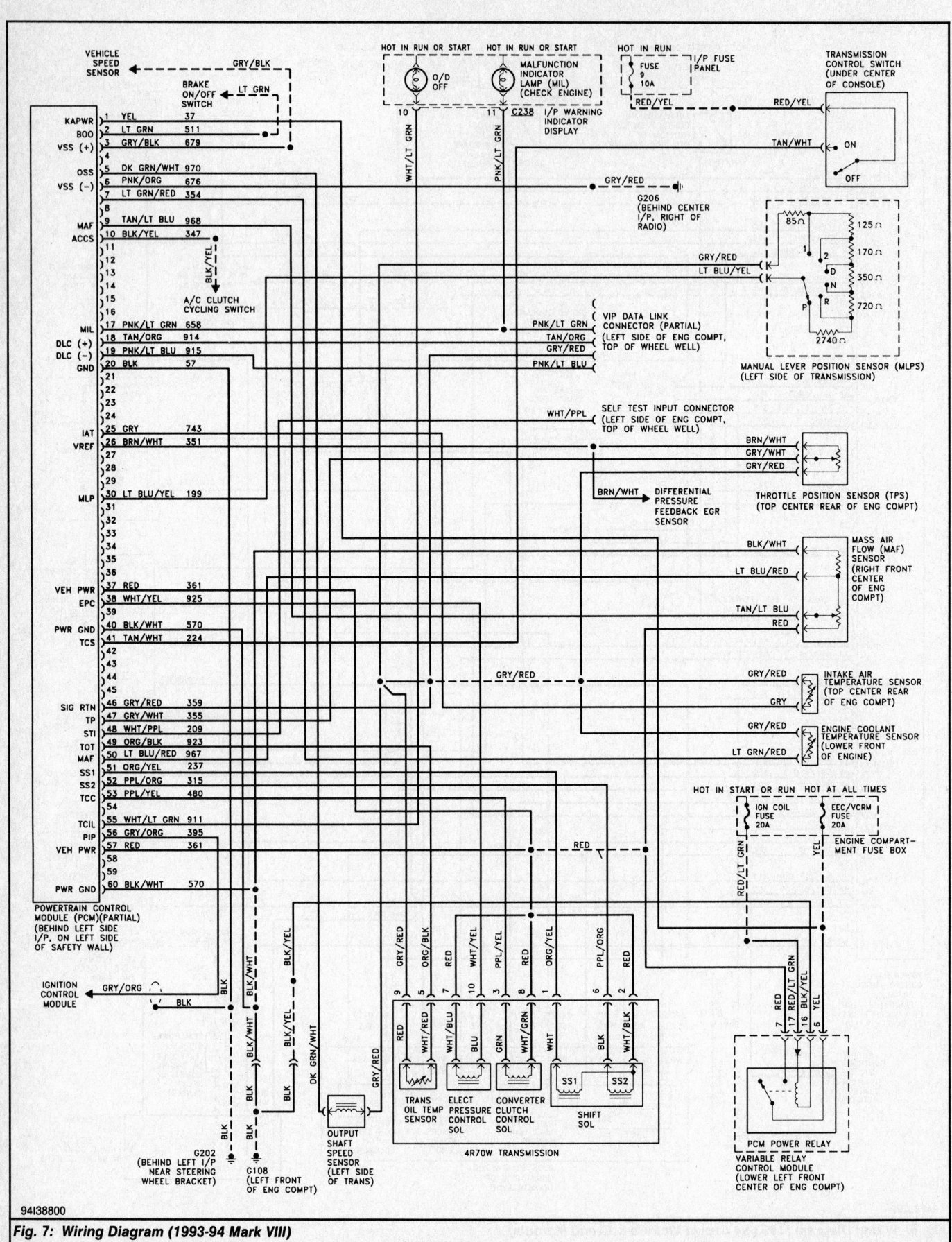

Fig. 7: Wiring Diagram (1993-94 Mark VIII)

AUTOMATIC TRANSMISSIONS
AODE & AODE-W EEC-IV Electronic Controls (Cont.)

3-587

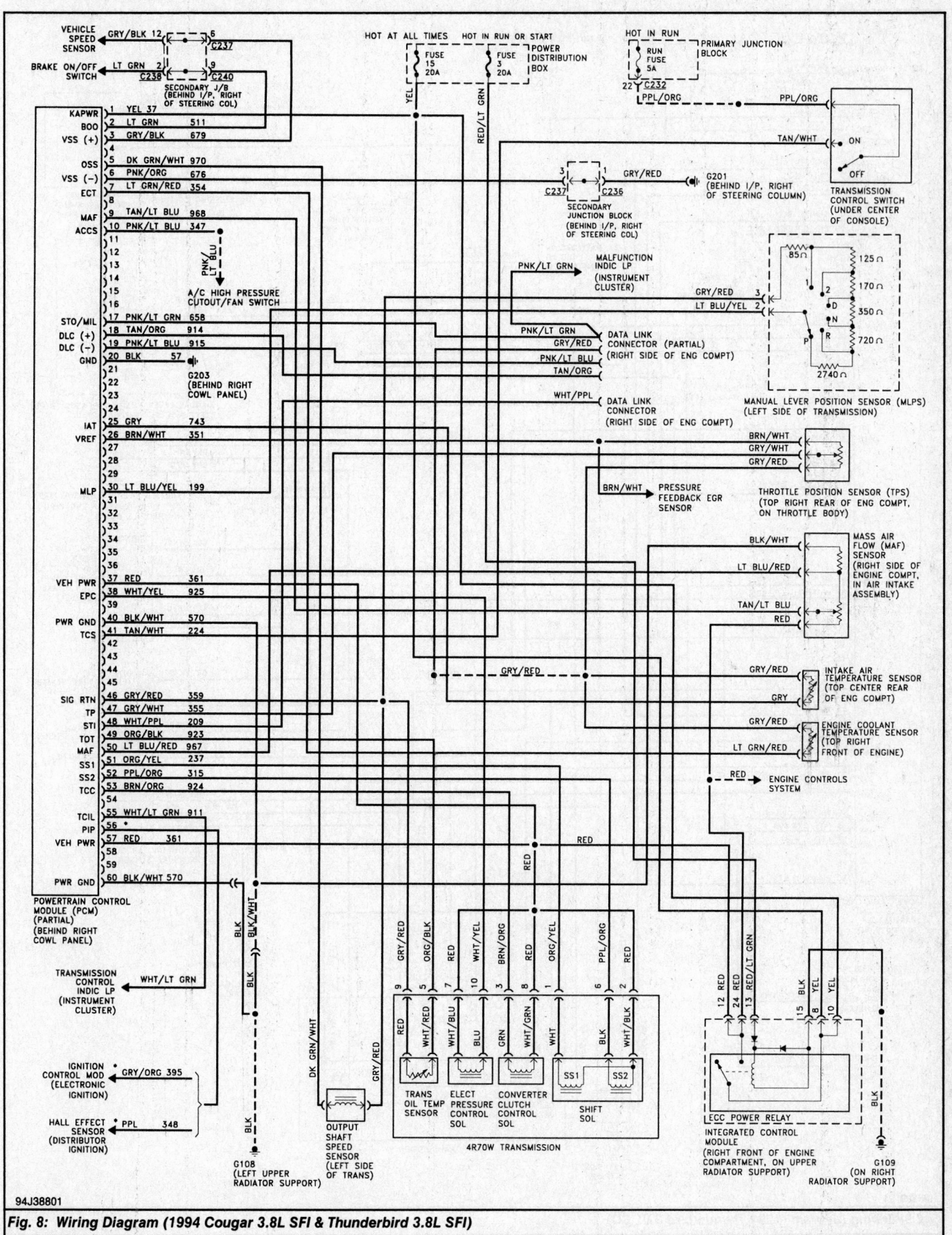

Fig. 8: Wiring Diagram (1994 Cougar 3.8L SFI & Thunderbird 3.8L SFI)

94J38801

3-588

AUTOMATIC TRANSMISSIONS
AODE & AODE-W EEC-IV Electronic Controls (Cont.)

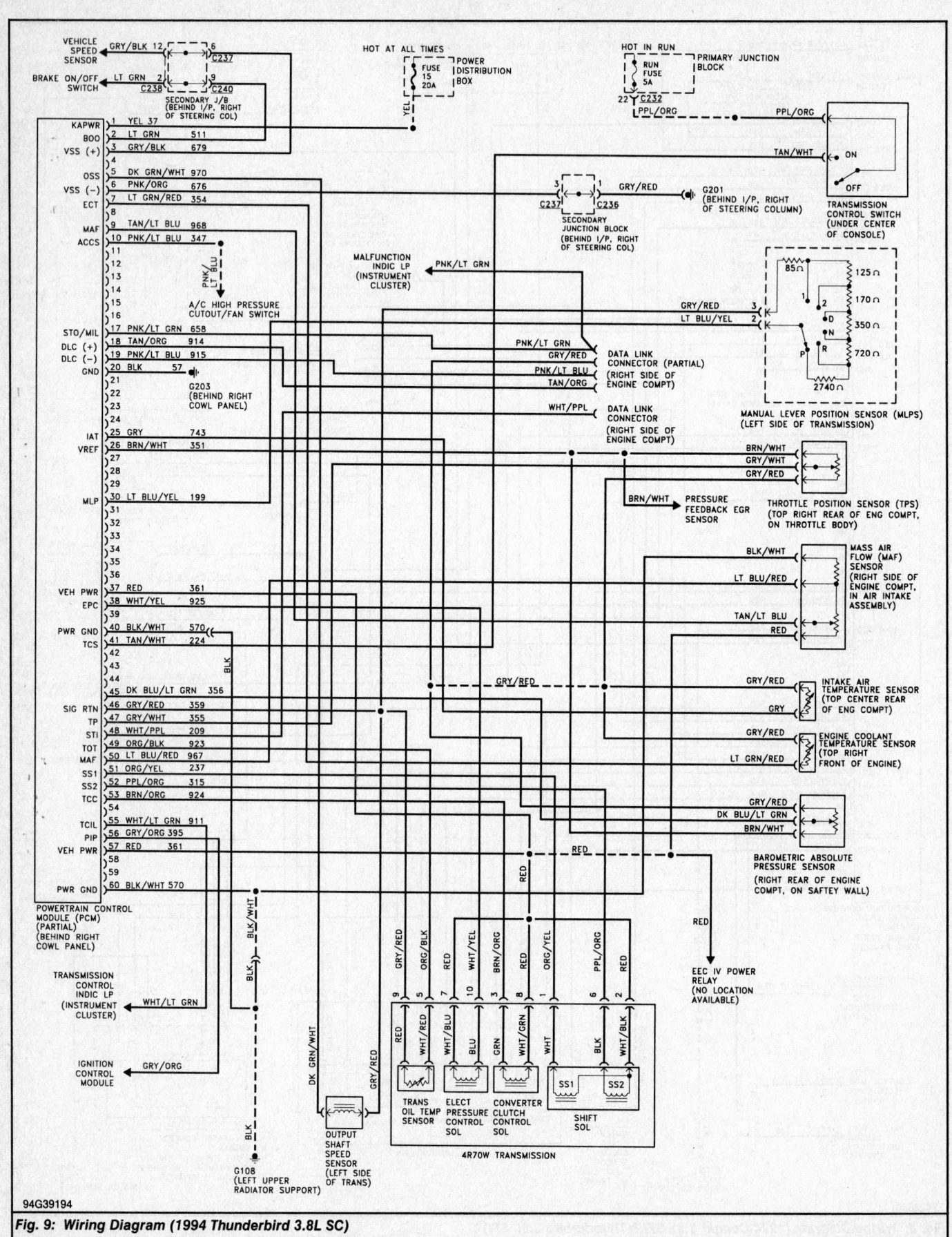

Fig. 9: Wiring Diagram (1994 Thunderbird 3.8L SC)

94G39194

AUTOMATIC TRANSMISSIONS
AODE & AODE-W EEC-IV Electronic Controls (Cont.)

3-589

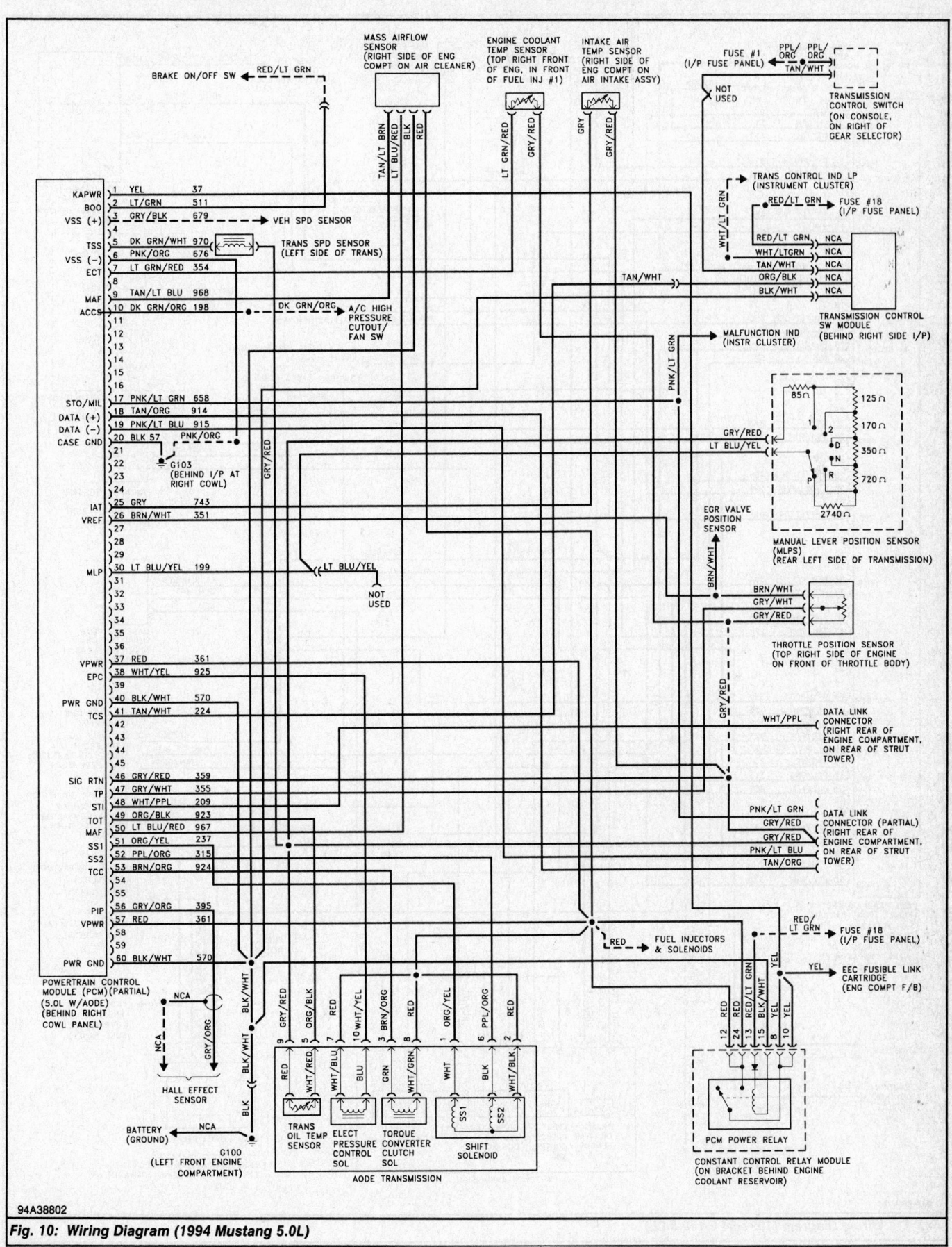

94A38802

Fig. 10: *Wiring Diagram (1994 Mustang 5.0L)*

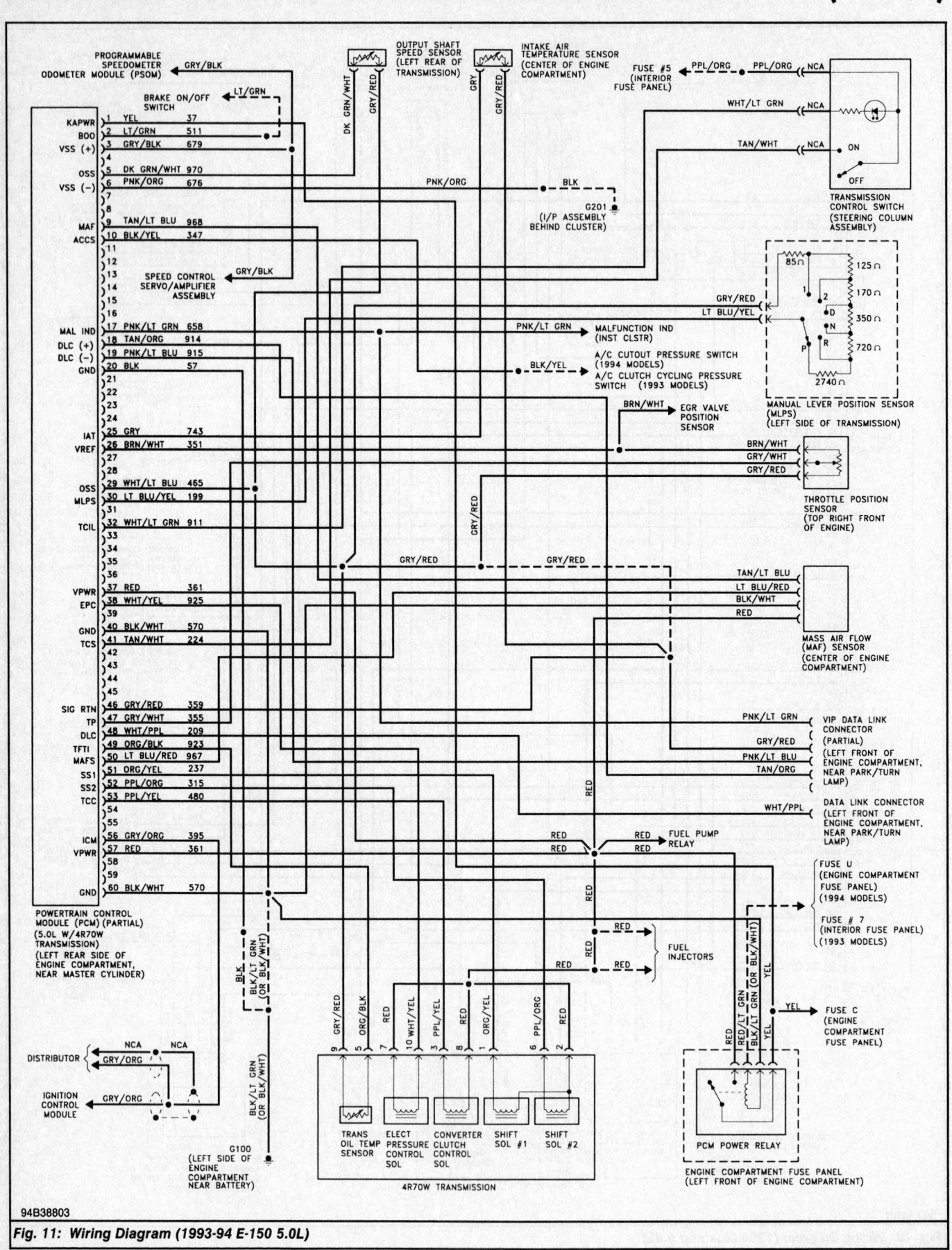

94B38803

Fig. 11: Wiring Diagram (1993-94 E-150 5.0L)

AUTOMATIC TRANSMISSIONS
AODE & AODE-W EEC-IV Electronic Controls (Cont.)

3-591

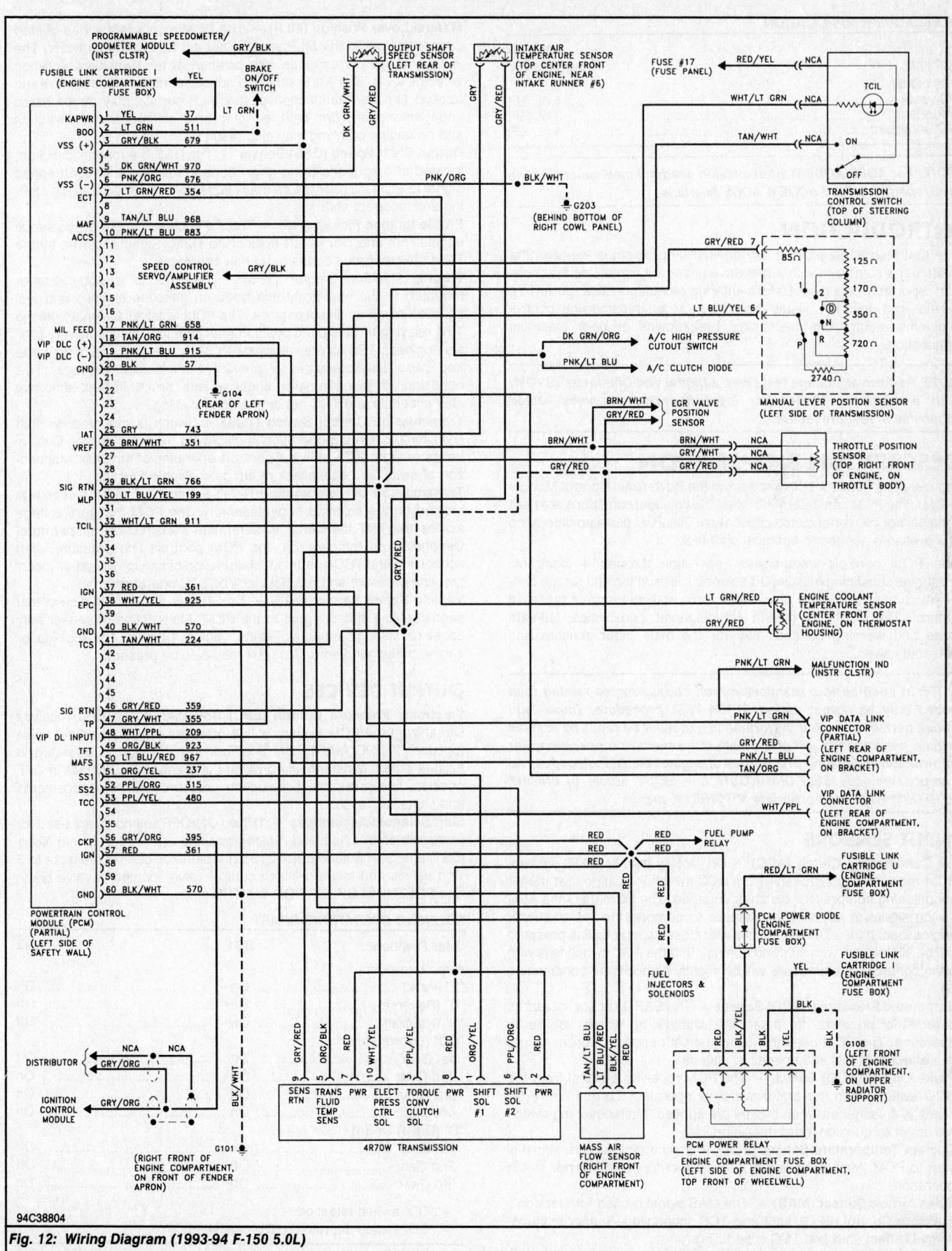

Fig. 12: Wiring Diagram (1993-94 F-150 5.0L)

94C38804

AODE/AODE-W APPLICATION

Vehicle	Engine Application
1994 Only	
Cougar	4.6L SFI
Mustang	3.8L SFI
Thunderbird	4.6L SFI

NOTE: For AODE/AODE-W transmission overhaul mechanical testing and repair, see Ford AODE & AODE-W article.

INTRODUCTION

The first step in diagnosing any driveability problem is verifying the customer's complaint with a test drive under the conditions the problem reportedly occurred. Before entering self-diagnostics, perform a careful and complete visual inspection. Most transmission control problems result from mechanical breakdowns or poor electrical connections.

NOTE: Perform all voltage tests with a Digital Volt-Ohmmeter (DVOM) with a minimum 10-megohm input impedance, unless stated otherwise in test procedure.

DESCRIPTION & OPERATION

Input signals from sensors are sent to the Powertrain Control Module (PCM). The PCM can determine when the time and conditions are right for a shift or converter clutch application. The PCM can also determine line pressure needed to optimize shift feel.

The PCM controls transmission operation through 4 electronic solenoids consisting of 3 On/Off solenoids for shifting and torque converter clutch control and one varible force solenoid for line pressure control. The PCM has built-in self-diagnosic capabilities, fail-safe code and warning code display for the main input sensors and solenoid valves.

NOTE: In addition to transmission fault codes, engine related fault codes may be output during QUICK TEST procedure. These fault codes pertain to engine performance and must be repaired first, as engine performance will greatly affect transmission operation. For information and testing procedures of engine related fault codes and components, see SELF-DIAGNOSTICS – EEC-V article in ENGINE PERFORMANCE of appropriate MITCHELL® manual.

INPUT SENSORS

Air Conditioning Clutch (ACC) – On factory installed A/C system, PCM receives signal voltage from ACC switch indication that the air conditioning compressor clutch is engaged. The PCM uses the ACC switch signal to adjust line pressure to compensate for additional engine load. If the ACC switch fails with closed contacts, line pressure will be slightly low with air conditioning off. If the ACC switch fails with open contacts, line pressure will be slightly high with air conditioning on.

Barometric Pressure (BARO) Sensor – The BARO sensor measures barometric pressure to determine altitude at which vehicle is operating. The PCM uses this to adjust shift speeds. Sensor failure can affect shift feel and speeds at altitude.

Brake On/Off (BOO) Switch – The PCM receives a signal from the BOO switch when the brake switch is operated. Torque converter clutch is disengaged when brakes are applied. Malfunctioning switch will affect torque converter operation.

Coolant Temperature Sensor (ECT) – Engine temperature signal is sent to PCM. Malfunctioning ECT will affect torque converter clutch operation.

Mass Airflow Sensor (MAS) – The MAS signal is used for Electronic Pressure Control (EPC), shift and TCC scheduling. Sensor malfunction will affect shift and TCC scheduling.

Manual Lever Position (MLP) – The PCM monitors a series of step down resistors in the MLP sensor that act as a voltage divider. The voltage signal corresponds with position of the transmission range selector lever. The MLP sensor also contains the neutral/start and backup circuits. Malfunction of the MLP sensor may cause harsh engagements and firm shift feel. Improper shifting or shift selection and no engine cranking may also result.

Output Shaft Speed (OSS) Sensor – The OSS is a magnetic pickup, located at output shaft ring gear. Sensor sends output shaft speed signal to PCM. Sensor failure may cause no TCC lock-up, harsh shifting and incorrect shift speeds.

Profile Ignition Pickup (PIP) – The PIP located in distributor, sends engine rpm and crankshaft position to PCM. Signal received by the PCM affects torque converter clutch operation.

Throttle Position Sensor (TPS) – The TPS is a potentiometer mounted to the engine throttle body on gasoline engines and fuel injection pump on diesel engines. The PCM receives a signal from the TPS relaying throttle plate position (gas engines) or fuel delivery (diesel engines). TPS failure will cause PCM to operate in fail safe mode and raise line pressure to prevent transmission damage. This condition will result in harsh engagements, firm shift feel, abnormal shift schedule and TCC not engaging or cycling.

Transmission Control Switch (TCS) – Switch is mounted on shift lever handle. On/Off operation is displayed by Transmission Control Indicator Light (TCIL). Switch controls operation of 4th gear. Malfunction of switch will cause lack of 4th gear disable function.

Transmission Oil Temperature (TOT) Sensor – The TOT sensor is located on the solenoid body assembly. The PCM monitors voltage across the TOT thermistor to determine transmission temperature. Depending on temperature, the PCM controls line pressure, shift scheduling and TCC operation. Malfunction of sensor will cause incorrect line pressure and possible lack of TCC operation.

Vehicle Speed Sensor (VSS) – The VSS is a magnetic pickup that sends vehicle speed signal to the PCM. Malfunction of sensor may cause harsh engagements of shifts. Lack of 4th gear, TCC lock-up, or engine braking in 2nd or 3rd gear may also be present.

OUTPUT DEVICES

Electronic Pressure Control (EPC) Solenoid – The EPC receives signal from the PCM to control line pressure and 2-3 backout valve function. If EPC fails in ON position, transmission is operated in failsafe mode. Minimum line pressure is present. If EPC fails in OFF position, line pressure at maximum pressure. Harsh engagements and shifts will result.

Shift Solenoid Assemblies – 1) Two ON/OFF solenoids are used for electronic shift scheduling. Solenoids used are Shift Solenoid No. 1 (SS1) and Shift Solenoid No. 2 (SS2). Solenoids control pressure to 3 shift valves and forward clutch control valve, located in valve body. See SOLENOID OPERATION CHART.

SOLENOID OPERATIONS CHART

Gear Position	SS1	SS2
Overdrive [1]		
"P" (Park)	On	Off
"R" (Reverse)	On	Off
"N" (Neutral)	On	Off
"OD" (Overdrive)		
1st Gear	On	Off
2nd Gear	Off	On
3rd Gear	Off	On
4th Gear	On	On
"D" (Drive) Or 3rd [2]		
1st Gear	On	Off
2nd Gear	Off	Off
3rd Gear	Off	On

[1] – "OD" switch released.
[2] – "OD" switch depressed (OD cancelled).

AUTOMATIC TRANSMISSIONS
AODE & AODE-W EEC-V Electronic Controls (Cont.)

3-593

SOLENOID OPERATIONS CHART (Cont.)

Gear Position	SS1	SS2
"2" (Manual 2)	Off	Off
"L" (Manual 1) [3]	On	Off
"L" (Manual 1)	Off	Off

[3] – Transmission is in 2nd gear until vehicle speed drops below calibrated speed.

2) When shift solenoid is "Always Off", failure could be due to PCM and/or vehicle wiring malfunction, and/or solenoid electrically stuck off, and/or hydraulically or mechanically stuck off. For shift symptoms, see Fig. 1.

3) When shift solenoid is "Always On", failure could be due to PCM and/or vehicle wiring malfunction, and/or solenoid electrically stuck off, and/or hydraulically or mechanically stuck off. For shift symptoms, see Fig. 2.

Torque Converter Clutch (TCC) Solenoid – The TCC receives signal from the PCM. The TCC controls application, modulation and release of torque converter clutch. If solenoid fails in ON position, vehicle engine will run rough (shudder) and engine stalls in Drive at low idle speeds (2nd, 3rd or 4th gear). If solenoid fails in OFF position, torque converter clutch will not engage.

PRELIMINARY INSPECTION

VISUAL INSPECTION

Visually inspect all electrical wiring, looking for chafed, stretched, cut or pinched wiring. Ensure electrical connectors fit tightly and are not corroded. Ensure vacuum hoses are properly routed and are not pinched or cut. Inspect air induction system for possible vacuum leaks. Check PCM, sensors and actuators for physical damage. Check engine coolant level. Check transmission fluid level and condition.

SS-1 ALWAYS OFF:	Transmission Range Selector Lever Position		
	D	2	1
PCM Gear Commanded	Actual Gear Obtained		
1	2	2	2
2	2	2	2
3	3	2*	2*
4	3	2*	2*

*No Engine Braking

SS-2 ALWAYS OFF:	Transmission Range Selector Lever Position		
	D	2	1
PCM Gear Commanded	Actual Gear Obtained		
1	1	1	1
2	2	2	2
3	2	2	2
4	1	1	1

94D38805 94E38806   Courtesy of Ford Motor Co.

Fig. 1: Shift Solenoid Failure Charts (Always Off)

SS-1 ALWAYS ON:	Transmission Range Selector Lever Position		
	D	2	1
PCM Gear Commanded	Actual Gear Obtained		
1	1	1	1
2	1	1	1
3	4	2*	2*
4	4	2*	2*

*No Engine Braking

SS-2 ALWAYS ON:	Transmission Range Selector Lever Position		
	D	2	1
PCM Gear Commanded	Actual Gear Obtained		
1	4	2*	2*
2	3	2*	2*
3	3	2*	2*
4	4	2*	2*

*No Engine Braking

94F38807 94G38808   Courtesy of Ford Motor Co.

Fig. 2: Shift Solenoid Failure Charts (Always On)

NOTE: In addition to transmission fault codes, engine-related fault codes may be output during QUICK TEST procedure. These fault codes pertain to engine performance and must be repaired first as engine performance will greatly affect transmission operation. For information and testing procedures of engine-related fault codes and components, see SELF-DIAGNOSTICS – EEC-V article in ENGINE PERFORMANCE of appropriate MITCHELL® manual.

SELF-DIAGNOSTIC SYSTEM

DIAGNOSTIC FORMATS

QUICK TEST and CIRCUIT/PINPOINT TESTS are diagnostic formats used to test and service EEC-V system. QUICK TEST allows technician to identify problems and retrieve diagnostic trouble codes. CIRCUIT TESTS check engine circuits, sensors and actuators. PINPOINT TESTS check transmission circuits, sensors and actuators.

Before starting any CIRCUIT/PINPOINT TEST, follow all steps under QUICK TEST to find correct CIRCUIT/PINPOINT TEST. If vehicle passes QUICK TEST and no driveability symptoms or intermittent faults exist, EEC-V system is okay.

DIAGNOSTIC TROUBLE CODES (DTC)

During QUICK TEST, 3 types of diagnostic trouble codes are retrieved: KOEO, KOER and Continuous Memory codes. See QUICK TEST for self-test procedures. Codes may be cleared from PCM memory after they have been recorded or repaired. See CLEARING CODES.

KOEO & KOER Codes (Hard Faults) – These codes indicate faults are present at time of testing. A hard fault may cause CHECK ENGINE or Malfunction Indicator Light (MIL) to go on and remain on until fault is repaired. If KOEO or KOER codes are retrieved during KOEO SELF-TEST or KOER SELF-TEST, use DIAGNOSTIC TROUBLE CODE REFERENCE CHARTS to find correct testing and repair procedures.

3-594

AUTOMATIC TRANSMISSIONS
AODE & AODE-W EEC-V Electronic Controls (Cont.)

Continuous Memory Codes (Intermittent Faults) – These codes are used to diagnose intermittent problems. Continuous Memory Codes are retrieved after KOEO SELF-TEST. These codes indicate a fault that may or may not be present at time of testing.

After noting and/or repairing fault, clear codes from memory. See CLEARING CODES. Intermittent faults may be caused by a sensor, connector or wiring-related problem.

CAUTION: Continuous Memory Codes should be recorded when retrieved. These codes may be used to identify intermittent problems that exist after all KOEO and KOER codes have been repaired. Some Continuous Memory Code faults may not be valid after KOEO and KOER codes are serviced.

RETRIEVING CODES

Fault codes are retrieved from EEC-V system through Data Link Connector (DLC). Self-diagnostic test procedures are for use with New Generation Star (NGS) scan tester. If a generic scan tester is used, ensure tool is certified ODB-II standard.

DATA LINK CONNECTOR (DLC) LOCATIONS

Application	Location
Cougar & Thunderbird	Below Instrument Panel To Right Of Steering Wheel
Mustang	Below Left Side Of Glove Compartment

READING CODES

KOEO & KOER SELF-TEST Codes – Record codes in order received. These codes indicate current faults in system and should be serviced in order of appearance. Use DIAGNOSTIC TROUBLE CODE REFERENCE CHARTS to identify correct CIRCUIT/PINPOINT TEST to perform.

NOTE: If self-test will not activate or TOOL COMMUNICATION ERROR is received, go to CIRCUIT TEST QA, step 1).

Pass Codes – SYSTEM PASS indicates no diagnostic trouble codes were recorded in that portion of test. If SYSTEM PASS is not retrieved in KOEO SELF-TEST, codes retrieved during KOER SELF-TEST may not be valid.

Continuous Memory Codes – These codes result from information stored by PCM during continuous self-test monitoring. Use these codes for diagnosis only when KOEO SELF-TEST and KOER SELF-TEST result in SYSTEM PASS and all steps under QUICK TEST are successfully completed. These codes indicate faults previously recorded. Fault may or may not be currently present. See DIAGNOSTIC TROUBLE CODE REFERENCE CHARTS.

CLEARING CODES

PCM Reset - After a PCM reset procedure, the following conditions will be met:
- All DTC's cleared from PCM memory
- All freeze frame data cleared from PCM memory
- All oxygen sensor test data cleared from PCM memory
- OBD II system monitor status is reset
- DTC P1000 set in PCM memory

To perform PCM reset using NGS scan tester, ensure connectors are properly connected. Program scan tester using the following steps:
- Select vehicle and engine selection menu (optional). *See Fig. 2.*
- Select year, engine, model and any additional information requested by scan tester (optional).
- Follow operating instructions from scan tester menu.
- Select GENERIC OBD II FUNCTIONS. Press CONT button if monitors are not complete.
- Turn ignition on.
- Select CLEAR DIAGNOSTIC CODES.

All codes should now be cleared from PCM memory. If problem has not been corrected or fault is still present, hard code will immediately be reset in PCM memory.

CAUTION: DO NOT disconnect vehicle battery to clear trouble codes. This will erase operating information from Keep-Alive Memory (KAM). To clear KAM, disconnect negative battery terminal for at least 5 minutes.

CAUTION: When battery is disconnected, vehicle computer may lose memory data. Driveability problems may exist until computer systems have completed a relearn cycle. See COMPUTER RELEARN PROCEDURES article in GENERAL INFORMATION before disconnecting battery.

QUICK TEST

Description – Following procedures are functional tests of EEC-V system. These basic test steps must be followed in sequence to avoid misdiagnosis:
- Visual Check
- Equipment Hookup
- KOEO (Key On Engine Off) SELF-TEST
- KOER (Key On Engine Running) SELF-TEST
- Computed Timing Check
- Continuous Memory Self-Test

Diagnostic Aids – After each service or repair procedure has been completed, repeat QUICK TEST to ensure all EEC-V systems work properly and diagnostic trouble codes are no longer present.

EQUIPMENT HOOKUP

Connect appropriate test equipment to vehicle as follows:

Generic Scan Tester – Ensure scan tester meets or exceeds OBD-II standard. Follow manufacturer's instructions to hook up equipment and record diagnostic trouble codes.

New Generation STAR (NGS) Tester – Turn ignition switch to OFF position. Connect adapter cable lead to diagnostic tester. *See Fig. 3.* Connect service connectors of adapter cable to vehicle Data Link Connector (DLC). Go to KOEO SELF-TEST.

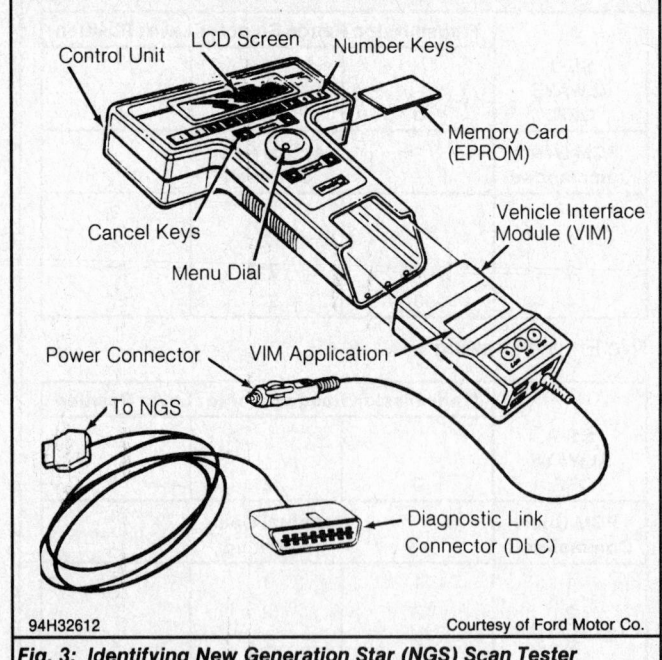

94H32612   Courtesy of Ford Motor Co.

Fig. 3: Identifying New Generation Star (NGS) Scan Tester

KOEO SELF-TEST

Ensure engine is at normal operating temperature. If engine does not start (or stalls after starting), continue KOEO SELF-TEST. Turn

AUTOMATIC TRANSMISSIONS
AODE & AODE-W EEC-V Electronic Controls (Cont.)

3-595

ignition switch to OFF position. Ensure test equipment is properly attached. Program scan tester using the following steps:
- Select vehicle and engine selection menu. *See Fig. 4.*
- Select year, engine, model and any additional information requested by scan tester.
- Select DIAGNOSTIC DATA LINK.
- Select PCM - POWERTRAIN CTRL MODULE.
- Select DIAGNOSTIC TEST MODE.
- Select KOEO ON-DEMAND SELF-TEST.
- Turn ignition on.
- Follow operating instructions from scan tester menu.

KOER SELF-TEST

Ensure engine is warmed to normal operating temperature. Turn ignition switch to OFF position. Ensure test equipment is properly attached. Program scan tester using the following steps:
- Select vehicle and engine selection menu. *See Fig. 4.*
- Select year, engine, model and any additional information requested by scan tester.
- Select DIAGNOSTIC DATA LINK.
- Select PCM – POWERTRAIN CTRL MODULE.
- Select DIAGNOSTIC TEST MODE.
- Select KOER ON-DEMAND SELF-TEST.
- Start engine and allow to idle.
- Follow operating instructions from scan tester menu.
- Perform BOO and TCS cycling (if equipped).

CONTINUOUS MEMORY SELF-TEST (EMISSION RELATED)

Turn ignition switch to OFF position. Ensure test equipment is properly attached. Program scan tester using the following steps:
- Select vehicle and engine selection menu (optional). *See Fig. 4.*
- Select year, engine, model and any additional information requested by scan tester (optional).
- Select GENERIC OBD II OPTIONS. Press CONT button if monitors are not complete.
- Select DIAGNOSTIC TROUBLE CODES.
- Turn ignition on.
- Follow operating instructions from scan tester menu.

CONTINUOUS MEMORY SELF-TEST (ENHANCED MODE)

Turn ignition switch to OFF position. Ensure test equipment is properly attached. Program scan tester using the following steps:
- Select vehicle and engine selection menu. *See Fig. 4.*
- Select year, engine, model and any additional information requested by scan tester.
- Select DIAGNOSTIC DATA LINK.
- Select PCM – POWERTRAIN CTRL MODULE.
- Select DIAGNOSTIC TEST MODES.
- Select RETRIEVE/CLEAR CONTINUOUS DTC's.
- Turn ignition on.
- Follow operating instructions from scan tester menu.

ADDITIONAL SYSTEM FUNCTIONS

NOTE: These additional diagnostic system features are available to help diagnose driveability problems and service EEC-V systems.
- *Generic OBD II Parameter Identification (PID)*
- *Non-Generic OBD II Parameter Identification (PID)*
- *On-Board System Readiness (OSR) Test Mode*
- *Freeze Frame Data Mode*
- *Oxygen Sensor Test Mode*
- *Transmission Drive Cycle Test*
- *Failure Mode Effects Management (FMEM)*
- *Hardware Limited Operational Strategy (HLOS)*

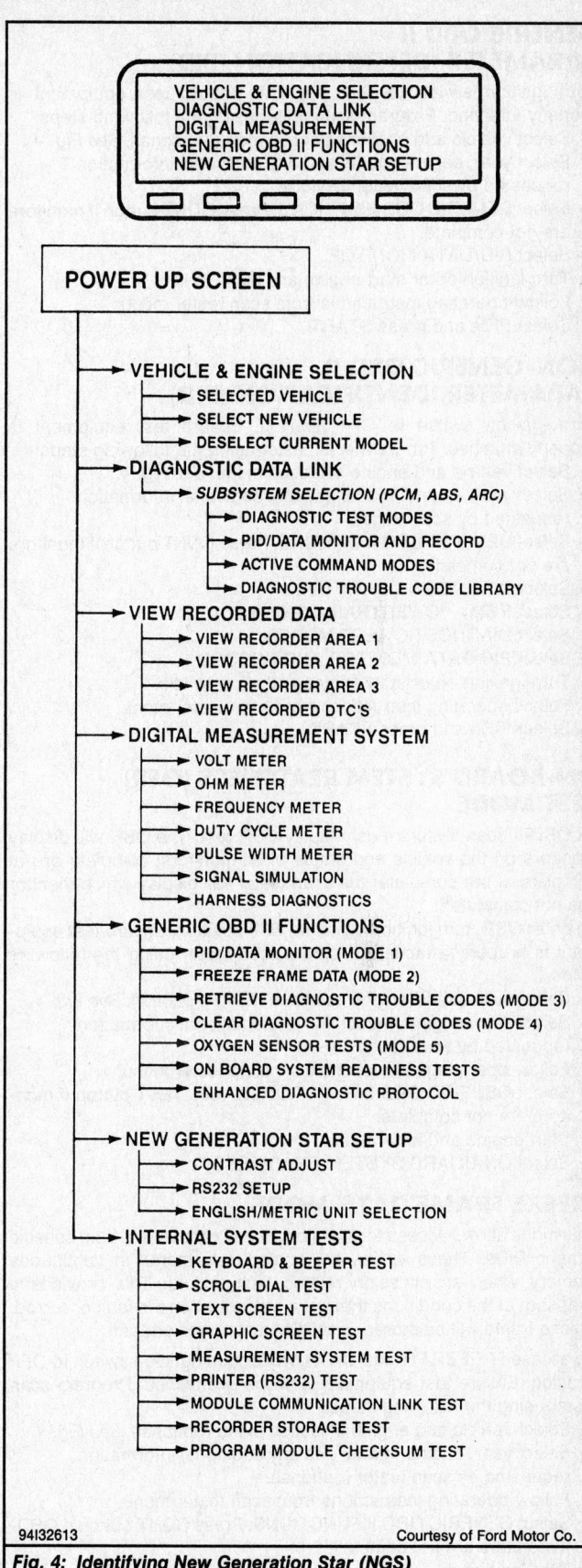

94132613   Courtesy of Ford Motor Co.

Fig. 4: Identifying New Generation Star (NGS) Main Menu & Mode Paths

3-596

AUTOMATIC TRANSMISSIONS
AODE & AODE-W EEC-V Electronic Controls (Cont.)

GENERIC OBD II
PARAMETER IDENTIFICATION (PID)

Turn ignition switch to OFF position. Ensure test equipment is properly attached. Program scan tester using the following steps:
- Select vehicle and engine selection menu (optional). *See Fig. 4.*
- Select year, engine, model and any additional information requested by scan tester (optional).
- Select GENERIC OBD II OPTIONS. Press CONT button if monitors are not complete.
- Select PID/DATA MONITOR.
- Turn ignition on or start engine and allow to idle.
- Follow operating instructions from scan tester menu.
- Select PIDs and press START.

NON-GENERIC OBD II
PARAMETER IDENTIFICATION (PID)

Turn ignition switch to OFF position. Ensure test equipment is properly attached. Program scan tester using the following steps:
- Select vehicle and engine selection menu. *See Fig. 4.*
- Select year, engine, model and any additional information requested by scan tester.
- Select GENERIC OBD II OPTIONS. Press CONT button if monitors are not complete.
- Select DIAGNOSTIC DATA LINK.
- Select PCM - POWERTRAIN CTRL MODULE.
- Select DIAGNOSTIC TEST MODES.
- Select PID DATA MONITOR AND RECORD.
- Turn ignition on or start engine and allow to idle.
- Follow operating instructions from scan tester menu.
- Select PIDs and press START.

ON-BOARD SYSTEM READINESS (OSR)
TEST MODE

All OBD-II scan testers must display OSR test. The OSR will display monitors on the vehicle and status of all monitors; complete or not complete. If not complete, the scan tester will display which monitor has not completed.

To enter OSR, turn ignition switch to OFF position. Ensure test equipment is properly attached. Program scan tester using the following steps:
- Select vehicle and engine selection menu (optional). *See Fig. 4.*
- Select year, engine, model and any additional information requested by scan tester.
- Follow operating instructions from scan tester menu.
- Select GENERIC OBD II FUNCTIONS. Press TEST button if monitors are not complete.
- Start engine and allow to idle.
- Select ON-BOARD SYSTEM READINESS

FREEZE FRAME DATA MODE

This mode allows access to emission related data values from specific generic PIDs. These values are immediately stored in continuous memory when an emission related fault occurs. This provides a snapshot of the conditions that were present when the fault occurred. Freeze frame will be stored until PCM memory is errased.

To access FREEZE FRAME DATA MODE, turn ignition switch to OFF position. Ensure test equipment is properly attached. Program scan tester using the following steps:
- Select vehicle and engine selection menu (optional). *See Fig. 4.*
- Select year, engine, model and any additional information requested by scan tester (optional).
- Follow operating instructions from scan tester menu.
- Select GENERIC OBD II FUNCTIONS. Press CONT button if OBD-II monitors are not complete.
- Turn ignition on.
- Select FREEZE FRAME PID TESTS.

OXYGEN SENSOR TEST MODE

This mode allows access to on-board sensor fault limits and actual values during test cycle. The test cycle has specific engine operating conditions that must be met for completion. This information is used to determine the efficiency of the catalytic converter.

To access OXYGEN SENSOR TEST mode, turn ignition switch to OFF position. Ensure test equipment is properly attached. Program scan tester using the following steps:
- Select vehicle and engine selection menu (optional). *See Fig. 4.*
- Select year, engine, model and any additional information requested by scan tester (optional).
- Follow operating instructions from scan tester menu.
- Select GENERIC OBD II FUNCTIONS.
- Select OXYGEN SENSOR TESTS.
- Select appropriate oxygen sensor test and follow menu instructions.

OUTPUT TEST MODE

This mode allows a technician to energize and de-energize most of the system output actuators on command. After accessing OUTPUT TEST MODE, outputs and cooling fans can be turned on and off separately.

To access OUTPUT TEST MODE, turn ignition switch to OFF position. Ensure test equipment is properly attached. Program scan tester using the following steps:
- Select vehicle and engine selection menu. *See Fig. 4.*
- Select year, engine, model and any additional information requested by scan tester.
- Follow operating instructions from scan tester menu.
- Select DIAGNOSTIC DATA LINK.
- Select PCM - POWERTRAIN CTRL MODULE.
- Select DIAGNOSTIC TEST MODE.
- Select ACTIVE COMMAND MODE.
- Select OUTPUT TEST MODE.
- Turn ignition on.
- Follow operating instructions from scan tester menu.
- Select either LOW SPEED FAN, HIGH SPEED FAN or ALL ON mode.
- Select START to turn outputs on. This step may cause link up to PIDs.
- Select STOP to turn outputs off.

TRANSMISSION DRIVE CYCLE TEST

NOTE: The transmission drive cycle test must be followed exactly. Malfunctions have to occur 4 times consecutively for codes 617, 618 and 619 to be set and 5 times consecutively for continuous code 628.

1) Record and then erase Quick Test codes. Warm engine to normal operating temperature. Ensure transmission fluid level is correct. Shift transmission to overdrive (OD).
2) Accelerate from stop to 50 mph. Hold speed for at least 15 seconds (30 seconds above 4000 ft.). Press TCS and accelerate to 50 mph. Hold speed for at least 15 seconds (30 seconds above 4000 ft.). Hold speed and throttle position steady for at least 15 seconds. While maintaining speed with transmission in 4th gear, lightly depress brake pedal and release. Maintain speed for additional 5 seconds. Bring vehicle to stop for at least 20 seconds. Repeat steps 1) and 2) at least 5 times. Perform Quick Test and record continuous codes.

FAILURE MODE EFFECTS MANAGEMENT
(FMEM)

FMEM mode allows system operation when sensors fail or transmit signals that are out of normal operating range. During FMEM mode, PCM substitutes a mid-range signal for defective sensor while continuing to monitor sensor. If faulty sensor's signals return to normal operating range, PCM will use those signals. Depending on specific failure, a fault code may be set in PCM memory.

AUTOMATIC TRANSMISSIONS
AODE & AODE-W EEC-V Electronic Controls (Cont.)

3-597

HARDWARE LIMITED OPERATIONAL STRATEGY (HLOS)

If a number of system or sensor failures are present and PCM is not receiving enough information to operate, PCM will switch to HLOS mode. PCM will output fixed values to allow operation of vehicle. Driveability concerns will be present. PCM will not output diagnostic trouble codes in this mode.

SUMMARY

If no service codes (or pass code 1111) is present but driveability problem still exists, return to TROUBLE SHOOTING in AODE/AODE-W overhaul article.

DIAGNOSTIC TROUBLE CODE (DTC) REFERENCE CHARTS

NOTE: In addition to transmission fault codes, engine-related fault codes may be output during QUICK TEST procedure. These fault codes pertain to engine performance and must be repaired first as engine performance will greatly affect transmission operation. For information and testing procedures of engine-related fault codes and components, see SELF-DIAGNOSTICS – EEC-V article in ENGINE PERFORMANCE of appropriate MITCHELL® manual.

CODE REFERENCE CHART

Fault Code	Code Definition	[1] Test
KOEO Codes		
No Code	N/A	QA1
1111	Pass Code	N/A
0103	IMAF Sensor Malfunction	DC20
0112	IAT Indicates 254° F (125° C)	DA20
0113	IAT Indicates -40° F (-40° C)	DA10
0117	ECT Indicates 254° F (125° C)	DA20
0118	ECT Indicates -40° F (-40° C)	DA10
0122	TPS Malfunction	DH8
0123	TPS Malfunction	DH5
0712	TOT Sensor Circuit Grounded	B1
0713	TOT Sensor Circuit Open	B1
0743	TCC Circuit Error	C1
0750	SS1 Solenoid Circuit Failure	A1
0755	SS2 Solenoid Circuit Failure	A1
1101	MAF Sensor Malfunction	DC1
1460	A/C Switch Failure	X105
1703	BOO Switch Malfunction	FD2
1709	MLP-No PARK Indication	A1
1711	TOT Out Of Range	B1
1746	Open PCM Output Driver	E1
1747	EPC Circuit Failure	E1
1751	SS1 Solenoid Circuit Failure	A1
1752	SS1 Solenoid Circuit Failure	A1
KOER Codes		
No Code	N/A	QA1
1111	Pass Code	N/A
0102	IMAF Sensor Malfunction	DC6
0103	IMAF Sensor Malfunction	DC20
0112	IAT Indicates 254° F (125° C)	DA20
0113	IAT Indicates -40° F (-40° C)	DA10
0117	ECT Indicates 254° F (125° C)	DA20
0118	ECT Indicates -40° F (-40° C)	DA10
0122	TPS Malfunction	DH8
0123	TPS Malfunction	DH5
0712	TOT Sensor Circuit Grounded	B1
0713	TOT Sensor Circuit Open	B1
1101	MAF Sensor Malfunction	DC1
1460	A/C Switch Failure	X105
1711	TOT Out Of Range	B1
1780	TCS Not Cycled	TB1

[1] – Circuit or Pinpoint test.

CODE REFERENCE CHART (Cont.)

Fault Code	Code Definition	[1] Test
Continuous Memory Codes		
No Code	N/A	QA1
1111	Pass Code	N/A
0102	IMAF Sensor Malfunction	DC6
0103	IMAF Sensor Malfunction	DC90
0112	IAT Indicates 254° F (125° C)	DA90
0113	IAT Indicates -40° F (-40° C)	DA90
0117	ECT Indicates 254° F (125° C)	DA90
0118	ECT Indicates -40° F (-40° C)	DA90
0122	TPS Malfunction	DH8
0123	TPS Malfunction	DH5
0125	TPS Malfunction	DA100
0500	Low VSS Output	DP1
0705	MLP Out Of Range	D1
0707	MLP Low Voltage	D1
0708	MLP High Voltage	D1
0712	TOT Sensor Circuit Grounded	B1
0713	TOT Sensor Circuit Open	B1
0720	Low OSS Output	F1
0743	TCC Circuit Error	C1
0750	SS1 Solenoid Circuit Failure	A1
0751	SS1 Solenoid Circuit Failure	A1
0755	SS2 Solenoid Circuit Failure	A1
0756	SS2 Solenoid Circuit Failure	A1
1100	MAF Sensor Malfunction	DC2
1460	A/C Switch Failure	X120
1709	MLP-No PARK Indication	A1
1731	1-2 Shift Error	A1
1732	2-3 Shift Error	A1
1733	3-4 Shift Error	A1
1741	TCC Engagement Error	C1
1742	TCC Failed On	C1
1743	TCC Failed On	C1
1746	Open PCM Output Driver	E1
1747	EPC Circuit Failure	E1
1783	TOT Overtemp Condition	A1

[1] – Circuit or Pinpoint test.

CIRCUIT/PINPOINT TESTS

NOTE: A breakout box, connected to vehicle harness at PCM, is necessary to perform most circuit tests. References to Test Pin No. found in CIRCUIT/PINPOINT TEST steps refer to test terminals on manufacturer's breakout box. Circuit diagrams at beginning of each test identify circuit and wire colors.

HOW TO USE CIRCUIT/PINPOINT TESTS

1) DO NOT perform any CIRCUIT/PINPOINT TEST unless specifically instructed by a QUICK TEST procedure. Follow each test step in order until fault is found. DO NOT replace any part unless directed to do so. When more than one code is retrieved, start with first code displayed.
2) CIRCUIT/PINPOINT TESTS ensure electrical circuits are okay before sensors or other components are replaced. Always test circuits for continuity between sensor and PCM. Test all circuits for short to power, opens or short to ground. Voltage Reference (VREF) and Voltage Power (VPWR) circuits should be tested with ignition on or as specified in CIRCUIT/PINPOINT TESTS.
3) DO NOT measure voltage or resistance at PCM. DO NOT connect any test light unless specified in testing procedure. All measurements are made by probing rear of connector (wiring harness side). Isolate both ends of a circuit and turn ignition off when checking for shorts or continuity, unless instructed otherwise.
4) Disconnect solenoids and switches from harness before measuring continuity and resistance or applying voltage. After each repair, check all component connections and repeat QUICK TEST.

5) An open circuit is defined as a resistance reading of greater than 5 ohms. This specification tolerance may be too high for some items in EEC-V system. If resistance approaches 5 ohms, always clean suspect connector and coat it with protective dielectric silicone grease. A short is defined as a resistance reading of less than 10 k/ohms to ground, unless stated otherwise in CIRCUIT/PINPOINT TEST.

NOTE: In following tests, circuit diagrams and illustrations are courtesy of Ford Motor Co.

PINPOINT TESTS

NOTE: PINPOINT TESTS are diagnostic formats used to test and service EEC-V system. PINPOINT TESTS check transmission circuits, sensors and actuators.

PINPOINT TEST A

SHIFT SOLENOID ELECTRICAL SYSTEM

1) AODE/AODE-W Electronic Diagnostics – Ensure transmission harness connector is in acceptable condition. Repair as necessary. Disconnect transmission harness connector. Connect Transmission Tester (007-0085A) or equivalent to transmission. Perform TRANSMISSION SOLENOID CYCLING & DRVE TEST. Perform KOEO test until Continuous Memory trouble code(s) have been displayed. See QUICK TEST. Depress throttle to WOT and release. If vehicle enters Output State, go to next step. If vehicle will not enter Output State, see SELF-DIAGNOSTICS – EEC-V article in ENGINE PERFORMANCE of appropriate MITCHELL® manual.

2) Check Electrical Signal Operation – Disconnect transmission harness connector. Inspect condition of connector and repair as needed. Using DVOM (20-volt scale), connect positive lead to transmission harness connector VPWR terminal. *See Fig. A1.* Connect negative lead to suspect solenoid circuit. Depress and release throttle to cycle solenoid output. If voltage changes at least .5 volts, go to step 5). If voltage is unaffected, go to next step.

94H38809

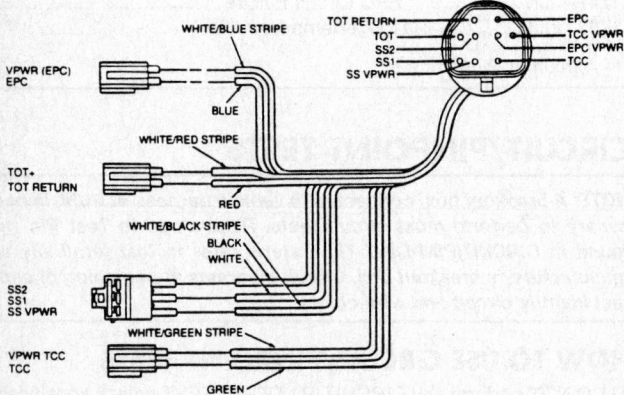

Fig. A1: Identifying Transmission Shift Solenoid Harness Connector

---

BREAKOUT BOX (BOB) TEST PIN REFERENCE CHART

Component Circuit [1]	BOB Test Pin
EPC	81
EPC VPWR	71/97
SS1	27
SS2	1
SS VPWR	71/97
TCC	82
TCC VPWR	71/97
TOT Return	91
TOT	37

[1] – *See Fig. A1.*

PINPOINT TEST A (Cont.)

3) Check Continuity Of Solenoid Signal & VPWR Harness Circuits – Ensure ignition is off. Disconnect PCM 60-pin connector, and inspect it for damaged pins, corrosion and loose wires. Repair as necessary. Install Breakout Box (007-00033), leaving PCM disconnected. Measure and record resistance between Breakout Box test pin No. 27 or 1 and corresponding transmission harness connector terminal. *See Fig. A1.* Measure and record resistance. Measure and record resistance between test pins No. 71 and 97 and transmission harness connector VPWR terminal. If any resistance is greater than 5 ohms, repair open circuit. Connect all components. Disconnect Breakout Box and repeat Quick Test. If resistance is 5 ohms or less, go to next step.

4) Check Solenoid Harness For Shorts To Power & Ground – Measure and record resistance between Breakout Box test pins No. 27 or 1 and test pins No. 71 and 97. Measure and record resistance between test pins No. 40, 46 and 60, and ground. If any resistance is less than 10 k/ohms, repair short circuit. Connect all components. Disconnect Breakout Box and repeat Quick Test. If resistance is 10 k/ohms or more, go to next step.

5) Solenoid Functional Test – Connect Transmission Tester (007-00085). Perform solenoid function test. See tester instructions. If solenoid activates (LED Green), go to next step. If solenoid does not activate, go to step 7).

6) Transmission Drive Test – Perform tester drive test. See tester instructions. If vehicle upshifts when operated with tester, go to TROUBLE SHOOTING in Ford AODE/AODE-W article. If vehicle does not upshift when operated by tester, go to next step.

7) Check Resistance Of Solenoid – Set tester Bench/Drive switch to Bench mode. Set Gear Selector switch to ohms check. Connect ohmmeter negative lead to SS1 jack and positive lead to VPWR jack on tester. Measure and record resistance. Connect ohmmeter negative lead to SS2 jack and positive lead to VPWR jack on tester. Measure and record resistance. Resistance for all solenoids should be 20-30 ohms. If resistance is within specification, go to next step. If resistance is not within specification, go to step 9).

8) Check Solenoid For Short To Ground – Check continuity between BAT(-) terminal and between SS1 and SS2. Check continuity between BAT(-) terminal and VPWR terminal. If continuity exists for any circuit, go to next step. If continuity does not exist, go to TROUBLE SHOOTING in Ford AODE/AODE-W article.

9) AODE/AODE-W Internal Electronic Diagnostics – Drain transmission fluid. See TRANSMISSION SERVICING section. Remove transmission side pan. See OIL PUMP & VALVE BODY ASSEMBLY under ON-VEHICLE SERVICE IN FORD AODE/AODE-W overhaul article. Inspect all internal harness connectors. Ensure all connectors are fully connected and not damaged. Repair as needed. Install all components in reverse order of disassembly. Fill transmission with fluid. Erase all trouble codes. See CLEARING CODES. Repeat QUICK TEST. If all connectors are okay, go to next step.

10) Check Internal Harness Continuity – Disconnect internal harness from solenoid assemblies. To test SS1, connect positive lead of ohmmeter to tester SS-1 jack and negative lead to SS1 White wire. Measure and record resistance. To test SS2, connect positive lead of ohmmeter to tester SS-2 jack and negative lead to SS2 Black wire. Measure and record resistance.

To test SS1 and SS2 VPWR circuits, connect positive lead of ohmmeter to selected solenoid White/Black wire. Connect negative lead to corresponding VPWR tester terminal. Measure and record resistance. If all resistances measured are .5 ohms or less, go to next step. If any resistance measured is more than .5 ohms, replace internal harness. Go to step 12).

11) Check Internal Harness For Shorts To Ground – Using transmission tester, check continuity between each solenoid lead and BAT(-) terminal of tester. If continuity does not exist in any circuit, go to next step. If continuity exists in any circuit, replace internal harness. Install all components in reverse order of disassembly. Fill transmission with fluid. Erase all trouble codes. See CLEARING CODES. Repeat QUICK TEST.

12) Check Solenoid Resistance – Using ohmmeter, check resistance between terminals of each solenoid. Resistance should be 20-30 ohms. If resistance is within specification, go to next step. If resistance measured for any solenoid is not within specification, replace solenoid assembly. Install all components in reverse order of disassembly. Fill transmission with fluid. Erase all trouble codes. See CLEARING CODES. Repeat QUICK TEST.

AUTOMATIC TRANSMISSIONS
AODE & AODE-W EEC-V Electronic Controls (Cont.)

3-599

PINPOINT TEST A (Cont.)

13) Check Solenoid For Short To Ground – Using ohmmeter, check continuity between each solenoid terminal and ground. If continuity exists, replace shift solenoid assembly. If continuity does not exist, go to TROUBLE SHOOTING in Ford AODE/AODE-W overhaul article. Install all components in reverse order of disassembly. Fill transmission with fluid. Erase all trouble codes. See CLEARING CODES. Repeat QUICK TEST.

PINPOINT TEST B

TOT ELECTRICAL SYSTEM

1) Visual Check – Check transmission harness connector. Inspect connector for damaged pins, corrosion and loose wires. Repair as necessary. Go to next step.

2) Check Electrical Signal Operation – Ensure ignition is off. Disconnect transmission connector. Using DVOM, connect positive lead to transmission harness connector TOT terminal and negative lead to SRTN terminal. *See Fig. A1.* Turn ignition on. If voltage is 4.75-5.25 volts, go to next step. If voltage is not within specification, see SELF-DIAGNOSTICS – EEC-V article in ENGINE PERFORMANCE of appropriate MITCHELL® manual to diagnose NO VREF voltage.

3) Check Continuity Of TOT & Signal Return (SIG RTN) Circuits – Turn ignition off. Disconnect PCM 60-pin connector, and inspect it for damaged pins, corrosion and loose wires. Repair as necessary. Install Breakout Box (007-00033), leaving PCM disconnected. Measure and record resistance between Breakout Box test pin No. 37 and transmission harness connector TOT terminal. *See Fig. A1.* Measure and record resistance between test pin No. 91 and transmission harness connector SRTN terminal. If resistances measured are less than 5 ohms, go to next step. If resistances are more than 5 ohms, repair open circuit. Connect all components. Erase trouble codes. See CLEARING CODES. Repeat QUICK TEST.

4) Check TOT Circuit For Short To VPWR & Ground – Ensure ignition is off. Disconnect PCM 60-pin connector, and inspect it for damaged pins, corrosion and loose wires. Repair as necessary. Install Breakout Box (007-00033), leaving PCM disconnected. Measure and record resistance between Breakout Box test pins No. 37 and test pins No. 71 and 97. If resistance is less than 10 k/ohms, repair short circuit. Disconnect Breakout Box and repeat Quick Test. If resistance is 10 k/ohms or more, go to next step.

NOTE: Code 637 is set if resistance measured exceeds 869 ohms (open circuit). Code 638 is set if resistance measured is below 597 ohms (short circuit).

5) Check Resistance Of TOT Sensor/Harness – Install Transmission Tester (007-00085). Set tester Bench/Drive switch to BENCH mode. Set Solenoid Select switch to OHMS CHECK. Connect ohmmeter lead to appropriate TOT jacks. Measure and record resistance. Resistance should be within specification. See TOT TEMPERATURE/RESISTANCE CHART. If resistance is within specification for specific temperature, either warm up transmission or allow transmission to cool to check resistance at different temperatures. If resistances measured remain within specification, go to next step. If resistances measured are not within specification, go to step 7).

TOT TEMPERATURE/RESISTANCE CHART

Temperature °F (°C)	Resistance-Ohms (K)
32-58 (0-20)	37-100
59-104 (21-40)	16-37
105-158 (41-70)	5-16
159-194 (71-90)	2.7-5
195-230 (91-110)	1.5-2.7
231-266 (111-130)	.8-1.5

6) Check TOT Sensor For Short To Ground – Check continuity between BAT (-) tester terminal and TOT terminals. If continuity exists, go to next step. If continuity does not exist, Erase all trouble codes. See CLEARING CODES. Repeat QUICK TEST. See FORD AODE/AODE-W overhaul article for non-electronic symptom diagnostics.

7) AODE/AODE-W Internal Electronic Diagnostics – Drain transmission fluid. See TRANSMISSION SERVICING section. Remove transmission side pan. See OIL PUMP & VALVE BODY ASSEMBLY under ON-VEHICLE SERVICE IN FORD AODE/AODE-W overhaul article. Inspect

PINPOINT TEST B (Cont.)

all internal harness connectors. Ensure all connectors are fully connected and not damaged. Repair as needed. Install all components in reverse order of disassembly. Fill transmission with fluid. Erase all trouble codes. See CLEARING CODES. Repeat QUICK TEST. If all connectors are okay, go to next step.

8) Check Internal Harness Continuity – Disconnect internal harness from TOT sensor. Connect positive lead of ohmmeter to tester TOT (+) jack and negative lead to TOT White/Red wire. Measure and record resistance. Connect positive lead of ohmmeter to tester TOT (–) jack and negative lead to TOT Red wire. If resistances measured are 5 ohms or less, go to next step. If any resistance measured is more than 5 ohms, replace internal harness. Go to step 10).

9) Check Internal Harness For Shorts To Ground – Using transmission tester, check continuity between each TOT sensor connector terminals and BAT (–) terminal of tester. If continuity does not exist in any circuit, go to next step. If continuity exists in any circuit, replace internal harness. Go to next step.

10) Check TOT Sensor Resistance – Using ohmmeter, check resistance between terminals TOT sensor. If resistance is within specification for specific temperature, go to next step. If resistances measured are not within specification, replace TOT sensor. Install all components in reverse order of disassembly. Fill transmission with fluid. Erase all trouble codes. See CLEARING CODES. Repeat QUICK TEST.

TOT TEMPERATURE/RESISTANCE CHART

Temperature °F (°C)	Resistance-k/ohms
32-58 (0-20)	37-100
59-104 (21-40)	16-37
105-158 (41-70)	5-16
159-194 (71-90)	2.7-5
195-230 (91-110)	1.5-2.7
231-266 (111-130)	.8-1.5

11) Check Solenoid For Short To Ground – Using ohmmeter, check continuity between each TOT sensor terminal and ground. If continuity exists, replace faulty TOT sensor. If continuity does not exist, install all components in reverse order of disassembly. Fill transmission with fluid. Erase all trouble codes. See CLEARING CODES. Repeat QUICK TEST, see SELF-DIAGNOSTICS – EEC-V article in ENGINE PERFORMANCE of appropriate MITCHELL® manual to diagnose vehicle harness or PCM malfunctions.

PINPOINT TEST C

TCC ELECTRICAL SYSTEM

NOTE: Transmission tester TCC terminals may be designated MCCC. Refer to tester instructions.

1) AODE/AODE-W Electronic Diagnostics – Ensure transmission harness connector is in acceptable condition. Repair as necessary. Disconnect transmission harness connector. Connect Transmission Tester (007-00085) or equivalent to transmission. Perform TRANSMISSION SOLENOID CYCLING & DRIVE TEST. Perform KOEO test until Continuous Memory trouble code(s) have been displayed. See QUICK TEST. Depress throttle to WOT and release. If vehicle enters Output State, go to next step. If vehicle will not enter Output State, see SELF-DIAGNOSTICS – EEC-V article in ENGINE PERFORMANCE of appropriate MITCHELL® manual.

2) Check Electrical Signal Operation – Disconnect transmission harness connector. Inspect condition of connector and repair as needed. Using DVOM (20-volt scale), connect positive lead to transmission harness connector VPWR terminal. *See Fig. A1.* Connect negative lead to TCC terminal. Depress and release throttle to cycle solenoid output. If voltage changes at least .5 volts, go to step 5). If voltage is unaffected, go to next step.

3) Check Continuity Of Solenoid Signal & VPWR Harness Circuits – Ensure ignition is off. Disconnect PCM 60-pin connector, and inspect it for damaged pins, corrosion and loose wires. Repair as necessary. Install Breakout Box (007-00033), leaving PCM disconnected. Measure and record resistance between Breakout Box test pin No. 82 and transmission harness connector TCC terminal. *See Fig. A1.* Measure and record resistance between test pins No. 71 and 97 and transmission harness connector VPWR terminal. If any resistance is greater than 5 ohms,

3-600

AUTOMATIC TRANSMISSIONS
AODE & AODE-W EEC-V Electronic Controls (Cont.)

PINPOINT TEST C (Cont.)

repair open circuit. Connect all components. Disconnect Breakout Box and repeat Quick Test. If resistance is 5 ohms or less, go to next step.

4) Check Solenoid Harness For Shorts To Power & Ground – Measure and record resistance between test pin No. 82 and test pins No. 71 and 97. Measure and record resistance between test pins No. 40, 91 and 60, and ground. If any resistance is less than 10 k/ohms, repair short circuit. Connect all components. Disconnect Breakout Box and repeat Quick Test. If resistance is 10 k/ohms or more, go to next step.

5) Solenoid Functional Test – Connect Transmission Tester (007-00085). Perform solenoid voltage test. See tester instructions. If solenoid activates (LED Green), go to next step. If solenoid does not activate, go to step 7).

6) Transmission Drive Test – Perform tester drive test. See tester instructions. When transmission has shifted into 2nd gear, depress MCCC switch on tester. If engine rpm decreases when operated with tester, see SELF-DIAGNOSTICS – EEC-V article in ENGINE PERFORMANCE of appropriate MITCHELL® manual to diagnose vehicle harness or PCM malfunctions. If engine rpm does not decrease when operated by tester, go to next step.

7) Check Resistance Of Solenoid – Set tester Bench/Drive switch to BENCH mode. Set Gear Selector switch to OHMS CHECK. Connect ohmmeter negative lead to MCCC jack and positive lead to MCCC VPWR jack on tester. Measure resistance. Resistance should be 1-3 ohms. If resistance is within specification, go to next step. If resistance is not within specification, go to step 9).

8) Check Solenoid For Short To Ground – Check continuity between BAT (–) tester terminal and MCCC terminals. If continuity exists, go to next step. If continuity does not exist, Erase all trouble codes. See CLEARING CODES. Repeat QUICK TEST. See TROUBLE SHOOTING in FORD AODE/AODE-W overhaul article for non-electronic symptom diagnostics.

9) AODE/AODE-W Internal Electronic Diagnostics – Drain transmission fluid. See TRANSMISSION SERVICING section. Remove transmission side pan. See OIL PUMP & VALVE BODY ASSEMBLY under ON-VEHICLE SERVICE IN FORD AODE/AODE-W overhaul article. Inspect all internal harness connectors. Ensure all connectors are fully connected and not damaged. Repair as needed. Install all components in reverse order of disassembly. Fill transmission with fluid. Erase all trouble codes. See CLEARING CODES. Repeat QUICK TEST. If all connectors are okay, go to next step.

10) Check Internal Harness Continuity – Disconnect internal harness from TCC sensor. Connect positive lead of ohmmeter to tester MCCC jack and negative lead to TCC Green wire. Measure and record resistance. Connect positive lead of ohmmeter to tester VPWR jack and negative lead to TCC White/Green wire. If resistances measured are 5 ohms or less, go to next step. If any resistance measured is more than 5 ohms, replace internal harness. Go to step 12).

11) Check Internal Harness For Shorts To Ground – Using transmission tester, check continuity between each TCC sensor connector terminals and BAT (–) terminal of tester. If continuity does not exist in either circuit, go to next step. If continuity exists in any circuit, replace internal harness. Go to next step.

12) Check TCC Solenoid Resistance – Using ohmmeter, check resistance between terminals TCC solenoid. If resistance is 1-3 ohms, go to next step. If resistance measured is not within specification, replace TCC solenoid assembly. Install all components in reverse order of disassembly. Fill transmission with fluid. Erase all trouble codes. See CLEARING CODES. Repeat QUICK TEST.

13) Check Solenoid For Short To Ground – Using ohmmeter, check continuity between each TCC solenoid terminal and ground. If continuity exists, replace faulty TCC solenoid. Install all components in reverse order of disassembly. Fill transmission with fluid. Erase all trouble codes. See CLEARING CODES. Repeat QUICK TEST. If continuity does not exist, install all components in reverse order of disassembly. Fill transmission with fluid. Erase all trouble codes. See CLEARING CODES. Repeat QUICK TEST. See TROUBLE SHOOTING in FORD AODE/AODE-W overhaul article for non-electronic symptom diagnostics.

PINPOINT TEST D

MLP Sensor

NOTE: Code 634 may be set if transmission is not in park or A/C is on when QUICK TEST is performed.

1) Preliminary Inspection – Disconnect MLP connector, and inspect it for damaged pins, corrosion and loose wires. Repair as necessary. Reconnect MLP connector. Ensure MLP sensor is correctly adjusted. See FORD AODE/AODE-W overhaul article. If sensor requires adjustment, clear trouble codes after adjustment. See CLEARING CODES. Repeat QUICK TEST. If sensor is correctly adjusted, go to next step.

2) Check Electrical Signal Operation – Ensure ignition is off. Disconnect MLP harness connector. Turn ignition on. Measure voltage between harness connector TOT terminal and SRTN terminal. See Fig. A1. If voltage is 4.75-5.25 volts, go to next step. If voltage is not within specification, see SELF-DIAGNOSTICS – EEC-V article in ENGINE PERFORMANCE of appropriate MITCHELL® manual for NO VREF voltage.

3) Check Continuity Of MLP Sensor Harness Circuits – Turn ignition off. Disconnect PCM 60-pin connector, and inspect it for damaged pins, corrosion and loose wires. Repair as necessary. Install Breakout Box (007-00033), leaving PCM disconnected. Measure and record resistance between Breakout Box test pin terminal No. 91 and MLP harness connector terminal No. 359. See Fig. D1. Measure and record resistance between Breakout Box test pin terminal No. 30 and MLP harness connector terminal No. 199. If resistance is less than 5 ohms, go to next step. If resistance is more than 5 ohms, repair open circuit(s). Remove Breakout Box and connect all components. Erase all trouble codes. See CLEARING CODES. Repeat QUICK TEST.

94A38810

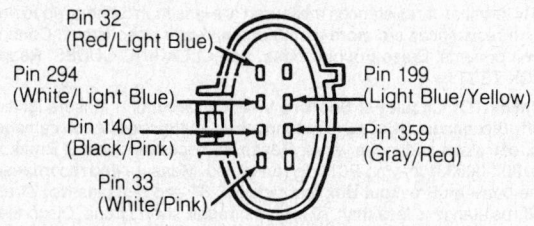

Pin 32 (Red/Light Blue)
Pin 294 (White/Light Blue)
Pin 140 (Black/Pink)
Pin 33 (White/Pink)
Pin 199 (Light Blue/Yellow)
Pin 359 (Gray/Red)

Fig. D1: Identifying Transmission Harness Connector

4) Check MLP Circuit For Shorts To Power & Ground – Ensure MLP sensor harness connector is disconnected. Measure resistance between Breakout Box test pin No. 30 and test pins No. 37, 40, 91, 57 and 60. Measure resistance between Breakout Box test pin No. 30 and ground. If each measurement is more than 10 k/ohms, go to next step. If any measurement is less than 10 k/ohms, repair short circuit. Remove Breakout Box and connect all components. Erase all trouble codes. See CLEARING CODES. Repeat QUICK TEST.

5) Operational Check Of MLP Sensor – Install MLP overlay on Transmission Tester (007-00085). Connect tester to MLP sensor. Check continuity and resistances in all positions. See Fig. D1. If MLP sensor does not operate within specification, replace sensor. Connect all components. Erase all trouble codes. See CLEARING CODES. Repeat QUICK TEST. If sensor operates within specification, connect all components. Erase all trouble codes. See CLEARING CODES. Repeat QUICK TEST. If code(s) 522, 634 or 659 are set, intermittent condition may be present. Attempt to duplicate malfunction by repeating previous steps.

AUTOMATIC TRANSMISSIONS
AODE & AODE-W EEC-V Electronic Controls (Cont.)

3-601

PINPOINT TEST D (Cont.)

94C38457

Transmission Range Selector Lever Position	Resistance (ohms)		Volts
	Min	Max	
P	3770	4607	4.41
R	1304	1593	3.60
N	660	807	2.83
D	361	442	2.90
2	190	232	1.37
1	78	95	0.68

Fig. D2: MLP Resistance Specification Chart

PINPOINT TEST E

EPC Solenoid

1) Check VPWR To Solenoid – Turn ignition off. Disconnect transmission harness connector. With KOEO, measure voltage between transmission harness connector EPC/TCC VPWR terminal and vehicle ground. *See Fig. A1.* If voltage is 10.5 volts or more, go to next step. If voltage is less than specification, repair open circuit. Connect all components. Erase all trouble codes. See CLEARING CODES. Repeat QUICK TEST.

2) Check Continuity Of Solenoid Signal & VPWR Harness Circuit – Turn ignition off, and wait 10 seconds. Disconnect PCM 60-pin connector, and inspect it for damaged pins, corrosion and loose wires. Repair as necessary. Install Breakout Box (007-00033), leaving PCM disconnected. Measure and record resistance between Breakout Box test pins No. 71 and 97, and transmission harness connector terminal EPC VPWR. *See Fig. A1.* Measure and record resistance between Breakout Box test pins No. 81, and transmission harness connector EPC terminal. If resistances measured are 5 ohms or less, go to next step. If resistances measured are more than 5 ohms, repair open circuit. Connect all components. Erase all trouble codes. See CLEARING CODES. Repeat QUICK TEST.

3) Check Harness For Short To Power Or Ground – Measure and record resistance between Breakout Box test pin No. 81 and test pins No. 71 and 97. Measure and record resistance between test pin No. 81 and test pins No. 40, 91 and 60. If any resistance measured is less than 10 k/ohms, repair short circuit. Disconnect Breakout Box and repeat Quick Test. If all resistances are 10 k/ohms or more, go to next step.

4) EPC Functional Test – Disconnect transmission harness connector. Connect Transmission Tester (007-00085). Connect line pressure gauge. See FORD AODE/AODE-W overhaul article. Set Bench/Drive switch to DRVE mode. Set Gear Selector switch to 1st gear position. Perform EPC function test. See tester instructions. Observe line pressure on gauge while depressing EPC switch (KOER). EPC solenoid should activate (LED Green) and line pressure should drop when EPC switch is depressed. If solenoid operates correctly, replace PCM. Connect all components. Erase all trouble codes. See CLEARING CODES. Repeat QUICK TEST. If solenoid is not operating, go to next step.

5) Check Resistance Of Solenoid – Ensure tester power is off. Set Bench/Drive switch to BENCH mode. Connect ohmmeter negative lead to EPC jack. Connect positive lead to VPWR jack. If resistance is 2.48-5.66 ohms, go to next step. If resistance is not within specifications, go to step 7).

6) Check Solenoid For Short To Ground – Check continuity between BAT (–) terminal of Transmission Tester and EPC jacks. If continuity exists, gp to next step. If continuity does not exist, see TROUBLE SHOOTING under FORD AODE/AODE-W overhaul overhaul article.

7) AODE/AODE-W Internal Electronic Diagnostics – Drain transmission fluid. See TRANSMISSION SERVICING section. Remove transmission side pan. See OIL PUMP & VALVE BODY ASSEMBLY under ON-

PINPOINT TEST E (Cont.)

VEHICLE SERVICE in FORD AODE/AODE-W overhaul article. Inspect all internal harness connectors. Ensure all connectors are fully connected and not damaged. Repair as needed. Install all components in reverse order of disassembly. Fill transmission with fluid. Erase all trouble codes. See CLEARING CODES. Repeat QUICK TEST. If all connectors are okay, go to next step.

8) Check Internal Harness Continuity – Disconnect internal harness from EPC solenoid assembly. Connect positive lead of ohmmeter to tester EPC jack and negative lead to EPC Blue wire. Measure and record resistance. Connect positive lead of ohmmeter to tester VPWR jack and negative lead to EPC White/Blue wire. If resistances measured are .5 ohms or less, go to next step. If any resistance measured is more than .5 ohms, replace internal harness. Go to step 10).

9) Check Internal Harness For Shorts To Ground – Using transmission tester, check continuity between each EPC sensor connector terminals and BAT(-) terminal of tester. If continuity does not exist in either circuit, go to next step. If continuity exists in any circuit, replace internal harness. Go to next step.

10) Check EPC Solenoid Resistance – Using ohmmeter, check resistance between EPC solenoid terminals. Resistance should be 2.48-5.66 ohms. If resistance is within specification, go to next step. If resistance measured is not within specification, replace EPC solenoid. Install all components in reverse order of disassembly. Fill transmission with fluid. Erase all trouble codes. See CLEARING CODES. Repeat QUICK TEST.

11) Check Solenoid For Short To Ground – Using ohmmeter, check continuity between each EPC solenoid terminal and ground. If continuity exists, replace faulty EPC solenoid. Install all components in reverse order of disassembly. Fill transmission with fluid. Erase all trouble codes. See CLEARING CODES. Repeat QUICK TEST. If continuity does not exist, install all components in reverse order of disassembly. Fill transmission with fluid. Erase all trouble codes. See CLEARING CODES. Repeat QUICK TEST. See TROUBLE SHOOTING in FORD AODE/AODE-W overhaul article for non-electronic symptom diagnostics.

PINPOINT TEST F

Output Shaft Speed Sensor

1) Preliminary Inspection – Inspect condition of OSS harness and component connector. Repair as needed.

2) Check Continuity Of OSS Harness Circuit – Ensure ignition is off. Turn ignition off, and wait 10 seconds. Disconnect PCM 60-pin connector, and inspect it for damaged pins, corrosion and loose wires. Repair as necessary. Install Breakout Box (007-00033), leaving PCM disconnected. Disconnect OSS harness connector. Measure and record resistance between Breakout Box test pin No. 84 and OSS harness connector positive terminal. *See Fig. F1.* Measure and record resistance between Breakout Box test pin No. 91 and OSS harness connector negative terminal. If resistances measured are 5 ohms or less, go to next step. If resistances measured are more than 5 ohms, repair open circuit(s). Connect all components. Erase all trouble codes. See CLEARING CODES. Repeat QUICK TEST.

94B38811

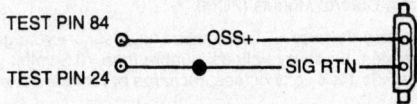

Fig. F1: Identifying OSS Harness Connector

3) Check OSS Circuit For Short To Power & Ground – Measure and record resistance between Breakout Box test pins No. 84 and 91, and test pins No. 71 and 97. Measure and record resistance between test pins No. 84, 71, 91 and 97, and test pins No. 40 and 60. If any resistance measured is less than 10 k/ohms, repair short circuit. Connect all components. Disconnect Breakout Box and repeat Quick Test. If resistance is 10 k/ohms or more, go to next step.

AUTOMATIC TRANSMISSIONS
AODE & AODE-W EEC-V Electronic Controls (Cont.)

3-602

PINPOINT TEST F (Cont.)

4) OSS Functional Test – Ensure OSS harness connector is disconnected. Connect Transmission Tester (007-00085) to OSS component connector. Connect voltmeter leads to appropriate tester OSS jacks. Set voltmeter to 20 volt A/C scale. Perform drive cycle test. See TRANSMISSION DRVE CYCLE TEST. If voltage increases with vehicle speed, replace PCM. Connect all components. Erase all trouble codes. See CLEARING CODES. Repeat QUICK TEST. If voltage does not increase with speed, go to next step.

5) Check Resistance Of OSS – Connect ohmmeter leads to appropriate Transmission Tester OSS jacks. If resistance is 450-750 ohms, go to next step. If resistance is not within specification, replace OSS. Connect all components. Erase all trouble codes. See CLEARING CODES. Perform drive cycle test. See TRANSMISSION DRVE CYCLE TEST. Repeat QUICK TEST.

6) Check OSS For Short To Ground – Check for continuity between Transmission Tester OSS jacks and tester BAT(-) jack. If continuity does not exist, go to next step. If continuity exists, replace OSS. Connect all components. Erase all trouble codes. See CLEARING CODES. Perform drive cycle test. See TRANSMISSION DRVE CYCLE TEST. Repeat QUICK TEST.

7) Check OSS Magnetism – Remove OSS from transmission. See FORD AODE/AODE-W overhaul article. Determine if OSS magnetically attracted to ferrous metal. If OSS acts like a magnet, go to next step. If OSS does not stick to ferrous metal surface, replace OSS. Connect all components. Erase all trouble codes. See CLEARING CODES. Perform drive cycle test. See TRANSMISSION DRVE CYCLE TEST. Repeat QUICK TEST.

8) Check Output Shaft Ring Gear – With OSS removed, inspect condition of ring gear. Rotate driveshaft and ensure all 6 holes or indentations of ring gear are not damaged. Replace ring gear if damaged. See FORD AODE/AODE-W overhaul article. If ring gear is not damaged, replace OSS. Connect all components. Erase all trouble codes. See CLEARING CODES. Perform drive cycle test. See TRANSMISSION DRVE CYCLE TEST. Repeat QUICK TEST.

CIRCUIT TESTS

NOTE: CIRCUIT TESTS are diagnostic formats used to test and service EEC-V system. CIRCUIT TESTS check engine circuits, sensors and actuators.

CIRCUIT TEST CA

REFERENCE VOLTAGE

Diagnostic Aids – SIG RTN is a dedicated ground used by most EEC-V system sensors. VREF is a 5-volt reference voltage that is continuously output by PCM. This consistent voltage signal is used on all 3-wire sensors.

This circuit test is only intended to diagnose the following components and circuits:
- Delta Pressure Feedback EGR (DPFE) sensor and TP sensor.
- Vehicle wiring harness circuits (SIG RTN and VREF).
- Powertrain Control Module (PCM).

1) Check Battery Voltage – Turn ignition on. Measure voltage between battery terminals. If battery voltage is more than 10.5 volts, go to next step. If voltage is 10.5 volts or less, recharge or replace battery as necessary.

2) Check SIG RTN Circuit – Perform the following procedure as appropriate:
- For DPFE sensor, disconnect DPFE wiring harness connector. Measure voltage between DPFE wiring harness connector SIG RTN terminal and positive battery terminal.
- For all except DPFE sensor, disconnect TP sensor wiring harness connector. Measure voltage between TP wiring harness connector SIG RTN terminal and positive battery terminal.

If voltage measurement is more than 10.5 volts and within one volt of battery voltage, go to next step. If voltage is less than 10.5 volts, go to step 11).

CIRCUIT TEST CA (Cont.)

94H32489

TEST PIN 89 — GY/W ———————— TP
TEST PIN 90 — BR/W ———————— VREF
TEST PIN 65 — BR/LG ———————— DPFE
TEST PIN 91 — GY/R ———————— SIG RTN

FROM OTHER SENSORS/SWITCHES

TEST PINS ARE LOCATED ON BREAKOUT BOX.
HARNESS CONNECTORS VIEWED INTO MATING SURFACE.

Fig. CA1: Identifying Reference Voltage Circuits & Connector Terminals

3) Check VREF To Idle Air Control (IAC) Solenoid – Turn ignition off. Disconnect DPFE and TP sensor wiring harness connector. Disconnect IAC solenoid. Turn ignition on. Measure voltage between VPWR terminal (Red wire) at IAC wiring harness connector and negative battery terminal. If voltage is 10.5 volts or more, go to next step. If voltage is less than 10.5 volts, reconnect wiring harness connector and go to CIRCUIT TEST X.

94A32490

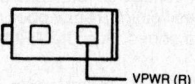

VPWR (R)

Fig. CA2: Identifying IAC Wiring Harness Connector Terminals

4) Check For Shorted DPFE Or TP Sensor – Disconnect DPFE and TP wiring harness connector. Perform the following procedure as appropriate:
- For vehicles with DPFE sensor trouble code, measure voltage between DPFE wiring harness connector SIG RTN terminal and VREF terminal.
- For vehicles without DPFE sensor trouble code, measure voltage between TP sensor wiring harness connector SIG RTN terminal and VREF terminal.

If voltage measurement is 4-6 volts perform the following procedure as appropriate:
- For vehicles with DPFE sensor trouble code, replace TP sensor.
- For vehicles without DPFE sensor trouble code, replace DPFE sensor and repeat QUICK TEST.

If voltage measurement is less than 4 volts go to next step. If voltage is more than 6 volts, go to step 16).

5) Check For VREF At Other Sensor – Leave DPFE and TP sensor disconnected. Turn ignition on. Perform the following procedure as appropriate:
- For vehicles with DPFE sensor trouble code, measure voltage between TP sensor wiring harness connector SIG RTN terminal and VREF terminal.
- For vehicles without DPFE sensor trouble code, measure voltage between DPFE sensor wiring harness connector SIG RTN terminal and VREF terminal.

If voltage measurement is 4-6 volts, repair open in VREF circuit. If voltage measurement is not 4-6 volts, go to next step.

6) Check VPWR To PCM – Turn ignition off. Leave DPFE and TP sensor disconnected. Disconnect PCM 104-pin connector. Inspect connector for damage and repair as necessary. Install Breakout Box (014-00950) leaving PCM disconnected. Turn ignition on. Measure voltage between test pins No. 71 (VPWR) and 77 (PWR GND). If voltage is 10.5 volts or more, go to next step. If voltage is less than 10.5 volts, repair open in VPWR circuit between IAC splice and PCM.

AUTOMATIC TRANSMISSIONS
AODE & AODE-W EEC-V Electronic Controls (Cont.)

3-603

CIRCUIT TEST CA (Cont.)

7) Check VREF Continuity To PCM – Turn ignition off. Leave PCM, DPFE and TP sensor disconnected. Measure resistance between test pin No. 90 (VREF) and VREF terminal at TP sensor wiring harness connector. See Fig. CA3. If resistance is less than 5 ohms, go to next step. If resistance is 5 ohms or more, repair open in VREF circuit between TP/DPFE sensor splice and PCM.

94H32547

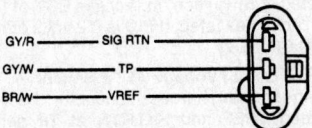

HARNESS CONNECTOR VIEW INTO MATING SURFACE.

Fig. CA3: Identifying TP Sensor Harness Connector Terminals

8) Check VREF Circuit For Short To Ground Or SIG RTN – Turn ignition off. Leave PCM, DPFE and TP sensor disconnected. Disconnect scan tester from DLC (if applicable). Measure resistance between test pin No. 90 (VREF) and test pins No. 51, 103 (PWR GND) and 91 (SIG RTN). If any resistance is less than 10 k/ohms, repair VREF short to ground and repeat QUICK TEST. If resistance is 10 k/ohms or more, replace PCM and repeat QUICK TEST.

NOTE: A break in step numbering sequence occurs at this point. Procedure skips from step 8) to step 11). No test procedures have been omitted.

11) Check SIG RTN Circuit Continuity To Ground At DPFE & TP Sensor – Turn ignition off. Leave PCM, DPFE and TP sensor disconnected. Disconnect scan tester from DLC (if applicable). Measure resistance between SIG RTN terminal of TP sensor wiring harness connector and negative battery terminal. Measure resistance between SIG RTN terminal of DPFE sensor wiring harness connector and negative battery terminal. If both resistances are less than 5 ohms, repeat step 1) and 2). If both resistances are 5 ohms or more, go to next step. If only one measurement is 5 ohms or more, repair open in SIR RTN circuit and repeat QUICK TEST.

12) Check SIG RTN Circuit Continuity PCM – Turn ignition off. Leave scan tester, PCM, DPFE and TP sensor disconnected. Install Breakout Box (014-00950) leaving PCM disconnected. Measure resistance between test pin No. 91 (SIG RTN) and SIG RTN terminal of TP sensor wiring harness connector. If resistance is less than 5 ohms, go to next step. If resistance is 5 ohms or more, repair open in SIG RTN circuit between TP/DPFE sensor splice and PCM.

13) Check PCM PWR GND Circuits – Turn ignition off. Leave scan tester, PCM, DPFE and TP sensor disconnected. Measure resistance between test pin No. 91 and test pins No. 51, 76, 77 and 103 (PWR GND). If resistance is less than 5 ohms, go to next step. If resistance is 5 ohms or more, repair open circuit and repeat QUICK TEST.

14) Check Ground Circuits In PCM – Ensure ignition is off. Connect PCM to breakout box. Measure resistance between test pin No. 91 (SIG RTN) and test pins No. 51, 76, 77 and 103 (PWR GND). If each resistance is less than 5 ohms, PWR GND and SIG RTN are okay; repeat step 11) to verify results. If any resistance is 5 ohms or more, replace PCM and repeat QUICK TEST.

NOTE: A break in step numbering sequence occurs at this point. Procedure skips from step 14) to step 16). No test procedures have been omitted.

16) Check VREF Circuit For Short To Power – Turn ignition off. Leave DPFE and TP sensor disconnected. Disconnect PCM. Turn ignition on. Measure voltage between VREF terminal at TP sensor wiring harness connector and negative battery terminal. If voltage is less than 0.5 volt, replace PCM and repeat QUICK TEST. If voltage is 0.5 volt or more, repair VREF short to power and repeat QUICK TEST.

CIRCUIT TEST DA

TEMPERATURE SENSOR TEST (IAT & ECT)

Diagnostic Aids – Perform this test only when directed by QUICK TEST. Ambient air temperature must be at least 50°F (10°C) to receive valid input from IAT sensor. Engine coolant temperature must be more than 50°F (10°C) to pass KOEO SELF-TEST and more than 180°F (82°C) to pass KOER SELF-TEST. Voltage values in this test are based on a 5-volt VREF signal. Values may vary up to 15 percent due to sensor and VREF variations.

This circuit test is intended to diagnose the following components and circuits:

• Intake Air Temperature (IAT) sensor.
• Engine Coolant Temperature (ECT) sensor.
• Wiring harness circuits (IAT, ECT and SIG RTN).
• Powertrain Control Module (PCM).

To prevent replacing good components, ensure the following non-EEC areas or components are not cause of problem:

• Coolant level low.
• Cooling system, water pump or fan.
• Engine operating temperature.
• Engine oil level low.
• Thermostat.
• Air cleaner duct.
• Ambient temperature.

94B32491

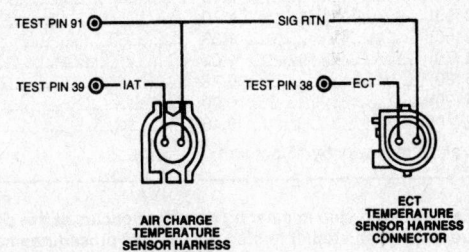

TEST PINS ARE LOCATED ON BREAKOUT BOX.
HARNESS CONNECTORS VIEWED INTO MATING SURFACE.

Fig. DA1: Identifying Temperature Sensor Circuits & Connector Terminals

1) Code P1116: – Code P1116 indicates sensor is out of self-test range. Correct range for measurement is .3-3.7 volts. Check for following possible causes:

• Low coolant level.
• Faulty harness connector.
• Faulty sensor.

Start engine and run until engine is at normal operating temperature. If vehicle cannot be started, go to step 3). Ensure upper radiator hose is hot and pressurized. Repeat QUICK TEST. If Code P1116 is present, go to step 2). If Code P1116 is not present, service other codes as necessary.

2) Check VREF Circuit Voltage At TP Sensor – Turn ignition off. Disconnect Throttle Position (TP) sensor. Turn ignition on. Measure voltage at TP sensor wiring harness connector between VREF and SIG RTN terminal. See Fig. DA2. If voltage is 4-6 volts, reconnect TP sensor and go to step 3). If voltage is not 4-6 volts, go to CIRCUIT TEST CA.

94G32488

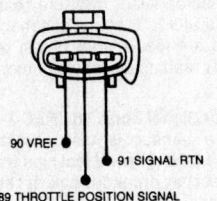

Fig. DA2: Identifying TP Sensor Harness Connector Terminals

3-604

AUTOMATIC TRANSMISSIONS
AODE & AODE-W EEC-V Electronic Controls (Cont.)

CIRCUIT TEST DA (Cont.)

3) Check Temperature Sensor Resistance – Turn ignition off. Disconnect suspect sensor. Measure resistance between signal circuit (ECT or IAT) terminal and SIG RTN terminal at sensor wiring harness connector. See ACT & ECT SENSOR SPECIFICATIONS table. If resistance is not within specification, replace suspected sensor and repeat QUICK TEST. If resistance is within specification, perform following step as applicable.

- For diagnosing vehicles with ECT sensor and a no-start condition, DO NOT service Code 116 at this time. Repair no-start condition and repeat QUICK TEST.
- For diagnosing vehicles without a no-start condition, go to step **4)**.

4) Check Temperature Sensor Resistance (KOER) – Warm engine to normal operating temperature. Turn ignition off. Disconnect suspect sensor. Start engine and operate at 2000 RPM for 2 minutes. Measure resistance between signal circuit (ECT or IAT) terminal and SIG RTN terminal at sensor wiring harness connector. See ACT & ECT SENSOR SPECIFICATIONS table. If resistance is within specification, replace PCM, and repeat QUICK TEST. If sensor is not within specification replace sensor, and repeat QUICK TEST.

ACT & ECT SENSOR SPECIFICATIONS

Temperature °F (°C)	¹ Volts	¹ Ohms
50 (10)	3.51	58,750
68 (20)	3.07	27,300
86 (30)	2.60	24,270
104 (40)	2.13	16,150
122 (50)	1.70	10,970
140 (60)	1.33	7700
158 (70)	1.02	5370
176 (80)	0.78	3840
194 (90)	0.60	2800
212 (100)	0.46	2070

¹ – Values may vary by 15 percent.

NOTE: A break in step numbering sequence occurs at this point. Procedure skips from step 4) to step 10). No test procedures have been omitted.

10) Code P0118 Or P0113: Induce Opposite Code (Code 117 Or 112) – Code P0118 (ECT) or P0113 (IAT) indicate corresponding sensor signal is more than self-test maximum. Maximum signal voltage for ECT and IAT sensor is 4.6 volts. Possible causes for excess voltage signals are:

- Open circuit in wiring harness (IAT or ECT).
- Faulty connection.
- Faulty sensor.
- Faulty PCM.

Turn ignition off. Disconnect suspect temperature sensor. Connect a jumper wire between signal circuit (ECT or IAT) terminal and SIG RTN terminal at sensor wiring harness connector. With scan tester installed, turn ignition on.

NOTE: If communication link error is displayed, remove jumper wire and go to step 12).

Access ECT or IAT PID. If the PID is less than 0.2 volt, replace sensor and repeat QUICK TEST. If PID is 0.2 volt or more, go to next step.

11) Check Continuity Of Sensor Signal & SIG RTN Circuits – Turn ignition off. Ensure suspect temperature sensor is disconnected. Disconnect PCM 104-pin connector. Check for damaged wiring, and repair as necessary. Install Breakout Box (014-00950), leaving PCM disconnected. Measure resistance between test pin No. 38 (ECT sensor) or test pin No. 39 (IAT sensor) at breakout box and SIG RTN terminal at sensor wiring harness connector. Also, measure resistance between test pin No. 91 (SIG RTN) and SIG RTN circuit at sensor wiring harness connector. If both readings are less than 5 ohms, replace PCM, and repeat QUICK TEST. If either reading is 5 ohms or more, repair open circuit and repeat QUICK TEST.

12) Check For Sensor Signal Short To VREF – Turn ignition off. Ensure suspect temperature sensor is disconnected. Measure resistance between test pin No. 90 (VREF) and test pins No. 38 (ECT sensor) or test pin No. 39 (IAT sensor) at breakout box. If resistance is 10 k/ohms or more, replace PCM and repeat QUICK TEST. If either resistance is less than 10 k/ohms, repair short circuit to VREF and repeat QUICK TEST.

NOTE: A break in step numbering sequence occurs at this point. Procedure skips from step 12) to step 20). No test procedures have been omitted.

CIRCUIT TEST DA (Cont.)

20) Code P0117 or P0112 – Code 117 (ECT) or 112 (IAT) indicates sensor signal is less than self-test minimum. Minimum signal for IAT and ECT sensor is 0.2 volt. Possible causes for this fault are:

- Circuit grounded in wiring harness.
- Faulty sensor.
- Faulty connection.
- Faulty PCM.

Turn ignition off. Disconnect wiring harness connector from suspect sensor. Check for damaged wiring, and repair as necessary. With scan tester connected, turn ignition on. Access ECT of IAT PID. If PID is less than 4.2 volts, go to next step. If PID is 4.2 volts or more, replace sensor and repeat QUICK TEST.

21) Check VREF Circuit Voltage At TP Sensor – Turn ignition off. Disconnect TP sensor wiring harness connector. Turn ignition on. Measure voltage between VREF and SIG RTN at TP sensor wiring harness connector. If voltage is 4-6 volts, connect TP sensor and go to next step. If voltage is not 4-6 volts, go to CIRCUIT TEST CA.

22) Check Signal Circuit For Short To Ground – Turn ignition off. Disconnect suspect sensor. Disconnect PCM 104-pin connector. Check for damaged wiring, and repair as necessary. Install Breakout Box (014-00950), leaving PCM disconnected. Measure resistance between test pin No. 38 (ECT) or 39 (IAT) and test pins No. 24 and 51 (PWR GND). If any reading is less than 10 k/ohms, repair short circuit, and repeat QUICK TEST. If all readings are 10 k/ohms or more, replace PCM and repeat QUICK TEST.

NOTE: A break in step numbering sequence occurs at this point. Procedure skips from step 22) to step 90). No test procedures have been omitted.

90) Continuous Memory Code P0112, P1112, P0113, P0117, P1117 Or P0118: Check Sensor – These trouble codes indicate possible intermittent fault. Possible causes for these faults are:

- Faulty sensor.
- Faulty sensor connector.
- Open or grounded circuit in harness.
- Faulty PCM.

With scan tester connected, turn ignition on. Access ECT or IAT PID. While observing PID, tap on sensor to simulate road shock. Wiggle sensor connector. If no change in temperature reading occurs, go to next step. If any change in temperature occurs, isolate fault and repair as necessary.

91) Check EEC-V Wiring Harness – While in PID, wiggle and bend small sections of wiring harness working toward PCM. If fault is indicated, isolate fault and repair as necessary. Clear memory, and repeat QUICK TEST. If no fault is found, go to step **92)**.

92) Inspect PCM & Wiring Harness Connectors – Turn ignition off. Disconnect PCM 104-pin connector. Inspect connector for damaged pins, corrosion and loose wires. If connectors and terminals are damaged, repair as necessary and repeat QUICK TEST. If connectors and terminals are okay, fault cannot be duplicated at this time and testing is complete.

NOTE: A break in step numbering sequence occurs at this point. Procedure skips from step 92) to step 100). No test procedures have been omitted.

100) Diagnostic Trouble Code P0125 – This code indicates ECT sensor has not reached normal operating temperature. Possible causes for this fault are:

- Thermostat leaking or stuck open.
- Low coolant.

Repair cooling system as necessary. Clear PCM memory, and repeat QUICK TEST.

AUTOMATIC TRANSMISSIONS
AODE & AODE-W EEC-V Electronic Controls (Cont.)

3-605

CIRCUIT TEST DC

MASS AIRFLOW (MAF) SENSOR

Diagnostic Aids – Perform this test when directed by QUICK TEST. This CIRCUIT TEST is intended to diagnose the following:

- MAF sensor.
- Wiring harness circuits (VPWR, PWR GND, MAF SIG and MAF RTN).
- Powertrain Control Module (PCM).

To prevent replacement of good components, be aware the following non-EEC related areas may be cause of problem:

- Air cleaner element.
- Inlet air duct.
- Throttle body.

94C32492

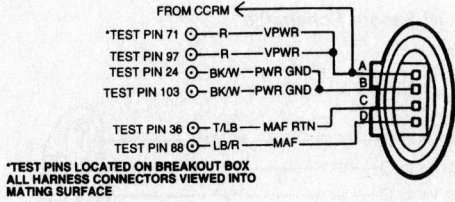

Fig. DC1: Identifying Mass Airflow (MAF) Sensor Circuits & Connector Terminals

94D32493

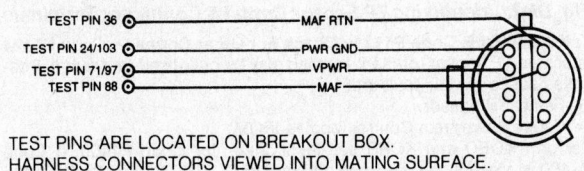

TEST PINS ARE LOCATED ON BREAKOUT BOX.
HARNESS CONNECTORS VIEWED INTO MATING SURFACE.

Fig. DC2: Identifying Mass Airflow (MAF) Sensor Extension Circuits & Connector Terminals (3.8L)

NOTE: Code P1101 may be caused by use of a garage exhaust ventilation system. Ensure vehicle is vented to outside atmosphere before repeating QUICK TEST.

1) Code P1101: MAF Output Voltage – Code P1101, retrieved during KOEO SELF-TEST, indicates voltage exceeded .2-volt test range. Code P1101, retrieved during KOER SELF-TEST, indicates voltage is not within .34-1.96 volts operating range. Possible causes for this fault are:

- Air leak before or after MAF sensor.
- Faulty MAF sensor.
- Faulty MAF sensor wiring harness connector.
- Open PWR GND or MAF RTN circuit.
- Faulty PCM.

Turn ignition off. Disconnect PCM 104-pin connector and inspect for damage. Repair as necessary. Install Breakout Box (014-00950) leaving PCM disconnected. With scan tester connected, turn ignition on. Measure voltage between test pin No. 88 (MAF SIG) and test pins No. 24 and 103 (PWR GND). If voltage is greater than 0.2 volt, go to step 12). If voltage is 0.2 volt or less, go to step 9).

2) Code P1100: Check MAF Circuit Intermittent Voltage Input – Code P1100, retrieved from continuous memory indicates voltage went out of range (0.39-4.70 volts) sometime during previous 40 warm-up cycles. Possible causes for this fault are:

- Faulty MAF sensor.
- Faulty MAF sensor wiring harness or connector.

Start engine and allow to idle. If engine does not idle smoothly, repair cause of rough idle condition before continuing. With scan tester connected, raise engine speed to 1500 RPM and return to idle. Access MAF PID. While observing PID, tap on sensor to simulate road shock. Wiggle sensor connector. If no MAF PID change in temperature reading occurs, go to next step. If any change in temperature occurs, isolate fault and repair as necessary.

CIRCUIT TEST DC (Cont.)

3) Check MAF Sensor Circuit Integrity – Turn ignition off. Disconnect PCM 104-pin connector and inspect for damage. Repair as necessary. Install Breakout Box (014-00950). Connect PCM to breakout box. Turn ignition on. Connect voltmeter between test pin No. 36 (MAF RTN) and No. 88 (MAF SIG). While observing voltmeter, wiggle and bend wiring harness between sensor and dash panel. Wiggle and bend wiring harness between dash panel and PCM. If voltage reading goes out of normal range (0.39-4.70 volts), isolate fault and repair as necessary. If voltage does not go out of normal range, fault cannot be duplicated or identified at this time. Testing is complete.

NOTE: A break in step numbering sequence occurs at this point. Procedure skips from step 3) to step 6). No test procedures have been omitted.

6) Continuous Memory & KOER Code P0102: Check MAF Low Input Signal To PCM – Code P0102 indicates MAF signal was less than 0.39 volt sometime during normal engine operation. Possible causes for this fault are:

- Open or closed MAF circuit.
- MAF circuit shorted to ground.
- Faulty MAF sensor or connector.
- Faulty TP system.

Ensure air induction system is okay. Repair if necessary. Start engine and allow to idle. If engine does not idle smoothly, repair cause of rough idle condition before continuing. With scan tester connected, raise engine speed to 1500 RPM and return to idle. Access MAF PID. If MAF PID is less than 0.39 volt, go to next step. If MAF PID is 0.60-1.0 volts, go to step 15). For all other MAF PIDs, go to step 2).

7) Check VPWR Circuit Voltage – Turn ignition off. Disconnect MAF sensor. Turn ignition on. Measure voltage between VPWR terminal of MAF sensor wiring harness connector and negative battery terminal. If voltage is 10.5 volts or more, go to next step. If voltage is less than 10.5 volts, repair open in VPWR circuit.

8) Check Continuity Of VPWR Circuit – Turn ignition off. Disconnect PCM 104-pin connector and inspect for damage. Repair as necessary. Install Breakout Box (014-00950), leaving PCM disconnected. Measure resistance between VPWR terminal of MAF sensor wiring harness connector and test pins No. 71 and 97 (VPWR) at breakout box. If resistance is less than 5 ohms, go to next step. If resistance is 5 ohms or more, repair open in VPWR circuit and repeat QUICK TEST.

9) Check MAF Circuit For Short To Ground & MAF RTN Circuit – Leave ignition off and MAF disconnected. Disconnect scan tester from DLC (if applicable). Measure resistance between test pin No. 88 (MAF SIG) and test pins No. 24, 36 (MAF RTN), and 103 (PWR GND) at breakout box. If resistance is 10 k/ohms or more, go to next step. If resistance is less than 10 k/ohms, repair circuit short to ground and repeat QUICK TEST.

10) Check Continuity Of MAF SIG Circuit – Leave ignition off and MAF disconnected. Measure resistance between MAF terminal of MAF sensor wiring harness connector and test pin No. 88 (MAF SIG) at breakout box. If resistance is less than 5 ohms, go to next step. If resistance is 5 ohms or more, repair open circuit in MAF SIG circuit and repeat QUICK TEST.

11) Check PWR GND Circuit To MAF Sensor – Leave ignition off and MAF disconnected. Turn ignition on. Measure voltage between VPWR and PWR GND terminal of MAF sensor wiring harness connector. If voltage is less than 10.5 volts, go to next step. If voltage is 10.5 volts or more, go to step 13).

12) Check PWR GND Circuit Continuity – Leave ignition off and MAF sensor disconnected. Disconnect scan tester from DLC (if applicable). Measure resistance between PWR GND terminal of MAF sensor wiring harness connector and negative battery terminal. If resistance is less than 10 ohms, go to next step. If resistance is 10 ohms or more, repair open in PWR GND circuit and repeat QUICK TEST.

13) Check MAF RTN Circuit Continuity – Leave ignition off and MAF disconnected. Measure resistance between MAF RTN terminal of MAF sensor wiring harness connector and test pin No. 36 (MAF RTN) at breakout box. If resistance is less than 5 ohms, go to next step. If resistance is 5 ohms or more, repair open in MAF RTN and repeat QUICK TEST.

14) Check MAF Circuit For Short To Ground In PCM – Leave ignition off and MAF disconnected. Connect PCM to breakout box. Disconnect scan tester from DLC (if applicable). Measure resistance between test pin No. 88 (MAF SIG) and test pins No. 24, 36 (MAF RTN) and 103 (PWR GND) at breakout box. If resistance is 10 k/ohms or more, go to next step. If resistance is less than 10 k/ohms, replace PCM and repeat QUICK TEST.

3-606

AUTOMATIC TRANSMISSIONS
AODE & AODE-W EEC-V Electronic Controls (Cont.)

CIRCUIT TEST DC (Cont.)

15) Check MAF Circuit Output – Ensure ignition is off. Reconnect MAF sensor. Connect PCM to breakout box. Start engine and alow to idle. If engine does not idle smoothly, repair cause of rough idle condition before continuing. Measure voltage between test pin No. 88 (MAF SIG) and negative battery cable. If voltage is 0.34-1.96 volts, go to next step. If voltage is not 0.34-1.96 volts replace MAF sensor and repeat QUICK TEST.

16) Check MAF Circuit Output With Scan Tester – Start engine and alow to idle. Access MAF PID on scan tester. If PID voltage is 0.34-1.96 volts, go to next step. If voltage is not 0.34-1.96 volts, replace PCM and repeat QUICK TEST.

17) Check MAF Circuit Input & Output – Turn ignition off. Leave MAF and PCM connected. Start engine and allow to idle. Measure voltage between test pin No. 36 (MAF RTN) and 88 (MAF SIG) at breakout box. If voltage is 0.34-1.96 volts, replace PCM and repeat QUICK TEST. If voltage is not 0.34-1.96 volts replace MAF sensor and repeat QUICK TEST.

NOTE: A break in step numbering sequence occurs at this point. Procedure skips from step 17) to step 20). No test procedures have been omitted.

20) Diagnostic Trouble Code (DTC) P0103: Check MAF High Input Signal To PCM – DTC P0103 indicates MAF signal was more than 4.70 volt sometime during normal engine operation. Possible causes for this fault are as follows:
- Restricted MAF sensor screen.
- MAF SIG circuit shorted to VPWR.
- Faulty MAF sensor or connector.
- Faulty PCM.

Ensure air induction system is okay. Repair if necessary. Start engine and allow to idle. If engine does not idle smoothly, repair cause of rough idle condition before continuing. With scan tester connected, raise engine speed to 1500 RPM and return to idle. Access MAF PID. PID reading should be more than 4.70 volts. Turn ignition off. Disconnect MAF sensor. Turn ignition on. Access MAF PID. If PID voltage reading does not drop to less than 0.39 volt, go to next step. If PID voltage reading does drops to less than 0.39 volt, replace MAF sensor.

21) Check MAF SIG Circuit For Short To Power – Leave ignition off and MAF sensor disconnected. Disconnect PCM 104-pin connector and inspect for damage. Repair as necessary. Install Breakout Box (014-00950). leaving breakout box disconnected. Turn ignition on. Measure voltage between test pin No. 88 (MAF SIG) and test pins No. 24 and 103 at breakout box. If voltage is less than 10.5 volts, go to next step. If voltage is 10.5 volts or more, repair MAF SIG circuit short to power.

22) Check MAF SIG Circuit For Short To Power In PCM – Leave ignition off and MAF sensor disconnected. Disconnect scan tester from DLC (if applicable). Measure resistance between test pin No. 88 (MAF SIG) and test pins No. 71 and 97 (VPWR) at breakout box. If resistance is more than 10 k/ohms, replace PCM and repeat QUICK TEST. If resistance is 10 k/ohms or less, repair short in MAF SIG circuit and repeat QUICK TEST.

CIRCUIT TEST DH

THROTTLE POSITION (TP) SENSOR

Diagnostic Aids – Perform this test only when directed by QUICK TEST. This test is intended to diagnose the following:
- TP sensor.
- Wiring harness circuits (PWR GND, SIG RTN, TP, VPWR and VREF).
- Powertrain Control Module (PCM).

Normal range of throttle angle measurement for TP sensor is 0-85 degrees. To pass QUICK TEST procedure, range of throttle rotation (in degrees) must be within 3 percent of specification.

To prevent replacement of good components, be aware the following non-EEC related areas may be at fault:
- Idle speed.
- Binding throttle shaft or linkage.
- TP sensor not seated.

CIRCUIT TEST DH (Cont.)

94J32549

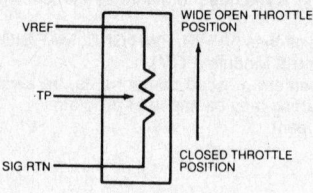

Fig. DH1: TP Sensor Schematic

94D32550

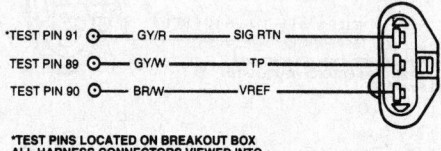

*TEST PINS LOCATED ON BREAKOUT BOX
ALL HARNESS CONNECTORS VIEWED INTO
MATING SURFACE

Fig. DH2: Identifying TP Sensor Circuit & Connector Terminals

1) KOEO/KOER Code P1124: Check For Other Codes – Code P1124 indicates TP sensor rotational setting may be out of self-test range. Possible causes for this fault are:
- Faulty TP sensor.
- Faulty Powertrain Control Module (PCM).

Perform KOEO and KOER self-test. Check for Code P1400. If Code P1400 is present, service code and repeat QUICK TEST. If Code P1400 is not present with Code P1124, go to step **2)**.

2) Code P1120: Check For Binding Throttle Plate – Code P1120 indicates TP sensor is below closed throttle position range of 9.8 percent (.49 volt) Possible causes for this fault are:
- Binding or bent throttle linkage.
- Throttle plate below closed throttle position.
- Faulty TP sensor.
- Faulty Powertrain Control Module (PCM).

Inspect throttle body for binding. If throttle body is binding, check for binding throttle or cruise control linkage, vacuum line or harness interference. Repair as necessary, and repeat QUICK TEST. If no mechanical problem is found, go to step **3)**.

3) Check For Stuck TP Sensor – Turn ignition off. Connect scan tester to DLC. Access TP PID on scan tester. While observing TP PID, slowly move throttle through range from closed to wide open throttle. If TP PID indicates any sudden drops to below 0.49 volt, replace TP sensor and repeat QUICK TEST. If TP PID increase and decrease is gradual and smooth, go to next step.

4) Check TP Sensor Signal To PCM – Turn ignition off. Disconnect PCM 104-pin connector. Inspect connector for damaged and repair as necessary. Install EEC-V Breakout Box (014-00950). Connect PCM to breakout box. Start engine and idle for 2 minutes. While slowly opening throttle, measure voltage between test pin No. 89 (TP) and 91 (SIG RTN) at breakout box. If at any time voltage enters 0.17-0.40 volt range, replace TP sensor. If voltage does not enter 0.17-0.40 volt range, go to next step.

5) Code P0123 – Code P0123 indicates TP signal is more than self-test maximum. Possible causes for this fault are:
- TP sensor not seated correctly.
- Faulty TP sensor.
- TP circuit shorted to VREF or VPWR.
- VREF circuit shorted to VPWR.
- Open in SIG RTN circuit.
- Faulty PCM.

Turn ignition off. Disconnect TP sensor wiring harness connector. Inspect for damage and repair as necessary. Turn ignition on. Access TP PID on scan tester. If PID voltage is 0.17 volt or more, go to step **7)**. If PID voltage is less than 0.17 volt, go to next step.

AUTOMATIC TRANSMISSIONS
AODE & AODE-W EEC-V Electronic Controls (Cont.)

3-607

CIRCUIT TEST DH (Cont.)

6) Check VREF Circuit Voltage – With TP sensor disconnected, turn ignition on. Measure voltage between VREF and SIG RTN terminals at TP sensor wiring harness connector. If voltage is 4-6 volts, replace TP sensor and repeat QUICK TEST. If voltage is not 4-6 volts, reconnect sensor and go to CIRCUIT TEST CA.

7) Check TP Circuit For Short To Power – Turn ignition off. Leave TP sensor disconnected. Disconnect PCM 104-pin connector. Inspect connector for damage and repair as necessary. Install EEC-V Breakout Box (014-00950), leaving PCM disconnected. Measure resistance between test pin No. 89 (TP) and test pins No. 71 and 97 (VPWR) at breakout box. If any resistance is less than 10 k/ohms, repair TP circuit short to VREF and repeat QUICK TEST. If both resistances are 10 k/ohms or more, replace PCM and repeat QUICK TEST.

8) Code P0122 – Code P0122 indicates TP signal is less than self-test minimum. Possible causes for this fault are:
* TP sensor not seated correctly.
* Faulty TP sensor.
* Open TP or VREF circuit.
* TP Circuit shorted to SIG RTN or PWR GND.
* Faulty PCM.

Turn ignition off. Disconnect TP sensor wiring harness connector. Inspect for damage and repair as necessary. Connect jumper wire between VREF and TP terminals at TP wiring harness connector. Turn ignition on. Access TP PID on scan tester. If PID voltage is more than 4.60 volts, replace TP sensor and repeat QUICK TEST. If PID voltage is 4.60 volts or less, go to next step.

9) Check VREF Circuit Voltage – With TP sensor disconnected, turn ignition on. Measure voltage between VREF and SIG RTN terminals at TP sensor wiring harness connector. If reading is 4-6 volts, go to next step. If reading is not 4-6 volts, reconnect sensor and go to CIRCUIT TEST CA.

10) Check TP Circuit Continuity – Turn ignition off. Leave TP sensor disconnected. Disconnect PCM 104-pin connector. Inspect connector for damage and repair as necessary. Install EEC-V Breakout Box (014-00950), leaving PCM disconnected. Measure resistance between test pin No. 89 (TP) and TP terminal of TP sensor wiring harness connector. If resistance is less than 5 ohms, go to next step. If resistance is 5 ohms or more, repair open in TP circuit.

11) Check TP Circuit For Short To SIG RTN Or PWR GND – Leave ignition off and TP sensor disconnected. Measure resistance between test pin No. 89 (TP) and test pins No. 91 (SIG RTN), 24 and 103 (PWR GND) at breakout box. If any resistance is less than 10 k/ohms, repair TP circuit short to SIG RTN or PWR GND and repeat QUICK TEST. If both resistances are 10 k/ohms or more, replace PCM and repeat QUICK TEST.

12) Continuous Memory Code P1121 – This code indicates TP signal is inconsistant with MAF sensor signal. Possible causes for this fault are as follows:
* TP sensor not seated correctly.
* Faulty TP sensor.
* Air leak between MAF sensor and throttle body.

If engine will start, go to next step. If engine is a no-start, check for cracks or openings in air induction system between MAF sensor and throttle body. If air induction system is okay, go to CIRCUIT TEST A under SELF-DIAGNOSTICS – EEC-V article in ENGINE PERFORMANCE of appropriate MITCHELL® manual.

13) Check Operation Of TP Sensor – Start engine and allow to idle. Access TP PID on scan tester. While observing TP PID, slowly move throttle through range from closed position to wide open throttle. If TP PID indicates any sudden drops to below 0.66 volt, or increases to more than 1.20 volts, replace TP sensor and repeat QUICK TEST. If TP PID increase and decrease is gradual and smooth, and within 0.66-1.20 volt range, go to next step.

14) Check Operation Of TP Sensor While Driving Vehicle – Connect scan tester to DLC. Drive vehicle while accessing TP PID and LOAD PID. If TP PID is 2.44 volts or less and LOAD PID is more than 25 percent, go to next step. If TP PID is more than 2.44 volts and LOAD PID is less than 25 percent, check for cracks or openings in air induction system between MAF sensor and throttle body. If air induction system is okay, replace TP sensor.

15) Check TP Sensor Low With Engine Under Load – Start engine and allow to idle. If engine does not start, go to CIRCUIT TEST A under SELF-DIAGNOSTICS – EEC-V article in ENGINE PERFORMANCE of appropriate MITCHELL® manual. Access TP PID and LOAD PID on scan

CIRCUIT TEST DH (Cont.)

tester. If TP PID is 0.24 volt or more and LOAD PID is more than 25 percent, go to next step. If TP PID is less than 2.44 volts and LOAD PID is 25 percent or more, clear PCM memory. Perform test drive utilizing all phases of vehicle operation. Perform QUICK TEST. If Code P1121 is present, replace MAF sensor.

16) Check Operation Of TP Sensor While Driving Vehicle – Connect scan tester to DLC. Drive vehicle while accessing TP PID and LOAD PID. If TP PID is 0.24 volt or less and LOAD PID is more than 60 percent, go to next step. If TP PID is more than 0.24 volt and LOAD PID is less than 60 percent, problem is intermittent and cannot be identified at this time. If vehicle will not start, go to CIRCIT TEST A.

17) Continuous Memory Code P1125 – This code indicates TP signal went below 0.49 volt or above 4.60 volts sometime during the last 80 drive cycles. Possible causes for this fault are:
* Faulty TP sensor wiring harness or connector.
* Faulty TP sensor.

With scan tester connected, start engine and allow to idle. Raise engine speed to 1500 RPM for 5 seconds and return to idle. Access TP PID. While observing PID, tap on TP sensor to simulate road shock. Wiggle sensor connector and wiring harness. If TP PID reading stays within normal operating range (0.49-4.60 volts), go to next step. If TP PID reading goes out of range, replace TP sensor.

18) Check Wiring Harness Between TP Sensor & PCM – Turn ignition off. Disconnect PCM 104-pin connector. Inspect connector for damage and repair as necessary. Install EEC-V Breakout Box (014-00950). Connect PCM to breakout box. Connect DVOM between test pin No. 89 (TP) and 91 (SIG RTN). While observing DVOM, wiggle small sections of wiring harness starting at the TP sensor and going to the PCM. If DVOM reading stays within normal operating range (0.49-4.60 volts), problem is intermittent and cannot be identified at this time. If DVOM reading goes out of range, isolate fault and repair as necessary. Clear PCM memory and repeat QUICK TEST.

CIRCUIT TEST DP

VEHICLE SPEED SENSOR (VSS)

Diagnostic Aids – Perform this test when directed by QUICK TEST. This CIRCUIT TEST is intended to diagnose:
* Vehicle Speed Sensor (VSS).
* VSS wiring harness circuits.
* Powertrain Control Module (PCM).

94E32494

*TEST PIN 58 — GY/BK — VSS(+)
*TEST PIN 33 — PK/O — VSS(-)

***TEST PINS LOCATED ON BREAKOUT BOX
ALL HARNESS CONNECTORS VIEWED IN
MATING SURFACE**

Fig. DP1: Identifying VSS Circuit & Connector Terminals

1) Code P0500 – This code indicates PCM detected incorrect output from VSS sometime during vehicle operation. Possible causes for this code are:
* Faulty VSS.
* Open or shorted circuit.
* Faulty PCM.

Turn ignition off. Disconnect VSS sensor. Remove PCM 104-pin connector. Inspect connector for damaged pins, corrosion and loose wires. Repair as necessary. Install EEC-V Breakout Box (014-000950), leaving PCM disconnected. Measure resistance between test pin No. 33 and VSS (-) terminal at VSS wiring harness connector. Measure resistance between test pin No. 58 and VSS (+) terminal at VSS wiring harness connector. If both resistance readings are less than 5 ohms, go to next step. If either resistance reading is 5 ohms or more, repair open circuit in VSS wiring harness. Clear PCM memory and go to step **20**).

3-608

AUTOMATIC TRANSMISSIONS
AODE & AODE-W EEC-V Electronic Controls (Cont.)

CIRCUIT TEST DP (Cont.)

2) Check VSS Circuits For Shorts To Power Or Ground – Turn ignition off. Ensure PCM and VSS are disconnected. Measure resistance between test pin No. 58 and test pins No. 51, 103 (PWR GND), 33, 71 (VPWR), and 91 (SIG RTN) at breakout box. If all readings are more than 500 ohms, go to next step. If any reading is less than 500 ohms, repair shorts in VSS wiring harness. Clear PCM memory and go to step 20).

3) Check VSS Resistance – Turn ignition off. Disconnect VSS wiring harness connector. Measure resistance between VSS terminals. If resistance is not 190-250 ohms, replace VSS and go to step 20). If resistance is 190-250 ohms, replace PCM and go to step 20).

NOTE: A break in step numbering sequence occurs at this point. Procedure skips from step 3) to step 10). No test procedures have been omitted.

10) Code P0500 – This code indicates PCM detected intermittent output from VSS. Possible causes for this code are:
• Intermittent open or shorted circuit.
• Faulty VSS.
• Faulty PCM.
Turn ignition off. Disconnect VSS sensor. Visually inspect VSS and VSS circuits for potential faults as follows:
• Loose VSS circuit connectors.
• Loose VSS circuit connector pins.
• Damaged VSS wiring harness insulation.
• Incorrect VSS circuit routing.
• Incorrect VSS installation.
If no faults are found, go to CIRCUIT TEST Z under SELF-DIAGNOSTICS – EEC-V article in ENGINE PERFORMANCE of appropriate MITCHELL® manual. If faults are found, repair or replace as necessary. Clear PCM memory and go to step 20).

NOTE: A break in step numbering sequence occurs at this point. Procedure skips from step 10) to step 20). No test procedures have been omitted.

20) VSS Drive Cycle – Record and clear continuous memory codes. Warm engine to normal operating temperature. Perform appropriate drive cycle as follows:
• On models with A/T, place gear selector in Drive position. Accelerate hard to 35 MPH and coast down to a stop. Repeat procedure 3 times. Shut off engine. Repeat QUICK TEST. Service codes as necessary. If no codes are present, testing is complete.
• On models with M/T, start in first gear, shifting no higher than second gear. Accelerate moderately to 40 MPH. Coast down to idle, and stop. Repeat procedure 3 times. Shut engine off. Repeat QUICK TEST. Service codes as necessary. If no codes are present, testing is complete.

CIRCUIT TEST FD

BRAKE ON-OFF (BOO) SWITCH

Diagnostic Aids – Perform this test when directed by QUICK TEST. This test is intended to diagnose a faulty BOO switch circuit or PCM. To prevent replacement of good components, be aware following non-EEC related areas may be at fault:
• Brakelight bulb.
• Brakelight switch or brakelight fuse.

1) Code P0703: Verify Brake Pedal Was Depressed – This code indicates that when brake pedal is applied during KOER SELF-TEST, BOO signal did not cycle high and low. Possible causes for this fault are as follows:
• Brake pedal not applied during self-test.
• Brake pedal applied during entire self-test.
• Open brakelight circuit.
• Short to ground or power.
• Faulty brakelight switch.
• Faulty Powertrain Control Module (PCM).
If brake was not applied during KOER SELF-TEST, repeat test. Depress and release brake pedal only once during test. If pedal was depressed, go to next step.

CIRCUIT TEST FD (Cont.)

94C32500

Fig. FD1: BOO Switch Circuit

2) Code P1703 – This code indicates that voltage was present at BOO circuit during KOEO SELF-TEST. Possible causes for this fault are as follows:
• Brake pedal applied during KOEO self-test.
• BOO circuit short to or power.
• Faulty brakelight switch.
• Faulty Powertrain Control Module (PCM).
If brake was applied during KOEO SELF-TEST, repeat test. If pedal was not depressed, go to next step.

3) Check Operation Of Brakelights – With ignition on, check operation of brakelights. If brakelights operate normally, go to next step. If brakelights do not operate, go to step 5). If brakelights are always on, go to step 6).

4) Check For BOO Switch Circuit Cycling – Turn ignition off. Disconnect PCM 104-pin connector. Inspect connector for damage and repair as necessary. Install EEC-V Breakout Box (014-000950), leaving PCM disconnected. Measure voltage between test pin No. 92 and test pins No. 76 and 77 while applying and releasing brake. If voltage cycles, replace PCM and repeat QUICK TEST. If voltage does not cycle, repair open circuit in BOO switch circuit between PCM and BOO switch connection to brakelight circuit. Repeat QUICK TEST.

5) Check For Power To Brakelight Switch – Ensure related fuses and brakelight bulbs are in good condition. Turn ignition off. Disconnect brakelight switch (located on brake pedal). Measure voltage between B+ input to brakelight switch and ground. If voltage is more than 10 volts, check condition of brakelight switch. If brakelight switch is okay, repair open circuit between brakelight switch and brakelight ground. Repeat QUICK TEST. If voltage is less than 10 volts, repair open in B+ circuit to brakelight switch and repeat QUICK TEST.

6) Verify Brake Switch Is Not Always Closed – Turn ignition off. Disconnect brakelight switch (located on brake pedal). Turn ignition on. If brakelights are still on, go to next step. If brakelights are not on, verify correct installation of brakelight switch. If installation is okay, replace brakelight switch and repeat QUICK TEST.

7) Check For Short To Power In PCM – Turn ignition off. Disconnect PCM. Turn ignition on. Check brakelights. If brakelights are on, go to next step. If brakelights are off, replace PCM and repeat QUICK TEST.

8) Check For Short To Power In Shift Lock Actuator – Turn ignition off. Ensure PCM and brakelight switch are disconnected. Disconnect shift lock actuator, cruise control module and ABS module (if equipped). Turn ignition on. If brakelights are still on, repair short to power in BOO circuit and repeat QUICK TEST. If brakelights are off, repair short circuit in shift lock actuator circuit, cruise control system circuit or ABS circuit. Reconnect all components and repeat QUICK TEST.

AUTOMATIC TRANSMISSIONS
AODE & AODE-W EEC-V Electronic Controls (Cont.)

3-609

CIRCUIT TEST QA

UNABLE TO ACTIVATE SELF-TEST/ SCP COMMUNICATION ERROR CODE NOT LISTED

Diagnostic Aids – Perform this test when instructed during QUICK TEST or if directed by other test procedures. This test is used to diagnose the following:

- Standard Corporate Protocol (SCP) communication circuits BUS (+) and BUS (-).
- Wiring harness circuits CHASSIS GROUND, PWR GND and VBAT.
- Faulty PCM.

94A32540

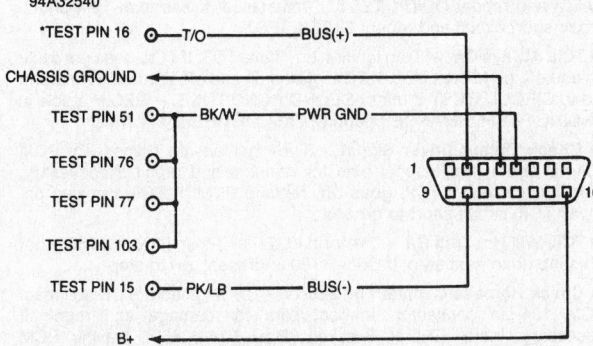

*TEST PIN LOCATIONS ON BREAKOUT BOX
ALL HARNESS CONNECTORS VIEWED INTO
MATING SURFACES

Fig. QA1: Identifying Data Link Connector (DLC) Circuit & Connector Terminals

1) Verify Self-Test Procedure Is Correct – Ensure scan tester is correctly attached to DLC located under dash panel. DO NOT use DLC located in engine compartment. Ensure correct self-test procedure is used. Correct as necessary. If correct procedures were used, go to next step.

2) Check For VREF At TP Sensor – Turn ignition off. Disconnect TP sensor. Turn ignition on. Measure voltage between SIG RTN terminal and VREF terminal at TP wiring harness connector. If voltage is 4-6 volts, go to next step. If voltage is not 4-6 volts, go to CIRCUIT TEST CA.

NOTE: KOER self-test failure or Communication Error message could result if a failure is present in MAF sensor, MLP sensor, VSS or related circuits.

94H32547

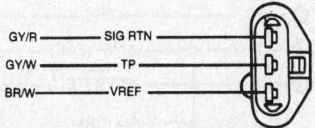

HARNESS CONNECTORS VIEWED INTO MATING SURFACE.

Fig. QA2: Identifying TP Sensor Harness Connector Terminals

3) Perform QUICK TEST. If any trouble codes are present, service as necessary before continuing. If unable to retrieve trouble codes, go to next step.

4) Check For Voltage At Data Link Connector (DLC) – Inspect DLC for damage and repair as necessary. Turn ignition on. Measure voltage between B+ terminal of DLC and engine ground. If 10.5 volts or more are present, go to next step. If less than 10.5 volts are present, repair open in B+ circuit and repeat QUICK TEST.

5) Check DLC Ground Circuit Continuity – Turn ignition off. Measure resistance between CHASSIS GROUND terminal of DLC and engine ground. If less than 5 ohms are present, go to next step. If 5 ohms or more are present, repair open in CHASSIS GROUND circuit and repeat QUICK TEST.

6) Turn ignition off. Disconnect PCM 104-pin connector. Inspect pins for damage and repair if necessary. Install EEC-V Breakout Box (014-00950), leaving PCM disconnected. Measure resistance between test pins No. 51 and 103 (PWR GND) at the breakout box and PWR GND ter-

CIRCUIT TEST QA (Cont.)

minal of DLC. If resistance is less than 5 ohms, go to next step. If resistance is 5 ohms or more, repair open in PWR GND circuit to DLC and repeat QUICK TEST.

7) Check BUS(-) Circuit – Leave ignition off. Measure resistance between test pin No. 15 (BUS-) at the breakout box and BUS(-) terminal of DLC. If resistance is less than 5 ohms, go to next step. If resistance is 5 ohms or more, repair open in BUS(-) circuit to DLC and repeat QUICK TEST.

8) Leave ignition off. Measure resistance between test pin No. 15 at the breakout box and engine ground. If resistance is 10 k/ohms or more, go to next step. If resistance is less than 10 k/ohms, repair short to ground in BUS(-) circuit and repeat QUICK TEST.

9) Turn ignition on. Measure voltage between test pin No. 15 and test pins No. 51 and 103 (PWR GND) at the breakout box and engine ground. If voltage is less than 1.0 volt, go to next step. If voltage is 1.0 volt or more, repair short to power in BUS(-) circuit and repeat QUICK TEST.

10) Check BUS (+) Circuit – Leave ignition off. Measure resistance between test pin No. 16 (BUS +) at the breakout box and BUS (+) terminal of DLC. If resistance is less than 5 ohms, go to next step. If resistance is 5 ohms or more, repair open in BUS (+) circuit to DLC and repeat QUICK TEST.

11) Turn ignition on. Measure voltage between engine ground and test pins No. 16, 51 and 103 (PWR GND) at the breakout box. If voltage is less than 1.0 volt, replace PCM. If voltage is 1.0 volt or more, repair short to power in BUS (+) circuit and repeat QUICK TEST.

CIRCUIT TEST QB

DIAGNOSTIC TROUBLE CODE P1605

Diagnostic Aids – KAPWR is interrupted when PCM or battery is disconnected. Code P1605 may be generated during the next PCM power-er-up.

Perform this test when instructed during QUICK TEST or if directed by other test procedures. This test is used to diagnose the following:

- Battery terminal condition.
- Keep Alive Power (KAPWR) circuit routing.
- KAPWR circuit condition.
- Faulty PCM.

94B32541

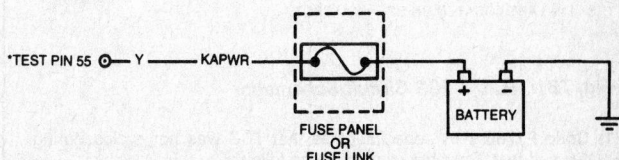

*TEST PIN LOCATED ON BREAKOUT BOX
ALL HARNESS CONNECTORS VIEWED INTO
MATING SURFACE

Fig. QB1: Keep Alive Power (KAPWR) Circuit Schematic

1) Check Battery Terminals – Inspect battery terminals for corrosion or loose connection. Service or replace as necessary. If battery terminals are okay, go to next step.

2) Check Wiring Harness – Inspect wiring harness and connectors for damage or corrosion. Ensure wiring harness is not improperly routed too close to ignition or exhaust components. Service or replace as necessary. If wiring harness looks okay, go to next step.

3) Check KAPWR Circuit – Turn ignition off. Disconnect PCM 104-pin connector. Inspect pins for damage. Install EEC-V Breakout Box (014-00959), leaving PCM disconnected. Connect DVOM between test pin No. 55 (KAPWR) and test pins No. 51 and 103 (PWR GND) at breakout box. Shake and bend small sections of wiring harness between PCM and dash panel. If DVOM continuously indicates 10.5 volts or more, go to next step. If DVOM indicates voltage drops to less than 10.5 volts, isolate open in KAPWR circuit and repair as necessary. Repeat QUICK TEST.

4) Check For Code P1605 – Perform KOEO self-test. If any trouble codes are present, service as necessary before continuing. If no trouble codes are present, testing is complete.

3-610

AUTOMATIC TRANSMISSIONS
AODE & AODE-W EEC-V Electronic Controls (Cont.)

CIRCUIT TEST QC

DIAGNOSTIC TROUBLE CODE P1000

Diagnostic Aids – Perform this test when instructed during QUICK TEST or if directed by other test procedures. This code indicates that On Board Diagnostics II (OBD II) monitor testing has not been completed. To erase code, a complete drive cycle, with sucessful OBD II monitor self-test, must occur.

A drive cycle consists of vehicle warmed to normal engine temperature and operating in all speed ranges. After all monitors test sucessfully, SYSTEM PASS can be retrieved from PCM.

Code P1000 will set in PCM memory when any of the following conditions occur:
• Battery or PCM has been disconnected.
• An OBD II monitor has failed before completion of drive cycle.
• PCM memory has been erased with a scan tester.

1) Check For Other Codes – If any trouble codes are present, service as necessary before continuing. If no trouble codes are present, go to next step.

2) Test drive vehicle to complete drive cycle. Cruise at 20-45 MPH for at least 4 minutes. Cruise at 30-40 MPH for at least 60 seconds. Cruise at 40-65 MPH for at least 80 seconds.

CIRCUIT TEST TB

TRANSMISSION CONTROL SWITCH (TCS)/ INDICATOR LAMP (TCIL)

Diagnostic Aids – Perform this test when instructed during QUICK TEST or if directed by other test procedures. This test is used to diagnose the following:
• Wiring harness circuits (TCIL & TCS).
• Faulty PCM.

94C32542

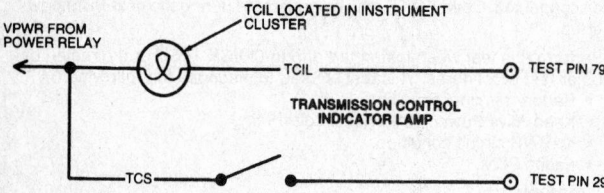

TEST PINS ARE LOCATED ON BREAKOUT BOX.

Fig. TB1: TCIL & TCS Circuit Schematic

1) Code P1780 This code indicates that TCS was not cycled during KOER self-test. Possible causes are as follows:
• TCS not cycled during KOER self-test.
• TCS circuit damage.
• Faulty TCS.
• Faulty PCM.
Repeat KOER self-test if TCS was not cycled in original test. If TCS was cycled during KOER self-test, go to next step.

2) Check TCS Circuit Voltage – Turn ignition off. Disconnect PCM 104-pin connector. Inspect pins for damage. Install EEC-V Breakout Box (014-00959), leaving PCM disconnected. Turn ignition on. Measure voltage between test pin No. 29 (TCS) and test pins No. 24 and 77 (PWR GND) at breakout box while cycling TCS. If voltmeter reading does not cycle when TCS is cycled, go to next step. If voltmeter reading cycles when TCS is cycled, replace PCM and repeat QUICK TEST.

3) Check Circuit For Short To Ground – Turn ignition off. Disconnect TCS. Inspect pins for damage and repair if necessary. Measure resistance between breakout box test pin No. 29 (TCS) and test pins No.

CIRCUIT TEST TB (Cont.)

24 and 77 (PWR GND). If resistance is 10 k/ohms or more, go to next step. If resistance is less than 10 k/ohms, repair short circuit and repeat QUICK TEST.

4) Check Continuity Of TCS Circuits – Leave ignition off. Connect ohmmeter positive lead to TCS keypower at the fuse panel. Connect negative lead to power terminal of TCS wiring harness connector. If resistance is less than 5 ohms, go to next step. If resistance is more than 5 ohms, repair open circuit and repeat QUICK TEST.

5) Check Circuit For Short To Power – Leave ignition off. Measure resistance between breakout box test pin No. 29 (TCS) and test pins No. 71 and 97 (VPWR). If resistance is 10 k/ohms or more, replace TCS switch and repeat QUICK TEST. If resistance is less than 10 k/ohms, repair short circuit and repeat QUICK TEST.

6) TCIL Always On – Turn ignition on. Cycle TCS. If TCIL does not cycle on and off, go to next step. If TCIL cycles on and off, fault is intermittent. Go to CIRCUIT TEST Z under SELF-DIAGNOSTICS – EEC-V article in ENGINE PERFORMANCE of appropriate MITCHELL® manual.

7) Check Output Driver Signal – Turn ignition off. Disconnect PCM 104-pin connector. Inspect pins for damage and repair if necessary. Turn ignition on. If TCIL goes off, replace PCM. If TCIL remains on, repair TCIL circuit short to ground.

8) TCIL Will Not Turn On – Perform KOER self-test. If Code 1780 is not present, go to next step. If Code 1780 is present, go to step 1).

9) Check Harness Circuits For Shorts – Turn ignition off. Disconnect PCM 104-pin connector. Inspect pins for damage and repair if necessary. Install EEC-V Breakout Box (014-00959), leaving PCM disconnected. Turn ignition on. Measure voltage between test pin No. 79 (TCIL) and test pins No. 24 and 76 (PWR GND) at breakout box. If voltage is 2 volts or more, replace PCM. If voltage is less than 2 volts, check indicator bulb and fuse. If bulb and fuse are okay, repair open circuit between test pin No. 79 and ignition switch.

CIRCUIT TEST TC

TRANSMISSION SOLENOIDS

Diagnostic Aids – Perform this test when instructed during QUICK TEST or if directed by other test procedures. This test is used to diagnose the following:
• Wiring harness circuits (CCS, EPC, SS1, SS2, TCC & VPWR).
• Faulty PCM.

94D32543

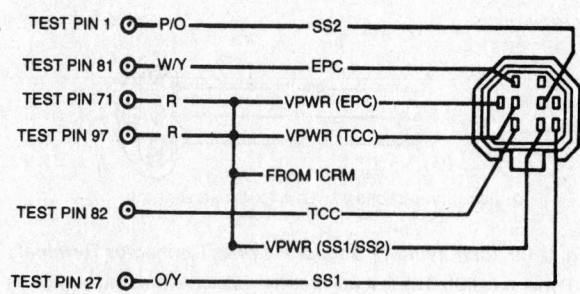

TEST PINS ARE LOCATED ON BREAKOUT BOX.
HARNESS CONNECTORS VIEWED INTO MATING SURFACE.

Fig. TC1: Identifying Transmission Circuit & Connector Terminals

TRANSMISSION SOLENOID IDENTIFICATION

Solenoid	Test Pin	KOEO Code
EPC	81	P1746 & P1747
SS1	27	P0750
SS2	1	P0755
TCC	82	P0743

AUTOMATIC TRANSMISSIONS
AODE & AODE-W EEC-V Electronic Controls (Cont.)

3-611

CIRCUIT TEST TC (Cont.)

1) Code P0743, P0746, P0747, P0750 & P0755 – These codes indicate that transmission electrical malfunctuion. Probable causes are as follows:

- Code P0743; Torque Converter Clutch (TCC) electrical fault.
- Code P0746; Electronic Pressure Control (EPC) circuit open.
- Code P0747; EPC circuit short.
- Code P0750; Shift Solenoid 1 (SS1) electrical fault.
- Code P0755; Shift Solenoid 2 (SS2) electrical fault.

Turn ignition off. Disconnect transmission wiring harness connector. Using a mirror, inspect connector terminals for damage, corrosion, loose wires or pushed out pins. Repair if necessary. Disconnect cruise control servo (if equipped). Connect DVOM positive lead to transmission wiring harness connector VPWR terminal. Connect negative lead to SS1 or SS2 terminal. Turn igniton on. Activate scan tester outputs. Observe and record transmission solenoid voltage. Cycle scan tester trigger button on and off. If transmission solenoid circuit voltage cycles 0.5 volt or more, fault is inside transmission. Circuit testing is complete. If transmission solenoid voltage is not as specified, go to next step.

2) Check VPWR Circuit At Solenoid – Leave transmission wiring harness connector disconnected. Turn ignition on. Measure voltage between VPWR terminal of transmission wiring harness connector and chassis ground. If voltage is 10.5 volts or more, go to next step. If voltage is less than 10.5 volts, repair open in VPWR circuit. Clear PCM memory and repeat QUICK TEST.

3) Check Circuit Continuity – Turn ignition off. Disconnect PCM 104-pin connector. Inspect pins for damage and repair if necessary. Install EEC-V Breakout Box (014-00959), leaving PCM disconnected. Measure and record resistance between VPWR terminal of transmission wiring harness connector and test pins No. 71 and 97 (VPWR) at breakout box. Measure and record resistance between suspect solenoid terminal of transmission wiring harness connector and suspect solenoid terminal at breakout box. If each resistance measurement is less than 5 ohms, go to next step. If any resistance measurement is 5 ohms or more, repair open circuit and repeat QUICK TEST.

4) Check For Circuit Short To Ground – Leave ignition off and transmission wiring harness connector disconnected. Measure and record resistance between suspect solenoid terminal of transmission wiring harness connector and test pins No. 51 and 76 (PWR GND) at breakout box. Measure and record resistance between suspect solenoid terminal of transmission wiring harness connector and test pins No. 71 and 97 (VPWR) at breakout box. If any resistance measurement is less than 10 k/ohms, repair open circuit and repeat QUICK TEST. If all resistance measurements are 10 k/ohms or more, replace PCM and repeat QUICK TEST.

CIRCUIT TEST TD

MANUAL LEVER POSITION (MLP) SENSOR

Diagnostic Aids – Perform this test when instructed during QUICK TEST or if directed by other test procedures. This test is used to diagnose the following:

- Wiring harness circuits (MLP & SIG RTN).
- Faulty PCM.

94E32544

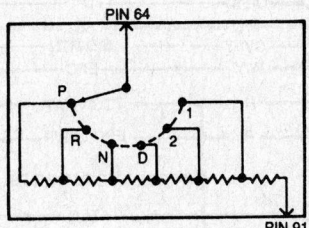

Fig. TD1: Manual Lever Position (MLP) Sensor Schematic

CIRCUIT TEST TD (Cont.)

94F32545

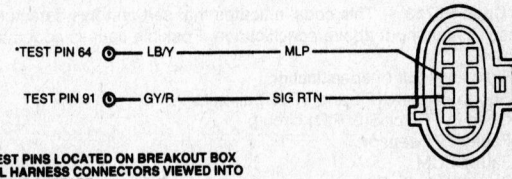

*TEST PINS LOCATED ON BREAKOUT BOX ALL HARNESS CONNECTORS VIEWED INTO MATING SURFACE

Fig. TD2: Identifying MLP Circuit & Connector Terminals

MLP SENSOR SPECIFICATIONS

Position	¹ Volts	¹ Ohms
Park	4.23-4.68	3770-4607
Reverse	3.52-3.89	1304-1593
Neutral	2.80-3.10	660-807
Overdrive	2.09-2.31	361-442
Drive	1.39-1.53	190-232
First	0.68-0.76	78-95

1) Code P0705, P0707 & P0708 – Probable causes for these codes are as follows:

- Code P0705; MLP not in Park during KOEO self-test.
- Code P0707; MLP sensor shorted to ground.
- Code P0708; MLP circuit open or shorted to power.

Turn ignition off. Ensure parking brake is applied. Place MLP in Neutral. Place MLP Sensor Gauge (T92P-7010-AH) in MLP sensor adjustment slot and go to next step. If gauge does fit in slot, loosen MLP sensor mounting screws and move sensor until gauge fits in slot. Tighten screws and verify shift linkage is properly adjusted. Repeat QUICK TEST.

2) Remove sensor adjustment gauge. Connect scan tester to DLC. Using scan tester, access MLP and MLPV PIDs. Turn ignition on. Cycle gear shift lever through all gear ranges while monitoring voltage. See MLP SENSOR SPECIFICATIONS table. If voltage is not within specification, go to next step. If voltage is within specification, go to step **5**).

3) Check Continuity Of MLP Circuits – Turn ignition off. Disconnect MLP sensor wiring harness connector. Disconnect PCM 104-pin connector. Inspect terminals for damage and repair if necessary. Install EEC-V Breakout Box (014-00959), leaving PCM disconnected. Measure resistance between test pin No. 64 (MLP) at breakout box and MLP terminal of MLP sensor wiring harness connector. Measure resistance between test pin No. 91 (SIG RTN) at breakout box and SIG RTN terminal of MLP sensor wiring harness connector. If resistance is less than 5 ohms, go to next step. If resistance is 5 ohms or more, repair open circuit and repeat QUICK TEST.

4) Leave ignition off and MLP sensor disconnected. Measure resistance between test pin No. 64 (MLP) and test pins No. 71, 76, 77, 91 and 97 at breakout box. Measure resistance between test pin No. 64 and chassis ground. If all resistance measurements are 10 k/ohms or more, go to next step. If any resistance measurement is less than 10 k/ohms, repair short circuit and repeat QUICK TEST.

5) Check MLP Sensor Resistance – Leave ignition off. Reconnect MLP sensor. Unlock steering column. Measure resistance between breakout box test pins No. 64 and 91 in each gear range. Resistance should be within specification. See MLP SENSOR SPECIFICATIONS table. If each resistance measurement is within specification, replace PCM and repeat QUICK TEST. If any resistance measurement is not within specification, replace MLP sensor and repeat QUICK TEST.

3-612

AUTOMATIC TRANSMISSIONS
AODE & AODE-W EEC-V Electronic Controls (Cont.)

CIRCUIT TEST TD (Cont.)

NOTE: A break in step numbering sequence occurs at this point. Procedure skips from step 3) to step 10). No test procedures have been omitted.

10) Code P0713 – This code indicates that self-test has detected TFT sensor circuit input above specification. Possible causes codes are as follows:
- Fluid level out of specification.
- Short between TFT and VPWR circuits.
- Open in TFT or SIG RTN circuit.
- Faulty TFT sensor.
- Faulty PCM.

Turn ignition off. Disconnect transmission wiring harness connector. Install jumper wire between TFT and SIG RTN terminal of connector. Perform KOEO and KOER self-test. If Code P0712 is present, replace TFT sensor. If Code P0712 is not present, go to next step. If no codes are present, go to step **12)**.

11) Check Circuit Continuity – Leave ignition off and transmission wiring harness connector disconnected. Disconnect PCM 104-pin connector. Inspect pins for damage and repair if necessary. Install EEC-V Breakout Box (014-00959), leaving PCM disconnected. Measure resistance between test pin No. 37 (TFT) at breakout box and TFT terminal at transmission wiring harness connector. Measure resistance between test pin No. 91 (SIG RTN) at breakout box and SIG RTN terminal at transmission wiring harness connector. If each resistance measurement is less than 5 ohms, go to next step. If either resistance measurement is 5 ohms or more, repair open circuit and repeat QUICK TEST.

12) Check TFT Circuit For Short To Power – Leave transmission wiring harness connector disconnected. Turn ignition on. Measure voltage between test pin No. 37 (TFT) and test pins No. 77 and 103 (PWR GND) at breakout box. If voltage is 2 volts or more, repair short to power in TFT circuit and repeat QUICK TEST. If voltage is less than 2 volts, replace PCM and repeat QUICK TEST.

NOTE: A break in step numbering sequence occurs at this point. Procedure skips from step 12) to step 20). No test procedures have been omitted.

20) Code P1711 – This code indicates that self-test has detected TFT sensor circuit input was out of range specification. Possible causes codes are as follows:
- Fluid level out of specification.
- Fluid not at operating temperature.
- Faulty TFT sensor.
- Faulty PCM.

Ensure transmission fluid temperature is at least 50°F (10°C). Perform KOEO and KOER self-test. If Code P1711 is present, go to next step. If Code P0713 is not present, testing is complete.

21) Check VREF At TP Sensor – Turn ignition off. Disconnect TP sensor wiring harness connector. Turn ignition on. Measure voltage between SIG RTN and VREF terminals at connecter. If voltage is 4-6 volts, go to next step. If voltage is not 4-6 volts, go to CIRCUIT TEST CA.

22) Check TFT Sensor Integrity – Warm transmission to normal operating temperature. Turn ignition off. Disconnect PCM 104-pin connector. Inspect pins for damage and repair if necessary. Install EEC-V Breakout Box (014-00959). Connect PCM to breakout box. As transmission cools, verify resistance increases as specified. See TFT SENSOR SPECIFICATIONS table. If resistance does not change as specified, replace TFT sensor. If resistance does change as specified, replace PCM and repeat QUICK TEST.

NOTE: A break in step numbering sequence occurs at this point. Procedure skips from step 22) to step 90). No test procedures have been omitted.

90) Continuous Memory Code P0712 – This code indicates that self-test has detected TFT sensor circuit input below specification. Possible causes codes are as follows:
- Fluid level out of specification.
- Short circuit in wiring harness.
- Faulty TFT sensor.
- Faulty PCM.

Turn ignition off. Connect scan tester to DLC. Using scan tester, access TFT PIDs. If TFT PID is 0.5 volt or more, go to next step. If TFT PID is less than 0.5 volt, return to step **1)**.

PINPOINT TEST TD (Cont.)

91) Wiggle Test TFT Sensor Circuits – Turn ignition off. Leave scan tester connected to DLC with TFT PIDs accessed. While shaking and bending TFT sensor wiring harness, observe TFT PIDs for indication of fault. A fault will be indicated by a sudden surge in PID voltage. If fault is indicated, isolate and repair as necessary. If fault is not indicated, problem cannot be duplicated or identified at this time. Testing is complete.

NOTE: A break in step numbering sequence occurs at this point. Procedure skips from step 91) to step 100). No test procedures have been omitted.

100) Continuous Memory Code P0713 – This code indicates that self-test has detected TFT sensor circuit input above specification. Possible causes for these codes are as follows:
- Fluid level out of specification.
- Short between TFT and VPWR circuits.
- Open in TFT or SIG RTN circuit.
- Faulty TFT sensor.
- Faulty PCM.

Turn ignition off. Connect scan tester to DLC. Using scan tester, access TFT PID. If TFT PID is 4.8 volts or less, go to next step. If TFT PID is more than 4.8 volts, return to step **10)**.

101) Wiggle Test TFT Sensor Circuits – Turn ignition off. Leave scan tester connected to DLC with TFT PIDs accessed. While shaking and bending TFT sensor wiring harness, observe TFT PIDs for indication of fault. A fault will be indicated by a sudden surge in PID voltage. If fault is indicated, isolate and repair as necessary. If fault is not indicated, problem cannot be duplicated or identified at this time. Testing is complete.

NOTE: A break in step numbering sequence occurs at this point. Procedure skips from step 101) to step 110). No test procedures have been omitted.

110) Continuous Memory Code P1783 – This code indicates that transmission has overheated. Possible causes codes are as follows:
- Incorrect transmission fluid level.
- Faulty transmission cooling system.
- Excessive load hauling.
- Faulty transmission connector.

Turn ignition off. Disconnect transmission wiring harness connector. Perform KOEO self-test. If Code P1783 is present, repair cause of transmission overheating as necessary. If Code P1783 is not present, testing is complete.

CIRCUIT TEST TE

TRANSMISSION FLUID TEMPERATURE (TFT) SENSOR

Diagnostic Aids – Perform this test when instructed during QUICK TEST or if directed by other test procedures. This test is used to diagnose the following:
- Wiring harness circuits (TFT SIG & SIG RTN).
- Faulty TFT sensor.
- Faulty PCM.

94D32543

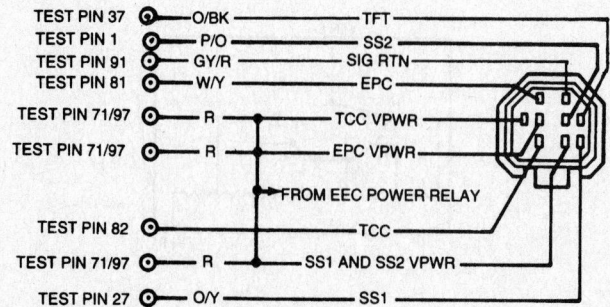

TEST PINS ARE LOCATED ON BREAKOUT BOX.
HARNESS CONNECTORS VIEWED INTO MATING SURFACE.

Fig. TE1: Identifying Transmission Circuit & Connector Terminals

AUTOMATIC TRANSMISSIONS
AODE & AODE-W EEC-V Electronic Controls (Cont.)

3-613

CIRCUIT TEST TE (Cont.)

94H32547

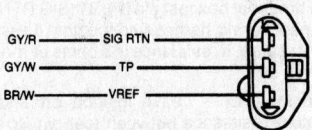

Fig. TE2: Identifying TP Sensor Wiring Harness Connector Terminals

TFT SENSOR SPECIFICATIONS [1]

Temperature °F (°C)	[1] Volts	[1] Ohms
32 (0)	3.88	96,255
59 (15)	3.32	46,883
104 (40)	2.15	16,043
158 (70)	1.03	5260
194 (90)	0.60	2750

[1] – Value may vary by 15 percent.

1) Code P0712 – This code indicates that self-test has detected TFT sensor circuit input below specification. Possible causes codes are as follows:
- Fluid level out of specification.
- Short circuit in wiring harness.
- Faulty TFT sensor.
- Faulty PCM.

Turn ignition off. Disconnect transmission wiring harness connector. Perform KOEO and KOER self-test. If Code P0713 is present, replace TFT sensor. If Code P0713 is not present, go to next step.

2) Check VREF At TP Sensor – Turn ignition off. Leave transmission connector disconnected. Disconnect TP sensor wiring harness connector. Turn ignition on. Measure voltage between SIG RTN and VREF terminals at connecter. If voltage is 4-6 volts, go to next step. If voltage is not 4-6 volts, go to CIRCUIT TEST CA.

3) Check For Short In TFT Circuit – Leave ignition off and transmission connector disconnected. Disconnect PCM 104-pin connector. Inspect pins for damage and repair if necessary. Install EEC-V Breakout Box (014-00959), leaving PCM disconnected. Measure resistance between test pins No. 37 (TFT) and test pins No. 91 (SIG RTN), 51 and 103 (PWR GND). If any resistance measurement is 10 k/ohms or less, repair short circuit and repeat QUICK TEST. If any resistance measurement is more than 10 k/ohms, replace PCM and repeat QUICK TEST.

CIRCUIT TEST TF

OUTPUT SHAFT SPEED (OSS) SENSOR

Diagnostic Aids – Perform this test when instructed during QUICK TEST or if directed by other test procedures. This test is used to diagnose the following:
- Wiring harness circuits (OSS & SIG RTN).
- Faulty OSS sensor.
- Faulty PCM.

94I32548

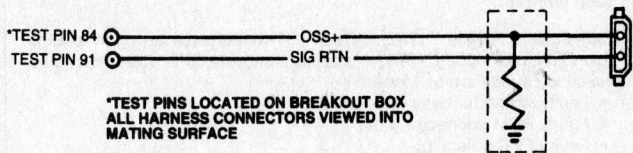

Fig. TF1: Identifying OSS Circuit & Connector Terminals

CIRCUIT TEST TF (Cont.)

Transmission Drive Cycle – Record codes and clear PCM memory. Warm engine to normal operating temperature. With vehicle stopped on open road, place gear selector in Drive and accelerate heavily to 35 MPH. Stop vehicle and turn ignition off.

1) Continuous Memory Code P0720 – Perform TRANSMISSION DRIVE CYCLE. Perform KOEO self-test. If Continuous Memory Code P0720 is present, go to next step. If no codes are present, go to CIRCUIT TEST Z under SELF-DIAGNOSTICS – EEC-V article in ENGINE PERFORMANCE of appropriate MITCHELL® manual.

2) Check OSS Circuit Continuity – Turn ignition off. Disconnect OSS sensor. Disconnect PCM 104-pin connector. Inspect pins for damage and repair if necessary. Install EEC-V Breakout Box (014-00959), leaving PCM disconnected. Measure resistance between breakout box test pin No. 84 (OSS) and OSS terminal at OSS wiring harness connector. If resistance is less than 5 ohms, go to next step. If resistance is 5 ohms or more, repair open circuit and repeat QUICK TEST.

3) Check OSS Circuit For Short To Ground – Leave ignition off and OSS sensor disconnected. Measure resistance between test pins No. 51 (GND) and 84 at breakout box. If resistance is more than 5 ohms, go to next step. If resistance is 5 ohms or less, repair faulty resistor or short circuit and repeat QUICK TEST.

4) Check OSS Circuit For Short To Power – Leave ignition off and OSS sensor disconnected. Measure resistance between test pins No. 71 (VPRW) and 84 at breakout box. If resistance is more than 5 ohms, go to next step. If resistance is 5 ohms or less, repair OSS circuit short to power and repeat QUICK TEST.

5) Check OSS Sensor Resistance – Leave ignition off and OSS sensor disconnected. Measure resistance between OSS sensor terminals. If resistance is not 450-650 ohms, replace OSS sensor. If resistance is 450-650 ohms, check transmission for mechanical faults. If transmission is okay, replace PCM and repeat QUICK TEST.

CIRCUIT TEST TG

ELECTRONIC TRANSMISSION CONTINUOUS MEMORY DIAGNOSTIC TROUBLE CODES (DTC)

Diagnostic Aids – Perform this test when instructed during QUICK TEST or if directed by other test procedures. This test is used to diagnose the following:
- Wiring harness circuits (EPC, MLP, SS1, SS2, TCC & TFT).
- Faulty PCM.

94F32545

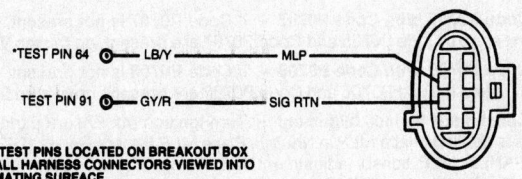

Fig. TG1: Manual Lever Position (MLP) Circuit Schematic

MLP SENSOR SPECIFICATIONS

Position	[1] Volts	[1] Ohms
Park	4.23-4.68	3770-4607
Reverse	3.52-3.89	1304-1593
Neutral	2.80-3.10	660-807
Overdrive	2.09-2.31	361-442
Drive	1.39-1.53	190-232
First	0.68-0.76	78-95

3-614

AUTOMATIC TRANSMISSIONS
AODE & AODE-W EEC-V Electronic Controls (Cont.)

CIRCUIT TEST TG (Cont.)

94D32543

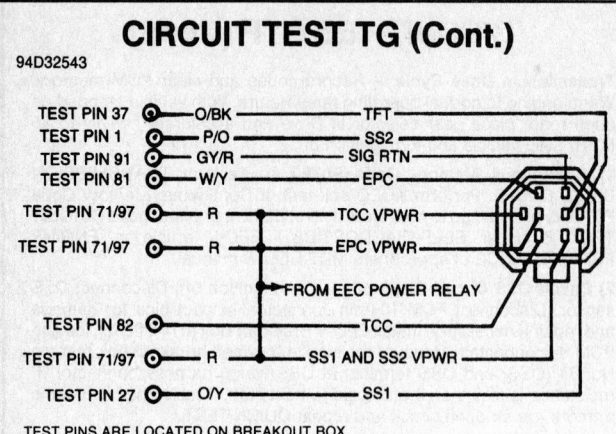

TEST PINS ARE LOCATED ON BREAKOUT BOX.
HARNESS CONNECTORS VIEWED INTO MATING SURFACE.

Fig. TG2: Identifying Transmission Wiring Harness Connector Terminals

Drive Cycle – Warm engine to normal operating temperature. With vehicle stopped on open road, place gear selector in Overdrive. Press Transmission Control Switch (TCS). TCIL should come on. Accelerate moderately to 40 MPH, allowing transmission to shift into 3rd gear. Hold speed steady for at least 30 seconds. Press TCS. TCIL should turn off. Accelerate to 60 MPH, allowing transmission to shift into 4th gear. With transmission in 4th gear, lightly apply and release brakes to operate brakelights. Hold speed steady for at least 5 more seconds. Stop vehicle with gear selector in still in "OD" (overdrive). Wait for at least 20 seconds and turn ignition off. Repeat entire procedure 5 times.

NOTE: Test procedure begins with step 90). No test procedures have been omitted.

90) – Ensure transmission fluid level is correct. Record all Continuous Memory Codes and clear PCM memory. Perform DRIVE CYCLE procedure. Repeat QUICK TEST. If no codes are present, check transmission for mechanical faults. Repair as necessary. If fault codes are present, proceed as appropriate:
- For Codes P0705, P0707, P0708 and P1706; go to step **91**).
- For Codes P0741, P0743, P1741 and P1744; go to step **110**).
- For Codes P0750 and P0755; go to step **120**).
- For Codes P0747 and P0747; go to step **130**).
- For all other codes; go to step **140**).

91) Code P1706 – Perform QUICK TEST. If Code P1706 is not present, go to next step. If Code P1706 is present, go to step **101**).

92) Code P0705 – If Code P0705 is present, go to next step. If Code P0705 is not present, go to step **96**).

93) Code P0705 With Code P0707 – If Code P0707 is not present, go to next step. If Code P0705 and Code P0707 are present, go to step **97**).

94) Code P0705 With Code P0708 – If Code P0708 is not present, go to next step. If Code P0705 and Code P0708 are present, go to step **99**).

95) Check MLP Sensor Alignment – Turn ignition off. Ensure parking brake is applied. Place MLP in Neutral. Place MLP Sensor Gauge (T92P-7010-AH) in MLP sensor adjustment slot. Remove sensor adjustment gauge and go to step **101**). If gauge does fit in slot, loosen MLP sensor mounting screws and move sensor until gauge fits in slot. Tighten screws and verify shift linkage is properly adjusted.

96) Code P0707 – If Code P0707 repeated after drive cycle, go to next step. If Code P0707 did not repeat after drive cycle, go to step **99**).

97) Turn ignition off. Disconnect MLP sensor. Disconnect PCM 104-pin connector. Inspect pins for damage and repair if necessary. Install EEC-V Breakout Box (014-00959), leaving PCM disconnected. Measure resistance between breakout box test pin No. 64 (MLP SIG) and MLP terminal of MLP sensor wiring harness connector. If resistance is less than 5 ohms, go to next step. If resistance is 5 ohms or more, repair open circuit and repeat step **90**).

98) Leave ignition off and MLP sensor disconnected. Measure resistance between breakout box test pin No. 64 and chassis ground. If resistance is less than 5 ohms, go to next step. If resistance is 5 ohms or more, repair open circuit and repeat step **90**).

CIRCUIT TEST TG (Cont.)

99) Code P0708; Check MLP SIG RTN Circuit Continuity – Turn ignition off. Disconnect MLP sensor. Disconnect PCM 104-pin connector. Inspect pins for damage and repair if necessary. Install EEC-V Breakout Box (014-00959), leaving PCM disconnected. Measure resistance between breakout box test pin No. 91 (SIG RTN) and SIG RTN terminal of MLP sensor wiring harness connector. If resistance is less than 5 ohms, go to next step. If resistance is 5 ohms or more, repair open circuit and repeat step **90**).

100) Check Circuit Integrity – Leave ignition off and MLP sensor disconnected. Measure resistance between test pin No. 64 (MLP SIG) test pins No. 24 (PWR GND), 91 (SIG RTN) and 97 (VPWR) at breakout box. If resistance is 10 k/ohms or more, go to next step. If resistance is less than 10 k/ohms or more, repair short circuit and repeat step **90**).

101) Check MLP Sensor Resistance – Leave ignition off. Reconnect MLP sensor. Unlock steering column. Measure resistance between breakout box test pins No. 64 and 91 in each gear range. Resistance should be within specification. See MLP SENSOR SPECIFICATIONS table. If each resistance measurement is within specification, replace PCM and repeat QUICK TEST. If any resistance measurement is not within specification, replace MLP sensor and repeat QUICK TEST.

NOTE: A break in step numbering sequence occurs at this point. Procedure skips from step 101) to step 110). No test procedures have been omitted.

110) Code P0741, P0743, P1741 and P1744 – These codes indicate a TCC solenoid or system performance error. Possible causes are as follows:
- Faulty wiring harness or connector.
- Faulty TCC solenoid.
- Interal transmission friction elements worn.

Turn ignition off. Disconnect PCM 104-pin connector. Inspect pins for damage and repair if necessary. Install EEC-V Breakout Box (014-00959). Connect PCM to breakout box. Connect DVOM test leads to breakout box test pins No. 71 (VPWR) and 82 (TCC). Turn ignition on. While shaking and bending TCC wiring harness, observe DVOM for indication of fault. A fault will be indicated by a sudden surge in DVOM voltage reading. Tap lightly on TCC connector to simulate road shock. If fault is indicated, isolate and repair as necessary and repeat step **90**). If fault is not indicated, check for transmission internal problem.

NOTE: A break in step numbering sequence occurs at this point. Procedure skips from step 110) to step 120). No test procedures have been omitted.

120) Code P0750 & P0755 – Code P0750 indicates a SS1 performance error. Code P0755 indicates a SS2 performance error. Possible causes are as follows:
- Faulty wiring harness or connector.
- Faulty PCM connector pins.
- Faulty shift solenoid.

Turn ignition off. Inspect shift solenoid wiring harness between transmission and PCM for damage and repair as necessary. Disconnect PCM 104-pin connector. Inspect pins for damage and repair if necessary. Install EEC-V Breakout Box (014-00959). Connect PCM to breakout box. For Code P0750, connect DVOM test leads to breakout box test pins No. 27 (SS1) and 71 (VPWR). For Code P0755, connect DVOM test leads to breakout box test pins No. 1 (SS2) and 71 (VPWR). Turn ignition on. While shaking and bending SS1/SS2 wiring harness, observe DVOM for indication of fault. A fault will be indicated by a sudden surge in DVOM voltage reading. Tap lightly on shift solenoid connector to simulate road shock. If fault is indicated, isolate and repair as necessary and repeat step **90**). If fault is not indicated, check for transmission internal problem.

NOTE: A break in step numbering sequence occurs at this point. Procedure skips from step 120) to step 130). No test procedures have been omitted.

130) Code P1746 & P1747 – Code P1746 indicates an open in EPC solenoid circuit. Code P0747 indicates a short in EPC solenoid circuit. Possible causes are as follows:
- Faulty wiring harness or connector.
- Faulty PCM connector pins.
- Faulty EPC solenoid.

Turn ignition off. Inspect EPC solenoid wiring harness between transmission and PCM for damage and repair as necessary. Disconnect PCM 104-pin connector. Inspect pins for damage and repair if

AUTOMATIC TRANSMISSIONS
AODE & AODE-W EEC-V Electronic Controls (Cont.)

3-615

CIRCUIT TEST TG (Cont.)

necessary. Install EEC-V Breakout Box (014-00959). Connect PCM to breakout box. Connect DVOM test leads to breakout box test pins No. 81 (EPC) and 97 (VPWR). Turn ignition on. While shaking and bending EPC wiring harness, observe DVOM for indication of fault. A fault will be indicated by a sudden surge in DVOM voltage reading. Tap lightly on EPC solenoid connector to simulate road shock. If fault is indicated, isolate and repair as necessary and repeat step 90). If fault is not indicated, check for transmission internal problem.

NOTE: A break in step numbering sequence occurs at this point. Procedure skips from step 130) to step 140). No test procedures have been omitted.

140) All Other Codes For Electronic Transmission – All other codes for electronic transmission code are defined as follows:
- Code P0731 indicates incorrect gear ratio after 1st gear was commanded.
- Code P0732 indicates incorrect gear ratio after 2nd gear was commanded.
- Code P0733 indicates incorrect gear ratio after 3rd gear was commanded.
- Code P0734 indicates incorrect gear ratio after 4th gear was commanded.
- Code P0735 indicates incorrect gear ratio after 5th gear was commanded.
- Code P0751 indicates shift solenoid No. 1 performance error.
- Code P0756 indicates shift solenoid No. 2 performance error.
- Code P1731 indicates incorrect 1-2 upshift.
- Code P1732 indicates incorrect 2-3 upshift.
- Code P1733 indicates incorrect 3-4 upshift.
- Code P1734 indicates incorrect 4-5 upshift.
- Code P1786 indicates incorrect 3-2 downshift.
- Code P1787 indicates incorrect 2-1 downshift.

Possible causes for these codes are as follows:
- Faulty wiring harness or connector.
- Worn internal transmission friction elements.
- Faulty shift solenoid.

Turn ignition off. Disconnect PCM 104-pin connector. Inspect pins for damage and repair if necessary. Install EEC-V Breakout Box (014-00959). Connect PCM to breakout box. Connect DVOM test lead to shift solenoid test pin (No. 1 or 27) at breakout box. Connect other DVOM test lead breakout box test pin No. 71 (VPWR). Turn ignition on. While shaking and bending wiring harness, observe DVOM for indication of fault. A fault will be indicated by a sudden surge in DVOM voltage reading. Tap lightly on connector to simulate road shock. If fault is indicated, isolate and repair as necessary and repeat step 90). If fault is not indicated, check for internal transmission problem.

CIRCUIT TEST X

CONSTANT CONTROL RELAY MODULE (CCRM)

Diagnostic Aids – CCRM interfaces with the EEC-V system to provide control for cooling fan and A/C clutch. CCRM also contains EEC-V power relay, which provides battery power (VPWR) to the Powertrain Control Module (PCM) and EEC-V system. Perform this test only when instructed by QUICK TEST or if directed by a CIRCUIT. This test is only intended to diagnose the following:
- CCRM including EEC power relay, Fan Control/Low Fan Control (FC/LFC) relay.
- Harness circuits (B+, FANM, FPM, FP, FC KPWR, PWR GND, LFC, HFC, A/C, ACCS and WAC).
- Powertrain Control Module (PCM).

To prevent replacing good components, be aware the following non-EEC related components or systems may be at fault:
- A/C system.
- Fuel system.
- Starting and charging system.

CIRCUIT TEST X (Cont.)

94D31693

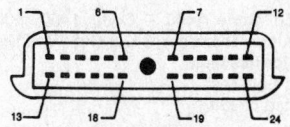

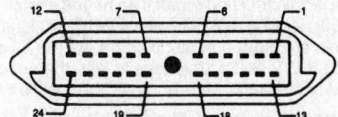

Fig. X1: Identifying CCRM Connector Terminals

94E31694

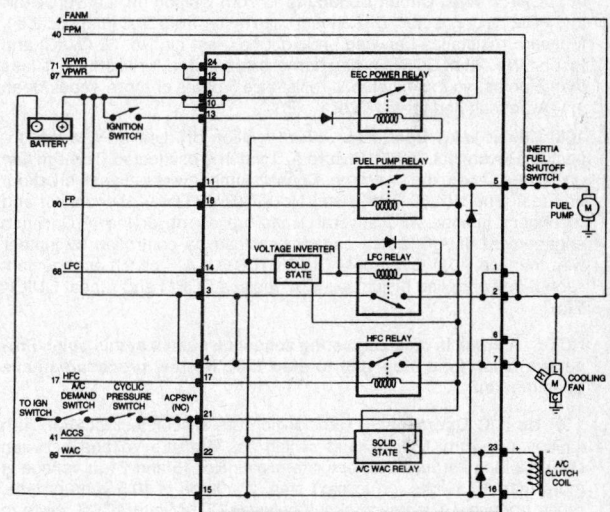

Fig. X2: CCRM Circuits (Cougar & Thunderbird 4.6L)

94F31695

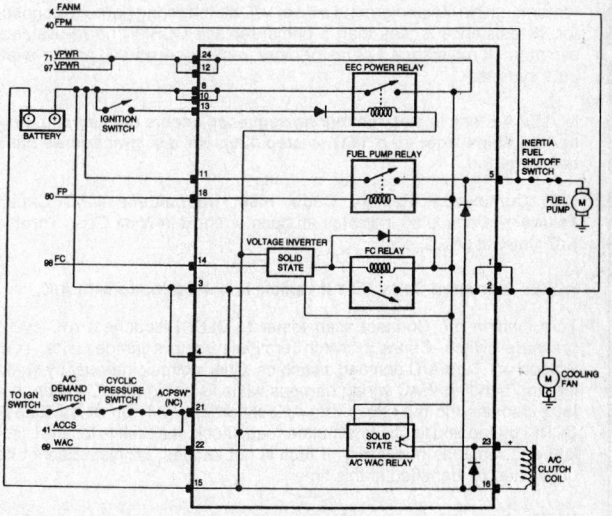

Fig. X3: CCRM Circuits (Mustang 3.8L)

3-616

AUTOMATIC TRANSMISSIONS
AODE & AODE-W EEC-V Electronic Controls (Cont.)

CIRCUIT TEST X (Cont.)

NOTE: Procedure begins at step 105). No test procedures have been omitted.

105) KOEO/KOER Code 1460 – Code 1460 indicates that a fault occured in Wide Open Throttle A/C Cut-Out (WAC) circuit. Following are possible causes for this fault.
- A/C on during Self-Test.
- Open or shorted circuit.
- Faulty CCRM.
- Faulty PCM.

Turn ignition off. Disconnect CCRM. Disconnect PCM wiring harness connector. Inspect wiring, and repair if damaged. Install EEC-V Breakout Box (014-00950), leaving PCM disconnected. Turn ignition on. Measure voltage between breakout box test pins No. 69 and test pins No. 51 and No. 103 (PWR GND). If voltage is less than one volt, go to next step. If voltage is one volt or more, repair WAC circuit short to power.

106) Check WAC Circuit For Short To Ground – Turn ignition off. Leave CCRM and PCM disconnected. Disconnect scan tool from DLC (if applicable). Measure resistance between breakout box test pins No. 69 (WAC) and test pins No. 51, 103 (PWR GND) and 91 (SIG RTN). If each resistance measurement is more than 10 k/ohms, go to next step. If any resistance measurement is 10 k/ohms or less, repair WAC circuit short to power and repeat QUICK TEST.

107) Check WAC Circuit Continuity – Turn ignition off. Leave CCRM and PCM disconnected. Disconnect scan tester from DLC (if applicable). Measure resistance between breakout box test pin No. 69 (WAC) and test pin No. 22 at CCRM wiring harness connector. If resistance is less than 5 ohms, go to next step. If resistance 5 ohms or more, repair open in WAC circuit and repeat QUICK TEST.

108) Check WAC Operation – Turn ignition off. Leave PCM disconnected. Reconnect CCRM. Ensure A/C clutch is connected. Turn ignition on. Turn A/C demand switch on. Connect jumper wire between breakout box test pins No. 69 (WAC) and No. 77 (PWR GND). Disconnect and reconnect jumper wire several times whiles observing A/C clutch engagement. If A/C clutch engagement can be controlled by jumper wire, replace PCM and repeat QUICK TEST. If A/C clutch engagement cannot be controlled by jumper wire, replace CCRM and repeat QUICK TEST.

NOTE: A break in step numbering sequence occurs at this point. Procedure skips from step 108) to step 110). No test procedures have been omitted.

110) No A/C Operation – Turn ignition off. Disconnect CCRM. Turn ignition on. Turn A/C demand switch on. Measure voltage between CCRM wiring harness connector terminals No. 15 and 21. If voltage is more than 10.5 volts, go to next step. If voltage is 10.5 volts or less, repair open in A/C demand circuit between CCRM and ACCS splice to PCM and re-evaluate symptom

111) Check Circuit Continuity – Turn ignition off. Leave CCRM disconnected. Disconnect scan tester from DLC (if applicable). Disconnect A/C clutch. Measure resistance between CCRM wiring harness connector terminal No. 16 and ground side of A/C clutch wiring harness connector. If resistance is less than 5 ohms, replace CCRM and re-evaluate symptom. If resistance 5 ohms or more, repair open circuit and re-evaluate symptom.

NOTE: A break in step numbering sequence occurs at this point. Procedure skips from step 111) to step 120). No test procedures have been omitted.

120) Continuous Memory Code 1460: Intermittent WAC Circuit Failure – Code 1460 indicates an open or short in Wide Open Throttle A/C Cut-Out (WAC) circuit.

NOTE: Disregard Code 1481 if vehicle is not equipped with A/C.

Turn ignition off. Connect scan tester to DLC. Disconnect A/C cyclic pressure switch. Connect switch terminals using a jumper wire. Turn ignition on. Turn A/C demand switch on. Check circuit integrity by shaking and bending WAC wiring harness while listening to A/C clutch. If a fault is located in the circuit, the A/C clutch will cycle on or off. Check CCRM by tapping lightly to simulate road shock. If a fault is located, isolate and repair as necessary. If fault is not located, problem cannot be duplicated or identified at this time.

NOTE: A break in step numbering sequence occurs at this point. Procedure skips from step 120) to step 125). No test procedures have been omitted.

CIRCUIT TEST X (Cont.)

125) ACCS PID On – Turn ignition off. Disconnect A/C Pressure Switch (ACPSW). Turn ignition on. Access ACCS PID. If ACCS PID does not go off, go to next step. If ACCS PID goes off, check ACPSW and repair or replace as necessary. If ACPSW is okay, repair short to power in A/C demand circuit to ACPSW.

126) Check A/C Clutch Circuit For Short To Power – Turn ignition off. Leave CCRM disconnected. Measure voltage between CCRM wiring harness connector terminals No. 16 and negative battery terminal. If voltage is less than one volt, go to next step. If voltage is one volt or more, repair circuit short to power and re-evaluate symptom.

127) Check ACCS Circuit For Short To Power – Turn ignition off. Leave ACPSW and CCRM disconnected. Disconnect PCM wiring harness connector. Inspect wiring, and repair if damaged. Install EEC-V Breakout Box (014-00950), leaving PCM disconnected. Turn ignition on. Measure voltage at breakout box test pin No. 41 (ACCS) and test pins No. 51 and 103 (PWR GND). If voltage is less than one volt, go to next step. If voltage is one volt or more, repair circuit for a short to power and re-evaluate symptom.

128) Check ACCS Circuit Voltage To PCM – Turn ignition off. Leave ACPSW and PCM disconnected. Reconnect CCRM. Turn ignition on. Measure voltage between breakout box test pin No. 41 (ACCS) and test pins No. 51 and 103 (PWR GND). If voltage is less than one volt, replace PCM and re-evaluate symptom. If voltage is one volt or more, replace CCRM and re-evaluate symptom.

NOTE: A break in step numbering sequence occurs at this point. Procedure skips from step 128) to step 130). No test procedures have been omitted.

130) No WAC & No DTCs – Turn ignition off. Leave ACPSW and CCRM disconnected. Disconnect PCM wiring harness connector. Inspect wiring, and repair if damaged. Install EEC-V Breakout Box (014-00950), leaving PCM disconnected. Reconnect CCRM and A/C clutch wiring harness connectors. Turn ignition on. Turn A/C demand switch on. Connect jumper wire between breakout box test pins No. 69 (WAC) and No. 77 (PWR GND). Disconnect and reconnect jumper wire several times while observing A/C clutch engagement. If A/C clutch engagement cannot be controlled by jumper wire, replace CCRM and re-evaluate symptom. If A/C clutch engagement can be controlled by jumper wire, EEC-V system is okay and testing is complete.

NOTE: A break in step numbering sequence occurs at this point. Procedure skips from step 130) to step 150). No test procedures have been omitted.

150) No Fuel Pressure – While listening for fuel pump operation, turn ignition on. Fuel pump should operate for about one second and then shut off. If fuel pump does not operate correctly, turn ignition off. With scan tester connected to DLC, enter Output Test Mode. While listening to fuel pump, turn outputs on. If fuel pump operates, fuel pump circuits are okay; check fuel pump and repair as necessary. If fuel pump does not operate, go to next step.

151) Check FPA PID During KOEO – Turn ignition on while viewing FPA PID. If FPA PID comes on when ignition is turned on, go to next step. If FPA PID does not come on when ignition is turned on, go to step **160)**.

152) Check FPA PID During KOEC – Crank engine while viewing FPA-PID. If FPA PID is on while engine is cranking, go to next step. If FPA PID is not on while engine is cranking, go to step **160)**.

153) Check FPM PID During KOEO – Turn ignition on while viewing FPM PID. If FPM PID comes on when ignition is turned on, go to next step. If FPM PID does not come on when ignition is turned on, turn ignition off. Verify Inertia Fuel Shutoff (IFS) switch is reset. If switch is okay, check for open in power-to-pump circuit, poor fuel pump ground or open in fuel pump or IFS. Repair as necessary.

154) Check FPM PID During KOEC – Crank engine while viewing FPM PID. If FPM PID is on while engine is cranking, electrical circuits are okay; check fuel system mechanical components. If FPM PID is not on while engine is cranking, go to step **165)**.

NOTE: A break in step numbering sequence occurs at this point. Procedure skips from step 154) to step 157). No test procedures have been omitted.

157) Check Fuel Pump Relay Coil Resistance – Turn ignition off. Disconnect CCRM. Measure resistance between CCRM wiring harness connector terminals No. 18 and 24. If resistance is 65-120 ohms, go to next step. If resistance is not 65-120 ohms, replace CCRM and re-evaluate symptom.

AUTOMATIC TRANSMISSIONS
AODE & AODE-W EEC-V Electronic Controls (Cont.)

3-617

CIRCUIT TEST X (Cont.)

158) Check FP Circuit Continuity – Turn ignition off. Leave CCRM disconnected. Disconnect PCM wiring harness connector. Inspect wiring, and repair if damaged. Install EEC-V Breakout Box (014-00950), leaving PCM disconnected. Measure resistance between breakout box test pin No. 18 and test pin No. 80 (FP). If resistance is less than 5 ohms, replace PCM and re-evaluate symptom. If resistance is 5 ohms or more, repair open in FP circuit and re-evaluate symptom.

NOTE: A break in step numbering sequence occurs at this point. Procedure skips from step 158) to step 160). No test procedures have been omitted.

160) Check FP Circuit For Short To Power In CCRM – Turn ignition off. Leave CCRM disconnected. Measure resistance between CCRM wiring harness connector terminals No. 18 and 24. Resistance should be 65-120 ohms. Measure resistance between CCRM wiring harness connector terminals No. 18 and the following terminals: No. 1-11 and No. 13. Resistance should be greater than 10 k/ohms. If all resistance checks are okay, go to next step. If any resistance is not okay, replace CCRM and re-evaluate symptom.

161) Check FP Circuit For Short To Power In CCRM – Leave CCRM disconnected. Turn ignition on. Measure voltage between CCRM wiring harness connector terminals No. 18 and negative battery terminal. If voltage is less than one volt, replace PCM and re-evaluate symptom. If voltage is one volt or more, repair FP circuit short to power and re-evaluate symptom.

NOTE: A break in step numbering sequence occurs at this point. Procedure skips from step 161) to step 165). No test procedures have been omitted.

165) Check For Power To Fuel Pump Relay – Turn ignition off. Disconnect CCRM wiring harness connector. Measure voltage between CCRM wiring harness connector terminal No. 11 and negative battery terminal. If voltage is 10.5 volts or more, go to next step. If voltage is less than 10.5 volts, repair open in B+ circuit to CCRM and re-evaluate symptom.

166) Check Power To Pump Circuit Continuity – Leave ignition off and CCRM disconnected. Measure resistance between CCRM wiring harness connector terminal No. 5 and negative battery terminal. If resistance is less than 10 ohms, replace CCRM and re-evaluate symptom. If resistance is 10 ohms or more, repair open in power to pump circuit between CCRM and FPM splice and re-evaluate symptom.

NOTE: A break in step numbering sequence occurs at this point. Procedure skips from step 166) to step 175). No test procedures have been omitted.

175) Fuel Pump Runs Continuously: Verify FPA PID Is Off – With ignition off, connect scan tester to DLC (if necessary). Turn ignition on and wait 5 seconds. Access FPA PID on scan tester. If FPA PID is off, go to next step. If FPA PID is on, go to step **180)**.

176) Check FPM PID – With scan tester connected and ignition on, access FPM PID. If FPM PID comes on, go to next step. If FPM PID does not comes on, EEC-V system is okay and testing is complete.

177) Check CCRM – Turn ignition off. Disconnect CCRM. Turn ignition on. If fuel pump is off, replace CCRM and re-evaluate symptom. If fuel pump is on, repair FPM circuit short to power and re-evaluate symptom.

NOTE: A break in step numbering sequence occurs at this point. Procedure skips from step 177) to step 180). No test procedures have been omitted.

180) Check PCM – Turn ignition off. Disconnect PCM wiring harness connector. Turn ignition on. If fuel pump is off, replace PCM and re-evaluate symptom. If fuel pump is on, go to next step.

181) Check FP Circuit For Short To Ground – Turn ignition off. Disconnect scan tester from DLC (if applicable). Disconnect CCRM and PCM wiring harness connector. Inspect wiring, and repair if damaged. Install EEC-V Breakout Box (014-00950), leaving PCM disconnected. Measure resistance between breakout box test pin No. 80 and test pins No. 51, 103 (PWR GND) and 91 (SIG RTN). If each resistance is more than 10 k/ohms, replace CCRM and re-evaluate symptom. If resistance is 10 k/ohms or less, repair FP circuit short to ground and re-evaluate symptom.

3-618

AUTOMATIC TRANSMISSIONS
AODE & AODE-W EEC-V Electronic Controls (Cont.)

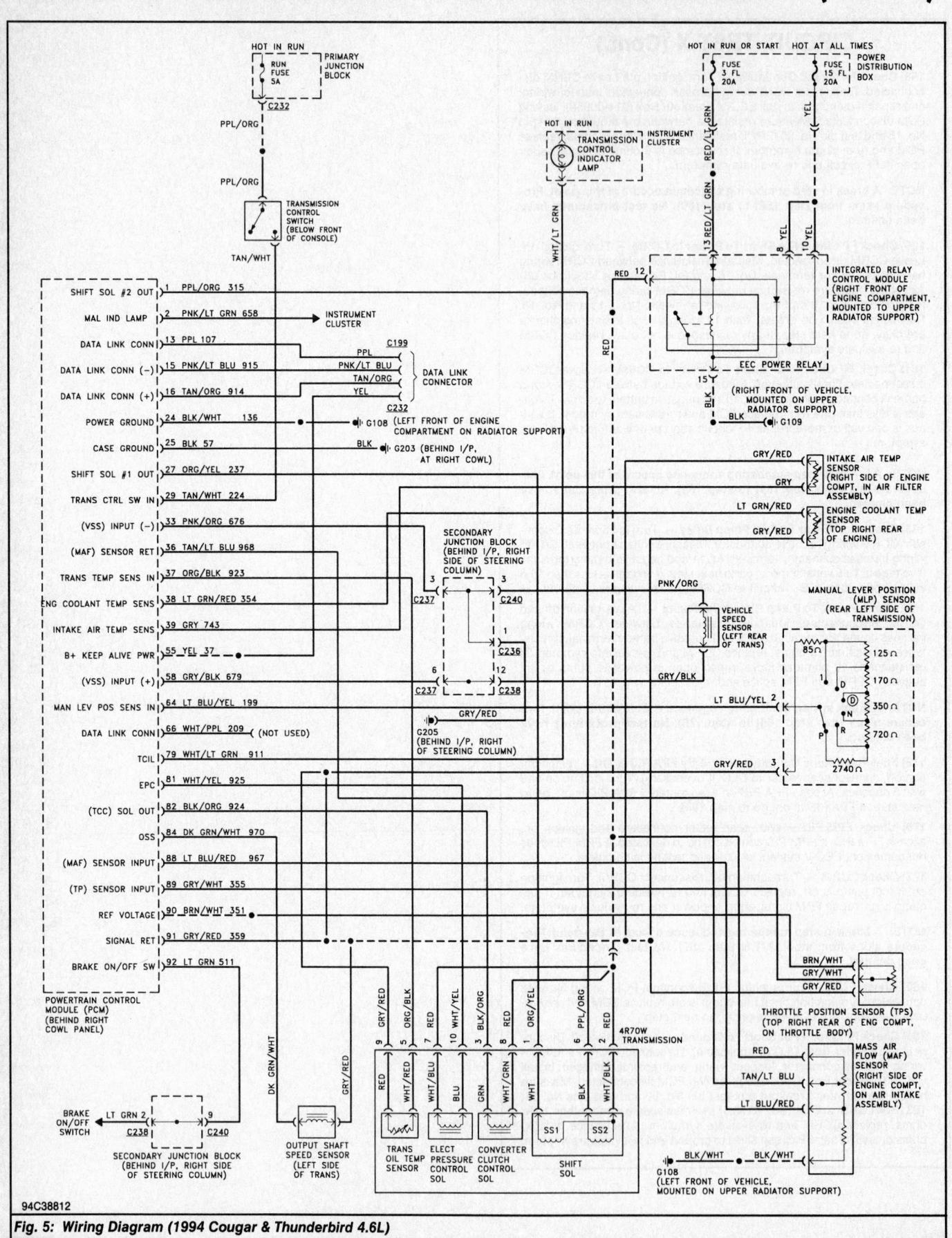

Fig. 5: *Wiring Diagram (1994 Cougar & Thunderbird 4.6L)*

94C38812

AUTOMATIC TRANSMISSIONS
AODE & AODE-W EEC-V Electronic Controls (Cont.)

3-619

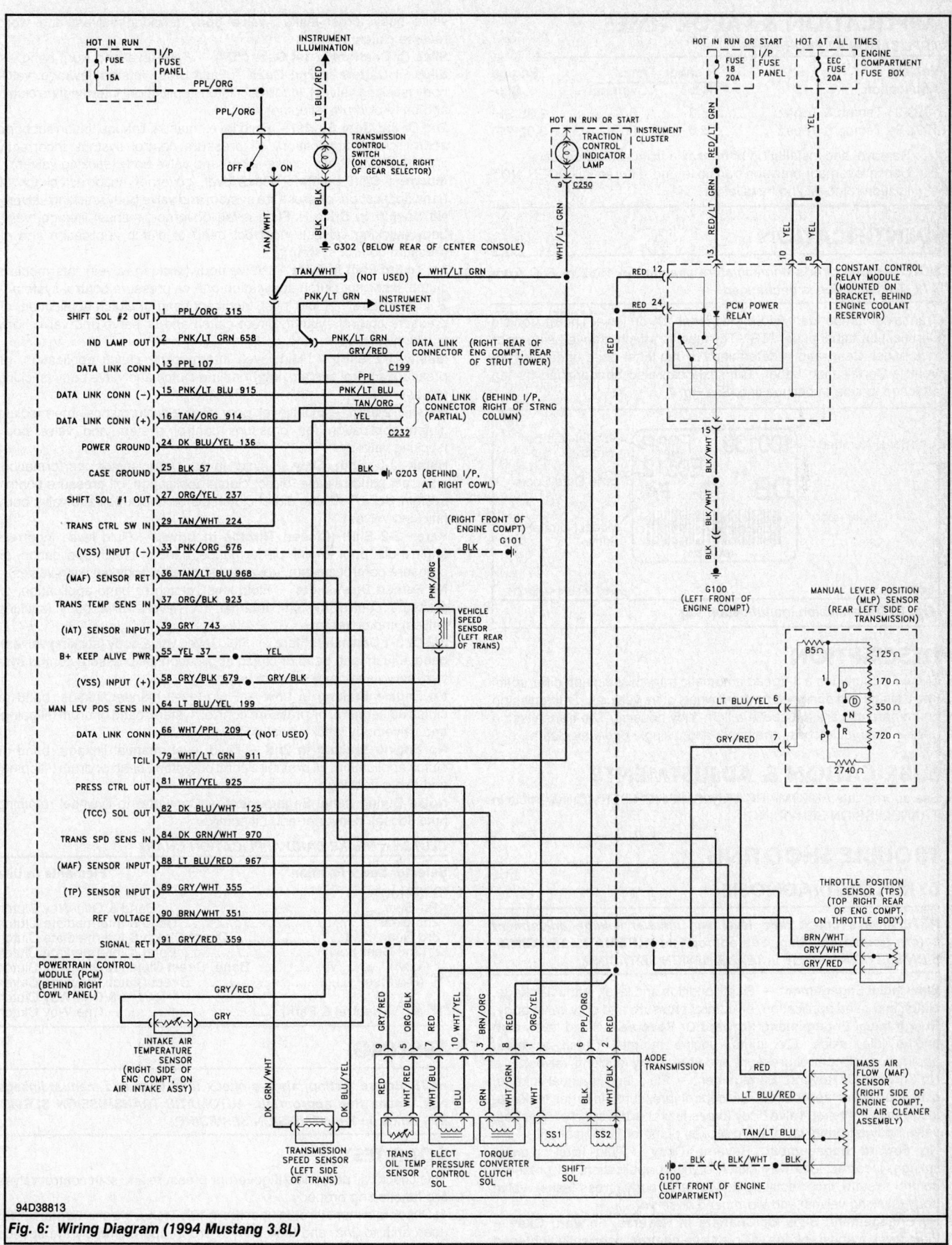

Fig. 6: *Wiring Diagram (1994 Mustang 3.8L)*

94D38813

AUTOMATIC TRANSMISSIONS
Ford ATX/FLC

APPLICATION & LABOR TIMES

APPLICATION & LABOR TIMES

Vehicle Application	Labor Times [1] R & I	[2] Overhaul	Engine Size
1993-94 Tempo & Topaz	5.0	6.7	2.3L SFI
1993-94 Tempo & Topaz	5.0	6.7	3.0L SFI

[1] – Removal and installation of transaxle from vehicle chassis.
[2] – Bench overhaul time for transaxle and differential. DOES NOT include removal and installation.

IDENTIFICATION

NOTE: *Manufacturer's nomenclature changed in 1992 to FLC from ATX. Transmission is unchanged.*

Transaxle can be identified by the letter "B" on lower line of Vehicle Certification Label under "TR". The label is attached to left side door lock panel. Gear ratio is determined by the letter code under "AX" of Vehicle Certification Label. Transaxle can also be identified by tag attached to side of bellhousing. *See Fig. 1.*

94I38719

Courtesy of Ford Motor Co.

Fig. 1: Transmission Identification Tag

DESCRIPTION

The ATX combines a 3-speed automatic transmission and differential into a single unit designed for front wheel drive vehicles. Transmission and differential are housed in a light-alloy housing. The transmission uses 3 friction clutches, one band, and a single one-way clutch.

LUBRICATION & ADJUSTMENTS

See appropriate AUTOMATIC TRANSMISSION SERVICING article in TRANSMISSION SERVICING.

TROUBLE SHOOTING

SYMPTOM DIAGNOSIS

NOTE: *Always check fluid level and manual linkage adjustment before trouble shooting. See appropriate AUTOMATIC TRANSMISSION SERVICING article in TRANSMISSION SERVICING.*

Slow Initial Engagement – Fluid condition and level, manual linkage, clutch and band application, oil control pressure and dirty valve body.
Rough Initial Engagement, Forward Or Reverse – Fluid level, high engine idle, axles, CV joints, engine mounts, clutch or band application, oil control pressure and valve body (sticking valves).
No Forward Or Reverse Engagement – Fluid level, manual linkage, clutch or band application, oil control pressure, internal leakage, incorrectly tightened valve body (cross-leaks), worn band or clutches, valve body (sticking valves) and broken pump or turbine shaft.
No Foward Engagement, Reverse Okay – Fluid level, manual linkage, incorrect one-way clutch or band application, oil pressure control system, incorrectly tightened valve body (cross-leaks), valve body (sticking valves) and worn band or servo.
No Engagement, Slips Or Chatters In Reverse, Forward Okay – Fluid level, manual linkage, oil pressure control, incorrectly tightened valve body (cross-leaks), valve body (sticking valves) and worn reverse clutch.
Slips Or Chatters In 1st Gear ("D") – Fluid level and worn band.
Slips Or Catters In 2nd Gear – Fluid Level, internal leakage, valve body (sticking valves), incorrect clutch application, intermediate clutch and band or drum (slipping).
2nd Or 3rd Gear Starts – Fluid level, manual linkage, incorrect band and/or clutch application, oil pressure control system, incorrectly tightened valve body (cross-leaks) and valve body (sticking valves)
Incorrect Shift Points – Fluid level, governor, incorrect clutch or band application, oil pressure system and valve body (sticking valves).
No Upshift In Drive – Fluid level, governor, manual linkage, valve body (sticking valves), incorrect band or clutch application and oil pressure control system.
1st To 3rd Shift In Drive – Valve body (sticking valves), intermediate clutch, incorrect clutch application and oil pressure control system.
2-3 Shift Flare – Fluid level, incorrect band or clutch application, oil pressure control system, direct clutch and/or servo and valve body (sticking valves).
Mushy 1-2 Shift – Fluid level, intermediate clutch application, oil pressure control system, intermediate clutch and valve body (sticking valves).
Harsh 1-2 Shift – Fluid level, poor engine performance, intermediate clutch application, oil pressure control system and valve body (sticking valves).
Harsh 2-3 Shift Only – Fluid level, poor engine performance, incorrect band release, direct clutch application, oil pressure control system, servo release, direct clutch piston check ball and valve body (sticking valves).
Harsh 3-2 Shift (Closed Throttle In Drive) – Fluid level, incorrect engine idle, poor engine performance, band or clutch application, oil pressure control system, governor and valve body (sticking valves).
No Forced Downshifts – Fluid level, clutch or band application, oil pressure control system, internal T.V. lever, valve body (sticking valves) and governor.
3-2 Or 3-1 Downshift Flare – Fluid level, valve body (sticking valves), band adjustment, band or clutch application, oil pressure control system, servo and band or drum (slipping).
No Engine Braking In Low – Fluid level, manual linkage, band or clutch adjustment, oil pressure control system, band or drum (slipping) and valve body (sticking valves).
No Engine Braking In 2nd – Fluid level, manual linkage, band or clutch application, oil pressure control system, band or drum (slipping) and servo (leaking).
Noise During Initial Engagement – Converter-to-flywheel retaining nuts (loose), converter and oil pump.

CLUTCH & BRAKE BAND APPLICATION CHART

Selector Lever Position	Elements In Use
"D" (Drive)	
1st Gear	Band & One-Way Clutch
2nd Gear	Band & Intermediate Clutch
3rd Gear	Direct Clutch & Intermediate Clutch
"2" (2nd Gear Low)	Band & Intermediate Clutch
"1" (Low)	Band, Direct Clutch & One-Way Clutch
"R" (Reverse)	Direct Clutch, Reverse Clutch & One-Way Clutch
"N" & "P" (Neutral & Park)	One-Way Clutch

TESTING

NOTE: *Before testing, always check fluid level and manual linkage adjustment. See appropriate AUTOMATIC TRANSMISSION SERVICING article in TRANSMISSION SERVICING.*

ROAD TEST

This check will determine if governor pressure and shift control valves are functioning properly.
1) Check minimum throttle upshifts in "D". Transaxle should start in 1st gear, shift to 2nd, and then shift to 3rd at approximately the speeds shown in ATX SHIFT SPEEDS tables.

2) With transaxle in 3rd, depress accelerator pedal to floor. Transaxle should shift from 3rd gear to 2nd gear or 1st gear, depending on vehicle speed. See ATX SHIFT SPEEDS tables.

3) Check closed throttle downshifts from 3rd to 1st by coasting down from approximately 35 MPH in 3rd gear. Shift should occur at approximate speed shown in ATX SHIFT SPEEDS tables.

4) With transaxle in 3rd and road speed above 35 MPH. transaxle should shift to 2nd gear when selector lever is moved from 3rd to 1st. Transaxle will shift into 1st when road speed is less than 20 MPH. When transaxle is shifted from Drive to 2nd, it should shift into 2nd gear regardless of vehicle speed.

NOTE: When "2" is selected, transaxle will operate in 1st and 2nd gears.

NOTE: Shift speeds are approximate. All shift speeds may vary somewhat due to production tolerances, rear axle ratios or emission control equipment.

ATX SHIFT SPEEDS

SHIFT SPEED CHART (2.3L HSC SFI)

Application	Shift	Speed Range/MPH
Closed Throttle		
"D" [1]	1-2	7-14
"D" [1]	2-3	12-27
"D"	3-2	12-21
"D"	2-1	4-10
"1"	2-1	11-29
Part Throttle		
"D"	1-2	11-27
"D"	2-3	29-46
"D"	3-2	17-36
"D"	2-1	14-21
Wide Open Throttle		
"D"	1-2	26-46
"D"	2-3	61-78
"D"	3-2	55-72
"D"	2-1	23-39

[1] – Speed Range/MPH is taken at 10-degree throttle opening.

SHIFT SPEED CHART (3.0L SFI)

Application	Shift	Speed Range/MPH
Closed Throttle		
"D" [1]	1-2	6-13
"D" [1]	2-3	11-26
"D"	3-2	10-19
"D"	2-1	4-10
"1"	2-1	11-29
Part Throttle		
"D"	1-2	9-25
"D"	2-3	27-44
"D"	3-2	12-31
"D"	2-1	10-17
Wide Open Throttle		
"D"	1-2	26-46
"D"	2-3	61-78
"D"	3-2	53-70
"D"	2-1	20-36

[1] – Speed Range/MPH is taken at 10-degree throttle opening.

GOVERNOR CHECK

Accelerate vehicle at full throttle to 30-40 MPH. Then back off throttle completely. If governor is functioning properly, transaxle will upshift to 3rd gear.

LINE PRESSURE TEST

1) Connect a 0-300 psi (0-2069 kPa) pressure gauge to line pressure test port on transaxle case. *See Fig. 2.* Run engine until normal operating temperature is reached.

2) Apply service and parking brakes. Check line pressure in all selector lever positions with engine at idle and then with engine at wide open throttle. Pressure should be as specified. See LINE PRESSURE SPECIFICATIONS table.

CAUTION: While performing this test, DO NOT hold throttle open for more than 5 seconds at a time.

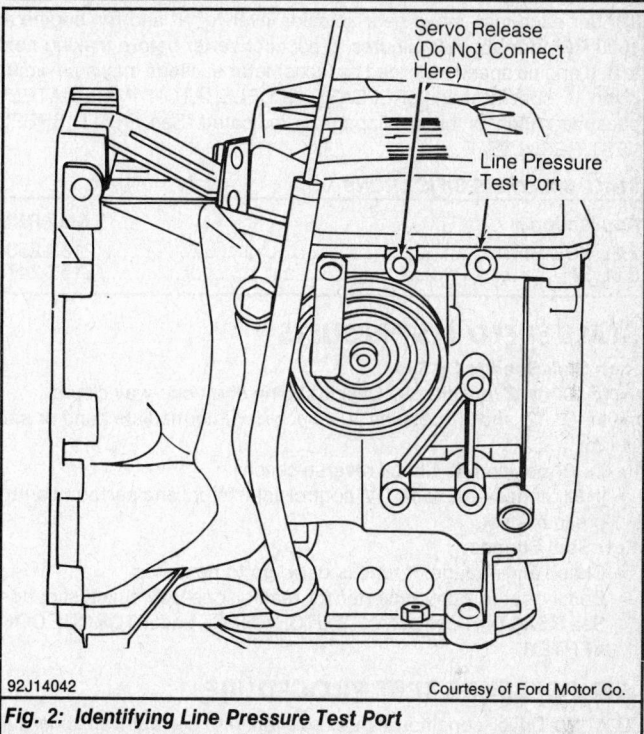

92J14042 — Courtesy of Ford Motor Co.

Fig. 2: Identifying Line Pressure Test Port

LINE PRESSURE SPECIFICATIONS

Application & Shift Range	Idle psi (kPa)	WOT @Stall RPM psi (kPa)
2.3L		
"D", "2", "P" & "N"	39-53 (269-365)	94-110 (648-758)
"R"	75-111 (517-765)	235-298 (1620-2055)
"1"	57-70 (393-483)	165-195 (1138-1345)
3.0L		
"D", "2", "P" & "N"	39-53 (269-365)	83-95 (572-655)
"R"	55-92 (379-634)	219-271 (1510-1869)
"1"	67-80 (461-551)	102-120 (703-827)

LINE PRESSURE TEST RESULTS

Low At Idle In All Ranges – Check engine idle. Check for low fluid level, restricted intake screen or filter, loose valve body or regulator-to-case bolts, loose oil tubes, excessive leakage in oil pump, case, valve body or sticking control pressure regulator valve.

High At Idle In All Ranges – Check throttle valve or control rod adjustment, and T.V. linkage return spring, or sticking regulator boost valve(s).

Low In "P" Or "N" – Faulty valve body.

Low In "D" – Faulty servo or valve body.

Low In "2" – Faulty valve body and/or intermediate servo.

Low In "1" – Faulty direct clutch and/or valve body.

Low In "R" – Faulty direct clutch and/or reverse clutch. Faulty valve body.

STALL SPEED TEST

1) Start engine and allow it to reach normal operating temperature. Apply both parking and service brakes. Stall test is made in all Drive ranges and Reverse at WOT throttle position.

2) Stall speed test checks engine performance, converter operation or installation and holding ability of the direct clutch, reverse clutch and low-intermediate band brake and gear train one-way clutch. See STALL SPEED SPECIFICATIONS table.

CAUTION: While performing this test, DO NOT hold throttle open for more than 5 seconds at a time.

3) After each test, move gear selector lever to "N" and run engine at 1000 RPM for about 2 minutes to cool converter before making next test. If engine speed recorded by tachometer exceeds maximum limits given in specifications, RELEASE ACCELERATOR IMMEDIATELY because clutch or band slippage is indicated. See STALL SPEED TEST RESULTS.

STALL SPEED SPECIFICATIONS

Application	Stall RPM
2.3L HSC SFI	2183-2534
3.0L SFI	2135-2474

STALL SPEED TEST RESULTS

High Stall Speeds Or Slip
- In "D" or "2" position – Check turbine shaft one-way clutch.
- In "D", "2" and "1" position – Check low-intermediate band or servo.
- In "R" position – Check reverse clutch.
- In all ranges – Check T.V. control adjustment and perform control pressure test.

Low Stall Speeds
- Check engine tune. If tune is okay, go to next step.
- Bench test torque converter for reactor one-way clutch slippage. See REACTOR ONE-WAY CLUTCH CHECK under TORQUE CONVERTER.

AIR PRESSURE TEST PROCEDURE

1) A "No Drive" condition can exist even with correct transaxle fluid pressure, because of inoperative clutches or band. Erratic shifts could be caused by a stuck governor valve. Inoperative units can be located through a series of checks by substituting air pressure for fluid pressure to determine location of malfunction.

2) To make air pressure checks, loosen valve body cover bolts. Remove cover and valve body assembly. Install Special Adapter Plate (T82P-7006-B) in place of valve body. Inoperative units can be located by applying air pressure to transaxle case passages, through adapter plate, leading to clutches, servo and governor. *See Fig. 3.*

NOTE: Air pressure test adapter plate should be installed with a new valve body gasket. Tighten attaching bolts to 80-97 INCH lbs. (9-11 N.m).

AIR PRESSURE TESTS

NOTE: See AIR PRESSURE TEST PROCEDURE before performing these tests.

Band Apply Servo – Apply air pressure to servo apply passage. Band should apply. A dull thud should be heard when air pressure is removed, allowing servo piston to return to release position.
Direct Clutch – Apply air pressure to direct clutch apply passage. A dull thud can be heard or movement of piston can be felt as piston is applied. If direct clutch seals are leaking, a hissing noise will be heard.
Intermediate Clutch – Apply air pressure to intermediate clutch apply passage. A dull thud can be heard or movement of piston can be felt on case as piston is applied. If intermediate clutch seals are leaking, a hissing noise will be heard.

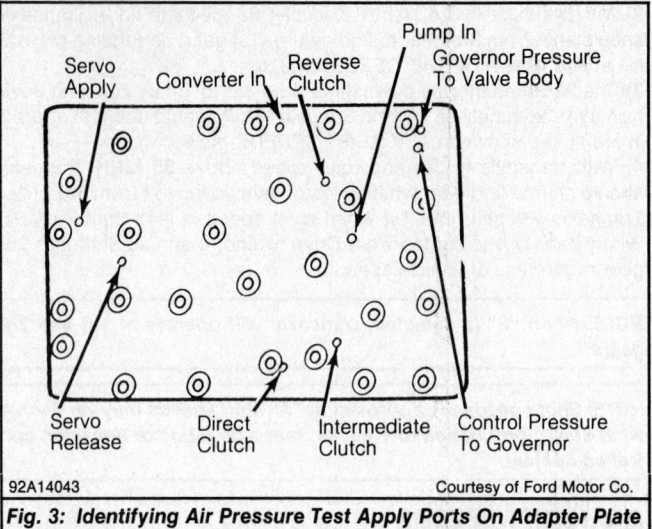

Fig. 3: Identifying Air Pressure Test Apply Ports On Adapter Plate

92A14043   Courtesy of Ford Motor Co.

Reverse Clutch – Apply air pressure to reverse clutch apply passage. A dull thud can be heard or movement of piston can be felt on case as piston is applied. If reverse clutch seals are leaking, a hissing noise will be heard.
Converter In – This passage can only be checked for blockage. If passage holds air pressure, remove adapter plate and check for an obstruction or damage.
Control Pressure-To-Governor – Remove governor cover. Apply air pressure to control pressure-to-governor apply passage. Watch for movement of governor valve.
Governor Pressure-To-Valve Body – This passage can only be checked for blockage. If passage holds air pressure, remove adapter plate and check for an obstruction or damage.
Pump In (Bench Test) – With transaxle removed from vehicle and converter removed, apply air pressure to pump in apply passage. Rotation of pump gears should be heard when air pressure is applied.

NOTE: PUMP IN check is normally performed during assembly of an overhauled transaxle.

TORQUE CONVERTER

LEAKAGE CHECK

With torque converter removed from transaxle, check for leakage using Leak Tester (Rotunda 021-00054).

STATOR-TO-IMPELLER INTERFERENCE CHECK

Position stator support assembly on bench. Splined end of stator shaft should face upward. Place converter on support. Splines on one-way clutch inner race should engage with mating splines on stator support. Holding stator support from rotating, turn converter counterclockwise. If converter does not turn freely, replace converter.

STATOR-TO-TURBINE INTERFERENCE CHECK

Place converter on bench with front side facing down. Install stator support, engaging splines. Install turbine shaft. Ensure splines engage with turbine hub. While holding stator support, rotate turbine with turbine shaft. If turbine does not rotate freely in both directions, replace converter. Ensure converter pilot bushing, in crankshaft, is okay.

REACTOR ONE-WAY CLUTCH CHECK

Position Holding Wire (T81P-7902-A) in thrust washer slot. Install Adapter (T81P-7902-B) in reactor spline. Rotate adapter counterclockwise, using a torque wrench. *See Fig. 4.* If adapter rotates with less than 10 ft. lbs. (14 N.m). applied, replace converter.

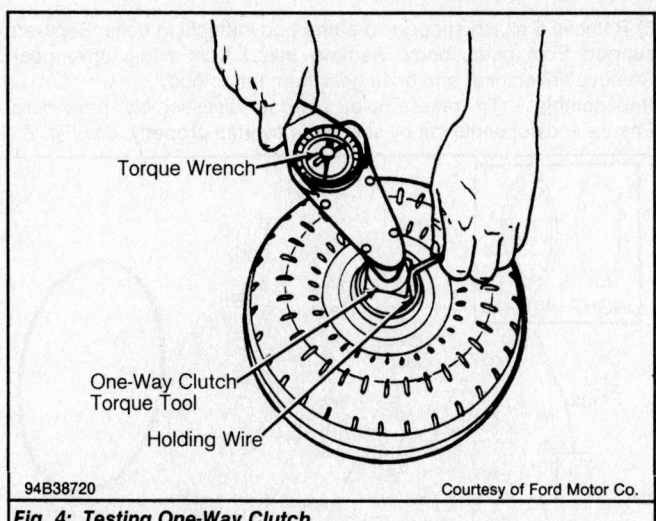

Fig. 4: Testing One-Way Clutch

Courtesy of Ford Motor Co.

94B38720

CONVERTER END PLAY CHECK

Position End Play Checking Device (T81P-7902-D) in converter hub. Tighten nut on device. Position a dial indicator on device. Position dial indicator pointer on converter shell. Lift up on device handles. See Fig. 5. If dial indicator reading exceeds .040" (1.02 mm), replace converter.

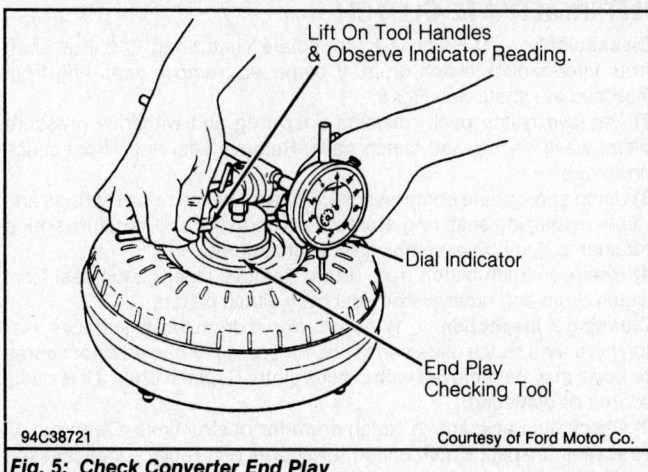

Fig. 5: Check Converter End Play

Courtesy of Ford Motor Co.

94C38721

ON-VEHICLE SERVICE

DRIVE AXLE SHAFTS

See appropriate AXLE SHAFTS article in AXLE SHAFTS & TRANSFER CASES.

VALVE BODY

Removal – Remove battery and battery tray. Remove ignition coil, transaxle dipstick and air cleaner assembly. Disconnect supply hoses and vacuum lines from air management valve (if equipped). Remove air management valve from valve body cover. Remove valve body cover and gasket. Remove valve body and gasket from transaxle case. For valve body repairs, see VALVE BODY ASSEMBLY under COMPONENT DISASSEMBLY & REASSEMBLY.

Installation – 1) Install 2 Alignment Pins (T80L-77100-A) into opposing valve body attaching bolt holes. Install valve body-to-case gasket. Install valve body assembly into case, removing one alignment pin to allow attachment of manual valve to "Z" link. Reinstall alignment pin.

NOTE: Ensure roller, located on end of throttle valve plunger has engaged cam, which is located on end of throttle lever shaft.

2) Connect throttle valve control spring. Remove alignment pins. Install valve body attaching bolts, detent spring, main oil pressure regulator baffle plate and transaxle control baffle plate. Tighten valve body attaching bolts, in sequence, to specification. See Fig. 23. See TORQUE SPECIFICATIONS.

3) Install new valve body cover gasket on case. Install cover attaching bolts. To complete installation, reverse removal procedure. Check transaxle fluid level and add fluid if necessary.

GOVERNOR

Removal – Remove air cleaner. Using a long screwdriver, remove governor retaining clip. Remove governor cover and pull out governor. For governor repairs, see GOVERNOR under COMPONENT DISASSEMBLY & REASSEMBLY.

Installation – To install governor, reverse removal procedure. Slide governor in carefully, allowing gear teeth to mesh. DO NOT force in. Install a new "O" ring seal on governor cover. Check transaxle fluid level and add fluid if necessary.

LOW-INTERMEDIATE SERVO

Removal – 1) Disconnect fan motor and water temperature sending unit wiring. Disconnect FM capacitor wiring (if equipped). Remove fan and shroud assembly.

2) Remove filler tube bolt and rotate filler tube to clear servo cover. Remove lower left mount-to-case attaching bolt from left front mount. Using Servo Compressor (T81P-70027-A), compress servo cover and remove retaining snap ring. Remove cover and servo assembly.

Installation – To install servo, reverse removal procedure. Refill transaxle with fluid.

OIL COOLER FLUSHING

Contaminates MUST be removed from oil cooler before transmission is put back into service. Replace cooler supply tubes if leaking. Thoroughly flush oil cooler and lines if a major service or transaxle removal has occurred. It is recommended that a mechanically agitated cleaner, such as Rotunda (014-00028) or equivalent be used.

TORQUE CONVERTER FLUSHING

Whenever transmission has been disassembled to replace worn or damaged parts or because valve body sticks due to foreign material, converter must be cleaned using a mechanically agitated cleaner, such as Rotunda (014-00028). Under no conditions should converter be cleaned by hand agitation using solvent. After converter is removed from cleaner, thoroughly drain solvent through hub. Add approximately 2 qts. (1.9L) clean ATF to converter. Agitate fluid by hand. Thoroughly flush ATF from converter.

REMOVAL & INSTALLATION

See appropriate AUTOMATIC TRANSMISSION REMOVAL article in TRANSMISSION SERVICING.

TRANSAXLE DISASSEMBLY

1) Mount transaxle in a holding stand. Pull torque converter from case. Remove oil pump drive shaft. Remove converter turbine sleeve (if equipped). Remove filler tube from case. Remove governor cover retainer from case. Pry off cover and remove governor from case. Remove lower pipe plug at side of governor housing. Remove filter. Note direction of filter for reassembly reference. Remove oil pan. Remove oil filter and seal.

2) Remove differential bearing retainer-to-case attaching bolts. Pry retainer from case. Remove differential bearing spacer shims located under bearing retainer. Remove differential assembly from transaxle case.

3) Remove valve body cover bolts and cover. Disconnect and remove throttle lever return spring. Remove valve body attaching bolts. Note length and location of bolts for reassembly reference. Remove main oil pressure regulator baffle plate. Remove transaxle control baffle plate. Remove detent spring and roller assembly. Disengage "Z" link from manual valve. Remove valve body assembly.

4) Lift governor screen from bore in case (located under valve body). Pry speedometer driven gear retaining pin partially out of case. Remove pin using side cutters. Using a hammer handle, tap driven gear from case.

5) Remove oil pump attaching bolts and washers. Remove pump from case using a slide hammer type puller. Remove selective thrust washer from under pump body, if equipped. Remove and discard pump gasket. Remove No. 11 thrust bearing (needle) from top of intermediate clutch. Remove clutch assembly from case. *See Fig. 25.*

NOTE: For thrust washer location, see Fig. 24.

---

6) Remove No. 10 thrust bearing (needle) from direct clutch. Remove direct clutch from case. Remove intermediate clutch hub and ring gear assembly. Remove No. 7 thrust washer from planetary assembly.

7) Remove large snap ring securing reverse clutch. Remove reverse clutch pack from case. Remove planetary assembly and No. 5 thrust washer from case. Remove reverse clutch return springs and holder assembly. Remove reverse clutch piston. Pry reverse clutch drum up to loosen and remove from case.

8) Using Servo Remover/Installer (T81P-70027-A), compress servo and remove retaining snap ring. *See Fig. 6.* Slowly release spring pressure. Remove servo remover/installer and servo assembly. Remove low-intermediate band.

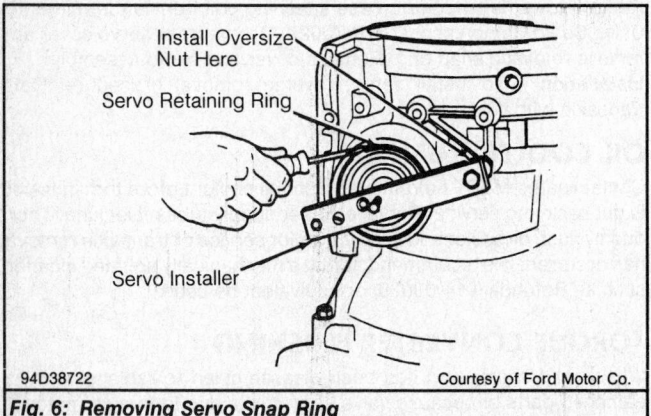

Fig. 6: *Removing Servo Snap Ring*

9) Remove sun gear and drum assembly from case. Remove No. 4 thrust washer from final drive housing. Remove 5 final drive housing retaining bolts. Using a screwdriver, pry housing from idler gear shaft and remove from case. DO NOT pry downward against idler gear teeth or damage will result.

NOTE: Discard final drive housing bolts. Replace with new bolts and use Loctite on threads.

---

10) Remove No. 3 thrust bearing (needle) from input gear. Remove input gear. Remove input gear caged needle bearing No. 2 and No. 1 thrust bearing (needle).

11) Position a 12-mm Allen wrench in idler gear shaft and allow wrench to catch on side of case. With wrench holding idler gear shaft, remove nut from rear of shaft using a 32-mm, 12 point socket. Tap idler gear shaft with a hammer handle to loosen "O" ring. Remove shaft from case.

12) Remove reactor support from case if damaged or unserviceable. Reactor support is pressed into case. Remove with Puller (T81P70363-A).

COMPONENT DISASSEMBLY & REASSEMBLY

OIL PUMP

Disassembly – 1) Remove No. 12 selective thrust washer and oil seal rings from clutch support. Remove pump-to-case oil seal ring from outside diameter of clutch support. *See Fig. 7.*

2) Remove 5 clutch support-to-pump body attaching bolts. Separate support from pump body. Remove insert from pump drive gear. Remove driven gear and drive gear from pump body.

Reassembly – To reassemble, reverse disassembly procedure. Ensure ends of angle-cut oil seal rings overlap properly. *See Fig. 7.*

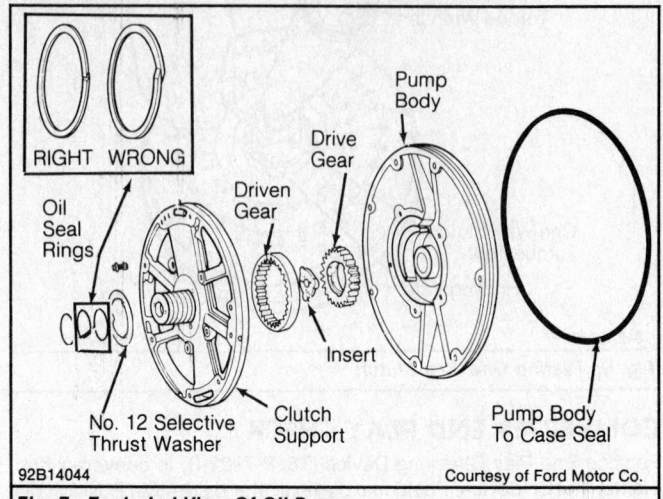

Fig. 7: *Exploded View Of Oil Pump*

INTERMEDIATE CLUTCH

Disassembly – 1) Remove intermediate shaft snap ring. Pull shaft from intermediate clutch drum. If damaged, remove snap ring from intermediate shaft. *See Fig. 8.*

2) Remove clutch pack retaining snap ring and withdraw pressure plate, wave spring. and clutch pack. Remove seal rings from clutch drum hub.

3) Using appropriate compressor, compress clutch return springs and remove retaining snap ring. Remove compressor and lift return spring retainer and spring assembly from clutch drum.

4) Remove clutch piston from drum. Remove inner piston seal from clutch drum and outer piston seal from clutch piston.

Cleaning & Inspection – 1) Inspect clutch drum thrust surfaces, piston bore, and clutch plate serrations for scores or burrs. Minor scores or burrs may be removed with crocus cloth. Replace drum if it is badly scored or damaged.

2) Check fluid passage in clutch drum for obstructions. Clean out all passages. Inspect clutch piston for scores and replace if necessary. Inspect piston check ball for freedom of movement and proper seating.

3) Inspect clutch return springs for distortion and cracks. Inspect friction plates, steel plates and pressure plate for worn or scored bearing surfaces. Replace all parts that are deeply scored.

4) Check clutch plates for flatness and fit on clutch drum hub serrations. Replace any plate that does not slide freely on serrations or that is not flat.

5) Check clutch hub thrust surfaces for scores and clutch hub splines for wear. Inspect shaft bearing surfaces for scoring. Check shaft splines for wear.

Reassembly – 1) Inspect piston check ball and ensure ball is free in cage. Install outer piston seal on piston with lip facing up and inner piston seal in clutch drum with lip facing down. Apply a light film of petroleum jelly to piston seals, drum seal area and piston inner seal area.

2) Install clutch piston into drum by pushing down on piston while rotating. Position return spring and retainer assembly into drum. Compress return springs and install retaining snap ring.

3) Install angle-cut seal rings on clutch drum hub. Ensure seals overlap at the bevel edge. Install wave spring into drum. Install clutch pack into drum starting with a steel plate. Alternate friction and steel plates until all plates are installed. Install pressure plate and clutch pack retaining snap ring.

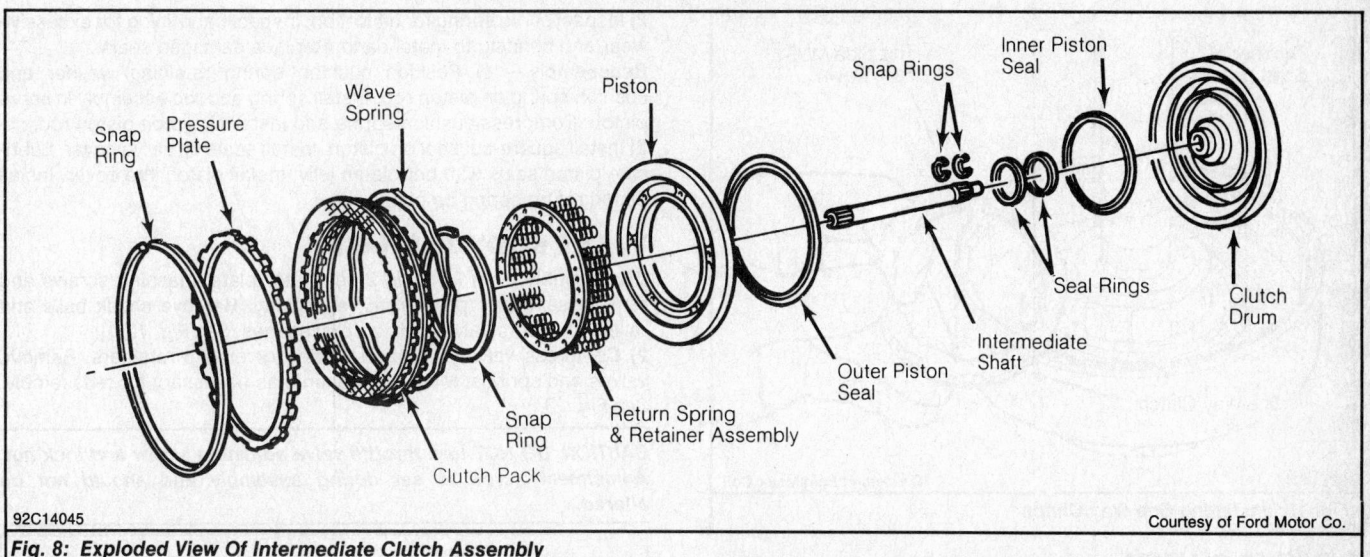

Fig. 8: Exploded View Of Intermediate Clutch Assembly

92C14045 — Courtesy of Ford Motor Co.

4) Use feeler gauge to measure clearance between clutch pack retaining snap ring and pressure plate with pressure plate held downward. Take 2 readings, 180 degrees apart and average readings. Ensure clearance is .030-.044" (.76-1.12 mm).

5) If clearance is not within specifications, install correct selective snap rings. Snap rings are available in thicknesses of .049-.053" (1.25-1.35 mm), .059-.063" (1.50-1.60 mm) and .070-.074" (1.79-1.88 mm). Once correct size snap ring is installed, recheck clearance.

6) If removed, install stop ring on intermediate shaft. Install shaft into clutch drum. Install intermediate shaft retaining snap ring.

DIRECT CLUTCH

Disassembly – 1) Remove sun gear/one-way clutch race assembly. Remove No. 8 thrust washer. Remove one-way clutch. *See Fig. 9.*

2) Remove clutch pack retaining snap ring. Remove pressure plate, clutch pack, and wave spring from clutch drum. Remove No. 9 thrust bearing. Note number of friction plates in clutch pack during disassembly for reassembly reference. Using appropriate compressor, compress piston return spring retainer. Remove retaining snap ring. Remove tool and piston return spring retainer.

3) Remove piston from clutch drum. Remove piston seals from clutch drum and piston.

Inspection – See CLEANING & INSPECTION under INTERMEDIATE CLUTCH.

Reassembly – 1) Inspect clutch drum check ball. Ensure ball is free in cage. Install seal on clutch drum with seal lip facing down. Install piston seal on piston with seal lip facing up. Apply a light film of petroleum jelly to piston seals. Install piston into drum using a rotating motion while applying downward pressure.

2) Position return springs, retainer and retaining snap ring in clutch drum. Compress retainer and install snap ring in groove. Install thrust bearing No. 9 on top of return spring retainer. See Fig. 9.

3) Install wave spring. Install clutch pack into drum starting with a steel clutch plate and alternating friction clutch plates and steel plates until all clutch plates have been installed. Install pressure plate and clutch pack snap ring.

4) Install one-way clutch over turbine shaft. Ensure one-way clutch is positioned correctly. See Fig. 10. Install No. 8 thrust washer into drum. See Fig. 9. Ensure tabs of washer are facing down against shoulder of one-way clutch inner race. Install clutch pack retaining snap ring.

5) Using feeler gauge or dial indicator, measure clearance between clutch pack retaining snap ring and pressure plate with pressure plate held down. Take 2 measurements 180 degrees apart. Ensure direct clutch clearance is .031-.047" (.79-1.20 mm) for 3 friction plate models and .040-.056" (1.01-1.43 mm) for 4 friction plate models.

6) If clearance is not within specification, install correct selective snap rings. Snap rings are available in thicknesses of .050-.054" (1.26-1.36 mm), .062-.066" (1.58-1.68 mm) and .075-.079" (1.90-2.00). Once correct size snap ring is installed, recheck clearance.

7) Install sun gear/one-way clutch outer race assembly over turbine shaft and into clutch drum. Check operation of one-way clutch. When properly assembled, the one-way clutch allows sun gear/outer race assembly to rotate in one direction only.

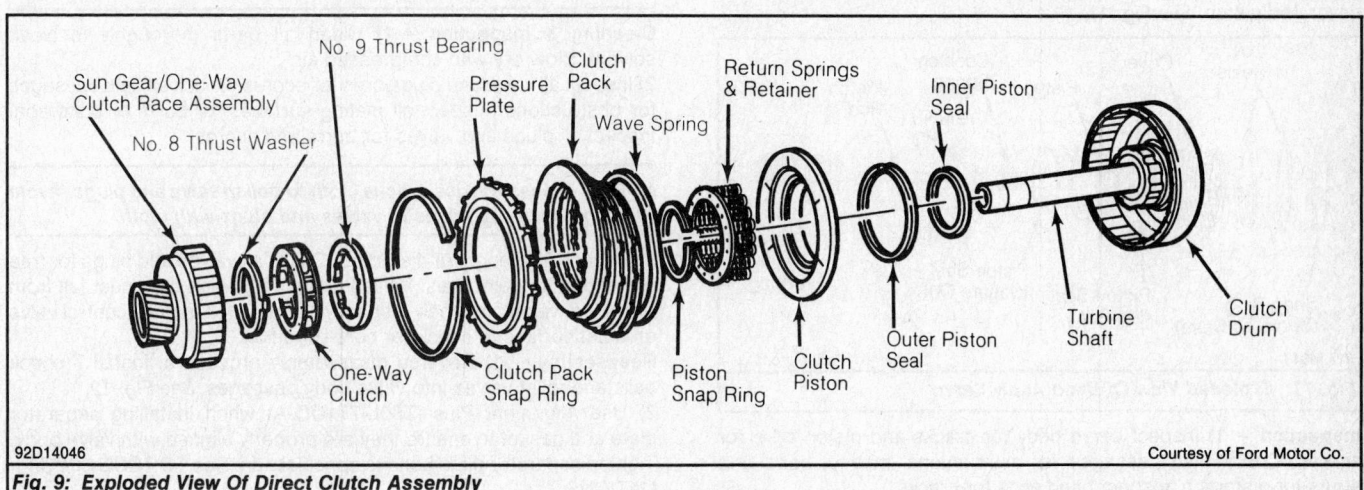

Fig. 9: Exploded View Of Direct Clutch Assembly

92D14046 — Courtesy of Ford Motor Co.

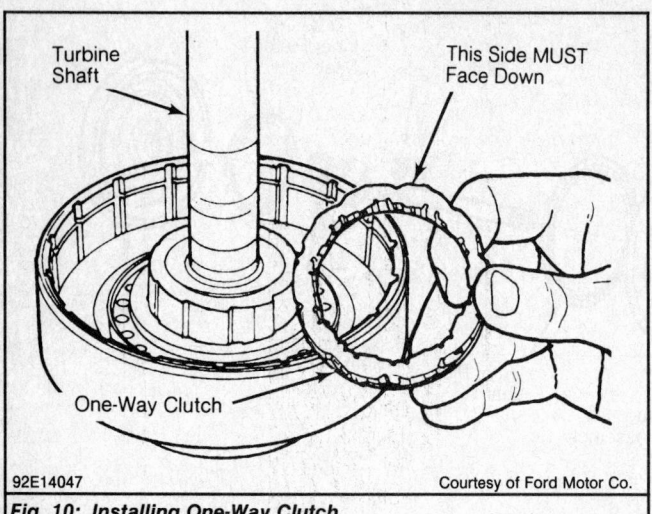

Fig. 10: Installing One-Way Clutch

92E14047

Courtesy of Ford Motor Co.

REVERSE CLUTCH

NOTE: Reverse clutch was disassembled under TRANSAXLE DISASSEMBLY and will be reassembled during TRANSAXLE REASSEMBLY. The following procedure is for replacing piston seals and inspecting components.

Piston Seal Replacement – Remove seals from clutch cylinder and clutch piston. Install new seal (large) on clutch cylinder with seal lips facing up. Install new inner seal (small) on piston with seal lip facing down. Install new outer seal on piston.

NOTE: Outer piston seal is square-cut and may be installed in either direction.

Inspection – **1)** Inspect clutch piston bore and piston inner and outer bearing surfaces for scores. Check air bleed ball valve in piston for free movement. Check orifice for obstructions.

2) Check fluid passages for obstructions. All passages must be clean and free of obstructions. Inspect clutch plates for wear, scoring and fit on clutch hub serrations. Replace all plates that are badly scored, worn, or do not fit freely in hub serrations.

3) Inspect clutch pressure plate for scores on clutch plate bearing surface. Check clutch return springs for distortion or collapsed coils.

BAND APPLY SERVO

Disassembly – Remove piston return spring. Separate servo piston from cover. Remove piston rod circlip. Slide piston rod, cushion spring and spring retaining washer from piston. Remove seals from servo cover and piston. *See Fig. 11.*

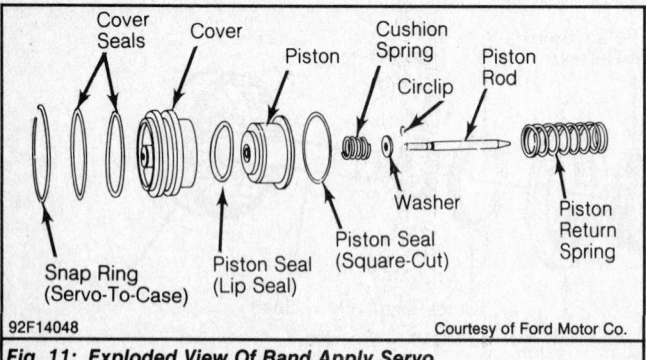

Fig. 11: Exploded View Of Band Apply Servo

92F14048

Courtesy of Ford Motor Co.

Inspection – **1)** Inspect servo body for cracks and piston bore for scores. Check fluid passages for obstructions. Inspect band and struts for distortion. Inspect band ends for cracks.

2) Inspect servo spring for distortion. Inspect band lining for excessive wear and bonding to metal band. Replace damaged seals.

Reassembly – **1)** Position cushion spring retaining washer and cushion spring on piston rod. Install spring and rod assembly in servo piston. Compress cushion spring and install circlip on piston rod.

2) Install square-cut seal on piston. Install seals on servo cover. Lubricate piston seals with petroleum jelly. Install piston into cover. Install piston return spring on piston rod.

VALVE BODY ASSEMBLY

Disassembly – **1)** Remove 2 separator plate attaching screws and remove separator plate from valve body. Remove check balls and relief valve from valve body core passages. *See Fig. 12.*

2) Compress valve plugs and valves to remove retainers. Remove valves and springs. Mark components as necessary for reassembly. *See Fig. 13.*

CAUTION: DO NOT turn throttle valve adjusting screw and lock nut. Adjustment screw is set during assembly and should not be altered.

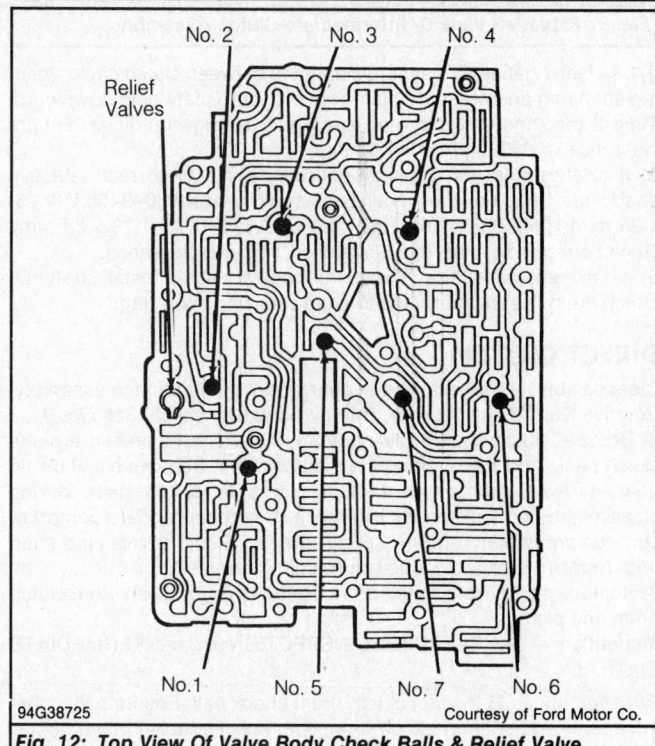

Fig. 12: Top View Of Valve Body Check Balls & Relief Valve

94G38725

Courtesy of Ford Motor Co.

Cleaning & Inspection – **1)** Clean all parts thoroughly in clean solvent. Blow dry with compressed air.

2) Inspect all valve and plug bores for scores. Check all fluid passages for obstructions. Inspect all mating surfaces for burrs or distortion. Inspect all plugs and valves for burrs and scores.

NOTE: If necessary, use crocus cloth to polish valve and plugs. Avoid rounding off sharp edges of valves and plugs with cloth.

3) Inspect all springs for distortion. Check all valves and plugs for free movement in their bores. Valves and plugs, when dry, must fall from their own weight into their respective bores. Roll manual control valve on a flat surface to check for bent condition.

Reassembly – **1)** Reverse disassembly procedure. Install 7 check balls and relief valves into valve body passages. *See Fig. 12.*

2) Use Alignment Pins (T80L-77100-A) when installing separator plate and gasket to ensure they are properly aligned with valve body. Tighten separator plate bolts to specification. See TORQUE SPECIFICATIONS.

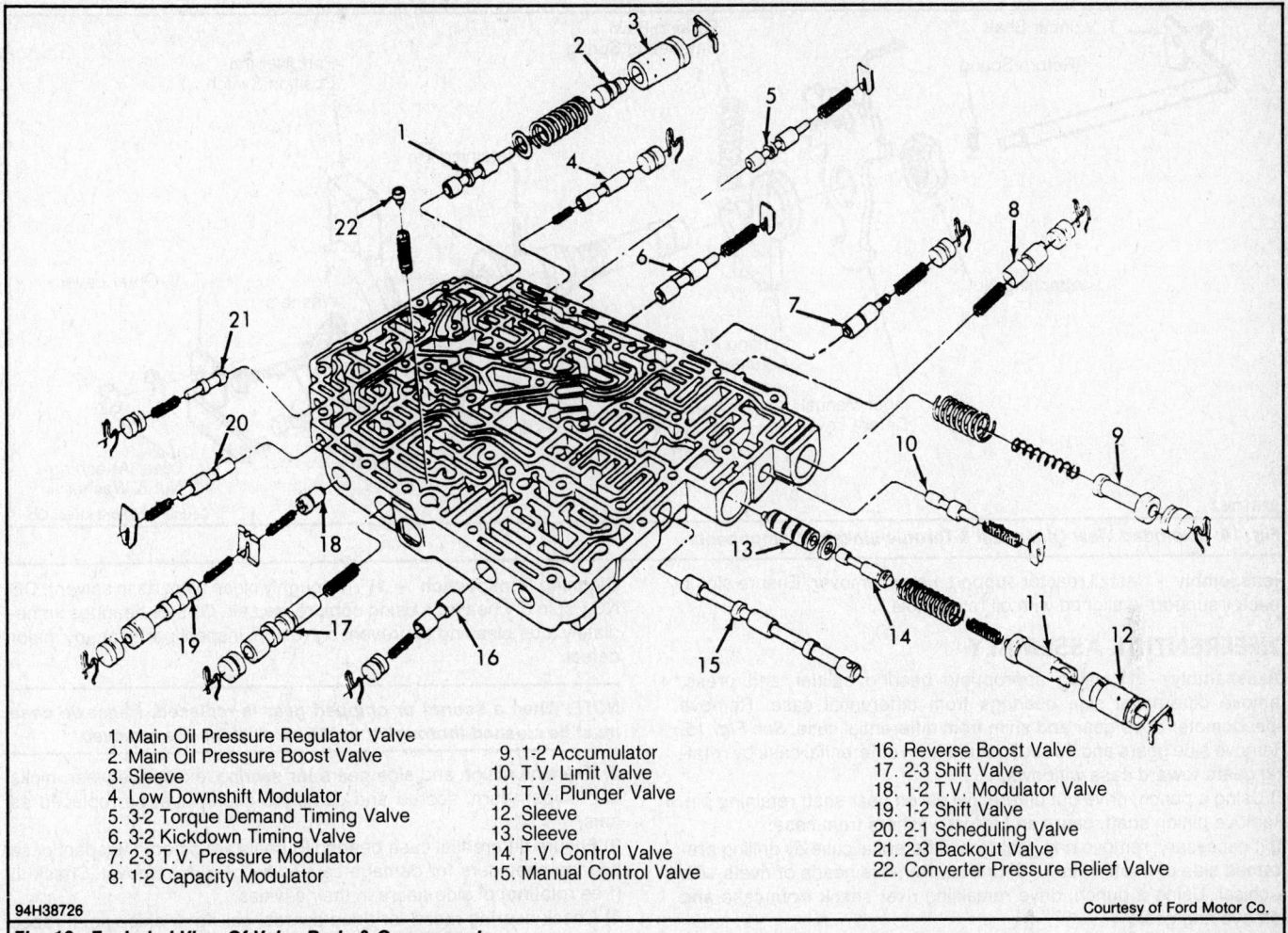

1. Main Oil Pressure Regulator Valve
2. Main Oil Pressure Boost Valve
3. Sleeve
4. Low Downshift Modulator
5. 3-2 Torque Demand Timing Valve
6. 3-2 Kickdown Timing Valve
7. 2-3 T.V. Pressure Modulator
8. 1-2 Capacity Modulator

9. 1-2 Accumulator
10. T.V. Limit Valve
11. T.V. Plunger Valve
12. Sleeve
13. Sleeve
14. T.V. Control Valve
15. Manual Control Valve

16. Reverse Boost Valve
17. 2-3 Shift Valve
18. 1-2 T.V. Modulator Valve
19. 1-2 Shift Valve
20. 2-1 Scheduling Valve
21. 2-3 Backout Valve
22. Converter Pressure Relief Valve

94H38726

Courtesy of Ford Motor Co.

Fig. 13: Exploded View Of Valve Body & Components

GOVERNOR

Disassembly – Support governor on a vise and remove 3/32" roll pin securing gear to shaft. DO NOT place governor assembly or governor shaft in vise jaws. DO NOT damage ring lands. Clamp plastic gear in vise. Grip shaft firmly and twist and pull to remove gear from shaft.

Inspection – 1) Inspect governor valve and bore for scores. Minor scores may be removed from valve with crocus cloth. Replace governor if valves or body are deeply scored.

2) Inspect governor screen for obstructions. Screen must be free of foreign material. If contaminated, clean thoroughly in solvent and blow dry with compressed air.

3) Check for free movement of valves in bores. Valves should slide freely of their own weight in bores when dry. Inspect fluid passages in valve body and counterweight for obstructions. All fluid passages must be clean.

4) Inspect governor drive gear and replace it if teeth are broken, chipped or excessively worn.

Reassembly – 1) Align driven gear to shaft gear bore. Ensure driven gear is properly aligned and tap gear into position using a plastic mallet. Gear is in correct position when shoulder is seated against governor shaft.

2) Support governor on a non-machined surface. Using a drill press, align drill bit to prevent damaging governor shaft and drill a 1/8" hole through driven gear. Install NEW roll pin.

MANUAL & THROTTLE LINKAGE

Disassembly – 1) Hold outer throttle lever stationary to prevent damage to throttle shaft cam and remove throttle valve outer lever nut and washer. Remove neutral safety switch. *See Fig. 14.*

2) Using needle nose pliers, remove manual lever retaining pin and parking pawl ratcheting spring. Remove nut attaching inner manual lever (detent) and parking pawl actuating lever to manual lever shaft.

3) Remove manual lever and shaft assembly. Remove throttle valve lever and components on throttle valve lever shaft. Remove parking pawl return spring. Using a screwdriver, pry manual lever shaft oil seal from case and throttle valve lever shaft seal from manual lever. Remove insulator from manual lever.

Reassembly – 1) Install new manual lever shaft seal in case. Install new seal on outer manual lever shaft. Install new insulator on outer manual lever. Install parking pawl return spring.

2) Install the following on T.V. inner shaft in this order: parking pawl actuator, inner manual detent lever, inner attaching nut. Position T.V. inner shaft in case. Install outer manual lever and shaft.

3) Position parking pawl actuator and inner manual detent lever on manual shaft. Install attaching nut. Tighten nut to specification. See TORQUE SPECIFICATIONS. Install parking pawl ratcheting spring. Install manual lever retaining pin.

4) Install neutral safety switch in case. Install, but do not tighten, attaching screws and washers. Adjust park/neutral position switch. See appropriate AUTOMATIC TRANSMISSION SERVICING article in TRANSMISSION SERVICING.

5) Install T.V. outer lever. Tighten attaching nut to specification while holding lever stationary to prevent damage to throttle shaft cam.

REACTOR SUPPORT

Disassembly – Remove reactor support attaching bolts. Install Remover (T81P-70363-A). Install collar washer and nut on outside side of reactor support. Remove reactor support.

AUTOMATIC TRANSMISSIONS
Ford ATX/FLC (Cont.)

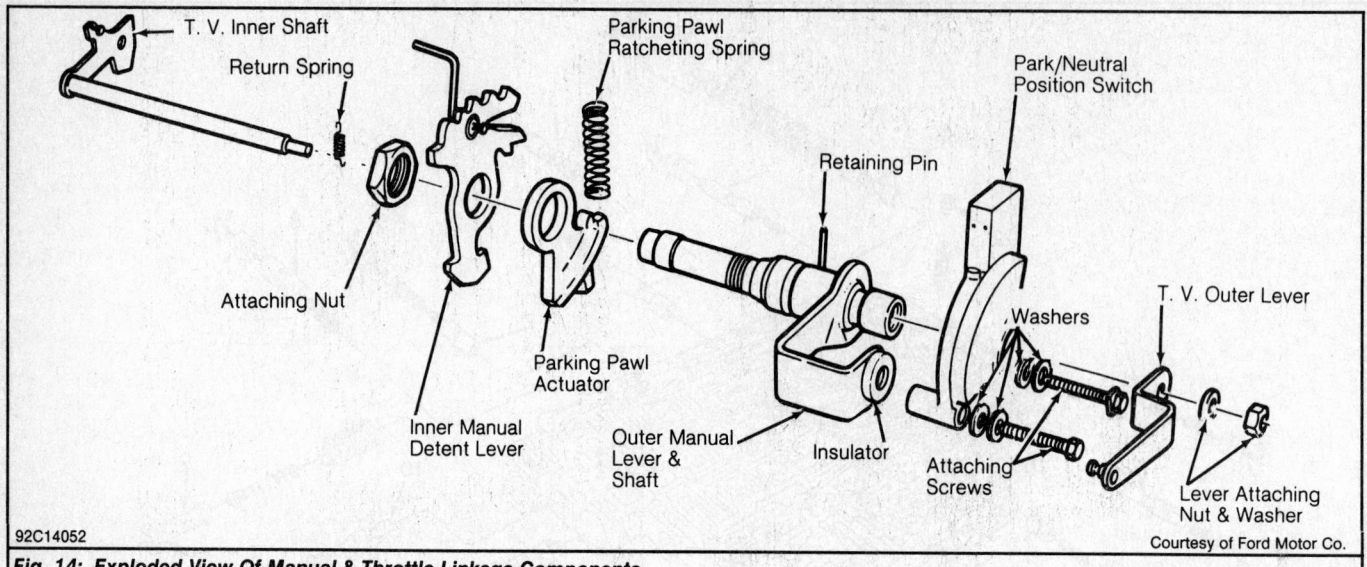

Fig. 14: Exploded View Of Manual & Throttle Linkage Components

Reassembly – Install reactor support, using remover. Ensure slot in reactor support is aligned with oil return hole.

DIFFERENTIAL ASSEMBLY

Disassembly – **1)** Using appropriate bearing splitter and press, remove differential side bearings from differential case. Remove speedometer drive gear and shim from differential case. *See Fig. 15.* Remove side gears and thrust washers from differential case by rotating gears toward case windows.

2) Using a punch, drive out differential pinion gear shaft retaining pin. Remove pinion shaft, gears and thrust washers from case.

3) If necessary, remove ring gear from differential case by drilling preformed side of rivets with 5/16" drill bit. Remove heads of rivets with a chisel. Using a punch, drive remaining rivet shank from case and remove ring gear.

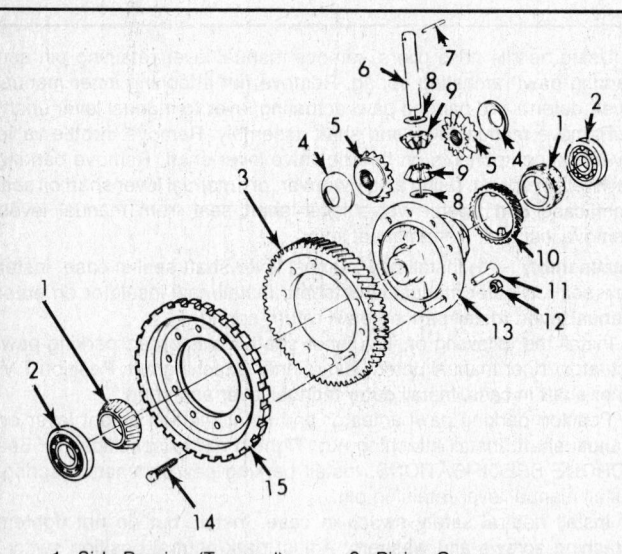

1. Side Bearing (Tapered)	9. Pinion Gears
2. Side Bearing (Roller)	10. Speedometer Drive Gear
3. Ring Gear	11. Rivet
4. Thrust Washers	12. Nut
5. Side Gears	13. Differential Case
6. Pinion Gear Shaft	14. Bolt
7. Retaining Pin	15. Parking Pawl Gear
8. Thrust Washers	

92D14053   Courtesy of Ford Motor Co.

Fig. 15: Exploded View Of Differential Assembly

Cleaning & Inspection – **1)** Thoroughly clean all parts in solvent. DO NOT spin dry bearings using compressed air. Oil side bearings immediately after cleaning to prevent corrosion. Inspect parts for any major defect.

NOTE: When a scored or chipped gear is replaced, transaxle case must be cleaned thoroughly to insure all chips are removed.

2) Examine pinion and side gears for scoring, excessive wear, nicks and chips. Worn, scored and damaged gears must be replaced as sets.

3) Ensure differential case bearing journals are smooth. Inspect case bearing shoulders for damage caused by bearing removal. Check fit (free rotation) of side gears in their cavities.

4) Check bearing races for deep scores, galling or chipping. If races are not damaged, DO NOT remove from transaxle case or differential retainer. If races must be replaced, remove and install with appropriate tools.

5) Check side bearings for smooth rotation in races. Examine bearing roller ends for step wear. If inspection reveals either a damaged race or bearing, both parts must be replaced as they are a matched set.

Reassembly – **1)** To reassemble differential assembly, reverse disassembly procedure. Lubricate all thrust washers and thrust surfaces on gears and in case with automatic transmission fluid.

2) If removed, press ring gear onto differential case and attach to case with service replacement nuts and bolts. Install bolts with heads on parking pawl gear side of ring gear. Tighten bolts to specification. See TORQUE SPECIFICATIONS.

3) Install speedometer drive gear and shim. Ensure bevel on inside diameter of speedometer drive gear is facing differential case.

NOTE: Differential side gears must be aligned in case. Use Shipping Plugs (T81P-1177-B) to maintain alignment. Failure to maintain alignment will make it impossible to install axle drive shafts through side gears.

TRANSAXLE CASE

Inspection – Inspect case for cracks and stripped threads. Inspect gasket surfaces and mating surfaces for burrs. Check vent for obstructions, and check all fluid passages for obstructions and leakage. Inspect case bushing for scores. Check all parking linkage parts for wear or damage.

NOTE: Repair kits are available for servicing damaged case threads.

TRANSAXLE REASSEMBLY

NOTE: Handle all parts carefully to avoid damaging bearings and mating surfaces. Lubricate all parts with clean ATF. Use petroleum jelly on gaskets, thrust washers and needle bearings to retain them in place. Use all new gaskets and seals, and tighten bolts evenly.

1) Clean idler gear shaft threads and install a new "O" ring. Place idler gear and shaft in case. Insert a 12-mm Allen wrench in idler gear shaft and position it to catch on band anchor strut.

2) Apply Loctite to idler shaft attaching nut. Install and tighten nut to specification using a 32-mm 12-point socket. See TORQUE SPECIFICATIONS. Install No. 1 thrust bearing and input gear No. 2 caged needle bearing. *See Fig. 16.*

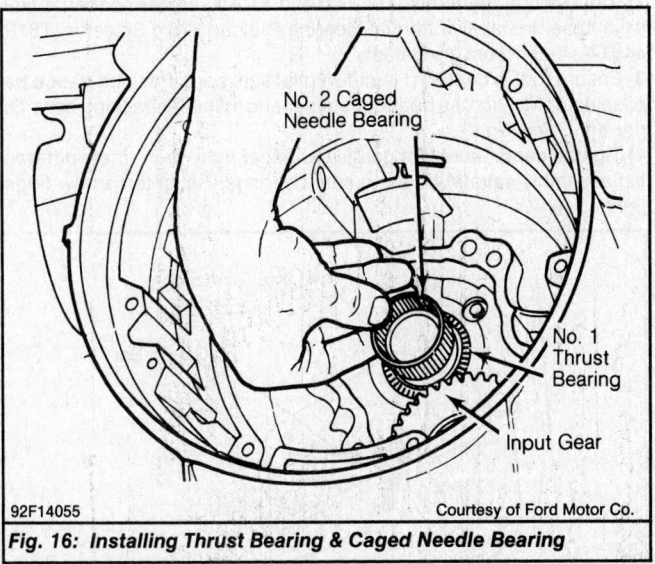

92F14055   Courtesy of Ford Motor Co.

Fig. 16: Installing Thrust Bearing & Caged Needle Bearing

NOTE: Before installing final drive housing, ensure band strut is rotated into its operating position. Transmission case and housing are matched parts. If one is damaged, both must be replaced.

3) Install input gear over reactor support. Install No. 3 thrust bearing (needle) on input gear. *See Fig. 24.* Position final drive (transfer) housing in case. Ensure it is firmly seated on alignment dowels. Install NEW final drive housing attaching bolts and tighten to specification. See TORQUE SPECIFICATIONS.

4) Install No. 4 thrust washer. Install sun gear and drum. Install intermediate band. Ensure band lug engages stud. Place servo piston in case and install Remover/Installer (T81P-70027-A).

NOTE: Servo travel check needs to be performed only if one of the following components has been replaced; transaxle case, band assembly, drum and sun gear assembly, servo piston rod, servo piston and band anchor strut. See BAND SERVO TRAVEL CHECK under TRANSAXLE REASSEMBLY.

5) Compress piston spring far enough to allow installation of retaining ring. Install servo retaining ring and before removing tool, ensure piston rod has engaged band lug.

6) Place reverse clutch cylinder in case and tap cylinder in using a hammer handle. Using Seal Protector (T81P-70402-A), apply even pressure and install reverse clutch piston in clutch cylinder. Remove seal protector. Install No. 5 thrust washer on planetary gear set. Install assembly on sun gear.

NOTE: Before installing reverse clutch piston return spring and holder assembly, reverse clutch clearance must be checked as described in steps 7) & 8).

7) Install clutch pack wave spring, clutch pack and pressure plate, then install clutch pack retaining ring. Clutch pack contains 3 friction and 3 steel plates. Using a feeler gauge, measure clearance between retaining ring and pressure plate at 2 places 180 degrees apart. *See Fig. 17.*

8) If average clearance is .030-.055" (.76-1.40 mm), clutch clearance is correct. If clearance is less than .030" (.76 mm). install a thinner retaining ring. If clearance is greater than .055" (1.40 mm), install a thicker retaining ring. Retaining ring are available in thicknesses of .049-.053" (1.24-1.34 mm), .066-.070" (1.68-1.78 mm), .083-.087" (2.11-2.21 mm) and .099-.103" (2.53-2.63 mm). Install correct retaining ring and recheck clearance.

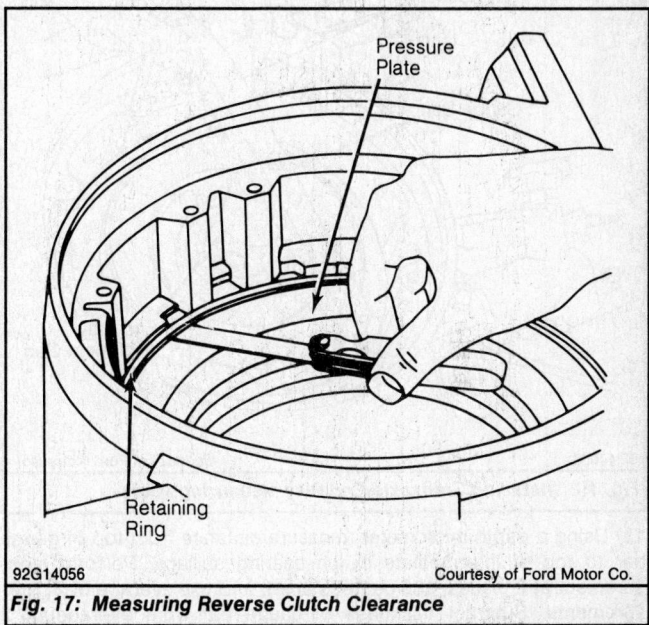

92G14056   Courtesy of Ford Motor Co.

Fig. 17: Measuring Reverse Clutch Clearance

9) Remove reverse clutch pack retaining ring, pressure plate, clutch pack and wave spring. Install reverse clutch return spring and holder assembly. Reinstall wave spring, clutch pack, pressure plate and retaining ring.

10) Install No. 7 thrust washer on planetary assembly. Install intermediate clutch hub and ring gear assembly into case. Install direct clutch assembly into case. Position No. 10 thrust bearing (needle type) on direct clutch.

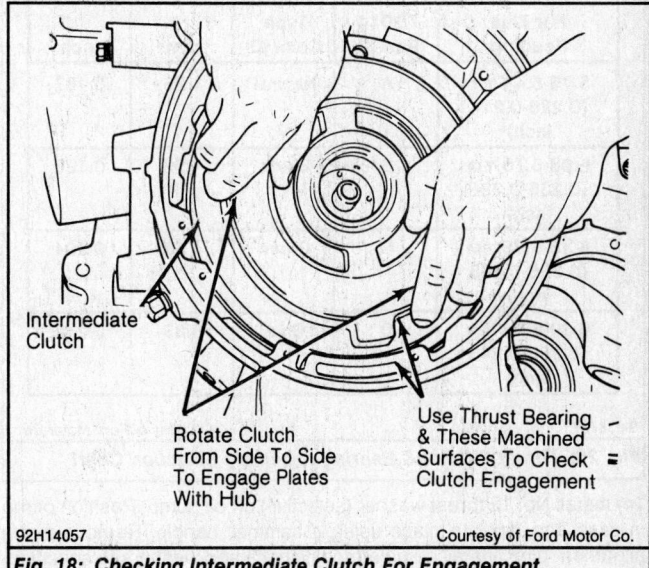

92H14057   Courtesy of Ford Motor Co.

Fig. 18: Checking Intermediate Clutch For Engagement

11) Install intermediate clutch assembly into case and check for proper clutch engagement as follows: position No. 11 thrust bearing on one of the machined tabs and push bearing up against case. If bearing is flush or slightly below machined pump housing surface in case, clutch is fully engaged. If clutch is not fully engaged, reposition clutch assembly. See Fig. 18. Position No. 11 thrust bearing on clutch drum.

12) Install pump Alignment Pins (T81P-77100-A) and pump housing gasket. Position transaxle End Play Checking Tools (T81P-77389-A and T80L-77003-A) in intermediate clutch. See Fig. 19.

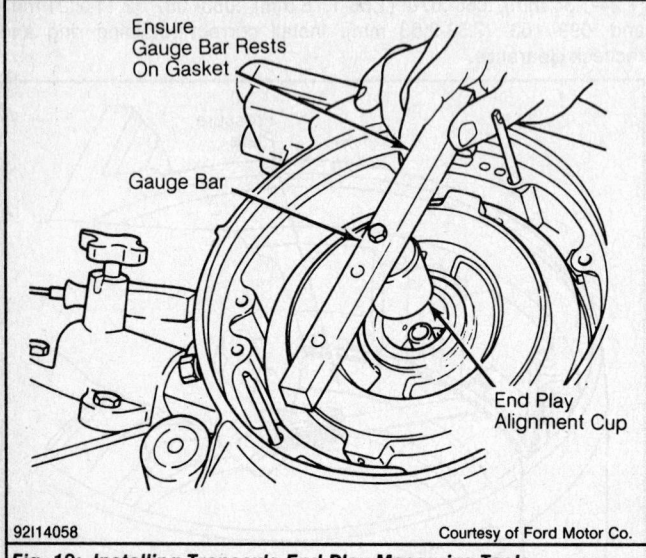

Ensure Gauge Bar Rests On Gasket

Gauge Bar

End Play Alignment Cup

92I14058   Courtesy of Ford Motor Co.

Fig. 19: Installing Transaxle End Play Measuring Tools

13) Using a depth micrometer, measure distance from top of gauge bar to top of intermediate clutch bearing surface. Perform measurement at 2 places, 180 degrees apart, and use average of 2 measurements. Subtract thickness of gauge bar from average of 2 measurements to determine end play. Choose proper end play thrust washer. See Fig. 20.

For This Reading	7D014 Part ID	Nylon Washer (Snap-On) Type Color ID	Bearing and Washer Assy Thickness	
			mm	Inch
5.75-5.44 mm (0.226-0.214 inch)	A	Natural	4.75	0.187
5.98-5.75 mm (0.235-0.226 inch)	B	Black	4.99	0.196
6.18-5.98 mm (0.235-0.226 inch)	C	Green	5.18	0.204
6.39-6.18 mm (0.252-0.243 inch)	D	Blue	5.38	0.212

94I38727   Courtesy of Ford Motor Co.

Fig. 20: Thrust Washer & Bearing Assembly Selection Chart

14) Install No. 12 thrust washer (selective) on oil pump. Position pump in case and tap into place using a hammer handle. Remove pump alignment pins. Install pump attaching bolts and washers to specification.

CAUTION: Oil pump attaching bolt washers provide bolt seal and must not be substituted. Failure to use sealing washers may result in fluid leak.

NOTE: Differential bearing preload is set at factory and need not be checked or adjusted unless one of the following parts are replaced; transaxle case, differential case, differential bearings, differential bearing retainer.

Differential Bearing Preload Adjustment – 1) Position differential assembly in transaxle case. Set bearing preload. Place Shim Spacer (T83P-4451-BH) on differential ball bearing outer race. Thickness of spacer should be .054-.055" (1.37-1.40 mm).

2) Remove bearing retainer oil seal and "O" ring. Install bearing retainer in case. Install Differential Bearing Preload Shim Selector (T81P-4451-A) in differential retainer.

3) Ensure tool is centered in differential seal bore. Position gauge bar of selector tool across bearing retainer and install 2 attaching bolts finger tight. See Fig. 21.

4) Tighten center screw of gauge bar finger tight, then rotate differential assembly several times to seat bearings. Retighten screw finger tight.

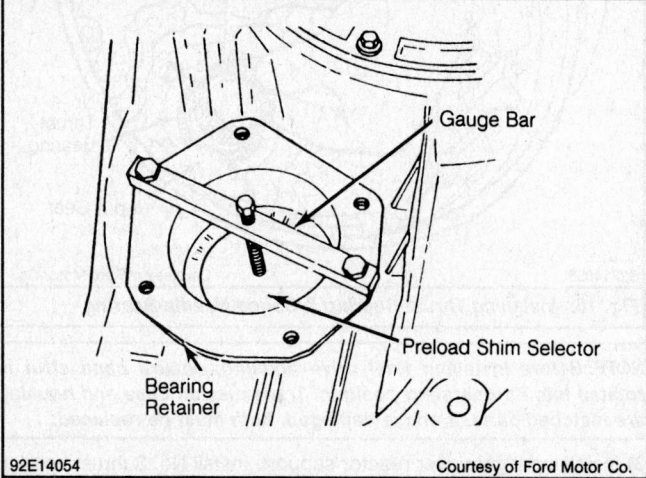

Gauge Bar

Preload Shim Selector

Bearing Retainer

92E14054   Courtesy of Ford Motor Co.

Fig. 21: Installing Of Differential Bearing Preload Tool

5) Using a feeler gauge, measure clearance between bearing retainer and transaxle case at 3 positions around retainer. Add the 3 measurements together and divide by 3 to obtain average of all measurements.

6) To determine shim needed for correct bearing preload, subtract average measurement obtained in step **5)** from .053" (1.35 mm). Then add compressed gasket thickness of .011" (.28 mm). Result is thickness of required preload shim to install.

7) Bearing preload shims are available in thickness of .012-.051" (.30-1.30 mm) in .02" (.05 mm) increments. If calculations result in shim thickness which falls between 2 available thicknesses, always use thinner shim.

8) Remove gauge bar, shim spacer and bearing retainer. Install new oil seal in retainer Position shim on ball bearing outer race. Install bearing retainer with new "O" ring by tapping evenly around outside edge of retainer face. Dip "O" ring in transmission fluid prior to installation.

9) Loctite bolt threads and install differential bearing retainer-to-case attaching bolts. Tighten bolts to specifications. See TORQUE SPECIFICATIONS.

Final Assembly – 1) Position new seal on oil filter and install filter in case. Install oil pan using a new gasket. Install new seal on speedometer driven gear retainer and position retainer in case. Tap retainer into position using a plastic hammer. Ensure retaining pin hole is aligned. With retainer properly positioned, tap retaining pin into case.

2) Install governor into case. Install new seal on governor cover and position cover on case. Tap cover into place using plastic hammer and install cover retaining wire.

3) Position governor screen into case bore. Position valve body gasket on case and install alignment pins to hold gasket in place. Place valve body in position in case and at the same time connect "Z" link to manual valve.

4) Connect throttle valve control spring to inner lever cam and to separator plate. With valve body correctly positioned, ensure roller on end of throttle valve plunger has engaged cam on end of throttle lever shaft.

5) Install detent roller assembly, baffle plates and remaining valve body attaching bolts. Tighten valve body attaching bolts in sequence to specification. *See Fig. 23.* See TORQUE SPECIFICATIONS. Connect throttle return spring to spring anchor on throttle lever.

6) Position a new valve body cover gasket on case. Install cover and tighten attaching bolts to specification. Install oil pump shaft. Install new seal on dipstick tube and install tube in case. Install torque converter into transaxle case.

BAND SERVO TRAVEL CHECK

1) Servo travel check needs to be performed only if one of the following components has been replaced:

- Transaxle Case
- Band Assembly
- Drum & Sun Gear Assembly
- Servo Piston Rod
- Servo Piston
- Band Anchor Strut

Clean and assemble servo piston without piston seals. Install Return Spring (T81P-70027-A) on piston rod and position piston in case.

2) Install Servo Piston Selector (T81P-70023-A) and secure in case using servo cover retaining snap ring. Tighten gauge screw to 120 INCH lbs. (14 N.m). *See Fig. 22.*

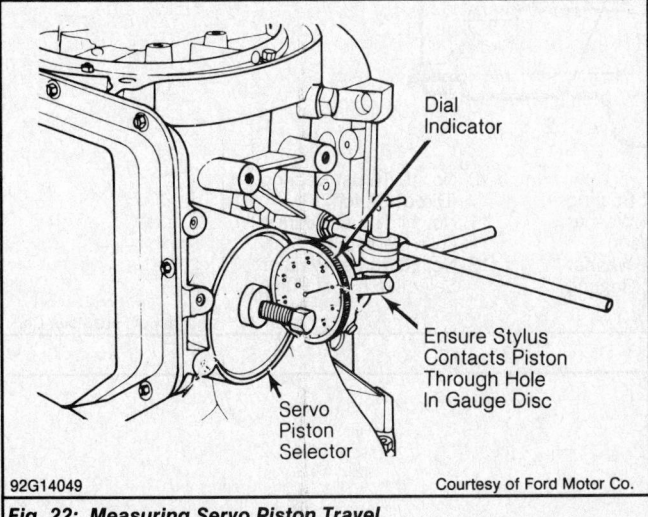

92G14049   Courtesy of Ford Motor Co.

Fig. 22: Measuring Servo Piston Travel

3) Mount a dial indicator and position indicator stylus through hole in gauge disc. Ensure stylus contacts servo piston. Zero dial indicator.
4) Back off gauge screw until piston movement stops and read dial indicator. Amount of piston travel shown on indicator will determine piston rod length to install.

5) If piston travel is .203-.247" (5.16-6.27 mm), correct piston rod is installed and no change is required. If travel is less than specifications, piston rod is too long and a shorter rod (more I.D. grooves) will have to be installed. If travel is more than specified, rod is too short and a longer rod (less grooves) will have to be installed.

6) Select new piston rod if necessary. See SERVO PISTON ROD SELECTION table. Install selected rod and recheck servo travel.

SERVO PISTON ROD SELECTION

Rod Length [1] In. (mm)	Rod I.D.
6.313-6.324 (160.35-160.63)	No Grooves
6.289-6.300 (159.74-160.02)	1 Groove
6.265-6.276 (159.13-159.41)	2 Grooves
6.240-6.252 (158.50-158.80)	3 Grooves
6.189-6.216 (157.20-157.89)	4 Grooves
6.197-6.209 (157.40-157.71)	5 Grooves

[1] – Measured from end of snap ring groove to end of rod.

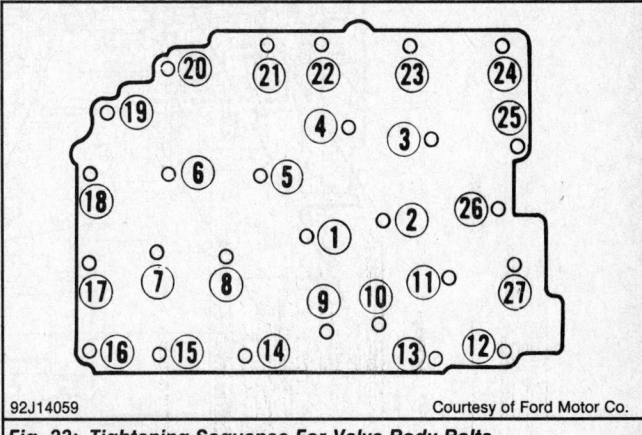

92J14059   Courtesy of Ford Motor Co.

Fig. 23: Tightening Sequence For Valve Body Bolts

TORQUE SPECIFICATIONS

TORQUE SPECIFICATIONS

Application	Ft. Lbs. (N.m)
Cooler Tube Fitting-To-Case	18-23 (24-31)
Differential Retainer-To-Case Bolt	15-19 (20-26)
Final Drive Housing-To-Case Bolt	18-23 (24-31)
Flex Plate-To-Crankshaft	54-64 (73-87)
Idler Shaft Nut	80-100 (108-136)
Inner Manual Lever-To-Shaft Nut	32-48 (43-65)
Oil Pan-To-Case Bolt	15-19 (20-26)
Ring Gear-To-Differential Case Bolt	55-70 (75-95)
Torque Converter-To-Flex Plate	23-39 (31-53)

	INCH Lbs. (N.m)
Filter-To-Case Bolt	84-108 (9-12)
Oil Pump Assembly-To-Case Bolt	72-96 (8-11)
Oil Pump Support-To-Pump Body Bolt	72-96 (8-11)
Outer Throttle Lever-To-Shaft Nut	90-114 (10-13)
Pressure Test Port Plug-To-Case	48-96 (5-11)
Reactor Support-To-Case Bolt	72-96 (8-11)
Separator Plate-To-Valve Body Bolt	72-96 (8-11)
Valve Body-To-Case Bolt	72-96 (8-11)
Valve Body Cover-To-Case Bolt	84-108 (9-12)

AUTOMATIC TRANSMISSIONS
Ford ATX/FLC (Cont.)

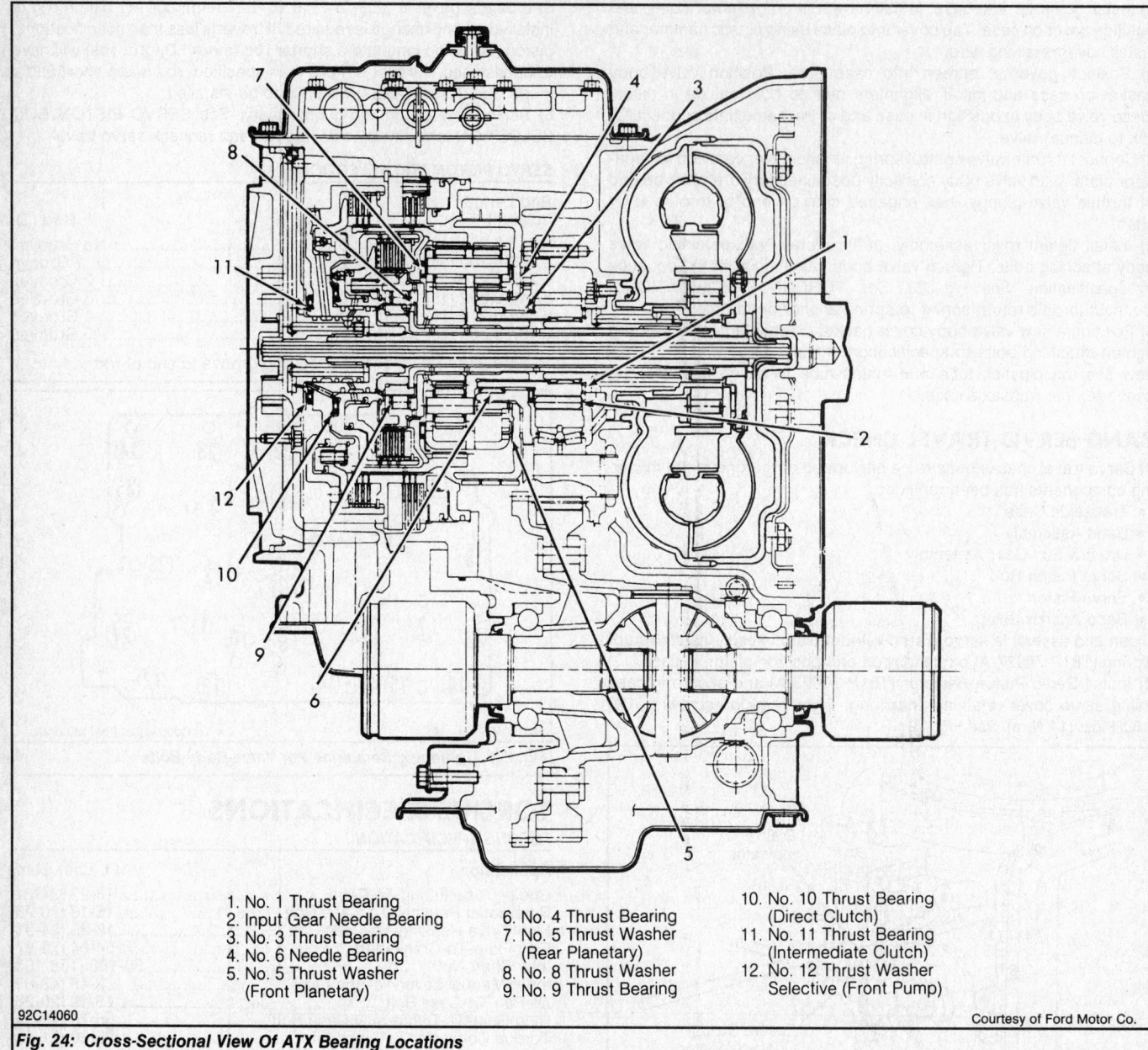

1. No. 1 Thrust Bearing
2. Input Gear Needle Bearing
3. No. 3 Thrust Bearing
4. No. 6 Needle Bearing
5. No. 5 Thrust Washer
   (Front Planetary)
6. No. 4 Thrust Bearing
7. No. 5 Thrust Washer
   (Rear Planetary)
8. No. 8 Thrust Washer
9. No. 9 Thrust Bearing
10. No. 10 Thrust Bearing
    (Direct Clutch)
11. No. 11 Thrust Bearing
    (Intermediate Clutch)
12. No. 12 Thrust Washer
    Selective (Front Pump)

92C14060

Courtesy of Ford Motor Co.

Fig. 24: Cross-Sectional View Of ATX Bearing Locations

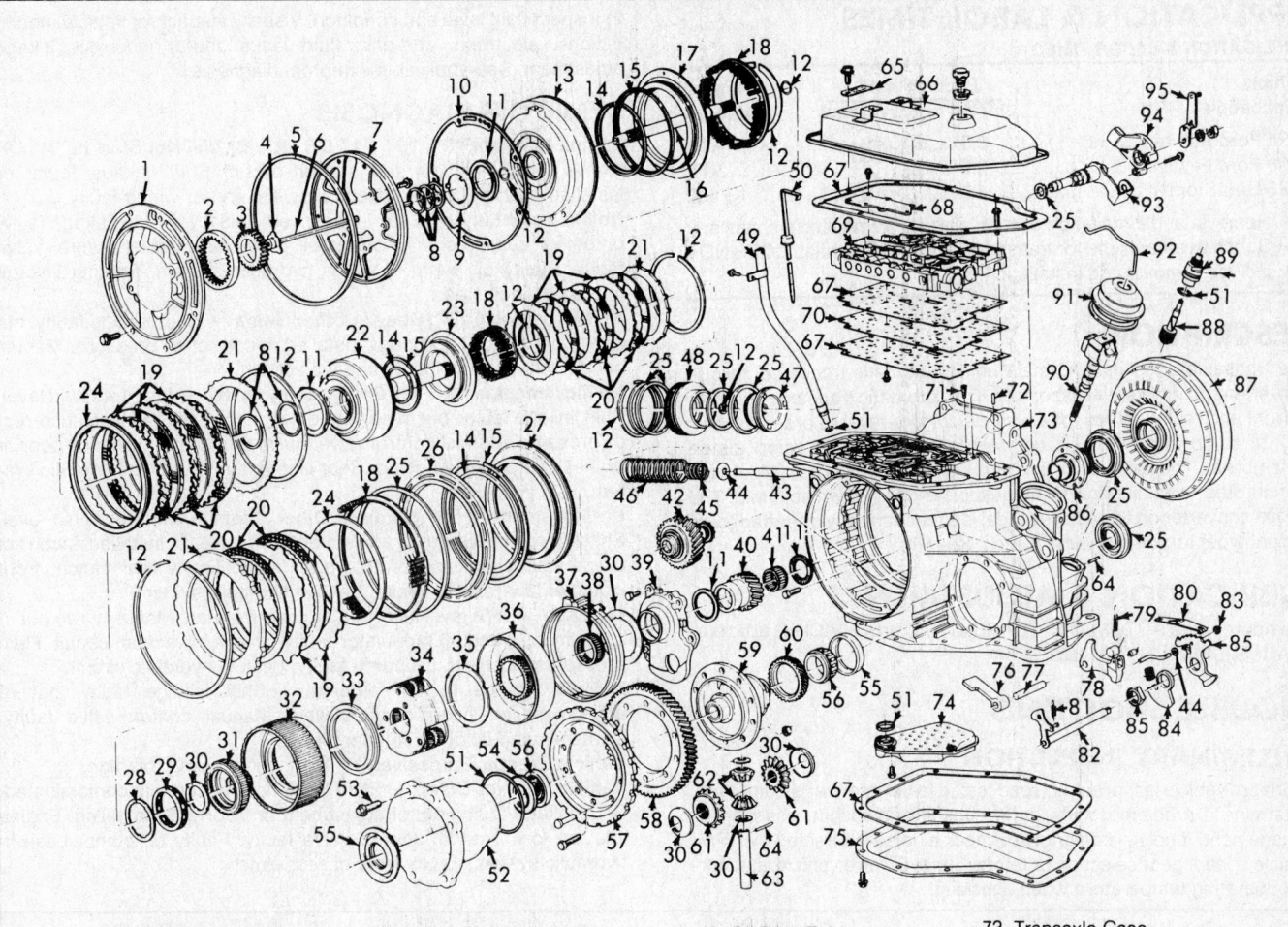

1. Oil Pump Body	26. Reverse Clutch Piston
2. Pump Driven Gear	27. Reverse Clutch Drum
3. Pump Drive Gear	28. One-Way Clutch Bearing
4. Pump Gear Insert	29. Spring & Roller Assembly
5. Oil Pump Seal	30. Thrust Washer
6. Oil Pump Drive Shaft	31. 1st-3rd Reverse Gear
7. Clutch Support	32. Intermediate Clutch Hub
8. Teflon Oil Seals	& Ring Gear
9. End Play Thrust Washer	33. Planetary Rear Thrust Bearing
10. Pump Gasket	34. Planetary Assembly
11. Thrust Bearing	35. Planetary Front Thrust Bearing
12. Retaining Ring	36. Sun Gear & Drum Assembly
13. Intermediate Clutch Drum	37. Band
14. Inner Piston Seal	38. Final Drive Housing Bearing
15. Outer Piston Seal	39. Final Drive Housing
16. Intermediate Clutch Shaft	40. Final Drive Input Gear
17. Intermediate Clutch Piston	41. Input Gear Bearing
18. Return Spring Assembly	42. Idler Gear
19. Steel Clutch Plates	43. Servo Rod
20. Friction Clutch Plates	44. Washer
21. Pressure Plate	45. Cushion Spring
22. Direct Clutch Drum	46. Piston Spring
23. Direct Clutch Piston	47. Servo Piston
24. Wave Spring	48. Servo Cover
25. Seal	

49. Oil Filler Tube	73. Transaxle Case
50. Dipstick	74. Oil Filter
51. "O" Ring	75. Oil Pan
52. Differential Retainer	76. Band Anchor Strut
53. Retainer Bolt	77. Park Pawl Shaft
54. Side Bearing Preload Shim	78. Park Pawl Assembly
55. Oil Seal	79. Park Pawl Return Spring
56. Differential Side Bearing	80. Manual Valve Detent Spring
57. Parking Pawl Gear	81. T.V. Lever Control Spring
58. Ring Gear	82. T.V. Lever Actuating Shaft
59. Differential Case	83. Nut
60. Speedometer Drive Gear	84. Park Pawl Actuating Lever
61. Side Gears	85. Manual Valve Inner Lever
62. Pinion Gears	86. Reactor Support
63. Pinion Gear Shafts	87. Torque Converter
64. Retaining Pin	88. Speedometer Driven Gear
65. Transaxle I.D. Tag	89. Speedometer Gear Retainer
66. Valve Body Cover	90. Governor
67. Gasket	91. Governor Cover
68. Baffle Plate	92. Retainer Wire
69. Valve Body Assembly	93. Manual Lever
70. Separator Plate	94. Neutral Safety Switch
71. Governor Screen	95. T.V. Outer Lever
72. Dowel Pin	

92D14061

Courtesy of Ford Motor Co.

Fig. 25: Exploded View Of ATX Automatic Transaxle Assembly

APPLICATION & LABOR TIMES

APPLICATION & LABOR TIMES

Vehicle Application	Labor Times ¹ R & I	² Overhaul	Trans. Model
1994 Ford Aspire	3.9	7.9	ATX
1993 Ford Festiva	3.9	7.9	ATX
1993 Geo Storm	4.7	7.9	KF400

¹ – Removal and installation of transmission from vehicle chassis.
² – Bench overhaul time for transmission and differential. DOES NOT include removal and installation.

DESCRIPTION

The transaxle consists of 3 main units: automatic transaxle, torque converter and differential assembly. The automatic transaxle consists of front and rear clutches, one-way clutch, low-reverse brake assembly, oil pump and hydraulic controls (valve body and servo piston assemblies). The valve body is controlled by the governor valve, vacuum throttle valve diaphragm (modulator) and kickdown solenoid. The torque converter on the Aspire model is a mechanically operated (centrifugal type) torque converter clutch. *See Fig. 1.*

LUBRICATION & ADJUSTMENTS

See appropriate AUTOMATIC TRANSMISSION SERVICING article in TRANSMISSION SERVICING.

TROUBLE SHOOTING

PRELIMINARY INSPECTION

1) Ensure vehicle is thoroughly road tested to verify driver's complaint. Determine if problem occurs during upshift, downshift, coasting or engagement. If noise is diagnosed, check if noise is affected by RPM, vehicle speed, gear selection or temperature. Ensure vehicle is at normal operating temperature when checking.

2) Inspect fluid level and condition. Visually inspect for vehicle modifications, electronic add-ons, fluid leaks and/or incorrect linkage adjustment. See applicable symptom diagnosis.

SYMPTOM DIAGNOSIS

Engine Starts In "D", "2", "1" OR "R", Or Will Not Start In "N" OR "P" – Check ignition and starter circuit. Shift linkage faulty or installed improperly. Park/Neutral switch and/or wiring faulty.

No Movement In Any Gear – Incorrect fluid level. Shift linkage faulty or out of adjustment. Incorrect oil pressure. Manual control valve faulty. Faulty oil pump. Leak in hydraulic system. Parking linkage improperly adjusted.

No Movement In "D", Okay In Other Gears – Shift linkage faulty, out of adjustment or improperly installed. Incorrect oil pressure. Manual control valve faulty. Faulty one-way clutch.

No Movement In "D", "2" Or "1", Okay In "R" – Incorrect fluid level. Shift linkage faulty, out of adjustment or incorrectly installed. Incorrect oil pressure. Manual control valve faulty. Engine performance poor or brakes improperly adjusted. Rear clutch faulty. Leak in hydraulic system.

No Movement In "R", Okay In Other Gears – Incorrect fluid level. Shift linkage faulty, out of adjustment or incorrectly installed. Incorrect oil pressure. Manual control valve faulty. Faulty rear clutch, front clutch or low-reverse brake. Leak in hydraulic system.

Slippage – ATF level incorrect or contaminated. Manual valve out of adjustment. Vacuum modulator faulty or leak in vacuum circuit. Fluid pressures incorrect. Oil pump faulty. Leak in hydraulic circuit.

Vehicle Creeps In "N" Position – Shift linkage faulty, out of adjustment or incorrectly installed. Manual control valve faulty. Contaminated fluid. Faulty rear clutch.

Vehicle Creeps Excessively – Engine idle speed too high.

Vehicle Will Not Creep – Fluid level incorrect or fluid contaminated. Shift linkage faulty, out of adjustment or incorrectly installed. Engine idle too low. Manual control valve faulty. Faulty oil pump. Leak in hydraulic system. Faulty front or rear clutch.

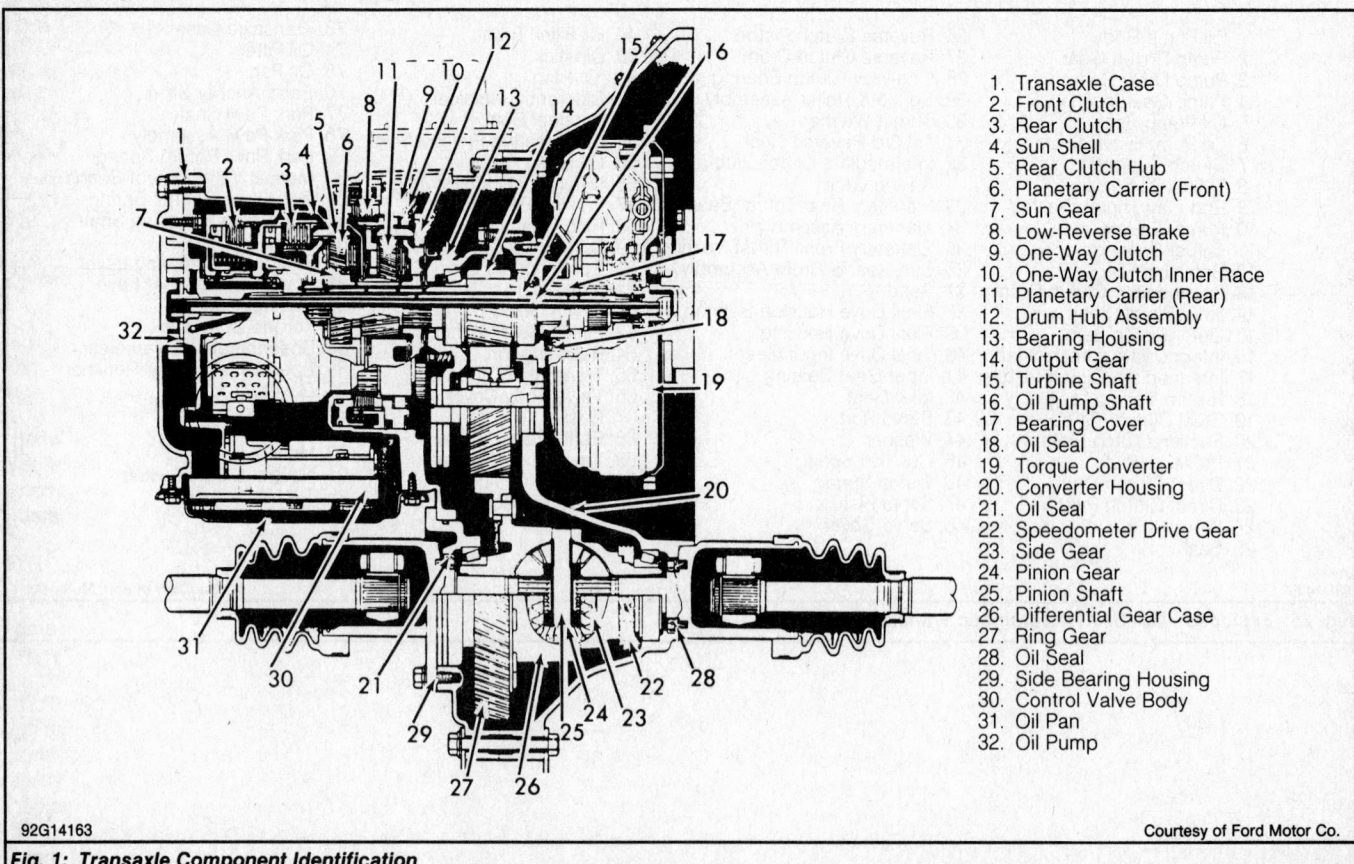

1. Transaxle Case
2. Front Clutch
3. Rear Clutch
4. Sun Shell
5. Rear Clutch Hub
6. Planetary Carrier (Front)
7. Sun Gear
8. Low-Reverse Brake
9. One-Way Clutch
10. One-Way Clutch Inner Race
11. Planetary Carrier (Rear)
12. Drum Hub Assembly
13. Bearing Housing
14. Output Gear
15. Turbine Shaft
16. Oil Pump Shaft
17. Bearing Cover
18. Oil Seal
19. Torque Converter
20. Converter Housing
21. Oil Seal
22. Speedometer Drive Gear
23. Side Gear
24. Pinion Gear
25. Pinion Shaft
26. Differential Gear Case
27. Ring Gear
28. Oil Seal
29. Side Bearing Housing
30. Control Valve Body
31. Oil Pan
32. Oil Pump

92G14163

Courtesy of Ford Motor Co.

Fig. 1: Transaxle Component Identification

Low Maximum Speed & Poor Acceleration – Incorrect ATF level or contaminated fluid. Selector linkage out of adjustment. Engine stall speed incorrect. Poor engine performance. Brake band faulty or out of adjustment. Faulty low-reverse brake, front clutch, rear clutch or hydraulic circuit.

Harsh "N" To "D" Engagement – Engine idle too high. Leak in vacuum circuit. Incorrect oil pressure. Manual control valve faulty. Faulty rear clutch. Low fluid level.

Harsh 1-2 Shift – Leak in vacuum circuit. Engine stall speed incorrect. Contaminated fluid. Manual control valve faulty. Band servo faulty. Brake band damaged or out of adjustment.

Harsh 2-3 Shift – Leak in vacuum circuit. Incorrect oil pressure. Manual control valve faulty. Band servo or front clutch faulty. Brake band faulty.

Shift Shock Felt On Kickdown Downshift – Shift linkage damaged, out of adjustment or incorrectly installed. Leak in vacuum circuit. Kickdown solenoid, switch or wiring faulty. Incorrect oil pressure. Manual control valve or governor valve faulty. Leak in hydraulic system.

2-1 Shift Shock With Lever In "1" Position – Leak in vacuum circuit. Engine stall speed incorrect. Manual control valve faulty. Contaminated fluid. Low-reverse brake faulty. Line pressure high.

Shift Shock On Deceleration – Range selector out of adjustment. Vacuum diaphragm or piping faulty. Kickdown solenoid out of adjustment or faulty. Excessive line pressure. Manual valve faulty. Governor valve faulty.

Vehicle Brakes In "R" Position – Band servo faulty. Contaminated fluid. Faulty rear clutch. Brake band damaged or out of adjustment. Parking linkage damaged or improperly adjusted.

Vehicle Brakes On 1-2 Shift – Manual control valve faulty. Contaminated fluid. Front clutch or low-reverse brake faulty. One-way clutch faulty.

Vehicle Brakes On 2-3 Shift – Manual control valve faulty. Band servo faulty. Contaminated fluid. Brake band out of adjustment or damaged.

No Engine Braking In "1" Position – Shift linkage damaged, out of adjustment or installed incorrectly. Incorrect oil pressure. Manual control valve faulty. Contaminated fluid. Low-reverse brake faulty. Leak in hydraulic system.

No Shift Shock; Slippage On 1-2 Shift – Incorrect fluid level. Shift linkage damaged, out of adjustment or incorrectly installed. Leak in vacuum circuit. Oil pressure incorrect. Manual control valve faulty. Band servo faulty. Contaminated fluid. Brake band faulty. Leakage in hydraulic system.

No Shift Shock; Slippage When Manually Shifted From "1" To "2" Position – Incorrect fluid level. Shift linkage damaged, out of adjustment or installed incorrectly. Leak in vacuum circuit. Engine idle speed incorrect. Engine stall speed incorrect. Manual control valve faulty. Contaminated fluid. Brake band out of adjustment or damaged. Oil pump faulty.

No Shift Shock; Slippage On 2-3 Shift – ATF contaminated or level incorrect. Shift linkage faulty. Vacuum modulator faulty or leak in vacuum circuit. Line pressure not correct. Band servo faulty. Front clutch faulty. Leak in hydraulic system.

Slippage On 3-2 Kickdown – Leak in vacuum circuit. Oil pressure incorrect. Manual valve faulty. Band servo faulty. Contaminated fluid. Front clutch faulty. Brake band out of adjustment or damaged. Leak in hydraulic system.

Transaxle Slips In 1st Gear – Incorrect fluid level. Shift linkage faulty, out of adjustment or incorrectly installed. Incorrect oil pressure. Manual control valve faulty. Contaminated fluid. Incorrect idle speed. Faulty kickdown solenoid, switch or wiring.

No 1-2 Shift – Shift linkage defective, out of adjustment or incorrectly installed. Leak in vacuum circuit. Faulty kickdown solenoid, switch or wiring. Contaminated fluid. Manual control valve faulty. Governor valve faulty. Band servo faulty. Brake band out of adjustment. Leak in hydraulic system. Rear clutch faulty.

No 2-3 Shift – Shift linkage defective, out of adjustment or incorrectly installed. Leak in vacuum circuit. Faulty kickdown solenoid, switch or wiring. Contaminated fluid. Manual control valve, governor valve or band servo faulty. Leak in hydraulic system. Front clutch faulty.

No Lock-Up – Faulty torque converter, wiring or solenoid.

1-3 Shift; Skips 2nd – Contaminated fluid. Brake band out of adjustment or damaged. Leak in hydraulic system.

No 3-2 Downshift – Leak in vacuum circuit. Manual control valve, governor valve or band servo faulty. Contaminated fluid. Faulty front clutch. Brake band out of adjustment of damaged. Leak in hydraulic system.

No 2-1 Or 3-1 Downshift – Leak in vacuum circuit. Manual control valve, governor valve or band servo faulty. Contaminated fluid. Brake band out of adjustment or damaged. One-way clutch faulty.

Slippage When Accelerating In 3rd Gear Above Kickdown Speed – Shift linkage damaged, out of adjustment or installed incorrectly. Leak in vacuum circuit. Oil pressure incorrect. Manual control valve or governor valve faulty. Contaminated fluid. Front clutch faulty. Leak in hydraulic system.

No Kickdown At Normal Speeds In 3rd Gear – Leak in vacuum circuit. Kickdown solenoid, switch or wiring faulty. Manual control valve or governor valve faulty. Contaminated fluid. Brake band out of adjustment or damaged. Leak in hydraulic system.

1-2 & 2-3 Shift Points Too High – ATF contaminated or level incorrect. Vacuum modulator faulty or leak in vacuum circuit. Line pressures incorrect. Manual valve out of adjustment. Governor valve faulty. Hydraulic circuit leaking.

3-2 & 2-1 Shift Points Too High – Shift linkage damaged, out of adjustment or incorrectly installed. Kickdown solenoid, switch or wiring faulty. Leak in vacuum circuit. Incorrect oil pressure. Manual control valve or governor valve faulty. Leak in hydraulic system.

1-2 Or 2-3 Shifts With Shift Lever In "1" Position – Shift linkage damaged, out of adjustment or installed incorrectly. Manual control valve faulty. Leak in hydraulic system.

2-1 Or 2-3 Shifts With Shift Lever In "2" Position – Shift linkage damaged, out of adjustment or installed incorrectly. Incorrect oil pressure. Manual control valve faulty.

Vehicle Moves In "P" Or Parking Gear Remains Engaged When Shifted Out Of "P" Position – Shift linkage damaged, out of adjustment or incorrectly installed. Parking linkage out of adjustment or damaged.

Transaxle Noisy In "P" Or "N" Position – Incorrect fluid level. Incorrect oil pressure. Faulty rear clutch, oil pump, one-way clutch or planetary gear.

Transaxle Noisy In "D", "1", "2" Or "R" – Oil pressure incorrect. Rear clutch, oil pump, one-way clutch or planetary gears faulty.

Transmission Overheats – ATF level incorrect. Engine stall speed and/or line pressure incorrect. Faulty band servo, front clutch, rear clutch, brake band, low-reverse brake, oil pump, torque converter or planetary gear. Leak in hydraulic circuit.

Differential Noise – ATF contaminated or level incorrect. Bearings worn or has excessive preload. Teeth on gears worn or damaged or has excessive backlash.

TESTING

PARK/NEUTRAL SWITCH

1) Ensure engine starts in "P" or "N". Ensure back-up lights glow when ignition is on and selector lever in "R". If park/neutral switch is not operating properly, disconnect connector at transaxle and check continuity between terminals. See Fig. 2. If continuity is not as indicated, replace park/neutral switch.

KICKDOWN (DOWNSHIFT) SOLENOID

1) **Check Fuse** – Ensure ignition is off. Inspect condition of 15 amp METER fuse located in interior fuse junction panel. If fuse is okay, go step 4). If fuse is blown, go to next step.

2) **Check System** – Ensure ignition is off. Replace 15 amp fuse. Turn ignition on. If fuse blows, go to next step. If fuse is okay, go to step 4).

3) **Check For Short To Ground** – Turn ignition off. Remove 15 amp METER fuse. Disconnect kickdown switch harness connector. Check continuity between Black/Yellow wire terminal of interior fuse holder and ground. If continuity exists, inspect and repair short circuit as needed. If continuity does not exist, replace 15 amp fuse. Go to next step.

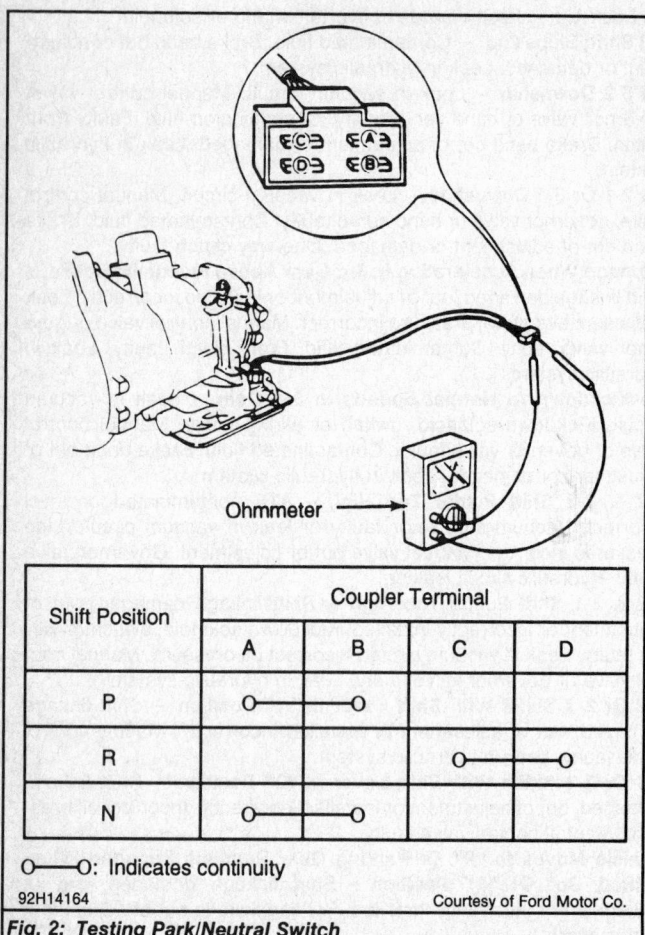

Ohmmeter

Shift Position	Coupler Terminal			
	A	B	C	D
P	O———O			
R			O———O	
N	O———O			

O———O: Indicates continuity

92H14164   Courtesy of Ford Motor Co.

Fig. 2: Testing Park/Neutral Switch

4) Check Power Supply To Kickdown Switch – Ensure ignition is off. Disconnect kickdown switch harness connector. Turn ignition on. Measure voltage between Black/Yellow wire terminal of kickdown switch harness connector and ground. If voltage is more than 10 volts, go to next step. If voltage is 10 volts or less, inspect and repair circuit between switch harness connector and fuse panel.

5) Check Kickdown Switch – Turn ignition off. Check continuity between kickdown switch terminals. Continuity should only exist with accelerator fully depressed. If switch is functioning correctly, go to next step. Replace switch if it failed testing. Road test vehicle to verify repair.

6) Check Circuit Between Kickdown Switch & Kickdown Solenoid – Ensure ignition is off. Disconnect kickdown switch harness connector. Disconnect kickdown solenoid harness connector. Check continuity of White/Black wire between switch harness connector and solenoid harness connector. If continuity does not exist, inspect and repair open circuit as needed. If continuity exists, check continuity between White/Black wire terminal at solenoid harness connector and ground. If continuity exists, inspect and repair short circuit as needed. If continuity does not exist, replace kickdown solenoid.

VACUUM THROTTLE VALVE DIAPHRAGM (MODULATOR)

1) Check System Integrity – Inspect all vacuum hoses and connections for leaks or damage. Disconnect vacuum hose at diaphragm connection and inspect for leaking ATF. Repair as needed. Go to next step.

2) Check Vacuum At Modulator – Ensure ignition is off. Disconnect vacuum hose at modulator valve and connect vacuum gauge to hose. Start and run engine at idle. Vacuum should be 15-22 In. Hg. If vacuum is not within specification, inspect and repair vacuum hose. If vacuum is within specification, go to next step.

3) Check Modulator Valve Function – Turn ignition off. Remove modulator valve from transaxle. Connect hand-held vacuum pump to valve. Apply 16-20 In. Hg of vacuum. Ensure vacuum is held by valve. Release vacuum and verify that valve moves freely. If valve is functioning correctly, go to next step. Replace valve if it fails testing.

4) Check Vacuum Diaphragm Rod – With modulator removed, measure depth of vacuum throttle valve (dimension "N"). See Fig. 3. Measure length of throttle control valve rod. Ensure correct length rod is installed. See THROTTLE VALVE ROD DIMENSION CHART. If correct rod is installed in transaxle, inspect operation of vacuum throttle valve in valve body. Install correct rod length as needed.

THROTTLE VALVE ROD DIMENSION CHART

"N" Dimension In. (mm)	Applicable Rod Length In. (mm)
1.0 (25.4)	1.16 (29.5)
1.0-1.02 (25.4-25.9)	1.18 (30.0)
1.02-1.04 (25.9-26.4)	1.20 (30.5)
1.04-1.06 (25.9-26.4)	1.22 (31.0)
1.06-1.08 (26.9-27.4)	1.24 (31.5)

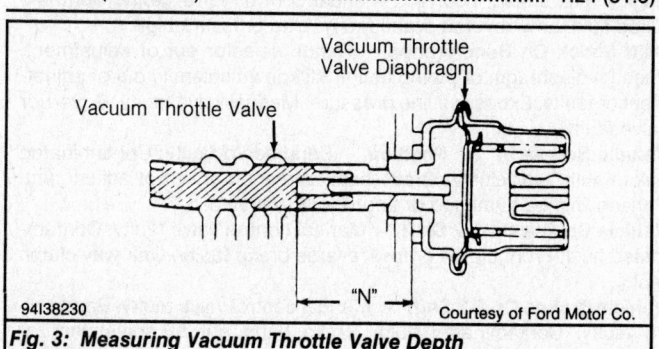

Vacuum Throttle Valve Diaphragm

Vacuum Throttle Valve

"N"

94I38230   Courtesy of Ford Motor Co.

Fig. 3: Measuring Vacuum Throttle Valve Depth

STALL TEST

Testing Precautions – When testing, DO NOT hold throttle open longer than 5 seconds. Shift to "N" and allow engine to idle for at least 2 minutes between tests to cool transaxle. If engine speed exceeds specification, release accelerator immediately as clutch or band slippage is indicated. See STALL SPEED SPECIFICATIONS table.

Testing Procedures – 1) With engine at normal operating temperature, tachometer installed and parking and service brakes applied, perform transaxle stall test in "D", "2", "1" and "R" ranges at full throttle and note maximum RPM obtained. Correct stall speed should occur at specified RPM. See STALL SPEED SPECIFICATIONS table.

STALL SPEED SPECIFICATIONS

Application	Engine RPM
Ford	
Aspire	2300-2500
Festiva	2300-2500
Geo Storm	2050-2350

2) If stall speed is too high in all shift ranges, the following components may be faulty:
- Worn Oil Pump.
- Oil leakage from oil pump, valve body or transaxle case.
- Sticking pressure regulator valve.

3) If stall speed is too high in "D", "2" and "1", the following component may be faulty:
- Slipping rear clutch.

4) If stall speed is too high in "D", the following component may be faulty:
- Slipping one-way clutch.

5) If stall speed is too high in "2", the following components may be faulty:
- Slipping intermediate band.

6) If stall speed is too high in "R", the following components may be faulty:
- Slipping Low/Reverse Clutch.
- Slipping Front Clutch.

7) If stall speed is too low in all shift ranges, the following components may be faulty:
- Slipping torque converter one-way clutch.

ROAD TEST

1) Before road test, ensure that fluid level, fluid condition and control linkage adjustments are okay. During test, transaxle should upshift or downshift at about same speed as specified. See appropriate VEHICLE SHIFT SPEED SPECIFICATIONS table.

2) All shifts may vary slightly due to production tolerances or tire size. The quality of the shifts are more important. All shifts should be smooth, responsive and with no slippage or engine flare. Slippage or engine flare in any gear usually indicates clutch or band problems.

3) The slipping clutch or band in a particular gear can usually be identified by noting transaxle operation in other selector positions and comparing internal units which are applied in these positions. See CLUTCH & BAND APPLICATION table.

VEHICLE SHIFT SPEED SPECIFICATIONS (ASPIRE & FESTIVA)

Operating Condition [1]	Shift Speed MPH (km/h)
Half Throttle (50%)	
1-2	9-17 (15-28)
2-3	16-34 (26-55)
Full Throttle (WOT) [2]	
1-2	28-33 (44-53)
2-3	55-63 (88-101)
3-2	53-48 (86-78)
2-1	24-22 (39-35)
Coasting	
2-1	9-6 (14-9)

[1] – Transmission is in "D" range.
[2] – To determine deceleration shift speeds, release throttle once transaxle has shifted into 3rd gear. Manually downshift shift lever into next lower gear and record speed at which downshift occurs. Continue downshifting and recording vehicle speed until transaxle has downshifted into low gear.

VEHICLE SHIFT SPEED SPECIFICATIONS (STORM)

Operating Condition [1]	Shift Speed MPH (km/h)
Half Throttle (50%) [2]	
1-2	15-21 (24-33)
2-3	33-39 (53-62)
3-2	18-12 (28-19)
2-1	12-7 (21-12)
Full Throttle (WOT) [2]	
1-2	32-38 (52-61)
2-3	67-73 (108-117)
3-2	71-59 (114-95)
2-1	28-22 (45-36)

[1] – Transmission is in "D" range.
[2] – To determine deceleration shift speeds, release throttle once transaxle has shifted into 3rd gear. Manually downshift shift lever into next lower gear and record speed at which downshift occurs. Continue downshifting and recording vehicle speed until transaxle has downshifted into low gear.

CLUTCH & BAND APPLICATION CHART

Selector Lever Position	Elements In Use
"P" (Park)	Low-Reverse Brake
"R" (Reverse)	Front Clutch & Low-Reverse Brake
"D" (Drive)	
First Gear	Rear Clutch & One-Way Clutch
Second Gear	Rear Clutch & Brake Band
Third Gear	Front Clutch & Rear Clutch
"2" (Intermediate)	
First Gear	Rear Clutch & One-Way Clutch
Second Gear	Rear Clutch & Brake Band
"1" (Low)	
First Gear	Rear Clutch & Low-Reverse Brake
"N" (Neutral)	All Clutches & Bands Released or Ineffective

HYDRAULIC PRESSURE TESTS

NOTE: DO NOT hold throttle open longer than 5 seconds. Shift to "N" and allow engine to idle for at least 2 minutes between tests to cool transaxle. If engine speed exceeds specification, release accelerator immediately as clutch or band slippage is indicated.

LINE PRESSURE TEST

1) Attach oil pressure gauge at line pressure checking port. *See Fig. 4.* Attach tachometer to engine. Position gauge so it can be seen from driver's seat.

2) With engine at normal operating temperature, transaxle fluid level correct and transaxle in "D", check line pressure at idle and at stall speed. Repeat test in "2", "1", and "R", allowing sufficient time for engine and transaxle to cool between tests. Record results. See LINE PRESSURE TEST SPECIFICATIONS table.

3) If Line Pressure Is Low In "D", "2", "1" & "R" – Check for worn oil pump, oil leaking from oil pump, control valve body or transaxle case and sticking pressure regulator valve.

4) If Line Pressure Is Low In "D" & "2" – Check for oil leakage from hydraulic circuit of rear clutch or governor.

5) If Line Pressure Is Low In "R" – Check for oil leakage from hydraulic circuit of low-reverse brake.

6) If Line Pressure Is High At Idle – Check for vacuum tube broken or disconnected or faulty vacuum modulator.

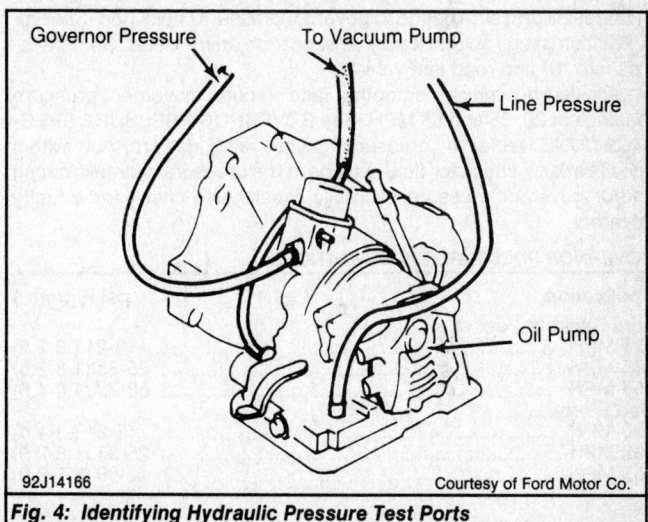

Governor Pressure — To Vacuum Pump — Line Pressure — Oil Pump

92J14166   Courtesy of Ford Motor Co.

Fig. 4: Identifying Hydraulic Pressure Test Ports

LINE PRESSURE TEST SPECIFICATIONS (ASPIRE)

Application	psi (kg/cm²)
At Idle	
"D"	46-54 (3.2-3.8)
"2"	150-166 (10.5-11.7)
"R"	76-95 (5.3-6.7)
At Stall Speed	
"D"	141-157 (9.9-11.0)
"2"	150-166 (10.5-11.7)
"R"	251-262 (17.6-18.4)

LINE PRESSURE TEST SPECIFICATIONS (FESTIVA & STORM)

Application	psi (kg/cm²)
At Idle	
"D"	43-57 (3.0-4.0)
"2"	114-171 (8.0-12.0)
"R"	57-110 (4.0-7.0)
At Stall Speed	
"D"	128-156 (9.0-11.0)
"2"	114-171 (8.0-12.0)
"R"	228-270 (16.0-19.0)

LINE PRESSURE CUT-BACK TEST

1) Connect oil pressure gauges to line pressure and governor pressure ports. *See Fig. 4*. Position gauges so they can be seen from driver's seat.

2) Connect a hand-held vacuum pump to vacuum modulator. *See Fig. 4*. Position vacuum pump so it can be operated from driver's seat. With shift lever in "D", gradually increase engine RPM and observe pressure gauge readings. Record results.

3) With shift lever in "D", gradually increase engine RPM, and apply 8 in. Hg to vacuum modulator. When line pressure reading suddenly decreases, observe governor pressure gauge. See LINE PRESSURE CUT-BACK TEST SPECIFICATIONS table.

4) If governor pressure gauge readings are not within specifications, ensure rod in vacuum modulator is installed. If a rod is installed, rod length may be incorrect or vacuum throttle valve is sticking. See VACUUM THROTTLE VALVE DIAPHRAGM (MODULATOR) under TESTING.

LINE PRESSURE CUT-BACK TEST SPECIFICATIONS

Vacuum Pump Reading	Governor Pressure psi (kg/cm²)
0 in. Hg (Atmosphere)	14-23 (.98-1.6)
8 in. Hg	6-14 (.42-.98)

GOVERNOR PRESSURE TEST

1) Attach oil pressure gauge to governor pressure check port. *See Fig. 4*. Position gauge so that it may be seen from driver's seat. Shift transaxle into "D" and road test vehicle.

2) Accelerate vehicle smoothly and record governor pressure readings at 20, 35 and 55 MPH. See GOVERNOR PRESSURE SPECIFICATIONS table. If pressure gauge readings are not within specifications, check for fluid leakage in line pressure hydraulic circuit and/or governor pressure hydraulic circuit. Also check for a faulty governor.

GOVERNOR PRESSURE SPECIFICATIONS

Application	psi (kg/cm²)
Ford Aspire & Festiva	
20 MPH	13-21 (.9-1.5)
35 MPH	25-35 (1.8-2.5)
55 MPH	58-70 (4.0-4.8)
Geo Storm	
20 MPH	13-21 (.9-1.5)
35 MPH	25-35 (1.8-2.5)
55 MPH	44-56 (3.1-3.9)

TORQUE CONVERTER

The torque converter is a sealed unit and cannot be serviced. Check for cracked or worn ring in seal area. Measure bushing in converter boss. If I.D. is larger than 2.090" (53.08 mm) on Aspire, 1.302" (33.075 mm) on Festiva and Storm, replace torque converter. If metal particles are found in ATF, replace torque converter.

Cleaning – Flush with solvent, drain and flush with ATF and drain ATF.

ON-VEHICLE SERVICE

BAND APPLY SERVO

Removal – **1)** Raise and support vehicle. Remove left front wheel. Drain transaxle fluid. Remove valve body. See VALVE BODY. Remove front stabilizer frame brackets. Carefully raise staked portion of left axle nut. Apply brakes and loosen, but DO NOT remove, axle nut. Remove left lower control arm ball joint clamp bolt. Pry downward on lower control arm to separate control arm from knuckle.

2) Insert pry bar between transaxle case and left axle flange. Carefully apply force to pry bar until axle circlip is disengaged. Slide knuckle assembly off axle shaft, and remove axle from vehicle. Quickly install appropriate plug in transaxle.

3) Loosen band adjusting stop and band adjusting stop nut. Remove band strut. Using "C" clamp and socket, compress servo piston into transaxle case. *See Fig. 5*. Remove snap ring. Remove servo retainer, servo piston and spring.

Installation – **1)** Lubricate servo piston with ATF. Assembly servo retainer, piston, piston large seal and spring. Insert assembly into transaxle. Using "C" clamp and socket, compress assembly and install snap ring. *See Fig. 5*. Install band strut to intermediate band. Install band adjusting stop to band and tighten to 9-10 ft. lbs. (12-15 N.m). Loosen adjusting stop 3 turns. Install and tighten band adjusting stop nut. See TORQUE SPECIFICATIONS.

2) Install remaining components in reverse order of disassembly. Fill transaxle with fluid.

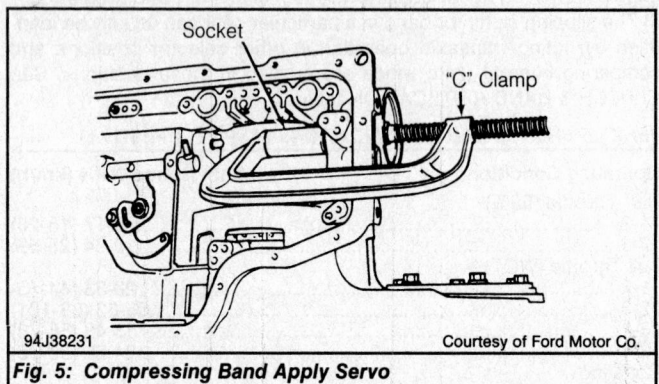

94J38231   Courtesy of Ford Motor Co.

Fig. 5: Compressing Band Apply Servo

DIFFERENTIAL OIL SEALS

Removal – **1)** Raise and support vehicle. Drain transaxle fluid. Carefully raise staked portion of axle nut. Apply brakes and loosen, but DO NOT remove, axle nut. Remove lower control arm ball joint clamp bolt. Pry downward on lower control arm to separate control arm from knuckle.

2) Insert pry bar between transaxle case and axle flange. Carefully apply force to pry bar until axle circlip is disengaged. Slide knuckle assembly off axle shaft, and remove axle from vehicle. Quickly install appropriate plug in transaxle. Using appropriate puller, remove seal.

Installation – **1)** Apply lubrication to new seal. Using appropriate driver, install seal. Install new circlip on transaxle end of axle. Remove transaxle plug, and carefully install axle into transaxle. Ensure circlip snaps into retaining groove.

2) Install axle into hub. Install NEW axle nut. Tighten bolts to specifications. See TORQUE SPECIFICATIONS. Stake NEW axle nut with blunt nose chisel. To complete installation, reverse removal procedure. Fill transaxle fluid to correct level.

OIL COOLER FLUSHING

Contaminates MUST be removed from oil cooler before transmission is put back into service. Replace cooler supply tubes if leaking. Thoroughly flush oil cooler and lines if a major service or transaxle removal has occurred. It is recommended that a mechanically agitated cleaner, such as Rotunda (014-00028), be used.

VACUUM THROTTLE VALVE DIAPHRAGM (MODULATOR)

NOTE: If replacing modulator, it is necessary to replace throttle control valve rod.

Removal – **1)** Drain transaxle fluid. Disconnect vacuum hose from modulator. Unscrew modulator from transaxle. Remove control rod. With beveled side out, insert Vacuum Diaphragm Rod Gauge (T87C-77000-A) into mounting hole until gauge bottoms out.

2) Place gauge rod through opening of gauge until rod bottoms out against vacuum throttle valve. Tighten lock knob on gauge and remove tool. Using depth gauge, measure distance from flat surface of gauge to end of rod. *See Fig. 6*. Select proper length throttle valve rod. See THROTTLE VALVE ROD DIMENSION CHART.

THROTTLE VALVE ROD DIMENSION CHART

Measurement In. (mm)	Applicable Rod Length In. (mm)
1.0 (25.4)	1.16 (29.5)
1.0-1.02 (25.4-25.9)	1.18 (30.0)
1.02-1.04 (25.9-26.4)	1.2 (30.5)
1.04-1.06 (25.9-26.4)	1.22 (31.0)
1.06-1.08 (26.9-27.4)	1.24 (31.5)

Installation – Install selected throttle valve rod. Coat threads of modulator with appropriate sealant. To install, reverse removal procedures.

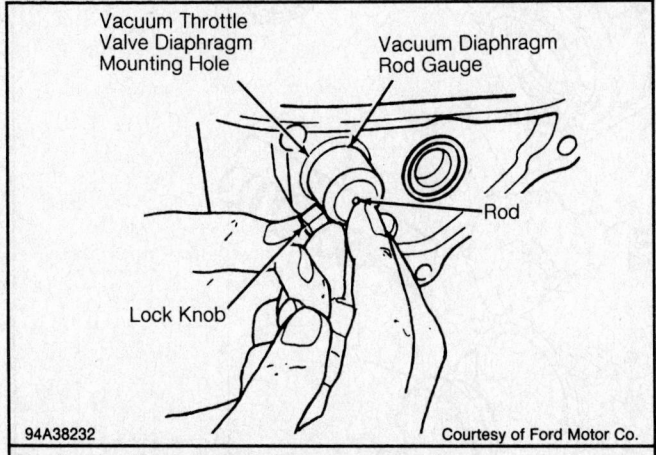

Fig. 6: Identifying Vacuum Diaphragm Rod Gauge

VALVE BODY

Removal & Installation – Disconnect battery ground cable. Raise and support vehicle. Remove front fender splash shield and front splash shield. Drain transaxle fluid. Unbolt and remove oil pan. Remove 9 valve body bolts. Remove valve body. Ensure care is used not to loose check ball and detent spring. To install, reverse removal procedure. Fill transaxle with fluid. Check for leaks.

REMOVAL & INSTALLATION

See appropriate AUTOMATIC TRANSMISSION REMOVAL article in TRANSMISSION SERVICING.

TRANSAXLE DISASSEMBLY

1) Remove torque converter. Attach transaxle to appropriate holding fixture. Remove park/neutral switch, kickdown solenoid and vacuum modulator with rod. Remove oil dipstick and tube. Remove speedometer driven gear retaining bolt and lift out gear assembly. Remove oil pump drive shaft and turbine shaft.

2) Remove oil pan. Remove valve body. DO NOT lose check ball and spring. Position transaxle with oil pump facing downward. With flat-blade screwdriver inserted in wide slot between front clutch drum and sun shell, pry down on front clutch drum. Do this several times as you rotate assembly 2 complete revolutions.

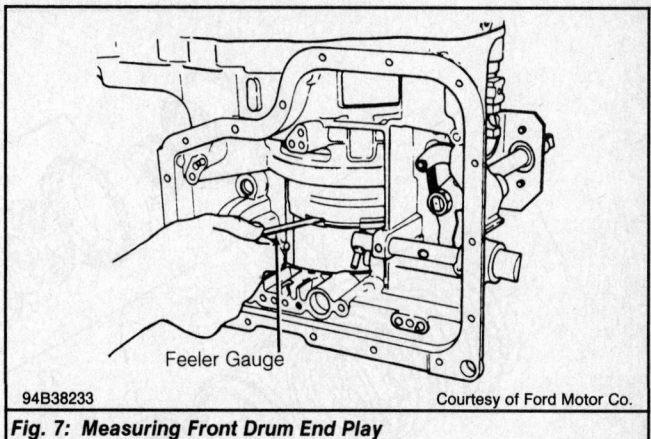

Fig. 7: Measuring Front Drum End Play

3) Using feeler gauge, measure front clutch drum end play. *See Fig. 7.* Check clearance of small slot between front clutch drum tabs and sun shell slots. Record measurement for reassembly reference. End play should be .020-.031" (.5-8 mm).

4) Remove oil pump. If oil pump is difficult to remove, tighten band adjusting stop bolt 106-133 INCH lbs. (12-15 N.m) and then remove oil pump. Remove brake band adjustment stop bolt, lock nut, band strut and band. *See Fig. 8.* Store band partially closed with a piece of wire.

5) Remove front clutch assembly. Remove rear clutch needle bearing and rear clutch drum. Remove front ring gear. Remove needle bearing and rear clutch hub assembly. Remove thrust bearing and sun gear spacer from front planetary gear. Remove planetary gear carrier.

6) Remove sun gear, spacer and connecting sun shell. *See Fig. 8.* Using "C" clamp and socket, compress servo piston with and remove snap ring. Release "C" clamp and remove servo piston. *See Fig. 5.* Remove governor cover and pull governor from transaxle case. Remove transaxle case-to-torque converter housing bolts. Separate case halves.

7) Remove differential assembly. Remove oil pipes and parking pawl assembly. Remove drum hub assembly. Remove one-way clutch inner race assembly. *See Fig. 8.* Remove rear planetary carrier with needle bearing and thrust washer. Before disassembling one-way clutch, measure and record clearance between one-way clutch and low-reverse brake retaining plate. Clearance should .032-.041" (.8-1.05 mm).

8) Remove snap ring, one-way clutch and low-reverse brake retaining plate. Remove low-reverse brake plates. Compress low-reverse brake piston with appropriate compressor. *See Fig. 9.* Remove snap ring with screwdriver and remove low-reverse brake hub and springs. Apply air pressure to low-reverse oil passage to remove piston. *See Fig. 10.*

9) Remove output bearing and idler support assembly by lightly tapping on idler shaft with a soft-faced hammer. Drive out idler gear roll pin and remove idler gear from output bearing and idler support. *See Fig. 11.* Remove output gear assembly, press out bearing race from output bearing and idler support and save adjusting shim for reassembly.

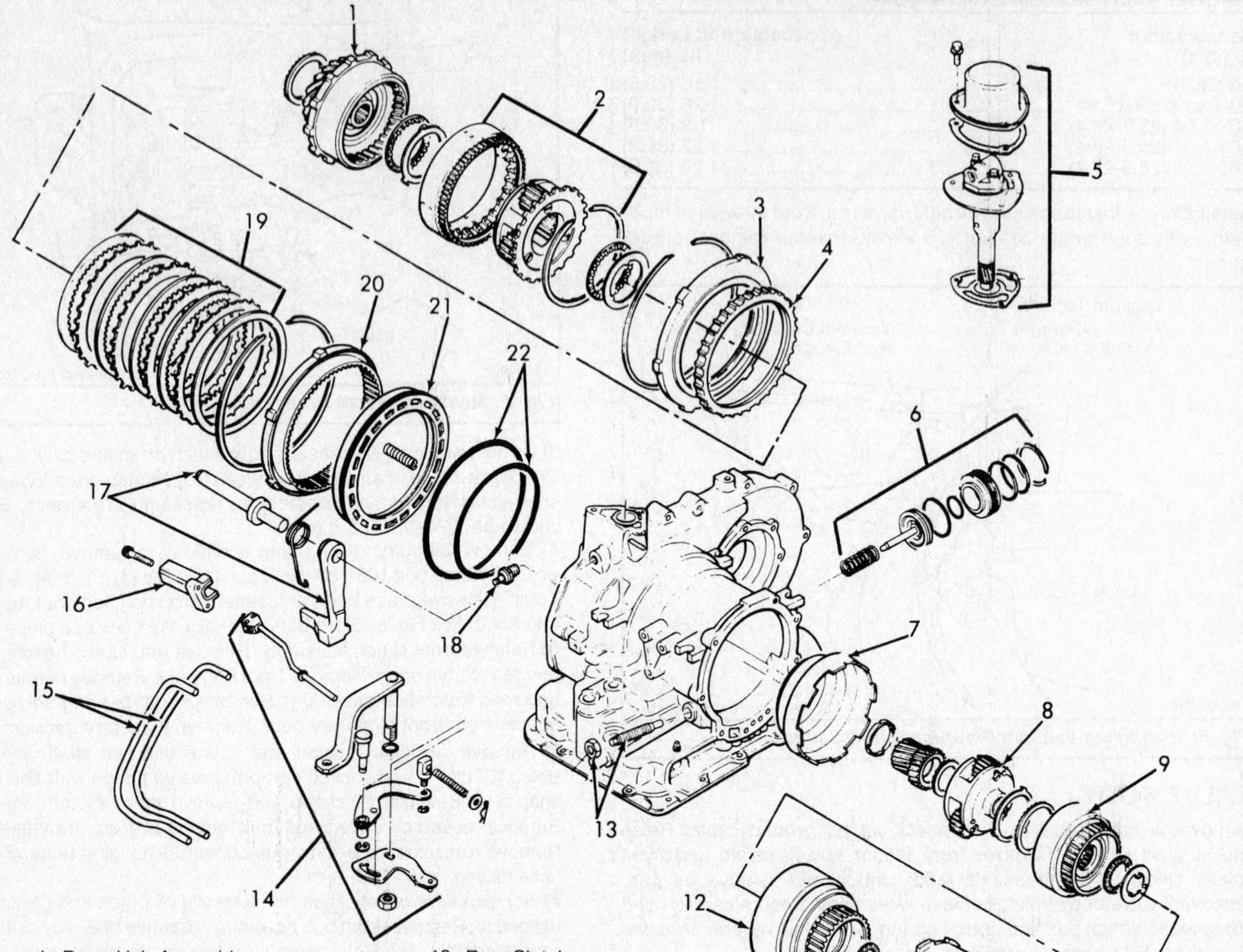

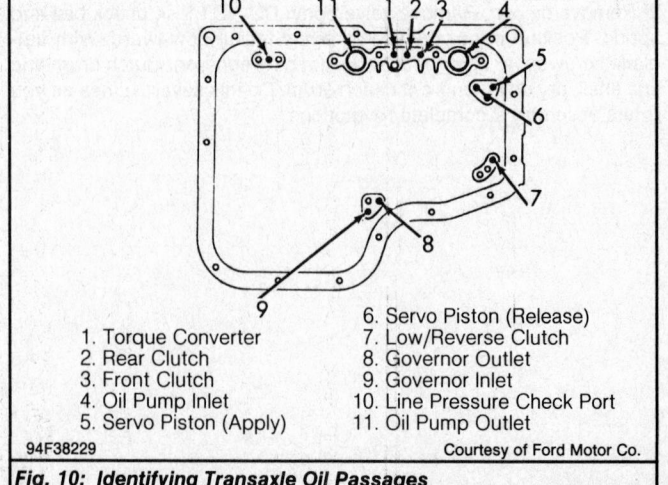

1. Drum Hub Assembly
2. One-Way Clutch Inner Race Assembly
3. One-Way Clutch
4. Low-Reverse Brake Retaining Plate
5. Governor
6. Servo Assembly
7. Connecting Shell
8. Planetary Carrier
9. Drum Hub Assembly
10. Brake Band
11. Front Clutch
12. Rear Clutch
13. Brake Band Stop Bolt & Lock Nut
14. Control Rod Assembly
15. Oil Pipes
16. Actuator Support
17. Parking Pawl Assembly
18. Park/Neutral Switch
19. Low-Reverse Brake Plate Assembly
20. Low-Reverse Brake Hub
21. Low-Reverse Brake Piston
22. Oil Seals

92B14168

Courtesy of Ford Motor Co.

Fig. 8: Exploded View Of Transaxle Housing & Primary Components

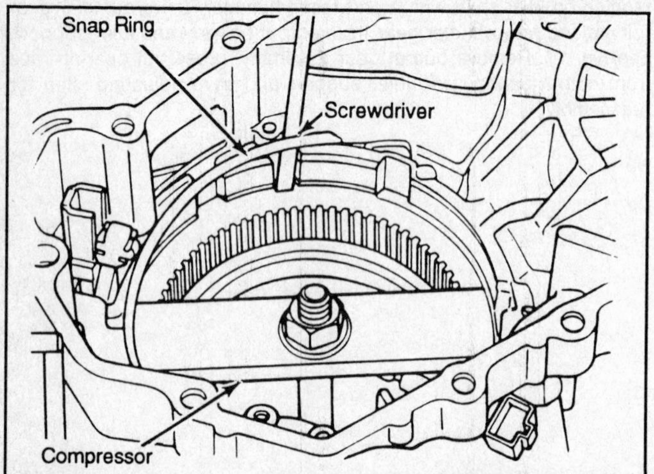

Snap Ring

Screwdriver

Compressor

92F14170

Courtesy of Ford Motor Co.

Fig. 9: Removing Snap Ring & Low-Reverse Brake

1. Torque Converter
2. Rear Clutch
3. Front Clutch
4. Oil Pump Inlet
5. Servo Piston (Apply)
6. Servo Piston (Release)
7. Low/Reverse Clutch
8. Governor Outlet
9. Governor Inlet
10. Line Pressure Check Port
11. Oil Pump Outlet

94F38229

Courtesy of Ford Motor Co.

Fig. 10: Identifying Transaxle Oil Passages

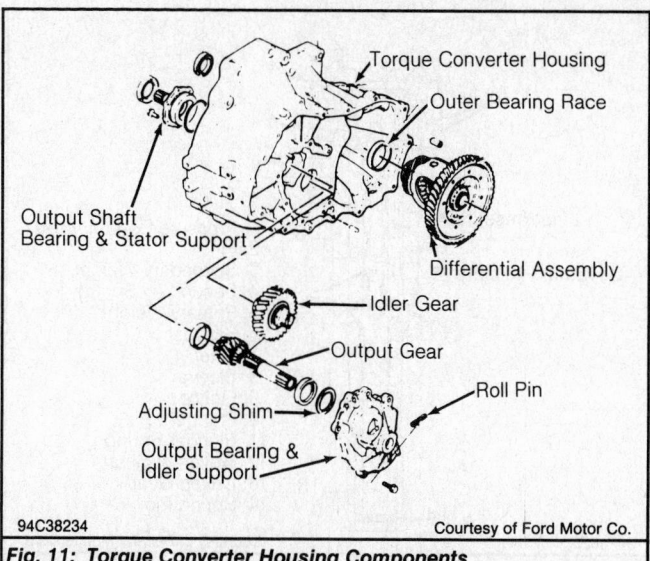

94C38234   Courtesy of Ford Motor Co.

Fig. 11: Torque Converter Housing Components

COMPONENT DISASSEMBLY & REASSEMBLY

BAND SERVO

Inspection – Remove seal rings and inspect piston for damaged or worn piston. Ensure spring free length is 1.890" (48.00 mm). If less than specified, replace spring. Install new seal rings on piston and servo retainer.

DIFFERENTIAL

Disassembly – **1)** Remove ring gear retaining bolts and ring gear. Using hammer and pin punch, drive out roll pin. See Fig. 12. Push out pinion gear shaft. Remove pinion and side gears, with washers, from differential housing.

2) Using appropriate puller, remove side bearings from differential housing. DO NOT remove speedometer drive gear unless damaged. Removal will damage speedometer drive gear.

Inspection – Check all gears for signs of excessive wear or damage. Check differential gear case for cracks or other damage. Replace as needed.

Reassembly – **1)** Reverse removal procedure to reassemble. Measure side gear and pinion gear backlash by inserting drive shafts into differential side gears and supporting shafts in "V" blocks. Position dial indicator with plunger resting on teeth of pinion gear. See Fig. 13. Measure backlash. Repeat procedure with plunger on other pinion gear.

2) Backlash readings should be less than .004" (.10 mm). If backlash is not within specification, adjust backlash by changing thrust washers. Thrust washers are available in .079" (2.00 mm), .083" (2.10 mm) and .087" (2.20 mm) thicknesses. Use thrust washers of the same thickness on both sides whenever possible.

DRUM HUB

Disassembly, Inspection & Reassembly – Remove parking gear spring from park gear. Push in parking gear retaining pins with screwdriver and remove parking gear. See Fig. 14. Remove snap ring and lift internal gear assembly from drive hub. Check gear for excessive wear or damage and replace if needed. Reverse disassembly procedure to reassemble drum hub.

FRONT CLUTCH

Disassembly – Remove retainer plate snap ring. Remove retainer plate, drive and driven plates and dished plate. See Fig. 15. Note position of dished plate for reassembly. Using appropriate compressor, compress return springs to remove spring retainer snap ring. Remove

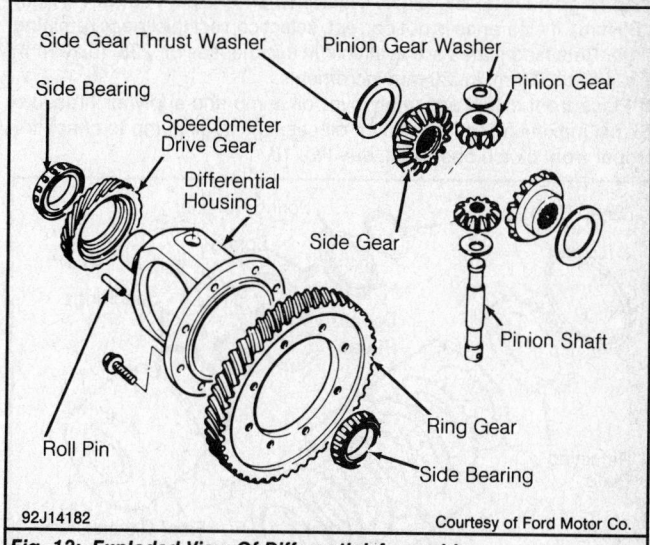

92J14182   Courtesy of Ford Motor Co.

Fig. 12: Exploded View Of Differential Assembly

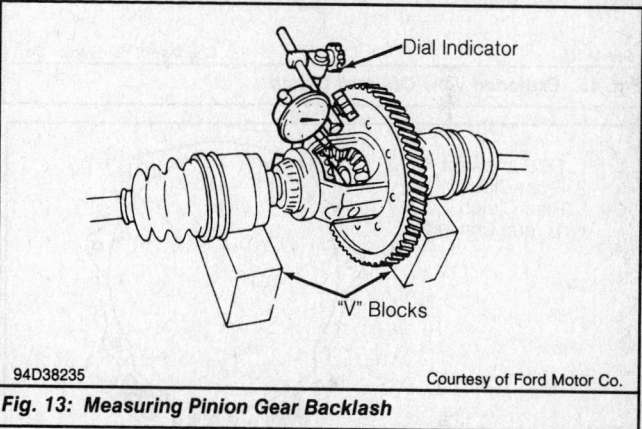

94D38235   Courtesy of Ford Motor Co.

Fig. 13: Measuring Pinion Gear Backlash

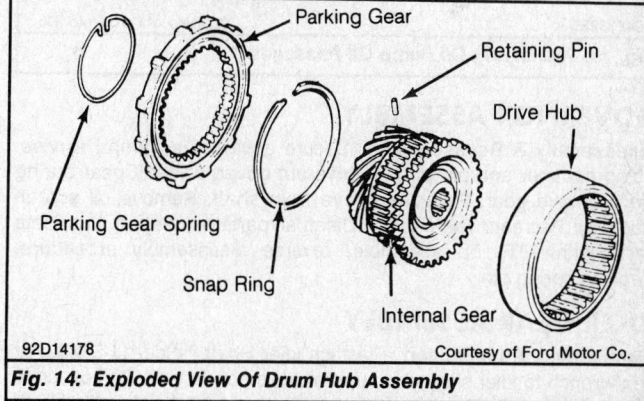

92D14178   Courtesy of Ford Motor Co.

Fig. 14: Exploded View Of Drum Hub Assembly

spring compressor. Remove spring retainer and return springs. Apply air pressure to front clutch oil passage and remove front clutch piston.

Inspection – Inspect all parts for wear or damage and replace as needed. Return springs must have free length of .992-1.071" (25.20-27.20 mm). If free length is not within specification, replace spring(s). Check inside diameter of clutch drum bushing. If diameter exceeds 1.735" (44.08 mm), replace bushing.

Reassembly – **1)** Reverse disassembly procedure to reassemble. Install new seal rings on piston and install piston by applying even pressure on perimeter while rotating piston. Install front clutch return springs and retainer. Compress spring retainer. Install snap ring.

2) Install dished plate. See Fig. 15. Install drive and driven clutch plates, retaining ring and snap ring. Using feeler gauge, measure between snap ring and retaining plate. Clearance should be .063-.071" (1.60-1.80 mm). If clearance is not correct, select correct thickness retaining plate. Retaining plates are available in thicknesses of .205" (5.20 mm) to .244" (6.20 mm) in .20 mm increments.

3) Place front clutch assembly over oil pump and apply air pressure (57 psi maximum) to front clutch oil passage in oil pump to check for proper front clutch operation. *See Fig. 16.*

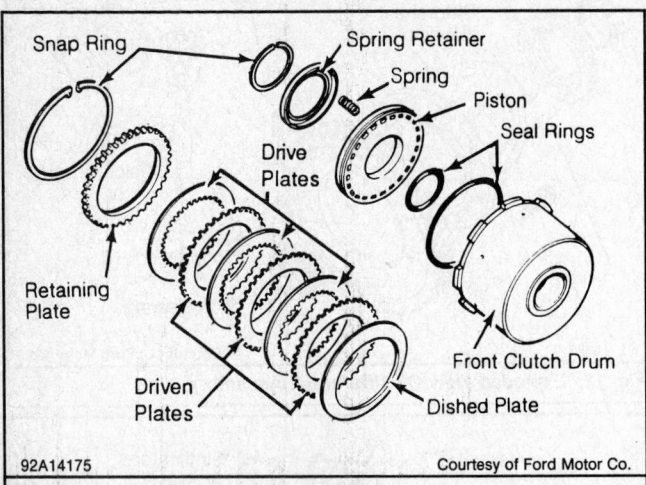

Fig. 15: Exploded View Of Front Clutch

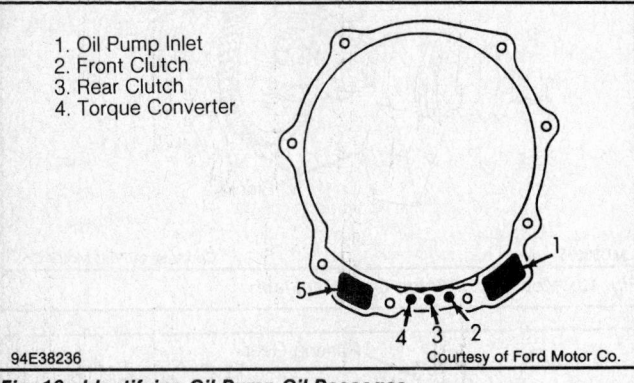

1. Oil Pump Inlet
2. Front Clutch
3. Rear Clutch
4. Torque Converter

Fig. 16: Identifying Oil Pump Oil Passages

GOVERNOR ASSEMBLY

Disassembly & Reassembly – Secure governor assembly in vise. Using hammer and pin punch, drive out governor shaft gear spring pin. Remove gear. Remove sleeve from shaft. Remove oil screen clamp and screen. *See Fig. 17.* Clean all parts as needed. Lubricate parts with ATF. To assemble, reverse disassembly procedure. Replace spring pin.

IDLER GEAR ASSEMBLY

Disassembly & Inspection – Attach Idler Shaft Holder (J-35286) or hex wrench to idler shaft and support assembly in vise. Remove lock nut. *See Fig. 18.* Remove bearing, spacer, idler gear, adjustment shim(s) and remaining bearing. Press bearing outer races from idler gear. Check all gear teeth for wear or damage and bearings for breakage or unusual wear.

Reassembly – 1) Place idler shaft holder or hex wrench in vise and place idler shaft on wrench. Install outer races in idler gear. Place bearing, idler gear, adjustment shim, spacers, bearing and nut on idler shaft and tighten nut to 94-130 ft. lbs. (127-176 N.m).

2) Measure bearing preload. Mount idler gear in vise. Using INCH lb. torque wrench, measure idler gear shaft turning torque. Turning torque should be .26-8.0 INCH lbs. (.03-.90 N.m). If preload is not within specification, change selective shims. Selective size shims are available from .004" (.10 mm) to .008" (.20 mm) in .04 mm increments.

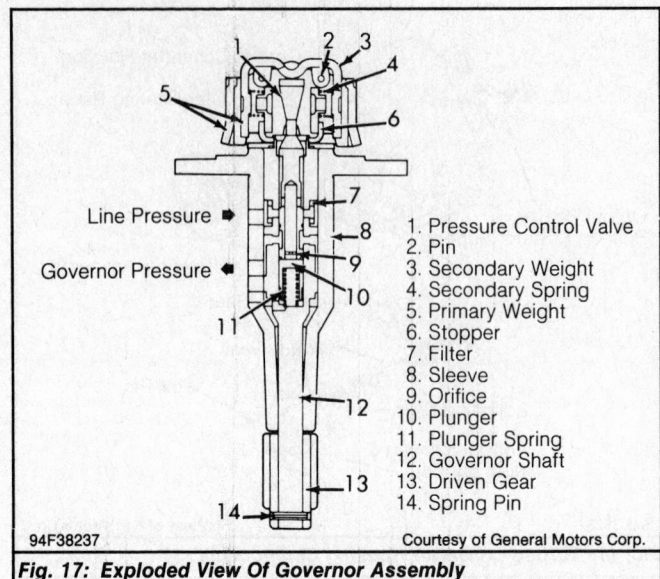

1. Pressure Control Valve
2. Pin
3. Secondary Weight
4. Secondary Spring
5. Primary Weight
6. Stopper
7. Filter
8. Sleeve
9. Orifice
10. Plunger
11. Plunger Spring
12. Governor Shaft
13. Driven Gear
14. Spring Pin

Fig. 17: Exploded View Of Governor Assembly

One .020" (.50 mm) shim is available. DO NOT use more than 7 shims. Once correct preload is obtained, retighten idler gear locknut to 94-130 ft. lbs. (128-177 N.m)

LOW-REVERSE BRAKE

Inspection – Check all components for signs of damage or excessive wear. Check free length of return springs. See LOW-REVERSE BRAKE SPRING SPECIFICATIONS table. If not correct, replace spring(s).

LOW-REVERSE BRAKE SPRING SPECIFICATIONS

Application	Free Length In. (mm)
Ford Aspire & Festiva	1.09 (27.7)
Geo Storm	1.051-1.130 (26.70-28.70)

OIL PUMP

Disassembly – Remove pump cover retaining bolts and separate cover from pump body. Remove pump flange. *See Fig. 19.* If gears are to be reused, match mark gears to reassemble in same position. Remove drive and driven gears.

Inspection – 1) Check condition of gear teeth and surfaces. Check seal rings for cracks or breaks and replace as needed. Check condition of pump housing sleeve and inner gear bushing. See OIL PUMP SPECIFICATIONS table. *See Fig. 20.* Check sleeve outer diameter and bushing inner diameter.

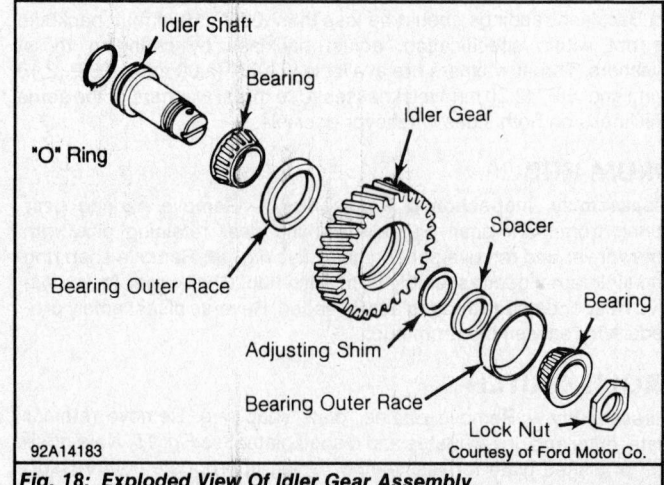

Fig. 18: Exploded View Of Idler Gear Assembly

2) If sleeve diameter is less than 1.492" (37.90 mm) or bushing diameter is greater than 1.499" (38.08 mm) replace sleeve and bushing as a set. Check pump clearances and compare with values shown in OIL PUMP SPECIFICATIONS table.

Reassembly – Apply ATF on all parts. To assemble, reverse disassembly procedure. Do Not tighten pump cover to oil pump housing. Oil pump reassembly is completed during transaxle reassembly.

OIL PUMP SPECIFICATIONS

Application	Clearance In. (mm)
Drive & Driven Gear-To-Pump Cover	.001-.003 (.025-.08)
Driven Gear-To-Crescent	.006-.010 (.14-.25)
Driven Gear-To-Pump Housing	.002-.003 (.04-.08)
Seal Ring Side	.002-.016 (.04-.40)

ONE-WAY CLUTCH

Disassembly, Inspection & Reassembly – 1) Record direction of rotation one-way clutch locks and turns. Remove snap ring and pull out planetary carrier from one-way clutch inner race. *See Fig. 8.* Check for worn or damaged parts. Bushing wear on one-way clutch must not exceed 5.120" (130.06 mm).

2) Check clearance between pinion gears and washers in planetary carrier. If clearance exceeds .031" (.80 mm), replace planetary carrier. Reverse disassembly procedure to reassemble. Install one-way clutch in inner race and ensure that it will turn in one direction (clockwise) only.

REAR CLUTCH

Disassembly – 1) Remove large snap ring. Lift out retaining plate, clutch plates, and dished plate. *See Fig. 21.* Using appropriate compressor, compress rear clutch spring retainer to remove small snap ring, spring retainer, and clutch return springs.

2) Place front clutch on oil pump and rear clutch hub on top of front clutch. Apply air pressure to rear clutch oil passage to remove piston. *See Fig. 16.* Remove and discard piston seal rings.

Inspection – Inspect for wear or damage. Ensure return spring free length is 1.031-1.071" (26.20-27.20 mm).

Reassembly – 1) Install seal rings on piston and install in clutch drum by applying even pressure on perimeter of piston and rotate piston slowly. Install return springs and spring retainer. Press spring retainer. Install snap ring. Note direction of dished plate and install. Install driven and drive plates, retainer plate and snap ring. *See Fig. 21.*

2) Ensure clearance between snap ring and retainer plate is .031-.039" (.80-1.00 mm). If clearance is not within specification, select correct retaining plate. Retaining plates are available in thicknesses .189" (4.80 mm) to .244" (6.20 mm) in .20 mm increments.

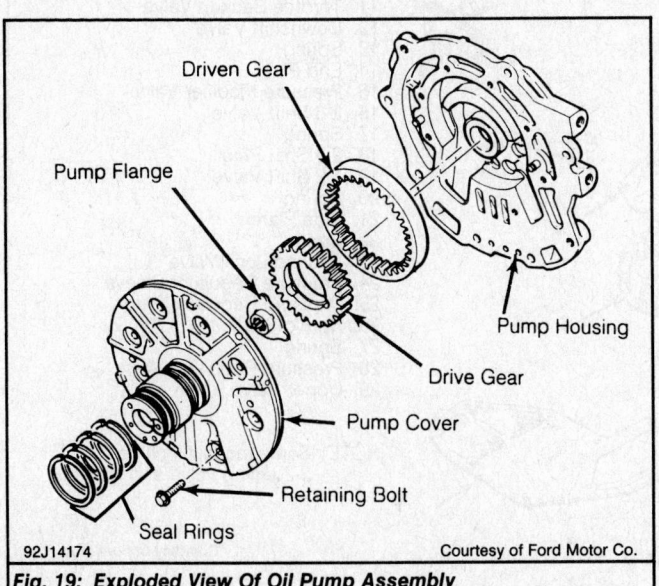

1. Gears-To-Cover Clearance
2. Cresent-To-Outer Gear Teeth Clearance
3. Outer Gear-To-Housing Clearance
4. Sealing Ring Side Clearance

94G38238   Courtesy of Ford Motor Co.

Fig. 20: Measuring Oil Pump Clearances

3) Check rear clutch operation by placing forward clutch on oil pump and then rear clutch. Apply compressed air (70 psi maximum) to rear clutch oil passage and check operation. *See Fig. 16.*

REAR CLUTCH HUB

Disassembly, Inspection & Reassembly – Remove snap ring and separate hub from internal gear. Check for worn or damaged snap ring or gear and replace as needed. Reverse disassembly procedure to reassemble hub.

VALVE BODY

NOTE: Remove and clean one valve at a time to avoid incorrect installation. If any valves, valve springs, or valve bodies are damaged, the entire valve body assembly must be replaced.

Disassembly – 1) Remove manual control valve. Remove oil strainer retaining bolts and oil strainer. Remove upper-to-lower valve body retaining bolts. Separate valve bodies, separator plate and sub-body. DO NOT lose check balls and springs or orifice valve and spring. *See Fig. 22.*

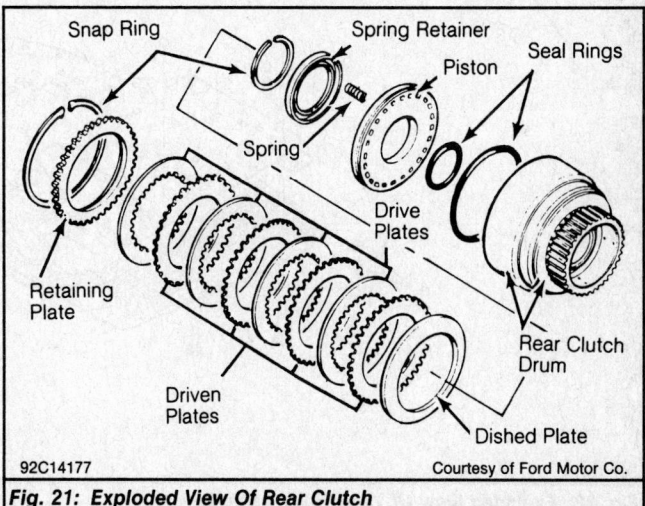

Snap Ring   Spring Retainer   Seal Rings   Piston   Spring   Drive Plates   Retaining Plate   Driven Plates   Rear Clutch Drum   Dished Plate

92C14177   Courtesy of Ford Motor Co.

Fig. 21: Exploded View Of Rear Clutch

Driven Gear   Pump Flange   Pump Housing   Drive Gear   Pump Cover   Retaining Bolt   Seal Rings

92J14174   Courtesy of Ford Motor Co.

Fig. 19: Exploded View Of Oil Pump Assembly

2) Remove, clean and install each valve individually as needed. *See Fig. 22.* Lubricate moving parts with ATF. Ensure all valves move (snap) freely. If valve sticks in its bore and cannot be freed, valve body must be replaced. Do not attempt to hone valve bores or polish valves.
3) Inspect valve springs for damage or deformation. Measure valve spring free length and diameter. See VALVE BODY SPRING DIMENSIONS table. Reassemble components in reverse order of disassembly.

VALVE BODY SPRING DIMENSIONS

Application	Free Length In. (mm)
Throttle Back-Up	1.417 (36.00)
Downshift	.862 (21.90)
2-3 Shift	
Ford Aspire & Festiva	1.614 (41.00)
Geo Storm	1.429 (36.30)
1-2 Shift	1.260 (32.00)
Second Lock	1.319 (33.50)
Pressure Regulator	1.693 (43.00)
Throttle Relief	.441 (11.20)
Orifice Check	
Ford Aspire & Festiva	.610 (15.50)
Geo Storm	.846 (21.50)
Steel Ball (Spring)	1.516 (26.80)

Reassembly – 1) To reassemble, reverse disassembly procedure. Coat all parts with clean transmission fluid. DO NOT force valves into position. Ensure orifice check valve, check ball and springs are located correctly.
2) Place separator plate on lower valve body and hold with clamps. Install upper valve body and bolt into place. Tighten upper valve body to lower valve body. See Fig. 23.

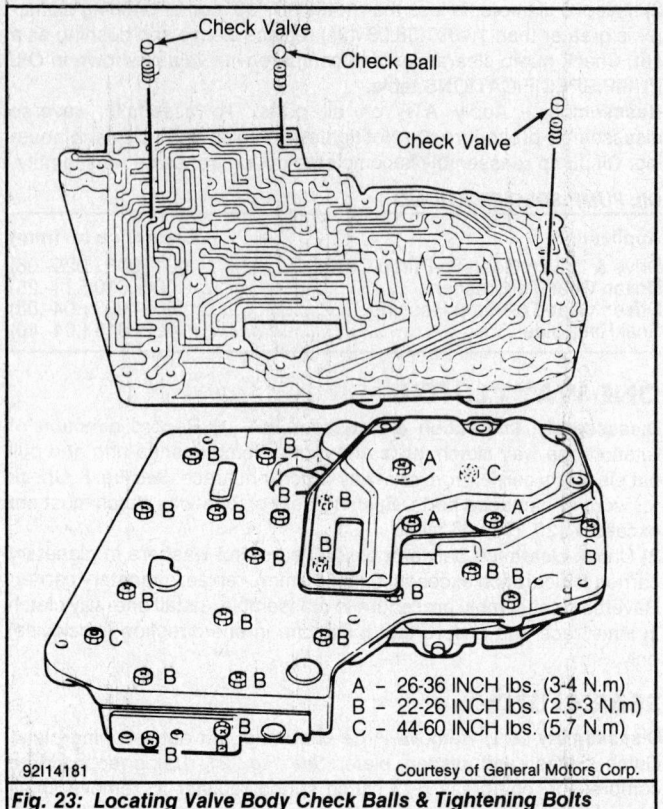

Check Valve
Check Ball
Check Valve

A – 26-36 INCH lbs. (3-4 N.m)
B – 22-26 INCH lbs. (2.5-3 N.m)
C – 44-60 INCH lbs. (5.7 N.m)

92I14181   Courtesy of General Motors Corp.

Fig. 23: Locating Valve Body Check Balls & Tightening Bolts

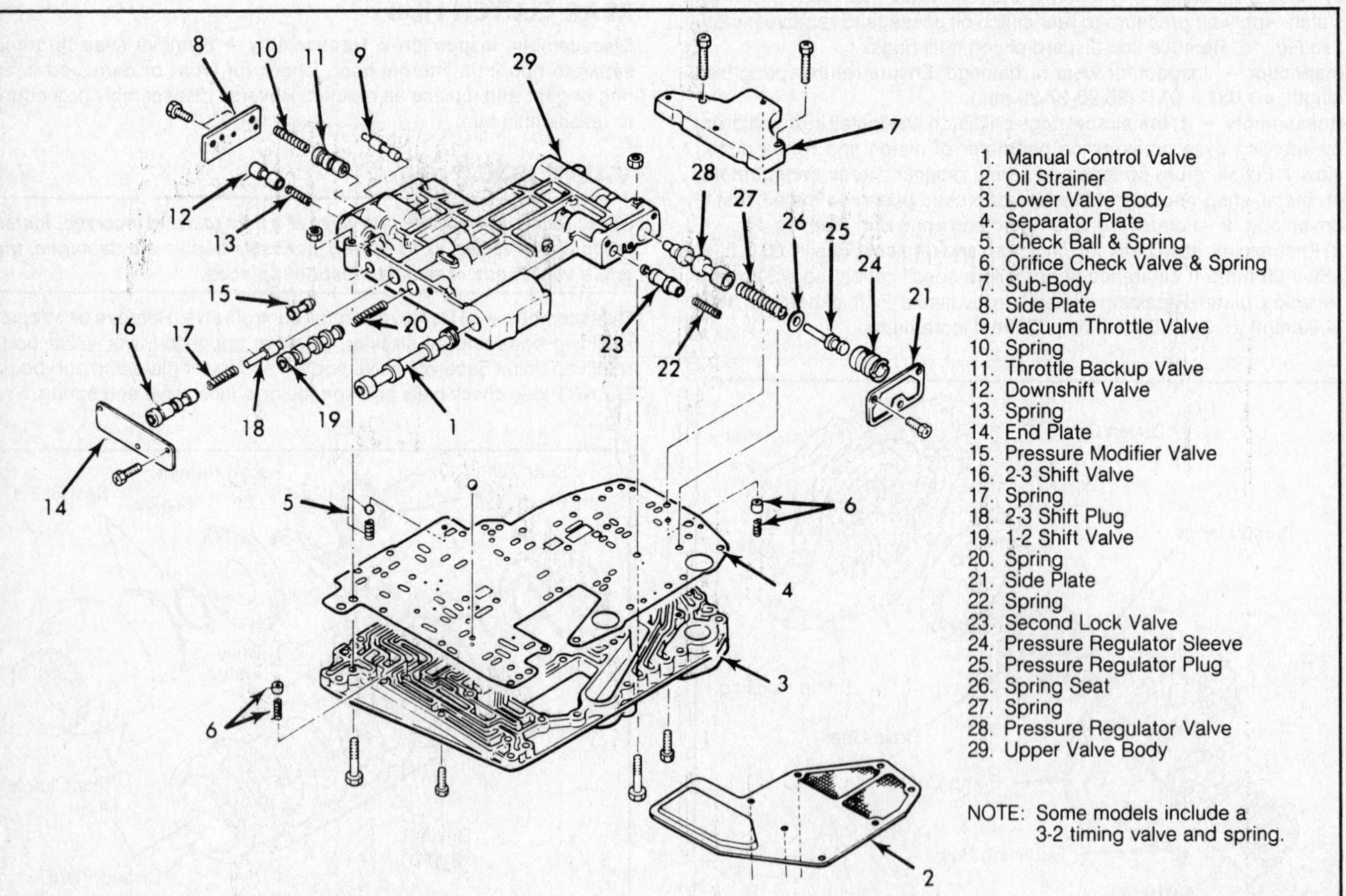

1. Manual Control Valve
2. Oil Strainer
3. Lower Valve Body
4. Separator Plate
5. Check Ball & Spring
6. Orifice Check Valve & Spring
7. Sub-Body
8. Side Plate
9. Vacuum Throttle Valve
10. Spring
11. Throttle Backup Valve
12. Downshift Valve
13. Spring
14. End Plate
15. Pressure Modifier Valve
16. 2-3 Shift Valve
17. Spring
18. 2-3 Shift Plug
19. 1-2 Shift Valve
20. Spring
21. Side Plate
22. Spring
23. Second Lock Valve
24. Pressure Regulator Sleeve
25. Pressure Regulator Plug
26. Spring Seat
27. Spring
28. Pressure Regulator Valve
29. Upper Valve Body

NOTE: Some models include a 3-2 timing valve and spring.

92H14180   Courtesy of Ford Motor Co.

Fig. 22: Exploded View Of Valve Body Assembly

TRANSAXLE CASE

Inspection – Inspect case for cracks and stripped threads. Inspect gasket surfaces and mating surfaces for burrs. Check vent for obstructions, and check all fluid passages for obstructions and leakage. Inspect case bushing for scores. Check all parking linkage parts for wear or damage.

TRANSAXLE REASSEMBLY

NOTE: Handle all parts carefully to avoid damaging bearings and mating surfaces. Lubricate all parts with clean ATF. Use petroleum jelly on gaskets, thrust washers and needle bearings to retain them in place. Soak all friction discs in ATF for at least 15 minutes. Use all new gaskets and seals, and tighten bolts evenly.

NOTE: For identification and position of thrust bearings and washers, see Fig. 27.

Output Shaft Bearing Preload – **1)** Position output shaft into torque converter housing. Position output shaft outer bearing race in recessed end of Gauge Tool (T87C-770002DJ). Place gauge tool over output shaft. *See Fig. 24.*
2) Ensure gauge tool is completely threaded together so that no gap is present. Position spacer collars and assemble output bearing and idler support to converter housing using supplied bolts and washers of tool set. *See Fig. 24.* Tighten bolts to 14-19 ft. lbs. (26 N.m).

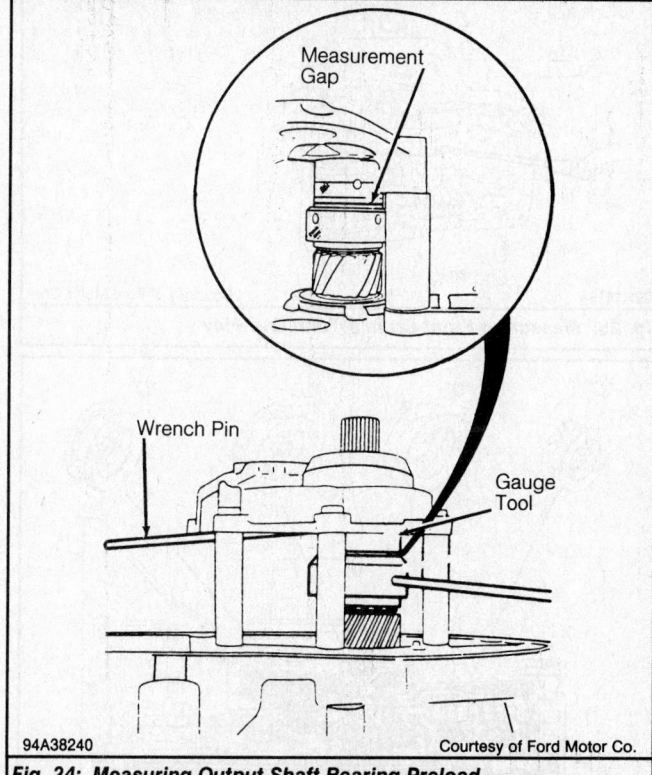

Fig. 24: *Measuring Output Shaft Bearing Preload*

3) Unthread gauge tool until output shaft bearings are seated and no play exists. Install Torque Adapter (T87C77000-E) over splined end of output shaft. Using INCH lb. torque wrench, rotate output shaft while unthreading gauge tool. Unthread gauge tool until 4.42-7.97 INCH lbs. (.5-.9 N.m) of turning torque is obtained.
4) Using feeler gauge, measure gap of gauge tool. Select correct thrust shim(s) that match measured gauge tool gap. Shims are available from in thicknesses of .004" (.10 mm) to .007" (.18 mm) in .02 mm increments. One shim is available in thickness of .019" (.50 mm).
5) Disassemble output bearing and idler support from converter housing. Remove gauge set and spacers. Install selected shim(s) in output bearing and idler support. DO NOT exceed 7 shims. Remove bearing

race from gauge tool and install race in support. Reassemble converter housing and output bearing and idler support. Install bolts and tighten bolts to specification. See TORQUE SPECIFICATIONS.
6) Install Torque Adapter (T87C77000-E) over splined end of output shaft. Using INCH lb. torque wrench, rotate output shaft to confirm correct bearing preload. Turning torque should be .26-7.96 INCH lbs. (.03-.9 N.m). If turning torque is not within specification, repeat steps **1)** through **6)**.
7) Once correct output shaft bearing preload is obtained, remove output bearing and idler gear support. Replace idler gear shaft seal on idler gear shaft. Install idler gear into converter housing. Install output gear and bearing support. Ensure alignment groove in idler gear shaft is aligned with support ridge of output bearing and idler support.
8) Install new idler gear shaft roll pin. Install output gear and bearing support bolts and tighten bolts to specification. See TORQUE SPECIFICATIONS.

Differential Bearing Preload Adjustment – **1)** Install differential assembly into converter housing. Position differential side bearing race in recessed end of Gauge Tool (T87-770002DJ). Place gauge tool on differential. *See Fig. 25.*
2) Ensure gauge tool is completely threaded together so that no gap is present. Position spacer collars and assemble case halves using supplied bolts and washers of tool set. *See Fig. 25.* Tighten bolts to 22-34 ft. lbs. (292D46 N.m).

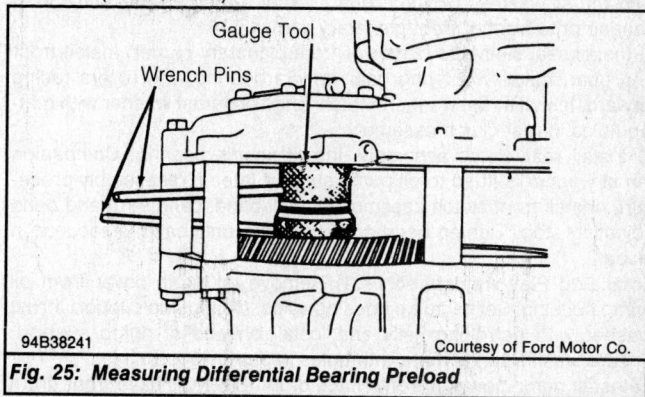

Fig. 25: *Measuring Differential Bearing Preload*

3) Unthread gauge tool until differential bearings are seated. Install Differential Rotator into differential assembly. Using INCH lb. torque wrench, rotate differential assembly while unthreading gauge tool. Unthread gauge tool until 4.3 INCH lbs. (.5 N.m) of turning torque is obtained.
4) Using feeler gauge, measure gap of gauge tool. Select correct thrust shim(s) by adding .006" (.15 mm) to measured gauge tool gap. Shims are available from in thicknesses of .043" (1.08 mm) to .079" (2.00 mm) in .040 mm increments.
5) Disassemble case halves. Remove gauge set and spacers. Install selected shim(s) in transaxle case. DO NOT exceed 3 shims. Remove bearing race from gauge tool and install race in transaxle case. Reassemble transaxle case halves. Install bolts and tighten bolts to specification. See TORQUE SPECIFICATIONS.
6) Install Differential Rotator (T88C-77000-L) into differential assembly. Using INCH lb. torque wrench, rotate differential assembly to confirm correct bearing preload. Turning torque should be 18-25 INCH lbs. (21.-2.8 N.m). If turning torque is not within specification, repeat steps **1)** through **6)**.

Final Reassembly – **1)** Install low-reverse brake piston by applying even pressure on perimeter of piston while rotating slowly. Install 20 return springs and low-reverse brake hub. Using appropriate compressor, compress return spring and install snap ring. *See Fig. 9.*
2) Install dished plate with small end of dish facing away from piston. Install clutch discs, retainer ring and one-way clutch. Install one-way clutch machined surface toward retainer ring. Install snap ring.

NOTE: Low/reverse snap ring may not have been installed during production. Snap ring is required during overhaul reassembly.

3) Using a feeler gauge, ensure clearance between one-way clutch and retainer plate is .031-.041" (.80-1.05 mm). If clearance is not within specification, select correct retainer plate to obtain correct clearance. Retainer plates are available in thicknesses of .063" (1.60 mm) to .102" (2.60 mm) in .20 mm increments. Apply air pressure to low-reverse oil passage and check for proper clutch operation. See Fig. 10.

4) Place converter housing on bench with output shaft facing upward. Install needle bearing over output shaft. Install drum hub assembly onto output shaft spline. Install needle bearing with thrust washer in recess of drum hub. Install rear planetary carrier onto one-way clutch race. Install snap ring. Install rear planetary assembly into drum hub. Install oil tubes into transaxle case.

5) Install governor into transaxle case. Ensure alignment mark on governor sleeve is aligned with mark on transaxle case. Install governor cover. Tighten bolts to specification. See TORQUE SPECIFICATIONS. Apply appropriate gasket sealant to converter housing and install transaxle case. Once case halves are secured in place, ensure all parts previously installed rotate without resistance.

6) Lubricate servo piston with ATF. Assembly servo retainer, piston, piston large seal and spring. Insert assembly into transaxle. Using "C" clamp and socket, compress assembly and install snap ring.

7) Install thrust bearing and thrust washer. Install sun gear shell with sun gear spacer and sun gear. See Fig. 8. Install front planetary carrier with thrust washer onto sun gear. Install thrust washer and thrust bearing onto front of front planetary carrier.

8) Install seal sleeve to center of front planetary carrier. Install front ring gear. Install front ring gear needle bearing with rollers facing upward. Install thrust washer. Match tangs on thrust washer with mating holes in rear clutch assembly.

9) Install rear clutch assembly. Install needle bearing. Companion thrust washer is fitted to oil pump support later in reassembly procedure. Install front clutch assembly. Install band, band strut and band adjusting stop. Tighten band adjusting stop until band is secured in place.

Total End Play Adjustment – 1) Remove oil pump cover from oil pump housing. Set oil pump housing aside. Coat pump support thrust washer with petroleum jelly and install on end of pump support. Ensure washer tangs mate with holes in pump support.

2) Install pump cover in front clutch drum. DO NOT have front drum adjusting thrust shim installed. Place a straightedge across transaxle case over pump cover. Measure clearance between straightedge and pump cover, or between straightedge and transaxle case. See Fig. 26.

3) If pump cover is below edge of transaxle case, clearance between straightedge and pump cover should not exceed .004" (.10 mm). If pump cover is above edge of transaxle case, clearance between straightedge and transaxle case should not exceed .006" (.15 mm).

4) If pump cover and/or transaxle case clearance is correct, total clutch assembly end play will be correct. Total clutch assembly end play should be .010-.020" (.25-.50 mm). If pump cover and/or transaxle case clearance is incorrect, remove pump cover and replace pump support thrust washer. Thrust washers are available in thicknesses from .047" (1.20 mm) to .087" (2.20 mm) in .20 mm increments.

5) Reassemble oil pump by aligning marks on oil pump gears. Place pump cover on pump housing. Install and tighten bolts to specification. See TORQUE SPECIFICATIONS. Install oil pump shaft in oil pump and check operation by turning shaft by hand. Gears should move freely without binding.

6) Install front clutch thrust washer over pump support. Install oil pump to transaxle. Install oil pump bolts. Apply sealant on 2 lower bolts and tighten bolts to specification. See TORQUE SPECIFICATIONS.

7) Position transaxle with oil pump facing down. Turn sun shell 2 revolutions. Insert screwdriver between tabs of front clutch and sun shell deep slots. Using a feeler gauge, measure in the shallow slots. See Fig. 26.

8) End play should be .020-.031" (.50-.80 mm). If end play is not within specification, remove oil pump and install correct thrust washer. Thrust washers are available in thicknesses of .051" (1.30 mm) to .106" (2.70 mm) in .20 mm increments.

9) Tighten band adjusting stop bolt to 106-133 INCH lbs. (12-15 N.m). Loosen bolt 3 turns and then tighten lock nut to 41-59 ft. lbs. (56-80 N.m). Install valve body steel check ball and spring in case. Install valve body and oil pan. Install turbine and oil pump shafts. Install speedometer driven gear, oil dipstick and tube.

10) Install vacuum modulator valve in transaxle. Ensure correct length control rod is installed in modulator. See VACUUM THROTTLE VALVE DIAPHRAGM (MODULATOR) under ON-VEHICLE SERVICE. Install kickdown solenoid and park/neutral switch. Install torque converter. With converter properly installed, distance between machined pad on torque converter and front edge of transaxle housing should be .50" (12.7 mm).

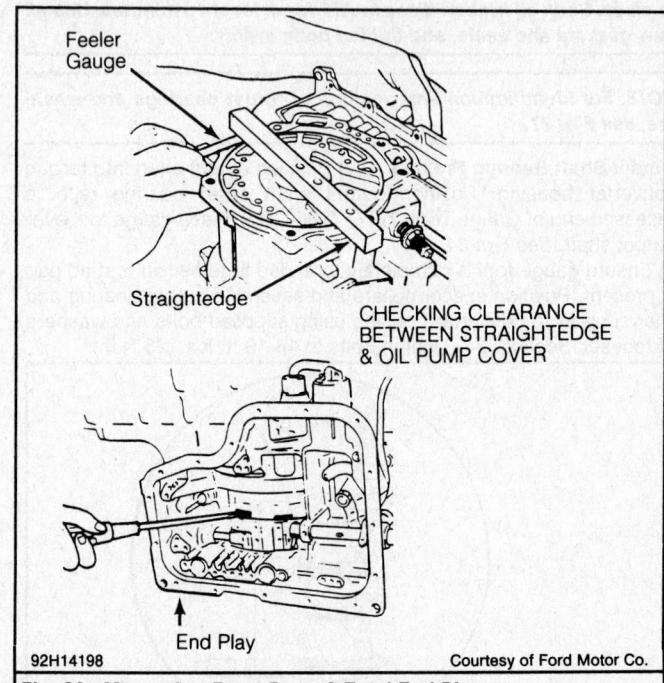

Feeler Gauge

Straightedge

CHECKING CLEARANCE BETWEEN STRAIGHTEDGE & OIL PUMP COVER

End Play

92H14198   Courtesy of Ford Motor Co.

Fig. 26: Measuring Front Drum & Total End Play

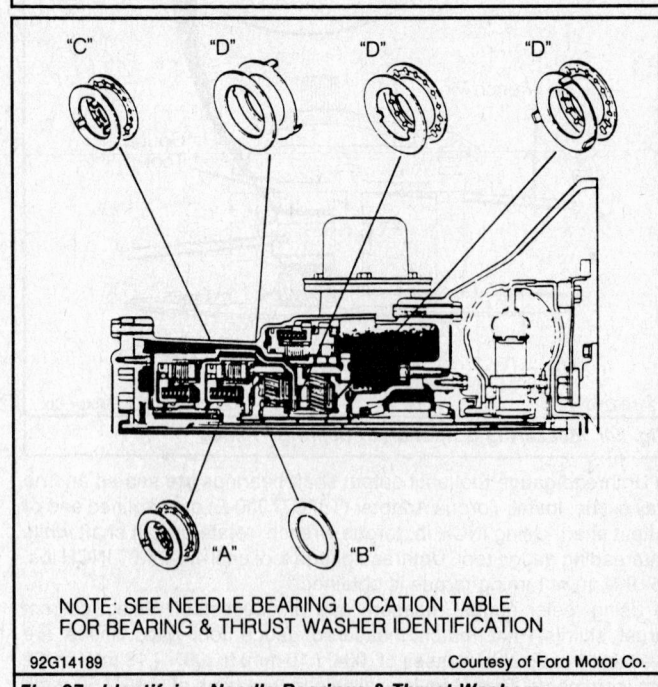

"C"   "D"   "D"   "D"

"A"   "B"

NOTE: SEE NEEDLE BEARING LOCATION TABLE FOR BEARING & THRUST WASHER IDENTIFICATION

92G14189   Courtesy of Ford Motor Co.

Fig. 27: Identifying Needle Bearings & Thrust Washers

NEEDLE BEARING LOCATION TABLE

Application	Dimension In. (mm)
Needle Bearing	
"A"	1.650 (41.90)
"B"	1.846 (46.90)
"C"	2.083 (52.90)
"D"	2.752 (69.90)
Thrust Washer	
"A"	1.614 (41.00)
"C"	2.028 (51.50)
"D"	2.756 (70.00)

TORQUE SPECIFICATIONS

TORQUE SPECIFICATIONS

Application	Ft. Lbs. (N.m)
Axle Nut	116-174 (157-235)
Ball Joint Clamp Bolt	40-50 (54-68)
Idler Gear Lock Nut	94-130 (127-176)
Lug Nut	65-87 (88-118)
Oil Pump-To-Transaxle Case	11-16 (15-22)
Output Bearing/Idler Support Bolt	14-19 (19-26)
Output Shaft/Stator Support Bolt	8-10 (11-14)
Ring Gear	51-62 (69-83)
Torque Converter-To-Drive Plate	25-36 (34-49)
Transaxle Case-To-Converter Housing	22-34 (29-46)

Application	INCH Lbs. (N.m)
Governor Cover Bolts	71-97 (8-11)
Oil Pan Bolts	71-97 (8-11)
Oil Pump Cover	97-124 (11-14)
Upper-To-Lower Valve Body	[1]
Valve Body Bolts	89 (10)

[1] – See Fig. 19.

TRANSAXLE SPECIFICATIONS

TRANSAXLE SPECIFICATIONS

Application	In. (mm)
Differential Backlash	.004 (.01)
Front Clutch Drum Bushing Diameter	1.735 (44.08)
Front Clutch Pack Clearance	.063-.071 (1.6-1.8)
Front Drum End Play	.020-.031 (.5-.8)
Front Planetary Pinion Clearance	.031 (.8)
Low/Reverse Clutch Pack Clearance	.032-.041 (.8-1.05)
Oil Pump Gear Clearance	.010 (.25)
Oil Pump Sealing Ring Clearance	.016 (.40)
Outer Gear-To-Housing Clearance [2]	.10 (.25)
Output Gear End Play	.003 (.08)
Rear Clutch Pack Clearance	.031-.039 (.8-1.0)
Rear Planetary Pinion Clearance	.031 (.8)

[1] – INCH lbs. (N.m).
[2] – Oil pump outer gear.

AUTOMATIC TRANSMISSIONS
Ford AXOD-E

Ford Motor Co: Continental, Sable, Taurus

NOTE: The AXOD-E transaxle is also known as AX4S.

APPLICATION & LABOR TIMES

APPLICATION & LABOR TIMES

Vehicle Application	Labor Times [1] R & I	Labor Times [2] Overhaul	Engine Size
1993-1994			
Continental	8.3	7.8	3.8L SFI
Sable	7.7	7.8	3.0L SFI
Sable	8.1	7.8	3.8L SFI
Taurus	7.7	7.8	3.0L SFI
Taurus	8.1	7.8	3.8L SFI
Taurus (Police)	8.1	7.8	3.8L SFI
Taurus (SHO)	7.9	7.8	3.2L SFI

[1] – Removal and installation of transmission from vehicle chassis.

[2] – Bench overhaul time for transmission and differential. DOES NOT include removal and installation.

IDENTIFICATION

The AXOD-E (Automatic Overdrive Transaxle-Electronic) is identified by the code letter "T", shown on the Vehicle Certification Label under "TR". The label is located on the driver's door lock panel or door pillar.

The transaxle also has an identification tag attached to the top of the converter housing. Use this information when servicing or ordering replacement parts. *See Fig. 2.*

Transaxle Model Number Designator Is Shown In Mirror Image (AAC)
Transaxle Assembly Number
Engine Size Designator
Serial Number
UDD
ASSY E9DP-CA
SN- 000050

92D12818 Courtesy of Ford Motor Co.

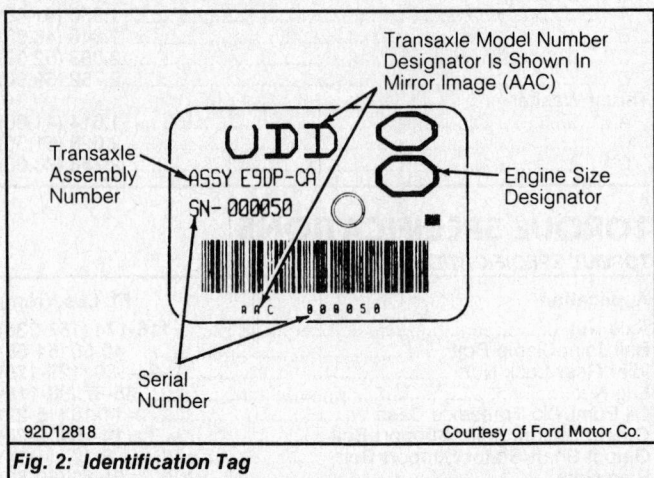

Fig. 2: Identification Tag

NOTE: For AXOD-E transaxle electronic testing and repair, see AXOD-E Electronic Controls article.

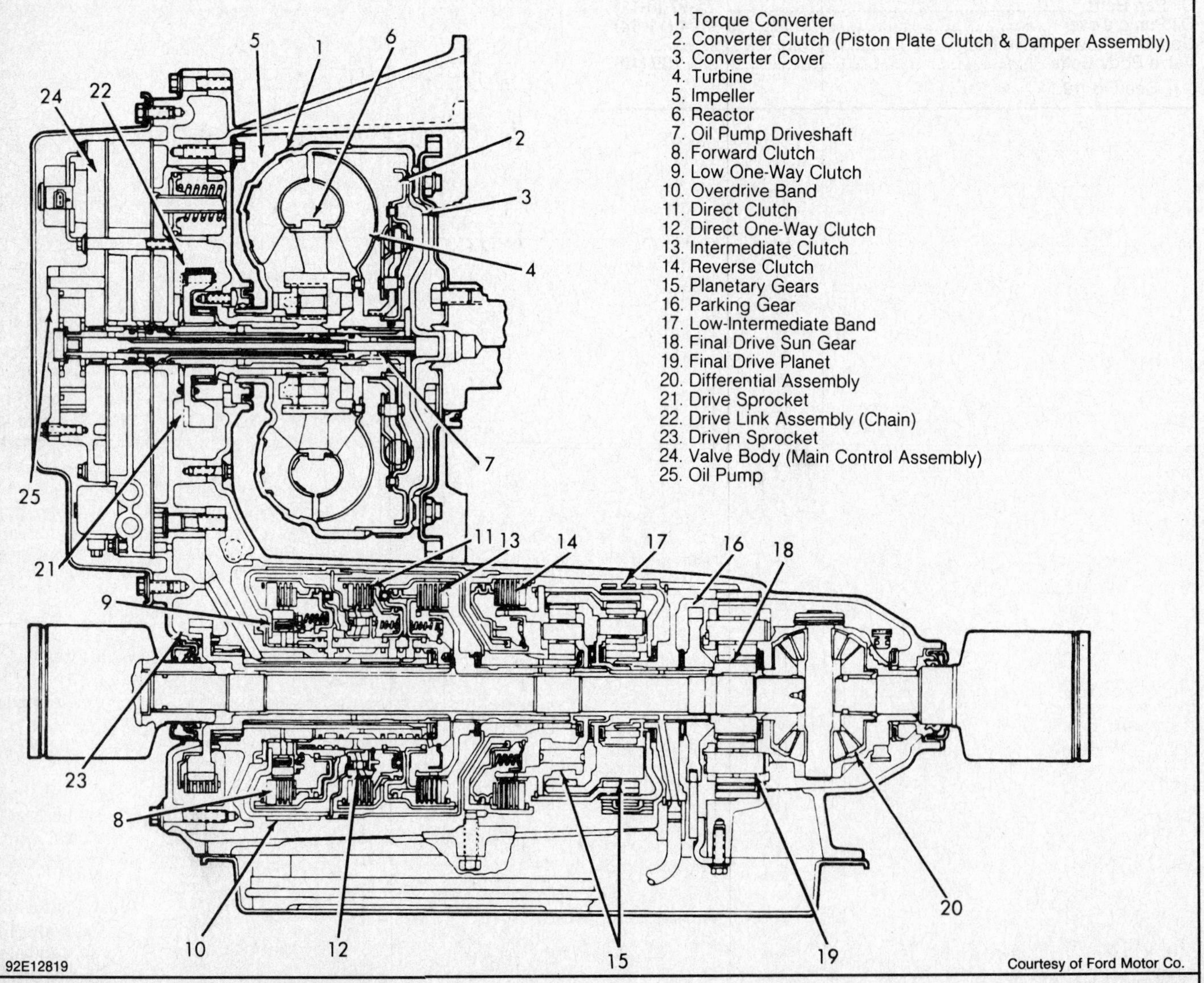

1. Torque Converter
2. Converter Clutch (Piston Plate Clutch & Damper Assembly)
3. Converter Cover
4. Turbine
5. Impeller
6. Reactor
7. Oil Pump Driveshaft
8. Forward Clutch
9. Low One-Way Clutch
10. Overdrive Band
11. Direct Clutch
12. Direct One-Way Clutch
13. Intermediate Clutch
14. Reverse Clutch
15. Planetary Gears
16. Parking Gear
17. Low-Intermediate Band
18. Final Drive Sun Gear
19. Final Drive Planet
20. Differential Assembly
21. Drive Sprocket
22. Drive Link Assembly (Chain)
23. Driven Sprocket
24. Valve Body (Main Control Assembly)
25. Oil Pump

92E12819 Courtesy of Ford Motor Co.

Fig. 1: Identifying Transmission Components

DESCRIPTION

The AXOD-E combines an automatic transaxle and differential into a single unit designed for front wheel drive vehicles. The transaxle is an electronically controlled, fully automatic unit with 4 forward speeds, one Reverse, Neutral and Park. Shift control solenoids provide gear selection and are controlled by the EEC-IV microprocessor. For additional information on the EEC-IV system, refer to SELF-DIAGNOSTICS – EEC-IV article in ENGINE PERFORMANCE of appropriate MITCHELL® manual.

The AXOD-E has 2 planetary gear sets and a combination planetary/differential gear set. Four multiple-plate clutches, 2 band assemblies, and 2 roller (one-way) clutches act as friction elements for operation of the planetary gear sets. See Fig. 1.

A lock-up torque converter couples the engine output to the planetary gears and overdrive unit. This is done by a chain which connects the drive and driven sprockets. The converter lock-up is controlled through the EEC-IV system. A piston plate clutch, inside converter, is activated by the computer and valve body.

LUBRICATION & ADJUSTMENTS

See appropriate AUTOMATIC TRANSMISSION SERVICING article in TRANSMISSION SERVICING.

TROUBLE SHOOTING

CAUTION: Vehicle should not be driven if fluid level is lower than DO NOT DRIVE hole on transmission dipstick.

FLUID LEVEL CHECK

Before vehicle is driven, ensure fluid is above DO NOT DRIVE hole on dipstick. Drive vehicle 15-20 miles, until transmission is at operating temperature (dipstick is hot to touch). Vehicle must be at operating temperature to ensure correct fluid level check.

Fluid level should be checked in Park position with engine at idle. Fluid level should be within cross-hatched are of dipstick. Ensure the following:

- Use only Mercon transmission fluid.
- If transmission fluid is excessively hot, allow vehicle to cool for 30 minutes prior to checking fluid level. Excessive heat build-up due to high speed operation, trailer towing, or operation in hot weather will effect fluid level.
- DO NOT overfill transmission. Fluid will foam and may cause transmission malfunction. Excessive fluid must be removed.
- If transmission is underfilled, slipping may occur.

PRELIMINARY INSPECTION

1) Ensure vehicle is thoroughly road tested to verify driver's complaint. Determine if problem occurs during upshift, downshift, coasting or engagement. If noise is diagnosed, check if noise is affected by RPM, vehicle speed, gear selection or temperature. Ensure vehicle is at normal operating temperature when checking.

2) Inspect fluid level and condition. Visually inspect for vehicle modifications, electronic add-ons, fluid leaks and/or incorrect linkage adjustment. Check for trouble codes before any mechanical repair is performed. See AXOD-E ELECTRONIC CONTROLS article for trouble code diagnosis and repair procedures. If no trouble codes are present, see applicable symptom diagnosis.

3) If the following symptoms are present, it is necessary to complete electronic diagnosis and repair before any mechanical diagnosis and repair is performed. See AXOD-E ELECTRONIC CONTROLS article for trouble code diagnosis and repair procedures.

- No Forward
- No Reverse
- Harsh Engagement
- All Or Some Shifts Not Present
- Early, Late, Erratic, Soft, Slipping And/Or Harsh Shifting
- No First Gear (In "D" Position).

- No Low Gear.
- No 2nd Gear (SHO only).
- No Torque Converter Clutch
- Torque Converter Clutch Always Engaged
- Torque Converter Cycling, Shudder Or Chatter
- Poor Vehicle Performance
- Transaxle Overheating
- No Engine Braking In Low ("L")
- No Engine Braking In 3rd (Overdrive Cancelled), (SHO only)

ENGAGEMENT FAULTS

No Forward Engagement, Reverse Okay – Check fluid level, drive axles, shift linkage, low internal pressure, oil pump external or internal (support sealing rings) leakage, filter or filter seal, valve body malfunction (gasket cross-leak, stuck regulator valve, 3-4 shift valve, forward clutch control valve and 2-3 servo regulator valve), forward clutch assembly, overrunning clutch, support assembly (driven sprocket), low intermediate servo assembly and output shaft.

No Reverse Engagement, Forward Okay – Check fluid level, drive axles, external and internal shift linkage, low line pressure, valve body (bolt torque, gasket cross-leak, forward clutch valve, manual control valve, main regulator valve and springs), oil pump assembly, support assembly (driven sprocket), forward clutch assembly, reverse clutch assembly, overrunning clutch assembly (planetary) and output shaft.

Harsh Reverse Engagement – Check fluid level, axle shafts and CV joints, engine/transaxle mounts, shift linkage, line pressure, restricted oil filter, valve body (improperly torqued bolts, gasket cross-leak, B1 check ball, pressure failsafe valve, manual control valve, main regulator valve), reverse clutch assembly and oil pump assembly.

Harsh Forward Engagement – Check fluid level, axle shafts and CV joints, engine/transaxle mounts, shift linkage, line pressure, valve body (improperly torqued bolts, gasket cross-leak, B2 or B3 check ball, pressure failsafe valve, main regulator valve, backout valve, EPC solenoid, 2-3 servo regulator valve, engagement valve), oil pump assembly, low and intermediate servo, drive shift accumulator, forward clutch assembly, and low and intermediate band/rear sun gear and drum.

Delayed Or Soft Reverse Engagement – Check fluid level, axle shafts and CV joints, engine/transaxle mounts, shift linkage, line pressure, restricted oil filter, valve body (improperly torqued bolts, gasket cross-leak, manual control valve, main regulator valve, B5 check ball, converter drain back valve, springs), oil pump assembly, support assembly (driven sprocket), neutral to drive accumulator, forward clutch assembly, reverse clutch assembly and drive shift accumulator.

Delayed Or Soft Forward Engagement – Check fluid level, axle shafts and CV joints, engine/transaxle mounts, shift linkage, line pressure, restricted oil filter, valve body (improperly torqued bolts, gasket cross-leak, manual control valve, main regulator valve, B5 check ball, 3-4 shift valve, backout valve, 2-3 servo regulator valve, engagement valve), oil pump assembly, low intermediate servo assembly, support assembly (driven sprocket), neutral to drive accumulator, forward clutch assembly, drive shift accumulator and low and intermediate band/rear sun gear and drum.

SHIFTING MALFUNCTION

All Or Some Shifts Not Present – Check fluid level, shift linkage, speedometer drive/driven gear, following symptoms.

Early Or Late Shifting – Check tire size, speedometer drive/driven gear and valve body.

Erratic/Hunting Shift Timing – Check fluid level, vehicle speed input, valve body and torque converter clutch (TCC).

Soft/Slipping Shift Feel – Check fluid condition and level, shift linkage, low line pressure and valve body (1-2 capacity modulator valve, accumulator/regulator valve, main regulator valve, 2-3 servo regulator valve, check balls, 3-2 shift timing valve, EPC solenoid, pressure failsafe valve and springs).

Harsh Shift Feel – Check fluid level and condition, axle shafts and CV joints, high line pressure, high EPC pressure and valve body (1-2 capacity modulator valve, accumulator regulator valve, main regulator valve, 2-3 servo regulator valve, 3-2 timing valve, springs, check balls).

No First Gear (In "D" Position) – Check shift linkage, valve body (shift valves, intermediate clutch shuttle valve, forward clutch control valve, springs) and internal seal(s) leakage and bands or clutches.

No Low Gear – Check shift linkage, valve body (improperly torqued bolts, gasket cross-leak, manual low relief valve, springs), low direct clutch pressure, low line pressure, low EPC pressure, support assembly (driven sprocket) and direct clutch.

No Manual 2nd Gear (3.2L SHO Only) – Check shift linkage/cable/MLP sensor, valve body (improperly torqued bolts, gasket cross-leak, shift valves, forward clutch control valve, shift solenoids), clutch assembly, low intermediate servo, support assembly (drive sprocket), low one-way clutch assembly and low intermediate band.

MISCELLANEOUS FAULTS

No Torque Converter Clutch – Check low line pressure, low EPC pressure, valve body (improperly torqued bolts, gasket cross-leak, valve body pilot sleeve, manual shift valve, TCC control valve and/or plunger, converter regulator valve, springs, solenoid regulator valve), turbine shaft, oil pump shaft and torque converter.

Torque Converter Clutch Always Engaged (Stalls Engine) – Check valve body (improperly torque bolts, gasket cross-leak, TCC control valve or plunger) and torque converter.

Torque Converter Clutch Cycling/Shudder/Chatter – Check fluid condition, low line pressure, low EPC pressure, valve body (improperly torque bolts, gasket cross-leak, TCC control valve or plunger, valve body output sleeve, manual shift valve, converter regulator valve), TCC solenoid, turbine shaft, oil pump shaft and torque converter.

No Engine Braking In 3rd Gear (OD Position) With OD Cancelled (3.2L SHO Only) – Check shift linkage, forward clutch pressure, line pressure, valve body (improperly torqued bolts, gasket cross-leak, shift valves, forward clutch control valve), forward clutch assembly and low one-way clutch assembly.

No Engine Braking In Manual Low Position – Check shift linkage, direct clutch pressure, valve body (improperly torqued bolts, gasket cross-leak, manual low relief valve, 1-2 shift valve, pull-in valve), direct clutch assembly and direct overrunning clutch assembly.

Stiff Shift Lever Operation – Check shift interlock system, shift linkage and manual valve (valve body).

Poor Vehicle Performance – Check correct shift linkage to shift lever indexing, torque converter (TCC applied and one-way clutch).

Transaxle Overheating – Check fluid condition and level, cooler line restriction, auxiliary cooler, valve body (TCC control valve and plunger, converter regulator valve) and seized converter clutch.

BAND & CLUTCH APPLICATION CHART

BAND & CLUTCH APPLICATION CHART

Selector Position (Gear)	Bands & Clutches Applied
"L" (1st Gear)	Lo-Int Band, Forward Clutch, Direct Clutch, Low One-Way Clutch
"D" (1st Gear)	Lo-Int Band, Forward Clutch Low One-Way Clutch
"D" (2nd Gear)	Lo-Int Band, Forward Clutch, Intermediate Clutch Low One-Way Clutch (Overrunning)
"D" (3rd Gear)	Intermediate Clutch, Direct Clutch
"OD" (4th Gear)	OD Band, Intermediate Clutch, Direct Clutch Direct One-Way Clutch (Overrunning)
"R" (Reverse)	Forward Clutch, Reverse Clutch Low One-Way Clutch
"N" (Neutral)	Forward Clutch
"P" (Park)	Forward Clutch

TESTING

AIR PRESSURE TEST

A NO DRIVE condition may exist even when line pressure is correct. This may be caused by an inoperative band or clutch. An erratic shift may be located by substituting air pressure for fluid pressure.

With gear selector lever in a forward gear position, a NO DRIVE condition may be caused by an inoperative forward clutch, low-intermediate one-way clutch or low-intermediate band.

A NO COAST condition in manual low (1st gear), could be caused by a faulty direct clutch or direct one-way clutch. Reverse failure may be caused by a malfunctioning reverse clutch, forward clutch or low-intermediate one-way clutch. Use the following procedure to perform air pressure tests:

1) Drain transaxle fluid and remove oil pan. Remove valve body cover, oil pump and valve body assembly. See OIL PUMP & VALVE ASSEMBLY under ON-VEHICLE SERVICE. Install Air Pressure Test Plate (T91P-7006-A) with valve body assembly-to-chain cover gasket.

2) Faulty clutches and bands may be located by applying air pressure to the indicated test ports. *See Fig. 3.* Refer to appropriate test procedure for listed components.

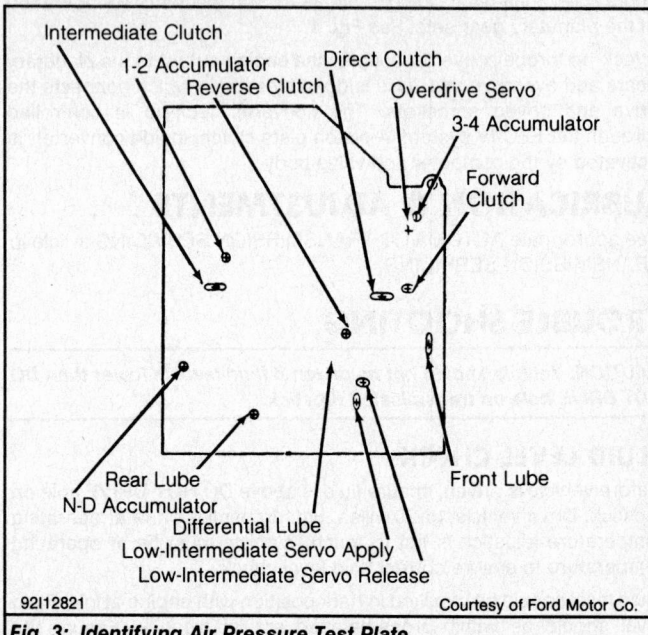

Fig. 3: Identifying Air Pressure Test Plate

Forward Clutch – Apply air pressure to forward clutch test port. A dull thud can be heard, or movement of piston felt when clutch piston is applied. If clutch seal(s) are leaking, a hissing sound will be heard.

Overdrive Servo – Apply air pressure to overdrive servo test port. Operation of servo is indicated by tightening of overdrive band around overdrive drum. Due to cushioning effect of servo release spring, this may not be heard or felt. Servo should hold air pressure and a dull thud should be heard when air pressure is released.

Direct Clutch – Apply air pressure to direct clutch test port. A dull thud can be heard, or movement of piston felt on case as piston is applied. A hissing sound indicates a leaking clutch seal.

Intermediate Clutch – Apply air pressure to intermediate clutch test port. A dull thud can be heard, or movement of piston felt on transmission case as piston is applied. If clutch seal(s) are leaking, a hissing sound will be heard.

NOTE: If air pressure fails to operate a clutch, or operates clutches simultaneously, remove and, using air pressure, check fluid passages in the clutches, chain cover and driven sprocket support.

Low-Intermediate Servo – **1)** Apply air pressure to low-intermediate servo apply test port. Low-intermediate band should tighten around sun gear of rear planetary gear set. Due to cushioning effect of the servo release spring, band application may not be heard or felt. Servo should hold air pressure and a dull thud should be heard when air pressure is released.

2) Apply air pressure to low-intermediate servo release test port while continuing to pressurize apply port. Servo piston should return to release position. Low-intermediate band should loosen and a dull thud should be heard. Release air pressure from apply test port. The release test port should hold air pressure. Any leakage or failure of piston movement requires servo servicing.

Lube & Rear Lube Passages – Apply air pressure to lube and rear lube test ports to check for blockage. If either passage holds air pressure, remove test plate and check for an obstruction or damage.

NOTE: If air pressure applied to the accumulator passages fails to operate an accumulator, remove and check fluid passages in the accumulator and chain cover.

1-2, 3-4 & N-D Accumulators – Apply air pressure to each accumulator test port. Accumulator should apply. Due to cushioning effect of release spring, application may not be heard or felt. Accumulator should hold air pressure without leaking and a dull thud should be heard when air pressure is released.

LINE PRESSURE TEST

1) Connect a pressure gauge to line pressure test port. *See Fig. 4.* Start engine. Apply service and parking brakes. Check pressure in all gears. See TRANSAXLE PRESSURE SPECIFICATIONS (PSI) table.
2) If pressure is not within specification, perform QUICK TEST and PINPOINT TEST E. See AXOD-E Electronic Controls article. Also perform air pressure checks and service valve body. See AIR PRESSURE TEST.
3) If line pressure is not within specification after servicing valve body and there are no fault codes present during EEC-IV Quick Test procedure, Electronic Pressure Control (EPC) solenoid may have a mechanical fault. Connect pressure gauge to EPC port. Start engine and check pressure at idle and at Wide Open Throttle (WOT). If pressure is not within specification, replace EPC solenoid.

TRANSAXLE PRESSURE SPECIFICATIONS (PSI)

Selector Position	@ Idle RPM	@ WOT Stall RPM
Line Pressure		
"P" & "N"	48-77	
"R"	61-99	252-316
"OD" & "D"	48-77	168-217
"L"	48-77	168-217
Direct Clutch [1]		
"L"	40-60	40-60
EPC		
"P" & "N"	10-20	
"R"	10-20	70-90
"OD" & "D"	10-20	70-90
"L"	10-20	70-90

[1] – Pressure is measured only in manual low position.

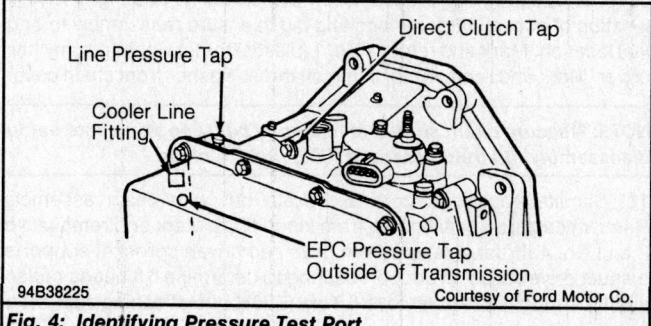

Line Pressure Tap

Direct Clutch Tap

Cooler Line Fitting

EPC Pressure Tap
Outside Of Transmission

94B38225   Courtesy of Ford Motor Co.

Fig. 4: Identifying Pressure Test Port

STALL SPEED TEST

NOTE: After each test, shift transaxle into Neutral and run engine for at least 2 minutes to cool torque converter and transmission fluid.

CAUTION: Do not maintain Wide Open Throttle (WOT) in any gear for more than 5 seconds. If engine RPM exceeds maximum specified stall speed, release accelerator immediately. Clutch or band slippage is indicated.

The stall speed test checks the operation of the following items:
- Converter One-Way Clutch
- Forward Clutch
- Low One-Way Clutch
- Reverse Clutch
- Low-Intermediate Band
- Engine Performance

1) Apply service and parking brakes. Connect tachometer to engine, and record RPM reached in each gear selector range (except Neutral) at WOT. Stall speed should be as indicated in STALL SPEED SPECIFICATIONS table.

STALL SPEED SPECIFICATIONS

Application	Stall RPM
3.0L V6	1881-2211
3.2L V6	2849-3252
3.8L V6	1791-2097

2) If stall speeds exceed specification, ensure engine is mechanically okay and tuned to specification. If engine is okay, remove torque converter and check torque converter one-way clutch for slippage.
3) If stall speed is too high in "OD", "D", "1", the following components may be faulty:
- Forward Clutch
- Low-Intermediate One-Way Clutch
- Low-Intermediate Band or Servo

4) If stall speed is too high in "R", the following components may be faulty:
- Forward Clutch
- Low-Intermediate One-Way Clutch
- Reverse Clutch

SHIFT POINT ROAD TEST

Use the following road test procedure to verify shift control valves are operating correctly:
1) Drive vehicle to bring engine and transaxle to operating temperature. Operate vehicle with gear selector in "OD" position.
2) Apply MINIMUM throttle and observe and record upshift speeds. Observe and record speed at which converter clutch applies.
3) Stop vehicle and move gear selector to "D" position. Repeat step **2)**. Transaxle should make all upshifts except 3rd-to-4th. Torque converter lock-up should occur above 27 MPH (43 km/h).
4) Depress throttle pedal to Wide Open Throttle (WOT) position. Converter clutch should release and transaxle should downshift to next lower gear.
5) With vehicle speed greater than 30 MPH (48 km/h), move gear selector from "D" to "1" position and release accelerator pedal. Transaxle should immediately downshift to 2nd gear. When vehicle speed drops to less than 20 MPH (32 km/h), transaxle should downshift into 1st gear.
6) If transaxle fails to shift as described above, perform EEC-IV QUICK TEST procedure. See AXOD-E ELECTRONIC CONTROLS article.

TORQUE CONVERTER

Torque converter is a sealed unit and cannot be disassembled. Replace converter assembly if defective. Perform the following procedures to ensure converter is defective before replacing unit.

LEAK TEST

If torque converter welds indicate leakage, attach Torque Converter Leak Test Kit (021-00054) to converter and follow directions supplied with kit.

TORQUE CONVERTER REACTOR ONE-WAY CLUTCH CHECK

Position Holding Wire (T77L-7902-R), into thrust washer slot. While holding wire in position, install One-Way Clutch Torque Tool (T81P-

7902-B) in reactor spline. Turn socket counterclockwise with a torque wrench. If socket begins to turn before torque wrench reads 10 ft. lbs. (14 N.m), replace converter. *See Fig. 5.*

TORQUE CONVERTER END PLAY CHECK

Position End Play Tester (T80L-7902-A) and Guide Sleeve (T86P-7902-A) in torque converter hub. Tighten tester nut. Mount a dial indicator on tester with stylus contacting converter shell. Zero indicator and lift on tester handles. If reading is above .05" (1.3 mm), replace converter.

ON-VEHICLE SERVICE

OIL COOLER FLUSHING

Contaminates MUST be removed from oil cooler before transmission is put back into service. Replace cooler supply tubes if leaking. Thoroughly flush oil cooler and lines if a major service or transaxle removal has occurred. It is recommended that a mechanically agitated cleaner such as Rotunda (014-00028) be used.

OIL PUMP & VALVE BODY ASSEMBLY

Removal – 1) Disconnect battery ground cable and electrical connectors from transaxle. Remove battery and battery tray. Remove and secure supply hoses, vacuum lines and wiring away from valve body cover, as necessary.

2) Disconnect shift lever and remove lever position sensor. Remove ABS cover and disconnect hoses, if equipped. Attach lifting equipment to support engine.

3) Remove left side transaxle mount. Remove side pan upper retaining bolts. Raise and support vehicle on hoist. Remove left wheel and inner fender splash shield. Remove transaxle-to-frame mount. Remove transaxle support bar.

CAUTION: Do not remove 2 bolts holding oil pump and valve body together. Do not remove 6 oil pump cover bolts.

---

4) Loosen valve body cover bolts and drain fluid. Remove cover and gasket. Using a screwdriver, position manual shift valve in Park position. Disconnect wiring to valve body. Remove valve body retaining bolts, disengage linkage and remove valve body. DO NOT remove 6 oil pump cover bolts. *See Fig. 6.*

Installation – 1) Install new valve body-to-chain cover gasket. Slide pump and valve body assembly onto oil pump shaft. Rotate pump and valve body assembly clockwise and connect manual valve link.

2) Slightly rotate or jiggle assembly to engage splines on oil pump shaft with splines in oil pump rotor. Valve body should slide flush onto chain cover without force. It may be necessary to rotate engine, using a 7/8" socket on crankshaft, to complete engagement of pump shaft to pump. If vehicle is equipped with ABS and valve body does not slide easily to flush position, go to next step.

3) If ABS-equipped, remove manual valve from valve body. Rotate valve body as necessary to allow full engagement. After engagement, return to installed position and install manual valve. Use Valve Body Alignment Pin (T86P-70100-C) to position valve body. Install bolts and tighten in sequence shown. *See Fig. 6.*

CAUTION: DO NOT use bolts to draw pump and valve body into position.

---

4) On all vehicles, install cover using a new gasket. To complete installation, reverse removal procedures. Refill transaxle and check for leaks.

REMOVAL & INSTALLATION

See appropriate AUTOMATIC TRANSMISSION REMOVAL article in TRANSMISSION SERVICING.

TRANSAXLE DISASSEMBLY

NOTE: For exploded view of transaxle, see Figs. 7-10.

---

1) Remove torque converter. Mount transaxle in a appropriate holding fixture. Place in vertical position and drain fluid.

2) Place in horizontal position. Remove 2 (8 mm) speedometer cover bolts, cover and seal. Discard seal. Lift speedometer drive gear assembly and bearing from case. Bearing sits on top of speedometer drive gear.

3) Remove 3 (8 mm) bolts from overdrive servo cover. Servo cover is under pressure and must be retained when removing bolts. Mark and remove cover, piston assembly and spring. Discard "O" ring from cover. Remove 3 low-intermediate servo cover bolts. Mark and remove cover, piston assembly and spring. Remove and discard gasket.

4) Install Step Plate Adapter (D80L-630-3) into right-hand output shaft opening; hold adapter in position with grease. Screw output shaft Seal Remover (T74P-6700-A) into metal seal and protector. Tighten screw on end of seal remover until metal seal protector is removed. Reinstall remover and repeat procedure to remove seal.

5) Remove 2 (8 mm) bolts from Manual Lever Position Sensor (MLPS) and remove sensor. Remove dipstick tube and dipstick from case. Remove 9 chain cover bolts from inside torque converter housing.

6) Using a slide hammer and Seal Puller (1175-AC), remove converter oil seal from input shaft. Rotate transaxle to vertical position. Remove 12 valve body cover bolts. Remove cover and discard gasket.

7) Disconnect electrical connectors from pressure switches and solenoid. Use both hands. DO NOT pull on wires. Compress tabs on both sides of bulkhead connector from inside of chain cover and remove connector and wiring. *See Fig. 6.*

8) Using a 9 mm wrench on flats of manual shaft, rotate shaft clockwise to position manual linkage in low detent (manual valve all the way in). Mark and remove 22 oil pump and valve body bolts, noting length and location. *See Fig. 6.*

CAUTION: Do not remove 2 bolts holding oil pump and valve body together. Do not remove 6 oil pump cover bolts.

---

9) Rotate valve body clockwise and remove manual valve link from manual valve. Disconnect manual valve link from detent lever. Remove pump and valve body assembly.

10) Pull oil pump drive shaft out of case and remove 4 Teflon seals from shaft. Discard seals.

11) Place transaxle in vertical position. Remove and discard left output shaft circlip. Screw Seal Remover (T74P-6700-A) into metal seal protector. Tighten screw of seal remover until metal seal protector is removed. Repeat procedure to remove seal.

12) Remove Turbine Speed Sensor (TSS) from chain cover. Mark and remove 16 chain cover bolts. Note length and location of bolts. Chain cover is under spring pressure; remove carefully. *See Fig. 11.* Note location of accumulator springs and tag to ensure reassembly to original location. Mark and remove No. 1 (plastic) thrust washer from chain cover. Mark and remove No. 3 (metal) thrust washer from chain cover.

NOTE: Measure chain stretch at mid-point between sprockets before disassembly. If stretch exceeds 7/8", replace chain.

---

13) Simultaneously lift both sprockets out with chain assembly. Remove cast iron sealing ring from input shaft. Mark and remove No. 2 and No. 4 thrust washers from drive and driven sprocket supports. Inspect drive sprocket support bearing to determine if it needs replacing. If bearing is okay, remove 6 Torx (T30) bolts attaching support to case.

14) Using Pin Remover (D81P-3504-N), remove lockpin and 2 roll pins from manual shaft. Be careful not to damage machined surfaces. Slide shaft out and pry seal from case. *See Fig. 12.*

15) Using a straightedge, note whether driven sprocket support machined bolt hole surface is above or below the case machined surface. Note for reassembly reference. Remove driven sprocket support assembly.

16) Remove 5 Teflon seals from support assembly. Mark and remove No. 5 selective thrust washer. Washer may stay on support assembly during removal. Using a wire hook, if necessary, remove No. 8 selective thrust washer and No. 9 needle bearing. Remove plastic overdrive

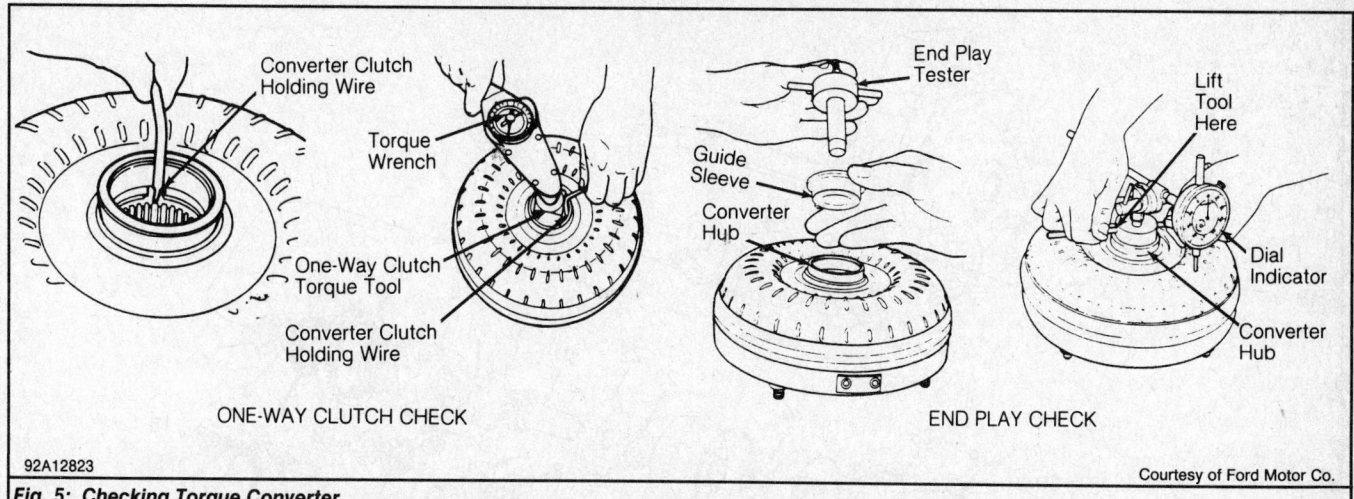

ONE-WAY CLUTCH CHECK

Converter Clutch Holding Wire
Torque Wrench
One-Way Clutch Torque Tool
Converter Clutch Holding Wire

END PLAY CHECK

End Play Tester
Guide Sleeve
Converter Hub
Lift Tool Here
Dial Indicator
Converter Hub

92A12823

Courtesy of Ford Motor Co.

Fig. 5: Checking Torque Converter

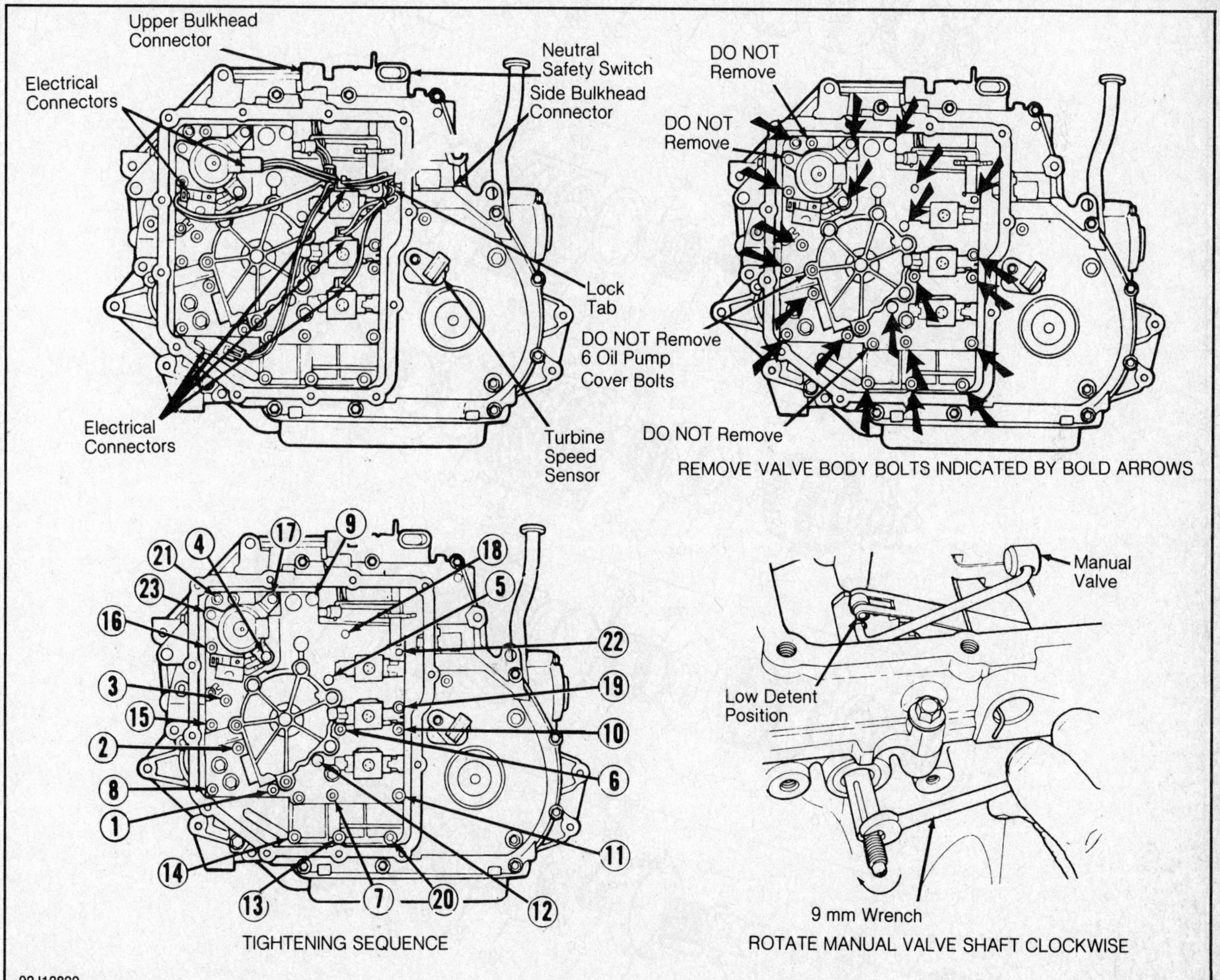

Upper Bulkhead Connector
Electrical Connectors
Neutral Safety Switch
Side Bulkhead Connector
Lock Tab
DO NOT Remove 6 Oil Pump Cover Bolts
Electrical Connectors
Turbine Speed Sensor

DO NOT Remove
DO NOT Remove
DO NOT Remove

REMOVE VALVE BODY BOLTS INDICATED BY BOLD ARROWS

TIGHTENING SEQUENCE

Manual Valve
Low Detent Position
9 mm Wrench
ROTATE MANUAL VALVE SHAFT CLOCKWISE

92J12822

Courtesy of Ford Motor Co.

Fig. 6: Removing & Installing Valve Body

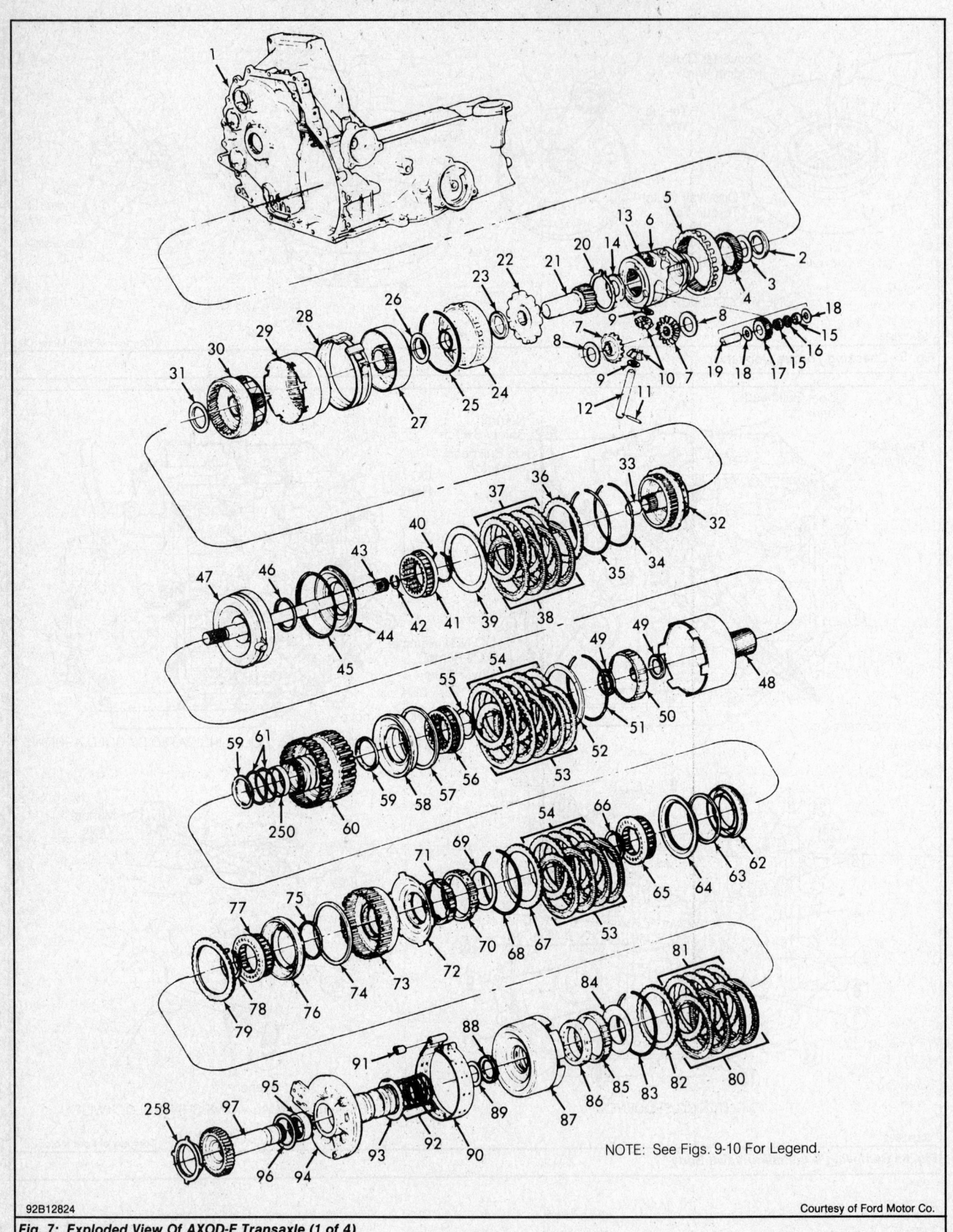

NOTE: See Figs. 9-10 For Legend.

92B12824

Courtesy of Ford Motor Co.

Fig. 7: Exploded View Of AXOD-E Transaxle (1 of 4)

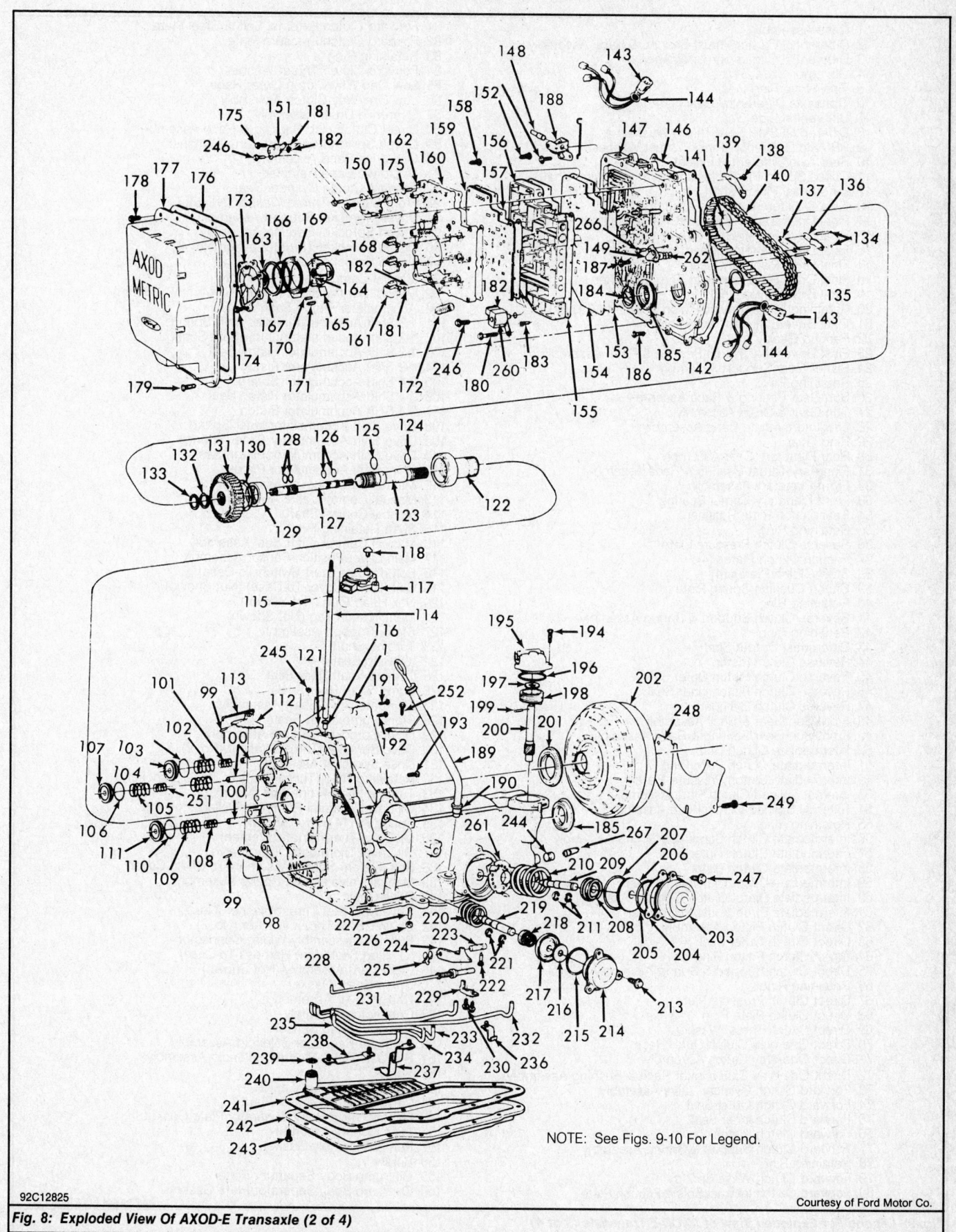

NOTE: See Figs. 9-10 For Legend.

92C12825

Courtesy of Ford Motor Co.

Fig. 8: Exploded View Of AXOD-E Transaxle (2 of 4)

1. Case Assembly
2. Differential Carrier Thrust Bearing & Race Assembly
3. Differential Carrier Thrust Washer
4. Governor Drive Gear
5. Final Drive Ring Gear
6. Transaxle Differential Gear Case
7. Differential Side Gear
8. Differential Side Gear Thrust Washer
9. RR Axle Differential Pinion Thrust Washer
10. Rear Axle Differential Pinion
11. Coiled Spring Pin (Retains Differential Pinion Shaft)
12. Differential Pinion Shaft
13. Gear & Differential Case Assembly
14. Final Drive Carrier Bearing & Race Assembly
15. Final Drive Planet Gear Needle Bearing
16. Final Drive Planetary Gear Spacer
17. Final Drive Planetary Gear
18. Final Drive Planetary Gear Thrust Washer
19. Final Drive Pinion Shaft
20. Retaining Ring (Retains Pinion Shaft Into Carrier)
21. Final Drive Sun Gear Assembly
22. Parking Gear
23. Final Drive Gear Thrust Bearing & Race Assembly
24. Planet Gear Support Assembly
25. Retaining Ring
26. Sun Gear Bearing & Race Assembly
27. Sun Gear & Drum Assembly
28. Low-Intermediate Band Assembly
29. Ring Gear
30. Rear Planetary Gear Assembly
31. Planetary Thrust Bearing & Race Assembly
32. Front Planetary Assembly
33. Front Planetary Carrier Bearing
34. Rear Clutch Plate Retainer
35. Retaining Ring
36. Reverse Clutch Pressure Plate
37. Friction Clutch Plates (4)
38. Steel Clutch Plates (4)
39. Clutch Cushion Spring Plate
40. Retaining Ring
41. Reverse Clutch Support & Spring Assembly
42. Retaining Ring
43. Differential Output Shaft
44. Reverse Clutch Piston
45. Reverse Clutch Piston Outer Seal
46. Reverse Clutch Piston Inner Seal
47. Reverse Clutch Cylinder
48. Front Sun Gear & Shell Assembly
49. Front Sun Gear Bearing & Race Assembly
50. Intermediate Clutch Hub
51. Intermediate Clutch Plate Ring
52. Intermediate Clutch Pressure Plate
53. Internal Splined Clutch Plate Assembly
54. External Splined Clutch Plate Assembly
55. Retaining Ring
56. Intermediate Clutch Support & Spring Assembly
57. Intermediate Clutch Outer Seal
58. Intermediate Clutch Piston
59. Intermediate-Direct Clutch Inner Seal
60. Intermediate-Direct Clutch Cylinder Assembly
61. Intermediate-Direct Clutch Hub Seal
62. Direct Clutch Piston Assembly
63. Direct Clutch Outer Seal
64. Direct Clutch Piston Ring
65. Direct Clutch Support & Spring Assembly
66. Retaining Ring
67. Direct Clutch Pressure Plate
68. Direct Clutch Plate Ring
69. Direct Clutch Thrust Washer
70. Direct One-Way Clutch Outer Race
71. Direct One-Way Clutch Assembly
72. Direct One-Way Clutch Inner Race & Bushing Assembly
73. Forward Clutch Cylinder Valve Assembly
74. Forward Clutch Outer Seal
75. Forward Clutch Inner Seal
76. Forward Clutch Piston
77. Forward Clutch Support & Spring Assembly
78. Retaining Ring
79. Forward Clutch Wave Spring
80. Forward Clutch Internal Spline Friction Plate
81. Forward Clutch External Spline Steel Plate
82. Forward Clutch Pressure Plate
83. Retaining Ring
84. Forward Clutch Thrust Washer
85. Low One-Way Clutch Outer Race
86. Low One-Way Clutch Assembly
87. Overdrive Drum Assembly
88. Direct Clutch Hub Bearing & Race Assembly
89. Driven Sprocket Support Thrust Washer
90. Overdrive Band Assembly
91. Overdrive Band Retainer
92. Forward Clutch Cylinder Seal
93. Front Support Thrust Washer (No. 5)
94. Driven Sprocket Support Assembly
95. Driven Sprocket Bearing Assembly
96. Driven Sprocket Thrust Washer (No. 4)
97. Driven Sprocket Assembly
98. Manual Control Lever Assembly
99. Manual Control Shaft Spring Pin (4 mm x 28 mm)
100. Accumulator Piston Shaft
101. 1-2 Shift Accumulator Inner Shift Spring
102. 1-2 Shift Accumulator Outer Shift Spring
103. 1-2 Shift Accumulator Piston Seal
104. 1-2 Shift Accumulator Piston
105. 3-4 Shift Accumulator Spring
106. 3-4 Shift Accumulator Piston Seal
107. 3-4 Shift Accumulator Piston
108. Drive Shift Accumulator Inner Spring
109. Drive Shift Accumulator Outer Spring
110. Drive Shift Accumulator Piston Seal
111. Drive Shift Accumulator Piston
112. Manual Detent Lever Assembly
113. Manual Control Valve Actuator Rod
114. Manual Control Shaft
115. Shaft Retaining Pin
116. Manual Control Shaft Seal Assembly
117. Main Lever Position Sensor Assembly
118. Bolt (Neutral Start Switch-To-Case)
119. Bolt (Chain Cover-To-Case) (Not Shown)
120. Hex Head Plug (Not Shown)
121. Identification Tag (Not Shown)
122. Stator Support Assembly
123. Turbine Shaft
124. "O" Ring Seal
125. Turbine Shaft Rear Seal
126. Pump Shaft Rear Seals
127. Oil Pump Drive Shaft Assembly
128. Front Pump Shaft Seals
129. Drive Sprocket Bearing Assembly
130. Drive Sprocket Thrust Washer (No. 2)
131. Drive Sprocket Assembly
132. Retaining Ring (Turbo Shaft-To-Drive Sprocket)
133. Turbine Shaft Front Seal (Metal)
134. Oil Level Thermal Retaining Collar
135. Spring Pin (4 mm x 22 mm)
136. Oil Level Thermostatic Element
137. Oil Level Thermostat Plate Valve
138. Bolt (Detent Spring Assembly-To-Chain Cover)
139. Manual Valve Detent Spring Assembly
140. Drive Chain
141. Drive Sprocket Thrust Washer (No. 1)
142. Chain Cover Thrust Washer (No. 3)
143. Bulkhead Assembly Wiring Connector
144. "O" Ring Seal (Wire Harness-To-Case)
145. Case Vent Assembly (Not Shown)
146. Chain Cover Gasket
147. Chain Cover Assembly
148. Connector Assembly
149. Turbine Speed Sensor
150. Pressure Regulator Solenoid Assembly
151. By-Pass Clutch Control Solenoid Assembly
152. Screw
153. Control Assembly Gasket
154. Valve Body Separator Plate
155. Control Valve Body Separator Plate Gasket
156. Main Control Assembly
157. Pump Assembly Gasket
158. Screw
159. Oil Pump Body Separator Plate
160. Oil Pump Body Separator Plate Gasket

Courtesy of Ford Motor Co.

92D12826

Fig. 9: Legend For Exploded View of AXOD-E Transaxle (3 of 4)

161. Switch Control Solenoid Assembly
162. Oil Pump Bearing & Seal Assembly
163. Oil Pump Vane Support Ring
164. Oil Pump Rotor
165. Oil Pump Vane
166. Oil Pump Bore Ring Side Seal
167. Oil Pump Bore Ring Side Seal Support
168. Pin (8 mm x 37.7 mm)
169. Oil Pump Body Ring
170. Oil Pump Bore Ring Radial Seal Support
171. Oil Pump Bore Ring Radial Seal
172. Oil Pump Bore Ring Spring
173. Oil Pump Cover & Sleeve Assembly
174. Bolt (Pump Cover-To-Pump Body)
175. Bolt (Pump Body & Main Control-To-Chain Cover)
176. Main Control Cover Gasket
177. Main Control Cover
178. Bolt (Chain Cover-To-Case)
179. Bolt (Main Control Cover-To-Chain Cover)
180. Bolt (Valve Body-To-Chain Cover & Solenoid Assembly)
181. "O" Ring Seal
182. "O" Ring Seal
183. Bypass Clutch Solenoid Screen Assembly
184. Output Shaft Retainer Circle Clip (Retains CV Joint)
185. Differential Seal Assembly
186. Bolt (Valve Body-To-Chain Cover & Solenoid Assembly)
187. Bolt (Chain Cover-To-Driven Support)
188. Oil Level Indicator Assembly
189. Oil Filler Tube Assembly
190. Oil Filler Grommet
191. Bolt (Chain Cover-To-Driven Support)
192. Bolt (Case-To-Chain Cover)
193. Screw (Case-To-Stator Support)
194. Bolt (Governor/Speedo Drive Cover-To-Case)
195. Governor/Speedo Drive Cover
196. "O" Ring (Governor/Speedo Drive Cover Seal)
197. Thrust Bearing & Race Assembly
198. Speedo Drive Gear
199. Spring Pin (Speedo Gear Drive Pin)
200. Gear & Shaft Assembly
201. Torque Converter Hub Seal
202. Torque Converter (10 1/4")
203. Low-Intermediate Band Servo Cover
204. Low-Intermediate Band Servo Gasket
205. Low-Intermediate Servo Piston Cover Seal
206. Low-Intermediate Band Servo Piston
207. Low-Intermediate Band Servo Piston Seal
208. Low-Intermediate Servo Spring & Retainer Assembly
209. Low-Intermediate Servo Piston Rod
210. Low-Intermediate Servo Piston Spring
211. Low-Intermediate Servo Piston Ring
212. Transfer Tube Seal Assembly (Not Shown)
213. Bolt (O/D Servo Cover-To-Case)
214. O/D Band Servo Cover

215. O/D Band Servo Cover Seal
216. O/D Servo Piston Retainer
217. O/D Servo Piston & Seal Assembly
218. O/D Servo Retainer & Cushion Spring Assembly
219. O/D Servo Piston Rod
220. O/D Servo Return Spring
221. O/D Servo retaining Ring
222. Shaft Retainer Pin
223. Parking Pawl Shaft
224. Parking Pawl
225. Parking Pawl Return Spring
226. Screw
227. Nut
228. Parking Pawl Actuating Rod Assembly
229. Parking Pawl Actuating Abutment
230. Bolt (Abutment Assembly-To-Case)
231. Rear Lube Oil Transfer Tube
232. Governor Oil Transfer Tube
233. Servo Apply Oil Transfer Tube
234. Servo Release Oil Transfer Tube
235. Reverse Clutch Apply Oil Transfer Tube
236. Governor Feed Tube Support Bracket Assembly
237. Reverse Clutch Tube Support Bracket Assembly
238. Tube Support Main Bracket Assembly
239. Oil Filter Seal
240. Oil Filter Assembly
241. Oil Pan Gasket
242. Oil Pan
243. Bolt (Oil Pan-To-Case)
244. Cup Plug
245. 1/4" Spring Nut (Retain I.D. Tag)
246. Bolt (Solenoid Assembly-To-Valve Body)
247. Bolt (Servo Cover-To-Case)
248. Converter Housing Lower Cover
249. Bolt (Converter Housing Cover-To-Case)
250. Direct/Intermediate Clutch Cylinder Bushing
251. 3-4 Shift Accumulator Inner Spring
252. Bolt (Filler Tube-To-Case)
253. Bolt (Oil Pump Assembly-To-Main Control) (Not Shown)
254. Hex Head Shoulder Stud (Not Shown)
255. Forward Clutch Wave Spring (3.8L Only)
256. Ceramic Magnet Case (Not Shown)
257. 1-2 Shift Accumulator Center Spring (3.8L Only)
258. Exciter Ring
259. Intermediate Circuit Case Screen (Not Shown)
260. Oil Temperature Sensor
261. Low-Intermediate Servo Return Spring Retainer
262. "O" Ring Seal (14.0 mm x 1.78 mm)
263. "O" Ring Seal (25.12 mm x 1.78 mm)
264. "O" Ring Seal (12.42 mm x 1.78 mm) (Not Shown)
265. Transmission Cooler Tube Retaining Clip
266. Bolt (Not Shown)
267. Stud

92E12827

Courtesy of Ford Motor Co.

Fig. 10: Legend For Exploded View of AXOD-E Transaxle (4 of 4)

band retainer and overdrive band. *See Fig. 13.* Remove filter screen. Clean filter with compressed air. Replace filter tube lip seal.

17) Position transaxle with oil pan up. Remove 17 oil pan cover bolts. Remove cover and discard gasket. Remove reverse apply tube/oil filter bolt and bracket. Remove oil filter screen and discard lip seal.

18) Remove tube retaining bracket bolts and brackets. If necessary, use Tube Remover (T86P-70001-A) and a slide hammer to remove lube tubes. Tubes are retained with Loctite. *See Fig. 14.*

NOTE: For complete transaxle disassembly, reverse apply tube MUST be removed prior to removing the reverse clutch or differential.

---

19) Remove 2 parking rod abutment bolts. Remove parking rod by lifting to clear abutment and lower from case. Remove parking pawl shaft roll pin. Use magnet to remove parking pawl shaft. Remove parking pawl and return spring. Loosen 19 mm reverse clutch anchor pin nut and remove 6 mm Allen head bolt.

NOTE: It is necessary to modify Front Clutch Loading Tool (T86P-70389-A) for use on 3.2L transaxle. Remove .02" (.5 mm) of material from hook end of tool.

---

20) Place transaxle in horizontal position. Install Front Clutch Loading Tool (T86P-70389-A). Lift front sun gear and shell assembly out of case. Install hook portion of Front Clutch Loading Tool (T86P-70389-A) on inner diameter of reverse clutch cylinder. Grasp outer diameter with fingertips and slide clutch assembly out of case.

21) Rotate transaxle to vertical position. Grasp front planetary shaft and lift out both front and rear planetary assemblies. Lift out low-intermediate drum and sun gear assembly. Remove low-intermediate band.

22) Remove final drive assembly snap ring from case using a screwdriver inserted through side of case. Lift out final drive assembly using output shaft. *See Fig. 15.*

23) Remove and discard rear lube tube seal using a 3/8" rod or drift. Remove final drive ring gear from case. Remove No. 18 thrust washer and No. 19 needle bearing. Thrust washer may remain on final drive next to speedometer gear. Tap seal towards inside of case. If case replacement is necessary, remove Torx bolts and converter support from old case at this time.

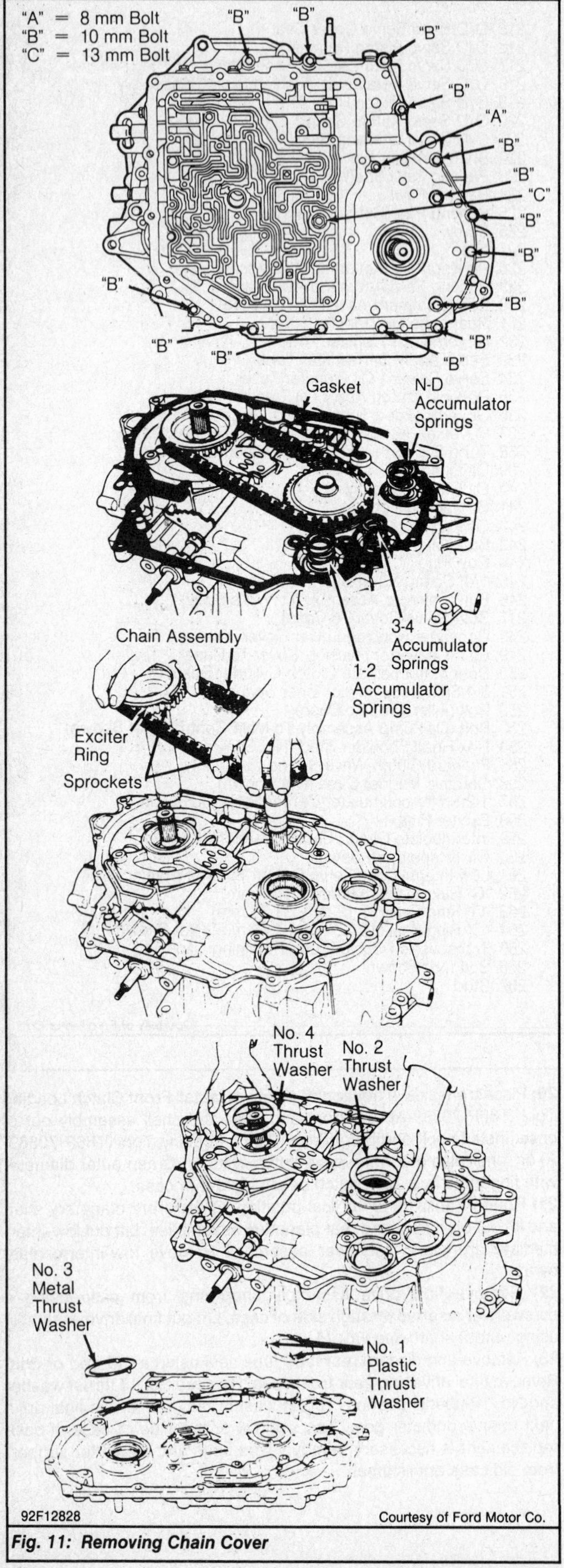

"A" = 8 mm Bolt
"B" = 10 mm Bolt
"C" = 13 mm Bolt

Gasket
N-D Accumulator Springs

3-4 Accumulator Springs

Chain Assembly

1-2 Accumulator Springs

Exciter Ring

Sprockets

No. 4 Thrust Washer
No. 2 Thrust Washer

No. 3 Metal Thrust Washer

No. 1 Plastic Thrust Washer

92F12828   Courtesy of Ford Motor Co.

Fig. 11: Removing Chain Cover

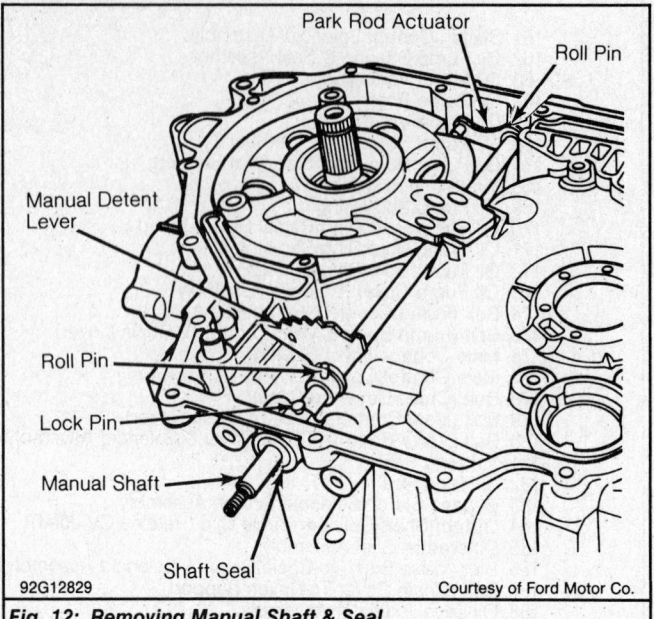

Park Rod Actuator
Roll Pin

Manual Detent Lever

Roll Pin

Lock Pin

Manual Shaft

Shaft Seal

92G12829   Courtesy of Ford Motor Co.

Fig. 12: Removing Manual Shaft & Seal

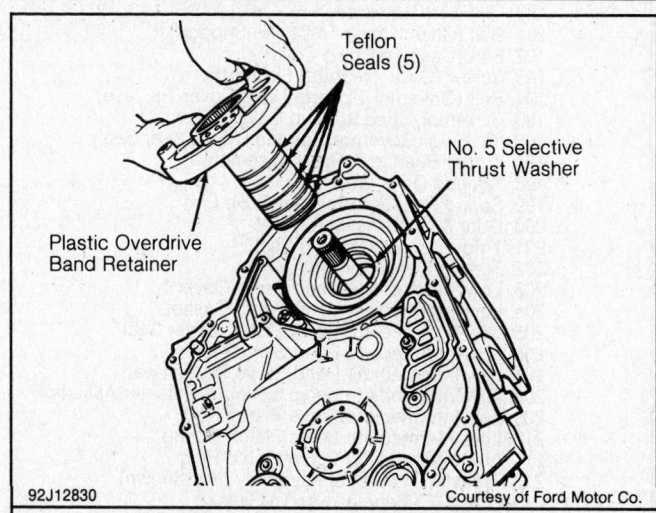

Teflon Seals (5)

No. 5 Selective Thrust Washer

Plastic Overdrive Band Retainer

92J12830   Courtesy of Ford Motor Co.

Fig. 13: Removing Driven Sprocket Support

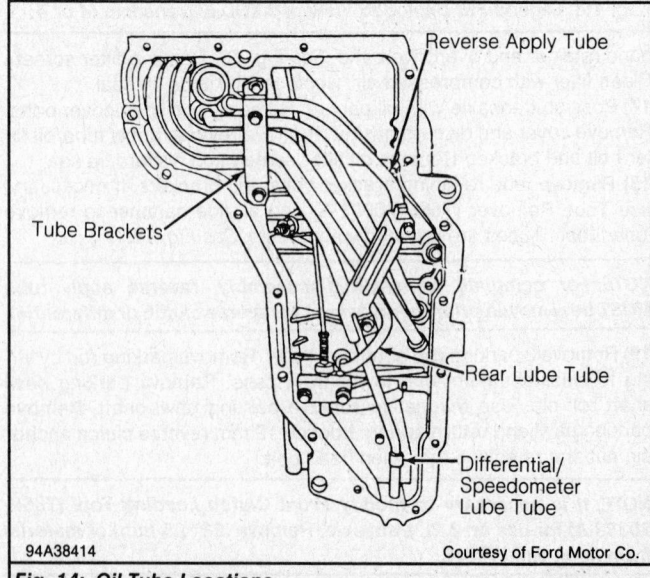

Reverse Apply Tube

Tube Brackets

Rear Lube Tube

Differential/Speedometer Lube Tube

94A38414   Courtesy of Ford Motor Co.

Fig. 14: Oil Tube Locations

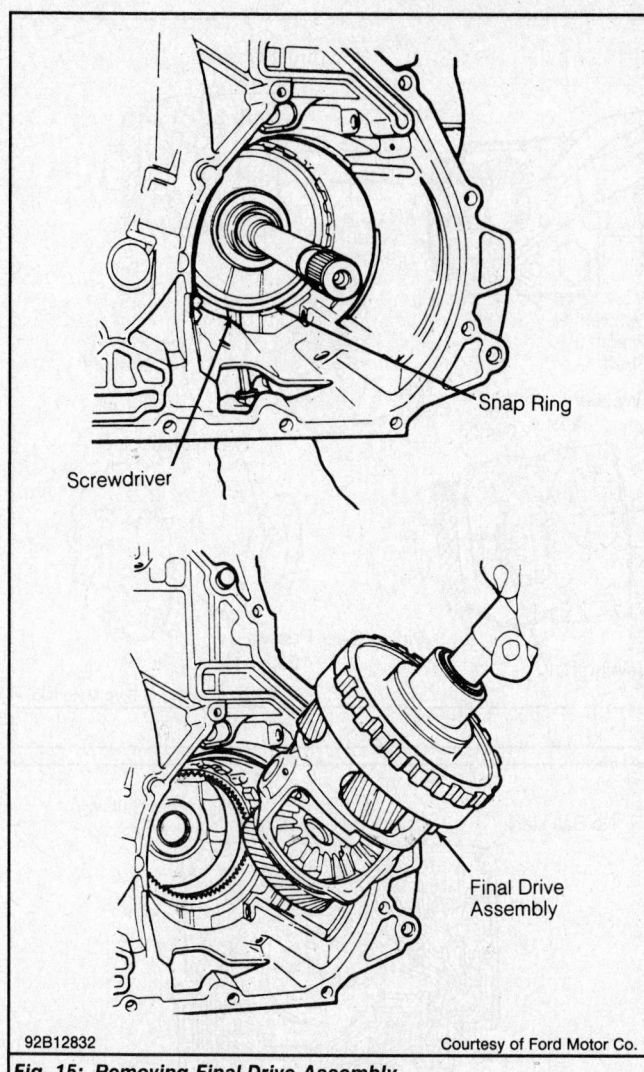

Fig. 15: Removing Final Drive Assembly

92B12832   Courtesy of Ford Motor Co.

COMPONENT DISASSEMBLY & REASSEMBLY

NOTE: When reassembling clutch packs, always soak clutch discs in ATF for 15 minutes before assembling.

CHAIN COVER

Disassembly – 1) If replacing wiring or chain cover, break off locating tab on bulkhead connectors and remove connectors from cover. DO NOT pull on wiring or connector. Only remove wiring if cover replacement is necessary. Mark and remove 3 accumulator piston shafts. Using flat-nose pliers, remove 3 accumulator pistons. Use care to avoid damaging piston bores.

2) Using side cutters, carefully remove retaining pin collars. *See Fig. 16.* Remove bimetallic strip and plate. Pull retaining pins from cover. Use care not to damage bimetallic strip or machined case surface.

3) Remove manual valve detent spring bolt and spring. Remove quick-disconnect oil cooler fittings from cover.

Reassembly – 1) Use a sealant on threads and install quick-disconnect fittings. Install manual valve detent spring and position tab in hole. Tighten bolt to 84-108 INCH lbs. (9-12 N.m). Start bimetallic strip retaining pins in cover. Gently tap center pin to bottom of hole. Center pin must not extend from case more than .26" (6.6 mm).

2) Position end of bimetallic strip with hole over front retaining pin. Install retaining collars. Place Height Gauge (T86P-70422-A) against

pin between bimetallic strip and case. Gently tap collar onto pin until it seats against bimetallic strip. *See Fig. 16.*

3) Engage slotted end of bimetallic strip under rear retaining pin. Use gauge and gently tap collar onto pin. Remove slotted end of bimetallic strip from pin. Position retaining plate onto rear and middle retaining pins. Place slotted end bimetallic strip under retaining collar.

4) Install new "O" rings and seals on accumulator pistons; lubricate with petroleum jelly. The N-D accumulator piston is fitted with an "O" ring. The 3-4 accumulator and 1-2 accumulator are fitted with square-cut seals. Install accumulator pistons; ensure pistons are inserted straight into bores. Install 3 accumulator piston shafts.

5) Install new "O" ring on electrical connectors. Connectors should "click" when they are installed. Black connector goes into top bore and White connector goes into side.

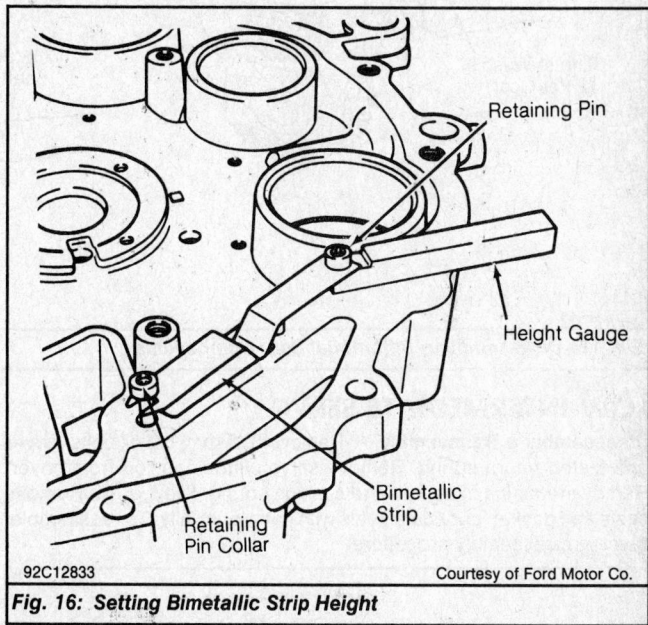

92C12833   Courtesy of Ford Motor Co.

Fig. 16: Setting Bimetallic Strip Height

DIFFERENTIAL & GEAR SET

Disassembly – 1) Remove rear planetary support, needle bearings (No. 15 and 16), and park wheel from output shaft. Ensure bushing lubrication hole is aligned with lube hole in rear planetary support. Replace bushing if necessary.

2) Remove planetary pinion shaft retaining snap ring. Using a magnet, work pinion shafts out of differential case housing. Slide out pinion gears and thrust washers. Inspect needle bearings and pinion shafts. Replace as necessary. Remove speedo drive gear by gently prying off with screwdriver, if necessary.

3) Remove No. 17 needle bearing from top of planetary. Drive out pinion shaft roll pin. Tap out pinion shaft. Remove pinion gears and thrust washers by rotating output shaft. Remove right side gear and thrust washer.

4) Push output shaft toward center of housing. Slide left side gear back and remove retaining ring. Slide shaft out of housing and remove side gear.

Reassembly – 1) With output shaft inside case, slide thrust washer and left side gear onto output shaft. Install retaining ring and slide gear down over ring. *See Fig. 17.* Install thrust washer and right side gear.

2) Install thrust washers on pinion gears. Ensure washer inner lip is seated in pinion gear recess. Position pinion gears on side gears. While rotating output shaft, walk pinion gears into position.

3) Tap pinion shaft through differential case and pinion gears. Tap in differential pinion shaft roll pin. Install No. 17 needle bearing over output shaft and seat on planetary housing with tabs facing up. Install upper and lower pinion gear thrust washers on gears. Install in case.

4) Push pinion shafts through case and gears until lower step on shaft is level with case. Lower step should face inward. Install snap ring.

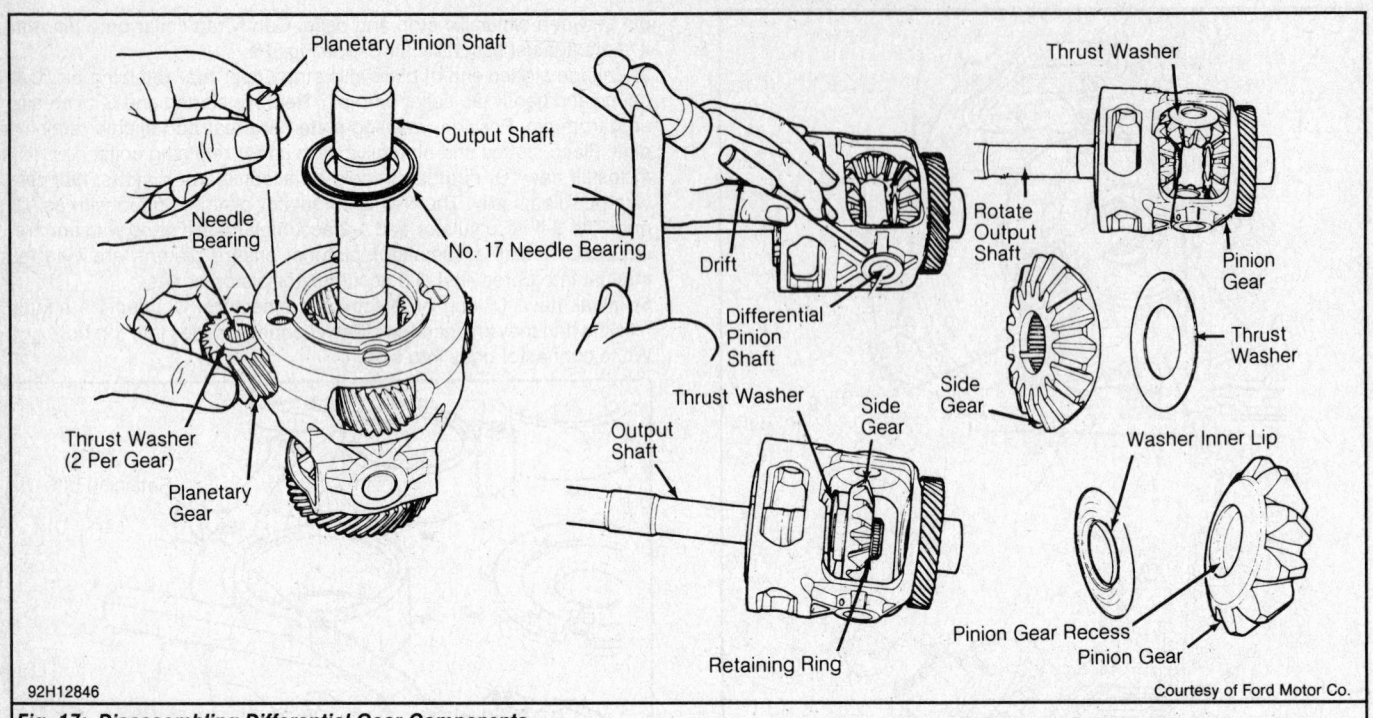

Fig. 17: Disassembling Differential Gear Components

LOW-INTERMEDIATE SERVO

Disassembly & Reassembly – Remove 3 (8 mm) cover bolts, cover and piston return spring. Remove servo piston and rod from cover. Remove retaining clips, rod and cushion spring. See Fig. 18. Remove seals and gasket. Lubricate seals with petroleum jelly. To reassemble, reverse disassembly procedure.

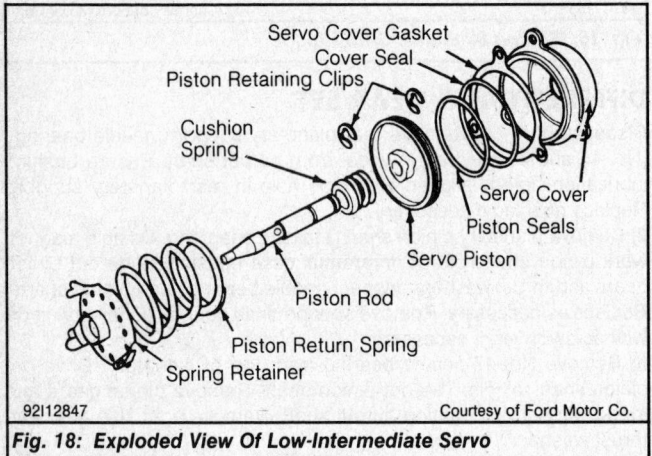

Fig. 18: Exploded View Of Low-Intermediate Servo

OIL PUMP

Removal & Installation – **1)** To separate oil pump housing from valve body, remove Torx bolts retaining oil pump housing to valve body. See Fig. 19. Separate valve body from oil pump. Remove and discard gasket. Clean gasket surface thoroughly.

2) Prior to installing oil pump housing to valve body, ensure check balls and relief valves are in correct position in pump housing. Position a new gasket and separator plate on oil pump housing.

3) Insert valve body Guide Pin Set (T86P-70100 "A" and "B") in valve body. See Fig. 19. Install 2 Torx bolts retaining separator plate to oil pump housing. Install pump housing on valve body.

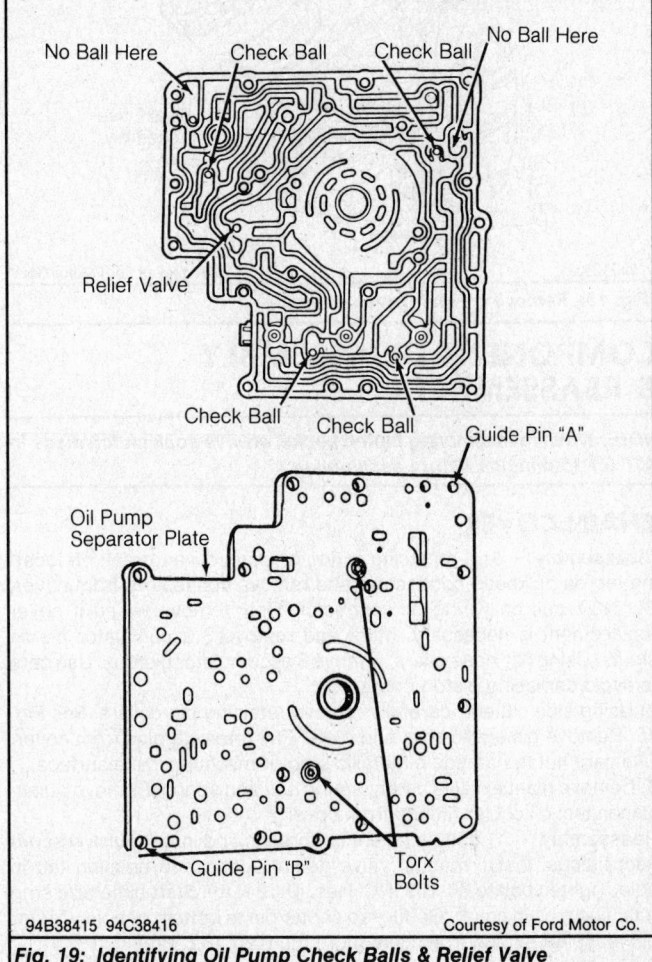

Fig. 19: Identifying Oil Pump Check Balls & Relief Valve

Disassembly – 1) Remove Torx bolts holding separator plate to oil pump housing. Remove separator plate and gasket. Remove 4 check balls and one relief valve. *See Fig. 19.*

2) Remove 6 bolts retaining cover to housing and remove. Remove bore spring by prying out of housing using a screwdriver. Place shop rag under screwdriver to prevent damage to housing surface.

CAUTION: Use extreme caution when removing bore spring to prevent injury.

---

3) Remove outside vane support retaining pin. Remove metal "O" ring retainer and "O" ring from outer vane support. Discard "O" ring.

4) Remove and discard side seal. Remove side seal support, top vane positioning ring and outer vane support. Remove 7 vanes from rotor. Remove inner vane support and bottom vane positioning ring. *See Fig. 20.*

5) Remove bolts retaining EPC and lock-up solenoids. Remove solenoids. Depress tabs and twist shift solenoids counterclockwise to remove. Use a socket on the rotor side of housing to press bearing and seal assembly out of valve body side of pump.

NOTE: The only serviceable parts in oil pump are seals. If any other parts are damaged or worn, replace entire assembly.

Reassembly – 1) To reassemble, reverse disassembly procedure. To install bearing and seal, use Output Shaft Seal Installation Tool (T89P-1177-AH). Install bearing from separator plate side of pump body. Bearing must be pressed in flush with pump body. Install seal from rotor side of pump body. *See Fig. 20.*

2) Install bottom vane positioning ring. Install inner vane support with small inside diameter counter bore facing up. Shiny portion of the 7 vane blades is installed toward outer vane support. Install outer vane support. Install top vane positioning ring. Install new side seal between outer vane support and housing. Install outer vane support retaining pin.

3) Install bore spring. Install "O" ring and metal retainer in outer vane support. Install oil pump cover while aligning pump gears with drive shaft. Install oil pump cover and tighten 6 retaining bolts to 84-108 INCH lbs. (9-12 N.m).

4) Install check balls and relief valve. Install separator plate and new gasket. Use valve body Guide Pins (T86P-70100-A or B) to align separator plate and pump housing. Install Torx bolts and tighten to 84-108 INCH lbs. (9-12 N.m). Remove guide pins.

OVERDRIVE SERVO

Disassembly & Reassembly – Remove 3 cover bolts, cover, return spring and rod. *See Fig. 21.* Remove piston from cover. Place piston assembly in a soft-jawed vise. Remove rear piston rod retaining clip and washer. Remove piston, seal and cushion spring. Piston and seal are an assembly and piston must be replaced if seal is damaged. Remove front rod clip, if necessary. Lubricate seals with petroleum jelly. To reassemble, reverse disassembly procedure. Ensure springs are correctly positioned in case.

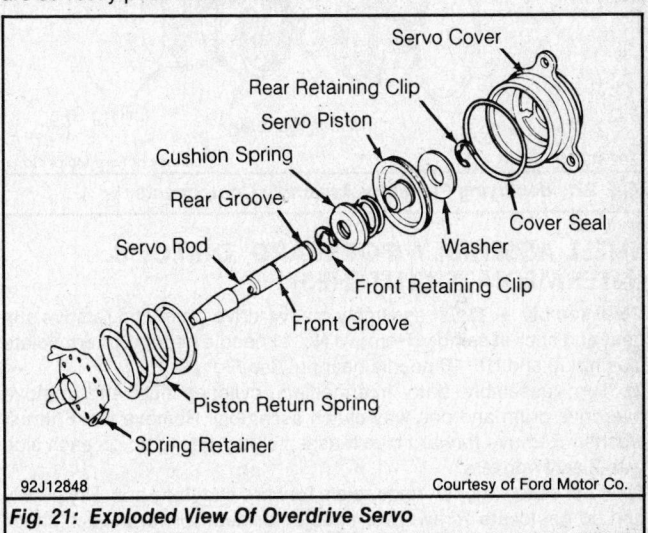

92J12848   Courtesy of Ford Motor Co.

Fig. 21: Exploded View Of Overdrive Servo

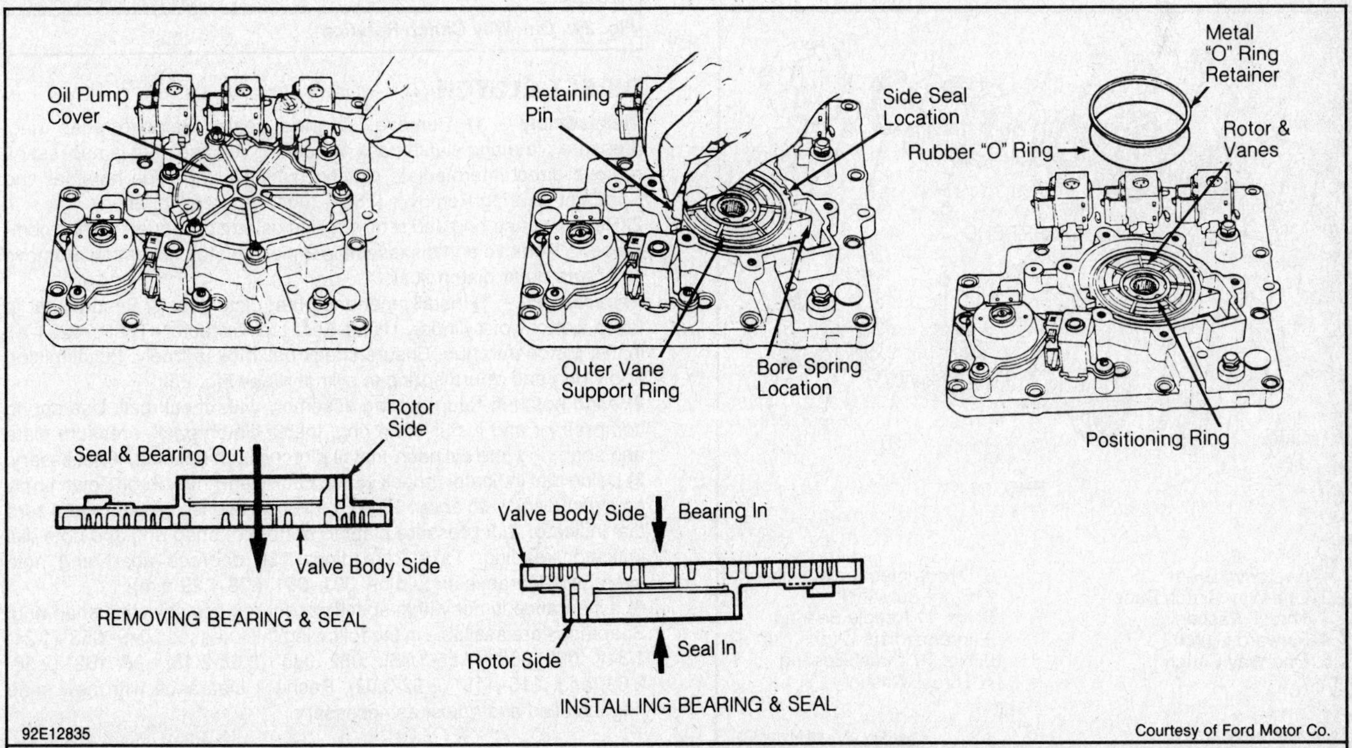

92E12835   Courtesy of Ford Motor Co.

Fig. 20: Identifying Oil Pump Components

PLANETARY ASSEMBLY

NOTE: Except for differential components, individual components of the planetary carrier are not serviceable.

Disassembly & Reassembly – Remove snap ring. Remove front planetary and No. 13 needle bearing from rear planetary. Remove rear planetary from shell and ring gear assembly. To reassemble, reverse disassembly procedure. *See Fig. 22.*

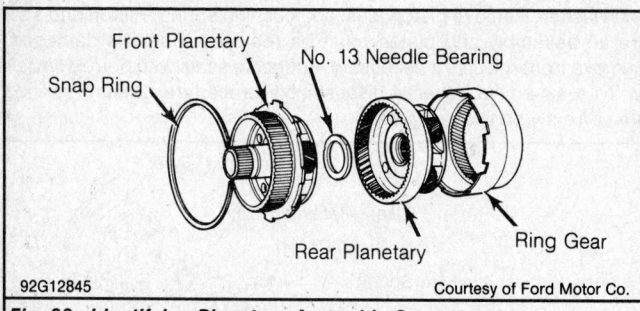

92G12845   Courtesy of Ford Motor Co.

Fig. 22: Identifying Planetary Assembly Components

SHELL ASSEMBLY (FORWARD, DIRECT & INTERMEDIATE CLUTCHES)

Disassembly – **1)** Set assembly on overdrive drum and remove sun gear and shell assembly. Remove No. 11 needle bearing, intermediate clutch hub and No. 10 needle bearing. *See Fig. 23.*
2) Turn assembly onto intermediate cylinder hub and remove overdrive drum and one-way clutch assembly. Remove No. 6 thrust washer. Remove forward clutch assembly by prying up on each side with 2 screwdrivers.
3) Direct clutch hub "O" rings retain forward clutch on hub. Pry evenly and do not locate screwdriver ends on or near forward clutch check ball. Remove direct one-way clutch and No. 7 thrust washer. Remove direct one-way clutch outer race and one-way clutch.
Reassembly – **1)** Ensure all clutch assemblies have been checked and overhauled as necessary before reassembling shell assembly.

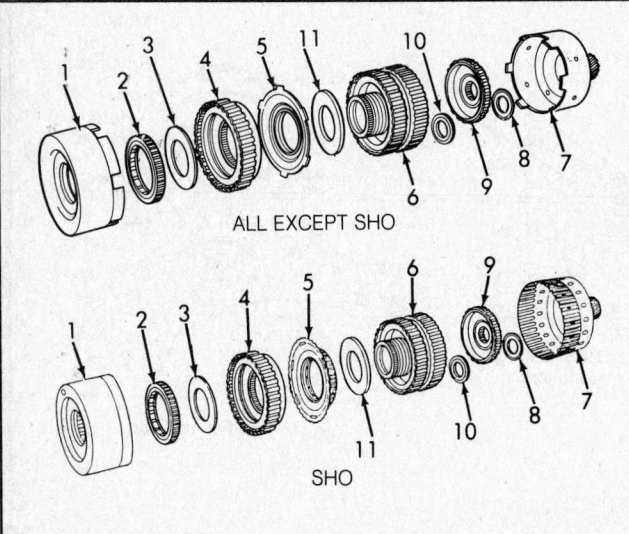

ALL EXCEPT SHO

SHO

1. Overdrive Drum
2. One-Way Clutch Race
3. Thrust Washer
4. Forward Clutch
5. One-Way Clutch
6. Direct/Intermediate Clutch
7. Front Sun Shell
8. No. 11 Needle Bearing
9. Intermediate Clutch Hub
10. No. 10 Thrust Bearing
11. Thrust Washer

92I12839 94B38423   Courtesy of Ford Motor Co.

Fig. 23: Exploded View Of Shell Assembly

Position shell with intermediate clutch facing down. Ensure No. 7 thrust washer tabs are aligned with slots in direct clutch.
2) Install one-way clutch on direct clutch, with clutch lip facing down and lip on outer race facing up. Outer race should turn clockwise and lock counterclockwise when direct clutch is facing up. Install one-way clutch and align onto clutch pack splines. Install "O" rings on hub.
3) Install forward clutch assembly, being careful not to damage "O" rings. Install No. 6 thrust washer on forward clutch assembly. Ensure one-way clutch is positioned in overdrive drum. One-way clutch should turn counterclockwise. Position overdrive drum over forward clutch. *See Fig. 24.*
4) Turn assembly over and set on overdrive drum. Install No. 10 needle bearing onto intermediate clutch hub. Use petroleum jelly to hold bearing in position.
5) Install intermediate clutch hub into forward clutch. Install No. 11 needle bearing on intermediate clutch hub with outer lip facing down. Install sun gear and shell assembly over forward clutch. Ensure tabs of sun gear shell and overdrive drum align.

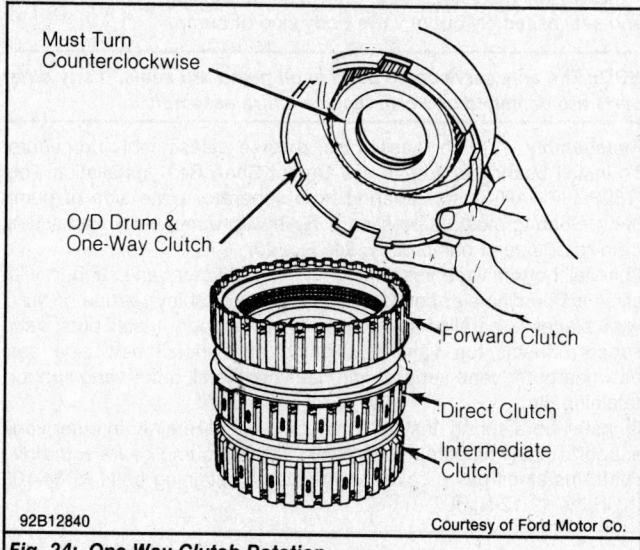

92B12840   Courtesy of Ford Motor Co.

Fig. 24: One-Way Clutch Rotation

DIRECT CLUTCH

Disassembly – **1)** Remove "O" ring seals. Remove snap ring, pressure plate and clutch pack. If bushing replacement is necessary, remove direct-intermediate clutch bushing using slide hammer and Sprocket Bearing Remover (T86P-70043-A). *See Fig. 25.*
2) Remove snap ring and return spring using appropriate spring compressor. Remove and disassemble 2-piece piston assembly. Remove inner and outer piston seals.
Reassembly – **1)** Install inner and outer piston seals. Ensure seal lip faces bottom of cylinder. Using Seal Lip Protector (T86P-70234-A), install piston into hub. Ensure check ball moves freely. Install piston apply ring and return spring in cylinder. *See Fig. 25.*
2) Align notch in return spring assembly with check ball. Use spring compressor and install snap ring. Install clutch pack, pressure plate and snap ring into cylinder. Install direct clutch bushing, if necessary.
3) Using dial indicator, check clutch pack clearance. Push down firmly on clutch pack with about 30 lbs. of force. Release pressure and zero dial indicator. Lift pressure plate to bottom of snap ring and note dial indicator reading. Take 2 readings 180 degrees apart and note average. Clearance should be .031-.051" (.78-1.29 mm).
4) If clearance is not within specification, replace selective snap ring. Snap rings are available in the following thicknesses; .049-.053" (1.24-1.34), .065-.069" (1.65-1.75), .082-.086" (2.08-2.18), .98-.102" (2.50-2.60) and .115-.119" (2.92-3.02). Recheck clearance with new snap ring installed and adjust as necessary.

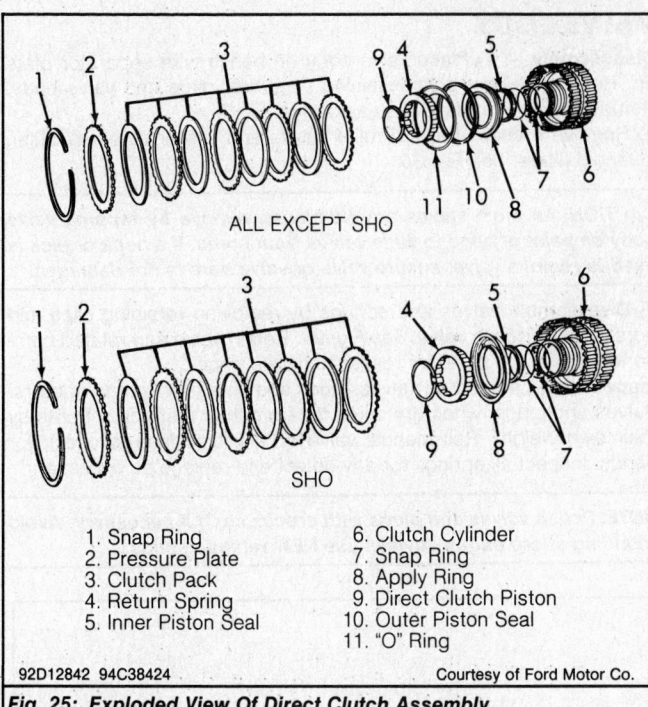

1. Snap Ring
2. Pressure Plate
3. Clutch Pack
4. Return Spring
5. Inner Piston Seal
6. Clutch Cylinder
7. Snap Ring
8. Apply Ring
9. Direct Clutch Piston
10. Outer Piston Seal
11. "O" Ring

92D12842 94C38424   Courtesy of Ford Motor Co.

Fig. 25: Exploded View Of Direct Clutch Assembly

FORWARD CLUTCH

NOTE: The number of plates and discs in the forward clutch and direct clutch assembly may vary with application.

Disassembly – Remove snap ring, pressure plate, clutch pack and wave spring. *See Fig. 26.* Using appropriate spring compressor to compress return spring, remove snap ring and return spring. Remove piston assembly from hub. Remove inner and outer piston seals.

Reassembly – 1) Install inner and outer piston seals. Ensure seal lips face bottom of cylinder. Using Seal Lip Protector (T86P-70548-A), install piston assembly. Using compressor, install return spring and snap ring. Install wave spring, clutch pack, pressure plate and snap ring. *See Fig. 26.*

2) Check clutch pack clearance using a dial indicator. Push down firmly on clutch pack with about 30 lbs. of force. Release pressure and zero dial indicator. Lift pressure plate to bottom of snap ring and note dial indicator reading. Take 2 readings 180 degrees apart and note average. Clearance should be .054-.072" (1.37-1.82 mm).

3) If clearance is not within specification, replace selective snap ring. Snap rings are available in the following thicknesses; .049-.053" (1.24-1.34), .063-.067" (1.60-1.70), .077-.081" (1.95-2.05), .091-.094" (2.31-2.38) and .104-.108" (2.65-2.75). Recheck clearance with new snap ring installed and adjust as necessary.

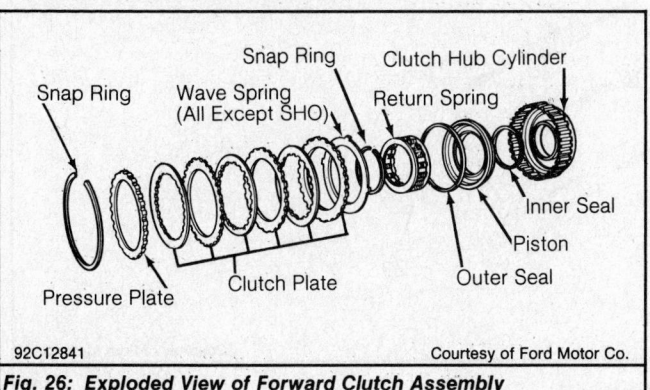

92C12841   Courtesy of Ford Motor Co.

Fig. 26: Exploded View of Forward Clutch Assembly

INTERMEDIATE CLUTCH

Disassembly – Remove snap ring, pressure plate and clutch pack assembly. Using appropriate spring compressor, remove snap ring and return spring. Remove piston assembly and inner and outer seals. *See Fig. 27.*

Reassembly – 1) Ensure check ball moves freely. Using Seal Lip Protector (T86P-70548-A), install inner and outer seals (lip facing bottom of cylinder). Install piston.

2) Using spring compressor, install return spring and snap ring. Install clutch pack, pressure plate and snap ring. *See Fig. 27.* Ensure step on pressure plate snap ring.

3) Check clutch pack clearance using a dial indicator. Push down firmly on clutch pack with about 30 lbs. of force. Release pressure and zero dial indicator. Lift pressure plate to bottom of snap ring and note dial indicator reading. Take 2 readings 180 degrees apart and note average. Clearance should be .040-.059" (1.02-1.50 mm). If clearance is not within specifications, replace selective snap ring. Snap rings are available in the following thicknesses; .047-.051" (1.20-1.30), .066-.070" (1.67-1.77), .084-.088" (2.14-2.24), .103-.107" (2.61-2.71) and .120-.124" (3.04-3.14). Recheck clearance with new snap ring installed and adjust as necessary.

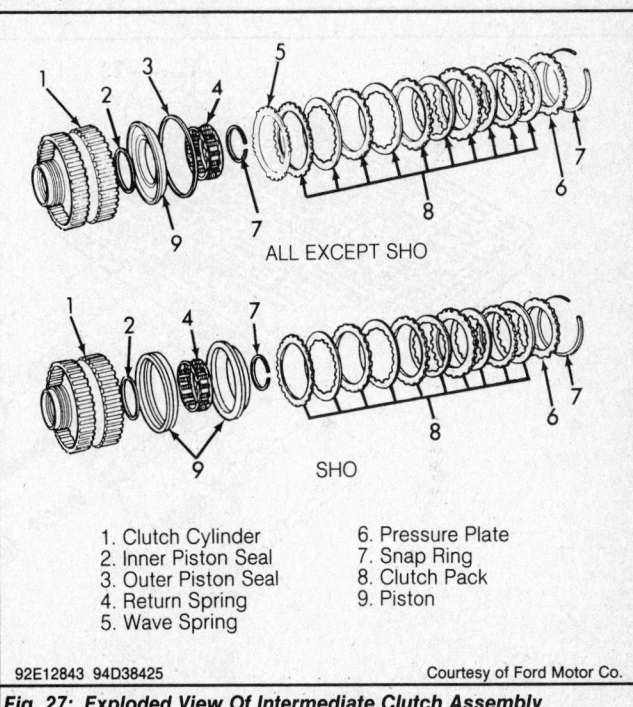

1. Clutch Cylinder
2. Inner Piston Seal
3. Outer Piston Seal
4. Return Spring
5. Wave Spring
6. Pressure Plate
7. Snap Ring
8. Clutch Pack
9. Piston

92E12843 94D38425   Courtesy of Ford Motor Co.

Fig. 27: Exploded View Of Intermediate Clutch Assembly

REVERSE CLUTCH

Disassembly – Remove snap ring, pressure plate, clutch pack and wave spring from clutch cylinder. Remove inner snap ring and return spring using appropriate spring compressor. Lift out piston and remove inner and outer seals. *See Fig. 28.*

Reassembly – 1) Install inner and outer piston seals (seal lip faces down) and install piston using Seal Protector (T86P-70403-A). Using spring compressor, install snap ring and return spring. Install wave spring, clutch pack, pressure plate and snap ring. *See Fig. 28.*

2) Check clutch pack clearance using a dial indicator. Push down firmly on clutch pack with about 30 lbs. of force. Release pressure and zero dial indicator. Lift pressure plate to bottom of snap ring and note dial indicator reading. Take 2 readings 180 degrees apart and note average. Clutch clearance should be .038-.064" (.97-1.63 mm). Snap rings are available in the following thicknesses; .059-.064" (1.52-1.62 mm), .078-.081" (1.98-2.08 mm), .096-.100" (2.45-2.55 mm) and .115-.119" (2.92-3.02 mm)

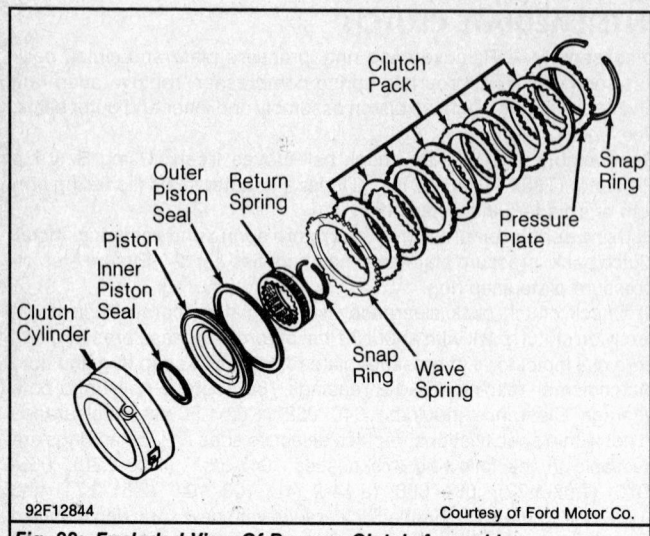

AUTOMATIC TRANSMISSIONS
Ford AXOD-E (Cont.)

Clutch Pack
Snap Ring
Outer Piston Seal
Return Spring
Pressure Plate
Piston
Inner Piston Seal
Clutch Cylinder
Snap Ring
Wave Spring
92F12844
Courtesy of Ford Motor Co.

Fig. 28: Exploded View Of Reverse Clutch Assembly

VALVE BODY

Disassembly – **1)** Place valve body on bench with separator plate up. Remove 2 Torx bolts retaining separator plate and valve body. Remove separator plate and gasket.

2) Remove 6 check balls, 2 relief valves and 2 filter screens. Clean solenoid filters. *See Fig. 30.*

CAUTION: As most valves are aluminum, remove by tapping valve body on palm of hand to slide valves from bores. If a hook or pick is used to remove valve, ensure valve or valve bore is not damaged.

3) Disassemble valves and springs by removing retaining clips and bore plugs for each valve. *See Fig. 29.* Retain valve and related components for each bore, for reassembly reference.

Inspection – Inspect all valves, plugs and bores for scores or burrs. Valves and plugs, when dry, must fall from their respective bores by their own weight. Roll manual valve on a flat surface to check for bends. Inspect all springs for any defect and replace as necessary.

NOTE: Polish valves and plugs with crocus cloth if necessary. Avoid rounding sharp edges. Always use NEW retaining clips.

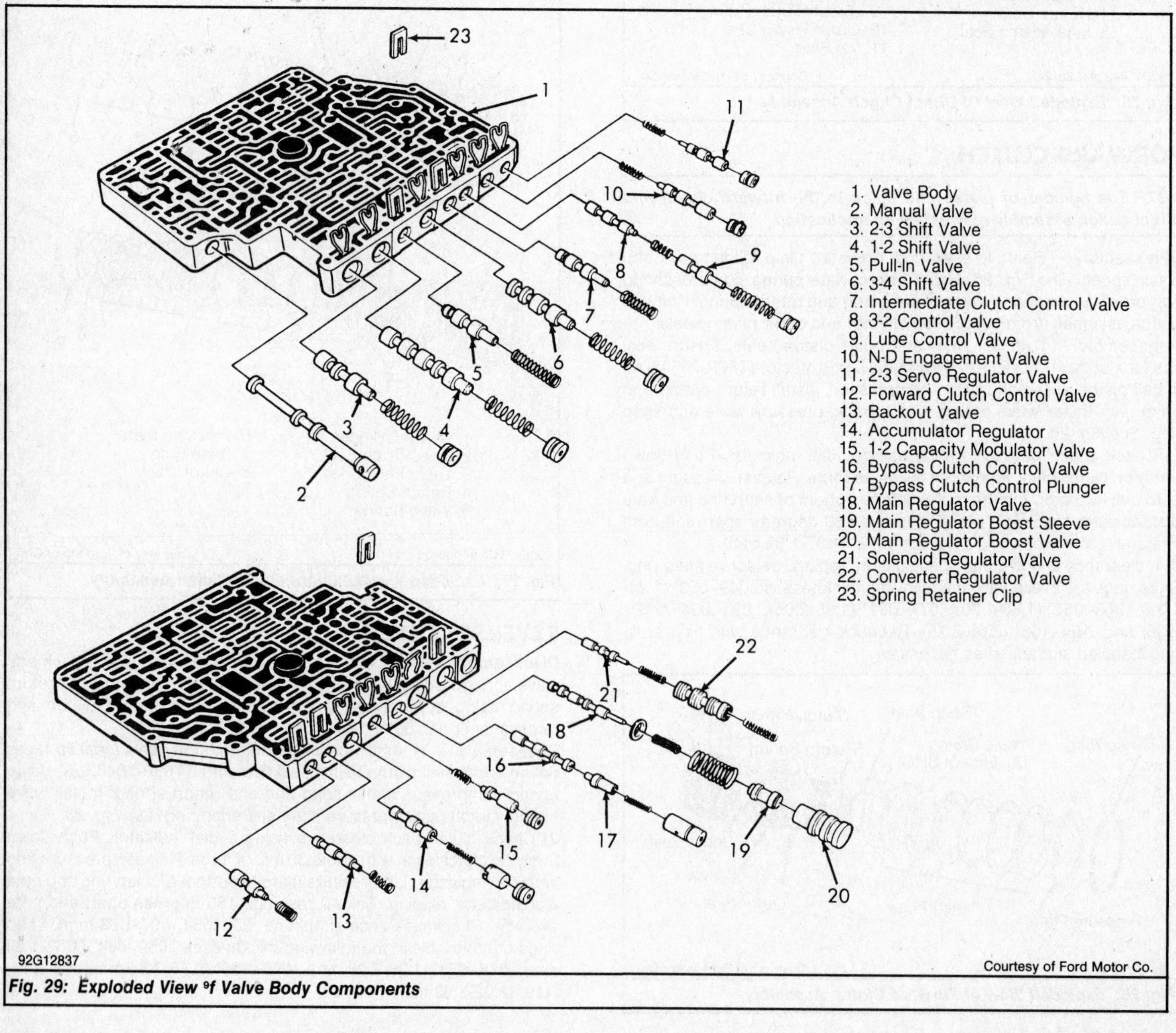

1. Valve Body
2. Manual Valve
3. 2-3 Shift Valve
4. 1-2 Shift Valve
5. Pull-In Valve
6. 3-4 Shift Valve
7. Intermediate Clutch Control Valve
8. 3-2 Control Valve
9. Lube Control Valve
10. N-D Engagement Valve
11. 2-3 Servo Regulator Valve
12. Forward Clutch Control Valve
13. Backout Valve
14. Accumulator Regulator
15. 1-2 Capacity Modulator Valve
16. Bypass Clutch Control Valve
17. Bypass Clutch Control Plunger
18. Main Regulator Valve
19. Main Regulator Boost Sleeve
20. Main Regulator Boost Valve
21. Solenoid Regulator Valve
22. Converter Regulator Valve
23. Spring Retainer Clip
92G12837
Courtesy of Ford Motor Co.

Fig. 29: Exploded View of Valve Body Components

Reassembly – To reassemble, reverse disassembly procedure. Install 6 check balls, 2 relief valves and 2 filters. Use a new valve body gasket. Use guide pins to align separator plate with valve body. Install Torx bolts and tighten to 84-108 INCH lbs. (9-12 N.m).

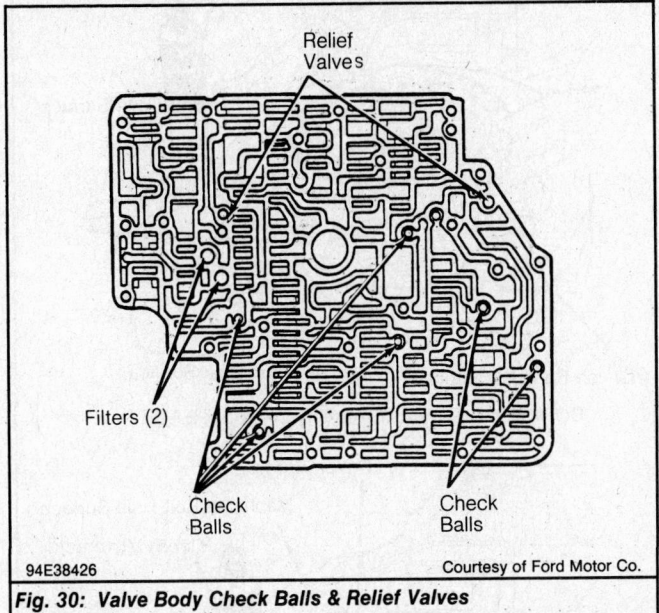

94E38426
Courtesy of Ford Motor Co.

Fig. 30: Valve Body Check Balls & Relief Valves

TRANSAXLE CASE

Inspection – Inspect case for cracks and stripped threads. Inspect gasket surfaces and mating surfaces for burrs. Check vent for obstructions, and check all fluid passages for obstructions and leakage. Inspect case bushing for scores. Check all parking linkage parts for wear or damage.

TRANSAXLE REASSEMBLY

NOTE: Handle all parts carefully to avoid damaging bearings and mating surfaces. Lubricate all parts with clean ATF. Use petroleum jelly on gaskets, thrust washers and needle bearings to retain them in place. Use all new gaskets and seals, and tighten bolts evenly.

NOTE: For identification and position of thrust bearings and washers, see Fig. 39.

1) Place case in horizontal position. Install drive sprocket support bearing, if necessary. Install drive sprocket support. Drive sprocket support bolt holes are offset. Sprocket support can only be aligned one way. Install and tighten 6 Torx (T-30) bolts to specification. See TORQUE SPECIFICATIONS.

2) Install converter oil seal using appropriate seal driver. Install right-hand output shaft seal using seal driver. After installation, ensure garter springs are present on seals.

3) Install AXOD End Play Tool (T87P-70014-AH) and Step Plate Adapter (D80L-630-3) over right-hand output shaft opening. *See Fig. 31.* This tool will be used to select thrust washers.

4) Position transaxle case in vertical position. Install No. 19 needle bearing over case boss with flat side facing up and outer lip facing down. Install final drive ring with external splines up. Lightly tap ring gear to fully seat in case splines.

5) Install speedometer drive gear, differential assembly, final drive sun gear, parking gear, No. 16 needle bearing, rear planet support, No. 15 needle bearing and No. 18 thrust washer. *See Fig. 32.*

6) Lower final drive assembly into case. Install snap ring and align end of snap ring with low-intermediate band anchor pin. Check end clearance at output shaft to select No. 18 thrust washer. Mount a dial indicator to end of output shaft. Back out screw on tool installed in step **3)**, until it no longer touches shaft. Zero dial indicator. Tighten screw to 35-44 INCH lbs. (4-5 N.m). Observe dial indicator. End clearance should be .004-.025" (.10-.63 mm). *See Fig. 33.*

7) If not within specification, replace No. 18 selective thrust washer. See NO. 18 THRUST WASHER SELECTION table.

NO. 18 THRUST WASHER SELECTION

Thickness/In. (mm)	Color Code
.048-.052 (1.20-1.28)	Red
.052-.054 (1.30-1.38)	Green
.056-.058 (1.40-1.48)	Blue
.060-.062 (1.50-1.58)	Black
.064-.066 (1.60-1.68)	White
.068-.070 (1.70-1.78)	Brown
.072-.074 (1.80-1.88)	Gold

8) After installing correct thrust washer, recheck clearance. If end clearance is within specifications, back off screw on tool and leave in position for No. 5 and No. 8 selective thrust washer clearance check.

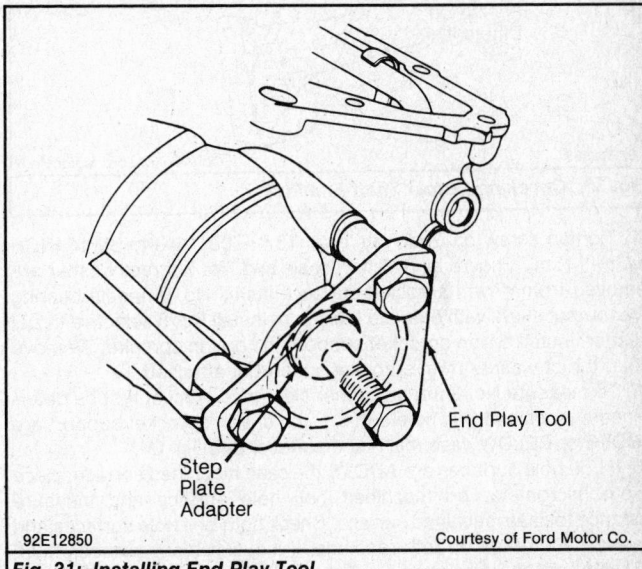

92E12850
Courtesy of Ford Motor Co.

Fig. 31: Installing End Play Tool

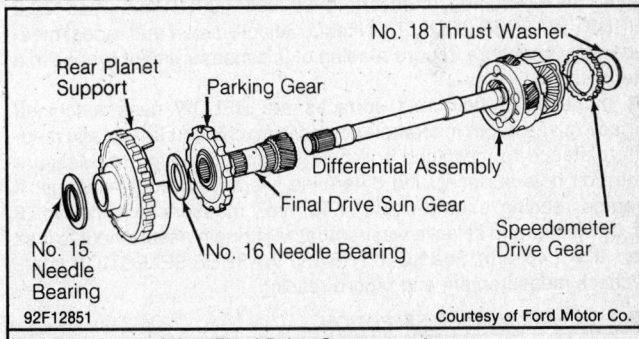

92F12851
Courtesy of Ford Motor Co.

Fig. 32: Assembling Final Drive Components

9) Install low-intermediate band and align anchor pin pocket with anchor pin. Install low-intermediate drum and sun gear assembly.

10) Reassemble ring gear and shell assembly, rear planetary, No. 13 needle bearing, front planetary and snap ring. *See Fig. 22.* Carefully slide planetary assembly over output shaft.

11) Lower reverse clutch into case and ensure clutch plates engage (intermediate clutch hub may be used as a tool to turn splines, if necessary). Align clutch cylinder anchor pin pocket with anchor pin case hole.

12) Start reverse anchor pin bolt, but do not tighten. Reassemble forward, direct and intermediate clutch assembly. Using Front Clutch Loading Tool (T86P-70389-A), lower assembly into case. Align shell and sun gear splines into forward planetary. Ensure assembly is fully seated before removing tool.

13) Install overdrive band into case. Install plastic retainer with cross-hairs facing up. Check end clearance for No. 5 and No. 8 thrust washer.

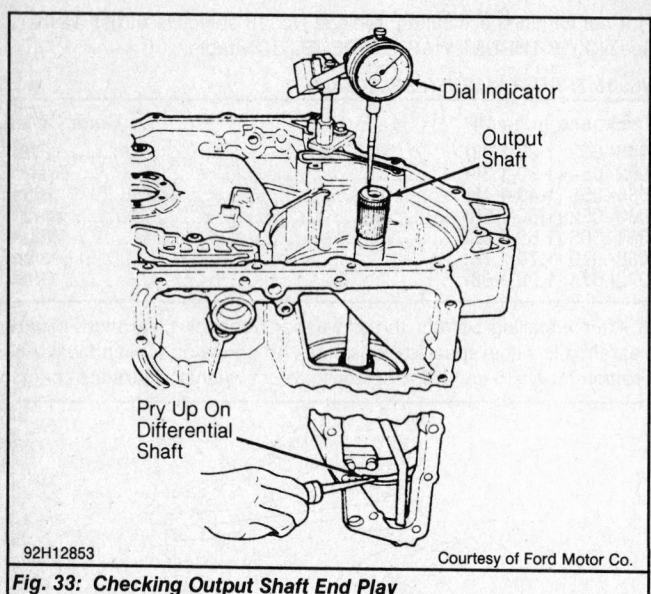

92H12853   Courtesy of Ford Motor Co.

Fig. 33: Checking Output Shaft End Play

14) Tighten screw on End Play Tool (T87P-7001-AH) to 35-44 INCH lbs. (4-5 N.m). Ensure all 5 Teflon seals and No. 5 thrust washer are removed from driven sprocket support. Install No. 9 needle bearing over output shaft, with outer lip facing up. Install No. 8 selective thrust washer. Install driven sprocket support and driven sprocket. Remove No. 5 thrust washer from sprocket support, if attached.

15) To measure No. 8 thrust washer clearance, it must first be determined if machined bolt hole surfaces on driven sprocket support are ABOVE or BELOW case machined surface. See Fig. 34.

16) If bolt hole surfaces are ABOVE the case machined surface, place depth micrometer on machined bolt hole surface and measure distance to case machined surface. Check both bolt hole surfaces and determine average of both readings. If measurement exceeds .008" (.21 mm), measure existing No. 8 thrust washer and select a washer that will ensure a measurement of .000-.008" (.00-.21 mm). See NO.8 THRUST WASHER SELECTION table. Select washer and repeat measurement procedure; record reading of this measurement for use in a later step.

17) If machined bolt hole surfaces are BELOW case machined surface, place depth micrometer on case machined surface and measure distance to machined bolt hole surface. See Fig. 34. Measure both bolt hole surfaces and determine average of both readings. If average reading exceeds .018" (.46 mm), measure existing No. 8 thrust washer and select a washer that will bring measurement to less than .018" (.46 mm). See NO. 8 THRUST WASHER SELECTION table. Recheck measurement and record reading.

NO. 8 THRUST WASHER SELECTION

Thickness/Inch (mm)	Color
.056-.060 (1.43-1.53)	Natural
.066-.070 (1.68-1.78)	Dark Green
.075-.079 (1.92-2.02)	Light Blue
.085-.089 (2.17-2.27)	Red

18) With correct No. 8 thrust washer selected, check end play and No. 5 thrust washer installation. Remove driven sprocket support, No. 8 thrust washer and No. 9 needle bearing. Apply petroleum jelly to No. 5 thrust washer and install on driven sprocket support. Align washer tab with mating slot in support. Install driven sprocket support. DO NOT install No. 8 thrust washer or No. 9 needle bearing at this time.

19) Determine if machined bolt hole surfaces of sprocket support are now ABOVE or BELOW machined case surface. If machined bolt hole surfaces are ABOVE case surface, add the distance of the final measurement taken in step 17) to the distance above the case. This distance should be .000-.033" (.00-.85 mm). If measurement exceeds specification, replace No. 5 thrust washer and recheck. See NO. 5 THRUST WASHER SELECTION table.

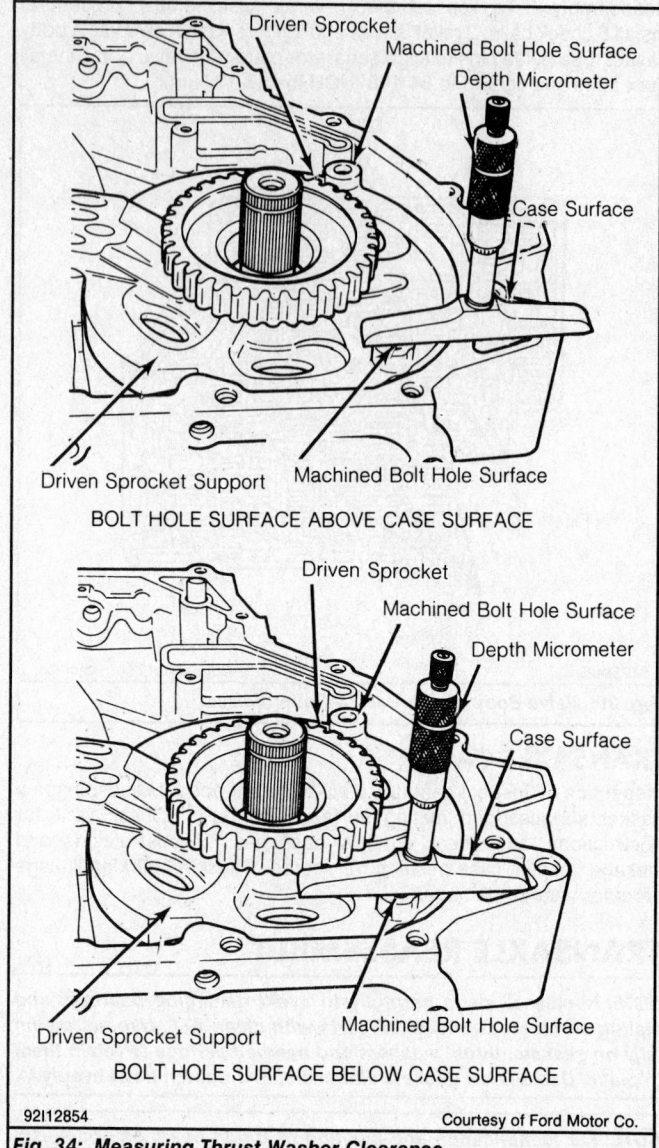

BOLT HOLE SURFACE ABOVE CASE SURFACE

BOLT HOLE SURFACE BELOW CASE SURFACE

92I12854   Courtesy of Ford Motor Co.

Fig. 34: Measuring Thrust Washer Clearance

20) If machined bolt hole surfaces are BELOW the case surface, record this measurement and the final measurement from step 17). Subtract the thickness of No. 8 thrust washer from No. 5 thrust washer. Result must be .000-.033" (.00-.84 mm). If measurement is not within specification, replace No. 5 thrust washer and recheck. See NO.5 THRUST WASHER SELECTION table.

NO. 5 THRUST WASHER SELECTION

Thickness	Color
.086-.090" (2.18-2.28 mm)	Green
.095-.099" (2.43-2.53 mm)	Black
.105-.109" (2.67-2.77 mm)	Natural
.115-.118" (2.92-3.02 mm)	Red

21) Remove tool from bottom of case. Remove dial indicator set-up. Remove driven sprocket support and install No. 9 needle bearing and correct No. 8 thrust washer. Install 5 Teflon seals on driven sprocket support. Install correct No. 5 thrust washer. Install driven sprocket support.

22) If manual shaft components have not been installed, tap manual shaft seal into case. Start manual shaft through seal, and slide manual detent lever onto shaft. Slide shaft through park rod actuating lever and tap into case hole. Install new lock pin through case hole, aligning with groove in shaft. Install new roll pins.

23) Install parking pawl, return spring, parking pawl shaft and locator pin. Ensure parking pawl engages park gear and returns freely. Install park rod actuating lever and park rod in case. Install park rod abutment and start abutment bolts. Push in parking pawl and locate rod between pawl and abutment.

24) Tighten reverse drum Allen head (6 mm) bolts to 89-106 INCH lbs. (10-12 N.m) and 19 mm lock nut to 26-35 ft. lbs. (35-47 N.m). Tighten park rod abutment bolts, reverse anchor pin bolt and lock nut to specification. Clean and lightly tap oil tubes into position until fully seated. Apply Threadlock (262) around tube-to-case surface. Install tube retaining brackets.

25) Install seal and oil filter into case. Install reverse apply tube/oil filter bracket and bolt. Install oil pan with new gasket. Tighten bolts to specification. See TORQUE SPECIFICATIONS. Position transaxle with input shaft and overdrive band facing up.

26) Align tabs of No. 2 and No. 4 thrust washers and install on drive and driven sprocket supports. Lubricate and install cast iron sealing ring on input shaft. Install chain on drive and driven sprockets. Lower assembly into sprocket supports, rotating to ensure components are fully seated.

27) Install No. 1 (plastic) and No. 3 (metal) thrust washers on chain cover, aligning tabs with slots in chain cover. Install new chain cover gasket. Install marked accumulator springs to correct position. Carefully align chain cover input shaft bore with input shaft. Ensure cast iron sealing ring is not damaged. Gently apply downward pressure, to overcome accumulator spring pressure, and start 2 chain cover bolts 180 degrees apart.

28) Install remaining chain cover bolts and tighten to specification in sequence. See Fig. 35. Input shaft should have end play and rotate freely. If it does not rotate freely, remove chain cover and check for damaged cast iron seal.

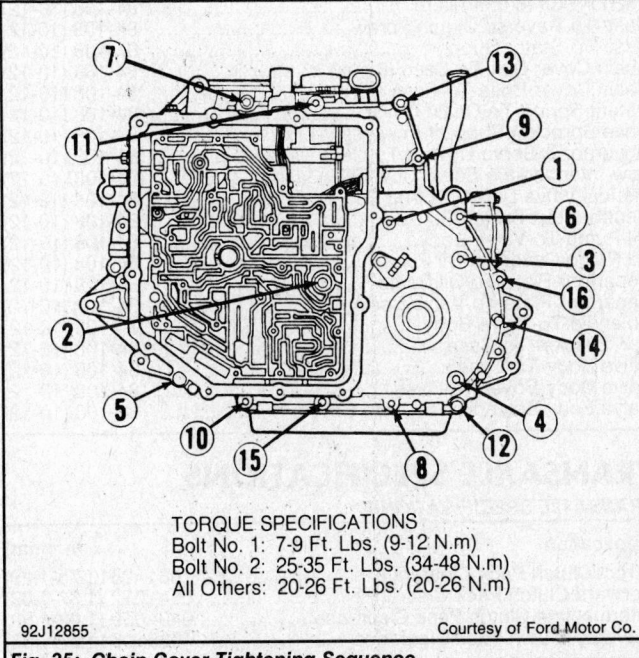

TORQUE SPECIFICATIONS
Bolt No. 1: 7-9 Ft. Lbs. (9-12 N.m)
Bolt No. 2: 25-35 Ft. Lbs. (34-48 N.m)
All Others: 20-26 Ft. Lbs. (20-26 N.m)

92J12855   Courtesy of Ford Motor Co.
Fig. 35: Chain Cover Tightening Sequence

29) Install turbine speed sensor. Install output shaft seal and circlip. Perform air pressure test. See AIR PRESSURE TEST under TESTING. Install new Teflon seals on pump driveshaft. Install shaft and connect manual valve link to detent lever.

30) Start oil pump and valve body assembly over pump shaft and connect manual valve link to manual valve. Push valve body down until seated. Install valve body bolts and tighten in sequence to 80-106 INCH lbs. (9-12 N.m). Ensure 3 short bolts are located in correct position. See Fig. 36.

31) Install bulkhead connector and electrical connectors. Ensure connectors "click" to lock position as they are installed. Place gear selector in Neutral position. Install Manual Lever Position Sensor (MLPS) and lightly tighten bolts. Align slots of MLPS using Gear Position Sensor Adjuster (T91P-70010-A). Tighten bolts to 80-106 INCH lbs. (9-12 N.m).

32) Install valve body cover with new self-adhesive gasket. Tighten bolts to specification. Install dipstick tube grommet and dipstick tube in case. Install speedometer driven gear and drive gear shaft. Install thrust bearing and race with black side of race facing upward. Install speedometer cover with new seal. Tighten bolts to specification. See TORQUE SPECIFICATIONS. Place transaxle in horizontal position. Install remaining chain cover bolts in bellhousing. Proceed to SERVO PISTON TRAVEL CHECK if any of the following components are being replaced:

- Transaxle Case Assembly
- Band Assembly
- Drum/Sun Gear Assembly
- Servo Piston Rod
- Servo Piston

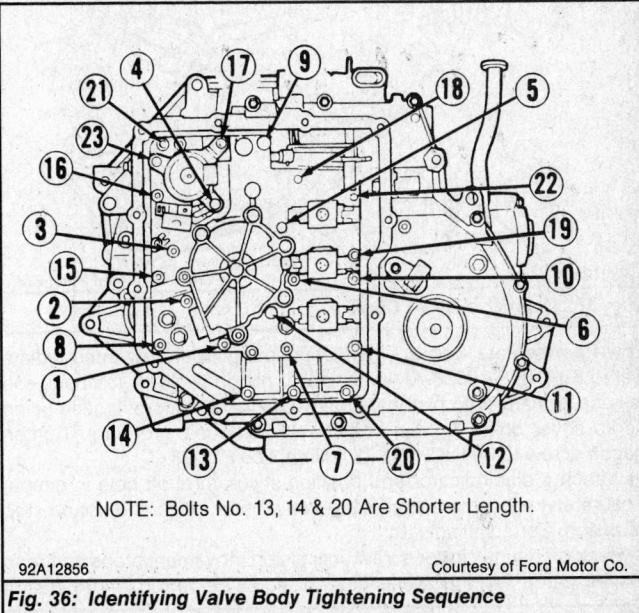

NOTE: Bolts No. 13, 14 & 20 Are Shorter Length.

92A12856   Courtesy of Ford Motor Co.
Fig. 36: Identifying Valve Body Tightening Sequence

NOTE: Servo piston travel check of both the overdrive and low-intermediate servos should only be performed if either the transaxle case, band assembly, drum and sun gear assembly, servo piston rod or servo piston were replaced.

NOTE: If test springs from servo tool kits are used in test procedure, ensure they are not interchanged with operational springs. Test springs are weaker and may be shorter or have smaller wire diameter. Spring color may be identical.

Servo Piston Travel Check-Overdrive Servo – **1)** Install spring from Overdrive Servo Rod Kit (T86P-70023-B) in case. Install servo piston and rod in case. Install servo piston gauge from kit and secure in case using servo cover bolts. Tighten bolts to 90 INCH lbs. (10 N.m). Tighten gauge center screw to 10 INCH lbs (1.13 N.m). See Fig. 37.

2) Attach a dial indicator and position stylus through hole in gauge. Ensure stylus contacts piston on a flat surface. DO NOT contact step on piston. Zero dial indicator.

3) Back off gauge center screw until piston movement stops and read piston travel on dial indicator. Piston travel is determined by servo rod length. Piston travel should be .070-.149" (1.8-3.8 mm).

4) If piston travel is not within specification, change piston rod and recheck. Piston rod is identified by number of grooves located on tip of rod. See OVERDRIVE SERVO ROD SELECTION table. Install overdrive servo assembly. Install new seals, cover and bolts. Tighten bolts to 84-108 INCH lbs. (10-12 N.m).

OVERDRIVE SERVO ROD SELECTION

Number Of Grooves In Rod Tip	Rod Length Inch (mm)
0 (No Grooves)	3.911 (99.33)
1	3.860 (98.05)
2	3.810 (96.78)

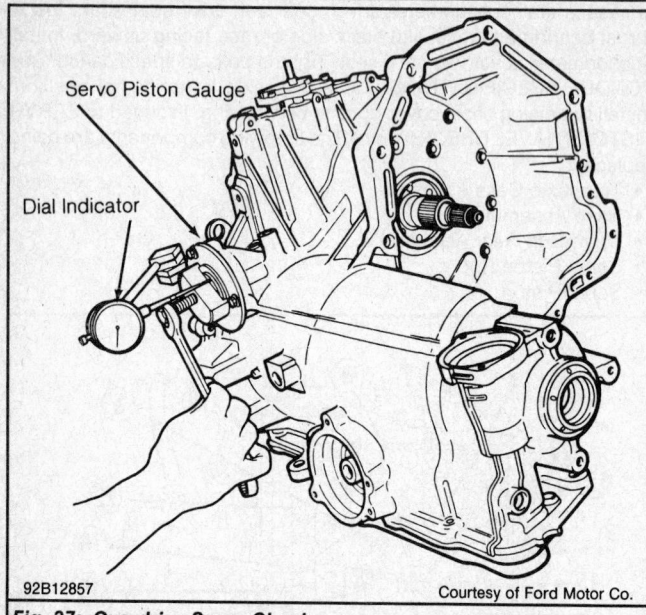

92B12857   Courtesy of Ford Motor Co.

Fig. 37: Overdrive Servo Check

Low-Intermediate Servo – 1) Install spring from Low-Intermediate Servo Kit (T86P-70023-A). Install servo piston (without seal) and rod in case. Install servo piston gauge from kit and secure in case using servo cover bolts. Tighten bolts to 90 INCH lbs. (10 N.m). Tighten gauge screw to 30 INCH lbs. (3.4 N.m). *See Fig. 38.*

2) Attach a dial indicator and position stylus through hole in gauge. Ensure stylus has contacted piston on a flat surface and not on step of piston. Zero dial indicator.

3) Back off gauge center screw until piston movement stops and read dial indicator. Piston travel is determined by servo rod length. Piston travel should be .217-.256" (5.5-6.5 mm) if a used low-intermediate band is installed. If low-intermediate band is new, reading should be .197-.236" (5.0-6.0 mm).

4) If piston travel is not within specification, change piston rod and recheck. Piston rod is identified by number of grooves located on tip of rod. See LOW-INTERMEDIATE SERVO ROD SELECTION table. Install servo assembly. Install new seals, cover and bolts. Tighten bolts to specification.

LOW-INTERMEDIATE SERVO ROD SELECTION

Number Of Grooves In Rod Tip	Rod Length Inch (mm)
0 (No Grooves)	4.498 (114.26)
1	4.477 (113.72)
2	4.456 (113.18)
3	4.435 (112.64)
4	4.413 (112.10)

NOTE: Ensure tab on low-intermediate servo cover is aligned with port on case.

TORQUE SPECIFICATIONS
TORQUE SPECIFICATIONS

Application	Ft Lbs. (N.m)
Anchor Bolt Lock Nut	25-35 (33-47)
Chain Cover Bolt-To-Case (13 mm)	20-22 (27-30)
Converter-To-Flywheel Bolts	23-39 (31-53)
Oil Pan-To-Case Bolts	10-12 (14-16)
Park Rod Abutment Bolts-To-Case	20-22 (27-30)

Application	INCH Lbs. (N.m)
Anchor Bolt (6 mm Allen)	84-108 (10-12)
Case-To-Reverse Clutch Screw	84-108 (10-12)
Case-To-Stator Support	84-108 (10-12)
Chain Cover Bolt-To-Case (8 mm)	84-108 (10-12)
Chain Cover Bolts-To-Case (10 mm)	84-108 (10-12)
Detent Spring-To-Chain Cover	84-108 (10-12)
Drive Sprocket Support-To-Case (Torx)	84-108 (10-12)
Governor & Servo Covers-To-Case	84-108 (10-12)
Low-Intermediate Servo Cover-To-Case	84-108 (10-12)
Manual Valve Detent Spring Bolt	84-108 (10-12)
Neutral Start Switch Bolt	84-108 (10-12)
Oil Pump-To-Valve Body	84-108 (10-12)
Oil Pump Cover-To-Oil Pump	84-108 (10-12)
Separator Plate-To-Oil Pump	84-108 (10-12)
Separator Plate-To-Valve Body	84-108 (10-12)
Solenoid-To-Valve Body	84-108 (10-12)
T.V. Bracket-To-Case	84-108 (10-12)
Valve Body-To-Case	84-108 (10-12)
Valve Body Cover-To-Case	84-108 (10-12)
Valve Body Solenoid-To-Chain Cover	84-108 (10-12)

TRANSAXLE SPECIFICATIONS
TRANSAXLE SPECIFICATIONS

Application	In. (mm)
Direct Clutch Pack Clearance	.031-.051 (.78-1.29)
Forward Clutch Pack Clearance	.054-.072 (1.37-1.82)
Intermediate Clutch Pack Clearance	.040-.059 (1.02-1.50)
Reverse Clutch Pack Clearance	.038-.064 (.97-1.63)

SERVICE BULLETINS

EXTENDED 3-2 OR 4-2 DOWNSHIFTS (3.2L TAURUS SHO)

Ford Motor Co. TSB 93-14-14 – On Ford Taurus SHO equipped with 3.2L engine, transaxle may have a extended 3-2 or 4-2 downshift with harsh bump. The symptom occurs above 55 MPH at wide open throttle. Condition is caused by PCM with calibration 3-10C-ROOA on vehicles built before 5/17/93. Replacement PCM part number is F3DZ-12A650-JC with calibration of 3-10C-R10.

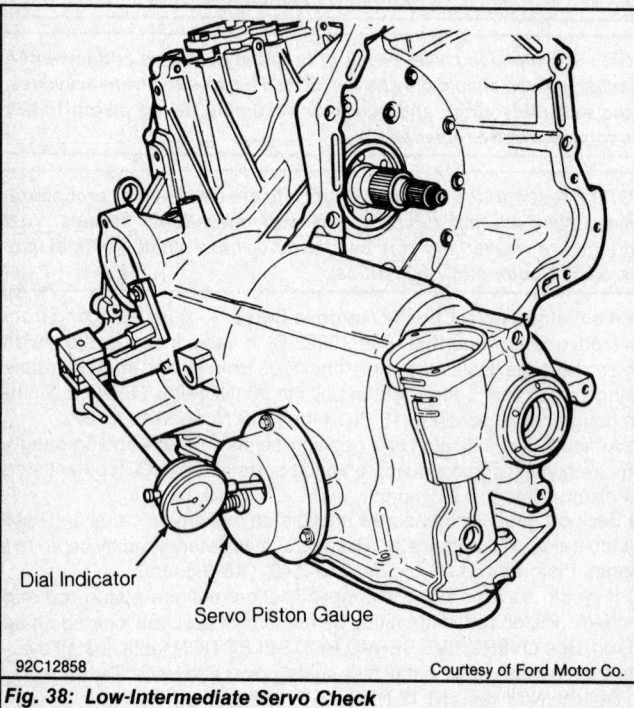

92C12858   Courtesy of Ford Motor Co.

Fig. 38: Low-Intermediate Servo Check

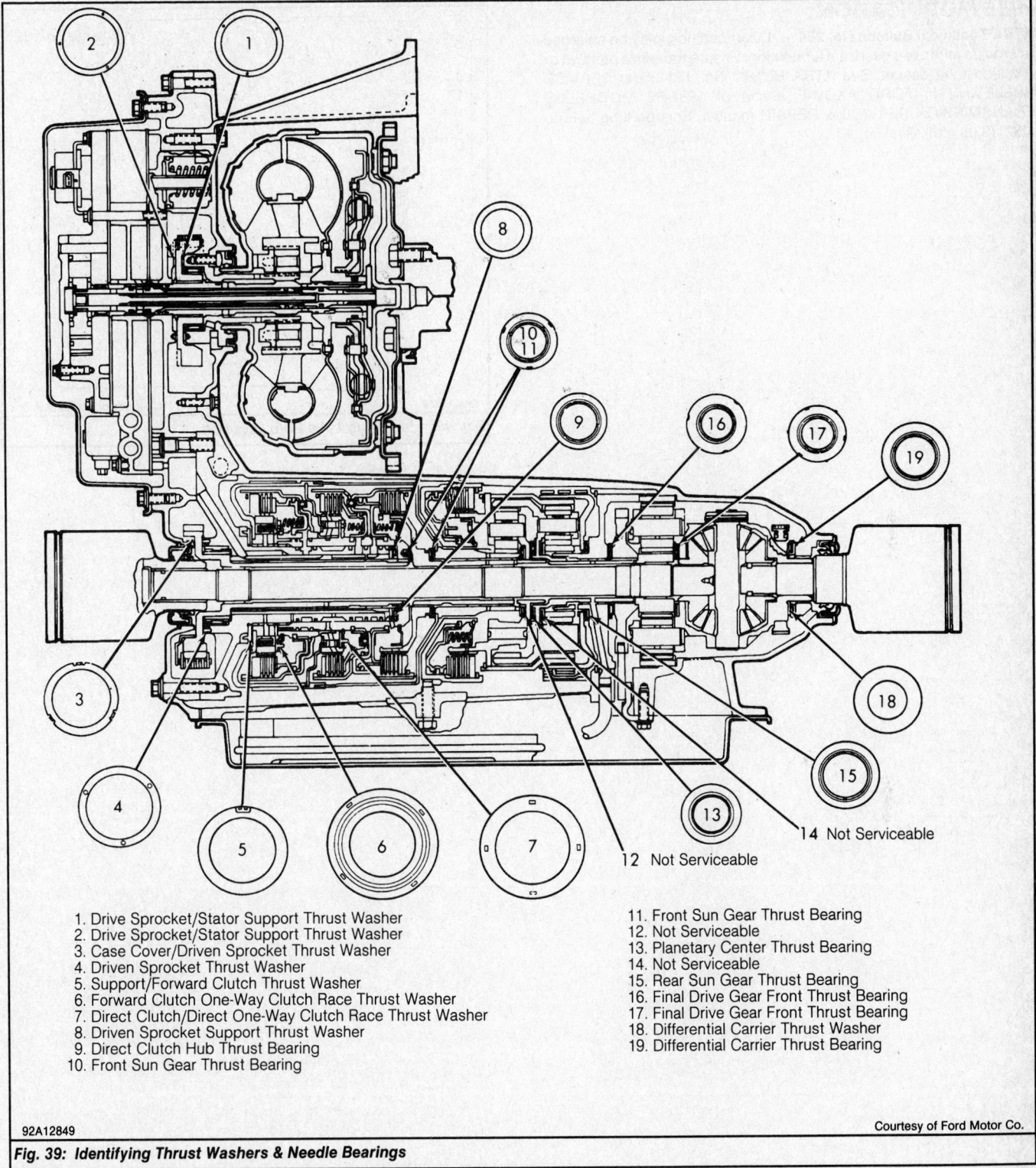

1. Drive Sprocket/Stator Support Thrust Washer
2. Drive Sprocket/Stator Support Thrust Washer
3. Case Cover/Driven Sprocket Thrust Washer
4. Driven Sprocket Thrust Washer
5. Support/Forward Clutch Thrust Washer
6. Forward Clutch One-Way Clutch Race Thrust Washer
7. Direct Clutch/Direct One-Way Clutch Race Thrust Washer
8. Driven Sprocket Support Thrust Washer
9. Direct Clutch Hub Thrust Bearing
10. Front Sun Gear Thrust Bearing
11. Front Sun Gear Thrust Bearing
12. Not Serviceable
13. Planetary Center Thrust Bearing
14. Not Serviceable
15. Rear Sun Gear Thrust Bearing
16. Final Drive Gear Front Thrust Bearing
17. Final Drive Gear Front Thrust Bearing
18. Differential Carrier Thrust Washer
19. Differential Carrier Thrust Bearing

92A12849

Courtesy of Ford Motor Co.

Fig. 39: Identifying Thrust Washers & Needle Bearings

LUBE MODIFICATION

ATRA Technical Bulletin No. 204 – Lube feed hole may be enlarged to provide improved geartrain lubrication. Ensure transaxle has 2nd or 3rd lube tube design. See ATRA Bulletin No. 121 under SERVICE BULLETINS in FORD AXOD-E article of 1991-92 MITCHELL® TRANSMISSION SERVICE & REPAIR manual. Enlarge lube hole to .082" (2.08 mm). *See Fig. 40.*

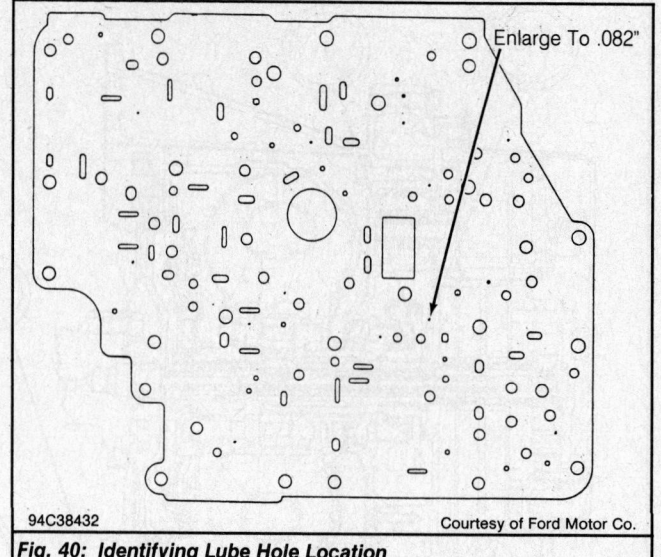

Enlarge To .082"

94C38432

Courtesy of Ford Motor Co.

Fig. 40: Identifying Lube Hole Location

Ford Motor Co: Continental, Sable, Taurus

NOTE: For AXOD-E transaxle mechanical testing and repair, see Ford AXOD-E article.

INTRODUCTION

The first step in diagnosing any driveability problem is verifying the customer's complaint with a test drive under the conditions the problem reportedly occurred. Before entering self-diagnostics, perform a careful and complete visual inspection. Most transmission control problems result from mechanical breakdowns or poor electrical connections.

NOTE: Perform all voltage tests with a Digital Volt-Ohmmeter (DVOM) with a minimum 10-megohm input impedance, unless stated otherwise in test procedure.

DESCRIPTION & OPERATION

Input signals from sensors are sent to the Powertrain Control Module (PCM). The PCM can determine when the time and conditions are right for a shift or converter clutch application. The PCM can also determine line pressure needed to optimize shift feel.

Five electronic solenoids accomplish these functions; 3 On/Off solenoids for shifting, 1 Pulse-Width Modulator solenoid for torque converter clutch control and Electronic Pressure Control (EPC) solenoid for line pressure control. The PCM has built-in self-diagnosis, fail-safe code and warning code display for the main input sensors and solenoid valves.

NOTE: In addition to transmission fault codes, engine-related fault codes may be output during QUICK TEST procedure. These fault codes pertain to engine performance and must be repaired first as engine performance will greatly affect transmission operation. For information and testing procedures of engine-related fault codes and components, see SELF-DIAGNOSTICS – EEC-IV article in ENGINE PERFORMANCE of appropriate MITCHELL® manual.

INPUT SENSORS

Air Conditioning Clutch (ACC) – On factory installed A/C system, PCM receives signal voltage from ACC switch indication that the air conditioning compressor clutch is engaged. The PCM uses the ACC switch signal to adjust line pressure to compensate for additional engine load. If the ACC switch fails with closed contacts, line pressure will be slightly low with air conditioning off. If the ACC switch fails with open contacts, line pressure will be slightly high with air conditioning on.

Brake On/Off (BOO) Switch – The PCM receives a signal from the BOO switch when the brake switch is operated. Torque converter clutch is disengaged when brakes are applied. Malfunctioning switch will affect torque converter operation.

Coolant Temperature Sensor (ECT) – Engine temperature signal is sent to PCM. Malfunctioning ECT will affect torque converter clutch operation.

Intake Air Temperature (IAT) Sensor – The IAT sensor monitors intake air temperature and sends signal to PCM to adjust air/fuel mixture and EPC pressure. IAT sensor malfunction will affect EPC pressure causing firm or soft shifts.

Mass Airflow Sensor (MAS) – The MAS signal is used for Electronic Pressure Control (EPC), shift and TCC scheduling. Sensor malfunction will affect shift and TCC scheduling.

Manual Lever Position (MLP) Sensor – The PCM monitors a series of step down resistors in the MLP sensor that act as a voltage divider. The voltage signal corresponds with position of the transaxle range selector lever. The MLP sensor also contains the neutral/start and backup circuits. Malfunction of the MLP sensor may cause harsh engagements and firm shift feel. Improper shifting or shift selection and no engine cranking may also result.

Power Steering Pressure Switch (PSPS) – The PCM receives signal from PSPS when power steering pressure exceeds a specific limit. The PCM compensates for increased engine load by adjusting idle speed. As idle speed is compensated, PCM also adjusts EPC pressure. If PSPS fails in ON position, EPC pressure will be increased causing firm engagements, firm upshifts and downshifts. If PSPS fails in OFF position, EPC pressure will be slightly low during increased loading of power steering system.

Profile Ignition Pickup (PIP) – The PIP located in distributor, sends engine rpm and crankshaft position to PCM. Signal received by the PCM affects torque converter clutch operation.

Throttle Position Sensor (TPS) – The TPS is a potentiometer mounted to the engine throttle body. The PCM receives a signal from the TPS relaying throttle plate position. TPS failure will cause PCM to operate in fail safe mode and raise line pressure to prevent transaxle damage. This condition will result in harsh engagements, firm shift feel, abnormal shift schedule and TCC not engaging or cycling.

Transmission Control Switch (TCS) – Switch is mounted on shift lever handle (Taurus SHO). Switch controls operation of 4th gear. Malfunction of switch will cause lack of 4th gear disable function.

Transmission Oil Temperature (TOT) Sensor – The TOT sensor is located on the solenoid valve body. The PCM monitors voltage across the TOT thermistor to determine transaxle temperature. Depending on temperature, the PCM controls line pressure, shift scheduling and TCC operation. Malfunction of sensor will cause incorrect line pressure and possible lack of TCC operation.

Transmission Speed Sensor (TSS) – The TSS is a magnetic pickup that sends turbine shaft speed signal to the PCM. Malfunction of sensor may cause harsh engagements of shifts. Lack of 4th gear or no engine braking in 2nd or 3rd gear may also be present.

Vehicle Speed Sensor (VSS) – The VSS is a magnetic pickup that sends vehicle speed signal to the PCM. Malfunction of sensor may cause harsh engagements of shifts. Lack of 4th gear, TCC lock-up, or engine braking in 2nd or 3rd gear may also be present.

OUTPUT DEVICES

Electronic Pressure Control (EPC) Solenoid – The EPC solenoid receives signal from the PCM to control line pressure and backout valve function. If EPC fails in ON position, transaxle is operated in fail-safe mode. Line pressure is approximately 120 psi. Harsh engagements and shifts will result. If EPC fails in OFF position, line pressure is approximately 90 psi. Harsh engagements and shifts will result.

Shift Solenoid Assemblies – 1) Three ON/OFF solenoids are used for electronic shift scheduling. Solenoids control pressure to 3 shift valves and forward clutch control valve, located in valve body. See SOLENOID OPERATION CHART.

SOLENOID OPERATIONS CHART

Gear Position	SS1	SS2	SS3
Overdrive [1]			
Park	Off	On	Off
Reverse	Off	On	Off
Neutral	Off	On	Off
OD1	Off	On	Off
OD2	On	On	Off
OD3	Off	Off	On
OD4	On	Off	On
"D" Or 3rd [2]			
D1	Off	On	Off
D2	On	On	Off
D3	Off	Off	Off

[1] – Transmission shift selector in Overdrive position, "OD" switch released (Taurus SHO).

[2] – Transmission shift selector in "D" or "3" position, "OD" switch depressed (Taurus SHO).

SOLENOID OPERATIONS CHART (Cont.)

Gear Position	SS1	SS2	SS3
SHO Only			
Manual 2 [3]	Off	Off	Off
Manual 2	On	On	Off
Manual 1 [4]	Off	Off	Off
Manual 1	Off	On	Off

[3] – Transmission is in 3rd gear until vehicle speed drops below calibrated speed.

[4] – Transmission is in 2nd gear until vehicle speed drops below calibrated speed.

2) When shift solenoid is "Always Off", failure could be due to PCM and/or vehicle wiring malfunction, and/or solenoid electrically stuck off, and/or hydraulically or mechanically stuck off. For shift symptoms, see Fig. 1.

3) When shift solenoid is "Always On", failure could be due to PCM and/or vehicle wiring malfunction, and/or solenoid electrically stuck off, and/or hydraulically or mechanically stuck off. For shift symptoms, see Fig. 2.

SS1 ALWAYS OFF	GEAR SELECTOR POSITION			
	D	D or 3rd w/O/D OFF (SHO)	2 SHO	1
PCM GEAR COMMANDED	**ACTUAL GEAR OBTAINED**			
1	1	1	1	1
2	1	1	1	1
3	3	3	3	
4	3			

SS2 ALWAYS OFF	GEAR SELECTOR POSITION			
	D	D or 3rd w/O/D OFF (SHO)	2 SHO	1
PCM GEAR COMMANDED	**ACTUAL GEAR OBTAINED**			
1	3	3	3	2
2	2	2	2	2
3	3	3	3	
4	4			

SS3 ALWAYS OFF	GEAR SELECTOR POSITION			
	D	D or 3rd w/O/D OFF (SHO)	2 SHO	1
PCM GEAR COMMANDED	**ACTUAL GEAR OBTAINED**			
1	1	1	1	1
2	2	2	2	2
3	3	3	3	
4	2			

94I38446 94J38447 94A38448   Courtesy of Ford Motor Co.

Fig. 1: Shift Solenoid Failure Charts (Always Off)

SS1 ALWAYS ON	GEAR SELECTOR POSITION			
	D	D or 3rd w/O/D OFF (SHO)	2 SHO	1
PCM GEAR COMMANDED	**ACTUAL GEAR OBTAINED**			
1	2	2	2	2
2	2	2	2	2
3	4	2		
4	4			

SS2 ALWAYS ON	GEAR SELECTOR POSITION			
	D	D or 3rd w/O/D OFF (SHO)	2 SHO	1
PCM GEAR COMMANDED	**ACTUAL GEAR OBTAINED**			
1	1	1	1	1
2	2	2	2	2
3	1	1		
4	2			

SS3 ALWAYS ON	GEAR SELECTOR POSITION			
	D	D or 3rd w/O/D OFF (SHO)	2 SHO	1
PCM GEAR COMMANDED	**ACTUAL GEAR OBTAINED**			
1	1	1	1	1
2	2	2	2	2
3	3	3		
4	4			

94B38449 94F38450 94G38451   Courtesy of Ford Motor Co.

Fig. 2: Shift Solenoid Failure Charts (Always On)

Torque Converter Clutch (TCC) Solenoid – The TCC receives signal from the PCM. The TCC controls application, modulation and release of torque converter clutch. If solenoid fails in ON position, vehicle engine will run rough (shudder) and engine stalls in Drive at low idle speeds (2nd, 3rd or 4th gear). If solenoid fails in OFF position, torque converter clutch will not engage.

PRELIMINARY INSPECTION
VISUAL INSPECTION

Visually inspect all electrical wiring, looking for chafed, stretched, cut or pinched wiring. Ensure electrical connectors fit tightly and are not corroded. Ensure vacuum hoses are properly routed and are not pinched or cut. Inspect air induction system for possible vacuum leaks. Check PCM, sensors and actuators for physical damage. Check engine coolant level. Check transmission fluid level and condition.

NOTE: In addition to transmission fault codes, engine-related fault codes may be output during QUICK TEST procedure. These fault codes pertain to engine performance and must be repaired first as engine performance will greatly affect transmission operation. For information and testing procedures of engine-related fault codes and components, see SELF-DIAGNOSTICS – EEC-IV article in ENGINE PERFORMANCE of appropriate MITCHELL® manual.

SELF-DIAGNOSTIC SYSTEM

DIAGNOSTIC FORMATS

QUICK TEST and CIRCUIT/PINPOINT TESTS are diagnostic formats used to test and service EEC-IV system. QUICK TEST allows technician to identify problems and retrieve service codes. CIRCUIT TESTS check engine circuits, sensors and actuators. PINPOINT TESTS check transaxle circuits, sensors and actuators.

Before starting any circuit test, follow all steps under QUICK TEST procedure to find correct circuit or pinpoint test. If vehicle passes QUICK TEST and no driveability symptoms or intermittent faults exist, EEC-IV system is okay.

DIAGNOSTIC TROUBLE CODES (DTC)

During QUICK TEST, 3 types of service codes are retrieved: Key On Engine Off (KOEO), Key On Engine Running (KOER) and Continuous Memory Codes. See QUICK TEST for self-test procedures. Codes may be cleared from PCM memory after they have been recorded or repaired. See CLEARING CODES.

KOEO & KOER Codes (Hard Faults) – These codes indicate faults are present at time of testing. A hard fault may cause CHECK ENGINE light or Malfunction Indicator Light (MIL) to glow and remain on until fault is repaired. If KOEO or KOER codes are retrieved during KOEO SELF-TEST or KOER SELF-TEST, use SERVICE CODE REFERENCE CHARTS to find correct testing and repair procedures.

Continuous Memory Codes (Soft Faults) – These codes indicate a fault that may or may not be present at time of testing. These codes are used to diagnose intermittent problems. Continuous Memory Codes are retrieved during KOEO SELF-TEST. Some codes may turn on MIL or CHECK ENGINE light. Corresponding soft trouble code will be retained in PCM memory. If fault does not reoccur within 40 warm-up cycles (80 cycles on some models), PCM will automatically clear code. Technician may clear service codes from memory. See CLEARING CODES. Intermittent faults may be caused by a sensor, connector or wiring-related problems.

CAUTION: Continuous Memory Codes should be recorded when retrieved during KOEO SELF-TEST. These codes may be used to identify intermittent problems that exist after all KOEO and KOER codes have been repaired and a Code 11 or 111 (pass code) has been obtained. Failure to follow this procedure may result in unnecessary testing. Some Continuous Memory Codes faults may not be valid after KOEO and KOER codes are repaired.

RETRIEVING CODES

Service codes are retrieved from EEC-IV system through self-test connector. Various methods and test equipment may be used to access these codes:
- Analog Volt-Ohmmeter (VOM)
- Scan Tester
- In-Dash Malfunction Indicator Light (MIL) Or CHECK ENGINE light
- STAR Series Tester
- Message Center (Continental)

DATA LINK CONNECTOR (DLC) LOCATIONS

Application	Location
Continental	Right Front Fender Apron
Sable & Taurus	Right Rear Of Engine, Below Map Sensor

READING CODES

KOEO & KOER SELF-TEST Codes – PCM outputs codes one digit at a time. Record codes in order received. These codes indicate current faults in system and should be serviced in order of appearance. Use SERVICE CODE REFERENCE CHARTS to find correct CIRCUIT/PIN-POINT TEST.

If using analog VOM, pay careful attention to length of pauses in order to read codes correctly. A 1/2-second pause occurs between number of sweeps in a digit. A 2-second pause occurs between digits in a code. A 4-second pause occurs between each code.

KOEO codes are separated from Continuous Memory codes by a 6-second delay, a 1/2-second sweep (separator) and another 6-second delay. *See Fig. 3.* If using MIL/CHECK ENGINE light, service codes are displayed as flashes. On Continental, message center may be used to display codes. *See Fig. 5.*

Scan tester, if used, will count pulses and display them as a digital code. STAR Series Tester will add a zero (0) to single-digit Separator Code (10) and Dynamic Response Code (10). Dynamic Response Code is displayed in KOER SELF-TEST. *See Fig. 3.*

Engine Identification (ID) Codes – Engine ID codes are issued at beginning of KOER SELF-TEST. Codes are one-digit numbers represented by number of pulses displayed. *See Fig. 3.* Engine ID code is equal to one-half the number of engine cylinders. For example, 2 pulses would indicate that engine is a 4 cylinder. ID code is used to verify proper PCM is installed and that SELF-TEST has been entered.

Separator Pulse – Single 1/2-second separator pulse is issued 6-9 seconds after last KOEO code. Continuous Memory Codes (soft faults) are then displayed 6-9 seconds after 1/2-second separator pulse. Some digital test equipment may display separator code as "10" instead of "1".

Pass Codes – A Code 11 or 111 indicates no service codes were recorded in that portion of test; system passes that portion of test. If Code 11 or 111 is not retrieved in KOEO SELF-TEST, codes retrieved during KOER SELF-TEST may not be valid. Code 11 or 111 (pass code) must be obtained in KOEO SELF-TEST. A Code 11-1-11 or 111-1-111 output during KOEO SELF-TEST indicates no KOEO code or Continuous Memory Code was recorded.

Continuous Memory Codes – These codes result from information stored by PCM during continuous self-test monitoring. Codes are displayed after separator pulse code in KOEO SELF-TEST. Use these codes for diagnosis only when KOEO SELF-TEST and KOER SELF-TEST result in Code 11 or 111 (pass code) and all steps under QUICK TEST are successfully completed. (A few codes are exceptions which may be checked after KOEO codes have been repaired). These codes indicate faults recorded within last 40 engine starts (80 engine starts on some models). Fault may or may not be currently present. See SERVICE CODE REFERENCE CHARTS.

Fast Codes – At start of KOEO SELF-TEST and after Wide Open Throttle (WOT) request in KOER SELF-TEST, PCM outputs short bursts of information, known as FAST CODES, which were used by manufacturer during assembly. With most equipment, these code bursts are not visible; an entire code sequence lasts less than 1/2 second. If this fluctuation is visible on test equipment, ignore it.

CLEARING CODES

To clear codes from PCM memory, start KOEO SELF-TEST under QUICK TEST. When service codes appear on test equipment or CHECK ENGINE light, disconnect jumper wire from Self-Test Input (STI) connector. If using STAR Series Tester, unlatch center button. This procedure erases Continuous Memory Codes from PCM memory. If problem has not been corrected or fault is still present, hard code will immediately be reset in PCM memory.

CAUTION: DO NOT disconnect vehicle battery to clear codes. This will erase stored operating information from Keep-Alive Memory (KAM). To clear KAM, disconnect negative battery terminal for at least 5 minutes.

WARNING: When battery is disconnected, vehicle computer and memory systems may lose memory data. Driveability problems may exist until computer systems have completed a relearn cycle. See COMPUTER RELEARN PROCEDURES in APPLICATIONS & IDENTIFICATION section before disconnecting battery.

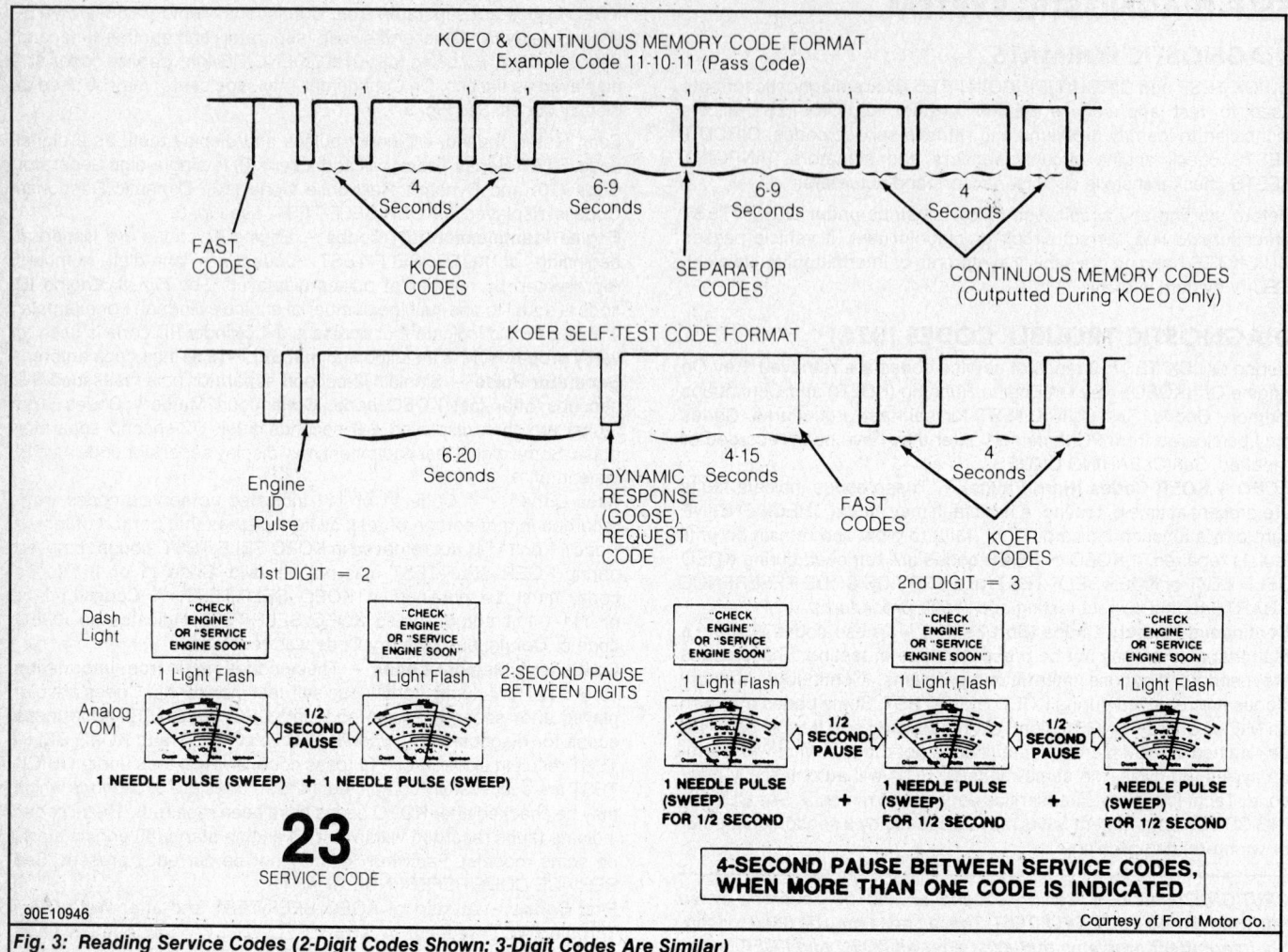

Fig. 3: Reading Service Codes (2-Digit Codes Shown; 3-Digit Codes Are Similar)

QUICK TEST

Description – Following procedures are functional tests of EEC-IV system. These following 4 basic test steps must be carefully followed in sequence, otherwise misdiagnosis or replacement of non-faulty components may result:

- VISUAL CHECK
- EQUIPMENT HOOKUP.
- KOEO (Key On Engine Off) SELF-TEST.
- KOER (Key On Engine Running) SELF-TEST.

Diagnostic Aids – After each service or repair procedure has been completed, repeat QUICK TEST to ensure all EEC-IV systems work properly and service codes are no longer present.

VISUAL CHECK

Complete a basic inspection of engine compartment and all components before proceeding to self-diagnostic tests. Ensure vacuum hoses and EEC-IV wiring harnesses are properly connected.

EQUIPMENT HOOKUP

Apply parking brake, and place shift lever in "P" position. Block drive wheels. Turn off all electrical loads. Connect appropriate test equipment to vehicle as follows:

Analog Volt-Ohmmeter (VOM) – **1)** Turn ignition switch to OFF position. Set VOM at 0-15V DC range. Connect positive lead of VOM to positive battery terminal.

2) Connect negative VOM lead to Self-Test Output (STO) terminal of self-test connector. *See Fig. 4.* Connect timing light, and go to KOEO SELF-TEST. Activate KOEO SELF-TEST by connecting jumper wire from Self-Test Input (STI) pigtail to signal return terminal of self-test connector with ignition on.

Scan Tester – Follow manufacturer instructions to hook up equipment and record service codes.

STAR Series Tester – Turn ignition switch to OFF position. Connect color-coded adapter cable leads to diagnostic tester. Connect 2 service connectors of adapter cable to vehicle self-test connector and STI pigtail connector. Connect timing light. Go to KOEO SELF-TEST.

CHECK ENGINE Light/Malfunction Indicator Light (MIL) – Turn ignition on. Connect a jumper wire between Self-Test Input (STI) pigtail and signal return (SIG RTN) terminal of Data Link Connector (DLC). *See Fig. 4.* Go to KOEO SELF-TEST.

Message Center (Continental) – **1)** To run SELF-TEST using the message center, located in the electronic instrument cluster, hold in all 3 buttons (Gauge Select, English Metric and Speed Alarm) at the same time. *See Fig. 5.*

2) To start Key On Engine Off (KOEO) Self-Test, hold in all 3 buttons, and turn ignition on. Release buttons. To start Key On Engine Running (KOER) Self-Test, hold in all 3 buttons and start engine. Release buttons.

3) After performing step **2)**, press Gauge Select button 3 times, until cluster mode "dEALEr 4" is displayed. To initiate Self-Test, jumper STI connector to SIG RTN terminal at the Data Link Connector (DLC), or use a STAR tester and latch center button in the down position.

4) Diagnostic trouble codes will be displayed on message center. To exit SELF-TEST, turn ignition off and remove jumper or unlatch STAR tester.

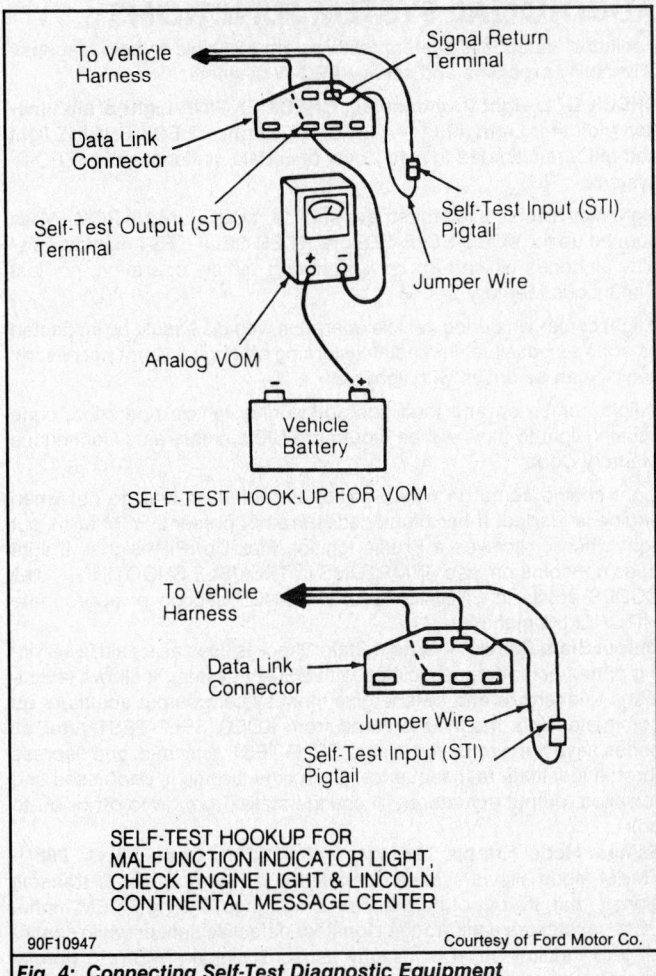

SELF-TEST HOOK-UP FOR VOM

SELF-TEST HOOKUP FOR
MALFUNCTION INDICATOR LIGHT,
CHECK ENGINE LIGHT & LINCOLN
CONTINENTAL MESSAGE CENTER

90F10947   Courtesy of Ford Motor Co.

Fig. 4: Connecting Self-Test Diagnostic Equipment

KOEO SELF-TEST

Ensure engine is at normal operating temperature. If engine does not start (or stalls after starting), continue KOEO SELF-TEST. DO NOT depress throttle on gasoline vehicles. Turn ignition off. Wait 10 seconds. Ensure test equipment is properly attached. Turn ignition on (engine off). Record all KOEO and Continuous Memory Codes.

If a Code 11 or 111 (pass code) is not retrieved in KOEO portion of test, service KOEO codes at this time. Service any engine codes recorded before servicing transmission codes (codes No. 566 and 629). If PCM will not output codes, see SELF-DIAGNOSTICS – EEC-IV article in ENGINE PERFORMANCE section of appropriate MITCHELL® manual. If service codes are retrieved observe the following procedures:

- If CHECK ENGINE or SERVICE ENGINE SOON light is on, service codes in order retrieved.
- On vehicles equipped with DIS and EDIS ignition systems, see SYSTEM & COMPONENT TESTING article in ENGINE PERFORMANCE section of appropriate MITCHELL® manual if Continuous Memory Code 211, 212, 215, 216, 217, 232 or 238 is retrieved during KOEO SELF-TEST. Repair ignition system as necessary.
- If vehicle has a no-start condition, go to CIRCUIT TEST AA, AB or AC in SELF-DIAGNOSTICS – EEC-IV article in ENGINE PERFORMANCE section of appropriate MITCHELL® manual.

KOER SELF-TEST

Diagnostic Aids – DO NOT enter this test sequence until a Code 11 or 111 (pass code) has been retrieved in KOEO SELF-TEST. If system has not passed KOEO SELF-TEST, codes recorded in KOER SELF-TEST may not be valid.

Deactivate self-test by removing and reconnecting jumper wire or by procedure specified by test equipment in use. Start engine, and run it for 2 minutes at 2000 RPM to warm Heated Exhaust Gas Oxygen (HEGO) sensor. Turn engine off, and wait 10 seconds. Activate KOER SELF-TEST using a jumper wire or appropriate procedure for test equipment used. Start engine. Record all service codes displayed. Check following items:

- If engine starts and stalls (or stalls during self-test), go to CIRCUIT TEST S. See SELF-DIAGNOSTICS – EEC-IV article in ENGINE PERFORMANCE section of appropriate MITCHELL® manual.
- If Code 98 or 998 is displayed, EEC-IV system is operating in Failure Management Effects Mode (FMEM) and vehicle has not passed KOEO SELF-TEST. Vehicle cannot be diagnosed while in FMEM mode. See Code 98 or 998 in SERVICE CODE REFERENCE CHARTS.
- If vehicle is equipped with a Brake On-Off (BOO) switch, brake pedal must be depressed and released after ID code portion of test.
- On vehicles with Power Steering Pressure Switch (PSPS), turn steering wheel at least 1/2 turn and release within 1-2 seconds after ID code portion of test.
- If Dynamic Response Code appears, perform a brief Wide Open Throttle (WOT). DO NOT perform WOT unless requested.

HOW TO RUN SELF-TEST USING THE CONTINENTAL MESSAGE CENTER

1. On the Electronic Instrument Cluster, hold in all 3 buttons (Gauge Select, English Metric and Speed Alarm) at the same time.

   a. Key On Engine Off (KOEO) Self-Test

   - While holding in all 3 buttons, place ignition switch in the ON position. Release buttons.

   b. Key On Engine Running (KOER) Self-Test

   - While holding in all 3 buttons, start engine. Release buttons.

2. Press Gauge Select button 3 times, until cluster mode "dEALEr 4" is displayed.

3. To initiate Self-Test, jumper STI to SIG RTN at the Self-Test connectors, or use a Star Tester and latch the center button in the down position.

91C06890

ELECTRONIC INSTRUMENT CLUSTER

GAUGE SELECT		MESSAGE CENTER
ENGLISH METRIC		1 1 1
		INST AVG ECON ECON
SPEED ALARM	dEALEr 4	CHECK ENGINE

4. Service code output will be displayed on the message center.

5. to exit Self-Test, turn ignition switch to OFF position and remove jumper or unlatch STAR Tester.

Courtesy of Ford Motor Co.

Fig. 5: Message Center Self-Test (Continental)

- If a Code 11 or 111 (pass code) is retrieved during KOER SELF-TEST, service Continuous Memory Codes retrieved in KOEO SELF-TEST. See SELF-DIAGNOSTICS – EEC-IV article in ENGINE PERFORMANCE section of appropriate MITCHELL® manual.
- If a Code 11 or 111 (pass code) is retrieved during Continuous Memory Code portion of KOEO SELF-TEST (Code 11-1-11 or Code 111-1-111) and no driveability problem exists, EEC-IV testing is complete. If driveability problems are still present, go to TROUBLE SHOOTING in AXOD-E transmission overhaul article.
- If KOER codes are present, see SERVICE CODE REFERENCE CHARTS. If system will not output codes, go to CIRCUIT TEST QA.

CONTINUOUS MONITOR MODE (WIGGLE TEST)

Continuous Monitor Mode allows technician to attempt to recreate an intermittent fault while monitoring system. This mode, also called wiggle test, may be used in both KOEO SELF-TEST and KOER SELF-TEST. CIRCUIT/PINPOINT TESTS specify use of this procedure to identify intermittent faults in specific circuits or components.

KOEO Wiggle Test Procedure – Connect test equipment. *See Fig. 4.* Turn ignition on, and activate self-test using jumper lead or diagnostic tester. Wait 10 seconds, and then deactivate and reactivate self-test. Wiggle test mode is now activated. Tap, move and wiggle suspect sensor and/or harness area. If a fault is detected, a service code may be stored in memory and indicated at diagnostic tester or scan tester. Retrieve code, and perform appropriate test. See SERVICE CODE REFERENCE CHARTS.

KOER Wiggle Test Procedure – Connect test equipment. *See Fig. 4.* Turn ignition off, and wait 10 seconds. Start engine. Activate self-test using jumper lead or diagnostic tester. Wait 10 seconds, and then deactivate and reactivate self-test. DO NOT turn engine off. KOER wiggle test mode is now activated. Tap, move and wiggle suspect sensor and/or harness area. If a fault is detected, a service code may be stored in memory and indicated at diagnostic tester or scan tester. Retrieve code, and perform appropriate test. See SERVICE CODE REFERENCE CHARTS.

TRANSMISSION DRIVE CYCLE TEST

NOTE: The transmission drive cycle test must be followed exactly. Malfunctions have to occur 4 times consecutively for codes 645, 646, 647 and 648 to be set and 5 times consecutively for continuous code 628.

Test Procedure (3.2L SHO) – **1)** Record and then erase Quick Test codes. Warm engine to normal operating temperature. Ensure transmission fluid level is correct. Shift transmission to overdrive (OD). **2)** Accelerate from stop to 50 mph. Hold speed for at least 15 seconds (30 seconds above 4000 ft.). Press TCS and accelerate to 50 mph. Hold speed for at least 15 seconds (30 seconds above 4000 ft.). Hold speed and throttle position steady for at least 15 seconds. While maintaining speed with transaxle in 4th gear, lightly depress brake pedal and release. Maintain speed for additional 5 seconds. Bring vehicle to stop for at least 20 seconds. Repeat steps **1)** and **2)** at least 5 times. Perform Quick Test and record continuous codes.

Test Procedure (3.2L SHO) – **1)** Record and then erase Quick Test codes. Warm engine to normal operating temperature. Ensure transmission fluid level is correct. Shift transmission to drive (D). Press TCS on shifter handle, O/D OFF light should illuminate. **2)** Accelerate from stop to 40 mph. Hold speed for at least 15 seconds (30 seconds above 4000 ft.). Press TCS and accelerate to 50 mph. Hold speed for at least 15 seconds (30 seconds above 4000 ft.). Hold speed and throttle position steady for at least 15 seconds. While maintaining speed with transaxle in 4th gear, lightly depress brake pedal and release. Maintain for additional 5 seconds. Bring vehicle to stop for at least 20 seconds. Repeat steps **1)** and **2)** at least 5 times. Perform Quick Test and record continuous codes.

ADDITIONAL SYSTEM FUNCTIONS

Additional diagnostic system features are available to help diagnose driveability problems and service EEC-IV systems.

CHECK DCL Light (Continental), CHECK ENGINE Light & Malfunction Indicator Light (MIL) – CHECK DCL light, CHECK ENGINE light and MIL are intended to alert driver of certain malfunctions in EEC-IV system.

Light may also be used to retrieve service codes stored in PCM. When hooked up for KOEO SELF-TEST or KOER SELF-TEST, light will display all codes which turn on light during vehicle operation, not just Continuous Memory Codes.

If light comes on during vehicle operation, vehicle should be inspected as soon as possible. Immediately turning off engine is not necessary; vehicle can be driven with light on.

If light comes on and then goes off during vehicle operation, code causing light to glow will be stored in PCM memory as a Continuous Memory Code.

Light should come on when ignition is turned on and go out when engine is started. If hard fault codes are not present, PCM turns out light when it receives a Profile Ignition Pick-Up (PIP) signal. If light does not come on, see SYMPTOMS in TROUBLE SHOOTING – NO CODES article in ENGINE PERFORMANCE section of appropriate MITCHELL® manual.

Output State Check – Output State Check is used as an aid in servicing output actuators associated with EEC-IV system. It allows technicians to energize and de-energize most system output actuators on command. This mode is entered from KOEO SELF-TEST after all codes have been retrieved. Leave SELF-TEST activated, and depress throttle to initiate test sequence. Each time throttle is depressed and released, output actuators will change state (from on to off or off to on).

Failure Mode Effects Management (FMEM), Code 98 Or 998 – FMEM mode allows system operation when sensors fail or transmit signals that are out of normal operating range. During FMEM mode, PCM substitutes a mid-range signal for defective sensor while continuing to monitor sensor. If faulty sensor's signals return to normal operating range, PCM will use those signals. A Code 98 or 998 will be displayed when FMEM mode is in effect.

Hardware Limited Operational Strategy (HLOS) – If a number of system or sensor failures are present and PCM is not receiving enough information to operate, PCM will switch to HLOS mode. PCM will output fixed values to allow operation of vehicle. Driveability concerns will be present. PCM will not output service codes in this mode.

SUMMARY

If no service codes (or pass code 11-1-11 or 111-1-111) is present but driveability problem still exists, return to TROUBLE SHOOTING in AXOD-E overhaul article.

SERVICE CODE REFERENCE CHARTS

NOTE: In addition to transmission fault codes, engine-related fault codes may be output during QUICK TEST procedure. These fault codes pertain to engine performance and must be repaired first as engine performance will greatly affect transmission operation. For information and testing procedures of engine-related fault codes and components, see SELF-DIAGNOSTICS – EEC-IV article in ENGINE PERFORMANCE of appropriate MITCHELL® manual.

NOTE: Trouble code 676 indicates failure of low one-way clutch. Code 677 indicates failure of low intermediate band. For both codes, see TROUBLE SHOOTING in FORD AXOD-E article.

CODE REFERENCE CHART

Fault Code	Code Definition	Circuit/Pinpoint Test
KOEO Codes		
No Code	N/A	QA1
111	Pass Code	N/A
112	IAT Indicates 254° F (125° C)	DA20
113	IAT Indicates -40° F (-40° C)	DA10
114	IAT Voltage High/Low	DA1
116	ECT Out Of Range	DA1
117	ECT Indicates 254° F (125° C)	DA20
118	ECT Indicates -40° F (-40° C)	DA10
121	TPS Voltage High/Low	DH2
122	TPS Malfunction	DH10
123	TPS Malfunction	DH3
158	MAF Sensor Malfunction	DC21
159	MAF Sensor Malfunction	DC1
519	PSP Open Circuit	FF1
522	MLP Open Circuit	D1
621	SS1 Solenoid Circuit Failure	A1
622	SS2 Solenoid Circuit Failure	A1
624	EPC Circuit Failure	E1
625	Open PCM Output Driver	E1
634	MLP Out Of Range	D1
636	TOT Out Of Range	B1
637	TOT Sensor Circuit Open	B1
638	TOT Sensor Circuit Grounded	B1
652	TCC Circuit Error	C1
998	FMEM Failure	TC10
Continuous Memory Codes		
No Code	N/A	QA1
111	Pass Code	N/A
112	IAT Indicates 254° F (125° C)	DA90
113	IAT Indicates -40° F (-40° C)	DA90
117	ECT Indicates 254° F (125° C)	DA90
118	ECT Indicates -40° F (-40° C)	DA90
121	TPS Voltage High/Low	G1
122	TPS Malfunction	DH94
123	TPS Malfunction	DH90
124	TPS Malfunction	G1
125	TPS Malfunction	G1
157	MAF Sensor Malfunction	DC10
158	MAF Sensor Malfunction	DC21
184	MAF Sensor Malfunction	G5
185	MAF Sensor Malfunction	G5
452	Insufficient VSS Input	DP1
536	BOO Switch Malfunction	FD90
624	EPC Solenoid Circuit Failure	E1
628	TCC Engagement Error	C1
634	MLP Sensor Voltage Error	D1
637	TOT Sensor Voltage High	B1
638	TOT Sensor Voltage Low	B1
639	Insufficient Input From TSS	F1
645	No 1st Gear	A1
646	No 2nd Gear	A1
647	No 3rd Gear	A1
648	No 4th Gear	A1
656	TCC Continuous Slip	C1
657	Transaxle Overtemp. Condition	A1
659	High Speed In Park	D1

CODE REFERENCE CHART (Cont.)

Fault Code	Code Definition	Circuit/Pinpoint Test
KOER Codes		
No Code	N/A	QA1
111	Pass Code	N/A
114	IAT Voltage High/Low	DA1
116	ECT Out Of Range	DA1
121	TPS Voltage High/Low	DH1
159	MAF Sensor Malfunction	DC1
167	TPS Malfunction	DH20
521	No PSP Flucuation	FF5
536	BOO Switch Malfunction	FD1
632	TCS Not Cycled	TB2
636	TOT Sensor Voltage Error	B1
639	Insufficient Input From TSS	F1

CIRCUIT/PINPOINT TEST PROCEDURES

NOTE: A breakout box, connected to vehicle harness at PCM, is necessary to perform most circuit tests. References to Test Pin No. found in CIRCUIT/PINPOINT TEST steps refer to test terminals on manufacturer breakout box. Circuit diagrams at beginning of each test identify circuit and wire colors.

HOW TO USE CIRCUIT/PINPOINT TESTS

1) Ensure all non-EEC related faults found while performing TROUBLE SHOOTING steps in AXOD-E overhaul article have been corrected. DO NOT perform any CIRCUIT/PINPOINT TEST unless specifically instructed by a QUICK TEST procedure. Follow each test step in order until fault is found. DO NOT replace any part unless directed to do so. When more than one code is retrieved, start with first code displayed.

2) CIRCUIT/PINPOINT TESTS ensure electrical circuits are okay before sensors or other components are replaced. Always test circuits for continuity between sensor and PCM. Test all circuits for short to power, opens or short to ground. Voltage Reference (VREF) and Voltage Power (VPWR) circuits should be tested with KOEO or as specified in CIRCUIT/PINPOINT TESTS.

3) DO NOT measure voltage or resistance at PCM. DO NOT connect any test light unless specified in testing procedure. All measurements are made by probing rear of connector. Isolate both ends of a circuit and turn ignition off when checking for shorts or continuity, unless instructed otherwise.

4) Disconnect solenoids and switches from harness before measuring continuity and resistance or applying voltage. After each repair, check all component connections and repeat QUICK TEST.

5) An open circuit is defined as a resistance reading of greater than 5 ohms. This specification tolerance may be too high for some items in EEC-IV system. If resistance approaches 5 ohms, always clean suspect connector and coat it with protective dielectric silicone grease. A short is defined as a resistance reading of less than 10 k/ohms to ground, unless stated otherwise in CIRCUIT/PINPOINT TEST.

Diagnostic Aids – Fuel-contaminated engine oil may set some codes and effect engine performance. If oil is suspect, remove PCV valve from valve cover and repeat QUICK TEST. If problem is corrected, change engine oil.

NOTE: In following tests, circuit diagrams and illustrations are courtesy of Ford Motor Co.

PINPOINT TESTS

NOTE: PINPOINT TESTS are diagnostic formats used to test and service EEC-IV system. PINPOINT TESTS check transaxle circuits, sensors and actuators.

PINPOINT TEST A

SHIFT SOLENOID ELECTRICAL SYSTEM

1) AXOD-E Electronic Diagnostics – Ensure transaxle harness connector is in acceptable condition. Repair as necessary. Disconnect transaxle harness connector. Connect Transmission Tester (007-0085A) or equivalent to transaxle. Perform TRANSMISSION SOLENOID CYCLING AND DRIVE TEST. Perform KOEO test until Continuous Memory trouble code(s) have been displayed. See QUICK TEST. Depress throttle to WOT and release. If vehicle enters Output State, go to next step. If vehicle will not enter Output State, see SELF-DIAGNOSTICS – EEC-IV article in ENGINE PERFORMANCE of appropriate MITCHELL® manual.

2) Check Electrical Signal Operation – Disconnect transaxle harness connector. Inspect condition of connector and repair as needed. Using DVOM (20-volt scale), connect positive lead to transaxle harness connector VPWR terminal. *See Fig. A1.* Connect negative lead to suspect solenoid circuit. Depress and release throttle to cycle solenoid output. If voltage changes at least .5 volts, go to step 5). If voltage is unaffected, go to next step.

94H38452

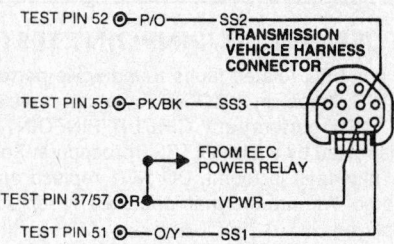

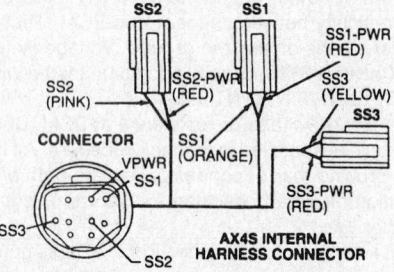

TEST PINS LOCATED ON BREAKOUT BOX. ALL HARNESS CONNECTORS VIEWED INTO MATING SURFACE.

Fig. A1: Identifying Transaxle Harness Connector

3) Check Continuity Of Solenoid Signal & VPWR Harness Circuits – Ensure ignition is off. Disconnect PCM 60-pin connector, and inspect it for damaged pins, corrosion and loose wires. Repair as necessary. Install Breakout Box (T83L-50-EEC-IV), leaving PCM disconnected. Measure and record resistance between Breakout Box test pin No. 51, 52 or 53 and corresponding transaxle harness connector terminal. *See Fig. A1.* Measure and record resistance. Measure and record resistance between test pins No. 37 and 57 and transaxle harness connector VPWR terminal. If any resistance is greater than 5 ohms, repair open circuit. Connect all components. Disconnect Breakout Box and repeat Quick Test. If resistance is 5 ohms or less, go to next step.

4) Check Solenoid Harness For Shorts To Power & Ground – Measure and record resistance between Breakout Box test pins No. 51 52 or 53 and test pins No. 37 and 57. Measure and record resistance between test pins No. 40, 46 and 60, and ground. If any resistance is less than 10 k/ohms, repair short circuit. Connect all components. Disconnect Breakout Box and repeat Quick Test. If resistance is 10 k/ohms or more, go to next step.

PINPOINT TEST A (Cont.)

5) Solenoid Functional Test – Connect Transaxle Tester (007-0085A). Perform solenoid voltage test. See tester instructions. If solenoid activates (LED green), go to next step. If solenoid does not activate, go to step **7)**.

6) Transaxle Drive Test – Perform tester drive test. See tester instructions. If vehicle upshifts when operated with tester, go to TROUBLE SHOOTING in Ford AXOD-E article. If vehicle does not upshift when operated by tester, go to next step.

7) Check Resistance Of Solenoid – Set tester Bench/Drive switch to Bench mode. Set Gear Selector switch to ohms check. Connect ohmmeter negative lead to SS1 jack and positive lead to VPWR jack on tester. Measure and record resistance. Connect ohmmeter negative lead to SS2 jack and positive lead to VPWR jack on tester. Measure and record resistance. Connect ohmmeter negative lead to SS3 jack and positive lead to VPWR jack on tester. Measure and record resistance. Resistance for all solenoids should be 15-25 ohms. If resistance is within specification, go to next step. If resistance is not within specification, go to step **9)**.

8) Check Solenoid For Short To Ground – Check continuity between BAT(-) terminal and between SS1, SS2 and SS3. Check continuity between BAT(-) terminal and VPWR terminal. If continuity exists for any circuit, go to next step. If continuity does not exist, go to TROUBLE SHOOTING in Ford AXOD-E article.

9) AXOD-E Internal Electronic Diagnostics – Drain transaxle fluid. See TRANSMISSION SERVICING section. Remove transaxle side pan. See OIL PUMP & VALVE BODY ASSEMBLY under ON-VEHICLE SERVICE IN FORD AXOD-E article. Inspect all internal harness connectors. Ensure all connectors are fully connected and not damaged. Repair as needed. Install all components in reverse order of disassembly. Fill transaxle with fluid. Erase all trouble codes. See CLEARING CODES. Repeat QUICK TEST. If all connectors are okay, go to next step.

10) Check Internal Harness Continuity – Disconnect internal harness from solenoid assemblies. To test SS1, connect positive lead of ohmmeter to tester SS-1 jack and negative lead to SS1 Orange wire. Measure and record resistance. To test SS2, connect positive lead of ohmmeter to tester SS-2 jack and negative lead to SS2 Pink wire. Measure and record resistance. To test SS3, connect positive lead of ohmmeter to tester SS-3 jack and negative lead to SS3 Yellow wire. Measure and record resistance.

To test SS1, SS2 and SS3 VPWR circuits, connect positive lead of ohmmeter to selected solenoid red wire. Connect negative lead to corresponding VPWR tester terminal. Measure and record resistance. If all resistances measured are 5 ohms or less, go to next step. If any resistance measured is more than 5 ohms, replace internal harness. Go to step **12)**.

11) Check Internal Harness For Shorts To Ground – Using transmission tester, check continuity between each solenoid lead and BAT(-) terminal of tester. If continuity does not exist in any circuit, go to next step. If continuity exists in any circuit, replace internal harness. Go to Install all components in reverse order of disassembly. Fill transaxle with fluid. Erase all trouble codes. See CLEARING CODES. Repeat QUICK TEST.

12) Check Resistance Of Solenoid – Using ohmmeter, check resistance between terminals of each solenoid. Resistance should be 15-25 ohms. If resistance is within specification, go to next step. If resistance measured for any solenoid is not within specification, replace suspected solenoid. Install all components in reverse order of disassembly. Fill transaxle with fluid. Erase all trouble codes. See CLEARING CODES. Repeat QUICK TEST.

13) Check Solenoid For Short To Ground – Using ohmmeter, check continuity between each solenoid terminal and ground. If continuity exists, replace faulty shift solenoid. If continuity does not exist, go to TROUBLE SHOOTING in Ford AXOD-E article. Install all components in reverse order of disassembly. Fill transaxle with fluid. Erase all trouble codes. See CLEARING CODES. Repeat QUICK TEST.

PINPOINT TEST B

TOT ELECTRICAL SYSTEM

1) Visual Check – Check transaxle harness connector. Inspect connector for damaged pins, corrosion and loose wires. Repair as necessary. Go to next step.

2) Check Electrical Signal Operation – Ensure ignition is off. Disconnect transaxle connector. Using DVOM, connect positive lead to transaxle harness connector TOT terminal and negative lead to SRTN terminal. *See Fig. B1.* Turn ignition on. If voltage is 4.5-5.25 volts, go to next step. If voltage is not within specification, see SELF-DIAGNOSTICS – EEC-IV article in ENGINE PERFORMANCE of appropriate MITCHELL® manual to diagnose NO VREF voltage.

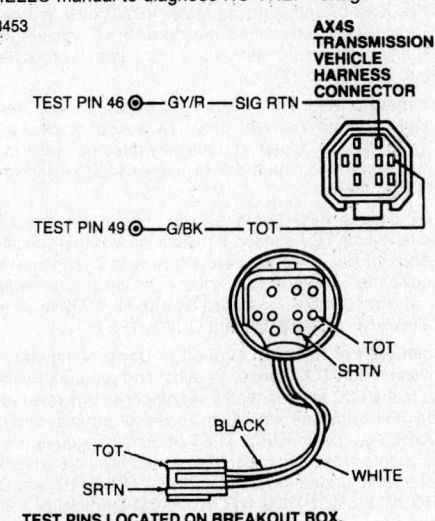

94I38453

AX4S TRANSMISSION VEHICLE HARNESS CONNECTOR

TEST PIN 46 — GY/R — SIG RTN

TEST PIN 49 — G/BK — TOT

TOT
SRTN

BLACK

TOT

SRTN

WHITE

TEST PINS LOCATED ON BREAKOUT BOX. ALL HARNESS CONNECTORS VIEWED INTO MATING SURFACE.

Fig. B1: Identifying Transaxle Harness Connector

3) Check Continuity Of TOT & Signal Return (SIG RTN) Circuits – Turn ignition off. Disconnect PCM 60-pin connector, and inspect it for damaged pins, corrosion and loose wires. Repair as necessary. Install Breakout Box (T83L-50-EEC-IV), leaving PCM disconnected. Measure and record resistance between Breakout Box test pin No. 49 and transaxle harness connector TOT terminal. *See Fig. B1.* Measure and record resistance between test pin No. 46 and transaxle harness connector SRTN terminal. If resistances measured are less than 5 ohms, go to next step. If resistances are more than 5 ohms, repair open circuit. Connect all components. Erase trouble codes. See CLEARING CODES. Repeat QUICK TEST.

4) Check TOT Circuit For Short To VPWR & Ground – Ensure ignition is off. Disconnect PCM 60-pin connector, and inspect it for damaged pins, corrosion and loose wires. Repair as necessary. Install Breakout Box (T83L-50-EEC-IV), leaving PCM disconnected. Measure and record resistance between Breakout Box test pins No. 49 and 57. If resistance is less than 10 k/ohms, repair short circuit. Disconnect Breakout Box and repeat Quick Test. If resistance is 10 k/ohms or more, go to next step.

NOTE: Code 637 is set if resistance measured exceeds 869 ohms (open circuit). Code 638 is set if resistance measured is below 597 ohms (short circuit).

5) Check Resistance Of TOT Sensor/Harness – Install Transmission Tester (007-0085A). Set tester Bench/Drive switch to BENCH mode. Set Solenoid Select switch to OHMS CHECK. Connect ohmmeter lead to appropriate TOT jacks. Measure and record resistance. Resistance should be within specification. See TOT TEMPERATURE/RESISTANCE CHART. If resistance is within specification for specific temperature, either warm up transaxle or allow transaxle to cool to check resistance at different temperatures. If resistances measured remain within specification, go to next step. If resistances measured are not within specification, go to step 7).

PINPOINT TEST B (Cont.)

TOT TEMPERATURE/RESISTANCE CHART

Temperature °F (°C)	Resistance-Ohms (K)
32-58 (0-20)	37-100
59-104 (21-40)	16-37
105-158 (41-70)	5-16
159-194 (71-90)	2.7-5
195-230 (91-110)	1.5-2.7
231-266 (111-130)	.8-1.5

6) Check TOT Sensor For Short To Ground – Check continuity between BAT (-) tester terminal and TOT terminals. If continuity exists, go to next step. If continuity does not exist, Erase all trouble codes. See CLEARING CODES. Repeat QUICK TEST. See FORD AXOD-E article for non-electronic symptom diagnostics.

7) AXOD-E Internal Electronic Diagnostics – Drain transaxle fluid. See TRANSMISSION SERVICING section. Remove transaxle side pan. See OIL PUMP & VALVE BODY ASSEMBLY under ON-VEHICLE SERVICE IN FORD AXOD-E article. Inspect all internal harness connectors. Ensure all connectors are fully connected and not damaged. Repair as needed. Install all components in reverse order of disassembly. Fill transaxle with fluid. Erase all trouble codes. See CLEARING CODES. Repeat QUICK TEST. If all connectors are okay, go to next step.

8) Check Internal Harness Continuity – Disconnect internal harness from TOT sensor. Connect positive lead of ohmmeter to tester TOT (+) jack and negative lead to TOT Black wire. Measure and record resistance. Connect positive lead of ohmmeter to tester TOT (-) jack and negative lead to TOT White wire. If resistances measured are 5 ohms or less, go to next step. If any resistance measured is more than 5 ohms, replace internal harness. Go to step 10).

9) Check Internal Harness For Shorts To Ground – Using transmission tester, check continuity between each TOT sensor connector terminals and BAT(-) terminal of tester. If continuity does not exist in any circuit, go to next step. If continuity exists in any circuit, replace internal harness. Go to next step.

10) Check TOT Sensor Resistance – Using ohmmeter, check resistance between terminals TOT sensor. If resistance is within specification for specific temperature, go to next step. If resistances measured are not within specification, replace TOT sensor. Install all components in reverse order of disassembly. Fill transaxle with fluid. Erase all trouble codes. See CLEARING CODES. Repeat QUICK TEST.

TOT TEMPERATURE/RESISTANCE CHART

Temperature °F (°C)	Resistance-K/Ohms
32-58 (0-20)	37-100
59-104 (21-40)	16-37
105-158 (41-70)	5-16
159-194 (71-90)	2.7-5
195-230 (91-110)	1.5-2.7
231-266 (111-130)	.8-1.5

11) Check Solenoid For Short To Ground – Using ohmmeter, check continuity between each TOT sensor terminal and ground. If continuity exists, replace faulty TOT sensor. If continuity does not exist, install all components in reverse order of disassembly. Fill transaxle with fluid. Erase all trouble codes. See CLEARING CODES. Repeat QUICK TEST, see SELF-DIAGNOSTICS – EEC-IV article in ENGINE PERFORMANCE of appropriate MITCHELL® manual to diagnose vehicle harness or PCM malfunctions.

PINPOINT TEST C

TCC ELECTRICAL SYSTEM

1) AXOD-E Electronic Diagnostics – Ensure transaxle harness connector is in acceptable condition. Repair as necessary. Disconnect transaxle harness connector. Connect Transmission Tester (007-0085A) or equivalent to transaxle. Perform TRANSMISSION SOLENOID CYCLING AND DRIVE TEST. Perform KOEO test until Continuous Memory trouble code(s) have been displayed. See QUICK TEST. Depress throttle to WOT and release. If vehicle enters Output State, go to next step. If vehicle will not enter Output State, see SELF-DIAGNOSTICS – EEC-IV article in ENGINE PERFORMANCE of appropriate MITCHELL® manual.

PINPOINT TEST C (Cont.)

2) Check Electrical Signal Operation – Disconnect transaxle harness connector. Inspect condition of connector and repair as needed. Using DVOM (20-volt scale), connect positive lead to transaxle harness connector VPWR terminal. *See Fig. C1.* Connect negative lead to TCC terminal. Depress and release throttle to cycle solenoid output. If voltage changes at least .5 volts, go to step **5)**. If voltage is unaffected, go to next step.

94J38454

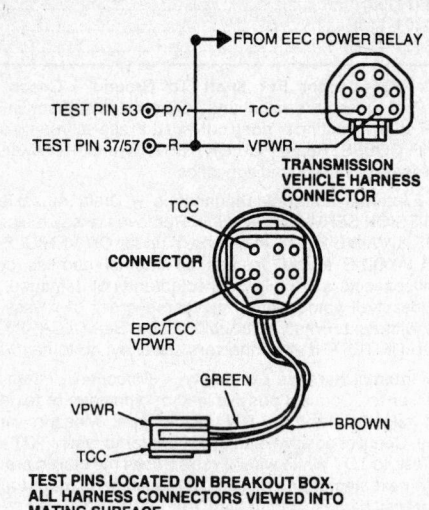

TEST PINS LOCATED ON BREAKOUT BOX. ALL HARNESS CONNECTORS VIEWED INTO MATING SURFACE.

Fig. C1: Identifying Transaxle Harness Connector

3) Check Continuity Of Solenoid Signal & VPWR Harness Circuits – Ensure ignition is off. Disconnect PCM 60-pin connector, and inspect it for damaged pins, corrosion and loose wires. Repair as necessary. Install Breakout Box (T83L-50-EEC-IV), leaving PCM disconnected. Measure and record resistance between Breakout Box test pin No. 53 and transaxle harness connector TCC terminal. *See Fig. C1.* Measure and record resistance between test pins No. 37 and 57 and transaxle harness connector VPWR terminal. If any resistance is greater than 5 ohms, repair open circuit. Connect all components. Disconnect Breakout Box and repeat Quick Test. If resistance is 5 ohms or less, go to next step.

4) Check Solenoid Harness For Shorts To Power & Ground – Measure and record resistance between test pin No. 53 and test pins No. 37 and 57. Measure and record resistance between test pins No. 40, 46 and 60, and ground. If any resistance is less than 10 k/ohms, repair short circuit. Connect all components. Disconnect Breakout Box and repeat Quick Test. If resistance is 10 k/ohms or more, go to next step.

5) Solenoid Functional Test – Connect Transaxle Tester (007-0085A). Perform solenoid voltage test. See tester instructions. If solenoid activates (LED green), go to next step. If solenoid does not activate, go to step **7)**.

6) Transaxle Drive Test – Perform tester drive test. See tester instructions. When transaxle has shifted into 2nd gear, depress TCC switch on tester. If engine rpm decreases when operated with tester, see SELF-DIAGNOSTICS – EEC-IV article in ENGINE PERFORMANCE of appropriate MITCHELL® manual to diagnose vehicle harness or PCM malfunctions. If engine rpm does not decrease when operated by tester, go to next step.

7) Check Resistance Of Solenoid – Set tester Bench/Drive switch to BENCH mode. Set Gear Selector switch to OHMS CHECK. Connect ohmmeter negative lead to TCC jack and positive lead to TCC VPWR jack on tester. Measure resistance. Resistance should be .98-1.6 ohms. If resistance is within specification, go to next step. If resistance is not within specification, go to step **9)**.

8) Check Solenoid For Short To Ground – Check continuity between BAT (-) tester terminal and TCC terminals. If continuity exists, go to next step. If continuity does not exist, Erase all trouble codes. See CLEARING CODES. Repeat QUICK TEST. See TROUBLE SHOOTING in FORD AXOD-E article for non-electronic symptom diagnostics.

PINPOINT TEST C (Cont.)

9) AXOD-E Internal Electronic Diagnostics – Drain transaxle fluid. See TRANSMISSION SERVICING section. Remove transaxle side pan. See OIL PUMP & VALVE BODY ASSEMBLY under ON-VEHICLE SERVICE IN FORD AXOD-E article. Inspect all internal harness connectors. Ensure all connectors are fully connected and not damaged. Repair as needed. Install all components in reverse order of disassembly. Fill transaxle with fluid. Erase all trouble codes. See CLEARING CODES. Repeat QUICK TEST. If all connectors are okay, go to next step.

10) Check Internal Harness Continuity – Disconnect internal harness from TCC sensor. Connect positive lead of ohmmeter to tester TCC jack and negative lead to TCC Brown wire. Measure and record resistance. Connect positive lead of ohmmeter to tester VPWR jack and negative lead to TCC Green wire. If resistances measured are 5 ohms or less, go to next step. If any resistance measured is more than 5 ohms, replace internal harness. Go to step **12)**.

11) Check Internal Harness For Shorts To Ground – Using transmission tester, check continuity between each TCC sensor connector terminals and BAT(-) terminal of tester. If continuity does not exist in either circuit, go to next step. If continuity exists in any circuit, replace internal harness. Go to next step.

12) Check TOT Sensor Resistance – Using ohmmeter, check resistance between terminals TOT sensor. If resistance is within specification for specific temperature, go to next step. If resistances measured are not within specification, replace TOT sensor. Install all components in reverse order of disassembly. Fill transaxle with fluid. Erase all trouble codes. See CLEARING CODES. Repeat QUICK TEST.

13) Check Solenoid For Short To Ground – Using ohmmeter, check continuity between each TCC sensor terminal and ground. If continuity exists, replace faulty TCC sensor. Install all components in reverse order of disassembly. Fill transaxle with fluid. Erase all trouble codes. See CLEARING CODES. Repeat QUICK TEST. If continuity does not exist, install all components in reverse order of disassembly. Fill transaxle with fluid. Erase all trouble codes. See CLEARING CODES. Repeat QUICK TEST. See TROUBLE SHOOTING in FORD AXOD-E article for non-electronic symptom diagnostics.

PINPOINT TEST D

MLP SENSOR

NOTE: Code 634 may be set if transaxle is not in park or A/C is on when QUICK TEST is performed.

1) Preliminary Inspection – Disconnect MLP connector, and inspect it for damaged pins, corrosion and loose wires. Repair as necessary. Reconnect MLP connector. Ensure MLP sensor is correctly adjusted. See FORD AXOD-E article. If sensor requires adjustment, clear trouble codes after adjustment. See CLEARING CODES. Repeat QUICK TEST. If sensor is correctly adjusted, go to next step.

2) Check Electrical Signal Operation – Ensure ignition is off. Disconnect MLP harness connector. Turn ignition on. Measure voltage between harness connector TOT terminal and SRTN terminal. *See Fig. B1.* If voltage is 4.75-5.25 volts, go to next step. If voltage is not within specification, see SELF-DIAGNOSTICS – EEC-IV article in ENGINE PERFORMANCE of appropriate MITCHELL® manual for NO VREF voltage.

3) Check Continuity Of MLP Sensor Harness Circuits – Turn ignition off. Disconnect PCM 60-pin connector, and inspect it for damaged pins, corrosion and loose wires. Repair as necessary. Install Breakout Box (T83L-50-EEC-IV), leaving PCM disconnected. Measure and record resistance between Breakout Box test pin terminal No. 46 and MLP harness connector terminal No. 359. *See Fig. D1.* Measure and record resistance between Breakout Box test pin terminal No. 30 and MLP harness connector terminal No. 199. If resistance is less than 5 ohms, go to next step. If resistance is more than 5 ohms, repair open circuit(s). Remove Breakout Box and connect all components. Erase all trouble codes. See CLEARING CODES. Repeat QUICK TEST.

PINPOINT TEST D (Cont.)

94A38455

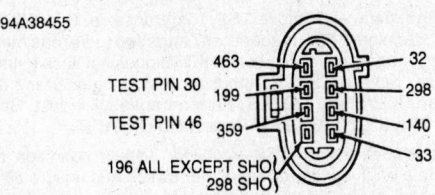

TEST PIN 30

TEST PIN 46

196 ALL EXCEPT SHO
298 SHO

	TERMINAL DESCRIPTIONS
196	Power Feed
199	MLP Sensor Signal
359	Sensor Signal Return
463	Liftgate Release Circuit
33	Start Circuit
140	Backup Lamp
298	Fused Accy Feed
32	Start Circuit

Fig. D1: Identifying Transaxle Harness Connector

4) Check MLP Circuit For Shorts To Power & Ground – Ensure MLP sensor harness connector is disconnected. Measure resistance between Breakout Box test pin No. 30 and test pins No. 37, 40, 46, 57 and 60. Measure resistance between Breakout Box test pin No. 30 and ground. If each measurement is more than 10 k/ohms, go to next step. If any measurement is less than 10 k/ohms, repair short circuit. Remove Breakout Box and connect all components. Erase all trouble codes. See CLEARING CODES. Repeat QUICK TEST.

5) Operational Check Of MLP Sensor – Install MLP overlay on Transmission Tester (007-0085A). Connect tester to MLP sensor. Check continuity and resistances in all positions. See Fig. D1. If MLP sensor does not operate within specification, replace sensor. Connect all components. Erase all trouble codes. See CLEARING CODES. Repeat QUICK TEST. If sensor operates within specification, connect all components. Erase all trouble codes. See CLEARING CODES. Repeat QUICK TEST. If code(s) 522, 634 or 659 are set, intermittent condition may be present. Attempt to duplicate malfunction by repeating previous steps.

94C38457

Transmission Range Selector Lever Position	Resistance (ohms)		Voltage**
	MIN	MAX	VOLTS
P	3770	4607	4.41
R	1304	1593	3.60
N	660	807	2.83
Ⓓ	361	442	2.09
2/D	190	232	1.37
1	78	95	.68

** May vary ± 10% due to sensor and VREF variations.

Fig. D2: MLP Resistance Specification Chart

PINPOINT TEST E

EPC SOLENOID

1) Check VPWR To Solenoid – Turn ignition off. Disconnect transaxle harness connector. With KOEO, measure voltage between transaxle harness connector EPC/TCC VPWR terminal and vehicle ground. See Fig. E1. If voltage is 10.5 volts or more, go to next step. If voltage is less than specification, repair open circuit. Connect all components. Erase all trouble codes. See CLEARING CODES. Repeat QUICK TEST.

PINPOINT TEST E (Cont.)

94B38456

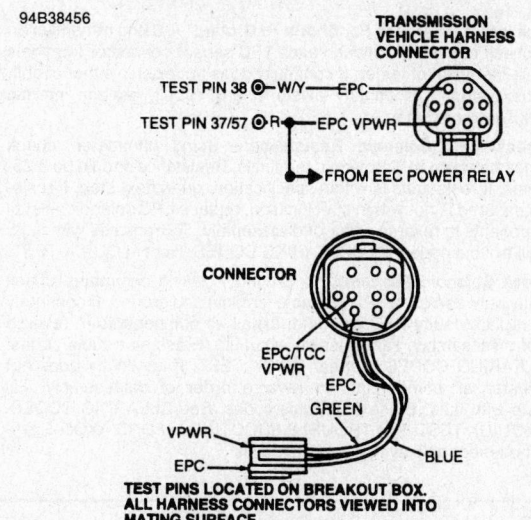

TRANSMISSION VEHICLE HARNESS CONNECTOR

TEST PIN 38 ⊚—W/Y—EPC
TEST PIN 37/57 ⊚—R—EPC VPWR
→FROM EEC POWER RELAY

CONNECTOR

EPC/TCC VPWR
EPC
GREEN
VPWR
EPC
BLUE

TEST PINS LOCATED ON BREAKOUT BOX. ALL HARNESS CONNECTORS VIEWED INTO MATING SURFACE.

Fig. E1: Identifying Transaxle Harness Connector

2) Check Continuity Of Solenoid Signal & VPWR Harness Circuit – Turn ignition off, and wait 10 seconds. Disconnect PCM 60-pin connector, and inspect it for damaged pins, corrosion and loose wires. Repair as necessary. Install Breakout Box (T83L-50-EEC-IV), leaving PCM disconnected. Measure and record resistance between Breakout Box test pins No. 37, and transaxle harness connector terminal EPC/TCC VPWR. See Fig. E1. Measure and record resistance between Breakout Box test pins No. 38, and transaxle harness connector EPC terminal. If resistances measured are 5 ohms or less, go to next step. If resistances measured are more than 5 ohms, repair open circuit. Connect all components. Erase all trouble codes. See CLEARING CODES. Repeat QUICK TEST.

3) Check Harness For Short To Power Or Ground – Measure and record resistance between Breakout Box test pin No. 38 and test pins No. 37 and 57. Measure and record resistance between test pin No. 38 and test pins No. 40, 46 and 60. If any resistance measured is less than 10 k/ohms, repair short circuit. Disconnect Breakout Box and repeat Quick Test. If all resistances are 10 k/ohms or more, go to next step.

4) EPC Functional Test – Disconnect transaxle harness connector. Connect Transaxle Tester (007-0085A). Connect line pressure gauge. See FORD AXOD-E article. Set Bench/Drive switch to DRIVE mode. Set Gear Selector switch to 1st gear position. Perform EPC function test. See tester instructions. Observe line pressure on gauge while depressing EPC switch (KOER). EPC solenoid should activate (LED green) and line pressure should drop when EPC switch is depressed. If solenoid operates correctly, replace PCM. Connect all components. Erase all trouble codes. See CLEARING CODES. Repeat QUICK TEST. If solenoid is not operating, go to next step.

5) Check Resistance Of Solenoid – Ensure tester power is off. Set Bench/Drive switch to BENCH mode. Connect ohmmeter negative lead to EPC jack. Connect positive lead to VPWR jack. If resistance is 3.23-5.50 ohms, go to next step. If resistance is not within specifications, go to step 7).

6) Check Solenoid For Short To Ground – Check continuity between BAT(-) terminal of Transmission Tester and EPC jacks. If continuity exists, go to next step. If continuity does not exist, see TROUBLE SHOOTING under FORD AXOD-E article.

7) AXOD-E Internal Electronic Diagnostics – Drain transaxle fluid. See TRANSMISSION SERVICING section. Remove transaxle side pan. See OIL PUMP & VALVE BODY ASSEMBLY under ON-VEHICLE SERVICE IN FORD AXOD-E article. Inspect all internal harness connectors. Ensure all connectors are fully connected and not damaged. Repair as needed. Install all components in reverse order of disassembly. Fill transaxle with fluid. Erase all trouble codes. See CLEARING CODES. Repeat QUICK TEST. If all connectors are okay, go to next step.

8) Check Internal Harness Continuity – Disconnect internal harness from EPC solenoid assembly. Connect positive lead of ohmmeter to tester EPC jack and negative lead to EPC Blue wire. Measure and record resistance. Connect positive lead of ohmmeter to tester VPWR jack and negative lead to EPC Green wire. If resistances measured are 5 ohms or less, go to next step. If any resistance measured is more than 5 ohms, replace internal harness. Go to step 10).

PINPOINT TEST E (Cont.)

9) Check Internal Harness For Shorts To Ground – Using transmission tester, check continuity between each EPC sensor connector terminals and BAT(-) terminal of tester. If continuity does not exist in either circuit, go to next step. If continuity exists in any circuit, replace internal harness. Go to next step.

10) Check EPC Solenoid Resistance – Using ohmmeter, check resistance between EPC solenoid terminals. Resistance should be 3.23-5.50 ohms. If resistance is within specification, go to next step. If resistance measured is not within specification, replace EPC solenoid. Install all components in reverse order of disassembly. Fill transaxle with fluid. Erase all trouble codes. See CLEARING CODES. Repeat QUICK TEST.

11) Check Solenoid For Short To Ground – Using ohmmeter, check continuity between each EPC solenoid terminal and ground. If continuity exists, replace faulty EPC solenoid. Install all components in reverse order of disassembly. Fill transaxle with fluid. Erase all trouble codes. See CLEARING CODES. Repeat QUICK TEST. If continuity does not exist, install all components in reverse order of disassembly. Fill transaxle with fluid. Erase all trouble codes. See CLEARING CODES. Repeat QUICK TEST. See TROUBLE SHOOTING in FORD AXOD-E article for non-electronic symptom diagnostics.

PINPOINT TEST F

TRANSMISSION SPEED SENSOR

1) Preliminary Inspection – Inspect condition of TSS harness and component connector. Repair as needed.

2) Check Continuity Of TSS Harness Circuit – Ensure ignition is off. Turn ignition off, and wait 10 seconds. Disconnect PCM 60-pin connector, and inspect it for damaged pins, corrosion and loose wires. Repair as necessary. Install Breakout Box (T83L-50-EEC-IV), leaving PCM disconnected. Disconnect TSS harness connector. Measure and record resistance between Breakout Box test pin No. 5 and TSS harness connector positive terminal. *See Fig. F1.* Measure and record resistance between Breakout Box test pin No. 46 and TSS harness connector negative terminal. If resistances measured are 5 ohms or less, go to next step. If resistances measured are more than 5 ohms, repair open circuit(s). Connect all components. Erase all trouble codes. See CLEARING CODES. Repeat QUICK TEST.

94J36730

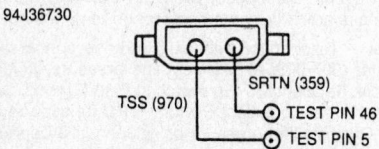

Fig. F1: Identifying TSS Harness Connector

3) Check TSS Circuit For Short To Power & Ground – Measure and record resistance between Breakout Box test pins No. 5 and 46, and test pins No. 37 and 57. Measure and record resistance between test pins No. 5, 37, 46 and 57, and test pins No. 40 and 60. If any resistance measured is less than 10 k/ohms, repair short circuit. Connect all components. Disconnect Breakout Box and repeat Quick Test. If resistance is 10 k/ohms or more, go to next step.

4) TSS Functional Test – Ensure TSS harness connector is disconnected. Connect Transmission Tester (007-0085A) to TSS component connector. Connect voltmeter leads to appropriate tester TSS jacks. Set voltmeter to 20 volt A/C scale. Perform drive cycle test. See TRANSMISSION DRIVE CYCLE TEST. If voltage increases with vehicle speed, replace PCM. Connect all components. Erase all trouble codes. See CLEARING CODES. Repeat QUICK TEST. If voltage does not increase with speed, go to next step.

5) Check Resistance Of TSS – Connect ohmmeter leads to appropriate Transmission Tester TSS jacks. If resistance is 100-200 ohms, go to next step. If resistance is not within specification, replace TSS. Connect all components. Erase all trouble codes. See CLEARING CODES. Perform drive cycle test. See TRANSMISSION DRIVE CYCLE TEST. Repeat QUICK TEST.

6) Check TSS For Short To Ground – Check for continuity between Transmission Tester TSS jacks and tester BAT(-) jack. If continuity does not exist, go to next step. If continuity exists, replace TSS. Connect all components. Erase all trouble codes. See CLEARING CODES. Perform drive cycle test. See TRANSMISSION DRIVE CYCLE TEST. Repeat QUICK TEST.

PINPOINT TEST F (Cont.)

7) Check TSS Magnetism – Remove TSS from transaxle. See FORD AXOD-E article. Determine if TSS magnetically attracted to ferrous metal. If TSS acts like a magnet, go to next step. If TSS does not stick to ferrous metal surface, replace TSS. Connect all components. Erase all trouble codes. See CLEARING CODES. Perform drive cycle test. See TRANSMISSION DRIVE CYCLE TEST. Repeat QUICK TEST.

8) Check Exciter Wheel – With TSS removed, inspect condition of exciter wheel. Rotate engine with remote starter switch and ensure all 4 teeth of exciter wheel are not damaged. Replace exciter wheel if any teeth are damaged. See FORD AXOD-E article. If exciter wheel is not damaged, replace TSS. Connect all components. Erase all trouble codes. See CLEARING CODES. Perform drive cycle test. See TRANSMISSION DRIVE CYCLE TEST. Repeat QUICK TEST.

CIRCUIT TESTS

CIRCUIT TEST CA

REFERENCE VOLTAGE

Diagnostic Aids – Perform this test when a check for VREF signal has failed in sensor input CIRCUIT TESTS AA-AC or QA. SIG RTN is a dedicated ground used by most EEC-IV system sensors. VREF is a 5-volt reference voltage that is continuously output by PCM. This consistent voltage signal is used on all 3-wire sensors.

This circuit test is only intended to diagnose the following components and circuits:
- Powertrain Control Module (PCM).
- Vehicle wiring harness circuits (SIG RTN and VREF).

93E40422

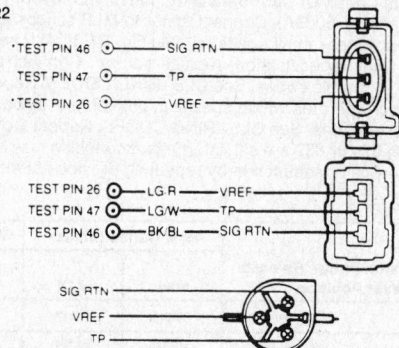

Fig. CA1: Identifying Reference Voltage Circuits & Connector Terminals

TEST PIN WIRE COLOR IDENTIFICATION

Terminal No.	Wire Color
No. 26 (VREF)	Brown/White
No. 46 (SIG RTN)	Gray/Red

1) Check Battery Power Circuit – Turn ignition off, and wait 10 seconds. Disconnect PCM 60-pin connector, and inspect it for damaged pins, corrosion and loose wires. Repair as necessary. Install Breakout Box (T83L-50-EEC-IV), leaving PCM connected. Turn ignition on. Measure and record voltage between breakout box test pin No. 37 and SIG RTN terminal of self-test connector. Measure and record voltage across battery terminals. If both readings are less than 10.5 volts or if they differ by more than 1.0 volt, reconnect sensor (if applicable). Go to CIRCUIT TEST X1 under SELF-DIAGNOSTICS – EEC-IV article in ENGINE PERFORMANCE of appropriate MITCHELL® manual. If voltages are 10.5 volts or more and do not differ from one another by more than 1.0 volt, go to step **2)**.

2) Check VREF Voltage – With breakout box installed and PCM connected, set DVOM on 20-volt scale. Turn ignition on. Measure voltage between test pins No. 26 and 46 at breakout box. If voltage is 4-6 volts, go to step **3)**. If voltage is more than 6 volts, go to step **4)**. If voltage is less than 4 volts, go to step **5)**.

3) Check VREF & SIG RTN Circuit Continuity – Turn ignition off. Disconnect PCM. If directed here by a sensor test, ensure sensor is disconnected. Measure resistance between Breakout Box test pin No. 26 and VREF terminal at wiring harness connector of applicable sensor.

CIRCUIT TEST CA (Cont.)

Measure resistance between test pin No. 46 and SIG RTN circuit terminal at wiring harness connector of applicable sensor. If both readings are less than 5 ohms, VREF circuit is okay. If either reading is 5 ohms or more, repair open in VREF or SIG RTN circuit. Remove breakout box, and repeat QUICK TEST.

4) Check For Excess VREF Circuit Voltage – Turn ignition off. Ensure PCM is disconnected. With breakout box installed, disconnect scan tester or STAR tester (if applicable). Turn ignition on. Measure voltage between test pin No. 26 and battery ground. If voltage is less than 0.5 volt, replace PCM and repeat QUICK TEST. If voltage is 0.5 volt or more, repair short to battery power in wiring harness. Remove breakout box, reconnect components and repeat QUICK TEST. Replace PCM if fault still occurs.

5) Check For Shorted TPS – Turn ignition off. Connect PCM to breakout box. Disconnect Throttle Position Sensor (TPS) from wiring harness. Turn ignition on. Measure voltage between test pins No. 26 and 46 at breakout box. If voltage is 4 volts or more, replace TPS, remove breakout box and repeat QUICK TEST. If voltage is less than 4 volts on models with EVP, PFE or DPFE sensor, go to step **6)**. If voltage is less than 4 volts on all other models, go to step **8)**.

6) Check For Shorted EVP/PFE/DPFE Sensor – Turn ignition off, and wait 10 seconds. Disconnect EVP/PFE/DPFE sensor. Turn ignition on. Measure voltage between test pins No. 26 and 46. If voltage is 4 volts or more, replace EVP/PFE/DPFE sensor and repeat QUICK TEST. If voltage is less than 4 volts, reconnect EVP/PFE/DPFE sensor and go to step **8)**.

NOTE: A break in step numbering sequence occurs at this point. Procedure skips from step 6) to step 8). No test procedures have been omitted.

8) Check VREF Circuit For Short To Ground – Turn ignition off. Disconnect PCM. Disconnect TPS, MAP/BARO sensor and EVP/PFE/DPFE sensor. Measure resistance between test pin No. 26 and test pins No. 20, 40, 46 and 60. If any resistance is less than 1000 ohms, repair short to ground. Remove breakout box, and repeat QUICK TEST. If original problem still exists, replace PCM and repeat QUICK TEST. If readings are 1000 ohms or more, replace PCM and repeat QUICK TEST.

CIRCUIT TEST DA

TEMPERATURE SENSOR TEST (IAT & ECT)

Diagnostic Aids – Perform this test only when directed by QUICK TEST. Ambient air temperature must be at least 50°F (10°C) to receive valid input from IAT sensor. Engine coolant temperature must be greater than 50°F (10°C) to pass KOEO SELF-TEST and greater than 180°F (82°C) to pass KOER SELF-TEST. Voltage values in this test are based on a 5-volt VREF signal. Values may vary up to 15% due to sensor and VREF variations.

This circuit test is intended to diagnose the following components and circuits:

- Intake Air Temperature (IAT) sensor.
- Engine Coolant Temperature (ECT) sensor.
- Wiring harness circuits (IAT, ECT and SIG RTN).
- Powertrain Control Module (PCM).

To prevent replacing good components, ensure the following non-EEC areas or components are not cause of problem:

- Coolant level low.
- Cooling system, water pump or fan.
- Engine operating temperature.
- Engine oil level low.
- Thermostat.
- Air cleaner duct.
- Ambient temperature.

CIRCUIT TEST DA (Cont.)

93J40427

*TEST PINS LOCATED ON BREAKOUT BOX.
ALL HARNESS CONNECTORS VIEWED INTO MATING SURFACE.

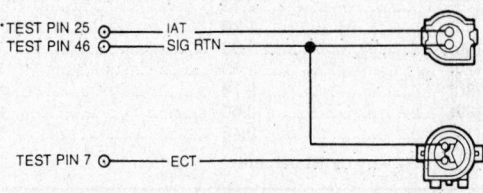

Fig. DA1: Identifying Temperature Sensor Circuits & Connector Terminals

TEST PIN WIRE COLOR IDENTIFICATION

Application	Wire Color
No. 7 (ECT)	Light Green/Red
No. 25 (IAT)	Gray
No. 46 (SIG RTN)	Gray/Red

1) Code 116 Or 114 – Code 116 (ECT) or 114 (IAT) indicates corresponding sensor is out of self-test range. Correct range for measurement is .3-3.7 volts. Check for following possible causes:

- Low ambient temperature (less than 50°F).
- Low coolant level.
- Faulty harness connector.
- Faulty sensor.

Ensure upper radiator hose is hot and pressurized. Repeat QUICK TEST. If Code 114 or 116 is present, go to step **2)**. If none of these codes are present, service other codes as necessary.

2) Check VREF Circuit Voltage At TPS – Turn ignition off. Disconnect Throttle Position Sensor (TPS). With ignition on and engine off, measure voltage at TPS wiring harness connector between VREF and SIG RTN. See Fig. DA2. If voltage is 4-6 volts, reconnect TPS and go to step **3)**. If voltage is not 4-6 volts, go to CIRCUIT TEST CA.

3) Check Temperature Sensor Resistance (KOEO) – Turn ignition off. Disconnect suspect sensor. Measure resistance between SIG RTN terminal at sensor and SIG RTN terminal at sensor wiring harness connector. If resistance is not within specification, replace suspected sensor and repeat QUICK TEST. If resistance is within specification, go to step **4)**.

93A40428

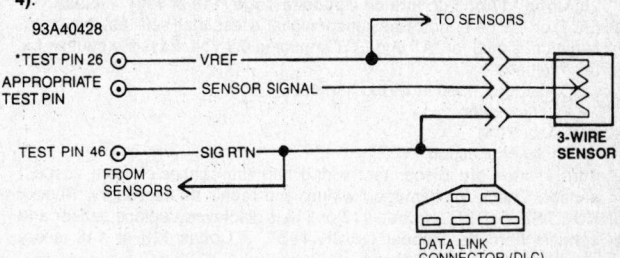

*TEST PINS LOCATED ON BREAKOUT BOX.
ALL HARNESS CONNECTORS VIEWED INTO MATING SURFACE.

Fig. DA2: Identifying TPS Harness Connector Terminals

4) Check Temperature Sensor Resistance (KOER) – Warm engine to normal operating temperature. Turn ignition off. Disconnect suspect sensor. Run engine at 2000 RPM for 2 minutes. Measure resistance between SIG RTN terminal at sensor and SIG RTN terminal at sensor wiring harness connector. See ACT & ECT SENSOR SPECIFICATIONS table. If resistance is within specification, replace PCM and repeat QUICK TEST. If sensor is not within specification, replace sensor and repeat QUICK TEST.

CIRCUIT TEST DA (Cont.)

ACT & ECT SENSOR SPECIFICATIONS

Temperature °F (°C)	¹ Volts	¹ Ohms
50 (10)	3.51	58,750
68 (20)	3.07	27,300
86 (30)	2.60	24,270
104 (40)	2.13	16,150
122 (50)	1.70	10,970
140 (60)	1.33	7700
158 (70)	1.33	7700
176 (80)	0.78	3840
194 (90)	0.60	2800
212 (100)	0.46	2070

¹ – Values may vary by 15 percent.

NOTE: A break in step numbering sequence occurs at this point. Procedure skips from step 4) to step 10). No test procedures have been omitted.

10) Code 118 Or 113 Induce Opposite Code (Code 117 Or 112) – Code 118 (ECT) or 113 (IAT) indicate corresponding sensor signal is greater than self-test maximum. Maximum signal voltage for ECT and IAT sensor is 4.6 volts. Possible causes for excess voltage signals are:
- Open circuit in wiring harness (IAT or ECT).
- Faulty connection.
- Faulty sensor.
- Faulty PCM.

Turn ignition off. Disconnect suspect temperature sensor. Connect a jumper wire between SIG RTN terminal at sensor and SIG RTN terminal at sensor wiring harness connector. Repeat QUICK TEST. If Code 112 or 117 is displayed, replace suspect sensor and repeat QUICK TEST. If Code 112 or 117 is not displayed, remove jumper wire and go to next step.

11) Check Continuity Of Sensor Signal & SIG RTN Circuits – Turn ignition off. Ensure suspect temperature sensor is disconnected. Disconnect PCM 60-pin connector. Check for damaged wiring, and repair as necessary. Install Breakout Box (T83L-50-EEC-IV), leaving PCM disconnected. Measure resistance between test pin No. 7 (ECT sensor) or test pin No. 25 (IAT sensor) at breakout box and SIG RTN terminal at sensor wiring harness connector. Also measure resistance between test pin No. 46 and SIG RTN circuit at sensor wiring harness connector. If both readings are less than 5 ohms, replace PCM and repeat QUICK TEST. If either reading is 5 ohms or more, repair open circuit and repeat QUICK TEST.

NOTE: A break in step numbering sequence occurs at this point. Procedure skips from step 11) to step 20). No test procedures have been omitted.

20) Code 117 or 112: Induce Opposite Code (118 or 113) – Code 117 (ECT) or 112 (IAT) indicates sensor signal is less than self-test minimum. Minimum signal for IAT and ECT sensor is 0.2 volt. Possible causes for this fault are:
- Circuit grounded in wiring harness.
- Faulty sensor.
- Faulty PCM.
- Faulty connection.

Turn ignition off. Disconnect wiring harness connector from suspect sensor. Check for damaged wiring, and repair as necessary. Repeat KOEO SELF-TEST. If Code 113 or 118 is displayed, replace sensor and connect harness. Repeat QUICK TEST. If Codes 113 or 118 is not displayed, go to step 21).

21) Check VREF Circuit Voltage At TPS – Turn ignition off. Disconnect wiring harness connector from suspect sensor. Disconnect TPS. Turn ignition on. Measure voltage between VREF and SIG RTN at TPS wiring harness connector. If voltage is not 4-6 volts, go to CIRCUIT TEST CA. If voltage is 4-6 volts, connect TPS and go to step 22).

22) Check Temperature Sensor Signal For Shorts To Ground – Turn ignition off. Disconnect suspect sensor. Disconnect PCM 60-pin connector. Check for damaged wiring, and repair as necessary. Install Breakout Box (T83L-50-EEC-IV), leaving PCM disconnected. Measure resistance between test pin No. 7 (ECT) or 25 (IAT) and pins No. 40, 46 and 60. If any reading is less than 10 k/ohms, repair short circuit and repeat QUICK TEST. If all readings are 10 k/ohms or more, replace PCM and repeat QUICK TEST.

CIRCUIT TEST DA (Cont.)

NOTE: A break in step numbering sequence occurs at this point. Procedure skips from step 22) to step 90). No test procedures have been omitted.

90) Continuous Memory Code 118, 113, 117 Or 112: Check Sensor – A Continuous Memory Code 118 or 113 indicates sensor signal is greater than self-test maximum of 4.6 volts. Code is set during normal driving conditions. Continuous Memory Code 117 or 112 indicates sensor signal is less than self-test minimum of 0.2 volt. Code is set during normal driving conditions. Possible causes for these faults are:
- Faulty sensor.
- Open or grounded circuit in harness.
- Faulty PCM.

SENSOR CODES

Sensor	Continuous Memory Code
IAT	113 Or 112
ECT	118 Or 117

Enter KOEO wiggle test mode. See CONTINUOUS MONITOR MODE (WIGGLE TEST) under QUICK TEST. Observe analog voltmeter or scan tester for indication of fault while tapping sensor lightly and wiggling sensor connector. If fault is indicated, disconnect and inspect connector and terminals. If connector and terminals are okay, replace sensor, clear continuous memory and repeat QUICK TEST. If fault is not indicated, go to step 91).

91) Check EEC-IV Wiring Harness – While in CONTINUOUS MONITOR MODE (WIGGLE TEST), observe analog voltmeter or scan tester while wiggling and bending wiring harness, a small section at a time, from sensor to cowl. Also check harness from cowl to PCM. If fault is indicated, isolate fault and repair as necessary. Clear continuous memory, and repeat QUICK TEST. If no fault is found, go to step 92).

92) Inspect PCM & Wiring Harness Connectors – Turn ignition off. Disconnect PCM 60-pin connector. Inspect both connector and connector terminals for damage. If connectors and terminals are damaged, repair as necessary and repeat QUICK TEST. If connectors and terminals are okay and fault cannot be duplicated at this time, see TROUBLE SHOOTING (EEC-IV) – NO CODES article in ENGINE PERFORMANCE in appropriate MITCHELL® manual.

NOTE: A break in step numbering sequence occurs at this point. Procedure skips from step 92) to step 100). No test procedures have been omitted.

100) Continuous Memory Code 338 – A Continuous Memory Code 338 indicates cooling system has not reached normal operating temperature. Possible causes for this fault are:
- Thermostat stuck open.
- Coolant outlet gasket leak.
- Water pump gasket leak.

Repair cooling system as necessary. Clear continuous memory, and repeat QUICK TEST.

101) Continuous Memory Code 339 – A Continuous Memory Code 339 indicates cooling system has overheated. Possible causes for this fault are:
- Coolant level low.
- Thermostat stuck closed.
- Coolant system clogged.
- Water pump damaged or worn.
- Radiator cap damaged or worn.
- Cooling fan damaged or worn.

Repair cooling system as necessary. Clear continuous memory, and repeat QUICK TEST.

CIRCUIT TEST DC

MASS AIRFLOW (MAF) SENSOR

Diagnostic Aids – Perform this test when directed by QUICK TEST. This CIRCUIT TEST is intended to diagnose the following:
- MAF sensor.
- Wiring harness circuits (VPWR, PWR GND, MAF and MAF RTN).
- Powertrain Control Module (PCM).

To prevent replacement of good components, be aware the following non-EEC related areas may be cause of problem:
- Air cleaner element.
- Inlet air duct.
- Throttle body.

Code 159, retrieved during KOEO SELF-TEST, indicates voltage exceeded .7-volt test range. Code 159, retrieved during KOER SELF-TEST, indicates voltage is not within .2-1.5 volts operating range. Possible causes are faulty MAF sensor or PCM.

93F40431

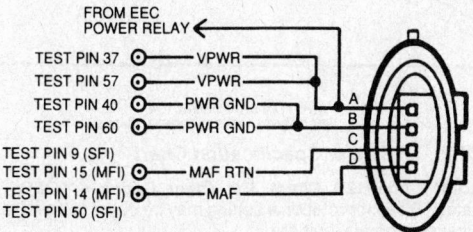

*TEST PINS LOCATED ON BREAKOUT BOX.
ALL HARNESS CONNECTORS VIEWED IN MATING SURFACE.

Fig. DC1: Identifying Mass Airflow (MAF) Sensor Circuits & Connector Terminals

TEST PIN WIRE COLOR IDENTIFICATION

Application	Wire Color
NO. 9 OR 15 (MAF RTN)	Tan/Light Blue
NO. 14 OR 50 (MAF)	Light Blue/Red
NO. 37 & 57 (VPWR)	Red
NO. 40 & 60 (PWR GND)	Black/Light Green

MAF SIGNAL VOLTAGE [1]

Application	Volts
Idle	.6
20 MPH	1.1
40 MPH	1.7
60 MPH	2.1

[1] – MAF signal voltage is typical for normal operating temperature. Voltage signal may vary due to engine load and temperature.

NOTE: Code 159 may be caused by use of a garage exhaust ventilation system. Ensure vehicle is vented to outside atmosphere before repeating QUICK TEST.

1) Code 159: Check VPWR Circuit Voltage – Code 159 indicates that MAF sensor was out of range during KOEO or KOER SELF-TEST. Possible causes for this fault are:
- Air leak before or after MAF sensor.
- Faulty MAF sensor.
- Faulty IAC solenoid.
- Open or grounded wiring harness.
- Faulty PCM.

Repeat QUICK TEST. If Code 412 is present, go to CIRCUIT TEST KE, step 1), and/or if Code 411 is present, go to CIRCUIT TEST KE, step 15) under SELF-DIAGNOSTICS – EEC-IV article in ENGINE PERFORMANCE of appropriate MITCHELL® manual. If Code 411 or 412 is not present, go to step 2).

2) VPWR Circuit Voltage Check – Turn ignition off. Disconnect MAF sensor connector. Set DVOM on 20-volt scale. Turn ignition on. Measure voltage between VPWR terminal at MAF sensor wiring harness connector and negative battery terminal. If voltage is less than 10.5 volts, repair open in VPWR circuit and repeat QUICK TEST. If voltage is 10.5 volts or more, go to step 3).

CIRCUIT TEST DC (Cont.)

3) Check MAF Sensor Ground – Turn ignition on. With MAF sensor disconnected, measure voltage between VPWR terminal and PWR GND terminal at MAF sensor connector. If voltage is less than 10.5 volts, repair open PWR GND circuit. Connect MAF sensor, and repeat QUICK TEST. If voltage is 10.5 volts or more, go to step 13).

NOTE: A break in step numbering sequence occurs at this point. Procedure skips from step 3) to step 10). No test procedures have been omitted.

10) Continuous Memory Code 157: Check For Intermittent Sensor Failure – Continuous Memory Code 157 indicates MAF signal was less than 0.4 volt sometime during last 80 warm-up cycles. Possible causes for this fault are:
- Open MAF circuit.
- MAF circuit shorted to ground.
- Faulty MAF sensor.
- MAF sensor disconnected.

Start engine and allow to idle for 5-10 minutes. Perform KOEO SELF-TEST. If Code 157 is present, go to step 13). If Code 157 is not present, go to next step.

11) Turn ignition off. Disconnect and inspect 60-pin connector at PCM. Service if necessary. Install EEC-IV Breakout Box (T83L-50-EEC-IV), leaving PCM connected. Connect DVOM between MAF test pin and MAF RTN test pin. See appropriate table at beginning of this CIRCUIT TEST. DVOM should read about 0.4 volt. Start engine and allow to idle. Lightly tap on MAF sensor and wiggle wiring harness to simulate road conditions. If sudden change in DVOM reading occurs, fault is indicated. If fault is indicated, replace MAF sensor and repeat QUICK TEST. If no fault is indicated, leave DVOM connected and go to next step.

12) Check Wiring Harness For Open Or Short Circuit – Turn ignition on. Shake and bend small sections of wiring harness starting at MAF sensor and working toward dash panel. Shake and bend small sections of wiring harness starting at dash panel and working toward PCM. If fault is indicated, isolate and repair as necessary. If fault is not indicated, problem is intermittent and cannot be duplicated at this time.

13) Codes 157 Or 129: Check For Air Leak At MAF Sensor – Check for broken or loose air outlet tube clamps at throttle body and air cleaner assembly. Repair or replace as necessary. If no faults are found, go to next step.

14) Check Continuity Of MAF & VPWR Circuit – Turn ignition off. Disconnect MAF sensor and PCM wiring harness connector. Install EEC-IV Breakout Box (T83L-50-EEC-IV), leaving PCM disconnected. Measure resistance between MAF terminal of MAF sensor wiring harness connector and test pins No. 37 and 57. Measure resistance between MAF terminal of MAF sensor wiring harness connector and test pin No. 50 (Sequential Fuel Injected engines) or test pin No. 14 (except Sequential Fuel Injected engines). If resistance is more than 5 ohms, repair open circuit and repeat QUICK TEST. If resistance is 5 ohms or more, go to next step.

15) Check MAF Signal For Short To Ground – Turn ignition off. Ensure MAF sensor and PCM wiring harness are disconnected. Measure resistance between test pin No. 50 and test pins No. 9, 40 and 60 (Sequential Fuel Injected engines) or between test pin No. 14 and test pins No. 15, 40 and 60 (except Sequential Fuel Injected engines). If resistance is less than 10 k/ohms, repair short circuit and repeat QUICK TEST. If resistance is 10 k/ohms or more, go to next step.

16) Check PWR/GND Circuit Continuity – Turn ignition off. Ensure MAP sensor and PCM wiring harness connector are disconnected. Measure resistance between PWR GND terminal at MAF sensor wiring harness connector and negative battery terminal. If resistance is 10 ohms or more, repair open PWR GND circuit and repeat QUICK TEST. If resistance is less than 10 ohms, go to next step.

17) Check Continuity Of MAF RTN Circuit – Ensure ignition is turned off. Measure resistance between MAF RTN terminal of MAF sensor wiring harness connector and test pin No. 9 (Sequential Fuel Injected engines) or test pin No. 15 (except Sequential Fuel Injected engines). If resistance is more than 5 ohms, repair open circuit and repeat QUICK TEST. If resistance is 5 ohms or more, go to next step.

18) Check MAF Circuit For Short To Ground – Turn ignition off. Ensure MAF sensor is disconnected. Connect PCM to breakout box. Measure resistance between test pin No. 50 and test pins No. 9, 40 and 60. If resistance is less than 10 k/ohms, replace PCM and repeat QUICK TEST. If resistance is 10 k/ohms or more, go to next step.

CIRCUIT TEST DC (Cont.)

19) Check MAF Circuit Output – Turn ignition off. Connect MAF sensor wiring harness connector. Start engine. Measure resistance between test pin No. 50 and negative battery terminal. If voltage is .36-1.50 volts, go to next step. If voltage is not .36-1.50 volts, replace MAF sensor and repeat QUICK TEST.

20) Check MAF Circuit Output (Cont.) – With engine running, measure resistance between test pin No. 9 and test pin No. 50. If voltage is .36-1.50 volts, replace PCM and repeat QUICK TEST. If voltage is not .36-1.50 volts, replace MAF sensor and repeat QUICK TEST.

21) Code 158 – Turn ignition off. Disconnect MAF sensor wiring harness connector. Start engine, and allow it to idle for one minute. Turn ignition off. Repeat KOEO SELF-TEST. If Code 157 is present, replace MAF sensor and repeat QUICK TEST. If Code 157 is not present, go to step **22)**.

22) Check MAF Circuit For Short To VPWR – Turn ignition off. Disconnect PCM 60-pin connector, and inspect it for damaged or corroded terminals. Service if necessary. Measure resistance between MAF and VPWR terminals at MAF sensor wiring harness connector. If resistance is 10 k/ohms or more, replace PCM and repeat QUICK TEST. If resistance is less than 10 k/ohms, repair short circuit and repeat QUICK TEST.

CIRCUIT TEST DH

THROTTLE POSITION (TP) SENSOR

Diagnostic Aids – Perform this test only when directed by QUICK TEST. This test is intended to diagnose the following:
- TP sensor.
- Wiring harness circuits (TP, SIG RTN and VREF).
- Powertrain Control Module (PCM).

Normal range of throttle angle measurement for TP sensor is 0-85 degrees. To pass QUICK TEST procedure, range of throttle rotation (in degrees) must be within 3 percent of specification. *See Fig. DH2.*

To prevent replacement of good components, be aware the following non-EEC related areas may be at fault:
- Idle speed.
- Binding throttle shaft or linkage.
- Choke cam adjustment (if equipped).
- TP sensor not seated.

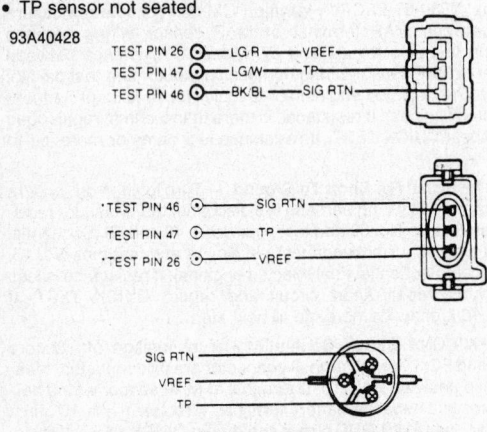

93A40428

NOTE: EITHER TYPE MAY BE FITTED

Fig. DH1: *Identifying TP Sensor Circuits & Connector Terminals*

TEST PIN WIRE COLOR IDENTIFICATION

Application	Wire Color
No. 26 (VREF)	Light Green/Red
No. 46 (SIG RTN)	Black/Blue
No. 47 (TP)	Light Green/White

CIRCUIT TEST DH (Cont.)

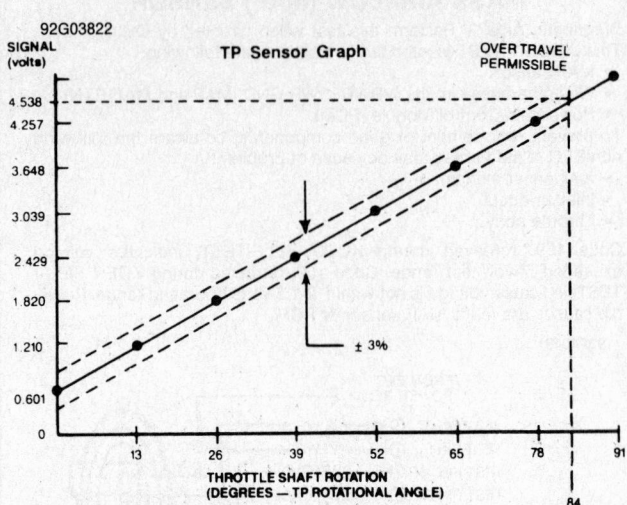

92G03822

Fig. DH2: *TP Sensor Specification Chart*

1) KOER Code 121: Check For Other Codes – KOER Code 121 indicates TP sensor rotational setting may be out of self-test range. Possible causes for this fault are:
- Binding throttle linkage.
- TP sensor not seated correctly.
- Faulty TP sensor.
- Faulty Powertrain Control Module (PCM).

Perform KOER SELF-TEST. Check for Code 327. If either of these codes are present with Code 121, service Code 327 and repeat QUICK TEST. If these codes are not present, go to step **2)**.

2) Code 121: Check For Binding Throttle Plate – Inspect throttle body for binding. If throttle body is binding, check for binding throttle or cruise control linkage, vacuum line or harness interference, etc. Repair as necessary, and repeat QUICK TEST. If no mechanical problem is found, go to step **3)**.

3) Code 123: Attempt To Generate Code 122 – Code 123 indicates TP sensor signal is greater than self-test maximum value. Possible causes for this fault are:
- TP sensor not seated properly.
- Faulty TP sensor.
- Short circuit to power.
- Faulty PCM.

Turn ignition off. Disconnect TP sensor wiring harness connector. Inspect and repair connector pins if damaged. Repeat KOEO SELF-TEST. Ignore all other codes at this time. If Code 63/122 is not displayed, go to step **5)**. If Code 122 is displayed, go to step **4)**.

4) Check VREF Circuit Voltage – Turn ignition on. Measure voltage between VREF and SIG RTN terminals at TP sensor wiring harness connector. If reading is 4-6 volts, replace TP sensor and repeat QUICK TEST. If reading is not 4-6 volts, reconnect sensor and go to CIRCUIT TEST CA.

5) Check TP Circuit For Short To Power – Turn ignition off. Leave TP sensor disconnected. Disconnect PCM 60-pin connector. Inspect it for damage and repair as necessary. Install EEC-IV Breakout Box (T83L-50-EEC-IV), leaving PCM disconnected. Measure resistance between test pin No. 47 and test pins No. 26 and 57. If either resistance is less than 10 k/ohms, repair short circuit in wiring harness and repeat QUICK TEST. If both resistances are 10 k/ohms or more, replace PCM and repeat QUICK TEST.

NOTE: A break in step numbering sequence occurs at this point. Procedure skips from step 5) to step 10). No test procedures have been omitted.

10) Code 122: Attempt To Generate Code 123 Or 121 – Code 122 indicates TP signal is less than minimum self-test value. *See Fig. DH2.* Possible causes for this fault are:
- TP sensor not seated correctly.
- Faulty TP sensor.
- Open circuit in wiring harness.
- Grounded circuit in wiring harness.
- Faulty PCM.

CIRCUIT TEST DH (Cont.)

Turn ignition off, and wait 10 seconds. Disconnect TP sensor from harness. Install a jumper wire between VREF and TP terminals at TP sensor wiring harness connector. Perform KOEO SELF-TEST. If no codes are generated, remove jumper wire and go to step 13). If Codes 123 and 121 are not present, remove jumper wire and go to step 11). If either Code 123 or 121 is displayed, replace TP sensor and repeat QUICK TEST.

11) Check VREF Circuit Voltage – Turn ignition on. Measure voltage between VREF and SIG RTN terminals at TP sensor wiring harness connector. If voltage is not 4-6 volts, reconnect all components and go to CIRCUIT TEST CA. If voltage is 4-6 volts, go to step 12).

12) Check TP Sensor Circuit Continuity – Turn ignition off. Leave TP sensor disconnected. Disconnect PCM 60-pin connector. Inspect connector and repair if necessary. Install EEC-IV Breakout Box (T83L-50-EEC-IV), leaving PCM disconnected. Measure resistance between TP terminal at TP sensor wiring harness connector and test pin No. 47. If resistance is 5 ohms or more, repair open circuit and repeat QUICK TEST. If resistance is less than 5 ohms, go to step 13).

13) Check TP Circuit For Shorts To Ground – Turn ignition off. Leave TP sensor disconnected. Ensure both 4EAT module wiring harness connectors are disconnected (if applicable). Disconnect PCM 60-pin connector. Inspect wiring, and repair as necessary. With breakout box installed and PCM disconnected, measure resistance between test pin No. 47 and test pins No. 40, 46 and 60. If any reading is less than 10 k/ohms, repair short circuit and repeat QUICK TEST. If all readings are 10 k/ohms or more, replace PCM and repeat QUICK TEST.

NOTE: A break in step numbering sequence occurs at this point. Procedure skips from step 13) to step 20). No test procedures have been omitted.

20) Code 167: Repeat Dynamic Response Test – KOER Code 167 indicates TP sensor did not exceed 25% rotation during dynamic response portion of KOER SELF-TEST. A complete Wide Open Throttle (WOT) must be performed during dynamic response portion of test. Perform KOER SELF-TEST. Ensure WOT is completed during dynamic response portion of test. If Code 167 is still present, go to step 21). If code is not present, system is unable to duplicate Code 167 at this time. Service any other KOER codes. If no other service codes are present, testing is complete.

21) Check TP Sensor Movement During Dynamic Response Test – Turn ignition off. Disconnect PCM 60-pin connector. Inspect wiring, and repair as necessary. Install EEC-IV Breakout Box (T83L-50-EEC-IV), leaving PCM connected. Set DVOM on 20-volt scale. Connect DVOM between test pins No. 46 and 47 at breakout box. Perform KOER SELF-TEST and ensure proper WOT is completed during dynamic response test. If DVOM reading exceeds 3.5 volts during dynamic response test, replace PCM and repeat QUICK TEST. If reading does not exceed 3.5 volts, ensure TP sensor is correctly installed and adjusted. If TP sensor is correctly installed and adjusted, replace TP sensor. Repeat QUICK TEST.

NOTE: A break in step numbering sequence occurs at this point. Procedure skips from step 21) to step 90). No test procedures have been omitted.

90) Continuous Memory Code 123 – This test monitors TP sensor under simulated road conditions. Enter wiggle test. See CONTINUOUS MONITOR MODE (WIGGLE TEST) under QUICK TEST. Connect DVOM or diagnostic tester to STO terminal of self-test connector. While slowly opening throttle to WOT, observe DVOM or diagnostic tester for indication of fault. Slowly bring throttle to closed position. Lightly tap TP sensor and wiggle harness connector. This test checks for open or short in TP sensor and wiring harness. If no fault is indicated, go to step 92). If fault is indicated, go to step 91).

91) Measure TP Circuit Voltage While Exercising TP Sensor – Turn ignition off, and wait 10 seconds. Disconnect PCM 60-pin connector. Inspect for damage and repair if necessary. Install EEC-IV Breakout Box (T83L-50-EEC-IV), leaving PCM connected. Stay in wiggle test (as in previous step). Connect DVOM between test pins No. 47 and 46. Set DVOM on 20-volt scale. With ignition on and engine off, observe DVOM and repeat step 90). If fault occurs at less than 4.25 volts, inspect TP sensor connectors and terminals. If connectors and terminals are okay, replace TP sensor, clear codes and repeat QUICK TEST. If fault does not occur at less than 4.25 volts, TP sensor over-travel may have caused Continuous Memory Code 123. TP sensor is okay. Go to step 92) to check wiring harness.

CIRCUIT TEST DH (Cont.)

92) Check EEC-IV Wiring Harness – While in wiggle test, bend and shake small sections of EEC-IV harness from TP sensor wiring harness connector to firewall and from firewall to PCM while observing analog voltmeter or scan tester. If fault is indicated, isolate fault in wiring and repair as necessary. Clear codes, and repeat QUICK TEST. If no fault is indicated, go to step 93).

93) Check PCM & Harness Connectors – Turn ignition off, and wait 10 seconds. Disconnect PCM 60-pin connector from breakout box. Inspect connectors and terminals for damage, and repair as necessary. Clear codes from PCM memory, and repeat QUICK TEST. If connectors and terminals are okay, fault cannot be duplicated at this time. Continuous Memory Code 123 testing is complete.

94) Continuous Memory Code 122 – Enter wiggle test. See CONTINUOUS MONITOR MODE (WIGGLE TEST) under QUICK TEST. Connect DVOM or diagnostic tester to STO terminal of self-test connector. Observe DVOM or diagnostic tester for indication of fault while performing the following:
- Slowly open throttle to WOT.
- Slowly bring throttle to closed position.
- Lightly tap TP sensor and wiggle connector.

If fault is indicated, disconnect TP sensor. Inspect connectors and terminals. If connectors and terminals are okay, replace TP sensor. Clear codes from PCM memory, and repeat QUICK TEST. If no fault is indicated, go to next step.

95) Check EEC-IV Wiring Harness – Stay in wiggle test (as in previous step). Bend, wiggle and shake small sections of EEC-IV harness from TP sensor wiring harness connector to firewall and from firewall to PCM while observing analog voltmeter or scan tester. If fault is indicated, isolate fault in wiring and repair as necessary. Clear codes from PCM memory, and repeat QUICK TEST. If no fault is indicated, go to step 96).

96) Check PCM & Harness Connectors – Turn ignition off. Inspect PCM 60-pin connector and terminals for damage. Repair connector terminals if necessary. Clear codes from PCM memory, and repeat QUICK TEST. If connectors and terminals are okay, fault cannot be duplicated at this time. Continuous Memory Code 122 testing is complete.

CIRCUIT TEST DP

VEHICLE SPEED SENSOR (VSS)

Diagnostic Aids – Perform this test when directed by QUICK TEST. This CIRCUIT TEST is intended to diagnose:
- Vehicle Speed Sensor (VSS).
- VSS wiring harness circuits.
- Powertrain Control Module (PCM).

93I40525

```
*TEST PIN 6 ○——————————— VSS (−)          VEHICLE
 TEST PIN 3 ○——————————— VSS (+)          SPEED
                                           SENSOR (VSS)
                                           VEHICLE
                                           HARNESS
                                           CONNECTOR
```

*TEST PINS LOCATED ON BREAKOUT BOX
ALL HARNESS CONNECTORS VIEWED IN MATING SURFACE

Fig. DP1: Vehicle Speed Sensor Circuit

TEST PIN WIRE COLOR IDENTIFICATION

Application	Wire Color
All Except Continental	
No. 3 (VSS +)	Dark Green/White
No. 6 (VSS −)	Orange/Yellow
Continental	
No. 3 (VSS +)	Gray/Black
No. 6 (VSS −)	Pink/Orange

Preliminary Instructions – Record and clear continuous memory codes. Warm engine to normal operating temperature. Place gear selector in Drive position. Accelerate hard to 35 MPH and coast down to a stop. Shut off engine. Perform KOEO SELF-TEST. Repeat step at least 2 more times. Go to step 1).

CIRCUIT TEST DP (Cont.)

1) Continuous Memory Code 452 – Code 452 indicates PCM detected incorrect output from VSS sometime during vehicle operation. Possible causes for this code are:
- Faulty VSS.
- Open or shorted circuit.
- Faulty PCM.

Perform appropriate TRANSMISSION DRIVE CYCLE TEST. Ensure driveability complaint can be verified. If Code 452 is still present or driveability complaint can be verified, go to step **2)**. If code is not present or complaint cannot be verified, fault cannot be duplicated at this time. Clear codes, and see SYMPTOMS in TROUBLE SHOOTING (EEC-IV) – NO CODES article in appropriate MITCHELL® manual.

2) Check VSS Circuit Continuity – Turn ignition off. Disconnect VSS sensor. Remove PCM 60-pin connector. Inspect terminals, and repair if damaged. Install EEC-IV Breakout Box (T83L-50-EEC-IV). Measure resistance between VSS (+) terminal at VSS wiring harness connector and test pin No. 3 at breakout box. Measure resistance between VSS (–) terminal at VSS wiring harness connector and test pin No. 6 at breakout box. If any resistance reading is more than 5 ohms, service open circuit in VSS wiring harness and repeat step **1)**. If both resistance readings are 5 ohms or less, go to step **3)**.

3) Check VSS Circuits For Shorts To Power Or Ground – Turn ignition off. Ensure PCM and VSS are disconnected. Measure resistance between test pin No. 3 and test pins No. 6, 37 and 40 at breakout box. If all readings are greater than 500 ohms, go to step **4)**. If any reading is less than 500 ohms, repair shorts in VSS wiring harness and repeat step **1)**.

4) Check VSS Resistance – Turn ignition off, and wait 10 seconds. Disconnect VSS wiring harness connector. Measure resistance across VSS terminals. If reading is not 190-250 ohms, replace VSS and repeat step **1)**. If resistance is 190-250 ohms, replace PCM and repeat step **1)**.

CIRCUIT TEST FD

BRAKE ON-OFF (BOO) SWITCH

Diagnostic Aids – Perform this test when directed by QUICK TEST. This test is intended to diagnose a faulty BOO switch circuit or PCM. To prevent replacement of good components, be aware following non-EEC related areas may be at fault:
- Brakelight bulb.
- Brakelight switch or brakelight fuse.

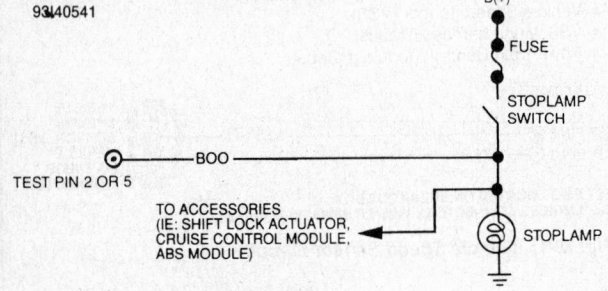

93140541

TEST PINS LOCATED ON BREAKOUT BOX

Fig. FD1: BOO Switch Circuit

TEST PIN WIRE COLOR IDENTIFICATION

Application	Wire Color
All Except Continental	
No. 2 (BOO) [1]	Red/Light Green
Continental	
No. 2 (BOO)	Light Green

[1] – Terminal No. 5 on Taurus SHO.

CIRCUIT TEST FD (Cont.)

1) Code 536: Verify Brake Pedal Was Depressed – Code 536 indicates that when brake pedal is applied during KOER SELF-TEST, BOO signal did not cycle high and low. Possible causes for this fault are:
- Brake pedal not applied during self-test.
- Brake pedal applied during entire self-test.
- Open brakelight circuit.
- Short to ground or power.
- Faulty Powertrain Control Module (PCM).

If brake was not applied during KOER SELF-TEST, repeat test. Depress and release brake pedal only once during test. If pedal was depressed, go to step **2)**.

2) Check Operation Of Brakelights – With ignition on, check operation of brakelights. If brakelights operate normally, go to step **3)**. If brakelights do not operate, go to step **4)**. If brakelights are always on, go to step **5)**.

3) Check For BOO Switch Circuit Cycling – Turn ignition off. Wait 10 seconds. Disconnect PCM 60-pin connector. Inspect terminals, and repair if damaged. Install EEC-IV Breakout Box (T83L-50-EEC-IV), leaving PCM disconnected. Measure voltage between BOO test pin (No. 2) and test pin No. 40 while applying and releasing brake. If voltage cycles, replace PCM and repeat QUICK TEST. If voltage does not cycle, repair open circuit in BOO switch circuit between PCM and BOO switch connection to brakelight circuit. Repeat QUICK TEST.

4) Check For Power To Brake Switch – Ensure related fuses and brakelight bulbs are in good condition. Turn ignition off. Disconnect brakelight switch (located on brake pedal). Measure voltage between BATT (+) input to brakelight switch and ground. If voltage is greater than 10 volts, check condition of brakelight switch. If brakelight switch is okay, repair open circuit between brakelight switch and brakelight ground. Repeat QUICK TEST. If voltage is less than 10 volts, repair open BATT (+) circuit to brakelight switch and repeat QUICK TEST.

5) Verify Brake Switch Is Not Always Closed – Turn ignition off. Disconnect brakelight switch (located on brake pedal). Turn ignition on. If brakelights are still on, go to step **6)**. If brakelights are not on, verify correct installation of brakelight switch. If installation is okay, replace brakelight switch and repeat QUICK TEST.

6) Check For Short To Power In PCM – Turn ignition off. Disconnect PCM. Turn ignition on. Check brakelights. If brakelights are on, go to step **7)**. If brakelights are not on, replace PCM and repeat QUICK TEST.

7) Check For Short To Power In Shift Lock Actuator – Turn ignition off. Ensure PCM and brakelight switch are disconnected. Disconnect shift lock actuator, cruise control module and ABS module (if equipped). Turn ignition on. If brakelights are still on, repair short to power in BOO or stoplight circuit and repeat QUICK TEST. If brakelights are not on, repair short circuit in shift lock actuator circuit, cruise control system circuit or ABS circuit. Repeat QUICK TEST.

NOTE: A break in step numbering sequence occurs at this point. Procedure skips from step 7) to step 90). No test procedures have been omitted.

90) Code 536: Check For Proper Brakelight Switch Installation – Continuous memory Code 536 indicates a BOO circuit failure. If BOO input does not cycle after a predetermined number of transitions from 0 mph to a specific speed, the BOO input is assumed to be damaged and continuous memory Code 536 is set. Possible causes of failure are:
- Incorrect brakelight switch installation.
- Open brakelight/BOO circuit.
- Brakelight/BOO circuit short.
- Damaged switch or ground circuit.

If switch is correctly installed and in good condition, go to next step. If switch or harness is damaged, service as needed and clear continuous memory. Repeat QUICK TEST.

91) Inspect Brakelight Ground – Inspect brakelight ground connection and harness connector. Repair as needed. If connections are okay, go to next step.

92) Inspect Brakelight/BOO Circuits For Shorts – With KOEO and brake pedal released, perform wiggle test of brakelight/BOO circuit harness and connectors while observing brakelights. If brakelights illuminate, inspect and repair circuits as needed. If brakelights do not illuminate, go to next step.

93) Inspect Brakelight Circuit Continuity – With ignition off, depress brake pedal and hold. Perform wiggle test of brakelight circuits while observing brakelights. Lightly tap brakelight switch while observing brakelights. If brakelights intermittently go out, inspect and repair circuits as needed. If brakelights remain illuminated, go to next step.

CIRCUIT TEST FD (Cont.)

94) Inspect BOO Circuit Continuity – With ignition off, ensure brake pedal is released. Disconnect PCM 60-pin connector. Inspect terminals, and repair if damaged. Install EEC-IV Breakout Box (T83L-50-EEC-IV), leaving PCM disconnected. Measure resistance between BOO test pin No. 2 and brakelight circuit at switch while performing wiggle test on harness and connector. If resistance intermittently increases above 5 ohms, inspect and repair open circuit. Repeat QUICK TEST. If resistance is within specification, go to next step for further diagnosis.

99) Road Test Vehicle – Purpose of this test is to identify faults by monitoring certain controlled parameters while trying to recreate a driveability or MIL symptom. To prepare for road test:
- Install fuel pressure gauge and if available, a MAP/BARO tester.
- Disconnect PCM 60-pin connector, install breakout box and reconnect PCM to breakout box.
- Connect "T" vacuum gauge into manifold vacuum line.
- Have DVOM, writing materials and appropriate schematics and pin voltage charts available.

With ignition on and negative lead of DVOM connected to negative battery terminal, ensure following signals are correct:
- POWERS: KAPWR (pin No. 1) is greater than 10.5 volts, VPWR (pins No. 37 and 57) is greater than 10.5 volts and VREF (pin No. 26) is 4-6 volts.
- GROUNDS: PWR GND (pins No. 40 and 60), SIG RTN (pin No. 46) and IGN GND (pin No. 16) are 0.0-0.5 volt.
- OPTIONAL GROUNDS: HO2S GND (pin No. 49), CSE GND (pin No. 20) and MAF RTN (pin No. 9 or 15) are 0.0-0.5 volt.

Diagnostic Aids – Test lights and DVOM are useful during diagnosis. For example:a testlight could be connected at brakelight switch between battery and ground and another testlight between switch bulb circuit and ground. Testlight to battery circuit should always illuminated and other testlight should only illuminate when brakelight is depressed.

With DVOM connected between test pin No. 2 and 40 at Breakout Box, check voltage. If voltage is between 6-7 volts with brake pedal released, possible open circuit between PCM and brakelight ground could exist.

CIRCUIT TEST FF

POWER STEERING PRESSURE (PSP) SWITCH

Diagnostic Aids – The PSP switch, is a normally closed switch that opens as pressure in the power steering system increases.

Perform this test when instructed during QUICK TEST or if directed by other test procedures. Some vehicles may not have power steering, but PCM may be equipped with PSP switch software strategy. If a KOEO Code 519 is displayed, check if vehicle is equipped with power steering. If vehicle is not equipped with power steering, disregard Code 519. This test is only intended to diagnose:
- Power Steering Pressure (PSP) switch.
- PSP and SIG RTN wiring harness circuits.
- Powertrain Control Module (PCM).

To prevent replacement of good components, be aware the following non-EEC related areas may be at fault:
- Idle speed/throttle stop adjustment.
- Binding throttle shaft/linkage.
- Cruise control linkage.
- Power steering hydraulic system.

93F40548

TEST PIN 28 ⊙——————— Y/LG ———— PSP

TEST PIN 2 FOR 3.0L TAURUS SHO,
TEST PIN 24 FOR 2.3L MUSTANG.

————— SIG RTN

TEST PIN 46 ⊙——————— GY/R

POWER STEERING PRESSURE (PSP) SWITCH VEHICLE HARNESS CONNECTOR

*TEST PINS LOCATED ON BREAKOUT BOX
ALL HARNESS CONNECTORS VIEWED IN MATING SURFACE

Fig. FF1: Power Steering Pressure (PSP) Switch Circuit

PSP SWITCH TEST PIN NUMBER IDENTIFICATION

Application	Test Pin No.
3.0L SHO	2
All Others	28

CIRCUIT TEST FF (Cont.)

1) KOEO Code 519: Attempt To Eliminate Code – Code 519 indicates PSP switch circuit is open. Possible causes for this fault are:
- Damaged PSP switch.
- Open circuit in wiring harness.
- Faulty PCM.

Turn ignition off. Disconnect PSP switch. Install jumper wire between PSP terminal and SIG RTN terminal at wiring harness connector. Repeat KOEO SELF-TEST. If Code 519 is not displayed, replace PSP switch and repeat QUICK TEST. If Code 519 is displayed, remove jumper wire and go to next step.

2) Check Continuity Of PSP Circuits – Turn ignition off. Disconnect PCM 60-pin connector. Inspect connector for damaged pins, corrosion and loose wires. Repair as necessary. Install EEC-IV Breakout Box (T83L-50-EEC-IV), leaving PCM disconnected. Measure resistance between test pin No. 46 and SIG RTN terminal at PSP switch wiring harness connector. Also measure resistance between PSP test pin at breakout box and PSP terminal at switch wiring harness connector. If both readings are less than 5 ohms, replace PCM. Remove breakout box, reconnect all components, and repeat QUICK TEST. If readings are 5 ohms or more, repair open circuit. Remove breakout box, reconnect all components, and repeat QUICK TEST.

3) Check PSP Switch Operation – Turn ignition off. Connect tachometer, and start engine. Allow engine to idle in Park or Neutral. Disconnect PSP switch wiring harness connector. If RPM increases, replace PSP switch and recheck system. If RPM does not increase, go to next step.

4) Check PSP Switch Circuits For Shorts – Turn ignition off. Disconnect PSP switch wiring harness connector. Disconnect PCM 60-pin connector. Inspect connector for damaged pins, corrosion and loose wires. Repair as necessary. Install EEC-IV Breakout Box (T83L-50-EEC-IV), leaving PCM disconnected. Measure resistance between PSP test pin at breakout box and test pin No. 46 at breakout box. If resistance is 10 k/ohms or less, repair short in harness and recheck symptom. If resistance is more than 10 k/ohms, replace PCM and recheck symptom.

5) KOER Code 521 – Disregard this code if vehicle does not have power steering. Code 521 indicates PSP switch did not change states due to open or closed circuit. Possible causes for this fault are:
- Damaged PSP switch.
- Open or shorted circuit in wiring harness.
- Front wheels turned but not centered.
- Faulty PCM.

If steering wheel was turned 1/2 turn within 2 seconds after engine ID code and then returned to center, go to next step. If steering wheel was not turned, repeat QUICK TEST.

6) Check PCM Open Circuit Identifying Capabilities – Turn ignition off. Disconnect PSP switch. Perform KOEO SELF-TEST. If Code 519 is present, go to step **8)**. If Code 519 is not present, go to next step.

7) Check PSP Switch Circuits For Shorts – Turn ignition off. Disconnect PSP switch. Disconnect PCM 60-pin connector. Inspect connector for damaged pins, corrosion and loose wires. Repair as necessary. Install EEC-IV Breakout Box (T83L-50-EEC-IV), leaving PCM disconnected. Measure resistance between PSP test pin and test pin No. 46 at breakout box. If resistance is 10 k/ohms or less, repair short circuit. Remove breakout box, reconnect all components, and repeat QUICK TEST. If resistance is more than 10 k/ohms, replace PCM. Remove breakout box, reconnect all components, and repeat QUICK TEST.

8) Check PSP Switch Position Comparison – Turn ignition off. Connect PCM connector to breakout box. With PSP switch connected, turn ignition on. Measure and record resistance between PSP test pin and test pin No. 46 at breakout box. Start engine. Measure and record resistance between PSP test pin and test pin No. 46 at breakout box. If reading shows less than 10 ohms difference between key off and key on engine running, go to next step. If reading is not as described, replace PSP switch and repeat QUICK TEST.

9) Check PSP Switch With Engine Running (Load & No Load) – Connect PSP switch. Start engine, and allow it to idle. On Taurus 3.0L SHO, ensure clutch is not depressed. On all models, measure resistance between PSP test pin and test pin No. 46 at breakout box. Turn steering wheel 1/2 turn and return to center position. If resistance changes from less than 10 ohms to infinity and then returns to 10 ohms or less (when steering wheel is centered), PSP switch system is okay. Testing is complete. If reading does not change as indicated, replace PSP switch. Repeat QUICK TEST.

CIRCUIT TEST G

MAF/TPS FUEL INJECTOR PULSE WIDTH TEST

Diagnostic Aids – Perform this test when instructed during QUICK TEST or if directed by other test procedures. To prevent replacement of good components, be aware the following non-EEC related areas may be at fault:

- Excessive blow-by.
- PCV malfunction.
- Vacuum leaks.
- Incorrect fuel pressure.
- Throttle binding.
- Improper fuel pressure.
- Idle air control solenoid.

This test is only intended to diagnose:

- MAP/BARO sensor.
- Throttle Position Sensor (TPS).
- Mass Airflow (MAF) sensor.
- Intake Air Temperature (IAT) sensor.
- Fuel injectors.

1) Check For Idle Air Codes – Code 121 indicates TPS is inconsistent with MAF value. Code 124 indicates TPS value is higher than expected. Code 125 indicates TPS value is lower than expected. Turn ignition on. Repeat KOEO SELF-TEST. If Code 411 or 412 is present, perform appropriate circuit test. See DIAGNOSTIC TROUBLE CODE REFERENCE CHARTS. If Code 411 or 412 is not present, go to next step.

2) Throttle Position (TP) Sensor: TP Sensor Integrity – Turn ignition off. Disconnect PCM 60-pin connector. Inspect connector for damaged pins, corrosion and loose wires. Repair as necessary. Install EEC-IV Breakout Box (T83L-50-EEC-IV). Connect PCM to breakout box. Connect DVOM to test pins No. 46 and 47 at breakout box. Turn ignition on. Slowly apply throttle to WOT, and release to closed position. Voltage should change smoothly from 0.4-4.5 volts. See CIRCUIT TEST DH for schematics and specific engine values. If voltage change is incorrect or erratic, ensure TP sensor is properly installed. If TP sensor is properly installed, replace TP sensor. Remove breakout box, reconnect all components, and repeat QUICK TEST. If voltage is okay, go to step **8)** for Code 121 or next step for all other codes.

3) Check Idle – Ensure idle is correct. If idle is correct, go to next step. If idle is incorrect, see IDLE SPEED in ON-VEHICLE ADJUSTMENTS article.

4) Check Throttle Body – Ensure idle is correct. Check throttle and/or cruise control linkage for binding and rough operation. Inspect throttle body for sludge build-up. Check engine vacuum hoses. Refer to Vehicle Emission Control Information (VECI) decal for proper vacuum hose routing. Check for air leak between ISC solenoid and MAF sensor. If problems are found, repair as necessary. Remove breakout box, reconnect all components, and repeat QUICK TEST. If no problems are found, go to next step.

5) Check MAP/BARO Sensor Output – On vehicles without MAP/BARO go to next step. On vehicles with MAP/BARO, see DIAGNOSTIC AIDS, then continue with this test. With tester connected and ignition on, measure sensor output voltage. If output voltage is within range for specified altitude, remove MAP/BARO tester and go to next step. See MAP SENSOR VOLTAGE OUTPUT table for specification. If output voltage is not within range, replace MAP/BARO sensor. Remove breakout box, reconnect all components, and repeat QUICK TEST.

Diagnostic Aids – If possible, measure several known good MAP/BARO sensors. Average voltage reading will be typical for location and day of testing. Also, refer to CIRCUIT TEST DF under SELF-DIAGNOSTICS – EEC-IV article in ENGINE PERFORMANCE of appropriate MITCHELL® manual for MAP/BARO sensor output check. See Fig. DF1 for connector terminal identification and MAP/BARO tester hookup.

MAP SENSOR VOLTAGE OUTPUT

Elevation (Feet)	Volts
0	1.55-1.63
1000	1.52-1.60
2000	1.49-1.57
3000	1.46-1.54
4000	1.43-1.51
5000	1.40-1.48
6000	1.37-1.45
7000	1.35-1.43

CIRCUIT TEST G (Cont.)

6) Check IAT Sensor – Ensure ambient temperature is more than 50°F (10°C) before performing this test. Also, check and repair any air leaks in front of IAT sensor. Turn ignition off. Connect breakout box to PCM. Set DVOM to 20-volt scale. Connect DVOM to test pins No. 25 and 46. Start engine, and let it idle. Observe voltage as engine warms up. See CIRCUIT TEST DA for voltage specifications. If voltage decreases smoothly and stabilizes when engine reaches operating conditions, system is operating properly at this time. Testing is complete. If voltage does not decrease smoothly and stabilize after engine reaches operating conditions, replace IAT sensor and repeat QUICK TEST.

7) Continuous Memory Code 184 & 185: Inspect MAF Sensor – Code 184 indicates MAF sensor signal is higher than expected. Code 185 indicates MAF sensor signal is lower than expected. Turn ignition off. Check for air leaks between Idle Air Control (IAC) solenoid and MAF sensor. Inspect MAF sensor for oil contamination caused by excessive blow-by or malfunctioning PCV. If problems are found, repair as necessary. Clear codes and repeat QUICK TEST. If no problems are found, go to step **10)**.

8) Check MAF Sensor Circuit Voltage – Turn ignition off. Disconnect PCM 60-pin connector. Inspect connector for damaged pins, corrosion and loose wires. Repair as necessary. Install EEC-IV Breakout Box (T83L-50-EEC-IV). Connect PCM to breakout box. Start engine, and warm it to normal operating temperature. Measure voltage between test pin No. 50 and test pin No. 40 or 60 at breakout box. If voltage is not within specification, replace MAF sensor. Remove breakout box, reconnect all components, and repeat QUICK TEST. See MAF SENSOR DATA table. If voltage is within acceptable range, system is operating normally at this time. Sometime during the last 80 warm-up cycles, MAF sensor signal was out of range.

MAF SENSOR DATA

Engine Condition	[1] Voltage
Idle	0.8
20 MPH	1.0
40 MPH	1.7
60 MPH	2.1

[1] – With engine at normal operating temperature.

9) Continuous Memory Code 186 & 187: Visual Vacuum Checks – Code 186 indicates pulse width is longer than expected (rich). Code 187 indicates pulse width is shorter than expected (lean). Inspect air cleaner and air inlet duct. Replace or repair an necessary. Check for unmetered air leaks between MAF sensor and IAC solenoid. Check all engine vacuum hoses for damage, blockage and improper routing. Repair as necessary, and repeat QUICK TEST. If all checks are okay, go to next step.

10) Check Fuel Pressure – Turn ignition off. Install fuel pressure gauge. Ensure vacuum hose is connected to fuel pressure regulator (if applicable). Start engine, and run it at idle. If fuel pressure is within specification, go to next step. See FUEL PRESSURE SPECIFICATIONS table. If fuel pressure is not within specifications, repair as necessary.

FUEL PRESSURE SPECIFICATIONS

Engine	KOER Pressure psi (kg/cm²)	KOEO Pressure psi (kg/cm²)
2.3L HSC SFI	45-60 (3.2-4.2)	50-60 (3.5-4.2)
3.0L SHO SFI	28-33 (2.0-2.3)	30-45 (2.1-3.2)
3.8L SC SFI	30-40 (2.1-3.1)	35-40 (2.4-3.1)
All Others	30-45 (2.1-3.2)	35-40 (2.4-3.1)

11) Verify Fuel Pressure Retention Ability – Turn ignition on. If fuel pressure remains at specification for 60 seconds, go to CIRCUIT TEST HB under SELF-DIAGNOSTICS – EEC-IV article in ENGINE PERFORMANCE of appropriate MITCHELL® manual. If fuel pressure does not remain at specification, repair fuel delivery system as necessary. For SFI equipped vehicles, go to next step.

12) Cylinder Balance Test – Perform KOER SELF-TEST. After last code, wait 5-10 seconds, and then goose throttle lightly (not wide open throttle). This will activate cylinder balance test. If Code 90 is present after test, go back to step **7)**. If Code 90 is not present after test, go to CIRCUIT TEST HB, step **5)** (Flex Fuel) under SELF-DIAGNOSTICS – EEC-IV article in ENGINE PERFORMANCE of appropriate MITCHELL® manual or CIRCUIT TEST H, step **4)** (except Flex Fuel).

CIRCUIT TEST ML

SELF-TEST OUTPUT (STO) OR MALFUNCTION INDICATOR LIGHT (MIL)

Diagnostic Aids – The MIL is turned on when PCM detects a fault in EEC circuit(s). The light will remain on as long as fault remains in system.

Perform this test only when instructed by QUICK TEST or if directed by CIRCUIT TEST QA. This test does not include procedure for models with electronic instrument panel. To prevent replacing good components, be aware that fuse, bulb or bulb socket may be cause of problem. This test is only intended to diagnose:

- STO/MIL circuit.
- Faulty PCM.

93H40433

Fig. ML1: Identifying Data Link Connector (DLC) Terminals

TEST PIN WIRE COLOR IDENTIFICATION

Terminal No.	Wire Color
All Except Continental	
No. 17 (STO/MIL)	Tan/Red
No. 48 (STI)	Brown
No. 18, Data (+)	[1] Tan/Orange
No. 19, Data (-)	[2] Pink/Light Blue
Continental	
No. 17 (STO/MIL)	Pink/Light Green
No. 48 (STI)	White/Pink
No. 18, Data (+)	Tan/Orange
No. 19, Data (-)	Pink/Light Blue

[1] – Wire color Orange/Black on 3.2L Taurus SHO.
[2] – Wire color Black/Orange on 3.2L Taurus SHO.

1) Malfunction Indicator Light (MIL) Always On – Service all KOEO and Continuous Memory Codes before proceeding with this test. Turn ignition off. Disconnect 60-pin PCM connector. Inspect terminals, and repair if damaged. Install EEC-IV Breakout Box (T83L-50-EEC-IV), leaving PCM disconnected. Measure resistance between test pins No. 17 and 40 at breakout box. If resistance is more than 5 ohms, replace PCM and repeat QUICK TEST. If reading is 5 ohms or less, repair short between test pin No. 17 and Diagnostic Link Connector (DLC) terminal No. 17 or MIL. Reconnect all components, and repeat QUICK TEST.

NOTE: A break in step numbering sequence occurs at this point. Procedure skips from step 1) to step 4). No test procedures have been omitted.

4) Malfunction Indicator Light (MIL) Does Not Light – Turn ignition on. Measure voltage between negative battery terminal and ground side of MIL fuse. If voltage is more than 10.5 volts, go to step 6). If voltage is 10.5 volts or less, go to step 5).

5) Check For Voltage At Fuse – Turn ignition on. Measure voltage from negative battery terminal to power side of MIL fuse. If voltage is more than 10.5 volts, replace fuse. Verify repair by turning ignition switch to RUN position. If voltage is 10.5 volts or less, repair open MIL/B+ circuit. Verify repair by turning ignition switch to RUN position.

6) Check Voltage At B+ Circuit – Turn ignition on. Measure voltage between B+ side of MIL bulb socket and negative battery terminal. If voltage is 10.5 volts or less, repair open in MIL circuit between fuse and bulb. Verify repair by turning ignition switch to RUN position. If voltage is more than 10.5 volts, go to step 7).

7) Check MIL Bulb Response To Grounding – Turn ignition off. Attach jumper wire between ground side of MIL bulb socket and chassis ground. Turn ignition on. If MIL light comes on, remove jumper wire, and go to step 8). If MIL light does not come on, remove jumper wire. Replace MIL bulb socket. Turn ignition on to verify correct MIL operation.

CIRCUIT TEST ML (Cont.)

8) Check Continuity Of MIL Circuit – Turn ignition off. Disconnect 60-pin PCM connector. Inspect terminals, and repair if damaged. Install EEC-IV Breakout Box (T83L-50-EEC-IV), leaving PCM disconnected. Measure resistance between test pin No. 17 at breakout box and MIL wiring harness connector terminal. If resistance is less than 5 ohms, replace PCM. If resistance is 5 ohms or more, repair open MIL circuit. Turn ignition on to verify correct MIL operation.

NOTE: A break in step numbering sequence occurs at this point. Procedure skips from step 8) to step 10). No test procedures have been omitted.

10) MIL On Intermittently, Check For Intermittent Short From STO To Ground – MIL comes on when a fault code is present. Service all fault codes before proceeding. If no codes are output, proceed with this test. Enter KOEO wiggle test. See CONTINUOUS MONITOR MODE (WIGGLE TEST) under QUICK TEST. Check DVOM for indication of fault while performing wiggle test on harness in the following areas:

- From Diagnostic Link Connector (DLC) to dash panel.
- Dash panel to PCM.
- Dash panel to Malfunction Indicator Light (MIL).

If a fault is indicated, repair short to ground and repeat QUICK TEST. If a fault is not indicated, fault cannot be duplicated at this time. Testing is complete.

NOTE: A break in step numbering sequence occurs at this point. Procedure skips from step 10) to step 15). No test procedures have been omitted.

15) MIL Flashes With Erratic Idle – Symptoms indicate STI is grounded and PCM is performing self-test without tester installed. Turn ignition off. Disconnect 60-pin PCM connector. Inspect terminals, and repair if damaged. Install EEC-IV Breakout Box (T83L-50-EEC-IV), leaving PCM disconnected. Measure resistance between STI connector and engine ground. If resistance is 10 k/ohms or less, repair short circuit. Reconnect PCM, and turn ignition on to verify correct MIL operation. If resistance is more than 10 k/ohms, MIL circuit is okay. Verify symptom, and test for other rough idle symptoms.

NOTE: A break in step numbering sequence occurs at this point. Procedure skips from step 15) to step 20). No test procedures have been omitted.

20) CHECK ENGINE Message Displayed – Perform KOEO SELF-TEST. If result is Code 111-10-111 (pass code), fault is in instrument cluster. If pass code is not displayed, service codes as necessary.

NOTE: A break in step numbering sequence occurs at this point. Procedure skips from step 20) to step 25). No test procedures have been omitted.

25) Continuous Memory Code 529 Or 533: CHECK ENGINE Or CHECK DLC Message Displayed – Codes 529 and 533 indicate circuit fault has occurred on Data Link Connector (DLC). These codes can occur alone or with another code. Fault will occur under following conditions:

- Code 529 indicates PCM or DLC circuit failure.
- Code 533 indicates DLC to electronic instrument cluster circuit failure.

If vehicle does not start, go to step 1). If vehicle starts, clear continuous memory codes. Wait 5 minutes, and repeat KOEO SELF-TEST. If result is pass code (Code 111-10-111), fault is in instrument cluster. If pass code is not displayed, service codes as necessary.

CIRCUIT TEST QA

NO CODES/CODES NOT LISTED

Diagnostic Aids – Aftermarket devices, such as alarm system, may cause SELF-TEST to abort if wiring is connected to certain EEC components. If a device is installed, disconnect it completely from EEC system. Before continuing with this circuit test, restore EEC circuits to original state and repeat QUICK TEST.

Perform this test when directed by QUICK TEST or other test procedures. This test is intended to diagnose:

- Powertrain Control Module (PCM).
- EEC power relay.
- Constant Control Relay Module (CCRM).
- Wiring harness circuits (HO2S, SIG RTN, STO, STI, VPWR and VREF).

CIRCUIT TEST QA (Cont.)

93A40808

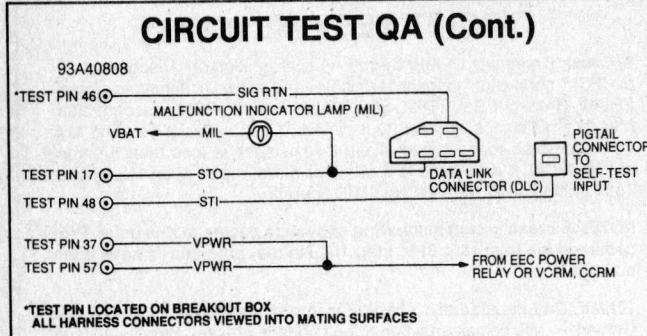

*TEST PIN LOCATED ON BREAKOUT BOX
ALL HARNESS CONNECTORS VIEWED INTO MATING SURFACES

Fig. QA1: No Codes/Codes Not Listed Circuits

TEST PIN WIRE COLOR IDENTIFICATION

Terminal No.	Wire Color
All Except Continental	
No. 17 (STO/MIL)	Tan/Red
No. 37 & 57 (VPWR)	Red
No. 46 (SIG RTN)	Black/White
No. 48 (STI)	Brown
Continental	
No. 17 (STO/MIL)	Pink/Light Green
No. 37 & 57 (VPWR)	Red
No. 46 (SIG RTN)	Black/White
No. 48 (STI)	White/Pink

1) Check VREF Voltage At Data Link Connector (DLC) – Turn ignition off. Disconnect 60-pin PCM connector. Inspect terminals, and repair if damaged. Install EEC-IV Breakout Box (T83L-50-EEC-IV). Connect PCM to breakout box. Turn ignition on. Measure voltage between test pin No. 26 at breakout box and SIG RTN terminal at DLC. If reading is 4-6 volts, go to step **3)**. If reading is not 4-6 volts, go to step **2)**.

2) Check SIG RTN Circuit Continuity – Turn ignition off. Disconnect PCM from breakout box. Measure resistance between test pin No. 46 at breakout box and SIG RTN terminal at DLC. If reading is less than 5 ohms, go to CIRCUIT TEST CA. If resistance is 5 ohms or more, repair open circuit and repeat QUICK TEST.

3) Check STI Circuit Continuity – Turn ignition off. Disconnect PCM from breakout box. Measure resistance between test pin No. 48 at breakout box and Self-Test Input (STI) terminal at pigtail connector. If resistance is 5 ohms or more, repair open circuit and repeat QUICK TEST. If reading is less than 5 ohms, go to step **4)**.

4) Check STO Circuit Continuity – Leave ignition off and PCM disconnected. Measure resistance between test pin No. 17 at breakout box and STO terminal at DLC. If reading is less than 5 ohms, go to step **5)**. If resistance is 5 ohms or more, repair open circuit and repeat QUICK TEST.

Diagnostic Aid – A right/rear HO2S short to power could prevent EEC system from entering self-diagnostics.

5) Check HO2S Signal For Short To Power – Leave PCM disconnected. Turn ignition on. Measure voltage between test pin No. 40 or 60 and HO2S SIGNAL test pin No. 29 or 44 at breakout box. For HO2S circuit schematics, see Figs. QA2 and QA3. If voltage is more than 2 volts, go to step **6)**. If voltage is 2 volts or less, go to step **7)**.

TEST PIN NO. 29 WIRE COLOR IDENTIFICATION

Application	Wire Color
3.0L SHO	Red/Black

TEST PIN NO. 43 WIRE COLOR IDENTIFICATION

Application	Wire Color
3.0L, 3.8L 4.6L & 5.0L	Red/Black
3.0L SHO & 3.2L SHO	Dark Blue/Light Green

TEST PIN NO. 44 WIRE COLOR IDENTIFICATION

Application	Wire Color
3.0L	Dark Blue/Light Green
2.3L & 3.2L SHO	Red/Black
3.0L & 3.8L	Gray/Light Blue

CIRCUIT TEST QA (Cont.)

94A31971

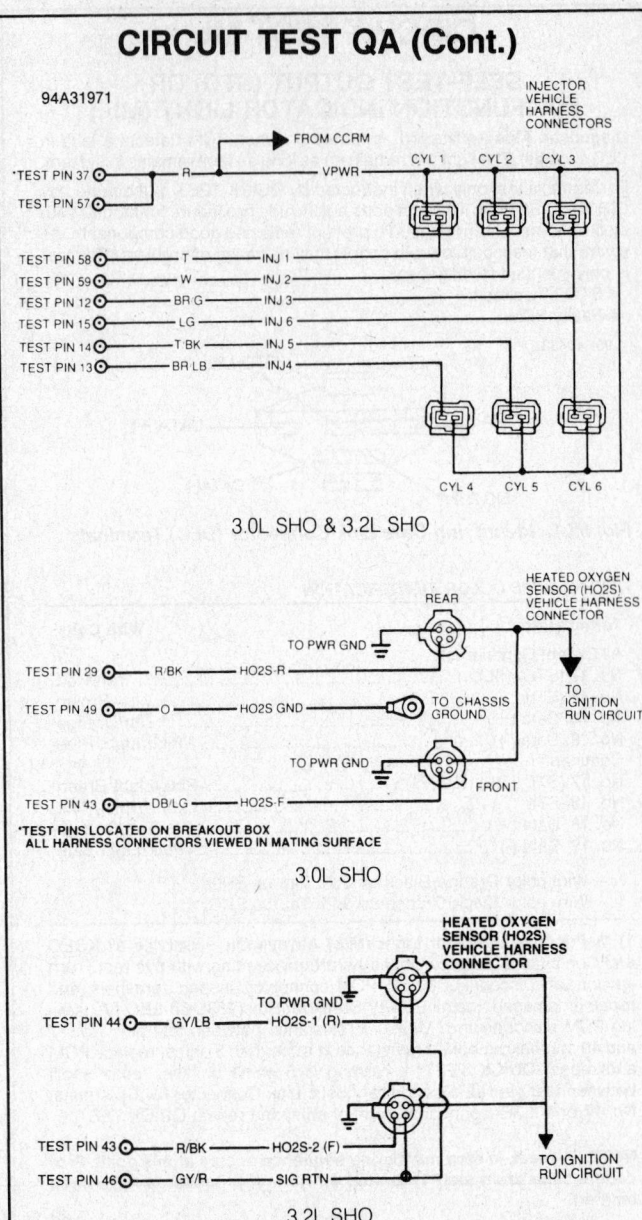

3.0L SHO & 3.2L SHO

3.0L SHO

3.2L SHO

*TEST PINS LOCATED ON BREAKOUT BOX
ALL HARNESS CONNECTORS VIEWED IN MATING SURFACE

Fig. QA2: Test Schematic (Taurus 3.0L SHO & 3.2L SHO)

6) Isolate Short To Harness Or HO2S Sensor – Turn ignition off. Leave PCM disconnected. Disconnect right/rear HO2S sensor connector. Turn ignition on. Measure voltage between HO2S SIGNAL test pin No. 29 or 44 and test pins No. 40 or 60 at breakout box. If any measurement is 2 volts or more, repair short to power in HO2S SIGNAL circuit, and repeat QUICK TEST. If voltage is less than 2 volts, replace right/rear HO2S sensor and repeat QUICK TEST.

7) Check STO Circuit For Short To Ground – Turn ignition off. Leave PCM disconnected. Measure resistance between STO at DLC and engine ground. If reading is more than 5 ohms, go to step **8)**. If resistance is 5 ohms or less, repair STO or MIL circuit for short to ground and repeat QUICK TEST.

8) Check If Power Relay Is Always On – Leave ignition off and PCM disconnected. Connect DVOM between test pin No. 37 or 57 and pin No. 40 or 60 at breakout box. Turn ignition on and then off. Wait 10 seconds. If voltage changes from 10.5 volts (or more) to less than 1.0 volt, go to step **10)**. If voltage does not change from 10.5 volts (or more) to less than 1.0 volt, go to step **9)**.

PINPOINT TEST QA (Cont.)

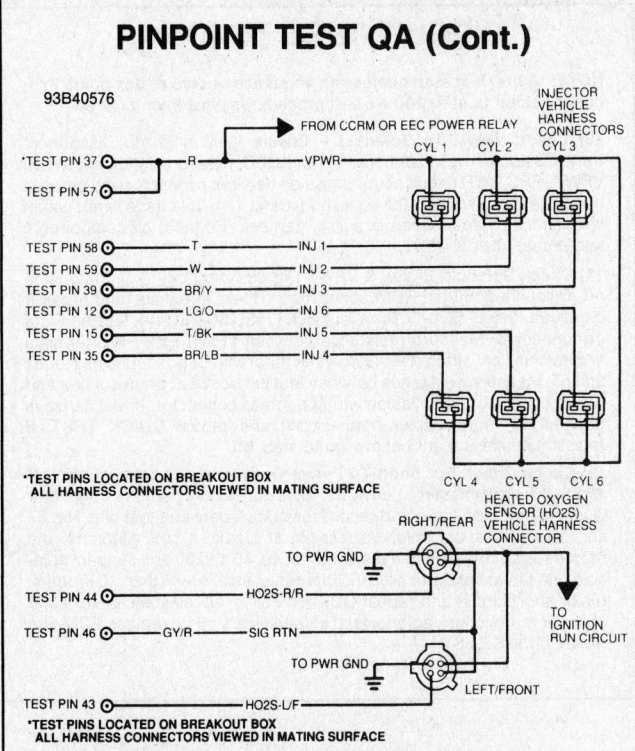

93B40576

*TEST PINS LOCATED ON BREAKOUT BOX
ALL HARNESS CONNECTORS VIEWED IN MATING SURFACE

*TEST PINS LOCATED ON BREAKOUT BOX
ALL HARNESS CONNECTORS VIEWED IN MATING SURFACE

Fig. QA3: Test Schematic (3.0L Except SHO & 3.8L)

9) Check VPWR Circuit For Short To Power – Turn ignition off. Leave PCM disconnected. Disconnect EEC power relay or Constant Control Relay Module (CCRM). Connect DVOM to test pin No. 37 or 57 and test pin No. 40 or 60 at breakout box. If voltage is more than 1.0 volt, repair VPWR circuit short to power and repeat QUICK TEST. If voltage is 1.0 volt or less, replace EEC power relay or CCRM and repeat QUICK TEST.

10) Check Malfunction Indicator Light (MIL) Function – If MIL is always on, go to CIRCUIT TEST ML, step 1). If MIL is always off, go to CIRCUIT TEST ML, step 4). If MIL is working normally, replace PCM and repeat QUICK TEST.

CIRCUIT TEST TB

TRANSMISSION CONTROL SWITCH (TCS), TRANSMISSION CONTROL SWITCH, MODULE (TCSM) & TRANSMISSION CONTROL INDICATOR LIGHT

Diagnostic Aids – Perform this test only when directed by QUICK TEST. This test is intended to diagnose:
- Powertrain Control Module (PCM).
- Wiring harness circuits (TCIL, TCS and TCSM).

To prevent replacing good components, be aware the following non-EEC related areas may be at fault:
- Basic engine condition (valves, vacuum leaks, valve timing, etc.).
- Charging system.
- Transmission (fluid, friction elements and cooling).

TEST PIN NO. 41 (TCS) WIRE COLOR IDENTIFICATION

Application	Wire Color
3.2L SHO	White/Light Green
All Others	Tan/Light Green

TEST PIN NO. 14 (TCIL) WIRE COLOR IDENTIFICATION

Application	Wire Color
3.2L SHO	Orange/Yellow

TEST PIN NO. 37 OR 57 (VPWR) WIRE COLOR IDENTIFICATION

Application	Wire Color
All Models	Red

CIRCUIT TEST TB (Cont.)

NOTE: A break in step numbering sequence occurs at this point. Procedure starts at step 2). No test procedures have been omitted.

2) Code 632 Or 653 – Code 632 or 653 indicates that the TCS was not cycled between engine ID Code and WOT check during KOER SELF-TEST. Possible causes for this fault are:
- Faulty TCS or switch was not cycled during SELF-TEST.
- Shorted wiring harness.
- Faulty Powertrain Control Module (PCM).
- Open in wiring harness or fuse.

If TCS cycled during KOER SELF-TEST, go to step 4). If TCS did not cycle during KOER SELF-TEST, repeat KOER SELF-TEST while cycling TCS.

3) Code 623 or 631 – Code 623 or 631 indicates transmission control indicator light circuit fault during KOEO SELF-TEST. Possible causes for this fault are:
- Burned out bulb.
- Open or shorted wiring harness.

If TCS cycled during KOEO SELF-TEST, go to step 5). If TCS did not cycle during KOEO SELF-TEST, repeat KOER SELF-TEST while cycling TCS.

4) Check TCS Circuit – Turn ignition off. Disconnect 60-pin PCM connector. Inspect connector for damaged pins, corrosion and loose wires. Repair as necessary. Install EEC-IV Breakout Box (T83L-50-EEC-IV), leaving PCM disconnected. Turn ignition on. Measure voltage between test pin No. 41 and test pin No 40 or 60 while cycling TCS several times. If voltage cycles replace PCM. Remove breakout box, reconnect all components, and repeat QUICK TEST. If voltage does not cycle, go to next step if diagnosing a trouble code or step 7) if diagnosing a driveability symptom.

5) Check Circuits For Short To Ground – Turn ignition off. Leave PCM disconnected from breakout box. Disconnect TCS connector. Inspect connector for damage and repair as necessary. Measure resistance between test pin No. 41 and test pin 40 or 60. Also, measure resistance between test pin No. 55 (14 on 3.2L SHO) and test pin No. 40 or 60. If each reading is more than 10 k/ohms, go to next step (Code 623 or 631) or step 8) (Code 632 or 653). If any reading is 10 k/ohms or less, repair short circuit. Repeat QUICK TEST. If code is still present, go to step 7).

6) Check Power Through TCIL Circuit – Turn ignition off. Leave PCM disconnected from breakout box. Measure voltage between test pin No. 55 (14 on 3.2L SHO) and test pin No. 40 or 60. If voltage is more than 10.5 volts, replace PCM. Remove breakout box, reconnect all components, and repeat QUICK TEST. If voltage is 10.5 volts or less, go to next step.

7) Check Output Driver Voltage Signal – Leave PCM disconnected from breakout box. Turn ignition on. Measure voltage between test pin No. 55 (14 on 3.2L SHO) and test pin No. 40 or 60. If voltage is 2 volts or more, go to next step. If voltage is less than 2 volts, check bulb and fuse. Replace as necessary. If bulb and fuse are okay, repair open circuit. Remove breakout box, reconnect all components, and repeat QUICK TEST.

8) Check TCS & TCIL Circuits – Turn ignition off. Leave PCM disconnected from breakout box. Ensure TCS is disconnected. Measure resistance of Purple/Orange wire between KEY POWER terminal of fuse No. 1 at instrument panel fuse block and TCS wiring harness connector. Also, measure resistance between test pin No. 41 at breakout box and Purple/Orange wire at TCS wiring harness connector. If any reading is 5 ohms or more, repair open circuit. Remove breakout box, reconnect all components, and repeat QUICK TEST. If each reading is less than 5 ohms, go to next step.

9) Check For Short To Power – Turn ignition off. Leave PCM disconnected from breakout box. Ensure TCS is disconnected. Measure resistance between test pin No. 41 and test pin 37 or 57. Also, measure resistance between test pin No. 55 (14 on 3.2L SHO) and test pin No. 37 or 57. If each reading is more than 10 k/ohms, replace TCS switch. Remove breakout box, reconnect all components, and repeat QUICK TEST. If any reading is 10 k/ohms or less, repair short circuit. Remove breakout box, reconnect all components, and repeat QUICK TEST.

CIRCUIT TEST TC

TRANSMISSION SOLENOIDS

Diagnostic Aids – Perform this test only when directed by QUICK TEST. To prevent replacing good components, be aware the following non-EEC areas may be at fault:

- Engine condition (compression, cam timing, valves, etc.).
- Charging system or battery.
- Transmission linkage, internal components or cooling.

This test is not intended to diagnose transmission. This test is intended to diagnose:

- Wiring harness circuits TCC, CCS, EPC, SS3/4, SS1, SS2, SS3, SIG RTN, EPC PWR and VPWR.
- Faulty Powertrain Control Module (PCM).

CIRCUIT TEST TC ACRONYMS

Acronym	Definition
CCC	Converter Clutch Control
CCS	Coast Clutch Control
EPC	Electronic Pressure Control
MCCC	Modulated Converter Clutch Control
SS	Shift Solenoid
TCC	Torque Converter Clutch

AXOD-E SERVICE CODE IDENTIFICATION

Application	PCM Pin No.	KOEO Code
EPC	38	624, 625
SS1	51	621
SS2	52	622
SS3	55	641
TCC	53	652

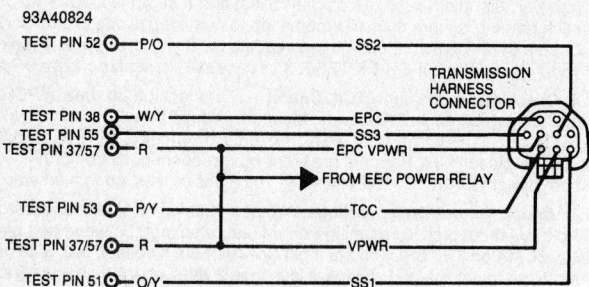

93A40824

Fig. TC1: AXOD-E Solenoid Circuits

CIRCUIT TEST TC (Cont.)

NOTE: A break in step numbering sequence occurs at this point. Procedure skips to step 10). No test procedures have been omitted.

10) Check VPWR To Solenoid – Ensure ignition is off. Disconnect transmission harness connector. With KOEO, measure voltage between VPWR, EPC PWR circuit at transmission harness connector and ground. If voltage is more than 10.5 volts, go to next step. If voltage is not within specification, repair open circuit in harness. Connect all components and repeat QUICK TEST.

11) Check Solenoid Signal & VPWR Circuit Continuity – Turn ignition off. Disconnect 60-pin PCM connector. Inspect terminals, and repair if damaged. Install EEC-IV Breakout Box (T83L-50-EEC-IV), leaving PCM disconnected. Measure resistance between VPWR/EPC PWR terminal at transmission wiring harness connector breakout box test pins No. 37 and 57. Measure resistance between test pin No. 38 at breakout box and EPC terminal at transmission wiring harness connector. If resistance is 5 ohms or more, repair open circuit and repeat QUICK TEST. If resistance is less than 5 ohms, go to step **12)**.

12) Check Circuit For Short To Power Or Ground – Leave ignition off and PCM disconnected. Leave transmission wiring harness connector disconnected. Measure and record resistance between test pins No. 37 and 57 and suspect solenoid test pin at breakout box. Measure and record resistance between test pins No. 40, 46 and 60 and suspect solenoid test pin at breakout box. If either resistance is less than 10 k/ohms, repair short circuit and repeat QUICK TEST. If all resistances are 10 k/ohms or more, check solenoids. If solenoids are okay, replace PCM and repeat QUICK TEST.

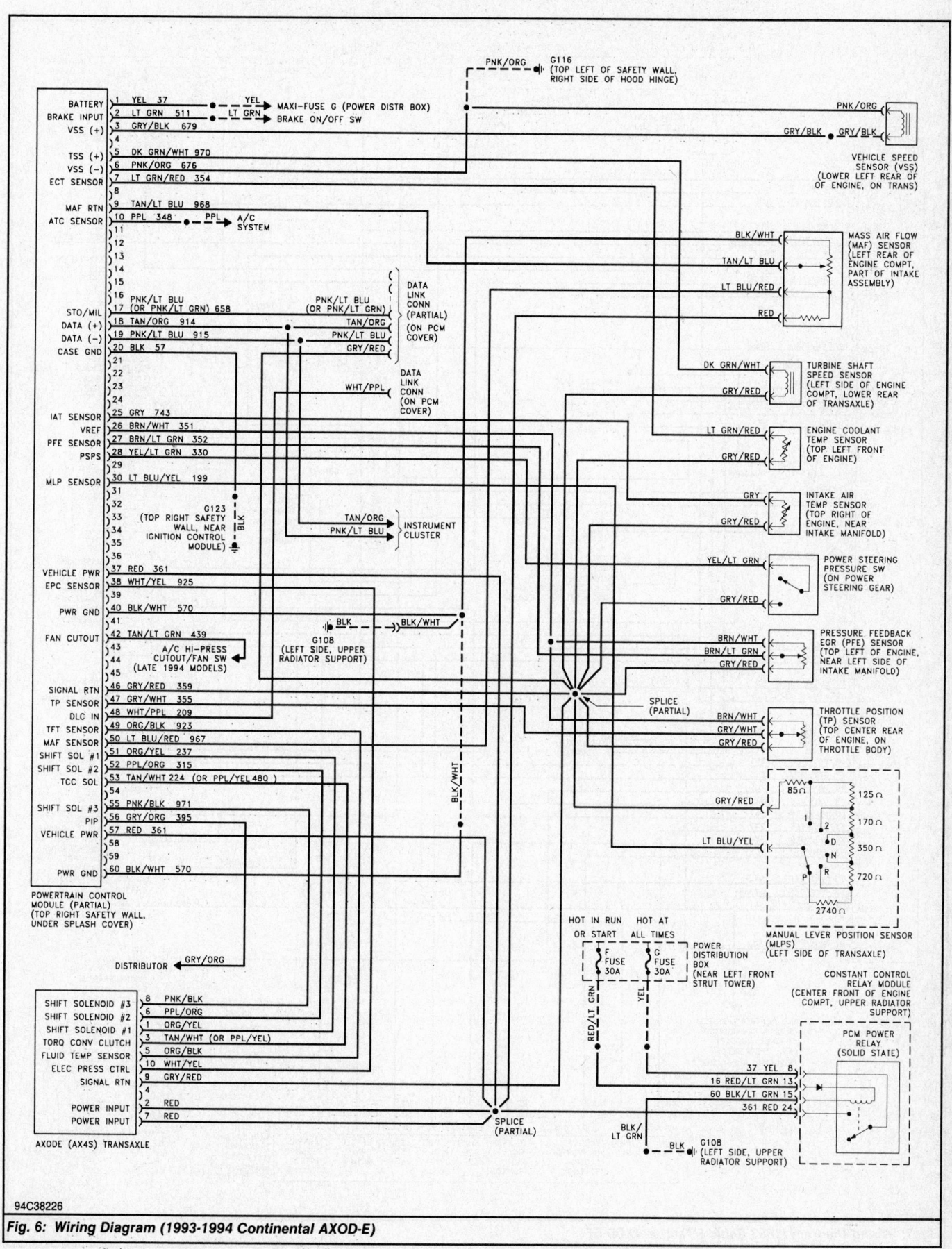

Fig. 6: Wiring Diagram (1993-1994 Continental AXOD-E)

94C38226

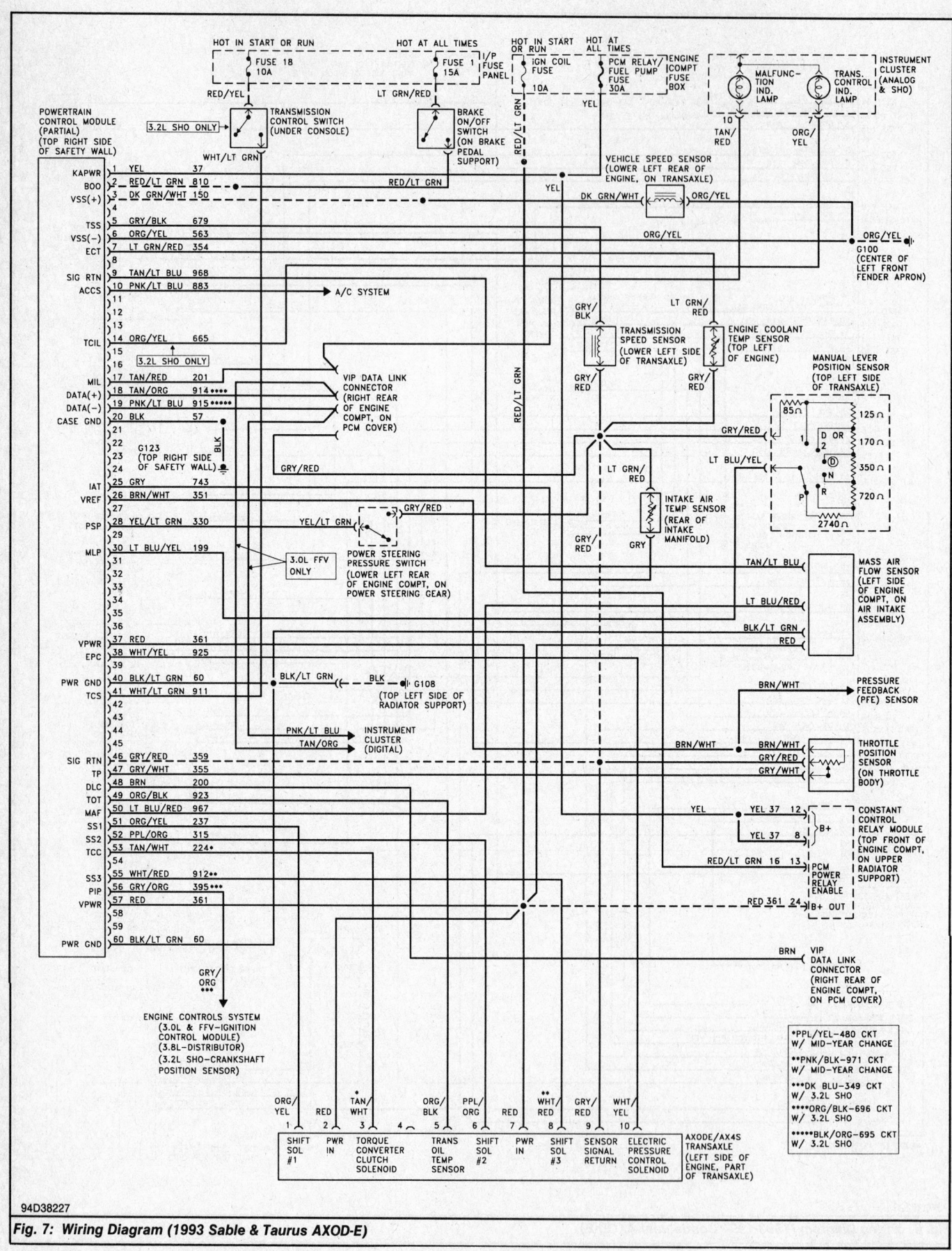

Fig. 7: Wiring Diagram (1993 Sable & Taurus AXOD-E)

94D38227

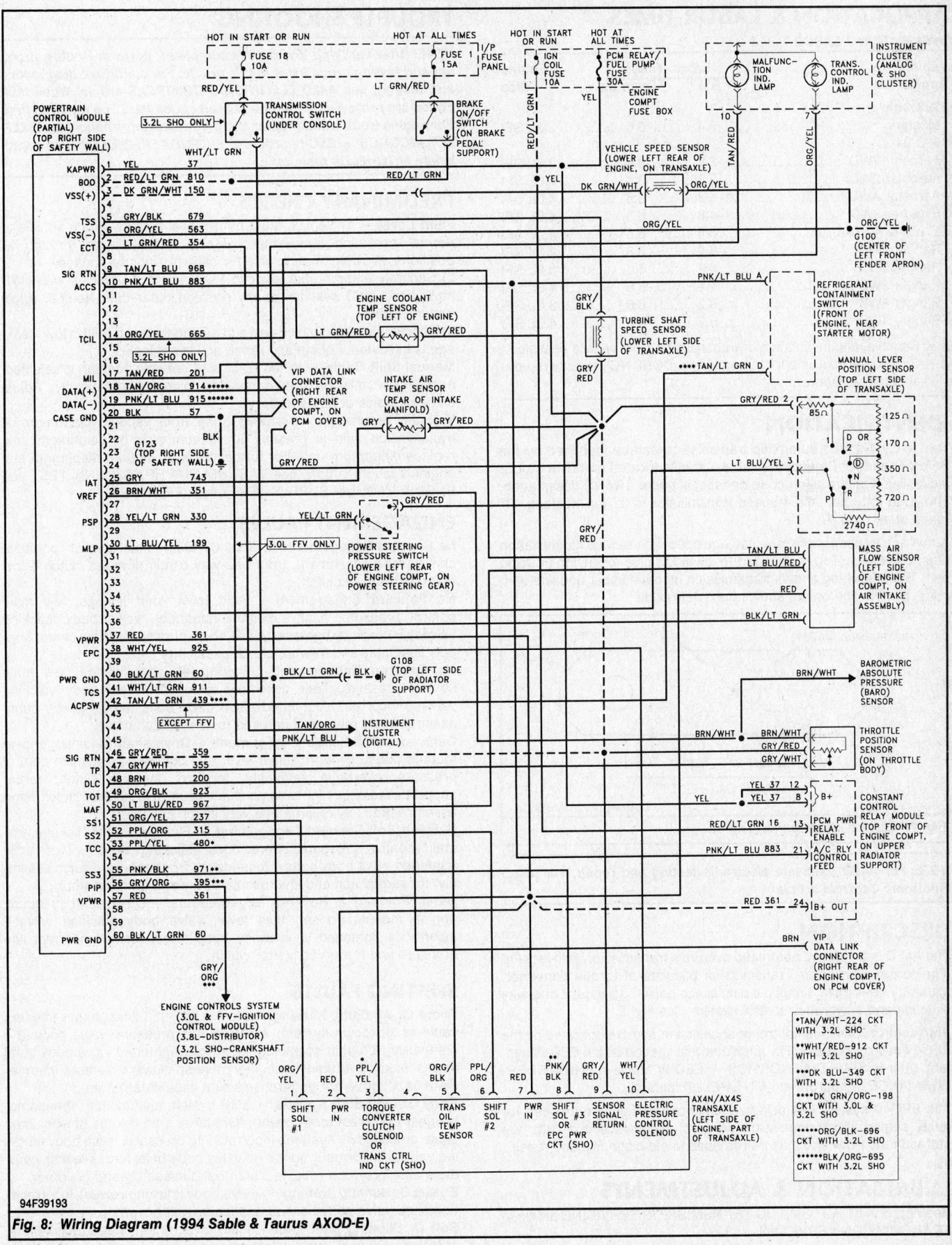

94F39193

Fig. 8: Wiring Diagram (1994 Sable & Taurus AXOD-E)

AUTOMATIC TRANSMISSIONS
Ford A4LD

APPLICATION & LABOR TIMES

APPLICATION & LABOR TIMES

Vehicle Application	Labor Times [1] R & I	[2] Overhaul	Engine Size
1993 Only			
Mustang	3.4	8.6	2.3L SFI
1993-94			
Aerostar 2WD	3.2	8.6	3.0L SFI
Aerostar 2WD	3.5	8.6	4.0L SFI
Aerostar AWD	5.3	8.6	4.0L SFI
Explorer 2WD	4.8	8.6	4.0L SFI
Explorer 4WD	5.8	8.6	4.0L SFI
Ranger 2WD	3.2	8.6	2.3L SFI
Ranger 2WD	4.2	8.6	3.0L SFI
Ranger 2WD	4.2	8.6	4.0L SFI
Ranger 4WD	5.2	8.6	3.0L SFI
Ranger 4WD	5.2	8.6	4.0L SFI

[1] – Removal and installation of transmission from vehicle chassis.
[2] – Bench overhaul time for transmission. DOES NOT include removal and installation.

IDENTIFICATION

The A4LD 4-speed automatic transmission can be identified by the Safety Standard Certification label. Label is located on driver's door lock pillar. Transmission code on label is under TRANS designation. The code for automatic 4-speed transmission is "L" for Mustang, "T" for all other models.

Automatic transmissions are also equipped with service identification tags. *See Fig. 1.* Tag is attached to lower left side extension housing bolt. Top line of tag shows transmission model number and line shift code. Bottom line on tag shows build date code.

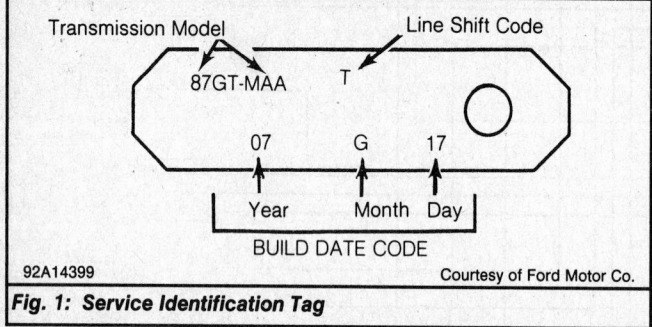

Fig. 1: Service Identification Tag

NOTE: For A4LD transaxle electronic testing and repair, see A4LD Electronic Controls article.

DESCRIPTION

The A4LD is a 4-speed automatic overdrive transmission with lock-up type torque converter. Transmission consists of torque converter, planetary gear train, 3 multiple disc clutch packs, 3 bands, 2 one-way clutches and a hydraulic control system. *See Fig. 2.*

Shift control solenoids control gear selection and are operated by the EEC-IV microprocessor. For additional information on the EEC-IV system, refer to SELF-DIAGNOSTICS – EEC-IV article in ENGINE PERFORMANCE of appropriate MITCHELL® manual.

The EEC-IV system has self-diagnostic capabilities. Fault codes for faulty engine and transmission sensors, switches and circuits are stored in the PCM and may be retrieved to aid diagnosis and repair.

LUBRICATION & ADJUSTMENTS

See appropriate AUTOMATIC TRANSMISSION SERVICING article in TRANSMISSION SERVICING.

TROUBLE SHOOTING

NOTE: After verifying driveability complaint, perform trouble shooting and testing procedures in this article. For electronic diagnostics and testing, see A4LD ELECTRONIC CONTROLS article. When fault codes are retrieved, all engine related codes MUST be repaired first. For engine trouble code repair and diagnostic information, see SELF-DIAGNOSTICS – EEC-IV article in ENGINE PERFORMANCE in appropriate MITCHELL® manual.

PRELIMINARY CHECKS

Fluid Level – 1) Vehicle must be on level surface. Bring vehicle to normal operating temperature. Move shift selector through all positions, allowing enough time for each position to engage.
2) Securely engage shift lever in Park position. Vehicles with 4WD must have 4WD selector in any position other than Neutral. Apply parking brake.
3) Check fluid with dipstick and add as necessary. If fluid is low, leakage is indicated. Locate and repair source of leak.
Manual Shift Cable – When column or console position is selected, ensure transmission detent position corresponds exactly. Adjust cable or indicator as necessary.
Vacuum Diaphragm – Remove hose from vacuum diaphragm. If transmission fluid is present on vacuum side of diaphragm unit, replace diaphragm unit. For further tests of vacuum diaphragm and engine vacuum supply, see VACUUM DIAPHRAGM UNIT TEST and ENGINE VACUUM SUPPLY TEST under TESTING.

ENGAGEMENT FAULTS

No Forward Engagements In "OD" Or "D" – Fluid level or condition, shift linkage adjustment, front one-way clutch, forward clutch & low reverse one-way clutch
No Forward Engagement – Fluid level, shift linkage, low main control pressure, filter assembly (plugged), valve body (sticking valves), incorrectly tightened valve body, pump assembly, center support assembly and forward clutch assembly.
No Reverse Engagement – Fluid level, shift linkage, low main control pressure, filter assembly (plugged), valve body (sticking valves), incorrectly tightened valve body bolts (cross-leaks), pump assembly, low reverse clutch and reverse clutch band.
Delayed/Soft Reverse Engagement – Drive shaft (u-joints), engine mounts (loose or worn), fluid level and condition, low main control pressure, overdrive assembly, forward one-way clutch, center support assembly, high reverse clutch drum, low reverse clutch/band assembly and low reverse one-way clutch assembly.
Delayed/Soft Forward Engagement – Fluid level, shift linkage, low main control pressure, valve body (sticking valves), incorrectly tightened valve body bolts (cross-leaks), front one-way clutch assembly, forward clutch and low reverse one-way clutch assembly.
Harsh Forward & Reverse Engagements – Drive shaft (u-joints), engine mounts (loose), fluid level, valve body (sticking valves), incorrectly tightened valve body bolts (cross-leaks), incorrect line pressure and torque converter clutch.

SHIFTING FAULTS

Some Or All Shifts Missing – Fluid level, shift linkage (misadjusted cable or kickdown system), incorrect line pressure, valve body (3-4 shift valve, 3/4 shift solenoid), incorrectly tightened valve body bolts (cross-leaks), overdrive band, high reverse clutch assembly, intermediate band, governor and transmission case (internal leaks).
Early Or Late Shift Speeds – EGR system malfunction, speedometer gear (incorrect tooth count), fluid level, shift linkage (misadjusted cable or kickdown system), incorrect line pressure, valve body (sticking valves), incorrectly tightened valve body bolts (cross-leaks), overdrive assembly, low reverse clutch/band assembly and governor.
Erratic Or Hunting Shifting – Valve body (sticking valves), incorrectly tightened valve body bolts (cross-leaks) and governor.
Soft Or Slipping Shift Feel – Fluid level, shift linkage (adjustment, kickdown linkage), modulator, incorrect line pressure, valve body

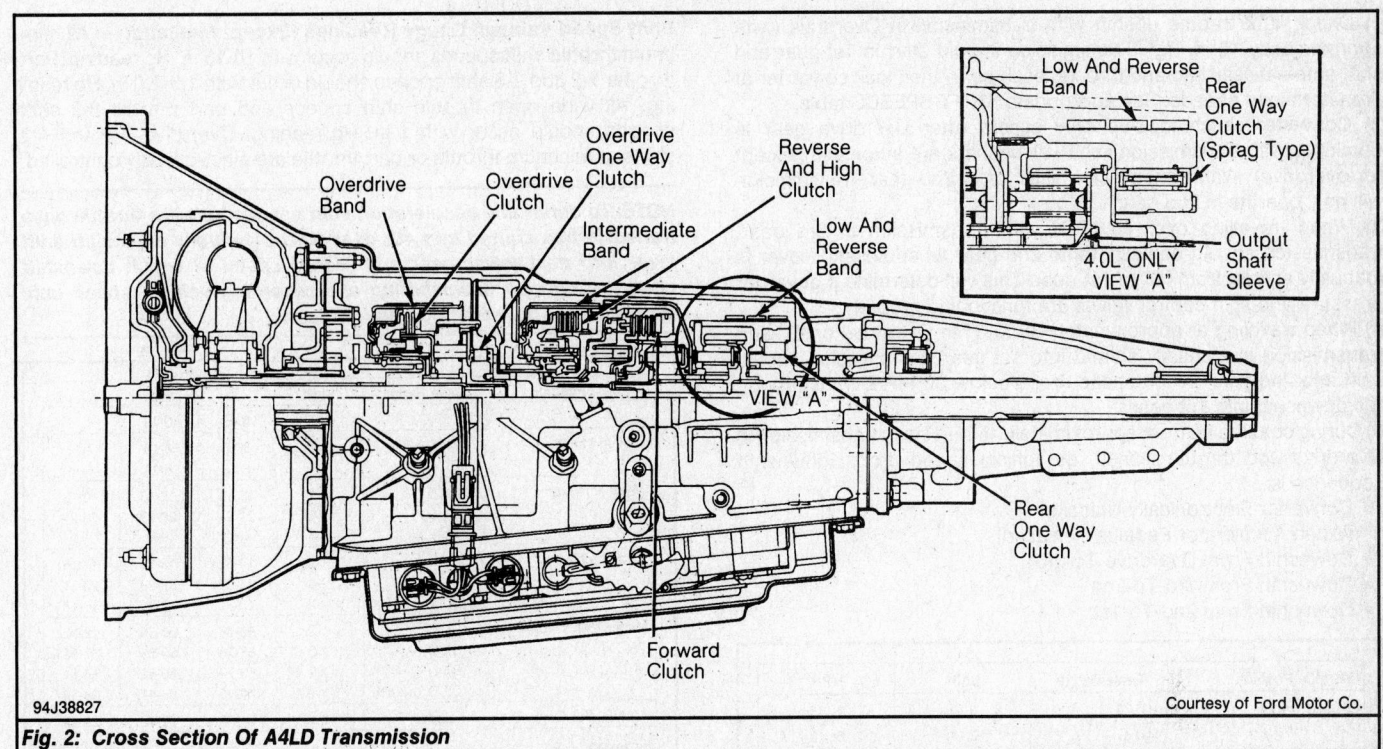

94J38827   Courtesy of Ford Motor Co.

Fig. 2: Cross Section Of A4LD Transmission

(throttle control valve, main regulator valve), incorrectly tightened valve body bolts (cross-leaks), overdrive assembly, high/reverse clutch drum, intermediate band and governor.

Harsh Shift Feel – Fluid level, shift linkage, incorrect line pressure, valve body (sticking valves, intermediate servo release check ball), incorrectly tightened valve body bolts (cross-leaks), high reverse clutch drum, intermediate band and governor.

No Manual 1st Gear – Incorrect line pressure, valve body (sticking valves), low reverse band and low reverse one-way clutch assembly.

No Manual 2nd Gear – Incorrect line pressure, valve body (sticking valves), intermediate band and low reverse one-way clutch assembly.

No Torque Converter Clutch (TCC) Application – Valve body (TCC solenoid stuck open, TCC shuttle valve stuck in unlock position, TCC shift valve stuck in downshift position), torque converter and pump assembly.

Torque Converter Clutch (TCC) Always Applied – Valve body (TCC shuttle valve stuck in locked position) and torque converter.

MISCELLANEOUS FAULTS

Transmission Overheating – Fluid level, incorrect line pressure, valve body (sticking valves), torque converter (seized one-way clutch) and cooler line restriction.

No Engine Braking In Manual 2nd Gear – Incorrect line pressure, overdrive assembly and intermediate band.

No Engine Braking In Manual 1st Gear – Fluid level, shift linkage, incorrect line pressure, coast clutch assembly, low reverse clutch/band and low reverse one-way clutch assembly.

Vehicle Movement With Gear Selector In Neutral Position – Fluid level, shift linkage (adjustment), front one-way clutch assembly, forward clutch assembly and low reverse one-way clutch.

Slips & Chatters In Manual 1st Position – Incorrect line pressure, valve body (sticking valves), low reverse band and low reverse one-way clutch.

Slips & Chatters In Manual 2nd Position – Incorrect line pressure, valve body (sticking valves), intermediate band and low reverse one-way clutch.

CLUTCH & BAND APPLICATION

CLUTCH & BAND APPLICATION CHART

Selector Lever Position	Elements In Use
"OD" (Overdrive)	
1st Gear	Forward Clutch, Front One-Way Clutch & Rear One-Way Clutch
2nd Gear	Forward Clutch, Front One-Way Clutch & Intermediate Band
3rd Gear	Forward Clutch, High/Reverse Clutch & Front One-Way Clutch
4th Gear	Forward Clutch, High/Reverse Clutch & Overdrive Band
"D" (Drive)	
1st Gear	Forward/Reverse Coast Clutch, Forward Clutch, Front One-Way Clutch & Rear One-Way Clutch
2nd Gear	Forward/Reverse Coast Clutch, Forward Clutch, Front One-Way Clutch & Intermediate Band
3rd Gear	Forward Clutch, High/Reverse Clutch, Front One-Way Clutch & Forward/Reverse Coast Clutch
"2"	Forward/Reverse Coast Clutch, Forward Clutch, Intermediate Band & Front One-Way Clutch
"1"	Forward/Reverse Coast Clutch, Forward Clutch, Low/Reverse Band, Front One-Way Clutch & Rear One-Way Clutch
"R"	Forward/Reverse Coast Clutch, Low/Reverse Band, High/Reverse Clutch & Front One-Way Clutch

TESTING

After completing PRELIMINARY CHECKS, use initial road test to verify malfunction of transmission. Ensure engine is operating properly.

SHIFT SPEED TEST

NOTE: Shift speeds into 4th gear are determined by engine calibration and are electronically controlled. Manufacturer does not supply 3-4 or 4-3 shift speed information.

Road Test – This test will determine if electronics, governor and shift control valves are functioning properly. Converter lock-up is difficult to detect. A vacuum gauge and tachometer should be used to determine lock-up speeds.

AUTOMATIC TRANSMISSIONS
Ford A4LD (Cont.)

1) Check light throttle upshift with transmission in Overdrive (with approximately 10 in. Hg). Transmission should start in 1st gear and shift automatically into and through each gear, then lock converter at predetermined speeds. See appropriate SHIFT SPEEDS table.

2) Converter clutch lock-up only occurs after Overdrive gear is obtained. With transmission in "D", all upshifts are automatic (except for overdrive). With transmission selector in 2nd gear, transmission will only operate in 2nd gear.

3) When travelling over 45 MPH with transmission in 3rd gear, transmission should downshift into 2nd gear when selector lever is manually shifted from "D" to 1st gear. This will determine if governor pressure and shift control valves are functioning properly.

4) When traveling at approximately 45 MPH in Overdrive or "D" and transmission is manually shifted into 1st gear, transmission should shift into 2nd gear. When speed drops below 30 MPH, transmission will downshift into 1st gear.

5) During coastdown from approximately 45 MPH with transmission in Overdrive and throttle closed, as vehicle speed drops, downshift sequence is:

- Converter Electronically Unlocks (When Accelerator Pedal Is Released)
- Downshift From Overdrive-To-3rd
- Downshift From 3rd-To-2nd
- Downshift From 2nd-To-1st

Throttle Position	Drive Range	Shift	MPH
Closed Throttle	Ⓓ, D	3 - 2	9 - 15
	Ⓓ, D	2 - 1	6 - 12
Minimum Throttle ①	Ⓓ, D	1 - 2	10 - 15
	Ⓓ, D	2 - 3	17 - 22
	Ⓓ	3 - 4	—
Part Throttle ②	Ⓓ, D	1 - 2	12 - 18
	Ⓓ, D	2 - 3	21 - 28
	Ⓓ	3 - 4	48 - 54
	Ⓓ ③	3 - 2	14 - 21
Wide Open Throttle ③ (WOT)	Ⓓ, D	1 - 2	36 - 41
	Ⓓ, D	2 - 3	61 - 67
	Ⓓ, D	3 - 2	58 - 63
	Ⓓ, D	3 - 1, 2 - 1	30 - 35
Manual Pull-Down	1	2 - 1	25 - 33

94A38828   Courtesy of Ford Motor Co.

Fig. 3: A4LD Shift Speeds (1993 2.3L Mustang)

Throttle Position	Drive Range	Shift	MPH
Closed Throttle	Ⓓ, D	3-2	9-17
	Ⓓ, D	2-1	5-13
Minimum Throttle①	Ⓓ, D	1-2	8-20
	Ⓓ, D	2-3	16-21
	Ⓓ	3-4	—
Part Throttle②	Ⓓ, D	1-2	10-27
	Ⓓ, D	2-3	18-27
	Ⓓ③	3-2	35-42
Wide Open Throttle④ (WOT)	Ⓓ, D	1-2	35-42
	Ⓓ, D	2-3	60-71
	Ⓓ, D	3-2	56-64
	Ⓓ, D	3-1, 2-1	28-35
Manual Pull-Down	1	2-1	28-36

94B38829   Courtesy of Ford Motor Co.

Fig. 4: A4LD Shift Speeds (1993-94 2.3L Ranger)

Shift Speed Vacuum Gauge Readings (Except Mustang) – All minimum throttle shift speeds should occur with 10-15 in. Hg reading. Part throttle 1-2 and 2-3 shift speeds should occur with 1.5-2.0 in. Hg reading. All wide open throttle shift speeds and part throttle 3-2 shift speeds should occur with 1 in. Hg reading. Overdrive 3-4 and 4-3 shifts at minimum throttle or part throttle are electronically controlled.

NOTE: To determine deceleration shift speeds, release throttle once transaxle has shifted into 4th gear (O/D). Manually downshift shift lever into next lower gear and record speed at which downshift occurs. Continue downshifting and recording vehicle speed until transaxle has downshifted into low gear.

Throttle Position	Drive Range	Shift	MPH		
			3.45	3.73	4.10
Closed Throttle	Ⓓ, D	3-2	8-15	8-14	7-13
	Ⓓ, D	2-1	6-12	6-11	5-11
Minimum Throttle ①	Ⓓ, D	1-2	12-14	12-13	10-12
	Ⓓ, D	2-3	21-24	20-22	18-21
	Ⓓ	3-4	—	—	—
Part Throttle ②	Ⓓ, D	1-2	14-21	13-19	11-18
	Ⓓ, D	2-3	23-32	22-29	20-27
	Ⓓ ③	3-2	12-21	12-19	10-18
Wide Open Throttle ④ (WOT)	Ⓓ, D	1-2	33-38	31-35	28-32
	Ⓓ, D	2-3	65-75	63-69	57-63
	Ⓓ, D	3-2	63-72	60-66	54-61
	Ⓓ, D	3-1, 2-1	40-45	38-41	34-39
Manual Pull-Down	1	2-1	34-46	32-42	29-39

94E38830   Courtesy of Ford Motor Co.

Fig. 5: A4LD Shift Speeds (1993-94 3.0L Aerostar & Ranger)

Throttle Position	Drive Range	Shift	MPH			
			3.08	3.27	3.55	3.73
Closed Throttle	Ⓓ, D	3-2	13-19	12-18	11-17	10-16
	Ⓓ, D	2-1	7-13	6-13	6-12	5-11
Minimum Throttle①	Ⓓ, D	1-2	13-17	12-17	11-15	10-15
	Ⓓ, D	2-3	19-26	17-25	16-23	15-22
	Ⓓ	3-4	—	—	—	—
Part Throttle②	Ⓓ, D	1-2	16-22	15-21	13-20	13-19
	Ⓓ, D	2-3	28-34	26-33	24-30	23-29
	Ⓓ③	3-2	19-27	18-26	16-24	15-23
Wide Open Throttle④ (WOT)	Ⓓ, D	1-2	39-44	36-42	33-39	32-37
	Ⓓ, D	2-3	69-75	64-71	59-66	56-62
	Ⓓ, D	3-2	66-72	62-68	57-63	54-60
	Ⓓ, D	3-1, 2-1	32-38	30-36	27-33	26-32
Manual Pull-Down	1	2-1	29-39	27-37	25-34	23-33

94F38831   Courtesy of Ford Motor Co.

Fig. 6: A4LD Shift Speeds (1993-94 4.0L Ranger)

Throttle Position	Drive Range	Shift	MPH		
			3.08	3.27	3.73
Closed Throttle	Ⓓ, D	3-2	14-18	13-17	11-15
	Ⓓ, D	2-1	8-12	7-12	6-10
Minimum Throttle①	Ⓓ, D	1-2	13-16	12-16	10-14
	Ⓓ, D	2-3	19-24	18-23	15-20
	Ⓓ	3-4	—	—	—
Part Throttle②	Ⓓ, D	1-2	17-21	16-20	14-18
	Ⓓ, D	2-3	29-38	27-36	23-32
	Ⓓ③	3-2	19-27	18-26	15-23
Wide Open Throttle④ (WOT)	Ⓓ, D	1-2	40-44	37-42	33-37
	Ⓓ, D	2-3	70-75	65-71	57-62
	Ⓓ, D	3-2	65-70	61-66	53-58
	Ⓓ, D	3-1, 2-1	32-37	30-35	26-31
Manual Pull-Down	1	2-1	30-38	28-36	29-32

94G38832   Courtesy of Ford Motor Co.

Fig. 7: A4LD Shift Speeds (1993-94 4.0L Explorer)

Throttle Position	Drive Range	Shift	MPH
Closed Throttle	Ⓓ, D	3-2	12-18
	Ⓓ, D	2-1	7-12
Minimum Throttle①	Ⓓ, D	1-2	13-22
	Ⓓ, D	2-3	18-38
	Ⓓ	3-4	—
Part Throttle②	Ⓓ, D	1-2	27-33
	Ⓓ, D	2-3	42-48
	Ⓓ③	3-2	33-39
Wide Open Throttle④ (WOT)	Ⓓ, D	1-2	38-42
	Ⓓ, D	2-3	67-72
	Ⓓ, D	3-2	62-67
	Ⓓ, D	3-1, 2-1	31-37
Manual Pull-Down	1	2-1	27-37

94H38833 — Courtesy of Ford Motor Co.

Fig. 8: A4LD Shift Speeds (1993-94 4.0L Aerostar-RWD)

Throttle Position	Drive Range	Shift	MPH
Closed Throttle	Ⓓ, D	3-2	11-16
	Ⓓ, D	2-1	6-11
Minimum Throttle①	Ⓓ, D	1-2	11-15
	Ⓓ, D	2-3	16-22
	Ⓓ	3-4	—
Part Throttle②	Ⓓ, D	1-2	23-28
	Ⓓ, D	2-3	36-41
	Ⓓ③	3-2	29-34
Wide Open Throttle④ (WOT)	Ⓓ, D	1-2	35-39
	Ⓓ, D	2-3	59-64
	Ⓓ, D	3-2	55-60
	Ⓓ, D	3-1, 2-1	27-33
Manual Pull-Down	1	2-1	24-33

94I38834 — Courtesy of Ford Motor Co.

Fig. 9: A4LD Shift Speeds (1993-94 4.0L Aerostar-AWD)

CONVERTER CLUTCH TEST

NOTE: Ensure engine coolant temperature is above 128°F (53°C) and below 240°F (116°C). Due to the difficulty of feeling converter clutch shift, a tachometer and/or vacuum gauge must be connected to engine.

1) To check converter for engagement and disengagement, drive vehicle at approximately 50 MPH. While maintaining this speed, lightly tap brake pedal. Engine RPM and vacuum should increase when clutch disengages, with light brake pedal application.
2) Engine RPM will decrease when pedal is released and clutch engages. If converter clutch does not engage or is engaged continuously, see A4LD ELECTRONIC CONTROLS article.

VACUUM DIAPHRAGM UNIT TEST

1) Remove hose from vacuum diaphragm. If transmission fluid is present on vacuum side of diaphragm unit, replace unit. Fluid indicates diaphragm in unit is defective.

NOTE: If replacing vacuum diaphragm unit, ensure correct replacement is used. Diaphragm units may appear identical, but cannot be interchanged.

2) Attach a vacuum pump to diaphragm unit. Apply 18 in. Hg of vacuum. If gauge reading holds steady, diaphragm unit is good. If gauge reading drops, diaphragm unit is defective and must be replaced.
3) Remove diaphragm unit from transmission. Apply 18 in. Hg of vacuum. Hold finger over end of unit control rod. When hose is removed, diaphragm unit should push control rod out. Replace as necessary.

ENGINE VACUUM SUPPLY TEST

1) Disconnect vacuum line at diaphragm unit. Connect vacuum line to gauge. At idle, engine vacuum must hold steady at an acceptable level for the altitude at which the vehicle is tested.

2) If vacuum reading is low, check for vacuum leaks in vacuum hoses and engine vacuum related components (power brake booster, etc.).
3) If vacuum reading is okay, press the accelerator pedal quickly, then release. Vacuum reading should drop rapidly then recover immediately when pedal is released.
4) If vacuum reading does not change or recover quickly, check supply line for restriction or incorrect connection.

CONTROL PRESSURE TEST

Using Engine Vacuum – 1) If vacuum diaphragm unit is working properly and linkage is adjusted correctly, all shifts should occur within specified road speed limits. See appropriate A4LD SHIFT SPEEDS table. If not within specifications or slipping occurs, check engine vacuum supply and vacuum operated units for possible defect.
2) Connect tachometer to engine. Connect vacuum gauge to manifold vacuum line, using "T" fitting at diaphragm unit. Attach pressure gauge to control pressure take-off located on left side of transmission case. *See Fig. 10.*
3) Apply parking brake firmly. Start engine and ensure idle RPM is correct. If engine idle cannot be brought within limits, check throttle and downshift linkages for binding. Check for vacuum leaks in hoses, tubes and all vacuum components such as power brake booster.
4) With engine at idle, read and record control pressures in all selector positions. Read and record control pressures with vacuum gauge reading at 10 in. Hg and at one in. Hg (wide open throttle). See appropriate CONTROL PRESSURE SPECIFICATIONS table and CONTROL PRESSURE TEST RESULTS.

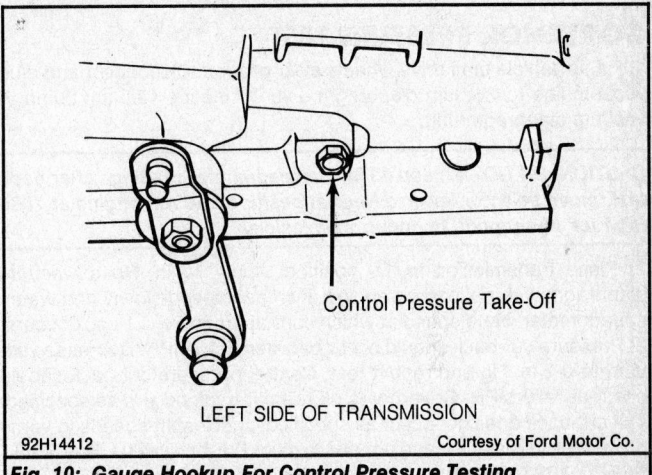

Control Pressure Take-Off

LEFT SIDE OF TRANSMISSION

92H14412 — Courtesy of Ford Motor Co.

Fig. 10: Gauge Hookup For Control Pressure Testing

NOTE: Governor can be checked at same time and in the same manner as control pressure test.

Using Vacuum Pump – 1) Disconnect vacuum line from diaphragm unit and attach vacuum pump. *See Fig. 10.* Apply parking and service brakes. Start engine and apply 15 in. Hg of vacuum to diaphragm unit. Read and record control pressures in all selector positions.
2) Bring engine RPM to 1000. Reduce vacuum to 10 in. Hg. Read and record control pressures in "OD", "D", "2" and "1" selector positions.
3) Reduce vacuum to one in. Hg. Read and record control pressures in "OD", "D", "2", "1" and "R" selector positions. See appropriate CONTROL PRESSURE SPECIFICATIONS table and CONTROL PRESSURE TEST RESULTS.

CONTROL PRESSURE SPECIFICATIONS (PSI @ SEA LEVEL)

Drive Range	15 in. Hg & Above	10 in. Hg	WOT Stall Thru Detent
OD, D,2,1	57-78	114-134	205-235
R	67-105	157-177	282-316
P, N	57-78	–	....

CONTROL PRESSURE SPECIFICATIONS (PSI @ 5000 FT.)

Drive Range	15 in. Hg & Above	10 in. Hg	WOT Stall Thru Detent
OD, D,2,1	57-67	90-110	180-210
R	67-77	124-144	247-280
P, N	57-67	–	–

CONTROL PRESSURE TEST RESULTS

Compare recorded control pressures to control pressures listed in table. See appropriate CONTROL PRESSURE SPECIFICATIONS table. If control pressures are outside of specified ranges, use symptoms to determine cause of trouble.

Low In "P" – Valve body.

Low In "R" – Reverse clutch, overdrive clutch or low-reverse servo leakage.

Low In "N" – Valve body.

Low In O/D - Forward clutch and overdrive servo.

Low In "D" – Forward clutch and overdrive clutch.

Low In "2nd" – Forward clutch, overdrive clutch or intermediate servo.

Low In "1st" – Forward clutch, overdrive clutch or low-reverse servo.

Low At Idle In All Ranges – Low fluid level, restricted intake screen or filter, loose valve body bolts, pump leakage, case leakage, faulty valve body, excessively low engine idle, fluid too hot or main regulator valve sticking.

GOVERNOR PRESSURE TEST

1) Raise vehicle until drive wheels clear ground. Disconnect and plug vacuum line to vacuum diaphragm unit. Connect a vacuum pump to vacuum diaphragm unit.

CAUTION: DO NOT exceed 60 MPH speedometer reading. After each test, move selector lever to Neutral position and run engine at 1000 RPM for 15 seconds to cool transmission.

2) Place transmission in "D" position. Apply 10 in. Hg to vacuum diaphragm with no load on engine. Increase speed slowly and watch speedometer. Note speed at which control pressure cut-back occurs.
3) Pressure cut-back should occur between 5-15 MPH. Decrease vacuum to 0-2 in. Hg and repeat test. Control pressure cut-back should occur at 7-20 MPH. Governor is okay if cut-back occurs as specified.
4) If cut-back does not occur as specified, check shift speeds to verify problem is in governor and not due to stuck cut-back valve. See SHIFT SPEED TEST. Repair or replace governor as necessary.

STALL SPEED TEST

Testing Precautions – 1) Engine coolant and transmission fluid must be at proper levels and operating temperatures. Linkages must be set properly. Hold accelerator down just long enough to get a stable tachometer reading. DO NOT floor accelerator for more than 5 seconds.
2) Do not exceed maximum specified RPM for vehicle. Before shifting into each selector position, run engine in Neutral at 1000 RPM for 2

STALL SPEEDS SPECIFICATIONS

Application	Engine Displacement	Stall Speed RPM Min.	Max.
1993			
Mustang	2.3L	2495	2885
1993-94			
Ranger (2WD)	2.3L	2437	2833
Aerostar (2WD)	3.0L	2720	3165
Ranger (2WD, 4WD)	3.0L	2781	3288
Aerostar (2WD, AWD)	4.0L	2550	2950
Explorer (2WD, 4WD)	4.0L	2550	2950
Ranger (2WD, 4WD)	4.0L	2550	2950

minutes to cool transmission. If engine speed exceeds specification, release accelerator immediately, as this is an indication of clutch or band slippage.

Testing Procedure – Connect tachometer to engine. Apply parking and service brakes firmly. Place selector lever in each gear. Press accelerator completely to floor and record tachometer reading in each gear. DO NOT exceed 5 second limit. Engine speed should be within specifications. See STALL SPEED SPECIFICATIONS table.

STALL TEST RESULTS

Low In All Ranges – Poor engine performance. Faulty torque converter stator one-way clutch.

High In All Ranges – General transmission problems are indicated. Perform control pressure tests.

High In "O/D" Only – Forward clutch faulty.

High In "O/D", "D" & "1" – Overdrive one-way clutch or rear one-way clutch faulty.

High In "D", "2" & "1" – Forward clutch or overdrive clutch faulty.

High In "2" Only – Overdrive one-way clutch, intermediate band or servo faulty.

High In "1" Only – Low-reverse band or servo faulty.

High In "R" Only – Overdrive clutch, overdrive one-way clutch. reverse and high clutch, low-reverse band or servo faulty.

AIR PRESSURE TESTS

A "No Drive" condition can exist, even with correct transmission fluid pressure, due to inoperative clutches or bands. Inoperative units can be located through a series of checks by substituting air pressure for fluid pressure to determine location of malfunction.

To check unit, drain transmission fluid. Remove oil pan, gasket and control valve body. See VALVE BODY removal procedure under ON-VEHICLE SERVICE. Using shop air, apply air to indicated points. *See Fig 11.* Check unit operation as follows.

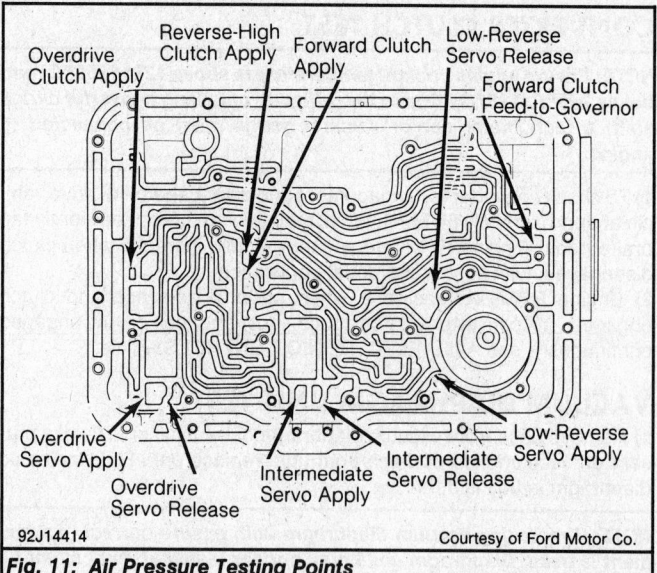

92J14414   Courtesy of Ford Motor Co.

Fig. 11: Air Pressure Testing Points

Forward Clutch – Apply air pressure into forward clutch passage. A dull thud can be heard when clutch piston is applied. If no thud is heard, movement of piston can be felt by placing fingertips on input shell.

Governor – Apply air pressure into the forward clutch control pressure-to-governor passage. Listen for sharp clicking or whistling noise indicating governor valve movement.

Overdrive Servo – 1) Apply air pressure to overdrive servo apply passage. Operation of servo is indicated by a tightening of overdrive band around overdrive drum.
2) While continuing to apply air pressure to servo apply passage, apply air pressure to overdrive servo release passage. The overdrive servo should release overdrive band.

Overdrive Clutch – Apply air pressure to overdrive clutch feed passage. A dull thud indicates the overdrive clutch piston has moved to the applied position.

NOTE: If air pressure applied to either clutch passage fails to operate clutch or operates both clutches at once, check fluid passages in case and oil pump. Use air pressure to detect obstructions.

Reverse-High Clutch – Apply air pressure into reverse-high clutch passage. A dull thud can be heard when clutch piston is applied. If no thud is heard, movement of piston can be felt by placing fingertips on clutch drum.

Intermediate Servo – 1) Hold air nozzle in intermediate servo apply passage. Operation of servo is indicated by tightening of intermediate band around drum.

2) While continuing to apply air pressure at servo apply passage, apply air pressure to intermediate servo release passage. Intermediate servo should release band against pressure in apply passage.

Low-Reverse Servo – Apply air pressure to low-reverse servo apply passage. Low-reverse band should tighten around drum if servo is operating properly.

TRANSMISSION FLUID COOLER FLOW CHECK

NOTE: Before performing TRANSMISSION FLUID COOLER FLOW CHECK, ensure shift cables and linkages are properly adjusted. Ensure fluid level is correct and control pressures are within specifications. See CONTROL PRESSURE TEST.

1) Remove transmission dipstick from filler tube. Install a funnel into filler tube. Raise and support vehicle. Disconnect transmission cooler return line (upper line) from transmission case fitting.

2) Connect one end of a hose to transmission cooler return line. Install other end of hose into filler tube funnel. With transmission in Neutral position, set idle speed to 1000 RPM.

3) Note fluid flow at funnel. Wait until flow is constant. This indicates air bleeding has been completed. Fluid flow should be free and heavy. If flow is intermittent or light, check flow from transmission fluid output line to determine source of restriction.

4) If transmission output line flow is good, restriction is in cooler. Repair as necessary. If output line flow is poor, check for main oil circuit leakage, oil pump defect or a stuck converter charge relief valve.

TORQUE CONVERTER

TORQUE CONVERTER FLUSHING

Whenever transmission has been disassembled to replace worn or damaged parts or because valve body sticks due to foreign material, converter must be cleaned using a mechanically agitated cleaner, such as Rotunda (014-00028). Under no conditions should converter be cleaned by hand agitation using solvent.

After removing torque converter from cleaning equipment, thoroughly drain remaining solvent from converter hub. Add 2 Qts. (1.9L) of clean transmission fluid to converter and agitate by hand. Thoroughly drain converter hub.

NOTE: Torque converter is a sealed unit and cannot be disassembled for service. Replace if found to be defective. Perform the following tests to ensure converter is defective before replacing unit.

LEAK TEST

If torque converter welds indicate leakage, attach Torque Converter Leak Detector (Rotunda 021-00054) to converter and follow detector kit instructions.

TURBINE & STATOR END PLAY CHECK

1) Insert Torque Converter End Play Tester (T80L-7902-A) into converter pump drive hub until it bottoms. Expand sleeve in turbine spline by tightening threaded inner post of tester until it is securely locked into spline. *See Fig. 12.*

2) Attach dial indicator to tester with dial indicator tip on converter housing. Zero dial face. Lift tester upward as far as it will go and note dial indicator reading.

3) Reading is total end play of turbine and stator. If end play exceeds .023" (.58 mm) on new or rebuilt converter, or .050" (1.27 mm) on used converter, replace torque converter assembly.

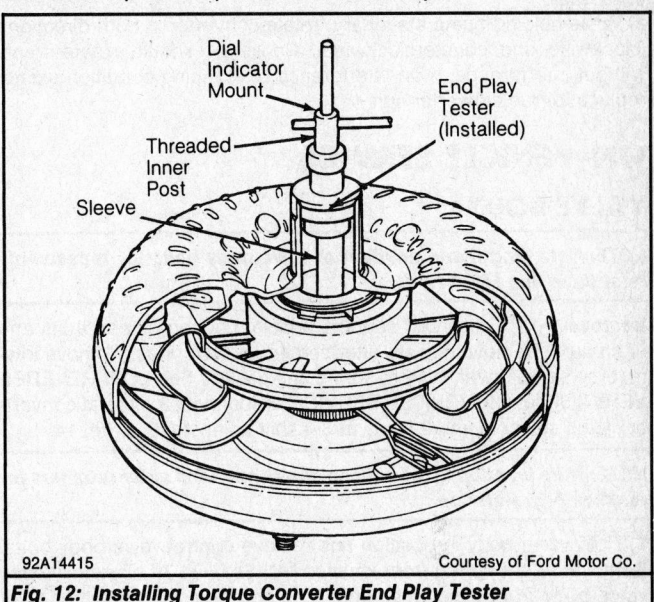

92A14415   Courtesy of Ford Motor Co.

Fig. 12: Installing Torque Converter End Play Tester

CONVERTER ONE-WAY CLUTCH CHECK

1) Insert one-way Clutch Holder (D84L-7902-A) into one of the grooves in the stator thrust washer. Insert Torque Adapter (T77L-7902-B) into converter impeller hub so as to engage one-way clutch inner race.

2) Attach a torque wrench to torque adapter. With clutch holder held stationary, turn torque wrench counterclockwise. *See Fig. 13.* Converter one-way clutch should lock-up and hold at 10 Ft. Lbs. (14 N.m). One-way clutch should rotate freely in a clockwise direction.

3) Repeat lock-up test in at least 5 different locations around torque converter. If clutch fails to lock-up and hold, replace torque converter.

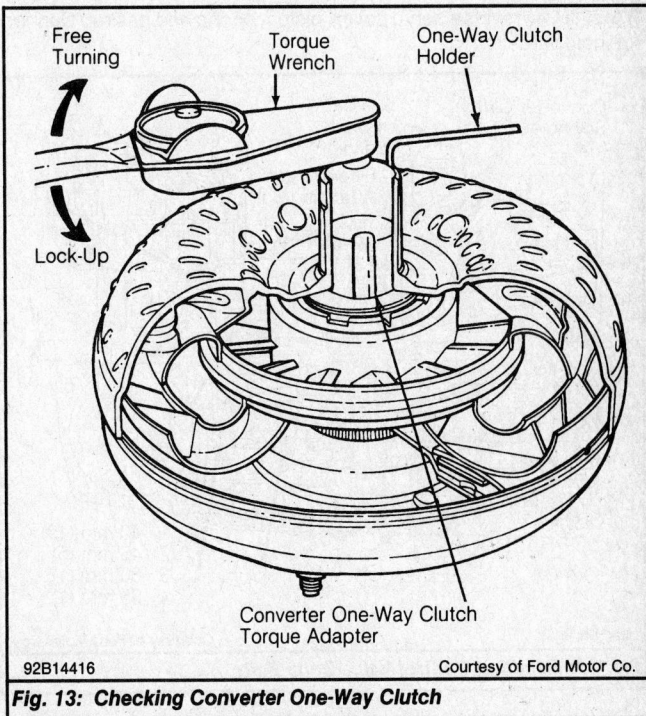

92B14416   Courtesy of Ford Motor Co.

Fig. 13: Checking Converter One-Way Clutch

STATOR INTERFERENCE CHECK

Stator-To-Impeller Interference Check – 1) Position front pump assembly on bench with spline end of stator shaft pointing upward. Mount converter on pump so splines of one-way clutch inner race engage splines of stator support and impeller hub engages pump drive gear.

2) While holding pump stationary, rotate converter in both directions (clockwise and counterclockwise). Converter should rotate freely without interference. If an interference or scraping condition exists, replace torque converter unit.

ON-VEHICLE SERVICE

VALVE BODY

NOTE: Note length and position of valve body bolts for reassembly reference. See Fig. 14.

Removal – 1) Raise and support vehicle. Loosen oil pan bolts and drain fluid. Remove oil pan, filter screen and "O" rings. Remove low-reverse servo cover, piston, spring and gasket. See LOW-REVERSE SERVO under ON-VEHICLE SERVICE. Disconnect 2 wires at converter clutch solenoid and 2 wires at 3-4 shift solenoid. *See Fig. 14.*

NOTE: Note location of 3-4 shift solenoid inner and outer retainers for reassembly reference.

2) Hold valve body in position and remove control valve body bolts. Remove detent spring from location "A". *See Fig. 14.* Carefully ease valve body from case while unlocking and detaching selector lever connecting rod ("Z" link). Clean and inspect valve body thoroughly. See CLEANING & INSPECTION.

Installation – 1) Attach and lock selector lever connecting rod ("Z" link) to manual valve. Using care not to deform "Z" link, ease valve body into case.

2) Install "A" and "B" bolts finger tight, to locate valve body into case. *See Fig. 14.* Install remaining bolts finger tight, except filter screen bolt and 3-4 shift solenoid bolts. Ensure proper bolts are installed in their correct location.

3) Tighten valve body bolts, starting from center bolts and working to outer edges. See TORQUE SPECIFICATIONS. Remove bolt "A" and install detent spring to bolt. Reinstall bolt "A" and tighten to specification.

4) Install low reverse servo cover, piston, spring and gasket. Connect solenoid wires.

5) Clean filter screen with solvent and install filter screen and "O" rings. Using a new gasket, install gasket and oil pan. Tighten oil pan bolts to specifications.

6) Add 3 Qts. (2.8L) of transmission fluid and start engine. Add fluid as necessary.

LOW-REVERSE SERVO

Removal & Installation – Remove transmission oil pan and filter screen with "O" rings. Remove low-reverse servo bolts. Remove servo cover, gasket, piston and spring. To install, reverse removal procedure.

EXTENSION HOUSING

Removal – 1) Raise and support vehicle. Mark drive shaft rear yoke and pinion flange for reassembly reference. Remove drive shaft. Disconnect speedometer cable from extension housing.

2) Support transmission with transmission jack. Remove rear support bolts. Raise transmission slightly and remove rear support from extension housing. Loosen extension housing bolts and allow transmission fluid to drain.

3) Remove bolts and slide extension housing off output shaft. See appropriate component under CLEANING & INSPECTION.

Installation – 1) Ensure parking pawl and spring are installed in housing correctly and are preloaded. Install new housing gasket and position extension housing on case.

2) Ensure parking pawl actuating rod is seated in extension housing guide cup bore. Install and tighten bolts. See TORQUE SPECIFICATIONS. To complete installation, reverse removal procedure.

EXTENSION HOUSING SEAL & BUSHING

Removal – 1) Raise and support vehicle. Mark drive shaft rear yoke and pinion flange for reassembly reference. Remove drive shaft.

2) Using Seal Remover (T71P-7657-A), remove extension housing oil seal. Using Bushing Remover (T77L-7697-E), remove extension housing bushing. See appropriate component under CLEANING & INSPECTION.

Installation – 1) Using Bushing Installer (T77L-7697-F), install bushing. Using Seal Installer (T74P-77052A), install seal.

2) Apply multipurpose long-life lubricant to seal lip and drive shaft yoke. Align index marks and install drive shaft. Add fluid as necessary.

GOVERNOR

Removal – 1) Raise and support vehicle. Remove extension housing. See EXTENSION HOUSING under ON-VEHICLE SERVICE. Remove governor body-to-oil collector body bolts. *See Fig. 15.*

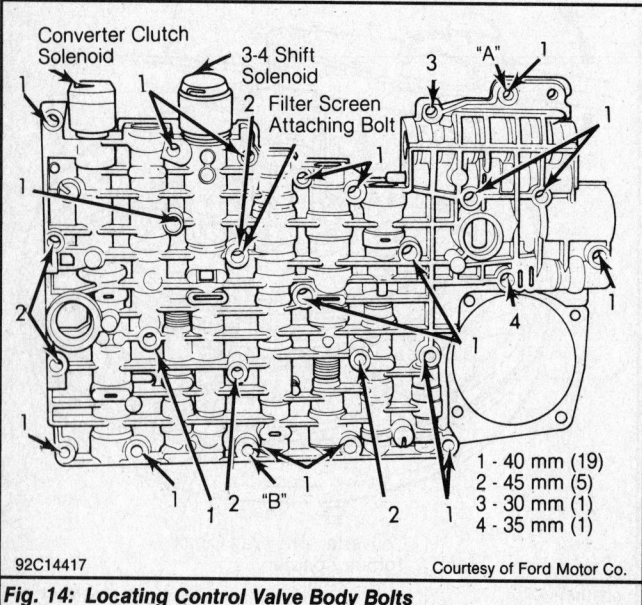

Converter Clutch Solenoid
3-4 Shift Solenoid
Filter Screen Attaching Bolt
"A"
"B"

1 - 40 mm (19)
2 - 45 mm (5)
3 - 30 mm (1)
4 - 35 mm (1)

92C14417   Courtesy of Ford Motor Co.

Fig. 14: Locating Control Valve Body Bolts

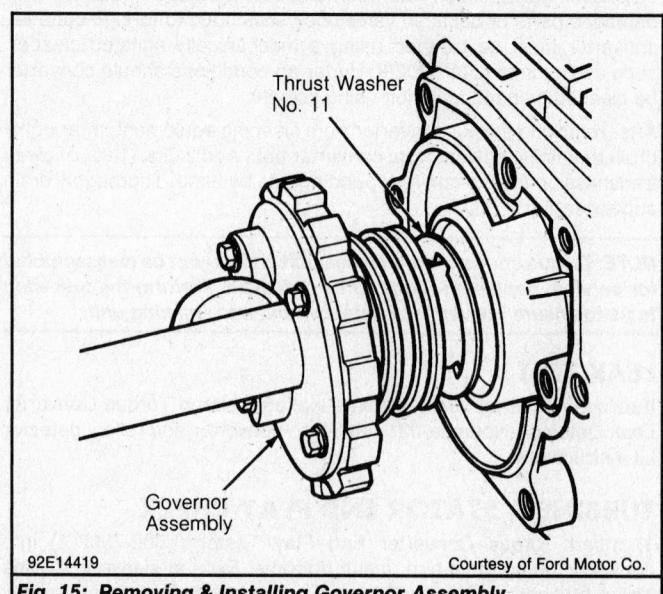

Thrust Washer No. 11

Governor Assembly

92E14419   Courtesy of Ford Motor Co.

Fig. 15: Removing & Installing Governor Assembly

NOTE: Components are not retained once governor body bolts have been removed. It is necessary to hold body and components together while removing and installing governor.

2) Remove governor body from collector body. Remove governor valve, spring and weight from governor body.

Installation – Reassemble governor body and components. Ensure correct spring is used for model application. Position governor body over oil feed holes of oil collector body. Install bolts and tighten to specifications. See TORQUE SPECIFICATIONS. To complete installation, reverse removal procedure.

PARK/NEUTRAL POSITION (PNP) SWITCH

Removal & Installation – Disconnect negative battery cable. Disconnect neutral switch wires from switch. Using Neutral Switch Socket (T74P-77247-A), remove switch and "O" ring from transmission. To install, reverse removal procedure. Tighten neutral switch to specification. See TORQUE SPECIFICATIONS.

VACUUM DIAPHRAGM

Removal & Installation – Remove heat shield (if equipped). Disconnect vacuum hose. Remove bolt and clamp. Remove vacuum diaphragm and control rod from case. To install, reverse removal procedure. Tighten bolt to specification. See TORQUE SPECIFICATIONS.

REMOVAL & INSTALLATION

See appropriate AUTOMATIC TRANSMISSION REMOVAL article in TRANSMISSION SERVICING.

TRANSMISSION DISASSEMBLY

NOTE: See Figs. 31, 32 and 33 for exploded view of internal parts, thrust washer and needle bearing locations.

1) Remove torque converter and input shaft. Splined input shaft ends are different. Note direction of installation for reassembly reference. Remove oil pan, filter screen and detent spring. Disconnect wires at converter clutch solenoid and 3-4 shift solenoid.

2) Remove valve body bolts. Unlock and remove selector connecting rod "Z" link and ease valve body and gasket from case. Remove 5 mm Allen head bolt retaining center support. Remove extension housing.

3) Remove parking pawl and return spring. Remove governor. Remove converter housing-to-case bolts. Remove converter housing and pump as an assembly. Use a twisting motion to keep clutches in place. Remove gasket and No. 1 thrust washer.

4) Remove oil pump seal from converter housing. Remove oil pump from converter housing. Remove steel plate with "O" ring from behind oil seal. See related components under CLEANING & INSPECTION.

5) Loosen overdrive band adjuster lock nut and back off adjusting screw. Discard lock nut. Remove anchor and apply struts. Lift out overdrive clutch and band. Tag band as overdrive. Tag anchor or apply end of band for reassembly reference.

6) Lift out overdrive one-way clutch and planetary assembly. Remove center support snap ring from case. Remove overdrive apply lever and shaft. Remove overdrive control bracket from valve body side of case.

NOTE: Mark apply lever and shaft for reassembly to overdrive assembly. Overdrive apply lever shaft is longer than the intermediate apply lever shaft.

7) Remove thrust washer from front of center support. Tag thrust washer for reassembly reference. Remove center support by pulling upward, carefully and evenly. Remove and tag thrust washer behind center support. See related components under CLEANING & INSPECTION.

8) Loosen intermediate band lock nut and back off adjusting screw. Discard lock nut. Remove anchor and apply struts. Remove reverse-high and forward clutch assembly. Remove intermediate band. Tag band as intermediate. Tag anchor or apply end of band for reassembly reference. Remove forward planet gear assembly. Tag thrust washer (or bearing) for reassembly reference. See related components under CLEANING & INSPECTION.

9) Remove sun gear shell. Remove large snap ring from reverse planet gear carrier (except 4.0L models). On all models, remove reverse planet assembly. Remove and tag thrust washers from both sides of assembly for reassembly reference.

10) On models with 4.0L engine, remove output shaft sleeve. On all models, remove small output shaft snap ring and remove output shaft ring gear. Remove low-reverse drum and one-way clutch assembly. If not previously removed, remove low-reverse servo. Remove low-reverse band.

11) Remove and tag thrust washer for reassembly reference. On 4.0L models, thrust washer is not removable. On all models, inner race of rear one-way clutch is not removable. Remove intermediate apply lever and shaft. Pull output shaft out from rear of transmission.

12) Remove park gear and collector body as an assembly from rear of case. Remove and tag thrust washer for reassembly reference. Remove vacuum diaphragm retaining bolt. Remove diaphragm and actuator rod. Ensure actuator rod moves freely in bore. Remove throttle valve.

13) Remove intermediate servo cover snap ring. Remove and mark intermediate servo cover, piston and spring. Remove overdrive servo cover snap ring. Remove and mark overdrive cover, piston and spring.

NOTE: Servo covers are under spring pressure. Use care during snap ring removal. If covers stick, lightly tap cover or side of case. Air pressure may be used, but DO NOT exceed 20 psi (1.4 kg/cm²). See Fig. 11.

14) Remove park/neutral position switch with appropriate switch socket. Remove kickdown lever nut, lever and "O" ring. Using care not to damage case gasket surface, remove manual linkage centering pin.

15) From inside case, remove 7/8" nut from shift lever. Remove lever, internal kickdown lever, park pawl rod and detent plate assembly. Remove lever shaft seal from case.

16) Depress tab on solenoid wire connector on outside of case. Remove solenoid wire connector. Do not remove solenoid wire connector unless replacing or degreasing case. See related components under CLEANING & INSPECTION.

COMPONENT DISASSEMBLY & REASSEMBLY

FORWARD GEAR TRAIN ASSEMBLY

Disassembly – **1)** Separate clutch hub and sun gear assembly from reverse high clutch and forward clutch assembly. Remove and tag needle bearing washer from forward planet gear carrier. See Fig. 16.

2) Remove forward planet assembly from forward clutch. Remove No. 6 needle bearing from forward clutch. Remove forward clutch thrust washer from internal gear. Tag bearing and thrust washers for reassembly reference.

3) Remove integral thrust washer from internal gear. Tag thrust washer for reassembly reference. Separate forward planet gear carrier and internal gear. Retain and mark No. 7 needle bearing thrust washer.

4) Separate reverse-high clutch assembly from forward clutch assembly. On all models except 4.0L models, remove and tag thrust washer No. 5.

Reassembly – To reassemble, reverse disassembly procedure. Ensure needle bearings and thrust washers are installed in their original location.

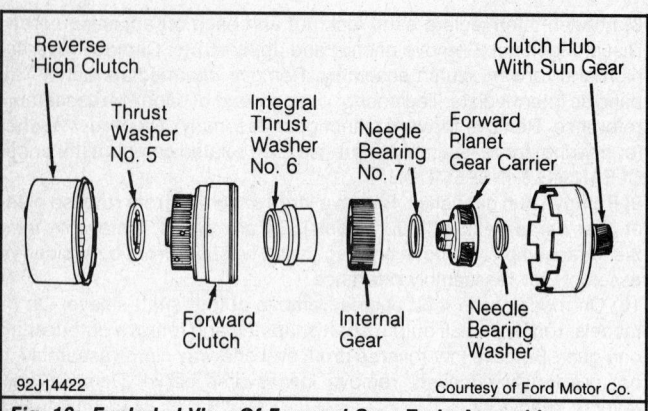

Reverse High Clutch
Thrust Washer No. 5
Integral Thrust Washer No. 6
Forward Clutch
Needle Bearing No. 7
Internal Gear
Forward Planet Gear Carrier
Needle Bearing Washer
Clutch Hub With Sun Gear

92J14422
Courtesy of Ford Motor Co.

Fig. 16: Exploded View Of Forward Gear Train Assembly (Standard Type Shown; 4.0L Model is Similar)

REVERSE-HIGH CLUTCH

Disassembly – 1) Remove pressure plate retaining snap ring. Remove pressure plate and clutch pack. Using appropriate spring compressor, compress clutch springs and remove retaining ring. Carefully release pressure on springs.

2) Remove spring compressor, spring retainer and clutch springs. Turn clutch body over and carefully force piston out with compressed air. Do not exceed 20 psi (1.4 kg/cm²). Hold finger over opposite hole. Remove "O" rings from piston and clutch body. See related components under CLEANING & INSPECTION.

Reassembly – 1) Install new "O" rings on clutch piston. Apply transmission fluid to "O" rings and install clutch piston into body. Install compression springs and spring retainer. Compress springs and install retaining snap ring. Carefully remove spring compressor.

2) Install a steel plate and then a friction plate. Alternately install remaining discs in clutch pack. Number of clutch discs varies with engine size. Install same number of discs as removed. See Fig. 17. Install pressure plate and secure pack with retaining snap ring.

3) While pushing downward on clutch pack, use a feeler gauge to check clearance between retaining snap ring and pressure plate. If clearance is not .051-.079" (1.3-2.0 mm), install correct thickness retaining snap ring.

4) Retaining snap rings are available in the following thicknesses: .0539" (1.37 mm), .0681" (1.73 mm), .0819" (2.08 mm) and .0961" (2.44 mm). Once correct retaining snap ring is installed, recheck clearance.

5) Apply air pressure to hole on back side of clutch assembly. Block opposite hole with finger. Piston must apply under pressure and release when air is removed.

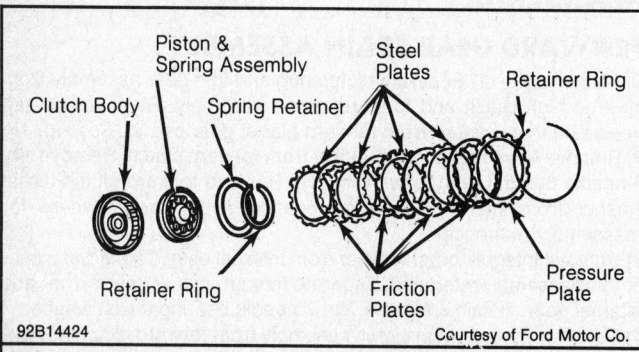

Clutch Body
Piston & Spring Assembly
Spring Retainer
Steel Plates
Retainer Ring
Retainer Ring
Friction Plates
Pressure Plate

92B14424
Courtesy of Ford Motor Co.

Fig. 17: Exploded View Of Reverse-High Clutch

FORWARD CLUTCH

Disassembly – 1) Remove pressure plate retaining snap ring. Remove pressure plate and clutch pack. Using appropriate spring compressor, compress clutch springs and remove retaining ring. Carefully release pressure on springs.

2) Remove spring compressor, spring retainer and clutch springs. Install center support on forward clutch cylinder. Apply air pressure to

left side (middle-sized) port. Piston will be forced out. See Fig. 18. Remove "O" rings from piston and clutch body. See related components under CLEANING & INSPECTION.

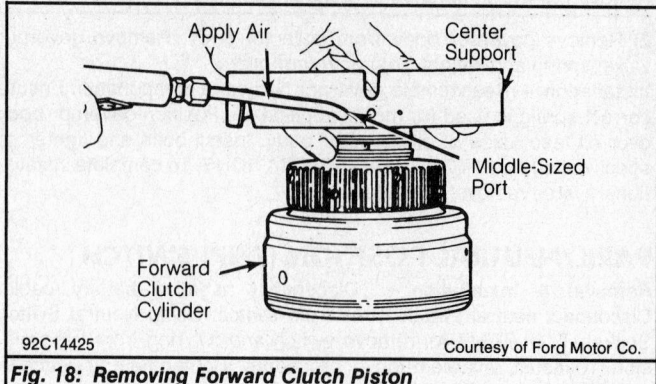

Apply Air
Center Support
Middle-Sized Port
Forward Clutch Cylinder

92C14425
Courtesy of Ford Motor Co.

Fig. 18: Removing Forward Clutch Piston

Reassembly – 1) Install new "O" rings on clutch piston. Apply transmission fluid to "O" rings and install clutch piston into body. Install compression springs and spring retainer. Compress springs and install retaining snap ring. Carefully remove spring compressor.

2) Ensure cushion is installed between steel clutch plate and piston. See Fig. 19. Install a steel plate and then a friction plate. Alternately install remaining discs in clutch pack. Number of clutch discs varies with engine size. Install same number of discs as removed. Install pressure plate and secure pack with retaining snap ring.

3) While pushing down on clutch pack, use a feeler gauge to check clearance between retaining snap ring and pressure plate. If clearance is not .055-.083" (1.4-2.1 mm), install correct thickness retaining snap ring.

4) Retaining snap rings are available in the following thicknesses: .0539" (1.37 mm), .0681" (1.73 mm), .0819" (2.08 mm) and .0961" (2.44 mm). Once correct retaining snap ring is installed, recheck clearance.

5) Apply air pressure to hole on back side of clutch assembly. Block opposite hole with finger. Piston must apply under pressure and release when air is removed.

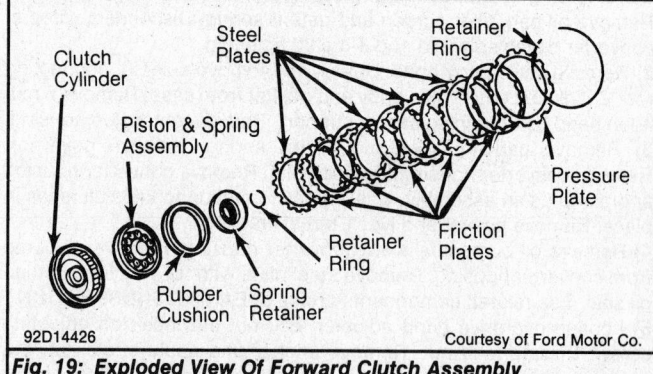

Clutch Cylinder
Piston & Spring Assembly
Rubber Cushion
Spring Retainer
Steel Plates
Retainer Ring
Retainer Ring
Friction Plates
Pressure Plate

92D14426
Courtesy of Ford Motor Co.

Fig. 19: Exploded View Of Forward Clutch Assembly

OVERDRIVE CLUTCH

Disassembly – Disassembly of overdrive clutch is the same as reverse-high clutch. See Fig. 20. See related components under CLEANING & INSPECTION.

Reassembly – 1) Reassembly of overdrive clutch is the same as reverse-high clutch, except for location of clutch springs during assembly. Ensure clutch springs are installed in 5 groups with 3 springs in each group and a single spring space between groups (5 spaces total).

2) Clearance between retaining snap ring and pressure plate must be .055-.083" (1.4-2.1 mm). Retaining snap rings are available in the following thicknesses: .0539" (1.37 mm), .0681" (1.73 mm), .0819" (2.08 mm) and .0961" (2.44 mm). Once correct retaining snap ring is installed, recheck clearance.

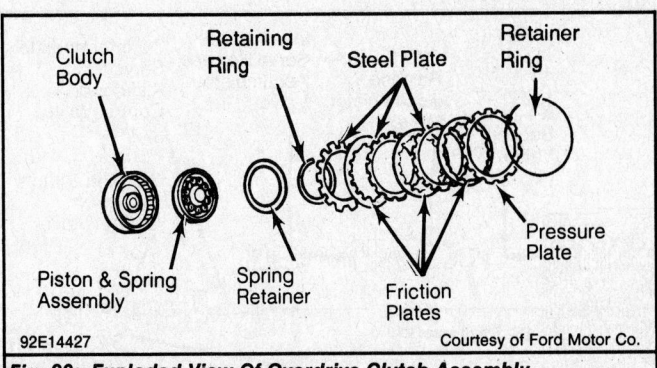

92E14427   Courtesy of Ford Motor Co.

Fig. 20: Exploded View Of Overdrive Clutch Assembly

OVERDRIVE ONE-WAY CLUTCH

Disassembly – 1) Mark and remove overdrive clutch adapter to ensure reassembly to original position. Remove sun overdrive gear and thrust bearing rear race. Mark thrust bearing race for reassembly reference. *See Fig. 22.*

2) Remove planet carrier and No. 2 needle bearing. Mark No. 2 needle bearing for reassembly. Remove retaining snap ring from overdrive center shaft and ring gear. Separate ring gear and center shaft.

3) Mark and remove washer. Note position of one-way clutch and remove from center shaft. One-way clutch must be installed properly or damage can occur. See related components under CLEANING & INSPECTION.

Reassembly – 1) For reassembly, reverse disassembly procedure. Ensure part number on adapter faces sun gear. Ensure No. 2 needle bearing is centered and lip faces toward sun gear.

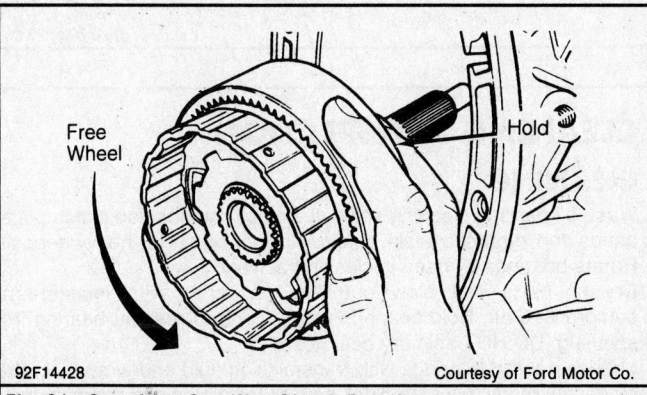

92F14428   Courtesy of Ford Motor Co.

Fig. 21: Overdrive One-Way Clutch Rotation

2) Ensure recessed I.D. of washer faces planet carrier. Ensure one-way clutch flange side faces planet carrier. Ensure one-way clutch rotates in proper direction. *See Fig. 21.*

LOW-REVERSE ONE-WAY CLUTCH

Disassembly & Reassembly – 1) Using a screwdriver, remove snap ring. Mark and lift out one-way clutch with springs and roller bearings as an assembly. Replace assembly if found defective. See related components under CLEANING & INSPECTION.

2) To reassemble, insert one-way clutch with springs. Using a screwdriver, separate springs and install roller bearings one at a time. Install snap ring. Ensure one-way clutch is installed properly as marked during disassembly.

GOVERNOR

Disassembly – 1) Remove governor body-to-oil collector body retaining bolts. When these bolts are removed, governor components are no longer secured in position. Care must be taken not to drop governor body and components when bolts are removed.

2) Remove outer weight, spring and primary valve from governor body. *See Fig. 31.* Remove 2 bolts holding counterweight to collector body and remove counterweight. Remove seals from oil collector body and discard. See related components under CLEANING & INSPECTION.

Reassembly – Clean and inspect all parts. Replace worn or damaged parts. Without excessive stretching, install new seals on oil collector. Reassemble counterweight, spring and primary valve in governor body. Reassemble governor body and counterweight to oil collector body.

VALVE BODY

NOTE: During disassembly, place individual parts in order and in relative position for reassembly reference. Tag all springs as they are removed for reassembly reference.

Disassembly – 1) Remove 3 Torx bolts and remove separator plate and gasket. Note location and remove check ball, shuttle balls, check valves and relief valves with springs. *See Fig. 24.*

2) Ensure small filter remains with separator plate when plate is removed from valve body. Filter is located in corner of separator plate near converter clutch solenoid connector. Remove retaining plates, dowels, plugs and valves with springs from valve body. *See Fig. 23.* See related components under CLEANING & INSPECTION.

Reassembly – Lubricate all parts with transmission fluid. Install valves, springs, plugs, and pins. *See Fig. 23.* Using new gasket, apply petroleum jelly to keep gasket in place during separator plate reassembly. Install separator plate.

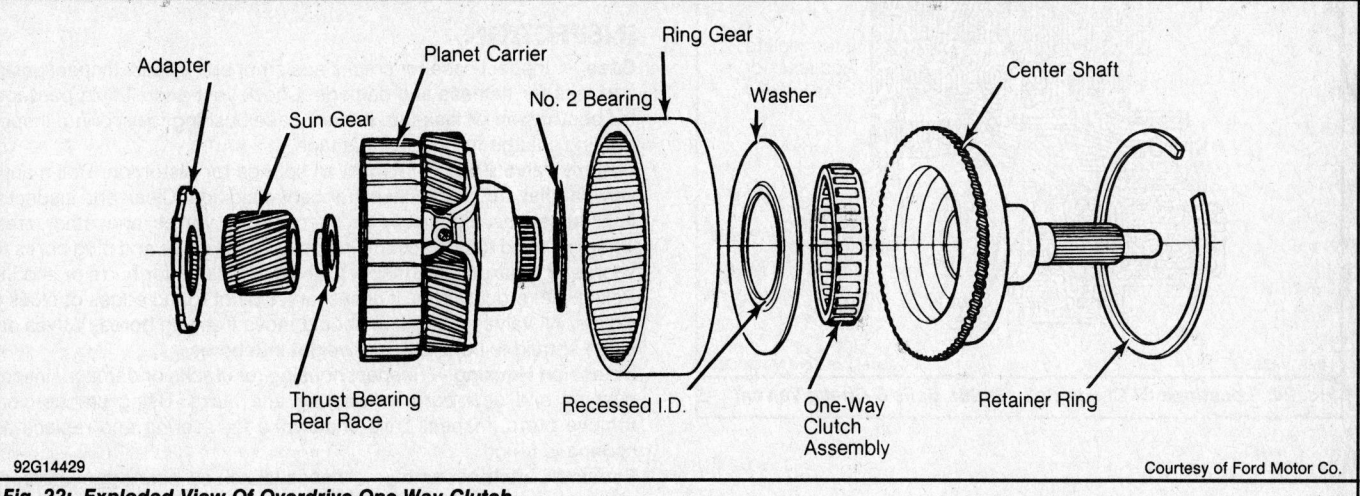

92G14429   Courtesy of Ford Motor Co.

Fig. 22: Exploded View Of Overdrive One-Way Clutch

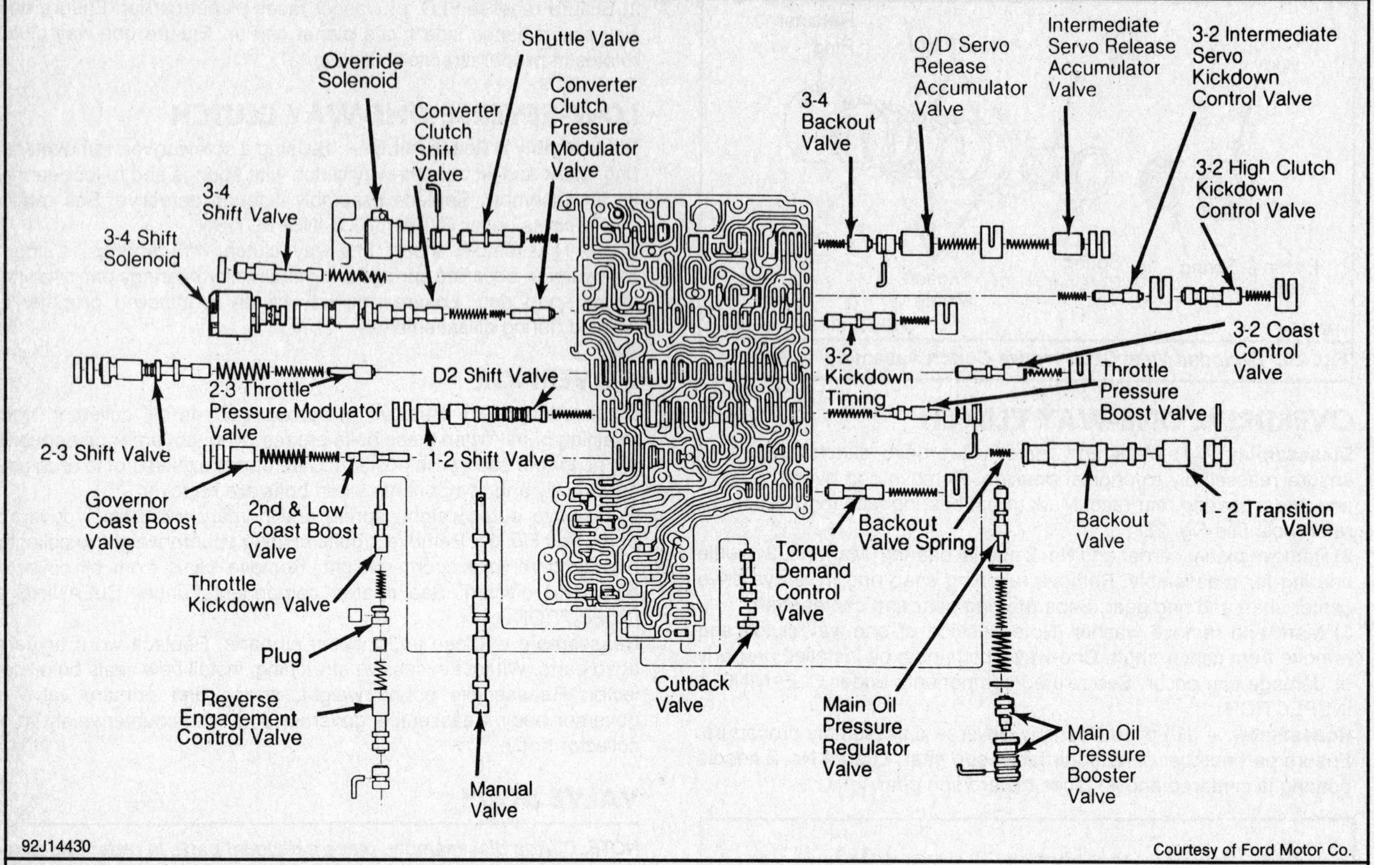

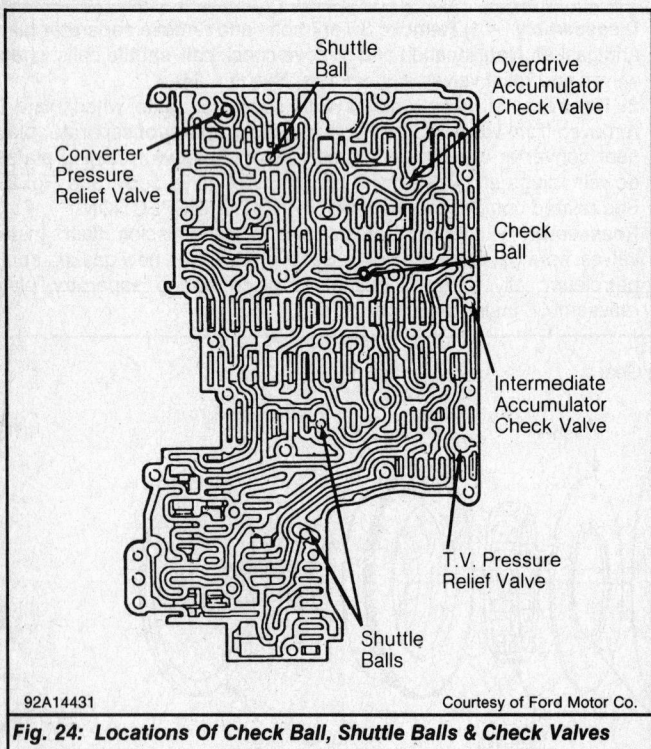

Override Solenoid
Shuttle Valve
Converter Clutch Shift Valve
Converter Clutch Pressure Modulator Valve
O/D Servo Release Accumulator Valve
Intermediate Servo Release Accumulator Valve
3-2 Intermediate Servo Kickdown Control Valve
3-4 Backout Valve
3-4 Shift Valve
3-2 High Clutch Kickdown Control Valve
3-4 Shift Solenoid
2-3 Throttle Pressure Modulator Valve
D2 Shift Valve
3-2 Coast Control Valve
3-2 Kickdown Timing
Throttle Pressure Boost Valve
2-3 Shift Valve
1-2 Shift Valve
Governor Coast Boost Valve
2nd & Low Coast Boost Valve
Backout Valve Spring
Backout Valve
1-2 Transition Valve
Throttle Kickdown Valve
Torque Demand Control Valve
Plug
Cutback Valve
Main Oil Pressure Regulator Valve
Main Oil Pressure Booster Valve
Reverse Engagement Control Valve
Manual Valve

92J14430 — Courtesy of Ford Motor Co.

Fig. 23: Exploded View Of Valve Body Assembly

Shuttle Ball
Overdrive Accumulator Check Valve
Converter Pressure Relief Valve
Check Ball
Intermediate Accumulator Check Valve
T.V. Pressure Relief Valve
Shuttle Balls

92A14431 — Courtesy of Ford Motor Co.

Fig. 24: Locations Of Check Ball, Shuttle Balls & Check Valves

CLEANING & INSPECTION

CLEANING

Wash all parts in cleaning solvent, except composition clutch plates, bands and synthetic seals. Use scraper or brush for heavy deposits. Rotate bearings by hand in cleaning solvent.

Dry all parts and blow out fluid passages with moisture-free compressed air. Hold bearings while drying to prevent bearing from spinning. DO NOT spin dry bearings.

Lubricate clean bearings with transmission fluid and wrap in lint-free cloth until ready to install. Soak new clutch plates and bands in transmission fluid for at least 15 minutes prior to installation.

INSPECTION

Case – Inspect case for cracks and stripped threads. Inspect gasket surfaces for flatness and damage. Check vent and all fluid passages for obstruction or leakage. Inspect case bushing for scoring. Inspect parking linkage for wear or damage.

Control Valve Body – Inspect all springs for distortion. Roll manual valve on flat surface to check for bent condition. Clean and inspect all fluid passages, especially at check balls, valves and other areas where dirt and debris accumulate. Inspect all valve and plug bores for scores or obstructions. Inspect valves and plugs for burrs or scoring. Polish with crocus cloth, if necessary. Do not round edges of plugs or valves. All valves and plugs should move freely in bores. Valves and plugs should fall of their own weight into bores.

Extension Housing – Inspect housing for cracks or damage. Inspect bushing and seal bore for scoring and burrs. Using crocus cloth, remove burrs. Inspect drive shaft yoke for scoring and replace it if scoring is found.

Forward Clutch Assembly – Inspect clutch cylinder thrust surfaces, piston, bore and clutch plates for scores or burrs. Minor burrs and scoring may be polished with crocus cloth. Inspect piston check ball for proper seating. Check clutch springs for distortion or cracks.

Check clutch plates for flatness and free movement on clutch hub. Check clutch hub thrust surfaces and splines for wear or scoring. Inspect input shaft for damaged or worn splines.

Governor – Inspect spring for distortion. Inspect fluid passages for obstruction. Inspect valve and bore for burrs or scoring. Polish with crocus cloth, if necessary. Do not round edges of valve. Valves should move freely in bore. Valve should fall of its own weight into bore.

Pinion Carrier – Inspect pins and shafts in planet assemblies for loose fit or complete disengagement. Ensure proper staking of shaft retaining pins before installation of planet assembly. Pins should be no more than .040" (1.0 mm) below surface of carrier. Inspect pinion gears for worn or damaged teeth. Check for free rotation of pinion gears.

Pump – Inspect fluid passages. Inspect mating surfaces of pump body and case for burrs. Inspect gear teeth for burrs. Inspect gear bearing surfaces and pump bushing for scoring. Minor burrs and scoring may be polished with crocus cloth.

One-Way Clutches – Inspect outer and inner races for scoring or damage. Inspect rollers and springs for damage. Inspect roller cage for damaged spring retainers.

Reverse-High and Overdrive Clutches – Inspect drum band surface, bushing and thrust surfaces for scoring. Minor burrs and scoring may be polished with crocus cloth. Inspect clutch piston, bore and inner and outer bearing surfaces for scoring. Inspect clutch plates for flatness and free movement on clutch hub. Check clutch plates for scoring or burrs. Check clutch springs for distortion. Replace as necessary. Inspect clutch cylinder check balls for proper seating.

Servos – Inspect band lining for excessive wear and proper bonding to metal band. Inspect fluid passages for obstructions. Inspect servo and piston bore for cracks, scoring or other damage. Inspect seals and sealing surfaces. Repair or replace as necessary.

Stator Support – Inspect stator support splines for burrs and wear. Inspect oil ring grooves in stator support for nicks or damaged edges. Check front pump support seal and seal rings for damage.

TRANSMISSION REASSEMBLY

NOTE: Lubricate all parts with transmission fluid during reassembly. Thrust washers and gaskets should be held in place with petroleum jelly. See Fig. 32 and 33 for location of thrust washers & bearings.

1) Before installing center support into case, install new high clutch seals on support hub. It is necessary to size these seals. Apply liberal amount of petroleum jelly to center support hub and seals.

NOTE: If sizing is not done, the seals may be cut or rolled over when entering intermediate brake drum cavity.

2) Use overdrive brake drum for sizing. Carefully rotate center support while inserting it into drum housing. Observe seals as they enter cavity to ensure that they do not roll over or get cut.

3) Ensure center support is seated fully into overdrive drum. Allow assembly to stand for several minutes for seals to seat in grooves. Set aside until required for reassembly.

NOTE: If new output shaft is being installed, ensure correct shaft is used. The shaft for the 4.0L model does not have a lubrication hole.

4) Position No. 11 thrust washer in rear of case. Install collector body in rear of case. Install output shaft. Install governor on collector body. Tighten bolts to specifications. See TORQUE SPECIFICATIONS.

5) Position No. 10 thrust washer into case from front. Using Clutch Replacement Guide (T74P-77193-A), install low-reverse brake drum (guide not required on 4.0L models). Install output shaft ring gear and new snap ring. On 4.0L models, install output shaft sleeve. On all models, install No. 9 thrust washer, reverse planet assembly and No. 8 thrust washer.

6) On all models except 4.0L, install snap ring in drum to hold planet assembly. On all models, install low-reverse band as marked at disassembly. Replace piston "O" ring and install low-reverse servo piston assembly to hold band in position.

CAUTION: DO NOT mix any of the servo piston assemblies or covers as transmission failure may occur.

7) Replace piston "O" ring and install intermediate servo piston assembly. Install piston cover and snap ring. Replace piston "O" ring and install overdrive servo piston assembly. Install piston cover and snap ring.

8) Install intermediate servo apply lever and shaft into case. Install complete forward clutch and reverse-high clutch assemblies (forward geartrain assembly). Turn transmission so output shaft points downward. Install intermediate band and apply strut. Install intermediate band anchor strut. Temporarily install input shaft.

9) Check transmission rear end play to determine amount of space between thrust washer surface of overdrive center support and intermediate brake drum. On all models except 4.0L clip together type assembly, the No. 4 thrust washer is used to obtain end play of .012-.022" (.30-.56 mm). On 4.0L clip together assembly, the No. 5 thrust bearing is used to obtain end play of .004-.024" (.10-.61 mm). *See Fig. 33.*

10) On all models except 4.0L, place appropriate gauge bar on case shoulder. *See Fig. 25.* Using depth micrometer, measure between gauge bar and No. 4 thrust washer mating surface at 2 locations, 180° apart. Average measurements and select correct thickness thrust washer. See NO. 4 SELECTIVE THRUST WASHER chart. Go to step **12)**.

NO. 4 SELECTIVE THRUST WASHER

Average Reading In. (mm)	Thrust Washer Thickness In. (mm)
.065-.073 (1.66-1.85)	.053-.055 (1.35-1.40)
.074-.077 (1.86-1.95)	.061-.063 (1.55-1.60)
.078-.081 (1.96-2.05)	.065-.067 (1.65-1.70)
.082-.085 (2.06-2.15)	.069-.071 (1.75-1.80)
.086-.089 (2.16-2.25)	.073-.075 (1.85-1.90)
.090-.093 (.077-.079)	.077-.079 (1.95-2.00)
.094-.100 (2.36-2.55)	.081-.083 (2.05-2.10)

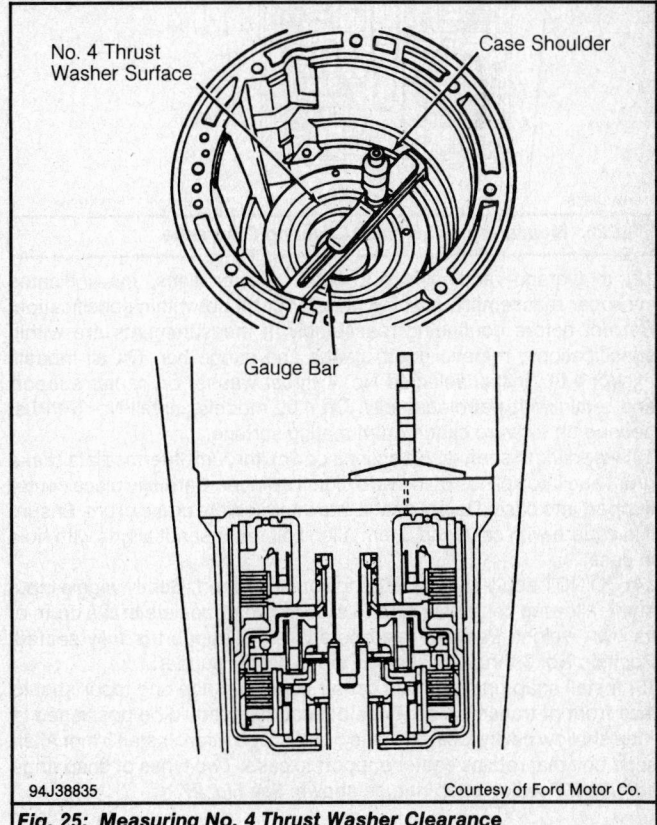

94J38835   Courtesy of Ford Motor Co.

Fig. 25: Measuring No. 4 Thrust Washer Clearance

11) On 4.0L models, place appropriate gauge bar on case shoulder. *See Fig. 26*. Using depth micrometer, measure between gauge bar and No. 5 thrust bearing mating surface at 2 locations, 180 degrees apart. Average measurements and select correct thickness thrust washer. See No. 5 SELECTIVE THRUST BEARING chart. Go to step **12)**.

NO. 5 SELECTIVE THRUST BEARING

Average Reading In. (mm)	Thrust Washer Thickness In. (mm)
1.773-1.780 (45.66-1.85)	.131-.135 (3.33-3.44)
1.781-1.788 (45.23-45.41)	.138-1.43 (3.51-3.62)
1.788-1.796 (45.42-45.61)	.146-.150 (3.70-3.81)
1.796-1.804 (45.62-45.81)	.154-.158 (3.90-4.01)

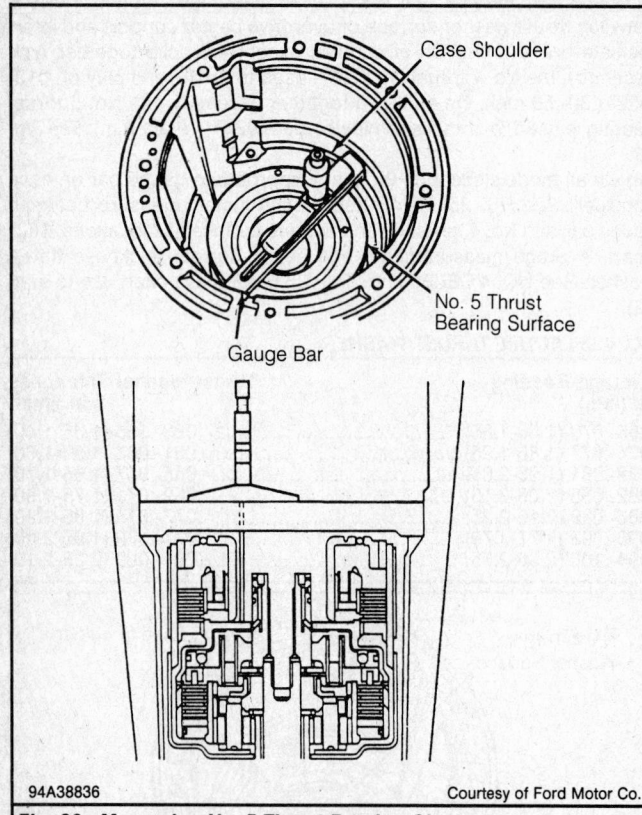

94A38836   Courtesy of Ford Motor Co.
Fig. 26: Measuring No. 5 Thrust Bearing Clearance

12) If average reading is not within specifications, this indicates improper reassembly, missing parts or parts not within specification. Correct before continuing reassembly. If measurements are within specifications, remove depth gauge and gauge bar. On all models except 4.0L, install selected No. 4 thrust washer on center support and retain with petroleum jelly. On 4.0L models, install No. 5 thrust bearing on forward clutch drum mating surface.

13) Insert input shaft (short splines down), through intermediate brake drum and into splines of forward clutch cylinder. Carefully place center support into case. Do not seat it into intermediate brake drum. Ensure it is square with case and 5 mm Allen bolt retainer nut aligns with hole in case.

14) DO NOT apply any pressure to center support. Gently wiggle input shaft, allowing center support to slide into intermediate brake drum of its own weight. Perform this operation until support is fully seated. Position No. 3 thrust washer on top of center support.

15) Install snap ring to retain center support. Snap ring taper should face front of transmission. Ends of snap ring should be positioned in wide shallow cavity located in the 5 o'clock position. Install 5 mm Allen head bolt that retains center support to case. Two types of snap rings are used. Position snap ring as shown. *See Fig. 27*.

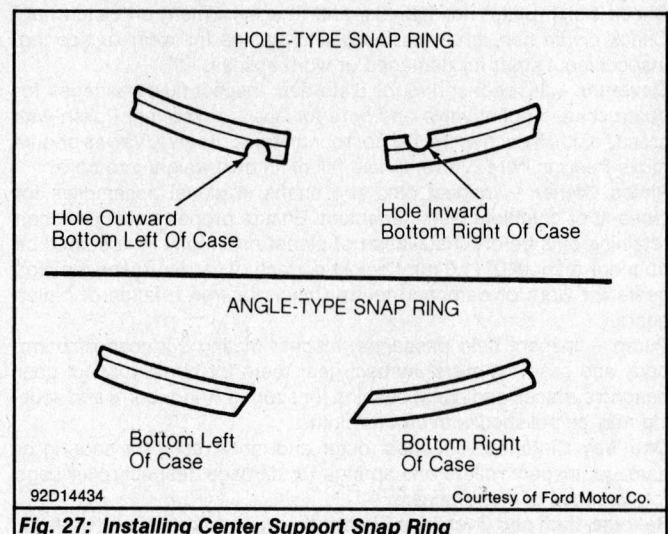

92D14434   Courtesy of Ford Motor Co.
Fig. 27: Installing Center Support Snap Ring

16) Install sun gear and adapter into overdrive planet assembly and one-way clutch. Take care to center needle bearing race inside of planetary assembly. Ensure it stays centered and is positioned with lip upward (toward sun gear).

17) Install overdrive planet assembly and one-way clutch into case. Install overdrive drum assembly. Install overdrive bracket, apply lever and shaft. Install overdrive band (tagged at disassembly), and apply strut. Install anchor strut.

18) Ensure needle bearing race in overdrive planetary assembly is centered and overdrive clutch is fully seated. Place No. 1 selective washer on top of overdrive clutch drum and temporarily install pump assembly (without gasket) into case. Ensure pump assembly is fully seated in case and pump body is below level of case gasket surface.

NOTE: Check for damaged or missing front pump support seal. Replace if necessary.

19) Mount a dial indicator on oil pump with tip resting on transmission housing. *See Fig. 28*. Zero dial indicator and swing indicator around so plunger contacts oil pump.

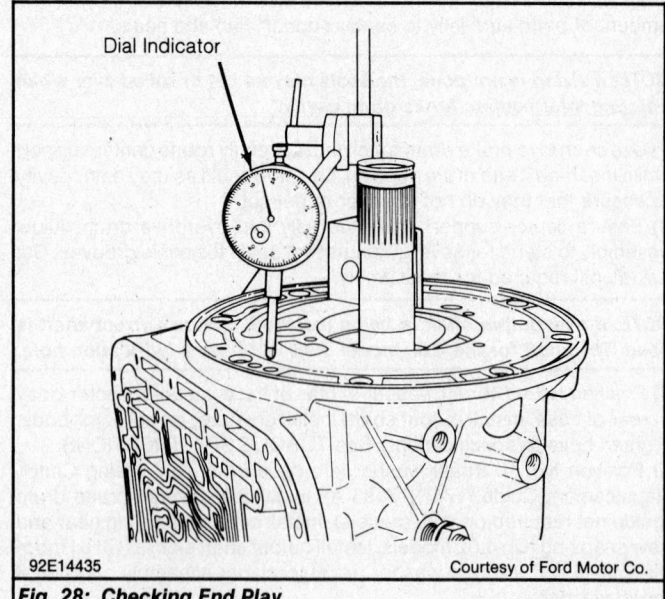

92E14435   Courtesy of Ford Motor Co.
Fig. 28: Checking End Play

20) Record dial indicator reading. Move dial indicator assembly to opposite side of pump (180 degrees). Take another end play reading. Average the 2 readings.

21) End play range is .007-.025" (.18-.64 mm). If end play exceeds limits, replace No. 1 selective thrust washer. No. 1 thrust washers are available in the following thicknesses: .053-.055" (1.35-1.40 mm), .061-.063" (1.55-1.60 mm), .065-.067" (1.65-1.70 mm), .069-.071" (1.75-1.80 mm), .073-.075" (1.85-1.90 mm), .077-.079" (1.95-2.00 mm) and .081-.083" (2.05-2.10 mm).

22) After end play check has been completed, remove oil pump and No. 1 selective thrust washer. Mark installed position of oil pump gears in relation to one another and remove.

23) Install new oil pump seal. Position separator plate on converter housing. Place pump gears into pump housing. The inside edge of small gear has a chamfer on one side. This chamfer must face toward front of transmission.

24) The larger gear has a dimple on one side which must face toward rear of transmission. Position pump assembly onto separator plate and converter housing. Install bolts finger tight.

NOTE: The rough appearance of pump stator casting is not a flaw. Do not replace casting due to this appearance.

---

25) To prevent seal leakage, pump gear breakage or bushing failure, align pump in converter housing with Pump Alignment Set (T74P-77103-X). Select smallest I.D. sleeve which will fit completely over pump shaft. Outside diameter of sleeve will center pump in converter housing.

26) Install 5 new Allen bolts. Tighten to specification. See TORQUE SPECIFICATIONS. Remove alignment tool. Install input shaft into pump. Install converter into pump gears. Rotate converter to check for free movement. Remove converter and input shaft.

27) Coat converter housing gasket with petroleum jelly and position on converter housing. Install seal ring on converter housing. Position No. 1 selected thrust washer on rear of pump. Align converter housing and pump to transmission case. Install bolts with new "O" rings and tighten to specification.

28) Install new lock nut on overdrive band adjusting screw. Tighten adjusting screw to 120 INCH lbs. (14 N.m) and back off exactly 2 turns. Hold adjusting screw and tighten lock nut to 35-45 ft. lbs. (47-61 N.m). Repeat procedure for intermediate band. Air pressure tests may be performed to ensure proper transmission operation. See AIR PRESSURE TESTS under TESTING.

29) Install shift lever oil seal. Install internal shift linkage, external manual control lever and centering pin. Tighten nut to 30-40 ft. lbs. (41-54 N.m). Install "O" ring, kickdown lever and 13 mm nut. Install Neutral switch using appropriate socket.

30) Install converter clutch solenoid connector. Install throttle valve, rod, vacuum diaphragm, retaining clamp and bolt. Tighten to specification. Ensure throttle valve moves freely in its bore.

31) Align valve body to separator plate and gasket using tapered punches. Use a small amount of petroleum jelly to hold gasket in place. Install 2 bolts and tighten to 53-71 INCH lbs. (6-8 N.m). Attach and lock "Z" link to manual valve. Carefully ease valve body into case using care not to bend "Z" link.

NOTE: Valve body bolts are of different lengths. Ensure each bolt is installed in its correct location.

---

32) Install and finger tighten bolts "A" and "B". *See Fig. 14.* Position solenoid retainer onto solenoid. Install and tighten remaining bolts except filter screen bolt. Remove bolt "A" and install detent spring.

33) Connect solenoid wires. Install reverse servo piston assembly into bore along with Servo Check Spring (D4ZZ-70031-A). Ensure piston rod is seated correctly in reverse band apply end. Install Servo Rod Selecting Gauge (T74P-77190-A) with new servo cover gasket. *See Fig. 29.*

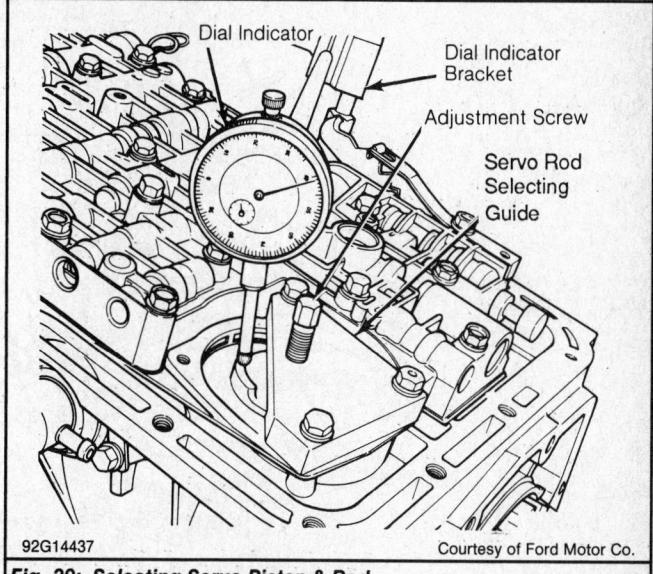

92G14437 · Courtesy of Ford Motor Co.

Fig. 29: Selecting Servo Piston & Rod

34) Tighten select guide adjusting screw to 35 INCH lbs. (4 N.m). Install dial indicator onto case. Position indicator tip on one of 3 servo piston pads accessible through cut-out of guide. Zero dial indicator.

35) Back out adjusting screw until servo piston bottoms out on guide. Record distance servo piston moved. Servo piston travel should be .120-.220" (3.05-5.59 mm). *See Fig. 30.*

36) If piston travel is greater than specification, use next longest piston and rod. If less than specification, use next shorter piston and rod. Rods are identified by their number of grooves. Rods with 2 grooves are shortest in length; rods with no grooves are medium in length; rods with one groove are longest.

37) Install selected piston and rod. Recheck piston travel. If correct, remove guide and auxiliary spring. Reinstall servo assembly, accumulator spring, gasket and cover. Install servo cover bolts and tighten to specification.

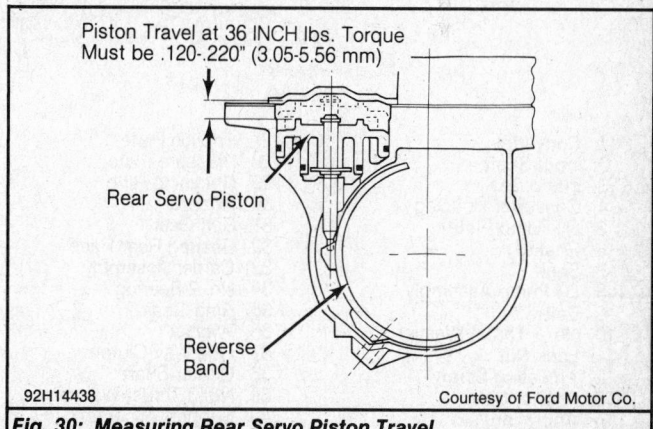

92H14438 · Courtesy of Ford Motor Co.

Fig. 30: Measuring Rear Servo Piston Travel

38) Install new "O" rings on filter screen and lube with petroleum jelly. Install filter screen and bolt. Install oil pan with new gasket. Tighten pan bolts to specification in 2 steps. See TORQUE SPECIFICATIONS.

39) Install parking pawl and return spring in extension housing and preload. Using new gasket, install extension housing. Ensure operating parking rod is correctly seated in extension guide cup. Install and tighten bolts.

40) Install input shaft and torque converter. Ensure torque converter is properly installed. When installation is correct, measurement between torque converter pilot nose and front face of housing will be .402-.568" (11.12-14.30 mm).

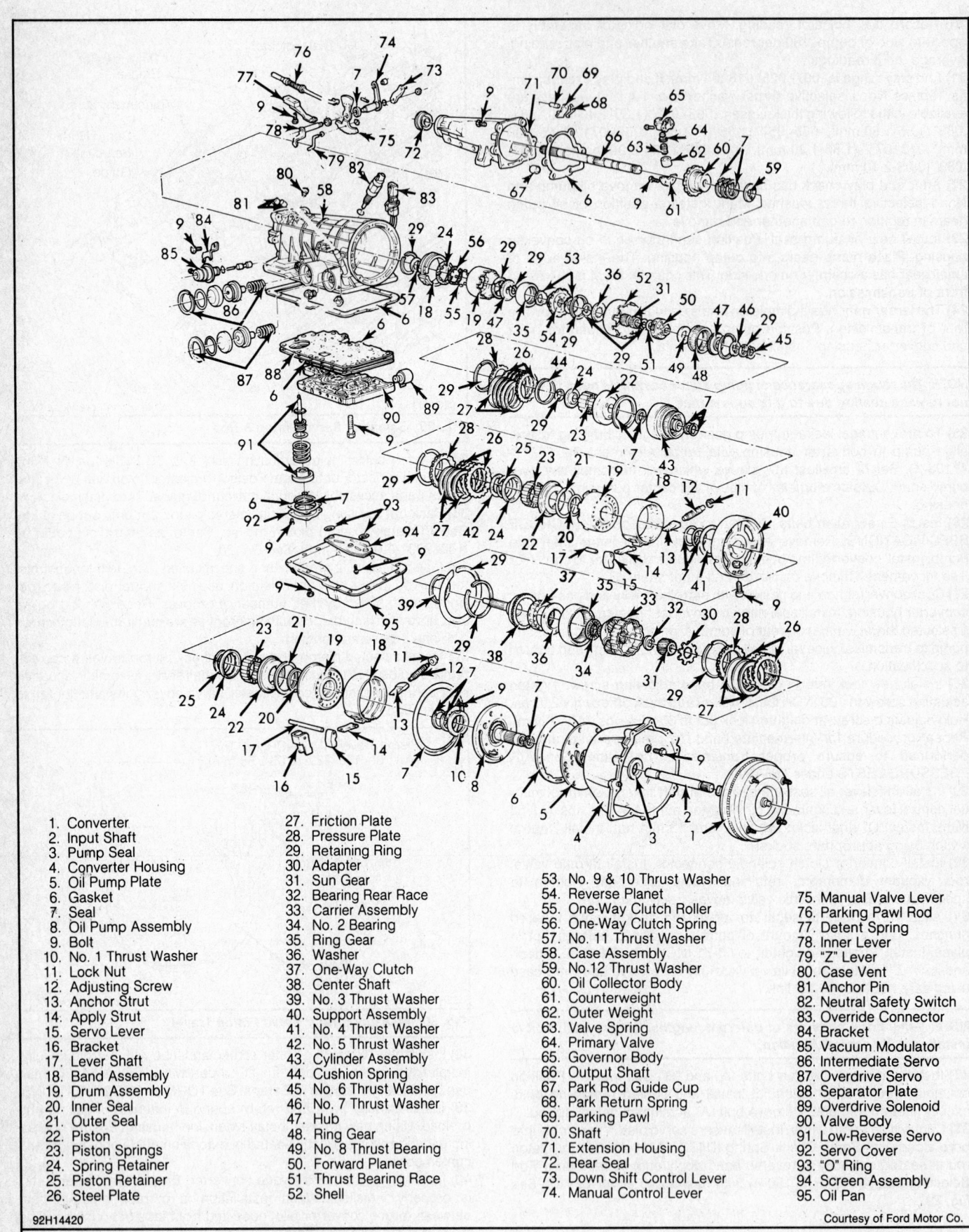

1. Converter	27. Friction Plate	53. No. 9 & 10 Thrust Washer
2. Input Shaft	28. Pressure Plate	54. Reverse Planet
3. Pump Seal	29. Retaining Ring	55. One-Way Clutch Roller
4. Converter Housing	30. Adapter	56. One-Way Clutch Spring
5. Oil Pump Plate	31. Sun Gear	57. No. 11 Thrust Washer
6. Gasket	32. Bearing Rear Race	58. Case Assembly
7. Seal	33. Carrier Assembly	59. No.12 Thrust Washer
8. Oil Pump Assembly	34. No. 2 Bearing	60. Oil Collector Body
9. Bolt	35. Ring Gear	61. Counterweight
10. No. 1 Thrust Washer	36. Washer	62. Outer Weight
11. Lock Nut	37. One-Way Clutch	63. Valve Spring
12. Adjusting Screw	38. Center Shaft	64. Primary Valve
13. Anchor Strut	39. No. 3 Thrust Washer	65. Governor Body
14. Apply Strut	40. Support Assembly	66. Output Shaft
15. Servo Lever	41. No. 4 Thrust Washer	67. Park Rod Guide Cup
16. Bracket	42. No. 5 Thrust Washer	68. Park Return Spring
17. Lever Shaft	43. Cylinder Assembly	69. Parking Pawl
18. Band Assembly	44. Cushion Spring	70. Shaft
19. Drum Assembly	45. No. 6 Thrust Washer	71. Extension Housing
20. Inner Seal	46. No. 7 Thrust Washer	72. Rear Seal
21. Outer Seal	47. Hub	73. Down Shift Control Lever
22. Piston	48. Ring Gear	74. Manual Control Lever
23. Piston Springs	49. No. 8 Thrust Bearing	75. Manual Valve Lever
24. Spring Retainer	50. Forward Planet	76. Parking Pawl Rod
25. Piston Retainer	51. Thrust Bearing Race	77. Detent Spring
26. Steel Plate	52. Shell	78. Inner Lever
		79. "Z" Lever
		80. Case Vent
		81. Anchor Pin
		82. Neutral Safety Switch
		83. Override Connector
		84. Bracket
		85. Vacuum Modulator
		86. Intermediate Servo
		87. Overdrive Servo
		88. Separator Plate
		89. Overdrive Solenoid
		90. Valve Body
		91. Low-Reverse Servo
		92. Servo Cover
		93. "O" Ring
		94. Screen Assembly
		95. Oil Pan

92H14420

Courtesy of Ford Motor Co.

Fig. 31: Exploded View Of A4LD Transmission

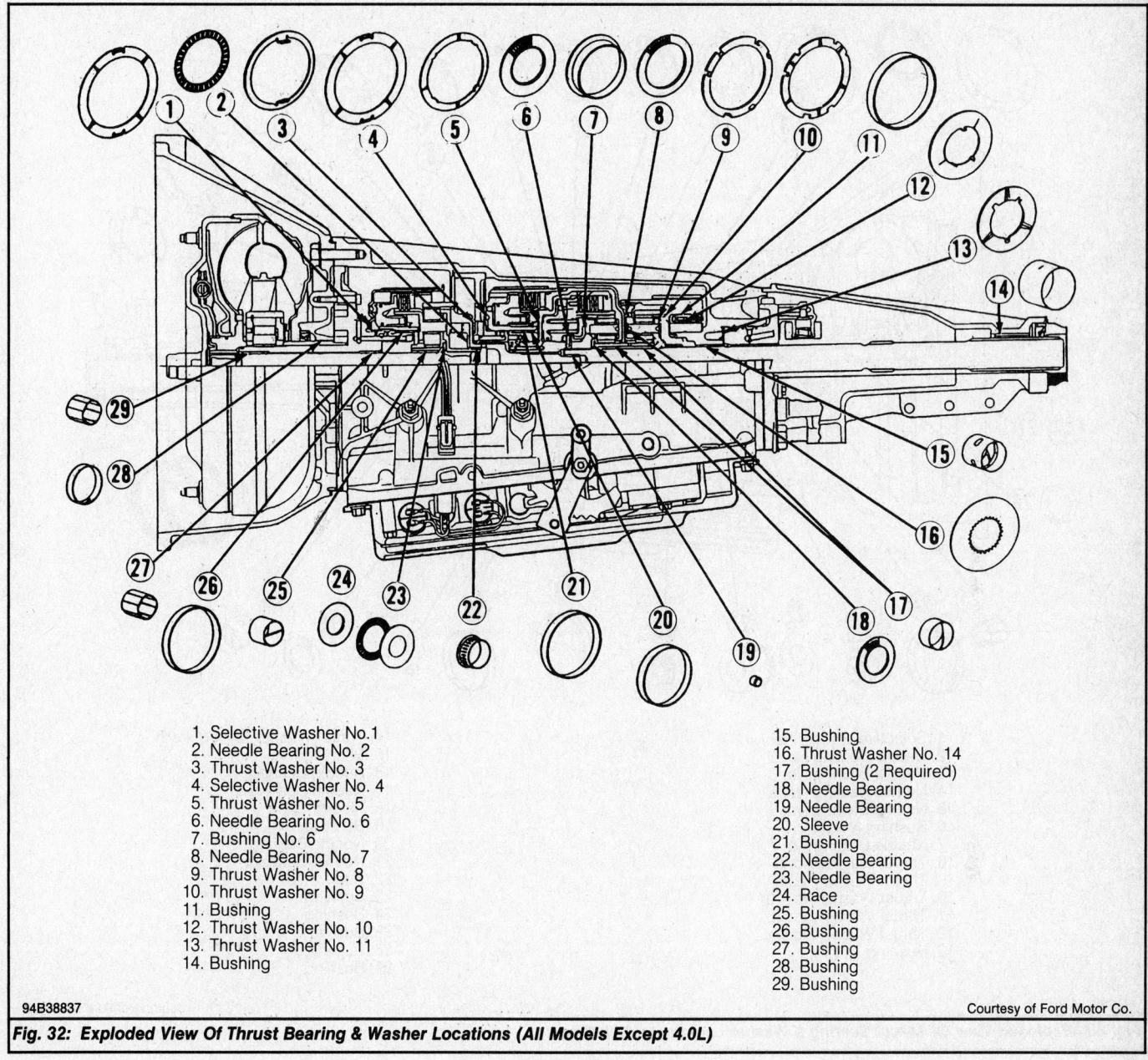

1. Selective Washer No.1
2. Needle Bearing No. 2
3. Thrust Washer No. 3
4. Selective Washer No. 4
5. Thrust Washer No. 5
6. Needle Bearing No. 6
7. Bushing No. 6
8. Needle Bearing No. 7
9. Thrust Washer No. 8
10. Thrust Washer No. 9
11. Bushing
12. Thrust Washer No. 10
13. Thrust Washer No. 11
14. Bushing

15. Bushing
16. Thrust Washer No. 14
17. Bushing (2 Required)
18. Needle Bearing
19. Needle Bearing
20. Sleeve
21. Bushing
22. Needle Bearing
23. Needle Bearing
24. Race
25. Bushing
26. Bushing
27. Bushing
28. Bushing
29. Bushing

94B38837

Courtesy of Ford Motor Co.

Fig. 32: Exploded View Of Thrust Bearing & Washer Locations (All Models Except 4.0L)

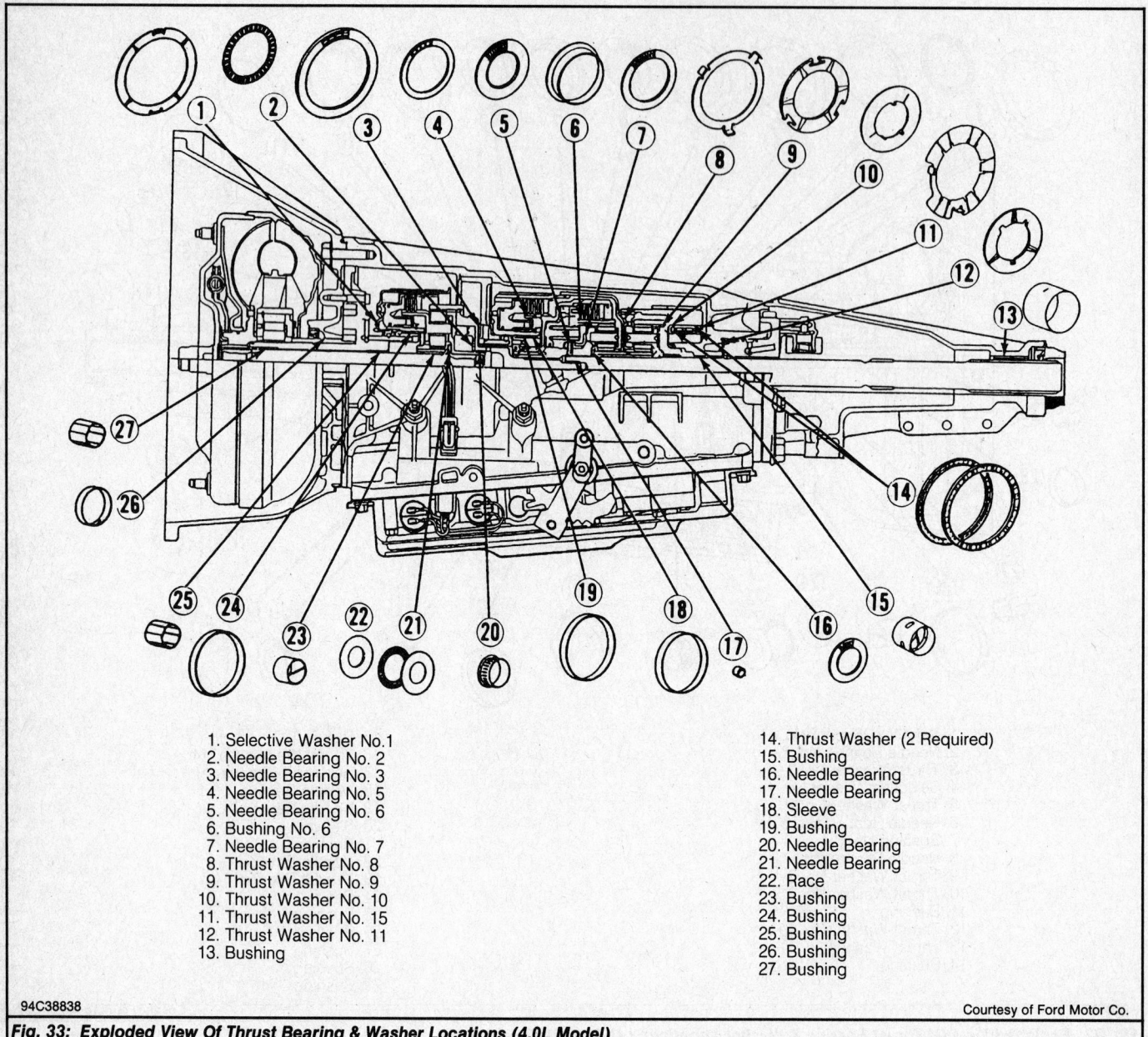

1. Selective Washer No.1
2. Needle Bearing No. 2
3. Needle Bearing No. 3
4. Needle Bearing No. 5
5. Needle Bearing No. 6
6. Bushing No. 6
7. Needle Bearing No. 7
8. Thrust Washer No. 8
9. Thrust Washer No. 9
10. Thrust Washer No. 10
11. Thrust Washer No. 15
12. Thrust Washer No. 11
13. Bushing

14. Thrust Washer (2 Required)
15. Bushing
16. Needle Bearing
17. Needle Bearing
18. Sleeve
19. Bushing
20. Needle Bearing
21. Needle Bearing
22. Race
23. Bushing
24. Bushing
25. Bushing
26. Bushing
27. Bushing

94C38838

Courtesy of Ford Motor Co.

Fig. 33: Exploded View Of Thrust Bearing & Washer Locations (4.0L Model)

TORQUE SPECIFICATIONS
TORQUE SPECIFICATIONS

Application	Ft. Lbs. (N.m)
Band Adjuster Lock Nut	35-45 (47-61)
Converter Housing Cover	
Except 2.3L Engine	12-16 (16-22)
Converter Housing-To-Case	27-39 (37-53)
Converter-To-Flywheel	20-34 (27-46)
Extension Housing-To-Case	27-39 (37-53)
Manual Lever Inner Nut	30-40 (41-54)
Oil Cooler Line-To-Connector	
Nut	18-23 (24-31)
5/16" Tube Nut	12-18 (16-24)
Oil Pump-To-Converter Housing	16-21 (22-28)
Transmission-To-Engine	
Except 3.0L Engine	28-38 (38-52)
3.0L Engine	33-44 (45-60)

Application	INCH Lbs. (N.m)
Center Support-to-Case Bolt	89-115 (10-13)
Converter Housing Cover Bolt	
2.3L Engine	27 (3)
Downshift Lever Outer Nut	89-133 (10-15)
Governor-To-Collector Body Bolt	89-115 (10-13)
Neutral Switch	89-115 (10-13)
Reverse Servo Cover Bolt	89-115 (10-13)
Separator Plate Bolt	54-71 (6-8)
Transmission Oil Pan Bolt	98-115 (11-13)
Vacuum Diaphragm Clip Bolt	89-106 (10-12)
Valve Body-to-Case Bolt	71-98 (8-11)

TRANSMISSION SPECIFICATIONS
TRANSMISSION SPECIFICATIONS

Application	In. (mm)
Converter End Play	.050-.077 (1.27-1.95)
Forward Clutch Pack Clearance	.055-.083 (1.40-2.10)
Overdrive Clutch Pack Clearance	.051-.079 (1.30-2.00)
Reverse/High Clutch Pack Clearance	.051-.079 (1.30-2.00)

SERVICE BULLETINS

PREMATURE CONVERTER BUSHING FAILURE

ATRA Technical Bulletin No. 182 (8-93) – Premature wear or repeat failure of converter hub, bellhousing bushing, converter seal and/or pump assembly may be caused by a worn or broken flywheel spacer. Remove flywheel and visually inspect spacer on every engine that requires it. Replacement spacer part number is D4ZZ-6434-A.

PUMP DAMAGE

ATRA Technical Bulletin No. 203 (1-94) – Pump gear damage may result after overhaul from warped bellhousing in the area around the bushing bore. Use appropriate straightedge to check for warpage in 4 locations across bellhousing. Machine or replace bellhousing as necessary to repair. Ensure after machining to check that mounting bolts do not bottom out in bolt holes. Also ensure pump gears have .0015-.0025" clearance to face of pump housing.

AUTOMATIC TRANSMISSIONS
A4LD Electronic Controls

Ford Motor Co: Aerostar, Explorer
Mustang (2.3L), Ranger

NOTE: For A4LD transaxle mechanical testing and repair, see Ford A4LD article.

INTRODUCTION

The first step in diagnosing any driveability problem is verifying the customer's complaint with a test drive under the conditions the problem reportedly occurred. Before entering self-diagnostics, perform a careful and complete visual inspection. Most transmission control problems result from mechanical breakdowns or poor electrical connections.

NOTE: Perform all voltage tests with a Digital Volt-Ohmmeter (DVOM) with a minimum 10-megohm input impedance, unless stated otherwise in test procedure.

DESCRIPTION & OPERATION

Input signals from sensors are sent to the Powertrain Control Module (PCM). The PCM can determine when the time and conditions are right for a shift or converter clutch application.

The PCM partially controls transmission operation through two electronic On/Off solenoids for 3-4 shifting and torque converter clutch control. The PCM has built-in self-diagnosis, fail-safe code and warning code display for the main input sensors and solenoid valves.

NOTE: In addition to transmission fault codes, engine related fault codes may be output during QUICK TEST procedure. These fault codes pertain to engine performance and must be repaired first, as engine performance will greatly affect transmission operation. For information and testing procedures of engine related fault codes and components, see SELF-DIAGNOSTICS – EEC-IV article in ENGINE PERFORMANCE of appropriate MITCHELL® manual.

INPUT SENSORS

Brake On/Off (BOO) Switch – The PCM receives a signal from the BOO switch when the brake switch is operated. Torque converter clutch is disengaged when brakes are applied. Malfunctioning switch will affect torque converter operation.

Profile Ignition Pickup (PIP) – The PIP located in distributor, sends engine RPM and crankshaft position to PCM. Signal received by the PCM affects torque converter clutch operation.

Programmable Speedometer/Odometer Module (PSOM) – The PSOM receives input from rear brake anti-lock sensor, which is mounted on rear axle differential housing. Vehicle speed (mph) signal is output to PCM. PSOM failure may cause harsh engagements, firm shift feel and abnormal shift schedule. Unexpected downshifts may occur at closed throttle and abnormal TCC operation or engages at WOT. Transmission Control Indicator Light (TCIL) may flash.

Throttle Position Sensor (TPS) – The TPS is a potentiometer mounted to the engine throttle body on gasoline engine. The PCM receives a signal from the TPS relaying throttle plate position. TPS failure will cause PCM to operate in fail safe mode and raise line pressure to prevent transaxle damage. This condition will result in abnormal 3-4 shift schedule and TCC not engaging or cycling.

Vehicle Speed Sensor (VSS) – The VSS is a magnetic pickup that sends vehicle speed signal to the PCM. Malfunction of sensor may cause harsh engagements of shifts. Lack of 4th gear or TCC lock-up.

OUTPUT DEVICES

Shift Solenoid Assemblies – **1)** One ON/OFF solenoid is used for 3-4 electronic shift scheduling. If solenoid fails in ON position, vehicle will have poor acceleration performance at all speeds. If solenoid fails in OFF position, transmission will not have a 3-4 or 4-3 shift.

Torque Converter Clutch (TCC) Solenoid – The TCC receives signal from the PCM. The TCC controls application, modulation and release of torque converter clutch. If solenoid fails in ON position, vehicle engine will run rough (shudder) and engine stalls in Drive at low idle speeds (2nd, 3rd or 4th gear). If solenoid fails in OFF position, torque converter clutch will not engage.

PRELIMINARY INSPECTION

VISUAL INSPECTION

Visually inspect all electrical wiring, looking for chafed, stretched, cut or pinched wiring. Ensure electrical connectors fit tightly and are not corroded. Ensure vacuum hoses are properly routed and are not pinched or cut. Inspect air induction system for possible vacuum leaks. Check PCM, sensors and actuators for physical damage. Check engine coolant level. Check transmission fluid level and condition.

NOTE: In addition to transmission fault codes, engine-related fault codes may be output during QUICK TEST procedure. These fault codes pertain to engine performance and must be repaired first as engine performance will greatly affect transmission operation. For information and testing procedures of engine-related fault codes and components, see SELF-DIAGNOSTICS – EEC-IV article in ENGINE PERFORMANCE of appropriate MITCHELL® manual.

SELF-DIAGNOSTIC SYSTEM

DIAGNOSTIC FORMATS

QUICK TEST, CIRCUIT/PINPOINT TESTS are diagnostic formats used to test and service EEC-IV system. QUICK TEST allows technician to identify problems and retrieve service codes. CIRCUIT TESTS check engine circuits, sensors and actuators. PINPOINT TESTS check transaxle circuits, sensors and actuators.

Before starting any circuit test, follow all steps under QUICK TEST to find correct circuit or pinpoint test. If vehicle passes QUICK TEST and no driveability symptoms or intermittent faults exist, EEC-IV system is okay.

DIAGNOSTIC TROUBLE CODES (DTC)

During QUICK TEST, 3 types of service codes are retrieved: Key On Engine Off (KOEO), Key On Engine Running (KOER) and Continuous Memory Codes. See QUICK TEST for self-test procedures. Codes may be cleared from PCM memory after they have been recorded or repaired. See CLEARING CODES.

KOEO & KOER Codes (Hard Faults) – These codes indicate faults are present at time of testing. A hard fault may cause CHECK ENGINE light or Malfunction Indicator Light (MIL) to glow and remain on until fault is repaired. If KOEO or KOER codes are retrieved during KOEO SELF-TEST or KOER SELF-TEST, use SERVICE CODE REFERENCE CHARTS to find correct testing and repair procedures.

Continuous Memory Codes (Soft Faults) – These codes indicate a fault that may or may not be present at time of testing. These codes are used to diagnose intermittent problems. Continuous Memory Codes are retrieved during KOEO SELF-TEST. Some codes may turn on MIL or CHECK ENGINE light. Corresponding soft trouble code will be retained in PCM memory. If fault does not reoccur within 40 warm-up cycles (80 cycles on some models), PCM will automatically clear code. Technician may clear service codes from memory. See CLEARING CODES. Intermittent faults may be caused by a sensor, connector or wiring-related problems.

CAUTION: Continuous Memory Codes should be recorded when retrieved during KOEO SELF-TEST. These codes may be used to identify intermittent problems that exist after all KOEO and KOER codes have been repaired and a Code 11 or 111 (pass code) has been obtained. Failure to follow this procedure may result in unnecessary testing. Some Continuous Memory Codes faults may not be valid after KOEO and KOER codes are repaired.

RETRIEVING CODES

Service codes are retrieved from EEC-IV system through self-test connector. Various methods and test equipment may be used to access these codes:

- Analog Volt-Ohmmeter (VOM)
- Scan Tester
- In-Dash Malfunction Indicator Light (MIL) Or CHECK ENGINE light
- STAR Series Tester

DATA LINK CONNECTOR (DLC) LOCATIONS

Application	Location
Aerostar	On Left Front Fender Panel, Near Starter Relay
Explorer	Right Rear Of Engine Compartment
Mustang	Left Shock Tower, Near Ignition Coil
Ranger	
4.0L	Right Rear Of Engine Compartment
All Others	Behind Engine Compartment Fuse/Relay Block

READING CODES

KOEO & KOER SELF-TEST Codes – PCM outputs codes one digit at a time. Record codes in order received. These codes indicate current faults in system and should be serviced in order of appearance. Use SERVICE CODE REFERENCE CHARTS to find correct CIRCUIT/PIN-POINT TEST.

If using analog VOM, pay careful attention to length of pauses in order to read codes correctly. A 1/2-second pause occurs between number of sweeps in a digit. A 2-second pause occurs between digits in a code. A 4-second pause occurs between each code. KOEO codes are separated from Continuous Memory codes by a 6-second delay, a 1/2-second sweep (separator) and another 6-second delay. See Fig. 1. If using MIL/CHECK ENGINE light, service codes are displayed as flashes.

Scan tester, if used, will count pulses and display them as a digital code. STAR Series Tester will add a zero (0) to single-digit Separator Code (10) and Dynamic Response Code (10). Dynamic Response Code is displayed in KOER SELF-TEST. See Fig. 1.

Engine Identification (ID) Codes – Engine ID codes are issued at beginning of KOER SELF-TEST. Codes are one-digit numbers represented by number of pulses displayed. See Fig. 1. Engine ID code is equal to one-half the number of engine cylinders. For example, 2 pulses would indicate that engine is a 4 cylinder. ID code is used to verify proper PCM is installed and that SELF-TEST has been entered.

Separator Pulse – Single 1/2-second separator pulse is issued 6-9 seconds after last KOEO code. Continuous Memory Codes (soft faults) are then displayed 6-9 seconds after 1/2-second separator pulse. Some digital test equipment may display separator code as "10" instead of "1".

Pass Codes – A Code 11 or 111 indicates no service codes were recorded in that portion of test; system passes that portion of test. If Code 11 or 111 is not retrieved in KOER SELF-TEST, codes retrieved during KOER SELF-TEST may not be valid. Code 11 or 111 (pass code) must be obtained in KOEO SELF-TEST. A Code 11-1-11 or 111-1-111 output during KOEO SELF-TEST indicates no KOEO code or Continuous Memory Code was recorded.

Continuous Memory Codes – These codes result from information stored by PCM during continuous self-test monitoring. Codes are displayed after separator pulse code in KOEO SELF-TEST. Use these

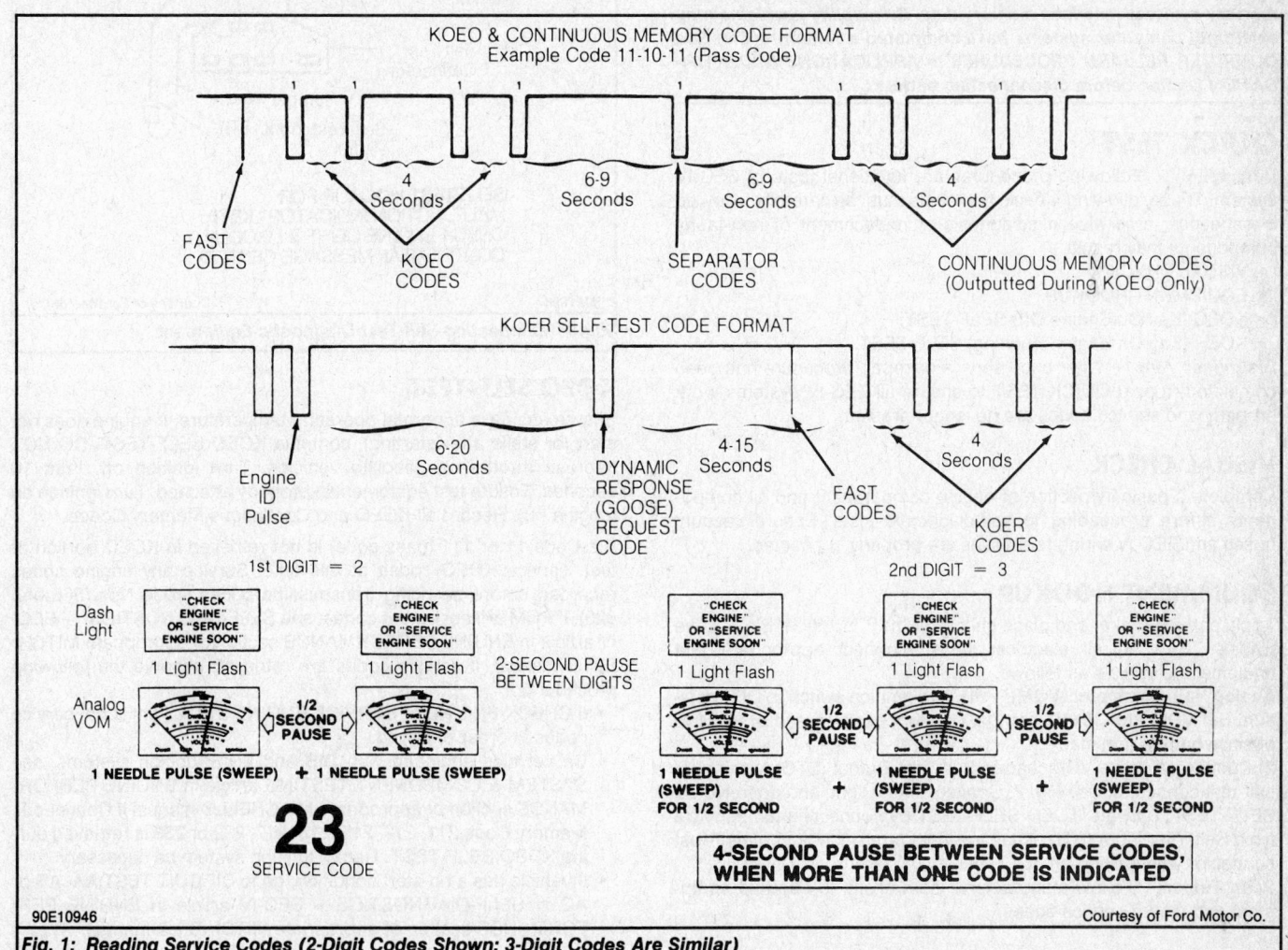

Fig. 1: Reading Service Codes (2-Digit Codes Shown; 3-Digit Codes Are Similar)

90E10946

Courtesy of Ford Motor Co.

codes for diagnosis only when KOEO SELF-TEST and KOER SELF-TEST result in Code 11 or 111 (pass code) and all steps under QUICK TEST are successfully completed. (A few codes are exceptions which may be checked after KOEO codes have been repaired). These codes indicate faults recorded within last 40 engine starts (80 engine starts on some models). Fault may or may not be currently present. See SERVICE CODE REFERENCE CHARTS.

Fast Codes – At start of KOEO SELF-TEST and after Wide Open Throttle (WOT) request in KOER SELF-TEST, PCM outputs short bursts of information, known as FAST CODES, which were used by manufacturer during assembly. With most equipment, these code bursts are not visible; an entire code sequence lasts less than 1/2 second. If this fluctuation is visible on test equipment, ignore it.

CLEARING CODES

To clear codes from PCM memory, start KOEO SELF-TEST under QUICK TEST. When service codes appear on test equipment or CHECK ENGINE light, disconnect jumper wire from Self-Test Input (STI) connector. If using STAR Series Tester, unlatch center button. This procedure erases Continuous Memory Codes from PCM memory. If problem has not been corrected or fault is still present, hard code will immediately be reset in PCM memory.

CAUTION: DO NOT disconnect vehicle battery to clear codes. This will erase stored operating information from Keep-Alive Memory (KAM). To clear KAM, disconnect negative battery terminal for at least 5 minutes.

WARNING: When battery is disconnected, vehicle computer and memory systems may lose memory data. Driveability problems may exist until computer systems have completed a relearn cycle. See COMPUTER RELEARN PROCEDURES in APPLICATIONS & IDENTIFICATION section before disconnecting battery.

QUICK TEST

Description – Following procedures are functional tests of EEC-IV system. These following 4 basic test steps must be carefully followed in sequence, otherwise misdiagnosis or replacement of non-faulty components may result:
- VISUAL CHECK
- EQUIPMENT HOOKUP.
- KOEO (Key On Engine Off) SELF-TEST.
- KOER (Key On Engine Running) SELF-TEST.

Diagnostic Aids – After each service or repair procedure has been completed, repeat QUICK TEST to ensure all EEC-IV systems work properly and service codes are no longer present.

VISUAL CHECK

Complete a basic inspection of engine compartment and all components before proceeding to self-diagnostic tests. Ensure vacuum hoses and EEC-IV wiring harnesses are properly connected.

EQUIPMENT HOOKUP

Apply parking brake, and place shift lever in "P" position. Block drive wheels. Turn off all electrical loads. Connect appropriate test equipment to vehicle as follows:

Analog Volt-Ohmmeter (VOM) – 1) Turn ignition switch to OFF position. Set VOM at 0-15V DC range. Connect positive lead of VOM to positive battery terminal.
2) Connect negative VOM lead to Self-Test Output (STO) terminal of self-test connector. *See Fig. 2.* Connect timing light, and go to KOEO SELF-TEST. Activate KOEO SELF-TEST by connecting jumper wire from Self-Test Input (STI) pigtail to signal return terminal of self-test connector with ignition on.

Scan Tester – Follow manufacturer instructions to hook up equipment and record service codes.

STAR Series Tester – Turn ignition switch to OFF position. Connect color-coded adapter cable leads to diagnostic tester. Connect 2 service connectors of adapter cable to vehicle self-test connector and STI pigtail connector. Connect timing light. Go to KOEO SELF-TEST.
CHECK ENGINE Light/Malfunction Indicator Light (MIL) – Turn ignition on. Connect a jumper wire between Self-Test Input (STI) pigtail and signal return (SIG RTN) terminal of Data Link Connector (DLC). *See Fig. 2.* Go to KOEO SELF-TEST.

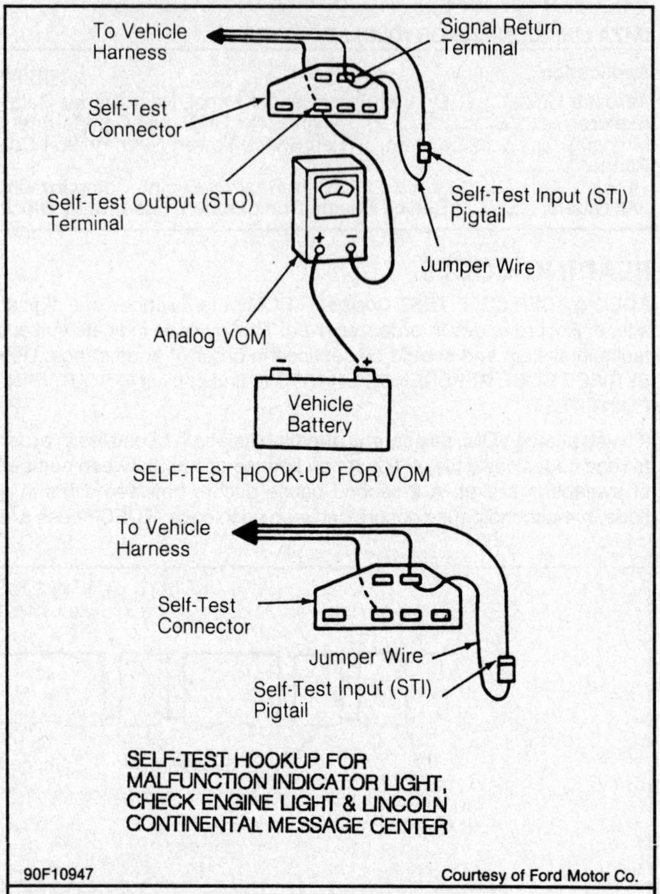

SELF-TEST HOOK-UP FOR VOM

SELF-TEST HOOKUP FOR MALFUNCTION INDICATOR LIGHT, CHECK ENGINE LIGHT & LINCOLN CONTINENTAL MESSAGE CENTER

90F10947   Courtesy of Ford Motor Co.

Fig. 2: Connecting Self-Test Diagnostic Equipment

KOEO SELF-TEST

Ensure engine is at normal operating temperature. If engine does not start (or stalls after starting), continue KOEO SELF-TEST. DO NOT depress throttle on gasoline vehicles. Turn ignition off. Wait 10 seconds. Ensure test equipment is properly attached. Turn ignition on (engine off). Record all KOEO and Continuous Memory Codes.

If a Code 11 or 111 (pass code) is not retrieved in KOEO portion of test, service KOEO codes at this time. Service any engine codes recorded before servicing transmission codes (code Nos. 566 and 629). If PCM will not output codes, see SELF-DIAGNOSTICS – EEC-IV article in ENGINE PERFORMANCE section of appropriate MITCHELL® manual. If service codes are retrieved observe the following procedures:
- If CHECK ENGINE or SERVICE ENGINE SOON light is on, service codes in order retrieved.
- On vehicles equipped with DIS and EDIS ignition systems, see SYSTEM & COMPONENT TESTING article in ENGINE PERFORMANCE section of appropriate MITCHELL® manual if Continuous Memory Code 211, 212, 215, 216, 217, 232 or 238 is retrieved during KOEO SELF-TEST. Repair ignition system as necessary.
- If vehicle has a no-start condition, go to CIRCUIT TEST AA, AB or AC in SELF-DIAGNOSTICS – EEC-IV article in ENGINE PERFORMANCE section of appropriate MITCHELL® manual.

KOER SELF-TEST

Diagnostic Aids – DO NOT enter this test sequence until a Code 11 or 111 (pass code) has been retrieved in KOEO SELF-TEST. If system has not passed KOEO SELF-TEST, codes recorded in KOER SELF-TEST may not be valid.

Deactivate self-test by removing and reconnecting jumper wire or by procedure specified by test equipment in use. Start engine, and run it for 2 minutes at 2000 RPM to warm Heated Exhaust Gas Oxygen (HEGO) sensor. Turn engine off, and wait 10 seconds. Activate KOER SELF-TEST using a jumper wire or appropriate procedure for test equipment used. Start engine. Record all service codes displayed. Check following items:

- If engine starts and stalls (or stalls during self-test), go to CIRCUIT TEST S. See SELF-DIAGNOSTICS – EEC-IV article in ENGINE PERFORMANCE section of appropriate MITCHELL® manual.
- If vehicle is equipped with a Brake On-Off (BOO) switch, brake pedal must be depressed and released after ID code portion of test.
- If Dynamic Response Code appears, perform a brief Wide Open Throttle (WOT). DO NOT perform WOT unless requested.
- If a Code 11 or 111 (pass code) is retrieved during KOER SELF-TEST, service Continuous Memory Codes retrieved in KOEO SELF-TEST. See SELF-DIAGNOSTICS – EEC-IV article in ENGINE PERFORMANCE section of appropriate MITCHELL® manual.
- If a Code 11 or 111 (pass code) is retrieved during Continuous Memory Code portion of KOEO SELF-TEST (Code 11-1-11 or Code 111-1-111) and no driveability problem exists, EEC-IV testing is complete. If driveability problems are still present, go to TROUBLE SHOOTING in A4LD article.
- If KOER codes are present, see SERVICE CODE REFERENCE CHARTS. If system will not output codes, go to CIRCUIT TEST QA. See SELF-DIAGNOSTICS – EEC-IV article in ENGINE PERFORMANCE of appropriate MITCHELL® manual.

CONTINUOUS MONITOR MODE (WIGGLE TEST)

Continuous Monitor Mode allows technician to attempt to recreate an intermittent fault while monitoring system. This mode, also called wiggle test, may be used in both KOEO SELF-TEST and KOER SELF-TEST. CIRCUIT/PINPOINT TESTS specify use of this procedure to identify intermittent faults in specific circuits or components.

KOEO Wiggle Test Procedure – Connect test equipment. See Fig. 2. Turn ignition on, and activate self-test using jumper lead or diagnostic tester. Wait 10 seconds, and then deactivate and reactivate self-test. Wiggle test mode is now activated. Tap, move and wiggle suspect sensor and/or harness area. If a fault is detected, a service code may be stored in memory and indicated at diagnostic tester or scan tester. Retrieve code, and perform appropriate test. See SERVICE CODE REFERENCE CHARTS.

KOER Wiggle Test Procedure – Connect test equipment. See Fig. 2. Turn ignition off, and wait 10 seconds. Start engine. Activate self-test using jumper lead or diagnostic tester. Wait 10 seconds, and then deactivate and reactivate self-test. DO NOT turn engine off. KOER wiggle test mode is now activated. Tap, move and wiggle suspect sensor and/or harness area. If a fault is detected, a service code may be stored in memory and indicated at diagnostic tester or scan tester. Retrieve code, and perform appropriate test. See SERVICE CODE REFERENCE CHARTS.

ADDITIONAL SYSTEM FUNCTIONS

Additional diagnostic system features are available to help diagnose driveability problems and service EEC-IV systems.

CHECK ENGINE Light & Malfunction Indicator Light (MIL) – CHECK DCL light, CHECK ENGINE light and MIL are intended to alert driver of certain malfunctions in EEC-IV system.

Light may also be used to retrieve service codes stored in PCM. When hooked up for KOEO SELF-TEST or KOER SELF-TEST, light will display all codes which turn on light during vehicle operation, not just Continuous Memory Codes.

If light comes on during vehicle operation, vehicle should be inspected as soon as possible. Immediately turning off engine is not necessary; vehicle can be driven with light on.

if light comes on and then goes off during vehicle operation, code causing light to glow will be stored in PCM memory as a Continuous Memory Code.

Light should come on when ignition is turned on and go out when engine is started. If hard fault codes are not present, PCM turns out light when it receives a Profile Ignition Pick-Up (PIP) signal. If light does not come on, see SYMPTOMS in TROUBLE SHOOTING – NO CODES article in ENGINE PERFORMANCE section of appropriate MITCHELL® manual.

Output State Check – Output State Check is used as an aid in servicing output actuators associated with EEC-IV system. It allows technicians to energize and de-energize most system output actuators on command. This mode is entered from KOEO SELF-TEST after all codes have been retrieved. Leave SELF-TEST activated, and depress throttle to initiate test sequence. Each time throttle is depressed and released, output actuators will change state (from on to off or off to on).

Failure Mode Effects Management (FMEM), Code 98 Or 998 – FMEM mode allows system operation when sensors fail or transmit signals that are out of normal operating range. During FMEM mode, PCM substitutes a mid-range signal for defective sensor while continuing to monitor sensor. If faulty sensor's signals return to normal operating range, PCM will use those signals. A Code 98 or 998 will be displayed when FMEM mode is in effect.

Hardware Limited Operational Strategy (HLOS) – If a number of system or sensor failures are present and PCM is not receiving enough information to operate, PCM will switch to HLOS mode. PCM will output fixed values to allow operation of vehicle. Driveability concerns will be present. PCM will not output service codes in this mode.

SUMMARY

If no service codes (or pass code 11-1-11 or 111-1-111) is present but driveability problem still exists, return to TROUBLE SHOOTING in A4LD overhaul article.

SERVICE CODE REFERENCE CHARTS

NOTE: In addition to transmission fault codes, engine-related fault codes may be output during QUICK TEST procedure. These fault codes pertain to engine performance and must be repaired first as engine performance will greatly affect transmission operation. For information and testing procedures of engine-related fault codes and components, see SELF-DIAGNOSTICS – EEC-IV article in ENGINE PERFORMANCE of appropriate MITCHELL® manual.

CODE REFERENCE CHART

Fault Code	Code Definition	Circuit Test
KOEO Codes		
111	Pass Code	N/A
116	ECT Voltage High/Low	DA1
117	ECT Voltage Low	DA20
118	ECT Voltage High	DA10
121	TPS Voltage High/Low	DH2
122	TPS Malfunction	DH10
123	TPS Malfunction	DH3
511	Replace PCM	....
513	Replace PCM	....
566	3/4 Solenoid Malfunction	A1
629	TCC Circuit Failure	C1
Continuous Memory Codes		
111	Pass Code	N/A
118	ECT Voltage High	DA90
121	TPS Voltage High/Low	G1
122	TPS Malfunction	DH94
123	TPS Malfunction	DH90
124	TPS Malfunction	G1
125	TPS Malfunction	G1
452	Insufficient VSS Input	[1] DP1
511	Replace PCM	....
513	Replace PCM	....
536	BOO Switch Malfunction	FD90
629	TCC Circuit Failure	C1
KOER Codes		
111	Pass Code	N/A
116	ECT Voltage High/Low	DA1
121	TPS Voltage High/Low	DH1
167	TPS Malfunction	DH20
511	Replace PCM	....
513	Replace PCM	....
536	BOO Switch Malfunction	FD1

[1] – On Aerostar models, perform CIRCUIT TEST DS1, for DTC 452.

CIRCUIT/PINPOINT TEST PROCEDURES

NOTE: A breakout box, connected to vehicle harness at PCM, is necessary to perform most circuit tests. References to Test Pin No. found in CIRCUIT/PINPOINT TEST steps refer to test terminals on manufacturer breakout box. Circuit diagrams at beginning of each test identify circuit and wire colors.

HOW TO USE CIRCUIT/PINPOINT TESTS

1) Ensure all non-EEC related faults found while performing TROUBLE SHOOTING steps in A4LD overhaul article have been corrected. DO NOT perform any CIRCUIT/PINPOINT TEST unless specifically instructed by a QUICK TEST procedure. Follow each test step in order until fault is found. DO NOT replace any part unless directed to do so. When more than one code is retrieved, start with first code displayed.
2) CIRCUIT/PINPOINT TESTS ensure electrical circuits are okay before sensors or other components are replaced. Always test circuits for continuity between sensor and PCM. Test all circuits for short to power, opens or short to ground. Voltage Reference (VREF) and Voltage Power (VPWR) circuits should be tested with KOEO or as specified in CIRCUIT/PINPOINT TESTS.
3) DO NOT measure voltage or resistance at PCM. DO NOT connect any test light unless specified in testing procedure. All measurements are made by probing rear of connector. Isolate both ends of a circuit and turn ignition off when checking for shorts or continuity, unless instructed otherwise.
4) Disconnect solenoids and switches from harness before measuring continuity and resistance or applying voltage. After each repair, check all component connections and repeat QUICK TEST.

5) An open circuit is defined as a resistance reading of greater than 5 ohms. This specification tolerance may be too high for some items in EEC-IV system. If resistance approaches 5 ohms, always clean suspect connector and coat it with protective dielectric silicone grease. A short is defined as a resistance reading of less than 10 k/ohms to ground, unless stated otherwise in CIRCUIT/PINPOINT TEST.

Diagnostic Aids – Fuel-contaminated engine oil may set some codes and effect engine performance. If oil is suspect, remove PCV valve from valve cover and repeat QUICK TEST. If problem is corrected, change engine oil.

NOTE: In following tests, circuit diagrams and illustrations are courtesy of Ford Motor Co.

PINPOINT TESTS

NOTE: PINPOINT TESTS are diagnostic formats used to test and service EEC-IV system. PINPOINT TESTS check transaxle circuits, sensors and actuators.

PINPOINT TEST A

SHIFT SOLENOID ELECTRICAL SYSTEM

1) A4LD Electronic Diagnostics – Ensure transmission harness connector is in acceptable condition. Repair as necessary. Perform KOEO test until Continuous Memory trouble code(s) have been displayed. See QUICK TEST. Depress throttle to WOT and release. If vehicle enters Output State, go to next step. If vehicle will not enter Output State, see SELF-DIAGNOSTICS – EEC-IV article in ENGINE PERFORMANCE of appropriate MITCHELL® manual.

2) Check Electrical Signal Operation – Disconnect transmission harness connector. Inspect condition of connector and repair as needed. Using DVOM (20-volt scale), connect positive lead to transmission harness connector VPWR terminal. See Fig. A1. Connect negative lead to solenoid circuit. Depress and release throttle to cycle solenoid output. If voltage changes at least .5 volts, go to step **5)**. If voltage is unaffected, go to next step.

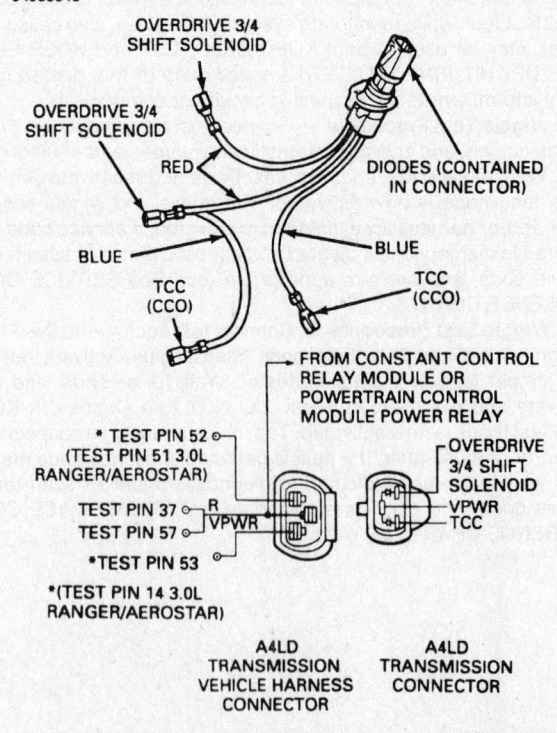

Fig. A1: Identifying Transmission Harness Connector

PINPOINT TEST A (Cont.)

3) Check Continuity Of Solenoid Signal & VPWR Harness Circuits – Ensure ignition is off. Disconnect PCM 60-pin connector, and inspect it for damaged pins, corrosion and loose wires. Repair as necessary. Install Breakout Box (T83L-50-EEC-IV), leaving PCM disconnected. On Aerostar and Ranger 3.0L models, measure and record resistance between Breakout Box test pin No. 51 and corresponding transmission harness connector terminal. On all other models, measure and record resistance between Breakout Box test pin No. 52 and corresponding transmission harness connector terminal. See Fig. A1. Measure and record resistance. Measure and record resistance between test pins No. 37 and 57 and transmission harness connector VPWR terminal. If any resistance is greater than 5 ohms, repair open circuit. Connect all components. Disconnect Breakout Box and repeat Quick Test. If resistance is 5 ohms or less, go to next step.

4) Check Solenoid Harness For Shorts To Power & Ground – On Aerostar and Ranger 3.0L models, measure and record resistance between Breakout Box test pins No. 51 and test pins No. 37 and 57. On all other models, measure and record resistance between Breakout Box test pins No. 52 and test pins No. 37 and 57. Measure and record resistance between test pins No. 40, 46 and 60, and ground. If any resistance is less than 10 k/ohms, repair short circuit. Connect all components. Disconnect Breakout Box and repeat Quick Test. If resistance is 10 k/ohms or more, go to next step.

5) Solenoid Functional Test – Connect Transmission Tester (007-0085A). Perform solenoid voltage test. See tester instructions. If solenoid activates (LED green), go to next step. If solenoid does not activate, check if diode test light is illuminated. If diode is okay, go to next step. If diode test light is not illuminated, replace solenoid harness assembly. Erase all trouble codes and road test vehicle. Repeat QUICK TEST.

6) Transmission Drive Test – Perform tester drive test. See tester instructions. If vehicle upshifts when operated with tester, erase all trouble codes. See CLEARING CODES. Perform tester drive cycle test. See tester instructions. Repeat QUICK TEST. If vehicle does not upshift when operated by tester, go to next step.

7) Check Resistance Of Solenoid – Set tester Bench/Drive switch to Bench mode. Set Gear Selector switch to OHMS/DIODE CHECK. Connect ohmmeter negative lead to SS3/4 jack and positive lead to VPWR jack on tester. Measure and record resistance. Resistance for solenoid should be 26-40 ohms. If resistance is within specification, go to next step. If resistance is not within specification, replace solenoid body assembly. Erase all codes. See CLEARING CODES. Repeat QUICK TEST.

8) Check Solenoid For Short To Ground – Check continuity between BAT(-) terminal and between SS3/4. Check continuity between BAT(-) terminal and VPWR terminal. If continuity exists for any circuit, go to next step. Erase all codes. See CLEARING CODES. Repeat QUICK TEST. If continuity does not exist, go to TROUBLE SHOOTING in Ford A4LD article.

9) A4LD Internal Electronic Diagnostics – Drain transaxle fluid. See TRANSMISSION SERVICING section. Remove transaxle side pan. See OIL PUMP & VALVE BODY ASSEMBLY under ON-VEHICLE SERVICE IN FORD A4LD article. Inspect all internal harness connectors. Ensure all connectors are fully connected and not damaged. Repair as needed. Install all components in reverse order of disassembly. Fill transaxle with fluid. Erase all trouble codes. See CLEARING CODES. Repeat QUICK TEST. If all connectors are okay, go to next step.

10) Check Internal Harness Continuity – Disconnect internal harness from solenoid assemblies. Connect positive lead of ohmmeter to tester SS 3/4 jack and negative lead to SS 3/4 Red wire. Measure and record resistance. To test SS 3/4 VPWR circuits, connect positive lead of ohmmeter to selected solenoid Red wire. Connect negative lead to corresponding VPWR tester terminal. Measure and record resistance. If all resistances measured are .5 ohms or less, go to next step. If any resistance measured is more than .5 ohms, replace internal harness.

11) Check Internal Harness For Shorts To Ground – Using transmission tester, check continuity between solenoid lead and BAT(-) terminal of tester. If continuity does not exist in any circuit, go to next step. If continuity exists in any circuit, replace internal harness. Install all components in reverse order of disassembly. Fill transaxle with fluid. Erase all trouble codes. See CLEARING CODES. Repeat QUICK TEST.

PINPOINT TEST A (Cont.)

12) Check Resistance Of Solenoid – Using ohmmeter, check resistance between terminals of each solenoid. Resistance should be 26-40 ohms. If resistance is within specification, go to next step. If resistance measured for any solenoid is not within specification, replace suspected solenoid. Install all components in reverse order of disassembly. Fill transaxle with fluid. Erase all trouble codes. See CLEARING CODES. Repeat QUICK TEST.

13) Check Solenoid For Short To Ground – Using ohmmeter, check continuity between each solenoid terminal and ground. If continuity exists, replace faulty shift solenoid. If continuity does not exist, go to TROUBLE SHOOTING in Ford A4LD article. Install all components in reverse order of disassembly. Fill transaxle with fluid. Erase all trouble codes. See CLEARING CODES. Repeat QUICK TEST.

PINPOINT TEST C

TCC ELECTRICAL SYSTEM

1) A4LD Electronic Diagnostics – Ensure transmission harness connector is in acceptable condition. Repair as necessary. Disconnect transmission harness connector. Connect Transmission Tester (007-0085A) or equivalent to transmission. Perform TRANSMISSION SOLENOID CYCLING AND DRIVE TEST. Perform KOEO test until Continuous Memory trouble code(s) have been displayed. See QUICK TEST. Depress throttle to WOT and release. If vehicle enters Output State, go to next step. If vehicle will not enter Output State, see SELF-DIAGNOSTICS – EEC-IV article in ENGINE PERFORMANCE of appropriate MITCHELL® manual.

2) Check Electrical Signal Operation – Disconnect transmission harness connector. Inspect condition of connector and repair as needed. Using DVOM (20-volt scale), connect positive lead to transmission harness connector VPWR terminal. See Fig. A1. Connect negative lead to TCC terminal. Depress and release throttle to cycle solenoid output. If voltage changes at least .5 volts, go to step 5). If voltage is unaffected, go to next step.

3) Check Continuity Of Solenoid Signal & VPWR Harness Circuits – Ensure ignition is off. Disconnect PCM 60-pin connector, and inspect it for damaged pins, corrosion and loose wires. Repair as necessary. Install Breakout Box (T83L-50-EEC-IV), leaving PCM disconnected. On Aerostar and Ranger 3.0L models, measure and record resistance between Breakout Box test pin No. 14 and transmission harness connector TCC terminal. On all other models, measure and record resistance between Breakout Box test pin No. 53 and transmission harness connector TCC terminal. See Fig. A1. Measure and record resistance between test pins No. 37 and 57 and transmission harness connector VPWR terminal. If any resistance is greater than 5 ohms, repair open circuit. Connect all components. Disconnect Breakout Box and repeat Quick Test. If resistance is 5 ohms or less, go to next step.

4) Check Solenoid Harness For Shorts To Power & Ground – On Aerostar and Ranger 3.0L models, measure and record resistance between Breakout Box test pin No. 14 and test pins No. 37 and 57. On all other models, measure and record resistance between test pin No. 53 and test pins No. 37 and 57. Measure and record resistance between test pins No. 40, 46 and 60, and ground. If any resistance is less than 10 k/ohms, repair short circuit. Connect all components. Disconnect Breakout Box and repeat Quick Test. If resistance is 10 k/ohms or more, go to next step.

5) Solenoid Functional Test – Connect Transmission Tester (007-0085A). Perform solenoid voltage test. See tester instructions. If solenoid activates (LED green), go to next step. If solenoid does not activate, check if diode test light is illuminated. If diode is okay, go to next step. If diode test light is not illuminated, replace solenoid body assembly. Erase all trouble codes and road test vehicle. Repeat QUICK TEST.

6) Transmission Drive Test – Perform tester drive test. See tester instructions. If engine RPM decreases when operated with tester, see SELF-DIAGNOSTICS – EEC-IV article in ENGINE PERFORMANCE of appropriate MITCHELL® manual to diagnose vehicle harness or PCM malfunctions. If engine RPM does not decrease when operated by tester, go to next step.

PINPOINT TEST C (Cont.)

7) Check Resistance Of Solenoid – Set tester Bench/Drive switch to BENCH mode. Set Gear Selector switch to OHMS/DIODE CHECK. Connect ohmmeter negative lead to CCO jack and positive lead to VPWR jack on tester. Measure resistance. Resistance should be 26-40 ohms. If resistance is within specification, go to next step. If resistance is not within specification, replace solenoid body assembly. Erase all trouble codes and road test vehicle. Repeat QUICK TEST.

8) Check Solenoid For Short To Ground – Check continuity between BAT (-) tester terminal and CCO terminals. If continuity exists, replace solenoid body assembly. Erase all trouble codes and road test vehicle. Repeat QUICK TEST. If continuity does not exist, Erase all trouble codes. See CLEARING CODES. Repeat QUICK TEST. See TROUBLE SHOOTING in FORD A4LD article for non-electronic symptom diagnostics.

9) A4LD Internal Electronic Diagnostics – Drain transaxle fluid. See TRANSMISSION SERVICING section. Remove transaxle side pan. See OIL PUMP & VALVE BODY ASSEMBLY under ON-VEHICLE SERVICE IN FORD A4LD article. Inspect all internal harness connectors. Ensure all connectors are fully connected and not damaged. Repair as needed. Install all components in reverse order of disassembly. Fill transaxle with fluid. Erase all trouble codes. See CLEARING CODES. Repeat QUICK TEST. If all connectors are okay, go to next step.

10) Check Internal Harness Continuity – Disconnect internal harness from TCC sensor. Connect positive lead of ohmmeter to tester TCC jack and negative lead to TCC Blue wire. Measure and record resistance. Connect positive lead of ohmmeter to tester VPWR jack and negative lead to TCC Blue/Red wire. If resistances measured are 5 ohms or less, go to next step. If any resistance measured is more than 5 ohms, replace internal harness. Go to step **12**).

11) Check Internal Harness For Shorts To Ground – Using transmission tester, check continuity between each TCC sensor connector terminals and BAT(-) terminal of tester. If continuity does not exist in either circuit, go to next step. If continuity exists in any circuit, replace internal harness. Go to next step.

12) Check TOT Sensor Resistance – Using ohmmeter, check resistance between TCC terminals. If resistance is 26-40 ohms, go to next step. If resistance measured is not within specification, replace TCC sensor. Install all components in reverse order of disassembly. Fill transaxle with fluid. Erase all trouble codes. See CLEARING CODES. Repeat QUICK TEST.

13) Check Solenoid For Short To Ground – Using ohmmeter, check continuity between each TCC sensor terminal and ground. If continuity exists, replace faulty TCC sensor. Install all components in reverse order of disassembly. Fill transaxle with fluid. Erase all trouble codes. See CLEARING CODES. Repeat QUICK TEST. If continuity does not exist, install all components in reverse order of disassembly. Fill transaxle with fluid. Erase all trouble codes. See CLEARING CODES. Repeat QUICK TEST. See TROUBLE SHOOTING in FORD A4LD article for non-electronic symptom diagnostics.

CIRCUIT TESTS

NOTE: CIRCUIT TESTS are diagnostic formats used to test and service EEC-IV system. CIRCUIT TESTS check engine circuits, sensors and actuators.

CIRCUIT TEST CA

REFERENCE VOLTAGE

Diagnostic Aids – Perform this test when a check for VREF signal has failed in sensor input CIRCUIT TESTS AA-AC or QA. See SELF-DIAGNOSTICS – EEC-IV article in ENGINE PERFORMANCE of appropriate MITCHELL® manual. SIG RTN is a dedicated ground used by most EEC-IV system sensors. VREF is a 5-volt reference voltage that is continuously output by PCM. This consistent voltage signal is used on all 3-wire sensors.

CIRCUIT TEST CA (Cont.)

This circuit test is only intended to diagnose the following components and circuits:
- Powertrain Control Module (PCM).
- Vehicle wiring harness circuits (SIG RTN and VREF).

93E40422

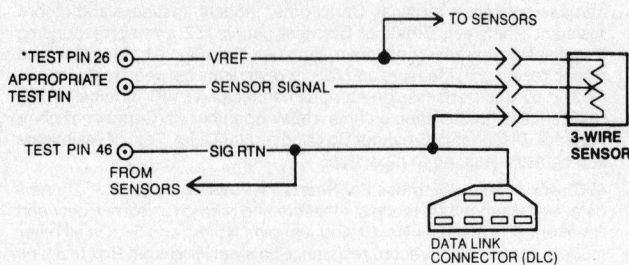

*TEST PINS LOCATED ON BREAKOUT BOX.
ALL HARNESS CONNECTORS VIEWED INTO MATING SURFACE.

Fig. CA1: Identifying Reference Voltage Circuits & Connector Terminals

TEST PIN WIRE COLOR IDENTIFICATION

Terminal No.	Wire Color
No. 26 (VREF)	Brown/White
No. 46 (SIG RTN)	Gray/Red

1) Check Battery Power Circuit – Turn ignition off, and wait 10 seconds. Disconnect PCM 60-pin connector, and inspect it for damaged pins, corrosion and loose wires. Repair as necessary. Install Breakout Box (007-00033), leaving PCM connected. Turn ignition on. Measure and record voltage between breakout box test pin No. 37 and SIG RTN terminal of self-test connector. Measure and record voltage across battery terminals. If both readings are less than 10.5 volts or if they differ by more than 1.0 volt, reconnect sensor (if applicable). Go to CIRCUIT TEST X for Mustang or CIRCUIT TEST B for all other models under SELF-DIAGNOSTICS – EEC-IV article in ENGINE PERFORMANCE of appropriate MITCHELL® manual. If voltages are 10.5 volts or more and do not differ from one another by more than 1.0 volt, go to step **2**).

2) Check VREF Voltage – With breakout box installed and PCM connected, set DVOM on 20-volt scale. Turn ignition on. Measure voltage between test pins No. 26 and 46 at breakout box. If voltage is 4-6 volts, go to step **3**). If voltage is more than 6 volts, go to step **4**). If voltage is less than 4 volts, go to step **5**).

3) Check VREF & SIG RTN Circuit Continuity – Turn ignition off. Disconnect PCM. If directed here by a sensor test, ensure sensor is disconnected. Measure resistance between Breakout Box test pin No. 26 and VREF terminal at wiring harness connector of applicable sensor. Measure resistance between test pin No. 46 and SIG RTN circuit terminal at wiring harness connector of applicable sensor. If both readings are less than 5 ohms, VREF circuit is okay. If either reading is 5 ohms or more, repair open in VREF or SIG RTN circuit. Remove breakout box, and repeat QUICK TEST.

4) Check For Excess VREF Circuit Voltage – Turn ignition off. Ensure PCM is disconnected. With breakout box installed, disconnect scan tester or STAR tester (if applicable). Turn ignition on. Measure voltage between test pin No. 26 and battery ground. If voltage is less than 0.5 volt, replace PCM and repeat QUICK TEST. If voltage is 0.5 volt or more, repair short to battery power in wiring harness. Remove breakout box, reconnect components and repeat QUICK TEST. Replace PCM if fault still occurs.

5) Check For Shorted TPS – Turn ignition off. Connect PCM to breakout box. Disconnect Throttle Position Sensor (TPS) from wiring harness. Turn ignition on. Measure voltage between test pins No. 26 and 46 at breakout box. If voltage is 4 volts or more, replace TPS, remove breakout box and repeat QUICK TEST. If voltage is less than 4 volts on models with EVP, PFE or DPFE sensor, go to step **6**). If voltage is less than 4 volts on all other models, go to step **8**).

CIRCUIT TEST CA (Cont.)

6) Check For Shorted EVP/PFE/DPFE Sensor – Turn ignition off, and wait 10 seconds. Disconnect EVP/PFE/DPFE sensor. Turn ignition on. Measure voltage between test pins No. 26 and 46. If voltage is 4 volts or more, replace EVP/PFE/DPFE sensor and repeat QUICK TEST. If voltage is less than 4 volts, reconnect EVP/PFE/DPFE sensor and go to step 8).

NOTE: A break in step numbering sequence occurs at this point. Procedure skips from step 6) to step 8). No test procedures have been omitted.

8) Check VREF Circuit For Short To Ground – Turn ignition off. Disconnect PCM. Disconnect TPS, MAP/BARO sensor and EVP/PFE/DPFE sensor. Measure resistance between test pin No. 26 and test pins No. 20, 40, 46 and 60. If any resistance is less than 1000 ohms, repair short to ground. Remove breakout box, and repeat QUICK TEST. If original problem still exists, replace PCM and repeat QUICK TEST. If readings are 1000 ohms or more, replace PCM and repeat QUICK TEST.

CIRCUIT TEST DA

TEMPERATURE SENSOR TEST (IAT & ECT)

Diagnostic Aids – Perform this test only when directed by QUICK TEST. Ambient air temperature must be at least 50°F (10°C) to receive valid input from IAT sensor. Engine coolant temperature must be greater than 50°F (10°C) to pass KOEO SELF-TEST and greater than 180°F (82°C) to pass KOER SELF-TEST. Voltage values in this test are based on a 5-volt VREF signal. Values may vary up to 15% due to sensor and VREF variations.

This circuit test is intended to diagnose the following components and circuits:

- Intake Air Temperature (IAT) sensor.
- Engine Coolant Temperature (ECT) sensor.
- Wiring harness circuits (IAT, ECT and SIG RTN).
- Powertrain Control Module (PCM).

To prevent replacing good components, ensure the following non-EEC areas or components are not cause of problem:

- Coolant level low.
- Cooling system, water pump or fan.
- Engine operating temperature.
- Engine oil level low.
- Thermostat.
- Air cleaner duct.
- Ambient temperature.

93J40427

    *TEST PINS LOCATED ON BREAKOUT BOX.
    ALL HARNESS CONNECTORS VIEWED INTO MATING SURFACE.

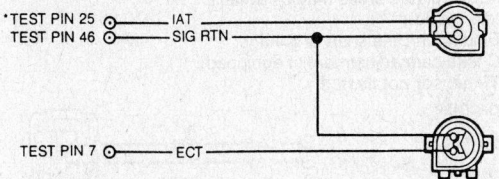

IAT SENSOR WIRING HARNESS CONNECTOR

ECT SENSOR WIRING HARNESS CONNECTOR

Fig. DA1: Identifying Temperature Sensor Circuits & Connector Terminals

TEST PIN WIRE COLOR IDENTIFICATION

Application	Wire Color
No. 7 (ECT)	Light Green/Red
No. 25 (IAT)	Gray
No. 46 (SIG RTN)	Gray/Red

CIRCUIT TEST DA (Cont.)

1) Code 116 Or 114: – Code 116 (ECT) or 114 (IAT) indicates corresponding sensor is out of self-test range. Correct range for measurement is .3-3.7 volts. Check for following possible causes:

- Low ambient temperature (less than 50°F).
- Low coolant level.
- Faulty harness connector.
- Faulty sensor.

Ensure upper radiator hose is hot and pressurized. Repeat QUICK TEST. If Code 114 or 116 is present, go to step 2). If none of these codes are present, service other codes as necessary.

2) Check VREF Circuit Voltage At TPS – Turn ignition off. Disconnect Throttle Position Sensor (TPS). With ignition on and engine off, measure voltage at TPS wiring harness connector between VREF and SIG RTN. *See Fig. DA2.* If voltage is 4-6 volts, reconnect TPS and go to step 3). If voltage is not 4-6 volts, go to CIRCUIT TEST CA.

3) Check Temperature Sensor Resistance – Ensure ignition is off. Disconnect suspect sensor. Measure resistance between signal and SIG RTN terminals at sensor. See ACT & ECT SENSOR SPECIFICATIONS table. If resistance is not within specification, replace suspected sensor and repeat QUICK TEST. If resistance is within specification, go to step 4).

93A40428

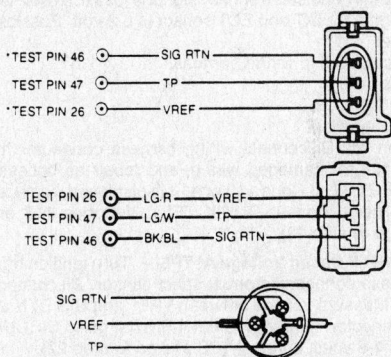

Fig. DA2: Identifying TPS Harness Connector Terminals

4) Check Temperature Sensor Resistance – Warm engine to normal operating temperature. Turn ignition off. Disconnect suspect sensor. Run engine at 2000 RPM for 2 minutes. Measure resistance between signal and SIG RTN terminal at sensor. See ACT & ECT SENSOR SPECIFICATIONS table. If resistance is within specification, replace PCM and repeat QUICK TEST. If sensor is not within specification, replace sensor and repeat QUICK TEST.

ACT & ECT SENSOR SPECIFICATIONS

Temperature °F (°C)	[1] Volts	[1] Ohms
50 (10)	3.51	58,750
68 (20)	3.07	27,300
86 (30)	2.60	24,270
104 (40)	2.13	16,150
122 (50)	1.70	10,970
140 (60)	1.33	7700
158 (70)	1.33	7700
176 (80)	0.78	3840
194 (90)	0.60	2800
212 (100)	0.46	2070

[1] – Values may vary by 15 percent.

NOTE: A break in step numbering sequence occurs at this point. Procedure skips from step 4) to step 10). No test procedures have been omitted.

10) Code 118 Or 113: Induce Opposite Code (Code 117 Or 112) – Code 118 (ECT) or 113 (IAT) indicate corresponding sensor signal is greater than self-test maximum. Maximum signal voltage for ECT and IAT sensor is 4.6 volts. Possible causes for excess voltage signals are:

- Open circuit in wiring harness (IAT or ECT).
- Faulty connection.
- Faulty sensor.
- Faulty PCM.

CIRCUIT TEST DA (Cont.)

Turn ignition off. Disconnect suspect temperature sensor. Connect a jumper wire between SIG RTN terminal at sensor and SIG RTN terminal at sensor wiring harness connector. Repeat QUICK TEST. If Code 112 or 117 is displayed, replace suspect sensor and repeat QUICK TEST. If Code 112 or 117 is not displayed, remove jumper wire and go to next step.

11) Check Continuity Of Sensor Signal & SIG RTN Circuits – Turn ignition off. Ensure suspect temperature sensor is disconnected. Disconnect PCM 60-pin connector. Check for damaged wiring, and repair as necessary. Install Breakout Box (T83L-50-EEC-IV), leaving PCM disconnected. Measure resistance between test pin No. 7 (ECT sensor) or test pin No. 25 (IAT sensor) at breakout box and SIG RTN terminal at sensor wiring harness connector. Also measure resistance between test pin No. 46 and SIG RTN circuit at sensor wiring harness connector. If both readings are less than 5 ohms, replace PCM and repeat QUICK TEST. If either reading is 5 ohms or more, repair open circuit and repeat QUICK TEST.

NOTE: A break in step numbering sequence occurs at this point. Procedure skips from step 11) to step 20). No test procedures have been omitted.

20) Code 117 or 112: Induce Opposite Code (118 or 113) –Code 117 (ECT) or 112 (IAT) indicates sensor signal is less than self-test minimum. Minimum signal for IAT and ECT sensor is 0.2 volt. Possible causes for this fault are:
- Circuit grounded in wiring harness.
- Faulty sensor.
- Faulty PCM.
- Faulty connection.

Turn ignition off. Disconnect wiring harness connector from suspect sensor. Check for damaged wiring, and repair as necessary. Repeat KOEO SELF-TEST. If Code 113 or 118 is displayed, replace sensor and connect harness. Repeat QUICK TEST. If Codes 113 or 118 is not displayed, go to step 21).

21) Check VREF Circuit Voltage At TPS – Turn ignition off. Disconnect wiring harness connector from suspect sensor. Disconnect TPS. Turn ignition on. Measure voltage between VREF and SIG RTN at TPS wiring harness connector. If voltage is not 4-6 volts, go to CIRCUIT TEST CA. If voltage is 4-6 volts, connect TPS and go to step 22).

22) Check Temperature Sensor Signal For Shorts To Ground – Turn ignition off. Disconnect suspect sensor. Disconnect PCM 60-pin connector. Check for damaged wiring, and repair as necessary. Install Breakout Box (T83L-50-EEC-IV), leaving PCM disconnected. Measure resistance between test pin No. 7 (ECT) or 25 (IAT) and pins No. 40, 46 and 60. If any reading is less than 10,000 ohms, repair short circuit and repeat QUICK TEST. If all readings are 10,000 ohms or more, replace PCM and repeat QUICK TEST.

NOTE: A break in step numbering sequence occurs at this point. Procedure skips from step 22) to step 90). No test procedures have been omitted.

90) Continuous Memory Code 118, 113, 117 Or 112: Check Sensor – A Continuous Memory Code 118 or 113 indicates sensor signal is greater than self-test maximum of 4.6 volts. Code is set during normal driving conditions. Continuous Memory Code 117 or 112 indicates sensor signal is less than self-test minimum of 0.2 volt. Code is set during normal driving conditions. Possible causes for these faults are:
- Faulty sensor.
- Open or grounded circuit in harness.
- Faulty PCM.

SENSOR CODES

Sensor	Continuous Memory Code
IAT	113 Or 112
ECT	118 Or 117

Enter KOEO wiggle test mode. See CONTINUOUS MONITOR MODE (WIGGLE TEST) under QUICK TEST. Observe analog voltmeter or scan tester for indication of fault while tapping sensor lightly and wiggling sensor connector. If fault is indicated, disconnect and inspect connector and terminals. If connector and terminals are okay, replace sensor, clear continuous memory and repeat QUICK TEST. If fault is not indicated, go to step 91).

CIRCUIT TEST DA (Cont.)

91) Check EEC-IV Wiring Harness – While in CONTINUOUS MONITOR MODE (WIGGLE TEST), observe analog voltmeter or scan tester while wiggling and bending wiring harness, a small section at a time, from sensor to cowl. Also check harness from cowl to PCM. If fault is indicated, isolate fault and repair as necessary. Clear continuous memory, and repeat QUICK TEST. If no fault is found, go to step 92).

92) Inspect PCM & Wiring Harness Connectors – Turn ignition off. Disconnect PCM 60-pin connector. Inspect both connector and connector terminals for damage. If connectors and terminals are damaged, repair as necessary and repeat QUICK TEST. If connectors and terminals are okay and fault cannot be duplicated at this time, see TROUBLE SHOOTING (EEC-IV) – NO CODES article in ENGINE PERFORMANCE in appropriate MITCHELL® manual.

NOTE: A break in step numbering sequence occurs at this point. Procedure skips from step 92) to step 100). No test procedures have been omitted.

100) Continuous Memory Code 338 – A Continuous Memory Code 338 indicates cooling system has not reached normal operating temperature. Possible causes for this fault are:
- Thermostat stuck open.
- Coolant outlet gasket leak.
- Water pump gasket leak.

Repair cooling system as necessary. Clear continuous memory, and repeat QUICK TEST.

101) Continuous Memory Code 339 – A Continuous Memory Code 339 indicates cooling system has overheated. Possible causes for this fault are:
- Coolant level low.
- Thermostat stuck closed.
- Coolant system clogged.
- Water pump damaged or worn.
- Radiator cap damaged or worn.
- Cooling fan damaged or worn.

Repair cooling system as necessary. Clear continuous memory, and repeat QUICK TEST.

CIRCUIT TEST DH

THROTTLE POSITION (TP) SENSOR

Diagnostic Aids – Perform this test only when directed by QUICK TEST. This test is intended to diagnose the following:
- TP sensor.
- Wiring harness circuits (TP, SIG RTN and VREF).
- Powertrain Control Module (PCM).

Normal range of throttle angle measurement for TP sensor is 0-85 degrees. To pass QUICK TEST procedure, range of throttle rotation (in degrees) must be within 3 percent of specification. See Fig. DH2.

To prevent replacement of good components, be aware the following non-EEC related areas may be at fault:
- Idle speed.
- Binding throttle shaft or linkage.
- Choke cam adjustment (if equipped).
- TP sensor not seated.

93A40428

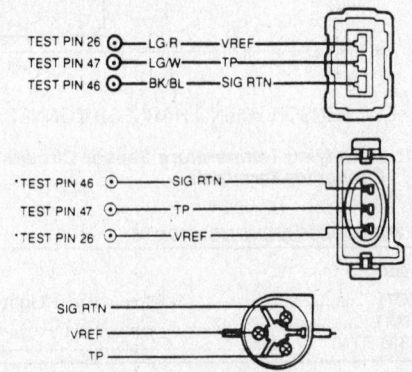

NOTE: EITHER TYPE MAY BE FITTED

Fig. DH1: Identifying TP Sensor Circuits & Connector Terminals

CIRCUIT TEST DH (Cont.)

TEST PIN WIRE COLOR IDENTIFICATION

Application	Wire Color
No. 26 (VREF)	Light Green/Red
No. 46 (SIG RTN)	Black/Blue
No. 47 (TP)	Light Green/White

92G03822

Fig. DH2: *TP Sensor Specification Chart*

1) KOER Code 121: Check For Other Codes – KOER Code 121 indicates TP sensor rotational setting may be out of self-test range. Possible causes for this fault are:
- Binding throttle linkage.
- TP sensor not seated correctly.
- Faulty TP sensor.
- Faulty Powertrain Control Module (PCM).

Perform KOER SELF-TEST. Check for Code 327. If either of these codes are present with Code 121, service Code 327 and repeat QUICK TEST. If these codes are not present, go to step **2)**.

2) Code 121: Check For Binding Throttle Plate – Inspect throttle body for binding. If throttle body is binding, check for binding throttle or cruise control linkage, vacuum line or harness interference, etc. Repair as necessary, and repeat QUICK TEST. If no mechanical problem is found, go to step **3)**.

3) Code 123: Attempt To Generate Code 122 – Code 123 indicates TP sensor signal is greater than self-test maximum value. Possible causes for this fault are:
- TP sensor not seated properly.
- Faulty TP sensor.
- Short circuit to power.
- Faulty PCM.

Turn ignition off. Disconnect TP sensor wiring harness connector. Inspect and repair connector pins if damaged. Repeat KOEO SELF-TEST. Ignore all other codes at this time. If Code 63/122 is not displayed, go to step **5)**. If Code 122 is displayed, go to step **4)**.

4) Check VREF Circuit Voltage – Turn ignition on. Measure voltage between VREF and SIG RTN terminals at TP sensor wiring harness connector. If reading is 4-6 volts, replace TP sensor and repeat QUICK TEST. If reading is not 4-6 volts, reconnect sensor and go to CIRCUIT TEST CA.

5) Check TP Circuit For Short To Power – Turn ignition off. Leave TP sensor disconnected. Disconnect PCM 60-pin connector. Inspect it for damage and repair as necessary. Install EEC-IV Breakout Box (T83L-50-EEC-IV), leaving PCM disconnected. Measure resistance between test pin No. 47 and test pins No. 26 and 57. If either resistance is less than 10,000 ohms, repair short circuit in wiring harness and repeat QUICK TEST. If both resistances are 10,000 ohms or more, replace PCM and repeat QUICK TEST.

NOTE: A break in step numbering sequence occurs at this point. Procedure skips from step 5) to step 10). No test procedures have been omitted.

CIRCUIT TEST DH (Cont.)

10) Code 122: Attempt To Generate Code 123 Or 121 – Code 122 indicates TP signal is less than minimum self-test value. *See Fig. DH2.* Possible causes for this fault are:
- TP sensor not seated correctly.
- Faulty TP sensor.
- Open circuit in wiring harness.
- Grounded circuit in wiring harness.
- Faulty PCM.

Turn ignition off, and wait 10 seconds. Disconnect TP sensor from harness. Install a jumper wire between VREF and TP terminals at TP sensor wiring harness connector. Perform KOEO SELF-TEST. If no codes are generated, remove jumper wire and go to step **13)**. If Codes 123 and 121 are not present, remove jumper wire and go to step **11)**. If either Code 123 or 121 is displayed, replace TP sensor and repeat QUICK TEST.

11) Check VREF Circuit Voltage – Turn ignition on. Measure voltage between VREF and SIG RTN terminals at TP sensor wiring harness connector. If voltage is not 4-6 volts, reconnect all components and go to CIRCUIT TEST CA. If voltage is 4-6 volts, go to step **12)**.

12) Check TP Sensor Circuit Continuity – Turn ignition off. Leave TP sensor disconnected. Disconnect PCM 60-pin connector. Inspect connector and repair if necessary. Install EEC-IV Breakout Box (T83L-50-EEC-IV), leaving PCM disconnected. Measure resistance between TP terminal at TP sensor wiring harness connector and test pin No. 47. If resistance is 5 ohms or more, repair open circuit and repeat QUICK TEST. If resistance is less than 5 ohms, go to step **13)**.

13) Check TP Circuit For Shorts To Ground – Turn ignition off. Leave TP sensor disconnected. Disconnect PCM 60-pin connector. Inspect wiring, and repair as necessary. With breakout box installed and PCM disconnected, measure resistance between test pin No. 47 and test pins No. 40, 46 and 60. If any reading is less than 10,000 ohms, repair short circuit and repeat QUICK TEST. If all readings are 10,000 ohms or more, replace PCM and repeat QUICK TEST.

NOTE: A break in step numbering sequence occurs at this point. Procedure skips from step 13) to step 20). No test procedures have been omitted.

20) Code 167: Repeat Dynamic Response Test – KOER Code 167 indicates TP sensor did not exceed 25% rotation during dynamic response portion of KOER SELF-TEST. A complete Wide Open Throttle (WOT) must be performed during dynamic response portion of test. Perform KOER SELF-TEST. Ensure WOT is completed during dynamic response portion of test. If Code 167 is still present, go to step **21)**. If code is not present, system is unable to duplicate Code 167 at this time. Service any other KOER codes. If no other service codes are present, testing is complete.

21) Check TP Sensor Movement During Dynamic Response Test – Turn ignition off. Disconnect PCM 60-pin connector. Inspect wiring, and repair as necessary. Install EEC-IV Breakout Box (T83L-50-EEC-IV), leaving PCM connected. Set DVOM on 20-volt scale. Connect DVOM between test pins No. 46 and 47 at breakout box. Perform KOER SELF-TEST and ensure proper WOT is completed during dynamic response test. If DVOM reading exceeds 3.5 volts during dynamic response test, replace PCM and repeat QUICK TEST. If reading does not exceed 3.5 volts, ensure TP sensor is correctly installed and adjusted. If TP sensor is correctly installed and adjusted, replace TP sensor. Repeat QUICK TEST.

NOTE: A break in step numbering sequence occurs at this point. Procedure skips from step 21) to step 90). No test procedures have been omitted.

90) Continuous Memory Code 123 – This test monitors TP sensor under simulated road conditions. Enter wiggle test. See CONTINUOUS MONITOR MODE (WIGGLE TEST) under QUICK TEST. Connect DVOM or diagnostic tester to STO terminal of self-test connector. While slowly opening throttle to WOT, observe DVOM or diagnostic tester for indication of fault. Slowly bring throttle to closed position. Lightly tap TP sensor and wiggle harness connector. This test checks for open or short in TP sensor and wiring harness. If no fault is indicated, go to step **92)**. If fault is indicated, go to step **91)**.

CIRCUIT TEST DH (Cont.)

91) Measure TP Circuit Voltage While Exercising TP Sensor – Turn ignition off, and wait 10 seconds. Disconnect PCM 60-pin connector. Inspect for damage and repair if necessary. Install EEC-IV Breakout Box (T83L-50-EEC-IV), leaving PCM connected. Stay in wiggle test (as in previous step). Connect DVOM between test pins No. 47 and 46. Set DVOM on 20-volt scale. With ignition on and engine off, observe DVOM and repeat step **90)**. If fault occurs at less than 4.25 volts, inspect TP sensor connectors and terminals. If connectors and terminals are okay, replace TP sensor, clear codes and repeat QUICK TEST. If fault does not occur at less than 4.25 volts, TP sensor over-travel may have caused Continuous Memory Code 123. TP sensor is okay. Go to step **92)** to check wiring harness.

92) Check EEC-IV Wiring Harness – While in wiggle test, bend and shake small sections of EEC-IV harness from TP sensor wiring harness connector to firewall and from firewall to PCM while observing analog voltmeter or scan tester. If fault is indicated, isolate fault in wiring and repair as necessary. Clear codes, and repeat QUICK TEST. If no fault is indicated, go to step **93)**.

93) Check PCM & Harness Connectors – Turn ignition off, and wait 10 seconds. Disconnect PCM 60-pin connector from breakout box. Inspect connectors and terminals for damage, and repair as necessary. Clear codes from PCM memory, and repeat QUICK TEST. If connectors and terminals are okay, fault cannot be duplicated at this time. Continuous Memory Code 123 testing is complete.

94) Continuous Memory Code 122 – Enter wiggle test. See CONTINUOUS MONITOR MODE (WIGGLE TEST) under QUICK TEST. Connect DVOM or diagnostic tester to STO terminal of self-test connector. Observe DVOM or diagnostic tester for indication of fault while performing the following:
* Slowly open throttle to WOT.
* Slowly bring throttle to closed position.
* Lightly tap TP sensor and wiggle connector.

If fault is indicated, disconnect TP sensor. Inspect connectors and terminals. If connectors and terminals are okay, replace TP sensor. Clear codes from PCM memory, and repeat QUICK TEST. If no fault is indicated, go to next step.

95) Check EEC-IV Wiring Harness – Stay in wiggle test (as in previous step). Bend, wiggle and shake small sections of EEC-IV harness from TP sensor wiring harness connector to firewall and from firewall to PCM while observing analog voltmeter or scan tester. If fault is indicated, isolate fault in wiring and repair as necessary. Clear codes from PCM memory, and repeat QUICK TEST. If no fault is indicated, go to step **96)**.

96) Check PCM & Harness Connectors – Turn ignition off. Inspect PCM 60-pin connector and terminals for damage. Repair connector terminals if necessary. Clear codes from PCM memory, and repeat QUICK TEST. If connectors and terminals are okay, fault cannot be duplicated at this time. Continuous Memory Code 122 testing is complete.

CIRCUIT TEST DP

VEHICLE SPEED SENSOR (VSS)

Diagnostic Aids – Perform this test when directed by QUICK TEST. This CIRCUIT TEST is intended to diagnose:
* Vehicle Speed Sensor (VSS).
* VSS wiring harness circuits.
* Powertrain Control Module (PCM).

93I40525

```
*TEST PIN 6 ○——————————————— VSS (–)
 TEST PIN 3 ○——————————————— VSS (+)
```

VEHICLE SPEED SENSOR (VSS) VEHICLE HARNESS CONNECTOR

*TEST PINS LOCATED ON BREAKOUT BOX
ALL HARNESS CONNECTORS VIEWED IN MATING SURFACE

Fig. DP1: Vehicle Speed Sensor Circuit

TEST PIN WIRE COLOR IDENTIFICATION

Application	Wire Color
All Except Aerostar & Mustang	
No. 3 (VSS +)	Gray/Black
No. 6 (VSS –)	Pink/Orange
Aerostar & Mustang	
No. 3 (VSS +)	Dark Green/White
No. 6 (VSS –)	Pink/Orange

CIRCUIT TEST DP (Cont.)

Preliminary Instructions – Record and clear continuous memory codes. Warm engine to normal operating temperature. Place gear selector in Drive position. Accelerate hard to 35 MPH and coast down to a stop. Shut off engine. Perform KOEO SELF-TEST. Repeat procedure at least 2 more times. Go to step **1)**.

1) Continuous Memory Code 452 – Code 452 indicates PCM detected incorrect output from VSS sometime during vehicle operation. Possible causes for this code are:
* Faulty VSS.
* Open or shorted circuit.
* Faulty PCM.

Perform appropriate TRANSMISSION DRIVE CYCLE TEST. Ensure driveability complaint can be verified. If Code 452 is still present or driveability complaint can be verified, go to step **2)**. If code is not present or complaint cannot be verified, fault cannot be duplicated at this time. Clear codes, and see SYMPTOMS in TROUBLE SHOOTING (EEC-IV) – NO CODES article in appropriate MITCHELL® manual.

2) Check VSS Circuit Continuity – Turn ignition off. Disconnect VSS sensor. Remove PCM 60-pin connector. Inspect terminals, and repair if damaged. Install EEC-IV Breakout Box (T83L-50-EEC-IV). Measure resistance between VSS (+) terminal at VSS wiring harness connector and test pin No. 3 at breakout box. Measure resistance between VSS (–) terminal at VSS wiring harness connector and test pin No. 6 at breakout box. If any resistance reading is more than 5 ohms, service open circuit in VSS wiring harness and repeat step **1)**. If both resistance readings are 5 ohms or less, go to step **3)**.

3) Check VSS Circuits For Shorts To Power Or Ground – Turn ignition off. Ensure PCM and VSS are disconnected. Measure resistance between test pin No. 3 and test pins No. 6, 37 and 40 at breakout box. If all readings are greater than 500 ohms, go to step **4)**. If any reading is less than 500 ohms, repair shorts in VSS wiring harness and repeat step **1)**.

4) Check VSS Resistance – Turn ignition off, and wait 10 seconds. Disconnect VSS wiring harness connector. Measure resistance across VSS terminals. If reading is not 190-250 ohms, replace VSS and repeat step **1)**. If resistance is 190-250 ohms, replace PCM and repeat step **1)**.

CIRCUIT TEST DS

PROGRAMMABLE SPEEDOMETER/ ODOMETER MODULE (PSOM)

Diagnostic Aids – Perform this test when directed by QUICK TEST. This CIRCUIT TEST is intended to diagnose:
* PSOM output to PCM.
* PSOM (+) and PSOM (-) wiring harness circuits.
* PCM.

To prevent replacement of good components, be aware following non EEC related areas and components may be cause of problem:
* Cruise Control system.
* Rear Anti-Lock Brake System (RABS).
* Ring gear inside differential.
* Instrumentation system.

93A75929

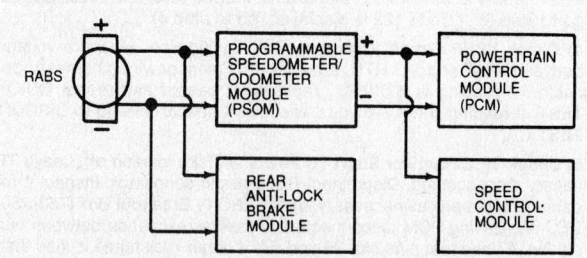

Fig. DS1 Programmable Speedometer/Odometer Module (PSOM) Circuit Logic

CIRCUIT TEST DS (Cont.)

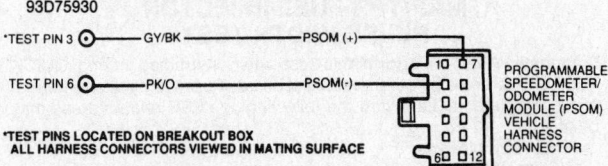

Fig. DS2 Identifying Programmable Speedometer/Odometer Module (PSOM) Circuit & Connector Terminals

TEST PIN NO. 3 (PSOM +) WIRE COLOR IDENTIFICATION

Application	Wire Color
All Models	Gray/Black

TEST PIN NO. 6 (PSOM -) WIRE COLOR IDENTIFICATION

Application	Wire Color
All Models	Pink/Orange

1) Continuous Memory Code 29/452 – Code 29/452 indicates PCM detected incorrect output from VSS sometime during vehicle operation. Following are possible causes of code.
- PSOM output to PCM.
- PSOM (+) and PSOM (-) wiring harness circuits.
- PCM.

Turn ignition off. Remove PCM 60-pin connector. Inspect terminals, and repair if damaged. Install Breakout Box (T83L-50-EEC-IV), leaving PCM disconnected. Measure resistance between test pins No. 3 and 6 at breakout box. If reading is 21-55 k/ohms, go to step **4)**. If resistance is not 21-55 k/ohms, go to next step.

2) Check PSOM Circuit Continuity • Ensure ignition is off. Disconnect PSOM wiring harness connector. Measure resistance between test pin No. 3 at breakout box and PSOM (+) circuit at PSOM wiring harness connector. Measure resistance between test pin No. 6 at breakout box and PSOM (-) circuit at PSOM wiring harness connector. If resistance is more than 5 ohms, repair open circuit and repeat QUICK TEST. If resistance is 5 ohms or less, go to next step.

3) Check PSOM Circuit For Open – Ensure ignition is off. Measure resistance between test pin No. 3 and test pins No. 6, 37 and 40 at breakout box. If resistance is 10 k/ohms or less, repair open circuit and repeat QUICK TEST. If resistance is more than 10 k/ohms, go to next step.

4) Check RABS Sensor Resistance – Turn ignition off. Remove RABS connector. *See Fig. DS1.* Measure resistance between connector terminals, If resistance is not 1300-1550 ohms, replace RABS and repeat QUICK TEST. If resistance is 1300-1550, go to next step.

5) Check PSOM Output Voltage – Turn ignition off. Connect PCM to breakout box. Connect wiring harness connector to PSOM. Set DVOM on 20-volt AC scale. Start engine, and warm to normal operating temperature. Using an assistant, measure voltage between test pins No. 3 and 6 while gradually increasing vehicle speed to 50 MPH. If maximum voltage is less than 4 volts, fault is in instrument cluster. If maximum voltage received is more than 4 volts, replace PCM.

CIRCUIT TEST FD

BRAKE ON-OFF (BOO) SWITCH

Diagnostic Aids – Perform this test when directed by QUICK TEST. This test is intended to diagnose a faulty BOO switch circuit or PCM. To prevent replacement of good components, be aware following non-EEC related areas may be at fault:
- Brakelight bulb.
- Brakelight switch or brakelight fuse.

CIRCUIT TEST FD (Cont.)

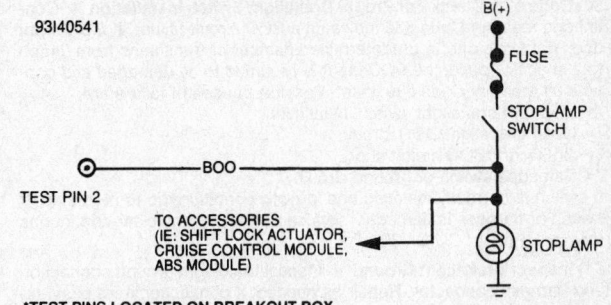

Fig. FD1: BOO Switch Circuit

TEST PIN WIRE COLOR IDENTIFICATION

Application	Wire Color
No. 2 (BOO)	Light Green

1) Code 536: Verify Brake Pedal Was Depressed – Code 536 indicates that when brake pedal is applied during KOER SELF-TEST, BOO signal did not cycle high and low. Possible causes for this fault are:
- Brake pedal not applied during self-test.
- Brake pedal applied during entire self-test.
- Open brakelight circuit.
- Short to ground or power.
- Faulty Powertrain Control Module (PCM).

If brake was not applied during KOER SELF-TEST, repeat test. Depress and release brake pedal only once during test. If pedal was depressed, go to step **2)**.

2) Check Operation Of Brakelights – With ignition on, check operation of brakelights. If brakelights operate normally, go to step **3)**. If brakelights do not operate, go to step **4)**. If brakelights are always on, go to step **5)**.

3) Check For BOO Switch Circuit Cycling – Turn ignition off. Wait 10 seconds. Disconnect PCM 60-pin connector. Inspect terminals, and repair if damaged. Install EEC-IV Breakout Box (T83L-50-EEC-IV), leaving PCM disconnected. Measure voltage between BOO test pin (No. 2) and test pin No. 40 while applying and releasing brake. If voltage cycles, replace PCM and repeat QUICK TEST. If voltage does not cycle, repair open circuit in BOO switch circuit between PCM and BOO switch connection to brakelight circuit. Repeat QUICK TEST.

4) Check For Power To Brake Switch – Ensure related fuses and brakelight bulbs are in good condition. Turn ignition off. Disconnect brakelight switch (located on brake pedal). Measure voltage between BATT (+) input to brakelight switch and ground. If voltage is greater than 10 volts, check condition of brakelight switch. If brakelight switch is okay, repair open circuit between brakelight switch and brakelight ground. Repeat QUICK TEST. If voltage is less than 10 volts, repair open BATT (+) circuit to brakelight switch and repeat QUICK TEST.

5) Verify Brake Switch Is Not Always Closed – Turn ignition off. Disconnect brakelight switch (located on brake pedal). Turn ignition on. If brakelights are still on, go to step **6)**. If brakelights are not on, verify correct installation of brakelight switch. If installation is okay, replace brakelight switch and repeat QUICK TEST.

6) Check For Short To Power In PCM – Turn ignition off. Disconnect PCM. Turn ignition on. Check brakelights. If brakelights are on, go to step **7)**. If brakelights are not on, replace PCM and repeat QUICK TEST.

7) Check For Short To Power In Shift Lock Actuator – Turn ignition off. Ensure PCM and brakelight switch are disconnected. Disconnect shift lock actuator, cruise control module and ABS module (if equipped). Turn ignition on. If brakelights are still on, repair short to power in BOO or stoplight circuit and repeat QUICK TEST. If brakelights are not on, repair short circuit in shift lock actuator circuit, cruise control system circuit or ABS circuit. Repeat QUICK TEST.

NOTE: A break in step numbering sequence occurs at this point. Procedure skips from step 7) to step 90). No test procedures have been omitted.

CIRCUIT TEST FD (Cont.)

90) Code 536: Check For Proper Brakelight Switch Installation – Continuous memory Code 536 indicates a BOO circuit failure. If BOO input does not cycle after a predetermined number of transitions from 0 mph to a specific speed, the BOO input is assumed to be damaged and continuous memory Code 536 is set. Possible causes of failure are:

- Incorrect brakelight switch installation.
- Open brakelight/BOO circuit.
- Brakelight/BOO circuit short.
- Damaged switch or ground circuit.

If switch is correctly installed and in good condition, go to next step. If switch or harness is damaged, service as needed and clear continuous memory. Repeat QUICK TEST.

91) Inspect Brakelight Ground – Inspect brakelight ground connection and harness connector. Repair as needed. If connections are okay, go to next step.

92) Inspect Brakelight/BOO Circuits For Shorts – With KOEO and brake pedal released, perform wiggle test of brakelight/BOO circuit harness and connectors while observing brakelights. If brakelights illuminate, inspect and repair circuits as needed. If brakelights do not illuminate, go to next step.

93) Inspect Brakelight Circuit Continuity – With ignition off, depress brake pedal and hold. Perform wiggle test of brakelight circuits while observing brakelights. Lightly tap brakelight switch while observing brakelights. If brakelights intermittently go out, inspect and repair circuits as needed. If brakelights remain illuminated, go to next step.

94) Inspect BOO Circuit Continuity – With ignition off, ensure brake pedal is released. Disconnect PCM 60-pin connector. Inspect terminals, and repair if damaged. Install EEC-IV Breakout Box (T83L-50-EEC-IV), leaving PCM disconnected. Measure resistance between BOO test pin No. 2 and brakelight circuit at switch while performing wiggle test on harness and connector. If resistance intermittently increases above 5 ohms, inspect and repair open circuit. Repeat QUICK TEST. If resistance is within specification, go to next step for further diagnosis.

NOTE: A break in step numbering sequence occurs at this point. Procedure skips from step 94) to step 99). No test procedures have been omitted.

99) Road Test Vehicle – Purpose of this test is to identify faults by monitoring certain controlled parameters while trying to recreate a driveability or MIL symptom. To prepare for road test:

- Install fuel pressure gauge and if available, a MAP/BARO tester.
- Disconnect PCM 60-pin connector, install breakout box and reconnect PCM to breakout box.
- Connect "T" vacuum gauge into manifold vacuum line.
- Have DVOM, writing materials and appropriate schematics and pin voltage charts available.

With ignition on and negative lead of DVOM connected to negative battery terminal, ensure following signals are correct:

- POWER: KAPWR (pin No. 1) is greater than 10.5 volts, VPWR (pins No. 37 and 57) is greater than 10.5 volts and VREF (pin No. 26) is 4-6 volts.
- GROUNDS: PWR GND (pins No. 40 and 60), SIG RTN (pin No. 46) and IGN GND (pin No. 16) are 0.0-0.5 volt.
- OPTIONAL GROUNDS: HO2S GND (pin No. 49), CSE GND (pin No. 20) and MAF RTN (pin No. 9 or 15) are 0.0-0.5 volt.

Diagnostic Aids – Test lights and DVOM are useful during diagnosis. For example: a testlight could be connected at brakelight switch between battery and ground and another testlight between switch bulb circuit and ground. Testlight to battery circuit should always be illuminated and other testlight should only illuminate when brakelight is depressed.

With DVOM connected between test pins No. 2 and 40 at Breakout Box, check voltage. If voltage is 6-7 volts with brake pedal released, possible open circuit between PCM and brakelight ground could exist.

CIRCUIT TEST G

MAF/TPS FUEL INJECTOR PULSE WIDTH TEST

Diagnostic Aids – Perform this test when instructed during QUICK TEST or if directed by other test procedures. To prevent replacement of good components, be aware the following non-EEC related areas may be at fault:

- Excessive blow-by.
- PCV malfunction.
- Vacuum leaks.
- Incorrect fuel pressure.
- Throttle binding.
- Improper fuel pressure.
- Idle air control solenoid.

This test is only intended to diagnose:

- MAP/BARO sensor.
- Throttle Position Sensor (TPS).
- Mass Airflow (MAF) sensor.
- Intake Air Temperature (IAT) sensor.
- Fuel injectors.

1) Check For Idle Air Codes – Code 121 indicates TPS is inconsistent with MAF value. Code 124 indicates TPS value is higher than expected. Code 125 indicates TPS value is lower than expected. Turn ignition on. Repeat KOEO SELF-TEST. If Code 411 or 412 is present, perform appropriate circuit test. See DIAGNOSTIC TROUBLE CODE REFERENCE CHARTS. If Code 411 or 412 is not present, go to next step.

2) Throttle Position (TP) Sensor: TP Sensor Integrity – Turn ignition off. Disconnect PCM 60-pin connector. Inspect connector for damaged pins, corrosion and loose wires. Repair as necessary. Install EEC-IV Breakout Box (T83L-50-EEC-IV). Connect PCM to breakout box. Connect DVOM to test pins No. 46 and 47 at breakout box. Turn ignition on. Slowly apply throttle to WOT, and release to closed position. Voltage should change smoothly from 0.4-4.5 volts. See CIRCUIT TEST DH for schematics and specific engine values. If voltage change is incorrect or erratic, ensure TP sensor is properly installed. If TP sensor is properly installed, replace TP sensor. Remove breakout box, reconnect all components, and repeat QUICK TEST. If voltage is okay, go to step **8)** for Code 121 or next step for all other codes.

3) Check Idle – Ensure idle is correct. If idle is correct, go to next step. If idle is incorrect, see IDLE SPEED in ON-VEHICLE ADJUSTMENTS article.

4) Check Throttle Body – Ensure idle is correct. Check throttle and/or cruise control linkage for binding and rough operation. Inspect throttle body for sludge build-up. Check engine vacuum hoses. Refer to Vehicle Emission Control Information (VECI) decal for proper vacuum hose routing. Check for air leak between ISC solenoid and MAF sensor. If problems are found, repair as necessary. Remove breakout box, reconnect all components, and repeat QUICK TEST. If no problems are found, go to next step.

5) Check MAP/BARO Sensor Output – On vehicles without MAP/BARO go to next step. On vehicles with MAP/BARO, see DIAGNOSTIC AIDS, then continue with this test. With tester connected and ignition on, measure sensor output voltage. If output voltage is within range for specified altitude, remove MAP/BARO tester and go to next step. See MAP SENSOR VOLTAGE OUTPUT table for specification. If output voltage is not within range, replace MAP/BARO sensor. Remove breakout box, reconnect all components, and repeat QUICK TEST.

Diagnostic Aids – If possible, measure several known good MAP/BARO sensors. Average voltage reading will be typical for location and day of testing. Also, refer to CIRCUIT TEST DF under SELF-DIAGNOSTICS – EEC-IV article in ENGINE PERFORMANCE of appropriate MITCHELL® manual for MAP/BARO sensor output check. See Fig. DF1 for connector terminal identification and MAP/BARO tester hookup.

MAP SENSOR VOLTAGE OUTPUT

Elevation (Feet)	Volts
0	1.55-1.63
1000	1.52-1.60
2000	1.49-1.57
3000	1.46-1.54
4000	1.43-1.51
5000	1.40-1.48
6000	1.37-1.45
7000	1.35-1.43

CIRCUIT TEST G (Cont.)

6) Check IAT Sensor – Ensure ambient temperature is more than 50°F (10°C) before performing this test. Also, check and repair any air leaks in front of IAT sensor. Turn ignition off. Connect breakout box to PCM. Set DVOM to 20-volt scale. Connect DVOM to test pins No. 25 and 46. Start engine, and let it idle. Observe voltage as engine warms up. See CIRCUIT TEST DA for voltage specifications. If voltage decreases smoothly and stabilizes when engine reaches operating conditions, system is operating properly at this time. Testing is complete. If voltage does not decrease smoothly and stabilize after engine reaches operating conditions, replace IAT sensor and repeat QUICK TEST.

7) Continuous Memory Code 184 & 185: Inspect MAF Sensor – Code 184 indicates MAF sensor signal is higher than expected. Code 185 indicates MAF sensor signal is lower than expected. Turn ignition off. Check for air leaks between Idle Air Control (IAC) solenoid and MAF sensor. Inspect MAF sensor for oil contamination caused by excessive blow-by or malfunctioning PCV. If problems are found, repair as necessary. Clear codes and repeat QUICK TEST. If no problems are found, go to step **10)**.

8) Check MAF Sensor Circuit Voltage – Turn ignition off. Disconnect PCM 60-pin connector. Inspect connector for damaged pins, corrosion and loose wires. Repair as necessary. Install EEC-IV Breakout Box (T83L-50-EEC-IV). Connect PCM to breakout box. Start engine, and warm it to normal operating temperature. Measure voltage between test pin No. 50 and test pin No. 40 or 60 at breakout box. If voltage is not within specification, replace MAF sensor. Remove breakout box, reconnect all components, and repeat QUICK TEST. See MAF SENSOR DATA table. If voltage is within acceptable range, system is operating normally at this time. Sometime during the last 80 warm-up cycles, MAF sensor signal was out of range.

MAF SENSOR DATA

Engine Condition	[1] Voltage
Idle	0.8
20 MPH	1.0
40 MPH	1.7
60 MPH	2.1

[1] – With engine at normal operating temperature.

9) Continuous Memory Code 186 & 187: Visual Vacuum Checks – Code 186 indicates pulse width is longer than expected (rich). Code 187 indicates pulse width is shorter than expected (lean). Inspect air cleaner and air inlet duct. Replace or repair an necessary. Check for unmetered air leaks between MAF sensor and IAC solenoid. Check all engine vacuum hoses for damage, blockage and improper routing. Repair as necessary, and repeat QUICK TEST. If all checks are okay, go to next step.

10) Check Fuel Pressure – Turn ignition off. Install fuel pressure gauge. Ensure vacuum hose is connected to fuel pressure regulator (if applicable). Start engine, and run it at idle. If fuel pressure is within specification, go to next step. See FUEL PRESSURE SPECIFICATIONS table. If fuel pressure is not within specifications, repair as necessary.

FUEL PRESSURE SPECIFICATIONS

Engine	KOER Pressure psi (kg/cm²)	KOEO Pressure psi (kg/cm²)
All	30-45 (2.1-3.2)	35-40 (2.4-3.1)

11) Verify Fuel Pressure Retention Ability – Turn ignition on. If fuel pressure remains at specification for 60 seconds, go to next step. If fuel pressure decreases, go to appropriate MITCHELL® manual for fuel systems diagnostic procedures.

12) Cylinder Balance Test – Perform KOER SELF-TEST. After last code, wait 5-10 seconds, and then goose throttle lightly (not wide open throttle). This will activate cylinder balance test. If Code 90 is present after test, go back to step **7)**. If Code 90 is not present after test, go to CIRCUIT TEST H under SELF-DIAGNOSTICS – EEC-IV article in ENGINE PERFORMANCE of appropriate MITCHELL® manual.

WIRING DIAGRAMS

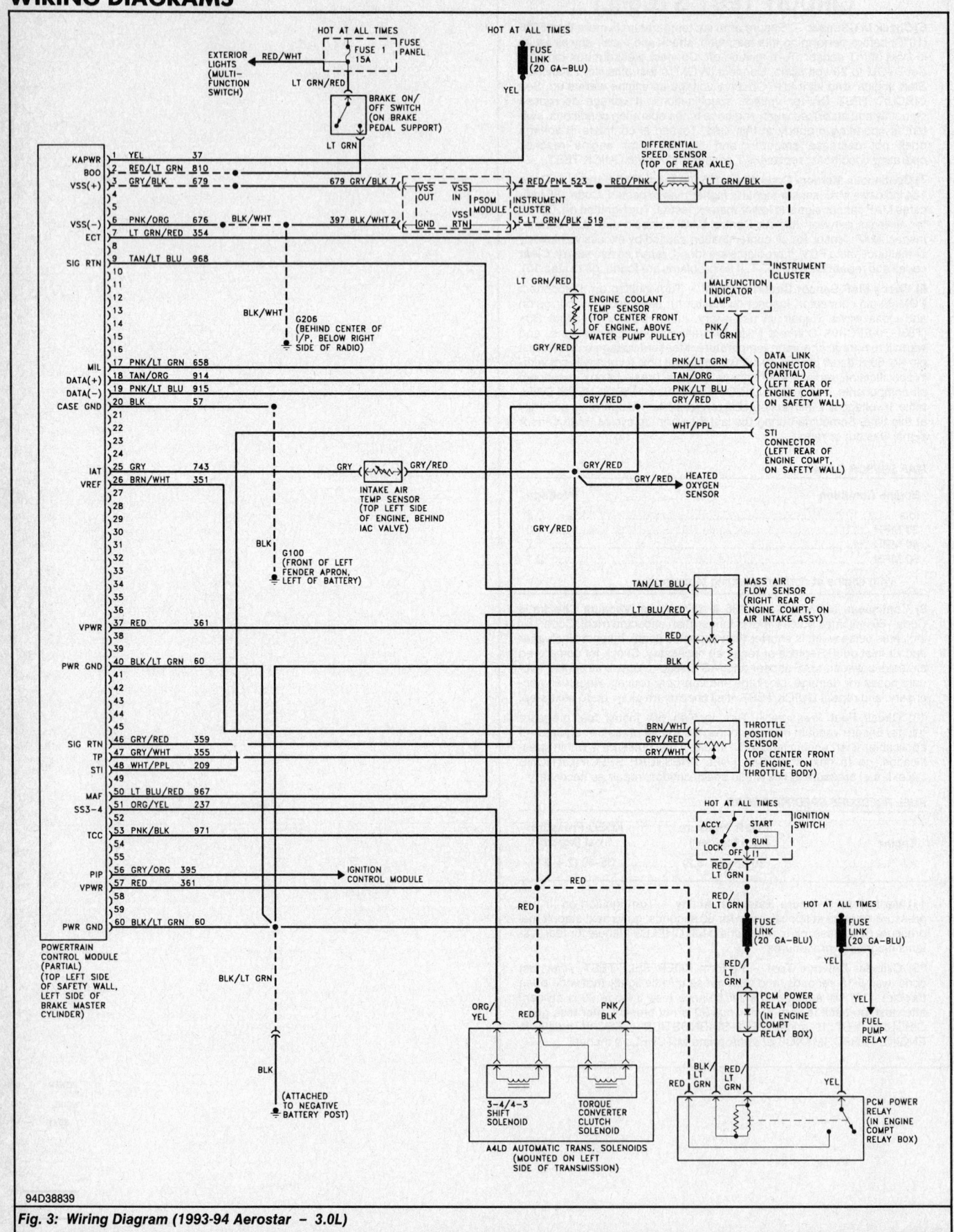

94D38839

Fig. 3: Wiring Diagram (1993-94 Aerostar – 3.0L)

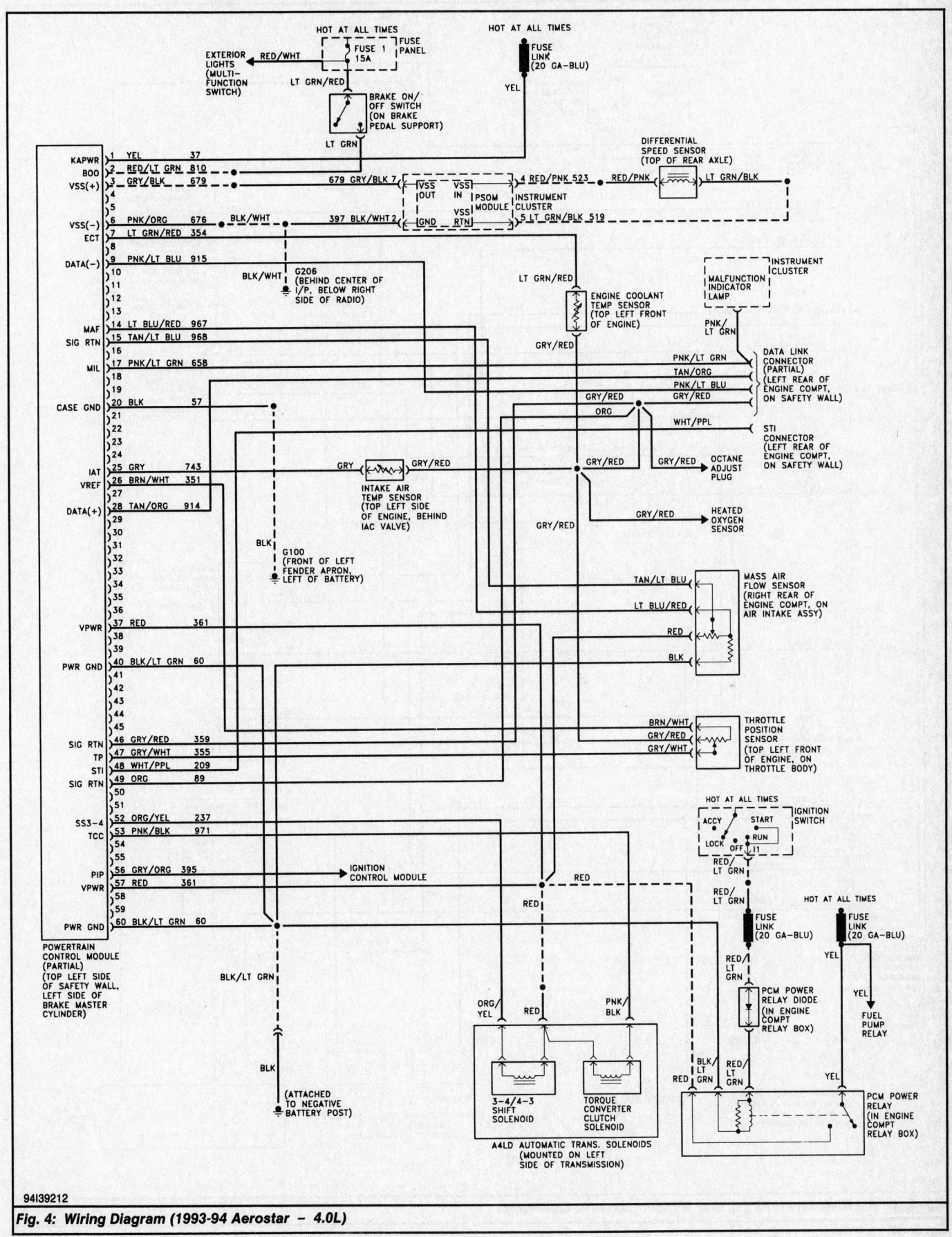

94139212

Fig. 4: Wiring Diagram (1993-94 Aerostar – 4.0L)

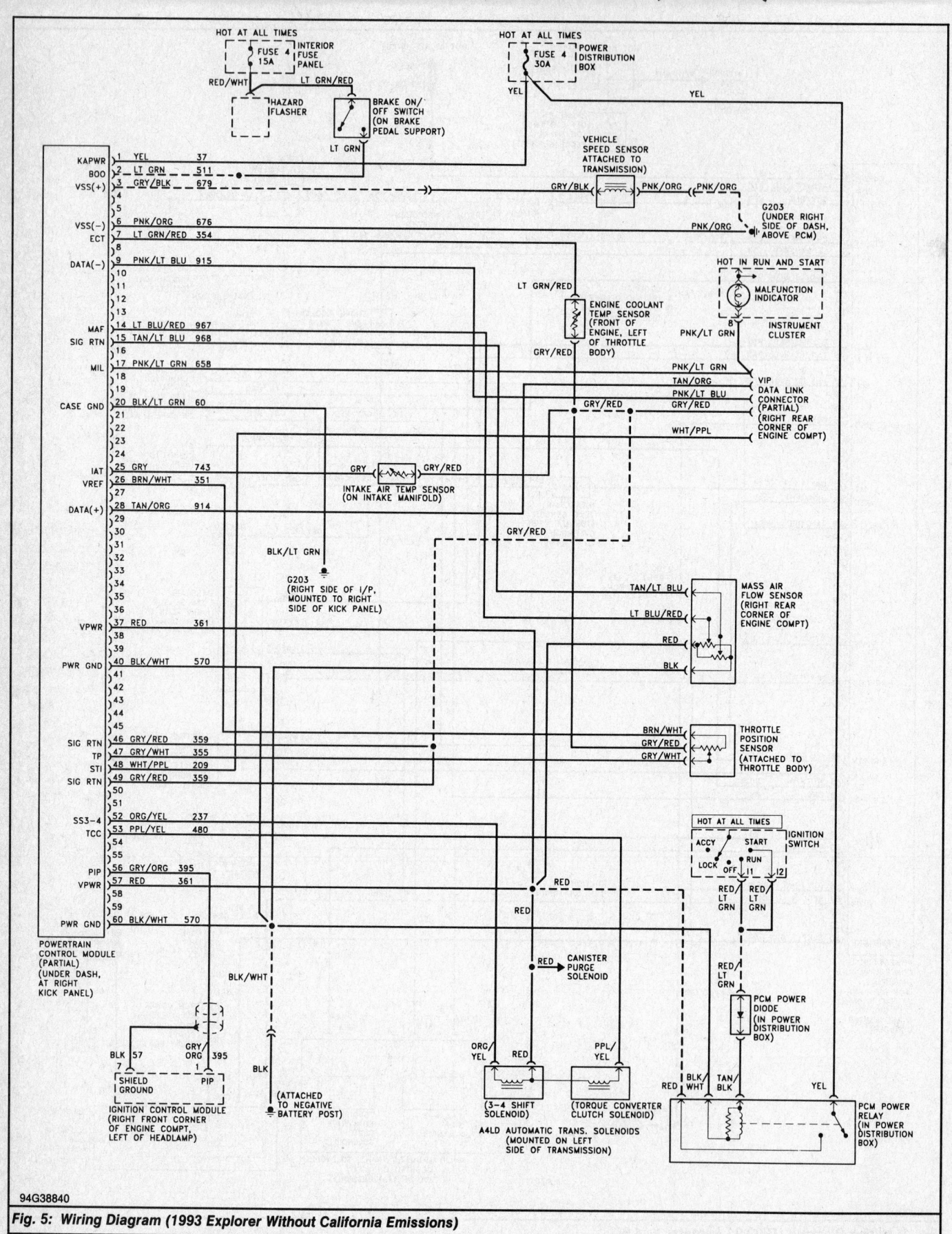

Fig. 5: *Wiring Diagram (1993 Explorer Without California Emissions)*

94G38840

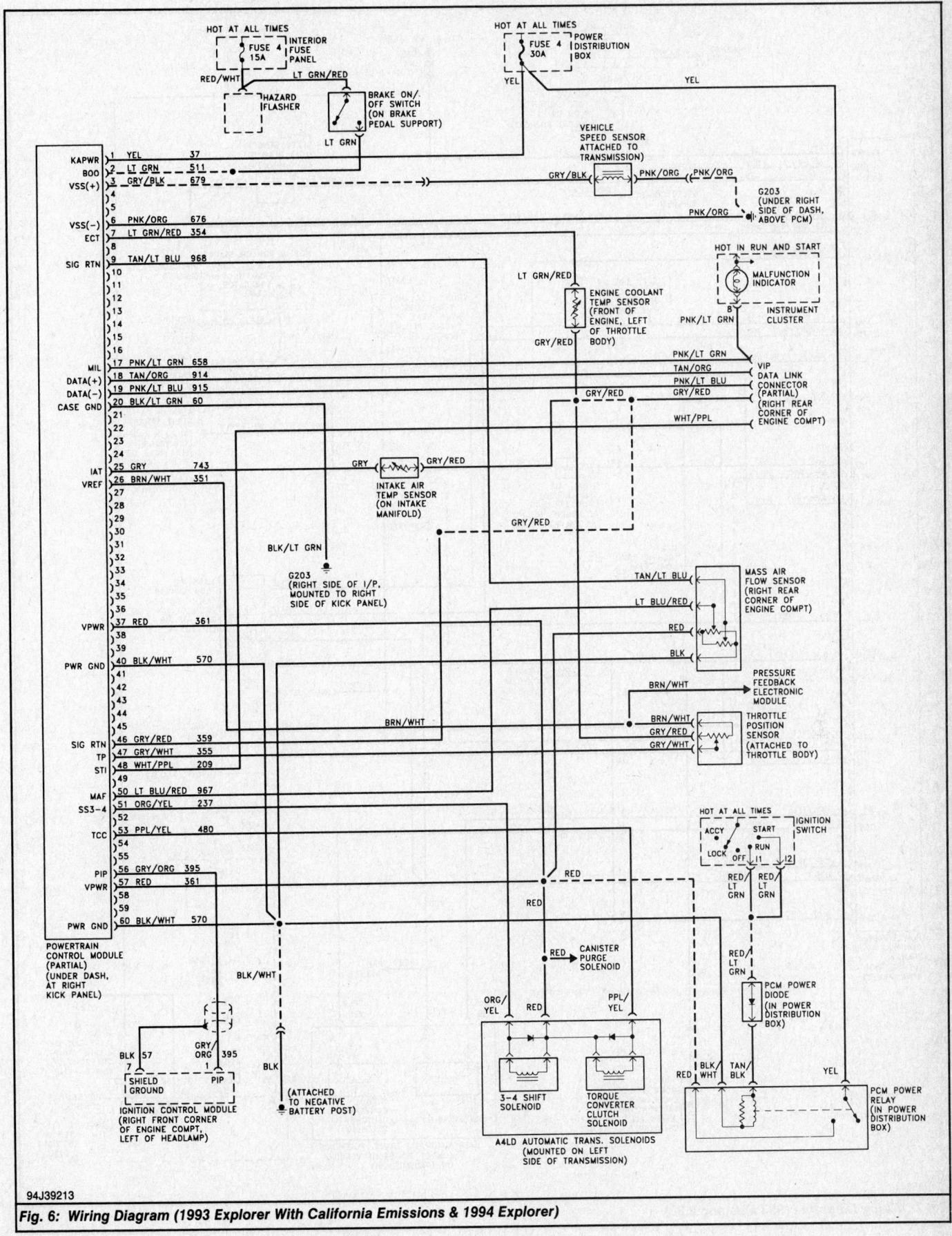

94J39213

Fig. 6: Wiring Diagram (1993 Explorer With California Emissions & 1994 Explorer)

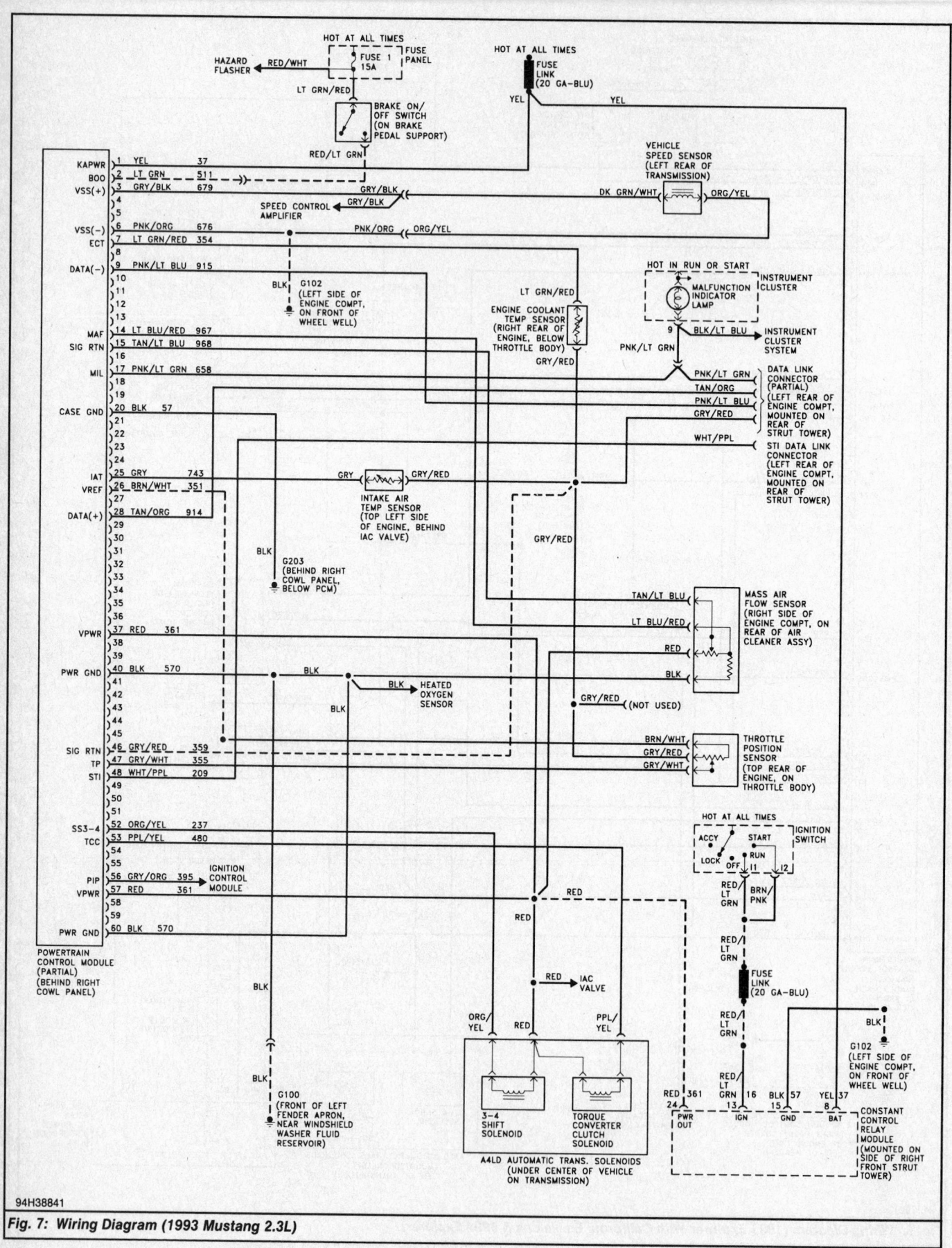

94H38841

Fig. 7: *Wiring Diagram (1993 Mustang 2.3L)*

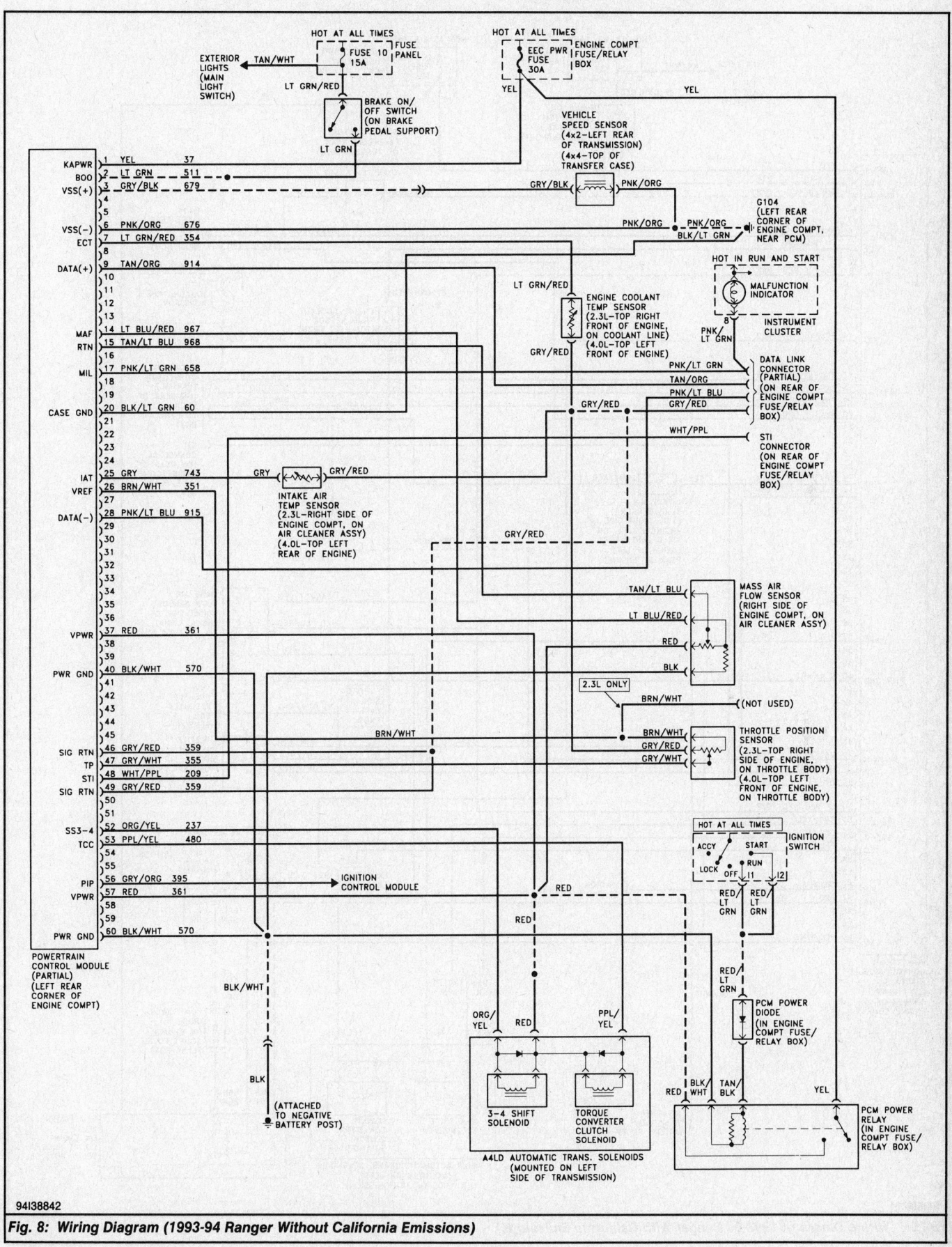

Fig. 8: Wiring Diagram (1993-94 Ranger Without California Emissions)

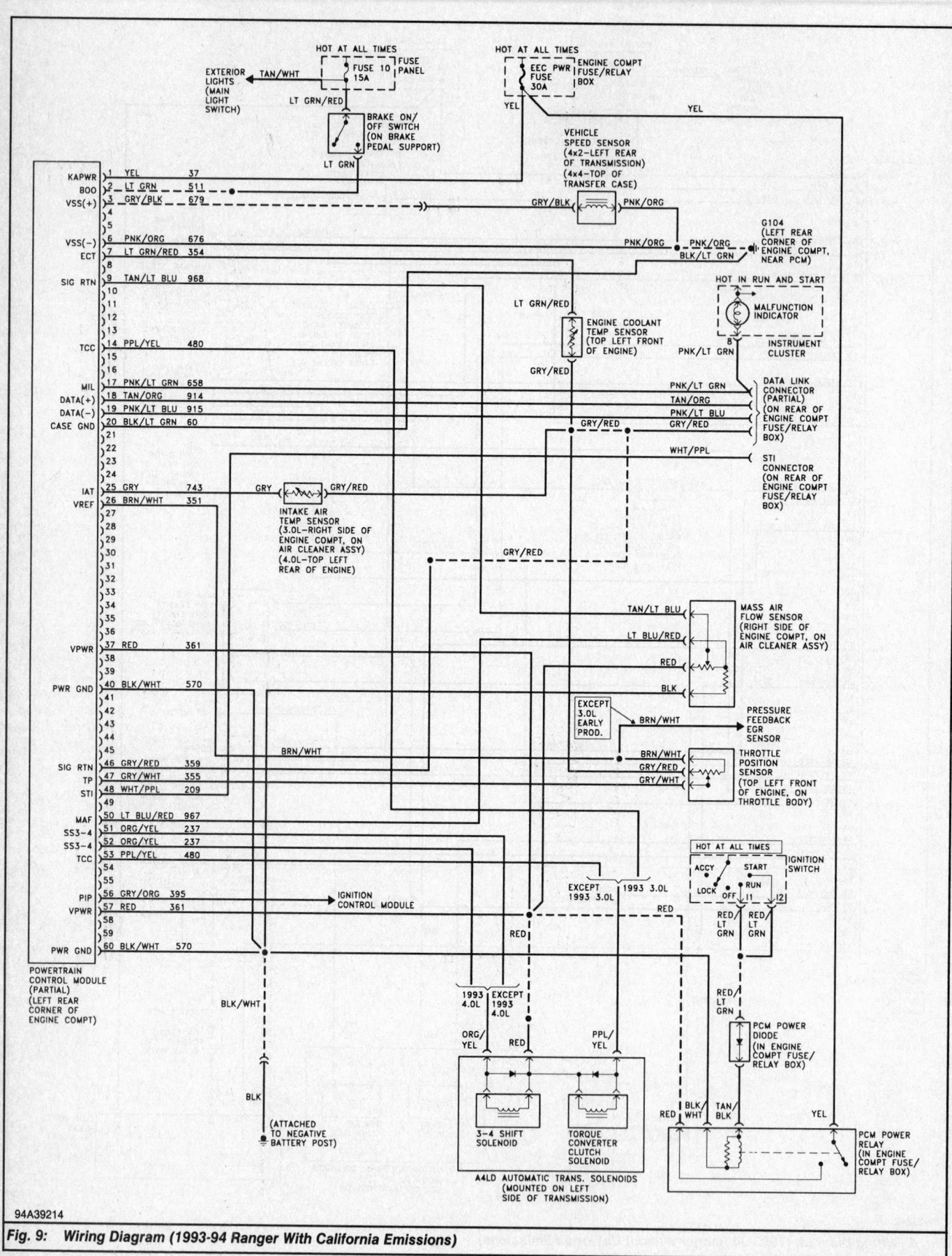

Fig. 9: *Wiring Diagram (1993-94 Ranger With California Emissions)*

94A39214

Ford Motor Co: 1994 Probe

APPLICATION & LABOR TIMES

APPLICATION & LABOR TIMES

Vehicle Application	Labor Times		Trans. Model
	[1] R & I	[2] Overhaul	
1994 Probe	5.0	8.6	CD4E

[1] – Removal and installation of transmission from vehicle chassis.

[2] – Bench overhaul time for transmission and differential. DOES NOT include removal and installation.

IDENTIFICATION

The CD4E automatic transmission is identified by identification tag located on rear of transaxle and bottom of main control assembly. *See Fig. 1.*

| Ford Model → | UM | FW5Ø19Ø9Ø | ← Ford Part Number Prefix & Suffix |
| | PTAJ | F4RP-BB | |

F4RPBB 21 3365 0001

Part Number Prefix & Suffix

Serial Number Includes Build Date, I.E. 1993 Dec. 31, Trans.No. 1

94F36611   Courtesy of Ford Motor Co.

Fig. 1: Identifying Vehicle Certification Label

NOTE: For CD4E transaxle electronic testing and repair, see CD4E ELECTRONIC CONTROLS article.

DESCRIPTION & OPERATION

The CD4E is a 4-speed transaxle assembly. The CD4E is controlled by both electronic and mechanical systems utilizing a compound planetary gearset, chain drive, final drive planetary gearset and an open differential. One band, 5 friction clutches, and 2 one-way clutches provide four forward gear ratios and reverse. *See Fig. 2.*

Input signals from sensors are sent to the Powertrain Control Module (PCM). The PCM can determine when the time and conditions are right for a shift or converter clutch application. The PCM can also determine line pressure needed to optimize shift feel.

Five electronic solenoids accomplish these functions; 2 On/Off solenoids for shifting, one Pulse-Width Modulator solenoid for torque converter clutch control, a Electronic Pressure Control (EPC) solenoid for line pressure control, and a 3-2 timing/coast clutch solenoid to control the release of the coast clutch and the coordinated release of the direct clutch and apply of the low and intermediate band. The PCM has built-in self-diagnosis, fail-safe code and warning code display for the main input sensors and solenoid valves.

LUBRICATION & ADJUSTMENTS

NOTE: See appropriate AUTOMATIC TRANSMISSION SERVICING article in TRANSMISSION SERVICING section.

TROUBLE SHOOTING

PRELIMINARY INSPECTION

1) Ensure vehicle is thoroughly road tested to verify driver's complaint. Determine if problem occurs during upshift, downshift, coasting or engagement. If noise is diagnosed, check if noise is affected by RPM, vehicle speed, gear selection or temperature. Ensure vehicle is at normal operating temperature when checking.

2) Inspect fluid level and condition. Visually inspect for vehicle modifications, electronic add-ons, fluid leaks and/or incorrect linkage adjustment. Check for trouble codes before any mechanical repair is performed. See CD4E ELECTRONIC CONTROLS article for trouble code diagnosis and repair procedures. If no trouble codes are present, see applicable symptom diagnosis.

3) If the following symptoms are present, it is necessary to complete electronic diagnosis and repair before any mechanical diagnosis and repair is performed. See CD4E ELECTRONIC CONTROLS article for trouble code diagnosis and repair procedures.

- No Reverse
- Harsh Engagement
- All Or Some Shifts Not Present
- Early, Late, Erratic, Soft, Slipping And/Or Harsh Shifting
- No First Gear (In "D" Position).
- No Low Gear.
- No Torque Converter Clutch
- Torque Converter Clutch Always Engaged
- Poor Vehicle Performance
- Engine Will Not Crank
- Transaxle Overheating
- No Engine Braking In Low ("L")
- No Engine Braking In Second ("2")

ENGAGEMENT FAULTS

No Forward Engagement, Reverse Okay – Check shift linkage, oil pump external or internal (support sealing rings) leakage, valve body malfunction (internal leak, stuck regulator valve and/or leaking forward accumulator), forward and coast clutch assembly, low one-way clutch, forward one-way clutch and low/intermediate planetary carrier.

No Reverse Engagement, Forward Okay – Check external and internal shift linkage, low line pressure, valve body (stuck valve), oil Pump internal leak (No. 6 and 7 sealing rings), reverse clutch assembly, low/reverse clutch assembly, forward/coast/direct clutch cylinder, case (oil passages cross leakage or porosity) and reverse/overdrive gear set.

Harsh Reverse &/Or Forward Engagement – Check fluid level, axle shafts and CV joints, engine/transaxle mounts, shift linkage, line pressure, restricted oil filter, valve body, forward clutch assembly, reverse clutch assembly, low/reverse clutch assembly and direct clutch assembly.

Delayed/Soft Reverse &/Or Forward Engagement – Check fluid level, axle shafts and CV joints, engine/transaxle mounts, shift linkage, line pressure, restricted oil filter, valve body, forward clutch assembly, reverse clutch assembly, low/reverse clutch assembly and direct clutch assembly.

No Forward Or Reverse Engagement – Check fluid level, shift linkage, line pressure, oil pump, restricted oil filter, valve body, torque converter, turbine shaft to forward/coast/direct clutch cylinder, chain and sprocket assembly, park pawl mechanism, axle shafts and CV joints, final drive assembly and planetary gear assemblies.

SHIFTING FAULTS

All Or Some Shifts Not Present – Check fluid level, shift linkage, speedometer drive/driven gear, valve body, band, low one-way clutch assembly, overdrive/reverse sun gear and shell, case, oil pump, direct clutch assembly, intermediate/overdrive servo, coast clutch assembly and forward one-way clutch assembly.

Early Or Late Shifting – Check tire size and speedometer drive/driven gear.

Erratic/Hunting Shift Timing – Check fluid, vehicle speed input, valve body and miscellaneous internal failures.

Soft/Slipping Shift Feel – Check fluid condition, shift linkage, low line pressure, valve body, oil pump assembly and leaking filter and/or seal.

Harsh Shift Feel – Check fluid level and condition, axle shafts and CV joints, high line pressure, valve body and torque converter.

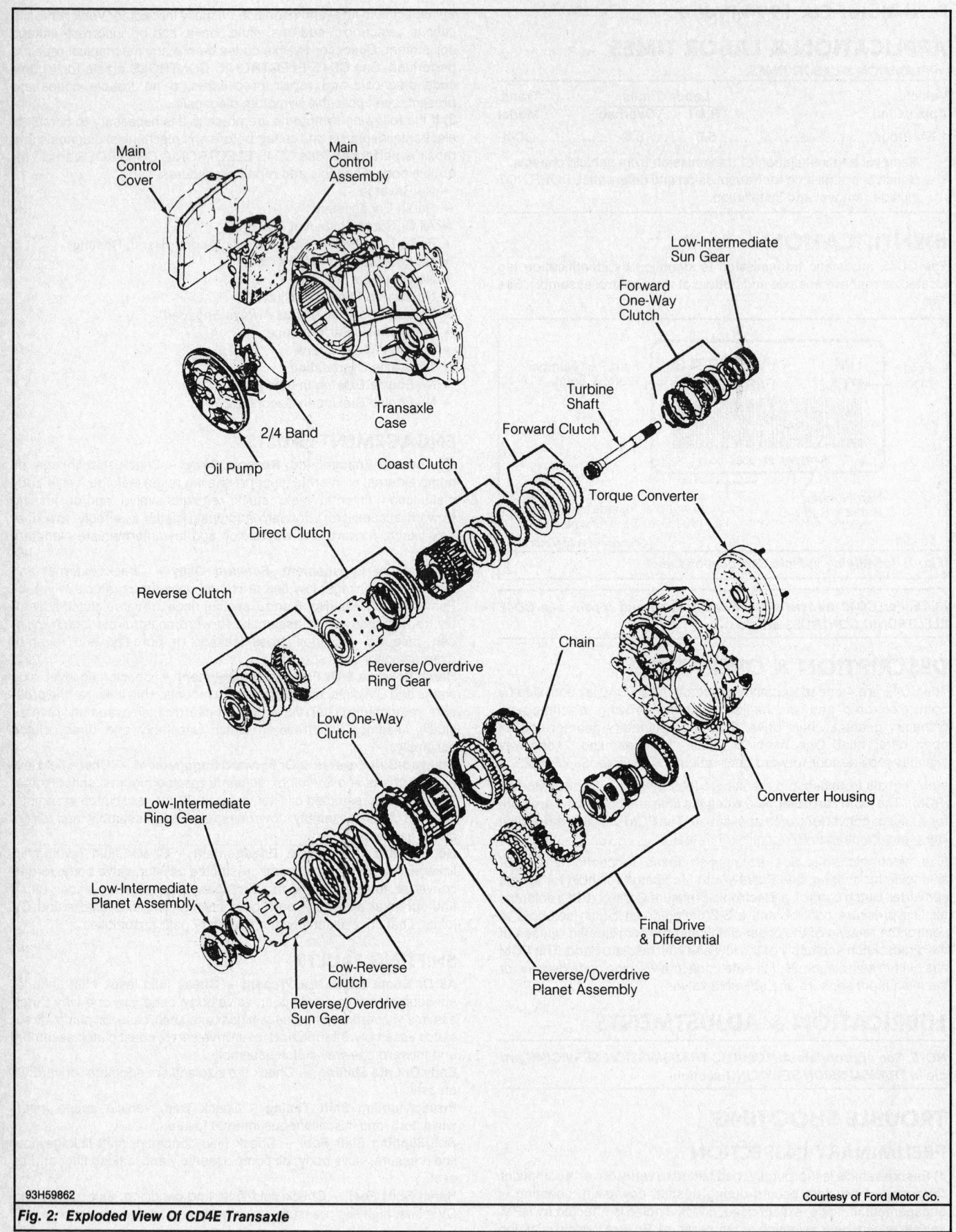

93H59862

Courtesy of Ford Motor Co.

Fig. 2: Exploded View Of CD4E Transaxle

No First Gear (In "D" Position) – Check shift linkage, valve body and internal seal(s) leakage.
No Low Gear – Check shift linkage and valve body.

MISCELLANEOUS FAULTS

No Torque Converter Clutch – Check valve body and torque converter.
Torque Converter Clutch Always Engaged – Check valve body, oil pump assembly, torque converter and transaxle case.
Stiff Shift Lever Operation – Check shift interlock system, shift linkage and manual valve (valve body).
Poor Vehicle Performance – Check correct shift linkage to shift lever indexing, torque converter (TCC applied and one-way clutch).
No Engine Braking In Manual Low Position – Check valve body, coast clutch assembly, low/reverse clutch assembly and oil pump assembly.
No Engine Braking In Manual 2nd Position – Check shift linkage, valve body, forward one-way clutch assembly, coast clutch assembly and oil pump assembly.
Vehicle Movement In Neutral Position – Check shift linkage, oil pump assembly and forward/coast clutch assembly.

CLUTCH & BAND APPLICATION

CLUTCH & BAND APPLICATION

Selector Lever Application	Elements In Use
Reverse ("R")	Low/Reverse Clutch & Reverse Clutch
Drive ("D")	
First Gear	Forward Clutch, Forward One-Way Clutch & Low One-Way Clutch
Second Gear	Low/Intermediate Band, Forward Clutch & Forward One-Way Clutch
Third Gear	Direct Clutch, Forward Clutch & Forward One-Way Clutch
Fourth Gear	Low/Intermediate Band, Direct Clutch & Forward Clutch
Manual Second ("2")	Low/Intermediate Band, Forward Clutch, Forward One-Way Clutch & Coast Clutch
Manual First ("1")	Forward Clutch, Forward One-Way Clutch, Coast Clutch, Low/Reverse Clutch & Low One-Way Clutch

TESTING

AIR PRESSURE CHECK

1) Disconnect negative battery cable. Remove air cleaner assembly. Disconnect transaxle harness connector. Compress tabs on transaxle electrical harness receptacle and push into case. Raise and support vehicle.
2) Remove drain plug and drain fluid. Remove left front fender splash shield. Secure cooler lines away from main control cover assembly (side cover). Remove cover and gasket. Remove 12 valve body bolts. Slightly lift valve body and remove "Z" link.
3) Remove valve body with wiring harness. Remove thermostatic oil level control valve bracket. Pull valve straight out of transaxle case.

CAUTION: Do not air check coast clutch since piston may be forced out of forward clutch piston.

4) Install Transmission Test Plate (T94P-77000-S). Air check clutch hydraulic circuits for function and leakage. *See Fig. 3*. If leakage is detected, disassemble transaxle and inspect. Remove test plate.
5) Install thermostatic oil level control valve in transaxle case. Install bracket. Tighten bolt to specification. See TORQUE SPECIFICATIONS. Install new "O" ring on valve body harness connector receptacle. Install receptacle in transaxle case.

6) Insert "Z" link into end of manual valve. Place valve body in position on transaxle case and install 12 valve body bolts. Tighten bolts in sequence. *See Fig. 4*. Tighten bolts to specification. See TORQUE SPECIFICATIONS.
7) Remove manual control lever bolt and lever assembly. Using Shifter Shaft Alignment Tool (T94P-77000-H), move manual control lever shaft to "D" position. Install pin to hold tool in position. *See Fig. 5*. Move manual valve detent lever assembly to "D" position.
8) Loosen nut on ball stud of manual valve detent lever actuating rod assembly. Snug nut on ball stud. Remove shifter pin. Rotate Shifter Shaft Alignment tool until socket can be installed on nut. Tighten bolt to specification. See TORQUE SPECIFICATIONS.
9) Rotate lever back to "D" position and recheck adjustment. Remove pin and alignment tool. Install manual control lever assembly. Tighten bolt to specification. See TORQUE SPECIFICATIONS. Install main control cover (side cover) with new gasket. Tighten bolts in sequence. *See Fig. 6*. Tighten bolts to specification. See TORQUE SPECIFICATIONS.
10) To complete installation, reverse removal procedures. Tighten drain plug to specification. See TORQUE SPECIFICATIONS. Add 6 qts. of ATF fluid. Start and run vehicle. Add fluid as necessary.

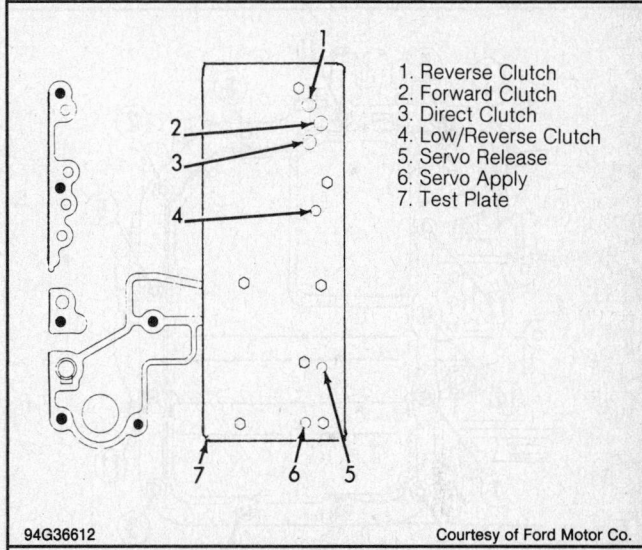

1. Reverse Clutch
2. Forward Clutch
3. Direct Clutch
4. Low/Reverse Clutch
5. Servo Release
6. Servo Apply
7. Test Plate

94G36612   Courtesy of Ford Motor Co.

Fig. 3: Air Checking Transaxle Assembly

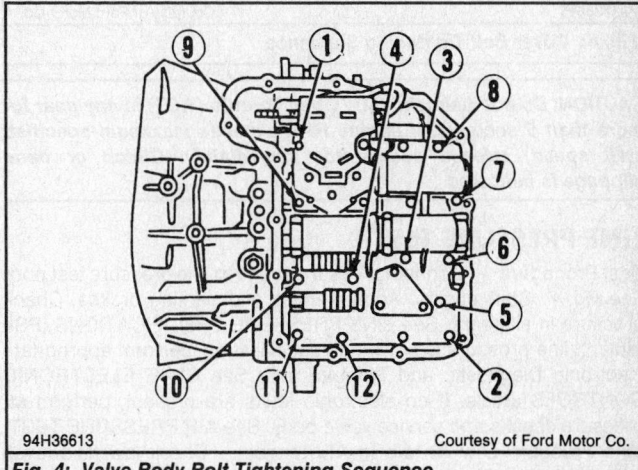

94H36613   Courtesy of Ford Motor Co.

Fig. 4: Valve Body Bolt Tightening Sequence

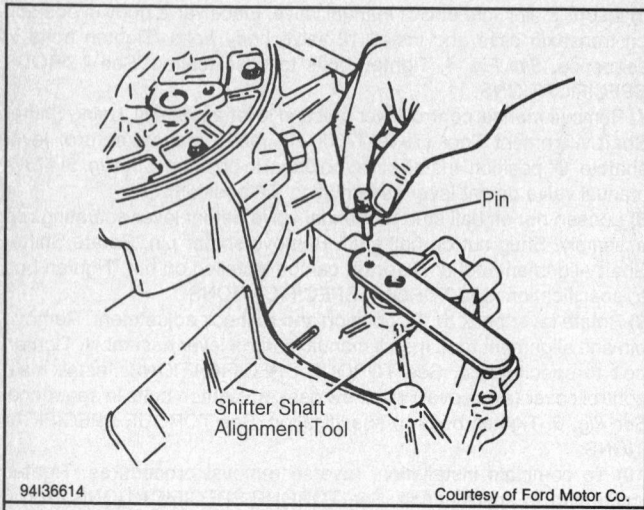

94I36614   Courtesy of Ford Motor Co.

Fig. 5: Installing Shifter Shaft Alignment Tool

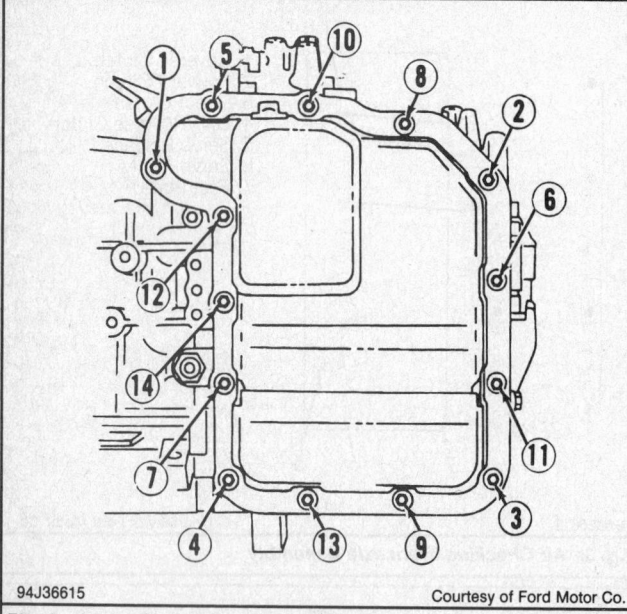

94J36615   Courtesy of Ford Motor Co.

Fig. 6: Cover Bolt Tightening Sequence

CAUTION: Do not maintain Wide Open Throttle (WOT) in any gear for more than 5 seconds. If engine RPM exceeds maximum specified stall speed, release accelerator immediately. Clutch or band slippage is indicated.

LINE PRESSURE TEST

Test Procedure – Connect pressure gauge to line pressure test port. See Fig. 7. Start engine. Apply service and parking brakes. Check pressure in all gears. See LINE PRESSURE SPECIFICATIONS (PSI) table. If line pressure is not within specification, perform appropriate electronic Diagnostic and Pinpoint test. See CD4E ELECTRONIC CONTROLS article. If no electronic faults are present, perform air pressure checks and service valve body. See AIR PRESSURE TEST.

Line Pressure Low At Idle In All Ranges – Check low fluid level, restricted inlet filter, loose valve body or valve body components, oil pump leakage and sticking main regulator valve.

Line Pressure High In All Ranges – Check main regulator valve, solenoid body and wiring harness and perform Quick Test procedure.

LINE PRESSURE SPECIFICATIONS (PSI)

Selector Position	Idle RPM	WOT Stall RPM
"P" & "N"	64-76	N/A
"R"	64-76	259-294
"D"	45-63	168-184
"2"	45-63	168-184
"L"	45-63	168-184

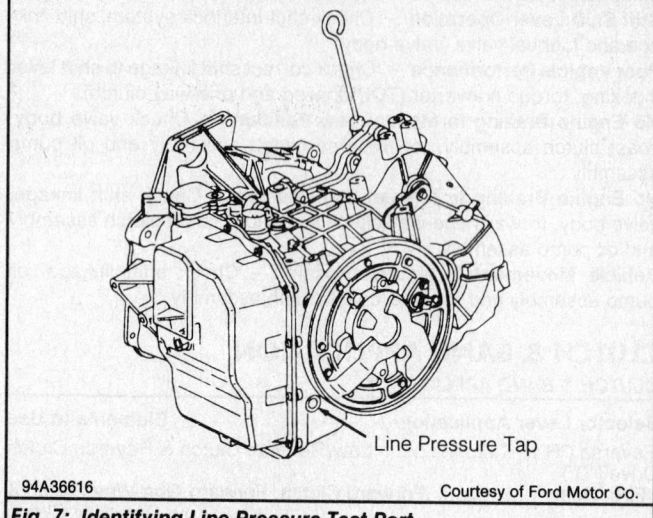

94A36616   Courtesy of Ford Motor Co.

Fig. 7: Identifying Line Pressure Test Port

STALL SPEED TEST

NOTE: After each test, shift transaxle into Neutral and run engine for at least 15 seconds to cool torque converter and transmission fluid.

CAUTION: Do not maintain Wide Open Throttle (WOT) in any gear for more than 5 seconds. If engine RPM exceeds maximum specified stall speed, release accelerator immediately. Clutch or band slippage is indicated.

The stall speed test checks the operation of the following items:
- Converter One-Way Clutch
- Forward Clutch
- Low One-Way Clutch
- Reverse Clutch
- Low-Intermediate Band
- Engine Performance

1) Apply service and parking brakes. Connect tachometer to engine, and record RPM reached in each gear selector range (except Neutral) at WOT. Stall speed should be 2200-2500 rpm. If stall speeds exceed specification, ensure engine is mechanically okay and tuned to specification. If engine is okay, remove torque converter and check torque converter one-way clutch for slippage.

2) If stall speed is too high in "D", "2", "1", the following components may be faulty:
- Forward Clutch
- Forward One-Way Clutch
- Low One-Way Clutch

3) If stall speed is too high in "R", the following components may be faulty:
- Low/Reverse Clutch
- Reverse Clutch

SHIFT POINT ROAD TEST

1) Ensure engine and transaxle is at normal operating temperature. Road test vehicle in "D". Apply minimum throttle and observe speeds at which upshift occurs and torque converter engages. See VEHICLE SHIFT SPEEDS table.

VEHICLE SHIFT SPEEDS

Operating Condition	Shift Speed MPH
Minimum Throttle [1]	
1-2	10-16
2-3	18-24
3-4	29-35
Partial Throttle [2]	
1-2	13-19
2-3	28-34
3-4	55-61
WOT	
1-2	31-37
2-3	63-69
3-4	98-104
Coast [3]	
4-3	18-24
3-2	N/A
2-1	6-12
Manual 2-1	28-34

[1] – Minimum throttle opening (13%).
[2] – Partial throttle opening (30%).
[3] – Closed throttle, coasting condition. Downshift may be imperceptible.

TORQUE CONVERTER

CONVERTER END PLAY CHECK

With torque converter removed from transaxle, position End Play Checking Device (T81P-7902-D) in converter hub. Tighten nut on device. Position a dial indicator on device. Position dial indicator pointer on converter shell. *See Fig. 8*. Lift up on device handles. If dial indicator reading exceeds .050" (1.27 mm), replace converter.

LEAKAGE CHECK

With torque converter removed from transaxle, check for leakage using torque converter leak tester.

ONE-WAY CLUTCH CHECK

Place 90 degree end of pick tool in slot on bottom of converter stator. While holding pick, rotate inner race with fingers. One-way clutch should not rotate in counter-clockwise direction and should rotate in clockwise direction. Replace converter if one-way clutch does not operate as specified.

PUMP INSERT CHECK

Install oil pump shaft into torque converter. Using torque wrench with 5/16" socket, ensure insert can hold up to 10 ft. lbs. Replace converter if insert turns.

TURBINE TORQUE CHECK

Install End Play Checking Tool (T81P-7902-D) with sleeve into turbine splines in converter. Using torque wrench, measure turbine turning torque. Replace converter is torque exceeds 53 INCH lbs. (6 N.m).

ON-VEHICLE SERVICE

DIFFERENTIAL OIL SEALS

Removal – 1) Raise and support vehicle. Remove front wheels and inner fender splash guards. Carefully raise staked portion of axle nut. Apply brakes and loosen, but DO NOT remove, axle nut. Remove stabilizer bar-to-control arm nut, spacer and bolt.
2) Remove lower control arm ball joint clamp bolt. Pry downward on lower control arm to separate control arm from knuckle. Remove knuckle-to-strut attaching bolts. Slide knuckle assembly off axle shaft, and remove from vehicle.

NOTE: If removing right drive axle, unbolt dynamic damper from engine block.

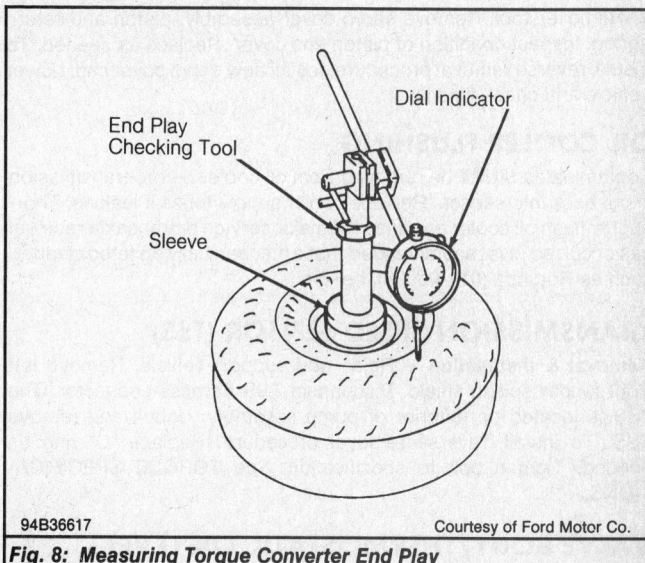

94B36617   Courtesy of Ford Motor Co.

Fig. 8: Measuring Torque Converter End Play

3) Insert pry bar between transaxle case and axle flange. Carefully apply force to pry bar until axle circlip is disengaged. On all models, carefully withdraw axle assembly from transaxle, and quickly install appropriate plug. Remove and discard axle nut. Pull axle from hub. Using appropriate puller, remove seal.
Installation – 1) Apply lubrication to new seal. Using appropriate driver, install seal. Install new circlip on transaxle end of axle. Remove transaxle plug, and carefully install axle into transaxle. Ensure circlip snaps into retaining groove.
2) Install axle into hub. Install NEW axle nut. Tighten bolts to specifications. See TORQUE SPECIFICATIONS. Stake NEW axle nut with blunt nose chisel. To complete installation, reverse removal procedure. Check transaxle fluid level and add as needed.

INTERMEDIATE & OVERDRIVE SERVO

NOTE: Manufacturer does not recommend removal of intermediate and overdrive servo while transaxle is installed in vehicle. On-vehicle removal of servo cover is only recommended for fluid leakage repair.

Removal & Installation – 1) Raise and support vehicle. Remove left front fender splash shield. Remove and discard servo cover cap. Using Servo Cover Remover/Replacer (T94P-77000-L), compress servo cover assembly. *See Fig. 9*. Remove retaining ring and release servo cover pressure.

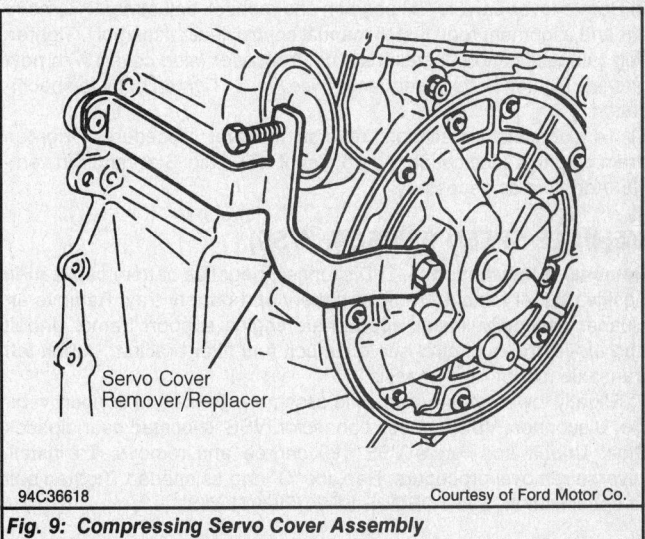

Servo Cover Remover/Replacer

94C36618   Courtesy of Ford Motor Co.

Fig. 9: Compressing Servo Cover Assembly

2) Remover tool. Remove servo cover assembly, piston and return spring. Inspect condition of piston and cover. Replace as needed. To install, reverse removal procedure. Install new servo cover cap. Lower vehicle and check fluid level.

OIL COOLER FLUSHING

Contaminates MUST be removed from oil cooler before transmission is put back into service. Replace cooler supply tubes if leaking. Thoroughly flush oil cooler and lines if a major service or transaxle removal has occurred. It is recommended that a mechanically agitated cleaner, such as Rotunda (014-00028), be used.

TRANSMISSION SPEED SENSOR (TSS)

Removal & Installation – Raise and support vehicle. Remove left front fender splash shield. Disconnect TSS harness connector. The TSS is located on exterior of pump assembly. Unbolt and remove TSS. To install, reverse removal procedure. Replace "O" ring as needed. Tighten bolt to specification. See TORQUE SPECIFICATIONS.

VALVE BODY/THERMOSTATIC OIL LEVEL CONTROL VALVE

Removal – **1)** Disconnect negative battery cable. Remove air cleaner assembly. Disconnect transaxle harness connector. Compress tabs on transaxle electrical harness receptacle and push into case. Raise and support vehicle.

2) Remove drain plug and drain fluid. Remove left front fender splash shield. Secure cooler lines away from main control cover assembly (side cover). Remove cover and gasket. Remove 12 valve body bolts. Slightly lift valve body and remove "Z" link.

3) Remove valve body with wiring harness. Remove thermostatic oil level control valve bracket. Pull valve straight out of transaxle case.

Installation – **1)** Install thermostatic oil level control valve in transaxle case. Install bracket. Tighten bolt to specification. See TORQUE SPECIFICATIONS. Install new "O" ring on valve body harness connector receptacle. Install receptacle in transaxle case.

2) Insert "Z" link into end of manual valve. Place valve body in position on transaxle case and install 12 valve body bolts. Tighten bolts in sequence. See Fig. 4. Tighten bolts to specification.

3) Remove manual control lever bolt and lever assembly. Using Shifter Shaft Alignment Tool (T94P-77000-H), move manual control lever shaft to "D" position. Install pin to hold tool in position. Move manual valve detent lever assembly to "D" position. See Fig. 5.

4) Loosen nut on ball stud of manual valve detent lever actuating rod assembly. Snug nut on ball stud. Remove shifter pin. Rotate Shifter Shaft Alignment tool until socket can be installed on nut. Tighten bolt to specification.

5) Rotate lever back to "D" position and recheck adjustment. Remove pin and alignment tool. Install manual control lever assembly. Tighten bolt to specification. Install main control cover (side cover) with new gasket. Tighten bolts in sequence. See Fig. 6. Tighten bolts to specification.

6) To complete installation, reverse removal procedures. Tighten drain plug to specification. Add 6 qts. of ATF fluid. Start and run vehicle. Add fluid as necessary.

VEHICLE SPEED SENSOR (VSS)

Removal & Installation – **1)** Disconnect negative battery cable, then positive battery cable. Remove battery and battery tray. Remove air cleaner assembly. Install appropriate engine support frame. Unbolt and move cruise control servo. Unbolt fuel filter bracket. Unbolt left transaxle mount from chassis.

2) Slightly lower engine/transaxle assembly. Raise and support vehicle. Disconnect VSS harness connector. VSS is located near dipstick tube. Unbolt and rotate VSS 180 degree and remove. To install, reverse removal procedure. Replace "O" ring as needed. Tighten bolt to specification. See TORQUE SPECIFICATIONS.

REMOVAL & INSTALLATION

See appropriate AUTOMATIC TRANSMISSION REMOVAL article in TRANSMISSION SERVICING.

TRANSAXLE DISASSEMBLY

NOTE: For identification and position verification of thrust bearings and washers, see Fig. 27.

1) Ensure outside of transaxle is thoroughly clean. Mount transaxle on appropriate stand. Remove and drain torque converter. Remove drain plug from transaxle if fluid was not drained before removal. Pull oil pump shaft from end of turbine shaft.

2) Using appropriate puller, remove torque convert hub seal. Remove differential seals. Unbolt and remove transmission speed sensor from outside of pump housing. Unbolt and remove dipstick tube and grommet. Remove vehicle speed sensor. Remove manual lever position sensor.

3) Remove main control cover assembly (side cover) bolts in crisscross pattern. Remove cover and gasket. Compress tabs on transaxle electrical harness receptacle and push into case. Remove 12 valve body bolts. Slightly lift valve body and remove "Z" link.

4) Remove valve body with wiring harness. Remove thermostatic oil level control valve bracket. Pull valve straight out of transaxle case. Remove and discard servo cover cap. Using Servo Cover Remover/Replacer (T94P-77000-L), compress servo cover assembly. Remove retaining ring and release servo cover pressure. Remove tool. Remove servo cover assembly, piston and return spring.

5) Position transaxle so converter housing is facing upward. Remove converter 23 housing-to-transaxle case bolts. Separate case halves. See Fig. 2. Remove No. 15 thrust bearing, No. 14 shim and speedometer drive gear from final drive/differential assembly.

6) Remove final drive/differential assembly. Unsnap and remove front chain cover. Remove driven sprocket No. 13 thrust bearing. Remove No. 10 thrust washer from reverse/overdrive ring gear assembly. Lift drive chain assembly, driven sprocket assembly and reverse/overdrive ring gear assembly together from case.

7) Remove rear chain cover with magnet attached. Using blind hole puller, remove oil filter recirculating regulator exhaust seal and discard. See Fig. 10. Remove and discard oil filter. Remove driven sprocket No. 12 thrust bearing assembly and No. 11 shim.

8) Unsnap socket end of manual valve detent lever actuating rod assembly from parking cam actuator lever assembly. Unsnap opposite end of actuating rod. Remove reverse/overdrive ring gear No. 9 thrust bearing assembly. Remove reverse/overdrive planetary carrier assembly with No. 8 thrust bearing. Inspect planetary pinion gear thrust clearance. Clearance should be .006-.028" (.15-.72 mm). Replace thrust bearing if clearance is not within specification.

9) Remove reverse/overdrive sun gear and shell assembly. See Fig. 2. Remove No. 7 thrust bearing. Remove low/intermediate ring gear assembly. Remove No. 6 thrust bearing. Remove low/intermediate planetary carrier assembly. Inspect planetary pinion gear thrust clearance. Clearance should be .006-.028" (.15-.72 mm). Replace as needed. Remove low/intermediate sun gear No. 5 thrust bearing, forward one-way clutch and low/intermediate sun gear assembly.

10) Remove No. 4 turbine shaft thrust bearing. Remove turbine shaft. Remove Forward/Coast/Direct (F/C/D) cylinder assembly and reverse clutch drum assembly. Remove pump support No. 1 thrust bearing assembly.

11) Remove low one-way clutch retaining snap ring. Remove thrust plate. Remove low one-way clutch assembly. Remove low/reverse clutch wave spring and clutch plates. Remove retaining snap ring. Remove low/reverse clutch return spring assembly. Pull out low/reverse clutch piston from bore.

12) Turn transaxle case over with pump facing upward. Remove 9 pump housing bolts. Using appropriate puller with slide hammer, remove pump assembly. Slide out intermediate and overdrive band from case. Remove final drive ring gear from converter housing.

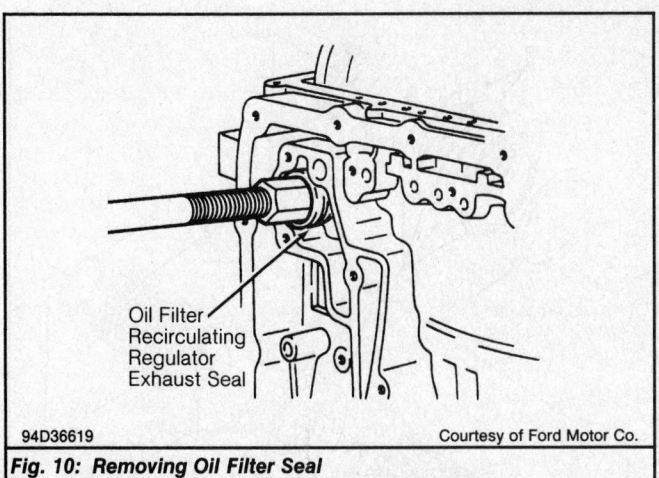

94D36619   Courtesy of Ford Motor Co.

Fig. 10: Removing Oil Filter Seal

COMPONENT DISASSEMBLY & REASSEMBLY

FORWARD ONE-WAY & LOW-INTERMEDIATE SUN GEAR ASSEMBLY

NOTE: Inspect clutch discs for wear and/or overheating. Individual clutch disc thicknesses are not supplied by manufacturer.

Disassembly – Remove coast clutch hub retaining ring. Remove coast clutch hub. Remove forward one-way clutch outer race and sprag assembly with end caps. Separate sprag assembly and end caps from outer race. Note position of end caps. End caps are different thicknesses. *See Fig. 11.* Remove forward one-way clutch retainer. Remove retaining ring from sun gear assembly. Inspect parts for wear or damage, replace as needed.

Reassembly – Install retaining ring gear on sun gear assembly. Install clutch retainer. Assemble sprag assembly and end caps. Ensure end caps are in correct position. Install remaining components in reverse order of disassembly. Check operation of assembly. With sun gear facing upward, sun gear should turn clockwise while holding outer race. *See Fig. 11.*

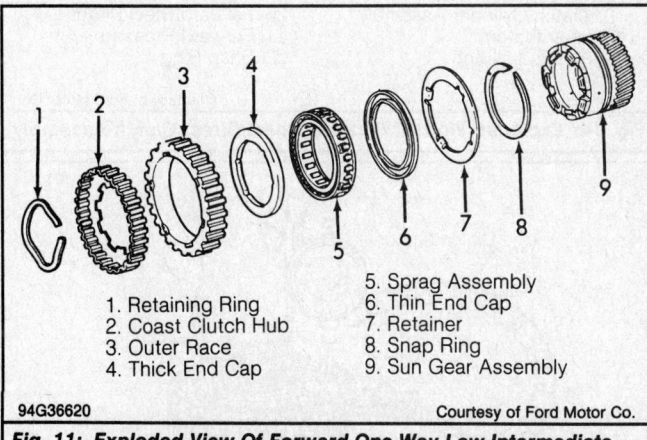

1. Retaining Ring
2. Coast Clutch Hub
3. Outer Race
4. Thick End Cap
5. Sprag Assembly
6. Thin End Cap
7. Retainer
8. Snap Ring
9. Sun Gear Assembly

94G36620   Courtesy of Ford Motor Co.

Fig. 11: Exploded View Of Forward One-Way Low-Intermediate Sun Gear Assembly

LOW ONE-WAY CLUTCH ASSEMBLY

Disassembly & Reassembly – Position clutch with inner and outer race grooves facing upward. Remove inner race. Remove roller assembly. Clean and inspect parts for wear or damage. Replace as needed. To reassemble, reverse disassembly procedures. Check operation of clutch assembly. Inner race should turn clockwise while holding outer race. *See Fig. 12.*

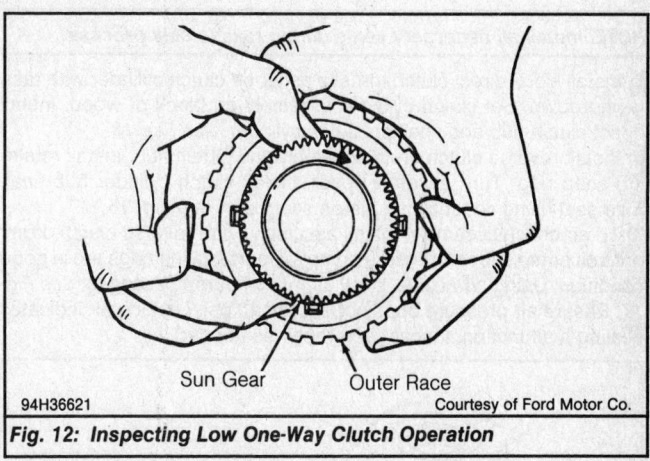

94H36621   Courtesy of Ford Motor Co.

Fig. 12: Inspecting Low One-Way Clutch Operation

FINAL DRIVE/DIFFERENTIAL ASSEMBLY

NOTE: Final drive differential backlash specification is not available from manufacturer.

Disassembly & Reassembly – Using pin punch, remove pinion shaft roll pin. Remove pinion shaft. Remove pinion gears, side gears and thrust washers. Clean and inspect parts for wear or damage. Replace as needed. To reassemble, reverse disassembly procedures. Check thrust clearance of final drive planetary pinion gears. Thrust clearance should be .006-.025" (.17-.65 mm). Replace thrust washers as needed.

FORWARD/COAST/DIRECT CLUTCH CYLINDER ASSEMBLY

Disassembly – **1)** Support assembly on block of wood (shell facing downward). Remove reverse clutch hub retaining ring. Remove reverse clutch hub. Remove reverse clutch drum assembly from direct clutch hub and shell assembly. See REVERSE CLUTCH DRUM. *See Fig. 13.* Remove direct clutch hub and shell from forward/coast/direct clutch cylinder. Remove No. 2 direct clutch thrust washer.

2) Remove direct clutch pressure plate retaining snap ring. *See Fig. 14.* Remove clutch plates. Using spring compressor, compress direct clutch support. Remove snap ring. Remove direct clutch return spring assembly. Remove direct clutch piston.

3) Turn assembly over. Remove forward clutch snap ring. Remove clutch plates. Using spring compressor, compress clutch return spring assembly. Remove snap ring and spring assembly. Remove forward/coast piston.

Reassembly – **1)** Before assembling reverse clutch drum, soak friction plates in transmission fluid for 15 minutes. Replace all necessary seals. Using Coast Clutch Piston Seal Protector (T94P-77000-D3), install coast clutch piston into forward clutch piston assembly.

2) Install clutch spring assembly. Compress spring assembly and install snap ring. Install clutch plates. *See Fig. 14.* Install pressure plate snap ring and measure clearance between pressure plate and snap ring. Forward/Coast clutch pack clearance should be .020-.043" (.50-1.09 mm). If clearance is not within specification, select proper thickness snap ring. Snap rings are available in the following thicknesses: .050-.054" (1.28-1.38 mm), .055-.059" (1.39-1.49 mm), .060-.064" (1.52-1.62 mm) and .065-.069" (1.65-1.75 mm).

3) Turn assembly over. Install direct clutch piston. Install spring assembly. Compress spring assembly and install snap ring. Install clutch plates. *See Fig. 14.* Mount dial indicator on clutch cylinder. Position dial indicator plunger on direct clutch pressure plate. *See Fig. 15.* Using 2 picks, pull pressure plate upward.

4) Record clearance measurement. Move dial indicator to opposite side of pressure plate. Measure clearance and average with previous measurement. Direct clutch pack clearance should be .020-.044" (.52-1.12 mm). If clearance is not within specification, select proper thickness snap ring. Snap rings are available in the following thicknesses: .050-.054" (1.28-1.38 mm), .055-.059" (1.39-1.49 mm), .060-.064" (1.52-1.62 mm) and .065-.069" (1.65-1.75 mm).

NOTE: Install all necessary seals during reassembly process.

5) Install No. 2 direct clutch thrust washer on clutch cylinder with tabs facing down. Set clutch cylinder assembly on block of wood. Install direct clutch hub and shell on clutch cylinder. *See Fig. 13.*

6) Install reverse clutch drum assembly and clutch hub. Install retaining snap ring. Turn assembly over. Install clutch cylinder hub seal. Size seal using coast clutch piston seal sizer. *See Fig. 16.*

7) To air check assembly, install assembly, with reverse clutch drum, onto oil pump support. Ensure pump support sealing rings are in good condition. Using air nozzle, blow air into oil pump passages. *See Fig. 17.* Ensure air pressure does not exceed 40 psi. Leaking air indicates sealing malfunction. Inspect and repair as needed.

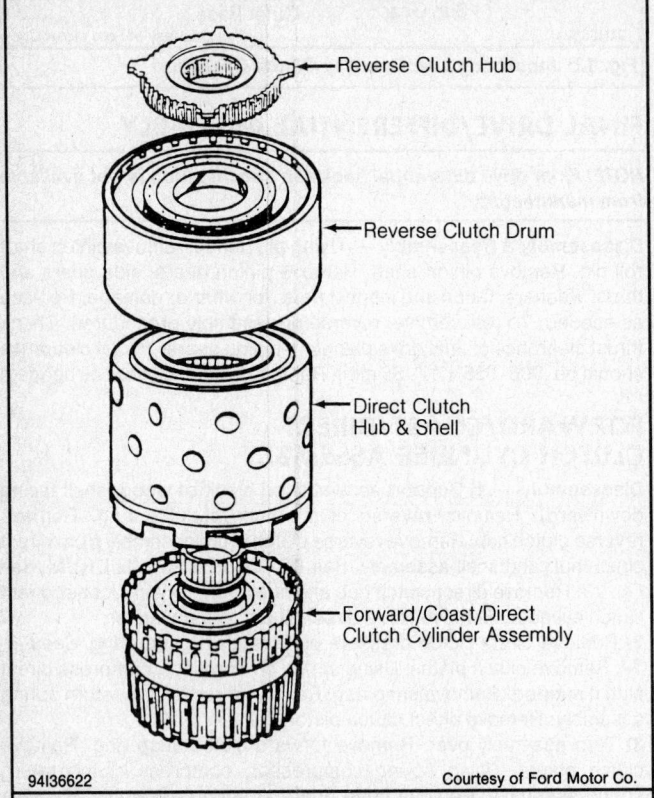

94I36622   Courtesy of Ford Motor Co.

Fig. 13: Identifying Forward/Coast/Direct Clutch Assembly With Reverse Clutch Assembly

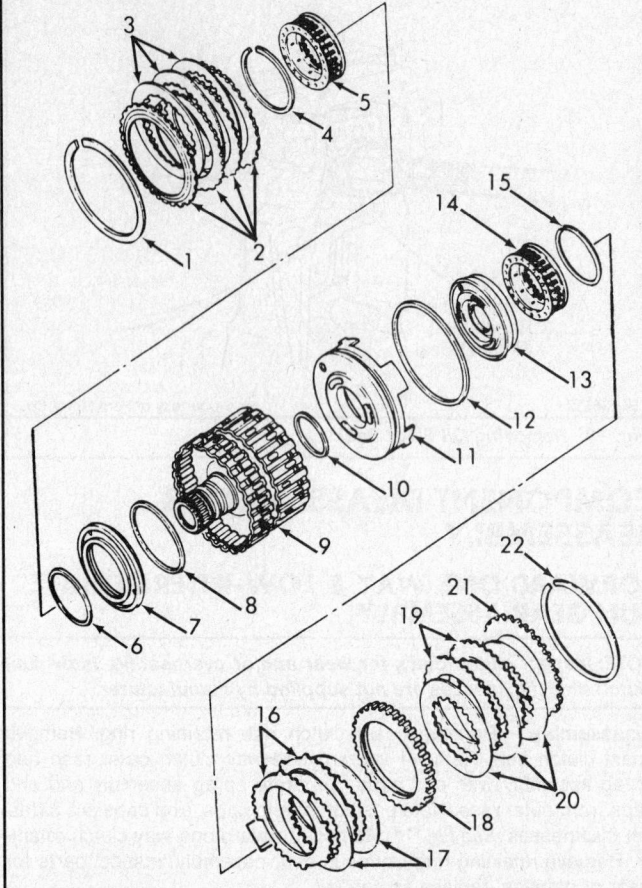

1. Snap Ring	12. Outer Piston Seal
2. Pressure Plate/Steel Plates	13. Coast Clutch Piston
3. Friction Plates	14. Return Spring Assembly
4. Snap Ring	15. Snap Ring
5. Return Spring Assembly	16. Steel Clutch Plates
6. Inner Piston Seal	17. Friction Clutch Plates
7. Direct Clutch Piston	18. Coast Pressure Plate
8. Outer Piston Seal	19. Forward Friction Plates
9. Clutch Cylinder Assembly	20. Forward Steel Plates
10. Inner Piston	21. Forward Pressure Plate
11. Forward Clutch	22. Snap Ring

94J36623   Courtesy of Ford Motor Co.

Fig. 14: Exploded View Of Forward/Coast/Direct Clutch Assembly

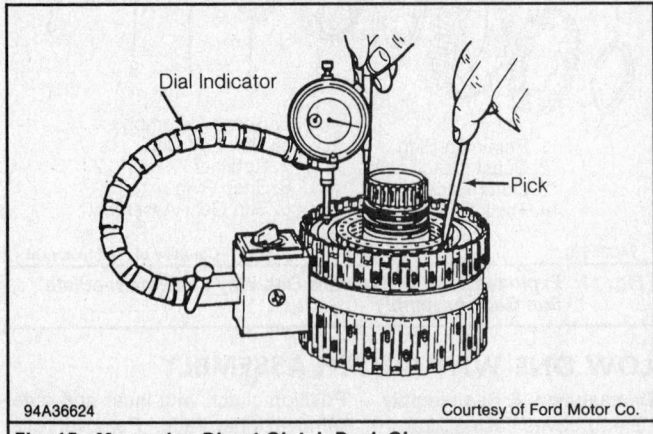

94A36624   Courtesy of Ford Motor Co.

Fig. 15: Measuring Direct Clutch Pack Clearance

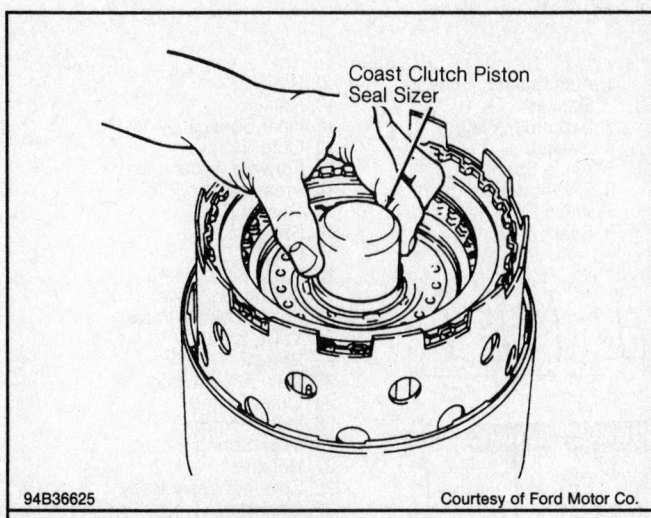

94B36625   Courtesy of Ford Motor Co.

Fig. 16: Installing Piston Seal Sizer

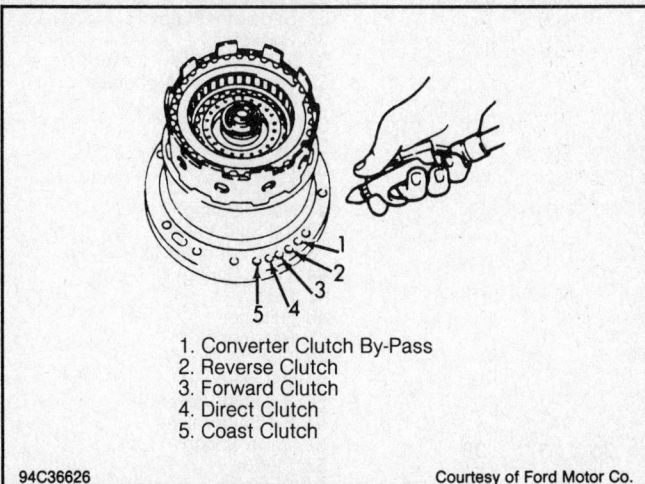

1. Converter Clutch By-Pass
2. Reverse Clutch
3. Forward Clutch
4. Direct Clutch
5. Coast Clutch

94C36626   Courtesy of Ford Motor Co.

Fig. 17: Air Checking Forward/Coast/Direct Clutch Assembly

REVERSE CLUTCH DRUM

Disassembly – 1) Remove reverse clutch pressure plate snap ring. Remove reverse clutch pressure plate with clutch plates. See Fig. 18. Using compressor, compress spring assembly and remove snap ring. Remove spring assembly. Remove reverse clutch piston.

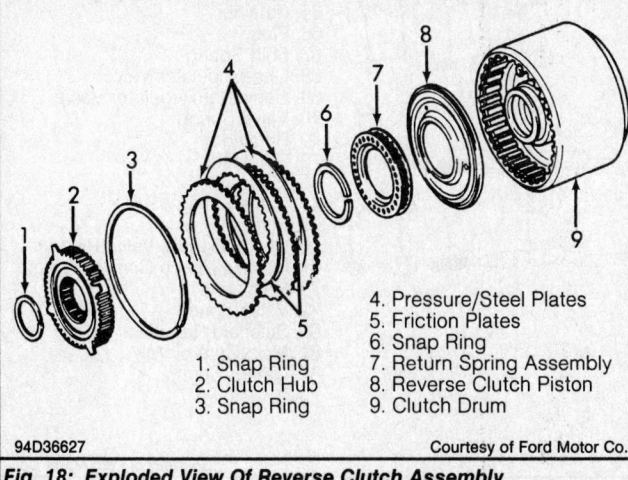

4. Pressure/Steel Plates
5. Friction Plates
6. Snap Ring
7. Return Spring Assembly
8. Reverse Clutch Piston
9. Clutch Drum

1. Snap Ring
2. Clutch Hub
3. Snap Ring

94D36627   Courtesy of Ford Motor Co.

Fig. 18: Exploded View Of Reverse Clutch Assembly

2) Before assembling reverse clutch drum, soak friction plates in transmission fluid for 15 minutes. Replace all necessary seals. Using Reverse Clutch Piston Seal Protector (T94P-77000-D2), install reverse clutch piston. See Fig. 19. Install spring assembly. Compress spring assembly and install retaining snap ring. Install clutch discs and pressure plate. See Fig. 18.

3) Install pressure plate snap ring and measure clearance between pressure plate and snap ring. Reverse clutch pack clearance should be .012-.035" (.33-.89 mm). If clearance is not within specification, select proper thickness snap ring. Snap rings are available in thicknesses; .055-.059" (1.39-1.49 mm), .060-.064" (1.53-1.63 mm) and .066-.070" (1.68-1.78 mm).

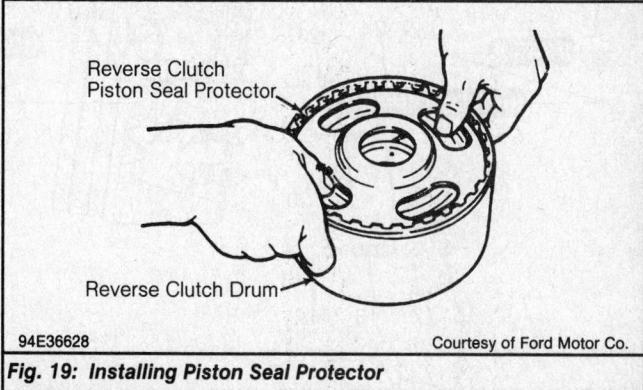

94E36628   Courtesy of Ford Motor Co.

Fig. 19: Installing Piston Seal Protector

OIL PUMP

Disassembly – Remove pump support sealing rings. Remove Torx T30 bolts. Separate pump assembly. Remove pump drive gear and insert. Remove pump driven gear. After components are cleaned, inspect components and housing for irregular wear or damage. Replace as needed.

Reassembly – 1) Install pump driven gear with identification dot facing pump body. Install pump drive gear with gear insert. Using gauge bar and depth micrometer, measure clearance between each gear and oil pump body facing.

2) Clearance should be .001-.002" (.027-.060 mm). If clearance is not within specification, replace oil pump assembly. Install Pump Alignment Pins (T94P-77000-P). Fill pump gear cavity with ATF to top of gears. Install separator plates and pump support assembly. Tighten bolts to specification. See TORQUE SPECIFICATIONS.

3) Install sealing rings. Install oil pump shaft. Using torque wrench, measure pump rotating torque. Maximum rotating torque is 2 INCH lbs. (.3 N.m). If rotating torque exceeds specification, disassembly and inspect pump assembly for contamination or improper end clearance.

VALVE BODY

NOTE: Remove and clean one valve at a time to avoid incorrect installation.

Disassembly & Reassembly – 1) Remove manual valve. Unbolt and remove solenoid valve body and gasket. Remove pressure tap plate and gasket. Remove manual valve detent spring assembly and adjacent bolt. Remove accumulator body-to-transfer plate bolts (3). Disassemble accumulator body assembly with separator plate and gaskets from main valve body. See Fig. 20.

2) Disassemble main valve body from separator plate and gaskets from transfer plate. Remove intermediate/overdrive accumulator valve plug retaining plate. Thread 6 mm bolt into plug and remove. Remove accumulator.

3) Remove, clean and install each valve individually as needed. Lubricate moving parts with ATF. Ensure all valves move (snap) freely. If valve sticks in its bore and cannot be freed, main valve body must be replaced. Do not attempt to hone valve bores. Reassemble components in reverse order of disassembly. Tighten bolts to specification. See TORQUE SPECIFICATIONS.

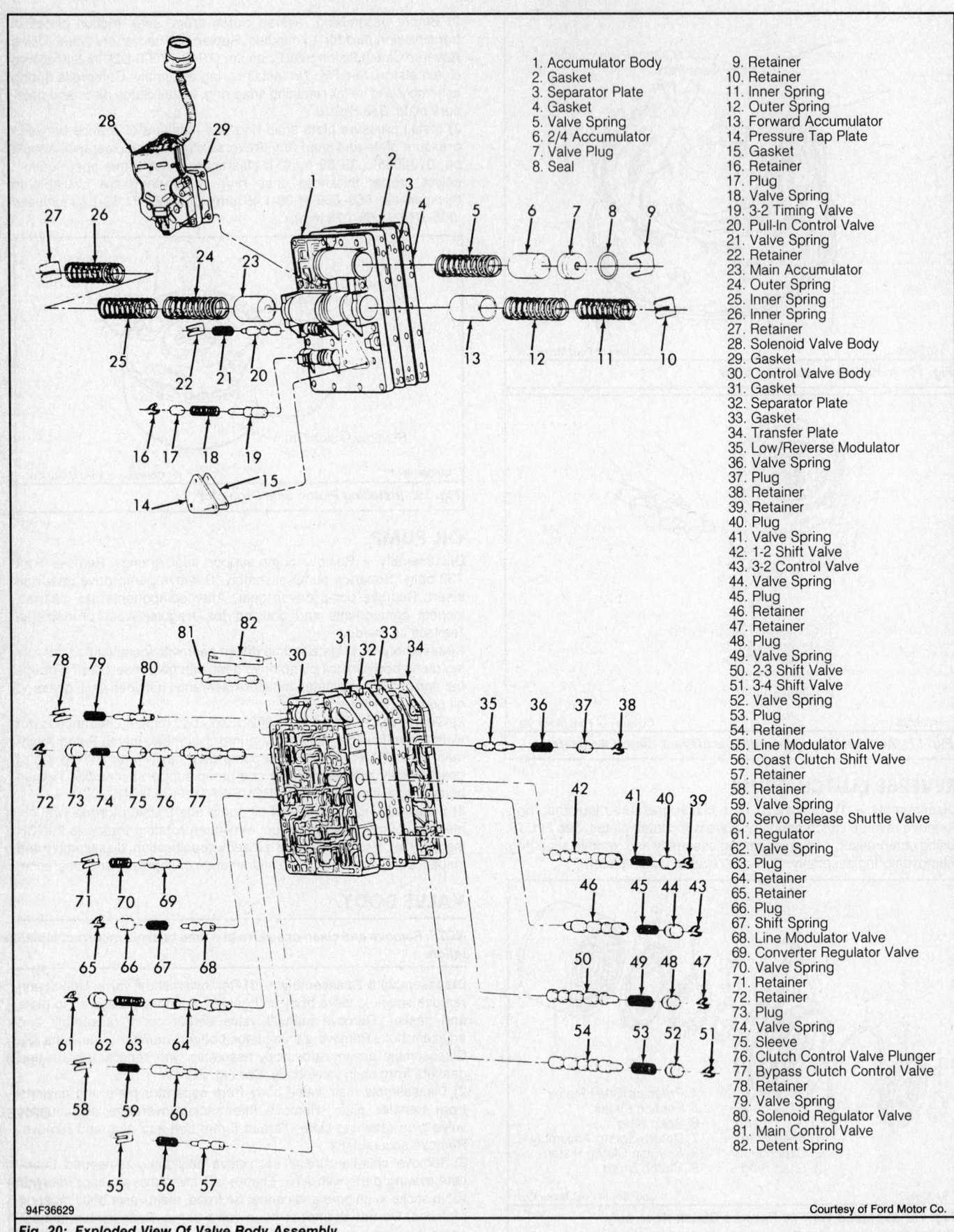

1. Accumulator Body
2. Gasket
3. Separator Plate
4. Gasket
5. Valve Spring
6. 2/4 Accumulator
7. Valve Plug
8. Seal
9. Retainer
10. Retainer
11. Inner Spring
12. Outer Spring
13. Forward Accumulator
14. Pressure Tap Plate
15. Gasket
16. Retainer
17. Plug
18. Valve Spring
19. 3-2 Timing Valve
20. Pull-In Control Valve
21. Valve Spring
22. Retainer
23. Main Accumulator
24. Outer Spring
25. Inner Spring
26. Inner Spring
27. Retainer
28. Solenoid Valve Body
29. Gasket
30. Control Valve Body
31. Gasket
32. Separator Plate
33. Gasket
34. Transfer Plate
35. Low/Reverse Modulator
36. Valve Spring
37. Plug
38. Retainer
39. Retainer
40. Plug
41. Valve Spring
42. 1-2 Shift Valve
43. 3-2 Control Valve
44. Valve Spring
45. Plug
46. Retainer
47. Retainer
48. Plug
49. Valve Spring
50. 2-3 Shift Valve
51. 3-4 Shift Valve
52. Valve Spring
53. Plug
54. Retainer
55. Line Modulator Valve
56. Coast Clutch Shift Valve
57. Retainer
58. Retainer
59. Valve Spring
60. Servo Release Shuttle Valve
61. Regulator
62. Valve Spring
63. Plug
64. Retainer
65. Retainer
66. Plug
67. Shift Spring
68. Line Modulator Valve
69. Converter Regulator Valve
70. Valve Spring
71. Retainer
72. Retainer
73. Plug
74. Valve Spring
75. Sleeve
76. Clutch Control Valve Plunger
77. Bypass Clutch Control Valve
78. Retainer
79. Valve Spring
80. Solenoid Regulator Valve
81. Main Control Valve
82. Detent Spring

94F36629

Courtesy of Ford Motor Co.

Fig. 20: Exploded View Of Valve Body Assembly

TRANSAXLE CASE

Inspection – Inspect case for cracks and stripped threads. Inspect gasket surfaces and mating surfaces for burrs. Check vent for obstructions, and check all fluid passages for obstructions and leakage. Inspect case bushing for scores. Check all parking linkage parts for wear or damage.

TRANSAXLE REASSEMBLY

NOTE: Handle all parts carefully to avoid damaging bearings and mating surfaces. Lubricate all parts with clean ATF. Use petroleum jelly on gaskets, thrust washers and needle bearings to retain them in place. Use all new gaskets and seals, and tighten bolts evenly.

NOTE: For identification and position of thrust bearings and washers, see Fig. 27.

1) Slide intermediate/overdrive band assembly into transaxle case. Install oil pump assembly in transaxle case. Tighten bolts to specification in crisscross pattern. See TORQUE SPECIFICATIONS.
2) Install low/reverse clutch piston into Low/Reverse Clutch Piston Outer Seal Protector (T94P-77000-D1). Install Low/Reverse Clutch Piston Inner Seal Protector (T94P-77000-D1) into piston. Install piston and remove protectors. *See Fig. 21.*

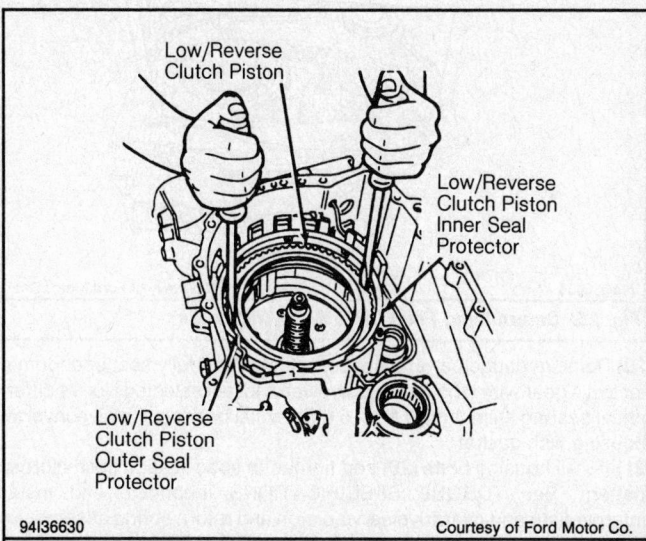

Low/Reverse Clutch Piston

Low/Reverse Clutch Piston Inner Seal Protector

Low/Reverse Clutch Piston Outer Seal Protector

94I36630   Courtesy of Ford Motor Co.

Fig. 21: Installing Low/Reverse Clutch Piston

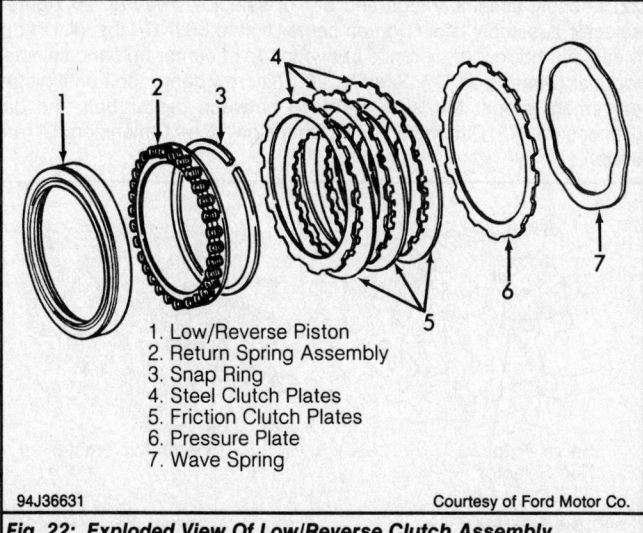

1. Low/Reverse Piston
2. Return Spring Assembly
3. Snap Ring
4. Steel Clutch Plates
5. Friction Clutch Plates
6. Pressure Plate
7. Wave Spring

94J36631   Courtesy of Ford Motor Co.

Fig. 22: Exploded View Of Low/Reverse Clutch Assembly

3) Install low/reverse clutch return spring assembly. Install snap ring. Install low/reverse clutch wave spring (measuring purposes only). Install low/reverse clutch plates, and pressure plate. *See Figs. 2 and 22.* Install low one-way clutch thrust plate (measuring purposes only).
4) Measure in 2 locations, clearance between low/reverse clutch pressure plate and thrust plate. Average measurements. Clearance should be .021-.046" (.54-1.17 mm). If clearance is not within specification, select proper thickness pressure plate. Pressure plates are available in the following thicknesses: .097-.101 (2.47-2.57), .089-.093 (2.26-2.36) and .081-.085 (2.06-2.16).
5) Remove low/reverse pressure plate, clutch discs and wave spring. Install No. 1 pump support thrust bearing. Remove seal sizer from forward/coast/direct cylinder assembly and install. Install turbine shaft assembly.
6) Install No. 4 turbine shaft thrust bearing. Install forward one-way clutch and low-intermediate sun gear assembly. Install No. 5 low-intermediate sun gear thrust bearing. Install low-intermediate planetary carrier assembly. Install No. 6 low-intermediate planetary thrust bearing. Install low-intermediate ring gear.
7) Install No. 7 reverse/overdrive sun gear thrust bearing. Install reverse/overdrive sun gear and shell assembly. Install reverse/overdrive planetary carrier assembly with No. 8 thrust bearing. Install low/reverse clutch plates.
8) Install low/reverse clutch pressure plate previously selected. Install low/reverse clutch wave spring. Install low one-way clutch assembly with I.D. ring on inner ring, facing upward. Install low one-way clutch thrust plate. Install low one-way clutch snap ring.
9) Install manual valve detent lever actuating rod. Install Preload Tool Adapter/Aligner Set (T94P-77000-R), on reverse/overdrive planetary carrier assembly. *See Fig. 23.* Tighten mounting bolts to 119 INCH lbs. (13.5 N.m).
10) Install Gauge Bar (T94P-77000-Q), with short spacers across transaxle case. Measure distance from top of gauge bar to No. 12 driven sprocket bearing assembly (Dimension "A"). *See Fig. 23.*
11) Measure distance from top of gauge bar to bearing surface on reverse/overdrive planetary carrier assembly (Dimension "B"). *See Fig. 24.* Dimension "B" - Dimension "A" = Dimension "C". Use Dimension "C" to select correct No. 11 driven sprocket shim. See DRIVEN SPROCKET SHIM SELECTION CHART.

DRIVEN SPROCKET SHIM SELECTION CHART

Dimension "C" In. (mm)	Shim Thickness In. (mm)
.558-.565 (14.17-14.34)	.083-.087 (2.10-2.20)
.551-.557 (14.00-14.16)	.076-.080 (1.92-2.02)
.544-.550 (13.83-13.99)	.069-.073 (1.75-1.85)
.538-.543 (13.66-13.82)	.062-.066 (1.57-1.67)
.531-.537 (13.49-13.65)	.055-.059 (1.40-1.50)
.524-.530 (13.32-13.48)	.048-.052 (1.22-1.32)

12) Install selected No. 11 shim. Remove gauge bar and preload tool. Install No. 12 driven sprocket bearing assembly. Ensure No. 18 needle bearing is lubricated. Install No. 9 reverse/overdrive ring gear thrust bearing. Install reverse/overdrive ring gear assembly (measuring purposes only).
13) Install Preload Tool Adapter/Aligner Set (T94P-77000-R) on reverse/overdrive ring gear. Tighten mounting bolts to 119 INCH lbs. (13.5 N.m). Install Gauge Bar (T94P-77000-Q), with short spacers across transaxle case. *See Fig. 23.*
14) Measure distance between top of gauge bar to face of reverse/overdrive ring gear assembly (Dimension "D"). Combined thickness of gauge bar and short spacers (1.00" (25.4 mm) is Dimension "E". Dimension "D" - Dimension "E" = Dimension "F". Use Dimension "F" to select correct No. 10 drive sprocket thrust washer. See DRIVE SPROCKET THRUST WASHER SELECTION CHART.

DRIVE SPROCKET THRUST WASHER SELECTION CHART

Dimension "E" In. (mm)	Washer Thickness In. (mm)
.034-.044 (.86-1.12)	.056-.059 (1.41-1.51)
.024-.033 (.60-.85)	.066-.070 (1.67-1.77)
.013-.023 (.34-.59)	.076-.080 (1.93-2.03)
.003-.013 (.08-.33)	.086-.090 (2.19-2.29)

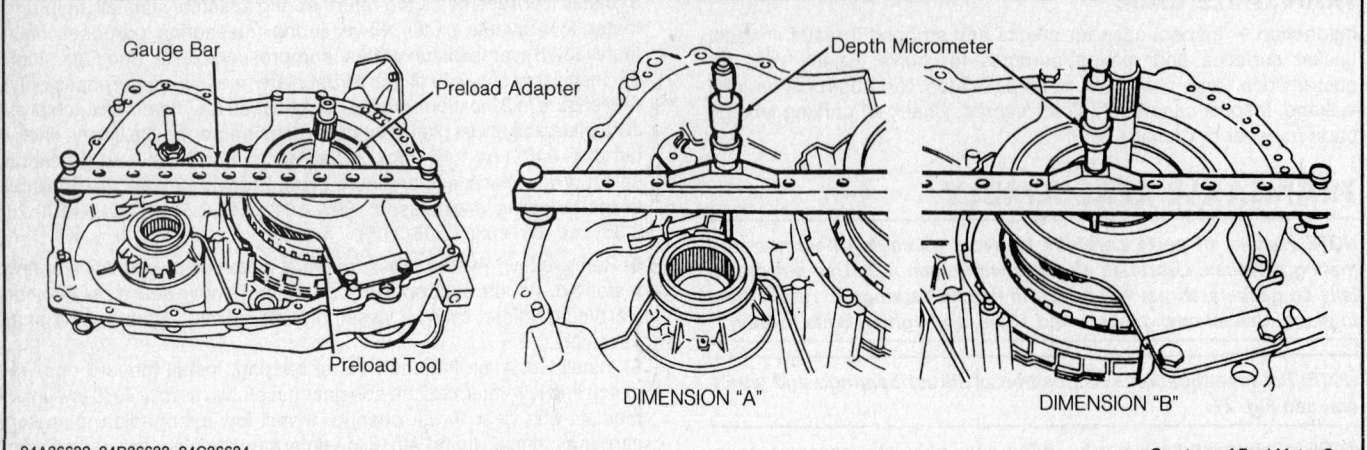

94A36632 94B36633 94C36634

DIMENSION "A"

DIMENSION "B"

Courtesy of Ford Motor Co.

Fig. 23: Determining Transaxle Thrust Washer & Shim Thickness

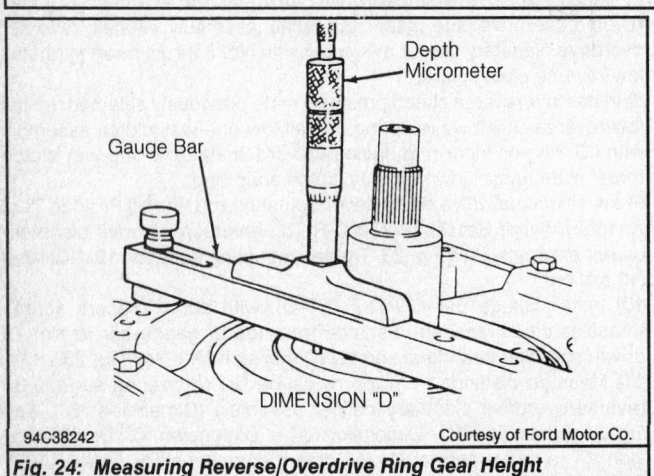

94C38242

DIMENSION "D"

Courtesy of Ford Motor Co.

Fig. 24: Measuring Reverse/Overdrive Ring Gear Height

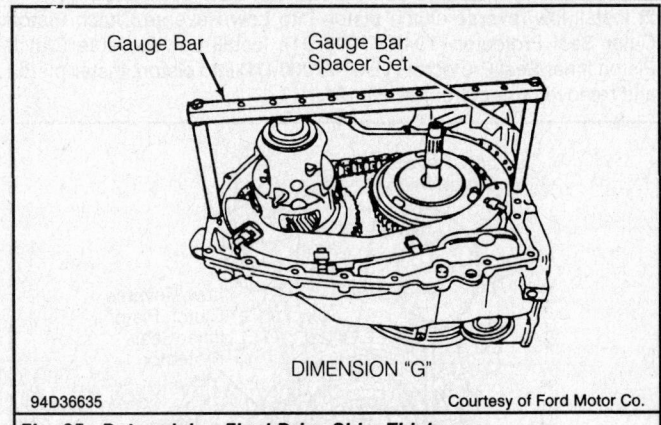

94D36635

DIMENSION "G"

Courtesy of Ford Motor Co.

Fig. 25: Determining Final Drive Shim Thickness

15) Remove gauge bar and preload tool. Apply petroleum jelly to selected No. 10 drive sprocket thrust washer and install on converter housing. Remove reverse/overdrive ring gear assembly. Install oil filter and seal assembly. Temporarily install appropriate guide pin through filter eyelet into transaxle case hole.

16) Install oil filter recirculating regulator exhaust seal. Remove guide pin. Install rear chain cover in transaxle case. Assembly drive chain assembly on driven sprocket assembly, and reverse/overdrive ring gear assembly. Install and fully seat chain and sprocket/ring gear assembly.

17) Install front chain cover. Install No. 13 driven sprocket thrust bearing assembly. Install final drive planetary/differential assembly. Install Gauge Bar (T94P-77000-Q) with Spacer Set (T94P-77000-T) on transaxle case. Tighten mounting bolts to 119 INCH lbs. (13.5 N.m). See Fig. 25.

18) Measure distance from top of gauge bar to shim surface area of final drive assembly. Measure in 2 places and average measurements (Dimension "G"). Combined thickness of gauge bar with long spacers (7.00" (177.8 mm) is Dimension "H".

19) Dimension "G" - Dimension "H" = Dimension "I". Use Dimension "I" to select correct No. 14 differential bearing shim. See DIFFERENTIAL BEARING SHIM SELECTION CHART.

DIFFERENTIAL BEARING SHIM SELECTION CHART

Dimension "I" In. (mm)	Washer Thickness In. (mm)
5.136-5.148 (130.46-130.76)	.039-.043 (.98-1.08)
5.124-5.136 (130.16-130.45)	.050-.054 (1.28-1.38)
5.113-5.123 (129.87-130.15)	.062-.066 (1.57-1.67)
5.101-5.123 (129.87-130.15)	.074-.078 (1.87-1.97)
5.089-5.101 (129.27-129.56)	.085-.089 (2.17-2.27)

20) Remove gauge bar and spacers. Install and fully seat speedometer drive gear with tabs facing downward. Install selected No. 14 differential bearing shim. Install No. 15 differential bearing. Install converter housing with gasket.

21) Install housing bolts (20) and tighten to specification in crisscross pattern. See TORQUE SPECIFICATIONS. Lubricate and install intermediate and overdrive servo piston and return spring assembly in transaxle case bore. Note number of grooves of servo apply rod. Install Servo Piston Rod Selector (T94P-77000-M) on piston.

22) Loosely assembly legs and bar of selector. See Fig. 26. Tighten selector assembly legs. Tighten center bolt to 36 INCH lbs. (4.1 N.m). Measure and record distance between top of center bolt and selector tool bar (Dimension "J"). See Fig. 26. Unscrew center bolt until piston movement stops. Measure distance between center bolt and bar (Dimension "K"). Dimension "J" - Dimension "K" = Dimension "L" (rod travel).

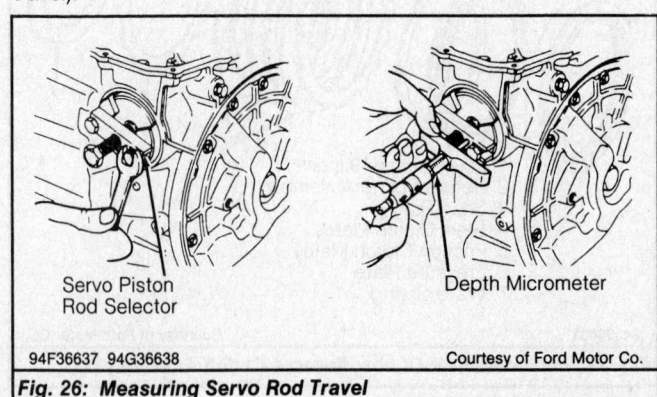

Servo Piston
Rod Selector

Depth Micrometer

94F36637 94G36638

Courtesy of Ford Motor Co.

Fig. 26: Measuring Servo Rod Travel

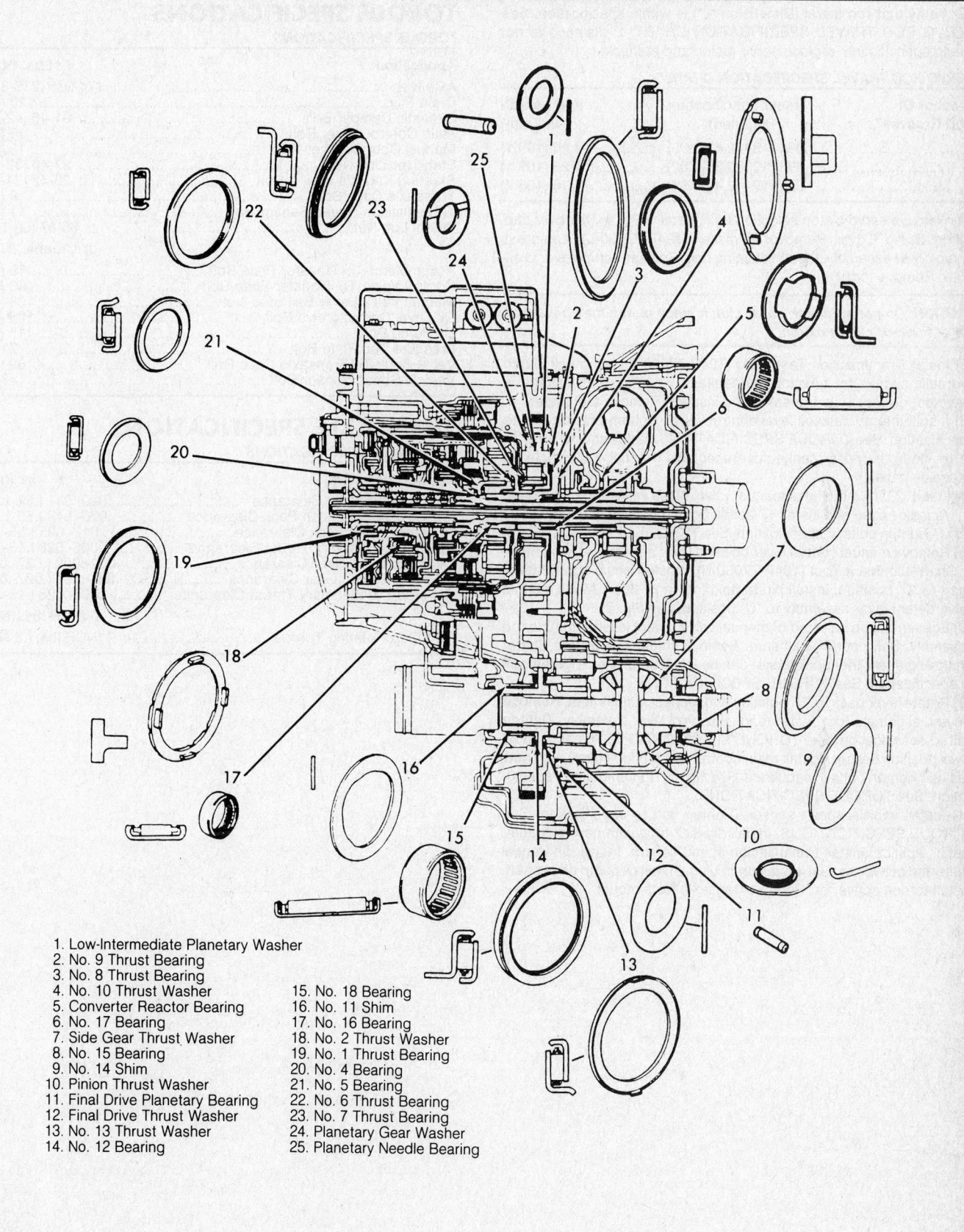

1. Low-Intermediate Planetary Washer
2. No. 9 Thrust Bearing
3. No. 8 Thrust Bearing
4. No. 10 Thrust Washer
5. Converter Reactor Bearing
6. No. 17 Bearing
7. Side Gear Thrust Washer
8. No. 15 Bearing
9. No. 14 Shim
10. Pinion Thrust Washer
11. Final Drive Planetary Bearing
12. Final Drive Thrust Washer
13. No. 13 Thrust Washer
14. No. 12 Bearing
15. No. 18 Bearing
16. No. 11 Shim
17. No. 16 Bearing
18. No. 2 Thrust Washer
19. No. 1 Thrust Bearing
20. No. 4 Bearing
21. No. 5 Bearing
22. No. 6 Thrust Bearing
23. No. 7 Thrust Bearing
24. Planetary Gear Washer
25. Planetary Needle Bearing

94H36639

Courtesy of Ford Motor Co.

Fig. 27: Identifying Thrust Bearing, Shims & Washers

23) Verify that rod travel (Dimension "L") is within specification. See SERVO ROD TRAVEL SPECIFICATION CHART. If distance is not within specification, replace servo piston and recheck.

SERVO ROD TRAVEL SPECIFICATION CHART

Number Of Rod Grooves	Travel Specification In. (mm)	Rod Length In. (mm)
0	.096-.194 (2.43-4.93)	4.26 (108.1)
1	.093-.190 (2.35-4.82)	4.22 (107.1)
2	.096-.194 (2.43-4.93)	4.16 (105.7)

24) Remove servo piston selection tool. Install NEW servo cover cap. Using Servo Cover Remover/Replacer (T94P-77000-L), compress servo cover assembly. Install retaining ring. Release servo cover pressure. Remove tool.

CAUTION: Do not air check coast clutch since piston may be forced out of forward clutch piston.

---

25) Install Transmission Test Plate (T94P-77000-S). Air check clutch hydraulic circuits for function and leakage. *See Fig. 3*. If leakage is detected, disassemble transaxle and inspect. Remove test plate.

26) Install thermostatic oil level control valve. Tighten bracket bolt to specification. See TORQUE SPECIFICATIONS. Install new "O" ring on valve body harness connector receptacle. Install receptacle in transaxle case.

27) Insert "Z" link into end of manual valve. Place valve body in position on transaxle case and install 12 bolts. Tighten bolts in sequence. *See Fig. 4*. Tighten bolts to specification. See TORQUE SPECIFICATIONS.

28) Remove manual control lever bolt and lever assembly. Using Shifter Shaft Alignment Tool (T94P-77000-H), move manual control lever shaft to "D" position. Install pin to hold tool in position. Move manual valve detent lever assembly to "D" position. *See Fig. 5*.

29) Loosen nut on ball stud of manual valve detent lever actuating rod assembly. Snug nut on ball stud. Remove shifter pin. Rotate Shifter Shaft Alignment tool until socket can be installed on nut. Tighten bolt to specification. See TORQUE SPECIFICATIONS.

30) Rotate lever back to "D" position and recheck adjustment. Remove pin and alignment tool. Install manual control lever assembly. Tighten bolt to specification. See TORQUE SPECIFICATIONS. Install manual lever position sensor. Install main control cover (side cover) with new gasket. Tighten bolts in sequence. *See Fig. 6*. Tighten bolts to specification. See TORQUE SPECIFICATIONS.

31) Install vehicle speed sensor. Tighten bolt to specification. See TORQUE SPECIFICATIONS. Install dipstick tube with new grommet. Install dipstick. Install transmission speed sensor. Install differential seals and converter seal. Install drain plug. Install oil pump drive shaft. Install torque converter. Remove transaxle from mount.

TORQUE SPECIFICATIONS
TORQUE SPECIFICATIONS

Application	Ft Lbs. (N.m)
Axle Nut	174-235 (235-319)
Drain Plug	20 (27)
Dynamic Damper Bolt	31-46 (42-62)
Main Control Cover Bolt	15 (20)
Manual Control Lever Bolt	18 (25)
Stabilizer Link Nut	27-40 (36-54)
Steering Knuckle Clamp Bolt	25-42 (34-57)
Transaxle Case Bolt	19 (26)
Transmission Speed Sensor Bolt	11 (15)
Wheel Lug Nut	65-87 (88-118)

	INCH Lbs. (N.m)
Accumulator-To-Transfer Plate Bolt	89 (10)
Control Valve-To-Transfer Plate Bolt	89 (10)
Manual Valve Lever Ball Stud Nut	106 (12)
Oil Level Control Valve Bolt	106 (12)
Oil Pump Bolt	115 (13)
Pressure Tap Plate Bolt	71 (8)
Valve Body-To-Transaxle Case Bolt	89 (10)
Vehicle Speed Sensor Bolt	43 (5)

TRANSAXLE SPECIFICATIONS
TRANSAXLE SPECIFICATIONS

Application	In. (mm)
Direct Clutch Pack Clearance	.020-.044 (.52-1.12)
Forward/Coast Clutch Pack Clearance	.020-.043 (.50-1.09)
Reverse Clutch Pack Clearance	.012-.035 (.33-.89)
Low/Inter. Planetary Thrust Clearance	.006-.028 (.15-.72)
Oil Pump Drive Gear Clearance	.001-.002 (.027-.060)
Oil Pump Driven Gear Clearance	.001-.002 (.027-.060)
Reverse/OD Planetary Thrust Clearance	.006-.028 (.15-.72)

	INCH lbs. (N.m)
Oil Pump Rotating Torque	2 INCH lbs. (.3 N.m)

Ford Motor Co: 1994 Probe

NOTE: For CD4E transaxle mechanical testing and repair, see Ford CD4E article.

INTRODUCTION

The first step in diagnosing any driveability problem is verifying the customer's complaint with a test drive under the conditions the problem reportedly occurred. Before entering self-diagnostics, perform a careful and complete visual inspection. Most transmission control problems result from mechanical breakdowns or poor electrical connections.

NOTE: Perform all voltage tests with a Digital Volt-Ohmmeter (DVOM) with a minimum 10-megohm input impedance, unless stated otherwise in test procedure.

DESCRIPTION & OPERATION

Input signals from sensors are sent to the Powertrain Control Module (PCM). The PCM controls shift or converter clutch application. The PCM can also determine line pressure needed to optimize shift feel.

Five electronic solenoids accomplish these functions; 2 On/Off solenoids for shifting, 1 Pulse-Width Modulate solenoid for torque converter clutch control, a Electronic Pressure Control solenoid for line pressure control, and a 3-2 timing/coast clutch solenoid to control the release of the coast clutch and the coordinated release of the direct clutch and apply of the low and intermediate band. The PCM has built-in self-diagnosis, fail-safe mode and fault code display for the main input sensors and solenoid valves.

INPUT SENSORS

Air Conditioning Clutch (ACC) – On factory installed A/C system, PCM receives signal voltage from ACC switch indication that the air conditioning compressor clutch is engaged. The PCM uses the ACC switch signal to adjust line pressure to compensate for additional engine load. If the ACC switch fails with closed contacts, line pressure will be slightly low with air conditioning off. If the ACC switch fails with open contacts, line pressure will be slightly higher with air conditioning on.

Brake On/Off (BOO) Switch – The PCM receives a signal from the BOO switch when the brake switch is operated. Torque converter clutch is disengaged when brakes are applied. Malfunctioning switch will affect torque converter operation.

Crankshaft Position (CKP) Sensor & Ignition Control Module (ICM) – The CKP sensor sends crankshaft position information to the ICM, which sends an engine speed signal to the PCM. Signal received by the PCM affects line pressure, shift scheduling, torque converter clutch and WOT shift control. Engine speed signal malfunction may result in harsh engagements, firm shifts, TCC lock-up and/or late WOT shifts.

Engine Coolant Temperature (ECT) Sensor – Engine temperature signal is sent to PCM. Malfunctioning ECT will affect torque converter clutch operation.

Mass Airflow Sensor (MAS) – The MAS signal is used for Electronic Pressure Control (EPC), shift and TCC operation and MAS malfunction will affect these areas.

Manual Lever Position (MLP) Sensor – The PCM monitors a series of step down resistors in the MLP sensor that act as a voltage divider. The voltage signal corresponds with position of the transaxle range selector lever. The MLP sensor also contains the neutral/start and backup light circuits. Malfunction of the MLP sensor may cause harsh engagements and firm shift feel. Improper shifting or shift selection and no engine cranking may also result.

Throttle Position Sensor (TPS) – The TPS is a potentiometer mounted to the engine throttle body. The PCM receives a signal from the TPS relaying throttle plate position. TPS failure will cause PCM to operate in fail safe mode and raise line pressure to prevent transaxle damage. This condition will result in harsh engagements, firm shift feel, abnormal shift schedule and TCC not engaging or cycling.

Transmission Control Switch (TCS) – Switch is mounted on shift lever handle. Switch controls operation of 4th gear. Malfunction of switch will cause lack of 4th disable function.

Transmission Oil Temperature (TOT) Sensor – The TOT sensor is located on the solenoid valve body. The PCM monitors voltage across the TOT thermistor to determine transaxle fluid temperature. Depending on temperature, the PCM controls line pressure, shift scheduling and TCC operation. Malfunction of sensor will cause incorrect line pressure and possible lack of TCC operation.

Transmission Speed Sensor (TSS) – The TSS is a magnetic pickup that sends turbine shaft speed signal to the PCM. Malfunction of sensor may cause harsh engagements of shifts. Lack of 4th gear or no engine braking in 2nd or 3rd gear may result.

Vehicle Speed Sensor (VSS) – The VSS is a magnetic pickup that sends output speed signal to the PCM. Malfunction of sensor may cause harsh engagements of shifts. Lack of 4th gear, TCC lock-up, or engine braking in 2nd or 3rd gear may result.

OUTPUT DEVICES

Solenoid Valve Body Assembly – 1) The solenoid valve body assembly contains EPC solenoid, Shift Solenoid No. 1 (SS1), Shift Solenoid No. 2 (SS2), 3-2 timing/coast clutch (3-2T/CCS) solenoid and Torque Converter Clutch (TCC) solenoid. See SOLENOID OPERATION CHART.

SOLENOID OPERATIONS CHART

Gear Position	SS1	SS2	3-2T/CCS
"P"	Off	On	N/A
"R"	Off	Off	N/A
"N"	Off	On	N/A
"OD" ON			
1st Gear	On	On	N/A
2nd Gear	Off	On	N/A
3rd Gear	Off	Off	N/A
4th Gear	On	Off	On
"OD" OFF			
1st Gear	On	On	On
2nd Gear	Off	On	Off
3rd Gear	Off	Off	Off
"2" [1]	Off	Off	Off
"2"	Off	On	Off
"1" [1]	Off	On	Off
"1" [2]	Off	Off	Off
"1"	On	Off	Off

[1] – Transmission is in 3rd gear until vehicle speed drops below calibrated speed.

[2] – Transmission is in 2nd gear until vehicle speed drops below calibrated speed.

2) When shift solenoid is Always Off, failure could be due to the PCM and/or vehicle wiring malfunction, and/or solenoid electrically stuck off, and/or solenoid hydraulically or mechanically stuck off. For shift symptoms, *see Fig. 1.*

3) When shift solenoid is Always On, failure could be due to the PCM and/or vehicle wiring malfunction, and/or solenoid electrically stuck off, and/or solenoid hydraulically or mechanically stuck off. For shift symptoms, *see Fig. 2.*

PRELIMINARY INSPECTION

VISUAL INSPECTION

Visually inspect all electrical wiring, looking for chafed, stretched, cut or pinched wiring. Ensure electrical connectors fit tightly and are not corroded. Ensure vacuum hoses are properly routed and are not pinched or cut. Inspect air induction system for possible vacuum leaks. Check PCM, sensors and actuators for physical damage. Check engine coolant level. Check transmission fluid level and condition.

SS1 Always OFF	Transaxle Range Selector Lever Position			
	OD	D˙	2	1˙˙
PCM Gear Commanded	Actual Gear Obtained			
1	2	2	-	2
2	2	2	2	2
3	3	3	3	3
4	3	-	-	-

˙ Overdrive cancelled
˙˙ When a manual pull-in occurs above a calibrated speed the transaxle will not downshift from the higher gear until the vehicle speed drops below this calibrated speed.

SS2 Always OFF	Transaxle Range Selector Lever Position			
	OD	D˙	2	1˙˙
PCM Gear Commanded	Actual Gear Obtained			
1	4	4	-	1
2	3	3	3	1
3	3	3	3	2
4	4	-	-	-

˙ Overdrive cancelled
˙˙ When a manual pull-in occurs above a calibrated speed the transaxle will not downshift from the higher gear until the vehicle speed drops below this calibrated speed.

94C36709 94F36710   Courtesy of Ford Motor Co.

Fig. 1: Shift Solenoid Failure Charts (Solenoid Always Off)

SS1 Always ON	Transaxle Range Selector Lever Position			
	OD	D˙	2	1˙˙
PCM Gear Commanded	Actual Gear Obtained			
1	1	1	-	1
2	1	1	1	1
3	4	4	4	4
4	4	-	-	-
Also No Reverse				

˙ Overdrive cancelled
˙˙ When a manual pull-in occurs above a calibrated speed the transaxle will not downshift from the higher gear until the vehicle speed drops below this calibrated speed.

SS2 Always ON	Transaxle Range Selector Lever Position			
	OD	D˙	2	1˙˙
PCM Gear Commanded	Actual Gear Obtained			
1	1	1	-	4
2	2	2	2	3
3	2	2	2	3
4	1	1	-	-

˙ Overdrive cancelled
˙˙ When a manual pull-in occurs above a calibrated speed the transaxle will not downshift from the higher gear until the vehicle speed drops below this calibrated speed.

94G36711 94H36712   Courtesy of Ford Motor Co.

Fig. 2: Shift Solenoid Failure Charts (Solenoid Always On)

NOTE: In addition to transmission fault codes, engine-related fault codes may be output during QUICK TEST procedure. These fault codes pertain to engine performance and must be repaired first as engine performance will greatly affect transmission operation. For information and testing procedures of engine-related fault codes and components, see SELF-DIAGNOSTICS – EEC-IV article in ENGINE PERFORMANCE of appropriate MITCHELL® manual.

SELF-DIAGNOSTIC SYSTEM

DIAGNOSTIC FORMATS

QUICK TEST and CIRCUIT/PINPOINT TESTS are diagnostic formats used to test and service EEC-IV system. QUICK TEST allows technician to identify problems and retrieve service codes. CIRCUIT/PINPOINT TESTS check circuits, sensors and actuators.

Before starting any CIRCUIT/PINPOINT TEST, follow all steps under QUICK TEST to find correct CIRCUIT/PINPOINT TEST. If vehicle passes QUICK TEST and no driveability symptoms or intermittent faults exist, EEC-IV system is okay.

SERVICE CODE TYPES

During QUICK TEST, 3 types of service codes are retrieved: Key On Engine Off (KOEO), Key On Engine Running (KOER) and Continuous Memory codes. See QUICK TEST for self-test procedures. Codes may be cleared from PCM memory after they have been recorded or repaired. See CLEARING CODES.

KOEO & KOER Codes (Hard Faults) – These codes indicate faults are present at time of testing. A hard fault may cause CHECK ENGINE or Malfunction Indicator Light (MIL) to go on and remain on until fault is repaired. If KOEO or KOER codes are retrieved during KOEO SELF-TEST or KOER SELF-TEST, use CODE REFERENCE CHART to find correct testing and repair procedures.

Continuous Memory Codes (Soft Faults) – These codes indicate a fault that may or may not be present at time of testing. These codes are used to diagnose intermittent problems. Continuous Memory Codes are retrieved after KOEO SELF-TEST. Some codes may turn on MIL/CHECK ENGINE light. Corresponding soft fault trouble code will be retained in PCM memory. If fault does not reoccur within 40 warm-up cycles, PCM will automatically clear code.

Technician may clear service codes from memory. See CLEARING CODES. Intermittent faults may be caused by a sensor, connector or wiring-related problem.

CAUTION: Continuous Memory Codes should be recorded when retrieved. These codes may be used to identify intermittent problems that exist after all KOEO and KOER codes have been repaired and a Code 11 or 111 (pass code) has been obtained. Some Continuous Memory Codes faults may not be valid after KOEO and KOER codes are serviced.

RETRIEVING CODES

NOTE: Data Link Connector (DLC) was previously referred to as Self-Test connector or VIP connector.

Service codes are retrieved from EEC-IV system through Data Link Connector (DLC). Various methods and test equipment may be used to access these codes:

- Analog Volt-Ohmmeter (VOM)
- Scan tester
- In-Dash Malfunction Indicator Light (MIL)/CHECK ENGINE light

READING CODES

KOEO & KOER SELF-TEST Codes – PCM outputs codes one digit at a time. Record codes in order received. These codes indicate current faults in system and should be serviced in order of appearance. Use CODE REFERENCE CHART to find correct CIRCUIT/PINPOINT TEST.

If using analog VOM, pay careful attention to length of pauses in order to read codes correctly. A 1/2-second pause occurs between number of sweeps in a digit. A 2-second pause occurs between digits in a code. A 4-second pause occurs between each code. KOEO codes are separated from Continuous Memory codes by a 6-second delay, a 1/2-second sweep (separator) and another 6-second delay. *See Fig. 3.* If using MIL/CHECK ENGINE light, service codes are displayed as flashes.

Scan tester, if used, will count pulses and display them as a digital code. STAR Series Tester will add a zero (0) to single-digit Separator Code (10) and Dynamic Response Code (10). Dynamic Response Code is displayed in KOER SELF-TEST. *See Fig. 3.*

Separator Pulse – Single 1/2-second separator pulse is issued 6-9 seconds after last KOEO code. Continuous Memory Codes (soft faults) are then displayed 6-9 seconds after 1/2-second separator pulse. Some digital test equipment may display separator code as "10" instead of "1".

Pass Codes – A Code 11 or 111 indicates no service codes were recorded in that portion of test; system passes that portion of test. If Code 11 or 111 is not retrieved in KOEO SELF-TEST, codes retrieved during KOER SELF-TEST may not be valid. Code 11 or 111 (pass code) must be obtained in KOEO SELF-TEST. A Code 11-1-11 or 111-1-111 output during KOEO SELF-TEST indicates no KOEO code or Continuous Memory Code was recorded.

Continuous Memory Codes – These codes result from information stored by PCM during continuous self-test monitoring. Codes are displayed after separator pulse code in KOEO SELF-TEST. Use these codes for diagnosis only when KOEO SELF-TEST and KOER SELF-TEST result in Code 11 or 111 (pass code) and all steps under QUICK TEST are successfully completed. These codes indicate faults recorded within last 40 engine starts (80 engine starts on some models). Fault may or may not be currently present. See CODE REFERENCE CHART.

Fast Codes – At start of KOEO SELF-TEST and after Wide Open Throttle (WOT) request in KOER SELF-TEST, PCM outputs short bursts of information, known as FAST CODES, which were used by manufacturer during assembly. With most equipment, these code bursts are not visible; an entire code sequence lasts less than 1/2 second. If this fluctuation is visible on test equipment, ignore it.

CLEARING CODES

To clear codes from PCM memory, start KOEO SELF-TEST. When service codes appear on test equipment or CHECK ENGINE light, disconnect jumper wire from Self-Test Input (STI) connector. If using STAR Series Tester, unlatch center button. This procedure erases Continuous Memory Codes from PCM memory. If problem has not been corrected or fault is still present, hard code will immediately be reset in PCM memory.

CAUTION: DO NOT disconnect vehicle battery to clear codes. This will erase stored operating information from Keep-Alive Memory (KAM). To clear KAM, disconnect negative battery terminal for at least 5 minutes.

CAUTION: When battery is disconnected, vehicle computer and memory systems may lose memory data. Driveability problems may exist until computer systems have completed a relearn cycle. See COMPUTER RELEARN PROCEDURES article in APPLICATIONS & IDENTIFICATION before disconnecting battery.

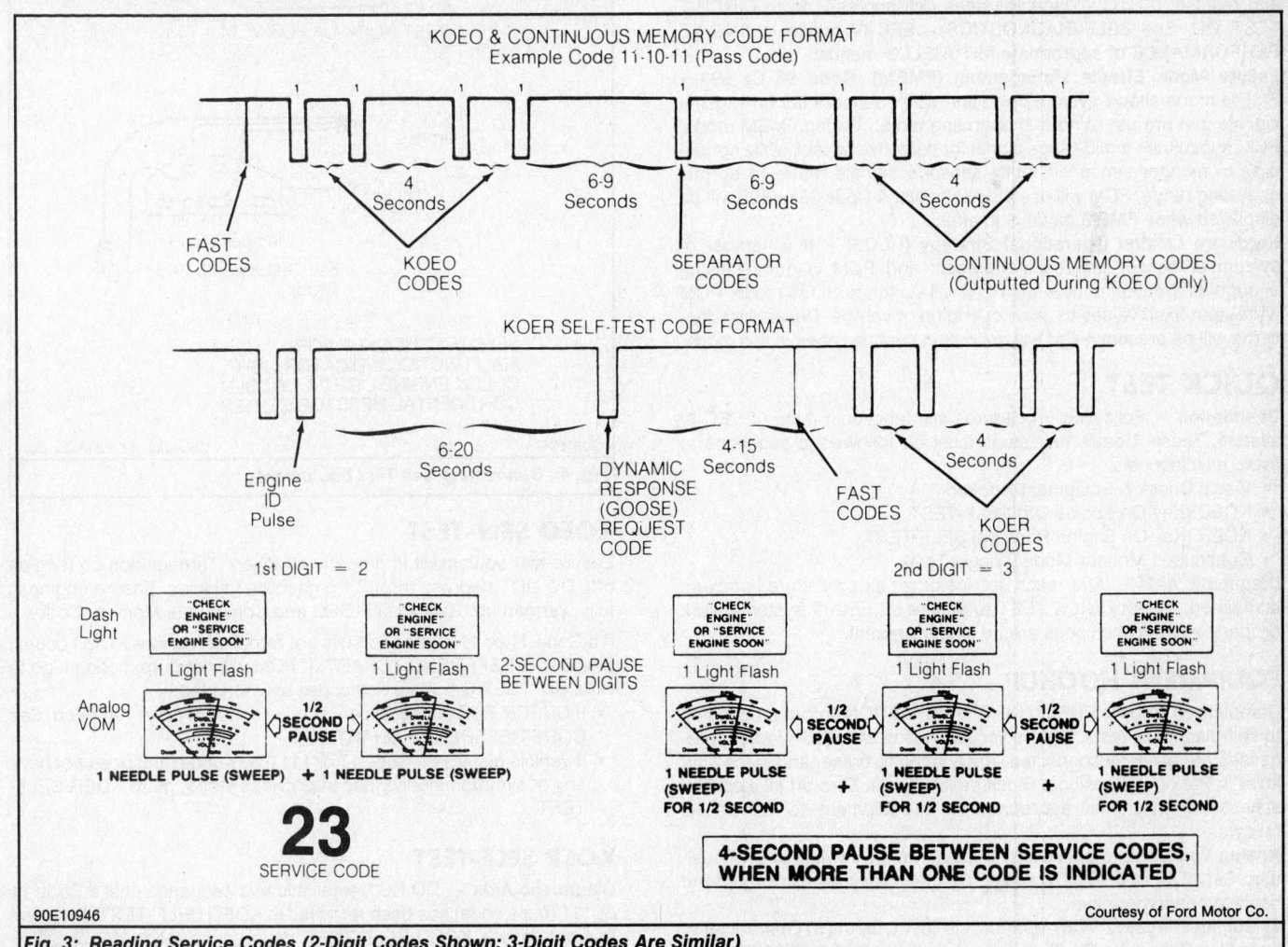

Fig. 3: Reading Service Codes (2-Digit Codes Shown; 3-Digit Codes Are Similar)

ADDITIONAL SYSTEM FUNCTIONS

Additional diagnostic system features are available to help diagnose driveability problems and service EEC-IV systems.

Malfunction Indicator Light (MIL) – The MIL is intended to alert driver of certain malfunctions in EEC-IV system. Light may also be used to retrieve service codes stored in PCM. When hooked up for KOEO SELF-TEST or KOER SELF-TEST, light will display all codes which turn on light during vehicle operation.

Light should come on when ignition is turned on and go out when engine is started. If light comes on and then goes off during vehicle operation, code causing light to come on will be stored in PCM memory as a Continuous Memory Code. If light comes on during vehicle operation, vehicle should be inspected as soon as possible. Immediately turning off engine is not necessary; vehicle can be driven with light on.

Output State Check – Output State Check is used as an aid in servicing output actuators associated with EEC-IV system. It allows technicians to energize and de-energize most system output actuators on command. This mode is entered from KOEO SELF-TEST after all codes have been retrieved.

Disconnect cruise control servo (if equipped). With DVOM on 20-volt scale, connect DVOM negative lead to STO terminal at Diagnostic Link Connector (DLC). Connect positive lead to positive battery terminal. Using jumper wire, connect STI to SIG RTN at Diagnostic Link Connector (DLC).

Perform KOEO SELF-TEST until continuous memory test is complete. DVOM will read less than 1.0 volt when test is complete. Depress and release throttle. If voltage increases, OUTPUT STATE CHECK has been entered. If voltage does not increase, depress throttle to WOT and release. If STO voltage still does not increase, go to CIRCUIT TEST QC. See SELF-DIAGNOSTICS – EEC-IV article in ENGINE PERFORMANCE of appropriate MITCHELL® manual.

Failure Mode Effects Management (FMEM), Code 98 Or 998 – FMEM mode allows system operation when sensors fail or transmit signals that are out of normal operating range. During FMEM mode, PCM substitutes a mid-range signal for defective sensor while continuing to monitor sensor. If faulty sensor's signals return to normal operating range, PCM will use those signals. A Code 98 or 998 will be displayed when FMEM mode is in effect.

Hardware Limited Operational Strategy (HLOS) – If a number of system or sensor failures are present and PCM is not receiving enough information to operate, PCM will switch to HLOS mode. PCM will output fixed values to allow operation of vehicle. Driveability concerns will be present. PCM will not output service codes in this mode.

QUICK TEST

Description – Following procedures are functional tests of EEC-IV system. These 4 basic test steps must be followed in sequence to avoid misdiagnosis:
- Visual Check & Equipment Hookup
- KOEO (Key On Engine Off) SELF-TEST
- KOER (Key On Engine Running) SELF-TEST
- Continuous Monitor Mode (Wiggle Test)

Diagnostic Aids – After each service or repair procedure has been completed, repeat QUICK TEST to ensure all EEC-IV systems work properly and service codes are no longer present.

EQUIPMENT HOOKUP

Complete all steps in PRELIMINARY INSPECTION before proceeding to self-diagnostic tests. Ensure vacuum hoses and EEC-IV wiring harnesses are properly connected. Apply parking brake, and place shift lever in Park (A/T position). Block drive wheels. Turn off all electrical accessories. Connect appropriate test equipment to vehicle as follows:

Analog Volt-Ohmmeter (VOM) – **1)** Turn ignition switch to OFF position. Set VOM at 0-15V DC range. Connect positive lead of VOM to positive battery terminal.

2) Connect negative VOM lead to Self-Test Output (STO) terminal of Data Link Connector (DLC). See Fig. 4. Activate KOEO SELF-TEST by connecting jumper wire from Self-Test Input (STI) pigtail to signal return terminal of Data Link Connector (DLC) with ignition on.

Scan Tester – Follow manufacturer's instructions to hook up equipment and record service codes.

STAR Series Tester – Turn ignition switch to OFF position. Connect color-coded adapter cable leads to diagnostic tester. Connect 2 service connectors of adapter cable to vehicle Data Link Connector (DLC) and STI pigtail connector. Connect timing light. Go to KOEO SELF-TEST. Ensure tester is switched to fast mode.

Malfunction Indicator Light (MIL) – Turn ignition on. Connect a jumper wire between Self-Test Input (STI) pigtail and signal return terminal of Data Link Connector (DLC). See Fig. 4. Go to KOEO SELF-TEST.

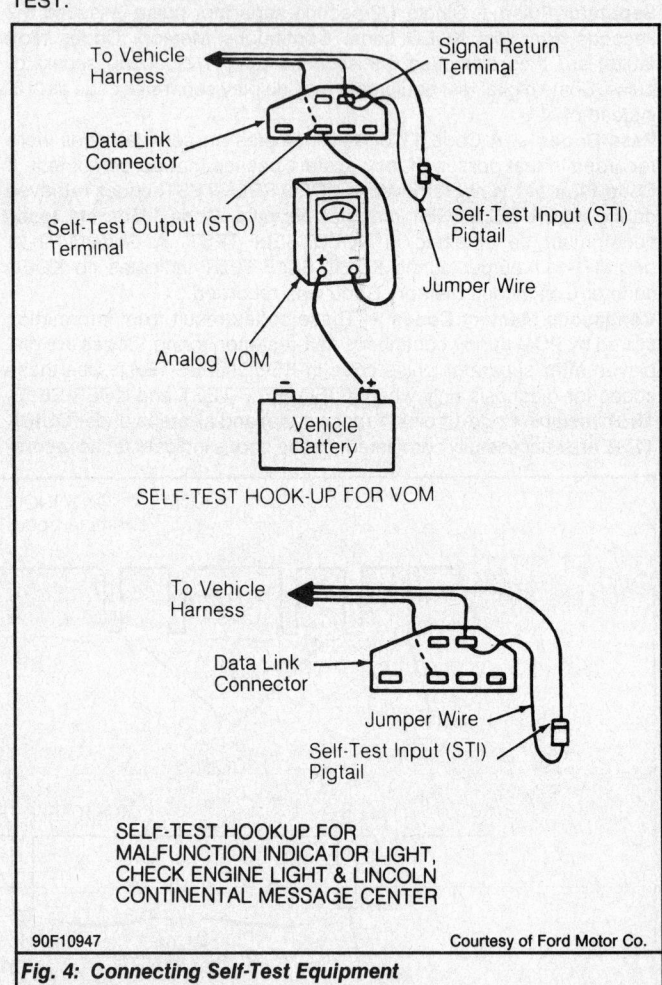

SELF-TEST HOOK-UP FOR VOM

SELF-TEST HOOKUP FOR
MALFUNCTION INDICATOR LIGHT,
CHECK ENGINE LIGHT & LINCOLN
CONTINENTAL MESSAGE CENTER

90F10947   Courtesy of Ford Motor Co.

Fig. 4: Connecting Self-Test Equipment

KOEO SELF-TEST

Ensure test equipment is properly attached. Turn ignition on (engine off). DO NOT depress throttle on gasoline vehicles. Ensure engine is fully warmed up. Record all KOEO and Continuous Memory Codes.

If a Code 11 or 111 (pass code) is not retrieved, service KOEO codes. See CODE REFERENCE CHART. If PCM will not output codes, go to CIRCUIT TEST QA. If service codes are retrieved:
- If CHECK ENGINE light is on, service codes in order retrieved. See CODE REFERENCE CHART.
- If vehicle displays a Code 11 or 111 (pass code) and does not have any of symptoms described in previous steps, go to KOER SELF-TEST.

KOER SELF-TEST

Diagnostic Aids – DO NOT enter this test sequence until a Code 11 or 111 (pass code) has been retrieved in KOEO SELF-TEST. If system has not passed KOEO SELF-TEST, codes recorded in KOER SELF-TEST may not be valid.

Deactivate self-test by removing and reconnecting jumper wire or by procedure specified by test equipment in use. Start engine, and run it for 2 minutes at 2000 RPM to warm Heated Exhaust Gas Oxygen Sensor (HO2S). Turn engine off, and wait 10 seconds. Activate KOER SELF-TEST using a jumper wire or appropriate procedure for test equipment used. Start engine. Record all service codes displayed. Check following items:

- If Code 98 or 998 is displayed, EEC-IV system is operating in Failure Management Effects Mode (FMEM) and vehicle has not passed KOEO SELF-TEST. Vehicle cannot be diagnosed while in FMEM mode.
- If vehicle is equipped with a Brake On-Off (BOO) switch, brake pedal must be depressed and released after ID code portion of test.
- On vehicles with Power Steering Pressure (PSP) switch, turn steering wheel at least 1/2 turn and release within 1-2 seconds after ID code portion of test.
- If Dynamic Response Code appears, perform a brief Wide Open Throttle (WOT). DO NOT perform WOT unless requested.
- If a Code 11 or 111 (pass code) is retrieved during KOER SELF-TEST, service Continuous Memory Codes retrieved in KOEO SELF-TEST. See CODE REFERENCE CHART.
- If KOER codes are present, see CODE REFERENCE CHART. If system will not output codes, go to CIRCUIT TEST QA.
- If a Code 11 or 111 (pass code) is retrieved during Continuous Memory Code portion of KOEO SELF-TEST and no driveability problem exists, EEC-IV testing is complete. If driveability problems are still present, go to Ford CD4E article.
- If a Code 11 or 111 (pass code) is retrieved during KOER SELF-TEST and intermittent fault(s) continue, go to CONTINUOUS MONITOR MODE (WIGGLE TEST).

CONTINUOUS MONITOR MODE (WIGGLE TEST)

Continuous Monitor Mode allows technician to attempt to recreate an intermittent fault while monitoring system. This mode, also called wiggle test, may be used in both KOEO SELF-TEST and KOER SELF-TEST. CIRCUIT/PINPOINT TESTS specify use of this procedure to identify intermittent faults in specific circuits or components.

KOEO Wiggle Test Procedure – Connect test equipment. See Fig. 4. Turn ignition on, and activate self-test using jumper lead or diagnostic tester. Wait 10 seconds, and then deactivate and reactivate self-test. Wiggle test mode is now activated. Tap, move and wiggle suspect sensor and/or harness area. If a fault is detected, a service code may be stored in memory and indicated at diagnostic tester or scan tester. Retrieve code, and perform appropriate test. See CODE REFERENCE CHART.

KOER Wiggle Test Procedure – Connect test equipment. See Fig. 4. Turn ignition off, and wait 10 seconds. Start engine. Activate self-test using jumper lead or diagnostic tester. Wait 10 seconds, and then deactivate and reactivate self-test. DO NOT turn engine off. KOER wiggle test mode is now activated. Tap, move and wiggle suspect sensor and/or harness area. If a fault is detected, a service code may be stored in memory and indicated at diagnostic tester or scan tester. Retrieve code, and perform appropriate test. See CODE REFERENCE CHART.

TRANSMISSION DRIVE CYCLE TEST

NOTE: The transmission drive cycle test must be followed exactly. Malfunctions have to occur 4 times consecutively for codes 645, 646, 647 and 648 to be set and 5 times consecutively for continuous code 628.

1) Ater repairing any engine performance trouble codes, erase remaining transmission codes. Warm engine to normal operating temperature. Ensure transmission fluid level is correct. Shift transmission to drive (D). Press TCS on shifter handle. O/D OFF light should illuminate.
2) Accelerate from stop to 40 mph. Hold speed for at least 15 seconds (30 seconds above 4000 ft.). Press TCS and accelerate to 50 mph.

Hold speed for at least 15 seconds (30 seconds above 4000 ft.). Hold speed and throttle position steady for at least 15 seconds. While maintaining speed with transaxle in 4th gear, lightly depress brake pedal and release. Bring vehicle to stop for at least 20 seconds. Repeat steps 1) and 2) at least 5 times. Perform Quick Test and record continuous codes.

TRANSMISSION SOLENOID CYCLING & DRIVE TEST (DYNAMIC TEST)

Preliminary Set Up – Connect Transaxle Tester (007-0085A). Install pressure gauge to line pressure tap. See FORD CD4E article. Set Bench/Drive switch to Drive mode. Set tester to Gear Select "1" position. Ensure vehicle is in park (P). Start vehicle.

CAUTION: Transaxle damage will occur if stall test is conducted with EPC switch depressed.

EPC Solenoid – Record line pressure. Line pressure should be 76 psi (maximum line pressure). If line pressure is not within specification, see TESTING in Ford CD4E article or PINPOINT TEST E. Depress EPC switch. Line pressure should be 64 psi (minimum line pressure). If line pressure is not within specification, see TESTING in Ford CD4E article or PINPOINT TEST E.

Engagements – Rotate gear select switch to 3/R position. Shift transaxle from park to reverse. Reverse should engage. Shift transaxle from reverse to park. Rotate gear select switch to "1" position. Depress EPC switch. Line pressure should drop to idle pressure (64 psi). While depressing EPC switch, shift vehicle from park to drive. Vehicle should shift into drive with smooth engagement. Vehicle shift engagement should be firm with EPC switch released.

NOTE: Ensure gear select switch is in 3/R position for reverse gear. Upshifts and downshifts will be firm during this procedure.

Upshift/Downshift – 1) Remove line pressure gauge. Set gear select switch to 1st position. Shift transmission to drive. Depress the 3-2T/CCS button and accelerate (road test) vehicle. If vehicle will not move, forward one-way clutch failure is possible. If vehicle will move go to next step.
2) Ensure gear select switch is in 1st position. Shift transmission to overdrive and accelerate to 15 mph. Rotate gear select switch to 2nd gear position. Vehicle should shift into 2nd gear. Accelerate to 25 mph and select 3rd gear. Vehicle should shift into 3rd gear. Accelerate to 35-45 mph and select 4th gear. Vehicle should shift into 4th gear.
3) Downshift as outlined in step 2). To prevent harsh 4-3 downshift depress 3-2T/CCS button during 4-3 downshift. Vehicle should downshift through each gear.

CAUTION: Do not depress TCC switch with transmission in gear and vehicle at a stop. Damage to TCC may result.

Torque Converter Engagement – Accelerate and upshift vehicle up into 3rd gear. Maintain constant speed and depress TCC switch. Torque converter clutch should engage and engine rpm should decrease.

3-2 Timing/Coast Clutch Engagement – Accelerate and upshift vehicle into 3rd gear. Release throttle and depress 3-2T/CCS switch. Coast clutch should disengage. Lightly depress throttle and release 3-2T/CCS switch. Engine braking should occur.

NOTE: This test may be performed on hoist.

Transmission Speed Sensor Function Check – Set voltmeter to 20 volts A/C. Connect voltmeter leads to appropriate TSS jacks. Slowly accelerate vehicle and monitor voltmeter reading. Voltage should increase with vehicle speed.

Transmission Tester Removal & Clearing Trouble Codes – Disconnect Transmission Tester from transaxle connector. Install vehicle wiring harness to transaxle connector. Install all heat shields that were removed. Disconnect tester power lead from vehicle. See CLEARING CODES to erase any trouble codes that were set. Run QUICK TEST to determine if any trouble codes are present.

SUMMARY

If no service code is present but driveability problem still exists, proceed to Ford CD4E article for symptom diagnosis procedures.

NOTE: CIRCUIT/PINPOINT TESTS are diagnostic formats used to test and service EEC-IV system. QUICK TEST allows technician to identify problems and retrieve service codes. CIRCUIT TESTS check engine circuits, sensors and actuators. PINPOINT TESTS check transaxle circuits, sensors and actuators.

CODE REFERENCE CHART

NOTE: In addition to transmission fault codes, engine-related fault codes may be output during QUICK TEST procedure. These fault codes pertain to engine performance and must be repaired first as engine performance will greatly affect transmission operation. For information and testing procedures of engine-related fault codes and components, see SELF-DIAGNOSTICS – EEC-IV article in ENGINE PERFORMANCE of appropriate MITCHELL® manual.

NOTE: No trouble code was available from manufacturer for 3-2T/CCS component malfunction. If component is suspected, see PINPOINT TEST G.

CODE REFERENCE CHART

Fault Code	Code Definition	Circuit/Pinpoint Test & Step
KOEO Codes		
No Code	N/A	QA1
111	Pass Code	N/A
116	ECT Out Of Range	DA1
117	ECT Indicates 254° F (125° C)	DA20
118	ECT Indicates -40° F (-40° C)	DA10
121	TPS Voltage High/Low	DH2
122	TPS Malfunction	DH10
123	TPS Malfunction	DH3
158	MAF Sensor Malfunction	DC21
159	MAF Sensor Malfunction	DC1
539	A/C Switch Error	KM40
621	SS1 Solenoid Circuit Failure	A1
622	SS2 Solenoid Circuit Failure	A1
624	EPC Circuit Failure	E1
625	Open PCM Output Driver	E1
634	MLP Out Of Range	D1
636	TOT Out Of Range	B1
637	TOT Sensor Circuit Open	B1
638	TOT Sensor Circuit Grounded	B1
652	TCC Circuit Error	C1
998	FMEM Failure	TC10
Continuous Memory Codes		
No Code	N/A	QA1
111	Pass Code	N/A
117	ECT Indicates 254° F (125° C)	DA90
118	ECT Indicates -40° F (-40° C)	DA90
121	TPS Voltage High/Low	GA1
122	TPS Malfunction	DH94
123	TPS Malfunction	DH90
124	TPS Malfunction	GA1
125	TPS Malfunction	GA1
157	MAF Sensor Malfunction	DC10
158	MAF Sensor Malfunction	DC21
184	MAF Sensor Malfunction	GA5
185	MAF Sensor Malfunction	GA5
452	Insufficient VSS Input	DP1
522	MLP Not In Park	D1

CODE REFERENCE CHART (Cont.)

Fault Code	Code Definition	Circuit/Pinpoint Test & Step
536	BOO Switch Malfunction	FD90
624	EPC Solenoid Circuit Failure	E1
628	TCC Engagement Error	C1
634	MLP Sensor Voltage Error	D1
637	TOT Sensor Voltage High	B1
638	TOT Sensor Voltage Low	B1
639	Insufficient Input From TSS	F1
645	No 1st Gear	A1
646	No 2nd Gear	A1
647	No 3rd Gear	A1
648	No 4th Gear	A1
KOER Codes		
No Code	N/A	QA1
111	Pass Code	N/A
116	ECT Out Of Range	DA1
121	TPS Voltage High/Low	DH1
159	MAF Sensor Malfunction	DC1
167	TPS Malfunction	DH20
536	BOO Switch Malfunction	FD1
539	A/C Switch Error	KM40
636	TOT Sensor Voltage Error	B1
639	Insufficient Input From TSS	F1
653	TCS Malfunction	TB2

CIRCUIT TESTS

NOTE: A breakout box, connected to vehicle harness at PCM, is necessary to perform most circuit tests. References to Test Pin No. found in CIRCUIT TEST steps refer to test terminals on manufacturer's breakout box. Circuit diagrams at beginning of each test identify circuit and wire colors.

HOW TO USE CIRCUIT TESTS

1) DO NOT perform any CIRCUIT TEST unless specifically instructed by a QUICK TEST procedure. Follow each test step in order until fault is found. DO NOT replace any part unless directed to do so. When more than one code is retrieved, start with first code displayed.

2) CIRCUIT TESTS ensure electrical circuits are okay before sensors or other components are replaced. Always test circuits for continuity between sensor and PCM. Test all circuits for short to power, opens or short to ground. Voltage Reference (VREF) and Voltage Power (VPWR) circuits should be tested with ignition on or as specified in CIRCUIT TESTS.

3) DO NOT measure voltage or resistance at PCM. DO NOT connect any test light unless specified in testing procedure. All measurements are made by probing rear of connector. Isolate both ends of a circuit and turn ignition off when checking for shorts or continuity, unless instructed otherwise.

4) Disconnect solenoids and switches from harness before measuring continuity and resistance or applying voltage. After each repair, check all component connections and repeat QUICK TEST.

5) An open circuit is defined as a resistance reading of greater than 5 ohms. This specification tolerance may be too high for some items in EEC-IV system. If resistance approaches 5 ohms, always clean suspect connector and coat it with protective dielectric silicone grease. A short is defined as a resistance reading of less than 10 k/ohms to ground, unless stated otherwise in CIRCUIT TEST.

Diagnostic Aids – Fuel-contaminated engine oil may affect some codes. If oil contamination is suspected, remove PCV valve from valve cover and repeat QUICK TEST. If problem is corrected, change engine oil.

NOTE: In following tests, circuit diagrams and illustrations are courtesy of Ford Motor Co.

PINPOINT TESTS

NOTE: PINPOINT TESTS are diagnostic formats used to test and service EEC-IV system. PINPOINT TESTS check transaxle circuits, sensors and actuators. For engine component testing and servicing, see CIRCUIT TESTS.

PINPOINT TEST A

SHIFT SOLENOID ELECTRICAL SYSTEM

1) CD4E Electronic Diagnostics – Ensure transaxle harness connector is in acceptable condition. Repair as necessary. Disconnect transaxle harness connector. Connect Transmission Tester (007-0085A) or equivalent to transaxle. Perform TRANSMISSION SOLENOID CYCLING AND DRIVE TEST. Perform KOEO test until Continuous Memory trouble code(s) have been displayed. See QUICK TEST. Depress throttle to WOT and release. If vehicle enters Output State, go to next step. If vehicle will not enter Output State, see SELF-DIAGNOSTICS – EEC-IV article in ENGINE PERFORMANCE of appropriate MITCHELL® manual.

2) Check Electrical Signal Operation – Disconnect transaxle harness connector. Inspect condition of connector and repair as needed. Using DVOM, connect positive lead to transaxle harness connector terminal No. 5. *See Fig. A1.* Connect negative lead to suspect solenoid circuit. Depress and release throttle to cycle solenoid output. If voltage changes at least .5 volts, go to step **5)**. If voltage is unaffected, go to next step.

94G36729

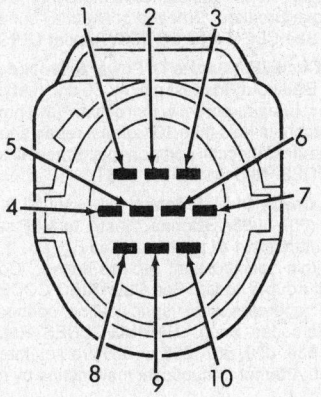

1. TCC Power (VPWR)
2. Signal Return
3. TOT Signal
4. SS1 Signal
5. Solenoid Power (VPWR)
6. SS2 Signal
7. TCC Signal
8. EPC Signal
9. EPC Power (VPWR)
10. 3-2T/CCS Signal

Fig. A1: Identifying Transaxle Harness Connector

3) Check Continuity Of Solenoid Signal & VPWR Harness Circuits – Ensure ignition is off. Disconnect PCM 60-pin connector, and inspect it for damaged pins, corrosion and loose wires. Repair as necessary. Install Breakout Box (T83L-50-EEC-IV), leaving PCM disconnected. Measure and record resistance between Breakout Box test pin No. 51 and transaxle harness connector terminal No. 4. *See Fig. A1.* Measure and record resistance between test pin No. 52 and transaxle harness connector terminal No. 6. Measure and record resistance between test pins No. 37 and 57 and transaxle harness connector terminals No. 1, 5 and 9. If any resistance is greater than 5 ohms, repair open circuit. Connect all components. Disconnect Breakout Box and repeat Quick Test. If resistance is 5 ohms or less, go to next step.

4) Check Solenoid Harness For Shorts To Power & Ground – Measure and record resistance between Breakout Box test pins No. 51 or 52 and test pins No. 37 and 57. Measure and record resistance between test pins No. 40, 47 and 60, and ground. If any resistance is less than 10K ohms, repair short circuit. Connect all components. Disconnect Breakout Box and repeat Quick Test. If resistance is 10K ohms or more, go to next step.

5) Solenoid Functional Test – Connect Transaxle Tester (007-0085A). Perform solenoid voltage test. See tester instructions. If solenoid activates (Green LED), go to next step. If solenoid does not activate, go to step **7)**.

PINPOINT TEST A (Cont.)

6) Transaxle Drive Test – Perform tester drive test. See tester instructions. If vehicle upshifts when operated with tester, erase all trouble codes. See CLEARING CODES. Perform drive test. See TRANSMISSION SOLENOID CYCLING & DRIVE TEST (DYNAMIC TEST). Repeat QUICK TEST. If vehicle does not upshift when operated by tester, go to next step.

7) Check Resistance Of Solenoid – Set tester Bench/Drive switch to Bench mode. Set Gear Selector switch to ohms check. Connect ohmmeter negative lead to SS1 jack and positive lead to VPWR jack on tester. Measure and record resistance. Connect ohmmeter negative lead to SS2 jack and positive lead to VPWR jack on tester. Measure and record resistance. Resistance for both solenoids should be 12-22 ohms. If resistance is within specification, go to next step. If resistance is not within specification, replace solenoid body assembly. Erase all trouble codes. See CLEARING CODES. Repeat QUICK TEST.

8) Check Solenoid For Short To Ground – Check continuity between BAT(-) terminal and between SS1 and SS2. If continuity exists, replace solenoid body assembly. Erase all trouble codes. See CLEARING CODES. Repeat QUICK TEST. If continuity does not exist, see FORD CD4E article for non-electronic symptom diagnostics.

PINPOINT TEST B

TOT ELECTRICAL SYSTEM

1) Visual Check – Check transaxle harness connector. Inspect connector for damaged pins, corrosion and loose wires. Repair as necessary. Go to next step.

2) Check Electrical Signal Operation – Ensure ignition is off. Disconnect transaxle connector. Using DVOM, connect positive lead to transaxle harness connector terminal No. 3 and negative lead to terminal No. 2. *See Fig. A1.* Turn ignition on. If voltage is 4.5-5.25 volts, go to next step. If voltage is not within specification, see SELF-DIAGNOSTICS – EEC-IV article in ENGINE PERFORMANCE of appropriate MITCHELL® manual to diagnose NO VREF voltage.

3) Check Continuity Of TOT Signal Return (SIG RTN) Circuits – Turn ignition off. Disconnect PCM 60-pin connector, and inspect it for damaged pins, corrosion and loose wires. Repair as necessary. Install Breakout Box (T83L-50-EEC-IV), leaving PCM disconnected. Measure and record resistance between Breakout Box test pin No. 49 and transaxle harness connector terminal No. 3. *See Fig. A1.* Measure and record resistance between test pin No. 46 and transaxle harness connector terminal No. 2. If resistances measured are less than 5 ohms, go to next step. If resistances are more than 5 ohms, repair open circuit. Connect all components. Erase trouble codes. See CLEARING CODES. Repeat QUICK TEST.

4) Check TOT Circuit For Short To VPWR & Ground – Ensure ignition is off. Disconnect PCM 60-pin connector, and inspect it for damaged pins, corrosion and loose wires. Repair as necessary. Install Breakout Box (T83L-50-EEC-IV), leaving PCM disconnected. Measure and record resistance between Breakout Box test pins No. 49 and test pins No. 37 and 57. Measure and record resistance between test pins No. 40, 46 and 60, and test pin No. 49. If any resistance is less than 10K ohms, repair short circuit. Disconnect Breakout Box and repeat Quick Test. If resistance is 10K ohms or more, go to next step.

NOTE: Code 637 is set if resistance measured exceeds 869 ohms. Code 638 is set if resistance measured is below 597 ohms.

5) Check Resistance Of TOT Sensor/Harness – Install Transmission Tester (007-0085A). Set tester Bench/Drive switch to Bench mode. Set Gear Selector switch to ohms check. Connect ohmmeter lead to appropriate TOT jacks. Measure and record resistance. Resistance should be within specification. See TOT TEMPERATURE/RESISTANCE CHART. If resistance is within specification for specific temperature, either warm up transaxle or allow transaxle to cool to check resistance at different temperatures. If resistances measured remain within specification, go to next step. If resistances measured are not within specification, replace solenoid body assembly. Erase all trouble codes. See CLEARING CODES. Repeat QUICK TEST.

PINPOINT TEST B (Cont.)

TOT TEMPERATURE/RESISTANCE CHART

Temperature °F (°C)	Resistance (k/Ohms)
32-58 (0-20)	37-100
59-104 (21-40)	16-37
105-158 (41-70)	5-16
159-194 (71-90)	2.7-5
195-230 (91-110)	1.5-2.7
231-266 (111-130)	.8-1.5

6) Check TOT Sensor For Short To Ground – Check continuity between BAT (-) tester terminal and TOT (TFT) terminals. If continuity exists, replace solenoid body assembly. Erase all trouble codes. See CLEARING CODES. Repeat QUICK TEST. If continuity does not exist, Erase all trouble codes. See CLEARING CODES. Repeat QUICK TEST. See FORD CD4E article for non-electronic symptom diagnostics.

PINPOINT TEST C

TCC ELECTRICAL SYSTEM

1) CD4E Electronic Diagnostics – Ensure transaxle harness connector is in acceptable condition. Repair as necessary. Disconnect transaxle harness connector. Connect Transmission Tester (007-0085A) or equivalent to transaxle. Perform TRANSMISSION SOLENOID CYCLING AND DRIVE TEST. Perform KOEO test until Continuous Memory trouble code(s) have been displayed. See QUICK TEST. Depress throttle to WOT and release. If vehicle enters Output State, go to next step. If vehicle will not enter Output State, see SELF-DIAGNOSTICS – EEC-IV article in ENGINE PERFORMANCE of appropriate MITCHELL® manual.

2) Check Electrical Signal Operation – Disconnect transaxle harness connector. Inspect condition of connector and repair as needed. Using DVOM, connect positive lead to transaxle harness connector terminal No. 5. *See Fig. A1.* Connect negative lead to terminal No. 7. Depress and release throttle to cycle solenoid output. If voltage changes at least .5 volts, go to step **5)**. If voltage is unaffected, go to next step.

3) Check Continuity Of Solenoid Signal & VPWR Harness Circuits – Ensure ignition is off. Disconnect PCM 60-pin connector, and inspect it for damaged pins, corrosion and loose wires. Repair as necessary. Install Breakout Box (T83L-50-EEC-IV), leaving PCM disconnected. Measure and record resistance between Breakout Box test pin No. 53 and transaxle harness connector terminal No. 7. *See Fig. A1.* Measure and record resistance between test pins No. 37 and 57 and transaxle harness connector terminals No. 1, 5 and 9. If any resistance is greater than 5 ohms, repair open circuit. Connect all components. Disconnect Breakout Box and repeat Quick Test. If resistance is 5 ohms or less, go to next step.

4) Check Solenoid Harness For Shorts To Power & Ground – Measure and record resistance between test pin No. 53 and test pins No. 37 and 57. Measure and record resistance between test pins No. 40, 46 and 60, and ground. If any resistance is less than 10K ohms, repair short circuit. Connect all components. Disconnect Breakout Box and repeat Quick Test. If resistance is 10K ohms or more, go to next step.

5) Solenoid Functional Test – Connect Transaxle Tester (007-0085A). Perform solenoid voltage test. See tester instructions. If solenoid activates (Green LED), go to next step. If solenoid does not activate, go to step **7)**.

6) Transaxle Drive Test – Perform tester drive test. See tester instructions. If engine rpm decreases when operated with tester, erase all trouble codes. See CLEARING CODES. Perform drive test. See TRANSMISSION SOLENOID CYCLING & DRIVE TEST (DYNAMIC TEST). Repeat QUICK TEST. If engine rpm does not decrease when operated by tester, go to next step.

7) Check Resistance Of Solenoid – Set tester Bench/Drive switch to Bench mode. Set Gear Selector switch to ohms check. Connect ohmmeter negative lead to TCC jack and positive lead to TCC VPWR jack on tester. Measure resistance. Resistance should be 1-2 ohms. If resistance is within specification, go to next step. If resistance is not within specification, replace solenoid body assembly. Erase all trouble codes. See CLEARING CODES. Repeat QUICK TEST.

8) Check Solenoid For Short To Ground – Check continuity between BAT (-) tester terminal and TCC terminals. If continuity exists, replace solenoid body assembly. Connect all components. Erase all trouble codes. See CLEARING CODES. Repeat QUICK TEST. If continuity does not exist, Erase all trouble codes. See CLEARING CODES. Repeat QUICK TEST. See FORD CD4E article for non-electronic symptom diagnostics.

PINPOINT TEST D

MLP Sensor

NOTE: Code 634 may be set if transaxle is not in park or A/C is on when QUICK TEST is performed.

1) Preliminary Inspection – Disconnect MLP connector, and inspect it for damaged pins, corrosion and loose wires. Repair as necessary. Reconnect MLP connector. Ensure MLP sensor is correctly adjusted. See FORD CD4E article. If sensor requires adjustment, clear trouble codes after adjustment. See CLEARING CODES. Repeat QUICK TEST. If sensor is correctly adjusted, go to next step.

2) Check Electrical Signal Operation – Ensure ignition is off. Disconnect MLP harness connector. Turn ignition on. Measure voltage between harness connector terminal No. 7 (Red/Black wire) and No. 1 (Black/Blue wire). If voltage is 4.75-5.25 volts, go to next step. If voltage is not within specification, see SELF-DIAGNOSTICS – EEC-IV article in ENGINE PERFORMANCE of appropriate MITCHELL® manual for NO VREF voltage.

3) Check Continuity Of MLP Sensor Harness Circuits – Turn ignition off. Disconnect PCM 60-pin connector, and inspect it for damaged pins, corrosion and loose wires. Repair as necessary. Install Breakout Box (T83L-50-EEC-IV), leaving PCM disconnected. Measure and record resistance between Breakout Box test pin terminal No. 46 and MLP harness connector terminal No. 1 (Black/Blue wire). Measure and record resistance between Breakout Box test pin terminal No. 30 and MLP harness connector terminal No. 7 (Red/Black wire). If resistance is less than 5 ohms, go to next step. If resistance is more than 5 ohms, repair open circuit(s). Remove Breakout Box and connect all components. Erase all trouble codes. See CLEARING CODES. Repeat QUICK TEST.

4) Check MLP Circuit For Shorts To Power & Ground – Measure resistance between Breakout Box test pin No. 30 and test pins No. 37, 40, 46, 57 and 60. If each measurement is more than 10K ohms, go to next step. If any measurement is less than 10K ohms, repair short circuit. Remove Breakout Box and connect all components. Erase all trouble codes. See CLEARING CODES. Repeat QUICK TEST.

5) Operational Check Of MLP Sensor – Install MLP overlay on Transmission Tester (007-0085A). Connect tester to MLP sensor. Check continuity and resistances in all positions. *See Fig. D1.* If MLP sensor does not operate within specification, replace sensor. Connect all components. Erase all trouble codes. See CLEARING CODES. Repeat QUICK TEST. If sensor operates within specification, connect all components. Erase all trouble codes. See CLEARING CODES. Repeat QUICK TEST. If code(s) 522, 634, 659, 667, 668 or 675 are set, intermittent condition may be present. Attempt to duplicate malfunction by repeating previous steps.

94F36728

Gearshift Selector Lever Position	Resistance (ohms)		Voltage
	min	max	range
P	3770	4607	3.97-4.85
R	1304	1593	3.24-3.46
N	660	807	2.55-3.11
D	361	442	1.88-2.30
2	190	232	1.23-1.51
1	78	95	0.61-0.75

Fig. D1: MLP Resistance Specification Chart

PINPOINT TEST E

EPC Solenoid

1) Check VPWR To Solenoid – Turn ignition off. Disconnect transaxle harness connector. With KOEO, measure voltage between transaxle harness connector terminals No. 9 and vehicle ground. *See Fig. A1.* If voltage is 10.5 volts or more, go to next step. If voltage is less than specification, repair open circuit. Connect all components. Erase all trouble codes. See CLEARING CODES. Repeat QUICK TEST.

PINPOINT TEST E (Cont.)

2) Check Continuity Of Solenoid Signal & VPWR Harness Circuit – Turn ignition off, and wait 10 seconds. Disconnect PCM 60-pin connector, and inspect it for damaged pins, corrosion and loose wires. Repair as necessary. Install Breakout Box (T83L-50-EEC-IV), leaving PCM disconnected. Measure and record resistance between Breakout Box test pins No. 37 and 57, and transaxle harness connector terminal No. 9. *See Fig. A1.* Measure and record resistance between Breakout Box test pins No. 38, and transaxle harness connector terminal No. 8. If resistances measured are 5 ohms or less, go to next step. If resistances measured are more than 5 ohms, repair open circuit. Connect all components. Erase all trouble codes. See CLEARING CODES. Repeat QUICK TEST.

3) Check Harness For Short To Power Or Ground – Measure and record resistance between Breakout Box test pin No. 38 and test pins No. 37 and 57. Measure and record resistance between test pin No. 38 and test pins No. 40, 46 and 60. If any resistance measured is less than 10K ohms, repair short circuit. Disconnect Breakout Box and repeat Quick Test. If any resistance is 10K ohms or more, go to next step.

4) EPC Functional Test – Disconnect transaxle harness connector. Connect Transaxle Tester (007-0085A). Connect line pressure gauge. See FORD CD4E article. Set Bench/Drive switch to Drive mode. Set Gear Selector switch to 1st gear position. Perform EPC function test. See tester instructions. Observe line pressure on gauge while depressing EPC switch (KOER). EPC solenoid should activate (Green LED) and line pressure should drop when EPC switch is depressed. If solenoid operates correctly, replace PCM. Connect all components. Erase all trouble codes. See CLEARING CODES. Repeat QUICK TEST. If solenoid is not operating, go to next step.

5) Check Resistance Of Solenoid – Ensure tester power is off. Connect ohmmeter to EPC jacks. If resistance is 3.75-5.92 ohms, go to next step. If resistance is not within specifications, replace solenoid body assembly. See FORD CD4E article. Connect all components. Erase all trouble codes. See CLEARING CODES. Repeat QUICK TEST.

6) Check Solenoid For Short To Ground – Check continuity between BAT(-) terminal of Transmission Tester and EPC jacks. If continuity exists, replace solenoid body assembly. See FORD CD4E article. Connect all components. Erase all trouble codes. See CLEARING CODES. Repeat QUICK TEST. If continuity does not exist, see TROUBLE SHOOTING in FORD CD4E article.

PINPOINT TEST F

Transmission Speed Sensor

1) Preliminary Inspection – Inspect condition of TSS harness and component connector. Repair as needed.

2) Check Continuity Of TSS Harness Circuit – Ensure ignition is off. Turn ignition off, and wait 10 seconds. Disconnect PCM 60-pin connector, and inspect it for damaged pins, corrosion and loose wires. Repair as necessary. Install Breakout Box (T83L-50-EEC-IV), leaving PCM disconnected. Disconnect TSS harness connector. Measure and record resistance between Breakout Box test pin No. 5 and TSS harness connector positive terminal. *See Fig. F1.* Measure and record resistance between Breakout Box test pin No. 46 and TSS harness connector negative terminal. If resistances measured are 5 ohms or less, go to next step. If resistances measured are more than 5 ohms, repair open circuit(s). Connect all components. Erase all trouble codes. See CLEARING CODES. Repeat QUICK TEST.

94J36730

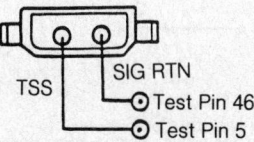

TSS SIG RTN
Test Pin 46
Test Pin 5

Fig. F1: Identifying TSS Harness Connector

3) Check TSS Circuit For Short To Power & Ground – Measure and record resistance between Breakout Box test pins No. 5 and 46, and test pins No. 37 and 57. Measure and record resistance between test pins No. 5, 37, 46 and 57, and test pins No. 40 and 60. If any resistance measured is less than 10K ohms, repair short circuit. Connect all components. Disconnect Breakout Box and repeat Quick Test. If resistance is 10K ohms or more, go to next step.

PINPOINT TEST F (Cont.)

4) TSS Functional Test – Ensure TSS harness connector is disconnected. Connect Transmission Tester (007-0085A) to TSS component connector. Connect voltmeter leads to appropriate tester TSS jacks. Set voltmeter to 20 volt AC scale. Perform drive cycle test. See TRANSMISSION DRIVE CYCLE TEST. If voltage increases with vehicle speed, replace PCM. Connect all components. Erase all trouble codes. See CLEARING CODES. Repeat QUICK TEST. If voltage does not increase with speed, go to next step.

5) Check Resistance Of TSS – Connect ohmmeter leads to appropriate Transmission Tester TSS jacks. If resistance is 140-290 ohms, go to next step. If resistance is not within specification, replace TSS. Connect all components. Erase all trouble codes. See CLEARING CODES. Repeat QUICK TEST.

6) Check TSS For Short To Ground – Check for continuity between Transmission Tester TSS jacks and tester BAT(-) jack. If continuity does not exist, go to next step. If continuity exists, replace TSS. Connect all components. Erase all trouble codes. See CLEARING CODES. Repeat QUICK TEST.

7) Check TSS Magnetism – Remove TSS from transaxle. See FORD CD4E article. Determine if TSS is magnetically attracted to ferrous metal. If TSS acts like a magnet, go to next step. If TSS does not stick to ferrous metal surface, replace TSS. Connect all components. Erase all trouble codes. See CLEARING CODES. Repeat QUICK TEST.

8) Check Exciter Wheel – With TSS removed, inspect condition of exciter wheel. Rotate engine with remote stater switch and ensure all 4 teeth of exciter wheel are not damaged. Replace exciter wheel if any teeth are damaged. See FORD CD4E article. If exciter wheel is not damaged, replace TSS. Connect all components. Erase all trouble codes. See CLEARING CODES. Repeat QUICK TEST.

PINPOINT TEST G

3-2T/CCS Solenoid

1) Check VPWR To Solenoid – Turn ignition off. Disconnect transaxle harness connector. With KOEO, measure voltage between transaxle harness connector terminals No. 5 and vehicle ground. *See Fig. A1.* If voltage is 10.5 volts or more, go to next step. If voltage is less than specification, repair open circuit. Connect all components. Erase all trouble codes. See CLEARING CODES. Repeat QUICK TEST.

2) Check Continuity Of Solenoid Signal & VPWR Harness Circuit – Turn ignition off, and wait 10 seconds. Disconnect PCM 60-pin connector, and inspect it for damaged pins, corrosion and loose wires. Repair as necessary. Install Breakout Box (T83L-50-EEC-IV), leaving PCM disconnected. Measure and record resistance between Breakout Box test pins No. 37 and 57, and transaxle harness connector terminal No. 5. *See Fig. A1.* Measure and record resistance between Breakout Box test pins No. 55, and transaxle harness connector terminal No. 10. If resistances measured are 5 ohms or less, go to next step. If resistances measured are more than 5 ohms, repair open circuit. Connect all components. Erase all trouble codes. See CLEARING CODES. Repeat QUICK TEST.

3) Check Harness For Short To Power Or Ground – Measure and record resistance between test pin No. 55 and test pins No. 37 and 57. Measure and record resistance between test pin No. 55 and test pins No. 40, 46 and 60. If any resistance is less than 10K ohms, repair short circuit. Disconnect Breakout Box and repeat Quick Test. If resistance is 10K ohms or more, go to next step.

4) 3-2T/CCS Functional Test – Disconnect transaxle harness connector. Connect Transaxle Tester (007-0085A). Set Bench/Drive switch to Drive mode. Set Gear Selector switch to 1st gear position. Perform 3-2T/CCS function test. See tester instructions. 3-2T/CCS solenoid should engage (LED off) and engine braking should occur when switch is released. If solenoid operates correctly, replace PCM. Connect all components. Erase all trouble codes. See CLEARING CODES. Repeat QUICK TEST. If solenoid is not operating, go to next step.

5) Check Resistance Of Solenoid – Ensure tester power is off. Connect ohmmeter to 3-2T/CCS jacks. If resistance is 3.75-5.92 ohms, go to next step. If resistance is not within specifications, replace solenoid body assembly. See FORD CD4E article. Connect all components. Erase all trouble codes. See CLEARING CODES. Repeat QUICK TEST.

6) Check Solenoid For Short To Ground – Check continuity between BAT(-) terminal of Transmission Tester and 3-2T/CCS jacks. If continuity exists, replace solenoid body assembly. See FORD CD4E article. Connect all components. Erase all trouble codes. See CLEARING CODES. Repeat QUICK TEST. If continuity does not exist, see TROUBLE SHOOTING in FORD CD4E article.

CIRCUIT TESTS

NOTE: CIRCUIT TESTS are diagnostic formats used to test and service EEC-IV system. CIRCUIT TESTS check engine circuits, sensors and actuators. For transaxle component testing and servicing, see PINPOINT TESTS.

CIRCUIT TEST BA

CHECKING VEHICLE BATTERY

Diagnostic Aids – Enter this CIRCUIT TEST only when directed by CIRCUIT TEST CA or CIRCUIT TEST PB.

This test is only intended to diagnose:
- Power Control Module (PCM).
- EEC Power Relay.
- Ignition Switch.
- Wiring Harness Circuits (SIG RTN, PWR GND, VPWR, KAPWR & VREF).

To prevent replacement of good components, be aware the following non-EEC related areas & components may be cause of problem:
- Battery cables & ground straps.
- Voltage regulator.
- Alternator.
- Ignition Switch.

93B39298

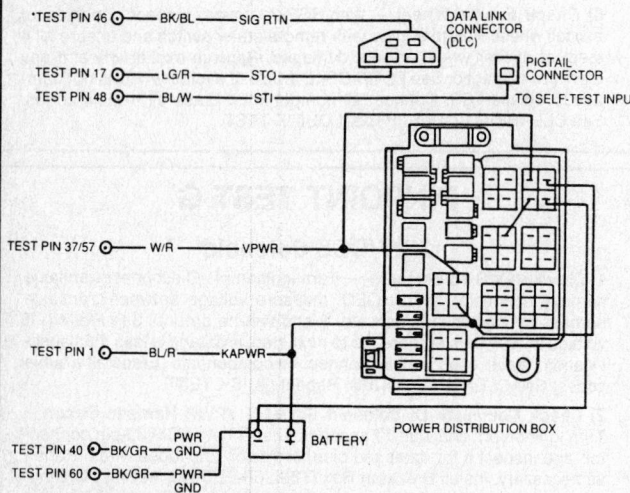

*TEST PINS LOCATED ON BREAKOUT BOX.
ALL HARNESS CONNECTORS VIEWED IN MATING SURFACE*

Fig. BA1: Identifying Power Relay Circuits (2.0L)

CAUTION: When battery is disconnected, PCM may lose memory data. Driveability problems may exist until computer systems have completed a relearn cycle. See COMPUTER RELEARN PROCEDURES article in APPLICATIONS & IDENTIFICATION before disconnecting battery.

1) Battery Voltage Check – Turn ignition on (engine off). Measure battery voltage. If voltage is less than 10.5 volts, recharge or replace battery. If voltage is 10.5 volts or more, go to step **2)**.

2) Check Continuity Of PWR GND Circuit – Turn ignition off. Wait 10 seconds. Disconnect PCM, and inspect connector pins. If PCM connector pins are damaged, loose or corroded, repair as necessary. Install Breakout Box (T83L-50-EEC-IV), leaving PCM connected. Measure resistance between test pins No. 40 and 60 at breakout box and negative battery terminal. If resistance is 5 ohms or more, repair open in PWR GND circuit, and repeat QUICK TEST. If both resistances are less than 5 ohms, go to step **3)**.

3) Check For Open Between SIG RTN & PWR GND Circuits At PCM – Ensure ignition is turned off. With breakout box installed and PCM connected, set DVOM on 200-ohm scale. Measure resistance between test pin No. 46 and test pins No. 40 and 60 at breakout box. If readings are 5 ohms or more, replace PCM and repeat QUICK TEST. If readings are less than 5 ohms, go to step **4)**.

4) Check Continuity Of SIG RTN Circuit – Ensure ignition is turned off. Measure resistance between test pin No. 46 at breakout box and SIG RTN terminal of Data Link Connector (DLC). If resistance is 5 ohms or more, repair open in SIG RTN circuit and repeat QUICK TEST. If reading is less than 5 ohms, go to step **5)**.

CIRCUIT TEST BA (Cont.)

5) Check KAPWR Circuit Voltage At EEC Power Relay – Turn ignition off. Locate relay block in engine compartment. Disconnect EEC power relay from relay block. Turn ignition on. Measure voltage between negative battery terminal and KAPWR terminal at EEC power relay connector. If voltage is 10.5 volts or less, check KAPWR circuit between EEC power relay and positive battery terminal for open circuit. If voltage is 10.5 volts or more, go to step **6)**.

NOTE: Vehicles equipped with Power Distribution Boxes use a diode to provide electrical surge protection for the ignition switch and Ignition Control Module (ICM). If a no-start/no-code condition exists, ensure diode continuity in one direction only is present before going to step 6).

6) Check Ignition Circuit Voltage At EEC Power Relay – Ensure PCM is connected to breakout box and EEC power relay is disconnected. Turn ignition on. Measure voltage between negative battery terminal and IGNITION terminal at EEC power relay connector. If voltage is less than 10.5 volts, repair open in ignition switch circuit and repeat QUICK TEST. If voltage is 10.5 volts or more, go to step **7)**.

7) Check PWR GND Circuit Continuity – Turn ignition off, and wait 10 seconds. With PCM connected to breakout box, measure resistance between negative battery terminal and PWR GND terminal at EEC power relay connector. If resistance is 10 ohms or more, repair open circuit and repeat QUICK TEST. If reading is less than 10 ohms, go to step **8)**.

8) Check VPWR Circuit Continuity – Turn ignition off. Measure resistance between test pins No. 37 and 57 (VPWR) at breakout box and VPWR terminal of EEC power relay connector. If resistance is 5 ohms or more, repair VPWR open circuit between EEC power relay and PCM. Repeat QUICK TEST. If reading is less than 5 ohms, go to step **9)**.

9) Check VPWR Circuit Voltage – Turn ignition off. Install EEC power relay. Turn ignition on. With PCM connected, measure voltage between test pins No. 37 and 57 (VPWR) and test pins No. 40 and 60 (PWR GND) and 46 (SIG RTN) at breakout box. If voltage is 10.5 volts or more, repair circuit between PCM and EEC power relay. Repeat QUICK TEST. If voltage is less than 10.5 volts, replace EEC power relay. Repeat QUICK TEST.

CIRCUIT TEST CA

REFERENCE VOLTAGE

Diagnostic Aids – Perform this test when a check for VREF signal has failed in sensor input CIRCUIT TEST QA. SIG RTN is a dedicated ground used by most EEC-IV system sensors. VREF is a 5-volt reference voltage that is continuously output by PCM. This consistent voltage signal is used on all 3-wire sensors.

This circuit test is only intended to diagnose the following components and circuits:
- Powertrain Control Module (PCM).
- Vehicle wiring harness circuits (SIG RTN and VREF).

93E40422

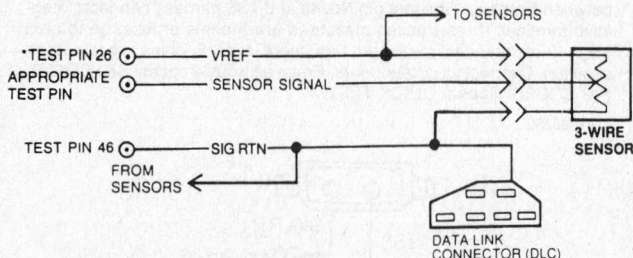

*TEST PINS LOCATED ON BREAKOUT BOX.
ALL HARNESS CONNECTORS VIEWED INTO MATING SURFACE.*

Fig. CA1: Identifying Reference Voltage Circuits & Connector Terminals

TEST PIN WIRE COLOR IDENTIFICATION

Terminal No.	Wire Color
No. 26 (VREF)	Light Green/Pink
No. 46 (SIG RTN)	Black/Blue

CIRCUIT TEST CA (Cont.)

1) Check Battery Power Circuit – Turn ignition off, and wait 10 seconds. Disconnect PCM 60-pin connector, and inspect it for damaged pins, corrosion and loose wires. Repair as necessary. Install Breakout Box (T83L-50-EEC-IV), leaving PCM connected. Turn ignition on. Measure and record voltage between breakout box test pin No. 37 and SIG RTN terminal of self-test connector. Measure and record voltage across battery terminals. If both readings are less than 10.5 volts or if they differ by more than 1.0 volt, reconnect sensor (if applicable). Go to CIRCUIT TEST BA. If voltages are 10.5 volts or more and do not differ from one another by more than 1.0 volt, go to step **2)**.

2) Check VREF Voltage – With breakout box installed and PCM connected, set DVOM on 20-volt scale. Turn ignition on. Measure voltage between test pins No. 26 and 46 at breakout box. If voltage is 4-6 volts, go to step **3)**. If voltage is more than 6 volts, go to step **4)**. If voltage is less than 4 volts, go to step **5)**.

3) Check VREF & SIG RTN Circuit Continuity – Turn ignition off. Disconnect PCM. If directed here by a sensor test, ensure sensor is disconnected. Measure resistance between Breakout Box test pin No. 26 and VREF terminal at wiring harness connector of applicable sensor. Measure resistance between test pin No. 46 and SIG RTN circuit terminal at wiring harness connector of applicable sensor. If both readings are less than 5 ohms, VREF circuit is okay. If either reading is 5 ohms or more, repair open in VREF or SIG RTN circuit. Remove breakout box, and repeat QUICK TEST.

4) Check For Excess VREF Circuit Voltage – Turn ignition off. Ensure PCM is disconnected. With breakout box installed, disconnect scan tester or STAR tester (if applicable). Turn ignition on. Measure voltage between test pin No. 26 and battery ground. If voltage is less than 0.5 volt, replace PCM and repeat QUICK TEST. If voltage is 0.5 volt or more, repair short to battery power in wiring harness. Remove breakout box, reconnect components and repeat QUICK TEST. Replace PCM if fault still occurs.

5) Check For Shorted TPS – Turn ignition off. Connect PCM to breakout box. Disconnect Throttle Position Sensor (TPS) from wiring harness. Turn ignition on. Measure voltage between test pins No. 26 and 46 at breakout box. If voltage is 4 volts or more, replace TPS, remove breakout box and repeat QUICK TEST. If voltage is less than 4 volts on models with EVP, PFE or DPFE sensor, go to step **6)**. If voltage is less than 4 volts on all other models, go to step **7)**.

6) Check For Shorted EVP/PFE/DPFE Sensor – Turn ignition off, and wait 10 seconds. Disconnect EVP/PFE/DPFE sensor. Turn ignition on. Measure voltage between test pins No. 26 and 46. If voltage is 4 volts or more, replace EVP/PFE/DPFE sensor and repeat QUICK TEST. If voltage is less than 4 volts, reconnect EVP/PFE/DPFE sensor and go to step **8)**.

NOTE: A break in step numbering sequence occurs at this point. Procedure skips from step 6) to step 8). No test procedures have been omitted.

8) Check VREF Circuit For Short To Ground – Turn ignition off. Disconnect PCM. Disconnect TPS, MAP/BARO sensor and EVP/PFE/DPFE sensor. Measure resistance between test pin No. 26 and test pins No. 20, 40, 46 and 60. If any resistance is less than 1000 ohms, repair short to ground. Remove breakout box, and repeat QUICK TEST. If original problem still exists, replace PCM and repeat QUICK TEST. If readings are 1000 ohms or more, replace PCM and repeat QUICK TEST.

CIRCUIT TEST DA

TEMPERATURE SENSOR TEST (IAT & ECT)

Diagnostic Aids – Perform this test only when directed by QUICK TEST. Ambient air temperature must be at least 50°F (10°C) to receive valid input from IAT sensor. Engine coolant temperature must be greater than 50°F (10°C) to pass KOEO SELF-TEST and greater than 180°F (82°C) to pass KOER SELF-TEST. Voltage values in this test are based on a 5-volt VREF signal. Values may vary up to 15% due to sensor and VREF variations.

This circuit test is intended to diagnose the following components and circuits:
- Intake Air Temperature (IAT) sensor.
- Engine Coolant Temperature (ECT) sensor.
- Wiring harness circuits (IAT, ECT and SIG RTN).
- Powertrain Control Module (PCM).

CIRCUIT TEST DA (Cont.)

To prevent replacing good components, ensure the following non-EEC areas or components are not cause of problem:
- Coolant level low.
- Cooling system, water pump or fan.
- Engine operating temperature.
- Engine oil level low.
- Thermostat.
- Air cleaner duct.
- Ambient temperature

93J40427

*TEST PINS LOCATED ON BREAKOUT BOX.
ALL HARNESS CONNECTORS VIEWED INTO MATING SURFACE.

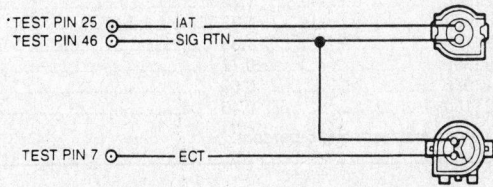

IAT SENSOR WIRING HARNESS CONNECTOR

ECT SENSOR WIRING HARNESS CONNECTOR

Fig. DA1: Identifying Temperature Sensor Circuits & Connector Terminals

TEST PIN WIRE COLOR IDENTIFICATION

Application	Wire Color
No. 7 (ECT)	Yellow/Black
No. 25 (IAT)	White/Light Green
No. 46 (SIG RTN)	Black/Blue

1) Code 116 Or 114: – Code 116 (ECT) or 114 (IAT) indicates corresponding sensor is out of self-test range. Correct range for measurement is .3-3.7 volts. Check for following possible causes:
- Low ambient temperature (less than 50°F).
- Low coolant level.
- Faulty harness connector.
- Faulty sensor.

Ensure upper radiator hose is hot and pressurized. Repeat QUICK TEST. If Code 114 or 116 is present, go to step **2)**. If none of these codes are present, service other codes as necessary.

2) Check VREF Circuit Voltage At TPS – Turn ignition off. Disconnect Throttle Position Sensor (TPS). With ignition on and engine off, measure voltage at TPS wiring harness connector between VREF and SIG RTN. See Fig. DA2. If voltage is 4-6 volts, reconnect TPS and go to step **3)**. If voltage is not 4-6 volts, go to CIRCUIT TEST CA.

3) Check Temperature Sensor Resistance (KOEO) – Turn ignition off. Disconnect suspect sensor. Measure resistance between SIG RTN terminal at sensor and SIG RTN terminal at sensor wiring harness connector. If resistance is not within specification, replace suspected sensor and repeat QUICK TEST. If resistance is within specification, go to step **4)**.

93A40428

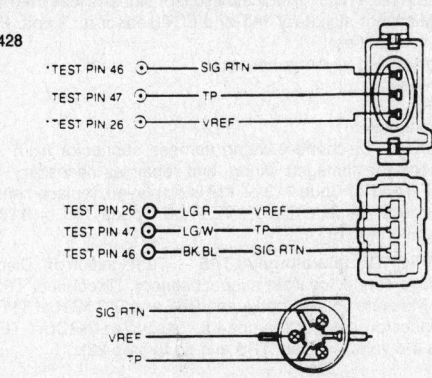

Fig. DA2: Identifying TPS Harness Connector Terminals

CIRCUIT TEST DA (Cont.)

4) Check Temperature Sensor Resistance (KOER) – Warm engine to normal operating temperature. Turn ignition off. Disconnect suspect sensor. Run engine at 2000 RPM for 2 minutes. Measure resistance between SIG RTN terminal at sensor and SIG RTN terminal at sensor wiring harness connector. See ACT & ECT SENSOR SPECIFICATIONS table. If resistance is within specification, replace PCM and repeat QUICK TEST. If sensor is not within specification, replace sensor and repeat QUICK TEST.

ACT & ECT SENSOR SPECIFICATIONS

Temperature °F (°C)	[1] Volts	[1] Ohms
50 (10)	3.51	58,750
68 (20)	3.07	27,300
86 (30)	2.60	24,270
104 (40)	2.13	16,150
122 (50)	1.70	10,970
140 (60)	1.33	7700
158 (70)	1.33	7700
176 (80)	0.78	3840
194 (90)	0.60	2800
212 (100)	0.46	2070

[1] – Values may vary by 15 percent.

NOTE: A break in step numbering sequence occurs at this point. Procedure skips from step 4) to step 10). No test procedures have been omitted.

10) Code 118 Or 113: Induce Opposite Code (Code 117 Or 112) – Code 118 (ECT) or 113 (IAT) indicate corresponding sensor signal is greater than self-test maximum. Maximum signal voltage for ECT and IAT sensor is 4.6 volts. Possible causes for excess voltage signals are:
- Open circuit in wiring harness (IAT or ECT)
- Faulty connection.
- Faulty sensor.
- Faulty PCM.

Turn ignition off. Disconnect suspect temperature sensor. Connect a jumper wire between SIG RTN terminal at sensor and SIG RTN terminal at sensor wiring harness connector. Repeat QUICK TEST. If Code 112 or 117 is displayed, replace suspect sensor and repeat QUICK TEST. If Code 112 or 117 is not displayed, remove jumper wire and go to next step.

11) Check Continuity Of Sensor Signal & SIG RTN Circuits – Turn ignition off. Ensure suspect temperature sensor is disconnected. Disconnect PCM 60-pin connector. Check for damaged wiring, and repair as necessary. Install Breakout Box (T83L-50-EEC-IV), leaving PCM disconnected. Measure resistance between test pin No. 7 (ECT sensor) or test pin No. 25 (IAT sensor) at breakout box and SIG RTN terminal at sensor wiring harness connector. Measure resistance between test pin No. 46 and SIG RTN circuit at sensor wiring harness connector. If both readings are less than 5 ohms, replace PCM and repeat QUICK TEST. If either reading is 5 ohms or more, repair open circuit and repeat QUICK TEST.

NOTE: A break in step numbering sequence occurs at this point. Procedure skips from step 11) to step 20). No test procedures have been omitted.

20) Code 117 or 112: Induce Opposite Code (118 or 113) – Code 117 (ECT) or 112 (IAT) indicates sensor signal is less than self-test minimum. Minimum signal for IAT and ECT sensor is .2 volt. Possible causes for this fault are:
- Circuit grounded in wiring harness.
- Faulty sensor.
- Faulty PCM.
- Faulty connection.

Turn ignition off. Disconnect wiring harness connector from suspect sensor. Check for damaged wiring, and repair as necessary. Repeat KOEO SELF-TEST. If Code 113 or 118 is displayed, replace sensor and connect harness. Repeat QUICK TEST. If Codes 113 or 118 is not displayed, go to step 21).

21) Check VREF Circuit Voltage At TPS – Turn ignition off. Disconnect wiring harness connector from suspect sensor. Disconnect TPS. Turn ignition on. Measure voltage between VREF and SIG RTN at TPS wiring harness connector. If voltage is not 4-6 volts, go to CIRCUIT TEST CA. If voltage is 4-6 volts, connect TPS and go to step 22).

CIRCUIT TEST DA (Cont.)

22) Check Temperature Sensor Signal For Shorts To Ground – Turn ignition off. Disconnect suspect sensor. Disconnect PCM 60-pin connector. Check for damaged wiring, and repair as necessary. Install Breakout Box (T83L-50-EEC-IV), leaving PCM disconnected. Measure resistance between test pin No. 7 (ECT) or 25 (IAT) and pins No. 40, 46 and 60. If any reading is less than 10 k/ohms, repair short circuit and repeat QUICK TEST. If all readings are 10 k/ohms or more, replace PCM and repeat QUICK TEST.

NOTE: A break in step numbering sequence occurs at this point. Procedure skips from step 22) to step 90). No test procedures have been omitted.

90) Continuous Memory Code 118, 113, 117 Or 112: Check Sensor – A Continuous Memory Code 118 or 113 indicates sensor signal is greater than self-test maximum of 4.6 volts. Code is set during normal driving conditions. Continuous Memory Code 117 or 112 indicates sensor signal is less than self-test minimum of .2 volt. Code is set during normal driving conditions. Possible causes for these faults are:
- Faulty sensor.
- Open or grounded circuit in harness.
- Faulty PCM.

SENSOR CODES

Sensor	Continuous Memory Code
IAT	113 Or 112
ECT	118 Or 117

Enter KOEO wiggle test mode. See CONTINUOUS MONITOR MODE (WIGGLE TEST) under QUICK TEST. Observe analog voltmeter or scan tester for indication of fault while tapping sensor lightly and wiggling sensor connector. If fault is indicated, disconnect and inspect connector and terminals. If connector and terminals are okay, replace sensor, clear continuous memory and repeat QUICK TEST. If fault is not indicated, go to step 91).

91) Check EEC-IV Wiring Harness – While in CONTINUOUS MONITOR MODE (WIGGLE TEST), observe analog voltmeter or scan tester while wiggling and bending wiring harness, a small section at a time, from sensor to cowl. Also check harness from cowl to PCM. If fault is indicated, isolate fault and repair as necessary. Clear continuous memory, and repeat QUICK TEST. If no fault is found, go to step 92).

92) Inspect PCM & Wiring Harness Connectors – Turn ignition off. Disconnect PCM 60-pin connector. Inspect both connector and connector terminals for damage. If connectors and terminals are damaged, repair as necessary and repeat QUICK TEST. If connectors and terminals are okay and fault cannot be duplicated at this time, see TROUBLE SHOOTING (EEC-IV) – NO CODES article in ENGINE PERFORMANCE in appropriate MITCHELL® manual.

NOTE: A break in step numbering sequence occurs at this point. Procedure skips from step 92) to step 100). No test procedures have been omitted.

100) Continuous Memory Code 338 – A Continuous Memory Code 338 indicates cooling system has not reached normal operating temperature. Possible causes for this fault are:
- Thermostat stuck open.
- Coolant outlet gasket leak.
- Water pump gasket leak.

Repair cooling system as necessary. Clear continuous memory, and repeat QUICK TEST.

101) Continuous Memory Code 339 – A Continuous Memory Code 339 indicates cooling system has overheated. Possible causes for this fault are:
- Coolant level low.
- Thermostat stuck closed.
- Coolant system clogged.
- Water pump damaged or worn.
- Radiator cap damaged or worn.
- Cooling fan damaged or worn.

Repair cooling system as necessary. Clear continuous memory, and repeat QUICK TEST.

CIRCUIT TEST DC

MASS AIRFLOW (MAF) SENSOR

Diagnostic Aids – Perform this test when directed by QUICK TEST. This CIRCUIT TEST is intended to diagnose the following:

- MAF sensor.
- Wiring harness circuits (VPWR, PWR GND, MAF and MAF RTN).
- Powertrain Control Module (PCM).

To prevent replacement of good components, be aware the following non-EEC related areas may be cause of problem:

- Air cleaner element.
- Inlet air duct.
- Throttle body.

Code 159, retrieved during KOEO SELF-TEST, indicates voltage exceeded .7-volt test range. Code 159, retrieved during KOER SELF-TEST, indicates voltage is not within .2-1.5 volts operating range. Possible causes are faulty MAF sensor or PCM.

93F40431

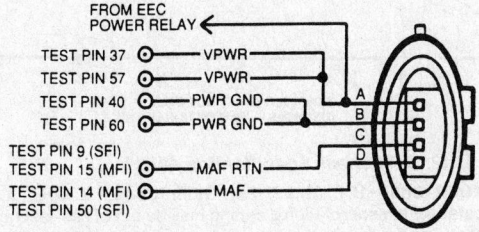

***TEST PINS LOCATED ON BREAKOUT BOX.
ALL HARNESS CONNECTORS VIEWED IN MATING SURFACE.**

Fig. DC1: Identifying Mass Airflow (MAF) Sensor Circuits & Connector Terminals

TEST PIN WIRE COLOR IDENTIFICATION

Application	Wire Color
No. 9 or 15 (MAF RTN)	Brown
No. 14 or 50 (MAF)	Red
No. 37 & 57 (VPWR)	White/Red
No. 40 & 60 (PWR GND)	Black/Green

MAF SIGNAL VOLTAGE [1]

Application	Volts
Idle	.6
20 MPH	1.1
40 MPH	1.7
60 MPH	2.1

[1] – MAF signal voltage is typical for normal operating temperature. Voltage signal may vary due to engine load and temperature.

NOTE: Code 159 may be caused by use of a garage exhaust ventilation system. Ensure vehicle is vented to outside atmosphere before repeating QUICK TEST.

1) Code 159: Check VPWR Circuit Voltage – Code 159 indicates that MAF sensor was out of range during KOEO or KOER SELF-TEST. Possible causes for this fault are:

- Air leak before or after MAF sensor.
- Faulty MAF sensor.
- Faulty IAC solenoid.
- Open or grounded wiring harness.
- Faulty PCM.

Repeat QUICK TEST. If Code 412 is present, go to CIRCUIT TEST KE, step 1). If Code 411 is present, go to CIRCUIT TEST KE, step 15). If Code 411 or 412 is not present, go to step 2).

2) VPWR Circuit Voltage Check – Turn ignition off. Disconnect MAF sensor connector. Set DVOM on 20-volt scale. Turn ignition on. Measure voltage between VPWR terminal at MAF sensor wiring harness connector and negative battery terminal. If voltage is less than 10.5 volts, repair open in VPWR circuit and repeat QUICK TEST. If voltage is 10.5 volts or more, go to step 3).

CIRCUIT TEST DC (Cont.)

3) Check MAF Sensor Ground – Turn ignition on. With MAF sensor disconnected, measure voltage between VPWR terminal and PWR GND terminal at MAF sensor connector. If voltage is less than 10.5 volts, repair open PWR GND circuit. Connect MAF sensor, and repeat QUICK TEST. If voltage is 10.5 volts or more, go to step 13).

NOTE: A break in step numbering sequence occurs at this point. Procedure skips from step 3) to step 10). No test procedures have been omitted.

10) Continuous Memory Code 157: Check For Intermittent Sensor Failure – Continuous Memory Code 157 indicates MAF signal was less than .4 volt sometime during last 80 warm-up cycles. Possible causes for this fault are:

- Open MAF circuit.
- MAF circuit shorted to ground.
- Faulty MAF sensor.
- MAF sensor disconnected.

Start engine and allow to idle for 5-10 minutes. Perform KOEO SELF-TEST. If Code 157 is present, go to step 13). If Code 157 is not present, go to next step.

11) Turn ignition off. Disconnect and inspect 60-pin connector at PCM. Service if necessary. Install EEC-IV Breakout Box (T83L-50-EEC-IV), leaving PCM connected. Connect DVOM between MAF test pin and MAF RTN test pin. See appropriate table at beginning of this CIRCUIT TEST. DVOM should read about 0.4 volt. Start engine and allow to idle. Lightly tap on MAF sensor and wiggle wiring harness to simulate road conditions. If sudden change in DVOM reading occurs, fault is indicated. If fault is indicated, replace MAF sensor and repeat QUICK TEST. If no fault is indicated, leave DVOM connected and go to next step.

12) Check Wiring Harness For Open Or Short Circuit – Turn ignition on. Shake and bend small sections of wiring harness starting at MAF sensor and working toward dash panel. Shake and bend small sections of wiring harness starting at dash panel and working toward PCM. If fault is indicated, isolate and repair as necessary. If fault is not indicated, problem is intermittent and cannot be duplicated at this time.

13) Codes 157 Or 129: Check For Air Leak At MAF Sensor – Check for broken or loose air outlet tube clamps at throttle body and air cleaner assembly. Repair or replace as necessary. If no faults are found, go to next step.

14) Check Continuity Of MAF & VPWR Circuits – Turn ignition off. Disconnect MAF sensor and PCM wiring harness connector. Install EEC-IV Breakout Box (T83L-50-EEC-IV), leaving PCM disconnected. Measure resistance between MAF terminal of MAF sensor wiring harness connector and test pins No. 37 and 57. Measure resistance between MAF terminal of MAF sensor wiring harness connector and test pin No. 50 (Sequential Fuel Injected engines) or test pin No. 14 (except Sequential Fuel Injected engines). If resistance is more than 5 ohms, repair open circuit and repeat QUICK TEST. If resistance is 5 ohms or less, go to next step.

15) Check MAF Signal For Short To Ground – Turn ignition off. Ensure MAF sensor and PCM wiring harness are disconnected. Measure resistance between test pin No. 50 and test pins No. 9, 40 and 60 (Sequential Fuel Injected engines) or between test pin No. 14 and test pins No. 15, 40 and 60 (except Sequential Fuel Injected engines). If resistance is less than 10 k/ohms, repair short circuit and repeat QUICK TEST. If resistance is 10 k/ohms or more, go to next step.

16) Turn ignition off. Ensure MAP sensor and PCM wiring harness connector are disconnected. Measure resistance between PWR GND terminal at MAF sensor wiring harness connector and negative battery terminal. If resistance is 10 ohms or more, repair open PWR GND circuit and repeat QUICK TEST. If resistance is less than 10 ohms, go to next step.

17) Check Continuity Of MAF RTN Circuit – Ensure ignition is turned off. Measure resistance between MAF RTN terminal of MAF sensor wiring harness connector and test pin No. 9 (Sequential Fuel Injected engines) or test pin No. 15 (except Sequential Fuel Injected engines). If resistance is more than 5 ohms, repair open circuit and repeat QUICK TEST. If resistance is 5 ohms or less, go to next step.

18) Check MAF Circuit For Short To Ground – Turn ignition off. Ensure MAF sensor is disconnected. Connect PCM to breakout box. Measure resistance between test pin No. 50 and test pins No. 9, 40 and 60. If resistance is less than 10 k/ohms, replace PCM and repeat QUICK TEST. If resistance is 10 k/ohms or more, go to next step.

19) Check MAF Circuit Output – Turn ignition off. Connect MAF sensor wiring harness connector. Start engine. Measure resistance between test pin No. 50 and negative battery terminal. If voltage is .36-1.50 volts, go to next step. If voltage is not .36-1.50 volts, replace MAF sensor and repeat QUICK TEST.

CIRCUIT TEST DC (Cont.)

20) With engine running, measure resistance between test pin No. 9 and test pin No. 50. If voltage is .36-1.50 volts, replace PCM and repeat QUICK TEST. If voltage is not .36-1.50 volts, replace MAF sensor and repeat QUICK TEST.

21) Code 158 – Turn ignition off. Disconnect MAF sensor wiring harness connector. Start engine, and allow it to idle for one minute. Turn ignition off. Repeat KOEO SELF-TEST. If Code 157 is present, replace MAF sensor and repeat QUICK TEST. If Code 157 is not present, go to step **22)**.

22) Check MAF Circuit For Short To VPWR – Turn ignition off. Disconnect PCM 60-pin connector, and inspect it for damaged or corroded terminals. Service if necessary. Measure resistance between MAF and VPWR terminals at MAF sensor wiring harness connector. If resistance is 10 k/ohms or more, replace PCM and repeat QUICK TEST. If resistance is less than 10 k/ohms, repair short circuit and repeat QUICK TEST.

CIRCUIT TEST DH

THROTTLE POSITION (TP) SENSOR

Diagnostic Aids – Perform this test only when directed by QUICK TEST. This test is intended to diagnose the following:
- TP sensor.
- Wiring harness circuits (TP, SIG RTN and VREF).
- Powertrain Control Module (PCM).

Normal range of throttle angle measurement for TP sensor is 0-85 degrees. To pass QUICK TEST procedure, range of throttle rotation (in degrees) must be within 3 percent of specification. *See Fig. DH2.*

To prevent replacement of good components, be aware the following non-EEC related areas may be at fault:
- Idle speed.
- Binding throttle shaft or linkage.
- Choke cam adjustment (if equipped).
- TP sensor not seated.

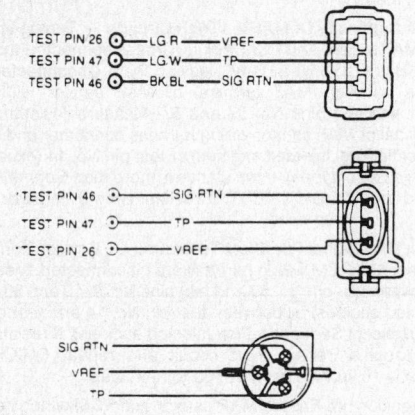

93A40428

TEST PIN 26 — LG R — VREF
TEST PIN 47 — LG W — TP
TEST PIN 46 — BK BL — SIG RTN

TEST PIN 46 — SIG RTN
TEST PIN 47 — TP
TEST PIN 26 — VREF

SIG RTN
VREF
TP

NOTE: EITHER TYPE MAY BE FITTED

Fig. DH1: **Identifying TP Sensor Circuits & Connector Terminals**

TEST PIN WIRE COLOR IDENTIFICATION

Application	Wire Color
No. 26 (VREF)	Light Green/Red
No. 46 (SIG RTN)	Black/Blue
No. 47 (TP)	Light Green/White

CIRCUIT TEST DH (Cont.)

92G03822

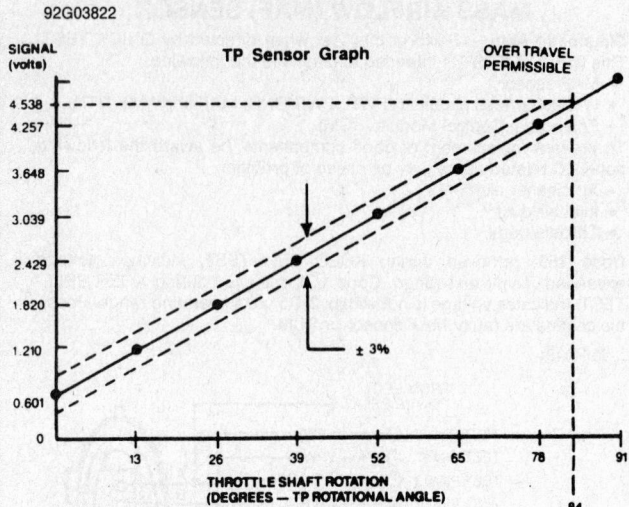

Fig. DH2: **TP Sensor Specification Chart**

1) KOER Code 121: Check For Other Codes – KOER Code 121 indicates TP sensor rotational setting may be out of self-test range. Possible causes for this fault are:
- Binding throttle linkage.
- TP sensor not seated correctly.
- Faulty TP sensor.
- Faulty Powertrain Control Module (PCM).

Perform KOER SELF-TEST. Check for Code 327. If either of these codes are present with Code 121, service Code 327 and repeat QUICK TEST. If these codes are not present, go to step **2)**.

2) Code 121: Check For Binding Throttle Plate – Inspect throttle body for binding. If throttle body is binding, check for binding throttle or cruise control linkage, vacuum line or harness interference, etc. Repair as necessary, and repeat QUICK TEST. If no mechanical problem is found, go to step **3)**.

3) Code 123: Attempt To Generate Code 122 – Code 123 indicates TP sensor signal is greater than self-test maximum value. Possible causes for this fault are:
- TP sensor not seated properly.
- Faulty TP sensor.
- Short circuit to power.
- Faulty PCM.

Turn ignition off. Disconnect TP sensor wiring harness connector. Inspect and repair connector pins if damaged. Repeat KOEO SELF-TEST. Ignore all other codes at this time. If Code 63/122 is not displayed, go to step **5)**. If Code 122 is displayed, go to step **4)**.

4) Check VREF Circuit Voltage – Turn ignition on. Measure voltage between VREF and SIG RTN terminals at TP sensor wiring harness connector. If reading is 4-6 volts, replace TP sensor and repeat QUICK TEST. If reading is not 4-6 volts, reconnect sensor and go to CIRCUIT TEST CA.

5) Check TP Circuit For Short To Power – Turn ignition off. Leave TP sensor disconnected. Disconnect PCM 60-pin connector. Inspect it for damage and repair as necessary. Install EEC-IV Breakout Box (T83L-50-EEC-IV), leaving PCM disconnected. Measure resistance between test pin No. 47 and test pins No. 26 and 57. If either resistance is less than 10 k/ohms, repair short circuit in wiring harness and repeat QUICK TEST. If both resistances are 10 k/ohms or more, replace PCM and repeat QUICK TEST.

NOTE: A break in step numbering sequence occurs at this point. Procedure skips from step 5) to step 10). No test procedures have been omitted.

10) Code 122: Attempt To Generate Code 123 Or 121 – Code 122 indicates TP signal is less than minimum self-test value. *See Fig. DH2.* Possible causes for this fault are:
- TP sensor not seated correctly.
- Faulty TP sensor.
- Open circuit in wiring harness.
- Grounded circuit in wiring harness.
- Faulty PCM.

CIRCUIT TEST DH (Cont.)

Turn ignition off, and wait 10 seconds. Disconnect TP sensor from harness. Install a jumper wire between VREF and TP terminals at TP sensor wiring harness connector. Perform KOEO SELF-TEST. If no codes are generated, remove jumper wire and go to step 13). If Codes 123 and 121 are not present, remove jumper wire and go to step 11). If either Code 123 or 121 is displayed, replace TP sensor and repeat QUICK TEST.

11) Check VREF Circuit Voltage – Turn ignition on. Measure voltage between VREF and SIG RTN terminals at TP sensor wiring harness connector. If voltage is not 4-6 volts, reconnect all components and go to CIRCUIT TEST CA. If voltage is 4-6 volts, go to step 12).

12) Check TP Sensor Circuit Continuity – Turn ignition off. Leave TP sensor disconnected. Disconnect PCM 60-pin connector. Inspect connector and repair if necessary. Install EEC-IV Breakout Box (T83L-50-EEC-IV), leaving PCM disconnected. Measure resistance between TP terminal at TP sensor wiring harness connector and test pin No. 47. If resistance is 5 ohms or more, repair open circuit and repeat QUICK TEST. If resistance is less than 5 ohms, go to step 13).

13) Check TP Circuit For Shorts To Ground – Turn ignition off. Leave TP sensor disconnected. Ensure both 4EAT module wiring harness connectors are disconnected (if applicable). Disconnect PCM 60-pin connector. Inspect wiring, and repair as necessary. With breakout box installed and PCM disconnected, measure resistance between test pin No. 47 and test pins No. 40, 46 and 60. If any reading is less than 10 k/ohms, repair short circuit and repeat QUICK TEST. If all readings are 10 k/ohms or more, replace PCM and repeat QUICK TEST.

NOTE: A break in step numbering sequence occurs at this point. Procedure skips from step 13) to step 20). No test procedures have been omitted.

20) Code 167: Repeat Dynamic Response Test – KOER Code 167 indicates TP sensor did not exceed 25% rotation during dynamic response portion of KOER SELF-TEST. A complete Wide Open Throttle (WOT) must be performed during dynamic response portion of test. Perform KOER SELF-TEST. Ensure WOT is completed during dynamic response portion of test. If Code 167 is still present, go to step 21). If code is not present, system is unable to duplicate Code 167 at this time. Service any other KOER codes. If no other service codes are present, testing is complete.

21) Check TP Sensor Movement During Dynamic Response Test – Turn ignition off. Disconnect PCM 60-pin connector. Inspect wiring, and repair as necessary. Install EEC-IV Breakout Box (T83L-50-EEC-IV), leaving PCM connected. Set DVOM on 20-volt scale. Connect DVOM between test pins No. 46 and 47 at breakout box. Perform KOER SELF-TEST and ensure proper WOT is completed during dynamic response test. If DVOM reading exceeds 3.5 volts during dynamic response test, replace PCM and repeat QUICK TEST. If reading does not exceed 3.5 volts, ensure TP sensor is correctly installed and adjusted. If TP sensor is correctly installed and adjusted, replace TP sensor. Repeat QUICK TEST.

NOTE: A break in step numbering sequence occurs at this point. Procedure skips from step 21) to step 90). No test procedures have been omitted.

90) Continuous Memory Code 123 – This test monitors TP sensor under simulated road conditions. Enter wiggle test. See CONTINUOUS MONITOR MODE (WIGGLE TEST) under QUICK TEST. Connect DVOM or diagnostic tester to STO terminal of self-test connector. While slowly opening throttle to WOT, observe DVOM or diagnostic tester for indication of fault. Slowly bring throttle to closed position. Lightly tap TP sensor and wiggle harness connector. This test checks for open or short in TP sensor and wiring harness. If no fault is indicated, go to step 92). If fault is indicated, go to step 91).

91) Measure TP Circuit Voltage While Exercising TP Sensor – Turn ignition off, and wait 10 seconds. Disconnect PCM 60-pin connector. Inspect for damage and repair if necessary. Install EEC-IV Breakout Box (T83L-50-EEC-IV), leaving PCM connected. Stay in wiggle test (as in previous step). Connect DVOM between test pins No. 47 and 46. Set DVOM on 20-volt scale. With ignition on and engine off, observe DVOM and repeat step 90). If fault occurs at less than 4.25 volts, inspect TP sensor connectors and terminals. If connectors and terminals are okay, replace TP sensor, clear codes and repeat QUICK TEST. If fault does not occur at less than 4.25 volts, TP sensor over-travel may have caused Continuous Memory Code 123. TP sensor is okay. Go to step 92) to check wiring harness.

CIRCUIT TEST DH (Cont.)

92) Check EEC-IV Wiring Harness – While in wiggle test, bend and shake small sections of EEC-IV harness from TP sensor wiring harness connector to firewall and from firewall to PCM while observing analog voltmeter or scan tester. If fault is indicated, isolate fault in wiring and repair as necessary. Clear codes, and repeat QUICK TEST. If no fault is indicated, go to step 93).

93) Check PCM & Harness Connectors – Turn ignition off, and wait 10 seconds. Disconnect PCM 60-pin connector from breakout box. Inspect connectors and terminals for damage, and repair as necessary. Clear codes from PCM memory, and repeat QUICK TEST. If connectors and terminals are okay, fault cannot be duplicated at this time. Continuous Memory Code 123 testing is complete.

94) Continuous Memory Code 122 – Enter wiggle test. See CONTINUOUS MONITOR MODE (WIGGLE TEST) under QUICK TEST. Connect DVOM or diagnostic tester to STO terminal of self-test connector. Observe DVOM or diagnostic tester for indication of fault while performing the following:
- Slowly open throttle to WOT.
- Slowly bring throttle to closed position.
- Lightly tap TP sensor and wiggle connector.

If fault is indicated, disconnect TP sensor. Inspect connectors and terminals. If connectors and terminals are okay, replace TP sensor. Clear codes from PCM memory, and repeat QUICK TEST. If no fault is indicated, go to next step.

95) Check EEC-IV Wiring Harness – Stay in wiggle test (as in previous step). Bend, wiggle and shake small sections of EEC-IV harness from TP sensor wiring harness connector to firewall and from firewall to PCM while observing analog voltmeter or scan tester. If fault is indicated, isolate fault in wiring and repair as necessary. Clear codes from PCM memory, and repeat QUICK TEST. If no fault is indicated, go to step 96).

96) Check PCM & Harness Connectors – Turn ignition off. Inspect PCM 60-pin connector and terminals for damage. Repair connector terminals if necessary. Clear codes from PCM memory, and repeat QUICK TEST. If connectors and terminals are okay, fault cannot be duplicated at this time. Continuous Memory Code 122 testing is complete.

CIRCUIT TEST DP

VEHICLE SPEED SENSOR (VSS)

Diagnostic Aids – Perform this test when directed by QUICK TEST. This CIRCUIT TEST is intended to diagnose:
- Vehicle Speed Sensor (VSS).
- VSS wiring harness circuits.
- Powertrain Control Module (PCM).

Fig. DP1: Vehicle Speed Sensor Circuit

TEST PIN WIRE COLOR IDENTIFICATION

Application	Wire Color
No. 3 (VSS +)	Black/White
No. 6 (VSS −)	Brown/Green

Preliminary Instructions – Record and clear continuous memory codes. Warm engine to normal operating temperature. Place gear selector in Drive position. Accelerate hard to 35 MPH and coast down to a stop. Shut off engine. Perform KOEO SELF-TEST. Repeat step at least 2 more times. Go to step 1).

1) Continuous Memory Code 452 – Code 452 indicates PCM detected incorrect output from VSS sometime during vehicle operation. Possible causes for this code are:
- Faulty VSS.
- Open or shorted circuit.
- Faulty PCM.

Perform appropriate drive cycle procedure. See PRELIMINARY INSTRUCTIONS. Ensure driveability complaint can be verified. If Code 452 is still present or driveability complaint can be verified, go to step 2). If code is not present or complaint cannot be verified, fault cannot be duplicated at this time. Clear codes, and see SYMPTOMS in TROUBLE SHOOTING (EEC-IV) – NO CODES article in appropriate MITCHELL® manual.

CIRCUIT TEST DP (Cont.)

2) Check VSS Circuit Continuity – Turn ignition off. Disconnect VSS sensor. Remove PCM 60-pin connector. Inspect terminals, and repair if damaged. Install EEC-IV Breakout Box (T83L-50-EEC-IV). Measure resistance between VSS (+) terminal at VSS wiring harness connector and test pin No. 3 at breakout box. Measure resistance between VSS (–) terminal at VSS wiring harness connector and test pin No. 6 at breakout box. If any resistance reading is more than 5 ohms, service open circuit in VSS wiring harness and repeat step **1)**. If both resistance readings are 5 ohms or less, go to step **3)**.

3) Check VSS Circuits For Shorts To Power Or Ground – Turn ignition off. Ensure PCM and VSS are disconnected. Measure resistance between test pin No. 3 and test pins No. 6, 37 and 40 at breakout box. If all readings are greater than 500 ohms, go to step **4)**. If any reading is less than 500 ohms, repair shorts in VSS wiring harness and repeat step **1)**.

4) Check VSS Resistance – Turn ignition off, and wait 10 seconds. Disconnect VSS wiring harness connector. Measure resistance across VSS terminals. If reading is not 190-250 ohms, replace VSS and repeat step **1)**. If resistance is 190-250 ohms, replace PCM and repeat step **1)**.

CIRCUIT TEST FD

BRAKE ON-OFF (BOO) SWITCH

Diagnostic Aids – Perform this test when directed by QUICK TEST. This test is intended to diagnose a faulty BOO switch circuit or PCM. To prevent replacement of good components, be aware following non-EEC related areas may be at fault:
- Brakelight bulb.
- Brakelight switch or brakelight fuse.

93I40541

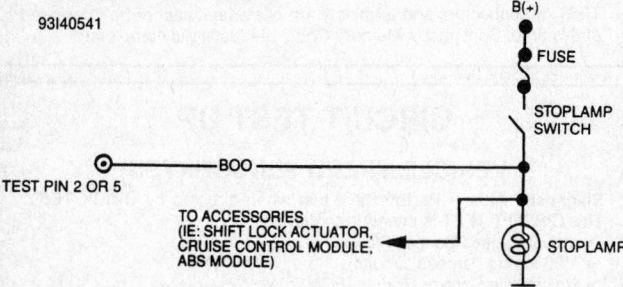

*TEST PINS LOCATED ON BREAKOUT BOX

Fig. FD1: BOO Switch Circuit

TEST Pin WIRE COLOR IDENTIFICATION

Application	Wire Color
No. 2 (BOO)	Light Green

1) Code 536: Verify Brake Pedal Was Depressed – Code 536 indicates that when brake pedal is applied during KOER SELF-TEST, BOO signal did not cycle high and low. Possible causes for this fault are:
- Brake pedal not applied during self-test.
- Brake pedal applied during entire self-test.
- Open brakelight circuit.
- Short to ground or power.
- Faulty Powertrain Control Module (PCM).

If brake was not applied during KOER SELF-TEST, repeat test. Depress and release brake pedal only once during test. If pedal was depressed, go to step **2)**.

2) Check Operation Of Brakelights – With ignition on, check operation of brakelights. If brakelights operate normally, go to step **3)**. If brakelights do not operate, go to step **4)**. If brakelights are always on, go to step **5)**.

3) Check For BOO Switch Circuit Cycling – Turn ignition off. Wait 10 seconds. Disconnect PCM 60-pin connector. Inspect terminals, and repair if damaged. Install EEC-IV Breakout Box (T83L-50-EEC-IV), leaving PCM disconnected. Measure voltage between BOO test pin (No. 2) and test pin No. 40 while applying and releasing brake. If voltage cycles, replace PCM and repeat QUICK TEST. If voltage does not cycle, repair open circuit in BOO switch circuit between PCM and BOO switch connection to brakelight circuit. Repeat QUICK TEST.

CIRCUIT TEST FD (Cont.)

4) Check For Power To Brake Switch – Ensure related fuses and brakelight bulbs are in good condition. Turn ignition off. Disconnect brakelight switch (located on brake pedal). Measure voltage between BATT (+) input to brakelight switch and ground. If voltage is greater than 10 volts, check condition of brakelight switch. If brakelight switch is okay, repair open circuit between brakelight switch and brakelight ground. Repeat QUICK TEST. If voltage is less than 10 volts, repair open BATT (+) circuit to brakelight switch and repeat QUICK TEST.

5) Verify Brake Switch Is Not Always Closed – Turn ignition off. Disconnect brakelight switch (located on brake pedal). Turn ignition on. If brakelights are still on, go to step **6)**. If brakelights are not on, verify correct installation of brakelight switch. If installation is okay, replace brakelight switch and repeat QUICK TEST.

6) Check For Short To Power In PCM – Turn ignition off. Disconnect PCM. Turn ignition on. Check brakelights. If brakelights are on, go to step **7)**. If brakelights are not on, replace PCM and repeat QUICK TEST.

7) Check For Short To Power In Shift Lock Actuator – Turn ignition off. Ensure PCM and brakelight switch are disconnected. Disconnect shift lock actuator, cruise control module and ABS module (if equipped). Turn ignition on. If brakelights are still on, repair short to power in BOO or stoplight circuit and repeat QUICK TEST. If brakelights are not on, repair short circuit in shift lock actuator circuit, cruise control system circuit or ABS circuit. Repeat QUICK TEST.

NOTE: A break in step numbering sequence occurs at this point. Procedure skips from step 7) to step 90). No test procedures have been omitted.

90) Code 536: Check For Proper Brakelight Switch Installation – Continuous memory Code 536 indicates a BOO circuit failure. If BOO input does not cycle after a predetermined number of transitions from 0 mph to a specific speed, the BOO input is assumed to be damaged and continuous memory Code 536 is set. Possible causes of failure are:
- Incorrect brakelight switch installation.
- Open brakelight/BOO circuit.
- Brakelight/BOO circuit short.
- Damaged switch or ground circuit.

If switch is correctly installed and in good condition, go to next step. If switch or harness is damaged, service as needed and clear continuous memory. Repeat QUICK TEST.

91) Inspect Brakelight Ground – Inspect brakelight ground connection and harness connector. Repair as needed. If connections are okay, go to next step.

92) Inspect Brakelight/BOO Circuits For Shorts – With KOEO and brake pedal released, perform wiggle test of brakelight/BOO circuit harness and connectors while observing brakelights. If brakelights illuminate, inspect and repair circuits as needed. If brakelights do not illuminate, go to next step.

93) Inspect Brakelight Circuit Continuity – With ignition off, depress brake pedal and hold. Perform wiggle test of brakelight circuits while observing brakelights. Lightly tap brakelight switch while observing brakelights. If brakelights intermittently go out, inspect and repair circuits as needed. If brakelights remain illuminated, go to next step.

94) Inspect BOO Circuit Continuity – With ignition off, ensure brake pedal is released. Disconnect PCM 60-pin connector. Inspect terminals, and repair if damaged. Install EEC-IV Breakout Box (T83L-50-EEC-IV), leaving PCM disconnected. Measure resistance between BOO test pin No. 2 and brakelight circuit at switch while performing wiggle test on harness and connector. If resistance intermittently increases above 5 ohms, inspect and repair open circuit. Repeat QUICK TEST. If resistance is within specification, go to next step for further diagnosis.

99) Road Test Vehicle – Purpose of this test is to identify faults by monitoring certain controlled parameters while trying to recreate a driveability or MIL symptom. To prepare for road test:
- Install fuel pressure gauge and if available, a MAP/BARO tester.
- Disconnect PCM 60-pin connector, install breakout box and reconnect PCM to breakout box.
- Connect "T" vacuum gauge into manifold vacuum line.
- Have DVOM, writing materials and appropriate schematics and pin voltage charts available.

With ignition on and negative lead of DVOM connected to negative battery terminal, ensure following signals are correct:
- POWER: KAPWR (pin No. 1) is greater than 10.5 volts, VPWR (pins No. 37 and 57) is greater than 10.5 volts and VREF (pin No. 26) is 4-6 volts.
- GROUND: PWR GND (pins No. 40 and 60), SIG RTN (pin No. 46) and IGN GND (pin No. 16) are 0.0-0.5 volt.
- OPTIONAL GROUNDS: HO2S GND (pin No. 49), CSE GND (pin No. 20) and MAF RTN (pin No. 9 or 15) are 0.0-0.5 volt.

CIRCUIT TEST FD (Cont.)

Diagnostic Aids – Test lights and DVOM are useful during diagnosis. For example: a testlight could be connected at brakelight switch between battery and ground and another testlight between switch bulb circuit and ground. Testlight to battery circuit should always illuminated and other testlight should only illuminate when brakelight is depressed.

With DVOM connected between test pin No. 2 and 40 at Breakout Box, check voltage. If voltage is between 6-7 volts with brake pedal released, possible open circuit between PCM and brakelight ground could exist.

CIRCUIT TEST KE

IDLE AIR CONTROL (IAC) SOLENOID

Diagnostic Aids – The IAC solenoid controls engine idle speed and dashpot functions by regulating the volume of air by-passing the throttle plate. IAC solenoid positioning is determined by signals sent from the PCM. On 2.0L models, a thermowax material is built into the unit to aid operation of IAC solenoid.

Perform this test when instructed by QUICK TEST or if directed by other test procedures. This test is intended to diagnose:
- RPM during SELF-TEST mode.
- IAC solenoid.
- Wiring harness circuits (IAC and VPWR).
- Powertrain Control Module (PCM).

To prevent replacement of good components, be aware the following non-EEC related areas may be at fault:
- Engine temperature outside correct operating range.
- A/C input (electrical problem).
- Incorrect throttle stop adjustment.
- Faulty throttle or cruise control linkage

93A40709

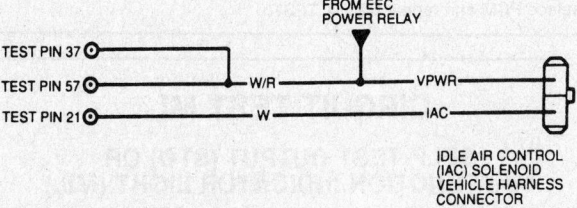

Fig. KE1: Idle Air Control Circuit

TEST PIN WIRE COLOR IDENTIFICATION

Application	Wire Color
No. 21 (IAC)	Light Green/Black
No. 37 & 57 (VPWR)	White/Red

1) Code 412 – Code 412 indicates engine RPM could not be controlled within upper RPM limit during KOER SELF-TEST. Possible causes for this fault are:
- Open or shorted circuit.
- Sticking or binding throttle linkage.
- Incorrect idle airflow setting.
- Throttle body or IAC solenoid contaminated.
- Faulty IAC solenoid.
- Faulty PCM.
- Mechanical faults unrelated to EEC-IV which could affect RPM..

Turn ignition off. Connect tachometer to engine. Start engine. Disconnect Idle Air Control (IAC) harness. If RPM drops or engine stalls, go to step **2**). If RPM does not drop or engine does not stall, go to step **3**).

2) Check For EGR Codes – If EGR service Code 213, 232, 326, 327, 328, 332, 334 or 336 is displayed, reconnect IAC solenoid. Go to appropriate KOER SELF-TEST. See SERVICE CODE REFERENCE CHARTS. If these codes are not displayed, go to step **3**).

3) Check For Other Diagnostic Test Codes – If Code 126, 136, 137, 172 or 173 is displayed, reconnect IAC solenoid. Go to appropriate KOER SELF-TEST. See SERVICE CODE REFERENCE CHARTS. If these codes are not displayed, go to step **4**).

CIRCUIT TEST KE (Cont.)

4) Measure IAC Solenoid Resistance – Turn ignition off. Disconnect IAC solenoid. Connect DVOM positive lead to VPWR terminal and negative lead to IAC terminal. See Fig. KE2. Measure resistance of IAC solenoid. If resistance is not 6-13 ohms, replace IAC solenoid and repeat QUICK TEST. If resistance is 6-13 ohms, go to step **5**).

93E40711

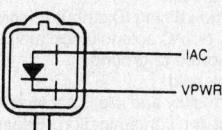

Fig. KE2: IAC Solenoid Connector

5) Check For Internal Short To IAC Solenoid Case – Turn ignition off. With IAC solenoid disconnected, measure resistance from either IAC terminal pin to IAC solenoid housing. If reading is more than 10 k/ohms, go to step **6**). If reading is 10 k/ohms or less, replace IAC solenoid. Repeat QUICK TEST.

6) Check VPWR Circuit Voltage – Leave IAC harness disconnected. Turn ignition on. Measure voltage between VPWR terminal at IAC harness connector and battery ground terminal. If voltage is 10.5 volts or more, go to step **7**). If voltage is less than 10.5 volts, repair open in circuit and repeat QUICK TEST.

7) Check IAC Circuit Continuity – Turn ignition off. Leave IAC solenoid disconnected. Disconnect 60-pin PCM connector. Inspect terminals, and repair if damaged. Install EEC-IV Breakout Box (T83L-50-EEC-IV), leaving PCM disconnected. Measure resistance between test pin No. 21 and IAC terminal at IAC wiring harness connector. If reading is 5 ohms or less, go to step **8**). If reading is more than 5 ohms, repair open circuit and repeat QUICK TEST.

8) Check IAC Circuit For Short To Ground – Turn ignition off. Leave IAC solenoid and PCM disconnected. Measure resistance between test pin No. 21 and test pins No. 40, 46 and 60. If any reading is less than 10 k/ohms, repair short to ground and repeat QUICK TEST. If all readings are 10 k/ohms or more, go to step **9**).

9) Check IAC Circuit For Short To Power – Leave IAC solenoid and PCM disconnected. Turn ignition on. Measure voltage between breakout box test pin No. 21 and chassis ground. If voltage is more than 1.0 volt, repair short circuit and repeat QUICK TEST. If code or symptom is still present, replace PCM. If voltage is 1.0 volt or less, go to step **10**).

10) Check IAC Signal From PCM – Turn ignition off. Reconnect IAC solenoid. Connect PCM to breakout box. Connect DVOM between test pins No. 21 and 40 at breakout box. Start engine. Observe DVOM while slowly increasing engine speed to 3000 RPM. If DVOM voltage reading is 3.0-11.5 volts, go to step **11**). If DVOM voltage reading is not 3.0-11.5 volts, remove IAC solenoid to confirm that it is not stuck open. If IAC is okay, replace PCM and repeat QUICK TEST.

11) Check Base Idle – Verify base idle speed is correct. If base idle speed is within specification, remove IAC solenoid and inspect for contamination. Repair or replace as necessary. Repeat QUICK TEST. If code or symptom is still present, replace IAC solenoid. If base idle speed is not correct, reset idle speed to specification. Repeat QUICK TEST. If unable to set idle to specification, go to step **12**).

12) Check For Faults Affecting Idle Speed – Check following mechanical items for faults:
- Throttle linkage and/or cruise control linkage (sticking or binding).
- Throttle body (contamination).
- Vacuum hoses. Check Vehicle Emission Control Information (VECI) label.
- Check for leaks around IAC solenoid (gaskets, etc.).

If any of these items are faulty, service as necessary, and repeat QUICK TEST. If all of these items are okay, remove IAC solenoid and inspect for contamination. Repair or replace as necessary. Repeat QUICK TEST. If code or symptom is still present, replace IAC solenoid. Repeat QUICK TEST.

NOTE: A break in step numbering sequence occurs at this point. Procedure skips from step 12) to step 15). No test procedures have been omitted.

CIRCUIT TEST KE (Cont.)

15) Code 411 – Code 411 indicates engine RPM could not be controlled within lower RPM limit during KOER SELF-TEST. Possible causes for this fault are:
- Incorrect idle airflow setting.
- Vacuum leaks.
- Sticking or binding throttle linkage.
- Throttle plates open.
- Incorrect ignition timing (Distributor ignition only).
- Throttle body or IAC solenoid contamination.
- IAC circuit shorted to ground.
- Faulty IAC solenoid.

If above items are okay and idle is set to specification, remove IAC solenoid and inspect for contamination. Repair or replace as necessary. Repeat QUICK TEST. If code or symptom is still present, replace IAC solenoid. If idle speed is not within specification, adjust as necessary and repeat QUICK TEST. If idle speed cannot be set to specification, go to next step.

16) Check For Conditions Affecting Idle Speed – Check the following mechanical components:
- Vacuum hoses. Check Vehicle Emission Control Information (VECI).
- Throttle linkage and/or cruise control linkage (sticking or binding).
- Ensure throttle plates are fully closed.
- Induction system (vacuum leaks).
- Throttle body (contamination).
- Ensure CANP solenoid is not stuck open.
- Ensure base ignition timing is to specification on emission decal

If everything checks okay, go to step **17)**. If fault is found, service as necessary and repeat QUICK TEST.

17) Check For Internal Short To IAC Solenoid Case – Turn ignition off. Disconnect IAC solenoid wiring harness connector. Measure resistance from either IAC terminal pin to IAC solenoid housing. If reading is more than 10 k/ohms, go to step **18)**. If reading is 10 k/ohms or less, replace IAC solenoid. Repeat QUICK TEST.

18) Check IAC Circuit For Short To Ground – Turn ignition off. Leave IAC solenoid disconnected. Disconnect 60-pin PCM connector. Inspect terminals, and repair if damaged. Install Breakout Box (T83L-50-EEC-IV), leaving PCM disconnected. Measure resistance between test pin No. 21 and test pins No. 40, 46 and 60. If any reading is less than 10 k/ohms, repair short to ground. Reconnect components, and repeat QUICK TEST. If all readings are 10 k/ohms or more, go to step **19)**.

19) Check IAC Signal From PCM – Turn ignition off. Connect PCM to breakout box. Reconnect IAC solenoid. Set DVOM on 20-volt scale. Connect DVOM between test pins No. 21 and 40. Start engine. Observe DVOM while slowly increasing and decreasing engine RPM. If voltage is 3.0-11.5 volts, remove IAC solenoid and inspect for contamination. Repair or replace as necessary, and repeat QUICK TEST. If code or symptom is still present, replace IAC solenoid. If voltage is not 3.0-11.5 volts, replace PCM and repeat QUICK TEST.

CIRCUIT TEST KM

A/C DEMAND SWITCH

Diagnostic Aids – Perform this test when diagnosing a symptom. To prevent replacing good components, check the following non-EEC components and systems:
- Refrigerant charge.
- Low ambient temperature (less than 45°F).

CIRCUIT TEST KM (Cont.)

93F40753

Fig. KM1: WOT A/C Cut-Out Circuit

40) Code 539: Check A/C Input – Code 539 indicates ACCS input to PCM was high during SELF-TEST. Turn ignition off. Disconnect 60-pin PCM connector. Inspect terminals, and repair if damaged. Install EEC-IV Breakout Box (T83L-50-EEC-IV), leaving PCM disconnected. Turn ignition on. Measure voltage between test pin No. 10 at breakout box and chassis ground. If voltage is 1.0 volt or more, repair short to power in A/C circuit and repeat QUICK TEST. If voltage is less than 1.0 volt, replace PCM and repeat QUICK TEST.

CIRCUIT TEST ML

SELF-TEST OUTPUT (STO) OR
MALFUNCTION INDICATOR LIGHT (MIL)

Diagnostic Aids – The MIL is turned on when PCM detects a fault in EEC circuit(s). The light will remain on as long as fault remains in system.

Perform this test only when instructed by QUICK TEST or if directed by CIRCUIT TEST QA. This test does not include procedure for models with electronic instrument panel. To prevent replacing good components, be aware that fuse, bulb or bulb socket may be cause of problem. This test is only intended to diagnose:
- STO/MIL circuit.
- Faulty PCM.

93H40433

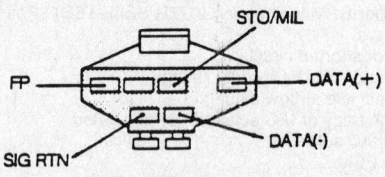

Fig. ML1: Identifying Data Link Connector (DLC) Terminals

CIRCUIT TEST ML (Cont.)

TEST PIN WIRE COLOR IDENTIFICATION

Terminal No.	Wire Color
No. 17 (STO/MIL)	Blue
No. 48 (STI)	Blue/Red
No. 18, Data (+)	Tan/Orange
No. 19, Data (-)	Pink/Light Blue

1) Malfunction Indicator Light (MIL) Always On – Service all KOEO and Continuous Memory Codes before proceeding with this test. Turn ignition off. Disconnect 60-pin PCM connector. Inspect terminals, and repair if damaged. Install EEC-IV Breakout Box (T83L-50-EEC-IV), leaving PCM disconnected. Measure resistance between test pins No. 17 and 40 at breakout box. If resistance is more than 5 ohms, replace PCM and repeat QUICK TEST. If reading is 5 ohms or less, repair short between test pin No. 17 and Diagnostic Link Connector (DLC) terminal No. 17 or MIL. Reconnect all components, and repeat QUICK TEST.

NOTE: A break in step numbering sequence occurs at this point. Procedure skips from step 1) to step 4). No test procedures have been omitted.

4) Malfunction Indicator Light (MIL) Does Not Light – Turn ignition on. Measure voltage between negative battery terminal and ground side of MIL fuse. If voltage is more than 10.5 volts, go to step 6). If voltage is 10.5 volts or less, go to step 5).

5) Check For Voltage At Fuse – Turn ignition on. Measure voltage from negative battery terminal to power side of MIL fuse. If voltage is more than 10.5 volts, replace fuse. Verify repair by turning ignition switch to RUN position. If voltage is 10.5 volts or less, repair open MIL/B+ circuit. Verify repair by turning ignition switch to RUN position.

6) Check Voltage At B+ Circuit – Turn ignition on. Measure voltage between B+ side of MIL bulb socket and negative battery terminal. If voltage is 10.5 volts or less, repair open in MIL circuit between fuse and bulb. Verify repair by turning ignition switch to RUN position. If voltage is more than 10.5 volts, go to step 7).

7) Check MIL Bulb Response To Grounding – Turn ignition off. Attach jumper wire between ground side of MIL bulb socket and chassis ground. Turn ignition on. If MIL light comes on, remove jumper wire, and go to step 8). If MIL light does not come on, remove jumper wire. Replace MIL bulb socket. Turn ignition on to verify correct MIL operation.

8) Check Continuity Of MIL Circuit – Turn ignition off. Disconnect 60-pin PCM connector. Inspect terminals, and repair if damaged. Install EEC-IV Breakout Box (T83L-50-EEC-IV), leaving PCM disconnected. Measure resistance between test pin No. 17 at breakout box and MIL wiring harness connector terminal. If resistance is less than 5 ohms, replace PCM. If resistance is 5 ohms or more, repair open MIL circuit. Turn ignition on to verify correct MIL operation.

NOTE: A break in step numbering sequence occurs at this point. Procedure skips from step 8) to step 10). No test procedures have been omitted.

10) MIL On Intermittently, Check For Intermittent Short From STO To Ground – MIL comes on when a fault code is present. Service all fault codes before proceeding. If no codes are output, proceed with this test. Enter KOEO wiggle test. See CONTINUOUS MONITOR MODE (WIGGLE TEST) under QUICK TEST. Check DVOM for indication of fault while performing wiggle test on harness in the following areas:
- From Diagnostic Link Connector (DLC) to dash panel.
- Dash panel to PCM.
- Dash panel to Malfunction Indicator Light (MIL).

If a fault is indicated, repair short to ground and repeat QUICK TEST. If a fault is not indicated, fault cannot be duplicated at this time. Testing is complete.

NOTE: A break in step numbering sequence occurs at this point. Procedure skips from step 10) to step 15). No test procedures have been omitted.

15) MIL Flashes With Erratic Idle – Symptoms indicate STI is grounded and PCM is performing self-test without tester installed. Turn ignition off. Disconnect 60-pin PCM connector. Inspect terminals, and repair if damaged. Install EEC-IV Breakout Box (T83L-50-EEC-IV), leaving PCM disconnected. Measure resistance between STI connector and engine ground. If resistance is 10 k/ohms or less, repair short circuit. Reconnect PCM, and turn ignition on to verify correct MIL operation. If resistance is more than 10 k/ohms, MIL circuit is okay. Verify symptom, and test for other rough idle symptoms.

CIRCUIT TEST ML (Cont.)

NOTE: A break in step numbering sequence occurs at this point. Procedure skips from step 15) to step 20). No test procedures have been omitted.

20) CHECK ENGINE Message Displayed – Perform KOEO SELF-TEST. If result is Code 111-10-111 (pass code), fault is in instrument cluster. If pass code is not displayed, service codes as necessary.

NOTE: A break in step numbering sequence occurs at this point. Procedure skips from step 20) to step 25). No test procedures have been omitted.

25) Continuous Memory Code 529 Or 533: CHECK ENGINE Or CHECK DLC Message Displayed – Codes 529 and 533 indicate circuit fault has occurred on Data Link Connector (DLC). These codes can occur alone or with another code. Fault will occur under following conditions:
- Code 529 indicates PCM or DLC circuit failure.
- Code 533 indicates DLC to electronic instrument cluster circuit failure

If vehicle does not start, go to step 1). If vehicle starts, clear continuous memory codes. Wait 5 minutes, and repeat KOEO SELF-TEST. If result is pass code (Code 111-10-111), fault is in instrument cluster. If pass code is not displayed, service codes as necessary.

CIRCUIT TEST QA

NO CODES/CODES NOT LISTED

Diagnostic Aids – Aftermarket devices, such as alarm system, may cause SELF-TEST to abort if wiring is connected to certain EEC components. If a device is installed, disconnect it completely from EEC system. Before continuing with this circuit test, restore EEC circuits to original state and repeat QUICK TEST.

Perform this test when directed by QUICK TEST or other test procedures. This test is intended to diagnose:
- Powertrain Control Module (PCM).
- EEC power relay.
- Constant Control Relay Module (CCRM).
- Wiring harness circuits (HO2S, SIG RTN, STO, STI, VPWR and VREF).

93A40808

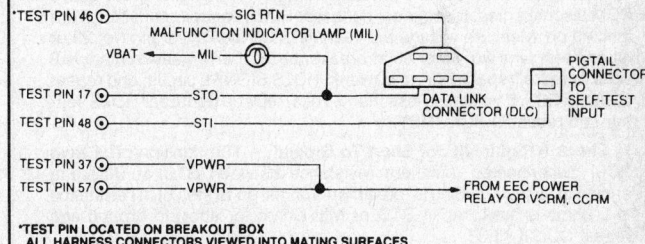

*TEST PIN LOCATED ON BREAKOUT BOX
ALL HARNESS CONNECTORS VIEWED INTO MATING SURFACES

Fig. QA1: No Codes/Codes Not Listed Circuits

TEST PIN WIRE COLOR IDENTIFICATION

Terminal No.	Wire Color
No. 17 (STO/MIL)	Blue
No. 37 & 57 (VPWR)	White/Red
No. 46 (SIG RTN)	Black/Blue
No. 48 (STI)	Blue/Red

1) Check VREF Voltage At Data Link Connector (DLC) – Turn ignition off. Disconnect 60-pin PCM connector. Inspect terminals, and repair if damaged. Install EEC-IV Breakout Box (T83L-50-EEC-IV). Connect PCM to breakout box. Turn ignition on. Measure voltage between test pin No. 26 at breakout box and SIG RTN terminal at DLC. If reading is 4-6 volts, go to step 3). If reading is not 4-6 volts, go to step 2).

2) Check SIG RTN Circuit Continuity – Turn ignition off. Disconnect PCM from breakout box. Measure resistance between test pin No. 46 at breakout box and SIG RTN terminal at DLC. If reading is less than 5 ohms, go to CIRCUIT TEST C. If resistance is 5 ohms or more, repair open circuit and repeat QUICK TEST.

CIRCUIT TEST QA (Cont.)

3) Check STI Circuit Continuity – Turn ignition off. Disconnect PCM from breakout box. Measure resistance between test pin No. 48 at breakout box and Self-Test Input (STI) terminal at pigtail connector. If resistance is 5 ohms or more, repair open circuit and repeat QUICK TEST. If reading is less than 5 ohms, go to step **4).**

4) Check STO Circuit Continuity – Leave ignition off and PCM disconnected. Measure resistance between test pin No. 17 at breakout box and STO terminal at DLC. If reading is less than 5 ohms, go to step **5).** If resistance is 5 ohms or more, repair open circuit and repeat QUICK TEST.

Diagnostic Aid – A right/rear HO2S short to power could prevent EEC system from entering self-diagnostics.

5) Check HO2S Signal For Short To Power – Leave PCM disconnected. Turn ignition on. Measure voltage between test pin No. 40 or 60 and HO2S SIGNAL test pin No. 29 or 44 at breakout box. For HO2S circuit schematics, *see Fig. QA2.* If voltage is more than 2 volts, go to step **6).** If voltage is 2 volts or less, go to step **7).**

93G40572

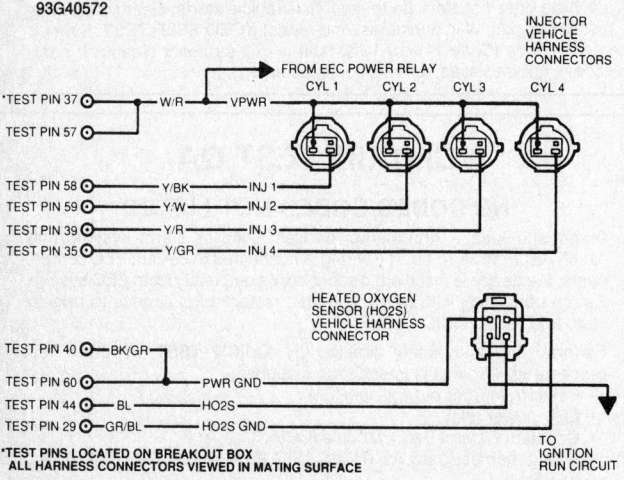

Fig. QA2: Test Schematic (Probe)

6) Isolate Short To Harness Or HO2S Sensor – Turn ignition off. Leave PCM disconnected. Disconnect right/rear HO2S sensor connector. Turn ignition on. Measure voltage between HO2S SIGNAL test pin No. 29 or 44 and test pins No. 40 or 60 at breakout box. If any measurement is 2 volts or more, repair short to power in HO2S SIGNAL circuit, and repeat QUICK TEST. If voltage is less than 2 volts, replace right/rear HO2S sensor and repeat QUICK TEST.

7) Check STO Circuit For Short To Ground – Turn ignition off. Leave PCM disconnected. Measure resistance between STO at DLC and engine ground. If reading is more than 5 ohms, go to step **8).** If resistance is 5 ohms or less, repair STO or MIL circuit for short to ground and repeat QUICK TEST.

8) Check If Power Relay Is Always On – Leave ignition off and PCM disconnected. Connect DVOM between test pin No. 37 or 57 and pin No. 40 or 60 at breakout box. Turn ignition on and then off. Wait 10 seconds. If voltage changes from 10.5 volts (or more) to less than 1.0 volt, go to step **10).** If voltage does not change from 10.5 volts (or more) to less than 1.0 volt, go to step **9).**

9) Check VPWR Circuit For Short To Power – Turn ignition off. Leave PCM disconnected. Disconnect EEC power relay or Constant Control Relay Module (CCRM). Connect DVOM to test pin No. 37 or 57 and test pin No. 40 or 60 at breakout box. If voltage is more than 1.0 volt, repair VPWR circuit short to power and repeat QUICK TEST. If voltage is 1.0 volt or less, replace EEC power relay or CCRM and repeat QUICK TEST.

10) Check Malfunction Indicator Light (MIL) Function – If MIL is always on, go to CIRCUIT TEST ML, step **1).** If MIL is always off, go to CIRCUIT TEST ML, step **4).** If MIL is working normally, replace PCM and repeat QUICK TEST.

CIRCUIT TEST TC

TRANSMISSION SOLENOIDS

Diagnostic Aids – Perform this test only when directed by QUICK TEST. To prevent replacing good components, be aware the following non-EEC areas may be at fault:
- Engine condition (compression, cam timing, valves, etc.).
- Charging system or battery.
- Transmission linkage, internal components or cooling.

This test is not intended to diagnose transmission. This test is intended to diagnose:
- Wiring harness circuits TCC, CCS, EPC, SS3/4, SS1, SS2, SS3, SIG RTN, EPC PWR and VPWR.
- Faulty Powertrain Control Module (PCM).

CIRCUIT TEST TC ACRONYMS

Acronym	Definition
CCC	Converter Clutch Control
CCS	Coast Clutch Control
EPC	Electronic Pressure Control
MCCC	Modulated Converter Clutch Control
SS	Shift Solenoid
TCC	Torque Converter Clutch

CD4E SERVICE CODE IDENTIFICATION

Application	PCM Pin No.	KOEO Code
EPC	38	624, 625
SS1	51	621
SS2	52	622
3-2T/CCS	55	641
TCC	53	652

94H36720

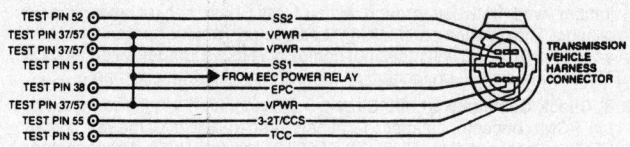

Fig. TC1: CD4E Solenoid Circuits

NOTE: A break in step numbering sequence occurs at this point. Procedure skips to step 10). No test procedures have been omitted.

10) Check VPWR To Solenoid – Ensure ignition is off. Disconnect transmission harness connector. With KOEO, measure voltage between VPWR, EPC PWR circuit at transmission harness connector and ground. If voltage is more than 10.5 volts, go to next step. If voltage is not within specification, repair open circuit in harness. Connect all components and repeat QUICK TEST.

11) Check Solenoid Signal & VPWR Circuit Continuity – Turn ignition off. Disconnect 60-pin PCM connector. Inspect terminals, and repair if damaged. Install EEC-IV Breakout Box (T83L-50-EEC-IV), leaving PCM disconnected. Measure resistance between VPWR/EPC PWR terminal at transmission wiring harness connector breakout box test pins No. 37 and 57. Measure resistance between test pin No. 38 at breakout box and EPC terminal at transmission wiring harness connector. If resistance is 5 ohms or more, repair open circuit and repeat QUICK TEST. If resistance is less than 5 ohms, go to step **12).**

12) Check Circuit For Short To Power Or Ground – Leave ignition off and PCM disconnected. Leave transmission wiring harness connector disconnected. Measure and record resistance between test pins No. 37 and 57 and suspect solenoid test pin at breakout box. Measure and record resistance between test pins No. 40, 46 and 60 and suspect solenoid test pin at breakout box. If either resistance is less than 10 k/ohms, repair short circuit and repeat QUICK TEST. If all resistances are 10 k/ohms or more, check solenoids. If solenoids are okay, replace PCM and repeat QUICK TEST.

WIRING DIAGRAMS

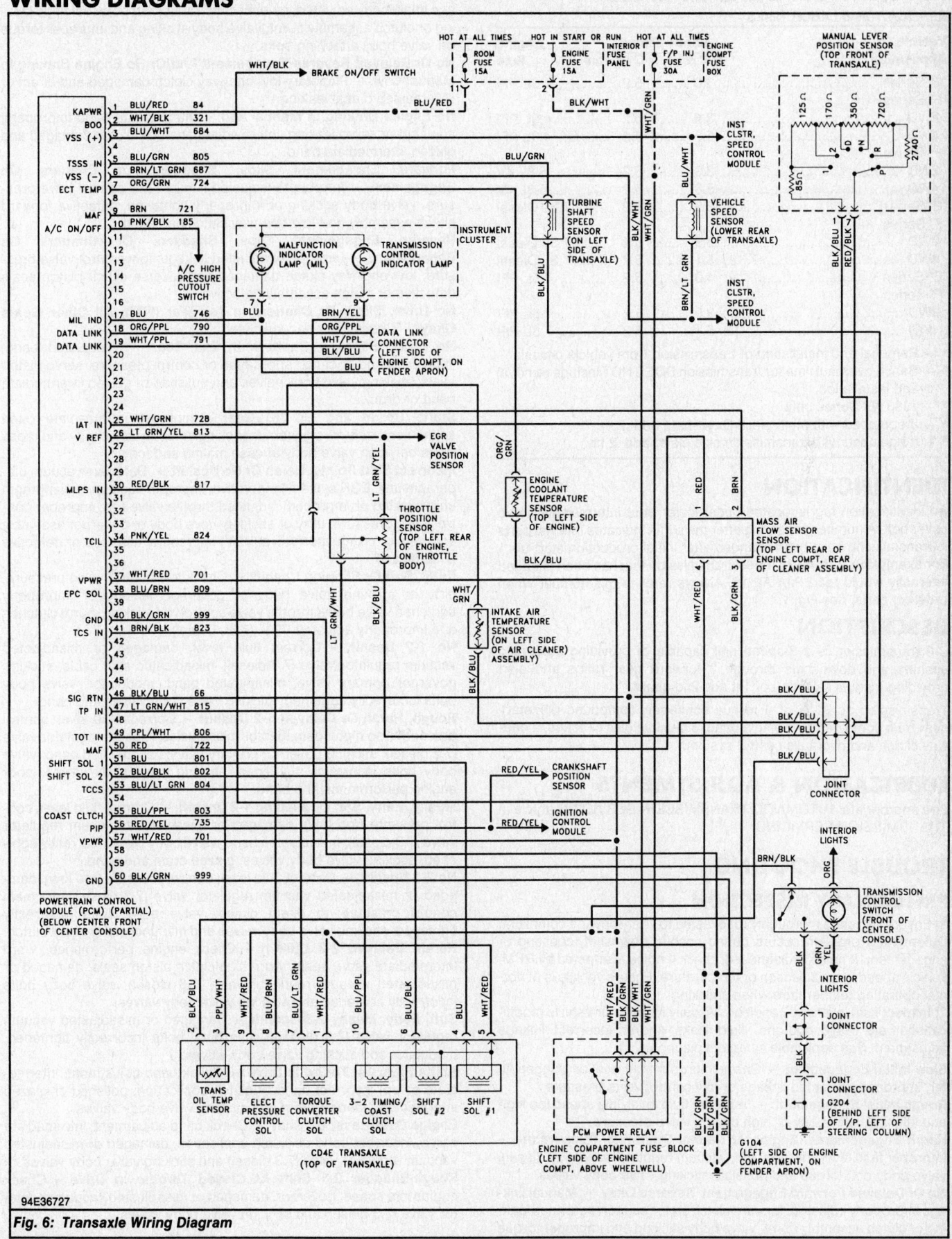

Fig. 6: Transaxle Wiring Diagram

94E36727

APPLICATION & LABOR TIMES

APPLICATION & LABOR TIMES

Vehicle Application	[1] [4] [5] R & I	[2] Overhaul	Engine Size
"E" Series	3.6	5.2	4.9L PFI
"F" Series			
2WD	3.5	5.2	4.9L PFI
4WD	5.5	5.2	4.9L PFI
"F" Series			
2WD	3.9	5.2	5.8L 4V
4WD	5.6	5.2	5.8L 4V
"E" Series	3.9	5.2	7.3L Diesel
"F" Series			
2WD	3.9	5.2	7.3L Diesel
4WD	5.1	5.2	7.3L Diesel
"E" Series [3]	4.0	5.2	7.5L PFI
"F" Series			
2WD	3.9	5.2	7.5L PFI
4WD	5.1	5.2	7.5L PFI

[1] – Removal and installation of transmission from vehicle chassis.
[2] – Bench overhaul time for transmission DOES NOT include removal and installation.
[3] – 1993 "E" Series only.
[4] – If equipped with multi-piece Driveshaft, add .2 hr.
[5] – If equipped with transmission skid plate, add .2 hr.

IDENTIFICATION

An identification tag is located under lower front intermediate servo cover bolt. A number appearing after the suffix indicates internal parts in transmission have been changed after initial production start-up. For example, a PJA-AL 15 model transmission that has been changed internally would read PJA-AL 16. Always refer to this number when ordering parts. *See Fig. 1.*

DESCRIPTION

C-6 transmission is a 3-speed unit capable of providing automatic upshifts and downshifts through 3 forward gear ratios and also providing manual selection of 1st and 2nd gears.

Transmission consists of a torque converter, compound planetary gear train controlled by a single band, 3 multiple disc clutches, a one-way clutch and hydraulic control system.

LUBRICATION & ADJUSTMENTS

See appropriate AUTOMATIC TRANSMISSION SERVICING article in TRANSMISSION SERVICING.

TROUBLE SHOOTING

PRELIMINARY INSPECTION

1) Ensure vehicle is thoroughly road tested to verify driver's complaint. Determine if problem occurs during upshift, downshift, coasting or engagement. If noise is diagnosed, check if noise is affected by RPM, vehicle speed, gear selection or temperature. Ensure vehicle is at normal operating temperature when checking.

2) Inspect fluid level and condition. Visually inspect for vehicle modifications, electronic add-ons, fluid leaks and/or incorrect linkage adjustment. See applicable symptom diagnosis.

Slow Initial Engagement – Check improper fluid level or plugged filter, improperly adjusted linkage or low control valve pressure.

Rough Initial Engagement – Improper fluid level, idle speed too high and sticking valve body or high control valve pressure.

Harsh Engagements, Engine At Normal Operating Temperature – Improper fluid level, idle too high, vacuum regulator valve (7.3 diesel), valve body bolt torque and possible sticking valve body valves.

No Or Delayed Forward Engagement, Reverse Okay – Manual linkage improperly adjusted, forward clutch stator support seal rings leaking or clutch assembly burnt, valve body sticking and improper torque on valve body attaching bolts.

No Or Delayed Reverse Engagement, Forward Okay – Manual linkage improperly adjusted, reverse clutch stator support seal rings leaking or clutch assembly burnt, valve body sticking and improper torque on valve body attaching bolts.

No Or Delayed Reverse Engagement And/Or No Engine Braking In Manual Low – Planetary low one-way clutch damaged and direct or reverse servo seal leaking.

No Engine Braking In Manual 2nd – Intermediate band improperly adjusted or servo leaking, intermediate one-way clutch damaged and glazed intermediate band.

Forward Engagement Slips, Shudders Or Chatters On Engagement – Improperly adjusted linkage, low control valve pressure, valve body sticking or improperly tightened, defective forward clutch assembly and low one-way clutch damaged.

Reverse Engagement Slips, Shudders Or Chatters On Engagement – Improperly adjusted linkage, low control valve pressure, low one-way clutch damaged and reverse clutch piston seals defective or clutch assembly defective.

No Drive, Slips, Or Chatters In 1st gear ("D"), All Other Gears Okay – Check low one-way clutch.

No Drive, Slips Or Chatters In 2nd Gear – Misadjusted band, improper band or clutch application or control pressure, servo piston seals, sticking valve body valves and polished or glazed intermediate band or drum.

Starts Up In 2nd Or 3rd Gear – Improper intermediate band adjustment, defective governor sticking or loose valve body and cross leaks between valve body at case mating surfaces.

Incorrect Shift Points, Harsh Or No Upshift – Defective vacuum diaphragm unit, EGR system inoperative, improper vacuum to diaphragm unit, sticking or improperly adjusted throttle valve rod, improper control valve pressure, dirty or sticking valve body or governor assembly and Vacuum Regulator Valve (VRV) improperly adjusted or defective (7.3L diesel).

Early, Soft Or Slipping Upshift – Check low control valve pressure, dirty or sticking valve body or governor, leaking or improperly tightened valve body, throttle valve control rod sticking, burnt clutches and improperly adjusted VRV. (7.3L Diesel).

No 1-2 Upshift – Correct fluid level, damaged or misadjusted vacuum regulator valve (7.3 diesel), misadjusted shift cable, sticking governor primary valve, misadjusted band, modulator, valve body bolts incorrectly tightened, sticking valve body valves and band.

Rough, Harsh Or Delayed 1-2 Upshift – Correct fluid level, control pressure (too high), damaged or misadjusted vacuum regulator valve (7.3 diesel), sticking governor primary valve, misadjusted band, valve body bolts incorrectly tightened, sticking valve body valves, poor engine performance and band.

Mushy, Early, Soft Or Slipping 1-2 Upshift – Correct fluid level, control pressure (too low), damaged or misadjusted vacuum regulator valve (7.3 diesel), misadjusted band, valve body bolts incorrectly tightened, sticking valve body valves, glazed drum and band.

No 2-3 Upshift – Correct fluid level, control pressure (too low), damaged or misadjusted vacuum regulator valve (7.3 diesel), low main control pressure to direct clutch, valve body bolts incorrectly tightened, sticking valve body valves and malfunctioning direct clutch.

Harsh, Delayed 2-3 Upshift – Check engine performance, worn intermediate servo seals, worn high clutch piston seals, damaged or misadjusted vacuum regulator valve (7.3 diesel), valve body bolts incorrectly tightened and sticking valve body valves.

Soft, Early, Mushy 2-3 Upshift – Damaged or misadjusted vacuum regulator valve (7.3 diesel), valve body bolts incorrectly tightened, modulator and sticking valve body valves.

Shifts From 1st To 3rd In Drive – Check band adjustment, intermediate servo, incorrect band or clutch application, polished or glazed intermediate band or drum and sticking valve body valves.

Engine Over-Revs, 2-3 Shift – Check band adjustment, intermediate servo, incorrect band or clutch application, damaged or misadjusted vacuum regulator valve (7.3 diesel) and sticking valve body valves.

Rough/Shudder 3-1 Shift At Closed Throttle In Drive – Check engine idle speed, governor, damaged or misadjusted vacuum regulator valve (7.3 diesel) and sticking valve body valves.

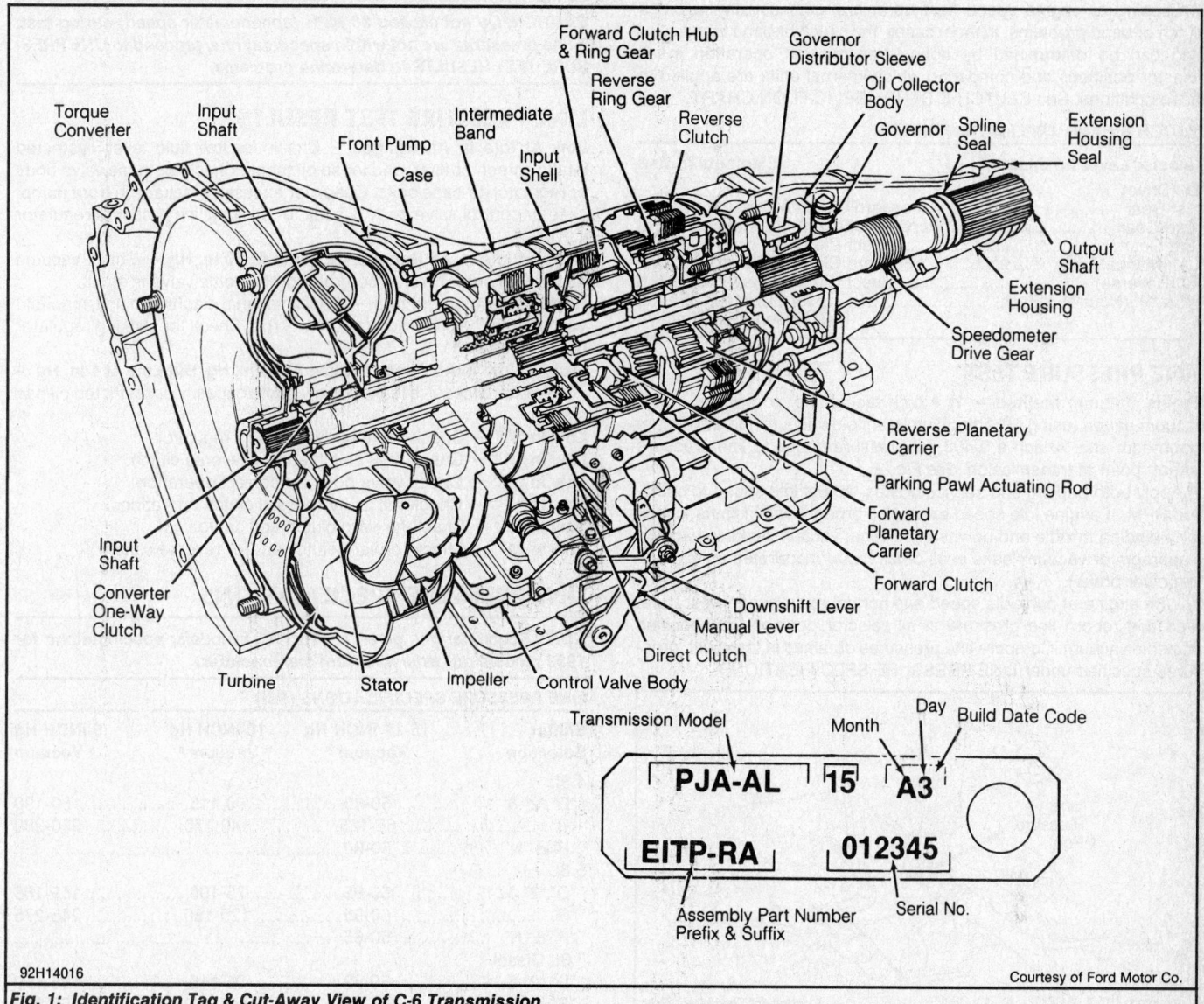

92H14016   Courtesy of Ford Motor Co.

Fig. 1: Identification Tag & Cut-Away View of C-6 Transmission

No Forced Downshifts – Downshift control lever or cable adjustment, internal kickdown linkage, governor, intermediate servo, incorrect band or clutch application and sticking valve body valves.

Engine Over-Revs, 2-3 Shift – Check band adjustment, intermediate servo, incorrect band or clutch application, polished or glazed band or drum and sticking valve body valves.

Erratic Shifts – Check poor engine performance, improper valve body bolt torque, valve body or governor sticking and governor collector body seal rings leaking.

No Forced Downshift – Improperly adjusted or sticking throttle valve rod, damaged internal linkage and dirty or sticking valve body or governor.

Engine Overrevs On 3-2 Downshifts – Intermediate band out of adjustment, leaking or damaged intermediate servo, sticking or leaking valve body, control valve pressure too low and glazed band or drum.

Transmission Overheats – Improper fluid level, engine idle too high, engine cooling system defective, transmission pressure too low, restriction in cooler or cooler lines and seized converter one-way clutch.

Poor Vehicle Acceleration – Check poor engine performance and torque converter (one-way clutch slipping).

Transmission Noisy (Valve Resonance) – Improper fluid level, improperly adjusted linkage, improper control valve pressure, internal oil pressure leaks and dirty or sticking valve body.

TESTING

NOTE: Before testing, always check fluid level, linkage adjustment and vacuum diaphragm.

ROAD TEST

1) Check minimum throttle upshift in Drive. Transmission should start in 1st gear, shift to 2nd and then shift to 3rd as speed increases. See SHIFT SPEEDS (MPH) under TESTING.

2) With transmission in 3rd gear, depress accelerator through detent (to floor). Transmission should shift from 3rd to 2nd or 3rd to 1st, depending on vehicle speed. See SHIFT SPEEDS (MPH) under TESTING.

3) Check closed throttle downshift from 3rd to 1st by coasting down from about 30 MPH in 3rd gear. Shift should occur as shown in table. With transmission selector lever in "2" position, transmission should operate only in 2nd gear.

4) With transmission in 3rd gear and road speed above 50 MPH, transmission should shift to 2nd gear when selector lever is moved from "D" into "2" or "1". When manual shift is made below 30 MPH, transmission should shift from 2nd or 3rd to 1st.

NOTE: This check will determine if governor pressure and shift control valve are operating properly.

5) Slipping or engine speed flare-up in any gear usually indicates clutch or band problems. In most cases, the clutch or band that is slipping can be determined by noting transmission operation in all selector positions and comparing which internal units are applied in those positions. See CLUTCH & BAND APPLICATION CHART.

CLUTCH & BAND APPLICATION CHART

Selector Lever Position	Elements In Use
"D" (Drive)	
1st Gear	Forward Clutch & One-Way Clutch
2nd Gear	Forward Clutch & Intermediate Band
3rd Gear	Direct Clutch & Forward Clutch
"L1" (Manual Low)	Forward Clutch & Reverse Clutch
"R" (Reverse)	Direct Clutch & Reverse Clutch
"N" & "P" (Neutral & Park)	All Clutches & Bands Released Or Ineffective

LINE PRESSURE TEST

Engine Vacuum Method – 1) Attach tachometer to engine. Install vacuum gauge (using "T" fitting) into manifold vacuum line at vacuum diaphragm unit. Attach a 0-400 psi pressure gauge to line pressure takeoff point at transmission. *See Fig. 2.*
2) Apply both parking and service brakes. Adjust idle speed to specified RPM. If engine idle speed cannot be brought within limits, check for a binding throttle and downshift linkage, vacuum leaks in vacuum diaphragm or vacuum leaks in all other vacuum operated units (such as power brake).
3) With engine at curb idle speed and normal operating temperature, read and record line pressure in all selector positions at specified manifold vacuum. Compare line pressures obtained in tests with pressures specified under LINE PRESSURE SPECIFICATIONS.

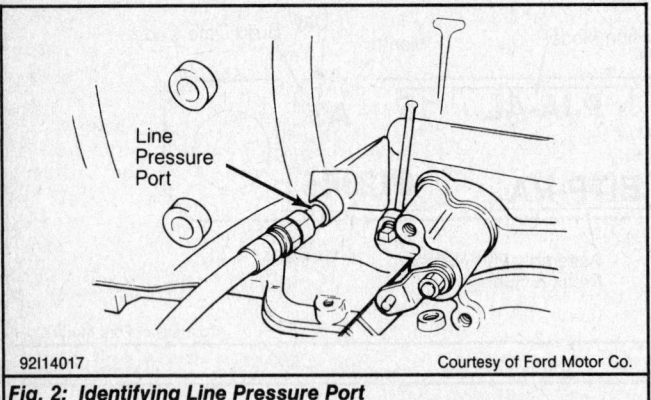

92I14017   Courtesy of Ford Motor Co.

Fig. 2: Identifying Line Pressure Port

Vacuum Pump Method – 1) Attach tachometer to engine and a 0-400 psi pressure gauge to pressure take-off point at transmission. *See Fig. 2.* Disconnect and plug manifold vacuum line at diaphragm unit.
2) Connect vacuum source to vacuum diaphragm. Apply parking and service brakes. Start engine and vacuum pump, setting vacuum to 15 in. Hg. Read and record line pressure in all shift selector positions with engine idling.
3) Increase engine speed to 1000 RPM, and reduce vacuum to 10 in. Hg. Read and record line pressure in "D", "2" and "1" shift selector positions.
4) With engine still at 1000 RPM, reduce vacuum to one in. Hg. Read and record line pressure in "D", "2", "1" and "R". Compare line pressures obtained in tests with pressures given in LINE PRESSURE SPECIFICATIONS.

NOTE: Governor pressure can be checked at same time line pressure test is performed.

5) With vehicle raised and no load on engine, place selector lever in "D" and apply 10 in. Hg. Increase speed slowly while watching speedometer. Check speed at which line pressure cutback occurs. It should occur between 10-20 MPH.
6) If cutback does not occur within specifications, check shift speeds to ensure problem is governor and not a stuck cutback valve.

CAUTION: Do not exceed 60 MPH (speedometer speed) during test. If line pressures are not within specifications, proceed to LINE PRESSURE TEST RESULTS to determine problems.

LINE PRESSURE TEST RESULTS

Low At Idle In All Ranges – Check for low fluid level, restricted intake screen or filter, and loose oil tubes. Check for loose valve body or regulator-to-case bolts. Check for excessive leakage in front pump, case or control valve body. Check for sticking line pressure regulator valve.
Okay At Idle In All Ranges, But Low At 10 In. Hg – Check vacuum diaphragm unit. Check if control rod or throttle valve is stuck.
High At Idle In All Ranges – Check vacuum diaphragm unit, manifold vacuum line, throttle rod, and control rod. Check for sticking regulator boost valve(s).
Okay At Idle In All Ranges, Okay At 10 In. Hg, But Low At 1 In. Hg – Check for excessive leakage, low pump capacity or restricted oil pan screen.
Low In "P" – Check valve body pressure regulator.
Low In "R" – Check high clutch and/or reverse clutch.
Low In "N" – Check valve body for correct operation.
Low In "D" – Check for faulty forward clutch operation.
Low In "2" – Check forward clutch and servo.
Low in "1" – Check forward clutch and/or reverse clutch.

LINE PRESSURE SPECIFICATIONS

NOTE: Specifications given are for 1994 models; specifications for 1993 models not available from manufacturer.

LINE PRESSURE SPECIFICATIONS (PSI)

Shifter Selection	15-17 INCH Hg Vacuum [1]	10 INCH Hg Vacuum [2]	.5 INCH Hg [3] Vacuum
4.9L			
"D","2" & "1"	50-80	90-115	160-190
"R"	65-125	140-170	250-280
"P" & "N"	50-80		
5.8L			
"D","2" & "1"	50-65	75-100	155-185
"R"	60-95	120-150	245-275
"P" & "N"	50-65		
7.3L Diesel			
"D","2" & "1"	50-82	95-115	165-190
"R"	60-120	140-170	250-280
"P" & "N"	50-80		
7.5L			
"D","2" & "1"	55-95	100-120	165-190
"R"	60-120	140-170	250-280
"P" & "N"	50-80		

[1] – Engine at idle.
[2] – Engine at partial throttle.
[3] – Engine at WOT, stall speed.

HIGH ALTITUDE LINE PRESSURE SPECIFICATIONS (PSI) [1]

Shifter Selection	15-17 INCH Hg Vacuum [2]	10 INCH Hg Vacuum [3]	.5 INCH Hg [4] Vacuum
5000 Ft.			
"D","2" & "1"	50-65	60-100	130-170
"R"	60-95	100-150	205-255
"P" & "N"	50-65		
Sea Level			
"D","2" & "1"	50-85	85-120	150-190
"R"	60-135	135-180	230-280
"P" & "N"	50-85		

[1] – All vehicles equipped with high altitude modulator.
[2] – Engine at idle.
[3] – Engine at partial throttle.
[4] – Engine at WOT, stall speed.

VACUUM DIAPHRAGM UNIT

Vacuum Supply & Diaphragm Check – 1) Disconnect vacuum line at diaphragm unit, and install a vacuum gauge in vacuum line using a "T" fitting. If transmission fluid is present in vacuum hose, diaphragm is leaking and vacuum diaphragm unit must be replaced. With engine idling, gauge must show a steady vacuum. If reading is low, unplug vacuum hose at diaphragm and plug. If vacuum is now acceptable, replace diaphragm. If vacuum is still not acceptable, check for vacuum leak or poor engine vacuum.

2) If reading is okay, rapidly accelerate engine momentarily. Vacuum must drop rapidly at acceleration and return upon deceleration. If vacuum reading does not change or changes slowly, vacuum line is plugged, restricted or connected to reservoir supply.

VACUUM REGULATOR VALVE (VRV) 7.3L DIESEL

Operational Check & Adjustment – 1) Shut engine off. Disconnect 2-port vacuum connector from VRV located on left side of fuel injection pump. Remove throttle cable from lever on right side of pump.

2) Remove throttle return spring. Install one end of spring over throttle lever ball stud and other end over throttle cable support bracket.

3) Attach a vacuum pump to upper port of VRV on vacuum supply side. Attach a vacuum gauge to lower port of VRV (labeled TRANS on VRV). Apply and maintain 20 in. Hg to VRV. *See Fig. 3.*

4) Pump vacuum up as it bleeds off. Cycle throttle lever 5 times from idle to wide open throttle with vacuum applied. Insert Gauge Block (T83T-7B200-AH) or .515" gauge block between pump boss and throttle wide open stop. Ensure lever stop is against block. Gauge attached to lower port should indicate 6-8 in. Hg. If reading is incorrect, adjust VRV to 7 in. Hg.

5) To adjust, loosen 2 adjustment screws that attach VRV to fuel injection pump. Rotate VRV until proper vacuum is obtained and tighten adjusting screws. If VRV cannot be adjusted to proper specifications, replace VRV and repeat procedure in step **2).**

6) Remove gauge block. Reattach throttle return spring and throttle cable. Apply and maintain 20 in. Hg to VRV. While maintaining vacuum, cycle the throttle lever from idle to wide open throttle 5 times. Vacuum gauge MUST indicate at least 13 in. Hg with throttle at idle position.

7) If vacuum gauge indicates less than 13 in. Hg, VRV must be replaced and procedure for adjustment must be repeated. After final adjustment, remove vacuum pump and gauge from VRV and reattach vacuum connector.

8) Start engine. Check throttle operation and transmission shift linkage.

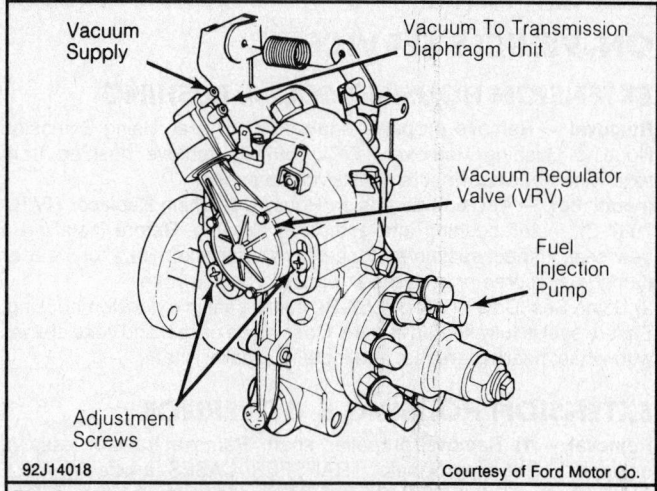

Fig. 3: Vacuum Regulator Valve (7.3L Diesel)

STALL SPEED TEST

CAUTION: Do not hold throttle open longer than 5 seconds at a time during testing. If engine speed exceeds maximum limit of stall speed, release throttle immediately as clutches or bands are slipping.

Testing Procedure – Install tachometer, and fully apply parking and service brakes. Start engine and run at curb idle at normal operating temperature. Stall transmission in each driving range at full throttle. Note maximum RPM obtained. Engine speed should be within limits shown in STALL SPEEDS table.

NOTE: Allow a cooling period of 2 minutes with transmission in Neutral and engine speed at 1000 RPM between each test.

STALL SPEEDS

Engine Application	Stall Speed RPM Range
4.9L EFI [1]	1622-1907
4.9L EFI [2]	1580-1855
4.9L EFI [3]	1580-1855
4.9L EFI [4]	1622-1907
5.8L 4V [5]	2271-2655
7.3L Diesel [5]	1825-2098
7.5L EFI [6]	1983-2315

[1] – E-150, E-250 (8850 GVW) & F-150.
[2] – F-250 (HD) & F-350
[3] – E-350
[4] – E-250 (LD)
[5] – F-250 (HD) & F-350
[6] – E-350 & F-350

SHIFT SPEEDS (MPH)

NOTE: Following tables are approximate. See Figs. 5-8. Shift speeds may vary due to production tolerances, rear axle ratios and emission control equipment.

SHIFT SPEED SPECIFICATIONS [1]

Throttle Opening	Shift	Low Limit MPH	High Limit MPH
4.9L E-150 [2]			
Minimum Throttle	1-2	7	16
Minimum Throttle	2-3	9	24
Closed Throttle	3-1	6	10
Part Throttle [3]	1-2	22	44
Part Throttle [3]	2-3	37	63
Part Throttle [3]	3-2	26	54
Wide Open Throttle	1-2	31	42
Wide Open Throttle	2-3	54	68
Max. Downshift [3]	3-2	47	60
Max. Downshift [3]	3-1	20	30
4.9L "E" & "F" Series [4]			
Minimum Throttle	1-2	6	13
Minimum Throttle	2-3	6	22
Closed Throttle	3-1	6	8
Part Throttle [3]	1-2	19	36
Part Throttle [3]	2-3	32	54
Part Throttle [3]	3-2	25	48
Wide Open Throttle	1-2	30	40
Wide Open Throttle	2-3	51	66
Max. Downshift [3]	3-2	47	62
Max. Downshift [3]	3-1	20	31

[1] – Shift selector is in "D" position.
[2] – 2.73 & 3.08 axle ratio.
[3] – Throttle open to detent.
[4] – 3.54, 3.55, 3.73 & 4.10 axle ratio.
[5] – 3.55 & 4.10 axle ratio.
[6] – 4.10 Axle ratio.
[7] – 3.54, 3.55 & 4.10 axle ratio.

SHIFT SPEED SPECIFICATIONS [1] (Cont.)

Throttle Opening	Shift	Low Limit MPH	High Limit MPH
5.8L F-250/350 [5]			
Minimum Throttle	1-2	6	16
Minimum Throttle	2-3	9	23
Closed Throttle	3-1	6	8
Part Throttle [3]	1-2	25	44
Part Throttle [3]	2-3	41	69
Part Throttle [3]	3-2	28	57
Wide Open Throttle	1-2	34	47
Wide Open Throttle	2-3	59	74
Max. Downshift [3]	3-2	50	65
Max. Downshift [3]	3-1	22	34
7.3L (Diesel)			
"E" & "F" 350 Series [6]			
Minimum Throttle	1-2	6	7
Minimum Throttle	2-3	11	16
Closed Throttle	3-1	6	7
Part Throttle [3]	1-2	19	26
Part Throttle [3]	2-3	35	43
Part Throttle [3]	3-2	29	38
Wide Open Throttle	1-2	24	28
Wide Open Throttle	2-3	42	47
Max. Downshift [3]	3-2	39	44
Max. Downshift [3]	3-1	15	20
7.5L F-250, 350 [7]			
Minimum Throttle	1-2	6	16
Minimum Throttle	2-3	9	26
Closed Throttle	3-1	6	8
Part Throttle [3]	1-2	26	45
Part Throttle [3]	2-3	45	70
Part Throttle [3]	3-2	25	48
Wide Open Throttle	1-2	34	46
Wide Open Throttle	2-3	60	75
Max. Downshift [3]	3-2	50	67
Max. Downshift [3]	3-1	22	33

[1] – Shift selector is in "D" position.
[2] – 2.73 & 3.08 axle ratio.
[3] – Throttle open to detent.
[4] – 3.54, 3.55, 3.73 & 4.10 axle ratio.
[5] – 3.55 & 4.10 axle ratio.
[6] – 4.10 Axle ratio.
[7] – 3.54, 3.55 & 4.10 axle ratio.

STALL SPEED TEST RESULTS

Stall Speed Too High – In "D", "2", "1", and "R": general transmission problems are indicated and a line pressure test should be made to locate faulty unit(s). In "D" only: planetary one-way clutch slippage is indicated. In "D", "2", and "1": forward clutch slippage is indicated. In "R" only: high and/or reverse clutch slippage indicated.

Stall Speed Too Low – Converter stator one-way clutch faulty. Ensure engine performance is satisfactory before condemning converter assembly. Converter cannot be overhauled and must be replaced if defective.

AIR PRESSURE CHECKS

1) A no-drive condition can exist, even with correct transmission fluid pressure, because of inoperative clutches or bands. Erratic shifts could be caused by stuck governor valve. Inoperative units can be located through a series of checks by substituting air pressure for fluid pressure to determine location of malfunction.

2) To make air pressure checks, remove oil pan and drain transmission fluid. Remove control valve body and apply air at points noted. *See Fig. 4.* Check unit operations as follows:

Forward Clutch – Apply air pressure to transmission case forward clutch passage. A dull thud can be heard when clutch piston is applied, or movement of piston can be felt by placing a finger on input shell.

Governor – Apply air pressure to governor line pressure passage and listen for sharp clicking or whistling noise, indicating governor valve movement.

Direct Clutch – Apply air pressure to Direct clutch passage. Dull thud should be heard when clutch piston is applied. If thud is not heard, place finger tips on clutch drum. Movement should be felt.

Intermediate Servo – Hold air nozzle in intermediate servo apply passages. Operation of servo will be indicated by tightening of intermediate band around drum. With air still applied at apply passage, use 2nd air nozzle to apply air at the servo release passage. Band should now release (combination of air pressure and spring on release side of piston should overcome apply pressure).

Reverse Clutch – Apply air pressure to reverse clutch apply passage. A dull thud should be heard if clutch is operating properly.

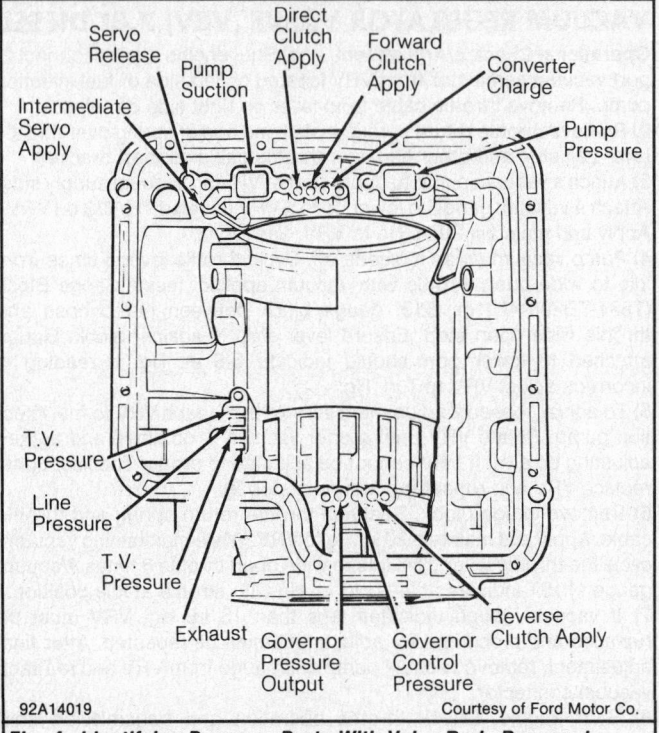

92A14019   Courtesy of Ford Motor Co.

Fig. 4: Identifying Pressure Ports With Valve Body Removed

ON-VEHICLE SERVICE

EXTENSION HOUSING SEAL & BUSHING

Removal – Remove propeller shaft. Pry out seal. Using Extension Housing Bushing Remover (T77L-7697-D), remove bushing from extension housing. Ensure seal is not damaged.

Installation – 1) Using Extension Housing Bushing Replacer (T77L-7697-C), install bushing into extension housing. Before installing a new seal, inspect sealing surface of propeller shaft yoke for wear or damage. If scores or grooves are found, replace yoke.

2) Using Seal Driver (T61L-7657-B), install seal in extension housing. Ensure seal is fully seated in bore. Coat inside of seal and yoke splines with wheel bearing grease, and install propeller shaft.

EXTENSION HOUSING & GOVERNOR

Removal – 1) Remove propeller shaft. Remove transfer case (if equipped). See appropriate TRANSFER CASES article in AXLE SHAFTS & TRANSFER CASES. Remove speedometer cable. Remove rear engine support-to-extension housing bolts. Raise transmission with jack to take weight off support. Remove support from crossmember.

2) Place drain pan under rear of transmission. Remove extension housing-to-case bolts. Slide housing off output shaft. Remove governor body-to-oil collector flange bolts. Separate governor from flange. For governor repairs, see GOVERNOR under COMPONENT DISASSEMBLY & REASSEMBLY.

Installation – To install, reverse removal procedure. Tighten all nuts and bolts to specification. See TORQUE SPECIFICATIONS. Ensure all mating surfaces are clean. Refill transmission to correct fluid level.

INTERMEDIATE SERVO

Removal – Remove engine rear support-to-crossmember bolt. Remove crossmember-to-frame retaining bolts and remove crossmember. Disconnect muffler Inlet pipe from exhaust manifolds and allow pipe to hang. Place a drain pan under servo and remove cover retaining bolts. Remove cover, piston, spring and gasket. See Fig. 5.

NOTE: As piston is being removed, screw in intermediate band adjustment screw. This keeps tension on band, keeping struts properly engaged in band end notches as piston is removed.

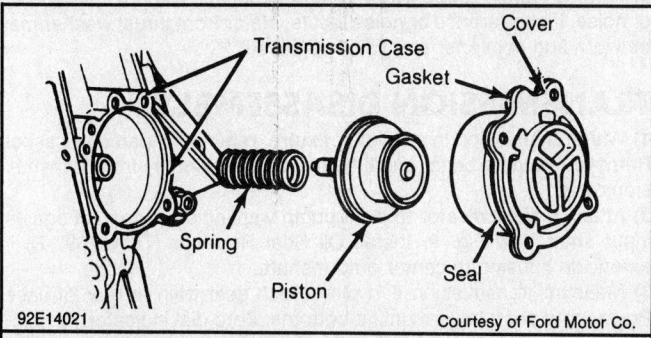

92E14021   Courtesy of Ford Motor Co.

Fig. 5: Exploded View Of Intermediate Servo

Seal Replacement – **1)** Apply air pressure to port in servo cover, and remove piston and rod. Remove seal from cover. Replace complete piston and rod assembly if piston or piston sealing lips are damaged.
2) Dip NEW seal in transmission fluid and install on cover. Coat NEW gasket with petroleum jelly and install on cover. Dip piston in transmission fluid and install in cover.
Installation – To install, reverse removal procedure. Install service identification tag and back off band adjusting screw as servo cover bolts are being tightened.
Intermediate Band Adjustment – Tighten intermediate band adjustment screw to specification. See TORQUE SPECIFICATIONS. Back off screw 1 1/2 turns. Hold adjustment screw in this position and tighten lock nut to specification. Refill transmission to correct fluid level.

OIL COOLER FLUSHING

Contaminates MUST be removed from oil cooler before transmission is put back into service. Replace cooler supply tubes if leaking. Thoroughly flush oil cooler and lines if a major service or transaxle removal has occurred. Use a mechanically agitated cleaner such as Rotunda (014-00028).

TORQUE CONVERTER FLUSHING

Whenever transmission has been disassembled to replace worn or damaged parts or because valve body sticks due to foreign material, converter must be cleaned using a mechanically agitated cleaner, such as Rotunda (014-00028). Under no conditions should converter be cleaned by hand agitation using solvent.

VALVE BODY

Removal – **1)** Loosen oil pan retaining bolts. Tap pan to break gasket loose, allowing fluid to drain. Remove oil pan and gasket. Remove and discard Nylon shipping plug from filler tube hole.

NOTE: Nylon plug is used to retain fluid in transmission during shipment and should be discarded when oil pan is removed.

2) Remove valve body retaining bolts and lower valve body from transmission case. For valve body repairs, see VALVE BODY under COMPONENT DISASSEMBLY & REASSEMBLY.
Installation – Position valve body on case, ensuring selector and downshift levers are engaged. Install and tighten valve body retaining bolts to specification. See TORQUE SPECIFICATIONS. See Fig. 6. Install oil pan with NEW gasket, and tighten bolts evenly to specification.

REMOVAL & INSTALLATION

TRANSMISSION

See appropriate AUTOMATIC TRANSMISSION REMOVAL article in TRANSMISSION SERVICING.

TORQUE CONVERTER

NOTE: Converter is a sealed unit and cannot be disassembled for service. Replace if found to be defective. Make the following tests to ensure converter is defective before replacing unit.

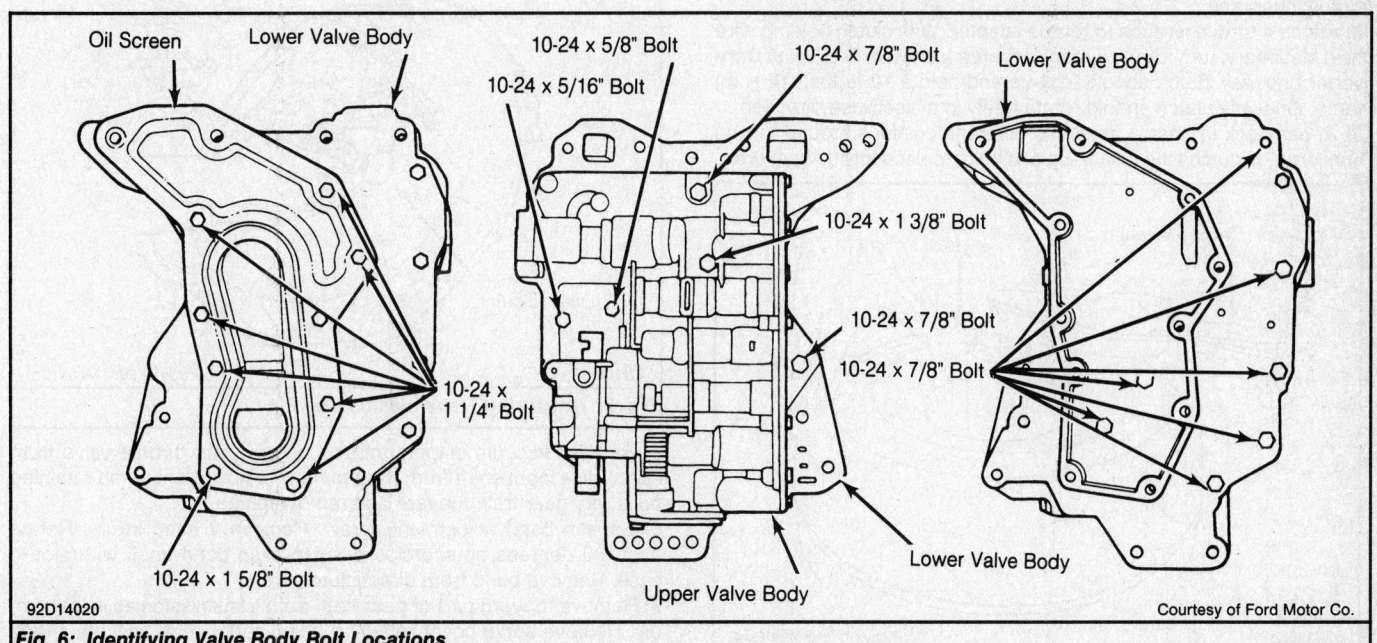

92D14020   Courtesy of Ford Motor Co.

Fig. 6: Identifying Valve Body Bolt Locations

LEAK TEST

If torque converter welds indicate leakage, attach Torque Converter Leak Detector (Rotunda 021-00054) to converter and follow detector kit instructions.

TURBINE & STATOR END PLAY CHECK

1) Insert Tester (T80L-7902-D) into converter pump drive hub until it bottoms. Expand sleeve in turbine spline by tightening threaded inner post of tester until it is securely locked into spline. See Fig. 7.
2) Attach dial indicator to tool with indicator button on converter pump drive hub. Zero dial face. Lift tool upward as far as possible and note indicator reading.
3) Reading is total end play of turbine and stator. If end play exceeds .021" (.53 mm) on new or rebuilt converter, or .040" (1.02 mm) on used converter, replace torque converter assembly.

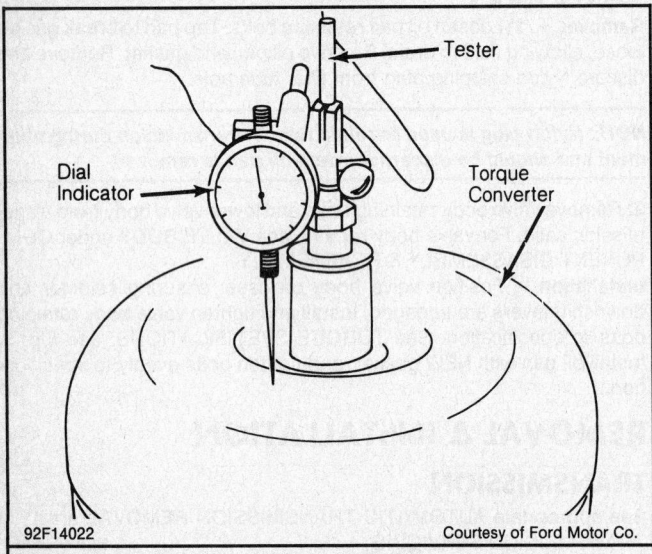

Fig. 7: Measuring Torque Converter End Play

CONVERTER ONE-WAY CLUTCH CHECK

1) Insert one-way Clutch Holding Tool (T77L-7902-R) into one of the grooves in the stator thrust washer. Insert Torque Adapter (T77L-7902-B) into converter pump drive hub so as to engage one-way clutch inner race.
2) Attach a torque wrench to torque adapter. With clutch holding wire held stationary, turn torque wrench counterclockwise. See Fig. 8. Converter one-way clutch should lock-up and hold a 10 ft. lbs. (14 N.m) force. One-way clutch should rotate freely in a clockwise direction.
3) Repeat lock-up test in at least 5 different locations around torque converter. If clutch fails to lock-up and hold, replace torque converter.

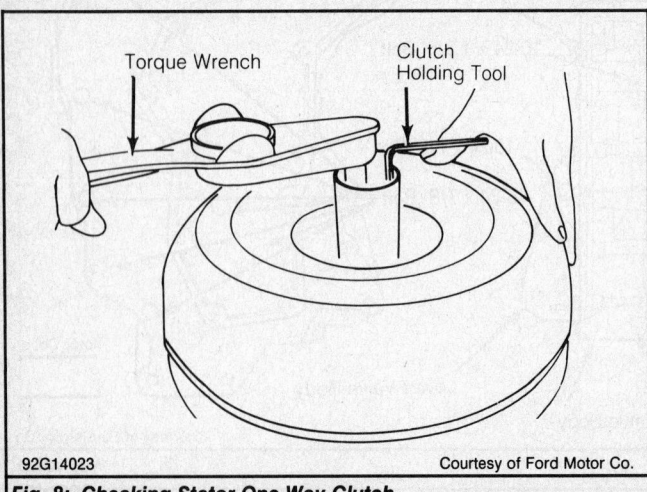

Fig. 8: Checking Stator One-Way Clutch

STATOR INTERFERENCE CHECK

Stator-To-Impeller Interference Check – 1) Position front pump assembly on bench with spline end of stator shaft pointing up. Mount converter on pump so splines of one-way clutch inner race engage splines of stator support and converter hub engages pump drive gear.
2) While holding pump stationary, rotate converter counterclockwise. Converter should rotate freely without interference or scraping within assembly. Should interference or a scraping condition within converter exist or if converter does not rotate freely, replace converter unit.
Stator-To-Turbine Interference Check – 1) Place converter on bench, front side down. Install front pump assembly to engage mating splines of stator support, stator and pump drive gear lugs.
2) Install input shaft, engaging the splines with turbine hub. While holding pump stationary, rotate turbine with input shaft.
3) Turbine should rotate freely in both directions without interference or noise. If interference or noise exists, stator front thrust washer may be worn and converter should be replaced.

TRANSMISSION DISASSEMBLY

1) With transmission in a holding fixture, remove oil pan and gasket. Remove retaining bolts, and lift valve body assembly from transmission case.
2) Attach a dial indicator to front pump with indicator contact against input shaft. See Fig. 9. Install Oil Seal Replacer (T61L-7697-B) in extension housing to center output shaft.
3) Measure transmission end play. Push gear train to rear of case. Press input shaft inward until it bottoms. Zero dial indicator.
4) Push gear train forward. Read and record end play for reassembly reference. Remove tools from transmission.

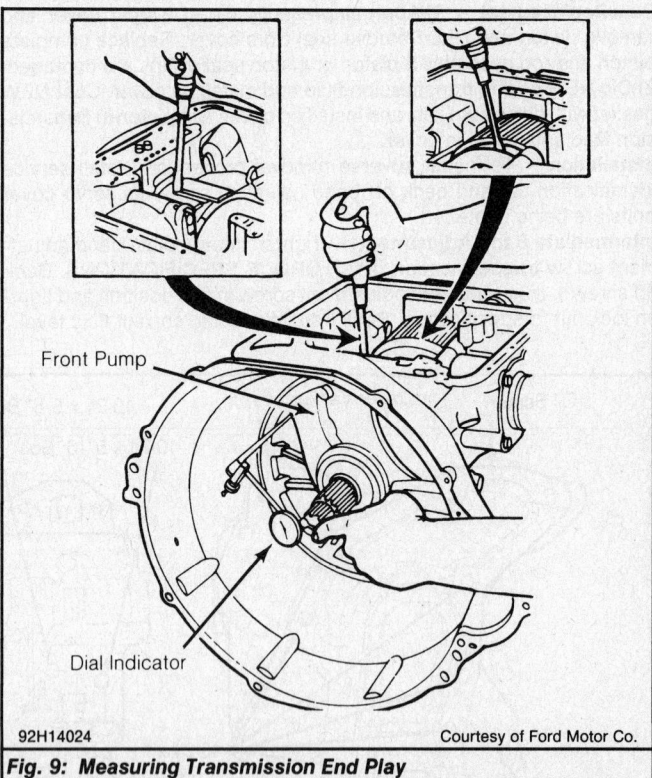

Fig. 9: Measuring Transmission End Play

5) Remove vacuum diaphragm, rod and primary throttle valve from case. Slide input shaft from front pump. Remove front pump retaining bolts, pry gear train forward and remove pump.
6) Loosen band adjustment screw. Remove 2 band struts. Rotate band 90 degrees counterclockwise to align band ends with slot in case. Remove band from direct clutch drum.
7) Remove forward part of gear train from transmission as an assembly. Remove servo cover retaining bolts, servo cover, piston, spring and gasket from case. Remove large snap ring securing reverse planet carrier in reverse clutch hub.

8) Lift carrier from drum. Remove snap ring securing reverse ring gear and hub on output shaft. Slide assembly from shaft. Rotate reverse hub in clockwise direction and remove from case.

9) Remove direct clutch snap ring and withdraw clutch discs, plates and pressure plate from case. See Fig. 17. Remove extension housing retaining bolts and vent tube from case.

10) Remove extension housing and gasket. Slide output shaft assembly from case. Remove distributor sleeve retaining bolts. Remove sleeve, parking pawl gear and thrust washer.

NOTE: If thrust washer is staked in place, use a sharp chisel to cut off metal from behind thrust washer. Remove any metal particles from case.

---

11) Compress reverse clutch piston release spring. Remove snap ring. Lift out springs and retainer assembly.

12) Remove one-way clutch inner race retaining bolts from rear of case. Remove inner race. Remove reverse clutch piston by applying air pressure to reverse clutch apply passage in case. See Fig. 4.

COMPONENT DISASSEMBLY & REASSEMBLY

DOWNSHIFT & MANUAL LINKAGE

Disassembly – 1) Remove nut and lock washer securing outer downshift lever to transmission and remove lever. Slide downshift lever out from inside case and remove seal from recess in manual lever shaft.

2) Remove park/neutral switch. Remove "C" clip securing parking pawl actuating rod to manual lever. Remove actuating rod from case. See Fig. 10.

3) Remove nut retaining inner manual lever to shaft. Remove inner lever from shaft. Slide outer lever and shaft from case. Remove seal from case using a puller and slide hammer.

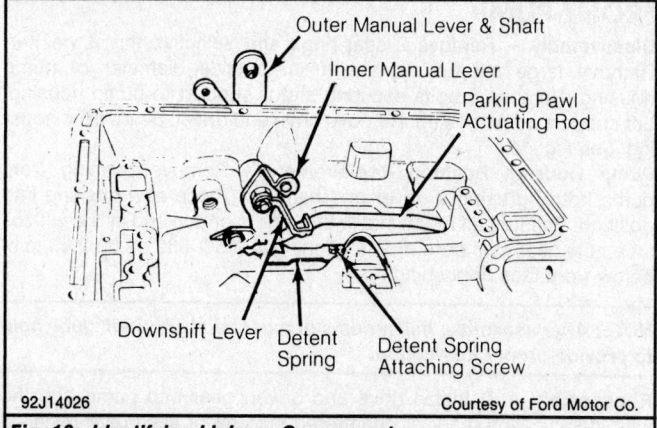

92J14026   Courtesy of Ford Motor Co.

Fig. 10: Identifying Linkage Components

Reassembly – 1) Dip new seal in transmission fluid, and install it into case. Slide outer manual lever and shaft into case. Position inner lever on shaft. Ensure leaf spring roller is positioned in inner manual lever detent.

2) Install retaining nut and tighten. Install parking pawl actuating rod and secure to inner manual lever with "C" clip. Slide neutral safety switch onto outer shaft lever.

3) Install retaining bolt. With manual lever in neutral, rotate switch and install gauge pin (No. 43 drill) into gauge pin hole. Tighten switch retaining bolt to specification. See TORQUE SPECIFICATIONS.

4) Install a NEW downshift lever seal in outer lever shaft recess. Slide downshift lever and shaft into position. Place outer downshift lever on shaft. Install and tighten lock washer and nut to specification.

PARKING PAWL LINKAGE

Disassembly – 1) Remove bolts retaining parking pawl guide plate in case. Remove plate. Remove spring, parking pawl and shaft from case. See Fig. 11.

2) Working from pan mounting surface, drill a 1/8" hole through center of cupped plug. Pull plug from case with a wire hook.

3) Unhook end of spring from park plate slot. Thread a 1/4"-20 x 1 1/4" screw into park plate shaft. Pull shaft from case with screw. Remove spring and park plate.

Reassembly – 1) Position spring and park plate in case, and install shaft. Place end of spring into slot of park plate. Install a new cupped plug to retain shaft. Install parking pawl shaft in case.

2) Slip parking pawl and spring into place on shaft. Position guide plate on case. Ensure actuating rod is seated in slot of plate. Secure plate with 2 bolts and lock washers.

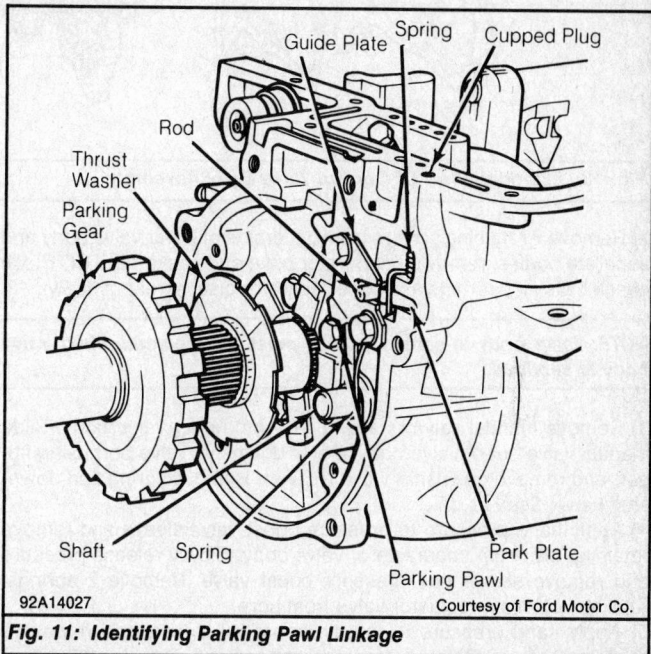

92A14027   Courtesy of Ford Motor Co.

Fig. 11: Identifying Parking Pawl Linkage

SERVO APPLY LEVER

Disassembly – Working from inside case, carefully tap servo apply lever shaft to remove the cup plug. Shaft can be withdrawn by hand.

NOTE: Cup plug should be coated with Loctite to prevent leakage.

Reassembly – Hold servo apply lever in position and install shaft. Using fabricated tool, drive cup plug into position in case. See Fig. 12. Ensure plug is flush with shoulder of counterbore.

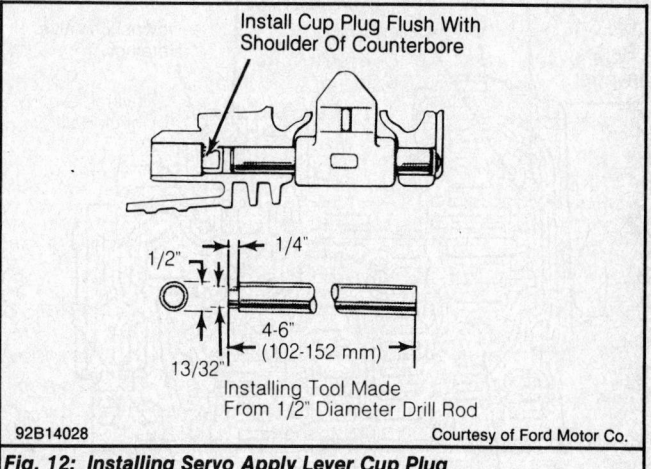

92B14028   Courtesy of Ford Motor Co.

Fig. 12: Installing Servo Apply Lever Cup Plug

VALVE BODY

Disassembly – 1) Remove 9 screws retaining screen-to-lower valve body and remove screen and gasket. See Fig. 6. Remove 5 upper-to-lower valve body and hold-down plate retaining screws.

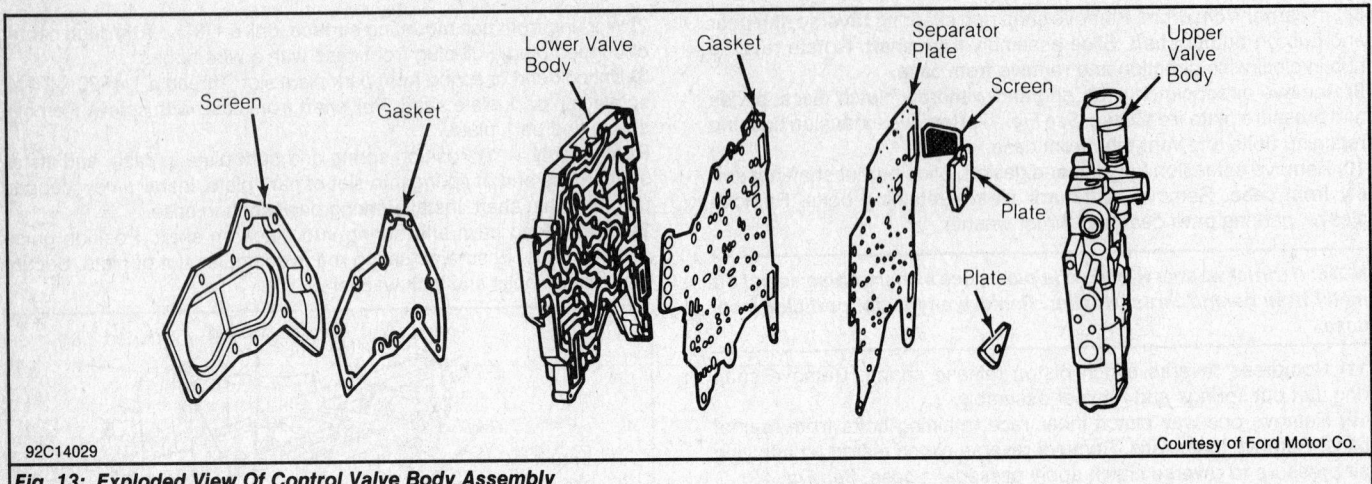

92C14029

Courtesy of Ford Motor Co.

Fig. 13: Exploded View Of Control Valve Body Assembly

2) Remove 7 retaining screws from underside of lower valve body and separate bodies, removing separator plate and gasket. DO NOT lose check balls and springs. Remove separator plate screen. *See Fig. 13.*

NOTE: Valve body-to-screen gasket must be replaced when valve body is serviced.

3) Remove manual valve retaining pin from upper valve body. Slide manual valve out of valve body. Cover downshift valve port using finger, and remove downshift valve retainer. Remove spring and downshift valve. *See Fig. 15.*

4) Apply hand pressure to pressure boost valve sleeve and remove retaining clip from underside of valve body. Slowly release pressure and remove sleeve and pressure boost valve. Remove 2 springs, retainer and main regulator valve from bore.

5) Apply hand pressure to throttle boost valve plate and remove 2 retaining screws. Release pressure and remove plate, throttle boost valve, spring, manual low 2-1 scheduling valve and spring from bore.

6) Apply hand pressure on remaining valve body plate and remove 8 retaining screws. Hold valve body so plate faces upward.

7) Release hand pressure on plate and remove. Remove spring and intermediate servo modulator valve from body. Remove intermediate servo accumulator valve and springs.

8) Remove 2-3 backout valve and spring. Remove 2-3 shift valve, spring and throttle modulator valve. Remove 1-2 shift valve, DR-2 shift valve and spring. Remove coasting regulator valve and cutback valve from body.

CAUTION: For gasoline and diesel applications, DO NOT interchange valve body repair kits or components. Cross-matching components may cause shift problems.

Reassembly – To reassemble, reverse disassembly procedure. Coat check balls with petroleum jelly to hold in place during reassembly. *See Fig. 14.* When installing screen in separator plate, ensure tabs are flush with separator plate surface. Tighten all bolts and screws evenly to specification. See TORQUE SPECIFICATIONS. *See Fig. 6.*

FRONT PUMP

Disassembly – Remove 2 seal rings and selective thrust washer. Remove large square cut seal from outside diameter of pump housing. Remove 5 bolts securing stator support to pump housing. Lift support from housing. Remove drive and driven gears from housing. *See Fig. 16.*

Pump Housing Bushing Replacement – Remove bushing from pump housing using a driver and hammer. Place new bushing into position. Ensure half moon slot in bushing is on top and in line with oil lube hole near seal bore. Press bushing in .060-.080" (1.52-2.03 mm) below front face of bushing bore.

NOTE: After assembly, half moon slot must be aligned with lube hole to provide proper lubrication.

Reassembly – 1) Install drive and driven gear into pump housing with identification mark or chamfered surface of each gear installed toward front of pump housing. Position stator support in pump housing. Install and tighten retaining bolts to specification. See TORQUE SPECIFICATIONS.

2) Carefully install 2 NEW seal rings on stator support. Ensure ends of rings are engaged to lock them in place. Install a NEW square cut seal on outside diameter of pump housing.

3) Install selective thrust washer. Place pump on torque converter. Ensure drive gear engages converter hub. Rotate pump to ensure gears rotate freely.

CAUTION: Different clutch assemblies are used in various models. When disassembling clutches, note number and location of plates used for reassembly reference.

DIRECT CLUTCH

Disassembly – 1) Remove pressure plate snap ring by prying up using screwdriver. Remove pressure, drive and driven plates. Using appropriate compressor, compress piston return springs.

Converter Pressure Relief Valve — **Pressure Boost Valve Sleeve** — **Converter Pressure Relief Spring** — **Downshift Valve & Spring** — **Throttle Pressure Relief Ball & Spring** — **Downshift Valve Retainer** — **Reverse Clutch Check Ball** — **2-3 Shift Check Valve** — **New Casting**

92G14031

Courtesy of Ford Motor Co.

Fig. 14: Identifying Valve Body Check Valves & Balls

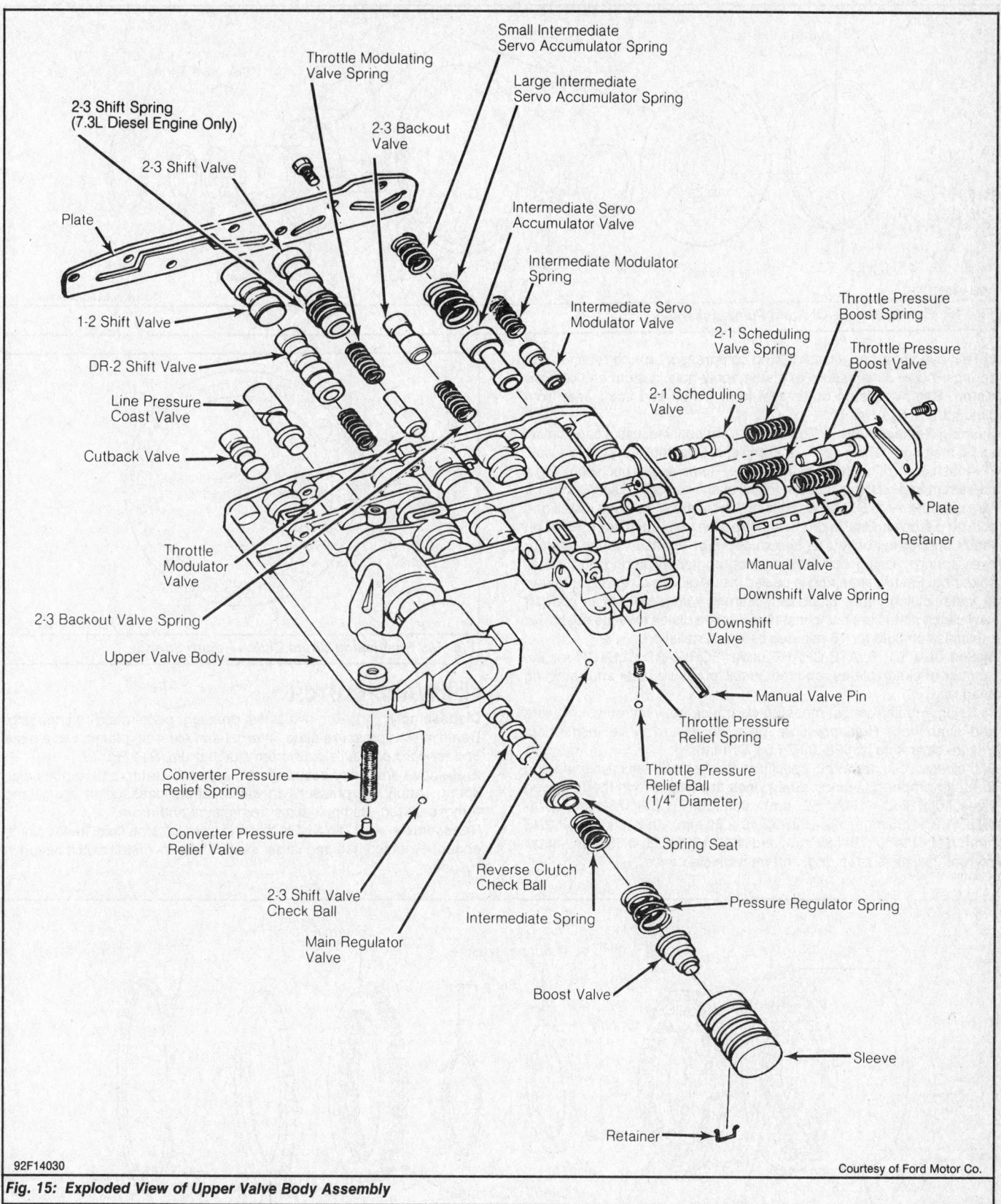

92F14030

Courtesy of Ford Motor Co.

Fig. 15: Exploded View of Upper Valve Body Assembly

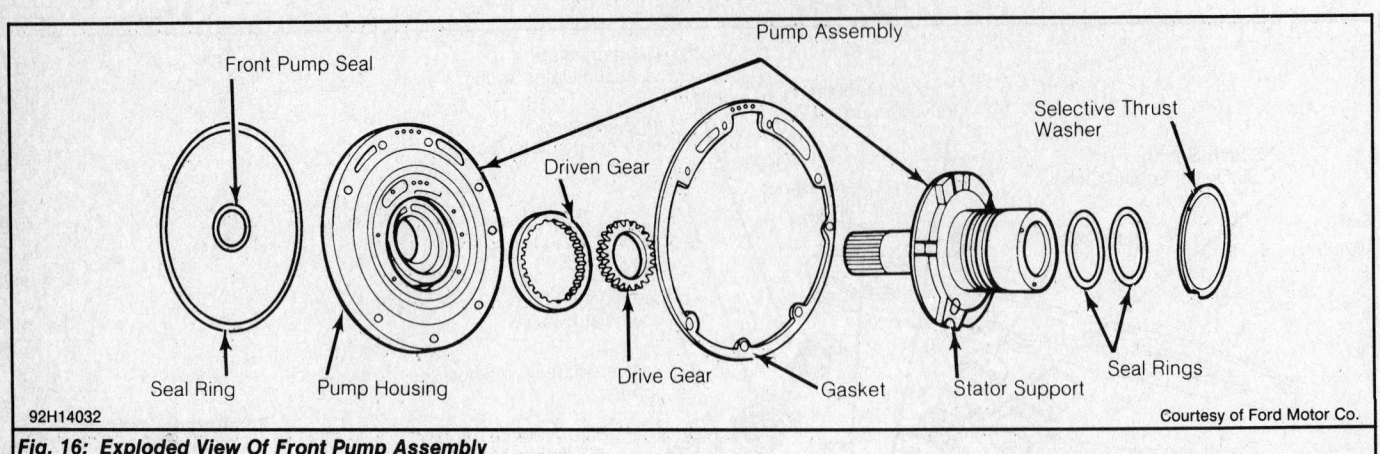

Fig. 16: *Exploded View Of Front Pump Assembly*

92H14032   Courtesy of Ford Motor Co.

2) Remove snap ring, clutch spring compressor, spring retainer and springs. Apply air pressure to piston apply hole in drum and remove piston. Remove piston outer seal from piston and inner seal from clutch drum. *See Fig. 17.*

Bushing Replacement – To remove front bushing, use a cape chisel and cut along bushing seam until chisel breaks through bushing wall. Pry loose ends of bushing up to remove. Remove rear bushing using a press ram and bushing adapter. Install bushings using bushing drivers.

Reassembly – **1)** Dip NEW seals in transmission fluid and install one seal on piston and one in drum. Install piston into clutch drum. Position return springs in pockets as shown. *See Fig. 18.* Place spring retainer over springs. Using compressor tool, compress spring and install snap ring. Ensure snap ring is sealed inside guides on spring retainer.

2) Install clutch plates alternately starting with a steel drive plate. If new clutch plates are being installed, friction plates must be soaked in transmission fluid for 15 minutes before installation.

3) See CLUTCH PLATE CHART under FORWARD CLUTCH for the number of clutch plates required. Install pressure plate and retaining snap ring.

4) Using a feeler gauge, measure clearance between pressure plate and snap ring. Hold pressure plate downward while measuring. Ensure clearance is .022-.036" (.56-.91 mm).

5) If clearance is not within specifications, replace selective snap ring to attain proper clearance. Snap rings are available in the following sizes; .056-.060" (1.42-1.52 mm), .065-.069" (1.65-1.75 mm), .074-.078" (1.87-1.98 mm), .083-.087" (2.10-2.20 mm), .092-.096" (2.33-2.43 mm), .110-.114" (2.79-2.89 mm) and .128-.132" (3.25-3.35 mm). Install correct thickness snap ring, and recheck clearance.

Springs Must Be Installed In Pockets Marked X only

92J14034   Courtesy of Ford Motor Co.

Fig. 18: *Positioning Direct Clutch Return Springs*

FORWARD CLUTCH

Disassembly – **1)** Remove clutch pressure plate retaining snap ring. Remove rear pressure plate, internal and external plates, wave plate and forward pressure plate from clutch drum. *See Fig. 19.*

2) Remove snap ring securing disc spring in drum, and remove disc spring. Apply air pressure to clutch apply passage in drum, and remove piston. Remove seals from piston and drum.

Reassembly – **1)** Dip 2 NEW seals in transmission fluid. Install smaller seal on clutch hub and larger seal on piston. Install clutch piston in cylinder.

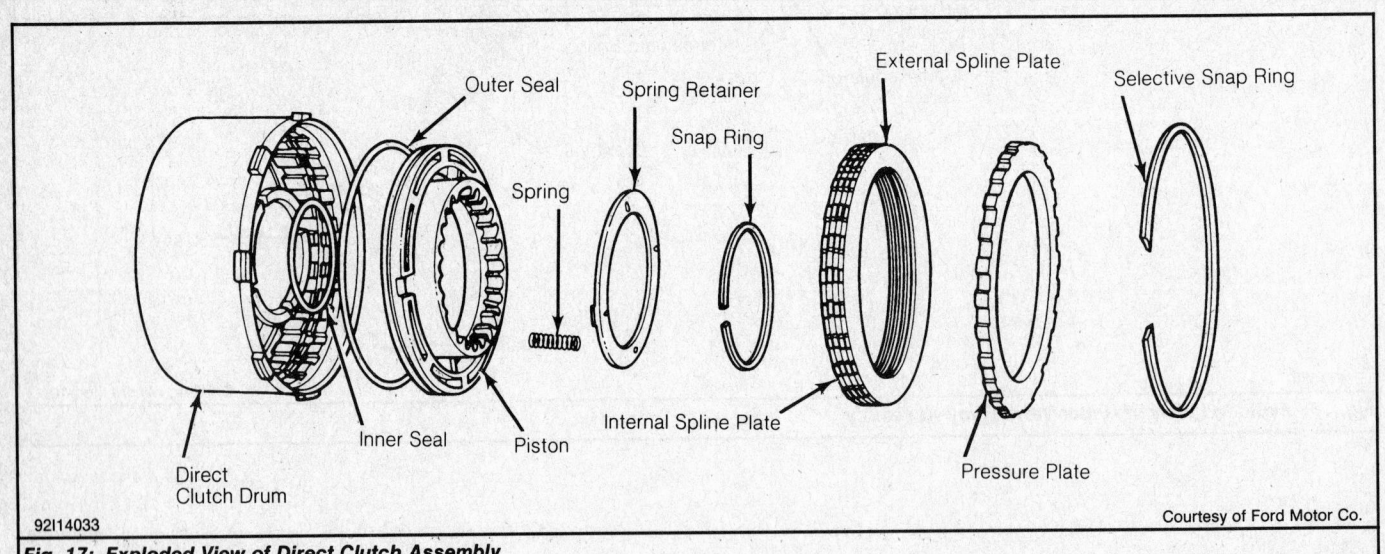

92I14033   Courtesy of Ford Motor Co.

Fig. 17: *Exploded View of Direct Clutch Assembly*

2) Ensure steel pressure ring is in groove on piston. Place disc spring in clutch drum with dished face downward. Secure in place with retaining snap ring.

NOTE: If new friction plates are being installed, soak them in transmission fluid for 15 minutes prior to installation.

3) Install forward pressure plate with flat side up and beveled side downward. Dip clutch plates in transmission fluid.

4) Install wave plate. Install clutch plates starting with a steel plate, then a friction plate. Install remaining plates in this sequence. See CLUTCH PLATE CHART for the number of clutch plates required. Install pressure plate and retaining snap ring.

CLUTCH PLATE CHART

Application/ Engine Size	Number Of Steel Plates	Number Of Friction Plates
Forward Clutch		
4.9L	[1] 3	3
5.8L	[1] 4	4
7.3L Diesel	[1] 4	4
7.5L	[1] 4	4
Direct Clutch		
4.9L	[1] 3	3
5.8L	[1] 4	4
7.3L Diesel	[1] 4	4
7.5L	[1] 4	4
Reverse Clutch		
4.9L	[1] 4	4
5.8L	[2] 5	5
7.3L Diesel	[2] 5	5
7.5L	[2] 6	6

[1] – Plus a wave plate next to inner pressure plate.
[2] – Plus a wave plate next to piston.

5) Using a feeler gauge, measure clearance between snap ring and pressure plate. Hold pressure plate down while measuring. Ensure clearance is .021-.046" (.53-1.17 mm). If clearance is not within specifications, replace selective snap ring to meet proper clearance. See SELECTIVE SNAP RINGS table under DIRECT CLUTCH. Install correct thickness snap ring and recheck clearance.

INPUT SHELL & SUN GEAR

Disassembly – Remove rear (external) snap ring from sun gear, and remove thrust washer from sun gear and input shell. Working inside input shell, remove sun gear. Remove forward (internal) snap ring from gear. See Fig. 20.

Reassembly – Install forward snap ring on short end of sun gear. Working inside input shell, slide sun gear and snap ring into place. Ensure longer end of gear is at rear. Place thrust washer on rear side of input shell. Install wear plate and rear snap ring.

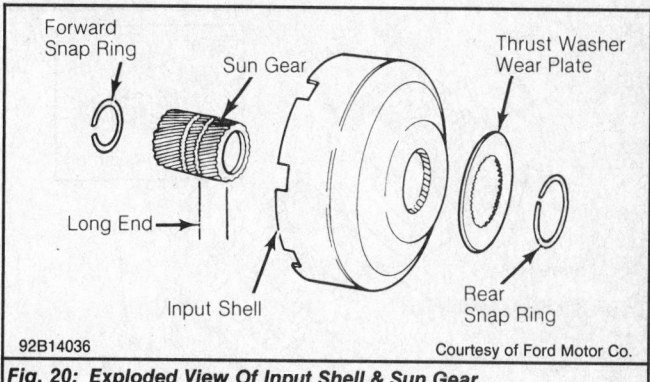

92B14036   Courtesy of Ford Motor Co.

Fig. 20: Exploded View Of Input Shell & Sun Gear

OUTPUT SHAFT HUB & RING GEAR

Disassembly & Reassembly – Remove hub retaining snap ring, and lift hub from ring gear. When installing, secure hub with retaining snap ring. Ensure snap ring is fully engaged in groove.

ONE-WAY CLUTCH

NOTE: One-way clutch assembly may be a non-serviceable type.

Disassembly – Remove snap ring and bushing from rear of reverse clutch hub. Remove rollers from spring assembly. Lift spring assembly from hub. Remove snap ring from hub. See Fig. 21.

Reassembly – **1)** Install snap ring in forward groove of reverse clutch hub. Place hub on bench with forward end down. Install clutch spring assembly on top of snap ring.

2) Install a roller into each spring assembly compartment. Install bushing on top of spring assembly. Install remaining snap ring at rear of clutch hub to secure assembly.

INTERMEDIATE SERVO

Disassembly – Apply air pressure to port in servo cover and remove piston assembly. Remove seal from cover.

NOTE: Piston and rod are serviced as an assembly. Replace if piston or sealing lip is damaged.

Reassembly – Dip new seal in transmission fluid, and install seal on cover. Dip piston assembly in transmission fluid, and install assembly in cover.

REVERSE CLUTCH PISTON

Clutch is assembled during transmission reassembly. Remove inner and outer seals from clutch piston. Dip NEW seals in transmission fluid and install on piston.

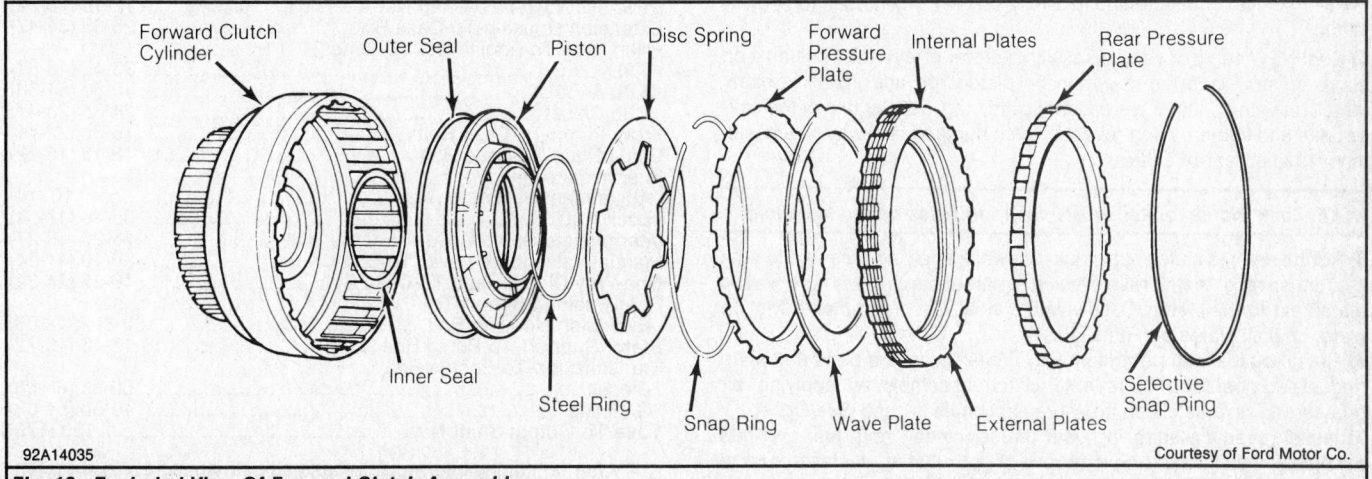

92A14035   Courtesy of Ford Motor Co.

Fig. 19: Exploded View Of Forward Clutch Assembly

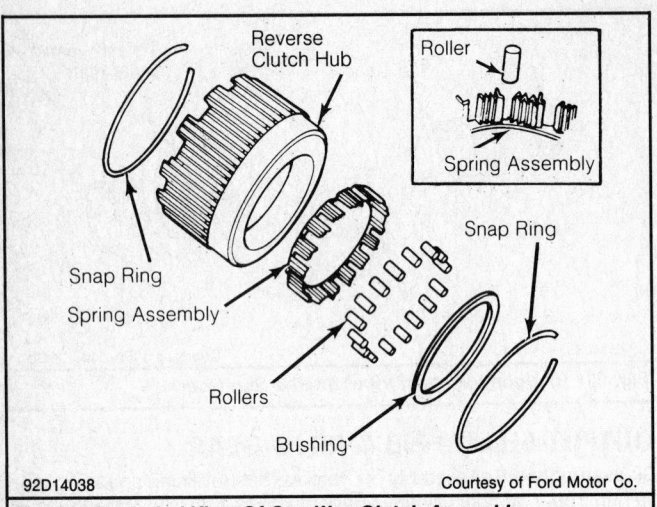

92D14038   Courtesy of Ford Motor Co.

Fig. 21: Exploded View Of One-Way Clutch Assembly

GOVERNOR

Disassembly – Remove governor retaining bolts and governor. Remove snap ring securing governor collector body to output shaft. Slide governor off front of shaft. Remove seal rings from collector body.

CAUTION: Diesel governor is NOT interchangeable with gasoline engine models.

Reassembly – **1)** Carefully install NEW seal rings on collector body. Working from front end of output shaft, slide collector body into place on shaft.

2) Secure in place with snap ring. Ensure snap ring is fully seated in groove. Position governor on collector body. Install and tighten retaining screws to specification. See TORQUE SPECIFICATIONS.

TRANSMISSION REASSEMBLY

1) With transmission mounted in fixture, tap reverse clutch piston into case using soft mallet. Install reverse clutch return spring and retainer assembly in clutch piston. Hold one-way clutch inner race in position, and install and tighten retaining bolts to specification. See TORQUE SPECIFICATIONS.

2) Place transmission case on bench with front end facing downward. Position parking gear thrust washer and gear on case. It is not necessary to restake thrust washer. Position oil distributor and tubes on rear of case.

3) Install and tighten retaining bolts. Install output shaft and governor as an assembly. *See Fig. 22.* Place a NEW gasket on rear of case. Install extension housing and retaining bolts. Tighten bolts to specification.

4) Coat NEW servo cover gasket with petroleum jelly and position it on servo cover. Place servo spring on piston rod and install in case. Install retaining bolts. Ensure identification tag is under one of the cover bolts and tighten. Align reverse clutch hub and one-way clutch with inner race at rear of case.

NOTE: Soak friction plates in ATF for 15 minutes before installing.

---

5) Rotate reverse clutch hub clockwise while applying pressure to seat it on inner race. Install reverse clutch plates, starting with the waved plate next to the piston. Follow with a steel plate, and then a friction plate, until all plates are installed.

6) Retain plates with petroleum jelly. Install pressure plate and snap ring. Test operation of reverse clutch assembly by applying air pressure to reverse clutch pressure apply hole in case. *See Fig. 4.*

7) Install reverse planet ring gear thrust washer, ring gear and hub assembly. Install snap ring in groove of output shaft. Install front and rear thrust washers onto reverse planet assembly. Retain with petroleum jelly.

8) Install assembly into ring gear, and install snap ring. Place direct clutch on bench with front end facing downward. Install thrust washer on rear end of assembly and retain washer with petroleum jelly.

9) Install splined end of forward clutch into open end of direct clutch with splines engaging direct clutch plates. Install thrust washer on front end of forward planet ring gear and hub. Retain with petroleum jelly.

10) Install ring gear into forward clutch. Install thrust washer on front end of forward planet assembly and retain with petroleum jelly. Install assembly into ring gear. Install input shell and sun assembly. Install reverse-high clutch, forward clutch, forward planet assembly, input shell and sun gear as an assembly, into case.

11) Install intermediate band around direct clutch drum. Install band struts and tighten band adjustment screw enough to retain band. Place selective bronze thrust washer on rear shoulder of stator support and retain with petroleum jelly. See STATOR SUPPORT SELECTIVE THRUST WASHERS table.

12) If end play was not within specifications when disassembled, replace washer at this time with one of proper thickness. Ensure end play is .008-.044" (.20-1.12mm)

STATOR SUPPORT SELECTIVE THRUST WASHERS

Color Code	Thickness In. (mm)
Blue	.056-.060 (1.42-1.52)
Natural (White)	.073-.077 (1.85-1.96)
Red	.088-.092 (2.24-2.34)

13) Using 5/16" x 3" bolts, make 2 alignment studs by cutting heads off and grinding a taper on cut end. Install studs opposite each other in case mounting holes.

14) Slide a NEW gasket onto studs. Position front pump on case, being careful not to damage seal on pump housing, and remove studs. Install 6 of the mounting bolts and tighten to specification.

15) Tighten intermediate band adjustment screw to specification. Back off screw 1 1/2 turns. Hold adjustment screw in this position and tighten lock nut to specification. See TORQUE SPECIFICATIONS.

16) Install input shaft with long splined end inserted into forward clutch assembly. Measure end play again to ensure correct assembly. Install control valve body into case, ensuring levers engage valves properly.

17) Install primary throttle valve, rod and vacuum diaphragm in case. Install oil pan with NEW gasket. Install retaining bolts and tighten to specification. Install torque converter.

TORQUE SPECIFICATIONS
TORQUE SPECIFICATIONS

Application	Ft. Lbs. (N.m)
Converter Cover-To-Housing Bolt	12-16 (16-22)
Converter Drain Plug	8-28 (11-38)
Converter-To-Flywheel Bolt	20-34 (27-46)
Cooler Tube Connector Lock Nut	20-35 (27-47)
Diaphragm Assembly-To-Case Bolt	12-16 (16-22)
Distributor Sleeve-To-Case Bolt	12-16 (16-22)
Downshift Lever-To-Shaft Nut	12-16 (16-22)
Extension Housing-To-Case Bolt	25-35 (34-47)
Filler Tube-To-Engine Bolt (E-Series)	
4.9L	33-42 (45-57)
5.8L & 7.5L	40-50 (54-68)
7.3L Diesel	24-35 (33-47)
Front Pump-To-Case Bolt	16-30 (22-41)
Guide Plate-To-Case Bolt	12-16 (16-22)
Intermediate Band	
Adjustment Screw	[1] 10 (14)
Lock Nut	35-40 (47-54)
Intermediate Servo Cover-To-Case Bolt	14-20 (19-27)
Manual Valve Inner Lever-To-Shaft Nut	30-40 (41-54)
One-Way Clutch Race-To-Case Bolt	18-25 (24-34)
Rear Engine Support-To-	
Extension Housing Bolt	60-80 (81-108)
Stator Support-To-Pump Bolt	12-16 (16-22)
Transmission-To-Engine Bolt	
Diesel	50-65 (68-88)
Gasoline	40-50 (54-68)
Yoke-To-Output Shaft Nut	130 (176)

[1] – After tightening intermediate band adjustment screw to specification, back off screw 1 1/2 turns.

TORQUE SPECIFICATIONS (Cont.)

Application	INCH Lbs. (N.m)
Converter Housing-To-Converter Cover Bolt	
7.5L Engine Only	30-60 (3.4-6.8)
Detent Spring-To-Case Bolt	80-120 (9.0-13.6)
End Plates-To-Valve Body Bolt	20-40 (2.3-4.5)
Governor Body-To-Oil Collector Flange Bolt	90-120 (10.2-13.6)
Inner Downshift Lever Stop Bolt	20-45 (2.3-5.1)
Neutral Safety Switch-To-Case Bolt	55-75 (6.2-8.5)
Oil Pan-To-Case Bolt	96-144 (10.8-16.3)
Reinforcement Plate-To-Valve Body Bolt	20-45 (2.3-5.1)
Screen & Lower-To-Upper Valve Body Bolt	40-55 (4.5-6.2)
Shift Valve Plate-To-Upper Body Bolt	20-45 (2.3-5.1)
Upper-To-Lower Body Bolt	40-55 (4.5-6.2)
Valve Body-To-Case Bolt	95-125 (10.7-14.1)

TORQUE SPECIFICATIONS (Cont.)

Application	INCH Lbs. (N.m)
VRV-To-Injection Pump Bolt	
7.3L Diesel Engine Only	75-90 (8.5-10.2)

TRANSAXLE SPECIFICATIONS

TRANSAXLE SPECIFICATIONS

Application	In. (mm)
Direct Clutch Pack Clearance	.022-.036 (.56-.91)
Forward Clutch Pack Clearance	.063-.071 (1.6-1.8)
Reverse Clutch Pack Clearance	.022-.036 (.56-.91)
Torque Converter End Play	.021 (.53)
Total End Play	.008-.044 (.20-1.12)

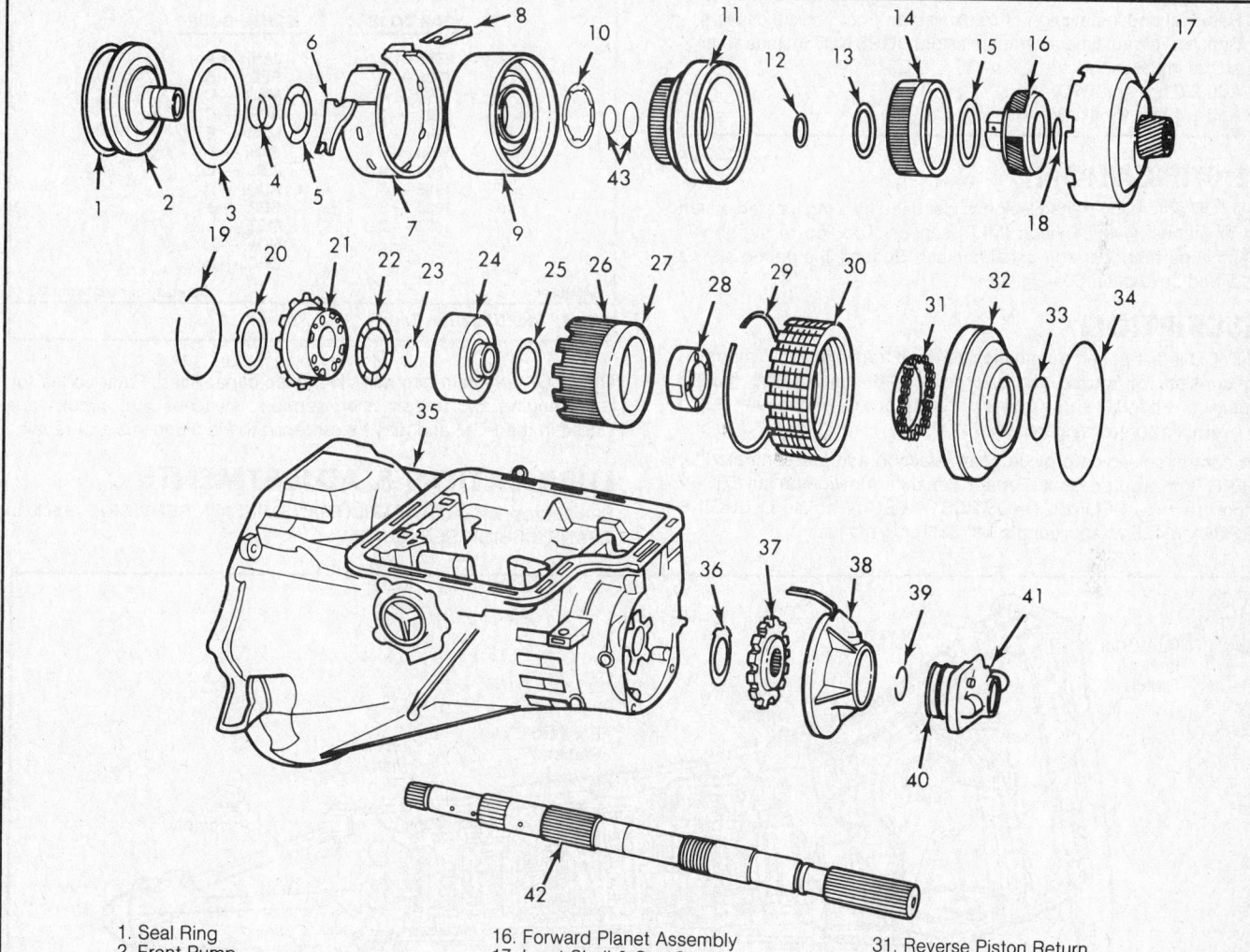

1. Seal Ring
2. Front Pump
3. Gasket
4. Seal Rings
5. No. 1 Thrust Washer
6. Strut Intermediate Brake Band
7. Intermediate Brake Band
8. Strut Intermediate Brake Band Anchor
9. Direct Clutch
10. No. 2 Thrust Washer
11. Forward Clutch Assembly
12. No. 3 Thrust Washer Needle Bearing
13. No. 4 Thrust Washer
14. Forward Planet Ring & Hub
15. No. 5 Thrust Washer
16. Forward Planet Assembly
17. Input Shell & Sun Gear
18. No. 6 Thrust Washer Needle Bearing
19. Snap Ring
20. No. 7 Thrust Washer
21. Reverse Planet Assembly
22. No. 8 Thrust Washer
23. Reverse Ring Gear & Hub Retaining Ring
24. Reverse Ring Gear & Hub
25. No. 9 Thrust Washer
26. Reverse Clutch Hub
27. One-Way Clutch
28. One-Way Clutch Inner Race
29. Snap Ring
30. Reverse Clutch Plates
31. Reverse Piston Return Spring & Retainer
32. Reverse Piston
33. Inner Seal
34. Outer Seal
35. Case
36. No. 10 Thrust Washer
37. Parking Gear
38. Governor Distributor Sleeve
39. Snap Ring
40. Governor Collector
41. Governor
42. Output Shaft
43. Forward Clutch Seal Rings

92H14040

Courtesy of Ford Motor Co.

Fig. 22: Exploded View Of Transmission Case & Drive Train Assembly

AUTOMATIC TRANSMISSIONS
Ford E4OD

APPLICATION & LABOR TIMES

APPLICATION & LABOR TIMES

Vehicle Application	Labor Times [1] R & I	[2] Overhaul	Engine Size
Bronco	5.6	8.2	5.0L PFI
Bronco	5.6	8.2	5.8L PFI
E150/250	3.6	8.2	4.9L PFI
E150/250/350	3.8	8.2	5.8L PFI
E350	3.8	8.2	7.3L Diesel
E350	3.8	8.2	7.5L PFI
F150/250 [3]	3.6	8.2	4.9L PFI
F150/250 [3]	3.6	8.2	5.0L PFI
F150/250/350 [3]	3.6	8.2	5.8L PFI
F250/350/Super Duty [4]	3.9	8.2	7.3L Diesel
F250/350/Super Duty [4]	3.9	8.2	7.5L PFI

[1] – Removal and installation of transmission from vehicle chassis.
[2] – Bench overhaul time for transmission. DOES NOT include removal and installation.
[3] – Add 2.0 hrs. for 4WD.
[4] – Add 1.4 hrs. for 4WD.

IDENTIFICATION

The E4OD automatic transmission is identified by a tag located on left side of manual lever position (MLP) sensor. Top line of tag shows assembly part number and serial number. Second line on tag shows model and build date. *See Fig. 1.*

DESCRIPTION

The E4OD is a 4-speed automatic overdrive transmission. Transmission consists of torque converter clutch, 6 multiple-disc friction clutches, one band, 2 sprag one-way clutches, a roller one-way clutch and hydraulic control system. *See Fig. 2.*

Shift control solenoids provide gear selection and are controlled by the EEC-IV microprocessor. For additional information on the EEC-IV system, refer to SELF-DIAGNOSTICS – EEC-IV article in ENGINE PERFORMANCE of appropriate MITCHELL® manual.

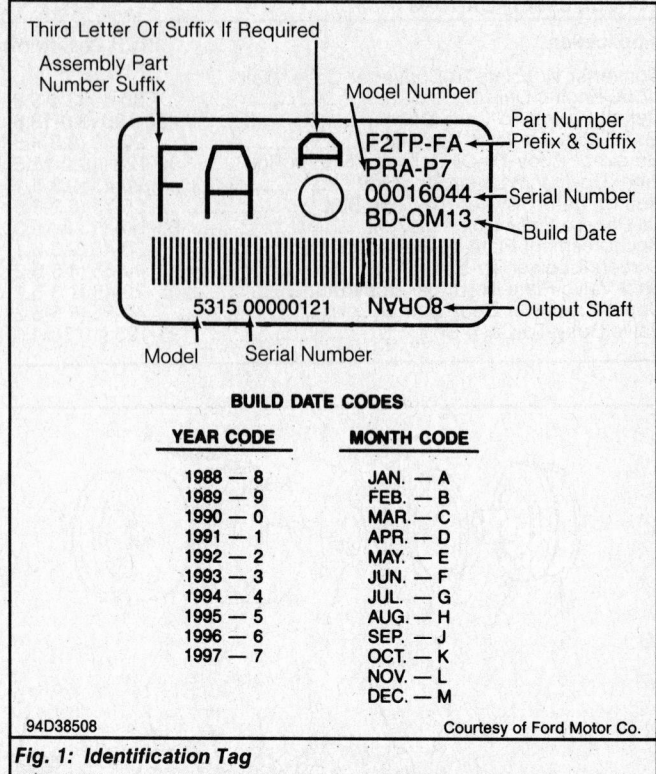

BUILD DATE CODES

YEAR CODE	MONTH CODE
1988 — 8	JAN. — A
1989 — 9	FEB. — B
1990 — 0	MAR. — C
1991 — 1	APR. — D
1992 — 2	MAY. — E
1993 — 3	JUN. — F
1994 — 4	JUL. — G
1995 — 5	AUG. — H
1996 — 6	SEP. — J
1997 — 7	OCT. — K
	NOV. — L
	DEC. — M

94D38508   Courtesy of Ford Motor Co.

Fig. 1: Identification Tag

The EEC-IV system has self-diagnostic capabilities. Fault codes for faulty engine and transmission sensors, switches and circuits are stored in the PCM and may be retrieved to aid diagnosis and repair.

LUBRICATION & ADJUSTMENTS

See appropriate AUTOMATIC TRANSMISSION SERVICING article in TRANSMISSION SERVICING.

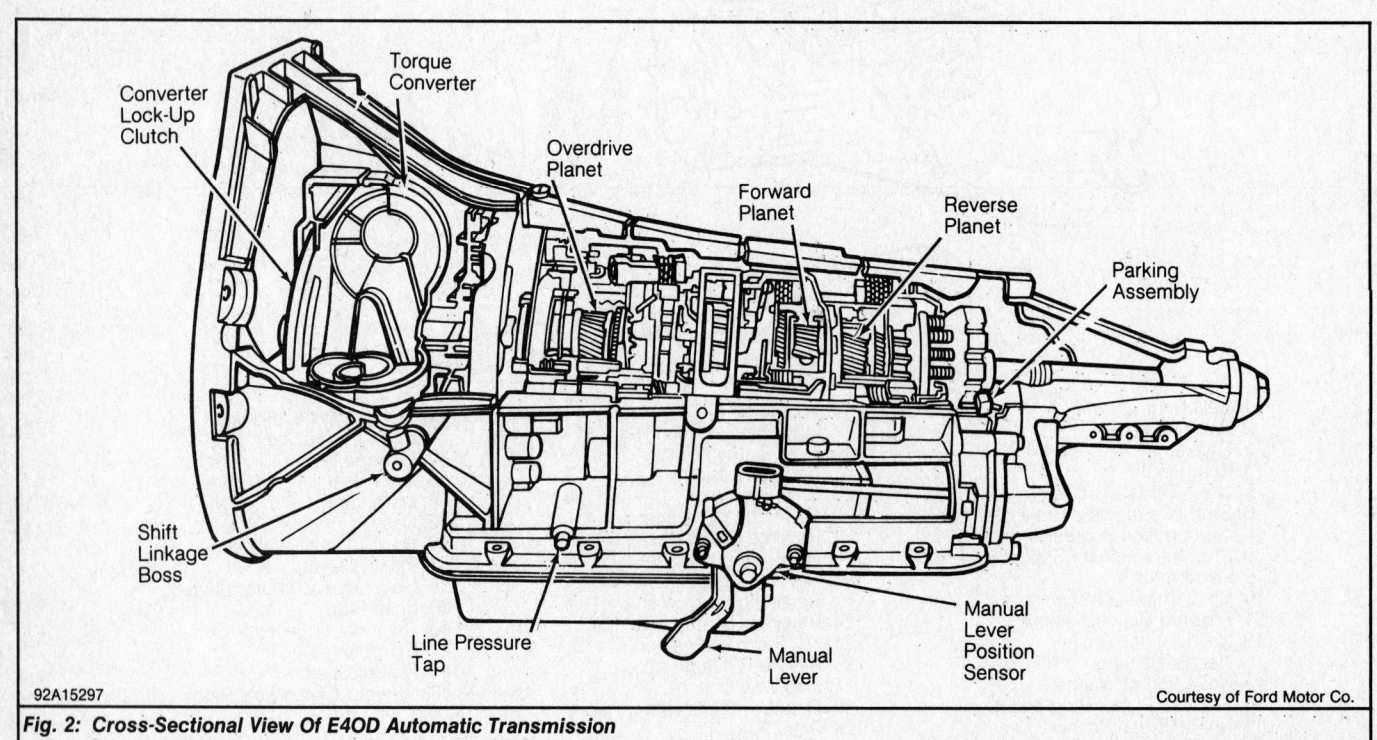

92A15297   Courtesy of Ford Motor Co.

Fig. 2: Cross-Sectional View Of E4OD Automatic Transmission

TROUBLE SHOOTING

NOTE: After verifying driveability complaint, perform trouble shooting and testing procedures in this article. For electronic diagnostics and testing, see E4OD ELECTRONIC CONTROLS article. When fault codes are retrieved, all engine related codes MUST be repaired first. For engine trouble code repair and diagnostic information, see SELF-DIAGNOSTICS – EEC-IV article in ENGINE PERFORMANCE in appropriate MITCHELL® manual.

ENGAGEMENT FAULTS

No Forward Engagement – Fluid level, shift linkage or cable, low line pressure, pump inlet filter and seal assembly, stuck manual valve, valve body leakage (gasket damage), improperly torqued valve body bolts, forward clutch assembly (damaged stator support, damaged check ball, loose feed bolt, damaged center support, worn clutch components), forward/reverse sun gear damaged, front planetary assembly damaged, output shaft splines and low one-way clutch assembly.

No Reverse Engagement – Fluid level, shift linkage or cable, low line pressure, pump inlet filter and seal assembly, stuck manual valve, valve body leakage (gasket damage), improperly torqued valve body bolts, coast clutch assembly, direct clutch assembly (only if 3rd gear is also inoperative), forward planetary assembly, reverse clutch assembly, reverse planet assembly and reverse ring gear.

Harsh Reverse Engagement – High line pressure, valve body leakage (gasket damage), improperly torqued valve body bolts, Electronic Pressure Control (EPC) solenoid stuck, stuck valve body components (direct clutch accumulator valve and plunger, engagement control valve, direct clutch accumulator regulator valve, springs), pump assembly and direct clutch assembly.

Harsh Forward Engagement – High line pressure, valve body leakage (gasket damage), improperly torqued valve body bolts, Electronic Pressure Control (EPC) solenoid stuck, valve body check ball No. 13 missing, pump assembly, direct clutch assembly and forward clutch assembly.

Delayed/Soft Reverse Engagement – Shift linkage or cable, improperly torqued valve body bolts, valve body components (direct clutch accumulator regulator valve, low reverse modulator valve, springs), coast clutch assembly, direct clutch assembly and reverse clutch assembly.

Delayed/Soft Forward Engagement – Fluid level, shift linkage or cable, low line pressure, pump inlet filter or seal assembly, improperly torqued valve body bolts, center support assembly and forward clutch assembly.

No Forward & No Reverse Engagement – Fluid level, internal or external shift linkage, low line pressure, pump inlet filter and seal assembly, manual valve, valve body leakage (improperly torqued bolts), pump assembly (main regulator/booster valve), center support assembly, forward/reverse sun gear, forward planetary assembly, input shaft, center shaft, output shaft, overdrive carrier assembly and overdrive overrunning clutch (shift selector in OD with OD switch in cancel mode).

Harsh Forward & Reverse Engagement – High line pressure, valve body bolts improperly torque, EPC solenoid stuck, valve body components (engagement control valve) and pump assembly (main regulator/booster valve).

Delayed/Soft Forward & Reverse Engagement – Shift linkage or cable, fluid level, low line pressure, pump inlet filter and seal assembly, valve body bolts improperly torqued (gasket damage) and torque converter drainback (initial engagement only).

SHIFTING FAULTS

No Shifting – Fluid level, internal or external shift linkage, pump inlet filter/seal assembly and valve body components.

Early/Late Shift Timing – Incorrect tire size, incorrect speedometer gear, mismatched axle ratio, poor engine performance and valve body components.

Erratic Or Hunting Shift Timing – Fluid level, pump inlet filter and seal assembly, valve body components and torque converter clutch.

Soft Or Slipping Shift Feel – Fluid level, low line pressure, valve body bolts improperly torqued (gasket damage, leaks), EPC solenoid, valve body components (line modulator valve, accumulator assembly) and pump assembly.

Harsh Shift Feel – Fluid level, high line pressure, valve body bolts improperly torqued (gasket damage), EPC solenoid, accumulator assembly, valve body components (line modulator valve) and pump assembly.

No 1st Gear, Engages In Higher Gear – Internal or external shift linkage, valve body bolts improperly torqued (gasket damage), shift solenoid 1 and/or 2, valve body components (solenoid regulator valve, 2-3 shift valve, 3-4 shift valve, D2 valve), air bleeds for S1 or S2 circuits missing, damaged band servo or clutches, reverse ring gear and low/reverse one-way clutch.

No Low (Manual 1st) Gear – Internal or external shift linkage, valve body bolts improperly torqued (gasket damage), shift solenoid No. 1, valve body components (manual control valve, low reverse modulator valve, 1-2 shift valve, 2-3 shift valve, BS1 check ball, 4-3-2 timing valve) and low/reverse one-way clutch assembly.

No 2nd (Manual 2nd) Gear – Internal or external shift linkage, improperly torque valve body bolts, valve body components (2-3 shift valve, 3-4 shift valve, manual 1-2 transition valve, BS2 or BS6 check ball) and intermediate clutch assembly and intermediate one-way clutch assembly.

No 1st To 2nd Shift – Internal or external shift linkage, improperly torque valve body bolts, valve body components (D2 valve, 1-2 shift valve, 1-2 manual transition valve, intermediate clutch accumulator regulator valves, springs), shift solenoid No. 2, intermediate clutch assembly and intermediate one-way clutch assembly.

No 2nd To 3rd Shift – Improperly torque valve body bolts, valve body components (2-3 shift valve, direct clutch accumulator regulator valves, springs), shift solenoid No. 1, direct clutch assembly and center support assembly.

No 3rd To 4th Shift – Improperly torqued valve body bolts (gasket damage), shift solenoid No. 1, shift solenoid No. 2, valve body components (overdrive accumulator regulator valve, 3-4 shift valve, overdrive one-way clutch assembly, overdrive clutch assembly and overdrive planetary assembly.

No 4th To 3rd Shift – Improperly torqued valve body bolts (gasket damaged), shift solenoid No. 2 and valve body components (check ball BS2, 3-4 shift valve).

No 3rd To 2nd Shift – Improperly torqued valve body bolts (gasket damaged), shift solenoid No. 1 and valve body components (3-2 shift valve).

No 2nd To 1st Shift – Improperly torqued valve body bolts (gasket damaged), shift solenoid No. 2 and valve body components (D2 shift valve).

Soft/Slipping 1st To 2nd Shift – Improperly torqued valve body bolts (gasket damaged), valve body components (intermediate clutch accumulator regulator valve or plunger) and intermediate clutch assembly.

Soft/Slipping 2nd To 3rd Shift – Improperly torqued valve body bolts (gasket damaged), valve body components (direct clutch accumulator regulator valve or plunger), center support assembly and direct clutch assembly.

Soft/Slipping 3rd To 4th Shift – Improperly torqued valve body bolts (gasket damaged), valve body components (overdrive accumulator regulator valve and spring, overdrive accumulator plunger and springs) and overdrive clutch assembly.

Soft/Slipping Downshifts – Improperly torqued valve body bolts (gasket damaged) and valve body components (check ball CB7, damage valve body separator plate).

Harsh 1st To 2nd Shift – Improperly torqued valve body bolts (gasket damaged), valve body components (intermediate clutch accumulator regulator valve or plunger springs) and intermediate clutch assembly.

Harsh 2nd To 3rd Shift – Improperly torqued valve body bolts (gasket damaged), valve body components (direct clutch accumulator valve or plunger), center support assembly and direct clutch assembly.

Harsh 3rd To 4th Shift – Improperly torqued valve body bolts (gasket damaged), valve body components (overdrive accumulator regulator valve or plunger) and overdrive clutch assembly.

Harsh 4th To 3rd Shift – Improperly torqued valve body bolts (gasket damaged), check ball CB7 missing and separator plate damaged.

Harsh 3rd To 2nd Shift – Improperly torqued valve body bolts (gasket damaged), check ball CB6 missing and separator plate damaged.

Harsh 2nd To 1st Shift – Improperly torqued valve body bolts (gasket damaged), check ball CB14 missing and separator plate damaged.

No Torque Converter Clutch Application – Improperly torqued valve body bolts (gasket damaged), torque converter clutch solenoid, transmission oil temperature sensor, pump assembly (converter clutch control valve and regulator valve stuck), stator support and torque converter assembly.

Torque Converter Clutch Always Applied (Stalls Vehicle In Drive & Manual 2nd Gear Only) – Low line pressure, improperly torqued valve body bolts (gasket damaged), torque converter clutch solenoid, pump assembly (converter clutch control valve) and torque converter assembly.

Torque Converter Clutch Cycling/Shudder/Chatter – Fluid condition, improperly torqued valve body bolts (gasket damaged), torque converter clutch solenoid, pump assembly, stator support and torque converter assembly.

MISCELLANEOUS FAULTS

No Park Range – Misadjusted internal or external shift linkage, park mechanism components and transfer case and linkages (4WD).

Transmission Overheating – Fluid level and condition, transmission cooling system, poor engine performance and torque converter clutch.

No Engine Braking In Manual 2nd Gear – Improperly torqued valve body bolts (gasket damaged), check balls BS1, BS2, BS6 and CB1 missing or damaged, valve body separator plate, valve body components (4-3-2 timing valve, D2 valve, 2-3 shift valve, coast clutch shift valve, 1-2 manual transition valve, 3-4 shift valve), coast clutch assembly and intermediate servo/band assembly.

No Engine Braking In Manual 1st Gear – Improperly torqued valve body bolts (gasket damaged), check balls BS1 and CB1 missing or damaged, valve body components (3-4 shift valve, low reverse clutch modulator valve, D2 valve, 4-3-2 timing valve, 2-3 shift valve, coast clutch shift valve), valve body separator plate, coast clutch assembly and low reverse clutch assembly.

No Engine Braking With Overdrive Switch Cancelled (Manual 1st & Manual 2nd Have Engine Braking) – Improperly torqued valve body bolts (gasket damaged) and valve body components (coast clutch solenoid, check balls BS2 and BS3, separator plate, 3-4 shift valve).

Fluid Venting/Foaming – Blocked or damaged vent, overfilled, fluid contamination (coolant or water), overheating, pump inlet filter and seal, and pump to case gasket damage.

CLUTCH & BAND APPLICATION
CLUTCH & BAND APPLICATION CHART

Selector Lever Position	Elements In Use
"OD" (Overdrive)	
1st Gear	Forward Clutch, Planetary One-Way Clutch
2nd Gear	Intermediate Clutch, Forward Clutch & Intermediate One-Way Clutch
3rd Gear	Forward Clutch, Intermediate Clutch Direct Clutch & Overdrive One-Way Clutch
4th Gear	Forward Clutch, Intermediate Clutch Overdrive Clutch & Direct Clutch
"2"	Coasting Clutch, Forward Clutch, Intermediate Clutch, Intermediate Band, Intermediate One-Way Clutch & Overdrive One-Way Clutch
"1"	Coasting Clutch, Forward Clutch, Low/Reverse Clutch, Overdrive One-Way Clutch & Low Reverse One-Way Clutch
"R"	Coasting Clutch, Direct Clutch, Low Reverse Clutch & Overdrive One-Way Clutch

TESTING

Check fluid level and correct if necessary. See appropriate AUTOMATIC TRANSMISSION SERVICING article in TRANSMISSION SERVICING. Use initial road test to verify transmission malfunction. Ensure engine is operating properly.

ROAD TEST

1) Check minimum throttle upshifts in overdrive. Transmission should start in 1st gear and shift automatically into and through each gear at pre-determined specifications. See appropriate SHIFT SPEEDS SPECIFICATIONS (MPH).
2) With transmission in 4th gear (overdrive), depress overdrive cancel switch. Transmission should downshift to 3rd gear.

Throttle Opening	Drive Range	Shift	Vehicle Speed①			
			Axle Ratios			
			3.08②	3.55③	3.54/3.55④	3.73⑤
Light Throttle⑥	Ⓓ or D	1-2	10-11	8.5-9.5	9.5-10.5	9-10
	Ⓓ or D	2-3	19.5-22	17.5-19	19.5-21	18-19
	Ⓓ	3-4	37.5-41	33-35.5	37-39	35-36
	Ⓓ	4-3	35-38.5	30.5-33.5	34.5-37	33-34
	Ⓓ or D	3-2	15-17	13-14.5	15-16	14-15
	Ⓓ or D	2-1	8.5-10	7.5-8.5	8.5-9.5	8-9
Wide Open Throttle (WOT)	Ⓓ or D	1-2	33-38.5	29-33.5	32.5-36.5	31-33
	Ⓓ or D	2-3	57-64.5	50-56	56.5-61.5	53.5-56
	Ⓓ	3-4	87.5-97	77-84.5	86.5-92.5	82-84
	Ⓓ	4-3	82-89.5	72-77.5	81-85.5	77-78
	Ⓓ or D	3-2	52-57	45.5-49.5	51.5-54.5	49-50
	Ⓓ or D	2-1	27-30.5	24-26.5	27-29	25.5-26.5

Note: D is the same as Ⓓ with the Ⓓ cancel switch actuated (light on).

① Nominal shift speed shown. Actual shift speed will depend on tire brand and size.
② E-150, F-150
③ E-150, F-150
④ F-250, E-250 ‹ 8500
⑤ E-250 ‹ 8500 GVW
⑥ Throttle position is less than 10°

3) Depress accelerator pedal to floor (WOT). Transmission should downshift from 3rd to 2nd or 1st gear, depending on vehicle speed. See appropriate SHIFT SPEEDS SPECIFICATIONS (MPH).

4) When traveling above 50 MPH at less than half throttle, move transmission from Overdrive to 2nd gear and release accelerator pedal. Transmission should immediately downshift into 2nd gear. With vehicle in 2nd gear, move selector to 1st gear and release accelerator pedal. Transmission should downshift to 1st gear at less than 30-35 MPH.

SHIFT SPEEDS SPECIFICATIONS (MPH)

NOTE: *Shift speeds are approximate. All shift speeds may vary somewhat due to production tolerances, rear axle ratios or emission control equipment.*

NOTE: *Specifications given are for 1994 models; 1993 models are similar. Ensure all tires are factory recommended sizes.*

Throttle Opening	Drive Range	Shift	Vehicle Speed①		
			Axle Ratios		
			3.55②	4.10③	4.10④
Light Throttle⑤	Ⓓ or D	1-2	9-10.5	8-9	8.5-10
	Ⓓ or D	2-3	18-21	16-18	18-20
	Ⓓ	3-4	36-40	33-35	34.5-37
	Ⓓ	4-3	31-34	29-30	30-32.5
	Ⓓ or D	3-2	15-17	14-15	14.5-16
	Ⓓ or D	2-1	8-9	7-8	7.5-8.5
Wide Open Throttle (WOT)	Ⓓ or D	1-2	33-39	30-32.5	31.5-35.5
	Ⓓ or D	2-3	61-68	56-58.5	58.5-64
	Ⓓ	3-4	86.5-94.5	80-82	83.5-89.5
	Ⓓ	4-3	81.5-87.5	75.5-76.5	78.5-83.5
	Ⓓ or D	3-2	55.5-62	51-52	53-56.5
	Ⓓ or D	2-1	26-29.5	24-25	25-27

Note: D is the same as Ⓓ with the Ⓓ cancel switch actuated (light on).

① Nominal shift speed is shown. Actual shift speed will depend on the tire brand and size.
② F-150, Bronco
③ F-150, Bronco
④ F-250 ‹ 8500
⑤ Throttle position is less than 10°.

94I38511   Courtesy of Ford Motor Co.

Fig. 4: 5.0L Bronco & F150/250

Throttle Opening	Drive Range	Shift	Vehicle Speed①					
			Axle Ratios					
			3.08②	3.55③	3.54/3.55④	3.73⑤	4.10⑥	4.10⑦
Light Throttle⑧	Ⓓ or D	1-2	10.5-12	9.5-11	9.5-11	8.5-10	8-9.5	10.5-11.5
	Ⓓ or D	2-3	21-24	18.5-21	18.5-21	17-19.5	16-18.5	19-20
	Ⓓ	3-4	43-49	38-43	38-43	35-40	32-37.5	36-37
	Ⓓ	4-3	38.5-44	34-38.5	34-38.5	31.5-34	29-34	32.5-33.5
	Ⓓ or D	3-2	17-19.5	15-17	15-17	13.5-16	12.5-14.5	15.5-16.5
	Ⓓ or D	2-1	7.5-9	6.5-7.5	6.5-7.5	6-7	5.5-7	7-8
Wide Open Throttle (WOT)	Ⓓ or D	1-2	38.5-44.5	34-38.5	34-38.5	31.5-36.5	29-33.5	37.5-38.5
	Ⓓ or D	2-3	69-79	61-69	61-69	56-64.5	52-60	65.5-66.5
	Ⓓ	3-4	95-108	84-95	84-95	77.5-88.5	71.5-83	98.5-100
	Ⓓ	4-3	89-102	79-89	79-89	72.5-83.5	67-78	91.5-92.5
	Ⓓ or D	3-2	62-71	55-62	55-62	50.5-58	47-54	59.5-60.5
	Ⓓ or D	2-1	31.5-36	28-31.5	28-31.5	25.5-30	23.5-27.5	27.5-28.5

Note: D is the same as Ⓓ with the Ⓓ cancel switch actuated (light on).

① Nominal shift speed is shown. Actual shift speed will depend on tire brand and size.
② E-150, F-150, Bronco
③ E-150, F-150, Bronco
④ E-250, F-250 ‹ 8500
⑤ E-250 ‹ 8500
⑥ E-250, F-250 ‹ 8500
⑦ Lightning
⑧ Throttle position is less than 10°.

94J38512   Courtesy of Ford Motor Co.

Fig. 5: 5.8L Bronco, E150/250, F150/250 & Lightning (Less Than 8500 GVW)

Throttle Opening	Drive Range	Shift	Vehicle Speed①	
			Axle Ratios	
			3.54/3.55②	4.10③
Light Throttle④	Ⓓ or D	1-2	10-12	8-10.5
	Ⓓ or D	2-3	19-22.5	17-19.5
	Ⓓ	3-4	38-43	32-36
	Ⓓ	4-3	34-37	28-32
	Ⓓ or D	3-2	17-20	15-17
	Ⓓ or D	2-1	8-9	7-8
Wide Open Throttle (WOT)	Ⓓ or D	1-2	36-41	31.5-35.5
	Ⓓ or D	2-3	65-70.5	56-61
	Ⓓ	3-4	93.5-99.5	80.5-86.5
	Ⓓ	4-3	88-92.5	78.5-80.5
	Ⓓ or D	3-2	60-63.5	51.5-55
	Ⓓ or D	2-1	32-34.5	27.5-30

Note: D is the same as Ⓓ with the Ⓓ cancel switch actuated (light on).

① Nominal shift speed is shown. Actual shift speed will depend on the tire brand and size.
② E-250, E-350, F-250, F-350
③ E-250, E-350, F-250, F-350
④ Throttle position is less than 10°.

94A38513   Courtesy of Ford Motor Co.

Fig. 6: 5.8L E250/350 & F250/350 (Greater Than 8500 GVW)

Throttle Opening	Drive Range	Shift	Vehicle Speed①	
			Axle Ratios	
			3.55/3.54②	4.10③
Light Throttle④	Ⓓ or D	1-2	9.5-10.5	8-9
	Ⓓ or D	2-3	17.5-18.5	15-16
	Ⓓ	3-4	37-39.5	32.5-34.5
	Ⓓ	4-3	35-37.5	30.5-32.5
	Ⓓ or D	3-2	16.5-17.5	14-15
	Ⓓ or D	2-1	8.5-9	7.5-8
Wide Open Throttle (WOT)	Ⓓ or D	1-2	28-31.5	24-27.5
	Ⓓ or D	2-3	50.5-55.5	43.5-48
	Ⓓ	3-4	79.5-85	68.5-73.5
	Ⓓ	4-3	69.5-73	60-63.5
	Ⓓ or D	3-2	45-47.5	39-41.5
	Ⓓ or D	2-1	24-25.5	21-22.5

Note: D is the same as Ⓓ with the Ⓓ cancel switch actuated (light on).

① Nominal shift speed is shown. Actual shift speed will depend on the tire brand and size.
② E-350, F-250, F-350
③ E-350, F-250, F-350
④ Throttle position is less than 10°.

94B38514   Courtesy of Ford Motor Co.

Fig. 7: 7.3L Diesel E350 & F250/350 (Greater Than 8500 GVW)

CAUTION: Do not maintain Wide Open Throttle (WOT) in any gear for more than 5 seconds. If engine RPM exceeds maximum specified stall speed, release accelerator immediately. Clutch or band slippage is indicated.

LINE PRESSURE TEST

1) Connect a 0-300 psi (0-21.1 kg/cm²) pressure gauge to line pressure tap on left side of transmission case just forward of control levers. *See Fig. 11.*

2) With engine at normal operating temperature, apply parking and service brakes. Check line pressure in all ranges. Pressure should be approximately as specified. See LINE PRESSURE SPECIFICATIONS table.

Throttle Opening	Drive Range	Shift	Vehicle Speed①
			Axle Ratios
			5.13
Light Throttle②	Ⓓ or D	1-2	8-8.5
	Ⓓ or D	2-3	13-13.5
	Ⓓ	3-4	26.5-27.5
	Ⓓ	4-3	25-26
	Ⓓ or D	3-2	11.5-12.5
	Ⓓ or D	2-1	7-7.5
Wide Open Throttle (WOT)	Ⓓ or D	1-2	20.5-22
	Ⓓ or D	2-3	37-38.5
	Ⓓ	3-4	57.5-59
	Ⓓ	4-3	51.5-53
	Ⓓ or D	3-2	31-32
	Ⓓ or D	2-1	16-17

Note: D is the same as Ⓓ with the Ⓓ cancel switch actuated (light on).

① Nominal shift speed is shown. Actual shift speed will depend on the tire brand and size.
② Throttle position is less than 10°.

94C38515

Courtesy of Ford Motor Co.

Fig. 8: 7.3L Diesel "F" Super Duty

Throttle Opening	Drive Range	Shift	Vehicle Speed①	
			Axle Ratios	
			3.55/3.54②	4.10③
Light Throttle④	Ⓓ or D	1-2	12.5-13	10.5-11.5
	Ⓓ or D	2-3	21.5-22.5	17.5-19.5
	Ⓓ	3-4	41-42	34-38
	Ⓓ	4-3	39.5-42	32-35.5
	Ⓓ or D	3-2	19.5-20.5	16-18
	Ⓓ or D	2-1	10-11	8.5-9.5
Wide Open Throttle (WOT)	Ⓓ or D	1-2	41-42	33.5-37
	Ⓓ or D	2-3	71-72.5	58-64.5
	Ⓓ	3-4	101-104	83-92
	Ⓓ	4-3	97-98	78-86.5
	Ⓓ or D	3-2	63-64.5	51-56.5
	Ⓓ or D	2-1	33-34	27-30

Note: D is the same as Ⓓ with the Ⓓ cancel switch actuated (light on).

① Nominal shift speed is shown. Actual shift speed will depend on the tire brand and size.
② E-350, F-250, F-350
③ E-350, F-250, F-350
④ Throttle position is less than 10°.

94D38516

Courtesy of Ford Motor Co.

Fig. 9: 7.5L E250/350 & F250/350 (Greater Than 8500 GVW)

LINE PRESSURE SPECIFICATIONS

Drive Range	Idle psi (kg/cm²)	WOT Stall psi (kg/cm²)
"P", "N"	55-65 (3.87-4.57)	(Not Applicable)
"R"	75-99 (5.27-6.96)	240-265 (16.87-18.63)
O/D, 2	55-65 (3.87-4.57)	156-174 (10.97-12.23)
1	75-99 (5.27-6.96)	161-186 (11.34-13.08)

LINE PRESSURE TEST RESULTS

Compare recorded line pressures with table. See LINE PRESSURE SPECIFICATIONS table under LINE PRESSURE TEST. If line pressures are outside of specified ranges, use following list to determine cause of trouble.

High At Idle In All Ranges – Check main regulator valve, solenoid body and wiring harness.

Throttle Opening	Drive Range	Shift	Vehicle Speed ①
			Axle Ratio 4.63
Light Throttle ②	Ⓓ or D	1-2	8-9.5
	Ⓓ or D	2-3	17-18
	Ⓓ	3-4	33-34
	Ⓓ	4-3	29-30.5
	Ⓓ or D	3-2	14-15
	Ⓓ or D	2-1	7-8
Wide Open Throttle (WOT)	Ⓓ or D	1-2	30.5-31.5
	Ⓓ or D	2-3	54-55
	Ⓓ	3-4	83-85
	Ⓓ	4-3	78-79
	Ⓓ or D	3-2	53-54
	Ⓓ or D	2-1	25-26

Note: D is the same as Ⓓ with the Ⓓ cancel switch actuated (light on).

① Nominal shift speed is shown. Actual shift speed will depend on the tire brand and size.
② Throttle position is less than 10°.

94E38517

Courtesy of Ford Motor Co.

Fig. 10: 7.5L "F" Super Duty

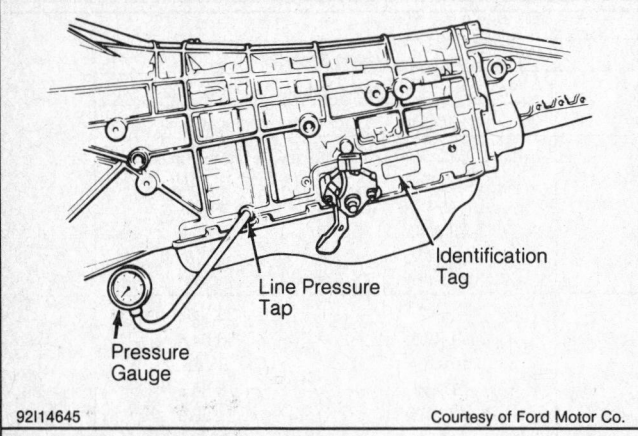

Pressure Gauge

Line Pressure Tap

Identification Tag

92I14645

Courtesy of Ford Motor Co.

Fig. 11: Testing With Pressure Gauge

Low At Idle In All Ranges – Check for low fluid level, restricted intake filter, loose main body, solenoid body or accumulator body-to-case bolts. Excessive leakage in pump, case control bodies, sticking main regulator valve or damaged inlet tube seal.

Low In "P" Or "N" – Check valve body.
Low In "O/D" – Check forward clutch.
Low In "2" – Check forward clutch, intermediate clutch, coast clutch and servo.
Low In "1" – Check forward clutch, low-reverse clutch and/or coast clutch.
Low In "R" – Check coast clutch, low-reverse clutch and/or direct clutch.

CONVERTER CLUTCH TEST

NOTE: Due to the difficulty of feeling converter clutch shift, a tachometer and/or vacuum gauge MUST be connected to engine.

1) To check converter for engagement and disengagement, drive vehicle at approximately 50 MPH and lightly tap brake pedal. Engine RPM and vacuum should increase when clutch disengages.
2) Engine RPM will increase when brake pedal is tapped and about 5 seconds after pedal is released. If this does not occur, see E4OD ELECTRONIC CONTROLS article.

STALL SPEED TEST

CAUTION: Do not maintain Wide Open Throttle (WOT) in any gear for more than 5 seconds. If engine RPM exceeds maximum specified stall speed, release accelerator immediately. Clutch or band slippage is indicated.

Testing Precautions – 1) Engine coolant and transmission fluid MUST be at proper level and operating temperature. Hold accelerator down long enough to stabilize tachometer. DO NOT hold at WOT for more than 5 seconds.
2) DO NOT exceed maximum specified RPM for vehicle. Before shifting into each selector position, run engine in Neutral at 1000 RPM for 2 minutes to cool transmission. If engine speed exceeds specification, release accelerator immediately, as this indicates clutch or band slippage.
Testing Procedure – Connect tachometer to engine. Apply parking and service brakes firmly. Stall test transmission in each driving range at WOT. Note maximum RPM obtained. Engine speed should be within limits. See STALL SPEED SPECIFICATIONS table. If maximum RPM obtained is not within specifications, see STALL SPEED TEST RESULTS.

STALL SPEED SPECIFICATIONS

Vehicle Application	Engine Size	Stall Speeds (RPM)
E150/250	4.9L PFI	1583-1900
E250 (8550 GVW)	4.9L PFI	1548-1855
F150/250	4.9L PFI	1590-1907
Bronco & F150/250	5.0L PFI	2068-2458
E150/250	5.8L PFI	2218-2666
F250/350	5.8L PFI	2215-2661
Bronco & F150/250	5.8L PFI	2217-2665
E250 (8550 GVW) & E350	5.8L PFI	2216-2662
F150	5.8L HP	2234-2701
E350 & F250/350/Super Duty	7.3L Diesel	1789-2096
F250/350/Super Duty	7.5L Turbo	1923-2256
E350 & F250/350/Super Duty	7.5L	1943-2315

STALL SPEED TEST RESULTS

Low In All Ranges – Poor engine performance. Faulty torque converter reactor one-way clutch.
High In All Ranges – General transmission problems are indicated. Perform control pressure tests.

High In "OD" Only – Forward clutch, overdrive one-way clutch or low-reverse one-way clutch faulty.

High In "2" Only – Forward clutch, or overdrive one-way clutch and coast clutch faulty.

High In "1" Only – Forward clutch, or reverse clutch and low-reverse one-way clutch, or coast clutch and overdrive one-way clutch faulty.

High In "R" Only – Direct clutch, or overdrive one-way clutch and coast clutch, or low-reverse clutch faulty.

AIR PRESSURE CHECKS

1) A "No Drive" condition can exist, even with correct transmission fluid pressure, due to inoperative clutches or bands. Inoperative units can be located by substituting air pressure for fluid pressure to determine location of malfunction.

2) To check unit, drain transmission fluid. Remove oil pan, filter, seal assembly, solenoid body and valve body.

3) Forward, coast, reverse, overdrive, direct and intermediate clutch operation may be checked as follows: Using shop air, apply air to proper points. *See Fig. 12.* A dull thud can be heard when clutch piston is applied. If no thud is heard, movement of piston can be felt by placing finger tips on input shell. If seals are leaking, a hissing sound will be heard.

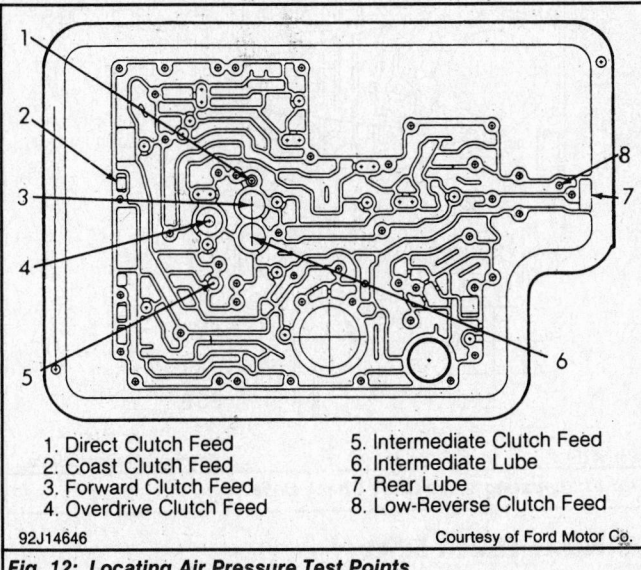

1. Direct Clutch Feed	5. Intermediate Clutch Feed
2. Coast Clutch Feed	6. Intermediate Lube
3. Forward Clutch Feed	7. Rear Lube
4. Overdrive Clutch Feed	8. Low-Reverse Clutch Feed

92J14646   Courtesy of Ford Motor Co.

Fig. 12: Locating Air Pressure Test Points

ON-VEHICLE SERVICE

EXTENSION HOUSING SEAL & BUSHING

Removal – Raise and support vehicle. Index and remove rear drive shaft. Remove extension seal, using appropriate seal remover. Using appropriate bushing remover, remove extension housing bushing. Ensure extension housing is not scored.

Installation – 1) Inspect extension housing bushing bore for burrs and remove burrs with an oil stone, as necessary. Install extension housing bushing, aligning lubrication slot to 6 o'clock position.

2) Install extension housing seal, aligning drain hole to 6 o'clock position. Ensure seal is seated against extension housing. Install drive shaft, aligning index marks.

EXTENSION HOUSING GASKET

Removal – Raise and support vehicle. Index and remove drive shaft(s). On 4WD vehicles, remove transfer case. See appropriate AUTOMATIC TRANSMISSION REMOVAL article under TRANSMISSION servicing. Remove transmission mount-to-transmission retaining bolts. Position transmission jack under transmission, and remove transmission mount-to-crossmember bolts. Remove 9 extension housing bolts. Remove extension housing and discard gasket.

Installation – Install NEW housing gasket and position extension housing on case. Ensure parking pawl spring is properly seated in

case. Install and tighten bolts to specification. See TORQUE SPECIFICATIONS. To complete installation, reverse removal procedure.

PARKING MECHANISM

Removal – Remove extension housing. See EXTENSION HOUSING GASKET. Remove parking rod guide plate retaining bolts. Remove parking pawl return spring, pin and parking pawl from case. Remove Torx head bolt (40A) and parking pawl abutment. *See Fig. 13.*

Installation – For installation, reverse removal procedure. Ensure return spring end rests on inside surface of case, and parking rod guide plate dimple is facing inward. Tighten bolts to specification. See TORQUE SPECIFICATIONS.

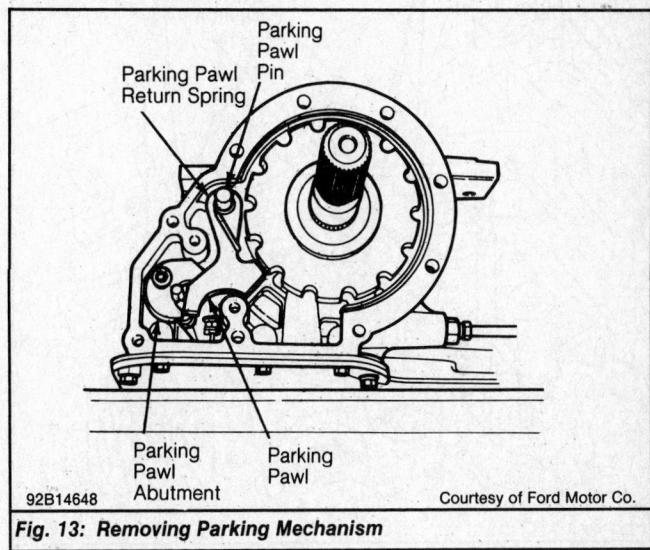

92B14648   Courtesy of Ford Motor Co.

Fig. 13: Removing Parking Mechanism

VALVE BODY & INTERMEDIATE BAND SERVO

NOTE: As valve body is disassembled, place individual parts in correct order and relation to valve body for reassembly. Tag all springs as they are removed.

Removal – 1) Remove solenoid body heat shield. Remove slotted heat shield. Remove solenoid body connector by pushing on center tab and pulling on wire harness. DO NOT attempt to pry tab with pry bar or screwdriver. Check electrical connectors for condition.

2) Loosen oil pan bolts and drain fluid. Remove oil pan, filter and "O" ring. DO NOT scratch or damage aluminum pump bore when removing "O" ring. Remove accumulator body. Remove main control body retaining bolts. Do not remove center 2 bolts. *See Fig. 14.* This keeps upper and lower valve body together during disassembly. Remove main control body.

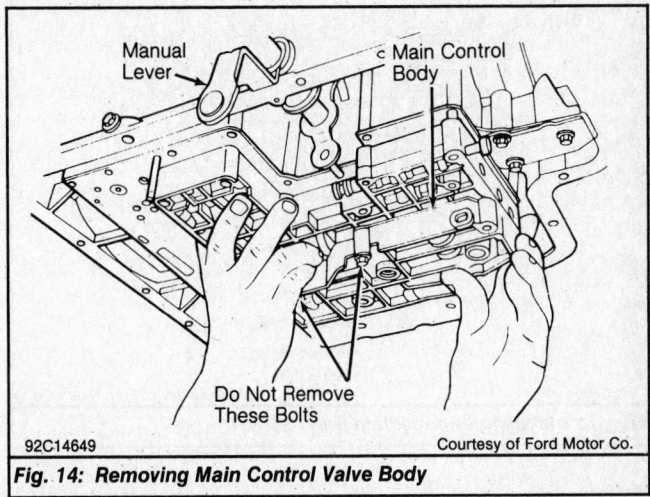

92C14649   Courtesy of Ford Motor Co.

Fig. 14: Removing Main Control Valve Body

3) Remove solenoid body Torx retaining bolts and one nut. Push down on solenoid body receptacle and remove solenoid body. Remove solenoid screen by rotating and pulling out. Remove reinforcing plate. Carefully lower separator plate and gasket so check balls, EPC ball and spring are retained.

4) Remove intermediate accumulator regulator filter and spring. See Fig. 15. Remove servo snap ring, retaining plate, servo piston and rod assembly, and servo spring.

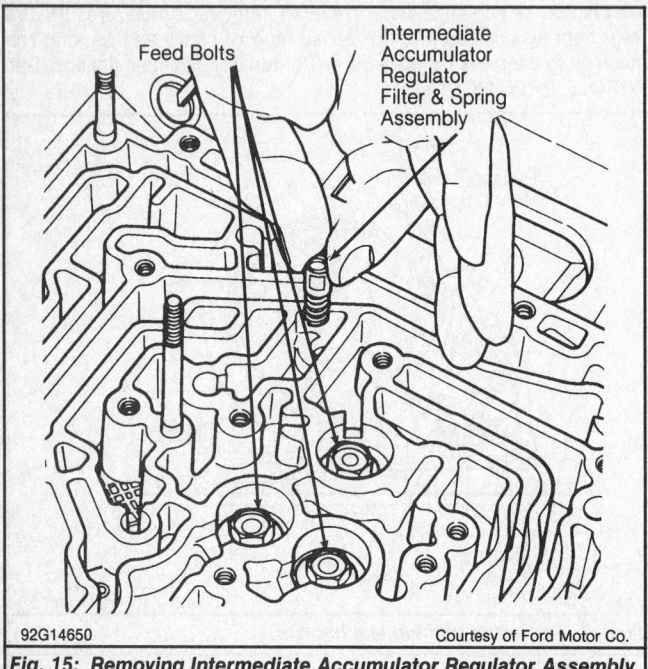

92G14650   Courtesy of Ford Motor Co.

Fig. 15: Removing Intermediate Accumulator Regulator Assembly

Installation – 1) Clean and inspect valve body thoroughly. DO NOT clean non-metallic check balls with solvent.

2) Install servo spring, servo piston and rod assembly. Install retaining plate and snap ring. See Fig. 16.

3) Lubricate valve body pockets with petroleum jelly. Place 9 check balls (rubber), Electronic Pressure Control (EPC) spring and EPC ball in position. See Fig. 17. Install separator plate and gaskets. Tighten retaining bolts to specifications. See TORQUE SPECIFICATIONS. Stamped "UP" on reinforcing plate MUST be visible.

4) Install solenoid screen and lock in place. Install valve body over studs. Align manual valve with manual lever. Install and tighten retaining bolts to specification. Install accumulator body retaining bolts. Tighten to specification. Coat case connector bore with grease and install solenoid body retaining bolts and nut. Tighten to specification.

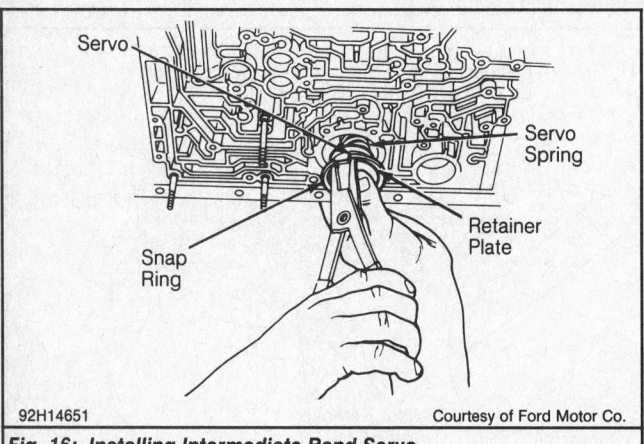

92H14651   Courtesy of Ford Motor Co.

Fig. 16: Installing Intermediate Band Servo

5) Install NEW filter and seal assembly. Install oil pan and NEW gasket. Check condition and placement of pan magnet. Tighten pan bolts to specification. Position solenoid body connector into receptacle. Audible click indicates full connection. Install solenoid body connector heat shield with offset bending inward.

6) Add transmission fluid and start engine. Fill transmission to proper level. Test vehicle for proper operation and ensure no leakage is present.

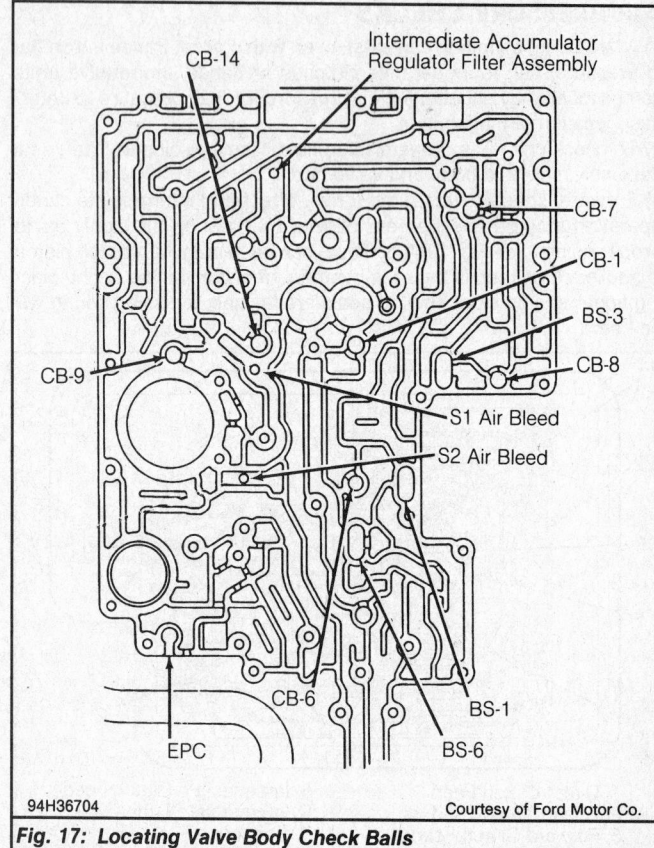

94H36704   Courtesy of Ford Motor Co.

Fig. 17: Locating Valve Body Check Balls

MANUAL LEVER SEAL

Removal – 1) Remove manual lever position sensor connector. Remove shift cable from transmission manual lever, using a large screwdriver, pry control cable and fitting from lever ball and stud. Remove sensor retaining bolts.

2) Loosen oil pan bolts and drain transmission fluid. Remove oil pan, filter and "O" ring. Discard filter and "O" ring. DO NOT scratch or damage aluminum pump bore.

3) Using Lock Nut Pin Remover (T78P-3504-N), remove manual lever roll pin. See Fig. 18. Using a 21-mm box wrench, remove Inner detent lever nut. Hold lever with crescent wrench. Remove inner detent lever and park actuating rod assembly from manual lever. Remove manual lever and seal.

Installation – 1) Clean seal bore opening with solvent. Using appropriate seal driver, install seal. Install manual lever, inner detent lever, park actuating rod assembly and NEW nut. Ensure inner detent lever is seated on flats of shaft, and rod assembly is through guide plate. Inner lever pin MUST BE aligned with manual valve.

2) Tighten inner detent lever nut to specification. See TORQUE SPECIFICATIONS. Ensure manual valve detent spring is on inner detent lever and aligned with inner detent.

3) Install manual lever roll pin. Install manual lever position sensor finger tight. Use Gear Position Sensor Adjustor (T89T-70010-J) to align manual lever position sensor for Neutral gear position. Tighten bolts to specification. Install manual lever position sensor connector. Install shaft linkage and adjust. See appropriate AUTOMATIC TRANSMISSION SERVICING article in TRANSMISSION SERVICING.

4) Install NEW filter and "O" ring assembly. Install oil pan and NEW gasket. Check condition and placement of pan magnet. Tighten oil pan retaining bolts to specifications. See TORQUE SPECIFICATIONS.

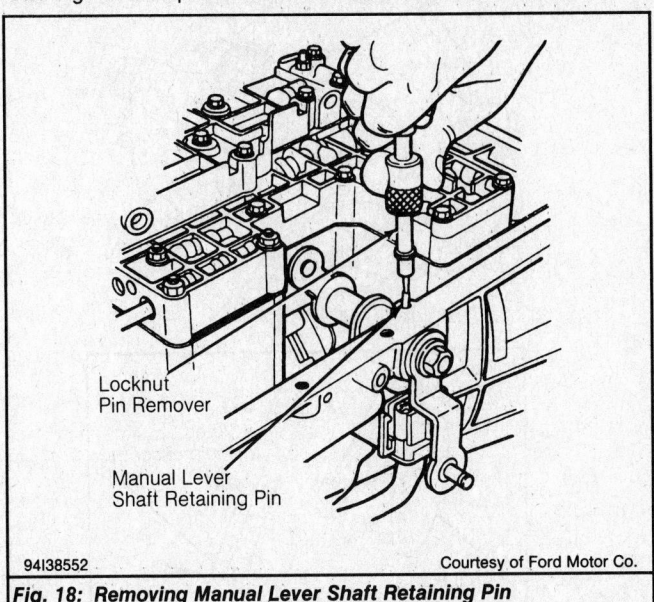

94I38552   Courtesy of Ford Motor Co.

Fig. 18: Removing Manual Lever Shaft Retaining Pin

REMOVAL & INSTALLATION

See appropriate AUTOMATIC TRANSMISSION REMOVAL article in TRANSMISSION SERVICING.

TORQUE CONVERTER

Whenever transmission has been disassembled to replace worn or damaged parts, converter and oil cooler MUST BE cleaned using a mechanically agitated cleaner (Rotunda 014-00028). Under NO conditions should converter or oil cooler be cleaned by hand agitation using solvent.

LEAK TEST

If torque converter welds indicate leakage, attach Torque Converter Leak Detector (Rotunda 021-00054) to converter and follow detector kit instructions.

TURBINE & STATOR END PLAY CHECK

1) Insert Tester (T80L-7902-D) into converter pump drive hub until tester bottoms. Expand sleeve in turbine spline by tightening threaded inner post of tester until tester is securely locked into spine.
2) Attach a dial indicator to tool with indicator button on converter pump drive hub. See Fig. 19. Zero dial face. Lift tool upward as far as possible and note indicator reading.
3) Reading is total end play of turbine and stator. If end play exceeds .038" (.96 mm) on new or rebuilt converter, or .071" (1.8 mm) on used converter, replace torque converter assembly.

CONVERTER ONE-WAY CLUTCH CHECK

1) Insert One-Way Clutch Holding Tool (T77L-7902-R) in one of stator thrust washer grooves. Insert Converter Clutch Torquing Tool (T76L-7902-C) with torque wrench in converter pump drive hub to engage one-way clutch inner race. See Fig. 20.
2) Hold holding tool stationary. Turn torque wrench counterclockwise. Converter one-way clutch should lock up and hold force of 10 ft. lbs. (13 N.m). One-way clutch should turn freely clockwise. Repeat procedure with holding tool in at least 5 locations. Replace converter if it fails testing.

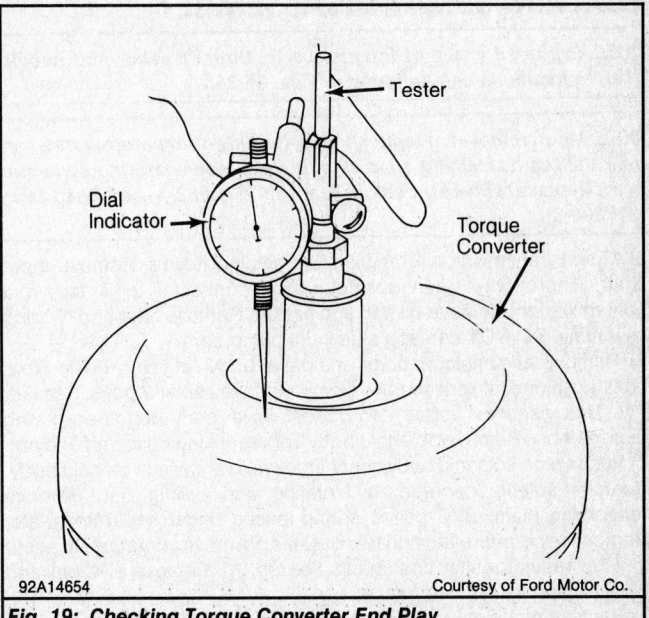

92A14654   Courtesy of Ford Motor Co.

Fig. 19: Checking Torque Converter End Play

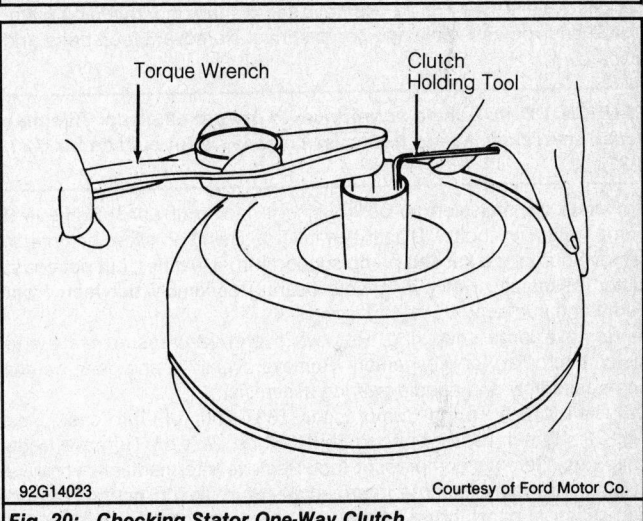

92G14023   Courtesy of Ford Motor Co.

Fig. 20: Checking Stator One-Way Clutch

STATOR INTERFERENCE CHECK

Stator-To-Impeller Interference Check – **1)** Position stator support on bench with spline end of stator shaft pointing up. Mount converter on stator support so splines of one-way clutch inner race engage splines of stator support.
2) While holding pump stationary, rotate converter counterclockwise. Converter should rotate freely without interference or scraping within assembly. Should interference or a scraping condition within converter exist or converter does not rotate freely, replace converter unit.
Stator-To-Turbine Interference Check – **1)** Place converter on bench, front side down. Install stator support to engage mating splines of stator support shaft.
2) Install input shaft, engaging splines with turbine hub. While holding stator shaft stationary, rotate turbine with input shaft.
3) Turbine should rotate freely in both directions without interference or noise. If interference or noise exists, stator front thrust washer may be worn and converter should be replaced.

NOTE: Stator support may remain in pump assembly during check.

TRANSMISSION DISASSEMBLY

NOTE: Exploded views of internal parts, thrust washer and needle bearing locations can be found in Figs. 35-36.

NOTE: Upon removal of input shell, determine if forward/reverse sun gear utilizes a retaining snap ring. Discard non-snap ring style sun gear. Replace with new design Gear (E9TZ-7D063-A) and Snap Ring (377300-S).

1) Mount transmission in appropriate holding fixture. Remove input shaft. Thoroughly clean solenoid body connector area to avoid contamination. Remove oil pan and gasket. Remove filter and "O" ring assembly. DO NOT damage aluminum pump bore.

2) Remove accumulator body and valve body retaining bolts. Note bolts positions for reassembly. Do not remove center 2 bolts. *See Fig. 14.* This secures upper and lower valve body together during disassembly. Remove solenoid body Torx retaining bolts and one nut.

3) Push up on solenoid body connector while removing solenoid body. Remove solenoid screen, by rotating and pulling out. Remove reinforcing plate. EPC ball is spring loaded under separator plate. Remove separator plate and two gaskets. Remove intermediate accumulator regulator filter and spring. *See Fig. 15.* Remove EPC ball and blow off spring. Discard gasket.

4) Remove one steel and 9 rubber check balls. DO NOT damage rubber check balls. *See Fig. 17.* Remove servo snap ring, retaining plate, piston and rod assembly and servo spring. Remove 3 feed bolts and discard.

CAUTION: DO NOT use a screwdriver to pry out oil pump. This may cause severe damage to transmission case (ATRA bulletin No. 123, 8-92).

5) Rotate transmission so bellhousing is facing upward. Remove 9 pump retaining bolts. Discard washers. Using 2 slide hammers, remove pump, gasket and pump support thrust washer. Lift out coast clutch assembly. Remove needle bearing assembly between front pump and sun gear.

6) Remove large snap ring. Remove overdrive pressure plate and clutch pack. Tag for reassembly. Remove overdrive ring gear, center shaft assembly and needle bearing assembly.

7) Install Clutch Spring Compressor (T89T-70010-F) into case. *See Fig. 21.* Tighten center bolts to 65 INCH lbs. (7 N.m). Remove large snap ring. Remove compressor tool. Remove Intermediate-overdrive cylinder assembly. Remove Intermediate return spring, center support and center support thrust washer.

8) Remove Intermediate pressure plate and clutch plates. Tag clutch plates for reassembly. Remove intermediate band. Using Clutch Remover/Installer (T89T-70010-E), remove direct clutch, forward clutch and shell. Hooks on crossbar MUST be rotated into notches on input shell. *See Fig. 32.*

9) Using large screwdriver, remove reverse planet assembly snap ring. Remove reverse planetary assembly and 2 planetary carrier thrust washers. Remove and discard output shaft snap ring.

10) Remove ring gear, hub assembly and needle bearing assembly. Remove reverse hub and one-way clutch assembly. Using large screwdriver, remove reverse clutch snap ring. Remove reverse pressure plate and clutch pack, tag for reassembly.

11) Rotate transmission so pan surface faces up. Remove 9 extension housing bolts. Remove wiring bracket, extension housing and gasket. Discard gasket.

12) Remove output shaft, park gear and output shaft thrust washer. Remove 5 retaining bolts from low-reverse one way clutch inner race. Remove reverse clutch return spring assembly and inner race.

NOTE: Reinstall reverse clutch pressure plate and snap ring to restrain reverse clutch piston during removal.

13) Using shop air in reverse clutch feed port, blow out reverse clutch piston against pressure plate. *See Fig. 12.* Remove snap ring, reverse clutch pressure plate and piston from case.

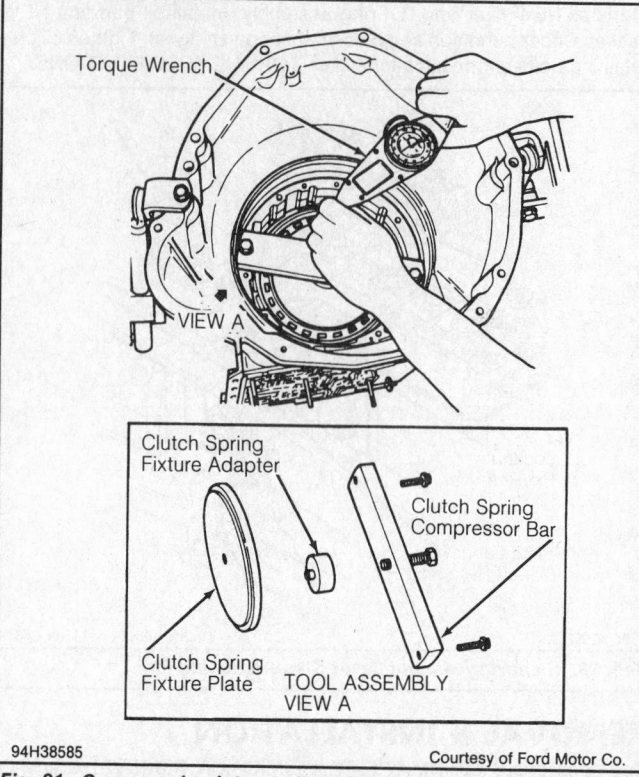

94H38585   Courtesy of Ford Motor Co.

Fig. 21: Compressing Intermediate/Overdrive Cylinder Assembly

14) Rotate transmission so pan surface faces downward. Remove parking pawl return spring, pin and parking pawl from case. Remove parking rod guide plate. Remove Torx head bolt and parking pawl abutment.

15) Using side cutters or remover tool, remove manual lever roll-pin from case. Remove inner detent lever nut, while holding lever with crescent wrench. Remove inner detent lever and parking pawl actuating rod assembly from manual lever.

16) Remove lever position sensor and manual lever. Remove manual valve detent spring. Using slide hammer, remove manual lever seal. If required, remove lube inlet short tube, using channel lock pliers.

COMPONENT DISASSEMBLY & REASSEMBLY

COAST CLUTCH ASSEMBLY

NOTE: All models use 2 steel and 2 friction plates on coast clutch cylinder assembly.

Disassembly – 1) Remove sun gear. Remove retaining ring and discard. Remove pressure and clutch plates, and tag for reassembly. Using appropriate spring compressor, remove return spring retaining ring. Remove tool.

2) Remove piston, return spring and apply plate. *See Fig. 22.* Remove piston from coast clutch cylinder. Remove outer seal from piston. Remove inner seal from cylinder.

Inspection – Inspect all parts for wear, damage and effects of overheating. Inspect coast clutch cylinder for damage and wear. Replace as necessary.

Reassembly – 1) Apply transmission fluid to "O" rings before installing. Soak all friction plates in ATF for 15 minutes before installing.

2) Install inner and outer seals with lips facing down in cylinder and piston respectively.

3) Install piston, piston apply plate and piston return spring. Use spring compressor and compress springs. Install retaining ring. Carefully remove spring compressor.

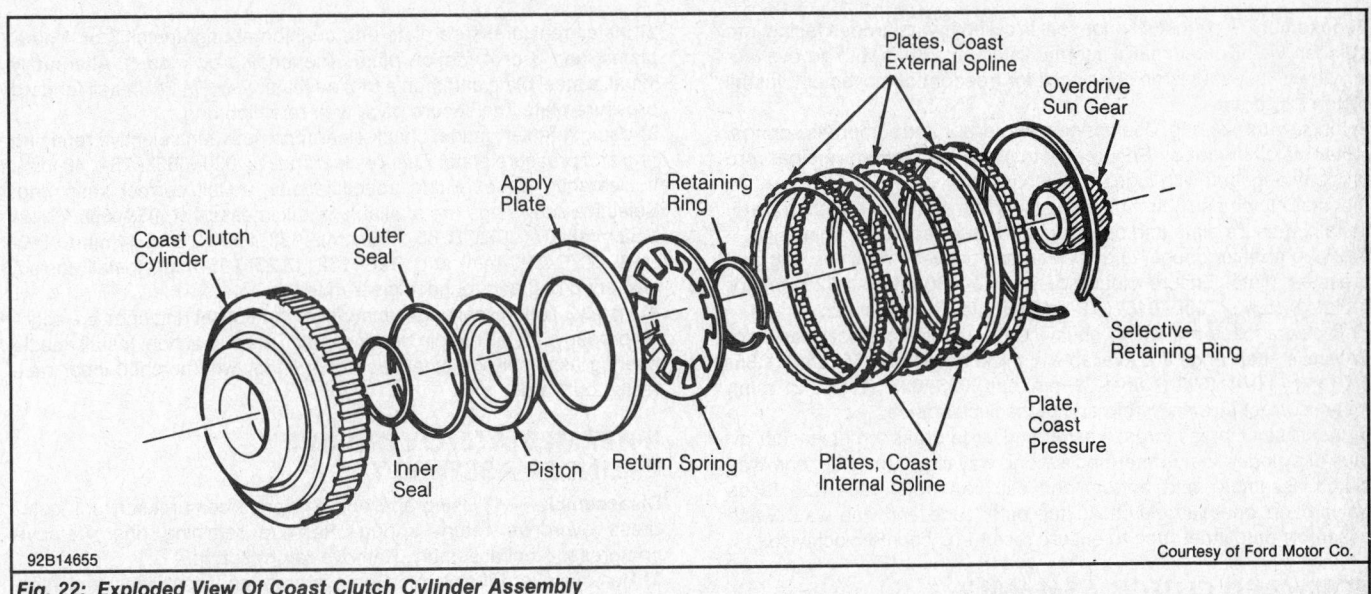

Fig. 22: Exploded View Of Coast Clutch Cylinder Assembly

92B14655

Courtesy of Ford Motor Co.

4) Install a steel plate and then a friction plate; alternately install remaining clutch pack. See Fig. 22. Install pressure plate and secure pack with retaining ring.

5) Using a feeler gauge, check clearance between retaining ring and pressure plate. Ensure clearance is .025-.045" (.62-1.14 mm). If clearance is not within specifications, install correct thickness snap ring. Selective snap rings are available in thicknesses of .053-.057" (1.35-1.45 mm), .069-.073" (1.75-1.85 mm) and .085-.089" (2.15-2.25 mm).

6) Install correct size snap ring and recheck clearance. Install overdrive sun gear assembly with short end down into cylinder.

DIRECT CLUTCH ASSEMBLY

Disassembly – 1) Remove outer race, one-way clutch and top end cap. Remove large brass thrust washer from rear face of cylinder. Remove small brass thrust washer from front face of cylinder. See Fig. 23.

2) Using a screwdriver, remove retaining ring. Remove pressure plate and clutch pack. Tag for reassembly.

3) Install appropriate spring compressor. Remove return spring retainer ring and return spring. Remove piston from intermediate brake drum. Remove inner and outer seals from drum.

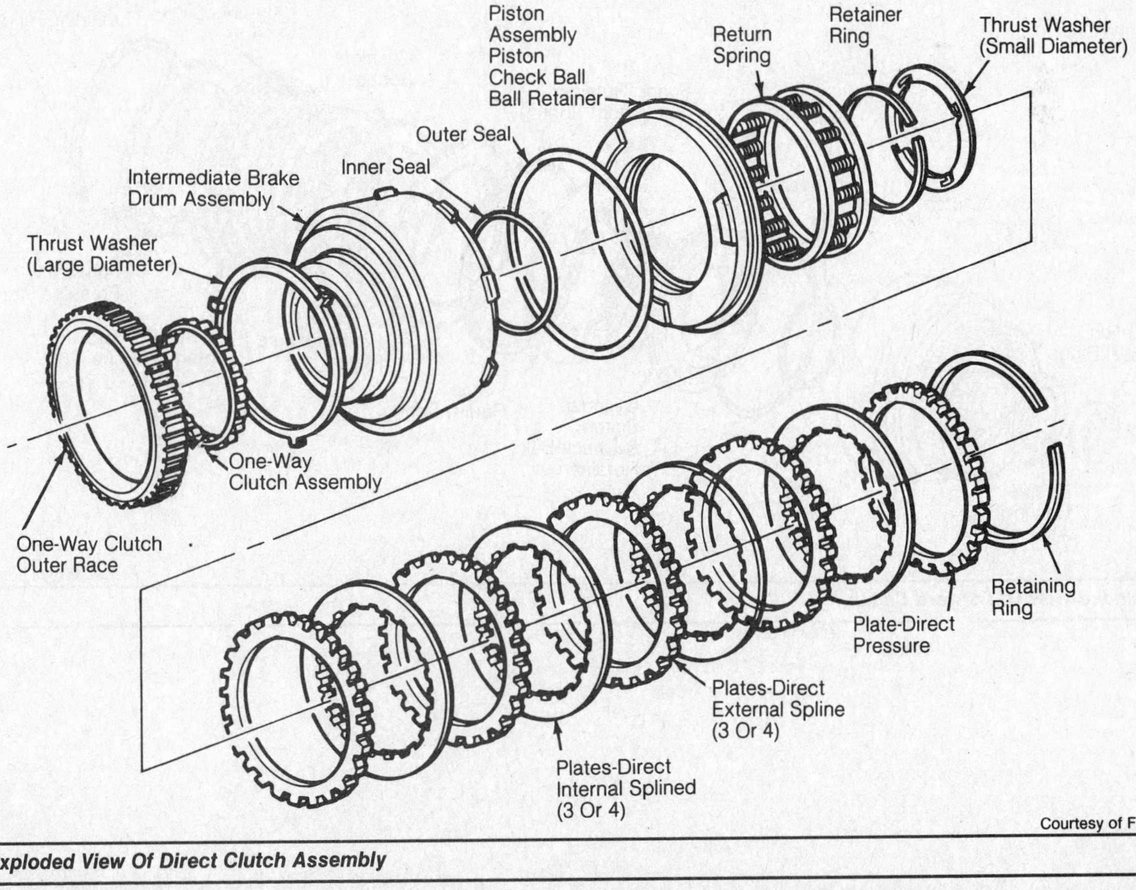

92E14658

Courtesy of Ford Motor Co.

Fig. 23: Exploded View Of Direct Clutch Assembly

Reassembly – 1) Install inner seal in cylinder with groove facing into cylinder. Install outer seal in intermediate brake drum with groove facing down. Inspect piston check ball for freedom of movement. Install piston into drum.

2) Install return spring. Use spring compressor and compress springs. Install retaining ring. Ensure protrusions on spring retainer are properly engaged with lugs on clutch piston.

3) Install clutch pack, first using a steel plate and then a friction plate. Install pressure plate and secure pack with selective retaining ring.

4) Using a feeler gauge, check clearance between retaining ring and pressure plate. Ensure clearance is .045-.060" (1.15-1.52 mm) for 4-plate clutch or .030-.045" (.76-1.15 mm) for 3-plate clutch.

5) If clearance is not within specifications, install correct snap ring. Selective snap rings are available in thicknesses of .065-.069" (1.65-1.75 mm), .074-.078" (1.88-1.98 mm) and .083-.087" (2.11-2.21 mm). Install correct size snap ring and recheck clearance.

6) Install small brass thrust washer and large brass thrust washer on face of cylinder. Install intermediate one-way clutch end cap, one-way clutch assembly, and bottom end cap into outer race. Lip faces upward on one-way clutch. Install outer race and one-way clutch assembly onto inner race to ensure race turns counterclockwise.

FORWARD CLUTCH ASSEMBLY

Disassembly – 1) Remove needle bearing and both Teflon seal rings. Remove retaining ring and rear pressure plate. Remove 3 or 4 plate clutch pack (depending on model), cushion spring and forward pressure plate. Tag for reassembly.

2) Remove spring retainer and piston return spring. Remove steel ring from piston groove. Remove cylinder piston with compressor.

Reassembly – 1) Install inner seal in cylinder and outer seal on cylinder piston. Inspect piston check ball for freedom of movement. Using Lip Seal Protector (T77L-7754A), install piston into cylinder. Install steel ring into groove on piston. Install piston return spring with fingers against piston and steel ring. Install spring retainer.

2) Install rear pressure plate and cushion spring. Install 3 or 4 steel plates, and 3 or 4 friction plates (depending on model). Alternately install a steel plate and then a friction plate. *See Fig. 24.* Install forward pressure plate and secure pack with retaining ring.

3) Using a feeler gauge, check clearance between selective retaining ring and pressure plate. Ensure clearance is .030-.055" (.76-1.40 mm). If clearance is not within specifications, install correct snap ring. Selective snap rings are available in thicknesses of .056-.060" (1.42-1.52 mm), .074-.078" (1.88-1.98 mm), .092-.096" (2.34-2.44 mm), .110-.114" (2.79-2.90 mm) and .128-.132" (3.25-3.35 mm). Install correct size snap ring and recheck clearance.

4) Install 2 Teflon seal rings, ensuring scarf cuts at ring ends are aligned properly. Install needle bearing over Teflon seal hub. Install needle bearing assembly on inner face of cylinder with notched inner race facing outward.

INTERMEDIATE/OVERDRIVE CYLINDER ASSEMBLY

Disassembly – 1) Using appropriate spring compressor tool, compress overdrive return spring. Remove retaining ring. Remove compressor tool assembly. Remove return spring.

2) Remove overdrive piston. Remove outer and inner seals and intermediate piston. *See Fig. 25.* Remove intermediate-overdrive inner seal from cylinder bore. Remove outer seal from intermediate piston. Remove 2 cast iron outer seal rings from center support.

3) Remove plastic thrust washer from front face of forward hub and ring gear. Using a screwdriver remove retaining ring. Remove forward hub from ring gear.

Reassembly – To reassemble, reverse disassembly procedure. Outer and inner seals are installed with lips facing down toward cylinder. Return spring fingers face up. Ensure plastic thrust washer is installed in correct location.

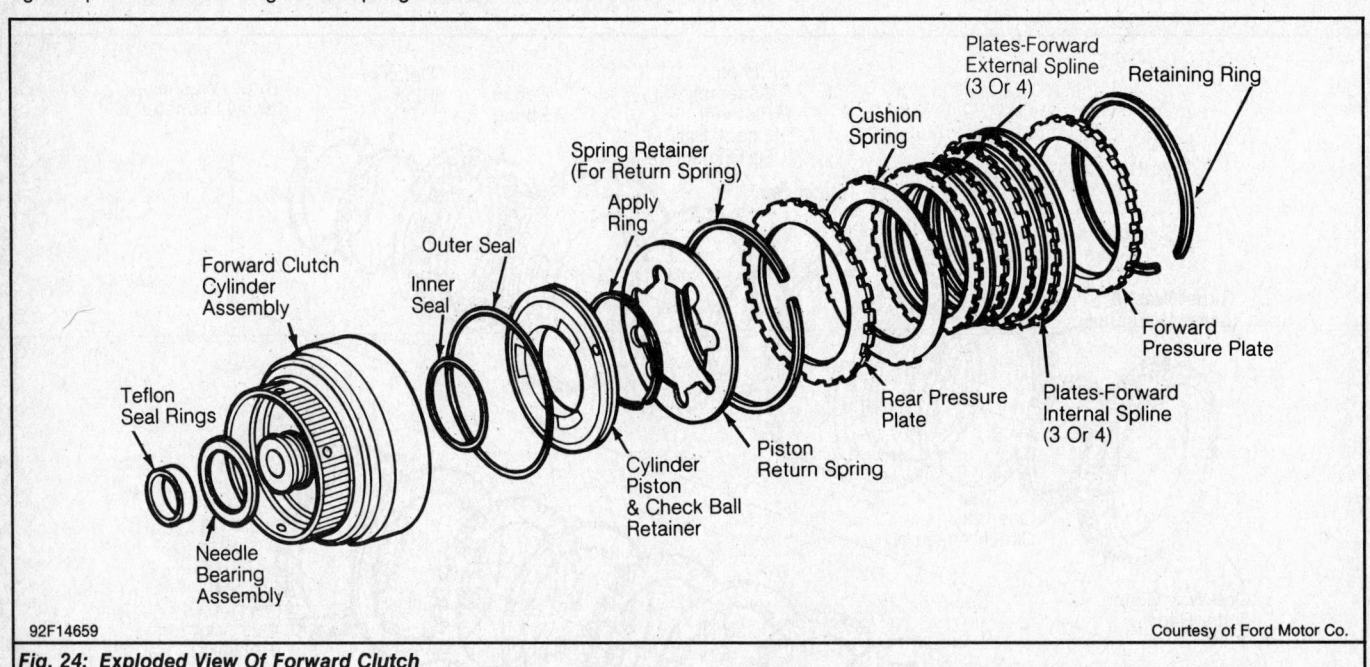

92F14659   Courtesy of Ford Motor Co.

Fig. 24: Exploded View Of Forward Clutch

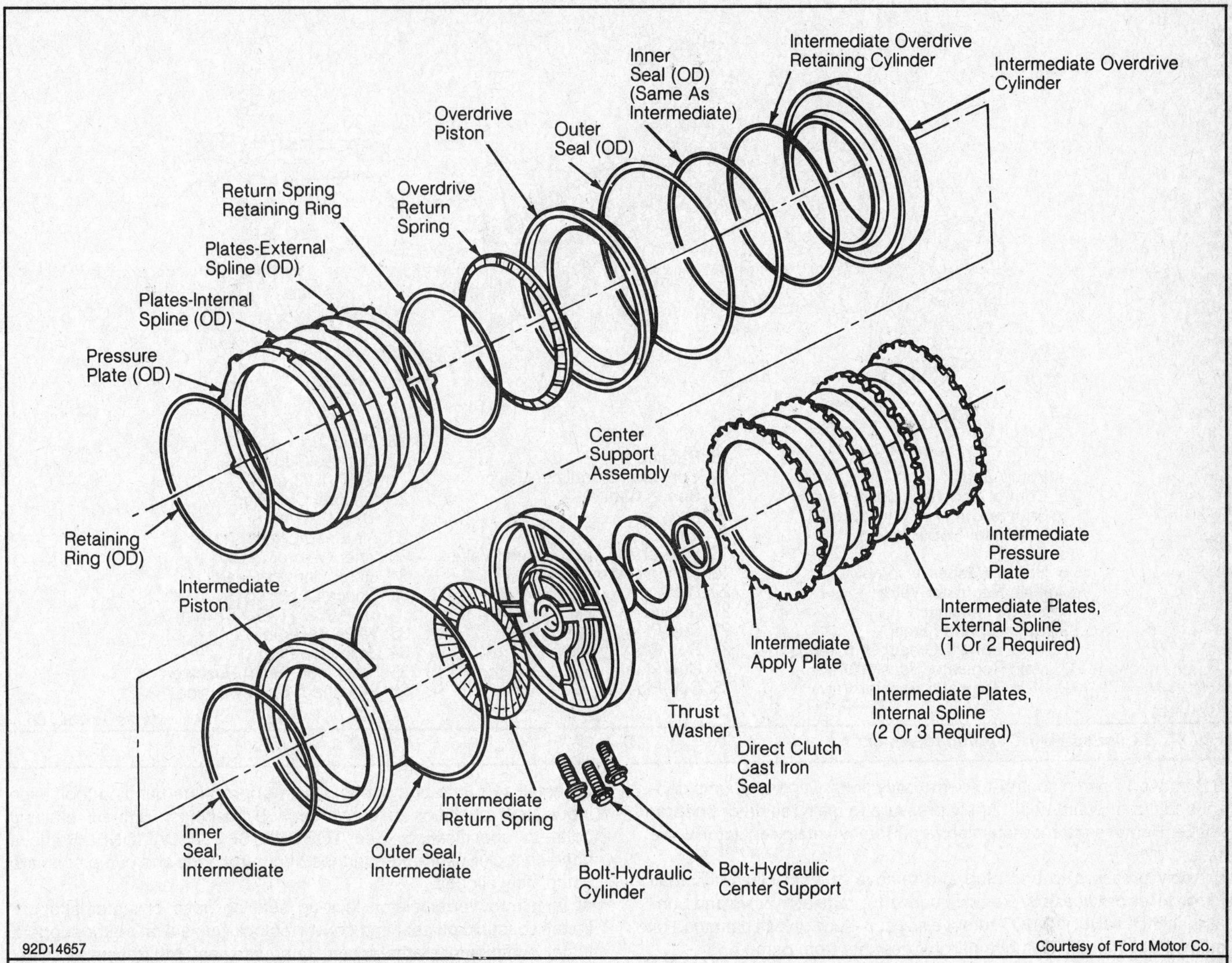

Fig. 25: Exploded View Of Intermediate-Overdrive Cylinder

92D14657

Courtesy of Ford Motor Co.

LOW REVERSE ONE-WAY CLUTCH

Disassembly – Remove reverse clutch hub assembly and needle bearing from hub. *See Fig. 26.* Remove retaining ring, brass thrust washer and rollers from reverse clutch hub.

Reassembly – To reassemble, reverse disassembly procedure. Install needle bearing with smooth race surface facing upward. Lightly grease thrust washer.

OIL PUMP ASSEMBLY

Disassembly – 1) Remove coast clutch and converter clutch seals from stator support. Remove large square cut seal from outside diameter of pump housing. Using internal puller, remove converter hub seal from pump body.

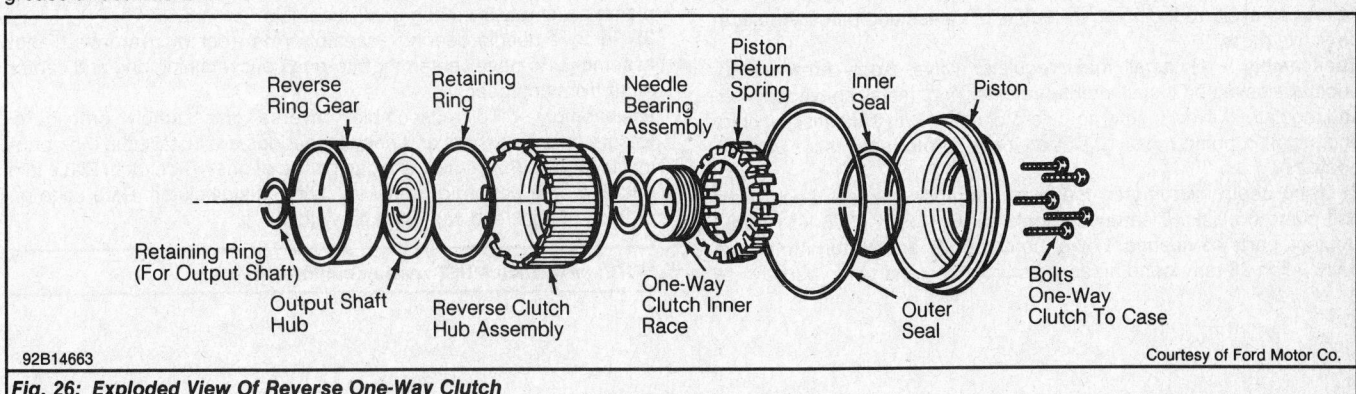

92B14663

Courtesy of Ford Motor Co.

Fig. 26: Exploded View Of Reverse One-Way Clutch

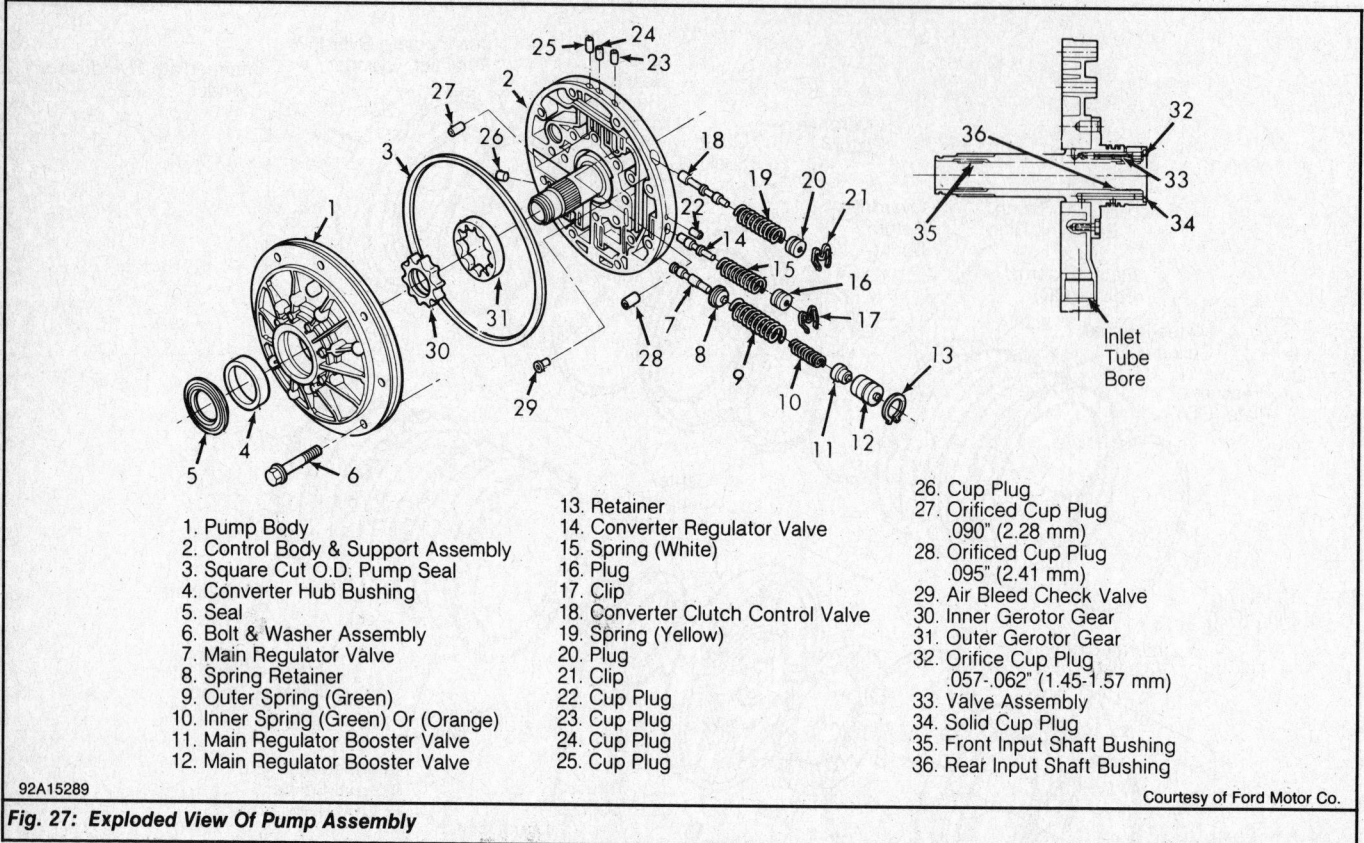

13. Retainer
14. Converter Regulator Valve
15. Spring (White)
16. Plug
17. Clip
18. Converter Clutch Control Valve
19. Spring (Yellow)
20. Plug
21. Clip
22. Cup Plug
23. Cup Plug
24. Cup Plug
25. Cup Plug

1. Pump Body
2. Control Body & Support Assembly
3. Square Cut O.D. Pump Seal
4. Converter Hub Bushing
5. Seal
6. Bolt & Washer Assembly
7. Main Regulator Valve
8. Spring Retainer
9. Outer Spring (Green)
10. Inner Spring (Green) Or (Orange)
11. Main Regulator Booster Valve
12. Main Regulator Booster Valve

26. Cup Plug
27. Orificed Cup Plug .090" (2.28 mm)
28. Orificed Cup Plug .095" (2.41 mm)
29. Air Bleed Check Valve
30. Inner Gerotor Gear
31. Outer Gerotor Gear
32. Orifice Cup Plug .057-.062" (1.45-1.57 mm)
33. Valve Assembly
34. Solid Cup Plug
35. Front Input Shaft Bushing
36. Rear Input Shaft Bushing

92A15289

Courtesy of Ford Motor Co.

Fig. 27: Exploded View Of Pump Assembly

2) Remove 11 pump control-to-pump body bolts. Separate pump control body from pump body. Apply pressure to main regulator booster sleeve. Remove internal retaining ring. Remove main regulator valve train.

3) Apply pressure to end plug and remove retainer clip with small screwdriver or tweezers. Remove converter regulator valve and converter clutch valve. DO NOT remove any cup plugs unless damaged or leaking. *See Fig. 27.* Remove gerotor gear set from pump body.

NOTE: To prevent distortion of control body surface, DO NOT remove stator support from control body.

Inspection – Thoroughly clean and inspect all components for damage, wear or scoring. Carefully check all teeth on gears. Replace pump assembly if any part is damaged or worn. Inspect converter hub bushing. Replace if defective. Stake bushing at notches. Inspect stator input shaft bushings. Replace control body assembly if bushings are worn. If necessary, use crocus cloth to polish components. Use caution to avoid rounding sharp edges of valves and plugs. Replace defective parts.

Reassembly – 1) Install main regulator valve. Apply pressure to booster sleeve and install internal retainer ring. Install converter shift and regulator valves. Lightly coat gerotor gears with transmission fluid and install in pump housing. Dot on inner gerotor gear faces control body.

2) Using depth micrometer, measure clearance between each gear and pump housing. Clearance should be .001-.002" (.025-.051 mm). Replace parts as needed. Lower control body and stator into pump body. Align 28-mm round holes in control body and pump body.

3) Install 11 pump body bolts. Using appropriate banding tool, align input shaft bushings to converter hub bushings. Tighten retaining bolts to specification. See TORQUE SPECIFICATIONS. Remove banding tool. Ensure outer edges of control body and pump body are completely aligned.

4) Install converter clutch lock-up seal on nose of stator support. Install coast clutch seal and converter lock-up seal on stator support. Install pump outer diameter seal. Lubricate seal with transmission fluid before installing pump into case.

OVERDRIVE RING GEAR & CENTER SHAFT ASSEMBLY

Disassembly – 1) Remove outer race-to-ring gear retaining ring. Remove one way clutch assembly with inner and outer races. Remove one way clutch assembly with inner race from outer race. *See Fig. 28.*

2) Remove inner race from one way clutch assembly. Remove thrust washer from front of overdrive planet assembly. Remove overdrive planet assembly from ring gear assembly.

3) Remove needle bearing assembly from rear of overdrive planet assembly. Remove center shaft to-ring gear retaining ring and center shaft from ring gear.

Reassembly – To reassemble, reverse disassembly procedure. Ensure thrust washers and needle bearings are installed in their original locations. Place thick end cap on top of one-way clutch. Place thin end cap onto bottom of one-way clutch. Install clutch. Date code on outside of thick end cap must be visible.

NOTE: Inner race MUST rotate counterclockwise.

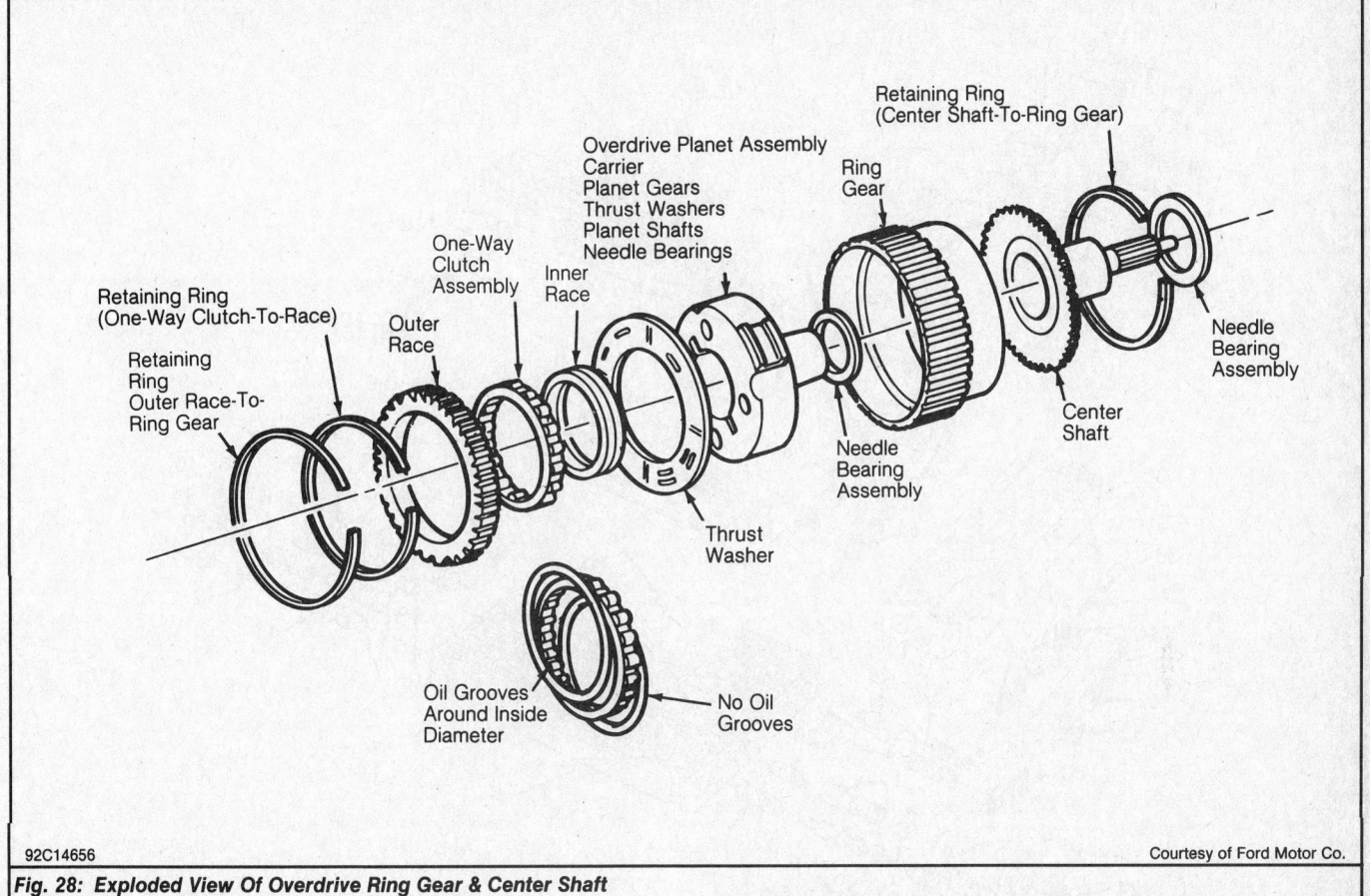

Retaining Ring
(Center Shaft-To-Ring Gear)

Overdrive Planet Assembly
Carrier
Planet Gears   Ring
Thrust Washers   Gear
Planet Shafts
Needle Bearings

One-Way
Clutch
Assembly   Inner
              Race
Retaining Ring
(One-Way Clutch-To-Race)
Outer
Race
                                        Needle
                                        Bearing
Retaining   Assembly
Ring
Outer Race-To-
Ring Gear
                                        Center
                            Needle   Shaft
                            Bearing
                            Assembly

                    Thrust
                    Washer

Oil Grooves
Around Inside   No Oil
Diameter   Grooves

92C14656   Courtesy of Ford Motor Co.

Fig. 28: Exploded View Of Overdrive Ring Gear & Center Shaft

VALVE BODY

Disassembly – Disassemble valve body. See VALVE BODY & INTERMEDIATE BAND SERVO under ON-VEHICLE SERVICE. Remove all valves, plungers, plugs and springs from control valve and accumulator bodies. *See Fig. 29.*

Inspection – **1)** Clean all parts, except non-metallic check balls, thoroughly in clean solvent. Blow dry with compressed air.

2) Inspect all valve and plunger bores for scores. Check all fluid passages for obstructions. Inspect all mating surfaces for burrs and scores. If necessary, use crocus cloth to polish valves and plungers. Avoid rounding sharp edges of valves and plungers with crocus cloth.

3) Inspect all springs for distortion. Check all valves and plungers for free movement in their respective bores. Valves and plungers, when dry, should fall by their own weight in their respective bores. Roll manual valve on a flat surface to check for bending.

Reassembly – Install all valves, plungers, plugs and springs into control valve and accumulator bodies. *See Fig. 29.* To complete reassembly, reverse disassembly procedure. See VALVE BODY & INTERMEDIATE BAND SERVO under ON-VEHICLE SERVICE.

TRANSMISSION REASSEMBLY

NOTE: Exploded views of internal parts, thrust washer and needle bearing locations can be found in Figs. 35-36. Lubricate all parts with transmission fluid during reassembly. Thrust washers and gaskets should be held in place with petroleum jelly.

NOTE: Thrust washers and needle bearings should be lubricated with petroleum jelly during reassembly.

Clutch & Drum Subassemblies – **1)** Install thrust washer on intermediate brake drum. Install forward clutch on intermediate brake drum and rotate until fully seated. Install needle bearing on intermediate brake drum and forward clutch assembly. Ensure Black side of needle bearing is facing up.

2) Install thrust washer on forward clutch hub. *See Fig. 30.* Insert forward clutch hub into intermediate brake drum and forward clutch assemblies. Place thrust washer on forward planet assembly. Insert planet assembly into clutch assembly. Install needle bearing into forward planet assembly. Ensure Black side of needle bearing is facing up.

3) Align input shell notches with intermediate brake drum. Install input shell on assembly and rotate until fully seated. *See Fig. 31.* Install needle bearing into front end of forward clutch assembly. Install Intermediate Brake Drum, Forward Clutch and Input Shell Remover-Installer (T89T-70010-E).

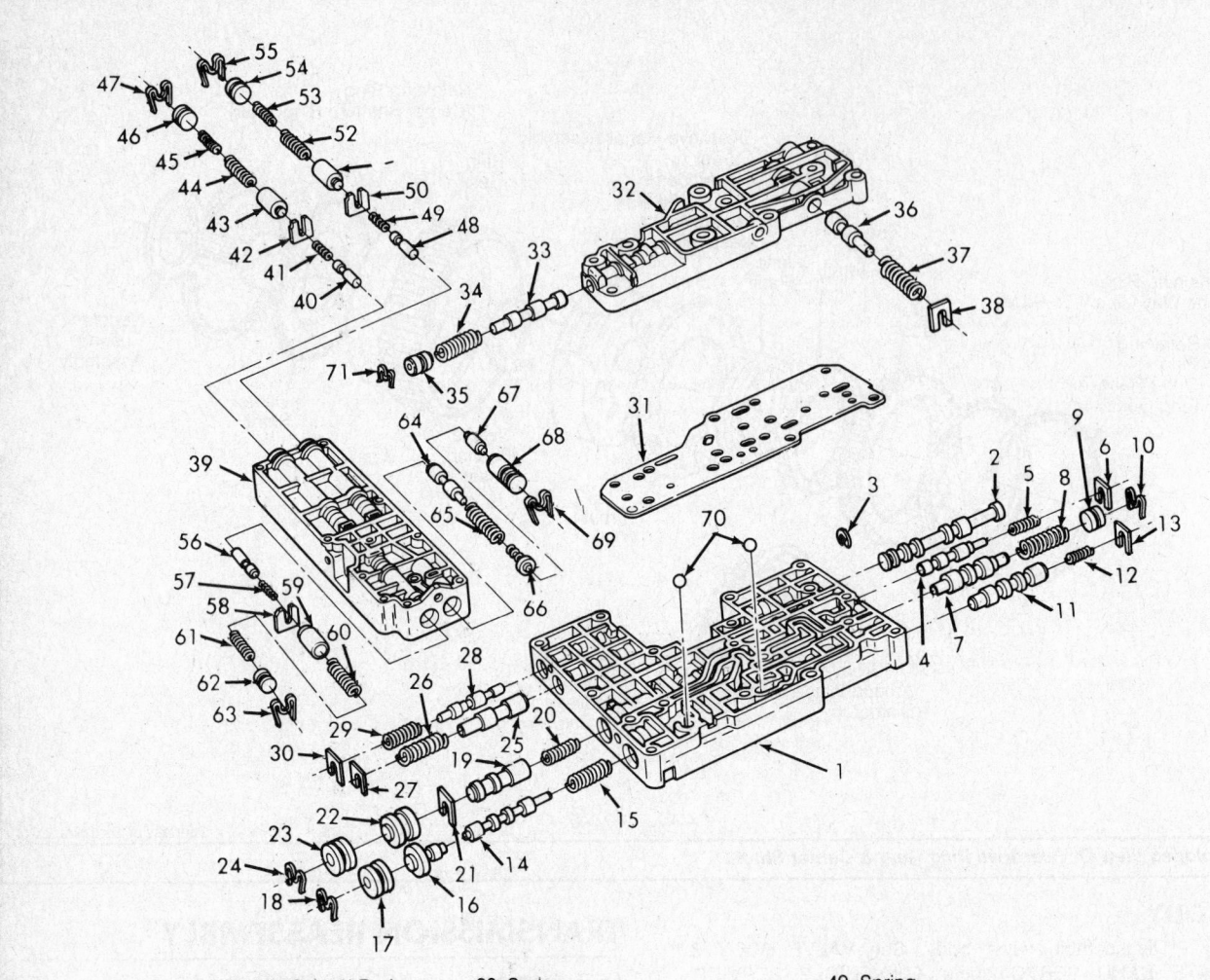

1. Main Control Body
2. Manual Valve
3. Retainer
4. Low/Reverse Modulator Valve
5. Spring
6. Retainer
7. 3-4 Shift Valve
8. Spring
9. Plug
10. Clip
11. 2-3 Shift Valve
12. Spring
13. Retainer
14. D2 Shift Valve
15. Spring
16. 1-2 Shift Valve
17. Plug
18. Clip
19. 4-3-2 Manual Timing Valve
20. Spring
21. Retainer
22. 4-3-2 Manual Timing Plunger
23. Plug
24. Clip
25. Coast Clutch Shift Valve

26. Spring
27. Retainer
28. Solenoid Regulator Valve
29. Spring
30. Retainer
31. Separator Plate
32. Lower Control Body
33. Engagement Control Valve
34. Spring
35. Plug
36. 1-2 Manual Transition Valve
37. Spring
38. Retainer
39. Accumulator Body
40. Overdrive Clutch Accumulator Regulator Valve
41. Spring
42. Retainer
43. Overdrive Clutch Accumulator Regulator Plunger
44. Outer Spring
45. Inner Spring
46. Plug
47. Clip
48. Direct Clutch Accumulator Regulator Valve

49. Spring
50. Retainer
51. Direct Clutch Accumulator Plunger
52. Outer Spring
53. Inner Spring
54. Plug
55. Clip
56. Intermediate Clutch Accumulator Regulator Valve
57. Spring
58. Retainer
59. Intermediate Clutch Accumulator Plunger
60. Outer Spring
61. Inner Spring
62. Plug
63. Clip
64. Line Pressure Modulator Valve
65. Outer Spring
66. Spring & Retainer Assembly
67. Line Pressure Modulator Plunger Valve
68. Line Pressure Modulator Sleeve
69. Clip
70. Check Balls
71. Clip

92D15290

Courtesy of Ford Motor Co.

Fig. 29: Exploded View Of Valve Body

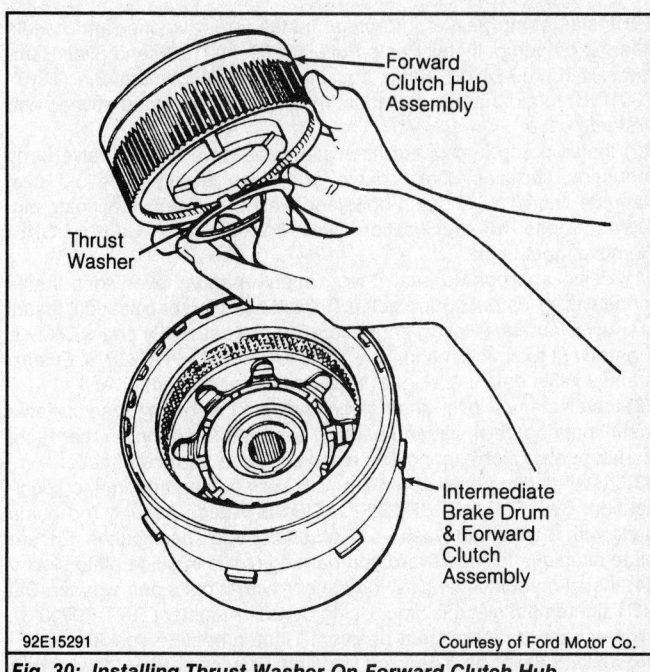

Fig. 30: Installing Thrust Washer On Forward Clutch Hub

92E15291   Courtesy of Ford Motor Co.

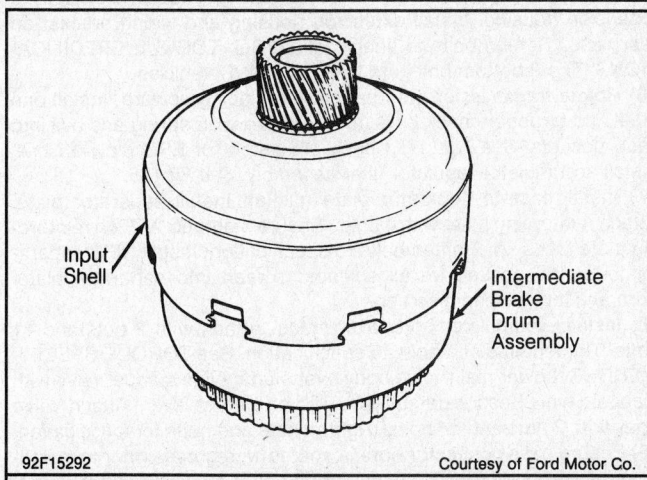

92F15292   Courtesy of Ford Motor Co.

Fig. 31: Assembling Direct Clutch, Forward Clutch & Input Shell

Final Reassembly – **1)** With transmission mounted in fixture, rotate bellhousing to face upward. Install inner and outer seals on reverse clutch piston. Using appropriate spring compressor, install reverse clutch piston. Remove spring compressor.

2) Install reverse piston return spring assembly and one-way clutch inner race. Ensure lubrication hole of inner race is in 6 o'clock position. Tighten bolts to specification. See TORQUE SPECIFICATIONS.

3) Install reverse clutch pack (5 or 6 plate assembly depending on model) starting with an external spline plate. Alternate external spline plates with internal spline plates. Install reverse clutch pressure plate and retaining ring. Ensure retaining ring is installed with opening between 12 and 3 o'clock. Clearance measurement is not required.

4) Rotate transmission to horizontal position. Lubricate steel side of thrust washer, and place on rear of case bronze side outward. Install retaining ring on output shaft. Slide park ear onto shaft with thrust surface opposite retaining ring. Install output shaft. DO NOT overextend retaining ring when installing. Ensure retaining ring is securely seated in groove.

5) Install reverse hub and low-reverse one-way clutch. Install output shaft hub and reverse ring gear with needle bearing on rear surface of hub. Hold bearing in place with petroleum jelly.

6) Install NEW retaining ring on output shaft. Rotate transmission with bellhousing facing upward. Install reverse planet into hub with thrust washer. Install retaining ring into low-reverse hub. Ensure retaining is securely seated in groove.

7) Using Clutch Remover-Installer (T89T-70010-E), install intermediate brake drum assembly, forward clutch assembly and input shell assembly into case as a unit. See Fig. 32. It may be necessary to rotate output shaft to seat reverse sun gear. Remove installer.

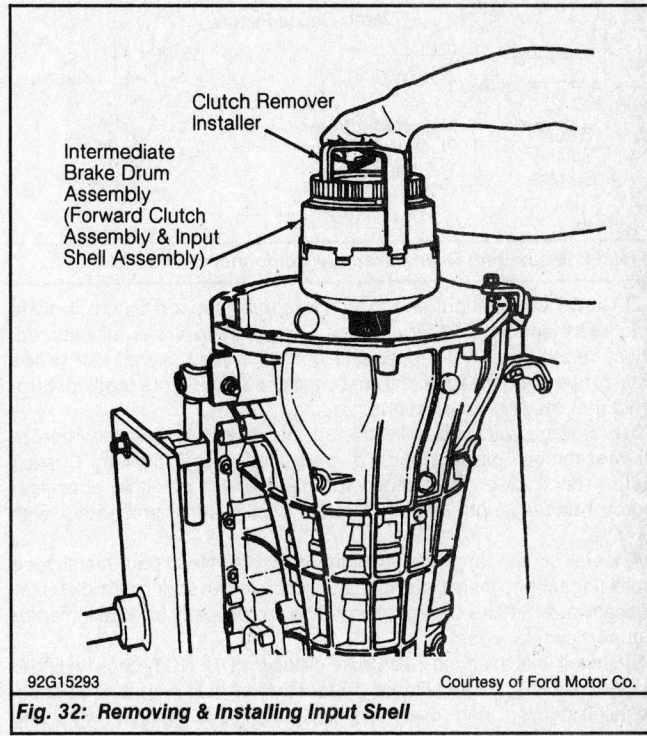

92G15293   Courtesy of Ford Motor Co.

Fig. 32: Removing & Installing Input Shell

8) Install intermediate band with one ear on reaction pin. Install servo retaining ring, retaining plate, piston and rod assembly, and servo spring. Install intermediate pressure plate. Install clutch pack starting with internal spline plate. Install apply plate.

9) Measure transmission rear end play to determine amount of space between thrust washer surfaces of center support and intermediate brake drum. Ensure transmission end play is .032-.081" (.81-2.06 mm).

10) Fabricate a depth gauge fixture from an overdrive center support. See Fig. 33. Drill a 1/8" hole through thrust washer surface of center support. This allows a measurement between thrust surfaces of support and intermediate brake drum to verify if components are correctly installed to this point.

NOTE: Remove cast iron seals from center support to allow easy insertion into intermediate brake drum.

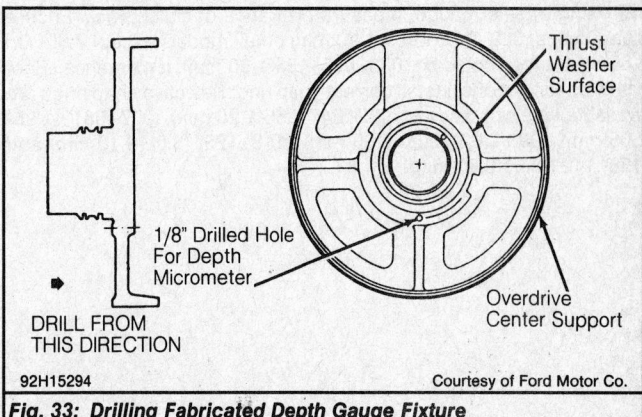

92H15294   Courtesy of Ford Motor Co.

Fig. 33: Drilling Fabricated Depth Gauge Fixture

11) Place depth micrometer over drilled hole. Extend micrometer probe until flush with thrust washer surface fixture and note reading. Install fabricated depth gauge fixture into intermediate brake drum. See Fig. 34.

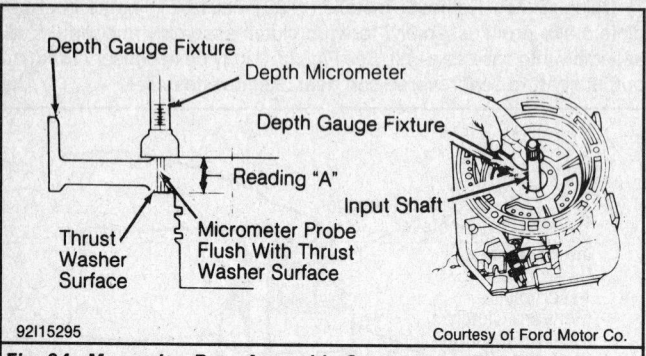

Depth Gauge Fixture
Depth Micrometer
Depth Gauge Fixture
Reading "A"
Input Shaft
Thrust Washer Surface
Micrometer Probe Flush With Thrust Washer Surface

92I15295   Courtesy of Ford Motor Co.

Fig. 34: Measuring Rear Assembly Components End Play

12) Gently wiggle input shaft to allow center support fixture to slide into intermediate brake drum. Ensure support fixture is fully seated. Place depth micrometer over drilled hole. Extend micrometer probe until probe bottoms against thrust washer surface. Note reading. Subtract first reading from second reading.

13) If average reading is not within specification, this indicates improper reassembly, missing parts or parts out of specification. Correct before continuing reassembly. If measurement is within specifications, remove depth gauge. Install thrust washer and retain with grease.

14) Install center support, and align with holes in feed port. Install feed bolts finger tight. Install intermediate clutch return spring with dish surface inward. Ensure spring locator legs are properly located in center support circular coast rib.

15) Install intermediate-overdrive cylinder. DO NOT cock cylinder when installing. Align cylinder threaded feed hole with hole in case. Install retaining ring over intermediate clutch cylinder with ring opening at bottom of case for proper oil drainback. Using Spring Compressor Plate (T89T-70010-F) and Spring Fixture (T89T-70010-C), tighten center bolt to 65 INCH lbs. (7 N.m). See Fig. 21.

16) Seat selective retaining ring in case ring groove. Install feed bolts finger tight. No clearance measurement is required. Remove spring tool assembly. Tighten all feed bolts to specification. See TORQUE SPECIFICATIONS.

CAUTION: Front feed bolt torque is lower than rear feed bolts. Ensure proper torque specification is used.

---

17) Coat needle bearing with grease and install on rear face of center shaft. Install center shaft, overdrive ring gear, overdrive planetary gear set and coast clutch cylinder as an assembly. Install overdrive clutch pack, starting with a steel plate. Install pressure plate with dot facing outward and toward top of case. Install trial selective retaining ring with opening at bottom of case.

18) Using a feeler gauge, measure clearance of clutch pack. Ensure clearance is .022-.047" (.055-1.20 mm) on all models except 7.5L. On 7.5L clearance should be .033-.059" (.85-1.50 mm). If clearance is not within specifications, install correct snap ring. Selective snap rings are available in thicknesses of .022-.047" (.55-1.20 mm), .077-.081" (1.95-2.05 mm), .098-.102" (2.50-2.60 mm), .118-.122" (3.00-3.10 mm) and .138-.142" (3.50-3.60 mm).

19) Install pump gasket into case. Install thrust washer and needle bearing on pump. Install Pump Puller (T89T-70010-A) and Slide Hammer (T59L-100-B) on pump housing. Install Alignment Pin (T89T-70010-B) to aid pump installation. Install input shaft long splined end first into case.

20) Install pump and orient filter inlet tube bore toward valve body mounting surfaces. Draw pump into case evenly to avoid seal damage. Install NEW pump bolts and washers. Remove aligning pin. Tighten bolts to specification. See TORQUE SPECIFICATIONS. Remove input shaft.

21) Using appropriate seal driver, install manual lever seal. Install manual lever detent spring bolts. Tighten bolts to specification. Install manual lever, inner lever, park actuating rod assembly and NEW nut. Tighten nut to specification. See TORQUE SPECIFICATIONS. Ensure manual valve detent spring is installed on inner detent lever.

22) Install manual lever and roll pin, with pin just below case surface. Install parking pawl, pin and parking pawl return spring on rear race. Parking pawl return spring end rests on inside surface of case.

23) Install parking pawl abutment with Torx bolt and tighten to specification. See TORQUE SPECIFICATIONS. Attach parking rod guide plate with 2 bolts and washers. Tighten bolts to specification. Ensure plate dimple is facing inward and parking rod is in guide plate slot.

24) Install manual lever position sensor with 2 bolts and washer. DO NOT tighten bolts at this time. Using Sensor Adjuster (T87T-70010-J), align sensor to neutral gear position. Tighten bolts to specification.

25) Install gasket on extension housing. Ensure parking pawl return spring is properly located on inside surface of case when installing extension housing. Install extension housing and wiring bracket on rear case. Tighten bolts to specification. See TORQUE SPECIFICATIONS. The 2 bottom bolts are longer on 4WD vehicles.

26) Rotate transmission with pan surface facing upward. Install one steel and 9 rubber check balls, and EPC blow-off spring and ball into case pockets. See Fig. 17. Check placement of EPC blow-off ball. Install accumulator regulator filter assembly. See Fig. 15.

27) Install case-to separator plate gasket. Install separator plate. Attach reinforcing plate with 3 bolts. Ensure stamped "UP" on reinforcing plate faces up. Tighten bolts to specification. Install NEW separator-to-control gasket. Install solenoid screen into separator plate. Turn and lock solenoid screen.

28) Install accumulator body over studs. Attach with 2 nuts and 11 bolts. Tighten nuts and bolts to specification. See TORQUE SPECIFICATIONS. Lower main valve body over studs. Align manual valve with manual lever. Ensure detent spring is on detent lever. Attach valve body with 2 nuts and 14 bolts. Tighten nuts and bolts to specification.

29) Ensure case connector bore is coated with grease prior to installing solenoid body. Install solenoid body over stud and attach with 9 Torx bolts and one nut. Tighten nut and bolts to specification.

30) Install NEW filter and seal assembly. Lubricate seal with ATF. Press filter into place. Install pan magnet on dimple in bottom of pan. Install NEW pan gasket on pan. Attach pan with bolts. Tighten bolts to specification. See TORQUE SPECIFICATIONS.

31) If necessary, install lube inlet short tube. Use stripe on side of tube for alignment. The stripe should be farthest outboard when installed. Reinstall input shaft, long splined end first.

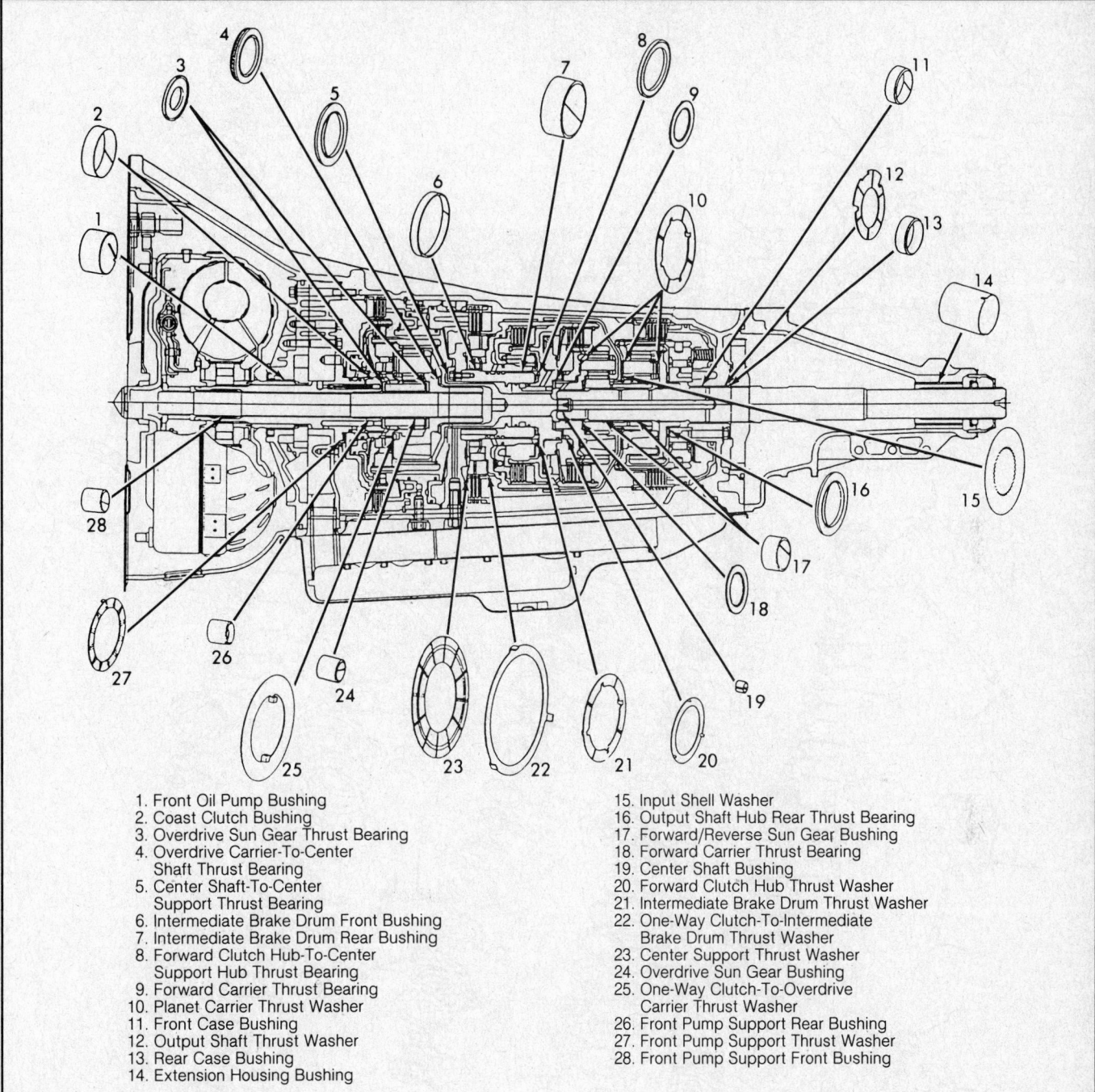

1. Front Oil Pump Bushing
2. Coast Clutch Bushing
3. Overdrive Sun Gear Thrust Bearing
4. Overdrive Carrier-To-Center Shaft Thrust Bearing
5. Center Shaft-To-Center Support Thrust Bearing
6. Intermediate Brake Drum Front Bushing
7. Intermediate Brake Drum Rear Bushing
8. Forward Clutch Hub-To-Center Support Hub Thrust Bearing
9. Forward Carrier Thrust Bearing
10. Planet Carrier Thrust Washer
11. Front Case Bushing
12. Output Shaft Thrust Washer
13. Rear Case Bushing
14. Extension Housing Bushing
15. Input Shell Washer
16. Output Shaft Hub Rear Thrust Bearing
17. Forward/Reverse Sun Gear Bushing
18. Forward Carrier Thrust Bearing
19. Center Shaft Bushing
20. Forward Clutch Hub Thrust Washer
21. Intermediate Brake Drum Thrust Washer
22. One-Way Clutch-To-Intermediate Brake Drum Thrust Washer
23. Center Support Thrust Washer
24. Overdrive Sun Gear Bushing
25. One-Way Clutch-To-Overdrive Carrier Thrust Washer
26. Front Pump Support Rear Bushing
27. Front Pump Support Thrust Washer
28. Front Pump Support Front Bushing

94l38586

Courtesy of Ford Motor Co.

Fig. 35: Locating Thrust Washers & Bearings

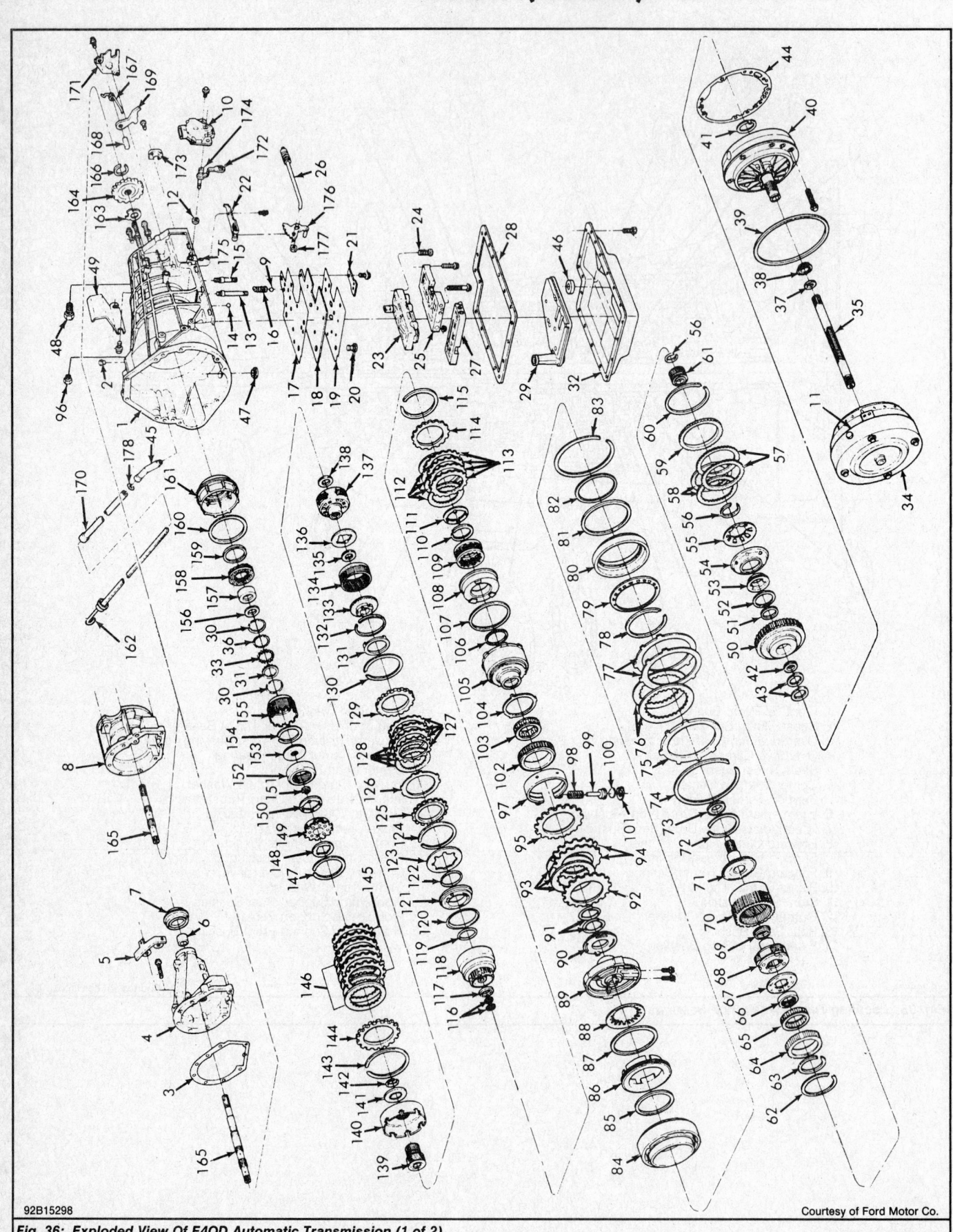

Courtesy of Ford Motor Co.

92B15298

Fig. 36: Exploded View Of E4OD Automatic Transmission (1 of 2)

1. Case Assembly
2. Vent Assembly
3. Extension Housing Gasket
4. Extension Housing
5. Wiring Bracket
6. Extension Housing Bushing
7. Extension Housing Seal
8. Extension Housing
9. EPC Blow-Off Ball
10. Manual Lever Position Sensor
11. Converter Drain
12. Manual Lever Seal
13. Case-To-Solenoid Body Stud
14. Rubber Check Ball
15. Case-To-Control Assembly Stud
16. EPC Blow-Off Spring
17. Case-To-Separator Plate Gasket
18. Separator Plate
19. Separator Plate-To-Control Gasket
20. Solenoid Screen
21. Separator Plate Reinforcement
22. Manual Valve Detent Spring Assembly
23. Solenoid Body Assembly
24. Torx Head Bolt
25. Main Control Body Assembly
26. Parking Pawl Actuating Rod Assembly
27. Accumulator Body Assembly
28. Oil Pan Gasket
29. Filter & Seal Assembly
30. Retaining Ring
31. Overrunning Clutch Spring Assembly
32. Oil Pan
33. Overrunning Clutch Roller
34. Torque Converter Assembly
35. Input Shaft
36. Overrunning Clutch Bushing
37. Teflon Seal Ring
38. Converter Hub Seal
39. Pump Seal
40. Pump Assembly
41. Pump Thrust Washer
42. Needle Bearing Assembly
43. Teflon Seal Ring
44. Pump Gasket
45. Lube Inlet Short Tube
46. Pan Magnet
47. Converter Access Plug
48. Oil Cooler Check Valve Assembly
49. Solenoid Body Connector Heat Shield
50. Coast Clutch Cylinder Assembly
51. Inner Seal
52. Outer Seal
53. Piston Coast Clutch
54. Piston Apply Ring
55. Piston Return Spring
56. Retaining Ring
57. Coast Clutch External Spline Plate
58. Coast Clutch Internal Spline Plate
59. Coast Clutch Pressure Plate

60. Selective Fit Retaining Ring
61. Overdrive Sun Gear Assembly
62. Retaining Ring
63. Retaining Ring
64. Overdrive One Way Clutch Outer Race
65. Overdrive One Way Clutch Assembly
66. Overdrive One Way Clutch Inner Race
67. Thrust Washer
68. Overdrive Planet Assembly
69. Needle Bearing Assembly
70. Overdrive Ring Gear
71. Center Shaft
72. Retaining Ring
73. Needle Bearing Assembly
74. Selective Fit Overdrive Retaining Ring
75. Overdrive Clutch Pressure Plate
76. Overdrive Clutch Internal Spline Plate
77. Overdrive Clutch External Spline Plate
78. Return Spring Retaining Ring
79. Overdrive Return Spring
80. Overdrive Piston
81. Overdrive Outer Seal
82. Overdrive Inner Seal
83. Cylinder Retaining Ring
84. Intermediate/Overdrive Cylinder
85. Intermediate Inner Seal
86. Intermediate Piston
87. Intermediate Outer Seal
88. Intermediate Return Spring
89. Center Support Assembly
90. Thrust Washer
91. Direct Clutch Cast Iron Seal
92. Intermediate Clutch Apply Plate
93. Intermediate Clutch Internal Spline Plate
94. Intermediate Clutch External Spline Plate
95. Intermediate Clutch Pressure Plate
96. Oil Tube Connector Assembly
97. Band Assembly
98. Servo Return Spring
99. Servo Piston Assembly
100. Servo Cover Plate
101. Servo Retaining Ring
102. Intermediate One Way Clutch Outer Race
103. Intermediate One Way Clutch Assembly
104. Thrust Washer
105. Intermediate Brake Drum Assembly
106. Inner Seal
107. Outer Seal
108. Piston Assembly
109. Piston Return Spring
110. Spring Retaining Ring
111. Thrust Washer
112. Direct Clutch Internal Spline Plate
113. Direct Clutch External Spline Plate
114. Direct Clutch Pressure Plate
115. Selective Fit Retaining Ring
116. Teflon Seal Ring
117. Needle Bearing Assembly
118. Forward Clutch Assembly Cylinder

119. Inner Seal
120. Outer Seal
121. Piston Assembly
122. Piston Apply Ring
123. Piston Return Spring
124. Retaining Ring
125. Forward Clutch Pressure Plate
126. Cushion Spring
127. Forward Clutch External Spline Plate
128. Forward Clutch Internal Spline Plate
129. Rear Clutch Pressure Plate
130. Selective Fit Retaining Ring
131. Plastic Thrust Washer
132. Retaining Ring
133. Forward Hub
134. Forward Ring Gear
135. Needle Bearing Assembly
136. Thrust Washer
137. Forward Planet Assembly
138. Needle Bearing Assembly
139. Forward/Reverse Sun Gear Assembly
140. Input Shell
141. Thrust Washer
142. Retaining Ring
143. Retaining Ring
144. Reverse Clutch Pressure Plate
145. Reverse Clutch External Spline Plate
146. Reverse Clutch Internal Spline Plate
147. Retaining Ring
148. Thrust Washer
149. Reverse Planet Assembly
150. Thrust Washer
151. Retaining Ring
152. Reverse Ring Gear
153. Output Shaft Hub
154. Retaining Ring
155. Reverse Clutch Hub Assembly
156. Needle Bearing Assembly
157. Low/Reverse One Way Clutch Inner Race
158. Piston Return Spring Assembly
159. Inner Seal
160. Outer Seal
161. Piston
162. Dipstick
163. Thrust Washer
164. Parking Gear
165. Output Shaft Assembly
166. Retaining Ring
167. Parking Pawl Return Spring
168. Parking Pawl Pin
169. Parking Pawl
170. Oil Filler Tube Assembly
171. Parking Rod Guide Plate
172. Insulator
173. Parking Pawl Actuating Abutment
174. Manual Control Lever Assembly
175. Manual Lever Retaining Pin
176. Inner Detent Lever
177. Inner Detent Lever Nut
178. Oil Filler Tube Seal

92C15299

Courtesy of Ford Motor Co.

Fig. 37: Legend For Exploded View Of E4OD Automatic Transmission (2 of 2)

TORQUE SPECIFICATIONS

TORQUE SPECIFICATIONS

Application	Ft. Lbs. (N.m)
Center Support Fluid Feed Bolts	8-12 (11-16)
Connector-To-Case Cooler Line Nut	18-23 (24-31)
Control Assembly-To-Pump Body Bolts	18-23 (24-31)
Converter Drain Plug	18-20 (24-27)
Extension Housing-To-Case	
(4X2) Bolts	20-29 (27-39)
(4X4) Bolts	24-40 (33-54)
Inner One-Way Clutch Race-To-Case Bolts	18-25 (24-34)
Inner & Outer Lever-To-Manual Control Shift Nut	30-40 (41-54)
Manual Detent Lever Nut	30-40 (41-54)
Oil Pan-To-Case Bolts	10-12 (14-16)
Oil Pump Body-To-Case Bolts	18-23 (24-31)
Parking Pawl Abutment-To-Case Bolts	16-20 (22-27)
Parking Rod Guide Plate-To-Case Bolts	16-20 (22-27)

TORQUE SPECIFICATIONS (Cont.)

Application	INCH Lbs. (N.m)
Center Support-To-Hub Bolts	
Front Bolt (1)	72-120 (9-14)
Rear Bolt (2)	96-144 (11-16)
Lower Body-To-Main Body Bolts	80-100 (9-11)
Main Accumulator And Solenoid	
Body-To-Case Bolts	80-100 (9-11)
Main And Lower Body-To-Case Bolts	80-100 (9-11)
MLP Sensor-To-Case Bolts	55-75 (6-8)
Overdrive Cylinder Fluid Feed Bolts	72-120 (8-14)
Plug Line Pressure Case	72-144 (8-16)
Plug Throttle Pressure Case	72-144 (8-16)
Positive Detent Spring-To-Case Bolts	80-100 (9-11)
Reinforcing Plate-To-Case Bolts	80-100 (9-11)
Solenoid Body-To-Case Bolts	80-100 (9-11)
Stator Support-To-Pump Body Bolts	80-100 (9-11)
Valve Body-To-Case Long Stud	80-100 (9-11)
Valve Body-To-Case Nut	80-100 (9-11)
Valve Body-To-Case Short Stud	80-100 (9-11)

TRANSMISSION SPECIFICATIONS

TRANSMISSION SPECIFICATIONS

Application	In. (mm)
Coast Clutch Pack Clearance	.025-.045 (.62-1.14)
Direct Clutch Pack Clearance	
3-Disc Clutch	.030-.045 (.76-1.15)
4-Disc Clutch	.045-.060 (1.15-1.52)
Forward Clutch Pack Clearance	.030-.055 (.76-1.40)
Inner/Outer Gear-To-Housing Clearance [1]	.004-.007 (.11-.18)
Intermediate Clutch Pack Clearance	
All Except 4.9L	.029-.063 (.74-1.60)
4.9L	.023-.057 (.59-1.44)
Overdrive Clutch Pack Clearance	
All Except 7.5L	.022-.047 (.55-1.20)
7.5L	.033-.059 (.85-1.50)
Reverse Clutch Pack Clearance	.047 (1.20)
5-Disc Clutch	.027-.104 (.68-2.64)
6-Disc Clutch	.027-.113 (.68-2.87)
Torque Converter End Play	
New Or Rebuilt	.014-.038 (.35-96)
Used	.071 (1.8)

[1] – Oil pump inner/outer gerotor gear.

SERVICE BULLETINS

CASE DAMAGE

ATRA Technical Bulletin No. 123 – Manufacturer's procedure uses 2 slide hammers to remove oil pump. Under no circumstances should a screwdriver be used to pry out oil pump. This procedure may cause severe damage to transmission case.

Ensure center support-to-hub bolts are properly tightened. Front bolt should be tightened to 72-120 INCH lbs. (9-14 N.m) and 2 rear bolts to 96-144 INCH lbs. (11-16 N.m). After bolts are tightened, check valve body mounting surface of case with straightedge. Flat file surface to correct minor warpage.

MANUAL VALVE INDEXING

ATRA Technical Bulletin No. 124 – Post overhaul malfunctions, such as no reverse, delayed reverse engagement and delayed forward engagement may be caused by manual valve misalignment. To check manual valve alignment, remove oil pan and shift transmission to neutral. The 2nd land of the manual valve should be within .030" (.76 mm) of being flush with surface of valve body. If manual valve is not correctly indexed, replace detent spring and recheck.

INTERMEDIATE SPRAG ROTATION

ATRA Technical Bulletin No. 138 – A bind-up occurring during 1-2 shift in "D", or 2-3 manual shift, may be caused by improper intermediate one-way clutch (sprag) rotation. With one-way clutch facing upward, outer race should rotate only counterclockwise.

FRONT SEAL BLOW OUT

ATRA Technical Bulletin No. 142 – Front seal blow-out may be caused by using a C6 front seal instead of a genuine E40D front seal. Seals differ slightly. For increased seal sealing to housing, wire brush paint off outside of seal and apply Locktite® prior to installation of seal.

OVERDRIVE PLANETARY FAILURE

ATRA Technical Bulletin No. 184 – Overdrive planetary failure may be caused by a melted drainback valve which is located under the orifice cup plug in rear of the stator support. The forked end of the valve will be melted. Replace valve with Ford replacement part No. E9TZ-7H132-A. The orifice cup plug must be reused.

FUEL INJECTION PUMP LEVER (FIPL) SENSOR TROUBLE SHOOTING & ADJUSTMENTS

ATRA Technical Bulletin No. 186 – On diesel vehicles, poor transmission performance and/or premature failure may be caused by a defective Fuel Injection Pump Lever (FIPL) sensor, or sensor signal. Sensor is located on injection pump. Ford Motor Co. recommends the FIPL be checked or replaced every 50K miles.

It is recommended to install "upgraded" FIPL (F2TZ-9B989-C) whenever a overhaul is performed on an E40D transmission. Also inspect condition of harness where it is routed across top of engine. For FIPL testing information, see E40D ELECTRONIC CONTROLS article.

SOLENOID HARNESS CONNECTOR FAULT

ATRA Technical Bulletin No. 216 – Incorrect installation of solenoid harness connector can cause high line pressure, 4th gear starts, 2nd gear starts in manual low and/or no torque converter clutch engagement. Connection problem usually occurs once solenoid body has been replaced. Solenoid body connector has inner sleeve that may stay connected to harness connector, preventing connector to fully seat on new solenoid body connector. Ensure connector lock is fully latched.

STACKED SHIFTS, NO KICKDOWN, INOPERATIVE O/D CANCEL SWITCH, SHIFT HUNTING

ATRA Technical Bulletin No. 219 – A blown No. 17 fuse can cause stacked shifts, no kickdown, inoperative O/D cancel switch and/or shift hunting. Common cause of blown No. 17 fuse is a short in wire located in steering column going to O/D cancel button. Repair wires as necessary or replace shifter lever assembly (F2TZ-7210-F).

NO TORQUE CONVERTER CLUTCH, TORQUE CONVERTER CLUTCH CYCLING, SHIFT HUNTING (DIESEL ONLY)

ATRA Technical Bulletin No. 220A – No torque converter clutch, torque converter clutch cycling and/or shift hunting can be caused by short or open of RPM sensor. To test sensor, see applicable test in E40D ELECTRONIC CONTROLS article.

EXTENSION HOUSING BUSHING FAILURE

ATRA Technical Bulletin No. 228 – The extension housing bushing may wear extensively in a relatively short period of time. There are 2 possible causes:
- Insufficient lube oil to bushing/yoke area.
- Inadequate transmission electrical grounding.

To check extension housing lube oil, ensure transmission is at normal operating temperature. Disconnect return cooler line. Start vehicle and check fluid volume from line. Flow should be 3 quarts per minute. Repair as needed.

Inspect output shaft bushing wear. Remove extension housing. Mount dial indicator on output shaft near park gear. Up and down movement of shaft should not exceed 1/16". Remove rear cooler line and apply compressed air to transmission case fitting. There should be minimal air escaping. Repair as needed.

Inspect lube oil passage. Passage is located on case below park gear. A small stream of fluid will be noticed when applying air to rear cooler line fitting. Reconnect cooler line and start vehicle. A steady stream of fluid should come from lube hole. Stop engine and using a .033", check diameter of opening. Repair as needed.

If electrical grounding problem is suspected, install additional grounding strap to transmission.

Ford Motor Co: Bronco, "E" Series, "F" Series

NOTE: For E4OD transmission mechanical testing and repair, see Ford E4OD article.

INTRODUCTION

The first step in diagnosing any driveability problem is verifying the customer's complaint with a test drive under the conditions the problem reportedly occurred. Before entering self-diagnostics, perform a careful and complete visual inspection. Most transmission control problems result from mechanical breakdowns or poor electrical connections.

NOTE: Perform all voltage tests with a Digital Volt-Ohmmeter (DVOM) with a minimum 10-megohm input impedance, unless stated otherwise in test procedure.

DESCRIPTION & OPERATION

Input signals from sensors are sent to the Powertrain Control Module (PCM). The PCM can determine when the time and conditions are right for a shift or converter clutch application. The PCM can also determine line pressure needed to optimize shift feel.

The PCM controls transmission operation through 5 electronic solenoids consisting of 4 On/Off solenoids for shifting and torque converter clutch control and one varible force solenoid for line pressure control. All components are part of the transmission solenoid body and are not serviceable individually. The PCM has built-in self-diagnostic capability, fail-safe code and warning code display for the main input sensors and solenoid valves.

NOTE: In addition to transmission fault codes, engine related fault codes may be output during QUICK TEST procedure. These fault codes pertain to engine performance and must be repaired first, as engine performance will greatly affect transmission operation. For information and testing procedures of engine related fault codes and components, see SELF-DIAGNOSTICS – EEC-IV article in ENGINE PERFORMANCE of appropriate MITCHELL® manual.

INPUT SENSORS

Air Conditioning Clutch (ACC) – On factory installed A/C system, PCM receives signal voltage from ACC switch indicating that the air conditioning compressor clutch is engaged. The PCM uses the ACC switch signal to adjust line pressure to compensate for additional engine load. If the ACC switch fails with closed contacts, line pressure will be slightly low with air conditioning off. If the ACC switch fails with open contacts, line pressure will be slightly high with air conditioning on.

Brake On/Off (BOO) Switch – The PCM receives a signal from the BOO switch when the brake switch is operated. Torque converter clutch is disengaged when brakes are applied. Malfunctioning switch will affect torque converter operation.

4WD Low Switch – Low range switch is located on transfer case cover. Switch modifies shift schedule for 4WD transfer case gear ratio. Early shifts will occur if switch fails in ON position. Delayed shifts will occur if switch fails in OFF position.

Mass Airflow Sensor (MAS) – The MAS signal is used for Electronic Pressure Control (EPC), shift and TCC scheduling. Sensor malfunction will affect shift and TCC scheduling.

Manual Lever Position (MLP) – The PCM monitors a series of step down resistors in the MLP sensor that act as a voltage divider. The voltage signal corresponds with position of the transmission range selector lever. The MLP sensor also contains the neutral/start and backup circuits. Malfunction of the MLP sensor may cause harsh engagements and firm shift feel. Improper shifting or shift selection and no engine cranking may also result.

Profile Ignition Pickup (PIP) – The PIP located in distributor, sends engine rpm and crankshaft position to PCM. Signal received by the PCM affects torque converter clutch operation.

Programmable Speedometer/Odometer Module (PSOM) – The PSOM receives input from rear brake anti-lock sensor, which is mounted on rear axle differential housing. Vehicle speed (mph) signal is output to PCM. PSOM failure may cause harsh engagements, firm shift feel and abnormal shift schedule. Unexpected downshifts may occur at closed throttle and abnormal TCC operation or engages at WOT. Transmission Control Indicator Light (TCIL) may flash.

Throttle Position Sensor (TPS) – The TPS is a potentiometer mounted to the engine throttle body on gasoline engines and fuel injection pump on diesel engines. The PCM receives a signal from the TPS relaying throttle plate position (gas engines) or fuel delivery (diesel engines). TPS failure will cause PCM to operate in fail safe mode and raise line pressure to prevent transmission damage. This condition will result in harsh engagements, firm shift feel, abnormal shift schedule and TCC not engaging or cycling.

Transmission Control Switch (TCS) – Switch is mounted on shift lever handle. On/Off operation is displayed by Transmission Control Indicator Light (TCIL). Switch controls operation of 4th gear. Malfunction of switch will cause lack of 4th gear disable function.

Transmission Oil Temperature (TOT) Sensor – The TOT sensor is located on the solenoid body assembly. The PCM monitors voltage across the TOT thermistor to determine transmission temperature. Depending on temperature, the PCM controls line pressure, shift scheduling and TCC operation. Malfunction of sensor will cause incorrect line pressure and possible lack of TCC operation.

Vehicle Speed Sensor (VSS) – The VSS is a magnetic pickup that sends vehicle speed signal to the PCM. Malfunction of sensor may cause harsh engagements of shifts. Lack of 4th gear, TCC lock-up, or engine braking in 2nd or 3rd gear may also be present.

OUTPUT DEVICES

Electronic Pressure Control (EPC) Solenoid – The EPC receives signal from the PCM to control line pressure and backout valve function. If EPC fails in ON position, transmission is operated in failsafe mode. Line pressure is approximately 120 psi. Harsh engagements and shifts will result. If EPC fails in OFF position, line pressure is approximately 90 psi. Harsh engagements and shifts will result.

Shift Solenoid Assemblies – 1) Three ON/OFF solenoids are used for electronic shift scheduling. Solenoids used are Shift Solenoid No. 1 (SS1), Shift Solenoid No. 2 (SS2) and Coast Clutch Solenoid (CCS). Solenoids control pressure to 3 shift valves and forward clutch control valve, located in valve body. See SOLENOID OPERATION CHART.

SOLENOID OPERATIONS CHART

Gear Position	SS1	SS2	CCS
Park	On	Off	Off
Reverse	On	Off	Off
Neutral	On	Off	Off
"OD" (Overdrive) [1]			
1st Gear	On	Off	Off
2nd Gear	On	On	Off
3rd Gear	Off	On	Off
4th Gear	Off	On	Off
"D" Or 3rd [2]			
1st Gear	On	Off	Off
2nd Gear	On	On	Off
3rd Gear	Off	On	On
Manual 2	Off	On	On
Manual 1 [3]	Off	Off	On
Manual 1	On	Off	On

[1] – "OD" switch released.
[2] – "OD" switch depressed (OD cancelled).
[3] – Transmission is in 2nd gear until vehicle speed drops below calibrated speed.

2) When shift solenoid is "Always Off", failure could be due to PCM and/or vehicle wiring malfunction, and/or solenoid electrically stuck off, and/or hydraulically or mechanically stuck off. For shift symptoms, see Fig. 1.

3) When shift solenoid is "Always On", failure could be due to PCM and/or vehicle wiring malfunction, and/or solenoid electrically stuck off, and/or hydraulically or mechanically stuck off. For shift symptoms, see Fig. 2.

Torque Converter Clutch (TCC) Solenoid – The TCC receives signal from the PCM. The TCC controls application, modulation and release of torque converter clutch. If solenoid fails in ON position, vehicle engine will run rough (shudder) and engine stalls in Drive at low idle speeds (2nd, 3rd or 4th gear). If solenoid fails in OFF position, torque converter clutch will not engage.

Shift Solenoid 1 ALWAYS OFF

Powertrain Control Module Gear Commanded	Position Selected: Overdrive	Position Selected: 2	Position Selected: 1
	Actual Gear Obtained		
1	4	2	1
2	3	2	2
3	3	2	2
4	4	2	2

Shift Solenoid 2 ALWAYS OFF

Powertrain Control Module Gear Commanded	Position Selected: Overdrive	Position Selected: 2	Position Selected: 1
	Actual Gear Obtained		
1	1	2	1
2	1	2	1
3	4	2	2
4	4	2	2

94E38707 94F38708   Courtesy of Ford Motor Co.

Fig. 1: Shift Solenoid Failure Charts (Solenoid Always Off)

Shift Solenoid 1 ALWAYS ON

Powertrain Control Module Gear Commanded	Position Selected: Overdrive	Position Selected: 2	Position Selected: 1
	Actual Gear Obtained		
1	1	2	1
2	2	2	1
3	2	2	1
4	1	2	1

Shift Solenoid 2 ALWAYS ON

Powertrain Control Module Gear Commanded	Position Selected: Overdrive	Position Selected: 2	Position Selected: 1
	Actual Gear Obtained		
1	2	1	1
2	2	2	1
3	3	2	2
4	3	2	2

94G38709 94J38710   Courtesy of Ford Motor Co.

Fig. 2: Shift Solenoid Failure Charts (Solenoid Always On)

PRELIMINARY INSPECTION

VISUAL INSPECTION

Visually inspect all electrical wiring, looking for chafed, stretched, cut or pinched wiring. Ensure electrical connectors fit tightly and are not corroded. Ensure vacuum hoses are properly routed and are not pinched or cut. Inspect air induction system for possible vacuum leaks. Check PCM, sensors and actuators for physical damage. Check engine coolant level. Check transmission fluid level and condition.

NOTE: In addition to transmission fault codes, engine-related fault codes may be output during QUICK TEST procedure. These fault codes pertain to engine performance and must be repaired first as engine performance will greatly affect transmission operation. For information and testing procedures of engine-related fault codes and components, see SELF-DIAGNOSTICS – EEC-IV article in ENGINE PERFORMANCE of appropriate MITCHELL® manual.

SELF-DIAGNOSTIC SYSTEM

DIAGNOSTIC FORMATS

QUICK TEST, CIRCUIT/PINPOINT TESTS are diagnostic formats used to test and service EEC-IV system. QUICK TEST allows technician to identify problems and retrieve service codes. CIRCUIT TESTS check engine circuits, sensors and actuators. PINPOINT TESTS check transmission circuits, sensors and actuators.

Before starting any circuit test, follow all steps under QUICK TEST to find correct circuit or pinpoint test. If vehicle passes QUICK TEST and no driveability symptoms or intermittent faults exist, EEC-IV system is okay.

DIAGNOSTIC TROUBLE CODES (DTC)

When CIRCUIT/PINPOINT TEST procedures apply to both 2-digit codes and 3-digit codes, the applicable codes will be separated by a diagonal mark (example: Code 31/327).

During QUICK TEST, 3 types of service codes are retrieved: Key On Engine Off (KOEO), Key On Engine Running (KOER) and Continuous Memory Codes. See QUICK TEST for self-test procedures. Codes may be cleared from PCM memory after they have been recorded or repaired. See CLEARING CODES.

KOEO & KOER Codes (Hard Faults) – These codes indicate faults are present at time of testing. A hard fault may cause CHECK ENGINE light or Malfunction Indicator Light (MIL) to glow and remain on until fault is repaired. If KOEO or KOER codes are retrieved during KOEO SELF-TEST or KOER SELF-TEST, use SERVICE CODE REFERENCE CHARTS to find correct testing and repair procedures.

Continuous Memory Codes (Soft Faults) – These codes indicate a fault that may or may not be present at time of testing. These codes are used to diagnose intermittent problems. Continuous Memory Codes are retrieved during KOEO SELF-TEST. Some codes may turn on MIL or CHECK ENGINE light. Corresponding soft trouble code will be retained in PCM memory. If fault does not reoccur within 40 warm-up cycles (80 cycles on some models), PCM will automatically clear code. Technician may clear service codes from memory. See CLEARING CODES. Intermittent faults may be caused by a sensor, connector or wiring-related problems.

CAUTION: *Continuous Memory Codes should be recorded when retrieved during KOEO SELF-TEST. These codes may be used to identify intermittent problems that exist after all KOEO and KOER codes have been repaired and a Code 11 or 111 (pass code) has been obtained. Failure to follow this procedure may result in unnecessary testing. Some Continuous Memory Codes faults may not be valid after KOEO and KOER codes are repaired.*

RETRIEVING CODES

Service codes are retrieved from EEC-IV system through self-test connector. Various methods and test equipment may be used to access these codes:

- Analog Volt-Ohmmeter (VOM)
- Scan Tester
- In-Dash Malfunction Indicator Light (MIL) Or CHECK ENGINE light
- STAR Series Tester

DATA LINK CONNECTOR (DLC) LOCATIONS

Application	Location
Bronco & "F" Series	Left Front Inner Fender Panel
"E" Series	Right Front Inner Fender Panel

READING CODES

KOEO & KOER SELF-TEST Codes – PCM outputs codes one digit at a time. Record codes in order received. These codes indicate current faults in system and should be serviced in order of appearance. Use SERVICE CODE REFERENCE CHARTS to find correct CIRCUIT/PINPOINT TEST.

If using analog VOM, pay careful attention to length of pauses in order to read codes correctly. A 1/2-second pause occurs between number of sweeps in a digit. A 2-second pause occurs between digits in a code. A 4-second pause occurs between each code. KOEO are separated from Continuous Memory codes by a 6-second delay, a 1/2-second sweep (separator) and another 6-second delay. *See Fig. 3.* If using MIL/CHECK ENGINE light, service codes are displayed as flashes.

Scan tester, if used, will count pulses and display them as a digital code. STAR Series Tester will add a zero (0) to single-digit Separator Code (10) and Dynamic Response Code (10). Dynamic Response Code is displayed in KOER SELF-TEST. *See Fig. 3.*

Engine Identification (ID) Codes – Engine ID codes are issued at beginning of KOER SELF-TEST. Codes are one-digit numbers represented by number of pulses displayed. *See Fig. 3.* Engine ID code is equal to one-half the number of engine cylinders. For example, 2 pulses would indicate that engine is a 4 cylinder. ID code is used to verify proper PCM is installed and that SELF-TEST has been entered.

Separator Pulse – Single 1/2-second separator pulse is issued 6-9 seconds after last KOEO code. Continuous Memory Codes (soft faults) are then displayed 6-9 seconds after 1/2-second separator pulse. Some digital test equipment may display separator code as "10" instead of "1".

Pass Codes – A Code 11 or 111 indicates no service codes were recorded in that portion of test; system passes that portion of test. If Code 11 or 111 is not retrieved in KOEO SELF-TEST, codes retrieved during KOER SELF-TEST may not be valid. Code 11 or 111 (pass code) must be obtained in KOEO SELF-TEST. A Code 11-1-11 or 111-1-111 output during KOEO SELF-TEST indicates no KOEO code or Continuous Memory Code was recorded.

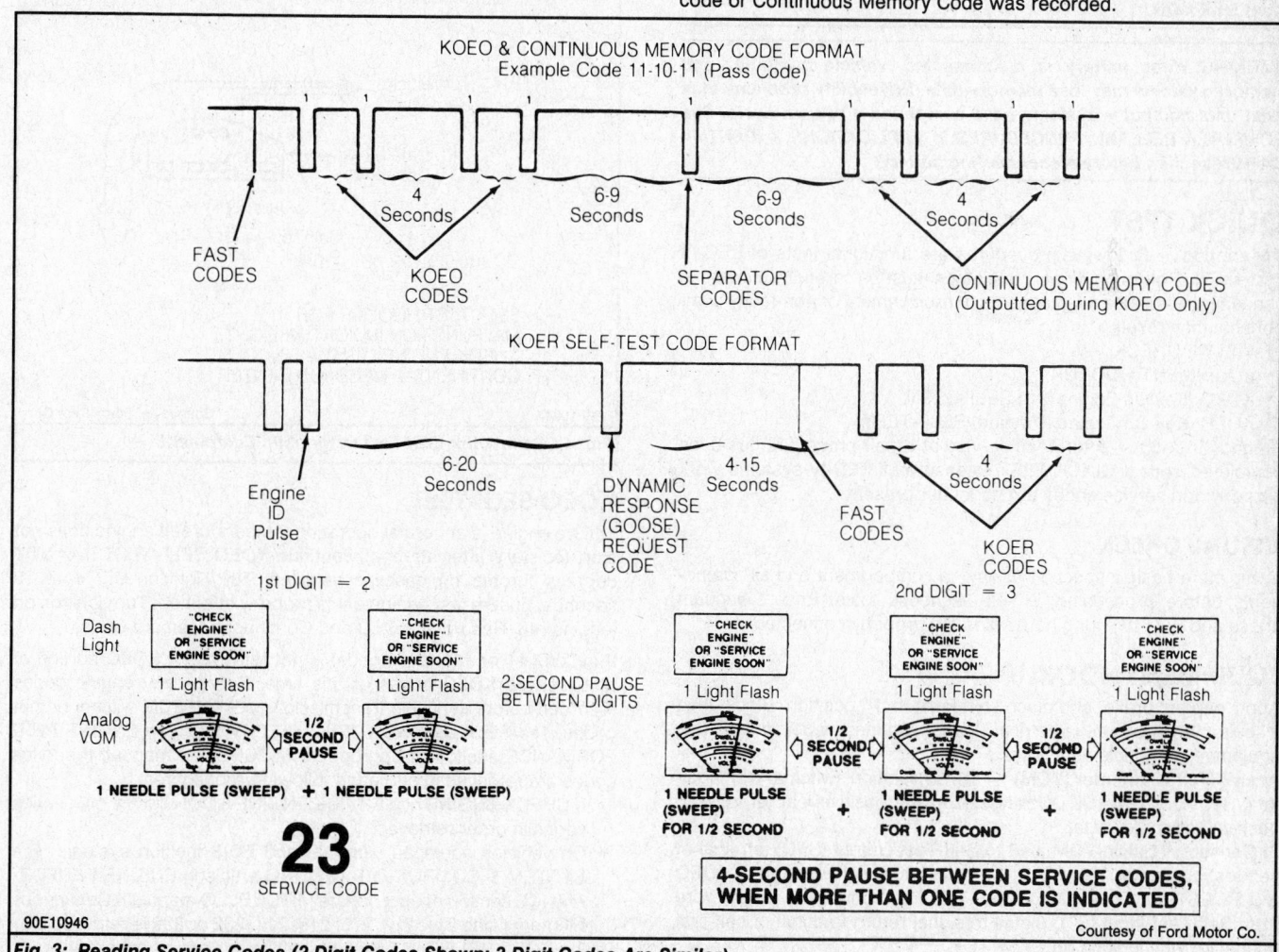

90E10946

Courtesy of Ford Motor Co.

Fig. 3: Reading Service Codes (2-Digit Codes Shown; 3-Digit Codes Are Similar)

Continuous Memory Codes – These codes result from information stored by PCM during continuous self-test monitoring. Codes are displayed after separator pulse code in KOEO SELF-TEST. Use these codes for diagnosis only when KOEO SELF-TEST and KOER SELF-TEST result in Code 11 or 111 (pass code) and all steps under QUICK TEST are successfully completed. A few codes are exceptions which may be checked after KOEO codes have been repaired. These codes indicate faults recorded within last 40 engine starts (80 engine starts on some models). Fault may or may not be currently present. See SERVICE CODE REFERENCE CHARTS.

Fast Codes – At start of KOEO SELF-TEST and after Wide Open Throttle (WOT) request in KOER SELF-TEST, PCM outputs short bursts of information, known as FAST CODES, which were used by manufacturer during assembly. With most equipment, these code bursts are not visible; an entire code sequence lasts less than 1/2 second. If this fluctuation is visible on test equipment, ignore it.

CLEARING CODES

To clear codes from PCM memory, start KOEO SELF-TEST under QUICK TEST. When service codes appear on test equipment or CHECK ENGINE light, disconnect jumper wire from Self-Test Input (STI) connector. If using STAR Series Tester, unlatch center button. This procedure erases Continuous Memory Codes from PCM memory. If problem has not been corrected or fault is still present, hard code will immediately be reset in PCM memory.

CAUTION: DO NOT disconnect vehicle battery to clear codes. This will erase stored operating information from Keep-Alive Memory (KAM). To clear KAM, disconnect negative battery terminal for at least 5 minutes.

WARNING: When battery is disconnected, vehicle computer and memory systems may lose memory data. Driveability problems may exist until computer systems have completed a relearn cycle. See COMPUTER RELEARN PROCEDURES in APPLICATIONS & IDENTIFICATION section before disconnecting battery.

QUICK TEST

Description – Following procedures are functional tests of EEC-IV system. The following 4 basic test steps must be carefully followed in sequence, otherwise misdiagnosis or replacement of non-faulty components may result:
- VISUAL CHECK
- EQUIPMENT HOOKUP.
- KOEO (Key On Engine Off) SELF-TEST.
- KOER (Key On Engine Running) SELF-TEST.

Diagnostic Aids – After each service or repair procedure has been completed, repeat QUICK TEST to ensure all EEC-IV systems work properly and service codes are no longer present.

VISUAL CHECK

Complete a basic inspection of engine compartment and all components before proceeding to self-diagnostic tests. Ensure vacuum hoses and EEC-IV wiring harnesses are properly connected.

EQUIPMENT HOOKUP

Apply parking brake, and place shift lever in "P" position. Block drive wheels. Turn off all electrical loads. Connect appropriate test equipment to vehicle as follows:

Analog Volt-Ohmmeter (VOM) – 1) Turn ignition switch to OFF position. Set VOM at 0-15V DC range. Connect positive lead of VOM to positive battery terminal.

2) Connect negative VOM lead to Self-Test Output (STO) terminal of self-test connector. *See Fig. 4.* Connect timing light, and go to KOEO SELF-TEST. Activate KOEO SELF-TEST by connecting jumper wire from Self-Test Input (STI) pigtail to signal return terminal of self-test connector with ignition on.

Scan Tester – Follow manufacturer instructions to hook up equipment and record service codes.

STAR Series Tester – Turn ignition switch to OFF position. Connect color-coded adapter cable leads to diagnostic tester. Connect 2 service connectors of adapter cable to vehicle self-test connector and STI pigtail connector. Connect timing light. Go to KOEO SELF-TEST.

CHECK ENGINE Light/Malfunction Indicator Light (MIL) – Turn ignition on. Connect a jumper wire between Self-Test Input (STI) pigtail and signal return (SIG RTN) terminal of Data Link Connector (DLC). *See Fig. 4.* Go to KOEO SELF-TEST.

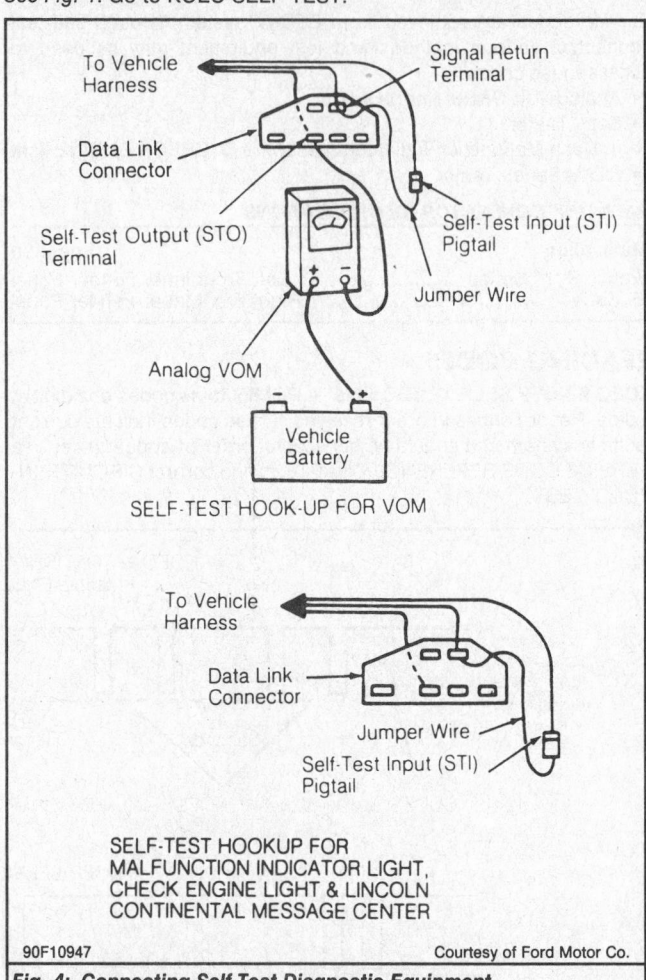

SELF-TEST HOOK-UP FOR VOM

SELF-TEST HOOKUP FOR MALFUNCTION INDICATOR LIGHT, CHECK ENGINE LIGHT & LINCOLN CONTINENTAL MESSAGE CENTER

90F10947   Courtesy of Ford Motor Co.

Fig. 4: Connecting Self-Test Diagnostic Equipment

KOEO SELF-TEST

Ensure engine is at normal operating temperature. If engine does not start (or stalls after starting), continue KOEO SELF-TEST. DO NOT depress throttle on gasoline vehicles. Turn ignition off. Wait 10 seconds. Ensure test equipment is properly attached. Turn ignition on (engine off). Record all KOEO and Continuous Memory Codes.

If a Code 11 or 111 (pass code) is not retrieved in KOEO portion of test, service KOEO codes at this time. Service any engine codes recorded before servicing transmission codes. If PCM will not output codes, see SELF-DIAGNOSTICS – EEC-IV article in ENGINE PERFORMANCE section of appropriate MITCHELL® manual. If service codes are retrieved observe the following procedures:
- If CHECK ENGINE or SERVICE ENGINE SOON light is on, service codes in order retrieved.
- On vehicles equipped with DIS and EDIS ignition systems, see SYSTEM & COMPONENT TESTING article in ENGINE PERFORMANCE section of appropriate MITCHELL® manual if Continuous Memory Code 211, 212, 215, 216, 217, 232 or 238 is retrieved during KOEO SELF-TEST. Repair ignition system as necessary.
- If vehicle has a no-start condition, go to CIRCUIT TEST AA, AB or AC in SELF-DIAGNOSTICS – EEC-IV article in ENGINE PERFORMANCE section of appropriate MITCHELL® manual.

KOER SELF-TEST

Diagnostic Aids – DO NOT enter this test sequence until a Code 11 or 111 (pass code) has been retrieved in KOEO SELF-TEST. If system has not passed KOEO SELF-TEST, codes recorded in KOER SELF-TEST may not be valid.

Deactivate self-test by removing and reconnecting jumper wire or by procedure specified by test equipment in use. Start engine, and run it for 2 minutes at 2000 RPM to warm Heated Exhaust Gas Oxygen (HEGO) sensor. Turn engine off, and wait 10 seconds. Activate KOER SELF-TEST using a jumper wire or appropriate procedure for test equipment used. Start engine. Record all service codes displayed. Check following items:

- If engine starts and stalls (or stalls during self-test), go to CIRCUIT TEST S. See SELF-DIAGNOSTICS – EEC-IV article in ENGINE PERFORMANCE section of appropriate MITCHELL® manual.
- If Code 98 or 998 is displayed, EEC-IV system is operating in Failure Management Effects Mode (FMEM) and vehicle has not passed KOEO SELF-TEST. Vehicle cannot be diagnosed while in FMEM mode. See Code 98 or 998 in SERVICE CODE REFERENCE CHARTS.
- If vehicle is equipped with a Brake On-Off (BOO) switch, brake pedal must be depressed and released after ID code portion of test.
- If Dynamic Response Code appears, perform a brief Wide Open Throttle (WOT). DO NOT perform WOT unless requested.
- If a Code 11 or 111 (pass code) is retrieved during KOER SELF-TEST, service Continuous Memory Codes retrieved in KOEO SELF-TEST. See SELF-DIAGNOSTICS – EEC-IV article in ENGINE PERFORMANCE section of appropriate MITCHELL® manual.
- If a Code 11 or 111 (pass code) is retrieved during Continuous Memory Code portion of KOEO SELF-TEST (Code 11-1-11 or Code 111-1-111) and no driveability problem exists, EEC-IV testing is complete. If driveability problems are still present, go to TROUBLE SHOOTING in E4OD overhaul article.
- If KOER codes are present, see SERVICE CODE REFERENCE CHARTS. If system will not output codes, go to CIRCUIT TEST QA.

CONTINUOUS MONITOR MODE (WIGGLE TEST)

Continuous Monitor Mode allows technician to attempt to recreate an intermittent fault while monitoring system. This mode, also called wiggle test, may be used in both KOEO SELF-TEST and KOER SELF-TEST. CIRCUIT/PINPOINT TESTS specify use of this procedure to identify intermittent faults in specific circuits or components.

KOEO Wiggle Test Procedure – Connect test equipment. *See Fig. 4.* Turn ignition on, and activate self-test using jumper lead or diagnostic tester. Wait 10 seconds, and then deactivate and reactivate self-test. Wiggle test mode is now activated. Tap, move and wiggle suspect sensor and/or harness area. If a fault is detected, a service code may be stored in memory and indicated at diagnostic tester or scan tester. Retrieve code, and perform appropriate test. See SERVICE CODE REFERENCE CHARTS.

KOER Wiggle Test Procedure – Connect test equipment. *See Fig. 4.* Turn ignition off, and wait 10 seconds. Start engine. Activate self-test using jumper lead or diagnostic tester. Wait 10 seconds, and then deactivate and reactivate self-test. DO NOT turn engine off. KOER wiggle test mode is now activated. Tap, move and wiggle suspect sensor and/or harness area. If a fault is detected, a service code may be stored in memory and indicated at diagnostic tester or scan tester. Retrieve code, and perform appropriate test. See SERVICE CODE REFERENCE CHARTS.

TRANSMISSION DRIVE CYCLE TEST

NOTE: The transmission drive cycle test must be followed exactly. Malfunctions have to occur 4 times consecutively for codes 49, 59, 617, 618 and 619 to be set and 5 times consecutively for continuous code 62/628.

1) Record and then erase Quick Test codes. Warm engine to normal operating temperature. Ensure transmission fluid level is correct. Shift transmission to Drive ("D"). Depress Transmission Control Switch (TCS). LED should illuminate.

2) Accelerate from stop to 40 mph. Hold speed for at least 30 seconds. Press TCS and accelerate to 50 mph. Hold speed for at least 30 seconds. Hold speed and throttle position steady for at least 30 seconds. While maintaining speed with transmission in 4th gear, lightly depress brake pedal and release. Maintain speed for additional 5 seconds. Bring vehicle to stop for at least 20 seconds. Repeat steps **1)** and **2)** at least 5 times. Perform Quick Test and record continuous codes.

ADDITIONAL SYSTEM FUNCTIONS

Additional diagnostic system features are available to help diagnose driveability problems and service EEC-IV systems.

CHECK ENGINE Light & Malfunction Indicator Light (MIL) – CHECK DCL light, CHECK ENGINE light and MIL are intended to alert driver of certain malfunctions in EEC-IV system.

Light may also be used to retrieve service codes stored in PCM. When hooked up for KOEO SELF-TEST or KOER SELF-TEST, light will display all codes which turn on light during vehicle operation, not just Continuous Memory Codes.

If light comes on during vehicle operation, vehicle should be inspected as soon as possible. Immediately turning off engine is not necessary; vehicle can be driven with light on.

If light comes on and then goes off during vehicle operation, code causing light to glow will be stored in PCM memory as a Continuous Memory Code.

Light should come on when ignition is turned on and go out when engine is started. If hard fault codes are not present, PCM turns out light when it receives a Profile Ignition Pick-Up (PIP) signal. If light does not come on, see SYMPTOMS in TROUBLE SHOOTING – NO CODES article in ENGINE PERFORMANCE section of appropriate MITCHELL® manual.

Output State Check – Output State Check is used as an aid in servicing output actuators associated with EEC-IV system. It allows technicians to energize and de-energize most system output actuators on command. This mode is entered from KOEO SELF-TEST after all codes have been retrieved. Leave SELF-TEST activated, and depress throttle to initiate test sequence. Each time throttle is depressed and released, output actuators will change state (from on to off or off to on).

Failure Mode Effects Management (FMEM), Code 98 Or 998 – FMEM mode allows system operation when sensors fail or transmit signals that are out of normal operating range. During FMEM mode, PCM substitutes a mid-range signal for defective sensor while continuing to monitor sensor. If faulty sensor's signals return to normal operating range, PCM will use those signals. A Code 98 or 998 will be displayed when FMEM mode is in effect.

Hardware Limited Operational Strategy (HLOS) – If a number of system or sensor failures are present and PCM is not receiving enough information to operate, PCM will switch to HLOS mode. PCM will output fixed values to allow operation of vehicle. Driveability concerns will be present. PCM will not output service codes in this mode.

SUMMARY

If no service codes (or pass code 11-1-11 or 111-1-111) is present but driveability problem still exists, return to TROUBLE SHOOTING in E4OD overhaul article.

AUTOMATIC TRANSMISSIONS
E4OD Electronic Controls (Cont.)

SERVICE CODE REFERENCE CHARTS

NOTE: In addition to transmission fault codes, engine-related fault codes may be output during QUICK TEST procedure. These fault codes pertain to engine performance and must be repaired first as engine performance will greatly affect transmission operation. For information and testing procedures of engine-related fault codes and components, see SELF-DIAGNOSTICS – EEC-IV article in ENGINE PERFORMANCE of appropriate MITCHELL® manual.

CODE REFERENCE CHART

Fault Code	Code Definition	¹ Test
KOEO Codes		
No Code	N/A	QA1
11/111	Pass Code	N/A
22/126	TOT Out Of Range	DF1
23	TPS Malfunction	DQ1
26/636	TOT Out Of Range	TE1
47/633	4WD Switch Closed	TB1
53	TPS High Voltage	DQ2
56/637	TOT Sensor Circuit Open	B1
63	TPS Malfunction	DQ10
66/638	TOT Sensor Circuit Grounded	B1
67/634	MLP Out Of Range	D1
91/621	SS1 Solenoid Circuit Failure	A1
92/622	SS2 Solenoid Circuit Failure	A1
93/626	CCS Circuit Failure	G1
94/627	TCC Circuit Failure	C1
97/631	TCIL Circuit Failure	TB3
98/998	FMEM Failure	TC10
99/624	EPC Circuit Failure	E1
121	TPS Voltage High/Low	DH2
122	TPS Malfunction	DH10
123	TPS Malfunction	DH3
158	MAF Sensor Malfunction	DC21
159	MAF Sensor Malfunction	DC1
539	A/C Switch Malfunction	KM40
625	Open PCM Output Driver	E1
629	TCC Circuit Failure	C1
654	MLP Not In Park	TD1

¹ – Circuit or Pinpoint test.

CODE REFERENCE CHART (Cont.)

Fault Code	Code Definition	¹ Test
Continuous Memory Codes		
No Code	N/A	QA1
11/111	Pass Code	N/A
14	RPM Sensor Malfunction	DJ1
22/126	TOT Out Of Range	DF90
29/452	Insufficient VSS Input	DS1
33	TPS Input Signal Noise	DQ97
49/617	1-2 Shift Error	A1
53	TPS Voltage High/Low	DQ90
56/637	TOT Sensor Voltage High	B1
59/618	2-3 Shift Error	A1
62/628	TCC Engagement Error	TG90
63	TPS Low Voltage	DQ94
66/638	TOT Sensor Voltage Low	B1
67/634	MLP Sensor Voltage Error	D1
68/657	Transaxle Overtemp. Condition	B1
69/619	3-4 Shift Error	A1
121	TPS Voltage High/Low	GA1
122	TPS Malfunction	DH94
123	TPS Malfunction	DH90
124	TPS Malfunction	GA1
125	TPS Malfunction	GA1
128	MAP Circuit Failure	DF11
157	MAF Sensor Malfunction	DC10
158	MAF Sensor Malfunction	DC21
184	MAF Sensor Malfunction	GA5
185	MAF Sensor Malfunction	GA5
536	BOO Switch Malfunction	FD90
624	EPC Solenoid Circuit Failure	E1
625	EPC Malfunction	E1
659	High Speed In Park	D1
667	MLP Low Voltage	D1
668	MLP High Voltage	D1
691	4 x 4L Switch Failure	TB1
KOER Codes		
No Code	N/A	QA1
11/111	Pass Code	N/A
22/126	MAP Failure	DF7
23	TPS Voltage High/Low	DQ1
26/636	TOT Sensor Voltage Error	TE1
65/632	TCS Not Cycled	TB2
74	BOO Circuit Failure	FD1
74/536	BOO Switch Malfunction	FD1
121	TPS Voltage High/Low	DH1
129	MAP Failure	² DF10
159	MAF Sensor Malfunction	DC1
167	TPS Malfunction	DH20
539	A/C Switch Malfunction	KM40

¹ – Circuit or Pinpoint test.
² – Circuit test DC13 on 5.0L "E" series.

CIRCUIT/PINPOINT TEST PROCEDURES

NOTE: A breakout box, connected to vehicle harness at PCM, is necessary to perform most circuit tests. References to Test Pin No. found in CIRCUIT/PINPOINT TEST steps refer to test terminals on manufacturer breakout box. Circuit diagrams at beginning of each test identify circuit and wire colors.

HOW TO USE CIRCUIT/PINPOINT TESTS

1) Ensure all non-EEC related faults found while performing TROUBLE SHOOTING steps in E4OD overhaul article have been corrected. DO NOT perform any CIRCUIT/PINPOINT TEST unless specifically instructed by a QUICK TEST procedure. Follow each test step in order until fault is found. DO NOT replace any part unless directed to do so. When more than one code is retrieved, start with first code displayed.

2) CIRCUIT/PINPOINT TESTS ensure electrical circuits are okay before sensors or other components are replaced. Always test circuits for continuity between sensor and PCM. Test all circuits for short to power, opens or short to ground. Voltage Reference (VREF) and Voltage Power (VPWR) circuits should be tested with KOEO or as specified in CIRCUIT/PINPOINT TESTS.

3) DO NOT measure voltage or resistance at PCM. DO NOT connect any test light unless specified in testing procedure. All measurements are made by probing rear of connector. Isolate both ends of a circuit and turn ignition off when checking for shorts or continuity, unless instructed otherwise.

4) Disconnect solenoids and switches from harness before measuring continuity and resistance or applying voltage. After each repair, check all component connections and repeat QUICK TEST.

5) An open circuit is defined as a resistance reading of greater than 5 ohms. This specification tolerance may be too high for some items in EEC-IV system. If resistance approaches 5 ohms, always clean suspect connector and coat it with protective dielectric silicone grease. A short is defined as a resistance reading of less than 10 k/ohms to ground, unless stated otherwise in CIRCUIT/PINPOINT TEST.

Diagnostic Aids – Fuel-contaminated engine oil may set some codes and effect engine performance. If oil is suspect, remove PCV valve from valve cover and repeat QUICK TEST. If problem is corrected, change engine oil.

NOTE: In following tests, circuit diagrams and illustrations are courtesy of Ford Motor Co.

PINPOINT TESTS

NOTE: PINPOINT TESTS are diagnostic formats used to test and service EEC-IV system. PINPOINT TESTS check transaxle circuits, sensors and actuators.

PINPOINT TEST A

SHIFT SOLENOID ELECTRICAL SYSTEM

1) E4OD Electronic Diagnostics – Ensure transmission harness connector is in acceptable condition. Repair as necessary. Perform KOEO test until Continuous Memory trouble code(s) have been displayed. See QUICK TEST. Depress throttle to WOT and release. If vehicle enters Output State, go to next step. If vehicle will not enter Output State, see SELF-DIAGNOSTICS – EEC-IV article in ENGINE PERFORMANCE of appropriate MITCHELL® manual.

2) Check Electrical Signal Operation – Disconnect transmission harness connector. Inspect condition of connector and repair as needed. Using DVOM (20-volt scale), connect positive lead to transmission harness connector VPWR terminal. *See Fig. A1.* Connect negative lead to suspect solenoid circuit. Depress and release throttle to cycle solenoid output. If voltage changes at least .5 volt, go to step **5)**. If voltage is unaffected, go to next step.

94E38715

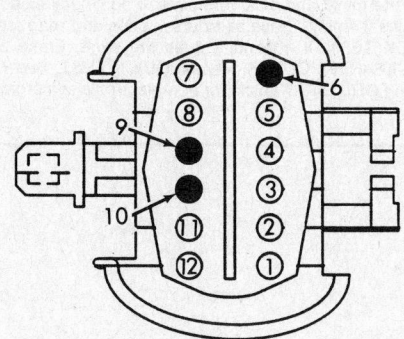

Fig. A1: Identifying Transmission Harness Connector

PINPOINT TEST A (Cont.)

HARNESS CONNECTOR TERMINAL IDENTIFICATION

Terminal Number	Circuit Description	[1] BOB Test Pin Number
1	VPWR	37/57
2	SS2	[2] 19
3	SS1	[3] 52
4	TCC Solenoid	53
5	CCS	55
6	Not Used	.....
7	TOT	[4], [5] 42
8	Sensor SRTN	46
9	Not Used	.....
10	Not Used	.....
11	EPC	38
12	EPC Power	[6] 37/57

[1] – Breakout Box.
[2] – Test pin No. 52, 5.0L models.
[3] – Test pin No. 51, 5.0L models.
[4] – Test pin No. 7, diesel models.
[5] – Test pin No. 49, 5.0L models.
[6] – Test pin No. 35, diesel models.

3) Check Continuity Of Solenoid Signal & VPWR Harness Circuits – Ensure ignition is off. Disconnect PCM 60-pin connector, and inspect it for damaged pins, corrosion and loose wires. Repair as necessary. Install Breakout Box (T83L-50-EEC-IV), leaving PCM disconnected. Measure and record resistance between Breakout Box test pin No. 19 or 52 and corresponding transmission harness connector terminal on all models except 5.0L. On 5.0L models, measure and record resistance between Breakout Box test pin No. 51 or 52 and corresponding transmission harness connector terminal. *See Fig. A1.* Measure and record resistance. Measure and record resistance between test pins No. 37 and 57 and transmission harness connector VPWR terminal. If any resistance is greater than 5 ohms, repair open circuit. Connect all components. Disconnect Breakout Box and repeat Quick Test. If resistance is 5 ohms or less, go to next step.

4) Check Solenoid Harness For Shorts To Power & Ground – Measure and record resistance between Breakout Box test pins No. 19 or 52 and test pins No. 37 and 57 on all models except 5.0L. On 5.0L models, measure and record resistance between Breakout Box test pins No. 51 or 52 and test pins No. 37 and 57. Measure and record resistance between test pins No. 40, 46 and 60, and ground. If any resistance is less than 10 k/ohms, repair short circuit. Connect all components. Disconnect Breakout Box and repeat Quick Test. If resistance is 10 k/ohms or more, go to next step.

5) Solenoid Functional Test – Connect Transmission Tester (007-0085A). Perform solenoid voltage test. See tester instructions. If solenoid activates (LED Green), go to next step. If solenoid does not activate, go to step **6)**. Check if diode test light is illuminated. If diode is okay, go to next step. If diode test light is not illuminated, replace solenoid body assembly. Erase all trouble codes and road test vehicle. Repeat QUICK TEST.

6) Transmission Drive Test – Perform tester drive test. See tester instructions. If vehicle upshifts when operated with tester, erase all trouble codes. See CLEARING CODES. Perform TRANSMISSION DRIVE CYCLE TEST. Repeat QUICK TEST. If vehicle does not upshift when operated by tester, go to next step.

7) Check Resistance Of Solenoid – Set tester Bench/Drive switch to Bench mode. Set Gear Selector switch to OHMS/DIODE CHECK. Connect ohmmeter negative lead to SS1 jack and positive lead to VPWR jack on tester. Measure and record resistance. Connect ohmmeter negative lead to SS2 jack and positive lead to VPWR jack on tester. Resistance for both solenoids should be 20-30 ohms. If resistance is within specification, go to next step. If resistance is not within specification, replace solenoid body assembly. Erase all codes. See CLEARING CODES. Repeat QUICK TEST.

8) Check Solenoid For Short To Ground – Check continuity between BAT(-) terminal and between SS1 and SS2. Check continuity between BAT(-) terminal and each VPWR terminal. If continuity exists for any circuit, replace solenoid body assembly. Erase all codes. See CLEARING CODES. Repeat QUICK TEST. If continuity does not exist, go to TROUBLE SHOOTING in Ford E4OD article.

PINPOINT TEST B

TOT ELECTRICAL SYSTEM

1) Visual Check – Check transmission harness connector. Inspect connector for damaged pins, corrosion and loose wires. Repair as necessary. Go to next step.

2) Check Electrical Signal Operation – Ensure ignition is off. Disconnect transmission connector. Using DVOM, connect positive lead to transmission harness connector TOT terminal and negative lead to SRTN terminal. See Fig. A1. Turn ignition on. If voltage is 4.75-5.25 volts, go to next step. If voltage is not within specification, see SELF-DIAGNOSTICS – EEC-IV article in ENGINE PERFORMANCE of appropriate MITCHELL® manual to diagnose NO VREF voltage.

3) Check Continuity Of TOT And Signal Return (SIG RTN) Circuits – Turn ignition off. Disconnect PCM 60-pin connector, and inspect it for damaged pins, corrosion and loose wires. Repair as necessary. Install Breakout Box (T83L-50-EEC-IV), leaving PCM disconnected. Measure and record resistance between applicable Breakout Box test pin and transmission harness connector TOT terminal. See TOT TEST PIN APPLICATION CHART. See Fig. A1. Measure and record resistance between test pin No. 46 and transmission harness connector SRTN terminal. If resistances measured are less than 5 ohms, go to next step. If resistances are more than 5 ohms, repair open circuit. Connect all components. Erase trouble codes. See CLEARING CODES. Repeat QUICK TEST.

TOT TEST PIN APPLICATION CHART

Application	Pin Number
5.0L	49
7.3L (Diesel)	7
All Others	42

4) Check TOT Circuit For Short To VPWR & Ground – Ensure ignition is off. Disconnect PCM 60-pin connector, and inspect it for damaged pins, corrosion and loose wires. Repair as necessary. Install Breakout Box (T83L-50-EEC-IV), leaving PCM disconnected. Measure and record resistance between applicable Breakout Box test pin and test pins No. 37 and 57. See TOT TEST PIN APPLICATION CHART. If resistance is less than 10 k/ohms, repair short circuit. Disconnect Breakout Box and repeat Quick Test. If resistance is 10 k/ohms or more, go to next step.

NOTE: Code 56/637 is set if resistance measured exceeds 869 ohms (open circuit). Code 66/638 is set if resistance measured is below 597 ohms (short circuit).

5) Check Resistance Of TOT Sensor/Harness – Install Transmission Tester (007-0085A). Set tester Bench/Drive switch to BENCH mode. Set Solenoid Select switch to OHMS/DIODE CHECK. Connect ohmmeter leads to appropriate TOT jacks. Measure and record resistance. Resistance should be within specification. See TOT TEMPERATURE/RESISTANCE CHART. If resistance is within specification for specific temperature, either warm up transmission or allow transmission to cool to check resistance at different temperatures. If resistances measured remain within specification, go to next step. If resistances measured are not within specification, replace solenoid assembly. Connect all components. Erase trouble codes. See CLEARING CODES. Repeat QUICK TEST.

TOT TEMPERATURE/RESISTANCE CHART

Temperature °F (°C)	Resistance-Ohms (K)
32-58 (0-20)	37-100
59-104 (21-40)	16-37
105-158 (41-70)	5-16
159-194 (71-90)	2.7-5
195-230 (91-110)	1.5-2.7
231-266 (111-130)	.8-1.5

6) Check TOT Sensor For Short To Ground – Check continuity between BAT (-) tester terminal and TOT terminals. If continuity exists, replace solenoid body assembly. Erase all trouble codes. See CLEARING CODES. Repeat QUICK TEST. If continuity does not exist, repeat QUICK TEST. If codes are still present, see TROUBLE SHOOTING in Ford E4OD article.

PINPOINT TEST C

TCC ELECTRICAL SYSTEM

1) E4OD Electronic Diagnostics – Ensure transmission harness connector is in acceptable condition. Repair as necessary. Disconnect transmission harness connector. Connect Transmission Tester (007-0085A) or equivalent to transmission. Perform TRANSMISSION SOLENOID CYCLING AND DRIVE TEST. Perform KOEO test until Continuous Memory trouble code(s) have been displayed. See QUICK TEST. Depress throttle to WOT and release. If vehicle enters Output State, go to next step. If vehicle will not enter Output State, see SELF-DIAGNOSTICS – EEC-IV article in ENGINE PERFORMANCE of appropriate MITCHELL® manual.

2) Check Electrical Signal Operation – Disconnect transmission harness connector. Inspect condition of connector and repair as needed. Using DVOM (20-volt scale), connect positive lead to transmission harness connector VPWR terminal. See Fig. A1. Connect negative lead to TCC terminal. Depress and release throttle to cycle solenoid output. If voltage changes at least .5 volt, go to step 5). If voltage is unaffected, go to next step.

3) Check Continuity Of Solenoid Signal & VPWR Harness Circuits – Ensure ignition is off. Disconnect PCM 60-pin connector, and inspect it for damaged pins, corrosion and loose wires. Repair as necessary. Install Breakout Box (T83L-50-EEC-IV), leaving PCM disconnected. Measure and record resistance between Breakout Box test pin No. 53 and transmission harness connector TCC terminal. See Fig. C1. Measure and record resistance between test pins No. 37 and 57 and transmission harness connector VPWR terminal. If any resistance is greater than 5 ohms, repair open circuit. Connect all components. Disconnect Breakout Box and repeat Quick Test. If resistance is 5 ohms or less, go to next step.

4) Check Solenoid Harness For Shorts To Power & Ground – Measure and record resistance between test pin No. 53 and test pins No. 37 and 57. Measure and record resistance between test pins No. 40, 46 and 60, and ground. If any resistance is less than 10 k/ohms, repair short circuit. Connect all components. Disconnect Breakout Box and repeat Quick Test. If resistance is 10 k/ohms or more, go to next step.

5) Solenoid Functional Test – Connect Transmission Tester (007-0085A). Perform solenoid voltage test. See tester instructions. If solenoid activates (LED Green), go to next step. If solenoid does not activate, go to step 6). Check if diode test light is illuminated. If diode is okay, go to next step. If diode test light is not illuminated, replace solenoid body assembly. Erase all trouble codes and road test vehicle. Repeat QUICK TEST.

6) Transmission Drive Test – Perform tester drive test. See tester instructions. If engine RPM decreases when operated with tester, see SELF-DIAGNOSTICS – EEC-IV article in ENGINE PERFORMANCE of appropriate MITCHELL® manual to diagnose vehicle harness or PCM malfunctions. If engine RPM does not decrease when operated by tester, go to next step.

7) Check Resistance Of Solenoid – Set tester Bench/Drive switch to BENCH mode. Set Gear Selector switch to OHMS/DIODE CHECK. Connect ohmmeter negative lead to CCC jack and positive lead to VPWR jack on tester. Measure resistance. Resistance should be 20-30 ohms. If resistance is within specification, go to next step. If resistance is not within specification, replace solenoid body assembly. Erase all trouble codes and road test vehicle. Repeat QUICK TEST.

8) Check Solenoid For Short To Ground – Check continuity between BAT (-) tester terminal and TCC terminals. If continuity exists, replace solenoid body assembly. Erase all trouble codes and road test vehicle. Repeat QUICK TEST. If continuity does not exist, Erase all trouble codes. See CLEARING CODES. Repeat QUICK TEST. See TROUBLE SHOOTING in FORD E4OD article for non-electronic symptom diagnostics.

PINPOINT TEST D

MLP SENSOR

94F38716

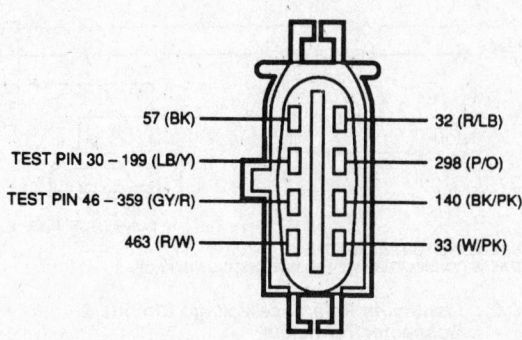

57 (BK) — 32 (R/LB)
TEST PIN 30 – 199 (LB/Y) — 298 (P/O)
TEST PIN 46 – 359 (GY/R) — 140 (BK/PK)
463 (R/W) — 33 (W/PK)

Fig. D1: MLP Harness Connector Resistance Specification Chart

HARNESS CONNECTOR TERMINAL IDENTIFICATION

Terminal Number	Description
32	Start Circuit
33	Start Circuit
57	Ground
140	Backup Lamp
199	MLP Sensor Circuit
298	Fused Accessory Feed
359	Sensor Signal Return
463	Neutral-To-Transfer Case

NOTE: Code 634 may be set if transmission is not in park or A/C is on when QUICK TEST is performed.

1) Preliminary Inspection – Disconnect MLP connector, and inspect it for damaged pins, corrosion and loose wires. Repair as necessary. Reconnect MLP connector. Ensure MLP sensor is correctly adjusted. See FORD E4OD article. If sensor requires adjustment, clear trouble codes after adjustment. See CLEARING CODES. Repeat QUICK TEST. If sensor is correctly adjusted, go to next step.

2) Check Electrical Signal Operation – Ensure ignition is off. Disconnect MLP harness connector. Turn ignition on. Measure voltage between harness connector MLP terminal and SRTN terminal. *See Fig. D1.* If voltage is 4.75-5.25 volts, go to next step. If voltage is not within specification, see SELF-DIAGNOSTICS – EEC-IV article in ENGINE PERFORMANCE of appropriate MITCHELL® manual for NO VREF voltage.

3) Check Continuity Of MLP Sensor Harness Circuits – Turn ignition off. Disconnect PCM 60-pin connector, and inspect it for damaged pins, corrosion and loose wires. Repair as necessary. Install Breakout Box (T83L-50-EEC-IV), leaving PCM disconnected. Measure and record resistance between Breakout Box test pin terminal No. 46 and MLP harness connector terminal No. 359. *See Fig. D1.* Measure and record resistance between Breakout Box test pin terminal No. 30 and MLP harness connector terminal No. 199. If resistance is less than 5 ohms, go to next step. If resistance is more than 5 ohms, repair open circuit(s). Remove Breakout Box and connect all components. Erase all trouble codes. See CLEARING CODES. Repeat QUICK TEST.

4) Check MLP Circuit For Shorts To Power & Ground – Ensure MLP sensor harness connector is disconnected. Measure resistance between Breakout Box test pin No. 30 and test pins No. 37, 40, 46, 57 and 60. Measure resistance between Breakout Box test pin No. 30 and ground. If each measurement is more than 10 k/ohms, go to next step. If any measurement is less than 10 k/ohms, repair short circuit. Remove Breakout Box and connect all components. Erase all trouble codes. See CLEARING CODES. Repeat QUICK TEST.

PINPOINT TEST D (Cont.)

5) Operational Check Of MLP Sensor – Install MLP overlay on Transmission Tester (007-0085A). Connect tester to MLP sensor. Check continuity and resistances in all positions. *See Fig. D2.* If MLP sensor does not operate within specification, replace sensor. Connect all components. Erase all trouble codes. See CLEARING CODES. Repeat QUICK TEST. If sensor operates within specification, connect all components. Erase all trouble codes. See CLEARING CODES. Repeat QUICK TEST. If code(s) 634 or 659 are set, intermittent condition may be present. Attempt to duplicate malfunction by repeating previous steps.

94C38457

Transmission Range Selector Lever Position	Resistance (ohms)		Voltage**
	MIN	MAX	VOLTS
P	3770	4607	4.41
R	1304	1593	3.60
N	660	807	2.83
Ⓓ	361	442	2.09
2 / D	190	232	1.37
1	78	95	.68

** May vary ± 10% due to sensor and VREF variations.

Fig. D2: MLP Resistance Specification Chart

PINPOINT TEST E

EPC SOLENOID

1) Check VPWR To Solenoid – Turn ignition off. Disconnect transmission harness connector. With KOEO, measure voltage between transmission harness connector EPC power terminal and vehicle ground. *See Fig. A1.* If voltage is 10.5 volts or more, go to next step. If voltage is less than specification, repair open circuit. Connect all components. Erase all trouble codes. See CLEARING CODES. Repeat QUICK TEST.

2) Check Continuity Of Solenoid Signal & VPWR Harness Circuit – Turn ignition off, and wait 10 seconds. Disconnect PCM 60-pin connector, and inspect it for damaged pins, corrosion and loose wires. Repair as necessary. Install Breakout Box (T83L-50-EEC-IV), leaving PCM disconnected. Measure and record resistance between Breakout Box test pins No. 37 and 57 (gas models) or pin 35 (diesel model), and transmission harness connector terminal for EPC power. *See Fig. A1.* Measure and record resistance between Breakout Box test pins No. 38, and transmission harness connector EPC terminal. If resistances measured are 5 ohms or less, go to next step. If resistances measured are more than 5 ohms, repair open circuit. Connect all components. Erase all trouble codes. See CLEARING CODES. Repeat QUICK TEST.

3) Check Harness For Short To Power Or Ground – Measure and record resistance between Breakout Box test pin No. 38 and test pins No. 37 and 57 (gas models) or pin 35 (diesel model). Measure and record resistance between test pin No. 38 and test pins No. 40, 46 and 60. If any resistance measured is less than 10 k/ohms, repair short circuit. Disconnect Breakout Box and repeat Quick Test. If all resistances are 10 k/ohms or more, go to next step.

4) EPC Functional Test – Disconnect transmission harness connector. Connect Transmission Tester (007-0085A). Connect line pressure gauge. See FORD E4OD article. Set Bench/Drive switch to DRIVE mode. Set Gear Selector switch to 1st gear position. Perform EPC function test. See tester instructions. Observe line pressure on gauge while depressing EPC switch (KOER). EPC switch should activate (LED green) and line pressure should drop when EPC switch is depressed. If solenoid operates correctly, replace PCM. Connect all components. Erase all trouble codes. See CLEARING CODES. Repeat QUICK TEST. If solenoid is not operating, go to next step.

5) Check Resistance Of Solenoid – Ensure tester power is off. Set Bench/Drive switch to BENCH mode. Connect ohmmeter negative lead to EPC jack. Connect positive lead to VPWR jack. If resistance is 3-5 ohms, go to next step. If resistance is not within specifications, replace solenoid body assembly. Connect all components. Erase all trouble codes. See CLEARING CODES. Repeat QUICK TEST.

6) Check Solenoid For Short To Ground – Check continuity between BAT(-) terminal of Transmission Tester and EPC jacks. If continuity exists, replace solenoid body assembly. Connect all components. Erase all trouble codes. See CLEARING CODES. Repeat QUICK TEST. If continuity does not exist, see TROUBLE SHOOTING in FORD E4OD article.

PINPOINT TEST G
CCS SOLENOID

1) E4OD Electronic Diagnostics – Ensure transmission harness connector is in acceptable condition. Repair as necessary. Perform KOEO test until Continuous Memory trouble code(s) have been displayed. See QUICK TEST. Depress throttle to WOT and release. If vehicle enters Output State, go to next step. If vehicle will not enter Output State, see SELF-DIAGNOSTICS – EEC-IV article in ENGINE PERFORMANCE of appropriate MITCHELL® manual.

2) Check VPWR To Solenoid – Turn ignition off. Disconnect transaxle harness connector. With KOEO, monitor voltage between transaxle harness connector VPWR terminal and vehicle ground. See Fig. A1. Depress and release throttle several times to cycle solenoid output On and Off. If output voltage changes by at least .5 volts, go to step 5). If voltage does change, go to next step.

3) Check Continuity Of Solenoid Signal & VPWR Harness Circuit – Turn ignition off, and wait 10 seconds. Disconnect PCM 60-pin connector, and inspect it for damaged pins, corrosion and loose wires. Repair as necessary. Install Breakout Box (T83L-50-EEC-IV), leaving PCM disconnected. Measure and record resistance between Breakout Box test pins No. 37 and 57, and transaxle harness connector VPWR terminal. See Fig. A1. Measure and record resistance between Breakout Box test pins No. 55, and transaxle harness connector CCS terminal. If resistances measured are 5 ohms or less, go to next step. If resistances measured are more than 5 ohms, repair open circuit. Connect all components. Erase all trouble codes. See CLEARING CODES. Repeat QUICK TEST.

4) Check Harness For Short To Power Or Ground – Measure and record resistance between test pin No. 55 and test pins No. 37 and 57. Measure and record resistance between test pins No. 40, 46 and 60, and vehicle ground . If any resistance is less than 10 k/ohms, repair short circuit. Disconnect Breakout Box and repeat Quick Test. If resistance is 10 k/ohms or more, go to next step.

5) CCS Solenoid Functional Test – Disconnect transaxle harness connector. Connect Transaxle Tester (007-0085A). Perform CCS function test. See tester instructions. CCS solenoid should engage (LED on) and engine braking should occur when switch is released. Perform solenoid diode test. If solenoid operates correctly and diode functions okay, go to next step. If either test fails, replace solenoid body assembly. Erase all trouble codes. See CLEARING CODES. Test drive vehicle and repeat QUICK TEST.

6) Check Resistance Of Solenoid – Set Bench/Drive switch to BENCH mode. Rotate gear select switch to OHMS/DIODE. Ensure tester power is off. Connect ohmmeter to CCS jacks. If resistance is 20-30 ohms, go to next step. If resistance is not within specifications, replace solenoid body assembly.Connect all components. Erase all trouble codes. See CLEARING CODES. Repeat QUICK TEST.

7) Check Solenoid For Short To Ground – Check continuity between BAT(-) terminal of Transmission Tester and CCS jacks. If continuity exists, replace solenoid body assembly. Connect all components. Erase all trouble codes. See CLEARING CODES. Repeat QUICK TEST. If continuity does not exist, see TROUBLE SHOOTING in FORD E4OD article.

CIRCUIT TESTS

NOTE: CIRCUIT TESTS are diagnostic formats used to test and service EEC-IV system. CIRCUIT TESTS check engine circuits, sensors and actuators.

CIRCUIT TEST CA
REFERENCE VOLTAGE

Diagnostic Aids – Perform this test when a check for VREF signal has failed in sensor input CIRCUIT TEST QA. SIG RTN is a dedicated ground used by most EEC-IV system sensors. VREF is a 5-volt reference voltage that is continuously output by PCM. This consistent voltage signal is used on all 3-wire sensors.

This circuit test is only intended to diagnose the following components and circuits:
- Powertrain Control Module (PCM).
- Vehicle wiring harness circuits (SIG RTN and VREF).

CIRCUIT TEST CA (Cont.)

93E40422

*TEST PINS LOCATED ON BREAKOUT BOX.
ALL HARNESS CONNECTORS VIEWED INTO MATING SURFACE.

Fig. CA1: Identifying Reference Voltage Circuits & Connector Terminals

TEST PIN WIRE COLOR IDENTIFICATION

Terminal No.	Wire Color
No. 26 (VREF)	Brown/White
No. 46 (SIG RTN)	Gray/Red

1) Check Battery Power Circuit – Turn ignition off, and wait 10 seconds. Disconnect PCM 60-pin connector, and inspect it for damaged pins, corrosion and loose wires. Repair as necessary. Install Breakout Box (T83L-50-EEC-IV), leaving PCM connected. Turn ignition on. Measure and record voltage between breakout box test pin No. 37 and SIG RTN terminal of self-test connector. Measure and record voltage across battery terminals. If both readings are less than 10.5 volts or if they differ by more than 1.0 volt, reconnect sensor (if applicable). Go to CIRCUIT TEST B1 under SELF-DIAGNOSTICS – EEC-IV article in ENGINE PERFORMANCE of appropriate MITCHELL® manual. If voltages are 10.5 volts or more and do not differ from one another by more than 1.0 volt, go to step 2).

2) Check VREF Voltage – With breakout box installed and PCM connected, set DVOM on 20-volt scale. Turn ignition on. Measure voltage between test pins No. 26 and 46 at breakout box. If voltage is 4-6 volts, go to step 3). If voltage is more than 6 volts, go to step 4). If voltage is less than 4 volts, go to step 5).

3) Check VREF & SIG RTN Circuit Continuity – Turn ignition off. Disconnect PCM. If directed here by a sensor test, ensure sensor is disconnected. Measure resistance between Breakout Box test pin No. 26 and VREF terminal at wiring harness connector of applicable sensor. Measure resistance between test pin No. 46 and SIG RTN circuit terminal at wiring harness connector of applicable sensor. If both readings are less than 5 ohms, VREF circuit is okay. If either reading is 5 ohms or more, repair open in VREF or SIG RTN circuit. Remove breakout box, and repeat QUICK TEST.

4) Check For Excess VREF Circuit Voltage – Turn ignition off. Ensure PCM is disconnected. With breakout box installed, disconnect scan tester or STAR tester (if applicable). Turn ignition on. Measure voltage between test pin No. 26 and battery ground. If voltage is less than 0.5 volt, replace PCM and repeat QUICK TEST. If voltage is 0.5 volt or more, repair short to battery power in wiring harness. Remove breakout box, reconnect components and repeat QUICK TEST. Replace PCM if fault still occurs.

5) Check For Shorted TPS – Turn ignition off. Connect PCM to breakout box. Disconnect Throttle Position Sensor (TPS) from wiring harness. Turn ignition on. Measure voltage between test pins No. 26 and 46 at breakout box. If voltage is 4 volts or more, replace TPS, remove breakout box and repeat QUICK TEST. If voltage is less than 4 volts on models with EVP, PFE or DPFE sensor, go to step 6). If voltage is less than 4 volts on all other models, go to step 8).

6) Check For Shorted EVP/PFE/DPFE Sensor – Turn ignition off, and wait 10 seconds. Disconnect EVP/PFE/DPFE sensor. Turn ignition on. Measure voltage between test pins No. 26 and 46. If voltage is 4 volts or more, replace EVP/PFE/DPFE sensor and repeat QUICK TEST. If voltage is less than 4 volts, reconnect EVP/PFE/DPFE sensor and go to step 8).

NOTE: A break in step numbering sequence occurs at this point. Procedure skips from step 6) to step 8). No test procedures have been omitted.

CIRCUIT TEST CA (Cont.)

8) Check VREF Circuit For Short To Ground – Turn ignition off. Disconnect PCM. Disconnect TPS, MAP/BARO sensor and EVP/PFE/DPFE sensor. Measure resistance between test pin No. 26 and test pins No. 20, 40, 46 and 60. If any resistance is less than 1000 ohms, repair short to ground. Remove breakout box, and repeat QUICK TEST. If original problem still exists, replace PCM and repeat QUICK TEST. If readings are 1000 ohms or more, replace PCM and repeat QUICK TEST.

CIRCUIT TEST DC
MASS AIRFLOW (MAF) SENSOR

Diagnostic Aids – Perform this test when directed by QUICK TEST. This CIRCUIT TEST is intended to diagnose the following:
- MAF sensor.
- Wiring harness circuits (VPWR, PWR GND, MAF and MAF RTN).
- Powertrain Control Module (PCM).

To prevent replacement of good components, be aware the following non-EEC related areas may be cause of problem:
- Air cleaner element.
- Inlet air duct.
- Throttle body.

Code 159, retrieved during KOEO SELF-TEST, indicates voltage exceeded .7-volt test range. Code 159, retrieved during KOER SELF-TEST, indicates voltage is not within .2-1.5 volts operating range. Possible causes are faulty MAF sensor or PCM.

93F40431

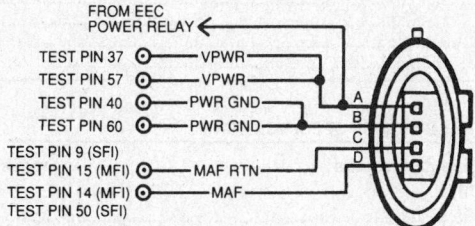

*TEST PINS LOCATED ON BREAKOUT BOX.
ALL HARNESS CONNECTORS VIEWED IN MATING SURFACE.

Fig. DC1: Identifying Mass Airflow (MAF) Sensor Circuits & Connector Terminals

TEST PIN WIRE COLOR IDENTIFICATION

Application	Wire Color
No. 9 OR 15 (MAF RTN)	Tan/Light Blue
No. 14 OR 50 (MAF)	Light Blue/Red
No. 37 & 57 (VPWR)	Red
No3. 40 & 60 (PWR GND)	Black/White

MAF SIGNAL VOLTAGE [1]

Application	Volts
Idle	.6
20 MPH	1.1
40 MPH	1.7
60 MPH	2.1

[1] – MAF signal voltage is typical for normal operating temperature. Voltage signal may vary due to engine load and temperature.

NOTE: Code 159 may be caused by use of a garage exhaust ventilation system. Ensure vehicle is vented to outside atmosphere before repeating QUICK TEST.

1) Code 159: Check VPWR Circuit Voltage – Code 159 indicates that MAF sensor was out of range during KOEO or KOER SELF-TEST. Possible causes for this fault are:
- Air leak before or after MAF sensor.
- Faulty MAF sensor.
- Faulty IAC solenoid.
- Open or grounded wiring harness.
- Faulty PCM.

CIRCUIT TEST DC (Cont.)

Repeat QUICK TEST. If Code 412 is present, go to CIRCUIT TEST KE, step **1)**, and/or if Code 411 is present, go to CIRCUIT TEST KE, step **15)** under SELF-DIAGNOSTICS – EEC-IV article in ENGINE PERFORMANCE of appropriate MITCHELL® manual. If Code 411 or 412 is not present, go to step **2)**.

2) VPWR Circuit Voltage Check – Turn ignition off. Disconnect MAF sensor connector. Set DVOM on 20-volt scale. Turn ignition on. Measure voltage between VPWR terminal at MAF sensor wiring harness connector and negative battery terminal. If voltage is less than 10.5 volts, repair open in VPWR circuit and repeat QUICK TEST. If voltage is 10.5 volts or more, go to step **3)**.

3) Check MAF Sensor Ground – Turn ignition on. With MAF sensor disconnected, measure voltage between VPWR terminal and PWR GND terminal at MAF sensor connector. If voltage is less than 10.5 volts, repair open PWR GND circuit. Connect MAF sensor, and repeat QUICK TEST. If voltage is 10.5 volts or more, go to step **13)**.

NOTE: A break in step numbering sequence occurs at this point. Procedure skips from step 3) to step 10). No test procedures have been omitted.

10) Continuous Memory Code 157: Check For Intermittent Sensor Failure – Continuous Memory Code 157 indicates MAF signal was less than 0.4 volt sometime during last 80 warm-up cycles. Possible causes for this fault are:
- Open MAF circuit.
- MAF circuit shorted to ground.
- Faulty MAF sensor.
- MAF sensor disconnected.

Start engine and allow to idle for 5-10 minutes. Perform KOEO SELF-TEST. If Code 157 is present, go to step **13)**. If Code 157 is not present, go to next step.

11) Monitor MAF Circuit Under Simulated Road Shock – Turn ignition off. Disconnect and inspect 60-pin connector at PCM. Service if necessary. Install EEC-IV Breakout Box (T83L-50-EEC-IV), leaving PCM connected. Connect DVOM between MAF test pin and MAF RTN test pin. See appropriate table at beginning of this CIRCUIT TEST. DVOM should read about 0.4 volt. Start engine and allow to idle. Lightly tap on MAF sensor and wiggle wiring harness to simulate road conditions. If sudden change in DVOM reading occurs, fault is indicated. If fault is indicated, replace MAF sensor and repeat QUICK TEST. If no fault is indicated, leave DVOM connected and go to next step.

12) Check Wiring Harness For Open Or Short Circuit – Turn ignition on. Shake and bend small sections of wiring harness starting at MAF sensor and working toward dash panel. Shake and bend small sections of wiring harness starting at dash panel and working toward PCM. If fault is indicated, isolate and repair as necessary. If fault is not indicated, problem is intermittent and cannot be duplicated at this time.

13) Codes 157 Or 129: Check For Air Leak At MAF Sensor – Check for broken or loose air outlet tube clamps at throttle body and air cleaner assembly. Repair or replace as necessary. If no faults are found, go to next step.

14) Check Continuity Of MAF & VPWR Circuit – Turn ignition off. Disconnect MAF sensor and PCM wiring harness connector. Install EEC-IV Breakout Box (T83L-50-EEC-IV), leaving PCM disconnected. Measure resistance between MAF terminal of MAF sensor wiring harness connector and test pins No. 37 and 57. Measure resistance between MAF terminal of MAF sensor wiring harness connector and test pin No. 50 (Sequential Fuel Injected engines) or test pin No. 14 (except Sequential Fuel Injected engines). If resistance is more than 5 ohms, repair open circuit and repeat QUICK TEST. If resistance is 5 ohms or more, go to next step.

15) Check MAF Signal For Short To Ground – Turn ignition off. Ensure MAF sensor and PCM wiring harness are disconnected. Measure resistance between test pin No. 50 and test pins No. 9, 40 and 60 (Sequential Fuel Injected engines) or between test pin No. 14 and test pins No. 15, 40 and 60 (except Sequential Fuel Injected engines). If resistance is less than 10 k/ohms, repair short circuit and repeat QUICK TEST. If resistance is 10 k/ohms or more, go to next step.

16) Check Power & Ground Circuit Continuity – Turn ignition off. Ensure MAP sensor and PCM wiring harness connector are disconnected. Measure resistance between PWR GND terminal at MAF sensor wiring harness connector and negative battery terminal. If resistance is 10 ohms or more, repair open PWR GND circuit and repeat QUICK TEST. If resistance is less than 10 ohms, go to next step.

CIRCUIT TEST DC (Cont.)

17) Check Continuity Of MAF RTN Circuit – Ensure ignition is turned off. Measure resistance between MAF RTN terminal of MAF sensor wiring harness connector and test pin No. 9 (Sequential Fuel Injected engines) or test pin No. 15 (except Sequential Fuel Injected engines). If resistance is more than 5 ohms, repair open circuit and repeat QUICK TEST. If resistance is 5 ohms or more, go to next step.

18) Check MAF Circuit For Short To Ground – Turn ignition off. Ensure MAF sensor is disconnected. Connect PCM to breakout box. Measure resistance between test pin No. 50 and test pins No. 9, 40 and 60. If resistance is less than 10 k/ohms, replace PCM and repeat QUICK TEST. If resistance is 10 k/ohms or more, go to next step.

19) Check MAF Circuit Output – Turn ignition off. Connect MAF sensor wiring harness connector. Start engine. Measure resistance between test pin No. 50 and negative battery terminal. If voltage is .36-1.50 volts, go to next step. If voltage is not .36-1.50 volts, replace MAF sensor and repeat QUICK TEST.

20) Check MAF Circuit Output – With engine running, measure resistance between test pin No. 9 and test pin No. 50. If voltage is .36-1.50 volts, replace PCM and repeat QUICK TEST. If voltage is not .36-1.50 volts, replace MAF sensor and repeat QUICK TEST.

21) Code 158 – Turn ignition off. Disconnect MAF sensor wiring harness connector. Start engine, and allow it to idle for one minute. Turn ignition off. Repeat KOEO SELF-TEST. If Code 157 is present, replace MAF sensor and repeat QUICK TEST. If Code 157 is not present, go to step **22**).

22) Check MAF Circuit For Short To VPWR – Turn ignition off. Disconnect PCM 60-pin connector, and inspect it for damaged or corroded terminals. Service if necessary. Measure resistance between MAF and VPWR terminals at MAF sensor wiring harness connector. If resistance is 10 k/ohms or more, replace PCM and repeat QUICK TEST. If resistance is less than 10 k/ohms, repair short circuit and repeat QUICK TEST.

CIRCUIT TEST DF

MAP ABSOLUTE PRESSURE (MAP)/ BAROMETRIC PRESSURE (BARO) SENSOR

Diagnostic Aids – Perform this test when directed by QUICK TEST. Barometric pressure sensor output is digital and must be measured using an oscilloscope or MAP/BARO tester. To prevent replacement of good components, be aware the following non-EEC related areas may be cause of problem:

* Unusually high or low atmospheric barometric pressure.
* Kinked or blocked vacuum lines.
* Engine mechanical condition (valves, vacuum leaks, timing, EGR valve, etc.).

This test is intended to diagnose the following:

* MAP/BARO sensor.
* Wiring harness circuits (VREF, MAP/BARO SIG and SIG RTN).
* MAP vacuum line.
* Powertrain Control Module (PCM).

93A40444

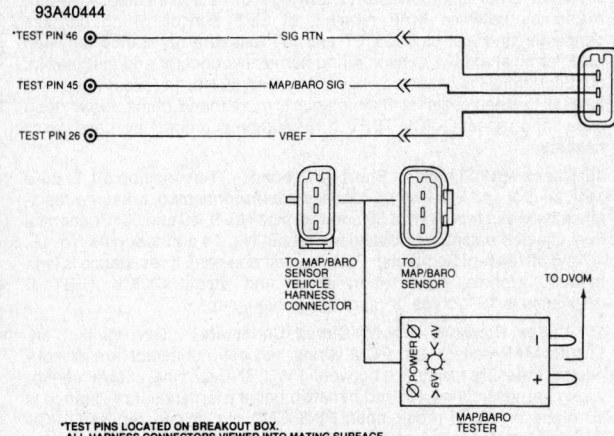

*TEST PINS LOCATED ON BREAKOUT BOX.
ALL HARNESS CONNECTORS VIEWED INTO MATING SURFACE.

Fig. DF1: Identifying MAP/BARO Sensor Circuits, Connector Terminals & Tester Hookup

CIRCUIT TEST DF (Cont.)

TEST PIN NO. 26 (VREF) WIRE COLOR IDENTIFICATION

Application	Wire Color
All Models	Brown/White

TEST PIN NO. 45 (MAP/BARO SIG) WIRE COLOR IDENTIFICATION

Application	Wire Color
All Models	Light Green/Black

TEST PIN NO. 46 (SIG RTN) WIRE COLOR IDENTIFICATION

Application	Wire Color
All Models	Gray/Red

MAP SENSOR SPECIFICATIONS

Manifold Vacuum In. Hg	Frequency/Hz
0	159
3	150
6	141
9	133
12	125
15	117
18	109
21	102
24	95
27	88
30	80

MAP/BARO SENSOR SPECIFICATIONS

Barometric Pressure In. Hg	Frequency/Hz
17.1	122.4
18.3	125.5
19.5	128.7
20.7	131.9
21.8	135.1
23.0	138.3
24.2	141.8
25.4	145.4
26.6	148.9
27.7	152.5
28.9	156.1
30.1	159.6
31.0	162.4

1) Code 126: Check Power To MAP/BARO Sensor – Code 126 indicates MAP/BARO sensor is out of self-test voltage range (1.4-1.6 volts). Following are possible causes of this code:

* Vacuum trapped at MAP/BARO sensor.
* High atmospheric pressure.
* MAP/BARO signal circuit open between sensor and PCM.
* MAP/BARO signal circuit shorted to VREF, SIG RTN or GND.
* VREF circuit open at sensor.
* SIG RTN circuit open at sensor.
* Faulty MAP/BARO sensor.
* Faulty PCM.

Turn ignition off. Disconnect MAP/BARO sensor from wiring harness. Connect MAP/BARO tester between wiring harness and MAP/BARO sensor. Connect banana plugs of tester into DVOM. Set DVOM on 20-volt scale. Turn ignition on. If Red light or no light is on, VREF is out of range. Go to next step. If Green light is on, VREF is okay. Go to step **3**).

2) Check Power At Sensor Wiring Harness Connector – Disconnect MAP/BARO sensor. Turn ignition on. If tester Green light is on, replace MAP/BARO sensor and repeat QUICK TEST. If Green light is off, remove MAP/BARO tester. Connect MAP/BARO sensor, and go to CIRCUIT TEST CA.

3) Check MAP/BARO Sensor Output – With MAP/BARO tester connected and ignition on, measure sensor output voltage. If output voltage is within range for altitude in which vehicle is being tested, remove MAP/BARO tester and go to next step. If output reading is not within range, remove MAP/BARO tester and go to step **5**).

CIRCUIT TEST DF (Cont.)

Diagnostic Aids – If possible, measure output voltage of several known good MAP/BARO sensors on available vehicles. Average voltage reading will be typical for location and time of testing.

MAP SENSOR VOLTAGE OUTPUT

Elevation (Feet)	Volts
0	1.59
1000	1.56
2000	1.53
3000	1.50
4000	1.47
5000	1.44
6000	1.41
7000	1.39

4) Check MAP/BARO SIG Circuit Continuity – Turn ignition off. Disconnect MAP/BARO sensor wiring harness connector. Disconnect PCM 60-pin connector. Inspect connector for damaged pins, corrosion and loose wires. Repair as necessary. Install EEC-IV Breakout Box (T83L-50-EEC-IV), leaving PCM disconnected. Measure resistance between MAP/BARO SIG terminal at sensor wiring harness connector and test pin No. 45. If reading is less than 5 ohms, replace PCM and repeat QUICK TEST. If reading is 5 ohms or more, repair open MAP/BARO SIG circuit and repeat QUICK TEST.

5) Check MAP/BARO SIG Circuit For Short To VREF, SIG RTN & Ground – Turn ignition off. Disconnect PCM 60-pin connector. Inspect connector for damaged pins, corrosion and loose wires. Repair as necessary. Install EEC-IV Breakout Box (T83L-50-EEC-IV), leaving PCM disconnected. Disconnect wiring harness at MAP/BARO sensor. Measure resistance between test pin No. 45 and test pins No. 26, 40, 46 and 60. If any reading is less than 10 k/ohms, repair short circuit. Remove breakout box, reconnect all components, and repeat QUICK TEST. If all readings are 10 k/ohms or more, replace MAP/BARO sensor. Remove breakout box, reconnect all components, and repeat QUICK TEST.

NOTE: A break in step numbering sequence occurs at this point. Procedure skips from step 5) to step 7). No test procedures have been omitted.

7) KOER Code 126: Check For EGR-Related Codes – Code 126 indicates MAP/BARO signal is out of self-test range during KOER SELF-TEST. Possible causes for this code are:
- Excess EGR flow.
- Damaged or misrouted MAP/BARO sensor vacuum hose.
- Faulty MAP/BARO sensor.

If Code 326, 327, 328, 332, 334, 336 or 337 is present, perform applicable CIRCUIT TEST. See SERVICE CODE REFERENCE CHARTS. If codes are not present, go to next step.

8) Check MAP Sensor Operation – Turn ignition off. Disconnect vacuum hose from MAP sensor. Connect vacuum pump to MAP sensor, and apply 18 in. Hg. If vacuum does not hold, replace sensor and repeat QUICK TEST. If MAP sensor holds vacuum, release vacuum and go to next step.

9) Attempt To Eliminate Code 126 – Plug MAP sensor vacuum supply hose. Start engine, and run it at 1400-1600 RPM. Slowly apply 15 in. Hg to MAP sensor. Perform KOER SELF-TEST. Check for Code 126, disregarding any other codes at this time. If Code 126 is still present, replace MAP sensor. If Code 126 is not present, inspect MAP sensor vacuum supply hose. If hose is okay, service other codes at this time. If no other code is present, check engine mechanical condition for cause of low vacuum.

10) Code 129: Repeat Dynamic Response Test – Code 129 indicates MAP sensor output did not change enough during dynamic response test. Possible causes for this code are:
- System failed to detect Wide Open Throttle (WOT).
- Damaged or misrouted MAP/BARO sensor vacuum hose.
- Faulty MAP sensor.

Repeat KOER SELF-TEST. Ensure complete WOT is performed during dynamic response portion of test. If KOER Code 129 is still present, go to next step. If code is not present, service any other codes as necessary.

11) Continuous Memory Code 128: Check Vacuum Hoses – Continuous Memory Code 128 indicates MAP sensor vacuum has not changed more than 2 in. Hg during normal vehicle operation. Possible causes for this code are:
- MAP sensor vacuum hose is improperly routed, blocked or is leaking.
- MAP sensor is leaking.

CIRCUIT TEST DF (Cont.)

Check vacuum lines for correct routing. Refer to Vehicle Emission Control Identification (VECI) decal. Check for loose connections, kinks and blockage. Repair vacuum lines as necessary. If vacuum lines are okay, go to next step.

12) Check MAP Sensor Operation – Turn ignition off. Disconnect vacuum supply hose from MAP sensor. Attach vacuum pump to MAP sensor. Apply 18 in. Hg to MAP sensor. If MAP sensor holds vacuum, release vacuum and go to next step. If sensor does not hold vacuum, replace MAP sensor and repeat QUICK TEST.

13) Verify Vacuum To MAP Sensor Decreases During Dynamic Response Test – Turn ignition off. Use a "T" fitting to install a vacuum gauge in MAP sensor vacuum hose. Perform KOER SELF-TEST while observing vacuum gauge. If vacuum decreases by more than 10 in. Hg during dynamic response test, replace MAP sensor and repeat QUICK TEST. If vacuum does not decrease by more than 10 in. Hg, EEC-IV system is okay. Check for engine mechanical problems affecting engine vacuum.

NOTE: A break in step numbering sequence occurs at this point. Procedure skips from step 13) to step 90). No test procedures have been omitted.

90) Continuous Memory Code 126 – Code 126 indicates MAP/BARO sensor was out of self-test range (1.4-1.6 volts) during normal driving conditions. Possible causes for this code are:
- Faulty MAP/BARO sensor.
- Faulty wiring harness or connectors.
- Unusually high or low barometric pressure.

Enter CONTINUOUS MONITOR MODE (WIGGLE TEST). Observe test equipment while performing the following:
- Connect a vacuum pump to MAP/BARO sensor.
- Slowly apply 25 in. Hg to sensor.
- Slowly bleed off vacuum from sensor.
- Lightly tap on sensor (to simulate road shock).
- Wiggle sensor connector.

If a fault is indicated, disconnect sensor and inspect connectors. Repair if necessary. If connectors are okay, replace MAP/BARO sensor. Repeat QUICK TEST. If a fault is not indicated, go to next step.

91) Check EEC-IV Wiring Harness – Stay in wiggle test. Observe analog VOM or scan tester for indication of fault while bending or wiggling small sections of harness from sensor connector to firewall, and from firewall to PCM. If fault is indicated, isolate fault in harness and repair as necessary. Repeat QUICK TEST. If no fault is indicated, go to next step.

92) Check PCM & Wiring Harness Connectors – Turn ignition off. Disconnect PCM 60-pin connector. Inspect connectors and terminals for damage. Repair if necessary. If connectors and terminals are okay, fault cannot be duplicated at this time. Testing is complete.

CIRCUIT TEST DH

THROTTLE POSITION (TP) SENSOR

Diagnostic Aids – Perform this test only when directed by QUICK TEST. This test is intended to diagnose the following:
- TP sensor.
- Wiring harness circuits (TP, SIG RTN and VREF).
- Powertrain Control Module (PCM).

Normal range of throttle angle measurement for TP sensor is 0-85 degrees. To pass QUICK TEST procedure, range of throttle rotation (in degrees) must be within 3 percent of specification. *See Fig. DH2.*

To prevent replacement of good components, be aware the following non-EEC related areas may be at fault:
- Idle speed.
- Binding throttle shaft or linkage.
- Choke cam adjustment (if equipped).
- TP sensor not seated.

CIRCUIT TEST DH (Cont.)

93A40428

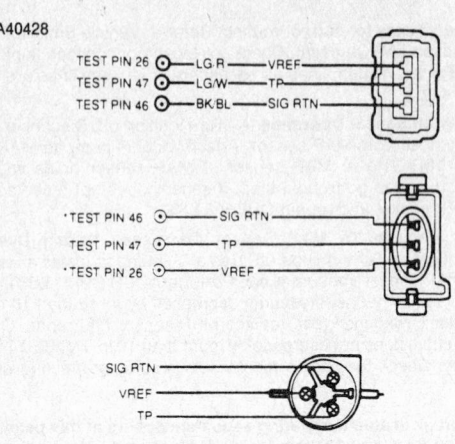

NOTE: EITHER TYPE MAY BE FITTED

Fig. DH1: Identifying TP Sensor Circuits & Connector Terminals

TEST PIN WIRE COLOR IDENTIFICATION

Application	Wire Color
No. 26 (VREF)	Light Green/Red
No. 46 (SIG RTN)	Black/Blue
No. 47 (TP)	Light Green/White

92G03822

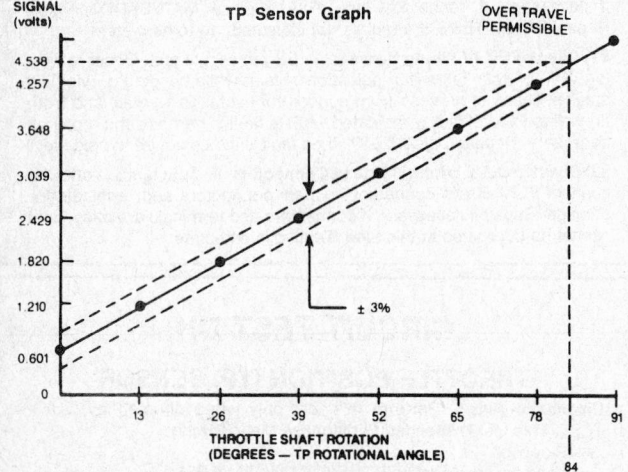

Fig. DH2: TP Sensor Specification Chart

1) KOER Code 121: Check For Other Codes – KOER Code 121 indicates TP sensor rotational setting may be out of self-test range. Possible causes for this fault are:
- Binding throttle linkage.
- TP sensor not seated correctly.
- Faulty TP sensor.
- Faulty Powertrain Control Module (PCM).

Perform KOER SELF-TEST. Check for Code 327. If either of these codes are present with Code 121, service Code 327 and repeat QUICK TEST. If these codes are not present, go to step 2).

2) Code 121: Check For Binding Throttle Plate – Inspect throttle body for binding. If throttle body is binding, check for binding throttle or cruise control linkage, vacuum line or harness interference, etc. Repair as necessary, and repeat QUICK TEST. If no mechanical problem is found, go to step 3).

CIRCUIT TEST DH (Cont.)

3) Code 123: Attempt To Generate Code 122 – Code 123 indicates TP sensor signal is greater than self-test maximum value. Possible causes for this fault are:
- TP sensor not seated properly.
- Faulty TP sensor.
- Short circuit to power.
- Faulty PCM.

Turn ignition off. Disconnect TP sensor wiring harness connector. Inspect and repair connector pins if damaged. Repeat KOEO SELF-TEST. Ignore all other codes at this time. If Code 63/122 is not displayed, go to step 5). If Code 122 is displayed, go to step 4).

4) Check VREF Circuit Voltage – Turn ignition on. Measure voltage between VREF and SIG RTN terminals at TP sensor wiring harness connector. If reading is 4-6 volts, replace TP sensor and repeat QUICK TEST. If reading is not 4-6 volts, reconnect sensor and go to CIRCUIT TEST CA.

5) Check TP Circuit For Short To Power – Turn ignition off. Leave TP sensor disconnected. Disconnect PCM 60-pin connector. Inspect it for damage and repair as necessary. Install EEC-IV Breakout Box (T83L-50-EEC-IV), leaving PCM disconnected. Measure resistance between test pin No. 47 and test pins No. 26 and 57. If either resistance is less than 10 k/ohms, repair short circuit in wiring harness and repeat QUICK TEST. If both resistances are 10 k/ohms or more, replace PCM and repeat QUICK TEST.

NOTE: A break in step numbering sequence occurs at this point. Procedure skips from step 5) to step 10). No test procedures have been omitted.

10) Code 122: Attempt To Generate Code 123 Or 121 – Code 122 indicates TP signal is less than minimum self-test value. See Fig. DH2. Possible causes for this fault are:
- TP sensor not seated correctly.
- Faulty TP sensor.
- Open circuit in wiring harness.
- Grounded circuit in wiring harness.
- Faulty PCM.

Turn ignition off, and wait 10 seconds. Disconnect TP sensor from harness. Install a jumper wire between VREF and TP terminals at TP sensor wiring harness connector. Perform KOEO SELF-TEST. If no codes are generated, remove jumper wire and go to step 13). If Codes 123 and 121 are not present, remove jumper wire and go to step 11). If either Code 123 or 121 is displayed, replace TP sensor and repeat QUICK TEST.

11) Check VREF Circuit Voltage – Turn ignition on. Measure voltage between VREF and SIG RTN terminals at TP sensor wiring harness connector. If voltage is not 4-6 volts, reconnect all components and go to CIRCUIT TEST CA. If voltage is 4-6 volts, go to step 12).

12) Check TP Sensor Circuit Continuity – Turn ignition off. Leave TP sensor disconnected. Disconnect PCM 60-pin connector. Inspect connector and repair if necessary. Install EEC-IV Breakout Box (T83L-50-EEC-IV), leaving PCM disconnected. Measure resistance between TP terminal at TP sensor wiring harness connector and test pin No. 47. If resistance is 5 ohms or more, repair open circuit and repeat QUICK TEST. If resistance is less than 5 ohms, go to step 13).

13) Check TP Circuit For Shorts To Ground – Turn ignition off. Leave TP sensor disconnected. Ensure both 4EAT module wiring harness connectors are disconnected (if applicable). Disconnect PCM 60-pin connector. Inspect wiring, and repair as necessary. With breakout box installed and PCM disconnected, measure resistance between test pin No. 47 and test pins No. 40, 46 and 60. If any reading is less than 10 k/ohms, repair short circuit and repeat QUICK TEST. If all readings are 10 k/ohms or more, replace PCM and repeat QUICK TEST.

NOTE: A break in step numbering sequence occurs at this point. Procedure skips from step 13) to step 20). No test procedures have been omitted.

20) Code 167: Repeat Dynamic Response Test – KOER Code 167 indicates TP sensor did not exceed 25% rotation during dynamic response portion of KOER SELF-TEST. A complete Wide Open Throttle (WOT) must be performed during dynamic response portion of test. Perform KOER SELF-TEST. Ensure WOT is completed during dynamic response portion of test. If Code 167 is still present, go to step 21). If code is not present, system is unable to duplicate Code 167 at this time. Service any other KOER codes. If no other service codes are present, testing is complete.

CIRCUIT TEST DH (Cont.)

21) Check TP Sensor Movement During Dynamic Response Test – Turn ignition off. Disconnect PCM 60-pin connector. Inspect wiring, and repair as necessary. Install EEC-IV Breakout Box (T83L-50-EEC-IV), leaving PCM connected. Set DVOM on 20-volt scale. Connect DVOM between test pins No. 46 and 47 at breakout box. Perform KOER SELF-TEST and ensure proper WOT is completed during dynamic response test. If DVOM reading exceeds 3.5 volts during dynamic response test, replace PCM and repeat QUICK TEST. If reading does not exceed 3.5 volts, ensure TP sensor is correctly installed and adjusted. If TP sensor is correctly installed and adjusted, replace TP sensor. Repeat QUICK TEST.

NOTE: A break in step numbering sequence occurs at this point. Procedure skips from step 21) to step 90). No test procedures have been omitted.

90) Continuous Memory Code 123 – This test monitors TP sensor under simulated road conditions. Enter wiggle test. See CONTINUOUS MONITOR MODE (WIGGLE TEST) under QUICK TEST. Connect DVOM or diagnostic tester to STO terminal of self-test connector. While slowly opening throttle to WOT, observe DVOM or diagnostic tester for indication of fault. Slowly bring throttle to closed position. Lightly tap TP sensor and wiggle harness connector. This test checks for open or short in TP sensor and wiring harness. If no fault is indicated, go to step **92)**. If fault is indicated, go to step **91)**.

91) Measure TP Circuit Voltage While Exercising TP Sensor – Turn ignition off, and wait 10 seconds. Disconnect PCM 60-pin connector. Inspect for damage and repair if necessary. Install EEC-IV Breakout Box (T83L-50-EEC-IV), leaving PCM connected. Stay in wiggle test (as in previous step). Connect DVOM between test pins No. 47 and 46. Set DVOM on 20-volt scale. With ignition on and engine off, observe DVOM and repeat step **90)**. If fault occurs at less than 4.25 volts, inspect TP sensor connectors and terminals. If connectors and terminals are okay, replace TP sensor, clear codes and repeat QUICK TEST. If fault does not occur at less than 4.25 volts, TP sensor over-travel may have caused Continuous Memory Code 123. TP sensor is okay. Go to step **92)** to check wiring harness.

92) Check EEC-IV Wiring Harness – While in wiggle test, bend and shake small sections of EEC-IV harness from TP sensor wiring harness connector to firewall and from firewall to PCM while observing analog voltmeter or scan tester. If fault is indicated, isolate fault in wiring and repair as necessary. Clear codes, and repeat QUICK TEST. If no fault is indicated, go to step **93)**.

93) Check PCM & Harness Connectors – Turn ignition off, and wait 10 seconds. Disconnect PCM 60-pin connector from breakout box. Inspect connectors and terminals for damage, and repair as necessary. Clear codes from PCM memory, and repeat QUICK TEST. If connectors and terminals are okay, fault cannot be duplicated at this time. Continuous Memory Code 123 testing is complete.

94) Continuous Memory Code 122 – Enter wiggle test. See CONTINUOUS MONITOR MODE (WIGGLE TEST) under QUICK TEST. Connect DVOM or diagnostic tester to STO terminal of self-test connector. Observe DVOM or diagnostic tester for indication of fault while performing the following:
- Slowly open throttle to WOT.
- Slowly bring throttle to closed position.
- Lightly tap TP sensor and wiggle connector.

If fault is indicated, disconnect TP sensor. Inspect connectors and terminals. If connectors and terminals are okay, replace TP sensor. Clear codes from PCM memory, and repeat QUICK TEST. If no fault is indicated, go to next step.

95) Check EEC-IV Wiring Harness – Stay in wiggle test (as in previous step). Bend, wiggle and shake small sections of EEC-IV harness from TP sensor wiring harness connector to firewall and from firewall to PCM while observing analog voltmeter or scan tester. If fault is indicated, isolate fault in wiring and repair as necessary. Clear codes from PCM memory, and repeat QUICK TEST. If no fault is indicated, go to step **96)**.

96) Check PCM & Harness Connectors – Turn ignition off. Inspect PCM 60-pin connector and terminals for damage. Repair connector terminals if necessary. Clear codes from PCM memory, and repeat QUICK TEST. If connectors and terminals are okay, fault cannot be duplicated at this time. Continuous Memory Code 122 testing is complete.

CIRCUIT TEST DJ

ENGINE RPM SENSOR (7.3 DIESEL)

Diagnostic Aids – Perform this test when Code 14 is displayed during QUICK TEST or when directed here by other test procedures. This test is intended to diagnose only the following components:
- Engine RPM Sensor (RPMS).
- PCM.
- RPMS (+) And RPMS (-) Vehicle Harness Circuits.

To prevent replacement of good components, verify RPM sensor is correctly installed and circuits/connectors are in good condition:

91F14253   Courtesy of Ford Motor Co.

*TEST PINS LOCATED ON BREAKOUT BOX.
ALL HARNESS CONNECTORS VIEWED INTO MATING SURFACE.

Fig. DJ1 Identifying RPM Sensor Circuit & Connector Terminals

TEST PIN 4 (RPMS +) WIRE COLOR IDENTIFICATION

Application	Wire Color
"E" Series	Pink/Orange
"F" Series	Tan/Yellow

TEST PIN 44 (RPMS -) WIRE COLOR IDENTIFICATION

Application	Wire Color
All Models	Dark Green

1) Code 14: Erratic RPM Signal – Code 14 indicates RPM signal output was missing pulses while engine was running. Check EEC-IV system for loose wires or connectors. If vehicle is equipped with 2-way radio or telephone, check for correct installation. Enter KOER CONTINUOUS MONITOR MODE (WIGGLE TEST). See QUICK TEST. Observe VOM or diagnostic tester while lightly tapping engine RPM sensor and wiggling RPM sensor connector. If fault is detected, repair as necessary and repeat QUICK TEST. If fault is not detected, go to next step.

2) Inspect EEC-IV Harness – Remain in KOER CONTINUOUS MONITOR MODE. Observe VOM or diagnostic tester for indication of fault while bending or wiggling small sections of harness from sensor connector to dash panel and from dash panel to PCM. If fault is detected, repair as necessary. Clear memory and repeat QUICK TEST to verify repair. If fault is not detected, go to next step.

3) Check Continuity Of Engine RPM Sensor Harness Circuits – Turn ignition off. Disconnect PCM 60-pin connector. Inspect connector for damage and repair as necessary. Install EEC-IV Breakout Box (T83L-50-EEC-IV), leaving PCM disconnected. Disconnect engine RPM sensor connector. Use ohmmeter to measure resistance between test pin No. 4 and RPMS (+) terminal at sensor. Measure resistance between test pin No. 44 and RPMS (-) terminal at sensor. If either circuit resistance is 5 ohms or more, repair open circuit and repeat QUICK TEST. If resistance is less than 5 ohms, go to next step.

4) Check Engine RPM Sensor Harness Circuits For Short To Power Or Ground – Ensure ignition is off and RPM sensor is disconnected. Measure resistance between test pin No. 4 and test pins No. 37, 40, 44 and 57 at breakout box. Measure resistance between test pin No. 44 and test pins No. 37 and 57 at breakout box. If either resistance is less than 10 k/ohms, repair short circuit and repeat QUICK TEST. If resistance is 10 k/ohms or more, go to next step.

5) Check RPM Sensor Resistance – Ensure ignition is off and RPM sensor is disconnected. Measure resistance between engine RPM sensor terminals. If resistance is 2400-2800 ohms, replace PCM and repeat QUICK TEST. If resistance is not 2400-2800 ohms, sensor and circuit are okay. Test is complete.

CIRCUIT TEST DQ

THROTTLE POSITION (TP) SENSOR
(7.3L DIESEL)

91G14254

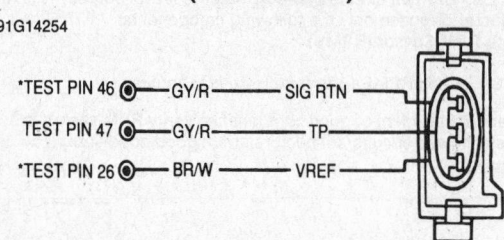

Fig. DQ1 Identifying Throttle Position (TP) Sensor Connector & Circuits (7.3 Diesel)

Diagnostic Aids – Enter this CIRCUIT TEST only when instructed during QUICK TEST. If you were direct here from KOEO Code 23 but an engine ID code of 5.0 was not received, go to CIRCUIT TEST DJ.

1) Code 23: Throttle Linkage Check – Inspect throttle linkage for binding, sticking or interference. If throttle linkage does not operate smoothly, service as necessary and repeat QUICK TEST. If throttle does operate smoothly, go to next step.

2) Code 53: Attempt To Generate Code 63 – With ignition off, and TP sensor disconnected, inspect and repair any corroded or damaged pins. Perform KOEO self test. If Code 63 is present, go to next step. If Code 63 is not present, go to step **4)**.

3) VREF Circuit Voltage Check – With ignition off and TP sensor disconnected, measure voltage at SIG RTN and VREF circuit at connector. If voltage is not 4-6 volts, connect all components and go to CIRCUIT TEST CA. If voltage is 4-6 volts, connect all components and go to step **14)**.

4) Check For Shorts To Power – With ignition off and TP sensor disconnected, remove PCM 60-pin connector. Inspect terminals, and repair if damaged. Install EEC-IV Breakout Box (T83L-50-EEC-IV), leaving PCM disconnected. Set DVOM on 200 k/ohm scale. Measure resistance between test pin No. 47 and test pins No. 26 and 57. If resistance is 10 k/ohms or more, replace PCM. Remove breakout box and reconnect components. Repeat QUICK TEST. If resistance is less than 10 k/ohms, repair shout circuit. Remove breakout box and reconnect components. Repeat QUICK TEST.

NOTE: A break in step numbering sequence occurs at this point. Procedure skips from step 4) to step 10). No test procedures have been omitted.

10) Code 63: Attempt To Generate Code 23/53 – With ignition off, disconnect TP sensor wiring harness connector. Inspect connector and harness for damage, and service as necessary. Connect jumper wire between VREF and TP circuit at TP sensor wiring harness connector. See Fig. DQ1. Perform KOEO SELF TEST. If no codes are present, go to step **13)**. If Code 23 or 53 is present, remove jumper wire and go to step **14)**. If any code but Code 23 or 25 is present, go to next step.

11) VREF Circuit Voltage Check – With ignition off and TP sensor disconnected, measure voltage at SIG RTN and VREF circuit at connector. If voltage is not 4-6 volts, connect all components and go to CIRCUIT TEST CA. If voltage is 4-6 volts, connect all components and go to next step.

12) TP Sensor Circuit Continuity Check – With ignition off and TP sensor disconnected, remove PCM 60-pin connector. Inspect terminals, and repair if damaged. Install EEC-IV Breakout Box (T83L-50-EEC-IV), leaving PCM disconnected. Measure resistance between test pin No. 47 and TP circuit at TP sensor wiring harness connector. See Fig. DQ1. If resistance is 5 ohms or more, repair open circuit and repeat QUICK TEST. If resistance is less than 5 ohms, go to next step.

13) Check For Shorts To Ground – Ensure ignition is off. Disconnect TP sensor harness connector. Remove PCM 60-pin connector. Inspect terminals, and repair if damaged. Install EEC-IV Breakout Box (T83L-50-EEC-IV), leaving PCM disconnected. Set DVOM on 200 k/ohms scale. Measure resistance between test pin No. 47 and test pins No. 40, 46 and 60 at breakout box. If resistance is 10 k/ohms or more, replace PCM. Connect all components and repeat QUICK TEST. If resistance is less than 10 k/ohms, repair short circuit and connect all components. Repeat QUICK TEST.

CIRCUIT TEST DQ (Cont.)

NOTE: Super Star II scan tester is used in step 14).

14) TP Sensor Adjustment – Perform KOEO SELF-TEST while holding throttle fully open. After last service code has been received, remain in self-test. Place .515" gauge between fuel pump lever travel screw and gauge block. Cycle Transmission Control Switch (TCS). Observe Super Star II tester for one of the following modes:
• Constant tone, solid light or consistent STO LO readout indicates TP sensor is within range. Cycle TCS to exit test.
• Beeping tone, flashing light or erratic STO readout indicates adjustment is required. See TRANSMISSION SERVICING section.
• If tone is undetectable, TP sensor may be worn.
• If adjustment is required, see TRANSMISSION SERVICING section. Repeat QUICK TEST. If service codes are still present or constant tone cannot be obtained, replace TP sensor.

91H14255

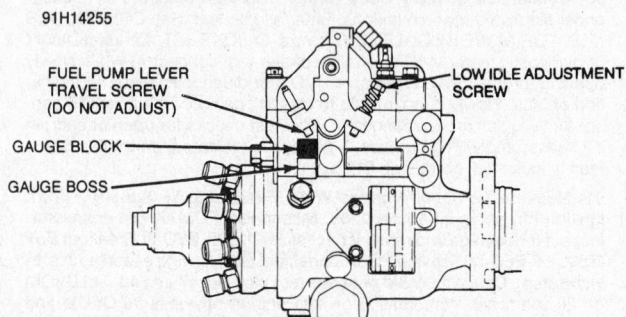

Fig. DQ2: Adjusting Fuel Pump Lever Travel Screw

NOTE: A break in step numbering sequence occurs at this point. Procedure skips from step 14) to step 90). No test procedures have been omitted.

90) Continuous Memory Code 53: Monitor TP Circuit Under Simulated Road Conditions – Enter KOEO wiggle test. See CONTINUOUS MONITOR MODE (WIGGLE TEST) under QUICK TEST. Observe DVOM or diagnostic tester for indication of fault while slowly opening throttle to WOT. Slowly bring throttle to closed position, and lightly tap TP sensor and wiggle harness connector. This test checks for open or short in TP sensor, connectors and wiring harness. If no fault is indicated, go to step 92). If fault is indicated, go to next step.

91) Measure TP Circuit Voltage While Exercising TP Sensor – Turn ignition off and wait 10 seconds. Remove PCM 60-pin connector. Inspect terminals, and repair if damaged. Install EEC-IV Breakout Box (T83L-50-EEC-IV), leaving PCM connected. Stay in KOEO wiggle test (as in previous step). Connect DVOM between test pins No. 46 and 47. Turn ignition on. Observe DVOM and repeat step 90). If fault occurs at less than 4.25 volts, inspect TP sensor connectors and terminals. If connectors and terminals are okay, go to step 14). If fault does not occur at less than 4.25 volts, go to next step.

92) Check ECC-IV Wiring Harness – While in KOEO wiggle test, shake, bend and wiggle small sections of wiring harness from TP sensor wiring harness connector to firewall, and from firewall to PCM. If fault is indicated, isolate fault in wiring and repair as necessary. Connect all components. Clear codes and repeat QUICK TEST. If no fault is indicated, go to next step.

93) Check PCM & Harness Connectors – Turn ignition off. Inspect PCM 60-pin connector and terminal for damage. Repair as necessary. Clear continuous memory codes and repeat QUICK TEST. See CLEARING CODES. If connectors and terminals are okay, fault cannot be duplicated at this time. Testing is complete.

94) Continuous Memory Code 63: Monitor TP Circuit Under Simulated Road Conditions – Enter KOEO wiggle test. See CONTINUOUS MONITOR MODE (WIGGLE TEST) under QUICK TEST. Check VOM or diagnostic tester for fault while performing the following:
• Slowly open throttle to WOT.
• Slowly bring throttle to closed position.
• Lightly tap TP sensor and wiggle connector.
If fault is indicated, disconnect TP sensor. Inspect connector and terminal. If connector and terminals are okay, go to step 14). If no fault is indication, go to next step.

CIRCUIT TEST DQ (Cont.)

95) Check EEC-IV Wiring Harness – While in KOEO wiggle test (CONTINUOUS MONITOR MODE), shake, bend and wiggle small section of wiring harness from TP sensor wiring harness connector to firewall, and from firewall to PCM. If fault is indicated, isolate fault in wiring and repair as necessary. Clear continuous memory codes and repeat QUICK TEST. See CLEARING CODES. If no fault is indicated, go to next step.

96) Check PCM & Harness Connectors – Turn ignition off and wait 10 seconds. Disconnect PCM 60-pin connector. Inspect connector and terminal for damage. Repair as necessary. Clear continuous memory codes and repeat QUICK TEST. If connectors and terminals are okay, fault cannot be duplicated at this time. Continuous Memory Code 63/122 testing is complete.

97) Continuous Memory Code 33: Continuous TP Sensor Noise – Code 33 is set when TP sensor becomes excessively worn, causing incorrect voltage fluctuation. If Code 33 is present, replace TP sensor and repeat QUICK TEST.

NOTE: A break in step numbering sequence occurs at this point. Procedure skips from step 97) to step 100). No test procedures have been omitted.

100) Code 43: Check TP Circuit Continuity – When TP circuit voltage drops below calibrated value at idle, Code 43 is set. Possible causes are as follows:
- Increased TP circuit resistance.
- Damaged or misadjusted TP sensor.

Turn ignition off. Disconnect PCM 60-pin connector. Install EEC-IV Breakout Box (T83L-50-EEC-IV), leaving PCM connected. Measure resistance between test pin No. 47 and test pins No. 40,46 and 60. If resistance is greater than 10 k/ohms, return to step 14). If resistance is 10 k/ohms or less, repair short circuit and repeat QUICK TEST.

CIRCUIT TEST DS

PROGRAMMABLE SPEEDOMETER/ ODOMETER MODULE (PSOM)

Diagnostic Aids – Perform this test when directed by QUICK TEST. This CIRCUIT TEST is intended to diagnose:
- PSOM output to PCM.
- PSOM (+) and PSOM (-) wiring harness circuits.
- PCM.

To prevent replacement of good components, be aware following non-EEC related areas and components may be cause of problem:
- Cruise Control system.
- Rear anti-lock brake system.
- Ring gear inside differential.
- Instrumentation system.

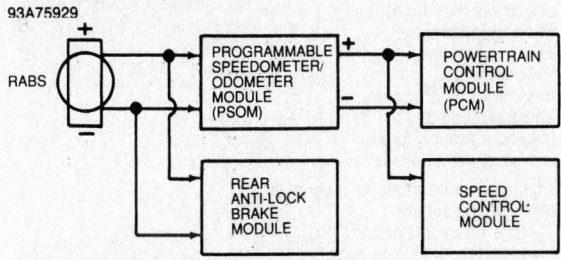

Fig. DS1 Programmable Speedometer/Odometer Module (PSOM) Circuit Logic

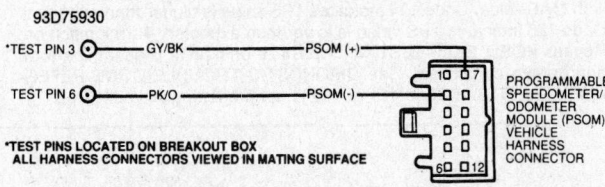

Fig. DS2 Identifying Programmable Speedometer/Odometer Module (PSOM) Circuit & Connector Terminals

CIRCUIT TEST DS (Cont.)

TEST PIN NO. 3 (PSOM +) WIRE COLOR IDENTIFICATION

Application	Wire Color
All Models	Gray/Black

TEST PIN NO. 6 (PSOM -) WIRE COLOR IDENTIFICATION

Application	Wire Color
All Models	Pink/Orange

1) Continuous Memory Code 29/452 – Code 29/452 indicates PCM detected incorrect output from VSS sometime during vehicle operation. Following are possible causes of code.
- PSOM output to PCM.
- PSOM (+) and PSOM (-) wiring harness circuits.
- PCM.

Turn ignition off. Remove PCM 60-pin connector. Inspect terminals, and repair if damaged. Install Breakout Box (T83L-50-EEC-IV), leaving PCM disconnected. Measure resistance between test pins No. 3 and 6 at breakout box. If reading is 21-55 k/ohms, go to step 4). If resistance is not 21-55 k/ohms, go to next step.

2) Check PSOM Circuit Continuity – Ensure ignition is off. Disconnect PSOM wiring harness connector. Measure resistance between test pin No. 3 at breakout box and PSOM (+) circuit at PSOM wiring harness connector. Measure resistance between test pin No. 6 at breakout box and PSOM (-) circuit at PSOM wiring harness connector. If resistance is more than 5 ohms, repair open circuit and repeat QUICK TEST. If resistance is 5 ohms or less, go to next step.

3) Check PSOM Circuit For Open – Ensure ignition is off. Measure resistance between test pin No. 3 and test pins No. 6, 37 and 40 at breakout box. If resistance is 10 k/ohms or less, repair open circuit and repeat QUICK TEST. If resistance is more than 10 k/ohms, go to next step.

4) Check RABS Sensor Resistance – Turn ignition off. Remove RABS connector. See Fig. DS1. Measure resistance between connector terminals. If resistance is not 1300-1550 ohms, replace RABS and repeat QUICK TEST. If resistance is 1300-1550, go to next step.

5) Check PSOM Output Voltage – Turn ignition off. Connect PCM to breakout box. Connect wiring harness connector to PSOM. Set DVOM on 20-volt AC scale. Start engine, and warm to normal operating temperature. Using an assistant, measure voltage between test pins No. 3 and 6 while gradually increasing vehicle speed to 50 MPH. If maximum voltage is less than 4 volts, fault is in instrument cluster. If maximum voltage received is more than 4 volts, replace PCM.

CIRCUIT TEST FD

BRAKE ON-OFF (BOO) SWITCH

Diagnostic Aids – Perform this test when directed by QUICK TEST. This test is intended to diagnose a faulty BOO switch circuit or PCM. To prevent replacement of good components, be aware following non-EEC related areas may be at fault:
- Brakelight bulb.
- Brakelight switch or brakelight fuse.

Fig. FD1: BOO Switch Circuit

TEST PIN NO. 2 WIRE COLOR IDENTIFICATION

Application	Wire Color
All Models	Red/Light Green

CIRCUIT TEST FD (Cont.)

1) Code 536: Verify Brake Pedal Was Depressed – Code 536 indicates that when brake pedal is applied during KOER SELF-TEST, BOO signal did not cycle high and low. Possible causes for this fault are:
- Brake pedal not applied during self-test.
- Brake pedal applied during entire self-test.
- Open brakelight circuit.
- Short to ground or power.
- Faulty Powertrain Control Module (PCM).

If brake was not applied during KOER SELF-TEST, repeat test. Depress and release brake pedal only once during test. If pedal was depressed, go to step **2)**.

2) Check Operation Of Brakelights – With ignition on, check operation of brakelights. If brakelights operate normally, go to step **3)**. If brakelights do not operate, go to step **4)**. If brakelights are always on, go to step **5)**.

3) Check For BOO Switch Circuit Cycling – Turn ignition off. Wait 10 seconds. Disconnect PCM 60-pin connector. Inspect terminals, and repair if damaged. Install EEC-IV Breakout Box (T83L-50-EEC-IV), leaving PCM disconnected. Measure voltage between BOO test pin (No. 2) and test pin No. 40 while applying and releasing brake. If voltage cycles, replace PCM and repeat QUICK TEST. If voltage does not cycle, repair open circuit in BOO switch circuit between PCM and BOO switch connection to brakelight circuit. Repeat QUICK TEST.

4) Check For Power To Brake Switch – Ensure related fuses and brakelight bulbs are in good condition. Turn ignition off. Disconnect brakelight switch (located on brake pedal). Measure voltage between BATT (+) input to brakelight switch and ground. If voltage is greater than 10 volts, check condition of brakelight switch. If brakelight switch is okay, repair open circuit between brakelight switch and brakelight ground. Repeat QUICK TEST. If voltage is less than 10 volts, repair open BATT (+) circuit to brakelight switch and repeat QUICK TEST.

5) Verify Brake Switch Is Not Always Closed – Turn ignition off. Disconnect brakelight switch (located on brake pedal). Turn ignition on. If brakelights are still on, go to step **6)**. If brakelights are not on, verify correct installation of brakelight switch. If installation is okay, replace brakelight switch and repeat QUICK TEST.

6) Check For Short To Power In PCM – Turn ignition off. Disconnect PCM. Turn ignition on. Check brakelights. If brakelights are on, go to step **7)**. If brakelights are not on, replace PCM and repeat QUICK TEST.

7) Check For Short To Power In Shift Lock Actuator – Turn ignition off. Ensure PCM and brakelight switch are disconnected. Disconnect shift lock actuator, cruise control module and ABS module (if equipped). Turn ignition on. If brakelights are still on, repair short to power in BOO or stoplight circuit and repeat QUICK TEST. If brakelights are not on, repair short circuit in shift lock actuator circuit, cruise control system circuit or ABS circuit. Repeat QUICK TEST.

NOTE: A break in step numbering sequence occurs at this point. Procedure skips from step 7) to step 90). No test procedures have been omitted.

90) Code 536: Check For Proper Brakelight Switch Installation – Continuous memory Code 536 indicates a BOO circuit failure. If BOO input does not cycle after a predetermined number of transitions from 0 MPH to a specific speed, the BOO input is assumed to be damaged and continuous memory Code 536 is set. Possible causes of failure are:
- Incorrect brakelight switch installation.
- Open brakelight/BOO circuit.
- Brakelight/BOO circuit short.
- Damaged switch or ground circuit.

If switch is correctly installed and in good condition, go to next step. If switch or harness is damaged, service as needed and clear continuous memory. Repeat QUICK TEST.

91) Inspect Brakelight Ground – Inspect brakelight ground connection and harness connector. Repair as needed. If connections are okay, go to next step.

92) Inspect Brakelight/BOO Circuits For Shorts – With KOEO and brake pedal released, perform wiggle test of brakelight/BOO circuit harness and connectors while observing brakelights. If brakelights illuminate, inspect and repair circuits as needed. If brakelights do not illuminate, go to next step.

93) Inspect Brakelight Circuit Continuity – With ignition off, depress brake pedal and hold. Perform wiggle test of brakelight circuits while observing brakelights. Lightly tap brakelight switch while observing brakelights. If brakelights intermittently go out, inspect and repair circuits as needed. If brakelights remain illuminated, go to next step.

CIRCUIT TEST FD (Cont.)

94) Inspect BOO Circuit Continuity – With ignition off, ensure brake pedal is released. Disconnect PCM 60-pin connector. Inspect terminals, and repair if damaged. Install EEC-IV Breakout Box (T83L-50-EEC-IV), leaving PCM disconnected. Measure resistance between BOO test pin No. 2 and brakelight circuit at switch while performing wiggle test on harness and connector. If resistance intermittently increases above 5 ohms, inspect and repair open circuit. Repeat QUICK TEST. If resistance is within specification, go to next step for further diagnosis.

NOTE: A break in step numbering sequence occurs at this point. Procedure skips from step 94) to step 99). No test procedures have been omitted.

99) Road Test Vehicle – Purpose of this test is to identify faults by monitoring certain controlled parameters while trying to recreate a driveability or MIL symptom. To prepare for road test:
- Install fuel pressure gauge and if available, a MAP/BARO tester.
- Disconnect PCM 60-pin connector, install breakout box and reconnect PCM to breakout box.
- Connect "T" vacuum gauge into manifold vacuum line.
- Have DVOM, writing materials and appropriate schematics and pin voltage charts available.

With ignition on and negative lead of DVOM connected to negative battery terminal, ensure following signals are correct:
- POWERS: KAPWR (pin No. 1) is greater than 10.5 volts, VPWR (pins No. 37 and 57) is greater than 10.5 volts and VREF (pin No. 26) is 4-6 volts.
- GROUNDS: PWR GND (pins No. 40 and 60), SIG RTN (pin No. 46) and IGN GND (pin No. 16) are 0.0-0.5 volt.
- OPTIONAL GROUNDS: HO2S GND (pin No. 49), CSE GND (pin No. 20) and MAF RTN (pin No. 9 or 15) are 0.0-0.5 volt.

Diagnostic Aids – Test lights and DVOM are useful during diagnosis. For example:a testlight could be connected at brakelight switch between battery and ground and another testlight between switch bulb circuit and ground. Testlight to battery circuit should always illuminated and other testlight should only illuminate when brakelight is depressed.

With DVOM connected between test pin No. 2 and 40 at Breakout Box, check voltage. If voltage is between 6-7 volts with brake pedal released, possible open circuit between PCM and brakelight ground could exist.

CIRCUIT TEST GA

MAF/TPS FUEL INJECTOR PULSE WIDTH TEST

Diagnostic Aids – Perform this test when instructed during QUICK TEST or if directed here by other test procedures. To prevent replacement of good components, be aware the following non-EEC related areas may be at fault:
- Excessive blow-by.
- PCV malfunction.
- Vacuum leaks.
- Incorrect fuel pressure.
- Throttle binding.
- Improper fuel pressure.
- Idle air control solenoid.

This test is only intended to diagnose:
- MAP/BARO sensor.
- Throttle Position Sensor (TPS).
- Mass Airflow (MAF) sensor.
- Intake Air Temperature (IAT) sensor.
- Fuel injectors.

1) Check For Idle Air Codes – Code 121 indicates TPS is inconsistent with MAF value. Code 124 indicates TPS value is higher than expected. Code 125 indicates TPS value is lower than expected. Turn ignition on. Repeat KOEO SELF-TEST. If Code 411 or 412 is present, perform appropriate circuit test. See DIAGNOSTIC TROUBLE CODE REFERENCE CHARTS. If Code 411 or 412 is not present, go to next step.

CIRCUIT TEST GA (Cont.)

2) Throttle Position (TP) Sensor: TP Sensor Integrity – Turn ignition off. Disconnect PCM 60-pin connector. Inspect connector for damaged pins, corrosion and loose wires. Repair as necessary. Install EEC-IV Breakout Box (T83L-50-EEC-IV). Connect PCM to breakout box. Connect DVOM to test pins No. 46 and 47 at breakout box. Turn ignition on. Slowly apply throttle to WOT, and release to closed position. Voltage should change smoothly from 0.4-4.5 volts. See CIRCUIT TEST DH for schematics and specific engine values. If voltage change is incorrect or erratic, ensure TP sensor is properly installed. If TP sensor is properly installed, replace TP sensor. Remove breakout box, reconnect all components, and repeat QUICK TEST. If voltage is okay, go to step **8)** for Code 121 or next step for all other codes.

3) Check Idle – Ensure idle is correct. If idle is correct, go to next step. If idle is incorrect, adjust as necessary.

4) Check Throttle Body – Ensure idle is correct. Check throttle and/or cruise control linkage for binding and rough operation. Inspect throttle body for sludge build-up. Check engine vacuum hoses. Refer to Vehicle Emission Control Information (VECI) decal for proper vacuum hose routing. Check for air leak between ISC solenoid and MAF sensor. If problems are found, repair as necessary. Remove breakout box, reconnect all components, and repeat QUICK TEST. If no problems are found, go to next step.

5) Check MAP/BARO Sensor Output – On vehicles without MAP/BARO go to next step. On vehicles with MAP/BARO, see DIAGNOSTIC AIDS, then continue with this test. With tester connected and ignition on, measure sensor output voltage. If output voltage is within range for specified altitude, remove MAP/BARO tester and go to next step. See MAP SENSOR VOLTAGE OUTPUT table for specification. If output voltage is not within range, replace MAP/BARO sensor. Remove breakout box, reconnect all components, and repeat QUICK TEST.

Diagnostic Aids – If possible, measure several known good MAP/BARO sensors. Average voltage reading will be typical for location and day of testing. Also, refer to CIRCUIT TEST DF under SELF-DIAGNOSTICS – EEC-IV article in ENGINE PERFORMANCE of appropriate MITCHELL® manual for MAP/BARO sensor output check. See Fig. DF1 for connector terminal identification and MAP/BARO tester hookup.

MAP SENSOR VOLTAGE OUTPUT

Elevation (Feet)	Volts
0	1.55-1.63
1000	1.52-1.60
2000	1.49-1.57
3000	1.46-1.54
4000	1.43-1.51
5000	1.40-1.48
6000	1.37-1.45
7000	1.35-1.43

6) Check IAT Sensor – Ensure ambient temperature is more than 50°F (10°C) before performing this test. Also, check and repair any air leaks in front of IAT sensor. Turn ignition off. Connect breakout box to PCM. Set DVOM to 20-volt scale. Connect DVOM to test pins No. 25 and 46. Start engine, and let it idle. Observe voltage as engine warms up. See CIRCUIT TEST DA for voltage specifications under SELF-DIAGNOSTICS – EEC-IV article in ENGINE PERFORMANCE of appropriate MITCHELL® manual. If voltage decreases smoothly and stabilizes when engine reaches operating conditions, system is operating properly at this time. Testing is complete. If voltage does not decrease smoothly and stabilize after engine reaches operating conditions, replace IAT sensor and repeat QUICK TEST.

7) Continuous Memory Code 184 & 185: Inspect MAF Sensor – Code 184 indicates MAF sensor signal is higher than expected. Code 185 indicates MAF sensor signal is lower than expected. Turn ignition off. Check for air leaks between Idle Air Control (IAC) solenoid and MAF sensor. Inspect MAF sensor for oil contamination caused by excessive blow-by or malfunctioning PCV. If problems are found, repair as necessary. Clear codes and repeat QUICK TEST. If no problems are found, go to step **10)**.

8) Check MAF Sensor Circuit Voltage – Turn ignition off. Disconnect PCM 60-pin connector. Inspect connector for damaged pins, corrosion and loose wires. Repair as necessary. Install EEC-IV Breakout Box (T83L-50-EEC-IV). Connect PCM to breakout box. Start engine, and warm it to normal operating temperature. Measure voltage between test pin No. 50 and test pin No. 40 or 60 at breakout box. If voltage is not within specification, replace MAF sensor. Remove breakout box, reconnect all components, and repeat QUICK TEST. See MAF SENSOR DATA table. If voltage is within acceptable range, system is operating normally at this time. Sometime during the last 80 warm-up cycles, MAF sensor signal was out of range.

CIRCUIT TEST GA (Cont.)

MAF SENSOR DATA

Engine Condition	[1] Voltage
Idle	0.8
20 MPH	1.0
40 MPH	1.7
60 MPH	2.1

[1] – With engine at normal operating temperature.

9) Continuous Memory Code 186 & 187: Visual Vacuum Checks – Code 186 indicates pulse width is longer than expected (rich). Code 187 indicates pulse width is shorter than expected (lean). Inspect air cleaner and air inlet duct. Replace or repair an necessary. Check for unmetered air leaks between MAF sensor and IAC solenoid. Check all engine vacuum hoses for damage, blockage and improper routing. Repair as necessary, and repeat QUICK TEST. If all checks are okay, go to next step.

10) Check Fuel Pressure – Turn ignition off. Install fuel pressure gauge. Ensure vacuum hose is connected to fuel pressure regulator (if applicable). Start engine, and run it at idle. If fuel pressure is within specification, go to next step. See FUEL PRESSURE SPECIFICATIONS table. If fuel pressure is not within specifications, repair as necessary.

FUEL PRESSURE SPECIFICATIONS

Engine	KOER Pressure psi (kg/cm²)	KOEO Pressure psi (kg/cm²)
All Models	30-45 (2.1-3.2)	35-40 (2.4-3.1)

11) Verify Fuel Pressure Retention Ability – Turn ignition on. If fuel pressure remains at specification for 60 seconds, go to next step. If fuel pressure does not remain at specification, repair fuel delivery system as necessary.

12) Cylinder Balance Test – Perform KOER SELF-TEST. After last code, wait 5-10 seconds, and then goose throttle lightly (not wide open throttle). This will activate cylinder balance test. If Code 90 is present after test, go back to step **7)**. If Code 90 is not present after test, go to CIRCUIT TEST H, step **4)** under SELF-DIAGNOSTICS – EEC-IV article in ENGINE PERFORMANCE of appropriate MITCHELL® manual.

CIRCUIT TEST KM

WIDE OPEN THROTTLE A/C CUT-OUT (WAC) & A/C DEMAND SWITCH

Diagnostic Aids – Perform this test when instructed by QUICK TEST. To prevent replacing good components, check the following non-EEC components and systems:
- Refrigerant charge.
- Low ambient temperature (less than 45°F).

This test is only intended to diagnose:
- Wiring harness circuits (WAC, VPWR, GND, POWER-TO-CLUTCH and ACD).
- WAC relay.
- Faulty PCM.

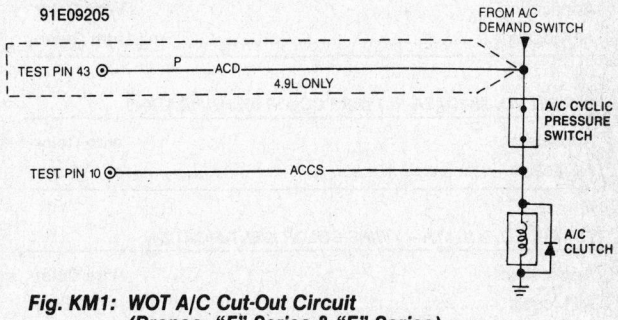

Fig. KM1: WOT A/C Cut-Out Circuit (Bronco, "F" Series & "E" Series)

TEST PIN NO. 10 (ACCS) WIRE COLOR IDENTIFICATION

Application	Wire Color
Bronco, "F" Series & "E" Series	Black/Yellow

CIRCUIT TEST KM (Cont.)

Diagnostic Aids – Before entering this test, ensure A/C selector is in OFF position and shift selector is in PARK (A/T). If A/C was on, repeat QUICK TEST. If Code 539 is present, continue with this test.

NOTE: Procedure begins at step 40). No test procedures have been omitted.

40) Code 539: Check A/C Input – Code 539 indicates ACCS input to PCM was high during SELF-TEST. Turn ignition off. Disconnect 60-pin PCM connector. Inspect connector for damaged pins, corrosion and loose wires. Repair as necessary. Install EEC-IV Breakout Box (T83L-50-EEC-IV), leaving PCM disconnected. Turn ignition on. Measure voltage between test pin No. 10 at breakout box and chassis ground. If voltage is more 1.0 volt, verify A/C switch operation. repair as necessary. If A/C switch is okay, repair short to power in A/C circuit. Remove breakout box, reconnect all components, and repeat QUICK TEST. If voltage is 1.0 volt or less on all models except 7.3L diesel, replace PCM. Remove breakout box, reconnect all components, and repeat QUICK TEST. If voltage is 1.0 volt or less on 7.3L diesel, go to next step.

41) Check For Short To Power In PCM – Ensure ignition is off. With Breakout Box still installed, connect PCM to Breakout Box. Disconnect A/C clutch electrical harness. With KOEO, measure voltage between breakout box test pin No. 10 and No. 40. If voltage is more than 5 volts, replace PCM. Connect all components and repeat QUICK TEST. If voltage is 5 volts or less, connect all components. Go to CIRCUIT TEST TD.

CIRCUIT TEST ML

SELF-TEST OUTPUT (STO) OR MALFUNCTION INDICATOR LIGHT (MIL)

Diagnostic Aids – The MIL is turned on when PCM detects a fault in EEC circuit(s). The light will remain on as long as fault remains in system.

Perform this test only when instructed by QUICK TEST or if directed by CIRCUIT TEST QA. This test does not include procedure for models with electronic instrument panel. To prevent replacing good components, be aware that fuse, bulb or bulb socket may be cause of problem. This test is only intended to diagnose:
- STO/MIL circuit.
- Faulty PCM.

93H40433

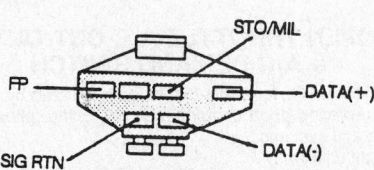

Fig. ML1: *Identifying Data Link Connector (DLC) Terminals*

TEST PIN NO. 17 (STO/MIL) WIRE COLOR IDENTIFICATION

Application	Wire Color
All Models	Pink/Light Green

TEST PIN NO. 28 (DATA +) WIRE COLOR IDENTIFICATION

Application	Wire Color
All Models	Tan/Orange

TEST PIN NO. 9 (DATA –) WIRE COLOR IDENTIFICATION

Application	Wire Color
All Models	Pink/Light Blue

1) Malfunction Indicator Light (MIL) Always On – Service all KOEO and Continuous Memory Codes before proceeding with this test. Turn ignition off. Disconnect 60-pin PCM connector. Inspect connector for damaged pins, corrosion and loose wires. Repair as necessary. Install EEC-IV Breakout Box (T83L-50-EEC-IV), leaving PCM disconnected.

CIRCUIT TEST ML (Cont.)

Measure resistance between test pins No. 17 and 40 at breakout box. If resistance is 5 ohms or more, replace PCM and repeat QUICK TEST. If reading is less than 5 ohms, repair short between test pin No. 17 and Diagnostic Link Connector (DLC) or MIL. Remove breakout box, reconnect all components, and repeat QUICK TEST.

NOTE: A break in step numbering sequence occurs at this point. Procedure skips from step 1) to step 4). No test procedures have been omitted.

4) Malfunction Indicator Light (MIL) Does Not Light – If vehicle will not start, go to step 1). Turn ignition on. Measure voltage between negative battery terminal and ground side of MIL fuse. If voltage is more than 10.5 volts, go to step 6). If voltage is 10.5 volts or less, go to next step.

5) Check For Voltage At Fuse – Turn ignition on. Measure voltage from negative battery terminal to power side of MIL fuse. If voltage is more than 10.5 volts, replace fuse. Verify repair by turning ignition switch to RUN position. If voltage is 10.5 volts or less, repair open MIL/B+ circuit. Verify repair by turning ignition switch to RUN position.

6) Check Voltage At B+ Circuit – Turn ignition on. Measure voltage between B+ side of MIL bulb socket and negative battery terminal. If voltage is 10.5 volts or less, repair open in MIL circuit between fuse and bulb. Verify repair by turning ignition switch to RUN position. If voltage is more than 10.5 volts, go to next step.

7) Check MIL Bulb Response To Grounding – Turn ignition off. Attach jumper wire between ground side of MIL bulb socket and chassis ground. Turn ignition on. If MIL light comes on, remove jumper wire, and go to next step. If MIL light does not come on, remove jumper wire. Replace MIL bulb socket. Turn ignition on to verify correct MIL operation.

8) Check Continuity Of MIL Circuit – Turn ignition off. Disconnect 60-pin PCM connector. Inspect connector for damaged pins, corrosion and loose wires. Repair as necessary. Install EEC-IV Breakout Box (T83L-50-EEC-IV), leaving PCM disconnected. Measure resistance between test pin No. 17 at breakout box and MIL wiring harness connector terminal. If resistance is less than 5 ohms, replace PCM. Turn ignition on to verify correct MIL operation. If resistance is 5 ohms or more, repair open in ground side of MIL circuit. Turn ignition on to verify correct MIL operation.

NOTE: A break in step numbering sequence occurs at this point. Procedure skips from step 8) to step 10). No test procedures have been omitted.

10) MIL On Intermittently, Check For Intermittent Short From STO To Ground – If vehicle does not start, go to step 1). MIL comes on when a fault code is present. Service all fault codes before proceeding. If no codes are output, proceed with this test. Enter KOEO wiggle test. See CONTINUOUS MONITOR MODE (WIGGLE TEST) under QUICK TEST. Check DVOM for indication of fault while performing wiggle test on harness in the following areas:
- From Diagnostic Link Connector (DLC) to dash panel.
- Dash panel to PCM.
- Dash panel to Malfunction Indicator Light (MIL).

If a fault is indicated, repair short to ground and repeat QUICK TEST. If a fault is not indicated, fault cannot be duplicated at this time. Testing is complete.

NOTE: A break in step numbering sequence occurs at this point. Procedure skips from step 10) to step 15). No test procedures have been omitted.

15) MIL Flashes With Erratic Idle – Symptoms indicate STI is grounded and PCM is performing self-test without tester installed. Turn ignition off. Disconnect 60-pin PCM connector. Inspect connector for damaged pins, corrosion and loose wires. Repair as necessary. Install EEC-IV Breakout Box (T83L-50-EEC-IV), leaving PCM disconnected. Measure resistance between STI connector and engine ground. If resistance is less than 10 k/ohms, repair short circuit. Reconnect PCM, and turn ignition on to verify correct MIL operation. If resistance is 10 k/ohms or more, MIL circuit is okay. Verify symptom, and test for other rough idle symptoms.

NOTE: A break in step numbering sequence occurs at this point. Procedure skips from step 15) to step 20). No test procedures have been omitted.

CIRCUIT TEST ML (Cont.)

20) CHECK ENGINE Message Displayed – Perform KOEO SELF-TEST. If result is Code 111-11-111 (pass code), fault is in instrument cluster. If pass code is not displayed, service codes as necessary.

NOTE: A break in step numbering sequence occurs at this point. Procedure skips from step 20) to step 25). No test procedures have been omitted.

25) Continuous Memory Code 529 Or 533: CHECK ENGINE Or CHECK DCL Message Displayed – Codes 529 and 533 indicate circuit fault has occurred on Data Communications Link (DCL). These codes can occur alone or with another code. Fault will occur under following conditions:
- Code 529 indicates PCM or DCL circuit failure.
- Code 533 indicates DCL to electronic instrument cluster circuit failure.

Clear continuous memory codes. Wait 5 minutes, and repeat KOEO SELF-TEST. If result is pass code (Code 111-11-111), fault is in instrument cluster. If pass code is not displayed, service codes as necessary.

CIRCUIT TEST QA

NO CODES/CODES NOT LISTED

Diagnostic Aids – Aftermarket devices, such as alarm system, may cause SELF-TEST to abort if wiring is connected to certain EEC components. If a device is installed, disconnect it completely from EEC system. Before continuing with this circuit test, restore EEC circuits to original state and repeat QUICK TEST.

Perform this test when directed by QUICK TEST or other test procedures. This test is intended to diagnose:
- Powertrain Control Module (PCM).
- EEC power relay.
- Constant Control Relay Module (CCRM).
- Wiring harness circuits (HO2S, SIG RTN, STO, STI, VPWR and VREF).

93A40808

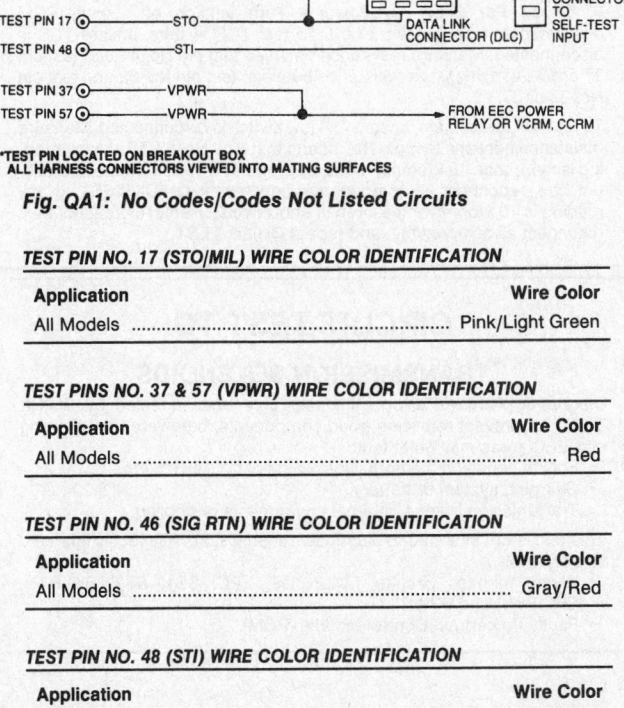

Fig. QA1: No Codes/Codes Not Listed Circuits

TEST PIN NO. 17 (STO/MIL) WIRE COLOR IDENTIFICATION

Application	Wire Color
All Models	Pink/Light Green

TEST PINS NO. 37 & 57 (VPWR) WIRE COLOR IDENTIFICATION

Application	Wire Color
All Models	Red

TEST PIN NO. 46 (SIG RTN) WIRE COLOR IDENTIFICATION

Application	Wire Color
All Models	Gray/Red

TEST PIN NO. 48 (STI) WIRE COLOR IDENTIFICATION

Application	Wire Color
All Models	White/Pink

CIRCUIT TEST QA (Cont.)

Diagnostic Aids – Thunderbird, Thunderbird SC and Cougar may be equipped with 2 Data Link Connectors (DLC). One underneath the dash and one in the engine compartment. Use the engine compartment DLC for testing.

1) Check VREF Voltage At Data Link Connector (DLC) – Turn ignition off. Disconnect 60-pin PCM connector. Inspect connector for damaged pins, corrosion and loose wires. Repair as necessary. Install EEC-IV Breakout Box (T83L-50-EEC-IV). Connect PCM to breakout box. Turn ignition on. Measure voltage between test pin No. 26 at breakout box and SIG RTN terminal at DLC. If reading is 4-6 volts, go to step 3). If reading is not 4-6 volts, go to next step.

2) Check SIG RTN Circuit Continuity – Turn ignition off. Disconnect PCM from breakout box. Measure resistance between test pin No. 46 at breakout box and SIG RTN terminal at DLC. If reading is less than 5 ohms, go to CIRCUIT TEST CA. If resistance is 5 ohms or more, repair open circuit and repeat QUICK TEST.

3) Check STI Circuit Continuity – Turn ignition off. Disconnect PCM from breakout box. Measure resistance between test pin No. 48 at breakout box and Self-Test Input (STI) terminal at pigtail connector. If resistance is 5 ohms or more, repair open circuit. Remove breakout box, reconnect all components, and repeat QUICK TEST. If reading is less than 5 ohms, go to next step.

4) Check STO Circuit Continuity – Leave ignition off and PCM disconnected. Measure resistance between test pin No. 17 at breakout box and STO terminal at DLC. If resistance is less than 5 ohms on all models except 7.3L diesel, go to step 5). If resistance is less than 5 ohms on 7.3L diesel, go to step 7). If resistance is 5 ohms or more, repair open circuit. Remove breakout box, reconnect all components, and repeat QUICK TEST.

5) Check HO2S Signal For Short To Power – Leave PCM disconnected. Turn ignition on. Measure voltage between test pin No. 40 or 60 and HO2S SIGNAL test pin No. 29 or 44 at breakout box. For HO2S circuit schematics, see CIRCUIT TEST H under SELF-DIAGNOSTICS – EEC-IV article in ENGINE PERFORMANCE of appropriate MITCHELL® manual. If voltage is more than 2 volts, go to step 6). If voltage is 2 volts or less, go to step 7).

6) Isolate Short To Harness Or HO2S Sensor – Turn ignition off. Leave PCM disconnected. Disconnect right/rear HO2S sensor connector. Turn ignition on. Measure voltage between HO2S SIGNAL test pin No. 29 or 44 and test pin No. 40 or 60 at breakout box. If any reading is more than 2 volts, repair short to power in HO2S SIGNAL circuit. Remove breakout box, reconnect all components, and repeat QUICK TEST. If voltage is 2 volts or less, replace right/rear HO2S sensor. Remove breakout box, reconnect all components, and repeat QUICK TEST.

7) Check STO Circuit For Short To Ground – Turn ignition off. Leave PCM disconnected. Measure resistance between STO at DLC and engine ground. If reading is 5 ohms or more, go to next step. If resistance is less than 5 ohms, repair STO or MIL circuit for short to ground. Remove breakout box, reconnect all components, and repeat QUICK TEST.

8) Check If Power Relay Is Always On – Leave ignition off and PCM disconnected. Connect DVOM between test pin No. 37 or 57 and test pin No. 40 or 60 at breakout box. Turn ignition on and then off. Wait 10 seconds. If voltage changes from more than 10.5 volts to less than 1.0 volt, go to step 10). If voltage does not change from more than 10.5 volts to less than 1.0 volt, go to next step.

9) Check VPWR Circuit For Short To Power – Turn ignition off. Leave PCM disconnected. Disconnect EEC power relay or Constant Control Relay Module (CCRM). Connect DVOM to test pin No. 37 or 57 and test pin No. 40 or 60 at breakout box. If voltage is more than 1.0 volt, repair VPWR circuit short to power. Remove breakout box, reconnect all components, and repeat QUICK TEST. If voltage is 1.0 volt or less, replace EEC power relay or CCRM. Remove breakout box, reconnect all components, and repeat QUICK TEST.

10) Check Malfunction Indicator Light (MIL) Function – If MIL is always on, go to CIRCUIT TEST ML, step 1). If MIL is always off, go to CIRCUIT TEST ML, step 4). If MIL is working normally, replace PCM and repeat QUICK TEST.

CIRCUIT TEST TB

TRANSMISSION CONTROL SWITCH (TCS), TRANSMISSION CONTROL SWITCH, MODULE (TCSM) & TRANSMISSION CONTROL INDICATOR LIGHT (TCIL)

Diagnostic Aids – Perform this test only when directed by QUICK TEST. This test is intended to diagnose:
- Powertrain Control Module (PCM).
- Wiring harness circuits (4x4 Low, TCIL and TCS).

To prevent replacing good components, be aware the following non-EEC related areas may be at fault:
- Basic engine condition (valves, vacuum leaks, valve timing, etc.).
- Charging system.
- Transmission (fluid, friction elements and cooling).

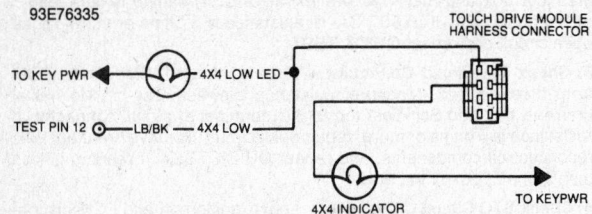

Fig. TB1: 4x4 Low & Overdrive Cancel Circuits (Touch Drive Option)

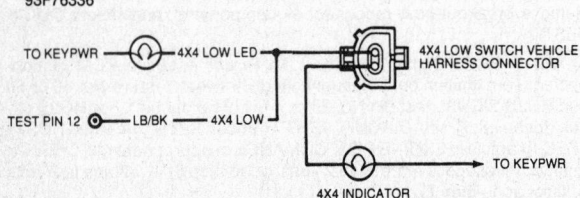

Fig. TB2: 4x4 Low & Overdrive Cancel Circuits (Without Touch Drive Option)

1) Code 47/633 & 691 – Code 47/633 indicates 4x4 low selector lever is not in 4x2 or 4x4 high position (KOEO). Code 691 is set when a stored Kam value for engine rpm or vehicle speed is compared to a calculated engine rpm/vehicle speed and do not match. Possible malfunction causes:
- Damaged 4x4 low switch or 4x4 selector lever position.
- Shorted harness.
- Damaged PCM.
- Internal damage to transfer case.

If 4x4 lever is in 4x2 or 4x4 high position, go to next step. If 4x4 lever is not in 4x2 or 4x4 high position, repeat QUICK TEST with shift lever in correct position.

2) Code 65/632 Or 653 – Code 65/632 or 653 indicates that the TCS was not cycled between engine ID Code and WOT check during KOER SELF-TEST. Possible causes for this fault are:
- Faulty TCS or switch was not cycled during SELF-TEST.
- Shorted wiring harness.
- Faulty Powertrain Control Module (PCM).
- Open in wiring harness or fuse.

If TCS cycled during KOER SELF-TEST, go to step **4)**. If TCS did not cycle during KOER SELF-TEST, repeat KOER SELF-TEST while cycling TCS.

3) Code 97/623 or 631 – Code 97/623 or 631 indicates transmission control indicator light circuit fault during KOEO SELF-TEST. Possible causes for this fault are:
- Burned out bulb.
- Open or shorted wiring harness.

If TCS cycled during KOEO SELF-TEST, go to step **5)**. If TCS did not cycle during KOEO SELF-TEST, repeat KOER SELF-TEST while cycling TCS.

4) Check TCS Circuit – Turn ignition off. Disconnect 60-pin PCM connector. Inspect connector for damaged pins, corrosion and loose wires. Repair as necessary. Install EEC-IV Breakout Box (T83L-50-EEC-IV), leaving PCM disconnected. Turn ignition on. For TCS circuit, measure voltage between test pin No. 41 and test pin No 40 or 60 while cycling TCS several times. For 4x4 low circuit, measure voltage between

CIRCUIT TEST TB (Cont.)

test pin No. 12 and test pin No 40 or 60 while moving lever between 4x2 and 4x4 low several times. If voltage cycles replace PCM. Remove breakout box, reconnect all components, and repeat QUICK TEST. If voltage does not cycle, go to next step if diagnosing a trouble code or step **7)** if diagnosing a driveability symptom.

5) Check Circuits For Short To Ground – Turn ignition off. Leave PCM disconnected from breakout box. To test 4x4 low circuit, disconnect 4x4 low switch connector. Inspect connector for damage and repair as necessary. Measure and record resistance between test pin No. 12 and test pin 40 or 60.

To test TCS circuit, disconnect TCS connector. Inspect connector for damage and repair as necessary. Measure resistance between test pin No. 41 and test pin 40 or 60. Also, measure resistance between test pin No. 55 and test pin No. 40 or 60. If each reading is more than 10 k/ohms, go to next step if Code 97/631 was originally present, or step **8)** if Codes 47/633, 65/632 or 691 were originally present. If any reading is 10 k/ohms or less, repair short circuit. Repeat QUICK TEST. If code is still present, go to step **7)**.

6) Check Power Through TCIL Circuit – Turn ignition off. Leave PCM disconnected from breakout box. Measure voltage between test pin No. 32 and test pin No. 40 or 60. If voltage is more than 10.5 volts, replace PCM. Remove breakout box, reconnect all components, and repeat QUICK TEST. If voltage is 10.5 volts or less, go to next step.

7) Check Output Driver Voltage Signal – Leave PCM disconnected from breakout box. Turn ignition on. Measure voltage between test pin No. 32 (TCS circuit) or test pin No. 12 (4x4 low circuit) and test pin No. 40 or 60. If voltage is 2 volts or more, go to next step. If voltage is less than 2 volts, check bulb and fuse. Replace as necessary. If bulb and fuse are okay, repair open circuit. Remove breakout box, reconnect all components, and repeat QUICK TEST.

8) Check 4x4 Low Or TCS Circuit Continuity – Turn ignition off. Leave PCM disconnected from breakout box. Ensure TCS is disconnected. To test 4x4 low circuit, check continuity between breakout box test pin No. 12 and 4x4 low switch touch drive module harness connector. To test TCS circuit, measure resistance between KEY POWER terminal of fuse (No. 5 on "E" series or No.17 on Bronco/"F" series) at instrument panel fuse block and TCS wiring harness connector. Also, measure resistance between test pin No. 41 at breakout box and signal wire at TCS wiring harness connector. If any reading is 5 ohms or more, repair open circuit. Remove breakout box, reconnect all components, and repeat QUICK TEST. If each reading is less than 5 ohms, go to next step.

9) Check For Short To Power – Turn ignition off. Leave PCM disconnected from breakout box. To test TCS system, ensure TCS is disconnected. Measure resistance between test pin No. 41 and test pin 37 or 57. Also, measure resistance between test pin No. 32 and test pin No. 37 or 57.

To test 4x4 low system, ensure 4x4 low switch is disconnected. Measure resistance between test pin No. 12 and test pins No. 37/57. If each reading is more than 10 k/ohms, replace appropriate switch. Remove breakout box, reconnect all components, and repeat QUICK TEST. If any reading is 10 k/ohms or less, repair short circuit. Remove breakout box, reconnect all components, and repeat QUICK TEST.

CIRCUIT TEST TC

TRANSMISSION SOLENOIDS

Diagnostic Aids – Perform this test only when directed by QUICK TEST. To prevent replacing good components, be aware the following non-EEC areas may be at fault:
- Engine condition (compression, cam timing, valves, etc.).
- Charging system or battery.
- Transmission linkage, internal components or cooling.

This test is not intended to diagnose transmission. This test is intended to diagnose:
- Wiring harness circuits TCC, CCS, EPC, SS1, SS2, SIG RTN, EPC PWR and VPWR.
- Faulty Powertrain Control Module (PCM).

CIRCUIT TEST TC (Cont.)

CIRCUIT TEST TC ACRONYMS

Acronym	Definition
CCC	Converter Clutch Control
CCS	Coast Clutch Control
EPC	Electronic Pressure Control
MCCC	Modulated Converter Clutch Control
SS	Shift Solenoid
TCC	Torque Converter Clutch

93A40824

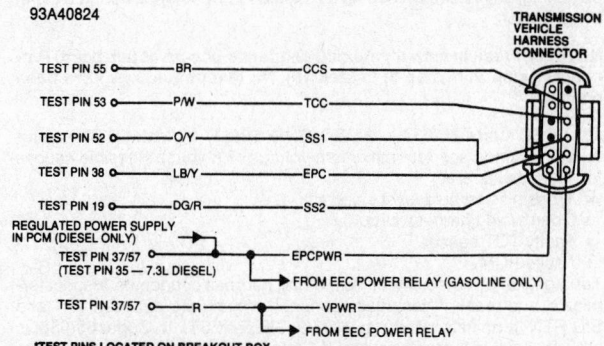

***TEST PINS LOCATED ON BREAKOUT BOX.
ALL HARNESS CONNECTORS VIEWED INTO MATING SURFACE.**

***Fig. TC1: Identifying E4OD Solenoid Circuits
(Bronco, "E" Series & "F" Series)***

E4OD DIAGNOSTIC TROUBLE CODE IDENTIFICATION

Application	PCM Pin No.	KOEO Code
EPC	38	99/624 & 625
SS1	52	91/621
SS2	19	92/622
CCS	55	93/626
TCC	53	94/629

TEST PIN NO. 35, 37 & 57 WIRE COLOR IDENTIFICATION

Application	Wire Color
4.9L, 5.0L, 5.8L & 7.5L	Red Or Red/White
7.3L Diesel	White/Red

NOTE: Procedure begins at step 10). No test procedures have been omitted.

10) Code 99/624 Or 625: Check VPWR To Solenoid – Code 624 indicates failure of EPC circuit. Code 625 indicates EPC driver failure. Possible causes for these faults are:
- Faulty solenoid.
- Circuit open or grounded.

Turn ignition off. Disconnect transmission wiring harness connector. Turn ignition on. Measure voltage between VPWR and EPC PWR terminal at transmission wiring harness connector and chassis/battery ground. If voltage is less 10.5 volts or less, repair open circuit. Reconnect all components and repeat QUICK TEST. If voltage is more than 10.5 volts, go to next step.

11) Check Solenoid Signal & VPWR Circuit Continuity – Turn ignition off. Disconnect 60-pin PCM connector. Inspect connector for damaged pins, corrosion and loose wires. Repair as necessary. Install EEC-IV Breakout Box (T83L-50-EEC-IV), leaving PCM disconnected. Measure resistance between VPWR/EPC PWR terminal at transmission wiring harness connector breakout box test pins No. 37 and 57 (All models except 7.3L diesel) or test pin No. 35 (7.3L diesel). Also, measure resistance between test pin No. 38 at breakout box and EPC terminal at transmission wiring harness connector. If resistance is 5 ohms or more, repair open circuit. Remove breakout box, reconnect all components, and repeat QUICK TEST. If resistance is less than 5 ohms, go to next step.

CIRCUIT TEST TC (Cont.)

12) Check Circuit For Short To Power Or Ground – Leave ignition off and PCM disconnected. Leave transmission wiring harness connector disconnected. Measure resistance between test pins No. 37 and 57 (All models except 7.3L diesel) or test pin No. 35 (7.3L diesel) and suspect solenoid test pin at breakout box. Also, measure resistance between test pins No. 40, 46 and 60 and suspect solenoid test pin at breakout box. If any reading is 10 k/ohms or less, repair short circuit. Remove breakout box, reconnect all components, and repeat QUICK TEST. If all readings are more than 10 k/ohms, check solenoids. If solenoids are okay, replace PCM. Remove breakout box, reconnect all components, and repeat QUICK TEST.

CIRCUIT TEST TD

MANUAL LEVER POSITION (MLP) SENSOR

Diagnostic Aids – Perform this test only when directed by QUICK TEST. To prevent replacing good components, be aware the following non-EEC areas may be at fault:
- Transmission linkage and internal components.
- Electrical (alternator, battery, add-on devices, etc.).

This test is not intended to diagnose transmission. This test is intended to diagnose:
- Wiring harness circuits MLP, TRD, TRL, TRR, TROD and SIG RTN.
- Powertrain Control Module (PCM).

93I76339

***TEST PINS LOCATED ON BREAKOUT BOX.
ALL HARNESS CONNECTORS VIEWED INTO MATING SURFACE.**

Fig. TD1: Identifying MLP Connector Terminals (E4OD)

1) Codes 67/634 & 654: Check MLP Sensor Alignment – KOEO Code 67/634 indicates MLP sensor is out of self-test range (3770-4607 ohms) when gear selector is in Park position. KOEO Codes 654 indicate gear selector was not in Park position during self-test. Possible causes for these faults are:
- Linkage not adjusted correctly.
- Faulty Manual Lever Position (MLP) sensor.
- Circuit open or grounded.
- Faulty Powertrain Control Module (PCM).

Turn ignition off. Apply parking brake. Place transmission gear selector in Neutral position. Place MLP Sensor Gauge (T91P-7010-AHT) in sensor slot. If gauge does not fit, loosen MLP mounting bolts and adjust sensor as necessary. If gauge fits, remove gauge and go to next step.

2) Check MLP Sensor Circuit Continuity – Turn ignition off. Disconnect MLP sensor wiring harness connector. Disconnect 60-pin PCM connector. Inspect connector for damaged pins, corrosion and loose wires. Repair as necessary. Install EEC-IV Breakout Box (T83L-50-EEC-IV), leaving PCM disconnected. Measure resistance between MLP terminal at MLP sensor wiring harness connector and test pin No. 30 at breakout box. Also, measure resistance between SIG RTN terminal at MLP sensor wiring harness connector and test pin No. 46 at breakout box. If any reading is 5 ohms or more, repair open circuit. Remove breakout box, reconnect all components, and repeat QUICK TEST. If both readings are less than 5 ohms, go to next step.

3) Check MLP Sensor For Short To Power & Ground – Turn ignition off. Leave PCM and MLP sensor disconnected. Measure resistance between test pin No. 30 and test pins No. 37, 57, 40, 46 and 60 at breakout box. Also, measure resistance between test pin No. 30 and chassis ground. If any reading is 10 k/ohms or less, repair short circuit. Remove breakout box, reconnect all components, and repeat QUICK TEST. If resistance is more than 10 k/ohms, go to next step.

4) Check MLP Sensor Resistance – Turn ignition off. Connect MLP sensor. Leave PCM disconnected. Unlock steering column. Measure resistance between test pins No. 30 and 46 at breakout box while cycling gear selector. See MLP SENSOR RESISTANCE table. If resistance is within specification, replace PCM and repeat QUICK TEST. If resistance is not within specification, replace MLP sensor and repeat QUICK TEST.

CIRCUIT TEST TD (Cont.)

MLP SENSOR RESISTANCE

Gear Selected	Ohms
Park	3770-4607
Reverse	1304-1593
Neutral	660-807
Overdrive	361-442
Drive	190-232
First	78-95

CIRCUIT TEST TE

TRANSMISSION OIL TEMPERATURE (TOT) SENSOR

Diagnostic Aids – Perform this test only when directed by QUICK TEST. To prevent replacing good components, be aware the following non-EEC areas may be at fault:
- Engine and/or transmission fluid level.
- Engine and/or transmission fluid temperature.
- Ambient temperature.

This test is intended to diagnose:
- TOT sensor.
- Wiring harness circuits TOT and SIG RTN.
- Faulty Powertrain Control Module (PCM).

93B76340

*TEST PIN 42
(TEST PIN 7 — 7.3L DIESEL) O——— O/BK ——— TOT
TEST PIN 46 O——— GY/R ——— SIG RTN

*TEST PINS LOCATED ON BREAKOUT BOX.
ALL HARNESS CONNECTORS VIEWED INTO MATING SURFACE.

E4OD TRANSMISSION VEHICLE HARNESS CONNECTOR

Fig. TE1: Transmission Oil Temperature (TOT) Sensor Circuit (E4OD)

TOT SENSOR (E4OD) SPECIFICATIONS

Temperature °F (°C)	[1] Volts	[1] Ohms
32 (0)	3.88	96,255
59 (15)	3.32	46,883
104 (40)	2.15	16,043
158 (60)	1.03	5260
194 (90)	0.60	2750

[1] – Values may vary by 15 percent.

1) **KOEO Code 26/636** – KOEO Code 26/636 indicate TOT sensor is out of self-test range. Possible causes for these faults are:
- Transmission fluid level incorrect.
- Transmission fluid temperature incorrect.
- Sensor resistance out of specification.
- Faulty Powertrain Control Module (PCM).

Ensure transmission fluid temperature is more than 50°F (10°C). Repeat QUICK TEST. If Code 26/636 is present, go to next. If Code 26/636 is not present, no problem is indicated at this time. Test is complete.

2) **Check VREF At Throttle Position (TP) Sensor** – Turn ignition off. Disconnect TP sensor wiring harness connector. Disconnect 60-pin PCM connector. Inspect connector for damaged pins, corrosion and loose wires. Repair as necessary. Install EEC-IV Breakout Box (T83L-50-EEC-IV). Connect PCM to breakout box. Turn ignition on. Measure voltage between VREF and SIG RTN terminals at TP sensor wiring harness connector. *See Fig. DH1.* If voltage is 4-6 volts, go to next step. If voltage is not 4-6 volts, go to CIRCUIT TEST CA.

CIRCUIT TEST TE (Cont.)

3) **Check TOT Sensor Resistance** – Turn ignition off. Disconnect PCM from breakout box. Allow transmission to cool. Measure and record resistance between test pin No. 46 and TOT test pin at breakout box. Reconnect PCM. Drive vehicle until transmission fluid is normal operating temperature. Disconnect PCM from breakout box. Measure resistance voltage between test pin No. 46 and TOT test pin at breakout box. If cold resistance measurement is higher than warm resistance measurement, and warm resistance is within specification, replace PCM and repeat QUICK TEST. See TOT SENSOR SPECIFICATIONS table at beginning of this circuit test. If resistance is not as specified, fault is in transmission.

NOTE: A break in step numbering sequence occurs at this point. Procedure skips from step 3) to step 10). No test procedures have been omitted.

10) **KOEO Code 56/637** – KOEO Code 56/637 indicates TOT sensor output exceeds self-test maximum voltage (4.8 volts). Possible causes for these faults are:
- Transmission fluid level incorrect.
- Open wiring harness circuit.
- Faulty TOT sensor.
- Faulty PCM.

Turn ignition off. Disconnect TOT wiring harness connector. Inspect terminals, and repair if damaged. Connect jumper wire between TOT and SIG RTN terminals. Perform KOEO SELF-TEST. If Code 66/638 is present, fault is in transmission. If Code 66/638 is not present, remove jumper wire and go to next step.

11) **Check TOT & SIG RTN Circuit Continuity** – Turn ignition off. Leave TOT sensor disconnected. Disconnect 60-pin PCM connector. Inspect connector for damaged pins, corrosion and loose wires. Repair as necessary. Install EEC-IV Breakout Box (T83L-50-EEC-IV), leaving PCM disconnected. Measure resistance between TOT circuit at TOT wiring harness connector and TOT test pin at breakout box. Also, measure resistance between SIG RTN circuit at TOT wiring harness connector and test pin No. 46 at breakout box. If any reading 5 ohms or more, repair open circuit. Remove breakout box, reconnect all components, and repeat QUICK TEST. If all readings are less than 5 ohms, go to next step.

12) **Check TOT Sensor For Short To VPWR** – Turn ignition off. Leave PCM and TOT sensor disconnected. Measure resistance between TOT test pin and test pins No. 37 and 57 at breakout box. If all readings are more than 10 k/ohms, replace PCM. Remove breakout box, reconnect all components, and repeat QUICK TEST. If any reading is 10 k/ohms or less, repair short circuit. Remove breakout box, reconnect all components, and repeat QUICK TEST.

CIRCUIT TEST TG

ELECTRONIC TRANSMISSION CONTINUOUS MEMORY DIAGNOSTIC TROUBLE CODES

Diagnostic Aids – Perform this test only when directed by QUICK TEST. To prevent replacing good components, be aware the following non-EEC areas may be at fault:
- Transmission fluid level.
- Engine/transmission fluid temperature.
- Ambient temperature.
- Faulty wiring harness connectors.

This test is intended to diagnose:
- Wiring harness circuits CCS, SS1, SS2, EPC, TCC, TOT, and MLP.
- Powertrain Control Module (PCM).

CIRCUIT TEST TG (Cont.)

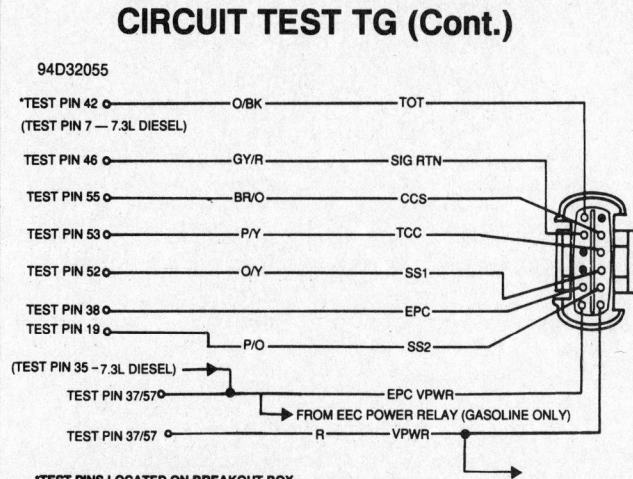

Fig. TG1: Identifying E4OD Transmission Circuit & Wiring Connector Terminals (Bronco, "E" Series, "F" Series)

TEST PINS NO. 35 & 37/57 WIRE COLOR IDENTIFICATION

Application	Wire Color
7.3L Diesel	White/Red
All Other Models	Red

TEST PINS NO. 38 WIRE COLOR IDENTIFICATION

Application	Wire Color
4.9L "E" Series	White
All Other Models	White/Yellow

NOTE: Procedure begins with step 90). No test procedures have been omitted.

90) Perform Drive Cycle Test – Ensure all components are connected. Ensure transmission fluid is correct level. Warm engine to normal operating temperature. Perform KOEO and CONTINUOUS MEMORY CODE SELF-TEST. Clear all codes. Perform DRIVE CYCLE TEST.

Drive Cycle Test (E4OD) – With transmission gear selector in Drive position, press Transmission Control Switch (TCS). Transmission Control Indicator Light (TCIL) should come on. Moderately accelerate vehicle to 40 MPH for at least 15 seconds (30 seconds above 4000' elevation). Transmission should be in 3rd gear. While holding speed steady, press TCS. TCIL should go off. Accelerate from 40 MPH to 50 MPH. Transmission should shift from 3rd gear to 4th gear. Hold speed steady for 15 seconds. While holding speed steady, lightly apply and release brakes to turn brakelights on. Maintain 50 MPH for about 5 seconds. Stop and park vehicle for a minimum of 20 seconds with transmission gear selector in Drive position. Repeat procedure 5 times. After completing drive cycle test, perform KOEO and CONTINUOUS MEMORY CODE SELF-TEST. If Code 111 is present, fault cannot be duplicated at this time. If Code 99/624, 67/634 or 651 is present, go to next step. If Code 29/452 is present, go to CIRCUIT TEST DS. If Code 659, 667, 668 or 675 is present, go to step **93)**. If any other code(s) is present, go to step **92)**.

91) Code 99/624, 67/634 Or 651 – Code 99/624 and 651 indicate Electronic Pressure Control (EPC) failure. Code 67/634 indicates that Manual Lever Position (MLP) sensor is out of calibration. Possible causes for these faults are:
- Faulty EPC solenoid.
- Faulty MLP sensor.
- Circuit open or grounded.
- Damaged PCM connector pins.

Turn ignition off. Disconnect 60-pin PCM connector. Inspect connector for damaged pins, corrosion and loose wires. Repair as necessary. Install EEC-IV Breakout Box (T83L-50-EEC-IV). Connect PCM to breakout box. To test EPC solenoid, connect DVOM to EPC test pin and EPC VPWR test pin at breakout box. To test MLP sensor, connect DVOM to MLP test pin and test pin No. 46 at breakout box. For EPC solenoid and MLP sensor, turn ignition on. Voltage for EPC should be less than 10 volts. Voltage for MLP should be less than 5 volts. Shake and

CIRCUIT TEST TG (Cont.)

bend EPC/MLP wiring harness. Lightly tap on components to simulate road shock. Voltage should remain stable. If voltage changes or exceeds specification, fault in circuit is indicated. If fault is indicated, isolate and repair as necessary. Clear continuous memory codes, and repeat QUICK TEST. If no faults are found, problem cannot be located at this time.

92) Check Circuit Harness & Connectors – Enter CONTINUOUS MONITOR MODE. Shake and bend EEC wiring harness while observing analog VOM or scan tool. Lightly tap on components to simulate road shock. If VOM indicator has erratic movement or scan tool beep, fault is indicated. If fault is indicated, isolate and repair as necessary. Clear continuous memory codes, and repeat QUICK TEST. If no faults are found, problem cannot be located at this time.

CIRCUIT TEST KOEO CONTINUOUS MEMORY CODES

Code	Fault
49/617	Improper 1-2 Shift
59/618	Improper 2-3 Shift
69/619	Improper 3-4 Shift
62/628	Excessive Converter Clutch Slippage
66/638	Inadequate TOT Circuit Voltage
645	Inadequate 1st Gear Command Response
646	Inadequate 2nd Gear Command Response
647	Inadequate 3rd Gear Command Response
648	Inadequate 4th Gear Command Response
656	Continuous Slippage Detected

93) Check For Code 659 – Code 659 indicates high vehicle speed detected while vehicle was in Park. Possible causes for this fault are:
- Faulty Manual Lever Position (MLP) sensor.
- Faulty Powertrain Control Module (PCM)

If Code 659 was present after performing drive cycle test in step **90)**, go to step **103)**. If Code 659 was not present after performing drive cycle test in step **90)**, go to next step.

94) Check For Code 675 – Code 675 indicates MLP circuit voltage was out of range. Possible causes for this fault are:
- Faulty MLP sensor.
- Open or short circuit.
- Short to power or ground in SIG RTN circuit.
- Faulty Powertrain Control Module (PCM).

If Code 675 was present after performing drive cycle test in step **90)**, go to next step. If Code 675 was not present after performing drive cycle test in step **90)**, go to step **98)**.

95) Check For Codes 675 & 667 – Code 667 indicates MLP circuit voltage was less than self-test minimum voltage allowed. Possible causes for this fault are:
- Faulty MLP sensor.
- Open or short in MLP circuit.
- Short to power in MLP circuit.
- Faulty Powertrain Control Module (PCM).

If Codes 675 and 667 were present after performing drive cycle test in step **90)**, go to step **99)**. If Codes 675 and 667 were not present after performing drive cycle test in step **90)**, go to next step.

96) Check For Codes 675 & 668 – Code 668 indicates MLP circuit voltage was more than self-test maximum voltage allowed. Possible causes for this fault are:
- Faulty MLP sensor.
- Open MLP circuit.
- Short to power in SIG RTN circuit.
- Faulty Powertrain Control Module (PCM).

If Codes 675 and 668 were present after performing drive cycle test in step **90)**, go to step **101)**. If Codes 675 and 668 were not present after performing drive cycle test in step **90)**, go to next step.

97) Check MLP Alignment – Turn ignition off. Apply parking brake. Place transmission gear selector in Neutral position. Place MLP Sensor Gauge (T91P-7010-AHT) in sensor slot. If gauge does not fit, loosen MLP mounting bolts and adjust sensor as necessary. Clear codes and repeat QUICK TEST. If gauge fits, remove gauge and go to next step.

98) Check For Code 667 – Code 667 indicates MLP circuit voltage less than self-test minimum voltage allowed. Possible causes for this fault are:
- Faulty MLP sensor.
- Open or short to ground in MLP circuit.
- Faulty Powertrain Control Module (PCM).

If Code 667 was present after performing drive cycle test in step **90)**, go to next step. If Code 667 was not present after performing drive cycle test in step **90)**, go to step **101)**.

CIRCUIT TEST TG (Cont.)

99) Check MLP Circuit Resistance – Turn ignition off. Disconnect 60-pin PCM connector. Disconnect MLP sensor. Inspect connectors for damaged pins, corrosion and loose wires. Repair as necessary. Install EEC-IV Breakout Box (T83L-50-EEC-IV), leaving PCM disconnected. Measure resistance between test pin No. 30 at breakout box and MLP terminal at MLP sensor connector. If resistance is less than 5 ohms, go to next step. If resistance is 5 ohms or more, repair open circuit. Remove breakout box, reconnect all components, and repeat QUICK TEST.

100) Check For Short To Ground In MLP Circuit – Turn ignition off. Ensure breakout box is installed and MLP sensor and PCM are disconnected. Measure resistance between test pin No. 30 and chassis ground. If resistance is more than 10 k/ohms, go to step **103)**. If resistance is 10 k/ohms or less, repair short circuit. Remove breakout box, reconnect all components, and repeat QUICK TEST.

101) Code 668 – Code 668 indicates MLP circuit voltage was more than self-test maximum voltage allowed. Possible causes for this fault are:
- Faulty MLP sensor.
- Open MLP circuit.
- Faulty MLP sensor circuit.
- Faulty Powertrain Control Module (PCM).

Turn ignition off. Disconnect 60-pin PCM connector. Disconnect MLP sensor. Inspect connectors for damaged pins, corrosion and loose wires. Repair as necessary. Install EEC-IV Breakout Box (T83L-50-EEC-IV), leaving PCM disconnected. Measure resistance between test pins No. 46 at breakout box and SIG RTN terminal at MLP sensor connector. If resistance is less than 5 ohms, go to next step. If resistance is 5 ohms or more, repair open circuit. Remove breakout box, reconnect all components, and repeat QUICK TEST.

102) Check For Short To Power – Ensure PCM and MLP sensor are disconnected. Measure resistance between test pin No. 30 and test pins No. 37, 40, 46, 57 and 60 at breakout box. If all readings are more than 10 k/ohms, go to next step. If any reading is 10 k/ohms or less, repair short circuit. Remove breakout box, reconnect all components, and repeat QUICK TEST.

103) Check MLP Sensor Resistance – Turn ignition off. Connect MLP sensor. Leave PCM disconnected. Unlock steering column. Measure resistance between test pins No. 30 and 46 at breakout box while cycling gear selector. See MLP SENSOR RESISTANCE table. If resistance is within specification, replace PCM and repeat QUICK TEST. If resistance is not within specification, replace MLP sensor and repeat QUICK TEST.

MLP SENSOR RESISTANCE

Gear Selected	Ohms
Park	3770-4607
Reverse	1304-1593
Neutral	660-807
Overdrive	361-442
2/Drive	190-232
First	78-95

WIRING DIAGRAMS

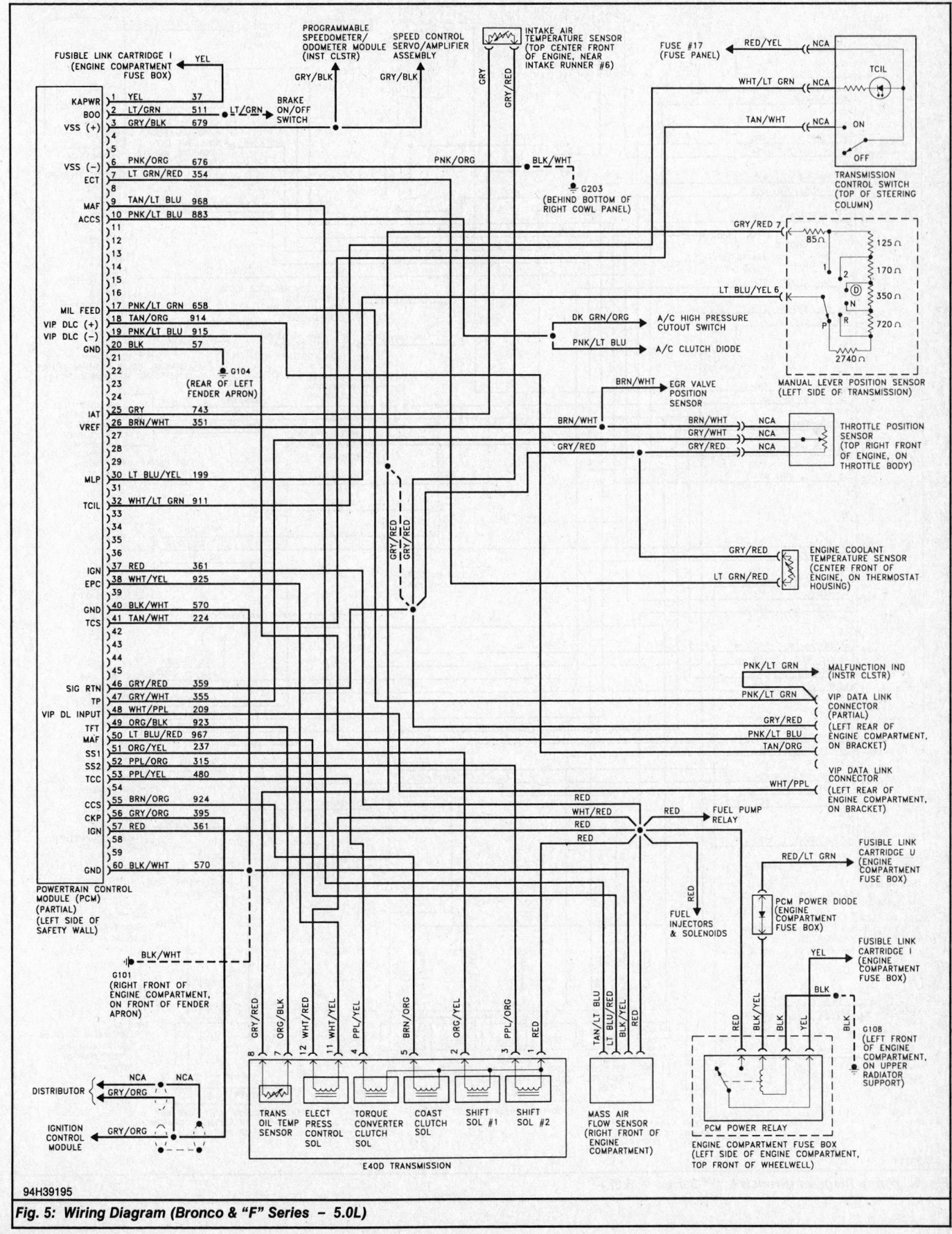

94H39195

Fig. 5: Wiring Diagram (Bronco & "F" Series - 5.0L)

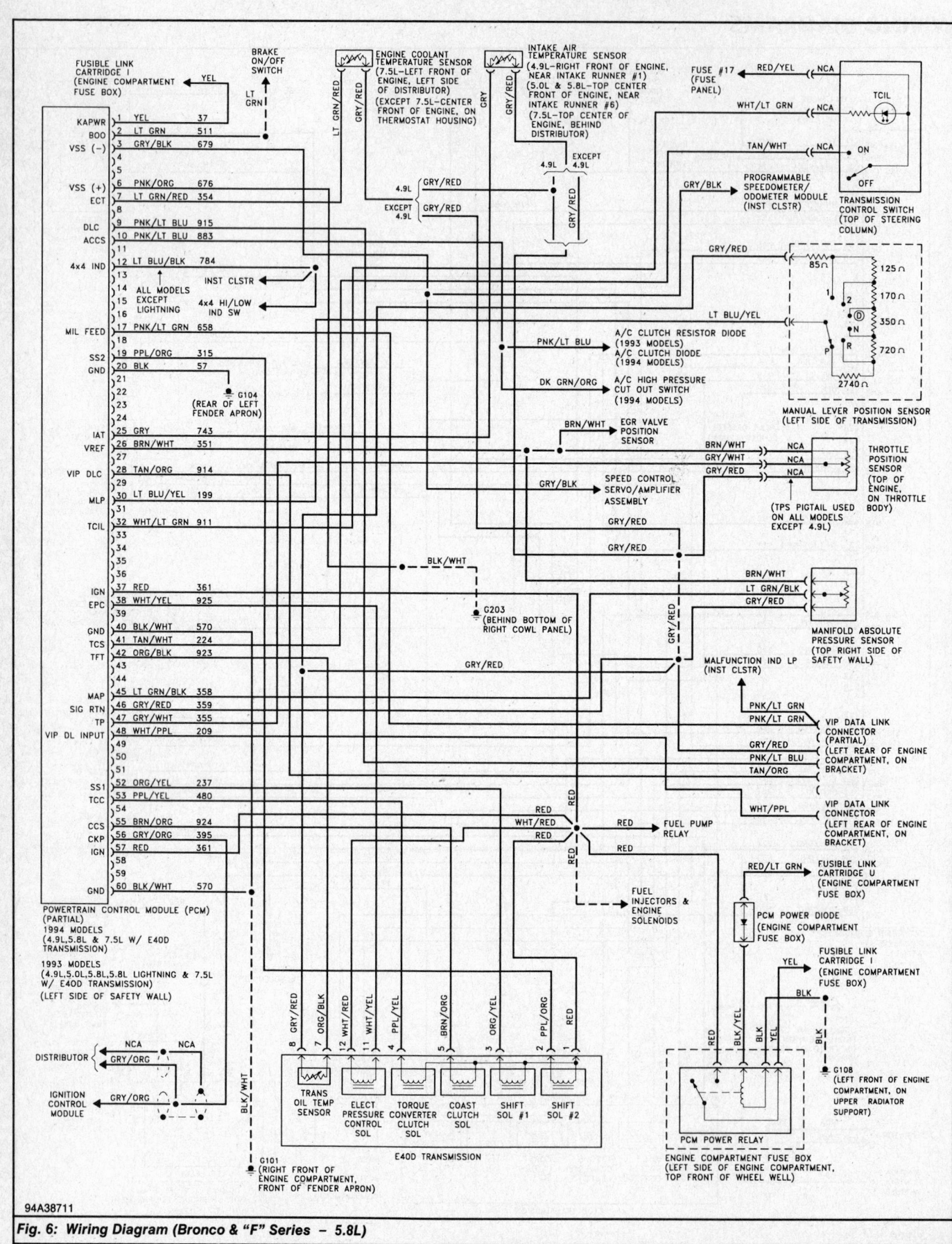

Fig. 6: Wiring Diagram (Bronco & "F" Series – 5.8L)

94A38711

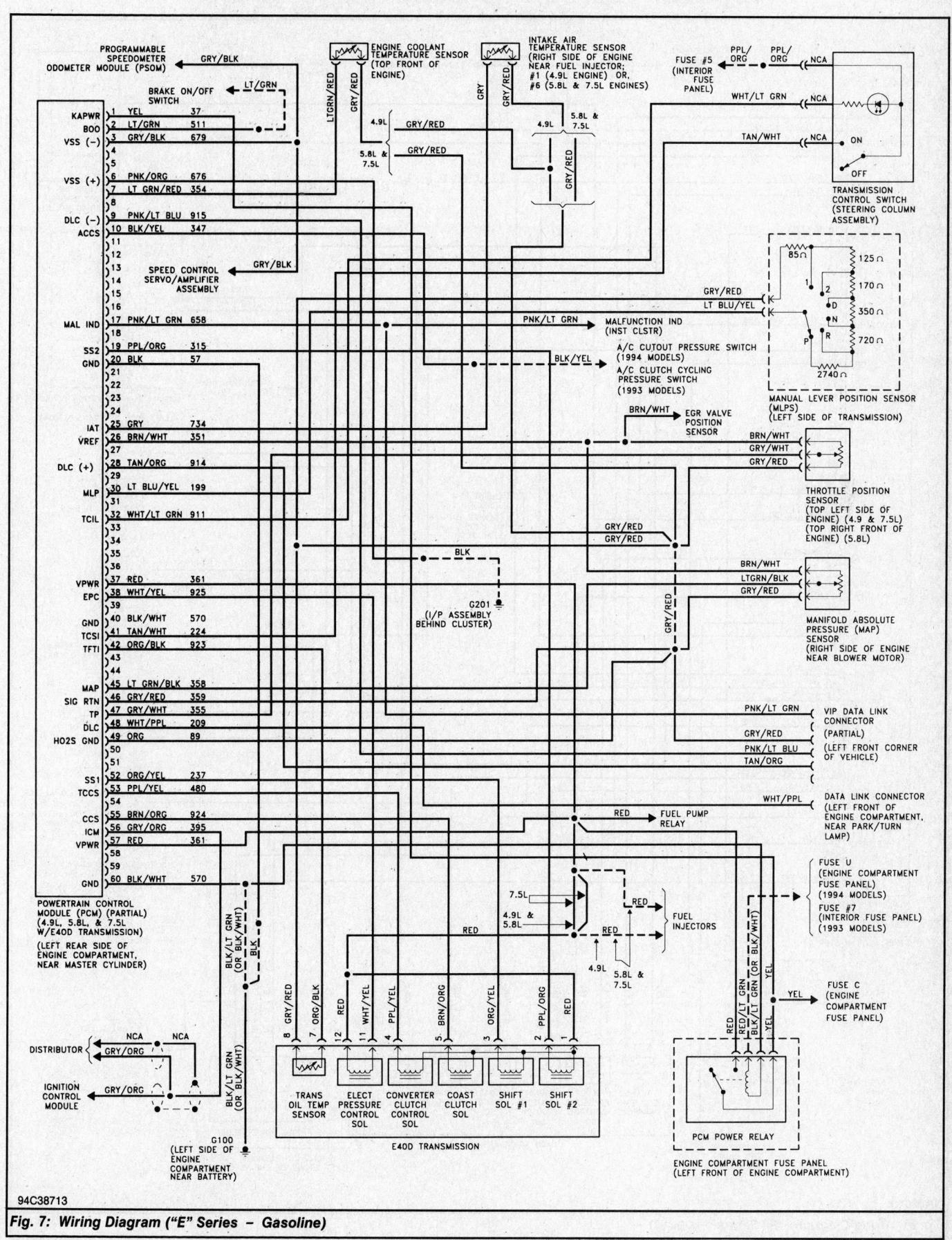

Fig. 7: Wiring Diagram ("E" Series - Gasoline)

94C38713

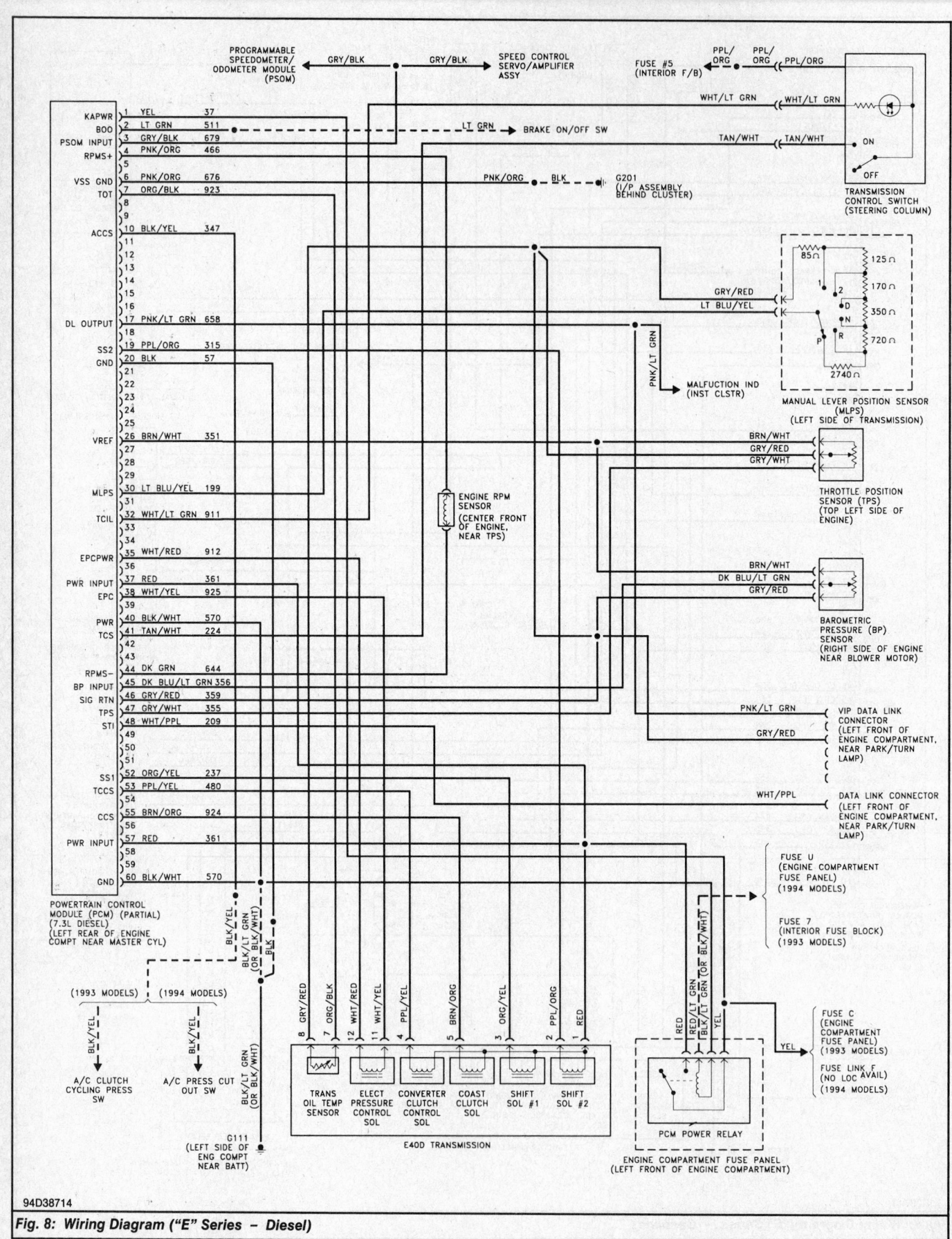

Fig. 8: Wiring Diagram ("E" Series – Diesel)

94D38714

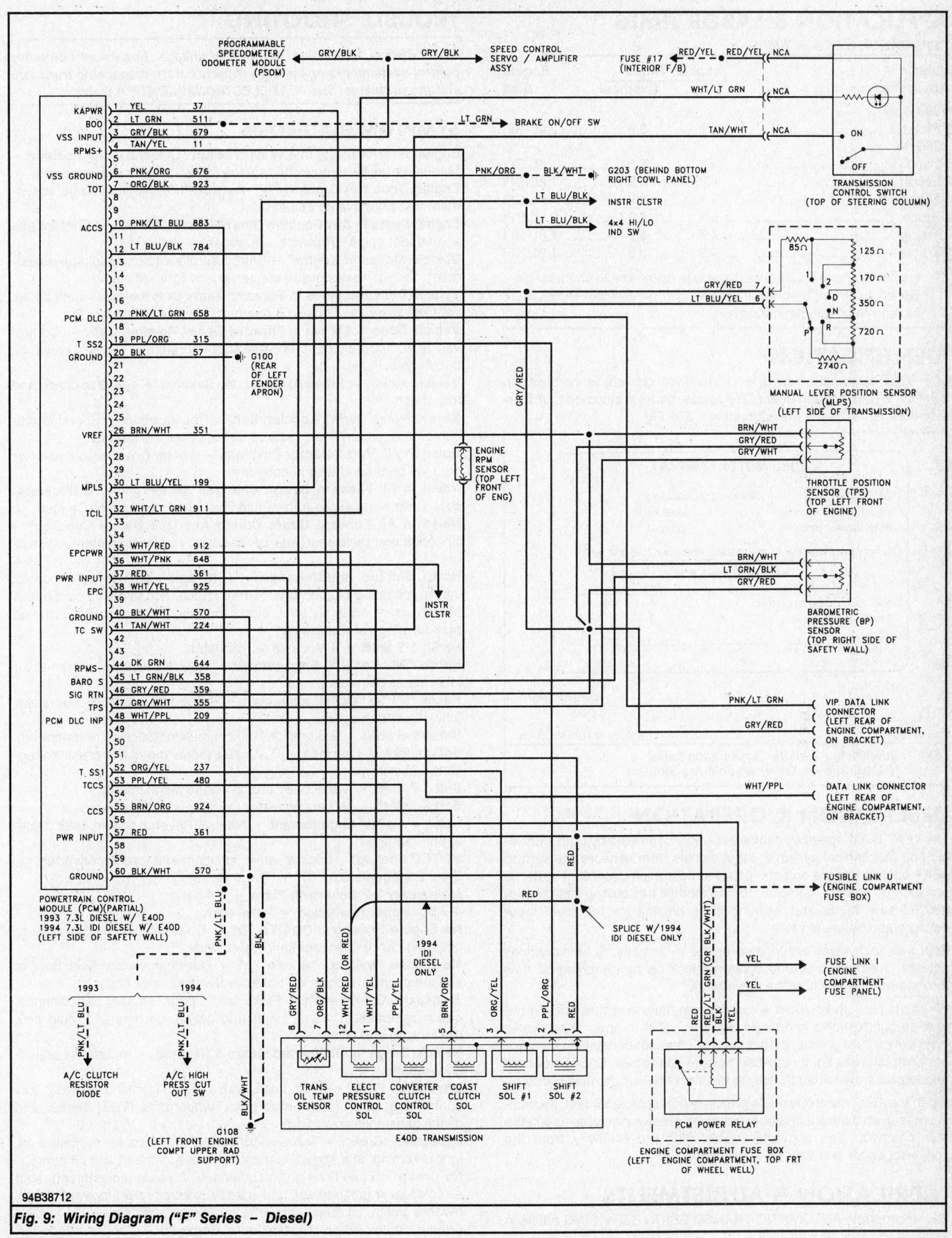

Fig. 9: Wiring Diagram ("F" Series – Diesel)

94B38712

AUTOMATIC TRANSMISSIONS
Ford 4EAT

APPLICATION & LABOR TIMES

APPLICATION & LABOR TIMES

Vehicle Application	Labor Times [1] R & I	[2] Overhaul	Engine Size
1993 Only			
Probe	4.8	8.9	2.0L SFI
1993-94			
Capri	3.9	8.9	1.6L SFI
Escort	4.7	8.9	1.8L SFI
Escort	4.9	8.9	1.9L SFI
Probe	5.1	8.9	2.5L SFI
Tracer	4.7	8.9	1.8L SFI
Tracer	4.9	8.9	1.9L SFI

[1] – Removal and installation of transaxle from vehicle chassis.
[2] – Bench overhaul time for transaxle and differential. DOES NOT include removal and installation.

IDENTIFICATION

The 4EAT automatic transaxle is identified on vehicle certification label by "E" designation under "TR" space. Label is attached to driver-side door jamb, below the latch striker. *See Fig. 1.*

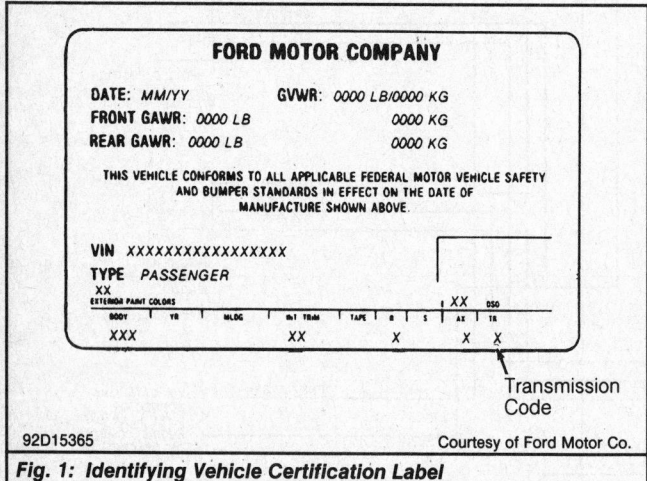

FORD MOTOR COMPANY

DATE: *MM/YY*   GVWR: *0000 LB/0000 KG*
FRONT GAWR: *0000 LB*   *0000 KG*
REAR GAWR: *0000 LB*   *0000 KG*

THIS VEHICLE CONFORMS TO ALL APPLICABLE FEDERAL MOTOR VEHICLE SAFETY AND BUMPER STANDARDS IN EFFECT ON THE DATE OF MANUFACTURE SHOWN ABOVE.

VIN *XXXXXXXXXXXXXXXX*
TYPE *PASSENGER*

Transmission Code

92D15365   Courtesy of Ford Motor Co.

Fig. 1: Identifying Vehicle Certification Label (Capri Shown; Other Models Are Similar)

DESCRIPTION & OPERATION

The 4EAT is a 4-speed transaxle assembly controlled by both electronic and mechanical systems. Input signals from sensors are sent to 4EAT control module and computed to determine gear, shift patterns and lock-up timing. The 4EAT control module has built-in self-diagnosis, fail-safe mode and warning code display for the main input sensors and solenoid valves.

Four solenoid valves are located on the valve body. Solenoid valves actuate shifting and torque converter lock-up by switching oil flow through passages within the valve body.

When the lock-up solenoid is switched on, fluid pressure holding the lock-up control valve is drained, allowing valve to open. When valve opens, hydraulic pressure from the rear chamber causes the converter clutch to press tightly against the converter cover. Lock-up occurs and force is transmitted directly to the transaxle with no fluid slippage.

When the 4EAT control module switches lock-up solenoid off, hydraulic pressure in the front chamber becomes greater than pressure in the rear chamber. The converter clutch then moves away from the converter cover and lock-up is released.

LUBRICATION & ADJUSTMENTS

See appropriate AUTOMATIC TRANSMISSION SERVICING article in TRANSMISSION SERVICING.

TROUBLE SHOOTING

NOTE: Always check fluid levels and linkage. Ensure all computer control systems are operating properly before diagnosing transaxle shifting problems. See 4EAT ELECTRONIC CONTROLS article.

SYMPTOM DIAGNOSIS

Engine Will Not Crank In Any Shift Control Selector Lever Position – Manual Lever Position (MLP) switch malfunction or disconnected.

Engine Does Not Crank In "P" And/Or "N" – Shift linkage adjustment and MLP switch adjustment.

Engine Starts In Any Position Other Than "P" Or "N" – Shift linkage adjustment and MLP switch adjustment.

Vehicle Moves In Neutral – Shift control selector or linkage adjustment, control valve, torque converter and forward clutch.

Vehicle Does Not Move In Forward Gears Or Reverse – Shift cable, control valves, fluid level, oil pump and torque converter.

Vehicle Does Not Move In Forward Gears, Reverse Okay – Control valves, forward clutch, one-way clutch (sprag) and forward clutch oil supply (blocked).

Vehicle Moves In Forward Gears, No Reverse – Reverse clutch and low clutch.

Severe Noise During Acceleration Or Deceleration – Speedometer cable, torque converter, reverse clutch or engine mounts.

Noise In All Shift Selector Positions – Loose flywheel-to-converter nuts, oil pump and torque converter.

Noise In All Forward Gears, Changes Acceleration To Deceleration – Differential assembly, fluid level and front axle or CV joint.

Noise In All Forward Gears During Any Operational Condition – Speedometer drive gear, internal bearings and front planetary assembly.

Harsh Shifting In All Ranges – T.V. cable (adjustment), control valves, coasting clutch, low/reverse clutch, accumulator piston, 3-4 clutch, axle shaft or CV joint, motor mounts, 2-4 band and servo, and pressure regulator (sticking).

Harsh 1-2 Shift – T.V. cable (adjustment).

Harsh "N" To "R" Engagement – Neutral/Reverse accumulator (sticking or damaged).

Harsh "N" To "OD" Engagement – Neutral/Overdrive accumulator (sticking or damaged).

Harsh 2-3 Shift – 2-3 and/or 1-2 accumulator (sticking or damaged).

Soft Shifts In All Ranges – T.V. cable (adjustment) and pressure regulator (sticking).

Soft 1-2 Shift – Valve body and 2-4 band (adjustment).

Soft 2-3 Shift – 2-3 accumulator (sticking) and valve body.

Soft "N" To "R" Engagement – Neutral/Reverse accumulator (sticking or damaged).

No TCC Lockup – Lockup valve (sticking) and torque converter.

Slow Engagement In "R" – Reverse clutch.

Momentary 3-2 Downshift Flare – 2-4 band.

3-2 Downshift Hesitation – Valve body.

No Engine Braking - "OD" To "D" – Coasting clutch, fluid flow to coasting clutch (blockage) and valve body.

No Engine Braking - "D" To "L" – Coasting clutch, fluid flow to coasting clutch (blockage), control valve and valve body.

Transaxle Overheating – Fluid level, poor engine performance, clutch assemblies (worn), band application, oil pressure, fluid flow (restriction) and oil cooler.

Vehicle Drags In All Forward Gears & Reverse – Incorrectly adjusted 2-4 band.

Upshifting Flare – Fluid level, valve body (sticking valves), low control pressure, Transmission Oil Temperature (TOT) sensor and clutch assemblies (slipping).

Excessive Creep – Torque converter, T.V. cable (adjustment), ignition timing, idle speed, manual valve (adjustment) and oil pump.

No Creep – Fluid level and condition, T.V. cable (adjustment), shift selector lever (adjustment), valve body, control valve, forward clutch, reverse clutch, oil pump and vehicle brake adjustment.

Engine Stalls When Transaxle Is Engaged – Torque converter, valve body, control valve and oil pump.

No Kickdown – Valve body.
Poor Performance – Torque converter, TCC solenoid and reverse clutch.

CLUTCH & BAND APPLICATION

CLUTCH & BAND APPLICATION

Selector Lever Application	Elements In Use
"P" & "N"	No Elements
"R" (Reverse)	Low/Reverse Clutch & Reverse Clutch
"D" (Drive) [1]	
1st Gear	Forward Clutch, One-Way Clutch (Sprag) & One-Way Clutch (Roller)
2nd Gear	Low/Intermediate Band, Forward Clutch & One-Way Clutch (Sprag)
3rd Gear	Coasting Clutch, Forward Clutch, 3-4 Clutch & One-Way Clutch (Sprag)
4th Gear	Low/Intermediate Band, 3-4 Clutch, Forward Clutch & One-Way Clutch (Sprag)
"2"	Low/Intermediate Band, Forward Clutch, One-Way Clutch (Sprag) & Coasting Clutch
"1"	Forward Clutch, One-Way Clutch (Sprag), Coasting Clutch, Low/Reverse Clutch & One-Way Clutch (Roller)

TESTING

Perform Preliminary Inspection – Inspect fluid level and condition. Visually inspect for vehicle modifications, electronic add-ons, fluid leaks and/or incorrect linkage adjustment. Check for trouble codes before any mechanical repair is performed. See 4EAT ELECTRONIC CONTROLS article for trouble code diagnosis and repair procedures. If no trouble codes are present, see applicable symptom diagnosis.

LINE PRESSURE TEST

CAUTION: Do not allow engine to run at maximum stall speed for more than 5 seconds. Run engine in "N" for one minute to cool transmission after each test is completed.

1) Block wheels. Connect tachometer to engine. Connect appropriate pressure gauge to line pressure port (square head plug, marked "L"). *See Figs. 2 and 3.*
2) Run engine until normal operating temperature is obtained. Ensure engine is idling within specification. Consult underhood emissions label. Shift transaxle to "OD" or "D" as applicable and record line pressure. Firmly apply brake pedal. Steadily increase engine RPM to maximum speed and record line pressure (when engine speed stabilizes). Release accelerator. DO NOT allow engine to operate at full stall speed for more than 5-second limit.
3) Repeat step 2) for each gear. Before shifting into each selector position, run engine in Neutral for one minute to cool transmission. If line pressure is within specification, go to THROTTLE PRESSURE TEST. See LINE PRESSURE SPECIFICATIONS. If line pressure is not within specification, go to LINE PRESSURE TEST RESULTS.

LINE PRESSURE SPECIFICATIONS (PSI)

Selector Position	@ Idle RPM PSI (kPa)	@ WOT Stall RPM PSI (kPa)
Capri, Escort & Tracer		
"R"	85-107 (586-738)	220-253 (1517-1744)
"OD", "D" & "L"	53-65 (365-448)	136-155 (938-1068)
Probe		
"R"	110-146 (758-1006)	276-294 (1903-2027)
"D" & "L"	60-78 (413-538)	160-170 (1103-1172)

LINE PRESSURE TEST RESULTS

Ensure line pressure is correctly adjusted. See LINE PRESSURE ADJUSTMENT under ON-VEHICLE SERVICE. If line pressure cannot be adjusted to specification, use following list to determine cause of trouble.

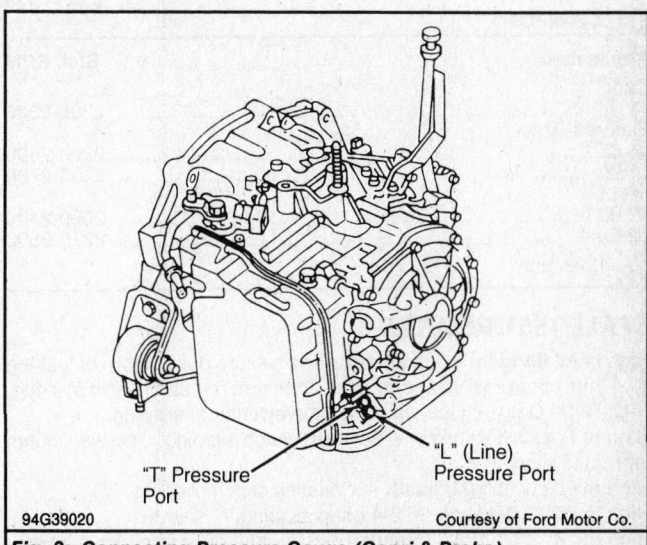

"T" Pressure Port
"L" (Line) Pressure Port
94G39020
Courtesy of Ford Motor Co.

Fig. 2: Connecting Pressure Gauge (Capri & Probe)

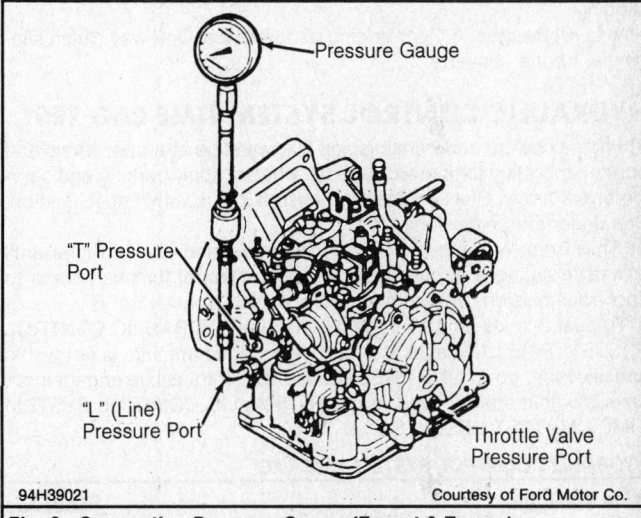

Pressure Gauge
"T" Pressure Port
"L" (Line) Pressure Port
Throttle Valve Pressure Port
94H39021
Courtesy of Ford Motor Co.

Fig. 3: Connecting Pressure Gauge (Escort & Tracer)

Low In All Ranges – Worn oil pump, leaking oil pump, valve body and/or case. Pressure regulator valve sticking.
Low In "OD" & "D" – Fluid leaking from reverse clutch.
Low In "R" Only – Fluid leaking from low and reverse band.
High In All Ranges – Throttle valve sticking. Throttle modulator valve sticking. Pressure regulator valve sticking.

STALL TEST

CAUTION: Do not allow engine to run at maximum stall speed for more than 5 seconds. Run engine in "N" for one minute to cool transmission after each test is completed.

1) Engine coolant and transmission fluid must be at proper levels and normal operating temperatures. Connect tachometer to engine. Apply parking and service brakes firmly. Block wheels and place selector in "R" position.
2) While observing tachometer, steadily increase engine RPM to maximum speed and release within 5 seconds. DO NOT exceed 5-second limit. Engine speed should be within specification. See STALL SPEEDS table.
3) Run engine in Neutral for one minute to cool transmission. Repeat procedure in each gear. If engine speed is not within specification, release accelerator immediately. See STALL TEST RESULTS. If engine speed is within specification, go to HYDRAULIC CONTROL SYSTEM TIME LAG TEST.

STALL SPEEDS

Application	Stall RPM
Capri	
1.6L	2200-2500
Escort & Tracer	
1.8L	2200-2500
1.9L	2400-2700
Probe	
2.0L [1]	2090-2400
2.5L	2270-2500

[1] – 1993 Only.

STALL TEST RESULTS

High In All Ranges – Insufficient line pressure due to worn or leaking oil pump, control valve and/or case. Pressure regulator valve sticking.

High "OD" Only – One-way clutch (overrunning) slipping.

High In Forward Ranges – Forward clutch slipping. One-way clutch (sprag) is slipping.

High In "D" & "L" (Manual) – Coasting clutch slipping.

High In "OD" (Manual) – 2-4 band slipping.

High In "R", "L" & "L" (Manual) – Low and reverse clutch slipping.

High In "R" – Low and reverse clutch slipping. Reverse clutch slipping.

Low In All Ranges – Poor engine performance. One-way clutch slipping in torque converter.

HYDRAULIC CONTROL SYSTEM TIME LAG TEST

1) Engine coolant and transmission fluid must be at proper levels and normal operating temperature. Block wheels, apply parking and service brake firmly. Start engine, and ensure idle is within specification. See underhood emissions label.

2) Shift from "N" range to "OD" while measuring elapsed time until transaxle engages in gear. Run engine in Neutral for one minute to cool transmission. Repeat procedure shifting from "N" to "R".

3) Repeat 3 times, and average results. See HYDRAULIC CONTROL SYSTEM TIME LAG table. If transaxle engagement time is not within specification, go to LINE PRESSURE TEST. If transaxle engagement time is within specification, go to HYDRAULIC CONTROL SYSTEM TIME LAG TEST RESULTS.

HYDRAULIC CONTROL SYSTEM TIME LAG

Gear Selection	[1] Seconds
Capri, Escort (1993) & Tracer (1993)	
"N" To "OD"	.5-.6
"N" To "R"	.6-.7
Escort (1994), Probe & Tracer (1994)	
"N" To "OD"	.9
"N" To "R"	1.1

[1] – If transaxle engagement is below specification, go to LINE PRESSURE TEST.

HYDRAULIC CONTROL SYSTEM TIME LAG TEST RESULTS

"N" To "OD" High – Insufficient line pressure. Forward clutch or one-way clutch (sprag) slipping & one-way clutch (overrunning) slipping.

"N" To "OD" Selection High – N-D accumulator faulty. Excessive line pressure.

"N" To "OD" (Manual) Selection High – Insufficient line pressure. Forward clutch, 2-4 band or one-way clutch (sprag) slipping.

"N" To "OD" (Manual) Selection Low – 1-2 accumulator faulty. Excessive line pressure.

"N" To "R" Selection High – Insufficient line pressure. Low and reverse clutch or reverse clutch slipping.

"N" To "R" Selection Low – N-R accumulator faulty. Excessive line pressure.

THROTTLE PRESSURE TEST

CAUTION: DO NOT allow engine to run at maximum stall speed for more than 5 seconds. Run engine in "N" for one minute to cool transmission after each test is completed.

NOTE: Stall test procedure is not conducted on Probe.

1) Connect tachometer to engine. Connect gauge and adapter to throttle valve pressure port (square head plug "T"). *See Figs. 2 and 3.*

2) Start engine and ensure engine idle is within specification. See underhood emission label. On Probe model, shift transaxle to "P" and record throttle pressure at idle. On all other models, shift to transaxle to "OD" or "D" and record throttle pressure at idle. On all models except Probe, firmly apply brake pedal. Steadily increase engine RPM to maximum speed and record line pressure (when engine speed stabilizes). Release accelerator. DO NOT allow engine to operate at full stall speed for more than 5-second limit.

3) Repeat step 2) for each gear. Before shifting into each selector position, run engine in Neutral for one minute to cool transmission. If throttle pressure is within specification, go to SHIFT POINT ROAD TEST. See THROTTLE PRESSURE SPECIFICATIONS. If throttle pressure is not within specification, go to THROTTLE PRESSURE TEST RESULTS.

THROTTLE PRESSURE SPECIFICATIONS (PSI)

Selector Position	@ Idle RPM	@ WOT Stall RPM
Capri, Escort & Tracer		
"OD" Or "D"	5-15	78-96
Probe		
"P"	52-58	Not Applicable

THROTTLE PRESSURE TEST RESULTS

Too High Or Low – Throttle valve (sticking), pressure regulator valve and improperly adjusted throttle cable.

SHIFT POINT ROAD TEST

1) Ensure engine and transaxle is at normal operating temperature. Road test vehicle with transaxle shift selector in gear specified by shift table. Apply throttle and observe speeds at which upshift occurs and torque converter is applied. See appropriate VEHICLE SHIFT SPEEDS table.

CAPRI (1.6L) VEHICLE SHIFT SPEEDS

Operating Condition	Shift Speed MPH
Half Throttle [1]	
1-2	24
2-3	47
3-4	70
WOT [2]	
1-2	35
2-3	65
3-4	103
Coast [3]	
Manual 2-1	24
Lockup (Full Throttle)	
On	106
Lockup (Half Throttle)	
On	80
Kickdown	
4-3	98
3-2	58
2-1	26

[1] – TPS voltage 1.6-2.2 volts.
[2] – TPS voltage 4.0 volts.
[3] – Manufacturer does not supply downshift shift speeds.

ESCORT & TRACER (1.8L) VEHICLE SHIFT SPEEDS

Operating Condition	Shift Speed MPH
Half Throttle [1]	
1-2	22-25
2-3	43-51
3-4	108-114
WOT [2]	
1-2	38-42
2-3	66-71
3-4	108-114
Coast [3]	
4-3	17-21
3-2	7-11
2-1	7-11
Manual 2-1	27-30
Lockup (4th Gear)	
On	74-85
Off	60-65
Kickdown	
4-3	100-107
3-2	61-66
2-1	34-38

[1] – TPS voltage 1.6-2.2 volts.
[2] – TPS voltage 4.0 volts.
[3] – Closed throttle, coasting condition. Downshift may be imperceptible.

ESCORT & TRACER (1.9L) VEHICLE SHIFT SPEEDS

Operating Condition	Shift Speed MPH
Half Throttle [1]	
1-2	17-21
2-3	33-41
3-4	51-61
WOT [2]	
1-2	34-38
2-3	65-70
3-4	82-88
Coast [3]	
4-3	17-20
3-2	6-10
2-1	6-10
Manual 2-1	27-30
Lockup (4th Gear) [1]	
On	50-61
Off	50-55
Lockup (3rd Gear) [1]	
On	41-52
Off	42-47
Kickdown	
4-3	100-107
3-2	61-66
2-1	34-38

[1] – TPS voltage 1.6-2.2 volts.
[2] – TPS voltage 4.0 volts.
[3] – Closed throttle, coasting condition. Downshift may be imperceptible.

PROBE (1993 2.0L) VEHICLE SHIFT SPEEDS

Operating Condition [1]	Shift Speed MPH
Half Throttle [2]	
1-2	17-22
2-3	34-44
3-4	68-84
WOT [3]	
1-2	36-40
2-3	65-70
3-4	100-107
Coast [4]	
4-3	10-14
3-1	5-9
Lockup (Full Throttle)	
On	100-107
Lockup (Half Throttle)	
On	68-74
Kickdown	
4-3	96-102
3-2	60-64
2-1	27-30

[1] – Transaxle operation is in NORMAL mode. Operational mode is controlled by the Transmission Control Module (TCM) and determined by speed the accelerator is depressed. Do not rapidly depress accelerator pedal when performing road test.
[2] – TPS voltage 1.6-2.2 volts.
[3] – TPS voltage 3.0-4.4 volts.
[4] – Closed throttle, coasting condition. Downshift may be imperceptible.

PROBE (2.5L) VEHICLE SHIFT SPEEDS

Operating Condition [1]	Shift Speed MPH
Half Throttle [2]	
1-2	25-30
2-3	43-54
3-4	71-86
WOT [3]	
1-2	36-40
2-3	65-70
3-4	105-111
Coast [4]	
4-3	10-14
3-1	7-11
Lockup (Full Throttle)	
On	105-111
Lockup (Half Throttle)	
On	77-92
Kickdown	
4-3	84-90
3-2	53-58
2-1	27-31

[1] – Transaxle operation is in NORMAL mode. Operational mode is controlled by the Transmission Control Module (TCM) and determined by speed the accelerator is depressed. Do not rapidly depress accelerator pedal when performing road test.
[2] – TPS voltage 1.6-2.2 volts.
[3] – TPS voltage 3.0-4.4 volts.
[4] – Closed throttle, coasting condition. Downshift may be imperceptible.

TORQUE CONVERTER

CLEANING & INSPECTION

NOTE: DO NOT clean torque converter by hand using solvent.

1) Torque converter is a sealed unit and cannot be disassembled for service. Replace torque converter if it is found to be defective. Remove any rust from pilot hub and boss of converter. Measure pilot bushing inner diameter. If measurement exceeds 2.090" (53.076 mm), replace torque converter.
2) Using Converter Cleaner (Rotunda 014-00028), flush torque converter. After converter is removed from cleaner, thoroughly drain solvent through hub. Add about .53 qt. (.5L) clean ATF to converter. Agitate fluid by hand. Thoroughly flush ATF from converter hub.

END PLAY CHECK

Insert fingers into converter hub opening and move one-way clutch up and down. If end play is greater than .04", replace converter.

STATOR INTERFERENCE CHECK

Stator-To-Impeller Interference Check – 1) Position front pump assembly on bench with spline end of stator shaft pointing up. Mount converter on pump so splines of one-way clutch inner race engage splines of stator support and converter hub engages pump drive gear.
2) While holding pump stationary, rotate converter counterclockwise. Converter should rotate freely without interference or scraping within assembly. Should interference or a scraping condition exist, or if converter does not rotate freely, replace converter unit.

Stator-To-Turbine Interference Check – 1) Place converter on bench, front side down. Install front pump assembly to engage mating splines of stator support, stator and pump drive gear lugs.
2) Install input shaft, engaging splines with turbine hub. While holding pump stationary, rotate turbine with input shaft.
3) Turbine should rotate freely in both directions without interference or noise. If interference or noise exists, stator front thrust washer may be worn; converter should be replaced.

ON-VEHICLE SERVICE

DIFFERENTIAL OIL SEALS

NOTE: Support engine with appropriate 3-bar engine support if rear engine mount removal is necessary.

Disassembly – 1) Raise and support vehicle. Remove front wheels and splash shields. Drain transaxle fluid. Disconnect tie rods from steering arms. Disconnect stabilizer link (if equipped).
2) Remove ball joint stud clamp bolts and nuts. Pull down lower control arms to separate lower arms from knuckles. Remove right joint shaft bracket (if equipped).
3) Remove half-shafts by carefully prying between shaft and transaxle case. Support half-shafts using wire. Remove oil seals.
Reassembly – 1) Using appropriate seal replacer, install oil seals. Replace circlip on end of half-shafts. Install half-shafts. Attach ball joints to knuckles. Install tie rod ends, and tighten nuts to specification. See TORQUE SPECIFICATIONS.
2) Install ball joint bolts and nuts. Install stabilizer link assemblies (if applicable). Turn nuts on each link assembly until 1.00 (25.4 mm) of bolt thread can be measured from upper nut. Secure upper nut, and back off lower nut until torque of 12-17 ft. lbs. (16-23 N.m) is reached.
3) Install splash shields and front wheels. Refer to appropriate automatic transmission servicing article in TRANSMISSION SERVICING for specified transaxle fluid. Check for leaks.

2-4 SERVO

Removal & Installation (Capri & Probe) – 1) Remove transaxle oil pan and filter assembly. Loosen servo piston stem lock nut while holding stem. Remove stem assembly from servo cover. Push in servo cover and remove retaining snap ring.
2) Reverse removal procedure to install servo assembly. Tighten piston stem to 105-130 INCH lbs. (11-14 N.m). Loosen stem 1 1/2 turns. Tighten lock nut to specification. See TORQUE SPECIFICATIONS. Install oil pan and fill transaxle with fluid.

Removal & Installation (Escort & Tracer) – Remove air cleaner assembly. Remove upper radiator hose. Depress servo assembly with large pair of slide-lock pliers. Remove retaining snap ring. Remove servo assembly. Coat new seals with fluid before assembly. To install, reverse removal procedure. Check fluid level.

VALVE BODY

Disassembly (Capri) – 1) Disconnect negative battery cable. Remove air cleaner assembly. Disconnect 5 transaxle harness connectors and separate harness from mounting clips.
2) Raise and support vehicle. Drain transaxle fluid. Disconnect oil cooler outlet and inlet hoses. Remove oil cooler inlet tube from trans-

axle. Remove valve body cover and gasket.
3) Remove kickdown cable from throttle cam. Pinch tangs of mating connector mounted on case to disconnect solenoid connector. Push connector inward, and remove connector. Remove valve body retaining bolts, and carefully remove body.
Reassembly – Place shift selector in "R" position. Install valve body using a mirror to align groove of manual valve with manual plate. To complete installation, reverse removal procedure. Tighten bolts to specification. See TORQUE SPECIFICATIONS. Fill transaxle with fluid. Confirm shift selector is indexed correctly.

Disassembly (Escort & Tracer) – Raise and support vehicle. Remove transaxle pan bolts and drain fluid. Remove pan. Disconnect harness connectors at valve body assembly. Remove valve body bolts securing wiring harness. Remove remaining bolts and remove valve body assembly.
Reassembly – Place shift selector lever in "R" position. Install valve body using a mirror to align groove of manual valve with manual valve detent lever. To complete installation, reverse removal procedure. Tighten bolts to specification. See TORQUE SPECIFICATIONS. Fill transaxle with fluid. Confirm shift selector is indexed correctly.

Disassembly (Probe) – 1) Disconnect negative battery cable. Raise and support vehicle. Remove left inner fender splash shield. Remove drain plug and drain fluid. Disconnect and plug inlet and outlet oil cooler tubes. Remove oil cooler mounting bracket from top right side of main cover.
2) Disconnect vent hose from top left side of cover. Loosen cover bolts and allow any residual fluid to drain. Remove cover bolts, cover and gasket. Disconnect Transmission Oil Temperature (TOT) sensor harness connector. Disconnect solenoid harness connectors. Remove valve body bolts and remove valve body.
Reassembly – Place shift selector lever in "R" position. Install valve body using a mirror to align groove of manual valve with manual valve detent lever. To complete installation, reverse removal procedure. Tighten bolts to specification. See TORQUE SPECIFICATIONS. Fill transaxle with fluid. Confirm shift selector is indexed correctly.

REMOVAL & INSTALLATION

See appropriate AUTOMATIC TRANSMISSION REMOVAL article in TRANSMISSION SERVICING.

TRANSAXLE DISASSEMBLY

1) Mount transaxle in a stand. Carefully remove torque converter from case. Remove oil pump drive shaft. Remove dipstick tube from case. Remove Manual Lever Position (MLP) sensor and Pulse Signal Generator (PSG). On Capri models, remove external Transmission Oil Temperature (TOT) sensor. On Probe models, remove backup light switch.
2) On all models, disconnect solenoid connector. Remove 4EAT external wiring harness and clip. Remove oil pipes, oil hoses as necessary. Use a magnet to remove converter drain-back ball and spring from cooler plug hole.
3) Remove oil pan and gasket. Remove oil strainer (filter) and "O" ring. On Capri and Probe models, remove valve body cover and gasket. On all models, remove kickdown cable and bracket. Remove throttle cam from cable. Pinch teeth of solenoid connector, and remove by pushing inward.
4) Remove retaining bolts from valve body, and carefully remove valve body. Ensure all electrical harness connectors are disconnected. Remove oil pump and gasket. Remove planetary gear thrust washer and thrust bearing. See Fig. 4.
5) Remove turbine shaft retaining ring. Remove reverse clutch assembly and thrust bearing. Remove primary sun gear and one-way clutch assembly. Remove thrust bearing from primary sun gear and one-way clutch assembly. Remove thrust washer from carrier hub. Remove and secure 2-4 band using wire to prevent warping.
6) Pull anchor shaft while holding strut, and remove strut. On Capri and Probe models, remove 2-4 servo. Using a "C" clamp and socket, compress servo. Remove retaining ring, servo and spring. On Escort and Tracer models, depress servo assembly with large pair of slide-lock pliers. Remove retaining snap ring. Remove servo assembly.

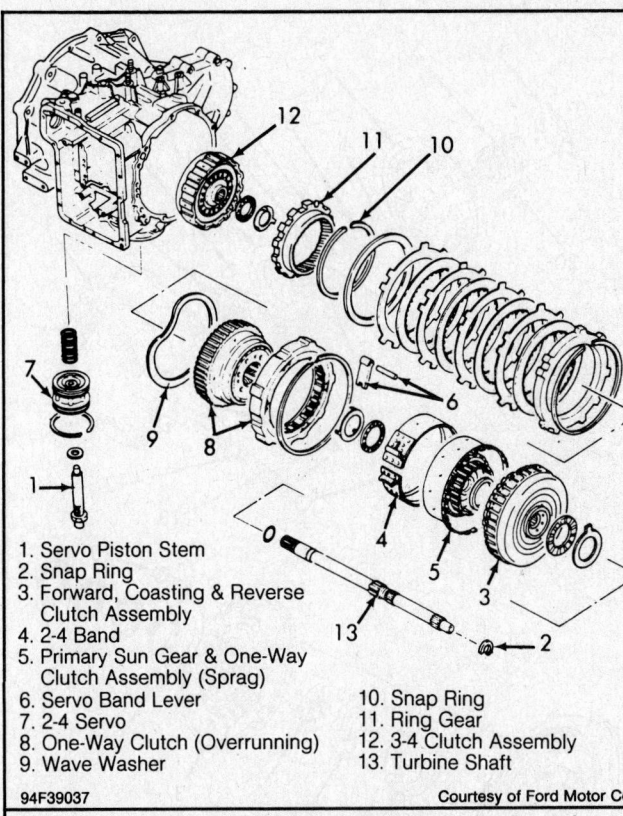

1. Servo Piston Stem
2. Snap Ring
3. Forward, Coasting & Reverse Clutch Assembly
4. 2-4 Band
5. Primary Sun Gear & One-Way Clutch Assembly (Sprag)
6. Servo Band Lever
7. 2-4 Servo
8. One-Way Clutch (Overrunning)
9. Wave Washer
10. Snap Ring
11. Ring Gear
12. 3-4 Clutch Assembly
13. Turbine Shaft

94F39037   Courtesy of Ford Motor Co.

Fig. 4: Exploded View Of Transaxle Assembly

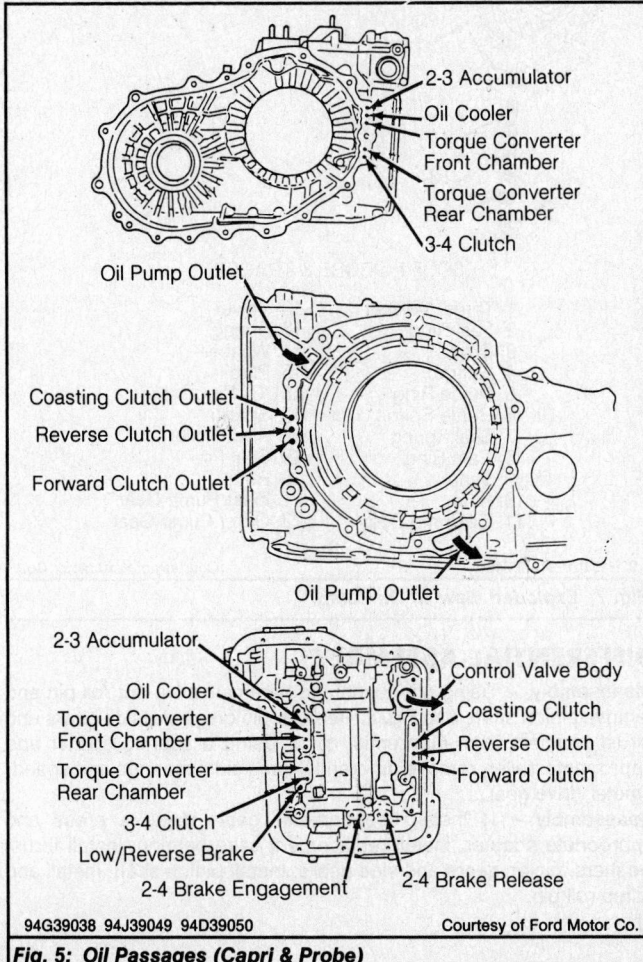

94G39038 94J39049 94D39050   Courtesy of Ford Motor Co.

Fig. 5: Oil Passages (Capri & Probe)

7) Remove one-way clutch retaining snap ring. Remove one-way clutch and carrier hub assembly. Remove wave washer. Remove low and reverse clutch pressure plate retaining snap ring. Remove low and reverse clutch retaining plate and drive and driven plates.

8) Remove internal gear snap ring, and remove ring gear. Remove "O" ring located on converter housing side of turbine shaft. Pull out turbine shaft, and remove 3-4 clutch assembly from shaft.

9) Remove transaxle case retaining bolts. Tap lightly using a plastic hammer to remove case from converter housing. Remove output shell from output gear with thrust washer and thrust bearing.

10) Using appropriate spring compressor, compress low/reverse clutch piston return spring. Remove retainer snap ring, return spring and retainer. Remove spring compressor tool. Apply compressed air through low and reverse clutch fluid passage to remove low/reverse clutch piston. See Figs. 5 and 6.

11) Remove oil pressure relief plug, washer, spring and detent ball. Remove differential assembly. On Capri and Probe models, remove 2-3 accumulator from converter housing. Remove bearing housing bolt to access roll pin. On all models, remove roll pin using a pin punch. Tapping lightly using a plastic hammer, remove bearing housing. Use a socket to tap out idler and output gear assemblies from torque converter housing.

12) Remove converter housing from holding fixture. Remove bearing-stator support bolts. Press bearing-stator support out of torque converter housing using Step Plate (D80L-630-10).

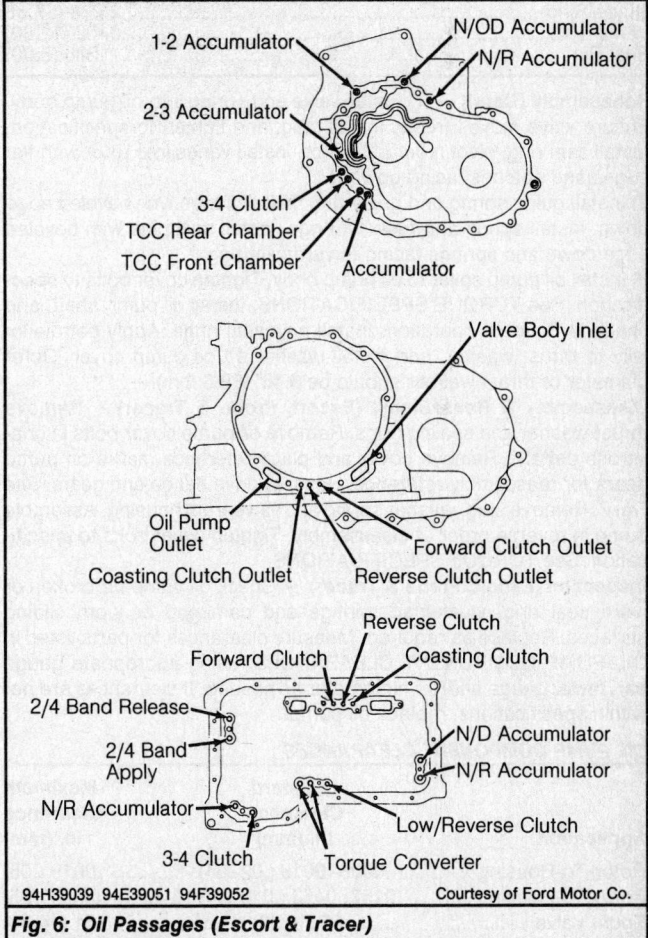

94H39039 94E39051 94F39052   Courtesy of Ford Motor Co.

Fig. 6: Oil Passages (Escort & Tracer)

COMPONENT DISASSEMBLY & REASSEMBLY

OIL PUMP

Disassembly (Capri) – 1) Remove oil pump cover, flange, spring and pivot roller. See Fig. 11. Remove guide ring and guide spring.

2) Remove vanes from rotor. Remove cam ring and rotor. Remove seal pin and spring. Remove plug, spring and valve from side of cover. Remove thrust washer, "O" rings and seal rings from cover. *See Fig. 7.*

Inspection (Capri) – Check oil pump for broken or worn seal ring, weakened springs and damaged or worn sliding surfaces. Replace as required. Measure clearances for parts listed in OIL PUMP COMPONENT CLEARANCES, using appropriate gauge bar, feeler gauge and/or micrometer as needed. If clearances are not within specifications, replace oil pump.

OIL PUMP COMPONENTS CLEARANCES

Application	Standard Clearance In. (mm)	Maximum Clearance In. (mm)
Seal Pin-To-Cover	.0002-.0008 (.005-.020)	.002 (.060)
Rotor-To-Cover	.0002-.0008 (.005-.020)	.002 (.060)
Cam Ring-To-Cover	.0002-.0008 (.005-.020)	.002 (.060)
Vane-To-Cover	.0006-.0020 (.015-.050)	.003 (.080)
Vane-To-Rotor Slot	.004-.0018 (.010-.045)	.0026 (.065)

OIL PUMP COMPONENTS CLEARANCES

Application	Standard Diameter In. (mm)
Sleeve	1.102 (28.00)
Rotor Bushing	1.102 (28.00)
Guide Ring	2.278 (57.85)
Valve	.0472 (12.00)
Seal Pin	.236 (6.00)

Reassembly (Capri) – **1)** Install valve and spring into oil pump body. Ensure valve moves freely. Install plug, and tighten to specification. Install cam ring, pivot roller and rotor. Install vanes into rotor with flat edges and notches facing upward.

2) Install guide spring and guide ring. Install flange with beveled edge down. Install spring and new "O" rings. Install seal pins with beveled edge down and springs facing toward cam ring.

3) Install oil pump cover to oil pump body. Tighten cover bolts to specification. See TORQUE SPECIFICATIONS. Install oil pump shaft, and check for smooth operation. Install new seal rings. Apply petroleum jelly to thrust washer, and install washer on oil pump cover. Outer diameter of thrust washer should be 3.46" (88.0 mm).

Disassembly & Reassembly (Escort, Probe & Tracer) – Remove thrust washer and sealing rings. Remove oil pump cover bolts in criss-cross pattern. Remove cover and place reference marks on pump gears for reassembly reference. Remove drive flange and gears. *See Fig. 7.* Remove plug, washer spring and valve from housing. Assemble pump in reverse order of disassembly. Tighten cover bolts to specification. See TORQUE SPECIFICATIONS.

Inspection (Escort, Probe & Tracer) – Check oil pump for broken or worn seal ring, weakened springs and damaged or worn sliding surfaces. Replace as required. Measure clearances for parts listed in OIL PUMP COMPONENT CLEARANCES, using appropriate gauge bar, feeler gauge and/or micrometer as needed. If clearances are not within specifications, replace oil pump.

OIL PUMP COMPONENT CLEARANCES

Application	Standard Clearance In. (mm)	Maximum Clearance In. (mm)
Rotor-To-Housing [1]	.0008-.0015 (.02-.04)	.0019 (.05)
Rotor-To-Housing	.0157-.0453 (.040-.115)	.0492 (.125)
Spool Valve	.55 (13.98) [2]	[2] .551 (14.00)

[1] – Outer and inner rotors.
[2] – Diameter.

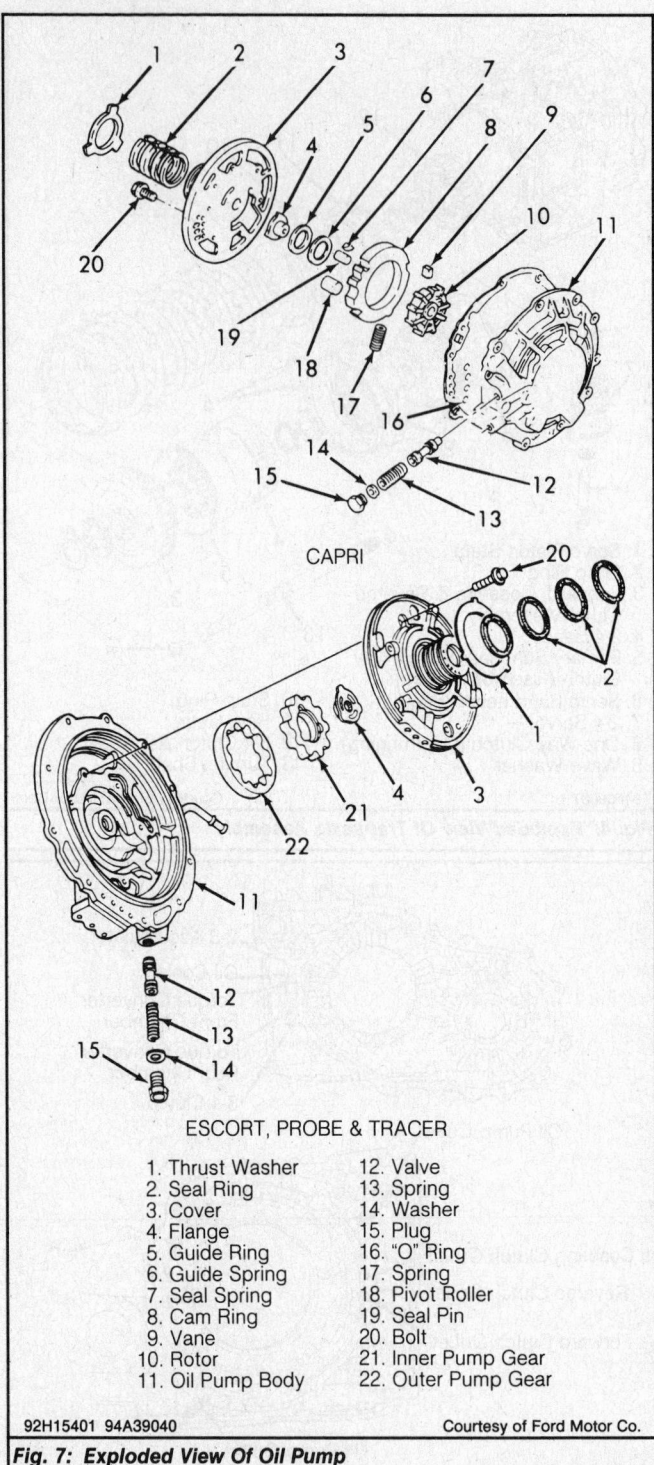

1. Thrust Washer	12. Valve
2. Seal Ring	13. Spring
3. Cover	14. Washer
4. Flange	15. Plug
5. Guide Ring	16. "O" Ring
6. Guide Spring	17. Spring
7. Seal Spring	18. Pivot Roller
8. Cam Ring	19. Seal Pin
9. Vane	20. Bolt
10. Rotor	21. Inner Pump Gear
11. Oil Pump Body	22. Outer Pump Gear

92H15401 94A39040   Courtesy of Ford Motor Co.

Fig. 7: Exploded View Of Oil Pump

DIFFERENTIAL ASSEMBLY

Disassembly – Using pin punch and hammer, drive out roll pin and remove pinion shaft. *See Fig. 8.* Remove pinion gears, side gears and thrust washers from differential case. Using a bearing splitter and appropriate puller, remove differential case side bearings and speedometer drive gear.

Reassembly – **1)** Install speedometer gear. Using a press and appropriate adapter, install replacement case bearing. Install thrust washers, pinion gears and side gears. Install pinion shaft. Install and crimp roll pin.

2) Install left and right half-shafts into differential assembly. Support half-shafts on "V" blocks. *See Fig. 9.* Using a dial indicator, measure backlash of both pinion gears. Backlash should be 0-.004" (0-.10 mm). Replace differential assembly if specification is exceeded.

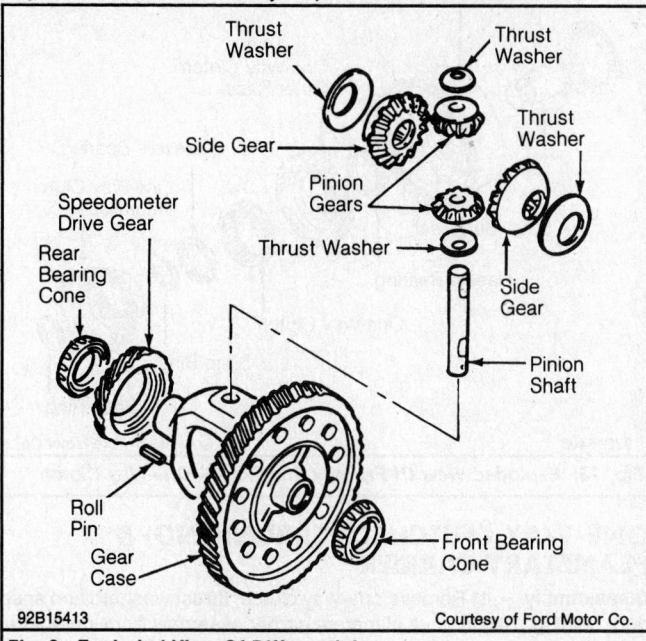

92B15413

Courtesy of Ford Motor Co.

Fig. 8: Exploded View Of Differential

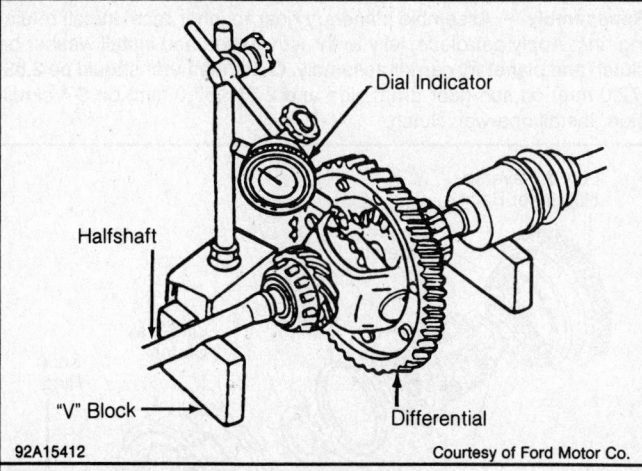

92A15412

Courtesy of Ford Motor Co.

Fig. 9: Checking Side Gear & Pinion Backlash

FORWARD CLUTCH

Disassembly – Remove retaining snap ring and pressure plate. Remove forward clutch pack and dished plate. *See Fig. 10.*

Inspection – Inspect all parts for wear, damage and effects of overheating. Check body thoroughly for wear and damage. Replace all parts as necessary.

Reassembly – **1)** Install dished plate with beveled side facing up. Install forward clutch pack. Install pressure plate and retaining ring.

2) Using a feeler gauge, check clearance between retaining ring and pressure plate. If clearance is not .040-.047" (1.0-1.2 mm), install correct thickness snap ring.

3) Snap rings are available in following thicknesses: .079" (2.00 mm), .085" (2.15 mm), .091" (2.30 mm), .097" (2.45 mm), .102" (2.60 mm) and .108" (2.75 mm). Set forward/reverse drum on pump support. Check clutch operation by applying air pressure through forward clutch fluid passages.

4) Clutch pack should compress. Pour in specified transmission fluid until reverse piston, coasting clutch drum and coasting piston are submerged. Apply short burst of air through fluid passages. No bubbles

should appear between piston and drum seal. Pressure should not exceed 57 psi (392 kPa).

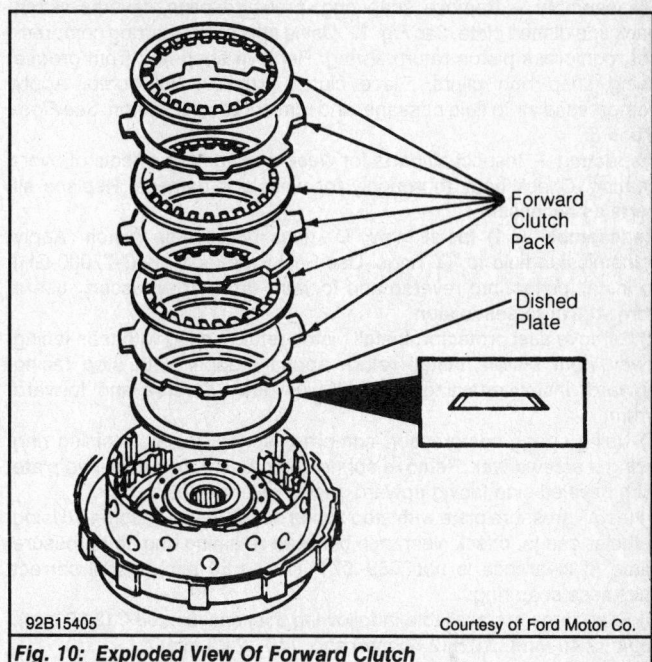

92B15405

Courtesy of Ford Motor Co.

Fig. 10: Exploded View Of Forward Clutch

COASTING CLUTCH

Disassembly – Remove retaining ring, pressure plate, coasting clutch pack and dished plate. *See Fig. 11.* Install appropriate spring compressor, and compress return spring and retainer. Remove retaining ring. Remove spring compressor. Remove return spring and retainer. Remove coasting clutch drum piston from clutch assembly using compressed air.

Inspection – Inspect all parts for wear, damage and effects of overheating. Inspect body for damage and wear. Replace as necessary.

Reassembly – **1)** Install new "O" rings on coasting piston. Apply transmission fluid to "O" rings, and install piston into coasting clutch drum. Roll outer "O" ring lip down to ease installation.

2) Install coasting clutch drum into reverse and forward drum. Install return spring and retainer. Use spring compressor to compress spring and retainer. Install snap ring.

3) Carefully remove spring compressor. Install dished plate with beveled side down. Install coasting clutch pack. Install pressure plate, and secure pack using snap ring.

4) Using a feeler gauge, check clearance between retaining ring and pressure plate. If clearance is not .040-.047" (1.00-1.20 mm), install correct thickness snap ring.

5) Snap rings are available in following thicknesses: .059" (1.50 mm), .065" (1.65 mm), .071" (1.80 mm), .077" (1.95 mm), .083" (2.10 mm) and .089" (2.25 mm).

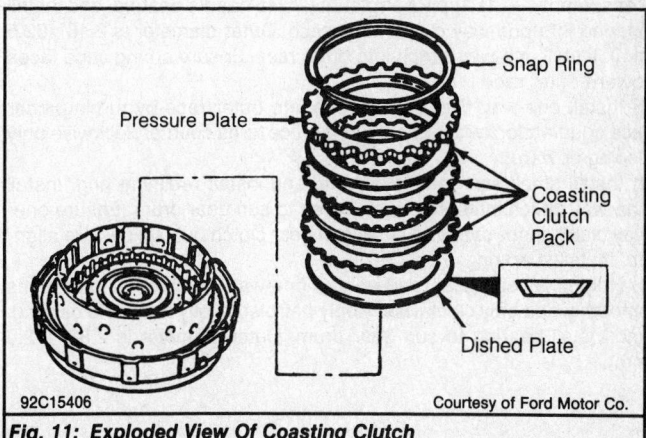

92C15406

Courtesy of Ford Motor Co.

Fig. 11: Exploded View Of Coasting Clutch

REVERSE CLUTCH

Disassembly – Remove snap ring, pressure plate, reverse clutch pack and dished plate. *See Fig. 12.* Using appropriate spring compressor, compress piston return spring. Remove snap ring from groove using snap ring pliers. Place clutch drum on oil pump. Apply compressed air to fluid passage, and remove reverse piston. *See Figs. 5 and 6.*

Inspection – Inspect all parts for wear, damage and effects of overheating. Check body thoroughly for wear and damage. Replace all parts as necessary.

Reassembly – 1) Install new "O" rings on reverse piston. Apply transmission fluid to "O" rings. Use Seal Protector (T88C-77000-GH) to install piston into reverse and forward drum. If necessary, use a screwdriver to seat piston.

2) Remove seal protector. Install piston return spring with tabs facing away from piston. Install return spring stopper with step facing upward. Install retaining ring half-way down reverse and forward drum.

3) Using spring compressor, compress spring. Install retaining ring using a screwdriver. Remove spring compressor. Install dished plate with beveled side facing upward. Install reverse clutch pack.

4) Install pressure plate with step facing down. Install snap ring. Using a feeler gauge, check clearance between retaining ring and pressure plate. If clearance is not .059-.071" (1.50-1.80 mm), install correct thickness snap ring.

5) Snap rings are available in following thicknesses: .087" (2.20 mm), .094" (2.40 mm), .102" (2.60 mm) and .110" (2.80 mm).

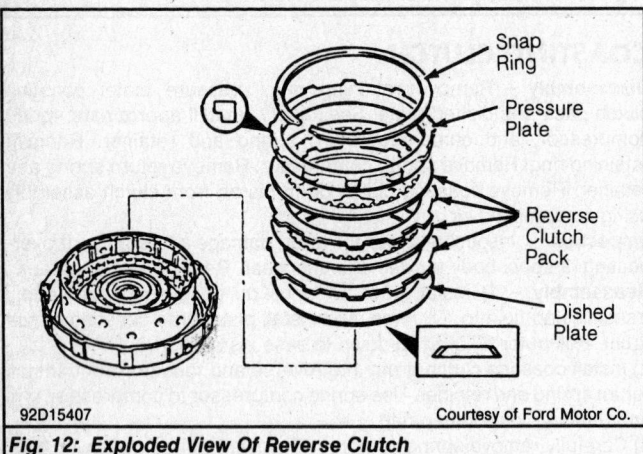

Fig. 12: Exploded View Of Reverse Clutch

PRIMARY SUN GEAR & ONE-WAY CLUTCH (SPRAG)

Disassembly – Remove snap ring and one-way clutch inner and outer races. *See Fig. 13.* Remove snap ring and small sun gear from drum. Separate one-way clutch inner race from outer race. Remove one-way clutch and needle bearing.

Reassembly – 1) Apply petroleum jelly to needle bearing, and install bearing into one-way clutch inner race. Outer diameter is 2.46" (62.5 mm). Install one-way clutch into outer race. Ensure spring cage faces toward outer race.

2) Install one-way clutch inner race into outer race by turning inner race counterclockwise. Ensure inner race turns counterclockwise only (facing upward).

3) Install small sun gear into drum, and install retaining ring. Install one-way clutch inner and outer races to sun gear drum. Ensure one-way clutch inner race and small sun gear clutch hub splines are aligned. Install snap ring.

4) Hold small sun gear, and ensure one-way clutch outer race turns smoothly and only clockwise. Apply petroleum jelly to needle bearing, and install bearing to sun gear drum. Outer diameter is 2.83" (72.0 mm).

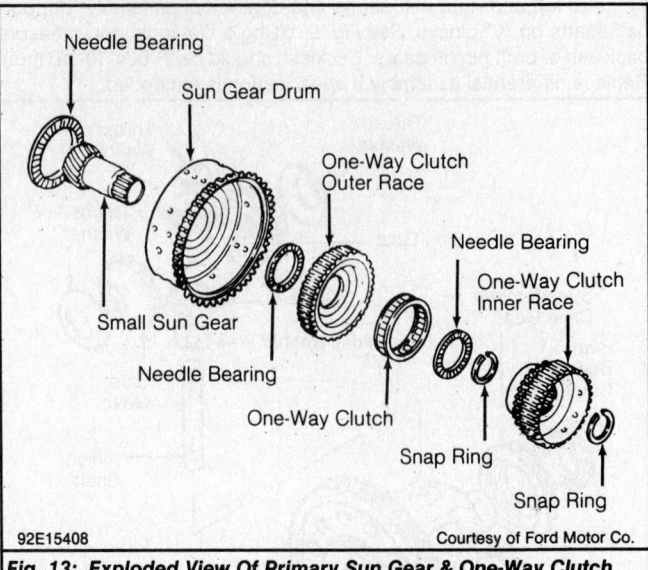

Fig. 13: Exploded View Of Primary Sun Gear & One-Way Clutch

ONE-WAY CLUTCH (OVERRUNNING) & PLANETARY CARRIER

Disassembly – 1) Remove one-way clutch, thrust washers and snap ring. *See Fig. 14.* Remove planetary carrier assembly from inner race. Place one-way clutch on inner race, and ensure clutch rotates smoothly and clockwise only.

Reassembly – Assemble planetary gear to inner race. Install retaining ring. Apply petroleum jelly to thrust washer, and install washer on clutch and planetary carrier assembly. Outer diameter should be 2.83" (72.0 mm) on sun gear drum side and 2.21" (57.0 mm) on 3-4 clutch side. Install one-way clutch.

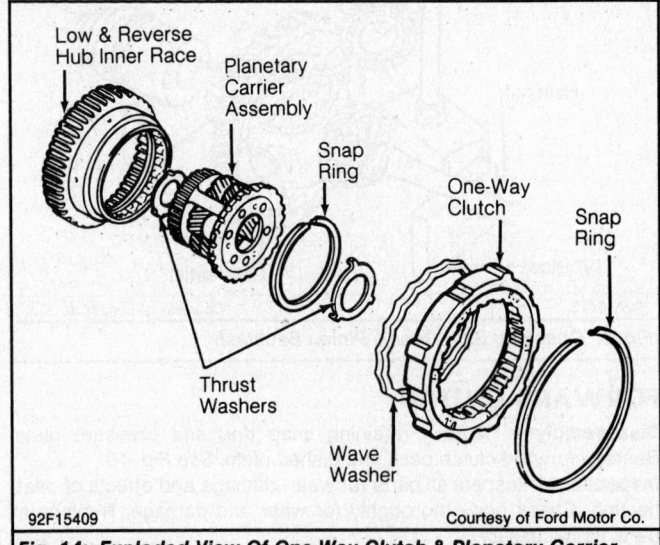

Fig. 14: Exploded View Of One-Way Clutch & Planetary Carrier

3-4 CLUTCH

Disassembly – Remove snap ring, pressure plate and clutch pack. *See Fig. 15.* Using appropriate spring compressor, compress return spring and retainer assembly and remove snap ring. Remove compressor. Remove return spring and retainer. Using Leak Check Adapter (T88C-77000-JH), remove piston using compressed air. Remove inner and outer seals from piston.

Reassembly – 1) Install new "O" rings on 3-4 clutch piston. Apply transmission fluid. Using spring compressor, compress return spring and retainer assembly. Install retaining ring. Remove compressor.

2) Install 3-4 clutch pack. Install pressure plate with step facing upward. Install snap ring. Using a feeler gauge, check clearance between snap ring and pressure plate. If clearance is not .051-.059" (1.30-1.50 mm), install correct thickness pressure plate.

3) Pressure plates are available in following thicknesses: .149" (3.80 mm), .157" (4.00 mm), .165" (4.20 mm), 1.73" (4.40 mm), .181 (4.60 mm) and .189" (4.80 mm). Install leak check adapter, and apply compressed air to check clutch operation. DO NOT apply over 57 psi (392 kPa) air pressure for more than 3 seconds.

4) Pour specified transmission fluid into clutch drum so 3-4 piston is fully submerged. Apply compressed air and ensure no bubbles come from clutch piston seal.

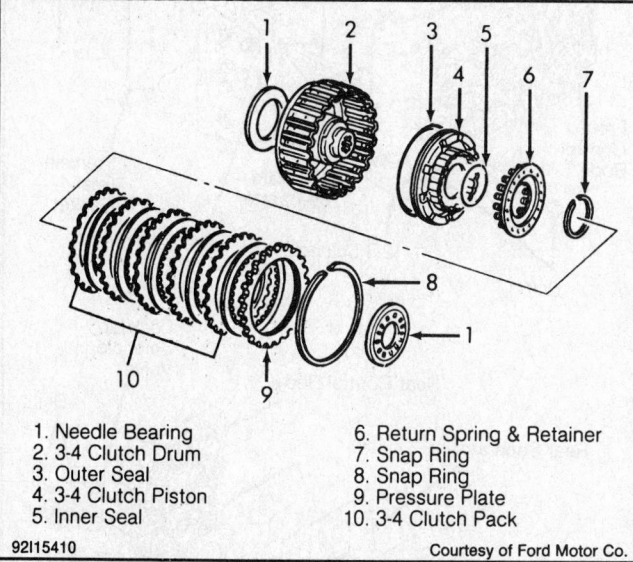

1. Needle Bearing
2. 3-4 Clutch Drum
3. Outer Seal
4. 3-4 Clutch Piston
5. Inner Seal
6. Return Spring & Retainer
7. Snap Ring
8. Snap Ring
9. Pressure Plate
10. 3-4 Clutch Pack

92I15410   Courtesy of Ford Motor Co.

Fig. 15: Exploded View Of 3-4 Clutch

2-3 ACCUMULATOR (CAPRI & PROBE)

Disassembly – **1)** Remove snap ring while holding in stopper plug. Remove stopper plug. *See Fig. 16.* Remove spring, piston, stopper plug "O" ring and seals from piston.

Inspection – Check for damaged or worn piston or stopper plug. Check for broken or worn spring. On Capri models, free length should be 3.280" (83.30 mm) for non-turbo models and 2.968" (75.40 mm) for turbo models. On Probe models, free spring length is 3.06" (77.7 mm). To assemble, reverse disassembly procedure.

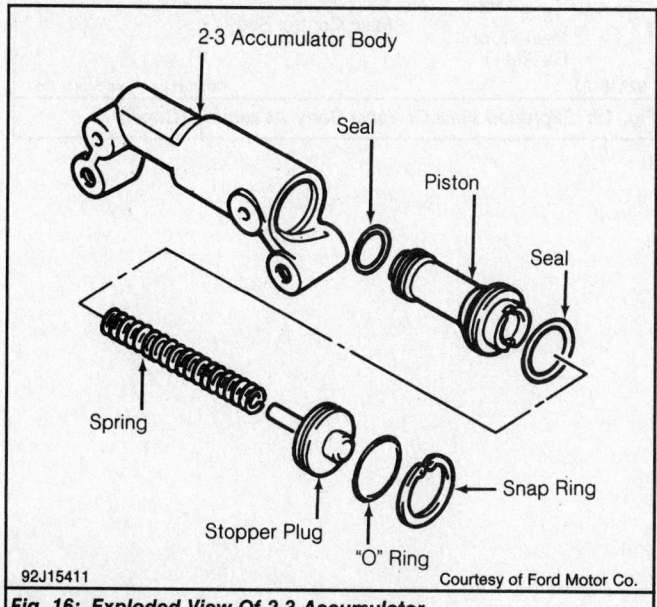

92J15411   Courtesy of Ford Motor Co.

Fig. 16: Exploded View Of 2-3 Accumulator

ACCUMULATORS (ESCORT & TRACER)

Disassembly & Reassembly – For exploded view of accumulator assemblies, *See Fig. 17.* Lubricate all seal and "O" ring with transmission fluid before reassembly.

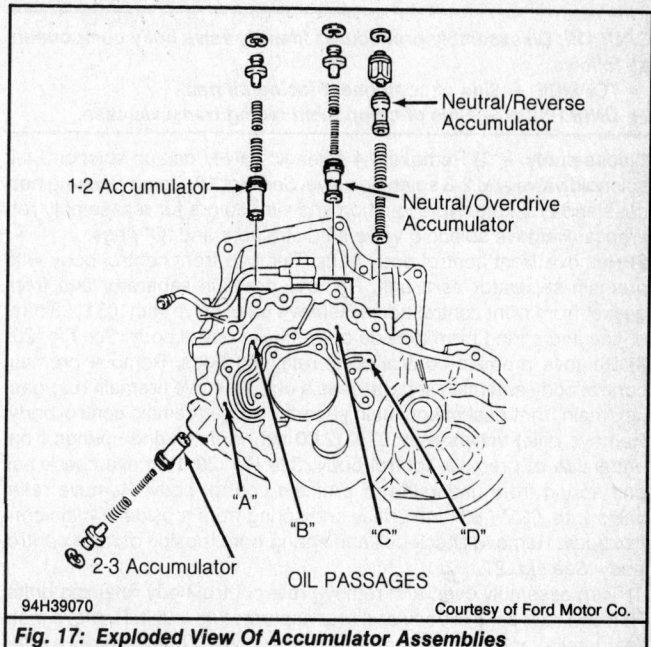

94H39070   Courtesy of Ford Motor Co.

Fig. 17: Exploded View Of Accumulator Assemblies (Escort & Tracer)

IDLER GEAR

Disassembly – **1)** Using Torque Adapter (T87C-77000-E), secure idler shaft in a vise. Using Mainshaft Lock Nut Wrench (T88T-7025-A) and a 1 5/8" socket, remove lock nut.

2) Remove bearing, spacer and idler gear from idler shaft. *See Fig 18.* Remove adjustment shim and other bearing. Using puller and slide hammer, remove bearing cups.

Reassembly – **1)** Press bearing cups into Idler gear. Install bearing on idler shaft. Install adjust shim, spacer and idler gear. Install remaining bearing.

2) Secure idler shaft in a vise using adapter. Use protective plates to prevent damage to adapter. Tighten lock nut to 94 ft. lbs. (128 N.m).

3) Turn idler gear and adapter over, with gear mounted in vise. Measure bearing preload by turning shaft with INCH lb. torque wrench. Turning torque should be .26-.78 INCH lbs. (.03-.9 N.m). If turning torque is not within specification, tighten lock nut. DO NOT exceed 94-130 ft. lbs. (128-177 N.m).

4) If preload is not within specified range, adjustment shim assortment pack is available. Shims range in thickness between .1787-.1966" (4.540-4.995 mm) in .0013" (.035 mm) increments. DO NOT use more than 7 shims.

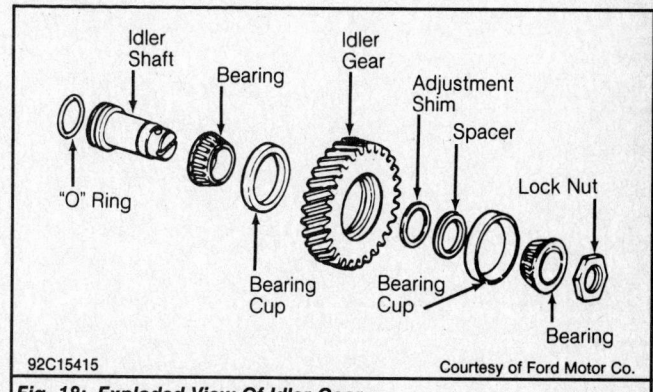

92C15415   Courtesy of Ford Motor Co.

Fig. 18: Exploded View Of Idler Gear

VALVE BODY (CAPRI)

NOTE: Each valve body bolt has a letter on bolt head which matches letter placed near bolt hole.

CAUTION: Disassembly procedures identify valve body components as follows:

- *TOPSIDE – Side of component facing oil pan.*
- *UNDERSIDE – Side of component facing transaxle case.*

Disassembly – 1) Remove 3-4 solenoid valve, lock-up solenoid, 1-2 solenoid valve and 2-3 solenoid valve. *See Fig. 19.* Remove wiring harness and brackets. Note location and wire colors for reassembly reference. Remove solenoid valve fluid strainers and "O" rings.

2) Remove front control body bolts. Remove front control body with premain separator as a unit. Remove premain separator and front gasket from front control body. Remove relief valve with .031" (.8 mm) orifice and spring from topside of premain control body. *See Fig. 20.*

3) Remove premain control body retaining bolts. Remove premain control body and main separator as a unit. Remove premain rear gasket, main front gasket and main separator from premain control body. Remove relief valves with .079" (2.00 mm) orifices and springs from underside of premain control body. *See Fig. 20.* Remove check ball and spring from underside of premain control body. Remove relief valve with .031" (.80 mm) orifice and spring from topside of main control body. Remove check ball and spring from topside of main control body. *See Fig. 21.*

4) Turn assembly over, and remove rear control body retaining bolts. Remove rear control body and rear separator as a unit. Remove main rear gasket and rear separator from rear control body. Remove relief valves with .039" (1.00 mm), .059" (1.50 mm) and .078" (2.00 mm) orifices and springs from topside of rear control body. *See Fig. 22.*

5) Remove relief valve with .098" (2.50 mm) orifice and spring from main control body. Remove rubber ball from main control body.

6) Individual valves and springs are removed by removing retaining clips and bore plugs. Some valves are aluminum and cannot be removed using a magnet. Tap valve body on palm of hand to slide valve out of bore. If using a pick becomes necessary to remove valves and springs, use extreme caution to prevent damage to valves and bores.

NOTE: DO NOT turn throttle valve adjusting screw on main control body. Adjusting screw is set during manufacture and MUST NOT be altered.

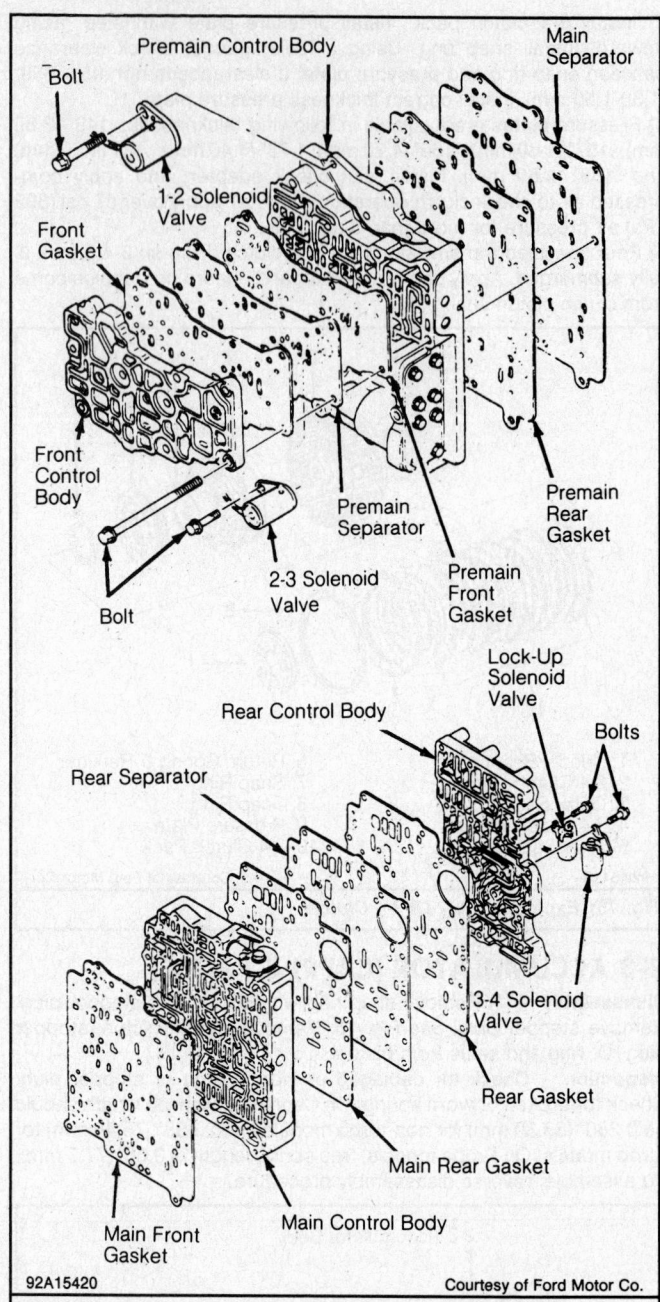

92A15420   Courtesy of Ford Motor Co.

Fig. 19: Exploded View Of Valve Body Assembly (Capri)

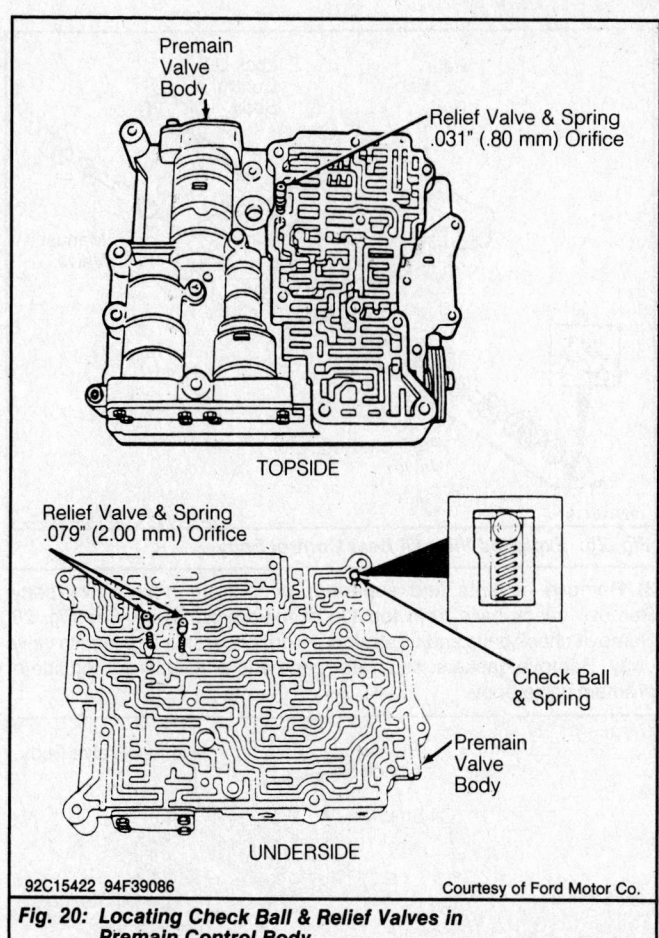

Fig. 20: Locating Check Ball & Relief Valves in Premain Control Body

92C15422 94F39086   Courtesy of Ford Motor Co.

CAUTION: *Avoid rounding off sharp edges of valves and plugs when using crocus cloth. These edges perform a cleaning action.*

Cleaning & Inspection – 1) Clean all parts thoroughly in clean solvent, and blow dry using moisture-free compressed air. Inspect all valves and plug bores for scores. Check all fluid passages for obstructions. Inspect all mating surfaces, plugs and valves for burrs and scores. If necessary, use crocus cloth to polish valves and plugs.

2) Inspect all springs for distortion. Check all valves and plugs for free movement in respective bores. Valves and plugs, when dry, must fall free from their own weight in respective bores.

Reassembly – 1) Install all valve trains into respective bores using illustrations as assembly guides. *See Figs. 23-25.* When installing throttle valve assembly into main control body, ensure groove is aligned with bolt hole. Install throttle return spring on throttle cam. Tighten retaining bolts to 69-95 INCH lbs. (8-11 N.m).

2) Install neutral-reverse/neutral-overdrive accumulator plate on premain control body. Tighten retaining bolts to 57-69 INCH lbs. (6-8 N.m). Install 1-2 accumulator plate. Tighten retaining bolts to 57-69 INCH lbs. (6-8 N.m). DO NOT install harness bracket bolt yet. To complete reassembly, reverse disassembly procedures.

NOTE: *Match bolt head letter with corresponding letter on valve body. DO NOT mix gaskets during assembly.*

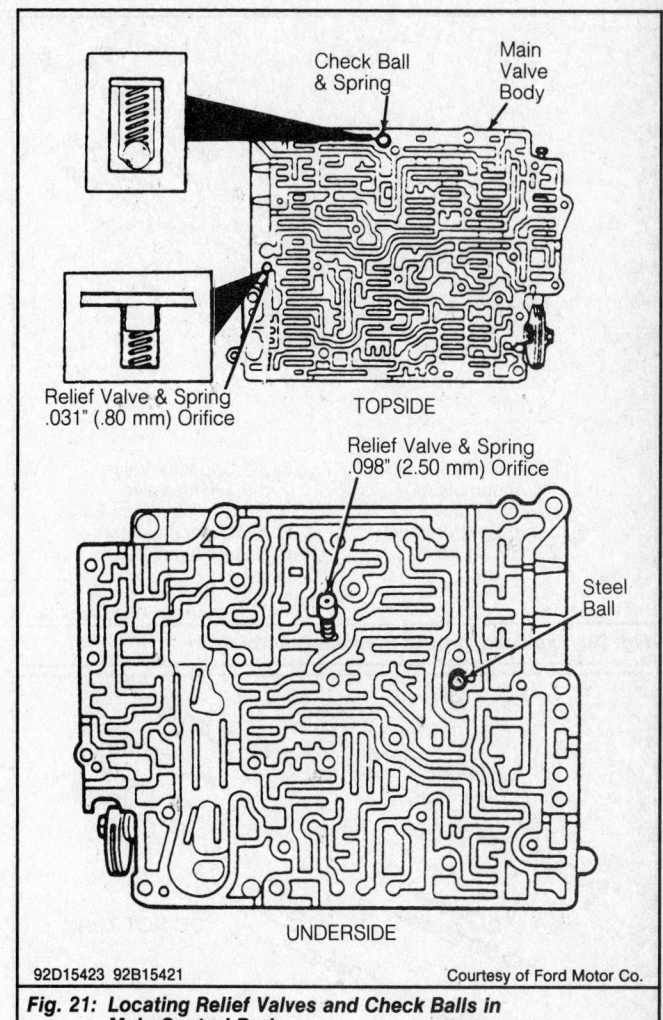

92D15423 92B15421   Courtesy of Ford Motor Co.

Fig. 21: Locating Relief Valves and Check Balls in Main Control Body

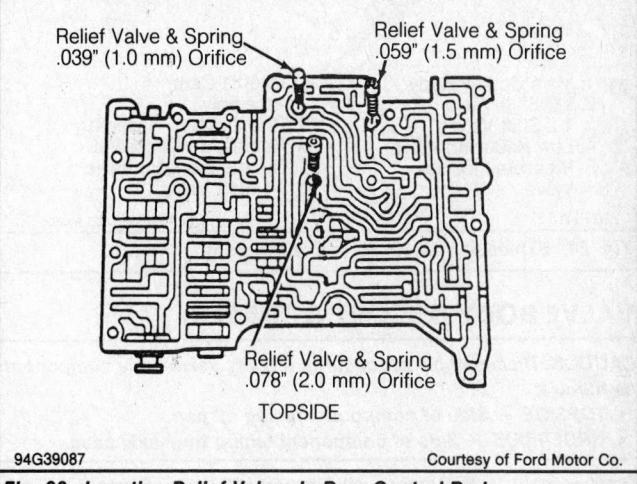

94G39087   Courtesy of Ford Motor Co.

Fig. 22: Locating Relief Valves In Rear Control Body

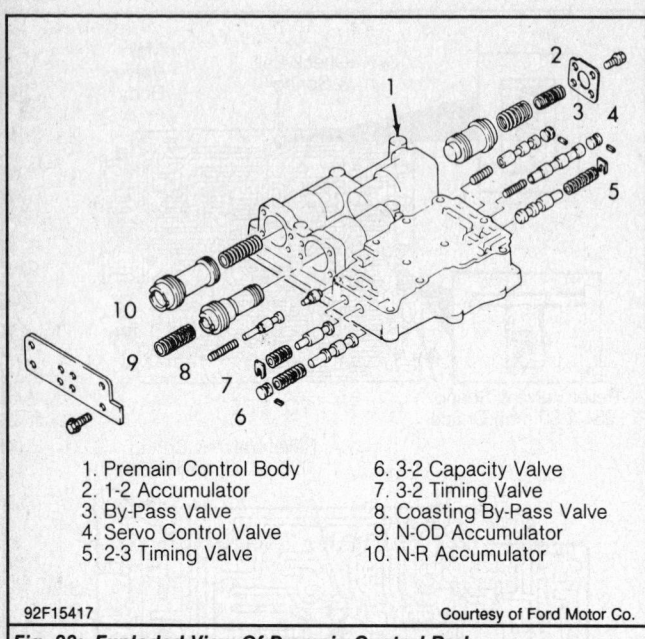

1. Premain Control Body
2. 1-2 Accumulator
3. By-Pass Valve
4. Servo Control Valve
5. 2-3 Timing Valve
6. 3-2 Capacity Valve
7. 3-2 Timing Valve
8. Coasting By-Pass Valve
9. N-OD Accumulator
10. N-R Accumulator

92F15417

Courtesy of Ford Motor Co.

Fig. 23: Exploded View Of Premain Control Body

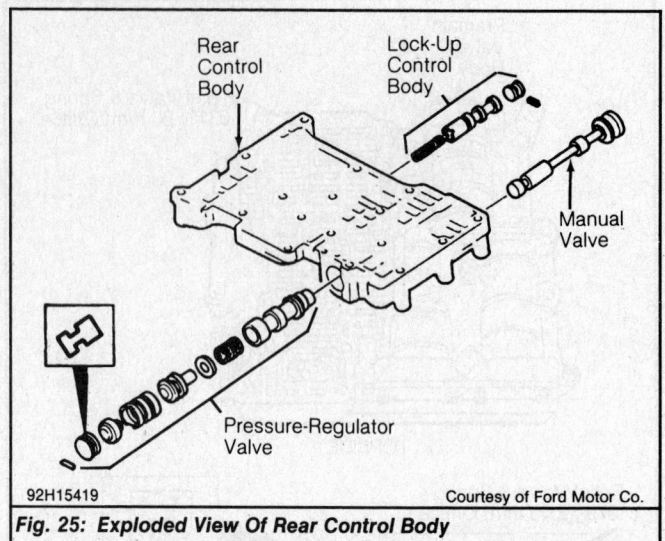

92H15419

Courtesy of Ford Motor Co.

Fig. 25: Exploded View Of Rear Control Body

3) Remove gaskets and separator plate from main valve body. Remove check balls from topside of main valve body. *See Fig. 28.* Remove check balls and oil strainers from underside of premain valve body. Remove gaskets, separator plate and oil filter from topside of premain valve body.

1. Main Control Body
2. 2-3 Shift Valve
3. 1-2 Shift Valve
4. Low Reducing Valve
5. Pressure-Modifier Valve
6. Throttle Cam Assembly
7. Throttle Valve Assembly
8. Throttle-Modulator Valve
9. Throttle Back-Up Valve
10. 3-4 Shift Valve

92G15418

Courtesy of Ford Motor Co.

Fig. 24: Exploded View Of Main Control Body

VALVE BODY (ESCORT & TRACER)

CAUTION: Disassembly procedures identify valve body components as follows:

- *TOPSIDE – Side of component facing oil pan.*
- *UNDERSIDE – Side of component facing transaxle case.*

Disassembly – 1) Remove oil filter and "O" ring. Remove oil pipe from lower valve body. Remove 1-2 solenoid and lockup solenoid with oil strainers. Remove 2-3 solenoid and 3-4 solenoid with oil strainers. *See Figs. 26 and 27.*

2) Unbolt and remove upper valve body. Remove gaskets and separator plate from upper valve body. Remove throttle relief check ball and spring from underside of upper valve body. Unbolt and remove main valve body from premain valve body.

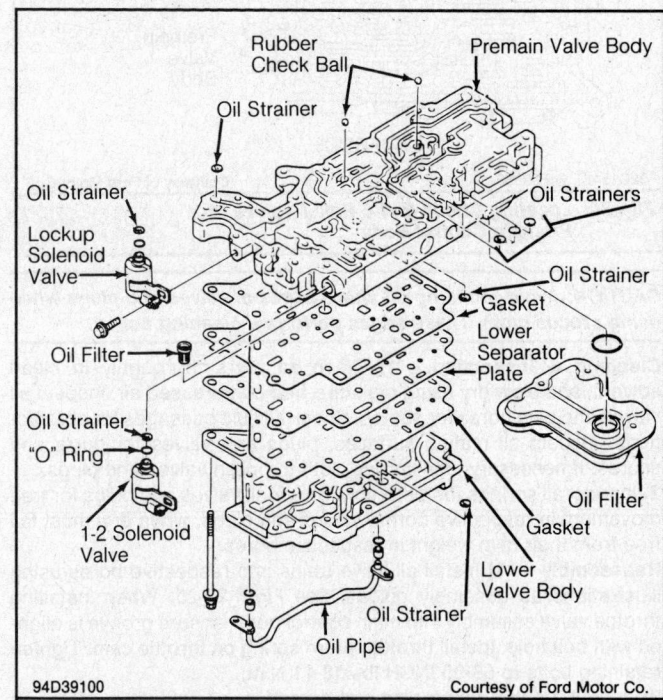

94D39100

Courtesy of Ford Motor Co.

Fig. 26: Exploded View Of Premain & Lower Valve Body (Escort & Tracer)

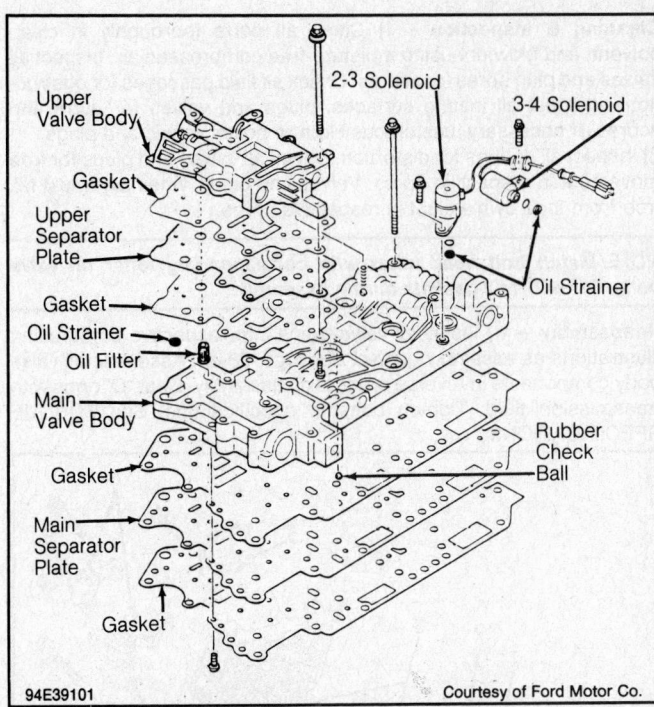

Fig. 27: Exploded View Of Main & Upper Valve Body (Escort & Tracer)

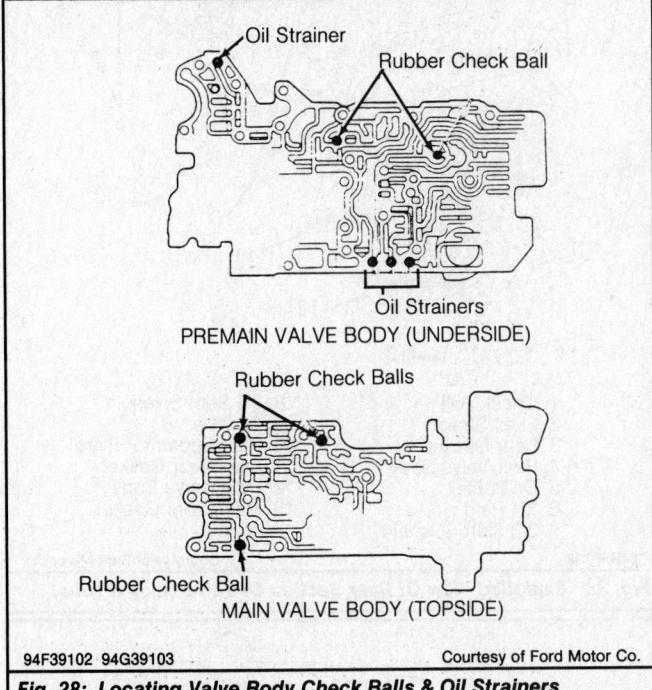

Fig. 28: Locating Valve Body Check Balls & Oil Strainers (Escort & Tracer)

Cleaning & Inspection – 1) Clean all parts thoroughly in clean solvent, and blow dry using moisture-free compressed air. Inspect all valves and plug bores for scores. Check all fluid passages for obstructions. Inspect all mating surfaces, plugs and valves for burrs and scores. If necessary, use crocus cloth to polish valves and plugs. **2)** Inspect all springs for distortion. Check all valves and plugs for free movement in respective bores. Valves and plugs, when dry, must fall free from their own weight in respective bores.

NOTE: Match bolt head letter with corresponding letter on valve body. DO NOT mix gaskets during assembly.

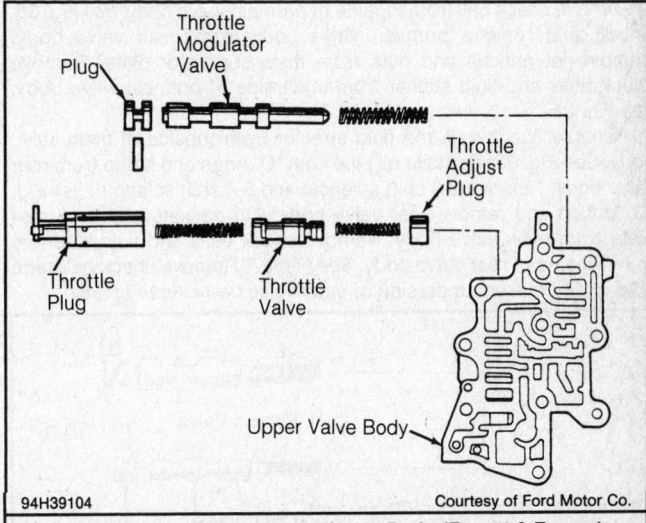

Fig. 29: Exploded View Of Upper Valve Body (Escort & Tracer)

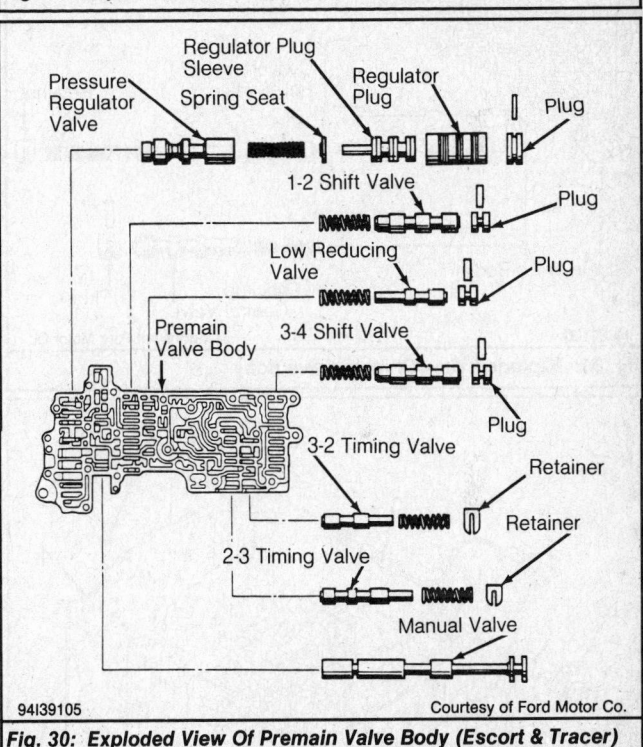

Fig. 30: Exploded View Of Premain Valve Body (Escort & Tracer)

Reassembly – 1) Install all valve trains into respective bores using illustrations as assembly guides. *See Figs. 29-31.* Assemble all valve body components in reverse order of disassembly. Coat "O" rings with transmission fluid. Tighten bolts to specifications. See TORQUE SPECIFICATIONS.

VALVE BODY (PROBE)

CAUTION: Disassembly procedures identify valve body components as follows:
- *TOPSIDE – Side of component facing oil pan.*
- *UNDERSIDE – Side of component facing transaxle case.*

Disassembly – 1) Remove Transmission Oil Temperature (TOT) sensor using appropriate socket. Remove line pressure solenoid, TCC solenoid, downshift solenoid, 1-2 shift solenoid and TCC control solenoid. *See Figs. 32 and 33.* **2)** Ensure all solenoid fluid stainers and "O" rings are removed. Remove front valve body with gaskets and separator plates. Remove check ball from underside of front valve body. *See Fig. 34.*

3) Remove check ball from topside of premain valve body. *See Fig. 35.* Unbolt and remove premain valve body from main valve body. Remove jet orifices and nuts from main separator plate. Remove check balls and fluid stainer from underside of premain valve body. *See Fig. 35.*

4) Remove check ball and fluid strainer from topside of main valve body. *See Fig. 36.* Remove oil pipe with "O" rings and baffle from rear valve body. Remove 2-3 shift solenoid and 3-4 shift solenoid. *See Fig. 33.* Unbolt and remove rear valve body with gaskets and separator plate from main valve body. Remove check balls and fluid strainers from topside of rear valve body. *See Fig. 37.* Remove check balls and fluid strainers from underside of main valve body. *See Fig. 36.*

Cleaning & Inspection – 1) Clean all parts thoroughly in clean solvent, and blow dry using moisture-free compressed air. Inspect all valves and plug bores for scores. Check all fluid passages for obstructions. Inspect all mating surfaces, plugs and valves for burrs and scores. If necessary, use crocus cloth to polish valves and plugs.
2) Inspect all springs for distortion. Check all valves and plugs for free movement in respective bores. Valves and plugs, when dry, must fall free from their own weight in respective bores.

NOTE: Match bolt head letter with corresponding letter on valve body. DO NOT mix gaskets during assembly.

Reassembly – 1) Install all valve trains into respective bores using illustrations as assembly guides. *See Figs. 38-40.* Assemble all valve body components in reverse order of disassembly. Coat "O" rings with transmission fluid. Tighten bolts to specifications. See TORQUE SPECIFICATIONS.

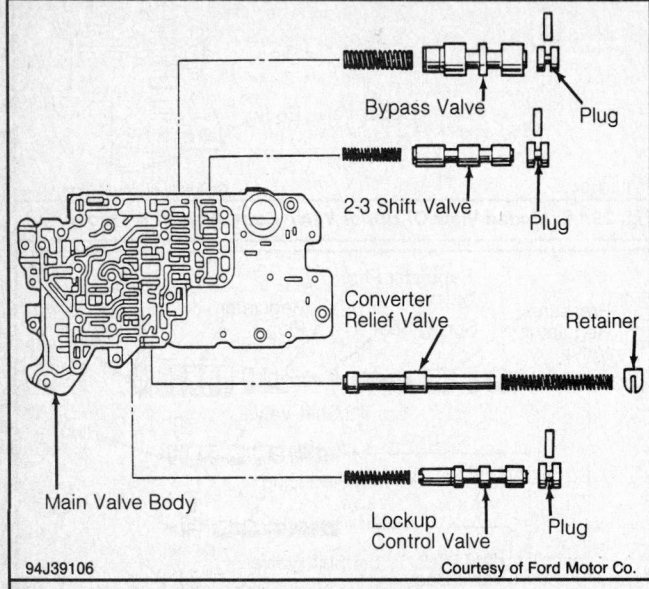

Bypass Valve
Plug
2-3 Shift Valve
Plug
Converter Relief Valve
Retainer
Main Valve Body
Lockup Control Valve
Plug

94J39106 Courtesy of Ford Motor Co.

Fig. 31: Exploded View Of Main Valve Body

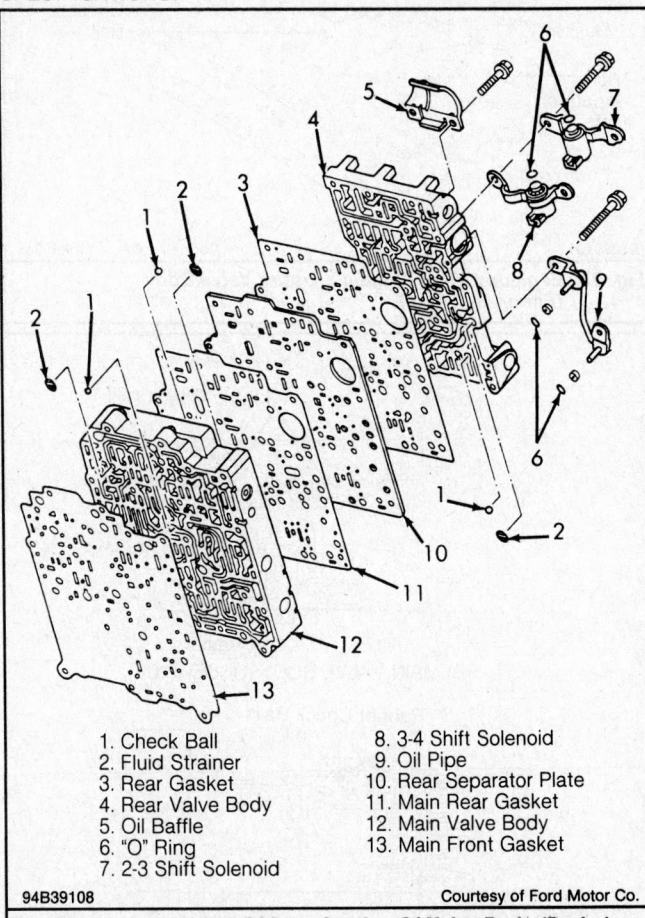

1. Check Ball
2. Fluid Strainer
3. Rear Gasket
4. Rear Valve Body
5. Oil Baffle
6. "O" Ring
7. 2-3 Shift Solenoid
8. 3-4 Shift Solenoid
9. Oil Pipe
10. Rear Separator Plate
11. Main Rear Gasket
12. Main Valve Body
13. Main Front Gasket

94B39108 Courtesy of Ford Motor Co.

Fig. 33: Exploded View Of Rear Section Of Valve Body (Probe)

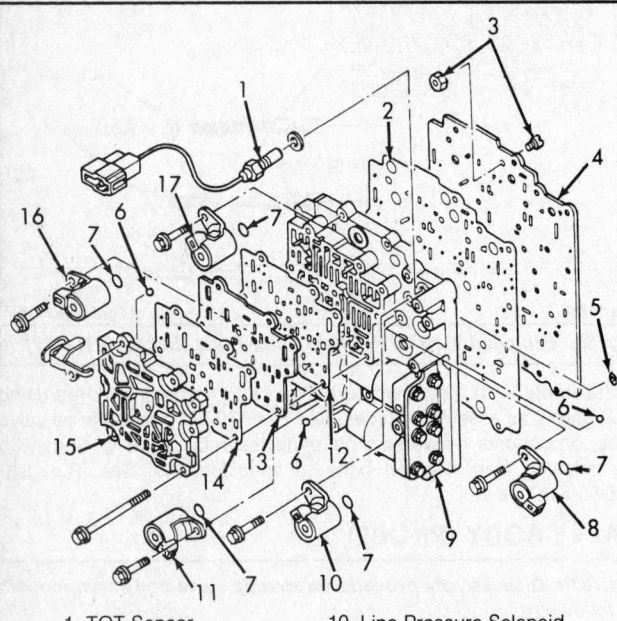

1. TOT Sensor
2. Premain Rear Gasket
3. Jet Orifice & Nut
4. Main Separator Plate
5. Fluid Strainer
6. Check Ball
7. "O" Ring
8. Downshift Solenoid
9. Premain Valve Body
10. Line Pressure Solenoid
11. TCC Control Solenoid
12. Premain Front Gasket
13. Front Separator Plate
14. Front Gasket
15. Front Valve Body
16. 1-2 Shift Solenoid
17. TCC Solenoid

94A39107 Courtesy of Ford Motor Co.

Fig. 32: Exploded View Of Front Section Of Valve Body (Probe)

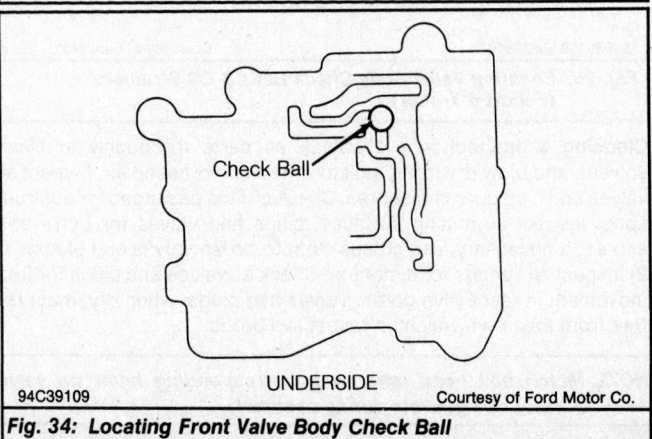

Check Ball

UNDERSIDE

94C39109 Courtesy of Ford Motor Co.

Fig. 34: Locating Front Valve Body Check Ball

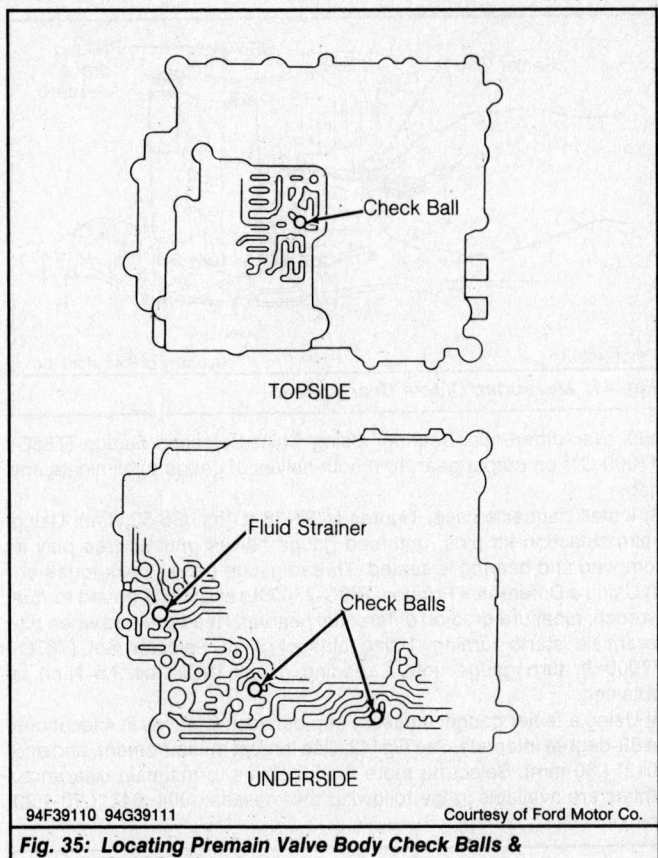

Fig. 35: Locating Premain Valve Body Check Balls & Fluid Strainers

94F39110 94G39111   Courtesy of Ford Motor Co.

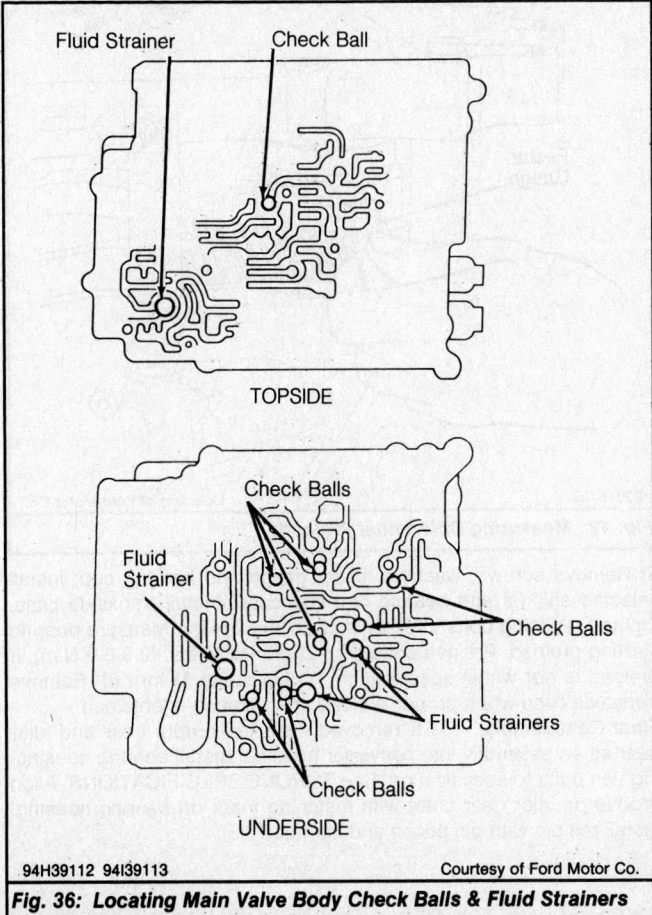

Fig. 36: Locating Main Valve Body Check Balls & Fluid Strainers

94H39112 94I39113   Courtesy of Ford Motor Co.

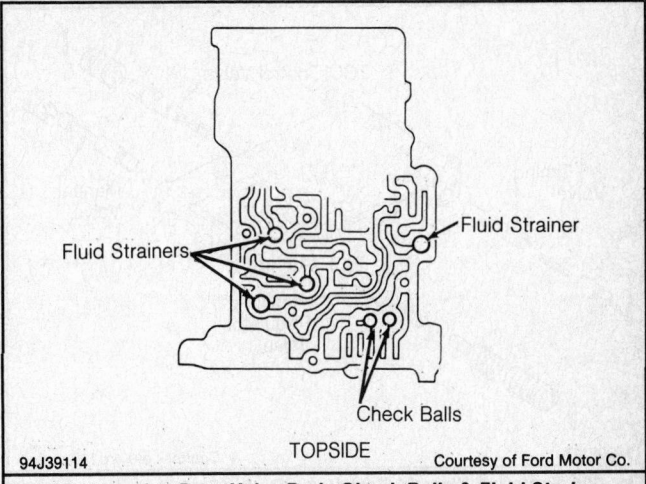

94J39114   Courtesy of Ford Motor Co.

Fig. 37: Locating Rear Valve Body Check Balls & Fluid Strainers

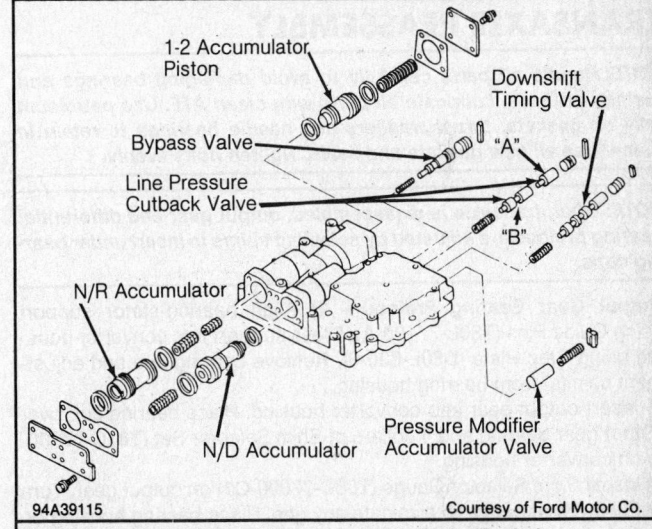

94A39115   Courtesy of Ford Motor Co.

Fig. 38: Exploded View Of Premain Valve Body (Probe)

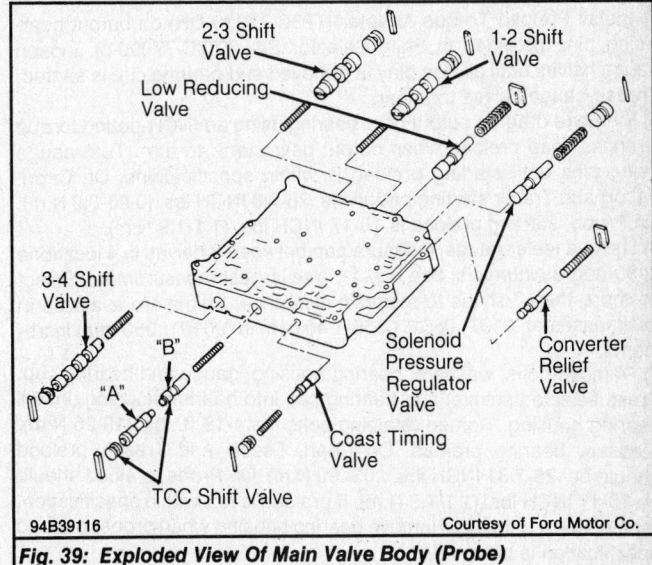

94B39116   Courtesy of Ford Motor Co.

Fig. 39: Exploded View Of Main Valve Body (Probe)

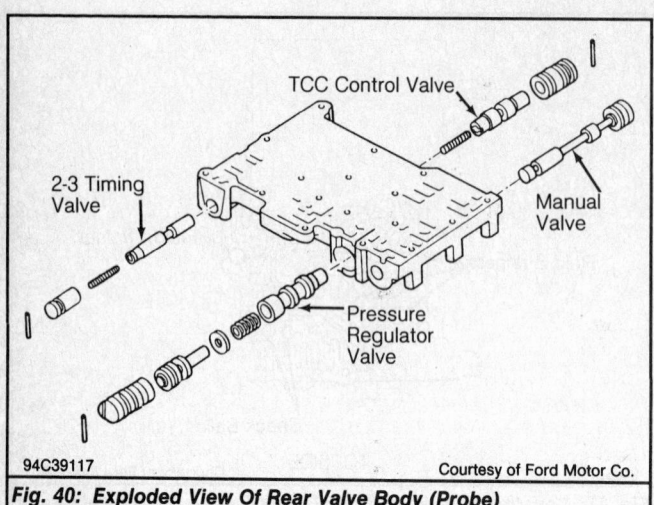

Fig. 40: Exploded View Of Rear Valve Body (Probe)

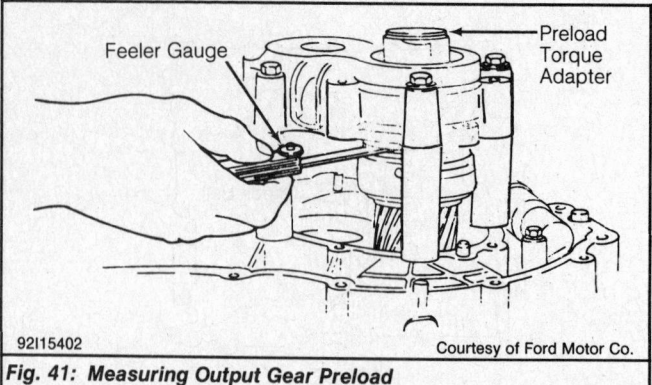

Fig. 41: Measuring Output Gear Preload

TRANSAXLE REASSEMBLY

NOTE: Handle all parts carefully to avoid damaging bearings and mating surfaces. Lubricate all parts with clean ATF. Use petroleum jelly on gaskets, thrust washers and needle bearings to retain in place. Use all new gaskets and seals. Tighten bolts evenly.

NOTE: When transaxle is disassembled, output gear and differential bearing preload are adjusted by selecting shims to insert under bearing cups.

Output Gear Bearing Preload – 1) Align bearing-stator support using Guide Pins (T80L-77100-A). Press support into converter housing using Step Plate (D80L-630-6). Remove bearing cup and adjustment shim(s) from bearing housing.
2) Insert output gear into converter housing. Place bearing cup over output gear bearing and 4 collars of Shim Selector Set (T87C-77000-J) on converter housing.
3) Install Shim Selector Gauge (T88C-77000-C1) on output gear. Turn both halves of gauge to eliminate any gap. Place bearing housing on collars. Install 4 bolts with washers. Tighten bolts to 19-22 ft. lbs. (26-30 N.m).
4) Install Preload Torque Adapter (T88C-77000-DH) on output gear. Using pins provided in Shim Selector Set (T87C-77000-J), loosen gauge halves until all free play is removed and bearing cup is seated. Thread gauge halves together.
5) Measure drag on output gear bearing using an INCH-pound torque wrench. Read preload when output gear starts to turn. Turn gauge using pins until starting preload is within specifications. On Capri, Escort and Tracer starting preload is .26-7.8 INCH lbs. (0.03-0.9 N.m). On Probe, starting preload is 10-17 INCH lbs. (1.1-1.9 N.m).
6) Using a feeler gauge, measure gap between 2 halves in 4 locations at 90-degree intervals. See Fig. 41. Use largest measurement. Select no more than 7 shims to maintain clearance. Shims are available in thicknesses of .0137-.0551" (.350-1.40 mm) in .0019" (.050 mm) increments.
7) Remove bolts, washers, bearing housing, gauge and bearing cup. Press selected shim(s) and bearing cup into bearing housing. Install bearing housing. Tighten retaining bolts to 14-19 ft. lbs. (19-26 N.m). Measure bearing preload. On Capri, Escort and Tracer, preload should be .26-7.81 INCH lbs. (.03-.90 N.m). On Probe, preload should be 10-17 INCH lbs. (1.1-1.9 N.m). If preload is not within specification, repeat steps **1)** thru **6)**. Remove bearing housing when proper preload specification is obtained.
Differential Bearing Preload – 1) Using appropriate bearing remover, remove rear bearing cup and shims from case. Install front bearing cup into converter housing using appropriate bearing cup replacer.
2) Insert differential into converter housing. Place 6 collars of Shim Selector Set (T87C-77000-J) on converter housing. Install rear bearing

cup over differential bearing. Using Shim Selection Gauge (T88C-77000-C1) on output gear, turn both halves of gauge to eliminate any gap.
3) Install transaxle case. Tighten to 27-38 ft. lbs. (36-52 N.m). Using shim selection kit pins, unthread gauge halves until all free play is removed and bearing is seated. Thread gauge halves back together.
4) Using a Differential Rotator (T88C-77000L) and INCH-pound torque wrench, measure drag on differential bearing. Read preload when differentials starts to turn. Using pins of Shim Selector Set (T87C-77000-J), turn gauge until a reading of 4.3 INCH lbs. (.5 N.m) is obtained.
5) Using a feeler gauge, measure gap between 2 halves in 4 locations at 90-degree intervals. See Fig. 42. Use largest measurement, and add .012" (.30 mm). Select no more than 3 shims to maintain clearance. Shims are available in the following thicknesses: .004-.048" (.10-1.20 mm) in .001" (.02 mm).

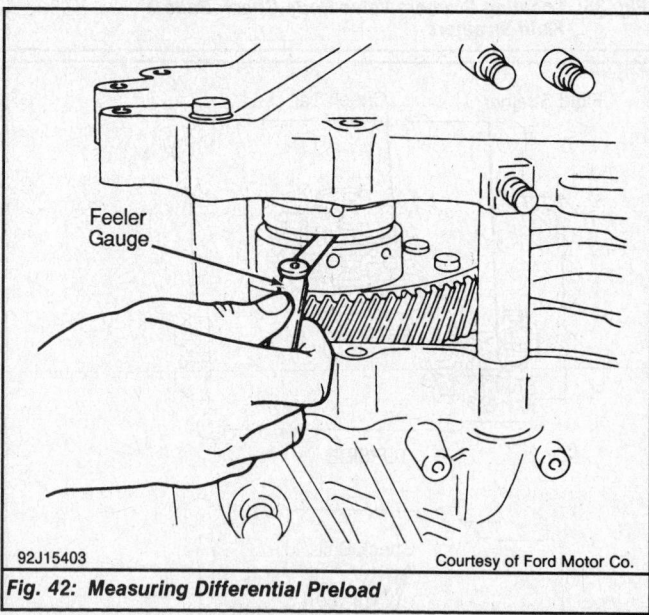

Fig. 42: Measuring Differential Preload

6) Remove screws, washers, case, gauge and bearing cup. Install selected shim(s) and bearing cup into case. Install transaxle case. Tighten retaining bolts to 27-38 ft. lbs. (36-52 N.m). Measure bearing starting preload. Preload should be 26-35 INCH lbs. (2.9-3.9 N.m). If preload is not within specification, repeat steps **1)** thru **6)**. Remove transaxle case when proper preload specification is obtained.
Final Reassembly – 1) If removed, installed output gear and idler gear as an assembly into converter housing. Install bearing housing. Tighten bolts to specification. See TORQUE SPECIFICATIONS. Align groove on idler gear shaft with matching mark on bearing housing. Install roll pin with pin punch and hammer.

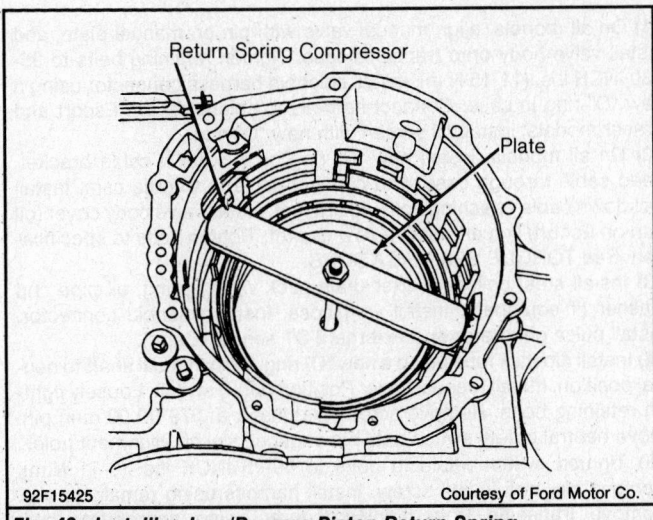

Fig. 43: Installing Low/Reverse Piston Return Spring

92F15425   Courtesy of Ford Motor Co.

2) On Capri and Probe models, install orifice check valve spring, check valve and lower accumulator seal. Install 2-3 accumulator. Install detent ball, spring, washer and oil pressure relief plug. Install differential assembly.

3) Using Seal Protector (T88C-77000-GH), carefully install low and reverse clutch piston by pushing evenly around circumference. DO NOT damage outer seal. Remove protector. Install return spring and retainer. Compress return spring and retainer using Spring Compressor (T88C-77000-AH) and Plate (T87C-77000-B). *See Fig. 43.* Install snap ring. Remove spring compressor.

4) Air check reverse clutch operation. *See Figs. 5 and 6.* Install output shell to output gear with 2.83" (72.0 mm) thrust washer on output shell. Apply thin coat of silicone sealant to contact surfaces of converter housing and transaxle case. Install new "O" rings. Install case to converter housing, and tighten retaining bolts to specification.

5) Install Transaxle Plugs (T88C-7025-AH) to differential side gears. Failure to install plugs may allow differential side gears to become mispositioned. Install 3-4 clutch and turbine shaft assembly with thrust bearing into case. *See Fig. 44.* Install internal gear and snap ring.

1. Oil Pump & Clutch Assembly
2. Clutch Assembly
3. One-Way Clutch Inner Race
4. One-Way Clutch Outer Race
5. Small Sun Gear & One-Way Clutch
6. Planetary Carrier Assembly
7. 3-4 Clutch Assembly

Fig. 44: Locating Thrust Washers & Needle Bearings

92E15424   Courtesy of Ford Motor Co.

6) Install Turbine Shaft Holder (T88C-77000-KH) to turbine shaft. Install ring gear and secure with snap ring. Install thrust bearing and carrier hub assembly. Ensure thrust washer is installed facing 3-4 clutch assembly.

7) Install low and reverse clutch pack, pressure plate and snap ring. Using a feeler gauge, check clearance between retaining snap ring and pressure plate. On Capri, Escort and Tracer models, clearance should be .083-.094" (2.10-2.40 mm). On Probe models, clearance should be .059-.071" (1.5-1.8 mm).

8) If clearance is not within specification on Capri and Probe models, install correct pressure plate. Pressure plates are available in following thicknesses: .268" (6.80 mm), .276" (7.00 mm), .283" (7.20 mm), .291" (7.40 mm), .299" (7.60 mm) and .307" (7.80 mm). Recheck clearance.

9) If clearance is not within specification on Escort and Tracer models, install correct snap ring. Snap rings are available in following thicknesses: .079" (2.0 mm), .087" (2.2 mm), .095" (2.4 mm), .102" (2.6 mm), .110" (2.8 mm) and .118" (3.0 mm). Recheck clearance.

CAUTION: Ensure carrier hub rotates counterclockwise while turning from rear of transaxle when one-way clutch is installed.

11) On all models, install wave washer. Turn carrier hub assembly counterclockwise, and carefully install one-way clutch. Install snap ring. On Capri and Probe models, install servo spring and servo. Compress servo using a "C" clamp and install retaining snap ring. Remove "C" clamp. Install piston stem.

12) On all models, install anchor strut. Install 2-4 band in case fully expanded. Interlock 2-4 band and anchor strut. On Escort and Tracer models, install servo assembly and servo piston spring into case. Compress servo assembly into bore and install piston snap ring.

13) Install dial indicator with Adapter (T75L-4201-A) to measure servo travel. *See Fig. 45.* Apply air pressure to 3rd fluid passage (2-4 band apply) beneath throttle control lever. *See Fig. 6.* Servo piston stem should move .039-.067" (1.0-1.7 mm).

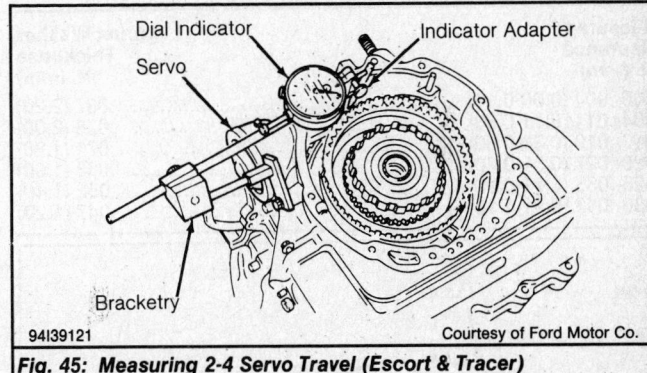

Fig. 45: Measuring 2-4 Servo Travel (Escort & Tracer)

94I39121   Courtesy of Ford Motor Co.

14) If stem movement is not within specification, disassemble servo assembly and replace stem with correct length replacement. Stem lengths range from 3.74" (95.0mm) to 3.90" (99.0 mm) in .5 mm increments. Recheck servo movement once stem is installed.

15) On all models, install primary sun gear and one-way clutch by rotating. Ensure planet gear bearing thrust washer and sun gear thrust bearing are installed. *See Fig. 44.*

16) On Capri and Probe models, pull 2-4 band using pliers, and loosely tighten piston stem by hand. On all models, install reverse clutch assembly with thrust bearing. Install turbine shaft snap ring. Remove turbine shaft holder. Measure height difference between reverse drum and transaxle case. *See Fig. 46.* Maximum height difference should be .032" (.80 mm) for Capri, .035" (.90 mm) for Escort and Tracer and .028-.075" (.7-1.9 mm) for Probe models. If assembly height is not within specification, recheck all assembled components.

17) Place needle bearing on reverse clutch assembly. To adjust total end play, remove previous thrust washer and gasket from oil pump. Place a .087" (2.20 mm) thrust washer on oil pump. Set oil pump on clutch assembly.

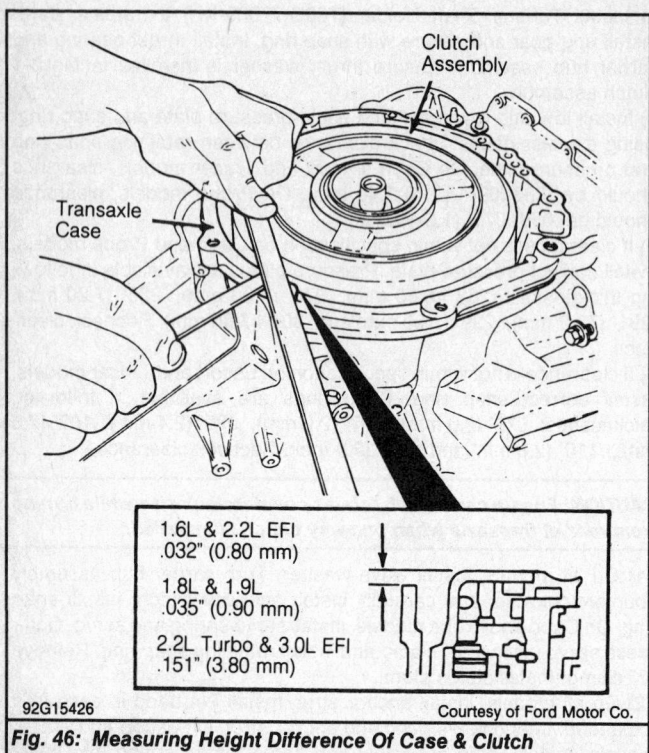

1.6L & 2.2L EFI
.032" (0.80 mm)

1.8L & 1.9L
.035" (0.90 mm)

2.2L Turbo & 3.0L EFI
.151" (3.80 mm)

92G15426   Courtesy of Ford Motor Co.

Fig. 46: Measuring Height Difference Of Case & Clutch

18) Using a feeler gauge, measure clearance between transaxle case and oil pump in several locations. *See Fig. 47.* Average measurements. Select correct end play thrust washer to install. See END PLAY THRUST WASHER SELECTION CHART.

END PLAY THRUST WASHER SELECTION CHART

Measured Clearance IN. (mm)	Thrust Washer Thickness IN. (mm)
.000-.004 (0.00-0.11)	.087 (2.20)
.004-.011 (0.11-0.30)	.078 (2.00)
.012-.019 (0.31-0.50)	.071 (1.80)
.020-.027 (0.51-0.70)	.063 (1.60)
.028-.035 (0.71-0.90)	.055 (1.40)
.036-.043 (0.91-1.10)	.047 (1.20)

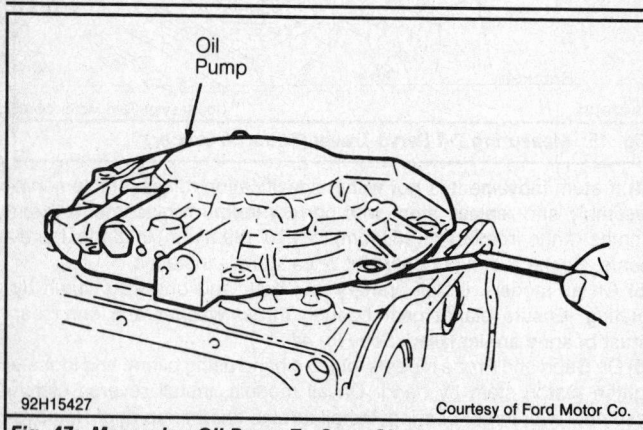

92H15427   Courtesy of Ford Motor Co.

Fig. 47: Measuring Oil Pump-To-Case Clearance

19) Remove oil pump. Place selected thrust washer and new gasket on oil pump. Install oil pump on clutch assembly, and tighten retaining bolts. On Capri and Probe models, loosen lock nut, and tighten piston stem to 105-130 INCH lbs. (11-14 N.m). Loosen stem 1 1/2 turns. Tighten lock nut to 18-29 ft. lbs. (25-39 N.m).

20) On Capri and Probe models, install oil strainer using new "O" ring. Ensure magnets are correctly positioned in oil pan. Install oil pan and new gasket. Tighten bolts to specification. See TORQUE SPECIFICATIONS.

21) On all models, align manual valve with pin on manual plate, and install valve body onto transaxle case. Tighten retaining bolts to 95-130 INCH lbs. (11-15 N.m). Install solenoid harness connector using a new "O" ring in case. Connect harness to solenoids. On Escort and Tracer models, install oil screen with new "O" ring.

22) On all models, install new "O" ring on kickdown cable bracket. Feed cable through case, and connect cable to throttle cam. Install kickdown cable attaching bolt and bracket. Install valve body cover (oil pan on Escort/Tracer) using a new gasket. Tighten bolts to specification. See TORQUE SPECIFICATIONS.

23) Install steel ball, converter drain-back valve spring, oil pipe and washer (if equipped). Install vent hose. Install solenoid connector. Install pulse generator and external TOT sensor (Capri).

24) Install dipstick tube using a new "O" ring. Turn manual shaft to neutral position. Install Manual Lever Position (MLP) switch. Loosely tighten retaining bolts. Remove screw, and insert a .079" (2.00 mm) pin. Move neutral safety switch until pin engages switch alignment hole.

25) Tighten switch retaining bolts to 69-95 INCH lbs. (8-11 N.m). Remove pin, and install screw. Install harness using remaining clip. Remove transaxle from holding fixture. Using appropriate seal replacer, install converter seal.

26) Install new "O" ring on turbine shaft. Install oil pump shaft. Fill torque converter with specified transaxle fluid. Carefully install torque converter in converter housing while rotating to align splines.

27) Measure distance between torque converter and end of converter housing. See TORQUE CONVERTER SETBACK table.

TORQUE CONVERTER SETBACK

Application	Setback In. (mm)
Capri	.98 (25)
Escort & Tracer	.54 (13.6)
Probe	.55 (14.0)

28) Install right transaxle mount, and tighten retaining bolts to 43-49 ft. lbs. (58-67 N.m). Using Differential Seal Replacer (T87C-77000-H), install differential oil seals.

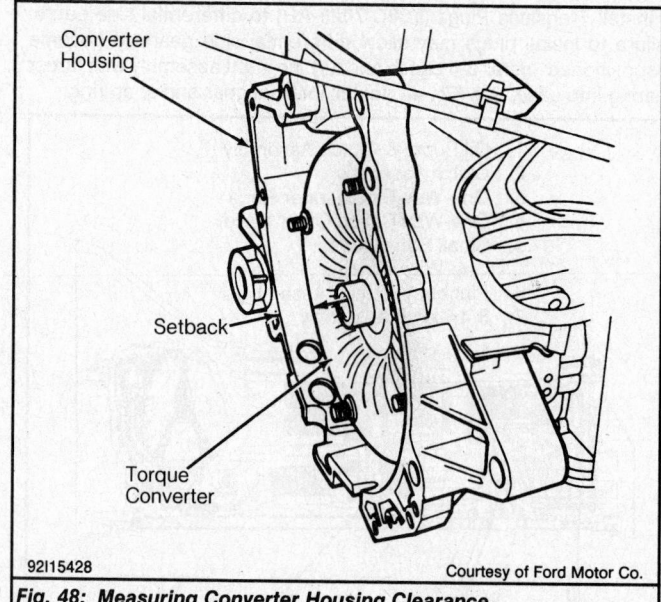

92I15428   Courtesy of Ford Motor Co.

Fig. 48: Measuring Converter Housing Clearance

TORQUE SPECIFICATIONS

TORQUE SPECIFICATIONS

Application	Ft. Lbs. (N.m)
Bearing Housing Bolts	14-19 (19-26)
Center Transaxle Mount Bolt	27-40 (37-54)
Center Transaxle Mount Nuts	47-66 (64-89)
Drain Plug	29-36 (39-50)
TOT Sensor Bolt	22-29 (29-39)
Manual Plate Nut	30-41 (41-56)
Oil Line Plug	23-35 (31-47)
Oil Pump Bolts	14-19 (19-26)
MLP Switch Bolts	22-29 (29-39)
Right Transaxle Mount Bolts	43-49 (58-66)
Switch Box Bolts	12-17 (16-23)
Torque Cable Bracket Bolt	32-45 (43-61)
Torque Converter Nuts	32-45 (43-61)
Transaxle Case-To-Converter Housing	27-38 (37-52)
Transaxle-To-Engine Bolts	66-86 (89-117)
Transaxle-To-Left Mount Bolts	63-86 (85-117)

Application	INCH Lbs. (N.m)
Actuator Support Bolts	95-120 (11-14)
Converter Cover Bolts	69-95 (8-11)
Dipstick Tube Bolt	61-87 (7-10)
Front Face & Rear Face Valve Body Bolts	57-69 (6-8)
Line Pressure Plug	43-87 (5-10)
N-R/N-OD Accumulator Plate Bolts	57-69 (6-8)
Oil Pan Bolts	69-95 (8-11)
Oil Pump Cover Bolts	69-95 (8-11)
Pulse Generator Bolt	69-95 (8-11)
Solenoid Valve Bolts	57-69 (6-8)
Throttle Cam Bolts	69-95 (8-11)
Valve Body Bolts	95-130 (11-15)
Valve Body Cover Bolts	69-95 (8-11)
1-2 Accumulator Plate Bolts	57-69 (6-8)
2-3 Accumulator Bolts	69-95 (8-11)

TRANSMISSION SPECIFICATIONS

TRANSMISSION SPECIFICATIONS

Application	In. (mm)
Coasting Clutch Pack Clearance	.040-.047 (1.0-1.2)
Converter Setback	
Capri	.98 (25)
Escort & Tracer	.54 (13.6)
Probe	.55 (14.0)
Differential Pinion Backlash	0-.004 (0-.10)
Forward Clutch Pack Clearance	.040-.047 (1.0-1.2)
Low/Reverse Clutch Pack Clearance	
Capri, Escort & Tracer	.54 (13.6)
Probe	.55 (14.0)
Reverse Clutch Pack Clearance	.059-.071 (1.5-1.8)
3/4 Clutch Pack Clearance	.051-.059 (1.3-1.5)

APPLICATION & IDENTIFICATION

TRANSAXLE APPLICATION

Vehicle	Engine Application
1993 Only	
Probe	2.0L SFI
1993-1994	
Capri	1.6L SFI
Escort	1.8L SFI
Probe	2.5L SFI
Tracer	1.8L SFI

INTRODUCTION

NOTE: The CHECK ENGINE light, located on the instrument cluster, is referred to as Malfunction Indicator Light (MIL) in this article.

The first step in diagnosing any driveability problem is verifying the customer's complaint with a test drive under the conditions the problem reportedly occurred. Before entering self-diagnostics, perform a careful and complete visual inspection. Most transmission control problems result from mechanical breakdowns or poor electrical connections.

NOTE: Perform all voltage tests with a Digital Volt-Ohmmeter (DVOM) with a minimum 10-megohm input impedance, unless stated otherwise in test procedure.

DESCRIPTION & OPERATION

Input signals from sensors are sent to the Powertrain Control Module (PCM). The PCM can determine when the time and conditions are right for a shift or converter clutch application. The PCM can also determine line pressure needed to optimize shift feel. Capri and Probe models utilize a separate Transmission Control Module (TCM) in conjunction with the PCM.

The PCM controls transmission operation through electronic solenoids consisting of On/Off solenoids for shifting and torque converter clutch control and variable force solenoid for line pressure control. The PCM has built-in self-diagnosis, fail-safe code and warning code display for the main input sensors and solenoid valves.

NOTE: In addition to transmission fault codes, engine related fault codes may be output during QUICK TEST procedure. These fault codes pertain to engine performance and must be repaired first, as engine performance will greatly affect transmission operation. For information and testing procedures of engine related fault codes and components, see SELF-DIAGNOSTICS – EEC article in ENGINE PERFORMANCE of appropriate MITCHELL® manual.

SELF-DIAGNOSTIC SYSTEM

Hard Failures – Hard failures cause Malfunction Indicator Light (MIL) to come on and trouble codes to be set in Powertrain Control Module (PCM) memory. Trouble code remains until problem is repaired. To retrieve trouble codes, see READING SELF-DIAGNOSTIC CODES. Use circuit tests to determine cause of malfunction.

If a sensor fails, PCM will use a substitute value in its calculations to continue engine operation. PCM can estimate failed sensor values based on feedback from working sensors. In this condition, known as Limited Operating Strategy (LOS), vehicle runs but driveability will not be optimum.

Intermittent Failures – Intermittent failures may cause Malfunction Indicator Light (MIL) to flicker or glow. Light will go out after intermittent fault goes away. These faults indicate that a defect may or may not be present at time of testing, however corresponding trouble code will be retained in PCM memory.

If related fault does not reoccur within a certain time frame, trouble code will be erased from PCM memory. Intermittent failures may be caused by a sensor, connector or wiring problems.

ENTERING SELF-DIAGNOSTICS

Diagnostic Trouble Codes (DTCs) can be retrieved using one of the following methods.
- Analog Volt-Ohmmeter (VOM).
- Malfunction Indicator Light (MIL).
- Overdrive Off Light (ODL).
- Superstar II (007-0041B) scan tester.
- New Generation Star (007-00500) scan tester.

Codes are accessed from PCM using Data Link Connector (DLC). *See Fig. 1.* Procedure to retrieve codes varies with each method. Follow QUICK TEST procedure for specific method being used to retrieve codes. If no code or only intermittent fault is found after performing QUICK TEST, proceed to SWITCH MONITOR TEST.

NOTE: Before hooking up equipment to diagnose EEC system, prepare and visually inspect vehicle. See VISUAL CHECK & VEHICLE PREPARATION.

Visual Check & Vehicle Preparation – Before hooking up any equipment to diagnose EEC system, visually check following and perform preparation procedures:
- Perform all necessary safety precautions to prevent personal injury or vehicle damage.
- Block drive wheels. Set parking brake. Place shift lever in "P" (Park). DO NOT move shift lever during test unless specifically directed to do so.
- Check condition of air cleaner and air ducting.
- Check all vacuum hoses for leaks, restrictions and proper routing.
- Check EEC system wiring harness connections for corrosion, damaged pins, loose wires and improper routing.
- Check PCM, sensors and actuators for physical damage.
- Check engine coolant and oil level.
- Check battery condition. Turn off all lights and accessories. Ensure vehicle doors are closed when measuring voltage.
- Ensure engine is at operating temperature.
- Check exhaust system for leaks.

DATA LINK CONNECTOR LOCATION

Data Link Connector (DLC) is located in engine compartment. *See Fig 1.*

EQUIPMENT HOOKUP

NOTE: After performing equipment hookup, follow appropriate quick test procedures based on type of equipment being used. See QUICK TEST.

Using Analog Volt-Ohmmeter (VOM) (Capri & Probe) – Turn ignition off. Locate Data Link Connector (DLC). *See Fig 1.* Connect positive (+) lead of VOM to TCM STO terminal at DLC and negative (–) test lead to engine ground (GND). *See Figs. 2 and 3.* Set VOM to 0-20V DC range. Connect a jumper wire between ground and TCM STI terminal of DLC.

Using Analog Volt-Ohmmeter (VOM) (Escort & Tracer) – Turn ignition off. Locate Data Link Connector (DLC). *See Fig 1.* Connect positive (+) lead of VOM to PCM STO terminal at DLC and negative (–) test lead to engine ground (GND). *See Fig. 3.* Set VOM to 0-20V DC range. Connect a jumper wire between ground and PCM STI terminal of DLC.

Using Malfunction Indicator Light (MIL) (Escort & Tracer) – Check MIL operation. Turn ignition on. If MIL is on, MIL circuit is okay. Go to next step. If MIL is off, go to CIRCUIT TEST MIL. See SELF-DIAGNOSTICS – EEC article in ENGINE PERFORMANCE of appropriate MITCHELL® manual. After performing CIRCUIT TEST MIL, return to this procedure. Connect a jumper wire between ground and PCM STI terminal of DLC. *See Fig. 2.*

Using Overdrive Off Light (ODL) (Capri & Probe) – Connect a jumper wire between ground and TCM STI terminal of DLC. *See Fig. 2.*

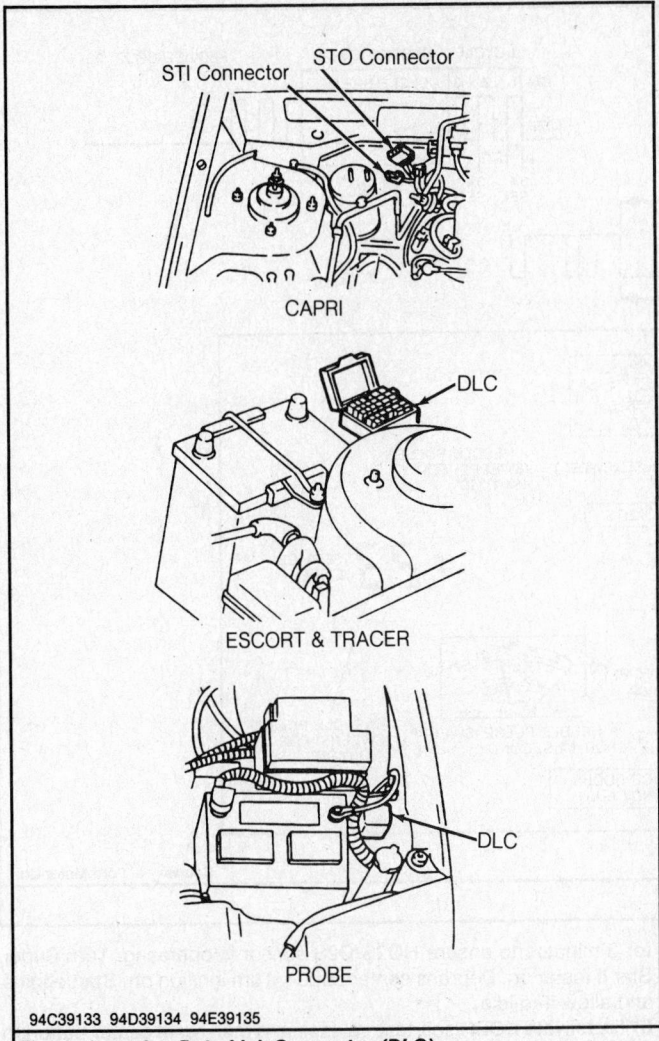

CAPRI

DLC

ESCORT & TRACER

DLC

PROBE

94C39133 94D39134 94E39135

Fig. 1: Locating Data Link Connector (DLC)

1. VPWR
2. PCM STI
3. SML
4. PCM STO
5. TCM STO (Probe)
6. GND
7. TCM STI (Probe)

94G39137 — Courtesy of Ford Motor Co.

Fig. 3: Identifying Data Link Connector Terminals (Escort, Probe & Tracer)

Using Super Star II Tester – 1) Turn ignition off. Connect color-coded adapter cable leads to Super Star II tester. Connect service adapter cables to vehicle Data Link Connector (DLC) (Escort, Probe and Tracer) or STO and STI connectors (Capri). See Figs. 1 and 2.
2) Connect Super MECS Adapter (007-00049 or 007-00052) between adapter cables and vehicle DLC. On Capri, connect adapter cable ground clip to negative (–) battery terminal. Slide adapter switch to EEC/MECS position (Capri, Escort and Tracer) or TCM position (Probe). Slide Super Star II tester switch to EEC/MECS position.

Using New Generation Star Tester – 1) Turn ignition off. Connect power cable and data cable to scan tester. Connect Rotunda Super MECS Adapter (007-00052) to scan tester data cable.
2) Plug matching connector on Super MECS adapter into vehicle DLC (Escort, Probe and Tracer) or STO and STI connectors (Capri). See Figs. 1 and 2. On Capri, connect adapter cable ground clip to negative (–) battery terminal. Slide switch on Super MECS adapter to PCM position (Capri, Escort and Tracer) or TCM position (Probe). Plug power cable on scan tester into cigar lighter or use battery adapter.

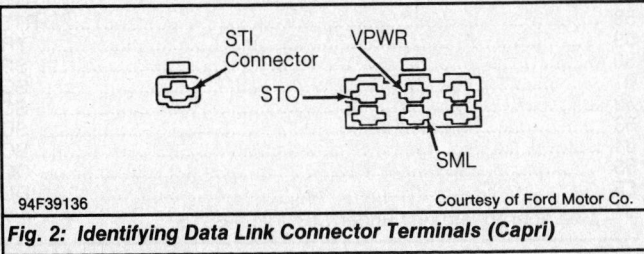

94F39136 — Courtesy of Ford Motor Co.

Fig. 2: Identifying Data Link Connector Terminals (Capri)

READING SELF-DIAGNOSTIC CODES

NOTE: Accuracy of self-diagnostics depends on correct operation of non-EEC components and systems. Correct all non-EEC problems in engine, ignition or fuel system attempting to diagnose EEC system.

NOTE: EEC system will not display a PASS code.

PCM outputs self-diagnostic codes one digit at a time. Record codes in order received. These codes indicate current faults in system and should be serviced in order of appearance. Use appropriate CODE REFERENCE table to find correct CIRCUIT TEST.

Using Analog VOM – Watch voltmeter and count needle sweeps (between 0-12 volts) to determine code. Pay careful attention to length of pauses in order to read codes correctly. A 2-second pause occurs between digits in a code. A 4-second pause occurs between each code. See Fig. 4.

Using MIL/CHECK ENGINE light – Service codes are displayed as flashes. Code flashes are read in the same manner as with using an analog VOM.

Using New Generation Star or Super Star II Scan Tester – Codes will be displayed digitally. KOEO codes include hard and intermittent failures. To determine failure type (hard or intermittent), record and clear codes stored in PCM memory. Operate vehicle, and repeat KOEO self-test. Codes that reappear immediately are hard failures. Codes that do not reappear are intermittent failures.

Repair hard failures in order of code appearance before performing KOER self-test. Use appropriate CODE REFERENCE table to determine circuit test to perform. Clear codes from PCM memory after they have been recorded and/or faults have been repaired. See CLEARING CODES. When performing quick test, if no trouble codes are found during KOEO self-test, proceed to KOER self-test.

CLEARING CODES

CAUTION: When battery is disconnected, vehicle computer and memory systems may lose memory data. Driveability problems may exist until computer systems have completed a relearn cycle. See COMPUTER RELEARN PROCEDURES article in APPLICATIONS & IDENTIFICATION.

To clear trouble codes, deactivate self-test by disconnecting jumper wire from PCM STI or TCM STI terminal at Data Link Connector (DLC). Disconnect negative (–) battery cable. Depress brake pedal for 5-10 seconds. All hard codes and intermittent codes will be erased from PCM memory.

QUICK TEST

NOTE: Reading codes using MIL pulses is similar to reading codes using VOM needle sweeps.

Analog VOM Or MIL – 1) To perform Key On Engine Off (KOEO) test, turn ignition on and observe voltmeter or MIL. Count voltmeter needle sweeps or MIL flashes. If codes are not present, go to step **3)**. If codes are present, record codes, turn ignition off and go to next step.

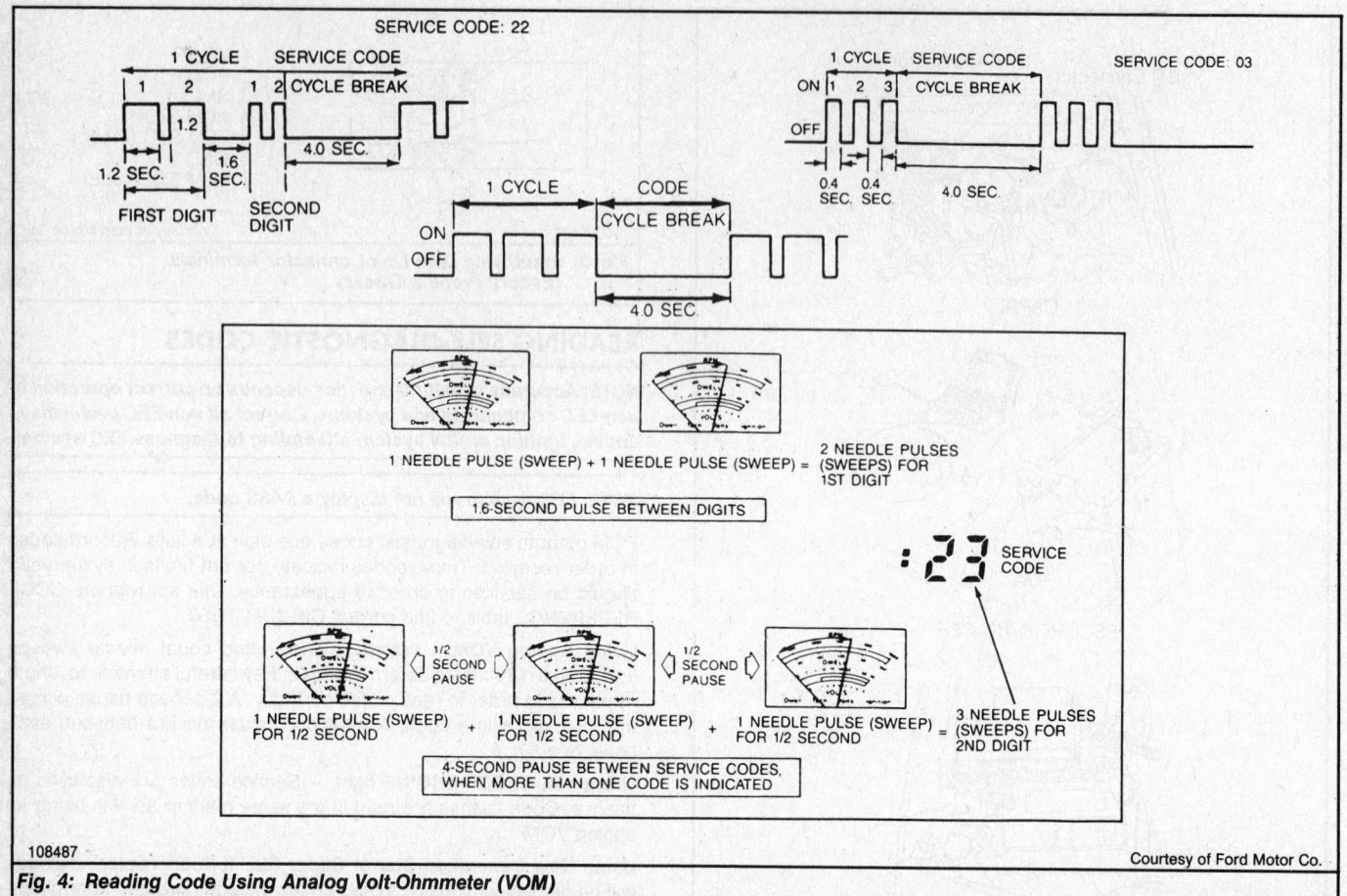

108487   Courtesy of Ford Motor Co.

Fig. 4: Reading Code Using Analog Volt-Ohmmeter (VOM)

NOTE: If code repeats immediately it is considered a "hard fault". If code does not immediately repeat the fault is intermittent and is not failing during self-testing.

2) Erase codes from PCM memory. See CLEARING CODES. Repeat step 1). If no codes are present go to next step. If any codes are present, refer to appropriate CODE REFERENCE table to determine circuit test to perform. After performing repair, return to start of quick test.

3) To perform Key On Engine Running (KOER) test, remove jumper wire from DLC. Start engine and run at 3000 RPM for 3 minutes. Reconnect jumper wire at DLC and read codes. If no codes are present, go to ANALOG VOM OR MIL under SWITCH MONITOR TEST. See SELF-DIAGNOSTICS – EEC article in ENGINE PERFORMANCE of appropriate MITCHELL® manual. If codes are present, refer to appropriate CODE REFERENCE table to determine circuit test to perform.

Super Star II Tester – **1)** To initiate KOEO self-test, depress center button to TEST position. Turn Super Star II tester on. Tester should display 888 for 2 seconds when activated. Turn ignition on.

2) Release and then depress center button to TEST position. After all codes have been received by tester, release center button.

3) Read and record all codes in tester memory, and then go to next step. If no code exists, go to step 5).

4) Erase codes from PCM memory. See CLEARING CODES. Repeat steps 1) and 2). If code does not reappear, fault is intermittent. Go to next step to begin KOER self-test. If code reappears, indicating hard fault, repair fault as necessary. Refer to appropriate CODE REFERENCE table to determine circuit test to perform. After performing repair, return to beginning of QUICK TEST. Repeat quick test until no hard codes exist.

5) To initiate KOER self-test, ensure center button on Super Star II tester is released and tester is OFF. Start and run engine at 2000 RPM

for 3 minutes to ensure HO2S/O2S sensor is operating. Turn Super Star II tester on. Depress center button. Turn ignition off. Start engine and allow it to idle.

6) To activate KOER self-test, release and then reset center button to TEST position. Record all codes displayed. Refer to appropriate CODE REFERENCE table to determine circuit test to perform. If no code is displayed, go to SUPER STAR II TESTER under SWITCH MONITOR TEST.

New Generation Star Tester – See manufacturer's instructions provided with tester.

CODE REFERENCE (CAPRI, ESCORT & TRACER)

Service Code	[1] Circuit Test
55	PSG
60	SCP
61	SCP
62	SCP
63	SCP

[1] – See appropriate test under CIRCUIT TESTS.

CODE REFERENCE (PROBE)

Service Code	[1] Circuit Test
55	PSG
56	TOT
57	RTS1
58	RTS2
59	TRS
60	SCP
61	SCP
62	SCP
63	SCP
64	SCP
65	DCS
66	DCS

[1] – See appropriate test under CIRCUIT TESTS.

SUMMARY

If no hard fault codes are present and driveability symptoms exist see TROUBLE SHOOTING in 4EAT overhaul article for diagnosis by symptom.

CIRCUIT TESTS

HOW TO USE CIRCUIT TESTS

1) DO NOT perform any circuit test unless specifically instructed by a procedure under QUICK TEST. Ensure all non-EEC related faults are corrected. Follow each test step in order until fault is found. When more than one code is received, start with first code displayed.

2) Use circuit tests to check electrical circuits before replacing sensors or any other components. Always test circuits for continuity between sensor and PCM. Test all circuits for short to power, opens or short to ground.

3) DO NOT connect any test light or measure voltage or resistance at PCM unless specified in testing procedure. DO NOT pierce wiring. If backprobing is specified, always backprobe harness side of connector. DO NOT probe connector side.

4) Isolate both ends of circuit and turn ignition off whenever checking for shorts or continuity, unless specified otherwise. Disconnect solenoids and switches before checking circuit continuity or energizing solenoids.

TEST EQUIPMENT

Following equipment is recommended for testing EEC system. DO NOT attempt to test this system without proper equipment. Damage to vehicle components may result if improper equipment is used.

- Digital Volt-Ohmmeter (DVOM) with minimum 10-megohm input impedance.
- 4EAT Tester (007-0037B) with appropriate overlays. Harness adapters available are; Capri (00700095A), Escort/Tracer (007-00100B) and Probe (007-00100A).
- A breakout box and breakout box adapter (007-00057 or T92C-6000) is required to perform certain tests on system. Test pin number mentioned in circuit tests refers to test pin number on breakout box. Breakout box Adapter (T92C-6000-AH) has an A/B position selector switch. Ensure switch is in correct position for each test step. If no switch position is given, switch can be in either position. Once breakout box has been installed during a test sequence, it may stay connected for remainder of that test, unless stated otherwise. Aftermarket breakout boxes are also available.
- Vacuum gauge with 0-30 in. Hg range and resolution (units on scale) of 1 in. Hg.
- Tachometer with 0-6000 RPM range, ± 40 RPM accuracy, and a resolution of 20 RPM.
- Vacuum pump with 0-30 in. Hg range.
- Timing light.
- Spark Tester (D81P-6666-A or ST-125) is required. A modified side electrode spark plug is not sufficient for these procedures.
- Fuel Injection Pressure Gauge (T80L-9974-A).
- 12-volt test light (non-powered type).
- Jumper wire about 15" long.

NOTE: Following circuit tests and illustrations are provided courtesy of Ford Motor Co.

CIRCUIT TEST DCS

DUTY CYCLE SOLENOID

NOTE: The PCM on all models is located behind center console, below radio. The TCM on Capri models is located behind glove box. The TCM on Probe (2.5L) models is located next to PCM.

Diagnostic Aids – This circuit test diagnoses the Torque Converter Clutch (TCC) solenoid and Line Pressure Solenoid (LPS).

DCS CIRCUIT IDENTIFICATION

Circuit	TCM Pin [1]	Wire Color
LPS	2N	Red/Green
TCC	2C	Red/Black

[1] – *See Fig. DCS1.*

92B15355

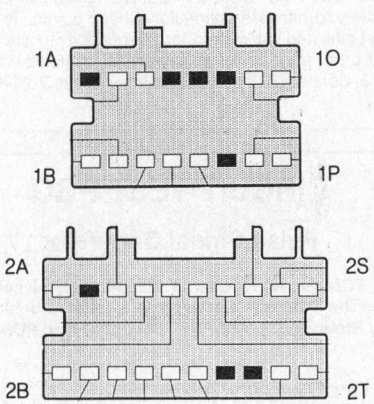

Fig. DCS1: Identifying TCM Harness Connector Terminals

1) Check Solenoid Voltage – Ensure ignition is off. Install 4EAT tester. Test drive vehicle to activate TCC lockup and operate vehicle at full throttle. Using DVOM, measure voltage between LPS and TCC test pins and GND test pin. LPS voltage with throttle closed should be 8 volts and 1-2 volts with WOT. TCC voltage should be 5 volts during engagement and 10 volts or greater when TCC has achieved lockup. If all voltages are within specification, solenoids are functioning correctly. Replace TCM. Reconnect all components and repeat QUICK TEST. If any voltage is not within specification, go to next step.

2) Check Solenoid Resistance – Turn ignition off. Measure resistance between LPS and GND test pins, and TCC and GND test pins. Resistance should be 9-18 ohms. If resistance is within specification, go to step 4). If resistance is not within specification, go to next step.

3) Check For Open Circuits – Ensure ignition is off. Disconnect transaxle solenoid harness connector. Check continuity between LPS and TCC terminal at harness connector and corresponding test pin of 4EAT tester. *See Fig. DCS2.* If continuity does not exist in either circuit, inspect and repair wire(s) as needed. If continuity exists, replace suspect solenoid. See ON-VEHICLE SERVICE in 4EAT overhaul article. Connect all components and repeat QUICK TEST.

CIRCUIT TEST DCS (Cont.)

94I39139

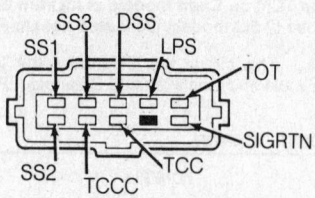

Fig. DCS2: Identifying Solenoid Harness Connector Terminals (2.0L & 2.5L Probe)

4) Check For Short To Ground – Ensure ignition is off. Disconnect transaxle solenoid harness connector. Check continuity between LPS and TCC test pins and vehicle ground. If continuity exists with either circuit, inspect and repair circuit as needed. If continuity does not exist, replace TCM. Connect all components and repeat QUICK TEST.

CIRCUIT TEST PSG

Pulse Signal Generator

NOTE: The PCM on all models is located behind center console, below radio. The TCM on Capri models is located behind glove box. The TCM on Probe (2.5L) models is located next to PCM.

PSG CIRCUIT IDENTIFICATION (Capri)

Circuit	TCM Pin [1]	Wire Color
PSG (+)	2J	Green
PSG (–)	2L	Yellow/Black

[1] – See Fig. DCS1.

PSG CIRCUIT IDENTIFICATION (Escort & Tracer)

Circuit	PCM Pin [1]	Wire Color
PSG (+)	2M	White/Black
PSG (–)	2N	Yellow/Black

[1] – See Figs. PSG1 and PSG2.

PSG CIRCUIT IDENTIFICATION (Probe 2.0L)

Circuit	PCM Pin [1]	Wire Color
PSG (+)	3F	White
PSG (–)	3H	Red

[1] – See Figs. PSG1 and PSG2.

PSG CIRCUIT IDENTIFICATION (Probe 2.5L)

Circuit	TCM Pin [1]	Wire Color
PSG (+)	2J	White
PSG (–)	2L	Red

[1] – See Fig. DCS1.

CIRCUIT TEST PSG (Cont.)

92C15356

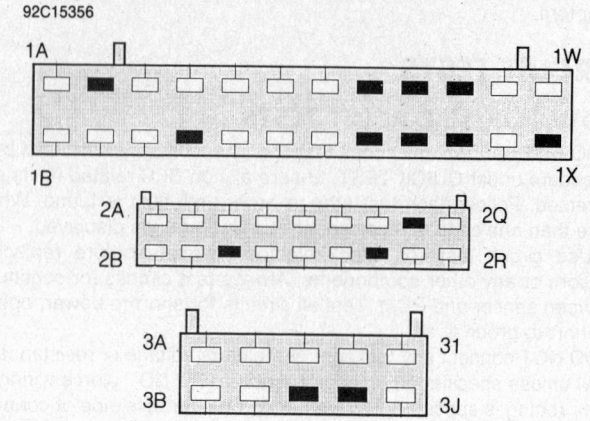

Fig. PSG1: Identifying PCM Harness Connector Terminals (Capri)

92F15359

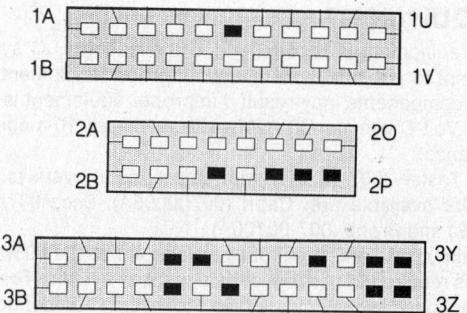

Fig. PSG2: Identifying PCM Harness Connector Terminals (Escort, Probe & Tracer)

1) Check Solenoid Voltage – Ensure ignition is off. Install 4EAT tester. Start and run engine in "P" (Park). Using DVOM (AC range), measure voltage between PSG (+) and PSG (–) test pins. Voltage with throttle closed should be 0 volts and .1-1.5 volts with 1/4 throttle. If all voltages are within specification, replace TCM or PCM (as applicable). Reconnect all components and repeat QUICK TEST. If any voltage is not within specification, go to next step.

2) Check Solenoid Resistance – Turn ignition off. Measure resistance between PSG (+) and PSG (–) test pins. Resistance should be 200-600 ohms for Capri, Escort and Tracer models, and 253-604 ohms for Probe models. If resistance is within specification, go to step **4)**. If resistance is not within specification, go to next step.

3) Check For Open Circuits – Ensure ignition is off. Disconnect PSG harness connector. Check continuity between PSG (+) and PSG (–) terminal at harness connector and corresponding test pin of 4EAT tester. See Fig. PSG3. If continuity does not exist in either circuit, inspect and repair wire(s) as needed. If continuity exists, replace PSG. Connect all components and repeat QUICK TEST.

CIRCUIT TEST PSG (Cont.)

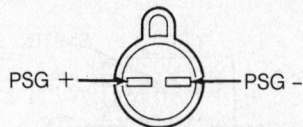

94D39142 94E39143 94F39144

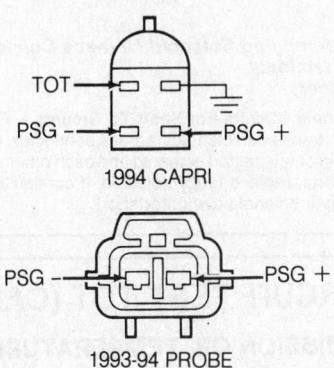

1993 CAPRI, 1993-94 ESCORT & TRACER

1994 CAPRI

1993-94 PROBE

Fig. PSG3 Identifying PSG Harness Connector Terminals

4) Check For Short To Ground – Ensure ignition is off. Disconnect PSG harness connector. Check continuity between PSG (+) and PSG (–) test pins and vehicle ground. If continuity exists with either circuit, inspect and repair circuit as needed. If continuity does not exist, replace PSG. Connect all components and repeat QUICK TEST.

CIRCUIT TEST RTS1

REDUCE TORQUE SIGNAL NO. 1

NOTE: The PCM on all models is located behind center console, below radio. The TCM on Capri models is located behind glove box. The TCM on Probe (2.5L) models is located next to PCM.

RTS1 CIRCUIT IDENTIFICATION

Circuit	TCM Pin [1]	Wire Color
RTS1	1J	Green

[1] – See Fig. DCS1.

1) Check RTS1 Signal – Ensure ignition is off. Install Breakout Box with PCM connected. Connect DVOM between test pin No. 8 and ground. Test drive vehicle and monitor voltage. Voltage should decrease from 10 volts or more to less than 1 volt during 1-2, 2-3 shift with 1/2 throttle opening or greater. If voltage does not decrease during transaxle upshifting, replace TCM. Connect all components and repeat QUICK TEST. If voltage decreases during upshifting, go to next step.

2) Check RTS1 Circuit For Open – Turn ignition off. Install 4EAT Tester with TCM connected. Check continuity between Breakout Box test pin No. 8 and 4EAT Tester test pin 1J. If continuity exists, go to next step. If continuity does not exist, inspect and repair circuit as needed. Connect all components and repeat QUICK TEST.

3) Check RTS1 Circuit For Short – Ensure ignition is off. Check continuity between Breakout Box test pin No. 8 and vehicle ground. If continuity exists, replace TCM. Connect all components and repeat QUICK TEST. If continuity exists, inspect and repair short to ground. Connect all components and repeat QUICK TEST.

CIRCUIT TEST RTS2

REDUCE TORQUE SIGNAL NO. 2

NOTE: The PCM on all models is located behind center console, below radio. The TCM on Capri models is located behind glove box. The TCM on Probe (2.5L) models is located next to PCM.

RTS2 CIRCUIT IDENTIFICATION

Circuit	TCM Pin [1]	Wire Color
RTS2	1L	Light Green/White

[1] – See Fig. DCS1.

1) Check RTS2 Signal – Ensure ignition is off. Install Breakout Box with PCM connected. Connect DVOM between test pin No. 11 and ground. Test drive vehicle and monitor voltage. Voltage should decrease from 10 volts or more to less than 1 volt during 3-2, 2-1 downshift with 1/2 throttle opening or greater. If voltage does not decrease during transaxle downshifting, replace PCM. Connect all components and repeat QUICK TEST. If voltage decreases during downshifting, go to next step.

2) Check RTS2 Circuit For Open – Turn ignition off. Install 4EAT Tester with TCM connected. Check continuity between Breakout Box test pin No. 11 and 4EAT Tester test pin 1L. If continuity exists, go to next step. If continuity does not exist, inspect and repair circuit as needed. Connect all components and repeat QUICK TEST.

3) Check RTS2 Circuit For Short – Ensure ignition is off. Check continuity between Breakout Box test pin No. 11 and vehicle ground. If continuity exists, replace TCM. Connect all components and repeat QUICK TEST. If continuity exists, inspect and repair short to ground. Connect all components and repeat QUICK TEST.

CIRCUIT TEST SCP

SOLENOID CONTROLLED BY POWER

NOTE: The PCM on all models is located behind center console, below radio. The TCM on Capri models is located behind glove box. The TCM on Probe (2.5L) models is located next to PCM.

Diagnostic Aids – This Circuit Test is intended to diagnose the following components:
- 1-2 Shift Solenoid (SS1)
- 2-3 Shift Solenoid (SS2)
- 3-4 Shift Solenoid (SS3)
- Torque Converter Clutch Control Solenoid (TCCC)
- Downshift Solenoid (DSS)

SCP CIRCUIT IDENTIFICATION (Capri)

Circuit	TCM Pin [1]	Wire Color
SS1	2E	Blue/Orange
SS2	2G	Blue/Yellow
SS3	2I	Orange
TCCC	2K	Blue

[1] – See Fig. DCS1.

PSG CIRCUIT IDENTIFICATION (Escort & Tracer)

Circuit	PCM Pin [1]	Wire Color
SS1	3W	Blue/Orange
SS2	3X	Blue/Yellow
SS3	3Y	Orange
TCCC	3Z	Blue

[1] – See Fig. PSG2.

CIRCUIT TEST SCP (Cont.)

PSG CIRCUIT IDENTIFICATION (Probe 2.0L)

Circuit	PCM Pin [1]	Wire Color
SS1	3P	Blue
SS2	3Q	Blue/Black
SS3	3R	Green/Black
TCCC	3S	Blue/White
DSS	3T	Red/White

[1] – See Fig. PSG2.

SCP CIRCUIT IDENTIFICATION (Probe 2.5)

Circuit	TCM Pin [1]	Wire Color
SS1	2E	Blue
SS2	2G	Blue/Black
SS3	2I	Green/Black
TCCC	2K	Blue/White
DSS	2K	Red/White

[1] – See Fig. DCS1.

1) Perform SCP Click Test – Turn ignition off. Install 4EAT Tester with PCM or TCM (as applicable) disconnected. Place tester in engine compartment. Apply 12 volts to each solenoid test pin. Use 12 volt test pin for voltage supply. Listen for a "click" at transaxle. If all solenoids can be heard operating, replace either PCM or TCM (as applicable). If any solenoid does not pass click test, go to next step.

2) Check SCP Resistance – Ensure ignition is off. Measure resistance between each solenoid test pin and BODY GND. Resistance should be 11-27 ohms. If resistance is within specifications, go to step **4)**. If resistance is not within specifications, go to next step.

3) Check Solenoid Circuits For Opens – Ensure ignition is off. Disconnect transaxle solenoid harness connector. Check continuity between each solenoid harness connector terminal and corresponding 4EAT Tester test pin. See Figs. DCS2, SCP1 and SCP2. If continuity exists is all circuits, replace suspect solenoid. See ON-VEHICLE SERVICE IN 4EAT overhaul article. Connect all components and repeat QUICK TEST. If continuity does not exist in any circuit, inspect and repair suspect circuit as needed. Connect all components and repeat QUICK TEST.

92H15344 94C39141

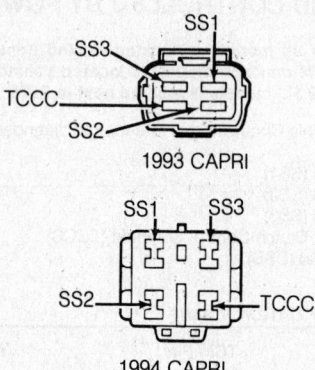

Fig. SCP1: Identifying Solenoid Harness Connector Terminals (Capri)

CIRCUIT TEST SCP (Cont.)

94H39146

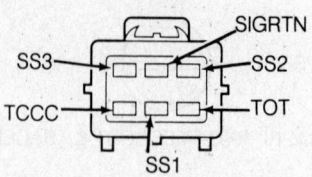

Fig. SCP2: Identifying Solenoid Harness Connector Solenoid Terminals (Escort & Tracer)

4) Check Solenoid Circuits For Short To Ground – Ensure ignition is off. Disconnect transaxle solenoid harness connector. Check continuity between test pin of suspected solenoid and each other solenoid test pin. If continuity exists, replace faulty solenoid. If continuity does not exist, inspect and repair solenoid circuit for short.

CIRCUIT TEST TOT (CAPRI)
TRANSMISSION OIL TEMPERATURE SWITCH

NOTE: The PCM on all models is located behind center console, below radio. The TCM on Capri models is located behind glove box. The TCM on Probe (2.5L) models is located next to PCM.

TOT CIRCUIT IDENTIFICATION (Capri)

Circuit	TCM Pin [1]	Wire Color
TOT	1M	Black/Blue

[1] – See Fig. DCS1.

1) Check TOT Voltage Output – Operate vehicle until transaxle fluid is at normal operating temperature. Turn ignition off. Install 4EAT Tester leaving TCM disconnected. Measure voltage between TOT test pin and ground. Allow transaxle fluid to cool. Voltage should increase from less than 1.5 volts to more than 10 volts as fluid temperature decreases below 302 °F (150 °C). If voltage is within specification, system is functioning properly. Connect all components and repeat QUICK TEST. If voltage is not within specification, go to next step.

2) Check TOT Switch – Operate vehicle until transaxle fluid is at normal operating temperature. Turn ignition off. Disconnect TOT switch harness connector. Measure resistance between TOT terminals. See Fig. TOT1. Allow transaxle fluid to cool. Resistance should increase from less than 5 ohms to more than 10 k/ohms as fluid temperature decreases below 302 °F (150 °C). If voltage is within specification, go to next step. If voltage is not within specification, replace TOT switch. Connect all components and repeat QUICK TEST.

94H39138

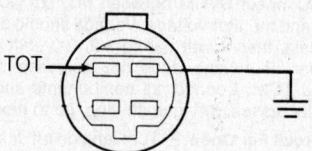

Fig. TOT1: Identifying TOT Harness Connector Terminals

3) Check TOT Switch Ground – Ensure ignition is off. Check continuity between switch Black wire and vehicle ground. If continuity does not exist, inspect and repair circuit as needed. If continuity exists, go to next step.

4) Check TOT Switch Circuit To TCM – Ensure ignition is off. Check continuity between TOT switch harness connector TOT terminal and TOT test pin. If continuity exists, replace TCM. Connect all components and repeat QUICK TEST. If continuity does not exist, inspect and repair circuit as needed.

CIRCUIT TEST TOT
(ESCORT, PROBE & TRACER)

TRANSMISSION OIL TEMPERTURE SENSOR

NOTE: The PCM on all models is located behind center console, below radio. The TCM on Capri models is located behind glove box. The TCM on Probe (2.5L) models is located next to PCM.

TOT CIRCUIT IDENTIFICATION (Escort & Tracer)

Circuit	PCM Pin [1]	Wire Color
TOT	2G	White/Black
SIGRTN	3A	Black/Orange

[1] – See Fig. PSG1.

TOT CIRCUIT IDENTIFICATION (Probe 2.0L)

Circuit	PCM Pin [1]	Wire Color
TOT	2H	Blue/Yellow
SIGRTN	3D	Black/Blue

[1] – See Fig. PSG1.

TOT CIRCUIT IDENTIFICATION (Probe 2.5L)

Circuit	TCM Pin [1]	Wire Color
TOT	1G	Blue/Yellow
SIGRTN	2P	

[1] – See Fig. DCS1.

1) Check TOT Voltage Output (Capri) Or Resistance (Escort, Probe & Tracer) – Operate vehicle until transaxle fluid is at normal operating temperature. Turn ignition off. Install 4EAT Tester leaving PCM or TCM disconnected (as applicable). On Escort, Probe and Tracer, measure resistance between TOT and SIGRTN test pins. Allow transaxle fluid to cool. Determine if sensor resistance increases as fluid cools. See TOT SENSOR SPECIFICATIONS chart. If resistance is within specification, replace PCM or TCM (as applicable). If resistance is not within specifications, go to next step.

TOT SENSOR SPECIFICATIONS (Escort & Tracer)

Temperature °F (°C)	Resistance k/ohms
-40 (-40)	325
32 (0)	52
68 (20)	23
104 (40)	11
140 (60)	6
212 (100)	2
266 (130)	1

TOT SENSOR SPECIFICATIONS (Probe)

Temperature °F (°C)	Resistance k/ohms
-20 (-4)	13-17
32 (0)	5-7
68 (20)	2.4-2.9
104 (40)	1.2-1.4
140 (60)	.63-.71
176 (80)	.35-.39
212 (100)	.21-.23
248 (120)	.13-.14
266 (130)	.10-.11

CIRCUIT TEST TOT (Cont.)

2) Check TOT & SIGRTN Circuits For Opens – Ensure ignition is off. Disconnect transaxle solenoid harness connector. Check continuity between harness connector TOT and SIGRTN terminals and corresponding 4EAT Tester test pins. See Figs. DCS2 and SCP2. If continuity does not exist in either circuit, inspect and repair suspect circuit as needed. If continuity exists in both circuits, go to next step.

3) Check TOT Circuit For Short To Ground – Ensure ignition is off. Check continuity between TOT test pin and vehicle ground. If continuity exists, inspect and repair circuit for short to ground. If continuity does not exist, replace PCM or TCM (as applicable).

CIRCUIT TEST TRS

TORQUE REDUCE/ENGINE COOLANT TEMPER-ATURE SIGNAL

NOTE: The PCM on all models is located behind center console, below radio. The TCM on Capri models is located behind glove box. The TCM on Probe (2.5L) models is located next to PCM.

TRS CIRCUIT IDENTIFICATION

Circuit	TCM Pin [1]	Wire Color
TRS	1K	White/Black

[1] – See Fig. DCS1.

1) Check TRS Signal – Turn ignition off. Install 4EAT Tester. Connect DVOM between TRS test pin and ground. Test drive vehicle. Monitor voltage as engine reaches normal operating temperature. Voltage should range from 0 volts with coolant temperature below 140°F (60°C) to battery voltage with coolant temperature above 140°F (60°C). Test drive vehicle above 40 MPH. Once engine has reached normal operating temperature, depress throttle until transaxle downshifts into next lower gear. Voltage should drop to 1 volt during downshift. If all voltage measurements are within specifications, replace TCM. Connect all components and repeat QUICK TEST. If any voltage measurement is not within specification, go to next step.

2) Check TRS Circuit For Open – Turn ignition off. Install Breakout Box, leaving PCM disconnected. Check continuity between Breakout Box test pin No. 19 and 4EAT Tester test pin No. 1K. If continuity exists, go to next step. If continuity does not exist, inspect and repair circuit as needed. Connect all components and repeat QUICK TEST.

3) Check TRS Circuit For Short To Ground – Ensure ignition is off. Check continuity between Breakout Box test pin No. 19 and ground. If continuity does not exist, replace PCM. If continuity exists, inspect and repair circuit as needed. Connect all components and repeat QUICK TEST.

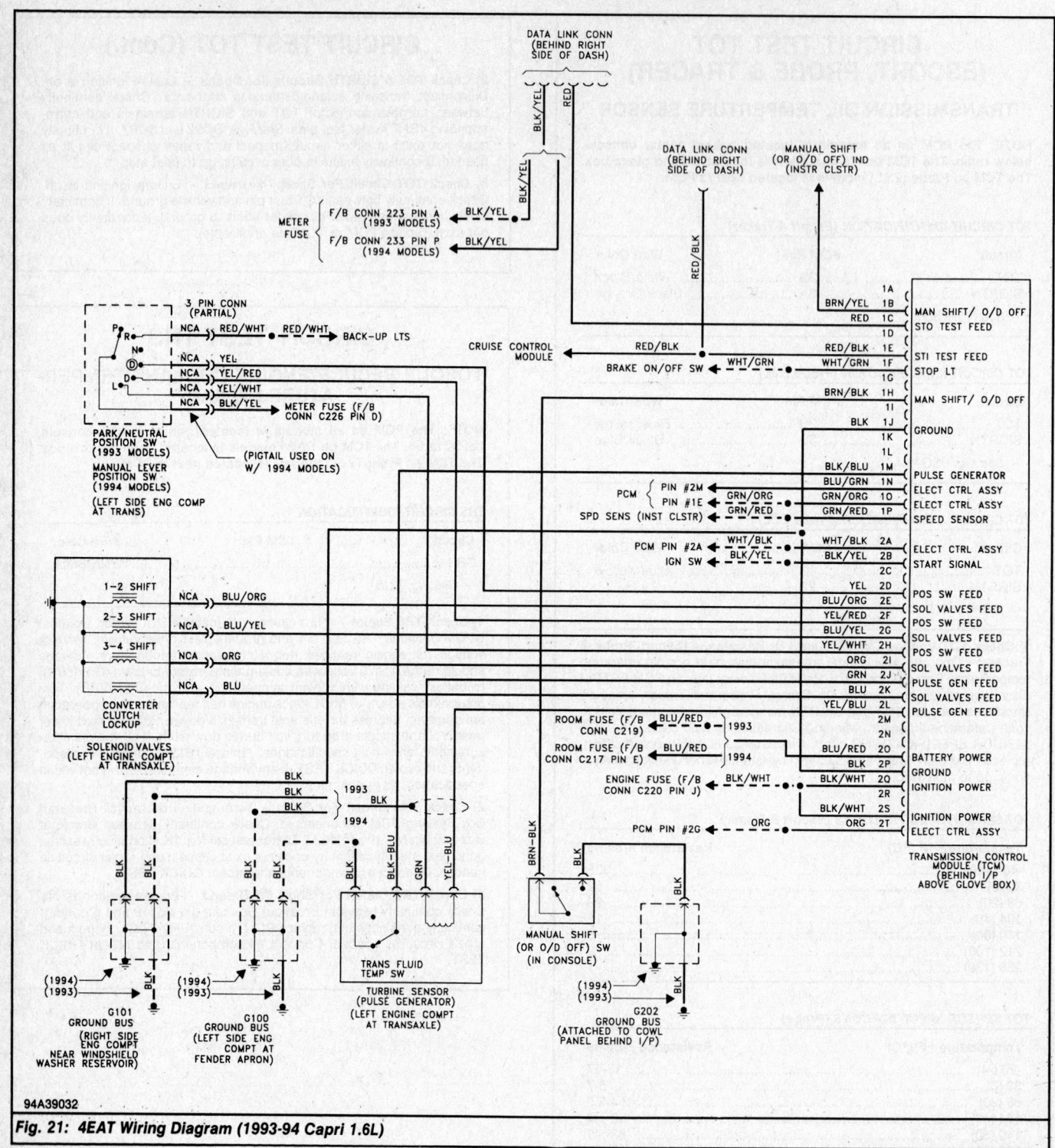

Fig. 21: 4EAT Wiring Diagram (1993-94 Capri 1.6L)

94A39032

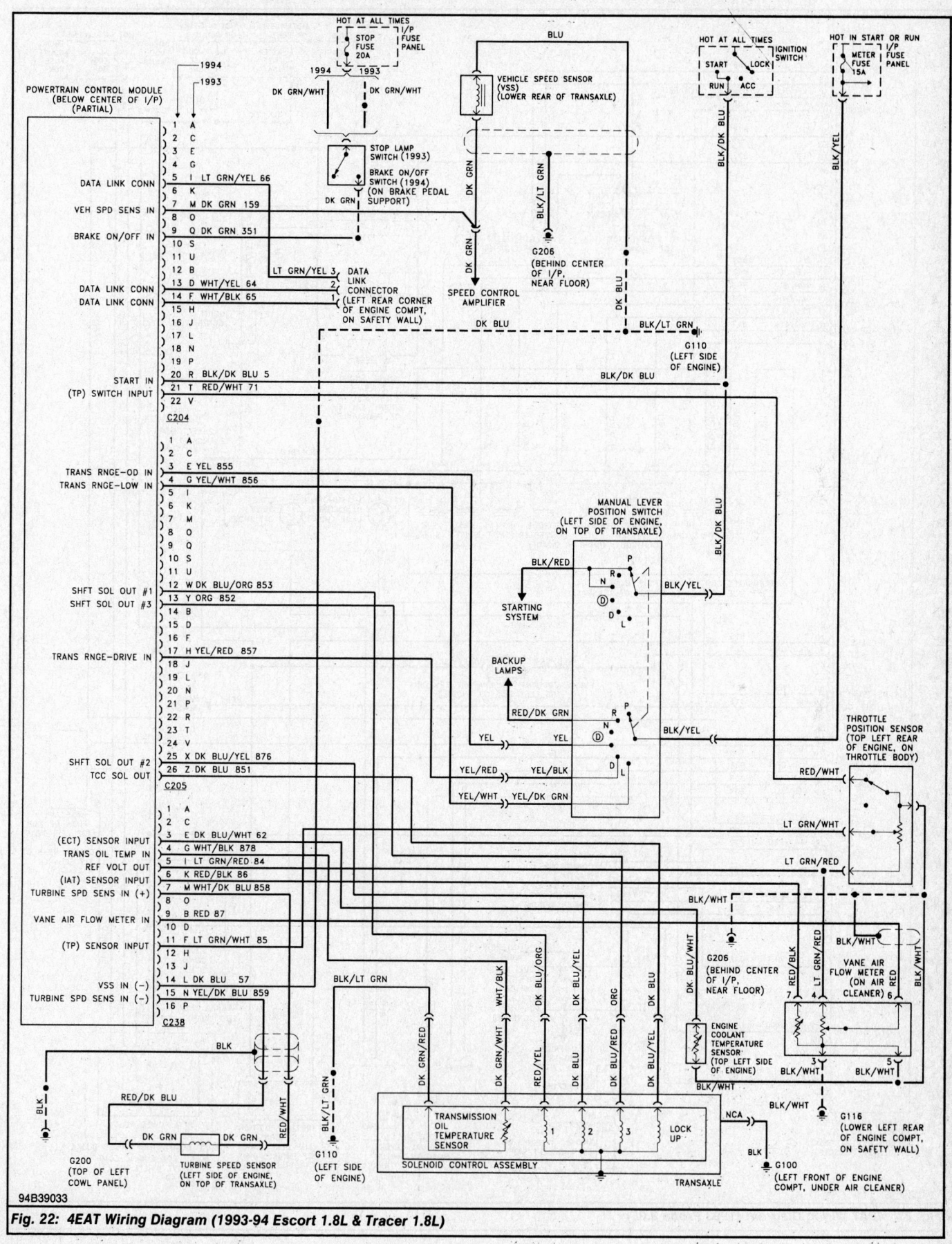

Fig. 22: 4EAT Wiring Diagram (1993-94 Escort 1.8L & Tracer 1.8L)

94B39033

AUTOMATIC TRANSMISSIONS
4EAT EEC Electronic Controls (Cont.)

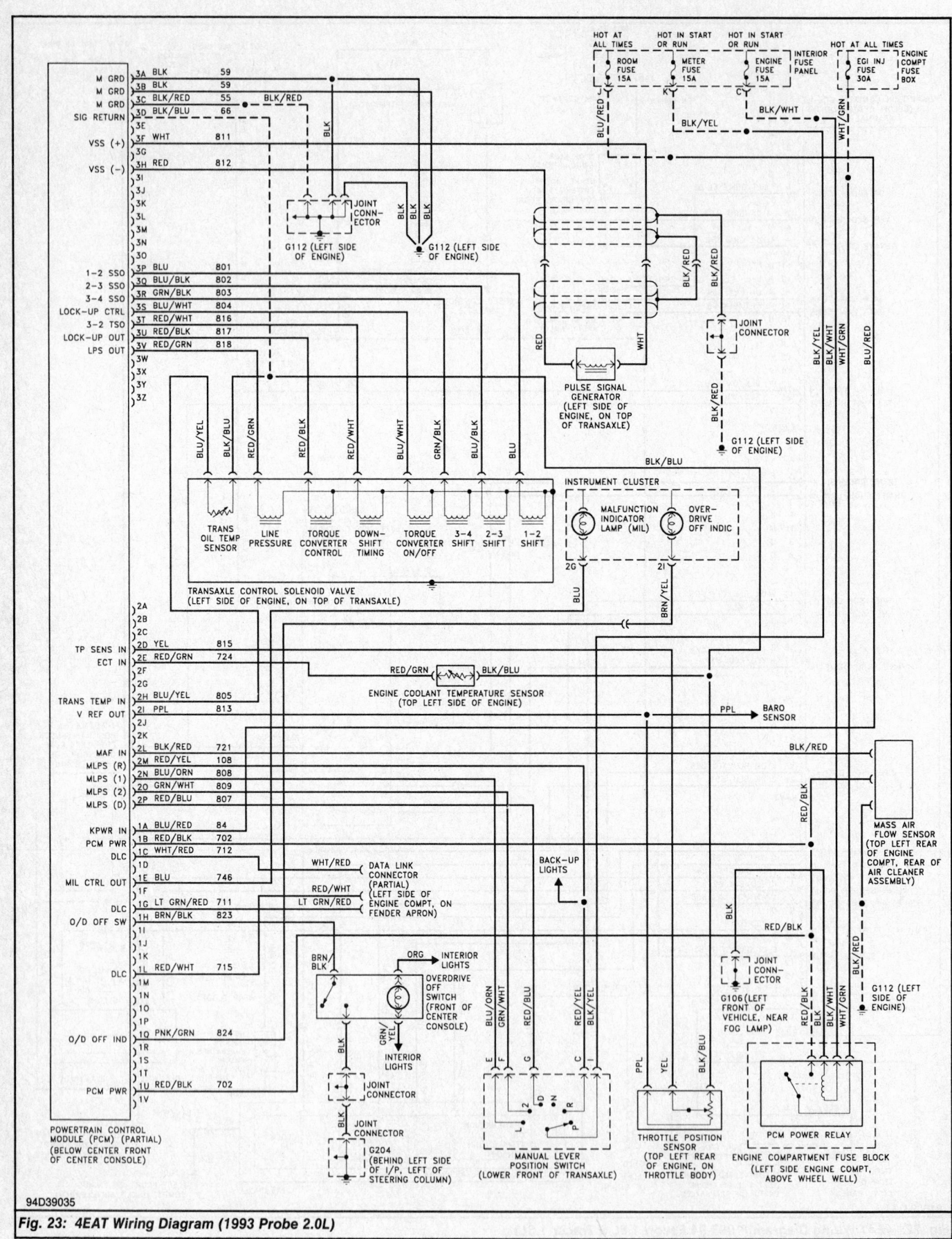

94D39035

Fig. 23: 4EAT Wiring Diagram (1993 Probe 2.0L)

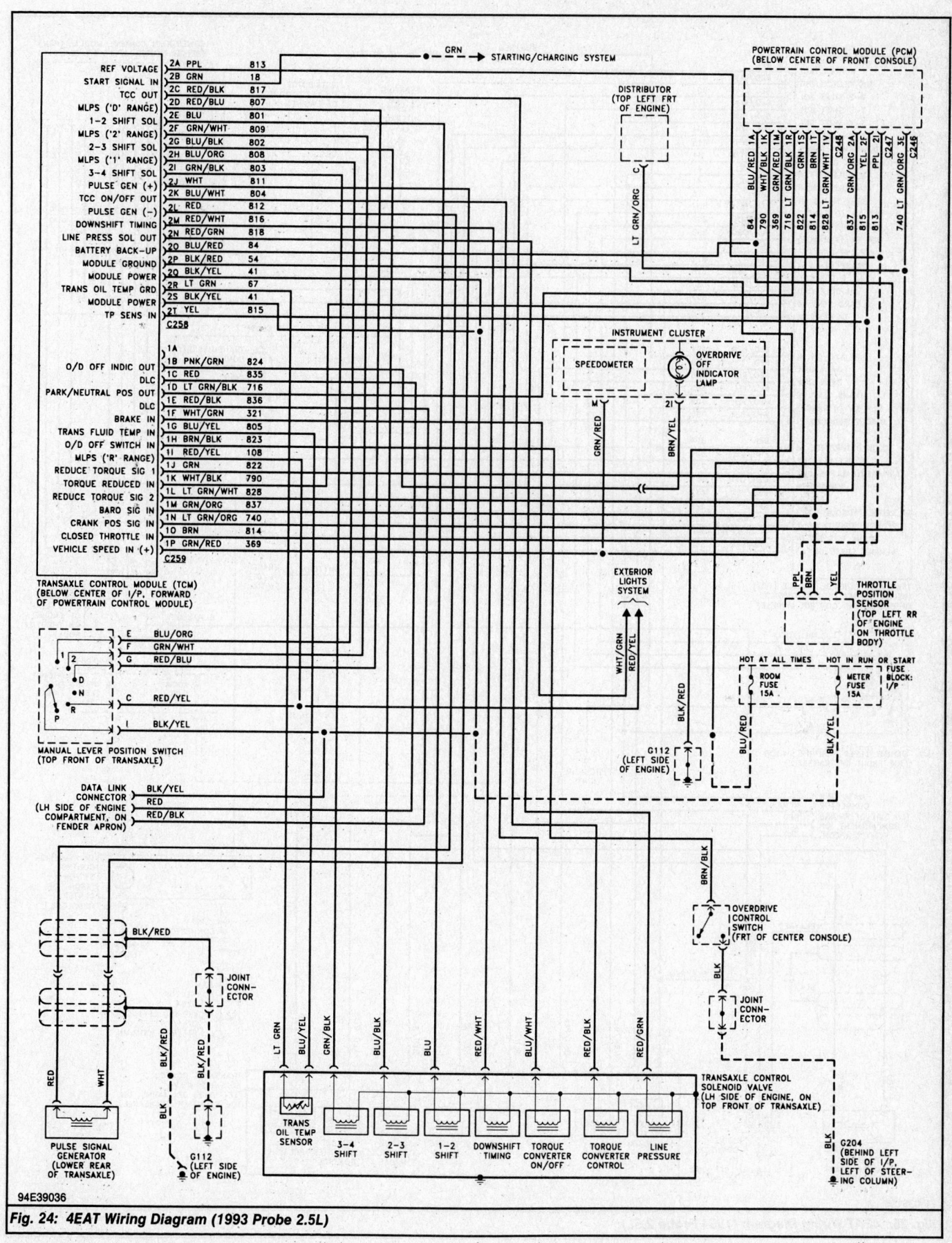

Fig. 24: 4EAT Wiring Diagram (1993 Probe 2.5L)

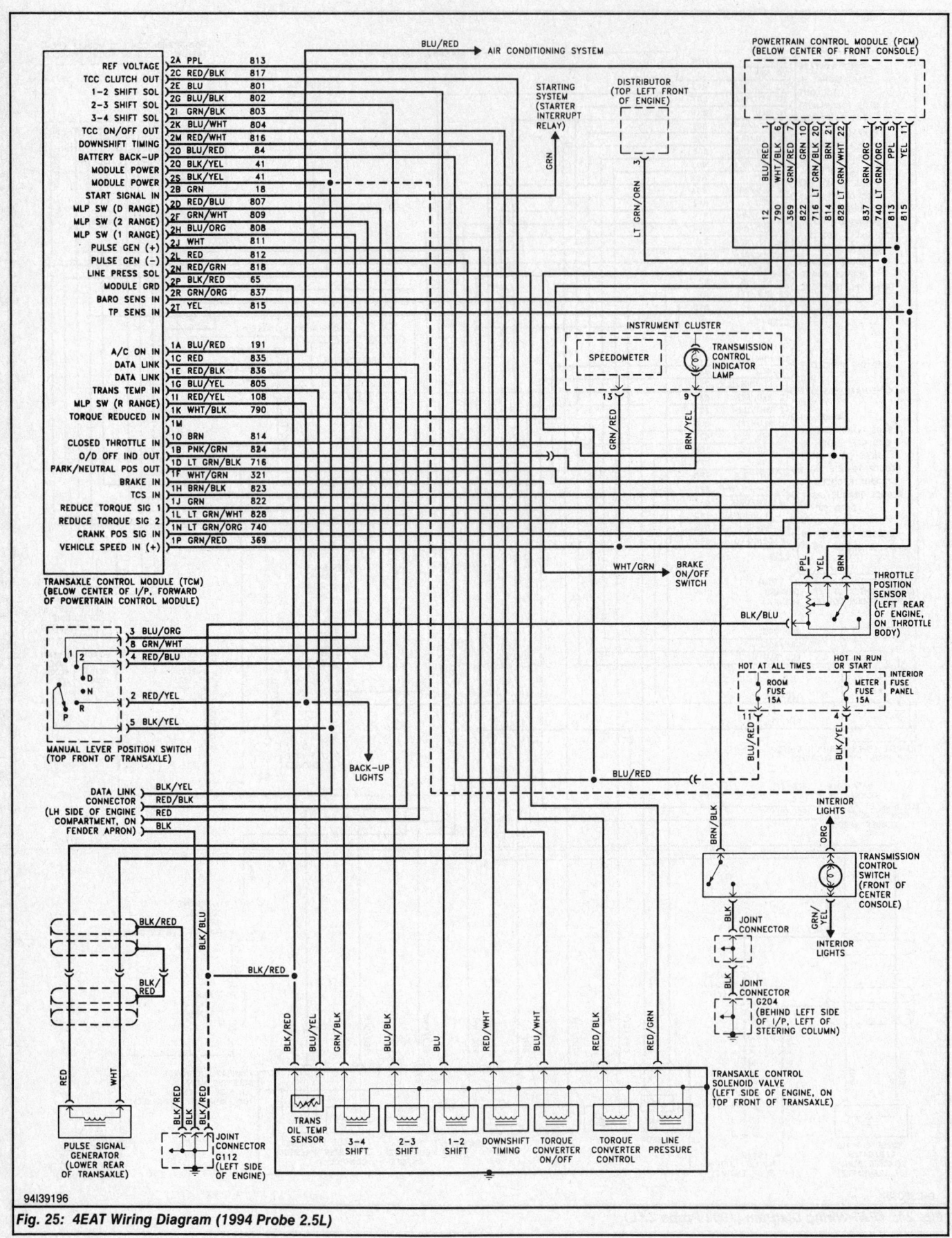

Fig. 25: 4EAT Wiring Diagram (1994 Probe 2.5L)

94I39196

Ford Motor Co: Escort, Tracer (1.9L)

NOTE: For 4EAT transaxle mechanical testing and repair, see Ford 4EAT overhaul article. For other models that use 4EAT transmissions, see 4EAT EEC ELECTRONIC CONTROLS article.

INTRODUCTION

The first step in diagnosing any driveability problem is verifying the customer's complaint with a test drive under the conditions the problem reportedly occurred. Before entering self-diagnostics, perform a careful and complete visual inspection. Most transmission control problems result from mechanical breakdowns or poor electrical connections.

NOTE: Perform all voltage tests with a Digital Volt-Ohmmeter (DVOM) with a minimum 10-megohm input impedance, unless stated otherwise in test procedure.

DESCRIPTION & OPERATION

Input signals from sensors are sent to the Powertrain Control Module (PCM). The PCM can determine when the time and conditions are right for a shift or converter clutch application.

Four electronic solenoids accomplish these functions; 3 On/Off solenoids for shifting and one On/Off solenoid for torque converter clutch control. The PCM has built-in self-diagnosis, fail-safe code and warning code display for the main input sensors and solenoid valves.

NOTE: In addition to transmission fault codes, engine-related fault codes may be output during QUICK TEST procedure. These fault codes pertain to engine performance and must be repaired first as engine performance will greatly affect transmission operation. For information and testing procedures of engine-related fault codes and components, see SELF-DIAGNOSTICS – EEC-IV article in ENGINE PERFORMANCE of appropriate MITCHELL® manual.

INPUT SENSORS

Brake On/Off (BOO) Switch – The PCM receives a signal from the BOO switch when the brake switch is operated. Torque converter clutch is disengaged when brakes are applied. Faulty switch will affect torque converter operation.

Manual Lever Position (MLP) Sensor – The PCM monitors a series of step down resistors in the MLP sensor that act as a voltage divider. The voltage signal corresponds with position of the transaxle range selector lever. The MLP sensor also contains the neutral/start and backup circuits. Malfunction of the MLP sensor may cause harsh engagements and firm shift feel. Improper shifting or shift selection and no engine cranking may also result.

Throttle Position Sensor (TPS) – The TPS is a potentiometer mounted to the engine throttle body. The PCM receives a signal from the TPS relaying throttle plate position. TPS failure will cause PCM to operate in fail safe mode and raise line pressure to prevent transaxle damage. This condition will result in harsh engagements, firm shift feel, abnormal shift schedule and TCC not engaging or cycling.

Transmission Oil Temperature (TOT) Sensor – The TOT sensor is located on the solenoid valve body. The PCM monitors voltage across the TOT thermistor to determine transaxle temperature. Depending on temperature, the PCM controls line pressure, shift scheduling and TCC operation. Malfunction of sensor will cause incorrect line pressure and possible lack of TCC operation.

Transmission Speed Sensor (TSS) – The TSS is a magnetic pickup that sends turbine shaft speed signal to the PCM. Malfunction of sensor may cause harsh engagements of shifts.

Vehicle Speed Sensor (VSS) – The VSS is a magnetic pickup that sends vehicle speed signal to the PCM. Malfunction of sensor may cause harsh engagements of shifts.

OUTPUT DEVICES

Shift Solenoid Assemblies – Three ON/OFF solenoids are used for electronic shift scheduling. Solenoids control pressure to 3 shift valves and forward clutch control valve, located in valve body. See SOLENOID OPERATIONS CHART.

SOLENOID OPERATIONS CHART

Gear Position	SS1	SS2	SS3
"P" (Park)	Off	Off	On
"R" (Reverse)	Off	Off	On
"N" (Neutral)	Off	Off	On
"OD" (Overdrive)			
OD1	Off	On	On
OD2	On	On	On
OD3	On	Off	Off
OD4	On	Off	On
"D" Or "3"			
D1	Off	On	On
D2	On	On	On
D3	On	Off	Off

Torque Converter Clutch (TCC) Solenoid – The TCC receives signal from the PCM. The TCC controls application, modulation and release of torque converter clutch. If solenoid fails in ON position, vehicle engine will run rough (shudder) and engine stalls in Drive at low idle speeds (2nd, 3rd or 4th gear). If solenoid fails in OFF position, torque converter clutch will not engage.

PRELIMINARY INSPECTION

VISUAL INSPECTION

Visually inspect all electrical wiring, looking for chafed, stretched, cut or pinched wiring. Ensure electrical connectors fit tightly and are not corroded. Ensure vacuum hoses are properly routed and are not pinched or cut. Inspect air induction system for possible vacuum leaks. Check PCM, sensors and actuators for physical damage. Check engine coolant level. Check transmission fluid level and condition.

NOTE: In addition to transmission fault codes, engine-related fault codes may be output during QUICK TEST procedure. These fault codes pertain to engine performance and must be repaired first as engine performance will greatly affect transmission operation. For information and testing procedures of engine-related fault codes and components, see SELF-DIAGNOSTICS – EEC-IV article in ENGINE PERFORMANCE of appropriate MITCHELL® manual.

SELF-DIAGNOSTIC SYSTEM

DIAGNOSTIC FORMATS

QUICK TEST and CIRCUIT TESTS are diagnostic formats used to test and service EEC-IV system. QUICK TEST allows technician to identify problems and retrieve service codes. CIRCUIT TESTS check engine circuits, sensors and actuators. CIRCUIT TESTS check transaxle circuits, sensors and actuators.

Before starting any circuit test, follow all steps under QUICK TEST procedure to find correct circuit or pinpoint test. If vehicle passes QUICK TEST and no driveability symptoms or intermittent faults exist, EEC-IV system is okay.

DIAGNOSTIC TROUBLE CODES (DTC)

During QUICK TEST, 3 types of service codes are retrieved: Key On Engine Off (KOEO), Key On Engine Running (KOER) and Continuous Memory Codes. See QUICK TEST for self-test procedures. Codes may be cleared from PCM memory after they have been recorded or repaired. See CLEARING CODES.

KOEO & KOER Codes (Hard Faults) – These codes indicate faults are present at time of testing. A hard fault may cause CHECK ENGINE light or Malfunction Indicator Light (MIL) to glow and remain on until fault is repaired. If KOEO or KOER codes are retrieved during KOEO SELF-TEST or KOER SELF-TEST, use SERVICE CODE REFERENCE CHARTS to find correct testing and repair procedures.

Continuous Memory Codes (Soft Faults) – These codes indicate a fault that may or may not be present at time of testing. These codes are used to diagnose intermittent problems. Continuous Memory Codes are retrieved during KOEO SELF-TEST. Some codes may turn on MIL or CHECK ENGINE light. Corresponding soft trouble code will be retained in PCM memory. If fault does not reoccur within 40 warm-up cycles (80 cycles on some models), PCM will automatically clear code. Technician may clear service codes from memory. See CLEAR-ING CODES. Intermittent faults may be caused by a sensor, connector or wiring-related problems.

CAUTION: Continuous Memory Codes should be recorded when retrieved during KOEO SELF-TEST. These codes may be used to iden-tify intermittent problems that exist after all KOEO and KOER codes have been repaired and a Code 111 (pass code) has been obtained. Failure to follow this procedure may result in unnecessary testing. Some Continuous Memory Codes faults may not be valid after KOEO and KOER codes are repaired.

RETRIEVING CODES

Service codes are retrieved from EEC-IV system through self-test connector. Various methods and test equipment may be used to access these codes:

- Analog Volt-Ohmmeter (VOM)
- Scan Tester
- In-Dash Malfunction Indicator Light (MIL) Or CHECK ENGINE light
- STAR Series Tester
- Message Center (Continental)

DATA LINK CONNECTOR (DLC) LOCATIONS

Application	Location
Escort & Tracer (1.9L)	Left Shock Tower

READING CODES

KOEO & KOER SELF-TEST Codes – PCM outputs codes one digit at a time. Record codes in order received. These codes indicate current faults in system and should be serviced in order of appearance. Use SERVICE CODE REFERENCE CHARTS to find correct CIRCUIT TEST.

If using analog VOM, pay careful attention to length of pauses in order to read codes correctly. A 1/2-second pause occurs between number of sweeps in a digit. A 2-second pause occurs between digits in a code. A 4-second pause occurs between each code.

KOEO codes are separated from Continuous Memory codes by a 6-second delay, a 1/2-second sweep (separator) and another 6-second delay. *See Fig. 1.* If using MIL/CHECK ENGINE light, service codes are displayed as flashes.

Scan tester, if used, will count pulses and display them as a digital code. STAR Series Tester will add a zero (0) to single-digit Separator

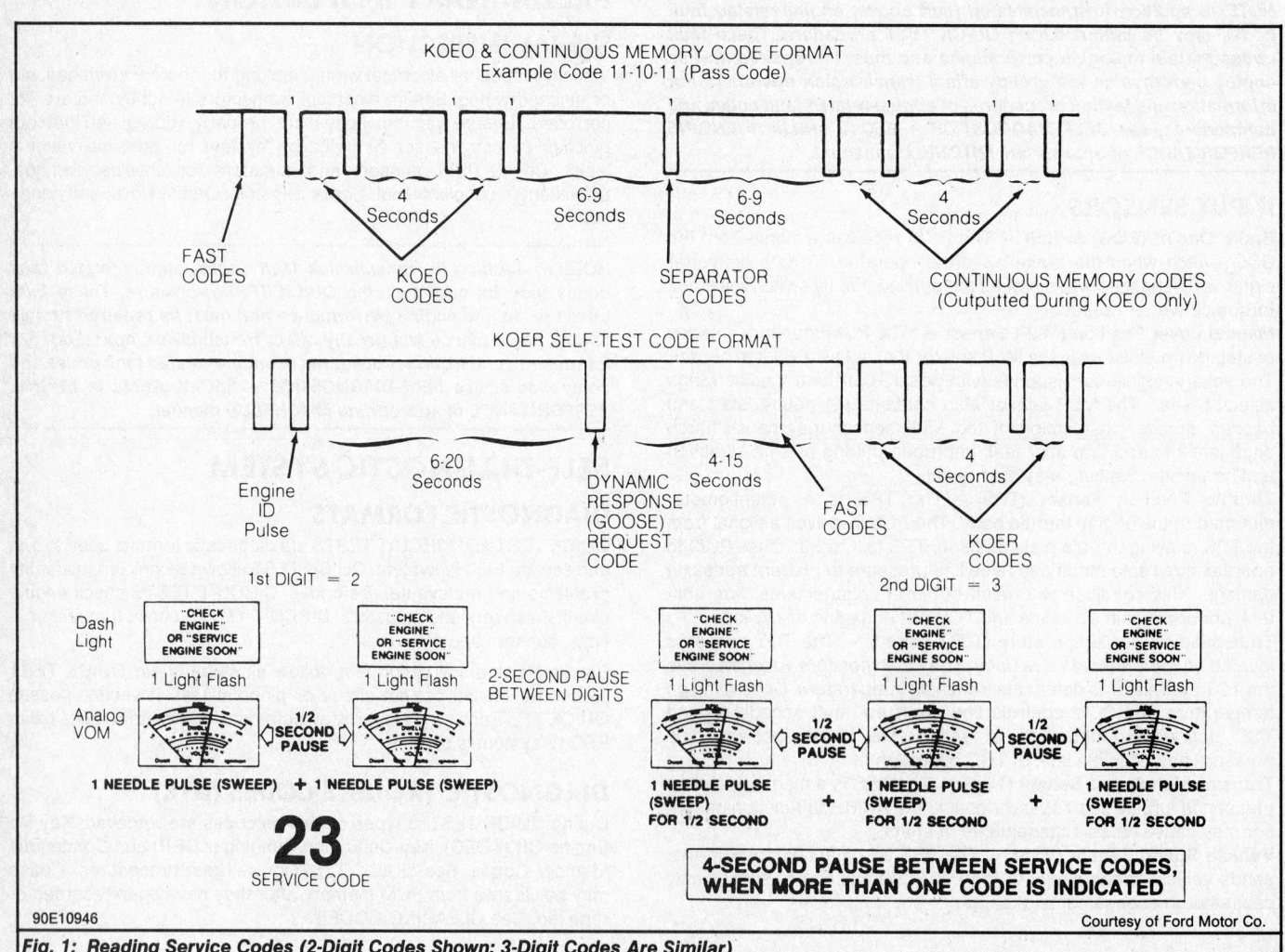

Fig. 1: Reading Service Codes (2-Digit Codes Shown; 3-Digit Codes Are Similar)

90E10946

Courtesy of Ford Motor Co.

Code (10) and Dynamic Response Code (10). Dynamic Response Code is displayed in KOER SELF-TEST. See Fig. 1.

Engine Identification (ID) Codes – Engine ID codes are issued at beginning of KOER SELF-TEST. Codes are one-digit numbers represented by number of pulses displayed. See Fig. 1. Engine ID code is equal to one-half the number of engine cylinders. For example, 2 pulses would indicate that engine is a 4 cylinder. ID code is used to verify proper PCM is installed and that SELF-TEST has been entered.

Separator Pulse – Single 1/2-second separator pulse is issued 6-9 seconds after last KOEO code. Continuous Memory Codes (soft faults) are then displayed 6-9 seconds after 1/2-second separator pulse. Some digital test equipment may display separator code as "10" instead of "1".

Pass Codes – A Code 111 indicates no service codes were recorded in that portion of test; system passes that portion of test. If Code 111 is not retrieved in KOEO SELF-TEST, codes retrieved during KOER SELF-TEST may not be valid. Code 111 (pass code) must be obtained in KOEO SELF-TEST. A Code 111-1-111 output during KOEO SELF-TEST indicates no KOEO code or Continuous Memory Code was recorded.

Continuous Memory Codes – These codes result from information stored by PCM during continuous self-test monitoring. Codes are displayed after separator pulse code in KOEO SELF-TEST. Use these codes for diagnosis only when KOEO SELF-TEST and KOER SELF-TEST result in Code 111 (pass code) and all steps under QUICK TEST are successfully completed. (A few codes are exceptions which may be checked after KOEO codes have been repaired). These codes indicate faults recorded within last 40 engine starts (80 engine starts on some models). Fault may or may not be currently present. See SERVICE CODE REFERENCE CHART.

Fast Codes – At start of KOEO SELF-TEST and after Wide Open Throttle (WOT) request in KOER SELF-TEST, PCM outputs short bursts of information, known as FAST CODES, which were used by manufacturer during assembly. With most equipment, these code bursts are not visible; an entire code sequence lasts less than 1/2 second. If this fluctuation is visible on test equipment, ignore it.

CLEARING CODES

To clear codes from PCM memory, start KOEO SELF-TEST under QUICK TEST. When service codes appear on test equipment or CHECK ENGINE light, disconnect jumper wire from Self-Test Input (STI) connector. If using STAR Series Tester, unlatch center button. This procedure erases Continuous Memory Codes from PCM memory. If problem has not been corrected or fault is still present, hard code will immediately be reset in PCM memory.

CAUTION: DO NOT disconnect vehicle battery to clear codes. This will erase stored operating information from Keep-Alive Memory (KAM). To clear KAM, disconnect negative battery terminal for at least 5 minutes.

WARNING: When battery is disconnected, vehicle computer and memory systems may lose memory data. Driveability problems may exist until computer systems have completed a relearn cycle. See COMPUTER RELEARN PROCEDURES in APPLICATIONS & IDENTIFICATION section before disconnecting battery.

QUICK TEST

Description – Following procedures are functional tests of EEC-IV system. These following 4 basic test steps must be carefully followed in sequence, otherwise misdiagnosis or replacement of non-faulty components may result:
- VISUAL CHECK
- EQUIPMENT HOOKUP.
- KOEO (Key On Engine Off) SELF-TEST.
- KOER (Key On Engine Running) SELF-TEST.

Diagnostic Aids – After each service or repair procedure has been completed, repeat QUICK TEST to ensure all EEC-IV systems work properly and service codes are no longer present.

VISUAL CHECK

Complete a basic inspection of engine compartment and all components before proceeding to self-diagnostic tests. Ensure vacuum hoses and EEC-IV wiring harnesses are properly connected.

EQUIPMENT HOOKUP

Apply parking brake, and place shift lever in "P" position. Block drive wheels. Turn off all electrical loads. Connect appropriate test equipment to vehicle as follows:

Analog Volt-Ohmmeter (VOM) – **1)** Turn ignition switch to OFF position. Set VOM at 0-15V DC range. Connect positive lead of VOM to positive battery terminal.

2) Connect negative VOM lead to Self-Test Output (STO) terminal of self-test connector. See Fig. 2. Connect timing light, and go to KOER SELF-TEST. Activate KOEO SELF-TEST by connecting jumper wire from Self-Test Input (STI) pigtail to signal return terminal of self-test connector with ignition on.

Scan Tester – Follow manufacturer instructions to hook up equipment and record service codes.

STAR Series Tester – Turn ignition switch to OFF position. Connect color-coded adapter cable leads to diagnostic tester. Connect 2 service connectors of adapter cable to vehicle self-test connector and STI pigtail connector. Connect timing light. Go to KOEO SELF-TEST.

CHECK ENGINE Light/Malfunction Indicator Light (MIL) – Turn ignition on. Connect a jumper wire between Self-Test Input (STI) pigtail and signal return (SIG RTN) terminal of Data Link Connector (DLC). See Fig. 2. Go to KOEO SELF-TEST.

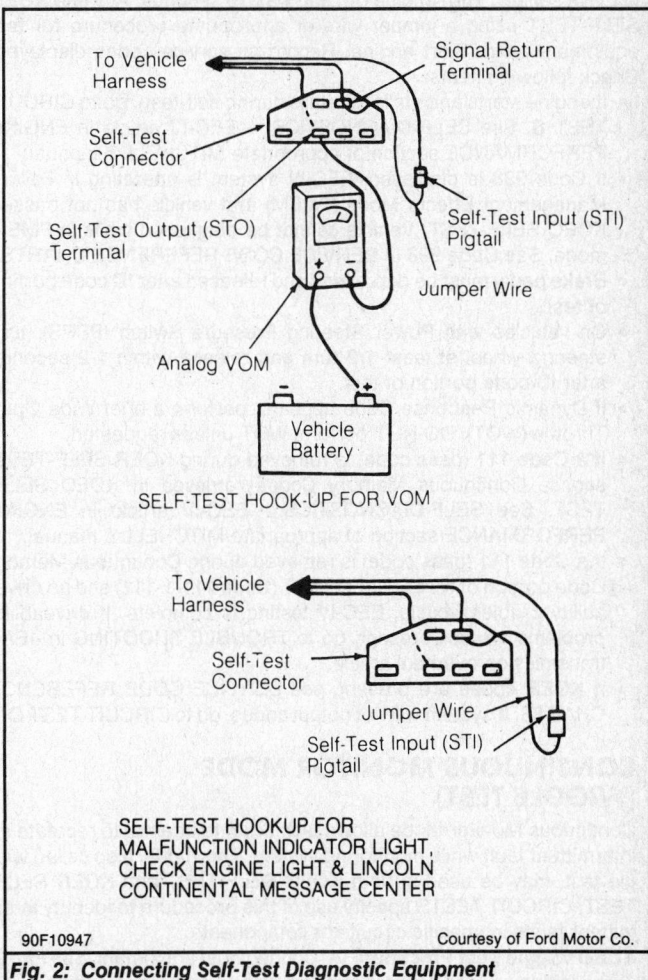

SELF-TEST HOOK-UP FOR VOM

SELF-TEST HOOKUP FOR MALFUNCTION INDICATOR LIGHT, CHECK ENGINE LIGHT & LINCOLN CONTINENTAL MESSAGE CENTER

90F10947   Courtesy of Ford Motor Co.

Fig. 2: Connecting Self-Test Diagnostic Equipment

KOEO SELF-TEST

Ensure engine is at normal operating temperature. If engine does not start (or stalls after starting), continue KOEO SELF-TEST. DO NOT depress throttle on gasoline vehicles. Turn ignition off. Wait 10 seconds. Ensure test equipment is properly attached. Turn ignition on (engine off). Record all KOEO and Continuous Memory Codes.

If a Code 111 (pass code) is not retrieved in KOEO portion of test, service KOEO codes at this time. Service any engine codes recorded before servicing transmission codes. If PCM will not output codes, see SELF-DIAGNOSTICS – EEC-IV article in ENGINE PERFORMANCE section of appropriate MITCHELL® manual. If service codes are retrieved observe the following procedures:

- If CHECK ENGINE or SERVICE ENGINE SOON light is on, service codes in order retrieved.
- If vehicle has a no-start condition, go to CIRCUIT TEST AA, AB or AC in SELF-DIAGNOSTICS – EEC-IV article in ENGINE PERFORMANCE section of appropriate MITCHELL® manual.

KOER SELF-TEST

Diagnostic Aids – DO NOT enter this test sequence until a Code 111 (pass code) has been retrieved in KOEO SELF-TEST. If system has not passed KOEO SELF-TEST, codes recorded in KOER SELF-TEST may not be valid.

Deactivate self-test by removing and reconnecting jumper wire or by procedure specified by test equipment in use. Start engine, and run it for 2 minutes at 2000 RPM to warm Heated Exhaust Gas Oxygen (HEGO) sensor. Turn engine off, and wait 10 seconds. Activate KOER SELF-TEST using a jumper wire or appropriate procedure for test equipment used. Start engine. Record all service codes displayed. Check following items:

- If engine starts and stalls (or stalls during self-test), go to CIRCUIT TEST S. See SELF-DIAGNOSTICS – EEC-IV article in ENGINE PERFORMANCE section of appropriate MITCHELL® manual.
- If Code 998 is displayed, EEC-IV system is operating in Failure Management Effects Mode (FMEM) and vehicle has not passed KOEO SELF-TEST. Vehicle cannot be diagnosed while in FMEM mode. See Code 998 in SERVICE CODE REFERENCE CHARTS.
- Brake pedal must be depressed and released after ID code portion of test.
- On vehicles with Power Steering Pressure Switch (PSPS), turn steering wheel at least 1/2 turn and release within 1-2 seconds after ID code portion of test.
- If Dynamic Response Code appears, perform a brief Wide Open Throttle (WOT). DO NOT perform WOT unless requested.
- If a Code 111 (pass code) is retrieved during KOER SELF-TEST, service Continuous Memory Codes retrieved in KOEO SELF-TEST. See SELF-DIAGNOSTICS – EEC-IV article in ENGINE PERFORMANCE section of appropriate MITCHELL® manual.
- If a Code 111 (pass code) is retrieved during Continuous Memory Code portion of KOEO SELF-TEST (Code 111-1-111) and no driveability problem exists, EEC-IV testing is complete. If driveability problems are still present, go to TROUBLE SHOOTING in 4EAT transmission overhaul article.
- If KOER codes are present, see SERVICE CODE REFERENCE CHARTS. If system will not output codes, go to CIRCUIT TEST QA.

CONTINUOUS MONITOR MODE (WIGGLE TEST)

Continuous Monitor Mode allows technician to attempt to recreate an intermittent fault while monitoring system. This mode, also called wiggle test, may be used in both KOEO SELF-TEST and KOER SELF-TEST. CIRCUIT TESTS specify use of this procedure to identify intermittent faults in specific circuits or components.

KOEO Wiggle Test Procedure – Connect test equipment. See Fig. 2. Turn ignition on, and activate self-test using jumper lead or diagnostic tester. Wait 10 seconds, and then deactivate and reactivate self-test. Wiggle test mode is now activated. Tap, move and wiggle suspect sensor and/or harness area. If a fault is detected, a service code may be stored in memory and indicated at diagnostic tester or scan tester. Retrieve code, and perform appropriate test. See SERVICE CODE REFERENCE CHART.

KOER Wiggle Test Procedure – Connect test equipment. See Fig. 2. Turn ignition off, and wait 10 seconds. Start engine. Activate self-test using jumper lead or diagnostic tester. Wait 10 seconds, and then deactivate and reactivate self-test. DO NOT turn engine off. KOER wiggle test mode is now activated. Tap, move and wiggle suspect sensor and/or harness area. If a fault is detected, a service code may be stored in memory and indicated at diagnostic tester or scan tester. Retrieve code, and perform appropriate test. See SERVICE CODE REFERENCE CHART.

ADDITIONAL SYSTEM FUNCTIONS

Additional diagnostic system features are available to help diagnose driveability problems and service EEC-IV systems.

Output State Check – Output State Check is used as an aid in servicing output actuators associated with EEC-IV system. It allows technicians to energize and de-energize most system output actuators on command. This mode is entered from KOEO SELF-TEST after all codes have been retrieved. Leave SELF-TEST activated, and depress throttle to initiate test sequence. Each time throttle is depressed and released, output actuators will change state (from on to off or off to on).

Failure Mode Effects Management (FMEM), Code 998 – FMEM mode allows system operation when sensors fail or transmit signals that are out of normal operating range. During FMEM mode, PCM substitutes a mid-range signal for defective sensor while continuing to monitor sensor. If faulty sensor's signals return to normal operating range, PCM will use those signals. A Code 98 or 998 will be displayed when FMEM mode is in effect.

SUMMARY

If no service codes (or pass code 111-1-111) is present but driveability problem still exists, return to TROUBLE SHOOTING in 4EAT overhaul article.

SERVICE CODE REFERENCE CHART

NOTE: In addition to transmission fault codes, engine-related fault codes may be output during QUICK TEST procedure. These fault codes pertain to engine performance and must be repaired first as engine performance will greatly affect transmission operation. For information and testing procedures of engine-related fault codes and components, see SELF-DIAGNOSTICS – EEC-IV article in ENGINE PERFORMANCE of appropriate MITCHELL® manual.

CODE REFERENCE CHART

Fault Code	Code Definition	Circuit/Pinpoint Test
KOEO Codes		
No Code	N/A	QA1
111	Pass Code	N/A
122	TPS Malfunction	DH10
123	TPS Malfunction	DH3
621	SS1 Solenoid Circuit Failure	TC20
622	SS2 Solenoid Circuit Failure	TC20
641	SS3 Solenoid Circuit Failure	TC20
636	TOT Out Of Range	TE1
637	TOT Sensor Circuit Open	TE10
638	TOT Sensor Circuit Grounded	TE20
998	FMEM Failure	TC20
Continuous Memory Codes		
No Code	N/A	QA1
111	Pass Code	N/A
122	TPS Malfunction	DH94
123	TPS Malfunction	DH90

CODE REFERENCE CHART (Cont.)

Fault Code	Code Definition	Circuit/Pinpoint Test
KOEO Codes		
452	Insufficient VSS Input	DP1
536	BOO Switch Malfunction	FD90
621	SS1 Solenoid Circuit Failure	TC30
622	SS2 Solenoid Circuit Failure	TC30
634	MLP Sensor Voltage Error	TD10
637	TOT Sensor Voltage High	TE90
638	TOT Sensor Voltage Low	TE90
639	Insufficient Input From TSS	TF95
641	SS3 Solenoid Circuit Failure	TC30
643	SS4 Solenoid Circuit Failure	TC30
KOER Codes		
No Code	N/A	QA1
111	Pass Code	N/A
536	BOO Switch Malfunction	FD1
636	TOT Sensor Voltage Error	TE1
639	Insufficient Input From TSS	TF10

CIRCUIT TEST PROCEDURES

NOTE: A breakout box, connected to vehicle harness at PCM, is necessary to perform most circuit tests. References to Test Pin No. found in CIRCUIT TEST steps refer to test terminals on manufacturer breakout box. Circuit diagrams at beginning of each test identify circuit and wire colors.

HOW TO USE CIRCUIT TESTS

1) Ensure all non-EEC related faults found while performing TROUBLE SHOOTING steps in 4EAT overhaul article have been corrected. DO NOT perform any CIRCUIT TEST unless specifically instructed by a QUICK TEST procedure. Follow each test step in order until fault is found. DO NOT replace any part unless directed to do so. When more than one code is retrieved, start with first code displayed.

2) CIRCUIT TESTS ensure electrical circuits are okay before sensors or other components are replaced. Always test circuits for continuity between sensor and PCM. Test all circuits for short to power, opens or short to ground. Voltage Reference (VREF) and Voltage Power (VPWR) circuits should be tested with KOEO or as specified in CIRCUIT TESTS.

3) DO NOT measure voltage or resistance at PCM. DO NOT connect any test light unless specified in testing procedure. All measurements are made by probing rear of connector. Isolate both ends of a circuit and turn ignition off when checking for shorts or continuity, unless instructed otherwise.

4) Disconnect solenoids and switches from harness before measuring continuity and resistance or applying voltage. After each repair, check all component connections and repeat QUICK TEST.

5) An open circuit is defined as a resistance reading of greater than 5 ohms. This specification tolerance may be too high for some items in EEC-IV system. If resistance approaches 5 ohms, always clean suspect connector and coat it with protective dielectric silicone grease. A short is defined as a resistance reading of less than 10 k/ohms to ground, unless stated otherwise in CIRCUIT TEST.

NOTE: In following tests, circuit diagrams and illustrations are courtesy of Ford Motor Co.

NOTE: In addition to transmission fault codes, engine-related fault codes and circuit tests may be referred to during CIRCUIT TEST procedures. These fault codes and circuit test pertain to engine performance and must be repaired first as engine performance will greatly affect transmission operation. For information and testing procedures of engine-related fault codes, circuit tests and components, see SELF-DIAGNOSTICS – EEC-IV article in ENGINE PERFORMANCE of appropriate MITCHELL® manual.

CIRCUIT TEST DH

THROTTLE POSITION (TP) SENSOR

Diagnostic Aids – Perform this test only when directed by QUICK TEST. This test is intended to diagnose the following:
- TP sensor.
- Wiring harness circuits (TP, SIG RTN and VREF).
- Powertrain Control Module (PCM).

Normal range of throttle angle measurement for TP sensor is 0-85 degrees. To pass QUICK TEST procedure, range of throttle rotation (in degrees) must be within 3 percent of specification. *See Fig. DH2.*

To prevent replacement of good components, be aware the following non-EEC related areas may be at fault:
- Idle speed.
- Binding throttle shaft or linkage.
- TP sensor not seated.

93A40428

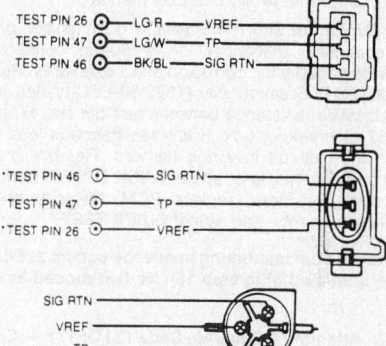

NOTE: EITHER TYPE MAY BE FITTED

Fig. DH1: Identifying TP Sensor Circuits & Connector Terminals

WIRE COLOR IDENTIFICATION

Application	Wire Color
Test Pin No. 26 (VREF)	Light Green/White
Test Pin No. 46 (SIG RTN)	Light Green/Black
Test Pin No. 47 (TP)	Red/White

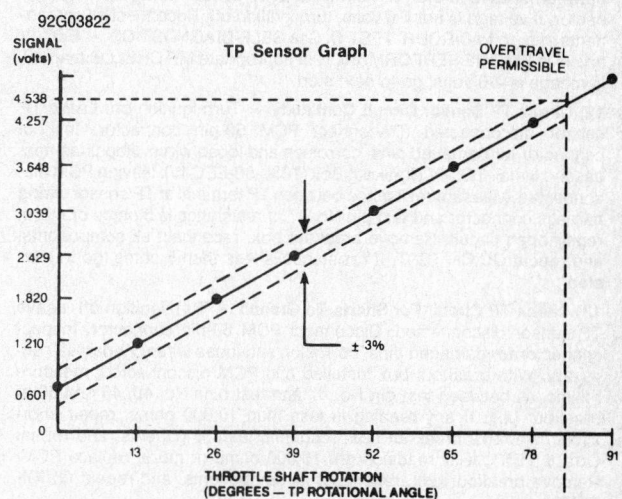

Fig. DH2: TP Sensor Specification Chart

NOTE: A break in step numbering sequence occurs at this point. Procedure skips from step 1) to step 3). No test procedures have been omitted.

CIRCUIT TEST DH (Cont.)

3) Code 123: Attempt To Generate Code 122 – Code 123 indicates TP sensor signal is more than self-test maximum value. Possible causes for this fault are:
- TP sensor not seated properly.
- Faulty TP sensor.
- Short circuit to power.
- Faulty PCM.

Turn ignition off. Disconnect TP sensor wiring harness connector. Inspect and repair connector pins if damaged. Repeat KOEO SELF-TEST. Disregard all other codes at this time. If Code 122 is not displayed, go to step 5). If Code 122 is displayed, go to next step.

4) Check VREF Circuit Voltage – Turn ignition on. Measure voltage between VREF and SIG RTN terminals at TP sensor wiring harness connector. If reading is 4-6 volts, replace TP sensor and repeat QUICK TEST. If reading is not 4-6 volts, reconnect sensor and go to CIRCUIT TEST C. See SELF-DIAGNOSTICS – EEC-IV article in ENGINE PERFORMANCE of appropriate MITCHELL® manual.

5) Check TP Circuit For Short To Power – Turn ignition off. Leave TP sensor disconnected. Disconnect PCM 60-pin connector. Inspect connector for damaged pins, corrosion and loose wires. Repair as necessary. Install EEC-IV Breakout Box (T83L-50-EEC-IV), leaving PCM disconnected. Measure resistance between test pin No. 47 and test pins No. 26 and 57 at breakout box. If any resistance is less than 10,000 ohms, repair short circuit in wiring harness. Remove breakout box, reconnect all components, and repeat QUICK TEST. If both resistances are 10,000 ohms or more, replace PCM. Remove breakout box, reconnect all components, and repeat QUICK TEST.

NOTE: A break in step numbering sequence occurs at this point. Procedure skips from step 5) to step 10). No test procedures have been omitted.

10) Code 122: Attempt To Generate Code 123 Or 121 – Code 122 indicates TP signal is less than minimum self-test value. *See Fig. DH2.* Possible causes for this fault are:
- TP sensor not seated correctly.
- Faulty TP sensor.
- Open circuit in wiring harness.
- Grounded circuit in wiring harness.
- Faulty PCM.

Turn ignition off. Disconnect TP sensor from harness. Install a jumper wire between VREF and TP terminals at TP sensor wiring harness connector. Perform KOEO SELF-TEST. If no codes are generated, remove jumper wire and go to step 13). If Codes 123 and 121 are not present, remove jumper wire and go to next step. If either Code 123 or 121 is displayed, replace TP sensor and repeat QUICK TEST.

11) Check VREF Circuit Voltage – Turn ignition on. Measure voltage between VREF and SIG RTN terminals at TP sensor wiring harness connector. If voltage is not 4-6 volts, turn ignition off. Reconnect all components and go to CIRCUIT TEST C. See SELF-DIAGNOSTICS – EEC-IV article in ENGINE PERFORMANCE of appropriate MITCHELL® manual. If voltage is 4-6 volts, go to next step.

12) Check TP Sensor Circuit Continuity – Turn ignition off. Leave TP sensor disconnected. Disconnect PCM 60-pin connector. Inspect connector for damaged pins, corrosion and loose wires. Repair as necessary. Install EEC-IV Breakout Box (T83L-50-EEC-IV), leaving PCM disconnected. Measure resistance between TP terminal at TP sensor wiring harness connector and test pin No. 47. If resistance is 5 ohms or more, repair open circuit. Remove breakout box, reconnect all components, and repeat QUICK TEST. If resistance is less than 5 ohms, go to next step.

13) Check TP Circuit For Shorts To Ground – Turn ignition off. Leave TP sensor disconnected. Disconnect PCM 60-pin connector. Inspect connector for damaged pins, corrosion and loose wires. Repair as necessary. With breakout box installed and PCM disconnected, measure resistance between test pin No. 47 and test pins No. 40, 46 and 60 at breakout box. If any reading is less than 10,000 ohms, repair short circuit. Remove breakout box, reconnect all components, and repeat QUICK TEST. If all readings are 10,000 ohms or more, replace PCM. Remove breakout box, reconnect all components, and repeat QUICK TEST.

NOTE: A break in step numbering sequence occurs at this point. Procedure skips from step 13) to step 90). No test procedures have been omitted.

CIRCUIT TEST DH (Cont.)

90) Continuous Memory Code 123 – This test monitors TP sensor under simulated road conditions. Enter wiggle test. See CONTINUOUS MONITOR MODE (WIGGLE TEST) under QUICK TEST. Connect DVOM or diagnostic tester to STO terminal of Data Link Connector (DLC). While slowly opening throttle to WOT, observe DVOM or diagnostic tester for indication of fault. Slowly bring throttle to closed position. Lightly tap TP sensor and wiggle harness connector. This test checks for open or short in TP sensor and wiring harness. If no fault is indicated, go to step 92). If fault is indicated, go to next step.

91) Measure TP Circuit Voltage While Exercising TP Sensor – Turn ignition off. Disconnect PCM 60-pin connector. Inspect connector for damaged pins, corrosion and loose wires. Repair as necessary. Install EEC-IV Breakout Box (T83L-50-EEC-IV), leaving PCM connected. Stay in wiggle test (as in previous step). Connect DVOM between test pins No. 47 and 46. Set DVOM on 20-volt scale. With ignition on and engine off, observe DVOM and repeat step 90). If fault occurs at less than 4.25 volts, inspect TP sensor connectors and terminals. If connectors and terminals are okay, replace TP sensor, clear codes and repeat QUICK TEST. If fault does not occur at less than 4.25 volts, TP sensor over-travel may have caused Continuous Memory Code 123. TP sensor is okay. Go to step 92) to check wiring harness.

92) Check EEC-IV Wiring Harness – While in wiggle test, bend and shake small sections of EEC-IV harness from TP sensor wiring harness connector to firewall and from firewall to PCM while observing analog voltmeter or scan tester. If fault is indicated, isolate fault in wiring and repair as necessary. Clear codes, and repeat QUICK TEST. If no fault is indicated, go to next step.

93) Check PCM & Harness Connectors – Turn ignition off. Disconnect PCM 60-pin connector from breakout box. Inspect connector for damaged pins, corrosion and loose wires. Repair as necessary. Clear codes from PCM memory, and repeat QUICK TEST. If connectors and terminals are okay, fault cannot be duplicated at this time. Continuous Memory Code 123 testing is complete.

94) Continuous Memory Code 122 – Enter wiggle test. See CONTINUOUS MONITOR MODE (WIGGLE TEST) under QUICK TEST. Connect DVOM or diagnostic tester to STO terminal of Data Link Connector (DLC). Observe DVOM or diagnostic tester for indication of fault while performing the following:
- Slowly open throttle to WOT.
- Slowly bring throttle to closed position.
- Lightly tap TP sensor and wiggle connector.

If fault is indicated, disconnect TP sensor. Inspect connectors and terminals. If connectors and terminals are okay, replace TP sensor. Clear codes from PCM memory, and repeat QUICK TEST. If no fault is indicated, go to next step.

95) Check EEC-IV Wiring Harness – Stay in wiggle test (as in previous step). Bend, wiggle and shake small sections of EEC-IV harness from TP sensor wiring harness connector to firewall and from firewall to PCM while observing analog voltmeter or scan tester. If fault is indicated, isolate fault in wiring and repair as necessary. Clear codes from PCM memory, and repeat QUICK TEST. If no fault is indicated, go to next step.

96) Check PCM & Harness Connectors – Turn ignition off. Disconnect PCM 60-pin connector. Inspect connector for damaged pins, corrosion and loose wires. Repair as necessary. Clear codes from PCM memory, and repeat QUICK TEST. If connectors and terminals are okay, fault cannot be duplicated at this time. Continuous Memory Code 122 testing is complete.

CIRCUIT TEST DP

VEHICLE SPEED SENSOR (VSS)

Diagnostic Aids – Perform this test when directed by QUICK TEST. This CIRCUIT TEST is intended to diagnose:
- Vehicle Speed Sensor (VSS).
- VSS wiring harness circuits.
- Powertrain Control Module (PCM).

93I40525

*TEST PIN 6 — VSS (—)
*TEST PIN 3 — VSS (+)

VEHICLE SPEED SENSOR (VSS) VEHICLE HARNESS CONNECTOR

*TEST PINS LOCATED ON BREAKOUT BOX
ALL HARNESS CONNECTORS VIEWED IN MATING SURFACE

Fig. DP1: Vehicle Speed Sensor Circuit

CIRCUIT TEST DP (Cont.)

WIRE COLOR IDENTIFICATION

Application	Wire Color
Test Pin No. 3 (VSS +)	White/Black
Test Pin No. 6 (VSS –)	Blue

Preliminary Instructions – Record and clear continuous memory codes. Warm engine to normal operating temperature. Place gear selector in Drive position. Accelerate hard to 35 MPH and coast down to a stop. Shut off engine. Perform KOEO SELF-TEST. Go to step 1).

1) Continuous Memory Code 452 – Code 452 indicates PCM detected incorrect output from VSS sometime during vehicle operation. Possible causes for this code are:
- Faulty VSS.
- Open or shorted circuit.
- Faulty PCM.

Perform appropriate drive cycle procedure. See PRELIMINARY INSTRUCTIONS (A/T) or PRELIMINARY INSTRUCTIONS (M/T). Ensure driveability complaint can be verified. If Code 452 is still present or driveability complaint can be verified, go to next step. If code is not present or complaint cannot be verified, fault cannot be duplicated at this time. Clear codes, and see SYMPTOMS under TROUBLE SHOOTING in 4EAT overhaul article.

2) Check VSS Circuit Continuity – Turn ignition off. Disconnect VSS sensor. Remove PCM 60-pin connector. Inspect connector for damaged pins, corrosion and loose wires. Repair as necessary. Install EEC-IV Breakout Box (T83L-50-EEC-IV), leaving PCM connector disconnected. Measure resistance between VSS (+) terminal at VSS wiring harness connector and test pin No. 3 at breakout box. Also, measure resistance between VSS (–) terminal at VSS wiring harness connector and test pin No. 6 at breakout box. If any resistance reading is more than 5 ohms, repair open circuit in VSS wiring harness. Remove breakout box reconnect all components. Repeat step 1). If both resistance readings are 5 ohms or less, go to next step.

3) Check VSS Circuits For Shorts To Power Or Ground – Turn ignition off. Ensure PCM and VSS are disconnected. Measure resistance between test pin No. 3 and test pins No. 6, 37 and 40 at breakout box. If all readings are more than 500 ohms, go to next step. If any reading is 500 ohms or less, repair shorts in VSS wiring harness and repeat step 1).

4) Check VSS Resistance – Turn ignition off. Disconnect VSS wiring harness connector. Measure resistance between VSS terminals. If resistance is not 190-250 ohms, replace VSS and repeat step 1). If resistance is 190-250 ohms, replace PCM and repeat step 1).

CIRCUIT TEST FD

BRAKE ON-OFF (BOO) SWITCH

Diagnostic Aids – Perform this test when directed by QUICK TEST. This test is intended to diagnose a faulty BOO switch circuit or PCM. To prevent replacement of good components, be aware following non-EEC related areas may be at fault:
- Brakelight bulb.
- Brakelight switch or brakelight fuse.

93I40541

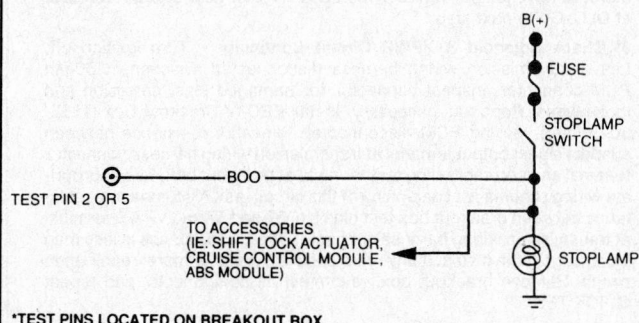

TEST PIN 2 OR 5

B(+)

FUSE

STOPLAMP SWITCH

BOO

TO ACCESSORIES (IE: SHIFT LOCK ACTUATOR, CRUISE CONTROL MODULE, ABS MODULE)

STOPLAMP

*TEST PINS LOCATED ON BREAKOUT BOX

Fig. FD1: BOO Switch Circuit

CIRCUIT TEST FD (Cont.)

WIRE COLOR IDENTIFICATION

Application	Wire Color
Test Pin No. 5 (BOO)	Dark Green

NOTE: A break in step numbering sequence occurs at this point. Procedure skips from step 1) to step 90). No test procedures have been omitted.

90) Continuous Memory Code 536: Check For Proper Brakelight Switch Installation – Code 536 indicates a BOO circuit failure. Possible causes for this fault are:
- Brakelight switch installed improperly.
- Open brakelight circuit.
- Short to ground or power.
- Faulty brakelight switch.
- Faulty brakelight switch ground connection.

Check brakelight switch for proper installation (alignment with brake pedal, corrosion or frayed wires). If brakelight switch is okay, go to next step. If brakelight switch is not okay, repair as necessary. Clear codes and repeat QUICK TEST.

91) Check Brakelight Switch Ground – Check brakelight switch ground connection. Also, check brakelight connector wires for corrosion or damage. Repair as necessary. Clear codes and repeat QUICK TEST. If connector and wires are okay, go to next step.

92) Check Brakelight BOO Circuits For Short To Power – Turn ignition on. Observe brakelights. With brake pedal released, wiggle brakelight BOO circuit wires and connectors. If brakelights flash, isolate short to power and repair as necessary. Clear codes and repeat QUICK TEST. If brakelights do not flash, go to next step.

93) Check Brakelight Circuit Continuity – Turn ignition off. Depress and hold-down brake pedal. Observe brakelights and wiggle brakelight circuit wires and connectors. Also, lightly tap on brakelight switch (to simulate road shock). If brakelights flash or go off, isolate open in brakelight circuit and repair as necessary. Clear codes and repeat QUICK TEST. If brakelights stay on (normal operation), go to next step.

94) Check BOO Circuit Continuity – Turn ignition off. Release brake pedal. Disconnect PCM 60-pin connector. Inspect connector for damaged pins, corrosion and loose wires. Repair as necessary. Install EEC-IV Breakout Box (T83L-50-EEC-IV), leaving PCM disconnected. Connect DVOM between BOO test pin (No. 2 or 5) at breakout box and BOO terminal at brakelight switch. Observe DVOM and wiggle BOO circuit wires and connectors. If resistance at anytime was more than 5 ohms, isolate open in BOO circuit and repair as necessary. Remove breakout box, reconnect all components, and repeat QUICK TEST. If resistance was 5 ohms or less at all times, fault is intermittent and cannot be duplicated at this time. Testing is complete.

CIRCUIT TEST QA

NO CODES/CODES NOT LISTED

Diagnostic Aids – Aftermarket devices, such as alarm system, may cause SELF-TEST to abort if wiring is connected to certain EEC components. If a device is installed, disconnect it completely from EEC system. Before continuing with this circuit test, restore EEC circuits to original state and repeat QUICK TEST.

Perform this test when directed by QUICK TEST or other test procedures. This test is intended to diagnose:
- Powertrain Control Module (PCM).
- EEC power relay.
- Constant Control Relay Module (CCRM).
- Wiring harness circuits (SIG RTN, STO, STI, VPWR and VREF).

CIRCUIT TEST QA (Cont.)

93A40808

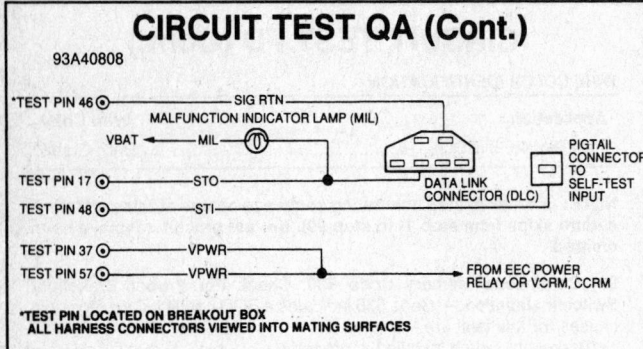

*TEST PIN LOCATED ON BREAKOUT BOX
ALL HARNESS CONNECTORS VIEWED INTO MATING SURFACES

Fig. QA1: No Codes/Codes Not Listed Circuits

WIRE COLOR IDENTIFICATION

Application	Wire Color
Test Pin No. 17 (STO/MIL)	Yellow/Black
Test Pins No. 37 & 57 (VPWR)	White/Red
Test Pin No. 46 (SIG RTN)	Light Green/Black
Test Pin No. 48 (STI)	Light Green/Yellow

1) Check VREF Voltage At Data Link Connector (DLC) – Turn ignition off. Disconnect 60-pin PCM connector. Inspect connector for damaged pins, corrosion and loose wires. Repair as necessary. Install EEC-IV Breakout Box (T83L-50-EEC-IV). Connect PCM to breakout box. Turn ignition on. Measure voltage between test pin No. 26 at breakout box and SIG RTN terminal at DLC. If reading is 4-6 volts, go to step **3)**. If reading is not 4-6 volts, go to next step.

2) Check SIG RTN Circuit Continuity – Turn ignition off. Disconnect PCM from breakout box. Measure resistance between test pin No. 46 at breakout box and SIG RTN terminal at DLC. If reading is less than 5 ohms, go to CIRCUIT TEST C. See SELF-DIAGNOSTICS – EEC-IV article in ENGINE PERFORMANCE of appropriate MITCHELL® manual. If resistance is 5 ohms or more, repair open circuit and repeat QUICK TEST.

3) Check STI Circuit Continuity – Turn ignition off. Disconnect PCM from breakout box. Measure resistance between test pin No. 48 at breakout box and Self-Test Input (STI) terminal at pigtail connector. If resistance is 5 ohms or more, repair open circuit. Remove breakout box, reconnect all components, and repeat QUICK TEST. If reading is less than 5 ohms, go to next step.

4) Check STO Circuit Continuity – Leave ignition off and PCM disconnected. Measure resistance between test pin No. 17 at breakout box and STO terminal at DLC. If resistance is less than 5 ohms, ensure Oxygen sensor circuit is not shorted and then go to step **5)**. If resistance is 5 ohms or more, repair open circuit. Remove breakout box, reconnect all components, and repeat QUICK TEST.

5) Check STO Circuit For Short To Ground – Turn ignition off. Leave PCM disconnected. Measure resistance between STO at DLC and engine ground. If reading is 5 ohms or more, go to next step. If resistance is less than 5 ohms, repair STO or MIL circuit for short to ground. Remove breakout box, reconnect all components, and repeat QUICK TEST.

6) Check If Power Relay Is Always On – Leave ignition off and PCM disconnected. Connect DVOM between test pin No. 37 or 57 and test pin No. 40 or 60 at breakout box. Turn ignition on and then off. Wait 10 seconds. If voltage changes from more than 10.5 volts to less than 1.0 volt, go to step **8)**. If voltage does not change from more than 10.5 volts to less than 1.0 volt, go to next step.

7) Check VPWR Circuit For Short To Power – Turn ignition off. Leave PCM disconnected. Disconnect EEC power relay or Constant Control Relay Module (CCRM). Connect DVOM to test pin No. 37 or 57 and test pin No. 40 or 60 at breakout box. If voltage is more than 1.0 volt, repair VPWR circuit short to power. Remove breakout box, reconnect all components, and repeat QUICK TEST. If voltage is 1.0 volt or less, replace EEC power relay or CCRM. Remove breakout box, reconnect all components, and repeat QUICK TEST.

8) Check Malfunction Indicator Light (MIL) Function – If MIL is always on, go to CIRCUIT TEST ML, step **1)**. If MIL is always off, go to CIRCUIT TEST ML, step **4)**. See SELF-DIAGNOSTICS – EEC-IV article in ENGINE PERFORMANCE of appropriate MITCHELL® manual. If MIL is working normally, replace PCM and repeat QUICK TEST.

CIRCUIT TEST TC

TRANSMISSION SOLENOIDS

Diagnostic Aids – Perform this test only when directed by QUICK TEST. To prevent replacing good components, be aware the following non-EEC areas may be at fault:
- Engine condition (compression, cam timing, valves, etc.).
- Charging system or battery.
- Transmission linkage, internal components or cooling.

This test is not intended to diagnose transmission. This test is intended to diagnose:
- Wiring harness circuits TCC, SS1, SS2, SS3, SIG RTN and VPWR.
- Faulty Powertrain Control Module (PCM).

CIRCUIT TEST TC ACRONYMS

Acronym	Definition
SS	Shift Solenoid
TCC	Torque Converter Clutch

93C40826

Fig. TC1: 4EAT Solenoid Circuits (Escort & Tracer)

1) OUTPUT STATE CHECK – Codes 621, 622 and 641 indicates shift solenoid did not respond to PCM command. Possible causes for these faults are:
- Faulty solenoid assembly.
- Circuit open or grounded.
- Faulty Powertrain Control Module (PCM).

To enter OUTPUT STATE CHECK, use only VOM or DVOM. DO NOT use scan tester. Turn ignition off. Disconnect cruise control servo wiring harness connector. Connect DVOM negative lead to STO terminal at Data Link Connector (DLC). Connect positive lead to positive battery terminal. Install a jumper wire between SIG RTN terminal and STI terminal at DLC. See Fig. QA1. Perform KOEO SELF-TEST until continuous memory test is complete. DVOM will read less than 1.0 volt when test is complete to indicate PCM has entered OUTPUT STATE CHECK. Depress and release throttle. If voltage increases, remain in OUTPUT STATE CHECK and go to next step. If voltage does not increase, depress throttle to WOT and release. If STO voltage goes high, go to next step. If STO voltage does not go high, leave test equipment connected and go to CIRCUIT TEST QC. See SELF-DIAGNOSTICS – EEC-IV article in ENGINE PERFORMANCE of appropriate MITCHELL® manual.

2) Check Solenoid Electrical Condition – Turn ignition off. Disconnect transmission wiring harness connector. Inspect terminals, and repair if damaged. Connect VOM or DVOM positive test lead to solenoid wiring harness connector VPWR terminal. Connect negative test lead to appropriate shift solenoid terminal at transmission wiring harness connector. Turn ignition on. Cycle solenoid output on and off by depressing and releasing throttle 3-5 times. If voltage output changes 0.5 volt or more, fault is in transmission. If voltage output does not change 0.5 volt or more, remove jumper wire between SIG RTN terminal and STI terminal at DLC. Go to next step.

3) Check Solenoid & VPWR Circuit Continuity – Turn ignition off. Leave transmission wiring harness disconnected. Disconnect 60-pin PCM connector. Inspect connector for damaged pins, corrosion and loose wires. Repair as necessary. Install EEC-IV Breakout Box (T83L-50-EEC-IV), leaving PCM disconnected. Measure resistance between suspect signal output terminal at transmission wiring harness connector terminal and corresponding test terminal at breakout box. See appropriate wiring schematic at beginning of this circuit test. Also, measure resistance between breakout box test pins No. 37 and 57 and VPWR terminal at transmission wiring harness connector. If each resistance is less than 5 ohms, go to next step. If any resistance is 5 ohms or more, repair open circuit. Remove breakout box, reconnect all components, and repeat QUICK TEST.

4) Check Solenoid Circuit For Short To Power Or Ground – Leave ignition off and PCM disconnected. Leave transmission wiring harness disconnected. Measure resistance between PCM output signal test pin and test pins No. 37 and 57 at breakout box. Also, measure resistance

CIRCUIT TEST TC (Cont.)

between PCM output signal test pin and pins No. 40, 46 and 60 at breakout box and chassis ground. Measure resistance between PCM output signal test pin and chassis ground. If any reading is less than 10,000 ohms, repair short circuit. Remove breakout box, reconnect all components, and repeat QUICK TEST. If all readings are 10,000 ohms or more, check solenoids. If solenoids are okay, replace PCM. Remove breakout box, reconnect all components, and repeat QUICK TEST.

NOTE: A break in step numbering sequence occurs at this point. Procedure skips from step 4) to step 20). No test procedures have been omitted.

20) Code 621, 622, 641 Or 643: Check Solenoid Resistance – KOEO Code 621 (SS1), 622 (SS2), 641 (SS3) or 643 (TCC) indicate failure in shift solenoid circuit. Possible causes for these faults are:
- Faulty shift solenoid.
- Circuit open or grounded.
- Faulty PCM.

Turn ignition off. Disconnect transmission wiring harness connector. Measure resistance between suspect shift solenoid at transmission wiring harness connector and chassis ground. If resistance is 13-27 ohms, go to next step. If resistance is not 13-27 ohms, go to step 25).

21) Check Shift Solenoid For Short To Power – Leave ignition off and transmission wiring harness connector disconnected. Disconnect 60-pin PCM connector. Inspect connector for damaged pins, corrosion and loose wires. Repair as necessary. Turn ignition on. Measure voltage between suspect shift solenoid at transmission wiring harness connector and chassis ground. If voltage is 0.5 volt or more, repair short to power and repeat QUICK TEST. If voltage is less than 0.5 volt, go to next step.

22) Check Shift Solenoid For Short To Ground – Turn ignition off. Leave transmission wiring harness connector disconnected. Measure resistance between suspect shift solenoid at transmission wiring harness connector and chassis ground. Also, measure resistance between suspect shift solenoid and other circuits at transmission wiring harness connector. If any reading is 10,000 ohms or less, repair short circuit. Reconnect all components and repeat QUICK TEST. If all readings are more than 10,000 ohms, go to next step.

23) Check Shift Solenoid Circuit Continuity – Turn ignition off. Leave transmission wiring harness connector disconnected. Install EEC-IV Breakout Box (T83L-50-EEC-IV) or 4EAT tester, leaving PCM disconnected. Measure resistance between suspect shift solenoid test pin at breakout box and suspect shift solenoid terminal at transmission wiring harness connector. If resistance is 5 ohms or more, repair open circuit. Reconnect all components and repeat QUICK TEST. If resistance is less than 5 ohms, go to next step.

24) Check Shift Solenoid For Short To Power In Transmission – Leave ignition off and PCM disconnected. Reconnect transmission wiring harness connector. Measure voltage between test pin No. 60 and suspect shift solenoid test pin at breakout box. If voltage is 0.5 volt or more, replace or repair solenoid short to power. Remove breakout box, reconnect all components, and repeat QUICK TEST. If voltage is less than 0.5 volt, replace PCM. Remove breakout box, reconnect all components, and repeat QUICK TEST.

25) Check Transmission Wiring – Leave ignition off. Check transmission wiring harness circuits and connectors breaks or corrosion in insulation. Check for open or grounded circuits. Repair or replace as necessary. If connectors and circuits are okay, replace suspect solenoid and repeat QUICK TEST.

NOTE: A break in step numbering sequence occurs at this point. Procedure skips from step 25) to step 30). No test procedures have been omitted.

30) Continuous Memory Codes 621, 622, 641 & 643 – Continuous Memory Code 621 (SS1), 622 (SS2), 641 (SS3) or 643 (TCC) indicates a failure was detected in shift solenoid circuit during last 80 warm-up cycles. Possible causes for these faults are:
- Faulty shift solenoid.
- Circuit open or grounded.

Turn ignition off. Check shift solenoid circuit between PCM and transmission. Repair or replace wiring as necessary. If circuits are okay, go to next step.

31) Check For Intermittent Short Or Open – Turn ignition off. Disconnect 60-pin PCM connector. Inspect connector for damaged pins, corrosion and loose wires. Repair as necessary. Install EEC-IV Breakout Box (T83L-50-EEC-IV) or 4EAT tester, leaving PCM disconnected. Turn igni-

CIRCUIT TEST TC (Cont.)

tion on. Connect test light between test pin No. 37 and suspect shift solenoid test pin at breakout box. See IDENTIFYING SHIFT SOLENOID TEST CIRCUITS table. Test light should be at partial brightness. Observe test light while wiggling and bending shift solenoid circuit between transmission and PCM. An open or short to power will be indicated by light going off. A short to ground will be indicated by light getting brighter. Repeat procedure for all solenoids. If fault is indicated, isolate and repair as necessary. If no fault is indicated, go to next step.

IDENTIFYING SHIFT SOLENOID TEST CIRCUITS

Shift Solenoid	Test Pin No.
SS1	11
SS2	51
SS3	52
TCC	55

32) Check For Intermittent Short To Ground – Leave ignition off and PCM disconnected. Disconnect transmission wiring harness connector. Turn ignition on. Connect test light between test pin No. 37 and suspect shift solenoid test pin at breakout box. Test light should be off. Observe test light while wiggling and bending shift solenoid circuit between transmission and PCM. A short to ground will be indicated by light turning on. Repeat procedure for all solenoids. If fault is indicated, isolate and repair as necessary. Remove breakout box, reconnect all components, and repeat QUICK TEST. If no fault is indicated, problem is intermittent and cannot be duplicated at this time.

CIRCUIT TEST TD

MANUAL LEVER POSITION (MLP) SENSOR

Diagnostic Aids – Perform this test only when directed by QUICK TEST. To prevent replacing good components, be aware the following non-EEC areas may be at fault:
- Transmission linkage and internal components.
- Electrical (alternator, battery, add-on devices, etc.).

This test is not intended to diagnose transmission. This test is intended to diagnose:
- Wiring harness circuits PNP, TRD, TRL, TRR and TROD.
- Powertrain Control Module (PCM).

93B40841

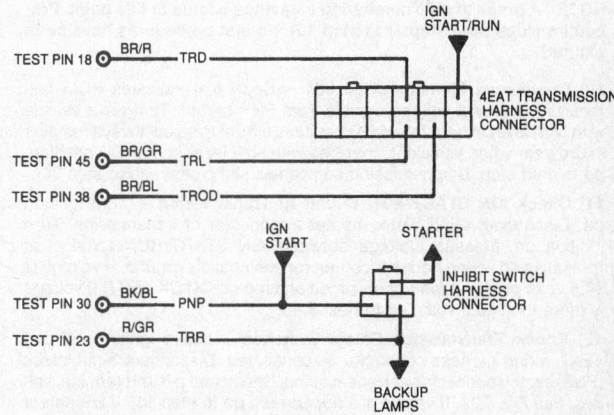

Fig. TD1: Identifying Inhibit Switch & 4EAT Module Circuits (4EAT – Escort & Tracer)

1) Code 634: Check MLP Sensor Alignment – KOEO Code 634 indicates MLP sensor is out of self-test range when gear selector is in Park position. Turn ignition off. Apply parking brake. Place transmission gear selector in Neutral position. Place MLP Sensor Gauge (T91P-7010-AHT) in sensor slot. If gauge does not fit, loosen MLP mounting bolts and adjust sensor as necessary. If gauge fits, remove gauge and go to next step.

CIRCUIT TEST TD (Cont.)

93D40843

4EAT Transmission Range Switch State

Switch (at transmission 12-pin connector)	Reference (at transmission 12-pin connector)	Switch State (Closed: Less than 5.0 ohms Open: Greater than 10,000 ohms)
TROD	IGN START/RUN	Closed in "OD", open in all other positions
TRD	IGN START/RUN	Closed in "D", open in all other positions
TRL	IGN START/RUN	Closed in "L", open in all other positions
Switch (at inhibit SW 3-pin connector)	Reference (at trans 12-pin connector)	
TRR	IGN START/RUN	Closed in "R", open in all other positions
Switch (at inhibit SW 3-pin connector)	Reference (at inhibit 12-pin connector)	
PNP	To Starter	Closed in "P" and "N", open in all other positions

Table heading: Transmission Switch (at transmission connector)

4EAT Transmission Range Switch Voltage at EEC-IV Breakout Box

Circuit	Pin	Reference (Pin)	Voltage at EEC-IV Breakout Box (Key on) (All voltages ± 0.5 volts)
TRR	23	GND (40)	VBAT in "R", 0V in all other positions
TRL	45	GND (40)	VBAT in "L", 0V in all other positions
TRD	18	GND (40)	VBAT in "D", 0V in all other positions
TROD	38	GND (40)	VBAT in "OD", 0V in all other positions

Fig. TD2: 4EAT Transmission Select Switch Specifications

CIRCUIT TEST TD (Cont.)

NOTE: A break in step numbering sequence occurs at this point. Procedure skips from step 1) to step 10). No test procedures have been omitted.

10) Continuous Memory Code 634 – Code 634 indicates PCM has received incorrect voltage signals from PNP switch. Test drive vehicle with shift lever in both D and OD position. If transmission always remains in 3rd gear when vehicle is operated with shift lever in D or OD position, go to next step. If transmission sometimes shifts okay, go to step 20).

11) Check IGN START/RUN Circuit At Transmission – Turn ignition off. Disconnect 4EAT wiring harness connector at transmission. Turn ignition on. Measure voltage between IGN START/RUN terminal at transmission wiring harness connector and chassis ground. If voltage is 10.5 volts or less, repair open circuit and repeat QUICK TEST. If voltage is more than 10.5 volts, go to next step.

12) Check Transmission Select Switches – Leave ignition off and 4EAT wiring harness connector disconnected. Disconnect 3-pin inhibit (PNP) switch connector at transmission. Check test pin and terminal values. See Fig. TD1. If values are not correct, go to step 14). If connector terminal values are correct, go to next step.

13) Check Transmission Switch Input Voltage – Turn ignition off. Disconnect 60-pin PCM connector. Inspect connector for damaged pins, corrosion and loose wires. Repair as necessary. Install EEC-IV Breakout Box (T83L-50-EEC-IV) or 4EAT tester, leaving PCM disconnected. Reconnect inhibit switch and transmission switch connectors. Turn ignition on. Check test pin and terminal values. See Figs. TD1 and TD2. If values are correct and no other problems can be found, replace PCM and repeat QUICK TEST. If values are not correct, repair circuit(s) and check system operation.

CIRCUIT TEST TD (Cont.)

With ignition on and negative lead of DVOM connected to negative battery terminal, ensure following signals are correct:
- **POWERS**: KAPWR (pin No. 1) is more than 10.5 volts, VPWR (pins No. 37 and 57) is more than 10.5 volts and VREF (pin No. 26) is 4-6 volts.
- **GROUNDS**: PWR GND (pins No. 40 and 60), SIG RTN (pin No. 46) and IGN GND (pin No. 16) are 0.0-0.5 volt.
- **OPTIONAL GROUNDS**: HO2S GND (pin No. 49), CSE GND (pin No. 20) and MAF RTN (pin No. 9 or 15) are 0.0-0.5 volt.

Diagnostic Aids – PNP input (pin No. 30) should be monitored. With PNP switch referenced to GND, the voltage should be about zero volts in Park or Neutral and more than 3.0 volts in all other gear positions.

Drive vehicle to create conditions so that symptom will occur. Information provided by vehicle operator may help when trying to recreate symptom. When symptom occurs, assistant should observe and record changes in voltage signals.

Information about symptom, operating condition value of voltage signal and any other information available should be recorded for analysis. After test is completed, analyze results to locate and repair fault causing symptom. If problem cannot be identified, go to TROUBLE SHOOTING (EEC-IV) – NO CODES article in ENGINE PERFORMANCE of appropriate MITCHELL® manual for other possible causes of symptom.

14) MLP Switch – Turn ignition off. Check MLP switch circuits and connectors for damage and corrosion. Ensure MLP switch is adjusted correctly. See step 1). If any faults are found, repair or replace as necessary and check system operation. If no faults are found, replace MLP switch. Reconnect all components and check system operation.

NOTE: A break in step numbering sequence occurs at this point. Procedure skips from step 14) to step 20). No test procedures have been omitted.

CIRCUIT TEST TD (Cont.)

20) Inspect 4EAT Circuit – Turn ignition off. Inspect transmission switches and harness connectors between PCM and transmission for corrosion or damage. Inspect wiring harness for correct routing. If any faults are found, repair or replace as necessary. If no faults are found, go to next step.

21) Check Wiring Harness & Connectors For Intermittent Open Or Short Circuit – Turn ignition off. Disconnect 60-pin PCM connector. Inspect connector for damaged pins, corrosion and loose wires. Repair as necessary. Install EEC-IV Breakout Box (T83L-50-EEC-IV) or 4EAT tester, leaving PCM disconnected. Turn ignition on. Connect test light between test pin No. 40 and transmission test pin as follows:

- Test pin No. 18 (TRD) with gear selector in D.
- Test pin No. 23 (TRR) with gear selector in R.
- Test pin No. 38 (TROD) with gear selector in OD.
- Test pin No. 45 (TRL) with gear selector in L.

Test light should be on when gear selector is in the same gear as the circuit being tested. Shake and wiggle transmission switch wiring harness between PCM and transmission. Lightly tap on inhibit switch to simulate road shock. If test light dims, flickers or goes off, fault is indicated. Isolate fault and repair as necessary. Remove breakout box, reconnect all components and check system operation. If test light stays on, fault cannot be duplicated at this time.

CAUTION: Following road test is an optional procedure. Follow all applicable safety procedures and traffic laws. This road test requires a driver and an assistant. Assistant should make measurements, observe changes and record notes. If this test is not performed, go to TROUBLE SHOOTING in 4EAT overhaul article for other possible causes.

22) Road Test Vehicle – Purpose of this test is to identify faults by monitoring certain controlled parameters while trying to recreate a driveability or MIL symptom. To prepare for road test:

- Install fuel pressure gauge and, if available, a MAP/BARO tester.
- Disconnect PCM 60-pin connector, install breakout box and reconnect PCM to breakout box.
- Have DVOM, writing materials and appropriate schematics and pin voltage charts available.

CIRCUIT TEST TE

TRANSMISSION FLUID TEMPERATURE (TFT) SENSOR

Diagnostic Aids – Perform this test only when directed by QUICK TEST. To prevent replacing good components, be aware the following non-EEC areas may be at fault:

- Engine and/or transmission fluid level.
- Engine and/or transmission fluid temperature.
- Ambient temperature.

This test is intended to diagnose:

- TFT sensor.
- Wiring harness circuits TFT and SIG RTN.
- Faulty Powertrain Control Module (PCM).

92F03893

TEST PIN 2 ⊙— W ——————— TOT

4EAT TRANSMISSION HARNESS CONNECTOR

TEST PIN 46 ⊙— LG/BK ——————— SIG RTN

Fig. TE1: Transmission Fluid Temperature (TFT) Sensor Circuit (Escort & Tracer)

CIRCUIT TEST TE (Cont.)

TFT SENSOR (4EAT) SPECIFICATIONS

Temperature °F (°C)	¹ Volts	¹ Ohms
32 (0)	4.8	52,000
68 (20)	4.6	23,000
104 (40)	4.3	11,000
140 (60)	3.7	5600
212 (100)	2.4	1711
266 (130)	1.5	860

¹ – Values may vary by 15 percent.

1) KOEO Code 636 – KOEO Code 636 indicate TFT sensor is out of self-test range. Possible causes for these faults are:

- Transmission fluid level incorrect.
- Transmission fluid temperature incorrect.
- Sensor resistance out of specification.
- Faulty Powertrain Control Module (PCM).

Ensure transmission fluid temperature is more than 50°F (10°C). Repeat QUICK TEST. If Code 636 is present, go to next. If Code 636 is not present, no problem is indicated at this time. Test is complete.

2) Check VREF At Throttle Position (TP) Sensor – Turn ignition off. Disconnect TP sensor wiring harness connector. Disconnect 60-pin PCM connector. Inspect connector for damaged pins, corrosion and loose wires. Repair as necessary. Install EEC-IV Breakout Box (T83L-50-EEC-IV). Connect PCM to breakout box. Turn ignition on. Measure voltage between VREF and SIG RTN terminals at TP sensor wiring harness connector. See Fig. DH1. If voltage is 4-6 volts, go to next step. If voltage is not 4-6 volts, go to CIRCUIT TEST C. See SELF-DIAGNOSTICS – EEC-IV article in ENGINE PERFORMANCE of appropriate MITCHELL® manual.

3) Check TFT Sensor Resistance – Turn ignition off. Disconnect PCM from breakout box. Allow transmission to cool. Measure and record resistance between test pin No. 46 and TFT test pin at breakout box. Reconnect PCM. Drive vehicle until transmission fluid is normal operating temperature. Disconnect PCM from breakout box. Measure resistance voltage between test pin No. 46 and TFT test pin at breakout box. If cold resistance measurement is higher than warm resistance measurement, and warm resistance is within specification, replace PCM and repeat QUICK TEST. See appropriate TFT SENSOR SPECIFICATIONS table at beginning of this circuit test. If resistance is not as specified, go to step 25).

NOTE: A break in step numbering sequence occurs at this point. Procedure skips from step 3) to step 10). No test procedures have been omitted.

10) KOEO Code 637 – KOEO Code 637 indicates TFT sensor output exceeds self-test maximum voltage (4.8 volts). Possible causes for these faults are:

- Transmission fluid level incorrect.
- Open wiring harness circuit.
- Faulty TFT sensor.
- Faulty PCM.

Turn ignition off. Disconnect TFT wiring harness connector. Inspect terminals, and repair if damaged. Connect jumper wire between TFT and SIG RTN terminals. Perform KOEO SELF-TEST. If Code 638 is present, remove jumper wire and go to step 25). If Code 638 is not present, remove jumper wire and go to next step.

11) Check TFT & SIG RTN Circuit Continuity – Turn ignition off. Leave TFT sensor disconnected. Disconnect 60-pin PCM connector. Inspect connector for damaged pins, corrosion and loose wires. Repair as necessary. Install EEC-IV Breakout Box (T83L-50-EEC-IV), leaving PCM disconnected. Measure resistance between TFT circuit at TFT wiring harness connector and TFT test pin at breakout box. Also, measure resistance between SIG RTN circuit at TFT wiring harness connector and test pin No. 46 at breakout box. If any reading 5 ohms or more, repair open circuit. Remove breakout box, reconnect all components, and repeat QUICK TEST. If all readings are less than 5 ohms, go to next step.

12) Check TFT Sensor For Short To VPWR – Turn ignition off. Leave PCM and TFT sensor disconnected. Measure resistance between TFT test pin and test pins No. 37 and 57 at breakout box. If all readings are more than 10,000 ohms, replace PCM. Remove breakout box, reconnect all components, and repeat QUICK TEST. If any reading is 10,000 ohms or less, repair short circuit. Remove breakout box, reconnect all components, and repeat QUICK TEST.

CIRCUIT TEST TE (Cont.)

NOTE: A break in step numbering sequence occurs at this point. Procedure skips from step 12) to step 20). No test procedures have been omitted.

20) KOEO Code 638 – KOEO Code 638 indicates TFT sensor output is lower than self-test minimum voltage. Possible causes for these faults are:
- Damaged TFT sensor.
- Shorted wiring harness circuit.
- Faulty PCM.

Turn ignition off. Disconnect transmission wiring harness connector. Inspect terminals, and repair if damaged. Perform KOEO SELF-TEST. If Code 637 is present, go to step 25). If Code 637 is not present, go to step 21).

21) Check VREF At Throttle Position (TP) Sensor – Turn ignition off. Disconnect TP sensor wiring harness connector. Disconnect 60-pin PCM connector. Inspect connector for damaged pins, corrosion and loose wires. Repair as necessary. Install EEC-IV Breakout Box (T83L-50-EEC-IV). Connect PCM to breakout box. Turn ignition on. Measure voltage between VREF and SIG RTN terminals at TP sensor wiring harness connector. Go to CIRCUIT TEST DH. If voltage is 4-6 volts, go to next step. If voltage is not 4-6 volts, go to CIRCUIT TEST C. See SELF-DIAGNOSTICS – EEC-IV article in ENGINE PERFORMANCE of appropriate MITCHELL® manual.

22) Check TFT Circuit For Short To Ground – Turn ignition off. Disconnect PCM from breakout box. Measure resistance between TFT test pin at breakout box and test pins No. 40, 46 and 60. If all readings are more than 10,000 ohms, replace PCM. Remove breakout box, reconnect all components, and repeat QUICK TEST. If any reading is 10,000 ohms or less, repair short circuit. Remove breakout box, reconnect all components, and repeat QUICK TEST.

NOTE: A break in step numbering sequence occurs at this point. Procedure skips from step 22) to step 25). No test procedures have been omitted.

25) Check Transmission Wiring Harness – Turn ignition off. Check transmission internal and external wiring and connectors for damage and corrosion. Repair or replace if necessary. If wiring is okay, replace TFT sensor and repeat QUICK TEST.

NOTE: A break in step numbering sequence occurs at this point. Procedure skips from step 25) to step 90). No test procedures have been omitted.

90) Continuous Memory Code 637 Or 638 – Continuous Memory Code 637 or 638 indicates a fault has been detected in TFT circuit during previous 80 warm-up cycles. Possible causes for these faults are:
- Incorrect fluid level.
- Intermittent fault in TFT sensor.
- Intermittent short or open in wiring harness.

Turn ignition off. Disconnect 60-pin PCM connector. Inspect connector for damaged pins, corrosion and loose wires. Repair as necessary. Install EEC-IV Breakout Box (T83L-50-EEC-IV). Connect PCM to breakout box. Connect DVOM between test pins No. 2 and 46 at breakout box. Turn ignition on. Shake and bend TFT and SIG RTN wires between transmission and PCM. Voltage should remain stable or change gradually. If voltage drops to zero, a short to ground is indicated. If voltage increases up to 5 volts, an open circuit is indicated. If voltage increases to more than 5 volts, a short to power is indicated. If fault is indicated, isolate and repair as necessary. If no faults are found, go to CIRCUIT TEST TD, step 22).

CIRCUIT TEST TF

TURBINE SHAFT SPEED SENSOR

Diagnostic Aids – Perform this test only when directed by QUICK TEST. This test is intended to diagnose:
- Wiring harness circuit TSS.
- Faulty Powertrain Control Module (PCM).

NOTE: A break in step numbering sequence occurs at this point. Procedure skips from step 1) to step 10). No test procedures have been omitted.

10) Code 639: Check TSS Resistance – Code 639 indicates incorrect input signal from TSS. Possible causes for this fault are:
- Faulty TSS.
- Circuit open or grounded.
- Faulty PCM.

CIRCUIT TEST TF (Cont.)

92A03895

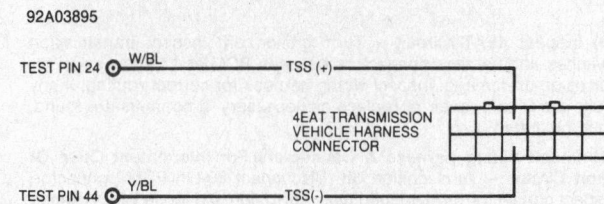

Fig. TF1: Turbine Shaft Speed Sensor Circuit

Turn ignition off. Disconnect transmission 12-pin connector. Measure resistance between TSS (–) and TSS (+) terminal at sensor wiring harness connector. If resistance is not 200-600 ohms, check wiring for damage and corrosion. If wiring is okay, replace TSS and repeat QUICK TEST. If resistance is 200-600 ohms, go to next step.

93A40873

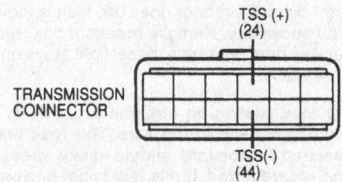

Fig. TF2: Identifying Transmission 12-Pin Connector Terminals

11) Check TSS Circuit For Short To Power – Leave ignition off and transmission 12-pin connector disconnected. Disconnect 60-pin PCM connector. Inspect connector for damaged pins, corrosion and loose wires. Repair as necessary. Turn ignition on. Measure voltage between TSS (+) terminal at sensor wiring harness connector and chassis ground. Also, measure voltage between TSS (–) terminal at sensor wiring harness connector and chassis ground. If both readings are less than 0.5 volt, go to next step. If any reading is 0.5 volt or more, repair short circuit. Reconnect all components and repeat QUICK TEST.

12) Turn ignition off. Leave transmission connector and PCM disconnected. Measure resistance between TSS (+) terminal at sensor wiring harness connector and chassis ground. Measure resistance between TSS (–) terminal at sensor wiring harness connector and chassis ground. Also, measure resistance between TSS (+) terminal and TSS (–) terminal at 12-pin connector. If any reading is 10,000 ohms or less, repair short circuit and repeat QUICK TEST. If any reading is more than 10,000 ohms, go to next step.

13) Check TSS Circuit Continuity – Leave ignition off and transmission 12-pin connector removed. Install EEC-IV Breakout Box (T83L-50-EEC-IV) or 4EAT tester, leaving PCM disconnected. Measure resistance between TSS (+) terminal at 12-pin connector and test pin No. 24 at breakout box. Also, measure resistance between TSS (–) terminal at 12-pin connector and test pin No. 44 at breakout box. If any reading is 5 ohms or more, repair open circuit and repeat QUICK TEST. If both readings are less than 5 ohms, go to next step.

14) Check PCM For Internal Shorts – Turn ignition off. Connect PCM to breakout box. Leave transmission wiring harness connector disconnected. Measure resistance between test pin No. 24 and pins No. 37, 40, 44, 57 and 60 at breakout box. If any reading is 500 ohms or less, replace PCM. Remove breakout box, reconnect all components, and repeat QUICK TEST. If all readings are more than 500 ohms, go to next step.

15) Check TSS Output – Turn ignition off. Leave PCM connected to breakout box. Reconnect transmission 12-pin connector. Set DVOM on AC voltage scale. Start engine. Measure voltage between breakout box test pins No. 24 and 44 while varying engine speed. If AC voltage varies more than 0.5 volt, replace PCM. Remove breakout box, reconnect all components, and repeat QUICK TEST. If AC voltage does not vary more than 0.5 volt, replace TSS. Remove breakout box, reconnect all components, and repeat QUICK TEST.

NOTE: A break in step numbering sequence occurs at this point. Procedure skips from step 15) to step 95). No test procedures have been omitted.

CIRCUIT TEST TF (Cont.)

95) Continuous Memory Code 639: Check TSS Wiring – Continuous Memory Code 639 indicates an error in TSS sensor output during previous 80 warm-up cycles. Possible causes for this fault are:

- Intermittent fault in TSS sensor.
- Intermittent short or open in wiring harness.
- Transmission placed in gear when fluid level is low.

Turn ignition off. Visually inspect TSS wires and connectors for damage. Disconnect 60-pin PCM connector. Inspect connector for damaged pins, corrosion and loose wires. Repair as necessary. Install EEC-IV Breakout Box (T83L-50-EEC-IV). Connect PCM to breakout box. Connect DVOM between test pins No. 24 and 44 at breakout box. Start engine. Shake and bend TSS wires between transmission and PCM. Lightly tap circuit connectors. Voltage should remain stable or change gradually. If voltage drops or surges abruptly, fault in circuit is indicated. If fault is indicated, isolate and repair as necessary. If no faults are found, go to next step.

96) Check PCM & Harness Connectors – Turn ignition off. Disconnect all connectors related to TSS circuit. Inspect circuits and connectors for damage. Repair as necessary and repeat QUICK TEST. If fault cannot be found, problem is intermittent and cannot be duplicated at this time.

CAUTION: Following road test is an optional procedure. Follow all applicable safety procedures and traffic laws. This road test requires a driver and an assistant. Assistant should make measurements, observe changes and record notes. If this test is not performed, go to TROUBLE SHOOTING (EEC-IV) – NO CODES article in ENGINE PER-FORMANCE of appropriate MITCHELL® manual for other possible causes.

97) Road Test Vehicle – Purpose of this test is to identify faults by monitoring certain controlled parameters while trying to recreate a drive-ability or MIL symptom. To prepare for road test:

- Install fuel pressure gauge and, if available, a MAP/BARO tester.
- Disconnect PCM 60-pin connector, install breakout box and recon-nect PCM to breakout box.
- Have DVOM, writing materials and appropriate schematics and pin voltage charts available.

With ignition on and negative lead of DVOM connected to negative bat-tery terminal, ensure following signals are correct:

- POWERS: KAPWR (pin No. 1) is more than 10.5 volts, VPWR (pins No. 37 and 57) is more than 10.5 volts and VREF (pin No. 26) is 4-6 volts.
- GROUNDS: PWR GND (pins No. 40 and 60), SIG RTN (pin No. 46) and IGN GND (pin No. 16) are 0.0-0.5 volt.
- OPTIONAL GROUNDS: HO2S GND (pin No. 49), CSE GND (pin No. 20) and MAF RTN (pin No. 9 or 15) are 0.0-0.5 volt.

Diagnostic Aids – Drive vehicle to create conditions so that symptom will occur. Information provided by vehicle operator may help when try-ing to recreate symptom. When symptom occurs, assistant should observe and record changes in voltage signals.

Information about symptom, operating condition value of voltage signal and any other information available should be recorded for analysis. After test is completed, analyze results to locate and repair fault causing symptom. If problem cannot be identified, go to TROUBLE SHOOTING (EEC-IV) – NO CODES article in ENGINE PERFORMANCE of appropri-ate MITCHELL® manual for other possible causes of symptom.

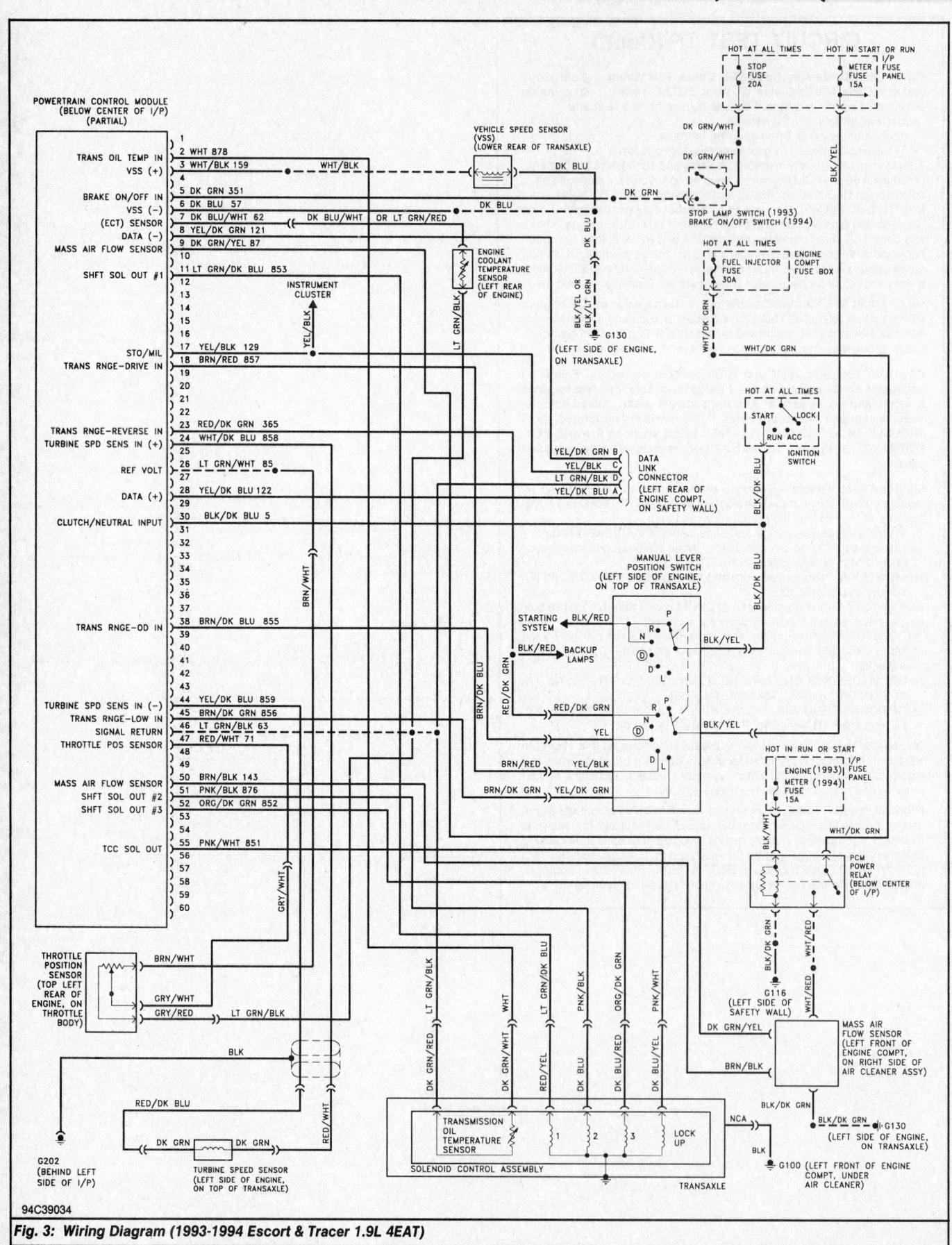

Fig. 3: Wiring Diagram (1993-1994 Escort & Tracer 1.9L 4EAT)

94C39034

Ford Motor Co: Villager

APPLICATION & LABOR TIMES

APPLICATION & LABOR TIMES

Vehicle Application	Labor Times		Trans. Model
	[1] R & I	[2] Overhaul	
1993-94 Villager	4.6	9.0	4F20E

[1] – Removal and installation of transmission from vehicle chassis.

[2] – Bench overhaul time for transmission and differential. DOES NOT include removal and installation.

IDENTIFICATION

The 4F20E automatic transmission is identified by identification tag located on rear of transaxle and bottom of main control assembly. *See Fig. 1.*

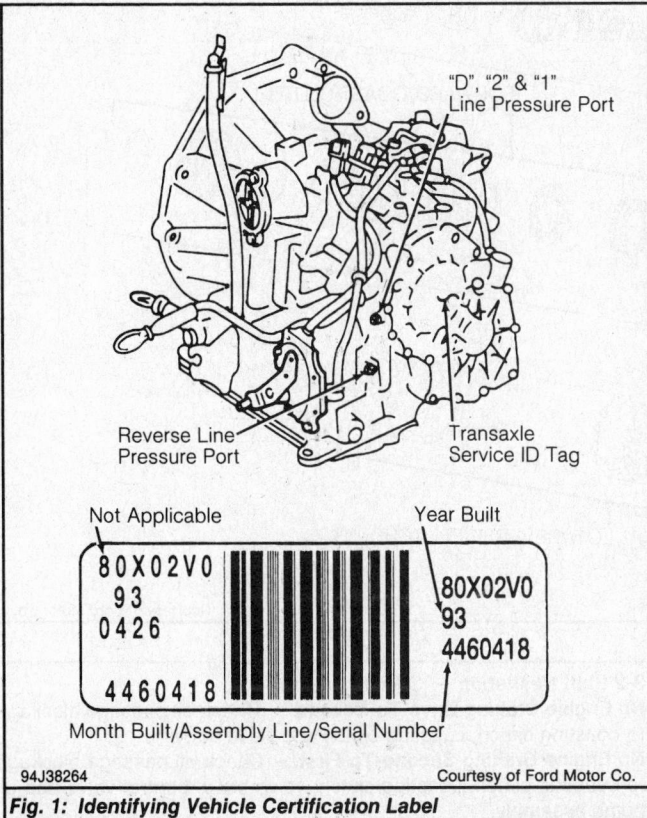

"D", "2" & "1" Line Pressure Port

Reverse Line Pressure Port

Transaxle Service ID Tag

Not Applicable

Year Built

```
80X02V0
93
0426
4460418
```

```
80X02V0
93
4460418
```

Month Built/Assembly Line/Serial Number

94J38264   Courtesy of Ford Motor Co.

Fig. 1: Identifying Vehicle Certification Label

NOTE: *For 4F20E transaxle electronic testing and repair, 4F20E Electronic Controls article.*

DESCRIPTION & OPERATION

The 4F20E is a 4-speed transaxle assembly controlled by both electronic and mechanical systems utilizing a compound planetary gearset, gear drive, and an open differential. One band, 5 friction clutches, and 2 one-way clutches provide 4 forward gear ratios and reverse. *See Fig. 2.*

Input signals from sensors are sent to the Transmission Control Module (TCM). The TCM can determine when the time and conditions are right for a shift or converter clutch application. The TCM can also determine line pressure needed to optimize shift feel.

Five electronic solenoids accomplish these functions; 2 On/Off solenoids for shifting, a Pulse-Width Modulator solenoid for torque converter clutch control, a Electronic Pressure Control (EPC) solenoid for line pressure control, and a coasting clutch solenoid to control the release of the coast clutch and the coordinated release of the direct clutch and apply of the low and intermediate band. The TCM has built-in self-diagnosis, fail-safe code and warning code display for the main input sensors and solenoid valves.

LUBRICATION & ADJUSTMENTS

NOTE: *See appropriate AUTOMATIC TRANSMISSION SERVICING article in TRANSMISSION SERVICING section.*

TROUBLE SHOOTING

PRELIMINARY INSPECTION

1) Ensure vehicle is thoroughly road tested to verify driver's complaint. Determine if problem occurs during upshift, downshift, coasting or engagement. If noise is diagnosed, check if noise is affected by RPM, vehicle speed, gear selection or temperature. Ensure vehicle is at normal operating temperature when inspecting.

2) Inspect fluid level and condition. Visually inspect for vehicle modifications, electronic add-ons, fluid leaks and/or incorrect linkage adjustment. Check for trouble codes before any mechanical repair is performed. See 4F20E ELECTRONIC CONTROLS article for trouble code diagnosis and repair procedures. If no trouble codes are present, see applicable symptom diagnosis.

SYMPTOM DIAGNOSIS

Engine Will Not Crank In Any Shift Lever Position – Check for stuck, inoperative, damaged or disconnected MLP switch.

Engine Does Not Crank In Park &/Or Neutral – Check shift lever and transmission shift cable adjustment, MLP switch alignment and possible ignition system damage.

Engine Starts In Shift Lever Position Other Than Park Or Neutral – Check shift lever and shift cable adjustment and MLP switch.

Vehicle Moves In Park Or Remains In Park When Shift Lever Is Not In Park Position – Check shift lever and shift cable adjustment, parking pawl and idler gear.

Vehicle Moves In Neutral – Check shift lever and shift cable adjustment, valve body, ATF fluid level, torque converter, MLP switch adjustment, reverse clutch and coasting clutch.

Vehicle Does Not Move In Any Shift Lever Position – Check valve body, shift cable, ATF fluid level, oil pump, torque converter, solenoid valves, clutches and parking mechanism.

Vehicle Does Not Move In Any Forward Gear, Reverse Okay – Check valve body, forward clutch, one-way clutch and forward clutch oil passage.

Vehicle Does Not Move In Reverse, Forward Gears Okay – Check reverse clutch and low/reverse clutch.

Severe Noise Under Acceleration Or Deceleration – Check torque converter, gear or clutch failure and damaged or worn engine mounts.

Constant Noise In Any Shift Lever Position – Check for loose torque converter mounting bolts, oil pump and torque converter failure.

Variable Pitch Noise, Changes Upon Deceleration – Check differential, ATF fluid level, C.V. joints, speedometer gear, internal bearings and planetary gear.

Overheating Transaxle – Check ATF fluid level, engine performance, clutch (worn), band application, oil pressure control, oil cooler (restriction), TOT sensor, valve body and solenoid valves.

Drags In Reverse – Check 2-4 band and vehicle braking system.

Drags In Forward Gears – Check 2-4 band and vehicle braking system.

Engine Runaway (Rapid Engine RPM Increase) On Upshift Or Accelerating – Check ATF fluid level, valve body, TOT sensor, oil pump and slipping clutches.

Engine Runaway (Rapid Engine RPM Increase) On Downshift – Check slipping clutches, ATF fluid level and oil pump.

Excessive Creep – Check torque converter, ignition timing and idle speed, line pressure solenoid and oil pump assembly.

No Creep – Check ATF fluid level and condition, shift lever and shift cable adjustment, valve body, shift control valve, forward clutch, reverse clutch, oil pump, forward one-way clutch (sprag), low one-way

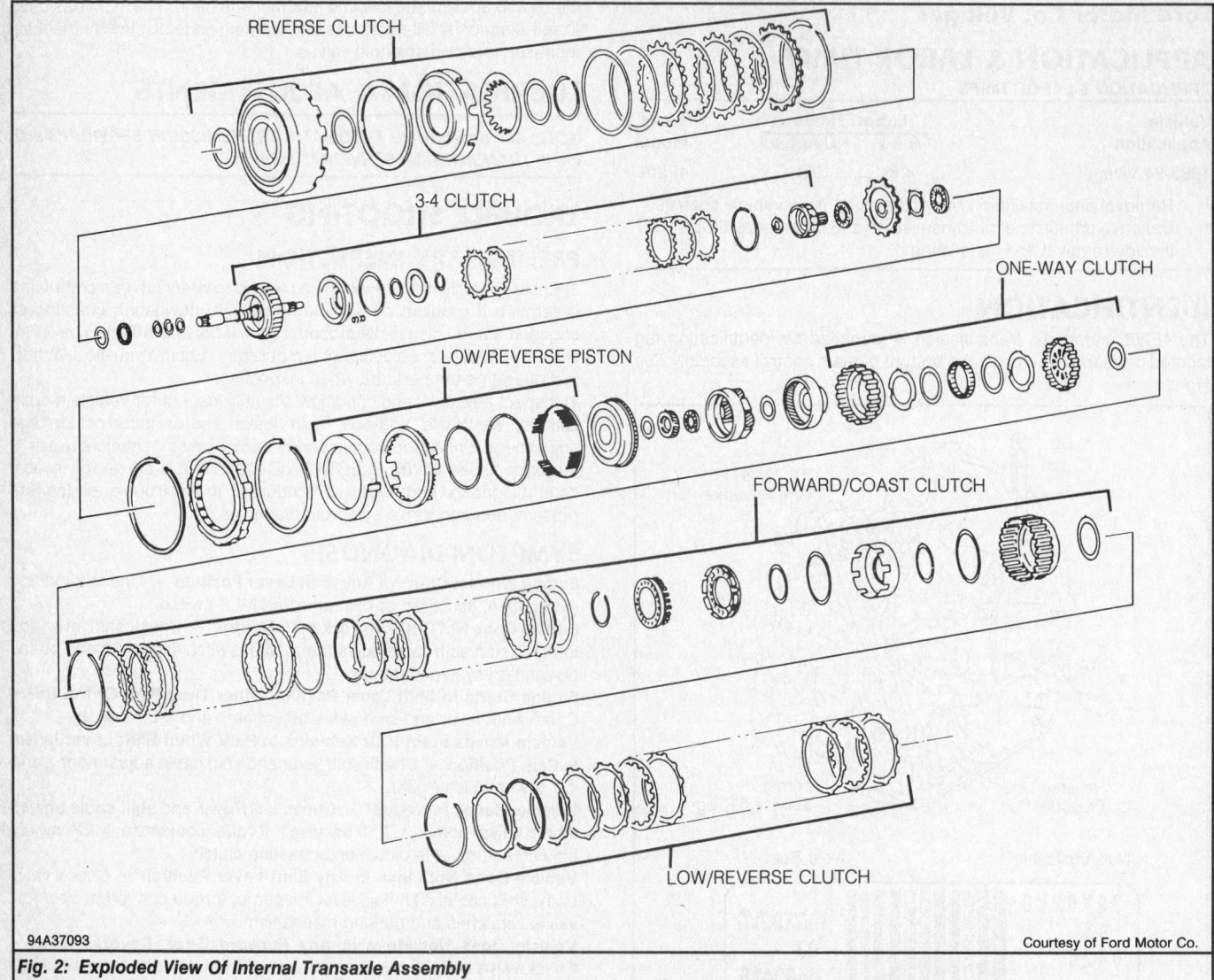

REVERSE CLUTCH

3-4 CLUTCH

ONE-WAY CLUTCH

LOW/REVERSE PISTON

FORWARD/COAST CLUTCH

LOW/REVERSE CLUTCH

94A37093   Courtesy of Ford Motor Co.

Fig. 2: Exploded View Of Internal Transaxle Assembly

clutch, low/reverse clutch, torque converter, 3-4 clutch and line pressure solenoid.

Engine Stalls When Transaxle Is Shifted Into Gear – Check torque converter, valve body and oil pump.

No Kickdown – Check line pressure solenoid and valve body.

Poor Fuel Economy – Check TCC solenoid, TCC control solenoid and torque converter.

Lack Of Power – Check torque converter and reverse clutch.

Surges While Cruising – Check valve body.

Poor Acceleration – Check TCC control solenoid and valve body.

SHIFT FAULTS

Shift Shock In All Ranges – Check line pressure solenoid, sticking pressure modulator valve, blocked control valve, coasting clutch, low/reverse clutch, front pump support, valve body, C.V. joints, engine mounts, 2-4 band and servo and sticking pressure regulator valve.

Harsh 1-2 Shift – Check line pressure solenoid.

Neutral-To-Reverse Shift Shock – Check sticking N-R accumulator, valve body and line pressure solenoid.

2-3 Shift Shock – Check sticking 2-3 accumulator and sticking 1-2 accumulator.

1-2 Soft Shift – Check valve body and loose 2-4 band.

2-3 Soft Shift – Check sticking 2-3 accumulator and valve body.

Neutral-To-Reverse Soft Shift – Check sticking N-R accumulator.

Delayed Engagement Into Reverse – Check reverse clutch.

Momentary Engine Runaway (Rapid RPM Increase) During 3-2 Downshift – Check 2-4 band and servo.

3-2 Shift Hesitation – Check valve body.

No Engine Braking Drive-To-Second – Check oil passage blockage to coasting clutch, coasting clutch and valve body.

No Engine Braking Second-To-First – Check oil passage blockage to coasting clutch, coasting clutch, valve body, control valve and oil pump assembly.

No 2-3 Upshift – Check 3-4 clutch, pressure reducing valve and valve body.

No Second Gear, 1-3 Shift – Check valve body and 2-4 band.

No Lockup – Check TCC solenoid, torque converter, TCC control solenoid and pressure reducing valve.

Incorrect Shift Points – Check valve body, 2-4 band adjustment and forward clutch.

Engine Runaway (Rapid RPM Increase) During Upshifting – Check MLP switch, valve body, forward one-way clutch, 2-4 band and servo, 3-4 clutch and forward clutch.

No 1st Gear, Second Gear Start – Check valve body, shift valve "A", shift valve "B", forward clutch, forward one-way clutch, low one-way clutch, 3-4 clutch, torque converter, oil pump and pressure reducing valve.

No 1-2 Shift – Check 2-4 band, front pump support and gear, shift solenoid valve "A", pressure reducing valve and servo piston assembly.

No 3-4 Shift – Check 2-4 band, torque converter, oil pump, servo piston assembly, valve body, shift solenoid "B" and pressure reducing valve.

Delayed 1-2 Shift – Check valve body.

CLUTCH & BAND APPLICATION

CLUTCH & BAND APPLICATION

Selector Lever Application	Elements In Use
Reverse ("R")	Low/Reverse Clutch & Reverse Clutch
Drive ("D")	
First Gear	Forward Clutch, Coasting Clutch [1], Forward One-Way Clutch & Low One-Way Clutch
Second Gear	2-4 Band, Forward Clutch, Coasting Clutch [1] & Forward One-Way Clutch
Third Gear	Coasting Clutch [1], Forward Clutch, Forward One-Way Clutch & 3-4 Clutch
Fourth Gear	2-4 Band, 3-4 Clutch & Forward Clutch
Manual Second ("2")	2-4 Band, Forward Clutch, Forward One-Way Clutch & Coasting Clutch
Manual First ("1")	Forward Clutch, Forward One-Way Clutch, Coast Clutch & Low/Reverse Clutch

[1] – Coasting clutch operates when O/D switch is in OFF position and 1/4 or less throttle opening.

TESTING

LINE PRESSURE TESTING

Test Procedure – Connect a pressure gauge to line pressure test port. *See Fig. 1.* Start engine. Apply service and parking brakes. Check pressure in all gears. See LINE PRESSURE SPECIFICATIONS (PSI) table. If line pressure is not within specification, perform QUICK TEST. See 4F20E ELECTRONIC CONTROLS article. If no electronic malfunctions are present, perform air pressure checks and service valve body. *See Fig. 3.*

LINE PRESSURE SPECIFICATIONS – PSI (kPa)

Selector Position	Idle RPM	WOT Stall RPM
"R"	113 (779)	284 (1958)
"D"	73 (503)	176 (1213)
"2"	73 (503)	176 (1213)
"L"	73 (503)	176 (1213)

LINE PRESSURE TEST RESULTS

Line Pressure Low At Idle In All Ranges – Check low fluid level, worn front pump support and gear, valve body and valve body components.

Line Pressure Low At Idle In Drive & 2nd – Check for leaking forward clutch hydraulic circuit.

Line Pressure Low At Idle In Reverse & Low – Check for leaking low/reverse clutch hydraulic circuit.

Line Pressure Low At Idle In Reverse – Check for leaking reverse clutch hydraulic circuit.

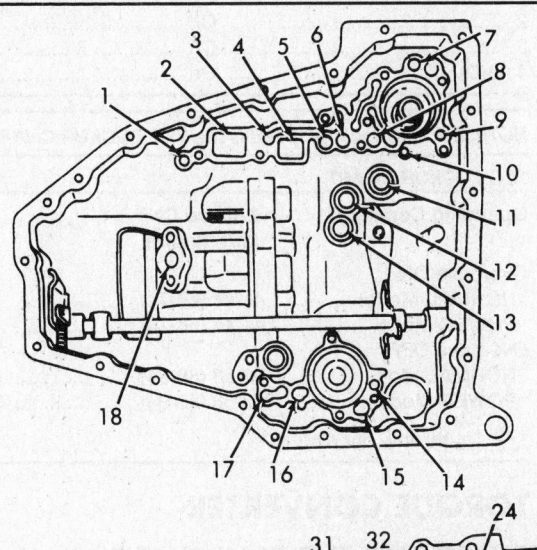
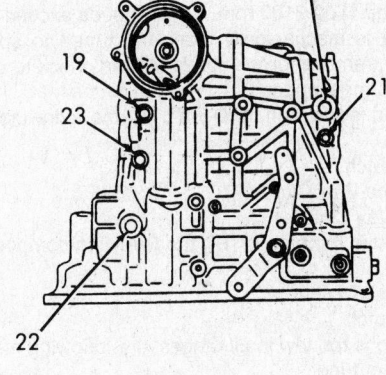
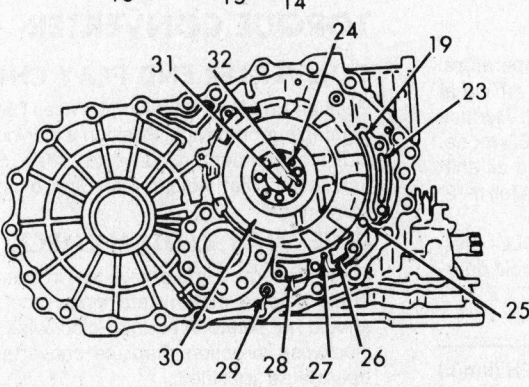
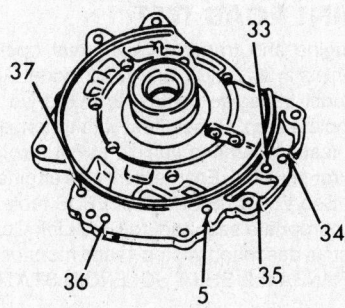

1. Differential Lubrication Feed	25. 3-4 Clutch Release Pressure
2. Oil Pump Assembly Suction	26. Oil Pump Discharge
3. Reverse Clutch Pressure	27. Reverse Clutch Pressure
4. Oil Pump Assembly Discharge	28. Oil Pump Suction
5. 3-4 Clutch Pressure	29. Differential Lubrication
6. TCC Lockup Released Pressure	30. Low/Reverse Clutch Pressure
7. D-R Accumulator	31. Coasting Clutch Pressure
8. TCC Lockup Applied Pressure	32. Forward Clutch
9. Transaxle Oil Cooler	33. Reverse Clutch Pressure
10. D-R Accumulator Back Pressure	34. Oil Pump Suction
11. 4th Gear Band Apply	35. Oil Pump Discharge
12. 2nd Gear Band Apply	36. TCC Lockup Applied Pressure
13. 2-4 Band Release	37. TCC Lockup Released Pressure
14. N-D Accumulator Shoulder Pressure	
15. N-D Accumulator Back Pressure	
16. Forward Clutch Pressure	
17. Coasting Clutch Pressure	
18. Low/Reverse Clutch Pressure	
19. TCC Lockup Released Pressure	
20. Transaxle Oil Cooler	
21. Line Pressure ("D", "2" & "1")	
22. Transaxle Oil Cooler	
23. TCC Lockup Trapplied Pressure	
24. Transaxle Oil Cooler	

94D37088 94E37089 94H37090 94I37091

Fig. 3: Identifying Oil Passageway Locations

Line Pressure High In All Ranges – Check pressure regulator valve, pressure modulator valve, TOT sensor, line pressure solenoid and TPS adjustment.

Line Pressure Low At Stall (WOT) In All Ranges – Check pressure reducing valve, line pressure solenoid, pressure modulator valve, pressure regulator valve and TPS adjustment.

STALL SPEED TEST

NOTE: After each test (5 seconds maximum), shift transaxle into Neutral and run engine for at least 1 minute to cool torque converter and transmission fluid.

CAUTION: Do not maintain Wide Open Throttle (WOT) in any gear for more than 5 seconds. If engine RPM exceeds maximum specified stall speed, release accelerator immediately. Clutch or band slippage is indicated.

The stall speed test checks the operation of the following items:
- Forward Clutch
- Reverse Clutch
- Low One-Way Clutch (Roller)
- Forward One-Way Clutch (Sprag)
- Engine Performance

Test Procedure – 1) Apply service and parking brakes. Connect tachometer or appropriate scan tester to engine, and record RPM reached in each gear selector range (except Neutral) at WOT. Stall speed should be 1800-2100 rpm. If stall speeds exceed specification, ensure engine is mechanically okay and tuned to specification. If engine is okay, remove torque converter and check torque converter one-way clutch for slippage.

2) If stall speed is too high in "D", "2", "1", the following components may be faulty:
- Forward Clutch
- Forward One-Way Clutch
- Low One-Way Clutch

3) If stall speed is too high in "R", the following components may be faulty:
- Low/Reverse Clutch
- Reverse Clutch

4) If stall speed is too low in all ranges, the following may be faulty:
- Engine out of tune
- Forward one-way clutch

SHIFT POINT ROAD TEST

1) Ensure engine and transaxle is normal operating temperature. Road test vehicle in drive "D", NORMAL mode. Accelerate vehicle at half throttle until transaxle shifts into overdrive (4th gear). Reduce speed to complete stop. Repeat test with transaxle in POWER mode. Repeat both tests, operating vehicle at full throttle. Record all shift speeds. Monitor shift feel. Ensure transaxle engine braking is felt in "2" and "1" gear. See VEHICLE SHIFT SPEEDS table and *Fig. 4.*

2) Connect appropriate scan tool to Data Link Connector (DLC). Perform road test as described in step **1)** and monitor shift solenoid operation. See TRANSAXLE SHIFT SOLENOID STATUS CHART.

VEHICLE SHIFT SPEEDS

Operating Condition [1]	Shift Speed MPH (km/h)
NORMAL Mode	
Half Throttle (50%)	
1-2	22-27 (56-64)
2-3	39-44 (63-71)
3-4	63-68 (101-104)
4-3	45-40 (73-65)
3-2	27-22 (44-36)
2-1	10-5 (16-8)
Full Throttle (WOT)	
1-2	35-40 (56-64)
2-3	62-67 (100-108)
3-4	102-108 (164-174)
4-3	103-98 (166-158)
3-2	61-56 (98-90)
2-1	31-26 (16-8)

VEHICLE SHIFT SPEEDS (Cont.)

Operating Condition [1]	Shift Speed MPH (km/h)
POWER Mode	
Half Throttle (50%)	
1-2	23-28 (37-45)
2-3	45-50 (72-80)
3-4	73-78 (117-125)
4-3	54-42 (87-79)
3-2	30-26 (49-41)
2-1	10-5 (16-8)
Full Throttle (WOT)	
1-2	35-40 (56-64)
2-3	62-67 (100-108)
3-4	103-108 (166-174)
4-3	103-98 (166-158)
3-2	61-56 (98-90)
2-1	31-26 (50-42)

[1] – To determine deceleration shift speeds, release throttle once transaxle has shifted into 4th gear (O/D). Manually downshift shift lever into next lower gear and record speed at which downshift occurs. Continue downshifting and recording vehicle speed until transaxle has downshifted into low gear.

TRANSAXLE SHIFT SOLENOID STATUS CHART

Gear	Shift Solenoid "A"	Shift Solenoid "B"
1	On	On
2	Off	On
3	Off	Off
4 (O/D)	On	Off

NOTE: For TCC lockup speeds, see TCC LOCKUP CHART

TCC LOCKUP CHART

Operating Condition [1]	Lockup ON MPH (km/h)	Lockup OFF MPH (km/h)
Overdrive ON		
NORMAL Mode	41-46 (66-74)	44-39 (71-63)
POWER Mode	41-46 (66-74)	44-39 (71-63)
Overdrive OFF		
NORMAL Mode	53-58 (86-94)	57-52 (91-83)
POWER Mode	53-58 (86-94)	57-52 (91-83)

[1] – 1/4 throttle opening.

TORQUE CONVERTER

CONVERTER END PLAY CHECK

Position End Play Checking Device (T94P-7902-AH) in converter hub. Tighten nut on device. Position a dial indicator on device. Position dial indicator pointer on converter shell. *See Fig. 5.* Lift up on device handles. If dial indicator reading exceeds .019" (.05 mm), replace converter.

ONE-WAY CLUTCH CHECK

Place 90 degree end of pick tool in slot on bottom of converter stator. While holding pick, rotate inner race with fingers. One-way clutch should not rotate in counter-clockwise direction and should rotate in clockwise direction. Replace converter if one-way clutch does not operate as specified.

ON-VEHICLE SERVICE

DIFFERENTIAL OIL SEALS

Removal & Installation – 1) Raise and support vehicle. Remove front wheels. Remove engine and transaxle splash shield. Remove axle cotter pin and nut retainer. Remove axle nut and washer. Loosen lower ball joint. Strike steering knuckle at ball joint with hammer while pulling down on lower control arm until ball joint stud separates from knuckle.

2) Remove stabilizer bar link from lower control arm. Separate lower control arm from steering knuckle. Separate outer CV joint from hub assembly.

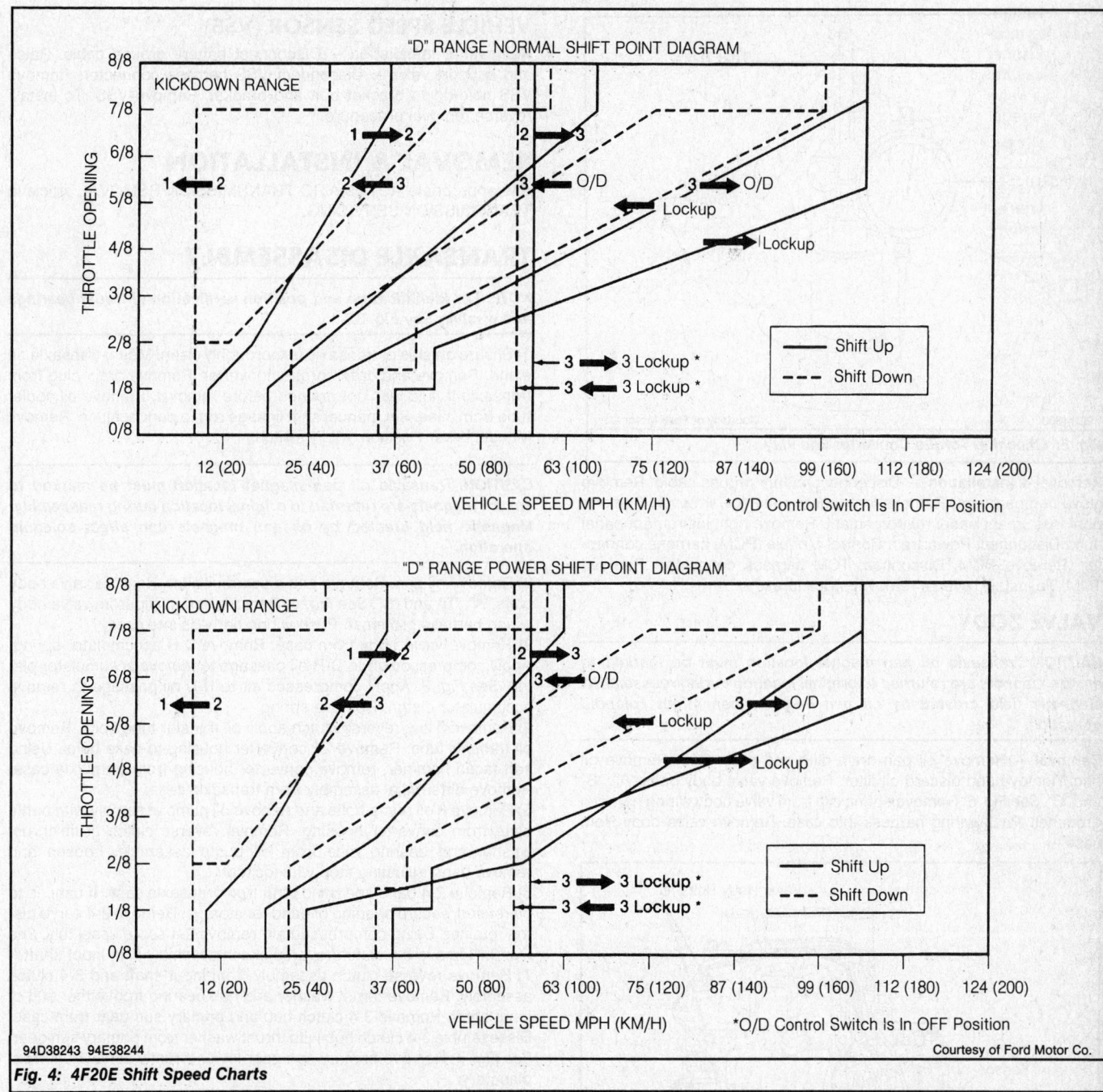

Fig. 4: 4F20E Shift Speed Charts

94D38243 94E38244

Courtesy of Ford Motor Co.

3) To remove left axle, pry between transaxle case and inner CV joint with 2 pry bars until axle snaps free. To remove right axle, unbolt center bearing assembly from bracket. Remove axle from transaxle with pry bars.

4) Using appropriate puller with slide hammer, remove selected seal. Using appropriate seal driver, install new seal. Install left axle with new inner CV joint circlip. Right axle does not have circlip. Install remaining components in reverse order of disassembly. Tighten bolts to specification. See TORQUE SPECIFICATIONS.

OIL COOLER FLUSHING

Contaminates MUST be removed from oil cooler before transmission is put back into service. Replace cooler supply tubes if leaking. Thoroughly flush oil cooler and lines if a major service or transaxle removal has occurred. It is recommended that a mechanically agitated cleaner, such as Rotunda (014-00028), be used.

PULSE SIGNAL GENERATOR (PSG)

Removal & Installation – Disconnect battery ground cable. Disconnect PSG harness connector, located on top of transaxle, next to side cover. Raise and support vehicle. Remove lower splash shield and left inner fender splash shield. Unbolt and remove PSG. To install, reverse removal procedure.

TRANSAXLE SHIFT SOLENOIDS & SENSOR

Removal of transaxle solenoids or TOT sensor requires removal of valve body. See VALVE BODY.

TRANSMISSION CONTROL MODULE (TCM)

CAUTION: Avoid touching module connector pins. Do not allow module to contact a conductive surface. Manufacturer recommends use of ground cable with wrist band when handling electronic modules to avoid damage due to static electricity.

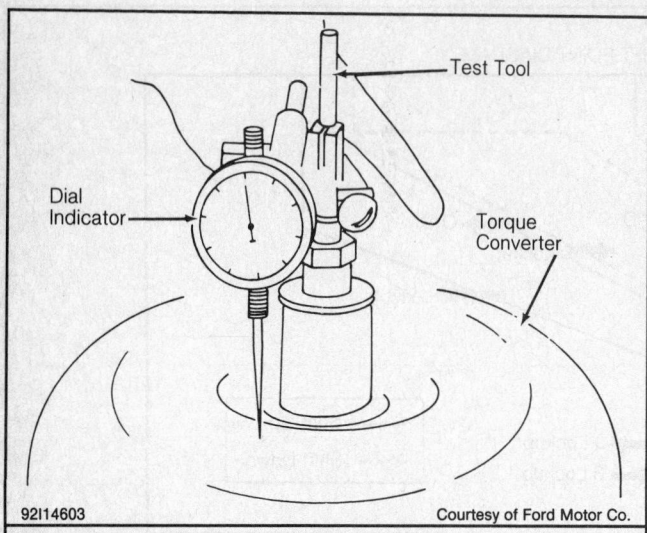

92I14603   Courtesy of Ford Motor Co.

Fig. 5: Checking Torque Converter End Play

Removal & Installation – Disconnect battery ground cable. Remove glove compartment. Remove instrument panel lower cover. Remove right instrument panel reinforcement. Remove right instrument panel duct. Disconnect Powertrain Control Module (PCM) harness connector. Remove PCM. Disconnect TCM harness connector. Remove TCM. To install, reverse removal procedures.

VALVE BODY

CAUTION: Transaxle oil pan magnet location must be marked to ensure magnets are returned to original location during reassembly. Magnetic field created by oil pan magnets can affect solenoid operation.

Removal – Remove oil pan drain plug and drain fluid. Remove oil pan. Remove and discard oil filter. Remove valve body bolts "A", "B" and "C". *See Fig. 6.* Remove spring clip from valve body wiring harness grommet. Push wiring harness into case. Remove valve body from case.

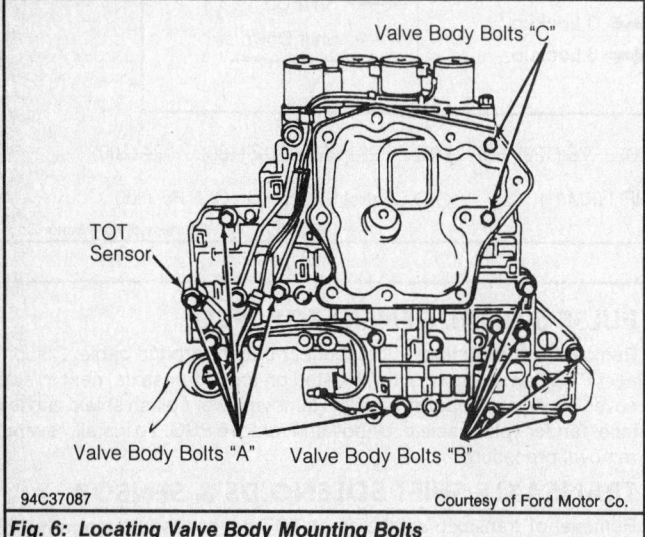

94C37087   Courtesy of Ford Motor Co.

Fig. 6: Locating Valve Body Mounting Bolts

Installation – Route valve body wiring harness up through transaxle case and secure with spring clip. Set manual shift linkage rod in neutral position. Install valve body into transaxle case while aligning manual valve with manual detent lever. Tighten bolts to specification. See TORQUE SPECIFICATIONS. Install oil filter. Place oil pan magnets in locations marked during disassembly. Install oil pan. Tighten bolts in crisscross pattern to specification. Install drain plug. Fill transaxle with fluid.

VEHICLE SPEED SENSOR (VSS)

Removal & Installation – Disconnect battery ground cable. Raise and support vehicle. Disconnect VSS harness connector. Remove VSS hold-down bracket bolt and bracket. Remove VSS. To install, reverse removal procedure.

REMOVAL & INSTALLATION

See appropriate AUTOMATIC TRANSMISSION REMOVAL article in TRANSMISSION SERVICING.

TRANSAXLE DISASSEMBLY

NOTE: For identification and position verification of thrust bearings and washer, See Fig. 32.

1) Ensure outside of transaxle is thoroughly clean. Mount transaxle on stand. Remove and drain torque converter. Remove drain plug from transaxle if fluid was not drained before removal. Remove oil cooler tube from case. Set manual shift linkage rod to park position. Remove Manual Lever Position (MLP) switch.

CAUTION: Transaxle oil pan magnet location must be marked to ensure magnets are returned to original location during reassembly. Magnetic field created by oil pan magnets can affect solenoid operation.

2) Remove oil pan. Remove and discard oil filter. Remove valve body bolts "A", "B" and "C". *See Fig. 6.* Remove spring clip from valve body wiring harness grommet. Push wiring harness into case.

3) Remove valve body from case. Remove D-R accumulator spring. Apply compressed air to D-R oil passage to remove accumulator piston. *See Fig. 3.* Apply compressed air to N-D oil passage to remove accumulator piston. Remove spring.

4) Remove 3 low/reverse clutch apply oil transfer tube bolts. Remove oil transfer tube. Remove 21 converter housing-to-case bolts. Using soft-faced hammer, remove converter housing from transaxle case. Remove differential assembly from transaxle case.

5) Remove 8 oil pump bolts and remove oil pump assembly with baffle plate from converter housing. Remove reverse clutch drum thrust washer and bearing race from oil pump assembly. Loosen and remove band adjusting stop with locknut.

6) Remove 2-4 band and band strut from transaxle case. If band is to be reused, secure opening of band for storage. Remove 2-4 servo piston retainer. Using compressed air, remove 2-4 servo assembly. *See Fig. 3.* Remove 3-4 clutch/reverse clutch assembly with input shaft.

7) Remove reverse clutch assembly from input shaft and 3-4 clutch assembly. Remove thrust washer and hub bearing from either end of input shaft. Remove 3-4 clutch hub and primary sun gear from case. Disassemble 3-4 clutch hub with thrust washer from primary sun gear. *See Fig. 7.* Remove primary sun gear lower thrust washer from front planetary.

8) Remove low one-way clutch pressure plate snap ring. Hold one-way clutch and turn transaxle case over. Assistance may be required.

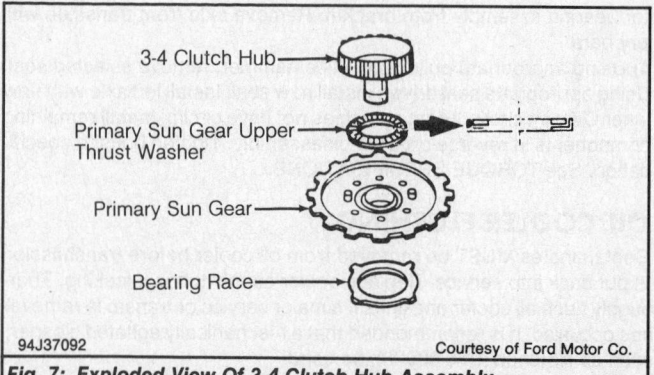

94J37092   Courtesy of Ford Motor Co.

Fig. 7: Exploded View Of 3-4 Clutch Hub Assembly

Rotate front planetary and remove low one-way clutch. Tap case with soft-faced hammer to aid in removal if clutch is stuck.

9) Turn transaxle over. Remove low/reverse clutch piston pressure plate snap ring. Remove front planetary gear and low/reverse clutch piston assembly and disassemble. *See Fig. 2.* Remove piston spring retainer. Remove rear sun gear front thrust bearing from front planetary gear. Remove rear planetary gear with rear sun gear from case. Remove 2 thrust bearings from planetary gear.

10) Remove forward clutch hub and ring gear assembly. Remove coasting clutch hub with thrust washer. Remove forward clutch hub assembly with thrust washer. Remove low/reverse clutch pressure plate snap ring. Remove low/reverse clutch pressure plate, steel and friction plates. *See Fig. 2.* Measure thickness of low/reverse friction discs. Thickness should be .071" (1.8 mm). Wear limit is .063" (1.6 mm). Replace low/reverse friction discs as needed.

11) Remove side cover bolts and lightly tap side cover with soft-faced hammer to remove. If output shaft is removed with side cover, separate shaft from cover by tapping with soft-faced hammer. Remove output shaft bearing shim. Remove output shaft if not previously removed.

12) Remove output shaft hub thrust washer. Remove output shaft bearing retainer bolts and retainer. Place manual shift linkage rod into park position to lock idler gear.

NOTE: *Only remove idler gear, idler gear shaft and reduction gear if components or bearings are worn.*

---

13) Using appropriate chisel and hammer, unstake idler gear locknut. Remove and discard locknut. Using appropriate puller, remove idler gear from shaft. Remove reduction gear. Remove adjusting shim from reduction gear shaft.

COMPONENT DISASSEMBLY & REASSEMBLY

DIFFERENTIAL ASSEMBLY

NOTE: *Only disassemble differential assembly if gears or bearings are worn.*

Disassembly & Reassembly – 1) Remove final drive ring gear. Using appropriate puller, remove differential housing side bearings. Remove speedometer drive gear. Using pin punch and hammer, drive out pinion shaft roll pin. Remove and inspect pinion shaft, pinion gears and thrust washers, and side gears and thrust washers. *See Fig. 8.* Replace worn parts as needed.

2) Install components in reverse order of disassembly. Mount dial indicator with Differential Rotator (T92P-77000-BH) onto differential housing. Insert rotator into selected side gear. *See Fig. 9.* Measure each side gear deflection (thrust clearance). Thrust clearance should be .004-.008" (.1-.2 mm). If side gear thrust clearance is not within specification, select and install correct thrust washer. Thrust washers are available in thicknesses from .030" (.75 mm) to .037" (.95 mm) in .05 mm increments.

FORWARD & COASTING CLUTCH ASSEMBLY

Disassembly – 1) Remove pressure plate snap ring. Remove forward pressure plate, steel clutch discs, friction discs and dish plate. Remove coasting clutch snap ring, pressure plate, steel clutch discs, friction discs and dish plate. *See Fig. 10.* Using appropriate compressor, compress spring retainer and remove snap ring. Remove remaining components. Inspect condition of clutch discs.

2) Measure thickness of forward and coasting friction discs. Thickness should be .063" (1.6 mm). Wear limit is .055" (1.4 mm). Replace forward and coasting clutch discs as needed. Measure height of dish plates. Height should be .106" (2.70 mm). Replace dish plates as needed.

Reassembly – 1) Assemble coasting clutch components in reverse order of disassembly. Apply ATF to new seals. Ensure alignment mark on spring retainer is aligned with check ball of coasting clutch piston. Using feeler gauge, measure clearance between snap ring and coasting pressure plate. Clearance should be .028-.043" (.70-1.10 mm).

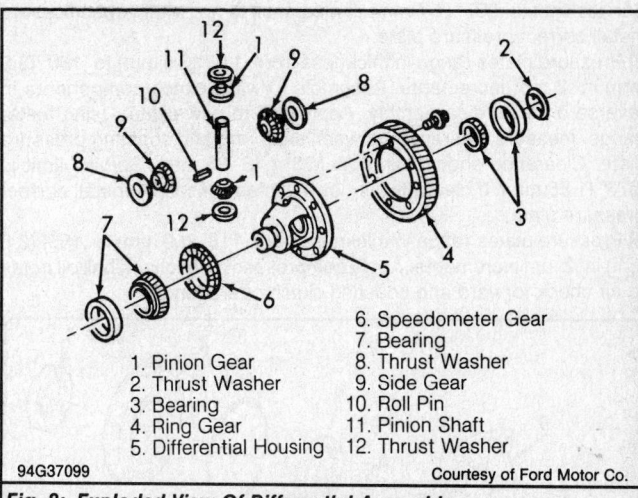

1. Pinion Gear
2. Thrust Washer
3. Bearing
4. Ring Gear
5. Differential Housing
6. Speedometer Gear
7. Bearing
8. Thrust Washer
9. Side Gear
10. Roll Pin
11. Pinion Shaft
12. Thrust Washer

94G37099   Courtesy of Ford Motor Co.

Fig. 8: Exploded View Of Differential Assembly

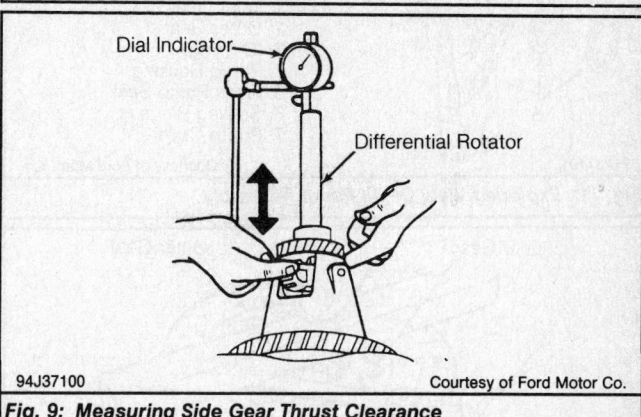

Dial Indicator

Differential Rotator

94J37100   Courtesy of Ford Motor Co.

Fig. 9: Measuring Side Gear Thrust Clearance

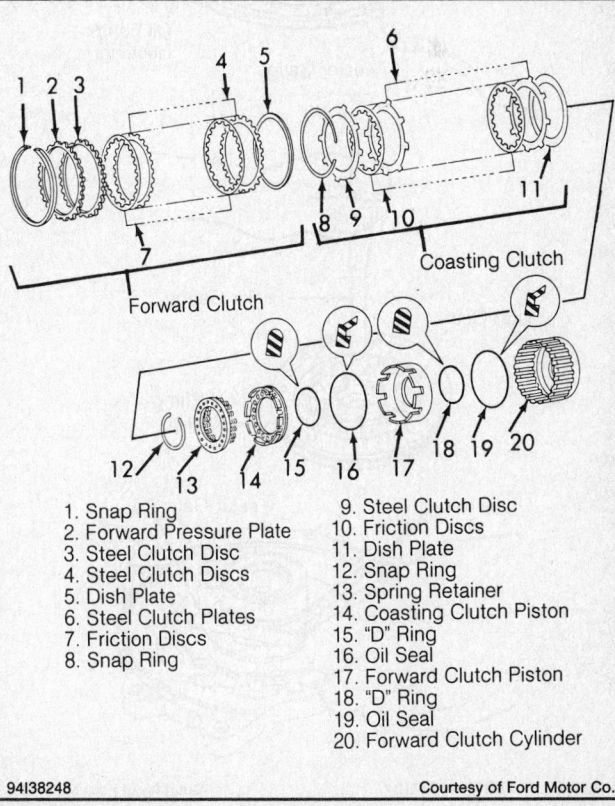

Coasting Clutch

Forward Clutch

1. Snap Ring
2. Forward Pressure Plate
3. Steel Clutch Disc
4. Steel Clutch Discs
5. Dish Plate
6. Steel Clutch Plates
7. Friction Discs
8. Snap Ring
9. Steel Clutch Disc
10. Friction Discs
11. Dish Plate
12. Snap Ring
13. Spring Retainer
14. Coasting Clutch Piston
15. "D" Ring
16. Oil Seal
17. Forward Clutch Piston
18. "D" Ring
19. Oil Seal
20. Forward Clutch Cylinder

94I38248   Courtesy of Ford Motor Co.

Fig. 10: Exploded View Of Forward & Coasting Clutch Assembly

Service limit is .067" (1.7 mm). If clearance is not within specification, install correct pressure plate.

2) Pressure plates range in thickness from .118" (3.0 mm) to .150" (3.8 mm) in .2 mm increments. Assemble forward clutch components in reverse order of disassembly. Apply ATF to new seals. Using feeler gauge, measure clearance between snap ring and coasting pressure plate. Clearance should be .018-.033" (.45-.85 mm). Service limit is .073" (1.85 mm). If clearance is not within specification, install correct pressure plate.

3) Pressure plates range in thickness from .118" (3.0 mm) to .150" (3.8 mm) in .2 mm increments. Apply compressed air to check ball oil holes to air check forward and coasting clutch operation.

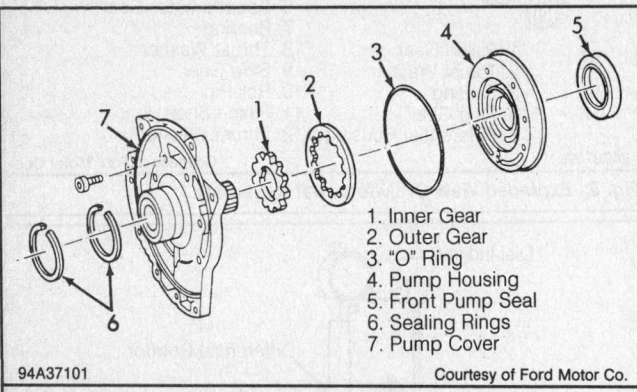

1. Inner Gear
2. Outer Gear
3. "O" Ring
4. Pump Housing
5. Front Pump Seal
6. Sealing Rings
7. Pump Cover

94A37101   Courtesy of Ford Motor Co.

Fig. 11: Exploded View Of Oil Pump Assembly

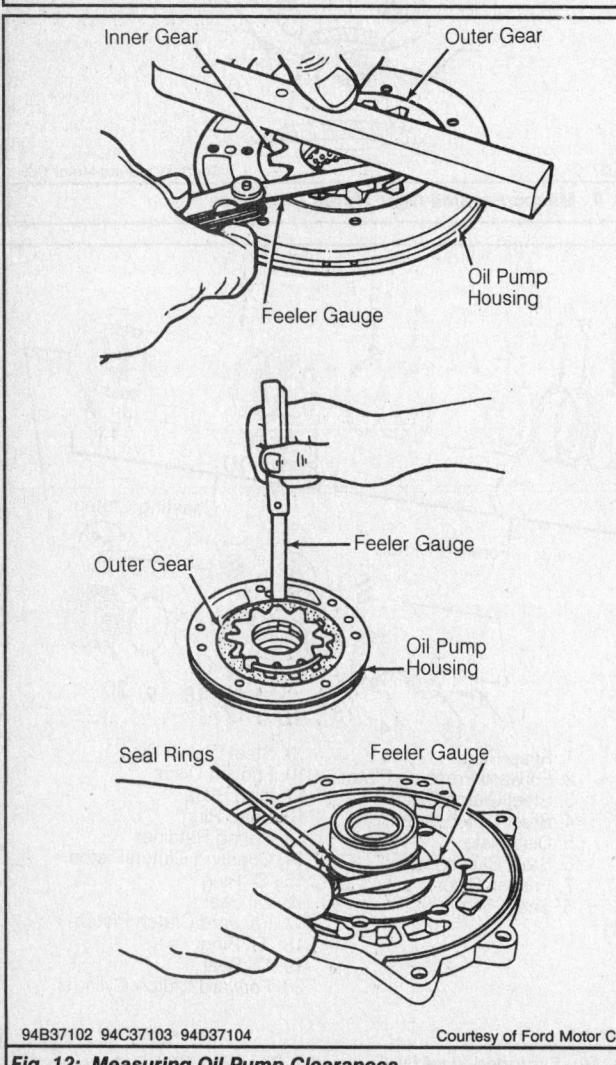

94B37102 94C37103 94D37104   Courtesy of Ford Motor Co.

Fig. 12: Measuring Oil Pump Clearances

OIL PUMP

Disassembly & Reassembly – 1) Remove and discard 2 sealing rings. Remove oil pump cover. *See Fig. 11.* Remove and inspect condition of pump gears and housing. Pump gears are replaced as matched set.

2) Measure side clearance between edge of oil pump housing and inner and outer pump gears. *See Fig. 12.* Clearance should be .001-.002" (.03-.05 mm). If clearance is not within specification, replace oil pump assembly.

3) Measure clearance between outer pump gear and pump housing. *See Fig. 12.* Clearance should be .004-.007" (.11-.18 mm). If clearance is not within specification, replace oil pump assembly.

4) Replace seal rings on pump support. Using feeler gauge, measure clearance between seal ring and groove. *See Fig. 12.* Clearance should be .001-.007" (.04-.18 mm). If clearance is not within specification, replace oil pump cover assembly.

5) Assemble oil pump in reverse order of disassembly. Ensure drive tangs of inner pump gear face toward center of pump. Tighten bolts in crisscross pattern to specification. See TORQUE SPECIFICATIONS.

REVERSE CLUTCH

Disassembly – 1) Remove and discard snap ring. Remove pressure plate, steel clutch discs, friction discs and dish plates. *See Fig. 13.* Using appropriate compressor, compress spring retainer and remove snap ring. Remove remaining components. Inspect condition of clutch discs.

2) Measure thickness of friction discs. Thickness should be .079" (2.0 mm). Wear limit is .071" (1.8 mm). Replace discs as needed. Measure height of dish plates. Height should be .121" (3.08 mm). Replace dish plates as needed.

Reassembly – 1) Assemble components in reverse order of disassembly. Apply ATF to new seals. Using feeler gauge, measure clearance between snap ring and pressure plate. Clearance should be .020-.031" (.50-.80 mm). Service limit is .047" (1.2 mm).

2) If clearance is not within specification, install correct snap ring. Snap rings range in thickness from .260" (6.6 mm) to .307" (7.8 mm) in .2 mm increments. Place assembled reverse clutch assembly on oil pump support and air check assembly. *See Fig. 3.*

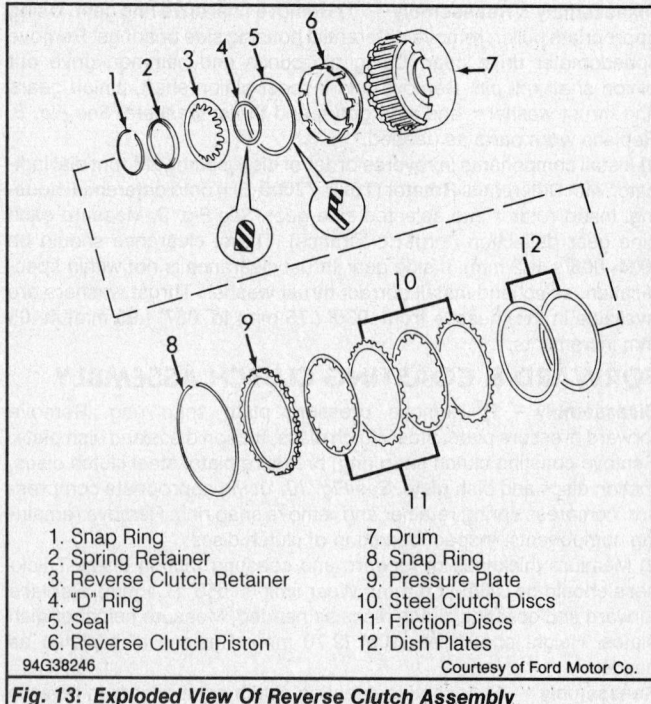

1. Snap Ring
2. Spring Retainer
3. Reverse Clutch Retainer
4. "D" Ring
5. Seal
6. Reverse Clutch Piston
7. Drum
8. Snap Ring
9. Pressure Plate
10. Steel Clutch Discs
11. Friction Discs
12. Dish Plates

94G38246   Courtesy of Ford Motor Co.

Fig. 13: Exploded View Of Reverse Clutch Assembly

RING GEAR & FORWARD/COAST CLUTCH HUB

Disassembly & Reassembly – Disassemble ring gear, forward clutch hub and coasting clutch hub. *See Fig. 14*. Inspect all contacting components and sprag for wear or damage. Assemble components in reverse order of disassembly. Check operation of forward one-way (sprag) clutch. With ring gear facing downward, forward clutch hub should rotate only counterclockwise while ring gear is prevented from turning.

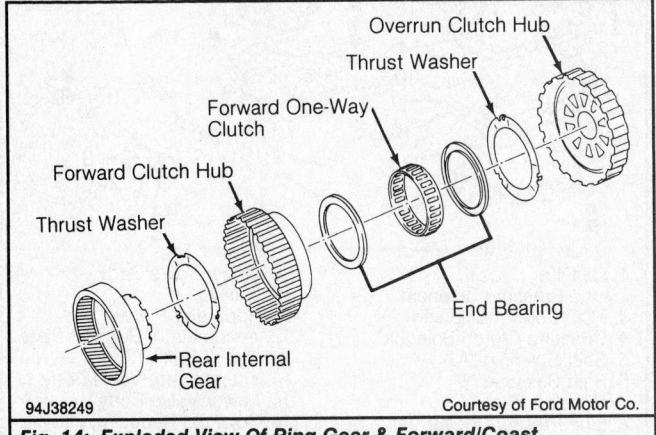

94J38249   Courtesy of Ford Motor Co.

Fig. 14: Exploded View Of Ring Gear & Forward/Coast Clutch Hub Assembly

3-4 CLUTCH

Disassembly – Remove 3-4 pressure plate snap ring. Remove pressure plate, steel clutch discs and friction discs. *See Fig. 15*. Using appropriate press, compress spring retainer and return snap ring. Remove remaining components. Inspect condition of clutch discs. Measure thickness of friction discs. Thickness should be .063" (1.6 mm). Wear limit is .055" (1.4 mm). Replace discs as needed.

Reassembly – 1) Assemble components in reverse order of disassembly. Apply ATF to new seals. Replace seal rings on input shaft. Using feeler gauge, measure clearance between each seal ring and groove. Clearance should be .003-.009" (.08-.23 mm). If clearance is not within specification, replace 3-4 clutch drum and input shaft.

2) Using feeler gauge, measure clearance between snap ring and pressure plate. Clearance should be .071-.087" (1.80-2.20 mm). Service limit is .118" (3.0 mm). If clearance is not within specification, install correct pressure plate. Pressure plates range in thickness from .118" (3.0 mm) to .150" (3.8 mm) in .2 mm increments. Hold assembled 3-4 clutch drum assembly and apply compressed air to port and air check assembly.

3) Apply petroleum jelly to new oil distributor sleeve seals. Wrap seals with thick paper and tape securely to prevent seals spreading prior to reassembly.

2-4 SERVO

Disassembly & Reassembly – 1) Hold 2-4 servo piston and 2-4 servo piston retainer with cloth and apply compressed air to oil hole in 2-4 servo piston retainer to remove piston from retainer. Push servo piston assembly out of piston retainer. Place servo piston stem end on wooden block. Depress servo piston spring retainer and remove "E" ring. Separate piston spring retainer, return spring, band piston, band thrust washer and piston stem. *See Fig. 16*.

2) Clean and inspect all components for excessive wear or damage. Inspect springs for deformation or damage. Measure servo spring free length and diameter. See 2-4 SERVO SPRING DIMENSIONS table. Reassemble components in reverse order of disassembly. Lubricate new seals with ATF.

2-4 SERVO SPRING DIMENSIONS

Application	Diameter In. (mm)	Length In. (mm)
Servo Piston Spring	1.02 (25.9)	1.28 (32.5)
Piston Return Spring	.85 (21.7)	1.02 (25.9)

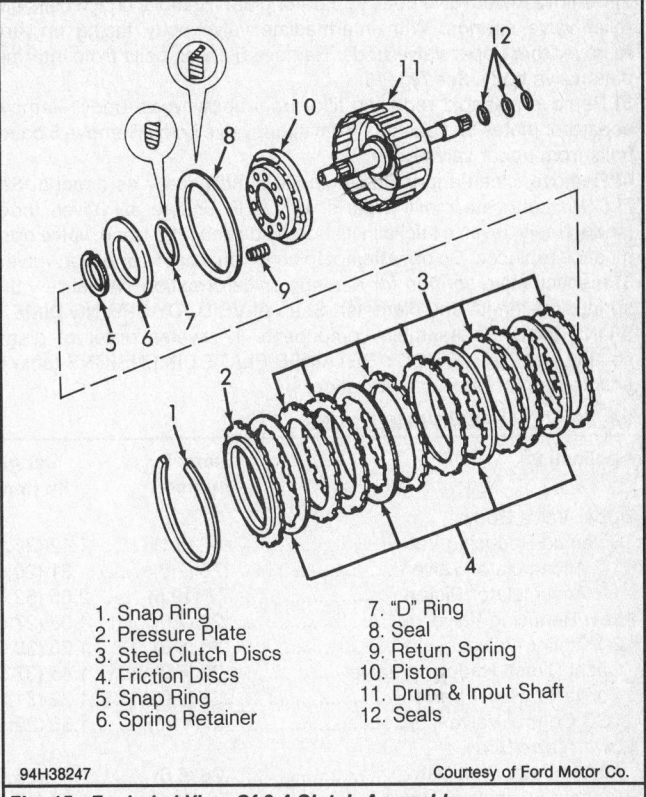

1. Snap Ring
2. Pressure Plate
3. Steel Clutch Discs
4. Friction Discs
5. Snap Ring
6. Spring Retainer
7. "D" Ring
8. Seal
9. Return Spring
10. Piston
11. Drum & Input Shaft
12. Seals

94H38247   Courtesy of Ford Motor Co.

Fig. 15: Exploded View Of 3-4 Clutch Assembly

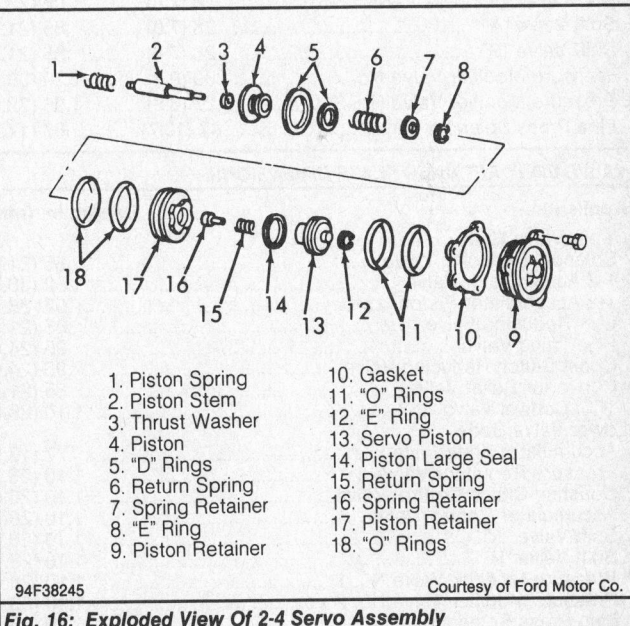

1. Piston Spring
2. Piston Stem
3. Thrust Washer
4. Piston
5. "D" Rings
6. Return Spring
7. Spring Retainer
8. "E" Ring
9. Piston Retainer
10. Gasket
11. "O" Rings
12. "E" Ring
13. Servo Piston
14. Piston Large Seal
15. Return Spring
16. Spring Retainer
17. Piston Retainer
18. "O" Rings

94F38245   Courtesy of Ford Motor Co.

Fig. 16: Exploded View Of 2-4 Servo Assembly

VALVE BODY

NOTE: Remove and clean one valve at a time to avoid incorrect installation. If any valves, valve springs, or valve bodies are damaged, the entire valve body assembly must be replaced.

Disassembly – 1) Remove solenoid assembly, line pressure solenoid, Transmission Oil Temperature (TOT) sensor and valve body wiring harness from valve body. Unbolt and remove lower valve body from intermediate and upper valve body. Turn lower valve body with inner side facing upward. Remove 2 accumulator support plates. *See Fig. 17.*

2) Remove lower valve body separator plate. Remove check balls and relief valve springs. With intermediate valve body facing upward, remove from upper valve body. Remove 6 check balls from intermediate valve body. *See Fig. 18.*

3) Remove solenoid reducing filter from upper valve body. Remove separator plates and gaskets from upper valve body. Remove 5 check balls from upper valve body.

4) Remove, clean and install each valve individually as needed. *See Fig. 19.* Lubricate moving parts with ATF. Ensure all valves move (snap) freely. If valve sticks in its bore and cannot be freed, valve body must be replaced. Do not attempt to hone valve bores or polish valves.

5) Inspect valve springs for damage or deformation. Measure valve spring free length and diameter. See VALVE BODY SPRING DIMENSIONS table. Reassemble components in reverse order of disassembly. See VALVE BODY RETAINER PLATE DIMENSIONS table to ensure correct retainer installation.

VALVE BODY SPRING DIMENSIONS

Application	Diameter In. (mm)	Length In. (mm)
Upper Valve Body		
Solenoid Reducing Valve	.32 (8.1)	1.42 (36.0)
1-2 Accumulator Valve	.28 (7.0)	.81 (20.5)
1-2 Accumulator Piston	.77 (19.6)	2.05 (52.0)
Low Reducing Valve	.28 (7.0)	1.06 (27.0)
2-3 Timing Valve	.26 (6.6)	1.20 (30.5)
Coast Clutch Reducing Valve	.27 (6.9)	1.45 (37.5)
Converter Relief Valve	.35 (9.0)	1.22 (31.0)
TCC Control Valve	.43 (11.0)	1.56 (39.5)
Lower Valve Body		
Accumulator Shift Valve	.26 (6.6)	.91 (23.0)
Pressure Regulator Valve	.59 (15.0)	1.77 (45.0)
Coasting Clutch Control Valve	.28 (7.0)	.85 (21.7)
Accumulator Control Valve	.28 (7.0)	1.06 (27.0)
Shift Valve "A"	.28 (7.0)	.85 (21.7)
Shift Valve "B"	.28 (7.0)	.85 (21.7)
Pressure Modifier Valve No. 1	.39 (9.8)	1.20 (30.5)
Pressure Modifier Valve No. 2	.27 (6.9)	1.26 (32.0)
Line Press Solenoid Valve	.42 (10.7)	.67 (17.0)

VALVE BODY RETAINER PLATE DIMENSIONS

Application	Length In. (mm)
Upper Valve Body	
Solenoid Reducing Valve	.85 (21.5)
1-2 Accumulator Valve	1.52 (38.5)
1-2 Accumulator Piston	.52 (38.5)
Low Reducing Valve	.85 (21.5)
2-3 Timing Valve	.95 (24.0)
Coast Clutch Reducing Valve	.95 (24.0)
Converter Relief Valve	.85 (21.5)
TCC Control Valve	1.10 (28.0)
Lower Valve Body	
Accumulator Shift Valve	.77 (19.5)
Pressure Regulator Valve	1.10 (28.0)
Coasting Clutch Control Valve	1.10 (28.0)
Accumulator Control Valve	1.10 (28.0)
Shift Valve "A"	1.10 (28.0)
Shift Valve "B"	1.10 (28.0)
Pressure Modifier Valve No. 1	1.10 (28.0)
Pressure Modifier Valve No. 2	1.10 (28.0)
Line Press Solenoid Valve	1.10 (28.0)

Installation – 1) Install 5 check balls in upper valve body. Secure check balls in place with vaseline. *See Fig. 18.* Install upper intermediate separator plate with gaskets on upper valve body. Install solenoid reducing filter into upper valve body. Install 6 check balls in intermediate valve body. *See Fig. 17.*

2) Use long reamer bolts as guide to place intermediate valve body onto upper valve body. Install line pressure valve springs and check balls into lower valve body. Install lower intermediate separator plate with gaskets on lower valve body. Install accumulator support plates onto lower valve body. Install lower valve body onto intermediate valve body and lightly tighten reamer bolts.

3) Lubricate all O-rings with ATF. Install solenoid valve assembly, TOT sensor and line pressure solenoid. *See Fig. 17.* Install remaining components in reverse order of disassembly. Install remaining bolts. Tighten bolts to specification. See TORQUE SPECIFICATIONS.

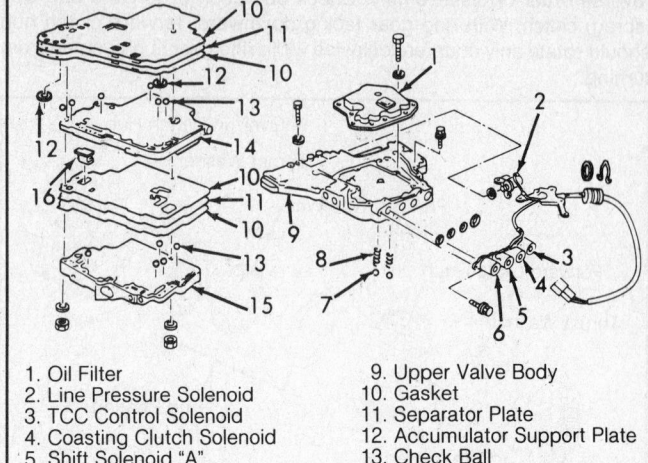

1. Oil Filter
2. Line Pressure Solenoid
3. TCC Control Solenoid
4. Coasting Clutch Solenoid
5. Shift Solenoid "A"
6. Shift Solenoid "B"
7. Check Ball
8. Line Pressure Relief Valve Spring
9. Upper Valve Body
10. Gasket
11. Separator Plate
12. Accumulator Support Plate
13. Check Ball
14. Intermediate Valve Body
15. Lower Valve Body
16. Solenoid Reducing Filter

94B37094   Courtesy of Chrysler Corp.

Fig. 17: Exploded View Of Valve Body Assembly

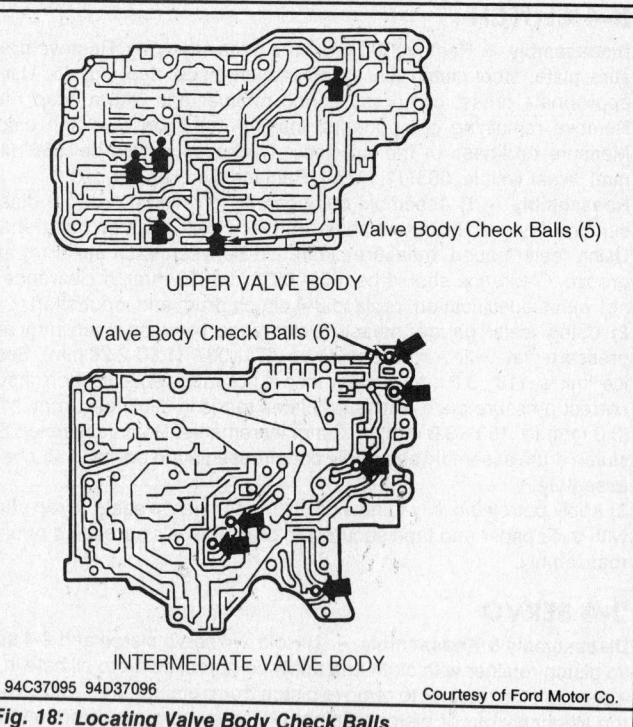

Valve Body Check Balls (5)

UPPER VALVE BODY

Valve Body Check Balls (6)

INTERMEDIATE VALVE BODY

94C37095 94D37096   Courtesy of Ford Motor Co.

Fig. 18: Locating Valve Body Check Balls

TRANSAXLE CASE

Inspection – Inspect case for cracks and stripped threads. Inspect gasket surfaces and mating surfaces for burrs. Check vent for obstructions, and check all fluid passages for obstructions and leakage. Inspect case bushing for scores. Check all parking linkage parts for wear or damage.

TRANSAXLE REASSEMBLY

NOTE: Handle all parts carefully to avoid damaging bearings and mating surfaces. Lubricate all parts with clean ATF. Use petroleum jelly on gaskets, thrust washers and needle bearings to retain them in place. Soak all friction discs in ATF for at least 15 minutes. Use all new gaskets and seals, and tighten bolts evenly.

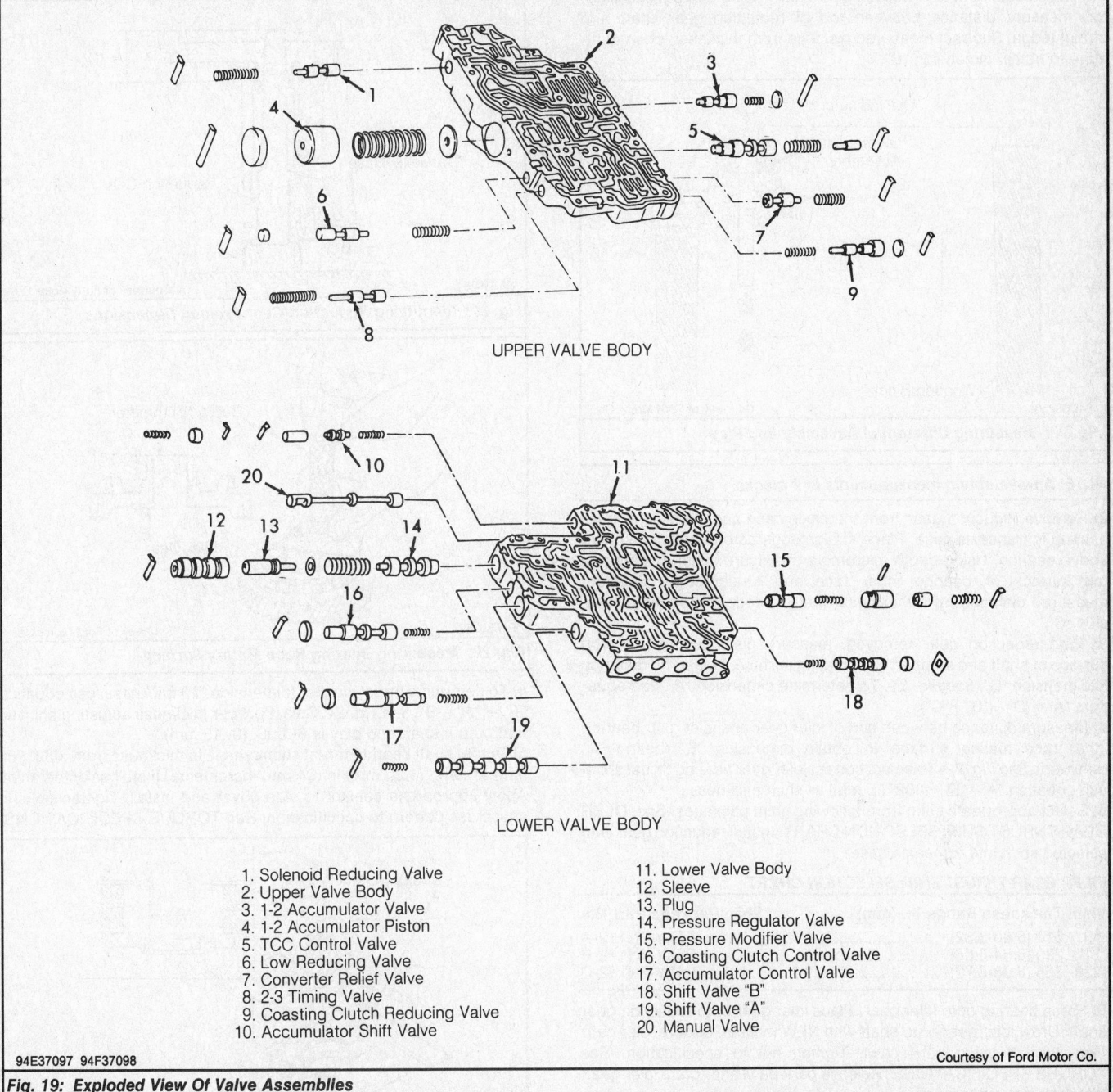

UPPER VALVE BODY

LOWER VALVE BODY

1. Solenoid Reducing Valve
2. Upper Valve Body
3. 1-2 Accumulator Valve
4. 1-2 Accumulator Piston
5. TCC Control Valve
6. Low Reducing Valve
7. Converter Relief Valve
8. 2-3 Timing Valve
9. Coasting Clutch Reducing Valve
10. Accumulator Shift Valve
11. Lower Valve Body
12. Sleeve
13. Plug
14. Pressure Regulator Valve
15. Pressure Modifier Valve
16. Coasting Clutch Control Valve
17. Accumulator Control Valve
18. Shift Valve "B"
19. Shift Valve "A"
20. Manual Valve

94E37097 94F37098

Courtesy of Ford Motor Co.

Fig. 19: Exploded View Of Valve Assemblies

NOTE: Perform transaxle reassembly procedure steps in order. Do not skip any steps.

NOTE: For identification and position of thrust bearings and washers, see Fig. 32.

Differential Bearing Preload Adjustment – 1) Differential bearing preload must be determined prior to reassembly. Ensure bearing race is installed without shim into transaxle case. Place differential into transaxle case.
2) Assemble case halves and tighten bolts to specification. See TORQUE SPECIFICATIONS. Support transaxle assembly with wooden blocks. Mount dial indicator on differential assembly. *See Fig. 20.* Use appropriate tool to move differential assembly up and down. Measure and record maximum deflection.
3) Add measured deflection and specified bearing preload. Differential bearing preload should be .002-.004" (.05-.09 mm). Select proper adjusting shim to obtain correct preload. Example: measured deflection is .026". .026" + .003" = .029" (shim thickness). Differential bearing preload adjusting shims range in thickness from .019" (.48 mm) to .036" (.92 mm) in .04 mm increments.
4) Disassemble transaxle case halves. Remove differential bearing race from transaxle case. Install selected shim and bearing race. Reinstall differential assembly. Assemble case halves and tighten bolts to specification. See TORQUE SPECIFICATIONS.
5) Insert Differential Rotator (T92P-770000-BH) into differential assembly. Using INCH lb. torque wrench, measure turning torque of differential assembly. With new bearings installed, turning torque should be 6.9-12.2 INCH lbs. (.78-1.37 N.m). With used bearings installed, turning torque should be 6.0-11.1 INCH lbs. (.70-1.23 N.m).
6) If turning torque is not within specification, select adjusting shim to obtain correct preload and recheck turning torque.

Reduction Gear/Idler Gear Bearing Preload Adjustment – 1) Install reduction gear into transaxle case. *See Fig. 21.* Measure dimension "B", "C" and "D" to determine dimension "A". Place straightedge across transaxle case, next to reduction gear shaft. Using a depth micrometer, measure distance between top of reduction gear shaft and straightedge. Subtract measured distance from thickness of straightedge to obtain dimension "B".

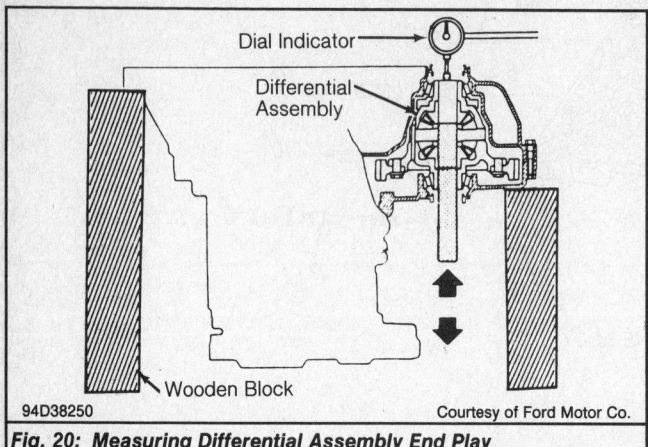

Fig. 20: Measuring Differential Assembly End Play

NOTE: Always obtain measurements in 2 places.

2) Remove reduction gear from transaxle case and install idler gear bearing in transaxle case. Place straightedge across transaxle case, above bearing. Using depth micrometer, measure distance between top surface of bearing inner race and straightedge. Subtract measured distance from thickness of straightedge to obtain dimension "C".

3) With reduction gear removed, measure distance between top surface of shaft and stepped shim mating surface. Measured distance is dimension "D". See Fig. 21. To determine dimension "A", use equation, "A"="D" - ("B"+"C").

4) Measure distance between end of idler gear and idler gear bearing inner race mating surface to obtain dimension "E" (bearing is removed). See Fig. 22. To select correct idler gear bearing thrust shim, use equation "A" - "E" - .002" (.5 mm) = shim thickness.

5) Select appropriate shim from following shim packages. See IDLER GEAR THRUST SHIM SELECTION CHART. Install reduction gear with selected shim into transaxle case.

IDLER GEAR THRUST SHIM SELECTION CHART

Shim Thickness Range In. (mm)	Shim Package Part No.
.197-.217 (5.00-5.52)	F3XY-7N112-A
.218-.239 (5.54-6.06)	F3XY-7N112-B
.239-.265 (6.08-6.72)	F3XY-7N112-C

6) Press bearing onto idler gear. Place idler gear onto reduction gear shaft. Draw idler gear onto shaft with NEW locknut. Secure idler gear from turning using park pawl. Tighten nut to specification. See TORQUE SPECIFICATIONS. Release park pawl and rotate idler gear. Recheck locknut torque.

7) Using INCH lb. torque wrench, measure idler gear turning torque. Ensure reduction gear can turn freely. Turning torque should be .4-1.4 INCH lbs. (.049-.162 N.m). Increase or decrease thickness of thrust shim to adjust turning torque if not within specification. Stake locknut.

Output Shaft Bearing Preload Adjustment – 1) Install output shaft bearing retainer with new sealing rings into transaxle case. Tighten bolts to specification. See TORQUE SPECIFICATIONS. Install output shaft hub thrust washer. Install output shaft into transaxle case.

2) Place equal height gauge blocks of either side of side cover. Place straightedge across gauge blocks. Measure distance from straightedge to thrust washer mating surface. See Fig. 23. Subtract measured distance from thickness of gauge block and straightedge. This is dimension "A".

3) Place equal height gauge blocks of either side of transaxle case. Place straightedge across gauge blocks. Measure distance from straightedge to output shaft bearing outer race thrust washer mating surface. See Fig. 23. Subtract measured distance from thickness of gauge block and straightedge. This is dimension "B".

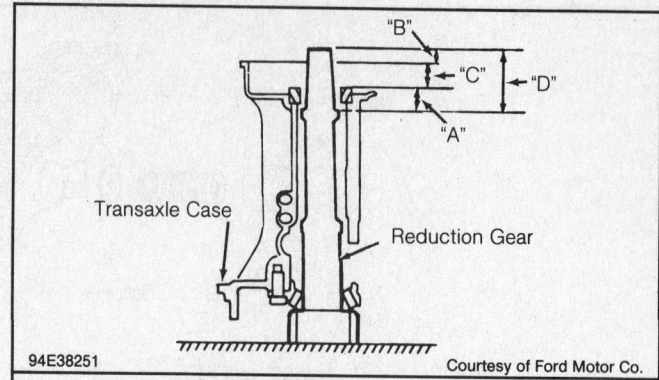

Fig. 21: Identifying Reduction Gear Preload Dimensions

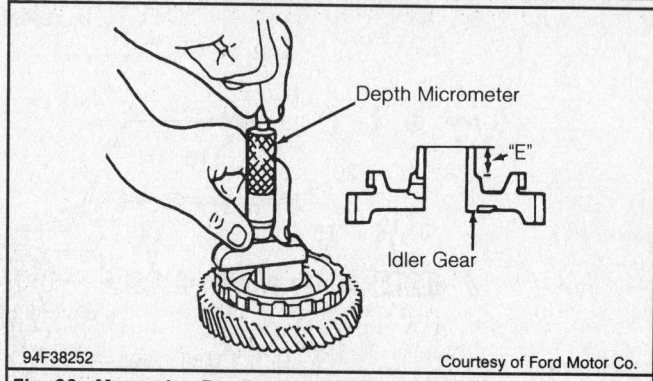

Fig. 22: Measuring Bearing Race Mating Surface

4) To determine thrust washer (dimension "T") thickness, use equation "T" = "A" - "B". See Fig. 24. Select proper thickness adjusting shim so that output shaft end play is 0-.006" (0-.15 mm).

5) Output shaft bearing thrust shims range in thickness from .032" (.80 mm) to .047" (1.20 mm) in .04 mm increments. Install selected shim. Apply appropriate sealant to side cover and install. Tighten bolts in crisscross pattern to specification. See TORQUE SPECIFICATIONS.

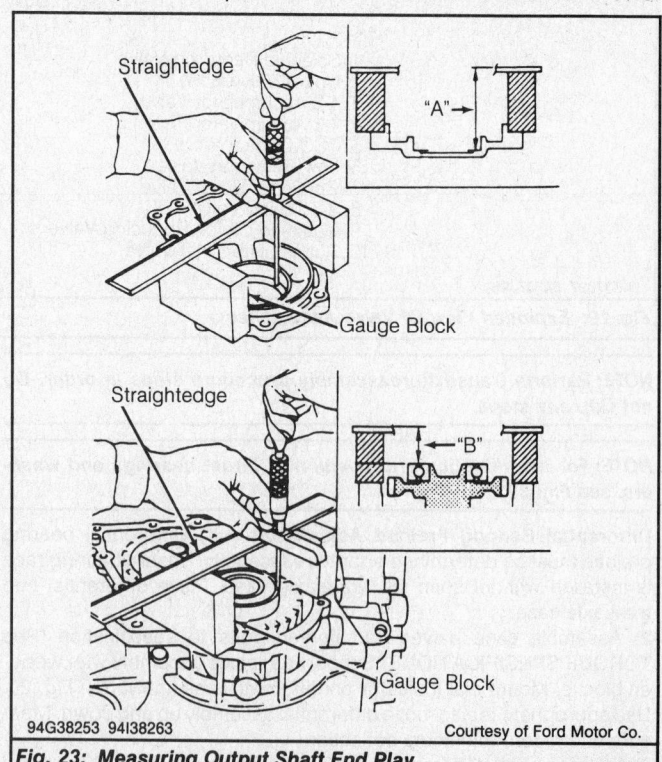

Fig. 23: Measuring Output Shaft End Play

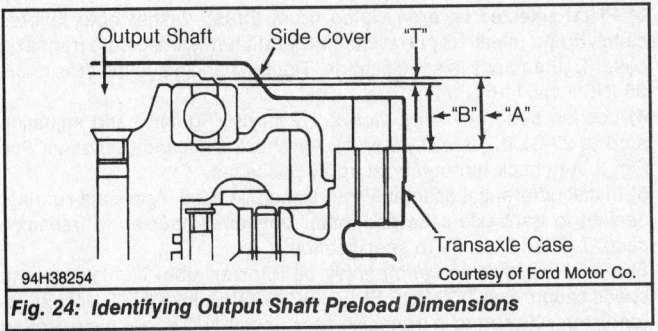

Fig. 24: Identifying Output Shaft Preload Dimensions

NOTE: For identification and position of thrust bearings and washers, see Fig. 32.

Final Reassembly – 1) Install low/reverse clutch plates, dish plate, pressure plate and snap ring. *See Fig. 25.* Using feeler gauge, measure clearance between bottom steel clutch plate and transaxle case. Clearance should be .067-.083" (1.7-2.1 mm).

2) If clearance is not within specification, select proper thickness pressure plate. Pressure plates range in thickness from .079" (2.0 mm) to .134" (3.4 mm) in .20 mm increments.

3) Install forward clutch hub lower thrust washer into transaxle case with black side of washer facing upward. Install forward clutch assembly. Install forward clutch hub upper thrust washer. Install coasting clutch upper thrust washer on coasting clutch hub. Install coasting clutch hub. *See Fig. 2.*

4) Before installing forward clutch hub/ring gear, ensure sprag is correctly installed. While holding forward clutch hub, ring gear (facing upward) should only rotate clockwise. Install forward clutch hub and ring gear assembly into transaxle case. Ensure thrust washer tabs are protruding through holes in forward clutch hub.

5) Place lower thrust bearing on outside of rear planetary gear. Place rear sun gear thrust bearing inside rear planetary gear. Install rear sun gear in rear planetary gear. Install assembly in transaxle.

6) Install sun gear front thrust bearing with black side of bearing facing upward. Install front planetary gear. Install low/reverse clutch piston spring retainer. Install low/reverse clutch piston into transaxle case. Ensure single tang of outer piston is centered in middle of double tang of inner piston.

7) Push down piston and retainer assembly and install snap ring (appropriate spring compressor may be necessary). Install low one-way clutch into front planetary gear. Rotate one-way clutch clockwise to aid installation. Install snap ring. Install primary sun gear lower thrust washer onto front planetary gear.

8) Install 3-4 clutch hub with primary sun gear upper thrust washer, primary sun gear and bearing race into transaxle case. *See Fig. 7.* Install 3-4 clutch hub bearing and input shaft upper thrust washer onto 3-4 clutch drum and input shaft assembly.

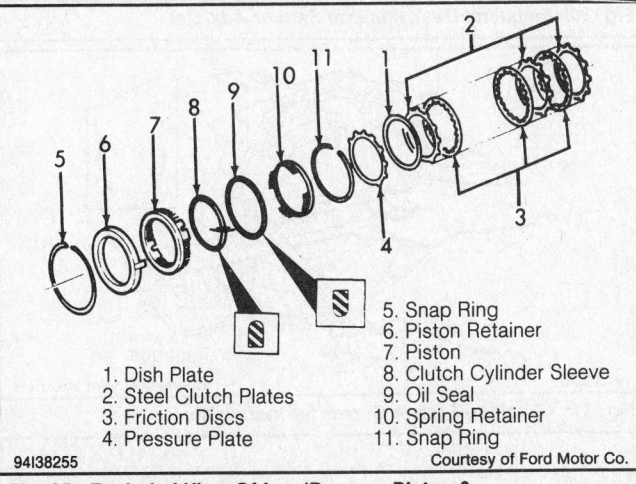

5. Snap Ring
6. Piston Retainer
7. Piston
8. Clutch Cylinder Sleeve
9. Oil Seal
10. Spring Retainer
11. Snap Ring

1. Dish Plate
2. Steel Clutch Plates
3. Friction Discs
4. Pressure Plate

Courtesy of Ford Motor Co.

Fig. 25: Exploded View Of Low/Reverse Piston & Clutch Assembly

9) Install reverse clutch assembly onto 3-4 clutch assembly and install into transaxle case. Adjust total end play and reverse clutch drum end play.

Total End Play Adjustment – 1) Place straightedge across output shaft rear bearing surface (pump support). *See Fig. 26.* Measure from top of straightedge to mating surface of oil pump assembly. Subtract thickness of straightedge from measured distance to obtain dimension "A".

CAUTION: Ensure oil pump gasket is in place during measuring procedure.

2) Place straightedge across oil pump mounting surface of transaxle case. Ensure oil pump gasket is installed between straightedge and transaxle case. Using depth micrometer, measure distance from top of straightedge to reverse clutch bearing roller. *See Fig. 27.* Subtract thickness of straightedge from distance measured to obtain dimension "B".

3) Subtract dimension "A" from dimension "B" ("B" - "A" = total end play). Total end play should be .010-.022" (.25-.55 mm). Select proper thickness bearing race to obtain correct total end play. Bearing races range in thickness from .031" (.80 mm) to .075" (1.90 mm) in .20 mm increments. Install bearing race.

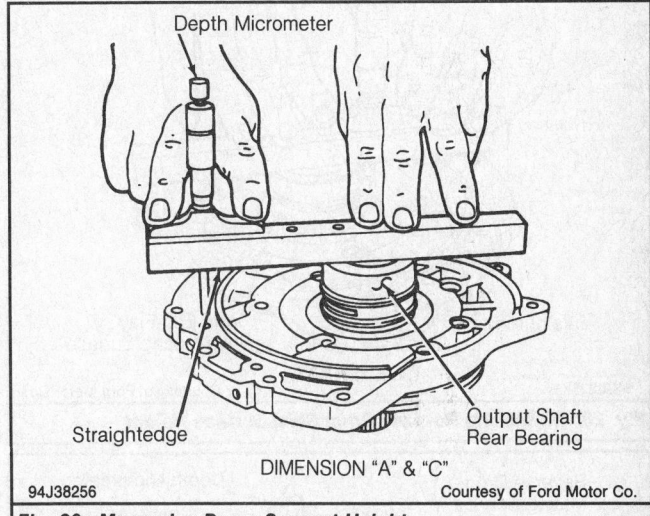

Fig. 26: Measuring Pump Support Height

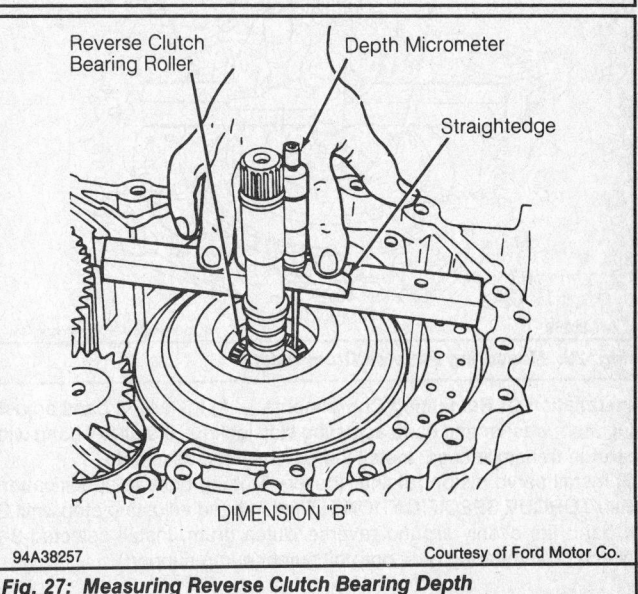

Fig. 27: Measuring Reverse Clutch Bearing Depth

CAUTION: Ensure oil pump gasket is in place during measuring procedure.

Reverse Clutch Drum End Play Adjustment – 1) Place straightedge across output shaft rear bearing surface (pump support). *See Fig. 26.* Measure from top of straightedge to mating surface of oil pump assembly. Subtract thickness of straightedge from measured distance to obtain dimension "C".

2) Maintain straightedge in same position and measure to drum end play shim surface. *See Fig. 28.* Subtract thickness of straightedge from measured distance to obtain dimension "D". Dimension "D" subtracted from dimension "C" equals dimension "E".

3) Place straightedge across oil pump mounting surface of transaxle case. Ensure oil pump gasket is in place during measuring procedure. Measure distance from straightedge to reverse drum mating surface. *See Fig. 29.* Subtract thickness of straightedge from measured distance to obtain dimension "F". Dimension "E" subtracted from dimension "F" equals reverse clutch drum end play.

4) Reverse drum end play should be .022-.035" (.55-.90 mm). Select and install proper thrust washer to obtain correct end play. Reverse clutch drum end play thrust washers range in thickness from .32" (.80mm) to .073" (1.85 mm) in .15 mm increments.

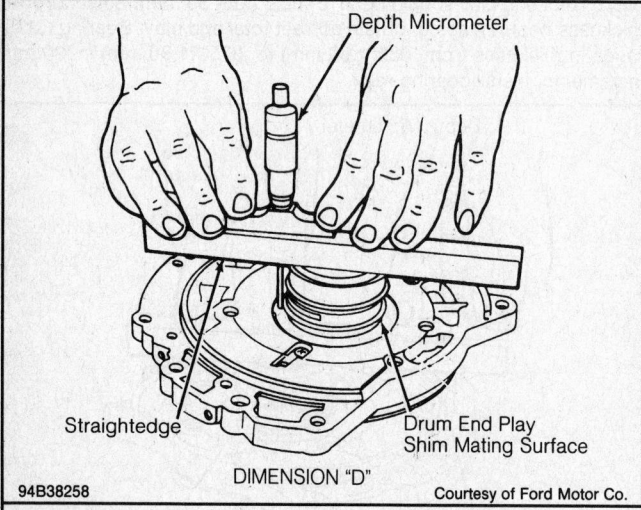

Fig. 28: *Measuring Reverse Drum Shim Surface Height*

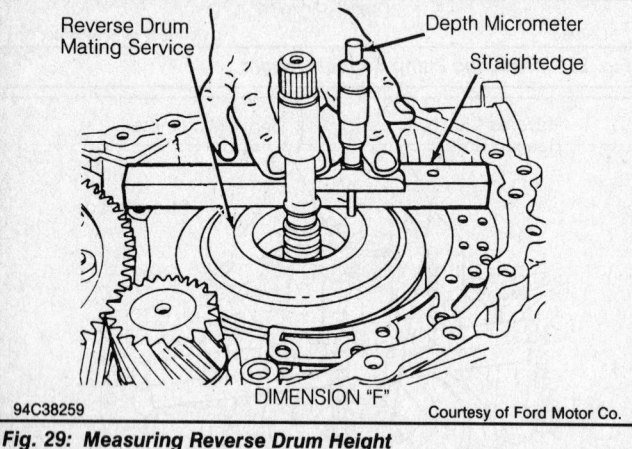

Fig. 29: *Measuring Reverse Drum Height*

Installation Of Remaining Components – 1) Install 2-4 band adjusting stop, washer and band adjusting stop locknut. Install 2-4 band with strut in transaxle case. Install 2-4 servo piston assembly.

2) Install servo piston retainer (cover). Tighten bolts to specification. See TORQUE SPECIFICATIONS. Tighten band adjusting stop until 2-4 band fits evenly around reverse clutch drum. Install selected 3-4 clutch drum bearing race onto oil pump (pump support).

3) Place selected reverse clutch drum thrust washer onto reverse clutch drum. Install oil pump assembly and baffle plate onto transaxle case. Tighten bolts to specification. Tighten band adjusting stop to 27-35 INCH lbs. (4-6 N.m).

4) Loosen band adjusting stop 2 1/2 turns. Tighten band adjusting stop to 23-31 ft. lbs. (31-42 N.m). Air check 2-4 band operation. *See Fig. 3.* Air check through both apply passages.

5) Install differential assembly into transaxle case. Apply appropriate sealant to transaxle case and install converter housing to transaxle case. Tighten 21 bolts to specification.

6) Install low/reverse clutch apply oil transfer tube. Tighten bolts to specification. See TORQUE SPECIFICATIONS. Install D-R accumulator piston with spring in transaxle case. Install N-D accumulator spring with piston in case. Air check transaxle assembly prior to install valve body. *See Fig. 3.*

7) Route valve body wiring harness up through transaxle case and secure with spring clip. Set manual shift linkage rod in neutral position. Install valve body into transaxle case while aligning manual valve with manual detent lever. Tighten bolts to specification. Install oil filter.

8) Place oil pan magnets in locations marked during disassembly. Install oil pan. Tighten bolts in crisscross pattern to specification. Install drain plug. Place manual shift linkage rod in park position. Install Manual Lever Position (MLP) switch. Move shift rod to neutral position.

9) Insert Gear Position Sensor Adjuster (T92P-70010-CH) into MLP switch and manual shaft adjustment hole. *See Fig. 30.* Ensure adjuster pin is vertical. Tighten MLP bolts to specification. Remove pin. Install oil cooler tube. Install oil filler tube.

10) Fill torque converter with 1.0 liter of ATF. Install converter into housing. Ensure oil pump inner gear tangs are inserted into converter hub notches. To verify torque converter is properly seated, place straightedge across converter housing. Measure distance from straightedge to converter mounting surface. *See Fig. 31.* Subtract thickness of straightedge to obtain distance. Distance should be .55" (14 mm).

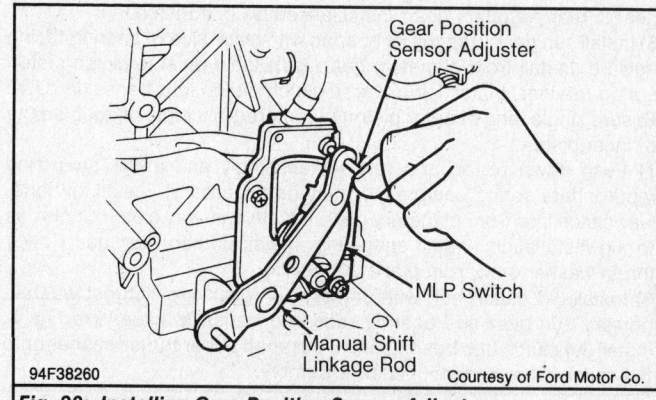

Fig. 30: *Installing Gear Position Sensor Adjuster*

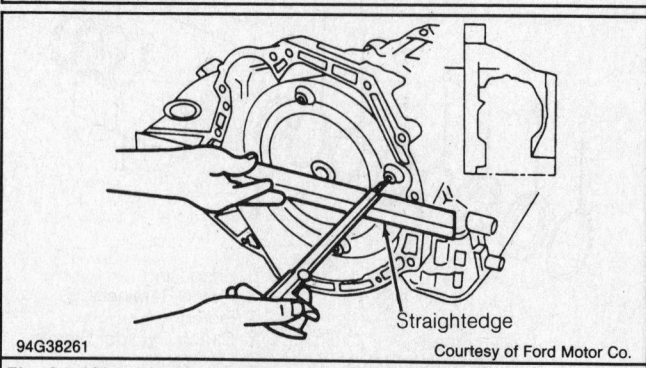

Fig. 31: *Checking Torque Converter Installation*

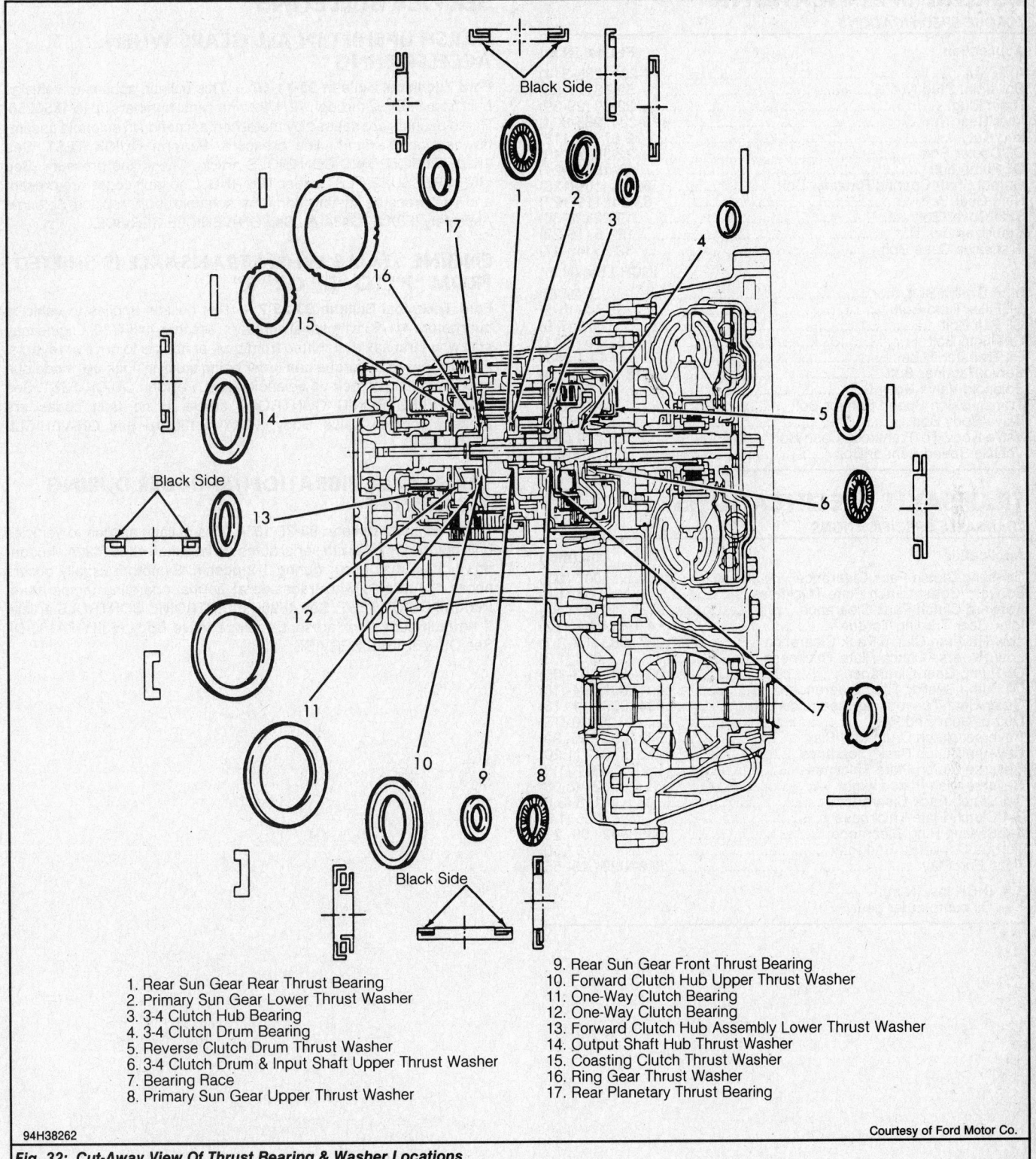

1. Rear Sun Gear Rear Thrust Bearing
2. Primary Sun Gear Lower Thrust Washer
3. 3-4 Clutch Hub Bearing
4. 3-4 Clutch Drum Bearing
5. Reverse Clutch Drum Thrust Washer
6. 3-4 Clutch Drum & Input Shaft Upper Thrust Washer
7. Bearing Race
8. Primary Sun Gear Upper Thrust Washer
9. Rear Sun Gear Front Thrust Bearing
10. Forward Clutch Hub Upper Thrust Washer
11. One-Way Clutch Bearing
12. One-Way Clutch Bearing
13. Forward Clutch Hub Assembly Lower Thrust Washer
14. Output Shaft Hub Thrust Washer
15. Coasting Clutch Thrust Washer
16. Ring Gear Thrust Washer
17. Rear Planetary Thrust Bearing

94H38262

Courtesy of Ford Motor Co.

Fig. 32: Cut-Away View Of Thrust Bearing & Washer Locations

TORQUE SPECIFICATIONS

TORQUE SPECIFICATIONS

Application	Ft Lbs. (N.m)
Axle Nut	174-231 (235-314)
Ball Joint Stud Nut	52-63 (71-86)
Drain Plug	22-29 (29-39)
Idler Gear Nut	195-224 (265-304)
Lug Nut	72-87 (98-118)
Oil Cooler Bolt	22-36 (29-49)
Oil Pump bolt	13-15 (18-21)
Output Shaft Bearing Retainer Bolt	80-90 (109-123)
Ring Gear Bolt	83-94 (113-127)
Side Cover Bolt	19-22 (26-30)
Stabilizer Link Nut	12-16 (16-22)
Transaxle Case Bolt	32-35 (43-47)

Application	INCH Lbs. (N.m)
MLP Switch Bolt	27 (3)
Oil Filler Tube Bolt	35-44 (14-5)
Oil Pan Bolt	62-79 (7-9)
Oil Pump Bolt	62-79 (7-11)
Oil Transfer Tube	44-61 (5-7)
Servo Retainer Bolt	18-21 (2.0-2.4)
Solenoid Valve Body Bolt	62-79 (7-9)
Transmission Speed Sensor Bolt	44-61 (5-7)
Valve Body Bolt	62-79 (7-9)
Valve Body-To-Transaxle Case Bolt	62-79 (7-9)
Vehicle Speed Sensor Bolt	43 (5)

TRANSAXLE SPECIFICATIONS

TRANSAXLE SPECIFICATIONS

Application	In. (mm)
Coasting Clutch Pack Clearance	.067 (1.7)
Forward/Coast Clutch Plate Thickness	.055 (1.4)
Forward Clutch Pack Clearance	.073 (1.85)
Idler Gear Turning Torque	[1].4-1.4 (.049-.162)
Low/Reverse Clutch Pack Clearance	.067-.083 (1.7-2.1)
Low/Reverse Clutch Plate Thickness	.063 (1.6)
Oil Pump Gear Clearance	.001-.002 (.03-.05)
Oil Pump Sealing Ring Clearance	.001-.007 (.04-.18)
Outer Gear-To-Housing Clearance [2]	.004-.007 (.11-.18)
Output Gear End Play	0-.006 (0-.15)
Reverse Clutch Drum End Play	.022-.035 (.55-.90)
Reverse Clutch Pack Clearance	.047 (1.20)
Reverse Clutch Plate Thickness	.071 (1.8)
Reverse Dish Plate Height	.121 (3.08)
3-4 Clutch Pack Clearance	.118 (3.0)
3-4 Clutch Plate Thickness	.055 (1.4)
3-4 Sealing Ring Clearance	.003-.009 (.09-.23)
Torque Converter End Play	.019 (.50)
Total End Play	.010-.022 (.25-.55)

[1] – INCH lbs. (N.m).
[2] – Oil pump outer gear.

SERVICE BULLETINS

HARSH UPSHIFT IN ALL GEARS WHEN ACCELERATING

Ford Technical Bulletin 93-11-10 – This bulletin applies to vehicles built from 4/13/92 through 12/1/92 with serial numbers up to 4X56258. Harsh upshifts are caused by metal contamination in solenoid assembly causing maximum line pressure. Perform QUICK TEST. See 4F20E ELECTRONIC CONTROLS article. Check line pressure. See LINE PRESSURE TEST under TESTING. If no fault codes are present and line pressure testing confirms solenoid fault, replace Solenoid Assembly (F3XY-7G484-A). See ON-VEHICLE SERVICE.

ENGINE STALLS WHEN TRANSAXLE IS SHIFTED FROM "P" TO "D" OR "R"

Ford Technical Bulletin 93-25-7 – This bulletin applies to vehicles built before 4/1/93 with serial numbers less than 4454720. Engine may stall when transaxle is shifted from park or neutral to drive or reverse. Fault is caused by torque converter being stuck in "lock-up" mode due to poor seating of lock-up solenoid valve. Perform QUICK TEST. See 4F20E ELECTRONIC CONTROLS article. If no fault codes are present, replace Valve Body (F3XY-7A100-D). See ON-VEHICLE SERVICE.

TRANSAXLE VIBRATION/SHUDDER DURING 1-2 UPSHIFT

Ford Technical Bulletin 93-25-13 – This bulletin applies to vehicles built before 11/1/92 with serial numbers less than 4Y59142. A shudder or vibration may occur during 1-2 upshift. Symptom usually occurs above 1/2 throttle with transaxle at normal operating temperature. Perform QUICK TEST. See 4F20E ELECTRONIC CONTROLS article. If no fault codes are present, replace Valve Body (F3XY-7A100-D). See ON-VEHICLE SERVICE.

Ford Motor Co: 1993-94 Villager

NOTE: For 4F20E transaxle mechanical testing and repair, see Ford 4F20E article.

INTRODUCTION

The first step in diagnosing any driveability problem is verifying the customer's complaint with a test drive under the conditions the problem occurred. Before entering self-diagnostics, perform a careful and complete visual inspection. Most transmission control problems result from mechanical breakdowns or poor electrical connections.

NOTE: Perform all voltage tests with a Digital Volt-Ohmmeter (DVOM) with a minimum 10-megohm input impedance, unless stated otherwise in test procedure.

DESCRIPTION & OPERATION

Input signals from sensors are sent to the Transaxle Control Module (TCM). The TCM can determine when the time and conditions are right for a shift or converter clutch application. The TCM can also determine line pressure needed to optimize shift feel.

Five electronic solenoids accomplish these functions; 2 On/Off solenoids for shifting, a Pulse-Width Modulate solenoid for torque converter clutch control, a Electronic Pressure Control solenoid for line pressure control, and a coasting clutch solenoid to control the release of the coast clutch and the coordinated release of the direct clutch and apply of the low and intermediate band. The TCM has built-in self-diagnosis, fail-safe code and warning code display for the main input sensors and solenoid valves.

INPUT SENSORS

Brake On/Off (BOO) Switch – The TCM receives a signal from the BOO switch when the brake switch is operated. Torque converter clutch is disengaged when brakes are applied. A faulty switch will affect torque converter operation.

Manual Lever Position (MLP) – The TCM monitors a series of step down resistors in the MLP sensor that act as a voltage divider. The voltage signal corresponds with position of the transaxle range selector lever. The MLP sensor also contains the neutral/start and backup circuits. Malfunction of the MLP sensor may cause harsh engagements and firm shift feel. Improper shifting or shift selection and no engine cranking may also result.

Overdrive Control Switch – The O/D control switch is used to inhibit 4th gear operation. Indicator light will illuminate when 4th gear is "locked out". Switch failure may affect 4th gear operation.

Power E-AT Switch – The power E-AT switch allows for selection of 2 shift schedules, NORMAL (early, low RPM shifts) and POWER (delayed, higher RPM shifts). The TCM has the capability to override the power schedule depending on driving conditions.

Pulse Signal Generator (PSG) – The PSG is a magnetic pickup that sends turbine shaft speed signal to the TCM. Turbine shaft speed is determined by monitoring reverse drum speed. Malfunction of sensor may cause harsh engagements of shifts. Lack of 4th gear or no engine braking in 2nd or 3rd gear may also be present.

Throttle Position Sensor (TPS) – The TPS is a potentiometer mounted to the engine throttle body. The PCM receives a signal from the TPS relaying throttle plate position. TPS failure will cause PCM to operate in fail safe mode and raise line pressure to prevent transaxle damage. This condition will result in harsh engagements, firm shift feel, abnormal shift schedule and TCC not engaging or cycling.

Transmission Control Switch (TCS) – Switch is mounted on shift lever handle. Switch controls operation of 4th gear. Malfunction of switch will cause lack of 4th gear disable function.

Transmission Oil Temperature (TOT) Sensor – The TOT sensor is hard wired to the solenoid valve body. The TCM monitors voltage across the TOT thermistor to determine transaxle temperature. Depending on temperature, the TCM controls line pressure, shift scheduling and TCC operation. Malfunction of sensor will cause incorrect line pressure and possible lack of TCC operation.

Vehicle Speed Sensor (VSS) – The VSS is a magnetic pickup that sends vehicle speed signal to the PCM and TCM. Malfunction of sensor may cause harsh engagements of shifts. Lack of 4th gear, TCC lock-up, or engine braking in 2nd or 3rd gear may also be present.

OUTPUT DEVICES

Solenoid Valve Body Assembly – 1) The solenoid valve body assembly contains Line Pressure Control (LPC) solenoid, Shift Solenoid "A" (SSA), Shift Solenoid "B" (SSB), Coasting Clutch (CCS) solenoid and Torque Converter Clutch (TCC) solenoid. See TRANSAXLE SHIFT SOLENOID STATUS CHART.

TRANSAXLE SHIFT SOLENOID STATUS CHART

Gear	Shift Solenoid "A"	Shift Solenoid "B"
1st	On	On
2nd	Off	On
3rd	Off	Off
4th (O/D)	On	Off

PRELIMINARY INSPECTION

VISUAL INSPECTION

Visually inspect all electrical wiring, looking for chafed, stretched, cut or pinched wiring. Ensure electrical connectors fit tightly and are not corroded. Inspect air induction system for possible vacuum leaks. Check TCM, sensors and actuators for physical damage. Check engine coolant level. Check transmission fluid level and condition.

NOTE: In addition to transmission fault codes, other engine-related fault codes may be present. These fault codes pertain to engine performance and must be repaired first as engine performance will greatly affect transmission operation. For information and testing procedures of engine-related fault codes and components, see SELF-DIAGNOSTICS – Villager article in ENGINE PERFORMANCE of appropriate MITCHELL® manual.

SELF-DIAGNOSTIC SYSTEM

DIAGNOSTIC FORMATS

QUICK TEST and PINPOINT TESTS are diagnostic formats used to test and service EEC system. QUICK TEST allows technician to identify problems and retrieve service codes. PINPOINT TESTS check circuits, sensors and actuators.

Before starting any PINPOINT TEST, follow all steps under QUICK TEST to find correct PINPOINT TEST. If vehicle passes QUICK TEST and no driveability symptoms or intermittent faults exist, EEC system is okay.

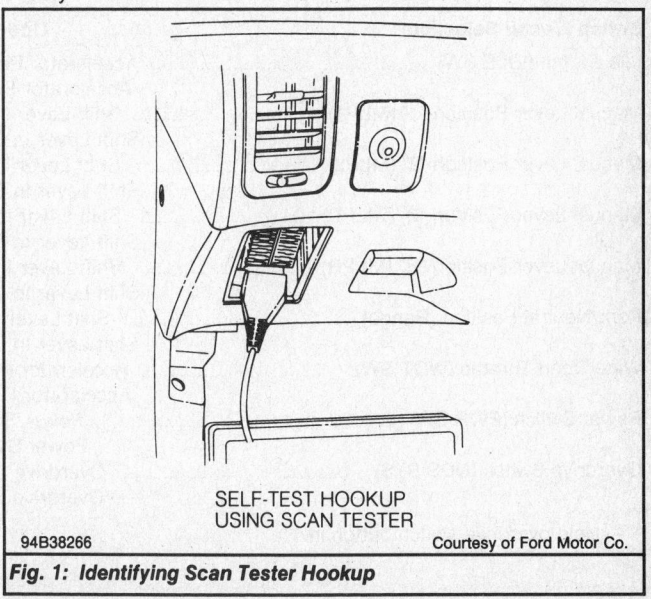

SELF-TEST HOOKUP
USING SCAN TESTER

94B38266   Courtesy of Ford Motor Co.

Fig. 1: Identifying Scan Tester Hookup

QUICK TEST

NOTE: *Following diagnostic procedures utilize a Ford New Generation STAR (NGS) tester. If using other applicable scan tester, refer to manufacturers instruction manual for appropriate procedure.*

1) Perform Visual Test – Ensure coolant and engine oil level is correct. Ensure transaxle fluid level is correct. Check shift linkage operation. Inspect wiring harnesses, connectors and fuses. Check condition of battery and charging system output. Ensure all repairs needed are completed before proceeding. Go to next step.

2) Perform Vehicle Preparation – Set parking brake. Ensure shift selector is in Park position. Block drive wheels. Ensure all accessories are off (no switched electrical loads). Go to next step.

3) Perform Equipment Hookup – Ensure ignition is off. Connect Rotunda New Generation STAR (NGS) tester (007-00500). See Fig. 1. Connect power leads to battery. If using Overdrive ON/OFF Light (ODL) for reading fault codes, no equipment hookup is needed.

NOTE: *If NGS tester is not able to access TCM - TRANSAXLE CTRL MODULE, see Pinpoint Test DLC.*

4) Perform Switch Monitor Test – Turn ignition on. Using NGS tester, select DIAGNOSTIC DATA LINK. Select TCM - TRANSAXLE CTRL MODULE. Select PID/DATA MONITOR AND RECORD. Select individual switches. See SWITCH MONITOR TEST CHART. If all switches are operating correctly, go to next step. If any switch is malfunctioning, go to appropriate PINPOINT TEST for diagnosis of selected faulty switch.

NOTE: *If ODL will not illuminate, see PINPOINT TEST ODL.*

5) Perform Diagnostic Test Mode – If using NGS tester, turn ignition on. Select DIAGNOSTIC DATA LINK. Select TCM - TRANSAXLE CTRL MODULE. Select DIAGNOSTIC TEST MODE RESULTS. Record any failed components and trouble codes.

If using ODL, ensure ignition is off. Place shift selector lever in "P". Turn ignition on. ODL should illuminate for 2 seconds. Turn ignition off (not in LOCK position). Move shift selector lever to "D". Hold OD On/Off switch button in and turn ignition on. Wait 2 seconds. Continue to hold OD On/Off switch button in and move shift selector to "2". Release OD button. Set OD On/Off switch to ON position. Move shift selector lever to "1". Set OD On/Off switch to OFF position. Depress accelerator to WOT and release. Monitor ODL and record flashing trouble codes. See READING CODES.

If any trouble codes are present, go to next step. If NGS tester displays NO FAILURES or if using ODL, initial flash signal is followed by 10 similar flashes signals, go to step 7). If unable to initiate DIAGNOSTIC TEST MODE RESULTS with NGS tester or ODL stays illuminated, see PINPOINT TESTS MLP, ODS, IDL and WOT for diagnosis of selected faulty switch.

NOTE: *Erasing trouble codes and retesting will indicate whether hard or intermittent codes are present.*

6) Erase & Retest System – Using NGS tester, press clear in DIAGNOSTIC TEST MODE RESULTS. Using O/D light, trouble codes are cleared when ignition is turned off after performing Diagnostic Test Mode (Step 5)). Repeat step 5). If all or some codes cannot be retrieved, it may be necessary to lightly tap suspect sensors, shake or wiggle harnesses, or drive vehicle in order to induce failure. Repeat step 5). If any trouble codes are recorded, go to appropriate PINPOINT TEST. See CODE REFERENCE CHART. If no codes are recorded, go to next step.

7) Perform Code Generation – Code generation is performed by individually disconnecting each component in order listed in CODE REFERENCE CHART. Repeat step 5) to verify that TCM recognizes open sensor or solenoid circuit and sets trouble code. If all components listed in chart set trouble code, go to next step. If no codes are set using ODL, replace TCM. Connect all components and repeat QUICK TEST. If no codes are set using NGS tester, perform PINPOINT TEST DLC.

8) Perform Component Verification Test – Perform PINPOINT TEST for suspected component(s). Inspect and service component(s) as needed. If component tests okay, repeat QUICK TEST.

CODE REFERENCE CHART

Fault Code	Code Definition	Pinpoint Test
01	Pulse Signal Generator	PSG
02	Vehicle Speed Sensor	VSS
03	Throttle Position Sensor	TPS
04	Shift Solenoid "A"	SCP
05	Shift Solenoid "B"	SCP
06	Coasting Clutch Solenoid	SCP
07	TCC Solenoid	SCP
08	TOT Sensor	TOT
09	Engine RPM	RPM
10	Line Pressure Solenoid	SCP
12 [1]	Transaxle Control Module	TCM
13 [1]	Transaxle Control Module	TCM

[1] – Replace Transaxle Control Module

SWITCH MONITOR TEST CHART

Switch (Tester Selection)	Operation	Tester Display	Pinpoint Test
Idle Switch (IDLE SW)	Accelerator Pedal Depressed	Off	IDL
	Accelerator Pedal Released	On	MLP
Manual Lever Position "1" (MLP1)	Shift Lever In "1" Position	On	MLP
	Shift Lever In Other Positions	Off	MLP
Manual Lever Position "2" (MLP2)	Shift Lever In "2" Position	On	MLP
	Shift Lever In Other Positions	Off	MLP
Manual Lever Position "D" (MLPD)	Shift Lever In "D" Position	On	MLP
	Shift Lever In Other Positions	Off	MLP
Manual Lever Position "R" (MLPR)	Shift Lever In "R" Position	On	MLP
	Shift Lever In Other Positions	Off	MLP
Park/Neutral Position (Range)	Shift Lever In "P" Or "N"	P Or N	MLP
	Shift Lever In Other Positions	1, 2, D Or R	MLP
Wide Open Throttle (WOT SW)	Accelerator Pedal 50-100%	On	WOT
	Accelerator Pedal Released	Off	WOT
Power Switch (PWR SW)	Power Switch ON	On	PWRS
	Power Switch OFF	Off	PWRS
Overdrive Switch (ODS STS)	Overdrive Switch ON [1]	On	ODS
	Overdrive Switch OFF	Off	ODS

[1] – Hold overdrive switch button in.

READING CODES
USING OVERDRIVE LIGHT)

After following Diagnostic Test Mode (QUICK TEST step **5**), the ODL will flash trouble codes. The ODL will first flash initial signal followed by 10 flashes. The longest flash indicates the trouble code. For example, if the first flash is longer than the next 9 flashes, trouble code 01 is indicated. *See Fig. 2.* The ODL will remain ON while overdrive is off if system is okay.

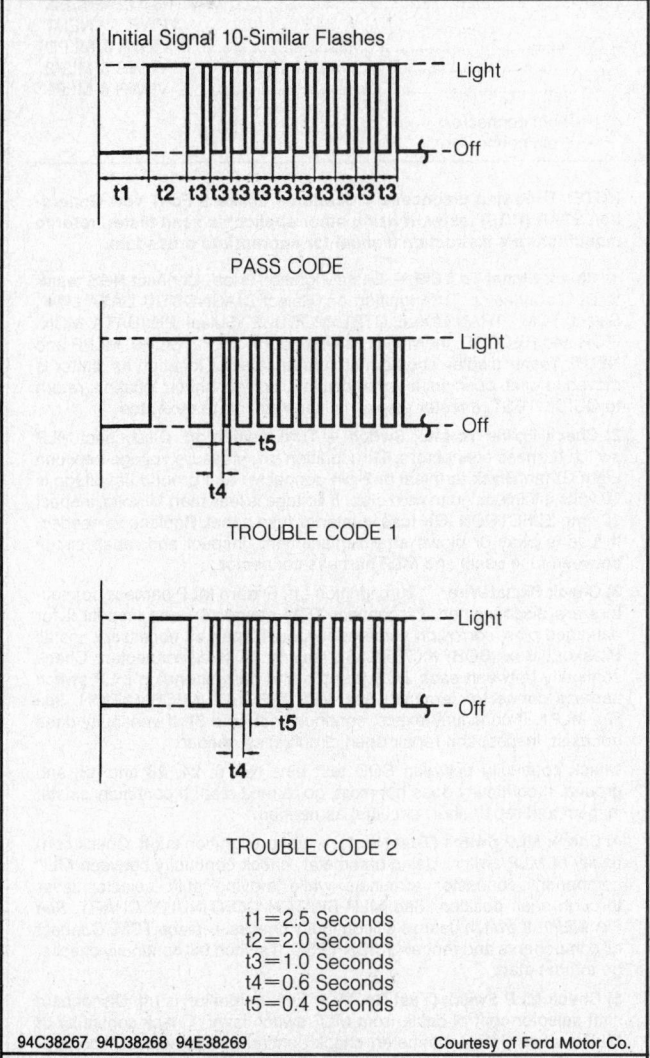

Initial Signal 10-Similar Flashes

PASS CODE

TROUBLE CODE 1

TROUBLE CODE 2

t1=2.5 Seconds
t2=2.0 Seconds
t3=1.0 Seconds
t4=0.6 Seconds
t5=0.4 Seconds

94C38267 94D38268 94E38269   Courtesy of Ford Motor Co.

Fig. 2: Reading Diagnostic Flash Codes

HOW TO USE PINPOINT TESTS

NOTE: Rotunda Breakout Box (007-00033) is frequently used during PINPOINT TESTS. See TRANSMISSION CONTROL MODULE (TCM) under ON-VEHICLE SERVICE in Ford 4F20E article for information regarding disconnecting TCM.

1) DO NOT perform any PINPOINT TEST unless specifically instructed by a QUICK TEST procedure. Follow each test step in order until fault is found. DO NOT replace any part unless directed to do so. When more than one code is retrieved, start with first code displayed.
2) PINPOINT TESTS ensure electrical circuits are okay before sensors or other components are replaced. Always test circuits for continuity between sensor and PCM. Test all circuits for short to power, opens or short to ground. Voltage Reference (VREF) and Voltage Power (VPWR) circuits should be tested with ignition on or as specified in PINPOINT TESTS.
3) DO NOT measure voltage or resistance at PCM or TCM. DO NOT connect any type of test light unless specified in testing procedure. All

measurements are made by probing rear of connector. Isolate both ends of a circuit and turn ignition off when checking for shorts or continuity, unless instructed otherwise.
4) Disconnect solenoids and switches from harness before measuring continuity and resistance or applying voltage. After each repair, check all component connections and repeat QUICK TEST.
5) An open circuit is defined as a resistance reading of greater than 5 ohms. This specification tolerance may be too high for some items in EEC-4F20E system. If resistance approaches 5 ohms, always clean suspected connector and coat it with protective dielectric silicone grease. A short is defined as a resistance reading of less than 10 k/ohms to ground, unless stated otherwise in PINPOINT TEST.

NOTE: In following tests, circuit diagrams and illustrations are courtesy of Ford Motor Co.

PINPOINT TEST DLC
DATA LINK CONNECTOR (DLC)

94G38279

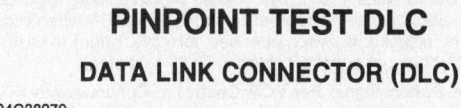

DATA LINK CONNECTOR (DLC)
FOR NGS HARNESS CONNECTOR
(INTERIOR FUSE PANEL)

Fig. DLC1: Identifying DLC Terminal Location

DLC CIRCUIT INFORMATION

Circuit	TCM Pin No.	¹ BOB Pin No.	Wire Color
DLC	28	45	Yel/Red
DLC	29	48	Yel/Blu
DLC	30	32	Yel/Blk
GND	15	39, 40, 46, 49 & 60	Blk

¹ – Rotunda Breakout Box (007-00033)

1) Check Ground At DLC – Ensure ignition is off. Access DLC. *See Fig. 1.* Check continuity between DLC ground terminal and vehicle ground. *See Fig. DLC1.* If continuity does not exist, inspect and repair circuit as needed. If continuity exists, go to next step.

2) Check DLC Circuits – Ensure ignition is off. Disconnect TCM connector, and inspect it for damaged pins, corrosion and loose wires. Repair as necessary. Install Breakout Box (BOB) (007-00033), leaving TCM disconnected. Check continuity between BOB test pins No. 45, 48 and 32, and corresponding DLC terminals. See DLC CIRCUIT INFORMATION table. If continuity does not exist, inspect and repair open circuit(s) as needed. If continuity exists, continue with step **2)**.

Check continuity between BOB test pins No. 45 and ground, and No. 32 and ground. If continuity exists, inspect and repair short circuit(s) as needed. If continuity does not exist, continue with step **2)**.

Measure resistance between BOB test pin No. 48 and ground. If resistance is less than 2000 ohms, inspect and repair circuit as needed. If resistance is more than 2000 ohms, circuit is okay. If all above circuit tests are okay, go to PINPOINT TEST PGC.

PINPOINT TEST IDL
IDLE SWITCH (IDL)

94J38280

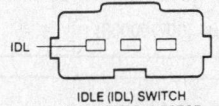

IDLE (IDL) SWITCH
HARNESS CONNECTOR

Fig. IDL1: Identifying IDL Terminal Location

PINPOINT TEST IDL (Cont.)

IDL CIRCUIT INFORMATION

Circuit	TCM Pin No.	[1] BOB Pin No.	Wire Color
IDL	14	2	Brn/Yel

[1] – Rotunda Breakout Box (007-00033)

NOTE: Following diagnostic procedures utilize a Ford New Generation STAR (NGS) tester. If using other applicable scan tester, refer to manufacturers instruction manual for appropriate procedure.

1) Check Idle Switch Signal – Ensure ignition is off. Connect NGS tester to DLC connector. Turn ignition on. Select DIAGNOSTIC DATA LINK. Select TCM - TRANSAXLE CTRL MODULE. Select PID/DATA MONITOR and RECORD. Select IDLE SW. Tester should display IDLE SW OFF when accelerator pedal is depressed and IDLE SW ON when accelerator pedal is released. If switch operates correctly, return to QUICK TEST. If switch does not operate correctly, go to next step.

2) Check Idle Switch Signal For PCM Control – Continue with NGS tester connected to DLC connector. Turn ignition on. Select DIAGNOSTIC DATA LINK. Select PCM - POWERTRAIN CTRL MODULE. Select PID/DATA MONITOR and RECORD. Select IDLE SW. Tester should display IDLE SW OFF when accelerator pedal is depressed and IDLE SW ON when accelerator pedal is released. If switch operates correctly, go to next step. If switch does not operate correctly, go to EEC PINPOINT TEST IDL under SELF-DIAGNOSTICS – Villager article in ENGINE PERFORMANCE of appropriate MITCHELL® manual.

3) Check IDL Circuit To TCM – Turn ignition off. Disconnect TCM connector, and inspect it for damaged pins, corrosion and loose wires. Repair as necessary. Install Breakout Box (BOB) (007-00033), leaving TCM disconnected. Disconnect IDL switch connector. Using ohmmeter, check continuity between IDL terminal of IDL harness connector and BOB test pin No. 2. If continuity exists, continue with step **3)**. If continuity does not exist, inspect and repair open circuit as needed.

Measure resistance between BOB test pin No. 2 and ground. If resistance is less than 4000 ohms, inspect and repair circuit as needed. If resistance is more than 4000 ohms, replace TCM. Connect all components and repeat QUICK TEST.

PINPOINT TEST MLP

MANUAL LEVER POSITION SWITCH (MLP)

94A38281

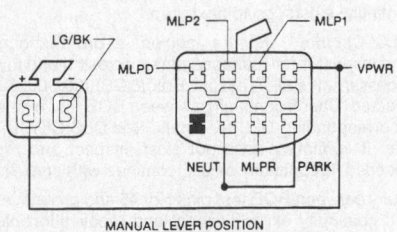

MANUAL LEVER POSITION
(MLP) HARNESS CONNECTORS

Fig. MLP1: Identifying MLP Terminal Location

MLP CIRCUIT INFORMATION

Circuit	TCM Pin No.	[1] BOB Pin No.	Wire Color
MLP1	16	6	Blu/Blk
MLP2	17	24	Blu/Yel
MLPD	18	43	Blu/Wht
MLPR	20	30	Blu/Red
PARK/NEUT	19	28	Blu

[1] – Rotunda Breakout Box (007-00033)

PINPOINT TEST MLP (Cont.)

MLP SWITCH CONTINUITY CHART

Selector Lever Position	Continuity Between Terminals
"P"	VPWR & [1] Lt. Grn/Blk
	VPWR & [2] PARK
"R"	VPWR & MLPR
"N"	VPWR & [1] Lt. Grn/Blk
	VPWR & [2] NEUT
"D"	VPWR & MLPD
"2"	VPWR & MLP2
"1"	VPWR & MLP1

[1] – 2-pin connector.
[2] – 8-pin connector.

NOTE: Following diagnostic procedures utilize a Ford New Generation STAR (NGS) tester. If using other applicable scan tester, refer to manufacturers instruction manual for appropriate procedure.

1) Check Signal To TCM – Ensure ignition is off. Connect NGS tester to DLC connector. Turn ignition on. Select DIAGNOSTIC DATA LINK. Select TCM - TRANSAXLE CTRL MODULE. Select PID/DATA MONITOR and RECORD. Individually select MLP1, MLP2, MLPD, MLPR and NEUT. Tester display should match shift selector location as shifter is moved to each position. If tester displays correct shifter location, return to QUICK TEST. If tester display is incorrect, go to next step.

2) Check Power To MLP Switch – Turn ignition off. Disconnect MLP switch harness connectors. Turn ignition on. Measure voltage between Light Green/Black terminal of 2-pin connector and ground. If voltage is 10 volts minimum, go to next step. If voltage is less than 10 volts, inspect 10 amp ELECTRON IGN fuse in interior fuse panel. Replace as needed. If fuse is okay or blows after replacement, inspect and repair circuit between fuse panel and MLP harness connector.

3) Check Signal Wire – Turn ignition off. Ensure MLP harness connectors are disconnected. Disconnect TCM connector, and inspect it for damaged pins, corrosion and loose wires. Repair as necessary. Install Breakout Box (BOB) (007-00033), leaving TCM disconnected. Check continuity between each BOB test pin and corresponding MLP switch harness connector terminal. See MLP CIRCUIT INFORMATION. See Fig. MLP1. If continuity exists, continue with step **3)**. If continuity does not exist, inspect and repair open circuit(s) as needed.

Check continuity between BOB test pins No. 6, 24, 28 and 43, and ground. If continuity does not exist, go to next step. If continuity exists, inspect and repair short circuit(s) as needed.

4) Check MLP Switch (Test No. 1) – Ensure ignition is off. Check continuity of MLP switch. Using ohmmeter, check continuity between MLP component connector terminals while moving shift selector lever through each position. See MLP SWITCH CONTINUITY CHART. See Fig. MLP1. If switch passes all continuity checks, replace TCM. Connect all components and repeat QUICK TEST. If switch fail continuity checks, go to next step.

5) Check MLP Switch (Test No. 2) – Ensure ignition is off. Disconnect shift selector control cable from MLP switch lever. Check continuity of MLP switch. Using ohmmeter, check continuity between MLP component connector terminals while moving MLP switch lever through each position. See MLP SWITCH CONTINUITY CHART. See Fig. MLP1. If switch passes all continuity checks, adjust control cable. See FORD 4F20E article. Connect all components and repeat QUICK TEST. If switch fails continuity checks, go to next step.

6) Check MLP Switch (Test No. 3) – Ensure ignition is off. Remove MLP switch from transaxle. Check continuity of MLP switch. Using ohmmeter, check continuity between MLP component connector terminals while moving MLP switch lever through each position. See MLP SWITCH CONTINUITY CHART. See Fig. MLP1. If switch passes all continuity checks, install and adjust MLP switch. See ON-VEHICLE SERVICE in FORD 4F20E article. Connect all components and repeat QUICK TEST. If switch fails continuity checks, replace MLP switch. Connect all components and repeat QUICK TEST.

PINPOINT TEST ODL

OVERDRIVE LIGHT (ODL)

94E38277 94F38278

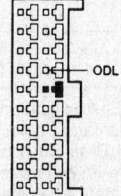

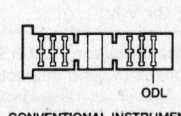

CONVENTIONAL INSTRUMENT
CLUSTER HARNESS CONNECTOR

ELECTRONIC INSTRUMENT
CLUSTER HARNESS CONNECTOR

Fig. ODL1: Identifying ODL Terminal Location

ODL CIRCUIT INFORMATION

Circuit	TCM Pin No.	[1] BOB Pin No.	Wire Color
ODL	3	17	Blu/Orn

[1] – Rotunda Breakout Box (007-00033)

1) Check ODL Operation – Ensure ignition is off. Disconnect TCM connector, and inspect it for damaged pins, corrosion and loose wires. Repair as necessary. Install Breakout Box (BOB) (007-00033), leaving TCM disconnected. Turn ignition on. Connect a jumper wire between BOB test pin No. 17 and ground. If ODL illuminates, go to PINPOINT TEST PGC. If ODL does not illuminate, go to next step.

2) Check ODL Bulb – Turn ignition off. Remove instrument cluster. Remove ODL bulb. Using ohmmeter, measure resistance between bulb terminals. If resistance is approximately 17 ohms, go to next step. If resistance is greater than 17 ohms, replace bulb. Connect all components and repeat QUICK TEST.

3) Check For Open ODL Circuit – Ensure ignition is off. Disconnect TCM connector, and inspect it for damaged pins, corrosion and loose wires. Repair as necessary. Install Breakout Box (BOB) (007-00033), leaving TCM disconnected. Disconnect instrument cluster harness connector. Using ohmmeter, check continuity between BOB test pin No. 17 and ODL terminal of instrument harness connector. See Fig. ODL1. If continuity does not exist, inspect and repair open circuit as needed. If continuity exists, go to next step.

4) Check For Shorted ODL Circuit – Continue with Breakout Box connected to TCM harness connector. Check continuity between BOB test pin No. 17 and ground. If continuity exists, inspect and repair short circuit as needed. If continuity does not exist, replace instrument cluster circuit board on analog cluster or entire instrument cluster for electronic type.

PINPOINT TEST ODS

OVERDRIVE ON/OFF SWITCH (ODS)

94B38282

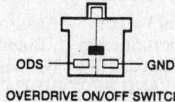

OVERDRIVE ON/OFF SWITCH
HARNESS CONNECTOR

Fig. ODS1: Identifying ODS Terminal Location

ODS CIRCUIT INFORMATION

Circuit	TCM Pin No.	[1] BOB Pin No.	Wire Color
ODS	39	18	Grn/Orn
GND	N/A	N/A	Blk

[1] – Rotunda Breakout Box (007-00033)

NOTE: Following diagnostic procedures utilize a Ford New Generation STAR (NGS) tester. If using other applicable scan tester, refer to manufacturers instruction manual for appropriate procedure.

PINPOINT TEST ODS (Cont.)

1) Check Overdrive On/Off Switch Signal – Ensure ignition is off. Connect NGS tester to DLC connector. Turn ignition on. Select DIAGNOSTIC DATA LINK. Select TCM - TRANSAXLE CTRL MODULE. Select PID/DATA MONITOR AND RECORD. Select ODS STS and OD ENA. Set the ODS to OFF position. Tester should display OFF when OD ENA is selected. O/D light on instrument cluster should be illuminated. Hold in ODS button. Tester should display ON when ODS STS is selected. O/D light on instrument cluster should be off. If tester display is correct for both ODS modes, return to QUICK TEST. If tester display does not match ODS operation, go to next step.

2) Check ODS Circuit – Ensure ignition is off. Disconnect TCM connector, and inspect it for damaged pins, corrosion and loose wires. Repair as necessary. Install Breakout Box (BOB) (007-00033), leaving TCM disconnected. Disconnect ODS harness connector. Check continuity between BOB test pin No. 18 and ODS harness connector terminal. See Fig. ODS1. If continuity exists, continue with step 2). If continuity does not exist, inspect and repair open circuit as needed.

Check continuity between BOB test pin No. 18 and ground. If continuity does not exist, go to next step. If continuity exists, inspect and repair short circuit as needed.

3) Check ODS – Ensure ignition is off. With ODS harness connector disconnected, check continuity between ODS component terminals. Continuity should exist only when button is depressed. If switch operates correctly, go to next step. Replace switch if faulty.

4) Check Ground – Ensure ignition is off. Check continuity between ODS harness connector ground terminal and vehicle ground. If continuity exists, replace TCM. Connect all components and repeat QUICK TEST. If continuity does not exist, inspect and repair open circuit as needed.

PINPOINT TEST PGC

POWER & GROUND CONNECTION (PGC)

PGC CIRCUIT INFORMATION

Circuit	TCM Pin No.	[1] BOB Pin No.	Wire Color
KAPWR	23	1	Pink
GND	15	39, 40, 46, 49 & 60	Blk
GND	48	20	Blk
SIGRTN	35	27	Wht/Blk

[1] – Rotunda Breakout Box (007-00033)

1) Check Voltage – Ensure ignition is off. Disconnect TCM connector, and inspect it for damaged pins, corrosion and loose wires. Repair as necessary. Install Breakout Box (BOB) (007-00033), leaving TCM disconnected. Turn ignition on. Measure voltage between BOB test pin No. 1 and ground. If voltage is greater than 10 volts, go to next step. If voltage is 10 volts or less, check 10 amp ELECTRON BAT fuse. Replace as needed. If fuse is okay or blows after replacement, inspect and repair KAPWR circuit. Connect all components and repeat QUICK TEST.

2) Check Ground Circuits – Check continuity between each BOB ground test pin and vehicle ground. If continuity exists, replace TCM. Connect all components and repeat QUICK TEST. If continuity does not exist, inspect and repair open ground circuit(s).

PINPOINT TEST PWRS

POWER E-AT SWITCH (PWRS)

94C38283

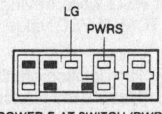

POWER E-AT SWITCH (PWRS)
HARNESS CONNECTOR

Fig. PWRS 1: Identifying PWRS Connector Terminals

PINPOINT TEST PWRS (Cont.)

PWRS CIRCUIT INFORMATION

Circuit	TCM Pin No.	¹ BOB Pin No.	Wire Color
PWRS	36	23	Red/Blk

¹ – Rotunda Breakout Box (007-00033)

NOTE: Following diagnostic procedures utilize a Ford New Generation STAR (NGS) tester. If using other applicable scan tester, refer to manufacturers instruction manual for appropriate procedure.

1) **Check Signal To TCM** – Ensure ignition is off. Connect NGS tester to DLC connector. Turn ignition on. Select DIAGNOSTIC DATA LINK. Select TCM - TRANSAXLE CTRL MODULE. Select PID/DATA MONITOR AND RECORD. Select PWR SW. Depress and release POWER E-AT switch. If tester display matches switch operation, return to QUICK TEST. If tester display does not match switch operation, go to next step.

2) **Check Power E-AT Switch Operation** – Turn ignition off. Disconnect PWRS harness connector. Check continuity between PWRS and Light Green (LG) wire terminals of component connector. If continuity exists only with switch in ON position, go to next step. Replace switch if faulty. Connect all components and repeat QUICK TEST,

3) **Check Voltage At POWER E-AT Switch** – Turn ignition on. Measure voltage between PWRS harness connector "LG" terminal and ground. If voltage is greater than 10 volts, go to next step. If voltage is 10 volts or less, inspect and repair circuit as needed.

4) **Check PWRS Circuit** – Ensure ignition is off. Disconnect TCM connector, and inspect it for damaged pins, corrosion and loose wires. Repair as necessary. Install Breakout Box (BOB) (007-00033), leaving TCM disconnected. Check continuity between BOB test pin No. 23 and PWRS terminal of PWRS harness connector. See Fig. PWRS1. If continuity exists, continue with step 4). If continuity does not exist, inspect and repair open circuit as needed.

Check continuity between BOB test pin No. 23 and ground. If continuity exists, inspect and repair short circuit as needed. If continuity does not exist, replace TCM. Connect all components and repeat QUICK TEST.

PINPOINT TEST PSG

PULSE SIGNAL GENERATOR (PSG)

94H38270

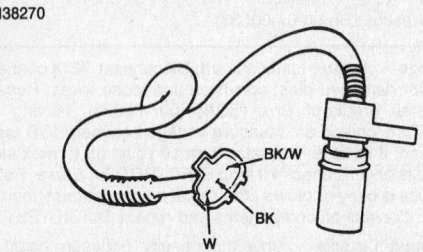

Fig. PSG1: Identifying PSG Connector Terminals

NOTE: Following diagnostic procedures utilize a Ford New Generation STAR (NGS) tester. If using other applicable scan tester, refer to manufacturers instruction manual for appropriate procedure.

1) **Check Transaxle Control Module Input Signal** – Ensure ignition is off. Connect NGS tester to DLC connector. See Fig. 1. Turn ignition on. Select DIAGNOSTIC DATA LINK. Select TCM - TRANSAXLE CTRL MODULE. Select PID/DATA MONITOR AND RECORD. Select PSG. Drive vehicle. Read value of PSG while driving. If PSG value changes with driving speed, replace TCM. If PSG value does not change, go to next step.

2) **Check PSG Resistance** – Turn ignition off. Disconnect PSG harness connector. Using ohmmeter, measure resistance between PSG connector terminals. See Fig. PSG1. See PSG CONTINUITY CHART. If resistance is within specification, go to next step. If continuity is not within specification, replace PSG.

PINPOINT TEST PSG (Cont.)

PSG CONTINUITY CHART

Terminal ID (Wire Color)	Ohms
PSG (Wht) & SIGRTN (Blk)	500-600
SIGRTN (Blk & Blk/Wht)	No Continuity
PSG (Wht & Blk/Wht)	No Continuity

3) **Check Signal Between TCM & PSG** – Ensure ignition is off. Disconnect TCM connector, and inspect it for damaged pins, corrosion and loose wires. Repair as necessary. Install Breakout Box (BOB) (007-00033), leaving TCM disconnected. Ensure PSG harness connector is disconnected. Using ohmmeter, check resistance between BOB test pin No. 56 and PSG harness connector White wire terminal. Measure check resistance between BOB test pin No. 27 and PSG harness connector Black wire terminal. If either resistance measured is 5 ohms or more, inspect and repair open circuit as needed. Check resistance between BOB test pins No. 27 and 56, and ground. If resistance is less than 10 K ohms, inspect and repair shorted circuit as needed. If all resistances checked are okay, replace TCM. Connect all components and repeat QUICK TEST.

PINPOINT TEST RPM

ENGINE RPM (RPM)

94A38273

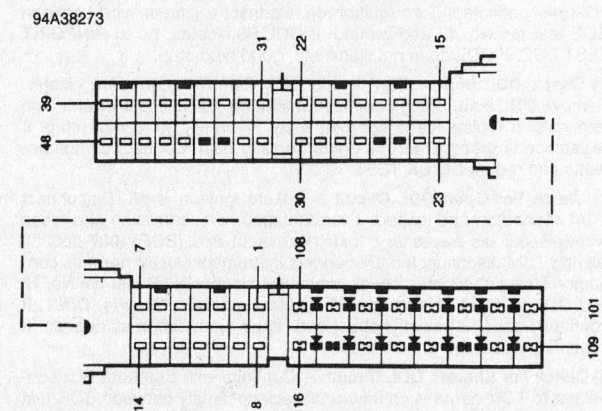

Fig. RPM1: Identifying PCM Harness Connector Terminals

NOTE: Following diagnostic procedures utilize a Ford New Generation STAR (NGS) tester. If using other applicable scan tester, refer to manufacturers instruction manual for appropriate procedure.

1) **Check EEC Pinpoint Test IGNS For PCM Control** – Perform EEC QUICK TEST (engine related trouble code retrieval). See SELF-DIAGNOSTICS – Villager article in ENGINE PERFORMANCE of appropriate MITCHELL® manual. If trouble code 21 is present, go to EEC PINPOINT TEST IGNS. If code 21 is not present, go to next step.

2) **Check Engine RPM Signal To TCM** – Ensure ignition is off. Connect NGS tester to DLC connector. See Fig. 1. Start and run engine. Select DIAGNOSTIC DATA LINK. Select TCM - TRANSAXLE CTRL MODULE. Select PID/DATA MONITOR AND RECORD. Select ENG RPM. Monitor engine RPM while depressing accelerator pedal. If RPM is reading is unaffected, replace TCM and repeat QUICK TEST. If engine RPM changes with accelerator pedal movement, go to next step.

3) **Check RPM Circuit** – Turn ignition off. Disconnect TCM connector, and inspect it for damaged pins, corrosion and loose wires. Repair as necessary. Install Breakout Box (BOB) (007-00033), leaving TCM disconnected. Disconnect PCM harness connector. Check continuity between BOB test pin No. 36 and PCM harness connector terminal No. 2. See Fig. RPM1. If continuity does not exist, inspect and repair open circuit as needed. Check continuity between BOB test pin No. 36 and ground. If continuity exists, inspect and repair short circuit as needed. If all circuits tested are okay, replace TCM. Connect all components and repeat QUICK TEST.

PINPOINT TEST SC

SPEED CONTROL (SC)

94D38284

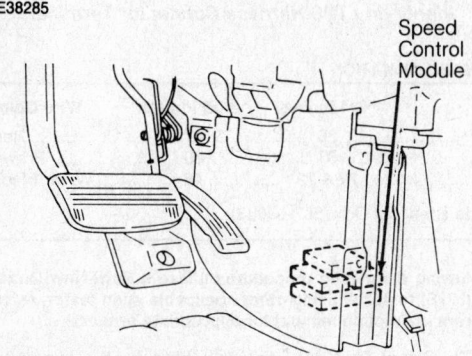

Fig. SC1: Identifying SC Module Connector Terminals

94E38285

Fig. SC2: Locating SC Module

SC CIRCUIT INFORMATION

Circuit	TCM Pin No.	[1] BOB Pin No.	Wire Color
SCI [2]	37	29	Red/Yel
SCODC [3]	40	19	Lt Grn/Red

[1] – Rotunda Breakout Box (007-00033)
[2] – Speed Control Indicator.
[3] – Speed Control OD Cut.

NOTE: Following diagnostic procedures utilize a Ford New Generation STAR (NGS) tester. If using other applicable scan tester, refer to manufacturers instruction manual for appropriate procedure.

1) Check Signal Between SC & TCM – Ensure ignition is off. Connect NGS tester to DLC connector. Start and run engine. Select DIAGNOSTIC DATA LINK. Select TCM - TRANSAXLE CTRL MODULE. Select PID/DATA MONITOR AND RECORD. Select SC STS and SCODC. Drive vehicle. Press CRUISE CONT. ON button to activate Speed Control (SC). Monitor tester display when setting cruise control and applying ACCEL switch. See NGS TESTER SPEED CONTROL DISPLAY CHART. If both speed control modes are correctly displayed on tester, return to QUICK TEST. If either mode is incorrectly displayed, go to next step.

NGS TESTER SPEED CONTROL DISPLAY CHART

Switch Position	NGS Display
SC CRUISE ON	SC STS ON
SC CRUISE OFF	SC STS OFF
ACCEL Released	[1] SCODC OFF
ACCEL Applied	SCODC OFF

[1] – SCODC is on only when vehicle speed cannot be maintained.

2) Check Signal Wire – Ensure ignition is off. Disconnect TCM connector, and inspect it for damaged pins, corrosion and loose wires. Repair as necessary. Install Breakout Box (BOB) (007-00033), leaving TCM disconnected. Disconnect SC module harness connector. See Fig. SC2. Check continuity between BOB test pins No. 19 and 29, and corresponding SC harness connector terminals. See Fig. SC1. If continuity exists, check cruise control system. If continuity does not exist, inspect and repair open circuit(s) as needed. Check continuity between BOB test pins No. 19 and 29, and ground. If continuity does not exist, check cruise control system. If continuity exists, inspect and repair short circuit(s) as needed.

PINPOINT TEST SCP

SOLENOID CONTROLLED BY POWER (SCP)

94B38274

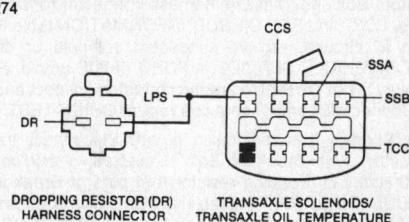

DROPPING RESISTOR (DR)
HARNESS CONNECTOR

TRANSAXLE SOLENOIDS/
TRANSAXLE OIL TEMPERATURE
HARNESS CONNECTOR

Fig. SCP1: Identifying SCP Connector Terminals

94C38275

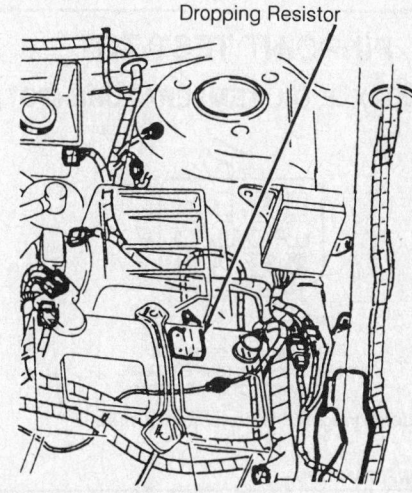

Dropping Resistor

Fig. SCP2: Locating Dropping Resistor

SCP CIRCUIT INFORMATION

Circuit	TCM Pin No.	[1] BOB Pin No.	Wire Color
SSA [2]	6	41	Orn/Blk
SSB [3]	7	21	Yel/Grn
CCS [4]	8	54	Yel/Pnk
TCC [5]	5	52	Orn/Blu
LPS [6]	1	33	Grn/Red
DR [7]	2	38	Yel

[1] – Rotunda Breakout Box (007-00033)
[2] – Shift Solenoid "A", trouble code 04.
[3] – Shift Solenoid "B", trouble code 05.
[4] – Coasting Clutch Solenoid, trouble code 06.
[5] – Torque Converter Clutch Solenoid, trouble code 07.
[6] – Line Pressure Solenoid, trouble code 10.
[7] – Dropping Resistor, no trouble code.

1) Perform Solenoid Click Tests – Ensure ignition is off. Disconnect TCM connector, and inspect it for damaged pins, corrosion and loose wires. Repair as necessary. Install Breakout Box (BOB) (007-00033), leaving TCM disconnected. Apply battery voltage to BOB test pins No. 33 and ground, and No. 52 and ground only. Listen for solenoid clicking sound. If clicking sound is heard, replace TCM. Connect all components and repeat QUICK TEST. If no clicking sound is heard from either solenoid, go to next step.

2) Check Solenoid Or Dropping Resistor Resistance At TCM – With Breakout Box installed, measure resistance between each solenoid test pin and ground. Ensure ignition is off. Measure resistance between DR test pin and ground. Resistance for SSA, SSB and CCS should be 26-30 ohms. Resistance for TCC should be 14-16 ohms. Resistance for LPS should be 2.5-5.0 ohms. Resistance for DR should be 16-17 ohms. If all resistances measured are within specification, go to step 4). If any resistance measured is not within specification, go to next step.

PINPOINT TEST SCP (Cont.)

3) Check Continuity – Ensure ignition is off. Disconnect transaxle harness connector. With Breakout Box connected, measure resistance between Breakout Box and transaxle harness connector for each component. *See Fig. SCP1* and SCP CIRCUIT INFORMATION table. If continuity exists in all circuits, replace suspected solenoid or dropping resistor. See ON-VEHICLE SERVICE in FORD 4F20E article. *See Fig. SCP2.* If continuity is not present in any circuit tested, inspect and repair faulty circuit. Connect all components and repeat QUICK TEST.

4) Check For Short – Ensure ignition is off. Disconnect transaxle harness connector. With Breakout Box connected, check continuity between any 2 solenoid/dropping resistor test pins of Breakout Box. See SCP CIRCUIT INFORMATION table. If continuity does not exist, replace TCM. Connect all components and repeat QUICK TEST. If continuity exists between any component test pins, inspect and repair circuit(s) as needed.

PINPOINT TEST TOT

TRANSAXLE OIL TEMPERATURE (TOT)

94D38276

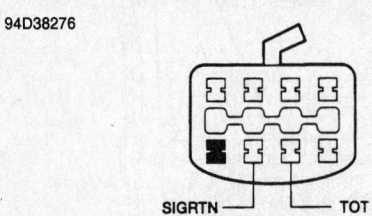

SIGRTN — TOT

TRANSAXLE SOLENOIDS/
TRANSAXLE OIL TEMPERATURE
HARNESS CONNECTOR

Fig. TOT1: Identifying TOT Connector Terminals

TOT CIRCUIT INFORMATION

Circuit	TCM Pin No.	¹ BOB Pin No.	Wire Color
TOT	33	7	Light Blue
SIGRTN	35	27	White/Black

¹ – Rotunda Breakout Box (007-00033)

NOTE: Following diagnostic procedures utilize a Ford New Generation STAR (NGS) tester. If using other applicable scan tester, refer to manufacturers instruction manual for appropriate procedure.

1) Check TCM Signal – Ensure ignition is off. Connect NGS tester to DLC connector. *See Fig. 1.* Start and run engine. Select DIAGNOSTIC DATA LINK. Select TCM - TRANSAXLE CTRL MODULE. Select PID/DATA MONITOR AND RECORD. Select TOT. Monitor transaxle oil temperature. Voltage should decrease from 1.5 volts (68° F) to .5 volts (186° F). If voltage decreases within specification, replace TCM. Repeat QUICK TEST. If voltage does not decrease, go to next step.

2) Check TOT Sensor – Continue to run engine until normal operating temperature is obtained. Turn ignition off. Disconnect transaxle harness connector. Measure resistance between TOT terminal and SIGRTN terminal of transaxle connector. *See Fig. TOT1.* Resistance should increase from 300 ohms (176° F) to 1125 ohms (68° F) as temperature decreases. If resistance measured is within specification, go to next step. If resistance is not within specification, replace TOT sensor. See ON-VEHICLE SERVICE in FORD 4F20E article. Connect all components and repeat QUICK TEST.

3) Check Continuity Between TCM & Transaxle Solenoids/TOT Connector – Ensure ignition is off. Disconnect TCM connector, and inspect it for damaged pins, corrosion and loose wires. Repair as necessary. Install Breakout Box (BOB) (007-00033), leaving TCM disconnected. With transaxle harness connector disconnected, check continuity between BOB test pin No. 7 and ground. If continuity exists, inspect and repair short as needed. Check continuity between transaxle harness connector TOT terminal and BOB test pin No. 7. *See Fig. TOT1.* Check continuity between transaxle harness connector SIGRTN terminal and BOB test pin No. 27. If continuity exists in both circuits and no short to ground is present in test pin No. 7 circuit, replace TCM. Connect all components and repeat QUICK TEST. If continuity of either TOT or SIGRTN circuit does not exist, inspect and repair open circuit as needed.

PINPOINT TEST TPS

THROTTLE POSITION SENSOR (TPS)

93F76534

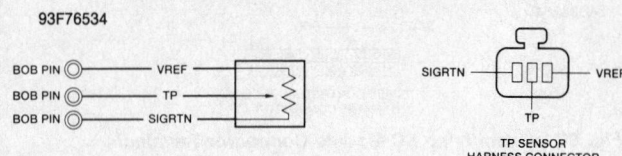

Fig. TPS1: Identifying TPS Harness Connector Terminals

TPS CIRCUIT INFORMATION

Circuit	PCM Pin No.	¹ BOB Pin No.	Wire Color
TP	20	47	Red
VREF	37	26	Brown
SIGRTN	21 & 29	46	White/Black

¹ – Rotunda Breakout Box (007-00033)

NOTE: Following diagnostic procedures utilize a Ford New Generation STAR (NGS) tester. If using other applicable scan tester, refer to manufacturers instruction manual for appropriate procedure.

1) Check TPS Signal To PCM – Ensure ignition is off. Connect NGS tester to DLC connector. Turn ignition on. Select DIAGNOSTIC DATA LINK. Select PCM - POWERTRAIN CTRL MODULE. Select WORK SUPPORT. Select THROTTLE SENSOR ADJUST. Monitor TPS voltage while gradually depressing accelerator pedal. Voltage should increase smoothly from .4 volt at zero throttle opening to 4.1 volts at WOT. If voltage increase is within specification, replace PCM. If voltage increase is erratic or not within specification, go to next step.

2) Check VREF Signal – Turn ignition off. Disconnect TPS harness connector. Turn ignition on. Measure voltage between TPS harness connector VREF terminal and ground. If voltage is 4-5 volts, go to next step. If voltage is not within specification, go to PINPOINT TEST VREF.

3) Check TPS – Turn ignition off. Using ohmmeter, measure resistance between TPS component connector terminals SIGRTN and TP. *See Fig. TPS1.* Resistance should be within specification at following positions:
- Closed throttle: 1 k/ohms.
- 1/2 open throttle: 1-10 k/ohms.
- Fully open throttle: approximately 10 k/ohms.

If resistance measured is within specification, go to next step. Replace TPS, if resistance is not within specification. Connect all components and repeat QUICK TEST.

4) Check TP & SIGRTN Circuits – Ensure ignition is off. Disconnect PCM connector, and inspect it for damaged pins, corrosion and loose wires. Repair as necessary. Install Breakout Box (007-00033), leaving PCM disconnected. Using ohmmeter, measure and record resistance between BOB test pin No. 46 and TPS harness connector SIGRTN terminal. *See Fig. TPS1.* Measure and record resistance between BOB test pin No. 47 and TPS harness connector TP terminal. If resistances measured are more than 5 ohms, inspect and repair open circuits as needed. Check continuity between BOB test pin No. 47 and ground. If continuity exists, inspect and repair short circuit. If resistance and continuity checks are okay, replace PCM. Connect all components and repeat QUICK TEST.

PINPOINT TEST VSS

VEHICLE SPEED SENSOR (VSS)

94I38271 94J38272

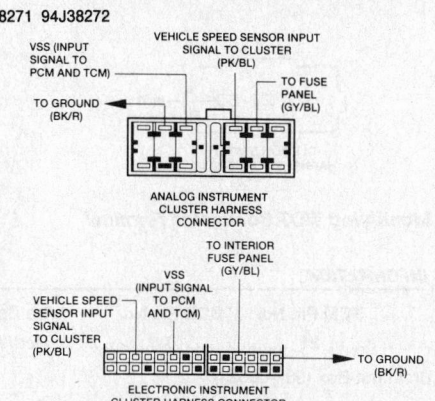

Fig. VSS1: Identifying VSS Harness Connector Terminals

NOTE: Following diagnostic procedures utilize a Ford New Generation STAR (NGS) tester. If using other applicable scan tester, refer to manufacturers instruction manual for appropriate procedure.

1) Check VSS Input Signal To TCM – Ensure ignition off. Connect NGS tester to DLC connector. Turn ignition on. Select DIAGNOSTIC DATA LINK. Select TCM - TRANSAXLE CTRL MODULE. Select PID/DATA MONITOR AND RECORD. Select VSS. Drive vehicle. Read value of VSS while driving. If VSS value is above zero and matches speedometer, replace TCM. Connect all components and repeat QUICK TEST. If VSS value does not change or match speedometer, go to next step.

2) Check Power To Instrument Cluster – Turn ignition off. Remove instrument cluster. Disconnect instrument cluster connector. Turn ignition on. Measure voltage between instrument cluster harness connector Gray/Blue wire terminal and ground. *See Fig. VSS1.* If voltage is less than 10 volts, inspect and repair circuit between fuse panel and instrument cluster. If voltage is 10 volts is greater, go to next step.

3) Check Ground Circuit – Turn ignition off. Using ohmmeter, check continuity between instrument cluster harness connector Black/Red wire terminal and ground. If continuity exists, go to next step. If continuity does not exist, inspect and repair circuit as needed.

4) Check VSS Signal To Instrument Cluster – Ensure ignition is off. Disconnect VSS harness connector. Connect jumper wire between VSS harness connector Pink/Blue wire and ground. Check continuity between instrument cluster harness connector Pink/Blue wire and ground. If continuity does not exist, inspect and repair circuit as needed. Connect jumper wire between VSS harness connector Black/Red wire and ground. Check continuity between instrument cluster harness connector Black/Red wire and ground. If continuity does not exist, inspect and repair circuit as needed. Disconnect jumper wire. Check continuity between instrument cluster harness connector Pink/Blue wire and ground. If continuity exists, inspect and repair shorted circuit as needed. If circuits test okay, go to next step.

5) Check Vehicle Speed Sensor – Ensure ignition is off. Remove VSS. See ON-VEHICLE SERVICE in FORD 4F20E article. Connect voltmeter (A/C range) leads to VSS component terminals. Turn VSS driven gear and monitor output. If voltage is approximately .5 volt, go to next step. If voltage is not within specification, replace VSS. Connect all components and repeat QUICK TEST.

6) Check VSS Wire Between TCM & Instrument Cluster – Ensure ignition is off. Disconnect TCM connector, and inspect it for damaged pins, corrosion and loose wires. Repair as necessary. Install Breakout Box (007-00033), leaving TCM disconnected. Using ohmmeter, check continuity between BOB test pin No. 3 and VSS harness connector Pink/Blue wire. If continuity does not exist, inspect and repair open circuit as needed. Check continuity between BOB test pin No. 3 and ground. If continuity exists, inspect and repair shorted circuit as needed. If circuits pass testing, replace TCM. Connect all components and repeat QUICK TEST.

PINPOINT TEST VREF

POWER E-AT SWITCH (VREF)

94F38286

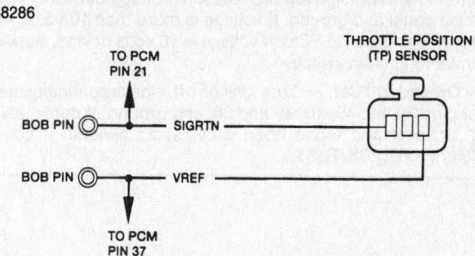

Fig. VREF1: Identifying VREF Connector Terminals

VREF CIRCUIT INFORMATION

Circuit	TCM Pin No.	¹ BOB Pin No.	Wire Color
VREF	31	26	Brn
SIGRTN	35	27	Wht/Blk

¹ – Rotunda Breakout Box (007-00033)

NOTE: Following diagnostic procedures utilize a Ford New Generation STAR (NGS) tester. If using other applicable scan tester, refer to manufacturers instruction manual for appropriate procedure.

1) Check Voltage At TCM – Ensure ignition is off. Disconnect TCM connector, and inspect it for damaged pins, corrosion and loose wires. Repair as necessary. Install Breakout Box (007-00033), leaving TCM disconnected. Turn ignition on. Measure voltage between BOB test pins No. 26 and 27. If voltage is 4.5-5.5, return to QUICK TEST. If voltage is not within specification, go to next step.

2) Check Signal From PCM – Turn ignition off. Disconnect PCM harness connector. Check continuity between BOB test pin No. 26 and PCM harness connector terminal No. 37. *See Fig. RPM1.* If continuity does not exist, inspect and repair circuit as needed. If continuity does exist, check power and ground circuits at PCM. See SELF-DIAGNOSTICS – Villager article in ENGINE PERFORMANCE of appropriate MITCHELL® manual. Check continuity between BOB test pin No. 26 and ground. If continuity exists, inspect and short repair circuit as needed. If continuity does not exist, check power and ground circuits at PCM. See SELF-DIAGNOSTICS – Villager article in ENGINE PERFORMANCE of appropriate MITCHELL® manual. If power and ground circuits are okay, replace PCM.

PINPOINT TEST VPWR

VEHICLE POWER (VPWR)

VPWR CIRCUIT INFORMATION

Circuit	TCM Pin No.	¹ BOB Pin No.	Wire Color
VPWR	4	57	Lt. Grn
VPWR	9	37	Lt. Grn
GND	15	39, 40, 46, 49 & 60	Blk
GND	48	20	Blk

¹ – Rotunda Breakout Box (007-00033)

NOTE: Following diagnostic procedures utilize a Ford New Generation STAR (NGS) tester. If using other applicable scan tester, refer to manufacturers instruction manual for appropriate procedure.

1) Check VPWR To TCM – Ensure ignition is off. Disconnect TCM connector, and inspect it for damaged pins, corrosion and loose wires. Repair as necessary. Install Breakout Box (007-00033), leaving TCM disconnected. Turn ignition on. Measure voltage between BOB test pins No. 4 and 9, and ground. If voltage is more than 10 volts, go to step **3)**. If voltage is 10 volts or less, check IGN 10 amp fuse, then proceed to next step.

PINPOINT TEST VPWR (Cont.)

2) Check Voltage At Interior Fuse Panel – Turn ignition off. Remove IGN 10 amp fuse. Turn ignition on. Measure voltage between VPWR at interior fuse panel and ground. If voltage is more than 10 volts, inspect and repair VPWR circuit to TCM. If voltage is 10 volts or less, inspect and repair circuit to ignition switch.

3) Check Ground At TCM. – Turn ignition off. Check continuity between BOB test pins 20, 39, 40, 46, 49 and 60, and ground. If continuity does not exist, inspect and repair open circuit(s) as needed. If continuity exists, return to QUICK TEST.

PINPOINT TEST WOT

POWER E-AT SWITCH (WOT)

94G38287

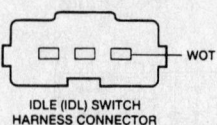

IDLE (IDL) SWITCH
HARNESS CONNECTOR

Fig. WOT1: Identifying WOT Connector Terminal

WOT CIRCUIT INFORMATION

Circuit	TCM Pin No.	¹ BOB Pin No.	Wire Color
WOT	21	10	Red/Wht

¹ – Rotunda Breakout Box (007-00033)

NOTE: Following diagnostic procedures utilize a Ford New Generation STAR (NGS) tester. If using other applicable scan tester, refer to manufacturers instruction manual for appropriate procedure.

1) Check WOT SWITCH Signal – Ensure ignition off. Connect NGS tester to DLC connector. Turn ignition on. Select DIAGNOSTIC DATA LINK. Select TCM - TRANSAXLE CTRL MODULE. Select PID/DATA MONITOR AND RECORD. Select WOT SW and TPOD (throttle position opening data). Read WOT SW signal while fully depressing accelerator pedal. Tester should display WOT SW ON at 1/2 throttle. If switch is operating correctly, return to QUICK TEST. If switch is not functioning correctly, go to next step.

2) Check WOT Switch Operation – Turn ignition off. Disconnect IDL switch connector (TPS harness connector). Check continuity between WOT and IDL terminal of component connector. There should be continuity only when throttle is depressed. If switch if functioning correctly, go to next step. Replace TPS, if it fails testing.

3) Check Continuity – Ensure ignition is off. Disconnect TCM connector, and inspect it for damaged pins, corrosion and loose wires. Repair as necessary. Install Breakout Box (007-00033), leaving TCM disconnected. Check continuity between BOB test pin No. 10 and WOT terminal of TPS harness connector. If continuity exists, continue with step **3)**. If continuity does not exist, inspect and repair open circuit as needed.

Check continuity between BOB test pin No. 10 and ground. If continuity exists, inspect and repair short circuit as needed. If continuity does not exist, replace TCM. Connect all components and repeat QUICK TEST.

WIRING DIAGRAMS

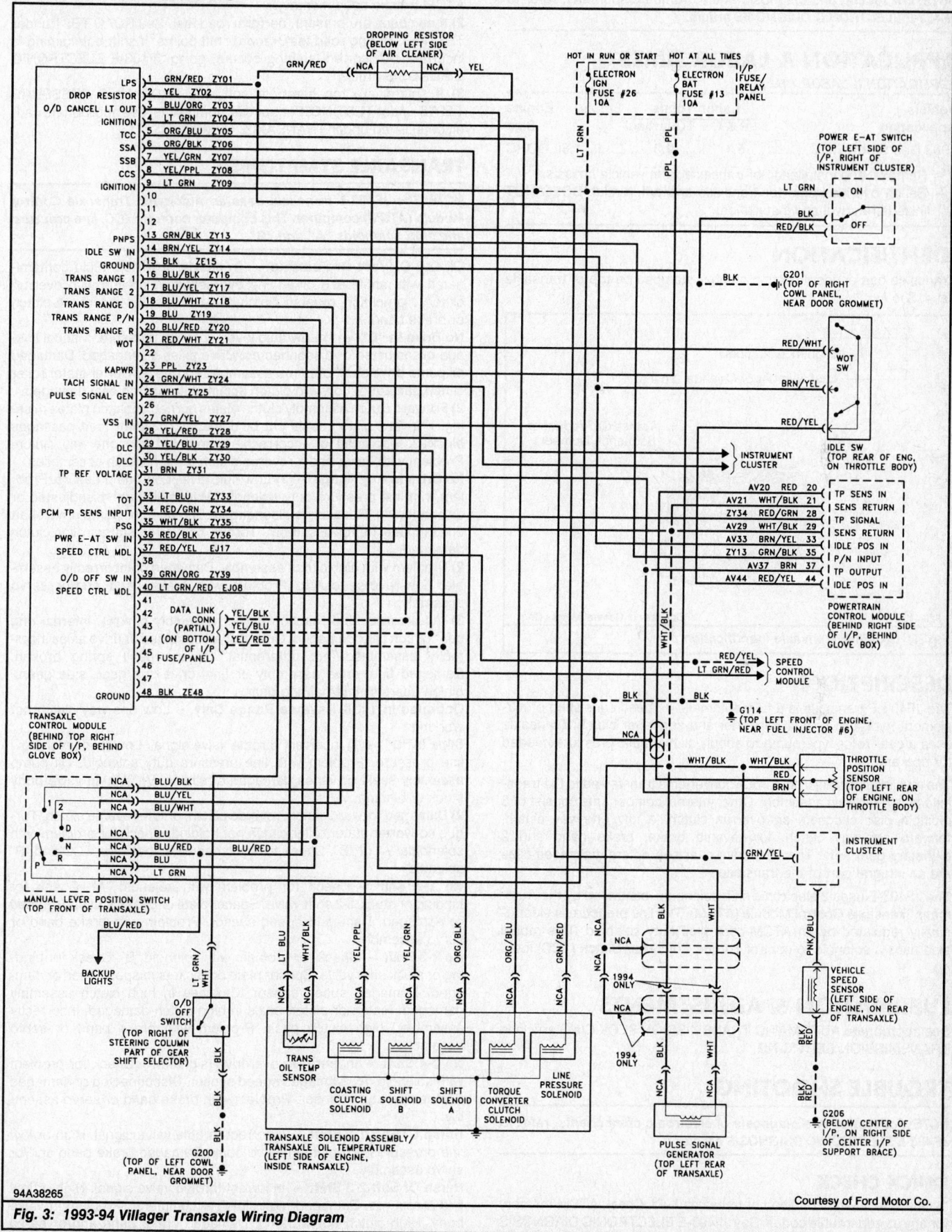

94A38265

Courtesy of Ford Motor Co.

Fig. 3: 1993-94 Villager Transaxle Wiring Diagram

NOTE: For testing and diagnosis of electronic components, refer to JF403-E ELECTRONIC DIAGNOSIS article.

APPLICATION & LABOR TIMES

APPLICATION & LABOR TIMES

Vehicle Application	Labor Times		Engine Size
	[1] R & I	[2] Overhaul	
1993 Geo Storm	5.1	9.9	1.8L DOHC

[1] – Removal and installation of transaxle from vehicle chassis.
[2] – Bench overhaul time for transaxle and differential. DOES NOT include removal and installation.

IDENTIFICATION

Transaxle has an identification number stamped on top of transaxle case. *See Fig. 1.*

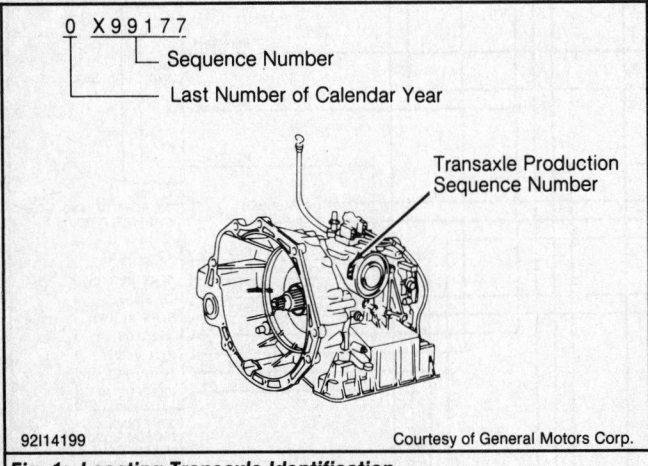

92I14199   Courtesy of General Motors Corp.

Fig. 1: Locating Transaxle Identification

DESCRIPTION

The JF403-E transaxle is a fully automatic 4-speed consisting of a 3-element hydraulic torque converter and converter clutch. Transaxle uses a gear rotor-type pump to supply all hydraulic pressure needed for operation.

The multiplied torque from torque converter is transferred to the transaxle by a gear train assembly. Other internal components consist of 3 multiple disc clutches, an overrun clutch, a low one-way clutch, forward one-way clutch, low-reverse brake, brake band and 2 planetary gear sets. The final drive gear and differential assemblies are an integral part of the transaxle.

The JF403-E uses 2 electronic shift solenoids, controlled by the Automatic Transaxle Control Module (ATCM). The line pressure is electronically regulated by an ATCM-controlled duty solenoid. This model also uses a solenoid to control Torque Converter Clutch (TCC) lock-up.

LUBRICATION & ADJUSTMENTS

See appropriate AUTOMATIC TRANSMISSION SERVICING article in TRANSMISSION SERVICING.

TROUBLE SHOOTING

NOTE: For testing and diagnosis of electronic components, refer to JF403-E ELECTRONIC DIAGNOSIS article.

QUICK CHECK

1) Check level and condition of transaxle fluid. Check ATCM memory for any stored trouble codes. See JF403-E ELECTRONIC DIAGNOSIS article. If no trouble codes are present, go to next step. If codes are present, diagnose and repair all ATCM-related trouble codes. Clear ATCM trouble code memory.

2) If no codes are present, perform road test. See ROAD TEST under TESTING. During road test, record shift points. If shift point timing is incorrect or incorrect shifting occurs, go to JF403-E ELECTRONIC DIAGNOSIS article.

3) If shift(s) are too harsh or soft, see HYDRAULIC PRESSURE TESTS under TESTING. For specific complaints, see appropriate condition(s) listed under TRANSAXLE SYMPTOMS.

TRANSAXLE SYMPTOMS

NOTE: The JF403-E transaxle uses an Automatic Transaxle Control Module (ATCM) computer. This computer controls TCC, line pressure and shift solenoids "A" and "B".

Oil Out Of Vent Or Foaming – Transaxle overfilled. Fluid contaminated with antifreeze or engine overheating. Problem with overrun clutch, high clutch, reverse clutch, low-reverse clutch forward clutch or brake band.

No Drive In "D" – **1)** Low fluid level. Low line pressure. Manual linkage misadjusted or disconnected. Drive axles disengaged. Damaged oil pump drive shaft or pump assembly. Torque converter stator roller clutch damaged. Forward clutch accumulator piston seal damaged.
2) Forward clutch assembly clutch plates burned or clutch plates missing. Forward piston seals cut or damaged, or shaft feed passages blocked. Damaged or incorrectly assembled low one-way clutch. Problem with valve body, reverse clutch or high clutch assemblies.

No Drive In Any Range – **1)** Low fluid level. Low line pressure. Problem with line pressure duty solenoid. Manual linkage misadjusted or disconnected. Drive axles disengaged. Damaged oil pump drive shaft or complete pump assembly. Torque converter stator roller clutch damaged.
2) Problem with high clutch assembly. Damaged or incorrectly assembled low-reverse clutch. Problem with brake band and/or servo assembly.
3) Input carrier and reaction carrier assembly pinions, internal ring gear or sun gear damaged. Output shaft damaged or drive axles incorrectly assembled into differential. Parking pawl spring broken. Damaged final drive assembly or final drive sun gear, side gears, pinion gears or internal ring gear.

Operates In 1st & Reverse Range Only – Low one-way clutch not working.

Slips in "D" – **1)** Incorrect throttle valve signal. Low fluid level. Low line pressure. Problem with line pressure duty solenoid. Oil pump assembly seals or vanes damaged or sliding. Valve(s) in valve body stuck or binding.
2) Damaged forward clutch, reverse clutch, or low-reverse clutch. Torque converter stator roller clutch not holding. Check for problem with solenoids "A" or "B". Check for switched wires between TCC and "B" solenoid.

No 1-2 Shift – Check for problem with solenoid "A". Check for binding or stuck 1-2 shift valve. Spacer plate or gaskets mispositioned or damaged. Damaged speed sensor. Problem with brake band or servo assembly.

No 2-3 Shift – Check for problem with solenoid "B". Check for binding or stuck shift valve. Spacer plate or gaskets mispositioned or damaged. Damaged speed sensor. Clutches in high clutch assembly damaged. Piston or piston seals in high clutch damaged. Incorrectly assembled high clutch pack. Problem with brake band or servo assembly.

No 3-4 Shift – Inoperative overdrive (signal off). Check for problem with solenoid "A". Damaged speed sensor. Disconnected or damaged fluid temperature sensor. Problem with brake band or servo assembly.

Harsh Or Soft 1-2 Shift – Incorrect throttle valve signal. High or low line pressures. Problem in valve body. Damaged brake band and/or servo assembly.

Harsh Or Soft 2-3 Shift – Incorrect throttle valve signal. High or low line pressures. Damaged high clutch accumulator. Problem in valve body. High clutch not working. Damaged brake band and/or servo assembly.

Harsh Or Soft 3-4 Shift – Incorrect throttle valve signal. High or low line pressures. Problem in valve body. Damaged brake band and/or servo assembly. Overrun clutch not working.

1-3 Shift – Damaged brake band and/or servo assembly.

1-2 Upshift Slip – High or low line pressures. Problem in valve body. Damaged brake band and/or servo assembly.

2-3 Upshift Slip – Incorrect throttle valve signal. High or low line pressures. Damaged high clutch accumulator. Problem in valve body. High clutch not working. Damaged brake band and/or servo assembly.

3-4 Upshift Slip – Incorrect throttle valve signal. High or low line pressures. Damaged high clutch accumulator. Problem in valve body. High clutch not working. Damaged brake band and/or servo assembly.

Late 1-2 Or 2-3 Shift – Incorrect throttle valve signal. Damaged speed sensor. Shift solenoid "A" or "B" not working.

No Reverse – **1)** Low fluid level. Low line pressure. Damaged line pressure duty solenoid. Manual linkage misadjusted or disconnected. Problem in valve body. Reverse clutch damaged.

2) Forward clutch assembly clutch plates burned or missing. Forward piston seals cut or damaged, or shaft feed passages blocked. Damaged or incorrectly assembled high clutch. Problem with overrun clutch or low-reverse clutch assemblies.

Binds In "R" – Incorrect line pressure. Damaged line pressure duty solenoid. Manual linkage misadjusted or disconnected. Problem in valve body. Problem with brake band and/or servo assembly. High clutch assembly clutch plates locked. Damaged or incorrectly assembled forward clutch. Problem with overrun clutch assembly.

Vehicle Moves In Park – Manual linkage damaged or disconnected. Broken final drive park pawl spring, park pawl or park pawl gear in final drive internal gear assembly. Park actuator spring damaged.

Vehicle Moves In Neutral – Problem with forward clutch, overrun clutch or reverse clutch being applied.

Harsh Engagement Neutral To Drive – Engine idle too high. Incorrect throttle valve signal. Incorrect line pressure. Transmission temperature sensor not working. Damaged line pressure duty solenoid. Problem in valve body. Problem with vehicle speed sensor or engine speed sensor. Loss of forward clutch accumulator pressure. Forward clutch applied at wrong time.

No Engine Breaking In Manual 1st – Incorrect throttle valve signal. Shift solenoid "A" not working. Problem in valve body. Overrun clutch or low-reverse clutch assemblies not working.

No Kickdown Shift From "D4" – Incorrect throttle valve signal. Vehicle speed sensor damaged. Shift solenoid "A" or "B" not working.

Unwanted Kickdown Shift Occurs From "D4" – Incorrect throttle valve signal. Vehicle speed sensor damaged. Shift solenoid "A" or "B" not working.

No 4-3 Downshift – Incorrect throttle valve signal. Shift solenoid "A" not working. Problem in valve body.

No Manual Selected 2nd Gear Kickdown (Stays in 3rd Gear) – Incorrect throttle valve signal. Overrun clutch solenoid not working. Shift solenoid "A" or "B" not working. Problem in valve body. Problem with overrun clutch or brake band assemblies.

No 4-2 Or 3-2 Downshift – Incorrect throttle valve signal. Shift solenoid "A" or "B" not working. Problem in valve body. Problem with high clutch or brake band assemblies.

No 3-1 Or 2-1 Downshift – Incorrect throttle valve signal. Overdrive off signal not working. Shift solenoid "A" or "B" not working. Problem in valve body. Problem with one-way clutch, high clutch or brake band assemblies.

No 2-1 Downshift In 1st Range – Vehicle speed sensor damaged. Shift solenoid "A" not working. Problem in valve body. Damaged overrun clutch or low-reverse clutch assemblies.

Harsh Downshifts On Downhill Deceleration – Incorrect throttle valve signal. Incorrect line pressure. Problem in valve body. Problem with overrun clutch assembly.

Downshift Shift Speeds Too High – Incorrect throttle valve signal. Vehicle speed sensor damaged. Economy mode switch not working.

Harsh 4-3 Downshift – Incorrect throttle valve signal. Incorrect line pressure. Damaged line pressure duty solenoid. Problem in valve body. Damaged high clutch or forward clutch assemblies.

Harsh 4-2 Downshift – Incorrect throttle valve signal. Incorrect line pressure. Damaged line pressure duty solenoid. Shift solenoid "A" not working. Problem in valve body. Damaged brake band, band servo or forward clutch assemblies.

Harsh 4-1 Or 3-1 Downshift – Incorrect throttle valve signal. Incorrect line pressure. Damaged line pressure duty solenoid. Problem in valve body. Damaged brake band, band servo or forward clutch assemblies. Damaged overrun clutch, high clutch or high clutch accumulator assemblies.

Harsh 3-2 Downshift – Incorrect throttle valve signal. Incorrect line pressure. Damaged line pressure duty solenoid. Problem in valve body. Damaged brake band, band servo or forward clutch assemblies. Damaged overrun clutch, high clutch or high clutch accumulator assemblies.

Harsh 4-1 Or 3-1 Downshift – Incorrect throttle valve signal. Incorrect line pressure. Damaged line pressure duty solenoid. Problem in valve body. Damaged forward one-way clutch or forward clutch assemblies. Damaged low one-way clutch assembly.

Harsh 2-1 Downshift – Problem in valve body. Low-reverse clutch not working.

NOTE: *The JF403-E transaxle uses an Automatic Transaxle Control Module (ATCM) computer. This computer controls TCC application.*

No TCC – Incorrect throttle valve signal. Vehicle speed sensor damaged. Engine speed sensor damaged. Automatic transaxle temperature switch damaged. Problem in valve body. Incorrect line pressure. Damaged TCC solenoid. Oil pump damaged.

Engine Stops – Damaged TCC solenoid. Problem in valve body.

Converter Clutch Apply Rough, Slips or Shudders – Incorrect throttle valve signal. Problem in valve body. Incorrect line pressure. Damaged TCC solenoid. Damaged line pressure duty solenoid. Defective converter clutch.

Incorrect Converter Clutch Lock-Up Speed – Incorrect throttle valve signal. Problem in valve body. Vehicle speed sensor damaged. TCC solenoid not working.

CLUTCH & BAND APPLICATION CHART

Selector Lever Position	Elements In Use
"D4" (Drive)	
First Gear	Forward Clutch, [1] Overrun Clutch, [2] Forward One-Way Clutch & [2] Low One-Way Clutch
Second Gear	Forward Clutch, [1] Overrun Clutch, Brake Band & [2] Forward One-Way Clutch
Third Gear	High Clutch, Forward Clutch, [1] Overrun Clutch, [3] Brake Band, [2] Forward One-Way Clutch
Fourth Gear	High Clutch, [3] Forward Clutch & Brake Band
"3" (Manual Third)	
First Gear	Forward Clutch, [4] Overrun Clutch, [2] Forward One-Way Clutch & [2] Low One-Way Clutch
Second Gear	Forward Clutch, [4] Overrun Clutch, Brake Band & [2] Forward One-Way Clutch
Third Gear	High Clutch, Forward Clutch, [4] Overrun Clutch, [3] Brake Band, [2] Forward One-Way Clutch
Fourth Gear [5]	High Clutch, [3] Forward Clutch & Brake Band
"2" (Manual Second)	
First Gear	Forward Clutch, [4] Overrun Clutch, [2] Forward One-Way Clutch & [2] Low One-Way Clutch
Second Gear	Forward Clutch, [4] Overrun Clutch, Brake Band & [2] Forward One-Way Clutch
Third Gear [5]	High Clutch, Forward Clutch, [4] Overrun Clutch, [3] Brake Band, [2] Forward One-Way Clutch
"1" (Manual Low)	
First Gear	Forward Clutch, Overrun Clutch, [2] Forward One-Way Clutch & Low-Reverse Brake
Second Gear [5]	Forward Clutch, Overrun Clutch, Brake Band & [2] Forward One-Way Clutch
"R" (Reverse)	Reverse Clutch & Low-Reverse Brake
"N" or "P" (Neutral or Park)	All Clutches & Bands Released or Ineffective

[1] – On during cruise and when OD off signal is present.
[2] – On during acceleration.
[3] – Applied but not effective.
[4] – Applied. Also engine braking effect during closed throttle.
[5] – Forced upshift.

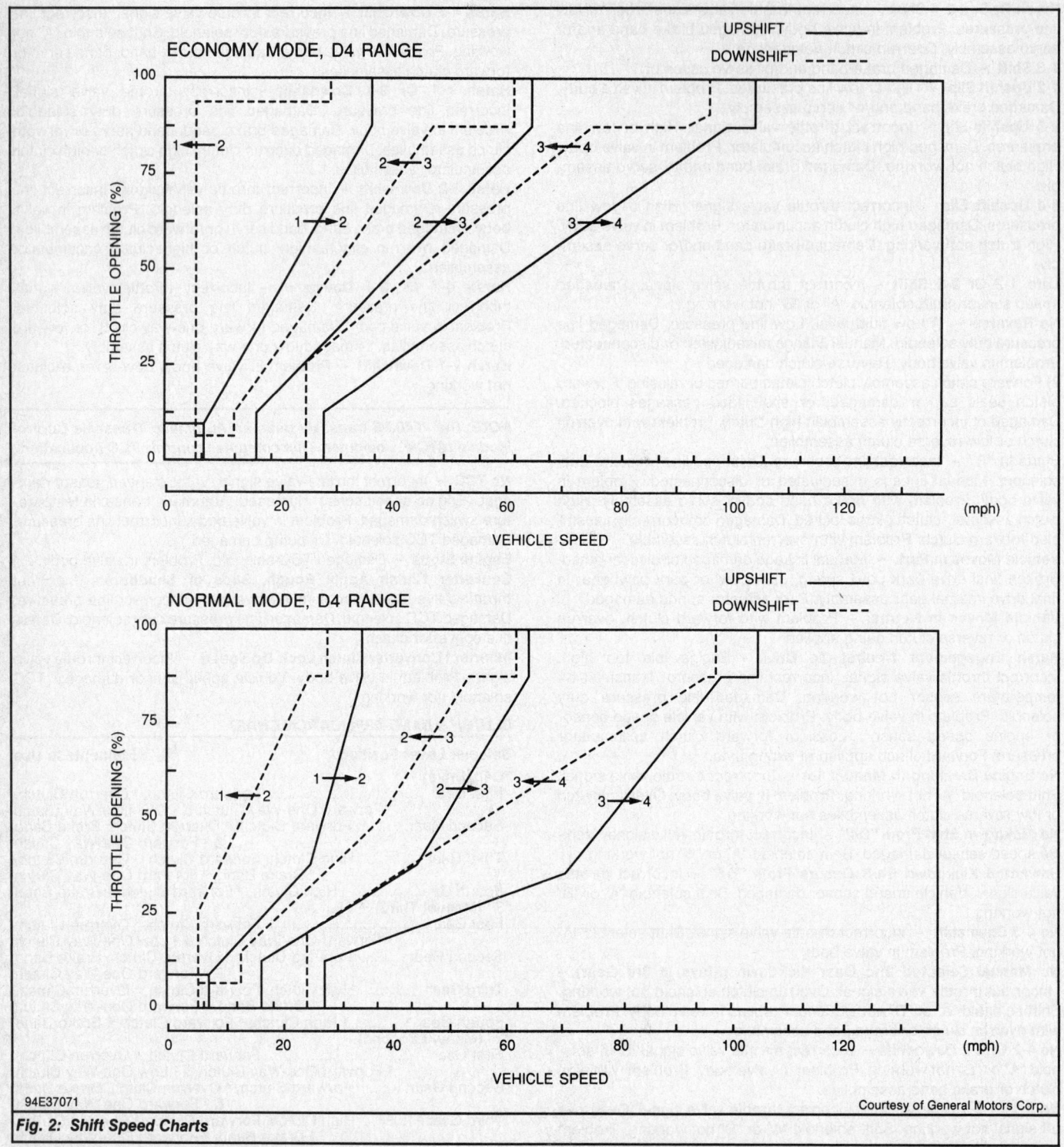

Fig. 2: Shift Speed Charts

94E37071

Courtesy of General Motors Corp.

ELECTRONIC SELF-DIAGNOSTICS & ELECTRONIC TESTING

NOTE: See JF403-E ELECTRONIC DIAGNOSIS article.

TESTING

ROAD TEST

NOTE: Before road testing vehicle, engine and transaxle must be at operating temperature. Torque converter clutch will not engage if transaxle temperature has not reached operating temperature.

Gear Selector Position "D4" (Overdrive) – 1) With gear selector in "D4" (overdrive) position, accelerate vehicle steadily increasing throttle pressure. Note shift speed engagement points in 2nd gear, 3rd gear and overdrive gear. Use shift speed charts as a reference for proper shift speeds. See Fig. 2. Also note when Torque Converter Clutch (TCC) applies while in 3rd gear or overdrive. If torque converter clutch does not apply as specified, see JF403-E ELECTRONIC DIAGNOSIS article.

NOTE: Ensure TCC applies in 3rd gear or overdrive during the following steps.

2) At vehicle speeds of 40-55 MPH, quickly depress accelerator to half open position (part throttle detent downshift). The TCC should release and transaxle should immediately downshift to 3rd gear.

3) At vehicle speeds of 48-55 MPH, quickly depress accelerator to wide open position (full throttle detent downshift). The TCC should release and transaxle should immediately downshift to 2nd gear.

4) At vehicle speeds of 40-55 MPH, release accelerator pedal while moving gear selector to the "D3" (third gear) position. The TCC should release, transaxle should downshift into 3rd gear and engine braking should slow vehicle.

5) Move gear selector to the "D4" (overdrive) position and accelerate to 40-45 MPH. Release accelerator pedal while moving gear selector to the "2" (2nd gear) position. The TCC should release, transaxle should downshift to 2nd gear immediately and engine braking should slow vehicle.

6) Move gear selector to the "D4" (overdrive) position and accelerate to 25 MPH. Release accelerator pedal while moving gear selector to the "1" (1st gear) position. The TCC should release, transaxle should downshift to 1st gear and engine braking should slow vehicle.

7) With gear selector in the "D4" (overdrive) position, accelerate vehicle to overdrive gear with TCC applied. Release accelerator pedal and lightly apply brakes. The TCC should release. Note speeds at which vehicle downshifts. See Fig. 2.

Gear Selector Position "D3" (3rd Gear) – With vehicle stopped, move gear selector to the "3" (3rd gear) position and accelerate vehicle, steadily increasing throttle pressure. Ensure transaxle upshifts from 1st to 2nd, and from 2nd to 3rd gear. Also note when TCC applies while in 3rd gear.

Gear Selector Position "2" (2nd Gear) – With vehicle stopped, move gear selector to the "2" (2nd gear) position. Accelerate vehicle and note 1st-2nd shift speeds. Accelerate vehicle to 25 MPH. Transaxle should not shift into 3rd gear and TCC should not apply.

Gear Selector Position "1" (1st Gear) – With vehicle stopped, move gear selector to the "1" (1st gear) position. Accelerate vehicle to 15 MPH. Transaxle should not upshift and TCC application should not occur.

STALL SPEED TEST

Testing Precautions – When performing test, DO NOT hold throttle open longer than 5 seconds. Shift to "N" position and allow engine to idle for at least one minute between tests to cool transaxle. If engine speed exceeds specification, release accelerator immediately as clutch or band slippage is indicated. See STALL SPEED SPECIFICATIONS table.

Testing Procedures – With engine at normal operating temperature, tachometer installed and parking and service brakes applied, perform transaxle stall speed test in "D4", "D3", "2", "1" and "R" ranges at full throttle and note maximum RPM obtained. See STALL SPEED SPECIFICATIONS table.

STALL SPEED SPECIFICATIONS

Application	Engine RPM
Geo Storm	2050-2350

Stall Speed Test Results – 1) If stall speed is below specifications, engine performance is unsatisfactory or torque converter one-way clutch is slipping. If stall speed is high in all drive ranges, line pressure is low. Check oil pump. Check oil pump control valve and transaxle case for leaks. Check line pressure duty solenoid for damage.

2) If stall speed is high in 1st gear only, the low one-way clutch is slipping. If stall speed is high in all other ranges, the forward clutch is slipping.

3) If stall speed is high in "R" only, either the low-reverse brake or reverse clutch is slipping. Road test vehicle to determine whether it is the low-reverse brake or the front clutch. If engine brakes in first gear position, the reverse clutch is slipping. If engine does not brake in first gear position, the low-reverse brake is slipping.

4) If stall speed is within specifications, but transaxle slips in 3rd and 4th gears in "D4" range, high clutch is slipping. If stall speed is within specifications, but transaxle slips in 2nd and 4th gears in "D4" range, brake band is slipping. If stall speed is within specifications but vehicle speed will not exceed 50 MPH, torque converter one-way clutch is seized. High fluid temperature will exist.

HYDRAULIC PRESSURE TESTS

CAUTION: Parking and service brakes must be applied at all times during hydraulic pressure test. Total testing time with vehicle in any driving gear should not exceed 2 minutes.

Before performing hydraulic pressure tests, check fluid level and condition. Connect a tachometer to engine and an oil pressure gauge to line pressure test port. *See Fig. 3.* See LINE PRESSURE SPECIFICATIONS table for correct line pressure at specified engine RPM.

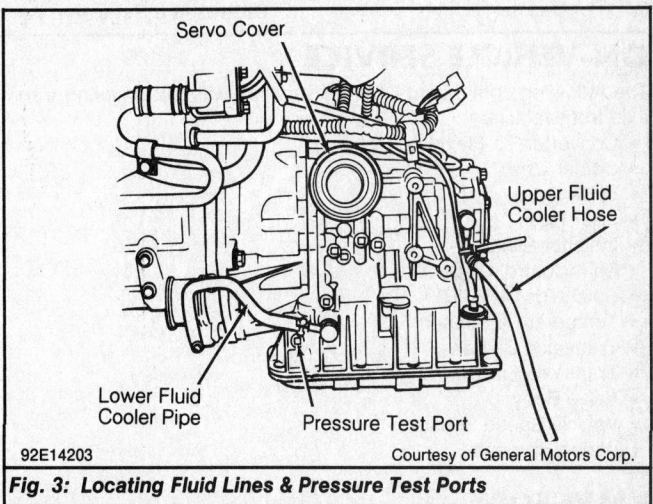

92E14203   Courtesy of General Motors Corp.

Fig. 3: Locating Fluid Lines & Pressure Test Ports

NOTE: Hydraulic pressure is controlled by pump output and is regulated by line pressure duty solenoid.

Minimum Line Pressure Check – Start engine, apply brakes and allow engine to idle. Record line pressure readings in all gear selector positions with engine at idle RPM, and compare recorded pressures to specifications. See LINE PRESSURE SPECIFICATIONS table. If recorded pressure is incorrect, see appropriate HIGH OR LOW LINE PRESSURE table.

Full Line Pressure – With brakes applied, engage each gear. Press throttle to wide open throttle position (stall speed RPM) only long enough to record pressure reading and release throttle. Record line pressure readings in all gear selector positions with engine at stall speed RPM. Compare recorded pressures to specifications. See LINE PRESSURE SPECIFICATIONS table. If recorded pressure is incorrect, see appropriate HIGH OR LOW LINE PRESSURE table.

LINE PRESSURE SPECIFICATIONS

Application RPM & Range	Line Pressure psi (kg/cm²)
1993	
950-1050 (Idle)	
"D4", "D3", "2" & "1"	63-77 (3.4-5.4)
"R"	78-92 (5.4-6.4)
2050-2350 (Stall)	
"D4", "D3", "2" & "1"	186-200 (12.9-13.9)
"R"	224-239 (15.6-16.5)

HIGH OR LOW LINE PRESSURE (IDLE OR STALL)

Condition	Cause
Low All Ranges	Worn Pump, Internal Leak Or Sticking Pressure Regulator Valve

HIGH OR LOW LINE PRESSURE (AT IDLE)

Condition	Cause
Low "1" Range Only	Problem In Related Device See CLUTCH & BAND APPLICATION table.
High All Ranges	Incorrect Throttle Signal, A/T Temperature Sensor, Line Pressure Duty Solenoid, Sticking Pressure Modifier Valve Or Pressure Regulator Valve

HIGH OR LOW LINE PRESSURE (AT STALL)

Condition	Cause
Same As At Idle	Incorrect Throttle Signal, ATCM Or Line Pressure Duty Solenoid, Sticking Pilot Valve, Pressure Modifier Valve Or Pressure Regulator Valve
Low All Ranges	Incorrect Throttle Signal Or Line Pressure Duty Solenoid, Sticking Pilot Valve, Pressure Modifier Valve Or Pressure Regulator Valve

ON-VEHICLE SERVICE

The following components can be serviced without removing transaxle from vehicle:

- Converter-To-Flexplate Bolts
- Cooler Lines
- Drive Axles
- Filler Pipe
- Inhibitor Switch
- Shift Control Cable
- Solenoids "A" & "B"
- Temperature Sensor
- Transaxle Oil Pan
- Transaxle Filter
- Valve Body
- Vehicle Speed Sensor
- Wiring Harness

VALVE BODY

See VALVE BODY under COMPONENT DISASSEMBLY & REASSEMBLY.

DRIVE AXLE SHAFTS

See appropriate AXLE SHAFTS article in AXLE SHAFTS & TRANSFER CASES.

OIL COOLER FLUSHING

1) If available, fill Line Flusher (J-35944) with solution and install oil cooler and line flusher to top transaxle cooler line on transaxle. Follow manufacturer's instructions to flush oil cooler and cooler lines.
2) If line flusher is not available, flush cooler and cooler lines with a mixture of clean solvent and water. Flush cooler in both directions until all old fluid and debris is removed. If necessary, replace plugged or damaged cooler and/or lines.

REMOVAL & INSTALLATION

See appropriate AUTOMATIC TRANSMISSION REMOVAL article in TRANSMISSION SERVICING.

TORQUE CONVERTER
INSPECTION

Torque converter must be replaced for any of the following conditions:

- Damage To Pump Assembly
- Metal Particles Present In Oil
- Leaks In Hub Weld Area
- Crankshaft Pilot Broken Or Damaged
- Hub Scored Or Damaged
- Stator Failure
- Torque Converter Imbalance
- Engine Coolant Contamination
- Excessive End Play

END PLAY CHECK

NOTE: End play checking procedure is not available from manufacturer.

TRANSAXLE DISASSEMBLY

TRANSAXLE UNIT

1) Thoroughly clean transaxle exterior. Drain fluid and remove torque converter. Place transaxle in holding fixture. Remove selector bracket, vehicle speed sensor and oil level gauge.
2) Remove oil pan, oil filter and side cover. Remove wiring harness grommet. Remove valve body assembly. See Fig. 30. Remove converter housing. Remove differential assembly.
3) Remove oil pump, brake band, and input shaft assembly with high and reverse clutches. See Fig. 30. Compress servo cover and remove servo snap ring. Remove servo assembly.
4) Remove low one-way clutch from transaxle case. Remove output gear. Using Low-Reverse Brake Spring Compressor and Bridge (J-38298 and J-35279-1), compress low-reverse brake piston. See Fig. 47. Remove snap ring and tools. Remove front planetary and low-reverse brake assembly. See Fig. 30. Remove remaining planetary, snap rings, clutch assemblies and thrust washers. See Fig. 30.
5) Remove staking from idler gear lock nut. Move shift lever to Park position. Remove lock nut and remove idler gear. Remove reduction gear race housing bolts. Using Gear Puller (J-38297), remove reduction gear. Remove idler gear outer bearing race from housing. See Fig. 30. Remove drum support.

NOTE: An exploded view of all internal parts can be seen in Fig. 30. Thrust washer and bearing locations can be found in Fig. 38.

COMPONENT DISASSEMBLY & REASSEMBLY
TRANSAXLE CASE

Cleaning & Inspection – Clean transaxle case thoroughly with solvent, then air dry. Inspect transaxle case for damage to band lugs, snap ring grooves, drive sprocket bearings, interconnected or damaged oil passages and servo bores. See Figs. 35 and 36. Inspect case for stripped threads in bolt holes or casting porosity. Repair or replace case if necessary.

NOTE: DO NOT remove these parts unless replacement is necessary. For installation procedures, see TRANSAXLE REASSEMBLY.

Removing Bearing Races & Seals – If removal of idler or differential bearing races from case is necessary, use Bearing Puller (J-33367) and Puller Bridge (J-35280). See Fig. 4. Remove axle shaft seals. If necessary, also remove differential outer bearing races from converter housing. See Fig. 5.

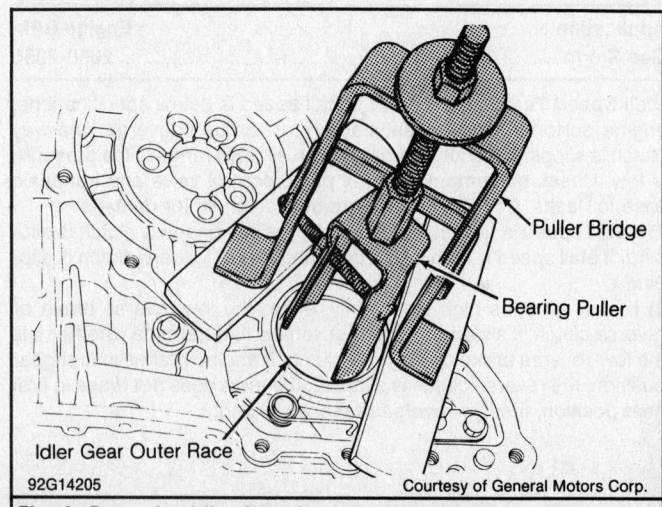

92G14205   Courtesy of General Motors Corp.

Fig. 4: Removing Idler Gear Outer Bearing Race

Removing Manual Shaft, Parking Pawl & Actuator Support – If manual shaft, parking pawl or parking actuator support removal is necessary, remove clip and bolt from parking lever. Remove parking lever and rod. Remove return spring from case. *See Fig. 6.* Remove actuator support from case. Remove manual plate and "O" ring from manual shaft. Remove support plate. *See Fig. 7.*

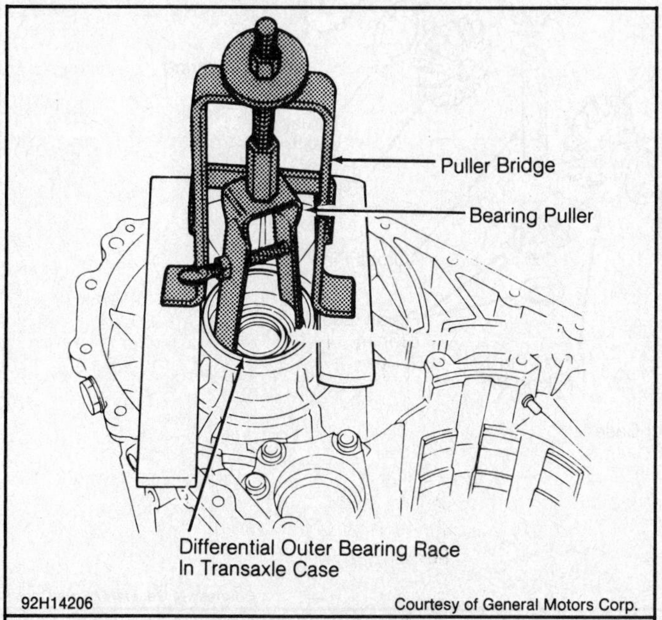

Fig. 5: Removing Differential Outer Bearing Race

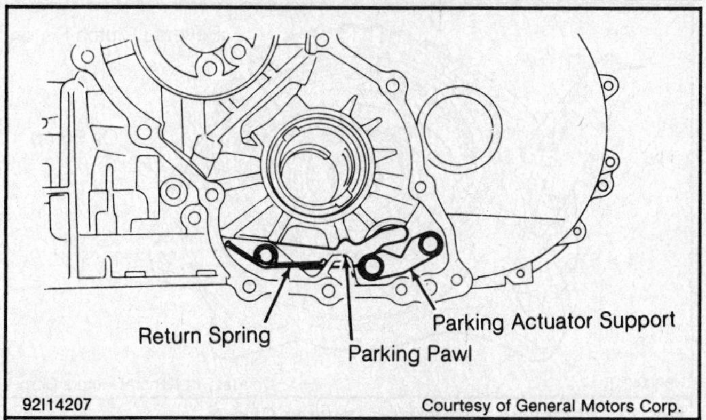

Fig. 6: Removing Parking Pawl Support & Return Spring

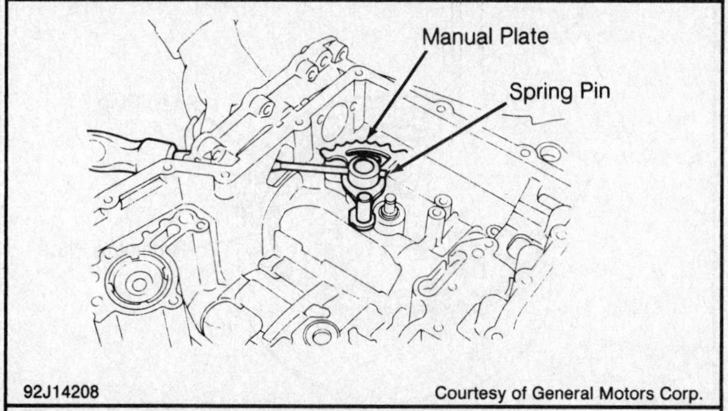

Fig. 7: Removing Manual Plate & Spring Pin

FINAL DRIVE ASSEMBLY

Disassembly & Inspection – **1)** Inspect final drive gear for damaged teeth or worn bearing surfaces. Inspect thrust bearings and speedometer drive gear for wear or damage. If necessary, remove differential side bearings. *See Fig. 8.*

2) Check differential carrier pinion gear backlash. Use a dial indicator and measure backlash between side gear and pinion gear thrust washer. *See Fig. 9.* Backlash should be less than .019" (.48 mm).

3) If necessary, replace thrust washers. Using a pin punch, drive cross pin locking pin from differential. Remove cross pin, pinion and side gears, and thrust washers. *See Fig. 10.* Inspect all parts for damage or abnormal wear.

Reassembly – **1)** Assemble differential side gears and thrust washers into carrier. Set thrust washers onto pinion gears. Assemble pinion gears and washers into carrier. *See Fig. 10.*

2) Rotate pinion gears into position, then install cross pin. Tap cross pin locking pin into position. Tap speedometer drive gear into position (if removed). Install side bearings on differential (if removed).

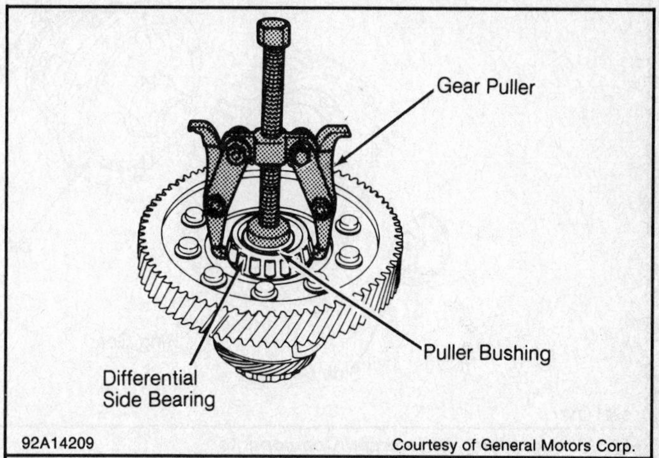

Fig. 8: Removing Differential Side Bearing

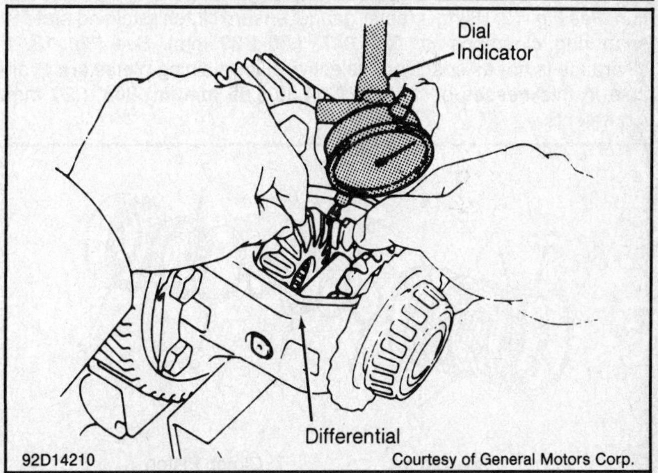

Fig. 9: Checking Differential Pinion Gear Backlash

REVERSE CLUTCH

Disassembly – Remove large snap ring. Lift out retaining plate, clutch plates, and dished plate. *See Fig. 11.* Compress reverse clutch spring retainer to remove small snap ring, spring retainer, and clutch return spring. Apply air pressure to rear clutch oil passage to remove piston. *See Fig. 12.* Remove and discard piston seal rings.

Inspection – Inspect for wear or damage. Ensure clutch piston check ball holds air pressure on drum side and allows air pressure through on clutch side of clutch piston. Ensure drive plate thickness is more than .055" (1.40 mm). If drive plate thickness is less than specified, replace drive plate.

Reassembly – **1)** Install seal rings on clutch piston and install in clutch drum by placing even pressure on perimeter of piston and slowly rotating piston. Install return spring and spring retainer. Compress spring retainer and install snap ring. Install dished plate. Install driven and drive plates, retainer plate and snap ring. *See Fig. 11.*

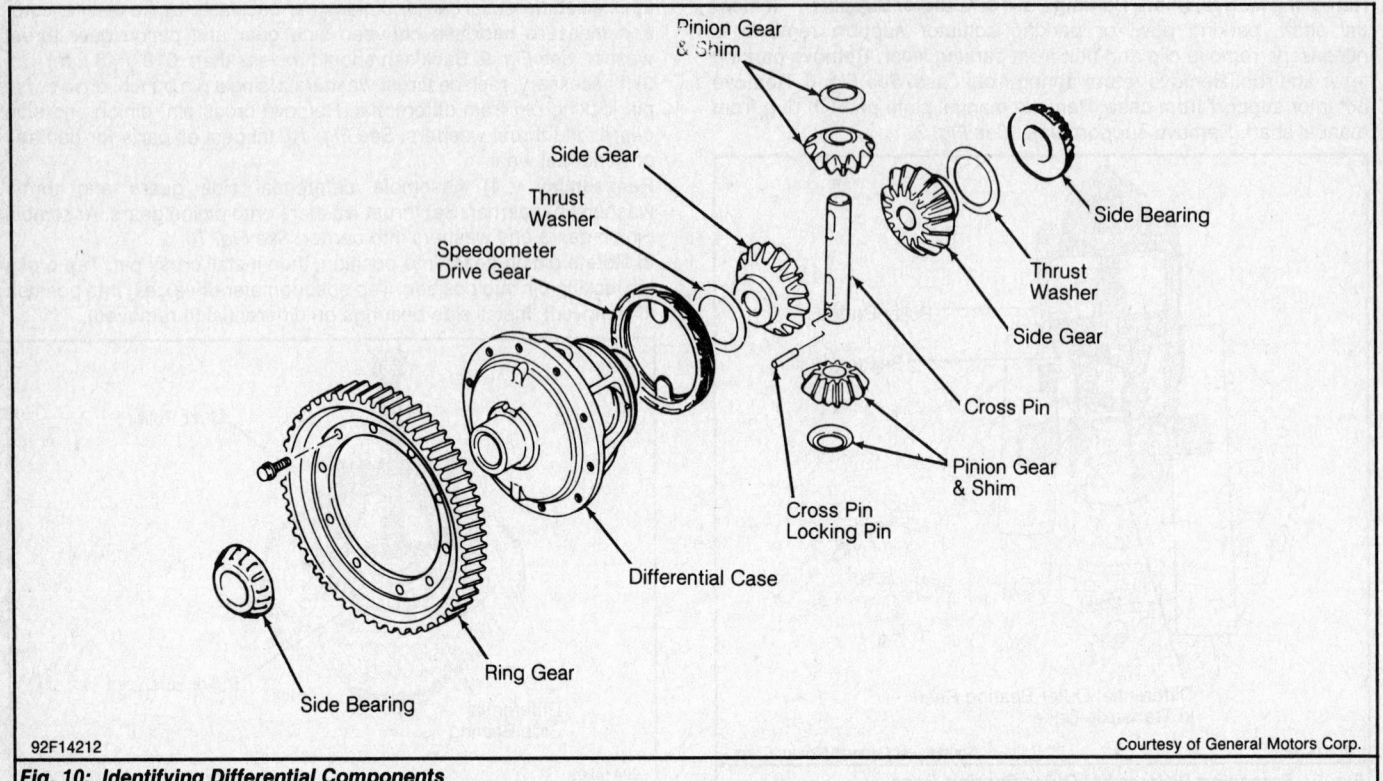

92F14212

Courtesy of General Motors Corp.

Fig. 10: Identifying Differential Components

2) Apply compressed air to rear clutch oil passage and check operation. *See Fig. 12.* Using a feeler gauge, ensure clutch retaining plate to snap ring clearance is .020-.047" (.50-1.20 mm). *See Fig. 13.* If clearance is not as specified, selective size retaining plates are available in thicknesses of .189-.220" (4.80-5.60 mm) in .008" (.20 mm) increments.

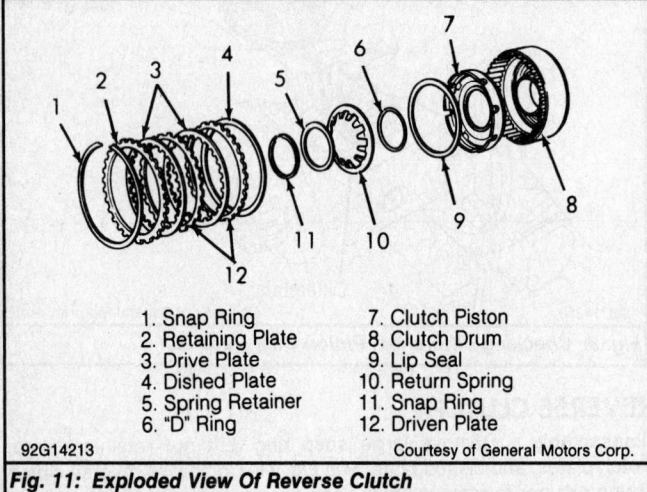

1. Snap Ring
2. Retaining Plate
3. Drive Plate
4. Dished Plate
5. Spring Retainer
6. "D" Ring
7. Clutch Piston
8. Clutch Drum
9. Lip Seal
10. Return Spring
11. Snap Ring
12. Driven Plate

92G14213

Courtesy of General Motors Corp.

Fig. 11: Exploded View Of Reverse Clutch

HIGH CLUTCH

Disassembly – 1) Remove retainer plate snap ring. Remove retainer plate, drive and driven plates and spacer plate. *See Fig. 16.* Compress return springs to remove spring retainer snap ring.

2) Remove spring compressor. Remove spring retainer and return springs. Apply air pressure to high clutch oil passage to remove high clutch piston. *See Fig. 14.*

Inspection – Inspect for wear or damage. Ensure clutch piston check ball holds air pressure on drum side and allows air pressure through on clutch side of clutch piston. Ensure drive plate thickness is greater than .055" (1.40 mm). If drive plate thickness is less than specified, replace drive plate.

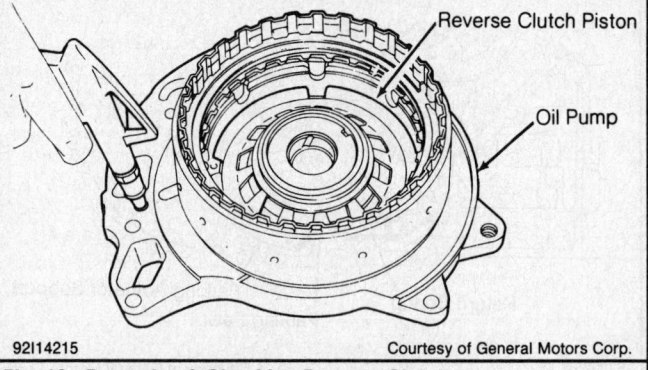

92I14215

Courtesy of General Motors Corp.

Fig. 12: Removing & Checking Reverse Clutch

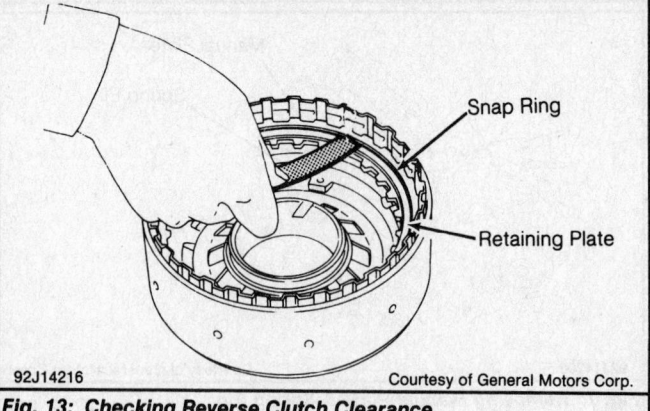

92J14216

Courtesy of General Motors Corp.

Fig. 13: Checking Reverse Clutch Clearance

Reassembly – 1) To reassemble, reverse disassembly procedure. Install new seal rings on piston and install piston by applying even pressure on perimeter while rotating piston. Install high clutch return springs and retainer. Compress spring retainer. Install snap ring.

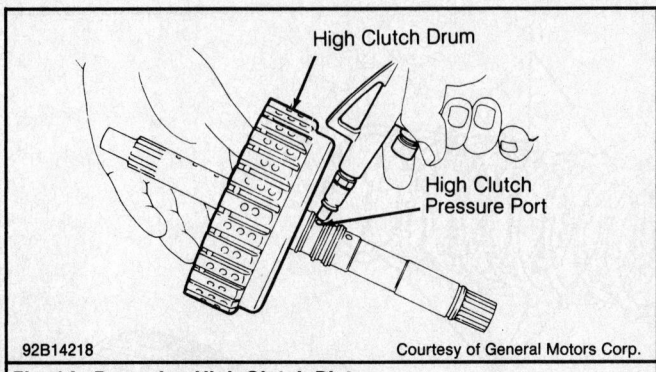

92B14218   Courtesy of General Motors Corp.

Fig. 14: Removing High Clutch Piston

2) Install spacer plate. *See Fig. 16*. Install 4 drive and 6 driven clutch plates, retaining plate and snap ring. Using a feeler gauge, check clearance between snap ring and retaining plate. *See Fig. 15*. Clearance should be .071-.110" (1.80-2.80 mm).

3) If clearance is not as specified, selective size retaining plates are available in thicknesses of .142-.173" (3.60-4.40 mm) in .008" (.20 mm) increments. Place high clutch assembly over oil pump. Apply air pressure to high clutch oil passage and check high clutch operation.

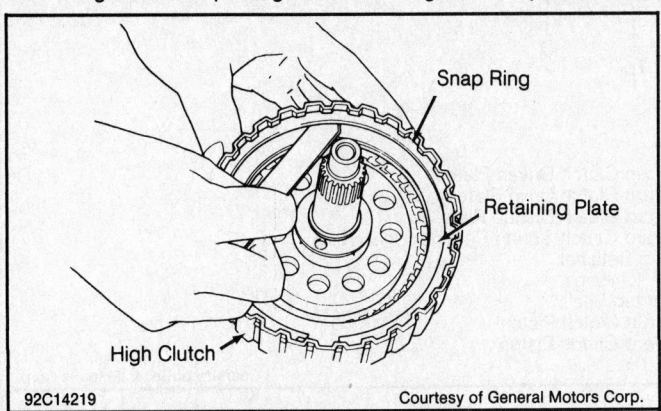

92C14219   Courtesy of General Motors Corp.

Fig. 15: Checking High Clutch Clearance

FORWARD & OVERRUN CLUTCH

Disassembly – 1) Remove forward clutch retaining plate snap ring. Remove retaining plate, spacer, drive and driven plates and dished plate. *See Fig. 17*.

2) Remove overrun clutch retaining plate snap ring. Remove retaining plate, drive and driven plates and dished plate. *See Fig. 17*. Compress return springs to remove forward clutch spring retainer snap ring.

3) Remove spring compressor. Remove spring retainer and return springs. Remove forward and overrun clutch pistons from forward clutch drum. *See Fig. 17*.

Inspection – Inspect for wear or damage. Ensure each clutch piston check ball holds air pressure on drum side and allows air pressure through on clutch side of clutch piston. *See Figs. 18-21*. Ensure forward and overrun drive plate thicknesses are greater than .055" (1.4 mm). If any drive plate is less than specified, replace drive plate.

Reassembly – 1) To reassemble, reverse disassembly procedure. Install new seal rings on forward and overrun pistons by applying even pressure on perimeter while rotating each piston. Install forward clutch return springs and retainer. Compress spring retainer. Install snap ring.

2) Install overrun clutch dished plate. *See Fig. 17*. Install 3 drive and 5 driven clutch plates, overrun retaining plate and snap ring. Install forward clutch dished plate. *See Fig. 17*. Install 4 drive and 4 driven clutch plates, spacer, forward retaining plate and snap ring.

3) Using a feeler gauge, check clearance between overrun clutch snap ring and overrun clutch retaining plate. *See Fig. 22*. Clearance should be .039-.079" (1.00-2.00 mm). If clearance is not as specified, selective size retaining plates are available in thicknesses of .118-.150" (3.00-3.80 mm) in .008" (.20 mm) increments.

4) Using a feeler gauge, check clearance between forward snap ring and forward retaining plate. Clearance should be .018-.099" (.45-2.51 mm). If clearance is not as specified, selective size retaining plates are available in thicknesses of .142-.181" (3.60-4.60 mm) in .008" (.20 mm) increments.

5) Place forward and overrun clutch assemblies and drum assembly into transaxle case. Apply air pressure to forward clutch and overrun clutch oil passage to check operation of each clutch.

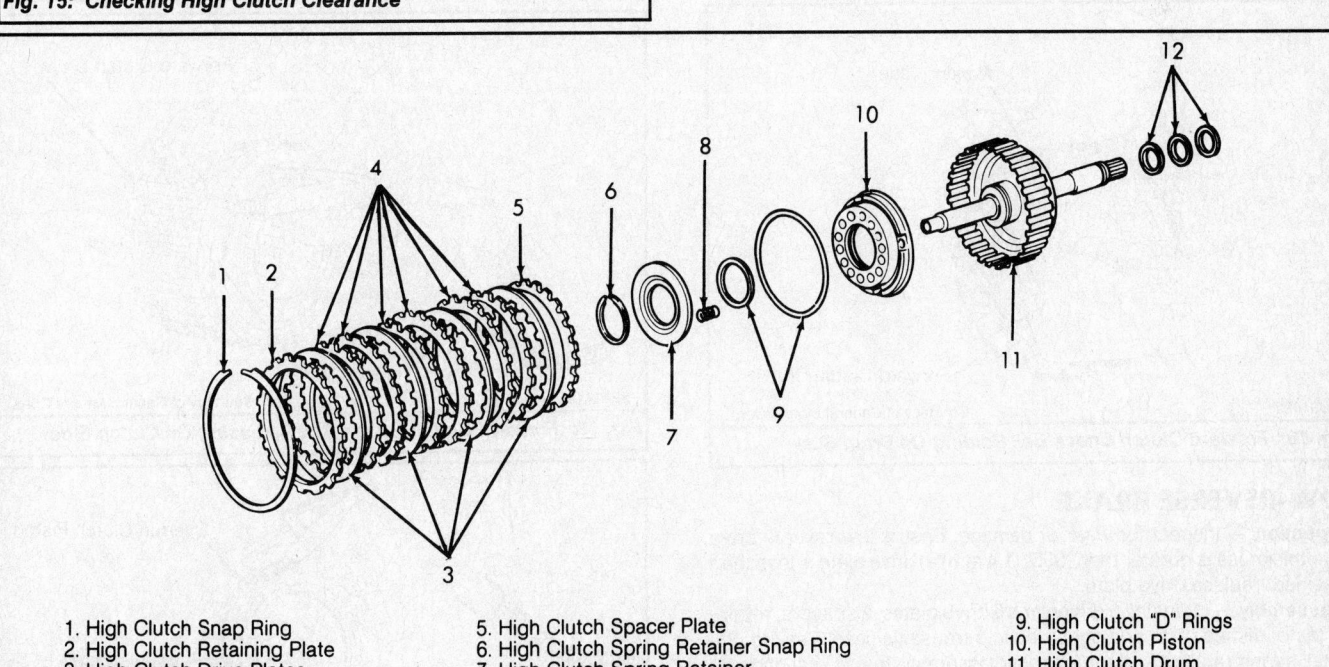

1. High Clutch Snap Ring
2. High Clutch Retaining Plate
3. High Clutch Drive Plates
4. High Clutch Driven Plates
5. High Clutch Spacer Plate
6. High Clutch Spring Retainer Snap Ring
7. High Clutch Spring Retainer
8. High Clutch Return Spring
9. High Clutch "D" Rings
10. High Clutch Piston
11. High Clutch Drum
12. Input Shaft Seal Rings

92A14217   Courtesy of General Motors Corp.

Fig. 16: Exploded View Of High Clutch

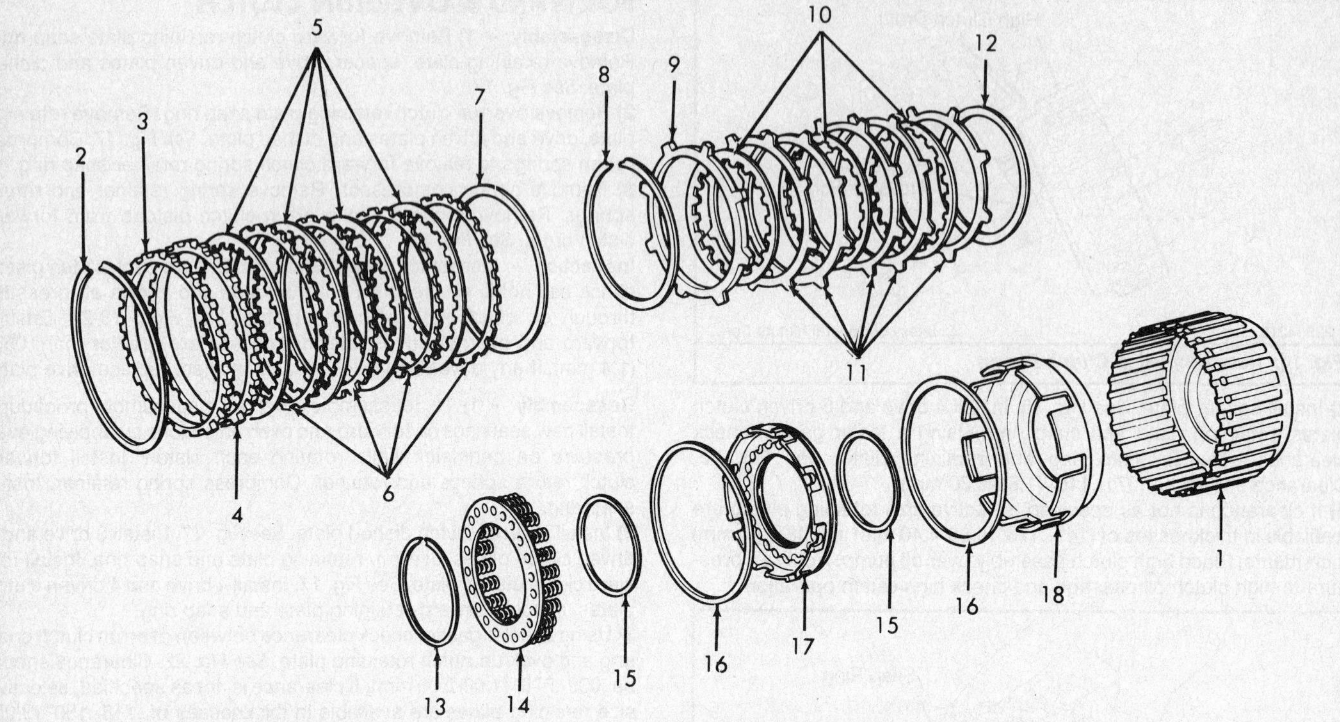

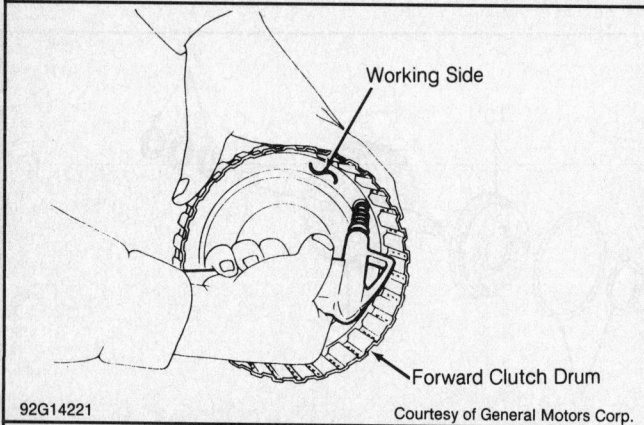

1. Forward Clutch Drum
2. Forward Clutch Snap Ring
3. Forward Clutch Retaining Plate
4. Forward Clutch Spacer
5. Forward Clutch Driven Plates
6. Forward Clutch Drive Plates
7. Forward Clutch Dished Plate
8. Overrun Clutch Snap Ring
9. Overrun Clutch Retaining Plate
10. Overrun Clutch Driven Plates
11. Overrun Clutch Drive Plates
12. Overrun Clutch Dished Plate
13. Forward Clutch Spring Retainer Snap Ring
14. Spring Retainer
15. Inner "D" Rings
16. Outer Lip Seals
17. Overrun Clutch Piston
18. Forward Clutch Piston

92F14220

Courtesy of General Motors Corp.

Fig. 17: Exploded View Of Forward & Overrun Clutch Assembly

92G14221   Courtesy of General Motors Corp.

Fig. 18: Forward Clutch Check Ball Holding On Drum Side

LOW-REVERSE BRAKE

Inspection – Inspect for wear or damage. Ensure low-reverse drive plate thickness is greater than .055" (1.4 mm). If drive plate is less than specified, replace drive plate.

Reassembly – **1)** Install 6 driven and 6 drive plates, 2 spacers, retaining plate, dished plate and snap ring into transaxle case. See Fig. 23. Install spring retainer and return spring assembly. Install seal rings on piston.

2) Install piston in piston retainer by placing even pressure on perimeter of piston and slowly rotating piston. Install piston retainer and compress. Install snap ring to transaxle case.

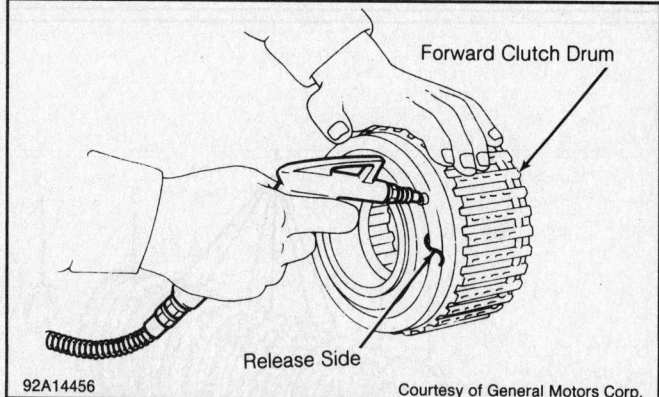

92A14456   Courtesy of General Motors Corp.

Fig. 19: Forward Clutch Check Ball Releasing On Clutch Side

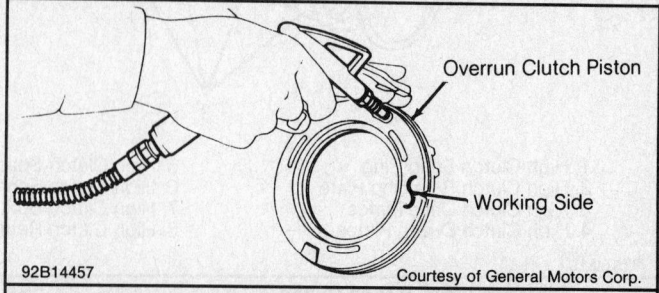

92B14457   Courtesy of General Motors Corp.

Fig. 20: Overrun Clutch Check Ball Holding On Drum Side

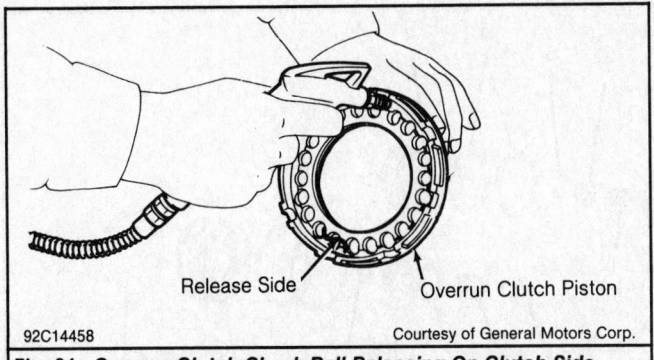

Release Side   Overrun Clutch Piston

92C14458   Courtesy of General Motors Corp.

Fig. 21: Overrun Clutch Check Ball Releasing On Clutch Side

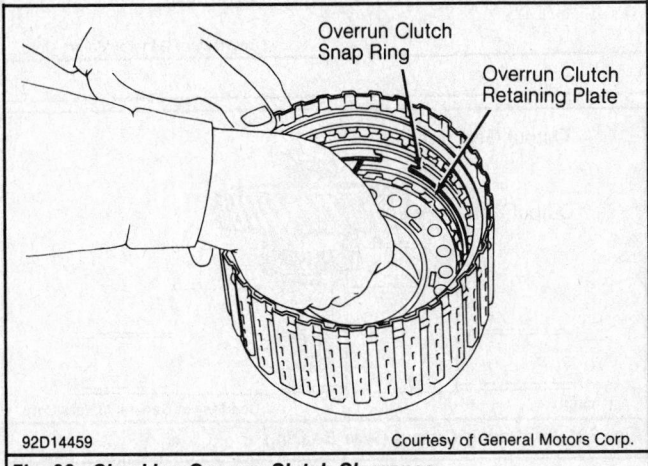

Overrun Clutch Snap Ring

Overrun Clutch Retaining Plate

92D14459   Courtesy of General Motors Corp.

Fig. 22: Checking Overrun Clutch Clearance

3) Using a feeler gauge, check clearance between snap ring and spring retaining plate. See Fig. 24. Clearance should be .043-.114" (1.10-2.90 mm). If clearance is not as specified, selective size retaining plates are available in thicknesses of .079-.134" (2.00-3.40 mm) in .008" (.20 mm) increments. Apply air pressure to low-reverse clutch oil passage, and check clutch operation. See Fig. 26.

BRAKE BAND & SERVO

Inspection & Reassembly – Inspect servo pistons and seals for damage or cracks. See Fig. 25. Inspect springs for damaged or weak coils. See BRAKE BAND SERVO SPRING SPECIFICATIONS table. If spring free length is less than specification, replace spring(s). Check brake band for wear. If necessary, replace brake band. To reassemble, reverse disassembly procedure. See Fig. 25.

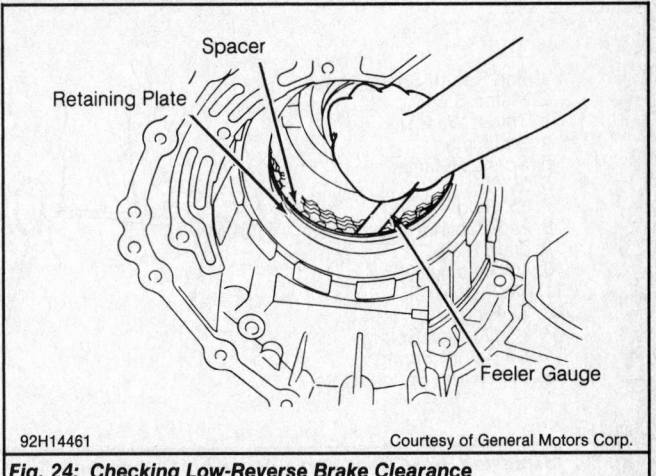

Spacer

Retaining Plate

Feeler Gauge

92H14461   Courtesy of General Motors Corp.

Fig. 24: Checking Low-Reverse Brake Clearance

BRAKE BAND SERVO SPRING SPECIFICATIONS

Application	Free Length
2nd Return Spring (Inner)	1.5" (38 mm)
2nd Return Spring (Outer)	1.5" (38 mm)
4th Return Spring	1.1" (28 mm)
4th Cushion Spring	.9" (23 mm)

FORWARD ONE-WAY CLUTCH

Disassembly, Inspection & Reassembly – 1) Record direction one-way clutch locks and turns. Pull rear internal gear out from forward clutch hub. Remove forward one-way clutch and separate remaining parts. See Fig. 27. Check for worn or damaged parts and replace as necessary.

2) To reassembly, reverse disassembly procedure. Install forward one-way clutch in forward clutch hub and ensure that internal gear will turn in one direction (clockwise) only.

DRUM SUPPORT

Disassembly, Inspection & Reassembly – Remove seal rings and thrust bearing. See Fig. 28. Remove snap ring and needle bearing assembly from drum support. Check drum support and needle bearing for wear or damage and replace if needed. To reassemble, reverse disassembly procedure.

OUTPUT GEAR, REDUCTION GEAR & IDLER GEAR

Cleaning & Inspection – Inspect all gears and bearings for wear or damage. See Fig. 30. Replace all worn parts as necessary. If necessary, use Bearing Remover (J-38288) and Bearing Pilot (J-38289) to remove output gear bearing. See Fig. 29.

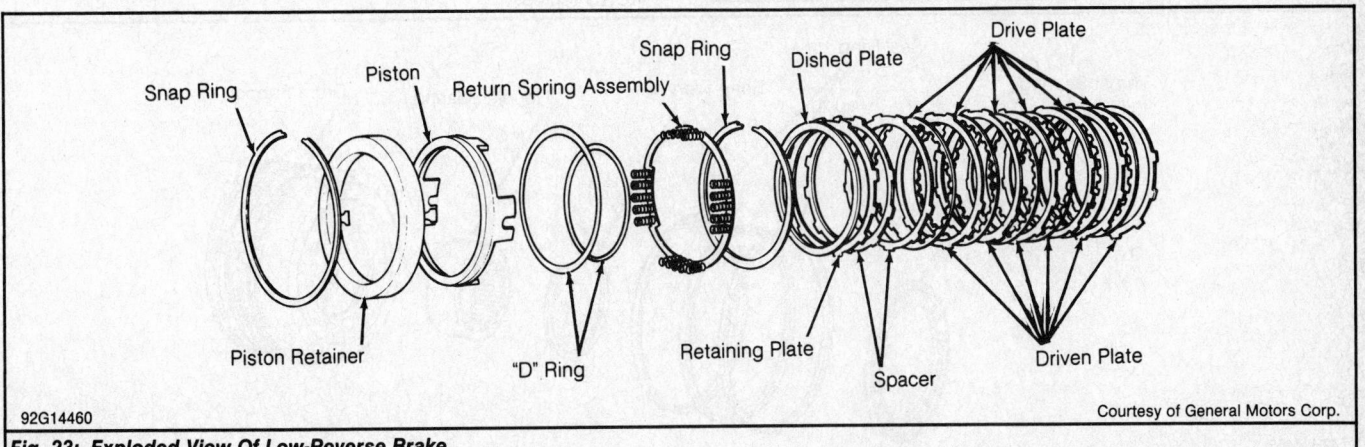

Snap Ring   Piston   Return Spring Assembly   Snap Ring   Dished Plate   Drive Plate

Piston Retainer   "D" Ring   Retaining Plate   Spacer   Driven Plate

92G14460   Courtesy of General Motors Corp.

Fig. 23: Exploded View Of Low-Reverse Brake

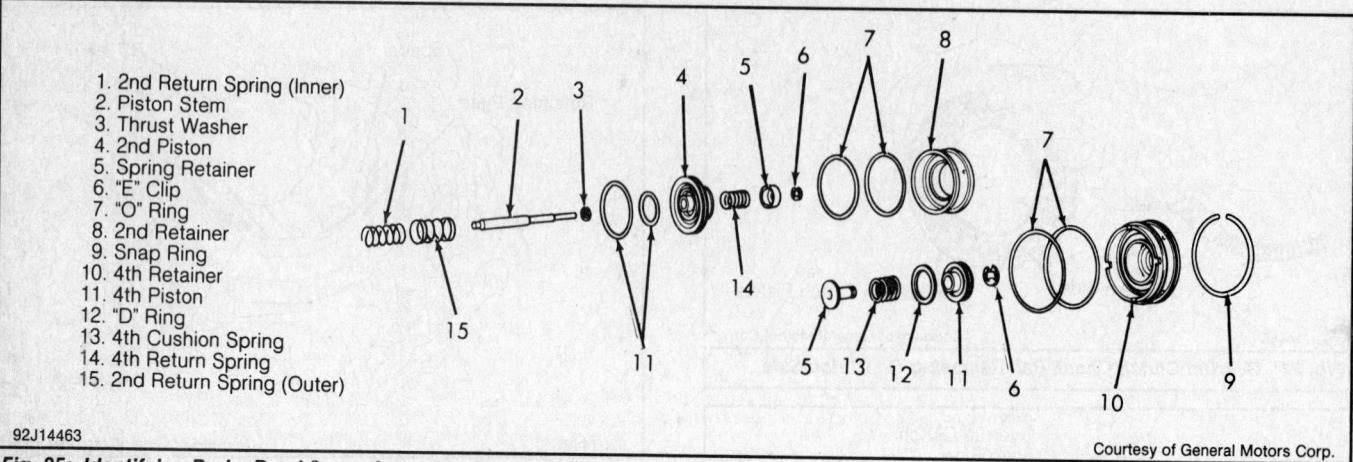

1. 2nd Return Spring (Inner)
2. Piston Stem
3. Thrust Washer
4. 2nd Piston
5. Spring Retainer
6. "E" Clip
7. "O" Ring
8. 2nd Retainer
9. Snap Ring
10. 4th Retainer
11. 4th Piston
12. "D" Ring
13. 4th Cushion Spring
14. 4th Return Spring
15. 2nd Return Spring (Outer)

92J14463

Courtesy of General Motors Corp.

Fig. 25: Identifying Brake Band Servo Assembly Components

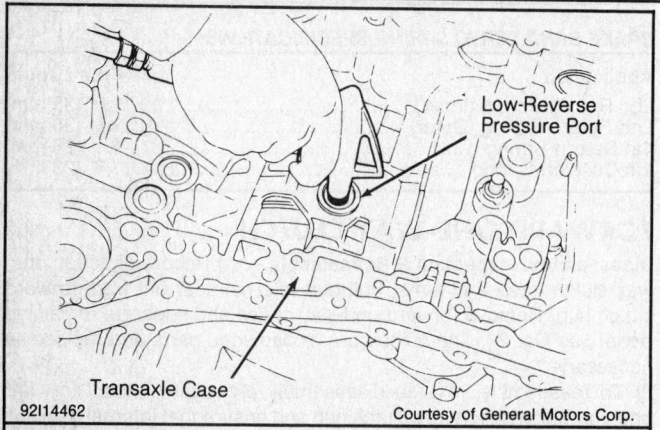

92I14462

Courtesy of General Motors Corp.

Fig. 26: Checking Low-Reverse Brake Operation

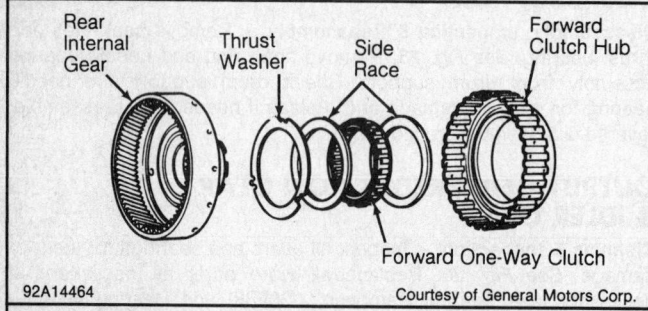

92A14464

Courtesy of General Motors Corp.

Fig. 27: Identifying Forward One-Way Clutch Assembly

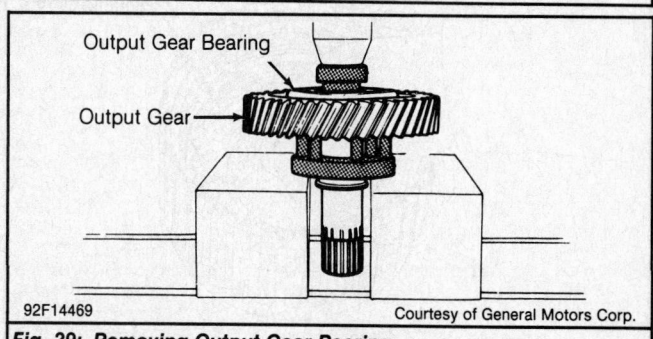

92F14469

Courtesy of General Motors Corp.

Fig. 29: Removing Output Gear Bearing

VALVE BODY

Disassembly – 1) Remove terminal assembly (solenoids and temperature sensor). Remove fluid filter screen bolts, support plates and fluid filter screen. *See Fig. 31.*

2) Remove through bolts, upper valve body and separator plate. Remove intermediate valve body, lower gasket and separator plate. Remove steel balls, one-way cup, spring and pilot filter.

3) Remove manual valve, spring, plug and key. For disassembly of upper and lower valve bodies, remove respective key, spring, plug and valve. Retain in proper order for reassembly. *See Figs. 32 and 33.*

Cleaning & Inspection – Inspect valves and bushings for scoring, nicks and scratches. Inspect springs for damaged or distorted coils. Inspect valve body casting for porosity, interconnected oil passages and damaged machined surfaces. Inspect transaxle case oil passages and machined surfaces for damage. *See Figs. 35 and 36.* Inspect springs for free length. See UPPER VALVE BODY SPRING SPECIFICATIONS and LOWER VALVE BODY SPRING SPECIFICATIONS tables.

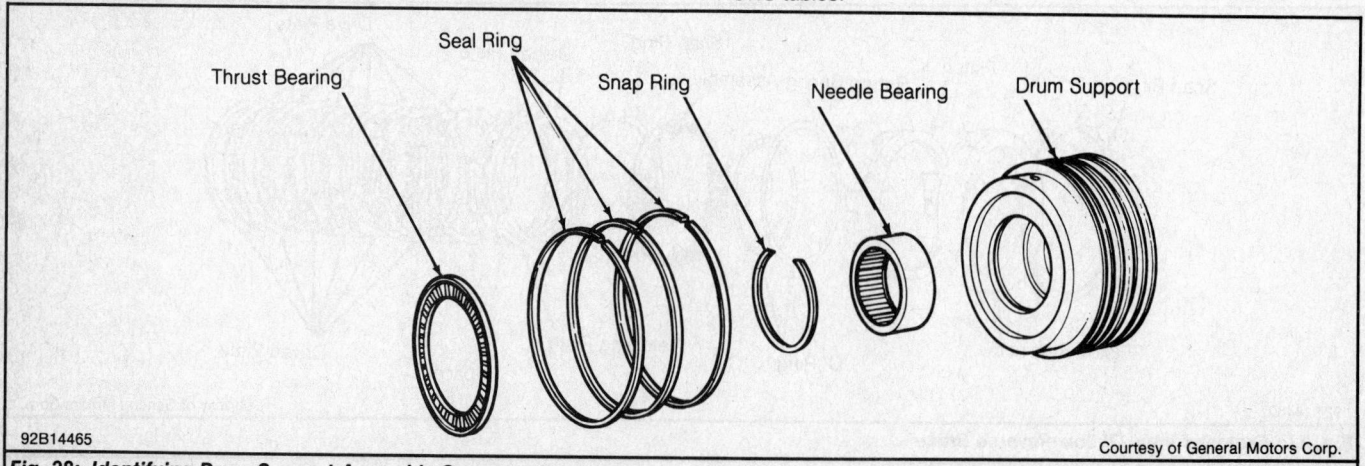

92B14465

Courtesy of General Motors Corp.

Fig. 28: Identifying Drum Support Assembly Components

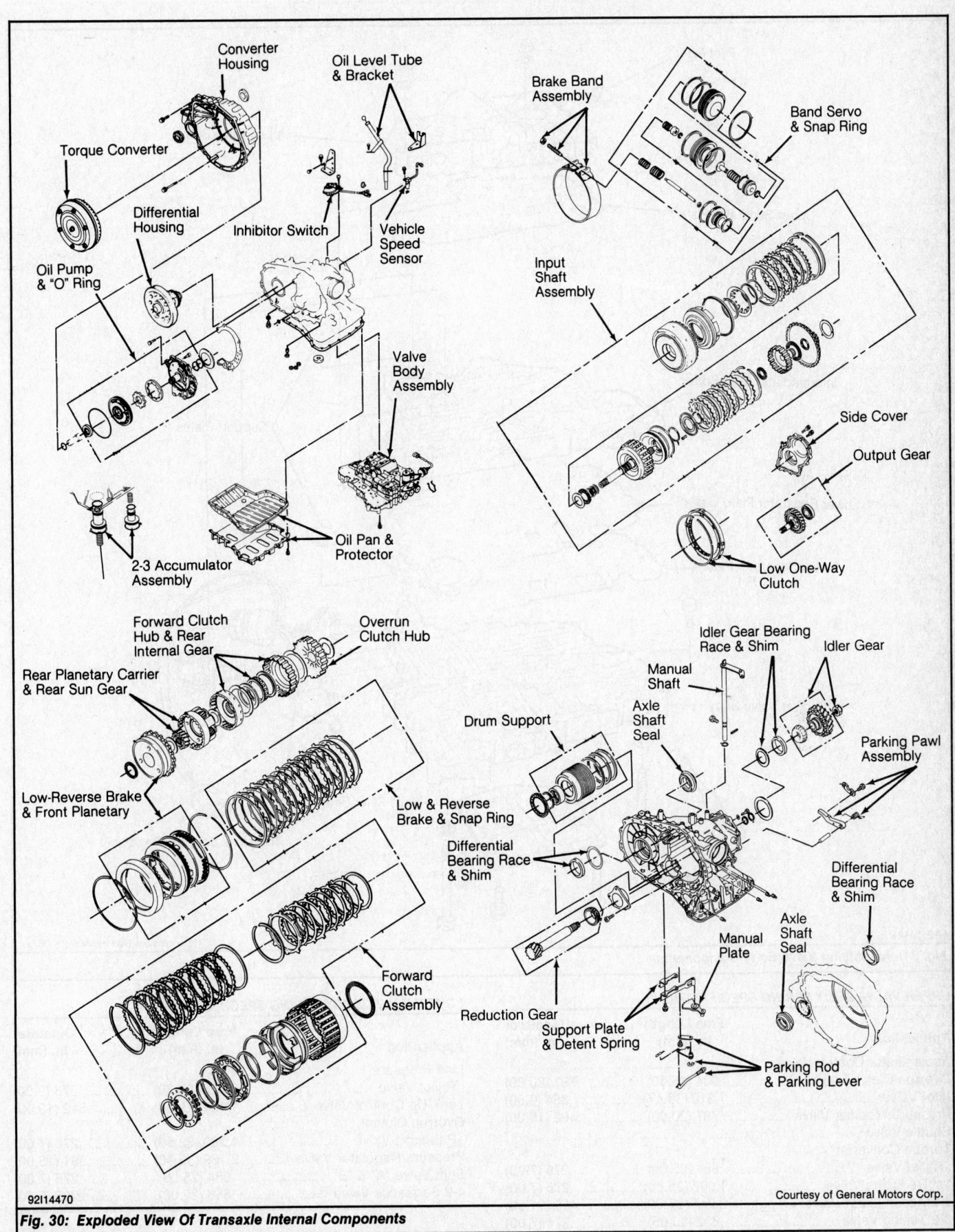

92I14470

Fig. 30: Exploded View Of Transaxle Internal Components

AUTOMATIC TRANSMISSIONS
Geo JF403-E (Cont.)

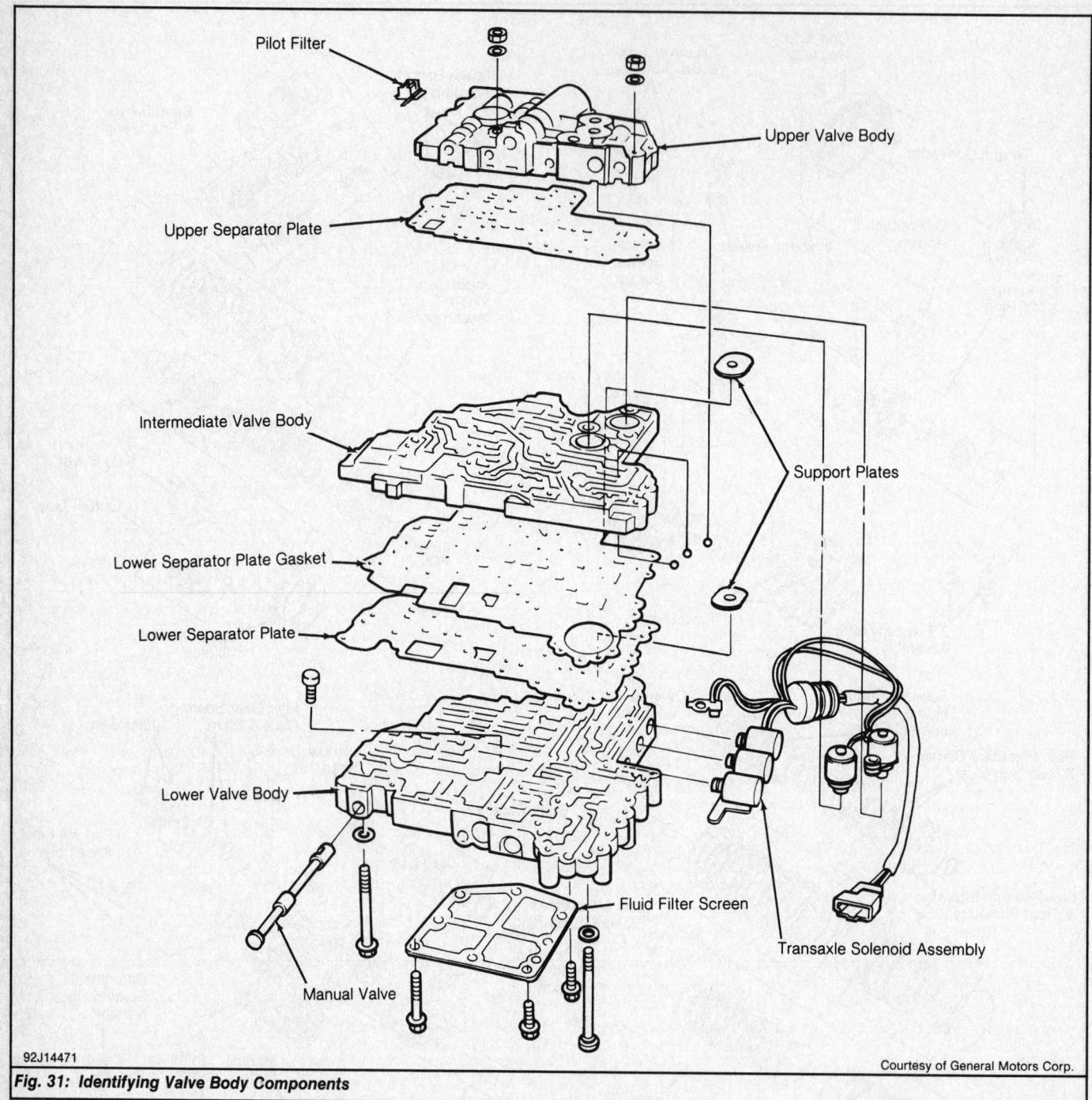

Fig. 31: Identifying Valve Body Components

92J14471

Courtesy of General Motors Corp.

UPPER VALVE BODY SPRING SPECIFICATIONS

Application	Free Length In. (mm)	Diameter In. (mm)
Accumulator Control Valve	[1]	[1]
Overrun Clutch Valve	.984 (25.00)	.787 (20.00)
Pilot Valve	1.318 (33.47)	.354 (9.00)
Pressure Modifier Valve	.787 (20.00)	.402 (10.20)
Shuttle Valve	[1]	[1]
Torque Converter		
Relief Valve	.984 (25.00)	.276 (7.00)
1st Reducing Valve	1.008 (25.60)	.276 (7.00)
1-2 Accumulator Valve	2.244 (57.00)	.453 (11.50)
3-2 Timing Valve	.632 (16.05)	.276 (7.00)

[1] – Valve does not use a valve spring.

LOWER VALVE BODY SPRING SPECIFICATIONS

Application	Free Length In. (mm)	Diameter In. (mm)
Line Pressure		
Relief Valve	2.728 (69.30)	.378 (9.60)
Lock-Up Control Valve	1.161 (29.50)	.512 (13.00)
Overrun Clutch		
Reducing Valve	1.280 (32.50)	.276 (7.00)
Pressure Regulator Valve	2.169 (55.10)	.591 (15.00)
Shift Valve "A" & "B"	.984 (25.00)	.276 (7.00)
4-2 Sequence Valve	.866 (22.00)	.205 (5.20)

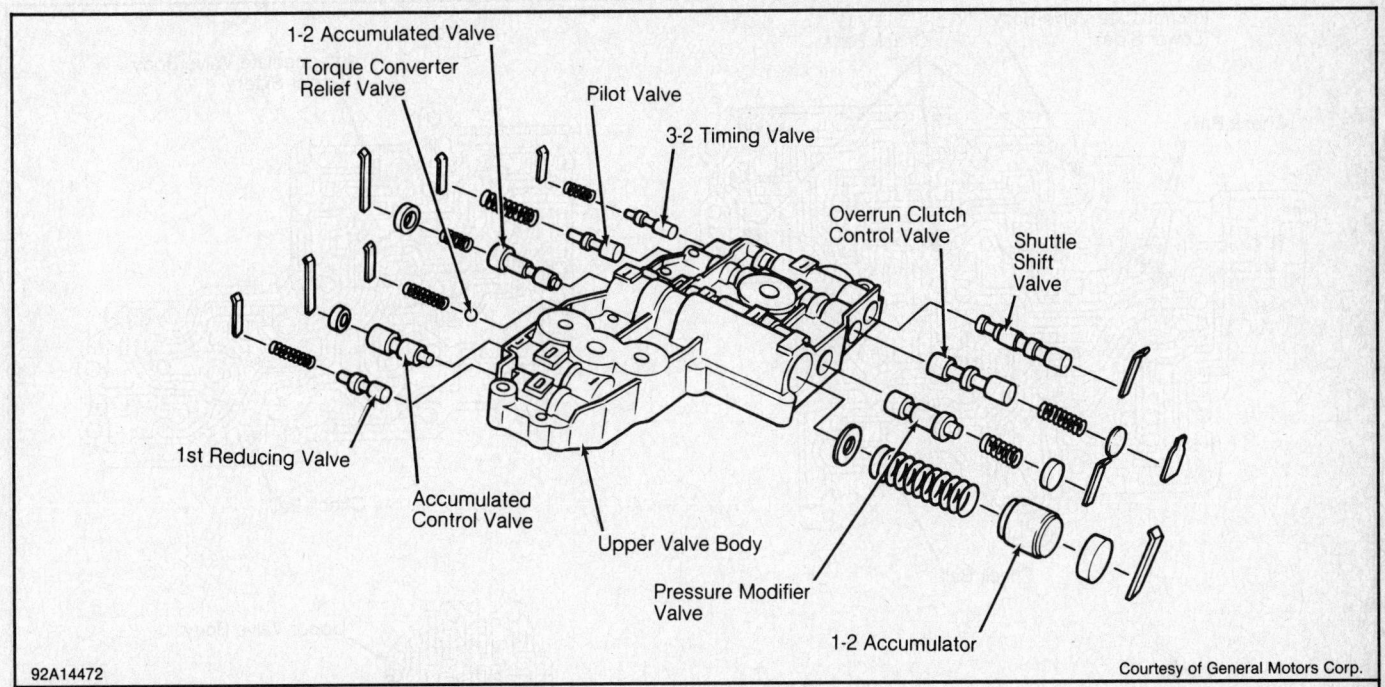

Fig. 32: Identifying Upper Valve Body Components

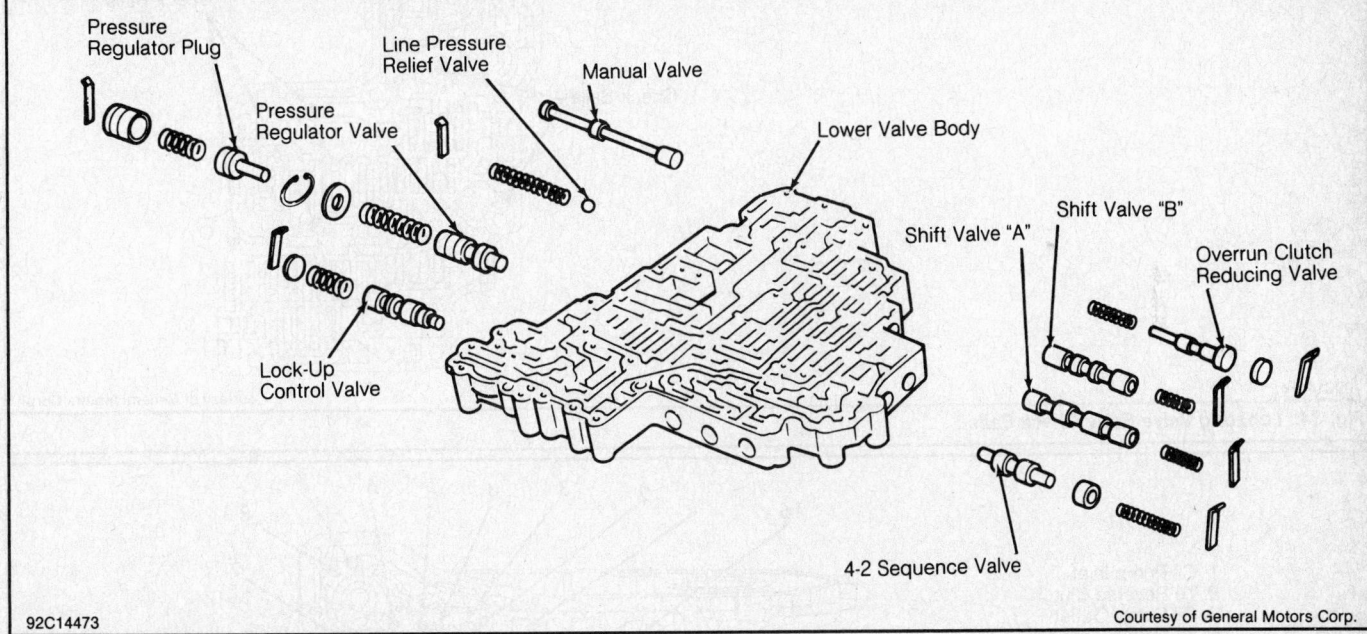

Fig. 33: Identifying Lower Valve Body Components

Reassembly – 1) To reassemble, reverse disassembly procedures. Assemble each valve, spring, plug and key. *See Figs. 31-33.* DO NOT push any part in with excessive force. Install pilot filter to separator plate. Install one-way cup and spring into lower valve body.

2) Install separator plate, gasket and intermediate body to lower valve body. Install steel balls into each valve body and intermediate body. *See Fig. 34.* Install separator plate and stack valve bodies. Install valve body bolts, but do not tighten at this time. Install solenoids and temperature sensor. *See Fig. 55.*

OIL PUMP ASSEMBLY

Disassembly – Remove oil pump cover bolts. Remove cover from housing. Remove outer rotor, inner rotor, "O" ring, seal rings and oil seal.

Inspection – Inspect inner and outer rotor surfaces and bushings for wear or damage. Replace any defective part. Measure oil pump clearances. Using straightedge and feeler gauge, measure inner rotor-to-oil pump housing and outer rotor-to-oil pump housing clearances. *See Fig. 37.* Measure with feeler gauge between inner rotor lobe and outer rotor lobe. See OIL PUMP SPECIFICATIONS table. Replace any part not within specification.

OIL PUMP SPECIFICATIONS

Application	Clearance In. (mm)
Inner Rotor-To-Oil Pump Housing	.0008-.0020 (.020-.050)
Outer Rotor-To-Oil Pump Housing	.0008-.0020 (.020-.050)
Inner Rotor-To-Outer Rotor	.0008-.0059 (.020-.150)

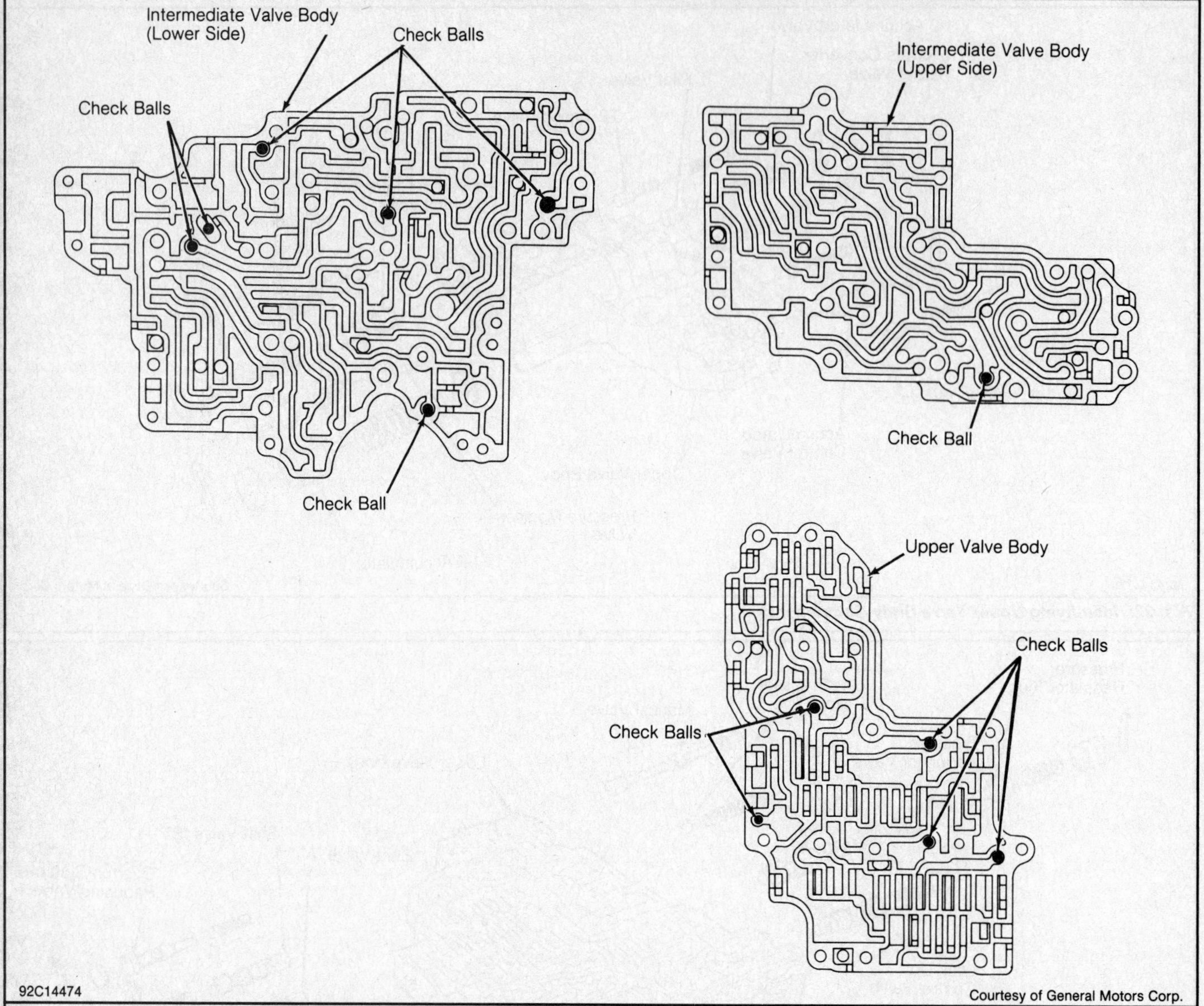

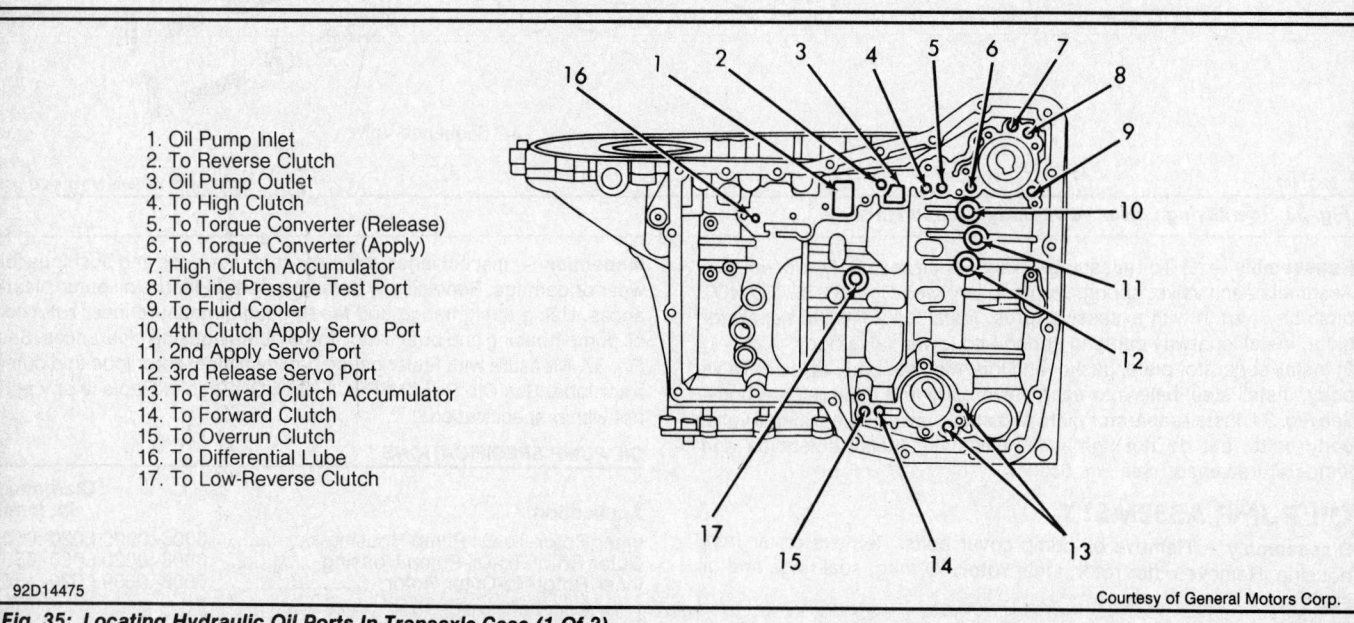

Intermediate Valve Body
(Lower Side)
Check Balls
Check Balls
Check Ball
Intermediate Valve Body
(Upper Side)
Check Ball
Upper Valve Body
Check Balls
Check Balls
92C14474
Courtesy of General Motors Corp.

Fig. 34: Locating Valve Body Check Balls

1. Oil Pump Inlet
2. To Reverse Clutch
3. Oil Pump Outlet
4. To High Clutch
5. To Torque Converter (Release)
6. To Torque Converter (Apply)
7. High Clutch Accumulator
8. To Line Pressure Test Port
9. To Fluid Cooler
10. 4th Clutch Apply Servo Port
11. 2nd Apply Servo Port
12. 3rd Release Servo Port
13. To Forward Clutch Accumulator
14. To Forward Clutch
15. To Overrun Clutch
16. To Differential Lube
17. To Low-Reverse Clutch

1
2
3
4
5
6
7
8
9
10
11
12
13
14
15
16
17
92D14475
Courtesy of General Motors Corp.

Fig. 35: Locating Hydraulic Oil Ports In Transaxle Case (1 Of 2)

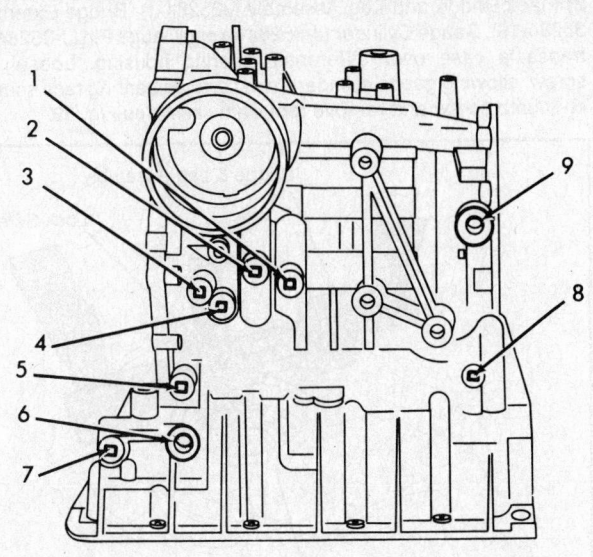
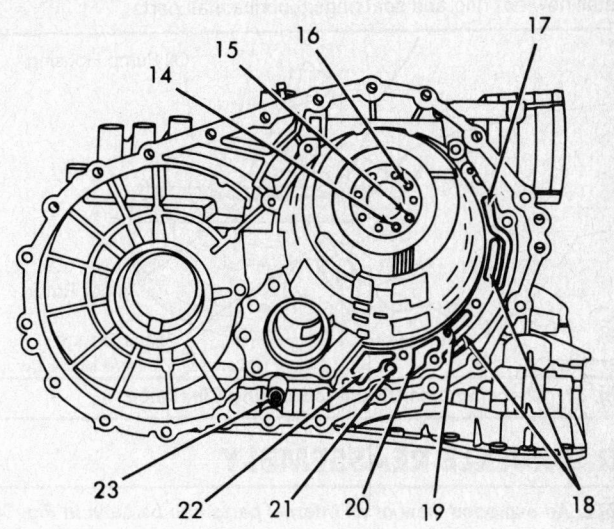
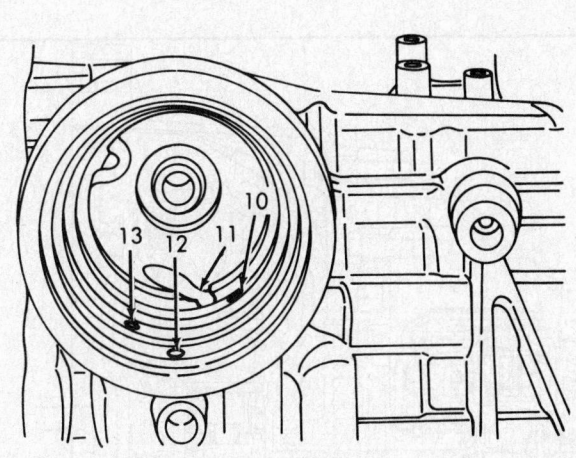
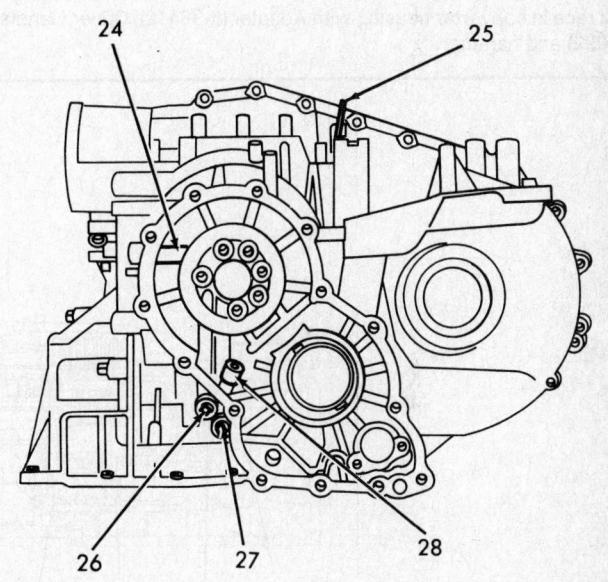

1. 3rd Release Servo Test Port
2. 2nd Apply Servo Test Port
3. Torque Converter Release Test Port
4. 4th Apply Servo Test Port
5. Torque Converter Apply Test Port
6. Fluid Cooler Inlet
7. Line Pressure Test Port
8. Accumulator Pressure Test Port
9. Fluid Cooler Outlet
10. 2nd Apply Servo Port
11. 3rd Release Servo Port
12. 4th Apply Servo Port
13. Servo Exhaust
14. To Overrun Clutch

15. To Forward Clutch
16. From Fluid Cooler
17. To Torque Converter Apply Side
18. Torque Converter Release Side
19. To High Clutch
20. Oil Pump Outlet
21. To Reverse Clutch
22. Oil Pump Inlet
23. To Differential Lube
24. From Fluid Cooler (Rear Lube)
25. Transaxle Case Vent
26. Forward Clutch Test Port
27. Overrun Clutch Test Port
28. Overrun Clutch Vent Check Valve

92E14476

Courtesy of General Motors Corp.

Fig. 36: Locating Hydraulic Oil Ports In Transaxle Case (2 Of 2)

Reassembly – To reassemble, reverse disassembly procedure. Install new "O" ring and seal rings. Lubricate all parts.

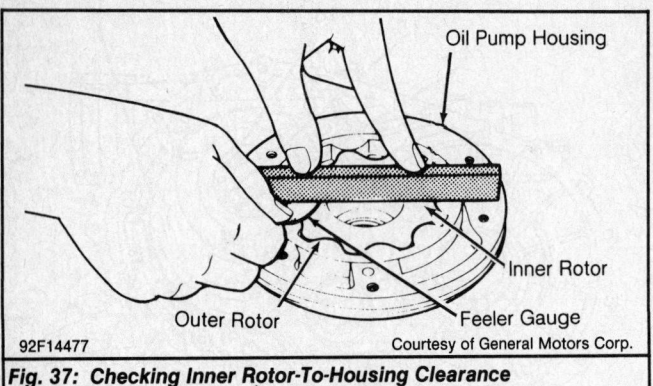

92F14477
Courtesy of General Motors Corp.

Fig. 37: Checking Inner Rotor-To-Housing Clearance

TRANSAXLE REASSEMBLY

NOTE: An exploded view of all internal parts can be seen in Fig. 30. Thrust washer and bearing locations can be found in Fig. 38. Location of hydraulic oil ports can be seen in Figs. 35 and 36.

Differential Bearing Preload – **1)** Install differential side bearing outer race in converter housing with Adapter (J-38412), Driver Handle (J-8092) and hammer.

2) Place Bridge and Leg Assembly (J35284-1), Bridge Extension (J-35284-19), Gauge Cylinder (J-35284-4) and Gauge Pin (J-35284-24) on transaxle case over differential bearing housing. Loosen thumb screw, allowing gauge cylinder to rest on side bearing race seat. Tighten thumb screw and remove tool from case. *See Fig. 39.*

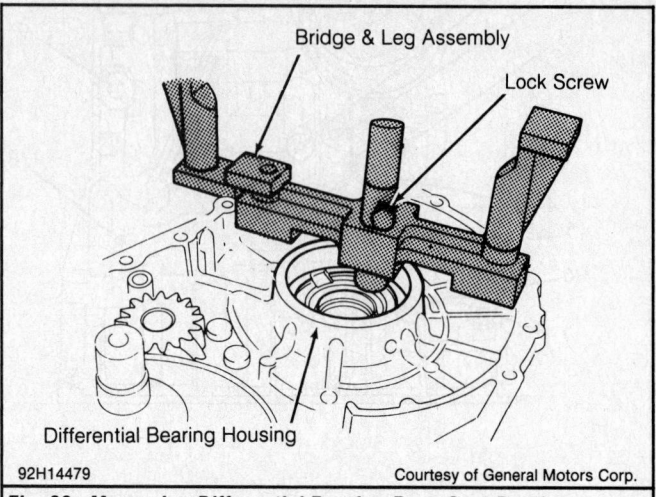

92H14479
Courtesy of General Motors Corp.

Fig. 39: Measuring Differential Bearing Race Seat Depth

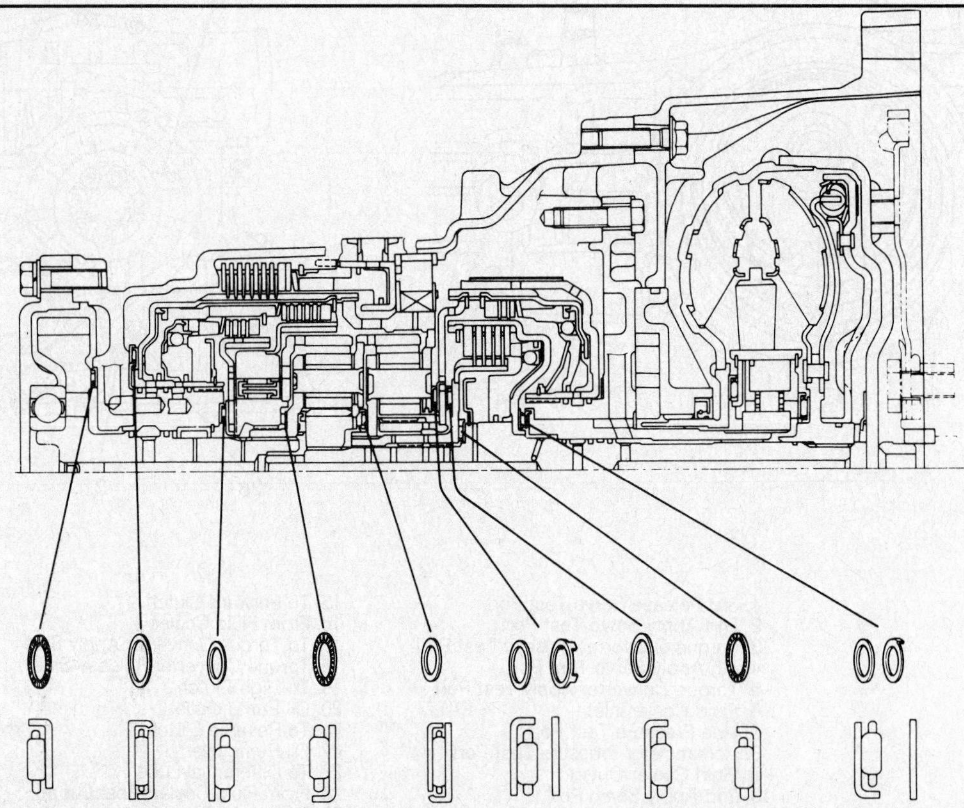

THRUST BEARING DIMENSIONS

Outer diameter	mm (in)	87.0 (3.425)	108.0 (4.252)	56.5 (2.224)	50.0 (1.969)	51.0 (2.008)	70.0 (2.756)	70.0 (2.756)	42.0 (1.654)	50.6 (1.992)
Inner diameter	mm (in)	70.1 (2.760)	85.15 (3.352)	40.0 (1.575)	35.1 (1.382)	33.1 (1.303)	50.1 (1.972)	50.1 (1.972)	23.0 (0.906)	34.7 (1.366)

92G14478
Courtesy of General Motors Corp.

Fig. 38: Locating Thrust Bearings & Washers

3) Install differential case assembly in converter housing. Install differential side bearing race on exposed side bearing. Set gauge assembly on converter housing over differential case. Loosen thumb screw, allowing gauge pin to rest on bearing race. Lock gauge pin with thumb screw.

4) Using a feeler gauge, measure gap between gauge cylinder and gauge pin or measure gap with available shims. See Fig. 40. Selective size shims are available in thicknesses of .005-.036" (.12-.92 mm) in .002" (.04 mm) increments. Install selected shim into side bearing race bore of transaxle case. Install bearing race with Installer (J-38412), driver handle and hammer.

5) Install transaxle case to torque converter housing with 4 bolts. Install Adaptor (J-35259-2A) into differential from torque converter side. Install INCH lb. torque wrench to adaptor. Measure rotational torque. Torque specification is 7-10 INCH lbs. (.78-1.13 N.m).

6) If rotational torque is less than specified, select next thicker size shim. If rotational torque is within specification, remove transaxle case from differential case assembly.

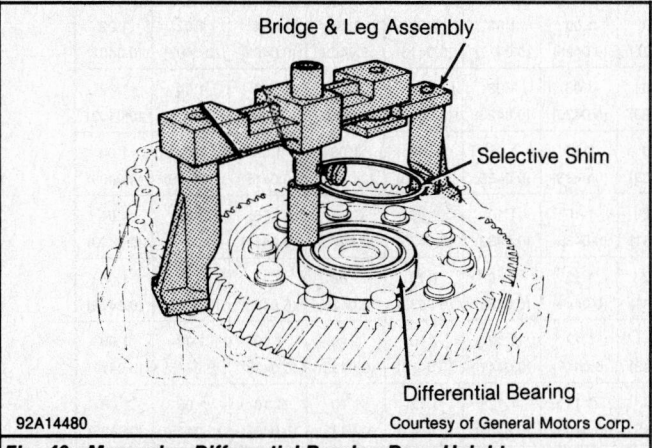

Fig. 40: *Measuring Differential Bearing Race Height*

92A14480   Courtesy of General Motors Corp.

Idler Gear Bearing Preload – **1)** Install reduction gear bearing outer race in transaxle case and tighten bolts. Install reduction gear in transaxle case.

2) Place Bridge and Leg Assembly (J-35284-1), Gauge Cylinder (J-35284-4), Gauge Pin (J-35284-26) and dial indicator on transaxle case over reduction gear shaft. See Fig. 41. Measure distance of idler gear bearing seat; this is dimension "A". Measure distance to shoulder on reduction gear shaft; this is dimension "B". Subtract dimension "B" from dimension "A"; this is dimension "C". See Fig. 42.

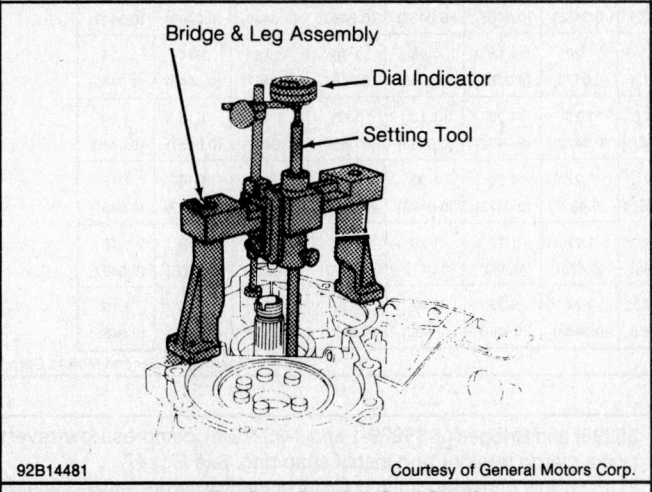

Fig. 41: *Measuring Idler Gear Bearing Seat Depth*

92B14481   Courtesy of General Motors Corp.

3) Place bearing outer race onto bearing on idler gear. Using bridge and leg assembly, gauge cylinder and dial indicator, measure dimensions "X" and "Y". See Figs. 43 and 45. Subtract dimension "X" from dimension "Y". This equals dimension "Z". See Fig. 45. Using

dimension "Z" and dimension "C" from step **2)**, select appropriate shim from IDLER GEAR BEARING SHIM SIZE CHART. See Fig. 44.

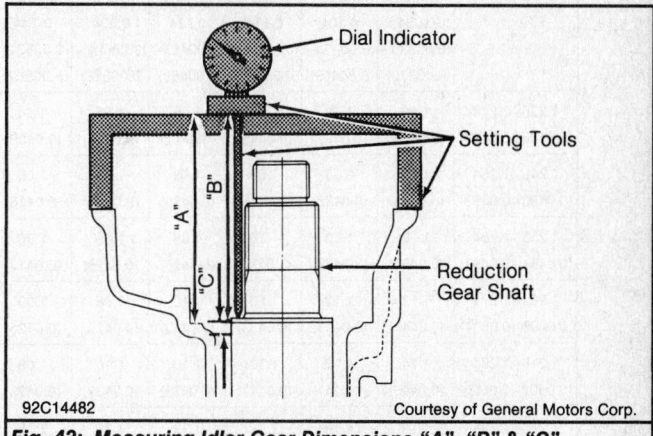

Fig. 42: *Measuring Idler Gear Dimensions "A", "B" & "C"*

92C14482   Courtesy of General Motors Corp.

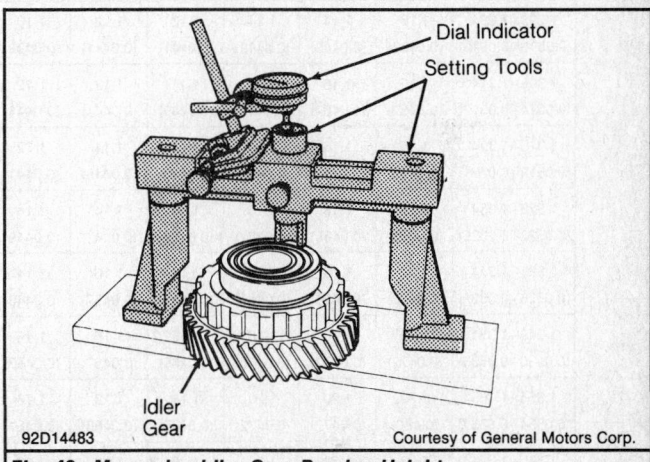

Fig. 43: *Measuring Idler Gear Bearing Height*

92D14483   Courtesy of General Motors Corp.

4) Install selected shim into transaxle case. Using Bearing Race Installer (J-35290), Handle (J-8092) and hammer, install bearing race into transaxle case.

5) Install new "O" ring on manual shaft. Install manual shaft and new locating bolt. Start spring pin into manual plate. Install manual plate on manual shaft and drive in spring pin. See Fig. 7. Install parking actuator support in transaxle case. Install parking pawl, parking shaft and return spring. See Fig. 6. Install parking rod and parking lever and secure with "E" ring.

6) Install new "O" rings on accumulator pistons. Install accumulator piston return spring. Install accumulator pistons into transaxle case. Using Installer (J-33411) and hammer, install idler gear on reduction gear shaft. See Fig. 30. Wipe all oil off lock nut seat on idler gear. Engage parking pawl to parking gear and tighten lock nut to 167 ft. lbs. (226 N.m). Ensure idler gear turns smoothly with a torque of 14 INCH lbs. (1.58 N.m). If not, install appropriate shims. Stake lock nut to idler gear shaft with a punch.

Sub-Assemblies – **1)** If necessary, install drum support and low-reverse brake. Align oil holes between drum support and transaxle case, and install drum support. See Fig. 30. Install low-reverse brake drive and driven plate and snap ring. See Fig. 46.

2) Apply petroleum jelly to forward clutch-to-transaxle case thrust bearing. Install bearing on forward clutch. Install forward clutch assembly into case. See Fig. 30. Ensure end face of drum support and inner side of forward clutch drum are flush with each other.

3) Apply petroleum jelly to thrust washer and bearing race and install on overrun clutch hub. Install overrun clutch hub into case until it contacts thrust bearing on drum support. Install forward clutch hub and rear internal gear. Apply petroleum jelly to thrust bearing and place over rear planetary carrier hub. Install rear planetary carrier into rear internal gear. Install rear sun gear. See Fig. 30.

mm (in)

C \ Z	0.085~0.094 (0.00330~0.00370)	0.095~0.104 (0.00374~0.00409)	0.105~0.114 (0.00413~0.00449)	0.115~0.124 (0.00453~0.00488)	0.125~0.134 (0.00492~0.00528)	0.135~0.144 (0.00531~0.00567)	0.145~0.154 (0.00571~0.00606)	0.155~0.164 (0.00610~0.00646)	0.165~0.174 (0.00650~0.00685)	0.175~0.184 (0.00689~0.00724)	0.185~0.194 (0.00728~0.00764)	0.195~0.204 (0.00768~0.00803)	0.205~0.214 (0.00807~0.00843)	0.215~0.224 (0.00846~0.00882)
1.235~1.244 (0.0486~0.0489)	1.10 (0.0433)	1.08 (0.0425)	1.08 (0.0425)	1.06 (0.0417)	1.06 (0.0416)	1.04 (0.0409)	1.04 (0.0409)	1.02 (0.0402)	1.02 (0.0402)	1.00 (0.0394)	1.00 (0.0394)	0.98 (0.0386)	0.98 (0.0386)	0.96 (0.0378)
1.245~1.254 (0.0490~0.0493)	1.10 (0.0433)	1.10 (0.0433)	1.08 (0.0425)	1.08 (0.0425)	1.06 (0.0417)	1.06 (0.0416)	1.04 (0.0409)	1.04 (0.0409)	1.02 (0.0402)	1.02 (0.0402)	1.00 (0.0394)	1.00 (0.0394)	0.98 (0.0386)	0.98 (0.0386)
1.255~1.264 (0.0494~0.0497)	1.12 (0.0441)	1.10 (0.0433)	1.10 (0.0433)	1.08 (0.0425)	1.08 (0.0425)	1.06 (0.0417)	1.06 (0.0416)	1.04 (0.0409)	1.04 (0.0409)	1.02 (0.0402)	1.02 (0.0402)	1.00 (0.0394)	1.00 (0.0394)	0.98 (0.0386)
1.265~1.274 (0.0498~0.0501)	1.12 (0.0441)	1.12 (0.0441)	1.10 (0.0433)	1.10 (0.0433)	1.08 (0.0425)	1.08 (0.0425)	1.06 (0.0417)	1.06 (0.0416)	1.04 (0.0409)	1.04 (0.0409)	1.02 (0.0402)	1.02 (0.0402)	1.00 (0.0394)	1.00 (0.0394)
1.275~1.284 (0.0502~0.0505)	1.14 (0.0449)	1.12 (0.0441)	1.12 (0.0441)	1.10 (0.0433)	1.10 (0.0433)	1.08 (0.0425)	1.08 (0.0425)	1.06 (0.0417)	1.06 (0.0416)	1.04 (0.0409)	1.04 (0.0409)	1.02 (0.0402)	1.02 (0.0402)	1.00 (0.0394)
1.285~1.294 (0.0506~0.0509)	1.14 (0.0449)	1.14 (0.0449)	1.12 (0.0441)	1.12 (0.0441)	1.10 (0.0433)	1.10 (0.0433)	1.08 (0.0425)	1.08 (0.0425)	1.06 (0.0417)	1.06 (0.0416)	1.04 (0.0409)	1.04 (0.0409)	1.02 (0.0402)	1.02 (0.0402)
1.295~1.304 (0.0510~0.0513)	1.16 (0.0457)	1.14 (0.0449)	1.14 (0.0449)	1.12 (0.0441)	1.12 (0.0441)	1.10 (0.0433)	1.10 (0.0433)	1.08 (0.0425)	1.08 (0.0425)	1.06 (0.0417)	1.06 (0.0416)	1.04 (0.0409)	1.04 (0.0409)	1.02 (0.0402)
1.305~1.314 (0.0514~0.0517)	1.16 (0.0457)	1.16 (0.0457)	1.14 (0.0449)	1.14 (0.0449)	1.12 (0.0441)	1.12 (0.0441)	1.10 (0.0433)	1.10 (0.0433)	1.08 (0.0425)	1.08 (0.0425)	1.06 (0.0417)	1.06 (0.0416)	1.04 (0.0409)	1.04 (0.0409)
1.315~1.324 (0.0518~0.0521)	1.18 (0.0465)	1.16 (0.0457)	1.16 (0.0457)	1.14 (0.0449)	1.14 (0.0449)	1.12 (0.0441)	1.12 (0.0441)	1.10 (0.0433)	1.10 (0.0433)	1.08 (0.0425)	1.08 (0.0425)	1.06 (0.0417)	1.06 (0.0416)	1.04 (0.0409)
1.325~1.334 (0.0522~0.0525)	1.18 (0.0465)	1.18 (0.0465)	1.16 (0.0457)	1.16 (0.0457)	1.14 (0.0449)	1.14 (0.0449)	1.12 (0.0441)	1.12 (0.0441)	1.10 (0.0433)	1.10 (0.0433)	1.08 (0.0425)	1.08 (0.0425)	1.06 (0.0417)	1.06 (0.0416)
1.335~1.344 (0.0526~0.0529)	1.20 (0.0472)	1.18 (0.0465)	1.18 (0.0465)	1.16 (0.0457)	1.16 (0.0457)	1.14 (0.0449)	1.14 (0.0449)	1.12 (0.0441)	1.12 (0.0441)	1.10 (0.0433)	1.10 (0.0433)	1.08 (0.0425)	1.08 (0.0425)	1.06 (0.0417)
1.345~1.354 (0.0530~0.0533)	1.20 (0.0472)	1.20 (0.0472)	1.18 (0.0465)	1.18 (0.0465)	1.16 (0.0457)	1.16 (0.0457)	1.14 (0.0449)	1.14 (0.0449)	1.12 (0.0441)	1.12 (0.0441)	1.10 (0.0433)	1.10 (0.0433)	1.08 (0.0425)	1.08 (0.0425)
1.355~1.364 (0.0534~0.0537)	1.22 (0.480)	1.20 (0.0472)	1.20 (0.0472)	1.18 (0.0465)	1.18 (0.0465)	1.16 (0.0457)	1.16 (0.0457)	1.14 (0.0449)	1.14 (0.0449)	1.12 (0.0441)	1.12 (0.0441)	1.10 (0.0433)	1.10 (0.0433)	1.08 (0.0425)
1.365~1.374 (0.0538~0.0541)	1.22 (0.480)	1.22 (0.480)	1.20 (0.0472)	1.20 (0.0472)	1.18 (0.0465)	1.18 (0.0465)	1.16 (0.0457)	1.16 (0.0457)	1.14 (0.0449)	1.14 (0.0449)	1.12 (0.0441)	1.12 (0.0441)	1.10 (0.0433)	1.10 (0.0433)
1.375~1.384 (0.0542~0.0544)	1.24 (0.0488)	1.22 (0.480)	1.22 (0.480)	1.20 (0.0472)	1.20 (0.0472)	1.18 (0.0465)	1.18 (0.0465)	1.16 (0.0457)	1.16 (0.0457)	1.14 (0.0449)	1.14 (0.0449)	1.12 (0.0441)	1.12 (0.0441)	1.10 (0.0433)
1.385~1.394 (0.0545~0.0548)	1.24 (0.0488)	1.24 (0.0488)	1.22 (0.480)	1.22 (0.480)	1.20 (0.0472)	1.20 (0.0472)	1.18 (0.0465)	1.18 (0.0465)	1.16 (0.0457)	1.16 (0.0457)	1.14 (0.0449)	1.14 (0.0449)	1.12 (0.0441)	1.12 (0.0441)
1.395~1.404 (0.0549~0.0552)	1.26 (0.0496)	1.24 (0.0488)	1.24 (0.0488)	1.22 (0.480)	1.22 (0.480)	1.20 (0.0472)	1.20 (0.0472)	1.18 (0.0465)	1.18 (0.0465)	1.16 (0.0457)	1.16 (0.0457)	1.14 (0.0449)	1.14 (0.0449)	1.12 (0.0441)
1.405~1.414 (0.0553~0.0556)	1.26 (0.0496)	1.26 (0.0496)	1.24 (0.0488)	1.24 (0.0488)	1.22 (0.480)	1.22 (0.480)	1.20 (0.0472)	1.20 (0.0472)	1.18 (0.0465)	1.18 (0.0465)	1.16 (0.0457)	1.16 (0.0457)	1.14 (0.0449)	1.14 (0.0449)
1.415~1.424 (0.0557~0.0560)	1.28 (0.0504)	1.26 (0.0496)	1.26 (0.0496)	1.24 (0.0488)	1.24 (0.0488)	1.22 (0.480)	1.22 (0.480)	1.20 (0.0472)	1.20 (0.0472)	1.18 (0.0465)	1.18 (0.0465)	1.16 (0.0457)	1.16 (0.0457)	1.14 (0.0449)
1.425~1.434 (0.0561~0.0564)	1.28 (0.0504)	1.28 (0.0504)	1.26 (0.0496)	1.26 (0.0496)	1.24 (0.0488)	1.24 (0.0488)	1.22 (0.480)	1.22 (0.480)	1.20 (0.0472)	1.20 (0.0472)	1.18 (0.0465)	1.18 (0.0465)	1.16 (0.0457)	1.16 (0.0457)
1.435~1.444 (0.0565~0.0568)	1.30 (0.0512)	1.28 (0.0504)	1.28 (0.0504)	1.26 (0.0496)	1.26 (0.0496)	1.24 (0.0488)	1.24 (0.0488)	1.22 (0.480)	1.22 (0.480)	1.20 (0.0472)	1.20 (0.0472)	1.18 (0.0465)	1.18 (0.0465)	1.16 (0.0457)
1.445~1.454 (0.0569~0.0572)	1.30 (0.0512)	1.30 (0.0512)	1.28 (0.0504)	1.28 (0.0504)	1.26 (0.0496)	1.26 (0.0496)	1.24 (0.0488)	1.24 (0.0488)	1.22 (0.480)	1.22 (0.480)	1.20 (0.0472)	1.20 (0.0472)	1.18 (0.0465)	1.18 (0.0465)

92F14485

Courtesy of General Motors Corp.

Fig. 44: Idler Gear Bearing Shim Size Chart

4) Apply petroleum jelly to thrust bearings and install on front planetary carrier. See Fig. 30. Install low-reverse brake return springs to low-reverse brake piston.

5) Assemble low-reverse brake piston to low-reverse brake piston retainer. Install low-reverse brake piston, piston retainer and front planetary carrier into case. See Fig. 30.

6) Both oil passages in low-reverse brake piston retainer and transaxle case must be aligned after assembly. Using Compressor (J-38298) and Bridges (J-35279-1 and J-35279-5), compress low-reverse brake piston retainer and install snap ring. See Fig. 47.

7) Install low one-way clutch on front planetary carrier with retainer tab positioned to front. Install front sun gear to engage front pinion gear. Engage parking pawl with parking gear, insert output gear and engage it with rear carrier.

8) Install one-way clutch into correct position while rotating front sun gear clockwise. Remove output gear and front sun gear. Ensure one-

way clutch is flush with front planetary carrier and install snap ring.
9) Install servo return spring, servo piston, servo piston retainer and snap ring. Apply petroleum jelly to thrust bearing and install in reverse clutch.
10) Install high clutch in reverse clutch. Install thrust bearing into high clutch and install high clutch hub. Install thrust bearing to high clutch hub. Install front sun gear and bearing race. Install reverse and high clutch assembly with input shaft into transaxle case. *See Fig. 30.* Install brake band and tighten anchor end bolt lightly. *See Figs. 48 and 49.*

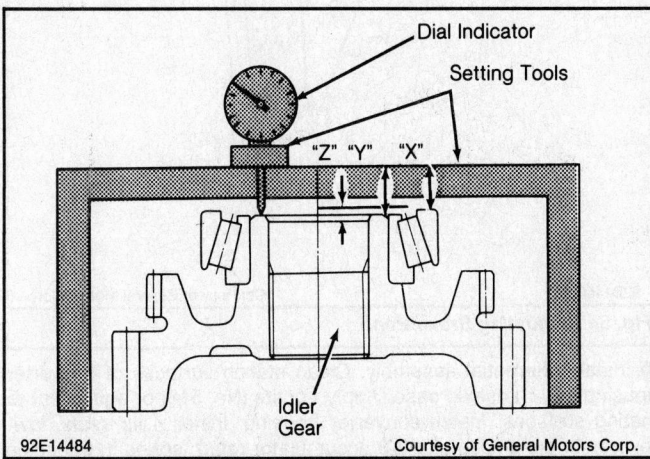

92E14484   Courtesy of General Motors Corp.

Fig. 45: Measuring Idler Gear Dimension "X", "Y" & "Z"

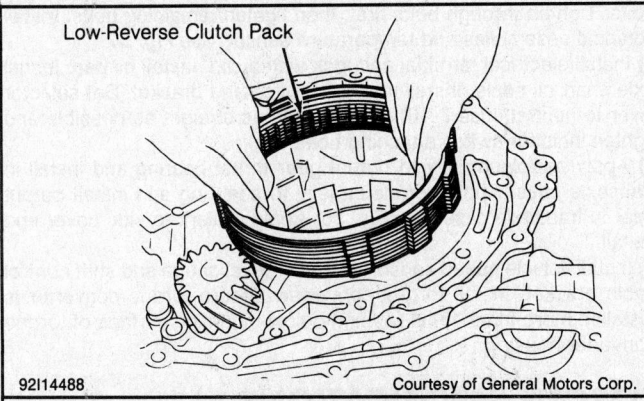

92I14488   Courtesy of General Motors Corp.

Fig. 46: Installing Low-Reverse Brake Assembly

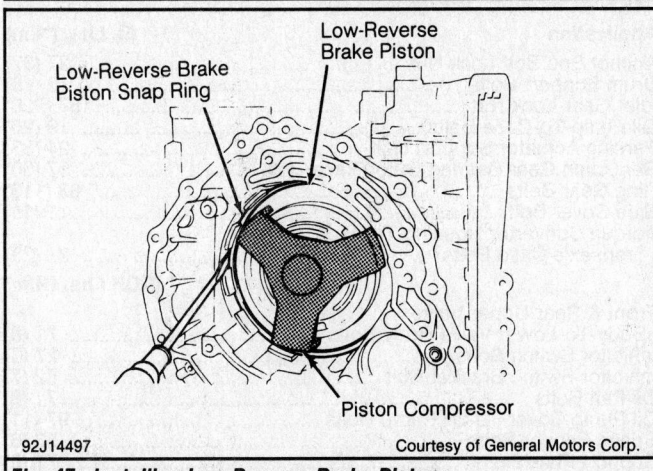

92J14497   Courtesy of General Motors Corp.

Fig. 47: Installing Low-Reverse Brake Piston

Total End Play Adjustment – 1) Set Bridge and Leg Assembly (J-35284-1), Bridge Extension (J35284-20), Gauge Cylinder (J-35284-4) and Gauge Pin (J-35284-32) on oil pump gasket surface with gasket removed. *See Fig. 50.*

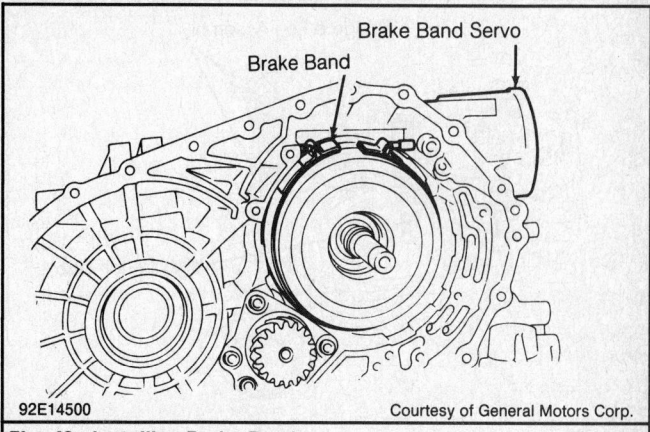

92E14500   Courtesy of General Motors Corp.

Fig. 48: Installing Brake Band

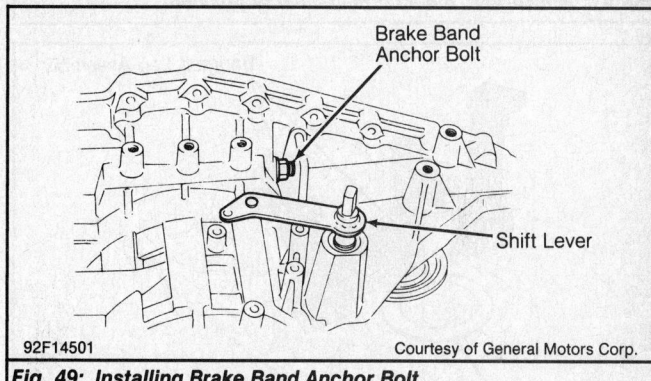

92F14501   Courtesy of General Motors Corp.

Fig. 49: Installing Brake Band Anchor Bolt

2) Loosen thumb screw to allow gauge cylinder to rest on pump hub and tighten thumb screw. Install bridge and leg assembly on transaxle. Loosen thumb screw to allow gauge pin to rest on high clutch hub thrust bearing and tighten thumb screw. *See Fig. 51.*
3) Loosen thumb screw and remove gauge cylinder and gauge pin. Measure gap between gauge cylinder and gauge pin. This measurement will be size of selective shim. Selective shims are available in thicknesses of .031-.079" (.78-2.00 mm) in .008" (.20 mm) increments.

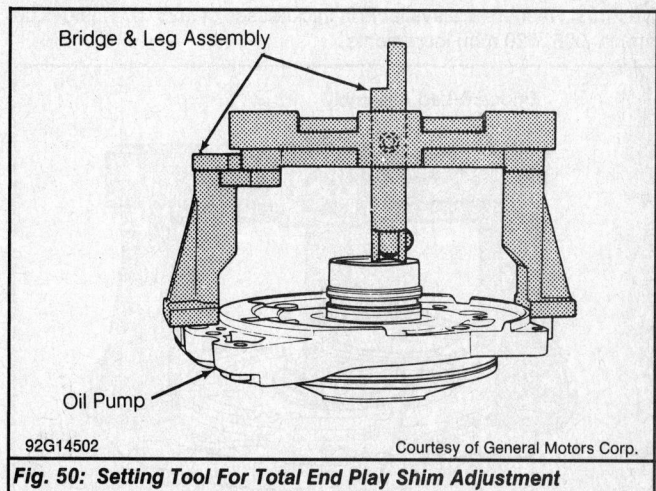

92G14502   Courtesy of General Motors Corp.

Fig. 50: Setting Tool For Total End Play Shim Adjustment

Reverse Clutch End Play Adjustment – 1) Place Bridge and Leg Assembly (J-35284-1), Gauge Cylinder (J-35284-4) and Reverse Clutch Gauge Pin (J-35284-33) on transaxle case. *See Fig. 52.* Loosen thumb screw to allow gauge cylinder to rest on reverse clutch hub and tighten thumb screw.

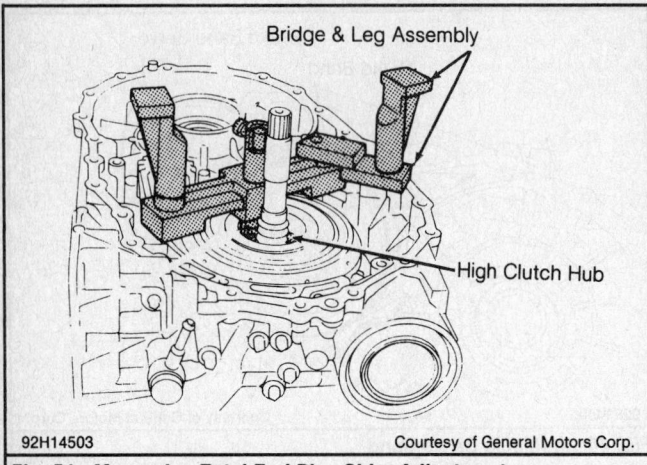

Fig. 51: **Measuring Total End Play Shim Adjustment**

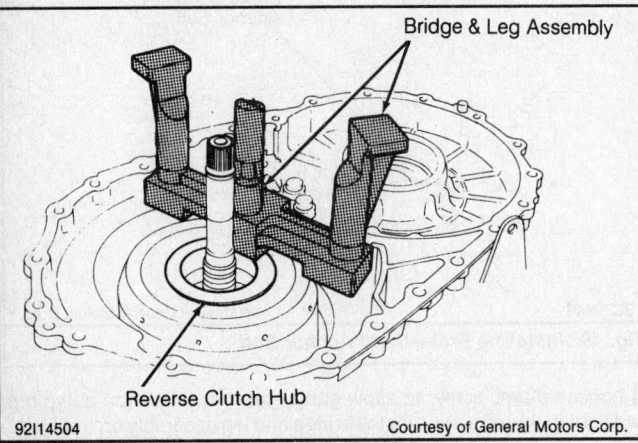

Fig. 52: **Positioning Tool For Reverse Clutch End Play**

2) Place gauge assembly on oil pump gasket surface (without gasket). Set selected total end play shims on oil pump hub. Loosen thumb screw so gauge pin rests on oil pump thrust washer surface and tighten thumb screw. Measure gap between gauge cylinder and gauge pin. *See Fig. 53.* This will determine size of selective thrust washer. Selective thrust washers are available in thicknesses of .025-.071" (.80-1.80 mm) in .008" (.20 mm) increments.

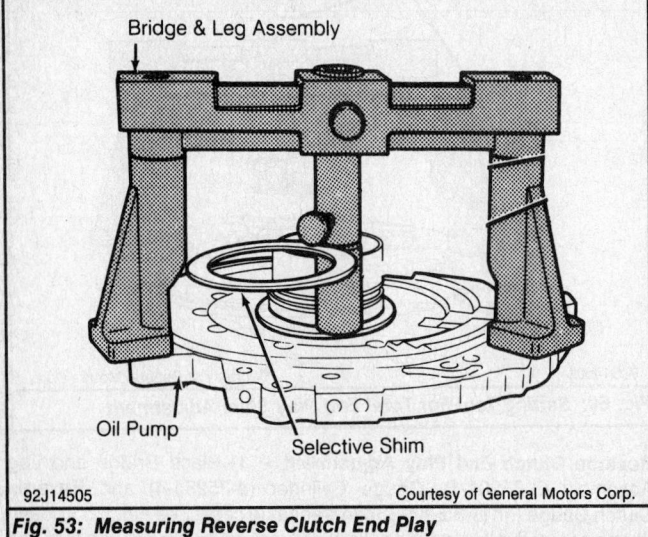

Fig. 53: **Measuring Reverse Clutch End Play**

Final Assembly − 1) Apply petroleum jelly to selected shims and thrust washer, and install on oil pump. Apply petroleum jelly to selected thrust bearing and install on high clutch hub.

2) Install oil pump gasket and oil pump. Install "O" ring on input shaft. Install "O" ring into oil hole for differential gear lubrication in transaxle case. Tighten brake band anchor bolt to 44 INCH lbs. (5 N.m). Loosen brake band anchor bolt 2 1/2 turns and tighten lock nut. *See Fig. 54.*

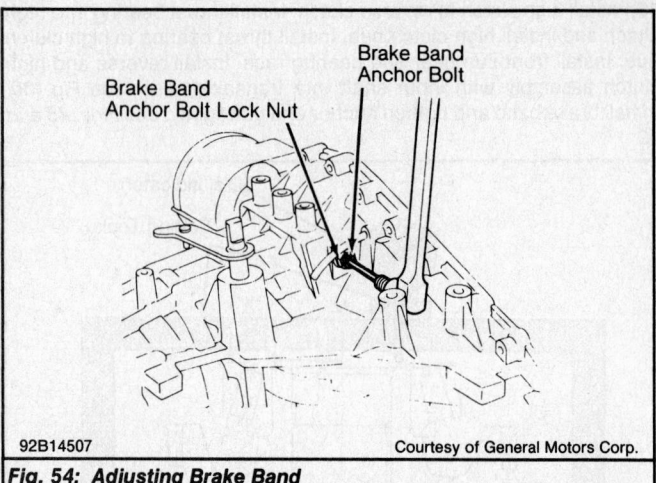

Fig. 54: **Adjusting Brake Band**

3) Install differential assembly. Clean mating surfaces of converter housing and transaxle case. Apply Loctite (No. 518) or equivalent to mating surfaces. Install converter housing. Install 4 lip seals, low-reverse brake sleeve and 2-3 accumulator return spring in transaxle case.

4) Align notch in manual valve with manual plate. Install valve body and bolts. Tighten through bolts first, then tighten remaining bolts. Install solenoid assemblies and temperature sensor. *See Fig. 55.*

5) Install electrical terminal and lock with a clip. Install oil pan. Install axle shaft oil seals. Install inhibitor switch and bracket. Set selector lever to neutral, insert .16" (4.0 mm) pin as straight as possible and tighten inhibitor switch attaching bolts.

6) Apply petroleum jelly to output gear thrust bearing and install in transaxle case. Apply petroleum jelly to seal ring and install output gear in transaxle case. *See Fig. 30.* Apply sealant to side cover and install.

7) Install vehicle speed sensor. Install oil level gauge and shift control cable bracket. Install torque converter. Ensure torque converter is installed more than .46" (11.7 mm) below mounting surface of torque converter housing.

TORQUE SPECIFICATIONS
TORQUE SPECIFICATIONS

Application	Ft. Lbs. (N.m)
Anchor End Bolt Lock Nut	27 (37)
Drum Support Bolts	13 (18)
Idler Gear Lock Nut	167 (226)
Oil Pump-To-Case Bolts	19 (26)
Parking Actuator Support Bolt	24 (33)
Reduction Gear Bearing Outer Race Bolt	37 (50)
Ring Gear Bolts	83 (113)
Side Cover Bolt	11 (15)
Torque Converter Housing-To- Transaxle Case Bolts	21 (28)

	INCH Lbs. (N.m)
Front & Rear Upper Valve Body-To-Lower Valve Body Bolts	71 (8)
Inhibitor Switch Bolts	27 (3)
Inhibitor Switch Bracket Bolt	62 (7)
Oil Pan Bolts	71 (8)
Oil Pump Cover-To-Oil Pump Bolts	97 (11)
Speed Sensor Bolts	53 (6)
Support Plate Bolts	71 (8)
Valve Body-To-Case Bolts	71 (8)

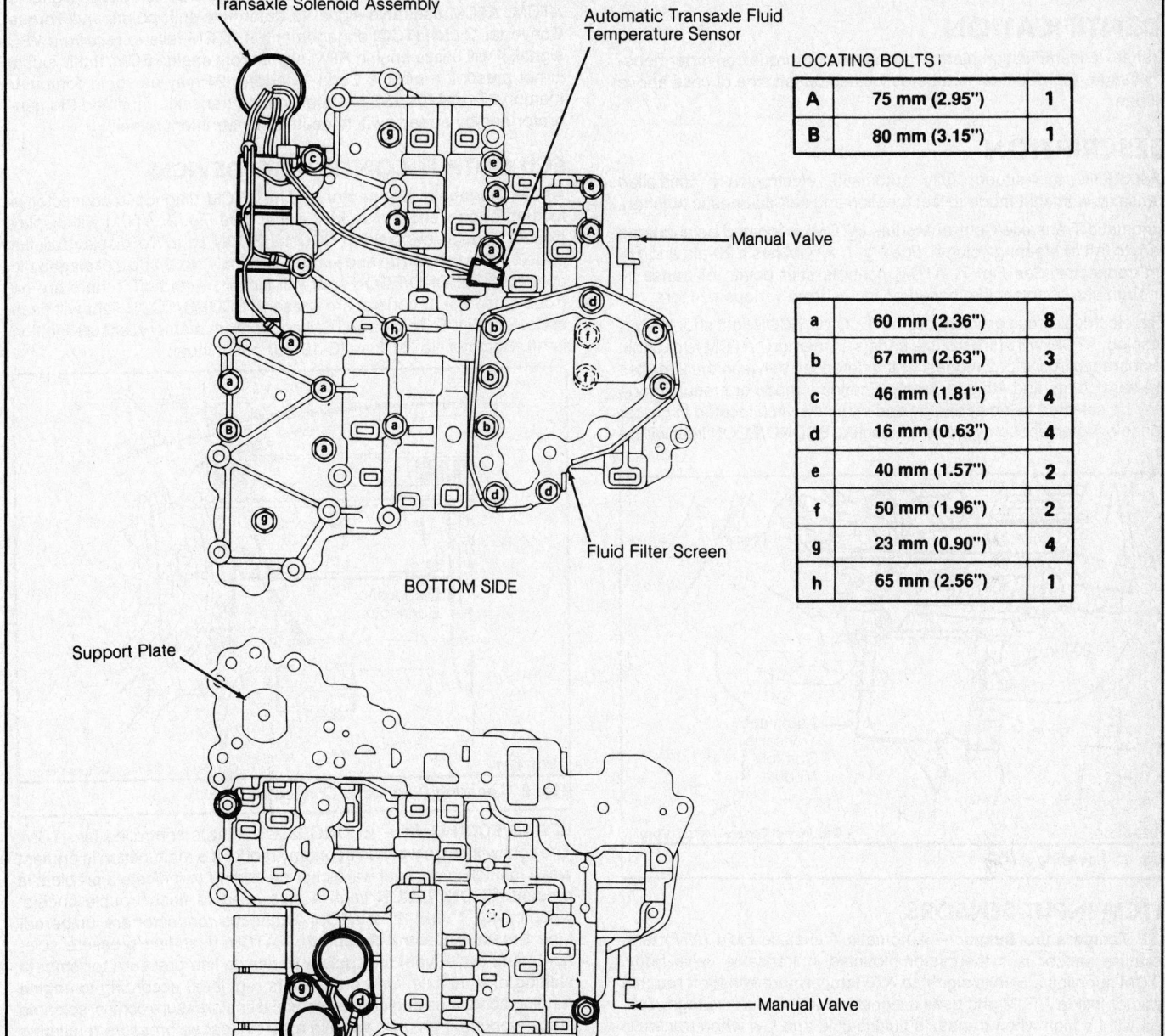

A	75 mm (2.95")	1
B	80 mm (3.15")	1

a	60 mm (2.36")	8
b	67 mm (2.63")	3
c	46 mm (1.81")	4
d	16 mm (0.63")	4
e	40 mm (1.57")	2
f	50 mm (1.96")	2
g	23 mm (0.90")	4
h	65 mm (2.56")	1

BOTTOM SIDE

TOP SIDE

92C14508

Courtesy of General Motors Corp.

Fig. 55: *Locating Valve Body Tightening Bolts*

TRANSAXLE SPECIFICATIONS

TRANSAXLE SPECIFICATIONS

Application	In. (mm)
Clutch Clearances	
Forward Clutch	.018-.099 (.45-2.51)
High Clutch	.071-.110 (1.80-2.80)
Low-Reverse	.043-.114 (1.10-2.90)
Overrun Clutch	.039-.079 (1.00-2.00)
Reverse Clutch	.020-.047 (.50-1.20)

TRANSAXLE SPECIFICATIONS (Cont.)

Application	In. (mm)
Oil Pump Clearance	
Inner Rotor-To-Oil Pump Housing	.0008-.0020 (.020-.050)
Outer Rotor-To-Oil Pump Housing	.0008-.0020 (.020-.050)
Inner Rotor-To-Outer Rotor	.0008-.0059 (.020-.150)

Geo: 1993 Storm

IDENTIFICATION

Transaxle identification plate is on left side of torque converter housing flange. A production number is located on left side of case above oil pan.

DESCRIPTION

JF403-E is a 4-speed, fully automatic, electronically controlled transaxle with shift mode select function and self-diagnostic function.

Automatic Transaxle Control Module (ATCM) is located behind knee pad, to left of steering column. *See Fig. 1*. ATCM has a 20-pin and 16-pin connector. *See Fig. 7*. ATCM controls shift points of transaxle through use of solenoids, based on inputs from various sensors.

If an electrical circuit problem occurs, ECONO/ECON light should start flashing. ATCM will store trouble code(s) in memory. ATCM is capable of operating in one of 2 modes. The differences between the 2 modes are shift points and 4th gear apply. Economy mode or manual mode may be selected using economy and manual switch located in center console. When economy mode is selected, ECONO/ECON light will be on.

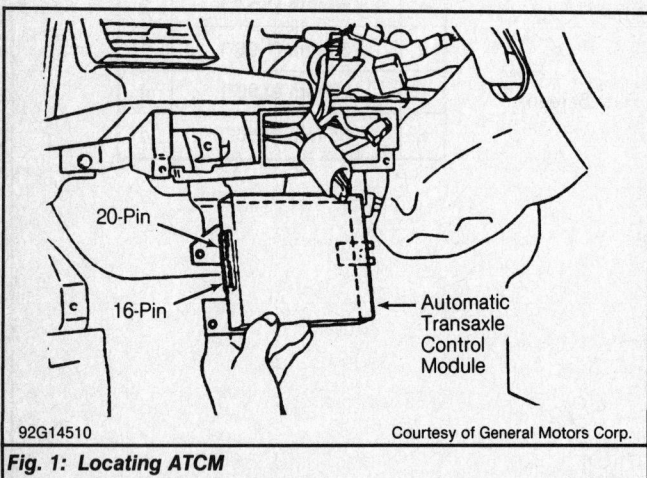

92G14510   Courtesy of General Motors Corp.
Fig. 1: Locating ATCM

ATCM INPUT SENSORS

ATF Temperature Sensor – Automatic Transaxle Fluid (ATF) temperature sensor is a thermistor mounted in transaxle valve body. ATCM supplies a 5 volts signal to ATF temperature sensor through a resistor inside ATCM and uses a signal line to measure voltage. Voltage will be high when transaxle fluid is cold and low when transaxle fluid is warm. A failure in ATF temperature sensor circuit may result in a trouble Code 15. For ATF temperature sensor testing, see COMPONENT TESTING.

Economy Switch – Economy switch allows driver to select ECONOMY mode or NORMAL mode. When depressed, economy switch provides a signal to ATCM. ATCM will adjust proper shift points and lock-up schedule for mode selected.

Inhibitor Switch Signal – This signal is used by ATCM to detect what position transaxle selector lever is in. If selector lever is misadjusted, shifting of transaxle would be affected. For adjustment procedures, see appropriate AUTOMATIC TRANSMISSION SERVICING article in TRANSMISSION SERVICING. For inhibitor switch testing, see COMPONENT TESTING.

RPM Signal – Engine RPM (tachometer) signal is supplied to ATCM by ECU. ATCM uses this signal to determine when lock-up (torque converter clutch) should occur for best fuel economy. If RPM signal is not present, ATCM may store a trouble Code 13 in memory.

Throttle Position Sensor Signal (TPS) – Engine ECM supplies a throttle position sensor signal to ATCM. This signal is used to detect rate at which throttle plates are opening, to determine shift points and, when necessary, to downshift transaxle. If no signal is present, ATCM may set a trouble Code 21.

Vehicle Speed Sensor (VSS) – VSS sends a pulse voltage signal to ATCM. ATCM uses this signal to determine shift points and Torque Converter Clutch (TCC) engagement. If ATCM fails to receive a VSS signal, it will utilize engine RPM signal from engine ECM. If this signal is not present, a trouble Code 11 and/or 24 may be set in computer memory. Signal for VSS is supplied by a transaxle-mounted PM generator and by a reed switch located in instrument panel.

ECU OUTPUT CONTROLLED DEVICES

ATCM Diagnostic Connector – The ATCM diagnostic connector is located at passenger side kick panel. *See Fig. 2*. ATCM will display trouble code(s) by flashing ECONO/ECON light. To display trouble code(s), turn ignition on and jumper terminals No. 1 and 2 of diagnostic connector. ECONO/ECON light will flicker on and off if there are no trouble code(s). If code(s) are present, ECONO/ECON light will flash code. *See Fig. 6*. To clear ATCM codes from memory, ensure ignition is off. Remove No. 11 fuse (C-19) for one minute.

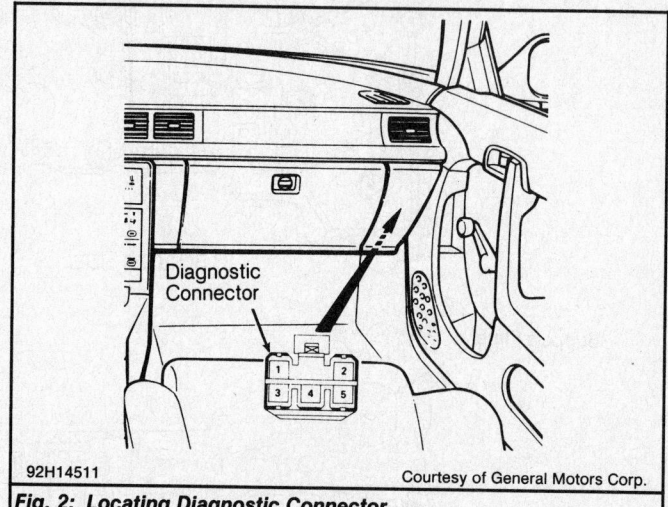

92H14511   Courtesy of General Motors Corp.
Fig. 2: Locating Diagnostic Connector

ECONO/ECON Light – ECONO/ECON light is controlled by ATCM. The light will be on when in economy mode. If a malfunction is present when ignition is on, light will flicker on and off to indicate a problem is present. ECONO/ECON light is also used to flash trouble code(s) when cavity "1" and "2" of ATCM diagnostic connector are jumpered.

Line Pressure Control Solenoid – ATCM uses line pressure solenoid (duty-cycle type) to regulate transaxle line pressure for smooth shifting of transaxle. Line pressure is regulated according to engine running conditions and engine torque. If line pressure control solenoid stops working, transaxle will use a spring loaded pressure regulating valve to control line pressure. If a problem is detected, a trouble Code 35 may be set in ATCM memory.

Lock-Up Duty Solenoid (TCC) – Lock-up duty solenoid is used for applying Torque Converter Clutch (TCC). Lock-up will occur during 2nd, 3rd and 4th gear. ATCM will delay TCC until transaxle temperature is at normal operating range. If ATCM detects a problem with lock-up duty solenoid, trouble Code 34 may be set in ATCM memory.

Overrun Clutch Solenoid – Overrun clutch solenoid is used to control transaxle engine braking on deceleration. ATCM will not supply battery voltage to solenoid when throttle position signal, VSS and RPM signal indicates vehicle is slowing down and throttle is closed.

If solenoid fails, overrun clutch solenoid will always be in a non-energized state. Overrun clutch will be engaged on forward driving position (except 4th gear position) so engine braking will be present during deceleration. If a problem is detected, a trouble Code 33 may be set in ATCM memory.

Shift Solenoids "A" & "B" – Shift solenoids "A" and "B" are controlled by ATCM. Shift solenoids control delivery of fluid line pressure to mechanical shift valve in transaxle valve body. If a malfunction is detected in either solenoid "A" or "B", ATCM will turn off solenoid that is not defective. If a solenoid is not working, a trouble Code 31 for solenoid "A" or a trouble Code 32 for solenoid "B" may be set in ATCM memory. If both solenoids are not working, transaxle will use governor pressure to shift transaxle.

COMPONENT TESTING

INPUT SENSORS

ATF Temperature Sensor – Wrap ATF sensor with nylon cloth. *See Fig. 3.* Place sensor in a container of ATF. Measure resistance across terminals No. 6 and 7 at temperature of 68°F (20°C). Resistance should be about 2500 ohms. With temperature at 176°F (80°C), resistance should be about 300 ohms. If sensor value is not within specified range, replace ATF temperature sensor. *See Fig. 3.*

Inhibitor Switch – Ensure engine starts in "P" and "N" position and back-up light is on when selector lever is in reverse detent position. To test for faulty inhibitor switch, disconnect switch connector at transaxle and check for continuity between each terminal as indicated. *See Fig. 4.* If continuity is not present at indicated terminals, adjust or replace inhibitor switch.

Vehicle Speed Sensor (VSS) – Disconnect VSS connector at transaxle. Measure resistance between terminals. Resistance should be 504-616 ohms. If not within specification, replace VSS.

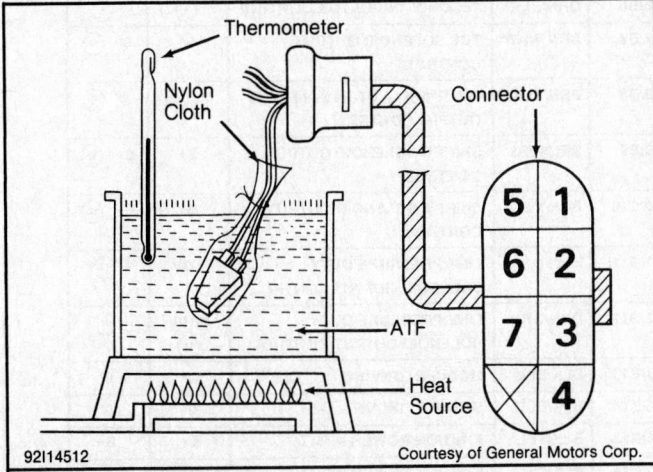

92I14512   Courtesy of General Motors Corp.

Fig. 3: Testing ATF Temperature Sensor

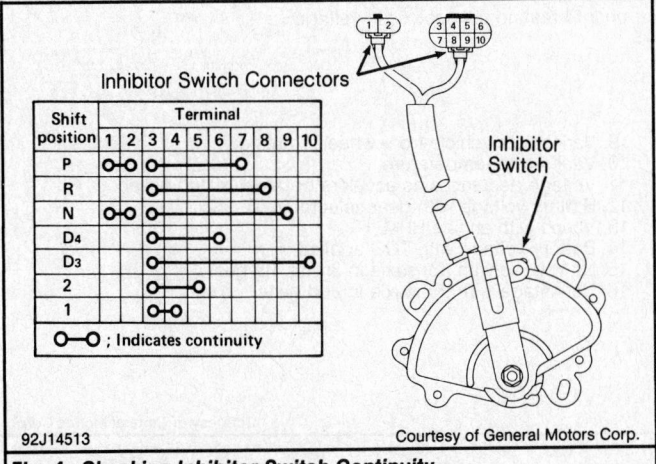

92J14513   Courtesy of General Motors Corp.

Fig. 4: Checking Inhibitor Switch Continuity

CONTROLLED DEVICES

Solenoid Valves – Disconnect solenoid connector at transaxle. Measure resistance between connector terminals and ground. *See Fig. 5.* If measured value is not within specification, replace solenoid.

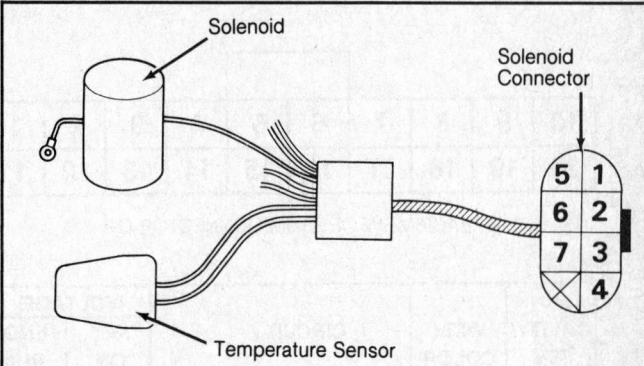

Solenoid	Terminal No.	Resistance (Ω)
Shift solenoid B	1	20.0 - 30.0
Shift solenoid A	2	20.0 - 30.0
Overrun clutch solenoid	3	20.0 - 30.0
Pressure line solenoid	4	2.5 - 5.0
Lockup solenoid	5	10.0 - 16.0

92A14514   Courtesy of General Motors Corp.

Fig. 5: Testing Solenoid Valve Resistance

SELF-DIAGNOSTICS

To display trouble code(s), turn ignition on and jumper terminals No. 1 and 2 of diagnostic connector. ECONO/ECON light will flicker on and off if there are no trouble code(s). If code(s) are present, ECONO/ECON light will flash code. *See Fig. 6.* To clear ATCM codes from memory, ensure ignition is off. Remove No. 11 fuse (C-19) for one minute.

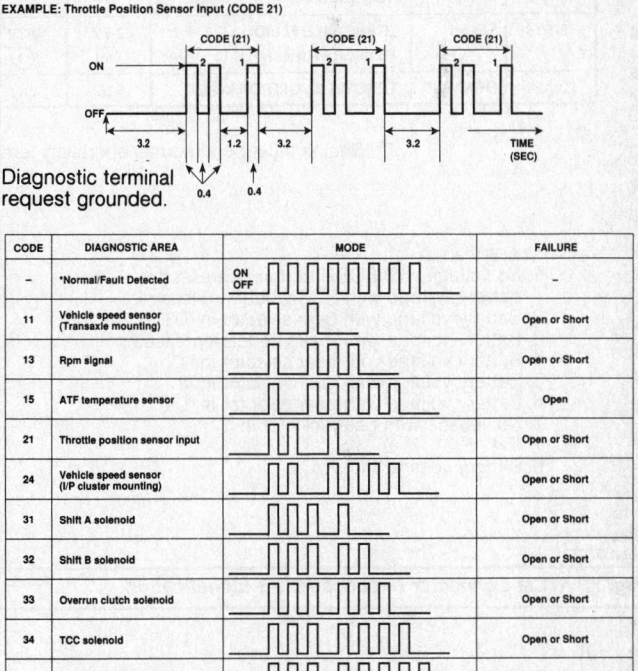

CODE	DIAGNOSTIC AREA	MODE	FAILURE
–	*Normal/Fault Detected	ON OFF	–
11	Vehicle speed sensor (Transaxle mounting)		Open or Short
13	Rpm signal		Open or Short
15	ATF temperature sensor		Open
21	Throttle position sensor input		Open or Short
24	Vehicle speed sensor (I/P cluster mounting)		Open or Short
31	Shift A solenoid		Open or Short
32	Shift B solenoid		Open or Short
33	Overrun clutch solenoid		Open or Short
34	TCC solenoid		Open or Short
35	Line pressure duty solenoid		Open or Short

* Normal with diagnostic request terminal grounded.
  Fault detected without diagnostic request terminal grounded.

92B14515   Courtesy of General Motors Corp.

Fig. 6: JF403-E Trouble Code Table

AUTOMATIC TRANSMISSIONS
JF403-E Electronic Diagnosis (Cont.)

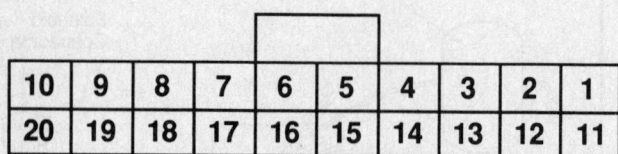

10	9	8	7	6	5	4	3	2	1
20	19	18	17	16	15	14	13	12	11

BACK VIEW OF ATCM CONNECTOR C1

8	7	6	5	4	3	2	1
16	15	14	13	12	11	10	9

BACK VIEW OF ATCM CONNECTOR C2

CAVITY/ PIN	WIRE COLOR	CIRCUIT	VOLTAGE KEY "ON"	VOLTAGE ENG. RUN
1/A1	–	NOT USED	–	–
2/A2	PNK/GRN	ECON SWITCH SIGNAL	①	①
3/A3	YEL/BLU	D3 SIGNAL	0* ②	0* ②
4/A4	–	NOT USED	–	–
5/A5	–	NOT USED	–	–
6/A6	BLK/WHT	DIAGNOSTIC REQUEST SIGNAL	4-6V	4-6V
7/A7	–	NOT USED	–	–
8/A8	GRN/YEL	BRAKE SIGNAL	0* ③	0* ③
9/A9	BLU/WHT	1 SIGNAL	0* ④	0* ④
10/A10	BLU/RED	2 SIGNAL	0* ⑤	0* ⑤
11/A11	BLU/ORN	D4 SIGNAL	0* ⑥	0* ⑥
12/A12	WHT/BLU	P/N SIGNAL	B+ ⑦	B+ ⑦
13/A13	–	NOT USED	–	–
14/A14	GRN	A/C ON SIGNAL	0*	0* ⑧
15/A15	BLU/GRN	VEHICLE SPEED INPUT	1-4V ⑨	1-4V ⑨
16/A16	BLU/YEL	SENSOR GROUND	0*	0*
17/A17	–	NOT USED	–	–
18/A18	–	NOT USED	–	–
19/A19	YEL	TRANSAXLE FLUID TEMPERATURE INPUT	2-3V ⑩	2-3V ⑩
20/A20	ORN/WHT	THROTTLE POSITION INPUT	6-8V	⑪

CAVITY/ PIN	WIRE COLOR	CIRCUIT	VOLTAGE KEY "ON"	VOLTAGE ENG. RUN
1/B1	GRN	MEMORY POWER INPUT	B+	B+
2/B2	–	NOT USED	–	–
3/B3	RED/BLU	R SIGNAL	0* ⑫	0* ⑫
4/B4	BLK/RED	ENGINE SPEED INPUT	B+	6-11V ⑬
5/B5	WHT	VEHICLE SPEED BACKUP INPUT	0-12V ⑨	0-12V ⑨
6/B6	ORN/BLK	"ECONO" INDICATOR CONTROL	①	①
7/B7	BRN/WHT	TCC SOLENOID OUTPUT CONTROL	0*	0* ⑭
8/B8	BRN/BLK	OVERRUN CLUTCH SOLENOID OUTPUT CONTROL	0* ⑥	0* ⑥
9/B9	BRN/RED	SHIFT B SOLENOID OUTPUT CONTROL	B+	B+ ⑮
10/B10	BRN/YEL	SHIFT A SOLENOID OUTPUT CONTROL	B+	B+ ⑯
11/B11	BRN	LINE PRESSURE DUTY SOLENOID OUTPUT CONTROL	2-3V	⑪
12/B12	BRN/GRN	LINE PRESSURE DUTY SOLENOID OUTPUT CONTROL	8-10V ⑪	⑪
13/B13	BLK/BLU	MODULE GROUND	0*	0*
14/B14	BLK/BLU	MODULE GROUND	0*	0*
15/B15	BLK/YEL	IGNITION POWER INPUT	B+	B+
16/B16	BLK/YEL	IGNITION POWER INPUT	B+	B+

Engine must be at normal operating temperature prior to testing connector pin voltage.

* Less than .5 volt.
1. No voltage with ECON button depressed, battery voltage with ECON button released.
2. Battery voltage with gear selector in "D3".
3. Battery voltage with brake pedal depressed.
4. Battery voltage with gear selector in "1".
5. Battery voltage with gear selector in "2".
6. Battery voltage with gear selector in "D4".
7. No voltage with gear selector in "R", "D4", "D3", "2" Or "1".
8. Battery voltage with A/C on.

9. Varies with vehicle front wheels rotating.
10. Varies with temperature.
11. Voltage decreases as accelerator pedal is depressed.
12. Battery voltage with gear selector in "R".
13. Varies with engine RPM.
14. Battery voltage with TCC applied.
15. No voltage with transaxle in 3rd or 4th gear.
16. No voltage with transaxle in 2nd gear.

94F37072

Fig. 7: ATCM Connector Pin Locations & Identification

DIAGNOSTIC CHARTS

Following charts include flow charts, testing information and related electrical circuits. For complete wiring diagram, see WIRING DIAGRAM.

NOTE: DIAGNOSTIC AIDS, located in following trouble code charts, can help diagnose trouble codes when circuit checks do not find a problem.

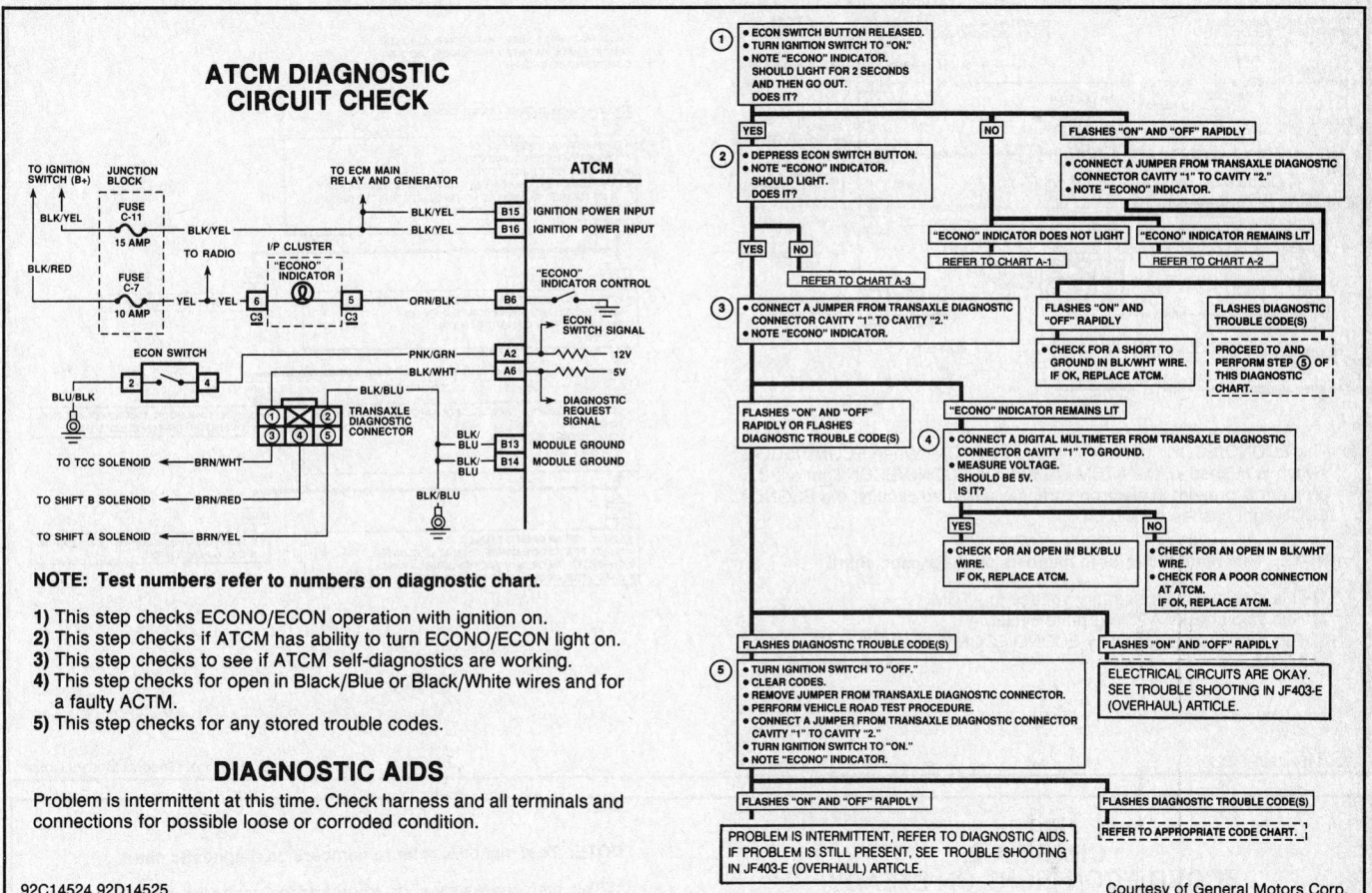

ATCM DIAGNOSTIC CIRCUIT CHECK

NOTE: Test numbers refer to numbers on diagnostic chart.

1) This step checks ECONO/ECON operation with ignition on.
2) This step checks if ATCM has ability to turn ECONO/ECON light on.
3) This step checks to see if ATCM self-diagnostics are working.
4) This step checks for open in Black/Blue or Black/White wires and for a faulty ACTM.
5) This step checks for any stored trouble codes.

DIAGNOSTIC AIDS

Problem is intermittent at this time. Check harness and all terminals and connections for possible loose or corroded condition.

92C14524 92D14525

Courtesy of General Motors Corp.

CHART A-1,
ECONO/ECON LIGHT NOT ON

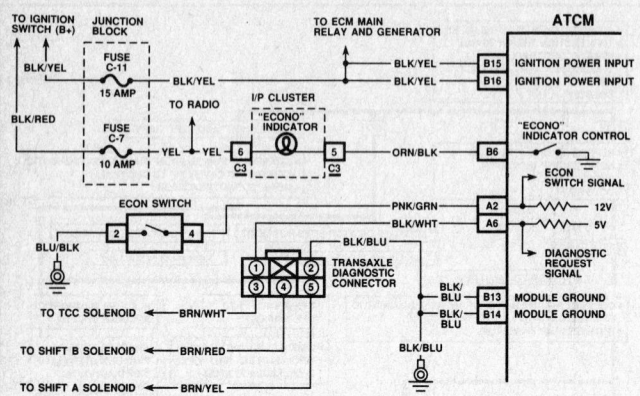

The ECONO/ECON light is controlled by ATCM. When ECONO/ECON switch is pushed in, the ATCM will turn the ECONO/ECON light on. If a problem is present in electronic transaxle related circuits, the ECONO/ECON light flashes on and off.

NOTE: Test numbers refer to numbers on diagnostic chart.

1) This step checks for battery voltage to ATCM.
2) This step checks ATCM ground circuit.
3) This step checks for faulty ECONO/ECON light circuit or for a faulty ATCM.

92C14524 92F14527

DIAGNOSTIC AIDS

Problem is intermittent at this time. Check harness and all terminals and connections for possible loose or corroded condition.

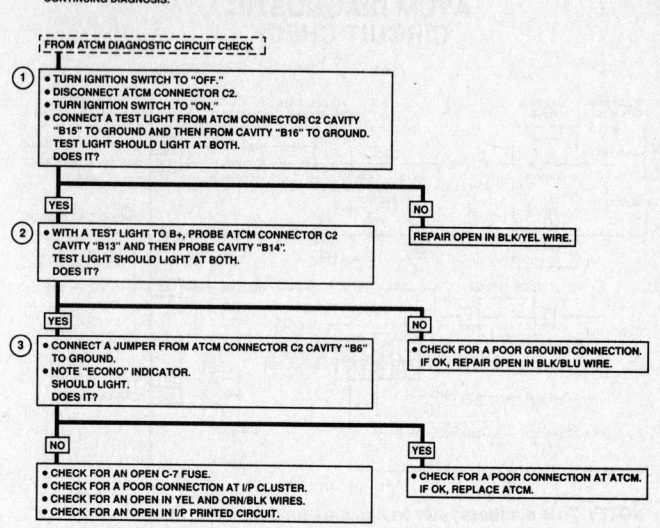

Courtesy of General Motors Corp.

CHART A-2,
ECONO/ECON LIGHT ON STEADY

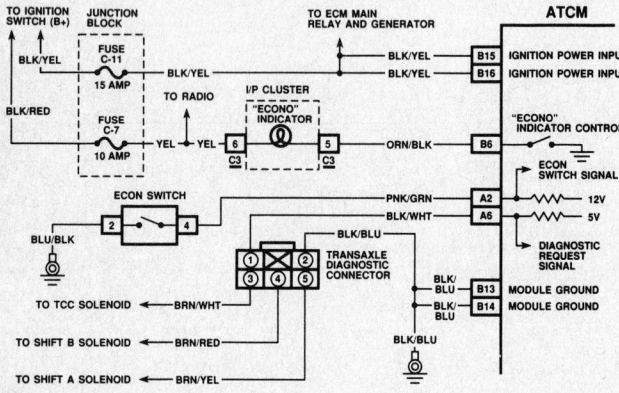

The ECONO/ECON light is controlled by ATCM. When ECONO/ECON switch is pushed in, the ATCM will turn the ECONO/ECON light on. When the ECONO/ECON switch is not pushed in, the ECONO/ECON light should be off. If a problem is present in electronic transaxle related circuits, the ECONO/ECON light flashes on and off.

NOTE: Test numbers refer to numbers on diagnostic chart.

1) This step checks for short to ground in Orange/Black wire.
2) This step checks for a faulty ATCM.
3) This step checks for short to ground in Pink/Green wire and for a faulty ECONO/ECON switch.

DIAGNOSTIC AIDS

Problem is intermittent at this time. Check harness and all terminals and connections for possible loose or corroded condition.

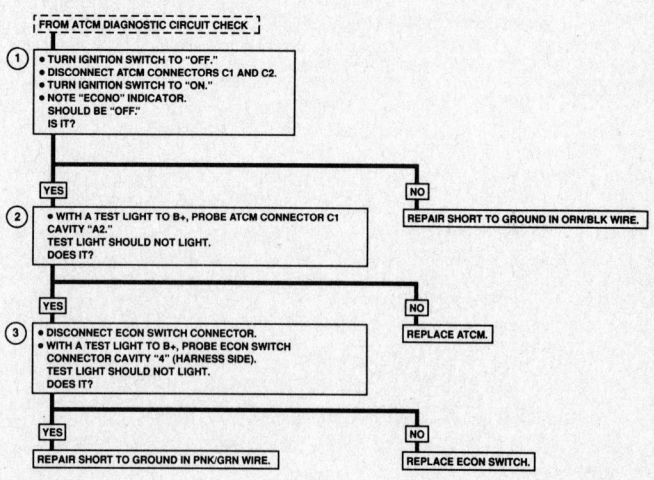

92C14524 92H14529

Courtesy of General Motors Corp.

CHART A-3,
ECONO/ECON LIGHT DOES NOT GLOW
WHEN BUTTON IS PUSHED IN

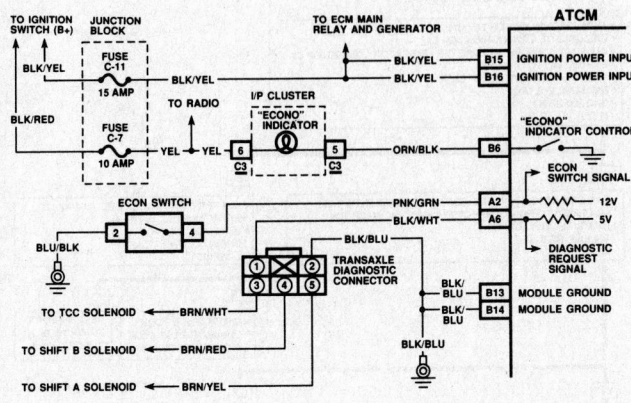

The ECONO/ECON light is controlled by ATCM. When ECONO/ECON switch is pushed in, the ATCM should turn the ECONO/ECON light on. If a problem is present in electrical transaxle related circuits, the ECONO/ECON light flashes on and off.

92C14524 92B14531

Courtesy of General Motors Corp.

NOTE: Test numbers refer to numbers on diagnostic chart.

1) This step checks for a poor ATCM connection or for a faulty ATCM.
2) This step checks for an open in Pink/Black and Blue/Black wires and for a faulty ECONO/ECON switch.

DIAGNOSTIC AIDS

Problem is intermittent at this time. Check harness and all terminals and connections for possible loose or corroded condition.

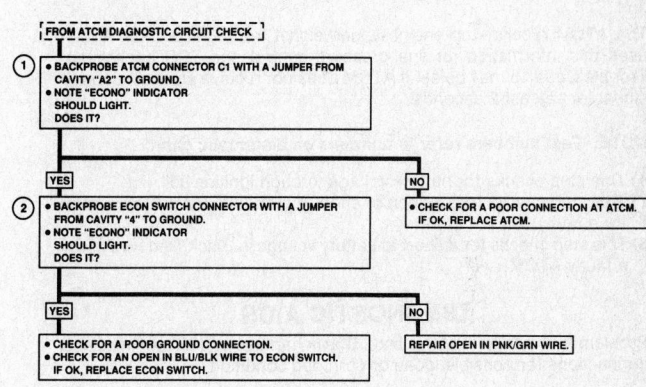

CODE 11, VEHICLE SPEED SENSOR (VSS)
OPEN OR SHORT INDICATED

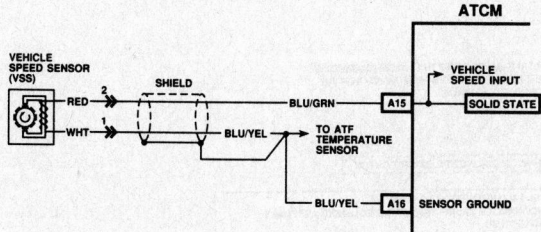

The ATCM receives an A/C signal from VSS (located on transaxle). ATCM uses this information to select shift points and TCC application. Trouble Code 11 may be set if ATCM does not receive a VSS signal when vehicle speed is greater than 19 MPH.

NOTE: Test numbers refer to numbers on diagnostic chart.

1) This step checks if conditions for trouble code 11 are still present.
2) This step checks for a faulty VSS.
3) This step checks for an open or short to ground in Blue/Yellow or Blue/Green wire.

DIAGNOSTIC AIDS

Problem is intermittent at this time. Check harness and all terminals and connections for possible loose or corroded condition.

IMPORTANT: MAKE SURE THAT ATCM DIAGNOSTIC CIRCUIT CHECK HAS BEEN PERFORMED BEFORE CONTINUING DIAGNOSIS.

FROM ATCM DIAGNOSTIC CIRCUIT CHECK

① • RAISE VEHICLE DRIVE WHEELS.
• NOTICE: DO NOT PERFORM THIS TEST WITHOUT SUPPORTING THE LOWER CONTROL ARMS SO THAT THE DRIVE AXLES ARE IN A NORMAL HORIZONTAL POSITION.
• START AND RUN ENGINE AT IDLE IN GEAR.
• BACKPROBE ATCM CONNECTOR C1 WITH A DIGITAL MULTIMETER FROM CAVITY "A15" TO CAVITY "A16".
• MEASURE VOLTAGE.
SHOULD VARY FROM 0-3V (VOLTAGE INCREASES WITH ENGINE SPEED).
DOES IT?

NO
② • DISCONNECT VSS CONNECTOR.
• CONNECT A DIGITAL MULTIMETER FROM VSS CONNECTOR TERMINAL "1" TO TERMINAL "2" (VSS SIDE).
• MEASURE VOLTAGE.
SHOULD VARY FROM 0-3V (VOLTAGE INCREASES WITH ENGINE SPEED).
DOES IT?

YES
PROBLEM IS INTERMITTENT.
REFER TO DIAGNOSTIC AIDS.

YES
③ • WITH A TEST LIGHT TO B+, PROBE VSS CONNECTOR CAVITY "1" (HARNESS SIDE).
• NOTE TEST LIGHT.
SHOULD LIGHT.
DOES IT?

NO
REPLACE VEHICLE SPEED SENSOR.

YES
• CHECK FOR AN OPEN OR A SHORT TO GROUND IN BLU/GRN WIRE.
• CHECK FOR A POOR CONNECTION AT ATCM.
IF OK, REPLACE ATCM.

NO
• CHECK FOR AN OPEN IN BLU/YEL WIRE.
• CHECK FOR A POOR CONNECTION AT ATCM.
IF OK, REPLACE ATCM.

92C14532 92D14533

Courtesy of General Motors Corp.

CODE 13, NO ENGINE SPEED INPUT

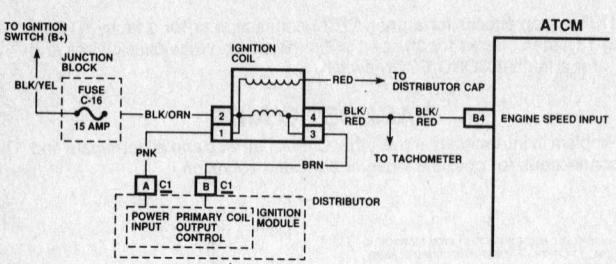

The ATCM receives an engine speed signal from ignition coil. ATCM uses this information for line pressure control and TCC application. Trouble Code 13 may be set if ATCM does not receive an engine speed signal for at least 2 seconds.

NOTE: Test numbers refer to numbers on diagnostic chart.

1) This step checks for battery voltage through ignition coil.
2) This step checks for an open or short to ground in Black/Red wire or for a faulty coil.
3) This step checks for a short to battery voltage in Black/Red wire or for a faulty ATCM.

DIAGNOSTIC AIDS

Problem is intermittent at this time. Check harness and all terminals and connections for possible loose or corroded condition.

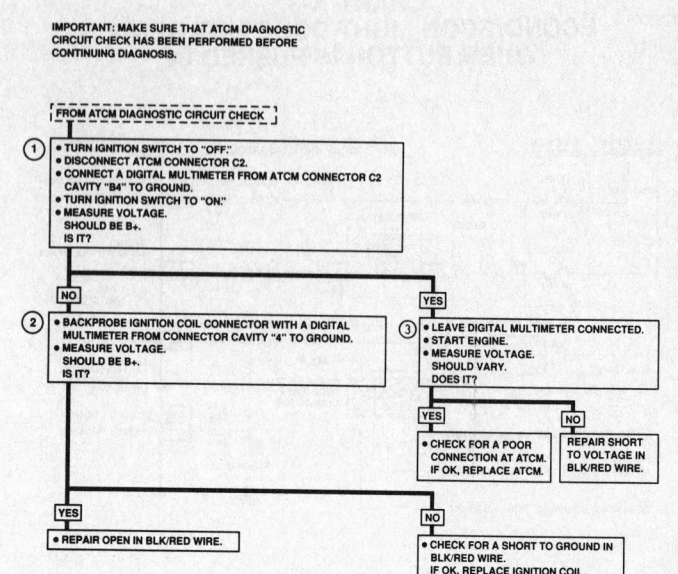

92E14534 92F14535

Courtesy of General Motors Corp.

CODE 15, ATF TEMPERATURE SENSOR OPEN OR SHORT INDICATED

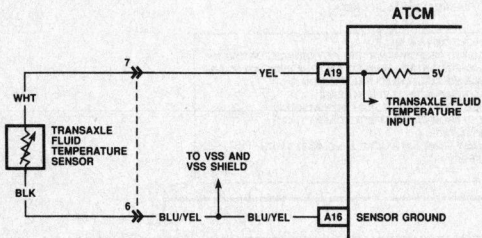

The ATCM reads the transaxle temperature by monitoring the voltage change across an internal resistor. When fluid temperature is cold, ATF sensor resistance is high and ATCM detects a high voltage signal. When fluid temperature is warm, ATF sensor resistance is low and ATCM detects a low voltage signal. The ATCM uses this information to control line pressure which affects shift points.

NOTE: Test numbers refer to numbers on diagnostic chart.

1) This step checks for system voltage at ATF sensor.
2) This tests for grounded sensor signal line between ATCM and ATF sensor.

DIAGNOSTIC AIDS

Problem is intermittent at this time. Check harness and all terminals and connections for possible loose or corroded condition.

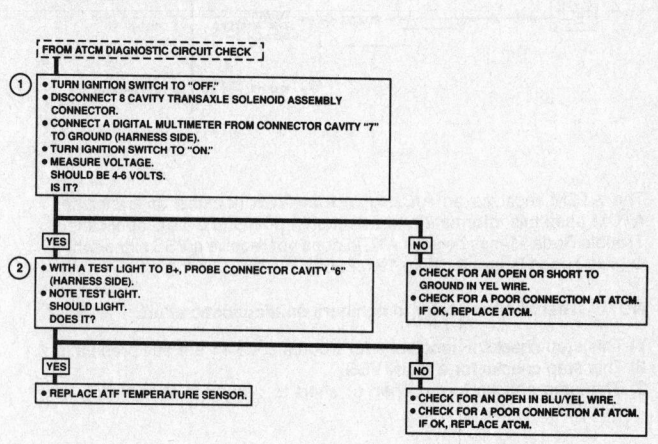

92G14536 92H14537

Courtesy of General Motors Corp.

CODE 21, THROTTLE POSITION SENSOR
OPEN OR SHORT INDICATED

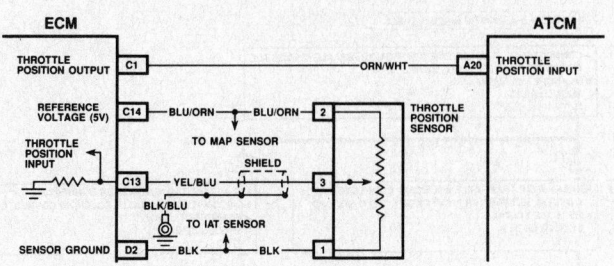

The ATCM receives an output signal from the Engine Control Module (ECM). The ECM reads the throttle position by monitoring the voltage change across an internal resistor. When throttle opening is near idle, TPS resistance is high and ATCM is sent a high voltage signal. When throttle opening is near wide open, TPS resistance is low and ATCM is sent a low voltage signal. The ATCM uses this information to control line pressure and TCC lock-up.

NOTE: Test numbers refer to numbers on diagnostic chart.

1) This step checks for 6-7 volts at ATCM.
2) This tests for a voltage drop when throttle is opened.
3) This tests for short in Orange/White wire or for a faulty ECM or ATCM.

DIAGNOSTIC AIDS
Problem is intermittent at this time. Check harness and all terminals and connections for possible loose or corroded condition.

IMPORTANT: MAKE SURE THAT ATCM DIAGNOSTIC CIRCUIT CHECK HAS BEEN PERFORMED BEFORE CONTINUING DIAGNOSIS.

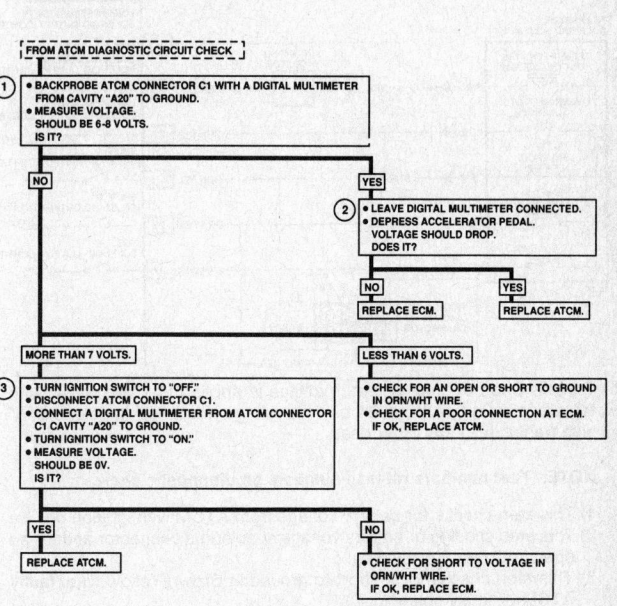

92I14538 92J14539

Courtesy of General Motors Corp.

CODE 24, VEHICLE SPEED SENSOR (VSS)
OPEN OR SHORT INDICATED

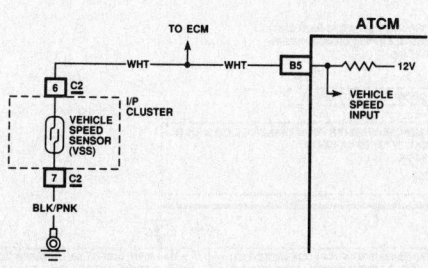

The ATCM sends a 12 volts signal to VSS (located in instrument panel). A reed switch in the VSS opens and closes 4 times with each revolution. ATCM monitors and converts this information to a vehicle speed. Trouble Code 24 may be set if ATCM does not receive a VSS signal with engine running and transaxle speed sensor signal present (vehicle moving).

NOTE: Test numbers refer to numbers on diagnostic chart.

1) This step checks for an open in White wire and for a faulty VSS.
2) This step checks for an open in Black/Pink wire and for VSS power circuit.

DIAGNOSTIC AIDS
Problem is intermittent at this time. Check harness and all terminals and connections for possible loose or corroded condition.

IMPORTANT: MAKE SURE THAT ATCM DIAGNOSTIC CIRCUIT CHECK HAS BEEN PERFORMED BEFORE CONTINUING DIAGNOSIS.

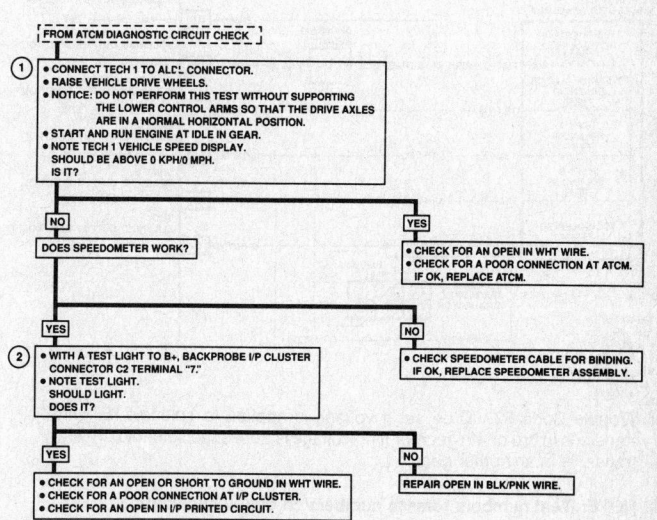

92C14540 92D14541

Courtesy of General Motors Corp.

CODE 31, SOLENOID "A"
OPEN OR SHORT INDICATED

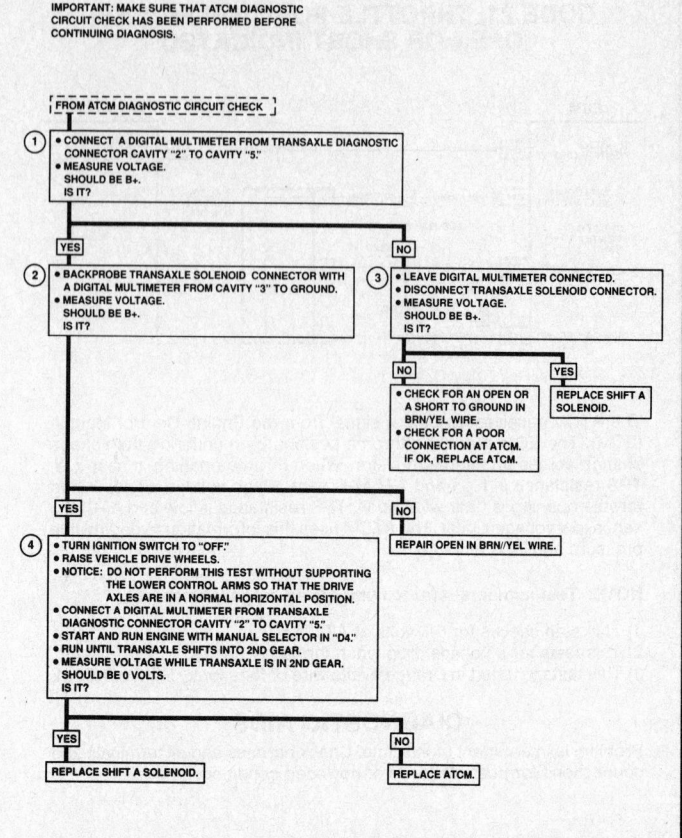

Trouble Code 31 may be set if voltage is applied to solenoid "A" with transaxle in 2nd or 3rd gear, or if no voltage is applied to solenoid "A" with transaxle in any other gear.

NOTE: Test numbers refer to numbers on diagnostic chart.

1) This step checks for battery voltage from ATCM with ignition on.
2) This step checks for battery voltage at solenoid connector and for an open in Brown/Yellow wire.
3) This step checks for a short to ground in Brown/Yellow wire, faulty ATCM or faulty solenoid.
4) This step checks for a faulty ATCM or faulty solenoid.

DIAGNOSTIC AIDS

Problem is intermittent at this time. Check harness and all terminals and connections for possible loose or corroded condition.

92E14542 92F14543

Courtesy of General Motors Corp.

CODE 32, SOLENOID "B"
OPEN OR SHORT INDICATED

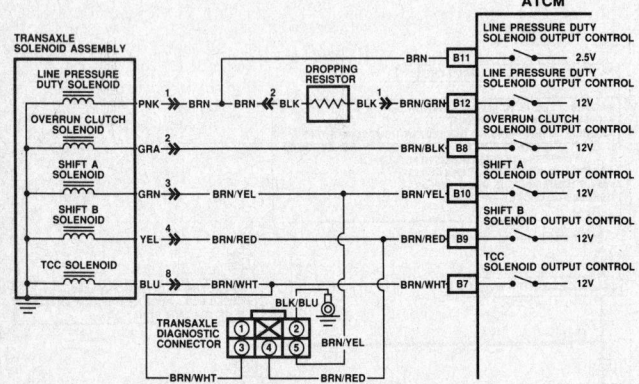

Trouble Code 32 will be set if voltage is applied to solenoid "B" with transaxle in 3rd or 4th gear, or if no voltage is applied to solenoid "B" with transaxle in any other gear.

NOTE: Test numbers refer to numbers on diagnostic chart.

1) This step checks for battery voltage from ATCM with ignition on.
2) This step checks for battery voltage at solenoid connector and for an open in Brown/Red wire.
3) This step checks for a short to ground in Brown/Red wire, faulty ATCM or faulty solenoid.
4) This step checks for a faulty ATCM or faulty solenoid.

DIAGNOSTIC AIDS

Problem is intermittent at this time. Check harness and all terminals and connections for possible loose or corroded condition.

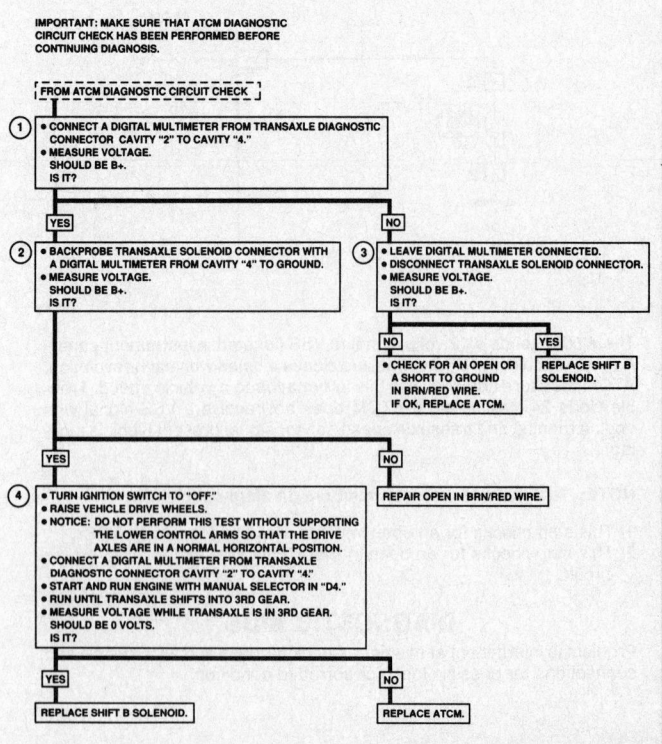

92E14542 92H14545

Courtesy of General Motors Corp.

CODE 33, OVERRUN CLUTCH SOLENOID OPEN OR SHORT INDICATED

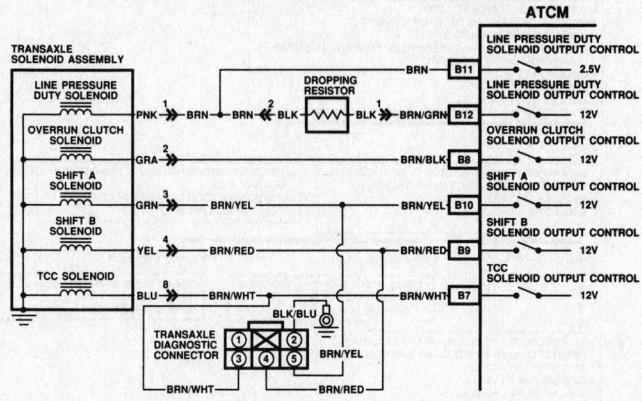

IMPORTANT: MAKE SURE THAT ATCM DIAGNOSTIC CIRCUIT CHECK HAS BEEN PERFORMED BEFORE CONTINUING DIAGNOSIS.

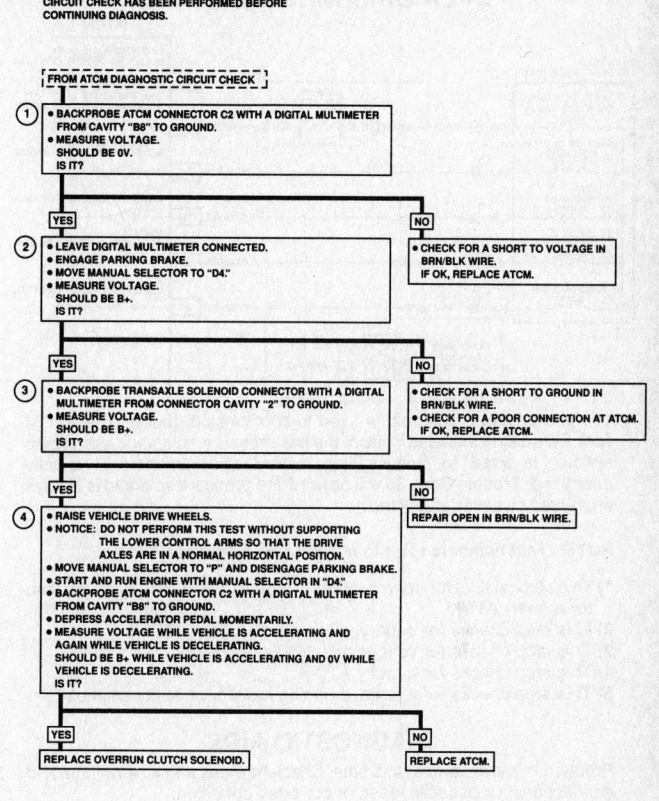

Trouble Code 33 will be set if overrun clutch is always engaged or never engaged.

NOTE: Test numbers refer to numbers on diagnostic chart.

1) This step checks for short to voltage in Brown/Black wire and for a faulty ATCM.
2) This step checks for short to ground in Brown/Black wire and for a faulty ATCM.
3) This step checks for an open in Brown/Black wire.
4) This step checks for a faulty ATCM or faulty solenoid.

DIAGNOSTIC AIDS

Problem is intermittent at this time. Check harness and all terminals and connections for possible loose or corroded condition.

92E14542 92J14547

Courtesy of General Motors Corp.

CODE 34, TCC SOLENOID OPEN OR SHORT INDICATED

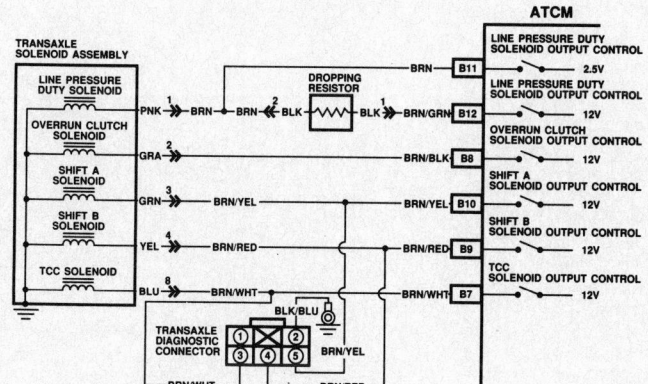

Trouble Code 34 will be set if voltage is applied to TCC solenoid with vehicle speed below 40 MPH. Trouble code 34 will also be set if voltage is not applied to TCC solenoid with vehicle speed above 40 MPH.

NOTE: Test numbers refer to numbers on diagnostic chart.

1) This step checks for short to voltage in Brown/White wire and for a faulty ATCM.
2) This step checks for short to ground in Brown/White wire and for a faulty ATCM or faulty solenoid.

DIAGNOSTIC AIDS

Problem is intermittent at this time. Check harness and all terminals and connections for possible loose or corroded condition.

IMPORTANT: MAKE SURE THAT "TCM DIAGNOSTIC CIRCUIT CHECK" HAS BEEN PERFORMED BEFORE CONTINUING DIAGNOSIS.

NOTICE: TCC WILL NOT LOCKUP WITH VEHICLE DRIVE WHEELS RAISED. VEHICLE MUST BE DRIVEN IN ORDER TO PERFORM SOME DIAGNOSTIC PROCEDURES.

FROM TCM DIAGNOSTIC CIRCUIT CHECK

1) • BACKPROBE TCM CONNECTOR C2 WITH A DIGITAL MULTIMETER FROM CAVITY "B7" TO GROUND.
   • MEASURE VOLTAGE.
     SHOULD BE 0 VOLTS.
     IS IT?

YES

2) • CONNECT A DIGITAL MULTIMETER FROM TRANSAXLE DLC CAVITY "2" TO CAVITY "3".
   • ROAD TEST VEHICLE ABOVE 80 km/h (50 mph).
   • NOTE VOLTAGE WITH VEHICLE SPEED ABOVE 80 km/h (50 mph). VOLTAGE SHOULD INCREASE TO ABOVE 10 VOLTS AT STEADY THROTTLE.
     DOES IT?

NO
• CHECK FOR AN OPEN OR SHORT TO VOLTAGE IN BRN/WHT WIRE.
  IF VOLTAGE IS OKAY, REPLACE ATCM.

YES
• CHECK FOR AN OPEN IN BRN/WHT WIRE.
  IF OK, REPLACE TCC SOLENOID.

NO
• CHECK FOR A SHORT TO GROUND IN BRN/WHT WIRE.
• CHECK FOR A POOR CONNECTION AT TCM.
  IF OK, REPLACE TCM.

92E14542 94G37073

Courtesy of General Motors Corp.

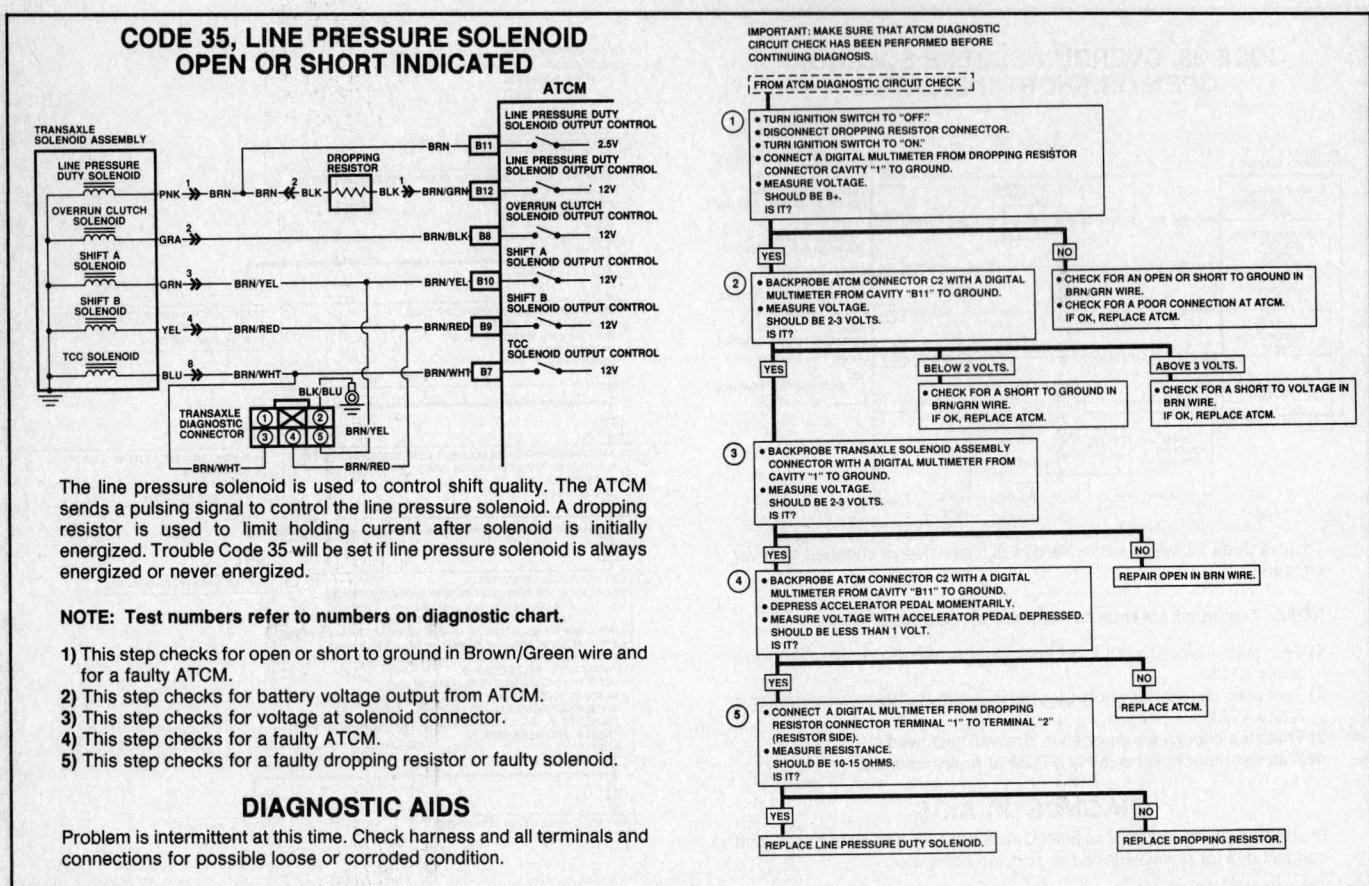

CODE 35, LINE PRESSURE SOLENOID OPEN OR SHORT INDICATED

The line pressure solenoid is used to control shift quality. The ATCM sends a pulsing signal to control the line pressure solenoid. A dropping resistor is used to limit holding current after solenoid is initially energized. Trouble Code 35 will be set if line pressure solenoid is always energized or never energized.

NOTE: Test numbers refer to numbers on diagnostic chart.

1) This step checks for open or short to ground in Brown/Green wire and for a faulty ATCM.
2) This step checks for battery voltage output from ATCM.
3) This step checks for voltage at solenoid connector.
4) This step checks for a faulty ATCM.
5) This step checks for a faulty dropping resistor or faulty solenoid.

DIAGNOSTIC AIDS

Problem is intermittent at this time. Check harness and all terminals and connections for possible loose or corroded condition.

92E14542 92G14551

Courtesy of General Motors Corp.

WIRING DIAGRAM

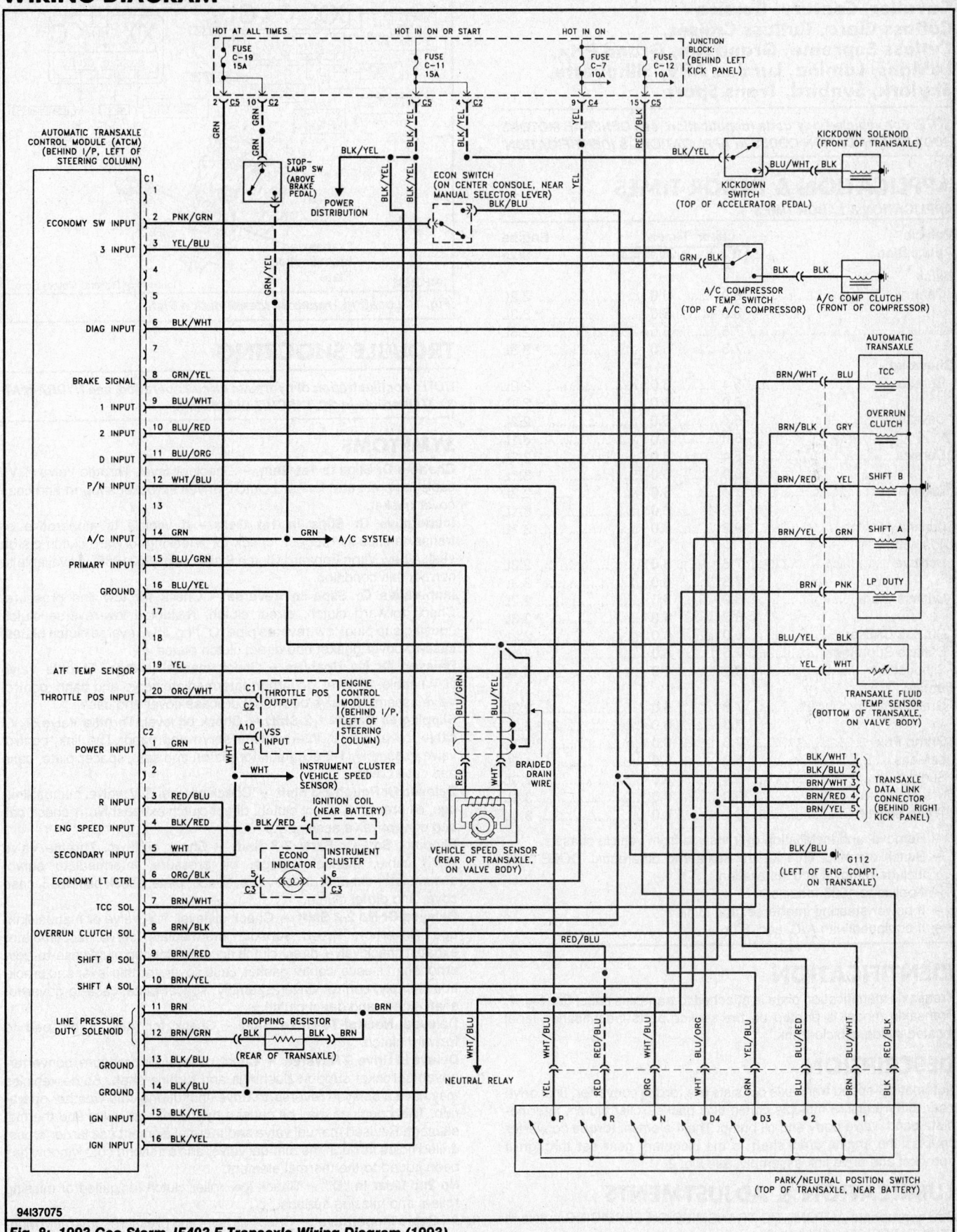

Fig. 8: 1993 Geo Storm JF403-E Transaxle Wiring Diagram (1993)

94I37075

AUTOMATIC TRANSMISSIONS
Hydra-Matic 3T40

General Motors: Achieva, Beretta, Cavalier, Century, Corsica Cutlass Ciera, Cutlass Cruiser, Cutlass Supreme, Grand Am, Grand Prix, LeMans, Lumina, Lumina APV, Silhouette, Skylark, Sunbird, Trans Sport

NOTE: For vehicle body code identification, see GENERAL MOTORS BODY IDENTIFICATION CODES in APPLICATIONS & IDENTIFICATION.

APPLICATION & LABOR TIMES

APPLICATION & LABOR TIMES

Vehicle Application	Labor Times [1] [4] R & I	[2] Overhaul	Engine Size
Buick			
Century	6.0	6.0	2.2L
	6.5	6.0	[3] 3.3L
Skylark	7.8	6.0	2.3L
	7.8	6.0	[3] 3.3L
Chevrolet			
Beretta	5.4	6.0	2.2L
	6.0	6.0	[3] 3.1L
Cavalier	5.4	6.0	2.2L
	6.0	6.0	3.1L
Corsica	5.4	6.0	2.2L
	6.0	6.0	[3] 3.1L
Lumina	7.4	6.0	[3] 2.2L
	7.6	6.0	3.1L
Lumina APV [5]	9.2	6.0	3.1L
Oldsmobile			
Achieva	7.8	6.0	2.3L
	7.8	6.0	[3] 3.3L
Cutlass Ciera	6.0	6.0	2.2L
	6.5	6.0	[3] 3.3L
Cutlass Cruiser	6.0	6.0	2.2L
Cutlass Supreme	7.6	6.0	[3] 3.1L
Silhouette [5]	9.2	6.0	3.1L
Pontiac			
Grand Am	7.8	6.0	2.3L
	7.8	6.0	[3] 3.3L
Grand Prix	7.6	6.0	[3] 3.1L
LeMans	5.0	6.0	1.6L
Sunbird	5.4	6.0	2.0L
	6.0	6.0	3.1L
Trans Sport [5]	9.2	6.0	3.1L

[1] – Removal and installation of transaxle from vehicle chassis.
[2] – Bench overhaul time for transaxle and differential. DOES NOT include removal and installation.
[3] – Applies to 1993 models.
[4] – If power steering interferes, add .3 hr.
[5] – If equipped with A/C, add .8 hr.

IDENTIFICATION

Transaxle identification plate is attached to transaxle case. *See Fig. 1.* Transaxle model is printed on the service parts identification label located inside vehicle trunk.

DESCRIPTION

Automatic 3-speed transaxle consists of a torque converter, final drive gear, differential, 3 multiple clutch disc packs, roller clutch, intermediate band, valve body and oil pump. The 4-element torque converter couples the engine crankshaft to the planetary gear set through a sprocket and drive link assembly. *See Fig. 2.*

LUBRICATION & ADJUSTMENTS

See appropriate AUTOMATIC TRANSMISSION SERVICING article in TRANSMISSION SERVICING.

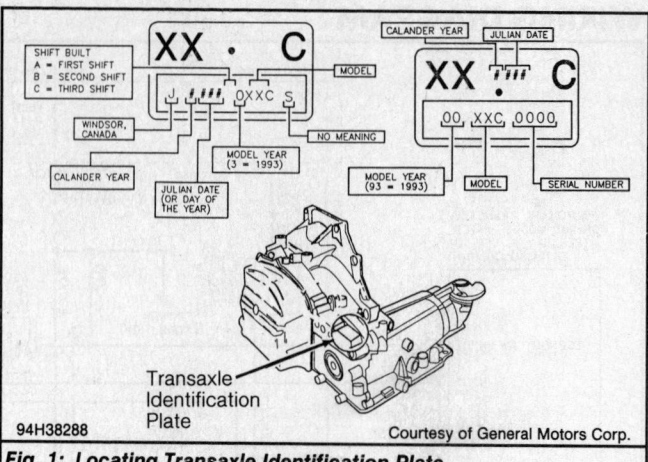

Fig. 1: Locating Transaxle Identification Plate

Courtesy of General Motors Corp.

TROUBLE SHOOTING

NOTE: For illustration of hydraulic circuit operation, see HYDRA-MATIC 3T40 article in OIL CIRCUIT DIAGRAMS.

SYMPTOMS

Chatters Or Slips In 1st Gear – Check oil level, Throttle Valve (T.V.) cable, oil pressure, forward clutch, driven sprocket support and case cover gasket.

Inoperative Or Slips In 1st Gear – If vehicle is inoperative or transaxle slips in 1st gear, check for a leaking forward clutch piston seal. A new Viton Forward Clutch Piston Seal (8631986) is available to correct this condition.

Inoperative Or Slips In Reverse – Check for low line pressure. Check forward clutch, direct clutch, restricted low-reverse clutch housing cup plug, low-reverse pipe "O" ring, low-reverse clutch plates, case-to-cover gasket and direct clutch plates.

Delayed Or No Upshifts – Check manual linkage, Throttle Valve (T.V.) cable, oil level, governor, intermediate servo and band, control valve assembly, valve body spacer, case cover and case.

Slipping Or Rough 1-2 Shift – Check oil level, Throttle Valve (T.V.) cable, oil pressure, intermediate servo and band, T.V. link, control valve assembly, 1-2 accumulator piston and seal, spacer plate, case and case cover.

Delayed Or Rough 2-3 Shift – Check oil level, T.V. valve, manual linkage, oil pressure, direct clutch, direct clutch exhaust No. 1 check ball and control valve assembly.

Slipping, Soft Or Early 2-3 Shift – Check oil level, Throttle Valve (T.V.) cable, manual linkage, oil pressure, intermediate servo, accumulator exhaust check valve, spacer plate, check ball No. 5, case cover and direct clutch.

Delayed Or No 2-3 Shift – Check oil level, T.V. valve or manual linkage, governor, speed sensor, intermediate servo, accumulator exhaust check valve, direct clutch accumulator cup plug, case-to-governor shaft sleeve, center gasket, case cover, throttle lever and bracket assembly, control valve assembly, spacer plate, case-to-governor shaft sleeve and direct clutch.

Delayed Neutral-To-Drive Shift – Check for lack of oil feed to forward clutch.

Delays In Drive & Reverse – Check oil level, oil pressure, converter-driven sprocket support bushings and turbine shaft. Some vehicles may have a delayed reverse-to-drive shift during cold weather operation. This condition may be caused by the manual valve and thermal element. Revised manual valve and thermal element use larger cross-drilled holes through the manual valve, and a second cold window has been added to the thermal element.

No 2nd Gear In "D" – Check low roller clutch for galled or missing rollers and missing springs.

All Gears Inoperative – Check oil level and pressure, drive link, manual linkage, input shaft, reaction carrier, differential and torque converter.

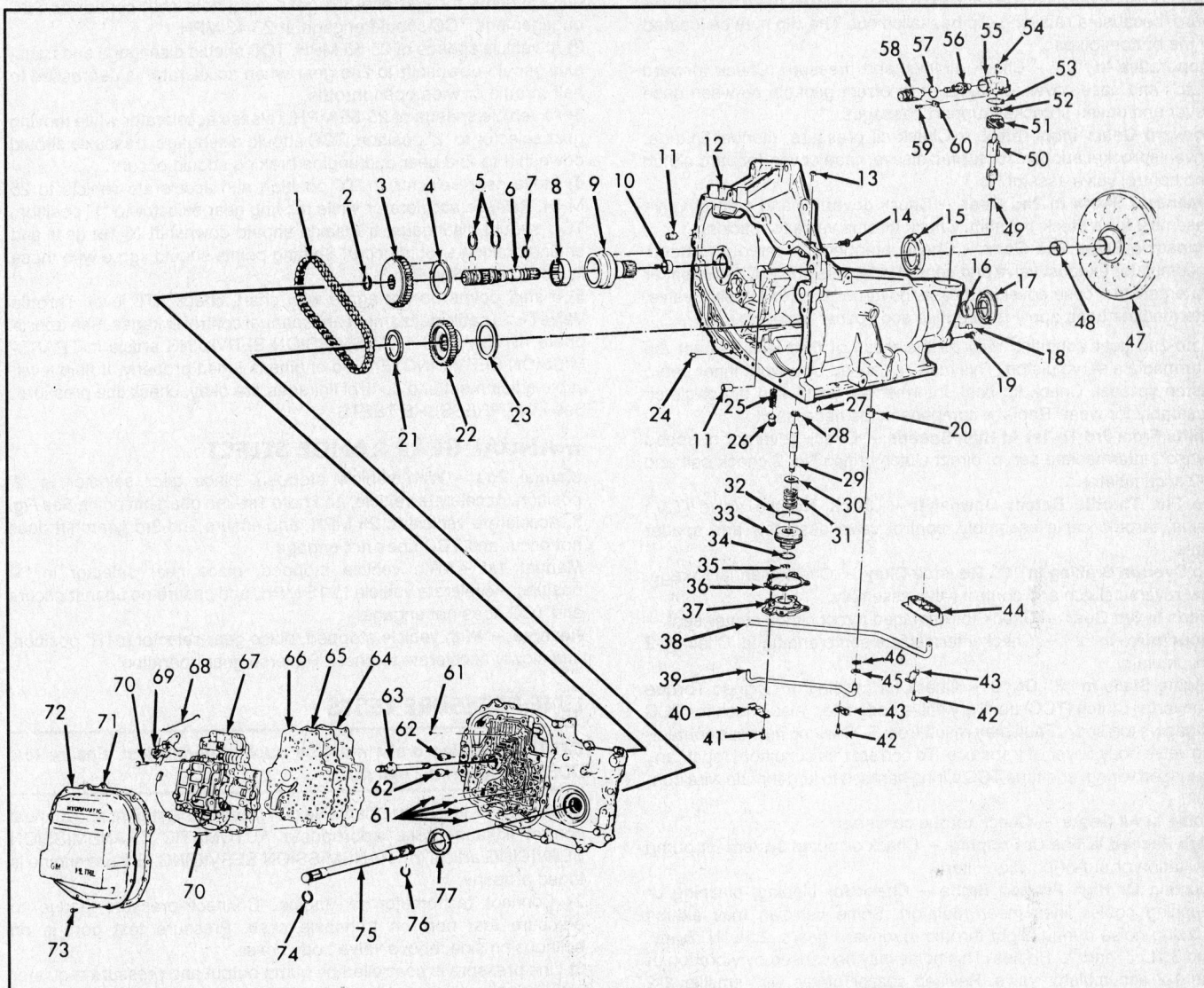

1. Drive Link	27. Low-Reverse Orifice Cup Plug	53. "O" Ring
2. Snap Ring	28. Oil Seal Ring	54. Screw
3. Drive Sprocket	29. Intermediate Band Apply Pin	55. Governor Cover
4. Thrust Washer	30. Intermediate Spring Retainer	56. Speedometer Driven Gear
5. Seal Ring	31. Intermediate Servo Spring	57. "O" Ring
6. Turbine Shaft	32. Intermediate Oil Seal Ring	58. Sleeve
7. "O" Ring	33. Intermediate Servo Piston	59. Gear Retainer
8. Drive Sprocket Support Bearing	34. Intermediate Oil Seal Ring	60. Gear Retainer Bolt
9. Drive Sprocket Support	35. Intermediate Snap Ring	61. Valve Body Check Balls
10. Bushing	36. Intermediate Gasket	62. Cooler Line Connector
11. Dowel Pin	37. Intermediate Servo Cover	63. Oil Pump Drive Shaft
12. Transaxle Case	38. Governor Oil Pipe	64. Spacer Plate Gasket
13. Manual Shift Seal Assembly	39. Rev. Oil Pipe	65. Spacer Plate
14. Screw	40. Rev. Oil Pipe Retainer	66. Spacer Plate Gasket
15. Converter Seal	41. Servo Cover Bolt	67. Cont. Valve & Oil Pump Assembly
16. Bushing	42. Pipe Retaining Bolt	68. Throttle Cable Link
17. Axle Seal	43. Pipe Retainer	69. Throttle Lever & Bracket
18. Cup Plug	44. Oil Weir	70. Valve Body Bolt
19. Plug	45. Seal Ring	71. Gasket
20. Case Oil Seal	46. Seal	72. Valve Body Cover
21. Thrust Bearing	47. Converter	73. Cover Screw
22. Driven Sprocket	48. Converter Pump Bushing	74. Retaining Ring
23. Thrust Washer	49. Oil Seal Ring	75. Output Shaft
24. 3rd Oil Cup Plug	50. Governor Assembly	76. Snap Ring
25. 3rd Accumulator Exhaust Spring	51. Speedometer Drive Gear	77. Axle Seal
26. 3rd Accumulator Exhaust Valve	52. Thrust Bearing	

92H12663

Courtesy of General Motors Corp.

Fig. 2: Exploded View Of Transaxle Case & Related Components

This condition may also be caused by the thermal element moving forward, because a retaining clip has fallen out. The clip may be located in the bottom oil pan.

Inoperative In "D" – Check oil level and pressure. Check forward clutch and case cover for leaks or incorrect gaskets between case cover and driven sprocket support passages.

Forward Gears Inoperative – Check oil pressure, manual linkage, driven sprocket support for turned sleeve, case cover, forward clutch and control valve assembly.

Transaxle Starts In 2nd Gear – Check governor and control valve assembly for a stuck 1-2 shift. Check throttle valve for sticking.

Transaxle Skips 2nd Gear – Check intermediate servo and band, accumulator exhaust valve and control valve assembly. Check spacer plate gaskets, case cover and case, governor feed to 1-2 shift valve, intermediate band apply feed orifice and spacer plate.

A no-2nd gear condition may be the result of fluid leaking past the intermediate servo piston. This may be caused by a worn inner servo piston lip seal. Check lip seal, intermediate band and direct clutch assembly for wear. Replace components as necessary.

Shifts From 3rd To 1st At High Speeds – Check governor or speed sensor, intermediate servo, direct clutch orifice No. 2 check ball and 1-2 accumulator.

No Full Throttle Detent Downshift – Check Throttle Valve (T.V.) cable, throttle cable assembly, control valve assembly and spacer plate.

No Overrun Braking In "1", Reverse Okay – Check manual linkage, low-reverse clutch and control valve assembly.

Binds In 3rd Gear – Check for damaged direct clutch center seal.

Inoperative In "2" – Check intermediate servo and band. Check 1-2 accumulator.

Engine Stalls In "R" Or "D" – Check for missing or clogged Torque Converter Clutch (TCC) auxiliary valve body filter. Also check for TCC engaging too soon. Fault may result from TCC wiring harness contacting valve body cover of transaxle. To correct this condition, repair any damaged wiring, and tape TCC wiring harness to larger main wire conduit.

Noise In All Gears – Check torque converter.

High Pitched Whine Or Popping – Check oil pump system for pump cavitation or out-of-position filter.

Buzzing Or High Pitched Rattle – Check for binding, pinching or touching cooler lines (near radiator). Some vehicles may exhibit buzzing noise during slight throttle in forward gears: 2.3L "N" Body, and 3.1L "J" and "L" Bodies. This noise may be caused by vibration of the 1-2 accumulator valve. Revised spacer plates with smaller 1-2 accumulator orifice are now available to correct this problem.

Whine Or Growl Under Light Accessories – Check drive link assembly, sprockets, chain and related bearings.

Noise In 1st Or Reverse Gear – Check input gear, input internal gear, input carrier or input sun gear for damage.

Noise In 2nd Gear – Check for worn or pitted reaction gear set, reaction internal gear, reaction carrier, reaction sun gear, or related bearings and thrust washers.

Hum During Light Acceleration (All Gears) – Check differential or final drive gear and related parts for wear or damage.

Light Rattle In 2nd Or 3rd At 25-40 MPH – Check for warped steel plates, excess clutch pack clearance or parallel-grooved fiber plates in low-reverse clutch pack. Also check case for excess case-to-plate spline clearance.

TESTING

NOTE: Ensure engine is at normal operating temperature. Engine coolant temperature must be greater than 130°F (54°C) before Torque Converter Clutch (TCC) will engage. If temperature is not as specified, check and repair cooling system as necessary. If TCC will not engage, see TCC TESTING.

ROAD TEST

1) Shift gear selector to each shift position. Ensure shifts are immediate and not harsh. With gear selector in "D" position, accelerate vehicle using increasing throttle pressure. Note shift speed gear

engagements for 2nd and 3rd gear. Also note shift speed for TCC engagement. TCC should engage at 23-42 MPH.

2) At vehicle speeds of 25-55 MPH, TCC should disengage and transaxle should downshift to 2nd gear when accelerator is depressed to half throttle or wide open throttle.

3) At vehicle speeds of 25-55 MPH, release accelerator while moving gear selector to "2" position. TCC should disengage, transaxle should downshift to 2nd gear and engine braking should occur.

4) Move gear selector to "D" position and accelerate vehicle to 25 MPH. Release accelerator while moving gear selector to "1" position. TCC should disengage, transaxle should downshift to 1st gear and engine braking should occur. Shifting points should agree with those listed in chart. *See Fig. 3.*

5) If shift points do not agree with chart, check ATF level, Throttle Valve (T.V.) cable adjustment and manual control linkages. See appropriate AUTOMATIC TRANSMISSION SERVICING article in TRANSMISSION SERVICING. Ensure engine is tuned properly. If fluid level, cable adjustment and control linkages are okay, check line pressure. See LINE PRESSURE TESTS.

MANUAL GEAR RANGE SELECT

Manual 2nd – With vehicle stopped, place gear selector in "2" position. Accelerate vehicle, and note 1st-2nd gearshift point. *See Fig. 3.* Accelerate vehicle to 25 MPH, and ensure 2nd-3rd gearshift does not occur and TCC does not engage.

Manual 1st – With vehicle stopped, place gear selector in "1" position. Accelerate vehicle to 15 MPH, and ensure no upshift occurs and TCC does not engage.

Reverse – With vehicle stopped, place gear selector in "R" position, and slowly accelerate to check Reverse gear operation.

LINE PRESSURE TESTS

CAUTION: Parking brake must be applied during test. Ensure test DOES NOT exceed 2 minutes.

1) Check ATF level, Throttle Valve (T.V.) cable adjustment and manual control linkages. See appropriate AUTOMATIC TRANSMISSION SERVICING article in TRANSMISSION SERVICING. Ensure engine is tuned properly.

2) Connect tachometer to engine. Connect pressure gauge to pressure test port on transaxle case. Pressure test port is on bellhousing side, above valve body cover.

3) Line pressure is controlled by pump output and pressure regulator valve. Line pressure is boosted by reverse boost valve in "R", "2" and "1" positions. Line pressure should increase with throttle opening in "N", "D" and "R" positions.

Minimum Throttle Valve (T.V.) Pressure Check – Ensure T.V. cable is properly adjusted. See appropriate AUTOMATIC TRANSMISSION SERVICING article in TRANSMISSION SERVICING. Check line pressure with transaxle and engine speed in the indicated gears and RPM, respectively. *See Fig. 4.*

Maximum Throttle Valve (T.V.) Pressure Check – With T.V. cable supported at full extent of travel, check line pressure with transaxle and engine speed in the indicated gears and RPM, respectively. *See Fig. 4.*

LINE PRESSURE TEST RESULTS

Line Pressure Too Low – **1)** Check fluid level. Check oil strainer "O" ring seal for leakage or damage. Check for plugged oil strainer. If pressure is low in "N" and "D" positions, and low to normal in "2" and "R" positions, Throttle Valve (T.V.) cable may be out of adjustment or bound.

2) Inspect control valve and pump assembly for loose bolts or internal leaks. Check T.V. valve and plunger, shift T.V. valve, pressure regulator valve, T.V. boost valve and pressure relief valve for sticking or damage. Check for missing or misplaced No. 5 or 6 check ball.

3) Check 1-2 accumulator piston and/or seal. If pressure is low in "1" position only, check for damaged low blow-off valve and missing or misplaced No. 4 check ball. If pressure is low in "R" position only, inspect low-reverse clutch housing-to-case cup plug for leaks.

HYDRA-MATIC 3T40 SHIFT SPEED CHART
UPSHIFTS

MODEL	TPS	1-2 SHIFT SPEED IN TPS ± 3 MPH									2-3 SHIFT SPEED IN TPS ± 4 MPH								
		10	15	20	25	30	35	40	45	50	10	15	20	25	30	35	40	45	50
AJC	MPH	14.0	16.0	17.0	18.0	20.0	21.0	22.0	23.0	24.0	26.0	27.0	30.0	32.0	33.0	36.0	37.0	39.0	41.0
AKC	MPH	14.0	15.0	18.0	21.0	22.0	23.0	24.0	25.0	25.0	24.0	26.0	27.0	28.0	33.0	36.0	40.0	43.0	45.0
ARC	MPH	17.0	18.0	20.0	22.0	23.0	24.0	25.0	26.0	28.0	25.0	28.0	29.0	34.0	37.0	42.0	46.0	48.0	52.0
BUC	MPH	16.0	18.0	19.5	20.8	22.2	23.4	24.7	25.9	27.2	25.0	26.8	29.4	33.8	38.1	41.8	45.0	48.2	50.9
BYC	MPH	16.0	17.8	19.5	20.7	22.1	23.2	24.5	25.7	26.9	24.8	27.3	32.5	36.6	41.2	44.5	47.9	51.0	53.9
CHC	MPH	14.6	15.9	17.3	18.4	20.0	20.8	22.1	23.1	24.1	24.2	25.5	26.8	28.7	32.7	35.8	39.2	41.8	44.9
CWC	MPH	16.0	18.0	21.0	23.0	26.0	30.0	33.0	36.0	39.0	27.0	33.0	37.0	41.0	45.0	51.0	53.0	55.0	58.0
CYC	MPH	16.0	18.0	18.0	19.0	21.0	22.0	23.0	24.0	25.0	25.0	26.0	28.0	30.0	33.0	37.0	41.0	43.0	46.0
HBC	MPH	16.0	18.0	20.0	20.0	22.0	23.0	24.0	25.0	26.0	26.0	28.0	29.0	31.0	36.0	40.0	42.0	43.0	46.0
HLC	MPH	14.0	16.0	17.0	17.5	18.0	19.0	21.0	22.0	22.5	22.5	23.0	24.0	25.0	27.0	30.0	32.5	34.0	37.0
HNC	MPH	14.0	16.0	17.0	18.0	18.0	19.0	20.0	21.0	22.0	21.0	23.0	23.0	26.0	30.0	33.0	36.0	38.0	41.0
JAC	MPH	16.0	17.0	18.0	19.0	20.0	21.0	22.0	23.0	23.0	26.0	28.0	31.0	33.0	36.0	38.0	40.0	43.0	44.0
KDC	MPH	16.7	18.7	20.4	22.1	23.3	24.6	28.8	30.4	33.8	26.0	31.7	35.7	40.2	44.2	47.8	51.2	54.1	57.5
KKC	MPH	15.2	17.3	19.1	20.3	21.8	22.9	24.3	25.0	27.4	24.7	27.4	32.7	36.9	41.4	45.4	48.9	51.9	54.9
KLC	MPH	16.0	17.0	19.0	20.0	21.0	23.0	24.0	26.0	28.0	25.0	28.0	33.0	38.0	42.0	46.0	47.0	53.0	56.0
KNC	MPH	15.0	16.0	17.0	18.0	21.0	23.0	26.0	27.0	29.0	25.0	26.0	27.0	28.0	30.0	36.0	41.0	44.0	46.0
KSC	MPH	16.0	18.0	20.0	22.0	24.0	25.0	26.0	29.0	34.0	25.0	27.0	29.0	32.0	34.0	36.0	38.0	41.0	44.0
LFC	MPH	16.0	18.0	19.0	21.0	22.0	24.0	25.0	26.0	26.0	25.0	27.0	29.0	32.0	35.0	37.0	40.0	43.0	45.0
LJC	MPH	16.2	17.7	19.2	20.6	21.9	23.1	24.4	25.6	26.7	26.2	27.8	29.4	32.9	36.9	41.0	44.7	48.4	51.4
LKC	MPH	16.0	17.0	19.0	21.0	22.0	23.0	24.0	26.0	28.0	25.0	27.0	30.0	33.0	35.0	37.0	40.0	43.0	44.0
LLC	MPH	15.8	17.5	19.1	20.4	21.6	22.8	24.1	25.4	26.6	24.7	27.0	31.9	36.3	40.1	43.6	46.7	49.8	52.9
LUC	MPH	16.3	17.7	19.4	20.7	22.0	23.1	24.5	25.6	26.8	26.2	27.8	29.4	30.7	33.4	36.8	40.0	43.2	45.9
PTC	MPH	14.3	15.5	16.1	17.2	18.1	19.1	20.0	20.6	21.5	21.7	24.2	28.1	31.3	34.1	36.9	39.1	41.6	43.7
PXC	MPH	16.0	16.0	18.0	20.0	22.0	23.0	24.0	26.0	27.0	23.0	25.0	27.0	30.0	33.0	35.0	37.0	40.0	43.0
SWC	MPH	16.0	17.0	18.0	19.0	21.0	22.0	23.0	24.0	26.0	25.0	26.0	27.0	31.0	36.0	40.0	46.0	48.0	51.0
TKC	MPH	14.0	16.0	17.0	18.0	18.0	19.0	20.0	21.0	22.0	21.0	24.0	28.0	31.0	33.0	36.0	38.0	41.0	43.0

FINAL DRIVE / SPROCKETS / OVERALL RATIOS / COASTDOWNS

MODEL	RATIOS FINAL DRIVE	SPROCKETS*	OVERALL	3-2 PART THROTTLE	3-2 COAST DOWN	2-1 COAST DOWN	2-1 MAN LOW
AJC	2.84	33/37	3.18	42-50	18-20	6-10	50-57
AKC	2.84	33/37	3.18	42-50	18-20	6-10	30-37
ARC	2.84	38/32	3.37	48-55	17-19	6-11	44-52
BUC	2.84	38/32	2.39	47-54	17-19	6-11	46-52
BYC	3.06	37/33	2.73	45-51	17-19	6-11	46-51
CHC	2.84	35/35	2.84	44-52	18-20	6-10	36-43
CWC	2.84	37/33	3.18	46-52	17-19	3-10	49-56
CYC	2.84	33/37	2.53	44-51	19-21	6-11	33-42
HBC	3.06	33/37	2.73	51-57	21-23	7-12	28-33
HLC	3.06	33/37	2.73	38-43	18-19	8-11	25-30
HNC	3.33	35/35	3.33	43-49	17-19	8-11	25-34
JAC	3.06	33/37	2.73	43-48	19-20	9-12	28-36
KDC	2.84	35/35	2.84	46-52	17-19	6-12	37-43
KKC	2.84	33/37	3.18	43-50	17-19	5-9	31-38
KLC	2.84	33/37	2.53	40-48	19-21	6-10	38-47
KNC	2.84	33/37	3.18	43-52	19-21	6-11	31-41
KSC	2.84	35/35	2.84	47-53	17-19	5-11	38-44
LFC	2.84	37/33	2.53	48-55	20-22	6-11	41-48
LJC	2.84	37/33	2.53	54-62	20-22	6-11	40-48
LKC	2.84	35/35	2.84	42-48	16-18	6-11	45-50
LLC	2.84	35/35	2.84	42-48	16-18	6-11	45-50
LUC	2.84	33/37	3.18	46-53	20-22	6-11	36-43
PTC	3.06	33/37	3.43	42-48	18-19	9-12	32-38
PXC	2.84	33/37	3.18	58-64	19-22	5-10	39-44
SWC	3.06	33/35	2.89	49-57	19-21	6-11	28-39
TKC	3.06	33/37	2.73	43-48	18-19	9-12	29-37

1. ALL SPEEDS INDICATED ARE IN MILES PER HOUR. CONVERSION TO KM/h = MPH x 1.609.
2. SHIFT POINTS WILL VARY SLIGHTLY DUE TO ENGINE LOAD AND VEHICLE OPTIONS.
3. 1-2 AND 2-3 SHIFT SPEEDS ARE BASED USING THROTTLE POSITION SENSOR (TP SENSOR) DATA AS A REFERENCE - USE A TECH 1 OR OTHER SCAN TOOL TO MONITOR THIS DATA.
* DESIGNATES THE NUMBER OF TEETH ON THE DRIVE/DRIVEN SPROCKETS, RESPECTIVELY.

94138289

Courtesy of General Motors Corp.

Fig. 3: Shift Speed Chart

PRELIMINARY CHECK PROCEDURE

CHECK TRANSMISSION FLUID LEVEL • CHECK AND ADJUST TV CABLE • CHECK OUTSIDE MANUAL LINKAGE AND CORRECT
CHECK ENGINE TUNE • INSTALL PRESSURE GAGE* • CONNECT TACHOMETER TO ENGINE

CHECK FLUID PRESSURES IN THE FOLLOWING MANNER:

Minimum TV Line Pressure Check

Set the TV cable to specification; and with the brakes applied, take the line pressure readings in the ranges and at the engine RPM indicated in the chart below.

Full TV Line Pressure Check

Full TV line pressure readings are obtained by tying or holding the TV cable to the full extent of its travel; and with the brakes applied, take the line pressure readings in the ranges and at the engine RPM indicated in the chart below.

CAUTION: Brakes must be applied at all times. | **NOTICE: Total running time for this combination not to exceed 2 minutes.**

Range	Model	MINIMUM TV		MAXIMUM TV	
		kPa	P.S.I.	kPa	P.S.I.
Park @ 1000 RPM	AJC, AKC, BUC, BYC, CHC, KDC, KKC, KNC, KSC, KXC, LFC, LJC, LUC, PXC	459-505	66-73	459-505	66-73
	ARC, CWC, CYC, HBC, JAC, KLC	460-506	67-73	460-506	67-73
	HLC	459-505	67-73	459-506	67-73
	HNC, SWC, TKC	396-436	58-63	396-436	58-63
	PTC	396-436	57-62	396-436	57-62
Reverse @ 1000 RPM	AKC, ANC, KNC, KSC, LFC, PXC	781-859	113-124	1553-1726	225-250
	ARC, CYC, KLC	781-859	113-125	781-859	113-125
	BUC	805-885	116-128	1882-2101	272-294
	BYC, CHC	805-885	116-128	1827-2034	264-294
	CWC, HBC, JAC	805-886	117-128	805-886	117-128
	HLC	753-949	109-138	753-949	109-138
	HNC	760-837	110-121	760-837	110-121
	KDC	805-885	116-128	1763-1966	255-285
	KKC, LLC	805-885	116-128	1636-1824	237-264
	LJC	805-885	116-128	1643-1831	238-265
	LUC	805-885	116-128	805-885	116-128
	PTC	693-764	100-110	1524-1702	221-246
	SWC	673-741	98-107	673-741	98-107
	TKC	694-764	101-111	694-764	101-111
Neutral/ Drive @ 1000 RPM	AJC, AKC, KDC, KNC, KSC, LFC, PXC	459-505	66-73	1006-1122	145-162
	ARC, CWC, CYC, HBC, JAC, KLC	460-506	67-73	460-506	67-73
	AYC	396-436	57-62	943-1053	136-152
	BUC	459-505	66-73	1075-1200	155-174
	BYC, CHC	459-505	66-73	1043-1161	151-168
	HLC	459-505	67-73	459-505	67-73
	HNC, SWC, TKC	396-436	58-63	396-436	58-63
	KKC, LLC, LUC	459-505	66-73	934-1042	135-151
	LJC, PDC	459-505	66-73	938-1045	136-151
	PTC	396-436	57-62	870-972	126-140
Intermediate/ Lo @ 1000 RPM	AJC, AKC, KNC, KSC, LFC, PXC	788-868	114-125	788-868	114-125
	ARC, CYC, HLC, KLC,	959-1055	139-153	959-1055	139-153
	BUC, BYC, CHC, KDC, KKC, LJC, LLC, PDC, PJC, TRC	959-1055	139-153	959-1055	139-153
	CWC, HBC, JAC	789-868	114-126	789-868	114-126
	HNC	826-910	120-132	826-910	120-132
	PTC	679-748	98-108	679-748	98-108
	SWC	827-910	120-132	827-910	120-132
	TKC	680-749	99-109	680-749	99-109

Line pressure is basically controlled by pump output and the pressure regulator valve. In addition, line pressure is boosted in Reverse, Intermediate and Lo by the reverse boost valve.

Also, in the Neutral, Drive and Reverse positions of the selector lever, the line pressure should increase with throttle opening because of the TV system. The TV system is controlled by the TV cable, the throttle lever and bracket assembly and the TV link, as well as the control valve pump assembly.

94B38290

Fig. 4: Checking Throttle Valve Line Pressure

4) Inspect oil pump for loose bolts and damaged or missing pump valve seals. Check intermediate oil passages to pressure regulator for blockage. Check driven sprocket support-to-case cover for leaks.

Line Pressure Too High – **1)** With pressure high in "N" and "D" positions, and normal to high in "2" and "R" positions, check for broken, sticking or misadjusted Throttle Valve (T.V.) cable.

2) Inspect T.V. linkage for binding or incorrect cable. Check throttle valve or shift T.V. valve for sticking. Inspect T.V. lifter for bend or damage. Check if lifter length is too short.

3) Inspect components of control valve and pump assembly for sticking or damaged T.V. valve and plunger, shift T.V. valve, pressure regulator valve, T.V. boost valve and/or pump slide.

4) Check for worn or missing pressure regulator valve retaining pin. If line pressure is too high in "1" position only, check low blow-off valve for sticking. Inspect internal pump case or case cover for leaks.

CLUTCH & BAND APPLICATION CHART

CLUTCH & BAND APPLICATION CHART [1]

Selector Lever Position	Elements In Use
"D" (Drive)	
1st Gear	Forward Clutch & Low Roller Clutch
2nd Gear	Forward Clutch & Intermediate Band
3rd Gear	Direct Clutch & Forward Clutch
"2" (Intermediate)	
1st Gear	Forward Clutch & Low Roller Clutch
2nd Gear	Forward Clutch & Intermediate Band
"1" (Low)	
1st Gear	Forward Clutch, Low-Reverse Clutch & Low Roller Clutch
"R" (Reverse)	Direct Clutch & Low-Reverse Clutch
"N" & "P" (Neutral & Park)	All Clutches & Bands Released Or Ineffective

[1] – For clutch assembly locations, *See Fig. 46.*

TORQUE CONVERTER

NOTE: Torque converter is a sealed unit and CANNOT be disassembled.

TORQUE CONVERTER INSPECTION

In-Vehicle Test – Install a tachometer, and warm engine to normal operation temperature. With vehicle in 3rd gear and speed between 50-55 MPH, converter clutch should engage. Engine speed should drop 200 RPM when clutch is engaged.

Bench Test – **1)** With converter removed from vehicle, insert fingers into splined inner race of roller clutch, and ensure stator turns freely clockwise, but does not turn or is very difficult to turn counterclockwise. DO NOT use driven sprocket support or shafts to turn race, as result may not be correct.

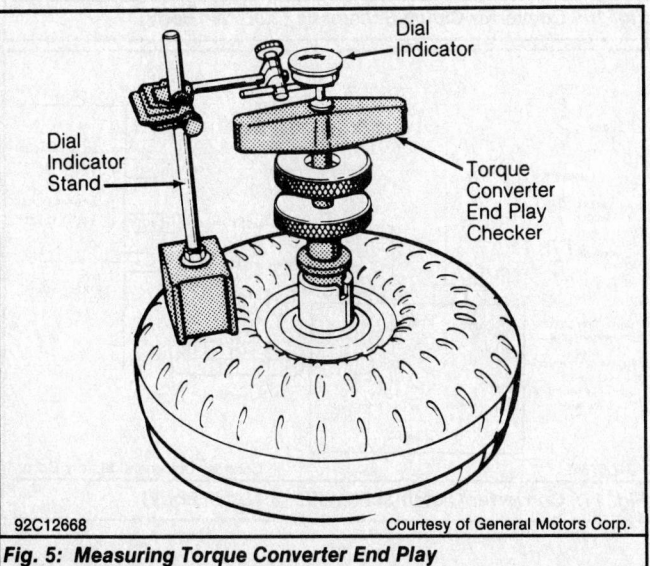

92C12668   Courtesy of General Motors Corp.

Fig. 5: Measuring Torque Converter End Play

2) Using Torque Converter End Play Checker (J-35138), measure torque converter end play. *See Fig. 5.* End play for 245-mm torque converter is 0-.020" (0-.5 mm). End play for 298-mm torque converter is 0-.024" (0-.6 mm). Converter must be replaced if it leaks, is imbalanced or is contaminated with antifreeze.

3) Check torque converter bushing-to-stator support clearance by cutting a narrow strip of paper about .003" (.07 mm) thick. Lay paper against the inside diameter of torque converter bushing. Install stator support into torque converter. No clearance should be present.

TORQUE CONVERTER CLUTCH

TORQUE CONVERTER CLUTCH (TCC) CONTROL COMPONENTS

NOTE: PCM may also be referred to as ECM.

The following components are used in TCC system. Not all components will be present on all vehicles.

Brake Switch – Power from ignition switch passes through brake switch to TCC solenoid. When brake pedal is depressed with TCC engaged, power to TCC solenoid is interrupted, releasing converter clutch and preventing engine from stalling.

Coolant Temperature Sensor – This sensor provides PCM with engine coolant temperature information. PCM will not allow TCC operation until signal from this sensor indicates coolant temperature greater than 130-150°F (55-65°C).

Powertrain Control Module (PCM) – To determine application of torque converter clutch, PCM receives and processes information from various input devices. These devices may include the vehicle speed sensor, coolant temperature sensor, throttle position sensor, 3rd and 4th gear switches and brake switch. The PCM controls application of torque converter clutch by providing a ground circuit for the TCC solenoid circuit.

TCC Solenoid Assembly – Solenoid is energized by PCM to redirect transmission fluid to the converter clutch apply valve in the auxiliary control valve assembly.

TCC Pulse-Width Modulated Solenoid – Acts with TCC regulator valve to control the apply and release of TCC.

Throttle Position Sensor (TPS) – Provides PCM with throttle position information. TCC operation is prevented when throttle position signal is less than a specified value.

Vacuum Sensor – Sends engine vacuum (load) information to PCM.

Vehicle Speed Sensor (VSS) – This sensor sends vehicle speed information to PCM. Vehicle speed must be greater than a certain value before TCC can be applied. Two types of speed sensor are used. A light emitting diode type is used in the instrument cluster on some models. Other models use a Permanent Magnet (PM) generator mounted in the transmission.

3rd & 4th Gear Switches – When open, 3rd and 4th gear switches prevent TCC operation. Switch status may be monitored by PCM, or switch may be an integral portion (series circuit) of TCC solenoid power supply.

NOTE: Diagnostic codes for coolant temperature sensor, throttle position sensor or vehicle speed sensor may be present while performing TCC electrical diagnosis. See ENGINE PERFORMANCE in appropriate MITCHELL® manual for complete information on General Motors Computerized Engine Control systems.

TCC TESTING

NOTE: When diagnosing converter clutch problems, ensure engine and vacuum systems are operating properly.

Converter Clutch Solenoid – Disconnect harness connector to Torque Converter Clutch (TCC) solenoid. Measure resistance between TCC solenoid terminals "A" and "D". Solenoid resistance should be greater than 20 ohms. *See Figs. 6-16.*

NOTE: Some solenoids have an internal pressure switch in series with the solenoid winding and will not show continuity until that pressure switch is applied by transmission hydraulic pressure.

Converter Lock-Up Signal At Transmission – 1) Warm engine to operating temperature. Raise vehicle and support drive wheels. Support suspension where necessary to prevent damage to drive axles.
2) Disconnect converter clutch connector at transmission. Connect a test light across terminals "A" and "D" of converter clutch harness. Start engine and place transmission in Drive. Accelerate vehicle to 45 MPH and note test light.
3) If test light is not on, check solenoid power supply wire of harness for open or short to ground. Check ground circuit for open between harness connector and PCM. If harness is okay, see CONVERTER LOCK-UP SIGNAL FROM PCM.

Converter Lock-Up Signal From PCM – 1) Warm engine to operating temperature. Raise vehicle and support drive wheels. Support suspension where necessary to prevent damage to drive axles.

2) Connect a test light to battery voltage. Touch TCC control driver terminal with test light. On some vehicles, this is terminal "F" of the ALDL connector. See Figs. 6-16. Accelerate vehicle to 45 MPH and note test light. If test light does not illuminate, problem is a faulty PCM connector or PCM.

NOTE: In the following schematics, Assembly Line Data Link (ALDL) connector is also referred to by manufacturer as Data Link Connector (DLC).

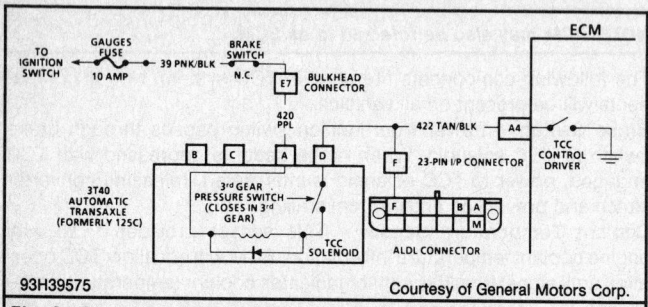

93H39575   Courtesy of General Motors Corp.

Fig. 6: Converter Clutch Schematic (2.0L "J" Body)

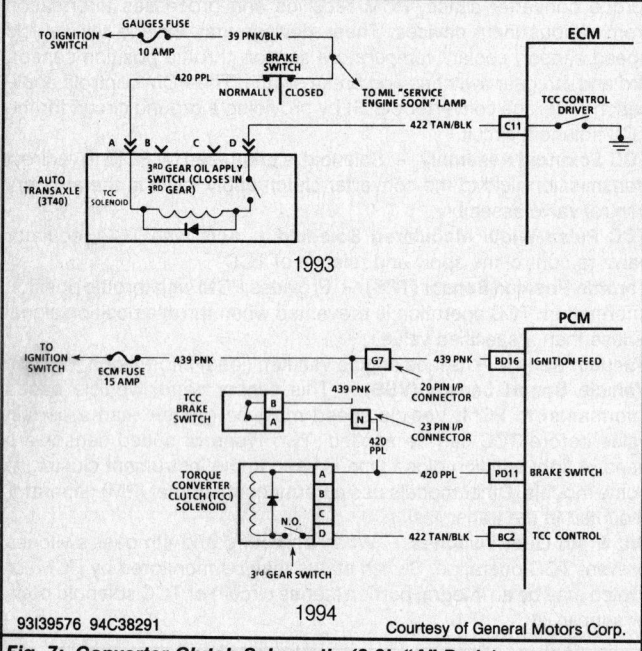

93I39576   94C38291   1994   Courtesy of General Motors Corp.

Fig. 7: Converter Clutch Schematic (2.2L "A" Body)

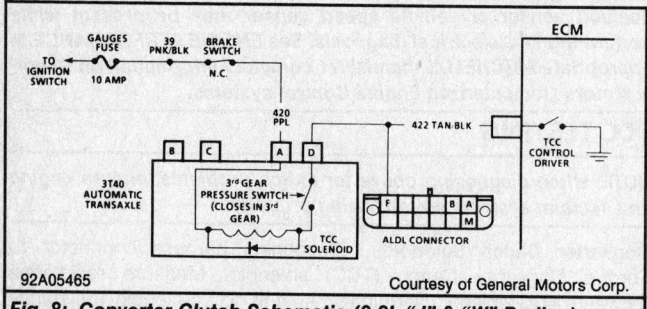

92A05465   Courtesy of General Motors Corp.

Fig. 8: Converter Clutch Schematic (2.2L "J" & "W" Bodies)

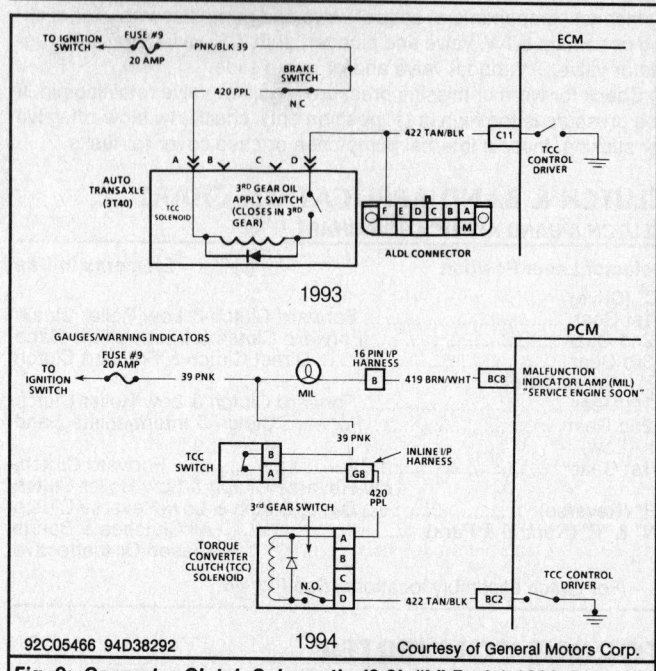

92C05466   94D38292   1994   Courtesy of General Motors Corp.

Fig. 9: Converter Clutch Schematic (2.2L "L" Body) 1993 Only

93J39577   Courtesy of General Motors Corp.

Fig. 10: Converter Clutch Schematic (2.3L "N" Body)

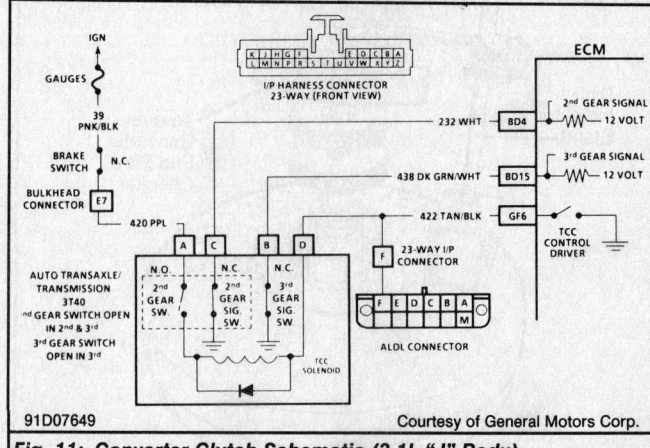

91D07649   Courtesy of General Motors Corp.

Fig. 11: Converter Clutch Schematic (3.1L "J" Body)

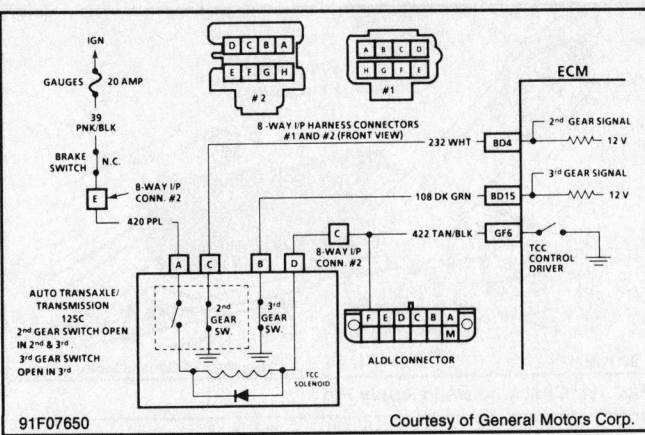

Fig. 12: Converter Clutch Schematic (3.1L "L" Body) 1993 Only

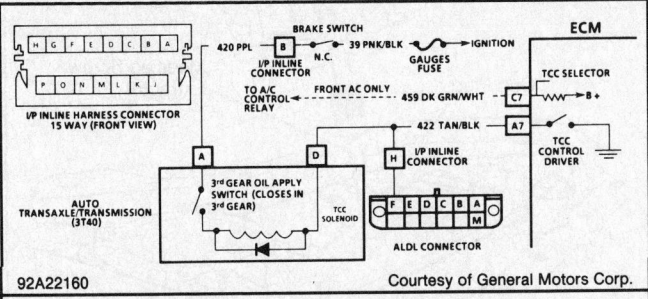

Fig. 13: Converter Clutch Schematic (3.1L "U" Body)

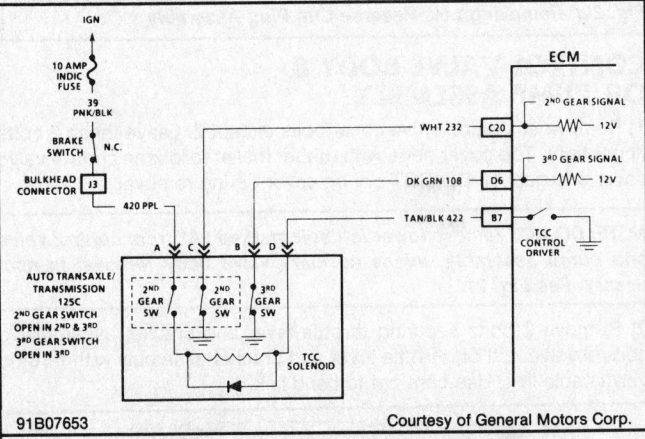

Fig. 14: Converter Clutch Schematic (3.1L "W" Body)

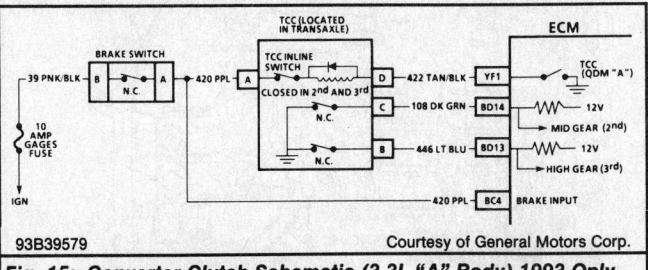

Fig. 15: Converter Clutch Schematic (3.3L "A" Body) 1993 Only

ON-VEHICLE SERVICE

CONTROL VALVE BODY

See CONTROL VALVE BODY & OIL PUMP ASSEMBLY under TRANSAXLE DISASSEMBLY.

DRIVE AXLE SHAFTS

See FWD AXLE SHAFTS article in AXLE SHAFTS & TRANSFER CASES.

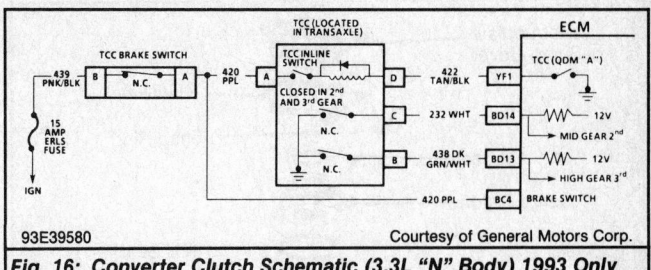

Fig. 16: Converter Clutch Schematic (3.3L "N" Body) 1993 Only

OIL COOLER FLUSHING

1) If flusher tool is available, fill line flusher with solution, and install Oil Cooler and Line Flusher (J-35944) to top transaxle cooler line on transaxle. Follow manufacturer's instructions to flush oil cooler and cooler lines.

2) If flusher tool is not available, flush cooler and cooler lines with a mixture of clean solvent and water. Flush cooler in both directions until all old fluid and debris are removed. If necessary, replace plugged or damaged cooler and/or lines.

REMOVAL & INSTALLATION

See appropriate AUTOMATIC TRANSMISSION REMOVAL article in TRANSMISSION SERVICING.

TRANSAXLE DISASSEMBLY

Clean exterior of transaxle case. Clean parts with solvent and dry with compressed air. Never use rags to dry parts. Remove torque converter by pulling straight out. Place transaxle in Holding Fixture (J-28664) and Bench Base (J-3289-20) so right axle end is down to drain fluid.

SPEEDOMETER DRIVE GEAR/SPEED SENSOR & GOVERNOR ASSEMBLY

Internal Transaxle Speed Sensor (ITSS) – Remove speed sensor housing bolts, speed sensor housing and oil seal. Remove thrust bearing, speed sensor rotor and governor assembly. See Fig. 45.

Speedometer Drive Gear – Remove speedometer driven gear mount bolt with retainer. Withdraw speedometer driven gear assembly from governor cover. Remove governor cover bolts, cover and "O" ring. Lift out unit as an assembly. See Fig. 44.

INTERMEDIATE SERVO ASSEMBLY

1) Remove all, except 2, oil pan bolts. Leave these 2 bolts finger tight. Tap oil pan loose with rubber mallet. Remove oil pan and oil strainer. Discard oil strainer "O" ring.

NOTE: DO NOT remove servo piston oil seals unless servo piston is to be replaced.

2) Remove reverse oil pipe retaining bracket-to-servo cover bolt. Remove remaining servo cover bolts. Lift off intermediate servo cover and gasket. Remove intermediate servo assembly. See Fig. 17.

3) If necessary, detach snap ring, and remove intermediate band apply pin from intermediate servo piston. Discard oil seals. Remove 3rd accumulator exhaust valve and spring. See Fig. 17. Inspect spring and exhaust valve for wear or damage. See Fig. 18.

NOTE: Perform BAND APPLY PIN SELECTION CHECK to determine correct pin to be used during reassembly.

Band Apply Pin Selection Check – **1)** Install Band Apply Pin Gauge (J-28535) over intermediate servo bore, and retain it with 2 servo cover bolts. See Fig. 19. Remove band apply pin from intermediate servo assembly.

2) Install Band Apply Pin Gauge Extension (J-28535-4) onto servo piston end of band apply pin. Install band apply pin and gauge extension into gauge on servo bore.

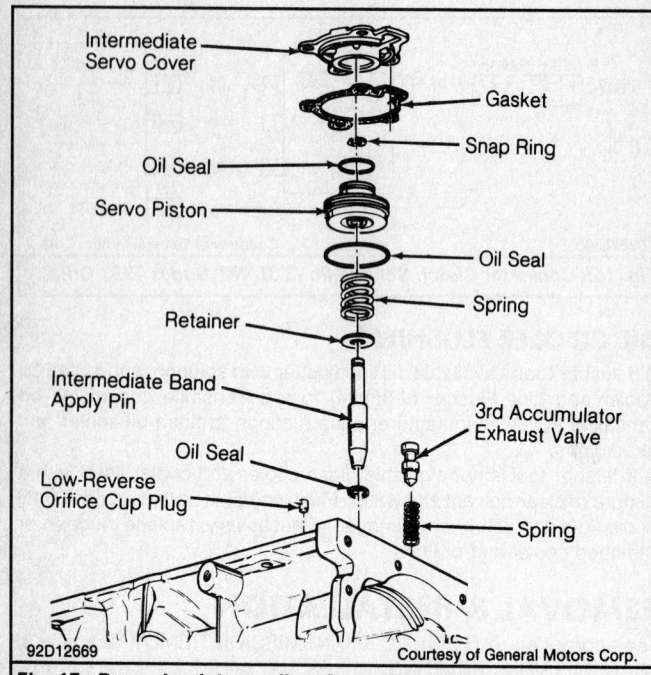

Fig. 17: Removing Intermediate Servo Assembly

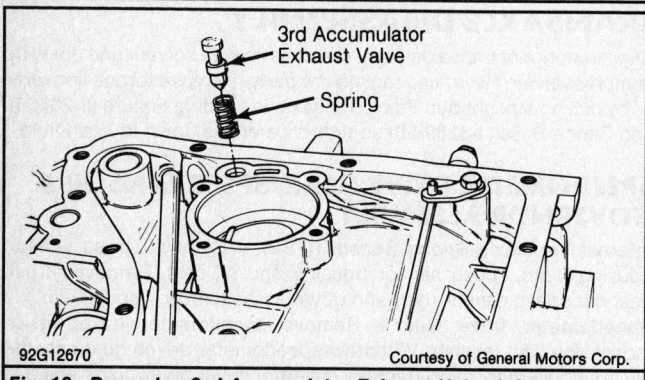

Fig. 18: Removing 3rd Accumulator Exhaust Valve & Spring

3) Using an INCH lb. torque wrench, apply torque of 100 INCH lbs. (11.3 N.m) to hex nut on gauge tool. If pin is correct size, White line on gauge extension will appear in window.

4) If White line does not appear in window, use a longer or shorter pin as necessary. See INTERMEDIATE BAND APPLY PIN table. Repeat step 3) to ensure pin size is correct. Set selected pin aside until transaxle reassembly procedure.

INTERMEDIATE BAND APPLY PIN

Length	Identification
Short	2 Grooves
Medium	1 Groove
Long	No Groove

OUTPUT SHAFT & LOW-REVERSE SEAL

1) Detach low-reverse oil pipe, oil pipe seal back-up washer and "O" ring seal. Grind about 3/4" from end of a No. 4 screw extractor. Insert modified screw extractor into low-reverse cup plug. *See Fig. 20.* DO NOT hammer or force screw extractor into cup plug. Carefully twist screw extractor to remove cup plug.

2) Remove dipstick stop and parking lock bracket from above parking pawl and parking pawl actuator rod. Rotate final drive unit until open ends of output shaft retaining "C" ring are visible.

3) Using output shaft "C" Ring Remover (J-34757), push both ends of retaining "C" ring down to partially dislodge from output shaft. Rotate output shaft/final drive until "C" ring is visible. Carefully remove "C" ring with needle-nose pliers. Remove output shaft.

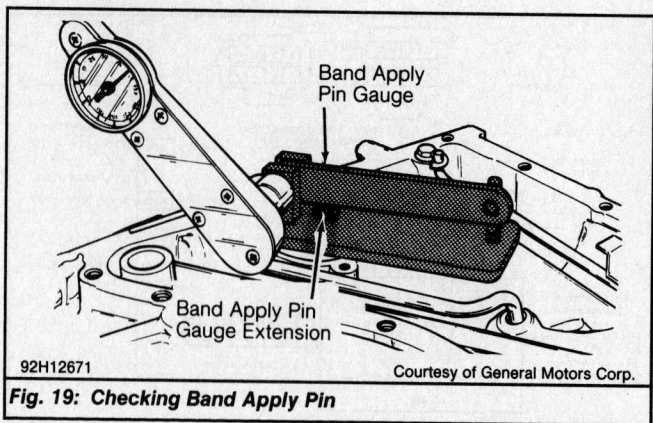

Fig. 19: Checking Band Apply Pin

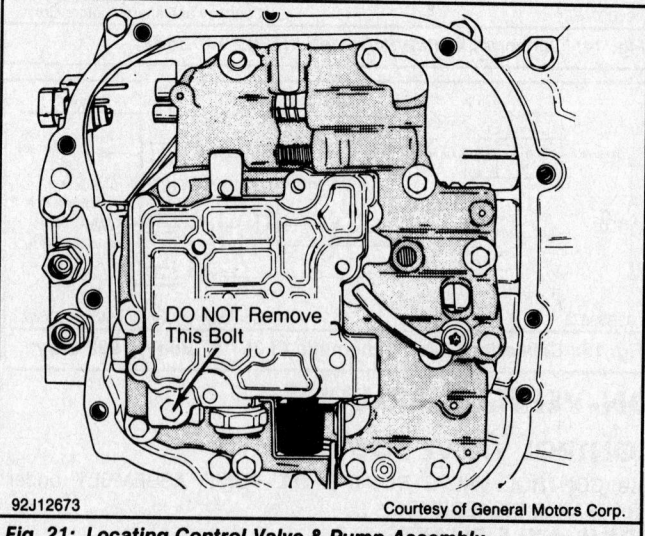

Fig. 20: Removing Low-Reverse Cup Plug Assembly

CONTROL VALVE BODY & OIL PUMP ASSEMBLY

1) Remove all control valve cover bolts except 2. Leave these 2 bolts finger tight. Tap cover edge with rubber mallet to loosen control valve cover and gasket. DO NOT pry on cover during removal.

NOTE: DO NOT remove lower left bolt marked "A" from control valve and pump assembly unless auxiliary valve body removal is necessary. See Fig. 21.

2) Remove 2 bolts securing throttle lever and bracket assembly to control valve. Lift off throttle lever and bracket assembly with throttle valve cable link. Use care not to bend link.

Fig. 21: Locating Control Valve & Pump Assembly Lower Left Bolt

3) Remove all auxiliary valve body bolts except lower left bolt. *See Fig. 21.* Remove remaining control valve assembly bolts. Carefully lift off control valve and pump assembly. Place assembly on bench with machined surface up.

4) Remove No. 1 check ball from direct clutch passage on spacer plate. Lift out oil pump drive shaft. Remove spacer plate and spacer plate gaskets. Remove 5 check balls from case cover. *See Fig. 22.*

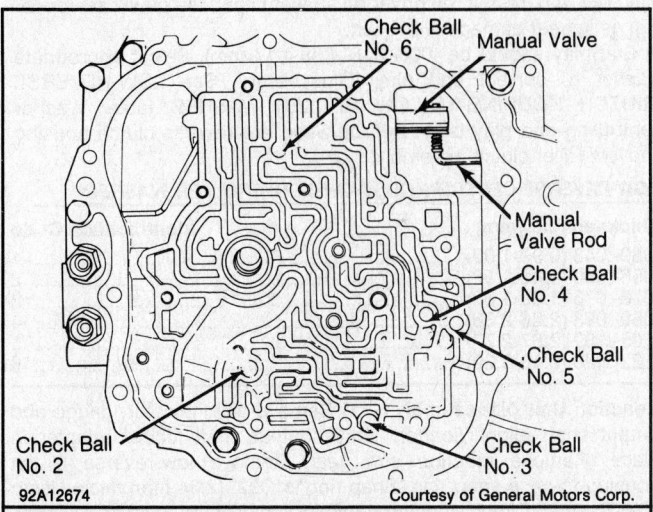

Fig. 22: Locating Case Cover Check Balls

Input Shaft-To-Case Cover End Play – **1)** Install Output Shaft Loader Adapter Plug (J-26958-10) into right axle end. *See Fig. 23.* Mount Output Shaft Aligner/Loader (J-26958) and Bracket (J-26958-11) to right axle end of case. Adjust loader by turning handle until knob bottoms.

2) Install Input Shaft Lifter (J-28544) into input shaft bore and tighten. Install dial indicator with Extension Post (J-25025-7). Place indicator plunger on end of lifter. Press down on lifter, zero dial indicator, and lift up tool. End play should be .004-.033" (.10-.84 mm). End play snap ring is located on input shaft, beneath driven sprocket. If end play is not as specified, replace snap ring. See INPUT SHAFT END PLAY SELECTIVE SNAP RINGS table.

CAUTION: Oil soaked snap rings may discolor. Measure snap ring for actual thickness.

INPUT SHAFT END PLAY SELECTIVE SNAP RINGS

Thickness In. (mm)	Color Code
.071-.076 (1.80-1.93)	White
.078-.084 (1.98-2.13)	Blue
.088-.092 (2.23-2.33)	Red
.095-.099 (2.41-2.51)	Yellow
.103-.107 (2.62-2.72)	Green

TRANSAXLE CASE COVER & INPUT UNIT ASSEMBLY

1) Disconnect manual valve rod from manual valve. Remove remaining transmission case cover mount bolts. Install 2 bolts (12 x 1.75 x 50 mm) into case cover dowel pin holes. *See Fig. 24.*

2) Bolts will bottom out on dowel pins and separate case cover from case. DO NOT pry cover from case. Remove case cover, and lay side with 1-2 accumulator up, as 1-2 accumulator pin may drop out of cover.

3) Remove 1-2 accumulator spring, piston and center case-to-cover gasket. Remove case cover-to-drive sprocket thrust washer and driven sprocket thrust bearing assembly. Case cover-to-drive sprocket thrust washer may come off with case cover.

4) Remove and discard turbine shaft "O" ring. Remove drive sprocket, driven sprocket and chain as an assembly. *See Fig. 2.* Remove drive and driven sprocket-to-support thrust washers. These washers may come off with sprockets.

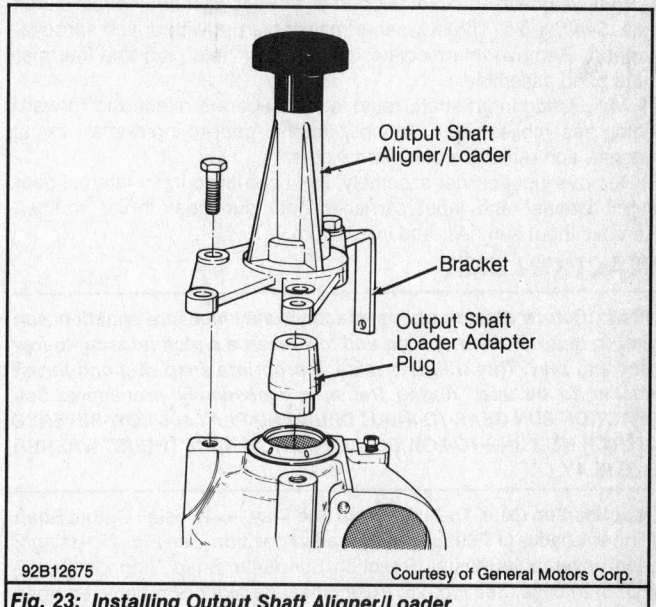

Fig. 23: Installing Output Shaft Aligner/Loader

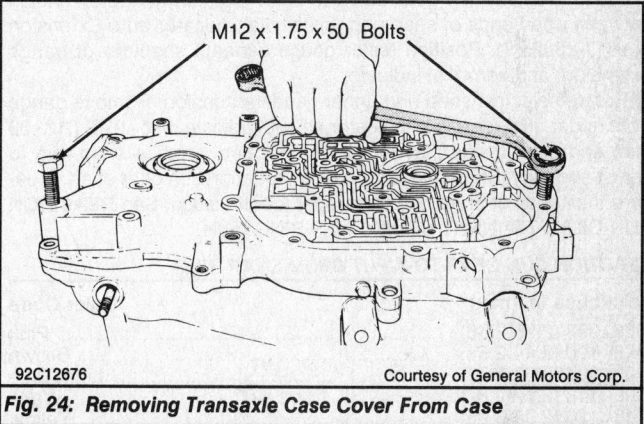

Fig. 24: Removing Transaxle Case Cover From Case

5) Using 3/16" drift, remove detent lever-to-manual shaft pin. Remove manual shaft-to-case nail. *See Fig. 25.* Withdraw manual shaft from case, and lift out manual valve rod and detent lever assembly. Remove park lock actuator rod.

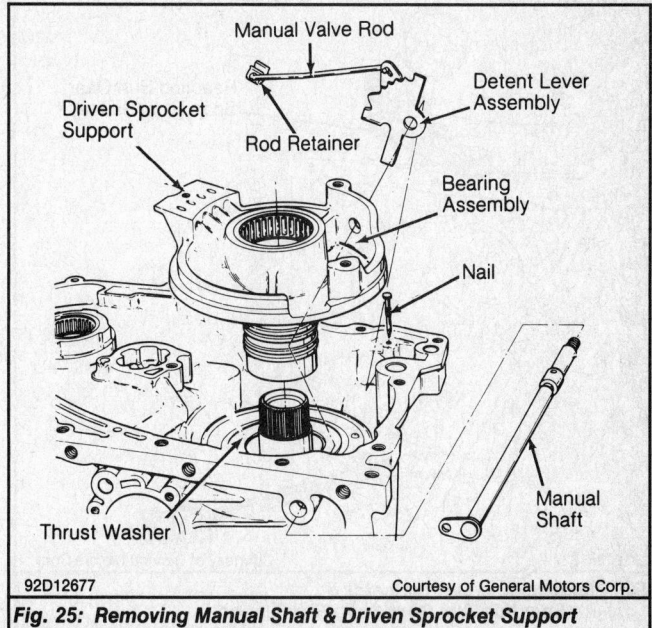

Fig. 25: Removing Manual Shaft & Driven Sprocket Support

6) Remove driven sprocket support and thrust washer on direct clutch side. *See Fig. 25.* Thrust washer may come out with driven sprocket support. Remove intermediate band anchor hole plug and intermediate band assembly.

7) While lifting input shaft, remove and separate direct and forward clutch assemblies. Remove input internal gear-to-input shaft thrust washer, and remove input internal gear.

8) Remove input carrier assembly, input carrier-to-input internal gear thrust washer and input carrier-to-input sun gear thrust washer. Remove input sun gear and input drum.

REACTION UNIT

NOTE: Before disassembling reaction unit, measure reaction sun gear-to-input drum snap ring and low-reverse clutch housing-to-low race end play. This will determine appropriate snap ring and thrust washer to be used during transaxle reassembly procedure. See REACTION SUN GEAR-TO-INPUT DRUM END PLAY and LOW-REVERSE CLUTCH HOUSING-TO-LOW ROLLER CLUTCH RACE THRUST WASHER END PLAY.

Reaction Sun Gear-To-Input Drum End Play – **1)** Install Output Shaft Aligner/Loader (J-26958) in fully loaded position. *See Fig. 23.* Using 2 case cover bolts, install Reaction Sun Gear Snap Ring Gauge (J-28588) to case. *See Fig. 26.* Position gauge extension between open ends of selective snap ring.

2) Press reaction sun gear down to seat. Position gauge extension between open ends of snap ring. Install dial indicator onto Extension Post (J-25025-7). Position feeler gauge beneath shoulder of gauge extension, and zero dial indicator.

3) Rotate selective snap ring under gauge extension. Remove gauge from under shoulder. Dial indicator should indicate .005-.013" (.13-.33 mm) end play. If end play is not as specified, replace snap ring to adjust end play. Snap ring is located on reaction sun gear shaft. Measure thickness of snap ring for proper identification. See REACTION SUN GEAR-TO-INPUT DRUM SNAP RING table.

REACTION SUN GEAR-TO-INPUT DRUM SNAP RING

Thickness In. (mm)	Color Code
.089-.093 (2.26-2.36)	Pink
.096-.100 (2.44-2.54)	Brown
.103-.107 (2.62-2.72)	Light Blue
.109-.113 (2.77-2.87)	White
.116-.120 (2.95-3.05)	Yellow
.123-.127 (3.12-3.22)	Light Green
.129-.133 (3.28-3.38)	Orange
.136-.140 (3.45-3.56)	No Color

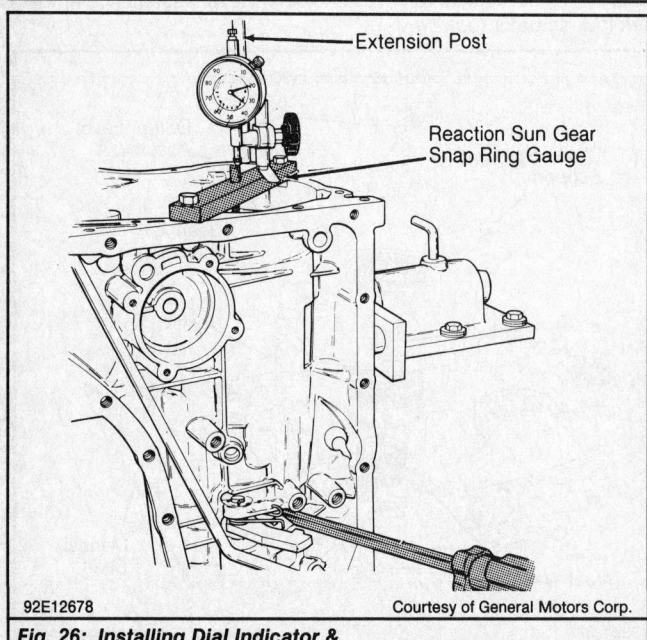

92E12678   Courtesy of General Motors Corp.

Fig. 26: Installing Dial Indicator & Reaction Sun Gear Snap Ring Gauge

Low-Reverse Clutch Housing-To-Low Roller Clutch Race Thrust Washer End Play – **1)** With dial indicator, gauge and output shaft aligner/loader still installed from previous procedure (REACTION SUN GEAR-TO-INPUT DRUM END PLAY), press down reaction sun gear to seat and zero dial indicator.

2) Insert screwdriver through parking pawl case opening. *See Fig. 26.* Lift reaction internal gear, and read low-reverse clutch selective end play. DO NOT rest screwdriver on spacer in parking pawl case opening, as spacer damage will result.

3) End play should be .003-.046" (.08-1.17 mm). Select appropriate washer to correct end play if necessary. See LOW-REVERSE CLUTCH HOUSING-TO-LOW ROLLER WASHER table. Washer controlling end play is located between low-reverse clutch housing and low roller clutch assembly.

LOW-REVERSE CLUTCH HOUSING-TO-LOW ROLLER WASHER

Thickness In. (mm)	Identification Code
.039-.043 (0.99-1.09)	1
.056-.060 (1.42-1.52)	2
.072-.076 (1.83-1.93)	3
.089-.093 (2.26-2.36)	4
.105-.109 (2.67-2.77)	5
.122-.126 (3.10-3.20)	6

Reaction Unit Disassembly – **1)** Remove dial indicator, gauge and output shaft aligner/loader. Leave output shaft loader adapter in place. Remove reaction sun gear. Remove low-reverse clutch housing-to-case snap ring. Snap ring is .092" (2.34 mm) thick. Using Low-Reverse Clutch Housing Remover/Installer (J-28542 or J-34008), remove low-reverse clutch housing. *See Fig. 27.*

2) Remove low-reverse clutch housing-to-case spacer ring from groove in case. Lift out final drive sun gear shaft and reaction gear set as an assembly. Remove roller clutch and reaction carrier assembly from final drive sun gear shaft.

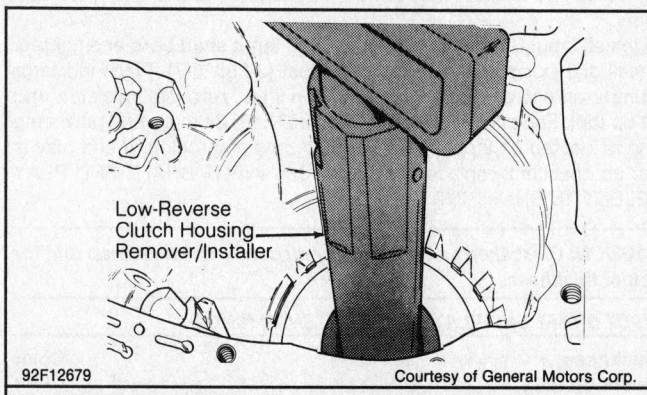

Low-Reverse Clutch Housing Remover/Installer

92F12679   Courtesy of General Motors Corp.

Fig. 27: Removing & Installing Low-Reverse Clutch Housing

FINAL DRIVE UNIT

NOTE: Before disassembling unit, check final drive-to-case end play. This will determine the appropriate final drive differential-to-case thrust washer to be used during transaxle reassembly procedure. See FINAL DRIVE-TO-CASE END PLAY.

Final Drive-To-Case End Play – **1)** Position transaxle so right axle is up. Using Output Shaft Aligner/Loader Adapter Plug (J-26958-10), press down adapter to seat final drive onto final drive internal gear-to-case snap ring.

2) Install dial indicator onto post, and install post in motor mount bolt hole. *See Fig. 29.* Ensure indicator plunger rests on top of adapter. Zero dial indicator while pressing down on adapter.

3) Insert large screwdriver into transaxle governor bore, and lift final drive by prying up on governor drive gear. Dial indicator should indicate .005-.032" (.12-.81 mm) end play.

4) Select appropriate thrust washer to correct end play if necessary. See FINAL DRIVE-TO-CASE THRUST WASHER table. Thrust washer controlling end play is located between differential carrier and differential carrier case thrust bearing assembly.

FINAL DRIVE-TO-CASE THRUST WASHER

Thickness In. (mm)	Identification Number (Color Code)
.055-.059 (1.40-1.50)	0 (Orange)
.059-.062 (1.50-1.60)	1 (White)
.062-.066 (1.60-1.70)	2 (Blue)
.066-.070 (1.70-1.80)	3 (Pink)
.070-.074 (1.80-1.90)	4 (Brown)
.074-.078 (1.90-2.00)	5 (Green)
.078-.082 (2.00-2.10)	6 (Black)
.082-.086 (2.10-2.20)	7 (Purple)
.086-.091 (2.20-2.30)	8 (Purple/White)
.091-.095 (2.30-2.40)	9 (Purple/Blue)

Final Drive Unit Disassembly – 1) Remove dial indicator, indicator post and loader/aligner adapter. Remove final drive internal gear spacer-to-case snap ring. Snap ring is .092" (2.34 mm) thick. Remove final drive internal gear spacer. Use care not to deform or bend spacer.

2) Using Final Drive Unit Remover/Installer (J-33381), lift final drive unit from case. Remove final drive differential-to-case selective thrust washer. Remove differential carrier-to-case thrust roller bearing assembly from final drive assembly. If thrust washer and thrust bearing did not come out with final drive assembly, remove from case.

COMPONENT DISASSEMBLY & REASSEMBLY

NOTE: Some procedures in COMPONENT DISASSEMBLY & REASSEMBLY may provide instructions for installing component(s) in transaxle case.

TRANSAXLE CASE

NOTE: Disassembly procedures provide instructions for removing drive sprocket roller bearing, drive sprocket support, 3rd oil cup plug, parking pawl and governor oil pipe. DO NOT remove components unless necessary.

Disassembly – 1) Using slide hammer and Adapter (J-26941), remove driven sprocket support bearing. *See Fig. 2 or 47.* Inspect bearing bore and roller bearing race on driven sprocket for wear or damage and replace if necessary.

2) To remove drive sprocket support, remove converter oil seal. Remove Torx bolts, and remove drive sprocket support. Using a screw extractor, remove parking pawl shaft cup plug from oil pan side of case. Remove parking pawl components as necessary.

3) To remove governor pipe, remove governor oil pipe clamp screw and clamp. *See Fig. 2.* Remove right axle end first. Use a piece of wood to protect machined case surface if pipe must be pried out. Grind 1/2" from end of No. 3 screw extractor. Install No. 3 screw extractor into 3rd oil cup plug. Remove cup plug. *See Fig. 2.*

4) With final drive assembly and right axle shaft removed from case, inspect final drive case bushing for wear or scoring. Use Bushing Remover (J-28537-6) and Driver Handle (J-8092) to remove bushing.

Inspection – 1) Inspect case assembly for damage, cracks, porosity and interconnected oil passages. Ensure exhaust vent holes are open. Inspect for stripped bolt holes.

2) Check case lugs, intermediate servo bore and snap ring grooves. Inspect case bushings for wear or scoring. Inspect drive and driven sprocket support bearing assemblies for pitting and scoring to carrier and rollers. Check rollers for excessive clearance.

3) Inspect drive and driven sprocket supports for damage to journal splines. Check for heat discoloration and cracks on support assembly. Inspect governor pipe for damage, cracks and leakage. Check parking pawl shaft cup plug, parking pawl shaft and parking pawl for damage and excessive wear. Inspect 3rd oil cup plug for tightness in bore or damage. Check all sealing and mating surfaces for straightness.

Reassembly – 1) Install new final drive case bushing using Bushing Installer (J-28537-2) and Driver Handle (J-8092). Drive in bushing until tool bottoms. Using Seal Driver (J-26938 or J-29130) and driver handle, install new right axle seal assembly. DO NOT damage seal guard during installation. Using a 9/16" socket, install manual shaft oil seal with lip up.

2) Using a 1/4" drift, install new cup plug. *See Fig. 2.* Cup plug should seat fully in bore. Before installing, coat ends of governor oil pipe with Loctite sealer. Install governor pipe and retaining clamp.

3) Install parking pawl and spring, parking pawl shaft and retainer. Ensure large loop of pawl spring is positioned on right side of pawl. Coat parking pawl shaft cup plug with sealant, and install plug using a 3/8" drift.

4) Install driven sprocket support roller bearing assembly with bearing identification facing up. Lightly tap driven sprocket support bearing into position using Bearing Installer (J-28677). Install new converter oil seal using Driver (J-28540).

DIFFERENTIAL & FINAL DRIVE

Disassembly & Inspection – 1) Remove final drive internal gear and final drive internal gear thrust bearing. Lift out final drive sun gear and thrust bearing. *See Fig. 28.* Inspect final drive internal gear and sun gear for cracks, damage, heat discoloration and worn or missing teeth.

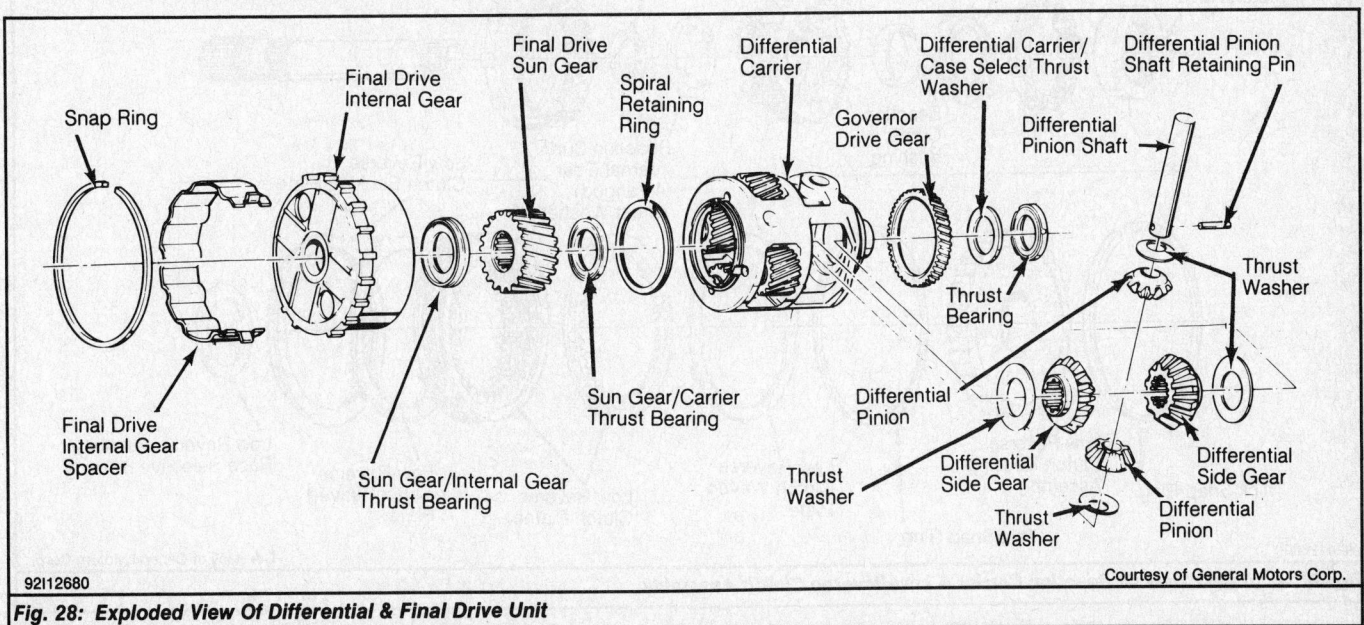

Courtesy of General Motors Corp.

Fig. 28: Exploded View Of Differential & Final Drive Unit

92I12680

2) Inspect differential side gears and pinions for wear or damage. Using a 3/16" pin punch, drive out differential pinion shaft retaining pin. Remove differential pinion gears and thrust washers. Push pinion gears from differential carrier. Ensure dished pinion thrust washers are removed with pinion gears. *See Fig. 28.*

3) Slide differential side gears toward center of carrier and remove. Remove side gear thrust washers. Keep thrust washers with gears for reassembly reference. Ensure end play between carrier and final drive pinion is .009-.025" (.23-.64 mm).

4) Inspect final drive pinions for damage. If pinions must be removed, detach spiral retaining snap ring, and withdraw pinion pins. Carefully remove pinion gears and thrust washers together to prevent dropping needle roller bearings. Remove needle bearings from each pinion gear and check for damage. Remove governor drive gear only if replacement is necessary. Using Puller (J-8433) and a thick, flat washer, pull governor drive gear from differential.

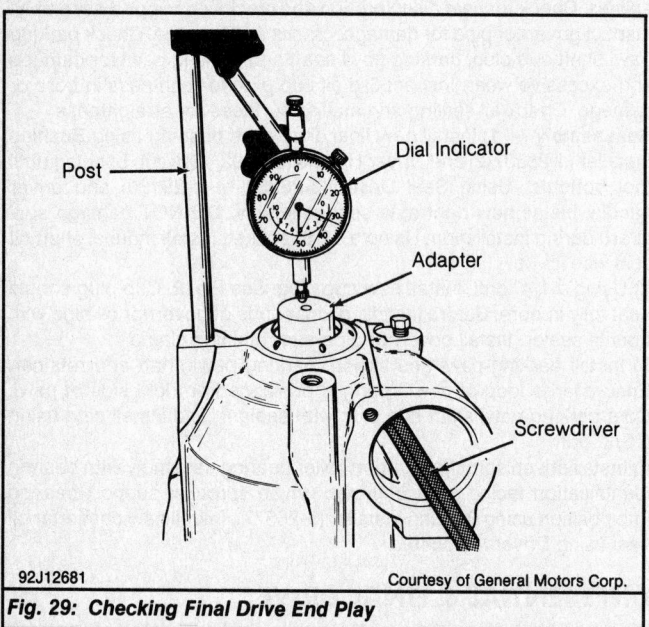

92J12681   Courtesy of General Motors Corp.

Fig. 29: Checking Final Drive End Play

Reassembly – **1)** If governor drive gear is removed, lightly tap it into place with a plastic mallet. Install needle bearings. Install steel pinion thrust washer onto end of pin (side opposite first thrust washer). Install one bronze pinion thrust washer to each end of pin. Slide pinion pin from assembly, keeping bearings intact in gear.

2) Install pinion gear assembly into differential carrier. Install pinion pin (stepped end last) into carrier through pinion gear assembly. Install other final drive pinion gears using same procedure. Install spiral retaining snap ring.

3) Install pinion pin so step is outside. Ensure bronze thrust washer is present on each end of final drive pinion, between carrier and steel thrust washer.

4) Install internal gear thrust bearing, sun gear with stepped side facing upward, thrust bearing with outside race to internal gear, and internal gear into final drive internal carrier. Install differential side gear thrust washers and side gears. Hold them in place with petroleum jelly. Coat side gear pinion dished thrust washers with petroleum jelly, and install them onto side gear pinions. Install pinion gears in differential carrier windows.

5) Install differential carrier case selective thrust washer into differential carrier case. Install thrust bearing into carrier assembly. Use petroleum jelly to hold bearing in place. Using Final Drive Unit Remover/Installer (J-33381), install differential carrier assembly into final drive internal case.

6) Install final drive internal gear spacer into case. Ensure parking pawl moves freely after spacer installation. Install snap ring into groove. Ensure final drive-to-case end play is .005-.032" (.12-.81 mm). See FINAL DRIVE UNIT under TRANSAXLE DISASSEMBLY. *See Fig. 29.*

REACTION INTERNAL GEAR

Inspection – Check final drive sun gear shaft, reaction internal gear and reaction sun/internal gear thrust bearing for excessive wear or damage. *See Fig. 30.* Check rear portion of center spline. If spline has a step (due to wear), replace reaction internal gear and shaft.

LOW ROLLER CLUTCH & REACTION CARRIER ASSEMBLY

Disassembly – Remove selective bearing and low roller clutch race. Pull low roller clutch from reaction carrier assembly. Remove reaction carrier-to-low roller clutch thrust washer from carrier. Pull final drive sun gear shaft from reaction internal gear. *See Fig. 30.*

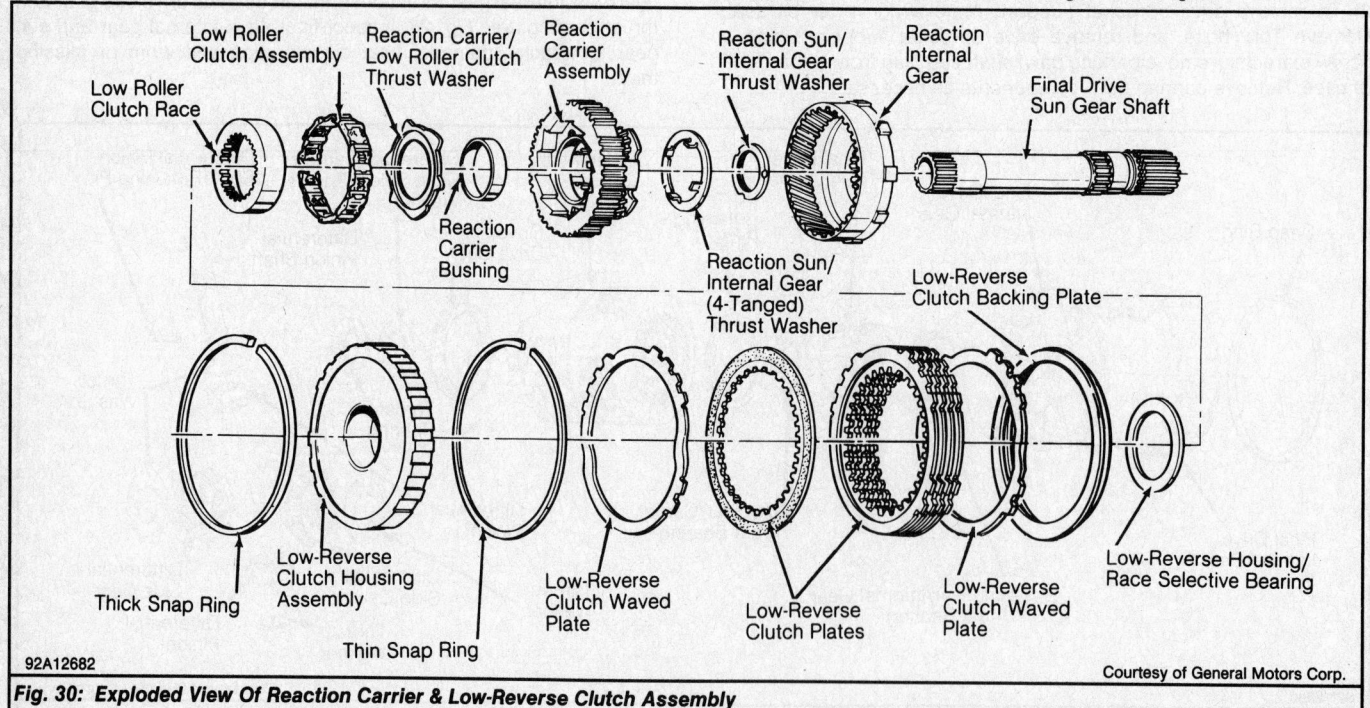

92A12682   Courtesy of General Motors Corp.

Fig. 30: Exploded View Of Reaction Carrier & Low-Reverse Clutch Assembly

Inspection – 1) Inspect low roller clutch race and roller clutch bearings for damage. Inspect 4-tanged thrust washer for scoring, excessive wear and distorted tangs. Inspect reaction carrier, roller clutch cam ramps and bushing for damage or scoring.

2) Inspect reaction carrier pinions for damage, rough bearings or excessive wear. Ensure pinion pins DO NOT rotate. Using a feeler gauge, check pinion end play. Pinion end play should be .009-.027" (.23-.69 mm).

Reassembly – 1) Install thrust washer into reaction carrier. Ensure all rollers are installed in cage, and install roller clutch into carrier. Install clutch race. See Fig. 30. Install 4-tanged thrust washer. Use petroleum jelly to hold washer in position.

2) Install reaction carrier and clutch assembly into reaction internal gear. Install selective bearing and reaction gear assembly. Ensure gear does not contact final drive internal gear spacer.

3) Install low-reverse clutch backing plate into case with stepped side down. Install low-reverse clutch waved plate. Lubricate composition plates with ATF. Install composition plates first and then install steel plate. See Fig. 30. Install low-reverse clutch waved plate and snap ring. Snap ring is .042" (1.07 mm) thick.

LOW-REVERSE CLUTCH HOUSING

Disassembly – Compress low-reverse clutch spring retainer, and remove snap ring. Lift out low-reverse clutch spring retainer. Remove waved release spring and clutch piston from housing. Remove inner and outer piston seals. See Figs. 30 and 31.

Inspection – Inspect clutch housing for damage or plugged feed hole. Check backing plate for cracks, damage or warpage. Inspect clutch splines and snap ring groove for damage or burrs. Remove any burrs on splines or snap ring groove. Inspect clutch piston and apply ring for distortion, cracks or damage. Inspect piston seals for nicks, cuts or hardening.

Reassembly – 1) Install seals onto piston. Using Inner/Outer Seal Installer (J-26744-A), install clutch piston. See Fig. 32. Install clutch release spring and retainer (cupped side down). Compress retainer, and install snap ring. Apply maximum air pressure of 50 psi (3.5 kg/cm²) to feed hole to check for proper operation.

2) Using Handle (J-34008), install low-reverse clutch housing. See Fig. 27. Ensure oil feed hole in housing lines up with feed hole in case. If housing does not go past snap ring groove, remove tool and install sun gear. Rotate sun gear back and forth until housing is in place. Install .092" (2.36 mm) thick snap ring.

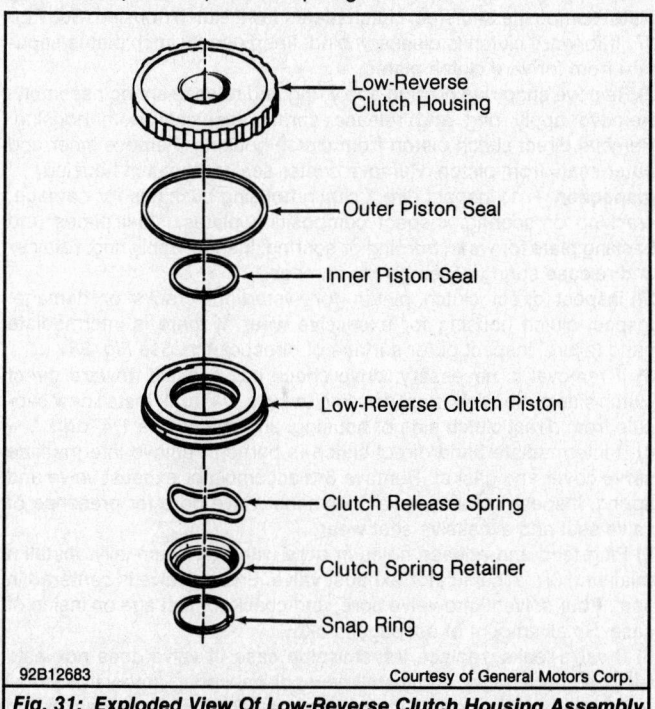

Fig. 31: Exploded View Of Low-Reverse Clutch Housing Assembly (1993 Shown; 1994 Is Similar)

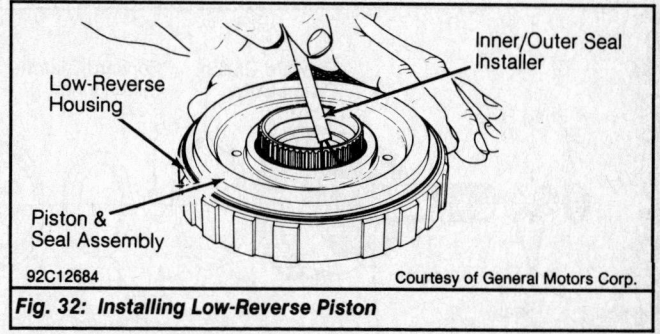

Fig. 32: Installing Low-Reverse Piston

REACTION SUN GEAR & INPUT DRUM END PLAY

Inspection – 1) Check reaction sun gear for cracks, splits, spline damage, gear-to-journal wear and plugged lubrication passages. Inspect input drum for distortion, damaged splines and pins. To check and adjust reaction sun gear-to-input drum end play, see REACTION UNIT under TRANSAXLE DISASSEMBLY.

2) Install correct thickness low-reverse housing/low race selective washer as previously determined. See LOW-REVERSE CLUTCH HOUSING-TO-LOW ROLLER CLUTCH RACE THRUST WASHER END PLAY under REACTION UNIT. See Figs. 26 and 30.

INPUT CARRIER, INPUT SUN GEAR & INTERNAL GEAR

Inspection – Check all parts for pitting, scoring, damaged gear teeth and cracks. Ensure lubrication holes are open. Check input carrier thrust washers for wear and distortion of tangs. See Fig. 33. Check carrier pinion pins for tightness. Ensure pins DO NOT rotate. Ensure input carrier pinion end play is .009-.027" (.23-.69 mm).

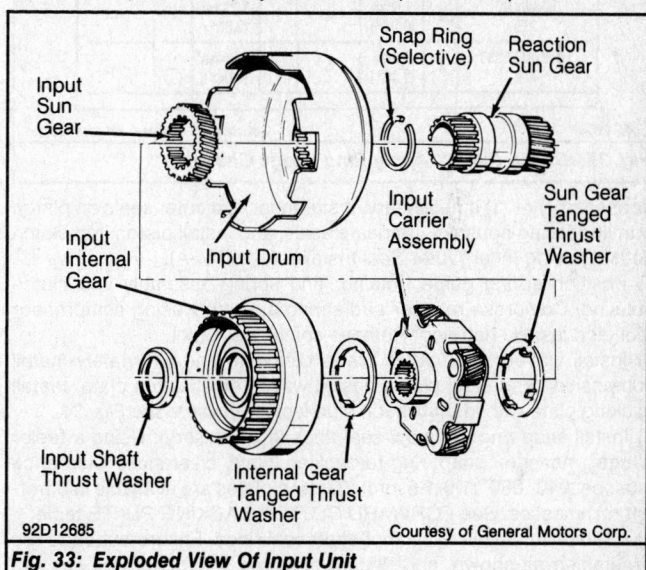

Fig. 33: Exploded View Of Input Unit

FORWARD CLUTCH ASSEMBLY

Disassembly – 1) Place forward clutch housing in a holding fixture with clutch pack facing up. Remove snap ring, backing plate, waved steel clutch plate, composite and steel clutch plates from housing. See Fig. 34. Remove other waved steel clutch plates.

2) Using Clutch Pack Compressor (J-23456) and Adapter (J-23327-1), compress retainer and spring assembly in order to remove snap ring. Remove tools, retainer and spring assembly from clutch housing. Remove piston and insert from housing, and remove seals from piston.

Inspection – Inspect input shaft oil seal rings for damage. DO NOT remove seal rings unless replacement is necessary. Inspect clutch plates and all components for excessive wear or damage and replace if necessary. See Fig. 35.

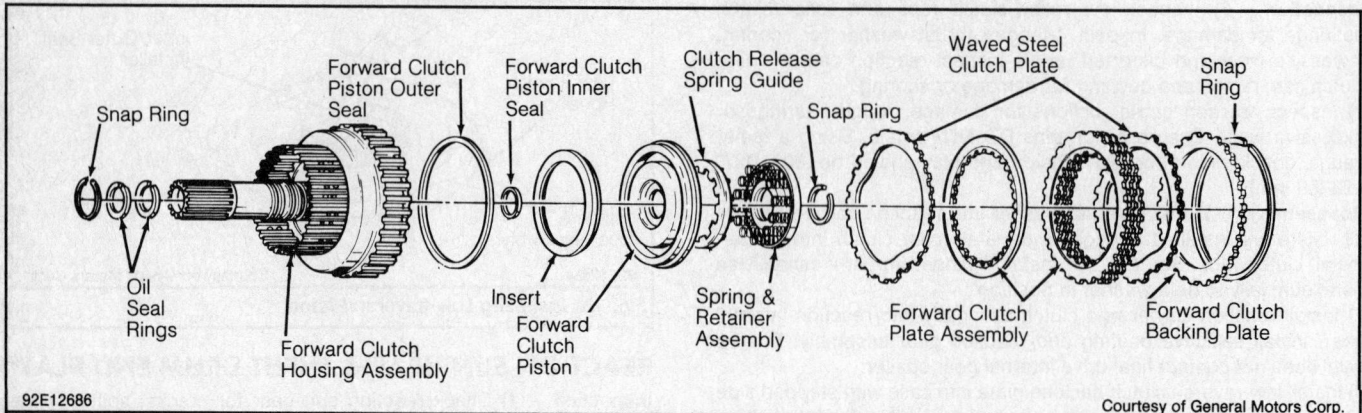

Snap Ring

Oil Seal Rings

Forward Clutch Piston Outer Seal

Forward Clutch Housing Assembly

Forward Clutch Piston Inner Seal

Insert

Forward Clutch Piston

Clutch Release Spring Guide

Spring & Retainer Assembly

Snap Ring

Waved Steel Clutch Plate

Forward Clutch Plate Assembly

Snap Ring

Forward Clutch Backing Plate

92E12686

Courtesy of General Motors Corp.

Fig. 34: Exploded View Of Forward Clutch Assembly

3T40 CLUTCH PLATE AND APPLY RING USAGE CHART

CLUTCH	FLAT STEEL PLATE		COMP. FACED PLATE	WAVED PLATE		APPLY RING	
	No.	Thickness	No.	No.	Thickness	I.D.	Thickness
DIRECT	5	2.3mm (0.09")	5	—	---	7	19.0mm (0.75")
	3	2.3mm (0.09")	3	—	---	2	27.4mm (1.08")
	4	2.3mm (0.09")	4	—	---	1	23.1mm (0.91")
FORWARD ALL	3	1.9mm (0.07")	4	2	1.25mm (0.05")	—	---
LO & REVERSE ALL	4	2.2mm (0.09")	5	2	1.94mm (0.08")	—	---

92F12687

Courtesy of General Motors Corp.

Fig. 35: Clutch Plate & Apply Ring Usage Chart

Reassembly – 1) If necessary, install inner and outer seals on piston with lips facing housing. Lubricate seals, and install piston into clutch housing using Inner/Outer Seal Installer (J-26744-A).
2) Position spring guide, retainer and spring assembly into clutch housing. Compress retainer and spring assembly using compressor tool, and install snap ring. Remove compressor tool.
3) Install waved steel clutch plate. Lubricate and alternately install composition and steel plates. Install waved steel clutch plate. Install backing plate with identification side facing upward. See Fig. 34.
4) Install snap ring and new seal rings (if necessary). Using a feeler gauge, measure snap ring-to-backing plate clearance. Clearance must be .040-.060" (1.0-1.5 mm). Backing plates are available in different thicknesses. See FORWARD CLUTCH BACKING PLATE table.
5) If removed, install new input shaft seal rings. Ensure cut ends are assembled as shown, and rings are seated in groove. See Fig. 36. Hold rings in place with petroleum jelly.

NOTE: Forward clutch backing plates are available in 2 materials, steel or powered metal. See FORWARD CLUTCH BACKING PLATE table for appropriate thickness code.

FORWARD CLUTCH BACKING PLATE

Thickness In. (mm)	Code Steel/Powered Metal
.191-.197 (4.9-5.0)	A/6
.170-.175 (4.3-4.4)	B/7
.148-.154 (3.8-3.9)	C/8
.126-.132 (3.2-3.3)	D/9

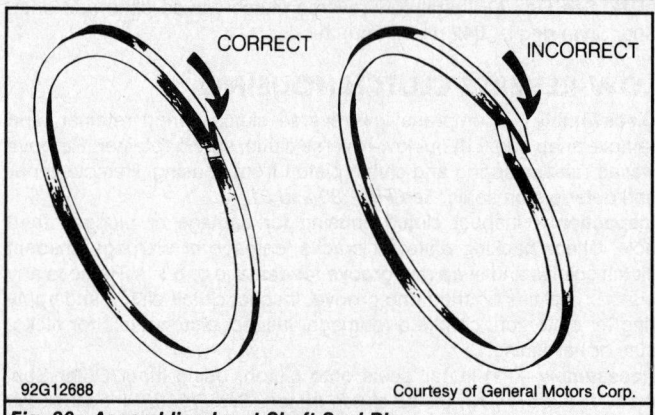

CORRECT

INCORRECT

92G12688

Courtesy of General Motors Corp.

Fig. 36: Assembling Input Shaft Seal Ring

DIRECT CLUTCH ASSEMBLY

NOTE: If transaxle is being serviced for a burnt intermediate band and direct clutch, new dual-land 3rd accumulator exhaust valve and conical spring must be installed.

Disassembly – 1) Remove clutch pack snap ring. Remove backing plate, composite and steel clutch plates from clutch housing. See Fig. 37. If forward clutch is disassembled, keep direct clutch plates separate from forward clutch plates.
2) Remove snap ring holding apply ring and release spring assembly. Remove apply ring and release spring assembly from housing. Remove direct clutch piston from clutch housing. Remove inner and outer seals from piston. Remove center seal from clutch housing.
Inspection – 1) Inspect direct clutch housing bushings for damage, cracking or scoring. Inspect composition plates, steel plates and backing plate for wear, burning or scoring. Inspect apply ring, retainer and release spring assembly for damage.
2) Inspect direct clutch piston for distortion, cracks or damage. Inspect clutch housing for excessive wear. If there is intermediate band failure, inspect outer surface of direct clutch. See Fig. 38.
3) If removal is necessary, drive check ball capsule (toward direct clutch side of housing) from housing using a 1/4" drift. Install new capsule from direct clutch side of housing, and seat with a 1/4" drift.
4) If intermediate band/direct clutch is burned, remove intermediate servo cover and gasket. Remove 3rd accumulator exhaust valve and spring. Inspect 3rd accumulator exhaust valve bore for presence of valve seat and excessive seat wear.
5) Plug feed and release holes in bore with petroleum jelly. Install a dual-land 3rd accumulator exhaust valve. Ensure valve is centered in seat. Pour solvent into valve bore, and check for leakage on inside of case. Small amount of seepage is okay.
6) If valve leaks, replace transmission case. If valve does not leak, remove check valve, and install new conical spring onto valve (small end first). Install valve with spring into bore. Replace servo gasket and cover.

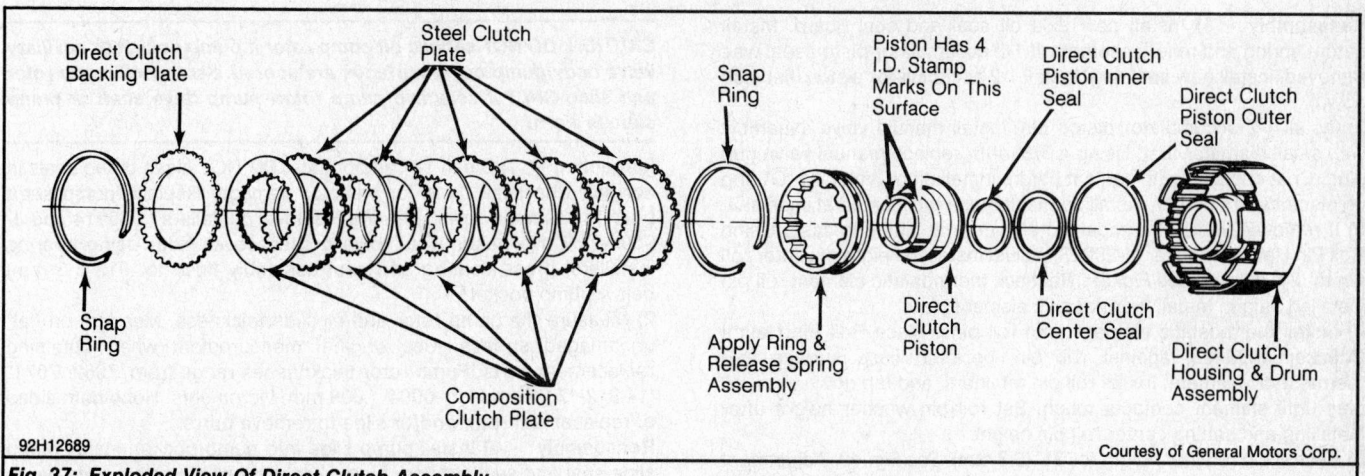

Fig. 37: Exploded View Of Direct Clutch Assembly

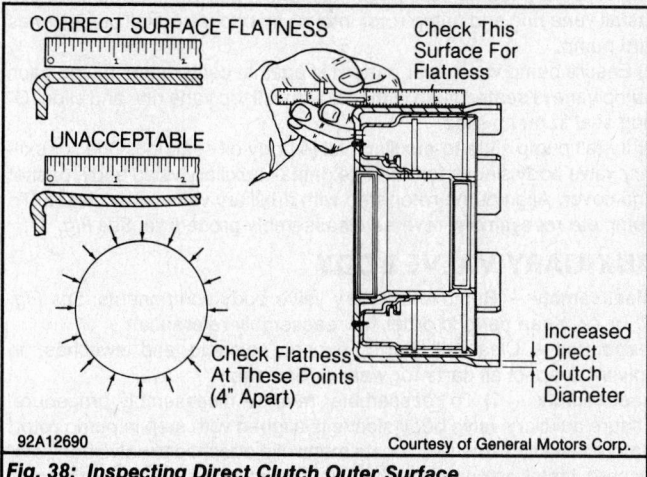

Fig. 38: Inspecting Direct Clutch Outer Surface

Reassembly – 1) Install inner and outer seals onto pistons with lips facing away from capsule. Install center seal on housing with lip facing away from capsule. Lubricate all seals, then install piston into clutch housing.

2) Install apply ring, retainer and release spring assembly, and snap ring. Lubricate direct clutch plates with ATF and install into housing, starting with a flat steel plate, and then alternating between composition and flat steel plates. Ensure smooth fiber composition plates are used. *See Figs. 35 and 37.*

3) Install snap ring. Install backing plate into housing with chamfered or polished side facing up. Install second snap ring. Ensure composition plates turn freely.

INTERMEDIATE BAND

Inspection – Inspect intermediate band for burns, flakes or damage. Install intermediate band, aligning lugged end with apply pin bore. Install band anchor hole plug.

DRIVEN SPROCKET SUPPORT

Inspection – 1) Inspect driven sprocket support and sleeve for damage. Ensure sleeve is tight in bore and aligns with holes in support. Inspect driven sprocket support bushing and bearing assembly for damage and wear. *See Fig. 25.*

2) Pull out bearing assembly using slide hammer and Bearing Remover (J-26941). Using Bearing Installers (J-28677 and J-8092), install bearing with identification facing up.

3) Check bearing race on driven sprocket. If race needs replacement, replace driven sprocket support. Inspect seal rings for nicks or cuts. Replace worn or damaged components as needed.

MANUAL SHAFT

Inspection – 1) Inspect manual valve rod, rod retainer and detent lever for damage. *See Fig. 25.* Check threads of manual shaft, and file any raised edges.

2) Inspect parking lock actuator rod for damage or broken retainer lugs. If removed, install parking lock actuator rod into manual shaft lever. Use a 3/16" drift and install roll pin into detent lever. Tap nail into place.

DRIVE LINK ASSEMBLY
(CHAIN, SPROCKETS & TURBINE SHAFT)

Inspection – 1) Inspect drive chain for damage. With drive link assembly installed, check chain slack. If slack is more than 1 1/16", replace drive chain.

2) Inspect driven sprocket thrust bearing race. *See Fig. 47.* If damaged, replace driven sprocket, drive sprocket (flat side up) and drive support bearing assembly. Inspect drive sprocket teeth for nicks, burrs, scoring and wear.

3) Check internal splines for nicks, burrs and excessive wear. Inspect turbine shaft for excessive wear or damage. Inspect turbine shaft seal ring grooves and seal rings for damage.

4) DO NOT remove seal rings unless they are being replaced. If turbine shaft seal ring removal is necessary, carefully cut old seals from turbine shaft. Install new seals.

5) Use Sizer (J-29569-2) on 2 seal rings on valve body side of sprocket. Use seal installer on seal ring on case side of sprocket. Push sizer down over seal and turn. Remove sizer, and inspect seal to ensure it is seated in groove.

CASE COVER

NOTE: DO NOT disassemble case cover unless repair or replacement of cover or components is necessary.

Disassembly – Remove detent spring/roller assembly retaining screw, and remove spring/roller assembly. Remove 2 thermostatic roll pin retainers. Remove thermostatic element and plate. Remove axle oil seal and guard if necessary. Using a drift, drive out manual valve cup plug. Carefully withdraw manual valve. DO NOT use manual valve to drive out cup plug.

Inspection – 1) Inspect case cover and threads for damage. Inspect vent assembly for damage and clogging. Check manual valve movement. Check manual valve electrical connector and replace if necessary. Inspect manual detent spring and roller assembly. Check case cover sleeve. Ensure hole in sleeve aligns with case cover passages that intersect case cover (pump shaft) bore.

2) Inspect 1-2 accumulator piston seals for damage and free fit in grooves. Inspect thermostatic element for damage or distortion. Inspect vent assembly and cooler line connectors for damage. Replace components if necessary.

Reassembly – 1) Install new axle oil seal and seal guard. Install detent spring and roller assembly. If 1-2 accumulator piston seal was removed, install new seal ring. Install 1-2 accumulator piston (flat side down).

2) Install 1-2 accumulator piston pin. Install manual valve assembly with small diameter first. Using a 3/8" drift, replace manual valve cup plug. Coat cup plug with sealant before installation. With new "O" ring on electrical connector, install connector with tab located at case slot.

3) If removed, install thermostatic element roll pins into case. Using Roll Pin Height Checker (J-29023), adjust installed height of center roll pin to .24" (6 mm). *See Fig. 39.* Recheck thermostatic element roll pin installed height. Install thermostatic element plate.

4) Install thermostatic element onto roll pins. Place Roll Pin Height Checker (J-29023) against roll pin, between case surface and thermostatic element. Install roll pin retainers, and tap down onto roll pins until element contacts touch. Set roll pin washer height after installing and setting center roll pin height.

5) Set roll pin retainer height to .21" (5.3 mm). *See Fig. 40.* Adjustment is important for thermostatic element operation. Thermostatic element controls fluid level in control valve cover oil sump.

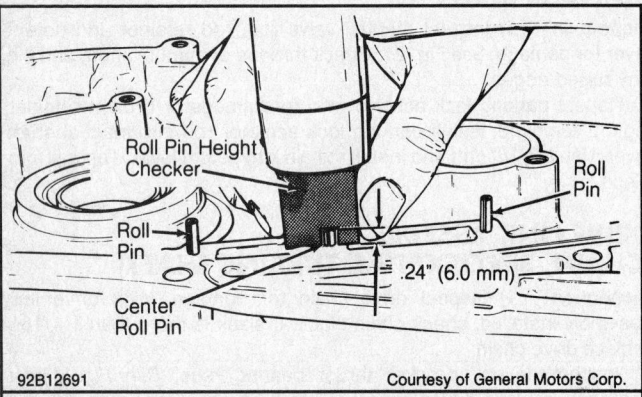

92B12691   Courtesy of General Motors Corp.

Fig. 39: Measuring Center Roll Pin Installed Height

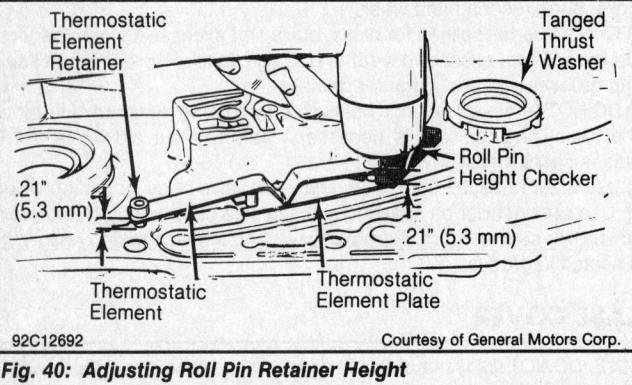

92C12692   Courtesy of General Motors Corp.

Fig. 40: Adjusting Roll Pin Retainer Height

CONTROL VALVE BODY & OIL PUMP ASSEMBLIES

NOTE: As valve components are removed from valve body bore, place individual parts, in correct order, in relative position to valve body. Valves, bushings and springs are not interchangeable. See Fig. 41.

Disassembly – 1) Position control valve body with cored face up and line boost valve at top. Remove roll pins. Pull all blind hole roll pins from valve body. If valve body is cleaned in solvent, low blow-off assembly must be replaced.

CAUTION: Many roll pins in valve body have pressure exerted against them. Use caution when removing pins.

2) Remove auxiliary valve body cover screw, auxiliary valve body, gasket and cover. Remove pump slide, rotor, vanes and vane rings.

CAUTION: DO NOT service oil pump rotor if pump pocket or auxiliary valve body/pump cover surfaces are scored. Service oil pump rotor and slide ONLY if selective pump rotor, pump drive shaft or pump slide is worn.

Inspection – 1) Clean all components. DO NOT clean pump seals in solvent. Check all parts for wear or damage. Replace pump shaft bearing assembly using Bearing Remover/Installers (J-35914 and J-7092-2). Drive bearing out toward case cover side. Using bearing installers, press bearing and seal assembly flush to .012" (.3 mm) below pump pocket.

2) Measure the pump rotor and/or slide thickness. Measure on flat, undamaged surface. Use original measurement when obtaining replacement parts. Pump rotor thicknesses range from .7052-.7071" (17.912-17.962 mm) in .0004" (.009 mm) increments. Hone both sides of replacement rotor and/or slide to remove burrs.

Reassembly – 1) Install pump slide into pump pocket. Install pump slide seal and seal support. Use petroleum jelly to retain slide parts. Align slide with pump slide pivot hole, and install pump slide pivot pin. Install vane ring and pump rotor into pump pocket. Install pump vanes into pump.

2) Ensure pump vane wear pattern is against centering ring, and each pump vane is seated flush with rotor. Install top vane ring and slide "O" ring seal in pump slide.

3) Install pump slide-to-auxiliary valve body oil seal ring. Check auxiliary valve body sleeve for damage. Install auxiliary valve body, gasket and cover. Align pump rotor step with auxiliary valve body sleeve. To complete reassembly, reverse disassembly procedure. *See Fig. 41.*

AUXILIARY VALVE BODY

Disassembly – Remove auxiliary valve body components. *See Fig. 41 or 42.* Keep parts in order for reassembly reference.

Inspection – Clean all parts, except solenoid and switches, in solvent. Inspect all parts for wear or damage.

Reassembly – 1) To reassemble, reverse disassembly procedure. Ensure auxiliary valve body sleeve is aligned with step in pump rotor. Before installing solenoid, locate metal clip attached to valve body and discard. Install solenoid with new "O" ring and plastic wire routing clip. Install cover gasket and screw.

2) Ensure valve body bolt sizes are correct. Coat threads of bolt "F" with sealant before installation. *See Fig. 52.* Tighten bolts to specifications. See TORQUE SPECIFICATIONS.

INTERMEDIATE SERVO

Disassembly & Reassembly – Remove snap ring from apply pin (if not previously done). Separate intermediate servo piston, spring retainer and apply pin. Remove and discard "O" ring seals. *See Fig. 43.* Check all parts for wear or damage. Intermediate servo is assembled during transaxle assembly. See TRANSAXLE REASSEMBLY.

GOVERNOR/SPEEDOMETER GEAR OR GOVERNOR/SPEED SENSOR ASSEMBLY

Inspection – 1) Check governor assembly for wear or damage. Ensure governor weights operate freely and independently of each other. Check for damaged, mispositioned or tilted springs.

2) Install governor cover with new "O" ring. Ensure governor shaft is piloted in cover before tightening retaining bolts. Install speedometer drive gear/speed sensor housing. *See Fig. 44 or 45.*

TRANSAXLE REASSEMBLY

NOTE: Note location of all gear sets, clutch plates, thrust bearings, thrust washers and bushings. See Figs. 46 and 47. Recheck snap ring and thrust washer measurements taken during disassembly. See appropriate procedures under **1)** Lubricate all bushings, seals, thrust bearings and internal mating surfaces with ATF during reassembly. Use petroleum jelly to hold thrust washers in place.

2) Install selected differential carrier/case thrust washer. *See Fig. 28.* Install thrust bearing assembly to final drive unit (inner race of bearing against selective washer). Install differential and final drive assembly into case.

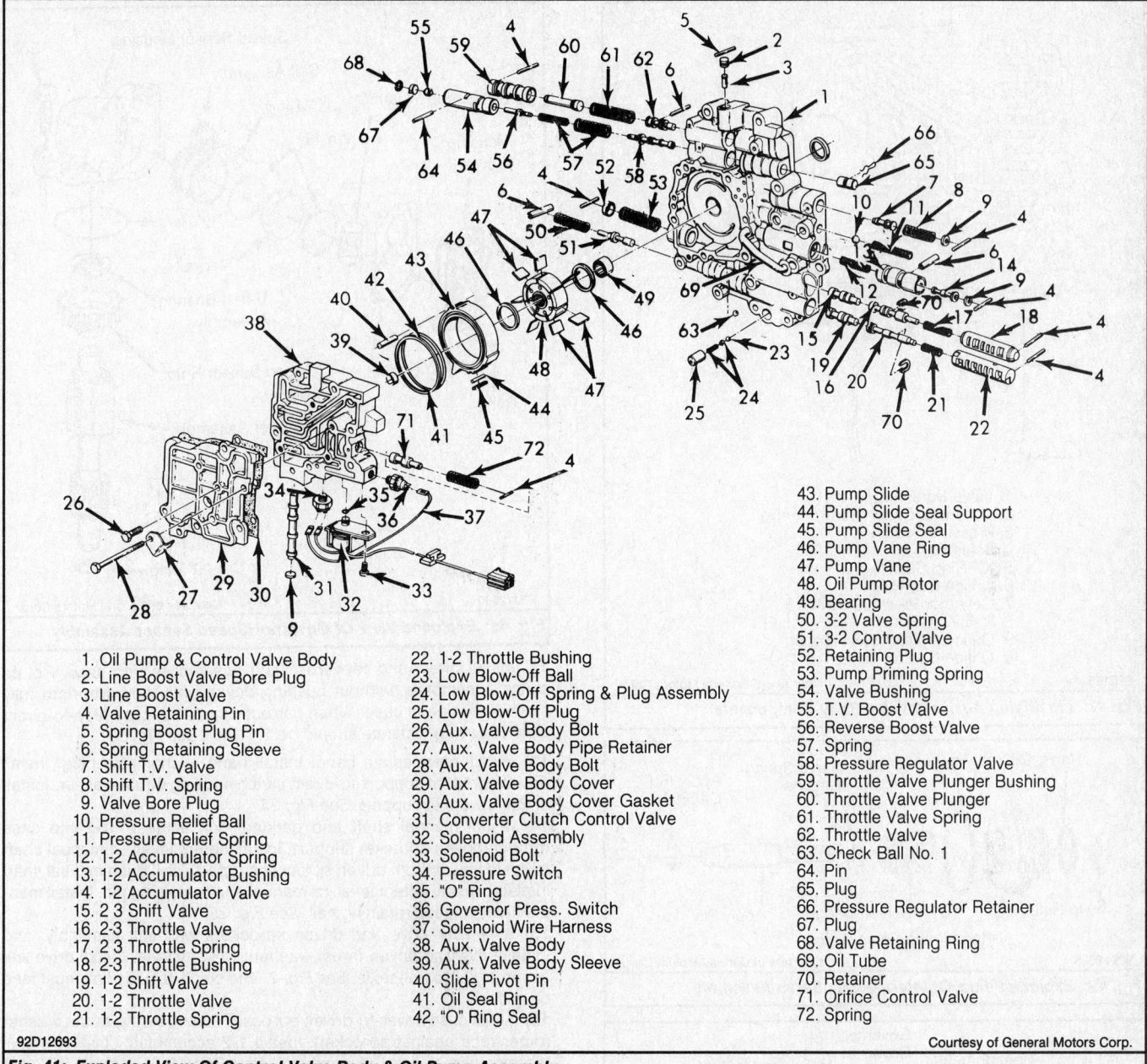

1. Oil Pump & Control Valve Body
2. Line Boost Valve Bore Plug
3. Line Boost Valve
4. Valve Retaining Pin
5. Spring Boost Plug Pin
6. Spring Retaining Sleeve
7. Shift T.V. Valve
8. Shift T.V. Spring
9. Valve Bore Plug
10. Pressure Relief Ball
11. Pressure Relief Spring
12. 1-2 Accumulator Spring
13. 1-2 Accumulator Bushing
14. 1-2 Accumulator Valve
15. 2 3 Shift Valve
16. 2-3 Throttle Valve
17. 2 3 Throttle Spring
18. 2-3 Throttle Bushing
19. 1-2 Shift Valve
20. 1-2 Throttle Valve
21. 1-2 Throttle Spring

22. 1-2 Throttle Bushing
23. Low Blow-Off Ball
24. Low Blow-Off Spring & Plug Assembly
25. Low Blow-Off Plug
26. Aux. Valve Body Bolt
27. Aux. Valve Body Pipe Retainer
28. Aux. Valve Body Bolt
29. Aux. Valve Body Cover
30. Aux. Valve Body Cover Gasket
31. Converter Clutch Control Valve
32. Solenoid Assembly
33. Solenoid Bolt
34. Pressure Switch
35. "O" Ring
36. Governor Press. Switch
37. Solenoid Wire Harness
38. Aux. Valve Body
39. Aux. Valve Body Sleeve
40. Slide Pivot Pin
41. Oil Seal Ring
42. "O" Ring Seal

43. Pump Slide
44. Pump Slide Seal Support
45. Pump Slide Seal
46. Pump Vane Ring
47. Pump Vane
48. Oil Pump Rotor
49. Bearing
50. 3-2 Valve Spring
51. 3-2 Control Valve
52. Retaining Plug
53. Pump Priming Spring
54. Valve Bushing
55. T.V. Boost Valve
56. Reverse Boost Valve
57. Spring
58. Pressure Regulator Valve
59. Throttle Valve Plunger Bushing
60. Throttle Valve Plunger
61. Throttle Valve Spring
62. Throttle Valve
63. Check Ball No. 1
64. Pin
65. Plug
66. Pressure Regulator Retainer
67. Plug
68. Valve Retaining Ring
69. Oil Tube
70. Retainer
71. Orifice Control Valve
72. Spring

92D12693

Courtesy of General Motors Corp.

Fig. 41: Exploded View Of Control Valve Body & Oil Pump Assembly

3) Install final drive internal gear spacer (cupped side against final drive internal gear). Ensure opening in spacer aligns with parking pawl opening in case. Ensure parking pawl passes through spacer.

4) Install final drive spacer-to-case snap ring with ring gap away from parking pawl opening in case. Install reaction sun gear set into case. *See Fig. 30.*

5) Install low-reverse clutch backing plate (stepped side down) and clutch plates into case. *See Fig. 30.* Start with a composition plate, and then alternate between steel and composition plates.

6) Install low-reverse clutch wave plate and thin housing-to-case spacer ring. Install low-reverse clutch housing assembly into transaxle case. *See Fig. 30.* Ensure clutch feed hole in housing lines up with clutch feed hole in case.

7) Install selective snap ring onto reaction sun gear. Install reaction sun gear onto final drive sun gear shaft in transaxle. *See Figs. 30 and 33.* Rotate reaction sun gear while pushing down on low-reverse clutch housing until clutch housing drops below snap ring groove in case.

8) Install thick low-reverse clutch housing-to-case snap ring. *See Fig. 30.* Install input drum onto reaction sun gear. *See Fig. 33.* Install input sun gear into input drum. Install input sun gear tanged thrust washer to pinion side of carrier.

9) Install input internal gear tanged thrust washer to internal gear side of carrier (input internal gear tanged thrust washer is larger than input sun gear tanged thrust washer). *See Fig. 33.* Install input pinion carrier onto input sun gear.

10) Install input internal gear over input carrier. Place forward clutch assembly on bench with input shaft up. Install direct clutch assembly over input shaft, onto forward clutch housing. When clutch housings are fully seated, distance from tang end of direct clutch housing to end of forward clutch housing should be 1.406" (35.71 mm). *See Fig. 49.*

11) Install input shaft-to-input internal gear thrust washer onto forward and direct clutch assembly. *See Figs. 33 and 46.* Ensure rounded side is against input shaft, and stepped side faces outward, onto forward and direct clutch assembly.

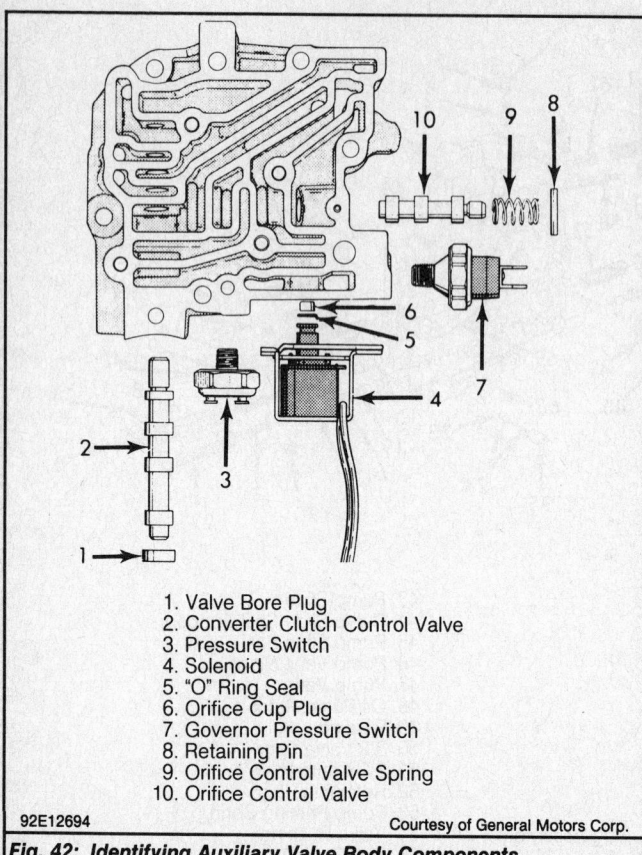

1. Valve Bore Plug
2. Converter Clutch Control Valve
3. Pressure Switch
4. Solenoid
5. "O" Ring Seal
6. Orifice Cup Plug
7. Governor Pressure Switch
8. Retaining Pin
9. Orifice Control Valve Spring
10. Orifice Control Valve

92E12694   Courtesy of General Motors Corp.

Fig. 42: Identifying Auxiliary Valve Body Components

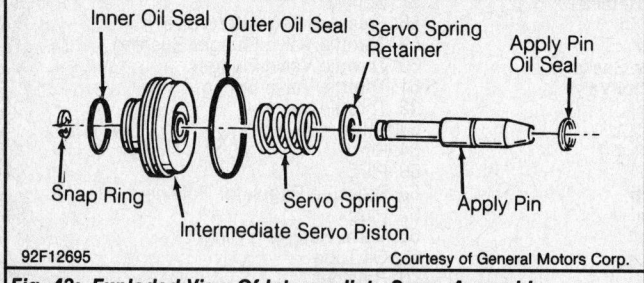

92F12695   Courtesy of General Motors Corp.

Fig. 43: Exploded View Of Intermediate Servo Assembly

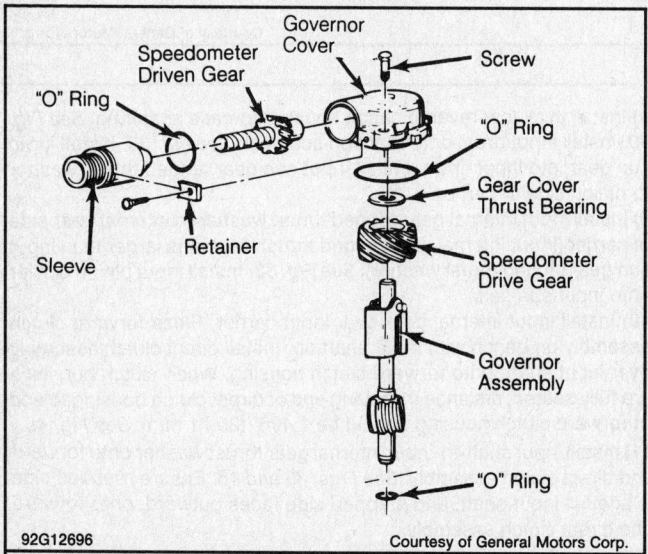

92G12696   Courtesy of General Motors Corp.

Fig. 44: Exploded View Of Governor/Speedometer Gear Assembly

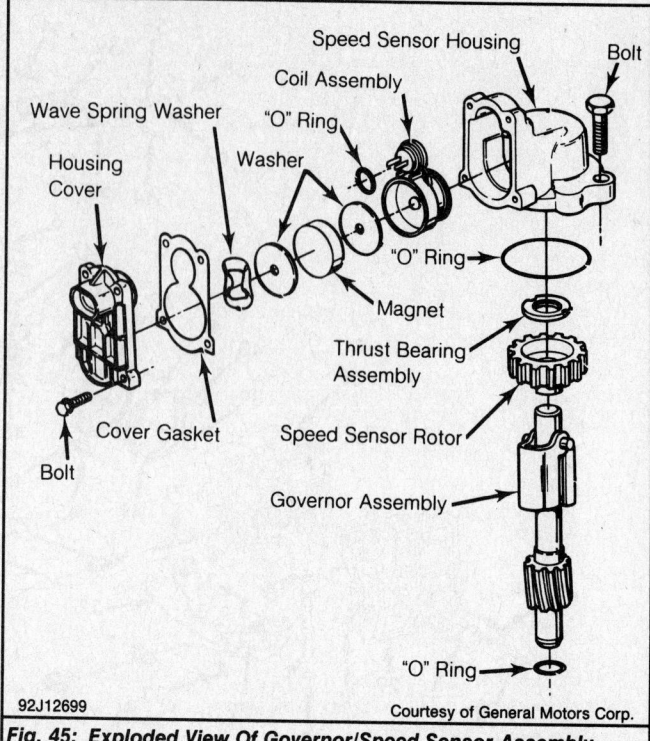

92J12699   Courtesy of General Motors Corp.

Fig. 45: Exploded View Of Governor/Speed Sensor Assembly

12) Install direct and forward clutch assemblies into case. Rotate clutch assemblies, without pushing down, until they drop into fully seated position in case. When correctly installed, case face-to-direct clutch housing distance should be 1 11/16". See Fig. 50.

13) Install intermediate band. Install band anchor hole plug. Install driven sprocket support-to-direct clutch housing thrust washer. Install driven sprocket support. See Fig. 25.

14) Install manual shaft and parking lock actuator rod into case through driven sprocket support. Install detent lever on manual shaft (hub side away from driven sprocket support), and push manual shaft in place. Install detent lever-to-manual shaft retaining pin. Install manual shaft-to-case retaining nail. See Fig. 25.

15) Assemble drive and driven sprockets with link assembly, and install drive and driven thrust washers to sprockets. Install drive link assembly onto transaxle. See Fig. 2. The colored guide link must face case cover.

16) Install case cover-to-driven sprocket roller bearing thrust washer (outer race against sprocket). Install 1-2 accumulator piston. Install thermostatic element (if removed). See CONTROL VALVE BODY & OIL PUMP ASSEMBLIES under COMPONENT DISASSEMBLY & REASSEMBLY.

17) Install 1-2 accumulator spring into bore in case. Install inner and outer case-to-cover gaskets and case cover. Install and tighten all case cover bolts. See Fig. 51. Install 2 case cover bolts from inside torque converter housing (M8 x 1.25 x 14 mm). Install remaining case cover bolts. The 3 bolts that mate sprocket support-to-case cover must be tightened evenly to avoid cocking sprocket support.

18) Connect manual valve rod to manual valve. Install check balls No. 2-6 into case cover. See Fig. 22. Install No. 1 check ball on direct clutch passage on spacer plate. Install oil pump shaft into bore in case cover. Install 2 guide pins (M6 x 1.0 x 75 mm) in case cover-to-valve body bolt holes.

19) Install control valve body and bolts. See Fig. 52. Tighten bolts to specification. See TORQUE SPECIFICATIONS. Install valve body wiring harness. Ensure wiring harness is routed properly. See Fig. 54. Connect lever link to T.V. bracket. Install T.V. bracket onto valve body.

20) Remove guide bolts used to install valve body, and install remaining 2 valve body bolts. Thoroughly clean valve body cover. Install cover with new gasket. Apply Loctite sealant to indicated cover bolts. See Fig. 53.

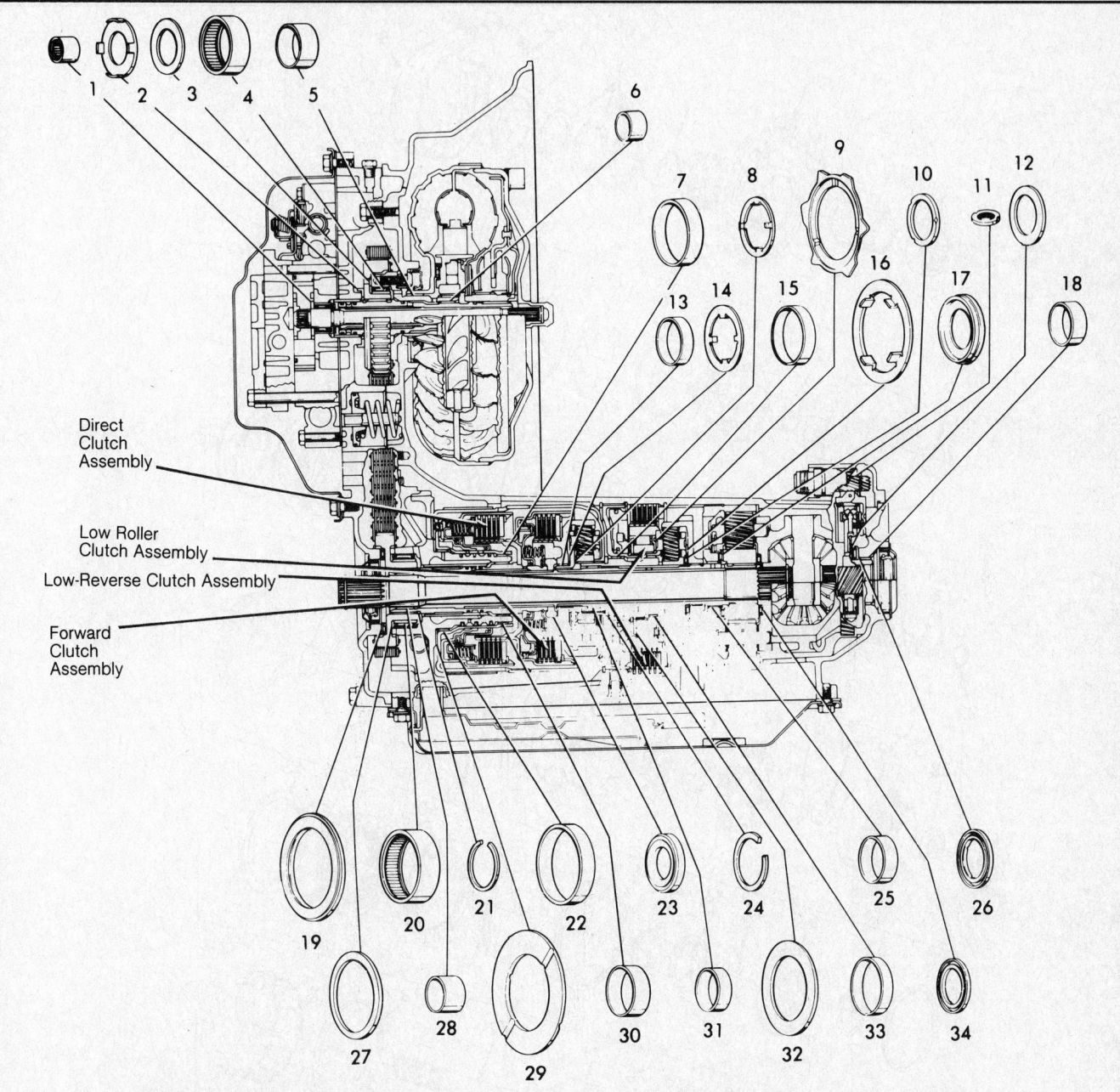

Direct Clutch Assembly

Low Roller Clutch Assembly

Low-Reverse Clutch Assembly

Forward Clutch Assembly

1. Pump Shaft Bearing Assembly
2. Case Cover-To-Driven Sprocket Thrust Washer
3. Drive Sprocket Support-To-Drive Sprocket Washer
4. Drive Sprocket Support Bearing Assembly
5. Converter Bushing
6. Drive Sprocket Support Bushing
7. Direct Clutch Drum Bushing
8. Input Carrier-To-Input Sun Gear Thrust Washer
9. Reaction Carrier-To-Low Race Thrust Washer
10. Reaction Sun Gear-To-Internal Gear Thrust Bearing
11. Thrust Bearing Assembly
12. Differential Carrier-To-Case Selective Thrust Washer
13. Input Internal Gear Bushing
14. Input Carrier-To-Input Internal Gear Thrust Washer
15. Reaction Carrier Bushing
16. Reaction Carrier-To-Internal Gear Thrust Washer
17. Sun Gear-To-Internal Gear Thrust Bearing
18. Case Bushing

19. Driven Sprocket Thrust Bearing Assembly
20. Driven Sprocket Support Sleeve
21. Selective Snap Ring
22. Direct Clutch Bushing
23. Input Shaft Thrust Washer
24. Selective Snap Ring
25. Case Bushing
26. Differential Case Thrust Bearing Assembly
27. Driven Sprocket Support Thrust Washer
28. Input Shaft Bushing
29. Thrust Washer
30. Driven Sprocket Support Bushing
31. Reaction Sun Gear Bushing
32. Reverse Housing-To-Low Race Selective Thrust Washer
33. Reaction Carrier Bushing
34. Sun Gear-To-Carrier Thrust Bearing

94G38717

Fig. 46: Locating Clutch Assemblies, Thrust Bearings, Thrust Washers & Bushings

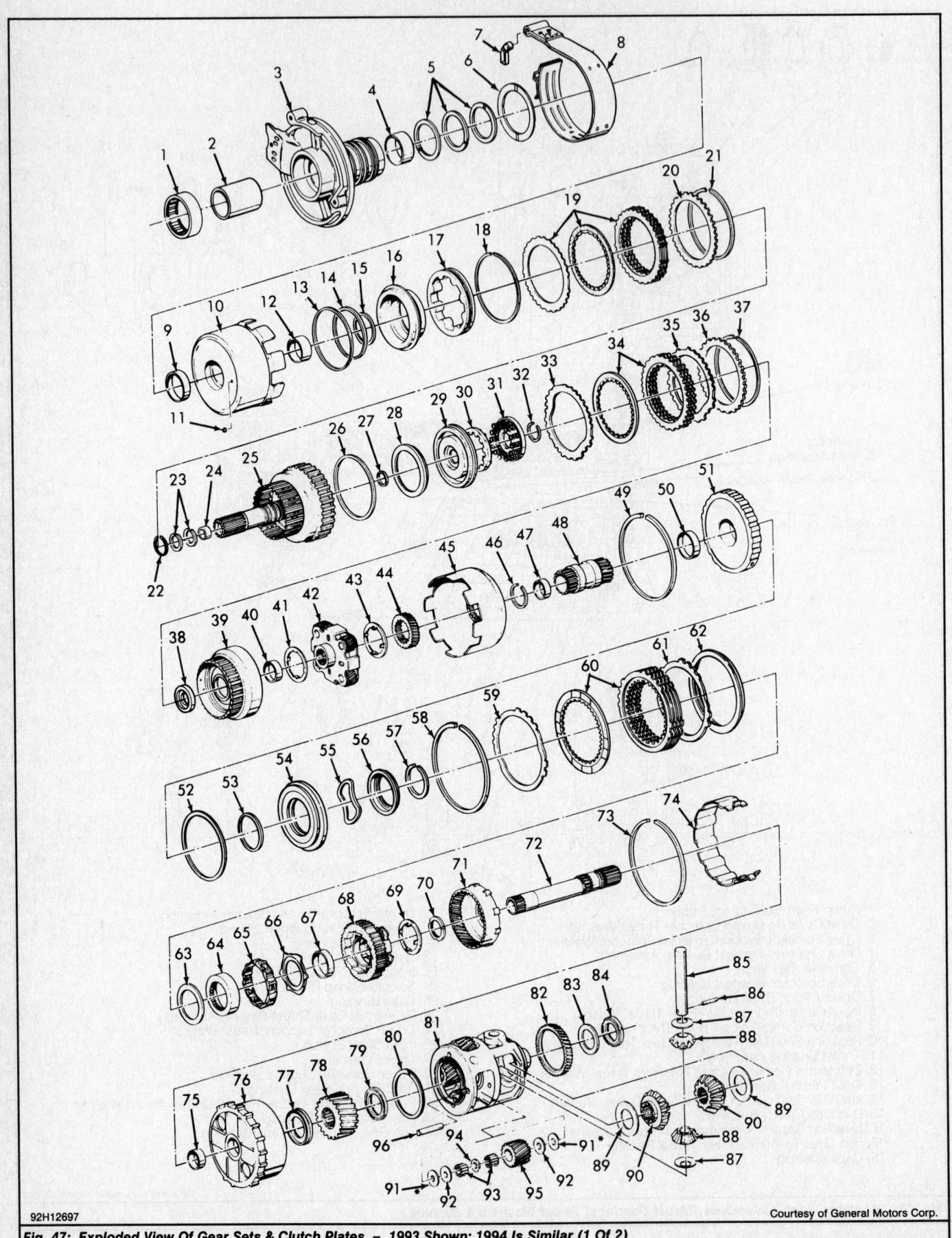

Courtesy of General Motors Corp.

Fig. 47: Exploded View Of Gear Sets & Clutch Plates – 1993 Shown; 1994 Is Similar (1 Of 2)

1. Driven Sprocket Support Bearing
2. Driven Sprocket Support Sleeve
3. Driven Sprocket Support Assembly
4. Driven Sprocket Support Bushing
5. Driven Sprocket Support Ring Oil Seals
6. Driven Sprocket Support-To-Direct Clutch Washer
7. Band Anchor Hole Plug
8. Intermediate Band
9. Direct Clutch Housing Bushing
10. Direct Clutch Housing & Drum
11. Direct Clutch Check Valve Retainer & Ball Assembly
12. Direct Clutch Drum Bushing
13. Direct Clutch Piston Outer Lip Seal
14. Direct Clutch Center Lip Seal
15. Direct Clutch Piston Inner Lip Seal
16. Direct Clutch Piston
17. Apply Ring & Release Spring Assembly
18. Snap Ring
19. Direct Clutch Plate Assembly
20. Direct Clutch Backing Plate
21. Snap Ring
22. Input Shaft Selective Snap Ring
23. Input Shaft Seal Rings
24. Input Shaft Bushing
25. Forward Clutch Housing Assembly
26. Forward Clutch Piston Outer Lip Seal
27. Forward Clutch Piston Inner Lip Seal
28. Forward Clutch Piston Insert
29. Forward Clutch Piston
30. Forward Clutch Release Spring Guide
31. Forward Clutch Retainer & Spring Assembly
32. Forward Clutch Snap Spring Retainer Ring
33. Forward Clutch Waved Plate
34. Forward Clutch Plate Assembly
35. Forward Clutch Waved Plate
36. Forward Clutch Selective Backing Plate
37. Snap Ring
38. Input Shaft Thrust Washer
39. Input Internal Gear
40. Input Internal Gear Bushing
41. Input Carrier/Input Internal Gear Tanged Thrust Washer
42. Input Carrier Assembly
43. Input Carrier/Input Sun Gear Tanged Thrust Washer
44. Input Sun Gear
45. Input Drum
46. Input Drum/Sun Gear Selective Snap Ring
47. Reaction Sun Gear Bushing
48. Reaction Sun Gear
49. Case Splines Snap Ring (Thick)
50. Reaction Carrier Bushing

51. Low-Reverse Clutch Housing Assembly
52. Low-Reverse Piston Outer Lip Seal
53. Low-Reverse Piston Inner Lip Seal
54. Low-Reverse Clutch Piston
55. Low-Reverse Clutch Release Spring
56. Low-Reverse Clutch Spring Retainer
57. Low-Reverse Piston Snap Ring
58. Case Splines Snap Ring (Thin)
59. Low-Reverse Clutch Waved Plate
60. Low-Reverse Clutch Plate Assembly
61. Low-Reverse Clutch Waved Plate
62. Low-Reverse Clutch Selective Backing Plate
63. Reverse Housing/Low Roller Race Selective Spacer
64. Low Roller Clutch Race
65. Low Roller Clutch Roller Assembly
66. Reaction Carrier/Low Roller Race Thrust Washer
67. Reaction Carrier Bushing
68. Reaction Carrier Assembly
69. Reaction Carrier/Reaction Internal Gear 4-Tanged Thrust Washer
70. Reaction Sun/Reaction Internal Gear Thrust Bearing
71. Reaction Internal Gear
72. Final Drive Sun Gear Shaft
73. Case Splines Snap Ring (Thick)
74. Final Drive Internal Gear Spacer
75. Final Drive Internal Gear Bushing
76. Final Drive Internal Gear
77. Sun Gear/Final Drive Internal Gear Thrust Bearing
78. Final Drive Sun Gear
79. Sun Gear/Differential Carrier Thrust Bearing
80. Spiral Pinion Retainer Ring
81. Carrier Assembly Differential
82. Governor Drive Gear
83. Differential Carrier/Case Selective Thrust Washer
84. Differential Carrier/Case Thrust Bearing Assembly
85. Differential Pinion Shaft
86. Differential Pinion Shaft Retainer Pin
87. Differential Pinion Thrust Washer
88. Differential Pinion
89. Differential Side Gear Thrust Washer
90. Differential Side Gear
91. Pinion Thrust Washer
   * Bronze – (Steel For Replacement)
92. Pinion Thrust Washer (Steel)
93. Needle Bearing Roller
94. Pinion Needle Bearing Spacer
95. Final Drive Planetary Pinion
96. Planetary Pinion Pin

92H12705

Courtesy of General Motors Corp.

Fig. 48: Legend For Exploded View Of Gear Sets & Clutch Plates (2 Of 2)

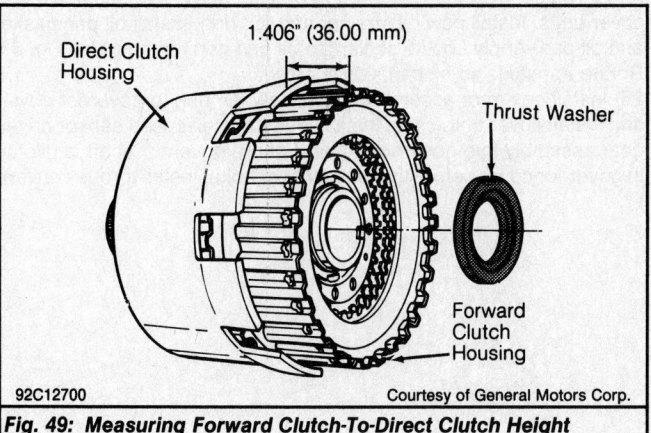

92C12700

Courtesy of General Motors Corp.

Fig. 49: Measuring Forward Clutch-To-Direct Clutch Height

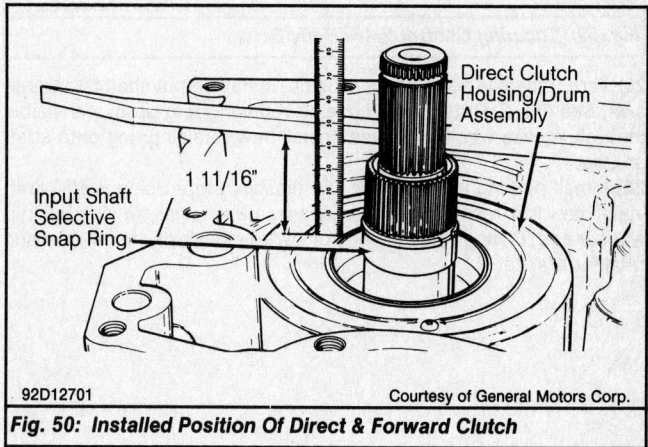

92D12701

Courtesy of General Motors Corp.

Fig. 50: Installed Position Of Direct & Forward Clutch

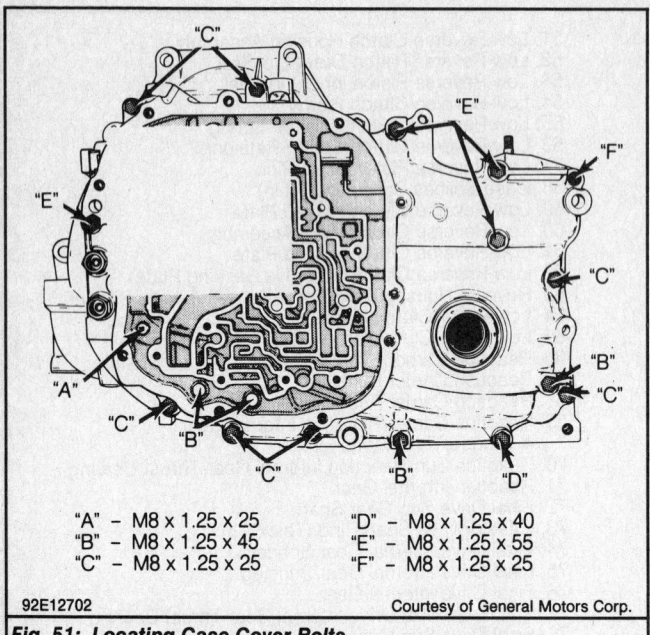

"A" — M8 x 1.25 x 25   "D" — M8 x 1.25 x 40
"B" — M8 x 1.25 x 45   "E" — M8 x 1.25 x 55
"C" — M8 x 1.25 x 25   "F" — M8 x 1.25 x 25

92E12702   Courtesy of General Motors Corp.

Fig. 51: Locating Case Cover Bolts

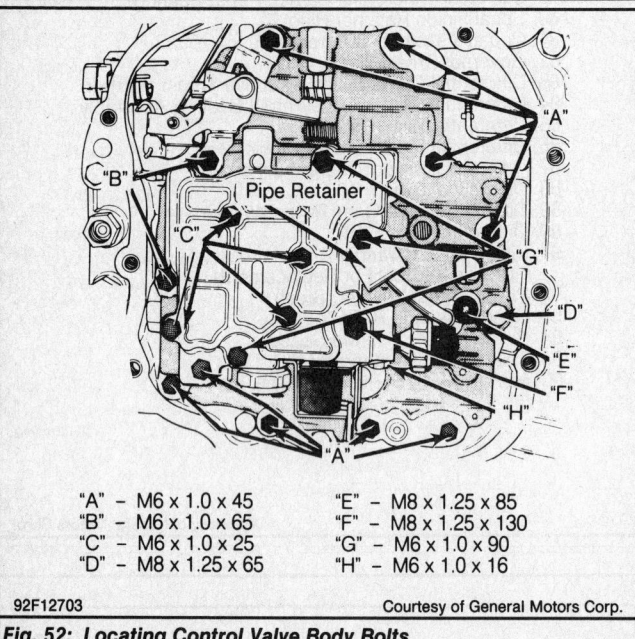

"A" — M6 x 1.0 x 45   "E" — M8 x 1.25 x 85
"B" — M6 x 1.0 x 65   "F" — M8 x 1.25 x 130
"C" — M6 x 1.0 x 25   "G" — M6 x 1.0 x 90
"D" — M8 x 1.25 x 65   "H" — M6 x 1.0 x 16

92F12703   Courtesy of General Motors Corp.

Fig. 52: Locating Control Valve Body Bolts

21) Turn transaxle so oil pan side is up. Install output shaft into transaxle. *See Fig. 2*. Rotate final drive so retaining ring groove is visible through access window in case. Install new retaining ring onto shaft groove.

22) Install parking lock bracket and dipstick stop. Using a 3/8" drift, install new low-reverse oil pipe seal assembly. Install "O" ring backup washer and "O" ring seal onto end of low-reverse pipe. Install pipe and retainer bracket.

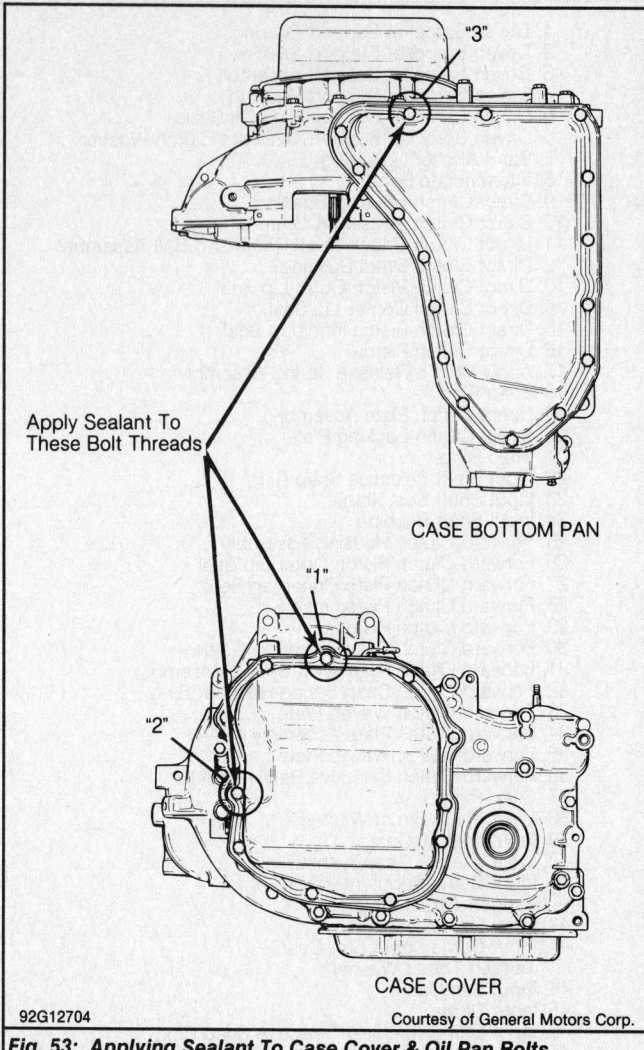

Apply Sealant To
These Bolt Threads

CASE BOTTOM PAN

CASE COVER

92G12704   Courtesy of General Motors Corp.

Fig. 53: Applying Sealant To Case Cover & Oil Pan Bolts

23) Install intermediate servo piston assembly. Use new inner and outer oil seals on piston and new seal on apply pin (apply pin size was determined during transaxle disassembly procedure). Install 3rd accumulator exhaust valve and spring into check valve bore next to servo piston. Install intermediate servo cover and 3 bolts. *See Fig. 17*.

24) Install reverse oil pipe bracket to oil pipe and servo cover. Install remaining servo cover bolt through bracket and cover. Tighten servo cover bolts. Install new oil strainer and "O" ring. Install oil pan gasket and oil pan. Apply Loctite sealant to oil pan bolt threads. *See Fig. 53*. Rotate transaxle so oil pan side is down.

25) Install governor assembly. Install new "O" ring to governor cover, and install cover onto case. Install speedometer/speed sensor driven gear assembly into governor cover. Ensure governor shaft is piloted in governor cover before tightening cover bolts. Install torque converter.

TORQUE SPECIFICATIONS

TORQUE SPECIFICATIONS

Application	Ft. Lbs. (N.m)
Auxiliary Valve Body-To-Case Bolt	
M6 Bolt	1
M8 Bolt	18 (24)
Case Cover-To-Case Bolt	18 (24)
Case-To-Drive Sprocket Support Bolt	18 (24)
Cooling Line Connector	26 (38)
Engine-To-Transaxle	55 (75)
Flywheel-To-Torque Converter Bolt	45-59 (61-80)
Parking Lock Bracket-To-Case Bolt	18 (24)
Pipe Retainer-To-Case Bolt	18 (24)
Pump Cover-To-Case Cover Bolt	18 (24)
Transaxle Mount Assembly-To-Body Bolt	49 (66)
Transaxle Support Assembly-To-Transaxle Bolt	55 (75)
Transaxle Support Assembly-To-Transaxle Mount Assembly Expansion Bolt	41 (55)
Valve Body-To-Case Bolt	
M6 Bolt	1
M8 Bolt	18 (24)

Application	INCH Lbs. (N.m)
Governor Cover-To-Case Bolt	96 (11)
Intermediate Servo Cover Bolt	96 (11)
Line Pressure Take-Off Bolt	96 (11)
Manual Detent Spring Assembly-To-Case Bolt	96 (11)
Oil Pan & Valve Body Cover Bolt	96 (11)
Pressure Switch	96 (11)
Pump Cover-To-Valve Body Bolt	96 (11)
Solenoid-To-Valve Body Bolt	96 (11)
Speedometer Driven Gear-To-Governor Cover Bolt	75 (8)
T.V. Cable-To-Case Bolt	75 (8)

1 – Tighten bolt to 96 INCH lbs. (11 N.m).

TRANSAXLE SPECIFICATIONS

TRANSAXLE SPECIFICATIONS

Application	In. (mm)
End Play	
Carrier-To-Final Drive Pinion	.009-.025 (.23-.64)
Final Drive-To Case	.005-.032 (.12-81)
Input Carrier Pinion	.009-.027 (.23-.69)
Input Shaft-To-Case Cover	.004-.033 (.10-.84)
Low Reverse Clutch Housing-To-Low Roller Clutch Race Thrust Washer	.003-.046 (.08-1.17)
Reaction Sun Gear-To-Input Drum	.005-.013 (.13-.33)
Torque Converter	
245 mm Converter	0-.020 (0-.50)
298 mm Converter	0-.024 (0-.60)
Forward Clutch Clearance	.040-.060 (1.0-1.5)

WIRING DIAGRAMS

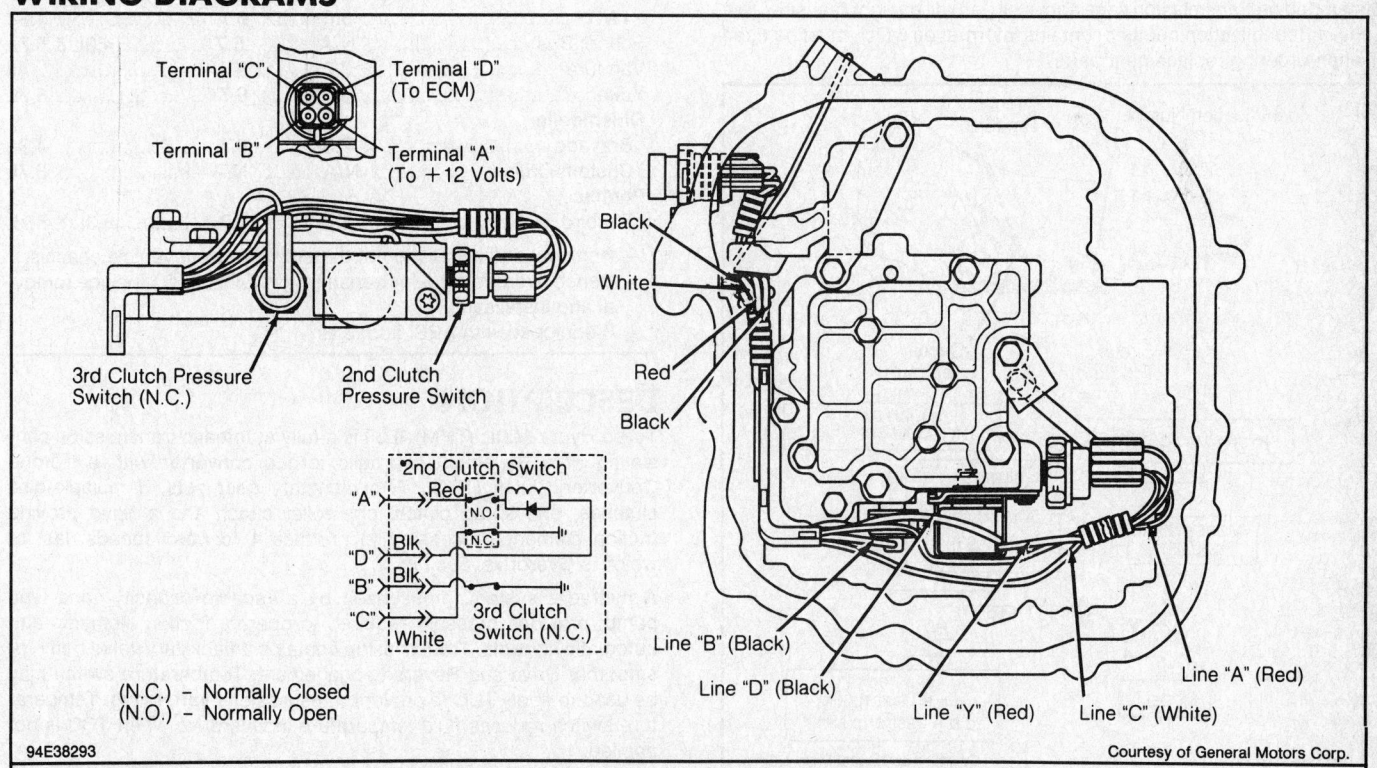

(N.C.) – Normally Closed
(N.O.) – Normally Open

94E38293

Courtesy of General Motors Corp.

Fig. 54: THM 3T40 Torque Converter Clutch Solenoid & Wiring Diagram (Typical – Wire Colors Will Vary)

AUTOMATIC TRANSMISSIONS
Hydra-Matic 4L60/4L60-E

APPLICATION & LABOR TIMES

THM 4L60 APPLICATION & LABOR TIMES (1993)

Vehicle Application	[1][3] R & I	[2] Overhaul	Engine Size
Buick			
Roadmaster	3.7	7.0	5.0L & 5.7L
Cadillac			
Brougham	3.9	7.0	5.0L & 5.7L
Chevrolet			
Blazer S/T			
2WD			
4-Cylinder	3.8	7.0	2.5L
V6	4.7	7.0	4.3L
4WD			
4-Cylinder	6.5	7.0	2.5L
V6 (2.8L)	6.5	7.0	4.3L
V6 (4.3L)	7.3	7.0	4.3L
Camaro	5.0	7.0	3.4L & 5.7L
Caprice	3.7	7.0	5.0L & 5.7L
Corvette [4]	6.0	7.0	5.7L
Pontiac			
Firebird	5.0	7.0	3.4L & 5.7L

[1] – Removal and installation of transmission from vehicle chassis.
[2] – Bench overhaul time for transmission. DOES NOT include removal and installation.
[3] – If equipped with ABS, add .3 Hr.
[4] – If vehicle has a convertible top add .9 Hr.

IDENTIFICATION

Turbo Hydra-Matic (THM) 4L60 transmission can be identified by a letter code contained in identification number. Identification number is stamped on transmission case above oil pan rail on right rear side. See Fig. 1. Identification number contains information which must be used when ordering replacement parts.

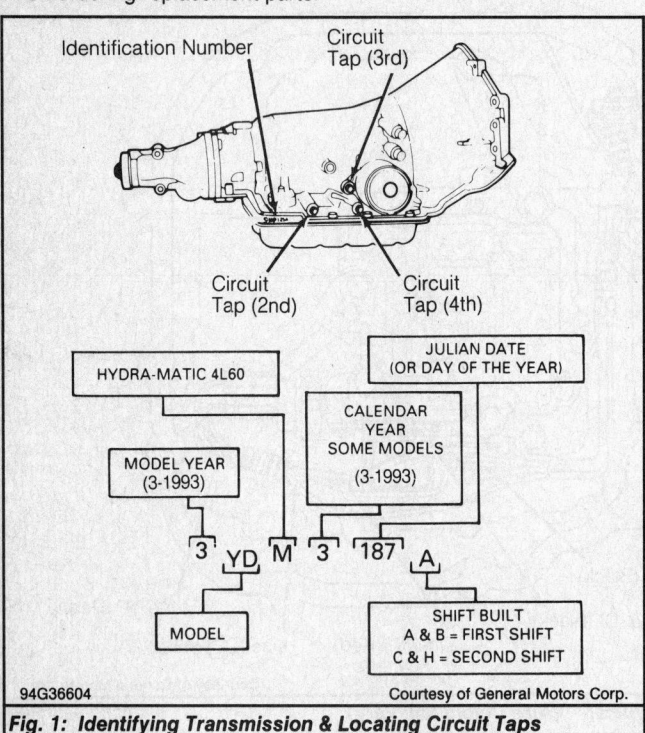

94G36604   Courtesy of General Motors Corp.

Fig. 1: Identifying Transmission & Locating Circuit Taps

THM 4L60-E APPLICATION & LABOR TIMES (1993-94)

Vehicle Application	[1][4] R & I	[2] Overhaul	Engine Size
Buick			
Roadmaster	3.7	6.7	5.7L
Cadillac			
Brougham	3.9	6.7	5.7L
Chevrolet			
Astro			
2WD	3.8	6.7	4.3L
4WD	5.0	6.7	4.3L
Blazer S/T			
4-Cylinder			
2WD	4.6	6.7	2.5L
4WD	7.8	6.7	2.5L
V6			
2WD	5.2	6.7	4.3L
4WD	7.8	6.7	4.3L
Blazer C/K			
4WD	5.7	6.7	All
GMC			
Jimmy			
2WD	5.2	6.7	All
4WD	7.8	6.7	All
Cutaway Van	3.7	6.7	5.7L
Hi-Cube Van	3.7	6.7	5.7L & 6.2L
Passenger Vans	3.7	6.7	All
Sports Vans	3.7	6.7	All
Suburban & Pickup			
2WD	4.9	6.7	5.7L
4WD	5.7	6.7	5.7L
Safari			
2WD	3.8	6.7	4.3L
4WD	5.0	6.7	4.3L
School Bus	N/A	6.7	4.3L & 5.7L
Vandura	3.7	6.7	All
Yukon	5.7	6.7	5.7L
Oldsmobile			
Bravada	7.8	6.7	4.3L
Custom Cruiser	N/A	N/A	5.7L
Pontiac			
Firebird	5.0	6.7	4.3L & 5.7L

[1] – Removal and installation of transmission from vehicle chassis.
[2] – Bench overhaul time for transmission. DOES NOT include removal and installation.
[3] – If equipped with ABS, add .3 Hr.

DESCRIPTION

Turbo Hydra-Matic (THM) 4L60 is a fully automatic transmission consisting of a 3-element hydraulic torque converter with a Torque Converter Clutch (TCC). Two planetary gear sets, 5 multiple-disc clutches, one sprag clutch, one roller clutch and a band provide friction elements necessary to produce 4 forward speeds, last of which is Overdrive. See Fig. 2.

A hydraulic system, pressurized by a variable capacity vane type pump, provides pressure required to operate friction elements and automatic controls. Transmission contains an auxiliary valve body for smoother Drive and Reverse engagement. Temperature switch may be used to apply TCC to prevent transmission overheating. Temperature switch reduces fluid temperature in Overdrive when TCC is not applied.

Temperature switch mounts on valve body and sits in transmission pan fluid. See Fig. 18. At normal operating temperature or less, switch is open. As fluid in pan heats to 270-286°F (134-140°C), switch closes to allow TCC to apply until fluid in pan cools to 250-268°F (121-131°C). Heat is reduced when TCC is applied and torque multiplication function of converter is by-passed.

The 4L60-E transmission, uses clutch and band elements which are very similar to the 4L60 transmission. The 4L60-E, also contains electronic solenoids to control hydraulic operations. The 4L60-E does not use a governor valve or throttle valve assemblies. A Powertrain Control Module (PCM) receives signals from Vehicle Speed Sensor (VSS), Throttle Position Sensor (TPS), fluid pressure switch assembly, and temperature switch. These signals help PCM determine when to switch the 2 shift solenoids, 3-2 downshift solenoid, and/or TCC solenoid on or off. The PCM can also control line pressure via pressure control solenoid (force motor).

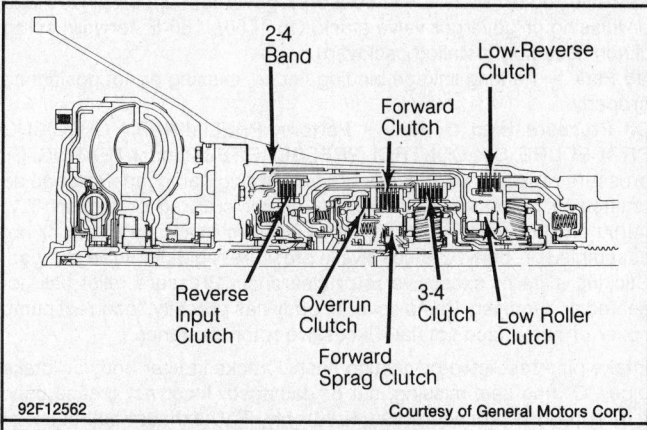

Fig. 2: Cut-Away View Of 4L60 Transmission; (4L60-E Transmission Is Similar)

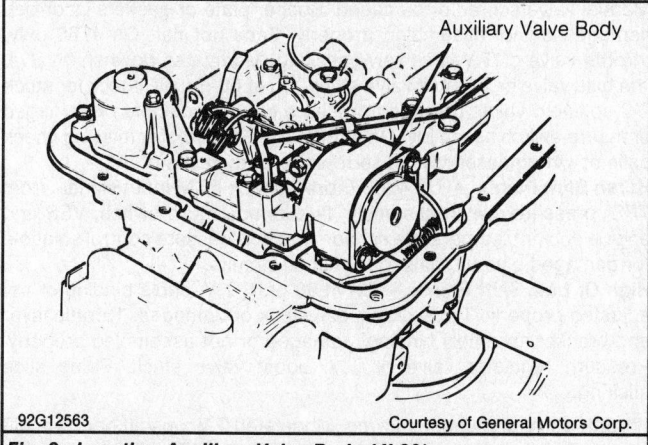

Fig. 3: Locating Auxiliary Valve Body (4L60)

LUBRICATION & ADJUSTMENTS

See appropriate AUTOMATIC TRANSMISSION SERVICING article in TRANSMISSION SERVICING.

TROUBLE SHOOTING

NOTE: Models with 4L60-E transaxle use Powertrain Control Module (PCM) computer, which controls TCC, pressure control solenoid and shifting solenoids 1-2 and 2-3. Models with 4L60 transaxle, use PCM to control TCC only.

NOTE: For electrical trouble shooting, see ELECTRICAL DIAGNOSIS 4L60-E article in AUTOMATIC TRANSMISSIONS.

NOTE: For additional trouble shooting, see SERVICE BULLETINS at end of article. For clutch and band application, see CLUTCH & BAND APPLICATION CHART under CLUTCH & BAND APPLICATION.

SYMPTOM DIAGNOSIS

1st Gear Only, No Upshift – On 4L60 only, check governor assembly. Governor valve sticking. Driven gear loose or damaged. Drive gear retaining pin missing. Nicks or burrs on output shaft, governor sleeve or case bore. Improper support pin length. Governor weights or springs missing, damaged or binding.

On 4L60/4L60-E, check 1-2 shift valve sticking in valve body. Spacer plate or gaskets damaged or not positioned properly. Case-to-valve body face damaged or not flat. Governor screen restricted or damaged. 2-4 servo assembly restricted or blocked case passages. Nicks or burrs on servo pin or case pin bore. Missing or damaged piston or pin seals. 4th servo piston installed backward. 2-4 band worn or damaged or band anchor pin not engaged. On 4L60-E only, check shift solenoids.

1st Gear Start In 2nd Gear Start Mode (Camaro & Firebird Only) – On 4L60-E only, check second gear start switch. Check technical service bulletins.

Slips In 1st – Defective forward clutch assembly. Clutch plates worn. Piston porous or damaged. Piston seals missing or damaged. Input housing-to-forward clutch housing "O" ring seal missing or damaged. Damaged housing. Housing retainer and ball assembly damaged or not seating. Input housing and shaft assembly turbine shaft seals missing or damaged. Accumulator valve stuck in valve body.

Valve body face not flat, damaged lands, or interconnected passages. Spacer plate or gaskets incorrect, damaged or not positioned properly. Binding or broken T.V. cable (4L60). On 4L60/4L60-E, check for defective 1-2 accumulator piston assembly. Porosity in piston or cover and pin assembly. Damaged piston ring grooves. Piston seal missing or damaged. Cover gasket missing or damaged. Broken accumulator spring.

Improper oil pressure. Torque converter stator roller clutch not holding or 4th servo piston in backward. Damage to low roller clutch lugs or inner ramps. Rollers not free moving, inadequate spring tension or damage to inner splines. Oil passage plugged. Forward clutch accumulator piston seal missing or damaged. Piston out of its bore. Porosity in piston or auxiliary valve body. Abuse valve stuck in auxiliary valve body (4L60).

High Or Low 1-2 Shift Speeds – On 4L60 only, check T.V. cable binding, broken or improperly adjusted. Governor assembly valve sticking. Driven gear loose or damaged. Drive gear retaining pin missing. Nicks or burrs on output shaft, governor sleeve or case bore. Improper support pin length. Governor weights or springs missing, damaged or binding.

Throttle lever and bracket assembly damaged, binding or not installed properly. T.V. link missing, binding or damaged. Valve body face not flat, T.V. exhaust check ball stuck or T.V. plunger sticking. Oil pump assembly or case face not flat.

Slipping Or Rough 1-2 Shift – On 4L60 only, check throttle lever and bracket assembly damaged, not installed properly or T.V. cable broken or binding. Valve body assembly throttle valve sticking. T.V. bushing turned in bore. On 4L60/4L60-E, check defective valve body assembly. 1-2 shift valve train, line bias valve, accumulator valve or T.V. limit valve stuck. Gaskets or spacer plate incorrect, damaged or not installed properly. Body face not flat.

Defective 2-4 servo assembly. Apply pin incorrect length. Servo seals or "O" ring seals missing or damaged. Restricted or missing oil passages. Case servo bore damaged. Defective 2nd accumulator. Porosity in 1-2 accumulator housing or piston. Piston seal or groove damaged. Nicks or burrs in 1-2 accumulator housing. Missing or restricted oil passages or 2-4 band worn or not positioned properly. Oil pump assembly or case faces not flat.

Slipping, Rough Or No 2-3 Shift – Internal converter damage. On 4L60 only, governor valve sticking. Drive gear retaining pin missing or loose. Governor weights binding. Governor drive gear damaged. Support pin in case incorrect length. On 4L60/4L60-E, oil pump stator shaft sleeve scored or not located properly. Valve body 2-3 valve train or accumulator valve stuck. Spacer plate or gaskets incorrect, damaged or not positioned properly. Throttle valve or T.V. limit valve stuck. Input housing assembly forward or 3-4 clutch plates worn. Excessive clutch plate travel.

Forward or 3-4 piston seals damaged. Porosity in 3-4 clutch housing or piston, or 3-4 piston check ball stuck, damaged or not sealing. Restricted apply passages. Forward clutch piston or 3rd accumulator retainer and ball assembly not seating. Sealing balls loose or missing. 2-4 servo assembly or 2nd apply piston seals missing or damaged.

1st & 4th Or 2nd & 3rd Gear Only – On 4L60-E only, check shift solenoids for dirt, damaged seals or electrical connections.

3rd Gear Only – On 4L60-E only, check 2-3 shift solenoid and 3-2 control solenoid circuits, damaged seals or electrical connections.

3-2 Flare Or Tie Up – On 4L60-E only, check 3-2 control solenoid for dirt, damaged seals or electrical connections.

Slipping, Rough Or No 3-4 Shift – On 4L60 only, check governor weights for binding. Governor valve sticking. Drive gear damaged or retaining pin missing or loose. Support pin in case incorrect length. On 4L60/4L60-E, check oil pump assembly faces not flat or pump cover retainer and ball assembly omitted or damaged. Valve body assembly 2-3 valve train, accumulator valve, throttle valve, T.V. limit valve (4L60 only), 1-2 shift valve or 3-2 control valve stuck. Manual valve link bent or damaged. Spacer plate or gaskets incorrect, damaged or not positioned properly. Defective 2-4 servo assembly.

Incorrect band apply pin. Servo seals missing or damaged. Porosity in pistons, cover or case. Plugged or missing orifice cup plug. Case 3rd accumulator retainer and ball assembly leaking. Porosity in 3-4 accumulator piston or bore. 3-4 accumulator piston seal or seal grooves damaged. Restricted oil passage. Defective input housing assembly. Forward or 3-4 clutch plates worn, or excessive plate travel.

Forward or 3-4 piston seals damaged. Porosity in 3-4 clutch housing or piston. 3-4 piston check ball stuck, damaged or not sealing. Restricted apply passages. Forward clutch piston retainer and ball assembly not seating. 2-4 band worn or not positioned properly. Sealing balls loose or missing.

No "R" Or Slips In "R" – Defective input housing assembly. 3-4 apply ring stuck in applied position. Forward clutch not releasing. Turbine shaft seals missing or damaged. Manual valve link disconnected. Defective oil pump assembly. Retainer and ball assembly missing or damaged. Stator shaft seal rings or ring grooves damaged. Stator shaft sleeve scored or damaged. Reverse boost valve stuck, damaged or not assembled properly. Cup plug missing.

Restricted oil passage. Faces not flat. Converter clutch apply valve stuck. Defective valve body assembly. 2-3 shift valve stuck. Manual linkage out of adjustment. Spacer plate and gaskets incorrect, damaged or not positioned properly. Defective reverse input clutch assembly. Clutch plate worn. Housing and drum assembly cracked at weld. Clutch plate or return spring assembly retaining ring out of groove. Piston deformed or dished.

Seals damaged or missing. Retainer and ball assembly not sealing. Restricted apply passage. Defective low-reverse clutch. Clutch plates worn or retaining ring not positioned properly. Porosity in piston. Seals damaged. Return spring assembly retaining ring not positioned properly. Case porosity. Case cover plate not tightened properly or gasket missing or damaged. On 4L60 only, auxiliary valve body low overrun valve stuck. Cup plug restricted, missing or damaged.

No Part-Throttle Or Delayed Downshifts – On 4L60 only, T.V. cable loose or not adjusted properly. T.V. bracket assembly bent. On 4L60/4L60-E, check for defective 2-4 servo assembly. Servo cover retaining ring missing or not assembled properly. 4th apply piston damaged or not assembled properly. Inner housing damaged or not assembled properly. Governor weights binding or governor valve stuck (4L60 only). Defective valve body assembly. Throttle valve, 3-2 control valve stuck. On 4L60 only, T.V. modulated downshift valve stuck. T.V. sleeve turned in bore. On 4L60/4L60-E, 4-3 sequence valve body channel blocked. No. 5 check ball missing.

Harsh Garage Shifts – On 4L60-E only, check valve body for missing check ball, or orifice cup plug.

No Overrun Braking In Manual 3-2-1 – T.V. cable loose or not adjusted properly (4L60 only). Defective valve body assembly. 4-3 sequence

valve or throttle valve stuck. No. 3 check ball not positioned properly. Spacer plate and gaskets incorrect, damaged or not positioned properly. Defective input clutch assembly. Turbine shaft oil passages plugged or not drilled. Turbine shaft seal rings damaged. Turbine shaft sealing balls loose or missing. Porosity in forward or overrun clutch piston. Overrun piston seals damaged or cut. Overrun piston check ball not sealing.

Drives (Creeps) In Neutral – Forward clutch not releasing. Manual valve link disconnected. Converter clutch apply valve stuck in oil pump. Face of transmission case not flat or internal leakage in case.

Starts In 2nd In "D" – On 4L60-E only, governor support pin too long or missing or governor valve stuck. On 4L60/4L60-E, forward sprag clutch assembly installed backward.

No Park – Parking linkage binding, loose, missing or not positioned properly.

Oil Pressure High Or Low – Perform PRELIMINARY CHECKING PROCEDURE. See CONTROL PRESSURE TEST under TESTING. Oil pressure regulator valve stuck or valve spring damaged. Rotor guide omitted or not assembled properly. Rotor cracked or broken. T.V. (4L60 only) or reverse boost valve or sleeve stuck, damaged or not assembled properly. Orifice valve in pressure regulator valve plugged. Sticking slide or excessive rotor clearance. Pressure relief ball not seated or damaged. Pump cover or body has porosity. Incorrect pump cover or pump face not flat. Excessive rotor clearance.

Intake pipe restricted by casting flash. Cracks in filter body or intake pipe. "O" ring seal missing, cut or damaged. Incorrect grease used during rebuild procedure. On 4L60 only, T.V. exhaust ball stuck or damaged. On 4L60/4L60-E, throttle link, lever and bracket assembly binding, damaged or not assembled properly.

Manual valve scored or damaged. Spacer plate or gaskets incorrect, damaged or not assembled properly. Face not flat. On 4L60 only, throttle valve or T.V. limit valve sticking. Modulated downshift valve, line bias valve or 2-3 shift valve stuck. On 4L60-E only, check for stuck 2-3 solenoid valve, damaged pressure control solenoid or damaged pressure switch assembly. On 4L60/4L60-E, check for missing check balls or wrong assembly. Case-to-valve body face not flat.

Harsh Shift Points – On 4L60-E only, check PCM input signals from TPS, pressure switch assembly, fluid temperature switch, VSS and engine coolant temperature sensor. Inspect pressure control solenoid for damaged pins or seals, or dirt in oil circuits.

High Or Low Shift Points – On 4L60 only, T.V. cable binding or not adjusted properly. T.V. exhaust ball stuck or damaged. Throttle lever and bracket assembly binding, damaged or not assembled properly. Pressure regulator valve or T.V. boost valve stuck. Pump slide sticking.

Throttle valve or plunger sticking. Modulated T.V. upshift or downshift valves, T.V. limit valve or line bias valve sticking. Spacer plate or gaskets damaged, incorrect or not assembled properly.

Valve body pad porous or damaged. Governor filter restricted or damaged. 2-4 accumulator has porosity. Servo piston seals damaged. Apply pin damaged or has improper length. 2-4 band burned or anchor pin not engaged.

On 4L60-E only, check for stuck pressure regulator valve or pump slide sticking. Spacer plate or gaskets damaged, incorrect or not assembled properly.

Valve body pad porous or damaged. 2-4 accumulator has porosity. Servo piston seals damaged. Apply pin damaged or has improper length. 2-4 band burned or anchor pin not engaged. Throttle Position (TP) sensor, VSS and/or 4WD low switch (if equipped) disconnected or damaged.

NOTE: Models with 4L60-E transaxle use Powertrain Control Module (PCM) computer, which controls TCC, pressure control solenoid and shifting solenoids 1-2 and 2-3. Models with 4L60 transaxle, use PCM to control TCC only.

No Converter Clutch Apply – Transmission not supplied 12 volts. Outside electrical connector damaged. Inside electrical connector wiring harness or solenoid damaged. Solenoid wire pinched. Solenoid not grounded. Pressure switches incorrect or damaged. Temperature switch damaged. Engine speed sensor or pressure switch assembly (4L60-E only). Converter internal damage.

Converter clutch valve stuck or assembled backward, or retaining ring not positioned properly. Pump-to-case gasket not positioned properly. Orifice cup plug restricted or damaged. Solenoid "O" ring seal cut or damaged. Pump-to-body cover high or uneven bolt torque.Turbine shaft "O" ring seal cut or damaged. Turbine shaft retainer and ball assembly restricted or damaged. TCC shift valve or apply valve stuck. Solenoid "O" ring leaking. Solenoid screen is blocked.

Converter Shudder – Torque converter has internal damage. Converter clutch valve stuck. Restricted oil passages. Crack in filter body. Flash restricting filter neck. "O" ring seal cut or damaged. Turbine shaft "O" ring cut or damaged. Turbine shaft retainer and ball assembly restricted or damaged. Low oil pressure. Engine not tuned properly.

No Converter Clutch Release – Solenoid external ground. Converter internal damage. Converter clutch valve stuck. Converter clutch apply valve stuck in apply position. PCM external ground.

Converter Clutch Apply Cold – On 4L60-E only, check engine coolant temperature sensor and trouble codes.

Ratcheting Noise – Parking pawl return spring weak, damaged or not assembled properly.

Oil Leaking Out Vent – Chamfer in pump body rotor pocket too large. T.V. limit valve stuck (4L60 only). Fluid level overfilled. Cross leak out of pump body and cover.

Vibration In Reverse & Whining Noise In Park – Oil pump broken vane rings.

Front Oil Leak – Torque converter welded seam leaking. Damaged torque converter hub. Damaged front seal.

No Reverse, Slips In Reverse, Bad Engagement (No Braking Or Weak Braking In Manual Low) – No. 5 check ball missing. Faulty low-reverse clutch. Reverse boost valve sticking. Reverse boost valve installed backward.

Pump Bushing Spins Out, "Walks" Into Seal, Or Seizes To Converter Hub – Transmission and engine center lines do not match. Excessive crankshaft runout. Bent flexplate (drive plate). Excessive converter hub runout. Pump bushing I.D. not centered in pump. Bushing too loose in pump. Not enough hub-to-bushing clearance.

Slip On 2-3 Shift, Falling Out Of 3rd, Repeated 3-4 Clutch Or 2-4 Band Failure – Leaking No. 7 check ball (direct clutch accumulator check valve located in case, visible through servo). Cracked input shaft. Input shaft sealing rings leaking. Leak at base of input shaft where shaft is pressed into drum. Pump cover bore (sealing ring surface) worn. Servo air bleed cup plug loose or blown out of case. Pump-to-case gasket misaligned or ripped. 3-4 air bleed ball in back of input drum leaking. 3-4 clutch piston seals leaking. Servo release side (large) sealing ring leaking in 2nd gear and dragging 3rd clutch. Band apply pin in case worn. Servo seized in case. Damaged pump. Stator sleeve turned in pump and partly blocking feed passage. Throttle valve sticking, causing delayed 3rd clutch circuit pressure rise during 2-3 shift.

Delayed Or No Forward Clutch Engagement, Slips Or Chatters In 1st Gear – Leak at forward clutch accumulator (auxiliary valve body; on 4L60) caused by accumulator pin "walking" out of oval hole in cover.

No 4th Gear, No 3-4 Upshift (Stays In 3rd, 2nd Usually Okay) – Leaking 4th gear piston sealing ring (inside servo cover). Excessive servo clearance allowing 4th piston to "walk" out of cover, leaking 4th apply oil out servo vent hole. Servo vent hole blocked (hole is at pan gasket surface). Leaking 4th signal switch. 3-4 relay valve installed backward. Aluminum disc missing from between 3-4 relay valve and hole pin. Servo feed tunnel cup missing from valve body. 3-4 shift valve stuck. Incorrect spring or spring too stiff at 3-4 shift valve. 3-4 accumulator air bleed cup plug blown out of case. Throttle valve sticks.

Falls Out Of 4th Gear During Coasting – Low line pressure at idle (weak pressure regulator spring).

Binds Up On 3-4 Shift (Feels Like Brake Drag) – Forward pressure plate installed incorrectly. Too many plates in overrun clutch. Incorrect top steel plate installed in overrun clutch.

Falls Out Of 4th Gear During Coasting – Low line pressure at idle (weak pressure regulator spring).

Binds Up On 3-4 Shift (Feels Like Brake Drag) – Forward pressure plate installed incorrectly. Too many plates in overrun clutch. Incorrect top steel plate installed in overrun clutch.

No Forward Or Reverse Gears (Line Pressure Reading Okay) – Mismatched converter input shaft or broken turbine hub.

No Drive In "D" Range – Torque converter stator roller clutch not holding.

No Drive In "OD" Range – Faulty output sprag. Teeth "hammered" out of forward friction plates.

CLUTCH & BAND APPLICATION

CLUTCH & BAND APPLICATION CHART (4L60)

Selector Lever Position	Elements In Use
"D" (Overdrive)	
First Gear	Forward Clutch, Forward Sprag & Low Roller Clutch
Second Gear	Forward Clutch, Forward Sprag & 2-4 Band
Third Gear	Forward Clutch, Forward Sprag & 3-4 Clutch
Overdrive	Forward Clutch, 2-4 Band & 3-4 Clutch
"D" (Drive)	
First Gear	Forward Clutch, Forward Sprag, Low Roller Clutch & Overrun Clutch
Second Gear	Forward Clutch, Forward Sprag, Overrun Clutch & 2-4 Band,
Third Gear	Forward Clutch, Forward Sprag, Overrun Clutch & 3-4 Clutch
"2" (Intermediate)	
First Gear	Forward Clutch, Forward Sprag, Low Roller Clutch & Overrun Clutch
Second Gear	Forward Clutch, Forward Sprag, Overrun Clutch & 2-4 Band
"1" (Low)	
First Gear	Forward Clutch, Forward Sprag, Low Reverse Clutch, Low Roller Clutch & Overrun Clutch
"R" (Reverse)	Low Reverse Clutch & Reverse Input Clutch
"N" Or "P" (Neutral Or Park)	All Clutches & Bands Released Or Ineffective

TESTING

NOTE: The following tests are for 4L60 transmission only. For complete testing of 4L60-E, see ELECTRONIC DIAGNOSIS 4L60-E article in AUTOMATIC TRANSMISSIONS.

ROAD TEST

1) Operate vehicle in Overdrive. Accelerate using steady throttle pressure. Note shift points for 2nd, 3rd, Overdrive and TCC application. TCC application should occur in 3rd or Overdrive.

2) Torque converter clutch will not engage until engine coolant has reached a temperature of 130°F (54°C). Compare shift points to shift speed charts. *See Fig. 4.* If TCC application is not obtained, see ELECTRONIC DIAGNOSIS 4L60-E article in AUTOMATIC TRANSMISSIONS.

3) Operate vehicle in Overdrive normally at 40-55 MPH with throttle in half-open position. Ensure TCC releases, and note 3rd gear downshift point. Repeat procedure with wide open throttle. Ensure TCC releases, and note 2nd gear downshift point.

4) Operate vehicle in Overdrive normally at 40-55 MPH. Release accelerator while manually shifting transmission to 3rd gear. Ensure TCC releases and engine braking is felt, and note 3rd gear downshift point.

5) Operate vehicle in Overdrive normally at 40-45 MPH. Release accelerator while manually shifting transmission into 2nd gear. Ensure TCC releases and engine braking is felt, and note 2nd gear downshift point.

6) With transmission in Overdrive, accelerate normally to 25 MPH, allowing vehicle to upshift normally. Release accelerator while

CLUTCH & BAND APPLICATION CHART (4L60-E)

Selector Lever Position	Shift Solenoid Position	Elements In Use
"D" (Overdrive)		
First Gear	1-2 ON/2-3 ON	Forward Clutch, Forward Sprag & Low Roller Clutch
Second Gear	1-2 OFF/2-3 ON	Forward Clutch, Forward Sprag & 2-4 Band
Third Gear	1-2 OFF/2-3 OFF	Forward Clutch, Forward Sprag & 3-4 Clutch
Overdrive	1-2 ON/2-3 OFF	Forward Clutch 2-4 Band & 3-4 Clutch
"D" (Drive)		
First Gear	1-2 ON/2-3 ON	Forward Clutch, Forward Sprag, Low Roller Clutch & Overrun Clutch
Second Gear	1-2 OFF/2-3 ON	Forward Clutch, Forward Sprag, Overrun Clutch & 2-4 Band,
Third Gear	1-2 OFF/2-3 OFF	Forward Clutch, Forward Sprag, Overrun Clutch & 3-4 Clutch
"2" (Intermediate)		
First Gear	1-2 ON/2-3 ON	Forward Clutch, Forward Sprag, Low Roller Clutch & Overrun Clutch
Second Gear	1-2 OFF/2-3 ON	Forward Clutch, Forward Sprag, Overrun Clutch & 2-4 Band
"1" (Low)		
First Gear	1-2 ON/2-3 ON	Forward Clutch, Forward Sprag, Low Reverse Clutch, Low Roller Clutch & Overrun Clutch
"R" (Reverse)	1-2 ON/2-3 ON	Low Reverse Clutch & Reverse Input Clutch
"N" Or "P" (Neutral Or Park)	1-2 ON/2-3 ON	All Clutches & Bands Released Or Ineffective

1993 HYDRA-MATIC 4L60 SHIFT SPEED CHART

MODEL	1-2 MIN THROTTLE	2-3 MIN THROTTLE	3-4 MIN THROTTLE	1-2 W.O.T.	4-3 COAST DOWN	3-2 COAST DOWN	2-1 COAST DOWN
AAM	11-14	23-26	36-46	27-30	25-29	13-20	6-8
ADM	13-15	23-26	36-45	40-44	30-38	18-26	9-12
AFM	15-18	26-31	38-52	34-39	28-33	16-24	9-12
ASM	11-13	22-28	36-47	27-30	25-29	13-20	6-8
BAM	12-15	22-28	32-41	30-36	22-26	13-21	9-11
BBM	14-18	26-33	40-52	36-43	25-29	14-24	9-11
BCM	13-18	26-28	43-53	36-42	25-29	14-24	9-11
BFM	13-16	24-28	38-52	30-40	25-29	14-21	8-11
BHM	12-15	22-28	33-43	30-36	21-25	12-20	7-9
BRM	16-19	28-31	35-48	36-50	24-31	15-23	10-13
BWM	13-18	25-31	38-51	36-42	25-29	14-24	9-11
CPM	13-20	23-29	49-53	33-39	35-46	15-22	11-13
FDM	15-19	26-33	42-51	40-47	28-35	16-24	11-13
FFM	10-13	18-21	33-46	34-42	17-20	10-16	4-7
FMM	13-21	21-23	31-43	34-42	19-24	13-20	8-10
HBM	13-16	24-28	43-51	31-41	25-34	14-22	9-12
HDM	13-16	26-29	40-48	31-38	28-34	15-24	10-12
HJM	14-18	18-31	50-55	31-41	31-47	16-27	11-13
HLM	14-17	26-34	56-63	34-43	40-51	15-25	10-13
LHM	13-14	22-25	48-53	24-27	35-47	13-21	8-10
SAM	13-15	18-25	48-50	28-35	37-47	10-18	9-12
SFM	10-13	18-23	43-51	29-35	36-45	13-19	8-10
YAM	12-14	21-26	31-46	45-52	21-26	12-21	9-11
YCM	12-14	21-26	31-40	42-52	21-26	12-21	9-11
YDM	14-16	24-28	38-51	35-44	23-29	13-22	9-11

Notes:
1. All speeds indicated are in miles per hour. Conversion to KM/H = MPH x 1.609.
2. Shift points will vary slightly due to engine loads and vehicle options.
3. Speeds listed with + exceed 65 MPH.
4. Speeds are based on TPS of 10 to 20. Use scan tool to measure correct TPS.

For transmission model identification, see Fig. 1.

94H36605

Fig. 4: Shift Speed Chart

manually shifting transmission into 1st gear. Ensure TCC releases and engine braking is felt, and note 1st gear downshift point.

7) With transmission in Overdrive, accelerate to 4th gear with TCC applied. Release accelerator. Lightly apply brakes, and ensure TCC releases and note speed at which downshifts occur. Compare shift points noted to shift speed charts. *See Fig. 4.*

8) Place transmission in 3rd gear with vehicle stopped. Accelerate, and note 1st-2nd and 2nd-3rd shift points. Repeat procedure with transmission in 2nd gear. Note 1st-2nd shift point. Accelerate to 25 MPH. Ensure 2nd-3rd gear upshift does not occur and TCC does not engage.

9) Place transmission in 1st gear with vehicle stopped. Accelerate to 15 MPH. Ensure upshifts do not occur and TCC not engage. With vehicle stopped, place transmission in Reverse and slowly accelerate to observe reverse gear operation.

10) Compare all shift points to shift speed charts. *See Fig. 4.* If shift points are not within approximate speed listed, see TROUBLE SHOOTING. Control pressure can also be checked. See CONTROL PRESSURE TEST.

CONTROL PRESSURE TEST

Preliminary Checking Procedure – 1) Ensure fluid level is correct and engine is in good operating condition before performing control pressure test. Ensure shift linkage is properly adjusted. See appropriate AUTOMATIC TRANSMISSION SERVICING article in TRANSMISSION SERVICING.

2) Control pressure can be checked to ensure proper throttle valve cable adjustment. If control pressure is not within specification, adjust throttle valve cable before attempting any other corrections. See THROTTLE VALVE CONTROL PRESSURE CHECK.

Throttle Valve Control Pressure Check – 1) Install pressure gauge on transmission line pressure tap. *See Fig. 5.* Install tachometer on engine. Apply parking brake. Ensure engine is at normal operating temperature.

2) Operate engine at 1000 RPM. With gear selector in "P" position, note oil pressure reading. Move gear selector to "D" position, and note oil pressure reading.

3) Oil pressure "D" reading must be equal to "P" reading or must not exceed it by more than 10 psi (.70 kg/cm). Operate engine at 1400 RPM. Oil pressure should increase. Adjust throttle valve cable if pressure does not increase. See appropriate AUTOMATIC TRANSMISSION SERVICING article in TRANSMISSION SERVICING.

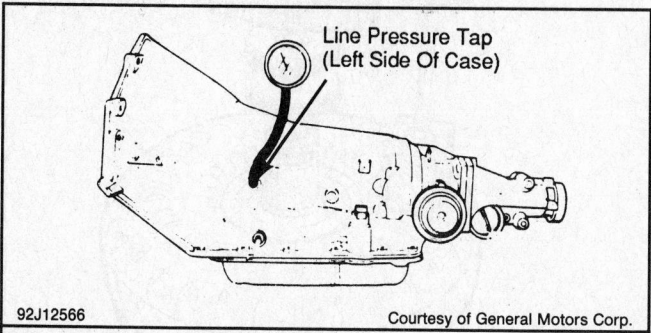

Line Pressure Tap (Left Side Of Case)

92J12566

Courtesy of General Motors Corp.

Fig. 5: Locating Line Pressure Tap

1993 HYDRA-MATIC 4L60 TRANSMISSION PRESSURES

RANGE	MODEL	NORMAL PRESSURE AT MINIMUM T.V.		NORMAL PRESSURE AT FULL T.V.	
		kPa	PSI	kPa	PSI
PARK, NEUTRAL, OVERDRIVE & MANUAL 3RD @ 1000 RPM	AAM	518-587	75-85	1016-1183	147-171
	ADM	518-587	75-85	1197-1389	174-201
	AFM, BWM	518-587	75-85	1028-1192	149-173
	ASM	518-587	75-85	952-1105	138-160
	BAM	451-518	65-75	944-1105	137-160
	BBM	518-587	75-85	965-1126	140-160
	BCM	518-587	75-85	931-1067	135-155
	BFM	518-587	75-85	1421-1689	206-245
	BHM	518-587	75-85	943-1085	137-157
	BRM	518-587	75-85	1061-1227	135-178
	CPM	451-515	65-75	1090-1273	158-184
	FDM	451-515	65-75	983-1142	142-166
	FFM, FMM	451-515	65-75	1311-1533	190-222
	LHM	518-587	75-85	1402-1669	203-242
	SAM	451-515	65-75	894-1038	130-150
	SFM	451-515	65-75	948-1104	137-160
	YAM, YCM, YDM	451-515	65-75	1354-1617	196-235
REVERSE @ 1000 RPM	AAM	738-836	107-121	1448-1685	210-244
	ADM	738-836	107-121	1706-1979	247-287
	AFM, BWM	738-836	107-121	1465-1698	212-246
	ASM	738-836	107-121	1356-1575	196-228
	BAM	742-847	108-123	1551-1816	225-263
	BBM	738-836	107-121	1375-1605	199-232
	BCM	738-836	107-121	1326-1520	192-220
	BFM	665-754	96-109	1825-2169	264-314
	BHM	738-836	107-121	1343-1545	195-224
	BRM	738-836	107-121	1511-1748	219-253
	CPM	742-847	108-123	1792-2092	260-303
	FDM	580-662	84-96	1263-1467	183-213
	FFM, FMM	580-662	84-96	1684-1969	244-286
	LHM	665-754	96-109	1801-2144	261-311
	SAM	580-662	84-96	1148-1333	166-193
	SFM	580-662	84-96	1217-1417	176-205
	YAM, YCM, YDM	580-662	84-96	1739-2077	252-301
MANUAL 2ND & MANUAL LO @ 1000 RPM	AAM, ADM, AFM, ASM, BBM, BCM, BHM, BRM, BWM	1121-1269	162-184	1121-1269	162-184
	BAM, CPM, FDM, FFM, FMM, SAM, SFM, YAM, YCM, YDM	1127-1286	163-187	1127-1286	163-187
	BFM, LHM	1293-1465	188-212	1293-1465	188-212

For transmission model identification, see Fig. 1.

94136606

Courtesy of General Motors Corp.

Fig. 6: Oil Pressure Specifications

CAUTION: DO NOT perform following pressure tests for longer than 2 minutes or transmission damage may occur.

Minimum Throttle Valve Pressure Check – 1) Ensure throttle valve cable is properly adjusted. Attach pressure gauge to line pressure tap. *See Fig. 5.* Apply parking brake and service brakes.

2) Check line pressure as specified. *See Fig. 6.* Pressure readings must be within specification. If pressure reading is not within specification, see TROUBLE SHOOTING.

Full Throttle Valve Pressure Check – 1) Attach pressure gauge to line pressure tap. *See Fig. 5.* Apply parking brake and service brakes. Ensure throttle valve cable is secured in fully extended position.

2) Check line pressure as specified. *See Fig. 6.* Pressure readings must be within specification. If pressure reading is not within specification, see TROUBLE SHOOTING.

Pressure Differential Check – 1) Possible leakage in clutch circuits may be determined by checking oil pressure differential between line pressure and 2nd, 3rd and 4th clutches. Attach pressure gauges to line pressure tap and appropriate clutch circuit tap on transmission.

2) Circuit tap for 2nd clutch is located on right rear side of transmission, above pan. Circuit tap for 3rd clutch is located next to 2-4 servo, above 4th clutch circuit tap. *See Fig. 1.* Drive vehicle, and note both pressure readings. Pressure differential between line pressure and clutch circuits exceeding 10 psi (0.70 kg/cm²) indicates possible leakage in clutch circuit.

TORQUE CONVERTER

NOTE: Torque converter is a sealed unit and must be serviced as complete assembly.

STALL TEST

1) Torque converter whine is usually noticed when vehicle is stopped and transmission is in Reverse or Drive. Whine will increase when engine RPM is increased and will stop when vehicle is moving or when torque converter clutch is applied. Stall test is to ensure whine is coming from torque converter.

2) Start engine, and allow it to reach normal operating temperature. Apply parking and service brakes. Put transmission in Drive. Depress accelerator to approximately 1200 RPM for less than 6 seconds. DO NOT depress accelerator for more than 6 seconds or transmission damage may occur. Torque converter noise will increase under this load.

NOTE: Torque converter whine should not be confused with pump whine, which is usually noticeable in Park, Neutral and all other gear ranges.

STATOR CHECK

1) Torque converter stator roller clutch can either remain locked up at all times or freewheel in both directions. If stator is freewheeling at all times, vehicle tends to have poor acceleration from a stop. Vehicle may act normal at speeds above 30-35 MPH.

2) If poor acceleration is noted, ensure exhaust system is not blocked, engine timing is correct and transmission is in 1st gear when starting from a stop. If stator is locked up at all times, performance from a stop appears normal. Engine RPM and acceleration is limited at high speeds. Engine may overheat from this condition.

3) A visual inspection of torque converter may reveal converter is Blue from overheating. If torque converter has been removed from vehicle, stator roller clutch can be checked by inserting a finger into splined inner race of roller clutch and trying to turn race in both directions. Inner race should turn freely clockwise but should not turn or should be difficult to turn counterclockwise.

END PLAY CHECK

1) Inspect torque converter for hub scoring, cracks or weld area cracks before checking end play. Install End Play Checking Tool (J-35138) on torque converter. *See Fig. 7.*

2) Note end play of torque converter. End play must be within specification. See TORQUE CONVERTER END PLAY SPECIFICATIONS table. Replace torque converter if end play is not within specification or damage to hub area exists.

TORQUE CONVERTER END PLAY SPECIFICATIONS

Converter Diameter In. (mm)	End Play In. (mm)
9.65 (245.0)	.000-.020 (.00-.50)
11.73 (298.0)	.000-.024 (.00-.61)

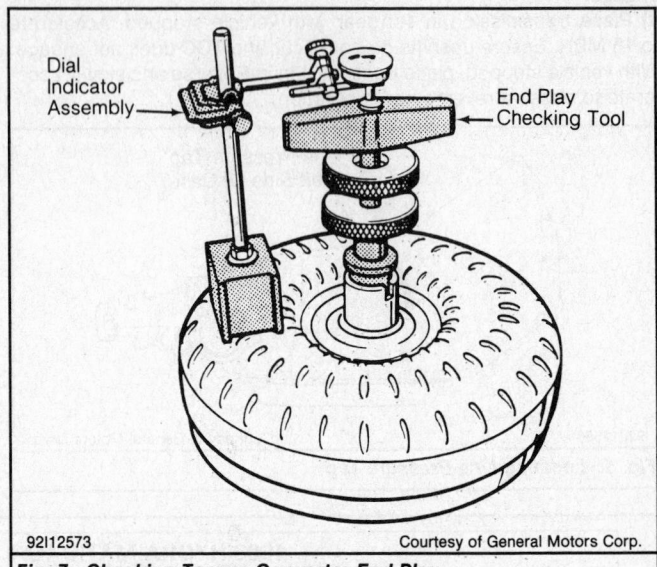

92I12573   Courtesy of General Motors Corp.

Fig. 7: Checking Torque Converter End Play

CONVERTER FLUSHING

Torque converter flushing is not recommended. Replace torque converter if contamination is found during oil cooler flushing procedure.

NOTE: For additional information on Torque Converter Clutch (TCC), see ELECTRONIC DIAGNOSIS 4L60-E article in AUTOMATIC TRANSMISSIONS.

ON-VEHICLE SERVICE

THROTTLE VALVE CABLE (4L60 ONLY)

Removal – Remove air cleaner. Disconnect throttle valve cable from throttle linkage. Compress locking tabs. Remove cable from mounting bracket. Raise and support vehicle. Remove cable retaining bolt from transmission. Disconnect cable from transmission. Remove seal.

Installation – To install, reverse removal procedure. Install NEW seal. Once cable is fully installed, pull upper end of cable. Slight resistance should be felt due to return spring. Ensure cable fully returns. Adjust cable. See appropriate AUTOMATIC TRANSMISSION SERVICING article in TRANSMISSION SERVICING.

GOVERNOR ASSEMBLY (4L60 ONLY)

Removal – Remove governor cover and "O" ring. Remove governor assembly.

Inspection – Inspect governor valve and sleeve for binding and scoring. *See Fig. 8.* Ensure weights operate freely. Inspect governor drive gear for damage and loose fit on shaft. Replace governor if necessary.

Installation – To install, reverse removal procedure. Install NEW cover seal or gasket. Apply thin coat of Loctite sealant on cover before installation. Ensure fluid level is correct.

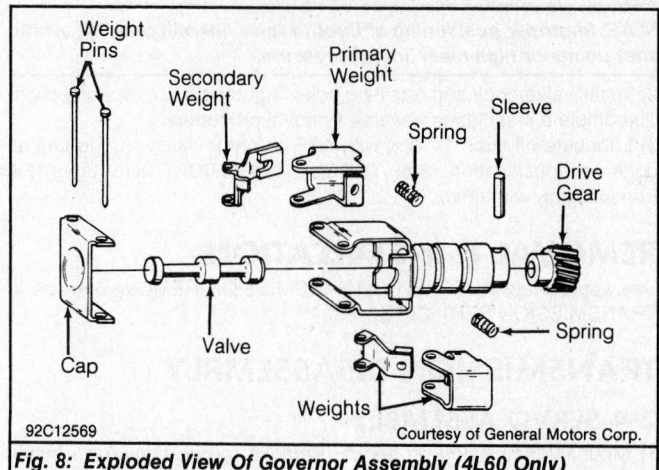

Fig. 8: *Exploded View Of Governor Assembly (4L60 Only)*

2-4 SERVO ASSEMBLY

Removal & Installation – Install Piston Compressor (J-29714) on oil pan. Compress servo cover, and remove retaining ring. *See Fig. 14.* Remove servo cover and "O" ring. Remove 2-4 servo assembly. To install, reverse removal procedure. For servo pin length check, see 2-4 SERVO ASSEMBLY under TRANSMISSION DISASSEMBLY.

REAR OIL SEAL

Removal & Installation – Remove drive shaft. Pry oil seal from extension housing. Coat outside edge of oil seal with non-hardening sealer. Using Seal Installer (J-21426), install oil seal. To complete installation, install drive shaft. Check fluid level.

AUXILIARY VALVE BODY (4L60 ONLY)

Removal – Remove transmission oil pan. Remove oil filter and "O" ring. Ensure "O" ring is removed from transmission case. Remove clamp and pressure tube. Remove auxiliary valve body retaining bolts. Remove auxiliary valve body and check ball. *See Fig. 9.* Note location of check ball.

Installation – Coat check ball with petroleum jelly before installation. Install check ball in auxiliary valve body. To complete installation, reverse removal procedure. Lubricate "O" ring with petroleum jelly. Install new filter and "O" ring. Tighten bolts to specification. See TORQUE SPECIFICATIONS table at end of article. Fill transmission with fluid.

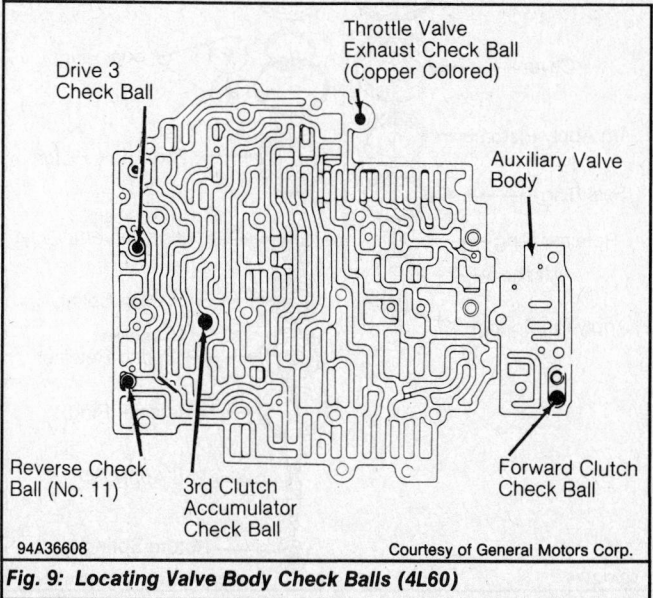

Fig. 9: *Locating Valve Body Check Balls (4L60)*

VALVE BODY

CAUTION: Note valve body bolt length and location during removal procedure. Transmission case damage may occur if bolts are incorrectly installed.

Removal (4L60) – **1)** Disconnect throttle valve cable from throttle lever. Raise and support vehicle, and remove transmission oil pan. Remove oil filter and "O" ring. Ensure "O" ring is removed from transmission case.
2) Remove electrical connectors from switches, and tag. Remove auxiliary valve tube to access valve body. Remove valve body bolts. Note length and location of bolts for installation.
3) Note direction of manual valve link. Remove manual valve link from manual valve at valve body. *See Fig. 10.* Note direction of throttle valve link. *See Fig. 11.* Remove throttle valve bracket and throttle valve link. Remove valve body. Note location of check balls. DO NOT lose balls. *See Fig. 9.*

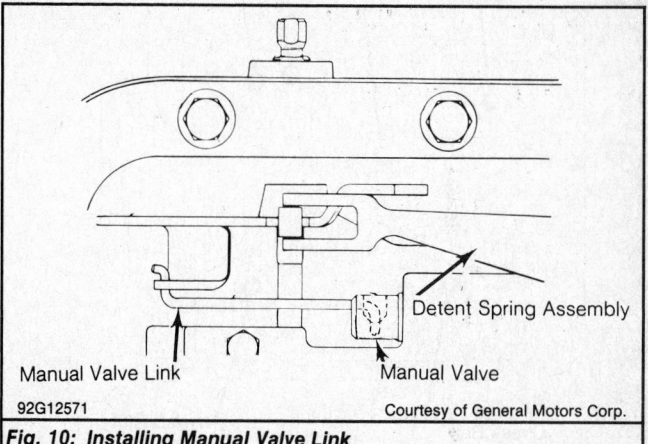

Fig. 10: *Installing Manual Valve Link*

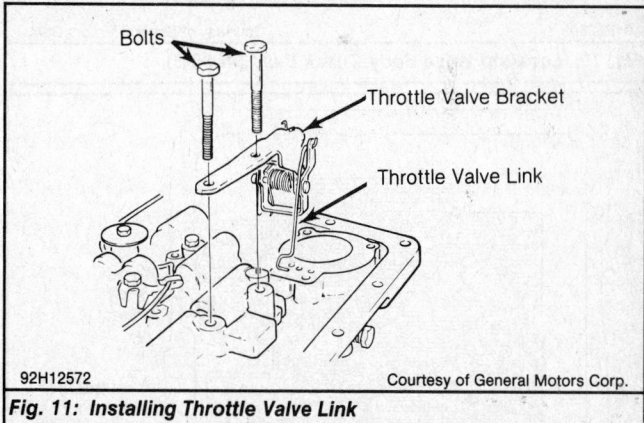

Fig. 11: *Installing Throttle Valve Link*

Installation – **1)** Coat check balls with petroleum jelly. Install check balls in proper locations on separator plate. *See Fig. 9.* Install manual valve link. Ensure manual valve link is properly seated in manual valve. *See Fig. 10.* Improper positioning may prevent vehicle operation in "D" range.

NOTE: Improper positioning of throttle valve link will result in erratic shift points or high main line oil pressure.

2) Install throttle link. Ensure link is properly positioned with lower hook facing outside of transmission case. *See Fig. 11.* Install valve body and retaining bolts. Tighten bolts to specification. To complete installation, reverse removal procedure.
3) Lubricate oil filter "O" ring with ATF before installation. Tighten all bolts to specification. See TORQUE SPECIFICATIONS table. Fill transmission with fluid.

Removal (4L60-E) – **1)** Remove transmission oil pan. Remove oil filter and "O" ring. Ensure "O" ring is removed from transmission case. **2)** Remove electrical connectors from switches and solenoids, and tag. Remove pressure switch assembly. Remove accumulator cover. Remove valve body bolts. Note length and location of bolts for installation.
3) Note direction of manual valve link. Remove manual valve link from manual valve at valve body. See Fig. 10. Remove valve body. Note location of check balls. DO NOT lose balls. See Figs. 12 and 13.

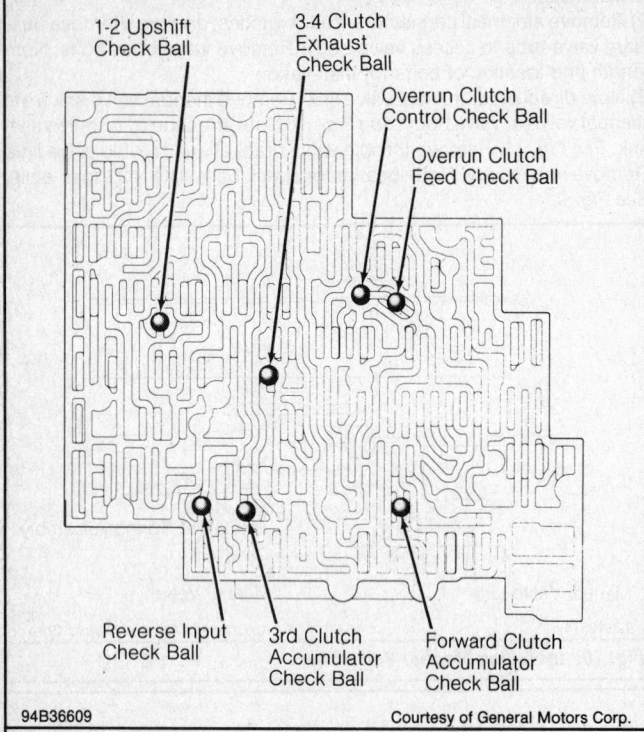

Fig. 12: Locating Valve Body Check Balls (4L60-E)

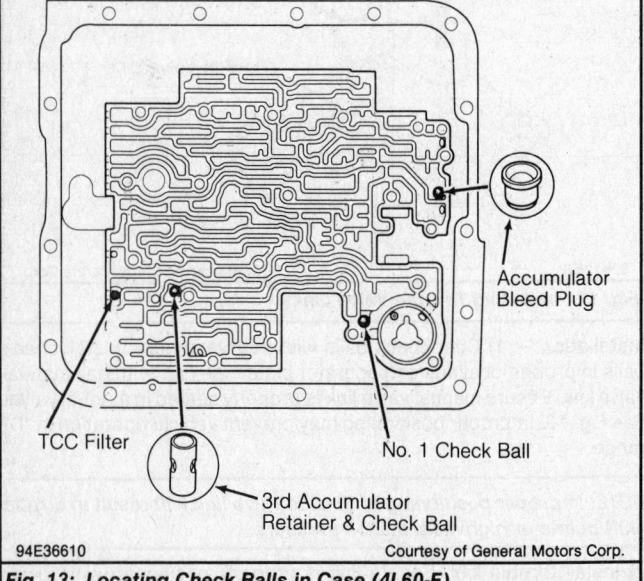

Fig. 13: Locating Check Balls in Case (4L60-E)

Installation – **1)** Coat check balls with petroleum jelly. Install check balls in proper locations on separator plate. See Figs. 12 and 13. Install manual valve link. Ensure manual valve link is properly seated in manual valve. See Fig. 10. Improper positioning may prevent vehicle operation in "D" range.

NOTE: *Improper positioning of throttle valve link will result in erratic shift points or high main line oil pressure.*

2) Install valve body and retaining bolts. Tighten bolts to specification. To complete installation, reverse removal procedure.
3) Lubricate oil filter "O" ring with ATF before installation. Tighten all bolts to specification. See TORQUE SPECIFICATIONS table. Fill transmission with fluid.

REMOVAL & INSTALLATION
See appropriate AUTOMATIC TRANSMISSION REMOVAL article in TRANSMISSION SERVICING.

TRANSMISSION DISASSEMBLY
2-4 SERVO ASSEMBLY
1) Mount transmission on bench. Remove torque converter. Install Servo Cover Compressor (J-29714) on oil pan. See Fig. 14. Compress servo cover. Remove servo cover and "O" ring.
2) Remove 2-4 servo assembly. Servo pin length should be checked before disassembling assembly to determine 2-4 band and reverse input drum wear or damage.

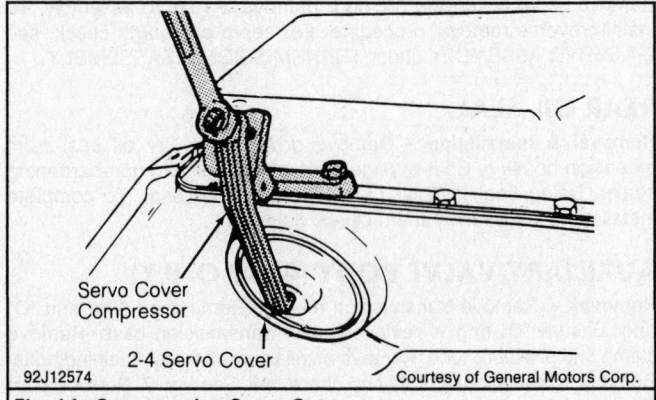

Fig. 14: Compressing Servo Cover

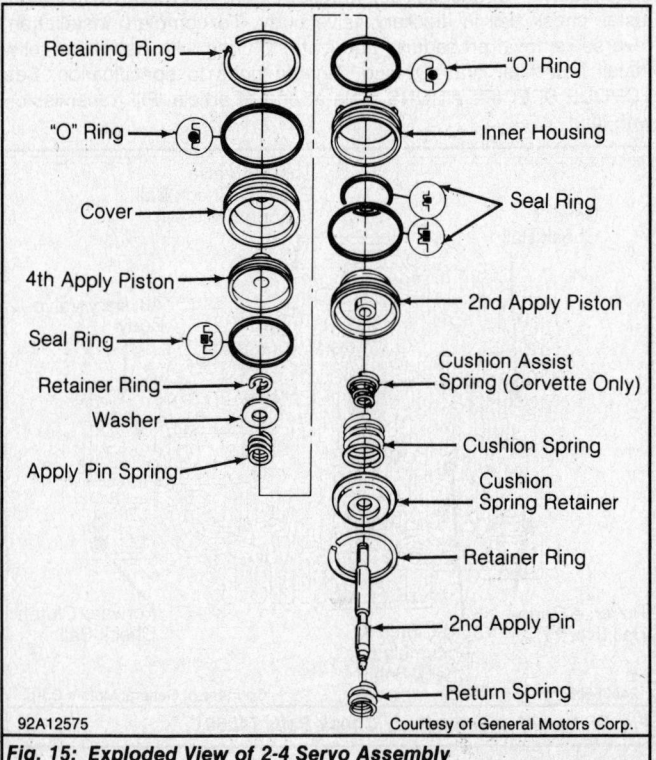

Fig. 15: Exploded View of 2-4 Servo Assembly

CHECKING SERVO PIN LENGTH

1) Remove 4th apply piston and return spring. *See Fig. 15.* Remove retainer ring, washer, apply pin spring and 2nd apply piston pin. Install Piston Compressor (J-22269-01) on 2nd apply piston. *See Fig. 16.*

2) Remove retainer ring, cushion spring and spring retainer. Install Band Apply Pin Tool (J-33037) and apply pin. *See Fig. 17.* Apply 100 INCH lbs. (11 N.m) torque.

3) White line on band apply tool should be within gauge slot if pin length is correct. If White line is not within gauge slot, inspect 2-4 band and reverse input drum for wear and damage during disassembly.

4) Servo pin length must be checked during reassembly. Servo pin is preset and must not be readjusted. See SERVO PIN SPECIFICATIONS table under 2-4 BAND & SERVO ASSEMBLY under TRANSMISSION REASSEMBLY.

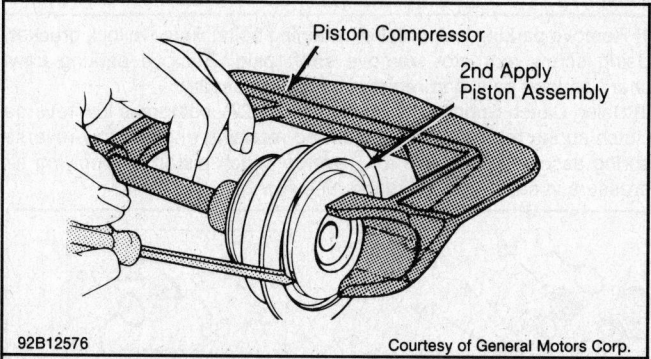

92B12576   Courtesy of General Motors Corp.

Fig. 16: Compressing 2nd Apply Piston

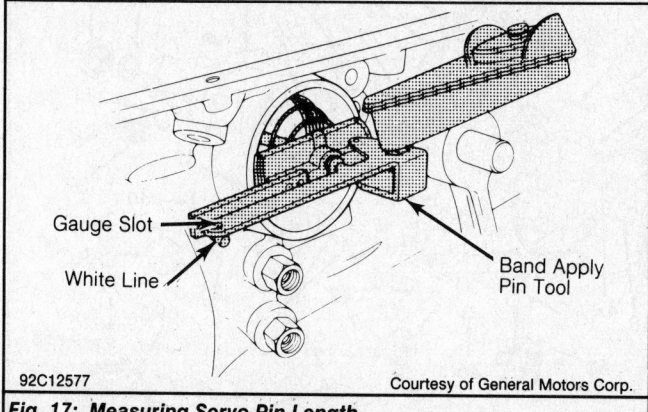

92C12577   Courtesy of General Motors Corp.

Fig. 17: Measuring Servo Pin Length

EXTENSION HOUSING

1) On 4L60 models, remove governor assembly. On models with mechanical speedometers, remove retaining bolt, washer and retainer. Remove speedometer driven gear assembly, driven gear and "O" ring.

2) On models with internal speed sensor, remove retaining bolt and washer. Remove speed sensor assembly and "O" ring. Remove extension housing and seal. Remove output shaft sleeve and "O" ring (if equipped). Speed sensor rotor must be removed from output shaft.

3) Install Gear Puller (J-21427-01) and Adapter (J-8433) on rotor. Pull rotor from output shaft. On models with mechanical speedometers, push retaining clip tab. Remove speedometer gear from output shaft.

4) On 4L60-E models, remove speed sensor assembly. Remove extension housing and seal.

VALVE BODY & AUXILIARY VALVE BODY (4L60 ONLY)

Remove valve body and auxiliary valve body (4L60). See VALVE BODY and AUXILIARY VALVE BODY (4L60 ONLY) under ON-VEHICLE SERVICE. Note bolt length and location during removal. Note check ball location for reassembly reference. *See Figs. 9 and 12.*

1-2 ACCUMULATOR & SPACER PLATES

1) Remove solenoid retaining bolts. Remove solenoid and "O" ring. Remove wiring harness, and note location for reassembly reference. Carefully remove accumulator cover retaining bolts, 1-2 accumulator cover and pin assembly.

2) Remove 1-2 accumulator piston, seal and spring. Remove spacer plate, and note check ball and filter locations. Remove spring, 3-4 accumulator piston and pin. Note spacer plate and gasket locations. *See Figs. 13 and 18* for check ball and filter locations.

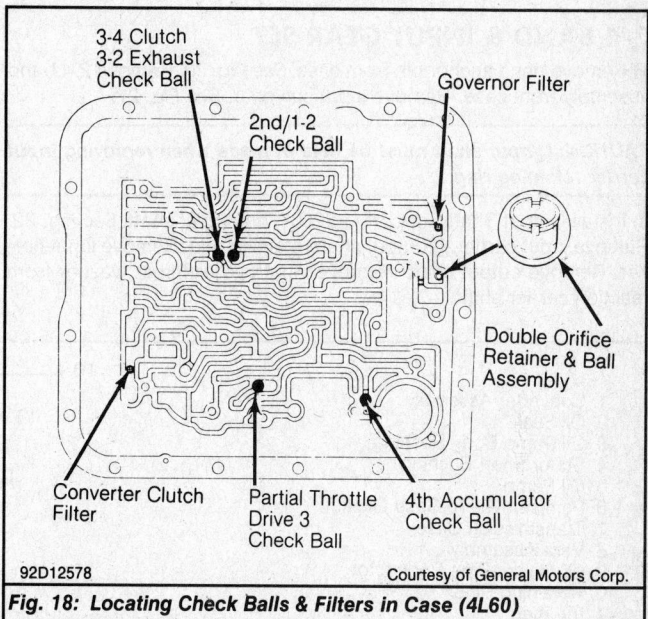

92D12578   Courtesy of General Motors Corp.

Fig. 18: Locating Check Balls & Filters in Case (4L60)

TRANSMISSION END PLAY CHECK

NOTE: Check transmission end play before disassembly. If end play is not within specification, check for damaged parts.

1) Install Pump Remover/End Play Fixture (J-24773-A) and End Play Adapter (J-25022-A) on end of turbine shaft. *See Fig. 19.*

2) Clamp dial indicator on long bolt with indicator tip on end play fixture. Measure transmission end play. Transmission end play should be .005-.036" (.13-.91 mm).

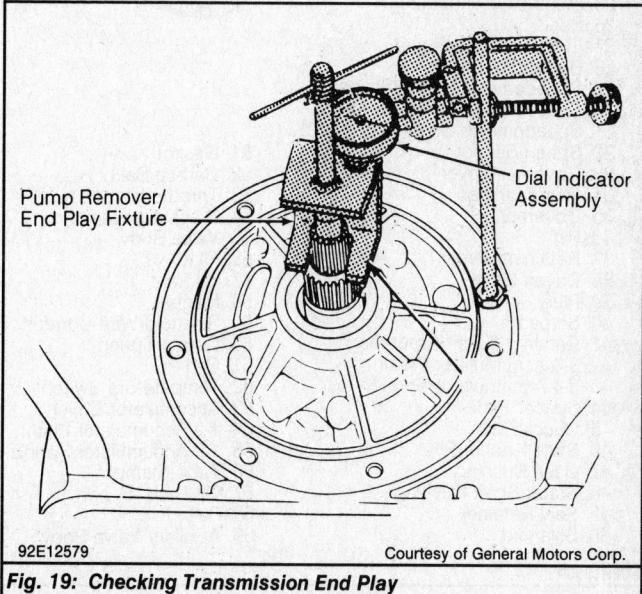

92E12579   Courtesy of General Motors Corp.

Fig. 19: Checking Transmission End Play

AUTOMATIC TRANSMISSIONS
Hydra-Matic 4L60/4L60-E (Cont.)

OIL PUMP, INPUT CLUTCH & REVERSE CLUTCH

1) Ensure TCC solenoid assembly and oil filter are removed before oil pump removal. Remove oil pump retaining bolts. Using Oil Pump Remover (J-37789-A) and Adapter (J-39119), pull pump assembly free from case.

2) Remove oil pump seal and gasket. Remove reverse input clutch-to-pump thrust washer from pump. Lift out turbine shaft with reverse and input clutch assembly.

2-4 BAND & INPUT GEAR SET

1) Remove band anchor pin from case. *See Fig. 20.* Remove 2-4 band assembly from case. Remove input sun gear. *See Fig. 21.*

CAUTION: Output shaft must be held in place when removing input carrier retaining ring.

2) Install Output Shaft Support (J-29837) on output shaft. *See Fig. 22.* Remove input carrier to output shaft retaining ring. Remove input carrier. Remove output shaft. Remove input carrier thrust washer from reaction carrier shaft.

REACTION GEAR SET

1) Remove input internal gear and reaction carrier shaft. Remove reaction sun shell and thrust washer. Remove sun shell-to-clutch race thrust washer. Remove support-to-case retaining ring.

2) Remove spring retainer from low-reverse support. Remove reaction sun gear, low-reverse clutch race, clutch roller, support assembly and reaction carrier assembly. *See Fig. 22.*

3) Remove low-reverse clutch assembly. Note locations of parts. Remove internal reaction gear and bearing assembly. Remove internal reaction support-to-case bearing assembly.

LOW-REVERSE CLUTCH

NOTE: Parking pawl may require removal to access low-reverse clutch.

1) Remove parking lock bracket retaining bolts. Remove lock bracket. Using screw extractor, remove shaft plug. Remove parking pawl shaft, parking pawl and return spring if necessary.

2) Using Clutch Spring Compressor (J-23327), compress low reverse clutch spring retainer. Remove spring retaining ring and low-reverse spring assembly. Remove low-reverse clutch piston by applying air pressure in case apply passage. *See Fig. 23.*

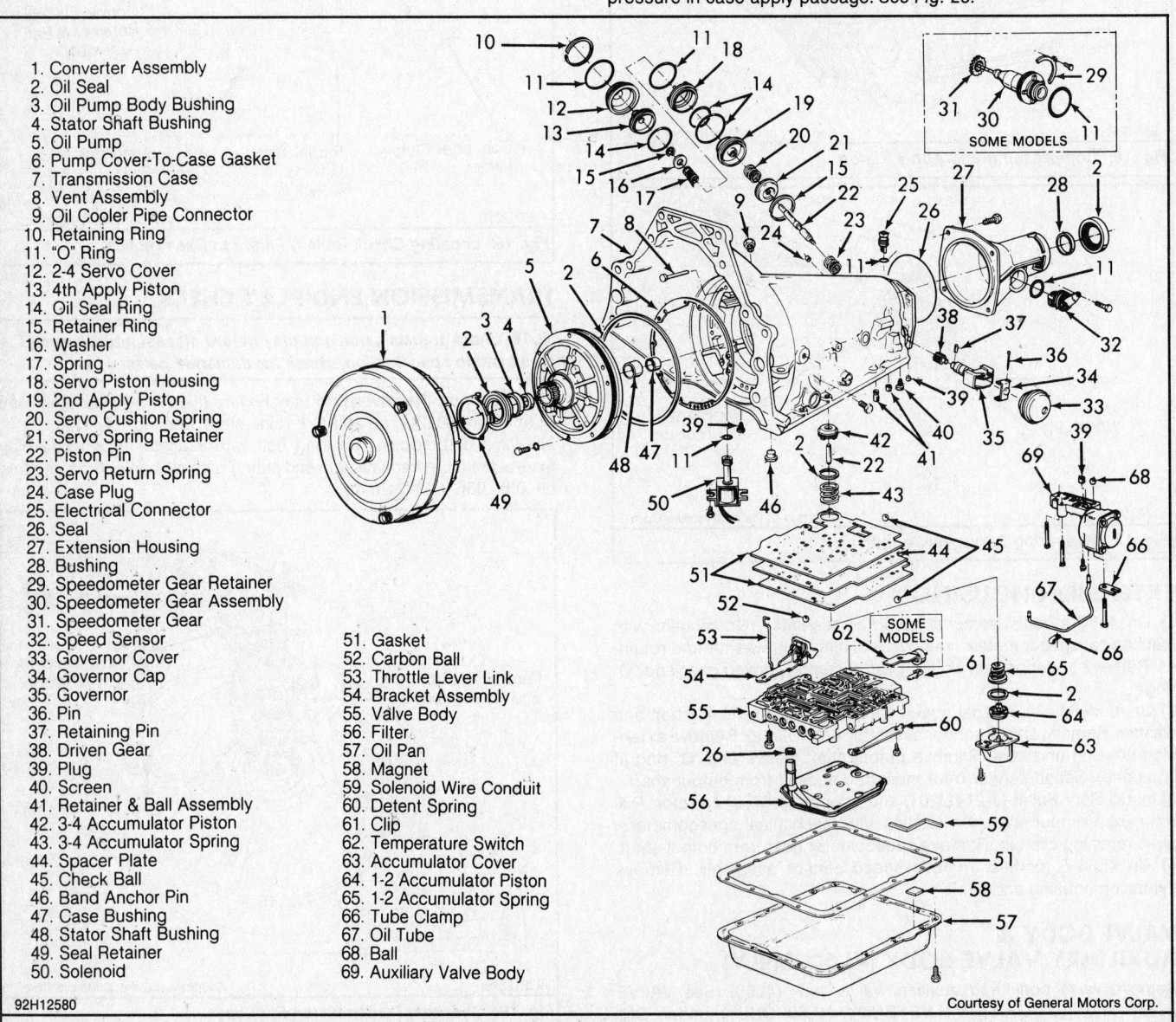

1. Converter Assembly
2. Oil Seal
3. Oil Pump Body Bushing
4. Stator Shaft Bushing
5. Oil Pump
6. Pump Cover-To-Case Gasket
7. Transmission Case
8. Vent Assembly
9. Oil Cooler Pipe Connector
10. Retaining Ring
11. "O" Ring
12. 2-4 Servo Cover
13. 4th Apply Piston
14. Oil Seal Ring
15. Retainer Ring
16. Washer
17. Spring
18. Servo Piston Housing
19. 2nd Apply Piston
20. Servo Cushion Spring
21. Servo Spring Retainer
22. Piston Pin
23. Servo Return Spring
24. Case Plug
25. Electrical Connector
26. Seal
27. Extension Housing
28. Bushing
29. Speedometer Gear Retainer
30. Speedometer Gear Assembly
31. Speedometer Gear
32. Speed Sensor
33. Governor Cover
34. Governor Cap
35. Governor
36. Pin
37. Retaining Pin
38. Driven Gear
39. Plug
40. Screen
41. Retainer & Ball Assembly
42. 3-4 Accumulator Piston
43. 3-4 Accumulator Spring
44. Spacer Plate
45. Check Ball
46. Band Anchor Pin
47. Case Bushing
48. Stator Shaft Bushing
49. Seal Retainer
50. Solenoid
51. Gasket
52. Carbon Ball
53. Throttle Lever Link
54. Bracket Assembly
55. Valve Body
56. Filter
57. Oil Pan
58. Magnet
59. Solenoid Wire Conduit
60. Detent Spring
61. Clip
62. Temperature Switch
63. Accumulator Cover
64. 1-2 Accumulator Piston
65. 1-2 Accumulator Spring
66. Tube Clamp
67. Oil Tube
68. Ball
69. Auxiliary Valve Body

92H12580

Courtesy of General Motors Corp.

Fig. 20: Exploded View Of 4L60 & 4L60-E Transmission External Components

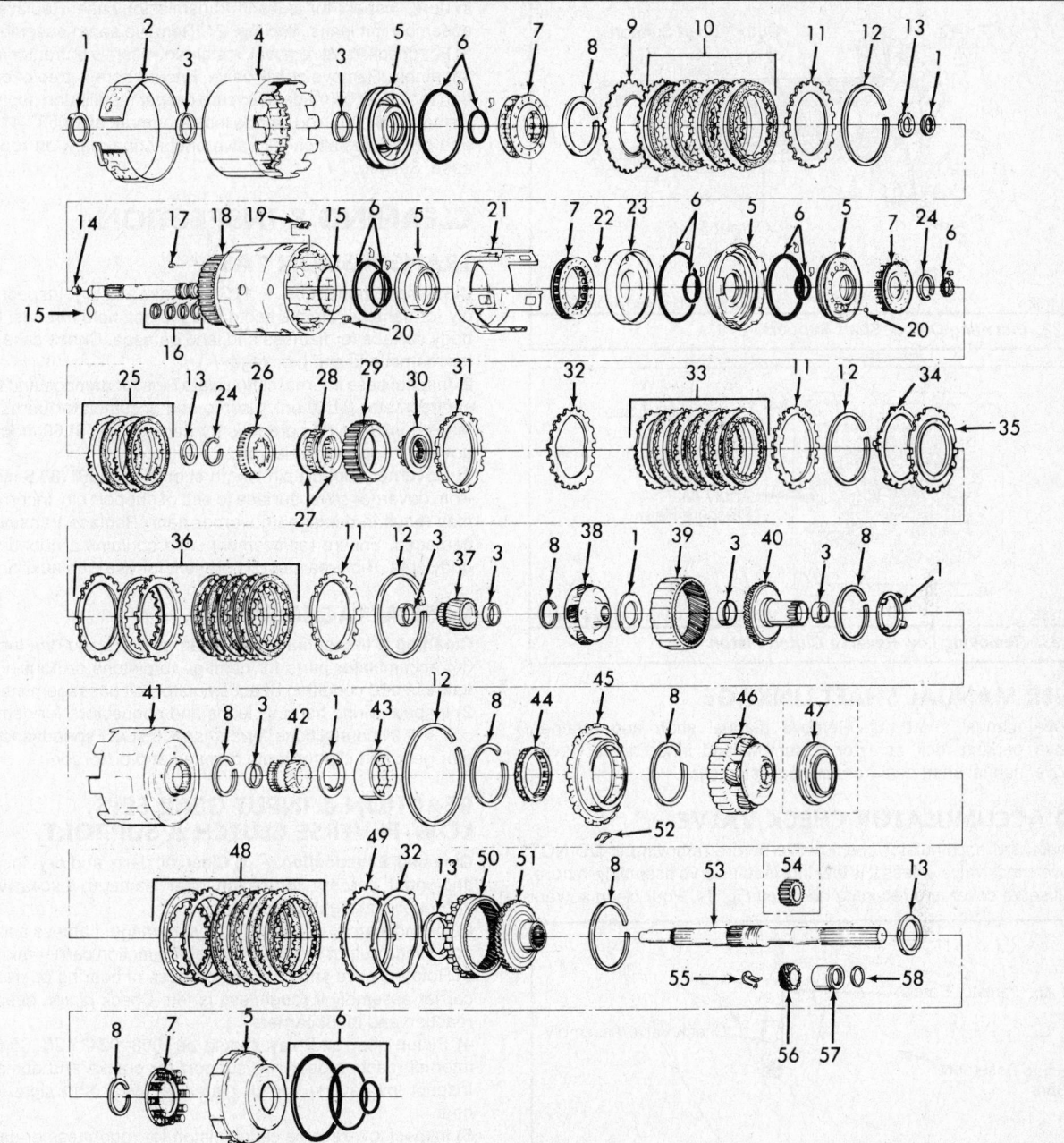

1. Thrust Washer	16. Oil Seal
2. 2-4 Band	17. Cup Plug
3. Bushing	18. Input Shaft Housing Assembly
4. Reverse Input Clutch Housing	19. Clutch Boost Spring Assembly
5. Piston	20. Check Ball
6. Seal	21. 3-4 Clutch Apply Ring
7. Spring Assembly	22. Retainer & Ball Assembly
8. Retainer Ring	23. Forward Clutch Housing
9. Belleville Plate	24. Snap Ring
10. Clutch Assembly	25. Overrun Clutch Assembly
11. Backing Plate	26. Overrun Clutch Hub
12. Retaining Ring	27. Sprag Retainer Rings
13. Bearing Assembly	28. Sprag Assembly
14. Check Valve	29. Forward Clutch Race
15. "O" Ring	30. Sprag Retainer & Race

31. Forward Clutch Apply Plate	46. Reaction Carrier Assembly
32. Waved Plate	47. Oil Deflector
33. Forward Clutch Assembly	48. Low-Reverse Clutch Assembly
34. Clutch Retainer Plate	49. Spacer Plate
35. 3-4 Clutch Apply Plate	50. Internal Reaction Gear
36. 3-4 Clutch Assembly	51. Internal Reaction Gear Support
37. Input Sun Gear	52. Retainer Spring
38. Input Carrier Assembly	53. Output Shaft
39. Input Internal Gear	54. Rotor
40. Reaction Carrier Shaft	55. Clip
41. Reaction Sun Gear Shell	56. Speedometer Drive Gear
42. Reaction Sun Gear	57. Output Shaft Sleeve
43. Low-Reverse Clutch Race	58. Output Shaft Seal
44. Low-Reverse Roller Clutch	
45. Support	

92I12581

Courtesy of General Motors Corp.

Fig. 21: Exploded View Of 4L60 & 4L60-E Transmission Internal Components

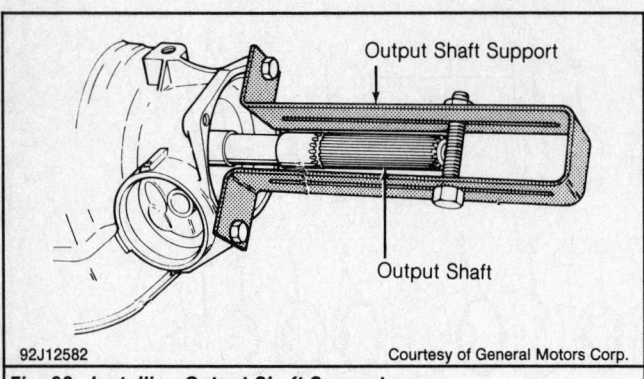

92J12582   Courtesy of General Motors Corp.

Fig. 22: Installing Output Shaft Support

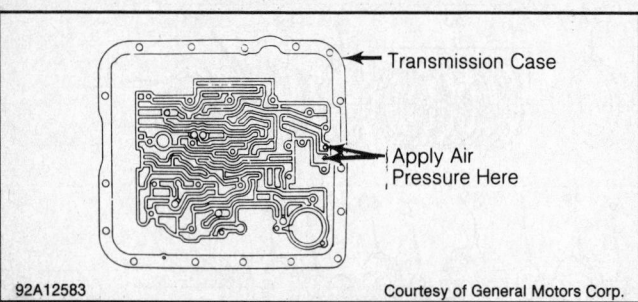

92A12583   Courtesy of General Motors Corp.

Fig. 23: Removing Low-Reverse Clutch Piston

INNER MANUAL SHAFT LINKAGE

Remove manual shaft nut. Remove manual shaft and retainer. Remove parking lock actuator assembly and inner detent lever. Remove manual shaft seal from transmission case.

3RD ACCUMULATOR CHECK VALVE

1) Check 3rd accumulator check valve before removing it. DO NOT remove check valve unless it is leaking. Install servo assembly in bore. Install servo cover and retaining ring. *See Fig. 14.* Pour clean solvent

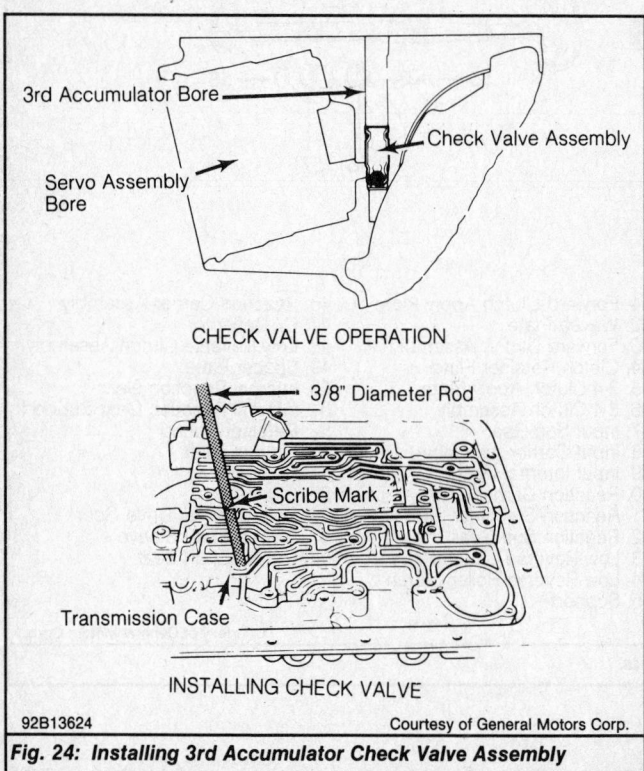

92B13624   Courtesy of General Motors Corp.

Fig. 24: Installing 3rd Accumulator Check Valve Assembly

in bore. Inspect for leaks in transmission case. Replace check valve assembly if it leaks. *See Fig. 24.* Remove servo assembly.

2) For check valve removal, install No. 4 screw extractor in check valve assembly. Remove check valve. Ensure bore is free of burrs. Installation tool must be made to ensure proper installation depth is obtained. Using a 3/8" O.D. rod, scribe indicator mark at 1.653" (41.98 mm) from end of rod. Install check valve until scribe mark on rod is flush with case. *See Fig. 24.*

CLEANING & INSPECTION

TRANSMISSION CASE

Cleaning & Inspection – 1) Clean case and dry. Inspect case assembly for damage, cracks and damaged bolt hole threads. Inspect valve body surface for flatness and land damage. Check case oil passages for restrictions and blockage.

2) Inspect case internal clutch plate lugs for damage and wear. Inspect speedometer (4L60 only), servo and accumulator bores for damage. Inspect all snap ring grooves for damage. On 4L60 models, measure governor support pin length.

3) Governor support pin length should be 3.30" (83.8 mm) measured from governor cover surface to end of support pin. Incorrect pin length may result in damaged governor gear. Replace transmission case if damaged. Ensure replacement case contains a ribbed area in valve body area. Rib area must be present for use with auxiliary valve body.

CASE ATTACHMENTS

Cleaning & Inspection – 1) Clean all parts and dry. Inspect 1-2 and 3-4 accumulator parts for damage to pistons or housing. Inspect for flatness and condition of accumulator, oil passage plate and gasket.

2) Inspect wiring harness leads and connectors for damage. Inspect coil and all connections for damage. Inspect speedsensor/speedometer gear and clip for tooth damage and distortion.

REACTION & INPUT GEAR SETS, LOW-REVERSE CLUTCH & SUPPORT

Cleaning & Inspection – 1) Clean all parts and dry. Inspect reaction and input carriers for pinion gear damage, excessive wear and improper staking of pinion pins.

2) Inspect carrier bearings for heat damage, flatness and roller condition. Place output shaft sleeve inside reaction carrier and input carrier.

3) Rotate sleeve and note smoothness of bearing operation. Replace carrier assembly if roughness is felt. Check pinion gear end play on reaction and input carriers.

4) Pinion gear end play should be .008-.024" (.20-.61 mm). Inspect internal reaction gear and support for cracks and damaged splines. Inspect low-reverse clutch plates for wear and signs of excessive heat.

5) Inspect low-reverse clutch piston for roughness or damage in seal ring area. Inspect retainer ring and spring assembly for damage. Inspect sun and internal gears and supports for spline and bushing wear and damage. Replace damaged parts as necessary.

COMPONENT DISASSEMBLY & REASSEMBLY

REVERSE INPUT CLUTCH

Disassembly – 1) Remove retaining ring from reverse input clutch housing. Remove selective backing plate, steel clutch plates, friction plates and Belleville plate. *See Fig. 21.* Note number of clutch plates used. Compress reverse input spring assembly.

2) Remove retaining ring. Remove spring assembly. Remove piston and seals. Thickness of friction plates should be .068-.074" (1.73-1.88 mm).

Inspection – Inspect all plates for damage, distortion, flatness and burred edges. Inspect spring retainer for distortion. Check piston for deformation or damage. Inspect clutch housing bushings for wear. Inspect clutch housing for dishing. Replace worn or damaged parts as necessary.

1. Valve Body
2. Pin
3. Throttle Valve
4. Spring
5. Throttle Valve Plunger
6. Sleeve
7. 3-4 Valve
8. 3-4 Relay Valve
9. Plug
10. Cup Plug
11. 4th Clutch Pressure Switch
12. Throttle Valve Limit Valve
13. Throttle Valve Plug
14. Retainer
15. 1-2 Accumulator Valve
16. Valve Sleeve
17. Line Bias Valve
18. 3-4 Pulse Pressure Switch
19. 3-2 Control Valve
20. 3rd Clutch Pressure Switch
21. Manual Valve
22. T.C.C. Pressure Switch
23. Modulator Downshift Valve
24. Modulator Upshift Valve
25. 3-4 Throttle Valve Sleeve
26. 3-4 Throttle Valve Spring
27. 3-4 Throttle Valve
28. 3-4 Shift Valve
29. 2-3 Shift Valve
30. 2-3 Throttle Valve
31. 2-3 Throttle Valve Spring
32. 2-3 Throttle Valve Sleeve
33. 1-2 Throttle Valve Sleeve
34. 1-2 Throttle Valve Spring
35. 1-2 Throttle Valve
36. 1-2 Shift Valve

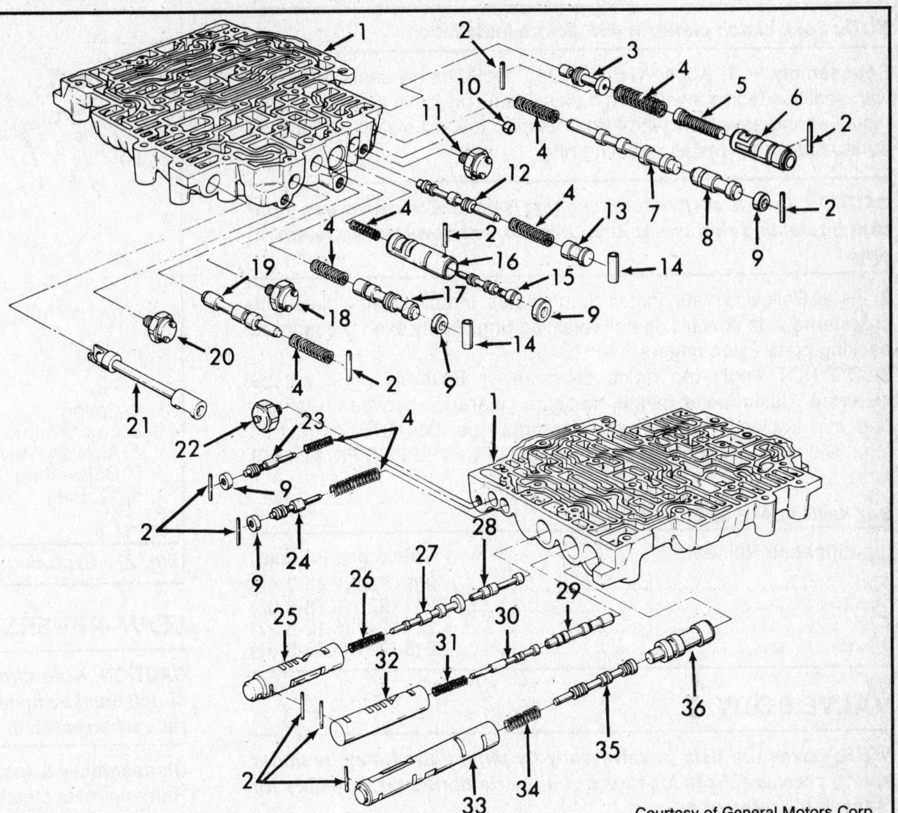

92C13625

Courtesy of General Motors Corp.

Fig. 25: Exploded View Of Valve Body (4L60)

1. Valve Body
2. Pin
3. Forward Accumulator Piston
4. Forward Accumulator Spring
5. Forward Accumulator Cover
6. Low Overrun Valve
7. Spring
8. Forward Abuse Valve
9. 1-2 Shift Solenoid
10. 1-2 Shift Valve
11. Bore Plug
12. 2-3 Shift Solenoid
13. 2-3 Shuttle Valve
14. Retainer
15. 2-3 Shift Valve
16. 1-2 Accumulator Valve Sleeve
17. 1-2 Accumulator Valve
18. 1-2 Accumulator Valve Spring
19. Pressure Control Solenoid
20. Actuator Feed Limit Valve Spring
21. Manual Valve
22. Actuator Feed Limit Valve Spring
23. 3-2 Control Solenoid
24. 3-2 Control Valve Spring
25. 3-2 Control Valve
26. 3-2 Downshift Valve Spring
27. 3-2 Downshift Valve
28. Reverse Abuse Valve Spring
29. Reverse Abuse Valve
30. 3-4 Shift Valve Spring
31. 3-4 Shift Valve
32. 3-4 Relay Valve
33. 4-3 Sequence Valve
34. 4-3 Sequence Valve Spring
35. Converter Clutch Signal Valve

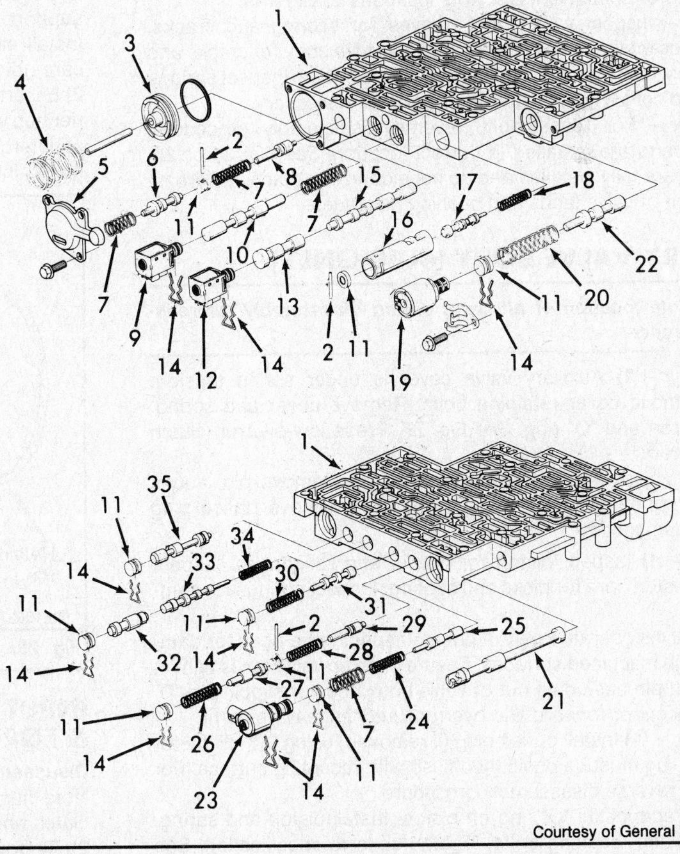

94E36636

Courtesy of General Motors Corp.

Fig. 26: Exploded View Of Valve Body (4L60-E)

NOTE: Soak clutch plates in ATF before installation.

Reassembly – 1) Apply ATF to piston seals. Install seals on piston with seal lips facing away from plates. Install piston in clutch housing. Install spring assembly with large opening toward piston. Compress spring assembly. Install retaining ring.

CAUTION: Ensure correct retaining ring is used. Ensure reverse input clutch retaining ring is not interchanged with low-reverse retaining ring.

2) Install Belleville plate. Install clutch plates. Install backing plate with chamfered side upward. Install retaining ring. Apply even pressure to backing plate using fingers.

3) DO NOT apply too much pressure or Belleville plate will be distorted. Using feeler gauge, measure clearance between retaining ring and backing plate. Clearance should be .040-.076" (1.02-1.94 mm). Select backing plate. See BACKING PLATE SPECIFICATIONS table.

BACKING PLATE SPECIFICATIONS

Identification Number	Thickness In. (mm)
5	.293-.299 (7.44-7.59)
6	.267-.273 (6.78-6.93)
7	.241-.247 (6.12-6.27)
8	.215-.221 (5.46-5.61)

VALVE BODY

NOTE: Valves are held in valve body by pins. Valves may be under spring pressure. Note locations of all parts during disassembly for reassembly reference.

Disassembly – Remove valve train, and note direction of valve installation. *See Fig. 25 or 26.* Remove all valve pins. Remove pressure switches and/or shift solenoids. Note locations of all parts.

Inspection – Inspect valves and sleeves for scoring and cracks. Ensure valves move freely in bores. Inspect valve body for cracks and scored bores. Inspect machined surfaces for damage. Inspect springs for damaged coils. Replace damaged parts as necessary.

Reassembly – For reassembly, reverse disassembly procedure. Ensure all parts are installed in correct location. *See Fig. 25 or 26.* Ensure pins are fully installed and do not extend into machined areas. Note position of valve lands and bushing passages.

AUXILIARY VALVE BODY (4L60 ONLY)

CAUTION: Note location of all parts during disassembly for reassembly reference.

Disassembly – 1) Auxiliary valve cover is under spring tension. Carefully remove cover retaining bolts. Remove cover and spring. Remove piston and "O" ring. *See Fig. 27.* Press low-overrun clutch valve downward.

2) Remove pin, spring and low-overrun valve. Remove pin, abuse valve stop, spring and abuse valve. DO NOT remove orifice plug unless it is damaged.

Inspection – 1) Inspect piston for cracks and roughness. Inspect valves and piston bore for nicks and scoring. Inspect springs for damaged coils.

2) Ensure valves operate freely in bores. Inspect valve body for damaged or rough machined surfaces. Ensure overrun valve pin is tight in valve body. If pin has come out of valve body, loss or slipping in "D" range may occur or forward and overrun clutches may be burnt.

Reassembly – 1) Install orifice plug (if removed) using 3/8" diameter rod. Orifice plug must be positioned flush with mounting surface. For reassembly, reverse disassembly procedure.

2) Lubricate and install "O" ring on piston. Install piston and spring. Install cover and retaining bolts. Tighten bolts to specification. See TORQUE SPECIFICATIONS table.

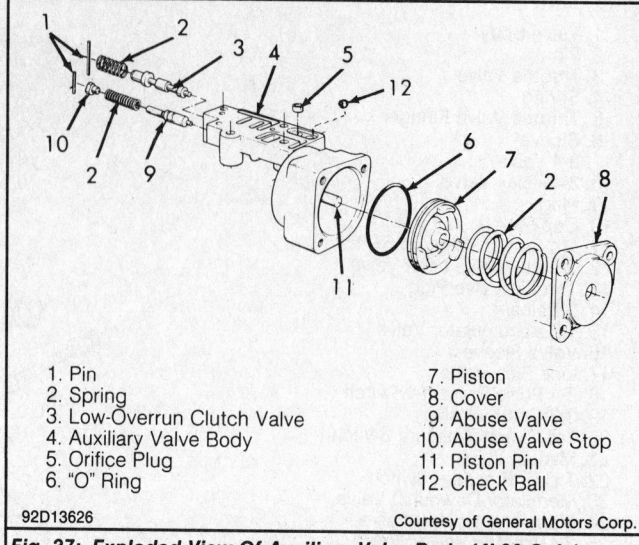

1. Pin
2. Spring
3. Low-Overrun Clutch Valve
4. Auxiliary Valve Body
5. Orifice Plug
6. "O" Ring
7. Piston
8. Cover
9. Abuse Valve
10. Abuse Valve Stop
11. Piston Pin
12. Check Ball

92D13626   Courtesy of General Motors Corp.

Fig. 27: Exploded View Of Auxiliary Valve Body (4L60 Only)

LOW-REVERSE SUPPORT ASSEMBLY

CAUTION: Note direction roller clutch is installed in support. Roller clutch must be installed in proper direction to provide lockup of inner race when rotated.

Disassembly & Inspection – Remove inner race and retainer ring. Remove roller clutch assembly. Check inner race for damage and surface finish. *See Fig. 28.* Inspect roller and springs for damage and distortion. Inspect support for loose cam, cracks and damaged surface finish. Replace damaged parts as necessary.

Reassembly – 1) Install roller clutch assembly in low-reverse support. *See Fig. 28.* Place support in case with hub facing downward. Install inner race. Rotate inner race while pushing downward. Use care not to damage roller and springs during installation.

2) Ensure inner race is fully seated. Bottom tangs will be flush with carrier hub when fully seated. Inner race should rotate clockwise and lock counterclockwise with clutch hub downward. Insert support retainer spring into case between case lug and open notch in support.

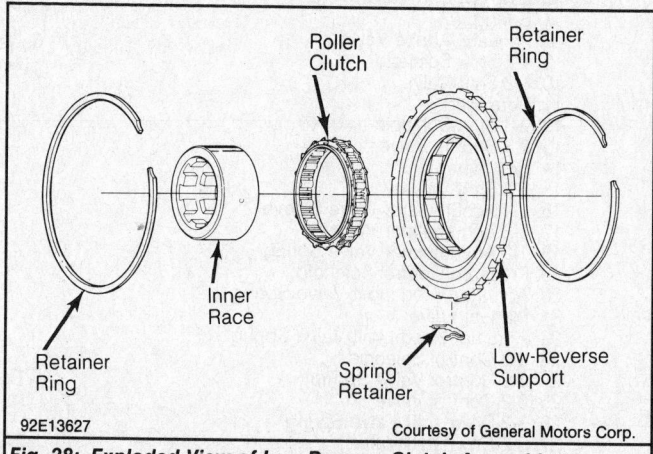

92E13627   Courtesy of General Motors Corp.

Fig. 28: Exploded View of Low-Reverse Clutch Assembly

INPUT CLUTCH & FORWARD CLUTCH HUB ASSEMBLY

Disassembly – 1) Remove backing plate. Remove 3-4 clutch plates. Note number and locations of parts. Remove 3-4 apply plate and clutch ring retainer. *See Fig. 21.*

2) Remove forward clutch retainer ring, and remove backing plate. Remove forward clutch sprag assembly and bearing. Remove input housing seal. Remove forward clutch plates. Note number and locations of parts.

3) Remove waved and apply plates. Remove overrun clutch plates (2 steel and 2 friction). Compress overrun clutch spring retainer.

4) Remove retainer ring. Remove overrun piston and forward clutch piston. Remove seals from pistons. Note direction of seals. Remove forward clutch housing. Remove 3-4 spring, 3-4 apply ring and piston. Remove "O" ring from input housing. Remove turbine shaft seal rings.

5) Remove forward clutch race. Remove snap ring and overrun clutch hub. Remove sprag retainer and race. Note direction race is installed. Use care not to lose rollers from roller cage.

Inspection – 1) Inspect sprag assembly for weak or damaged springs and retainers and worn rollers. Inspect overrun clutch hub for spline damage, excessive wear and open oil passages. Inspect retainer and race for spline damage, surface wear and damaged ring grooves.

2) Replace sprag assembly if damaged. Inspect forward clutch race for spline damage, excessive wear and open oil passages. Inspect input shaft and housing for spline damage, wear and open feed passages.

3) Inspect 3 sealing balls located in rear of turbine shaft for tightness. Turbine shaft contains one open lubrication hole. Ensure orifice plug is installed.

4) Inspect check valve located in end of turbine shaft for tightness in shaft. Check ball must move freely. Replace check valve if damaged. Inspect turbine shaft seal areas for roughness and burrs.

5) Inspect check ball located in input housing for free operation. Inspect pistons for wear, damage and porosity. Inspect spring assemblies for damage and distortion.

6) Inspect steel and friction clutch plates for damage. Inspect retainer rings for distortion and damage. Check backing plates for flatness and distortion. Inspect clutch apply rings for distortion and damaged tangs.

7) Inspect forward clutch housing check ball for proper operation (if equipped). Inspect housing for cracks and damage in seal areas. Inspect bearings for excessive wear, flatness, damage and flat rollers.

Reassembly – 1) If turbine shaft check valve requires replacement, straighten tangs of retainer and remove check ball. Using No. 4 screw extractor, remove check valve. Remove retainer from shaft by turning.

2) Position check valve in turbine shaft. Using a 3/8" diameter rod, drive retainer and check valve assembly into shaft. Check valve must be positioned 1/8" below top surface of turbine shaft. Ensure check ball is loose.

3) For input housing check ball replacement, drive retainer and ball assembly from housing using 1/4" diameter drift. Install NEW check ball assembly using 1/4" drift. Check ball assembly should seat on housing shoulder. Assemble forward clutch sprag assembly.

4) Install sprag assembly in forward clutch race. Notches located in sprag must face upward. See Fig. 29. Install retainer ring on sprag retainer and race. Retainer ring flange must face away from retainer and race.

5) Hold outer race in left hand. Support sprag assembly. Install sprag retainer and race in sprag assembly. Rotate retainer and race left. Install remaining retainer ring. Install overrun clutch hub. Install snap ring.

6) Check sprag operation. Holding forward clutch race, rotate overrun clutch hub. Overrun clutch hub should turn freely clockwise and lock counterclockwise. See Fig. 29.

7) Place input clutch housing with turbine shaft downward. Install 3-4 piston seals with lips facing away from hub. Install 3-4 piston in input housing.

8) Install 3-4 clutch apply ring. Install "O" ring in input clutch housing. Install forward clutch housing. Install seals on forward clutch piston with lips facing away from tangs.

9) Install forward clutch piston in forward clutch housing. Install 3-4 spring on 3-4 clutch apply ring. Install forward clutch assembly on 3-4 spring assembly. Align forward clutch piston legs with tangs of 3-4 apply ring. Install Seal Protector (J-29883) on input housing.

10) Install 3-4 apply ring and forward clutch assembly in input clutch housing. Hold apply ring tangs while installing. DO NOT allow forward clutch piston to separate from assembly. Ensure assembly is firmly seated.

11) Install Seal Protector (J-29883) on input housing. Install overrun clutch piston with hub facing upward. If fully seated, overrun piston should be 3/16" below top of snap ring groove in input housing hub.

12) Install spring assembly on overrun piston. Compress springs, and install snap ring. Install input housing seal.

NOTE: Soak clutch plates in ATF before installation. Coat all seals and "O" rings with ATF. Coat thrust washers and bearings with petroleum jelly.

---

13) Install 4 overrun clutch plates, starting with steel plate. Align wide notches with case lugs. Install remaining clutch plates, alternating steel and friction plates.

14) Install bearing assembly on input clutch hub. Bearing inner race must face input housing hub. Ensure bearing is centered. Align clutch plate tabs. Install forward clutch sprag assembly in input housing. Align overrun clutch hub with clutch plates.

15) Install forward clutch apply plate in input housing. Install waved forward clutch plate. Ensure all plates are aligned with input housing tangs. Starting with steel plate, install clutch plates, alternating steel and friction plates. Install backing plate and retainer ring. See FORWARD CLUTCH PLATE SPECIFICATIONS table.

16) Using 2 feeler gauges, measure clearance between backing plate and retainer ring. Clearance should be .030-.063" (.75-1.60 mm). Install proper size backing plate with chamfered side upward. See FORWARD CLUTCH BACKING PLATE SPECIFICATIONS table. Install retainer ring.

FORWARD CLUTCH PLATE SPECIFICATIONS

Plate Type	Quantity	Thickness In. (mm)
Apply	1	.169 (4.29)
Waved Steel	1	.070 (1.78)
Flat Steel	5	.090 (2.29)
Friction	5	.070 (1.78)
Backing	1	Selective

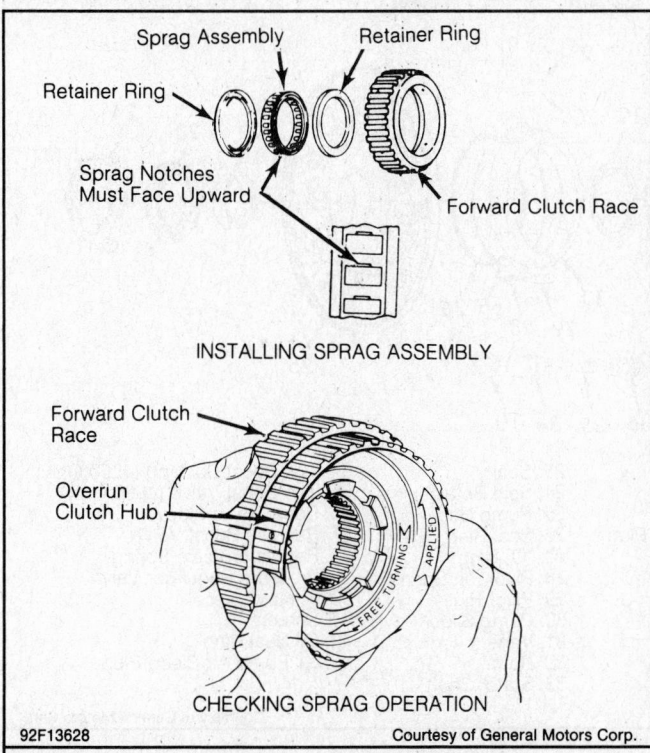

Sprag Assembly
Retainer Ring
Retainer Ring
Sprag Notches Must Face Upward
Forward Clutch Race

INSTALLING SPRAG ASSEMBLY

Forward Clutch Race
Overrun Clutch Hub
APPLIED
FREE TURNING

CHECKING SPRAG OPERATION

92F13628   Courtesy of General Motors Corp.

Fig. 29: Installing & Checking Clutch Sprag Assembly

FORWARD CLUTCH BACKING PLATE SPECIFICATIONS

Identification Letter	Thickness In. (mm)
A	.274-.278 (6.96-7.06)
B	.251-.255 (6.38-6.48)
C	.228-.232 (5.79-5.89)
D	.205-.208 (5.20-5.28)
E	.180-.185 (4.57-4.70)

17) Install 3-4 clutch plates and backing plate. Install clutch plates and backing plate with chamfered side upward. Install retainer ring.

18) Measure clearance between backing plate and first friction plate. Clearance should be .060-.095" (1.52-2.42 mm) on 4L60 or .035-.083" (.90-2.10 mm) on 4L60-E.

3-4 CLUTCH PLATE SPECIFICATIONS (4L60 ONLY)

Plate Type	Quantity	Thickness In. (mm)
Stepped Apply	1	.183 (4.65)
Flat Steel [1]	1	.070 (1.78)
Flat Steel [2]	5 Or 6	.070 (1.78)
Friction [3]	5 Or 6	.079 (2.01)
Backing	1	Selective

[1] – Same spline configuration as apply plate.
[2] – 6 plates on SAM models.
[3] – 5 plates on SAM models.

3-4 CLUTCH PLATE SPECIFICATIONS (4L60-E ONLY)

Plate Type	Quantity	Thickness In. (mm)
Stepped Apply	1	.220 (5.60)
Flat Steel [1]	1	.070 (1.78)
Flat Steel	5	.107 (2.71)
Friction	6	.079 (2.01)
Backing	1	Selective

[1] – Same spline configuration as apply plate.

19) Select proper backing plate to obtain correct clearance. See 3-4 BACKING PLATE SPECIFICATIONS table. Air check all clutches at feed holes in turbine shaft.

20) During overrun clutch test, air pressure will blow past forward clutch piston seals and exit out forward clutch feed hole in turbine shaft. Turbine shaft seals require sizing and should be installed just before oil pump installation.

3-4 BACKING PLATE SPECIFICATIONS (4L60 ONLY)

Identification	Thickness In. (mm)
5 [1]	.251-.259 (6.38-6.58)
6 [1]	.218-.226 (5.54-5.74)
7 [2]	.186-.194 (4.72-4.93)
8 [2]	.153-.161 (3.89-4.09)

[1] – FBM and SAM models only.
[2] – Except FBM and SAM models.

3-4 BACKING PLATE SPECIFICATIONS (4L60-E ONLY)

Identification	Thickness In. (mm)
A	.224-.231 (5.68-5.88)
B	.187-.196 (4.76-4.99)
C	.153-.161 (3.89-4.09)

OIL PUMP ASSEMBLY

Disassembly – 1) Remove reverse input clutch drum-to-pump thrust washer, pump-to-case gasket and pump-to-case oil seal ring from pump assembly. Remove pump cover retaining bolts. Separate pump cover from pump body.

CAUTION: Pump slide spring and pressure relief spring rivet are under high pressure. To prevent possible injury, cover springs during removal.

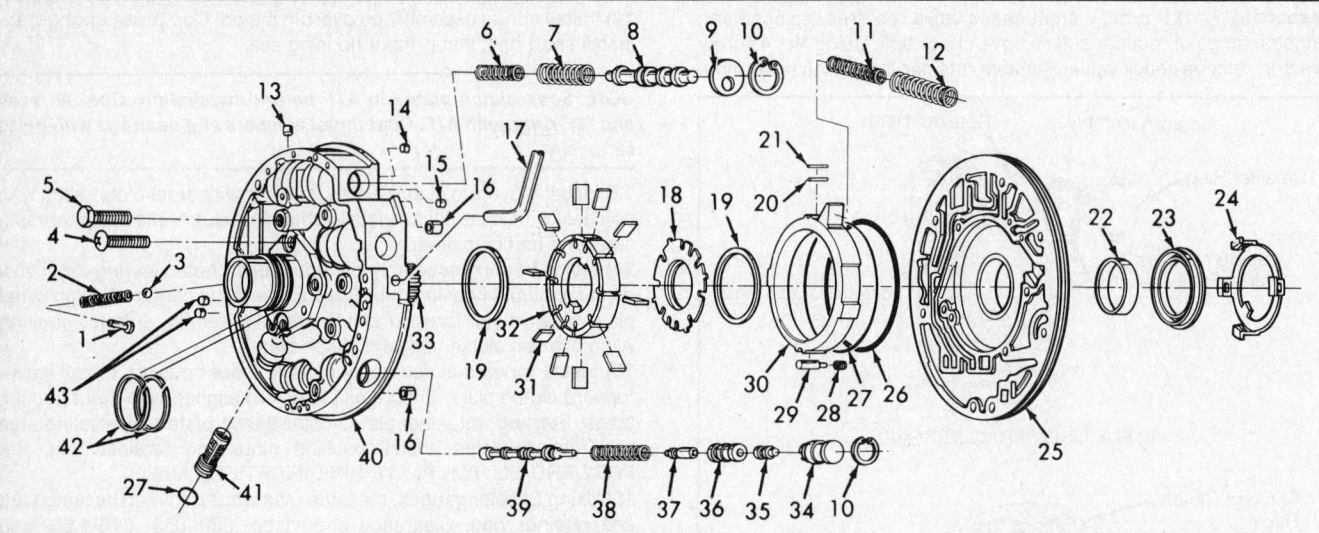

1. Rivet	12. Pump Slide Spring (Outer)	23. Seal	34. T.V. Boost Bushing (4L60 Only)
2. Pressure Relief Spring	13. Oil Pump Cover Plug	24. Seal Retainer	35. T.V. Boost Valve (4L60 Only)
3. Check Ball	14. Oil Pump Cooler Feed Plug	25. Pump Body	36. Boost Valve Sleeve
4. Stator Shaft Screw	15. Oil Pump Converter Clutch Signal Plug	26. Seal Ring	37. Reverse Boost Valve
5. Cover-To-Body Bolt	16. Retainer & Ball Assembly	27. "O" Ring	38. Regulator Valve Spring
6. Converter Clutch Spring (Inner)	17. Auxiliary Accumulator Valve Tube	28. Pivot Pin Spring	39. Pressure Regulator Valve
7. Converter Clutch Spring (Outer)	18. Rotor Guide	29. Pivot Pin	40. Pump Cover
8. Converter Clutch Valve	19. Pump Vane Ring	30. Pump Slide	41. Screen
9. Valve Stop	20. Seal Support	31. Vane	42. Oil Seal Ring
10. Snap Ring	21. Pump Slide Seal	32. Rotor	43. Oil Pump Air Bleed Plug
11. Pump Slide Spring (Inner)	22. Bushing	33. Stator Shaft	

94G36703

Fig. 30: Exploded View Of Oil Pump Assembly

2) Using needle-nose pliers, compress pump slide spring. Remove from pump by pulling straight out. Remove pump vane rings, pump vanes, pump rotor and rotor guide from pump pocket.

CAUTION: Keep pump vanes in installed position. If pump vanes are installed upside-down or backwards, they will quickly wear out.

3) Remove slide from pump pocket. Remove slide seal and seal support from pump slide. *See Fig. 30.* Remove pivot pin and pivot pin spring. Remove seal ring and "O" ring from pump slide. Remove seal retainer and seal from pump body.

4) Check condition of pump bushing. If bushing is in good condition, DO NOT remove it. Push inward on converter clutch valve stop to compress spring. Remove snap ring. Remove valve stop, converter clutch apply valve and springs.

5) Using a small punch, remove pressure relief spring retaining rivet. Remove relief spring and ball. Remove oil screen and "O" ring from pump cover. Using a small screwdriver, compress throttle valve boost valve bushing. Remove snap ring.

6) On 4L60 models, remove Throttle Valve (T.V.) boost bushing and throttle valve boost valve. On all models, remove reverse boost valve sleeve. Remove reverse boost valve, pressure regulator valve spring and pressure regulator valve.

Inspection – 1) Inspect all valves, springs, sleeves and bushings for chips, burrs, distortion and freeness in bores. Check pressure relief ball and spring for damage and distortion. Low main line pressure will exist if ball and spring are damaged.

NOTE: Use compressed air to blow out all passages, especially converter passage between TCC apply valve and stator support shaft.

2) Inspect pump cover screen and "O" ring for wear and damage. Clean pump body and cover. Check all bores for obstructions. Inspect mating sides of cover and body for scoring, flatness and damage between channels. Check channels for dirt and damaged passages. Inspect stator shaft and pump body bushings for damage.

3) Inspect rotor and slide for scoring, cracks and damage. Check rotor guide and pump vane rings for excessive wear and damage. Inspect all seals for damage. Measure pump rotor and slide thickness in undamaged area if replacement is required. Replacement parts must be same size as those removed to provide proper end clearance.

4) Lay pump body flat on bench, and install rotor into rotor and slide cavity. Lay straight edge over pump body and rotor. Use feeler gauge to check rotor-to-stator (cover) clearance. Specification is .0010-.0015" (.025-.038 mm). If pump cover is replaced, ensure reverse input feed hole in stator hub is same diameter as in hub removed.

Reassembly – 1) Install "O" ring and seal ring in groove on back side of pump slide. Retain seal ring using petroleum jelly. Install pivot pin and spring in pump body. Install pump slide. Notch in pump slide must align with pivot pin hole and with flat oil seal ring facing downward in pump pocket. Install slide seal and support.

CAUTION: Keep pump vanes in installed position. If pump vanes are installed upside-down or backwards, they will quickly wear out.

2) Install pump vane ring into pump pocket. Coat rotor guide with petroleum jelly. Install rotor guide on rotor. Install rotor and guide into pump pocket with guide toward pump pocket. Install vanes in rotor. Install vane guide ring. Compress pump slide spring and install into pump pocket. All parts must be even with pump body surface. Install "O" ring on pump screen, and install screen in pump cover with seal end last.

3) Install seal in pump body. Install seal retainer. Install pressure relief check ball and spring in pump cover. Install retaining rivet. Install converter clutch valve springs and converter clutch valve. Install valve stop and snap ring. Install pressure regulator valve and spring in pump cover. *See Fig. 30.*

4) On 4L60 models, coat T.V. boost valve with petroleum jelly. Install T.V. boost valve in throttle valve bushing. Long area on valve must be positioned in large hole of bushing. On all models, coat reverse boost

valve with petroleum jelly. Install reverse boost valve in boost valve sleeve with small end first. Install reverse boost valve sleeve in pump cover.

5) Install T.V. boost valve sleeve (4L60 only) in pump cover. Install snap ring. Ensure snap ring is fully seated. Install pump cover on pump body. Install retaining bolts finger tight. Align pump body and cover using Alignment Strap (J-21368). Place bolt through pump-to-case bolt hole. Tighten retaining bolts to specification. See TORQUE SPECIFICATIONS table. Remove alignment strap.

6) Position pump-to-case gasket on pump, and retain it using petroleum jelly. Install oil seal rings on stator hub. Retain oil seal rings using petroleum jelly. Install pump-to-case oil seal on cover. Ensure seal is not twisted. Coat seal with ATF. Install pump-to-drum thrust washer. Ensure tangs on washer engage with holes in hub.

2-4 SERVO ASSEMBLY

Disassembly – 1) Remove 4th apply piston and housing from 2nd apply piston assembly. Remove return spring from apply pin. Install Piston Compressor (J-22269-01) on second apply piston. *See Fig. 16.*

2) Compress 2nd servo apply piston assembly. Remove retainer ring. Separate 2nd apply piston, spring and retainer. Remove retainer ring, washer and spring from apply pin, and remove pin. Remove all oil seal rings. *See Fig. 15.*

Inspection – Inspect all pistons for porosity and damage. Check for ring groove damage and servo bore in case for any wear which may cut servo seals. Check all springs and oil seal rings for distortion and damage.

Reassembly – Different servo piston housings and 2nd apply pistons are used for different applications. If servo piston housing or 2nd apply piston is replaced, inside dimension of parts must be checked. Measure inside of piston housing and 2nd apply piston. Dimension must be same as original. To assemble, reverse disassembly procedure. Coat seals with petroleum jelly before assembly.

TRANSMISSION REASSEMBLY

NOTE: To identify seals, bearings and thrust washers locations, see SEALS, BEARINGS & THRUST WASHERS under TRANSMISSION REASSEMBLY. See Fig. 31.

LOW-REVERSE CLUTCH

1) Place transmission in a vertical position. Install seals on low-reverse clutch piston. Apply petroleum jelly to seals.

2) Align and install piston with notch in bottom of transmission case. Ensure piston is fully seated and parking pawl aligns with opening in piston wall. Install spring assembly with flat side of retainer upward. Compress springs and install retainer ring.

3) Coat bearing assembly with petroleum jelly. Install bearing assembly on case hub with outside bearing race toward case hub. Install internal reaction gear and support. Install bearing assembly onto support with outside bearing race toward support. Install oil deflector (if equipped) and reaction carrier assembly in case. *See Fig. 21.* Ensure clutch plates are proper thickness.

4) Install clutch plates. See LOW-REVERSE CLUTCH PLATE USAGE table. Ensure clutch plates align with splines of reaction carrier and case and that steel plates are aligned. Place waved plate on work bench. Install 5 friction plates and 4 steel plates alternately, starting with friction plate.

LOW-REVERSE CLUTCH PLATE USAGE

Type	No. Used	Thickness In. (mm)
Flat Steel	5	.069 (1.75)
Friction	5	.088 (2.24)

5) Install low-reverse support. Apply light pressure to low-reverse support. DO NOT flatten waved plate. Measure height of clutch pack from work bench to top of low-reverse support. Using height dimension, determine proper selective spacer plate to be used. See SPACER PLATE SELECTION table.

SPACER PLATE SELECTION [1] (4L60)

Measured Clutch Pack Height [2] In. (mm)	Plate Thickness In. (mm)
1.136-1.164 (28.85-29.57)	.066-.073 (1.67-1.85)
1.155-1.185 (29.35-30.09)	.046-.052 (1.17-1.31)
1.115-1.144 (28.32-29.06)	.087-.092 (2.19-2.34)

[1] – Spacer plates are available in select sizes. Plate .066-.073" (1.67-1.85 mm) thick has no identifying marks. Other plates are marked "0" or "1".

[2] – Clutch pack height is measured without spacer plate in position.

SPACER PLATE SELECTION [1] (4L60-E)

Measured Clutch Pack Height [2] In. (mm)	Plate Thickness In. (mm)
1.081-1.102 (27.55-28.06)	.066-.073 (1.67-1.85)
1.102-1.122 (28.06-28.59)	.046-.052 (1.17-1.31)
1.061-1.081 (27.03-27.54)	.087-.092 (2.19-2.34)

[1] – Spacer plates are available in select sizes. Plate .066-.073" (1.67-1.85 mm) thick has no identifying marks. Other plates are marked "0" or "1".

[2] – Clutch pack height is measured without spacer plate in position.

6) Place spacer plate between waved plate and first friction clutch plate with identification facing upward. Measure overall height of clutch pack. Overall height should be 1.20-1.24" (30.5-31.5 mm). Install clutch pack assembly in transmission case.

7) Install low-reverse support in case with hub downward. Install inner race by pushing downward while rotating until it is fully engaged. Bottom tangs will be flush with hub when fully installed. Install spring retainer in case between case lug and open notch in support. Install low-reverse retainer ring.

REACTION & INPUT GEAR SETS

1) Install snap ring on reaction sun gear (if removed). Install sun gear into reaction carrier. Install thrust washer on low-reverse clutch race. Install reaction sun gear shell on reaction sun gear.

2) Install thrust washer on reaction sun gear shell. Ensure thrust washer tangs engage on gear shell. Install input internal gear and reaction carrier shaft in sun gear shell. Carrier shaft splines must engage with reaction carrier. See Fig. 21.

3) Install thrust washer on reaction carrier shaft. Outer race must face toward reaction carrier shaft. Install output shaft in transmission. Ensure output shaft engages with all parts.

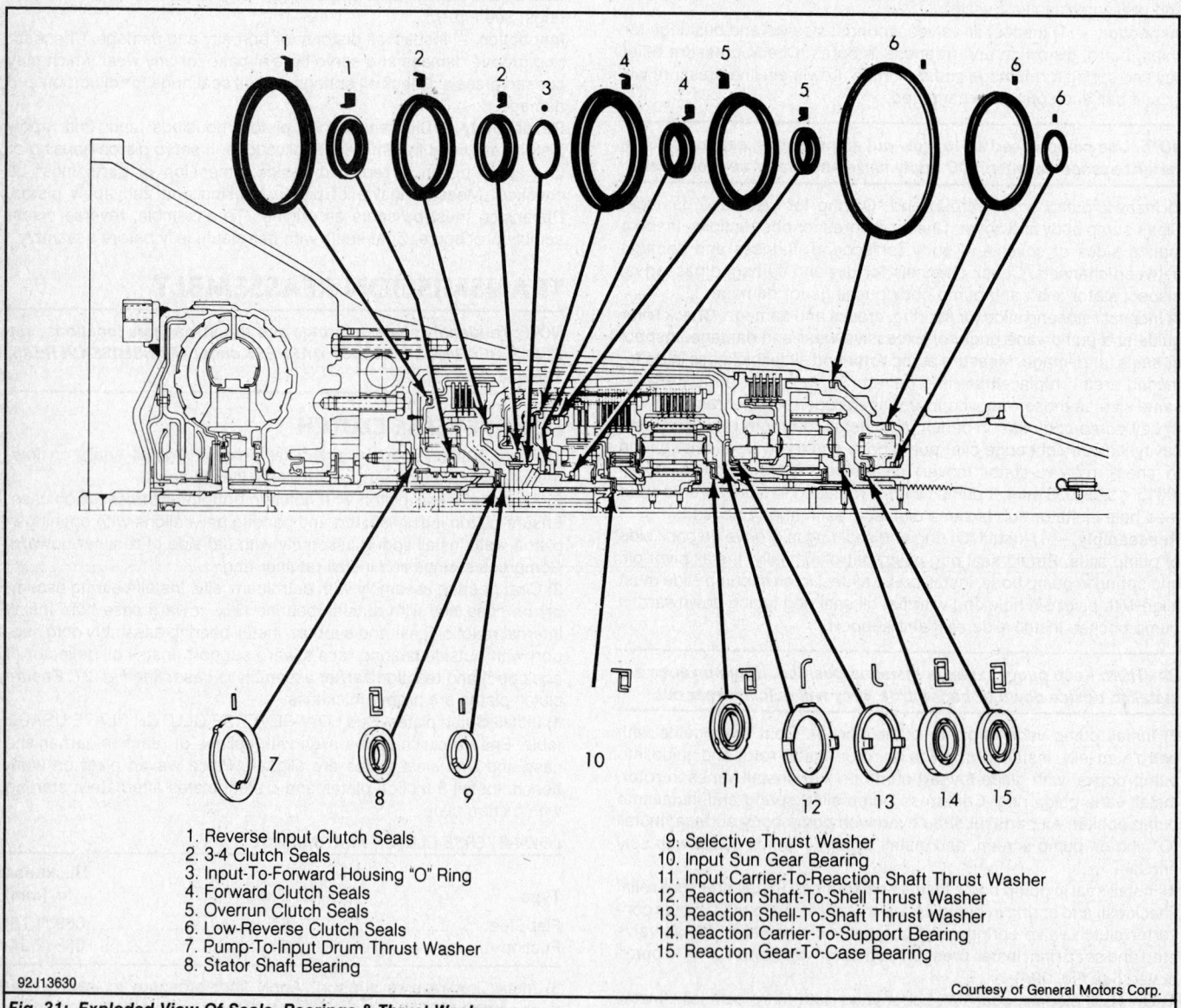

1. Reverse Input Clutch Seals
2. 3-4 Clutch Seals
3. Input-To-Forward Housing "O" Ring
4. Forward Clutch Seals
5. Overrun Clutch Seals
6. Low-Reverse Clutch Seals
7. Pump-To-Input Drum Thrust Washer
8. Stator Shaft Bearing
9. Selective Thrust Washer
10. Input Sun Gear Bearing
11. Input Carrier-To-Reaction Shaft Thrust Washer
12. Reaction Shaft-To-Shell Thrust Washer
13. Reaction Shell-To-Shaft Thrust Washer
14. Reaction Carrier-To-Support Bearing
15. Reaction Gear-To-Case Bearing

92J13630

Courtesy of General Motors Corp.

Fig. 31: Exploded View Of Seals, Bearings & Thrust Washers

4) Install Output Shaft Support (J-29837). Adjust support so output shaft is positioned upward as far as possible. Install input carrier assembly with hub end down on output shaft. Install NEW retainer ring on output shaft. Remove output shaft support. Install input sun gear, indexing gear end with input carrier pinions.

REVERSE INPUT ASSEMBLY & INPUT CLUTCH

Install selective thrust washer on input housing. Install bearing assembly on selective thrust washer. Inner race (Black) must go toward oil pump. Position reverse input assembly on input clutch assembly. Reverse input clutch plates must align with input clutch hub. Ensure all clutch plates are fully engaged.

REVERSE & INPUT CLUTCHES

Install reverse and input clutch assemblies in case as an assembly. Align 3-4 clutch plates of input assembly with input internal gear. Assembly is fully seated when reverse housing is just below oil pump face of case.

2-4 BAND & SERVO ASSEMBLY

1) Install 2-4 band in case. Align band anchor pin end with case pin hole. Install band anchor pin in case. Ensure band anchor pin aligns with end of 2-4 band.

2) Install 2-4 servo assembly into case, and index apply pin on band end. Check for proper engagement of apply pin on band end. Recheck 2-4 servo apply pin selection to ensure correct pin is installed. See CHECKING SERVO PIN LENGTH under TRANSMISSION DISASSEMBLY. Different length servo pins are available. See SERVO PIN SPECIFICATIONS table. Select proper length servo pin.

SERVO PIN SPECIFICATIONS

Pin Identification	Pin Length In. (mm)
1 Groove	2.59-2.60 (65.8-66.1)
3 Grooves [1]	2.65-2.66 (67.2-67.5)
No Groove	2.70-2.71 (68.6-68.9)

[1] – Pin has 2 grooves on 4L60-E transmission.

3) Install servo cover and "O" ring. Compress cover and install cover retaining ring. Index ring ends with slot in case.

SEALS, BEARINGS & THRUST WASHERS

NOTE: To identify seals, bearings and thrust washers locations, see Fig. 31.

OIL PUMP ASSEMBLY

1) Turbine shaft seals should be installed just before oil pump installation. Position Seal Installer (J-36418-1) on input shaft. *See Fig. 32.* Adjustment screw in seal installer must be adjusted to obtain correct height for each seal installation. Install 4 turbine shaft seals.

2) Turbine shaft seals must be sized using Seal Sizer (J-36418-2A) after installation. Install aligning pins in 2 opposing pump bolt holes in case. Ensure thrust washer is installed on rear of oil pump. Thrust washer can be retained using petroleum jelly.

3) Install pump into case, aligning filter and pressure regulator holes with holes in case. Install retaining bolts. Tighten bolts to specification. See TORQUE SPECIFICATIONS table. Place transmission in a horizontal position.

4) Turbine shaft should rotate by hand. If turbine shaft will not rotate, loosen pump retaining bolts and attempt to rotate shaft again. If shaft now turns, reverse and input assemblies have not been indexed properly or some other assembly problem has occurred, such as thrust washer not positioned properly.

5) Check transmission end play. See TRANSMISSION END PLAY CHECK under TRANSMISSION DISASSEMBLY. Transmission end play should be .005-.036" (.13-.91 mm). If transmission end play is not within specification, thrust washer must be changed between oil pump and input housing.

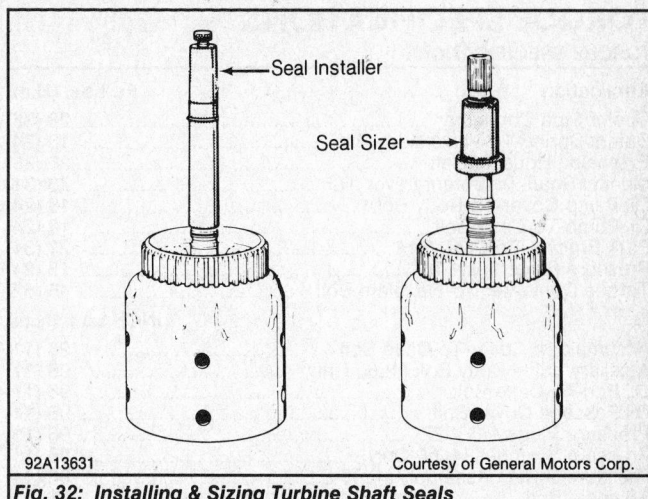

Fig. 32: Installing & Sizing Turbine Shaft Seals

92A13631   Courtesy of General Motors Corp.

6) See OIL PUMP THRUST WASHER SPECIFICATIONS table. Install thrust washer, and recheck end play. Install torque converter. Ensure converter hub is aligned with oil pump. Install torque converter retaining strap to hold converter.

OIL PUMP THRUST WASHER SPECIFICATIONS

Identification Number	Thickness In. (mm)
67	.074-.078 (1.88-1.98)
68	.080-.084 (2.03-2.13)
69	.087-.091 (2.21-2.31)
70	.094-.098 (2.39-2.49)
71	.100-.104 (2.54-2.64)
72	.107-.111 (2.72-2.82)
73	.113-.118 (2.87-3.00)
74	.120-.124 (3.05-3.15)

1-2 ACCUMULATOR & SPACER PLATES

CAUTION: If spacer plate and gasket replacement is required, ensure NEW spacer plate and gasket are identical as those removed.

1) Install 3-4 accumulator piston pin in case. Install 3-4 piston seal on piston. Install 3-4 accumulator piston on pin. Legs of piston must face valve body.

2) Install 3-4 accumulator spring. Install check balls and oil screens in proper locations. Install special retainer and ball assembly. *See Figs. 13 and 18* for check ball and filter installation locations. Install spacer plate gasket and spacer plate.

3) Install 1-2 accumulator spring, oil seal ring and 1-2 accumulator piston. Install accumulator cover and bolts. Tighten bolts to specification. See TORQUE SPECIFICATIONS table.

VALVE BODY & AUXILIARY VALVE BODY

Install valve body and auxiliary valve body. See VALVE BODY and AUXILIARY VALVE BODY under ON-VEHICLE SERVICE.

EXTENSION HOUSING

1) Install speed sensor wheel/speedometer gear and retaining clip on output shaft. On 4L60, if output shaft has 2 locating holes, use hole nearest yoke on Corvette only. Install "O" ring in output shaft sleeve.

2) On all models, install output sleeve on output shaft. DO NOT position output sleeve past machined surface of output shaft. Install seal ring on extension housing.

3) Position extension housing on transmission case. Install retaining bolts. Install oil seal in extension housing.

4) Install speed sensor/speedometer driven gear and fitting assembly. Install retainer and bolt. Tighten bolt to specification. See TORQUE SPECIFICATIONS table. Install outside electrical connector and manual shift lever.

TORQUE SPECIFICATIONS
TORQUE SPECIFICATIONS

Application	Ft. Lbs. (N.m)
Cooler Pipe Connector	28 (38)
Detent Spring-To-Valve Body Bolt	18 (24)
Extension Housing Bolt	26 (35)
Manual Shaft-To-Detent Lever Nut	23 (31)
Oil Pump Cover-To-Body Bolt	18 (24)
Oil Pump-To-Case Bolt	18 (24)
Park Bracket-To-Case Bolt	23 (31)
Pressure Plugs 1/4 X 18"	18 (24)
Torque Converter-To-Flexplate Bolt	46 (62)

	INCH Lbs. (N.m)
Accumulator Cover-To-Case Bolt	96 (11)
Auxiliary Valve Body Bolt (4L60 Only)	96 (11)
Oil Pan-To-Case Bolt	96 (11)
Oil Passage Cover Bolt	96 (11)
Pressure Plugs 1/8 X 27"	96 (11)
Pressure Switches (4L60 Only)	96 (11)
Pressure Switch Assembly (4L60-E Only)	96 (11)
Solenoid Bolt	96 (11)
Speed Sensor/Speedometer Bolt	89 (10)
T.V. Cable Bolt (4L60 Only)	75 (8.5)
Valve Body-To-Case Bolt [1]	96 (11)

[1] – Tighten valve body bolts in a spiral pattern starting in center of valve body.

SERVICE BULLETINS

NO UPSHIFT OR STUCK IN 1ST GEAR

1991 Custom Cruiser, 1991 Bravada & 1991-92 Roadmaster (GM TSB 177113R 6/28/91) — Some Hydra-Matic 4L60 transmissions may experience a no upshift or stuck in 1st gear condition. This condition may be caused by input carrier-to-output shaft retaining ring becoming unseated or retaining ring omitted during assembly.

Output shaft is able to move slightly and will cause wear on governor driven gear. Governor driven gear wear may be described as an "apple coring" condition. If governor driven gear is worn, transmission cannot upshift out of 1st gear.

Remove governor, and inspect governor driven gear. If "apple coring" condition exists, disassemble transmission to determine if retaining ring is unseated, broken or missing. *See Fig. 33.* Install NEW retaining ring as necessary. DO NOT over expand new retaining ring during installation.

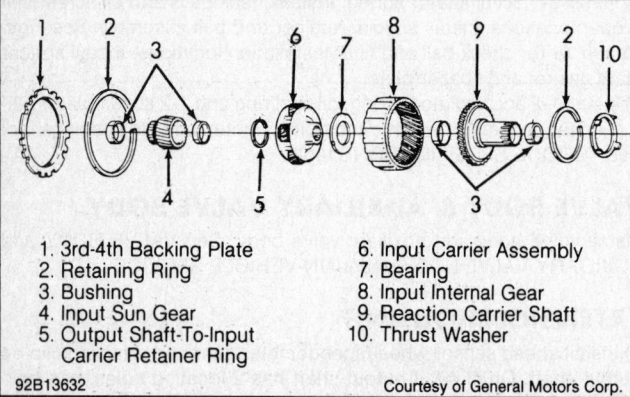

1. 3rd-4th Backing Plate
2. Retaining Ring
3. Bushing
4. Input Sun Gear
5. Output Shaft-To-Input Carrier Retainer Ring
6. Input Carrier Assembly
7. Bearing
8. Input Internal Gear
9. Reaction Carrier Shaft
10. Thrust Washer

92B13632   Courtesy of General Motors Corp.

Fig. 33: Exploded View Of Input Carrier-To-Output Shaft Assembly

NO 3RD OR 4TH GEAR OR SLIPPING IN 3RD OR 4TH GEAR

1991-92 All Models (GM TSB 177119 8/91) — Some Hydra-Matic 4L60 transmissions may experience a no 3rd or 4th gear or slipping in 3rd or 4th gear condition. Ensure T.V. cable is adjusted correctly and fluid level is filled to correct level. Check cooler lines to ensure lines are not restricted. Remove transmission pan, and check transmission filter neck seal for proper fit. If seal does not seal properly around filter, air can enter into oil pump and cause low line pressure or aerated fluid. Replace seal if necessary.

If overhaul is performed, disassemble oil pump and inspect pump body bushing for wear. Replace bushing if necessary. A worn bushing can create a large leak in oil pump and lower line pressure, which can cause oil flow to be cut off. If oil pump bore has excessive wear in one area (out-of-round), replace oil pump body. Inspect 3-4 clutch boost springs for signs of polishing on spring tabs. Polishing is caused by 3-4 clutch friction plates rubbing on boost springs. Replace boost springs as necessary.

Inspect input housing splines on inside of input housing. If splines show drag marks in middle spline, 3-4 clutch steel plates are binding in housing. New plates with smaller outer diameter are available to correct this condition. See REDESIGNED 3-4 STEEL CLUTCH PLATES under SERVICE BULLETINS. Check 2-4 band for a lube passage. If lube passage does not exist in 2-4 band, install new design 2-4 band with lube passage.

Inspect 1-2 and 3-4 accumulator piston and bore for scoring caused by metal particles in transmission. Inspect 3rd accumulator exhaust check ball and retainer (located in case servo bore). Check ball may not seat due to metal particles stuck in bore. This will cause 2-4 band to drag or 3-4 clutch to not fully apply on 2-3 upshift.

Ensure 3rd accumulator orifice cup plug (located in case servo bore) is not blocked. If metal particles block orifice, 3rd accumulator will not fill properly due to trapped air in cavity. This can effect 3-4 clutch. Orifice cup plug also lubricates 2-4 band through lube passage.

Check 3-4 clutch exhaust check ball and retainer (located in input housing). Check ball helps exhaust 3-4 clutch. If check ball does not seat, 3-4 clutch cannot fully apply. If check ball is stuck in seated position, 3-4 clutch cannot exhaust fully.

NO 4TH GEAR, LATE OR FALLS OUT OF 4TH GEAR

1991-92 All Models (ATRA TSB 043) – Ensure T.V. cable and manual linkage is adjusted correctly. Check line pressure at 4th gear transmission tap. If pressure does not exist, go to **STEP "A"**. If pressure is low, go to **STEP "B"**. If pressure is normal, go to **STEP "C"**.

Step "A" – If 4th gear pressure does not exist, check items which could keep transmission from shifting. Check for oversized tires. Oversized tires can reduce governor pressure. Ensure governor is operating correctly. Ensure valve body bolts are tightened to correct specification.

Ensure pressure regulator snap ring is installed in its groove. Air check into exhaust hole at 4-3 sequence valve to check 4th apply servo circuit. Air check into exhaust hole at 3-4 shift valve to check 4th gear switch, 4-3 relay and sequence valve for sticking and binding. Check for missing plug at relay valve.

Air check governor circuit for leaks, and check for sticking 3-4 shift valve. Check for missing cup plug. Remove valve body, and check for stuck valves, relay valve installed backward or plugs missing from upshift and downshift valves. Ensure gaskets are not covering separator plate holes. Check placement of check balls in case and 3-4 spring tension.

Step "B" – If 4th gear pressure is low, shift occurred but a leak exists in circuit. Remove transmission pan, and air check into exhaust hole at 4-3 sequence valve to check 4th apply servo circuit. Check for valve body leaks. Remove servo, and check for damaged seals, incorrect clearance and assembly errors. Check piston for cracks and pin bore for wear. Check 3-4 accumulator piston for cracks and damaged seal. Check for missing cup plug.

Step "C" – If 4th gear pressure is normal, a mechanical problem exists in transmission. Remove transmission pan, and check servo exhaust hole for blockage by pan gasket or sealant. Air check into 4th gear pressure tap. Air should come out 4-3 sequence exhaust hole, showing a clear circuit. Block 4-3 sequence exhaust hole, and air check again. Servo should apply. Remove servo, and check for stuck servo pin in second gear piston. Check for stripped sun gear shell. Stripped sun gear shell will cause loss of 2nd gear and Reverse.

LOSS OF WIDE OPEN THROTTLE 3-4 UPSHIFT WHEN HOT

1991 Caprice 5.7L Police (GM TSB 077155 1/91) – Some 1991 Hydra-Matic 4L60 transmissions, models BFM, BPM & YNM with 5.7L engine, may exhibit a loss of wide open throttle 3-4 upshift when hot. When servicing this condition, install new T.V. boost valve and spring into oil pump cover. Install new 3-4 throttle valve, sleeve and spring into valve body. *See Fig. 34.* If service is necessary on BFM model transmission, replacement of T.V. boost valve and sleeve in oil pump cover may not be required.

Beginning September 24,1991 (Julian Date 267), transmission contains updated boost valve and sleeve. Beginning October 19, 1990 (Julian Date 292), BFM model transmission was replaced by BJM model transmission. BJM model transmission contains updated components.

BFM, BPM & YNM MODEL TRANSMISSION SERVICE PARTS

Description	Part Number
Throttle Boost Valve & Bushing, 3-4 Throttle Valve, Bushing & Sleeve Service Package	8673948

NOTE: During high speed pursuit, vehicles should be driven in Overdrive for maximum power train performance. DO NOT install 1991 model transmission in earlier model vehicles. 1991 model transmission is not compatible with earlier model vehicles.

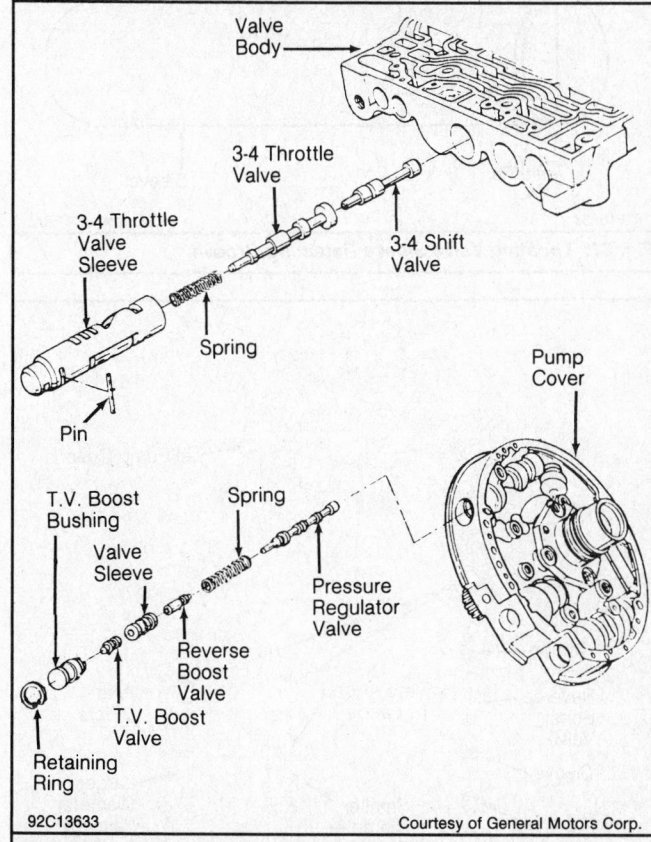

Valve Body

3-4 Throttle Valve

3-4 Throttle Valve Sleeve

3-4 Shift Valve

Spring

Pin

Pump Cover

T.V. Boost Bushing

Spring

Valve Sleeve

Pressure Regulator Valve

Reverse Boost Valve

T.V. Boost Valve

Retaining Ring

92C13633

Courtesy of General Motors Corp.

Fig. 34: Installing Throttle Valve & T.V. Boost Valve Assemblies

---

REDESIGNED OUTPUT SHAFT & INPUT HOUSING-TO-OUTPUT SHAFT SEAL

1991 All Models (GM TSB 177118 8/91) – Due to changes in lube passage locations, Hydra-Matic 4L60 transmission output shafts and input housing-to-output shaft seals have been redesigned to provide increased oil flow. Beginning January 28, 1991 (Julian Date 028), all

transmissions were built using new output shaft and seal. New seal can only be used on new output shaft. If new seal is used on previous model output shaft, seal will block one lube passage. Previous seal can be used on both shaft designs.

New output shaft and seal can be used as a set in all 4L60 transmissions manufactured. New output shaft can be identified by lube passage location. New shaft has a lube passage on chamfer at front of output shaft. Lube passage was previously located on shank of output shaft.

REDESIGNED 3-4 STEEL CLUTCH PLATES

1991 All Models (GM TSB 077138 11/90) – Redesigned 3-4 steel clutch plates have a slightly smaller outer radius. Design lets plates move freely in clutch housing. Beginning July 27,1990 (Julian Date 208), all Hydra-Matic 4L60 transmissions are equipped with new design plates. New clutch plates may be used on any 1989-91 4L60 transmission.

3-4 STEEL CLUTCH PLATES

Description	Part Number
3rd & 4th Plate (Set Of 5 Plates)	8678053
3rd & 4th Plate (Single Plate)	8678054

NEW 3-4 CLUTCH FRICTION MATERIAL

1991-92 All Models (GM TSB 177119 8/91) – New friction material on 3-4 clutch plates has been installed on limited applications of Hydra-Matic 4L60 transmission. New friction material has increased heat capacity but cannot be used interchangeably with previous friction material. New material was put into production during 1991 model year. Model codes changed as transmissions received new 3-4 clutch plates.

New plates cannot be used to service any transmissions except those 1991 models listed. See 1991 TRANSMISSION MODEL LIST table. Transmissions used with 5.7L engine were first to contain new plates, beginning in January 1991.

NOTE: DO NOT use new plates in any transmission which is not listed in 1991 TRANSMISSION MODEL LIST table. If new plates are used in incorrect application, shift quality will be poor and transmission damage could occur quickly.

1991 TRANSMISSION MODEL LIST

New [1]	Previous
AMM	AKM
APM	DBM
CNM	CHM
CYM	CJM
FYM	FUM
KWM	KRM
LHM	None
RCM	RAM
RDM	WCM
YHM	YDM

[1] – New models contain new material. Previous models are early 1991 models which do not contain new material.

PEENED SPACER PLATE

1991 All Models (GM TSB 177120 8/91) – Some valve body spacer plate peening is acceptable and preferred to help seat check balls. Excessive peening will cause uneven seating of check ball. Inspect spacer plate for raised material on opposite side of check ball seat. If material on opposite side is raised, peening is too severe and spacer plate must be replaced. *See Fig. 35*.

To verify spacer plate is peening evenly and check ball is sealing correctly, seat check ball on spacer plate. Shine beam of light on opposite side and inspect for light between spacer plate and check ball. Light should not be present. If light is present, check ball is not seated properly and spacer plate must be replaced.

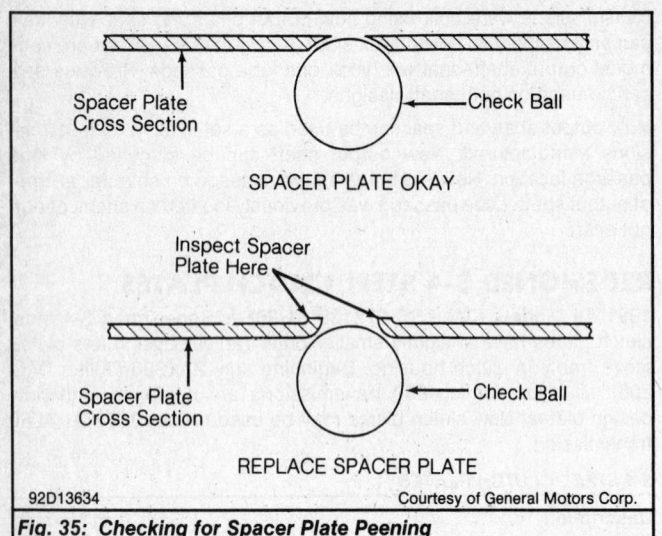

92D13634   Courtesy of General Motors Corp.

Fig. 35: Checking for Spacer Plate Peening

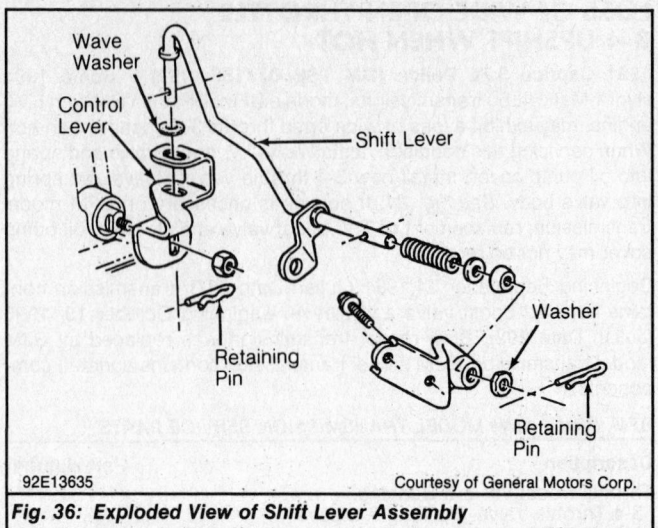

92E13635   Courtesy of General Motors Corp.

Fig. 36: Exploded View of Shift Lever Assembly

NOISE IN SHIFT LEVER

1991 Bravada (GM TSB 167103 8/21/91) – When driving vehicle, a squeak or buzz can be heard in shift lever. Possible cause can be found at connection of transmission shift lever and transmission control lever. Check for loose fitting of control lever to shift lever. A loose control lever can generate a vibration induced noise. To correct this condition, a wave washer should be installed on control lever.

A second source of noise is a possible grinding out of shift lever with end of slot in control lever. This condition can be corrected by adding one or 2 flat washers as necessary to end of shift lever that is secured to frame. *See Fig. 36.* Shift lever will center in slot in control lever, preventing grinding out condition. When wave and flat washers have been added to control lever, ensure shift linkage is adjusted correctly. Bravada vehicles built after Vehicle Identification Number (VIN) 1GHDT13Z2M2704746 have had new washers installed.

SHIFT LEVER SERVICE PARTS

Description	Part Number
Wave Washer	4722812
Flat Washer	14074908

VALVE BODY SLEEVE INSTALLATION

1991-92 All Models (ATRA TSB 058 7/91) – Valve body sleeves may be installed incorrectly if casting lines on end of sleeve are not within 10 degrees of vertical. Casting lines are visible without removing valve body. If casting lines are not within 10 degrees of vertical, retaining pin is installed into an oil slot, not into retaining groove. *See Fig. 37.*

NOTE: Sleeves can be installed incorrectly even if casting lines are within vertical position.

OIL PUMP REMOVAL TOOL

1991-92 Bravada, Custom Cruiser & Firebird (GM TSB 277107 2/7/92) – Due to product changes in 4L60 Hydra-Matic transmission stator shaft, a new tool has been developed to remove oil pump assembly. New tool is an adapter for use with current pump puller. Because groove under stator shaft has been removed, previous tool cannot fit onto new shaft.

With transmission removed from vehicle, remove torque converter. Position transmission in an upright position. Remove "O" ring and turbine shaft. Remove oil pump bolts, and install 4L60 Adapter (J 39119) by slipping adapter over stator shaft. Install 4L80E Pump Puller (J 37789-A) over adapter. Tighten small screw to secure pump puller to adapter. Turn forcing screw to lift oil pump out of case.

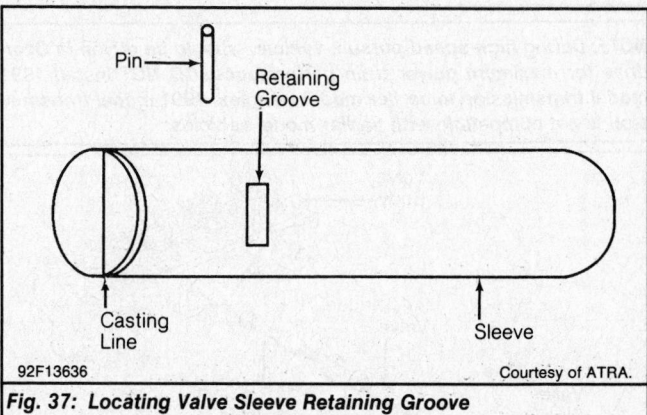

92F13636   Courtesy of ATRA.

Fig. 37: Locating Valve Sleeve Retaining Groove

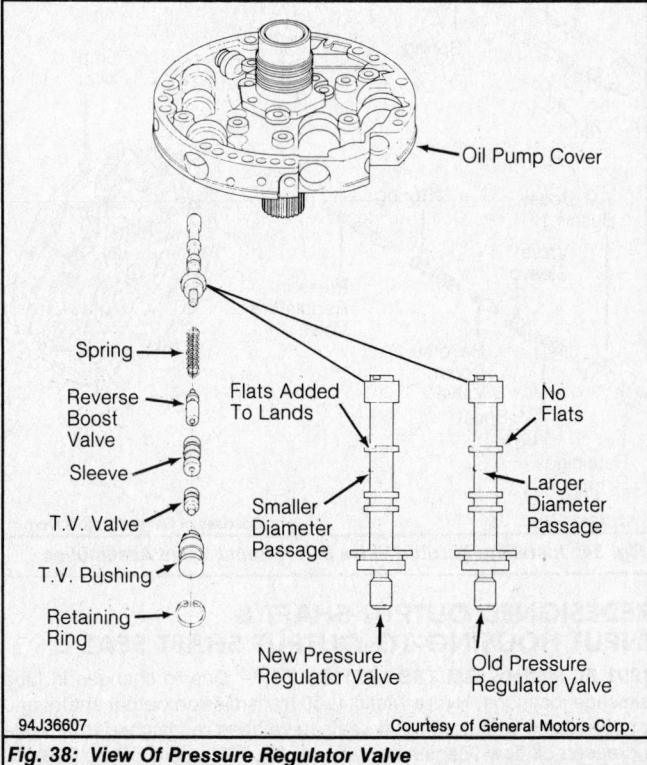

94J36607   Courtesy of General Motors Corp.

Fig. 38: View Of Pressure Regulator Valve

BUZZING NOISE AT IDLE IN GEAR

1982-93 Astro, "C", "G", "K", "S", Safari, "T" & "V" Light Trucks & Vans (GM TSB 277142 10/2/92) — Some Hydra-Matic 4L60 transmissions may have a buzzing noise at idle in gear. The noise may be louder while idling in Reverse. This condition may be caused by the pressure regulator valve. To correct this, install Pressure Regulator Valve (8684048). *See Fig. 38.*

3-2 COAST DOWN CLUNK

1993 Camaro & Firebird With 5.7L Engine (Chevrolet TSB 93-234-7A 6/3/93) – Some Hydra-Matic 4L60 transmissions built before February 8, 1993, may have a 3-2 coast down bump. To correct this, install a revised Valve Body Spacer Plate (8686065).

CLICK OR WHINE IN 3RD OR 4TH GEAR

1988-93 GM Passenger Vehicle, Light Trucks & Vans (Chevrolet TSB 93-228-7A 6/1/93) – Some Hydra-Matic 4L60 transmissions built before November 19, 1992, may have a click noise or whine in 3rd or 4th gear. This may be caused by the low and reverse friction plates. To correct this, install Low and Reverse Overhaul Package (8689951).

NEW 3-4 CLUTCH FRICTION MATERIAL & 3-4 BACKING PLATE

1987-93 All Models (GM TSB 377117 3/93) – New Friction Material (No. 2050) on 3-4 clutch plates has been installed on limited applications of Hydra-Matic 4L60 transmission. New friction material has increased heat capacity but cannot be used interchangeably with previous friction material.

New material was put into production during 1991 model year. Model codes changed as transmissions received new 3-4 clutch plates. New plates cannot be used to service any transmissions except those 1991-93 models listed. See TRANSMISSION MODEL LIST table.

As of January 5, 1993, transmissions received a revised 3-4 backing plate and 3-4 steel plates. The 1-piece backing plate takes the place of the 4th clutch apply plate, 3-4 backing plate and the top 3-4 steel plate. The 3-4 steel plates are thicker. Due to this change, 3-4 clutch pack clearance is revised to .35-.84" (.90-.2.14 mm). Measure 3-4 clutch clearance and install correct 3-4 backing plate. See SELECTIVE 3-4 BACKING PLATE table.

NOTE: DO NOT use new plates in any transmission which is not listed in TRANSMISSION MODEL LIST tables If new plates are used in incorrect application, shift quality will be poor and transmission damage could occur quickly.

1991 TRANSMISSION MODEL LIST

New [1]	Previous
1AMM	AKM
1APM	DBM
1CNM	CHM
1CYM	CJM
1FYM	FUM
1KWM	KRM
1LHM	None
1RCM	RAM
1RDM	WCM
1YHM	YDM

[1] – New models contain new material. Previous models are early 1991 models which do not contain new material.

1992 TRANSMISSION MODEL LIST

New [1]

2ADM, 2AKM, 2BFM, 2CHM, 2CJM, 2FUM, 2KJM, 2LHM, 2WCM, 2YCM, 2YDM

[1] – New models contain new material. Previous models are early 1991 models which do not contain new material.

1993 TRANSMISSION MODEL LIST

New [1]

3AAM, 3ADM, 3AFM, 3ASM, 3BAM, 3BBM, 3BCM, 3BHM, 3BRM, 3BWM, 3CPM, 3FAM, 3FDM, 3FMM, 3FMM, 3LHM, 3SFM, 2YAM, 3YCM, 3YDM

[1] – New models contain new material. Previous models are early 1991 models which do not contain new material.

SELECTIVE 3-4 BACKING PLATE

Identification	Thickness In. (mm)
A [1]	.224-.231 (5.68-5.88)
B	.187-.196 (4.76-4.99)
C [2]	.154-.161 (3.90-4.10)

[1] – SFM and SAM models only.
[2] – Except SFM and SAM models.

IMPROVED PARK TO REVERSE ENGAGEMENT

1993 Brougham, Caprice, Camaro, Corvette, Firebird, Roadmaster & S/T Pickups with 2.5L Engine (GM TSB 377116 3/93) – New spacer plate, spacer plate gaskets and additional valve body check ball No. 11 have been installed in Hydra-Matic 4L60 transmissions. These parts are used to improve the Park to Reverse gear engagement. Make sure earlier gaskets are not installed on 1993 transmission assemblies. The revised view of valve body check ball locations is

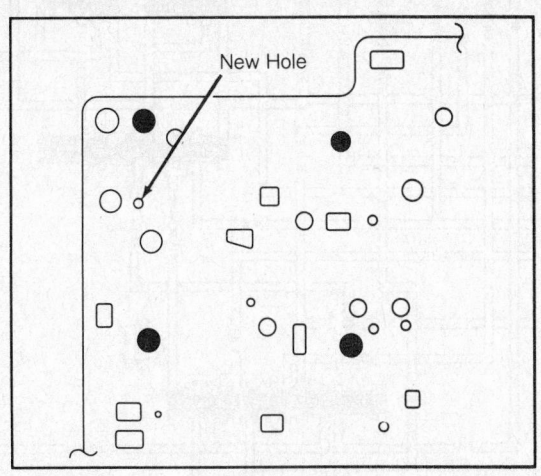

SPACER PLATE

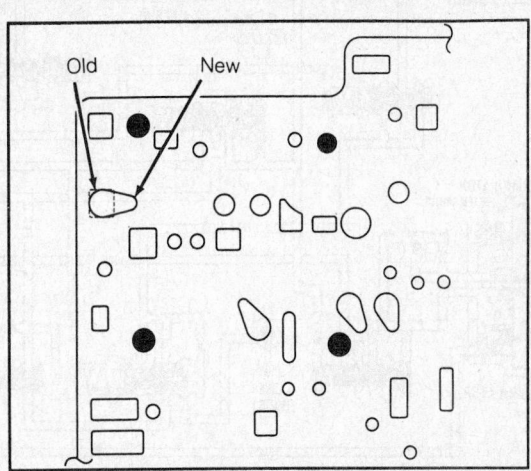

SPACER PLATE TO VALVE BODY GASKET

94I36705

Courtesy of General Motors Corp.

Fig. 39: View Of Revised Spacer Plate Gasket

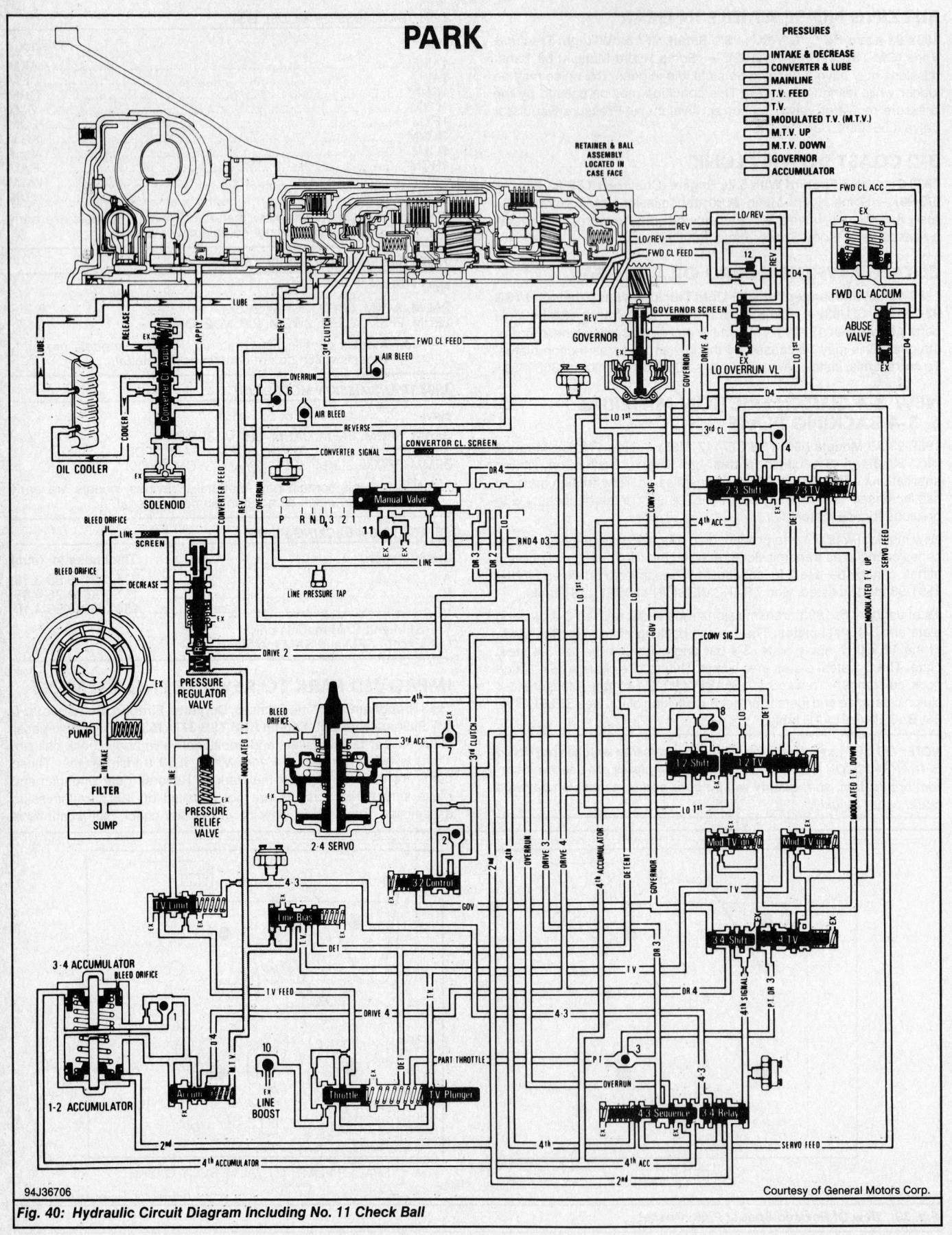

Fig. 40: *Hydraulic Circuit Diagram Including No. 11 Check Ball*

Courtesy of General Motors Corp.

94J36706

included in the 4L60 repair article. See HYDRA-MATIC 4L60 article in AUTOMATIC TRANSMISSION section. The correct 1993 gaskets can be identified by a pear shaped hole for reverse passage orifice. *See Fig. 39.* If the wrong parts are installed, reverse will not apply. Use accompanying hydraulic circuit diagram to help diagnosis valve body and oil circuit problems. *See Fig. 40.*

2ND GEAR START IN D2

1993 Camaro & Firebird With 5.7L Engine & Transmission Calibration 3FFM (GM TSB 377115 3/16/93) – During small to part throttle acceleration from a stop while in D2, transmission will, start in second gear. The transmission will start in first gear during full throttle acceleration from a stop while in D2. This is normal for 1993 Calibration 3FFM. With transmission in D3 or OD, transmission will start in first gear from a stop.

DIFFICULT GEAR SELECTION

1984-93 Camaro & Firebird (GM TSB 377105 2/15/93) – If problems with selecting gears is found, check the shift cable for damage at the transmission support bracket. If the shift cable is bent or twisted, replace the shift cable. DO NOT bend or twist shift cable during installation.

VIBRATION OR GEAR RATTLE W/TCC APPLIED

1992-93 "S" & "T" Pickups With 4.3L Engine & 4L60/4L60-E Transmission (GM TSB 277145 10/92) – Some 1992-93 "S" & "T" Pickups with 4.3L engine and 4L60/4L60-E transmission may have a vibration or gear rattle when TCC applies at 1000-2000 RPM. This problem may be caused by damper springs in the torque converter being too stiff. To correct this condition, install Torque Converter (8688904).

REVISED ACCUMULATOR ASSEMBLY

1993 Brougham, Caprice, Camaro, Corvette, Firebird, Roadmaster & S/T Pickups with 2.5L Engine (GM TSB 277140 9/92) – Starting in 1993, the 3-4 accumulator spring is no longer installed and the 1-2 accumulator piston and 1-2 accumulator spring are reversed on 4L60 transmissions. *See Fig. 41.*

HARSH 1-2 UPSHIFT

1992 Camaro & Firebird With Transmission Models 2FTM, 2FUM & 2FZM (GN TSB 277135 9/15/92) – Some Camaro and Firebird vehicles built between March and June 1992 may have a harsh 1-2 upshift. This condition may be caused by a sticking 1-2 accumulator valve. A revised 1-2 accumulator valve and valve sleeve are now available to correct this. See 1-2 ACCUMULATOR SERVICE PACKAGE table.

1-2 ACCUMULATOR SERVICE PACKAGE

Model	Service Kit No.
2FTM & 2FUM	8687992
2FZM	8688900

NO LINE PRESSURE RISE

All General Motor Vehicles with 4L60 (ATRA TSB 201) – Some General Motors vehicles may have a problem with no line pressure rise. This may be caused by an aftermarket or rebuilt oil pump. Disassemble the pump. Check oil pump body-to-slide end clearance. End clearance should be .0015-.0025" (.040-.060 mm). Check bottom surface of pump pocket. Outside edge of pump pocket surface should have a 90 degree cut or an under-cut groove (preferred) should be present. If any problems are found, replace pump assembly.

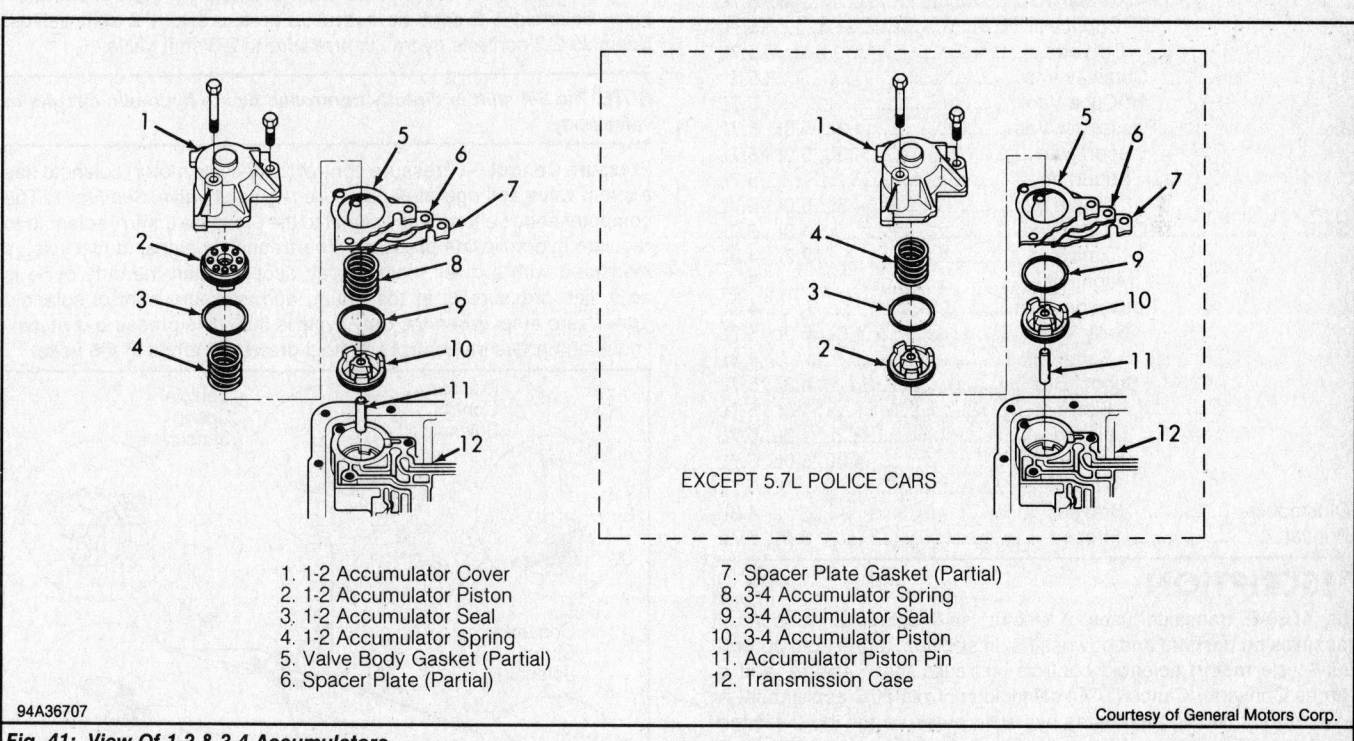

EXCEPT 5.7L POLICE CARS

1. 1-2 Accumulator Cover
2. 1-2 Accumulator Piston
3. 1-2 Accumulator Seal
4. 1-2 Accumulator Spring
5. Valve Body Gasket (Partial)
6. Spacer Plate (Partial)
7. Spacer Plate Gasket (Partial)
8. 3-4 Accumulator Spring
9. 3-4 Accumulator Seal
10. 3-4 Accumulator Piston
11. Accumulator Piston Pin
12. Transmission Case

94A36707

Courtesy of General Motors Corp.

Fig. 41: View Of 1-2 & 3-4 Accumulators

AUTOMATIC TRANSMISSIONS
4L60-E Electronic Controls

APPLICATION & IDENTIFICATION

THM 4L60-E APPLICATIONS (1993-94)

Manufacturer	Model	Engine
1993		
Chevrolet	Astro	4.3L
	Blazer	2.5L, 4.3L, 5.7L, 6.2L
	Cutaway Van	5.7L, 6.2L
	Hi-Cube Van	5.7L, 6.2L
	Passenger Van	4.3L, 5.0L, 5.7L, 6.2L
	Sport Van	4.3L, 5.0L, 5.7L, 6.2L
	Suburban	5.7L, 6.2L
	Pickup	2.5L, 4.3L, 5.0L, 5.7L, 6.2L
GMC	Cutaway Van	4.3L, 5.7L
	Jimmy	2.5L, 4.3L
	Magnavan	5.7L, 6.2L
	Passenger Van	4.3L
	Rally Van	4.3L, 5.0L, 5.7L, 6.2L
	Safari	4.3L
	School Bus	4.3L, 5.7L
	Sierra	4.3L, 5.7L, 6.2L
	Pickup	2.5L, 4.3L, 5.7L, 6.2L
	Vandura	4.3L, 5.0L, 5.7L, 6.2L
	Yukon	5.7L
Oldsmobile	Bravada	4.3L
1994		
Buick	Roadmaster	5.7L
Cadillac	Brougham	5.7L
Chevrolet	Astro	4.3L
	Blazer	2.2L, 4.3L, 5.7L
	Camaro	3.4L, 5.7L
	Caprice	5.7L
	Corvette	5.7L
	Cutaway Van	5.7L
	Hi-Cube Van	5.7L
	Passenger Van	4.3L, 5.0L, 5.7L
	Sport Van	4.3L, 5.0L, 5.7L
	Suburban	5.7L
	Pickup	2.2L, 4.3L, 5.0L, 5.7L
GMC	Cutaway Van	4.3L, 5.7L
	Jimmy	2.2L, 4.3L
	Magnavan	5.7L
	Passenger Van	4.3L
	Rally Van	4.3L, 5.0L, 5.7L
	Safari	4.3L
	School Bus	4.3L, 5.7L
	Sierra	4.3L, 5.7L
	Pickup	2.2L, 4.3L, 5.7L
	Vandura	4.3L, 5.0L, 5.7L
	Yukon	5.7L
Oldsmobile	Bravada	4.3L
Pontiac	Firebird	3.4L, 5.7L

DESCRIPTION

The 4L60-E transaxle uses 2 electric shift solenoids to control transmission upshifts and downshifts. In addition, a pressure control (duty-cycle motor) solenoid controls hydraulic line pressure, and a Torque Converter Clutch (TCC) solenoid controls TCC application. A 3-2 control solenoid modulates hydraulic pressure for the 2-4 band and 3-4 clutch to improve 3-2 downshift. Solenoids are turned on and off by the Powertrain Control Module (PCM).

The PCM receives signals from various transmission sensors. The sensors include engine speed and throttle position, transmission speed, hydraulic pressure and transmission fluid temperature. The PCM has on-board self-diagnostics to help identify any parts or circuits that may need further testing.

OPERATION

Shift solenoid holds hydraulic pressure when it is on and releases pressure when it is off. This action controls the shift valves inside valve body. By switching one or both solenoids on or off, different combinations of clutches, sprags and bands are operated. See CLUTCH & BAND APPLICATION CHART table under ELECTRONIC TESTING.

PCM

The PCM is located under air cleaner on Brougham, Caprice and Roadmaster; at right rear corner of engine compartment on Camaro and Firebird, and above power brake booster on Corvette. The PCM is located behind glove box on all light duty truck vehicles except "G" Series. On "G" Series, PCM is under driver's seat.

PCM controls TCC, pressure control solenoid (hydraulic pressure) and shifting solenoids 1-2 and 2-3. In addition, PCM also controls ignition, fuel and emission devices related to the engine.

The PCM receives electronic signals from sensors and switches. These signals help the PCM determine when to operate various relays and solenoids related to engine and transmission components.

SENSORS & SWITCHES

The PCM controls converter clutch lock-up, upshifts and downshifts based on transmission temperature, system voltage, throttle position, transmission oil pressure switches (5), and transmission output and input (engine) speed sensors. See Fig. 1. The system includes several other switches and sensors that are used for engine control (gasoline engines). For additional information and testing of engine components, see appropriate article in ENGINE PERFORMANCE of appropriate Mitchell® manual.

SOLENOIDS

Shift Solenoids 1-2 & 2-3 – Transmission is shifted up or down by 2 electric solenoids. Both solenoids are located on valve body. See Fig. 1. Ignition power is supplied to each solenoid by the transmission fuse. Solenoid 1-2 controls hydraulic pressure to 1-2 shift valves. Solenoid 2-3 controls hydraulic pressure to 2-3 shift valve.

NOTE: The 3-4 shift is directly controlled by the hydraulic circuits in valve body.

Pressure Control – Pressure control (duty-cycle motor) solenoid has a spool valve and operates pressure regulator valve. See Fig. 1. The computer sends a frequency signal to the pressure control solenoid to regulate hydraulic line pressure. The frequency signal (duty cycle) is measured with a dwell meter or lab scope. When the duty cycle is zero, line pressure is at maximum, and pressure control solenoid draws zero amp. When the duty cycle is 60%, line pressure is at minimum, and pressure control solenoid draws 1.1 amps at 4-5 volts.

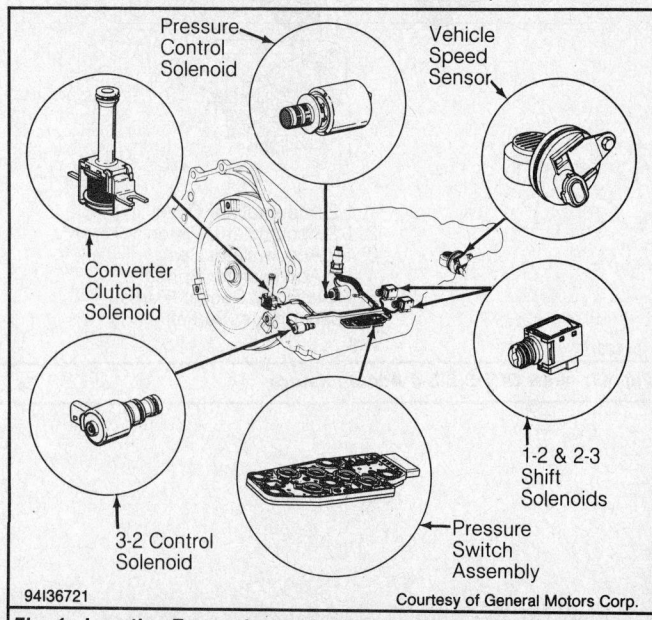

94I36721   Courtesy of General Motors Corp.

Fig. 1: Locating Transmission Solenoids, Sensors & Switches

ELECTRONIC TESTING

CLUTCH & BAND APPLICATION CHART

CLUTCH & BAND APPLICATION CHART

Selector Lever Position	Shift Solenoid Position	Elements In Use
"D" (Overdrive)		
First Gear	1-2 ON/2-3 ON	Forward Clutch, Forward Sprag & Low Roller Clutch
Second Gear	1-2 OFF/2-3 ON	Forward Clutch, Forward Sprag & 2-4 Band
Third Gear	1-2 OFF/2-3 OFF	Forward Clutch, Forward Sprag & 3-4 Clutch
Overdrive	1-2 ON/2-3 OFF	Forward Clutch 2-4 Band & 3-4 Clutch
"D" (Drive)		
First Gear	1-2 ON/2-3 ON	Forward Clutch, Forward Sprag, Low Roller Clutch & Overrun Clutch
Second Gear	1-2 OFF/2-3 ON	Forward Clutch, Forward Sprag, Overrun Clutch & 2-4 Band,
Third Gear	1-2 OFF/2-3 OFF	Forward Clutch, Forward Sprag, Overrun Clutch & 3-4 Clutch
"2" (Intermediate)		
First Gear	1-2 ON/2-3 ON	Forward Clutch, Forward Sprag, Low Roller Clutch & Overrun Clutch
Second Gear	1-2 OFF/2-3 ON	Forward Clutch, Forward Sprag, Overrun Clutch & 2-4 Band
"1" (Low)		
First Gear	1-2 ON/2-3 ON	Forward Clutch, Forward Sprag, Low Reverse Clutch, Low Roller Clutch & Overrun Clutch
"R" (Reverse)	1-2 ON/2-3 ON	Low Reverse Clutch & Reverse Input Clutch
"N" Or "P" (Neutral Or Park)	1-2 ON/2-3 ON	All Clutches & Bands Released Or Ineffective

TCC Solenoid – This solenoid is used to control TCC apply valve. The computer sends a frequency signal to the TCC solenoid to gradually apply or release the TCC. *See Fig. 1.*

3-2 Control Solenoid – PCM modulates current (duty cycle) to control 3-2 control solenoid. The 3-2 control solenoid is off in first gear. In all other gears, 3-2 control solenoid is 90 percent on. Hydraulic pressure is regulated to smoothly release the 3-4 clutch and 2-4 apply band during 3-2 downshift.

NOTE: The following tests are for 4L60-E transmission only. For complete testing of 4L60, see 4L60 & 4L60-E article in AUTOMATIC TRANSMISSIONS.

SHIFT SPEED TEST

1) Connect scan tool and observe throttle angle and vehicle speed at shift points. Operate vehicle in Overdrive. Accelerate using steady throttle pressure. Note shift points for 2nd, 3rd, Overdrive and TCC application. TCC application should occur in 3rd or Overdrive.

2) Torque converter clutch will not engage until engine coolant has reached a temperature of 140°F (60°C). Compare shift points to shift speed charts. *See Figs. 2-4.*

3) Operate vehicle in Overdrive normally at 40-55 MPH with throttle in half-open position. Ensure TCC releases, and note 3rd gear downshift point. Repeat procedure with wide open throttle. Ensure TCC releases, and note 2nd gear downshift point.

4) Operate vehicle normally in Overdrive, at 40-55 MPH. Release accelerator while manually shifting transmission to 3rd gear. Ensure TCC releases and engine braking is felt, and note 3rd gear downshift point.

5) Operate vehicle normally in Overdrive, at 40-45 MPH. Release accelerator while manually shifting transmission into 2nd gear. Ensure TCC releases and engine braking is felt, and note 2nd gear downshift point.

6) With transmission in Overdrive, accelerate normally to 25 MPH, allowing vehicle to upshift normally. Release accelerator while manually shifting transmission into 1st gear. Ensure TCC releases and engine braking is felt, and note 1st gear downshift point.

7) With transmission in Overdrive, accelerate to 4th gear with TCC applied. Release accelerator. Lightly apply brakes, and ensure TCC releases and note speed at which downshifts occur. Compare shift points noted to shift speed charts. *See Figs. 2-4.*

8) Place transmission in 3rd gear with vehicle stopped. Accelerate, and note 1st-2nd and 2nd-3rd shift points. Repeat procedure with transmission in 2nd gear. Note 1st-2nd shift point. Accelerate to 25 MPH. Ensure 2nd-3rd gear upshift does not occur and TCC does not engage.

9) Place transmission in 1st gear with vehicle stopped. Accelerate to 20 MPH. Ensure upshifts do not occur and TCC does not engage. With vehicle stopped, place transmission in Reverse and slowly accelerate to observe reverse gear operation.

10) Compare all shift points to shift speed charts. *See Figs. 2-4.* If shift points are not within speed listed, see TROUBLE SHOOTING. Control pressure can also be checked. See CONTROL PRESSURE TEST.

LINE PRESSURE TEST

CAUTION: DO NOT perform following pressure tests for longer than 2 minutes or transmission damage may occur.

1) Ensure fluid level is correct and engine is in good operating condition before performing line pressure test. Ensure shift linkage is properly adjusted. See appropriate AUTOMATIC TRANSMISSION SERVICING article in TRANSMISSION SERVICING.

2) Install a scan tester to diagnostic connector. *See Fig. 6.* Install pressure gauge on transmission line pressure tap. *See Fig. 5.* Apply parking brake. Ensure engine is at normal operating temperature.

3) Access PCS CONTROL test in scan tool. Place gear selector in "P" position. Increase DESIRED PCS in .1 amp increments. Note line pressure reading. Line pressure reading should be the same with gear selector to "D" or "N" position.

4) Check line pressure. See LINE PRESSURE SPECIFICATIONS table. Line pressure readings must be within specification. If line pressure reading is not within specification, see TROUBLE SHOOTING.

LINE PRESSURE SPECIFICATIONS

Current (Amps)	Line Pressure
.02	170-190 psi (11.7-13.1 kg/cm²)
.10	165-185 psi (11.3-12.7 kg/cm²)
.20	160-180 psi (11.0-12.4 kg/cm²)
.30	155-175 psi (10.7-12.1 kg/cm²)
.40	148-168 psi (10.4-11.7 kg/cm²)
.50	140-160 psi (9.6-11.0 kg/cm²)
.60	130-145 psi (8.9-10.0 kg/cm²)
.70	110-130 psi (7.5-8.9 kg/cm²)
.80	90-115 psi (6.2-7.9 kg/cm²)
.90	65-90 psi (4.5-6.2 kg/cm²)
.98	55-65 psi (3.8-4.5 kg/cm²)

SYMPTOM TROUBLE SHOOTING

Incorrect Shift Pattern – Check TP sensor, VSS, shift solenoids, 4WD low switch (light trucks and vans only) or performance switch (Camaro and Firebird with V8 only).

AUTOMATIC TRANSMISSIONS
4L60-E Electronic Controls (Cont.)

ENGINE	BODY	AXLE RATIO	1-2 SHIFT +/- 250 RPM					2-3 SHIFT +/- 200 RPM					3-4 SHIFT +/- 150 RPM					4-3 +/- 100 RPM	3-2 +/- 100 RPM	2-1 +/- 100 RPM
		TPS	10	20	30	40	50	10	20	30	40	50	10	20	30	40	50	0-10	0-10	0-10
5.7L (L05)	C10/G	3.08	466	622	738	816	894	835	1126	1282	1495	1670	1243	1554	1981	*	*	1127	699	369
	C20/K	3.42																		
	C10/G	3.42	466	678	762	889	953	847	1228	1440	1652	1800	1270	1567	2054	*	*	1122	762	381
	C20/K	3.73																		
	C10/G	3.73	514	700	817	911	981	934	1284	1518	1705	1845	1307	1635	2101	*	*	1121	841	373
	C/K	4.10																		

ENGINE	BODY	AXLE RATIO	1-2 SHIFT +/- 250 RPM					2-3 SHIFT +/- 200 RPM					3-4 SHIFT +/- 150 RPM					4-3 +/- 100 RPM	3-2 +/- 100 RPM	2-1 +/- 100 RPM
		TPS	10	20	30	40	50	10	20	30	40	50	10	20	30	40	50	0-10	0-10	0-10
5.0L (L03)	C10/G	3.08	486	660	758	855	893	835	1146	1360	1632	1768	1243	1535	1943	2311	*	1126	699	369
	C20/K	3.42																		
	C10/G	3.42	510	744	893	978	957	851	1233	1446	1680	1808	1276	1574	1914	2297	*	1127	765	383
	C20/K	3.73																		
	G	3.73	560	793	910	1004	980	934	1237	1517	1704	1844	1307	1611	1914	2311	*	1120	840	373
	C/K	4.10																		

ENGINE	BODY	AXLE RATIO	1-2 SHIFT +/- 250 RPM					2-3 SHIFT +/- 200 RPM					3-4 SHIFT +/- 150 RPM					4-3 +/- 100 RPM	3-2 +/- 100 RPM	2-1 +/- 100 RPM
		TPS	10	20	30	40	50	10	20	30	40	50	10	20	30	40	50	0-10	0-10	0-10
6.2L DIESEL (LH6)	C	3.08	369	369	505	582	757	757	757	893	1184	1437	1359	1359	1359	*	*	1223	679	330
	C20/K	3.42																		
	C10	3.42	361	382	489	595	744	744	744	872	1170	1425	1340	1340	1340	*	*	1212	680	319
	C20/K	3.73																		
	C10	3.73	373	373	467	607	747	747	747	887	1190	1424	1354	1354	1354	*	*	1214	677	326
	C/K	4.10																		
	G	3.08	352	389	519	556	723	723	723	871	1057	1317	1298	1298	1298	*	*	1168	649	315
		3.42	349	369	472	513	719	719	719	863	1068	1315	1294	1294	1294	*	*	1171	657	308
		3.73	359	381	516	561	718	718	718	853	1077	1324	1302	1302	1302	*	*	1167	651	314

ENGINE	BODY	AXLE RATIO	1-2 SHIFT +/- 250 RPM					2-3 SHIFT +/- 200 RPM					3-4 SHIFT +/- 150 RPM					4-3 +/- 100 RPM	3-2 +/- 100 RPM	2-1 +/- 100 RPM
		TPS	10	20	30	40	50	10	20	30	40	50	10	20	30	40	50	0-10	0-10	0-10
4.3L (L35)	M/L	3.42/3.73	566	784	828	893	915	981	1482	1656	1765	1787	1395	1918	3488	*	*	1242	588	348
	S/T	3.08/3.42	545	784	828	893	915	981	1460	1656	1765	1787	1438	2005	3488	*	*	1242	588	348
4.3L (LB4)	M/L	3.23/3.42	392	545	588	675	784	784	1111	1242	1417	1613	1395	1700	1918	*	*	1242	632	348
		3.73	479	719	937	1002	1046	850	1308	1526	1787	1940	1395	1765	1983	*	*	1242	654	348
	G	3.42/3.73	479	741	937	1002	1046	850	1329	1569	1787	1940	1395	1787	2005	*	*	1242	654	348
	S/T	3.08/3.42	436	545	588	675	784	784	1090	1220	1417	1613	1395	1678	1918	*	*	1242	654	348
	C10	3.08/3.42	479	588	654	741	784	850	1177	1308	1460	1613	1395	1678	1918	*	*	1242	654	348
		3.73/4.10	501	654	719	763	784	915	1242	1373	1526	1613	1395	1678	1918	*	*	1242	654	348

* – No shift at this TP sensor position.
1. All speeds are given in transmission output shaft RPM.
2. Speeds are based on percent of TP sensor position data.
3. Use a Scan tester to monitor data.
4. All shift speeds are approximate.

Fig. 2: Shift Speed Chart (1993 – All Models)

ENGINE	BODY	AXLE RATIO	1-2 SHIFT +/- 250 RPM TPS			2-3 SHIFT +/- 200 RPM TPS			3-4 SHIFT +/- 150 RPM TPS			2-1 +/- 100 RPM	1-2 WOT	2-3 WOT
			10	25	50	10	25	50	10	25	50			
3.4L (L32)	F	3.23	472	837	1072	815	1523	1994	1373	2016	N/A	1286	1501	2874
4.3L (L99)	B	2.93	376	581	924	650	992	1642	992	1300	N/A	1027	1505	2395
4.3L (L99)	B	2.73	376	615	1026	650	1026	1711	958	1403	N/A	1027	1711	2395

ENGINE	BODY	AXLE RATIO	1-2 SHIFT +/- 250 RPM TPS			2-3 SHIFT +/- 200 RPM TPS			3-4 SHIFT +/- 150 RPM TPS			2-1 +/- 100 RPM	1-2 WOT	2-3 WOT
			10	25	50	10	25	50	10	25	50			
5.7L (LT1)	B	3.08	457	724	1182	724	1220	2212	1106	1716	N/A	1258	1716	3051
5.7L (LT1)	B/D	2.93	317	570	951	570	951	1680	887	1268	N/A	982	1331	2250
5.7L (LT1)	B/D	2.56	348	602	1046	602	1077	1902	919	1458	N/A	951	1648	2536
5.7L (LT1)	F Normal Mode	2.73	434	543	1375	760	1303	2570	977	1448	N/A	1339	1737	3366
5.7L (LT1)	F Performance Mode (Pontiac Only)	2.73	434	651	1194	760	1267	2280	977	1737	N/A	1339	1520	3004
5.7L (LT1)	F Normal Mode	3.23	481	788	1182	832	1576	2190	1401	1883	N/A	1620	1664	3197
5.7L (LT1)	F Performance Mode (Pontiac Only)	3.23	481	788	1357	876	1357	2934	1401	1883	N/A	1620	1576	3197
5.7L (LT1)	Y	2.59	386	737	1193	751	1333	2211	1053	1860	N/A	1404	1755	3439
5.7L (LT1)	Y	3.07	456	830	1286	871	1618	2407	1203	2241	N/A	1618	1743	3237

1. All speeds are given in transmission output shaft RPM.
2. Speeds are based on percent of TP sensor position data.
3. Use a Scan tester to monitor data.
4. All shift speeds are approximate.

94A36723

Courtesy of General Motors Corp.

Fig. 3: Shift Speed Chart (1994 Passenger Vehicles)

Shift Quality – Check TP sensor, VSS, transmission temperature sensor, engine coolant temperature sensor, shift solenoids, pressure switch assembly, pressure control solenoid or manual and/or performance switches (Camaro and Firebird with V8 only).
Engine Rough – Check TP sensor.
Line Pressure Too High – Check pressure switch assembly, system voltage or pressure control solenoid.
Line Pressure Too Low – Check pressure control solenoid.
MIL Stuck On – Check engine speed (tachometer) sensor.

Erratic Manual Downshift – Check pressure switch assembly.
Unwanted Downshift (Corvette Only) – Check Acceleration Slip Regulation (ASR) system.
Wrong Gear, No Shift Or Two Gears Only – Check shift solenoids.
Second Gear Start (Camaro & Firebird With V6 Engine Only) – Check second gear start switch.
3rd Gear Only – Check system voltage or 3-2 control solenoid.
Delayed 3-4 Upshift & TCC Apply During Hard Acceleration – Check cruise control.

AUTOMATIC TRANSMISSIONS
4L60-E Electronic Controls (Cont.)

ENGINE	BODY	AXLE RATIO	1-2 SHIFT +/- 250 RPM (TPS)			2-3 SHIFT +/- 200 RPM (TPS)			3-4 SHIFT +/- 150 RPM (TPS)			3-2 +/- 100 RPM	2-1 +/- 100 RPM	1-2 WOT	2-3 WOT
			10	25	50	10	25	50	10	25	50				
2.2L (LM2)	S	4.10	596	795	1143	1043	1441	2137	1491	1988	3280	3081	1491	1689	3230

ENGINE	BODY	AXLE RATIO	1-2 SHIFT +/- 250 RPM (TPS)			2-3 SHIFT +/- 200 RPM (TPS)			3-4 SHIFT +/- 150 RPM (TPS)			3-2 +/- 100 RPM	2-1 +/- 100 RPM	1-2 WOT	2-3 WOT
			10	25	50	10	25	50	10	25	50				
4.3L (L35)	S/T	3.08/3.42	566	828	915	1090	1526	1787	1438	1918	2659	2441	1220	1526	2921
	M/L	3.42/3.73	566	828	915	1090	1526	1787	1438	1918	2659	2441	1220	1526	2921
4.3L (LB4)	G	3.42/3.73	479	654	959	872	1264	1918	1395	1831	2572	2267	1220	1351	2528
	C/K	3.08/3.42	479	654	959	959	1264	1918	1395	1831	2572	2267	1220	1351	2528
	C/K	3.73/4.10	523	697	784	1002	1351	1613	1395	1831	2572	2049	1220	1351	2528
	M	3.23	479	654	959	959	1526	1918	1395	1831	2572	2267	1220	1351	2528
	M	3.42	523	784	1046	915	1438	1962	1395	1918	2659	2049	1220	1351	2528
	S/T	3.08/3.42	479	654	959	915	1526	1918	1395	1831	2572	2267	1220	1351	2528

ENGINE	BODY	AXLE RATIO	1-2 SHIFT +/- 250 RPM (TPS)			2-3 SHIFT +/- 200 RPM (TPS)			3-4 SHIFT +/- 150 RPM (TPS)			3-2 +/- 100 RPM	2-1 +/- 100 RPM	1-2 WOT	2-3 WOT
			10	25	50	10	25	50	10	25	50				
5.0L (L03)	C10/G10/G20	3.08	481	666	851	777	1184	1591	1184	1665	2479	2035	962	1258	2368
	C20/K10/K20	3.42													
	C10/G10/G20	3.42	529	773	936	814	1302	1750	1221	1668	2482	2035	976	1261	2360
	C20/K10/K20	3.73													
	G20	3.73	536	849	938	894	1385	1788	1251	1698	2503	2011	983	1251	2369
	C20/K10/K20	4.10													

ENGINE	BODY	AXLE RATIO	1-2 SHIFT +/- 250 RPM (TPS)			2-3 SHIFT +/- 200 RPM (TPS)			3-4 SHIFT +/- 150 RPM (TPS)			3-2 +/- 100 RPM	2-1 +/- 100 RPM	1-2 WOT	2-3 WOT
			10	25	50	10	25	50	10	25	50				
5.7L (L05)	C10/G10/G20	3.08	444	629	851	777	1184	1591	1184	1628	2479	2035	962	1295	2368
	C20/K10/K20	3.42													
	C10/G10/G20	3.42	447	691	936	814	1302	1709	1221	1668	2482	2035	976	1261	2360
	C20/K10/K20	3.73													
	C10/G20	3.73	491	759	938	894	1385	1788	1251	1698	2503	2011	983	1251	2369
	C20/K20	4.10													

ENGINE	BODY	AXLE RATIO	1-2 SHIFT +/- 250 RPM (TPS)			2-3 SHIFT +/- 200 RPM (TPS)			3-4 SHIFT +/- 150 RPM (TPS)			3-2 +/- 100 RPM	2-1 +/- 100 RPM	1-2 WOT	2-3 WOT
		TPS	10	25	50	10	25	50	10	25	50				
6.5L (DIESEL)	G	3.42	370	534	822	698	1068	1644	1315	1561	2096	1767	945	1191	1931
	G	3.08	370	518	814	703	1073	1665	1295	1554	2109	1776	962	1147	1924
	C10	3.42	370	534	822	698	1068	1644	1315	1561	2096	2013	945	1191	2260
	C20/K	3.73													
	C10	3.08	370	518	814	703	1036	1665	1295	1517	2109	2035	962	1147	2257
	C20/K	3.42													
	G	3.73	358	537	806	716	1075	1657	1299	1568	2105	1792	940	1164	1926

1. All speeds are given in transmission output shaft RPM.
2. Speeds are based on percent of TP sensor position data.
3. Use a Scan tester to monitor data.
4. All shift speeds are approximate.

94B36724

Courtesy of General Motors Corp.

Fig. 4: Shift Speed Chart (1994 Light Trucks & Vans)

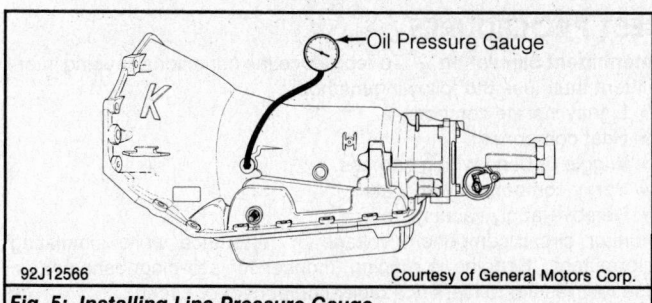

92J12566   Courtesy of General Motors Corp.

Fig. 5: Installing Line Pressure Gauge

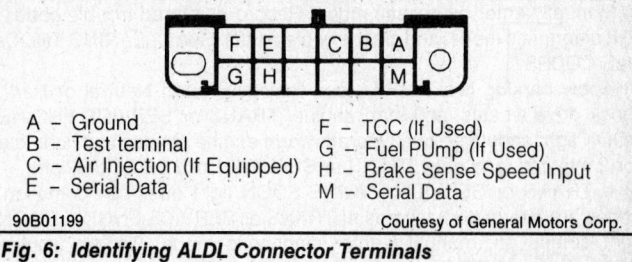

A – Ground
B – Test terminal
C – Air Injection (If Equipped)
E – Serial Data

F – TCC (If Used)
G – Fuel PUmp (If Used)
H – Brake Sense Speed Input
M – Serial Data

90B01199   Courtesy of General Motors Corp.

Fig. 6: Identifying ALDL Connector Terminals

No 4th Gear Hot – Check engine speed (tachometer) sensor, pressure switch assembly, brake switch, system voltage or TCC solenoid.

No TCC Apply – Check engine speed (tachometer) sensor, pressure switch assembly, brake switch, system voltage, or TCC solenoid.

TCC Apply Time Wrong – Check VSS, transmission temperature sensor.

SELF-DIAGNOSTICS

The PCM constantly monitors all electrical circuits. If the PCM detects circuit problem(s) or out-of-range sensor(s), a trouble code(s) will be recorded in computer memory. If problem continues for a preset time, the TRANS or SERVICE ENGINE SOON light will glow.

If the TRANS or SERVICE ENGINE SOON light is always on, trouble code(s) is currently being detected. If the TRANS or SERVICE ENGINE SOON light is off, but PCM has detected a circuit or sensor problem, trouble code(s) will be stored in computer memory.

Stored trouble codes may be retrieved from PCM memory using Scan tester or TRANS or SERVICE ENGINE SOON light. See appropriate RETRIEVING CODES procedure under ELECTRONIC SELF-DIAGNOSTICS.

NOTE: For complete PCM testing and diagnosis, see appropriate article in ENGINE PERFORMANCE of appropriate Mitchell® manual.

ELECTRONIC SELF-DIAGNOSTICS

NOTE: To test electronic control of transmission solenoids without using self-diagnostics, see COMPONENT TEST CHARTS (NO CODES) under COMPONENT TESTING. After repairs are made, trouble codes should be erased from computer memory. See CLEARING TROUBLE CODES under ELECTRONIC SELF-DIAGNOSTICS.

RETRIEVING CODES (WITHOUT SCAN TESTER)

1) Turn ignition on. DO NOT start engine. TRANS or SERVICE ENGINE SOON light should glow. Locate Assembly Line Data Link (ALDL) connector under dash, on driver's side of vehicle. Turn ignition on with engine not running.

2) Connect jumper wire from terminal "B" (diagnostic terminal) to terminal "A" (ground terminal) of ALDL connector. *See Fig. 6.* Some models do not have a wire connected to "B" terminal. These models must use a Scan tester to access trouble codes.

NOTE: Connecting terminals "A" and "B" of ALDL connector with engine running will cause fuel injected vehicles to enter field service mode. The TRANS or SERVICE ENGINE SOON light will not flash codes if this is done.

3) TRANS or SERVICE ENGINE SOON light should begin flashing codes. Each code will be repeated 3 times. Code 21 is identified by 2 flashes, a short pause followed by one flash; Code 53 is identified by 5 flashes, a short pause followed by 3 flashes. Trouble codes are separated by slightly longer pauses.

4) Trouble codes are displayed in numerical order. Each code is displayed 3 times. Codes will continue to repeat as long as ALDL test terminal is grounded.

5) If codes are not flashed, or TRANS or SERVICE ENGINE SOON light does not glow, self-diagnostics will not work. See CHART A-1 under DIAGNOSTIC CHARTS. If TRANS or SERVICE LIGHT SOON light glows steadily, see CHART A-2 under DIAGNOSTIC CHARTS. To exit diagnostic mode, turn ignition off, and remove jumper wire from ALDL connector.

NOTE: Trouble codes will be recorded at various operating times. Some codes require operation of sensor or switch for 5 seconds; others may require operation for 5 minutes or longer at normal operating temperature, road speed and load. Therefore, some codes may not set in a service bay operational mode, but may require road testing vehicle in order to duplicate condition under which code will set.

RETRIEVING CODES (WITH SCAN TESTER)

NOTE: To read trouble codes and check system voltages on serial data line, plug scan tester into ALDL.

The scan tester is a specialized tester which, when plugged into ALDL, can be used to diagnose on-board computer control systems by providing instant access to circuit voltage information without need to crawl under dash or hood to backprobe sensors and connectors.

Scan testers may also furnish information on status of output devices (solenoids and relays). However, status parameters are only an indication that output signals have been sent to devices by the control module. It does not indicate if devices have responded properly to that signal. This will need to be checked at output device using a voltmeter or test light.

NOTE: Code 12 should always exist when ALDL is grounded with key on and engine off, but may not be indicated by all makes of Scan testers.

If trouble code is not present, this is not an indication there is no problem. Driveability-related problems with codes displayed occur about 20 percent of the time, while driveability problems without codes occur about 80 percent of the time.

Out-of-specification sensors WILL NOT set trouble code, but WILL cause driveability problems. Using scan tester is the easiest method of checking sensor specifications and other data parameters. Intermittent wiring problems may be identified by wiggling wiring harnesses and connections (key on, engine off) while observing scan tester.

NOTE: If erroneous voltage signals are suspected, it will be necessary to verify tester information using digital voltmeter and wiring schematic. If non-existent codes are displayed, turn ignition off, remove tester, turn ignition on, and ground ALDL test terminal "B". The same codes should be retrieved whether scan tester or TRANS or SERVICE ENGINE SOON light is used.

HARD OR INTERMITTENT TROUBLE CODE DETERMINATION

During any diagnostic procedure, it must be determined if codes are hard failure codes or intermittent failure codes. A hard failure indicates that a problem is currently present. Diagnostic charts do not usually provide intermittent code diagnosis. To determine hard codes and intermittent codes, proceed as follows:

1) Manually enter diagnostic mode. Record all stored trouble codes. Exit diagnostic mode, and clear trouble codes. See CLEARING TROUBLE CODES.

2) Apply parking brake, and place transmission in Neutral or Park. Block drive wheels, and start engine. TRANS or SERVICE ENGINE SOON light should go out. Operate warm engine at specified curb idle for 2 minutes, and note TRANS or SERVICE ENGINE SOON light.

3) If TRANS or SERVICE ENGINE SOON light does not come on, codes are intermittent failures. If TRANS or SERVICE ENGINE SOON light comes on, manually enter diagnostic mode. Record trouble codes. If same codes reappear, they are hard failure codes. It may be necessary to road test vehicle in order to reset hard failure codes.

TROUBLE CODE DEFINITION
PCM TROUBLE CODE DEFINITION

Code No.	Circuit Affected
12 [1]	No RPM Reference Pulse
16 (Diesel Only)	Vehicle Speed Sensor
21	Throttle Position Switch Voltage High
22	Throttle Position Switch Voltage Low
24	Vehicle Speed Sensor Signal Low
28	Oil Pressure Switch Assembly Problem
39	[3][4][5] TCC Stuck OFF
58	Transmission Temperature High
59	Transmission Temperature Low
66	[5] 3-2 Control Solenoid Circuit
67	[5] TCC Solenoid Circuit
68	[3][4][5] Transmission Slipping
69	[5] TCC Stuck ON
72	Vehicle Speed Sensor Loss
73	[2] Pressure Control Solenoid Problem
74	[2][3][4] Transmission Input Speed Sensor Circuit
79	Transmission Fluid Too Hot
80	[3][7] Transmission Slipping
81	[2] Shift Solenoid "B" Circuit Error
82	[2] Shift Solenoid "A" Circuit Error
83	[3][4] TCC Solenoid Circuit Error
84	[2] 3-2 Control Solenoid Circuit
85	[3][4] Undefined Ratio Error Problem
85	[2][7] TCC Stuck ON
86	[3][4] Low Ratio Error Problem
87	[3][4] High Ratio Error Problem
90	[6][7] TCC Stuck ON
93	[6] Pressure Control Solenoid Problem

[1] – Display of a Code 12 is normal when no reference pulses are received by control module (engine not running).
[2] – Not on 3.4L Camaro and Firebird.
[3] – Applies to 1994 model year.
[4] – Applies to "C" and "K" light trucks only.
[5] – Not on passenger cars.
[6] – Used on 3.4L Camaro and Firebird only.
[7] – Used on passenger cars.

NOTE: Only transmission-mounted components related to transmission trouble codes are listed. If other trouble codes are present, see appropriate article in ENGINE PERFORMANCE of appropriate Mitchell® manual.

INTERMITTENT PROBLEM DIAGNOSIS

Intermittent fault testing requires duplicating circuit or component failure to identify fault. These procedures may lead to computer setting a fault code which may help in diagnosis.

If vehicle does not produce fault codes, monitor voltage or resistance values using a DVOM while attempting to reproduce conditions causing the intermittent fault. A status change on DVOM indicates a fault has been located.

Use DVOM to pinpoint faults. When monitoring voltage, ensure ignition is in ON position or engine is running. When monitoring resistance, ensure ignition switch is in the OFF position or negative battery cable is disconnected. A status change on DVOM while performing TEST PROCEDURES indicates area of fault.

TEST PROCEDURES

Intermittent Simulation – To reproduce the conditions causing intermittent fault, use the following methods:
- Lightly vibrate component.
- Heat component.
- Wiggle or bend wiring harness.
- Spray component with water.
- Remove/apply vacuum source.

Monitor circuit/component voltage or resistance while simulating intermittent. If engine is running, monitor for self-diagnostic codes. Use test results to identify a faulty component or circuit.

INTERMITTENT TROUBLE SHOOTING

Intermittent Symptom Definition – SERVICE ENGINE SOON light comes on but does not stay on. A stored code may or may not exist.

Possible Cause & Correction – To track down possible causes of an intermittent SERVICE ENGINE SOON light, check the following items:

- Check for poor mating of one connector to another. Terminals may not be fully seated. Check for improperly formed or damaged terminals. Check wire to terminal connections.
- Check wire from SERVICE ENGINE SOON light to PCM for short to ground.
- Check wire from test terminal "B" of ALDL for intermittent short to ground.
- Check for poor connections in PCM ground terminals.
- Check for loss of trouble code memory. To check code memory on fuel injected models, disconnect TP sensor and run engine at idle until SERVICE ENGINE SOON light comes on. Code 22 (or appropriate TP sensor code) should be stored and retained in memory when ignition is turned off. If code is not stored, PCM is faulty.
- Check for electrical system interference caused by a defective relay, or an PCM-driven solenoid or switch which may cause sharp electrical surge. This type of problem will normally occur when faulty component is operated.
- Check for aftermarket parts which may not have been produced to manufacturer's specifications. Solenoids without original-equipment diodes for circuit protection, and HEI-EST module or voltage regulator using transistors instead of silicon-chip circuitry may possibly cause voltage surges (up to 300 volts) in PCM wiring, causing temporary PCM shutdown. PCM shutdown is a normal response to system overvoltage (greater than 16-17 volts on most models). PCM will repower when condition no longer exists. This could cause a flickering SERVICE ENGINE SOON light and stumble, with no codes set in memory.
- Check for any open diodes in A/C or engine wiring.
- Check for improper installation of electrical accessories such as auxiliary lights or 2-way radios.
- Ensure EST (gas engine) wires are kept away from spark plug wires, distributor wires, distributor housing, ignition coil and generator. Ensure ground wire from PCM to distributor or ignition module is connected to a good ground.

CLEARING TROUBLE CODES

Turn ignition switch to ON position, and ground diagnostic test terminal "B" at ALDL connector. Turn ignition switch to OFF position, and remove control module fuse from fuse block for 30 seconds. Install fuse. Remove diagnostic terminal ground lead from terminal "B". If fuse cannot be located, pigtail at battery can be disconnected. When power to PCM is removed, poor driveability may occur until control module relearns operating parameters.

DIAGNOSTIC CHARTS

The following charts include flow charts, testing information and related wiring diagram. For complete transmission wiring diagrams, see WIRING DIAGRAMS at end of article. For additional engine diagnostic information, see appropriate article in ENGINE PERFORMANCE of appropriate MITCHELL® manual.

NOTE: DIAGNOSTIC AIDS in charts may help diagnose trouble codes when problem cannot be identified through circuit checks. ECM, PCM or TCM may be used in flow charts to describe the control module.

CHART A-1 (CAMARO & FIREBIRD W/4.3L)

1) If engine starts, go to step **3)**. If engine does not start, check for blown fuses in PCM ignition and PCM battery feed circuits. Check and repair circuits if blown fuses are present.

2) If fuses are okay, turn ignition off. Disconnect PCM connector and turn ignition on. Check for battery and ignition voltage at appropriate PCM connector terminals. If voltage is not present, repair open circuit. If voltage is present, check for faulty PCM grounds, faulty connections at PCM or faulty PCM.

3) If engine started in step **1)**, disconnect PCM connectors. Using a jumper wire, connect terminal B7 (Brown/White wire) of PCM connector to ground. If test light stays off, repair open circuit, burned bulb, or Brown/White wire shorted to voltage as necessary. If test light is on, PCM connector is faulty or PCM is faulty.

CHART A-1 (BROUGHAM, CAPRICE, CAMARO, CORVETTE, FIREBIRD & ROADMASTER W/5.7L)

1) If engine starts, go to step **3)**. If engine does not start, check for blown fuses in PCM ignition and PCM battery feed circuits. Check and repair circuits if blown fuses are present.

2) If fuses are okay, turn ignition off. Disconnect PCM connector and turn ignition on. Check for battery and ignition voltage at appropriate PCM connector terminals. If voltage is not present, repair open circuit. If voltage is present, check for faulty PCM grounds, faulty connections at PCM or faulty PCM.

3) If engine started in step **1)**, connect Scan tester to ALDL connector. If Scan tester can display serial data, go to CODE DTC-11. If Scan tester cannot display serial data, turn ignition off.

4) Disconnect PCM connector and turn ignition on. Check for ignition voltage at PCM connector terminal D3 (Pink or Pink/Black wires). If voltage is not present, repair open ignition circuit. If voltage is present, check for faulty PCM grounds, faulty connections at PCM or faulty PCM.

CHART A-2 (BROUGHAM, CAPRICE, CAMARO, CORVETTE, FIREBIRD & ROADMASTER W/5.7L)

1) If MIL lamp does not flash with engine at idle, go to step **3)**. If MIL lamp flashes with engine at idle, turn ignition off. Disconnect PCM connector "D" ("C" on Corvette).

2) Connect one end of test light to battery positive terminal. Touch other end to terminal "B" of the ALDL connector. If test light is on, repair circuit shorted to ground. If test light stays off, PCM is faulty.

3) If MIL lamp did not flash in step **1)**, check for 5 volts at terminal "B" of the ALDL connector. If 5 volts are present, repair faulty connector at PCM or replace PCM. If 5 volts are not present, turn ignition off.

CHART A-1 ("C", "G" & "K" W/DIESEL ENGINE)

CHART A-1, NO MIL (SERVICE ENGINE SOON) LIGHT (WITH AUTOMATIC TRANSMISSION)

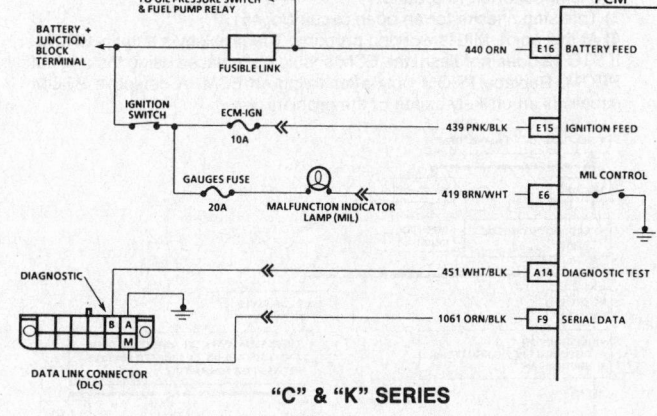

"C" & "K" SERIES

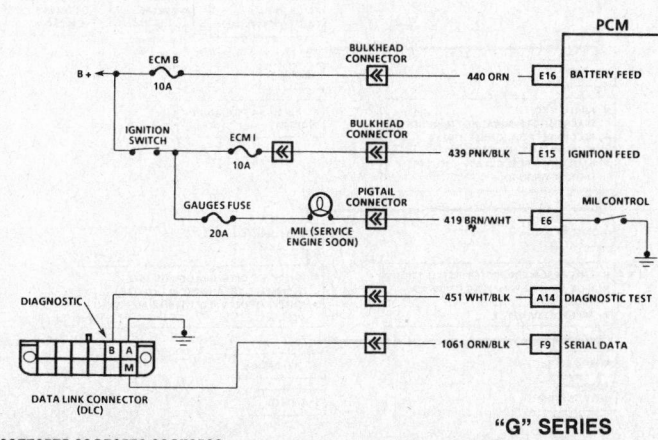

"G" SERIES

MIL should be on when engine is off and ignition is on. Switched battery voltage is supplied to MIL. The ECM turns light on by providing a ground path through circuit No. 419.

NOTE: Test numbers refer to numbers on diagnostic chart.

1) If fusible link is blown, see WIRING DIAGRAMS article for complete circuit.

2) Using a test light connected to 12 volts, probe each of the system ground circuits to ensure a good ground is present. See PIN VOLTAGE CHARTS article.

DIAGNOSTIC AIDS

If engine functions properly, check for a burned out bulb, blown gauges fuse, or circuit No. 419 open. If engine cranks but will not start, check for blown fusible link and for open circuit No. 440 to fuel pump relay.

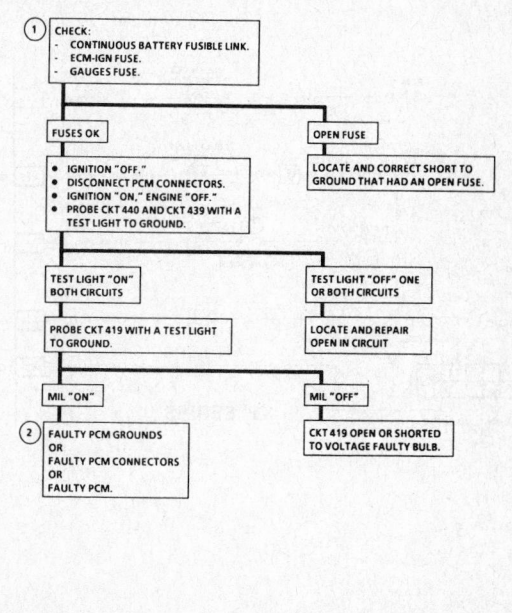

93F76575 93G76576 93C76580

Courtesy of General Motors Corp.

4) Disconnect PCM connector "D" ("C" on Corvette). Using a jumper wire, connect terminal "B" of ALDL connector to ground. Connect one end of test light to battery positive terminal. Touch other end to appropriate PCM terminal of the "D" connector ("C" on Corvette). If test light stays off, repair open circuit. If test light is on, PCM connector is faulty or PCM is faulty.

CHART A-1
("C", "G", "K", "L", "M", "S" & "T" W/GAS ENGINE)

1) If engine starts, go to step **3)**. If engine does not start, check for blown fuses in PCM ignition and PCM battery feed circuits. Check and repair circuits if blown fuses are present.

2) If fuses are okay, turn ignition off. Disconnect PCM connector and turn ignition on. Check for battery and ignition voltage at appropriate PCM connector terminals. If voltage is not present, repair open circuit. If voltage is present, check for faulty PCM grounds, faulty connections at PCM or faulty PCM.

CHART A-2
("C", "G" & "K" W/DIESEL ENGINE)

3) If engine started in step **1)**, turn ignition off. Disconnect PCM connector and turn ignition on. Using a test light, ground circuit at MIL control terminal of PCM connector (Brown/White wire). If MIL lamp does not go on, check MIL bulb, check related circuits and repair as necessary. If MIL lamp goes on, check for faulty PCM grounds, faulty connections at PCM or faulty PCM.

CHART A-2 ("C", "G", "K", "L", "M", "S" & "T" W/GAS ENGINE)

1) Turn ignition on, but leave engine off. If MIL lamp is off, go to CHART A-1. If MIL lamp is on, ground diagnostic connector. If MIL lamp does not flash code DTC-12, go to next step. If MIL lamp flashes code DTC-12, check serial data circuit for shorts or opens. If circuit is okay, PCM or PROM may be faulty.

2) If MIL lamp is off from step **1)**, turn ignition off. Disconnect PCM connectors. Turn ignition on. If MIL lamp goes on, check for short in circuit from MIL bulb to PCM connector.

3) If MIL lamp stays off, turn ignition off. Reconnect PCM connectors. Turn ignition on, but leave engine off. Make sure diagnostic connector is not grounded. Using a test light, back probe diagnostic connector terminal "B" at PCM (Black/White or White/Black wire).

CHART A-2, NO DLC DATA, MIL (SERVICE ENGINE SOON) LIGHT ON AT ALL TIMES OR WILL NOT FLASH DTC 12 (WITH AUTOMATIC TRANSMISSION)

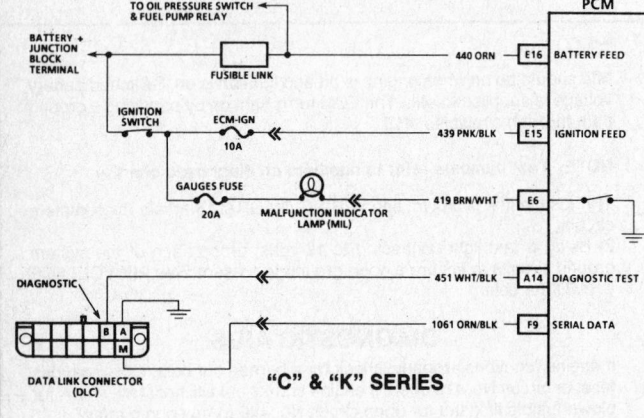

"C" & "K" SERIES

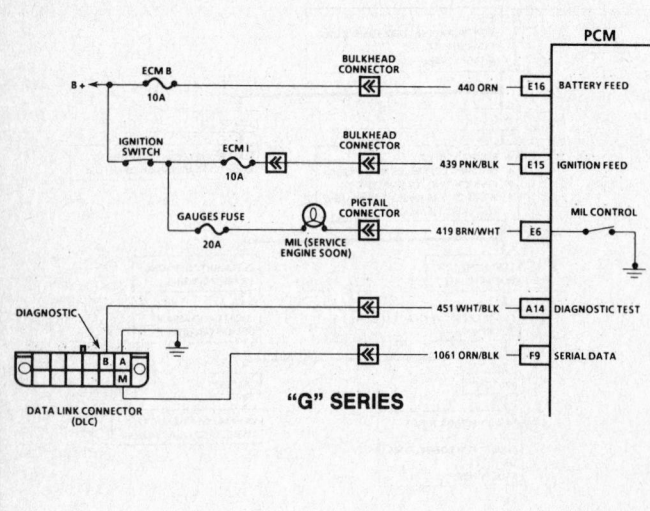

"G" SERIES

MIL should be on when engine is off and ignition is on. Switched battery voltage is supplied to MIL light. The ECM turns light on by providing a ground path through circuit No. 419. With diagnostic terminal grounded, MIL should flash DTC 12, followed by any other DTC stored in memory. A steady light on indicates a short to ground in circuit No. 419, or no engine speed sensor signal.

NOTE: Test numbers refer to numbers on diagnostic chart.

1) If there is a problem with ECM that causes scan tester not to read serial data, then the ECM should not flash DTC 12. If DTC 12 does flash, ensure scan tester is functioning properly (on another vehicle). If scan tester is functioning properly, and circuit No. 1061 is okay, the PROM or ECM may be at fault for no DLC data symptom.

2) If light goes off when ECM connector is disconnected, then circuit No. 419 is not shorted to ground.

3) This step checks for an open circuit No. 451.

4) At this point, MIL is working properly. The problem is a faulty PROM. If DTC 12 does not flash, the ECM should be replaced using the original PROM. Replace PROM only after trying an ECM. A defective PROM usually is an unlikely cause of the problem.

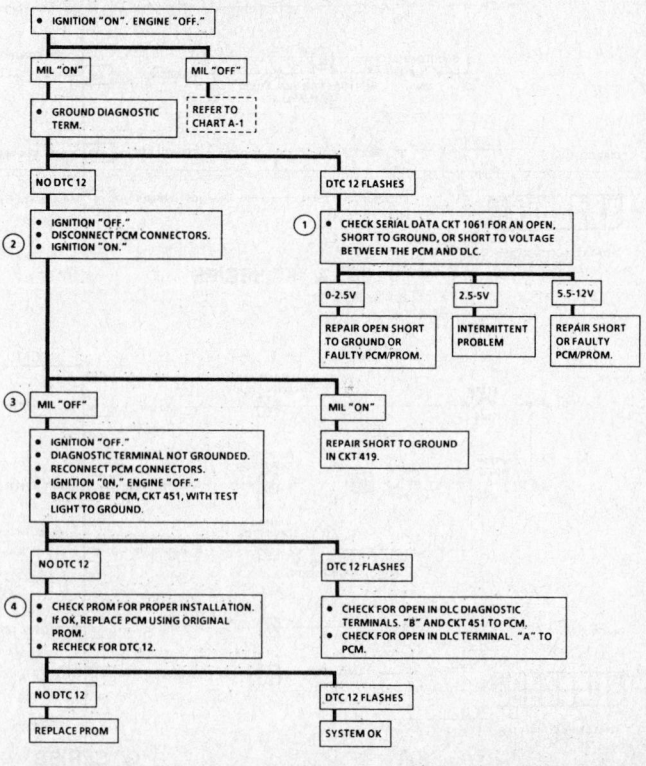

93F76583 93E76582 93J76587

Courtesy of General Motors Corp.

4) If MIL lamp does not flash DTC-12, go to next step. If MIL lamp flashes DTC-12, check circuit (Black/White or White/Black wire) between diagnostic connector terminal "B" and PCM connector for short to ground.

DIAGNOSTIC CODE CHARTS (PASSENGER VEHICLES)

5) If MIL lamp does not flash DTC-12 from step 4), check PROM installation. If PROM is installed correctly, replace PCM using original PROM. If code DTC-12 is now present, system is okay. If code DTC-12 is still not present, replace PROM.

CODE 11, MALFUNCTION INDICATOR LIGHT 5.7L "B", "D", "F" & "Y" BODIES

NOTE: Test numbers refer to numbers on diagnostic chart.

1) If MIL driver circuit or ignition feed circuit to bulb is open, MIL will not illuminate.
2) Jumper Harness (J 35616-A) should be used instead of directly probing harness. This will prevent damage to harness.
3) MIL should go off after engine starts. If it does, problem is not present at this time. If light does not go off, drive circuit is shorted to ground or PCM is faulty.
4) If other codes are also displayed, use other code charts first, then restart at beginning of this chart.

DIAGNOSTIC AIDS

If ignition feed circuit is suspected of being open, check and see if other bulbs on that circuit illuminate. Code 11 will cause MIL to remain on, even if malfunction clears.

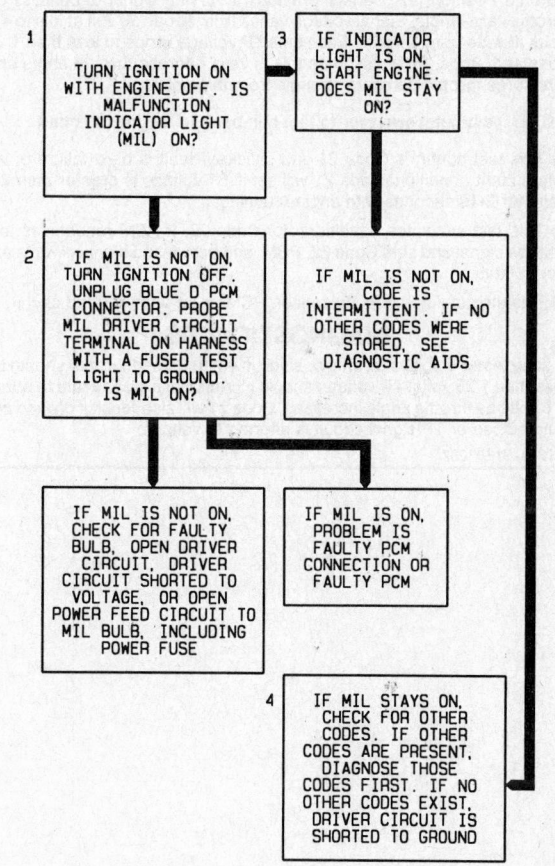

5.7L "B" BODY

5.7L "D" BODY

5.7L "F" BODY

5.7L "Y" BODY

MIL should always be on steady with ignition on and engine stopped. Ignition voltage is supplied directly to bulb. PCM turns on light by providing a path to ground.

94A31906 94B31907 94C31908 94D31909 94G31910

CODE 21, TPS SIGNAL VOLTAGE HIGH

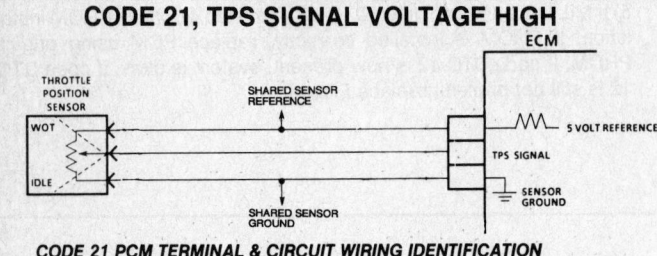

CODE 21 PCM TERMINAL & CIRCUIT WIRING IDENTIFICATION

Application	PCM Terminal	Wire Color
"C" & "K" Series Gas Engine		
TP Signal	C13	Dark Blue
TP Ground	D2	Black
TP Reference	C14	Gray
"C", "G", "K" & "P" Series Diesel Engine		
TP Signal	A15	Dark Blue
TP Ground	B3	Black
TP Reference	F14	Gray
"L", "M", "S" & "T" Series		
TP Signal	A15	Dark Blue
TP Ground	B3	Black
TP Reference	F14	Gray

Throttle Position (TP) sensor provides a varying signal depending on throttle valve angle. Signal voltage varies from about .50 volt at idle to 4.5 volts at wide open throttle. Each time TP voltage drops to less than 1.25 volts and stops, PCM assumes this is zero degrees throttle angle and measures throttle percentage angle from this point.

NOTE: Test numbers refer to test numbers on diagnostic chart.

1) This test confirms Code 21 and checks if fault is hard failure or an intermittent condition. Code 21 will set if TP voltage is greater than 2.5 volts for 2-10 seconds with engine running.

2) This test simulates conditions for Code 22. If PCM recognizes low voltage signal and sets Code 22, PCM, and power and signal circuits are not at fault.

3) This step isolates a faulty sensor, PCM or an open ground circuit.

DIAGNOSTIC AIDS

A scan tester displays throttle position in volts. Closed throttle should be less than 1.25 volts. TP voltage should increase at a steady rate to about 4.5 volts as throttle angle increases. Code 21 will also result if ground circuit is open or TP signal circuit is shorted to voltage.

91C07385 91E07287

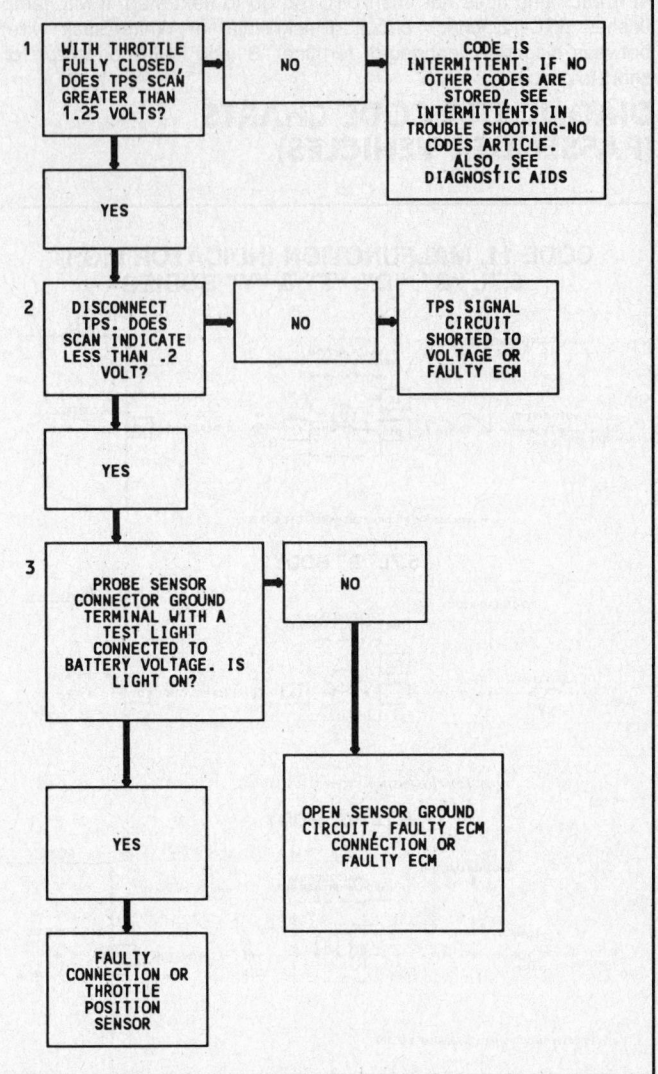

CODE 22, TPS SIGNAL VOLTAGE LOW

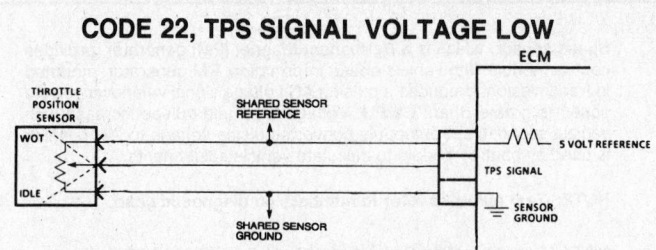

CODE 22 PCM TERMINAL & CIRCUIT WIRING IDENTIFICATION

Application	PCM Terminal	Wire Color
"C" & "K" Series Gas Engine		
TP Signal	C13	Dark Blue
TP Ground	D2	Black
TP Reference	C14	Gray
"C", "G", "K" & "P" Series Diesel Engine		
TP Signal	A15	Dark Blue
TP Ground	B3	Black
TP Reference	F14	Gray
"L", "M", "S" & "T" Series		
TP Signal	A15	Dark Blue
TP Ground	B3	Black
TP Reference	F14	Gray

Throttle Position (TP) sensor provides a varying signal depending on throttle valve angle. Signal voltage varies from about .50 volt at idle to 4.5 volts at wide open throttle.

NOTE: Test numbers refer to test numbers on diagnostic chart.

1) This test confirms Code 22 and checks if fault is hard failure or an intermittent condition. Code 22 will set if TP voltage is less than .2 volts for 2-4 seconds with engine running.

2) This test simulates conditions for Code 21. If PCM recognizes high voltage signal and sets Code 21, PCM wiring are not at fault. Replace TP.

3) This simulates a high voltage signal to check for an open TP signal circuit.

DIAGNOSTIC AIDS

A scan tester displays throttle position in volts. Closed throttle should be less than 1.25 volts. TP voltage should increase at a steady rate to about 4.5 volts as throttle angle increases. Code 22 will also result TP signal or ground circuits are open or grounded.

91C07385 91G07288

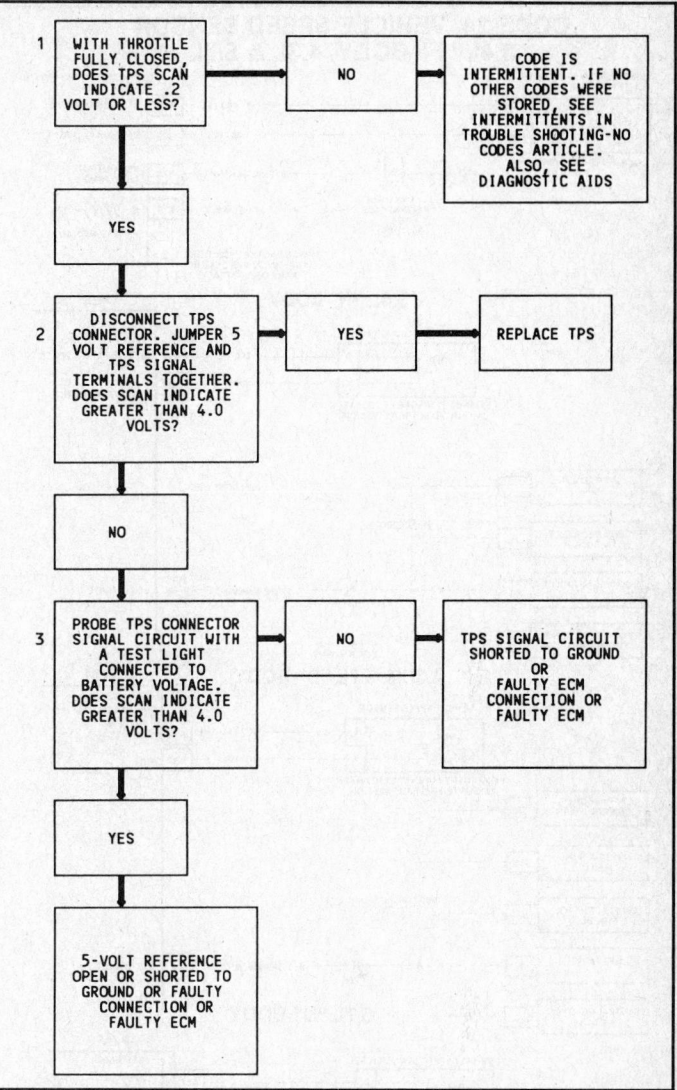

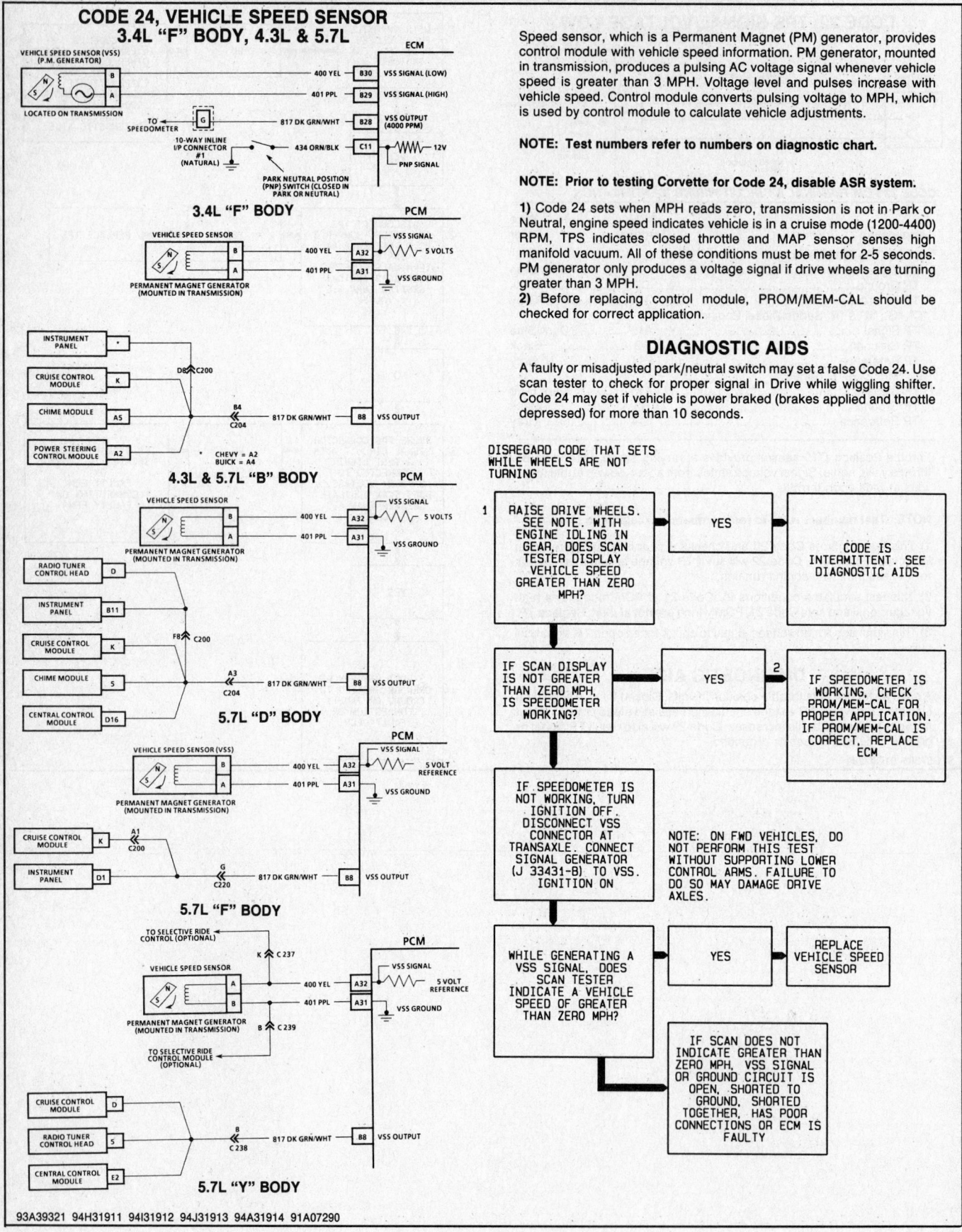

CODE 24, VEHICLE SPEED SENSOR
3.4L "F" BODY, 4.3L & 5.7L

Speed sensor, which is a Permanent Magnet (PM) generator, provides control module with vehicle speed information. PM generator, mounted in transmission, produces a pulsing AC voltage signal whenever vehicle speed is greater than 3 MPH. Voltage level and pulses increase with vehicle speed. Control module converts pulsing voltage to MPH, which is used by control module to calculate vehicle adjustments.

NOTE: Test numbers refer to numbers on diagnostic chart.

NOTE: Prior to testing Corvette for Code 24, disable ASR system.

1) Code 24 sets when MPH reads zero, transmission is not in Park or Neutral, engine speed indicates vehicle is in a cruise mode (1200-4400) RPM, TPS indicates closed throttle and MAP sensor senses high manifold vacuum. All of these conditions must be met for 2-5 seconds. PM generator only produces a voltage signal if drive wheels are turning greater than 3 MPH.

2) Before replacing control module, PROM/MEM-CAL should be checked for correct application.

DIAGNOSTIC AIDS

A faulty or misadjusted park/neutral switch may set a false Code 24. Use scan tester to check for proper signal in Drive while wiggling shifter. Code 24 may set if vehicle is power braked (brakes applied and throttle depressed) for more than 10 seconds.

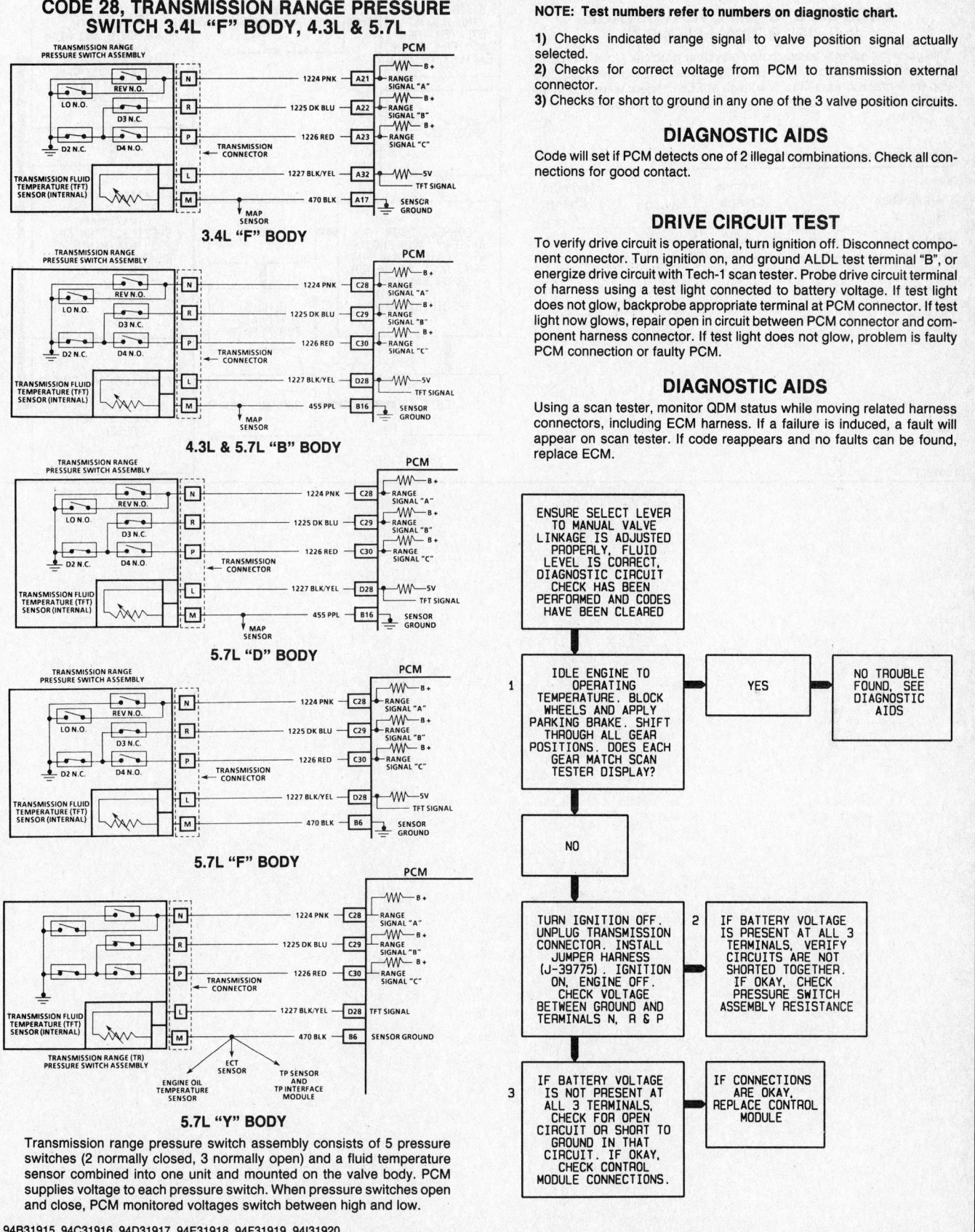

CODE 28, TRANSMISSION RANGE PRESSURE SWITCH 3.4L "F" BODY, 4.3L & 5.7L

3.4L "F" BODY

4.3L & 5.7L "B" BODY

5.7L "D" BODY

5.7L "F" BODY

5.7L "Y" BODY

Transmission range pressure switch assembly consists of 5 pressure switches (2 normally closed, 3 normally open) and a fluid temperature sensor combined into one unit and mounted on the valve body. PCM supplies voltage to each pressure switch. When pressure switches open and close, PCM monitored voltages switch between high and low.

94B31915 94C31916 94D31917 94E31918 94F31919 94I31920

NOTE: Test numbers refer to numbers on diagnostic chart.

1) Checks indicated range signal to valve position signal actually selected.
2) Checks for correct voltage from PCM to transmission external connector.
3) Checks for short to ground in any one of the 3 valve position circuits.

DIAGNOSTIC AIDS

Code will set if PCM detects one of 2 illegal combinations. Check all connections for good contact.

DRIVE CIRCUIT TEST

To verify drive circuit is operational, turn ignition off. Disconnect component connector. Turn ignition on, and ground ALDL test terminal "B", or energize drive circuit with Tech-1 scan tester. Probe drive circuit terminal of harness using a test light connected to battery voltage. If test light does not glow, backprobe appropriate terminal at PCM connector. If test light now glows, repair open in circuit between PCM connector and component harness connector. If test light does not glow, problem is faulty PCM connection or faulty PCM.

DIAGNOSTIC AIDS

Using a scan tester, monitor QDM status while moving related harness connectors, including ECM harness. If a failure is induced, a fault will appear on scan tester. If code reappears and no faults can be found, replace ECM.

CODE 53, SYSTEM OVERVOLTAGE
3.4L "F" BODY, 4.3L & 5.7L

This code indicates a basic charging system problem. Code 53 will set when voltage at control module terminal is greater or less than specification for a precalibrated time. If voltage at PCM battery voltage terminal is not within specification, check and repair charging system.

CHARGING SYSTEM SPECIFICATIONS

Application	Minimum Charge	Maximum Charge
3.4L	10	16.5
4.3L & 5.7L	9.6	17.1

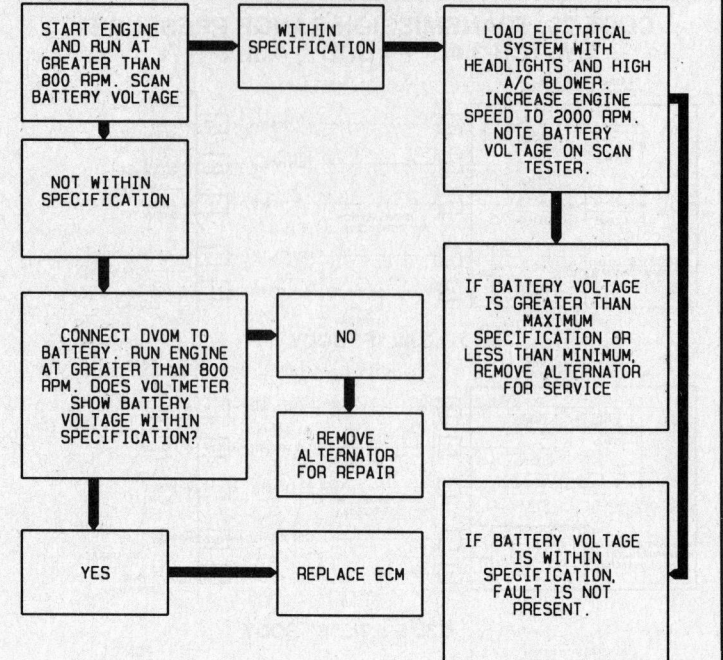

START ENGINE AND RUN AT GREATER THAN 800 RPM. SCAN BATTERY VOLTAGE

WITHIN SPECIFICATION

LOAD ELECTRICAL SYSTEM WITH HEADLIGHTS AND HIGH A/C BLOWER. INCREASE ENGINE SPEED TO 2000 RPM. NOTE BATTERY VOLTAGE ON SCAN TESTER.

NOT WITHIN SPECIFICATION

CONNECT DVOM TO BATTERY. RUN ENGINE AT GREATER THAN 800 RPM. DOES VOLTMETER SHOW BATTERY VOLTAGE WITHIN SPECIFICATION?

NO

REMOVE ALTERNATOR FOR REPAIR

IF BATTERY VOLTAGE IS GREATER THAN MAXIMUM SPECIFICATION OR LESS THAN MINIMUM, REMOVE ALTERNATOR FOR SERVICE

YES

REPLACE ECM

IF BATTERY VOLTAGE IS WITHIN SPECIFICATION, FAULT IS NOT PRESENT.

91D07357

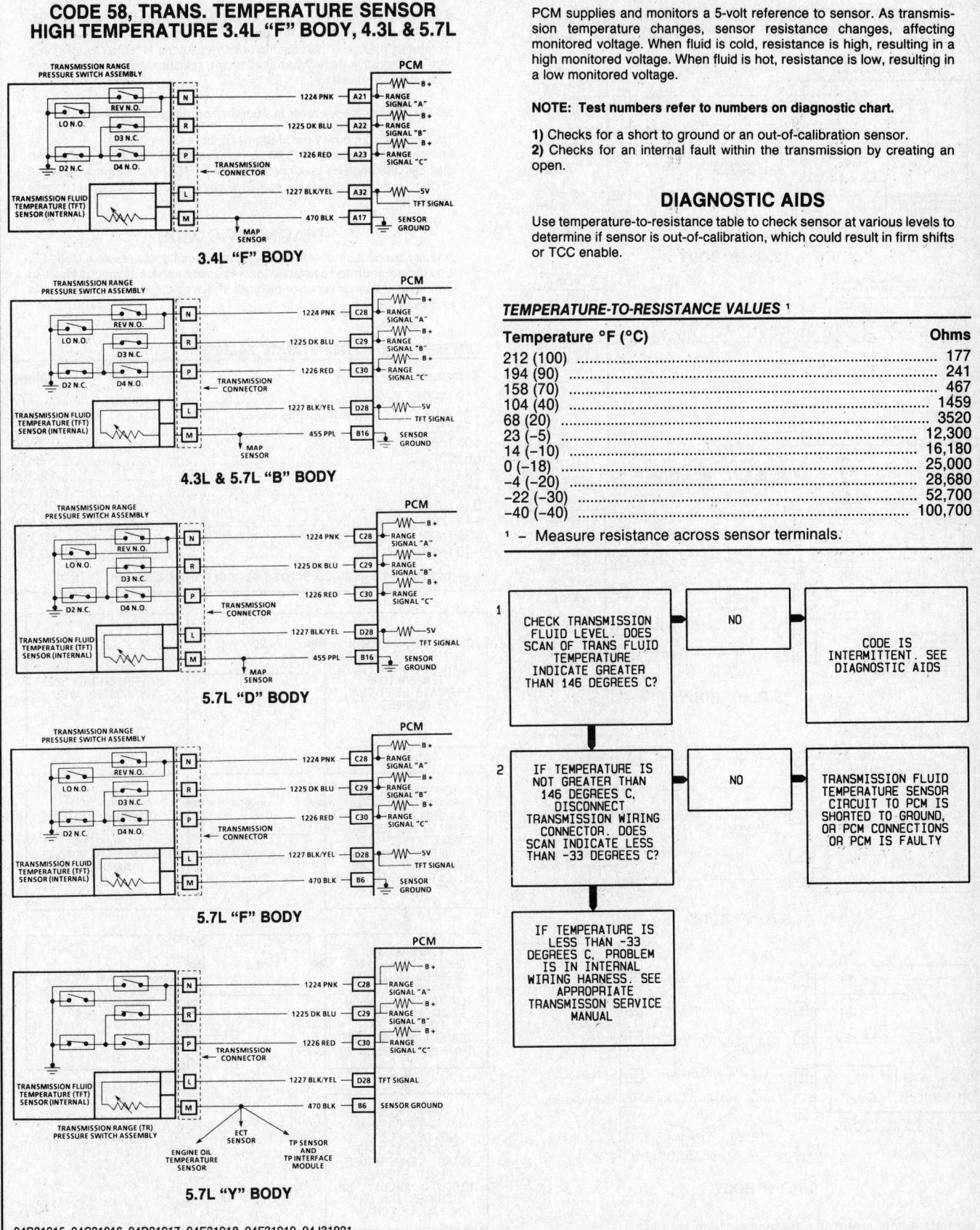

CODE 58, TRANS. TEMPERATURE SENSOR HIGH TEMPERATURE 3.4L "F" BODY, 4.3L & 5.7L

PCM supplies and monitors a 5-volt reference to sensor. As transmission temperature changes, sensor resistance changes, affecting monitored voltage. When fluid is cold, resistance is high, resulting in a high monitored voltage. When fluid is hot, resistance is low, resulting in a low monitored voltage.

NOTE: Test numbers refer to numbers on diagnostic chart.

1) Checks for a short to ground or an out-of-calibration sensor.
2) Checks for an internal fault within the transmission by creating an open.

DIAGNOSTIC AIDS

Use temperature-to-resistance table to check sensor at various levels to determine if sensor is out-of-calibration, which could result in firm shifts or TCC enable.

TEMPERATURE-TO-RESISTANCE VALUES [1]

Temperature °F (°C)	Ohms
212 (100)	177
194 (90)	241
158 (70)	467
104 (40)	1459
68 (20)	3520
23 (−5)	12,300
14 (−10)	16,180
0 (−18)	25,000
−4 (−20)	28,680
−22 (−30)	52,700
−40 (−40)	100,700

[1] – Measure resistance across sensor terminals.

94B31915 94C31916 94D31917 94E31918 94F31919 94J31921

AUTOMATIC TRANSMISSIONS
4L60-E Electronic Controls (Cont.)

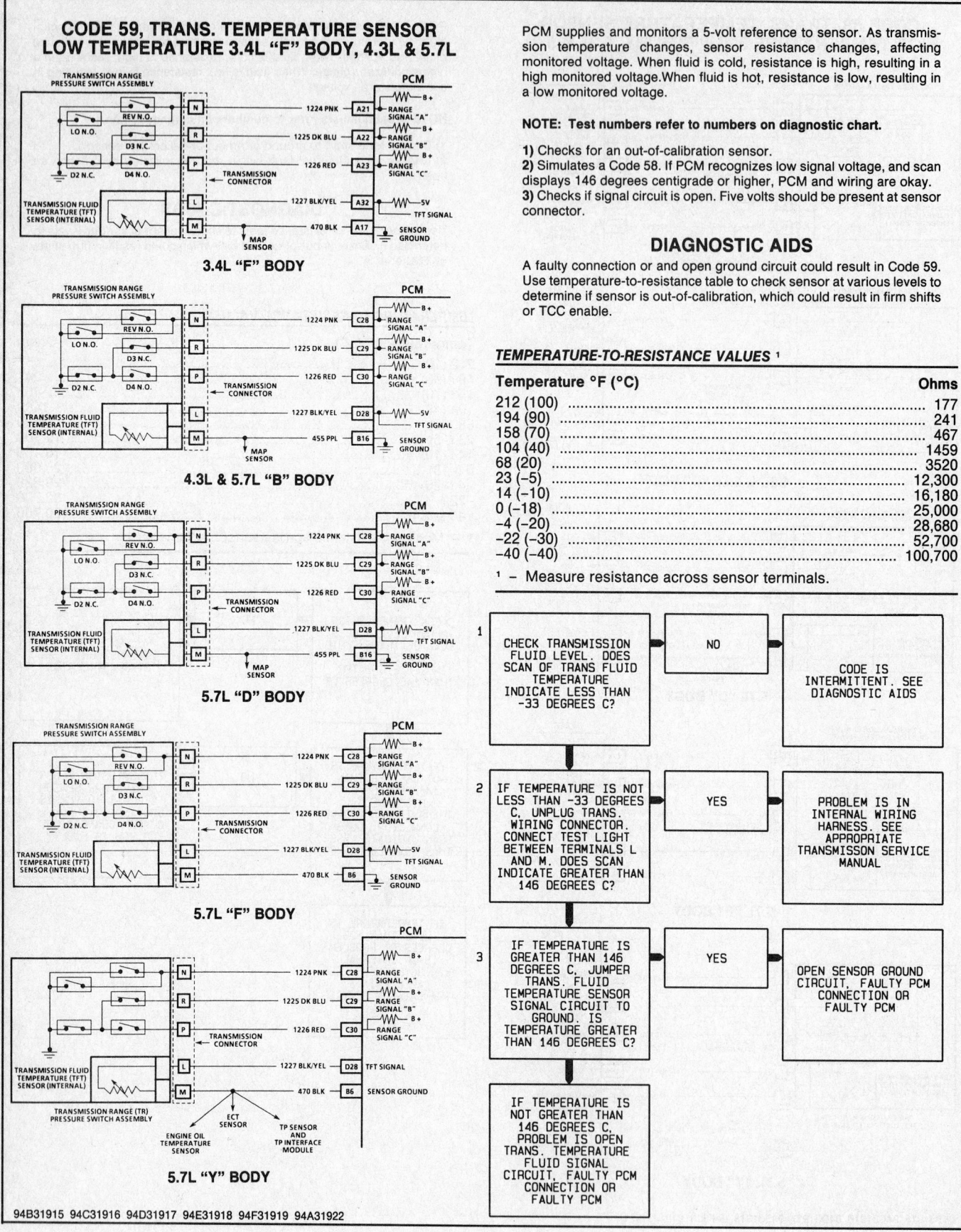

CODE 59, TRANS. TEMPERATURE SENSOR
LOW TEMPERATURE 3.4L "F" BODY, 4.3L & 5.7L

3.4L "F" BODY

4.3L & 5.7L "B" BODY

5.7L "D" BODY

5.7L "F" BODY

5.7L "Y" BODY

94B31915 94C31916 94D31917 94E31918 94F31919 94A31922

PCM supplies and monitors a 5-volt reference to sensor. As transmission temperature changes, sensor resistance changes, affecting monitored voltage. When fluid is cold, resistance is high, resulting in a high monitored voltage. When fluid is hot, resistance is low, resulting in a low monitored voltage.

NOTE: Test numbers refer to numbers on diagnostic chart.

1) Checks for an out-of-calibration sensor.
2) Simulates a Code 58. If PCM recognizes low signal voltage, and scan displays 146 degrees centigrade or higher, PCM and wiring are okay.
3) Checks if signal circuit is open. Five volts should be present at sensor connector.

DIAGNOSTIC AIDS

A faulty connection or and open ground circuit could result in Code 59. Use temperature-to-resistance table to check sensor at various levels to determine if sensor is out-of-calibration, which could result in firm shifts or TCC enable.

TEMPERATURE-TO-RESISTANCE VALUES [1]

Temperature °F (°C)	Ohms
212 (100)	177
194 (90)	241
158 (70)	467
104 (40)	1459
68 (20)	3520
23 (−5)	12,300
14 (−10)	16,180
0 (−18)	25,000
−4 (−20)	28,680
−22 (−30)	52,700
−40 (−40)	100,700

[1] – Measure resistance across sensor terminals.

1 CHECK TRANSMISSION FLUID LEVEL. DOES SCAN OF TRANS FLUID TEMPERATURE INDICATE LESS THAN −33 DEGREES C? → **NO** → CODE IS INTERMITTENT. SEE DIAGNOSTIC AIDS

2 IF TEMPERATURE IS NOT LESS THAN −33 DEGREES C, UNPLUG TRANS. WIRING CONNECTOR. CONNECT TEST LIGHT BETWEEN TERMINALS L AND M. DOES SCAN INDICATE GREATER THAN 146 DEGREES C? → **YES** → PROBLEM IS IN INTERNAL WIRING HARNESS. SEE APPROPRIATE TRANSMISSON SERVICE MANUAL

3 IF TEMPERATURE IS GREATER THAN 146 DEGREES C, JUMPER TRANS. FLUID TEMPERATURE SENSOR SIGNAL CIRCUIT TO GROUND. IS TEMPERATURE GREATER THAN 146 DEGREES C? → **YES** → OPEN SENSOR GROUND CIRCUIT, FAULTY PCM CONNECTION OR FAULTY PCM

IF TEMPERATURE IS NOT GREATER THAN 146 DEGREES C, PROBLEM IS OPEN TRANS. TEMPERATURE FLUID SIGNAL CIRCUIT, FAULTY PCM CONNECTION OR FAULTY PCM

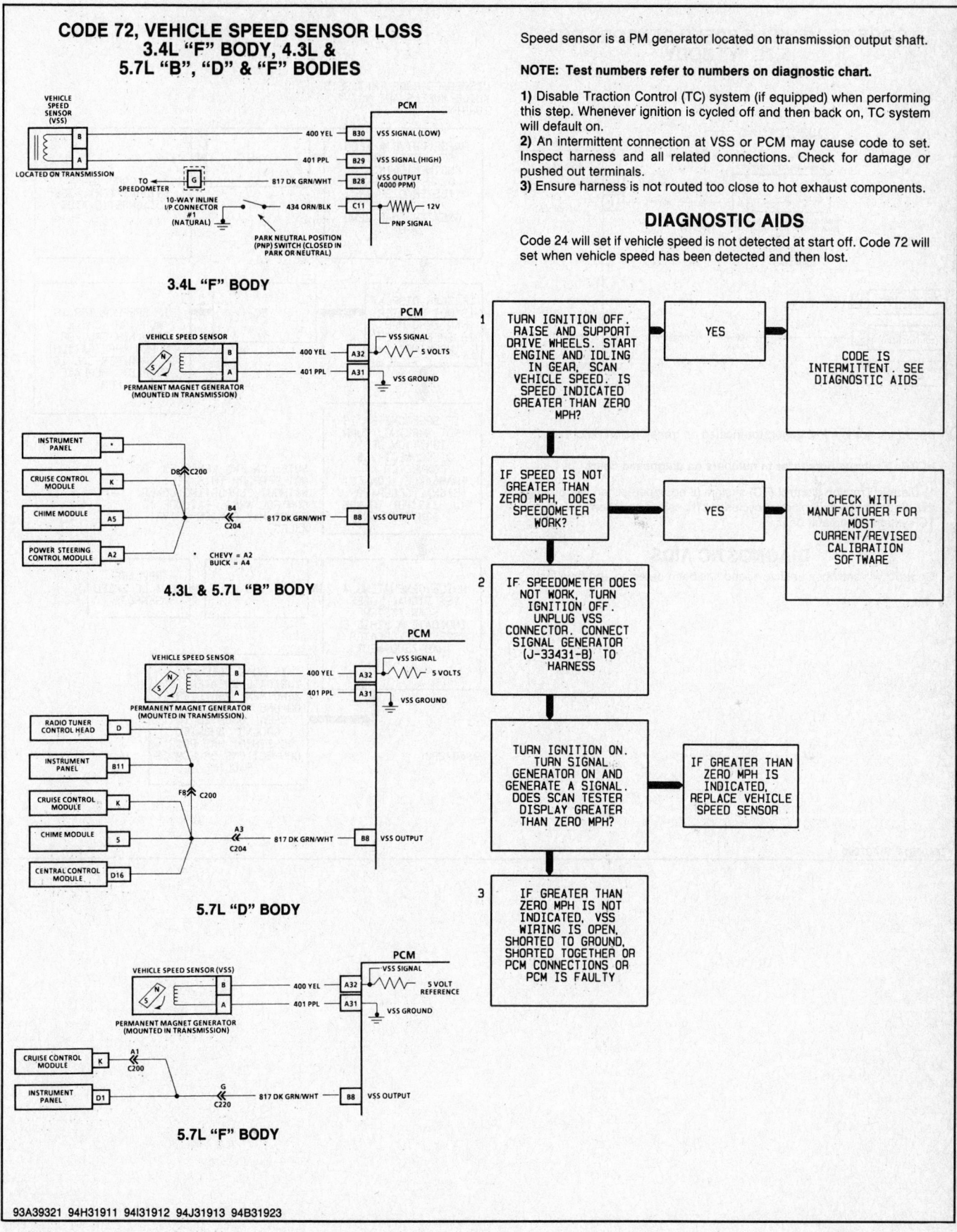

CODE 72, VEHICLE SPEED SENSOR LOSS 3.4L "F" BODY, 4.3L & 5.7L "B", "D" & "F" BODIES

Speed sensor is a PM generator located on transmission output shaft.

NOTE: Test numbers refer to numbers on diagnostic chart.

1) Disable Traction Control (TC) system (if equipped) when performing this step. Whenever ignition is cycled off and then back on, TC system will default on.
2) An intermittent connection at VSS or PCM may cause code to set. Inspect harness and all related connections. Check for damage or pushed out terminals.
3) Ensure harness is not routed too close to hot exhaust components.

DIAGNOSTIC AIDS

Code 24 will set if vehicle speed is not detected at start off. Code 72 will set when vehicle speed has been detected and then lost.

**CODE 72, VEHICLE SPEED SENSOR LOSS
5.7L "Y" BODY**

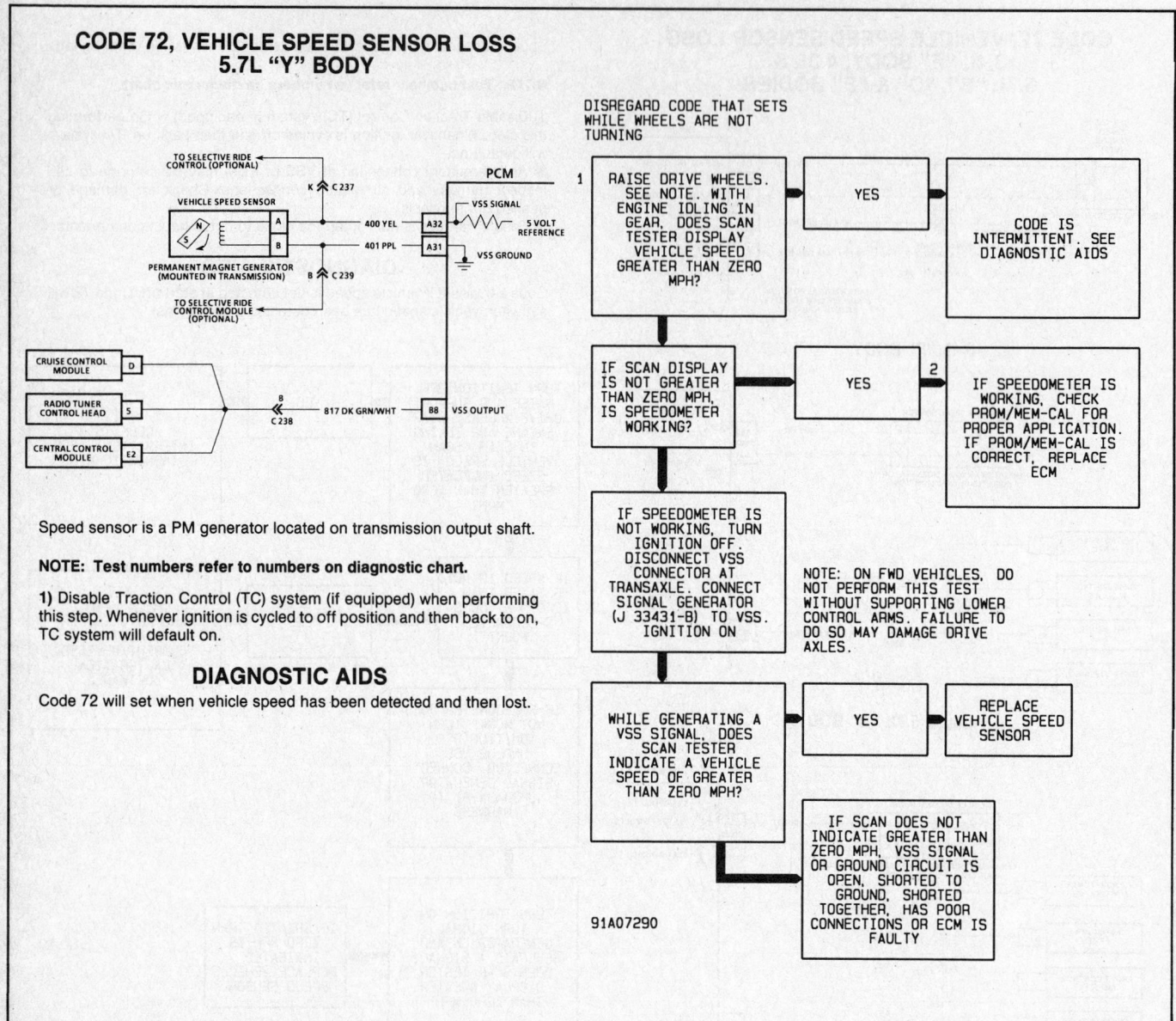

Speed sensor is a PM generator located on transmission output shaft.

NOTE: Test numbers refer to numbers on diagnostic chart.

1) Disable Traction Control (TC) system (if equipped) when performing this step. Whenever ignition is cycled to off position and then back to on, TC system will default on.

DIAGNOSTIC AIDS

Code 72 will set when vehicle speed has been detected and then lost.

94A31914 91A07290

CODE 73, PRESSURE CONTROL SOLENOID
4.3L & 5.7L

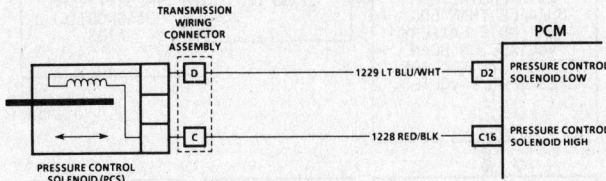

Pressure control solenoid is a PCM-controlled device used to regulate transmission line pressure. PCM compares TPS voltage, engine RPM and other inputs to determine proper line pressure for a given load. PCM regulates pressure by applying a varying amperage to pressure control solenoid. Amperage varies from 0.1 to 1.1 amps.

NOTE: Test numbers refer to numbers on diagnostic chart.

1) Checks ability of the PCM to command pressure control solenoid.
2) Checks for voltage at PCM.

DIAGNOSTIC AIDS

Check for poor connections at PCM and at transmission connector.

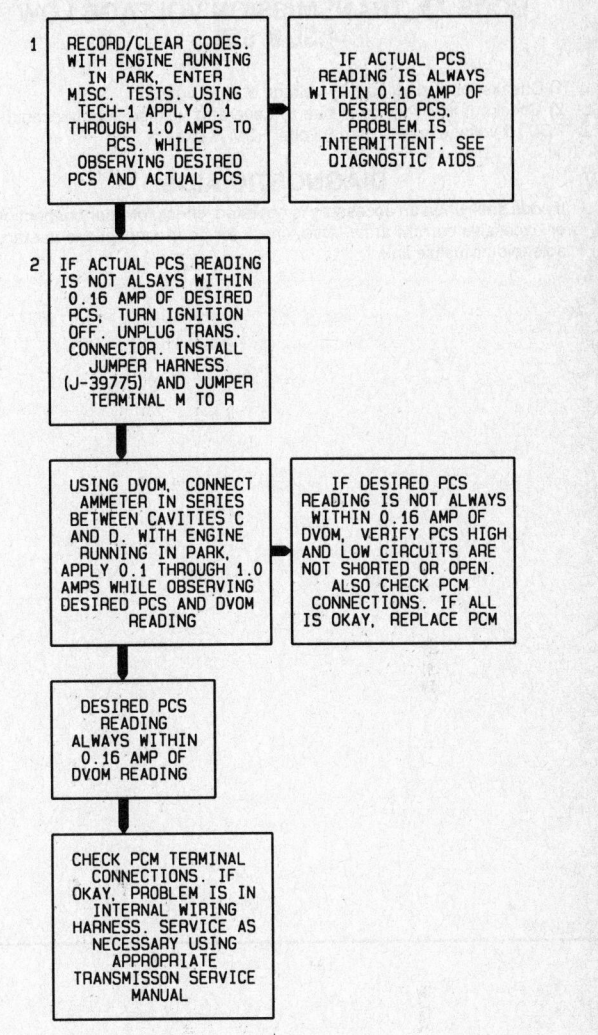

94C31924 94D31925

CODE 75, TRANSMISSION VOLTAGE LOW
4.3L & 5.7L

1) Checks for normal battery voltage of 9-15 volts.
2) Checks if low voltage is due to generator voltage supply circuit, or PCM. If voltage is less than 9 volts, PCM is okay.

DIAGNOSTIC AIDS

If code sets when an accessory is operated, check for poor connections or excessive current draw. Also, check for poor connections at starter solenoid or fusible link.

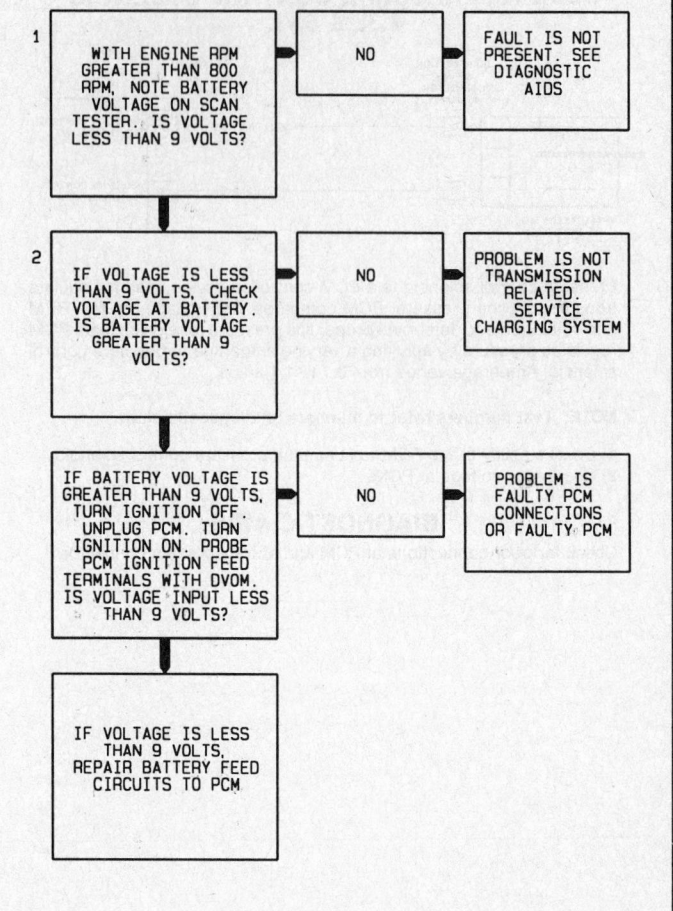

1. WITH ENGINE RPM GREATER THAN 800 RPM, NOTE BATTERY VOLTAGE ON SCAN TESTER. IS VOLTAGE LESS THAN 9 VOLTS? → NO → FAULT IS NOT PRESENT. SEE DIAGNOSTIC AIDS

2. IF VOLTAGE IS LESS THAN 9 VOLTS, CHECK VOLTAGE AT BATTERY. IS BATTERY VOLTAGE GREATER THAN 9 VOLTS? → NO → PROBLEM IS NOT TRANSMISSION RELATED. SERVICE CHARGING SYSTEM

IF BATTERY VOLTAGE IS GREATER THAN 9 VOLTS, TURN IGNITION OFF. UNPLUG PCM. TURN IGNITION ON. PROBE PCM IGNITION FEED TERMINALS WITH DVOM. IS VOLTAGE INPUT LESS THAN 9 VOLTS? → NO → PROBLEM IS FAULTY PCM CONNECTIONS OR FAULTY PCM

IF VOLTAGE IS LESS THAN 9 VOLTS, REPAIR BATTERY FEED CIRCUITS TO PCM

94E31926

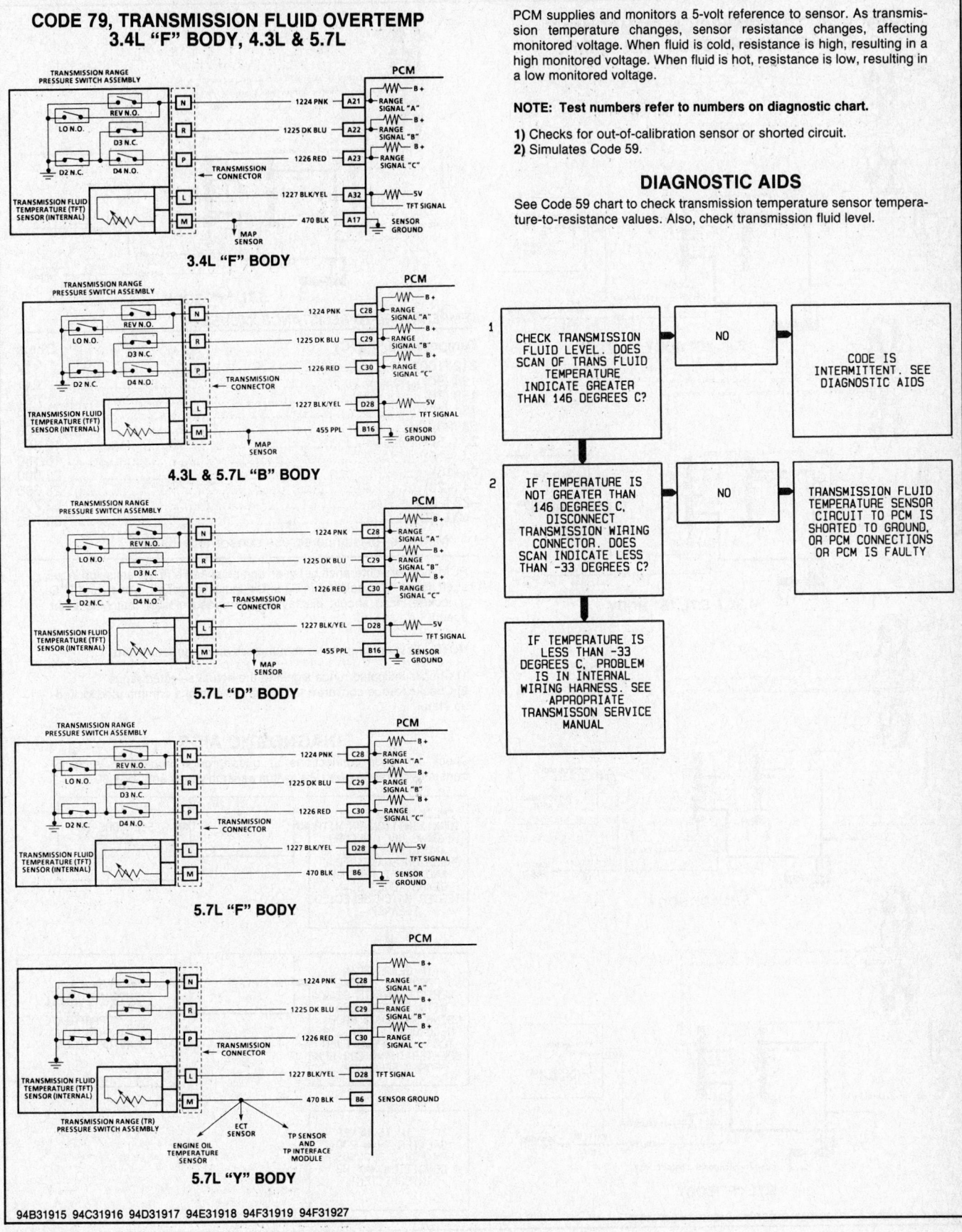

CODE 79, TRANSMISSION FLUID OVERTEMP
3.4L "F" BODY, 4.3L & 5.7L

3.4L "F" BODY

4.3L & 5.7L "B" BODY

5.7L "D" BODY

5.7L "F" BODY

5.7L "Y" BODY

PCM supplies and monitors a 5-volt reference to sensor. As transmission temperature changes, sensor resistance changes, affecting monitored voltage. When fluid is cold, resistance is high, resulting in a high monitored voltage. When fluid is hot, resistance is low, resulting in a low monitored voltage.

NOTE: Test numbers refer to numbers on diagnostic chart.

1) Checks for out-of-calibration sensor or shorted circuit.
2) Simulates Code 59.

DIAGNOSTIC AIDS

See Code 59 chart to check transmission temperature sensor temperature-to-resistance values. Also, check transmission fluid level.

1 — CHECK TRANSMISSION FLUID LEVEL. DOES SCAN OF TRANS FLUID TEMPERATURE INDICATE GREATER THAN 146 DEGREES C? — NO — CODE IS INTERMITTENT. SEE DIAGNOSTIC AIDS

2 — IF TEMPERATURE IS NOT GREATER THAN 146 DEGREES C, DISCONNECT TRANSMISSION WIRING CONNECTOR. DOES SCAN INDICATE LESS THAN -33 DEGREES C? — NO — TRANSMISSION FLUID TEMPERATURE SENSOR CIRCUIT TO PCM IS SHORTED TO GROUND, OR PCM CONNECTIONS OR PCM IS FAULTY

IF TEMPERATURE IS LESS THAN -33 DEGREES C, PROBLEM IS IN INTERNAL WIRING HARNESS. SEE APPROPRIATE TRANSMISSON SERVICE MANUAL

94B31915 94C31916 94D31917 94E31918 94F31919 94F31927

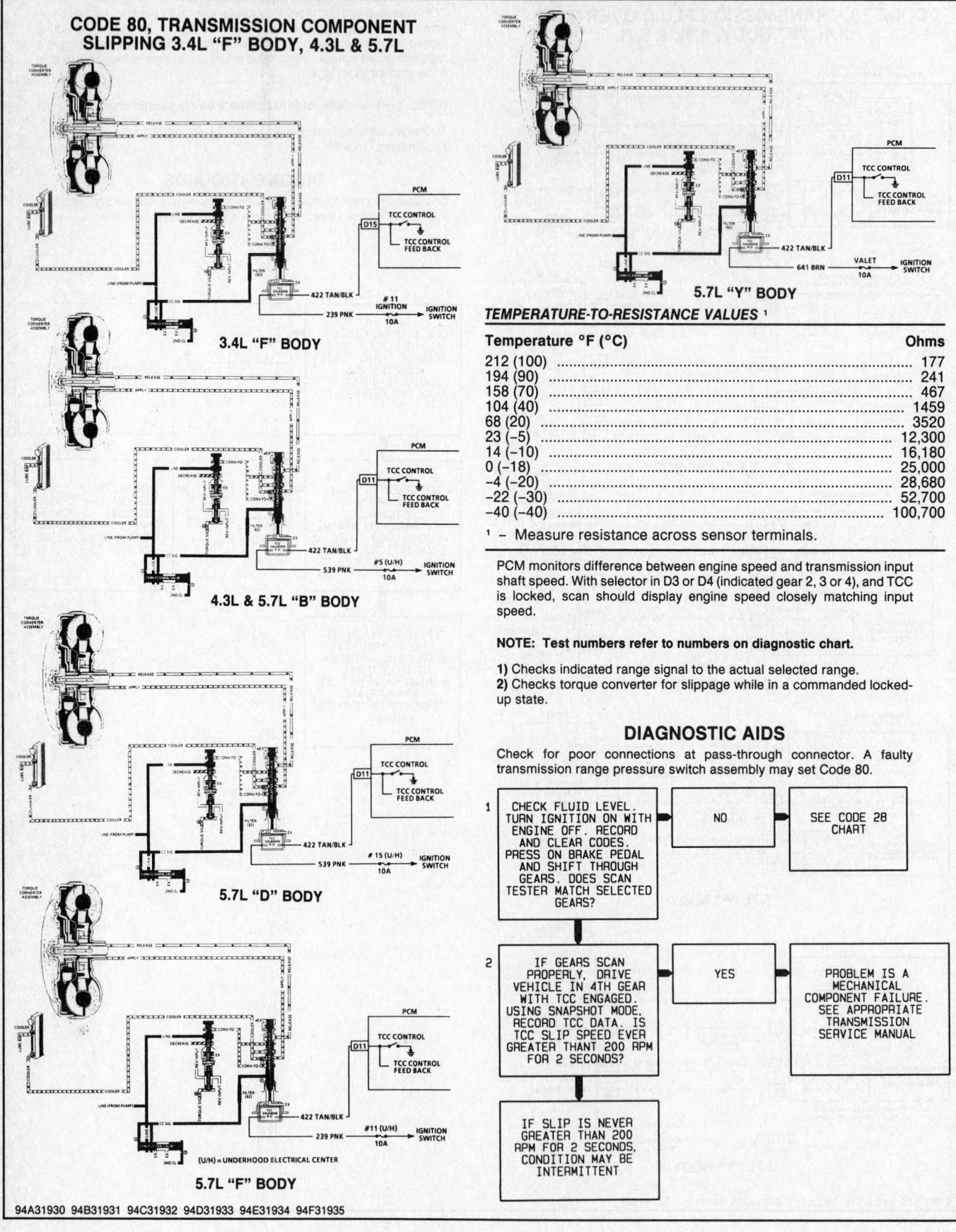

CODE 80, TRANSMISSION COMPONENT SLIPPING 3.4L "F" BODY, 4.3L & 5.7L

3.4L "F" BODY

4.3L & 5.7L "B" BODY

5.7L "D" BODY

5.7L "F" BODY

(U/H) = UNDERHOOD ELECTRICAL CENTER

5.7L "Y" BODY

TEMPERATURE-TO-RESISTANCE VALUES [1]

Temperature °F (°C)	Ohms
212 (100)	177
194 (90)	241
158 (70)	467
104 (40)	1459
68 (20)	3520
23 (−5)	12,300
14 (−10)	16,180
0 (−18)	25,000
−4 (−20)	28,680
−22 (−30)	52,700
−40 (−40)	100,700

[1] – Measure resistance across sensor terminals.

PCM monitors difference between engine speed and transmission input shaft speed. With selector in D3 or D4 (indicated gear 2, 3 or 4), and TCC is locked, scan should display engine speed closely matching input speed.

NOTE: Test numbers refer to numbers on diagnostic chart.

1) Checks indicated range signal to the actual selected range.
2) Checks torque converter for slippage while in a commanded locked-up state.

DIAGNOSTIC AIDS

Check for poor connections at pass-through connector. A faulty transmission range pressure switch assembly may set Code 80.

1. CHECK FLUID LEVEL. TURN IGNITION ON WITH ENGINE OFF. RECORD AND CLEAR CODES. PRESS ON BRAKE PEDAL AND SHIFT THROUGH GEARS. DOES SCAN TESTER MATCH SELECTED GEARS? — NO — SEE CODE 28 CHART

2. IF GEARS SCAN PROPERLY, DRIVE VEHICLE IN 4TH GEAR WITH TCC ENGAGED. USING SNAPSHOT MODE, RECORD TCC DATA. IS TCC SLIP SPEED EVER GREATER THANT 200 RPM FOR 2 SECONDS? — YES — PROBLEM IS A MECHANICAL COMPONENT FAILURE. SEE APPROPRIATE TRANSMISSION SERVICE MANUAL

IF SLIP IS NEVER GREATER THAN 200 RPM FOR 2 SECONDS, CONDITION MAY BE INTERMITTENT

94A31930   94B31931   94C31932   94D31933   94E31934   94F31935

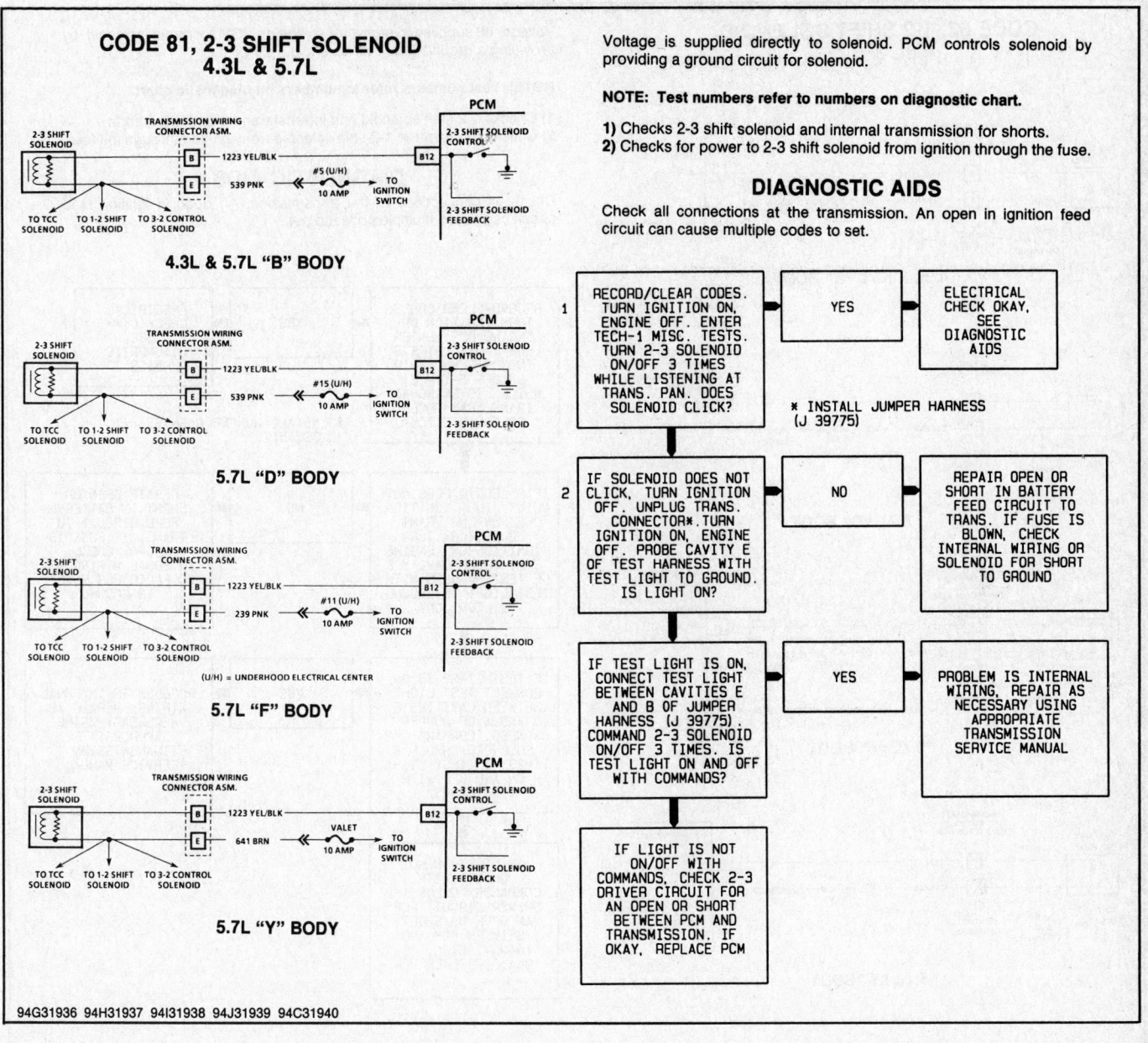

CODE 81, 2-3 SHIFT SOLENOID 4.3L & 5.7L

4.3L & 5.7L "B" BODY

5.7L "D" BODY

5.7L "F" BODY

(U/H) = UNDERHOOD ELECTRICAL CENTER

5.7L "Y" BODY

Voltage is supplied directly to solenoid. PCM controls solenoid by providing a ground circuit for solenoid.

NOTE: Test numbers refer to numbers on diagnostic chart.

1) Checks 2-3 shift solenoid and internal transmission for shorts.
2) Checks for power to 2-3 shift solenoid from ignition through the fuse.

DIAGNOSTIC AIDS

Check all connections at the transmission. An open in ignition feed circuit can cause multiple codes to set.

1. RECORD/CLEAR CODES. TURN IGNITION ON, ENGINE OFF. ENTER TECH-1 MISC. TESTS. TURN 2-3 SOLENOID ON/OFF 3 TIMES WHILE LISTENING AT TRANS. PAN. DOES SOLENOID CLICK? — **YES** → ELECTRICAL CHECK OKAY, SEE DIAGNOSTIC AIDS

* INSTALL JUMPER HARNESS (J 39775)

2. IF SOLENOID DOES NOT CLICK, TURN IGNITION OFF. UNPLUG TRANS. CONNECTOR*. TURN IGNITION ON, ENGINE OFF. PROBE CAVITY E OF TEST HARNESS WITH TEST LIGHT TO GROUND. IS LIGHT ON? — **NO** → REPAIR OPEN OR SHORT IN BATTERY FEED CIRCUIT TO TRANS. IF FUSE IS BLOWN, CHECK INTERNAL WIRING OR SOLENOID FOR SHORT TO GROUND

IF TEST LIGHT IS ON, CONNECT TEST LIGHT BETWEEN CAVITIES E AND B OF JUMPER HARNESS (J 39775). COMMAND 2-3 SOLENOID ON/OFF 3 TIMES. IS TEST LIGHT ON AND OFF WITH COMMANDS? — **YES** → PROBLEM IS INTERNAL WIRING, REPAIR AS NECESSARY USING APPROPRIATE TRANSMISSION SERVICE MANUAL

IF LIGHT IS NOT ON/OFF WITH COMMANDS, CHECK 2-3 DRIVER CIRCUIT FOR AN OPEN OR SHORT BETWEEN PCM AND TRANSMISSION. IF OKAY, REPLACE PCM

94G31936 94H31937 94I31938 94J31939 94C31940

CODE 82, 1-2 SHIFT SOLENOID 4.3L & 5.7L

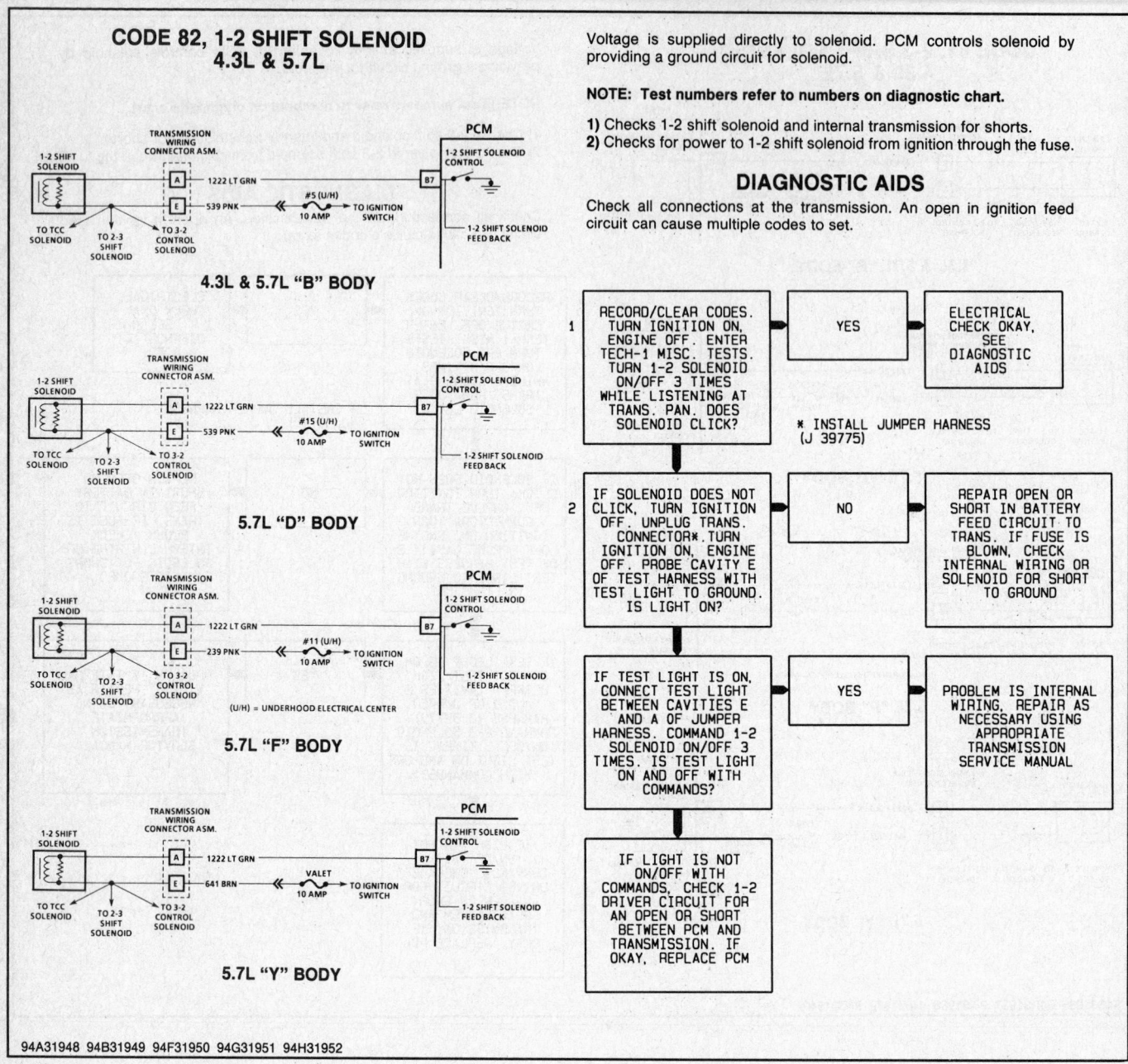

4.3L & 5.7L "B" BODY

5.7L "D" BODY

5.7L "F" BODY

(U/H) = UNDERHOOD ELECTRICAL CENTER

5.7L "Y" BODY

94A31948 94B31949 94F31950 94G31951 94H31952

Voltage is supplied directly to solenoid. PCM controls solenoid by providing a ground circuit for solenoid.

NOTE: Test numbers refer to numbers on diagnostic chart.

1) Checks 1-2 shift solenoid and internal transmission for shorts.
2) Checks for power to 1-2 shift solenoid from ignition through the fuse.

DIAGNOSTIC AIDS
Check all connections at the transmission. An open in ignition feed circuit can cause multiple codes to set.

1 RECORD/CLEAR CODES. TURN IGNITION ON, ENGINE OFF. ENTER TECH-1 MISC. TESTS. TURN 1-2 SOLENOID ON/OFF 3 TIMES WHILE LISTENING AT TRANS. PAN. DOES SOLENOID CLICK? — YES — ELECTRICAL CHECK OKAY, SEE DIAGNOSTIC AIDS

※ INSTALL JUMPER HARNESS (J 39775)

2 IF SOLENOID DOES NOT CLICK, TURN IGNITION OFF. UNPLUG TRANS. CONNECTOR※. TURN IGNITION ON, ENGINE OFF. PROBE CAVITY E OF TEST HARNESS WITH TEST LIGHT TO GROUND. IS LIGHT ON? — NO — REPAIR OPEN OR SHORT IN BATTERY FEED CIRCUIT TO TRANS. IF FUSE IS BLOWN, CHECK INTERNAL WIRING OR SOLENOID FOR SHORT TO GROUND

IF TEST LIGHT IS ON, CONNECT TEST LIGHT BETWEEN CAVITIES E AND A OF JUMPER HARNESS. COMMAND 1-2 SOLENOID ON/OFF 3 TIMES. IS TEST LIGHT ON AND OFF WITH COMMANDS? — YES — PROBLEM IS INTERNAL WIRING. REPAIR AS NECESSARY USING APPROPRIATE TRANSMISSION SERVICE MANUAL

IF LIGHT IS NOT ON/OFF WITH COMMANDS, CHECK 1-2 DRIVER CIRCUIT FOR AN OPEN OR SHORT BETWEEN PCM AND TRANSMISSION. IF OKAY, REPLACE PCM

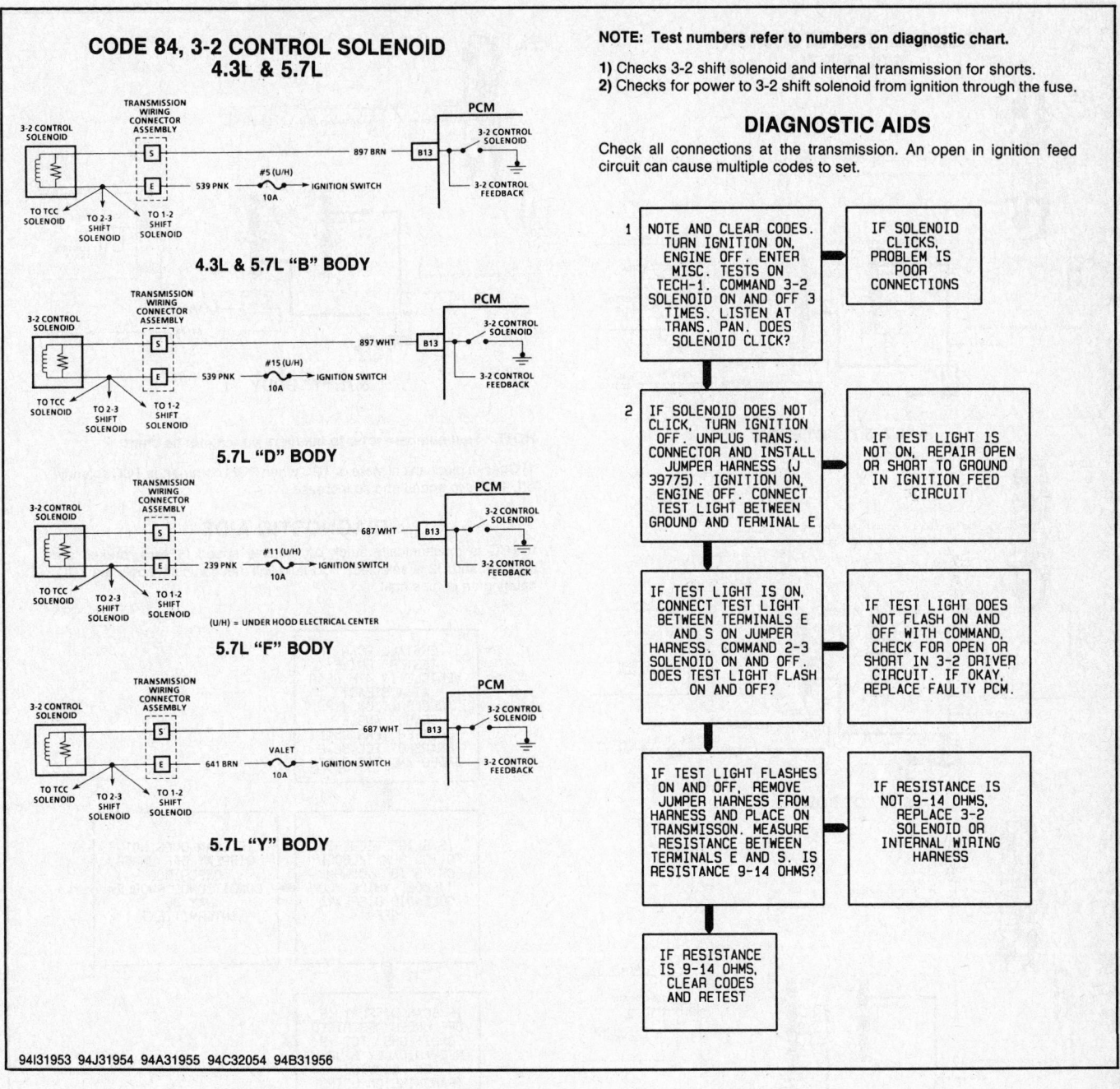

CODE 84, 3-2 CONTROL SOLENOID
4.3L & 5.7L

4.3L & 5.7L "B" BODY

5.7L "D" BODY

5.7L "F" BODY

(U/H) = UNDER HOOD ELECTRICAL CENTER

5.7L "Y" BODY

NOTE: Test numbers refer to numbers on diagnostic chart.

1) Checks 3-2 shift solenoid and internal transmission for shorts.
2) Checks for power to 3-2 shift solenoid from ignition through the fuse.

DIAGNOSTIC AIDS

Check all connections at the transmission. An open in ignition feed circuit can cause multiple codes to set.

1 — NOTE AND CLEAR CODES. TURN IGNITION ON, ENGINE OFF. ENTER MISC. TESTS ON TECH-1. COMMAND 3-2 SOLENOID ON AND OFF 3 TIMES. LISTEN AT TRANS. PAN. DOES SOLENOID CLICK?

→ IF SOLENOID CLICKS, PROBLEM IS POOR CONNECTIONS

2 — IF SOLENOID DOES NOT CLICK, TURN IGNITION OFF. UNPLUG TRANS. CONNECTOR AND INSTALL JUMPER HARNESS (J 39775). IGNITION ON, ENGINE OFF. CONNECT TEST LIGHT BETWEEN GROUND AND TERMINAL E

→ IF TEST LIGHT IS NOT ON, REPAIR OPEN OR SHORT TO GROUND IN IGNITION FEED CIRCUIT

IF TEST LIGHT IS ON, CONNECT TEST LIGHT BETWEEN TERMINALS E AND S ON JUMPER HARNESS. COMMAND 2-3 SOLENOID ON AND OFF. DOES TEST LIGHT FLASH ON AND OFF?

→ IF TEST LIGHT DOES NOT FLASH ON AND OFF WITH COMMAND, CHECK FOR OPEN OR SHORT IN 3-2 DRIVER CIRCUIT. IF OKAY, REPLACE FAULTY PCM.

IF TEST LIGHT FLASHES ON AND OFF, REMOVE JUMPER HARNESS FROM HARNESS AND PLACE ON TRANSMISSON. MEASURE RESISTANCE BETWEEN TERMINALS E AND S. IS RESISTANCE 9-14 OHMS?

→ IF RESISTANCE IS NOT 9-14 OHMS, REPLACE 3-2 SOLENOID OR INTERNAL WIRING HARNESS

IF RESISTANCE IS 9-14 OHMS, CLEAR CODES AND RETEST

94I31953 94J31954 94A31955 94C32054 94B31956

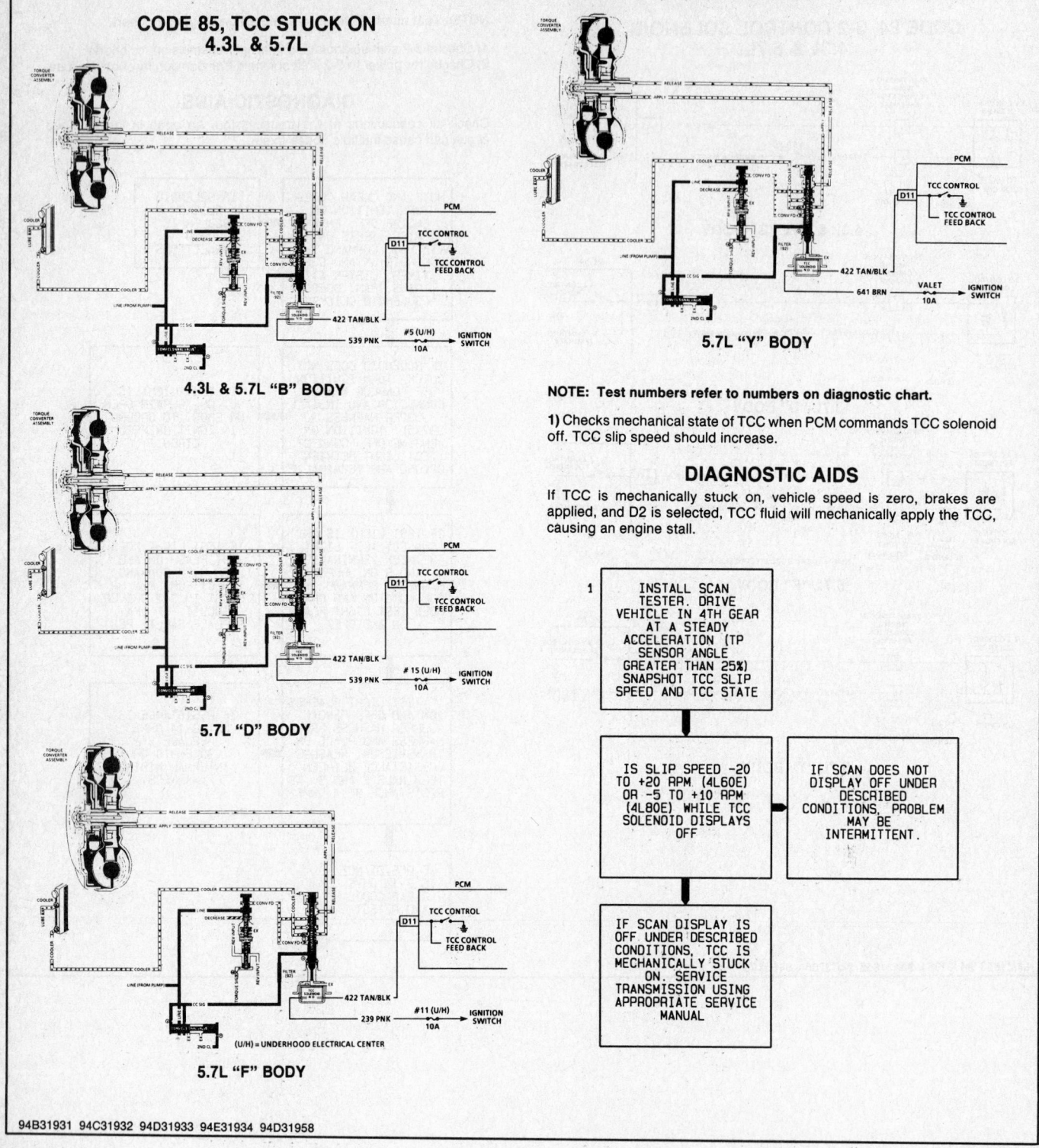

**CODE 85, TCC STUCK ON
4.3L & 5.7L**

4.3L & 5.7L "B" BODY

5.7L "D" BODY

5.7L "F" BODY

(U/H) = UNDERHOOD ELECTRICAL CENTER

5.7L "Y" BODY

NOTE: Test numbers refer to numbers on diagnostic chart.

1) Checks mechanical state of TCC when PCM commands TCC solenoid off. TCC slip speed should increase.

DIAGNOSTIC AIDS

If TCC is mechanically stuck on, vehicle speed is zero, brakes are applied, and D2 is selected, TCC fluid will mechanically apply the TCC, causing an engine stall.

1 — INSTALL SCAN TESTER. DRIVE VEHICLE IN 4TH GEAR AT A STEADY ACCELERATION (TP SENSOR ANGLE GREATER THAN 25%) SNAPSHOT TCC SLIP SPEED AND TCC STATE

IS SLIP SPEED -20 TO +20 RPM (4L60E) OR -5 TO +10 RPM (4L80E) WHILE TCC SOLENOID DISPLAYS OFF

IF SCAN DOES NOT DISPLAY OFF UNDER DESCRIBED CONDITIONS, PROBLEM MAY BE INTERMITTENT.

IF SCAN DISPLAY IS OFF UNDER DESCRIBED CONDITIONS, TCC IS MECHANICALLY STUCK ON. SERVICE TRANSMISSION USING APPROPRIATE SERVICE MANUAL

94B31931 94C31932 94D31933 94E31934 94D31958

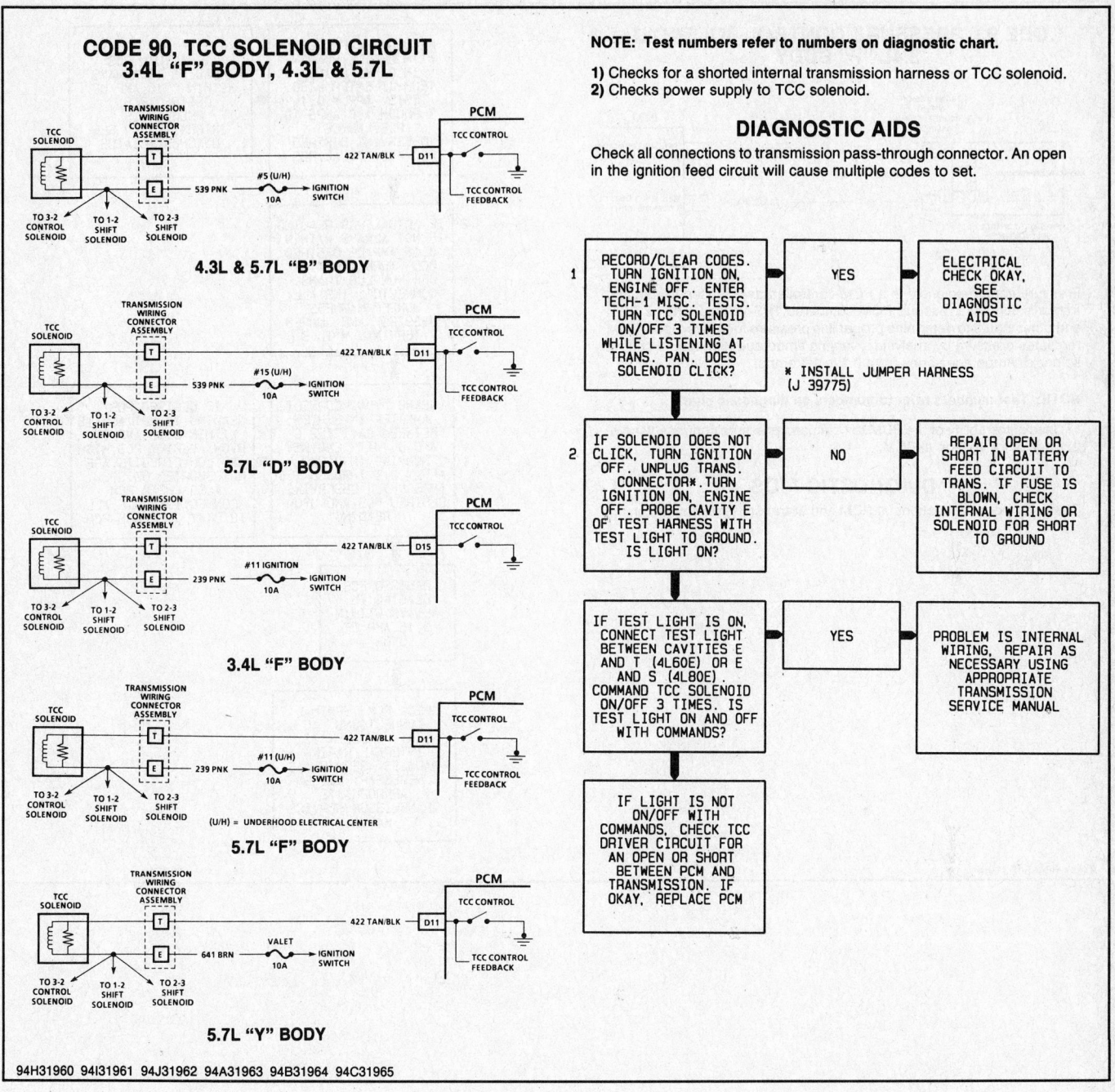

**CODE 90, TCC SOLENOID CIRCUIT
3.4L "F" BODY, 4.3L & 5.7L**

4.3L & 5.7L "B" BODY

5.7L "D" BODY

3.4L "F" BODY

(U/H) = UNDERHOOD ELECTRICAL CENTER

5.7L "F" BODY

5.7L "Y" BODY

94H31960 94I31961 94J31962 94A31963 94B31964 94C31965

NOTE: Test numbers refer to numbers on diagnostic chart.

1) Checks for a shorted internal transmission harness or TCC solenoid.
2) Checks power supply to TCC solenoid.

DIAGNOSTIC AIDS

Check all connections to transmission pass-through connector. An open in the ignition feed circuit will cause multiple codes to set.

1. RECORD/CLEAR CODES. TURN IGNITION ON, ENGINE OFF. ENTER TECH-1 MISC. TESTS. TURN TCC SOLENOID ON/OFF 3 TIMES WHILE LISTENING AT TRANS. PAN. DOES SOLENOID CLICK? → YES → ELECTRICAL CHECK OKAY, SEE DIAGNOSTIC AIDS

* INSTALL JUMPER HARNESS (J 39775)

2. IF SOLENOID DOES NOT CLICK, TURN IGNITION OFF. UNPLUG TRANS. CONNECTOR*. TURN IGNITION ON, ENGINE OFF. PROBE CAVITY E OF TEST HARNESS WITH TEST LIGHT TO GROUND. IS LIGHT ON? → NO → REPAIR OPEN OR SHORT IN BATTERY FEED CIRCUIT TO TRANS. IF FUSE IS BLOWN, CHECK INTERNAL WIRING OR SOLENOID FOR SHORT TO GROUND

IF TEST LIGHT IS ON, CONNECT TEST LIGHT BETWEEN CAVITIES E AND T (4L60E) OR E AND S (4L80E). COMMAND TCC SOLENOID ON/OFF 3 TIMES. IS TEST LIGHT ON AND OFF WITH COMMANDS? → YES → PROBLEM IS INTERNAL WIRING, REPAIR AS NECESSARY USING APPROPRIATE TRANSMISSION SERVICE MANUAL

IF LIGHT IS NOT ON/OFF WITH COMMANDS, CHECK TCC DRIVER CIRCUIT FOR AN OPEN OR SHORT BETWEEN PCM AND TRANSMISSION. IF OKAY, REPLACE PCM

CODE 93, PRESSURE CONTROL SOLENOID 3.4L "F" BODY

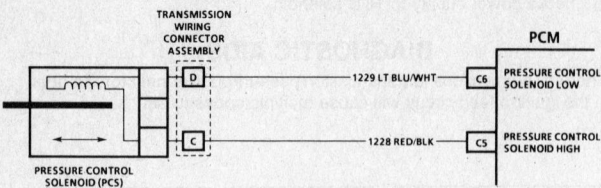

Pressure control solenoid is a PCM-controlled device used to regulate transmission line pressure. PCM compares TPS voltage, engine RPM and other inputs to determine proper line pressure for a given load. PCM regulates pressure by applying a varying amperage to pressure control solenoid. Amperage varies from 0.1 to 1.1 amps.

NOTE: Test numbers refer to numbers on diagnostic chart.

1) Checks the ability of the PCM to command pressure control solenoid.
2) Checks for voltage at PCM.

DIAGNOSTIC AIDS

Check for poor connections at PCM and at transmission connector.

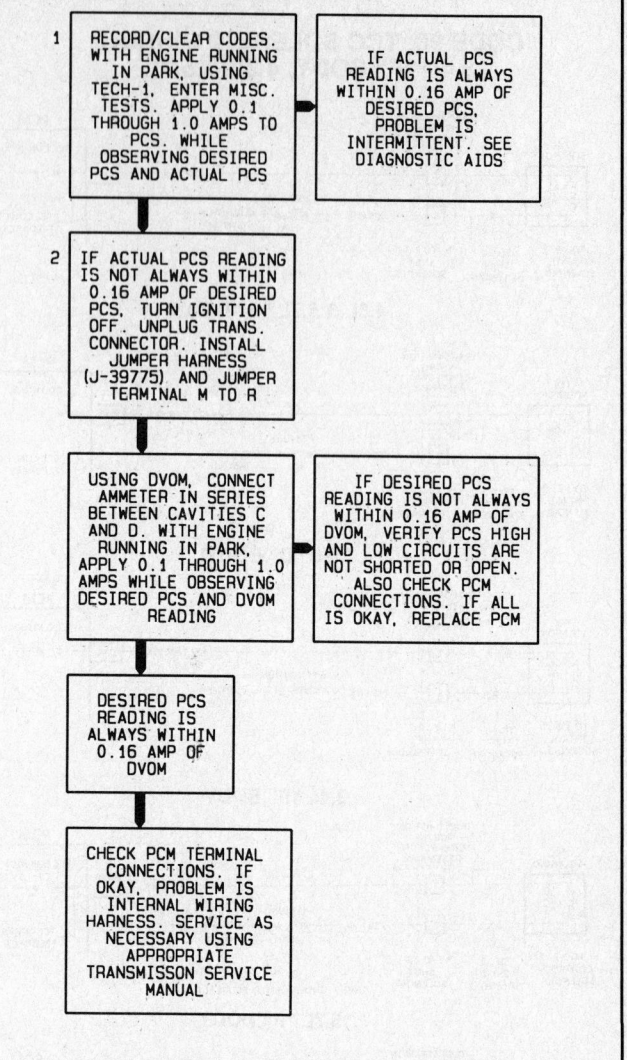

94D31966 94E31967

CODE 96, TRANSMISSION VOLTAGE LOW
3.4L "F" BODY

NOTE: Test numbers refer to numbers on diagnostic chart.

1) Checks for normal battery voltage of 9-15 volts.
2) Checks if low voltage is due to generator voltage supply circuit, or PCM. If voltage is less than 9 volts, PCM is okay.

DIAGNOSTIC AIDS

If code sets when an accessory is operated, check for poor connections or excessive current draw. Also, check for poor connections at starter solenoid or fusible link.

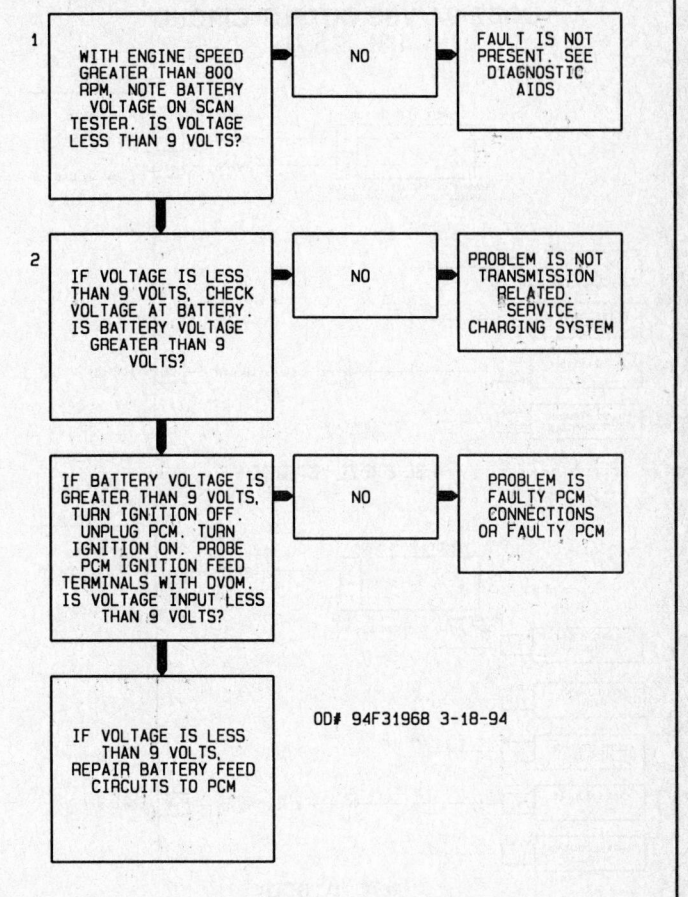

1 — WITH ENGINE SPEED GREATER THAN 800 RPM, NOTE BATTERY VOLTAGE ON SCAN TESTER. IS VOLTAGE LESS THAN 9 VOLTS? — NO → FAULT IS NOT PRESENT. SEE DIAGNOSTIC AIDS

2 — IF VOLTAGE IS LESS THAN 9 VOLTS, CHECK VOLTAGE AT BATTERY. IS BATTERY VOLTAGE GREATER THAN 9 VOLTS? — NO → PROBLEM IS NOT TRANSMISSION RELATED. SERVICE CHARGING SYSTEM

IF BATTERY VOLTAGE IS GREATER THAN 9 VOLTS, TURN IGNITION OFF. UNPLUG PCM. TURN IGNITION ON. PROBE PCM IGNITION FEED TERMINALS WITH DVOM. IS VOLTAGE INPUT LESS THAN 9 VOLTS? — NO → PROBLEM IS FAULTY PCM CONNECTIONS OR FAULTY PCM

IF VOLTAGE IS LESS THAN 9 VOLTS, REPAIR BATTERY FEED CIRCUITS TO PCM

OD# 94F31968 3-18-94

94F31968

CODE 97, VSS OUTPUT CIRCUIT
4.3L & 5.7L

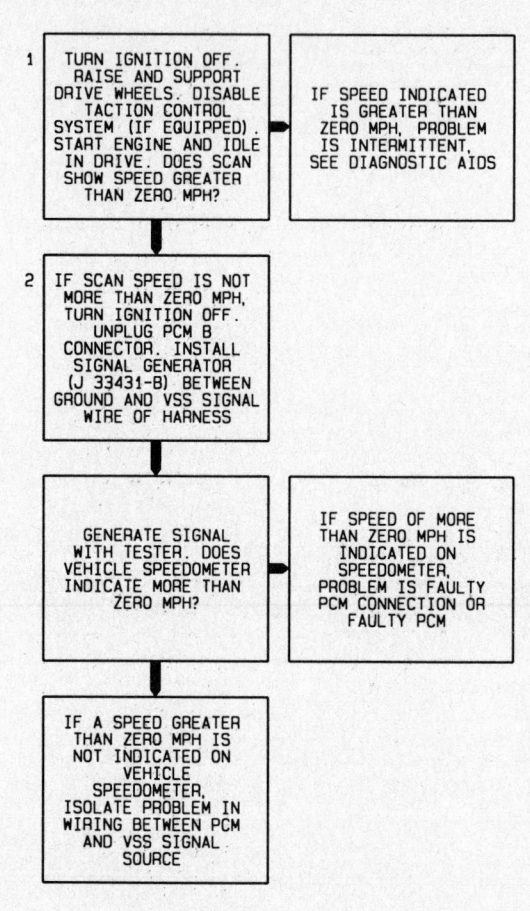

NOTE: Test numbers refer to numbers on diagnostic chart.

1) Disable Traction Control (TC) system (if equipped) prior to this step. Switch is located in glove box. Whenever ignition is cycled off and then on, TC system will default to on. If vehicle speed is indicated at this point, code is intermittent.

2) Use Jumper Harness (J 35616-A) to prevent damage to harness.

DIAGNOSTIC AIDS

Inspect harness and all related connections, including PCM connections.

1 TURN IGNITION OFF. RAISE AND SUPPORT DRIVE WHEELS. DISABLE TRACTION CONTROL SYSTEM (IF EQUIPPED). START ENGINE AND IDLE IN DRIVE. DOES SCAN SHOW SPEED GREATER THAN ZERO MPH?

→ IF SPEED INDICATED IS GREATER THAN ZERO MPH, PROBLEM IS INTERMITTENT, SEE DIAGNOSTIC AIDS

2 IF SCAN SPEED IS NOT MORE THAN ZERO MPH, TURN IGNITION OFF. UNPLUG PCM B CONNECTOR. INSTALL SIGNAL GENERATOR (J 33431-B) BETWEEN GROUND AND VSS SIGNAL WIRE OF HARNESS

GENERATE SIGNAL WITH TESTER. DOES VEHICLE SPEEDOMETER INDICATE MORE THAN ZERO MPH?

→ IF SPEED OF MORE THAN ZERO MPH IS INDICATED ON SPEEDOMETER, PROBLEM IS FAULTY PCM CONNECTION OR FAULTY PCM

IF A SPEED GREATER THAN ZERO MPH IS NOT INDICATED ON VEHICLE SPEEDOMETER, ISOLATE PROBLEM IN WIRING BETWEEN PCM AND VSS SIGNAL SOURCE

94H31911 94I31912 94J31913 94A31914 94G31969

DIAGNOSTIC CODE CHARTS
(LIGHT TRUCKS & VANS)

DTC 16,
TRANSMISSION OUTPUT SPEED
SIGNAL VOLTAGE LOW
(AUTOMATIC TRANSMISSION ONLY)

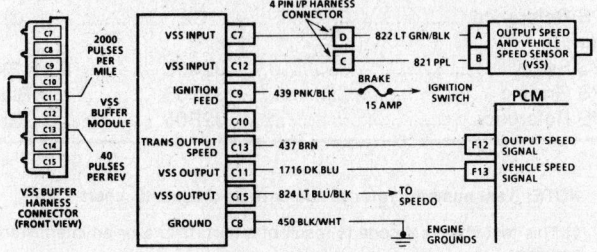

"C" & "K" SERIES

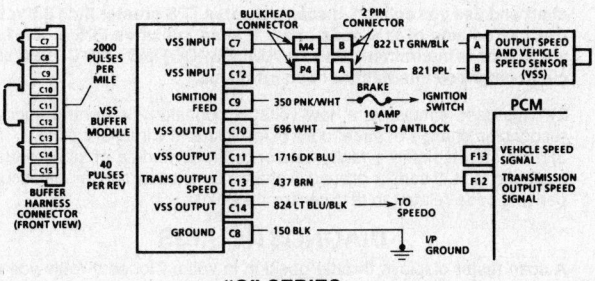

"G" SERIES

This DTC concerns itself with the loss of the 2002 pulses per mile signal to ECM terminal F13. This may be caused by a loss of power to the VSS buffer or an open or grounded circuit. Listed below are the conditions, which must be met for 3 seconds, under which the DTC will set:

- Vehicle speed less than 2 MPH.
- 1000-4000 RPM.
- Throttle angle less than 2 degrees.
- Engine coolant temperature greater than 140°F (60°C).
- Circuit No. 1716 open or grounded.

NOTE: Test numbers refer to numbers on diagnostic chart.

1) This tests for battery voltage at VSS buffer.
2) Tests for proper ground path for vehicle speed sensor signal buffer.
3) This tests for vehicle speed sensor signal buffer CM. Use Digital Volt-Ohmmeter (DVOM) on 20-volt DC scale.
4) This tests for a signal from VSS buffer to ECM.

DIAGNOSTIC AIDS

Check connections at VSS buffer and ECM. Check for codes DTC 24 or DTC 72.

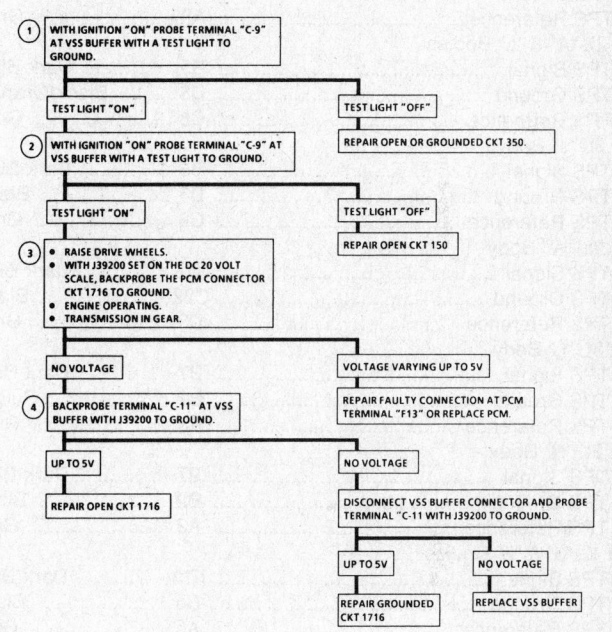

93I76602   93G76600   93E76608

Courtesy of General Motors Corp.

CODE 21, THROTTLE POSITION SENSOR SIGNAL VOLTAGE HIGH

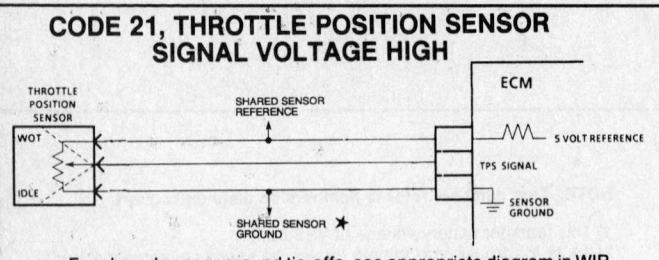

★ – For shared sensor ground tie-offs, see appropriate diagram in WIRING DIAGRAMS article.

CODE 21 ECM TERMINAL & CIRCUIT WIRING IDENTIFICATION

Application	ECM Terminal	Wire Color
2.0L		
TPS Signal	B12	Dark Blue
TPS Ground	D2	Black
TPS Reference	A8	Gray
2.2L "A" & "L" Bodies		
TPS Signal	B5	Dark Blue
TPS Ground	D3	Black/Orange
TPS Reference	C8	Gray
2.2L "J" Body		
TPS Signal	B5	Dark Blue
TPS Ground	D3	Black
TPS Reference	C8	Gray
2.2L "W" Body		
TPS Signal	C18	Dark Blue
TPS Ground	C22	Black
TPS Reference	D3	Gray
2.3L "L" Body		
TPS Signal	B7	Dark Blue
TPS Ground	B2	Purple
TPS Reference	A3	Gray
2.3L "N" Body		
TPS Signal	B7	Dark Blue
TPS Ground	B2	Black
TPS Reference	A3	Gray
3.1L "J" & "L" Bodies		
TPS Signal	F13	Dark Blue
TPS Ground	B5	Black
TPS Reference	A5	Gray
3.1L "W" Body (Exc. Calif.) **& 3.4L "W" Body**		
TPS Signal	C15	Dark Blue
TPS Ground	C10	Black
TPS Reference	C12	Gray
3.1L "W" Body (Calif.) **& 3.4L (VIN S) "F" Body**		
TPS Signal	A30	Dark Blue
TPS Ground	A17	Black
TPS Reference	B31	Gray
3.3L		
TPS Signal	F13	Dark Blue
TPS Ground	B6	Black
TPS Reference	A4	Gray
3.8L "C", "E" & "H" Bodies		
TPS Signal	B10	Dark Blue
TPS Ground	A8	Black
TPS Reference	B3	Gray
3.8L "W" Body		
TPS Signal	C19	Dark Blue
TPS Ground	C7	Black
TPS Reference	B4	Gray
4.3L, 5.0L & 5.7L "B" Body		
TPS Signal	C13	Dark Blue
TPS Ground	A11	Black
TPS Reference	C14	Gray

CODE 21 ECM TERMINAL & CIRCUIT WIRING IDENTIFICATION (Cont.)

Application	ECM Terminal	Wire Color
5.7L "D" Body		
TPS Signal	C5	Dark Blue
TPS Ground	D3	Black
TPS Reference	C4	Gray
5.7L "F" & "Y" Bodies		
TPS Signal	C3	Dark Blue
TPS Ground	B18	Black
TPS Reference	C2	Gray
Saturn		
TPS Signal	J2A08	Dark Blue
TPS Ground	J1D03	Black
TPS Reference	J2B05	Gray

NOTE: Test numbers refer to numbers on diagnostic chart.

1) This test checks if code is result of a hard failure or an intermittent condition.

NOTE: On 2.0L and 2.2L, Code 21 does not differentiate between high or low voltage. If scan indicates TPS less than .19 volt, go to Code 22 chart and use yes column. If scan indicates TPS greater than 3.9 volts, use yes column of this code chart. If scan indicates TPS is .33-1.33 volts, code is intermittent. See TROUBLE SHOOTING - NO CODES article to diagnose intermittent code problems.

2) This test simulates a low-voltage condition. If control module recognizes change of state, control module and wiring are okay.

3) This step isolates a faulty sensor, control module or open sensor ground circuit. If sensor ground is shared by another sensor, an accompanying code related to that sensor may exist.

DIAGNOSTIC AIDS

A scan tester displays throttle position in volts. Closed throttle voltage should be low. Voltage should increase gradually to about 4.5 volts at a steady rate as throttle angle is increased. If code is intermittent, see INTERMITTENTS in TROUBLE SHOOTING – NO CODES article.

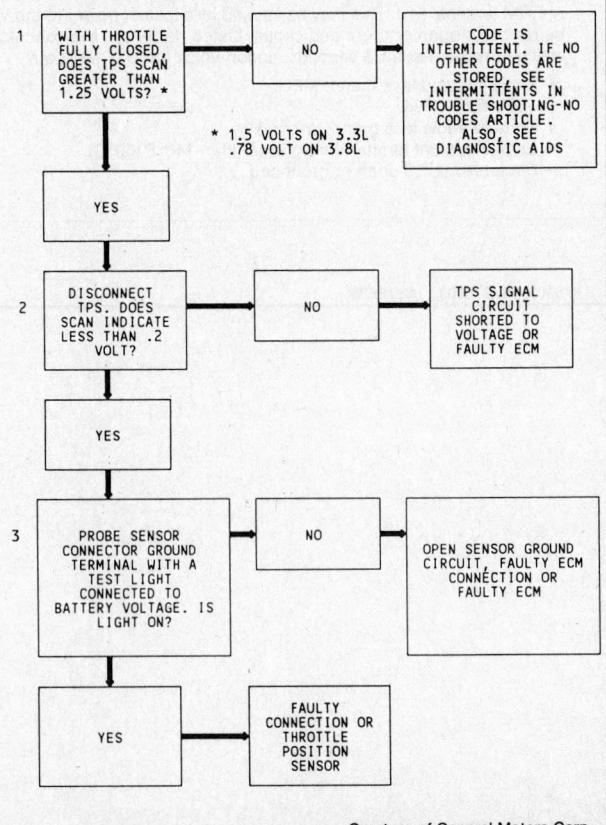

CODE 22, THROTTLE POSITION SENSOR SIGNAL VOLTAGE LOW

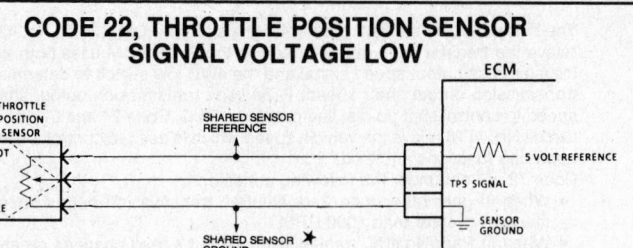

★ – For shared sensor ground tie-offs, see appropriate diagram in WIRING DIAGRAMS.

CODE 22 ECM TERMINAL & CIRCUIT WIRING IDENTIFICATION

Application	ECM Terminal	Wire Color
2.0L		
TPS Signal	B12	Dark Blue
TPS Ground	D2	Black
TPS Reference	A8	Gray
2.2L "A" & "L" Bodies		
TPS Signal	B5	Dark Blue
TPS Ground	D3	Black/Orange
TPS Reference	C8	Gray
2.2L "J" Body		
TPS Signal	B5	Dark Blue
TPS Ground	D3	Black
TPS Reference	C8	Gray
2.2L "W" Body		
TPS Signal	C18	Dark Blue
TPS Ground	C22	Black
TPS Reference	D3	Gray
2.3L "L" Body		
TPS Signal	B7	Dark Blue
TPS Ground	B2	Purple
TPS Reference	A3	Gray
2.3L "N" Body		
TPS Signal	B7	Dark Blue
TPS Ground	B2	Black
TPS Reference	A3	Gray
3.1L "J" & "L" Bodies		
TPS Signal	F13	Dark Blue
TPS Ground	B5	Black
TPS Reference	A5	Gray
3.1L "W" Body (Exc. Calif.) & 3.4L "W" Body		
TPS Signal	C15	Dark Blue
TPS Ground	C10	Black
TPS Reference	C12	Gray
3.1L "W" Body (Calif.) & 3.4L (VIN S) "F" Body		
TPS Signal	A30	Dark Blue
TPS Ground	A17	Black
TPS Reference	B31	Gray
3.3L		
TPS Signal	F13	Dark Blue
TPS Ground	B6	Black
TPS Reference	A4	Gray
3.8L "C", "E" & "H" Bodies		
TPS Signal	B10	Dark Blue
TPS Ground	A8	Black
TPS Reference	B3	Gray
3.8L "W" Body		
TPS Signal	C19	Dark Blue
TPS Ground	C7	Black
TPS Reference	B4	Gray
4.3L, 5.0L & 5.7L "B" Body		
TPS Signal	C13	Dark Blue
TPS Ground	A11	Black
TPS Reference	C14	Gray

CODE 22 ECM TERMINAL & CIRCUIT WIRING IDENTIFICATION (Cont.)

Application	ECM Terminal	Wire Color
5.7L "D" Body		
TPS Signal	C5	Dark Blue
TPS Ground	D3	Black
TPS Reference	C4	Gray
5.7L "F" & "Y" Bodies		
TPS Signal	C3	Dark Blue
TPS Ground	B18	Black
TPS Reference	C2	Gray
Saturn		
TPS Signal	J2A08	Dark Blue
TPS Ground	J1D03	Black
TPS Reference	J2B05	Gray

NOTE: Test numbers refer to numbers on diagnostic chart.

1) This test checks if code is result of a hard failure or an intermittent condition.
2) This test simulates conditions for a Code 21. If control module recognizes change of state, control module and wiring are okay.
3) This simulates a high signal voltage to check for an open in TPS signal line to control module. Scan tester should recognize this signal and display high TPS voltage.

DIAGNOSTIC AIDS

A scan tester displays throttle position in volts. Closed throttle voltage should be low. Voltage should increase gradually to about 4.5 volts at a steady rate as throttle angle is increased. If code is intermittent, see INTERMITTENTS in TROUBLE SHOOTING – NO CODES article.

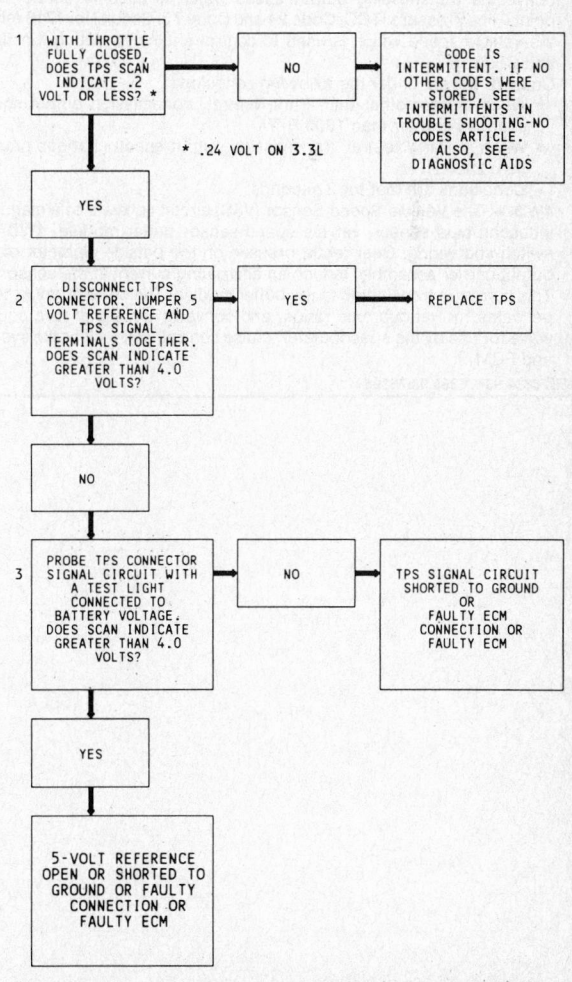

Courtesy of General Motors Corp.

CODE 24 & 72, VEHICLE SPEED SENSOR LOSS (2WD, AWD & 4WD)

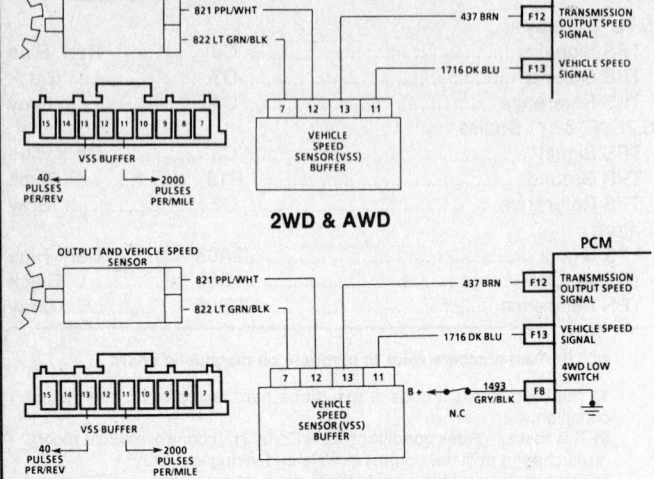

2WD & AWD

4WD

2WD & AWD – The Vehicle Speed Sensor (VSS) circuit consists of a magnetic induction-type sensor, vehicle speed sensor buffer module and wiring. Gear teeth, pressed on the outside diameter of the output carrier assembly, induce an alternating current in the sensor.

This current is transmitted to the buffer module. The buffer module compensates for various axle ratios, and converts the signal to a square wave for use by the speedometer, cruise control, anti-lock brake system and PCM.

The buffer module sends 2 different signals to the PCM. Circuit No. 437 relays the transmission output speed which is used to control shift points, line pressure, TCC, Code 24 and Code 72. Circuit No. 1716 relays the vehicle speed which is used to control engine operating functions and Code 16.

Code 72 will set under the following conditions.
- When in gear other than Park/Neutral, transmission output speed changes greater than 1000 RPM.
- When in Park/Neutral, transmission output speed changes greater than 2050 RPM.
- Conditions are met for 2 seconds.

4WD – The Vehicle Speed Sensor (VSS) circuit consists of a magnetic induction-type sensor, vehicle speed sensor buffer module, 4WD low switch and wiring. Gear teeth, pressed on the outside diameter of the output carrier assembly, induce an alternating current in the sensor.

This current is transmitted to the buffer module. The buffer module compensates for various axle ratios, and converts the signal to a square wave for use by the speedometer, cruise control, anti-lock brake system and PCM.

The buffer module sends 2 different signals to the PCM. Circuit No. 437 relays the transfer case output speed to the PCM. PCM uses both the transfer case output speed signal and the 4WD low switch to determine transmission output shaft speed. PCM uses transmission output shaft speed to control shift points, line pressure, TCC, Code 24 and Code 72. Circuit No. 1716 relays the vehicle speed which is used to control engine operating functions and Code 16.

Code 72 will set under the following conditions.
- When in gear other than Park/Neutral, transmission output speed changes greater than 1000 RPM.
- When in Park/Neutral, transmission output speed changes greater than 2050 RPM.
- Conditions are met for 2 seconds.

NOTE: Test numbers refer to numbers on diagnostic chart.

1) This test checks the VSS signal to the PCM.
2) This test checks the VSS signal to the buffer module.
3) This test checks the VSS signal.

DIAGNOSTIC AIDS

Check all connections, especially those at the transmission pass-thru connector. If code is intermittent, see INTERMITTENTS in TROUBLE SHOOTING – NO CODES article.

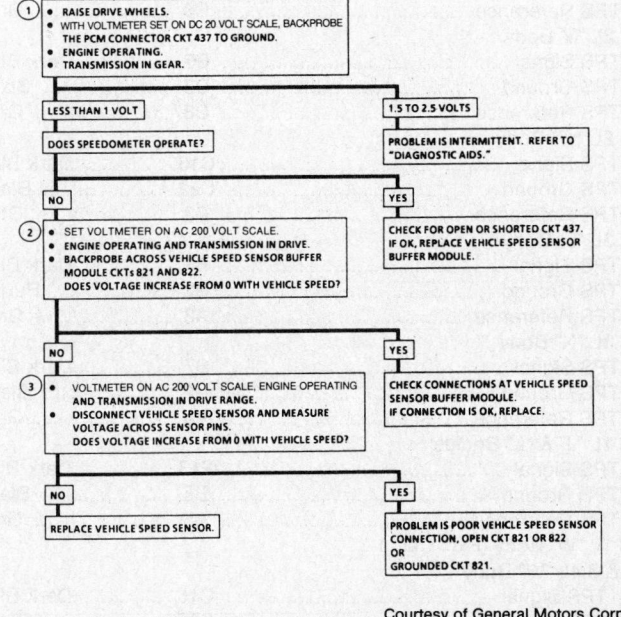

93E76384 93F76385 93I76396

Courtesy of General Motors Corp.

CODE 28, FLUID PRESSURE SWITCH ASSEMBLY FAULT

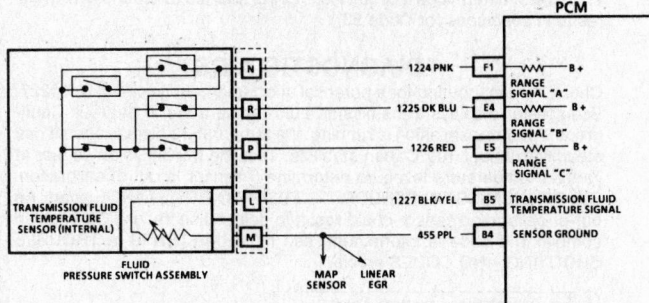

ASTRO, SAFARI & "C" & "K" SERIES

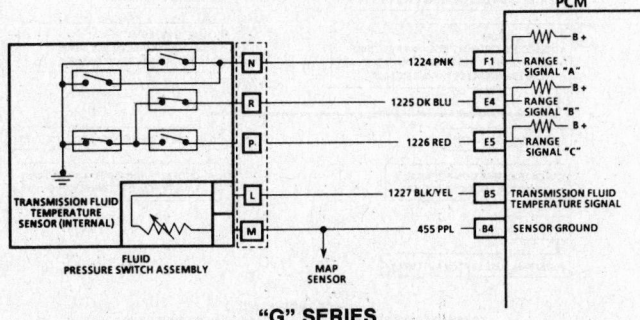

"G" SERIES

The fluid pressure switch assembly consists of a fluid temperature sensor and 5 pressure switches combined into one unit and mounted on the transmission valve body. The PCM supplies battery voltage to the fluid pressure switch on 3 separate wires. By grounding one or more of these circuits through various combinations of the pressure switches inside the fluid pressure switch assembly, the PCM detects what gear range has been selected by the vehicle operator while idling.

With engine off, PARK/NEUTRAL will be indicated. If range signals "A" and "C" are zero volts, or all 3 signals are zero volts for 1.5 seconds on diesel engine or 2 seconds on gasoline engine, Code 28 will set. When Code 28 is set, harsh shifts, no TCC, and possibly no 4th gear (if in hot mode) will occur.

NOTE: Test numbers refer to numbers on diagnostic chart.

1) This test compares the indicated range to the range actually selected.
2) This test checks for correct voltage from the PCM to the transmission pass-thru connector.
3) This test will detect a short to ground in any one of the 3 fluid pressure switch assembly range circuits.

DIAGNOSTIC AIDS

Code 28 will set if PCM detects one of 2 "illegal" fluid pressure switch assembly combinations. See VALID FLUID PRESSURE SWITCH ASSEMBLY COMBINATION table for various combinations. Check pass-thru connector for good contact.

VALID FLUID PRESSURE SWITCH ASSEMBLY COMBINATION CHART

	A	B	C
Park	Off	On	Off
Reverse	On	On	Off
Neutral	OFF	ON	OFF
4th	Off	On	On
3rd	Off	Off	On
2nd	Off	Off	Off
1st	On	Off	Off
Illegal	On	On	On
Illegal	On	On	On

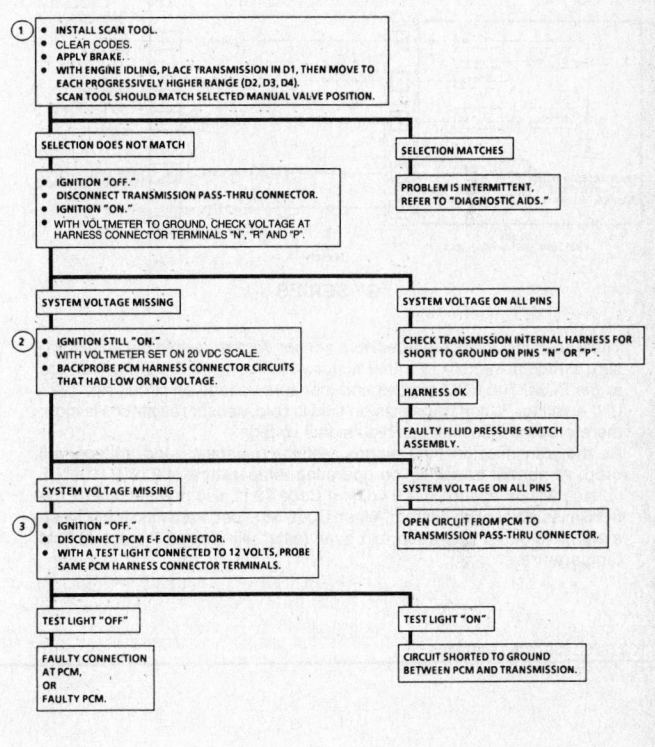

93E76392 93F76393 93H76403

Courtesy of General Motors Corp.

CODE 58, TRANSMISSION FLUID TEMPERATURE SENSOR CIRCUIT (HIGH TEMPERATURE INDICATED)

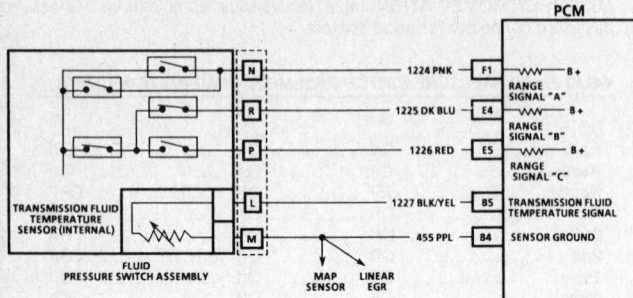

ASTRO, SAFARI & "C" & "K" SERIES

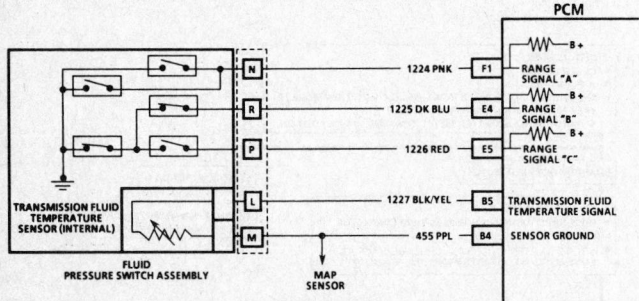

"G" SERIES

The transmission fluid temperature sensor, located within the fluid pressure switch assembly, is a thermistor which controls the signal voltage to the PCM. The PCM applies and monitors voltage on circuit No. 1227 to the sensor. When transmission fluid is cold, sensor resistance is high; therefore, the PCM will see high signal voltage.

As the transmission fluid warms, sensor resistance and voltage will drop. At normal transmission operating temperature of 212°F (100°C), voltage will be about 1.5-2.0 volts. If Code 79 is also present, check the transmission cooling system. When Code 58 is set, transmission will use a warm value for operation, but scan tester will display the actual fluid temperature.

93E76392 93F76393 93J76405

NOTE: Test numbers refer to numbers on diagnostic chart.

1) Code 58 will set if signal voltage indicates a transmission fluid temperature greater than 309°F (154°C) for one second.

2) This test determines if circuit No. 1227 is shorted to ground, which will result in conditions for Code 58.

DIAGNOSTIC AIDS

Check harness routing for a potential short to ground in circuit No. 1227. Scan tester displays transmission fluid temperature in degrees Centigrade. After transmission is running, the temperature display should rise steadily to about 100°C then stabilize. Test the transmission sensor at various temperature levels to determine if sensor is out of calibration. See TRANSMISSION SENSOR — TEMP TO RESISTANCE chart. An out-of-calibration sensor could result in delayed shifts, or TCC enabled complaint. If code is intermittent, see INTERMITTENTS in TROUBLE SHOOTING – NO CODES article.

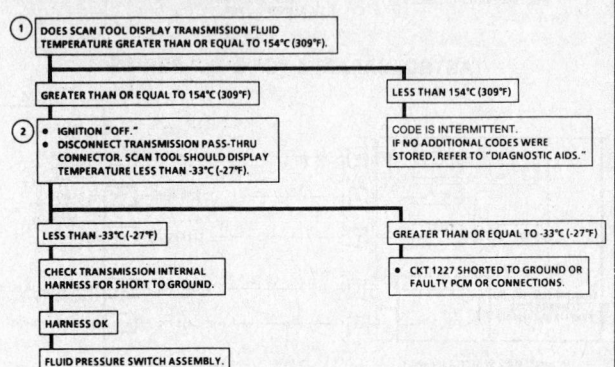

DIAGNOSTIC AID				
TRANSMISSION SENSOR - TEMP TO RESISTANCE (APPROXIMATE)				
°C	°F	MINIMUM RESISTANCE	NOMINAL RESISTANCE	MAXIMUM RESISTANCE
-40°C	-40°F	80965	100544	120123
-30°C	-20°F	42701	52426	62151
-20°C	-4°F	23458	28491	33524
-10°C	14°F	13366	16068	18770
0°C	32°F	7871	9370	10869
10°C	50°F	4771	5640	6508
20°C	68°F	2981	3500	4018
30°C	86°F	1915	2232	2550
40°C	104°F	1260	1460	1660
50°C	122°F	848.8	977.1	1105
60°C	140°F	584.1	668.7	753.4
70°C	158°F	410.3	467.2	524.2
80°C	176°F	293.7	332.7	371.7
90°C	194°F	213.9	241.0	268.2
100°C	212°F	158.1	177.4	196.8
110°C	230°F	118.8	132.6	146.5
120°C	248°F	90.40	100.6	110.8
130°C	266°F	69.48	77.29	85.11
140°C	284°F	53.96	60.13	66.29
150°C	304°F	42.43	47.31	52.20

Courtesy of General Motors Corp.

CODE 59, TRANSMISSION FLUID TEMPERATURE SENSOR CIRCUIT (LOW TEMPERATURE INDICATED)

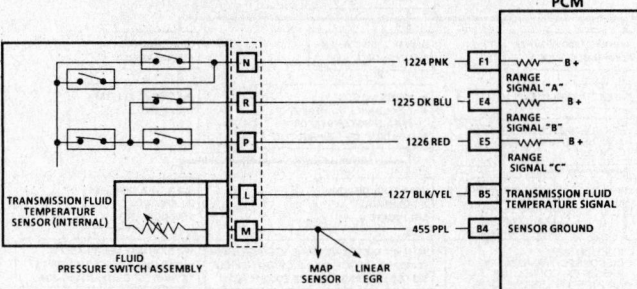

ASTRO, SAFARI & "C" & "K" SERIES

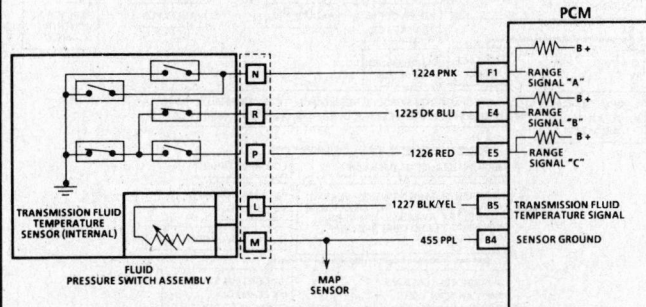

"G" SERIES

The transmission fluid temperature sensor, located within the fluid pressure switch assembly, is a thermistor which controls the signal voltage to the PCM. The PCM applies and monitors 5 volts to the sensor on circuit No. 1227. When transmission fluid is cold, sensor resistance is high; therefore, the PCM will see high signal voltage.

As the transmission fluid warms, sensor resistance and voltage will drop. At normal transmission operating temperature of 212°F (100°C), voltage will be about 1.5-2.0 volts. When Code 59 is set, transmission will use a warm value for operation, but scan tester will display the actual fluid temperature.

NOTE: Test numbers refer to numbers on diagnostic chart.

1) Code 59 will set if signal voltage indicates a transmission fluid temperature less than -27°F (-33°C) for one second.

2) This test simulates Code 58. If PCM recognizes the low signal voltage (high temperature) and scan tester reads 309°F (154°C) or greater, the PCM and wiring are okay.

93E76392 93F76393 93A76406

3) This test determines if circuit No. 1227 is open. There should be 5 volts present at the sensor connector if measuring with a DVOM.

DIAGNOSTIC AIDS

Scan tester displays transmission fluid temperature in degrees Centigrade. After transmission is running, the temperature display should rise steadily to about 100°C then stabilize. A faulty connection or an open in circuit No. 455 or circuit No. 1227 will result in a Code 59. Test the transmission sensor at various temperature levels to determine if sensor is out of calibration. See TRANSMISSION SENSOR — TEMP TO RESISTANCE chart. An out-of-calibration sensor could result in firm shifts, or TCC enabled complaint.

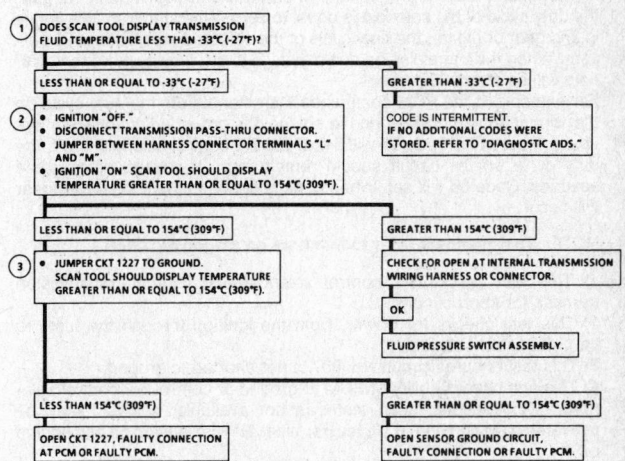

DIAGNOSTIC AID
TRANSMISSION SENSOR - TEMP TO RESISTANCE (APPROXIMATE)

°C	°F	MINIMUM RESISTANCE	NOMINAL RESISTANCE	MAXIMUM RESISTANCE
-40°C	-40°F	80965	100544	120123
-30°C	-20°F	42701	52426	62151
-20°C	-4°F	23458	28491	33524
-10°C	14°F	13366	16068	18770
0°C	32°F	7871	9370	10869
10°C	50°F	4771	5640	6508
20°C	68°F	2981	3500	4018
30°C	86°F	1915	2232	2550
40°C	104°F	1260	1460	1660
50°C	122°F	848.8	977.1	1105
60°C	140°F	584.1	668.7	753.4
70°C	158°F	410.3	467.2	524.2
80°C	176°F	293.7	332.7	371.7
90°C	194°F	213.9	241.0	268.2
100°C	212°F	158.1	177.4	196.8
110°C	230°F	118.8	132.6	146.5
120°C	248°F	90.40	100.6	110.8
130°C	266°F	69.48	77.29	85.11
140°C	284°F	53.96	60.13	66.29
150°C	304°F	42.43	47.31	52.20

Courtesy of General Motors Corp.

CODE 66, 3-2 CONTROL SOLENOID CIRCUIT FAULT

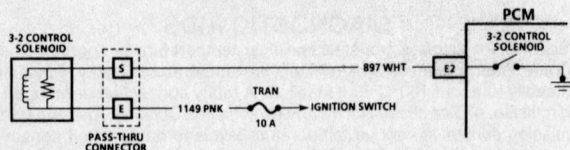

The 3-2 control solenoid hydraulically coordinates the apply rate of the 2-4 band with hydraulic release of the 3-4 clutch during a 3-2 downshift. 3-2 circuit duty cycle is continually monitored by the PCM depending on the command state of the circuit. When the transmission is in 1st gear the duty cycle of the solenoid is equal to zero. When the transmission is in 2nd gear or higher, the duty cycle of the solenoid will be about 90 percent. When the transmission downshifts 3-2, the duty cycle of the solenoid will be about 20 percent.

For example, if the PCM commands the solenoid on, the duty cycle on that circuit should drop when the solenoid is grounded. If voltage stays up for 4 seconds, Code 66 will set. If the 3-2 control solenoid is off, the duty cycle on the circuit should remain high. If voltage drops for 4 seconds, Code 66 will set. When code is set, a soft landing to 3rd gear will occur.

NOTE: Test numbers refer to numbers on diagnostic chart.

1) This test checks 3-2 control solenoid and internal transmission harness for short circuits.
2) This test checks for power, from the ignition through the fuse, to the 3-2 control solenoid.
3) This test ensures circuit No. 897 is not shorted to ground.
4) This test checks ability of PCM to ground or control 3-2 control solenoid. If bidirectional scan tester is not available, solenoid may be activated by grounding ALDL test terminal "B" with ignition on and engine off.

DIAGNOSTIC AIDS

Check all connections, especially those at the transmission pass-thru connector. If code is intermittent, see INTERMITTENTS in TROUBLE SHOOTING – NO CODES article. Some slight TCC slippage is normal. 3-2 control solenoid feedback normally oscillates on/off when the duty cycle is applied.

93I76388 93B76399

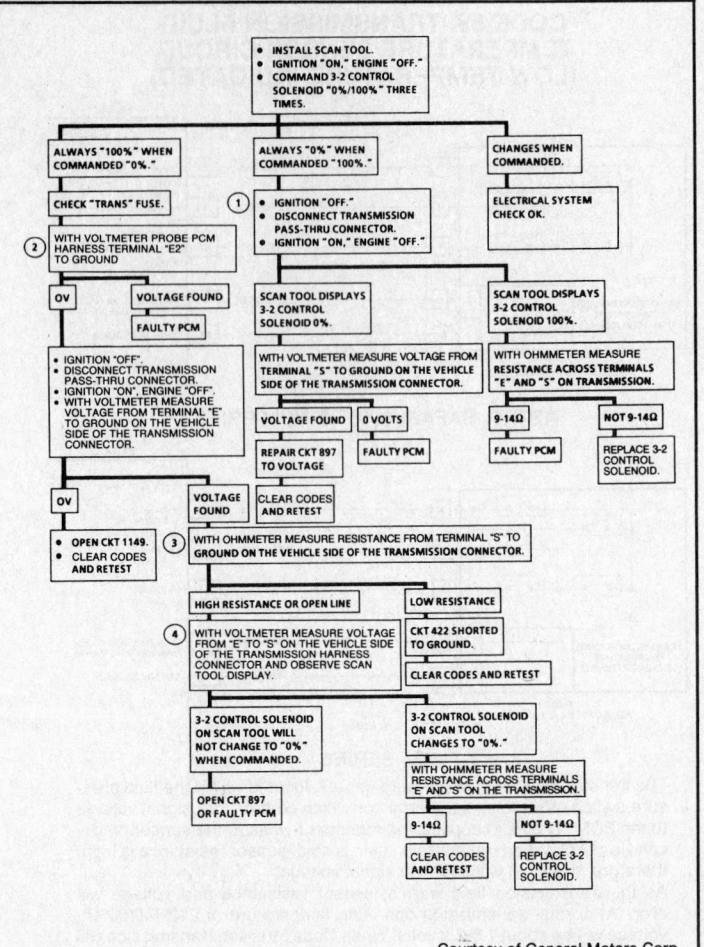

Courtesy of General Motors Corp.

CODE 67, TCC SOLENOID CIRCUIT CHECK

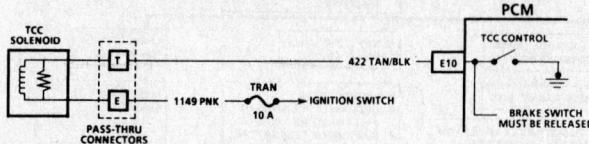

The TCC solenoid is a normally open exhaust valve. The PCM will engage the solenoid by grounding circuit No. 422 with an internal quad-driver. The PCM continually monitors voltage on TCC circuit for either low or high voltage, depending on the commanded state of the circuit. Code 67 will set if a fault is detected.

For example, If the PCM commands the TCC solenoid on, the voltage on that circuit should drop when the solenoid is grounded. If voltage stays up for 2 seconds, Code 67 will set. If solenoid is off, the voltage on that circuit should remain higher. If voltage drops for 2 seconds, Code 67 will set. When code is set, no TCC will occur and no 4th gear in hot mode.

NOTE: Test numbers refer to numbers on diagnostic chart.

1) This test checks TCC solenoid and the internal transmission harness for short circuits.
2) This test checks for power, from the ignition through the fuse, to the TCC solenoid.
3) This test ensures circuit No. 422 is not shorted to ground.
4) This test checks ability of PCM to ground or control TCC solenoid.

DIAGNOSTIC AIDS

Check all connections, especially those at the transmission pass-thru connector. If code is intermittent, see INTERMITTENTS in TROUBLE SHOOTING – NO CODES article. Some slight TCC slippage is normal.

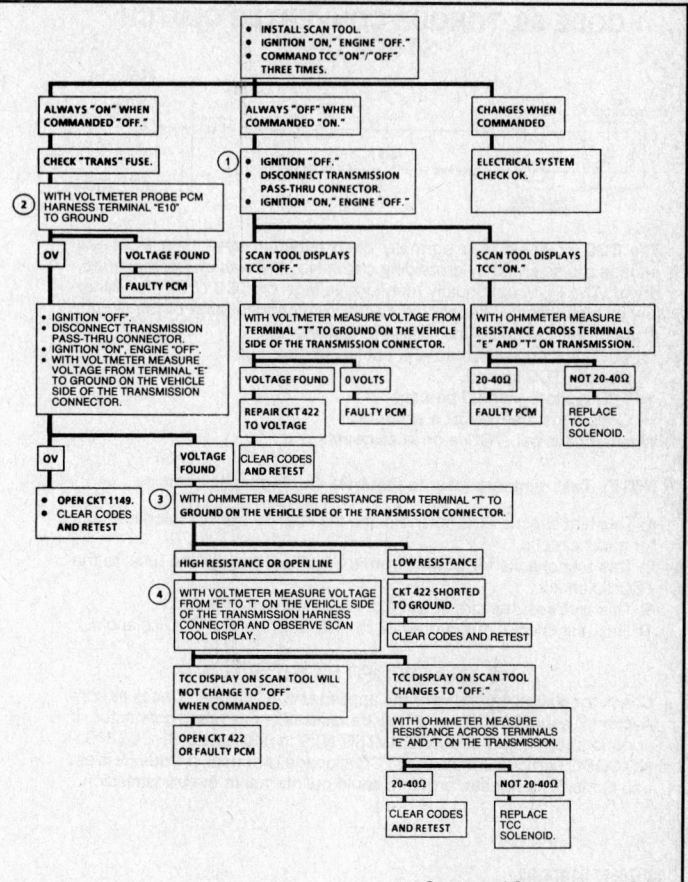

93H76387 93A76398

Courtesy of General Motors Corp.

CODE 69, TORQUE CONVERTER CLUTCH STUCK ON

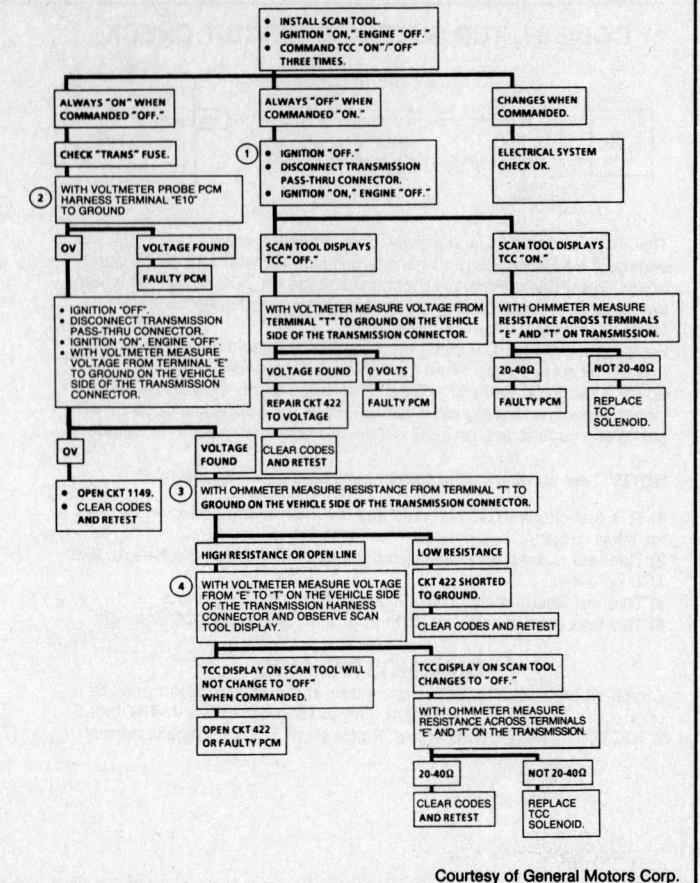

The TCC solenoid is a normally open exhaust valve. The PCM will engage the solenoid by grounding circuit No. 422 with an internal quad-driver. The PCM continually monitors voltage on TCC circuit for either low or high voltage, depending on the commanded state of the circuit. Code 69 will set under the following conditions:
- TCC slip is greater than -20, but less than 20.
- Without TCC locked.
- TPS is more than 25 percent.
- Conditions are met for 4 seconds.

When code is set, TCC is on in all gears.

NOTE: Test numbers refer to numbers on diagnostic chart.

1) This test checks TCC solenoid and the internal transmission harness for short circuits.
2) This test checks for power, from the ignition through the fuse, to the TCC solenoid.
3) This test ensures circuit No. 422 is not shorted to ground.
4) This test checks ability of PCM to ground or control TCC solenoid.

DIAGNOSTIC AIDS

Check for stall with parking brake applied and in 2nd gear. Check all connections, especially those at the transmission pass-thru connector. If code is intermittent, see INTERMITTENTS in TROUBLE SHOOTING – NO CODES article. Some slight TCC slippage is normal. If Code 69 is set and Code 67 is not set, problem could be internal to the transmission.

93H76387 93A76398

Courtesy of General Motors Corp.

CODE 73, PRESSURE CONTROL SOLENOID (CURRENT ERROR)

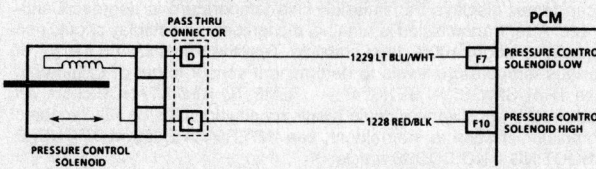

The pressure control solenoid is a PCM-controlled device used to regulate transmission line pressure. The PCM looks at TPS voltage, engine RPM and other inputs to determine the appropriate line pressure for a given load, then regulates the pressure by applying a variable amperage to the pressure control solenoid. Applied amperage varies from .1 to 1.1 amps.

The PCM then monitors the amperage at the return line. If the return amperage varies greater than .16 amp from the commanded amperage for at least one second, Code 73 will set. When Code 73 sets, the full line pressure will be applied, causing harsh shifts until the next ignition cycle. The code will remain stored in memory, and the pressure control solenoid will resume normal operation until conditions for the code reoccur.

NOTE: Test numbers refer to numbers on diagnostic chart.

1) This test checks ability of PCM to command pressure control solenoid.

2) This test checks for voltage at PCM.

3) This test checks internal transmission harness and pressure control solenoid for low resistance.

4) This test checks internal transmission harness and pressure control solenoid for high resistance.

DIAGNOSTIC AIDS

Check all connections, especially those at the transmission pass-thru connector and PCM.

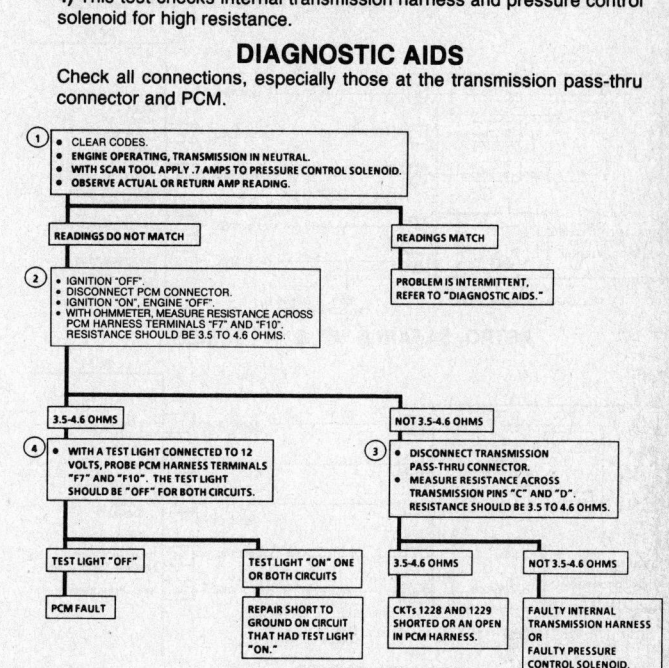

Courtesy of General Motors Corp.

CODE 79, TRANSMISSION FLUID OVERTEMP

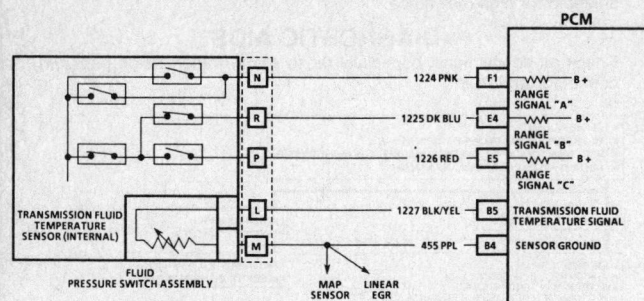

ASTRO, SAFARI & "C" & "K" SERIES

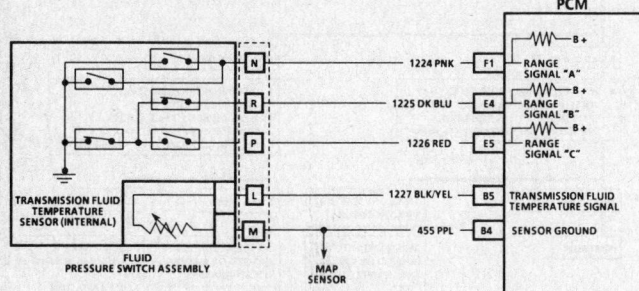

"G" SERIES

The transmission fluid temperature sensor, located within the fluid pressure switch assembly, is a thermistor which controls the signal voltage to the PCM. The PCM applies and monitors voltage on circuit No. 1227 to the sensor. When transmission fluid is cold, sensor resistance is high; therefore, the PCM will see high signal voltage.

As the transmission fluid warms, sensor resistance and voltage will drop. At normal transmission operating temperature of 212°F (100°C), voltage will be about 1.5-2.0 volts. If fluid temperature becomes greater than 304°F (150°C) but less than 309°F (154°C) for 15 minutes, Code 79 will set. If fluid temperature becomes greater than 309°F (154°C), Code 58 will also set.

NOTE: Test numbers refer to numbers on diagnostic chart.

1) Code 58 will set if signal voltage indicates a transmission fluid temperature greater than 309°F (154°C).
2) This test simulates a Code 59.

DIAGNOSTIC AIDS

Check harness routing for a potential short to ground in circuit No. 1227. Scan tester displays transmission fluid temperature in degrees Centigrade. After transmission is running, the temperature display should rise steadily to about 100°C then stabilize. Test the transmission sensor at various temperature levels to determine if sensor is out of calibration. See TRANSMISSION SENSOR — TEMP TO RESISTANCE chart. An out-of-calibration sensor could result in delayed shifts or TCC enabled complaint. If code is intermittent, see INTERMITTENTS in TROUBLE SHOOTING – NO CODES article.

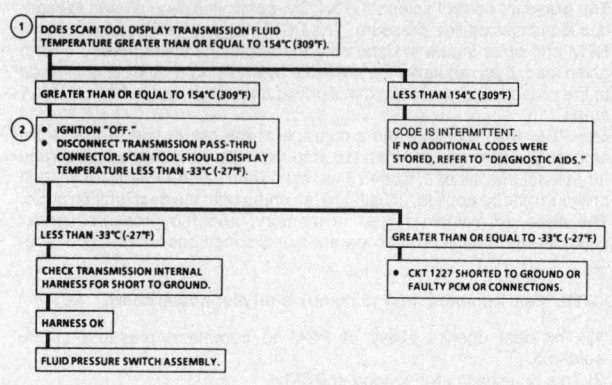

DIAGNOSTIC AID
TRANSMISSION SENSOR - TEMP TO RESISTANCE (APPROXIMATE)

°C	°F	MINIMUM RESISTANCE	NOMINAL RESISTANCE	MAXIMUM RESISTANCE
-40°C	-40°F	80965	100544	120123
-30°C	-20°F	42701	52426	62151
-20°C	-4°F	23458	28491	33524
-10°C	14°F	13366	16068	18770
0°C	32°F	7871	9370	10869
10°C	50°F	4771	5640	6508
20°C	68°F	2981	3500	4018
30°C	86°F	1915	2232	2550
40°C	104°F	1260	1460	1660
50°C	122°F	848.8	977.1	1105
60°C	140°F	584.1	668.7	753.4
70°C	158°F	410.3	467.2	524.2
80°C	176°F	293.7	332.7	371.7
90°C	194°F	213.9	241.0	268.2
100°C	212°F	158.1	177.4	196.8
110°C	230°F	118.8	132.6	146.5
120°C	248°F	90.40	100.6	110.8
130°C	266°F	69.48	77.29	85.11
140°C	284°F	53.96	60.13	66.29
150°C	304°F	42.43	47.31	52.20

93E76392 93E76393 93J76405

Courtesy of General Motors Corp.

CODE 81, 2-3 SHIFT SOLENOID CIRCUIT FAULT

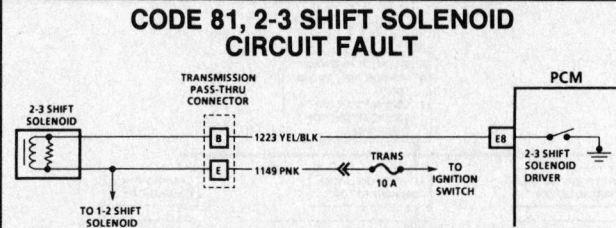

The PCM continually monitors voltage on each circuit connected to the quad-driver, looking for either low or high voltage, depending on the commanded state of the devices connected to it. Code 81 will set if a fault has been detected on the 2-3 shift solenoid circuit.

If 2-3 shift solenoid is commanded on by the PCM, voltage on that circuit should drop when solenoid is grounded. If 2-3 shift solenoid is off, voltage on the circuit should remain high. If solenoid is shorted off, 3rd gear only will occur. If solenoid is shorted on, 2nd gear only will occur. If voltage stays up for at least 2 seconds, Code 81 will set. If voltage drops for more than 2 seconds, Code 81 will set.

NOTE: Test numbers refer to numbers on diagnostic chart.

1) This test checks 2-3 shift solenoid and internal transmission wiring for short circuits.
2) This test checks for power, from the ignition through the fuse, to the shift solenoid.
3) This test ensures circuit No. 1223 is not shorted to ground.
4) This test checks ability of PCM to ground or control 2-3 shift solenoid. If bidirectional scan tester is not available, solenoid may be activated by grounding ALDL test terminal "B" with ignition on and engine off.

DIAGNOSTIC AIDS

Check all connections, especially those at the transmission pass-thru connector. If code is intermittent, see INTERMITTENTS in TROUBLE SHOOTING – NO CODES article. An open in the circuit can cause multiple codes to set.

SHIFT SOLENOID COMBINATION

Gear	1-2 Shift Solenoid	2-3 Shift Solenoid
1st	On	On
2nd	Off	On
3rd	Off	Off
4th	On	Off

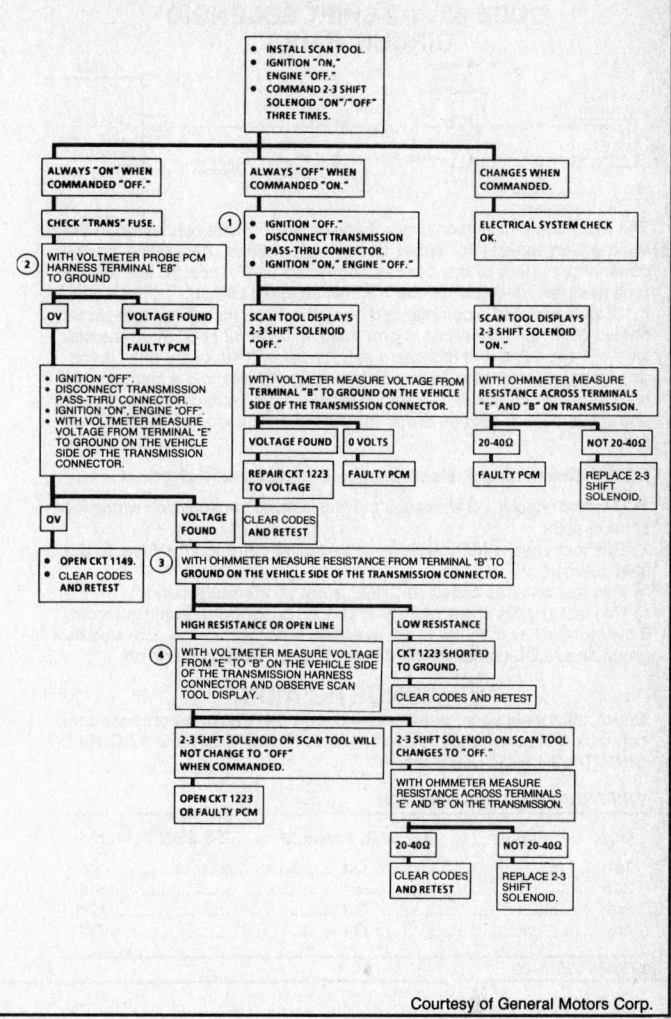

93C76390 93F76401

Courtesy of General Motors Corp.

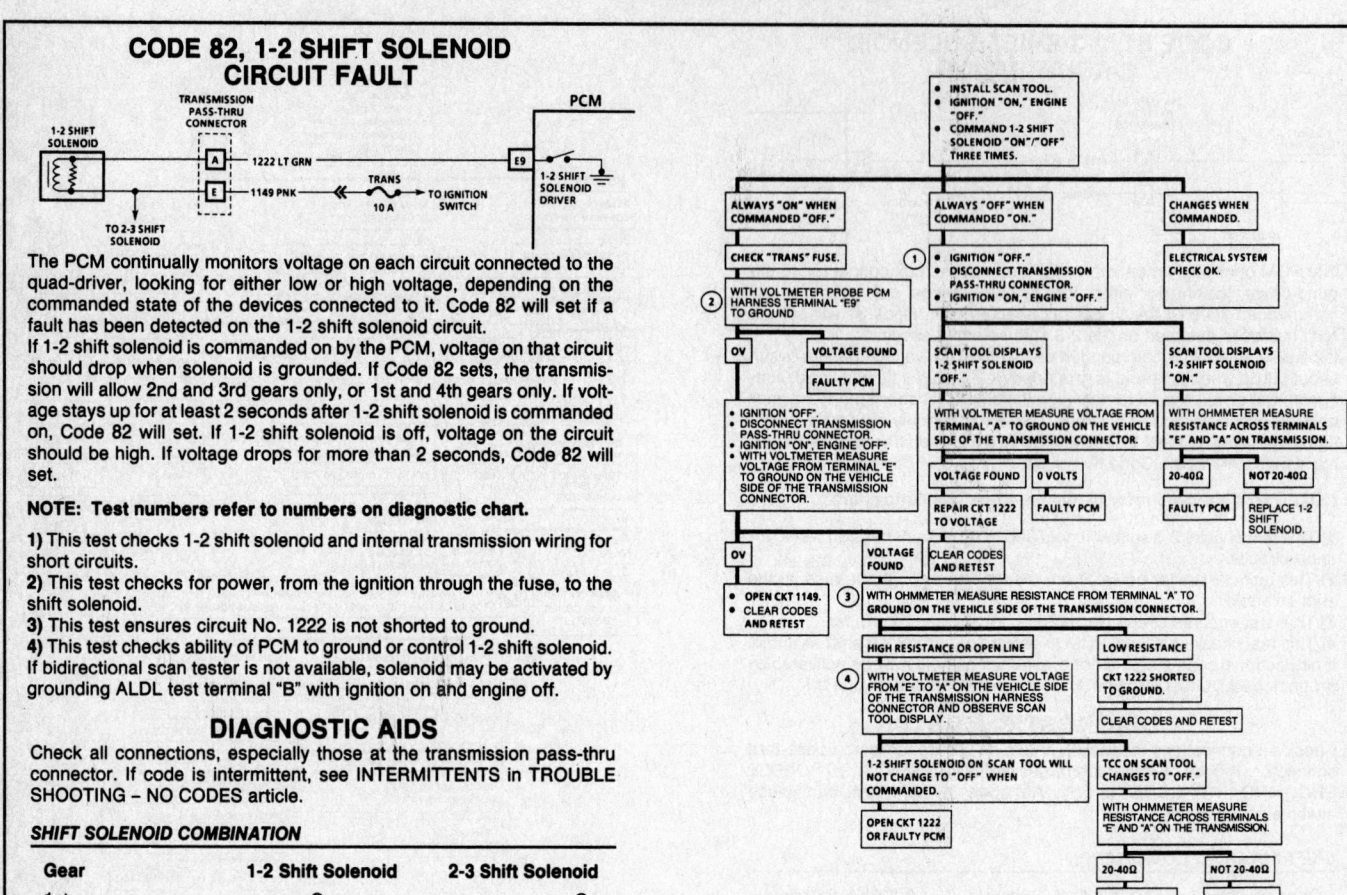

CODE 82, 1-2 SHIFT SOLENOID CIRCUIT FAULT

The PCM continually monitors voltage on each circuit connected to the quad-driver, looking for either low or high voltage, depending on the commanded state of the devices connected to it. Code 82 will set if a fault has been detected on the 1-2 shift solenoid circuit.

If 1-2 shift solenoid is commanded on by the PCM, voltage on that circuit should drop when solenoid is grounded. If Code 82 sets, the transmission will allow 2nd and 3rd gears only, or 1st and 4th gears only. If voltage stays up for at least 2 seconds after 1-2 shift solenoid is commanded on, Code 82 will set. If 1-2 shift solenoid is off, voltage on the circuit should be high. If voltage drops for more than 2 seconds, Code 82 will set.

NOTE: Test numbers refer to numbers on diagnostic chart.

1) This test checks 1-2 shift solenoid and internal transmission wiring for short circuits.

2) This test checks for power, from the ignition through the fuse, to the shift solenoid.

3) This test ensures circuit No. 1222 is not shorted to ground.

4) This test checks ability of PCM to ground or control 1-2 shift solenoid. If bidirectional scan tester is not available, solenoid may be activated by grounding ALDL test terminal "B" with ignition on and engine off.

DIAGNOSTIC AIDS
Check all connections, especially those at the transmission pass-thru connector. If code is intermittent, see INTERMITTENTS in TROUBLE SHOOTING – NO CODES article.

SHIFT SOLENOID COMBINATION

Gear	1-2 Shift Solenoid	2-3 Shift Solenoid
1st	On	On
2nd	off	on
3rd	Off	Off
4th	On	Off

93J76389 93E76400

Courtesy of General Motors Corp.

COMPONENT TESTING

COMPONENT TEST CHARTS
(NO CODES) – 1993

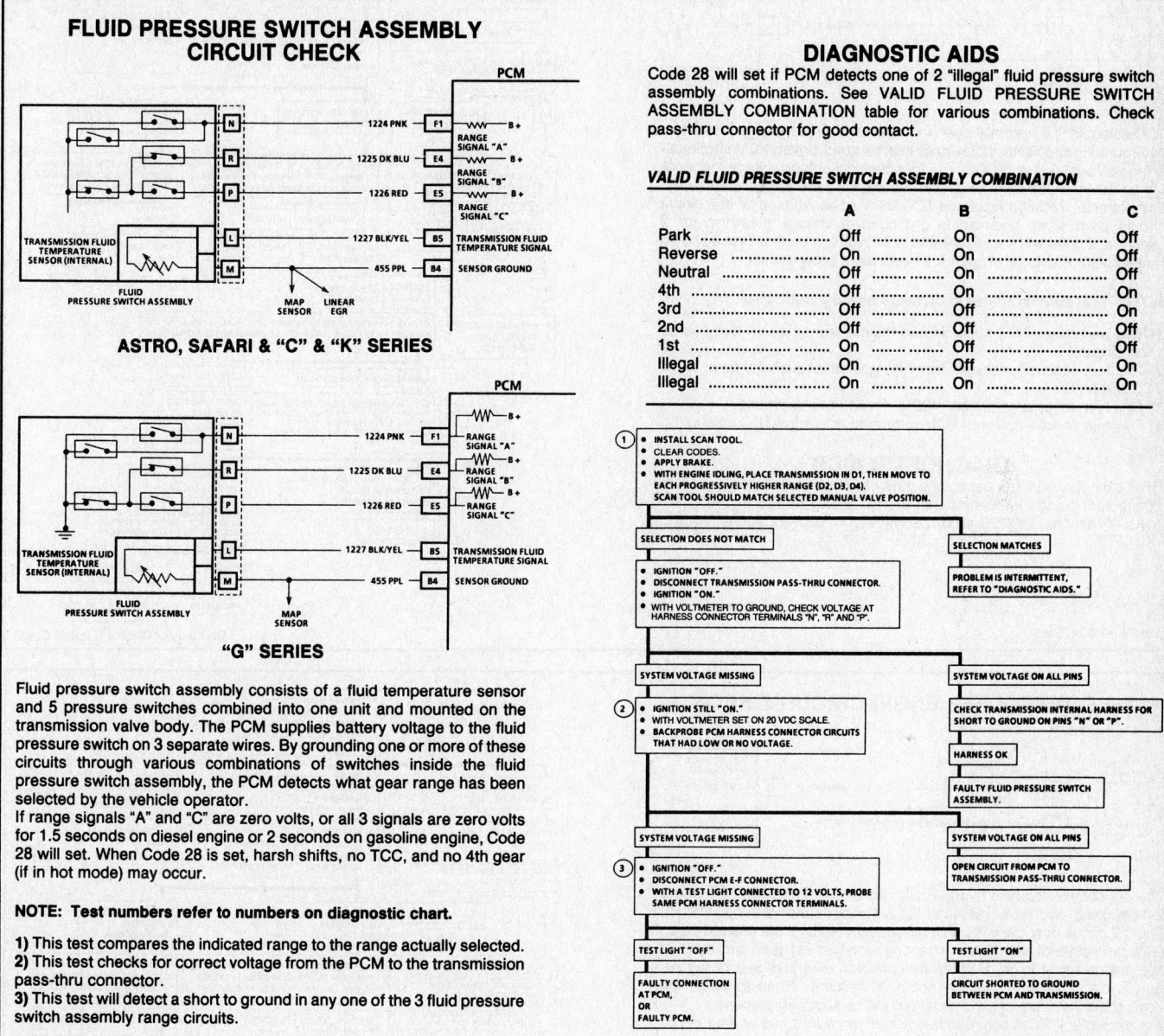

FLUID PRESSURE SWITCH ASSEMBLY CIRCUIT CHECK

ASTRO, SAFARI & "C" & "K" SERIES

"G" SERIES

Fluid pressure switch assembly consists of a fluid temperature sensor and 5 pressure switches combined into one unit and mounted on the transmission valve body. The PCM supplies battery voltage to the fluid pressure switch on 3 separate wires. By grounding one or more of these circuits through various combinations of switches inside the fluid pressure switch assembly, the PCM detects what gear range has been selected by the vehicle operator.

If range signals "A" and "C" are zero volts, or all 3 signals are zero volts for 1.5 seconds on diesel engine or 2 seconds on gasoline engine, Code 28 will set. When Code 28 is set, harsh shifts, no TCC, and no 4th gear (if in hot mode) may occur.

NOTE: Test numbers refer to numbers on diagnostic chart.

1) This test compares the indicated range to the range actually selected.
2) This test checks for correct voltage from the PCM to the transmission pass-thru connector.
3) This test will detect a short to ground in any one of the 3 fluid pressure switch assembly range circuits.

93E76392 93F76393 93H76403

DIAGNOSTIC AIDS

Code 28 will set if PCM detects one of 2 "illegal" fluid pressure switch assembly combinations. See VALID FLUID PRESSURE SWITCH ASSEMBLY COMBINATION table for various combinations. Check pass-thru connector for good contact.

VALID FLUID PRESSURE SWITCH ASSEMBLY COMBINATION

	A	B	C
Park	Off	On	Off
Reverse	On	On	Off
Neutral	Off	On	Off
4th	Off	On	On
3rd	Off	Off	On
2nd	Off	Off	Off
1st	On	Off	Off
Illegal	On	Off	On
Illegal	On	On	On

Courtesy of General Motors Corp.

TORQUE CONVERTER CLUTCH (TCC) SOLENOID CIRCUIT CHECK

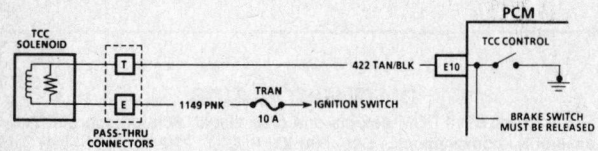

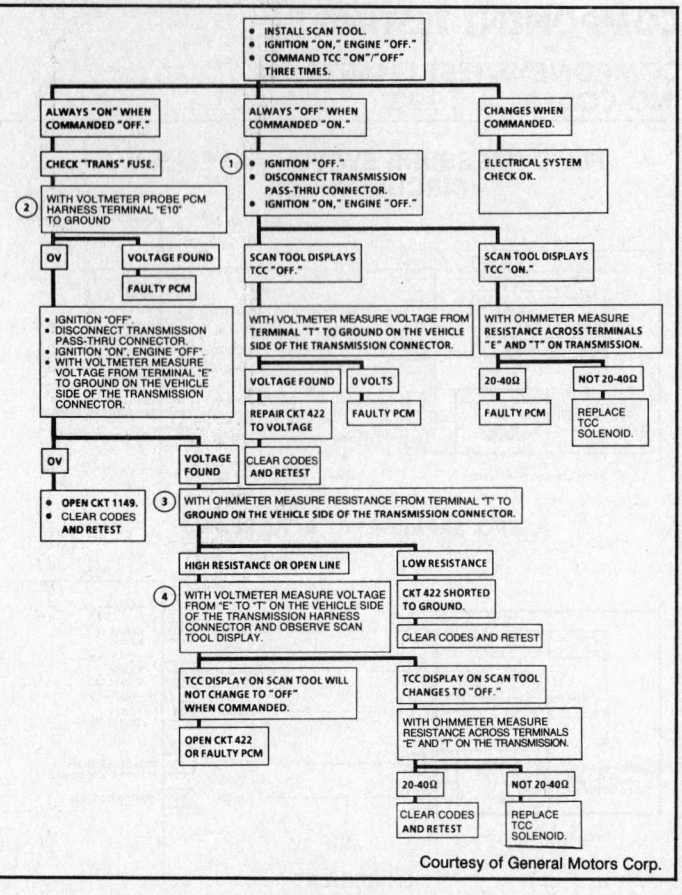

TCC solenoid is a normally open exhaust valve. PCM engages solenoid by grounding circuit No. 422 with an internal quad-driver. PCM continually monitors voltage on TCC circuit for either low or high voltage, depending on commanded state of circuit. A code will set if a fault is detected. For example, if PCM commands TCC solenoid on, voltage on that circuit should drop when solenoid is grounded. If voltage stays up for 2 seconds, a code will set. If solenoid is off, voltage on that circuit should remain high. If voltage drops for 2 seconds, a code will set.

NOTE: Test numbers refer to numbers on diagnostic chart.

1) This test check TCC solenoid and internal transmission harness for short circuits.
2) This test checks for power, from the ignition through the fuse, to the TCC solenoid.
3) This test ensures circuit No. 422 is not shorted to ground.
4) This test checks ability of PCM to ground or control TCC solenoid.

DIAGNOSTIC AIDS

Check all connections, especially those at the transmission pass-thru connector. If code is intermittent, see INTERMITTENTS in TROUBLE SHOOTING – NO CODES article. Some slight TCC slippage is normal.

93H76387 93A76398

Courtesy of General Motors Corp.

3-2 CONTROL SOLENOID CIRCUIT CHECK

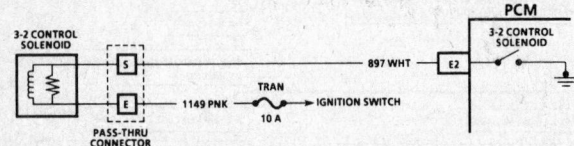

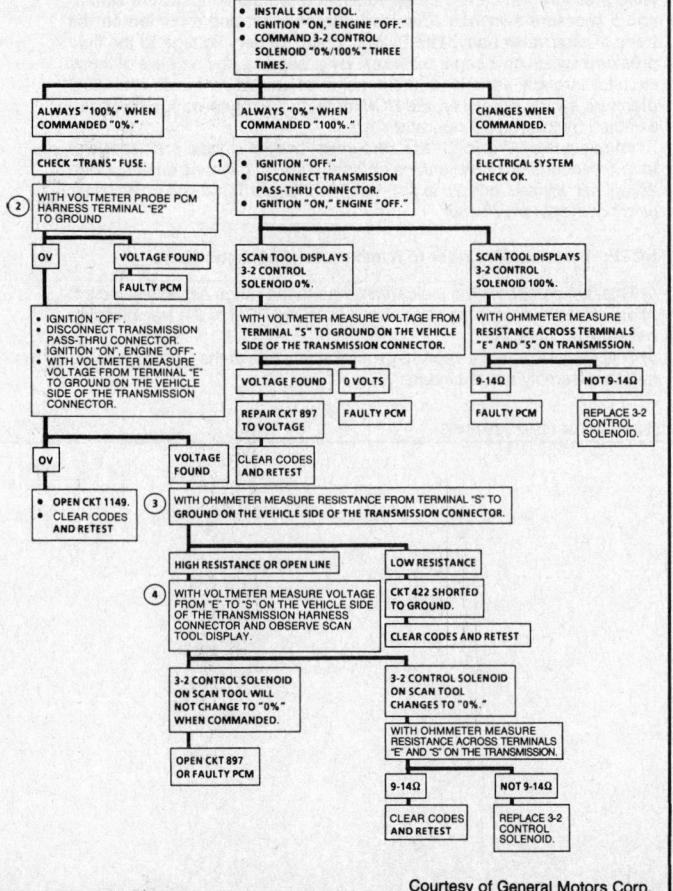

The 3-2 control solenoid hydraulically coordinates the apply rate of the 2-4 band with hydraulic release of the 3-4 clutch during a 3-2 downshift. The 3-2 circuit duty cycle is continually monitored by PCM depending on command state of circuit. When transmission is in 1st gear, duty cycle of solenoid is equal to zero. When transmission is in 2nd gear or higher, duty cycle of solenoid will be about 90 percent. When transmission downshifts 3-2, duty cycle of solenoid will be about 20 percent.
For example, if PCM commands solenoid on, duty cycle on that circuit should drop when solenoid is grounded. If voltage stays up for 4 seconds, a code will set. If 3-2 control solenoid is off, duty cycle on circuit should remain high. If voltage drops for 4 seconds, a code will set. When code is set, a soft landing to 3rd gear will occur.

NOTE: Test numbers refer to numbers on diagnostic chart.

1) This test check 3-2 control solenoid and internal transmission harness for short circuits.
2) This test checks for power, from the ignition through the fuse, to the 3-2 control solenoid.
3) This test ensures circuit No. 897 is not shorted to ground.
4) This test checks ability of PCM to ground or control 3-2 control solenoid. If bidirectional scan tester is not available, solenoid may be activated by grounding ALDL test terminal "B" with ignition on and engine off.

DIAGNOSTIC AIDS

Check all connections, especially those at the transmission pass-thru connector. If code is intermittent, see INTERMITTENTS in TROUBLE SHOOTING – NO CODES article.

93I76388 93B76399

Courtesy of General Motors Corp.

VEHICLE SPEED SENSOR CHECK (2WD & AWD)

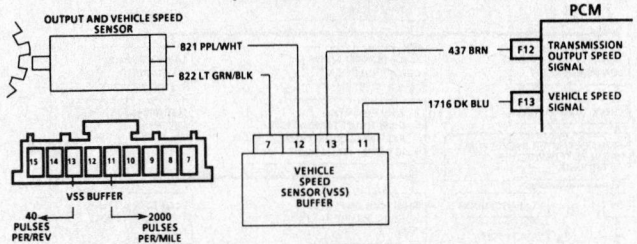

The Vehicle Speed Sensor (VSS) circuit consists of a magnetic induction-type sensor, vehicle speed sensor buffer module and wiring. Gear teeth, pressed on the outside diameter of output carrier assembly, induce an alternating current in the sensor.

This current is transmitted to the buffer module. Buffer module compensates for various axle ratios, and converts signal to a square wave for use by speedometer, cruise control, anti-lock brake system and PCM. Buffer module sends 2 different signals to PCM. Circuit No. 437 relays transmission output speed, which is used to control shift points, line pressure, TCC, Code 24 and Code 72. Circuit No. 1716 relays vehicle speed, which is used to control engine operating functions and Code 16.

NOTE: Test numbers refer to numbers on diagnostic chart.

1) This test checks the VSS signal to the PCM.
2) This test checks the VSS signal to the buffer module.
3) This test checks the VSS signal.

93E76384 93I76396

DIAGNOSTIC AIDS

Check all connections, especially at transmission pass-thru connector. If code is intermittent, see INTERMITTENTS in TROUBLE SHOOTING – NO CODES article.

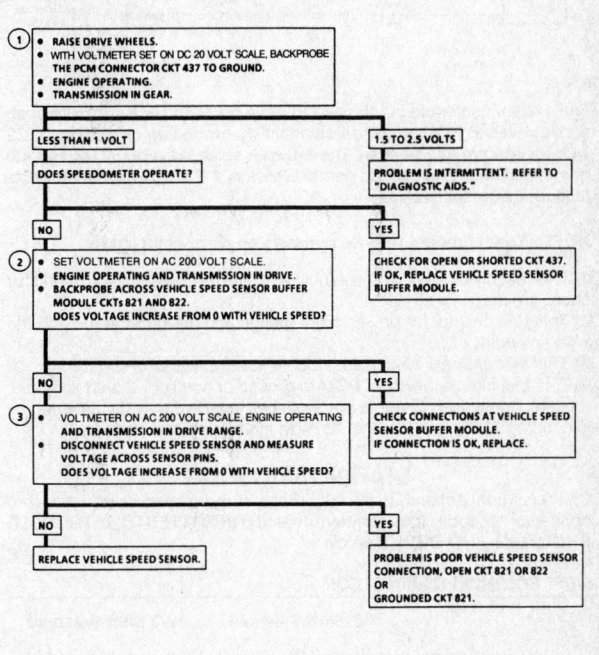

VEHICLE SPEED SENSOR CHECK (4WD)

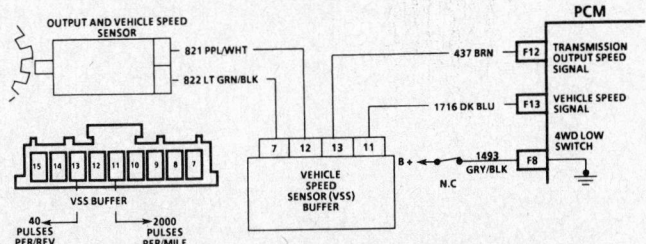

The Vehicle Speed Sensor (VSS) circuit consists of a magnetic induction-type sensor, vehicle speed sensor buffer module, 4WD low switch and wiring. Gear teeth, pressed on outside diameter of output carrier assembly, induce an alternating current in the sensor.

This current is transmitted to the buffer module. Buffer module compensates for various axle ratios, and converts signal to a square wave for use by speedometer, cruise control, anti-lock brake system and PCM. Buffer module sends 2 different signals to PCM. Circuit No. 437 relays transfer case output speed to PCM. PCM uses transfer case output speed signal and 4WD low switch to determine transmission output shaft speed. PCM uses transmission output shaft speed to control shift points, line pressure, TCC, Code 24 and Code 72. Circuit No. 1716 relays vehicle speed, which is used to control engine operating functions and Code 16.

NOTE: Test numbers refer to numbers on diagnostic chart.

1) This test checks VSS signal to PCM.
2) This test checks the VSS signal to the buffer module.
3) This test checks VSS signal.

93F76385 93I76396

DIAGNOSTIC AIDS

Check all connections, especially at transmission pass-thru connector. If code is intermittent, see INTERMITTENTS in TROUBLE SHOOTING – NO CODES article.

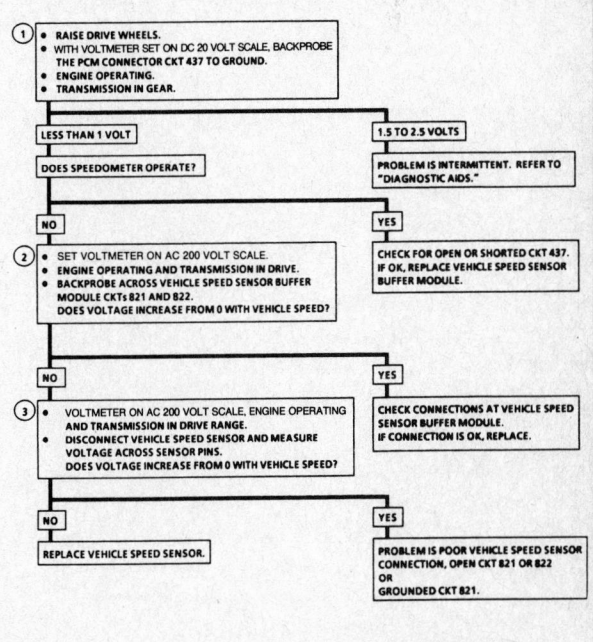

1-2 SHIFT SOLENOID CIRCUIT CHECK

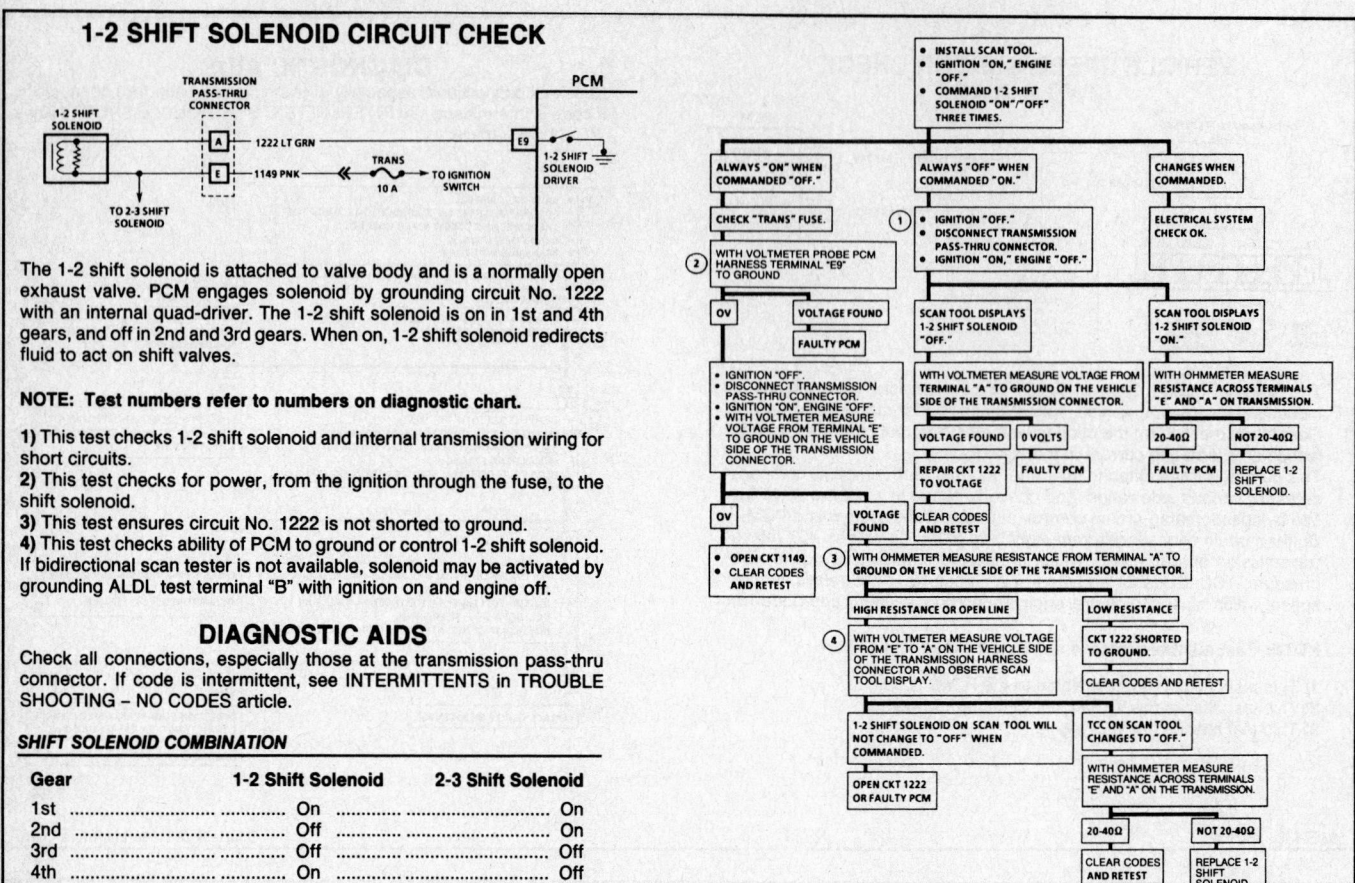

The 1-2 shift solenoid is attached to valve body and is a normally open exhaust valve. PCM engages solenoid by grounding circuit No. 1222 with an internal quad-driver. The 1-2 shift solenoid is on in 1st and 4th gears, and off in 2nd and 3rd gears. When on, 1-2 shift solenoid redirects fluid to act on shift valves.

NOTE: Test numbers refer to numbers on diagnostic chart.

1) This test checks 1-2 shift solenoid and internal transmission wiring for short circuits.
2) This test checks for power, from the ignition through the fuse, to the shift solenoid.
3) This test ensures circuit No. 1222 is not shorted to ground.
4) This test checks ability of PCM to ground or control 1-2 shift solenoid. If bidirectional scan tester is not available, solenoid may be activated by grounding ALDL test terminal "B" with ignition on and engine off.

DIAGNOSTIC AIDS

Check all connections, especially those at the transmission pass-thru connector. If code is intermittent, see INTERMITTENTS in TROUBLE SHOOTING – NO CODES article.

SHIFT SOLENOID COMBINATION

Gear	1-2 Shift Solenoid	2-3 Shift Solenoid
1st	On	On
2nd	Off	On
3rd	Off	Off
4th	On	Off

93J76389 93E76400

Courtesy of General Motors Corp.

2-3 SHIFT SOLENOID CIRCUIT CHECK

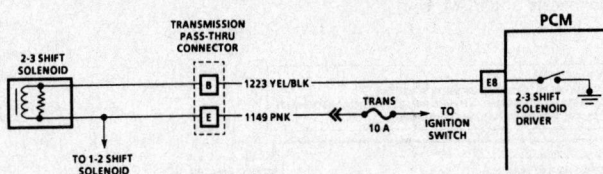

Shift solenoids are used inside valve body to control spool valves and determine transmission gear. The 2-3 shift solenoid is on in 1st and 2nd gears, and off in 3rd and 4th gears. Fused battery ignition voltage is supplied to 2-3 shift solenoid. PCM engages solenoid by grounding circuit No. 1223.

NOTE: Test numbers refer to numbers on diagnostic chart.

1) This test checks 2-3 shift solenoid and internal transmission wiring for short circuits.
2) This test checks for power, from the ignition through the fuse, to the shift solenoid.
3) This test ensures circuit No. 1223 is not shorted to ground.
4) This test checks ability of PCM to ground or control 2-3 shift solenoid. If bidirectional scan tester is not available, solenoid may be activated by grounding ALDL test terminal "B" with ignition on and engine off.

DIAGNOSTIC AIDS

Check all connections, especially those at the transmission pass-thru connector. If code is intermittent, see INTERMITTENTS in TROUBLE SHOOTING – NO CODES article.

SHIFT SOLENOID COMBINATION

Gear	1-2 Shift Solenoid	2-3 Shift Solenoid
1st	On	On
2nd	Off	On
3rd	Off	Off
4th	On	Off

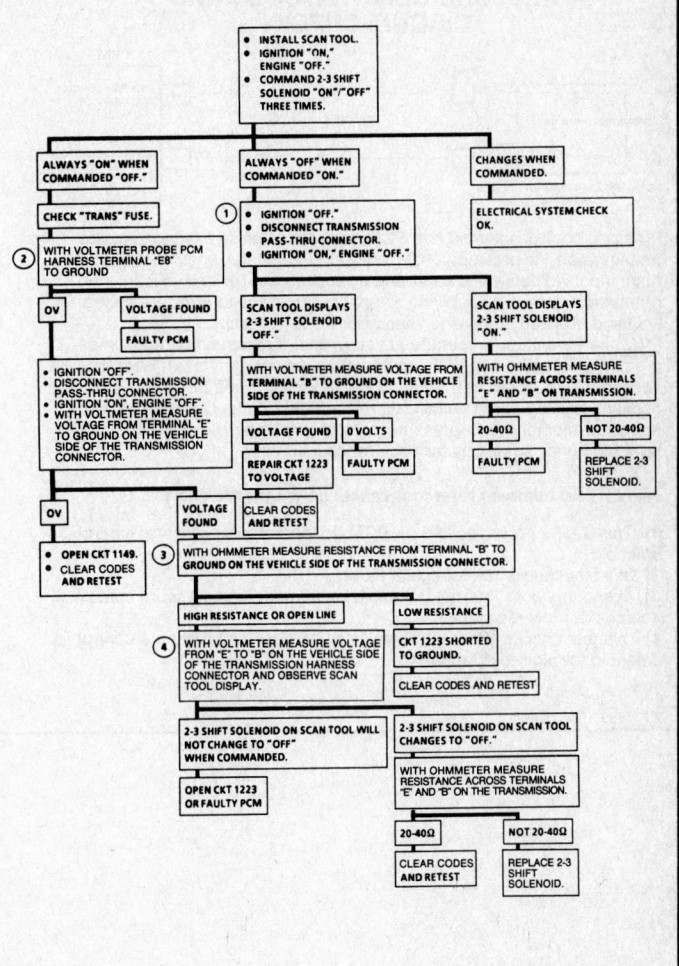

93C76390 93F76401

Courtesy of General Motors Corp.

PRESSURE CONTROL SOLENOID CIRCUIT CHECK

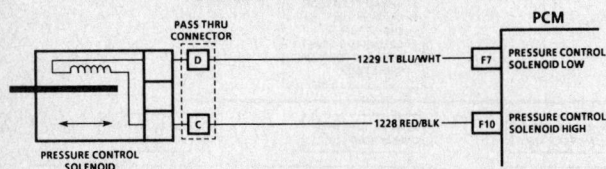

Pressure control solenoid is a PCM-controlled device used to regulate transmission line pressure. PCM looks at TPS voltage, engine RPM, and other inputs to determine appropriate line pressure for a given load, then regulates pressure by applying a variable amperage to pressure control solenoid. Applied amperage varies from .1 to 1.1 amps.

PCM then monitors amperage at return line. If return amperage varies greater than .16 amp from commanded amperage for at least one second, Code 73 will set. When Code 73 sets, full line pressure will be applied, causing harsh shifts until next ignition cycle. Code will remain stored in memory, and pressure control solenoid will resume normal operation until conditions for code reoccur.

NOTE: Test numbers refer to numbers on diagnostic chart.

1) This test checks ability of PCM to command pressure control solenoid.
2) This test checks for voltage at PCM.
3) This test checks internal transmission harness and pressure control solenoid for low resistance.
4) This test checks internal transmission harness and pressure control solenoid for high resistance.

93D76391 93G76402

DIAGNOSTIC AIDS

Check all connections, especially those at the transmission pass-thru connector and PCM.

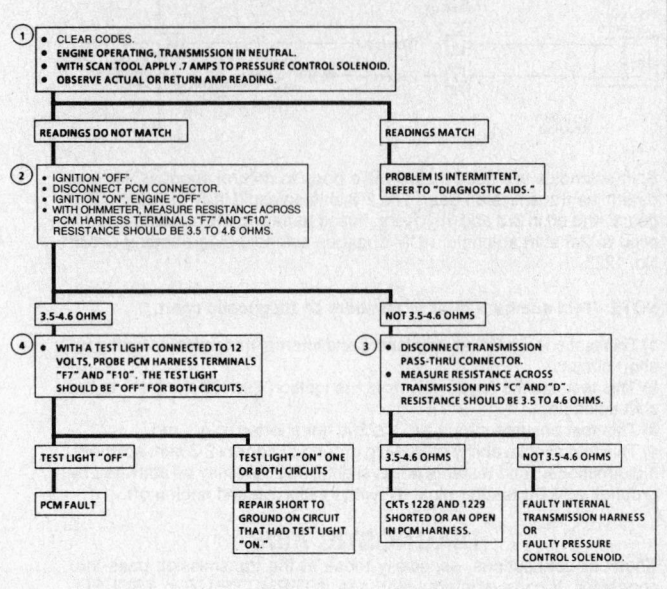

Courtesy of General Motors Corp.

COMPONENT TEST CHARTS (NO CODES) – 1994

Internal Harness Check Chart – 1) Install Test Harness (J-39775) to transmission connector. Compare resistance of each solenoid to known values. See TRANSMISSION SOLENOID RESISTANCE chart. **2)** If solenoid resistance is okay, go to step **3)**. If solenoid resistance is not okay, check harness from connector to solenoid. Repair harness if necessary. Check resistance of solenoid. If resistance is not okay, replace solenoid.

3) Measure resistance between each terminal at transmission connector and ground. See Fig. 7. If resistance is high, problem is intermittent. If resistance is low, remove harness from connector to solenoid.

4) Measure resistance between component and ground. If resistance is low, replace component. If resistance is high, check internal harness wiring for short to ground.

TRANSMISSION SOLENOID RESISTANCE

Application	Ohms
1-2 Shift, 2-3 Shift & TCC Solenoid	20-40
3-2 Control Solenoid	9-14
Pressure Control Solenoid	3.5-8

Oil Pressure Switch Assembly – Install Test Harness (J-39775) to transmission connector. Compare resistance of pressure switches with gear selector in each position to known values. See Fig. 8. If resistance values are the same as chart, problem is intermittent. If resistance values are not the same, complete test chart until problem is found. See Fig. 8.

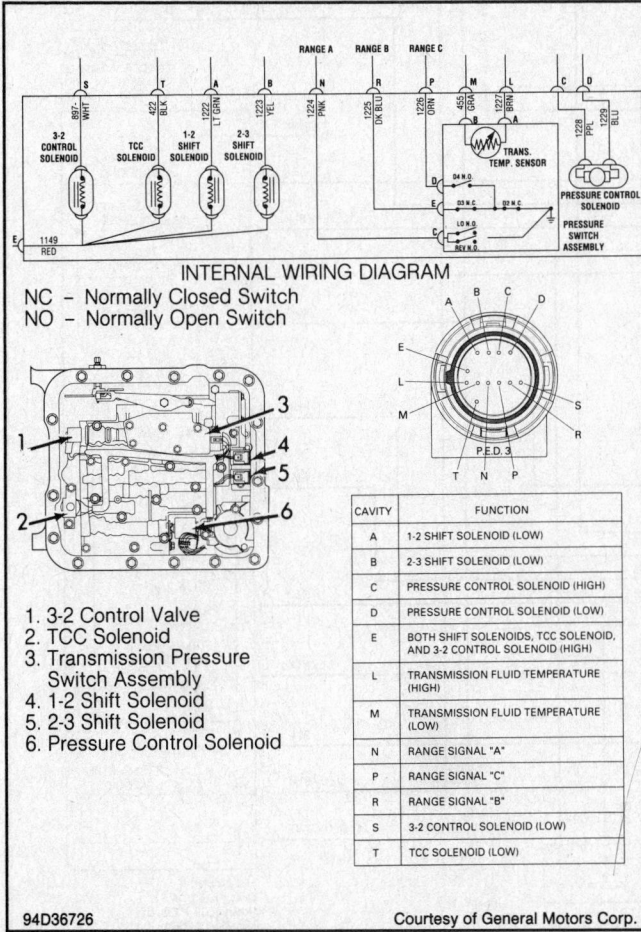

INTERNAL WIRING DIAGRAM
NC – Normally Closed Switch
NO – Normally Open Switch

1. 3-2 Control Valve
2. TCC Solenoid
3. Transmission Pressure Switch Assembly
4. 1-2 Shift Solenoid
5. 2-3 Shift Solenoid
6. Pressure Control Solenoid

CAVITY	FUNCTION
A	1-2 SHIFT SOLENOID (LOW)
B	2-3 SHIFT SOLENOID (LOW)
C	PRESSURE CONTROL SOLENOID (HIGH)
D	PRESSURE CONTROL SOLENOID (LOW)
E	BOTH SHIFT SOLENOIDS, TCC SOLENOID, AND 3-2 CONTROL SOLENOID (HIGH)
L	TRANSMISSION FLUID TEMPERATURE (HIGH)
M	TRANSMISSION FLUID TEMPERATURE (LOW)
N	RANGE SIGNAL "A"
P	RANGE SIGNAL "C"
R	RANGE SIGNAL "B"
S	3-2 CONTROL SOLENOID (LOW)
T	TCC SOLENOID (LOW)

94D36726   Courtesy of General Motors Corp.

Fig. 7: Internal Electrical Circuit Diagram

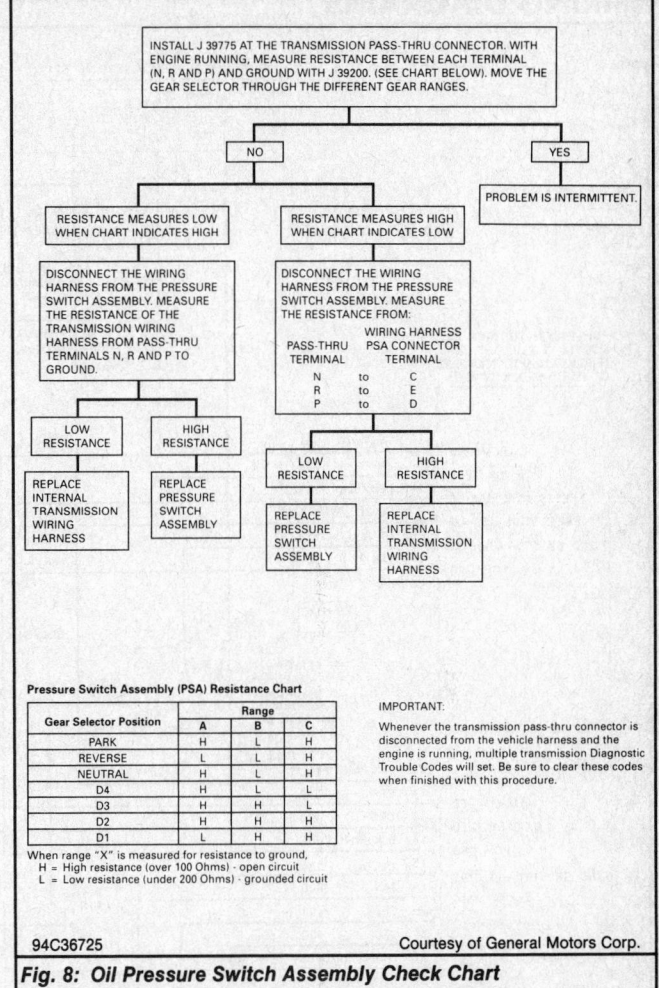

Pressure Switch Assembly (PSA) Resistance Chart

Gear Selector Position	Range A	Range B	Range C
PARK	H	L	H
REVERSE	L	L	H
NEUTRAL	H	L	H
D4	H	L	L
D3	H	H	L
D2	H	H	H
D1	L	H	H

When range "X" is measured for resistance to ground,
H = High resistance (over 100 Ohms) · open circuit
L = Low resistance (under 200 Ohms) · grounded circuit

IMPORTANT:
Whenever the transmission pass-thru connector is disconnected from the vehicle harness and the engine is running, multiple transmission Diagnostic Trouble Codes will set. Be sure to clear these codes when finished with this procedure.

94C36725   Courtesy of General Motors Corp.

Fig. 8: Oil Pressure Switch Assembly Check Chart

Transmission Fluid Temperature & Vehicle Speed Sensor – See appropriate trouble code test under SELF-DIAGNOSTICS.

Torque Converter Clutch – See appropriate trouble code test under SELF-DIAGNOSTICS.

AUTOMATIC TRANSMISSIONS
4L60-E Electronic Controls (Cont.)

WIRING DIAGRAMS

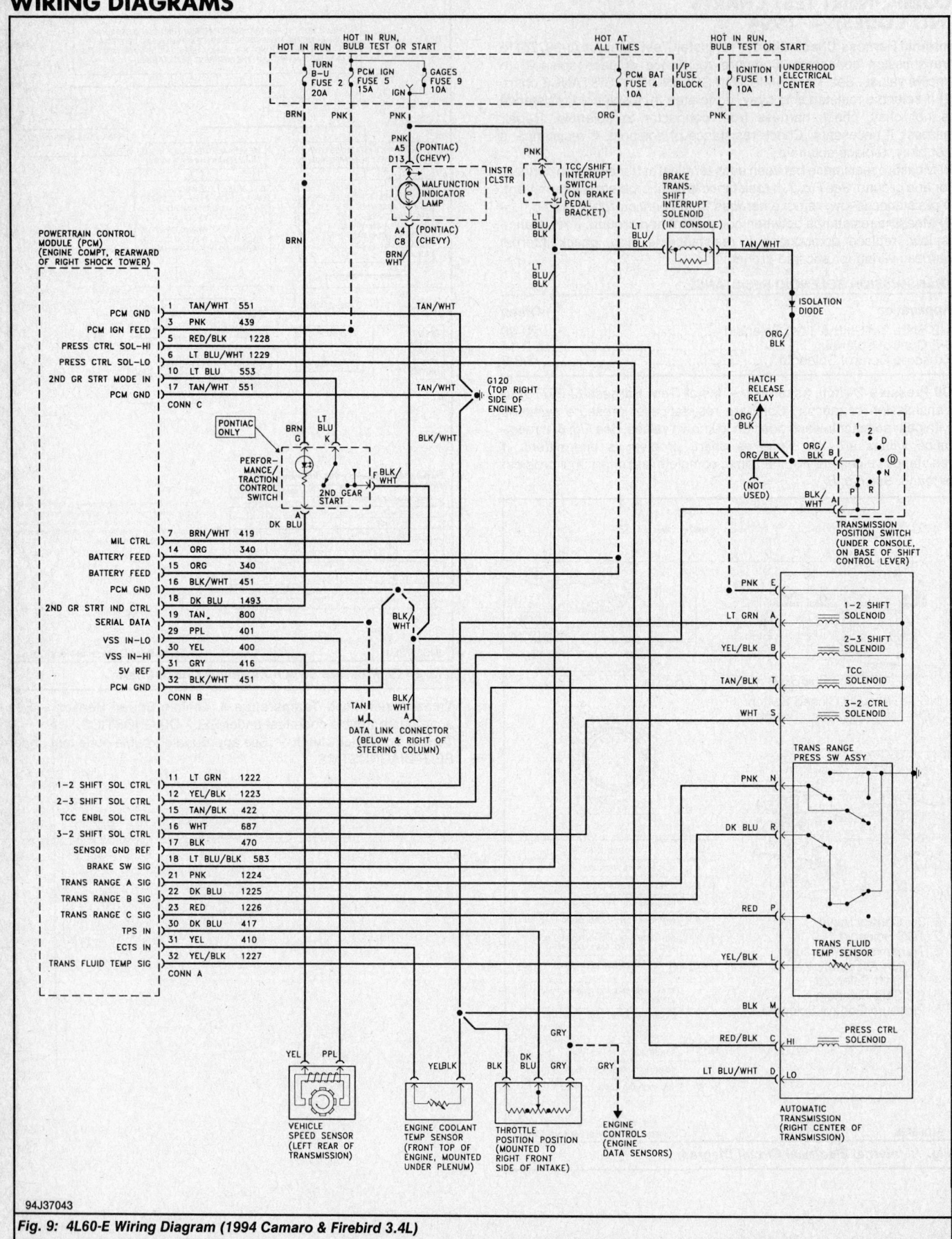

Fig. 9: 4L60-E Wiring Diagram (1994 Camaro & Firebird 3.4L)

94J37043

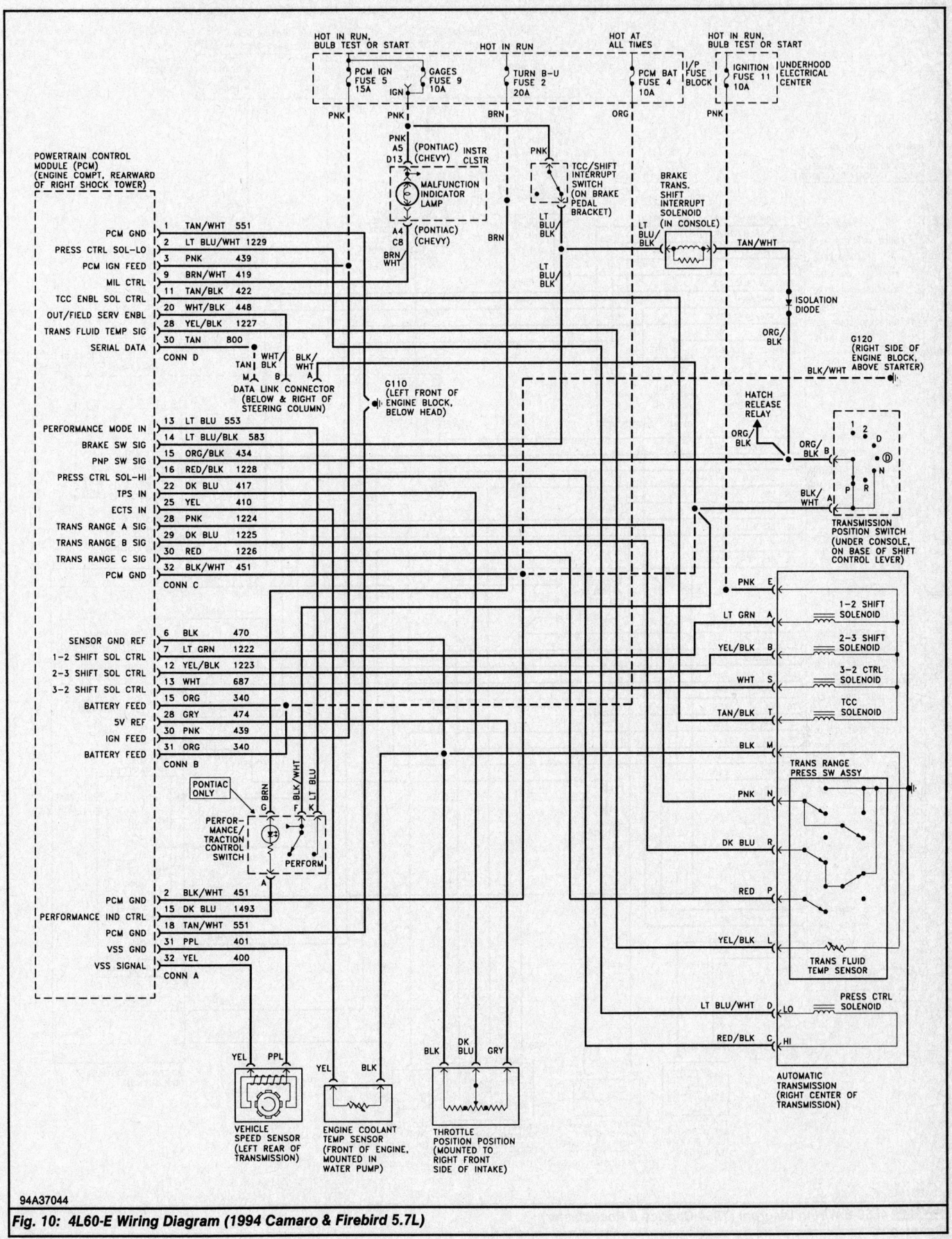

94A37044

Fig. 10: 4L60-E Wiring Diagram (1994 Camaro & Firebird 5.7L)

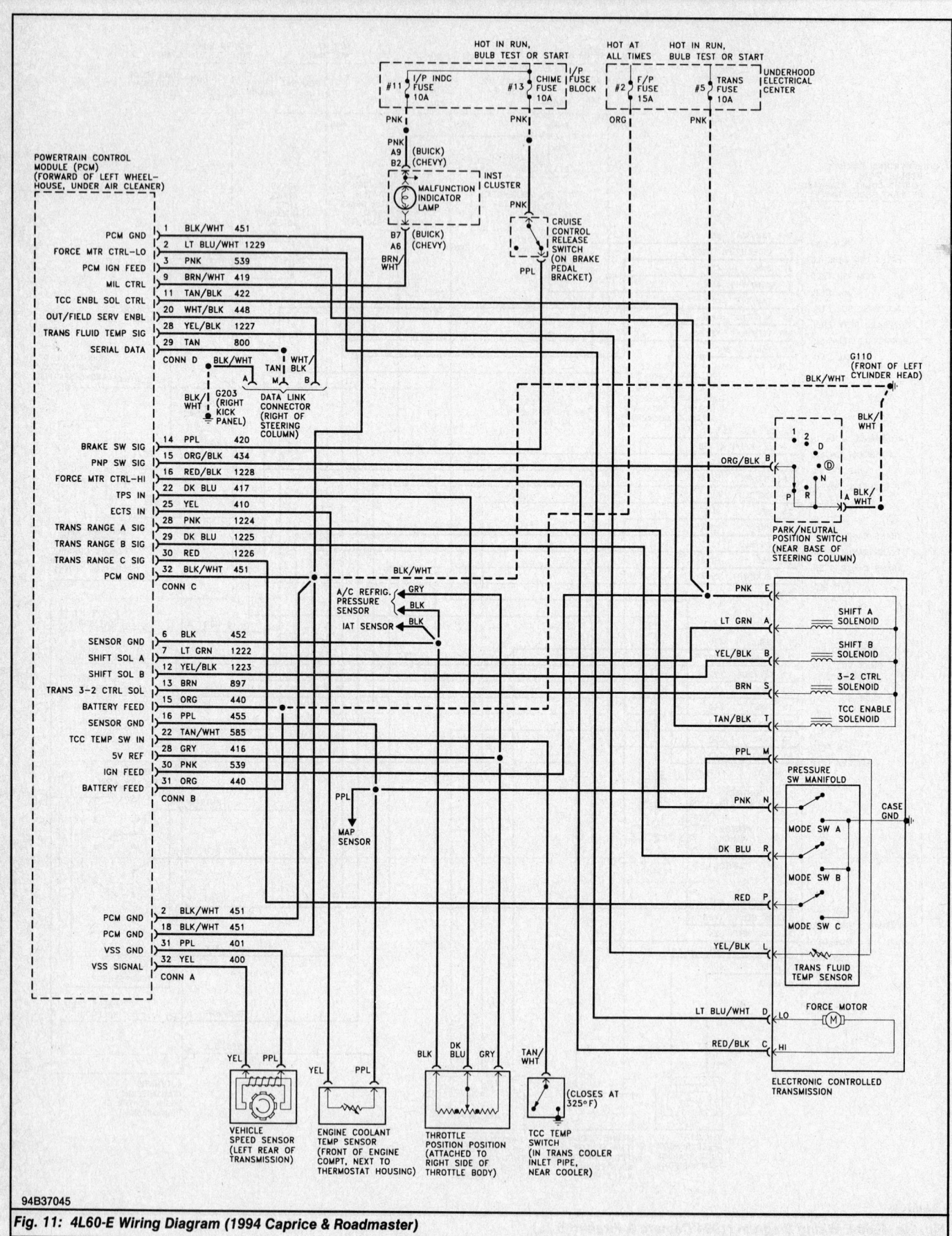

Fig. 11: *4L60-E Wiring Diagram (1994 Caprice & Roadmaster)*

94B37045

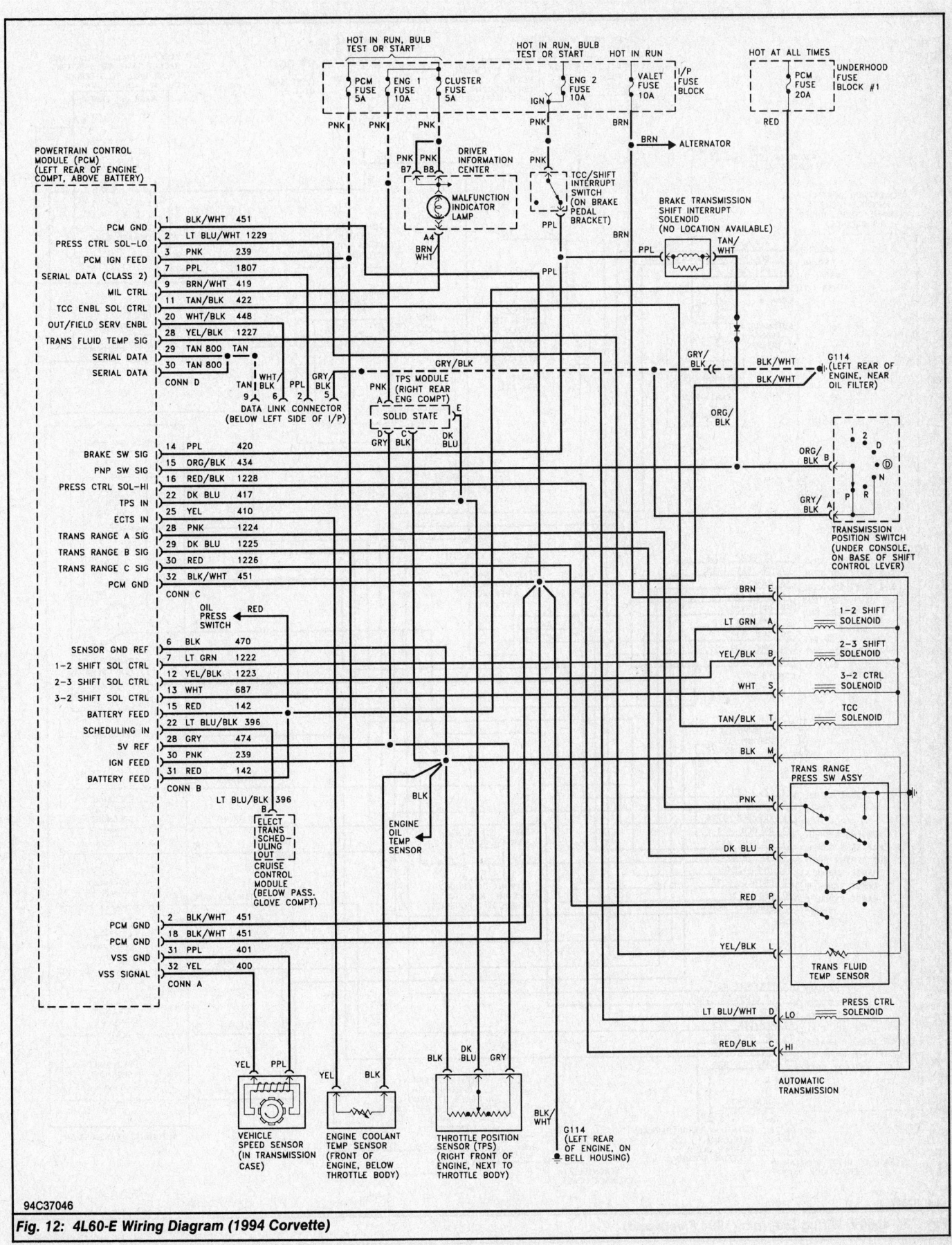

Fig. 12: 4L60-E Wiring Diagram (1994 Corvette)

94C37046

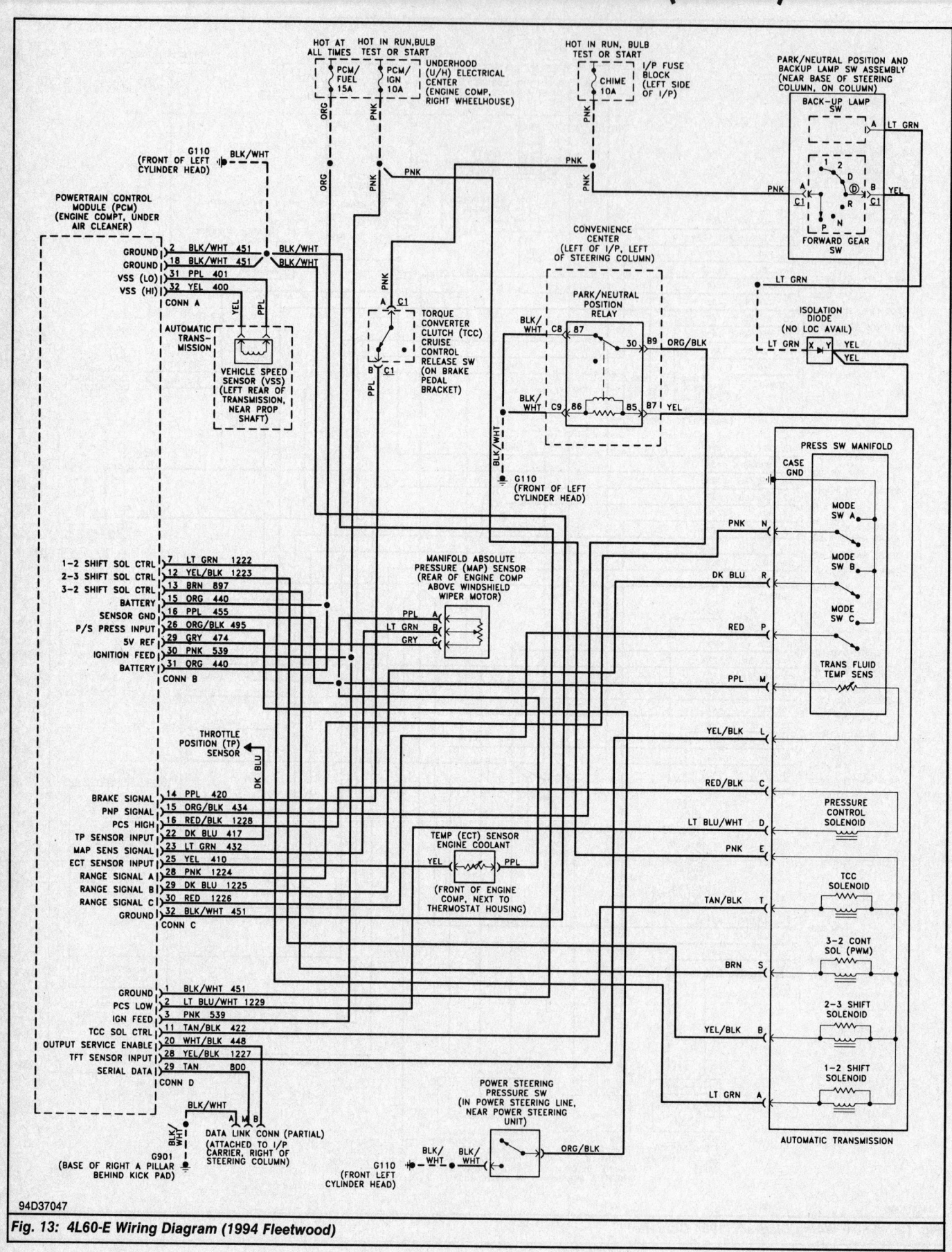

Fig. 13: 4L60-E Wiring Diagram (1994 Fleetwood)

94D37047

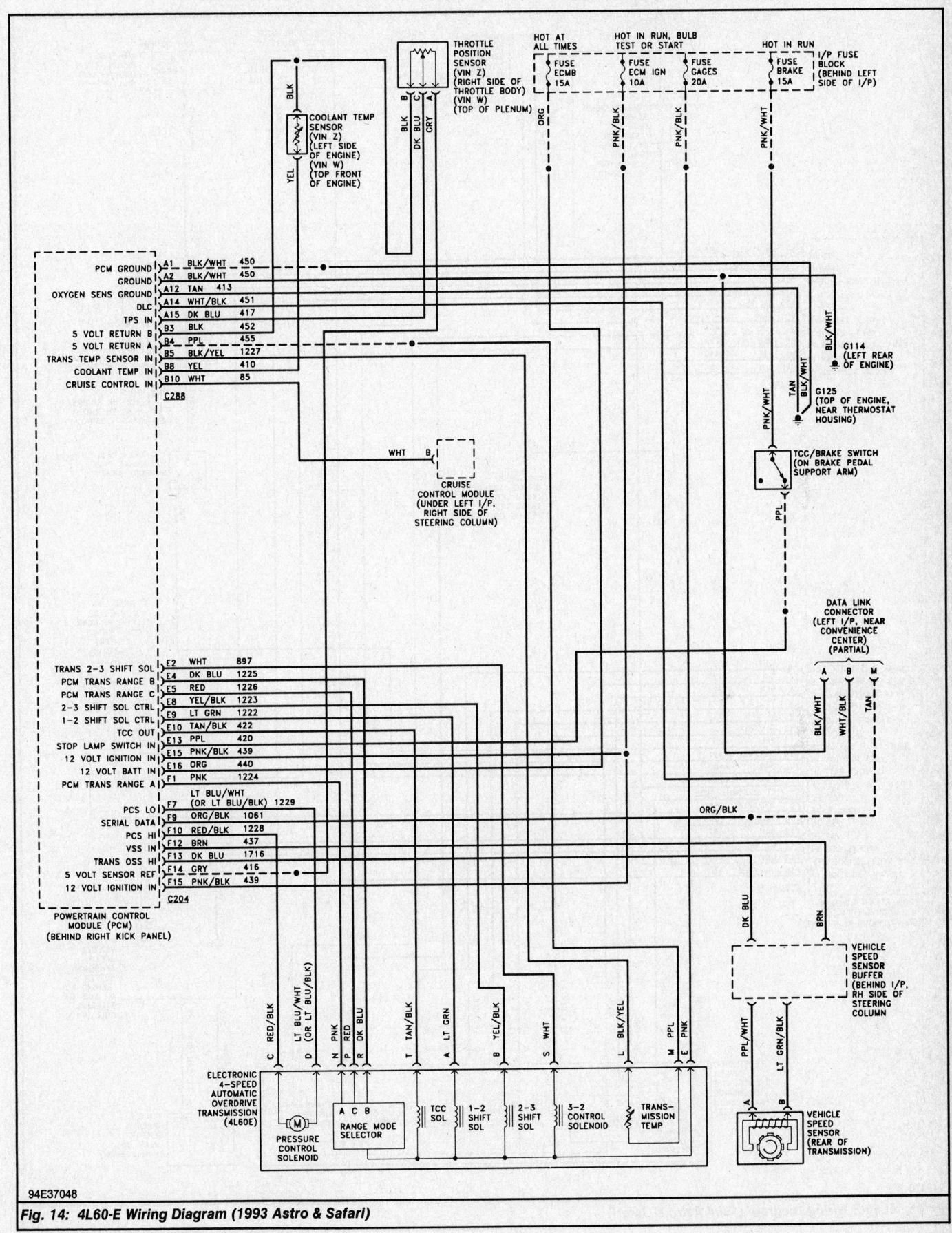

Fig. 14: 4L60-E Wiring Diagram (1993 Astro & Safari)

94E37048

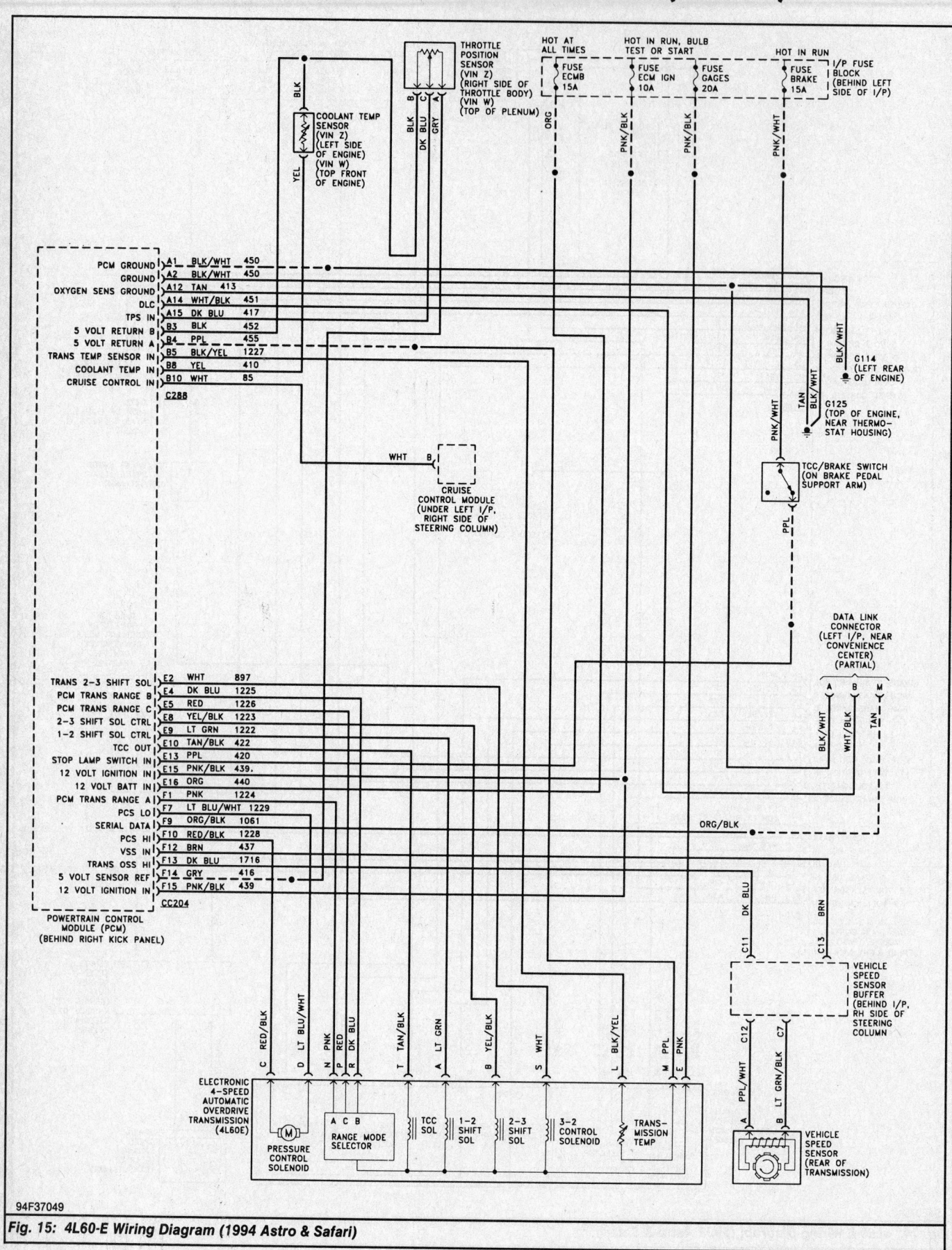

Fig. 15: 4L60-E Wiring Diagram (1994 Astro & Safari)

94F37049

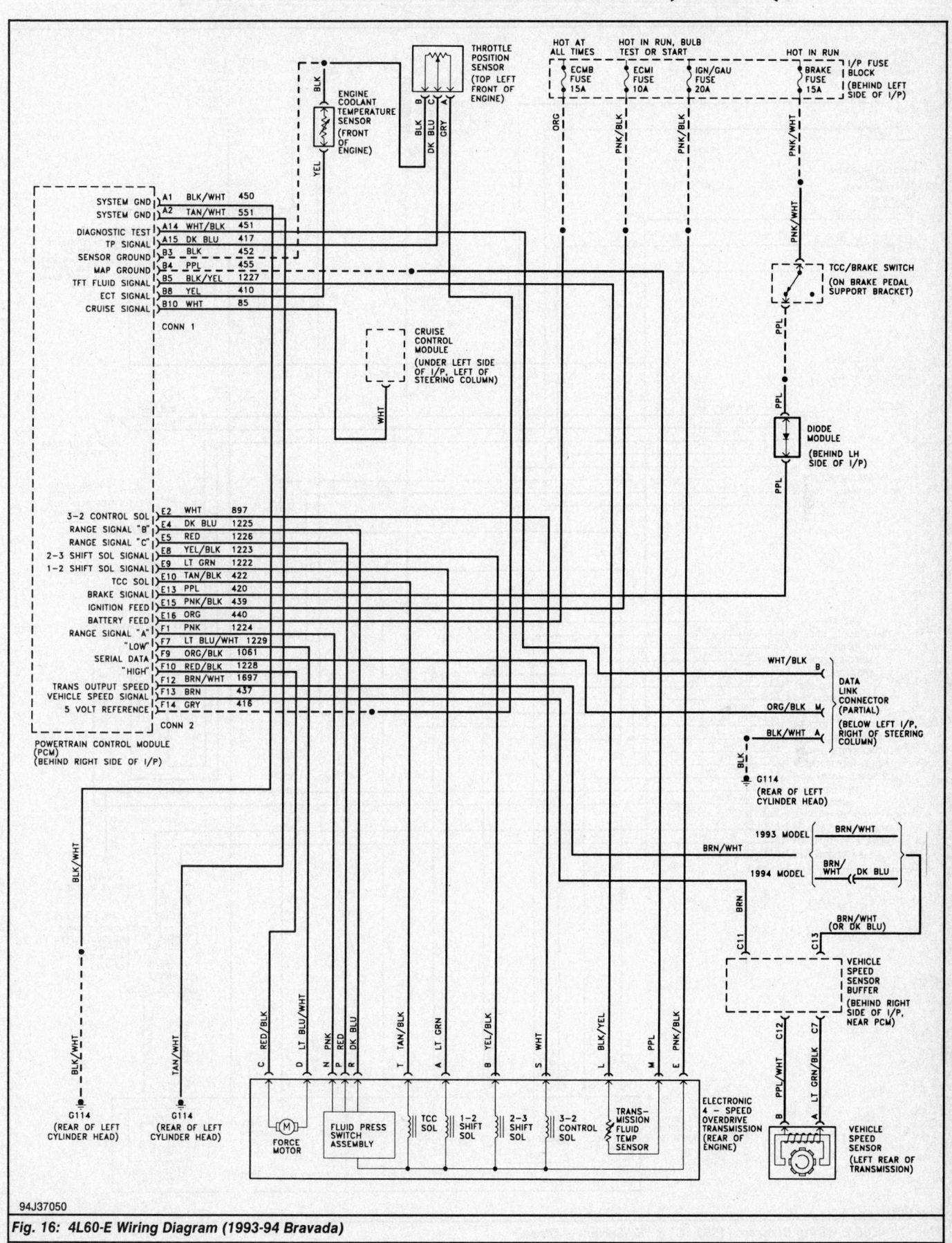

Fig. 16: 4L60-E Wiring Diagram (1993-94 Bravada)

94J37050

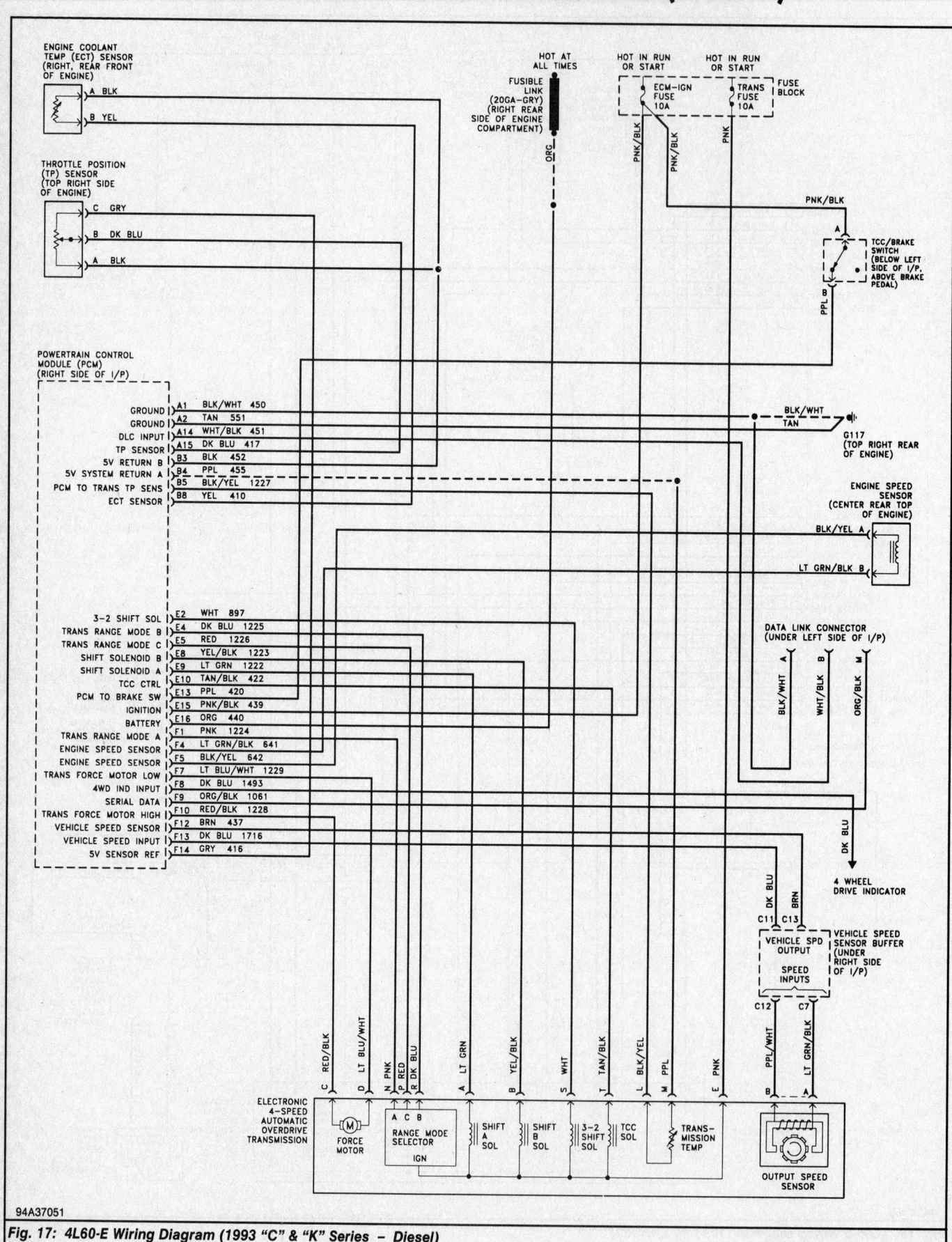

94A37051

Fig. 17: 4L60-E Wiring Diagram (1993 "C" & "K" Series – Diesel)

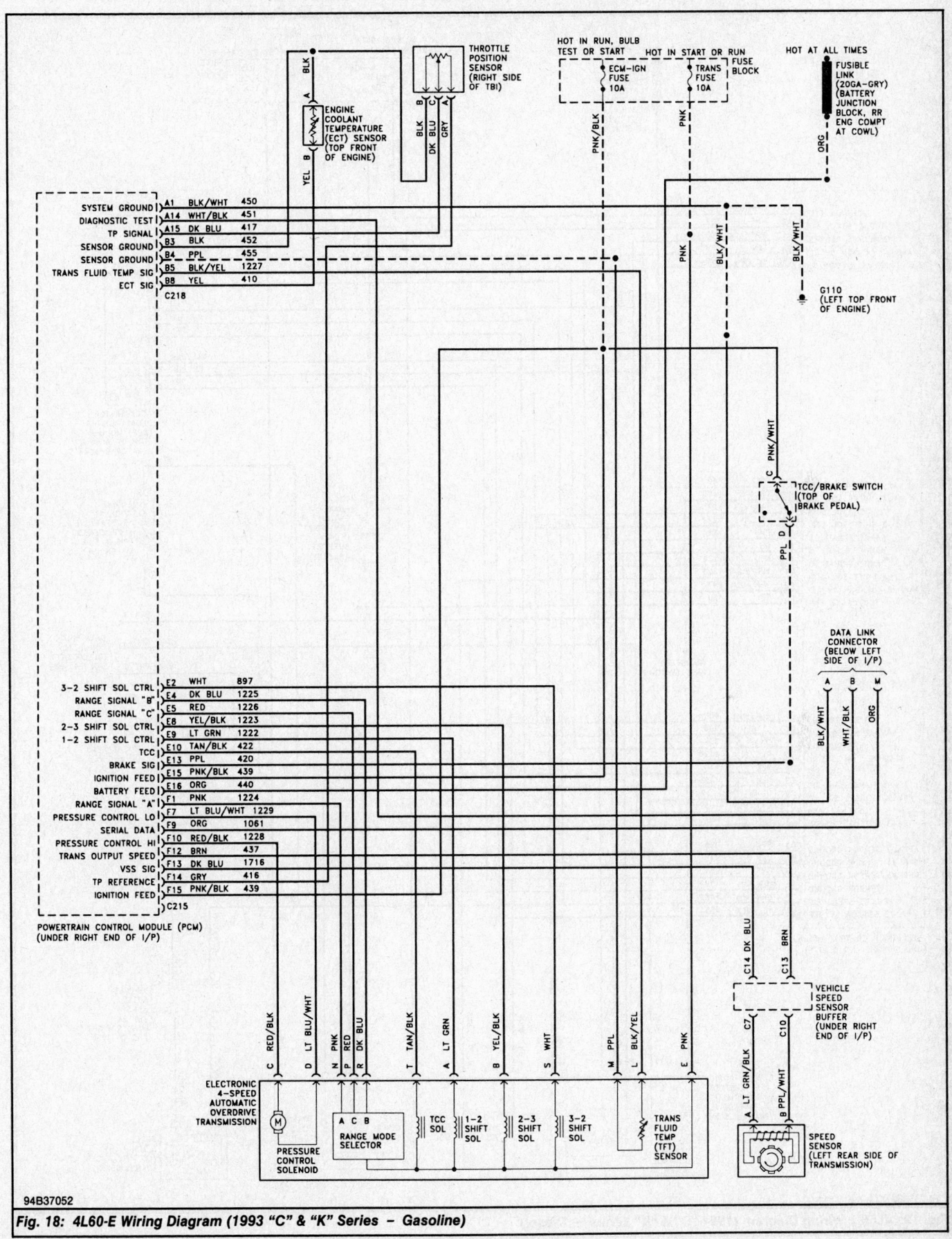

Fig. 18: 4L60-E Wiring Diagram (1993 "C" & "K" Series – Gasoline)

94B37052

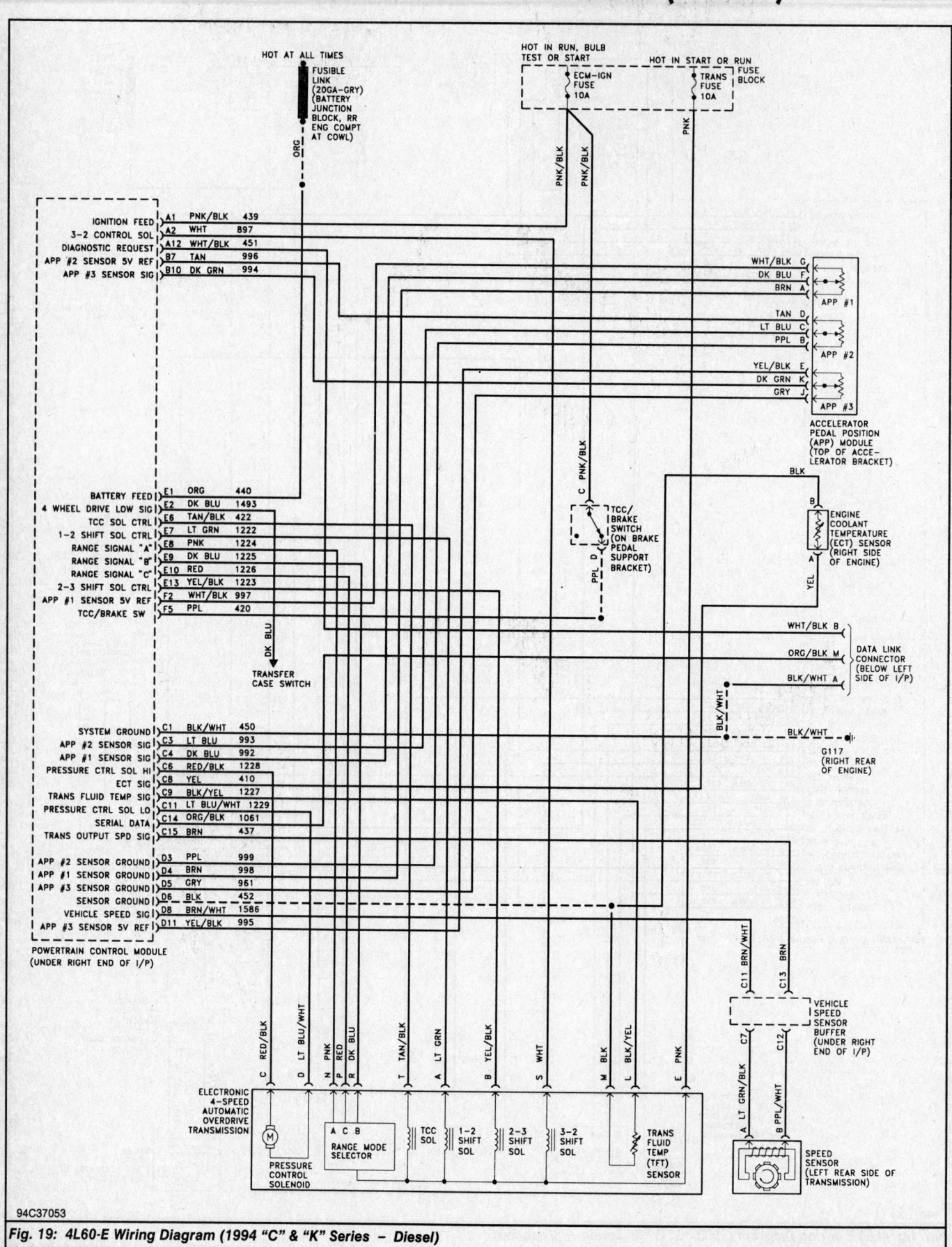

94C37053

Fig. 19: 4L60-E Wiring Diagram (1994 "C" & "K" Series – Diesel)

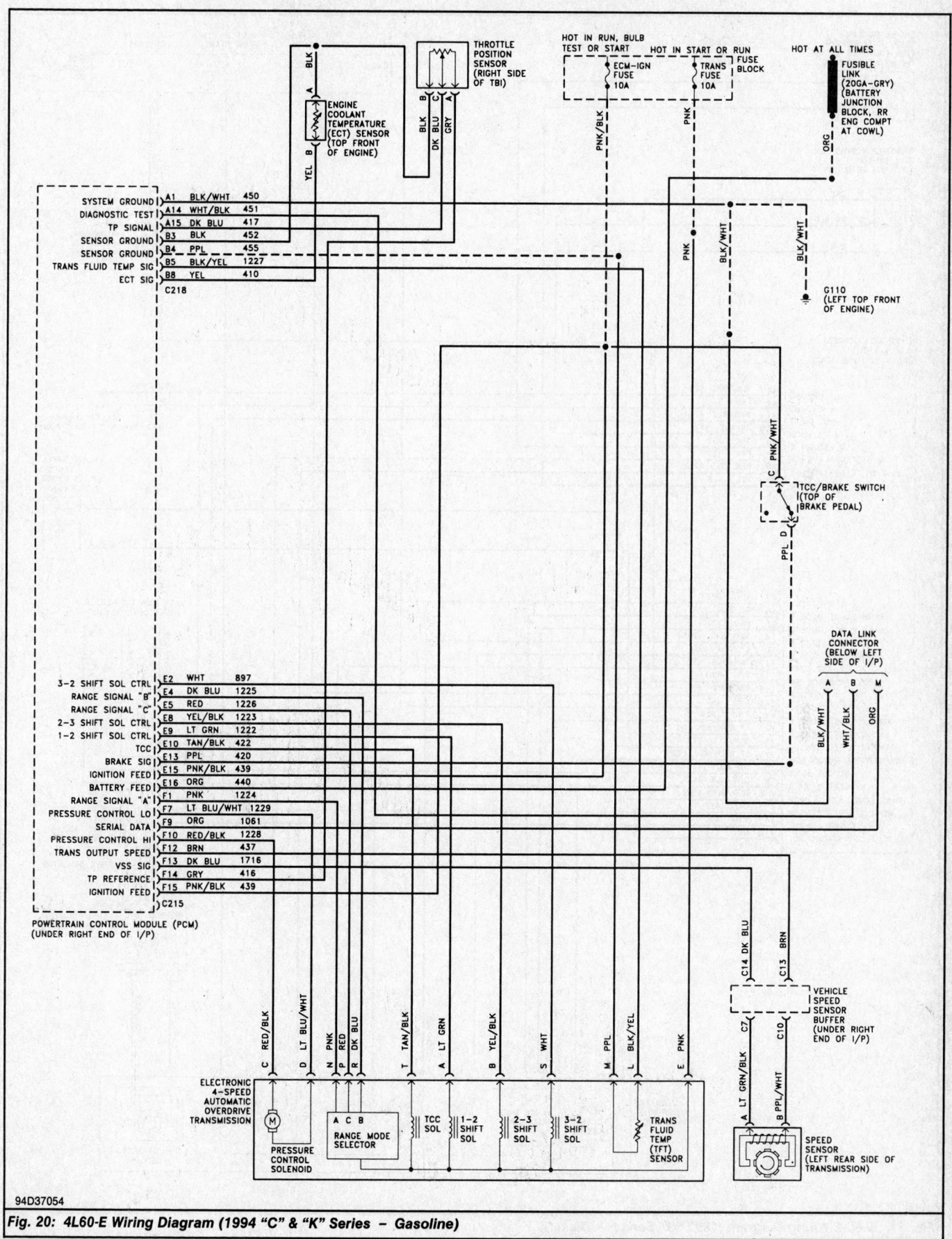

Fig. 20: 4L60-E Wiring Diagram (1994 "C" & "K" Series – Gasoline)

94D37054

AUTOMATIC TRANSMISSIONS
4L60-E Electronic Controls (Cont.)

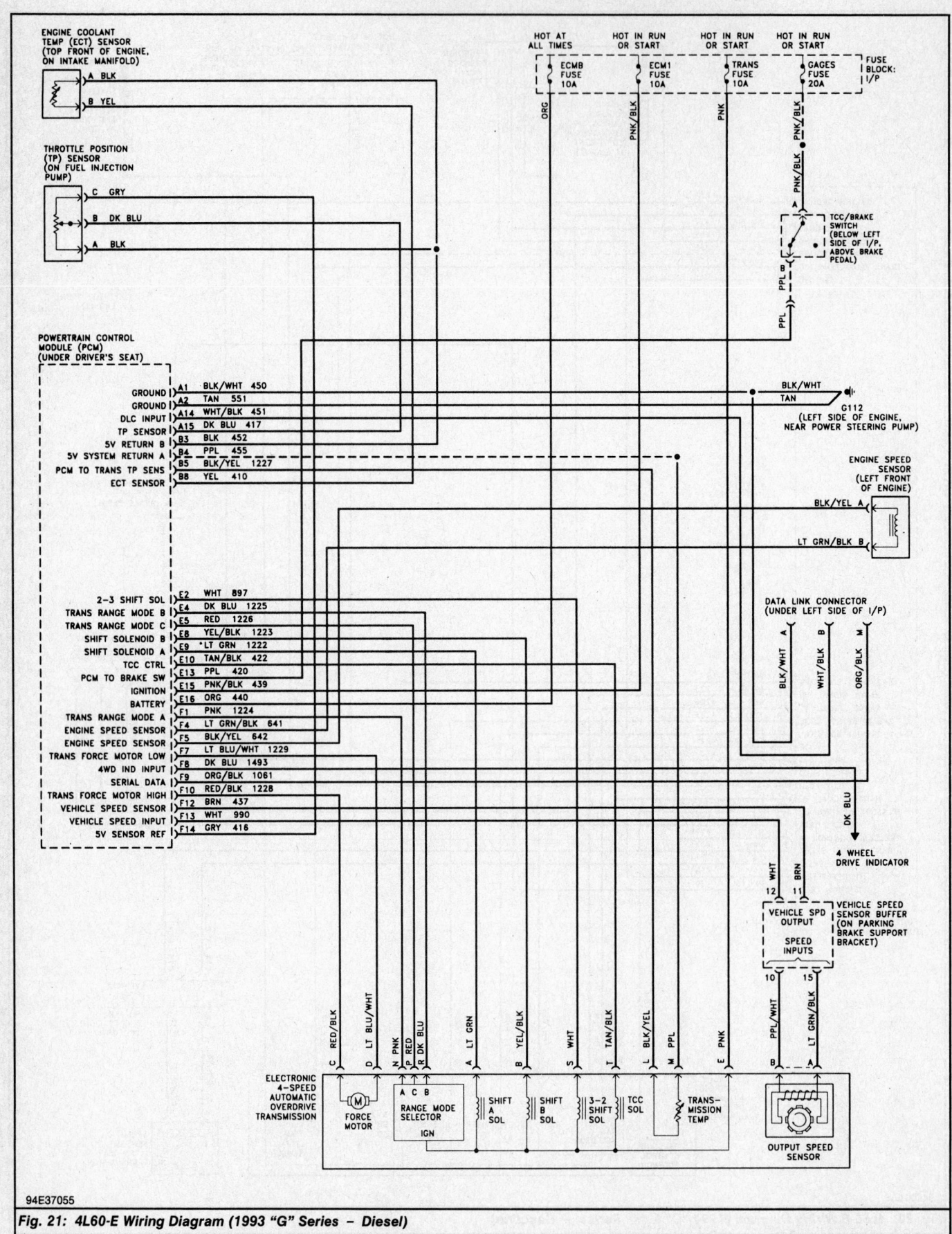

94E37055

Fig. 21: 4L60-E Wiring Diagram (1993 "G" Series – Diesel)

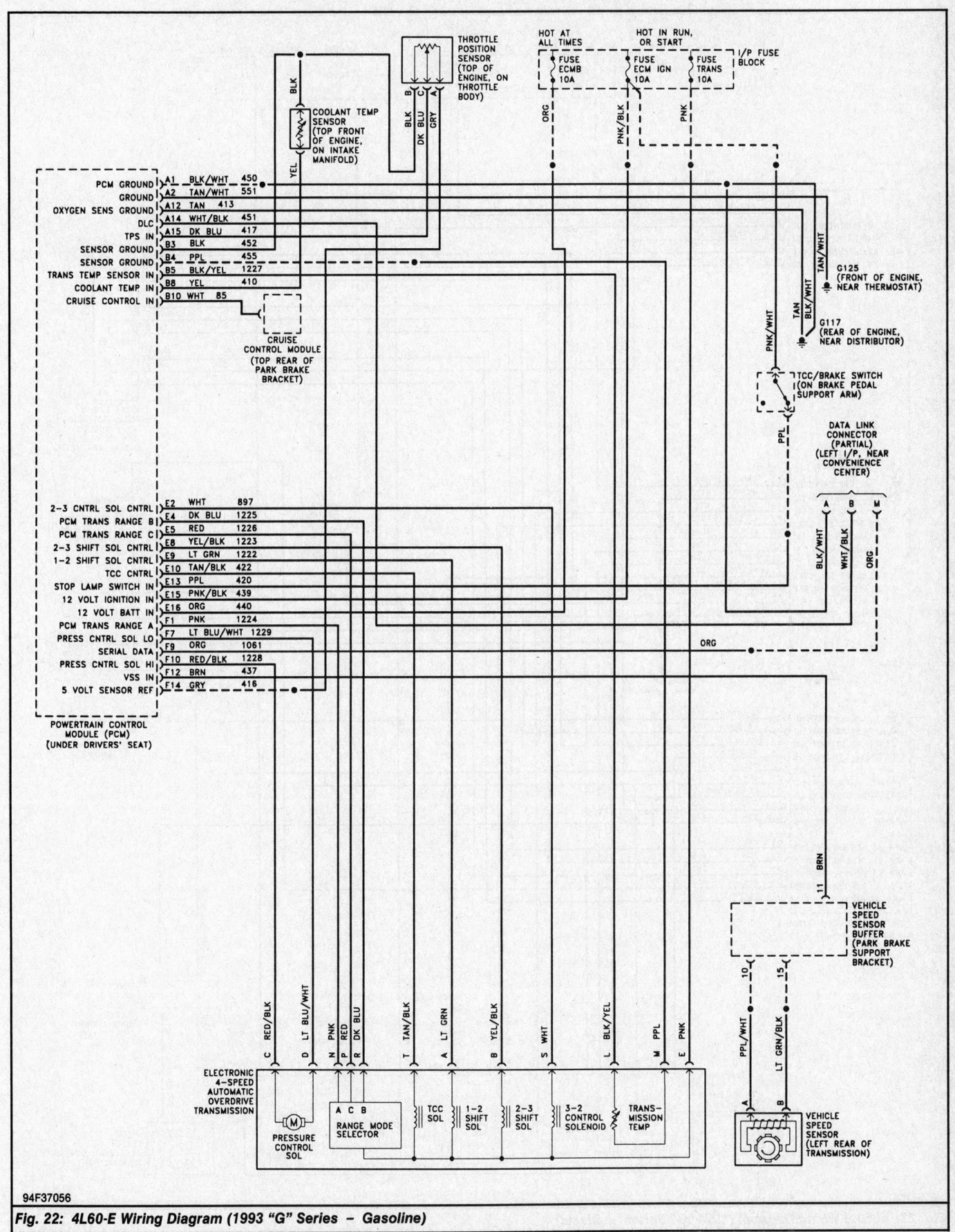

Fig. 22: 4L60-E Wiring Diagram (1993 "G" Series – Gasoline)

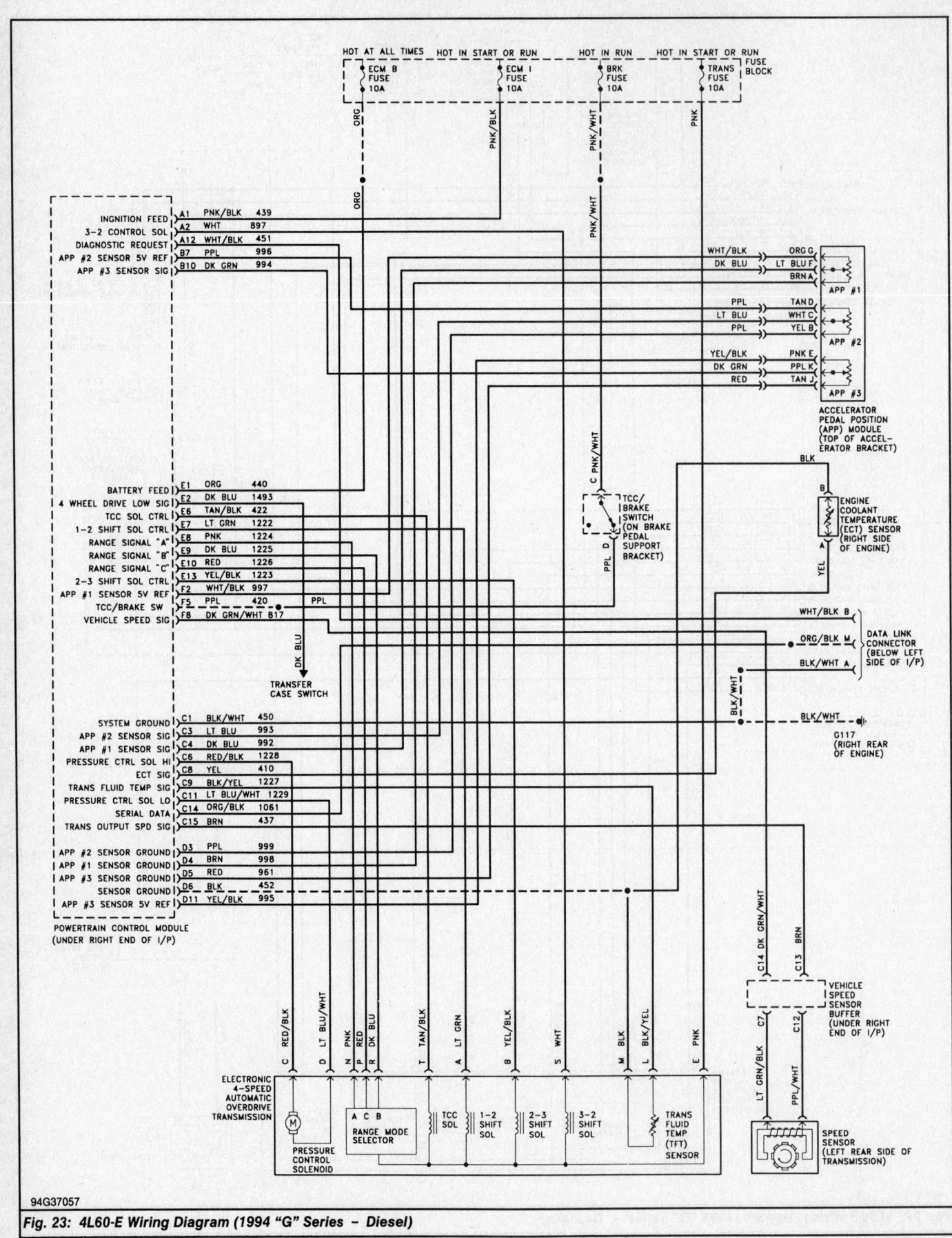

Fig. 23: 4L60-E Wiring Diagram (1994 "G" Series – Diesel)

94G37057

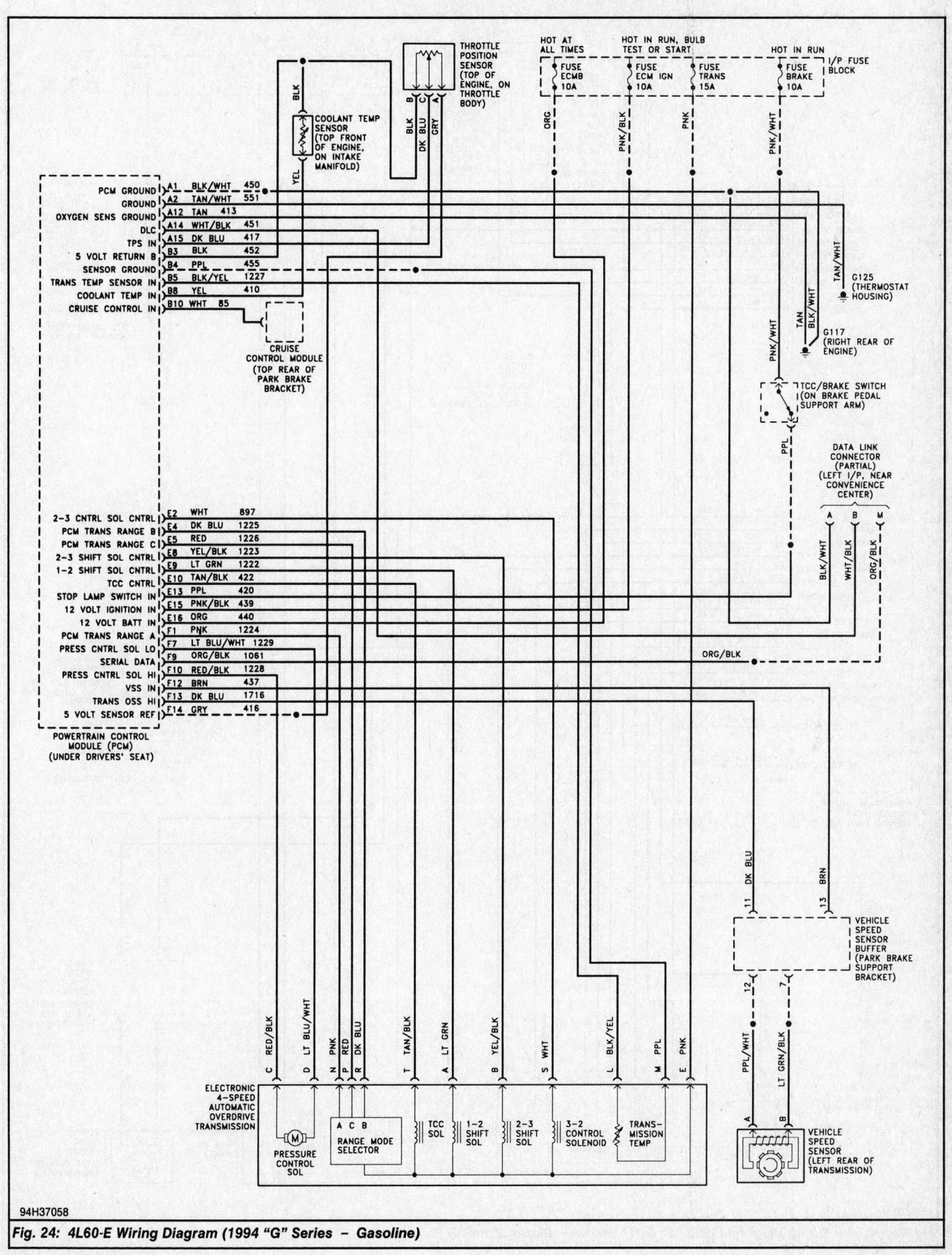

Fig. 24: 4L60-E Wiring Diagram (1994 "G" Series - Gasoline)

94H37058

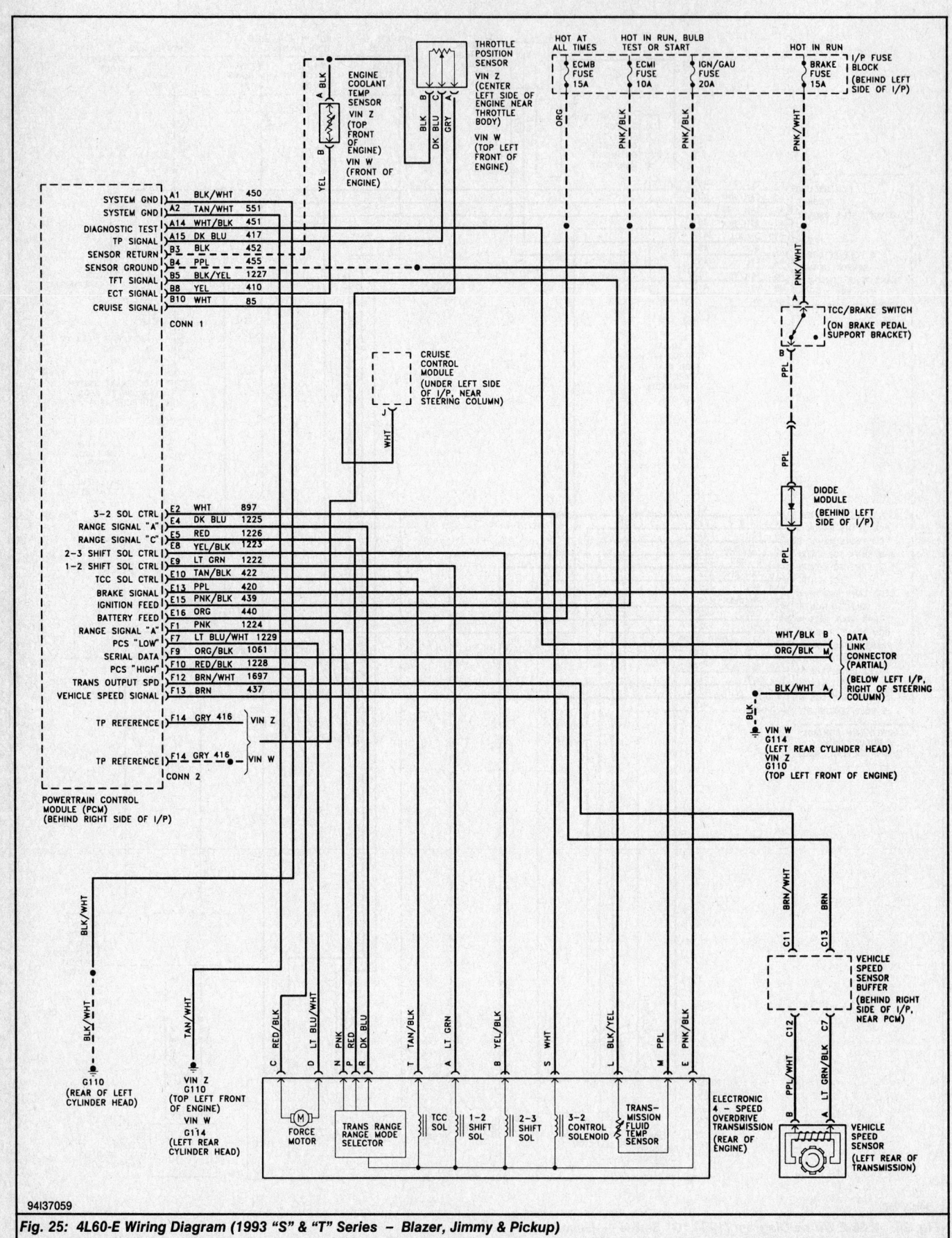

Fig. 25: 4L60-E Wiring Diagram (1993 "S" & "T" Series – Blazer, Jimmy & Pickup)

94I37059

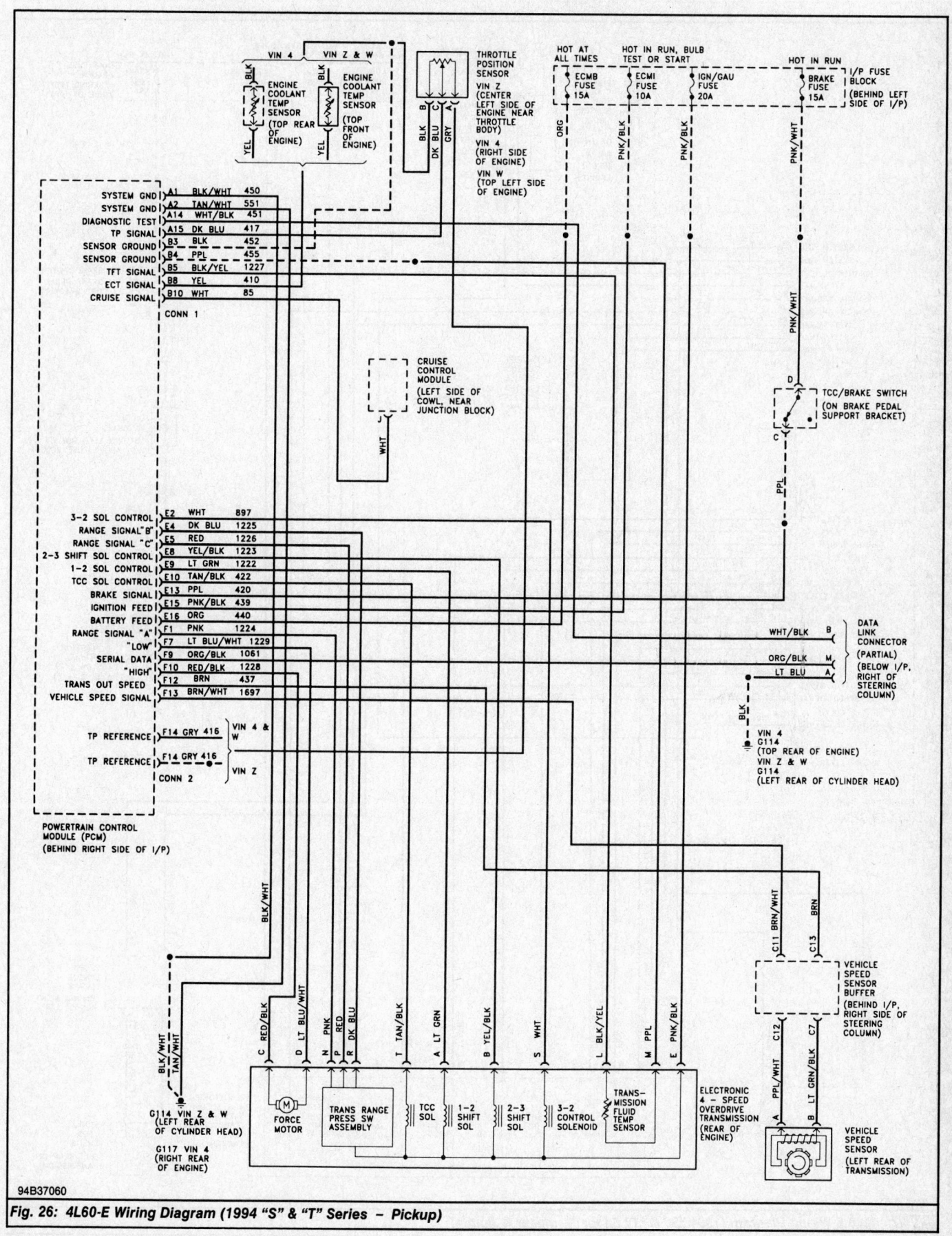

Fig. 26: 4L60-E Wiring Diagram (1994 "S" & "T" Series – Pickup)

94B37060

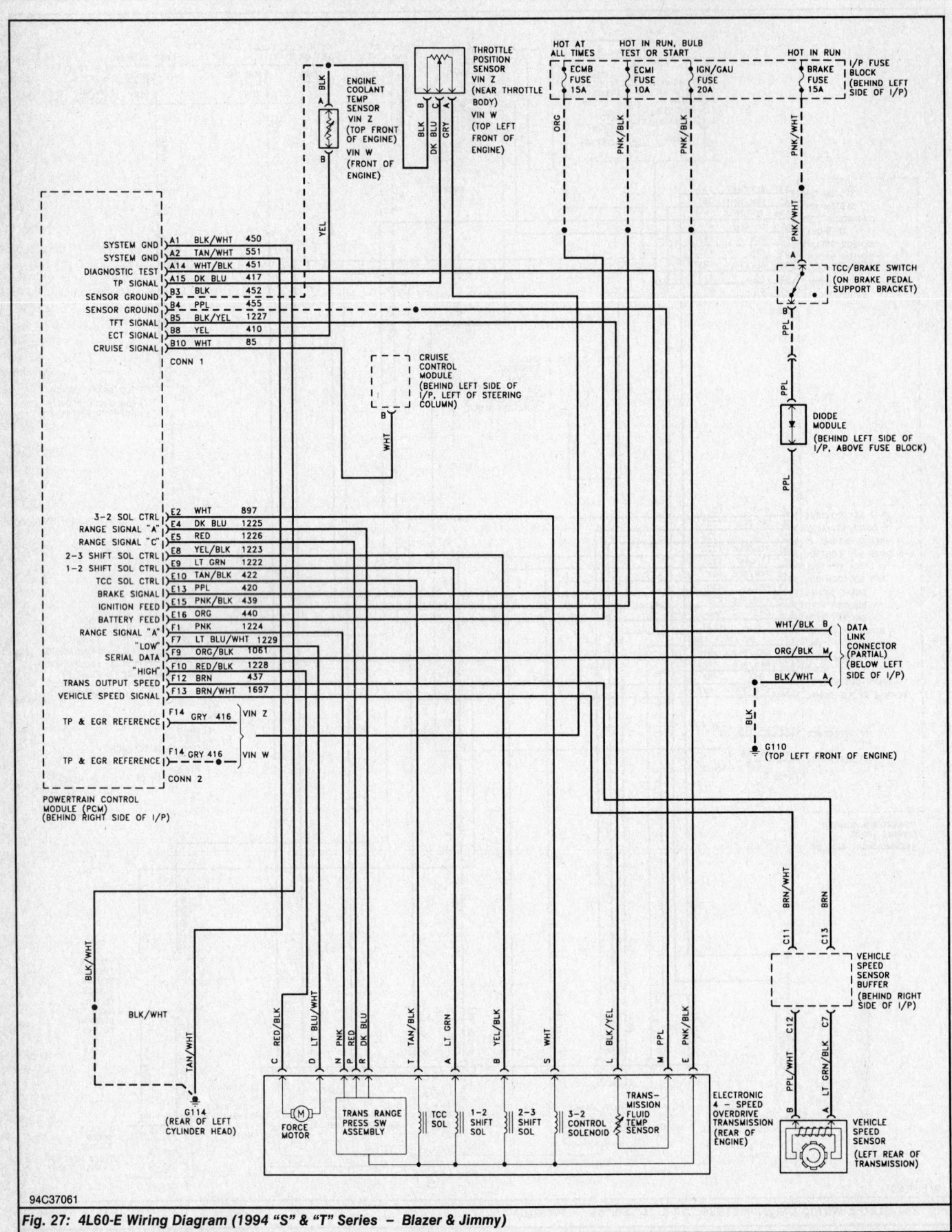

94C37061

Fig. 27: 4L60-E Wiring Diagram (1994 "S" & "T" Series – Blazer & Jimmy)

NOTE: For testing and diagnostic procedures of electronic components, see 4T60-E ELECTRONIC CONTROLS article in AUTOMATIC TRANSMISSIONS.

BODY CODE DESIGNATIONS (1993 PASSENGER CARS)

Body Designation	Model
"C" Body	DeVille, Fleetwood, Ninety-Eight & Park Avenue
"E" Body	Eldorado & Riviera
"H" Body	Bonneville, Eighty-Eight (Royale) & LeSabre
"K" Body	Seville
"W" Body	Cutlass Supreme, Grand Prix, Lumina & Regal

BODY CODE DESIGNATIONS (1994 PASSENGER CARS)

Body Designation	Model
"A" Body	Century & Cutlass Ciera
"C" Body	Ninety-Eight & Park Avenue
"H" Body	Bonneville, Eighty-Eight (Royale) & LeSabre
"K" Body	DeVille
"L" Body	Beretta & Corsica
"N" Body	Achieva, Grand Am & Skylark
"W" Body	Cutlass Supreme, Grand Prix, Lumina & Regal

SERIES CODE DESIGNATIONS (1993-94 VANS)

Series Designation	Model
"U" Series	Lumina APV, Silhouette & Trans Sport

APPLICATION & LABOR TIMES

APPLICATION & LABOR TIMES

Vehicle Application	Labor Times [1] R & I	Labor Times [2] Overhaul	Engine Size
Buick			
Century [3] (A)	6.5	9.0	3.1L
LeSabre (H)	7.0	9.0	3.8L
Park Avenue (C)	7.0	9.0	3.8L
Regal (W)	6.5	9.0	3.1L
	6.5	9.0	3.8L
Riviera [4] (E)	7.0	9.0	3.1L
	7.0	9.0	3.8L
Skylark [3] (N)	7.5	9.0	2.3L
	7.5	9.0	3.1L
Cadillac			
DeVille (C/K)	5.9	9.0	4.9L
Eldorado [4] (E)	8.3	9.0	4.9L
Fleetwood [4] (C)	5.9	9.0	4.9L
Seville [4] (K)	8.3	9.0	4.9L
Chevrolet			
Beretta [3] (L)	6.8	9.0	2.3L
	6.8	9.0	3.1L
Corsica [3] (L)	6.8	9.0	2.3L
	6.8	9.0	3.1L
Lumina (W)	6.5	9.0	3.1L
	6.5	9.0	3.4L
Lumina APV (U)	7.0	9.0	3.8L
Oldsmobile			
Achieva [3] (N)	7.5	9.0	2.3L
	7.5	9.0	3.1L
Ciera [3] (A)	6.5	9.0	3.1L
Cutlass (W)	6.5	9.0	3.1L
	6.5	9.0	3.4L
Eighty Eight Royale (H)	7.0	9.0	3.8L
Ninety Eight (C)	7.0	9.0	3.8L
Silhouette (U)	7.0	9.0	3.8L

[1] – Removal and installation of transaxle from vehicle chassis.
[2] – Bench overhaul time for transaxle and differential. DOES NOT include removal and installation.
[3] – 1994 model year.
[4] – 1993 model year.

APPLICATION & LABOR TIMES (Cont.)

Vehicle Application	Labor Times [1] R & I	Labor Times [2] Overhaul	Engine Size
Pontiac			
Bonneville (H)	7.0	9.0	3.8L
Grand Am [3] (N)	7.5	9.0	2.3L
	7.5	9.0	3.1L
Grand Prix (W)	6.5	9.0	3.1L
	6.5	9.0	3.4L
Trans Sport (U)	7.0	9.0	3.8L

[3] – 1994 model year.

IDENTIFICATION

All transaxles have a metal identification plate attached to the rear face of transaxle case. See Fig. 1.

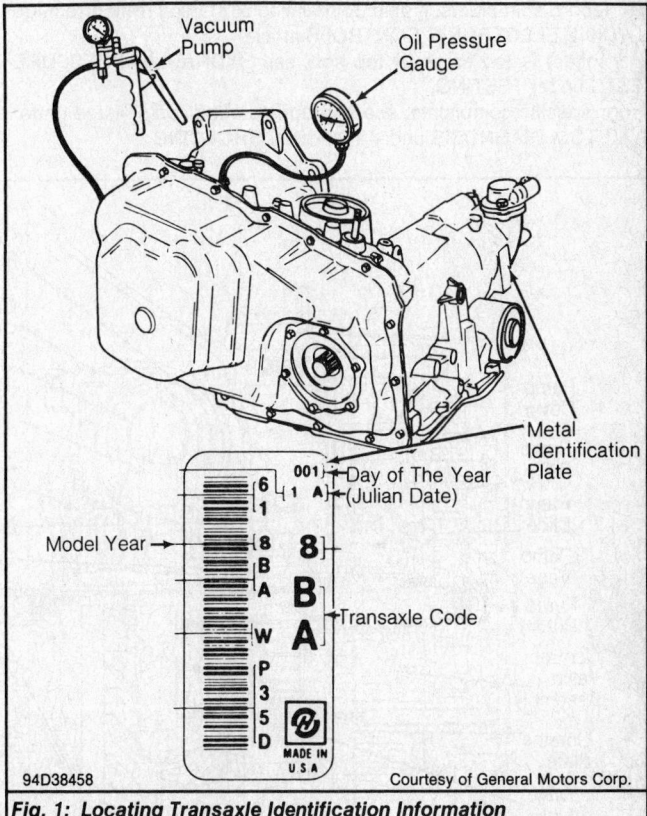

Fig. 1: Locating Transaxle Identification Information

DESCRIPTION

The Hydra-Matic 4T60-E transaxle is a fully automatic 4-speed unit consisting primarily of a 3-element hydraulic torque converter and converter clutch. Transaxle uses a variable capacity vane-type pump to supply all hydraulic pressure needed for operation.

The multiplied torque from torque converter is transferred to the transaxle by a sprocket and link chain assembly. Other internal components consist of 4 multiple-disc clutches, a roller clutch, a sprag clutch, 3 bands and a compound planetary gear set. The final drive gear and differential assemblies are an integral part of the transaxle.

The 4T60-E uses 2 electronic shift valves, controlled by the Powertrain Control Module (PCM), to switch hydraulic pressure on or off. Another electronic solenoid controls Torque Converter Clutch (TCC) lock-up. Some models also use a Pulse Width Modulated (PWM) solenoid to control rate of TCC apply.

LUBRICATION & ADJUSTMENTS

See appropriate AUTOMATIC TRANSMISSION SERVICING article in TRANSMISSION SERVICING.

TROUBLE SHOOTING

NOTE: For testing and diagnostic procedures of electronic components, see 4T60-E ELECTRONIC CONTROLS article in AUTOMATIC TRANSMISSIONS.

NOTE: For clutch and band applications, see CLUTCH & BAND APPLICATION CHART at end of TROUBLE SHOOTING.

QUICK CHECK

1) Check level and condition of transaxle fluid. Check PCM memory for stored trouble codes. See 4T60-E ELECTRONIC CONTROLS article in AUTOMATIC TRANSMISSIONS. If no trouble codes are present, go to next step. If codes are present, diagnose and repair all PCM-related trouble codes. Clear PCM trouble code memory.
2) Perform road test. See ROAD TEST under TESTING. During road test, record shift points. If shift point timing or shifting is incorrect, go to 4T60-E ELECTRONIC CONTROLS article.
3) If shift(s) is too harsh or too soft, see HYDRAULIC PRESSURE TESTS under TESTING.
4) For specific complaints, see appropriate condition(s) listed under SYMPTOM DIAGNOSIS under TROUBLE SHOOTING.

SYMPTOM DIAGNOSIS

NOTE: Transaxle uses a PCM computer, which controls TCC, PWM solenoid (if equipped) and shifting solenoids "A" and "B".

Oil Out Of Vent Or Foaming – Transaxle overfilled. Oil contaminated with antifreeze or engine overheating. Oil filter "O" ring damaged or missing. Thermo element in case does not close when hot, incorrect pin height or thermo element incorrectly installed. Modulator "O" ring incorrectly installed or damaged. Drive sprocket support drain back holes plugged.

High Or Low Line Pressure – Incorrect oil level. Vacuum line leaking, pinched, disconnected or cut. Aspirator "T" connection installed backward or blocked. Modulator diaphragm damaged. Modulator valve nicked, scored or stuck. Oil pump assembly seals or vanes damaged or slide stuck. Pump drive shaft damaged. Pressure regulator valve spring damaged or pressure regulator valve nicked or scored. Pressure relief valve spring damaged or ball missing. Check balls missing in control valve body. Pump or case cover leaking (bolts loose).

Delayed Engagement – Low fluid level. Oil cooler check ball not seating. Reverse servo or 1-2 servo seals cut or damaged. Cut or damaged input housing piston seal. Damaged forward servo seals or servo assembly.

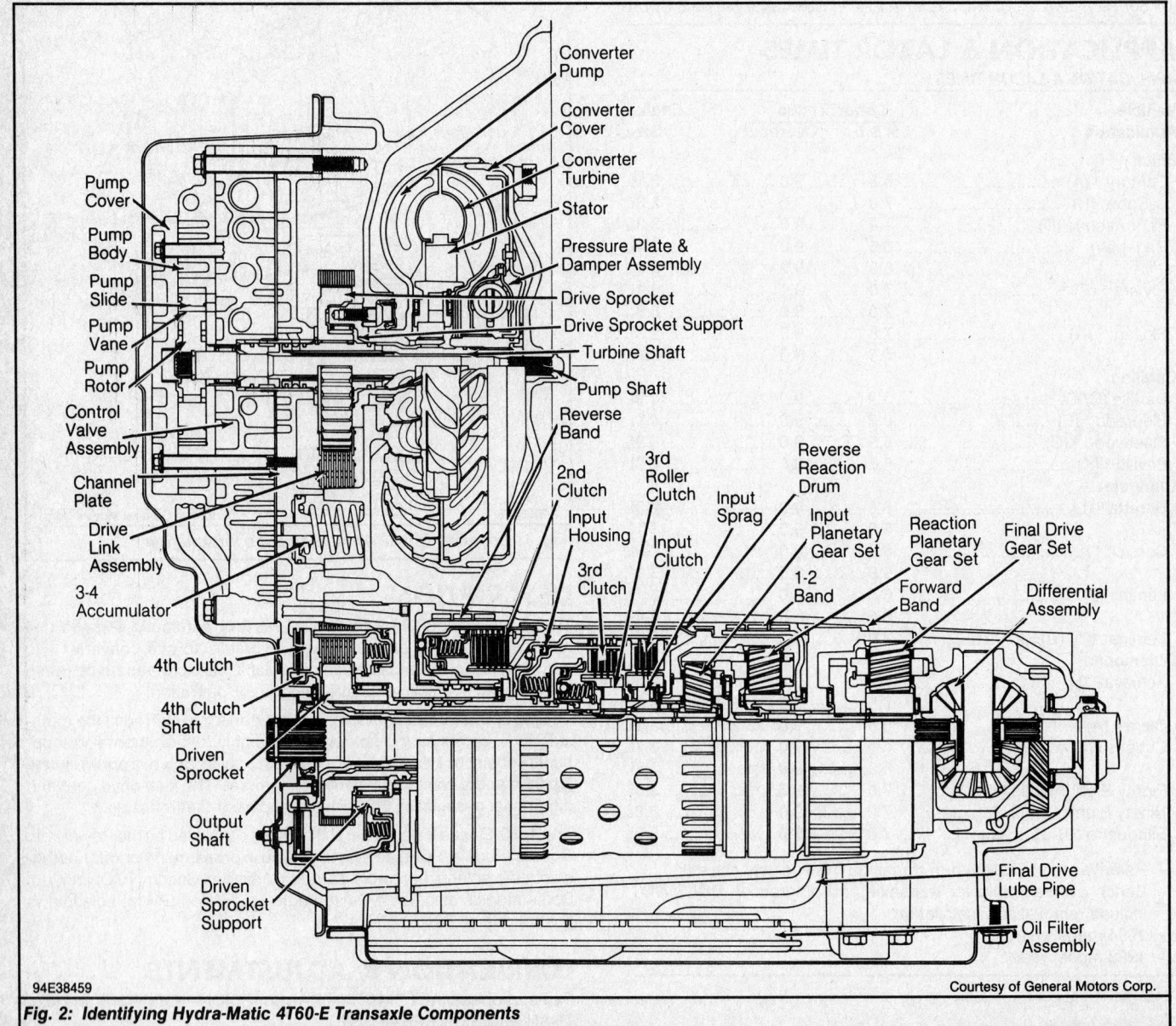

94E38459   Courtesy of General Motors Corp.

Fig. 2: Identifying Hydra-Matic 4T60-E Transaxle Components

1-2, 2-3 AND 3-4 SHIFT SPEEDS

MODEL	TPS IN %	1-2 SHIFT SPEED IN % TPS ±3 MPH									2-3 SHIFT SPEED IN % TPS ±4 MPH									3-4 SHIFT SPEED IN % TPS ±5 MPH								
		10	15	20	25	30	35	40	45	50	10	15	20	25	30	35	40	45	50	10	15	20	25	30	35	40	45	50
ABW	MPH	13	17	22	26	28	30	32	34	36	24	33	41	48	54	58	61	65	69	43	43	60	68	78	86	-	-	-
AMW	MPH	14	16	20	24	26	28	30	32	34	24	30	38	44	50	53	57	60	64	43	43	55	62	70	78	-	-	-
ANW	MPH	14	16	20	24	26	28	30	32	34	24	30	38	44	50	53	57	60	64	43	43	55	62	70	78	-	-	-
APW	MPH	14	16	20	24	26	28	30	32	34	24	30	38	44	50	53	57	60	64	43	43	55	62	70	78	-	-	-
AVW	MPH	13	17	22	26	28	30	32	34	36	24	33	41	48	54	58	61	65	69	43	43	60	68	78	86	-	-	-
AWW	MPH	14	16	20	23	25	28	30	32	34	24	30	38	44	50	53	57	60	64	43	43	55	62	70	78	-	-	-
AYW	MPH	14	16	20	24	26	28	30	32	34	24	30	38	45	50	52	54	57	59	41	43	49	54	62	71	-	-	-
AZW	MPH	14	17	22	26	28	35	33	35	37	24	33	41	48	54	58	62	66	71	43	43	60	69	78	87	-	-	-

FINAL DRIVE / SPROCKETS RATIOS AND SHIFT SPEEDS

MODEL	RATIOS			1-2 MIN THROTTLE	2-3 MIN THROTTLE	3-4 MIN THROTTLE	3-2 DET DOWNSHIFT (Over 90 % TPS)	2-1 DET DOWNSHIFT (Over 90 % TPS)	1-2 W.O.T. (100 % TPS)	2-3 W.O.T. (100 % TPS)	3-4 W.O.T. (100 % TPS)	4-3 COAST DOWN	3-2 COAST DOWN	2-1 COAST DOWN
	FINAL DRIVE	SPROCKETS*	OVERALL											
ABW	3.06	37/33	2.73	12	22	43	74	29/35	43	80	-	39	19	9
AMW	3.33	37/33	2.97	12	22	43	67	29/31	39	76	-	39	19	9
ANW	3.33	37/33	2.97	12	22	43	67	31	39	76	-	39	19	9
APW	3.33	37/33	2.97	12	22	43	67	31	39	76	-	39	19	9
AVW	3.06	37/33	2.73	12	22	43	74	29/35	43	80	-	39	19	9
AWW	3.33	37/33	2.97	12	22	43	67	31	39	76	-	39	19	9
AYW	3.33	35/35	3.33	12	22	41	62	27	34	70	-	39	19	9
AZW	3.06	37/33	2.73	12	22	43	74	35	43	80	-	39	19	9

NOTES:

1. ALL SPEEDS INDICATED ARE IN MILES PER HOUR. CONVERSION TO KM/h = MPH x 1.609.

2. SHIFT POINTS WILL VARY SLIGHTLY DUE TO ENGINE LOAD AND VEHICLE OPTIONS.

3. THE UPSHIFT SPEEDS FOR 1-2, 2-3 AND 3-4 ARE BASED ON THROTTLE POSITION SENSOR (TPS) DATA AS A REFERENCE – USE A TECH 1® OR OTHER SCAN TOOL THAT GIVES PERCENTAGE OF THROTTLE OPENING INSTEAD OF VOLTAGE TO MONITOR THIS DATA.

4. THE 1-2, 2-3 AND 3-4 SHIFT SPEED CHART INFORMATION IS BASED ON PERCENTAGE OF THROTTLE OPENING. THE CONVERSION FACTOR FOR THE OUPUT OF THE CADILLAC SELF-DIAGNOSTIC FEATURES FOR THE DRIVER INFORMATION CENTER (DIC) WOULD BE, PERCENT TPS X 0.819 TO GET THROTTLE ANGLE DATA. REFER TO SECTION 8D.

5. THE 3-2 AND 2-1 DETENT DOWNSHIFTS SPEEDS ARE THE MAXIMUM SPEEDS THAT A 3-2 OR 2-1 DETENT DOWNSHIFT (OVER 90 % TPS) WILL OCCUR. EUROPE AND JAPAN EXPORT VEHICLES WILL HAVE THE LOWER 2-1 DETENT VALVES.

* DESIGNATES THE NUMBER OF TEETH ON THE DRIVE/DRIVEN SPROCKETS, RESPECTIVELY.

NOTE: *See Fig. 1 for model ID.*

94H38460

Fig. 3: *Hydra-Matic 4T60-E Shift Speed Chart (1993 – 1 Of 3)*

AUTOMATIC TRANSMISSIONS
Hydra-Matic 4T60-E (Cont.)

1-2, 2-3 AND 3-4 SHIFT SPEEDS

MODEL	TPS IN %	1-2 SHIFT SPEED IN % TPS ±3 MPH									2-3 SHIFT SPEED IN % TPS ±4 MPH									3-4 SHIFT SPEED IN % TPS ±5 MPH								
		10	15	20	25	30	35	40	45	50	10	15	20	25	30	35	40	45	50	10	15	20	25	30	35	40	45	50
BTW	MPH	14	17	20	23	27	29	31	34	36	24	30	35	39	44	49	51	53	56	45	50	58	65	79	-	-	-	-
BYW	MPH	12	17	21	23	25	28	31	34	36	24	29	34	39	44	47	50	53	56	45	46	52	65	80	-	-	-	-
CLW	MPH	13	16	20	23	27	28	31	34	36	24	30	35	39	44	48	50	53	56	45	49	56	65	79	-	-	-	-
CSW	MPH	13	16	20	23	26	28	31	34	36	22	29	35	39	42	47	49	52	56	45	49	54	67	80	-	-	-	-
CTW	MPH	12	17	21	23	25	28	31	34	36	24	29	34	39	44	47	50	53	56	45	46	52	65	80	-	-	-	-
CXW	MPH	14	17	20	23	27	29	31	34	36	24	30	35	39	44	49	51	53	56	45	50	58	65	79	-	-	-	-
CZW	MPH	13	17	19	21	23	25	28	30	32	23	27	31	35	40	44	46	49	51	46	49	57	65	80	-	-	-	-
PHW	MPH	13	17	19	21	23	25	28	30	32	23	27	31	35	40	44	46	49	51	46	49	57	65	80	-	-	-	-
WAW	MPH	14	17	21	23	27	29	31	34	36	24	30	35	39	45	48	51	53	56	45	49	58	65	80	-	-	-	-
YLW	MPH	13	17	21	23	27	28	31	34	36	24	29	35	39	44	48	50	53	56	45	46	56	65	81	-	-	-	-
YMW	MPH	13	16	20	23	27	28	31	34	36	24	30	35	39	44	48	50	53	56	45	49	56	65	79	-	-	-	-
YRW	MPH	13	16	20	23	26	28	31	34	36	22	29	35	39	42	47	49	52	56	45	49	54	67	80	-	-	-	-
YZW	MPH	13	16	20	23	26	28	31	34	36	22	29	35	39	42	47	49	52	56	45	49	54	67	80	-	-	-	-

FINAL DRIVE / SPROCKETS RATIOS AND SHIFT SPEEDS

MODEL	RATIOS			1-2 MIN THROTTLE	2-3 MIN THROTTLE	3-4 MIN THROTTLE	3-2 DET DOWNSHIFT (Over 90 % TPS)	2-1 DET DOWNSHIFT (Over 90 % TPS)	1-2 W.O.T. (100 % TPS)	2-3 W.O.T. (100 % TPS)	3-4 W.O.T. (100 % TPS)	4-3 COAST DOWN	3-2 COAST DOWN	2-1 COAST DOWN
	FINAL DRIVE	SPROCKETS*	OVERALL											
BTW	3.33	37/33	2.97	11	20	45	62	35	39	74	-	40	16	10
BYW	3.06	35/35	3.06	11	20	45	62	35	39	74	-	40	19	10
CLW	2.84	35/35	2.84	11	20	45	62	35	39	74	-	40	19	10
CSW	3.06	35/35	3.06	11	20	45	62	35	39	74	-	40	19	10
CTW	3.06	35/35	3.06	11	20	45	62	35	39	74	-	40	19	10
CXW	3.33	37/33	2.97	11	20	45	62	35	39	74	-	40	16	10
CZW	3.33	37/33	2.97	11	19	45	62	35	37	64	-	40	18	10
PHW	3.33	37/33	2.97	11	19	45	62	35	37	64	-	40	18	10
WAW	3.06	35/35	3.06	11	20	45	62	35	39	74	-	40	16	10
YLW	2.84	35/35	2.84	11	20	45	62	35	39	74	-	40	19	10
YMW	2.84	35/35	2.84	11	20	45	62	35	39	74	-	40	19	10
YRW	2.84	35/35	2.84	11	20	45	62	35	39	74	-	40	19	10
YZW	3.06	35/35	3.06	11	20	45	62	35	39	74	-	40	19	10

NOTES:

1. ALL SPEEDS INDICATED ARE IN MILES PER HOUR. CONVERSION TO KM/h = MPH x 1.609.

2. SHIFT POINTS WILL VARY SLIGHTLY DUE TO ENGINE LOAD AND VEHICLE OPTIONS.

3. THE UPSHIFT SPEEDS FOR 1-2, 2-3 AND 3-4 ARE BASED ON THROTTLE POSITION SENSOR (TPS) DATA AS A REFERENCE – USE A TECH 1® OR OTHER SCAN TOOL THAT GIVES PERCENTAGE OF THROTTLE OPENING INSTEAD OF VOLTAGE TO MONITOR THIS DATA.

4. THE 3-2 AND 2-1 DETENT DOWNSHIFTS SPEEDS ARE THE MAXIMUM SPEEDS THAT A 3-2 OR 2-1 DETENT DOWNSHIFT (OVER 90 % TPS) WILL OCCUR. EUROPE AND JAPAN EXPORT VEHICLES WILL HAVE THE LOWER 2-1 DETENT VALVES.

* DESIGNATES THE NUMBER OF TEETH ON THE DRIVE/DRIVEN SPROCKETS, RESPECTIVELY.

NOTE: *See Fig. 1* for model ID.

94I38461

Fig. 4: Hydra-Matic 4T60-E Shift Speed Chart (1993 – 2 Of 3)

1-2, 2-3 AND 3-4 SHIFT SPEEDS

MODEL	TPS IN %	1-2 SHIFT SPEED IN % TPS ±3 MPH									2-3 SHIFT SPEED IN % TPS ±4 MPH									3-4 SHIFT SPEED IN % TPS ±5 MPH								
		10	15	20	25	30	35	40	45	50	10	15	20	25	30	35	40	45	50	10	15	20	25	30	35	40	45	50
CMW	MPH	9	14	16	17	19	21	23	25	27	20	22	25	31	37	43	47	50	54	32	35	39	44	50	56	59	65	72
CWW	MPH	11	14	16	17	19	22	24	27	29	22	23	27	31	34	37	41	45	48	32	34	39	43	50	60	70	–	–

FINAL DRIVE / SPROCKETS RATIOS AND DOWNSHIFT SPEEDS

MODEL	RATIOS			1-2 MIN THROTTLE	2-3 MIN THROTTLE	3-4 MIN THROTTLE	3-2 DET DOWNSHIFT (Over 90 % TPS)	2-1 DET DOWNSHIFT (Over 90 % TPS)	1-2 W.O.T. (100 % TPS) RPM	2-3 W.O.T. (100 % TPS) RPM	1-2 W.O.T. (100 % TPS) MPH	2-3 W.O.T. (100 % TPS) MPH	4-3 COAST DOWN	3-2 COAST DOWN	2-1 COAST DOWN
	FINAL DRIVE	SPROCKETS*	OVERALL												
CMW	3.33	35/35	3.33	9	19	32	48	8	5250	5150	36	67	31	17	8
CWW	3.06	33/37	3.43	7	22	22	71	8	6200	6000	41	80	21	17	6

NOTES:

1. ALL SPEEDS INDICATED ARE IN MILES PER HOUR. CONVERSION TO KM/h = MPH x 1.609.

2. SHIFT POINTS WILL VARY SLIGHTLY DUE TO ENGINE LOAD AND VEHICLE OPTIONS.

3. THE UPSHIFT SPEEDS FOR 1-2, 2-3 AND 3-4 ARE BASED ON THROTTLE POSITION SENSOR (TP SENSOR) DATA AS A REFERENCE – USE A TECH 1® OR OTHER SCAN TOOL THAT GIVES PERCENTAGE OF THROTTLE OPENING INSTEAD OF VOLTAGE TO MONITOR THIS DATA.

4. THE 3-2 AND 2-1 DETENT DOWNSHIFTS SPEEDS ARE THE MAXIMUM SPEEDS THAT A 3-2 OR 2-1 DETENT DOWNSHIFT (OVER 90 % TP SENSOR) WILL OCCUR.

5. THE 1-2, 2-3 WIDE OPEN THROTTLE (W.O.T.) SHIFT VALUES ARE GIVEN IN BOTH MPH's AND RPM's. (THE PCM USES RPM FOR THE W.O.T. SHIFTS – THE MPH IS GIVEN FOR A REFERENCE VALVE ONLY AND MAY VARY FROM VEHICLE TO VEHICLE.)

* DESIGNATES THE NUMBER OF TEETH ON THE DRIVE/DRIVEN SPROCKETS, RESPECTIVELY.

NOTE: *See Fig. 1* for model ID.

94J38462

Courtesy of General Motors Corp.

Fig. 5: Hydra-Matic 4T60-E Shift Speed Chart (1993 – 3 Of 3)

CLUTCH & BAND APPLICATION CHART (4T60-E)

Selector Lever Position	Solenoid Position	Elements In Use
"D" (Drive)		
1st Gear	"A" ON/"B" ON	Input Clutch, [1] Input Sprag, Forward Band & [1] 1-2 Support Roller Clutch
2nd Gear	"A" OFF/"B" ON	2nd Clutch, [2] Input Clutch, [3] Input Sprag, Forward Band & [1] 1-2 Support Roller Clutch
3rd Gear	"A" OFF/"B" OFF	2nd Clutch, 3rd Clutch, [1] 3rd Roller Clutch, Forward Band & [3] 1-2 Support Roller Clutch
Overdrive	"A" ON/"B" OFF	4th Gear, 2nd Clutch, [2] 3rd Clutch, [3] 3rd Roller Clutch, Forward Band & [3] 1-2 Support Roller Clutch
"3" (Manual 3rd)		
3rd Gear	"A" OFF/"B" OFF	2nd Clutch, 3rd Clutch, [1] 3rd Roller Clutch, Input Clutch, [1] Input Sprag, Forward Band & [3] 1-2 Support Roller Clutch
2nd Gear	"A" OFF/"B" ON	2nd Clutch, [2] Input Clutch, [3] Input Sprag, Forward Band & [1] 1-2 Support Roller Clutch
1st Gear	"A" ON/"B" ON	Input Clutch, [1] Input Sprag, Forward Band & [1] 1-2 Support Roller Clutch
"2" (Manual 2nd)		
2nd Gear	"A" OFF/"B" ON	2nd Clutch, [2] Input Clutch, [3] Input Sprag, Forward Band, [1] 1-2 Support Roller Clutch & 1-2 Band
1st Gear	"A" ON/"B" ON	Input Clutch, [1] Input Sprag, Forward Band, [1] 1-2 Support Roller Clutch & 1-2 Band
"1" (Manual Low)		
1st Gear	"A" ON/"B" ON	3rd Clutch, [1] 3rd Roller Clutch, Input Clutch, [1] Input Sprag, Forward Band, [1] 1-2 Support Roller Clutch & 1-2 Band
"R" (Reverse)	"A" ON/"B" ON	Reverse Band, Input Clutch & [1] Input Sprag
"N" Or "P" (Neutral Or Park)	"A" ON/"B" ON	All Clutches & Bands Released Or Ineffective

[1] – Holding.
[2] – Applied but not effective.
[3] – Overrunning.

AUTOMATIC TRANSMISSIONS
Hydra-Matic 4T60-E (Cont.)

1-2, 2-3 AND 3-4 SHIFT SPEEDS

MODEL	TPS %	1-2 SHIFT SPEED ± 3 MPH			2-3 SHIFT SPEED ± 4 MPH			3-4 SHIFT SPEED ± 5 MPH		
		10	25	50	10	25	50	10	25	50
AFW	MPH	12	20	30	22	32	54	34	48	72
AJW	MPH	14	21	31	24	36	57	36	47	74
ATW	MPH	13	26	38	24	48	70	43	68	–
BLW	MPH	13	22	36	24	39	56	45	65	–
CLW	MPH	11	19	32	19	32	59	26	46	75
CMW	MPH	9	17	27	20	31	54	32	44	72
CWW	MPH	11	17	29	22	31	45	32	43	–
KHW	MPH	14	25	38	22	41	59	40	50	–
KUW	MPH	13	22	36	24	39	56	45	65	–
PAW	MPH	14	21	31	24	36	57	36	47	74
PBW	MPH	11	17	29	22	31	45	32	43	–
PFW	MPH	13	22	36	24	39	56	45	65	–
PHW	MPH	10	17	28	17	29	52	24	38	71
PMW	MPH	13	22	36	24	39	56	45	65	–
WAW	MPH	13	22	36	24	39	56	45	65	–
WBW	MPH	11	19	31	22	34	57	34	47	72
WSW	MPH	11	19	31	22	34	57	34	47	72
YCW	MPH	13	22	36	23	39	56	45	65	–
YMW	MPH	13	22	36	24	39	56	45	65	–
YZW	MPH	13	22	36	24	39	56	45	65	–

FINAL DRIVE / SPROCKETS RATIOS AND SHIFT SPEEDS

MODEL	RATIOS			1-2 THROTTLE	2-3 THROTTLE	3-4 THROTTLE	3-2 DET DOWNSHIFT (Over 90 % TPS)	2-1 DET DOWNSHIFT (Over 90 % TPS)	1-2 W.O.T. (100 % TPS)	2-3 W.O.T. (100 % TPS)	4-3 COAST DOWN	3-2 COAST DOWN	2-1 COAST DOWN
	FINAL DRIVE	SPROCKETS*	OVERALL										
AFW	3.33	35/35	3.33	9	20	32	60	30	39	74	31	19	8
AJW	3.33	37/33	2.97	10	22	35	68	31	40	75	33	20	8
ATW	3.06	37/33	2.73	12	22	43	75	36	43	80	39	19	8
BLW	3.06	35/35	3.06	11	20	45	62	35	39	74	40	19	10
CLW	3.06	33/37	3.43	10	16	24	57	16	44	78	20	14	9
CMW	3.33	35/35	3.33	9	19	32	48	8	36	67	31	17	8
CWW	3.06	33/37	3.43	11	22	32	70	24	41	80	30	19	9
KHW	3.33	37/33	2.97	11	17	38	62	35	41	74	34	16	10
KUW	3.06	35/35	3.06	11	20	45	62	35	39	74	40	16	10
PAW	3.33	37/33	2.97	10	22	35	68	31	40	75	33	20	8
PBW	3.06	33/37	3.43	11	22	32	70	24	41	80	30	19	9
PFW	3.06	35/35	3.06	11	20	45	62	35	39	74	40	19	10
PHW	3.33	33/37	3.73	9	15	22	44	15	42	77	18	13	8
PMW	3.06	35/35	3.06	11	20	45	62	35	39	74	40	16	10
WAW	3.06	35/35	3.06	11	20	45	62	35	39	74	40	19	10
WBW	3.33	37/33	2.97	9	20	32	69	30	39	74	31	19	8
WSW	3.33	37/33	2.97	9	20	32	69	30	39	74	31	19	8
YCW	3.33	37/33	2.97	11	20	45	62	35	39	74	40	16	10
YMW	2.84	35/35	2.84	11	20	45	62	35	39	74	40	19	10
YZW	3.06	35/35	3.06	11	20	45	62	35	39	74	40	19	10

NOTES:

1. ALL SPEEDS INDICATED ARE IN MILES PER HOUR. CONVERSION TO KM/h = MPH x 1.609.
2. SHIFT POINTS WILL VARY SLIGHTLY DUE TO ENGINE LOAD AND VEHICLE OPTIONS.
3. THE UPSHIFT SPEEDS FOR 1-2, 2-3 AND 3-4 ARE BASED ON THROTTLE POSITION SENSOR (TPS) DATA AS A REFERENCE – USE A TECH 1® OR OTHER SCAN TOOL THAT GIVES PERCENTAGE OF THROTTLE OPENING INSTEAD OF VOLTAGE TO MONITOR THIS DATA. THE CONVERSION FACTOR TO GET THROTTLE ANGLE IN DEGREES IS PERCENT TPS x 0.9.
4. THE 3-2 AND 2-1 DETENT DOWNSHIFTS SPEEDS ARE THE MAXIMUM SPEEDS THAT A 3-2 OR 2-1 DETENT DOWNSHIFT (OVER 90 % TPS) WILL OCCUR.

* DESIGNATES THE NUMBER OF TEETH ON THE DRIVE/DRIVEN SPROCKETS, RESPECTIVELY.

NOTE: See Fig. 1 for model ID.

94A38463

Courtesy of General Motors Corp.

Fig. 6: Hydra-Matic 4T60-E Shift Speed Chart (1994)

No Drive In "D" – **1)** Low oil level or pressure. Manual linkage misadjusted or disconnected. Piston or seal damaged in 1-2 servo assembly. Drive axles disengaged. Leaking or damaged 1-2 servo oil pipe seals. Damaged oil pump drive shaft or pump assembly. Incorrect No. 3 check ball location. Torque converter stator roller clutch damaged. Input clutch accumulator piston seal damaged. Drive link assembly damaged, drive link chain broken or sprockets and bearings damaged.

2) Input clutch assembly clutch plates burned, clutch plates missing, check ball capsule leaking or missing. Input piston seals cut or damaged, or shaft feed passages blocked. Damaged or incorrectly assembled input sprag or input sun gear assembly. Burned 3rd roller clutch (due to lack of lubrication), oil lube pipe leaking or damaged.

3) Input carrier and reaction carrier assembly pinions, internal ring gear or sun gear damaged. Output shaft damaged or drive axles incorrectly assembled into differential. Burned 1-2 band assembly or band out of position. Parking pawl spring broken. Damaged final drive assembly or final drive sun gear, side gears, pinion gears or internal ring gear.

Slips In "D" – **1)** Low fluid level. Vacuum line pinched or cut. Damaged vacuum modulator. Low line pressure. Oil pump assembly seals or vanes damaged or slide stuck. Modulator valve stuck or binding. Damaged 1-2 servo assembly or leaking servo piston seal. Oil filter screen plugged. Leaking or damaged servo pipe seals. Torque converter stator roller clutch not holding. Input clutch accumulator piston or input shaft seals damaged. Leaking ball capsule or damaged input clutch assembly seals.

2) Check for problem with solenoid "A" or "B". Check for switched wires between TCC and solenoid "B".

No 1-2 Shift (1st Gear) – Check for binding or stuck 1-2 shift valve. Spacer plate or gaskets mispositioned or damaged. Drive sprocket support oil sealing rings damaged. Clutches in 2nd clutch assembly damaged. Piston or piston seals in 2nd clutch damaged. Incorrectly assembled 2nd clutch pack. Missing or damaged check ball capsule in 2nd clutch housing. Reverse reaction drum splines damaged or reverse reaction drum plate missing.

Harsh Or Soft 1-2 Shift – High or low line pressures. Damaged 1-2 accumulator piston seals or piston springs missing. Accumulator cover bolts improperly tightened or gaskets mispositioned. Accumulator valve in control valve body stuck. Incorrect No. 2 check ball location. Damaged seals on driven support sprocket.

1-2 Shift Shudder – Damaged 2nd clutch or driven sprocket support.

No 2-3 Shift (1st & 2nd Gears) – Depending on vehicle, check for trouble Code 26, 29, 36, 56, 755 or 1650. Solenoid "B" stuck on. Dirt in solenoid, PCM signal to solenoid "B" grounded or signal return wire shorted to ground.

1-4 Shift (Misses 2nd & 3rd Gears) – Depending on vehicle, check for trouble Code 26, 29, 56 or 1650. Solenoid "A" stuck on. Dirt in solenoid, PCM signal to solenoid "A" grounded or signal return wire shorted to ground.

2-3 Shift Only – Depending on vehicle, check for trouble code 26, 29, 56 or 1650. Failed "A" solenoid ("A" solenoid off). Dirt in filter, PCM not grounded, leaking "O" ring, no supply voltage to "A" solenoid or wire disconnected.

1-2-4 Shift (No 2-3 Shift) – Stuck 2-3 shift valve or 3-2 manual shift valve. Mispositioned or damaged channel plate gasket. Blocked 3rd clutch port in driven sprocket support. Seals damaged or leaking in input shaft. Burned 3rd clutch assembly. Damaged or incorrectly assembled 3rd roller clutch assembly.

Harsh Or Soft 2-3 Shift – Low or high oil pressures. Mispositioned No. 4 check ball causing soft shift. Leaking 2-3 accumulator piston. Missing No. 9 check ball causing harsh shift.

Early Or Late 2-3 Shift – Wrong PROM. See SERVICE BULLETINS.

3-4 Shift – (Misses 1st & 2nd Gears) – Depending on vehicle, check for trouble Code 26, 29, 36, 56, 755 or 1650. Solenoid "B" stuck off. Dirt in solenoid, "O" ring leaking, PCM signal to solenoid "B" grounded or signal return wire shorted to ground.

No 3-4 Shift – Check for manual shift linkage out of adjustment. Sticking 3-4 shift valve. Splines on 4th clutch shaft damaged. Burned

4th clutch assembly clutch plates, damaged piston seals or incorrect number of clutch plates.

Harsh Or Soft 3-4 Shift – High or low line pressures. Accumulator cover bolts improperly tightened. Damaged accumulator seals or pistons. Check for stuck 3-4 accumulator valve in control valve assembly or missing No. 10 check ball.

Early Or Late 3-4 Shift – Wrong PROM. See SERVICE BULLETINS.

No Reverse – **1)** Oil pressure low. Reverse servo incorrectly assembled, piston or seal damaged or apply pin incorrect. Damaged oil pump drive shaft or oil pump assembly. Input clutch accumulator piston seal damaged. Drive link assembly damaged or drive link chain broken. Burned, damaged or mispositioned reverse band. Input clutch assembly clutch plates burned, clutch plates missing or check ball capsule leaking or missing.

2) Input piston seals cut or damaged, or shaft feed passages blocked. Damaged or incorrectly assembled input sprag or input sun gear assembly. Reverse reaction drum splines damaged. Burned 3rd roller clutch (due to lack of lubrication), or oil lube pipe leaking or damaged.

3) Input carrier and reaction carrier assembly pinions, internal ring gear or sun gear damaged. Output shaft damaged or drive axles incorrectly assembled into differential assembly. Blown out "A" or TCC solenoid.

4) Parking pawl spring broken. Damaged final drive assembly or final drive sun gear, side gears, pinion gears or internal ring gear.

Locked In Reverse – Damaged parking pawl binding on final drive internal gear.

Slips In Reverse – Low oil pressure. Reverse servo seal damaged. Reverse reaction drum splines stripped.

Vehicle Moves In Park – Manual linkage damaged or disconnected. Broken final drive park pawl spring, park pawl or park pawl gear in final drive internal gear assembly. Park actuator spring damaged.

Harsh Neutral-To-Drive Engagement – Engine idle too high. Loss of vacuum due to damaged lines, aspirator "T" or vacuum modulator. Aspirator "T" installed backward or plugged. Reverse servo cushion spring weak or broken. Check ball No. 5 missing (also harsh engagement in Reverse). Check ball No. 6 is missing. Control valve body spacer plate mispositioned. Thermal element does not close when warm. Reverse servo apply pin too long.

Vehicle Starts In 2nd Gear – Stuck 1-2 shift valve.

Harsh Reverse – Scored 2nd clutch housing. Burned reverse band fiber. Check for missing or mispositioned check ball No. 5, or damaged or wrong servo cushion spring.

No Engine Breaking In Manual 2nd Or Low – Burned 2-1 manual band. Apply pin not engaging 2-1 manual band. Apply servo seals leaking, servo cover loose or piston binding in bore.

Harsh 4-3 Downshift – Missing No. 10 check ball in control valve body. 3-4 accumulator valve stuck or 3-4 accumulator seal cut.

Harsh 3-2 Downshift – No. 9 check ball in control valve body missing. 2-3 accumulator valve stuck or 2-3 accumulator seal cut.

Harsh 2-1 Downshift – Wrong spacer plate, stuck 1-2 accumulator valve or cut 1-2 accumulator seal.

NOTE: Transaxle uses a PCM computer. This computer controls TCC, PWM solenoid (if equipped) and shifting solenoids "A" and "B".

No Converter Clutch Apply – Verify proper PCM operation and vehicle wiring. Coolant temperature sensor damaged. Damaged wiring harness or pinched wires. Solenoid inoperative. Converter clutch shift valve of control valve assembly stuck. Converter clutch apply valve stuck. Solenoid "O" ring leaking or screen blocked.

Torque converter external leaks at hub weld area, or fluid unbalanced or contaminated. Turbine shaft seals damaged. Oil pump drive shaft seal damaged. Channel plate converter clutch blow-off check ball not seated or damaged. Damaged or missing TCC accumulator piston or seal (without PWM only).

Converter Clutch Does Not Release – PCM-controlled TCC solenoid does not exhaust. Control valve assembly converter clutch apply valve stuck in apply position. TCC orifice screen missing.

Converter Clutch Stuck On In 3rd & 4th – TCC solenoid stuck on. Dirt in TCC solenoid. Wire between TCC solenoid and PCM shorted to ground.

Converter Applied With Maximum Pressure (With PWM) – PWM solenoid always off. Dirt in solenoid. Leaky "O" ring. No voltage to PWM solenoid. Open wire or no apply signal from PCM.

Converter Clutch Apply Rough, Slips Or Shudders – Control valve assembly converter clutch regulator valve stuck. Turbine shaft seals damaged or missing. Converter clutch blow-off check ball not sealed or damaged. Damaged channel plate converter clutch accumulator piston or seal (if equipped). Spring damaged. Wrong blow-off spring. Seals damaged or missing. Defective converter clutch.

No TCC – Depending on vehicle, check for possible trouble Code 15, 26, 27, 31, 38, 56, 90, 90, 117, 740 or 1640. Check the following solenoids and switches for faulty operation, dirt or binding: TCC solenoid, PWM, brake switch, PRNDL ("P"/"N" switch) and coolant temperature sensor. Also check the same solenoid and switch circuits for open or shorted wires between voltage supply or PCM.

ELECTRONIC SELF-DIAGNOSTICS & ELECTRONIC TESTING

NOTE: See 4T60-E ELECTRONIC CONTROLS article in AUTOMATIC TRANSMISSIONS.

TESTING
ROAD TEST

NOTE: Before road testing vehicle, engine and transmission must be at operating temperature. Torque converter clutch will not engage if engine coolant has not reached operating temperature.

Gear Selector Position "D" (Overdrive) – **1)** With gear selector in "D" (overdrive) position, steadily increase throttle pressure to accelerate vehicle. Note shift speed engagement points in 2nd gear, 3rd gear and overdrive gear. Use chart as a reference for proper shift speeds. *See Figs. 3-6.* Also note Torque Converter Clutch (TCC) engagement point while in 3rd gear or Overdrive.

NOTE: Ensure TCC engages in 3rd gear or overdrive during the following steps. On vehicles with PWM solenoid, TCC engagement point may be hard to feel. Use scan tool to indicate TCC engagement and release points.

2) At vehicle speeds of 40-50 MPH, quickly depress accelerator to half-open position (part throttle detent downshift). TCC should release, and transaxle should immediately downshift to 3rd gear.

3) At vehicle speeds of 40-50 MPH, quickly depress accelerator to wide open position (full throttle detent downshift). TCC should release, and transaxle should immediately downshift to 2nd gear.

4) At vehicle speeds of 40-55 MPH, release accelerator pedal while moving gear selector to the "3" (third gear) position. The TCC should release, transaxle should downshift into 3rd gear, and engine braking should slow vehicle.

5) Move gear selector to the "D" (overdrive) position, and accelerate to 40-45 MPH. Release accelerator pedal while moving gear selector to the "2" (2nd gear) position. The TCC should release, transaxle should downshift to 2nd gear immediately, and engine braking should slow vehicle.

6) Move gear selector to the "D" (overdrive) position, and accelerate to 25 MPH. Release accelerator pedal while moving gear selector to "1" (1st gear) position. TCC should release, transaxle should downshift to 1st gear and engine braking should slow vehicle.

7) With gear selector in the "D" (overdrive) position, accelerate vehicle to overdrive gear with TCC applied. Release accelerator pedal, and lightly apply brakes. The TCC should release. Note speeds at which vehicle downshifts. *See Figs. 3-6.*

Gear Selector Position "3" (3rd Gear) – With vehicle stopped, move gear selector to "3" (3rd gear) position and steadily increase throttle pressure to accelerate vehicle. Note speeds at which vehicle shifts into 2nd and 3rd gears. *See Figs. 3-6.* Also note when TCC engages while in 3rd gear.

Gear Selector Position "2" (2nd Gear) – With vehicle stopped, move gear selector to the "2" (2nd gear) position. Accelerate vehicle and note speed at which vehicle shifts from 1st gear to 2nd gear. Accelerate vehicle to 25 MPH. Transaxle should not shift into 3rd gear, and TCC should not engage.

Gear Selector Position "1" (1st Gear) – With vehicle stopped, move gear selector to the "1" (1st gear) position. Accelerate vehicle to 15 MPH. Transaxle should not upshift, and TCC should not engage.

HYDRAULIC PRESSURE TESTS

CAUTION: Parking and service brakes must be applied throughout hydraulic pressure test. Total time for testing with vehicle in any driving gear should not exceed 2 minutes.

1) Before performing hydraulic pressure tests, check fluid level and condition. Check manual control linkages for correct adjustment, and ensure engine is properly tuned.

2) Connect tachometer to engine, hand-held vacuum pump to vacuum modulator and pressure gauge to line pressure test port. *See Fig. 1.* Check line pressure at specified engine RPM. *See Fig. 7 or 8.*

NOTE: Hydraulic pressure is controlled by pump output and regulated by pressure regulator valve. Line pressure is boosted by reverse boost valve when selector is in "R" and "D1" positions. Line pressure should increase with throttle opening due to decrease in engine vacuum to vacuum modulator.

	RANGE	kPa	PSI
MINIMUM LINE @ 1250 R.P.M. 61 kPa (18 In. Hg.) Vacuum At Modulator	D4,D3,D2	510 - 586	74 - 85
	D1	1088 - 1171	158 - 170
	P,R,N	544 - 654	79 - 95
FULL LINE @ 1250 R.P.M. 0 kPa (0 In. Hg.) Vacuum At Modulator	D4,D3,D2	1137 - 1412	165 - 205
	D1	1088 - 1171	158 - 170
	P,R,N	1757 - 2170	255 - 315

92A12716   Courtesy of General Motors Corp.

Fig. 7: Line Pressure (1993)

ON-VEHICLE SERVICE

The following components can be serviced without removing transaxle from vehicle.

- Case Side Cover Pan
- Converter-To-Flexplate Bolts
- Cooler Lines
- Drive Axles
- Filler Pipe
- Final Drive
- Forward Servo
- Reverse Servo
- Scavenger Oil Scoop
- Shift Control Cable
- Solenoid
- Speed Sensor
- Thermal Element
- Transaxle Pan
- Transaxle Filter
- Vacuum Modulator
- Valve Body
- Wiring Harness
- 1-2 Servo
- 1-2 Or 3-4 Accumulator Assemblies
- 3rd & 4th Gear Pressure Switches (if equipped)

VALVE BODY

See OIL PUMP & VALVE BODY under TRANSAXLE DISASSEMBLY.

DRIVE AXLE SHAFTS

See appropriate AXLE SHAFTS article in AXLE SHAFTS & TRANSFER CASES.

OIL COOLER FLUSHING

1) If available, fill Line Flusher (J-35944) with solution, and install oil cooler and line flusher to top transaxle cooler line on transaxle. Follow manufacturer instructions to flush oil cooler and cooler lines.

2) If line flusher is not available, flush cooler and cooler lines with a mixture of clean solvent and water. Flush cooler in both directions until all old fluid and debris are removed. If necessary, replace plugged or damaged cooler and/or lines.

REMOVAL & INSTALLATION

See appropriate AUTOMATIC TRANSMISSION REMOVAL article in TRANSMISSION SERVICING.

Minimum Line Pressure Check – Start engine, and apply 18 in. Hg to vacuum modulator. Record line pressure readings in all gear selector positions with engine running at specified RPM, and compare recorded pressures to specifications. *See Fig. 7 or 8.* If recorded pressure is incorrect, see HIGH OR LOW LINE PRESSURE under TROUBLE SHOOTING.

Full Line Pressure – Release vacuum applied to vacuum modulator. Record line pressure readings in all gear selector positions with engine running at specified engine RPM. Compare recorded pressures to specifications. *See Fig. 7 or 8.* If pressure recorded is incorrect, see HIGH OR LOW LINE PRESSURE under TROUBLE SHOOTING.

TORQUE CONVERTER

INSPECTION

Torque converter must be replaced for any of the following reasons.
- Damage To Pump Assembly
- Metal Particles Present In Oil
- Leaks In Hub Weld Area
- Crankshaft Pilot Broken Or Damaged
- Hub Scored Or Damaged
- Stator Failure
- Torque Converter Imbalance
- Engine Coolant Contamination
- Excessive End Play

END PLAY CHECK

Mount Torque Converter End Play Fixture (J-35138) and Dial Gauge (J-8001) on stand to check end play. End play should be 0-.020" (0-0.50 mm). *See Fig. 9.*

TRANSAXLE DISASSEMBLY

REAR TRANSAXLE ASSEMBLY

Thoroughly clean transaxle exterior. Drain fluid, and remove torque converter. Place transaxle in holding fixture. Remove speed sensor and rear extension housing.

LOWER TRANSAXLE ASSEMBLY

Remove bottom oil pan, oil filter, accumulator cover with 2-1 servo feed and return pipes. Remove modulator and modulator valve. Check modulator with known good modulator and Tester (36619). If necessary, replace modulator. Remove all retainers, gaskets, pipes and accumulator piston assemblies from bores (DO NOT interchange springs). *See Fig. 10.*

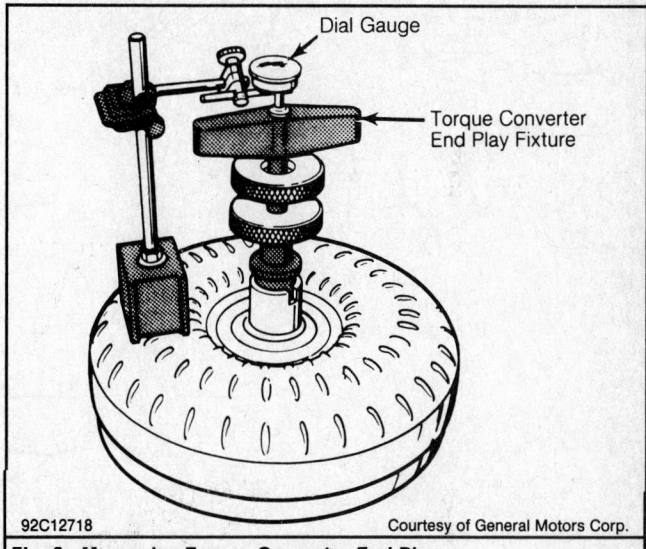

92C12718   Courtesy of General Motors Corp.

Fig. 9: Measuring Torque Converter End Play

	RANGE	MODELS	kPa	PSI
MINIMUM LINE PRESSURE **1250 RPM** **61 kPa (18" Hg) VACUUM**	D4, D3, D2	KUW, PMW, WAW, YMW, YZW	422-475	61-69
		AJW, ATW, BLW, CLW, CMW, CWW, KHW, PAW, PBW, PFW, PHW, WBW, WSW, YCW	512-592	74-86
		AFW	512-596	74-86
	D1	AFW, ATW, BLW, CMW, CWW, PBW, PFW	921-1333	134-193
		KUW, PMW, WAW, YMW, YZW	998-1276	145-185
		AJW, CLW, KHW, PAW, PHW, WBW, WSW, YCW	1005-1289	146-187
	P, R, N	KUW, PMW, WAW, YMW, YZW	423-536	61-78
		ATW, BLW, PFW	460-666	67-97
		AFW, CMW, CWW, PBW	512-666	74-97
		AJW, CLW, KHW, PAW, PHW, WBW, WSW, YCW	542-696	79-101
FULL LINE PRESSURE **1250 RPM** **0 kPa (0" Hg) VACUUM**	D4, D3, D2	AFW, ATW, BLW, CMW, CWW, PBW, PFW	1148-1400	166-203
		KUW, PMW, WAW, YMW, YZW	1150-1390	167-202
		AJW, CLW, KHW, PAW, PHW, WBW, WSW, YCW	1153-1400	167-203
	D1	AFW, ATW, BLW, CMW, CWW, PBW, PFW	921-1333	134-193
		KUW, PMW, WAW, YMW, YZW	998-1276	145-185
		AJW, CLW, KHW, PAW, PHW, WBW, WSW, YCW	1005-1289	146-187
	P, R, N	AJW, CLW, KHW, PAW, PHW, WBW, WSW, YCW	1540-1869	223-271
		KUW, PMW, WAW, YMW, YZW	1570-1898	228-275
		AFW, ATW, BLW, CMW, CWW, PBW, PFW	1774-2164	257-314

94B38464   Courtesy of General Motors Corp.

Fig. 8: Line Pressure Specification Chart (1994)

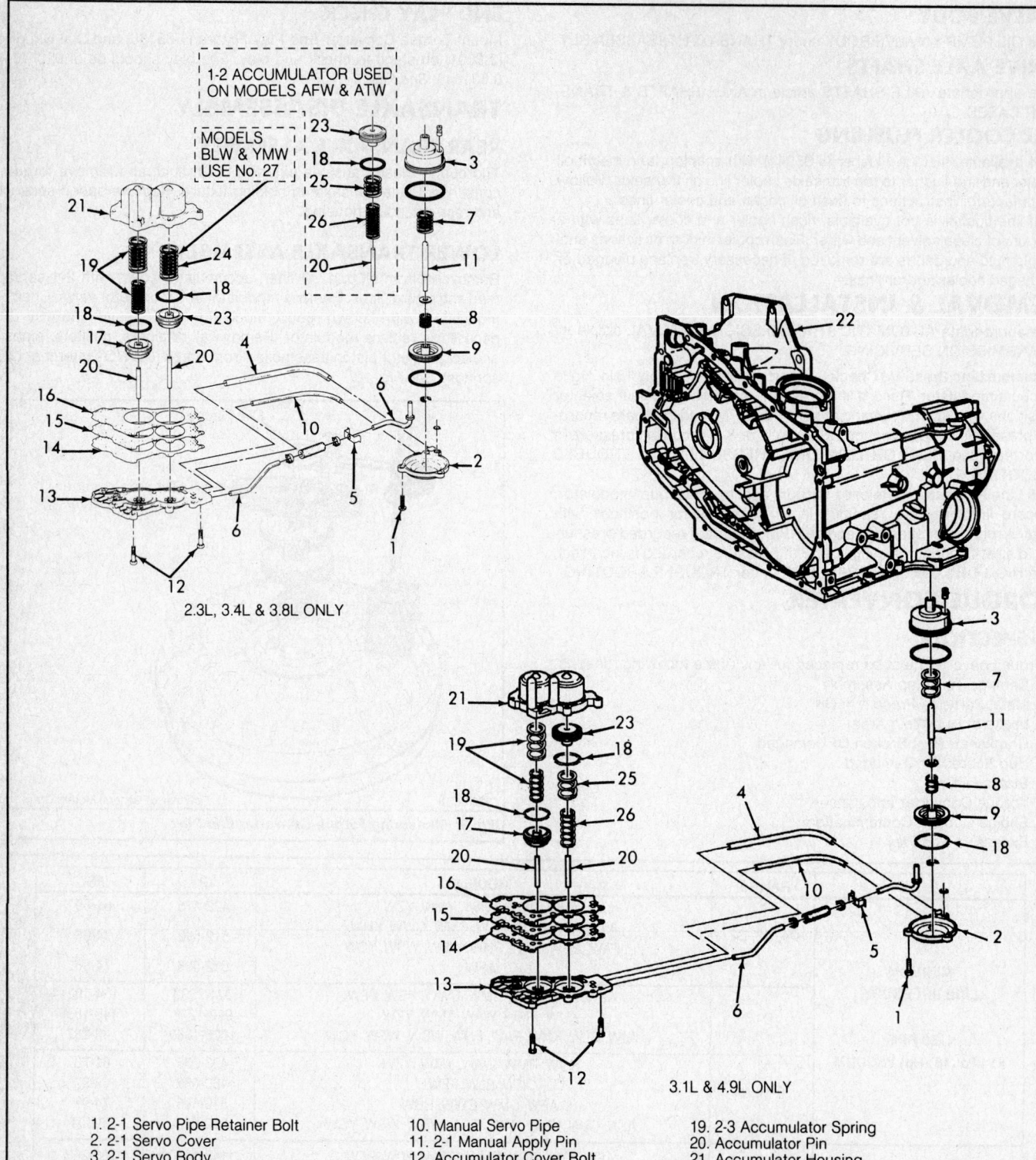

2.3L, 3.4L & 3.8L ONLY

3.1L & 4.9L ONLY

1-2 ACCUMULATOR USED ON MODELS AFW & ATW

MODELS BLW & YMW USE No. 27

1. 2-1 Servo Pipe Retainer Bolt
2. 2-1 Servo Cover
3. 2-1 Servo Body
4. Forward Servo Pipe
5. Lube Oil Retainer Clip
6. Lube Oil Pipe
7. 2-1 Manual Return Spring
8. 2-1 Manual Cushion Spring
9. 2-1 Manual Servo Piston

10. Manual Servo Pipe
11. 2-1 Manual Apply Pin
12. Accumulator Cover Bolt
13. Accumulator Cover
14. Gasket
15. Spacer Plate
16. Gasket
17. 2-3 Accumulator Piston
18. Piston Seal

19. 2-3 Accumulator Spring
20. Accumulator Pin
21. Accumulator Housing
22. Transaxle
23. 1-2 Accumulator Piston
24. 1-2 Accumulator Spring
25. 1-2 Accumulator Outer Spring
26. 1-2 Accumulator Inner Spring

94B38480

Fig. 10: Exploded View Of Lower Transaxle Assembly

SERVO ASSEMBLIES

1) Apply inward pressure to top of reverse servo cover, and remove cover retaining ring. Remove reverse servo cover and reverse servo assembly from case. *See Fig. 11.*

2) Apply inward pressure to top of 1-2 servo cover, and remove servo cover retaining ring. Remove 1-2 servo cover and 1-2 servo assembly from case.

OIL PUMP & VALVE BODY

1) Remove side cover attaching bolts, nuts and washers. Remove side cover and gaskets. Disconnect wiring harness from pressure switches, solenoid and case connector. Remove wiring harness.

2) Remove linkage and bracket from valve body assembly. Remove pump assembly cover bolts to remove pump cover from valve body. *See Fig. 12.* Remove servo pipe retainer bolt and retainer plate. Remove remaining mounting bolts from valve body, and remove valve body from channel plate.

3) Remove oil dam from cavity above 4th clutch assembly. Remove 4 check balls between spacer plate and valve body. Remove 8 check balls between channel plate and spacer plate.

Labels (Fig. 11 upper):
Cover Retaining Ring
Reverse Servo Cover
Servo Cover "O" Ring
Snap Ring
Reverse Servo Piston
Servo Spring Retainer
Cushion Spring
Apply Pin
Return Spring

Labels (Fig. 11 lower):
Apply Pin
1-2 Servo Piston
Retainer Servo
Return Spring
Snap Ring
Cushion Spring
Servo Cover "O" Ring
1-2 Servo Cover
Servo Cover Retaining Ring

92G12720   Courtesy of General Motors Corp.

Fig. 11: Exploded View Of Servo Assemblies

CHANNEL PLATE ASSEMBLY & 4TH CLUTCH

1) Disconnect manual valve link from manual valve, and pull spring back. Place detent lever in Park position for clip removal. Remove channel plate attaching bolts. Remove channel plate and channel plate gaskets.

2) Remove oil pump drive shaft. Remove input clutch accumulator piston assembly and converter clutch accumulator piston assembly. Remove 4th clutch plates and apply plate. Remove 4th clutch hub thrust bearing. Remove 4th clutch hub and shaft. *See Fig. 39.*

FINAL DRIVE ASSEMBLY

1) Rotate output shaft until "C" ring opening is visible from beneath lower tapered end of transaxle case. Using "C" Ring Remover/Installer (J-34757), push "C" ring partially off shaft, then rotate shaft and remove ring with needle-nose pliers. Ring can also be removed with 2 long thin screwdrivers.

2) Check final drive end play. See FINAL DRIVE ASSEMBLY under COMPONENT DISASSEMBLY & REASSEMBLY. *See Fig. 17.* Remove final drive assembly and selective thrust washer and bearing. Remove internal gear snap ring and internal gear from case.

DRIVE LINK ASSEMBLY

NOTE: See Fig. 36 for exploded view of all internal components (from drive link support to final drive assembly). See Fig. 37 for thrust washer and bearing locations. See Fig. 38 for lip seal locations.

1) Remove "O" ring from turbine shaft. *See Fig. 39.* Remove turbine shaft drive sprocket, driven sprocket and drive link chain together as an assembly. Note position of Copper-colored link on drive link chain; it should be installed facing up.

2) Remove drive sprocket and driven sprocket thrust washers from between sprockets and channel plate. Remove chain scavenging scoop and driven sprocket support with 2nd clutch thrust washer.

NOTE: If deflection of drive link chain exceeds 1 1/16", check drive link chain, sprockets and supports for wear; replace if necessary.

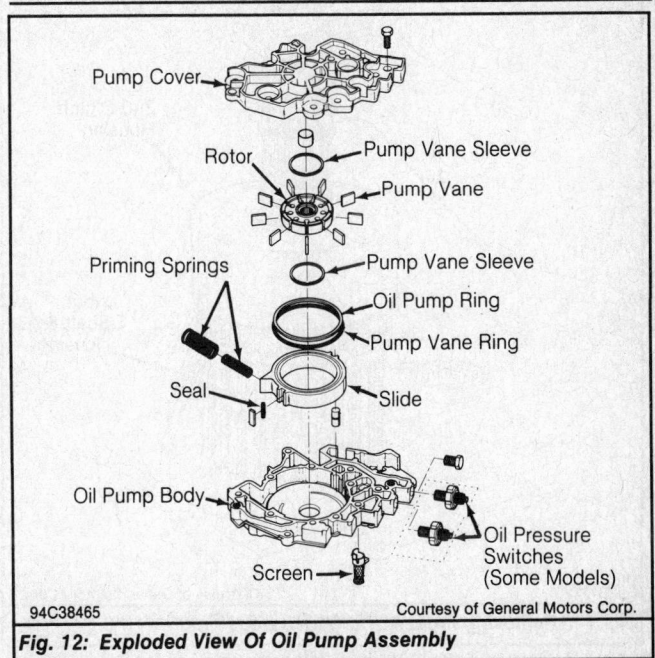

Labels (Fig. 12):
Pump Cover
Rotor
Pump Vane Sleeve
Pump Vane
Priming Springs
Pump Vane Sleeve
Oil Pump Ring
Pump Vane Ring
Seal
Slide
Oil Pump Body
Oil Pressure Switches (Some Models)
Screen

94C38465   Courtesy of General Motors Corp.

Fig. 12: Exploded View Of Oil Pump Assembly

INPUT & 2ND CLUTCH ASSEMBLIES

1) Using Final Drive/Clutch Assembly Remover/Installer (J-33381), remove 2nd clutch and input shaft clutch housings as an assembly. *See Fig. 14.* Remove reverse band if it did not come out with 2nd clutch housing.

2) Remove thrust washers. Install input housing and shaft assembly back in transaxle. Install Loading Tool (J-26958) to transaxle case. *See Fig. 13.*

3) Measure input shaft clutch housing end play using End Play Gauge (J-33386). Record measurements for proper end play clearances during reassembly. *See Fig. 13.*

4) Fit proper selective thrust washer and measure clearance. Record measurement, and set aside proper selective washer for reassembly. Remove 2nd clutch and reverse band assembly as described previously in step 1).

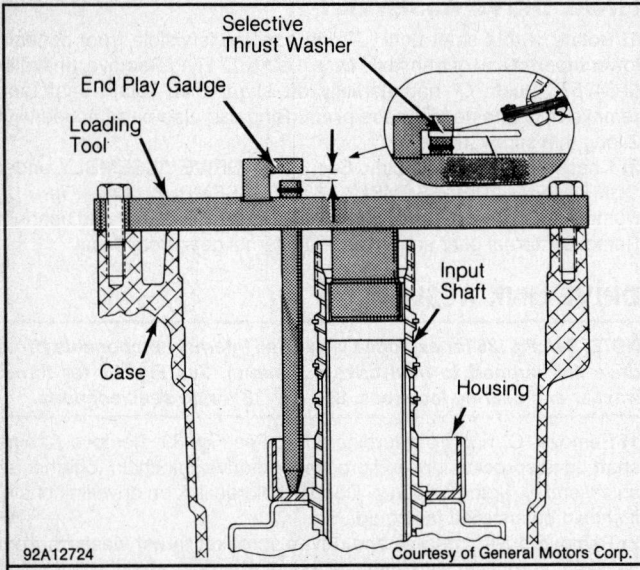

Fig. 13: Checking Input Clutch Housing End Play

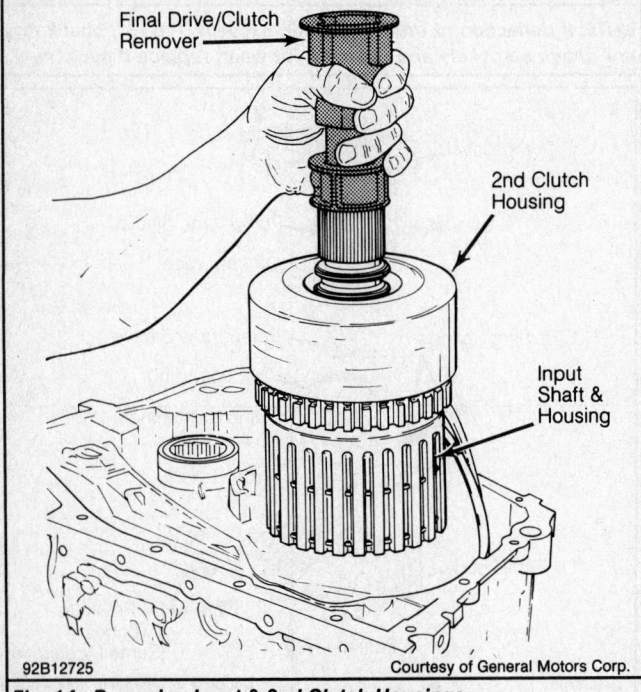

Fig. 14: Removing Input & 2nd Clutch Housings

INPUT SPRAG, SUN GEARS & 3RD ROLLER CLUTCH ASSEMBLIES

Remove input clutch sprag assembly, 3rd roller clutch assembly and input sun gear. Remove reverse band. Remove reverse reaction drum input carrier assembly and thrust bearing. Remove reaction carrier, reaction sun gear/drum assembly and 1-2 band. Remove reaction sun gear thrust bearing and final drive output shaft. Remove forward band. DO NOT clean assemblies in solvent.

FINAL DRIVE ASSEMBLY

Disassembly & Inspection – 1) Inspect final drive internal gear for damaged teeth, worn bearing surfaces, broken parking pawl spring or damage to parking pawl. Inspect sun gear, thrust bearings, parking gear and governor drive gear for wear or damage.

2) Check final drive carrier pinion gears for excessive end play. Use a feeler gauge and measure end play between carrier and pinion gear thrust washer. End play should be .009-.025" (.24-.63 mm).

3) Using a pin punch, drive differential pinion shaft retainer pin from carrier. Remove pinion shaft, pinion and side gears, and thrust washers. *See Fig. 16.* Inspect all parts for damage or abnormal wear. Inspect final drive sun gear shaft for damaged splines or journals.

COMPONENT DISASSEMBLY & REASSEMBLY

TRANSAXLE CASE

Cleaning & Inspection – Clean transaxle case thoroughly with solvent, and then air dry. Inspect transaxle case for damage to band lugs, snap ring grooves and drive sprocket bearings. Check for interconnected or damaged oil passages and servo bores. Inspect case for stripped threads in bolt holes or casting porosity. Repair or replace case if necessary.

Drive Sprocket Support – 1) If removal of drive sprocket bearing from case is necessary, use Bearing Puller (J-26941) and Slide Hammer (J6125-1B). *See Fig. 15.* Remove support bearing, and install new bearing with Bearing Installer (J-28677) and Driver Handle (J-8092).

2) If drive sprocket support replacement is necessary, remove attaching screws and remove support. Install new support, and tighten attaching screws to specifications. See TORQUE SPECIFICATIONS table at end of article.

NOTE: DO NOT remove these parts unless replacement is necessary.

Manual Shaft, Detent Lever & Actuator Rod – If manual shaft, detent lever or actuator rod removal is necessary, remove pin and lock nut from manual shaft. Remove actuator rod from detent lever. Remove retaining pin from case. Remove actuator rod assembly from case. Remove "O" ring from actuator rod guide.

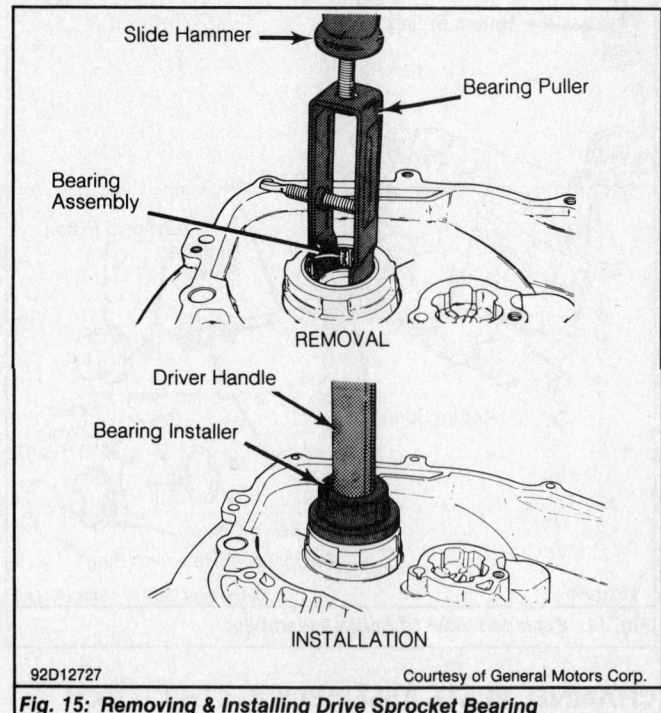

Fig. 15: Removing & Installing Drive Sprocket Bearing

Reassembly – 1) Assemble differential side gears and thrust washers into carrier. Using petroleum jelly, stick thrust washers onto pinion gears. Assemble pinion gears and washers into carrier.

2) Slide pinion shaft through both pinion gears for alignment, then remove shaft. Rotate pinion gears into position, then install pinion shaft. Tap retaining pin into position using a plastic hammer.

3) Tap speed sensor drive gear (if removed) into position using soft mallet. Install sun gear with stepped side facing out. Assemble parking gear on sun gear.

4) Inspect carrier-to-case selective thrust washer for damage. Install thrust washer onto carrier hub. Install thrust bearing onto thrust washer and retain with petroleum jelly.

5) Assemble thrust bearing on internal gear. Install internal gear to case and install snap ring. Move detent lever out of "P" position. Install final drive assembly into case.

6) To measure final drive end play, install dial indicator so pointer contacts Adapter (J-26958-10). *See Fig. 17.* Lift speed sensor drive gear with Snap Ring Remover (J-28585), and read dial indicator.

7) Correct end play is .005-.025" (.20-.62 mm). If necessary, adjust end play with selective carrier-to-case thrust washer. See CARRIER-TO-CASE SELECTIVE THRUST WASHER SIZES table.

CARRIER-TO-CASE SELECTIVE THRUST WASHER SIZES

Washer Identification	Thickness In. (mm)
1	.059-.062 (1.5-1.6)
2	.062-.066 (1.6-1.7)
3	.066-.070 (1.7-1.8)
4	.070-.074 (1.8-1.9)
5	.074-.078 (1.9-2.0)
6	.078-.082 (2.0-2.1)

SUN GEAR SHAFT

Inspection & Reassembly – Inspect final drive sun gear shaft for damaged splines or journals. *See Fig. 36.* Install thrust bearing. Install final drive sun gear shaft into final drive, ensuring splines engage with parking gear and sun gear.

NOTE: The 1-2 band assembly is presoaked in a friction solution. DO NOT wash band in solvent.

1-2 & FORWARD BANDS

Inspection – DO NOT wash 1-2 band in solvent. Inspect 1-2 and forward band assembly for heat damage, lining cracks and separation. Check band stop for damage and replace if necessary.

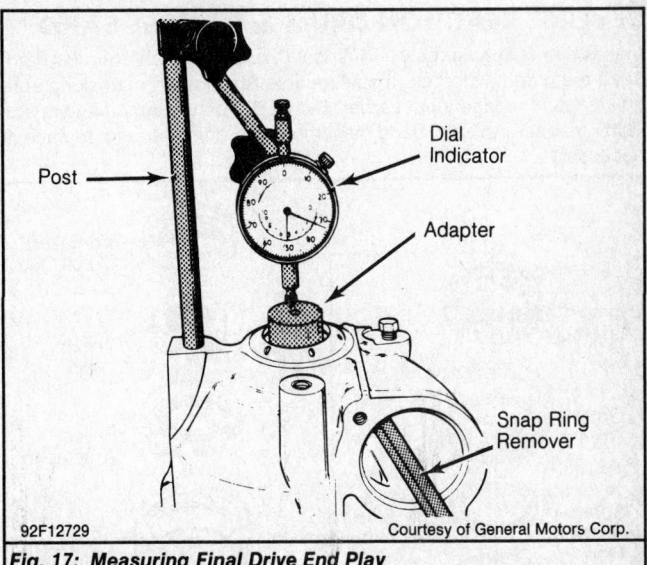

92F12729   Courtesy of General Motors Corp.

Fig. 17: Measuring Final Drive End Play

REACTION CARRIER & DRUM

Cleaning & Inspection – Inspect reaction carrier and reaction drum for damaged teeth, scoring or warpage. Check thrust bearing for damage. Using a feeler gauge, check reaction carrier pinion gear end play. End play should be .009-.030" (.23-.77 mm). Check for damage to reaction carrier internal gear.

Reassembly – 1) Install reaction sun gear-to-final drive internal gear thrust bearing, positioning inner race against internal gear. Assemble reaction sun gear and drum assembly onto final drive internal gear.

2) Install reaction carrier-to-sun gear thrust bearing, positioning inner race against reaction carrier. Retain bearing with petroleum jelly. Install reaction carrier, rotating carrier until pinions engage sun gear.

INPUT CARRIER ASSEMBLY

Inspection – Check input carrier pinion gears for proper end play. Pinion gear end play should be .009-.030" (.23-.77 mm). Inspect internal gear and pinion gears for worn or damaged teeth, and ensure pinions rotate freely. Inspect thrust bearing for damage (thrust bearing cannot be removed from carrier).

Reassembly – Install thrust bearing with inside race against carrier. Retain thrust bearing with petroleum jelly. Install input carrier into case, and rotate into position.

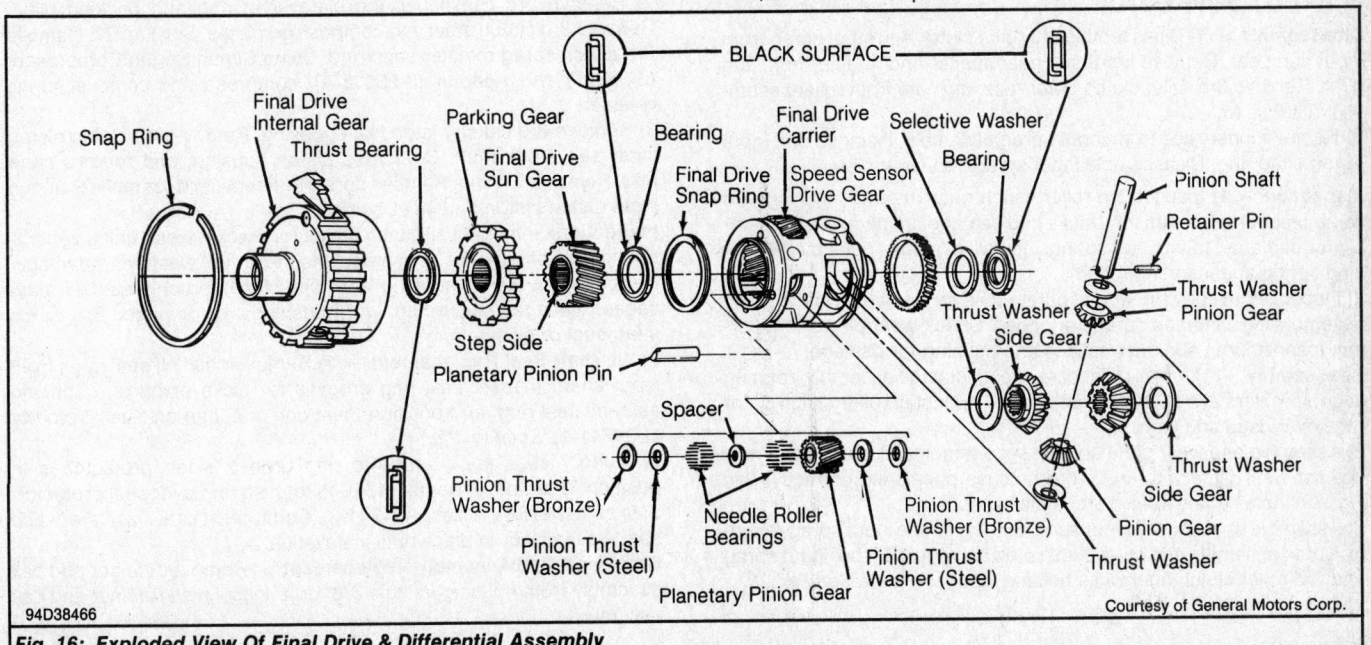

94D38466   Courtesy of General Motors Corp.

Fig. 16: Exploded View Of Final Drive & Differential Assembly

REVERSE REACTION DRUM & REVERSE BAND

Inspection & Reassembly – Inspect reverse reaction drum for damaged teeth and distortion. Install reverse reaction drum, making sure spline teeth engage input carrier. DO NOT wash reverse band in solvent. Inspect reverse band assembly for damage and replace if necessary.

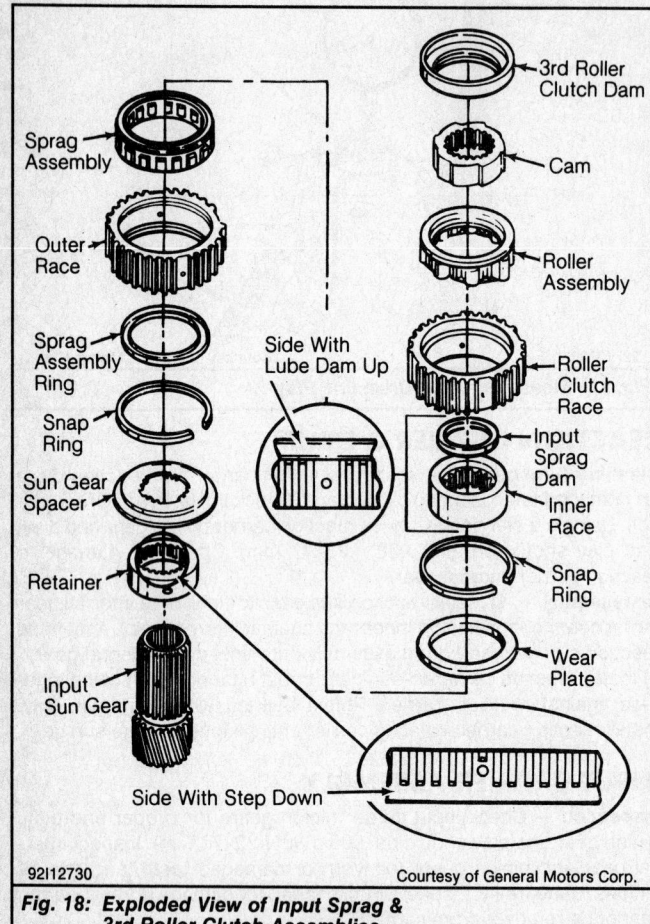

92I12730   Courtesy of General Motors Corp.

Fig. 18: Exploded View of Input Sprag & 3rd Roller Clutch Assemblies

3RD ROLLER CLUTCH, INPUT SPRAG & INPUT SUN GEAR

Disassembly – 1) Disassemble 3rd roller clutch and input sprag from input sun gear. Remove input sun gear spacer and retainer from sun gear. Remove 3rd roller clutch outer race and cam from roller assembly. *See Fig. 18.*

2) Remove inner race from input sprag assembly. Remove one input sprag snap ring. Disassemble input sprag and wear plate.

Inspection – 1) Inspect 3rd roller clutch outer race for scoring and wear. Inspect roller cam for cracks and damage. Inspect roller assembly for damaged rollers and springs. Install any loose roller by depressing spring and inserting roller.

2) Inspect input sprag inner and outer races for damage. Check sprag assembly for damaged sprags or cages. Check wear plates for scoring. Inspect input sun gear splines and bushing for damage.

Reassembly – 1) Install roller cam into roller cage assembly, rotating cage so rollers are at lowest ramp position. Install roller clutch outer race over cage and cam.

2) Assemble one wear plate against snap ring. Install sprag assembly against wear plate with cross bar notches positioned correctly. *See Fig. 19.* Install other wear plate. Install snap ring.

3) Assemble spacer onto input sun gear. Assemble input sprag retainer, sprag assembly and roller clutch onto sun gear. Ensure input sprag and 3rd roller clutch hold while holding input sun gear. *See Fig. 20.*

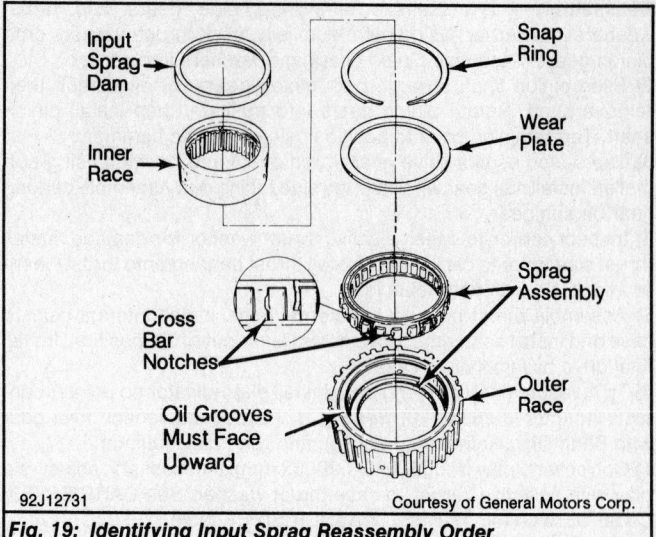

92J12731   Courtesy of General Motors Corp.

Fig. 19: Identifying Input Sprag Reassembly Order

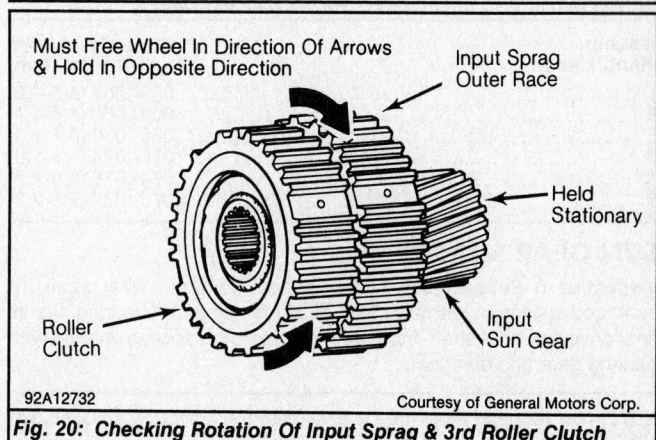

92A12732   Courtesy of General Motors Corp.

Fig. 20: Checking Rotation Of Input Sprag & 3rd Roller Clutch

INPUT CLUTCH ASSEMBLY

Disassembly – 1) Remove input shaft thrust washer and input clutch backing plate snap ring. Remove input clutch backing plate. Remove input clutch steel and composition plates. Remove input clutch apply plate.

2) Remove 3rd clutch backing plate snap ring and backing plate. Remove 3rd clutch steel and composition plates. *See Fig. 21.* Remove 3rd clutch sprag retainer snap ring. Using Clutch Spring Compressor (J-23327) and Adapter (J-25018-A), compress and remove spring retainer.

3) Remove 3rd clutch piston from housing. Remove 3rd clutch piston inner seal from shaft. Compress piston housing, and remove snap ring. Remove "O" ring. Remove spring and retainer assembly. Remove input clutch piston and inner seal.

Inspection – Inspect all clutch plates for cracks, wear, lining separation, pits or other signs of damage. Inspect thrust washer for damage. Inspect input clutch housing and shaft for interconnected oil passages, damaged clutch hub, worn bushings, or damaged 3rd clutch shaft seal or oil seal rings.

Input Shaft Seal Replacement – 1) Remove solid oil seal rings from input shaft. Inspect seal ring grooves for nicks or burrs. Lubricate each oil seal ring, and position them one at a time on Seal Protector (J-34741-1). *See Fig. 22.*

2) Quickly slide each seal into ring groove when protector is in position. Use Seal Driver (J-34741-2) to push ring over seal protector. Size seal with Seal Sizer (J-34741-3). Gently twist seal sizer over each seal. Leave sizer in place until installation.

Retainer & Ball Assembly Replacement – Remove retainer and ball assembly from housing using a 3/8" drift. Install new retainer and ball assembly.

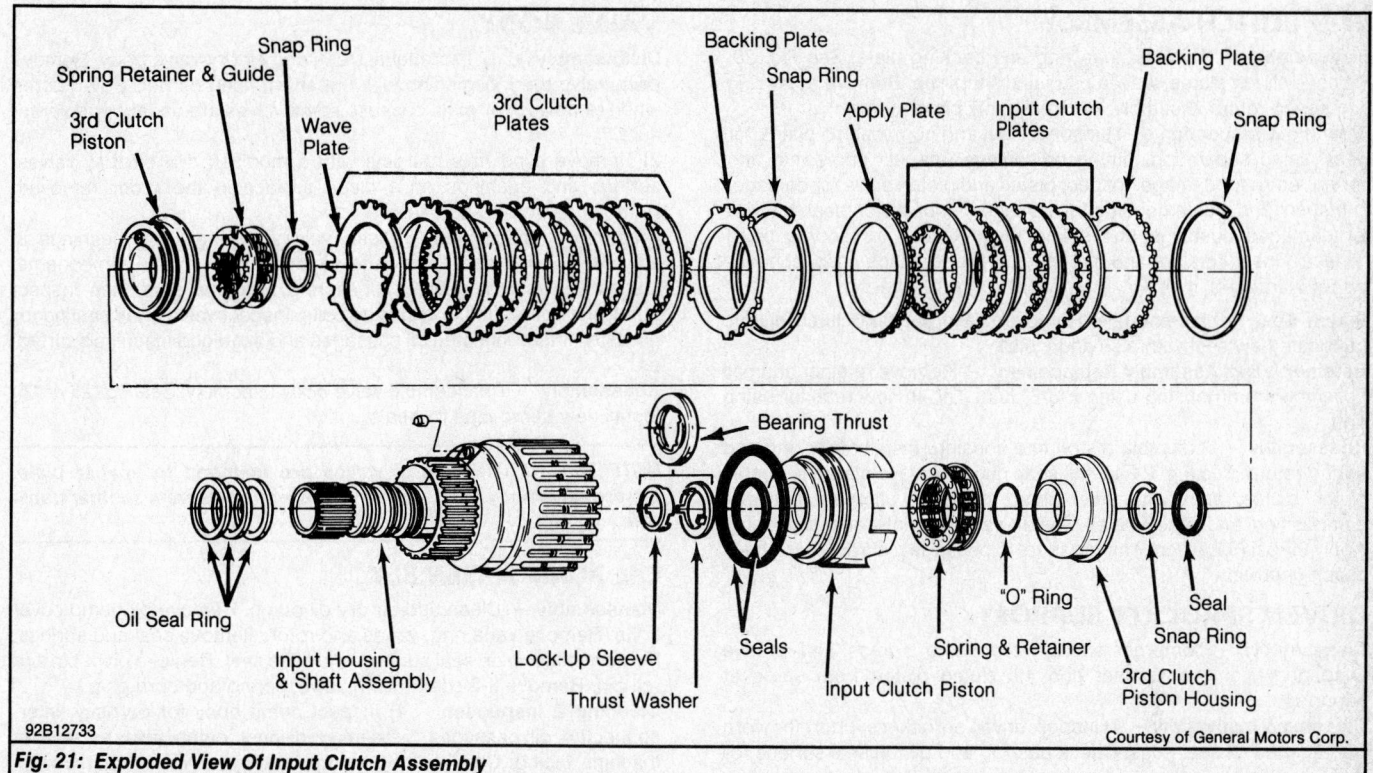

Fig. 21: *Exploded View Of Input Clutch Assembly*

Courtesy of General Motors Corp.

Piston Seal Replacement – Remove seals from input clutch piston or 3rd clutch piston. Lubricate new seals with ATF, and install seals.

Reassembly – **1)** Lubricate input clutch piston inner seal with ATF, and install seal using Seal Protector (J-37361). Assemble input piston into input housing. Assemble "O" ring seal onto input shaft.

2) Install spring retainer and guide in piston. *See Fig. 21.* Install 3rd clutch piston housing into input housing. Using spring compressor, compress 3rd clutch housing, and install snap ring.

3) Install 3rd clutch inner seal. Install 3rd clutch piston into housing. Compress 3rd clutch spring retainer, and install snap ring.

4) Install wave plate. Assemble 3rd clutch plates; start with steel plate, and then alternate between composition and steel plates. Install 3rd clutch backing plate with stepped side facing up. Install snap ring.

5) Assemble input clutch plates; start with composition plate, and then alternate between steel and composition plates. Install input clutch backing plate with identification mark facing up.

6) Install snap ring. Apply air pressure to oil passages in input shaft, and check for proper operation of clutch. Air pressure must not exceed 90 psi (6.2 kg/cm²).

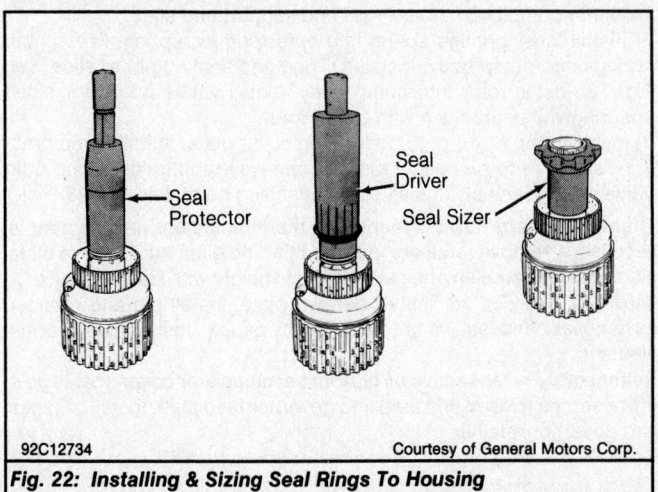

Fig. 22: *Installing & Sizing Seal Rings To Housing*

Courtesy of General Motors Corp.

Fig. 23: *Exploded View Of 2nd Clutch Housing*

Courtesy of General Motors Corp.

2ND CLUTCH ASSEMBLY

Disassembly – Remove snap ring and backing plate. *See Fig. 23.* Remove clutch plates, waved plate and snap ring. Remove apply ring and spring return assembly. Remove apply piston.

Cleaning & Inspection – 1) Inspect steel and composition plates for wear, lining separation, pitting or damage. Inspect apply ring and spring return for damage. Inspect piston and piston seals for damage.
2) Inspect 2nd clutch housing for damaged inner piston seal. Inspect for damaged bushings and spline teeth. Check for scored band surface. Check retainer and ball assembly for damage. Inspect housing for warpage.

Piston Seal Replacement – Remove seal from 2nd clutch piston. Lubricate new seal with ATF and install.

Retainer & Ball Assembly Replacement – Remove retainer and ball assembly from housing using a 3/8" drift. Tap in new retainer using drift.

Reassembly – Assemble piston into housing. Install apply ring and spring return. *See Fig. 24.* Install snap ring and wave plate. Assemble clutch plates; start with steel plate, and then alternate between composition and steel plates. Install backing plate and snap ring. Apply 90-psi (6.2 kg/cm²) air pressure to passage marked "2" to check clutch operation.

DRIVEN SPROCKET SUPPORT

Disassembly – Compress spring return using a press, and remove snap ring. Remove retainer and 4th clutch piston from sprocket support.

Cleaning & Inspection – 1) Inspect driven sprocket support for worn or damaged oil seal rings. Check bushing and piston seal surface for damage. Check for blocked or interconnected oil passages and cup plug.
2) Check chain scavenging scoop and baffle for cracks. Inspect piston, seals and thrust washer for damage. Check spring retainer for distorted springs. Inspect driven sprocket bearing for damage.

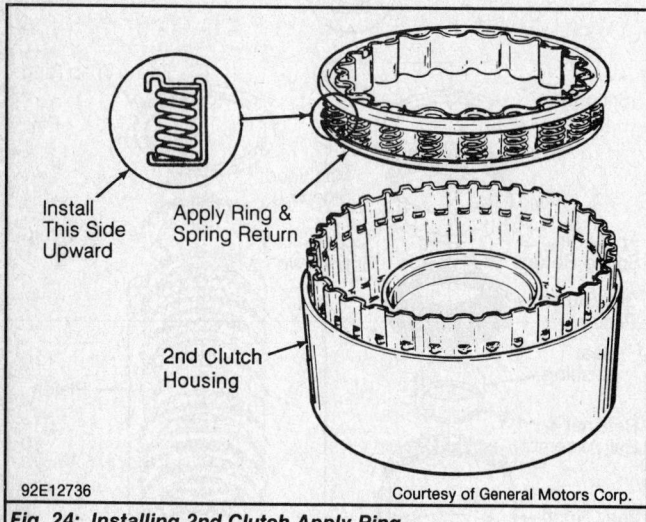

Install This Side Upward

Apply Ring & Spring Return

2nd Clutch Housing

92E12736

Courtesy of General Motors Corp.

Fig. 24: Installing 2nd Clutch Apply Ring

OUTPUT SHAFT

Inspection – Inspect output snap ring groove, splines, journal and bearings for damage. Replace if necessary.

DRIVE LINK ASSEMBLY & SPROCKETS

Cleaning & Inspection – Inspect drive and driven sprockets for damaged or chipped teeth. Check drive link chain for deflection greater than 1 1/16". Replace drive link chain if too much wear is present. Check sprockets for damaged bearing surfaces or splines. Check thrust washers and drive link for excessive wear or damage. Inspect 4th clutch shaft and turbine shaft for damaged bushings, splines or seals. Replace if necessary.

VALVE BODY

Disassembly – 1) Thoroughly clean and air dry valve body. Remove each valve train, beginning with upper left hand corner. Cover bores when removing roll pins, because some valves are under spring pressure.
2) Remove blind hole roll pins with a modified drill bit. Lay valves, springs and bushings on a clean surface in the order removed. Remove servo pipe lip seals.

Cleaning & Inspection – Clean valves, springs and bushings in solvent. NEVER use shop rags to clean valve body components. Inspect valves and bushings for scoring, nicks and scratches. Inspect springs for damaged or distorted coils. Inspect valve body casting for porosity, interconnected oil passages and damaged machined surfaces.

Reassembly – Reassemble valve body assembly. *See Fig. 25 or 26.* Install new servo pipe lip seals.

NOTE: The 3-2 line control valves are matched to spacer plate. Ensure valve body parts are not mixed with parts from another transaxle.

OIL PUMP ASSEMBLY

Disassembly – Clean and air dry oil pump. Remove oil pump cover bolts. Remove vane ring, vanes and rotor. Remove seal and springs. Remove slide, slide seal support and slide seal. Remove pivot pin and roll pin. Remove 3-2 coast-down valve, spring and bore plug.

Cleaning & Inspection – 1) Inspect pump body for porosity, interconnected oil passages, or damaged inner pump area surface or machine facing. Check slide, springs, rotor and vanes for damage. Inspect slide seal, slide support and seals for damage.
2) Measure undamaged area of rotor, vane or slide to check for proper size. See OIL PUMP COMPONENT THICKNESS CHART table. Ensure replacement parts are matched for exact fit. *See Fig. 27.*

NOTE: Oil pump components are matched sets. DO NOT mix old and new parts.

OIL PUMP COMPONENT THICKNESS CHART

Component	In. (mm)
Pump Rotor	.7068-.7072 (17.953-17.963)
	.7072-.7076 (17.963-17.973)
	.7076-.7080 (17.973-17.983)
Pump Slide	.7080-.7084 (17.983-17.993)
	.7084-.7088 (17.993-18.003)
	.7088-.7092 (18.003-18.013)
Pump Vane	.7064-.7071 (17.943-17.961)
	.7071-.7078 (17.961-17.979)
	.7078-.7085 (17.979-17.997)

Reassembly – 1) Install vane ring onto pump pocket. Install pump slide into pump body. Install seal and support into slide.
2) Install inner priming spring into outer priming spring. Press both springs into pump body. Install "O" ring and seal ring onto slide. *See Fig. 12.* Install rotor into pump body. Install vanes into rotor slots, ensuring vanes are flush with top of rotor.
3) Install pump cover onto body using cover bolts. Install pump pressure screen into pump (screen has one-way tab). Install pump onto valve body assembly. Install pump attaching bolts. *See Fig. 33.*

Thermo Element Replacement – If thermo element replacement is necessary, remove retainers, pins and thermo element. Remove plate element. For new element, set thermo pin height with Height Gauge (J-34094-A). *See Fig. 28.* Install element plate. Install pin and retainer assemblies, and set height with height gauge. Install new thermo element.

Reassembly – Assemble oil pipe into accumulator cover. Install governor screen (closed end first) into governor feed pipe. Install oil pipes into governor retainer.

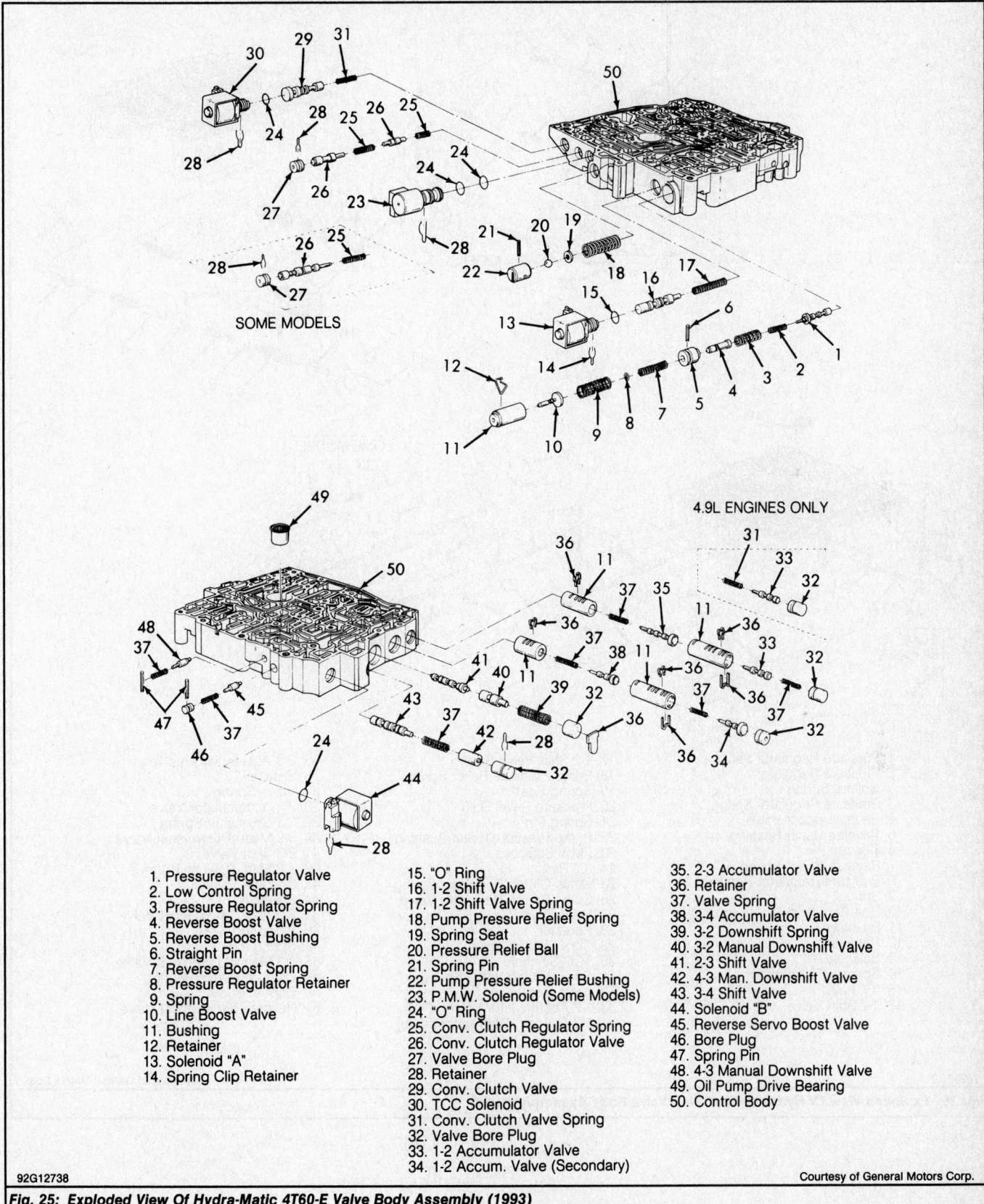

Fig. 25: Exploded View Of Hydra-Matic 4T60-E Valve Body Assembly (1993)

92G12738

1. Pressure Regulator Valve
2. Low Control Spring
3. Pressure Regulator Spring
4. Reverse Boost Valve
5. Reverse Boost Bushing
6. Straight Pin
7. Reverse Boost Spring
8. Pressure Regulator Retainer
9. Spring
10. Line Boost Valve
11. Bushing
12. Retainer
13. Solenoid "A"
14. Spring Clip Retainer

15. "O" Ring
16. 1-2 Shift Valve
17. 1-2 Shift Valve Spring
18. Pump Pressure Relief Spring
19. Spring Seat
20. Pressure Relief Ball
21. Spring Pin
22. Pump Pressure Relief Bushing
23. P.M.W. Solenoid (Some Models)
24. "O" Ring
25. Conv. Clutch Regulator Spring
26. Conv. Clutch Regulator Valve
27. Valve Bore Plug
28. Retainer
29. Conv. Clutch Valve
30. TCC Solenoid
31. Conv. Clutch Valve Spring
32. Valve Bore Plug
33. 1-2 Accumulator Valve
34. 1-2 Accum. Valve (Secondary)

35. 2-3 Accumulator Valve
36. Retainer
37. Valve Spring
38. 3-4 Accumulator Valve
39. 3-2 Downshift Spring
40. 3-2 Manual Downshift Valve
41. 2-3 Shift Valve
42. 4-3 Man. Downshift Valve
43. 3-4 Shift Valve
44. Solenoid "B"
45. Reverse Servo Boost Valve
46. Bore Plug
47. Spring Pin
48. 4-3 Manual Downshift Valve
49. Oil Pump Drive Bearing
50. Control Body

AUTOMATIC TRANSMISSIONS
Hydra-Matic 4T60-E (Cont.)

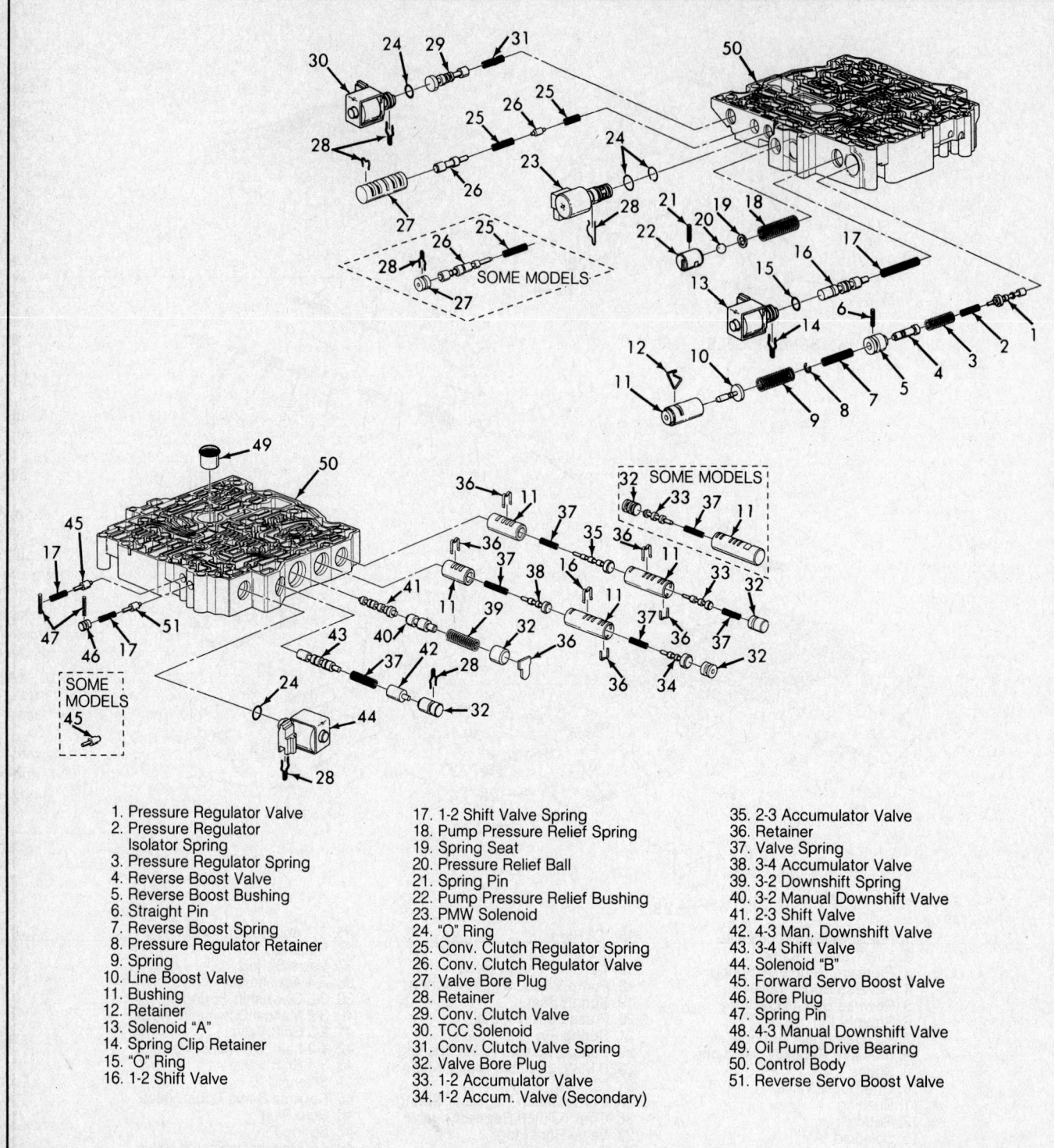

94E38467

Courtesy of General Motors Corp.

1. Pressure Regulator Valve
2. Pressure Regulator Isolator Spring
3. Pressure Regulator Spring
4. Reverse Boost Valve
5. Reverse Boost Bushing
6. Straight Pin
7. Reverse Boost Spring
8. Pressure Regulator Retainer
9. Spring
10. Line Boost Valve
11. Bushing
12. Retainer
13. Solenoid "A"
14. Spring Clip Retainer
15. "O" Ring
16. 1-2 Shift Valve

17. 1-2 Shift Valve Spring
18. Pump Pressure Relief Spring
19. Spring Seat
20. Pressure Relief Ball
21. Spring Pin
22. Pump Pressure Relief Bushing
23. PMW Solenoid
24. "O" Ring
25. Conv. Clutch Regulator Spring
26. Conv. Clutch Regulator Valve
27. Valve Bore Plug
28. Retainer
29. Conv. Clutch Valve
30. TCC Solenoid
31. Conv. Clutch Valve Spring
32. Valve Bore Plug
33. 1-2 Accumulator Valve
34. 1-2 Accum. Valve (Secondary)

35. 2-3 Accumulator Valve
36. Retainer
37. Valve Spring
38. 3-4 Accumulator Valve
39. 3-2 Downshift Spring
40. 3-2 Manual Downshift Valve
41. 2-3 Shift Valve
42. 4-3 Man. Downshift Valve
43. 3-4 Shift Valve
44. Solenoid "B"
45. Forward Servo Boost Valve
46. Bore Plug
47. Spring Pin
48. 4-3 Manual Downshift Valve
49. Oil Pump Drive Bearing
50. Control Body
51. Reverse Servo Boost Valve

Fig. 26: Exploded View Of Hydra-Matic 4T60-E Valve Body Assembly (1994)

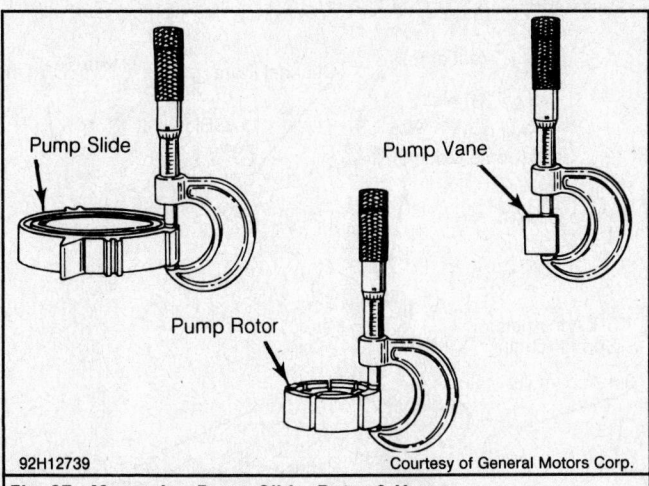

Fig. 27: Measuring Pump Slide, Rotor & Vanes

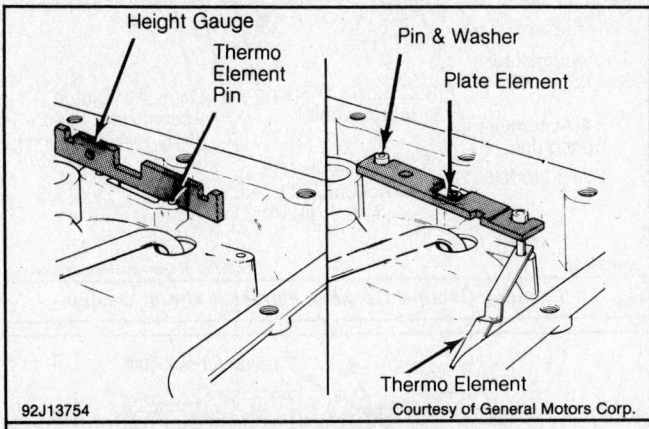

Fig. 28: Using Thermo Element Height Gauge

1-2 & REVERSE SERVOS

Inspection – Inspect servo pistons and seals for damage or cracks. DO NOT remove seals unless replacement is required. Inspect springs for damaged coils.

Reassembly – DO NOT interchange servo parts. Assemble spring retainer onto pin. 1-2 servo spring retainer step must face spring. Reverse servo wave spring must be installed between 2 spring retainers. Install cushion spring, servo piston and snap ring onto pin. *See Fig. 11.*

TRANSAXLE REASSEMBLY

NOTE: All selective snap ring and thrust washer measurements taken during disassembly must be rechecked at appropriate reassembly stage.

1) Install and ensure sun gear shaft, forward band, 1-2 band, reaction sun gear and reverse band drum are in place. Ensure 1-2 band anchor pins engage band, and 1-2 band assembly stop is in place.

2) Install reverse band, making sure anchor engages band. Recheck end play of final drive. See FINAL DRIVE ASSEMBLY under COMPONENT DISASSEMBLY & REASSEMBLY. Install thrust washer onto input shaft and hold it in position with petroleum jelly. Install sprag, roller clutch and input sun gear assembly into input clutch assembly. Clutch hubs must engage clutch plates.

3) Install input clutch roller clutch and sprag assemblies into case using Final Drive/Clutch Installer (J-33381). DO NOT install 2nd clutch housing, thrust bearing or thrust washer at this time.

4) Check input shaft end play. *See Fig. 13.* Install and tighten Aligner/Loader (J-26958-10). Install End Play Gauge (J-33386) and thrust washer. Using feeler gauge, check clearance between thrust washer and end play gauge. Clearance must be .000-.006" (.000-.152 mm). If

clearance is not as specified, use different thrust washer. See INPUT SHAFT THRUST WASHERS table.

INPUT SHAFT THRUST WASHERS

Washer Color	Thickness In. (mm)
Orange/Green	.114-.118 (2.90-3.00)
Orange/Black	.120-.124 (3.05-3.15)
Orange	.126-.130 (3.20-3.30)
White	.132-.136 (3.35-3.45)
Blue	.138-.142 (3.50-3.60)
Pink	.144-.148 (3.65-3.75)
Brown	.150-.154 (3.80-3.90)
Green	.155-.159 (3.95-4.05)
Black	.161-.165 (4.10-4.20)
Purple	.167-.171 (4.25-4.35)
Purple/White	.173-.177 (4.40-4.50)
Purple/Blue	.179-.183 (4.55-4.65)
Purple/Pink	.185-.189 (4.70-4.80)
Purple/Brown	.191-.195 (4.85-4.95)
Purple/Green	.197-.201 (5.00-5.10)

5) Install reverse reaction plate and thrust washer. Install thrust bearing with large race facing down. Install 2nd clutch assembly onto input clutch assembly. Clutch plates must engage input clutch hub, and clutch housing must engage reverse reaction drum splines.

6) Install reverse band into case, locating band on anchor pins. Install thrust washer to driven sprocket support, and hold washer in position with petroleum jelly. Install driven sprocket support into case, ensuring support lube hole aligns with hole in bottom of case.

7) If removed, install driven sprocket support assembly. Install output shaft into case. Install "C" ring onto output shaft through bottom of case. Push "C" ring onto output shaft.

8) Coat Seal Installer (J-29569-1 and J-29829-1) with petroleum jelly, and place seal installer over turbine shaft. Slide oil ring seals into position. Using Seal Sizer (J-29569-2 and J-29829-1), size seals by gently twisting sizer over seal.

9) Install thrust washer onto drive sprocket, and hold washer in position with petroleum jelly. Install sprockets and drive link onto case. Ensure colored link faces upward.

10) Install thrust washer onto driven sprocket and retain with petroleum jelly. Insert 4th clutch shaft through driven sprocket, and install clutch apply plate with identification mark facing down. Install 4th clutch plates. *See Fig. 29.*

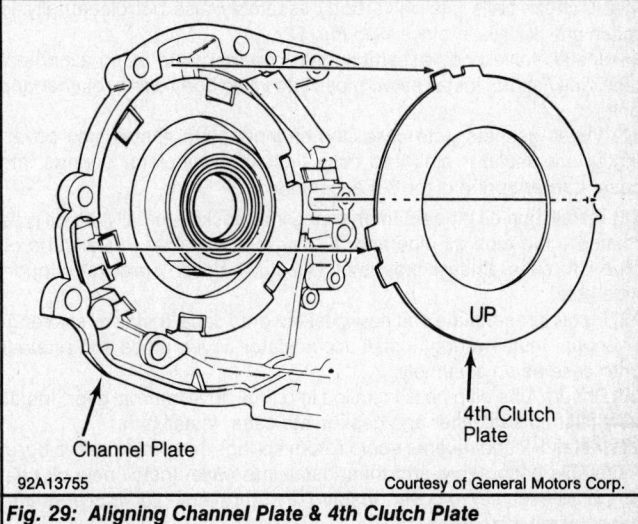

Fig. 29: Aligning Channel Plate & 4th Clutch Plate

11) If necessary, pry out axle seal, and tap new seal into place. Install pistons and pins into channel plate. Install springs into case. Install channel plate gaskets and modulator port gasket. Install thrust washer onto channel plate.

12) Install channel plate onto case. Channel plate lugs must align with tangs on 4th clutch plates and apply plate. *See Fig. 29.* Install sleeve into channel plate. Install oil reservoir baffle, detent spring and roller. Install channel plate gaskets.

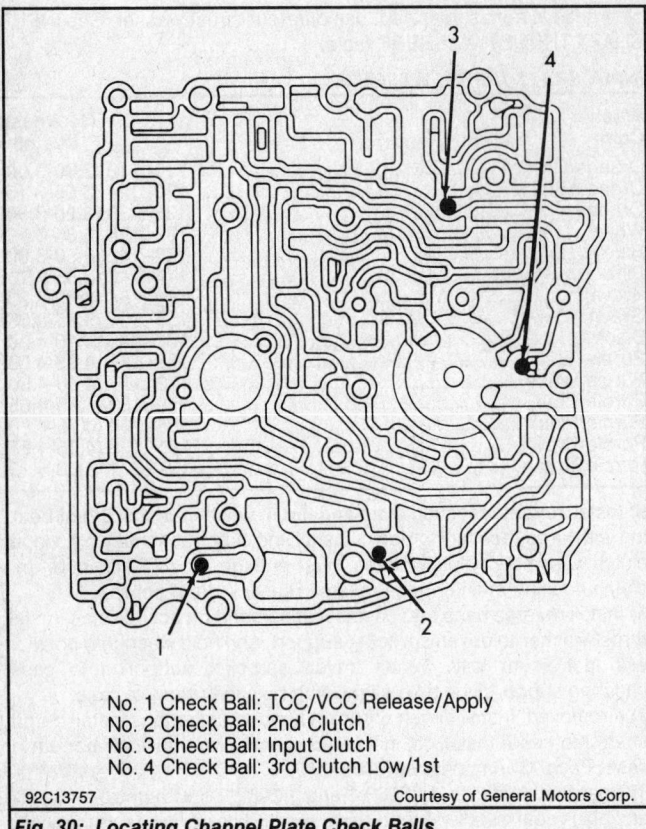

No. 1 Check Ball: TCC/VCC Release/Apply
No. 2 Check Ball: 2nd Clutch
No. 3 Check Ball: Input Clutch
No. 4 Check Ball: 3rd Clutch Low/1st

92C13757   Courtesy of General Motors Corp.

Fig. 30: Locating Channel Plate Check Balls

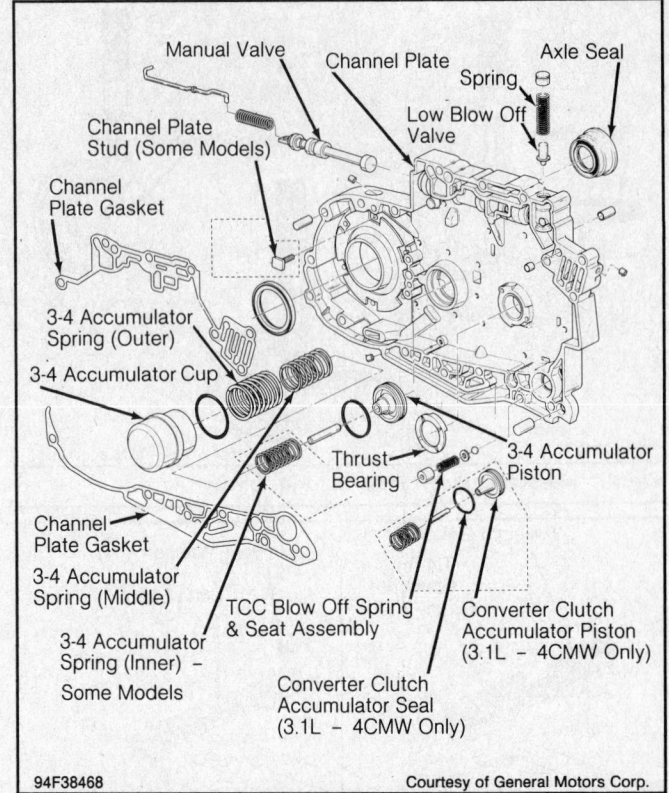

94F38468   Courtesy of General Motors Corp.

Fig. 31: Locating Channel Gaskets, Pistons & Thrust Washer

13) Install and tighten channel plate bolts. *See Fig. 34.* Install check balls in channel plate, using petroleum jelly to retain check balls. *See Fig. 30.* Install converter clutch screen. Install detent spring and roller assembly.

14) Install new spacer plate/channel plate gasket onto channel plate using alignment pins. Install spacer plate onto gasket. Install new spacer plate/valve body gasket onto spacer plate. *See Fig. 31.*

15) Install oil pump drive shaft and converter clutch solenoid screen. Install check balls into valve body assembly; use petroleum jelly to retain check balls in place. *See Fig. 32.*

16) Install valve body assembly onto channel plate using alignment pins. *See Fig. 35.* Install servo pipes into valve body using retainer and bolt.

17) Install gaskets onto case and channel plate. Install side cover. Install accumulator pins into case. Install accumulator springs into case. Larger spring is for 3-4 accumulator.

18) Install lube oil pipe retainer spring into pocket. Install lube oil pipe retainer onto lube oil pipe and "O" ring onto retainer. Install lube oil pipe into case. Ensure pipe is installed into driven sprocket support lube hole.

19) Install spacer plate and new gaskets onto case. Install oil scavenger scoop. Install wiring. Install accumulator cover, pipes and retainer onto case as an assembly.

20) Ensure lube oil pipe is installed into final drive internal gear. Install new filter lip seal, filter and gasket into case. Install pan.

21) Install 1-2 and reverse servo return springs into proper servo bore. Assemble each servo and then install into case. Install new oil seal ring onto each servo cover. Install 1-2 and reverse servo covers into case. Install snap rings.

22) Install speed sensor. Install modulator valve into case. Install new "O" ring seal onto modulator. Install modulator into case. Install retainer and bolt. Use Converter Holding Strap (J-21366) to hold torque converter in place for installation.

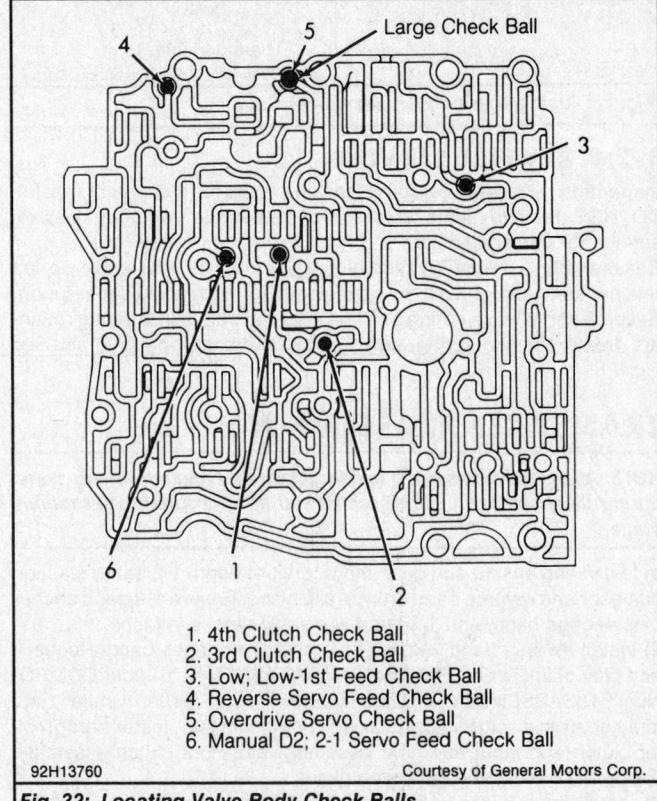

1. 4th Clutch Check Ball
2. 3rd Clutch Check Ball
3. Low; Low-1st Feed Check Ball
4. Reverse Servo Feed Check Ball
5. Overdrive Servo Check Ball
6. Manual D2; 2-1 Servo Feed Check Ball

92H13760   Courtesy of General Motors Corp.

Fig. 32: Locating Valve Body Check Balls

NOTE: *Use Figs. 33-39, following TORQUE SPECIFICATIONS, for disassembly and reassembly reference.*

TORQUE SPECIFICATIONS

TORQUE SPECIFICATIONS

Application	Ft. Lbs. (N.m)
Axle Shaft Nut	185 (251)
Case-To-Drive Sprocket Support Bolts	18 (24)
Channel Plate-To-Case Bolts	18 (24)
Channel Plate-To-Driven Sprocket Support Bolts	18 (24)
Connector Cooler Fitting Bolts	29 (39)
Converter-To-Flywheel Bolts	46 (62)
Manual Shaft-To-Detent Lever Bolts	24 (33)
Modulator-To-Case Bolts	18 (24)
Pump Body-To-Case Bolts	18 (24)
Pump Cover-To-Pump Body Bolts	18 (24)
Valve Body-To-Case 8 mm Bolts	18 (24)
	INCH Lbs. (N.m)
Accumulator Cover-To-Case Bolts	98 (11)
Case Side Cover-To-Channel Plate Bolts	98 (11)
Oil Scoop-To-Case Bolts	71 (8)
Pipe Plug	71 (8)
Pressure Switch Bolts	98 (11)
Pump Cover-To-Channel Plate Bolts	98 (11)
Pump Cover-To-Valve Body Bolts	98 (11)
Servo Pipe Bracket-To-Valve Body Bolts	98 (11)
Side Cover-To-Case Bolts	98 (11)
Solenoid-To-Valve Body Bolts	98 (11)
Valve Body-To-Case 6 mm Bolts	98 (11)
Valve Body-To-Channel Plate Bolts	98 (11)

WIRING DIAGRAMS

NOTE: *See 4T60-E ELECTRONIC CONTROLS article in AUTOMATIC TRANSMISSIONS.*

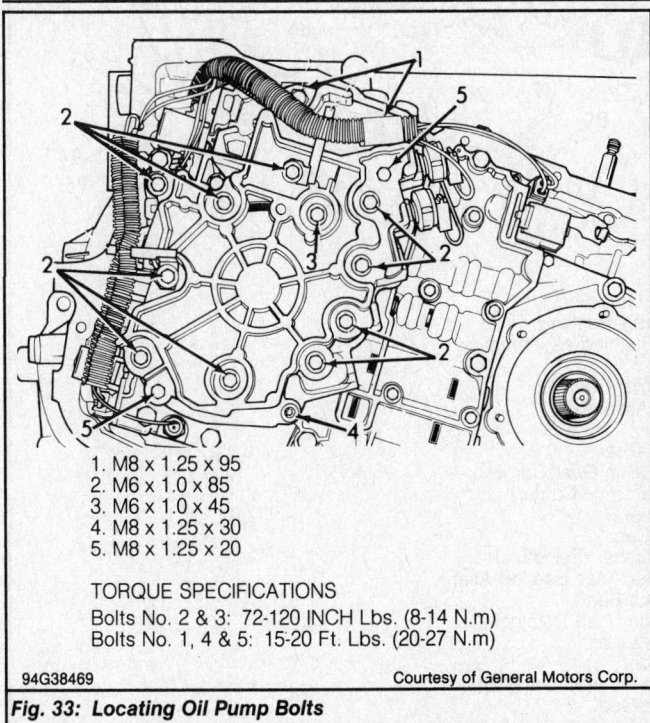

1. M8 x 1.25 x 95
2. M6 x 1.0 x 85
3. M6 x 1.0 x 45
4. M8 x 1.25 x 30
5. M8 x 1.25 x 20

TORQUE SPECIFICATIONS
Bolts No. 2 & 3: 72-120 INCH Lbs. (8-14 N.m)
Bolts No. 1, 4 & 5: 15-20 Ft. Lbs. (20-27 N.m)

94G38469   Courtesy of General Motors Corp.

Fig. 33: Locating Oil Pump Bolts

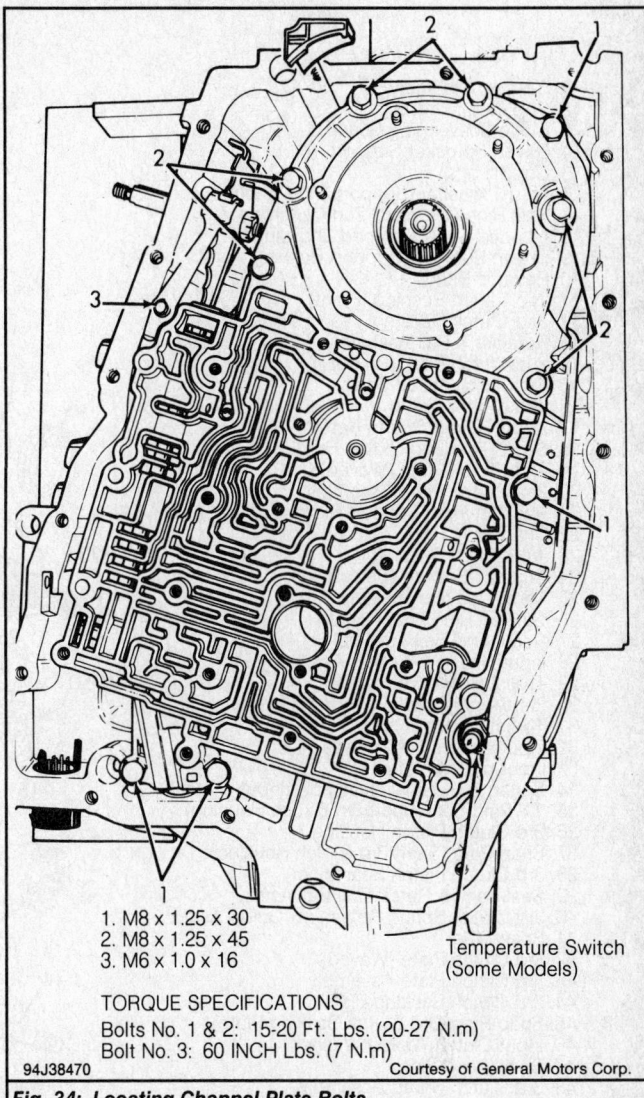

1. M8 x 1.25 x 30
2. M8 x 1.25 x 45
3. M6 x 1.0 x 16

Temperature Switch
(Some Models)

TORQUE SPECIFICATIONS
Bolts No. 1 & 2: 15-20 Ft. Lbs. (20-27 N.m)
Bolt No. 3: 60 INCH Lbs. (7 N.m)

94J38470   Courtesy of General Motors Corp.

Fig. 34: Locating Channel Plate Bolts

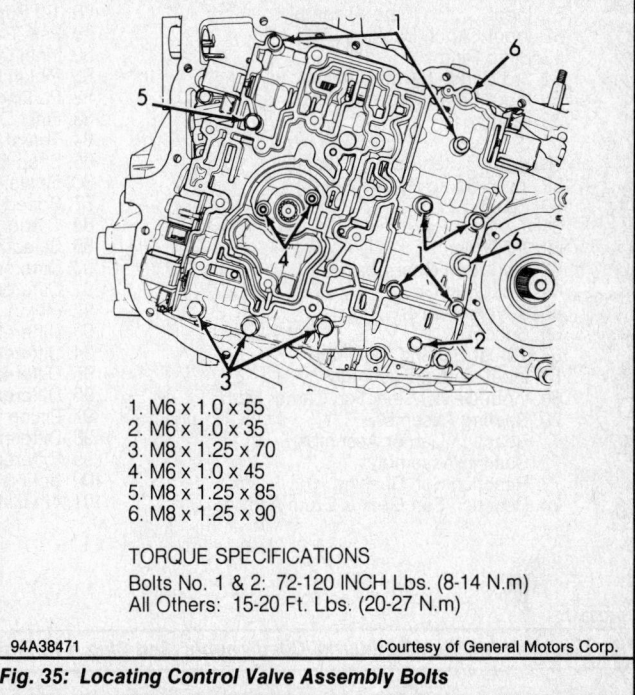

1. M6 x 1.0 x 55
2. M6 x 1.0 x 35
3. M8 x 1.25 x 70
4. M6 x 1.0 x 45
5. M8 x 1.25 x 85
6. M8 x 1.25 x 90

TORQUE SPECIFICATIONS
Bolts No. 1 & 2: 72-120 INCH Lbs. (8-14 N.m)
All Others: 15-20 Ft. Lbs. (20-27 N.m)

94A38471   Courtesy of General Motors Corp.

Fig. 35: Locating Control Valve Assembly Bolts

1. Bearing Assembly
2. Cup Plug (Orificed)
3. Chain Scavenging Scoop
4. Driven Sprocket Support
5. Cup Plug (4)
6. Thrust Washer (Support 2nd Clutch)
7. Seal Rings (Support 2nd Clutch)
8. 4-Lobed Seals (Support 2nd Clutch)
9. Driven Sprocket Support Bushing
10. Reverse Band
11. 2nd Clutch Bushing (Front)
12. 2nd Clutch Housing
13. Retainer & Ball Assembly
14. 2nd Clutch Bushing (Rear)
15. 4th Clutch Piston Seals
16. 2nd Clutch Piston
17. Apply Ring & Spring Return
18. Snap Ring (2nd Clutch Hub)
19. 2nd Clutch Plate (Waved)
20. 2nd Clutch Plate Assembly
21. Backing Plate Support Ring
22. Snap Ring
23. Input Shaft Bushing
24. Support Bearing (Selective)
25. Thrust Washer (Selective)
26. Oil Seal Ring (Input Shaft)
27. Retainer & Ball Assembly
28. Input Housing & Shaft Assembly
29. Thrust Bearing Assembly
30. 2nd Apply Reaction Tapered Plate
31. Thrust Washer
32. Input Clutch Piston Seals
33. Input Clutch Piston
34. Spring & Retainer Assembly (Input Clutch)
35. "O" Ring Seal (Shaft 3rd Clutch Housing)
36. 3rd Clutch Piston Housing
37. Snap Ring (Shaft 3rd Clutch Housing)
38. 3rd Clutch Piston Seal (Inner)
39. Seal Asm. & Retainer & Ball Asm.
40. 3rd Clutch Spring Retainer & Guide Asm.
41. Snap Ring
42. 3rd Clutch Plate (Waved)
43. 3rd Clutch Plate Assembly
44. 3rd Clutch Backing Plate
45. Snap Ring (3rd Clutch Backing Plate)
46. Input Clutch Waved Washer
47. Spiral Lock Ring
48. 3rd Clutch Sprag Assembly
49. 3rd Clutch Sprag Race
50. Input Clutch Apply Plate
51. Input Clutch Plate Assembly
52. Input Clutch Backing Plate
53. Snap Ring
54. 3rd Clutch Sprag Retainer
55. Input Sprag Race (Inner)
56. Bearing
57. 2-1 Band
58. Input Clutch Sprag Assembly
59. Input Sprag Race (Outer)
60. Bearing End
61. 1-2 Inner Race
62. 1-2 Roller
63. Input Sun Gear Spacer
64. Input Sun Gear
65. Reverse Action Drum
66. Spacer
67. Thrust Bearing Assembly
68. Input Carrier Assembly
69. Input Carrier/Reaction Carrier Dam
70. Bearing Assembly
71. Reaction Carrier Assembly
72. Bearing Assembly
73. Reaction Sun Bushing
74. Reaction Sun Gear & Drum Asm.

75. Forward Band
76. Final Drive Sun Gear Shaft
77. Final Drive Internal Bushing
78. 1-2 Support & Bushing Assembly
79. Park Pawl
80. Final Drive Internal Gear
81. Pinion Bearing Assembly
82. Parking Gear
83. Final Drive Sun Gear
84. Thrust Bearing (Sun Gear/Carrier)
85. Snap Ring (Final Drive Carrier)
86. Final Drive Carrier
87. Speed Sensor Gear
88. Carrier/Case Washer (Selective)
89. Selective Washer/Case Bearing Asm.
90. Differential Pinion Shaft
91. Differential Pinion Shaft Retainer
92. Pinion Thrust Washer
93. Differential Pinion
94. Differential Side Gear Thrust Washer
95. Differential Side Gear
96. Differential Pinion
97. Pinion Thrust Washer
98. Differential Side Gear
99. Differential Side Gear Thrust Washer
100. Spring Retainer
101. 4th Clutch Piston

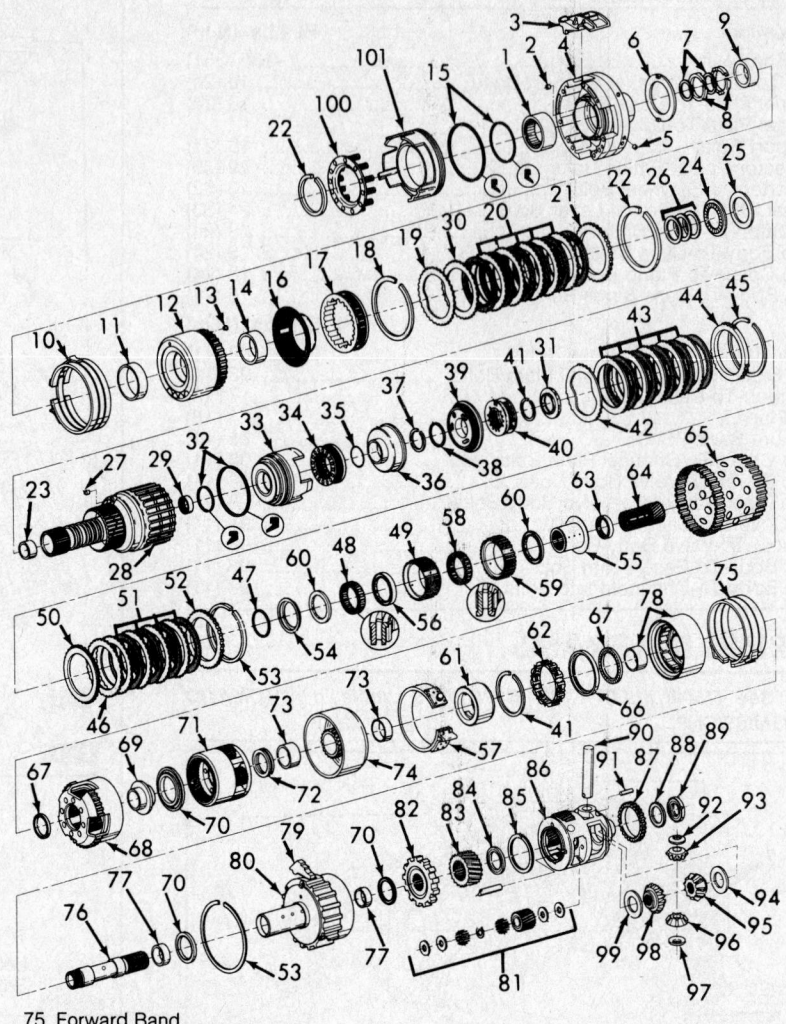

94B38472

Courtesy of General Motors Corp.

Fig. 36: _Exploded View Of Internal Components (2nd Clutch To Final Drive)_

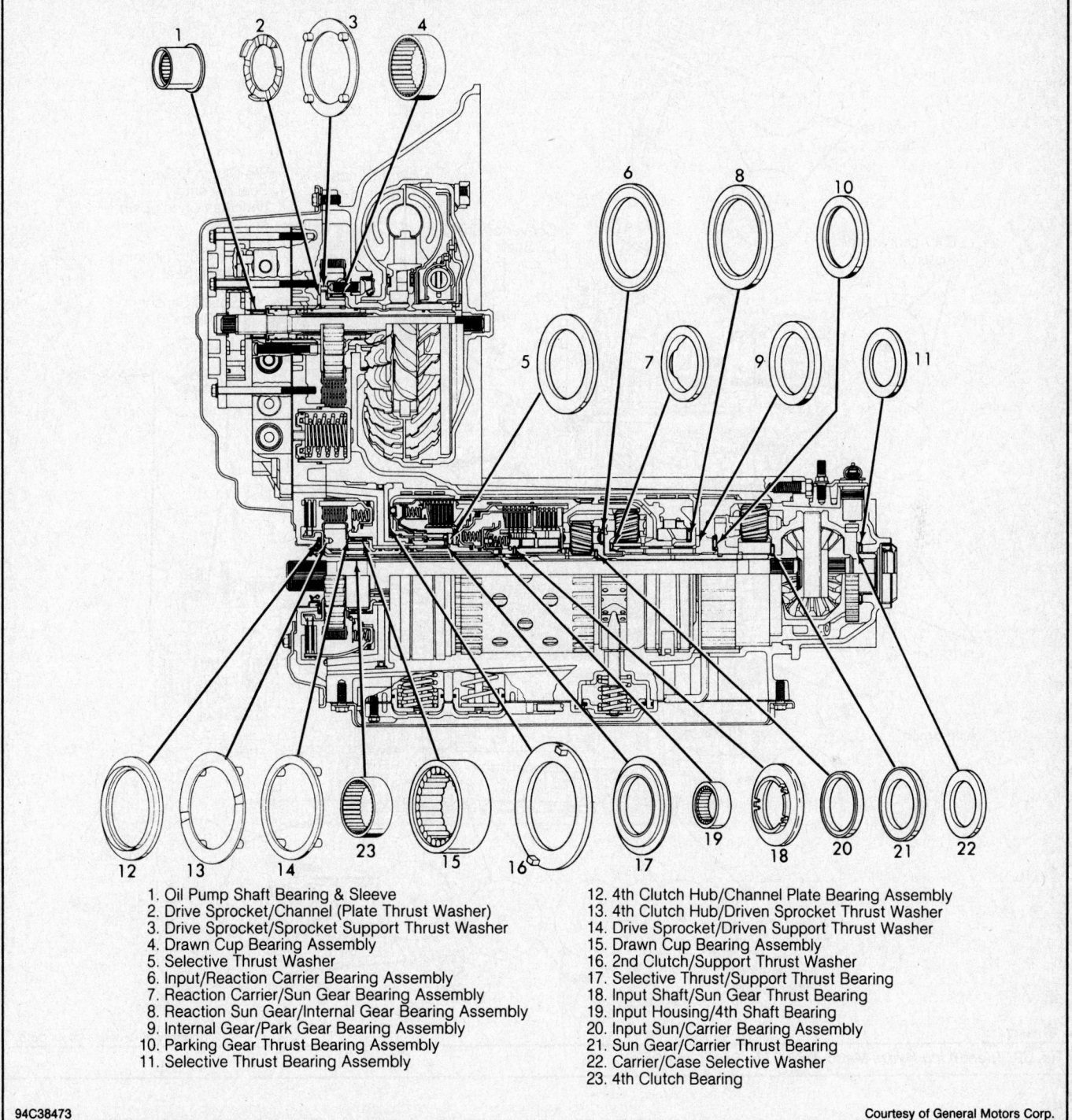

1. Oil Pump Shaft Bearing & Sleeve
2. Drive Sprocket/Channel (Plate Thrust Washer)
3. Drive Sprocket/Sprocket Support Thrust Washer
4. Drawn Cup Bearing Assembly
5. Selective Thrust Washer
6. Input/Reaction Carrier Bearing Assembly
7. Reaction Carrier/Sun Gear Bearing Assembly
8. Reaction Sun Gear/Internal Gear Bearing Assembly
9. Internal Gear/Park Gear Bearing Assembly
10. Parking Gear Thrust Bearing Assembly
11. Selective Thrust Bearing Assembly

12. 4th Clutch Hub/Channel Plate Bearing Assembly
13. 4th Clutch Hub/Driven Sprocket Thrust Washer
14. Drive Sprocket/Driven Support Thrust Washer
15. Drawn Cup Bearing Assembly
16. 2nd Clutch/Support Thrust Washer
17. Selective Thrust/Support Thrust Bearing
18. Input Shaft/Sun Gear Thrust Bearing
19. Input Housing/4th Shaft Bearing
20. Input Sun/Carrier Bearing Assembly
21. Sun Gear/Carrier Thrust Bearing
22. Carrier/Case Selective Washer
23. 4th Clutch Bearing

94C38473

Courtesy of General Motors Corp.

Fig. 37: Identifying Hydra-Matic 4T60-E Thrust Washers & Bearing Locations

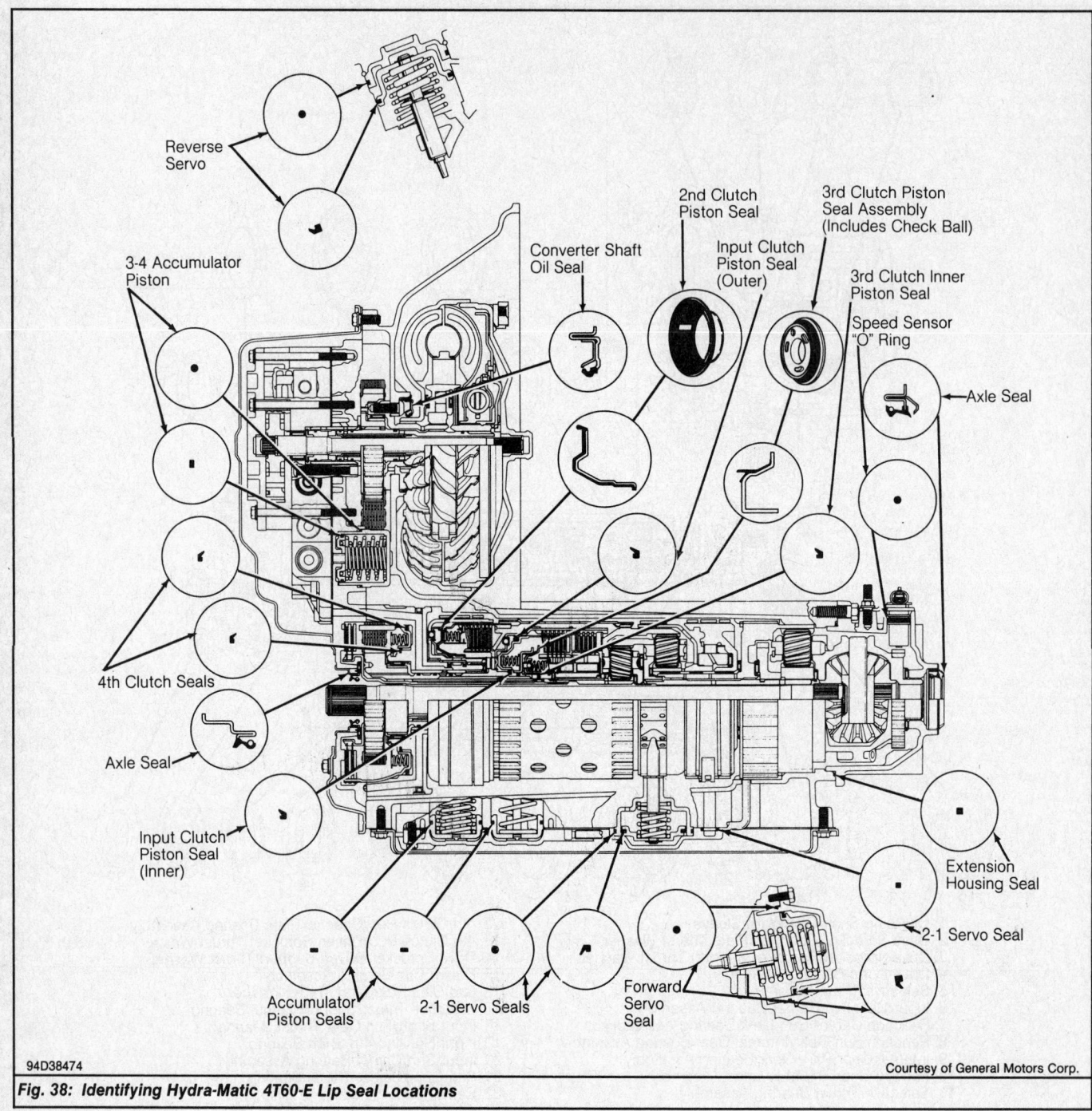

94D38474

Courtesy of General Motors Corp.

Fig. 38: Identifying Hydra-Matic 4T60-E Lip Seal Locations

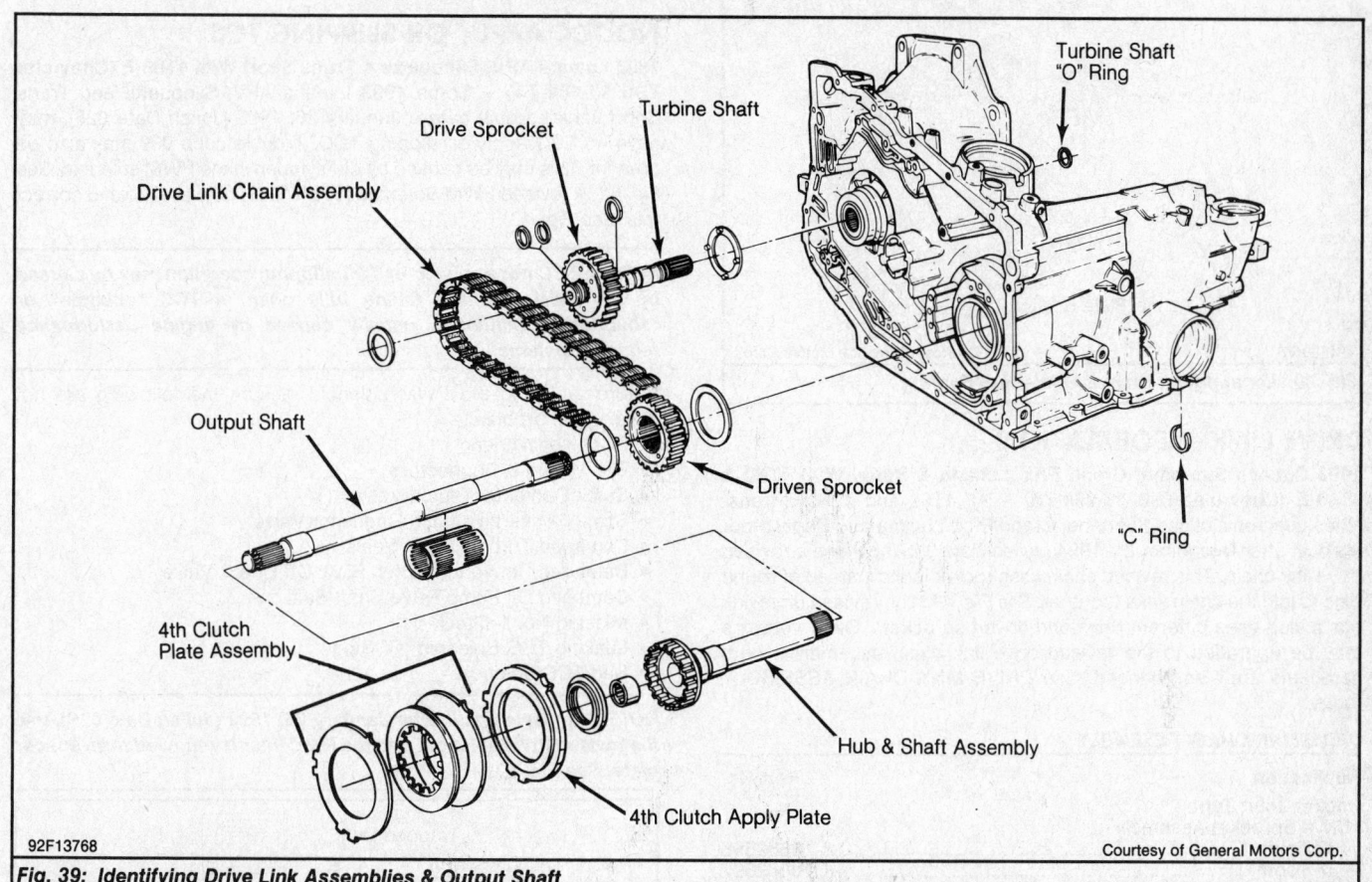

Fig. 39: Identifying Drive Link Assemblies & Output Shaft

92F13768

Courtesy of General Motors Corp.

SERVICE BULLETINS

NOISE OR VIBRATION DURING RIGHT TURNS UNDER HEAVY ACCELERATION

1994 Lumina With 3.1L & 4T60-E (Chevrolet TSB 437101) – Some transaxles built before VIN 2G1WL54T8R165535 (Oshawa No. 1) or 2G1WL54T8R1115524 (Oshawa No. 2), may have a noise or vibration during right turns under heavy acceleration. This may be caused by the upper rear transaxle mount bracket contacting transaxle. To correct this, install the revised Upper Rear Transaxle Mount Bracket (10262677).

2ND GEAR VIBRATION AT 40-55 MPH UNDER MEDIUM-TO-HEAVY ACCELERATION

1994 Achieva, Beretta, Corsica, Grand Am & Skylark with 3.1L & 4T60-E Models 4WBW or 4WSW (General Motors TSB 377135A) – Some transaxles built before September 24, 1993 (Julian Date 264), may vibrate in 2nd gear at 40-55 MPH under medium-to-heavy acceleration. This may be caused by the 4th hub and shaft bore being off center. To correct this, install the revised 4th Hub and Shaft Assembly (2420194). The revised 4th hub and shaft assembly is identified by an Purple stripe painted around the shaft.

UPDATED 4TH CLUTCH & HYDRAULIC CONTROL

1991-94 General Motors With 4T60-E (General Motors TSB 377132A) – Beginning with model year 1993, all 4T60-E transaxles were built with modified 4th clutch plates, 4th clutch apply piston, channel plate, control valve body, spacer plate and gaskets. Make sure the transaxle being overhauled or repaired is correctly identified. If gaskets or parts are mixed between 1991-92 and 1993-94 transaxles, early transaxle failure may result. If any components are replaced, ensure new part matches old part. Use the correct gaskets and seals kit, or overhaul kit for the transaxle being repaired. See 4T60-E SERVICE PACKAGES table.

4T60-E SERVICE PACKAGES

Application	Part No.
Complete Overhaul Package	
1991-92	8651901
1993-94	8651929
Seals & Gaskets	
1991-92	8651900
1993-94	8651928

FINAL DRIVE WHINE AT 20-40 MPH

1991-93 Eldorado, DeVille, Fleetwood & Seville With 4T60-E Models 1AHW, 1AVW, 2AVW, 2A5W Or 3AVW (General Motors TSB 217106) – Some 1991-93 Eldorado, DeVille, Fleetwood and Seville models may have a final drive whine at 20-40 MPH during light acceleration and closed throttle deceleration. If this condition is present and no other cause of problem is found, replace the transaxle with revised Transaxle Assembly (2420016). This kit includes a different mounting bracket.

BEARING WHINE IN 2ND, 3RD OR 4TH GEAR

1991-93 Cutlass Supreme, Grand Prix, Lumina, Lumina APV, Regal, Silhouette & Trans Sport (Chevrolet TSB 93-272-7A) – Some transaxles may have a bearing whine in 2nd, 3rd or 4th gear. The noise occurs mostly in 2nd gear under light throttle acceleration. This may be caused by an incorrectly installed 4th-channel-plate hub bearing. To correct this, inspect the bearing for signs of notch marks on the bearing race. If notch marks are present, replace with 4th-Channel-Plate Hub Bearing (8656393). See Fig. 40.

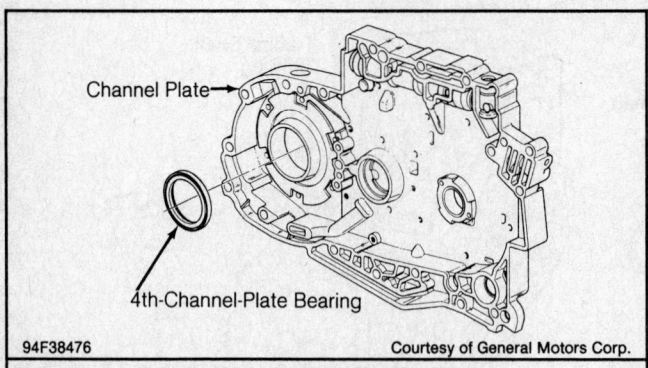

Fig. 40: Locating 4th-Channel-Plate Hub Bearing

DRIVE LINK INFORMATION

1993 Cutlass Supreme, Grand Prix, Lumina & Regal With 4T60 & 4T60-E (Chevrolet TSB 93-264-7A) – All 4T60 and 4T60-E transaxles used on Cutlass Supreme, Grand Prix, Lumina and Regal models built after December 21, 1994 (Julian Date 356) now use a revised drive link chain. This revised chain uses rocker joints instead of round pins to join the chain links together. See Fig. 41. The revised drive link chain also uses different drive and driven sprockets. Older versions may be upgraded to the revised drive link chain assembly if both sprockets are also changed. See DRIVE LINK CHAIN ASSEMBLY table.

DRIVE LINK CHAIN ASSEMBLY

Application	Part No.
Rocker Joint Type	
Drive Sprocket Assembly	
33 Tooth	8682599
37 Tooth	8682597
Driven Sprocket	
33 Tooth	8682600
37 Tooth	8682602
Drive Link Chain	8682603
Round Pin Type	
Drive Sprocket Assembly	
33 Tooth	8651568
37 Tooth	8644679
Driven Sprocket	
33 Tooth	8675035
37 Tooth	8678146
Drive Link Chain	8660099

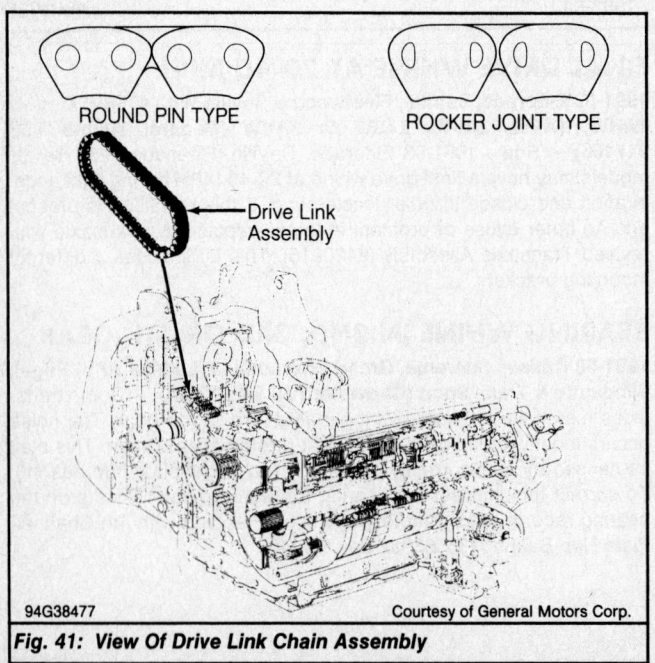

Fig. 41: View Of Drive Link Chain Assembly

NO TCC APPLY OR SLIPPING TCC

1993 Lumina APV, Silhouette & Trans Sport With 4T60-E (Chevrolet TSB 93-182-7A) – Some 1993 Lumina APV, Silhouette and Trans Sport vehicles built before January 26, 1993 (Julian Date 026), may have no TCC apply or slipping TCC. Trouble code 039 may also be present. This may be caused by dirt trapped in the PWM solenoid. See Fig. 42. A revised PWM Solenoid (8681523) is now available to correct this. See Fig. 43.

NOTE: A TCC not applying or TCC slipping condition may be caused by the PWM solenoid failing fully open. A TCC "chuggle" or "shudder" condition is usually caused by engine performance related problems.

Before replacing the PWM solenoid, ensure the following are not causing the problem,
- PCM Not Working
- Bad Wiring & Connectors
- Stuck Converter Clutch Valve
- Stuck Converter Clutch Regulator Valve
- Damaged Turbine Shaft Seals
- Damaged Converter Clutch Blow Off Check Valve
- Damaged Oil Pump Drive Shaft Seal
- Missing No. 1 Check Ball
- Leaking TCC Solenoid "O" Ring
- Bad TCC Solenoid

NOTE: Transaxles built after January 26, 1993 (Julian Date 026), use the revised PWM solenoid and the PWM filter is removed from spacer plate. See Fig. 43.

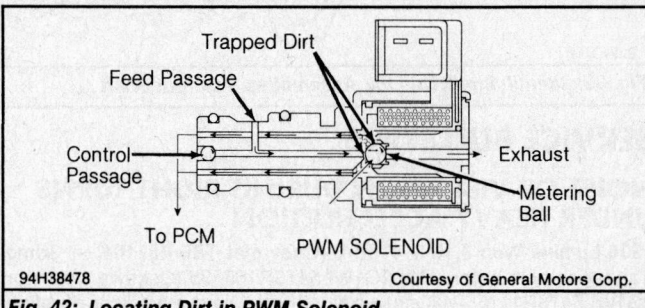

Fig. 42: Locating Dirt in PWM Solenoid

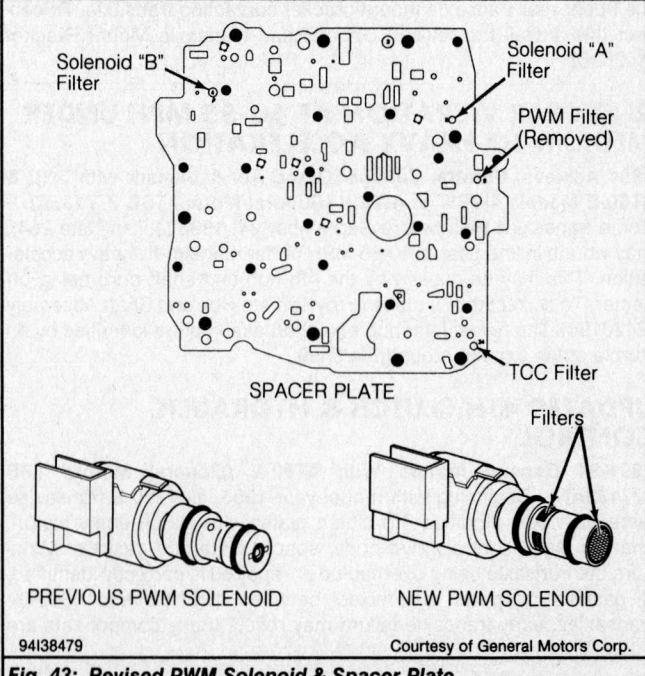

Fig. 43: Revised PWM Solenoid & Spacer Plate

CONVERTER SEAL LEAK

1991-93 Cutlass Supreme, Grand Prix, Lumina, Lumina APV, Regal, Silhouette & Trans Sport With 4T60-E (Chevrolet TSB 93-53-7A) – Some Cutlass Supreme, Grand Prix, Lumina, Lumina APV, Regal, Silhouette and Trans Sport vehicles with 4T60-E transaxle built on or before October 28, 1992 (Julian Date 302), may leak oil from the torque converter seal. To correct this, remove the seal. Clean seal bore and dry. Apply a bead of Red Loctite 272 to outer edge of torque converter seal. Install seal. Wait 30 minutes before allowing ATF to contact seal. Wait 24 hours before starting vehicle.

FLUID LEAK AT SIDE COVER

1993-94 Achieva, Beretta, Corsica, Cutlass Supreme, Grand Am, Grand Prix, Lumina, Regal & Skylark With 4T60-E (General Motors TSB 377139) – Some mentioned vehicles with 4T60-E transaxle and aluminum side covers may develop a fluid leak. This leak occurs at the lower back corner of the side cover. This information only pertains to transaxles with case No. 723, aluminum side covers and having an external fluid leak. *See Fig. 44.* To correct this condition, install Revised Side Cover Gasket (8651940).

INTERMITTENT OR NO TCC APPLY

1991-93 General Motors With 4T60-E (General Motors TSB 377136) – Some 1991-93 vehicles with 4T60-E transaxle may have intermittent or no TCC apply and also store Codes 26 and/or 39 in the PCM memory. This condition may be caused by a shorted wire harness in the transaxle. To check this, remove the lower oil pan. Connect a DVOM between transaxle connector pins "A" (Red wire) and "D" (Black wire). Wiggle transaxle harness. If continuity is present at any time, replace the wire harness. See WIRE HARNESS ASSEMBLY table.

WIRE HARNESS ASSEMBLY

Application	Part No.
1AHW, 1AMW, 1APW, 1AVW, 1AZW, 1YMW, 1YPW, 1YZW, 1BTW, 2AMW, 2APW, 2AVW, 2AYW, 2AZW, 2BTW, 2BYW, 2PHW, 2WAW, 2YLW, 2YMW, 2YLW, 2YZW, 3AMW, 3AVW, 3AZW, 3BTW, 3BYW, 3PHW, 3WAW, 3YLW, 3YMW, 3YRW, 3YZW	12121130
1CWW, 2CWW, 3CWW, 3CMW	12121131
2ABW, 2ANW, 2AWW, 2CLW, 2CSW, 2CTW, 2CXW, 2CZW, 3ABW, 3ANW, 3AWW, 3CLW, 3CSW, 3CTW, 3CXW, 3CZW	12109436
3BHW	12143000

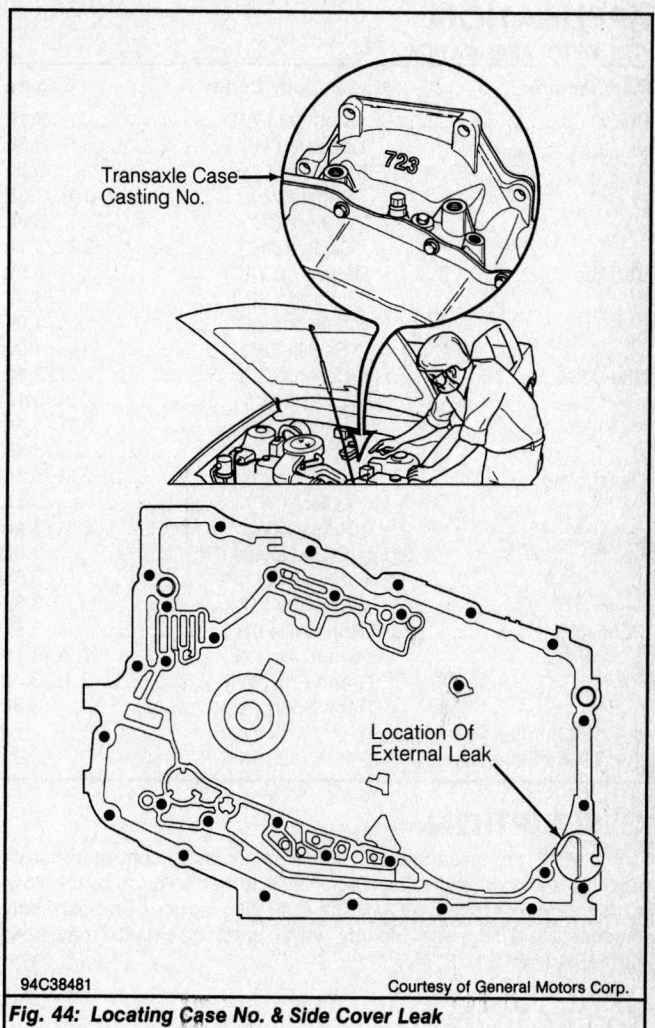

Fig. 44: Locating Case No. & Side Cover Leak

Transaxle Case Casting No.

Location Of External Leak

94C38481

Courtesy of General Motors Corp.

APPLICATION

THM 4T60-E APPLICATION

Manufacturer	Model (Body Code)	Engine
Buick	² Century ("A")	3.1L
	LeSabre ("H")	3.8L
	Park Avenue ("C")	3.8L
	Regal ("W")	3.1L/3.8L
	¹ Riviera ("E")	3.8L
	² Skylark ("N")	2.3L/3.1L
Cadillac	DeVille ("C"/"K")	4.9L
	¹ Eldorado ("E")	4.9L
	¹ Fleetwood ("C")	4.9L
	¹ Seville ("K")	4.9L
Chevrolet	² Beretta ("L")	2.3L/3.1L
	² Corsica ("L")	2.3L/3.1L
	Lumina ("W")	3.1L/3.4L
	Lumina APV ("U")	3.8L
Oldsmobile	² Achieva ("N")	2.3L/3.1L
	² Ciera ("A")	3.1L
	Cutlass ("W")	3.1L/3.4L
	Eighty Eight Royale ("H")	3.8L
	Ninety Eight ("C")	3.8L
	Silhouette ("U")	3.8L
Pontiac	Bonneville ("H")	3.8L
	² Grand Am ("N")	2.3L/3.1L
	Grand Prix ("W")	3.1L/3.4L
	Trans Sport ("U")	3.8L

¹ – 1993 model year.
² – 1994 model year.

DESCRIPTION

The 4T60-E transaxle uses 2 electric solenoids to control transaxle upshifts and downshifts. Each solenoid is turned on or off by the Powertrain Control Module (PCM). The PCM also includes on-board self-diagnostics. This helps identify which parts or circuits may need further testing.

OPERATION

Each solenoid either holds hydraulic pressure (solenoid on) or releases hydraulic pressure (solenoid off). This action controls the shift valves inside valve body. By switching one or both solenoids on or off, different combinations of clutches, sprags and bands are operated. See CLUTCH & BAND APPLICATION CHART (4T60-E) under ELECTRONIC TESTING.

COMPONENT DESCRIPTION

PCM

On Cutlass Supreme, Grand Prix, Lumina and Regal, PCM is located at right side of engine compartment. On other models, the PCM is located under right kick panel. PCM controls ignition, fuel and emission devices related to the engine and transaxle upshifts and downshifts.

The PCM receives electronic signals from sensors and switches. These signals help the PCM determine when to operate various relays and solenoids related to engine and transaxle control.

On Cadillac models, the PCM is also connected to one or more other computers, which operate the climate control system, anti-lock brake system, driver information center and supplemental restraint system.

SENSORS & SWITCHES

The PCM controls upshifts and downshifts based on coolant temperature (or transaxle temperature), throttle position, PRNDL or gear switch position, vehicle speed sensor and brake pedal switch. The system includes several other switches and sensors which are used for engine control. These are covered in ENGINE PERFORMANCE in appropriate MITCHELL® manual.

SOLENOIDS

Transaxle is shifted up or down by 2 electric solenoids. Both solenoids are located on the valve body. Ignition power is supplied to each solenoid by the cooling fan fuse (most models).

Solenoid "A" controls hydraulic pressure to 1-2 and 3-4 shift valves. Solenoid "B" controls hydraulic pressure to 3-2 down and 4-3 down shift valves.

SELF-DIAGNOSTICS

PCM constantly monitors all electrical circuits. If PCM detects circuit problems or sensors out of range, it will record trouble codes. If problem continues for a predetermined time, CHECK ENGINE or SERVICE ENGINE SOON light will glow.

If the CHECK ENGINE or SERVICE ENGINE SOON light is on all the time, trouble code(s) are currently being detected. If the CHECK ENGINE or SERVICE ENGINE SOON light is off, but PCM had detected a circuit or sensor problem, trouble code(s) will be stored in computer memory.

Stored trouble codes may be retrieved from PCM memory. Depending on the vehicle, several methods may be used. The most basic method (non-scan) uses a jumper wire and watching the CHECK ENGINE or SERVICE ENGINE SOON light flash a series of codes.

Other methods include using a factory recommended Tech 1 scan tool, aftermarket scan tool or instrument panel mounted display (Cadillac only).

NOTE: *Faulty engine sensors and actuators may cause transaxle related fault codes or driveability problems. Engine faults and related trouble codes must be diagnosed and repaired before transaxle codes are repaired. For additional information on diagnosing and repairing engine related PCM fault codes, see* ENGINE PERFORMANCE *section of appropriate* MITCHELL® *manual.*

ELECTRONIC SELF-DIAGNOSTICS (EXCEPT CADILLAC)

NOTE: To test electronic control of transaxle solenoids without using self-diagnostics or if self-diagnostics will not work, go to appropriate COMPONENT TESTS under ELECTRONIC TESTING. After repairs are made, trouble codes should be erased from computer memory. See CLEARING TROUBLE CODES under ELECTRONIC SELF-DIAGNOSIS (EXCEPT CADILLAC).

RETRIEVING CODES (WITHOUT SCAN TOOL)

1) Turn ignition on. DO NOT start engine. CHECK ENGINE or SERVICE ENGINE SOON light should glow. Locate Assembly Line Data Link (ALDL) connector attached to control module wiring harness. Most ALDL connectors are located under dash on driver's side of vehicle. Turn ignition on with engine not running. Insert jumper wire from terminal "B" (diagnostic test terminal) to terminal "A" (ground) of ALDL connector. See Fig. 1.

NOTE: Inserting jumper wire into test and ground terminals of ALDL connector with engine running will cause fuel injected vehicles to enter field service mode. The CHECK ENGINE or SERVICE ENGINE SOON light will not indicate codes if this is done.

NOTE: Code 12 should always exist when ALDL is grounded with key on and engine not running.

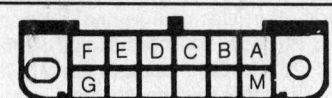

A – Ground
B – Test Terminal
C – Air Injection (If Equipped)
D – Service Engine Soon Light (If Used)
E – Serial Data
F – TCC (If Used)
G – Fuel Pump (If Used)
M – Serial Data (Some Models)

90B01199   Courtesy of General Motors Corp.

Fig. 1: ALDL Connector Terminal Identification

2) CHECK ENGINE or SERVICE ENGINE SOON light should begin to flash codes. Each code will be repeated 3 times. For example, FLASH, FLASH, pause, FLASH, longer pause, identifies Code 21. The first series of flashes is the first digit of trouble code. The second series of flashes is the second digit of trouble code.

3) Trouble codes are displayed starting with lowest numbered code. Each code is displayed 3 times. Codes will continue to repeat as long as ALDL test terminal is grounded.

4) If codes are not flashed, or CHECK ENGINE or SERVICE ENGINE SOON light does not glow, self-diagnostics will not work. See DIAGNOSTIC CIRCUIT CHECK in BASIC DIAGNOSTIC PROCEDURES article in ENGINE PERFORMANCE section of appropriate MITCHELL® manual. To exit diagnostic mode, turn ignition off and remove jumper wire from ALDL connector.

NOTE: Trouble codes will be recorded at various operating times. Some codes require operation of affected sensor or switch for 5 seconds; others may require operation for 5 minutes or longer at normal operating temperature, road speed and load. Therefore, some codes may not set in a service bay operational mode and may require road testing vehicle in order to duplicate condition under which code will set.

RETRIEVING CODES (WITH SCAN TOOL)

NOTE: Plugging scan tester into the ALDL enables user to read trouble codes and check voltages in the system on the serial data line.

The scan tester is a specialized tester which, when plugged into ALDL, can be used to diagnose on-board computer control systems by providing instant access to circuit voltage information, eliminating the need to crawl under dash or hood to backprobe sensors and connectors.

Scan testers may also furnish information on status of output devices (solenoids and relays). However, status parameters are only an indication that output signals have been sent to devices by control module; they do not indicate if devices have responded properly to signal. Check for proper response at output device using a voltmeter or test light.

NOTE: Code 12 should always exist when ALDL is grounded with key on and engine not running, but may not be indicated by all makes of scan tools. On 1994 models, Code 12 will not be present on vehicles which require the use of a scan tester to obtain codes.

If trouble codes are not present, this is not necessarily an indication that there is not a problem. Driveability related problems with codes displayed occur about 20 percent of the time, while driveability problems without codes occur about 80 percent of the time. Sensors that are out of specification WILL NOT set a trouble code but WILL cause driveability problems. Using the scan tool is the easiest method of checking sensor specifications and other data parameters. Scan tool is also useful in finding intermittent wiring problems by wiggling wiring harnesses and connections (key on, engine off) while observing scan tool.

NOTE: If erroneous voltage signals are suspected, it will be necessary to verify tester information using a digital voltmeter and wiring schematic. If non-existent codes are displayed, turn ignition off, remove tester, turn ignition on and ground ALDL test terminal "B". See Fig. 1. The same codes flashed by CHECK ENGINE or SERVICE ENGINE SOON light should be indicated by scan tool.

TROUBLE CODE DEFINITION

NOTE: Only transaxle-related trouble codes are listed. If other trouble codes are present, see ENGINE PERFORMANCE in appropriate MITCHELL® manual.

PCM TROUBLE CODE DEFINITION (1993)

Code No.	Circuit Affected
12 [1]	No RPM Reference Pulse
14	Coolant Temp. Signal Voltage Low
15	Coolant Temp. Signal Voltage High
21	Throttle Position Switch Voltage High
22	Throttle Position Switch Voltage Low
24	Vehicle Speed Sensor Circuit
26	Quad-Driver Error (Some Models)
31	Park/Neutral Switch (3.4L & 3.8L)
36	Trans. Shift Circuit
38	Brake Switch (3.4L & 3.8L)
39	TCC or VCC Problem
56	Quad-Driver Error (Lumina APV, Silhouette & Trans Sport)
62	Gear Switch (3.1L – Except Calif. & 3.4L)
79	VSS Voltage High (3.1L Calif.)
80	VSS Voltage Low (3.1L Calif.)

[1] – Display of a Code 12 is normal when no reference pulses are received by control module (engine not running).

PCM TROUBLE CODE DEFINITION (2.3L – 1994)

Code No.	Circuit Affected
12 [1]	No RPM Reference Pulse
14	Coolant Temp. Signal Voltage High
15	Coolant Temp. Signal Voltage Low
21	Throttle Position Switch Voltage High
22	Throttle Position Switch Voltage Low
24	Vehicle Speed Sensor Circuit
27	Quad Driver (TCC Problem)
29	Quad-Driver (Shift Solenoid Error)

[1] – Display of a Code 12 is normal when no reference pulses are received by control module (engine not running).

PCM TROUBLE CODE DEFINITION
(3.1L EXCEPT CENTURY & CIERA – 1994)

Code No.	Circuit Affected
12 [1]	No RPM Reference Pulse
14	Coolant Temp. Signal Voltage High
15	Coolant Temp. Signal Voltage Low
21	Throttle Position Switch Voltage High
22	Throttle Position Switch Voltage Low
24	Vehicle Speed Sensor Circuit
28	Gear Range Switch
58	Transaxle Temp. Signal Voltage High
59	Transaxle Temp. Signal Voltage Low
79	Transaxle Temp. Signal Voltage High

[1] – Display of a Code 12 is normal when no reference pulses are received by control module (engine not running).

PCM TROUBLE CODE DEFINITION
(3.1L CENTURY & CIERA, 3.4L & 3.8L – 1994)

Code No.	Circuit Affected
P0118	Coolant Temp. Signal Voltage High
P0117	Coolant Temp. Signal Voltage Low
P0122	Throttle Position Switch Voltage Low
P0123	Throttle Position Switch Voltage High
P0510/502	Vehicle Speed Sensor Circuit
P0703	TCC Brake Switch
P0705	Gear Range Switch
P0712	Transaxle Temp. Signal Voltage High
P0713	Transaxle Temp. Signal Voltage Low
P0740	TCC Fault
P0755	Transaxle Shift Problem
P01640	Quad Driver (TCC Problem)
P01650	Quad-Driver (Shift Solenoid Error)

HARD OR INTERMITTENT TROUBLE CODE DETERMINATION

During any diagnostic procedure, it must be determined if codes are hard failure codes or intermittent failure codes. Diagnostic charts will not usually help analyze intermittent codes. To determine hard codes and intermittent codes, proceed as follows:

1) Manually enter diagnostic mode. See RETRIEVING CODES (WITHOUT SCAN TOOL) Read and record all stored trouble codes. Exit diagnostic mode and clear trouble codes. See CLEARING TROUBLE CODES.

2) Apply parking brake and place transaxle in Neutral or Park. Block drive wheels and start engine. CHECK ENGINE or SERVICE ENGINE SOON light should go out. Run warm engine at specified curb idle for 2 minutes and note CHECK ENGINE or SERVICE ENGINE SOON light.

3) If CHECK ENGINE or SERVICE ENGINE SOON light comes on, MANUALLY enter diagnostic mode. Read and record trouble codes. This will reveal hard failure codes. Trouble codes may require a road test to reset hard failure after clearing trouble codes.

4) If CHECK ENGINE or SERVICE ENGINE SOON light does not come on, all stored trouble codes were intermittent failures.

CLEARING TROUBLE CODES

Turn ignition switch to ON position, and ground diagnostic test terminal "B" at ALDL connector. See Fig. 1. Turn ignition switch to OFF position, and remove control module fuse from fuse block for 10 seconds. Replace fuse. Remove diagnostic terminal ground lead. If fuse cannot be located, disconnect pigtail at battery. After power to PCM is removed, poor driveability may occur until control module "relearns" operating parameters.

DIAGNOSTIC CHARTS (EXCEPT CADILLAC)

Diagnostic Charts – Following charts are typical flow charts and testing information. For electrical wiring diagrams, see WIRING DIAGRAMS at end of article. For more engine diagnostic information, see ENGINE PERFORMANCE in appropriate MITCHELL® manual.

Diagnostic Aids – Diagnostic aids (located in many trouble code charts) are additional tips used to help diagnose trouble codes when circuit checks do not find a problem.

NOTE: For the purpose of the diagnostic charts, either Electronic Control Module (ECM) or Powertrain Control Module (PCM) may be used to describe the vehicle's computer.

CODE 14/P0118, COOLANT TEMP. SENSOR SIGNAL VOLTAGE LOW – 1993-94

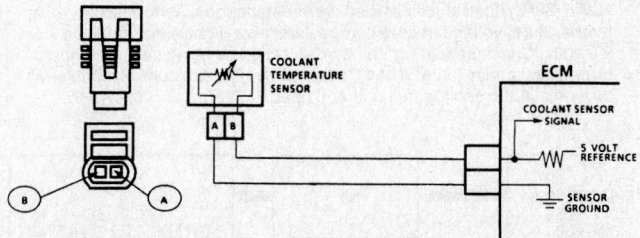

CODE 14/P0118 PCM TERMINAL & CIRCUIT WIRING IDENTIFICATION

Application	ECM Terminal	Wire Color
1993		
3.1L "W" Body (Except Calif.)		
& 3.4L "W" Body		
CTS Signal	C16	Yellow
CTS Ground	C10	Black
3.1L "W" Body (Calif.)		
CTS Signal	A31	Yellow
CTS Ground	A17	Black
3.8L "C", "E" & "H" Bodies		
CTS Signal	B9	Yellow
CTS Ground	A8	Black
3.8L "U" Body		
CTS Signal	BB9	Yellow
CTS Ground	BA8	Black
3.8L "W" Body		
CTS Signal	C13	Yellow
CTS Ground	C7	Black
1994		
2.3L		
CTS Signal	PC10	Yellow
CTS Ground	bb1	Black
3.1L "A" Body		
CTS Signal	BB9	Yellow
CTS Ground	BA8	Black
3.1L "L", "N" & "W" Bodies		
CTS Signal	A31	Yellow
CTS Ground	A17	Black
3.1L Lumina		
CTS Signal	C16	Yellow
CTS Ground	C10	Black
3.4L "W" Body		
CTS Signal	C13	Yellow
CTS Ground	C7	Black
3.8L "C", "H" & "U" Bodies		
CTS Signal	BF13	Yellow
CTS Ground	BE5	Black
3.8L "W" Body		
CTS Signal	C20	Yellow
CTS Ground	C12	Black

NOTE: This chart applies when engine cooling system is functioning properly (not overheating). Test numbers refer to test numbers on diagnostic chart.

1) Code 14/P0118 indicates the control module has seen low coolant sensor voltage signal (high temperature) at control module terminal for a precalibrated period of time. This checks if conditions for Code 14/P0118 still exist.

2) This tests for grounded sensor signal line between control module and coolant sensor.

91J07379 94J38587

DIAGNOSTIC AIDS

After the engine is started, temperature should rise steadily to about 190°F (88°C), then stabilize when thermostat opens. At normal operating temperature, signal voltage at control module terminal should be 1.5-2.0 volts. Check sensor for shifted calibration by using sensor TEMPERATURE-TO-RESISTANCE VALUES table. When Code 14/P0118 is set, control module will turn on electric cooling fan(s), if equipped.

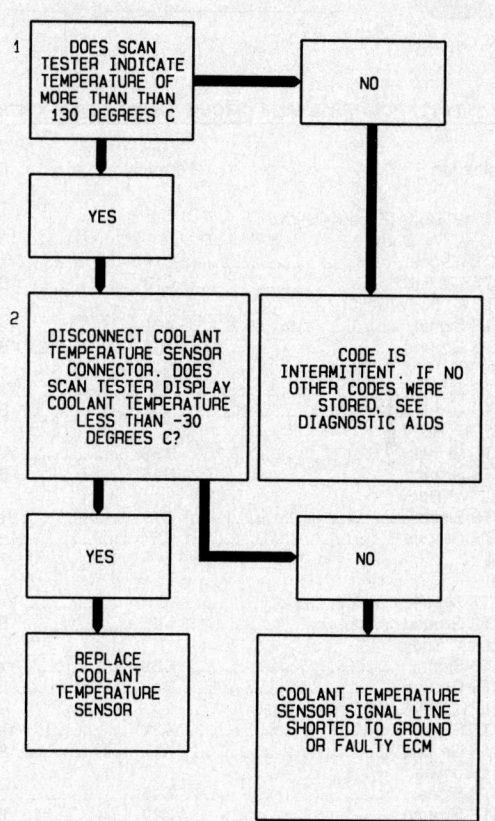

TEMPERATURE-TO-RESISTANCE VALUES [1]

Temperature °F (°C)	Ohms
210 (100)	185
160 (70)	450
100 (38)	1800
70 (20)	3400
20 (-7)	13,500
0 (-18)	25,000
-40 (-40)	100,700

[1] – Measure resistance across sensor terminals.

CODE 15/P0117, COOLANT TEMP. SENSOR SIGNAL VOLTAGE HIGH – 1993-94

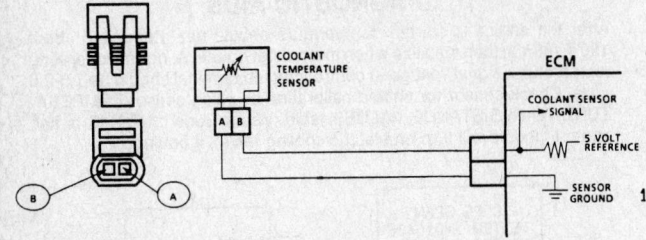

CODE 15/P0117 PCM TERMINAL & CIRCUIT WIRING IDENTIFICATION

Application	ECM Terminal	Wire Color
1993		
3.1L "W" Body (Except Calif.) & 3.4L "W" Body		
CTS Signal	C16	Yellow
CTS Ground	C10	Black
3.1L "W" Body (Calif.)		
CTS Signal	A31	Yellow
CTS Ground	A17	Black
3.8L "C", "E" & "H" Bodies		
CTS Signal	B9	Yellow
CTS Ground	A8	Black
3.8L "U" Body		
CTS Signal	BB9	Yellow
CTS Ground	BA8	Black
3.8L "W" Body		
CTS Signal	C13	Yellow
CTS Ground	C7	Black
1994		
2.3L		
CTS Signal	PC10	Yellow
CTS Ground	bb1	Black
3.1L "A" Body		
CTS Signal	BB9	Yellow
CTS Ground	BA8	Black
3.1L "L", "N" & "W" Bodies		
CTS Signal	A31	Yellow
CTS Ground	A17	Black
3.1L Lumina		
CTS Signal	C16	Yellow
CTS Ground	C10	Black
3.4L "W" Body		
CTS Signal	C13	Yellow
CTS Ground	C7	Black
3.8L "C", "H" & "U" Bodies		
CTS Signal	BF13	Yellow
CTS Ground	BE5	Black
3.8L "W" Body		
CTS Signal	C20	Yellow
CTS Ground	C12	Black

NOTE: Test numbers refer to test numbers on diagnostic chart.

1) Code 15/P0117 indicates control module has seen high resistance in coolant sensor circuit. This could be due to high resistance (cold temperature) or high voltage at coolant sensor terminal at control module for a precalibrated period of time. This checks if conditions for Code 15/P0117 still exist.

2) This test simulates conditions for a Code 14/P0118. If control module recognizes the low voltage signal, scan tester will display greater than 130°C. This indicates the control module and wiring are not at fault.

3) This test determines if coolant sensor ground or signal circuit is open.

DIAGNOSTIC AIDS

After the engine is started, temperature should rise steadily to about 190°F (88°C), then stabilize when thermostat opens. At normal operating temperature, voltage at control module sensor signal line should be 1.5-2.0 volts. Check sensor for shifted calibration by using sensor temperature-to-resistance table. When Code 14/P0118 is set, control module will turn on electric cooling fan(s), if equipped.

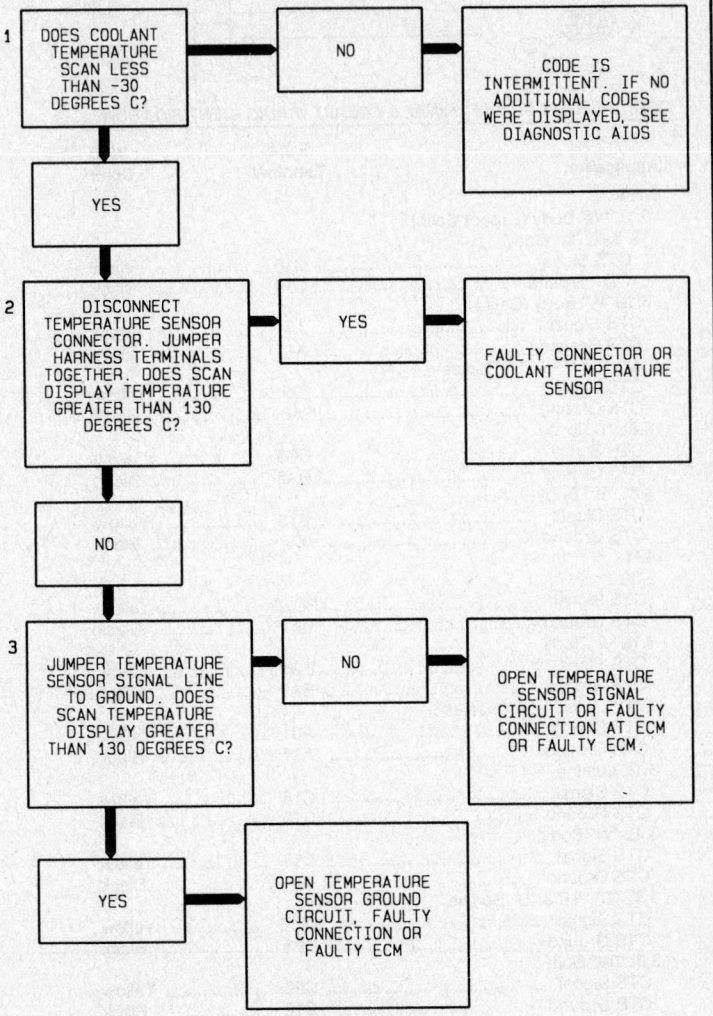

TEMPERATURE-TO-RESISTANCE VALUES [1]

Temperature °F (°C)	Ohms
210 (100)	185
160 (70)	450
100 (38)	1800
70 (20)	3400
20 (–7)	13,500
0 (–18)	25,000
–40 (–40)	100,700

[1] – Measure resistance across sensor terminals.

CODE 21/P0123, THROTTLE POSITION SENSOR SIGNAL VOLTAGE HIGH – 1993-94

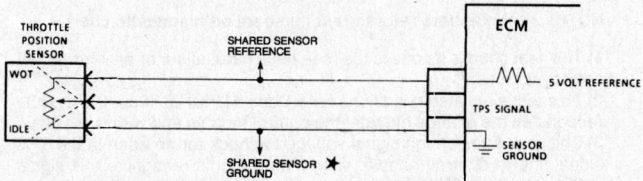

★ – For shared sensor ground tie-offs, see appropriate diagram in WIRING DIAGRAMS article.

CODE 21/P0123 PCM TERMINAL & CIRCUIT WIRING IDENTIFICATION

Application	PCM Terminal	Wire Color
1993		
3.1L "W" Body (Except Calif.)		
& 3.4L "W" Body		
TPS Signal	C15	Dark Blue
TPS Ground	C10	Black
TPS Reference	C12	Gray
3.1L "W" Body (Calif.)		
TPS Signal	A30	Dark Blue
TPS Ground	A17	Black
TPS Reference	B31	Gray
3.8L "C", "E" & "H" Bodies		
TPS Signal	B10	Dark Blue
TPS Ground	A8	Black
TPS Reference	B3	Gray
3.8L "U" Body		
TPS Signal	BB10	Dark Blue
TPS Ground	BA8	Black
TPS Reference	BB3	Gray
3.8L "W" Body		
TPS Signal	C19	Dark Blue
TPS Ground	C7	Black
TPS Reference	B4	Gray
1994		
2.3L		
TPS Signal	PB7	Dark Blue
TPS Ground	PB1	Black
TPS Reference	PA4	Gray
3.1L "A Body		
TPS Signal	BB10	Dark Blue
TPS Ground	BA8	Black
TPS Reference	BB3	Gray
3.1L "L", "N" & "W" Bodies		
TPS Signal	A30	Dark Blue
TPS Ground	A17	Black
TPS Reference	B31	Gray
3.1L Lumina		
TPS Signal	C15	Dark Blue
TPS Ground	C10	Black
TPS Reference	C12	Gray
3.4L "W" Body		
TPS Signal	C19	Dark Blue
TPS Ground	C7	Black
TPS Reference	B4	Gray
3.8L "C", "H" & "U" Bodies		
TPS Signal	BF11	Dark Blue
TPS Ground	BE5	Black
TPS Reference	BE6	Gray
3.8L "W" Body		
TPS Signal	C22	Dark Blue
TPS Ground	C12	Black
TPS Reference	C11	Gray

NOTE: Test numbers refer to test numbers on diagnostic chart.

1) This test checks if code is the result of a hard failure or an intermittent condition.
2) This test simulates conditions for a Code 22/P0122. If control module recognizes the change of state, the control module and wiring are okay.
3) This step isolates a faulty sensor, control module or open sensor ground circuit. If sensor ground is shared by another sensor, there may be an accompanying code related to that sensor.

DIAGNOSTIC AIDS

A scan tester displays throttle position in volts. Closed throttle voltage should be low. Voltage should increase gradually to about 4.5 volts at a steady rate, as throttle angle is increased.

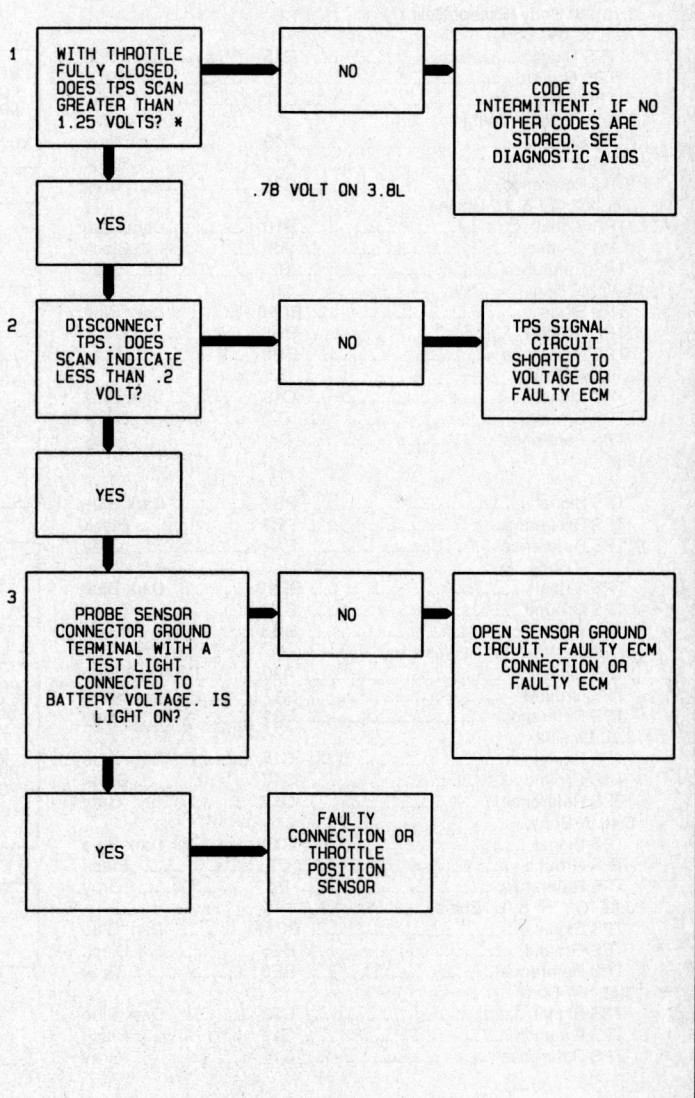

1 — WITH THROTTLE FULLY CLOSED, DOES TPS SCAN GREATER THAN 1.25 VOLTS? ★

.78 VOLT ON 3.8L

NO — CODE IS INTERMITTENT. IF NO OTHER CODES ARE STORED, SEE DIAGNOSTIC AIDS

YES

2 — DISCONNECT TPS. DOES SCAN INDICATE LESS THAN .2 VOLT?

NO — TPS SIGNAL CIRCUIT SHORTED TO VOLTAGE OR FAULTY ECM

YES

3 — PROBE SENSOR CONNECTOR GROUND TERMINAL WITH A TEST LIGHT CONNECTED TO BATTERY VOLTAGE. IS LIGHT ON?

NO — OPEN SENSOR GROUND CIRCUIT, FAULTY ECM CONNECTION OR FAULTY ECM

YES — FAULTY CONNECTION OR THROTTLE POSITION SENSOR

91C07385 94B38589

CODE 22/P0122, THROTTLE POSITION SENSOR SIGNAL VOLTAGE LOW – 1993-94

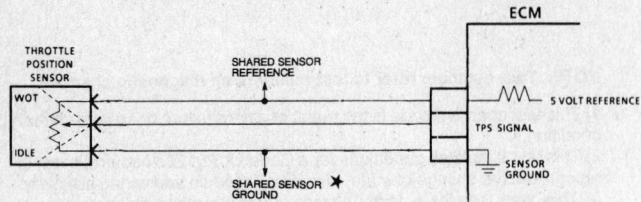

✳ – For shared sensor ground tie-offs, see appropriate diagram in WIRING DIAGRAMS.

CODE 22/P0122 PCM TERMINAL & CIRCUIT WIRING IDENTIFICATION

Application	PCM Terminal	Wire Color
1993		
3.1L "W" Body (Except Calif.) & 3.4L "W" Body		
TPS Signal	C15	Dark Blue
TPS Ground	C10	Black
TPS Reference	C12	Gray
3.1L "W" Body (Calif.)		
TPS Signal	A30	Dark Blue
TPS Ground	A17	Black
TPS Reference	B31	Gray
3.8L "C", "E" & "H" Bodies		
TPS Signal	B10	Dark Blue
TPS Ground	A8	Black
TPS Reference	B3	Gray
3.8L "U" Body		
TPS Signal	BB10	Dark Blue
TPS Ground	BA8	Black
TPS Reference	BB3	Gray
3.8L "W" Body		
TPS Signal	C19	Dark Blue
TPS Ground	C7	Black
TPS Reference	B4	Gray
1994		
2.3L		
TPS Signal	PB7	Dark Blue
TPS Ground	PB1	Black
TPS Reference	PA4	Gray
3.1L "A Body		
TPS Signal	BB10	Dark Blue
TPS Ground	BA8	Black
TPS Reference	BB3	Gray
3.1L "L", "N" & "W" Bodies		
TPS Signal	A30	Dark Blue
TPS Ground	A17	Black
TPS Reference	B31	Gray
3.1L Lumina		
TPS Signal	C15	Dark Blue
TPS Ground	C10	Black
TPS Reference	C12	Gray
3.4L W Body		
TPS Signal	C19	Dark Blue
TPS Ground	C7	Black
TPS Reference	B4	Gray
3.8L "C", "H" & "U" Bodies		
TPS Signal	BF11	Dark Blue
TPS Ground	BE5	Black
TPS Reference	BE6	Gray
3.8L "W" Body		
TPS Signal	C22	Dark Blue
TPS Ground	C12	Black
TPS Reference	C11	Gray

NOTE: Test numbers refer to test numbers on diagnostic chart.

1) This test checks if code is the result of a hard failure or an intermittent condition.
2) This test simulates conditions for a Code 21/P0123. If control module recognizes the change of state, the control module and wiring are okay.
3) This simulates a high signal voltage to check for an open in the TPS signal line to control module. scan tester should recognize this signal and display high TPS voltage.

DIAGNOSTIC AIDS

A scan tester displays throttle position in volts. Closed throttle voltage should be low. Voltage should increase gradually to about 4.5 volts at a steady rate, as throttle angle is increased.

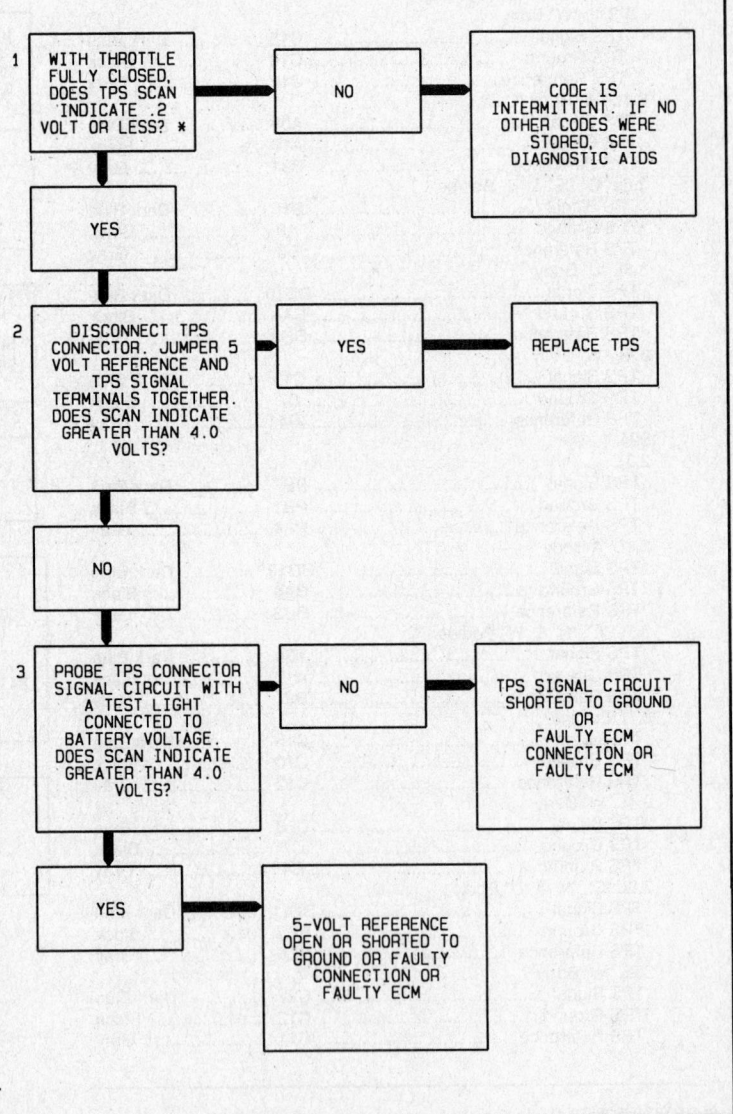

CODE 24, VEHICLE SPEED SENSOR (VSS) 3.1L, 3.4L & 3.8L "W" BODY – 1993

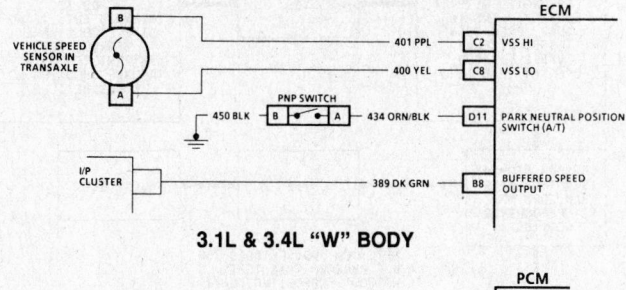

3.1L & 3.4L "W" BODY

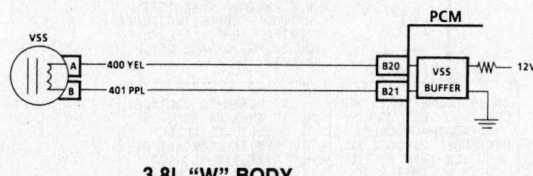

3.8L "W" BODY

The speed sensor, which is a Permanent Magnet (PM) generator, provides the control module with vehicle speed information. The PM generator, mounted in the transmission, produces a pulsing voltage signal whenever the vehicle speed is more than 3 MPH. The voltage level and pulses increase with vehicle speed. The control module converts the pulsing voltage to MPH, which is used by the control module in calculations to determine vehicle adjustments.

NOTE: Test numbers refer to test numbers on diagnostic chart.

1) A Code 24 will set when MPH reads zero, transmission is not in Park or Neutral, engine speed indicates vehicle is in a cruise mode (1200-4400) RPM, TPS indicates closed throttle and high manifold vacuum is sensed by the MAP sensor. All of these conditions must be met for 2-5 seconds. The PM generator only produces a voltage signal if drive wheels are turning greater than 3 MPH.
2) Before replacing the control module, PROM/MEM-CAL should be checked for correct application.

91A07389 93B39322 91A07290

DIAGNOSTIC AIDS

A faulty or misadjusted park/neutral switch may set a false Code 24. Use scan tester and check for proper signal in Drive, while wiggling shifter. Code 24 may set if vehicle is power braked (brakes applied and throttle depressed) for more than 10 seconds.

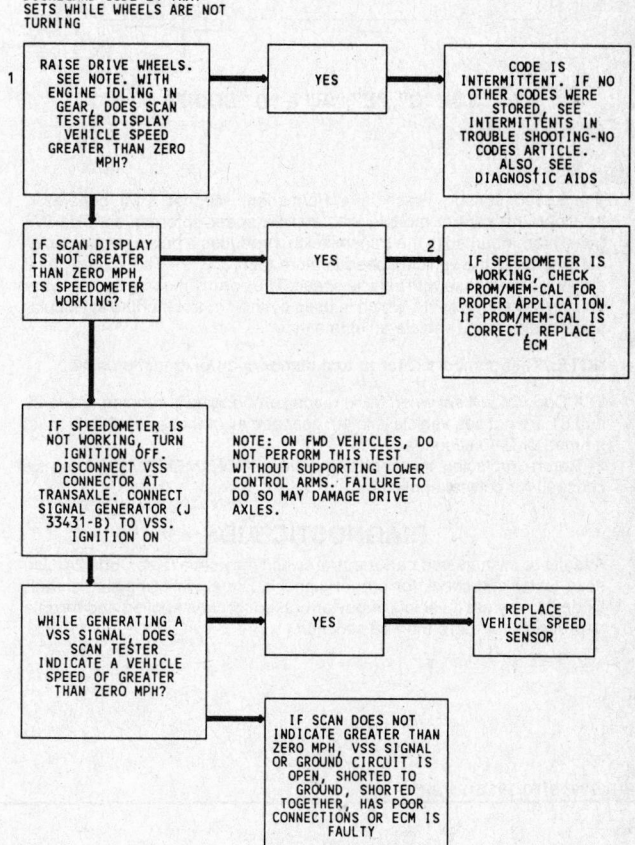

CODE 24, VEHICLE SPEED SENSOR (VSS)
3.8L "C", "E", "H" & "U" BODIES – 1993

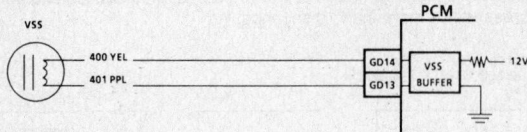

3.8L "C", "E", "H" & "U" BODIES

The speed sensor, which is a Permanent Magnet (PM) generator, provides the control module with vehicle speed information. The PM generator, mounted in the transmission, produces a pulsing voltage signal whenever the vehicle speed is more than 3 MPH. The voltage level and pulses increase with vehicle speed. The control module converts the pulsing voltage to MPH, which is used by the control module in calculations to determine vehicle adjustments.

NOTE: Test numbers refer to test numbers on diagnostic chart.

1) A Code 24 will set when MPH reads zero, engine is running, Code 29 and 31 are not set, vehicle is in 4th gear and all of these conditions must be met for 2-40 seconds.

2) Before replacing the control module, PROM/MEM-CAL should be checked for correct application.

DIAGNOSTIC AIDS

A faulty or misadjusted park/neutral switch may set a false Code 24. Use scan tester and check for proper signal in Drive, while wiggling shifter. Code 24 may set if vehicle is power braked (brakes applied and throttle depressed) for more than 10 seconds.

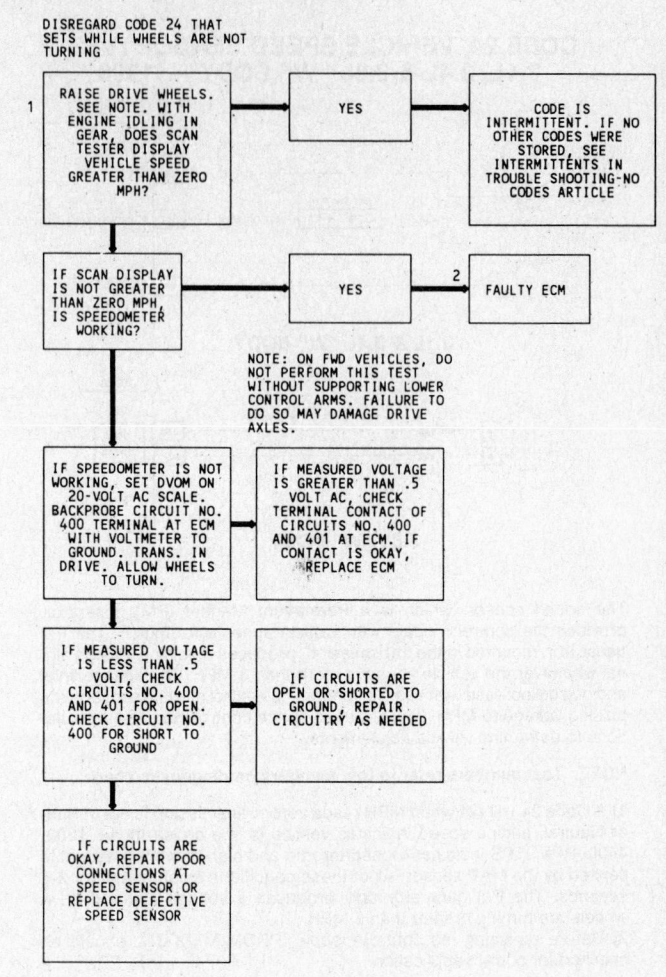

91D07395 91F07396 91E07292

CODE 24, VEHICLE SPEED SENSOR
2.3L, 3.1L "L", "N" & "W" BODIES
3.4L & 3.8L "W" BODIES – 1994

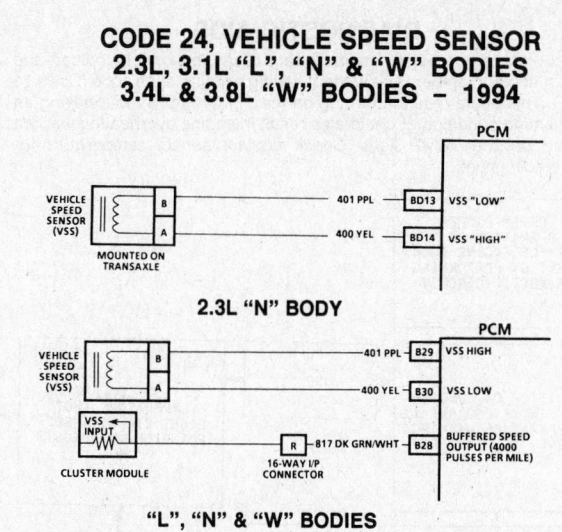

2.3L "N" BODY

"L", "N" & "W" BODIES

Speed sensor, which is a Permanent Magnet (PM) generator, provides control module with vehicle speed information. PM generator, mounted in transaxle, produces a pulsing AC voltage signal whenever vehicle speed is greater than 3 MPH. Voltage level and pulses increase with vehicle speed. Control module converts pulsing voltage to MPH, which is used by control module to calculate vehicle adjustments.

NOTE: Test numbers refer to numbers on diagnostic chart.

1) Code 24 sets when MPH reads zero, transaxle is not in Park or Neutral, engine speed indicates vehicle is in a cruise mode (1200-4400) RPM, TPS indicates closed throttle and MAP sensor senses high manifold vacuum. All of these conditions must be met for 2-5 seconds. PM generator only produces a voltage signal if drive wheels are turning greater than 3 MPH.
2) Before replacing control module, PROM/MEM-CAL should be checked for correct application.

DIAGNOSTIC AIDS

A faulty or misadjusted park/neutral switch may set a false Code 24. Use scan tester to check for proper signal in Drive while wiggling shifter. Code 24 may set if vehicle is power braked (brakes applied and throttle depressed) for more than 10 seconds.

94B38555   94D38565   94A07290

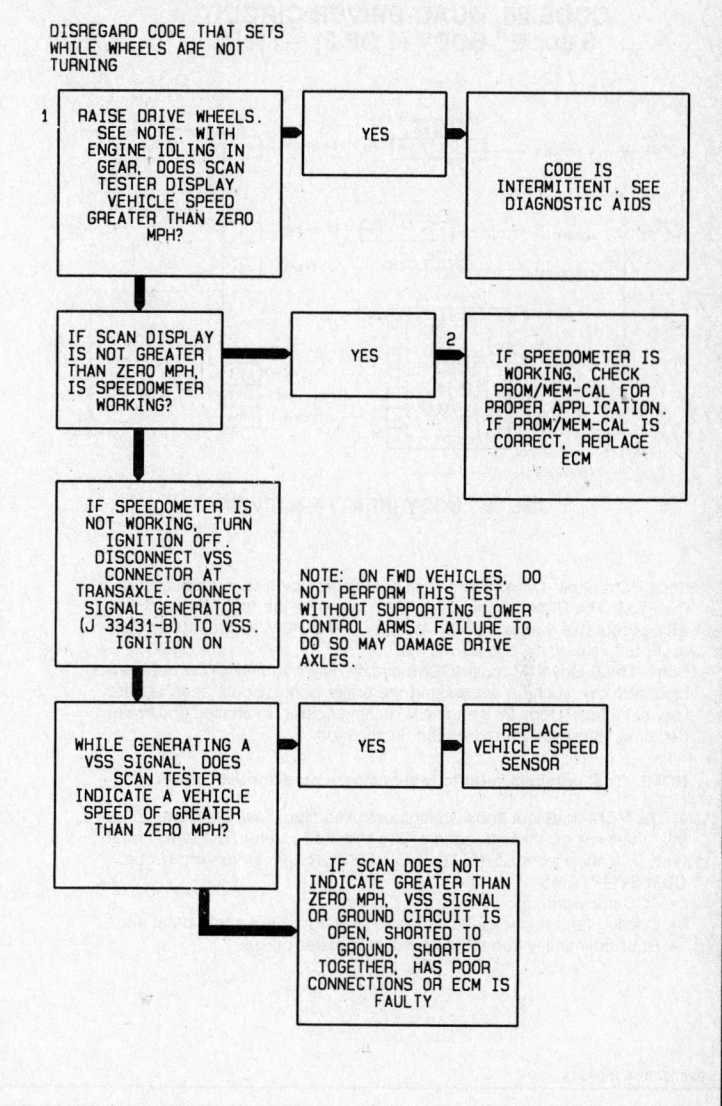

DISREGARD CODE THAT SETS WHILE WHEELS ARE NOT TURNING

1 | RAISE DRIVE WHEELS. SEE NOTE. WITH ENGINE IDLING IN GEAR, DOES SCAN TESTER DISPLAY VEHICLE SPEED GREATER THAN ZERO MPH? → YES → CODE IS INTERMITTENT. SEE DIAGNOSTIC AIDS

IF SCAN DISPLAY IS NOT GREATER THAN ZERO MPH, IS SPEEDOMETER WORKING? → YES → 2 | IF SPEEDOMETER IS WORKING, CHECK PROM/MEM-CAL FOR PROPER APPLICATION. IF PROM/MEM-CAL IS CORRECT, REPLACE ECM

IF SPEEDOMETER IS NOT WORKING, TURN IGNITION OFF. DISCONNECT VSS CONNECTOR AT TRANSAXLE. CONNECT SIGNAL GENERATOR (J 33431-B) TO VSS. IGNITION ON

NOTE: ON FWD VEHICLES, DO NOT PERFORM THIS TEST WITHOUT SUPPORTING LOWER CONTROL ARMS. FAILURE TO DO SO MAY DAMAGE DRIVE AXLES.

WHILE GENERATING A VSS SIGNAL, DOES SCAN TESTER INDICATE A VEHICLE SPEED OF GREATER THAN ZERO MPH? → YES → REPLACE VEHICLE SPEED SENSOR

IF SCAN DOES NOT INDICATE GREATER THAN ZERO MPH, VSS SIGNAL OR GROUND CIRCUIT IS OPEN, SHORTED TO GROUND, SHORTED TOGETHER, HAS POOR CONNECTIONS OR ECM IS FAULTY

CODE 26, QUAD-DRIVER CIRCUIT
3.8L "E" BODY (1 OF 3) – 1993

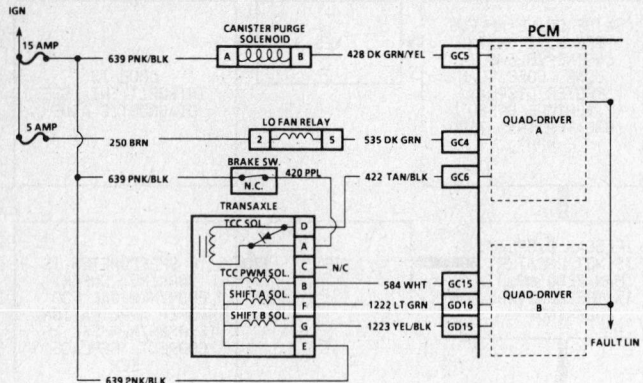

3.8L "E" BODY (REATTA & RIVIERA)

Each PCM Quad-Driver has a fault detect circuit which is monitored by the PCM. The PCM compares voltage values of the fault detect circuit with acceptable values in PCM memory. If the PCM senses other than accepted values, a Code 26 will set.

Some Quad-Driver Module (QDM) circuits will normally cycle between high and low, such as depressing the brake pedal. Some scan testers may set a false Code 26 if engine is running, tester is installed and brake pedal is depressed for more than 30 seconds.

NOTE: Test numbers refer to test numbers on diagnostic chart.

1) The PCM does not know which controlled circuit set the Code 26 so this chart will go through each of the circuits to determine which is at fault. This step tests SERVICE ENGINE SOON light driver and circuit.

QDM SYMPTOMS
- TCC not working.
- Cooling fan on low speed all of the time or will not come on at all.
- Poor driveability due to 100 percent canister purge.

DIAGNOSTIC AIDS

The coolant temperature sensor, in rare cases, may fail to indicate the correct coolant temperature without setting a malfunction code (Code 14 or 15). This could result in turning on the TEMP light without having an overheating condition. It could also result in engine overheating without turning on the TEMP light. Check coolant sensor temperature-to-resistance values.

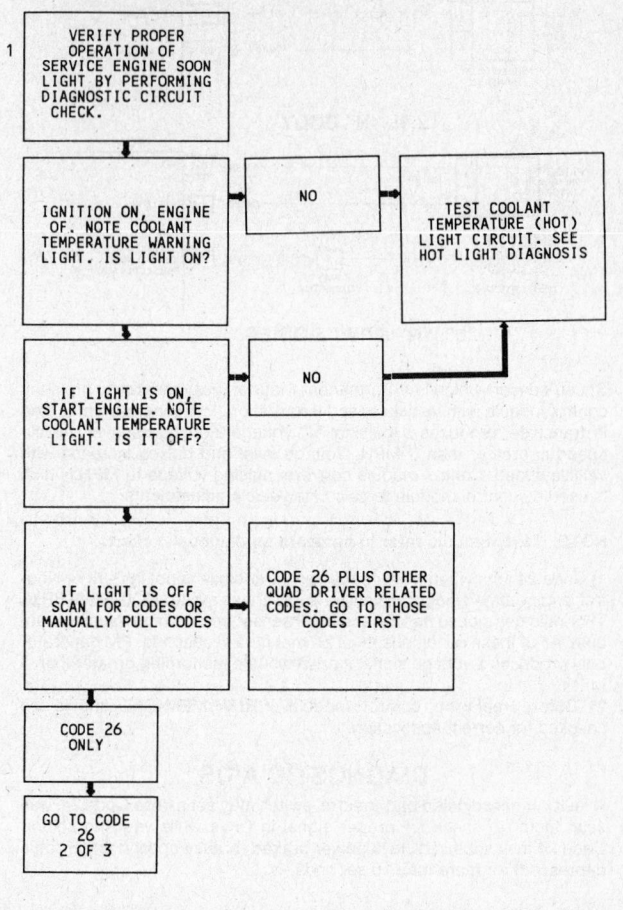

91A07488 91F07315

CODE 26, QUAD-DRIVER CIRCUIT
3.8L "E" BODY (2 OF 3) – 1993

2) This determines which circuit is out of specification. All circuits except GD16 and GD15 should have battery voltage with ignition on, engine not running and ALDL test terminal not grounded.

DIAGNOSTIC AIDS

Monitor the voltage of each terminal while moving related harness connectors, including PCM harness. If the fault is induced, the voltage will change. This may help locate intermittent problems. If code reappears with no problems present, replace PCM.

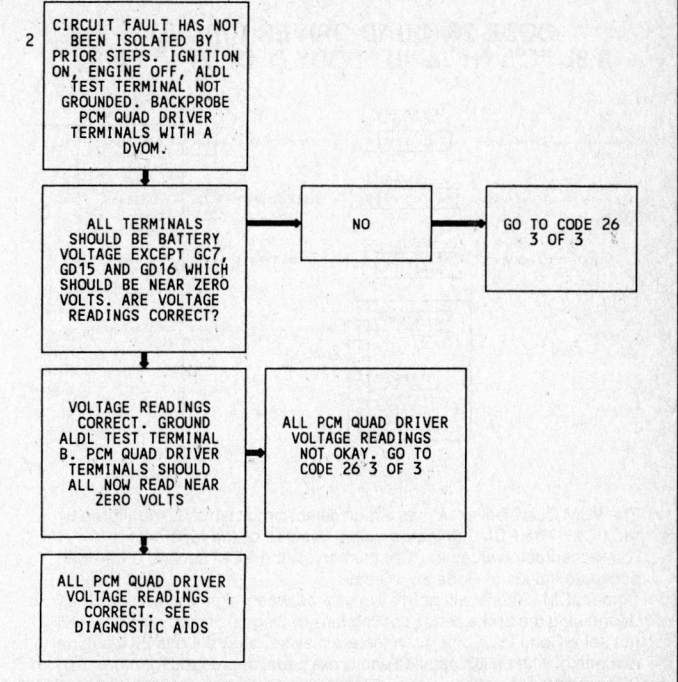

91H07316

CODE 26, QUAD-DRIVER CIRCUIT
3.8L "E" BODY (3 OF 3) – 1993

3) This determines if the problem is the circuit or the component. Factory-installed PCM has an internal circuit breaker and should not need replacing.

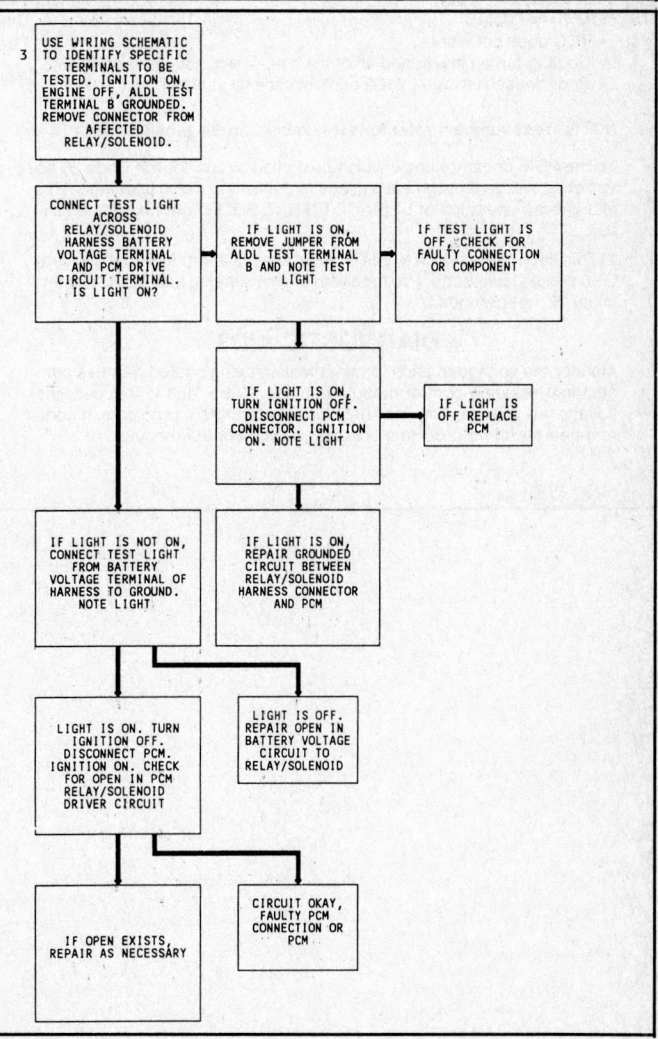

91J07317

CODE 26, QUAD-DRIVER CIRCUIT
3.8L "C", "H" & "U" BODY (1 OF 2) – 1993

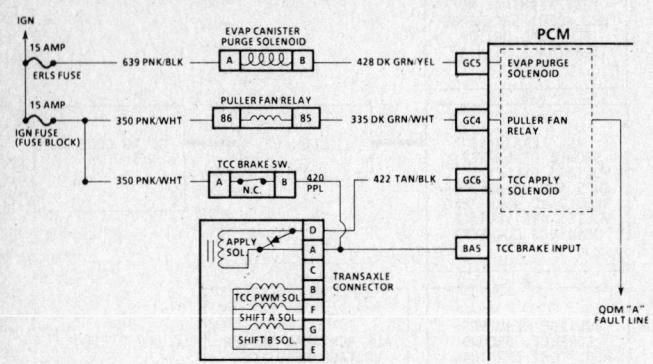

The PCM Quad-Driver "A" has a fault detect circuit which is monitored by the PCM. The PCM compares voltage values of the fault detect circuit with acceptable values in PCM memory. If the PCM senses other than accepted values, a Code 26 will set.

Some QDM circuits will normally cycle between high and low, such as depressing the brake pedal, cooling fans cycling on and off. QDM "A" will not set a Code 26. Some scan testers may set a false Code 26 if engine is running, with tester installed and brake pedal depressed for more than 30 seconds.

QDM SYMPTOMS
- TCC does not work.
- Cooling fan on low speed all of the time or will not come on at all.
- Poor driveability due to 100 percent canister purge.

NOTE: Test numbers refer to test numbers on diagnostic chart.

1) The PCM does not know which controlled circuit set the Code 26 so this chart will go through each circuit to determine which is at fault. This test checks operation of SERVICE ENGINE SOON light and related circuit.

2) This determines which circuit is out of specification. All circuits except GC6 should have battery voltage with engine running and ALDL test terminal "B" not grounded.

DIAGNOSTIC AIDS

Monitor the voltage of each terminal while moving related harness connectors, including control module harness. If the fault is induced, the voltage will change. This may help locate intermittent problems. If code reappears with no problems present, replace control module.

93J76363 93A76364

---

1 → VERIFY PROPER OPERATION OF SERVICE ENGINE SOON LIGHT BY PERFORMING DIAGNOSTIC CIRCUIT CHECK. SEE BASIC DIAGNOSTIC PROCEDURES ARTICLE

↓

SCAN FOR CODES OR MANUALLY PULL CODES → CODE 26 PLUS OTHER QUAD DRIVER RELATED CODES. GO TO THOSE CODES FIRST

↓

CODE 26 ONLY

↓

2 → FAULT HAS NOT BEEN ISOLATED BY PRIOR STEPS. IGNITION OFF, UNPLUG GREEN PCM CONNECTOR. IGNITION ON. PROBE PCM QUAD DRIVER HARNESS TERMINALS WITH POSITIVE AMMETER LEAD

↓

ALL TERMINALS SHOULD MEASURE LESS THAN .75 AMP, BUT NOT ZERO AMPS. DO THEY? → NO → GO TO CODE 26 2 OF 2

↓

YES

↓

ALL PCM QUAD DRIVER READINGS CORRECT. SEE DIAGNOSTIC AIDS

CODE 26, QUAD-DRIVER CIRCUIT
3.8L "C", "H" & "U" BODY (2 OF 2) – 1993

NOTE: Test number refer to test numbers on diagnostic chart.

3) This determines if the problem is the circuit or the component. Factory-installed PCM has an internal circuit breaker and should not need replacing.

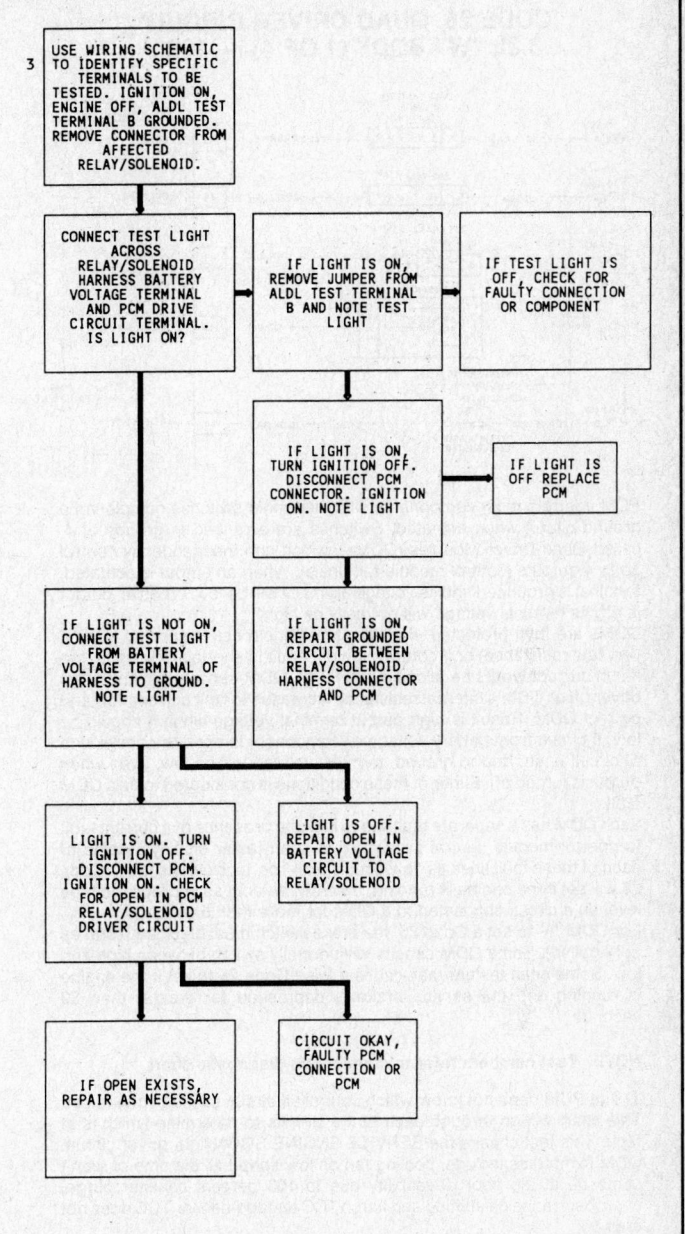

91J07317

CODE 26, QUAD-DRIVER CIRCUIT
3.8L "W" BODY (1 OF 4) – 1993

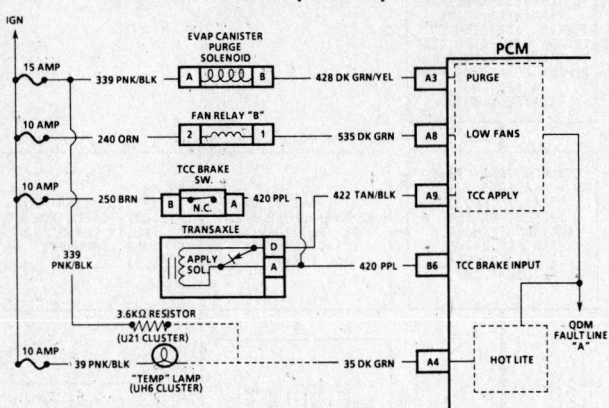

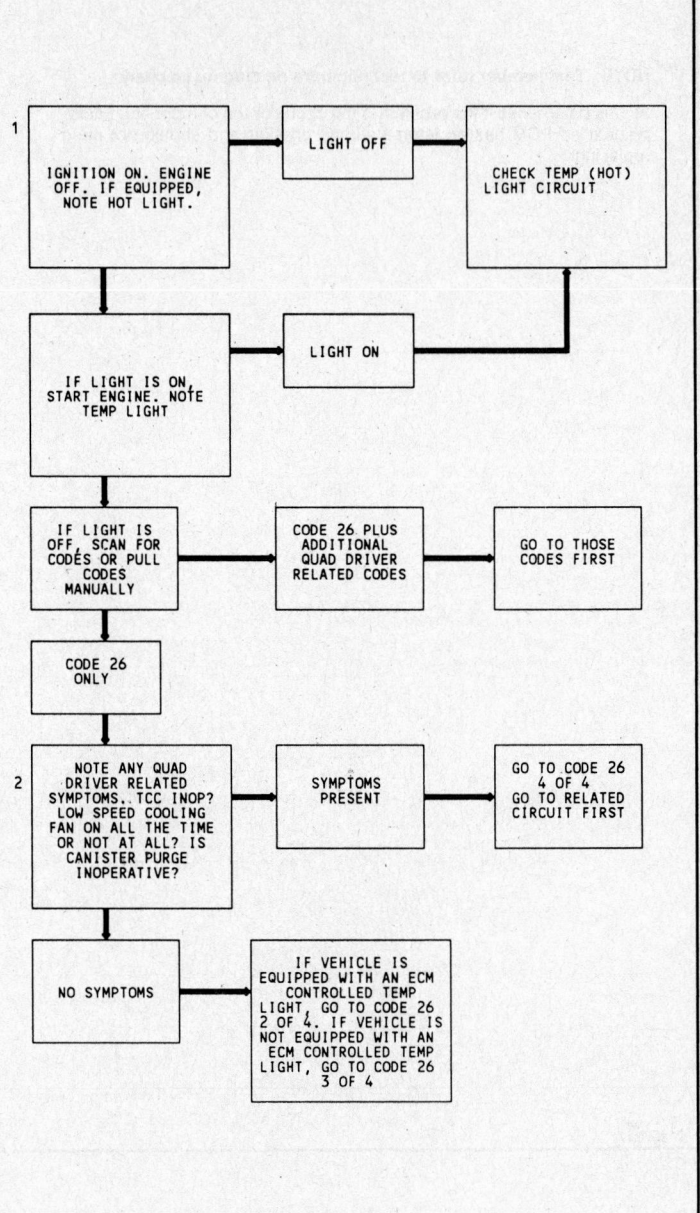

PCM controls most components with electronic switches completing a ground circuit when actuated. Switches are arranged in groups of 4, called Quad-Driver Modules (QDMs), which can independently control up to 4 outputs (control module terminals). When an output is actuated, terminal is grounded and its voltage normally will be low. When an output is off, its terminal voltage will normally be high.

QDMs are fault-protected. If a relay or solenoid coil is shorted (having very low resistance) or if control side of circuit is shorted to voltage, too much current would be allowed into QDM. QDM senses this and turns driver off or QDM's internal resistance increases to limit current flow and protect QDM. Result is high output terminal voltage when it should be low. If circuit from battery voltage or component is open or control side of circuit is shorted to ground, terminal voltage will be low, even when output is turned off. Either of these conditions is considered to be a QDM fault.

Each QDM has a separate fault line to indicate presence of a current fault to control module central processor. A scan tester displays status of each of these fault lines as "low equals okay" or "high equals fault". Code 26 will set if the engine is running, the PCM detects an improper voltage level on a circuit connected to a QDM for more than 5 seconds.

For QDM "A" to set a Code 26, the brake switch must be closed (brakes not applied). Some QDM circuits will normally switch between high and low. Some scan testers may cause a false Code 26 to set if the engine is running and the service brake is depressed for greater than 30 seconds.

NOTE: Test numbers refer to numbers on diagnostic chart.

1) The PCM does not know which controlled circuit caused code to set. This chart will go through each of the circuits to determine which is at fault. This test checks the SERVICE ENGINE SOON light driver circuit. QDM symptoms include: cooling fan on low speed all the time or won't come on at all, poor driveability due to 100 percent canister purge, improper transaxle shifting and harsh TCC engagement or TCC does not engage.

2) QDM-related codes include Codes 38 and 39. QDM symptoms include: TEMP light on all the time, off during bulb check, cooling fan on low speed all the time or won't come on at all, poor driveability due to 100 percent canister purge and TCC does not engage.

93F39334 91F07301

CODE 26, QUAD-DRIVER "A" ERROR
3.8L "W" BODY (2 OF 4) – 1993

NOTE: Test numbers refer to numbers on diagnostic chart.

3) This test determines which circuit is out of specification.

DIAGNOSTIC AIDS

Monitor voltage at each terminal while wiggling related harness connectors, including PCM harness. If the failure is induced, voltage will change. If no faults are found and code resets for no apparent reason, replace PCM.

93G39335

```
3  ┌─────────────────────────┐
   │ IGNITION OFF. REMOVE    │
   │ ECM CONNECTOR.          │
   │ IGNITION ON. DVOM SET   │
   │ TO 2-AMP SCALE. PROBE   │
   │ ECM HARNESS TERMINALS   │
   │ A3, A4, A8 AND A9       │
   │ WITH BLACK DVOM LEAD    │
   │ TO GROUND.              │
   └─────────────────────────┘
                │
                ▼
   ┌─────────────────────────┐      ┌──────────────────┐
   │ EACH TERMINAL           │      │ IF PROBLEMS ARE  │
   │ SHOULD MEASURE LESS     │─────▶│ INDICATED SEE    │
   │ THAN .75 AMP, BUT       │      │ CODE 26          │
   │ NOT ZERO. NOTE ANY      │      │ 4 OF 4           │
   │ TERMINAL THAT           │      └──────────────────┘
   │ MEASURES GREATER        │
   │ THAN .75 AMP, OR ZERO.  │
   └─────────────────────────┘
                │
                ▼
   ┌─────────────────────────┐
   │ IF NO PROBLEMS ARE      │
   │ FOUND, SEE              │
   │ INTERMITTENTS IN        │
   │ TROUBLE SHOOTING-NO     │
   │ CODES ARTICLE.          │
   │ ALSO, SEE               │
   │ DIAGNOSTIC AIDS         │
   └─────────────────────────┘
```

CODE 26, QUAD-DRIVER "A" ERROR
3.8L "W" BODY (3 OF 4) – 1993

NOTE: Test numbers refer to numbers on diagnostic chart.

3) This step will determine which circuit is out of specification. If all circuits check out okay, the in-line resistor (used in place of the hot light) and related wiring should be checked. The in-line resistor is taped into the engine harness between the engine electrical center and the PCM pigtails, about 2" from the PCM pigtail junction.

DIAGNOSTIC AIDS

Monitor voltage at each terminal while wiggling related harness connectors, including PCM harness. If the failure is induced, voltage will change. If no faults are found and code resets for no apparent reason, replace PCM.

93H39336

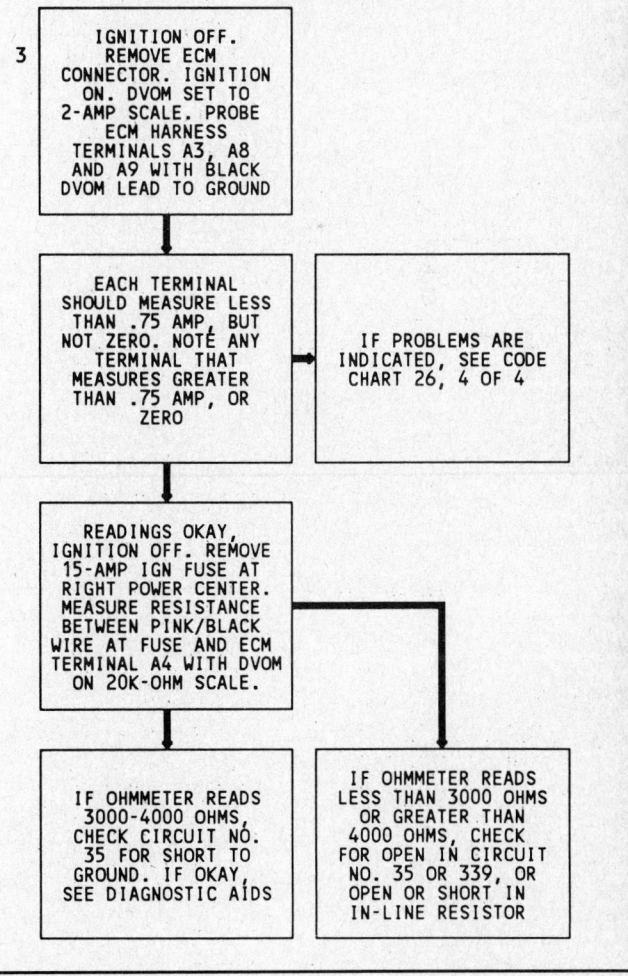

```
3  ┌─────────────────────────┐
   │ IGNITION OFF.           │
   │ REMOVE ECM              │
   │ CONNECTOR. IGNITION     │
   │ ON. DVOM SET TO         │
   │ 2-AMP SCALE. PROBE      │
   │ ECM HARNESS             │
   │ TERMINALS A3, A8        │
   │ AND A9 WITH BLACK       │
   │ DVOM LEAD TO GROUND     │
   └─────────────────────────┘
                │
                ▼
   ┌─────────────────────────┐      ┌──────────────────┐
   │ EACH TERMINAL           │      │ IF PROBLEMS ARE  │
   │ SHOULD MEASURE LESS     │─────▶│ INDICATED, SEE   │
   │ THAN .75 AMP, BUT       │      │ CODE CHART 26,   │
   │ NOT ZERO. NOTE ANY      │      │ 4 OF 4           │
   │ TERMINAL THAT           │      └──────────────────┘
   │ MEASURES GREATER        │
   │ THAN .75 AMP, OR ZERO   │
   └─────────────────────────┘
                │
                ▼
   ┌─────────────────────────┐
   │ READINGS OKAY,          │
   │ IGNITION OFF. REMOVE    │
   │ 15-AMP IGN FUSE AT      │────────────┐
   │ RIGHT POWER CENTER.     │            │
   │ MEASURE RESISTANCE      │            │
   │ BETWEEN PINK/BLACK      │            │
   │ WIRE AT FUSE AND ECM    │            │
   │ TERMINAL A4 WITH DVOM   │            │
   │ ON 20K-OHM SCALE.       │            │
   └─────────────────────────┘            │
                │                         │
                ▼                         ▼
   ┌─────────────────────────┐  ┌──────────────────────┐
   │ IF OHMMETER READS       │  │ IF OHMMETER READS    │
   │ 3000-4000 OHMS,         │  │ LESS THAN 3000 OHMS  │
   │ CHECK CIRCUIT NO.       │  │ OR GREATER THAN      │
   │ 35 FOR SHORT TO         │  │ 4000 OHMS, CHECK     │
   │ GROUND. IF OKAY,        │  │ FOR OPEN IN CIRCUIT  │
   │ SEE DIAGNOSTIC AIDS     │  │ NO. 35 OR 339, OR    │
   └─────────────────────────┘  │ OPEN OR SHORT IN     │
                                │ IN-LINE RESISTOR     │
                                └──────────────────────┘
```

CODE 26, QUAD-DRIVER "A" ERROR
3.8L "W" BODY (4 OF 4) – 1993

NOTE: Test numbers refer to numbers on diagnostic chart.

4) This test will determine if the problem is the circuit or the component. As the factory installed PCM is protected by an internal circuit breaker, it is unlikely that the PCM needs to be replaced.

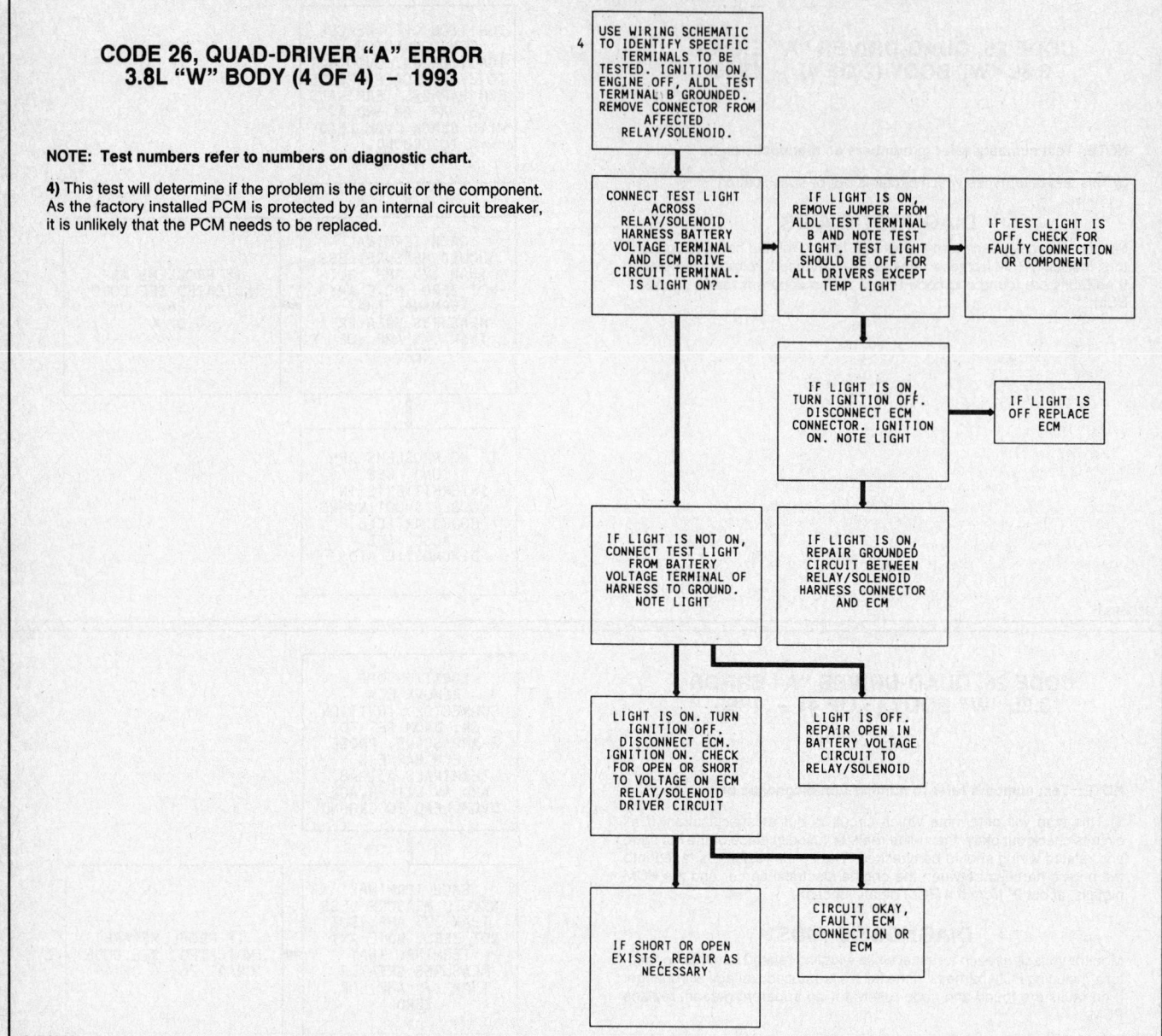

91B07304

CODE 27, QUAD-DRIVER NO. 1 ERROR
2.3L "N" BODY – 1994

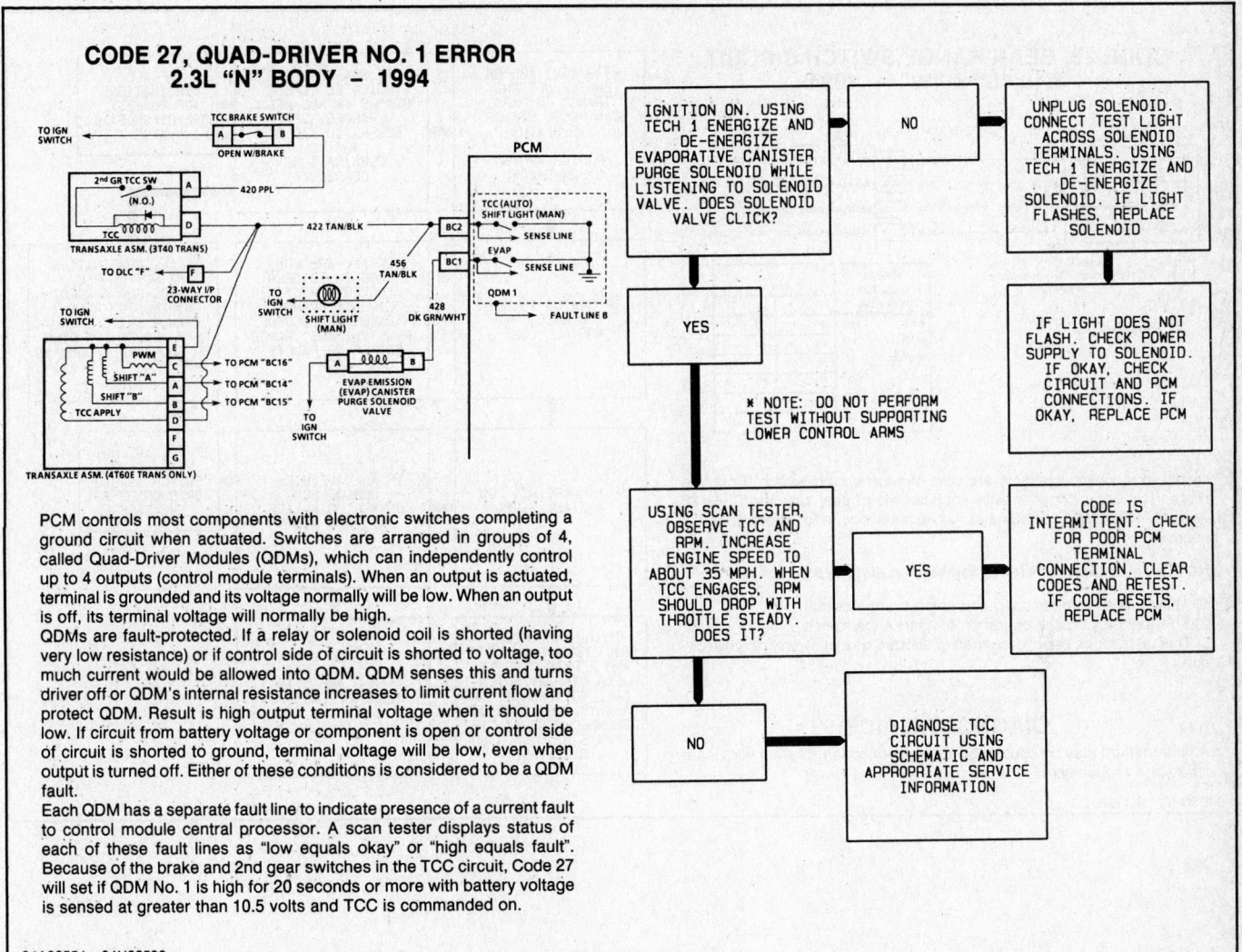

PCM controls most components with electronic switches completing a ground circuit when actuated. Switches are arranged in groups of 4, called Quad-Driver Modules (QDMs), which can independently control up to 4 outputs (control module terminals). When an output is actuated, terminal is grounded and its voltage normally will be low. When an output is off, its terminal voltage will be high.

QDMs are fault-protected. If a relay or solenoid coil is shorted (having very low resistance) or if control side of circuit is shorted to voltage, too much current would be allowed into QDM. QDM senses this and turns driver off or QDM's internal resistance increases to limit current flow and protect QDM. Result is high output terminal voltage when it should be low. If circuit from battery voltage or component is open or control side of circuit is shorted to ground, terminal voltage will be low, even when output is turned off. Either of these conditions is considered to be a QDM fault.

Each QDM has a separate fault line to indicate presence of a current fault to control module central processor. A scan tester displays status of each of these fault lines as "low equals okay" or "high equals fault". Because of the brake and 2nd gear switches in the TCC circuit, Code 27 will set if QDM No. 1 is high for 20 seconds or more with battery voltage is sensed at greater than 10.5 volts and TCC is commanded on.

94A38554   94H38593

CODE 28, GEAR RANGE SWITCH CIRCUIT
3.1L "L" & "W" – 1994

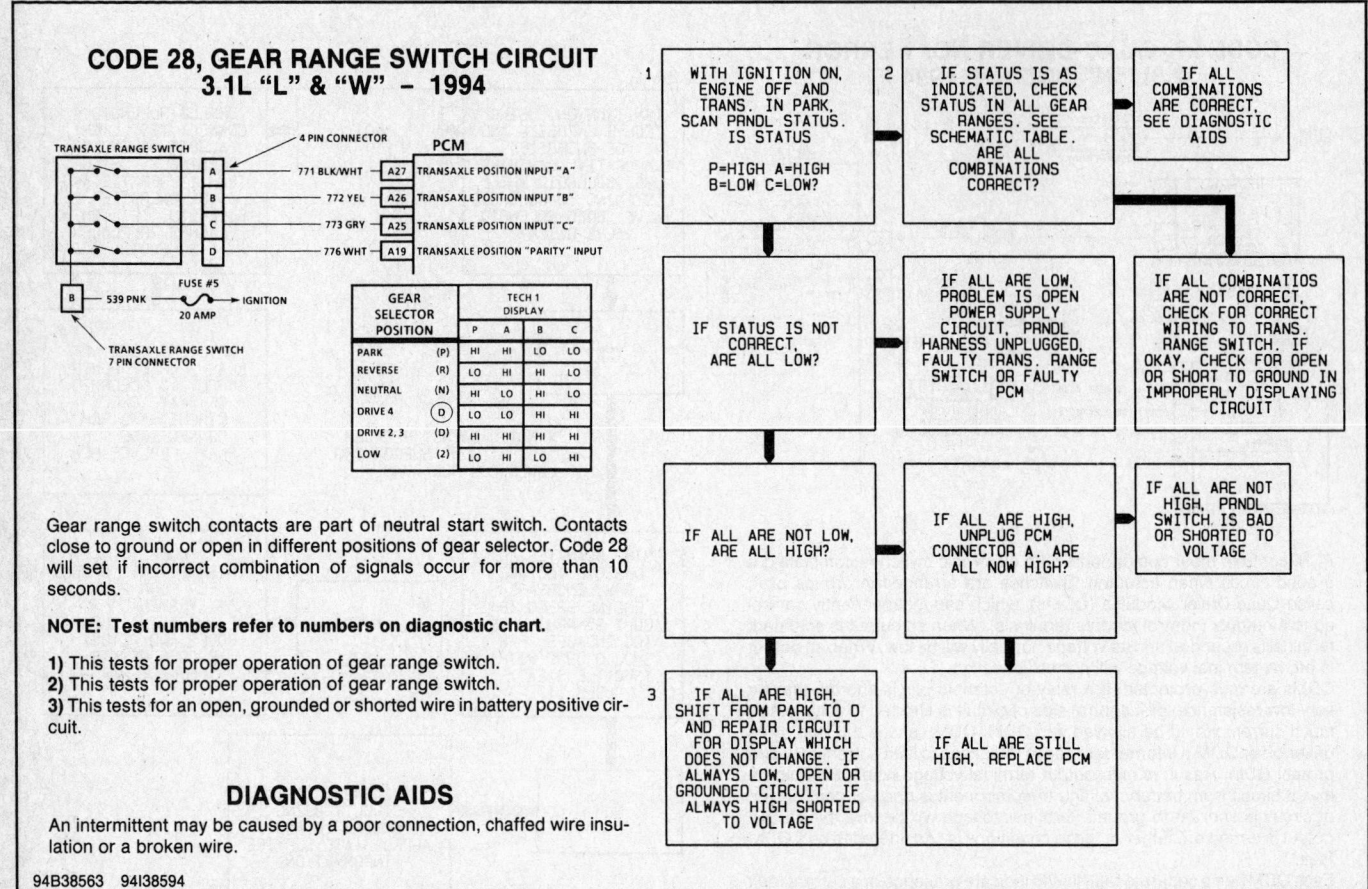

GEAR SELECTOR POSITION		TECH 1 DISPLAY			
		P	A	B	C
PARK	(P)	HI	HI	LO	LO
REVERSE	(R)	LO	HI	HI	LO
NEUTRAL	(N)	LO	LO	HI	LO
DRIVE 4	(D)	LO	LO	HI	HI
DRIVE 2, 3	(D)	HI	HI	HI	HI
LOW	(2)	LO	HI	LO	HI

Gear range switch contacts are part of neutral start switch. Contacts close to ground or open in different positions of gear selector. Code 28 will set if incorrect combination of signals occur for more than 10 seconds.

NOTE: Test numbers refer to numbers on diagnostic chart.

1) This tests for proper operation of gear range switch.
2) This tests for proper operation of gear range switch.
3) This tests for an open, grounded or shorted wire in battery positive circuit.

DIAGNOSTIC AIDS

An intermittent may be caused by a poor connection, chaffed wire insulation or a broken wire.

94B38563   94I38594

Diagnostic chart (right side):

1 — WITH IGNITION ON, ENGINE OFF AND TRANS. IN PARK, SCAN PRNDL STATUS. IS STATUS P=HIGH A=HIGH B=LOW C=LOW?

2 — IF STATUS IS AS INDICATED, CHECK STATUS IN ALL GEAR RANGES. SEE SCHEMATIC TABLE. ARE ALL COMBINATIONS CORRECT?

IF ALL COMBINATIONS ARE CORRECT, SEE DIAGNOSTIC AIDS

IF STATUS IS NOT CORRECT, ARE ALL LOW?

IF ALL ARE LOW, PROBLEM IS OPEN POWER SUPPLY CIRCUIT, PRNDL HARNESS UNPLUGGED, FAULTY TRANS. RANGE SWITCH OR FAULTY PCM

IF ALL COMBINATIOS ARE NOT CORRECT, CHECK FOR CORRECT WIRING TO TRANS. RANGE SWITCH. IF OKAY, CHECK FOR OPEN OR SHORT TO GROUND IN IMPROPERLY DISPLAYING CIRCUIT

IF ALL ARE NOT LOW, ARE ALL HIGH?

IF ALL ARE HIGH, UNPLUG PCM CONNECTOR A. ARE ALL NOW HIGH?

IF ALL ARE NOT HIGH, PRNDL SWITCH IS BAD OR SHORTED TO VOLTAGE

3 — IF ALL ARE HIGH, SHIFT FROM PARK TO D AND REPAIR CIRCUIT FOR DISPLAY WHICH DOES NOT CHANGE. IF ALWAYS LOW, OPEN OR GROUNDED CIRCUIT. IF ALWAYS HIGH SHORTED TO VOLTAGE

IF ALL ARE STILL HIGH, REPLACE PCM

CODE 28, GEAR RANGE SWITCH CIRCUIT
3.1L "N" – 1994

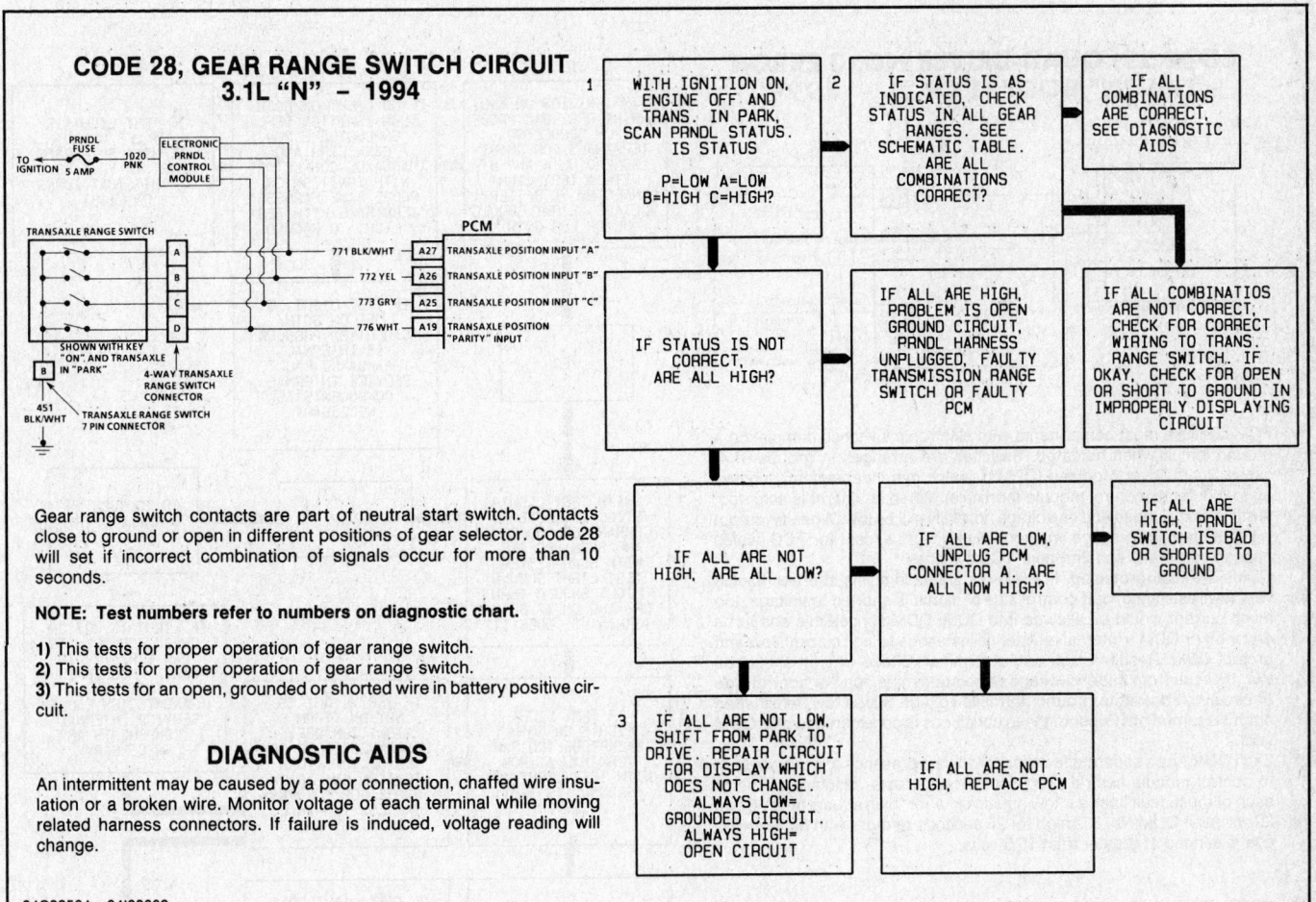

Gear range switch contacts are part of neutral start switch. Contacts close to ground or open in different positions of gear selector. Code 28 will set if incorrect combination of signals occur for more than 10 seconds.

NOTE: Test numbers refer to numbers on diagnostic chart.

1) This tests for proper operation of gear range switch.
2) This tests for proper operation of gear range switch.
3) This tests for an open, grounded or shorted wire in battery positive circuit.

DIAGNOSTIC AIDS

An intermittent may be caused by a poor connection, chaffed wire insulation or a broken wire. Monitor voltage of each terminal while moving related harness connectors. If failure is induced, voltage reading will change.

94C38564   94I38602

CODE 29, QUAD-DRIVER NO. 3 ERROR
2.3L "N" BODY (1 Of 2) – 1994

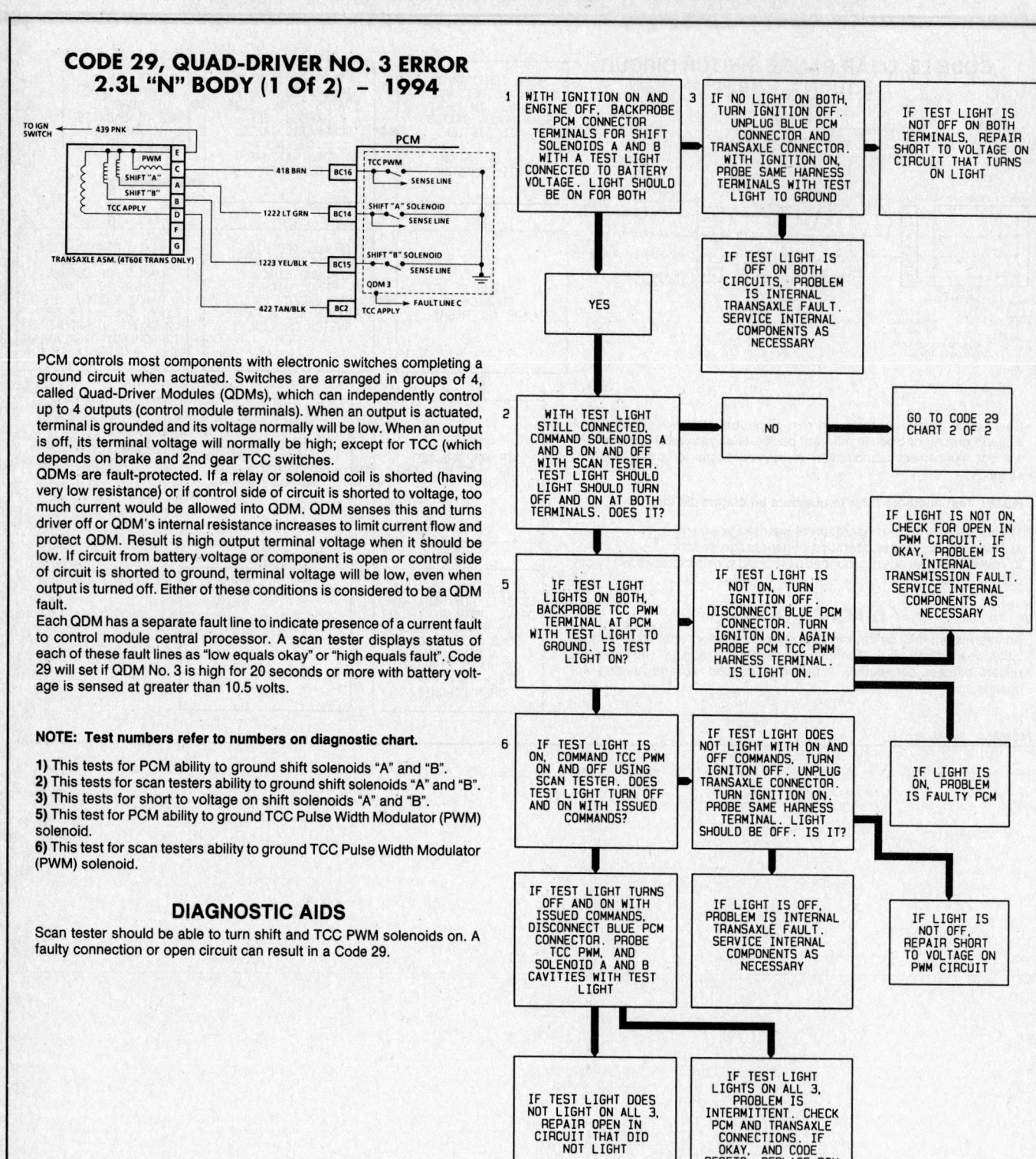

PCM controls most components with electronic switches completing a ground circuit when actuated. Switches are arranged in groups of 4, called Quad-Driver Modules (QDMs), which can independently control up to 4 outputs (control module terminals). When an output is actuated, terminal is grounded and its voltage normally will be low. When an output is off, its terminal voltage will normally be high; except for TCC (which depends on brake and 2nd gear TCC switches).

QDMs are fault-protected. If a relay or solenoid coil is shorted (having very low resistance) or if control side of circuit is shorted to voltage, too much current would be allowed into QDM. QDM senses this and turns driver off or QDM's internal resistance increases to limit current flow and protect QDM. Result is high output terminal voltage when it should be low. If circuit from battery voltage or component is open or control side of circuit is shorted to ground, terminal voltage will be low, even when output is turned off. Either of these conditions is considered to be a QDM fault.

Each QDM has a separate fault line to indicate presence of a current fault to control module central processor. A scan tester displays status of each of these fault lines as "low equals okay" or "high equals fault". Code 29 will set if QDM No. 3 is high for 20 seconds or more with battery voltage is sensed at greater than 10.5 volts.

NOTE: Test numbers refer to numbers on diagnostic chart.

1) This tests for PCM ability to ground shift solenoids "A" and "B".
2) This tests for scan testers ability to ground shift solenoids "A" and "B".
3) This tests for short to voltage on shift solenoids "A" and "B".
5) This test for PCM ability to ground TCC Pulse Width Modulator (PWM) solenoid.
6) This test for scan testers ability to ground TCC Pulse Width Modulator (PWM) solenoid.

DIAGNOSTIC AIDS

Scan tester should be able to turn shift and TCC PWM solenoids on. A faulty connection or open circuit can result in a Code 29.

94J38553   94J38595

CODE 29, QUAD-DRIVER NO. 3 ERROR
2.3L "N" BODY (2 Of 2) – 1994

NOTE: Test numbers refer to numbers on diagnostic chart.

4) This step tests for continuity of the shift solenoid circuits.

DIAGNOSTIC AIDS

Scan tester should be able to turn shift and TCC PWM solenoids on. A faulty connection or open circuit can result in a Code 29.

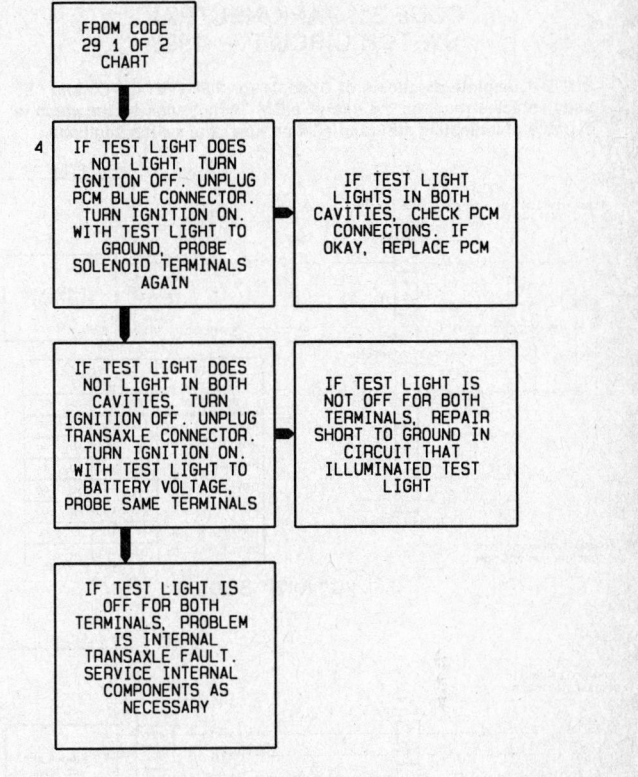

94A38596

CODE 31, PARK/NEUTRAL SWITCH CIRCUIT – 1993

NOTE: Complete diagnosis of Code 31 for 3.8L (VIN L) "C" and "E" body vehicles requires the use of a GM Tech 1 scan tester which is capable of indicating status of all 4 park/neutral switch positions.

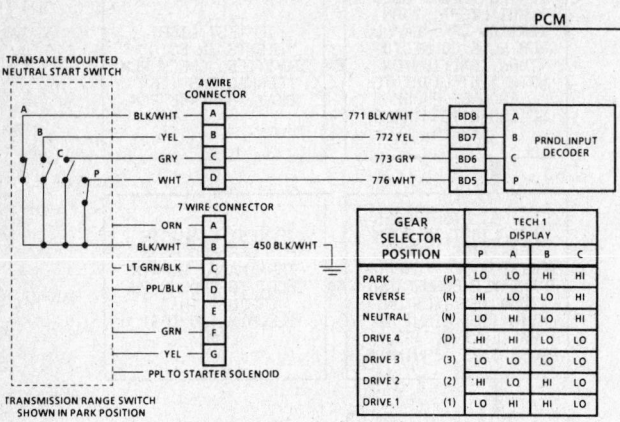

3.8L "C" & "H" BODIES

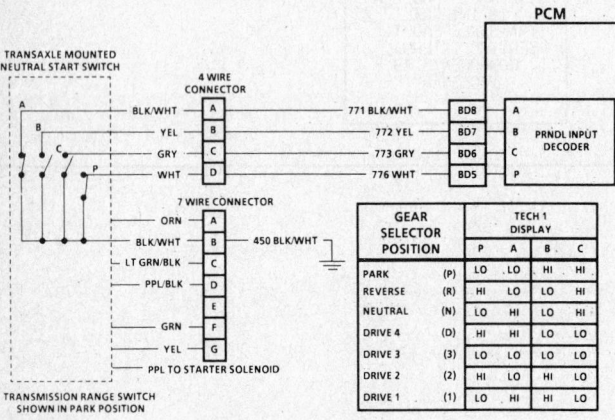

3.8L "E" & "U" BODIES

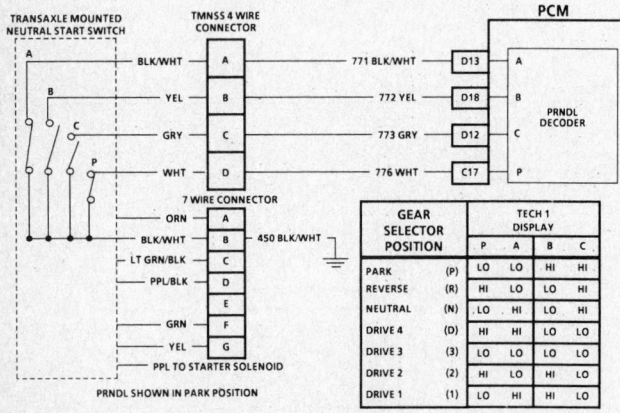

3.8L "W" BODY

The park/neutral switch contacts are part of the neutral start switch. The contacts close to ground in Park or Neutral and open in Drive. Code 31 will set if park/neutral signal circuit indicates an open for 3-4 consecutive starts or if conditions occur as follows:

- No 29 exists.
- Circuit No. 434 indicates ground.
- Transmission is in high gear.
- TCC is locked on.
- Vehicle speed is greater than 45 MPH and TPS is less than 15 percent.
- All above conditions have been met for at least 12 seconds.

NOTE: Test numbers refer to test numbers on diagnostic chart.

1) This tests for a closed switch to ground in Park.
2) This tests for proper operation of PRNDL.
3) Be sure scan tester indicates Drive, even when wiggling shifter.

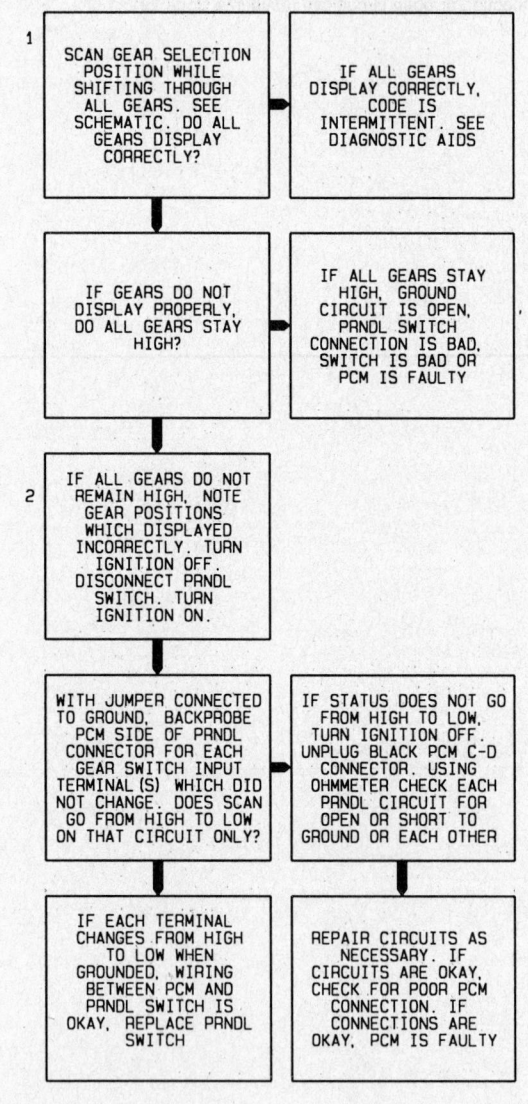

CODE 36, SHIFT PROBLEM
3.8L "C" & "H" BODIES – 1993

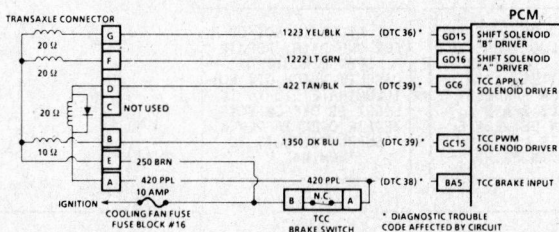

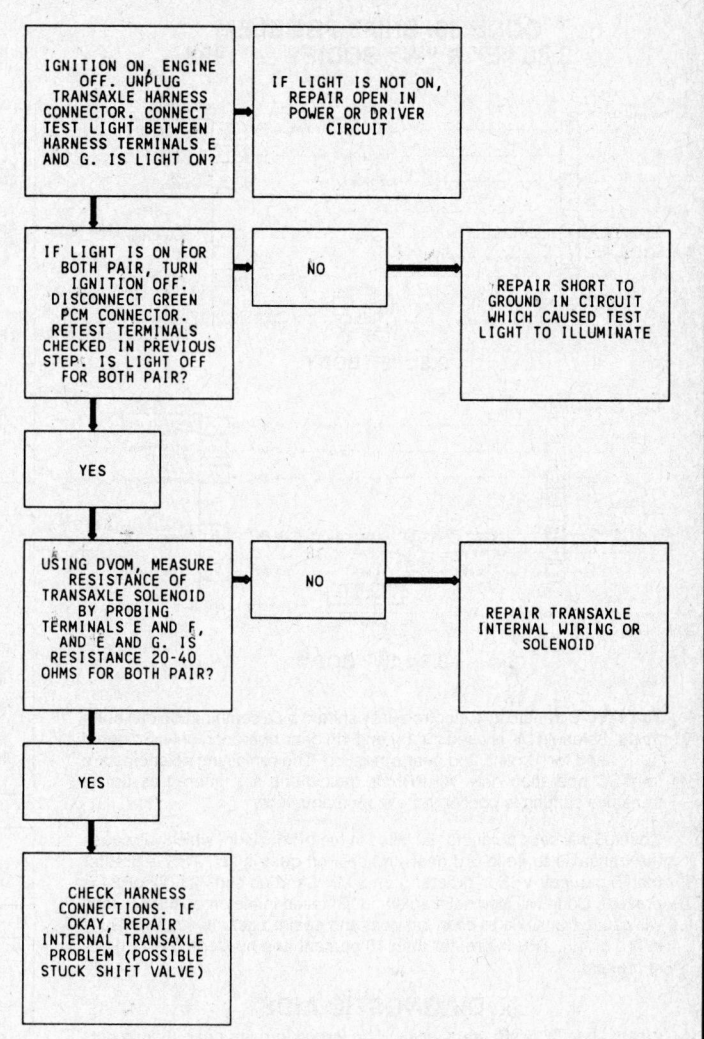

The 4T60-E transaxle is an electronically shifted transaxle. Within the transaxle are 3 or 4 solenoids. Solenoid "A" is used for 1st and 4th gear operation only. Solenoid "B" is used for 1st and 2nd gear operation. The remaining solenoid(s) are for TCC operation only. This trouble code chart deals with control solenoids only.

When ignition is turned on, solenoids "A" and "B" receive battery voltage. The PCM grounds signal drivers for both solenoids during 1st gear. When vehicle speed and TP sensor calibrated values are reached, PCM turns off ground for solenoid "A" and transaxle shifts into 2nd gear. To engage 3rd gear, PCM turns off ground for solenoid "B". When vehicle speed is high enough, PCM grounds solenoid "A" and 4th gear is engaged.

All PRNDL indications are ignored as far as transaxle shifting is concerned except manual low. Code 36 will set if solenoid "B" failed in the off position, which will cause the transaxle to be in 3rd gear and desired gear is 1st, TPS is greater than 5 percent, VSS is greater than 5 MPH and no code 21, 22 or 24 is present. Code will also set if solenoid "B" failed in the on position, which will cause transaxle to be in 1st gear and desired gear is 4th, PRNDL is in 3rd or 4th, TPS is greater than 10 percent and no Code 31, 21 or 22 is present.

DIAGNOSTIC AIDS

When Code 36 is set, transaxle will be forced into 3rd gear. If code sets due to a grounded circuit No. 1223, 1st and 2nd gear operation will be available only. If circuit No. 1223 is open, 3rd and 4th gear operation will be available only. If fault goes away, normal operation will be resumed for the duration of the key cycle.

93D39373 93E39374

CODE 36, SHIFT PROBLEM
3.8L "E" & "W" BODIES – 1993

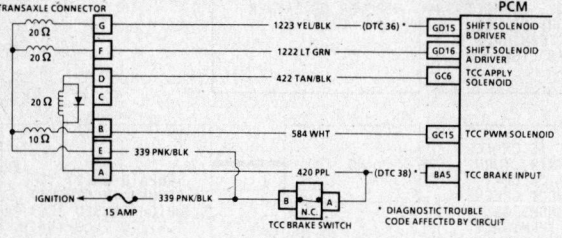

3.8L "E" BODY

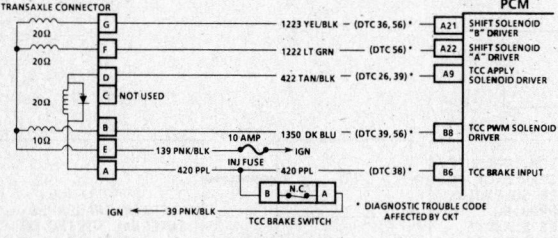

3.8L "W" BODY

The 4T60-E transaxle is electronically shifted by a combination of 4 solenoids. Solenoid "A" is used for 1st and 4th gear operation only. Solenoid "B" is used for 1st and 2nd gear operation. The remaining solenoids are for TCC operation only. All PRNDL indications are ignored as far as transaxle shifting is concerned except manual low.

Code 36 will set if solenoid "B" failed in the off position, which will cause the transaxle to be in 3rd gear and desired gear is 1st, TPS is greater than 5 percent, VSS is greater than 5 MPH and no code 21, 22 or 24 is present. Code will also set if solenoid "B" failed in the on position, which will cause transaxle to be in 1st gear and desired gear is 4th, PRNDL is in 3rd or 4th, TPS is greater than 10 percent and no Code 31, 21 or 22 is present.

DIAGNOSTIC AIDS

When Code 36 is set, transaxle will be forced into 3rd gear. If code sets due to a grounded circuit No. 1223, 1st and 2nd gear operation will be available only. If circuit No. 1223 is open, 3rd and 4th gear operation will be available only. If fault goes away, normal operation will be resumed for the duration of the key cycle.

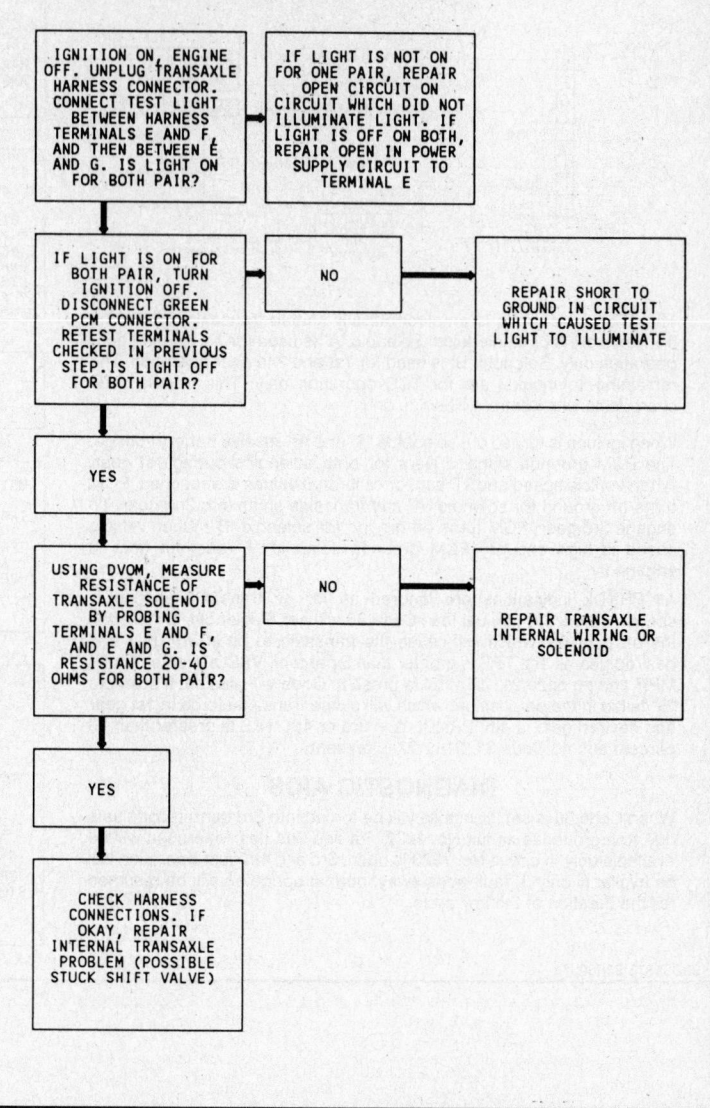

93F39375 93G39376 91H07335

CODE 36, SHIFT PROBLEM
3.8L "U" BODY – 1993

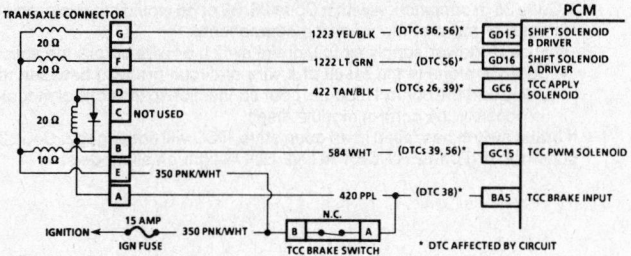

The 4T60-E transaxle is electronically shifted by a combination of 4 solenoids. Solenoid "A" is used for 1st and 4th gear operation only. Solenoid "B" is used for 1st and 2nd gear operation. The remaining solenoids are for TCC operation only. All PRNDL indications are ignored as far as transaxle shifting is concerned except manual low.

Code 36 will set if solenoid "B" failed in the off position, which will cause the transaxle to be in 3rd gear and desired gear is 1st, TPS is greater than 5 percent, VSS is greater than 5 MPH and no code 21, 22 or 24 is present. Code will also set if solenoid "B" failed in the on position, which will cause transaxle to be in 1st gear and desired gear is 4th, PRNDL is in 3rd or 4th, TPS is greater than 10 percent and no Code 31, 21 or 22 is present.

DIAGNOSTIC AIDS

When Code 36 is set, transaxle will be forced into 3rd gear. If code sets due to a grounded circuit No. 1223, 1st and 2nd gear operation will be available only. If circuit No. 1223 is open, 3rd and 4th gear operation will be available only. If fault goes away, normal operation will be resumed for the duration of the key cycle.

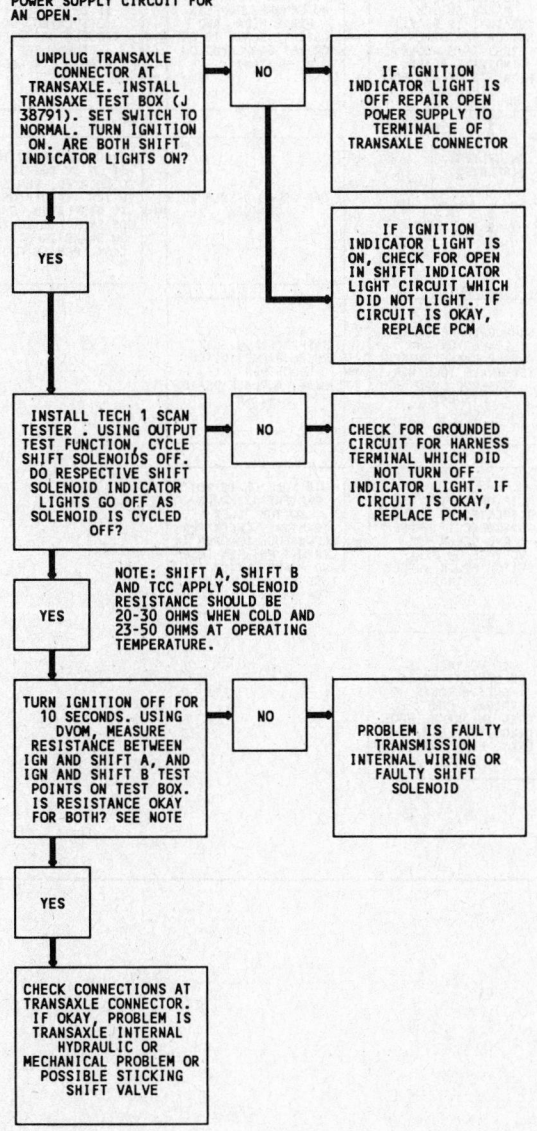

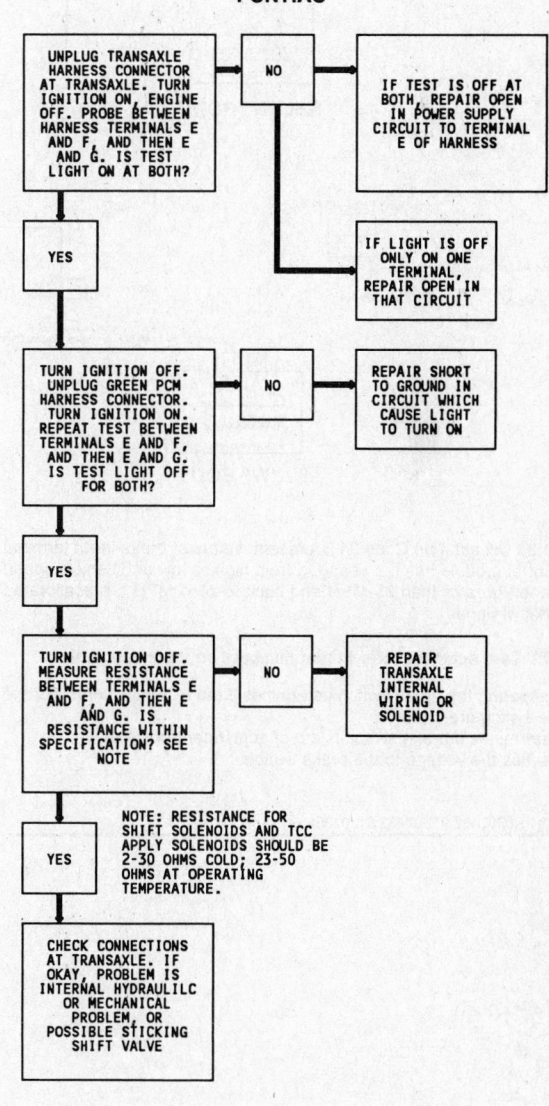

93C76408 93D76409 93H76411

CODE 38, BRAKE SWITCH CIRCUIT

3.8L "C" & "E" BODIES

3.8L "H" BODY

3.8L "W" BODY

Code 38 will set if no Code 24 is present, status at brake input terminal of control module has not changed from high to low and vehicle speed has been greater than 35 MPH and back to zero MPH a precalibrated number of times.

NOTE: Test numbers refer to test numbers on diagnostic chart.

1) Jumpering the brake switch determines if the PCM and wiring for the brake switch are okay.
2) Determines if brake switch is out of adjustment or is faulty.
3) Verifies the voltage to the brake switch.

91A07431 91C07432 91E07433 91J07336

DIAGNOSTIC AIDS

A Code 38 in conjunction with a Code 26, 39 or 56 would mean a problem with one or more of the following components.
• Fuse or power supply circuit, brake switch or wire before the splice.
• Code 38 alone is the result of a wire or circuit problem between the splice and the control module, poor connection to the control module, or possibly the control module, itself.

If brake switch has failed in an open state, TCC will not engage. Code 38 does not turn on SERVICE ENGINE SOON light on all models.

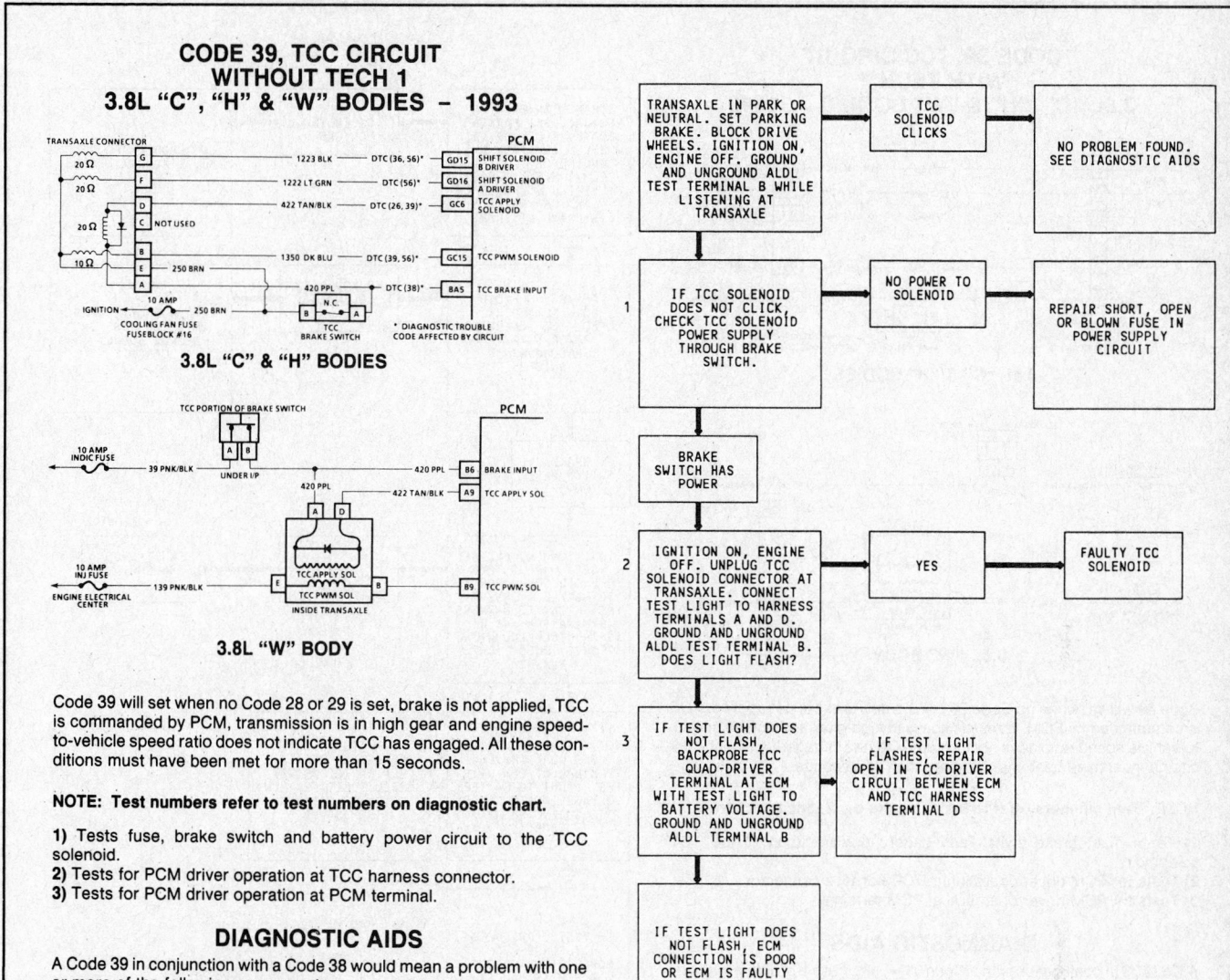

CODE 39, TCC CIRCUIT
WITHOUT TECH 1
3.8L "C", "H" & "W" BODIES – 1993

3.8L "C" & "H" BODIES

3.8L "W" BODY

Code 39 will set when no Code 28 or 29 is set, brake is not applied, TCC is commanded by PCM, transmission is in high gear and engine speed-to-vehicle speed ratio does not indicate TCC has engaged. All these conditions must have been met for more than 15 seconds.

NOTE: Test numbers refer to test numbers on diagnostic chart.

1) Tests fuse, brake switch and battery power circuit to the TCC solenoid.
2) Tests for PCM driver operation at TCC harness connector.
3) Tests for PCM driver operation at PCM terminal.

DIAGNOSTIC AIDS

A Code 39 in conjunction with a Code 38 would mean a problem with one or more of the following components:
• Fuse or power circuit, brake switch or wire before the splice.
Code 39 alone indicates a problem at:
• Circuit No. 420 between splice and TCC solenoid.
• Circuit No. 422 between TCC solenoid and PCM.
• Connection to the PCM or faulty PCM.

93E39382 93F39383 91F07339

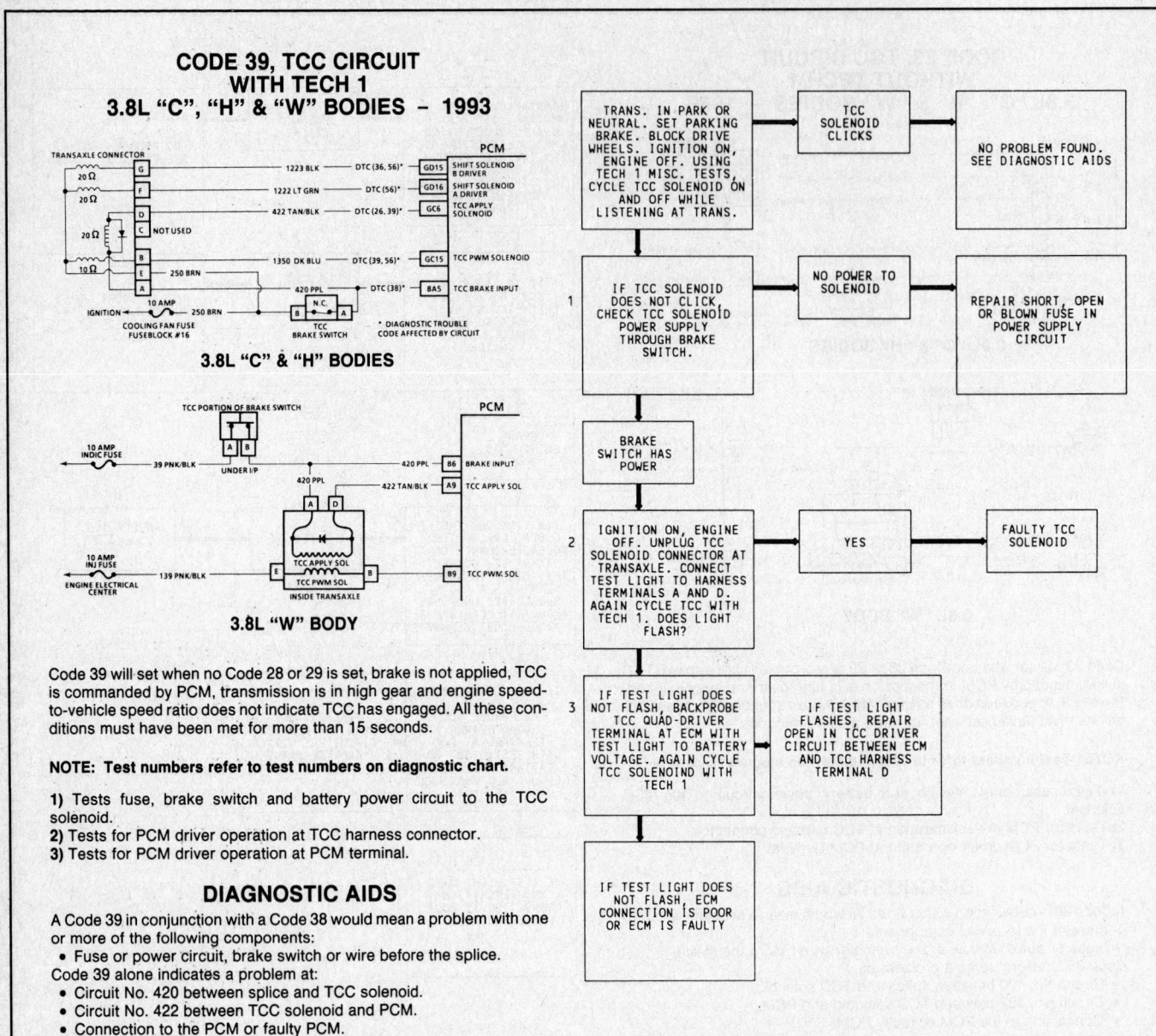

CODE 39, TCC CIRCUIT WITH TECH 1
3.8L "C", "H" & "W" BODIES – 1993

3.8L "C" & "H" BODIES

3.8L "W" BODY

Code 39 will set when no Code 28 or 29 is set, brake is not applied, TCC is commanded by PCM, transmission is in high gear and engine speed-to-vehicle speed ratio does not indicate TCC has engaged. All these conditions must have been met for more than 15 seconds.

NOTE: Test numbers refer to test numbers on diagnostic chart.

1) Tests fuse, brake switch and battery power circuit to the TCC solenoid.
2) Tests for PCM driver operation at TCC harness connector.
3) Tests for PCM driver operation at PCM terminal.

DIAGNOSTIC AIDS

A Code 39 in conjunction with a Code 38 would mean a problem with one or more of the following components:
• Fuse or power circuit, brake switch or wire before the splice.
Code 39 alone indicates a problem at:
• Circuit No. 420 between splice and TCC solenoid.
• Circuit No. 422 between TCC solenoid and PCM.
• Connection to the PCM or faulty PCM.

93E39382 93F39383 91H07340

CODE 39, TCC CIRCUIT
3.8L "U" BODY – 1993

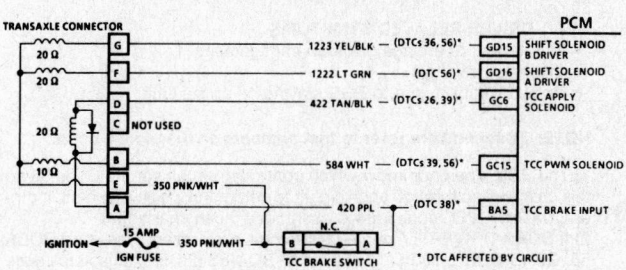

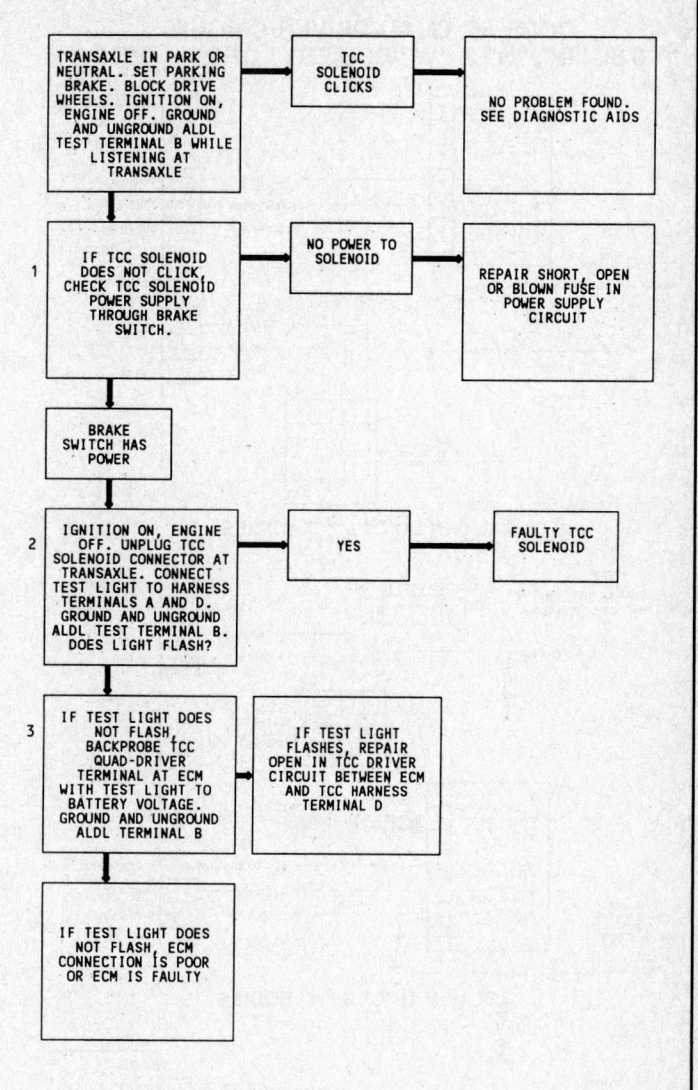

Code 39 will set when vehicle speed is greater than 35 MPH, brake is not applied, TCC is commanded by PCM, transmission is in high gear and engine speed-to-vehicle speed ratio does not indicate TCC has engaged. All these conditions must have been met for more than 10 seconds.

NOTE: Test numbers refer to test numbers on diagnostic chart.

1) Grounding ALDL connector casues PCM to ground TCC control citcuit. This step tests fuse, brake switch and battery power circuit to the TCC solenoid.

2) Tests for faulty solenoid, power suppply or driver circuit.

3) Tests for PCM driver operation at PCM terminal.

DIAGNOSTIC AIDS

Scan tester only indicates when PCM has commanded TCC on. This does not indicate TCC is actually engaged. To determine if TCC is engaged, road test vehicle. Engine RPM should decrease when scan tester indicates TCC engagement.

93C76408 91F07339

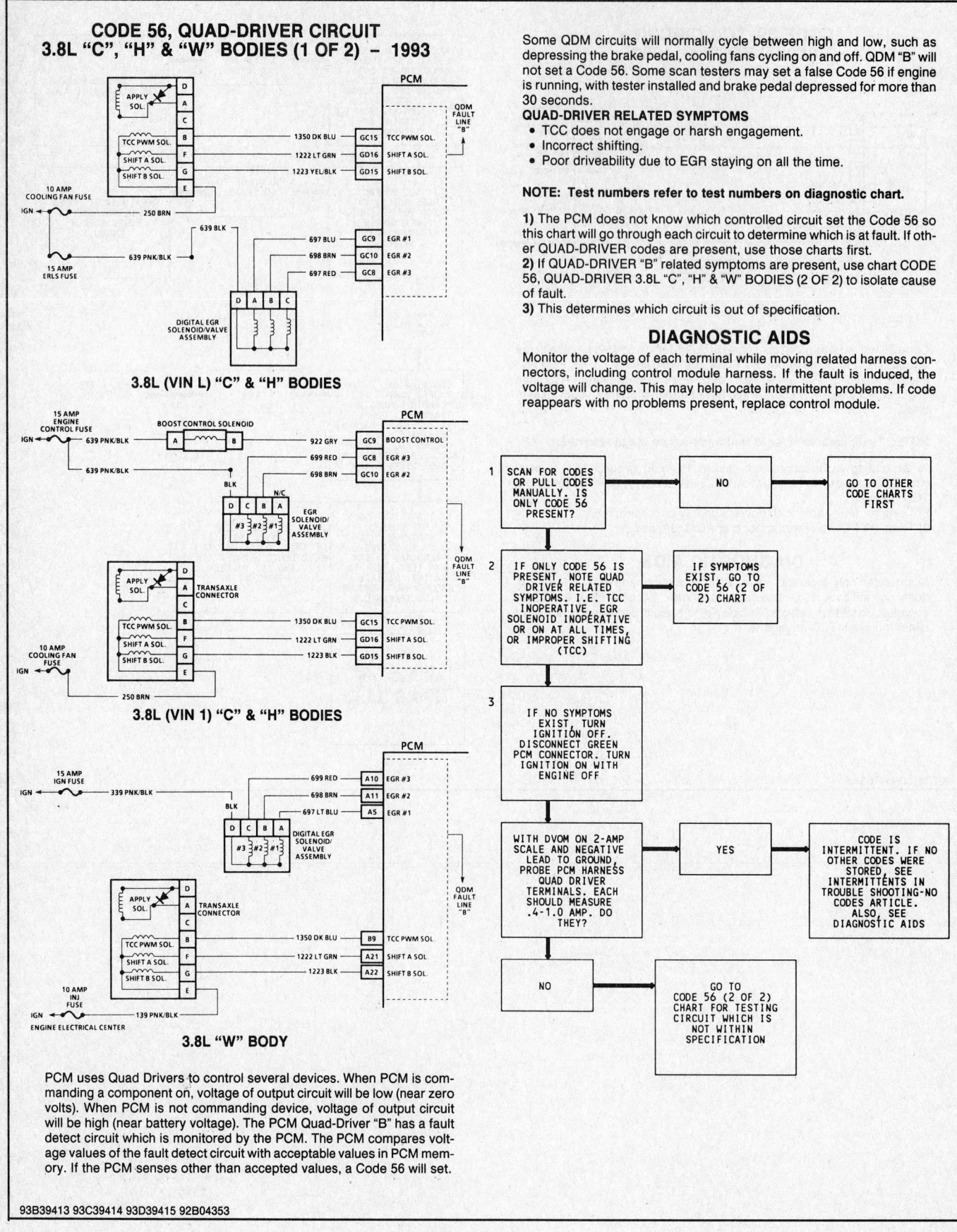

CODE 56, QUAD-DRIVER CIRCUIT
3.8L "C", "H" & "W" BODIES (1 OF 2) – 1993

3.8L (VIN L) "C" & "H" BODIES

3.8L (VIN 1) "C" & "H" BODIES

3.8L "W" BODY

PCM uses Quad Drivers to control several devices. When PCM is commanding a component on, voltage of output circuit will be low (near zero volts). When PCM is not commanding device, voltage of output circuit will be high (near battery voltage). The PCM Quad-Driver "B" has a fault detect circuit which is monitored by the PCM. The PCM compares voltage values of the fault detect circuit with acceptable values in PCM memory. If the PCM senses other than accepted values, a Code 56 will set.

Some QDM circuits will normally cycle between high and low, such as depressing the brake pedal, cooling fans cycling on and off. QDM "B" will not set a Code 56. Some scan testers may set a false Code 56 if engine is running, with tester installed and brake pedal depressed for more than 30 seconds.

QUAD-DRIVER RELATED SYMPTOMS
- TCC does not engage or harsh engagement.
- Incorrect shifting.
- Poor driveability due to EGR staying on all the time.

NOTE: Test numbers refer to test numbers on diagnostic chart.

1) The PCM does not know which controlled circuit set the Code 56 so this chart will go through each circuit to determine which is at fault. If other QUAD-DRIVER codes are present, use those charts first.
2) If QUAD-DRIVER "B" related symptoms are present, use chart CODE 56, QUAD-DRIVER 3.8L "C", "H" & "W" BODIES (2 OF 2) to isolate cause of fault.
3) This determines which circuit is out of specification.

DIAGNOSTIC AIDS
Monitor the voltage of each terminal while moving related harness connectors, including control module harness. If the fault is induced, the voltage will change. This may help locate intermittent problems. If code reappears with no problems present, replace control module.

CODE 56, QUAD-DRIVER CIRCUIT
3.8L "C", "H" & "W" BODIES (2 OF 2) – 1993

PCM uses Quad Drivers to control several devices. When PCM is commanding a component on, voltage of output circuit will be low (near zero volts). When PCM is not commanding device, voltage of output circuit will be high (near battery voltage). The PCM Quad-Driver "B" has a fault detect circuit which is monitored by the PCM. The PCM compares voltage values of the fault detect circuit with acceptable values in PCM memory. If the PCM senses other than accepted values, a Code 56 will set. Some QDM circuits will normally cycle between high and low, such as depressing the brake pedal, cooling fans cycling on and off. QDM "B" will not set a Code 56. Some scan testers may set a false Code 56 if engine is running, with tester installed and brake pedal depressed for more than 30 seconds.

NOTE: Test number refer to test number on diagnostic chart.

4) This determines if problem is circuit or component.

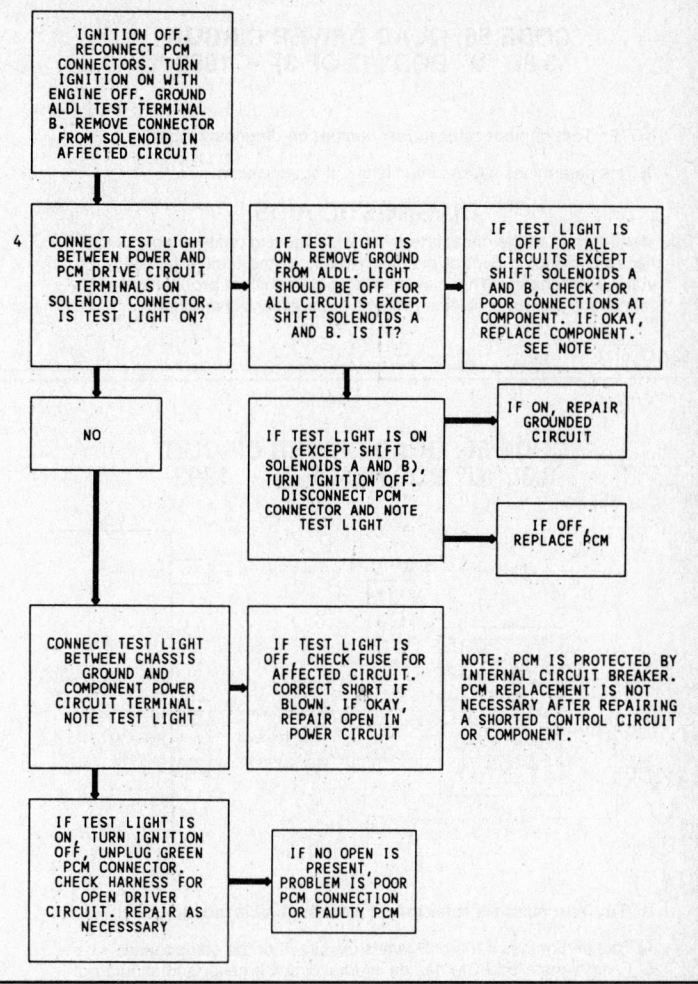

92D04354

CODE 56, QUAD-DRIVER CIRCUIT
3.8L "U" BODY (1 OF 3) – 1993

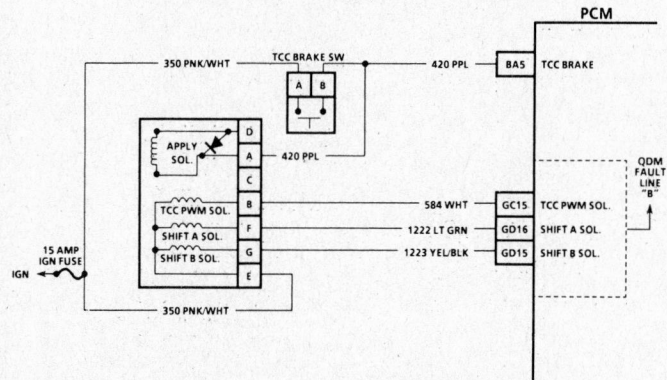

The PCM Quad-Driver "B" has a fault detect circuit which is monitored by the PCM. The PCM compares voltage values of the fault detect circuit with acceptable values in PCM memory. If the PCM senses other than accepted values, a Code 56 will set.
Some QDM circuits will normally cycle between high and low, such as depressing the brake pedal, cooling fans cycling on and off. QDM "B" will not set a Code 56. Some scan testers may set a false Code 56 if engine is running, with tester installed and brake pedal depressed for more than 30 seconds.

92H13794 92I13795

QDM SYMPTOMS
- TCC does not engage or harsh engagement.
- Incorrect shifting.
- Poor driveability due to EGR staying on all the time.

NOTE: Test numbers refer to test numbers on diagnostic chart.

1) The PCM does not know which controlled circuit set the Code 56 so this chart will go through each circuit to determine which is at fault.
2) If symptoms are present, use chart CODE 56, QUAD-DRIVER 3.8L U BODY (3 OF 3) to isolate cause of fault.

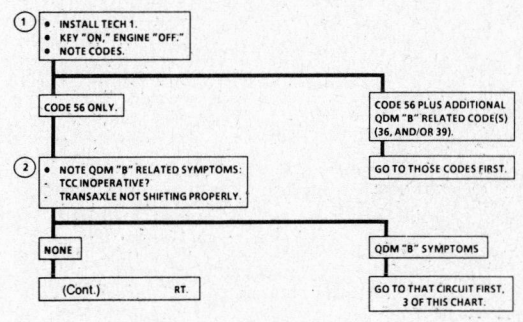

CODE 56, QUAD-DRIVER CIRCUIT
3.8L "U" BODY (2 OF 3) – 1993

NOTE: Test number refer to test number on diagnostic chart.

3) This determines which circuit is out of specification.

DIAGNOSTIC AIDS

Monitor the voltage of each terminal while moving related harness connectors, including control module harness. If the fault is induced, the voltage will change. This may help locate intermittent problems. If code reappears with no problems present, replace control module.

92J13796

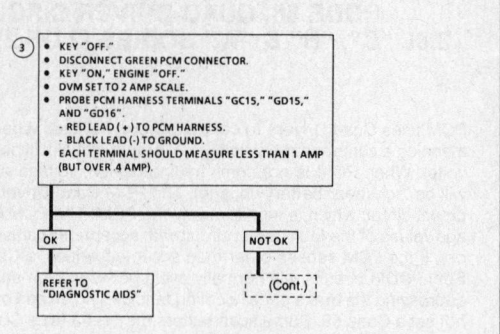

CODE 56, QUAD-DRIVER CIRCUIT
3.8L "U" BODY (3 OF 3) – 1993

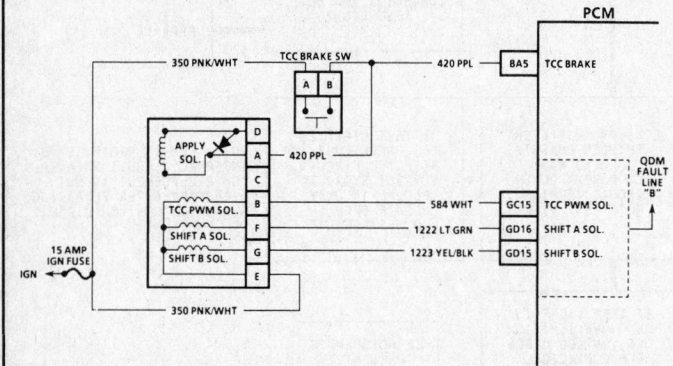

NOTE: Test numbers refer to test numbers on diagnostic chart.

4) This determines if the problem is the circuit or the component.
5) Factory-installed PCM has an internal circuit breaker and should not need replacing.

92H13794 92A13797

CIRCUIT ISOLATED FROM PRIOR CHARTS

④
- USE FACING PAGE WIRING DIAGRAM FOR SPECIFIC TERMINALS TO BE TESTED.
- RECONNECT PCM, IF APPLICABLE.
- KEY "ON," ENGINE "OFF," GROUND ALDL DIAGNOSTIC TEST TERMINAL OR SELECT FIELD SERVICE MODE WITH TECH 1.
- REMOVE CONNECTOR FROM TRANSAXLE.
- CONNECT TEST LIGHT BETWEEN TERMINAL "E" AND PCM DRIVER CIRCUIT.
- LIGHT SHOULD BE "ON," IS IT?

NO
- CONNECT TEST LIGHT FROM IGNITION CIRCUIT TO GROUND.
- NOTE LIGHT.

  "ON"
  - KEY "OFF."
  - DISCONNECT GREEN PCM CONNECTOR.
  - CHECK FOR OPEN IN DRIVER CIRCUIT.

    NOT OK → REPAIR OPEN.

  "OFF"
  - CHECK 15 AMP IGN FUSE AND CORRECT SHORT TO GROUND IF BLOWN –
  - IF FUSE IS OK, REPAIR OPEN IN CKT 350 TO SOLENOID.

    OK → POOR CONNECTION OR FAULTY PCM.

YES
- REMOVE GROUND AT DIAGNOSTIC TEST TERMINAL OR EXIT FIELD SERVICE MODE WITH TECH 1.
- NOTE LIGHT SHOULD BE "OFF" FOR CKT 584 (PWM SOL.) AND "ON" FOR CKT 1222 (SHIFT "A" SOLENOID) AND CKT 1223 (SHIFT "B" SOLENOID). IS IT?

  NO
  - DISCONNECT PCM CONNECTOR.
  - NOTE LIGHT.

    "ON" → REPAIR GROUNDED CIRCUIT.

  YES
  - CHECK FOR POOR CONNECTIONS. IF OK, REPLACE COMPONENT.

    "OFF" → **⑤** REPLACE PCM.

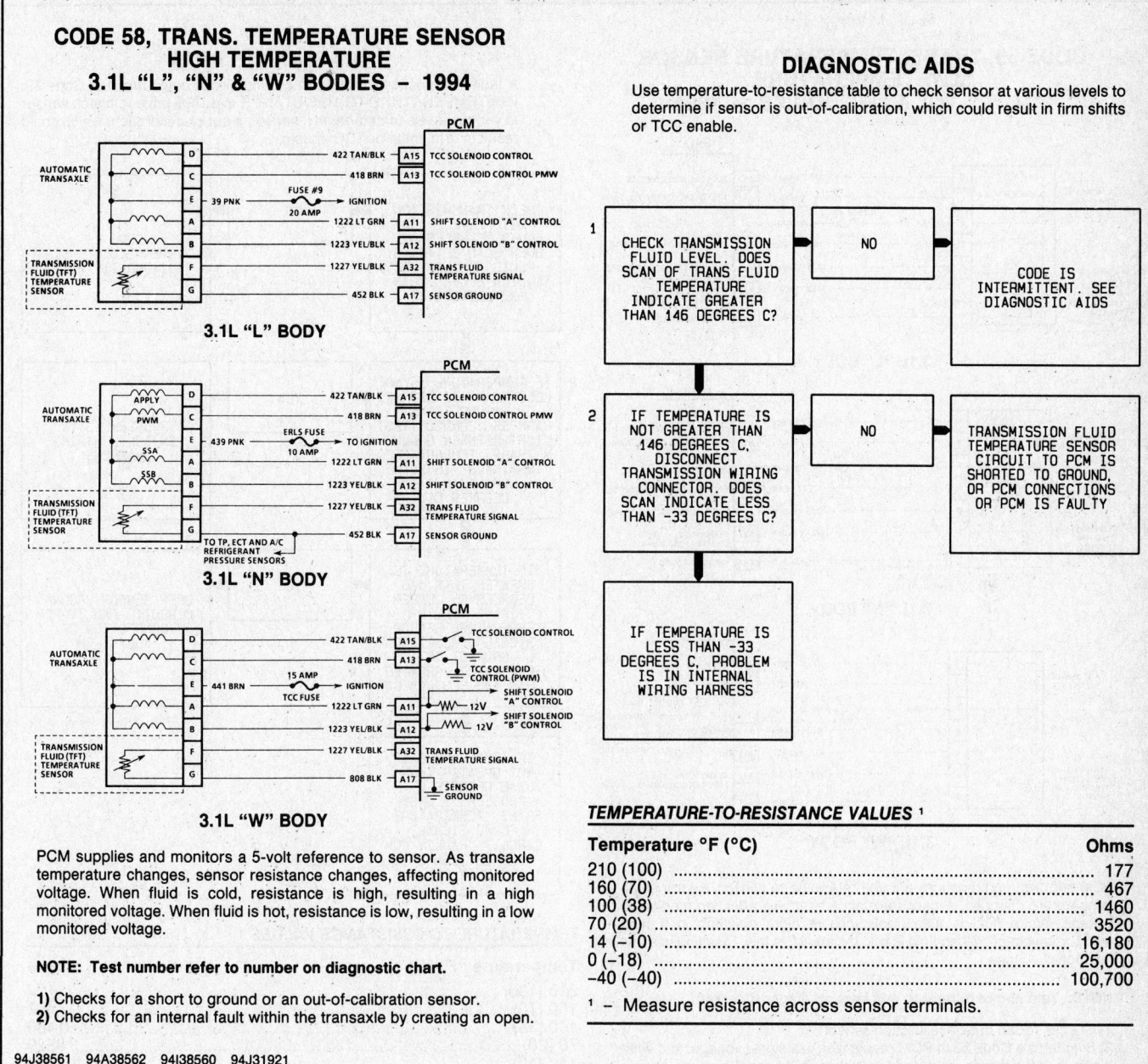

CODE 58, TRANS. TEMPERATURE SENSOR HIGH TEMPERATURE
3.1L "L", "N" & "W" BODIES – 1994

3.1L "L" BODY

3.1L "N" BODY

3.1L "W" BODY

PCM supplies and monitors a 5-volt reference to sensor. As transaxle temperature changes, sensor resistance changes, affecting monitored voltage. When fluid is cold, resistance is high, resulting in a high monitored voltage. When fluid is hot, resistance is low, resulting in a low monitored voltage.

NOTE: Test number refer to number on diagnostic chart.

1) Checks for a short to ground or an out-of-calibration sensor.
2) Checks for an internal fault within the transaxle by creating an open.

DIAGNOSTIC AIDS

Use temperature-to-resistance table to check sensor at various levels to determine if sensor is out-of-calibration, which could result in firm shifts or TCC enable.

1 CHECK TRANSMISSION FLUID LEVEL. DOES SCAN OF TRANS FLUID TEMPERATURE INDICATE GREATER THAN 146 DEGREES C? → NO → CODE IS INTERMITTENT. SEE DIAGNOSTIC AIDS

2 IF TEMPERATURE IS NOT GREATER THAN 146 DEGREES C, DISCONNECT TRANSMISSION WIRING CONNECTOR. DOES SCAN INDICATE LESS THAN -33 DEGREES C? → NO → TRANSMISSION FLUID TEMPERATURE SENSOR CIRCUIT TO PCM IS SHORTED TO GROUND, OR PCM CONNECTIONS OR PCM IS FAULTY

IF TEMPERATURE IS LESS THAN -33 DEGREES C, PROBLEM IS IN INTERNAL WIRING HARNESS

TEMPERATURE-TO-RESISTANCE VALUES [1]

Temperature °F (°C)	Ohms
210 (100)	177
160 (70)	467
100 (38)	1460
70 (20)	3520
14 (-10)	16,180
0 (-18)	25,000
-40 (-40)	100,700

[1] – Measure resistance across sensor terminals.

94J38561   94A38562   94I38560   94J31921

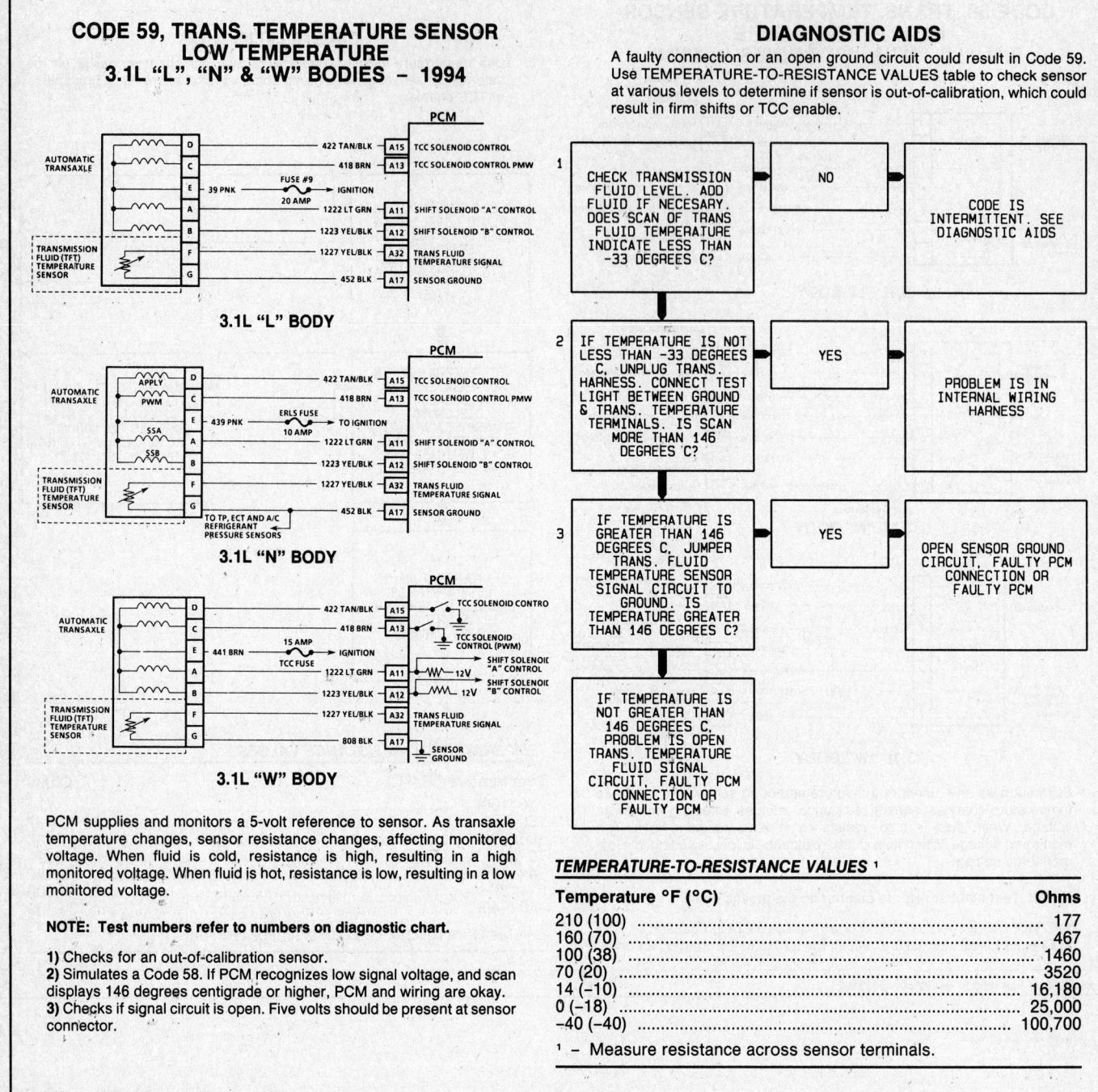

CODE 59, TRANS. TEMPERATURE SENSOR LOW TEMPERATURE
3.1L "L", "N" & "W" BODIES – 1994

3.1L "L" BODY

3.1L "N" BODY

3.1L "W" BODY

PCM supplies and monitors a 5-volt reference to sensor. As transaxle temperature changes, sensor resistance changes, affecting monitored voltage. When fluid is cold, resistance is high, resulting in a high monitored voltage. When fluid is hot, resistance is low, resulting in a low monitored voltage.

NOTE: Test numbers refer to numbers on diagnostic chart.

1) Checks for an out-of-calibration sensor.
2) Simulates a Code 58. If PCM recognizes low signal voltage, and scan displays 146 degrees centigrade or higher, PCM and wiring are okay.
3) Checks if signal circuit is open. Five volts should be present at sensor connector.

DIAGNOSTIC AIDS

A faulty connection or an open ground circuit could result in Code 59. Use TEMPERATURE-TO-RESISTANCE VALUES table to check sensor at various levels to determine if sensor is out-of-calibration, which could result in firm shifts or TCC enable.

1 CHECK TRANSMISSION FLUID LEVEL. ADD FLUID IF NECESARY. DOES SCAN OF TRANS FLUID TEMPERATURE INDICATE LESS THAN -33 DEGREES C? — **NO** → CODE IS INTERMITTENT. SEE DIAGNOSTIC AIDS

2 IF TEMPERATURE IS NOT LESS THAN -33 DEGREES C, UNPLUG TRANS. HARNESS. CONNECT TEST LIGHT BETWEEN GROUND & TRANS. TEMPERATURE TERMINALS. IS SCAN MORE THAN 146 DEGREES C? — **YES** → PROBLEM IS IN INTERNAL WIRING HARNESS

3 IF TEMPERATURE IS GREATER THAN 146 DEGREES C, JUMPER TRANS. FLUID TEMPERATURE SENSOR SIGNAL CIRCUIT TO GROUND. IS TEMPERATURE GREATER THAN 146 DEGREES C? — **YES** → OPEN SENSOR GROUND CIRCUIT, FAULTY PCM CONNECTION OR FAULTY PCM

IF TEMPERATURE IS NOT GREATER THAN 146 DEGREES C, PROBLEM IS OPEN TRANS. TEMPERATURE FLUID SIGNAL CIRCUIT, FAULTY PCM CONNECTION OR FAULTY PCM

TEMPERATURE-TO-RESISTANCE VALUES [1]

Temperature °F (°C)	Ohms
210 (100)	177
160 (70)	467
100 (38)	1460
70 (20)	3520
14 (−10)	16,180
0 (−18)	25,000
−40 (−40)	100,700

[1] – Measure resistance across sensor terminals.

94J38561 94A38562 94I38560 94A31922

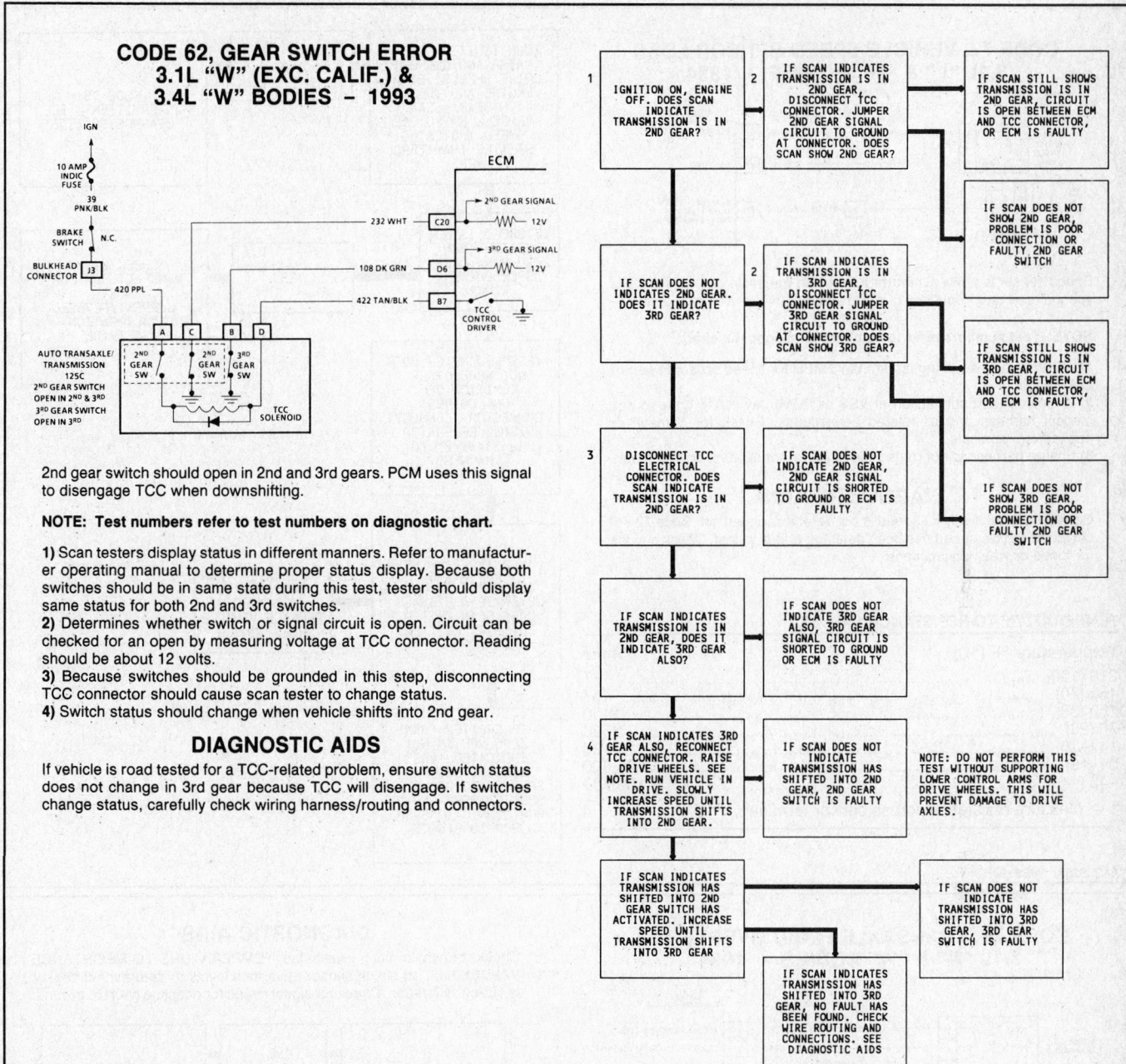

CODE 62, GEAR SWITCH ERROR
3.1L "W" (EXC. CALIF.) &
3.4L "W" BODIES – 1993

2nd gear switch should open in 2nd and 3rd gears. PCM uses this signal to disengage TCC when downshifting.

NOTE: Test numbers refer to test numbers on diagnostic chart.

1) Scan testers display status in different manners. Refer to manufacturer operating manual to determine proper status display. Because both switches should be in same state during this test, tester should display same status for both 2nd and 3rd switches.
2) Determines whether switch or signal circuit is open. Circuit can be checked for an open by measuring voltage at TCC connector. Reading should be about 12 volts.
3) Because switches should be grounded in this step, disconnecting TCC connector should cause scan tester to change status.
4) Switch status should change when vehicle shifts into 2nd gear.

DIAGNOSTIC AIDS

If vehicle is road tested for a TCC-related problem, ensure switch status does not change in 3rd gear because TCC will disengage. If switches change status, carefully check wiring harness/routing and connectors.

93G39426 91D07362

CODE 72, VEHICLE SPEED SENSOR LOSS
3.1L "L" & "W" BODIES – 1994

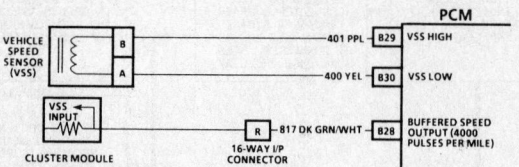

Speed sensor is a PM generator located on transaxle output shaft. The voltage level and frequency of pulses increases with vehicle speed.

NOTE: Test numbers refer to numbers on diagnostic chart.

1) Wheels must be turning faster than 3 MPH for speed sensor to generate a signal.
2) An intermittent connection at VSS or PCM may cause code to set. Inspect harness and all related connections. Check for damage or pushed out terminals.
3) Ensure harness is not routed too close to hot exhaust components.

DIAGNOSTIC AIDS

Code 24 will set if vehicle speed is not detected at start off. Code 72 will set when vehicle speed has been detected and then lost. Check circuits for loose or weak connections.

TEMPERATURE-TO-RESISTANCE VALUES [1]

Temperature °F (°C)	Ohms
210 (100)	177
160 (70)	467
100 (38)	1460
70 (20)	3520
14 (−10)	16,180
0 (−18)	25,000
−40 (−40)	100,700

[1] – Measure resistance across sensor terminals.

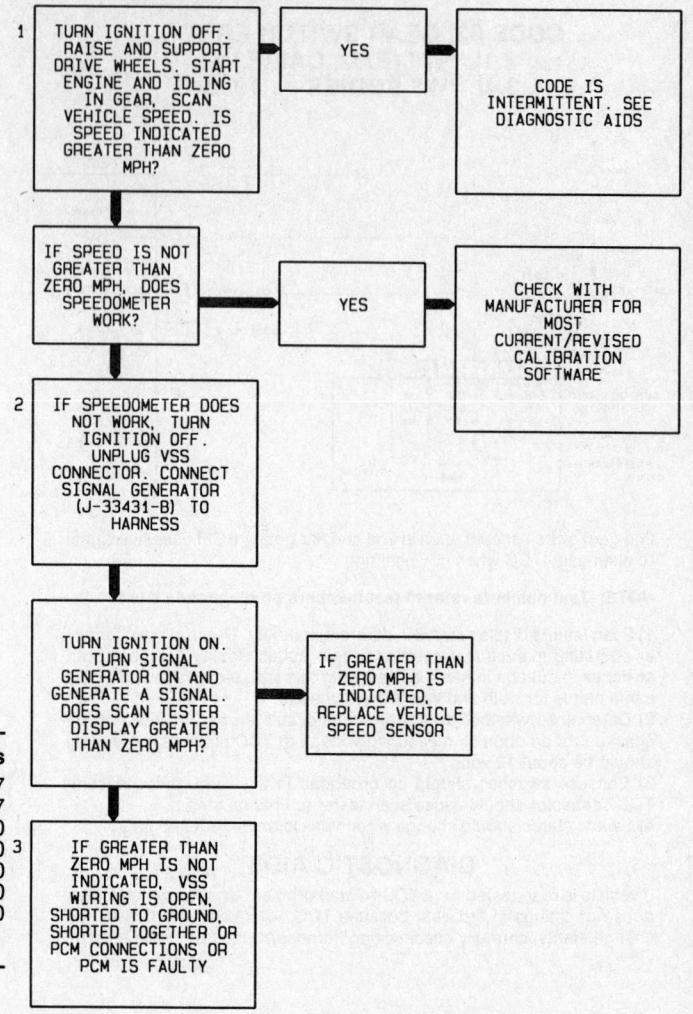

94D38565   94B31923

CODE 79, TRANSAXLE FLUID OVERTEMP
3.1L "N" & "W" BODIES – 1994

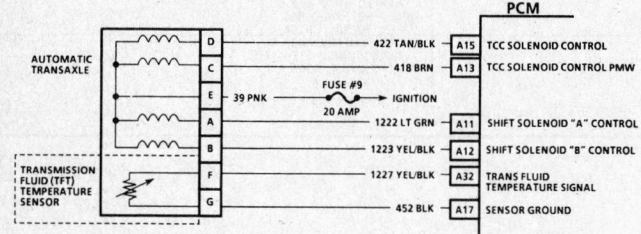

PCM supplies and monitors a 5-volt reference to sensor. As transaxle temperature changes, sensor resistance changes, affecting monitored voltage. When fluid is cold, resistance is high, resulting in a high monitored voltage. When fluid is hot, resistance is low, resulting in a low monitored voltage. If vehicle is driven hard for an extended period, Code 79 will be set to alert driver of transaxle fluid temperature being too high.

NOTE: Test number refer to number on diagnostic chart.

1) Simulates conditions for Code 79 to reappear.

DIAGNOSTIC AIDS

Check transaxle fluid level. Use TEMPERATURE-TO-RESISTANCE VALUES table to check sensor at various levels to determine if sensor is out-of-calibration. Check for signal circuit for possible short to ground.

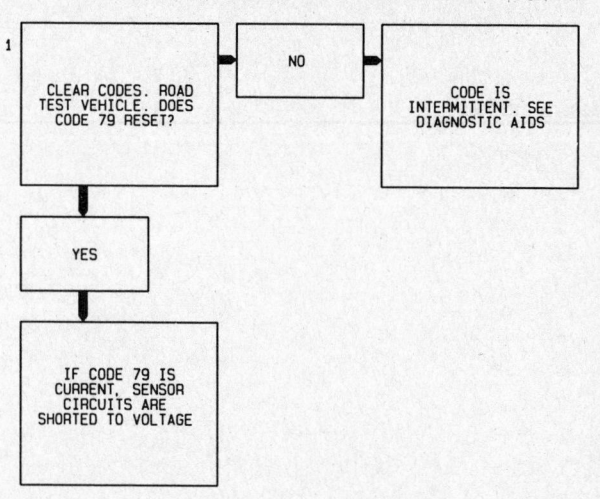

94J38561   94D38599

CODE 79, VSS SIGNAL VOLTAGE HIGH
3.1 CALIF. "W" BODY – 1993

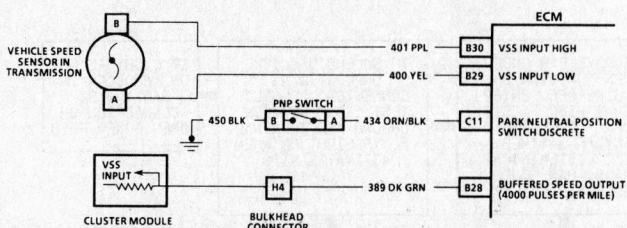

Vehicle speed information is provided to the PCM by the permanent magnet speed signal generator located in the transaxle. Generator produces a pulsing voltage signal whenever the vehicle speed is greater than 3 MPH. The generated AC voltage signal and pulse frequency increases with vehicle speed. PCM converts this pulsed signal to MPH. MPH is used in internal calculations and can be monitored on a scan tester. Output of signal generator can also be monitored using a DVOM set on the AC scale. The function of the VSS buffer is incorporated in the PCM which furnishes the instrument panel with a MPH signal (4000 pulses per mile). If vehicle is also equipped with cruise control, PCM will also furnish cruise control module with MPH signal (2000 pulses per mile). Disregard a Code 79 which sets when drive wheels are not turning.

NOTE: Test numbers refer to numbers on diagnostic chart.

1) PCM is programmed with a VSS (high) diagnostic check. The diagnostic check will be enabled when the throttle position is greater than 10 MPH. The diagnosis checks for discrepancy in vehicle speed.

93A39461 93B39462

DIAGNOSTIC AIDS

Scan tester should indicate vehicle speed whenever drive wheels are turning greater than 3 MPH. A problem in the PCM-supplied instrument panel signal circuit or PCM-supplied cruise control module signal circuit will not affect VSS input to PCM or scan tester. A faulty or misadjusted park/neutral switch can set a false code.

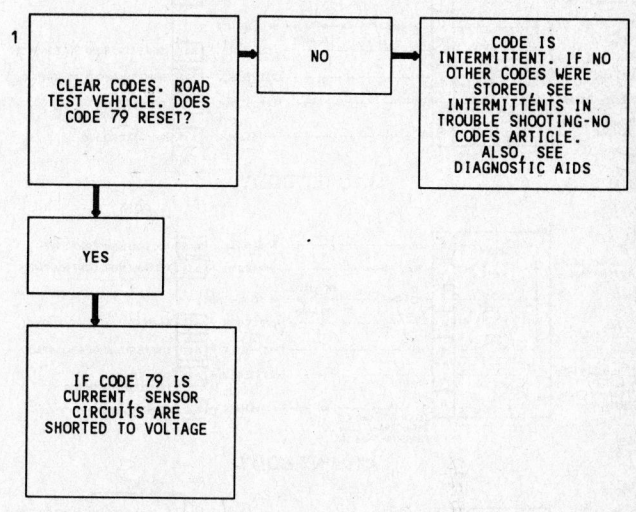

CODE 80, VSS SIGNAL VOLTAGE LOW
3.1L CALIF. "W" BODY – 1993

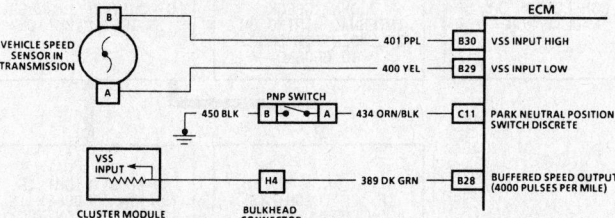

Vehicle speed information is provided to the PCM by the permanent magnet speed signal generator located in the transaxle. Generator produces a pulsing voltage signal whenever the vehicle speed is greater than 3 MPH. The generated AC voltage signal and pulse frequency increases with vehicle speed. PCM converts this pulsed signal to MPH. MPH is used in internal calculations and can be monitored on a scan tester. Output of signal generator can also be monitored using a DVOM set on the AC scale. The function of the VSS buffer is incorporated in the PCM which furnishes the instrument panel with a MPH signal (4000 pulses per mile). If vehicle is also equipped with cruise control, PCM will also furnish cruise control module with MPH signal (2000 pulses per mile). Disregard a Code 80 which sets when drive wheels are not turning.

NOTE: Test numbers refer to numbers on diagnostic chart.

1) Code 80 will set if vehicle speed is equal to zero MPH and conditions are met as follows: VSS indicates greater than 3 MPH, MAP is less than 30 kPa, engine speed is 2200-4400 RPM, TPS is greater than 2 percent, vehicle is not in Park or Neutral, Codes 21, 22, 33 or 34 are not set and all conditions have been met for 4 seconds. These conditions are met during a road load deceleration.
2) If VSS circuits and cluster signal circuit are okay, and speedometer works properly, code is being caused by faulty PCM, faulty PROM or incorrect PROM program.

DIAGNOSTIC AIDS

Scan tester should indicate vehicle speed whenever drive wheels are turning greater than 3 MPH. A problem in the PCM-supplied instrument panel signal circuit or PCM-supplied cruise control module signal circuit will not affect VSS input to PCM or scan tester. A faulty or misadjusted park/neutral switch can set a false code.

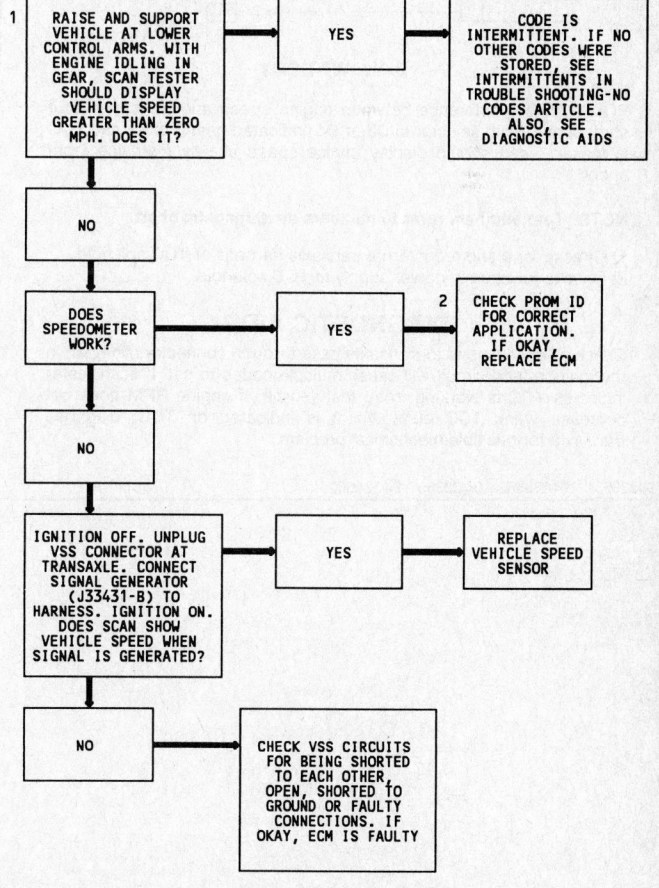

93A39461 93C39463

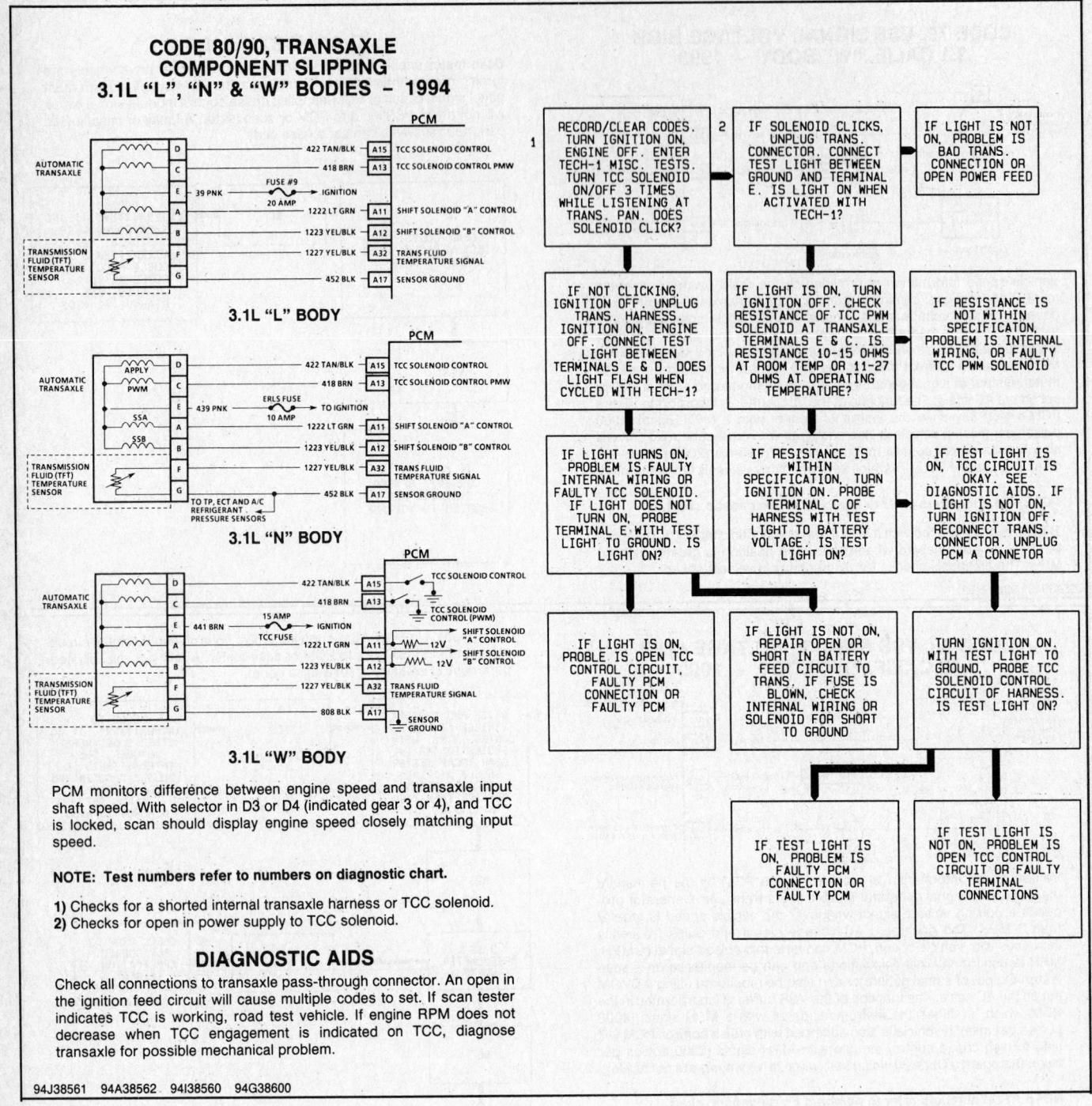

CODE 80/90, TRANSAXLE COMPONENT SLIPPING
3.1L "L", "N" & "W" BODIES – 1994

3.1L "L" BODY

3.1L "N" BODY

3.1L "W" BODY

PCM monitors difference between engine speed and transaxle input shaft speed. With selector in D3 or D4 (indicated gear 3 or 4), and TCC is locked, scan should display engine speed closely matching input speed.

NOTE: Test numbers refer to numbers on diagnostic chart.

1) Checks for a shorted internal transaxle harness or TCC solenoid.
2) Checks for open in power supply to TCC solenoid.

DIAGNOSTIC AIDS

Check all connections to transaxle pass-through connector. An open in the ignition feed circuit will cause multiple codes to set. If scan tester indicates TCC is working, road test vehicle. If engine RPM does not decrease when TCC engagement is indicated on TCC, diagnose transaxle for possible mechanical problem.

94J38561   94A38562   94I38560   94G38600

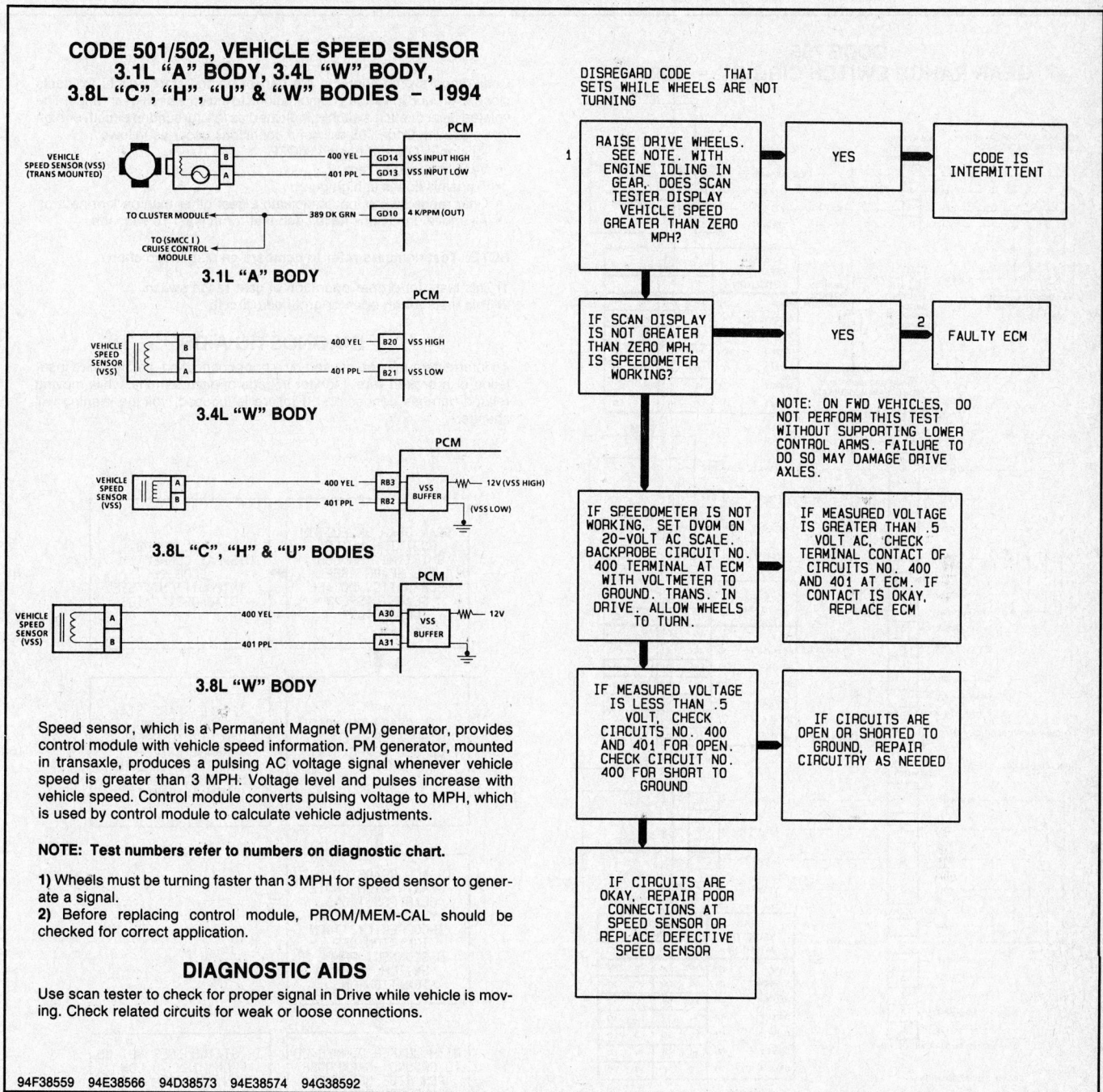

CODE 501/502, VEHICLE SPEED SENSOR
3.1L "A" BODY, 3.4L "W" BODY,
3.8L "C", "H", "U" & "W" BODIES – 1994

3.1L "A" BODY

3.4L "W" BODY

3.8L "C", "H" & "U" BODIES

3.8L "W" BODY

Speed sensor, which is a Permanent Magnet (PM) generator, provides control module with vehicle speed information. PM generator, mounted in transaxle, produces a pulsing AC voltage signal whenever vehicle speed is greater than 3 MPH. Voltage level and pulses increase with vehicle speed. Control module converts pulsing voltage to MPH, which is used by control module to calculate vehicle adjustments.

NOTE: Test numbers refer to numbers on diagnostic chart.

1) Wheels must be turning faster than 3 MPH for speed sensor to generate a signal.
2) Before replacing control module, PROM/MEM-CAL should be checked for correct application.

DIAGNOSTIC AIDS

Use scan tester to check for proper signal in Drive while vehicle is moving. Check related circuits for weak or loose connections.

DISREGARD CODE THAT SETS WHILE WHEELS ARE NOT TURNING

1. RAISE DRIVE WHEELS. SEE NOTE. WITH ENGINE IDLING IN GEAR, DOES SCAN TESTER DISPLAY VEHICLE SPEED GREATER THAN ZERO MPH? → YES → CODE IS INTERMITTENT

IF SCAN DISPLAY IS NOT GREATER THAN ZERO MPH, IS SPEEDOMETER WORKING? → YES → 2 FAULTY ECM

NOTE: ON FWD VEHICLES, DO NOT PERFORM THIS TEST WITHOUT SUPPORTING LOWER CONTROL ARMS. FAILURE TO DO SO MAY DAMAGE DRIVE AXLES.

IF SPEEDOMETER IS NOT WORKING, SET DVOM ON 20-VOLT AC SCALE. BACKPROBE CIRCUIT NO. 400 TERMINAL AT ECM WITH VOLTMETER TO GROUND. TRANS. IN DRIVE. ALLOW WHEELS TO TURN. → IF MEASURED VOLTAGE IS GREATER THAN .5 VOLT AC, CHECK TERMINAL CONTACT OF CIRCUITS NO. 400 AND 401 AT ECM. IF CONTACT IS OKAY, REPLACE ECM

IF MEASURED VOLTAGE IS LESS THAN .5 VOLT, CHECK CIRCUITS NO. 400 AND 401 FOR OPEN. CHECK CIRCUIT NO. 400 FOR SHORT TO GROUND → IF CIRCUITS ARE OPEN OR SHORTED TO GROUND, REPAIR CIRCUITRY AS NEEDED

IF CIRCUITS ARE OKAY, REPAIR POOR CONNECTIONS AT SPEED SENSOR OR REPLACE DEFECTIVE SPEED SENSOR

94F38559   94E38566   94D38573   94E38574   94G38592

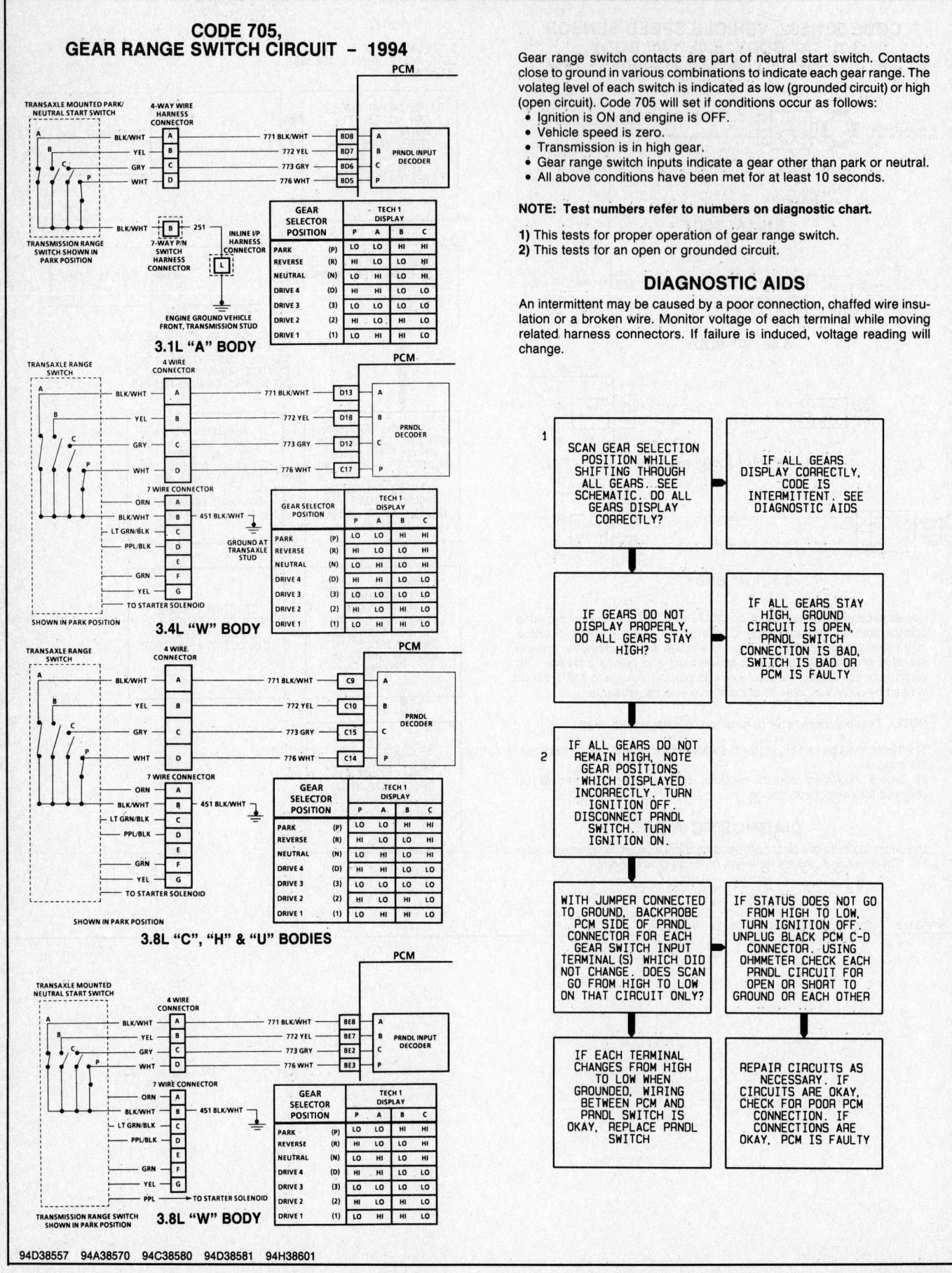

CODE 705,
GEAR RANGE SWITCH CIRCUIT – 1994

Gear range switch contacts are part of neutral start switch. Contacts close to ground in various combinations to indicate each gear range. The volateg level of each switch is indicated as low (grounded circuit) or high (open circuit). Code 705 will set if conditions occur as follows:
- Ignition is ON and engine is OFF.
- Vehicle speed is zero.
- Transmission is in high gear.
- Gear range switch inputs indicate a gear other than park or neutral.
- All above conditions have been met for at least 10 seconds.

NOTE: Test numbers refer to numbers on diagnostic chart.

1) This tests for proper operation of gear range switch.
2) This tests for an open or grounded circuit.

DIAGNOSTIC AIDS

An intermittent may be caused by a poor connection, chaffed wire insulation or a broken wire. Monitor voltage of each terminal while moving related harness connectors. If failure is induced, voltage reading will change.

CODE 712, TRANSAXLE TEMPERATURE SENSOR SIGNAL VOLTAGE LOW – 1994

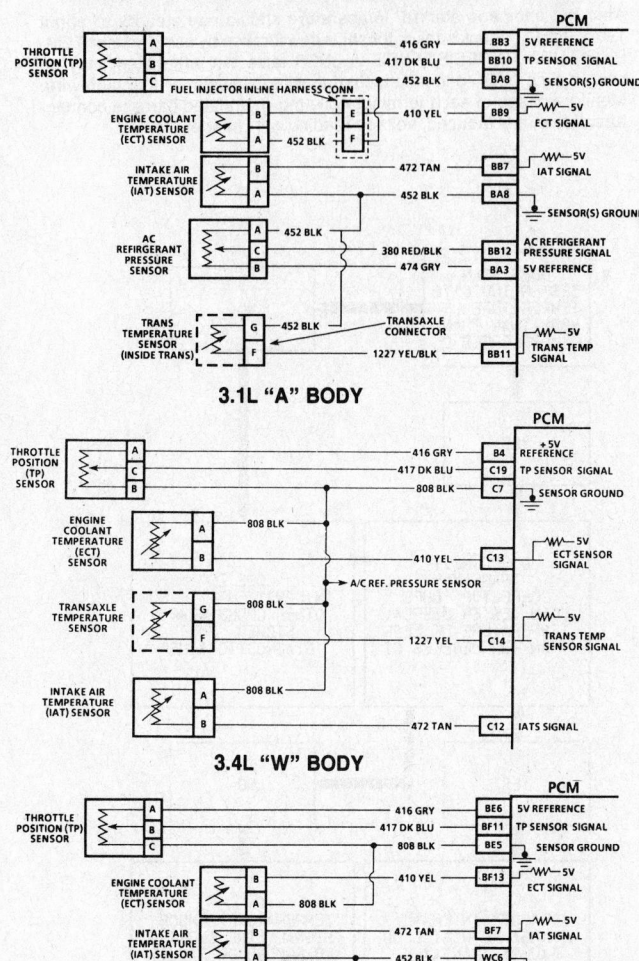

3.1L "A" BODY

3.4L "W" BODY

3.8L "C", "H", "U" & "W" BODIES

PCM sends a voltage signal to sensor and monitors the return voltage. Transaxle temperature sensor varies resistance as temperature of transaxle fluid changes. Temperature sensor resistance is high when transaxle fluid is cold. As fluid temperature increases, sensor resistance decreases. At normal operating temperature, transaxle temperature sensor signal voltage will be about 2 volts.

NOTE: Test numbers refer to test numbers on diagnostic chart.
1) Code 712 indicates the control module has seen low sensor voltage signal (low temperature) at control module terminal for a precalibrated period of time. This checks if conditions for Code 712 still exist.
2) This simulates conditions for a Code 713. If PCM sets Code 713, wiring between control module and sensor, and PCM are okay.

94C38556   94B38571   94E38582   94J38603

DIAGNOSTIC AIDS

After the engine is started, temperature should rise steadily to about 190°F (88°C). Check sensor for shifted calibration by using sensor TEMPERATURE-TO-RESISTANCE VALUES table. An intermittent may be caused by a poor connection, chaffed wire insulation or a broken wire. Monitor voltage of each terminal while moving related harness connectors. If failure is induced, voltage reading will change.

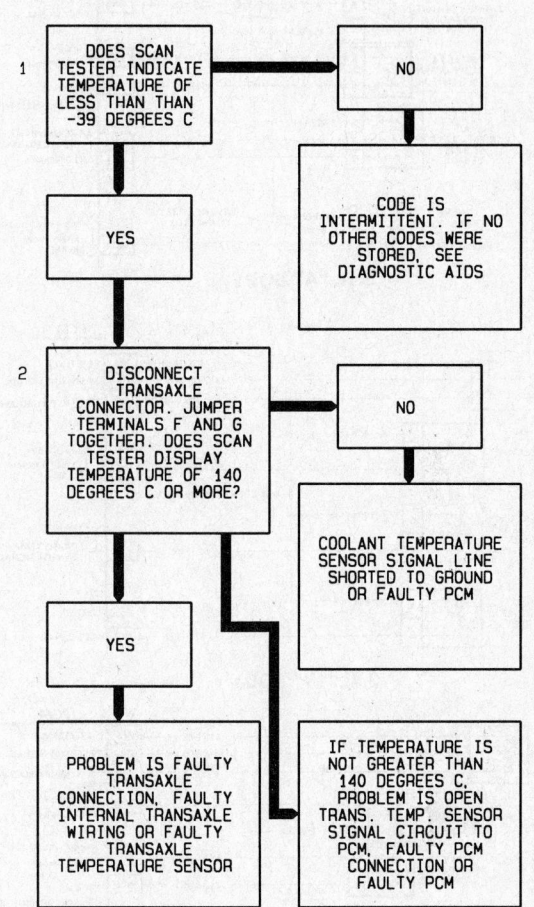

TEMPERATURE-TO-RESISTANCE VALUES [1]

Temperature °F (°C)	Ohms
210 (100)	177
160 (70)	467
100 (38)	1460
70 (20)	3520
14 (–10)	16,180
0 (–18)	25,000
–40 (–40)	100,700

[1] – Measure resistance across sensor terminals.

CODE 713, TRANSAXLE TEMPERATURE SENSOR SIGNAL VOLTAGE HIGH – 1994

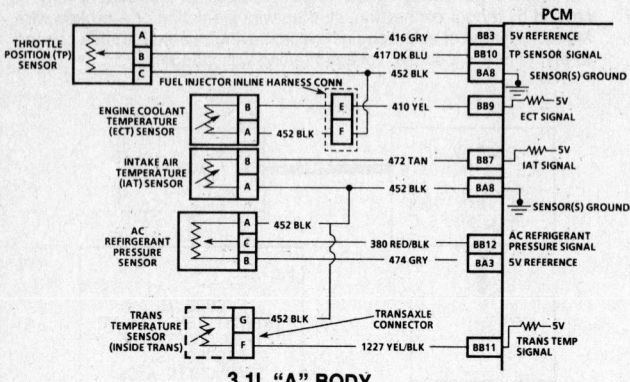

3.1L "A" BODY

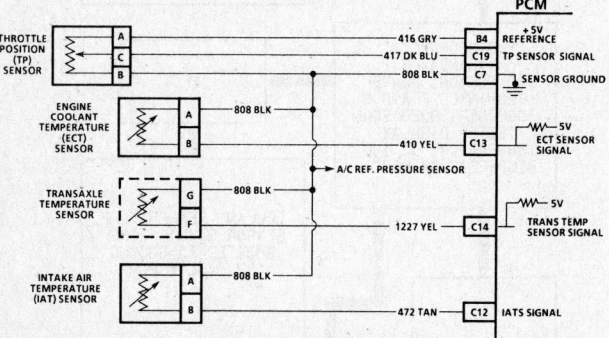

3.4L "W" BODY

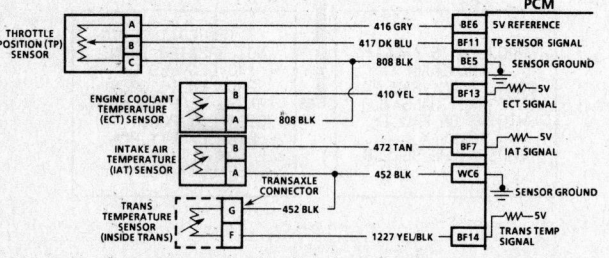

3.8L "C", "H", "U" & "W" BODIES

DIAGNOSTIC AIDS

After the engine is started, temperature should rise steadily to about 190°F (88°C). Check sensor for shifted calibration by using sensor TEMPERATURE-TO-RESISTANCE VALUES table. An intermittent may be caused by a poor connection, chaffed wire insulation or a broken wire. Monitor voltage of each terminal while moving related harness connectors. If failure is induced, voltage reading will change.

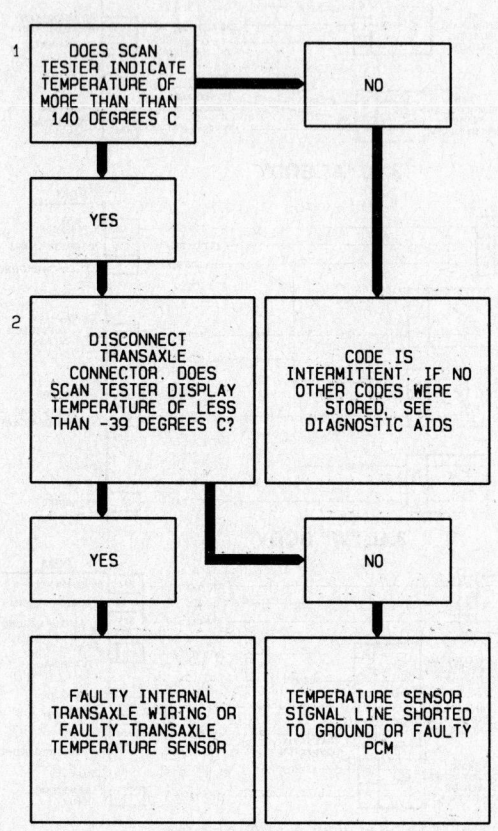

PCM sends a voltage signal to sensor and monitors the return voltage. Transaxle temperature sensor varies resistance as temperature of transaxle fluid changes. Temperature sensor resistance is high when transaxle fluid is cold. As fluid temperature increases, sensor resistance decreases. At normal operating temperature, transaxle temperature sensor signal voltage will be about 2 volts.

NOTE: Test numbers refer to test numbers on diagnostic chart.
1) Code 713 indicates control module has seen low resistance in transaxle temperature sensor circuit. This checks if conditions for Code 713 still exist.
2) This test determines if coolant sensor signal circuit is grounded.

TEMPERATURE-TO-RESISTANCE VALUES [1]

Temperature °F (°C)	Ohms
210 (100)	177
160 (70)	467
100 (38)	1460
70 (20)	3520
14 (–10)	16,180
0 (–18)	25,000
–40 (–40)	100,700

[1] – Measure resistance across sensor terminals.

94C38556   94B38571   94E38582   94A38604

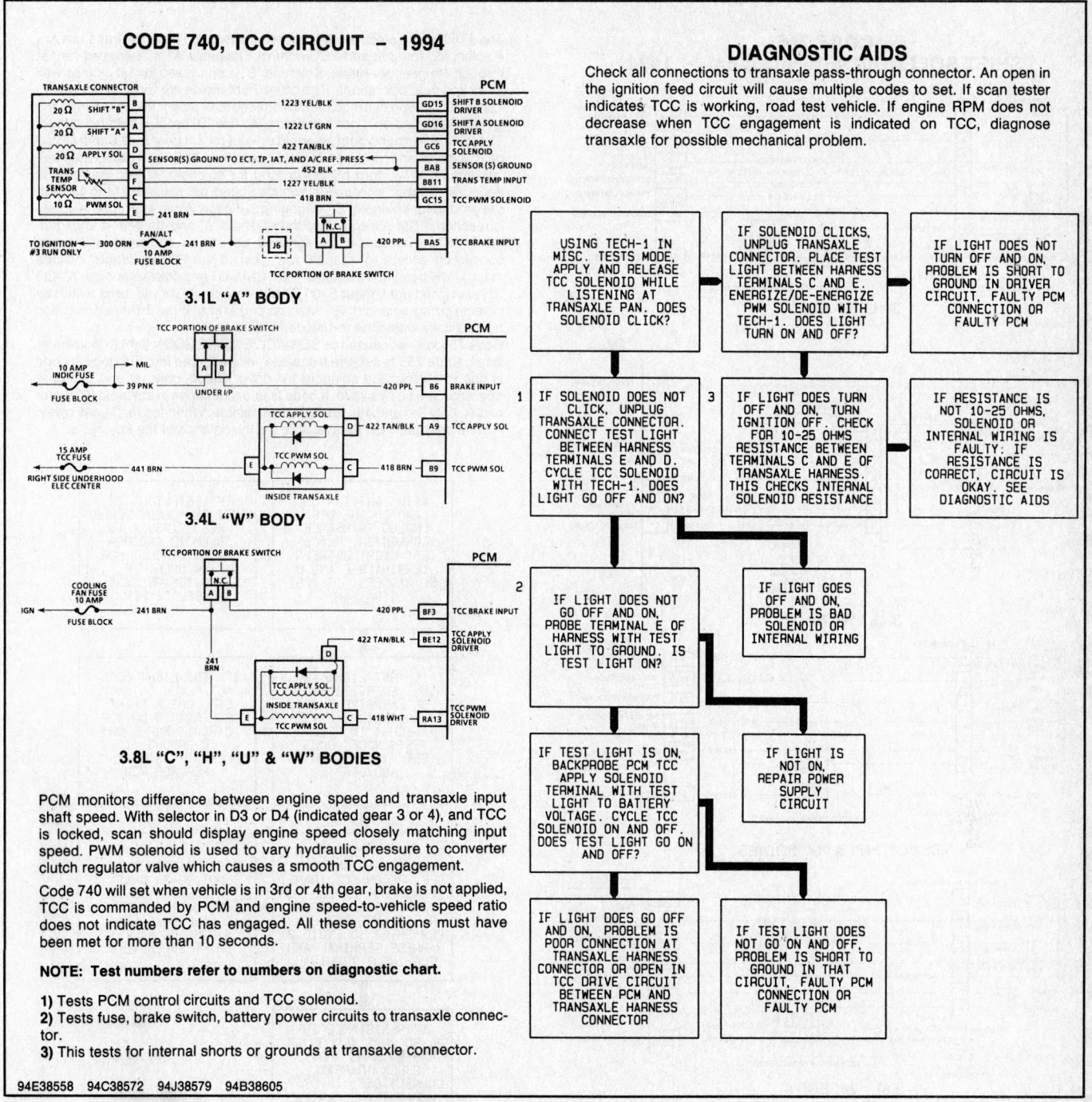

CODE 740, TCC CIRCUIT - 1994

3.1L "A" BODY

3.4L "W" BODY

3.8L "C", "H", "U" & "W" BODIES

DIAGNOSTIC AIDS

Check all connections to transaxle pass-through connector. An open in the ignition feed circuit will cause multiple codes to set. If scan tester indicates TCC is working, road test vehicle. If engine RPM does not decrease when TCC engagement is indicated on TCC, diagnose transaxle for possible mechanical problem.

PCM monitors difference between engine speed and transaxle input shaft speed. With selector in D3 or D4 (indicated gear 3 or 4), and TCC is locked, scan should display engine speed closely matching input speed. PWM solenoid is used to vary hydraulic pressure to converter clutch regulator valve which causes a smooth TCC engagement.

Code 740 will set when vehicle is in 3rd or 4th gear, brake is not applied, TCC is commanded by PCM and engine speed-to-vehicle speed ratio does not indicate TCC has engaged. All these conditions must have been met for more than 10 seconds.

NOTE: Test numbers refer to numbers on diagnostic chart.

1) Tests PCM control circuits and TCC solenoid.
2) Tests fuse, brake switch, battery power circuits to transaxle connector.
3) This tests for internal shorts or grounds at transaxle connector.

94E38558   94C38572   94J38579   94B38605

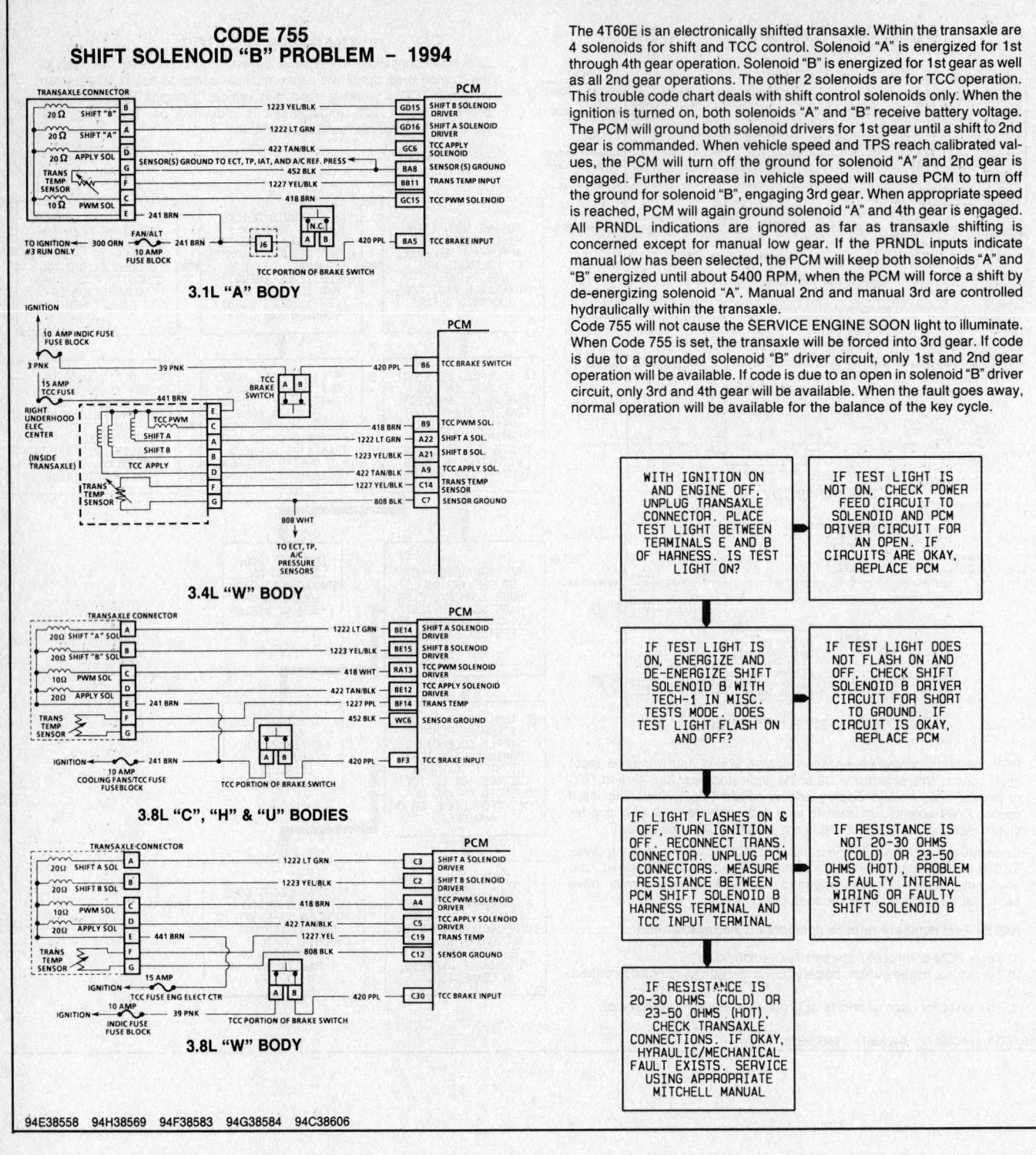

CODE 755
SHIFT SOLENOID "B" PROBLEM – 1994

The 4T60E is an electronically shifted transaxle. Within the transaxle are 4 solenoids for shift and TCC control. Solenoid "A" is energized for 1st through 4th gear operation. Solenoid "B" is energized for 1st gear as well as all 2nd gear operations. The other 2 solenoids are for TCC operation. This trouble code chart deals with shift control solenoids only. When the ignition is turned on, both solenoids "A" and "B" receive battery voltage. The PCM will ground both solenoid drivers for 1st gear until a shift to 2nd gear is commanded. When vehicle speed and TPS reach calibrated values, the PCM will turn off the ground for solenoid "A" and 2nd gear is engaged. Further increase in vehicle speed will cause PCM to turn off the ground for solenoid "B", engaging 3rd gear. When appropriate speed is reached, PCM will again ground solenoid "A" and 4th gear is engaged. All PRNDL indications are ignored as far as transaxle shifting is concerned except for manual low gear. If the PRNDL inputs indicate manual low has been selected, the PCM will keep both solenoids "A" and "B" energized until about 5400 RPM, when the PCM will force a shift by de-energizing solenoid "A". Manual 2nd and manual 3rd are controlled hydraulically within the transaxle.

Code 755 will not cause the SERVICE ENGINE SOON light to illuminate. When Code 755 is set, the transaxle will be forced into 3rd gear. If code is due to a grounded solenoid "B" driver circuit, only 1st and 2nd gear operation will be available. If code is due to an open in solenoid "B" driver circuit, only 3rd and 4th gear will be available. When the fault goes away, normal operation will be available for the balance of the key cycle.

94E38558   94H38569   94F38583   94G38584   94C38606

CODE 1640, QUAD-DRIVER ERROR
3.1L "A" BODY – 1994

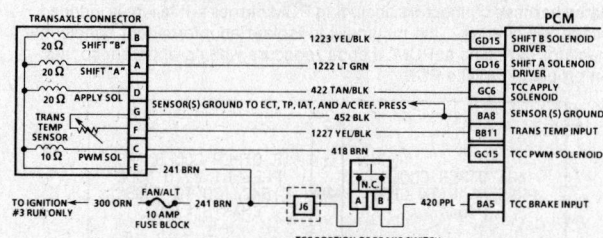

PCM uses Quad-Driver Modules (QDMs) to control several devices. When PCM is commanding a component on, voltage of output circuit will be low (near zero volts). When PCM is commanding component off, voltage of output circuit will be high (near battery voltage). Primary function of quad-driver module is to control ground circuit for component being controlled. PCM has an internal fault line for each quad-driver module. Fault line status can be displayed on a scan tester. If PCM detects an output voltage other than what is expected on fault line, PCM will set Code 1640.

QUAD-DRIVER RELATED SYMPTOMS

- Improper shifting.
- TCC will not apply or harsh engagement.
- Poor driveability due to constant EGR.

NOTE: Test numbers refer to numbers on diagnostic chart.

1) If other QDM-related codes are present, use those charts first. Repairing other related code problems will also fix Code 1640.
2) This step will check each circuit to determine which is at fault.

DIAGNOSTIC AIDS

Monitor voltage at each terminal shown in schematic while moving related harness connectors, including PCM harness. If failure is induced, voltage will change. This may help to isolate an intermittent condition. Check for bent pins at PCM. If code reoccurs with no apparent connection problem, replace PCM.

94E38558   94D38607

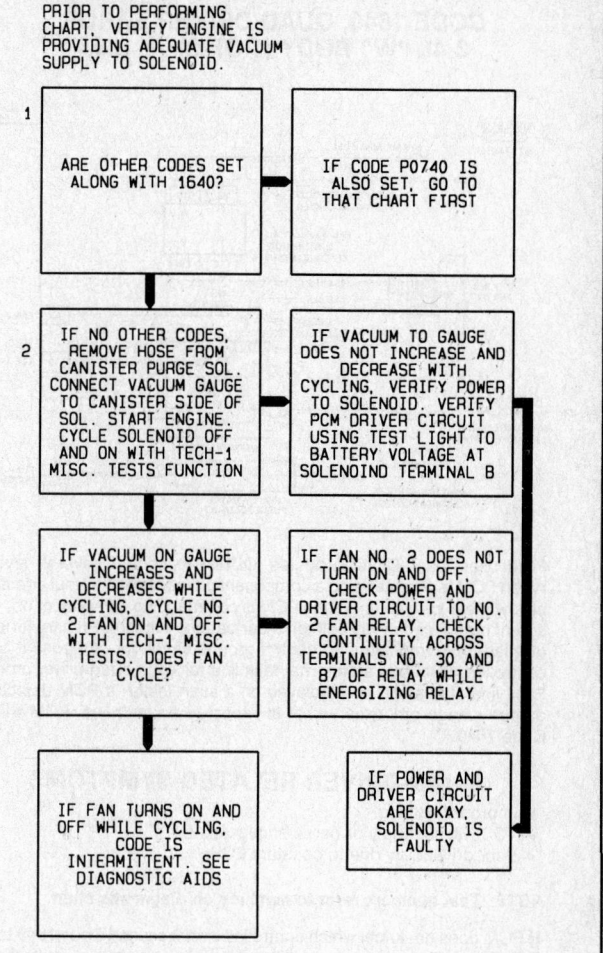

CODE 1640, QUAD-DRIVER ERROR
3.4L "W" BODY (1 OF 2) – 1994

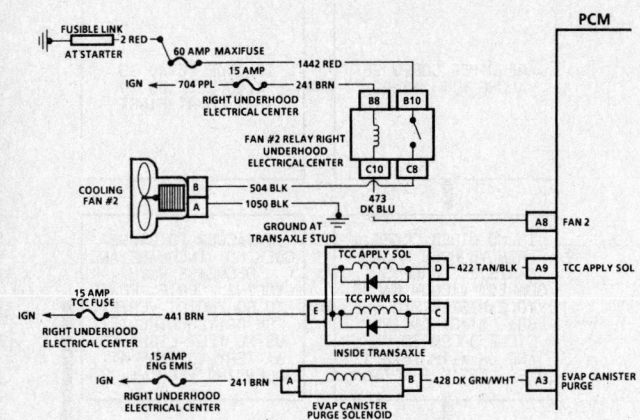

PCM uses Quad-Driver Modules (QDMs) to control several devices. When PCM is commanding a component on, voltage of output circuit will be low (near zero volts). When PCM is commanding component off, voltage of output circuit will be high (near battery voltage). Primary function of quad-driver module is to control ground circuit for component being controlled. PCM has an internal fault line for each quad-driver module. Fault line status can be displayed on a scan tester. If PCM detects an output voltage other than what is expected on fault line, PCM will set Code 1640.

QUAD-DRIVER RELATED SYMPTOMS

- Improper shifting.
- TCC will not apply or harsh engagement.
- Poor driveability due to constant EGR.

NOTE: Test numbers refer to numbers on diagnostic chart.

1) PCM does not know which controlled circuit caused Code 1640 to set. This chart will check each circuit to determine which is at fault. If other QDM-related codes are present, use those charts first.
2) If QDM "A" related symptoms are present, check for Code 740. If Code 740 is present, repair Code 740 first.
3) These steps help determine which circuit is out of specification.
4) This test will determine if the problem is the circuit or the component. As the factory installed PCM is protected by an internal circuit breaker, it is unlikely that the PCM needs to be replaced.

94F38567   94E38608

DIAGNOSTIC AIDS

Monitor voltage at each terminal shown in schematic while moving related harness connectors, including PCM harness. If failure is induced, voltage will change. This may help to isolate an intermittent condition. Check for bent pins at PCM. If code reoccurs with no apparent connection problem, replace PCM.

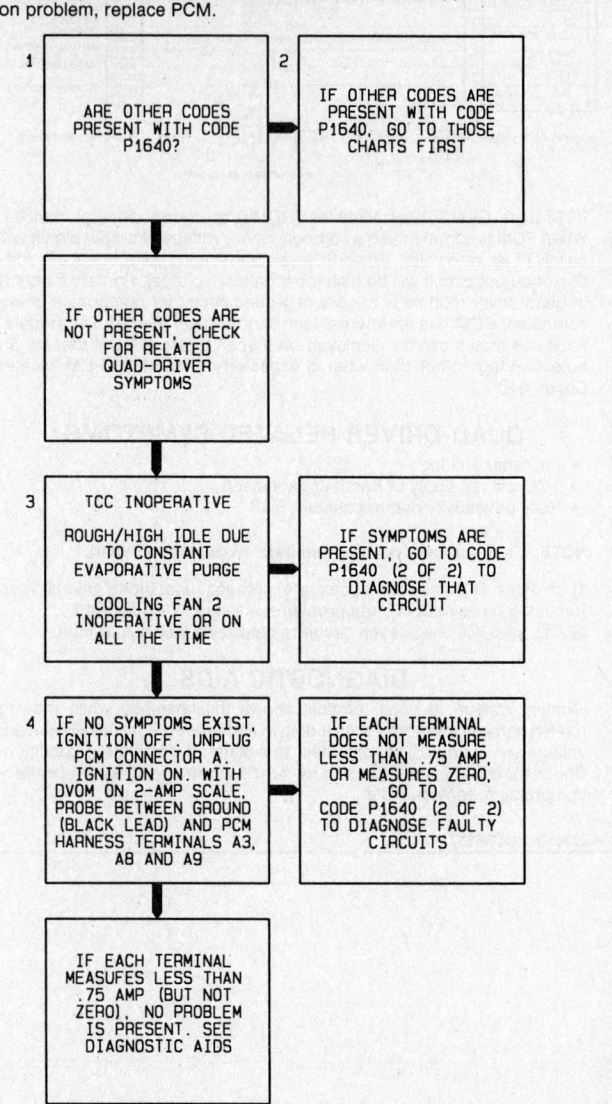

1 ARE OTHER CODES PRESENT WITH CODE P1640?

2 IF OTHER CODES ARE PRESENT WITH CODE P1640, GO TO THOSE CHARTS FIRST

IF OTHER CODES ARE NOT PRESENT, CHECK FOR RELATED QUAD-DRIVER SYMPTOMS

3 TCC INOPERATIVE

ROUGH/HIGH IDLE DUE TO CONSTANT EVAPORATIVE PURGE

COOLING FAN 2 INOPERATIVE OR ON ALL THE TIME

IF SYMPTOMS ARE PRESENT, GO TO CODE P1640 (2 OF 2) TO DIAGNOSE THAT CIRCUIT

4 IF NO SYMPTOMS EXIST, IGNITION OFF. UNPLUG PCM CONNECTOR A. IGNITION ON. WITH DVOM ON 2-AMP SCALE, PROBE BETWEEN GROUND (BLACK LEAD) AND PCM HARNESS TERMINALS A3, A8 AND A9

IF EACH TERMINAL DOES NOT MEASURE LESS THAN .75 AMP, OR MEASURES ZERO, GO TO CODE P1640 (2 OF 2) TO DIAGNOSE FAULTY CIRCUITS

IF EACH TERMINAL MEASUFES LESS THAN .75 AMP (BUT NOT ZERO), NO PROBLEM IS PRESENT. SEE DIAGNOSTIC AIDS

**CODE 1640, QUAD-DRIVER ERROR
3.4L "W" BODY (2 OF 2) – 1994**

NOTE: Test number refer to number on diagnostic chart.

5) This step determines which circuit is out of specification.

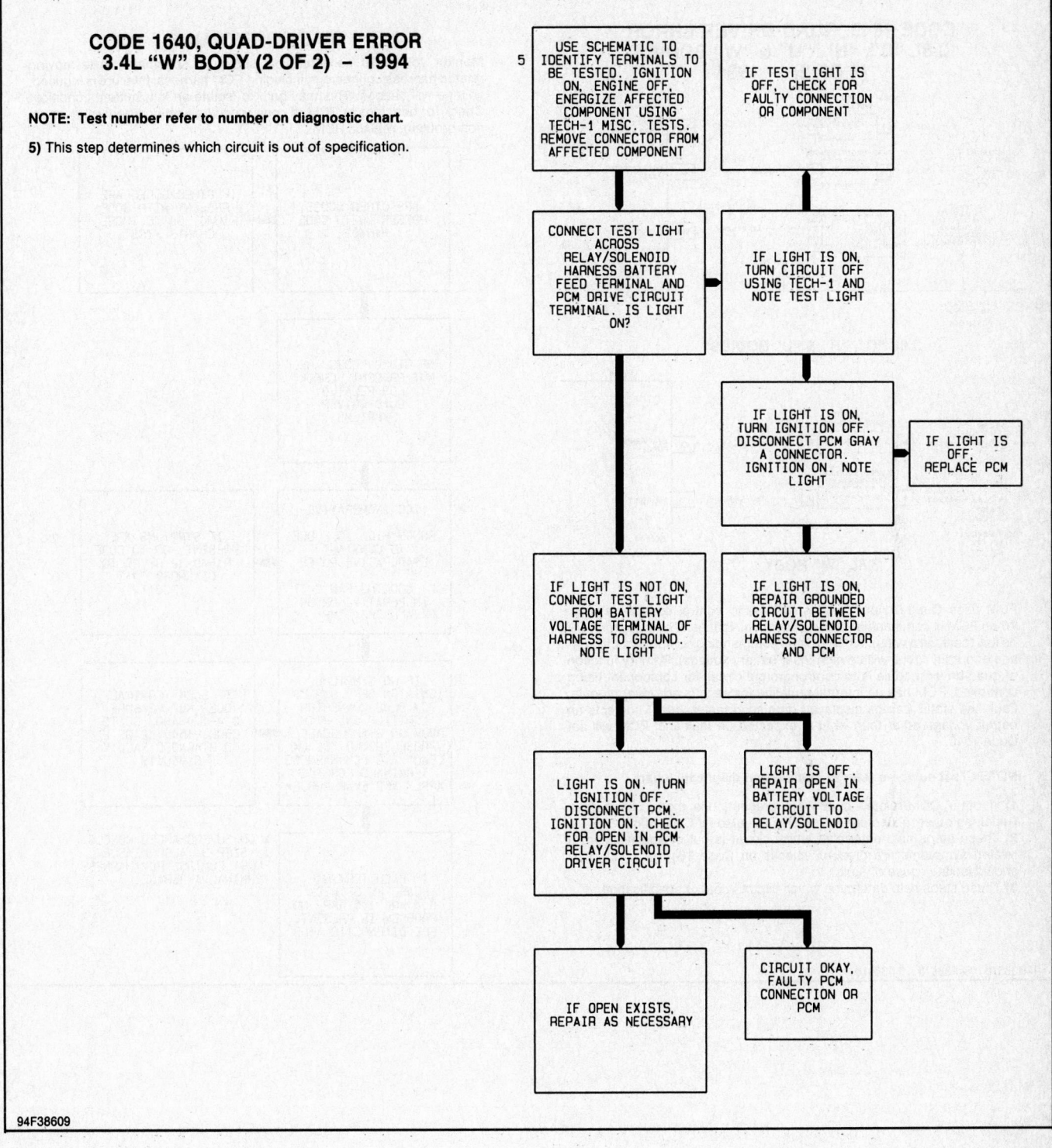

94F38609

CODE 1640, QUAD-DRIVER ERROR
3.8L "C", "H", "U" & "W" BODIES
(1 OF 2) – 1994

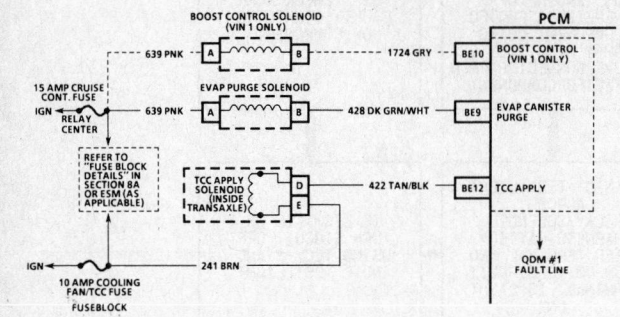

3.8L "C", "H" & "U" BODIES

3.8L "W" BODY

PCM uses Quad-Driver Modules (QDMs) to control several devices. When PCM is commanding a component on, voltage of output circuit will be low (near zero volts). When PCM is commanding component off, voltage of output circuit will be high (near battery voltage). Primary function of quad-driver module is to control ground circuit for component being controlled. PCM has an internal fault line for each quad-driver module. Fault line status can be displayed on a scan tester. If PCM detects an output voltage other than what is expected on fault line, PCM will set Code 1640.

NOTE: Test numbers refer to numbers on diagnostic chart.

1) If other QDM-related codes are present, use those charts first. Repairing other related code problems will also fix Code 1640.
2) These steps help determine which circuit is out of specification. If related symptoms are present, checks on Code 1640 (2 of 2) chart should isolate cause of fault.
3) These steps help determine which circuit is out of specification.

94G38576 94F38575 94I38610

DIAGNOSTIC AIDS

Monitor voltage at each terminal shown in schematic while moving related harness connectors, including PCM harness. If failure is induced, voltage will change. This may help to isolate an intermittent condition. Check for bent pins at PCM. If code reoccurs with no apparent connection problem, replace PCM.

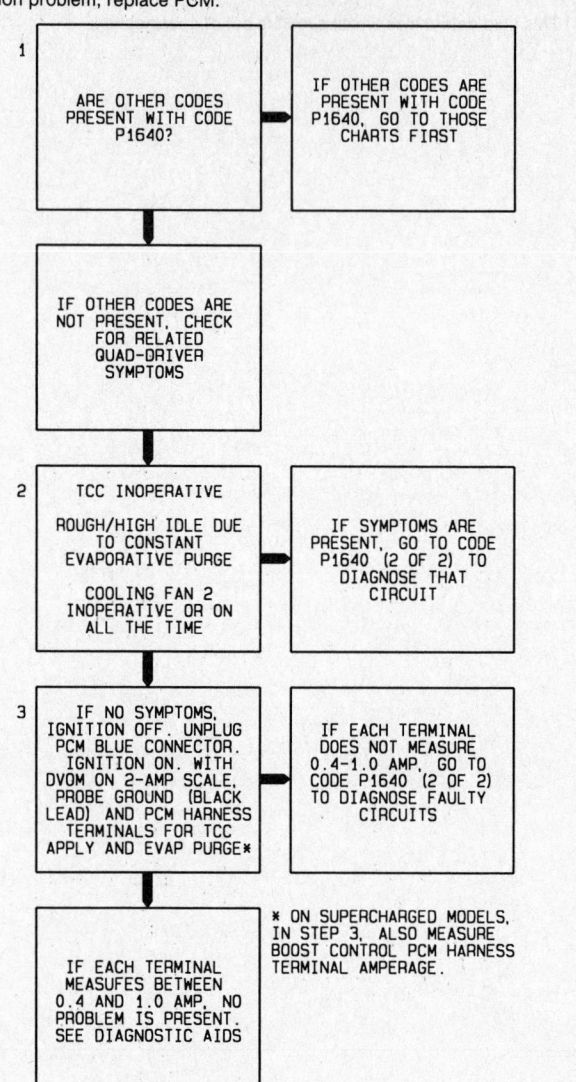

CODE 1640, QUAD-DRIVER ERROR
3.8L "C", "H", "U" & "W" BODIES
(2 OF 2) – 1994

NOTE: Test numbers refer to numbers on diagnostic chart.

4) This test will determine if the problem is the circuit or the component.
5) As the factory installed PCM is protected by an internal circuit breaker, it is unlikely that the PCM needs to be replaced.

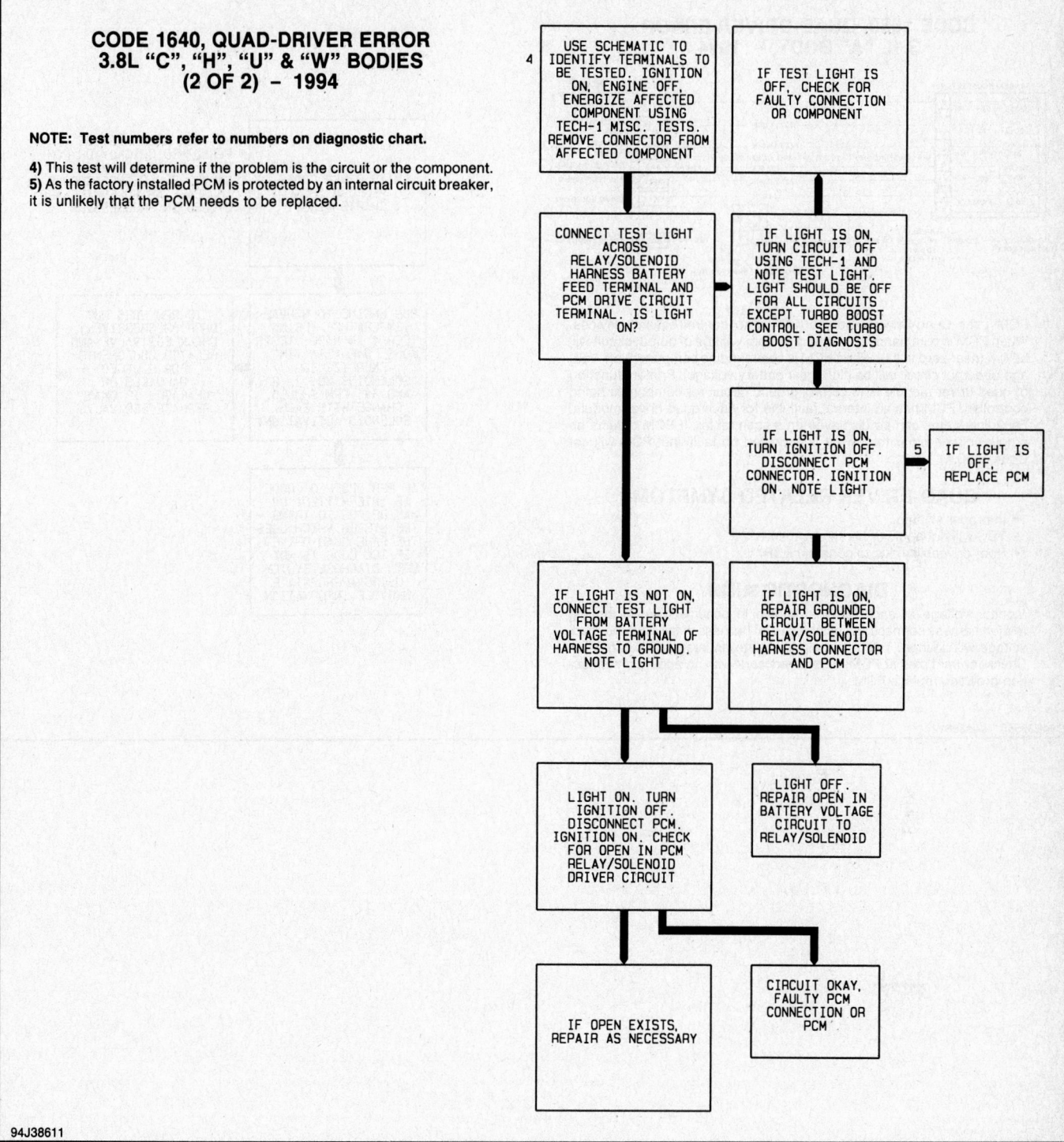

4 USE SCHEMATIC TO IDENTIFY TERMINALS TO BE TESTED. IGNITION ON, ENGINE OFF, ENERGIZE AFFECTED COMPONENT USING TECH-1 MISC. TESTS. REMOVE CONNECTOR FROM AFFECTED COMPONENT

IF TEST LIGHT IS OFF, CHECK FOR FAULTY CONNECTION OR COMPONENT

CONNECT TEST LIGHT ACROSS RELAY/SOLENOID HARNESS BATTERY FEED TERMINAL AND PCM DRIVE CIRCUIT TERMINAL. IS LIGHT ON?

IF LIGHT IS ON, TURN CIRCUIT OFF USING TECH-1 AND NOTE TEST LIGHT. LIGHT SHOULD BE OFF FOR ALL CIRCUITS EXCEPT TURBO BOOST CONTROL. SEE TURBO BOOST DIAGNOSIS

IF LIGHT IS ON, TURN IGNITION OFF. DISCONNECT PCM CONNECTOR. IGNITION ON. NOTE LIGHT

5 IF LIGHT IS OFF, REPLACE PCM

IF LIGHT IS NOT ON, CONNECT TEST LIGHT FROM BATTERY VOLTAGE TERMINAL OF HARNESS TO GROUND. NOTE LIGHT

IF LIGHT IS ON, REPAIR GROUNDED CIRCUIT BETWEEN RELAY/SOLENOID HARNESS CONNECTOR AND PCM

LIGHT ON. TURN IGNITION OFF. DISCONNECT PCM. IGNITION ON. CHECK FOR OPEN IN PCM RELAY/SOLENOID DRIVER CIRCUIT

LIGHT OFF. REPAIR OPEN IN BATTERY VOLTAGE CIRCUIT TO RELAY/SOLENOID

IF OPEN EXISTS, REPAIR AS NECESSARY

CIRCUIT OKAY, FAULTY PCM CONNECTION OR PCM

94J38611

CODE 1650, QUAD-DRIVER ERROR
3.1L "A" BODY – 1994

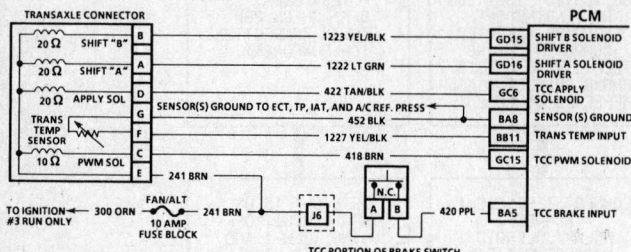

PCM uses Quad-Driver Modules (QDMs) to control several devices. When PCM is commanding a component on, voltage of output circuit will be low (near zero volts). When PCM is commanding component off, voltage of output circuit will be high (near battery voltage). Primary function of quad-driver module is to control ground circuit for component being controlled. PCM has an internal fault line for each quad-driver module. Fault line status can be displayed on a scan tester. If PCM detects an output voltage other than what is expected on fault line, PCM will set Code 1650.

QUAD-DRIVER RELATED SYMPTOMS

- Improper shifting.
- TCC will not apply or harsh engagement.
- Poor driveability due to constant EGR.

DIAGNOSTIC AIDS

Monitor voltage at each terminal shown in schematic while moving related harness connectors, including PCM harness. If failure is induced, voltage will change. This may help to isolate an intermittent condition. Check for bent pins at PCM. If code reoccurs with no apparent connection problem, replace PCM.

94E38558   94A38612

IF CODE IS STORED WITH OTHER CODES, PERFORM THOSE CHARTS FIRST.

↓

RUN ENGINE TO NORMAL TEMPERATURE. USING TECH-1 IN MISC. TESTS MODE, ONE AT A TIME, ENERGIZE EGR SOLENOIDS NO. 1, 2 AND 3*. RPM SHOULD CHANGE WITH EACH SOLENOID ACTIVATION

→ IF RPM DOES NOT DROP PROGRESSIVELY, CHECK EGR VALVE AND RELATED COMPONENTS FOR PLUGGED PASSAGES OR LEAKAGE. IF OKAY, REPLACE EGR VALVE

↓

IF RPM DROPPED, CODE IS INTERMITTENT OR MAY BE DUE TO TRANS. TCC SYSTEM WHICH USES THE SAME QUAD-DRIVER. IF TCC CODE IS NOT SET, DIAGNOSE SYSTEM USING APPROPRIATE SERVICE INFORMATION

*: THIS STEP MUST BE PERFORMED QUICKLY OR PCM WILL ADJUST RPM WITH IAC VALVE. RPM CHANGE SHOULD INCREASE AS SOLENOIDS ARE CYCLED IN PROGRESSION

CODE 1650, QUAD-DRIVER ERROR
3.4L "W" BODY (1 OF 2) – 1994

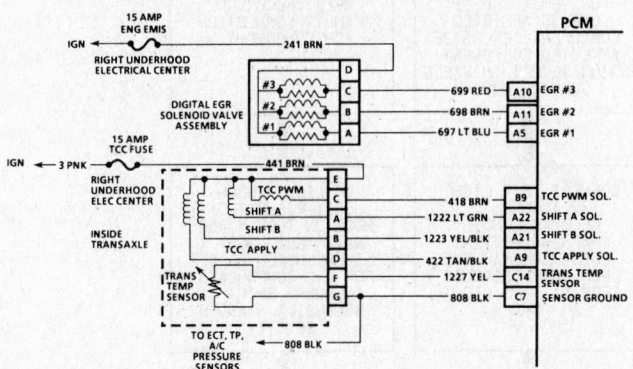

PCM uses Quad-Driver Modules (QDMs) to control several devices. When PCM is commanding a component on, voltage of output circuit will be low (near zero volts). When PCM is commanding component off, voltage of output circuit will be high (near battery voltage). Primary function of quad-driver module is to control ground circuit for component being controlled. PCM has an internal fault line for each quad-driver module. Fault line status can be displayed on a scan tester. If PCM detects an output voltage other than what is expected on fault line, PCM will set Code 1650.

NOTE: Test numbers refer to numbers on diagnostic chart.

1) If other QDM-related codes are present, use those charts first. Repairing other related code problems will also fix Code 1650.
2) These steps help determine which circuit is out of specification. If related symptoms are present, checks on Code 1650 (2 of 2) chart should isolate cause of fault.
3) These steps help determine which circuit is out of specification.

DIAGNOSTIC AIDS

Monitor voltage at each terminal shown in schematic while moving related harness connectors, including PCM harness. If failure is induced, voltage will change. This may help to isolate an intermittent condition. Check for bent pins at PCM. If code reoccurs with no apparent connection problem, replhis may help to isolate an intermittent condition. Check for bent pins at PCM. If code reoccurs with no apparent connection problem, replace PCM.

94G38568   94B38613

1

ARE OTHER CODES PRESENT WITH CODE P1650? → IF OTHER CODES ARE PRESENT WITH CODE P1650, GO TO THOSE CHARTS FIRST

IF OTHER CODES ARE NOT PRESENT, CHECK FOR RELATED QUAD-DRIVER SYMPTOMS

2

TCC INOPERATIVE

EGR INOPERATIVE OR ON ALL THE TIME

TRANSAXLE NOT SHIFTING PROPERLY → IF SYMPTOMS ARE PRESENT, GO TO CODE P1650 (2 OF 2) TO DIAGNOSE THAT CIRCUIT

3

IF NO SYMPTOMS EXIST, IGNITION OFF. UNPLUG PCM CONNECTORS. IGNITION ON. WITH DVOM ON 2-AMP SCALE, AND BLACK DVOM LEAD TO GROUND, PROBE PCM HARNESS TERMINALS A5/A10/A11/A21/A22/B9 → IF EACH TERMINAL DOES NOT MEASURE 0.4-1.0 AMP, GO TO CODE P1650 (2 OF 2) TO DIAGNOSE FAULTY CIRCUITS

IF EACH TERMINAL MEASUFES 0.4-1.0 AMP, NO PROBLEM IS PRESENT. SEE DIAGNOSTIC AIDS

CODE 1650, QUAD-DRIVER ERROR
3.4L "W" BODY (2 OF 2) – 1994

NOTE: Test numbers refer to numbers on diagnostic chart.

4) This test will determine if the problem is the circuit or the component.
5) As the factory installed PCM is protected by an internal circuit breaker, it is unlikely that the PCM needs to be replaced.

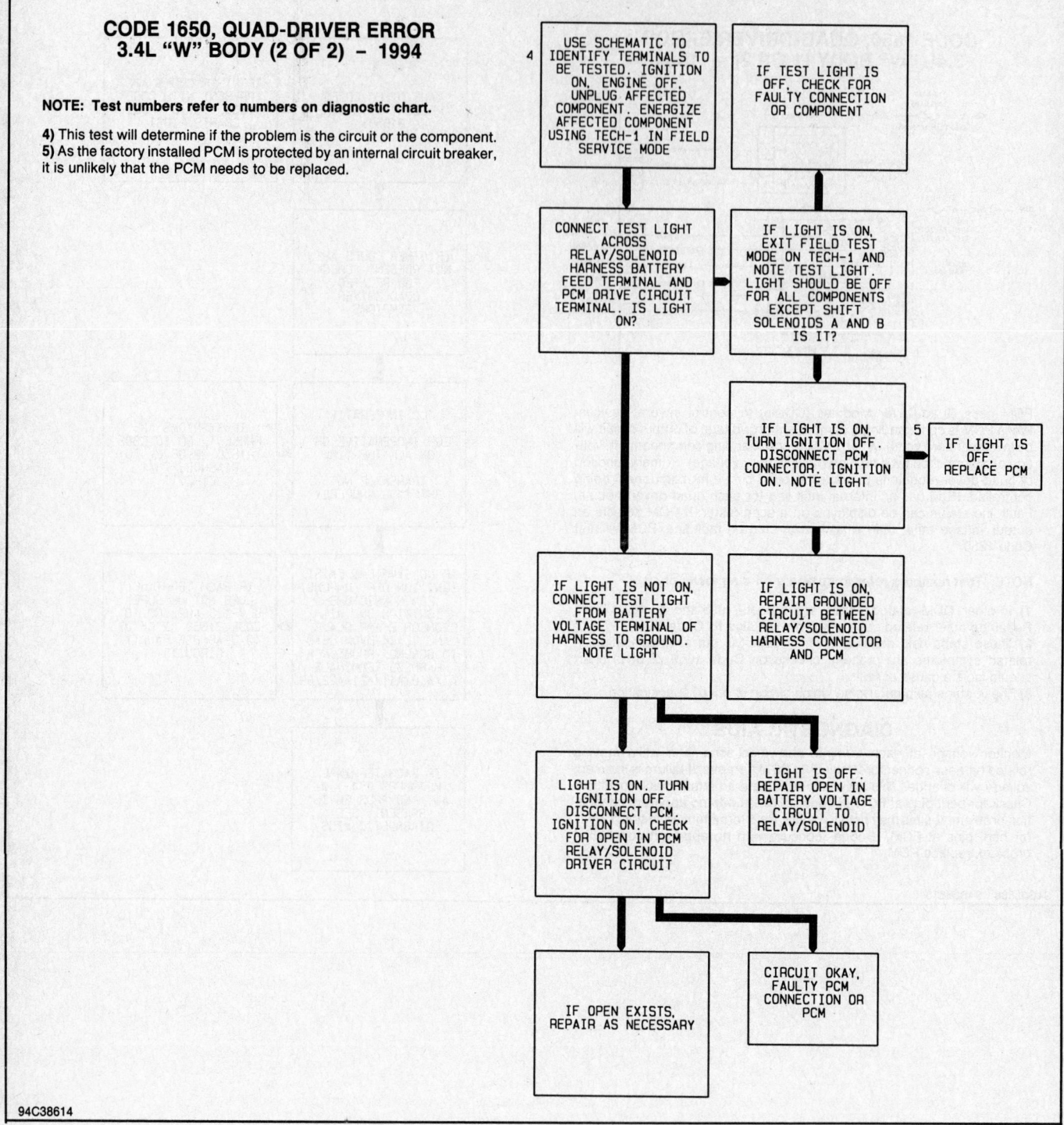

94C38614

CODE 1650, QUAD-DRIVER ERROR
3.8L "C", "H", "U" & "W" BODIES
(1 OF 2) – 1994

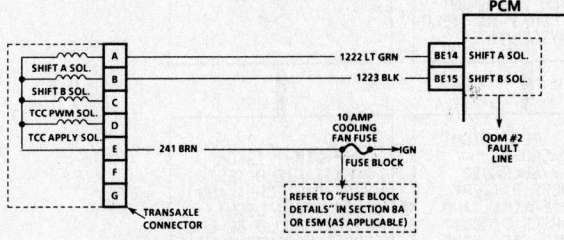

3.8L "C", "H" & "U" BODIES

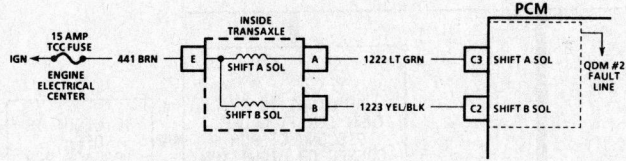

3.8L "W" BODY

PCM uses Quad-Driver Modules (QDMs) to control several devices. When PCM is commanding a component on, voltage of output circuit will be low (near zero volts). When PCM is commanding component off, voltage of output circuit will be high (near battery voltage). Primary function of quad-driver module is to control ground circuit for component being controlled. PCM has an internal fault line for each quad-driver module. Fault line status can be displayed on a scan tester. If PCM detects an output voltage other than what is expected on fault line, PCM will set Code 1650.

NOTE: Test numbers refer to numbers on diagnostic chart.

1) If other QDM-related codes are present, use those charts first. Repairing other related code problems will also fix Code 1650.
2) These step determines which circuit is out of specification.

94I38578   94H38577   94D38615

DIAGNOSTIC AIDS

Monitor voltage at each terminal shown in schematic while moving related harness connectors, including PCM harness. If failure is induced, voltage will change. This may help to isolate an intermittent condition. Check for bent pins at PCM. If code reoccurs with no apparent connection problem, replace PCM.

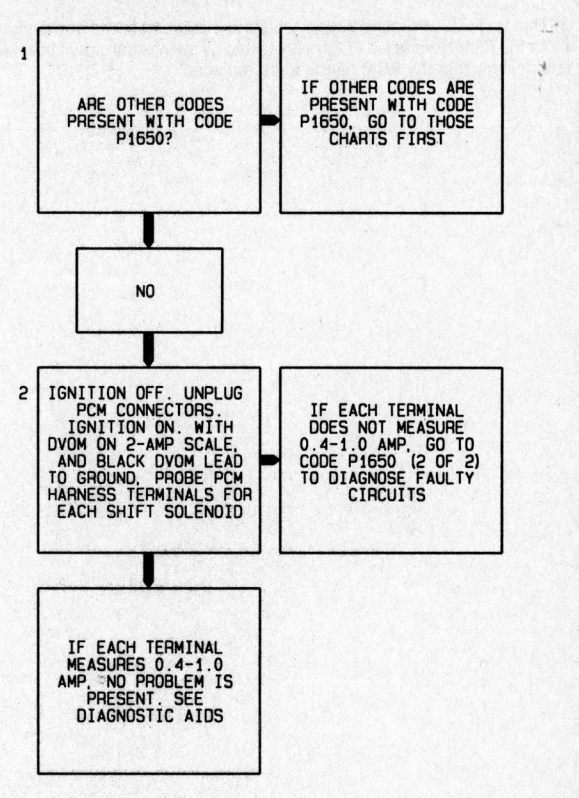

CODE 1650, QUAD-DRIVER ERROR
3.8L "C", "H", "U" & "W" BODIES
(2 OF 2) – 1994

NOTE: Test numbers refer to numbers on diagnostic chart.

3) This test will determine if the problem is the circuit or the component.
4) As the factory installed PCM is protected by an internal circuit breaker, it is unlikely that the PCM needs to be replaced.

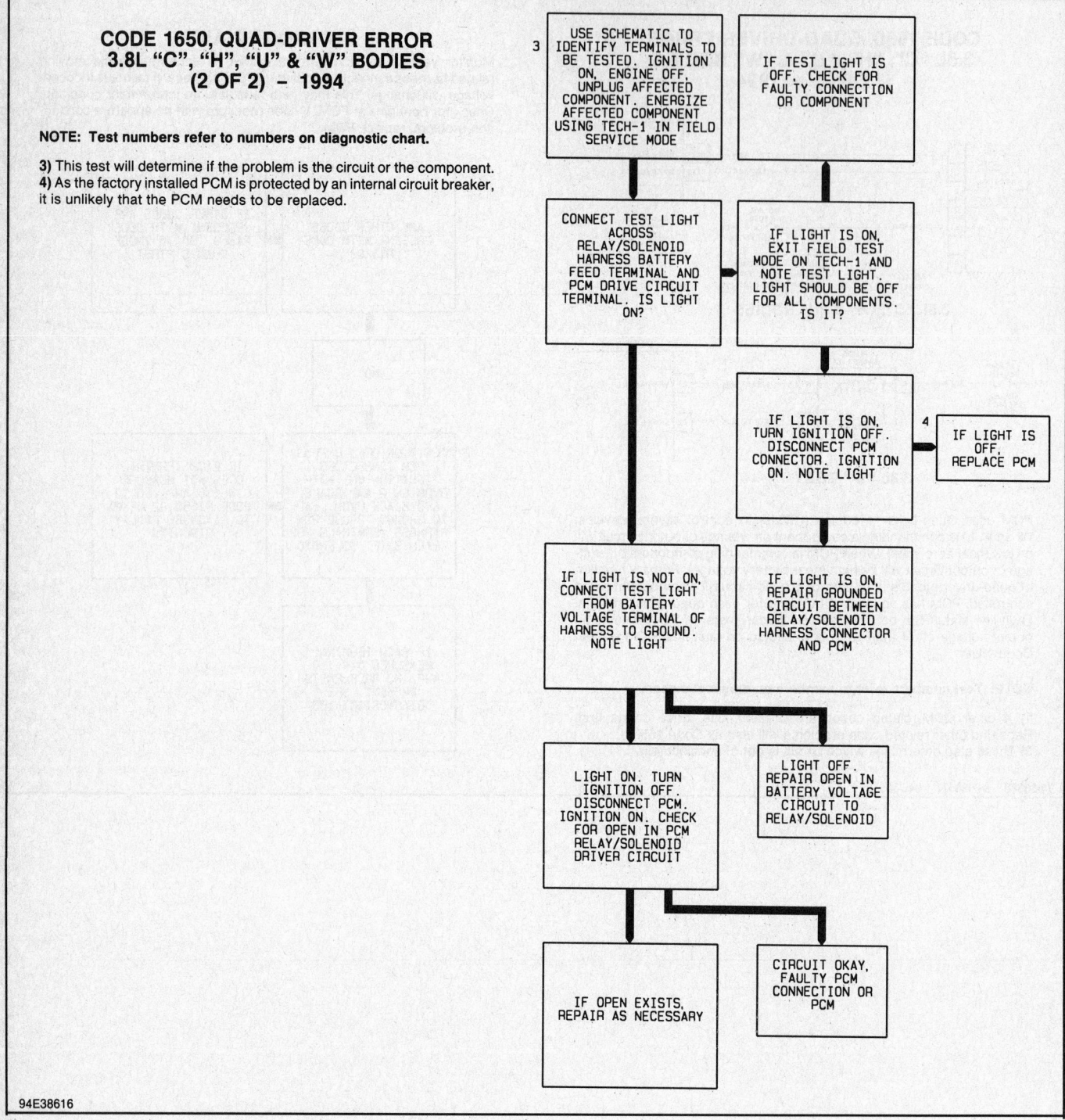

3 — USE SCHEMATIC TO IDENTIFY TERMINALS TO BE TESTED. IGNITION ON, ENGINE OFF, UNPLUG AFFECTED COMPONENT. ENERGIZE AFFECTED COMPONENT USING TECH-1 IN FIELD SERVICE MODE

IF TEST LIGHT IS OFF, CHECK FOR FAULTY CONNECTION OR COMPONENT

CONNECT TEST LIGHT ACROSS RELAY/SOLENOID HARNESS BATTERY FEED TERMINAL AND PCM DRIVE CIRCUIT TERMINAL. IS LIGHT ON?

IF LIGHT IS ON, EXIT FIELD TEST MODE ON TECH-1 AND NOTE TEST LIGHT. LIGHT SHOULD BE OFF FOR ALL COMPONENTS. IS IT?

IF LIGHT IS ON, TURN IGNITION OFF. DISCONNECT PCM CONNECTOR. IGNITION ON. NOTE LIGHT

4 — IF LIGHT IS OFF, REPLACE PCM

IF LIGHT IS NOT ON, CONNECT TEST LIGHT FROM BATTERY VOLTAGE TERMINAL OF HARNESS TO GROUND. NOTE LIGHT

IF LIGHT IS ON, REPAIR GROUNDED CIRCUIT BETWEEN RELAY/SOLENOID HARNESS CONNECTOR AND PCM

LIGHT ON. TURN IGNITION OFF. DISCONNECT PCM. IGNITION ON. CHECK FOR OPEN IN PCM RELAY/SOLENOID DRIVER CIRCUIT

LIGHT OFF. REPAIR OPEN IN BATTERY VOLTAGE CIRCUIT TO RELAY/SOLENOID

IF OPEN EXISTS, REPAIR AS NECESSARY

CIRCUIT OKAY, FAULTY PCM CONNECTION OR PCM

94E38616

ELECTRONIC SELF-DIAGNOSTICS (CADILLAC)

PCM constantly monitors all electrical circuits. If PCM detects circuit problems or sensors out of range, it will record trouble codes. If problem continues for a predetermined time, SERVICE ENGINE SOON light will glow.

If the SERVICE ENGINE SOON light is on all the time, trouble code(s) are currently being detected. If the SERVICE ENGINE SOON light is off, but PCM had detected a circuit or sensor problem, trouble code(s) will be stored in computer memory.

Stored trouble codes may be retrieved from PCM memory. On these models, trouble codes may be retrieved through the instrument panel.

NOTE: For complete PCM testing and diagnosis, see ENGINE PERFORMANCE in appropriate MITCHELL® manual.

RETRIEVING CODES

NOTE: These vehicles are capable of displaying trouble codes and computer data on the instrument panel. The information is similar to what a scan tool can provide. Use the following information to access transaxle-related trouble codes and to erase them from computer memory. If available, a bidirectional scan tool (Tech 1) can also be used on these vehicles.

In order to access and control the PCM self-diagnostic features, 2 electronic components are used, the Drivers Information Center (DIC) and the Electronic Climate Control Panel (ECCP). *See Fig. 2.* The SERVICE MODE for diagnostic information incorporates odometer/trip odometer as Driver Information Center (DIC) display. When a malfunction is sensed by the PCM, the SERVICE ENGINE SOON (SES) light will glow on DIC and stay on (with engine running) until code is cleared from PCM.

The ECCP becomes the controller by which to enter and access self-diagnostics. By pressing the appropriate buttons on the ECCP, data messages can be sent to the PCM, requesting specific diagnostic features. This process allows PCM to transfer any of its available diagnostic information to instrument panel DIC display during service mode operation.

PCM STATUS LIGHTS (1993 ELDORADO & SEVILLE; 1994 DEVILLE ONLY)

While in SYSTEM LEVEL of DIAGNOSTIC SERVICE MODE, mode indicators on ECCP are used to indicate status of certain operating modes. Different modes of operation are indicated by status light being on or off. Following is a description of various status lights.

- **AUTO A/C Status Indicator** – This indicator is used to signify operating mode of PCM. If AUTO is on, PCM is in closed loop. If AUTO is off, PCM is in open loop.
- **AUTO Fan Status Indicator** – This displays status of Park/Neutral switch. When Park/Neutral switch is closed, AUTO fan symbol is on. When Park/Neutral switch is open, AUTO fan symbol is off.
- **ECON Status Indicator** – This displays status of transaxle shift solenoid "B". When ECON is on, transaxle shift solenoid "B" is energized. When ECON is off, transaxle shift solenoid "B" is not energized.
- **"E" Temperature Status Indicator** – This displays status of shift adapt status. When the "E" symbol is on, transaxle shift adapts are disabled. When the "E" symbol is off, transaxle shift adapts are enabled.
- **DEFOG Status Indicator** – This displays status of transaxle shift solenoid "A". When DEFOG is on, transaxle shift solenoid "A" is energized. When DEFOG is off, transaxle shift solenoid "A" is not energized.
- **Front Defogger Status Indicator** – This indicator is used for A/C clutch command. *See Fig. 2.* Light should only be on when A/C clutch is engaged.

- **LO Fan Speed Status Indicator** – This indicator is used to indicate status of the throttle position switch. When the throttle position switch is closed, the LO fan symbol is on. When the throttle position switch is open, the LO fan symbol is off.
- **Rear Defogger Status Indicator** – This indicator is used for the Torque Converter Clutch (TCC) or Viscous Converter Clutch (VCC). *See Fig. 2.* Light only indicates TCC/VCC solenoid status requested by PCM; actual operation depends on condition of TCC/VCC system.

ENTERING SELF-DIAGNOSTICS

CAUTION: Accessing self-diagnostics for 30 minutes or longer without running engine will cause battery to discharge, resulting in a possible no-start condition and faulty diagnostic readings. To ensure proper operation, attach battery charger to battery.

1) Turn ignition switch on. Simultaneously depress OFF and WARMER buttons on the Electronic Climate Control Panel (ECCP). *See Fig. 2.*
2) Continue to depress OFF and WARMER buttons until all segments and bulbs of the DIC and ECCP illuminate. When all segments are lit, system has entered self-diagnostic mode. Release OFF and WARMER button.
3) If all segments of the DIC and ECCP glow, go to step 4). Failure of any segment to glow may result in inaccurate test results. All inoperative segments of the display must be made to operate before proceeding with self-diagnostic procedures.
4) Powertrain Control Module (PCM) trouble codes are automatically displayed after system enters self-diagnostics. Trouble codes (3-digit) appear in numerical order and are prefixed with letter "P". If no PCM trouble codes are stored, NO PCM CODES message will be displayed.
5) All PCM trouble codes are followed by letter "C" or "H". Letter "C" stands for current and indicates fault presently exists.
6) The letter "H" stands for history and indicates system failure was not present during last key cycle, but was present during one of previous 50 key cycles. For example: Code P024H is PCM Code 024, set in response to a malfunction that occurred in the past (history).

NOTE: After all trouble codes have been displayed, depressing OFF button on ECCP will activate a repeat of trouble code display.

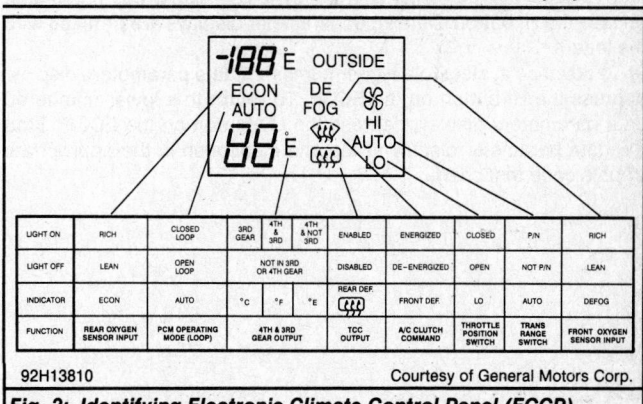

LIGHT ON	RICH	CLOSED LOOP	3RD GEAR	4TH & 3RD	4TH & NOT 3RD	ENABLED	ENERGIZED	CLOSED	P/N	RICH
LIGHT OFF	LEAN	OPEN LOOP	NOT IN 3RD or 4TH GEAR			DISABLED	DE-ENERGIZED	OPEN	NOT P/N	LEAN
INDICATOR	ECON	AUTO	°C	°F	°E	REAR DEF.	FRONT DEF.	LO	AUTO	DEFOG
FUNCTION	REAR OXYGEN SENSOR INPUT	PCM OPERATING MODE (LOOP)	4TH & 3RD GEAR OUTPUT			TCC OUTPUT	A/C CLUTCH COMMAND	THROTTLE POSITION SWITCH	TRANS RANGE SWITCH	FRONT OXYGEN SENSOR INPUT

92H13810   Courtesy of General Motors Corp.

Fig. 2: Identifying Electronic Climate Control Panel (ECCP)

NOTE: Information related to ICP and SIR trouble codes is provided here in case FDC or DIC begins to display them. For complete information, see ENGINE PERFORMANCE in appropriate MITCHELL® manual.

ICP Trouble Codes Display – Following the display of ICP trouble codes, 2 cycles of ICP trouble codes will be displayed. ICP trouble codes are prefixed by the letter(s) "I" or "I.I.". A single "I" precedes the first pass of ICP trouble codes, which is a display of both history and current trouble codes. The letters "I.I." precede the second pass of ICM trouble codes which is a display of current trouble codes only.

Supplemental Inflatable Restraint (SIR) Trouble Code Display – SIR system trouble codes are displayed last. These codes are displayed in ascending (3-digit) numerical order and are prefixed by "R".

NOTE: *If no codes are present or the communication link between a component and the ICP is not operating, a NO X DATA message will be displayed, indicating the ICP could not communicate with the particular component (X = the particular component).*

PCM TROUBLE CODES (CADILLAC)

Code	Circuit Affected
P012 [1]	No Distributor Signal
P014	Shorted Coolant Temp. Sensor Circuit
P015	Open Coolant Temp. Sensor Circuit
P021	Shorted Throttle Position Sensor (TPS) Circuit
P022	Open TPS circuit
P024	VSS Circuit Protection
P039	VCC Engagement Problem Electrical Check
P057	Shorted Transaxle Temp. Sensor Circuit
P059	Open Transaxle Temp. Sensor Circuit
P090	VCC Brake Switch Input Problem
P091	Park/Neutral Switch Problem

[1] – Code P012 is normal when no reference pulses are received by control module (engine not running).

NOTE: *After the display of all PCM and BCM trouble codes, ".7.0" will be displayed on the FDC or DIC. ".7.0" indicates the system is ready for a diagnostic feature (such as on-line data value) to be selected.*

ON-LINE DATA VALUE

Entering PCM Data Parameters Display – PCM data parameters (on-line data value) display allows technician to compare the present operating specifications of the malfunctioning vehicle with the specifications of a known good vehicle.

Eldorado & Seville – 1) With "PCM" displayed on the DIC, depress and release the HI button on the ECCP. This will switch display from "PCM" to "DATA", signaling the start of the available PCM data.

2) Several types of tests are available. To select different tests, press and release the LO button. With "INPUTS" displayed, press and release the HI button. Data input parameter displays are prefixed with the letters "P I".

3) To advance system to a higher numbered data parameters display, depress the HI button on the ECCP. To return to a lower numbered data parameters display, depress the LO button on the ECCP. Stop the data parameter display at the one mentioned in the appropriate trouble code test chart.

4) To exit data parameter series at any time and return to "PCM", press and release OFF button 3 times or complete procedures for clearing PCM or ICP trouble codes. See CLEARING TROUBLE CODES under ELECTRONIC SELF-DIAGNOSTICS (CADILLAC).

DeVille & Fleetwood – 1) With ".7.0" displayed on FDC, depress and release LO button on ECCP. This will switch display from ".7.0" to "E.9.0", signaling start of PCM data parameters display. Data parameter displays are prefixed by "P".

2) To advance system to a higher numbered data parameters display, depress HI button on ECCP. To return to a lower numbered data parameters display, depress LO button on ECCP. Stop data parameter display when parameter mentioned in appropriate trouble code test chart is found.

3) To exit data parameter series at any time and return to ".7.0", complete procedures for clearing PCM or ICP trouble codes. To exit data parameter without clearing codes in memory, go to exiting diagnostics. See CLEARING TROUBLE CODES or EXITING DIAGNOSTICS under ELECTRONIC SELF-DIAGNOSTICS (CADILLAC).

CLEARING CODES

To clear codes, depress LO button on the ECCP 4 times or until ECCP displays PCM CLEAR CODES. Press HI button on ECCP. PCM will clear codes within 3 seconds. Press LO button on ECCP to return to PCM DATA display. If ignition switch is turned to OFF position, trouble codes are not erased.

EXITING SELF-DIAGNOSTICS

To exit self-diagnostics, press BI-LEV button on ECCP. Another way to exit self-diagnostics is to turn ignition to OFF position. Trouble codes will not be cleared by exiting self-diagnostics.

NOTE: *Faulty engine sensors and actuators may cause transaxle related fault codes or driveability problems. Engine faults and related trouble codes must be diagnosed and repaired before transaxle codes are repaired. For additional information on diagnosing and repairing engine related PCM fault codes, see ENGINE PERFORMANCE section of appropriate MITCHELL® manual.*

DIAGNOSTIC CHARTS (CADILLAC)

Diagnostic Aids – Diagnostic aids (located in many trouble code charts) are additional tips to help diagnosis trouble codes when circuit checks do not find problem.

PCM CODE PO14,
SHORTED COOLANT SENSOR CIRCUIT – 1993
(FLEETWOOD & SEVILLE ONLY)

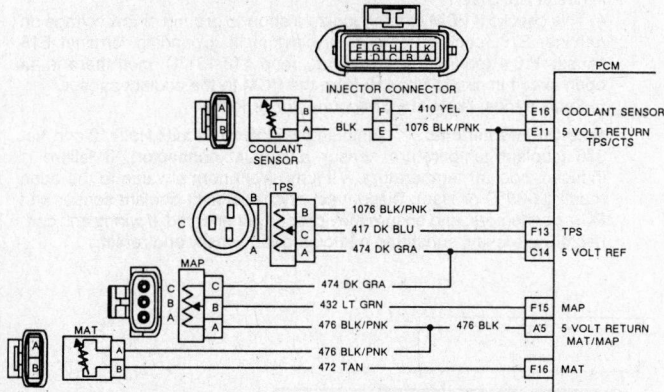

Failure Conditions: Coolant sensor value greater than or equal to 298°F (148°C).

Action: PCM turns on SERVICE ENGINE SOON light and uses MAT sensor value in place of coolant sensor value for all calculations for the first 4 minutes of operation. Then a value of 194°F (90°C) is used.

The coolant sensor is a 2-wire sensor with signal voltage coming from PCM to sensor terminal "B" (circuit No. 410), and a sensor reference ground on terminal "A" (circuit No. 976).

As sensor temperature increases, resistance decreases. Signal voltage from PCM to terminal "A" decreases as sensor temperature increases and current flows through sensor element to terminal "A" (sensor ground). Code PO14 sets because PCM assumes coolant temperature cannot be 298°F (148°C) or greater when MAT is 212°F (100°C) or less.

91E07541   91F07546

NOTE: Test numbers refer to test numbers on diagnostic chart.

1) With coolant sensor shorted, PCM parameter P.0.4 (on-line data value) should read 148°C or more. If not, sensor is not shorted. See NOTE ON INTERMITTENTS.

2) This checks for a shorted coolant sensor or a short in circuit No. 410. If parameter stays at 142°C or greater with sensor unplugged, then short is in circuit No. 410, between pin "B" and PCM terminal E16.

3) Fault is most likely at PCM connector or PCM.

Note On Intermittents – Manipulate wiring on circuit No. 410, coolant sensor, and PCM connector. If failure is induced, coolant temperature will jump from its normal value to the shorted reading of 148°C or greater. Disconnect and reconnect coolant sensor and PCM connectors, and ensure they are properly connected. If wiring and connectors are okay, substitute a known good sensor and retest.

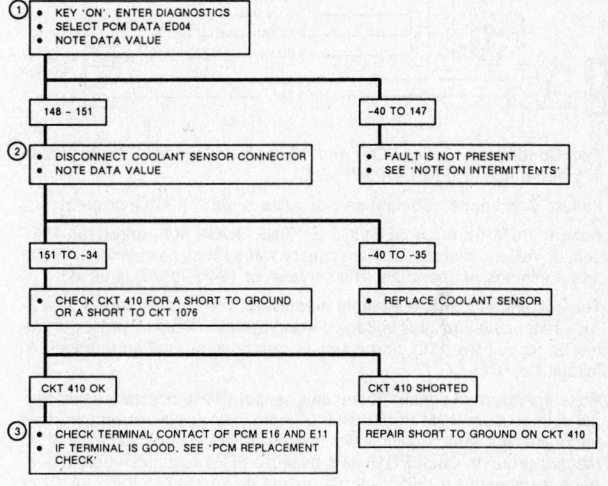

WHEN ALL DIAGNOSIS AND REPAIRS ARE COMPLETED, CLEAR CODES AND VERIFY OPERATION

Courtesy of General Motors Corp.

PCM CODE PO15,
OPEN COOLANT SENSOR CIRCUIT – 1993
(FLEETWODD & SEVILLE ONLY)

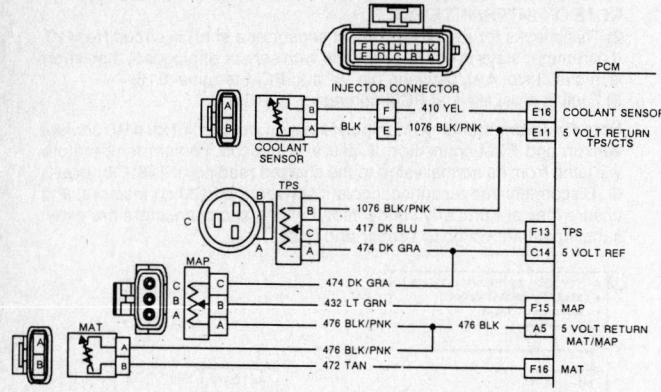

Test Conditions: Codes PO37 and PO38 not set and MAT sensor value is greater than or equal to 23°F (-5°C).

Failure Conditions: Coolant sensor value is -36°F (-38°C) or greater.

Action: PCM turns on SERVICE ENGINE SOON light and uses MAT sensor value in place of coolant sensor value for all calculations for the first 4 minutes of operation. Then a value of 194°F (90°C) is used.

The coolant sensor is a variable thermistor. The coolant sensor is a 2-wire sensor with a signal voltage coming from the PCM to sensor terminal "B" (circuit No. 410), and a sensor reference ground on terminal "A" (circuit No. 976).

As temperature of sensor decreases, sensor resistance increases. Signal voltage from PCM to terminal "B" increases as sensor temperature decreases and less current flows through sensor element to terminal "A" (sensor ground). Code PO15 sets because PCM assumes coolant temperature cannot be -36°F (-38°C) or less when MAT is 23°F (-5°C) or greater.

NOTE: Test numbers refer to test numbers on diagnostic chart.

1) If sensor is open, PCM parameter P.0.4 (on-line data value) should read -38°C or less. If not, then sensor signal is not open. See NOTE ON INTERMITTENTS.

2) This checks for open sensor signal in circuit No. 410 from PCM to sensor connector. If parameter or P.0.4 (on-line data value) reads 148-151°C with connector shorted, then circuit No. 410 is okay.

3) This checks for open in the sensor ground (circuit No. 1076 from sensor pin "A" to ground splice). If shorting pin "A" to ground causes parameter P.0.4 (on-line data value) to read 148-151°C, then there is an open in circuit No. 976.

4) This checks if PCM can recognize a short to ground or low voltage on terminal E16, coolant temperature signal. If grounding terminal E16 causes P.0.4 (on-line data value) to read 148-151°C, then there is an open circuit in circuit No. 410 from the PCM to the coolant sensor.

5) Fault is most likely at PCM connector or PCM.

Note On Intermittents – Manipulate wiring on circuits No. 410 and No. 976 (coolant temperature sensor and PCM connector). If failure is induced, coolant temperature will jump from normal value to the open reading (-38°C or less). Disconnect and reconnect coolant sensor and PCM connectors, and ensure they properly connected. If wiring and connectors are okay, substitute a known good sensor and retest.

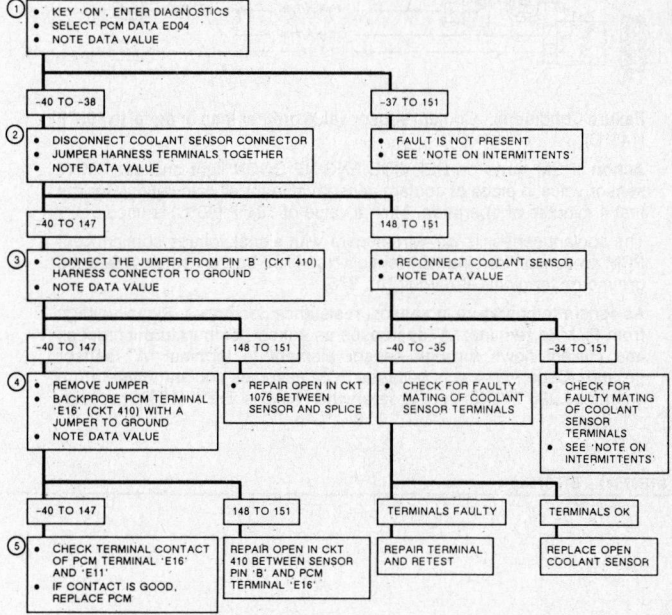

WHEN ALL DIAGNOSIS AND REPAIRS ARE COMPLETED, CLEAR CODES AND VERIFY OPERATION

91E07541   91J07548

Courtesy of General Motors Corp.

PCM CODE PO21, SHORTED TP SENSOR CIRCUIT (SIGNAL VOLTAGE HIGH) – 1993-94

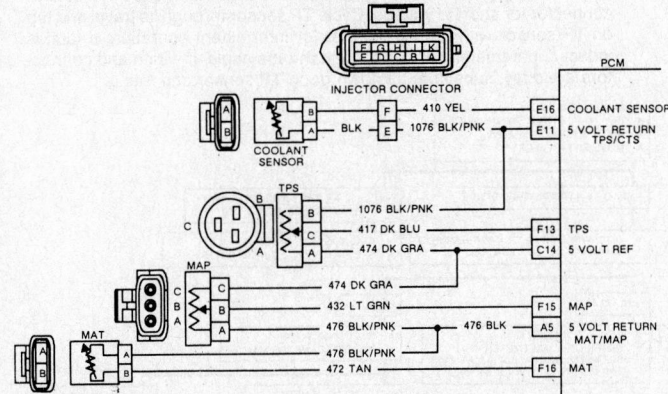

Test Conditions: Engine speed between 25-3000 RPM.

Failure Conditions: Throttle Position (TP) sensor value greater than or equal to 72 degrees for .7 second.

Action: PCM turns on SERVICE ENGINE SOON light and disables VCC. PCM sets TP sensor equal to 13 degrees when TP sensor is open and 6 degrees when TP sensor is closed. Fourth gear is disabled.

The TP sensor is a potentiometer. A 5-volt reference is provided on circuit No. 474 and ground is provided on circuit No. 1076. The TP sensor signal circuit No. 417 varies between ground and 5 volts based on throttle plate position. At low throttle angle, the TP sensor signal voltage is low. The PCM uses TP sensor information to determine idle, WOT, deceleration leanness and acceleration enrichment.

NOTE: Test numbers refer to test numbers on diagnostic chart.

1) This step checks for shorted TP sensor or shorted wiring. If data value stays greater than -7 with TP sensor disconnected, problem is in the wiring circuit.

2) This checks for an open in circuit No. 1076 between the TP sensor and PCM. An open in circuit No. 1076 will result in high TPS values whenever the TP sensor is plugged in.

Note On Intermittents – If Code PO21 is intermittent, manipulate related wiring. Check TP sensor connector for shorts to voltage. Cycle TP sensor through its travel and tap on TP sensor with a pencil to test for intermittent operation. If fault is induced, parameter will skip to high throttle angle. If wiring and connectors are okay, substitute a known good TP sensor and retest.

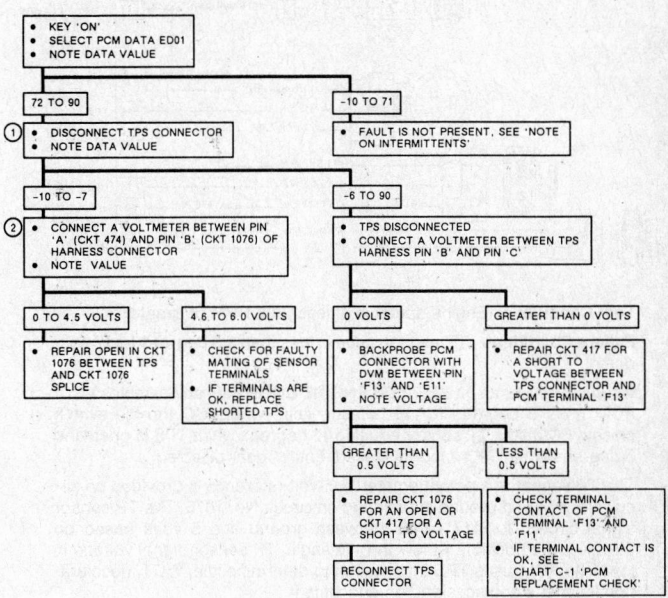

WHEN ALL DIAGNOSIS AND REPAIRS ARE COMPLETED, CLEAR CODES AND VERIFY OPERATION

91E07541 91A07558

Courtesy of General Motors Corp.

PCM CODE PO22, OPEN TP SENSOR CIRCUIT (SIGNAL VOLTAGE LOW) – 1993-94

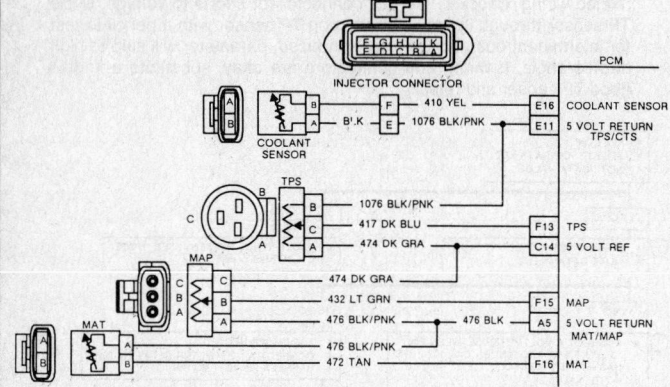

INJECTOR CONNECTOR

COOLANT SENSOR

TPS

MAP

MAT

410 YEL	E16	COOLANT SENSOR
1076 BLK/PNK	E11	5 VOLT RETURN TPS/CTS
1076 BLK/PNK		
417 DK BLU	F13	TPS
474 DK GRA	C14	5 VOLT REF
474 DK GRA		
432 LT GRN	F15	MAP
476 BLK/PNK	A5	5 VOLT RETURN MAT/MAP
476 BLK/PNK		
472 TAN	F16	MAT

Test Conditions: Engine speed is at least 600 RPM or greater.

Failure Conditions: TP sensor value is less than 1.3 degrees for .7 second.

Action: PCM turns on SERVICE ENGINE SOON light and disables VCC. PCM uses 6 degrees for TP sensor value when ISC throttle switch closes. PCM sets TP sensor equal to 13 degrees when TPS is open and 6 degrees when TP sensor is closed. Fourth gear disabled.

The TP sensor is a potentiometer. A 5-volt reference is provided on circuit No. 474 and ground is provided on circuit No. 1076. The TP sensor signal circuit No. 417 varies between ground and 5 volts based on throttle plate position. At low throttle angle, TP sensor signal voltage is low. The PCM uses TPS information to determine idle, WOT, deceleration leanness and acceleration enrichment.

NOTE: Test numbers refer to test numbers on diagnostic chart.

1) Checks for shorted TP sensor or wiring. If data value stays greater than -7 with TP sensor disconnected, problem is in the wiring circuit.

2) Checks for an open in circuit No. 1076 between TP sensor and PCM. An open in circuit No. 1076 will cause TP sensor signal to be always high whenever the TP sensor is plugged in.

Note On Intermittents – If Code PO22 is intermittent, manipulate related wiring, while observing PCM on-line data value. Check TP sensor connector for short to voltage. Cycle TP sensor through its travel and tap on TP sensor with a pencil to test for intermittent operation. If fault is induced, parameter will skip to high throttle angle. If wiring and connectors are okay, substitute a known good TP sensor and retest.

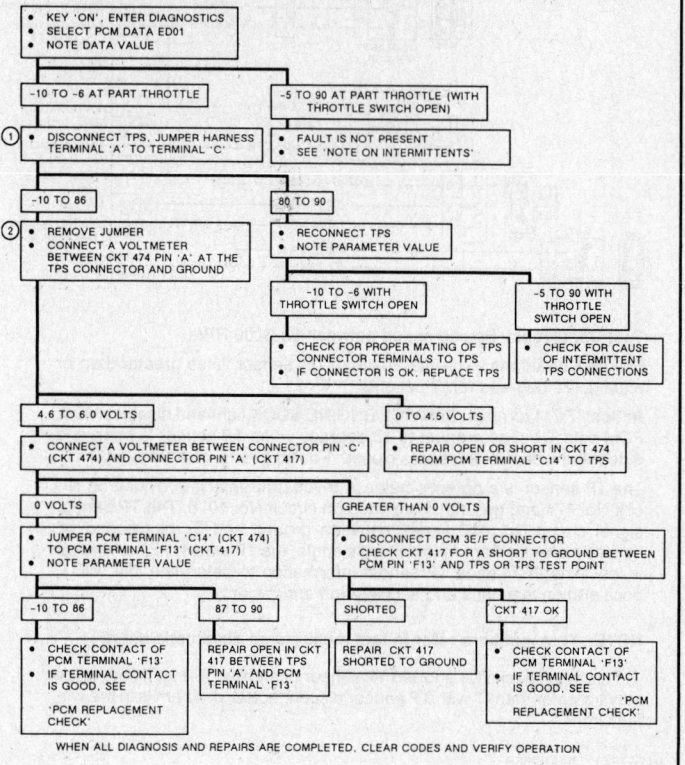

WHEN ALL DIAGNOSIS AND REPAIRS ARE COMPLETED, CLEAR CODES AND VERIFY OPERATION

91E07541   91C07559

Courtesy of General Motors Corp.

PCM CODE PO24,
SPEED SENSOR CIRCUIT PROBLEM – 1993-94

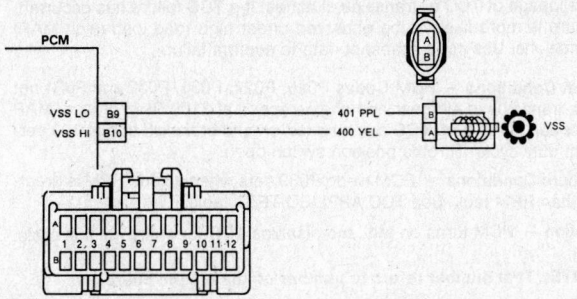

Test Conditions: Codes PO21, PO22, PO26 and PO27 not set. Transaxle in Reverse or Drive and brake switch off. Throttle switch open. Throttle angle greater than 17 degrees. Engine speed greater or at least 1400 RPM.

Failure Conditions: Vehicle speed equals zero MPH for 3 seconds.

Action: PCM turns on SERVICE ENGINE SOON light and disables Viscous Converter Clutch (VCC) and cruise control. Third and fourth gears are disabled. The Vehicle Speed Sensor (VSS) is a permanent magnet pulse generator mounted in transaxle. The PCM uses VSS input for VCC apply-and-release determinations, to select between RPM and throttle angle control of ISC, and as a test condition for many codes.

NOTE: Test number refers to test number on diagnostic chart.

1) Vehicle speed sensor provides 0-36 volts AC signal to the PCM, depending upon vehicle speed. With tires moving, signal to PCM should be at least .5 volt AC.

Note On Intermittents – If Code PO24 is stored as a history code, select parameter PD12 or P.0.9 (on-line data value). Lift drive wheels, place transaxle in Drive and allow wheels to turn. Manipulate affected wiring while observing on-line data value. If fault is induced, parameter ED12 (on-line data value) will momentarily drop to zero MPH. Check for intermittent opens or shorts to ground on circuits No. 400 and No. 401. Check terminal contact at VSS and at PCM connector.

NOTE: DO NOT USE THIS TROUBLE TREE WHILE VEHICLE IS CONNECTED TO A BATTERY CHARGER.

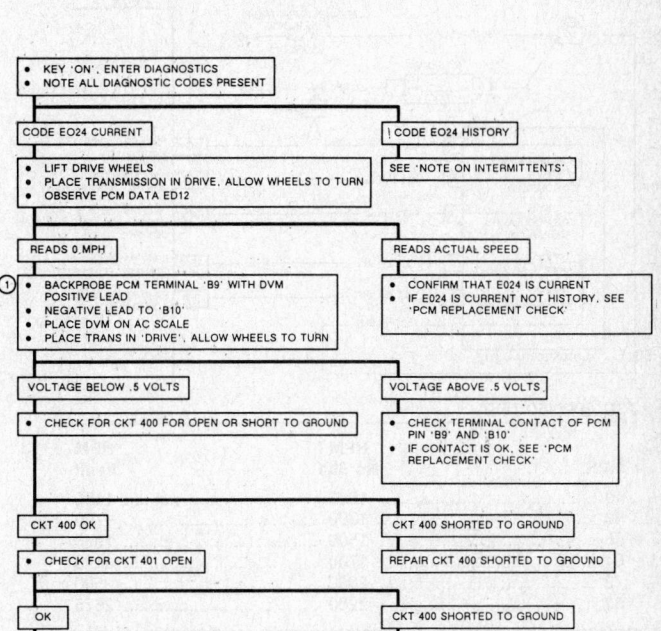

WHEN ALL DIAGNOSIS AND REPAIRS ARE COMPLETED, CLEAR CODES AND VERIFY OPERATION

91A07563   91C07564

Courtesy of General Motors Corp.

PCM CODE P039, TORQUE CONVERTER CLUTCH (TCC) ENGAGEMENT (1 OF 5) – 1993-94

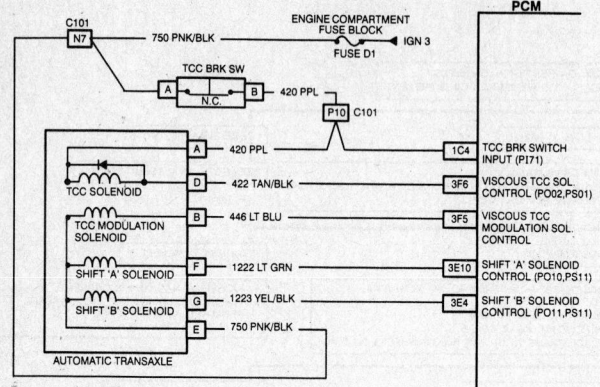

TCC APPLIED TEST

MPH	RPM No Slip	RPM Fault
40	1090	1450
48	1300	1700
56	1500	1950
64	1700	2175
72	2000	2500
80	2200	2675

PCM VOLTAGE CHART

PCM Terminal	Condition	Voltage
1C4	Brake Applied	0-0.3
	Brake Released	Battery
3F6	TCC Apply On	0-0.3
	TCC Apply Off	Battery
3F5	TCC Mod. On	0-0.3
	TCC Mod. Off	Battery
3E10	Shift Sol. "A" On	0-0.3
	Shift Sol. "A" Off	Battery
3E4	Shift Sol. "B" Off	0-0.3
	Shift Sol. "B" Off	Battery

This code test monitors engine RPM and vehicle speed and compares them. PCM will set code when engine speed exceeds fault value for a particular vehicle speed. This code can set due to an electrical problem or slippage of TCC or transaxle clutches. If a TCC failure has occurred, failure is more likely to be observed under high road load (high MAP) conditions. Use code snapshot data to confirm failure.

Test Conditions – PCM Codes P026, P027, P031, P032 and P034 not set, transaxle in 4th gear and engine speed at 3100 RPM or less. MAP between 29-80 kPa. TCC commanded on and brake off and at 100 percent duty cycle. Throttle position switch open.

Failure Conditions – PCM Code P039 sets when engine RPM is greater than RPM fault. See TCC APPLIED TEST table.

Action – PCM turns on MIL and disables TCC for entire ignition cycle.

NOTE: Test number refers to number on diagnostic chart.

1) Checks electrical operation of transaxle. Road test checks for proper operation of transaxle.

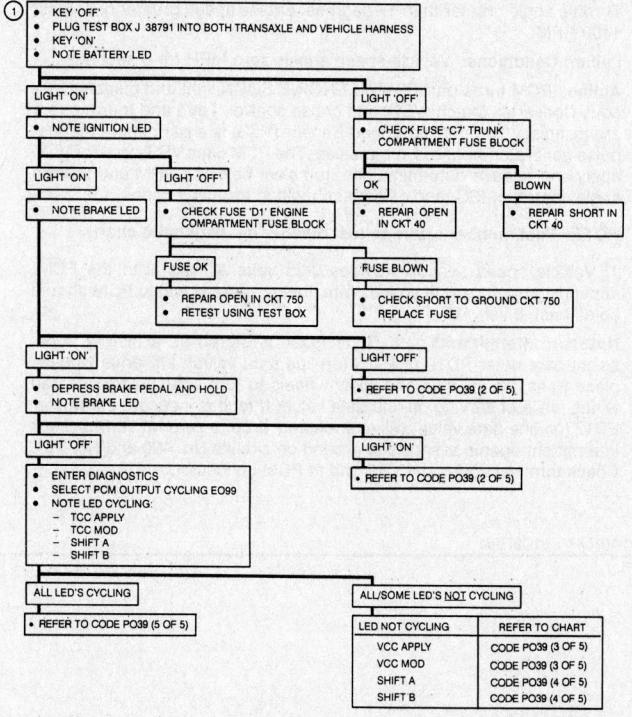

WHEN ALL DIAGNOSIS AND REPAIRS ARE COMPLETED, CLEAR CODES AND VERIFY OPERATION.

93A40311   93D40314   93C40313

Courtesy of General Motors Corp.

PCM CODE P039,
TCC ENGAGEMENT (2 OF 5) – 1993-94

NOTE: Test numbers refer to numbers on diagnostic chart.

1) This chart checks TCC brake switch or circuit problem. PCM input P171 should cycle from HI to LO if a problem exists. If P171 does not cycle, and test box LED is off, check test box for proper connection.
2) To adjust brake switch, first fully seat switch in its retainer, then pull up on brake pedal.

PCM VOLTAGE CHART

PCM Terminal	Condition	Voltage
1C4	Brake Applied	0-0.3
	Brake Released	Battery
3F6	TCC Apply On	0-0.3
	TCC Apply Off	Battery
3F5	TCC Mod. On	0-0.3
	TCC Mod. Off	Battery
3E10	Shift Sol. "A" On	0-0.3
	Shift Sol. "A" Off	Battery
3E4	Shift Sol. "B" Off	0-0.3
	Shift Sol. "B" Off	Battery

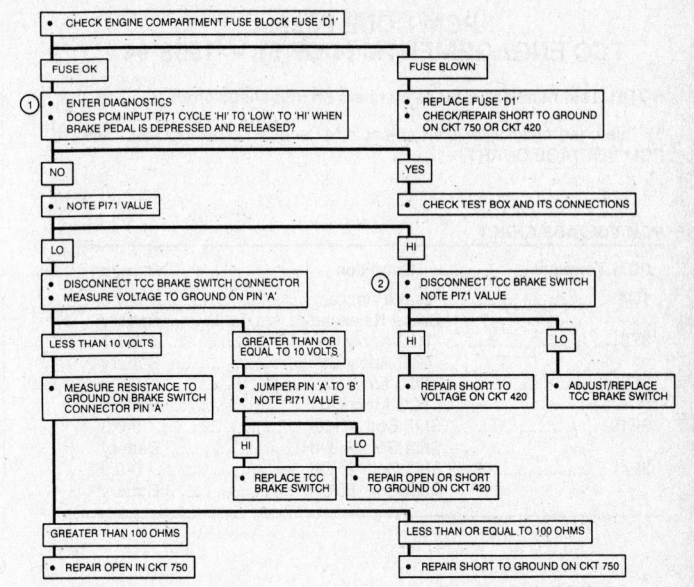

WHEN ALL DIAGNOSIS AND REPAIRS ARE COMPLETED, CLEAR CODES AND VERIFY OPERATION.

93D40314 93E40315

Courtesy of General Motors Corp.

PCM CODE P039,
TCC ENGAGEMENT (3 OF 5) – 1993-94

NOTE: Test numbers refer to numbers on diagnostic chart.

1) This chart checks for TCC MOD and TCC apply solenoid or wiring fault. See PCM VOLTAGE CHART.

PCM VOLTAGE CHART

PCM Terminal	Condition	Voltage
1C4	Brake Applied	0-0.3
	Brake Released	Battery
3F6	TCC Apply On	0-0.3
	TCC Apply Off	Battery
3F5	TCC Mod. On	0-0.3
	TCC Mod. Off	Battery
3E10	Shift Sol. "A" On	0-0.3
	Shift Sol. "A" Off	Battery
3E4	Shift Sol. "B" Off	0-0.3
	Shift Sol. "B" Off	Battery

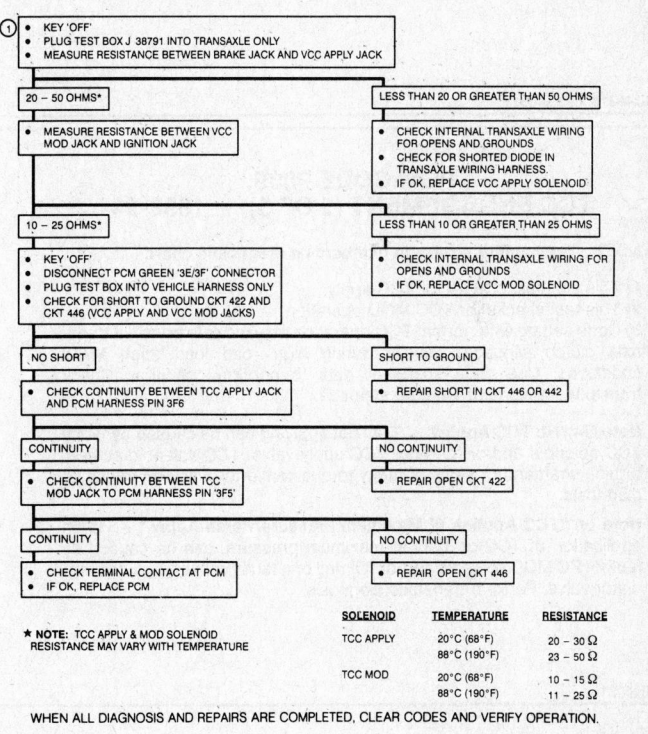

★ **NOTE:** TCC APPLY & MOD SOLENOID RESISTANCE MAY VARY WITH TEMPERATURE

SOLENOID	TEMPERATURE	RESISTANCE
TCC APPLY	20°C (68°F)	20 – 30 Ω
	88°C (190°F)	23 – 50 Ω
TCC MOD	20°C (68°F)	10 – 15 Ω
	88°C (190°F)	11 – 25 Ω

WHEN ALL DIAGNOSIS AND REPAIRS ARE COMPLETED, CLEAR CODES AND VERIFY OPERATION.

93D40314 93F40316

Courtesy of General Motors Corp.

PCM CODE P039,
TCC ENGAGEMENTM (4 OF 5) – 1993-94

NOTE: Test numbers refer to numbers on diagnostic chart.

1) This chart checks for shift solenoid "A" and "B" or wiring fault. See PCM VOLTAGE CHART.

PCM VOLTAGE CHART

PCM Terminal	Condition	Voltage
1C4	Brake Applied	0-0.3
	Brake Released	Battery
3F6	TCC Apply On	0-0.3
	TCC Apply Off	Battery
3F5	TCC Mod. On	0-0.3
	TCC Mod. Off	Battery
3E10	Shift Sol. "A" On	0-0.3
	Shift Sol. "A" Off	Battery
3E4	Shift Sol. "B" Off	0-0.3
	Shift Sol. "B" Off	Battery

① • KEY 'OFF'
• PLUG TEST BOX INTO TRANSAXLE ONLY
• MEASURE RESISTANCE BETWEEN IGNITION JACK AND SHIFT 'A' JACK

20–50 OHMS* → **LESS THAN 20 OR GREATER THAN 50 OHMS**
• CHECK INTERNAL TRANSAXLE WIRING FOR OPENS AND GROUNDS
• IF OK, REPLACE SHIFT 'A' SOLENOID

• KEY 'OFF'
• DISCONNECT GREEN PCM CONNECTOR '3E/3F'
• PLUG TEST BOX INTO VEHICLE HARNESS ONLY
• CHECK FOR SHORT TO GROUND CKT 1222 (SHIFT 'A' JACK)

NO SHORT / **SHORT**
REPAIR SHORT IN CKT 1222

• CHECK CONTINUITY BETWEEN SHIFT 'A' JACK AND PCM HARNESS PIN '3E10'

CONTINUITY / **NO CONTINUITY**
REPAIR OPEN CKT 1222

• KEY 'OFF'
• PLUG TEST BOX INTO TRANSAXLE ONLY
• MEASURE RESISTANCE BETWEEN IGNITION JACK AND SHIFT 'B' JACK

20 – 50 OHMS * → **LESS THAN 20 OR GREATER THAN 50 OHMS**
• CHECK TERMINAL TRANSAXLE WIRING FOR OPENS AND GROUNDS
• IF OK, REPLACE SHIFT 'B' SOLENOID

• KEY 'OFF'
• PLUG TEST BOX INTO VEHICLE HARNESS ONLY
• CHECK FOR SHORT TO GROUND ON CKT 1223 (SHIFT 'B' JACK)

NO SHORT / **SHORT**
REPAIR SHORT IN CKT 1223

• CHECK CONTINUITY BETWEEN SHIFT 'B' JACK AND PCM HARNESS PIN '3E4'

CONTINUITY / **NO CONTINUITY**
REPAIR OPEN IN CKT 1223

• CHECK PCM TERMINAL CONTACT
• IF OK, REPLACE PCM

★ NOTE: SHIFT 'A' AND 'B' SOLENOID RESISTANCE MAY VARY WITH TEMPERATURE

TEMPERATURE	RESISTANCE
20°C (68°F)	20 – 30 Ω
88°C (190°F)	23 – 50 Ω

WHEN ALL DIAGNOSIS AND REPAIRS ARE COMPLETED, CLEAR CODES AND VERIFY OPERATION.

93D40314   93G40317

Courtesy of General Motors Corp.

PCM CODE P039,
TCC ENGAGEMENT (5 OF 5) – 1993-94

NOTE: Test numbers refer to numbers on diagnostic chart.

1) This stall test checks for TCC apply.
2) This test checks for TCC MOD operation.
3) Code setting with normal TCC operation may indicate possible transaxle clutch slippage, usually during high road load (high MAP) conditions. Use code snapshot data to confirm condition. Check transaxle for signs of 4th gear slippage.

Note On "No TCC Apply" – TCC not applying can be caused by faulty TCC solenoid and/or "O" ring, TCC apply valve, TCC solenoid screen, turbine shaft and/or seals or faulty torque converter. Perform transaxle diagnosis.

Note on "TCC Applies W/Maximum Pressure/Harsh Apply" – Harsh application of TCC or TCC at maximum pressure, can be caused by faulty TCC MOD solenoid and/or "O" ring or a faulty converter clutch regulator valve. Perform transaxle diagnosis.

① • KEY 'OFF'
• PLUG TEST BOX INTO BOTH TRANSAXLE AND VEHICLE HARNESS
• START ENGINE
• APPLY BRAKES
• SHIFT TRANSAXLE TO D4 RANGE
• SELECT 3RD GEAR ON TEST BOX GEAR SELECTOR
• WHILE BRAKES APPLIED, TURN TEST BOX CONVERTER CLUTCH SWITCH TO 'ON' POSITION

ENGINE STALLED / **ENGINE DID NOT STALL**
• REFER TO NOTE ON 'NO TCC APPLY'

② • RESTART ENGINE
• APPLY BRAKES
• SHIFT TRANSAXLE TO D4 RANGE
• JUMPER VCC MOD JACK TO GROUND JACK
• SELECT 3RD GEAR ON TEST BOX SELECTOR
• WHILE BRAKES APPLIED, TURN TEST BOX CONVERTER CLUTCH SWITCH TO 'ON' POSITION

ENGINE DID NOT STALL / **ENGINE STALLED**
• REFER TO NOTE ON 'TCC APPLIES WITH MAX PRESSURE HARSH APPLY'

③ TCC NORMAL OPERATION AT THIS TIME

WHEN ALL DIAGNOSIS AND REPAIRS ARE COMPLETED, CLEAR CODES AND VERIFY OPERATION.

93H40318

Courtesy of General Motors Corp.

PCM CODE P057, SHORTED TRANSAXLE TEMPERATURE SENSOR CIRCUIT – 1993-94

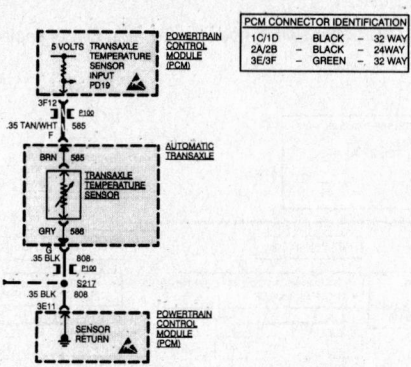

PCM CONNECTOR IDENTIFICATION		
1C/1D	– BLACK	– 32 WAY
2A/2B	– BLACK	– 24WAY
3E/3F	– GREEN	– 32 WAY

NOTE: Test numbers refer to numbers on diagnostic chart.

1) If transaxle temperature sensor is shorted, PCM data PD19 should read 298°F (148°C) or greater. If parameter does not show this, then sensor and circuit are okay. Fault is intermittent.

2) Checks circuit No. 585 for short. If parameter value stays at -18°F (-28°C) or greater with transaxle connector unplugged, check for short in circuit No. 585, PCM terminal 3F12 or transaxle connector terminal "F".

3) Checks circuits No. 585 for short to ground inside transaxle. If wiring is okay, replace shorted transaxle temperature sensor.

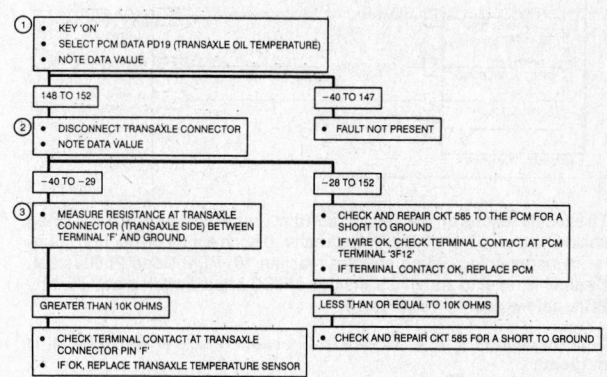

WHEN ALL DIAGNOSIS AND REPAIRS ARE COMPLETED, CLEAR CODES AND VERIFY OPERATION

Transaxle temperature sensor is a variable resistor whose resistance varies based on its temperature. As sensor temperature increases, resistance decreases. A high transaxle temperature will result in a low signal voltage on circuit No. 585. PCM Code P057 sets when PCM see transaxle temperature sensor reading of 298°F (148°C) or greater (0.8 volt or less).

Test Conditions – Tested continuously.

Failure Conditions – Transaxle temperature sensor value is 298°F (148°C) or greater for 5 seconds.

Action – PCM turns on MIL. PCM substitutes engine coolant temperature value for transaxle temperature until engine coolant temperature reaches 221°F (105°C), then transaxle will be set to hot mode operation.

94D33244   94C33292

Courtesy of General Motors Corp.

PCM CODE P059, OPEN TRANSAXLE TEMPERATURE SENSOR CIRCUIT – 1993-94

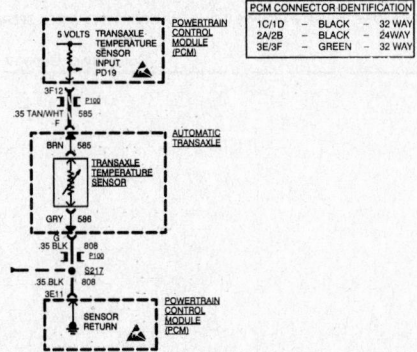

PCM CONNECTOR IDENTIFICATION		
1C/1D	– BLACK	– 32 WAY
2A/2B	– BLACK	– 24WAY
3E/3F	– GREEN	– 32 WAY

NOTE: Test numbers refer to numbers on diagnostic chart.

1) With transaxle temperature sensor or wiring open, PCM data PD77 will read -31°F (-35°C) or less. If parameter does not show this, sensor and circuit are okay.

2) Check for open in circuit No. 585 between PCM and sensor connector. If PCM data PD77 reads 298-303°F (148-151°C) with sensor terminal "F" jumpered to ground, circuit No. 585 and PCM are okay.

3) Checks circuit No. 808 for open to PCM terminal connector.

4) Checks PCM's ability to recognize low voltage on PCM terminal 3F12 (transaxle temperature sensor input). If grounding PCM terminal 3F12 caused PCM data PD1 to read 298-303°F (148-151°C), check for open in circuit No. 585 between PCM and sensor connector.

5) Checks for an open transaxle temperature sensor.

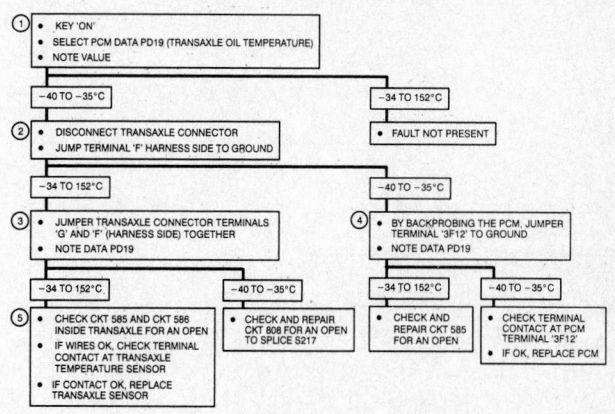

WHEN ALL DIAGNOSIS AND REPAIRS ARE COMPLETED, CLEAR CODES AND VERIFY OPERATION

Transaxle temperature sensor resistance varies based on its resistance. As sensor temperature increases, resistance decreases. A low transaxle temperature will result in high voltage in circuit No. 585. PCM Code sets when PCM sees a transaxle temperature sensor reading of -31°F (-35°C) or less (4.9 volts or greater).

Test Conditions – PCM Codes P014, P015 and P024 not set. Coolant temperature at -13.0°F (-25°C) or greater and vehicle speed greater than zero MPH.

Failure Conditions – Transaxle temperature sensor -31°F (-35°C) or less for 6 seconds.

Action – PCM turns on MIL. PCM substitutes coolant temperature value for transaxle temperature until coolant temperature reaches 221°F (105°C) then sets transaxle to hot mode operation.

94D33244   94E33294

Courtesy of General Motors Corp.

PCM CODE EO90,
VCC BRAKE SWITCH INPUT – 1993-94

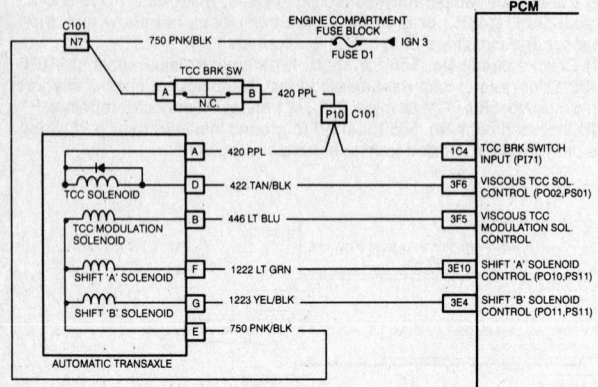

This test functions on the assumption that brake must be applied to bring vehicle to a stop from 30 MPH or greater. If such condition occurs, counter is incremented. When counter reaches 10, PCM Code P090 is set. Counter is reset to zero if a transition of TCC brake switch is detected by PCM before counter reaches 10.

Test Conditions – PCM Code P024 not set. Vehicle speed at 30 MPH or greater.

Failure Conditions – Vehicle speed cycles from 30 MPH or greater to zero MPH with no VCC brake switch input. PCM must record 10 of these events to set code.

Action – PCM turn on SERVICE VEHICLE SOON message. PCM disables cruise control.

NOTE: Test numbers refer to numbers on diagnostic chart.

1) Testing TCC brake switch input to PCM PI71 or E.7.1. If input is working correctly, display will change from HI to LO to HI. If display remains HI, check circuit No. 420 and TCC brake switch for short to voltage. If display remains LO, check circuit No. 420 for open or short to ground.
2) Checks for voltage at TCC brake switch terminal "A".

3) Checks for resistance between TCC brake switch terminal "A" and ground.
4) Checks for resistance between TCC brake switch terminal "B" and ground.
5) Checks if TCC brake switch needs to be adjusted or replaced, or if PCM is faulty.

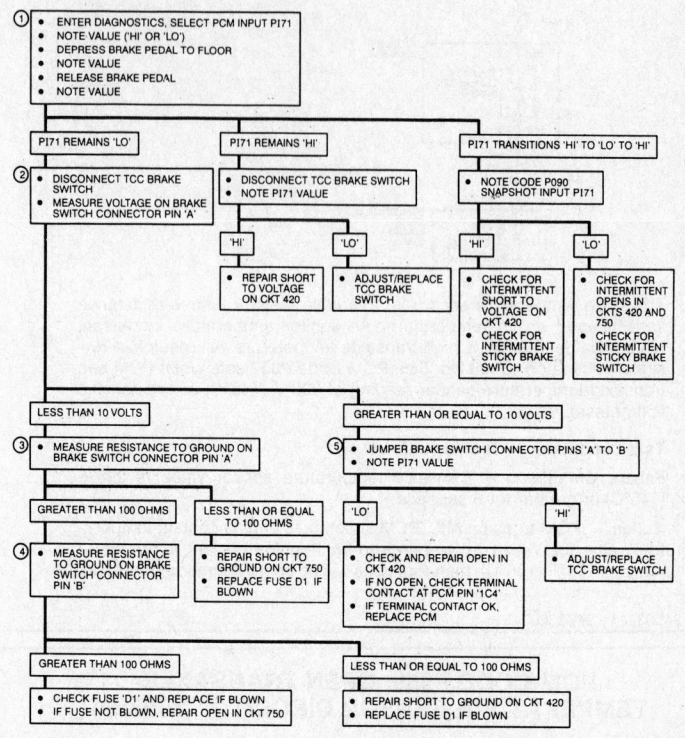

WHEN ALL DIAGNOSIS AND REPAIRS ARE COMPLETED, CLEAR CODES AND VERIFY OPERATION.

93A40311   93A40352

Courtesy of General Motors Corp.

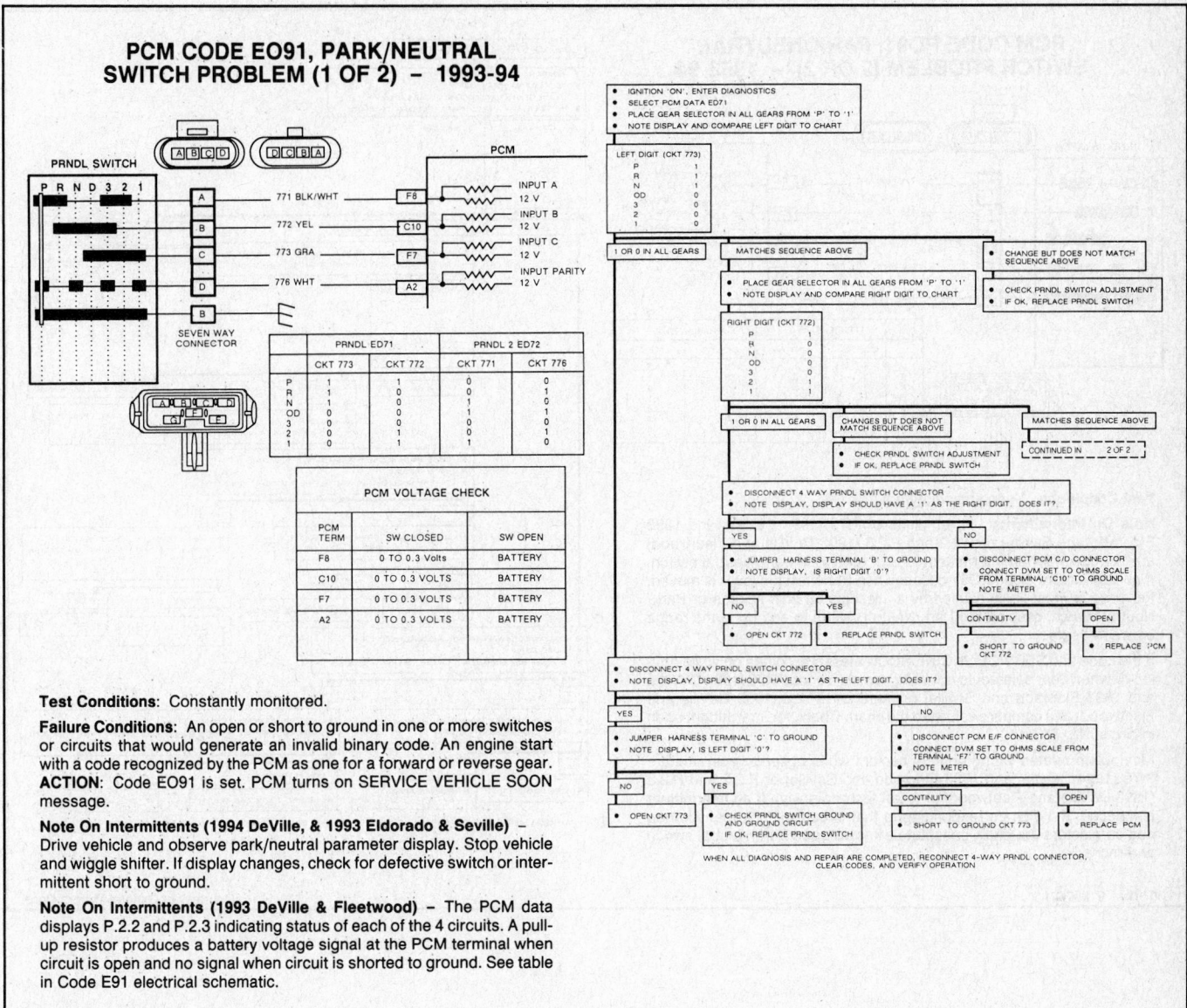

**PCM CODE EO91, PARK/NEUTRAL
SWITCH PROBLEM (1 OF 2) – 1993-94**

PCM VOLTAGE CHECK		
PCM TERM	SW CLOSED	SW OPEN
F8	0 TO 0.3 Volts	BATTERY
C10	0 TO 0.3 VOLTS	BATTERY
F7	0 TO 0.3 VOLTS	BATTERY
A2	0 TO 0.3 VOLTS	BATTERY

Test Conditions: Constantly monitored.

Failure Conditions: An open or short to ground in one or more switches or circuits that would generate an invalid binary code. An engine start with a code recognized by the PCM as one for a forward or reverse gear.

ACTION: Code EO91 is set. PCM turns on SERVICE VEHICLE SOON message.

Note On Intermittents (1994 DeVille, & 1993 Eldorado & Seville) – Drive vehicle and observe park/neutral parameter display. Stop vehicle and wiggle shifter. If display changes, check for defective switch or intermittent short to ground.

Note On Intermittents (1993 DeVille & Fleetwood) – The PCM data displays P.2.2 and P.2.3 indicating status of each of the 4 circuits. A pull-up resistor produces a battery voltage signal at the PCM terminal when circuit is open and no signal when circuit is shorted to ground. See table in Code E91 electrical schematic.

91I07618 91A07619 91C07620

Courtesy of General Motors Corp.

PCM CODE PO91, PARK/NEUTRAL SWITCH PROBLEM (2 OF 2) – 1993-94

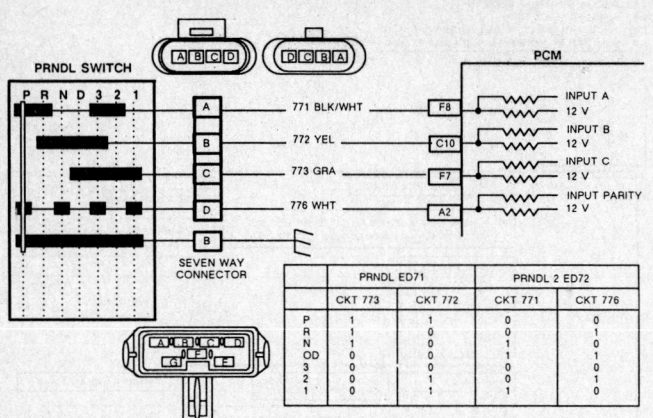

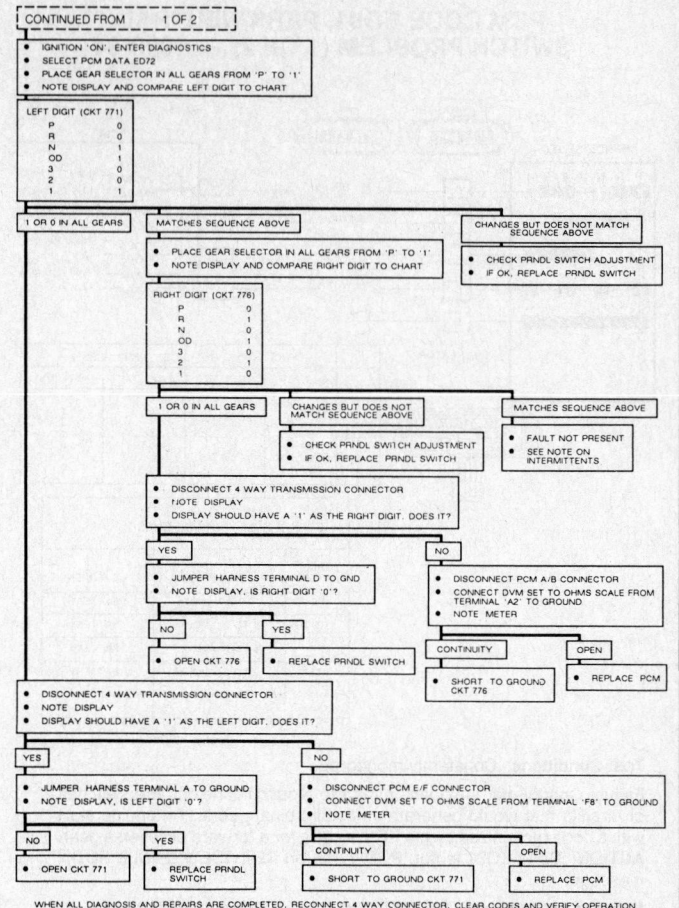

Test Conditions: Constantly monitored.

Note On Intermittents – If all digits of PI79 (1994 DeVille, and 1993 Eldorado and Seville) or P.2.2 and P.2.3 (1993 DeVille and Fleetwood) are "1", check for an intermittent loss of ground in Park/Neutral switch. If an intermittent Code PO91 occurs when transmission lever is moved, the code is most likely caused by a misadjusted shift linkage or Park/Neutral switch, causing the Park/Neutral switch to end up in the range between gears.

If the code and SERVICE ENGINE SOON message comes on while driving or when gear selector is not being moved, record PI79 (1994 DeVille, and 1993 Eldorado and Seville) or P.2.2 and P.2.3 (1993 DeVille and Fleetwood) and compare values to the chart. Check for intermittent open in circuit No. 773.

Manipulate related wiring and connectors while observing parameters PI79 (1994 DeVille, and 1993 Eldorado and Seville) or P.2.2 and P.2.3 (1993 DeVille and Fleetwood) or (scan tester display). If an intermittent is induced, the digit corresponding to that circuit will change. If wiring and connectors are okay, substitute a known good Park/Neutral switch and recheck.

91I07618   91E07621

Courtesy of General Motors Corp.

ELECTRONIC TESTING

NOTE: On all 1993 vehicles and 1994 vehicles with transaxle model CMW (used on 3.1L and 3.4L engines) cannot use the test box to diagnose components. On these vehicles, go to COMPONENT TESTS (WITHOUT TEST BOX).

NOTE: The following procedures check operation of electronic control of 4T60-E transaxle. These tests are also found in the appropriate SYSTEM & COMPONENT TESTING article in ENGINE PERFORMANCE section of appropriate MITCHELL® manual.

TESTING EQUIPMENT & PROCEDURES

1) Check PCM memory for trouble codes. If present, perform all tests and correct any PCM related trouble codes. Warm transaxle to normal operating temperature.
2) Using Transaxle Test Box (J-38791), connect test harness between transaxle case connector and vehicle harness connector. *See Fig. 3.* Connect a bidirectional scan tester or Tech 1 (94-00101 A) to ALDL or enter on-board self-diagnostics.

CAUTION: DO NOT accelerate vehicle from a standing start in 3rd or 4th gear. DO NOT shift into 1st gear above 25 MPH. DO NOT "brake torque" vehicle with test box tool attached. DO NOT engage TCC below 25 MPH. DO NOT manually shift into 1st, 2nd or 3rd gear with test box attached.

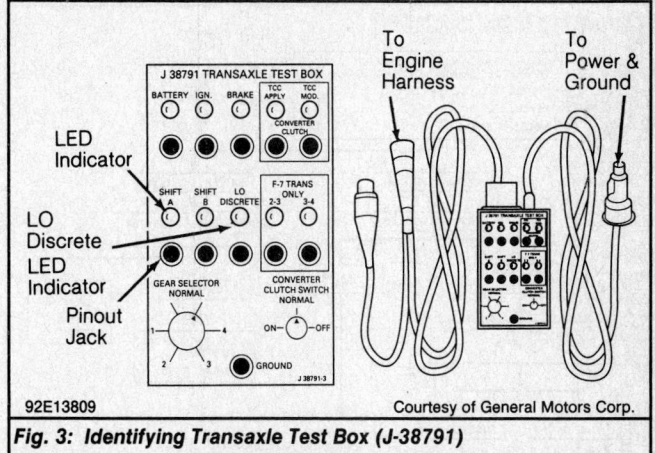

92E13809   Courtesy of General Motors Corp.

Fig. 3: Identifying Transaxle Test Box (J-38791)

3) Turn ignition on. If necessary, input vehicle information on scan tool. Place gear selector and TCC switches on test box to normal position. Follow test procedures outlined in TEST BOX DIAGNOSTIC FLOW CHART. *See Fig. 4.*
4) Road test the vehicle and note LED indicators on test box. If a problem is present (indicated by test box LEDs), the TEST BOX DIAGNOSTIC FLOW CHART will refer you to the next procedure or chart. *See Figs. 5-7. See appropriate COMPONENT TESTS procedures.*

CLUTCH & BAND APPLICATION CHART (4T60-E)

Selector Lever Position	Solenoid Position	Elements In Use
"D" (Drive)		
First Gear	"A" ON/"B" ON	Input Clutch, [1] Input Sprag, Forward Band & [1] 1-2 Support Roller Clutch
Second Gear	"A" OFF/"B" ON	2nd Clutch, [2] Input Clutch, [3] Input Sprag, Forward Band & [1] 1-2 Support Roller Clutch
Third Gear	"A" OFF/"B" OFF	2nd Clutch, 3rd Clutch, [1] 3rd Roller Clutch, Forward Band & [3] 1-2 Support Roller Clutch
Overdrive	"A" ON/"B" OFF	4th Gear, 2nd Clutch, [2] 3rd Clutch, [3] 3rd Roller Clutch, Forward Band & [3] 1-2 Support Roller Clutch
"3" – Manual Third		
Third Gear	"A" OFF/"B" OFF	2nd Clutch, 3rd Clutch, [1] 3rd Roller Clutch, Input Clutch, [1] Input Sprag, Forward Band & [3] 1-2 Support Roller Clutch
Second Gear	"A" OFF/"B" ON	2nd Clutch, [2] Input Clutch, [3] Input Sprag, Forward Band & [1] 1-2 Support Roller Clutch
First Gear	"A" ON/"B" ON	Input Clutch, [3] Input Sprag, Forward Band & [1] 1-2 Support Roller Clutch
"2" – Manual Second		
Second Gear	"A" OFF/"B" ON	2nd Clutch, [2] Input Clutch, [3] Input Sprag, Forward Band, [1] 1-2 Support Roller Clutch & 1-2 Band
First Gear	"A" ON/"B" ON	Input Clutch, [1] Input Sprag, Forward Band, [1] 1-2 Support Roller Clutch & 1-2 Band
"1" – Manual Low		
First Gear	"A" ON/"B" ON	3rd Clutch, [1] 3rd Roller Clutch, Input Clutch, [1] Input Sprag, Forward Band, [1] 1-2 Support Roller Clutch & 1-2 Band
"R" – Reverse	"A" ON/"B" ON	Reverse Band, Input Clutch & [1] Input Sprag
"N" or "P" (Neutral or Park)	"A" ON/"B" ON	All Clutches & Bands Released or Ineffective

[1] – Holding.
[2] – Applied but not effective.
[3] – Overrunning.

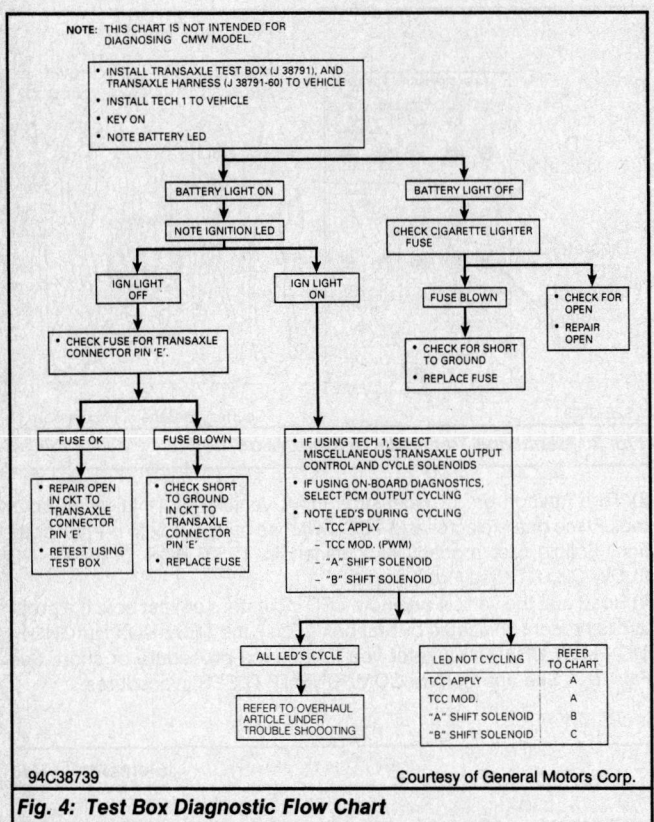

94C38739   Courtesy of General Motors Corp.

Fig. 4: Test Box Diagnostic Flow Chart

COMPONENT TESTS (WITH TEST BOX)

*NOTE: Before using the following charts, see TESTING EQUIPMENT &
PROCEDURES under ELECTRONIC TESTING. On all 1993 vehicles and
1994 vehicles with transaxle model CMW (used on 3.1L and 3.4L
engines), do not use the test box to diagnose components. On these
vehicles, go to COMPONENT TESTS (WITHOUT TEST BOX).*

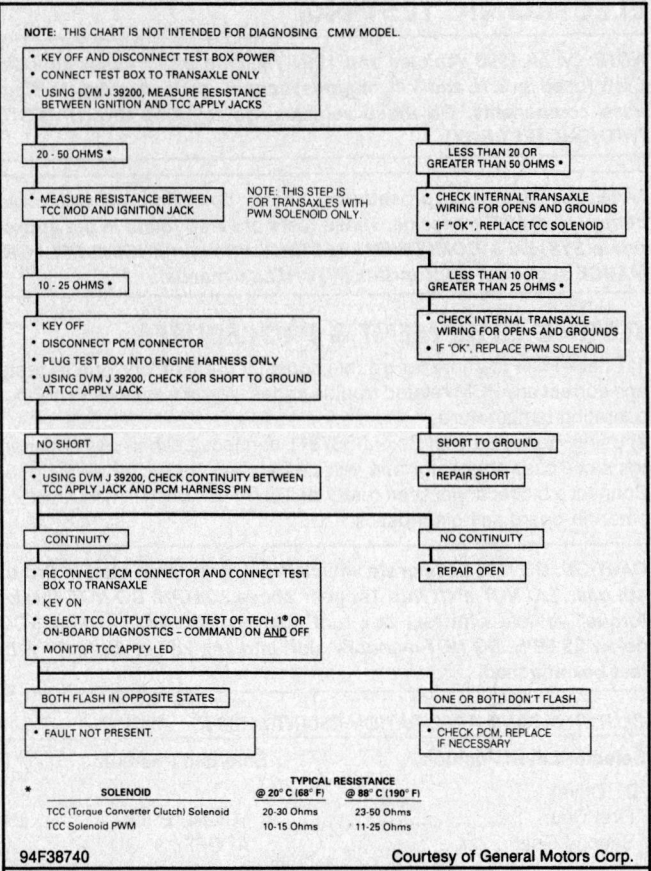

94F38740   Courtesy of General Motors Corp.

Fig. 5: Chart "A" TCC Diagnosis Flow Chart

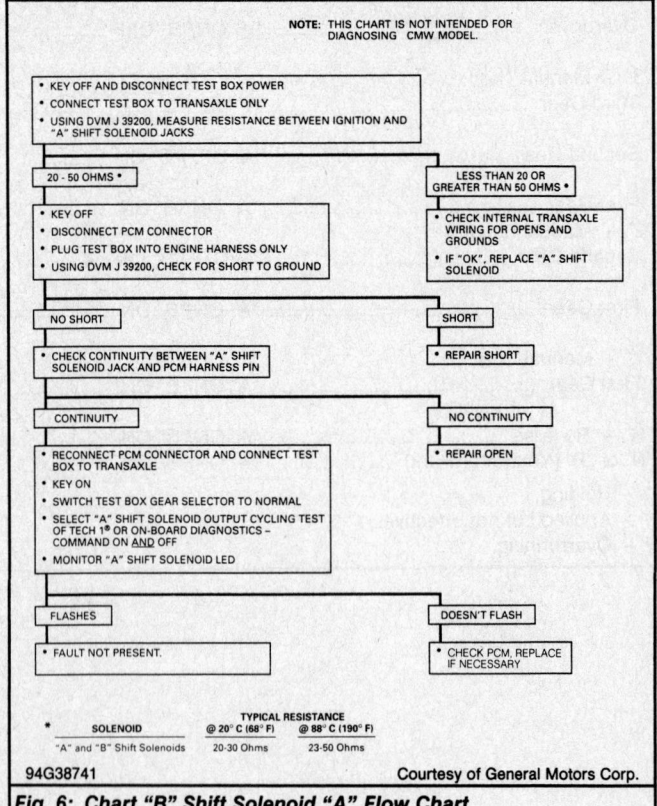

94G38741   Courtesy of General Motors Corp.

Fig. 6: Chart "B" Shift Solenoid "A" Flow Chart

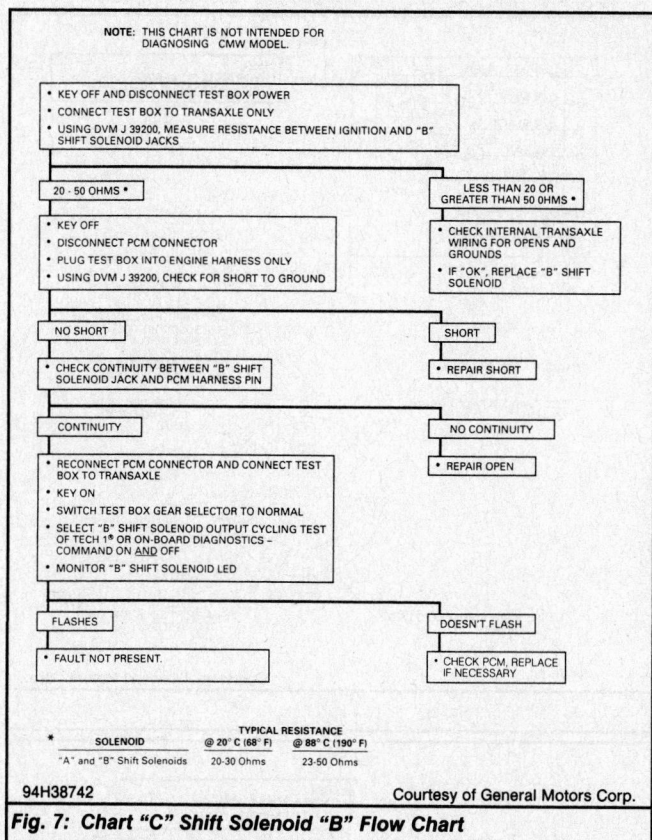

Fig. 7: Chart "C" Shift Solenoid "B" Flow Chart

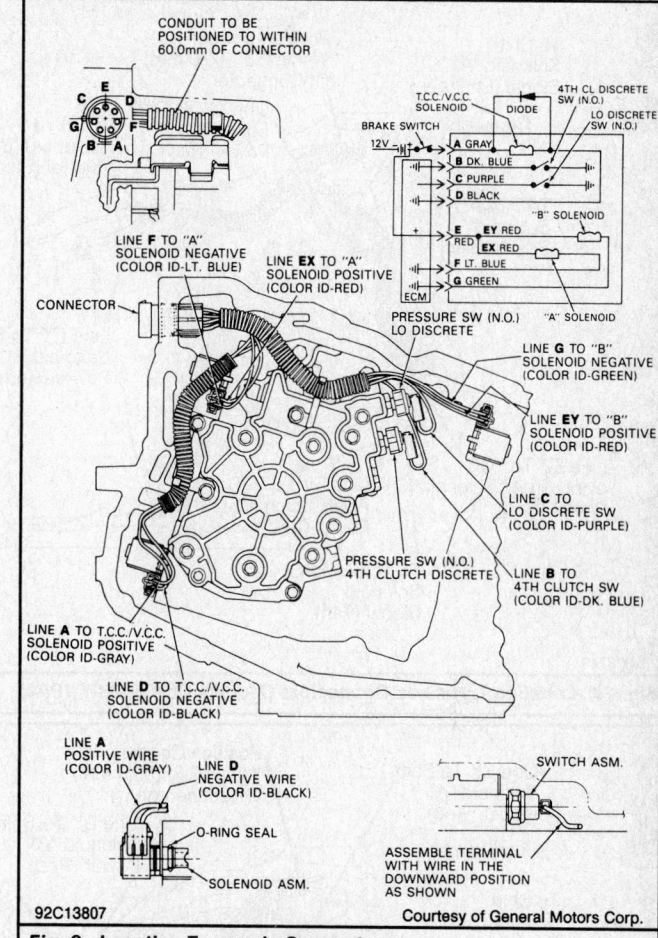

Fig. 9: Locating Transaxle Connectors
(With 3.1L & 3.4L Engines 1993)

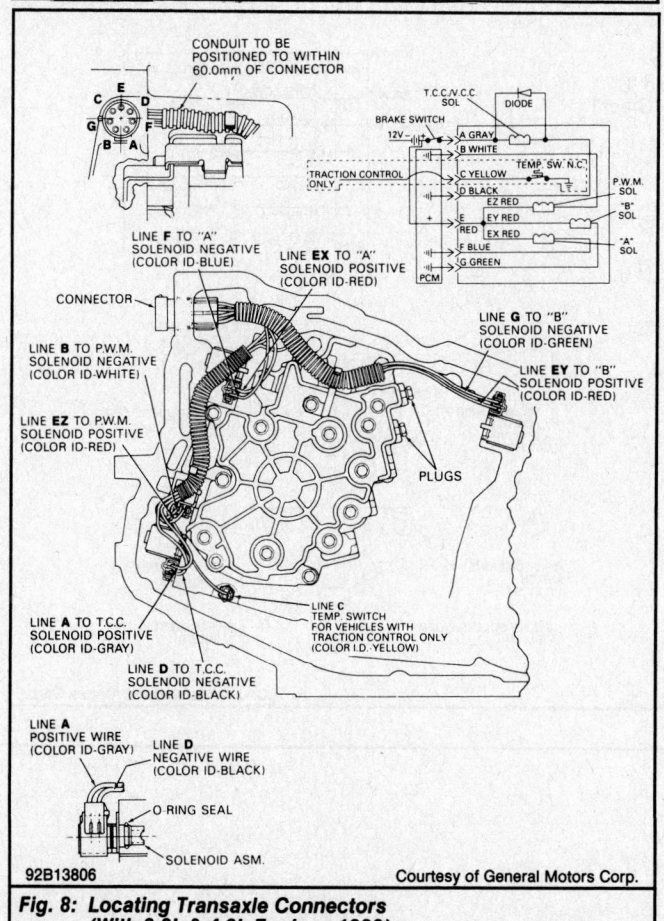

Fig. 8: Locating Transaxle Connectors
(With 3.8L & 4.9L Engines 1993)

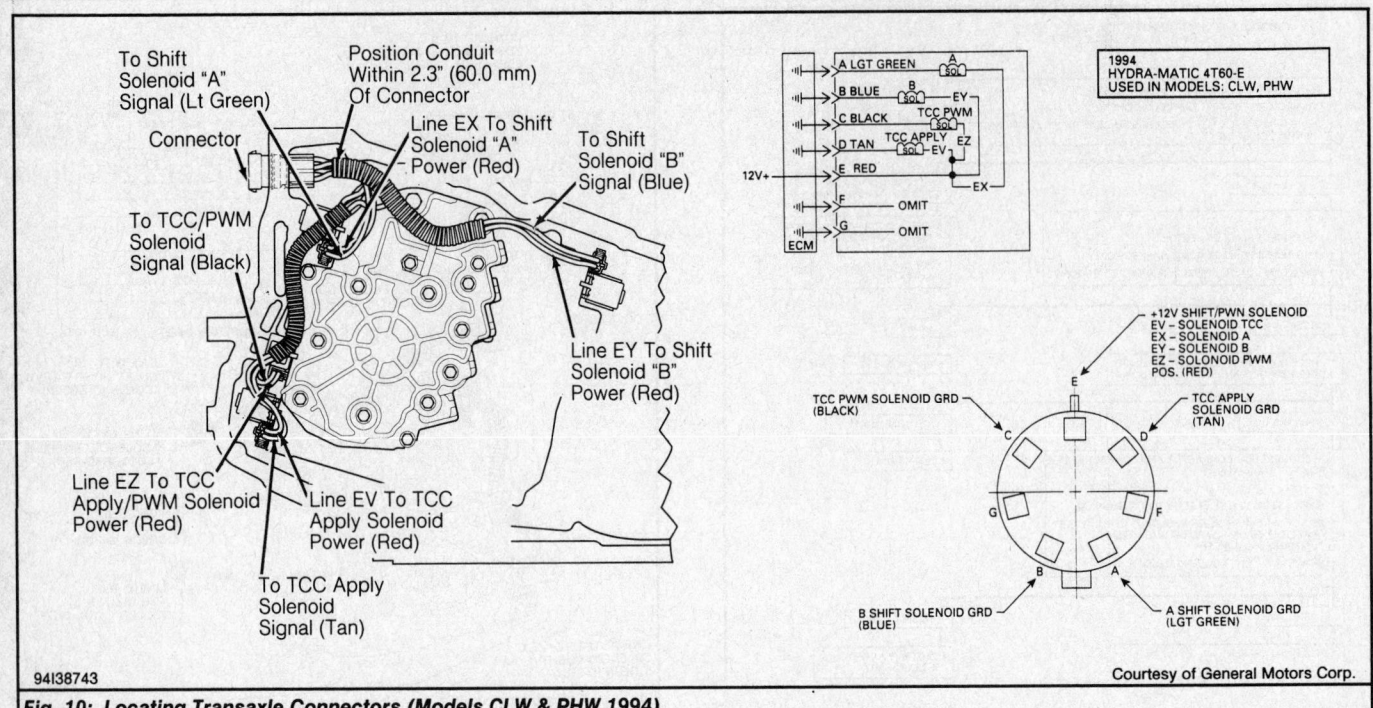

Fig. 10: *Locating Transaxle Connectors (Models CLW & PHW 1994)*

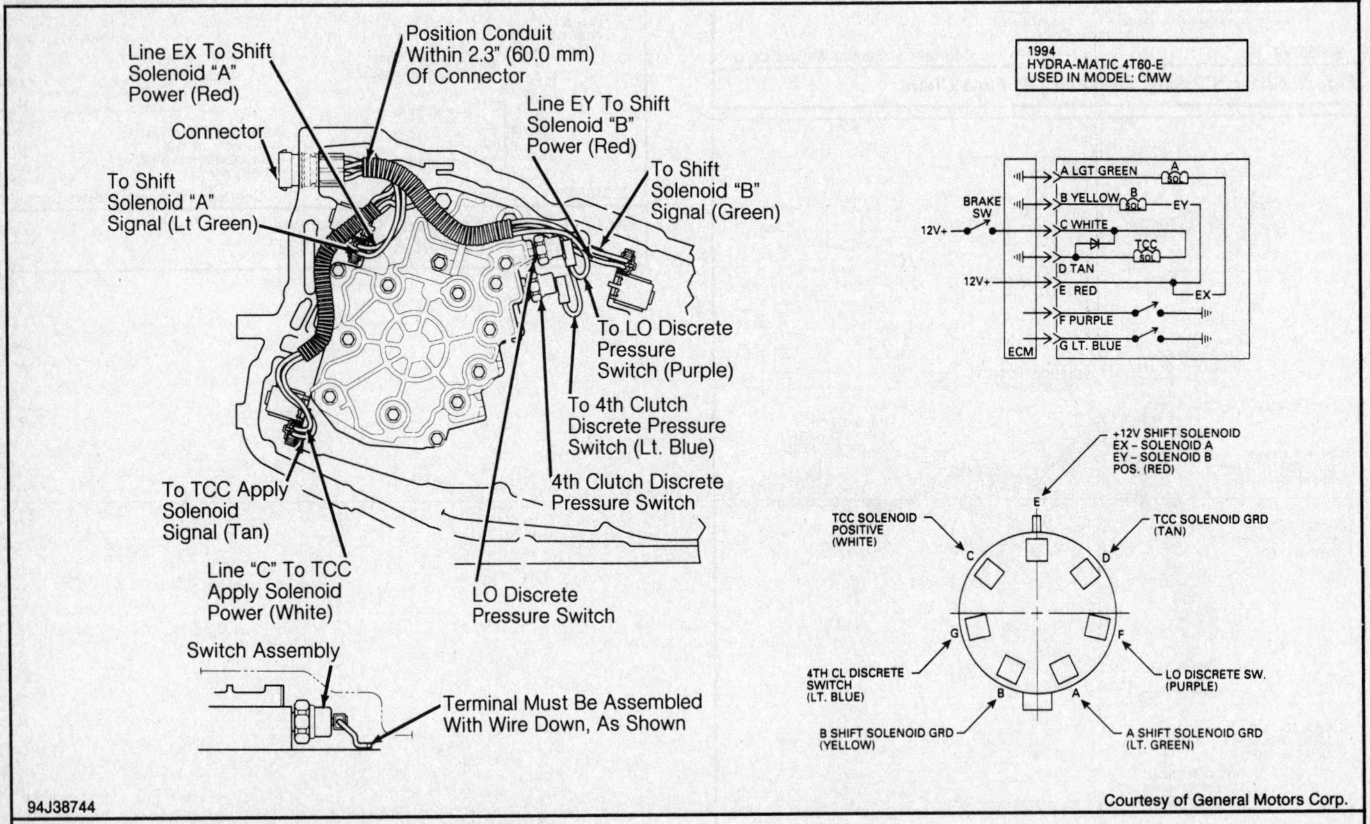

Fig. 11: *Locating Transaxle Connectors (Model CMW 1994)*

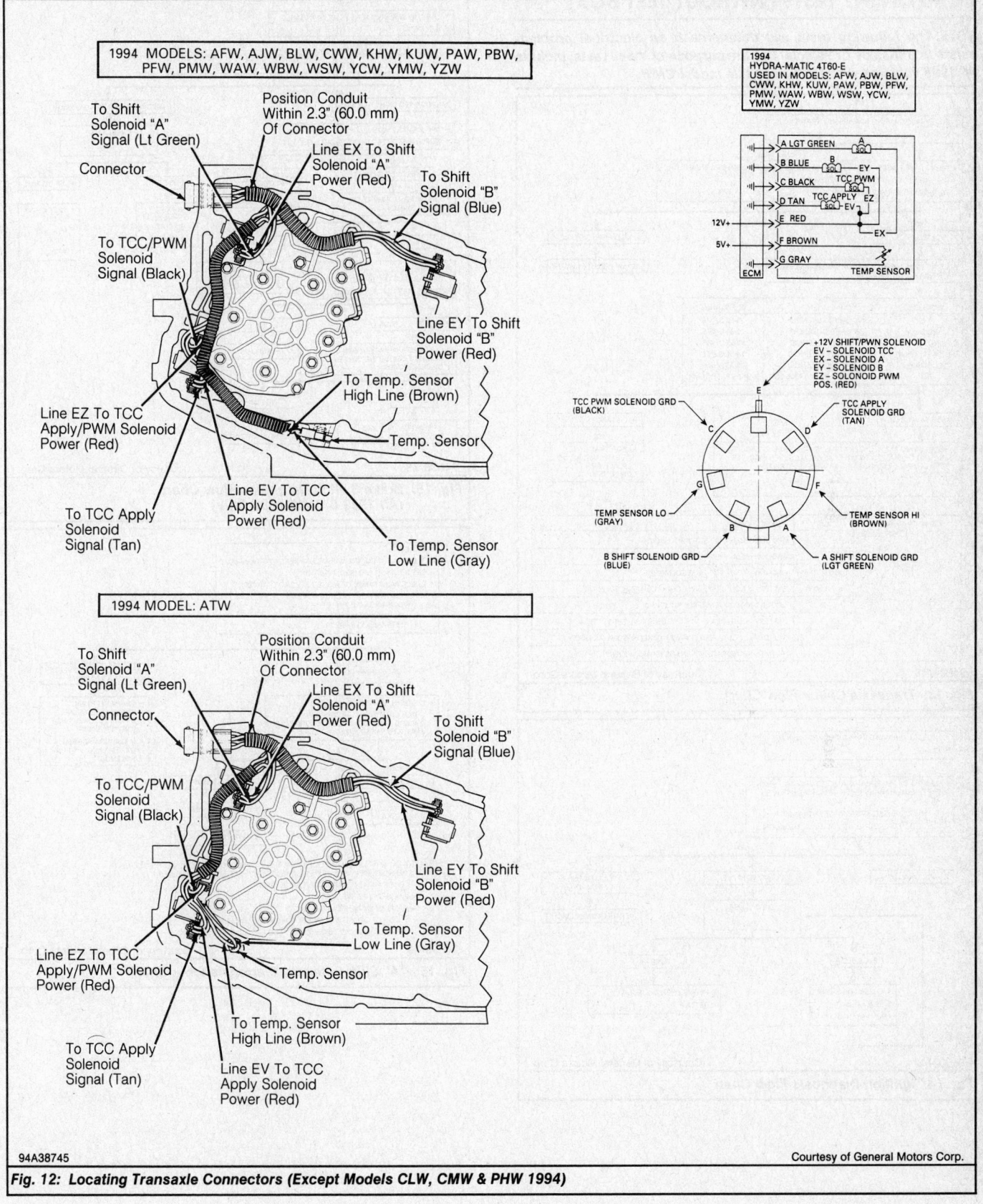

94A38745

Courtesy of General Motors Corp.

Fig. 12: Locating Transaxle Connectors (Except Models CLW, CMW & PHW 1994)

COMPONENT TESTS (WITHOUT TEST BOX)

NOTE: The following tests will determine if an electrical problem exists in transaxle or vehicle. For the purpose of these tests, include all 1993 vehicles with 1994 transaxle model CMW.

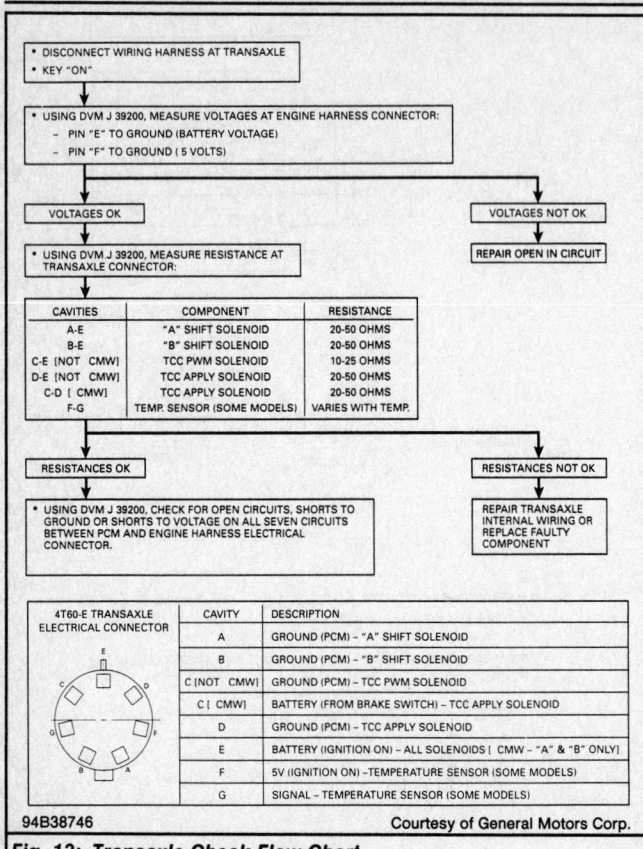

Fig. 13: **Transaxle Check Flow Chart**

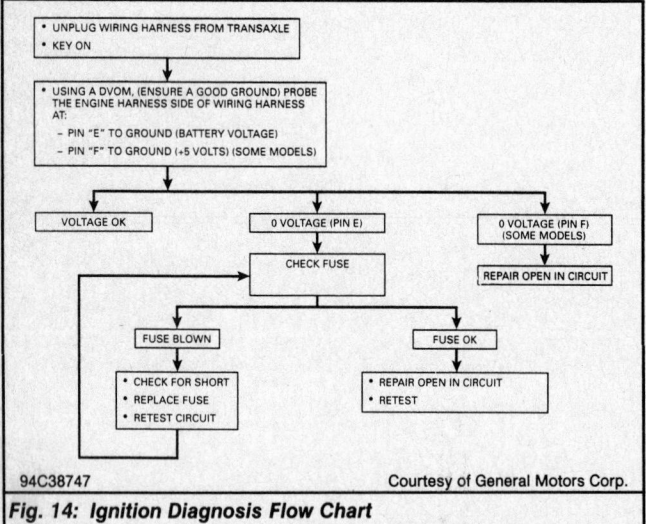

Fig. 14: **Ignition Diagnosis Flow Chart**

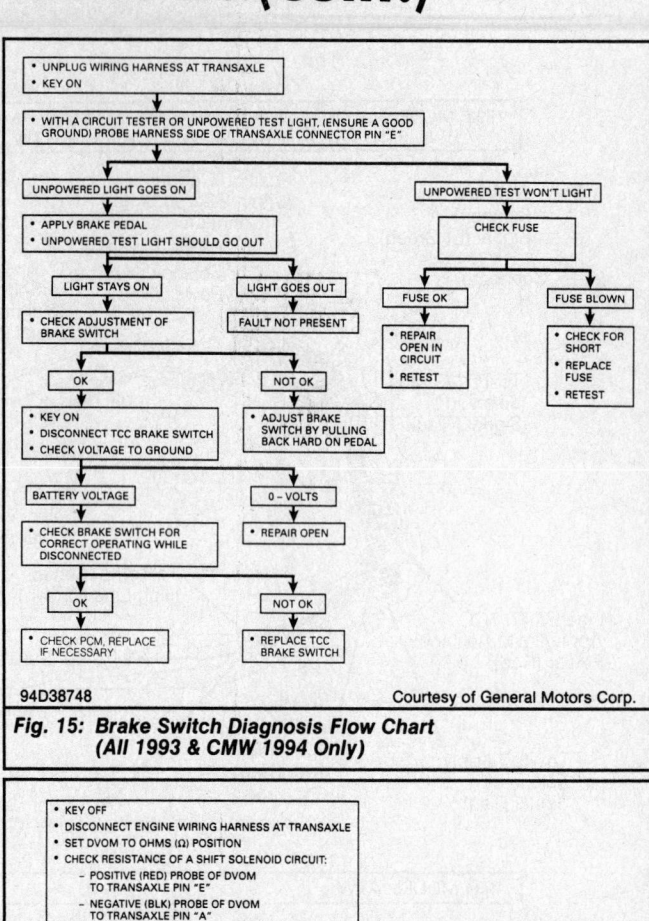

Fig. 15: **Brake Switch Diagnosis Flow Chart**
(All 1993 & CMW 1994 Only)

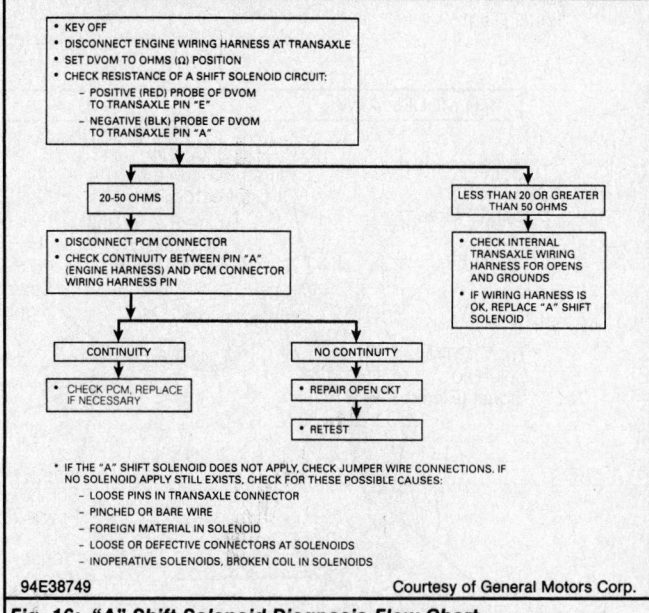

Fig. 16: **"A" Shift Solenoid Diagnosis Flow Chart**

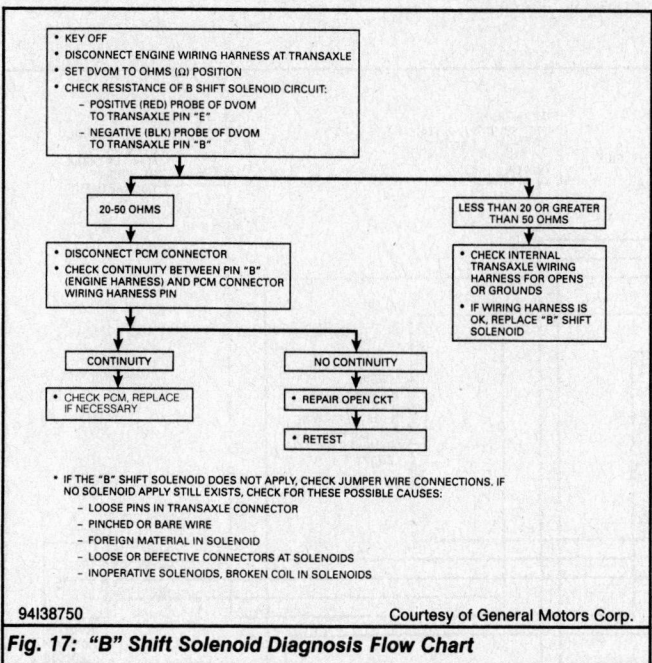

94I38750   Courtesy of General Motors Corp.

Fig. 17: "B" Shift Solenoid Diagnosis Flow Chart

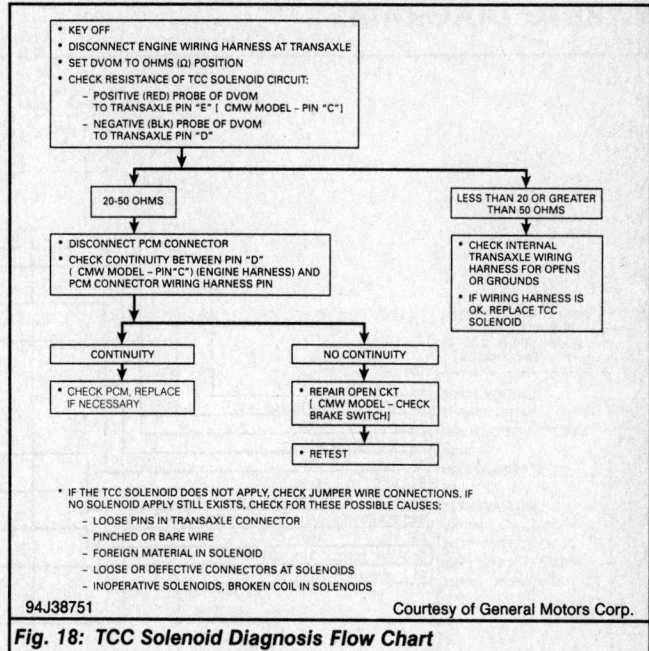

94J38751   Courtesy of General Motors Corp.

Fig. 18: TCC Solenoid Diagnosis Flow Chart

AUTOMATIC TRANSMISSIONS
4T60-E Electronic Controls (Cont.)

WIRING DIAGRAMS

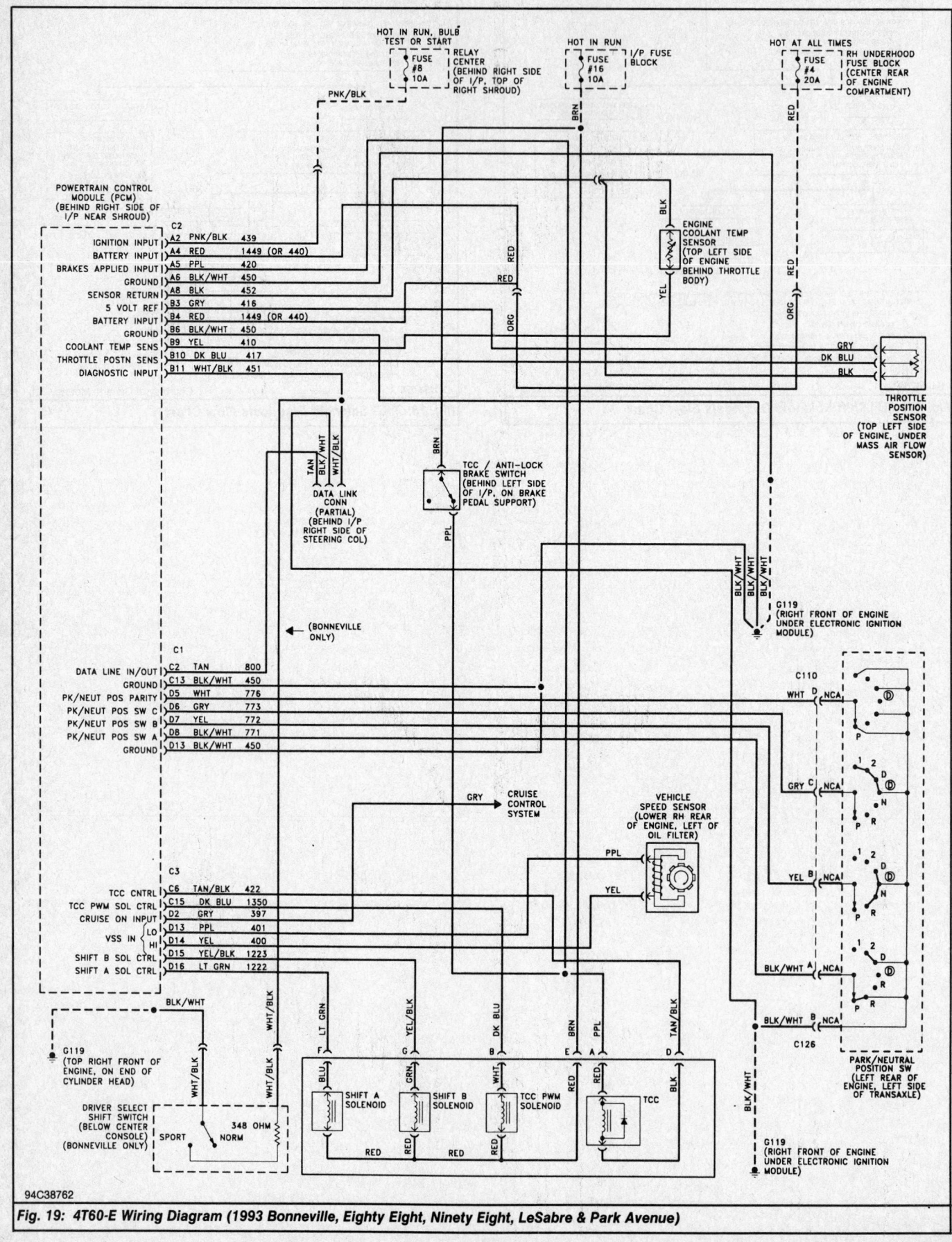

Fig. 19: 4T60-E Wiring Diagram (1993 Bonneville, Eighty Eight, Ninety Eight, LeSabre & Park Avenue)

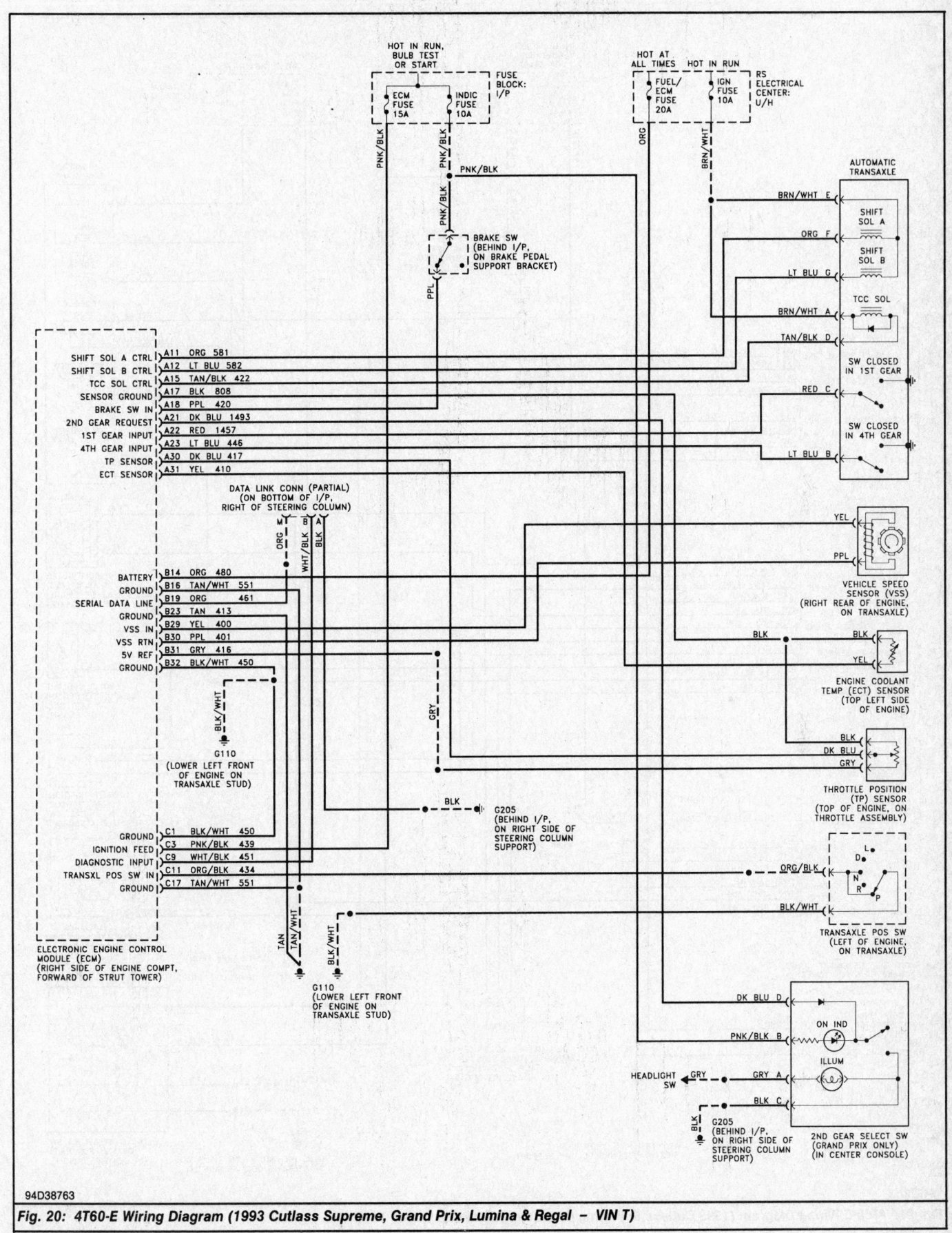

Fig. 20: 4T60-E Wiring Diagram (1993 Cutlass Supreme, Grand Prix, Lumina & Regal – VIN T)

94D38763

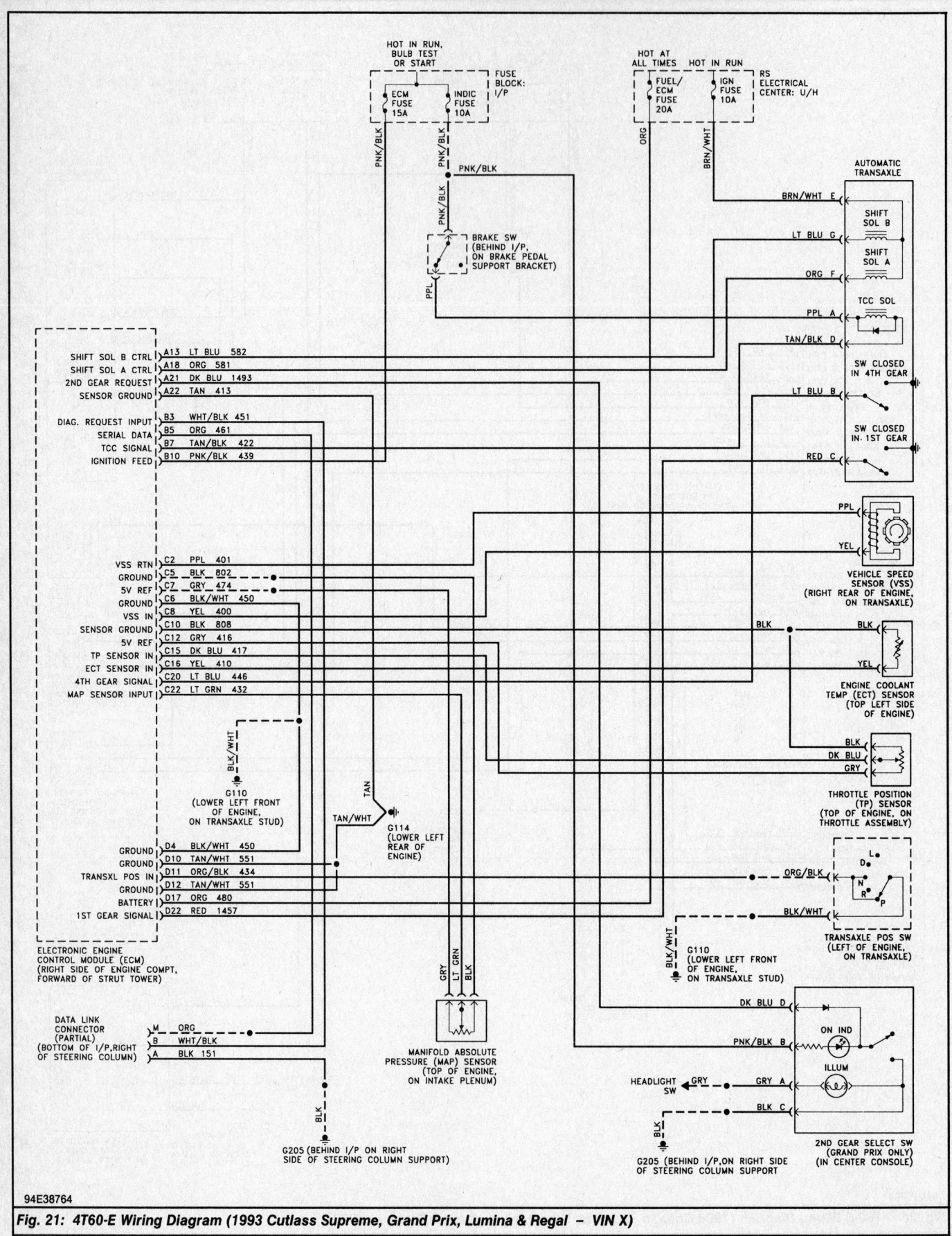

94E38764

Fig. 21: *4T60-E Wiring Diagram (1993 Cutlass Supreme, Grand Prix, Lumina & Regal – VIN X)*

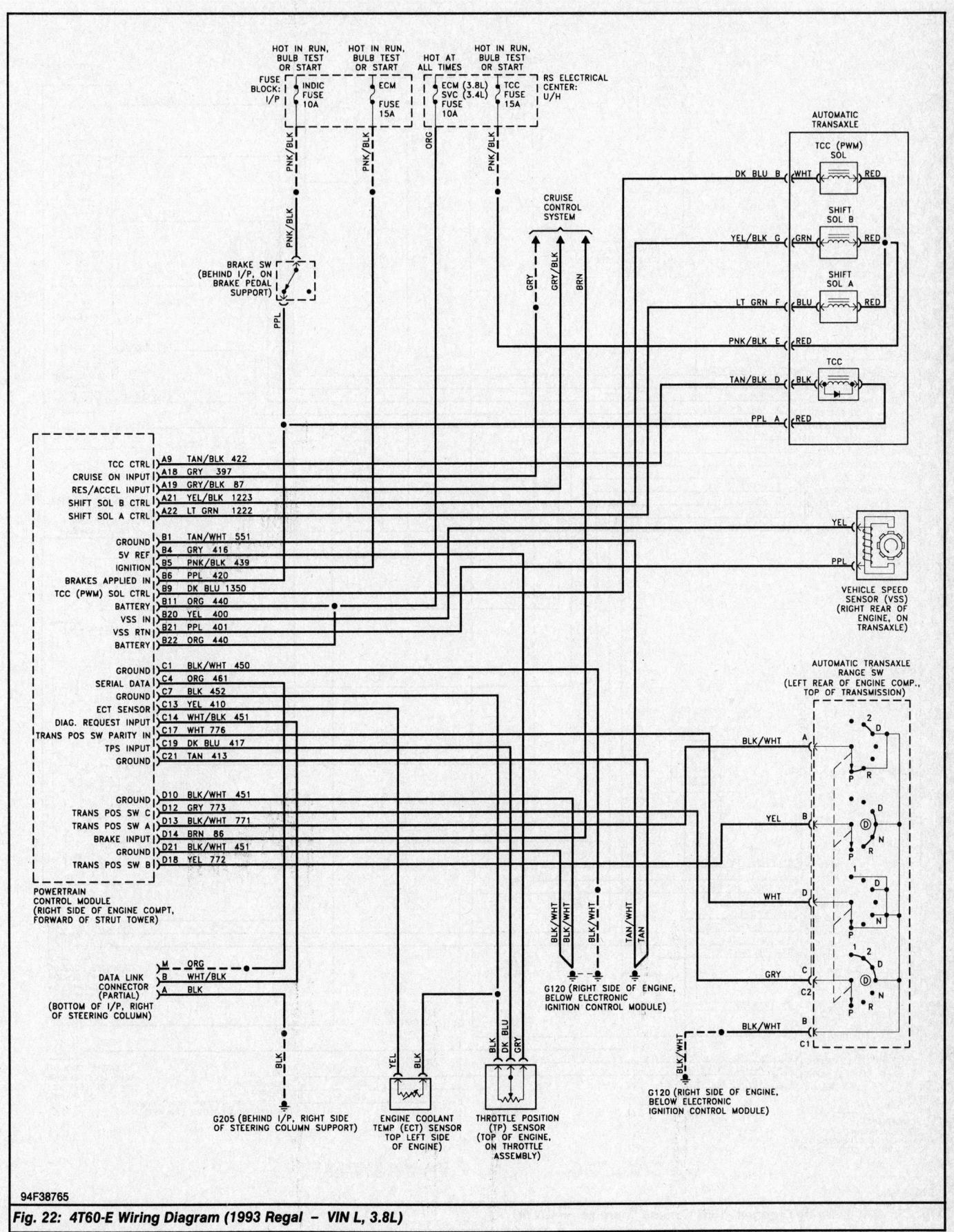

Fig. 22: 4T60-E Wiring Diagram (1993 Regal – VIN L, 3.8L)

94F38765

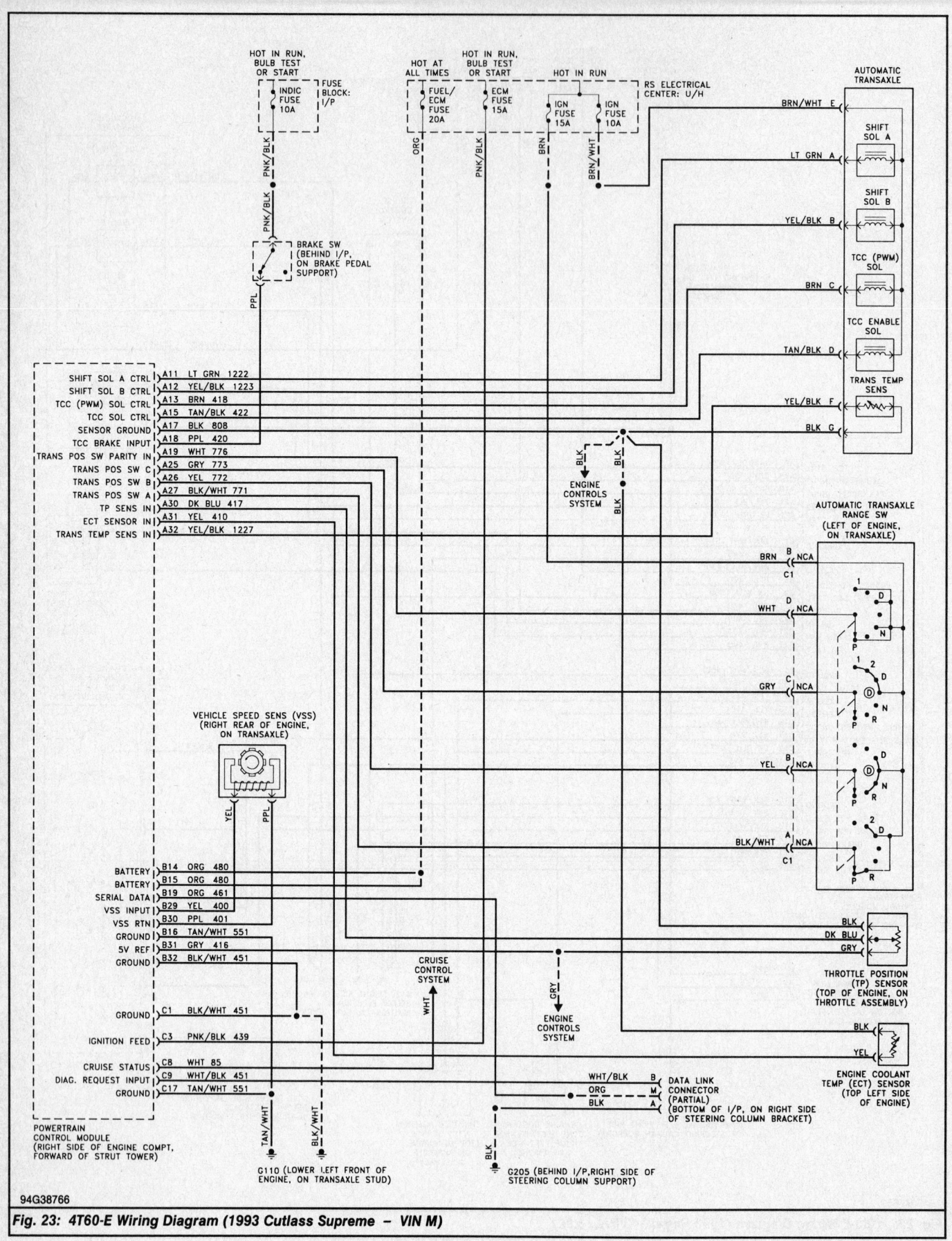

94G38766

Fig. 23: 4T60-E Wiring Diagram (1993 Cutlass Supreme – VIN M)

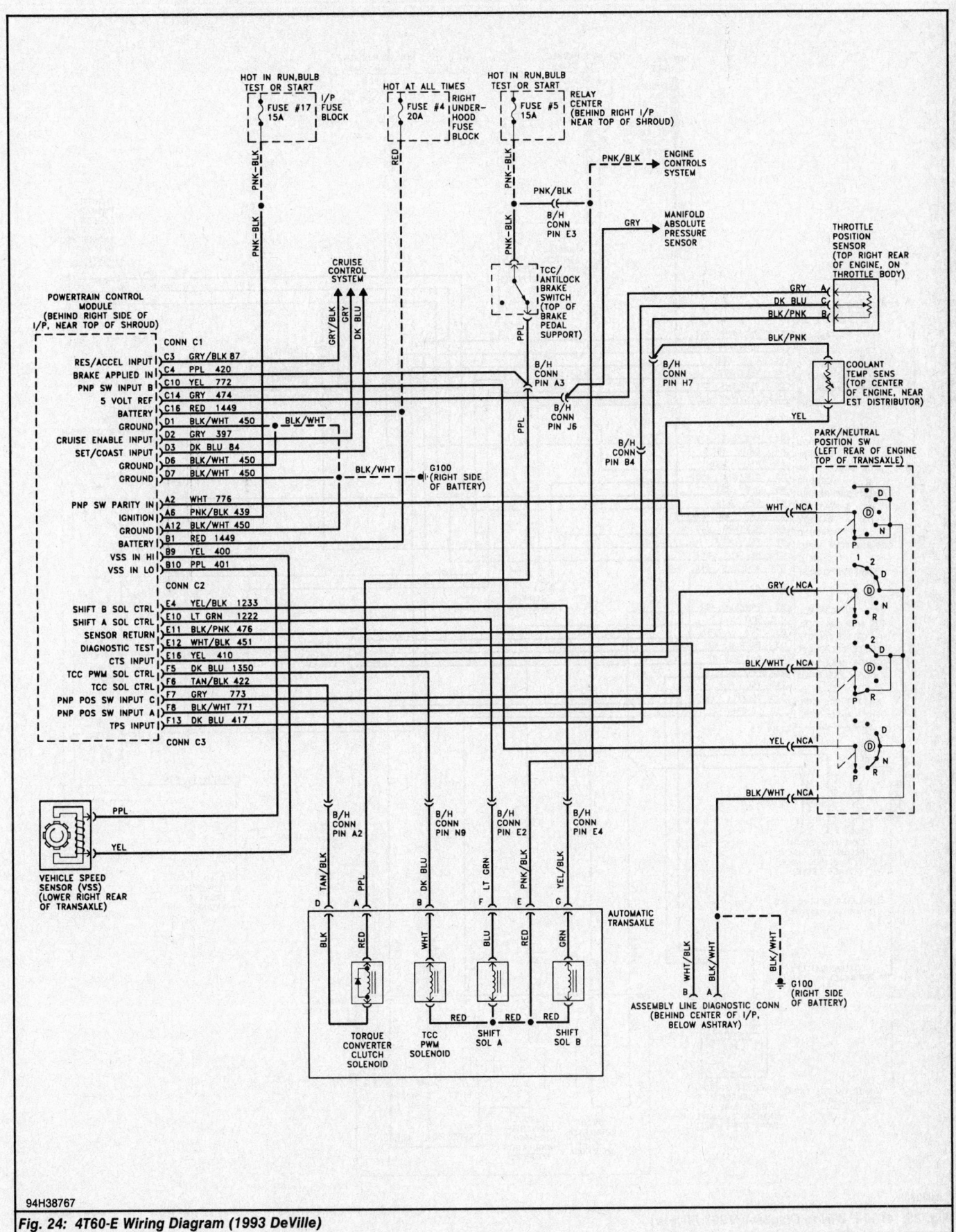

Fig. 24: 4T60-E Wiring Diagram (1993 DeVille)

94H38767

AUTOMATIC TRANSMISSIONS
4T60-E Electronic Controls (Cont.)

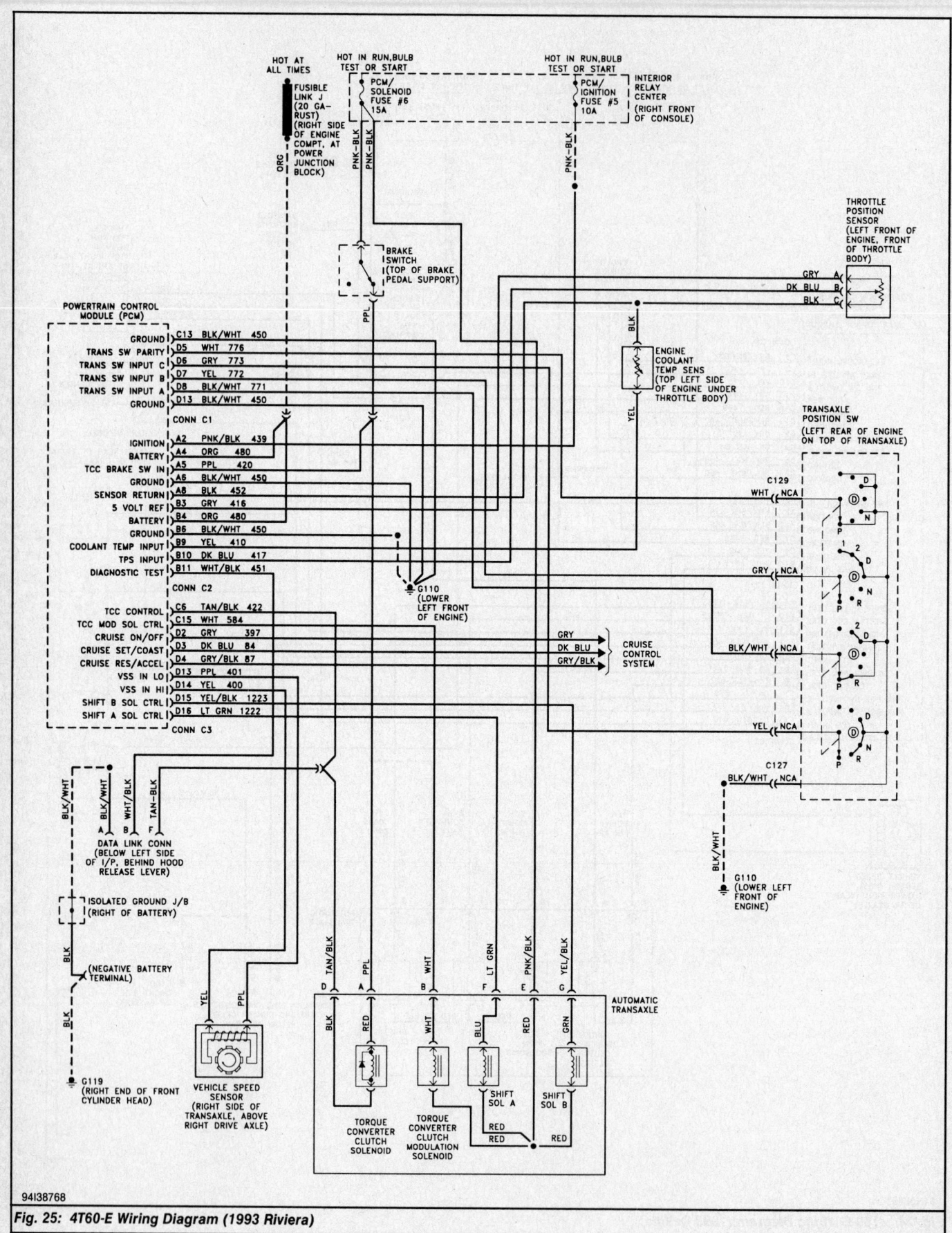

Fig. 25: 4T60-E Wiring Diagram (1993 Riviera)

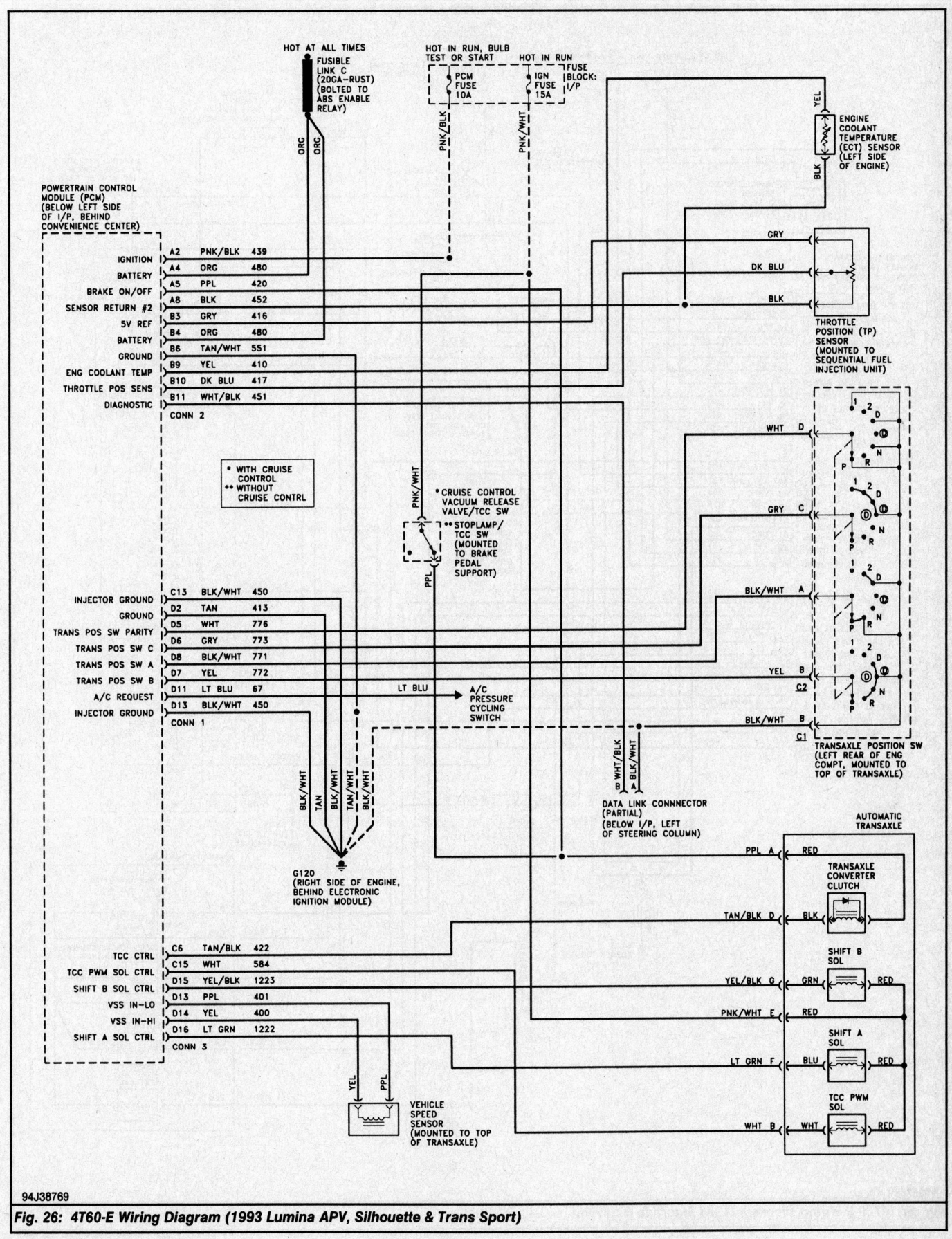

Fig. 26: 4T60-E Wiring Diagram (1993 Lumina APV, Silhouette & Trans Sport)

94J38769

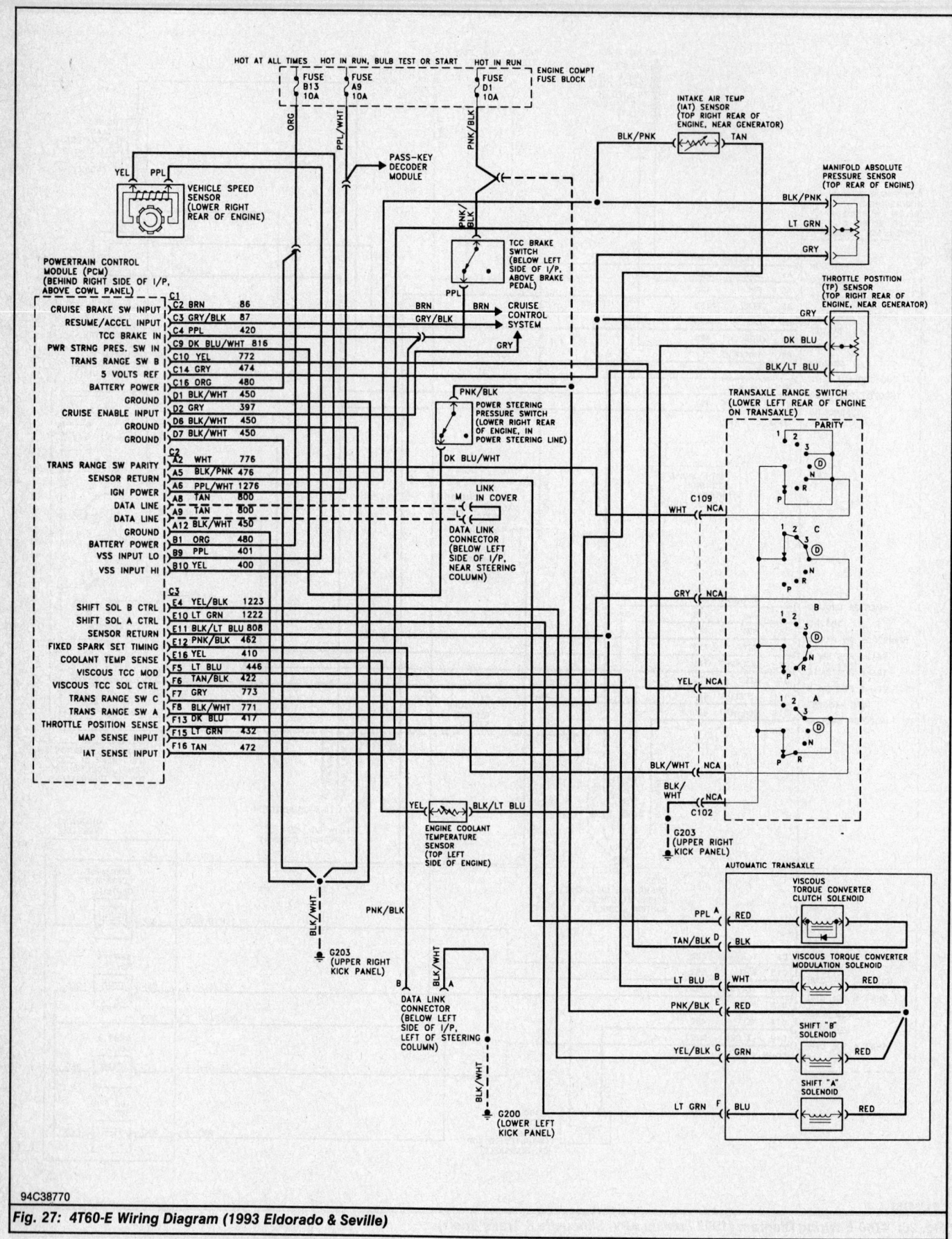

Fig. 27: 4T60-E Wiring Diagram (1993 Eldorado & Seville)

94C38770

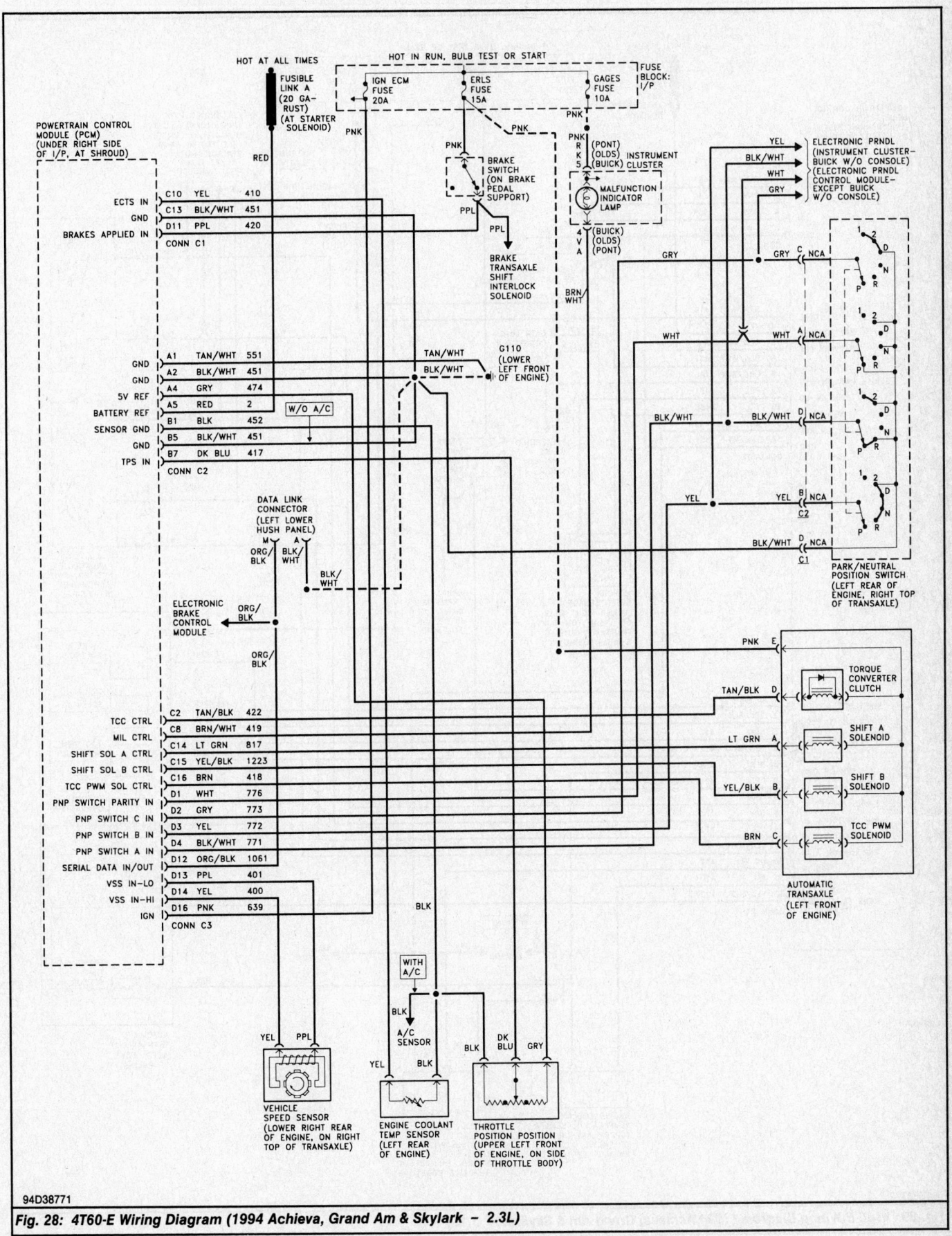

Fig. 28: 4T60-E Wiring Diagram (1994 Achieva, Grand Am & Skylark – 2.3L)

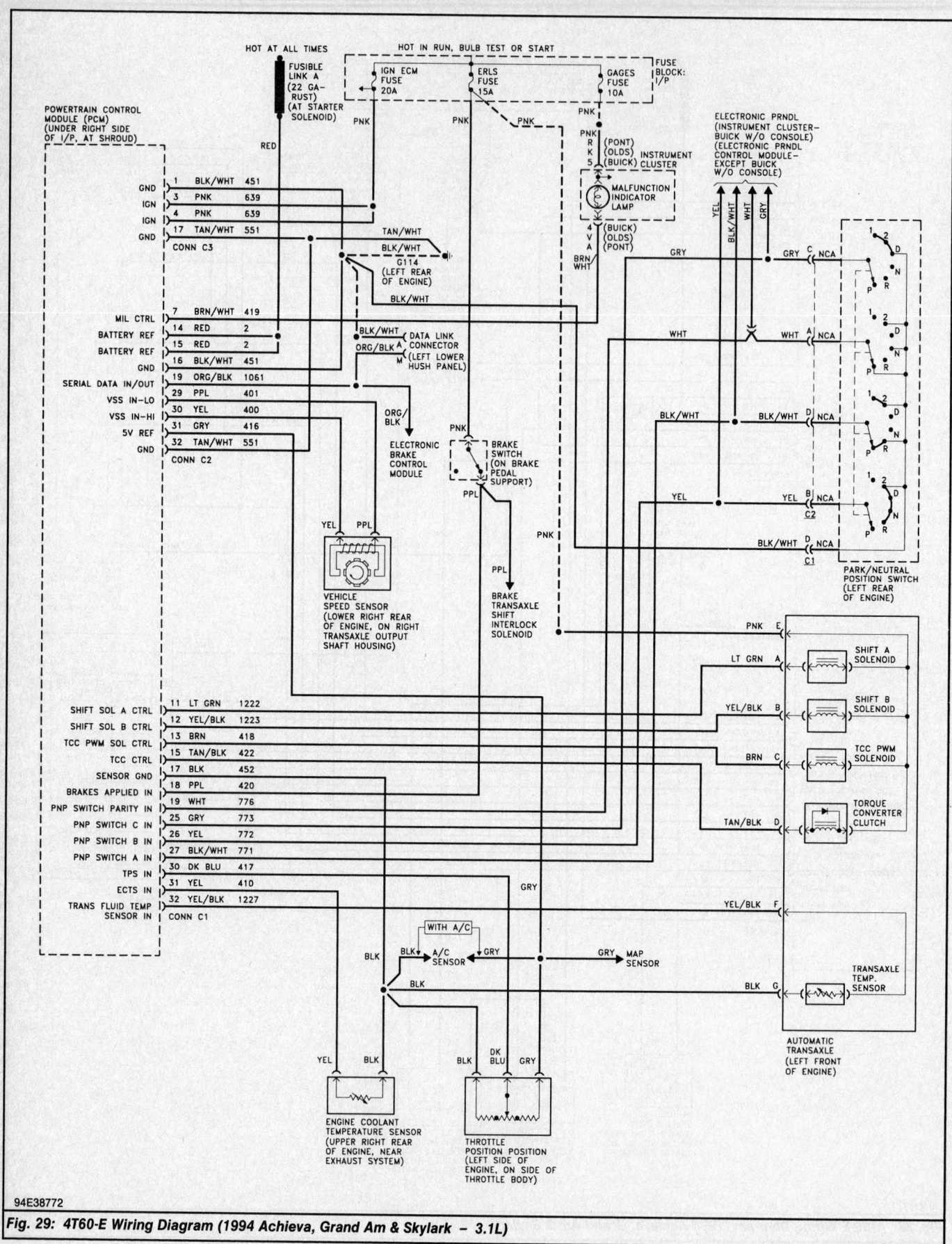

Fig. 29: 4T60-E Wiring Diagram (1994 Achieva, Grand Am & Skylark - 3.1L)

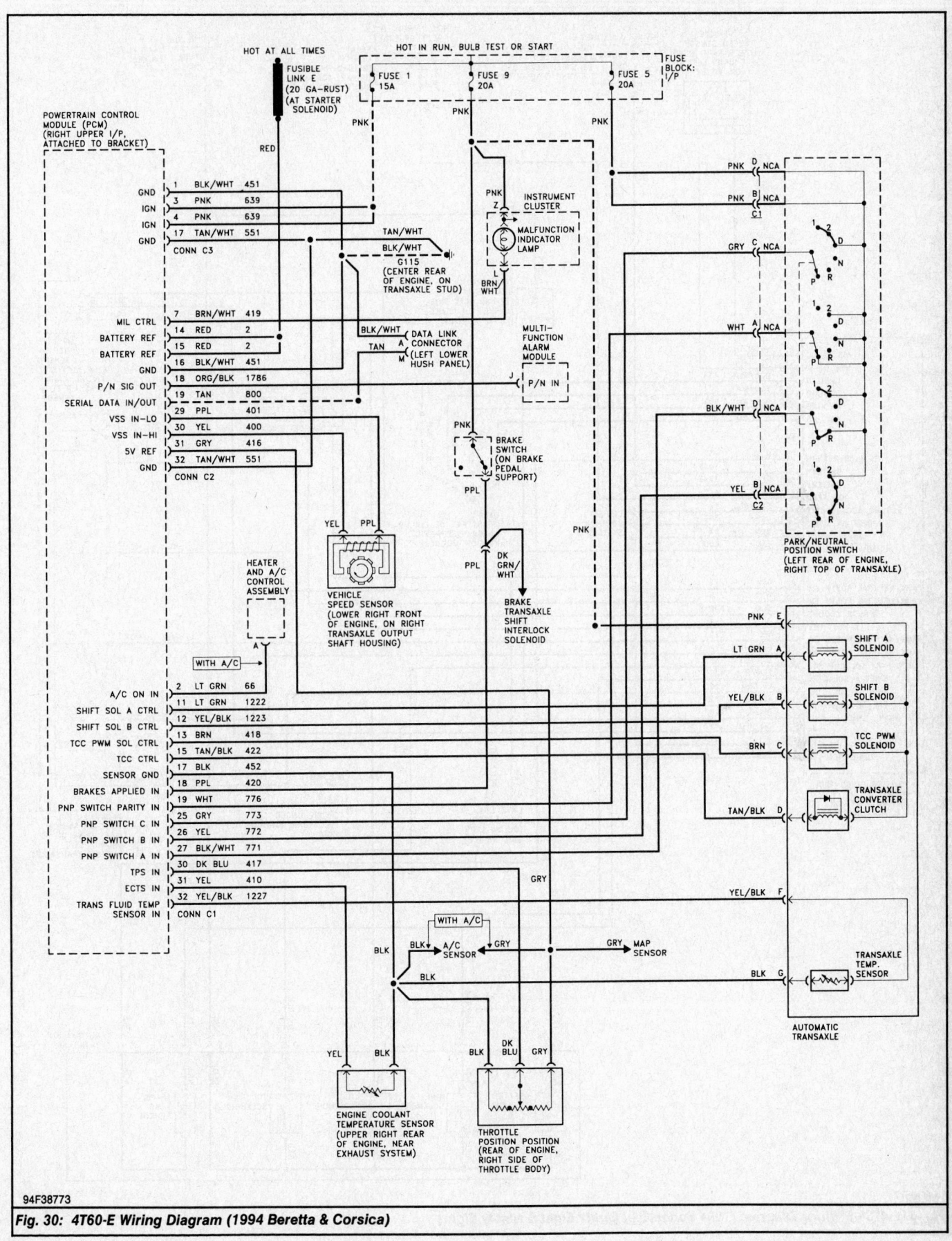

Fig. 30: 4T60-E Wiring Diagram (1994 Beretta & Corsica)

94F38773

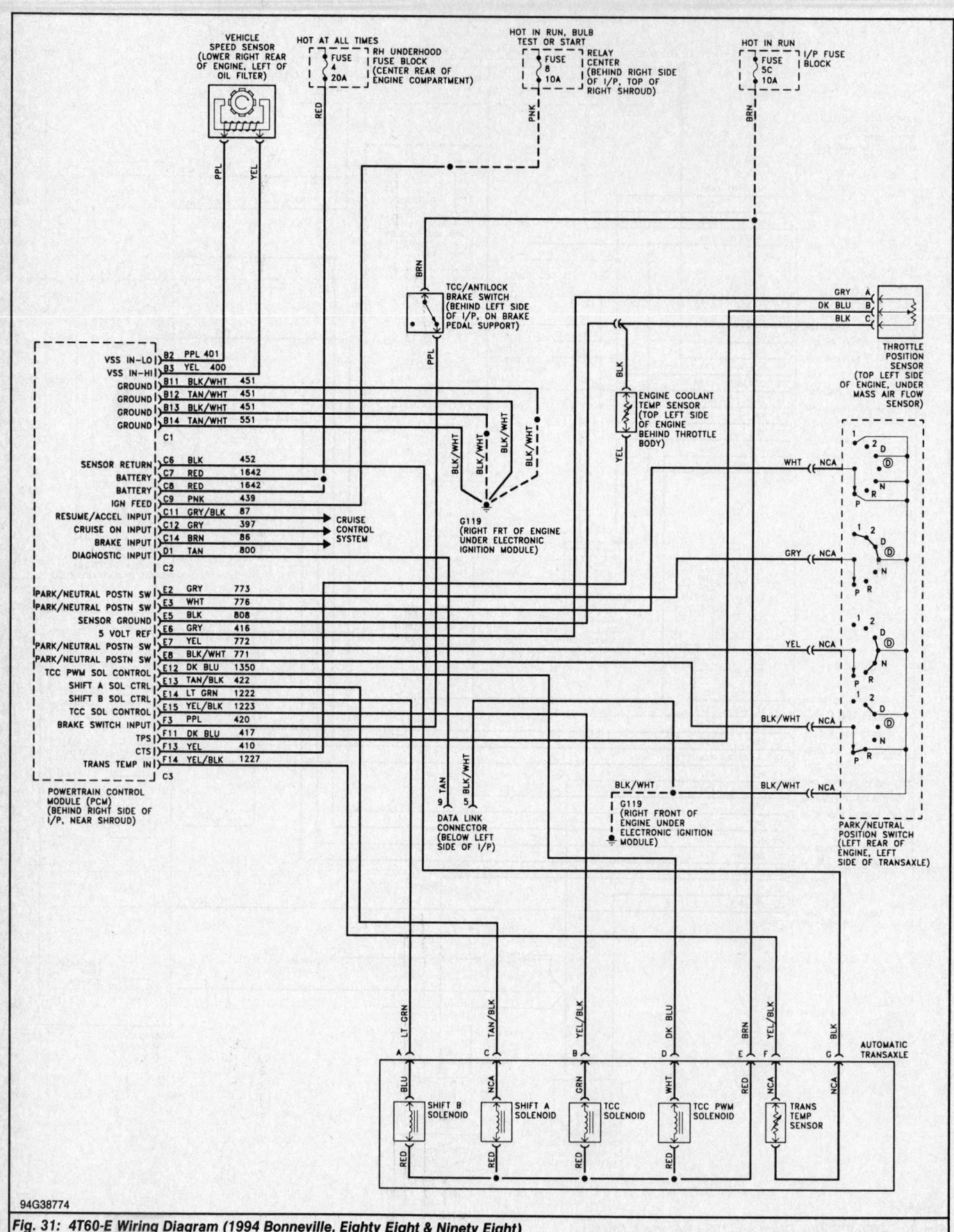

94G38774

Fig. 31: 4T60-E Wiring Diagram (1994 Bonneville, Eighty Eight & Ninety Eight)

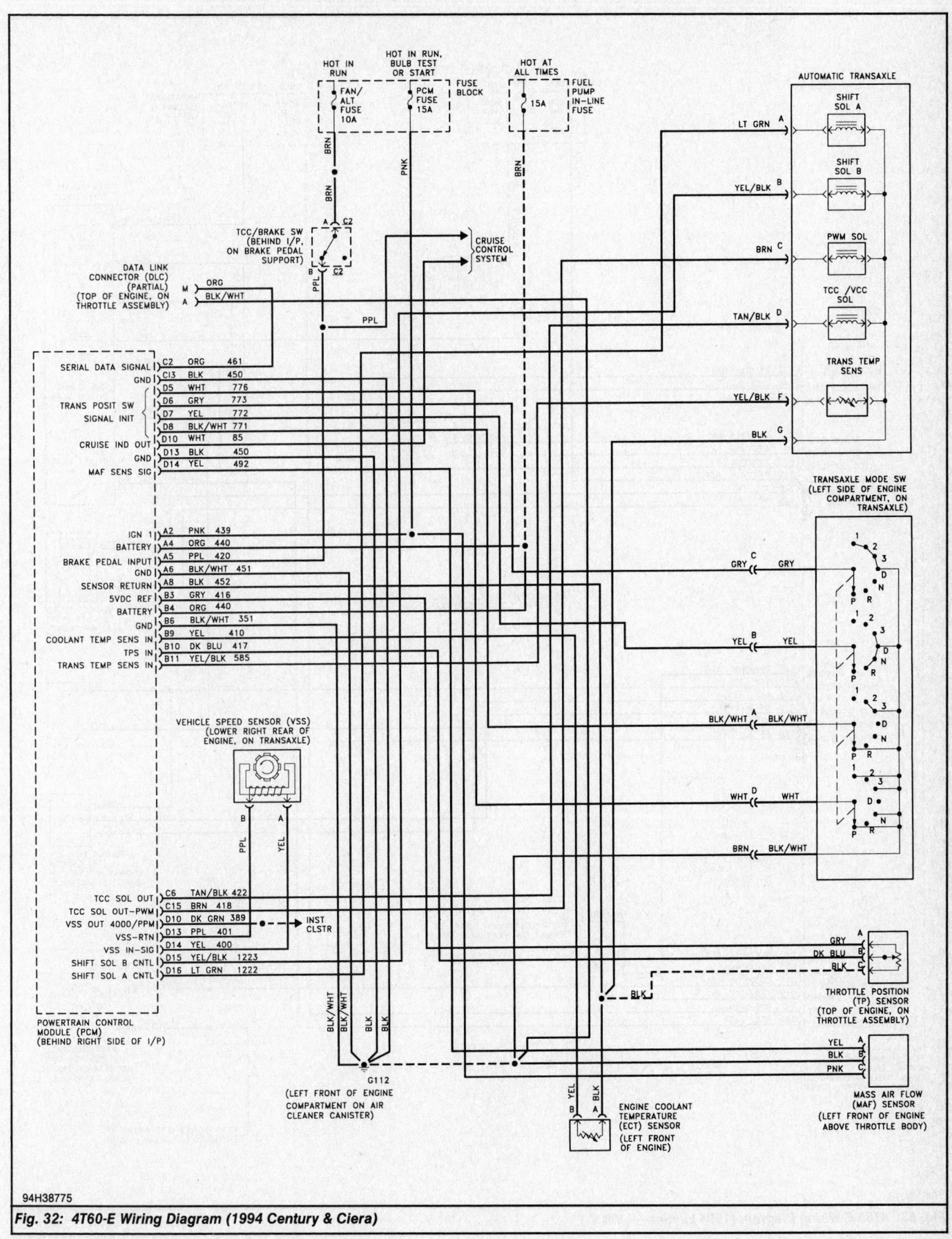

Fig. 32: 4T60-E Wiring Diagram (1994 Century & Ciera)

94H38775

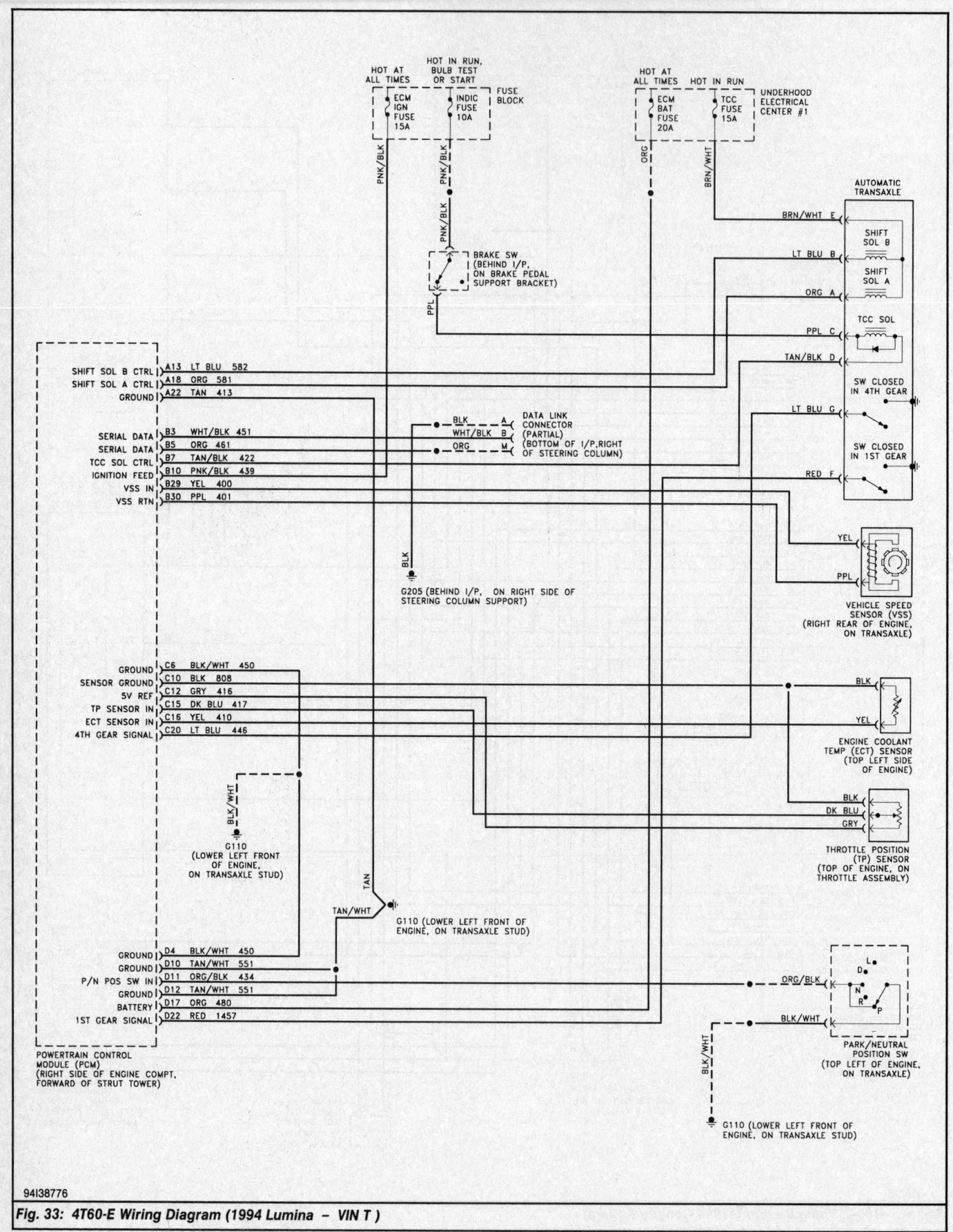

94138776

Fig. 33: *4T60-E Wiring Diagram (1994 Lumina – VIN T)*

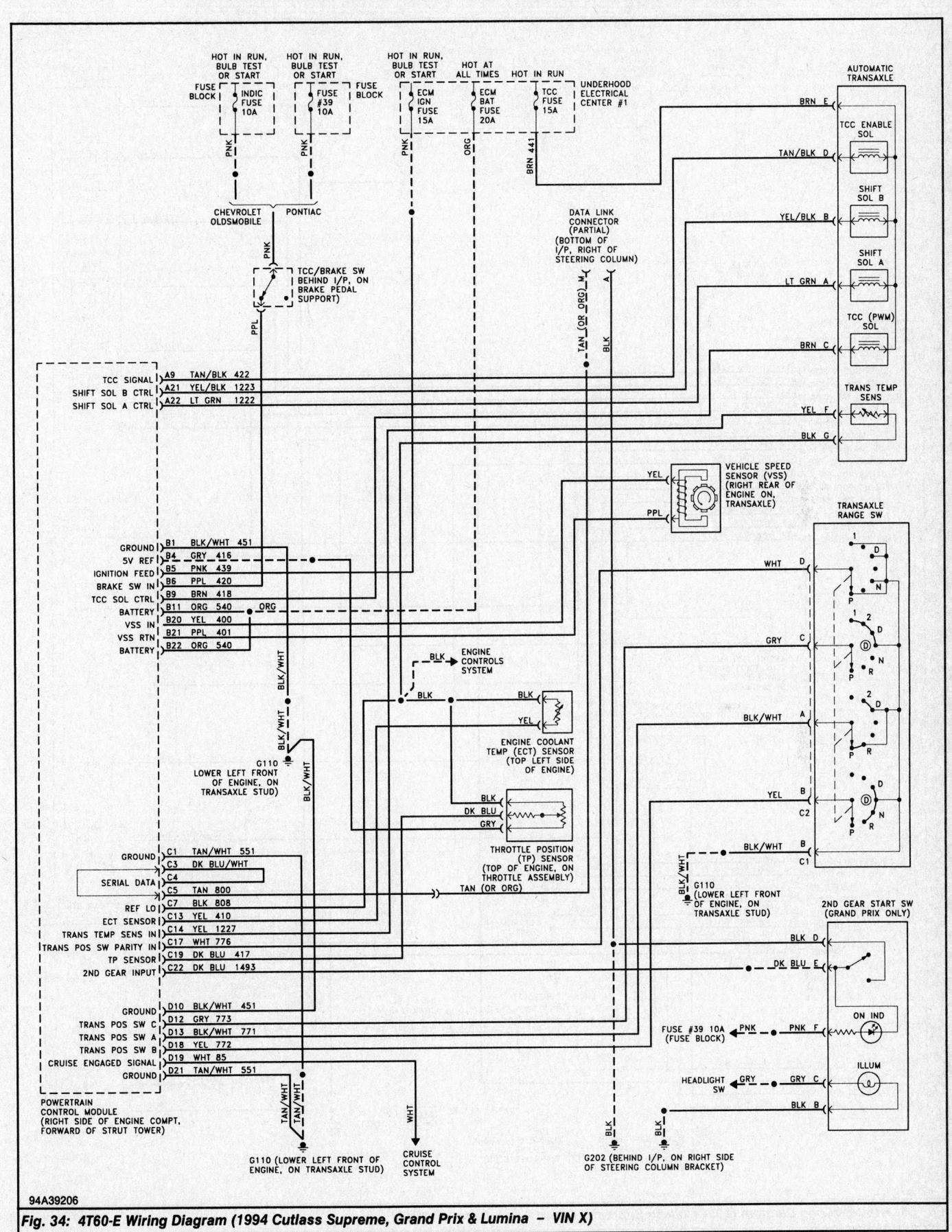

Fig. 34: 4T60-E Wiring Diagram (1994 Cutlass Supreme, Grand Prix & Lumina – VIN X)

94A39206

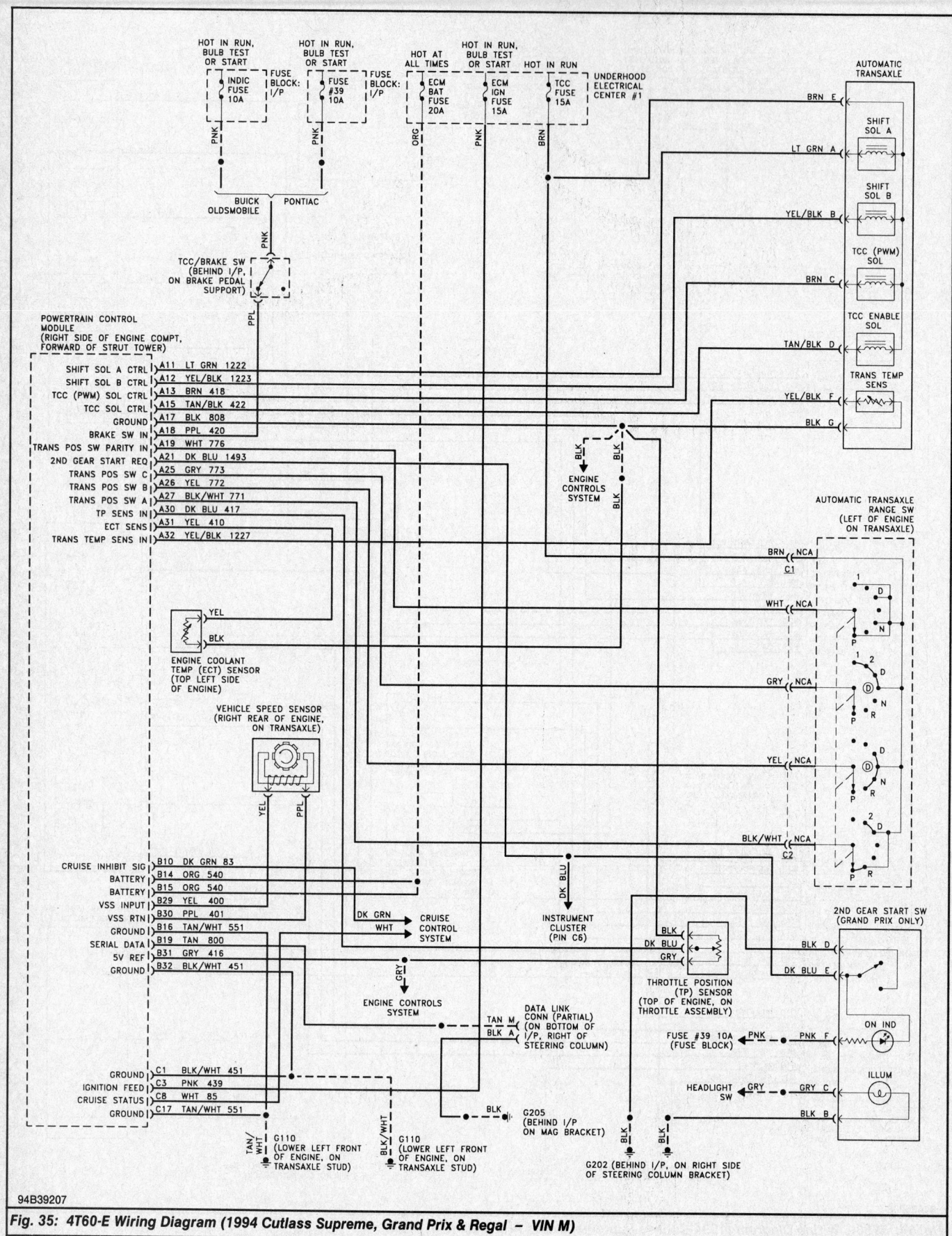

Fig. 35: 4T60-E Wiring Diagram (1994 Cutlass Supreme, Grand Prix & Regal – VIN M)

94B39207

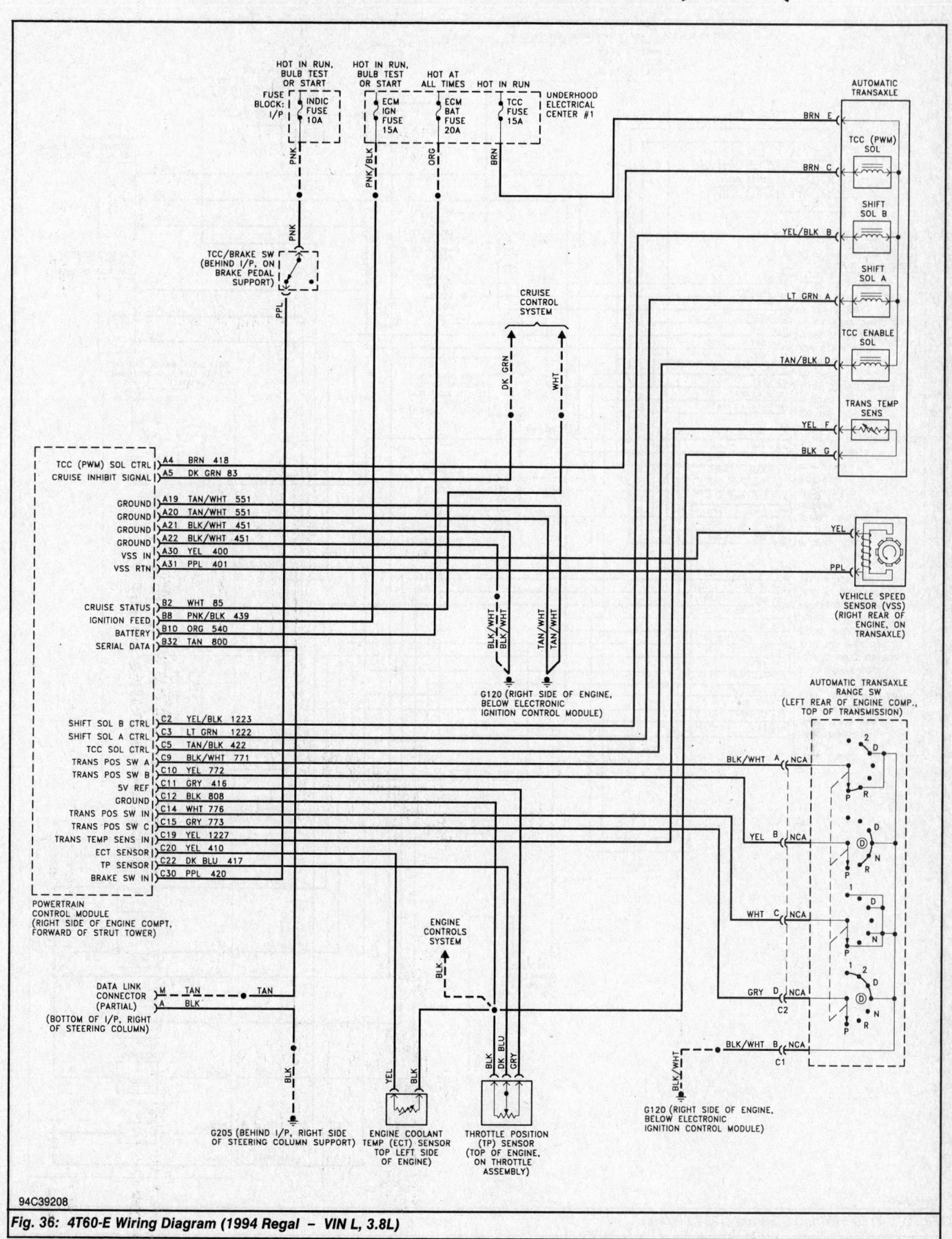

Fig. 36: 4T60-E Wiring Diagram (1994 Regal – VIN L, 3.8L)

94C39208

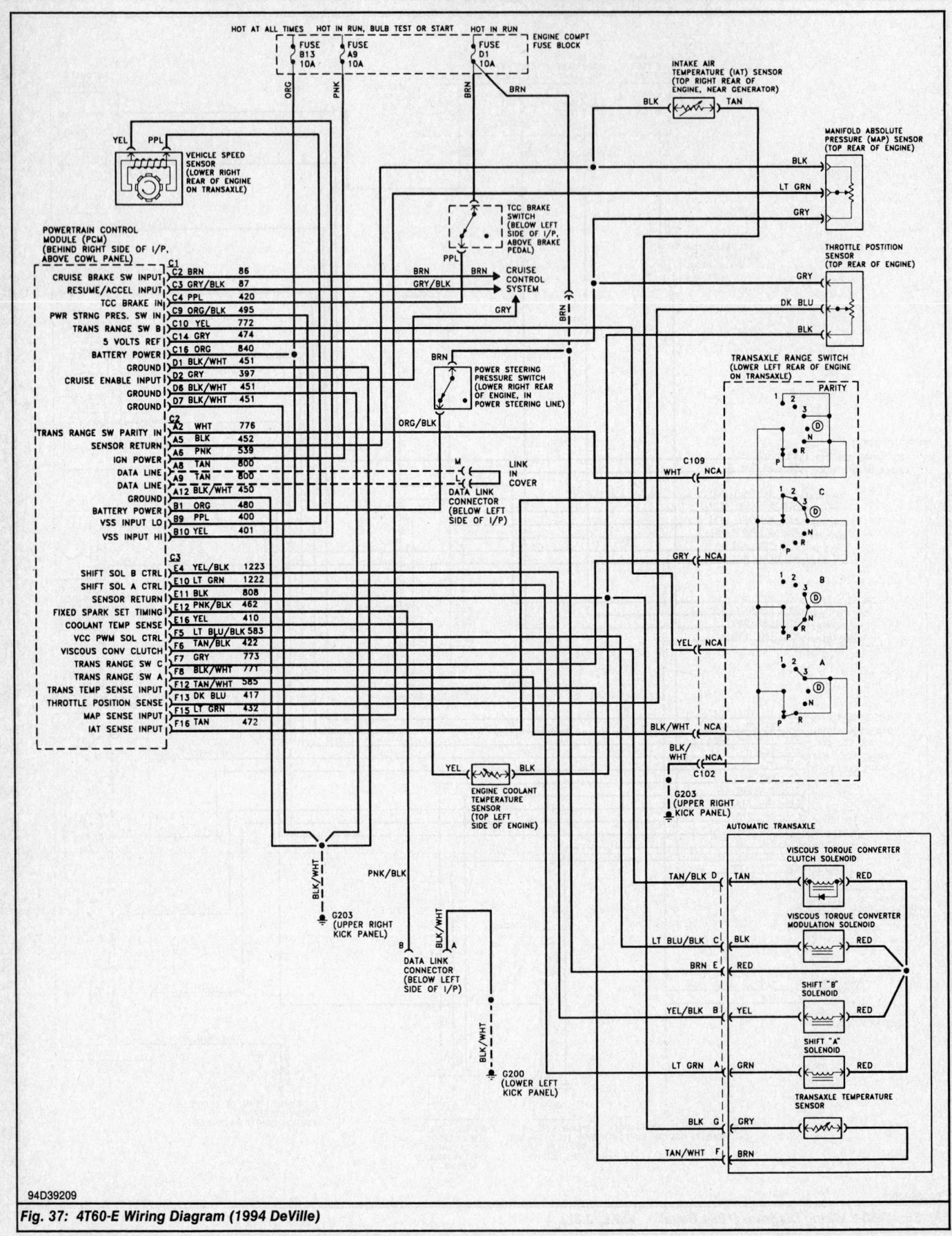

Fig. 37: 4T60-E Wiring Diagram (1994 DeVille)

94D39209

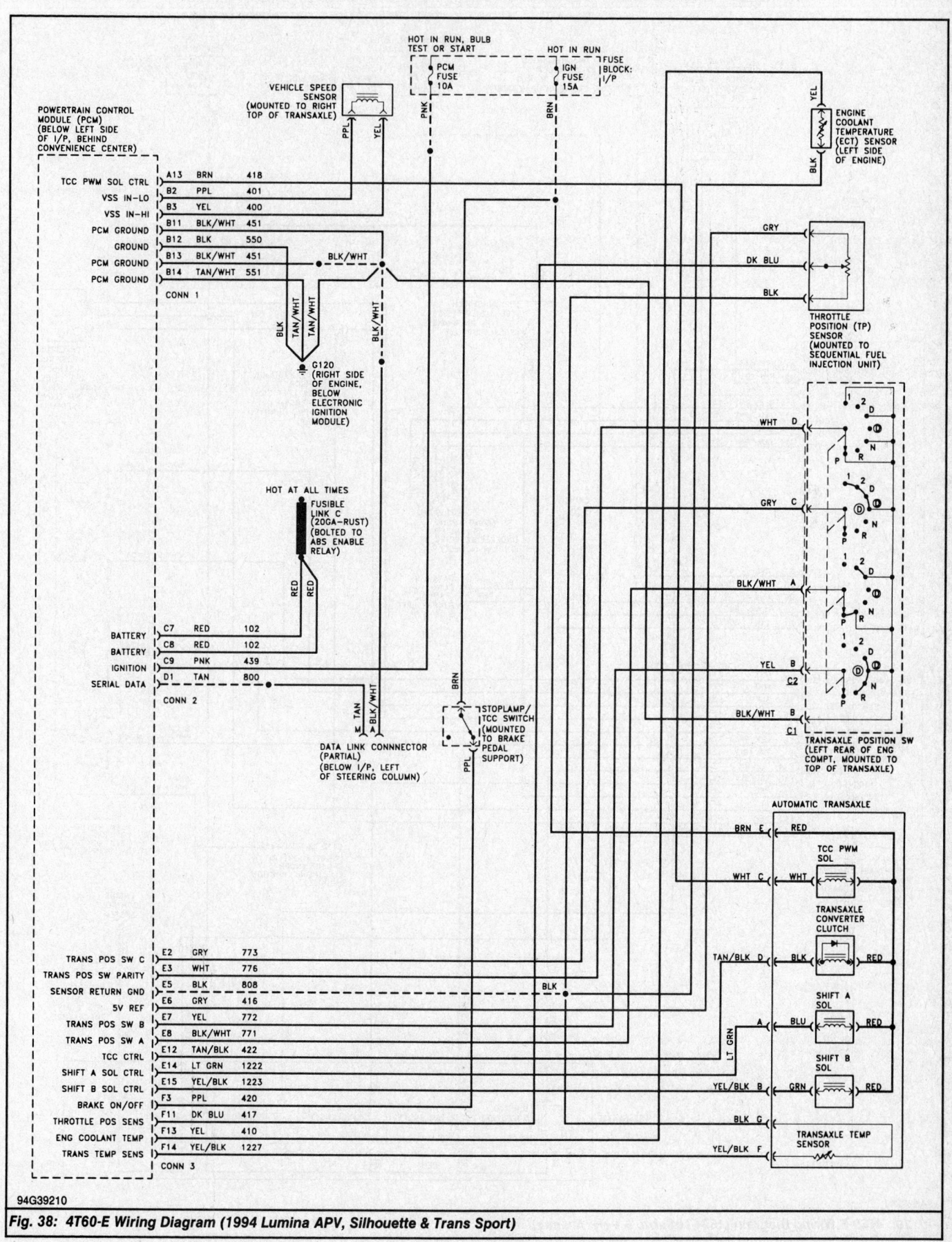

Fig. 38: 4T60-E Wiring Diagram (1994 Lumina APV, Silhouette & Trans Sport)

94G39210

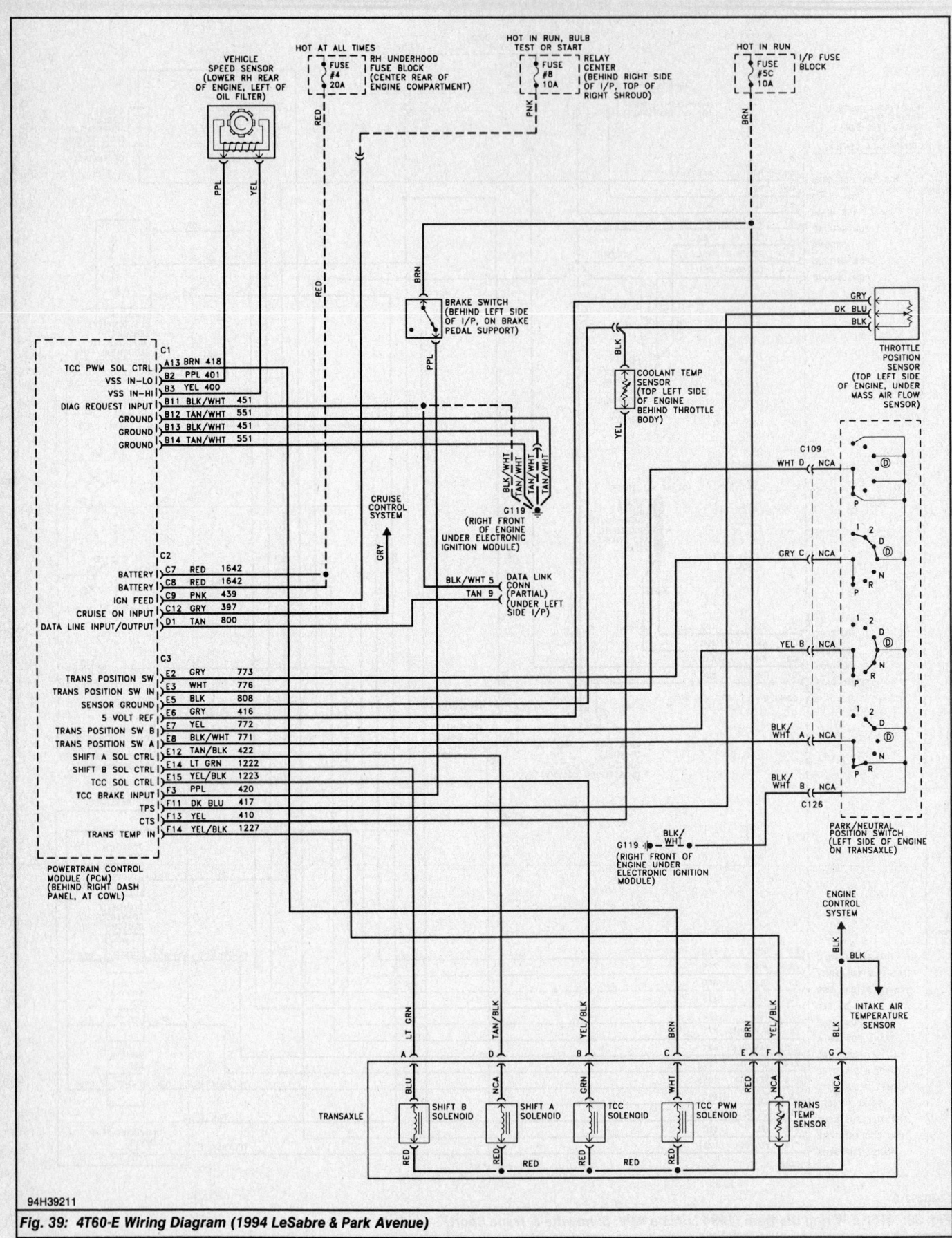

Fig. 39: 4T60-E Wiring Diagram (1994 LeSabre & Park Avenue)

94H39211

"C", "G", "K", "P" Series

NOTE: For testing and diagnostic procedures of electronic components, see 4L80-E ELECTRONIC CONTROLS article in AUTOMATIC TRANSMISSIONS.

APPLICATION & LABOR TIMES

APPLICATION & LABOR TIMES

Vehicle Application	[1] R & I	[2] Overhaul	Series
Blazer [3][4]	6.0	8.0	"K"
Parcel Van	4.3	8.0	"P"
Pickup			
2WD	4.7	8.0	"C"
4WD [3][4]	6.0	8.0	"K"
Sierra & Suburban			
2WD	4.7	8.0	"C"
4WD [3][4]	6.0	8.0	"K"
Van	4.3	8.0	"G"
Yukon [3][4]	6.0	8.0	"K"

[1] – Removal and installation of transmission from vehicle chassis.
[2] – Bench overhaul time for transmission. DOES NOT include removal and installation.
[3] – Add .3 hr. if equipped with skid plate (4WD).
[4] – Add .3 hr. if equipped with strut rods (K15/K35).

IDENTIFICATION

All transmissions have a metal identification plate attached to the rear face of transmission case. See Fig. 1.

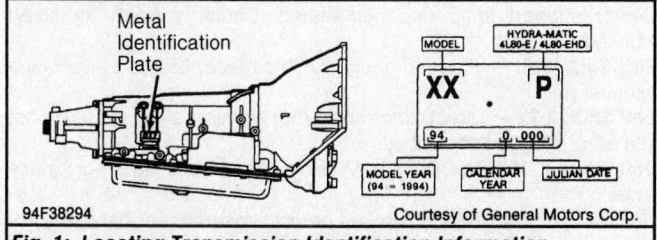

Fig. 1: Locating Transmission Identification Information

DESCRIPTION

The Hydra-Matic 4L80-E transmission is a fully automatic 4-speed unit consisting primarily of a hydraulic torque converter and converter clutch. Transmissions have dual stators inside the torque converter. Transmission uses a gear-type pump to supply all hydraulic pressure needed for operation.

Other internal parts include the following: 5 multiple disc clutches, a roller clutch, a sprag clutch, 2 bands and 3 compound planetary gear sets.

The Hydra-Matic 4L80-E also uses 2 electronic shift solenoids controlled by Powertrain Control Module (PCM) or Transmission Control Module (TCM). The transmission uses 2 speed sensors instead of a governor.

LUBRICATION & ADJUSTMENTS

See appropriate AUTOMATIC TRANSMISSION SERVICING article in TRANSMISSION SERVICING.

TROUBLE SHOOTING

NOTE: For testing and diagnostic procedures of electronic components, see 4L80-E ELECTRONIC CONTROLS article in AUTOMATIC TRANSMISSIONS.

QUICK CHECK

1) Check level and condition of transmission fluid. Check PCM or TCM memory for any stored trouble codes. See 4L80-E ELECTRONIC CONTROLS article in AUTOMATIC TRANSMISSIONS. If no trouble codes are present, go to next step. If codes are present, diagnose and repair all computer-related trouble codes. Clear PCM or TCM trouble code memory.
2) Perform road test. See ROAD TEST under TESTING. During road test, record shift points. If shift point timing or shifting is incorrect, go to 4L80-E ELECTRONIC CONTROLS article in AUTOMATIC TRANSMISSIONS.
3) If shift(s) is too harsh or too soft, see HYDRAULIC PRESSURE TESTS under TESTING. For specific complaints, see appropriate condition(s) listed under SYMPTOM DIAGNOSIS.

SYMPTOM DIAGNOSIS

NOTE: Models with gasoline engines use Powertrain Control Module (PCM) computer. Models with diesel engines use Transmission Control Module (TCM) computer. These computers control TCC, force motor (hydraulic pressure) and shift solenoids "A" and "B".

Fluid Out Of Vent Or Foaming – Transmission overfilled. Fluid contaminated with antifreeze or engine overheating. Filter not seated. Cross-channel leak allowing pressure to leak in to vent area of pump cover.
Transmission Overheats – Low fluid or blocked radiator. TCC stuck in apply or release. Broken TCC valve spring. Cross channel leakage in pump cover. Pressure regulator stuck in high demand. Blocked oil cooler. Problem with converter limit valve assembly. Loss of fluid. Problem with stator(s) or turbine seals.
Reduced Internal Lubrication – Cross channel leakage in pump cover. Pressure regulator stuck in high demand. Damaged oil pump mounting gasket. Stuck closed converter limit valve assembly (under heavy load).
High Or Low Line Pressure – Incorrect fluid level. Oil pump assembly seals or gears damaged. Pump drive shaft damaged. Pressure regulator valve spring damaged, pressure regulator valve nicked or scored. Pressure relief valve spring damaged. Pump cover leaking (bolts loose). Force motor off or on at all times. Loose connection at PCM or TCM. Possible trouble Code 73.
Inoperative In Drive – **1)** Low fluid level. Low fluid pressure. Manual linkage misadjusted or disconnected. Damaged torque converter. Leaking or damaged transmission case seals or gaskets. Damaged oil pump drive shaft or pump assembly. Broken bearing, pinion or carrier. Roller clutch damaged or locked.
2) Piston or seal damaged in forward clutch assembly. Forward clutch assembly clutch plates burned or missing, or check ball capsule leaking or missing. Burned reaction plate (due to lack of lubrication), broken snap ring or worn gear teeth.
3) Rear gear set assembly pinions, internal ring gear or sun gear damaged. Main shaft damaged. Parking pawl spring broken. Turbine shaft ball not seating.
Vehicle Moves Forward In "N" – Mis-positioned or stuck manual valve. Problem with forward clutch assembly.
Engine Stall – Seized forward clutch, 4th clutch or overrun clutch assembly. TCC stuck on or dragging.
No Torque In Reverse & 3rd – Broken forward clutch hub, housing or snap ring.
Locked In Park – Damaged parking pawl; binding, weak spring or stretched rod.
Vehicle Moves In Park – Manual linkage damaged or disconnected. Broken parking pawl spring, parking pawl or parking pawl gear assembly. Park actuator spring damaged.
Slips In Reverse – Low fluid pressure. Reverse servo seal damaged. Reverse reaction drum splines stripped.
No Reverse – Low fluid pressure. Reverse servo not correctly assembled, piston or seal damaged, or incorrect apply pin. Damaged rear band. Direct clutch assembly clutch plates burned or missing, or check ball capsule leaking or missing.

Slips In "D" – Low fluid level. Low fluid pressure.

No 1st Gear In "D4" – Low roller assembly not attached or race broken. Broken center support race or splines. Damaged case near center support. Center support snap rings not seated.

No 1st Gear In "D2" Or "D3" – Low roller assembly not attached or race broken. Broken center support race or splines. Damaged case near center support. Center support snap rings not seated. Stuck front band.

No 1st Gear In "D1" – Low roller assembly not attached or race broken. Broken center support race or splines. Damaged case near center support. Center support snap rings not seated. Broken housing, or mispositioned or broken rear band anchor pin. Misaligned detent lever.

No 1-2 Shift In "D4" (1st Gear Only) – Output or input speed sensor reads zero. Sun gear splines damaged or missing.

1st & 2nd Gear Only – Solenoid "B" stuck off or not connected to PCM or TCM. Dirt in filter, leaking "O" ring or no supply voltage to solenoid "B". Stuck 2-3 shift valve. Possible trouble Code 68, 81, 85 or 87.

1st & 4th Gear Only (Manual 2nd & 3rd Only) – Solenoid "A" stuck off. Dirt in filter, PCM or TCM not grounded, leaking "O" ring, no supply voltage to solenoid "A" or wire disconnected. Stuck 1-2 shift valve. Possible trouble Code 68, 82 or 85.

Late 1-2 Shift – Problem with input and/or output speed sensor(s). Faulty digital ratio adapter (2WD only). Incorrect PROM calibration. Possible trouble Code 24, 28 or 85.

No Engine Braking In "D1" – Problem with rear band assembly. Damaged main or output shafts.

No 2nd Gear – Intermediate clutch feed cup plug missing. Problem with intermediate clutch and center support assembly. Damaged intermediate sprag. Broken direct clutch housing or snap ring.

2nd Gear Only – Possible trouble Code 24, 53, 75 and 81.

No Torque In 2nd – Worn or damaged intermediate sprag.

Starts In 2nd Gear – Seized intermediate clutch plates. Problem with direct clutch or center support assemblies. Stuck 1-2 shift valve. PCM- or TCM-related problem. Possible trouble Code 82.

No 2nd Gear Braking In "D2" – Problem with direct clutch housing or front band assemblies.

No Engine Braking In "D2" – Problem with rear gear set assembly. Damaged main or output shafts.

No Overrun Braking In "D2" – Problem with overrun clutch or reaction sun gear assemblies.

No 1st Gear In "D3" – Low roller assembly not attached or race broken. Broken center support race or splines. Damaged case near center support. Center support snap rings not seated. Applied front band.

No 2nd Gear In "D3" – Intermediate clutch feed cup plug missing. Problem with intermediate clutch and center support assembly. Damaged intermediate sprag. Broken direct clutch housing or snap ring.

No 3rd Gear In "D3" – Direct clutch feed cup plug missing. Problem with direct clutch and center support assembly. Broken direct clutch housing or snap ring. Solenoid "B" stuck off. Dirt in filter, PCM or TCM not grounded, leaking "O" ring, no supply voltage to solenoid "B" or wire disconnected. Stuck 2-3 shift valve. PCM or TCM problem. Possible trouble Code 81, 85 or 87.

Starts In 3rd Gear – Seized forward clutch or oil holes in driving hub plugged. Damaged or seized direct clutch assembly.

No Engine Braking In "D3" – Damaged main shaft or main shaft bushing.

2nd & 3rd Gear Only – Stuck 1-2 shift valve. Solenoid "A" off. Dirt in filter, PCM or TCM not grounded, leaking "O" ring, no supply voltage to solenoid "A" or wire disconnected. Possible trouble Code 68, 82 or 85.

No 4th Gear – Problem with 4th clutch or overrun clutch related assemblies. 2-3 shift valve stuck. Solenoid "B" off. Dirt in filter, PCM or TCM not grounded, leaking "O" ring, no supply voltage to solenoid "B" or wire disconnected. Possible trouble Code 21, 22, 28, 68, 75 or 81.

Starts In 4th Gear – Solenoid "B" stuck on. Dirt in filter, PCM or TCM signal wire grounded. Possible trouble Code 86.

NOTE: Digital ratio adapter receives signals from electronic speedometer and sends them to PCM/TCM.

Incorrect Shift Points – Problem related to PCM or TCM signal inputs from TPS, speed sensors or pressure switch manifold. Faulty digital ratio adapter (2WD only). Possible trouble Code 21, 22, 24, 28 or 85. Incorrect tire size, axle ratio or PROM.

Harsh Shifts – High or low line pressures. Force motor stuck off. Accumulator piston seals damaged or piston springs missing. Accumulator cover bolts improperly tightened or gaskets mispositioned. Missing check balls. Incorrect PROM calibration. Possible trouble Code 21, 22, 24, 28, 53, 68, 73, 75, 81 or 85.

Harsh Shifts ("D" To "R") – Blocked direct lube exhaust. Forward clutch spring not working. Direct clutch snap ring broken or not seated. Plugged direct clutch check ball.

Harsh Shifts (3-4 Shift) – Binding 4th clutch spring assembly. Plugged air bleed hole. 4th clutch case bolt blocking oil feed hole.

Harsh Shifts (4-3 Shift) – 4th clutch snap ring not seated. 4th clutch spring assembly not working. Plugged 4th clutch housing cup plug. 4th clutch case bolt blocking oil feed hole. Blocked direct lube exhaust port.

Harsh Shifts ("D4" To "D3", "D2" Or "D1") – Overrun clutch return spring assembly not working. Plugged overrun clutch housing check ball. Snap ring not seated.

Soft Shifts – Low line pressures. Force motor stuck on. Accumulator piston seals damaged or piston springs missing. Accumulator cover bolts improperly tightened or gaskets mispositioned. PCM or TCM failure. Incorrect PROM calibration. Possible trouble Code 73.

Soft Shift (Into "R") – Plugged direct clutch oil feed. Blocked direct lube exhaust port.

Soft Shift (R To "D") – Direct clutch spring not working, large snap ring not seated or plugged check ball.

Soft Shift (2-1) – Intermediate clutch spring assembly not working. Center support snap ring not seated. Center support air bleed blocked.

Soft Shift (2-3) – Plugged direct clutch oil feed. Blocked direct lube exhaust port.

Soft Shift (3-2) – Direct clutch spring not working, small snap ring not seated or plugged check ball.

Soft Shift ("D3" To "D2") – Missing check ball. Incorrect orifice sizes.

No "D2" To "D1" Shift – Broken or disconnected rear band. Incomplete travel of detent lever.

No "D3" To "D2" Shift – Broken or disconnected front band.

No Converter Clutch Apply – Verify proper PCM or TCM operation and vehicle wiring. Damaged wiring harness or pinched wires. Brake switch not working or misadjusted. Solenoid inoperative. Oil pump valve assembly converter clutch shift valve stuck. Converter clutch apply valve stuck. Leaking solenoid "O" ring or blocked screen. Inspect torque converter for external leaks at hub weld area, or unbalanced or contaminated fluid. Turbine shaft seals damaged. Oil pump drive shaft seal damaged. Converter clutch release exhaust orifice cup plug not seated or damaged. Possible trouble Code 24, 27, 28, 37, 39, 53, 68, 75, 81 or 83.

Converter Clutch Does Not Release – PCM or TCM-controlled TCC solenoid stuck on or does not exhaust. Control valve assembly converter clutch apply valve stuck in apply position. Faulty PCM or TCM. Possible trouble Code 83.

Converter TCC Apply Soft Or Slipping – Leaking turbine shaft seals. Worn oil pump body bushing. Leaking oil hole transfer cup plug. Faulty TCC solenoid. Low fluid pressure.

Converter Clutch Apply Time Incorrect – Incorrect output speed sensor, engine speed or throttle position sensor signal. Faulty PCM or TCM. Faulty pressure switch or temperature sensor. Incorrect coolant or transmission temperature (diesel engine) signal. Possible trouble Code 14, 15, 21, 22, 24, 28, 58, 59 or 68. Problem with digital ratio adapter (2WD only). Faulty brake switch circuit or ignition module (gasoline vehicles) or faulty tachometer (diesel vehicles).

CLUTCH & BAND APPLICATION CHART

Selector Lever Position	Solenoid Positions	Elements In Use
"D" (Overdrive)		
1st Gear	"A" ON/"B" OFF	[1] Overdrive Roller Clutch, Forward Clutch, [2] Intermediate Sprag Clutch & Low Roller Clutch
2nd Gear	"A" OFF/"B" OFF	[1] Overdrive Roller Clutch, Forward Clutch, Intermediate Sprag Clutch, Intermediate Clutch & [3] Low Roller Clutch
3rd Gear	"A" OFF/"B" ON	[1] Overdrive Roller Clutch, Forward Clutch, Direct Clutch, [3] Intermediate Sprag Clutch, Intermediate Clutch & [3] Low Roller Clutch
Overdrive	"A" ON/"B" ON	4th Clutch, [3] Overdrive Roller Clutch, Forward Clutch, Direct Clutch, [3] Intermediate Sprag Clutch, Intermediate Clutch & [3] Low Roller Clutch
"D" (Manual 3rd)		
1st Gear	"A" ON/"B" OFF	Overrun Clutch, [1] Overdrive Roller Clutch, Forward Clutch, [2] Intermediate Sprag Clutch & [1] Low Roller Clutch
2nd Gear	"A" OFF/"B" OFF	Overrun Clutch, [1] Overdrive Roller Clutch, Forward Clutch, [1] Intermediate Sprag Clutch, Intermediate Clutch & [3] Low Roller Clutch
3rd Gear	"A" OFF/"B" ON	Overrun Clutch, [1] Overdrive Roller Clutch, Forward Clutch, Direct Clutch, [3] Intermediate Sprag Clutch, Intermediate Clutch & [3] Low Roller Clutch
"2" (Manual 2nd)		
1st Gear	"A" ON/"B" OFF	Overrun Clutch, [1] Overdrive Roller Clutch, Forward Clutch, [2] Intermediate Sprag Clutch & [1] Low Roller Clutch
2nd Gear	"A" OFF/"B" OFF	Overrun Clutch, [1] Overdrive Roller Clutch, Forward Clutch, Front Band, [1] Intermediate Sprag Clutch, Intermediate Clutch & [3] Low Roller Clutch
"1" (Manual Low)		
1st Gear	"A" ON/"B" OFF	Overrun Clutch, [1] Overdrive Roller Clutch, Forward Clutch, [2] Intermediate Sprag Clutch, [1] Low Roller Clutch & Rear Band
2nd Gear	"A" OFF/"B" OFF	Overrun Clutch, [1] Overdrive Roller Clutch, Forward Clutch, Front Band, [1] Intermediate Sprag Clutch, Intermediate Clutch & [3] Low Roller Clutch
"R" (Reverse)	"A" ON/"B" OFF	[1] Overdrive Roller Clutch, Direct Clutch & Rear Band
"N" Or "P" (Neutral Or Park)	"A" ON/"B" OFF	[1] Overdrive Roller Clutch; All Other Clutches & Bands Released Or Ineffective

[1] – Holding.
[2] – Applied but not effective.
[3] – Overrunning.

ELECTRONIC SELF-DIAGNOSTICS & ELECTRONIC TESTING

NOTE: Models with gasoline engines use Powertrain Control Module (PCM) computer. Models with diesel engines use Transmission Control Module (TCM) computer. These computers control hydraulic line pressure, shift solenoids "A" and "B", and TCC.

NOTE: For testing and diagnostic procedures of electronic components, see 4L80-E ELECTRONIC CONTROLS article in AUTOMATIC TRANSMISSIONS.

TESTING

ROAD TEST

NOTE: Before road testing vehicle, engine and transmission must be at operating temperature. Torque converter clutch will not engage if engine coolant has not reached operating temperature.

Gear Selector Position "D" (Overdrive) – **1)** With gear selector in "D" (overdrive) position, steadily increase throttle pressure to accelerate vehicle. Note shift speed engagement points in 2nd gear, 3rd gear and overdrive gear. Use shift speed charts as a reference for correct shift speeds. *See Figs. 2 and 3.* Also note when Torque Converter Clutch (TCC) engages while in 3rd gear or overdrive.

NOTE: Ensure TCC engages in 3rd gear or overdrive during the following steps. Transmission has a Pulse Width Modulated (PWM) solenoid, which may make TCC engagement point hard to detect. If necessary, a Tech 1 scan tool may be used to indicate TCC and shift solenoid operation.

2) At vehicle speeds of 40-50 MPH, quickly depress accelerator to half open position (part throttle detent downshift). TCC should release,

solenoid "A" turns off, and transmission should immediately downshift to 3rd gear.

3) At vehicle speeds of 40-50 MPH, quickly depress accelerator to wide open position (full throttle detent downshift). TCC should release, solenoids "A" and "B" turn off, and transmission should immediately downshift to 2nd gear.

4) At vehicle speeds of 40-55 MPH, release accelerator pedal while moving gear selector to "3" (3rd gear) position. TCC should release, transmission should downshift to 3rd gear, and engine braking should slow vehicle.

5) Move gear selector to "D" (overdrive) position, and accelerate to 40-45 MPH. Release accelerator pedal while moving gear selector to "2" (2nd gear) position. TCC should release, transmission should downshift to 2nd gear immediately, and engine braking should slow vehicle.

6) Move gear selector to "D" (overdrive) position, and accelerate to 30 MPH. Release accelerator pedal while moving gear selector to "1" (1st gear) position. TCC should release, transmission should downshift to 1st gear, and engine braking should slow vehicle.

7) With gear selector in "D" (overdrive) position, accelerate vehicle to overdrive gear with TCC applied. Release accelerator pedal, and lightly apply brakes. The TCC should release. Note speeds at which vehicle downshifts. *See Fig. 2 or 3.*

Gear Selector Position "3" (3rd Gear) – With vehicle stopped, move gear selector to "3" (3rd gear) position. Steadily increase throttle pressure to accelerate vehicle. Note speeds at which vehicle shifts into 2nd and 3rd gears. *See Fig. 2 or 3.* Ensure TCC engages while in 3rd gear.

Gear Selector Position "2" (2nd Gear) – With vehicle stopped, move gear selector to "2" (2nd gear) position. Accelerate vehicle, and note speed at which vehicle shifts from 1st gear to 2nd gear. Accelerate vehicle to 35 MPH. Transmission should not shift into 3rd gear, and TCC should not engage.

Gear Selector Position "1" (1st Gear) – With vehicle stopped, move gear selector to "1" (1st gear) position. Accelerate vehicle to 20 MPH. Transmission should not upshift, and TCC should not engage.

AUTOMATIC TRANSMISSIONS
Hydra-Matic 4L80-E (Cont.)

4.3L ENGINES			1-2 SHIFT +/-150 RPM					2-3 SHIFT +/-200 RPM					3-4 SHIFT +/-250 RPM					4-3 +/- 100 RPM	3-2 +/- 100 RPM	2-1 +/- 100 RPM
MODEL	BODY	TPS	10	20	30	40	50	10	20	30	40	50	10	20	30	40	50	0-10	0-10	0-10
ABP	P	TRAN RPM	560	672	769	950	1096	974	1159	1432	1739	1948	1705	1729	1924	2118	2313	1461	609	292
ABP, ACP	C, K	TRAN RPM	560	672	769	950	1096	1032	1242	1432	1739	1948	1705	1729	1924	2318	2630	1461	609	390
ADP, AJP	G	TRAN RPM	560	672	769	950	1096	974	1159	1432	1739	1948	2143	2143	2143	2289	2435	1705	609	438

5.7L ENGINES			1-2 SHIFT +/-150 RPM					2-3 SHIFT +/-200 RPM					3-4 SHIFT +/-250 RPM					4-3 +/- 100 RPM	3-2 +/- 100 RPM	2-1 +/- 100 RPM
MODEL	BODY	TPS	10	20	30	40	50	10	20	30	40	50	10	20	30	40	50	0-10	0-10	0-10
BSP, BUP, MJP	C, K	TRAN RPM	521	674	842	925	1023	939	1260	1500	1660	1810	1490	1760	2120	2380	2600	1350	744	419
BYP, BZP, JCP, MAP, MJP, MLP	G, P, ISUZU	TRAN RPM	465	550	660	770	880	884	1070	1274	1442	1628	1442	1632	1874	2148	2372	1302	744	395

6.2L ENGINES			1-2 SHIFT +/-150 RPM					2-3 SHIFT +/-200 RPM					3-4 SHIFT +/-250 RPM					4-3 +/- 100 RPM	3-2 +/- 100 RPM	2-1 +/- 100 RPM
MODEL	BODY	TPS	10	20	30	40	50	10	20	30	40	50	10	20	30	40	50	0-10	0-10	0-10
BAP, BJP, BMP, MBP, MCP	C, G, K, P	TRAN RPM	438	438	497	648	828	852	852	930	1213	1510	1266	1266	1403	1753	2167	1120	755	341
LAP	C, P	TRAN RPM	310	310	350	450	610	600	600	650	850	1090	880	880	980	1220	1510	780	530	240

6.5L ENGINES			1-2 SHIFT +/-150 RPM					2-3 SHIFT +/-200 RPM					3-4 SHIFT +/-250 RPM					4-3 +/- 100 RPM	3-2 +/- 100 RPM	2-1 +/- 100 RPM
MODEL	BODY	TPS	10	20	30	40	50	10	20	30	40	50	10	20	30	40	50	0-10	0-10	0-10
LAP, LFP, LLP	C, K	TRAN RPM	487	487	506	648	828	852	852	930	1213	1510	1266	1266	1403	1753	2167	1120	755	438

7.4L ENGINES			1-2 SHIFT +/-150 RPM					2-3 SHIFT +/-200 RPM					3-4 SHIFT +/-250 RPM					4-3 +/- 100 RPM	3-2 +/- 100 RPM	2-1 +/- 100 RPM
MODEL	BODY	TPS	10	20	30	40	50	10	20	30	40	50	10	20	30	40	50	0-10	0-10	0-10
DCP, DLP, DRP, MHP, TWP, TXP	C, G, K, P<12K	TRAN RPM	484	651	865	995	1070	990	1335	1576	1790	1930	1600	1897	2213	2497	2744	1302	651	419
DNP, DPP,	P>12K	TRAN RPM	553	660	865	995	1070	1083	1311	1590	1776	1907	1600	1897	2158	2427	2674	1302	651	419
DSP	C 5.6K	TRAN RPM	520	737	980	1212	1288	1000	1470	1894	2212	2348	1510	2081	2565	3040	3409	1313	732	404

NOTES: 1. All speeds given are in transmission output shaft RPM.
2. Speeds are based on percent of throttle position sensor opening.
3. Use a Tech 1 or other scan tester to monitor this data.

94G38295

Courtesy of General Motors Corp.

Fig. 2: Hydra-Matic 4L80-E Shift Speed Chart (1993)

4.3L ENGINES			1-2 SHIFT +/- 150 RPM			2-3 SHIFT +/- 200 RPM			3-4 SHIFT +/- 250 RPM			3-2 +/- 100 RPM	2-1 +/- 100 RPM	WOT 1-2
MODEL	BODY	TPS	10	25	50	10	25	50	10	25	50	0-10	0-10	
ABP, ACP, ADP, AFP, AHP	C, K P G	TRANS RPM	560	720	1100	1030	1340	1950	1700	1825	2630	610	390	1530

5.7L ENGINES			1-2 SHIFT +/- 150 RPM			2-3 SHIFT +/- 200 RPM			3-4 SHIFT +/- 250 RPM			3-2 +/- 100 RPM	2-1 +/- 100 RPM	WOT 1-2
MODEL	BODY	TPS	10	25	50	10	25	50	10	25	50	0-10	0-10	
BJP, BMP, BNP, JHP, MBP, MCP, MRP, MTP	C, K G, P ISUZU	TRANS RPM	520	775	1020	940	1380	1810	1490	1940	2600	740	420	1580

6.5L ENGINES			1-2 SHIFT +/- 150 RPM			2-3 SHIFT +/- 200 RPM			3-4 SHIFT +/- 250 RPM			3-2 +/- 100 RPM	2-1 +/- 100 RPM	WOT 1-2
MODEL	BODY	TPS	10	25	50	10	25	50	10	25	50	0-10	0-10	
LAP, LBP, LFP, LHP, LLP, LUP	G, P C, K	TRANS RPM	350	465	860	700	880	1510	1280	1345	2160	650	325	1260
LUP	DERATED P	TRANS RPM	360	385	720	700	730	1280	1040	1095	1780	620	280	920

7.4L ENGINES			1-2 SHIFT +/- 150 RPM			2-3 SHIFT +/- 200 RPM			3-4 SHIFT +/- 250 RPM			3-2 +/- 100 RPM	2-1 +/- 100 RPM	WOT 1-2
MODEL	BODY	TPS	10	25	50	10	25	50	10	25	50	0-10	0-10	
DLP, DNP, DPP, DRP, MSP, TWP, TXP	C, G, K, P	TRANS RPM	480	760	1070	990	1455	1930	1600	2055	2740	740	420	1530

NOTES: 1. All speeds given are in transmission output shaft RPM.
2. Speeds are based on percent of throttle position sensor opening.
3. Use a Tech 1 or other scan tester to monitor this data.

94H38296

Courtesy of General Motors Corp.

Fig. 3: Hydra-Matic 4L80-E Shift Speed Chart (1994)

HYDRAULIC PRESSURE TESTS

CAUTION: Parking and service brakes must be applied throughout hydraulic pressure test. Factory recommends using TECH 1 scan tool to test line pressure. Total time for testing should not exceed 2 minutes.

1) Before performing hydraulic pressure tests, check fluid level and condition. Check manual control linkages for correct adjustment. See appropriate article in TRANSMISSION SERVICING. Ensure engine is properly tuned.

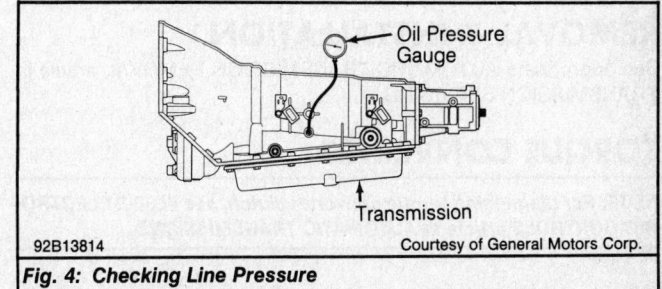

92B13814

Courtesy of General Motors Corp.

Fig. 4: Checking Line Pressure

2) Connect a tachometer to engine and an oil pressure gauge to line pressure test port. *See Fig. 4.* Compare line pressure to force motor current draw. See FORCE MOTOR VS. LINE PRESSURE table.

NOTE: Hydraulic pressure is controlled by pump output and regulated by computer-controlled force motor. Line pressure is boosted (pressure is doubled) by force motor in the "R" selector position.

Line Pressure Check – Start engine, and access OVERRIDE FORCE MOTOR on Tech 1 scan tool. Increase force motor current in .1-amp increments. Record line pressure readings and compare to specifications. See FORCE MOTOR VS. LINE PRESSURE table. If pressure recorded is incorrect, see HIGH OR LOW LINE PRESSURE under SYMPTOM DIAGNOSIS.

FORCE MOTOR VS. LINE PRESSURE

Force Motor Applied Current (Amps)	Line Pressure psi (kPa)
0.02	157-177 (1082-1220)
0.10	151-176 (1040-1213)
0.20	140-172 (965-1186)
0.30	137-162 (944-1117)
0.40	121-147 (834-1013)
0.50	102-131 (703-903)
0.60	88-113 (606-780)
0.70	63-93 (434-640)
0.80	43-73 (296-503)
0.90	37-61 (255-420)
0.98	35-55 (241-380)

ON-VEHICLE SERVICE

The following components can be serviced without removing transmission from vehicle:

- Converter-To-Flexplate Bolts
- Filler Pipe
- Front Servo
- Rear Servo
- Rear Extension Housing
- Shift Control Cable
- Solenoids
- Speedometer Driven Gear & Seal
- Speed Sensors
- Transmission Pan & Filter
- Valve Body
- Wiring Harness
- 3-4 Accumulator Assemblies

VALVE BODY

See OIL PUMP & VALVE BODY under TRANSMISSION DISASSEMBLY.

OIL COOLER FLUSHING

1) If available, fill line flusher with solution and install Oil Cooler and Line Flusher (J-35944) to top transaxle cooler line on transaxle. Follow manufacturer instructions to flush oil cooler and cooler lines.

2) If flusher tool is not available, flush cooler and cooler lines with a mixture of clean solvent and water. Flush cooler in both directions until all old fluid and debris are removed. If necessary, replace plugged or damaged cooler and/or lines.

REMOVAL & INSTALLATION

See appropriate AUTOMATIC TRANSMISSION REMOVAL article in TRANSMISSION SERVICING.

TORQUE CONVERTER

NOTE: For diagnosing torque converter clutch, see 4L80-E ELECTRONIC CONTROLS article in AUTOMATIC TRANSMISSIONS.

INSPECTION

Torque converter must be replaced for any of the following reasons.

- Damage To Pump Assembly
- Metal Particles Present In Oil
- Leaks In Hub Weld Area
- Crankshaft Pilot Broken Or Damaged
- Hub Scored Or Damaged
- Stator Failure
- Torque Converter Imbalance
- Engine Coolant Contamination
- Excessive End Play

END PLAY CHECK

Mount Torque Converter End Play Fixture (J-35138) and Dial Gauge (J-8001) on stand to check end play. End play should be 0-.024" (0-0.60 mm). *See Fig. 5.*

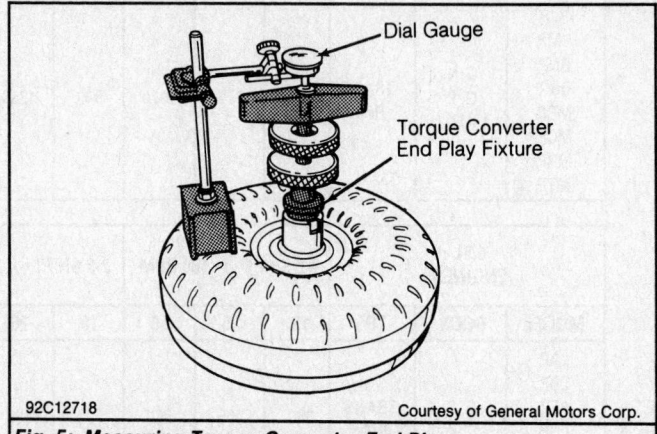

92C12718   Courtesy of General Motors Corp.

Fig. 5: Measuring Torque Converter End Play

TRANSMISSION DISASSEMBLY

SPEED SENSORS/REAR HOUSING

Thoroughly clean transmission exterior. Drain fluid, and remove torque converter. Place transmission in holding fixture. Remove rear extension housing. Remove speed sensors.

LOWER TRANSMISSION ASSEMBLY

Remove oil pan and oil filter. Remove accumulator assembly. *See Fig. 45.* Remove valve body assembly. *See Fig. 46.* Remove check balls from case. *See Fig. 59.* Remove wiring harness. *See Fig. 61.* Remove parking pawl and manual linkage. *See Fig. 6.*

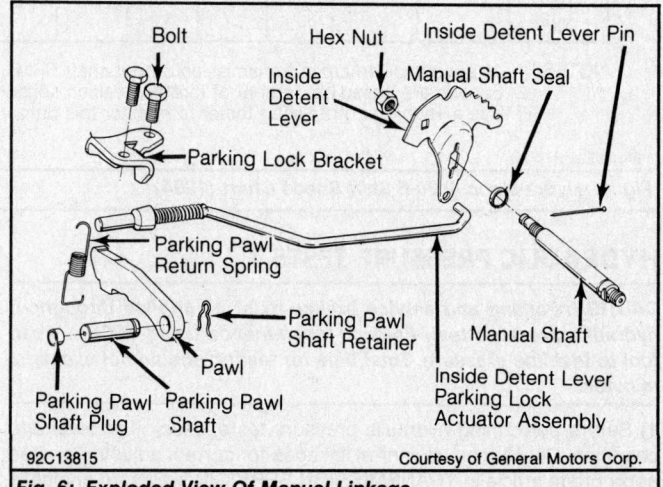

92C13815   Courtesy of General Motors Corp.

Fig. 6: Exploded View Of Manual Linkage

SERVO ASSEMBLIES

Remove servo covers and assemblies. *See Figs. 44 and 58.*
Rear Band Apply Pin Selection – 1) Install Band Apply Selector Pin (J-21370-10) into servo bore. *See Fig. 7.* Mount Band Apply Pin Selector Gauge (J-38737) and selector pin on transmission. *See Fig. 8.* Apply 25 ft. lbs. (34 N.m) of torque to hex nut on gauge.
2) Note which step on selector pin lines up with top edge of apply pin gauge; use this information to determine pin length. *See Figs. 7 and 9.* Record length for reassembly. Pins are available in various lengths. *See Fig. 9.*

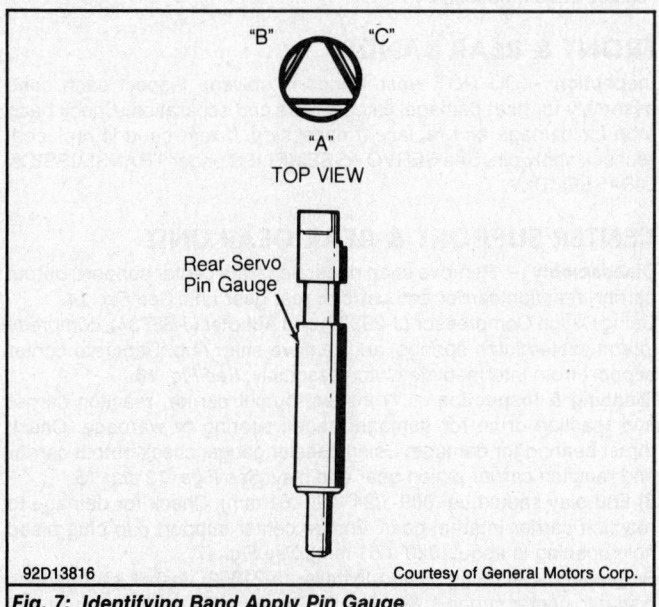

Courtesy of General Motors Corp.

92D13816

Fig. 7: Identifying Band Apply Pin Gauge

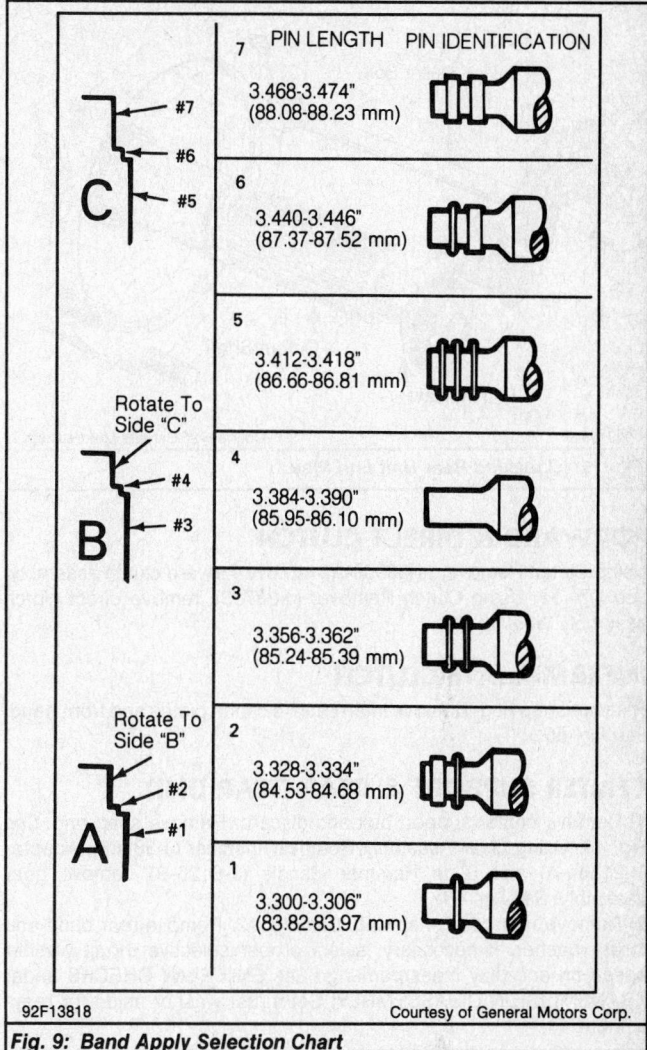

92F13818   Courtesy of General Motors Corp.

Fig. 9: Band Apply Selection Chart

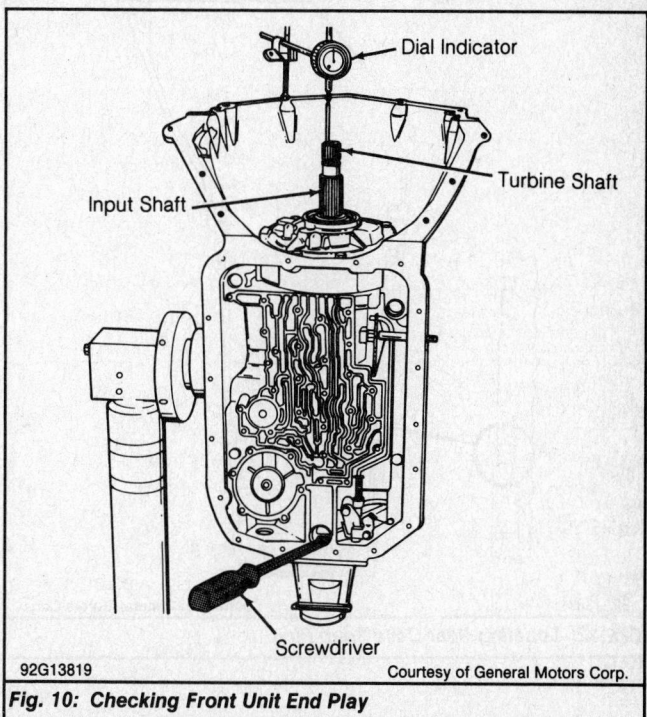

92E13817   Courtesy of General Motors Corp.

Fig. 8: Checking Band Apply Pin Length

END PLAY CHECKS

Using Dial Indicator (J-8001), check front and rear unit end play. *See Figs. 10 and 11.* Front unit end play should be .004-.022" (.10-.56 mm). Rear unit end play should be .005-.025" (.13-.63 mm). Record measurements for reassembly reference.

OIL PUMP & VALVE BODY

Remove oil pump assembly cover bolts. Remove oil pump assembly, gasket and thrust washer. *See Fig. 57.* Remove valve body assembly. *See Fig. 46.*

OVERDRIVE ASSEMBLY & 4TH CLUTCH

Remove turbine shaft and overdrive assembly. *See Fig. 33.* Using 40T Torx wrench, remove 4th clutch support bolt and discard. *See Fig. 49.* Remove 4th clutch snap ring and assembly. *See Fig. 55.*

92G13819   Courtesy of General Motors Corp.

Fig. 10: Checking Front Unit End Play

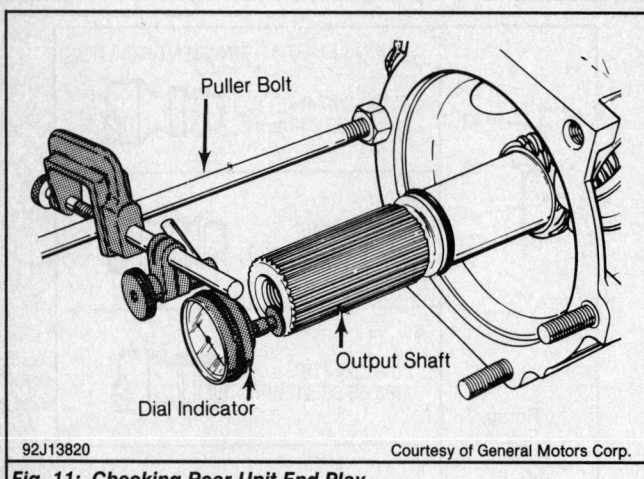

Fig. 11: Checking Rear Unit End Play

FORWARD & DIRECT CLUTCH

Using Clutch Remover (J-38358-A), remove forward clutch assembly. See Fig. 52. Using Clutch Remover (J-38733), remove direct clutch assembly. See Fig. 51.

INTERMEDIATE CLUTCH

Remove snap ring. Remove intermediate clutch plates and front band. See Fig. 50.

CENTER SUPPORT & REAR GEAR UNIT

1) Remove center support bolt and discard. Remove snap ring. See Fig. 49. Using Gear Assembly Remover/Installer (J-38868), Adapter (J-21364-A) and Slide Hammer Handle (J-6125-B), remove gear assembly. See Fig. 48.

2) Remove rear case snap ring. See Fig. 12. Remove rear band and thrust washer. If necessary, select proper selective thrust washer based on end play measurements. See END PLAY CHECKS under TRANSMISSION DISASSEMBLY. Set thrust washer aside for reassembly.

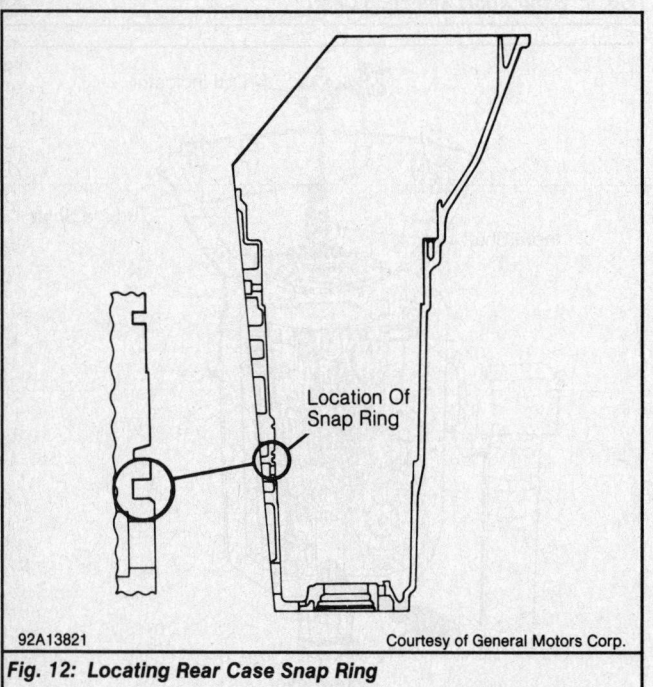

Fig. 12: Locating Rear Case Snap Ring

COMPONENT DISASSEMBLY & REASSEMBLY

TRANSMISSION CASE

Cleaning & Inspection – Thoroughly clean transmission case with solvent and dry using compressed air. Inspect transmission case for damage to band lugs, snap ring grooves, drive sprocket bearings, interconnected or damaged oil passages and servo bores. Inspect case for stripped threads in bolt holes or casting porosity. Repair or replace case if necessary.

FRONT & REAR BANDS

Inspection – DO NOT wash bands in solvent. Inspect each band assembly for heat damage, lining cracks and separation. Check band stop for damage and replace if necessary. If rear band is replaced, recheck apply pin. See SERVO ASSEMBLIES under TRANSMISSION DISASSEMBLY.

CENTER SUPPORT & REAR GEAR UNIT

Disassembly – Remove snap rings. Separate center support, output carrier, reaction carrier and parts of rear gear unit. See Fig. 14.
Using Clutch Compressor (J-23327) and Adapter (J-38734), compress intermediate clutch springs, and remove snap ring. Separate center support from intermediate clutch assembly. See Fig. 16.

Cleaning & Inspection – 1) Inspect output carrier, reaction carrier and reaction drum for damaged teeth, scoring or warpage. Check thrust bearing for damage. Using a feeler gauge, check output carrier and reaction carrier pinion gear end play. See Figs. 13 and 15.

2) End play should be .009-.024" (.23-.61 mm). Check for damage to reaction carrier internal gear. Ensure center support cup plug bleed hole opening is about .020" (.51 mm). See Fig. 17.

Reassembly – Using Piston Installer (J-21362), install intermediate piston to center support. See Fig. 18. Reassemble center support and rear gear unit. See Figs. 19-22. Install new oil seal rings to center support.

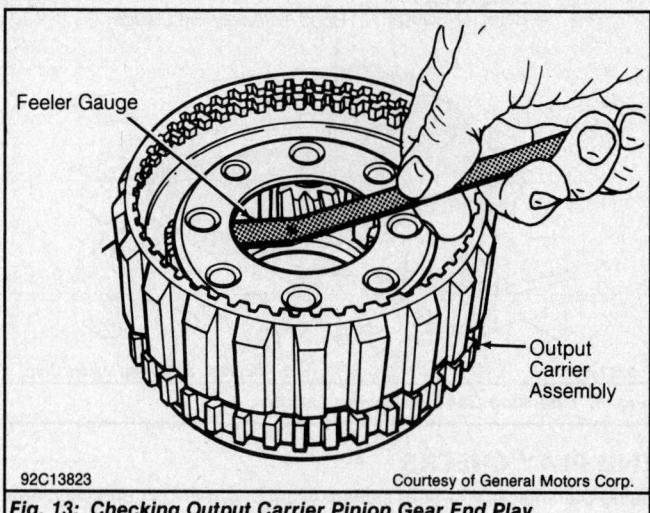

Fig. 13: Checking Output Carrier Pinion Gear End Play

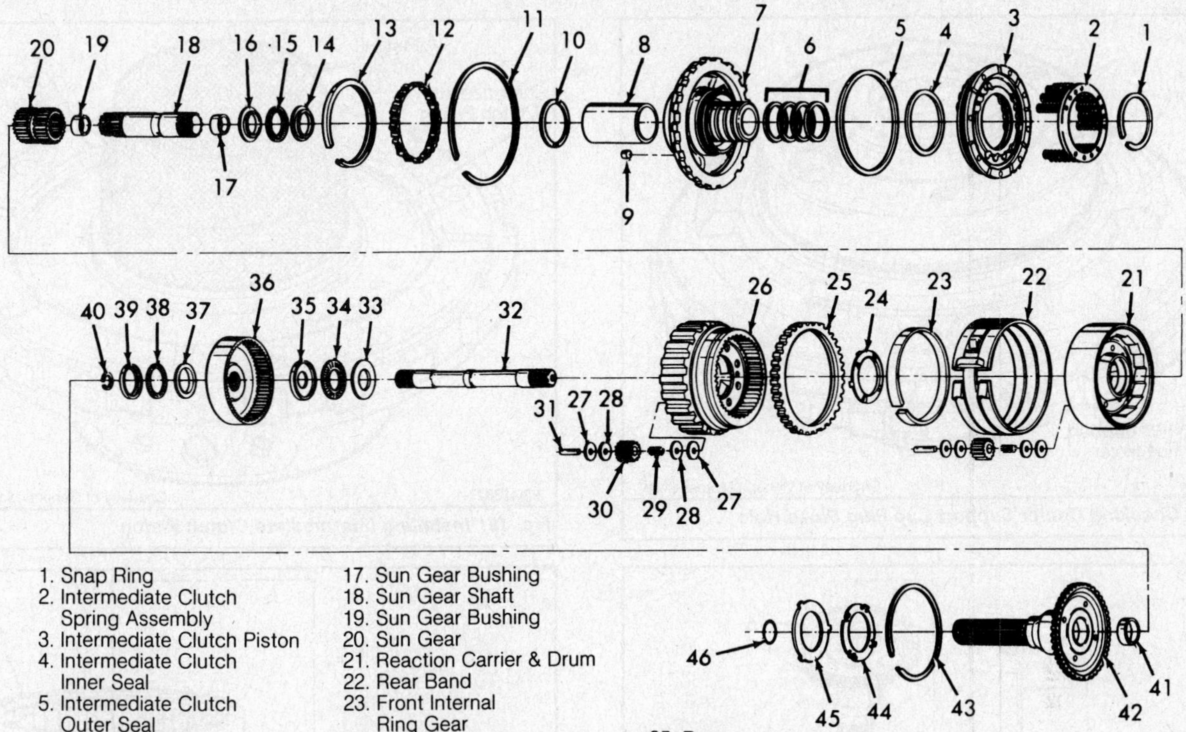

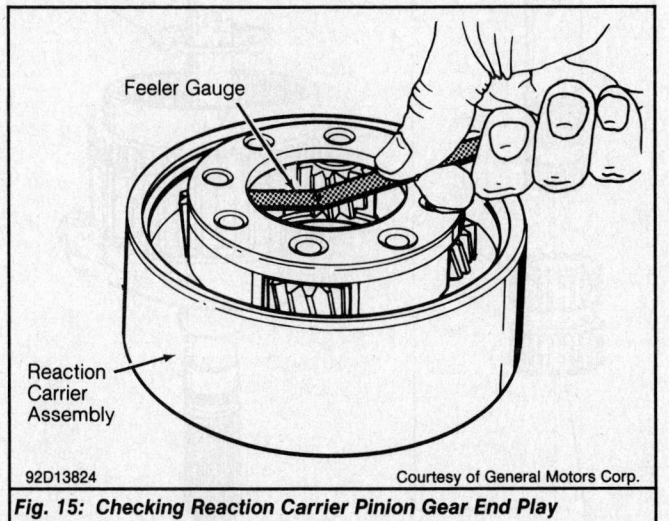

1. Snap Ring
2. Intermediate Clutch Spring Assembly
3. Intermediate Clutch Piston
4. Intermediate Clutch Inner Seal
5. Intermediate Clutch Outer Seal
6. Oil Seal Rings
7. Center Support
8. Center Support Bushing
9. Center Support Orifice Plug
10. Thrust Washer
11. Spacer Ring
12. Roller Clutch Assembly
13. Spacer Ring
14. Thrust Bearing Race
15. Needle Bearing
16. Race
17. Sun Gear Bushing
18. Sun Gear Shaft
19. Sun Gear Bushing
20. Sun Gear
21. Reaction Carrier & Drum
22. Rear Band
23. Front Internal Ring Gear
24. Washer
25. Output Speed Sensor Gear
26. Output Carrier
27. Thrust Washer
28. Thrust Washer (Steel)
29. Needle Bearings
30. Pinion
31. Pinion Pin
32. Main Shaft
33. Thrust Bearing Race
34. Needle Bearing
35. Race
36. Rear Internal Gear
37. Bearing Race
38. Needle Bearing
39. Bearing Race
40. Snap Ring
41. Output Shaft Bushing
42. Output Shaft
43. Snap Ring
44. Thrust Washer
45. Selective Thrust Washer
46. Output Shaft Seal (Some Models)

92B13822

Courtesy of General Motors Corp.

Fig. 14: Exploded View Of Center Support & Rear Gear Unit

92D13824

Courtesy of General Motors Corp.

Fig. 15: Checking Reaction Carrier Pinion Gear End Play

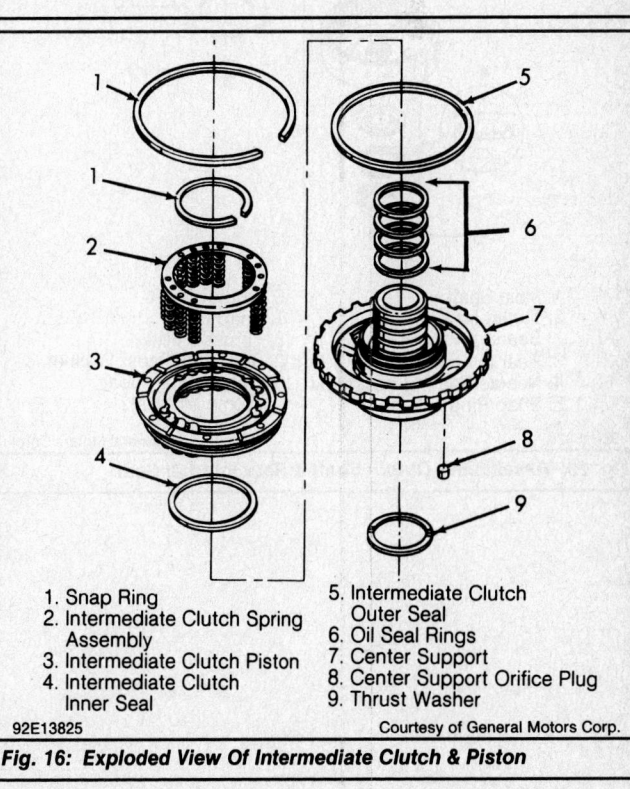

1. Snap Ring
2. Intermediate Clutch Spring Assembly
3. Intermediate Clutch Piston
4. Intermediate Clutch Inner Seal
5. Intermediate Clutch Outer Seal
6. Oil Seal Rings
7. Center Support
8. Center Support Orifice Plug
9. Thrust Washer

92E13825

Courtesy of General Motors Corp.

Fig. 16: Exploded View Of Intermediate Clutch & Piston

AUTOMATIC TRANSMISSIONS
Hydra-Matic 4L80-E (Cont.)

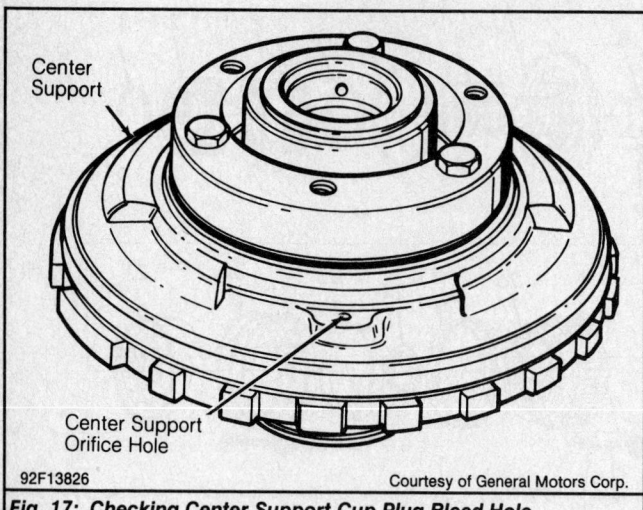

92F13826   Courtesy of General Motors Corp.

Fig. 17: Checking Center Support Cup Plug Bleed Hole

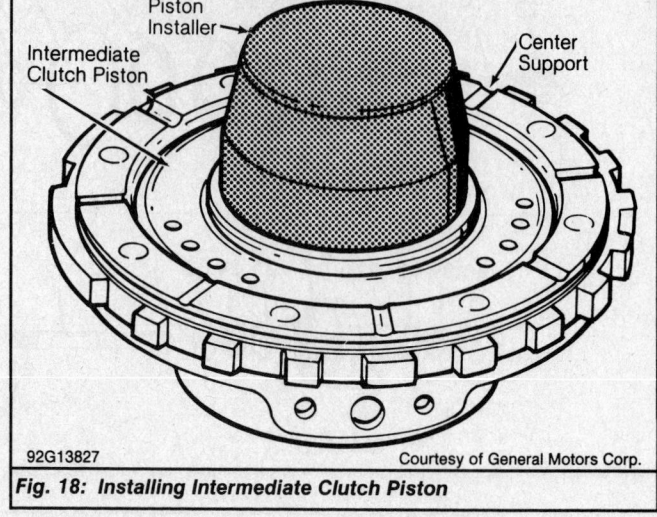

92G13827   Courtesy of General Motors Corp.

Fig. 18: Installing Intermediate Clutch Piston

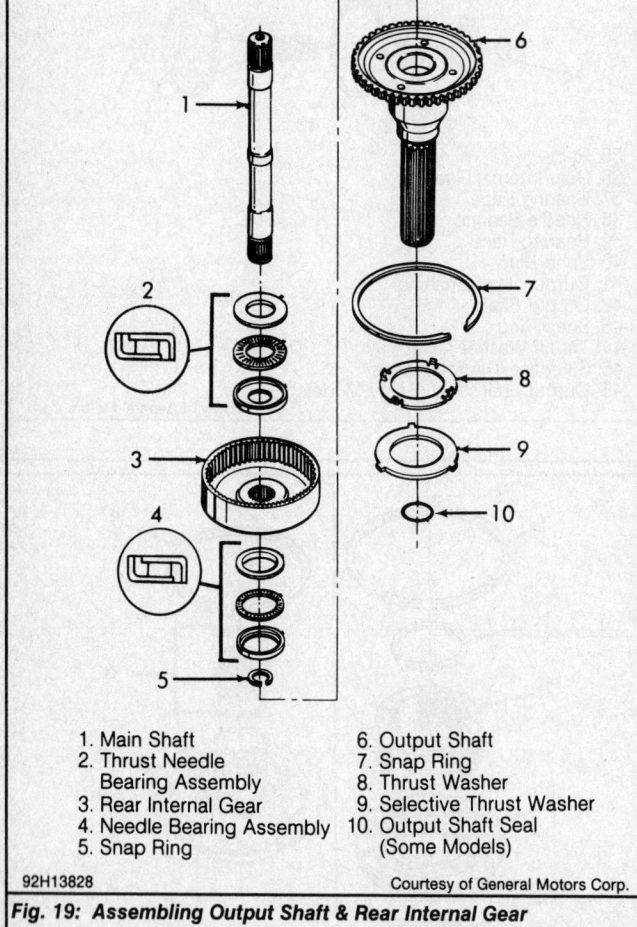

1. Main Shaft
2. Thrust Needle Bearing Assembly
3. Rear Internal Gear
4. Needle Bearing Assembly
5. Snap Ring
6. Output Shaft
7. Snap Ring
8. Thrust Washer
9. Selective Thrust Washer
10. Output Shaft Seal (Some Models)

92H13828   Courtesy of General Motors Corp.

Fig. 19: Assembling Output Shaft & Rear Internal Gear

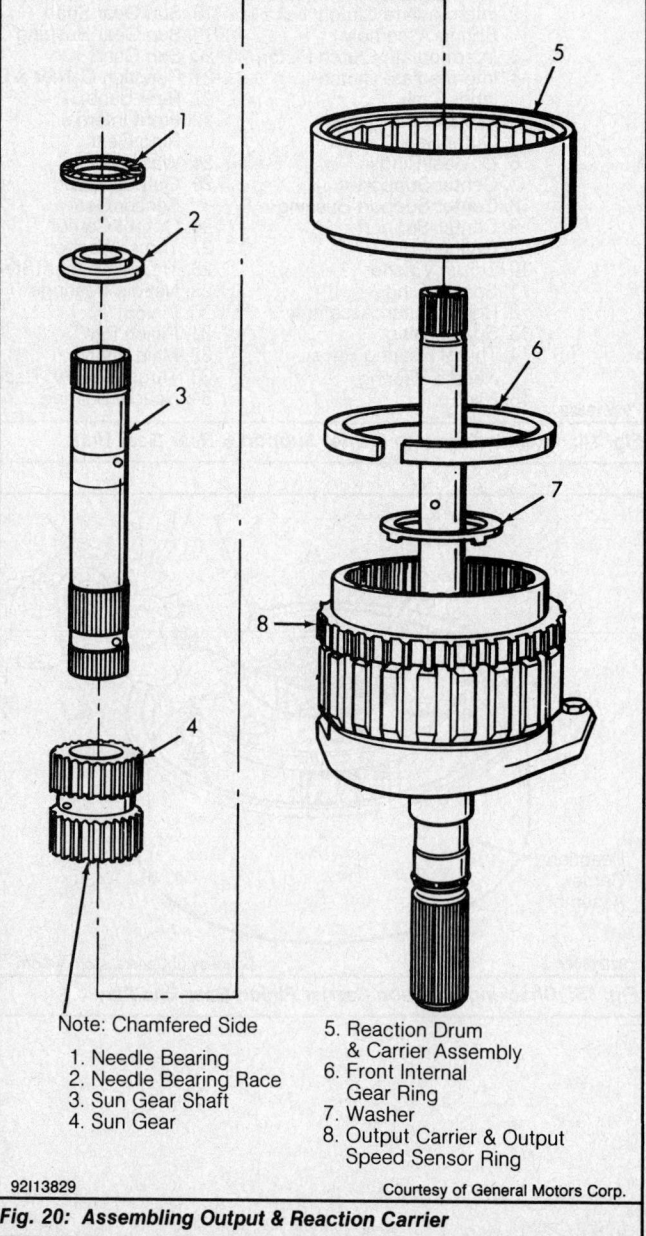

Note: Chamfered Side

1. Needle Bearing
2. Needle Bearing Race
3. Sun Gear Shaft
4. Sun Gear
5. Reaction Drum & Carrier Assembly
6. Front Internal Gear Ring
7. Washer
8. Output Carrier & Output Speed Sensor Ring

92I13829   Courtesy of General Motors Corp.

Fig. 20: Assembling Output & Reaction Carrier

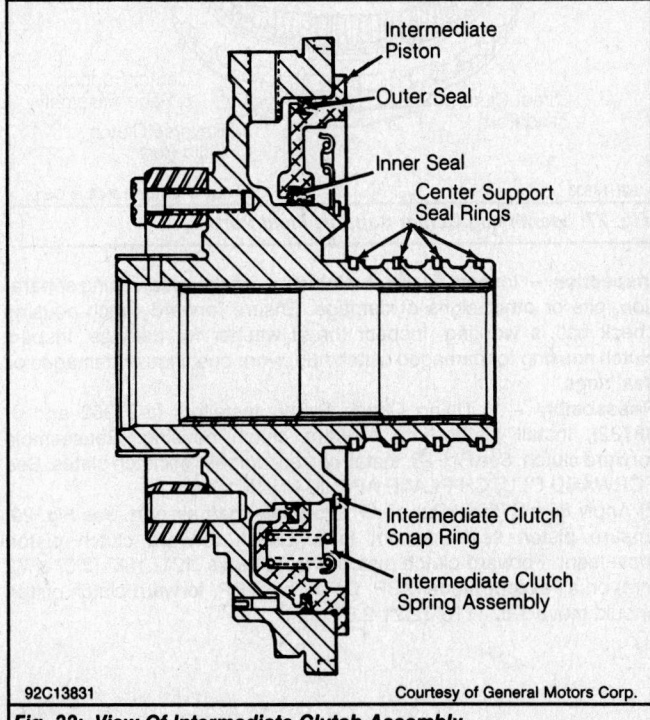

1. Snap Ring
2. Center Support
3. Snap Ring
4. Thrust Bearing Race
5. Thrust Washer
6. Roller Clutch Assembly
7. Snap Ring/Spacer
8. Sun Gear Shaft
9. Output Carrier & Output Speed Sensor Ring

92B13830

Courtesy of General Motors Corp.

Fig. 21: Assembling Center Support & Roller Clutch Assemblies

Intermediate Piston
Outer Seal
Inner Seal
Center Support Seal Rings
Intermediate Clutch Snap Ring
Intermediate Clutch Spring Assembly

92C13831

Courtesy of General Motors Corp.

Fig. 22: View Of Intermediate Clutch Assembly

DIRECT CLUTCH ASSEMBLY

Disassembly – Disassemble intermediate sprag clutch assembly. Discard the spiral snap ring. Remove the direct clutch pack. See Fig. 23. Using Clutch Compressor (J-23327) and Adapter (J-25018-A), compress direct clutch springs, and remove snap ring.

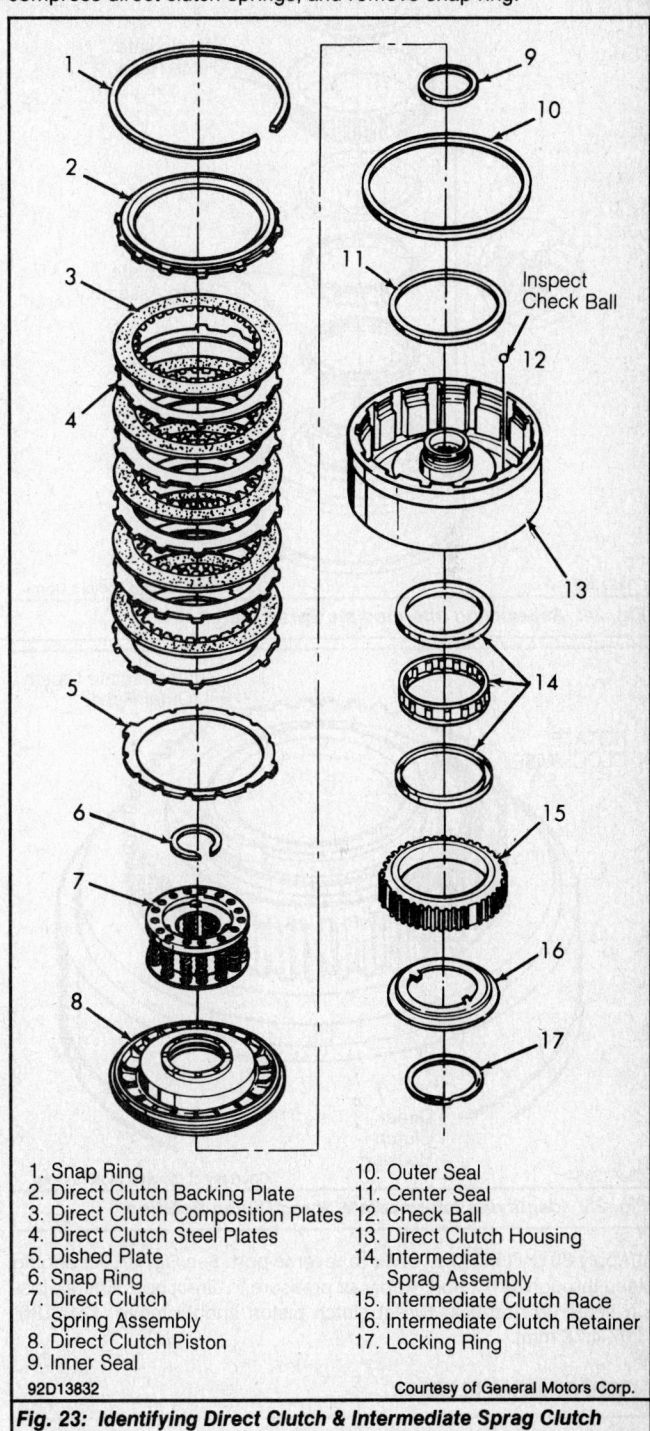

Inspect Check Ball

1. Snap Ring
2. Direct Clutch Backing Plate
3. Direct Clutch Composition Plates
4. Direct Clutch Steel Plates
5. Dished Plate
6. Snap Ring
7. Direct Clutch Spring Assembly
8. Direct Clutch Piston
9. Inner Seal
10. Outer Seal
11. Center Seal
12. Check Ball
13. Direct Clutch Housing
14. Intermediate Sprag Assembly
15. Intermediate Clutch Race
16. Intermediate Clutch Retainer
17. Locking Ring

92D13832

Courtesy of General Motors Corp.

Fig. 23: Identifying Direct Clutch & Intermediate Sprag Clutch

Inspection – Inspect all parts for wear, cracks, burned plates and scoring; replace if necessary.

Reassembly – **1)** Reassemble intermediate sprag clutch. See Fig. 24. Install new spiral snap ring. Ensure intermediate sprag rotates clockwise only. See Fig. 25.

2) Using Clutch Piston Installers (J-21362 and J-38732), install piston into direct clutch housing. Reassemble direct clutch. Direct clutch uses 5 steel plates, 5 composition plates and one dished plate. See Figs. 23 and 26.

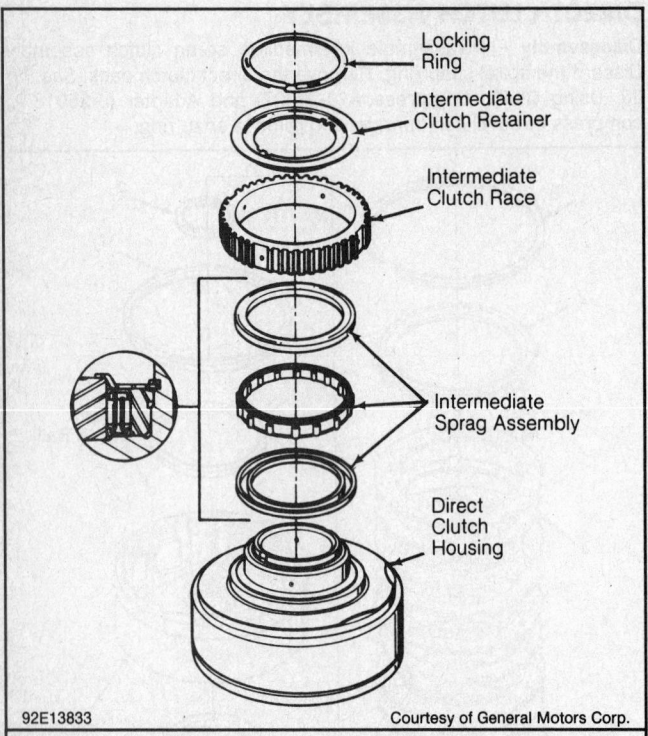

Locking Ring
Intermediate Clutch Retainer
Intermediate Clutch Race
Intermediate Sprag Assembly
Direct Clutch Housing

92E13833   Courtesy of General Motors Corp.

Fig. 24: Assembling Intermediate Sprag Clutch

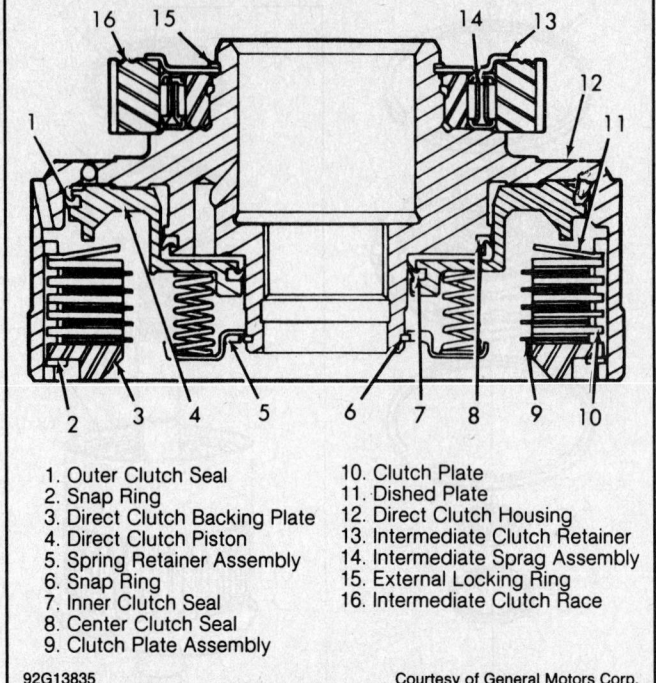

1. Outer Clutch Seal
2. Snap Ring
3. Direct Clutch Backing Plate
4. Direct Clutch Piston
5. Spring Retainer Assembly
6. Snap Ring
7. Inner Clutch Seal
8. Center Clutch Seal
9. Clutch Plate Assembly
10. Clutch Plate
11. Dished Plate
12. Direct Clutch Housing
13. Intermediate Clutch Retainer
14. Intermediate Sprag Assembly
15. External Locking Ring
16. Intermediate Clutch Race

92G13835   Courtesy of General Motors Corp.

Fig. 26: View Of Direct Clutch & Intermediate Sprag Clutch

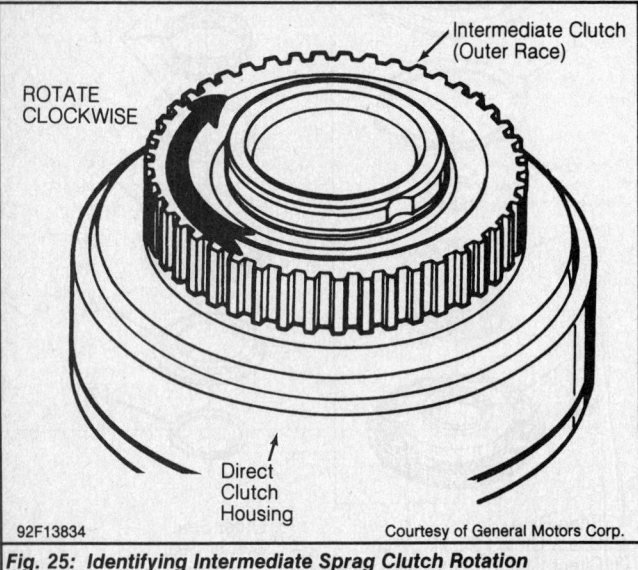

Intermediate Clutch (Outer Race)
ROTATE CLOCKWISE
Direct Clutch Housing

92F13834   Courtesy of General Motors Corp.

Fig. 25: Identifying Intermediate Sprag Clutch Rotation

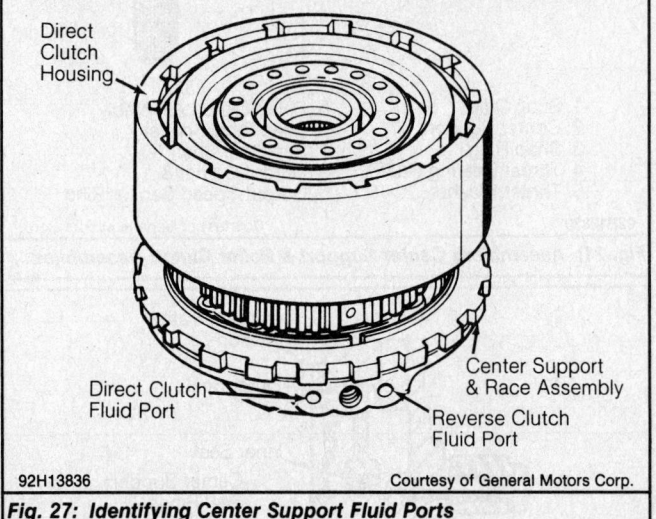

Direct Clutch Housing
Direct Clutch Fluid Port
Center Support & Race Assembly
Reverse Clutch Fluid Port

92H13836   Courtesy of General Motors Corp.

Fig. 27: Identifying Center Support Fluid Ports

3) Apply 80 psi (550 kPa) of air to reverse port. *See Fig. 27.* Air should bleed through direct port. Apply air pressure to direct port. Ensure piston seals do not leak. Direct clutch piston should move .121-.186" (3.07-4.72 mm).

FORWARD CLUTCH

NOTE: Prior to checking Forward Clutch piston movement, check identification plate attached to rear of transmission case. Units with ZBP identification are set to a different specification.

Disassembly – Disassemble forward clutch assembly. *See Fig. 28.* Using Clutch Spring Compressor (J-23327-1), compress and remove spring retainer. *See Fig. 30.* Remove clutch piston and seals from piston.

Inspection – Inspect all clutch plates for cracks, wear, lining separation, pits or other signs of damage. Ensure forward clutch housing check ball is working. Inspect thrust washer for damage. Inspect clutch housing for damaged clutch hub, worn bushings or damaged oil seal rings.

Reassembly – 1) Using Clutch Piston Installers (J-21362 and J-38732), install piston into forward clutch housing. Reassemble forward clutch. *See Fig. 28.* Install correct number of clutch plates. See FORWARD CLUTCH PLATE APPLICATION table.

2) Apply 80 psi (550 kPa) of air to turbine shaft air port. *See Fig. 29.* Ensure piston seals do not leak. Check forward clutch piston movement. Forward clutch piston should move .121-.186" (3.07-4.72 mm) on all except model ZBP. On model ZBP, forward clutch piston should move .087-.110" (2.21-2.81 mm).

FORWARD CLUTCH PLATE APPLICATION

Application	Quantity
Except Model ZBP	
Flat Steel Plate	5
Composition Plate	5
Dished Steel Plate	1
Model ZBP	
Flat Steel Plate	4
Composition Plate	5
Waved Steel Plate	1

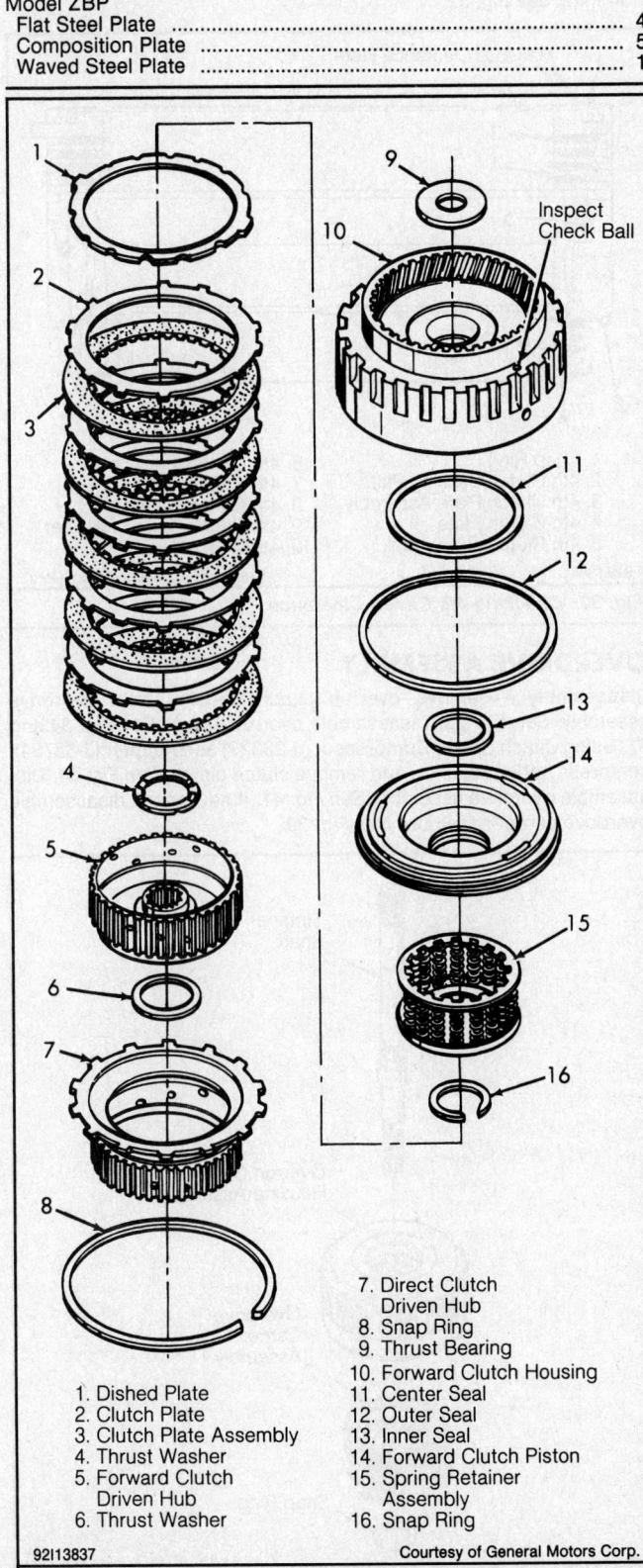

1
2
3
4
5
6
7
8
9
10
Inspect
Check Ball
11
12
13
14
15
16
1. Dished Plate
2. Clutch Plate
3. Clutch Plate Assembly
4. Thrust Washer
5. Forward Clutch Driven Hub
6. Thrust Washer
7. Direct Clutch Driven Hub
8. Snap Ring
9. Thrust Bearing
10. Forward Clutch Housing
11. Center Seal
12. Outer Seal
13. Inner Seal
14. Forward Clutch Piston
15. Spring Retainer Assembly
16. Snap Ring
92I13837
Courtesy of General Motors Corp.

Fig. 28: Exploded View Of Forward Clutch Assembly

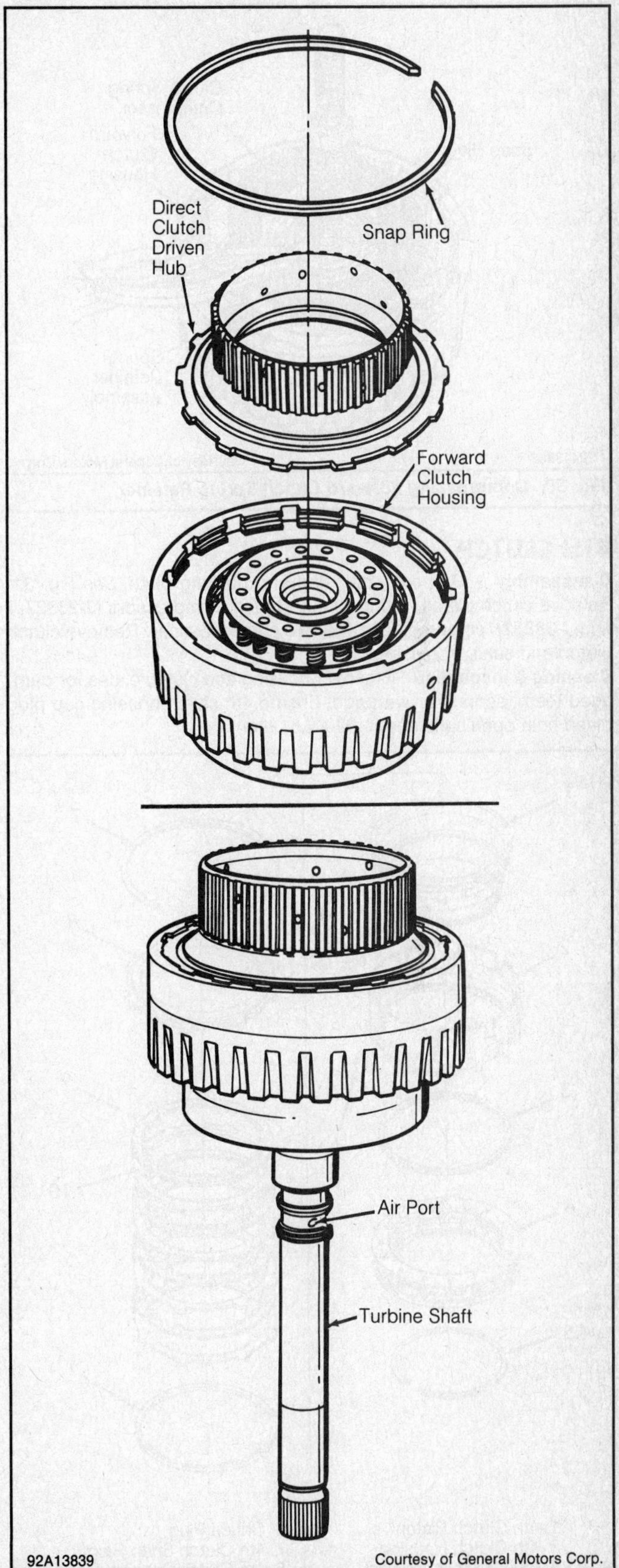

Direct
Clutch
Driven
Hub
Snap Ring
Forward
Clutch
Housing
Air Port
Turbine Shaft
92A13839
Courtesy of General Motors Corp.

Fig. 29: Checking Forward Clutch

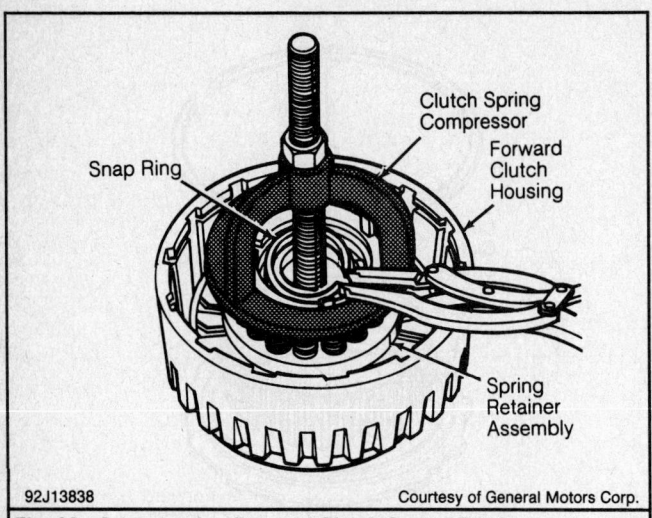

92J13838   Courtesy of General Motors Corp.

Fig. 30: Compressing Forward Clutch Spring Retainer

4TH CLUTCH

Disassembly – Remove snap ring and backing plate. *See Fig. 31.* Remove clutch plates. Using Clutch Spring Compressors (J-23327-1 and J-38882), compress and remove spring retainer. Remove clutch piston and seals from piston.

Cleaning & Inspection – Inspect housing and clutch plates for damaged teeth, scoring or warpage. Ensure 4th clutch housing cup plug bleed hole opening is about .020" (.51 mm).

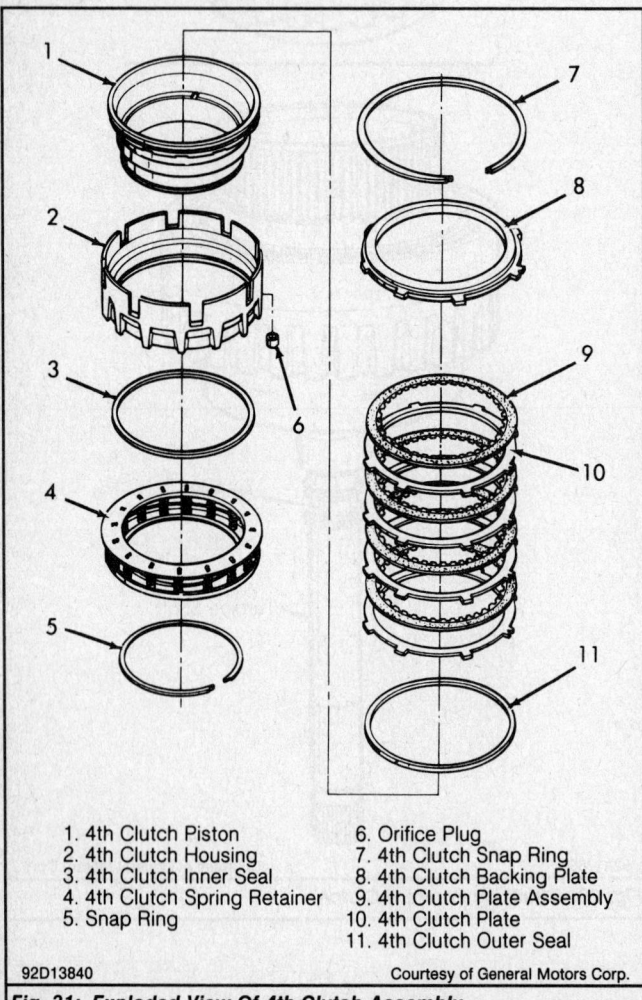

1. 4th Clutch Piston	6. Orifice Plug
2. 4th Clutch Housing	7. 4th Clutch Snap Ring
3. 4th Clutch Inner Seal	8. 4th Clutch Backing Plate
4. 4th Clutch Spring Retainer	9. 4th Clutch Plate Assembly
5. Snap Ring	10. 4th Clutch Plate
	11. 4th Clutch Outer Seal

92D13840   Courtesy of General Motors Corp.

Fig. 31: Exploded View Of 4th Clutch Assembly

Reassembly – **1)** Using Piston Seal Protectors (J-38731-1, J-38731-2 and J-38731-3), install piston into 4th clutch housing. Reassemble 4th clutch assembly. *See Fig. 31.*

2) Install snap ring. Install 4 steel and 4 composition plates. Ensure steel plate notches are indexed opposite 4th clutch bolt hole. Ensure clearance between backing plate and snap ring is .040-.100" (1.01-2.54 mm). *See Fig. 32.*

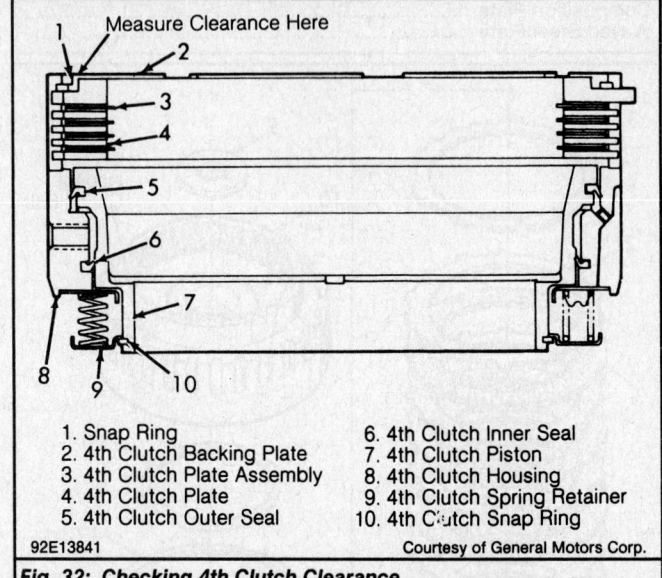

1. Snap Ring	6. 4th Clutch Inner Seal
2. 4th Clutch Backing Plate	7. 4th Clutch Piston
3. 4th Clutch Plate Assembly	8. 4th Clutch Housing
4. 4th Clutch Plate	9. 4th Clutch Spring Retainer
5. 4th Clutch Outer Seal	10. 4th Clutch Snap Ring

92E13841   Courtesy of General Motors Corp.

Fig. 32: Checking 4th Clutch Clearance

OVERDRIVE ASSEMBLY

Disassembly – Remove overrun clutch housing from overdrive assembly. *See Fig. 33.* Disassemble overrun clutch. *See Fig. 34 and 41.* Using Clutch Spring Compressor (J-23327) and Adapter (J-38734), compress spring retainer, and remove clutch piston. *See Fig. 34.* Disassemble overdrive assembly. *See Fig. 41.* If necessary, disassemble overdrive carrier assembly. *See Fig. 39.*

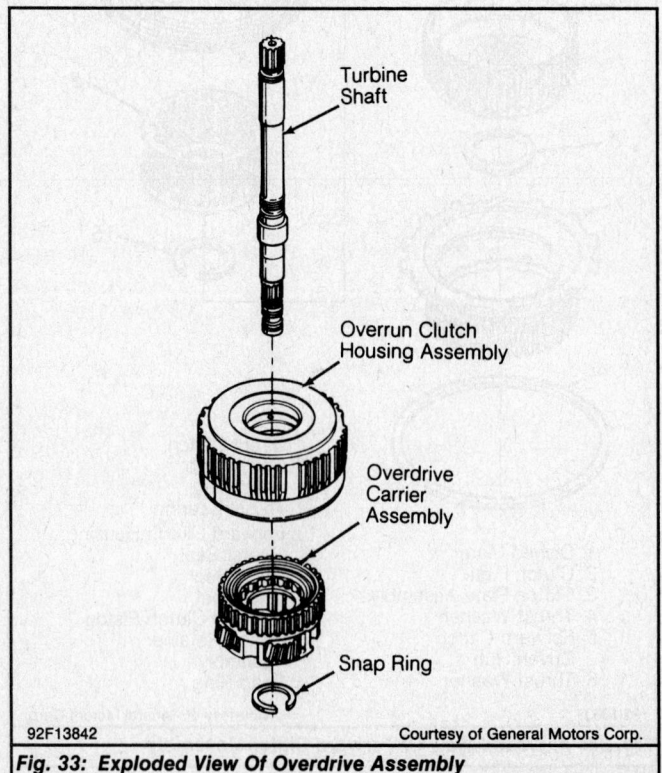

92F13842   Courtesy of General Motors Corp.

Fig. 33: Exploded View Of Overdrive Assembly

Inspection – Inspect housing and clutch plates for damaged teeth, scoring or warpage. Inspect spring and spring retainer for damage. Inspect overdrive carrier assembly and turbine shaft for wear or damage. Replace if necessary. Ensure end play of overdrive carrier pinions is .009-.024" (.23-.61 mm). *See Fig. 36.*

Turbine Shaft Seal Replacement – **1)** Remove oil seal rings from turbine shaft. Inspect seal ring grooves for nicks or burrs. Lubricate each oil seal ring. Place Seal Protector/Installer Kit (J-38736) on turbine shaft.

2) Quickly slide each seal into ring groove when protector is in position. Use seal driver from Kit (J-38736) to push ring over seal protector. Size seal with seal sizer from Kit (J-38736); gently twist seal sizer over each seal. Leave sizer in place.

Reassembly – **1)** Using Piston Seal Protector (J-38729), install piston into overrun clutch housing. *See Fig. 35.* Reassemble overrun clutch assembly. *See Fig. 34.*

2) Install snap ring. Install 3 steel and 3 composition plates. Ensure clearance between backing plate and snap ring is .033-.094" (.838-2.39 mm). *See Fig. 37.*

3) If necessary, reassemble overdrive carrier. *See Figs. 38, 39 and 41.* Install thrust washer to overdrive carrier. *See Fig. 38.* To complete reassembly, install turbine shaft and overdrive carrier to overrun clutch. *See Figs. 33 and 41.*

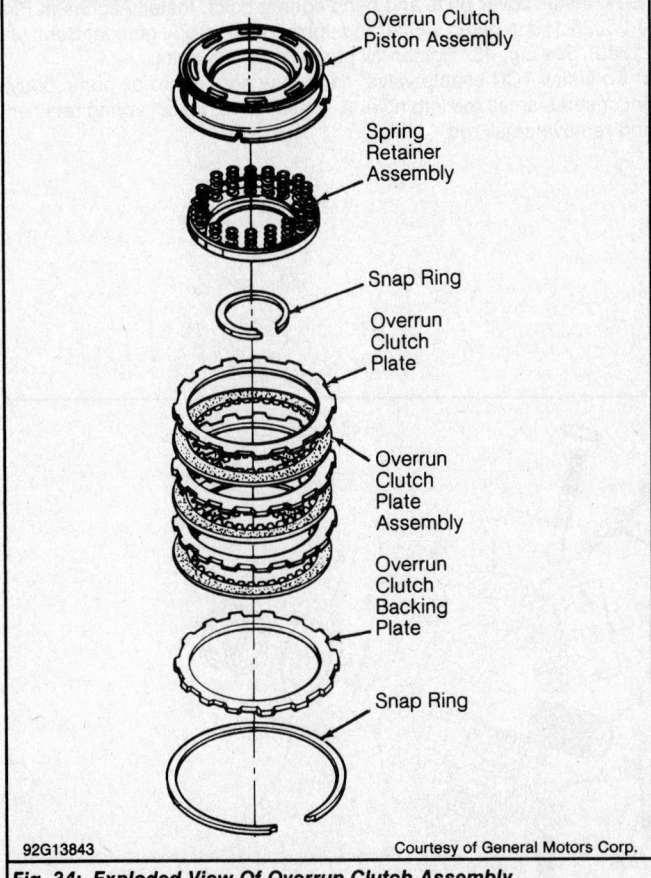

92G13843   Courtesy of General Motors Corp.

Fig. 34: Exploded View Of Overrun Clutch Assembly

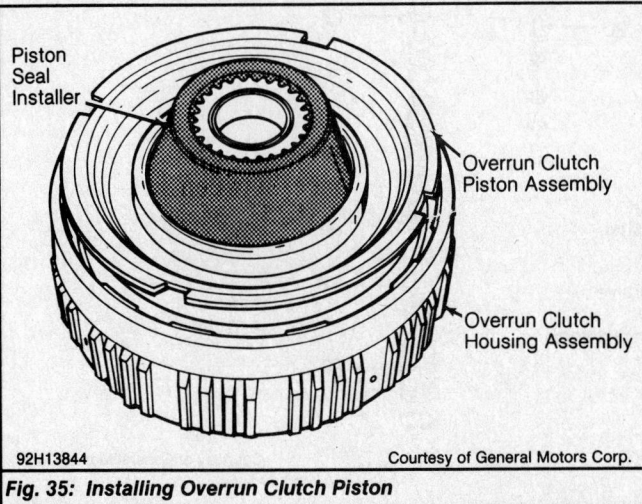

92H13844   Courtesy of General Motors Corp.

Fig. 35: Installing Overrun Clutch Piston

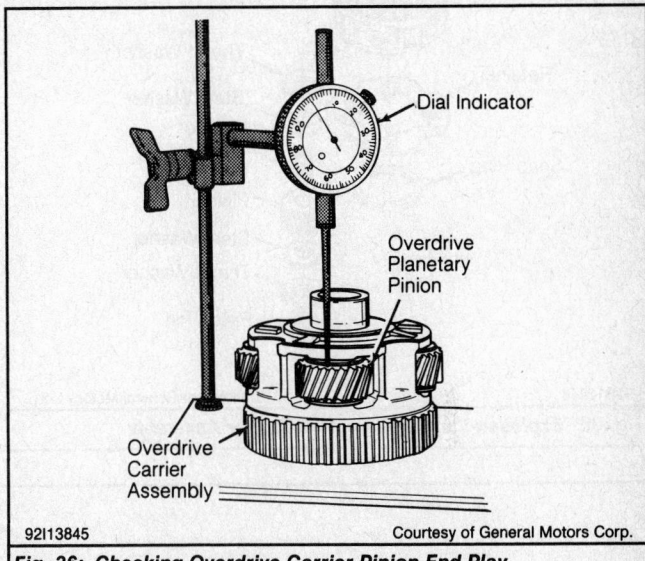

92I13845   Courtesy of General Motors Corp.

Fig. 36: Checking Overdrive Carrier Pinion End Play

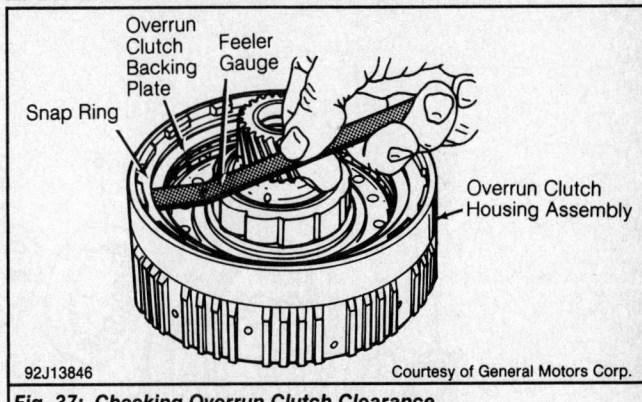

92J13846   Courtesy of General Motors Corp.

Fig. 37: Checking Overrun Clutch Clearance

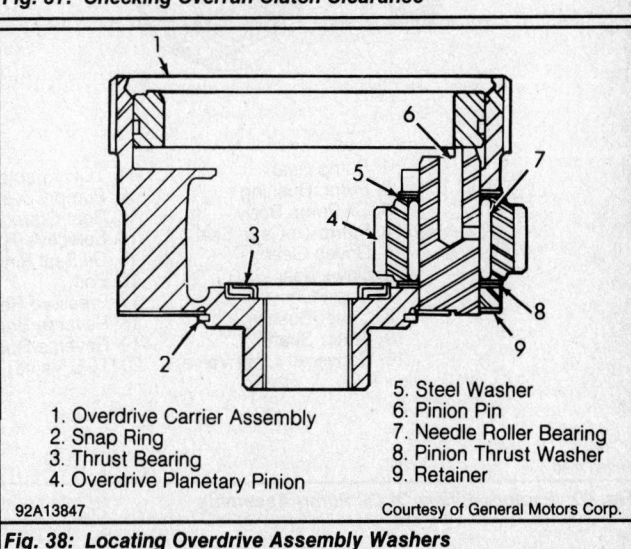

1. Overdrive Carrier Assembly
2. Snap Ring
3. Thrust Bearing
4. Overdrive Planetary Pinion
5. Steel Washer
6. Pinion Pin
7. Needle Roller Bearing
8. Pinion Thrust Washer
9. Retainer

92A13847   Courtesy of General Motors Corp.

Fig. 38: Locating Overdrive Assembly Washers

AUTOMATIC TRANSMISSIONS
Hydra-Matic 4L80-E (Cont.)

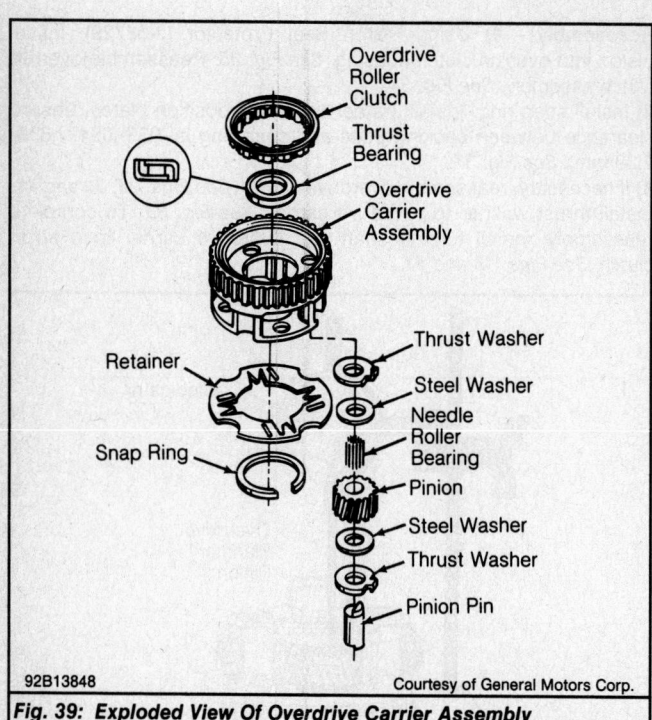

Overdrive Roller Clutch
Thrust Bearing
Overdrive Carrier Assembly
Retainer
Thrust Washer
Steel Washer
Needle Roller Bearing
Snap Ring
Pinion
Steel Washer
Thrust Washer
Pinion Pin

92B13848

Courtesy of General Motors Corp.

Fig. 39: Exploded View Of Overdrive Carrier Assembly

OIL PUMP ASSEMBLY

Disassembly – Clean and air dry oil pump. Disassemble oil pump. See Fig. 40 for exploded view of pump assembly. Use caution when removing reverse boost valve snap ring. Regulator spring is under extreme pressure.

Cleaning & Inspection – Inspect pump body for porosity, interconnected oil passages, damaged inner pump area surface or damaged machine facing. Check gears and bushings for damage.

Reassembly – **1)** Reassemble oil pump. See Fig. 40. Install oil pump gears into pump body with chamfered side down. Measure gear clearance between oil pump gears and pump body. Clearance should be .0007-.0028" (.017-.071 mm).

2) Ensure pump body mating surface is flat. Install pump cover onto body. Install cover bolts and hand tighten bolts. Install Alignment Pin (J-25025-1) into pump. Install and tighten oil pump Alignment Band (J-21368). See Fig. 43. Tighten oil pump attaching bolts.

3) To install TCC enable valve, compress spring into oil pump body, and insert a small rod into hole "A". See Fig. 42. Install spring retainer, and remove small rod.

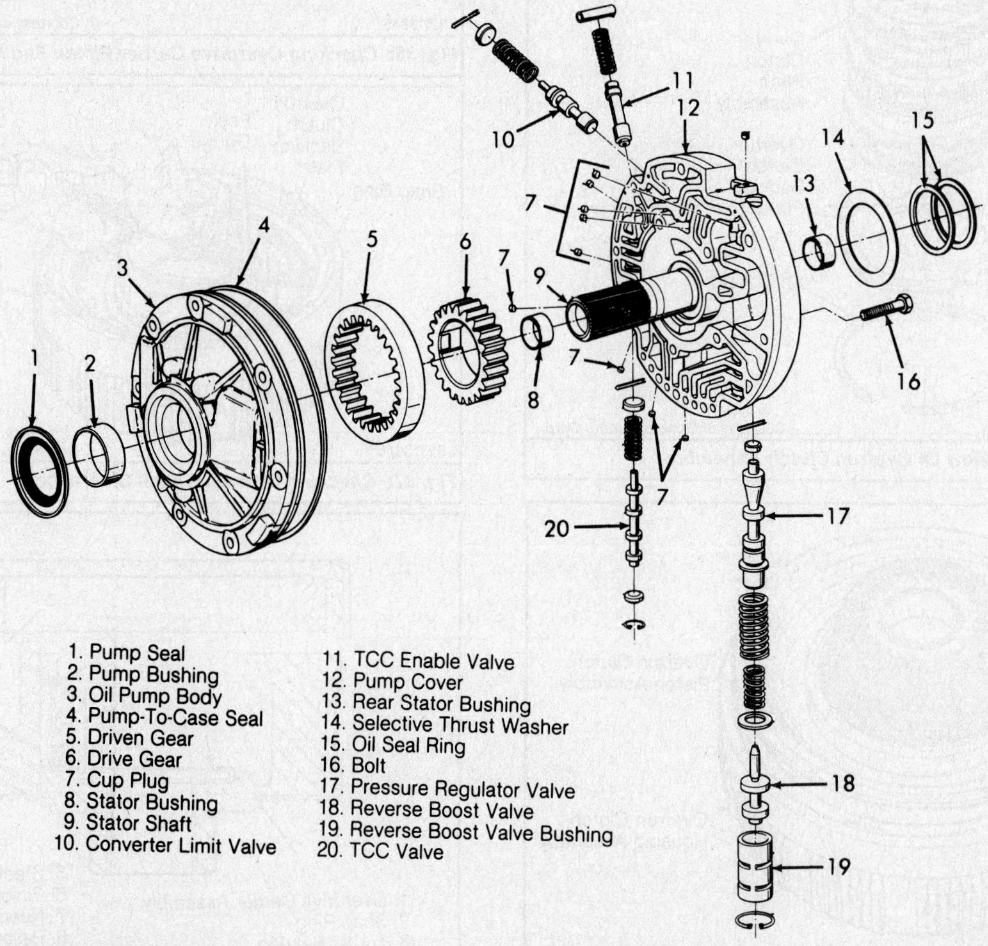

1. Pump Seal
2. Pump Bushing
3. Oil Pump Body
4. Pump-To-Case Seal
5. Driven Gear
6. Drive Gear
7. Cup Plug
8. Stator Bushing
9. Stator Shaft
10. Converter Limit Valve
11. TCC Enable Valve
12. Pump Cover
13. Rear Stator Bushing
14. Selective Thrust Washer
15. Oil Seal Ring
16. Bolt
17. Pressure Regulator Valve
18. Reverse Boost Valve
19. Reverse Boost Valve Bushing
20. TCC Valve

92G13850

Courtesy of General Motors Corp.

Fig. 40: Exploded View Of Oil Pump Assembly

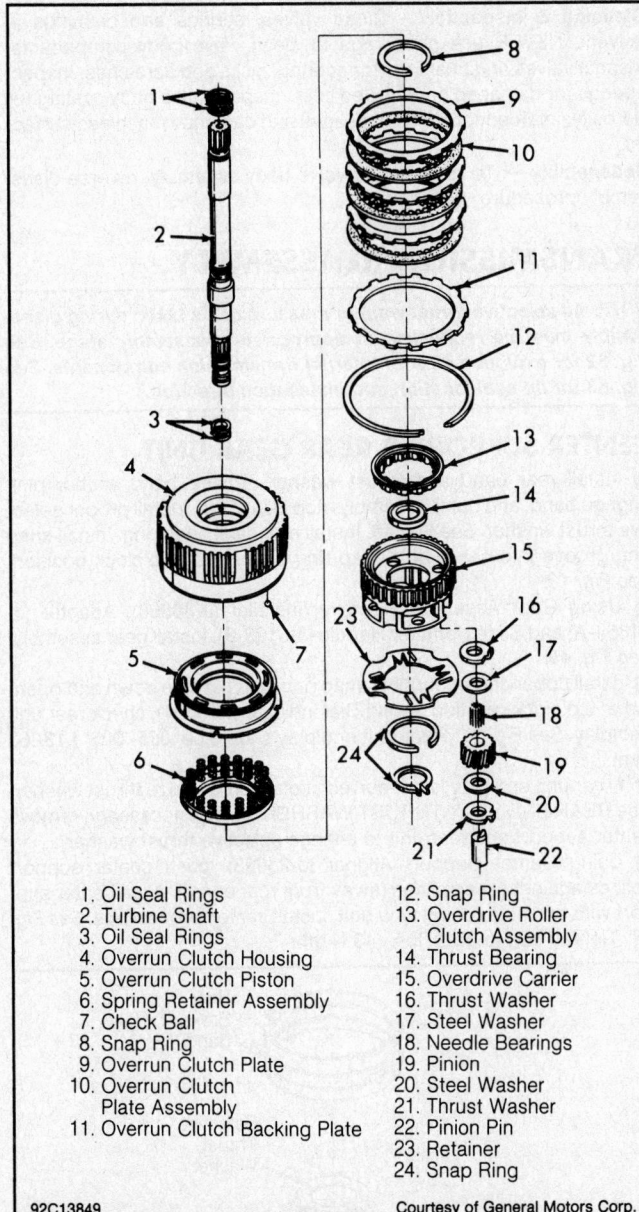

1. Oil Seal Rings
2. Turbine Shaft
3. Oil Seal Rings
4. Overrun Clutch Housing
5. Overrun Clutch Piston
6. Spring Retainer Assembly
7. Check Ball
8. Snap Ring
9. Overrun Clutch Plate
10. Overrun Clutch Plate Assembly
11. Overrun Clutch Backing Plate
12. Snap Ring
13. Overdrive Roller Clutch Assembly
14. Thrust Bearing
15. Overdrive Carrier
16. Thrust Washer
17. Steel Washer
18. Needle Bearings
19. Pinion
20. Steel Washer
21. Thrust Washer
22. Pinion Pin
23. Retainer
24. Snap Ring

92C13849   Courtesy of General Motors Corp.

Fig. 41: Exploded View Of Overdrive/Overrun Assembly

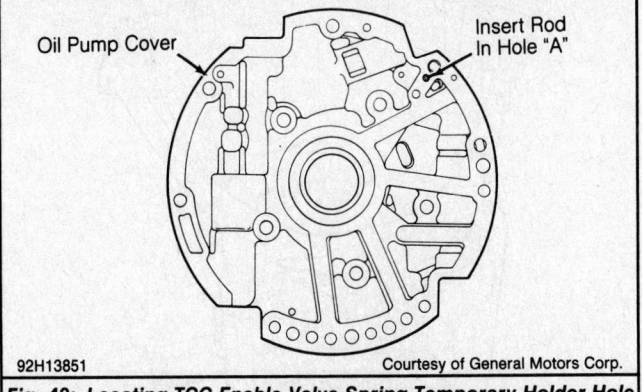

92H13851   Courtesy of General Motors Corp.

Fig. 42: Locating TCC Enable Valve Spring Temporary Holder Hole

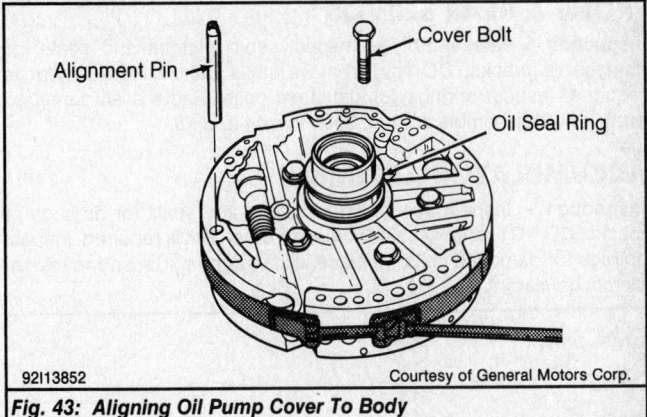

92I13852   Courtesy of General Motors Corp.

Fig. 43: Aligning Oil Pump Cover To Body

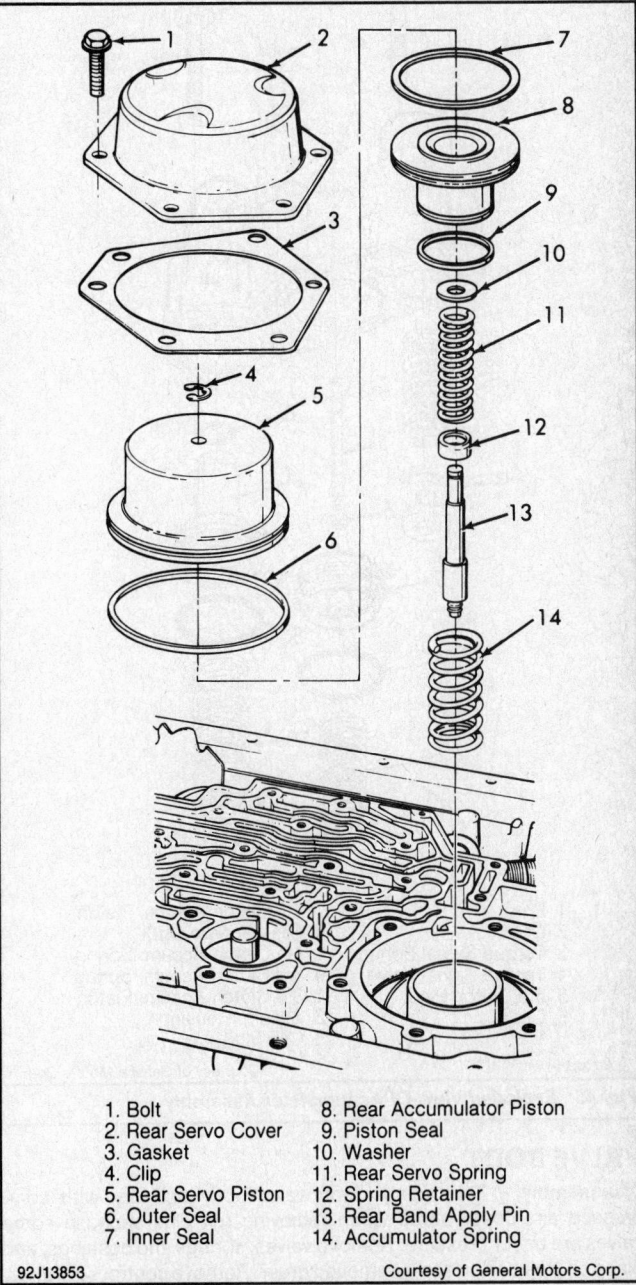

1. Bolt
2. Rear Servo Cover
3. Gasket
4. Clip
5. Rear Servo Piston
6. Outer Seal
7. Inner Seal
8. Rear Accumulator Piston
9. Piston Seal
10. Washer
11. Rear Servo Spring
12. Spring Retainer
13. Rear Band Apply Pin
14. Accumulator Spring

92J13853   Courtesy of General Motors Corp.

Fig. 44: Exploded View Of Rear Servo Assembly

FRONT & REAR SERVOS

Inspection & Reassembly – Inspect servo pistons and seals for damage or cracks. DO NOT remove seals unless replacement is required. Inspect springs for damaged coils. Replace all damaged parts, and reassemble servos. See Figs. 44 and 58.

ACCUMULATOR ASSEMBLY

Inspection – Inspect accumulator pistons and seals for damage or cracks. DO NOT remove seals unless replacement is required. Inspect springs for damaged coils. Replace all damaged parts, and reassemble accumulators. See Fig. 45.

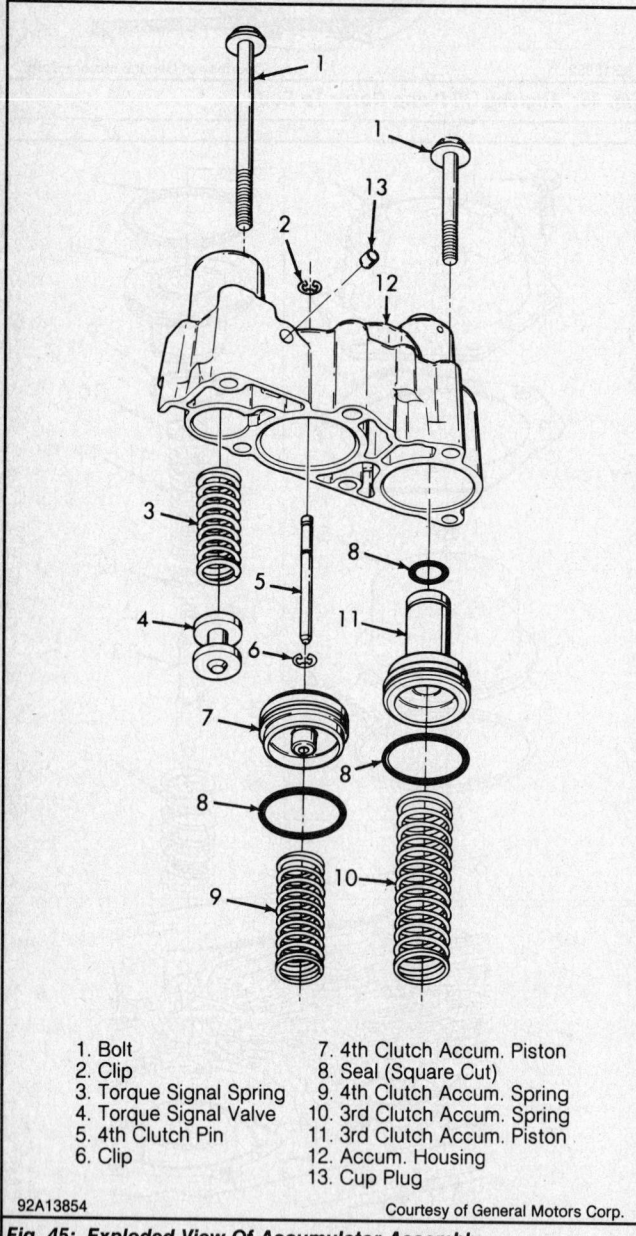

1. Bolt
2. Clip
3. Torque Signal Spring
4. Torque Signal Valve
5. 4th Clutch Pin
6. Clip
7. 4th Clutch Accum. Piston
8. Seal (Square Cut)
9. 4th Clutch Accum. Spring
10. 3rd Clutch Accum. Spring
11. 3rd Clutch Accum. Piston
12. Accum. Housing
13. Cup Plug

92A13854   Courtesy of General Motors Corp.

Fig. 45: Exploded View Of Accumulator Assembly

VALVE BODY

Disassembly – Thoroughly clean valve body and dry with compressed air. Cover bores when removing roll pins because some valves are under pressure. Remove valves, springs and bushings, and place on a clean surface in removed order. Remove control solenoids. Remove blind hole roll pins with a drill bit. Remove servo pipe lip seals.

Cleaning & Inspection – Clean valves, springs and bushings in solvent. NEVER use shop rags to clean valve body components. Inspect valves and bushings for scoring, nicks and scratches. Inspect springs for damaged or distorted coils. Inspect valve body casting for porosity, interconnected oil passages and damaged machined surfaces.

Reassembly – To reassemble valve body assembly, reverse disassembly procedure. See Fig. 47.

TRANSMISSION REASSEMBLY

NOTE: All selective thrust washer measurements taken during disassembly must be rechecked at appropriate reassembly stage. See Fig. 62 for exploded view of internal transmission components. See Fig. 63 for lip seal location and installation direction.

CENTER SUPPORT & REAR GEAR UNIT

1) Install rear band and thrust washer. Ensure band anchor pins engage band, and band assembly stop is in place. Install proper selective thrust washer. See Fig. 46. Install rear case snap ring. Install snap ring groove into case, with snap ring opening at 9 o'clock position. See Fig. 12.

2) Using Gear Assembly Remover/Installer (J-38868), Adapter (J-21364-A) and Slide Hammer Handle (J-6125-B), install gear assembly. See Fig. 49.

3) Install upper center support snap ring with flat side down and opening at 9 o'clock position. Using Dial Indicator (J-8001), check rear unit end play. See Fig. 11. Rear unit end play should be .005-.025" (.13-.63 mm).

4) If rear unit end play is not correct, select proper size thrust washer. See REAR END PLAY THRUST WASHER table. If necessary, remove center support and rear unit to change selective thrust washer.

5) Using Center Support Aligner (J-23093), push center support splines against case splines (away from rear servo). Align center support with bolt hole. Using new bolt, install center support bolt. See Fig. 48. Tighten bolt to 32 ft. lbs. (43 N.m).

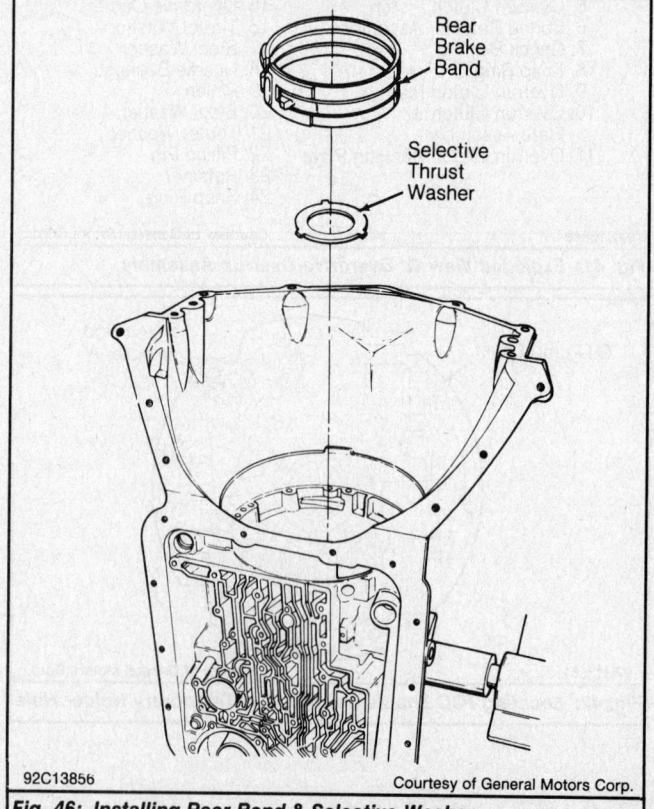

Rear Brake Band

Selective Thrust Washer

92C13856   Courtesy of General Motors Corp.

Fig. 46: Installing Rear Band & Selective Washer

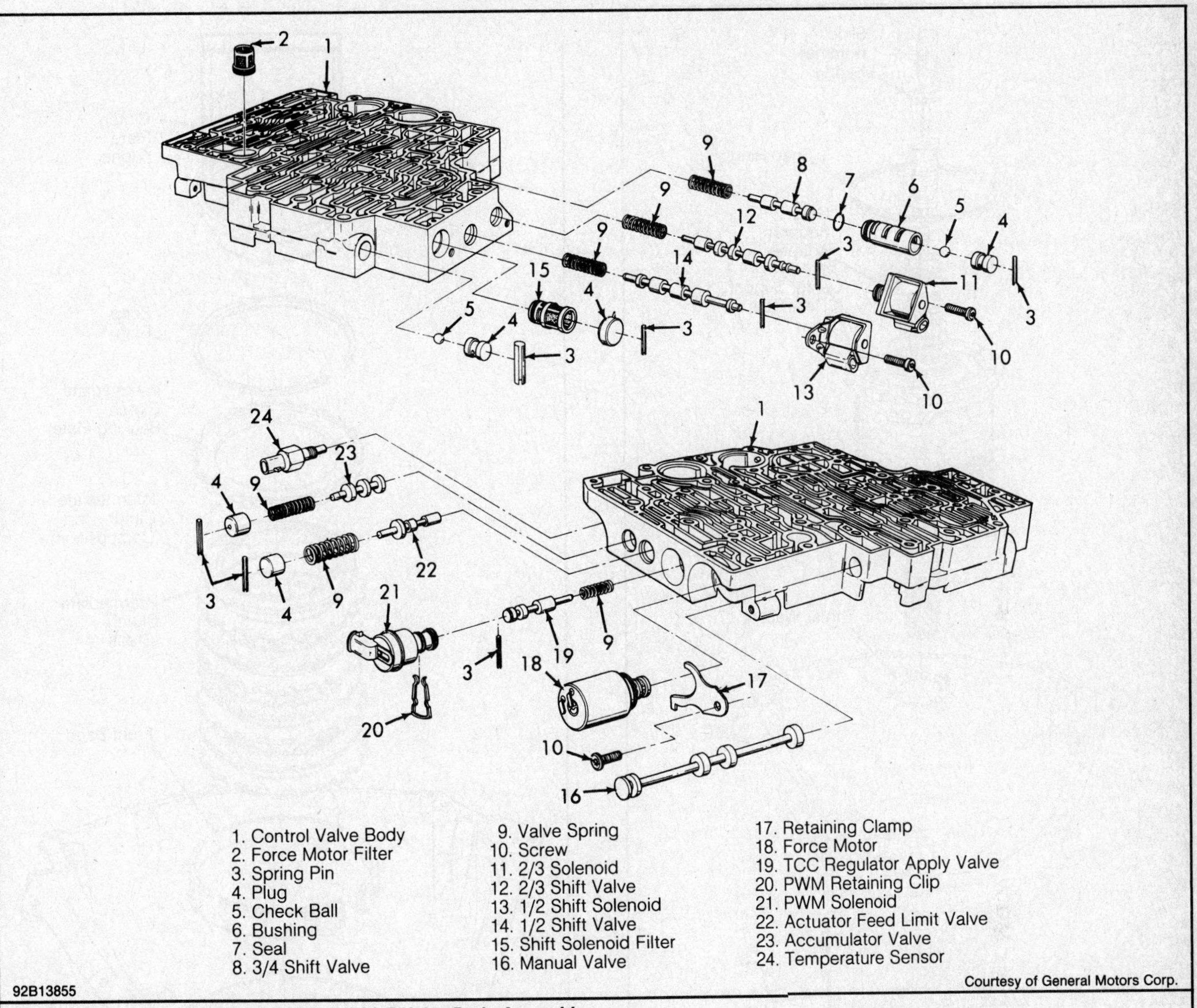

1. Control Valve Body
2. Force Motor Filter
3. Spring Pin
4. Plug
5. Check Ball
6. Bushing
7. Seal
8. 3/4 Shift Valve
9. Valve Spring
10. Screw
11. 2/3 Solenoid
12. 2/3 Shift Valve
13. 1/2 Shift Solenoid
14. 1/2 Shift Valve
15. Shift Solenoid Filter
16. Manual Valve
17. Retaining Clamp
18. Force Motor
19. TCC Regulator Apply Valve
20. PWM Retaining Clip
21. PWM Solenoid
22. Actuator Feed Limit Valve
23. Accumulator Valve
24. Temperature Sensor
92B13855
Courtesy of General Motors Corp.

Fig. 47: Exploded View Of Hydra-Matic 4L80-E Valve Body Assembly

REAR END PLAY THRUST WASHER

Identification	Thickness
No. 1	.074-.078" (1.88-1.98 mm)
No. 2 (Side Of Tab)	.082-.086" (2.08-2.18 mm)
No. 3 (Side Of Tab)	.090-.094" (2.29-2.39 mm)
No. 4 (End Of Tab)	.098-.102" (2.49-2.59 mm)
No. 5 (End Of Tab)	.106-.110" (2.69-2.79 mm)
No. 6 (End Of Tab)	.114-.118" (2.89-3.00 mm)

INTERMEDIATE CLUTCH

Install intermediate clutch plates (4 steel and 4 composition). *See Fig. 50.* Install backing plate with flat side down. Install snap ring at 9 o'clock position. Ensure clearance between clutch plates and backing plate is .040-.107" (1.02-2.72 mm). Using Clutch Plate Aligner (J-24396), align intermediate clutch assembly.

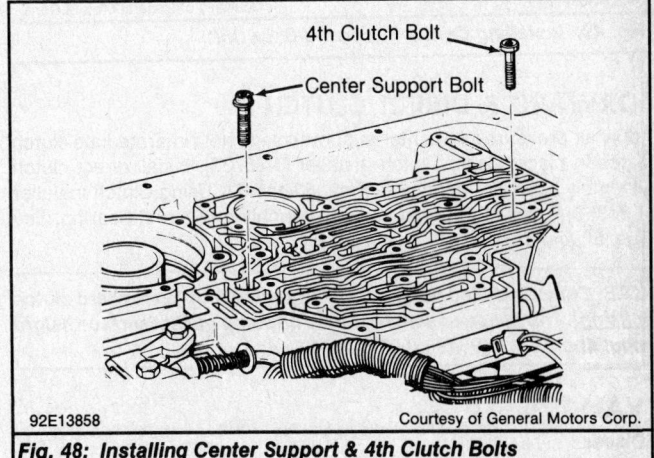

4th Clutch Bolt
Center Support Bolt
92E13858
Courtesy of General Motors Corp.

Fig. 48: Installing Center Support & 4th Clutch Bolts

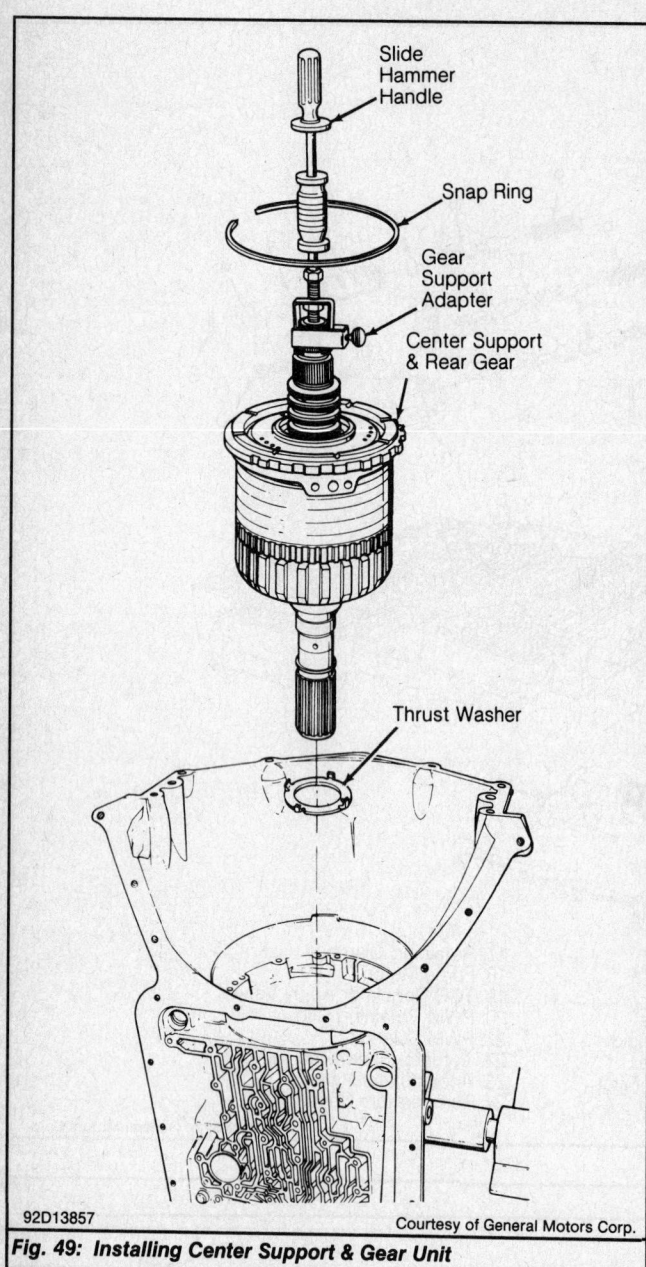

92D13857

Courtesy of General Motors Corp.

Fig. 49: Installing Center Support & Gear Unit

FORWARD & DIRECT CLUTCH

Apply air pressure into center support hole to hold intermediate clutch plates in place. Using Clutch Installer (J-38733), install direct clutch assembly and front band. *See Figs. 50 and 51.* Using Clutch Installer (J-38358-A), install forward clutch assembly and thrust bearing. *See Figs. 52 and 62.*

NOTE: Check installed height of speed sensor ring (on forward clutch housing). Top of speed sensor ring to oil pump gasket surface height should be 3.85-3.89" (98.0-99.0 mm).

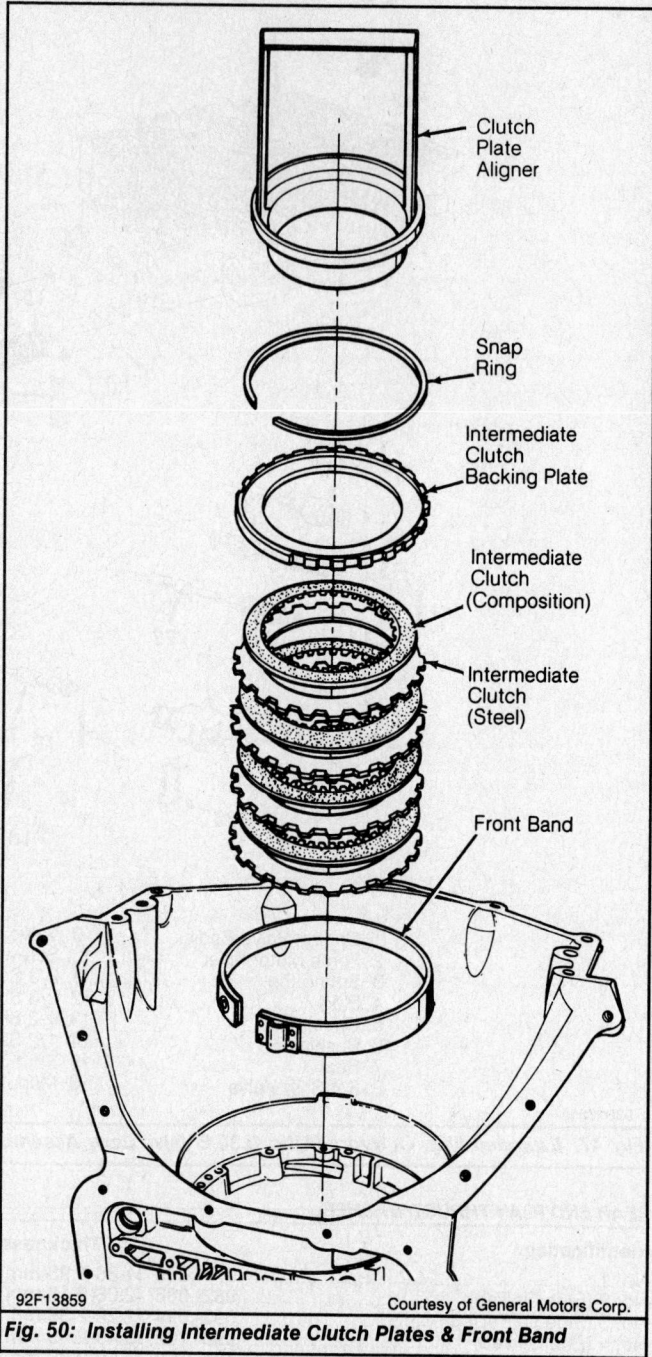

92F13859

Courtesy of General Motors Corp.

Fig. 50: Installing Intermediate Clutch Plates & Front Band

OVERDRIVE ASSEMBLY & 4TH CLUTCH

1) Install 4th clutch support (without clutch plates) into transmission case. Using 40T Torx wrench, install new 4th clutch support bolt. *See Fig. 53.* Tighten bolt to 12 ft. lbs. (16 N.m).

2) Remove turbine seal sizer from turbine shaft. Install turbine shaft and overdrive assembly. *See Fig. 33.* Ensure assembly is fully seated. Install 4th clutch plates (4 steel and 4 composition). Install steel plates with narrow tang "V" notch at 1 o'clock position in housing. *See Fig. 54.* Install backing plate and snap ring. *See Fig. 55.*

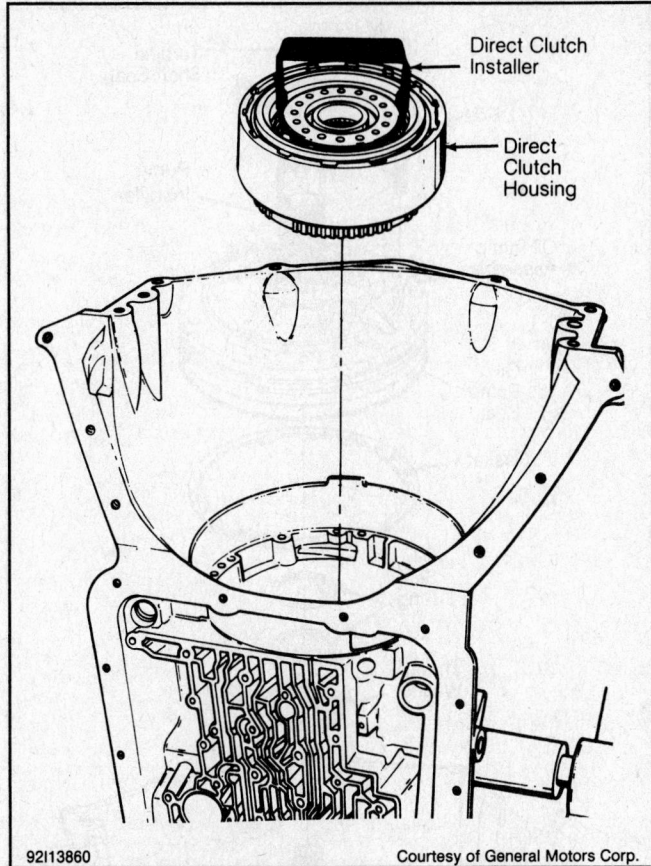

92I13860   Courtesy of General Motors Corp.

Fig. 51: Installing Direct Clutch

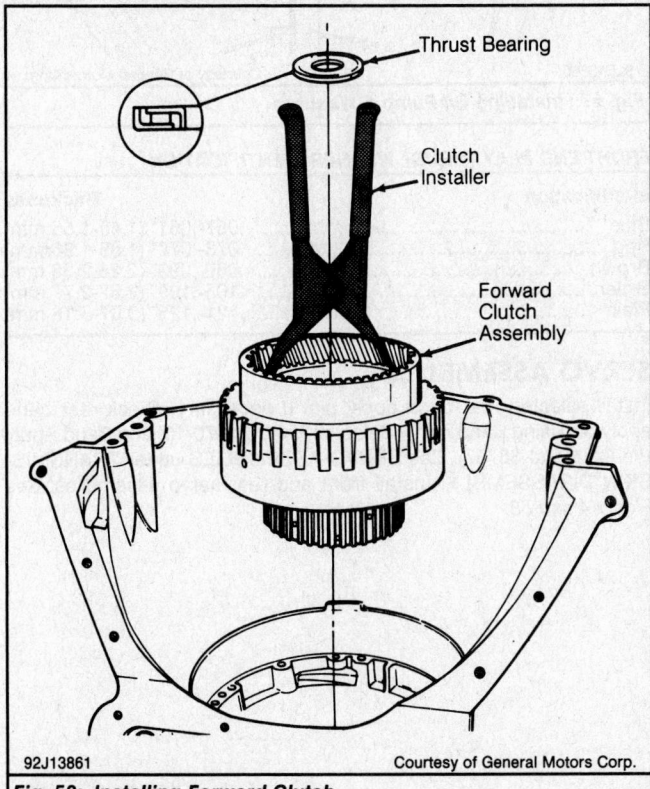

92J13861   Courtesy of General Motors Corp.

Fig. 52: Installing Forward Clutch

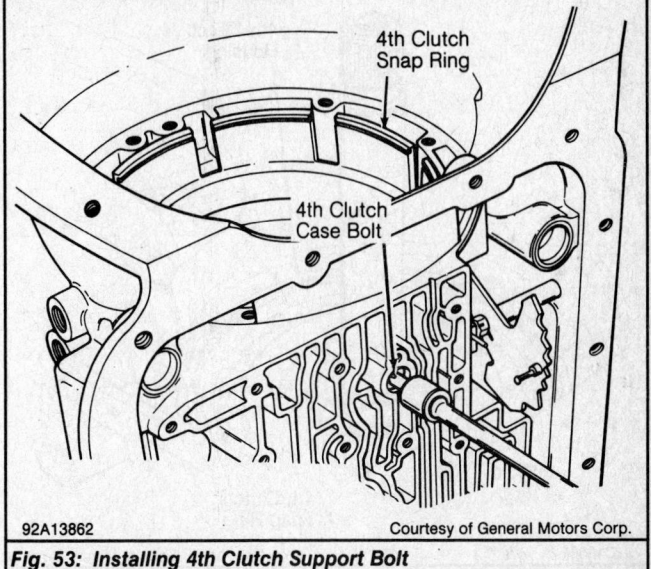

92A13862   Courtesy of General Motors Corp.

Fig. 53: Installing 4th Clutch Support Bolt

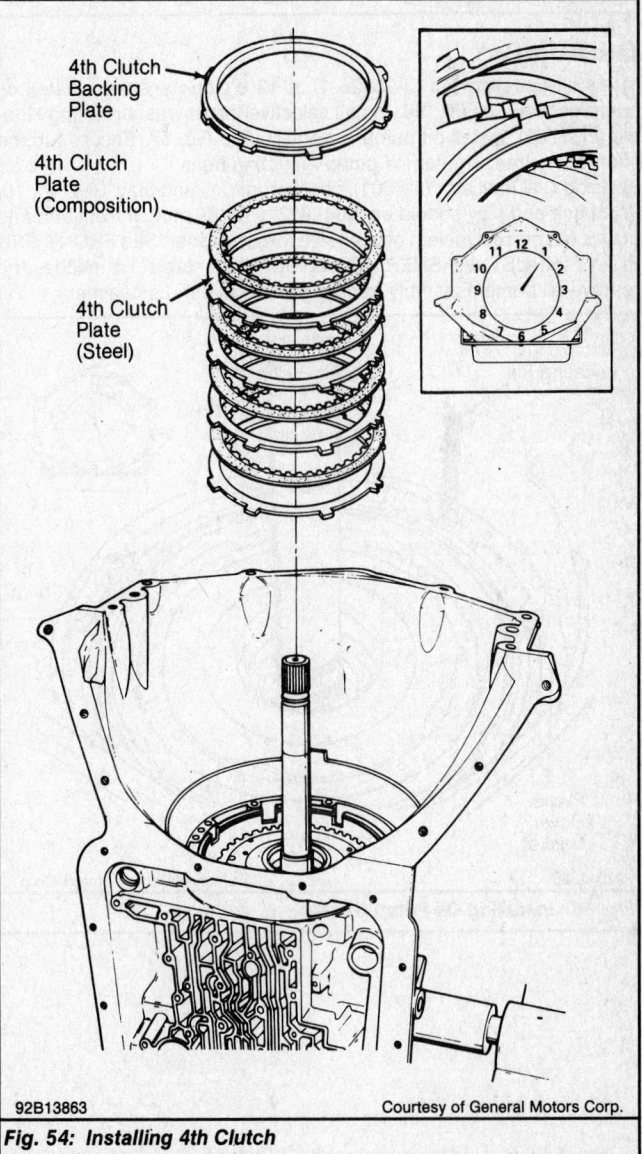

92B13863   Courtesy of General Motors Corp.

Fig. 54: Installing 4th Clutch

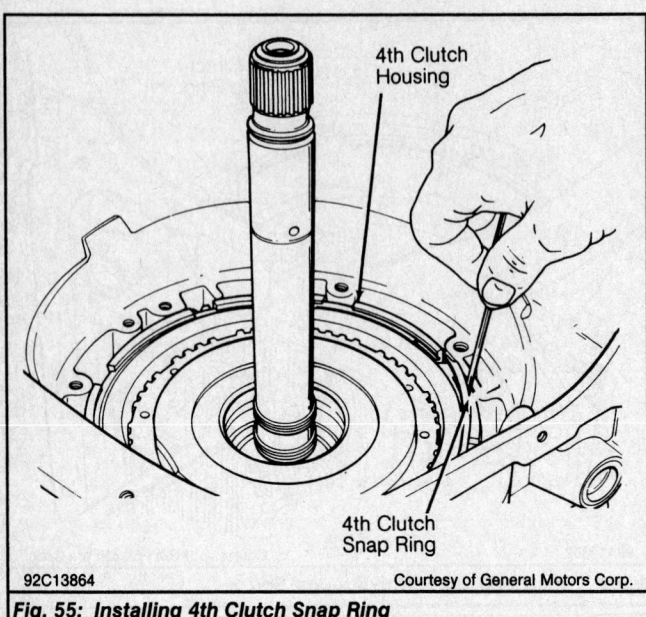

92C13864   Courtesy of General Motors Corp.

Fig. 55: Installing 4th Clutch Snap Ring

OIL PUMP

1) Install Locating Pin (J-25025-1) at 12 o'clock position. Install oil pump gasket. *See Fig. 56.* Install selective thrust washer. Using Handle (J-37789), install oil pump assembly. *See Fig. 57.* Ensure turbine shaft spins free. Tighten oil pump mounting bolts.

2) Using Dial Indicator (J-8001), check front unit end play. *See Fig. 10.* Front unit end play should be .004-.022" (.10-.56 mm). If front unit end play is not correct, select proper size thrust washer. See FRONT END PLAY THRUST WASHER IDENTIFICATION table. If necessary, remove oil pump assembly to change selective thrust washer.

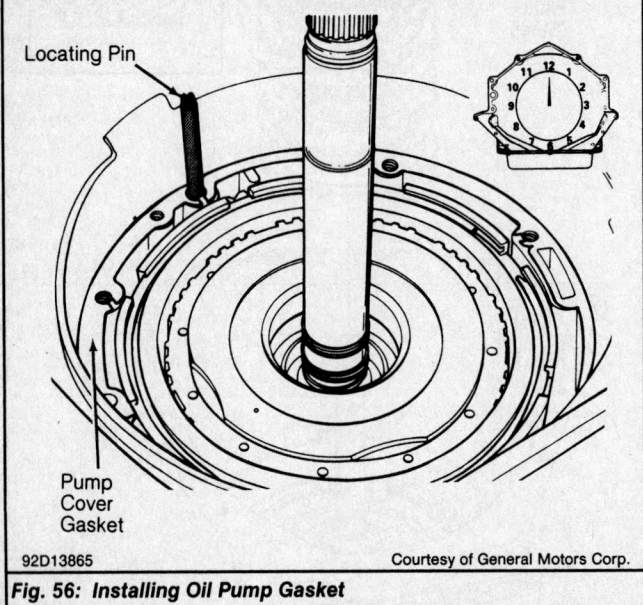

92D13865   Courtesy of General Motors Corp.

Fig. 56: Installing Oil Pump Gasket

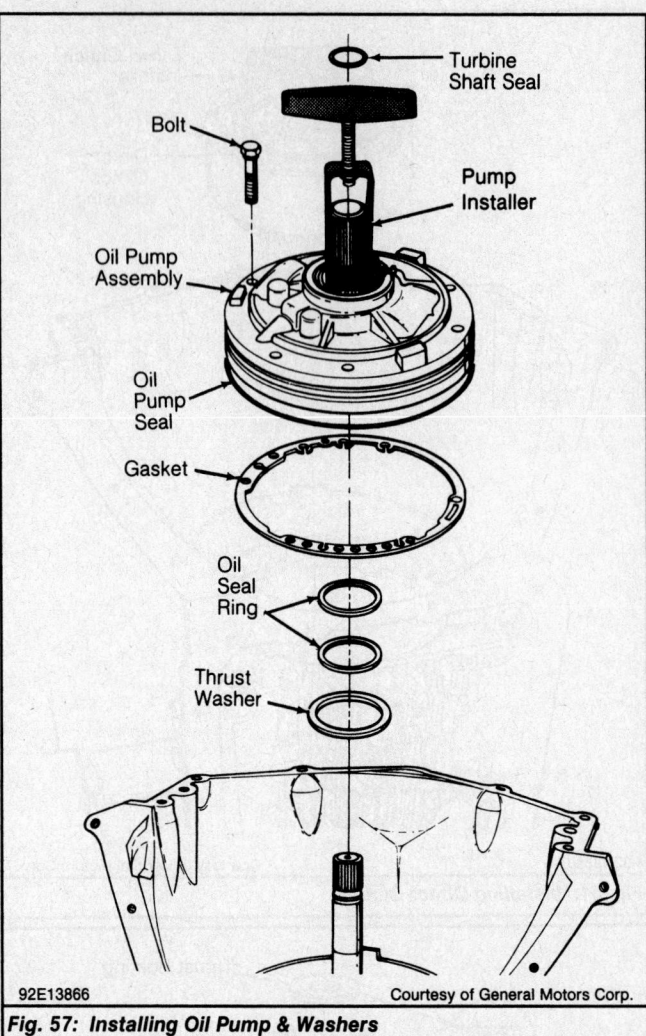

92E13866   Courtesy of General Motors Corp.

Fig. 57: Installing Oil Pump & Washers

FRONT END PLAY THRUST WASHER IDENTIFICATION

Identification	Thickness
Blue	.057-.061" (1.45-1.55 mm)
Red	.073-.077" (1.85-1.96 mm)
Brown	.089-.093" (2.26-2.36 mm)
Green	.105-.109" (2.67-2.77 mm)
Plain	.121-.125" (3.07-3.18 mm)

SERVO ASSEMBLIES

Install selected rear band apply pin. If necessary, check rear band apply pin using Band Apply Selector Pin (J-21370-10) and Band Apply Pin Gauge (J-38737). See SERVO ASSEMBLIES under TRANSMISSION DISASSEMBLY. Install front and rear servo assemblies. *See Figs. 44 and 58.*

LOWER TRANSMISSION ASSEMBLY

Install parking pawl and manual linkage. *See Fig. 6.* Install check balls in case. *See Fig. 59.* Assemble and install accumulator assembly. *See Fig. 45.* Tighten accumulator assembly bolts in sequence. *See Fig. 60.* Install valve body assembly. *See Fig. 46.* Install lube pipe and wiring harness. *See Fig. 61.* Install oil pan and oil filter.

SPEED SENSORS & REAR HOUSING

Install and secure torque converter. Install rear extension housing. Install speed sensors.

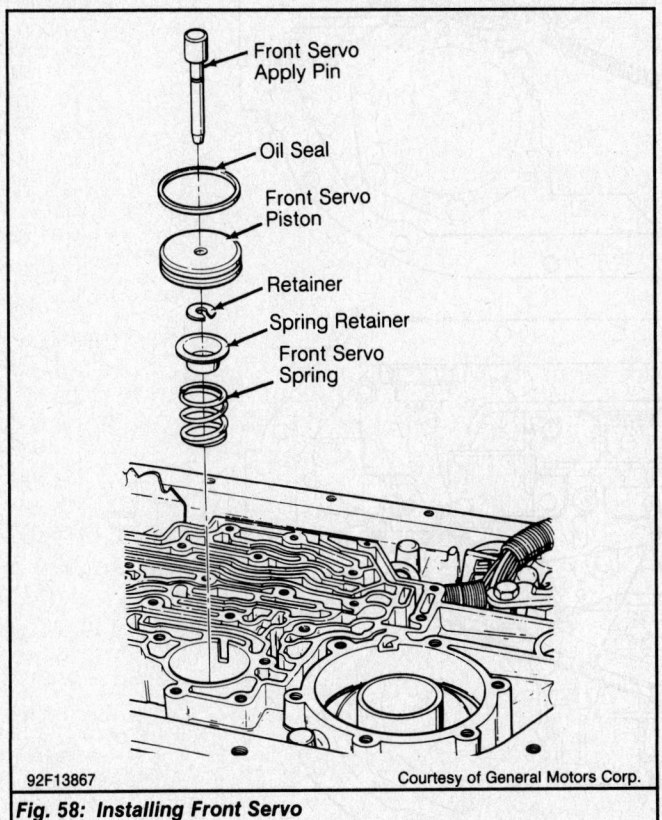

92F13867   Courtesy of General Motors Corp.

Fig. 58: Installing Front Servo

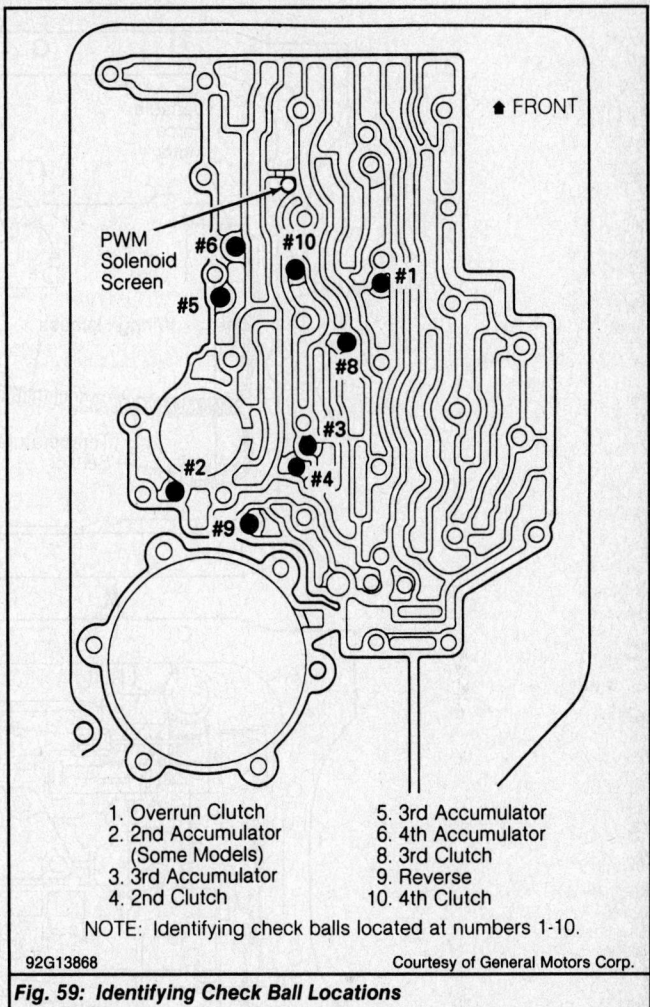

1. Overrun Clutch
2. 2nd Accumulator (Some Models)
3. 3rd Accumulator
4. 2nd Clutch
5. 3rd Accumulator
6. 4th Accumulator
8. 3rd Clutch
9. Reverse
10. 4th Clutch

NOTE: Identifying check balls located at numbers 1-10.

92G13868   Courtesy of General Motors Corp.

Fig. 59: Identifying Check Ball Locations

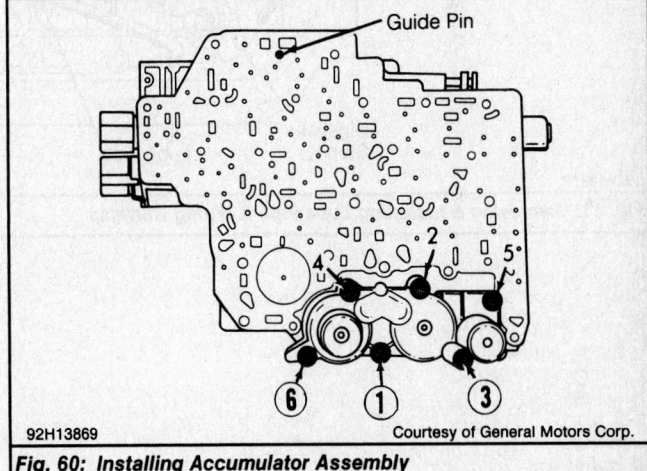

92H13869   Courtesy of General Motors Corp.

Fig. 60: Installing Accumulator Assembly

AUTOMATIC TRANSMISSIONS
Hydra-Matic 4L80-E (Cont.)

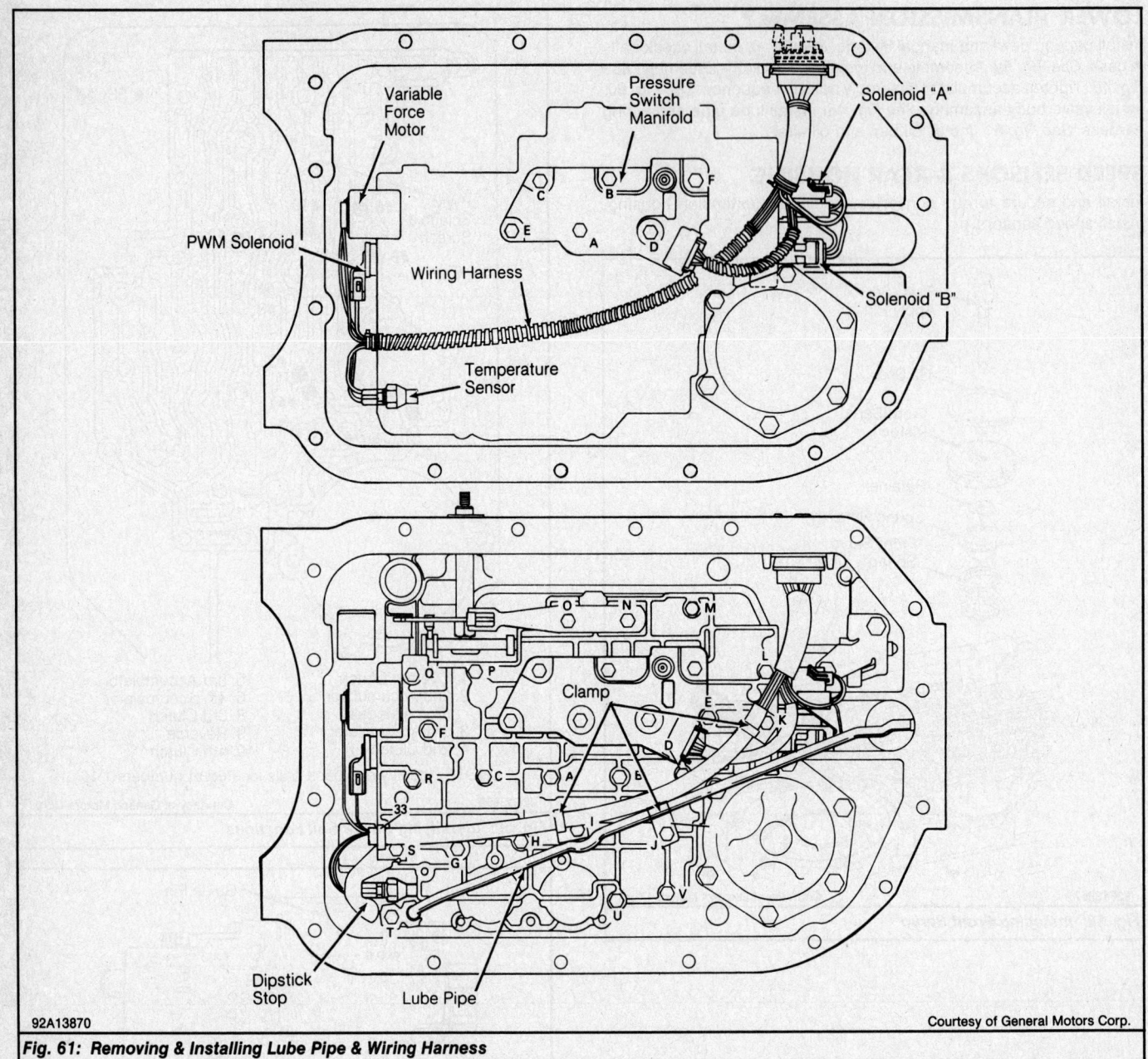

92A13870

Courtesy of General Motors Corp.

Fig. 61: Removing & Installing Lube Pipe & Wiring Harness

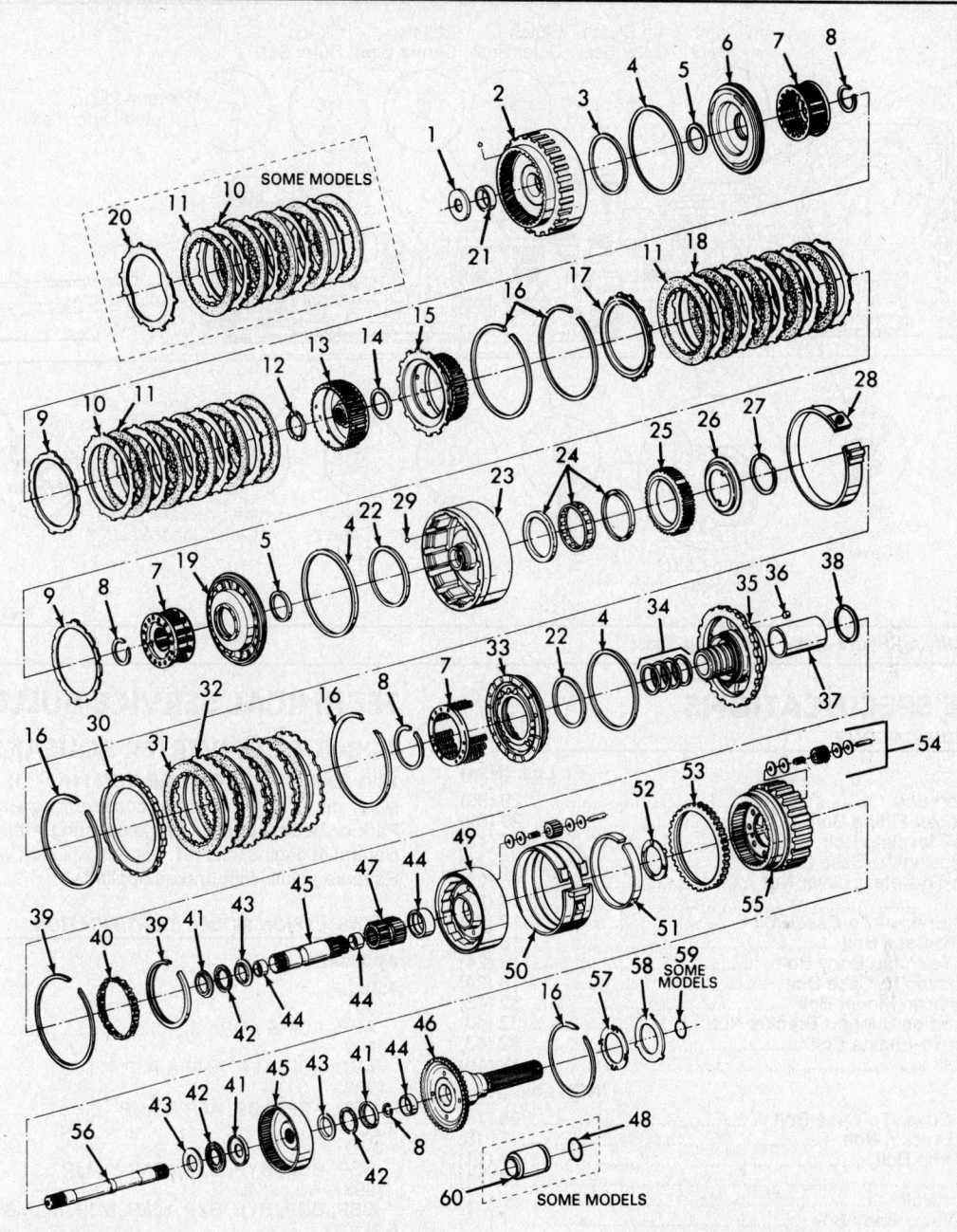

1. Forward Clutch Thrust Bearing
2. Forward Clutch Housing
3. Center Clutch Seal
4. Outer Clutch Seal
5. Inner Clutch Seal
6. Forward Clutch Piston
7. Spring Retainer
8. Snap Ring
9. Dished Clutch Plate
10. Clutch Plate
11. Clutch Plate Assembly
12. Thrust Washer
13. Forward Clutch Hub
14. Forward Clutch Thrust Washer
15. Direct Clutch Driven Hub
16. Snap Ring
17. Direct Clutch Backing Plate
18. Clutch Plate
19. Direct Clutch Piston
20. Waved Clutch Plate

21. Bushing
22. Center Clutch Seal
23. Direct Clutch Housing
24. Intermediate Sprag Assembly
25. Intermediate Clutch Outer Race
26. Intermediate Clutch Retainer
27. External Locking Ring
28. Front Band
29. Check Ball
30. Intermediate Clutch Backing Plate
31. Intermediate Clutch Plate Assembly
32. Intermediate Clutch Plate
33. Intermediate Clutch Piston
34. Oil Seal Ring
35. Center Support Assembly
36. Orifice Plug
37. Bushing
38. Reaction Drum Thrust Washer
39. Spacer
40. Roller Clutch Assembly

41. Thrust Bearing Race
42. Needle Bearing
43. Thrust Bearing Race
44. Sun Gear Bushing
45. Sun Gear Shaft
46. Output Shaft
47. Sun Gear
48. Output Shaft Seal
49. Reaction Drum & Carrier
50. Rear Brake Band
51. Front Internal Gear Ring
52. Reaction Carrier Washer
53. Output Speed Sensor Ring
54. Pinion Assembly
55. Output Carrier Assembly
56. Main Shaft
57. Thrust Washer
58. Selective Thrust Washer
59. Output Shaft Seal
60. Yoke Seal

92B13871

Courtesy of General Motors Corp.

Fig. 62: Exploded View Of Hydra-Matic 4L80-E Internal Components

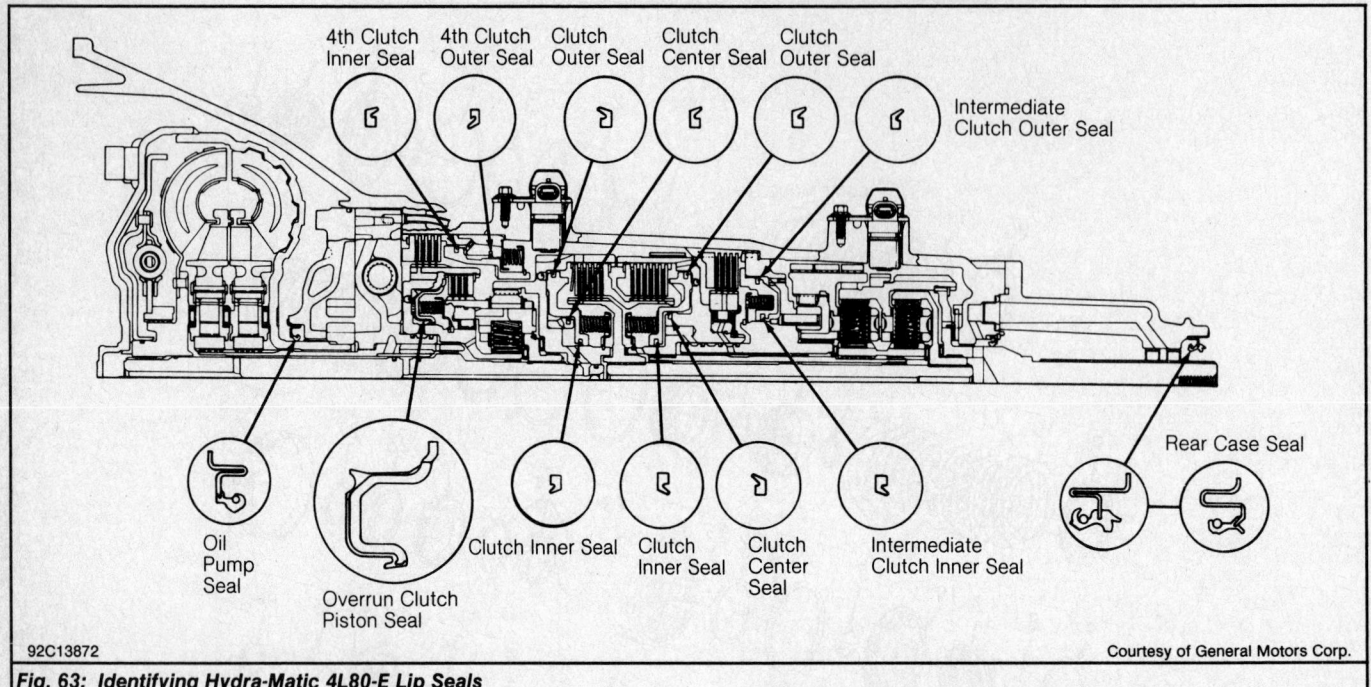

92C13872   Courtesy of General Motors Corp.

Fig. 63: Identifying Hydra-Matic 4L80-E Lip Seals

TORQUE SPECIFICATIONS
TORQUE SPECIFICATIONS

Application	Ft. Lbs. (N.m)
Center Support Bolt	29 (39)
Connector Cooler Fitting Bolt	29 (39)
Converter-To-Flexplate Bolt	32 (43)
Extension Housing-To-Case Bolt	25 (34)
Manual Shaft-To-Detent Lever Nut	18 (24)
Oil Pan Bolt	18 (24)
Parking Pawl Bracket-To-Case Bolt	18 (24)
Pump Body-To-Case Bolt	18 (24)
Pump Cover-To-Pump Body Bolt	18 (24)
Rear Servo Cover-To-Case Bolt	18 (24)
Rear Transmission Mount Bolt	32 (43)
Rear Transmission Support Bracket Nut	32 (43)
Transmission-To-Engine Bolt	32 (43)
4th Clutch Bolt	12 (16)

	INCH Lbs. (N.m)
Accumulator Cover-To-Case Bolt	98 (11)
Force Motor Bracket Bolt	71 (8)
Lube Pipe Clamp Bolt	98 (11)
Pipe Plug	98 (11)
Speed Sensor Bolt	98 (11)
Solenoid-To-Valve Body Bolt	71 (8)
Temperature Sensor	35 (4)
Valve Body-To-Case Bolt	98 (11)

TRANSMISSION SPECIFICATIONS
TRANSMISSION SPECIFICATIONS

Application	In. (mm)
Clutch Clearances	
Direct Clutch	.121-.186 (3.07-4.72)
Forward Clutch	
Except Model ZBP	.121-.186 (3.07-4.72)
Model ZBP	.087-.110 (2.21-2.81)
Intermediate Clutch	.040-.107 (1.02-2.72)
Overrun Clutch	.033-.094 (.838-2.39)
4th Clutch	.040-.100 (1.01-2.54)
End Play	
Front Unit	.004-.022 (.10-.56)
Output Carrier & Reaction Carrier	
Pinion Gear	.009-.024 (.023-.61)
Rear Unit	.005-.025 (.13-.63)
Torque Converter	0-.024 (0-.60)
Oil Pump Gears-To-Body Clearance	.007-.0028 (.017-.071)

TECHNICAL SERVICE BULLETINS
TORQUE CONVERTER SQUEAKS

1991-93 4L80-E – GM TSB 377111R – 1) Some 4L80-E transmissions may exhibit a torque converter squeak. Squeak is present in Park or Neutral at idle, during coasting with a light load or in Park or Neutral at engine shut off. Squeak will stop when vehicle is in Drive or Reverse at idle with brakes applied.

TRANSMISSION MODEL IDENTIFICATION

Application	Part No.
4.3L	
1991	
ABP, ACP & ADP	8690904
1992	
ABP, ACP, AFP, AHP & AJP	8690904
1993	
ABP, ACP, ADP, AFP & AHP	8690904
5.7L	
1992	
BSP, BUP, BYP, BZP, MAP & MJP	8689961
1993	
BSP, BUP, BYP, BZP, MAP, MJP, MLP & MXP	8689961
6.2L	
1991	
BAP, BBP, BJP, BMP, BNP, CAP, CBP, CKP & CRP	8690903
1992	
BAP, BJP, BMP, BNP, MBP, MKP & MPP	8690903
1993	
BAP, BJP, BMP, BNP, JPD, MBP, MCP & MPP	8690903
6.5L Turbo	
1992-93	
LAP, LAP & LLP	8689959
7.4L	
1991	
DCP, DDP, DLP, DNP, DPP, DRP & DSP	8689960
1992	
DCP, DLP, DNP, DPP, DRP, HTP, MHP, TSP & TWP	8689960
1993	
DCP, DLP, DNP, DPP, DRP, DSP, MHP, TVP, TWP & TXP	8689960

2) This condition is caused due to a high spring load in stator assembly of torque converter. To improve this condition, replace torque converter with converter with lower spring load in stator assembly. See TRANSMISSION MODEL IDENTIFICATION table for transmission model and torque converter part numbers. Beginning January 11, 1993 (Julian Date 011), all 1993 4L80-E transmissions will have new converter.

NO UPSHIFT, STUCK IN 1ST, NO CODES, FLUID LEAK

1993 4L80-E – GM TSB 377118 – 1) Some 4L80-E transmissions may experience no upshift or stuck in 1st gear with no Diagnostic Trouble Code (DTC) stored. This condition may be caused by an input/output speed sensor malfunction, or leaking fluid through speed sensor connector. If input speed sensor is not functioning correctly, output speed sensor is not used for reference by PCM/TCM, and an upshift cannot occur.
2) To correct this condition, diagnosis input speed sensor circuit. Repair circuit as necessary. If circuit is okay, replace sensor (No. 8685042). Beginning January 15, 1993 (Julian Date 015), all 1993 4L80-E transmissions will have new sensor assemblies.

FLUID LEAK OUT EXTENSION HOUSING OR VIBRATION

1993 4L80-E – GM TSB 377122 – 1) Some 4L80-E transmissions may leak fluid at extension housing, or a vibration may exist in all shift positions at all speeds. This condition is caused by the extension housing bushing not seating properly due to an oversized bore, possibly interfering with housing seal.
2) To correct this condition, inspect housing bushing for proper seating and seal for damage. If bushing has moved, replace extension housing and bushing (No. 8677464), and seal (No. 8681168). DO NOT attempt to repair existing extension housing by staking, sealing or securing bushing in place. Beginning January 14, 1993 (Julian Date 014), all 4L80-E transmissions will have corrected extension housing assembly.

FLUID LEAK AT OUTPUT SPEED SENSOR BORE PLUG

1993-94 4L80-E (All With 4WD – GM TSB 377145) – 1) Some transmissions (model ACP, BJP, DLP or LFP) may exhibit fluid leaking past the output speed sensor bore plug or bore plug is missing. To correct this condition, replace bore plug (No. 8684222).
2) On all 1994 4L80-E 4WD models, speed sensor has been removed and a plated steel bore plug has been installed. Output speed sensor reluctor ring also has been eliminated on these models. Vehicle speed is obtained from speed sensor in transfer case.

TRANSMISSION STARTS IN 2ND OR 3RD GEAR/BINDS

1993-94 4L80-E – ATRA TSB 126 – Some 4L80-E transmissions may start in 3rd gear and bind up in manual low. This condition may be caused by a broken dished plate in the direct clutch. See Fig. 23. Inspect plate and replace as necessary. If transmission starts in 2nd gear and binds in manual low, check for a clogged solenoid "B" or stuck 1-2 shift valve.

BUZZING NOISE

1991-94 4L80-E – ATRA TSB 139 – 1) Some 4L80-E transmissions may exhibit a buzzing noise. This condition may be caused by pressure instability in the oil pump pressure regulator circuit. Service package No. 8682998 is available to correct this condition. Beginning March 15, 1991 (Julian Date 074), all 4L80-E transmissions were built with new design pressure regulator assembly.

2) Pressure regulator assembly has 2 different designs. Early design regulator valve has a longer regulator valve stem, smaller inside diameter washer and shorter stem on boost valve than late design. Late design boost valve has an additional valve spring. See Fig. 40. Mixing design components will cause uncontrollable line pressure. DO NOT mix components.

NO LINE PRESSURE INCREASE

1993-94 4L80-E – ATRA TSB 140 – 1) Some 4L80-E transmissions may exhibit no line pressure increase. This condition may be caused by using early design transmission valve body gaskets on late design transmissions. Incorrect gaskets will cover a hole in the spacer plate which feeds the boost valve.
2) Late design gaskets fit both early and late design valve body spacer plates. When repairing valve body, ensure correct valve body gaskets are used. For early valve body gasket design, See Fig. 60. Early design has an banana shaped hole at corner opposite accumulator bolt No. 5. Late design has 2 round holes at this location.

BINDS IN MANUAL LOW

1993-94 4L80-E – ATRA TSB 189 – Some 4L80-E transmissions may exhibit bind-up in manual low. This condition may be caused by a leaking intermediate accumulator. Condition can be corrected by replacing rear accumulator piston and seals. An improved rear accumulator piston (No. 8680929) has been designed which uses rubber seals instead of Teflon seals. See Fig. 44.

LOW OR NO LINE PRESSURE INCREASE

1993-94 4L80-E – ATRA TSB 190 – Some 4L80-E transmissions may exhibit low or no line pressure increase. This condition may be caused by a dirty or damaged shift solenoid filter. See Fig. 47. A broken filter will create a fluid leak, causing low or no line pressure increase. Check filter for cracks or damage and replace filter as necessary (No. 8661709).

NO LINE PRESSURE INCREASE OR HIGH LINE PRESSURE

1993-94 4L80-E – ATRA TSB 209 – 1) Some 4L80-E transmissions may exhibit no line pressure increase or high line pressure (more than 400 psi). This condition may be caused by defective or incorrect parts. Transmission case, spacer plate and valve body gasket must be compatible to prevent this condition. Transmission case, spacer plate and valve body gasket has 2 designs.
2) Early design case does not have case dam at front right corner of case. See Fig. 59. Late design case has a dam at this location. Mixing early and late design components will cause this condition. Early design spacer plate and valve body gasket has a banana shaped hole at corner opposite accumulator bolt No. 5. Late design has 2 round holes at this location. For early valve body gasket design, See Fig. 60.
3) A defective force motor can also create no line pressure increase or high line pressure. Ensure force motor screens are not plugged. Insert a needle into center of motor screen to check valve movement. When 12 volts is connected and disconnected at force motor terminals, valve should move back and forth. DO NOT leave force motor on for more than 5 seconds. If force motor does not operate as described, valve is stuck. Replace force motor (No. 8677314).

WIRING DIAGRAMS

NOTE: See 4L80-E ELECTRONIC CONTROLS article.

APPLICATION

THM 4L80-E APPLICATION

Application	Engine
Chevrolet & GMC	
"C", "G", "K" &, "P" Series	4.3L, 5.7L, 6.2L, 6.5L & 7.4L

1993-94 SERIES CODE DESIGNATIONS

Model	Series
Blazer	"K"
Parcel Van	"P"
Pickup	
2WD	"C"
4WD	"K"
Sierra & Suburban	
2WD	"C"
4WD	"K"
Van	"G"
Yukon	"K"

DESCRIPTION

The 4L80-E transmission uses 2 electric shift solenoids to control transmission upshifts and downshifts. In addition, a force motor (also referred to as pressure control solenoid) controls hydraulic line pressure, and a Torque Converter Clutch (TCC) solenoid controls TCC application. Solenoid is turned on and off by the Powertrain Control Module (PCM) or Transmission Control Module (TCM). PCM/TCM has on-board self-diagnostics to help identify any components or circuits that may need further testing.

OPERATION

Shift solenoid holds hydraulic pressure when it is on and releases pressure when it is off. This action controls the shift valves inside valve body. By switching one or both solenoids on or off, different combinations of clutches, sprags and bands are operated. See CLUTCH & BAND APPLICATION CHART table under ELECTRONIC TESTING.

COMPONENT DESCRIPTION

PCM/TCM

NOTE: Models with gasoline engines use a Powertrain Control Module (PCM) computer. Models with diesel engines use a Transmission Control Module (TCM) computer. These computers control TCC, force motor (hydraulic pressure) and shift solenoids "A" and "B".

The PCM/TCM is located behind driver's seat riser ("G" Series Van and "P" Series Commercial Van) or behind right side of dash on all other vehicles. On ~"G" Series Van Motorhome, PCM/TCM has been relocated to behind left side "B" pillar. PCM/TCM controls TCC, force motor (hydraulic pressure) and shift solenoids "A" and "B". In addition, PCM also controls ignition, fuel and emission devices related to the engine.

The PCM/TCM receives electronic signals from sensors and switches. These signals help the PCM/TCM determine when to operate various relays and solenoids related to engine and transmission components.

SENSORS & SWITCHES

The PCM/TCM controls upshifts and downshifts based on coolant temperature, transmission fluid temperature, system voltage, throttle position, transmission oil pressure switches, and transmission output and input speed sensors. *See Fig. 1.* The system includes several other switches and sensors that are used for engine control (gasoline engines). For additional information and testing of engine components, see appropriate article in ENGINE PERFORMANCE of appropriate MITCHELL® manual.

SOLENOIDS

Shift Solenoids "A" & "B" – Transmission is shifted up or down by 2 electric solenoids. Both solenoids are located on valve body. *See Fig. 1.* Ignition power is supplied to each solenoid by the transmission fuse. Solenoid "A" controls hydraulic pressure to 1-2 and 3-4 shift valves (if equipped). Solenoid "B" controls hydraulic pressure to 2-3 shift valve.

Force Motor (Pressure Control Solenoid) – Force motor solenoid has a spool valve and operates pressure regulator valve. *See Fig. 1.* The computer sends a frequency signal to the force motor to regulate hydraulic line pressure. The frequency signal (duty cycle) is measured with a dwell meter or lab scope. When the duty cycle is zero, line pressure is at maximum, and force motor draws zero amp. When the duty cycle is 40 percent, line pressure is at minimum, and force motor draws 1.1 amps at 4-5 volts.

TCC (PWM) Solenoid – This solenoid is used to control TCC apply valve. The computer sends a frequency signal to the TCC solenoid to gradually apply or release the TCC. *See Fig. 1.*

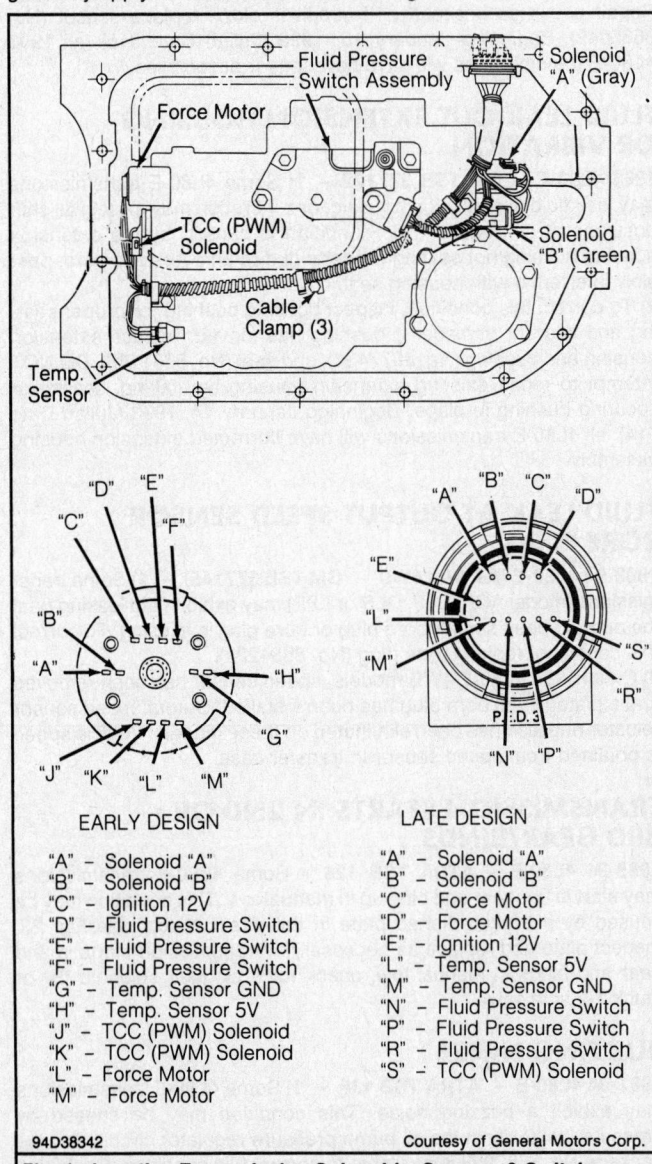

"A" – Solenoid "A"
"B" – Solenoid "B"
"C" – Ignition 12V
"D" – Fluid Pressure Switch
"E" – Fluid Pressure Switch
"F" – Fluid Pressure Switch
"G" – Temp. Sensor GND
"H" – Temp. Sensor 5V
"J" – TCC (PWM) Solenoid
"K" – TCC (PWM) Solenoid
"L" – Force Motor
"M" – Force Motor

EARLY DESIGN

"A" – Solenoid "A"
"B" – Solenoid "B"
"C" – Force Motor
"D" – Force Motor
"E" – Ignition 12V
"L" – Temp. Sensor 5V
"M" – Temp. Sensor GND
"N" – Fluid Pressure Switch
"P" – Fluid Pressure Switch
"R" – Fluid Pressure Switch
"S" – TCC (PWM) Solenoid

LATE DESIGN

94D38342   Courtesy of General Motors Corp.

Fig. 1: *Locating Transmission Solenoids, Sensors & Switches*

TORQUE CONVERTER CLUTCH (TCC) CONTROL COMPONENTS

NOTE: PCM may also be referred to as ECM.

The following components are used in TCC system. Not all components will be present on all vehicles.

Brake Switch – Power from ignition switch passes through brake switch to TCC solenoid. When brake pedal is depressed with TCC engaged, power to TCC solenoid is interrupted, releasing converter clutch and preventing engine from stalling.

Coolant Temperature Sensor – This sensor provides PCM with engine coolant temperature information. PCM will not allow TCC operation until signal from this sensor indicates coolant temperature greater than 130-150°F (55-65°C).

Powertrain Control Module (PCM) – To determine application of torque converter clutch, PCM receives and processes information from various input devices. These devices may include the vehicle speed sensor, coolant temperature sensor, throttle position sensor and brake switch. The PCM controls application of torque converter clutch by providing a ground circuit for the TCC solenoid circuit.

TCC Solenoid Assembly – Solenoid is energized by PCM to redirect transmission fluid to the converter clutch apply valve in the auxiliary control valve assembly.

TCC (PWM) Solenoid – Acts with TCC regulator valve to control the apply and release of TCC.

Throttle Position Sensor (TPS) – Provides PCM with throttle position information. TCC operation is prevented when throttle position signal is less than a specified value.

Vacuum Sensor – Sends engine vacuum (load) information to PCM.

Vehicle Speed Sensor (VSS) – This sensor sends vehicle speed information to PCM. Vehicle speed must be greater than a certain value before TCC can be applied. Two types of speed sensor are used. A light emitting diode type is used in the instrument cluster on some models. Other models use a Permanent Magnet (PM) generator mounted in the transmission.

NOTE: Diagnostic codes for coolant temperature sensor, throttle position sensor or vehicle speed sensor may be present while performing TCC electrical diagnosis. See ENGINE PERFORMANCE in appropriate MITCHELL® manual for complete information on General Motors Computerized Engine Control systems.

TCC TESTING

NOTE: When diagnosing converter clutch problems, ensure engine and vacuum systems are operating properly. For torque converter clutch electrical circuit information, see WIRING DIAGRAMS.

Converter Clutch Solenoid – Disconnect harness connector to Torque Converter Clutch (TCC) solenoid. Measure resistance between TCC solenoid terminals. Solenoid resistance should be greater than 20 ohms. *See Fig. 2.*

NOTE: Some solenoids have an internal pressure switch in series with the solenoid winding and will not show continuity until that pressure switch is applied by transmission hydraulic pressure.

Converter Lock-Up Signal At Transmission – **1)** Warm engine to operating temperature. Raise vehicle and support suspension where necessary to prevent damage to drive axles.
2) Disconnect converter clutch connector at transmission. Connect a test light across converter clutch harness terminals. Start engine and place transmission in Drive. Accelerate vehicle to 45 MPH and note test light.
3) If test light is not on, check solenoid power supply wire of harness for open or short to ground. Check ground circuit for open between harness connector and PCM. If harness is okay, see CONVERTER LOCK-UP SIGNAL FROM PCM.

Converter Lock-Up Signal From PCM – **1)** Warm engine to operating temperature. Raise vehicle and support suspension where necessary to prevent damage to drive axles.
2) Connect a test light to battery voltage. Touch TCC control driver terminal with test light. *See Fig. 2.* Accelerate vehicle to 45 MPH and note test light. If test light does not illuminate, problem is a faulty PCM connector or PCM.

SELF-DIAGNOSTICS

PCM/TCM constantly monitors all electrical circuits. If PCM/TCM detects circuit problem(s) or out-of-range sensor(s), a Diagnostic Trouble Code (DTC) will be recorded in computer memory. If problem continues for a preset time, the Malfunction Indicator Light (MIL) or SERVICE ENGINE SOON light will glow.

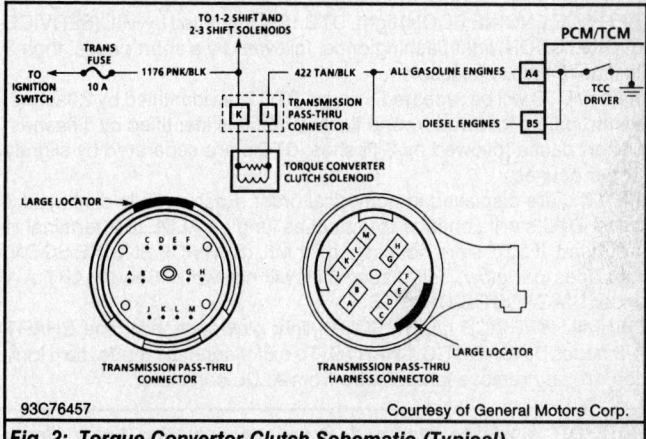

93C76457   Courtesy of General Motors Corp.

Fig. 2: Torque Converter Clutch Schematic (Typical)

If the MIL (SERVICE ENGINE SOON) light is always on, DTC is currently being detected. If the MIL (SERVICE ENGINE SOON) light is off, but PCM/TCM has detected a circuit or sensor problem, DTC's will be stored in computer memory.

Stored DTC's may be retrieved from PCM/TCM memory using scan tool or MIL (SERVICE ENGINE SOON) light. See appropriate RETRIEVING CODES procedure under ELECTRONIC SELF-DIAGNOSTICS.

NOTE: For complete PCM/TCM testing and diagnosis, see appropriate article in ENGINE PERFORMANCE of appropriate MITCHELL® manual.

ELECTRONIC SELF-DIAGNOSTICS

NOTE: To test electronic control of transmission solenoids without using self-diagnostics, go to COMPONENT TEST CHARTS (NO CODES) under ELECTRONIC TESTING. After repairs are made, trouble codes should be erased from computer memory. See CLEARING TROUBLE CODES under ELECTRONIC SELF-DIAGNOSTICS.

RETRIEVING CODES (WITHOUT SCAN TOOL)

NOTE: The Assembly Line Data Link (ALDL) may also be referred to as the Data Link Connector (DLC).

1) With key on and engine off, locate Assembly Line Data Link (ALDL) connector under dash, on driver's side of vehicle. Connect a jumper wire between ALDL terminal "B" (test terminal) and terminal "A" (ground terminal). *See Fig. 3.* This places control module in diagnostic mode.

NOTE: Connecting terminals "A" and "B" of ALDL connector with engine running will cause fuel injected vehicles to enter field service mode. The MIL (SERVICE ENGINE SOON) light will not flash codes if this is done.

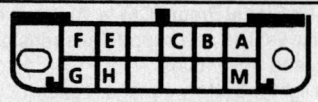

TERMINAL IDENTIFICATION

"A" – Ground
"B" – Diagnostic Terminal
"C" – Air Injection (If Used)
"E" – Serial Data Line

"F" – TCC
"G" – Fuel Pump
"H" – Brake Switch Sense Input
"M" – Serial Data Line

92G14130   Courtesy of General Motors Corp.

Fig. 3: Identifying ALDL Connector Terminals

2) In this mode, control module will display DTC 12 by flashing MIL (SERVICE ENGINE SOON) light. DTC 12 is identified by MIL (SERVICE ENGINE SOON) light flashing once, followed by a short pause, then 2 flashes in quick succession.

3) Each DTC will be repeated 3 times. DTC 21 is identified by 2 flashes, a short pause followed by one flash; DTC 53 is identified by 5 flashes, a short pause followed by 3 flashes. DTC's are separated by slightly longer pauses.

4) DTC's are displayed in numerical order. Each code is displayed 3 times. DTC's will continue to repeat as long as ALDL test terminal is grounded. If DTC's are not flashed, or MIL (SERVICE ENGINE SOON) light does not glow, self-diagnostics will not work. See CHART A-1 under DIAGNOSTIC CHARTS.

5) If MIL (SERVICE LIGHT SOON) light glows steadily, see CHART A-2 under DIAGNOSTIC CHARTS. To exit diagnostic mode, turn ignition off, and remove jumper wire from ALDL connector.

NOTE: DTC's will be recorded at various operating times. Some codes require operation of sensor or switch for 5 seconds; others may require operation for 5 minutes or longer at normal operating temperature, road speed and load. Therefore, some codes may not set in a service bay operational mode, but may require road testing vehicle in order to duplicate condition under which code will set.

RETRIEVING CODES (WITH SCAN TOOL)

NOTE: To read DTC's and check system voltages on serial data line, plug scan tool into ALDL.

The scan tool is a specialized tester which, when plugged into ALDL, can be used to diagnose on-board computer control systems by providing instant access to circuit voltage information without need to crawl under dash or hood to backprobe sensors and connectors.

Scan tools may also furnish information on status of output devices (solenoids and relays). However, status parameters are only an indication that output signals have been sent to devices by the control module. It does not indicate if devices have responded properly to that signal. This will need to be checked at output device using a voltmeter or test light.

NOTE: DTC 12 should always exist when ALDL is grounded with key on and engine off, but may not be indicated by all makes of scan tools.

If DTC is not present, this is not an indication that there is no problem. Driveability-related problems with codes displayed occur about 20 percent of the time, while driveability problems without codes occur about 80 percent of the time.

Out-of-specification sensors WILL NOT set trouble code, but WILL cause driveability problems. Using scan tool is the easiest method of checking sensor specifications and other data parameters. Intermittent wiring problems may be identified by wiggling wiring harnesses and connections (key on, engine off) while observing scan tool.

NOTE: If erroneous voltage signals are suspected, it will be necessary to verify tester information using digital voltmeter and wiring schematic. If non-existent codes are displayed, turn ignition off, remove scan tool, turn ignition on, and ground ALDL test terminal "B". The same codes should be retrieved whether scan tool or MIL (SERVICE ENGINE SOON) light is used.

TROUBLE CODE DEFINITION
PCM/TCM TROUBLE CODE DEFINITION

DTC No.	Circuit Affected
12 [1]	No RPM Reference Pulse
14	Coolant Temperature High
15	Coolant Temperature Low
21	Throttle Position Switch Voltage High
22	Throttle Position Switch Voltage Low
24	Output Speed Sensor Circuit
28	Pressure Switch Manifold Problem
37 [2]	Brake Switch Stuck ON
38 [2]	Brake Switch Stuck OFF
39	TCC Stuck OFF
51	Prom Error
52 [2]	System Voltage Too High (To Long)
53	System Voltage Too High
58	Fluid Temperature High
59	Fluid Temperature Low
63 [3]	Barometric Pressure Sensor Voltage High
64 [3]	Barometric Pressure Sensor Voltage Low
68	Overdrive Ratio Error Problem
69 [2]	TCC Stuck ON
71 [3]	Camshaft Position Sensor Circuit
72 [2]	Output Speed Signal Error
73	Force Motor Current Error
74 [2]	Input Speed Sensor Circuit Error
75	System Voltage Too Low
79	Fluid Temperature High
81	Shift Solenoid "B" Circuit Error
82	Shift Solenoid "A" Circuit Error
83	TCC (PWM) Solenoid Circuit Error
85	Undefined Ratio Error
86	Low Ratio Error
87	High Ratio Error

[1] – Display of a DTC 12 is normal when no reference pulses are received by control module (engine not running).
[2] – For 1994 diesel only.
[3] – For 1994 "G" and "P" series diesel only.

NOTE: Only transmission-related trouble codes are listed. If other trouble codes are present, see appropriate article in ENGINE PERFORMANCE of appropriate MITCHELL® manual.

HARD OR INTERMITTENT TROUBLE CODE DETERMINATION

During any diagnostic procedure, it must be determined if codes are hard failure codes or intermittent failure codes. A hard failure indicates that a problem is currently present. Diagnostic charts do not usually provide intermittent code diagnosis. To determine hard codes and intermittent codes, proceed as follows:

1) Manually enter diagnostic mode. Record all stored trouble codes. Exit diagnostic mode, and clear trouble codes. See CLEARING TROUBLE CODES.

2) Apply parking brake and place transmission in Neutral or Park. Block drive wheels and start engine. MIL (SERVICE ENGINE SOON) light should go out. Operate warm engine at specified curb idle for 2 minutes, and note MIL (SERVICE ENGINE SOON) light.

3) If MIL (SERVICE ENGINE SOON) light does not come on, codes are intermittent failures. If MIL (SERVICE ENGINE SOON) light comes on, manually enter diagnostic mode. Record trouble codes. If same codes reappear, they are hard failure codes. It may be necessary to road test vehicle in order to reset hard failure codes.

CLEARING TROUBLE CODES

Trouble codes should be cleared after repairs have been completed. Also, some diagnostic charts require that codes be cleared before using diagnostic chart. To clear codes, disconnect PCM/TCM power feed for 30 seconds.

DIAGNOSTIC CHARTS

The following charts include flow charts, testing information and related wiring diagram. Terminal numbers and wire colors may vary depending on model. For complete transmission wiring diagrams, see WIRING DIAGRAMS. For additional engine diagnostic information, see appropriate article in ENGINE PERFORMANCE of appropriate MITCHELL® manual.

NOTE: Some charts require the use of a bidirectional (Tech 1) scan tool. If a bidirectional scan tool is not available, the PCM/TCM-controlled relays and solenoids may be energized by grounding ALDL test terminal "B" with ignition on and engine off. DIAGNOSTIC AIDS in charts may help diagnose trouble codes when problem cannot be identified through circuit checks.

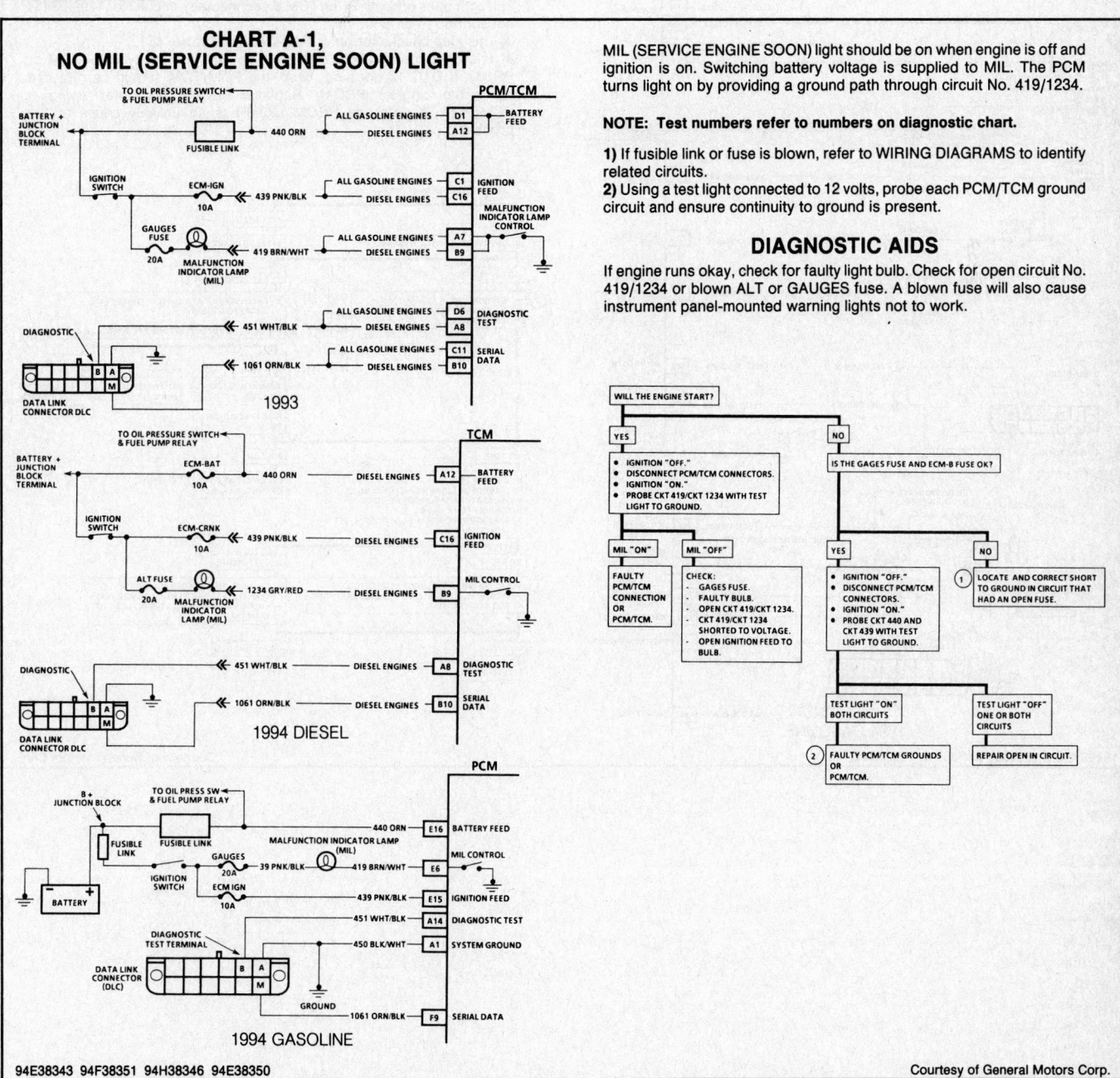

MIL (SERVICE ENGINE SOON) light should be on when engine is off and ignition is on. Switching battery voltage is supplied to MIL. The PCM turns light on by providing a ground path through circuit No. 419/1234.

NOTE: Test numbers refer to numbers on diagnostic chart.

1) If fusible link or fuse is blown, refer to WIRING DIAGRAMS to identify related circuits.
2) Using a test light connected to 12 volts, probe each PCM/TCM ground circuit and ensure continuity to ground is present.

DIAGNOSTIC AIDS

If engine runs okay, check for faulty light bulb. Check for open circuit No. 419/1234 or blown ALT or GAUGES fuse. A blown fuse will also cause instrument panel-mounted warning lights not to work.

94E38343 94F38351 94H38346 94E38350

Courtesy of General Motors Corp.

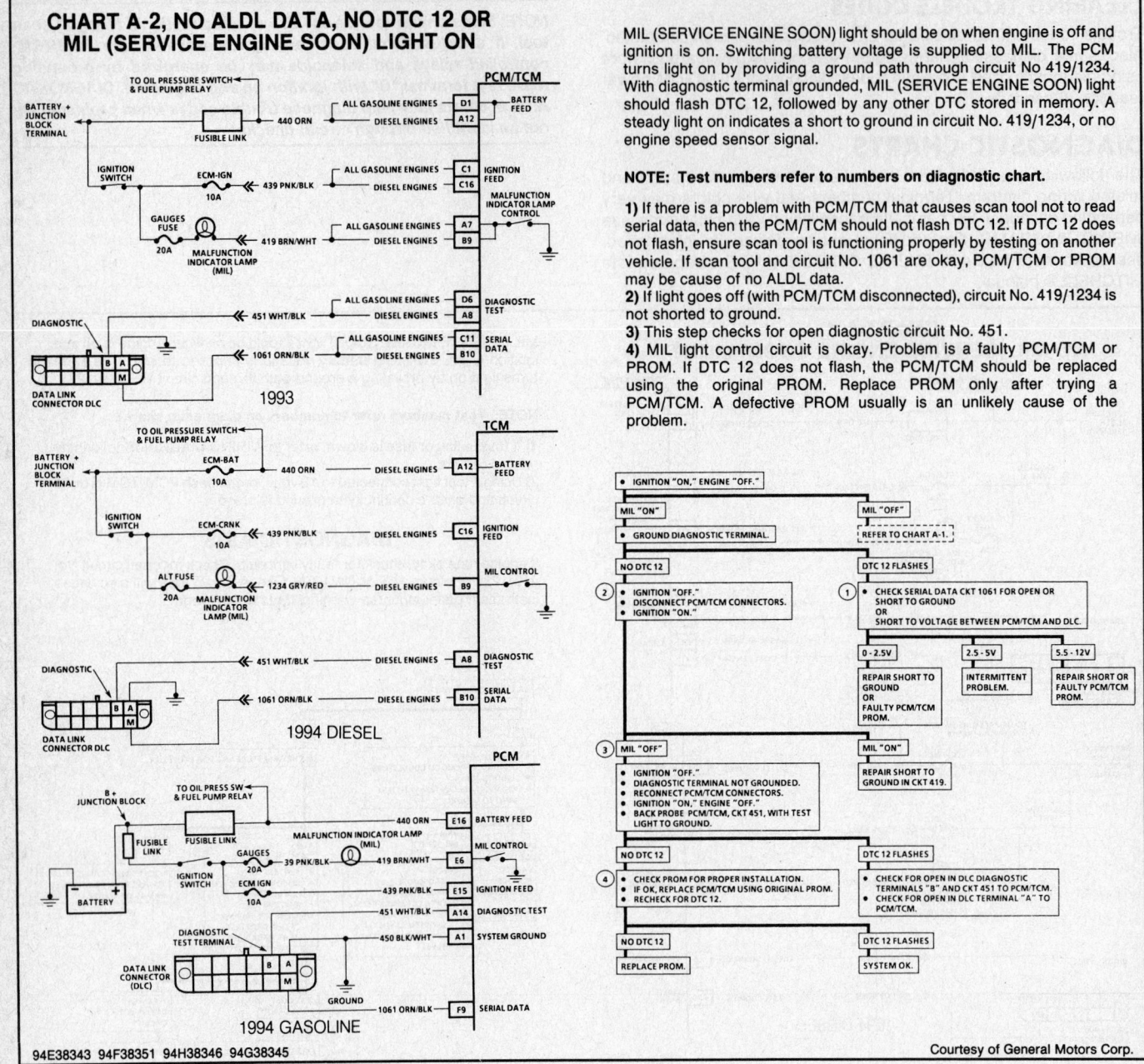

CHART A-2, NO ALDL DATA, NO DTC 12 OR MIL (SERVICE ENGINE SOON) LIGHT ON

MIL (SERVICE ENGINE SOON) light should be on when engine is off and ignition is on. Switching battery voltage is supplied to MIL. The PCM turns light on by providing a ground path through circuit No 419/1234. With diagnostic terminal grounded, MIL (SERVICE ENGINE SOON) light should flash DTC 12, followed by any other DTC stored in memory. A steady light on indicates a short to ground in circuit No. 419/1234, or no engine speed sensor signal.

NOTE: Test numbers refer to numbers on diagnostic chart.

1) If there is a problem with PCM/TCM that causes scan tool not to read serial data, then the PCM/TCM should not flash DTC 12. If DTC 12 does not flash, ensure scan tool is functioning properly by testing on another vehicle. If scan tool and circuit No. 1061 are okay, PCM/TCM or PROM may be cause of no ALDL data.
2) If light goes off (with PCM/TCM disconnected), circuit No. 419/1234 is not shorted to ground.
3) This step checks for open diagnostic circuit No. 451.
4) MIL light control circuit is okay. Problem is a faulty PCM/TCM or PROM. If DTC 12 does not flash, the PCM/TCM should be replaced using the original PROM. Replace PROM only after trying a PCM/TCM. A defective PROM usually is an unlikely cause of the problem.

94E38343 94F38351 94H38346 94G38345

Courtesy of General Motors Corp.

DTC 14, COOLANT TEMPERATURE SENSOR HIGH TEMPERATURE INDICATED (SIGNAL VOLTAGE LOW)

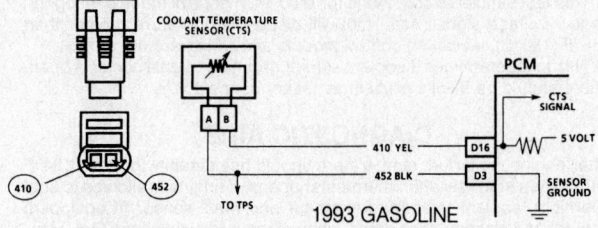

1993 GASOLINE

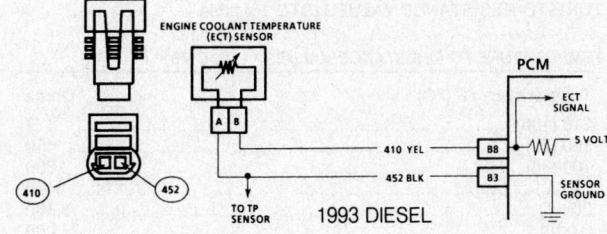

1993 DIESEL

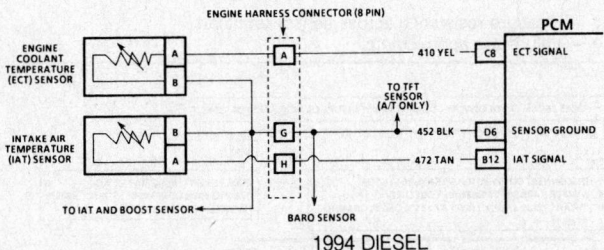

1994 DIESEL

PCM uses coolant temperature sensor inputs in determining control of fuel delivery, engine timing, idle and converter clutch (TCC). As engine warms, sensor resistance reduces. At normal operating temperature, voltage signal will be about 1.5-2.0 volts at PCM coolant sensor terminals.

NOTE: For 1994 gasoline, see appropriate wiring diagram under WIRING DIAGRAMS. Test numbers refer to numbers on diagnostic chart.

1) This checks if conditions for DTC 14 still exist. DTC 14 indicates control module has sensed low coolant sensor voltage signal (high temperature) at control module terminal for 6 seconds.

2) This tests for grounded sensor signal line between control module and coolant sensor.

DIAGNOSTIC AIDS

After engine is started, temperature should rise steadily to about 194°F (90°C), then stabilize when thermostat opens. If engine is allowed to cool overnight, coolant temperature sensor and MAT sensor (if equipped) should read close to each other, when measured with a scan tool. Measure sensor resistance to check for shifted calibration. See TEMPERATURE-TO-RESISTANCE VALUES (DTC 14) table.

TEMPERATURE-TO-RESISTANCE VALUES [1] [2] (DTC 14)

Temperature °F (°C)	Ohms
210 (100)	177
160 (70)	450
100 (38)	1800
70 (20)	3400
20 (-7)	13,500
0 (-18)	25,000
-40 (-40)	100,700

[1] – Measure resistance across sensor terminals.
[2] – Values are approximate.

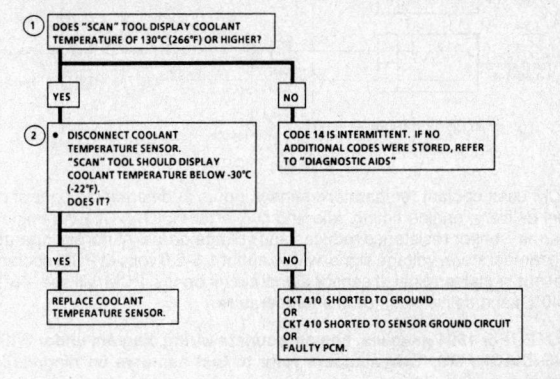

92E13874 93A76596 94B38399 92J13879

Courtesy of General Motors Corp.

DTC 15, COOLANT TEMPERATURE SENSOR LOW TEMPERATURE INDICATED (SIGNAL VOLTAGE HIGH)

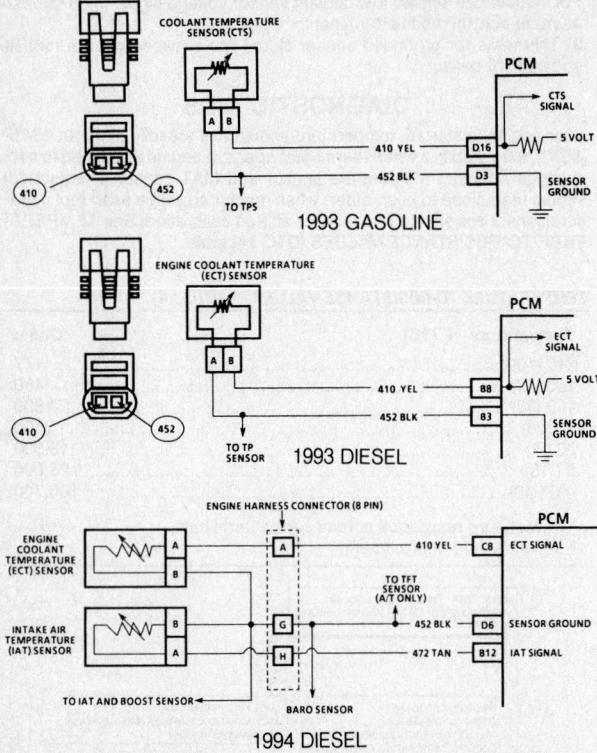

1993 GASOLINE

1993 DIESEL

1994 DIESEL

PCM uses coolant temperature sensor inputs in determining control of fuel delivery, engine timing, idle and converter clutch (TCC). As engine warms, sensor resistance reduces and voltage drops. At normal operating temperature, voltage signal will be about 1.5-2.0 volts at PCM coolant sensor signal terminal. If sensor signal circuit opens, PCM will see -40°F (-40°C) and deliver fuel for this temperature.

NOTE: For 1994 gasoline, see appropriate wiring diagram under WIRING DIAGRAMS. Test numbers refer to test numbers on diagnostic chart.

92E13874 93A76596 94B38399 92D13881

1) This checks if conditions for DTC 15 still exist. DTC 15 indicates control module has sensed high resistance in coolant sensor circuit. This could be due to high resistance (low temperature) or high voltage at coolant sensor terminal at control module for one second.
2) This test simulates conditions for DTC 14. If control module recognizes low voltage signal, scan tool will display temperature greater than 266°F (130°C), indicating control module and wiring are not at fault.
3) This test determines if coolant sensor ground or signal circuit is open. There should be 5 volts present at sensor connector.

DIAGNOSTIC AIDS

After engine is started, temperature should rise steadily to about 194°F (90°C) then stabilize when thermostat opens. If engine is allowed to cool overnight, coolant temperature sensor and MAT sensor (if equipped) should read close to each other, when measured with a scan tool. Measure sensor resistance to check for shifted calibration. See TEMPERATURE-TO-RESISTANCE VALUES (DTC 15) table.

TEMPERATURE-TO-RESISTANCE VALUES [1] [2] (DTC 15)

Temperature °F (°C)	Ohms
210 (100)	177
160 (70)	450
100 (38)	1800
70 (20)	3400
20 (-7)	13,500
0 (-18)	25,000
-40 (-40)	100,700

[1] – Measure resistance across sensor terminals.
[2] – Values are approximate.

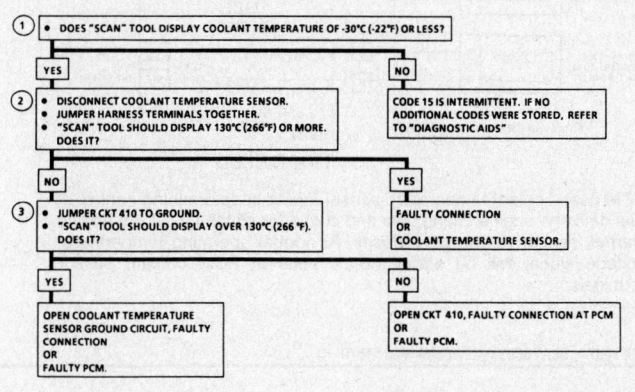

Courtesy of General Motors Corp.

DTC 21, THROTTLE POSITION SENSOR SIGNAL VOLTAGE HIGH

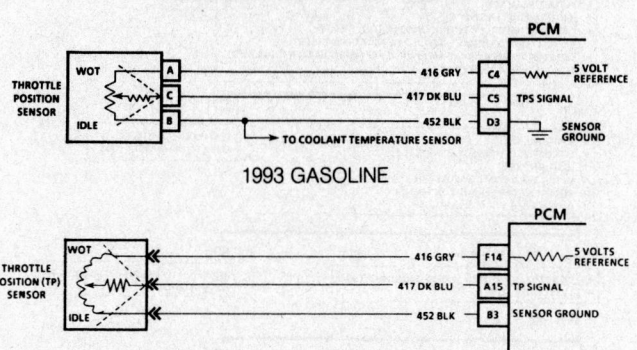

1993 GASOLINE

1993 DIESEL & 1994 GASOLINE

Throttle Position Sensor (TPS) provides a varying voltage signal depending on throttle valve angle. Signal voltage varies from about .50 volt at idle to 4.5 volts at wide open throttle. Each time TPS voltage drops to less than 1.25 volts and stops, PCM assumes this is zero degrees throttle angle and measures throttle percentage angle from this point. When DTC 21 sets, the following occurs:

- Torque converter clutch will not be applied.
- Pressure control solenoid current will be low, resulting in high line pressure.
- Fixed or harsh shift points, and no 4th gear when hot.

NOTE: Test numbers refer to numbers on diagnostic chart.

1) DTC 21 sets if TP signal voltage is greater than 4.9 volts at WOT for 4 seconds.
2) With TP sensor disconnected, TP voltage should go low if the PCM and wiring are okay.
3) Probing circuit No. 452 with a test light checks 5-volt return circuit.

DIAGNOSTIC AIDS

Scan tool displays throttle position in volts. Closed throttle voltage should be low. As throttle angle increase, voltage should increase gradually to about 4.5 volts at a steady rate.

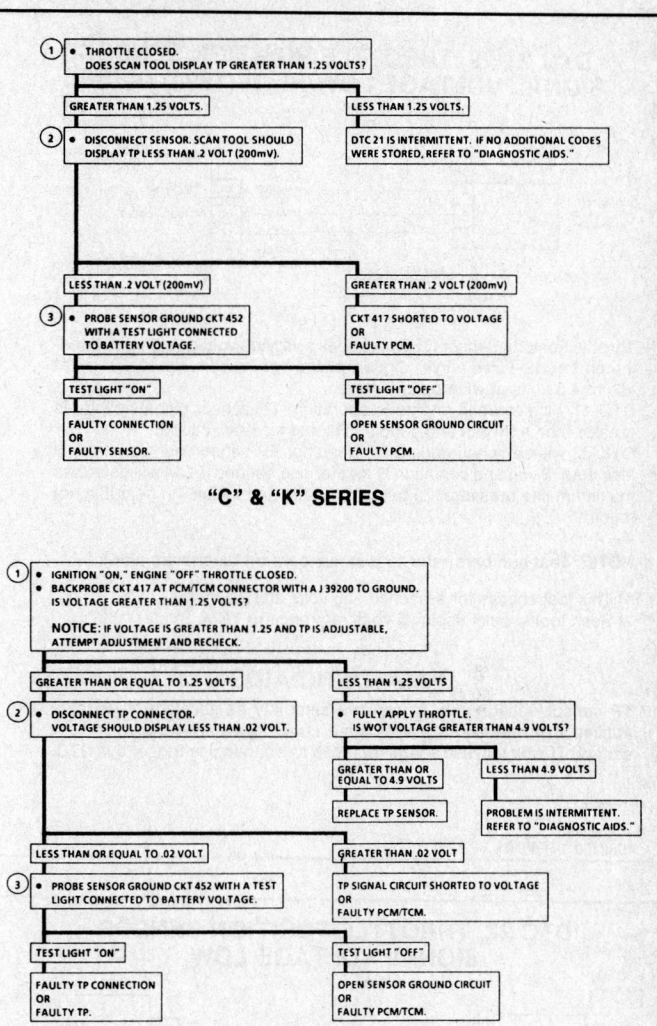

"C" & "K" SERIES

"G" & "P" SERIES

92E13882 93A76604 93F76609 93B76605

Courtesy of General Motors Corp.

DTC 21/22, THROTTLE POSITION SENSOR SIGNAL VOLTAGE LOW/HIGH (1994) DIESEL

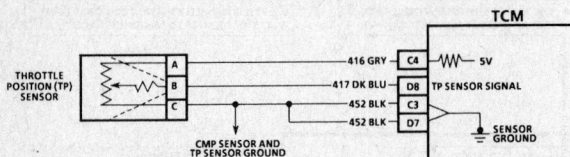

Throttle Position Sensor (TPS) provides a varying voltage signal depending on throttle valve angle. Signal voltage varies from about .50 volt at idle to 4.5 volts at wide open throttle.

DTC 21 will set when engine is operating, TP sensor signal voltage is greater than 4.9 volts and condition is met for one second.

DTC 22 will set when engine is operating, TP sensor signal voltage is less than .2 volt and condition is met for one second. PCM will default to maximum line pressure, 35 percent throttle and inhibit 4th gear if in hot mode.

NOTE: Test numbers refer to test numbers on diagnostic chart.

1) This test checks for presence of 5 volts at TP sensor.
2) Scan tool should display 5 volts reference to TCM.

DIAGNOSTIC AIDS

TP sensor voltage should increase smoothly as accelerator pedal is applied. If an intermittent is suspected, check terminal tension at TP sensor and TCM. Also, use snapshot mode on scan tool to trigger this DTC.

94E38400 94F38401

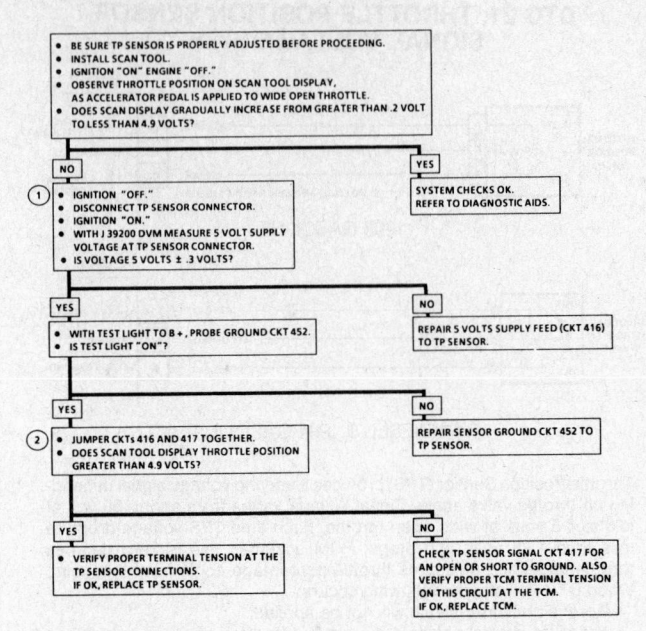

WHEN ALL DIAGNOSIS AND REPAIRS ARE COMPLETED, CLEAR DTC(s) AND VERIFY PROPER OPERATION.

Courtesy of General Motors Corp.

DTC 22, THROTTLE POSITION SENSOR SIGNAL VOLTAGE LOW

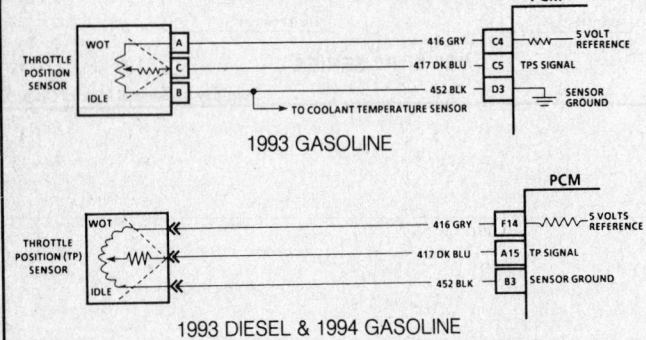

1993 GASOLINE

1993 DIESEL & 1994 GASOLINE

Throttle Position Sensor (TPS) provides a varying voltage signal depending on throttle valve angle. Signal voltage varies from about .50 volt at idle to 4.5 volts at wide open throttle. When DTC 22 sets, the following occurs:

- Torque converter clutch will not be applied.
- Pressure control solenoid current will be low, resulting in high line pressure and harsh shifts.

NOTE: Test numbers refer to test numbers on diagnostic chart.

1) DTC 22 will set if TP signal voltage is less than .06 volt for 4 seconds.
2) This test simulates conditions for DTC 21. If control module recognizes state change, control module and wiring are okay.
3) This simulates high signal voltage to check for open in TPS signal line to control module. Scan tool should recognize signal and display high TPS voltage.

92E13882 93A76604 93J76611

DIAGNOSTIC AIDS

Scan tool displays throttle position in volts. Closed throttle voltage should be low. As throttle angle increases, voltage should increase gradually to about 4.5 volts at a steady rate. Open or short to ground in circuits No. 416 or 417 will set DTC 22.

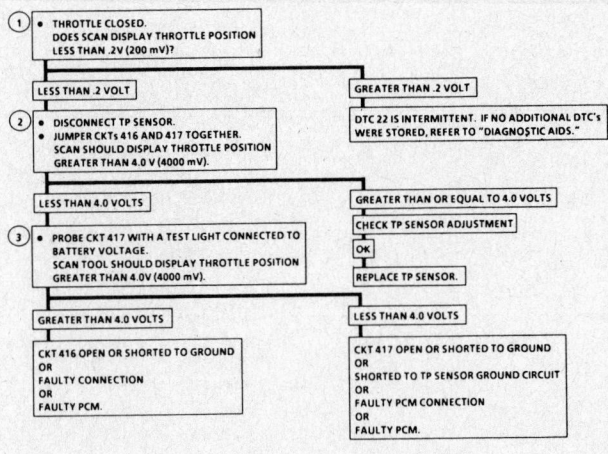

Courtesy of General Motors Corp.

DTC 24, OUTPUT SPEED SENSOR LOW
(1993 2WD)

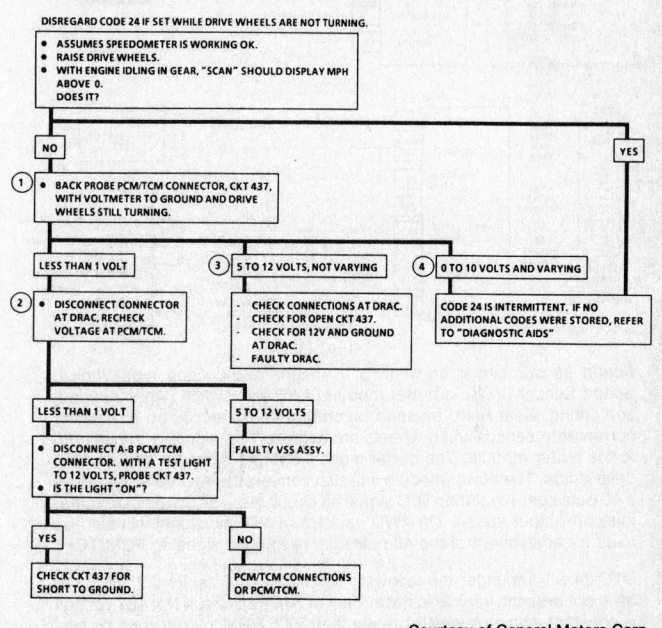

1) This tests for voltage variation while wheels are turning. Voltage will be low at low wheel speeds (4-6 volts at 20 MPH).
2) This step determines whether VSS assembly is faulty, circuit No. 437 is grounded, or PCM/TCM connector or PCM/TCM is faulty.
3) This signal indicates an open circuit No. 437 or faulty DRAC.
4) This is a normal voltage signal.

DIAGNOSTIC AIDS

Using scan tool, check for proper signal in Drive while wiggling wiring. Ensure all connectors are good. Check the pass-through connector at transmission.

The speed sensor, which is a Permanent Magnet (PM) generator, provides Digital Ratio Adapter Control (DRAC) with vehicle speed information. PM generator, mounted in transmission, produces a pulsing voltage signal whenever vehicle speed is more than 3 MPH. Voltage level and pulse increase with vehicle speed. DRAC converts PM generator signal to a pulsing signal by grounding circuit No. 437 (Brown wire) 2000 times per mile. Control module uses this signal in calculations to determine vehicle adjustments.

DTC 24 will set under following conditions: vehicle speed is zero, transmission is not in Park or Neutral, engine speed is greater than 3000 RPM, and PCM/TCM input circuit No. 437 is constant. All of these conditions must be met for 1.5 seconds. PM generator only produces voltage signal if drive wheels are turning faster than 3 MPH.

NOTE: Test numbers refer to numbers on diagnostic chart.

92A14100 92B14101

Courtesy of General Motors Corp.

DTC 24, OUTPUT SPEED SENSOR LOW
(1993 4WD)

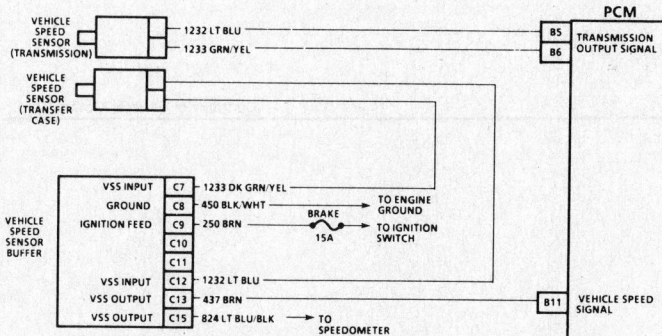

NOTE: Test numbers refer to numbers on diagnostic chart.

1) This step tests for voltage variation while wheels are turning. Voltage will be low at low wheel speeds (4-6 volts at 20 MPH).
2) This step tests operation of output sensor.

DIAGNOSTIC AIDS

Check the pass-through connector at transmission. If input sensor is not working at start-up, output sensor will read zero.

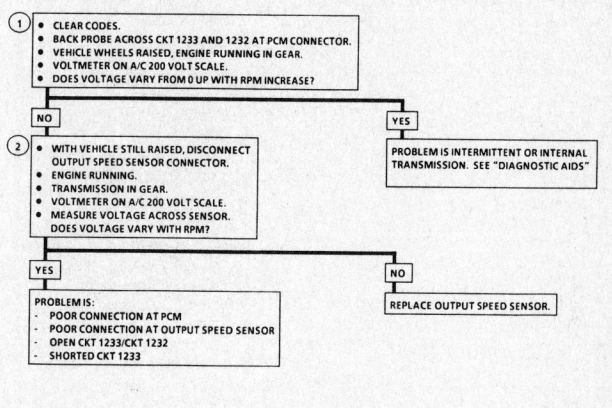

The speed sensor, which is a Permanent Magnet (PM) generator, provides PCM/TCM with vehicle speed information. PM generator, mounted in transfer case, produces a pulsing voltage signal whenever vehicle speed is greater than 3 MPH. Control module uses this signal in calculations to determine vehicle adjustments.

DTC 24 will set under following conditions: vehicle speed is less than 20 MPH, transmission is not in Park or Neutral, and engine speed is greater than 3000 RPM. All of these conditions must be met for 1.5 seconds. PM generator only produces voltage signal if drive wheels are turning faster than 3 MPH.

93H76361 92H14099

Courtesy of General Motors Corp.

DTC 24 & DTC 72, VEHICLE SPEED SENSOR (OUTPUT SPEED SIGNAL LOW) & (OUTPUT SPEED SIGNAL LOSS) 1994

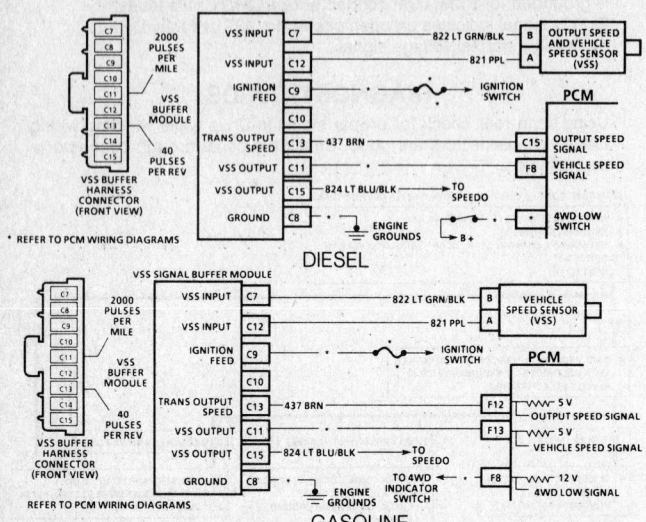

DIESEL

* REFER TO PCM WIRING DIAGRAMS

REFER TO PCM WIRING DIAGRAMS

GASOLINE

Speed sensor circuit consists of a magnetic induction type Vehicle Speed Sensor (VSS), a buffer module, 4WD low switch (when needed) and wiring. Gear teeth pressed on output shaft induces an alternating current into sensor when wheels are turning. This signal is transmitted to the buffer module. The buffer module compensates for various final drive ratios. The buffer module will also convert the A/C VSS signal into a 40 pulse per revolution D/C signal on circuit No. 437, to indicate transmission output speed. On 4WD vehicles, 4WD low signal will also be used for adjustment of the 40 pulse per revolution signal to PCM/TCM.

DTC 24 will set under the following conditions: DTC(s) 21, 22, 28, 33 or 34 is not present, vehicle is not in Park or Neutral, circuit No. 437 voltage is constant, engine speed is greater than 3000 RPM, output speed is less than 200 RPM, MAP pressure is greater than 5.8 psi, throttle position is between 10 percent and 100 percent, and all conditions are met for 3 seconds. PCM/TCM will default to 2nd gear only at maximum line pressure.

DTC 72 will set under the following conditions: with vehicle not in Park or Neutral, DTC 28 is not present, engine speed is greater than 300 RPM, output speed is greater than 1000 RPM, (2050 RPM in Park or Neutral) and all conditions are met for 2 seconds. PCM/TCM will default to maximum line pressure and a soft delayed shift to second gear will occur.

94J39189 94C38366 94D38376

NOTE: Test numbers refer to numbers on diagnostic chart.

1) This test checks for voltage to buffer module.
2) This test checks ground circuit to buffer module.
3) This test checks VSS circuit at buffer module.
4) This test checks for an output speed signal from buffer module.

DIAGNOSTIC AIDS

DTC 24 will set when no vehicle speed is detected at start off. DTC 72 will set when vehicle speed has been detected and is lost during vehicle operation.

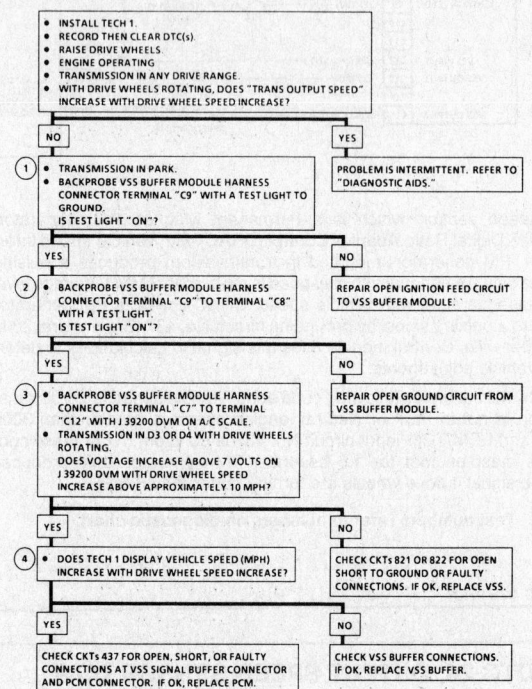

DTC 28, PRESSURE SWITCH MANIFOLD (PSM) ASSEMBLY FAULT (1993)

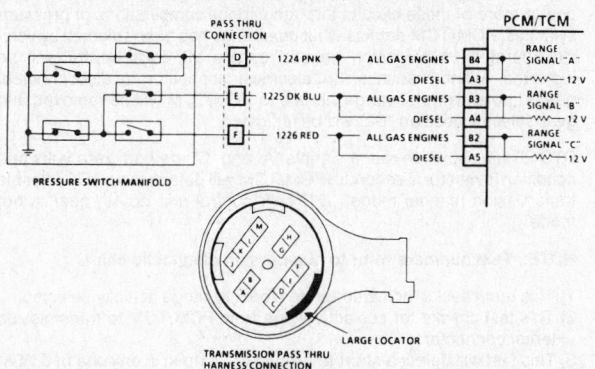

PRESSURE SWITCH MANIFOLD

TRANSMISSION PASS THRU
HARNESS CONNECTION

LARGE LOCATOR

Pressure Switch Manifold (PSM), also referred to as fluid pressure switch assembly, is actually 5 pressure switches combined into one unit and mounted on the transmission valve body. The PCM/TCM supplies battery voltage to the PSM on 3 separate wires. By grounding one or more of these circuits through various combinations of switches inside the pressure switch manifold, the PCM/TCM detects what gear range has been selected by the vehicle operator.

NOTE: Test numbers refer to numbers on diagnostic chart.

1) This step tests for proper operation of pressure switches.
2) This step tests for correct voltage from PCM/TCM to transmission pass-through connector.
3) This step tests for short to ground in any one of 3 pressure switch circuits.

DIAGNOSTIC AIDS

DTC 28 will set if PCM/TCM detects one of 2 "illegal" PSM assembly combinations. See PSM COMBINATION CHART for range combinations. Check all wiring connectors for proper terminal tension and location.

91B13673 92D14103

PSM COMBINATION CHART

Gear Shift Position	[1] Range Signal Circuit(s)
Park	"A" & "C"
Reverse	"C"
Neutral	"A" & "C"
4th	"A"
3rd	"A" & "B"
2nd	"A", "B" & "C"
1st	"B" & "C"
Illegal	"B"
Illegal	None

[1] – See mini-schematic to determine range signal circuits.

① • CLEAR CODES.
• RAISE DRIVE WHEELS.
• WITH ENGINE IDLING - PLACE TRANSMISSION IN MANUAL LOW, THEN MOVE ON TO EACH PROGRESSIVELY HIGHER RANGE.
"SCAN" SHOULD MATCH SELECTED RANGE.
DOES IT?

NO → • IGNITION "OFF."
• DISCONNECT TRANSMISSION PASS-THRU CONNECTOR.
• IGNITION "ON."
• WITH A VOLTMETER, CHECK VOLTAGE AT HARNESS CONNECTOR TERMINALS "D", "E" AND "F".
IS THERE SYSTEM VOLTAGE ON ALL PINS?

YES → PROBLEM IS INTERMITTENT, SEE "DIAGNOSTIC AIDS"

② NO → • IGNITION STILL "ON."
• DVM SELECTION SWITCH SET ON 20 VDC SCALE.
• BACKPROBE PCM/TCM HARNESS CONNECTOR RANGE CIRCUITS THAT HAD LOW OR NO VOLTAGE.
IS THERE SYSTEM VOLTAGE?

YES → CHECK TRANSMISSION INTERNAL HARNESS FOR OPEN OR SHORT TO GROUND.

HARNESS OK

FAULTY PRESSURE SWITCH MANIFOLD

③ NO → • IGNITION "OFF."
• DISCONNECT PCM/TCM A-B CONNECTOR.
• WITH A TEST LIGHT CONNECTED TO 12 VOLTS, PROBE SAME PCM/TCM HARNESS CONNECTOR TERMINALS.

YES → OPEN RANGE CIRCUIT FROM PCM/TCM TO TRANSMISSION PASS-THRU CONNECTOR.

LIGHT "OFF" → PROBLEM IS FAULTY CONNECTION AT PCM/TCM, OR PCM/TCM.

LIGHT "ON" → RANGE CIRCUIT SHORTED TO GROUND BETWEEN PCM/TCM AND TRANSMISSION.

Courtesy of General Motors Corp.

DTC 28, PRESSURE SWITCH MANIFOLD (PSM) ASSEMBLY FAULT (1994)

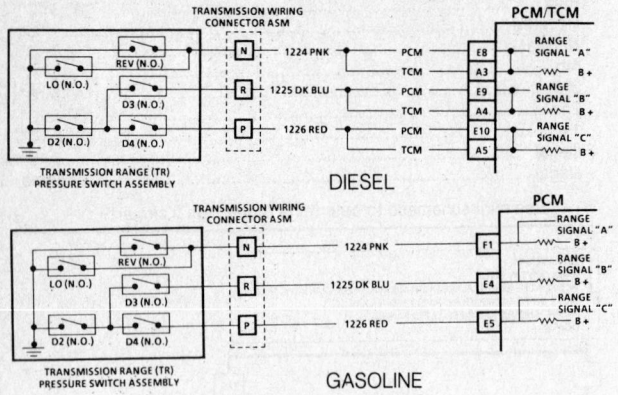

DIESEL

GASOLINE

DIAGNOSTIC AIDS

DTC 28 will set if PCM/TCM detects one of 2 "illegal" PSM assembly combinations. See PSM COMBINATION CHART for range combinations. Check all wiring connectors for proper terminal tension and location.

PSM COMBINATION CHART

Gear Shift Position	[1] Range Signal Circuit(s)
Park	"A" & "C"
Reverse	"C"
Neutral	"A" & "C"
4th	"A"
3rd	"A" & "B"
2nd	"A", "B" & "C"
1st	"B" & "C"
Illegal	"B"
Illegal	None

[1] – See mini-schematic to determine range signal circuits.

Pressure Switch Manifold (PSM) assembly, also referred to as fluid pressure switch assembly, consists of 5 normally open pressure switches. PCM/TCM supplies battery voltage to each range signal. By grounding one or more of these circuits through various combinations of pressure switches, PCM/TCM detects what gear range has been selected by vehicle operator. With ignition on and engine off, Park/Neutral will be indicated. When transmission electrical connector is disconnected, ground potential for 3 range signals to PCM/TCM will be removed and gear selector position "D2" will be indicated.

DTC 28 will set when range signals "A" and "C" are both zero volts and condition is met for 2 seconds. PCM/TCM will default to no TCC, disable transmission manual mode, "D4" shift control and no 4th gear in hot mode.

NOTE: Test numbers refer to numbers on diagnostic chart.

1) This test checks indicated range signal to range actually selected.
2) This test checks for correct voltage from PCM/TCM to transmission external connector.
3) This test will detect a short to ground or an open in any one of 3 PSM assembly range circuits.

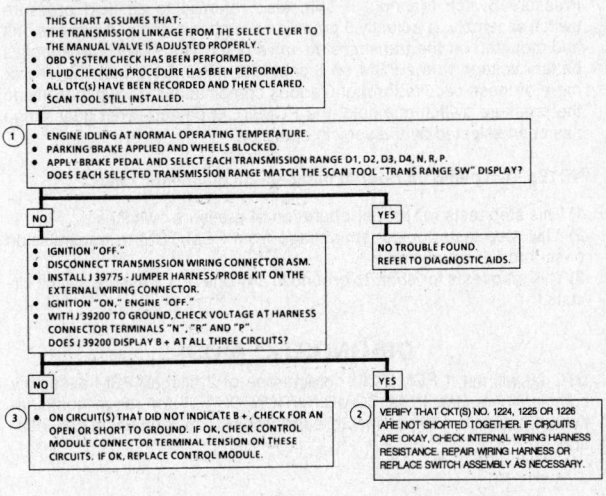

WHEN ALL DIAGNOSIS AND REPAIRS ARE COMPLETED, CLEAR DTC(s) AND VERIFY PROPER OPERATION.

94G38352 94E38368 94F38369

DTC 37 & 38, TCC BRAKE SWITCH STUCK ON OR OFF (1994)

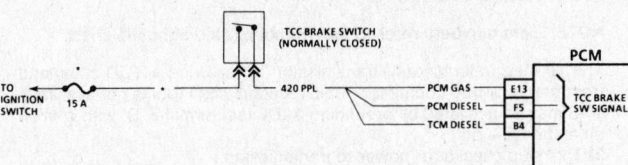

TCC BRAKE SWITCH (NORMALLY CLOSED)

TO IGNITION SWITCH — 15 A — 420 PPL — PCM GAS E13 / PCM DIESEL F5 / TCM DIESEL B4 — **PCM** — TCC BRAKE SW SIGNAL

Normally closed brake switch supplies battery voltage signal on circuit No. 420 to PCM/TCM. Signal voltage drops to zero volts when TCC brake switch is opened (brake pedal depressed).

DTC 37 will set when circuit No. 420 is open, vehicle speed is less than 5 MPH for greater than 6 seconds, then vehicle speed is between 5-20 MPH for greater than 6 seconds, then vehicle speed is greater than 20 MPH for greater than 6 seconds. Conditions must occur on 7 different occasions.

DTC 38 will set when circuit No. 420 has constant voltage, vehicle speed is greater than 20 MPH for greater than 6 seconds, then vehicle speed is between 5-20 MPH for greater than 6 seconds. Conditions must occur on 7 different occasions.
For both DTC's, PCM/TCM will default to no TCC and no 4th gear in hot mode.

NOTE: Test numbers refer to numbers on diagnostic chart.

1) This test checks for voltage at brake switch.
2) This test checks brake switch.
3) This test checks circuit No. 420 at PCM/TCM.

DIAGNOSTIC AIDS

Problem may be intermittent. Check brake switch connections. Check customer driving habits and/or unusual traffic conditions such as stop and go traffic conditions.

94I38370 94J38371

- INSTALL SCAN TOOL.
- IGNITION SWITCH "ON," ENGINE "OFF."
- RECORD THEN CLEAR DTC(s).
- APPLY THEN RELEASE BRAKE PEDAL.
- DOES SCAN TOOL DISPLAY TCC BRAKE SW "OPEN" WITH BRAKE PEDAL APPLIED, AND THEN DISPLAY "CLOSED" WHEN RELEASED?

NO →

(1) WITH A TEST LIGHT CONNECTED TO GROUND, BACKPROBE IGNITION FEED CIRCUIT ON BRAKE SWITCH. IS TEST LIGHT "ON"?

YES →

WITH TEST LIGHT CONNECTED TO GROUND, BACKPROBE HARNESS CKT 420 AT BRAKE SWITCH. IS TEST LIGHT "ON"?

YES →

(2) APPLY BRAKE PEDAL. IS TEST LIGHT "OFF" WHEN BRAKE PEDAL IS APPLIED?

YES →

- IGNITION "OFF."
- DISCONNECT CONTROL MODULE CONNECTORS.
- IGNITION "ON," ENGINE "OFF."
- WITH A TEST LIGHT CONNECTED TO GROUND, PROBE CONTROL MODULE CKT 420 HARNESS CONNECTOR. IS TEST LIGHT "ON"?

YES →

(3)
- IGNITION "OFF."
- RECONNECT CONTROL MODULE CONNECTIONS.
- IGNITION "ON."
- APPLY THEN RELEASE BRAKE PEDAL.
- DOES SCAN TOOL DISPLAY TCC BRAKE SW "OPEN" WITH BRAKE APPLIED, AND THEN DISPLAY "CLOSED" WHEN RELEASED?

YES →

ELECTRICAL SYSTEM CHECKS OK AT THIS TIME. THE MALFUNCTION MAY BE INTERMITTENT OR MAY HAVE BEEN CORRECTED DURING THIS DIAGNOSTIC PROCEDURE. REFER TO DIAGNOSTIC AIDS.

YES →

NO TROUBLE FOUND. REFER TO "DIAGNOSTIC AIDS."

NO →

REPAIR OPEN IN THE IGNITION FEED CIRCUIT TO THE BRAKE SWITCH. IF THE IGNITION VOLTAGE FEED FUSE IS OPEN, ALSO CHECK CKT 420 FOR A SHORT TO GROUND.

NO →

BRAKE SWITCH OUT OF ADJUSTMENT OR FAULTY BRAKE SWITCH.

NO →

CHECK CKT 420 FOR SHORT TO B +. IF OK, REPLACE BRAKE SWITCH.

NO →

REPAIR OPEN CKT 420 FROM TCC BRAKE SWITCH TO PCM.

NO →

FAULTY CONTROL MODULE.

WHEN ALL DIAGNOSIS AND REPAIRS ARE COMPLETED, CLEAR DTC(s) AND VERIFY PROPER OPERATION.

Courtesy of General Motors Corp.

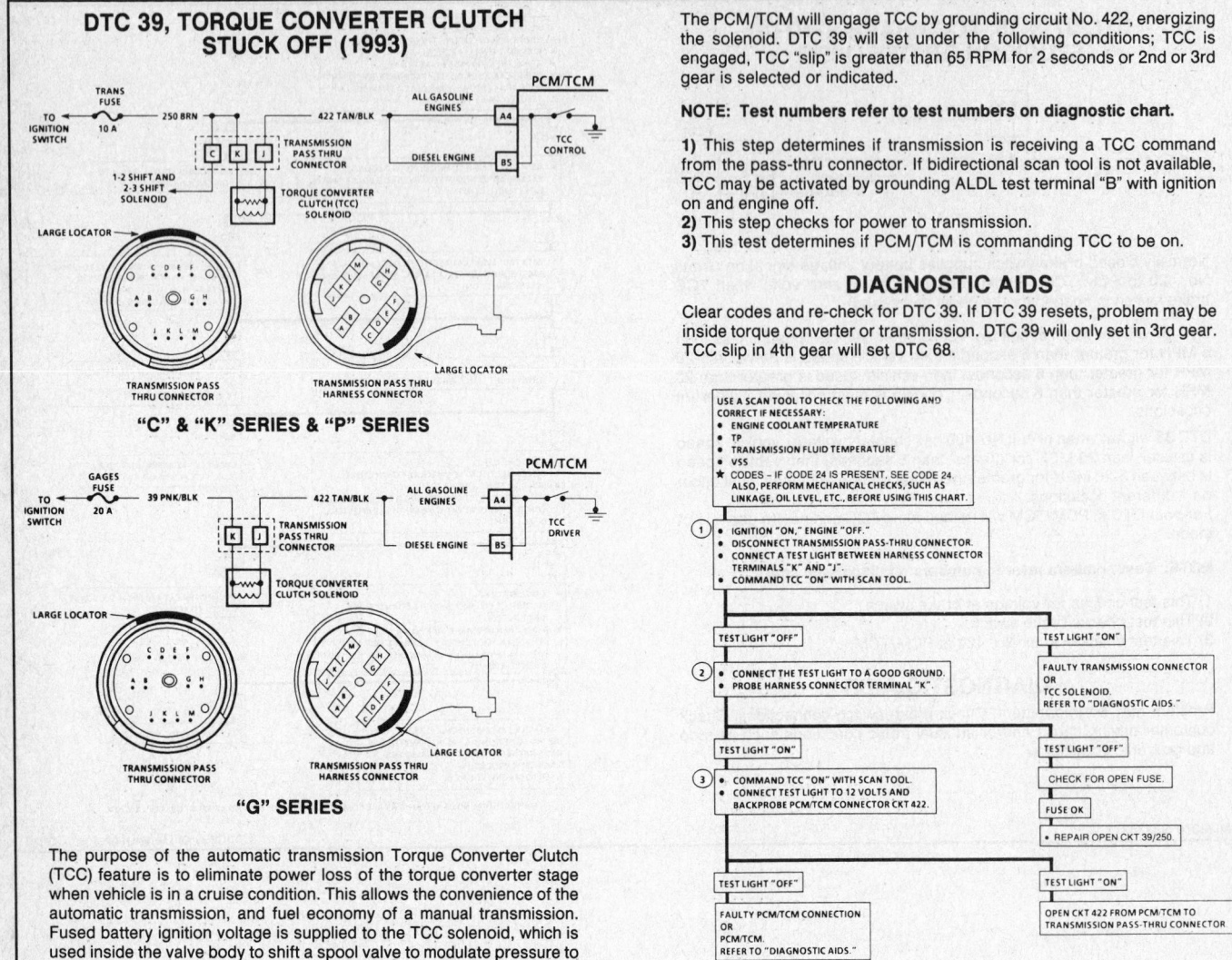

DTC 39, TORQUE CONVERTER CLUTCH STUCK OFF (1993)

"C" & "K" SERIES & "P" SERIES

"G" SERIES

The purpose of the automatic transmission Torque Converter Clutch (TCC) feature is to eliminate power loss of the torque converter stage when vehicle is in a cruise condition. This allows the convenience of the automatic transmission, and fuel economy of a manual transmission. Fused battery ignition voltage is supplied to the TCC solenoid, which is used inside the valve body to shift a spool valve to modulate pressure to the TCC. This modulated pressure normally allows some slight slippage of TCC.

The PCM/TCM will engage TCC by grounding circuit No. 422, energizing the solenoid. DTC 39 will set under the following conditions; TCC is engaged, TCC "slip" is greater than 65 RPM for 2 seconds or 2nd or 3rd gear is selected or indicated.

NOTE: Test numbers refer to test numbers on diagnostic chart.

1) This step determines if transmission is receiving a TCC command from the pass-thru connector. If bidirectional scan tool is not available, TCC may be activated by grounding ALDL test terminal "B" with ignition on and engine off.
2) This step checks for power to transmission.
3) This test determines if PCM/TCM is commanding TCC to be on.

DIAGNOSTIC AIDS

Clear codes and re-check for DTC 39. If DTC 39 resets, problem may be inside torque converter or transmission. DTC 39 will only set in 3rd gear. TCC slip in 4th gear will set DTC 68.

93F76302 93G76303 93H76304

Courtesy of General Motors Corp.

DTC 39, TORQUE CONVERTER CLUTCH STUCK OFF (1994)

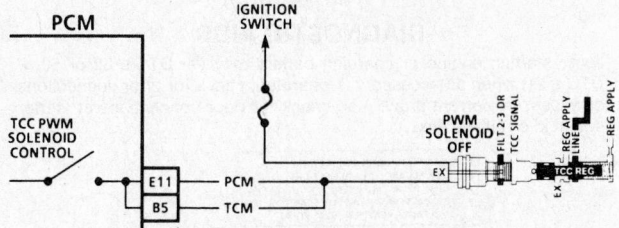

The purpose of the automatic transmission Torque Converter Clutch (TCC) feature is to eliminate power loss of the torque converter stage when vehicle is in a cruise condition. This allows the convenience of the automatic transmission, and fuel economy of a manual transmission.

PCM/TCM commands the TCC PWM solenoid on by modulating TCC signal fluid acting on converter clutch shift valve. TCC fluid applies torque converter clutch.

94B38557 94A38372

DTC 39 will set when DTC(s) 28, 71 or 74 is not present, TCC is commanded on, TCC slip speed is greater than 65 RPM, transmission range switch indicates "D3" or "D4", transmission is in 2nd or 3rd gear and all conditions are met for 2 seconds. PCM/TCM will inhibit 4th gear if in hot mode.

NOTE: Test number refers to number on diagnostic chart.

1) This test checks the mechanical and hydraulic operation of TCC, while commanded on by PCM/TCM.

DIAGNOSTIC AIDS

Snapshot mode will record 5 data parameters per second.

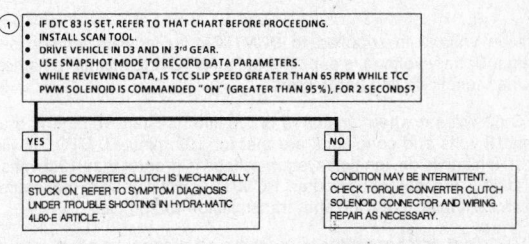

Courtesy of General Motors Corp.

DTC 51, PROM PROBLEM

Ensure all pins are fully inserted in socket. If pins are fully inserted, replace PROM and recheck. If problem is not corrected, replace PCM.

DTC 53, SYSTEM VOLTAGE HIGH (1993)

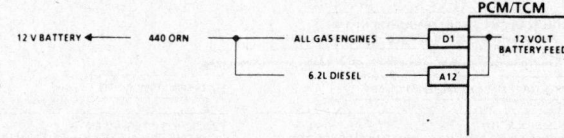

DTC 53 will set when ignition is on and PCM/TCM 12-volt battery feed voltage is greater than 19.5 volts for about 2 seconds. During the time the failure is present, the force motor is turned off, transmission immediately shifts to 2nd gear, and TCC operation is inhibited. The setting of additional codes may result.

NOTE: Test numbers refer to numbers on diagnostic chart.

1) Normal system charging voltage is 9-15 volts.
2) This test checks if high voltage reading is due to the alternator, circuit No. 440 or PCM/TCM. With engine running, check voltage at battery. If voltage is greater than 15 volts, the PCM/TCM is okay.
3) This step checks if alternator is faulty under load conditions. If voltage is greater than 15 volts, check alternator.

91F13677 93I76305

DIAGNOSTIC AIDS

Jump-starting engine or charging battery may set DTC 53. If DTC is set when an accessory is operated, check for poor connections or excessive current draw. Also check for poor connections at starter solenoid or fusible link.

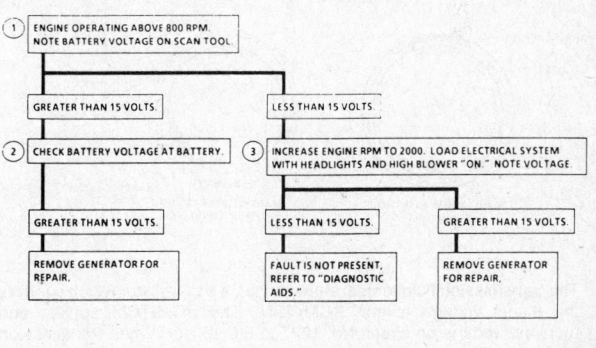

Courtesy of General Motors Corp.

AUTOMATIC TRANSMISSIONS
4L80-E Electronic Controls (Cont.)

DTC 52 & 53, LONG SYSTEM VOLTAGE HIGH OR SYSTEM VOLTAGE HIGH (1994)

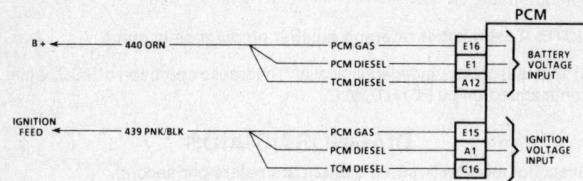

Ignition voltage is supplied to PCM/TCM to indicate ignition switch status. Battery voltage is supplied to PCM/TCM to maintain memory of learned functions and parameters.

DTC 52 will set when ignition is on, ignition system voltage is greater than 16 volts and conditions are met for 109 minutes. DTC 53 will set when ignition is on, ignition system voltage is greater than 19.5 volts and conditions are met for 2 minutes. PCM/TCM will default to maximum line pressure, inhibit TCC and shift transmission to 2nd gear.

NOTE: Test numbers refer to numbers on diagnostic chart.

94B38373 94C38374

1) Normal battery voltage is between 9-15 volts.
2) This test checks if alternator is faulty under load conditions. If voltage is more than 15 volts, check and repair charging system as necessary.

DIAGNOSTIC AIDS

Jump-starting engine or charging battery may set DTC's 52 or 53. If DTC's set when an accessory is operated, check for poor connections or excessive current draw. Also check for poor connections at starter solenoid or fusible link.

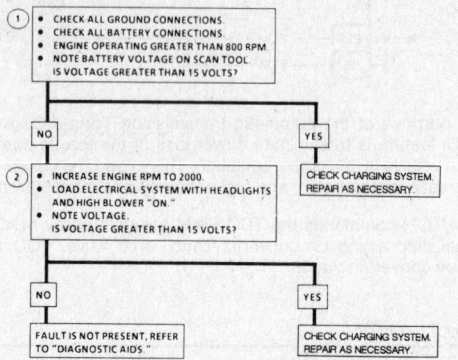

Courtesy of General Motors Corp.

DTC 58, TRANSMISSION FLUID TEMPERATURE SENSOR CIRCUIT (HIGH TEMPERATURE INDICATED) 1993

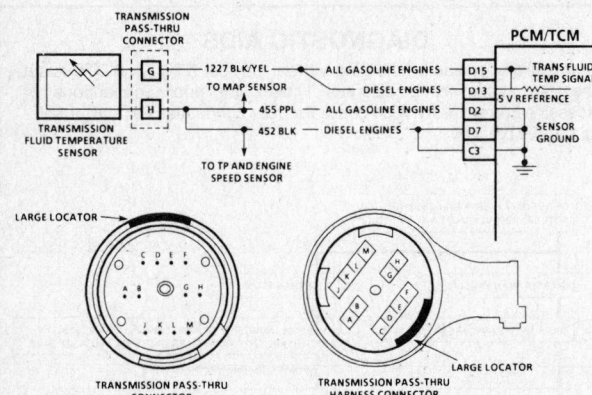

The transmission fluid temperature sensor is a thermistor which controls the signal voltage to the PCM/TCM. The PCM/TCM applies and monitors voltage on circuit No. 1227 to the sensor. When transmission fluid is cold, sensor resistance is high; therefore, the PCM/TCM will see high signal voltage. As the transmission fluid temperature warms up, sensor resistance and voltage will drop. At normal transmission operating temperature of 212°F (100°C), voltage will be about 1.5-2.0 volts.

NOTE: Test numbers refer to numbers on diagnostic chart.

1) DTC 58 will set if signal voltage indicates a transmission fluid temperature greater than 305°F (151°C) for one second.
2) This step determines if circuit No. 1227 is shorted to ground, which will result in conditions for DTC 58.

93J76306 93A76307

DIAGNOSTIC AIDS

Check harness routing for a potential short to ground in circuit No. 1227. Scan tool displays transmission fluid temperature in degrees Centigrade. After transmission has been in operation, temperature should rise steadily to about 212°F (100°C) then stabilize. Test transmission sensor at various temperature levels to determine if sensor is out of calibration. See TRANSMISSION SENSOR – TEMP TO RESISTANCE chart. An out-of-calibration sensor could result in delayed shifts or TCC enabled complaint.

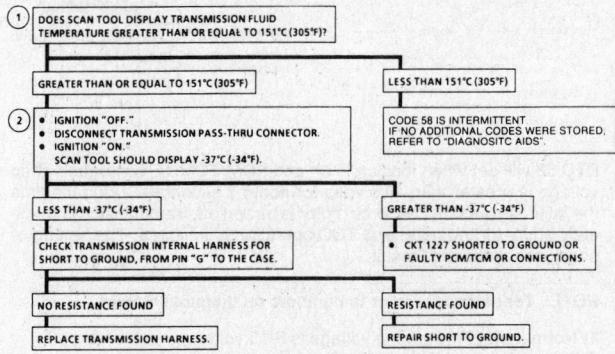

DIAGNOSTIC AID
TRANSMISSION FLUID SENSOR - TEMP TO RESISTANCE (APPROXIMATE)

°C	°F	MINIMUM RESISTANCE	NOMINAL RESISTANCE	MAXIMUM RESISTANCE
-40°C	-40°F	80965	100544	120123
-30°C	-20°F	42701	52426	62151
-20°C	-4°F	23458	28491	33524
-10°C	14°F	13366	16068	18770
0°C	32°F	7871	9370	10869
10°C	50°F	4771	5640	6508
20°C	68°F	2981	3500	4018
30°C	86°F	1915	2232	2550
40°C	104°F	1260	1460	1660
50°C	122°F	848.8	977.1	1105
60°C	140°F	584.1	668.7	753.4
70°C	158°F	410.3	467.2	524.2
80°C	176°F	293.7	332.7	371.7
90°C	194°F	213.9	241.0	268.2
100°C	212°F	158.1	177.4	196.8
110°C	230°F	118.8	132.6	146.5
120°C	248°F	90.40	100.6	110.8
130°C	266°F	69.48	77.29	85.11
140°C	284°F	53.96	60.13	66.29
150°C	304°F	42.43	47.31	52.20

Courtesy of General Motors Corp.

DTC 58, TRANSMISSION FLUID TEMPERATURE SENSOR CIRCUIT (HIGH TEMPERATURE INDICATED) 1994

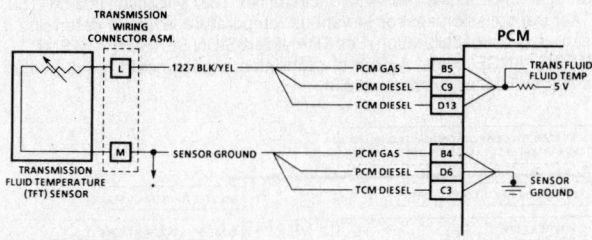

*REFER TO PCM WIRING DIAGRAMS

The transmission fluid temperature sensor is a thermistor which controls the signal voltage to the PCM/TCM. The PCM/TCM supplies a 5 volt reference signal to the sensor on circuit No. 1227. When transmission fluid is cold, sensor resistance is high and PCM/TCM will sense high signal voltage. As transmission fluid temperature warms to normal operating temperature of 212°F (100°C), sensor resistance becomes less and voltage decreases to about 1.5 to 2 volts. With a DTC 79 also set, check transmission cooling system. DTC 58 will set when signal voltage indicates fluid temperature greater than 306°F (151°C) for one second. PCM/TCM will default to warm fluid temperature value.

NOTE: Test numbers refer to numbers on diagnostic chart.

1) This test checks for short to ground or faulty sensor.
2) This test checks for an internal fault within transmission by creating an open.

DIAGNOSTIC AIDS

Check harness routing for potential short to ground in circuit No. 1227. Scan tool displayed temperature should rise steadily to about 212°F (100°C), then stabilize. Test transmission sensor at various temperature levels to determine if sensor is out of calibration. See TEMPERATURE-TO-RESISTANCE VALUES (DTC 58) table. An out-of-calibration sensor could result in firm shifts or TCC enable complaint.

TEMPERATURE-TO-RESISTANCE VALUES [1] (DTC 58)

Temperature °F (°C)	Ohms
300 (150)	43-52
248 (120)	90-110
212 (100)	158-196
160 (70)	410-524
104 (40)	1260-1660
70 (20)	2981-4018
15 (-10)	13,366-18,770
0 (-18)	23,458-33,524
-40 (-40)	80,965-120,123

[1] – Measure resistance across sensor terminals.

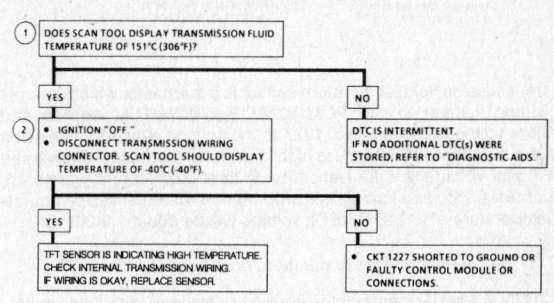

WHEN ALL DIAGNOSIS AND REPAIRS ARE COMPLETED, CLEAR DTC(s) AND VERIFY PROPER OPERATION.

94D38375 94E38376

DTC 59, TRANSMISSION FLUID TEMPERATURE SENSOR CIRCUIT (LOW TEMPERATURE INDICATED) 1993

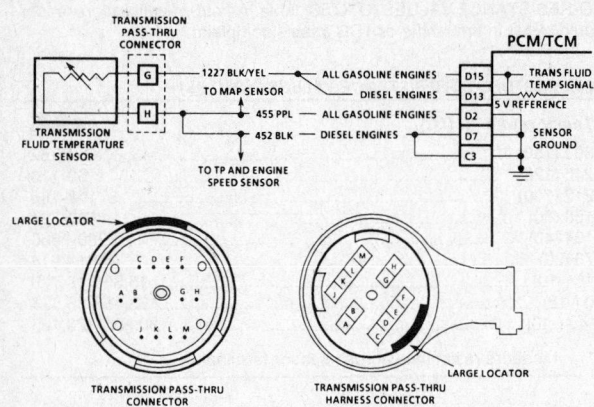

TRANSMISSION PASS-THRU CONNECTOR

TRANSMISSION FLUID TEMPERATURE SENSOR

PCM/TCM

1227 BLK/YEL — ALL GASOLINE ENGINES — D15 — TRANS FLUID TEMP SIGNAL
TO MAP SENSOR — DIESEL ENGINES — D13
455 PPL — ALL GASOLINE ENGINES — D2 — 5 V REFERENCE
452 BLK — DIESEL ENGINES — D7
TO TP AND ENGINE SPEED SENSOR — C3 — SENSOR GROUND

LARGE LOCATOR

TRANSMISSION PASS-THRU CONNECTOR

TRANSMISSION PASS-THRU HARNESS CONNECTOR

LARGE LOCATOR

The transmission fluid temperature sensor is a thermistor which controls the signal voltage to the PCM/TCM. The PCM/TCM applies and monitors voltage on circuit No. 1227 to the sensor. When transmission fluid is cold, sensor resistance is high: therefore, the PCM/TCM will see high signal voltage. As the transmission fluid temperature warms up, sensor resistance and voltage will drop. At normal transmission operating temperature of 212°F (100°C), voltage will be about 1.5-2.0 volts.

NOTE: Test numbers refer to numbers on diagnostic chart.

1) DTC 59 will set if signal voltage indicates a transmission fluid temperature less than -34°F (-37°C) for one second.
2) This test simulates conditions for DTC 58. If PCM/TCM recognizes low voltage signal, scan tool will display temperature greater than 304°F (151°C), indicating control module and wiring are not at fault.
3) This test determines if circuit No. 1227 is open. There should be 5 volts present at transmission sensor connector.

93J76306 93B76308

DIAGNOSTIC AIDS

Scan tool displays transmission fluid temperature in degrees Centigrade. After transmission has been in operation, temperature should rise steadily to about 212°F (100°C) then stabilize. A faulty connection or an open in circuit No. 455/452 or circuit No. 1227 will result in a DTC 59. Test transmission sensor at various temperature levels to determine if sensor is out of calibration. See TRANSMISSION SENSOR – TEMP TO RESISTANCE chart. An out-of-calibration sensor could result in firm shifts or TCC enabled complaint.

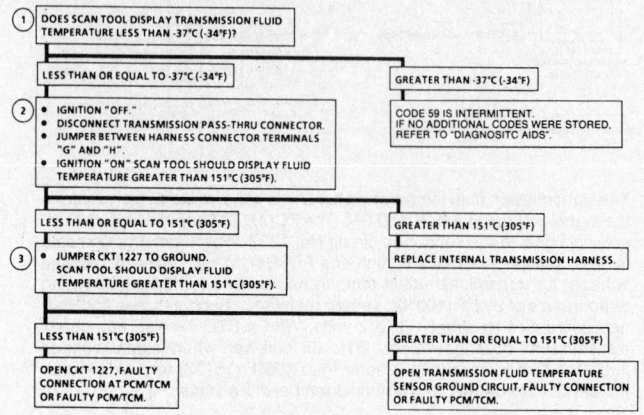

① DOES SCAN TOOL DISPLAY TRANSMISSION FLUID TEMPERATURE LESS THAN -37°C (-34°F)?

LESS THAN OR EQUAL TO -37°C (-34°F)

GREATER THAN -37°C (-34°F)

② • IGNITION "OFF."
• DISCONNECT TRANSMISSION PASS-THRU CONNECTOR.
• JUMPER BETWEEN HARNESS CONNECTOR TERMINALS "G" AND "H".
• IGNITION "ON" SCAN TOOL SHOULD DISPLAY FLUID TEMPERATURE GREATER THAN 151°C (305°F).

CODE 59 IS INTERMITTENT. IF NO ADDITIONAL CODES WERE STORED, REFER TO "DIAGNOSITC AIDS".

LESS THAN OR EQUAL TO 151°C (305°F)

GREATER THAN 151°C (305°F)

③ • JUMPER CKT 1227 TO GROUND. SCAN TOOL SHOULD DISPLAY FLUID TEMPERATURE GREATER THAN 151°C (305°F).

REPLACE INTERNAL TRANSMISSION HARNESS.

LESS THAN 151°C (305°F)

GREATER THAN OR EQUAL TO 151°C (305°F)

OPEN CKT 1227, FAULTY CONNECTION AT PCM/TCM OR FAULTY PCM/TCM.

OPEN TRANSMISSION FLUID TEMPERATURE SENSOR GROUND CIRCUIT, FAULTY CONNECTION OR FAULTY PCM/TCM.

DIAGNOSTIC AID
TRANSMISSION FLUID SENSOR - TEMP TO RESISTANCE (APPROXIMATE)

°C	°F	MINIMUM RESISTANCE	NOMINAL RESISTANCE	MAXIMUM RESISTANCE
-40°C	-40°F	80965	100544	120123
-30°C	-20°F	42701	52426	62151
-20°C	-4°F	23458	28491	33524
-10°C	14°F	13366	16068	18770
0°C	32°F	7871	9370	10869
10°C	50°F	4771	5640	6508
20°C	68°F	2981	3500	4018
30°C	86°F	1915	2232	2550
40°C	104°F	1260	1460	1660
50°C	122°F	848.8	977.1	1105
60°C	140°F	584.1	668.7	753.4
70°C	158°F	410.3	467.2	524.2
80°C	176°F	293.7	332.7	371.7
90°C	194°F	213.9	241.0	268.2
100°C	212°F	158.1	177.4	196.8
110°C	230°F	118.8	132.6	146.5
120°C	248°F	90.40	100.6	110.8
130°C	266°F	69.48	77.29	85.11
140°C	284°F	53.96	60.13	66.29
150°C	304°F	42.43	47.31	52.20

DTC 59, TRANSMISSION FLUID TEMPERATURE SENSOR CIRCUIT (LOW TEMPERATURE INDICATED) 1994

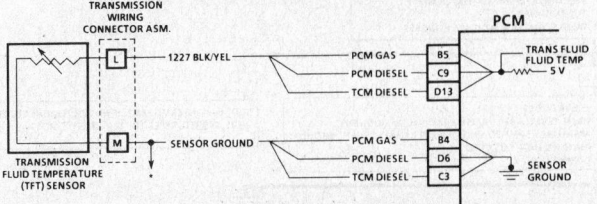

The transmission fluid temperature sensor is a thermistor which controls the signal voltage to the PCM/TCM. The PCM/TCM supplies a 5 volt reference signal to the sensor on circuit No. 1227. When transmission fluid is cold, sensor resistance is high and PCM/TCM will sense high signal voltage. As transmission fluid temperature warms to normal operating temperature of 212°F (100°C), sensor resistance becomes less and voltage decreases to about 1.5 to 2 volts. DTC 59 will set when signal voltage indicates fluid temperature less than -40°F (-40°C) for one second. PCM/TCM will default to warm fluid temperature value.

NOTE: Test numbers refer to numbers on diagnostic chart.

1) This checks entire circuit and indicates if malfunction is present.
2) This test simulates DTC 58. If PCM/TCM recognizes the low signal voltage (high temperature)) and scan tool displays 305°F (151°C) or more, PCM/TCM and wiring are okay.
3) This test determines if circuit No. 1227 is open. There should be 5 volts present at sensor connector if measuring with a DVOM.

DIAGNOSTIC AIDS

Scan tool displays transmission fluid temperature in degrees Centigrade. After transmission is operating, displayed temperature should rise steadily to about 212°F (100°C) then stabilize. A poor connection or an open circuits No. 455/1227 will result in DTC 59. Test transmission sensor at various temperature levels to determine if sensor is out of calibration. See TEMPERATURE-TO-RESISTANCE VALUES (DTC 59) table. An out-of-calibration sensor could result in firm shifts or TCC enable complaint.

94F38377 94G38378

TEMPERATURE-TO-RESISTANCE VALUES [1] (DTC 59)

Temperature °F (°C)	Ohms
300 (150)	43-52
248 (120)	90-110
212 (100)	158-196
160 (70)	410-524
104 (40)	1260-1660
70 (20)	2981-4018
15 (-10)	13,366-18,770
0 (-18)	23,458-33,524
-40 (-40)	80,965-120,123

[1] – Measure resistance across sensor terminals.

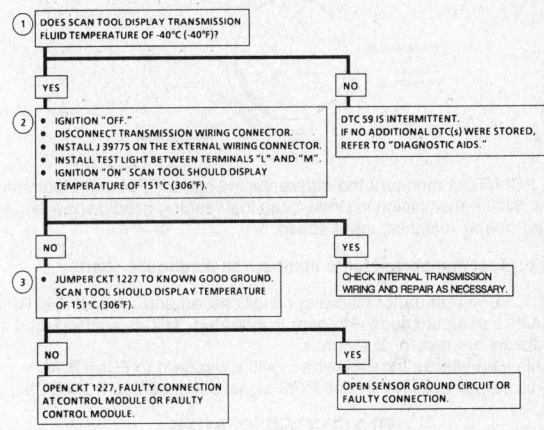

Courtesy of General Motors Corp.

DTC 63 & 64, BAROMETRIC PRESSURE SENSOR CIRCUIT HIGH OR LOW (1994) DIESEL

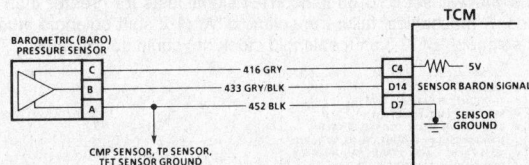

The TCM supplies 5 volts to the barometric pressure sensor. As the atmospheric pressure changes, the resistance within the sensor also changes, modifying the voltage on the sensor input signal. When atmospheric pressure is high, input signal voltage will also be high (about 4.5 volts). As atmospheric pressure decreases, input signal voltage decreases.

DTC 63 will set when sensor signal voltage is greater than 4.9 volts for greater than 2 seconds. DTC 64 will set when sensor signal voltage is less than 1.9 volts for greater than 2 seconds.

NOTE: Test numbers refer to numbers on diagnostic chart.

1) This verifies the 5 volt supply to barometric pressure sensor.
2) If entire circuit is okay, voltage measured will be 5 volts.

DIAGNOSTIC AIDS

If DTC will not set, use snapshot mode on scan tool to set DTC, then review data to identify malfunction.

94H38353 94I38354

Courtesy of General Motors Corp.

DTC 68, OVERDRIVE RATIO ERROR (1993)

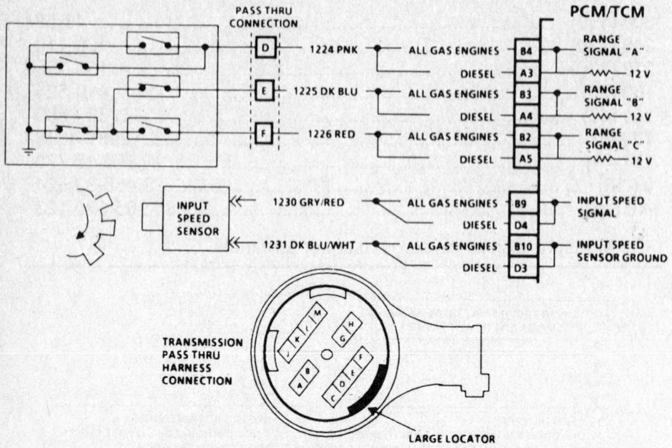

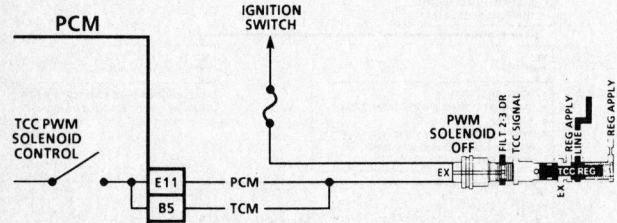

PASS THRU CONNECTION
PCM/TCM
D 1224 PNK ALL GAS ENGINES B4 RANGE SIGNAL "A"
DIESEL A3 12 V
E 1225 DK BLU ALL GAS ENGINES B3 RANGE SIGNAL "B"
DIESEL A4 12 V
F 1226 RED ALL GAS ENGINES B2 RANGE SIGNAL "C"
DIESEL A5 12 V
INPUT SPEED SENSOR
1230 GRY/RED ALL GAS ENGINES B9 INPUT SPEED SIGNAL
DIESEL D4
1231 DK BLU/WHT ALL GAS ENGINES B10 INPUT SPEED SENSOR GROUND
DIESEL D3
TRANSMISSION PASS THRU HARNESS CONNECTION
LARGE LOCATOR

The PCM/TCM monitors the difference in engine RPM and input shaft RPM. With transmission in Drive, scan tool reading should show engine speed closely matching input speed.

NOTE: Test numbers refer to numbers on diagnostic chart.

1) DTC 68 will set under following conditions: engine speed is 200 RPM greater than input speed, 4th gear is indicated, TCC is enabled, and all conditions are met for 2 seconds.
2) This step checks transmission signal being sent to PCM/TCM.
3) This step checks for engine RPM signal being sent to PCM/TCM.

DIAGNOSTIC AIDS

Check transmission pass-through connector. DTC 68 will set if transmission defaults to 2nd gear. If problems are still present, check for possible internal transmission problems.

1
• CLEAR CODES.
• RAISE DRIVE WHEELS.
• ENGINE RUNNING.
• TRANSMISSION AT OPERATING TEMPERATURE.
• RANGE SELECTOR IN (D).
• WHEELS TURNING.
• SPEEDOMETER INDICATING 45 MPH.
• TCC ENGAGED.
DOES SCAN TOOL INDICATE CODE 68?
YES
NO
CODE 68 IS INTERMITTENT. IF NO ADDITIONAL CODES WERE STORED, REFER TO "DIAGNOSTIC AIDS"
2
• CLEAR CODES.
• DRIVE WHEELS STILL RAISED AND ENGINE RUNNING.
• MANUALLY SHIFT TO EACH HIGHER RANGE. "SCAN" SHOULD MATCH RANGE SELECTED.
DOES IT?
NO
• IGNITION "OFF."
• DISCONNECT TRANSMISSION PASS-THRU CONN. HARNESS.
• IGNITION "ON."
• WITH DVM, CHECK VOLTAGE AT HARNESS CONNECTOR CKT 1224, CKT 1225 AND CKT 1226.
IS THERE SYSTEM VOLTAGE AT ALL PINS?
YES
CHECK INTERNAL TRANS-MISSION HARNESS FOR OPEN OR SHORTS.
OK
REPLACE PRESSURE SWITCH MANIFOLD
NO
• IGNITION STILL "ON."
• WITH A VOLTMETER ON 20V DC SCALE, BACKPROBE PCM/TCM CONN. CIRCUITS THAT HAD LOW OR NO VOLTAGE. METER SHOULD READ SYSTEM VOLTAGE.
DOES IT?
NO
• IGNITION "OFF."
• DISCONNECT PCM/TCM A-B CONNECTOR.
• WITH A TEST LIGHT CONNECTED TO 12 VOLTS, PROBE HARNESS CONNECTOR CIRCUIT(S) THAT HAD LOW OR NO VOLTAGE.
LIGHT "ON"
CIRCUIT SHORTED TO GND BETWEEN PCM/TCM AND TRANSMISSION.
LIGHT "OFF"
FAULTY CONNECTION AT PCM/TCM OR, PCM/TCM
YES
OPEN CIRCUIT FROM PCM/TCM TO TRANSMISSION
YES
3
• DRIVE WHEELS RAISED AND ENGINE RUNNING.
• SELECTOR IN "D".
• DVM ON AC 200V SCALE BACK PROBE ACROSS PCM/TCM CONNECTOR CKT 1230 AND 1231.
• SLOWLY INCREASE RPM.
• NOTE VOLT METER READING. VOLTAGE SHOULD VARY WITH RPM.
DOES IT?
NO
• DRIVE WHEELS RAISED
• TRANSMISSION IN DRIVE
• WITH DVM AT 200V AC SCALE MEASURE VOLTAGE ACROSS TRANSMISSION INPUT SENSOR TERMINALS.
• NOTE VOLTMETER. VOLTAGE SHOULD VARY. WITH RPM.
DOES IT?
YES
CHECK FOR:
- OPEN CKT 1230 OR 1231.
- SHORT TO GROUND CKT 1230.
- FAULTY PCM/TCM CONNECTION.
NO
FAULTY INPUT SENSOR
YES
INTERNAL TRANSMISSION PROBLEM, SEE "DIAGNOSTIC AIDS"

91C13682 92F14113

Courtesy of General Motors Corp.

DTC 68, OVERDRIVE RATIO ERROR (1994)

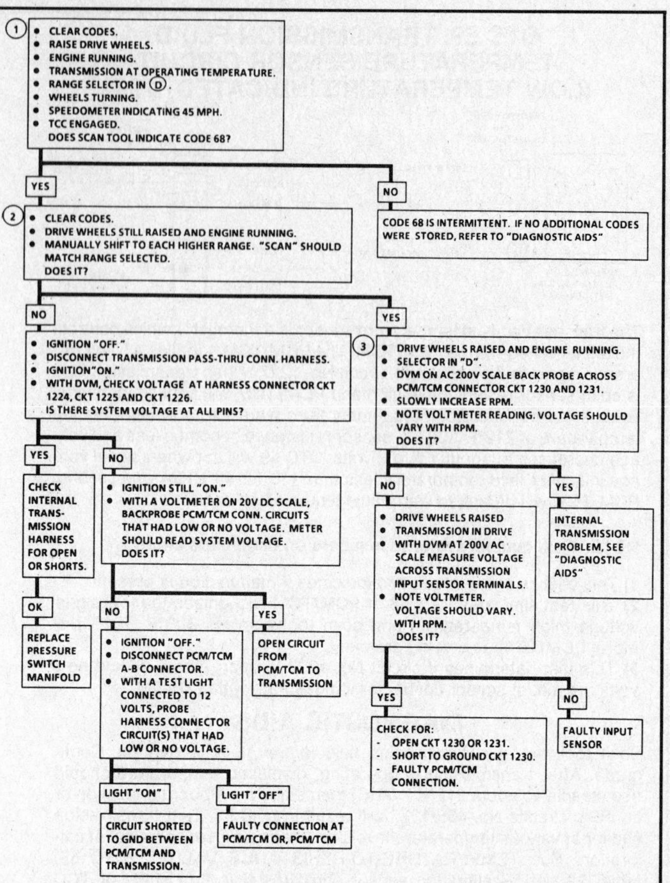

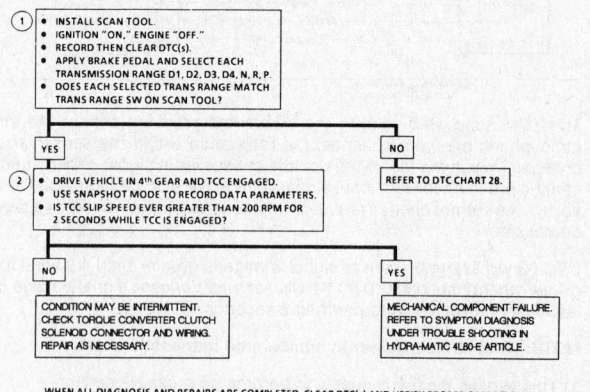

PCM
IGNITION SWITCH
TCC PWM SOLENOID CONTROL
E11 PCM
B5 TCM
PWM SOLENOID OFF
FILT 2-3 DR TCC SIGNAL
REG APPLY LINE
REG APPLY
EX
TCC REG

The PCM/TCM monitors the difference in engine RPM and input shaft RPM. With transmission in Drive, scan tool reading should show engine speed closely matching input speed. DTC 68 will set when DTC(s) 28, 71 or 74 is not present, TCC slip speed is greater than 200 RPM, 4th gear is indicated, TCC is locked, vehicle is not in Park or Neutral and all conditions are met for 2 seconds. PCM/TCM will inhibit TCC operation.

NOTE: Test numbers refer to numbers on diagnostic chart.

1) This test checks indicated range to actual selected range. A faulty switch could set DTC 68.
2) This test checks torque converter for slippage while in a commanded lock-up state.

DIAGNOSTIC AIDS

Check for deformed connections at pass-thru connector. DTC 68 will set when transmission defaults to 2nd gear. An intermittent incorrect engine speed signal will set DTC 68 if incorrect signal lasts for greater than 2 seconds. A mechanical failure in solenoid "A" (1-2 shift solenoid stuck off) or solenoid "B" (2-3 shift solenoid stuck on) could set DTC 68.

1
• INSTALL SCAN TOOL.
• IGNITION "ON," ENGINE "OFF."
• RECORD THEN CLEAR DTC(s).
• APPLY BRAKE PEDAL AND SELECT EACH TRANSMISSION RANGE D1, D2, D3, D4, N, R, P.
• DOES EACH SELECTED TRANS RANGE MATCH TRANS RANGE SW ON SCAN TOOL?
YES
NO
REFER TO DTC CHART 28.
2
• DRIVE VEHICLE IN 4th GEAR AND TCC ENGAGED.
• USE SNAPSHOT MODE TO RECORD DATA PARAMETERS.
• IS TCC SLIP SPEED EVER GREATER THAN 200 RPM FOR 2 SECONDS WHILE TCC IS ENGAGED?
NO
CONDITION MAY BE INTERMITTENT. CHECK TORQUE CONVERTER CLUTCH SOLENOID CONNECTOR AND WIRING. REPAIR AS NECESSARY.
YES
MECHANICAL COMPONENT FAILURE. REFER TO SYMPTOM DIAGNOSIS UNDER TROUBLE SHOOTING IN HYDRA-MATIC 4L80-E ARTICLE.
WHEN ALL DIAGNOSIS AND REPAIRS ARE COMPLETED, CLEAR DTC(s) AND VERIFY PROPER OPERATION.

94B38357 94H38379

Courtesy of General Motors Corp.

DTC 69, TORQUE CONVERTER CLUTCH (TCC) STUCK ON (1994)

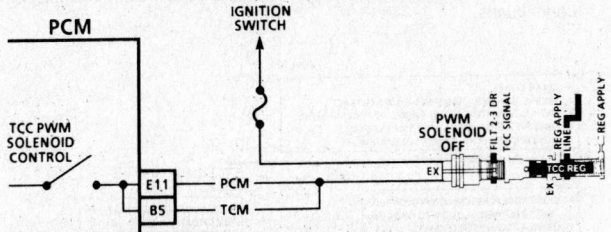

The purpose of the automatic transmission Torque Converter Clutch (TCC) feature is to eliminate power loss of the torque converter stage when vehicle is in a cruise condition. This allows the convenience of the automatic transmission, and fuel economy of a manual transmission.

PCM/TCM commands the TCC PWM solenoid on by modulating TCC signal fluid acting on converter clutch shift valve. TCC fluid applies torque converter clutch.

DTC 69 will set when DTC(s) 21, 22, 28, 71 or 74 is not present, TCC is commanded off, TCC slip speed is between -5 and 10 RPM, TPS signal is greater than 25 percent, transmission range switch indicates "D3" or "D4", transmission is in 2nd or 3rd gear and all conditions are met for 2 seconds.

94B38357 94A38380

NOTE: Test number refers to number on diagnostic chart.

1) This test checks mechanical state of TCC. When PCM/TCM commands TCC solenoid off, TCC slip speed should increase.

DIAGNOSTIC AIDS

If TCC is mechanically stuck on, vehicle speed is zero, brakes are applied and "D2" is selected, TCC fluid will mechanically apply TCC, causing engine to stall.

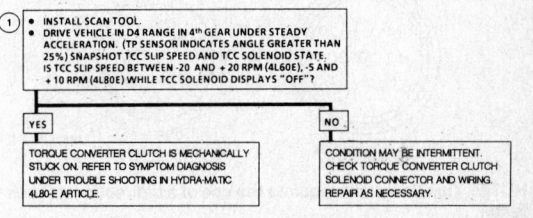

DTC 71, CAMSHAFT POSITION SENSOR CIRCUIT LOW (1994) DIESEL

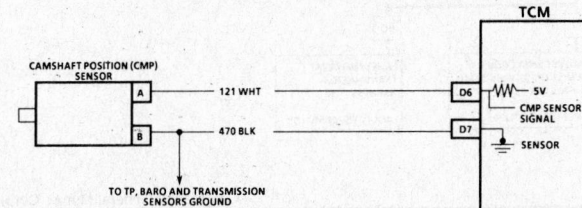

The Camshaft Position (CMP) sensor detects the rotational speed of the camshaft. As the camshaft rotates, an A/C signal is generated in the circuit. This signal provides the input to determine engine speed for use in various calculations including TCC slip speed and overdrive ratio. DTC 71 will set when DTC 28 is not present, engine speed is less than 50 RPM, transmission range switch indicates "D4", "D3", "D1" or Reverse and conditions are met for 2 seconds. TCM will inhibit TCC.

NOTE: Test numbers refer to numbers on diagnostic chart.

1) An out-of-range transmission fluid pressure switch could falsely indicate the actual transmission range.
2) This checks the entire CMP sensor circuit for proper signal.
3) A signal at this point indicates that the sensor is capable of inducing an AC voltage in the circuit.

DIAGNOSTIC AIDS

A mechanical problem with the camshaft may set DTC 71. With CMP sensor removed, check camshaft for damage.

94J38355 94A38356

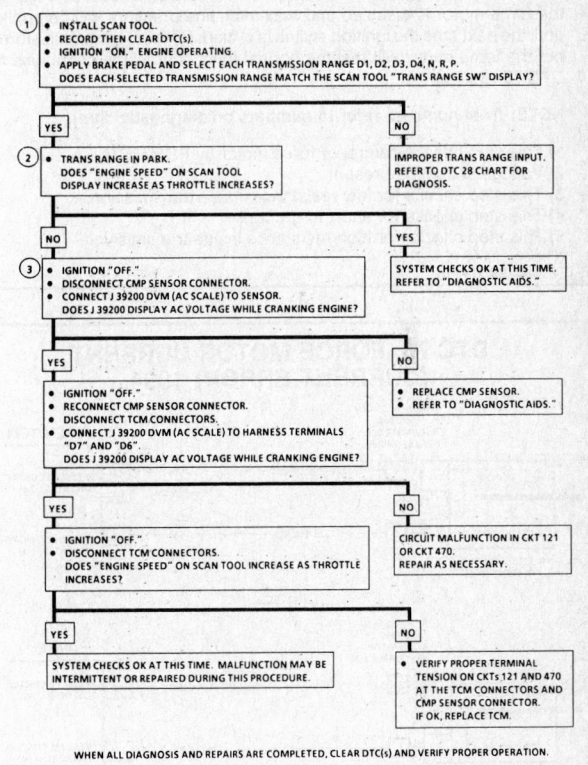

DTC 73, FORCE MOTOR CURRENT (CURRENT ERROR) 1993

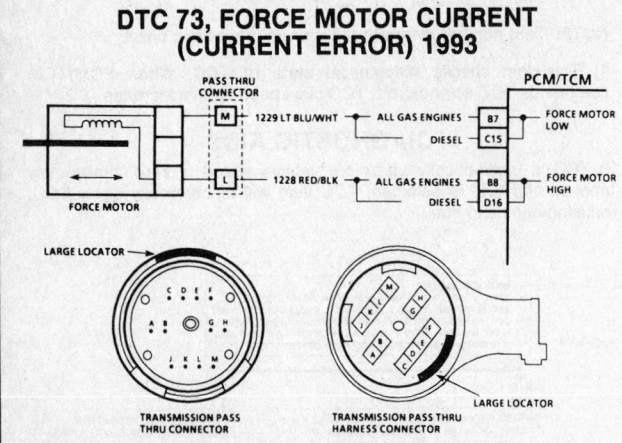

NOTE: This flow chart requires the use of a bidirectional (Tech 1) scan tester.

Force motor, also referred to as pressure control solenoid, is a PCM/TCM-controlled device used to regulate transmission line pressure. The PCM/TCM looks at TPS voltage, engine RPM and other inputs to determine appropriate line pressure for a given load, then regulates the pressure by applying a varying amperage. The applied amperage can vary from 1 to 1.1 amps.

The PCM/TCM then monitors amperage at the return line. If the return amperage varies more than .16 amp from the commanded amperage for the duration of at least one second, DTC 73 will set. Once DTC 73 is set, the force motor is disabled and maximum line pressure will be applied until the next time the ignition switch is cycled. DTC 73 will remain stored, but the force motor will resume normal function until the conditions for DTC 73 re-occur.

NOTE: Test numbers refer to numbers on diagnostic chart.

1) This step checks control of force motor by PCM/TCM.
2) Voltage should be present.
3) This step checks for low resistance inside transmission.
4) This step checks for short to ground.
5) This step checks for high resistance inside transmission.

91E13684 92H14115

DIAGNOSTIC AIDS

Check transmission pass-through connector and PCM/TCM for poor connections.

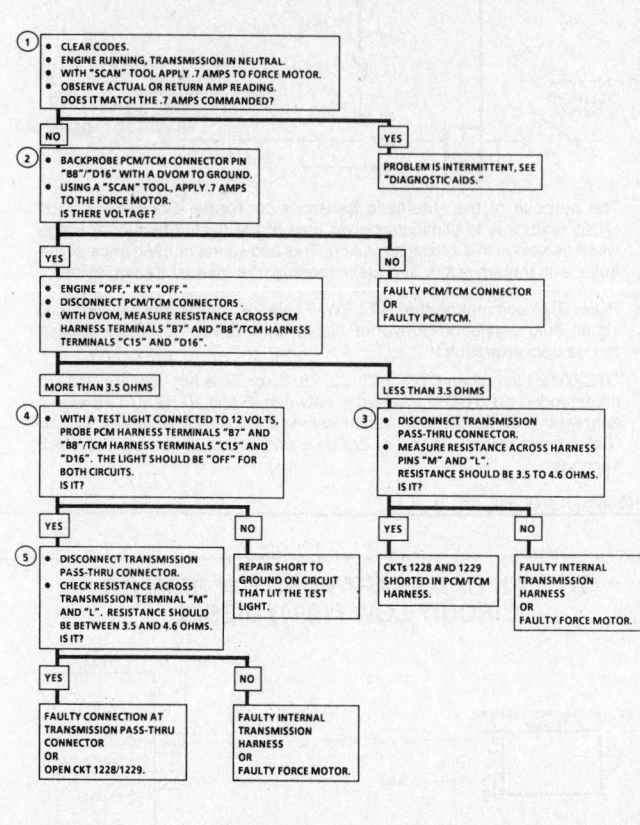

Courtesy of General Motors Corp.

DTC 73, FORCE MOTOR CURRENT (CURRENT ERROR) 1994

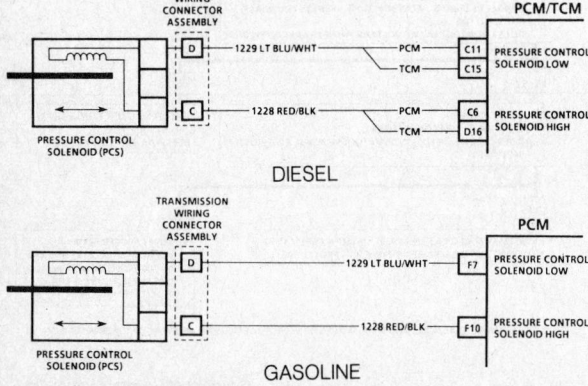

Force motor, also referred to as pressure control solenoid, is a PCM/TCM controlled device used to regulate transmission line pressure. PCM/TCM looks at TPS voltage, engine RPM and other inputs to determine the appropriate line pressure for a given load, then regulates the pressure by applying a variable amperage to the pressure control solenoid. Applied amperage varies from .1 to 1.1 amps.

PCM/TCM monitors amperage at the return line. DTC 73 will set if the return line amperage varies greater than .16 amp from the commanded amperage for at least one second, and DTC 75 is not present. When DTC 73 sets, maximum line pressure will be applied, causing harsh shifts until the next ignition cycle.

94C38358 94B38381 94C38382

NOTE: Test numbers refer to numbers on diagnostic chart.

1) This test checks ability of PCM/TCM to command pressure control solenoid.
2) This test checks internal transmission harness and pressure control solenoid for high resistance.

DIAGNOSTIC AIDS

Check for poor connection at all connections, especially those at the transmission pass-thru connector and PCM/TCM.

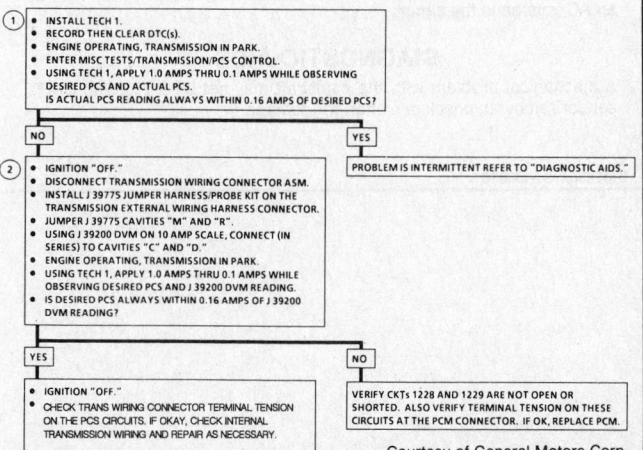

Courtesy of General Motors Corp.

DTC 74, INPUT SPEED SENSOR CIRCUIT (1994)

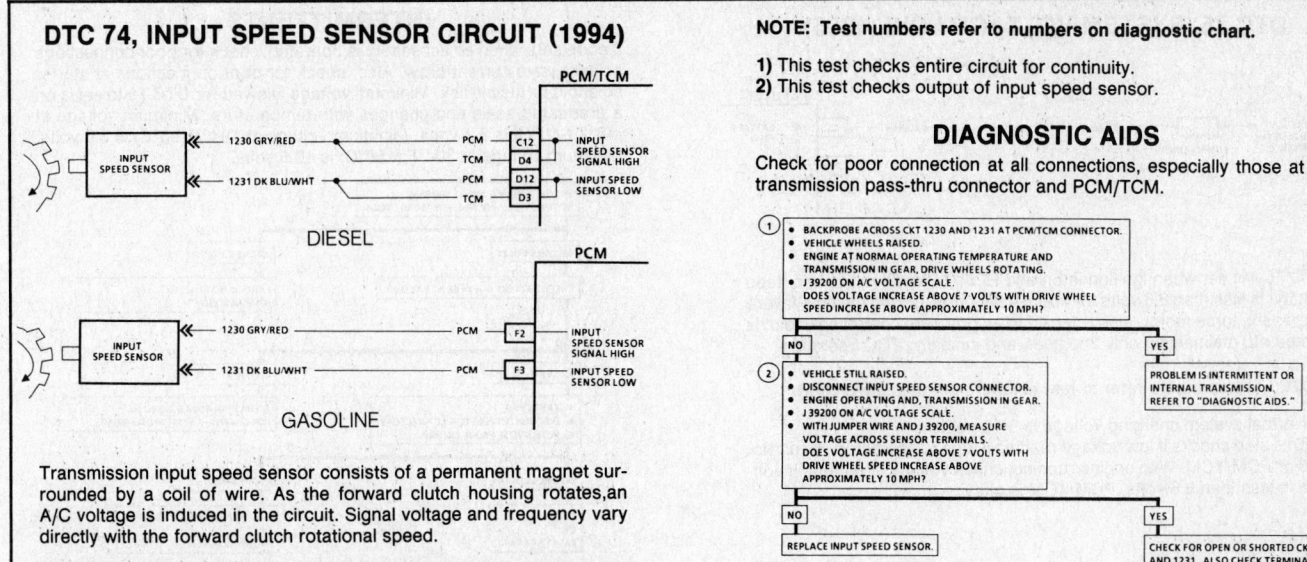

DIESEL

GASOLINE

Transmission input speed sensor consists of a permanent magnet surrounded by a coil of wire. As the forward clutch housing rotates,an A/C voltage is induced in the circuit. Signal voltage and frequency vary directly with the forward clutch rotational speed.

DTC 74 will set when DTC(s) 24, 28 or 71 is not present, transmission is not in Park or Neutral, engine speed is greater than 300 RPM, output speed is greater than 200 RPM, input speed is less than 50 RPM and all conditions are met for 2 seconds. PCM/TCM will inhibit TCC operation.

94D38359 94D38383 94E38384

NOTE: Test numbers refer to numbers on diagnostic chart.

1) This test checks entire circuit for continuity.
2) This test checks output of input speed sensor.

DIAGNOSTIC AIDS

Check for poor connection at all connections, especially those at the transmission pass-thru connector and PCM/TCM.

①
- BACKPROBE ACROSS CKT 1230 AND 1231 AT PCM/TCM CONNECTOR.
- VEHICLE WHEELS RAISED.
- ENGINE AT NORMAL OPERATING TEMPERATURE AND TRANSMISSION IN GEAR, DRIVE WHEELS ROTATING.
- J 39200 ON A/C VOLTAGE SCALE. DOES VOLTAGE INCREASE ABOVE 7 VOLTS WITH DRIVE WHEEL SPEED INCREASE ABOVE APPROXIMATELY 10 MPH?

NO

②
- VEHICLE STILL RAISED.
- DISCONNECT INPUT SPEED SENSOR CONNECTOR.
- ENGINE OPERATING AND, TRANSMISSION IN GEAR.
- J 39200 ON A/C VOLTAGE SCALE.
- WITH JUMPER WIRE AND J 39200, MEASURE VOLTAGE ACROSS SENSOR TERMINALS. DOES VOLTAGE INCREASE ABOVE 7 VOLTS WITH DRIVE WHEEL SPEED INCREASE ABOVE APPROXIMATELY 10 MPH?

YES

PROBLEM IS INTERMITTENT OR INTERNAL TRANSMISSION. REFER TO "DIAGNOSTIC AIDS."

NO

REPLACE INPUT SPEED SENSOR.

YES

CHECK FOR OPEN OR SHORTED CKTs 1230 AND 1231. ALSO CHECK TERMINAL TENSION OF THESE CIRCUITS AT THE PCM/TCM AND THE INPUT SPEED SENSOR CONNECTOR. IF OK, REPLACE PCM/TCM.

WHEN ALL DIAGNOSIS AND REPAIRS ARE COMPLETED, CLEAR DTC(s) AND VERIFY PROPER OPERATION.

Courtesy of General Motors Corp.

DTC 75, SYSTEM VOLTAGE LOW (1993)

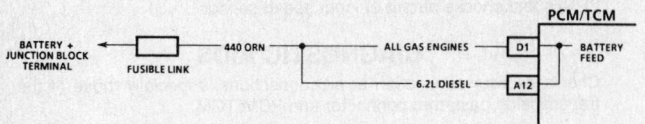

DTC 75 will set when ignition is on and PCM/TCM 12-volt battery feed voltage is less than 8.6 volts for about 4 seconds. During the time failure is present, force motor, also referred to as pressure control solenoid, is turned off, maintaining only 2nd gear, and inhibiting TCC operation.

NOTE: Test numbers refer to test numbers on diagnostic chart.

1) Normal system charging voltage is 9-15 volts.
2) This step checks if low voltage reading is due to alternator, circuit No. 440 or PCM/TCM. With engine running, check voltage at battery. If voltage is less than 8.6 volts, PCM/TCM is okay.

92I14116 92J4117

INTERMITTENTS

If code sets when an accessory is operated, check for poor connections or excessive current draw. Also, check for poor connections at starter solenoid or fusible link. Minimum voltage allowed for DTC 75 to set is on a graduated scale and changes with temperature. Minimum voltage at -40°F (-40°C) is 6.7 volts. Minimum voltage at 194°F (90°C) is 8.6 volts. Minimum voltage at 304°F (150°C) is 10.5 volts.

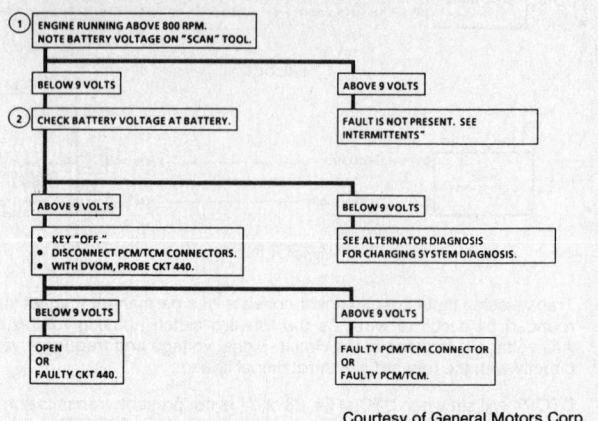

Courtesy of General Motors Corp.

DTC 75, SYSTEM VOLTAGE LOW (1994)

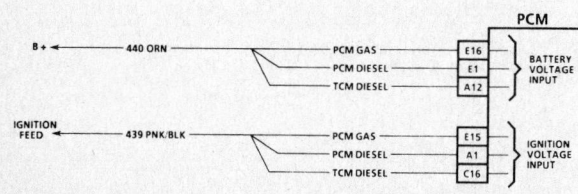

Ignition voltage is supplied to PCM/TCM to indicate ignition switch status. Battery voltage is supplied to PCM/TCM to maintain memory of learned functions and parameters. DTC 75 will set when ignition is on and engine speed is greater than 1000 RPM for 4 seconds. PCM/TCM will default to maximum line pressure, shift transmission to 2nd gear, and inhibit TCC and 4th gear.

NOTE: Test numbers refer to numbers on diagnostic chart.

1) Normal battery voltage is 9-15 volts.
2) This test checks if alternator is faulty under load conditions. With engine running, check voltage at battery. If voltage is more than 15 volts, repair malfunction in charging system.

94F38385 94G38386

DIAGNOSTIC AIDS

Jump-starting engine and charging battery may set DTC 52 or DTC 53. If DTC(s) set when accessory is operated, check for poor connections or excessive current draw. Also check for poor connections at starter solenoid and fusible link. Minimum voltage allowed for DTC 75 to set is on a graduated scale and changes with temperature. Minimum voltage at -40°F (-40°C) is 7.3 volts. Minimum voltage at 194°F (90°C) is 10.3 volts. Minimum voltage at 304°F (150°C) is 11.7 volts.

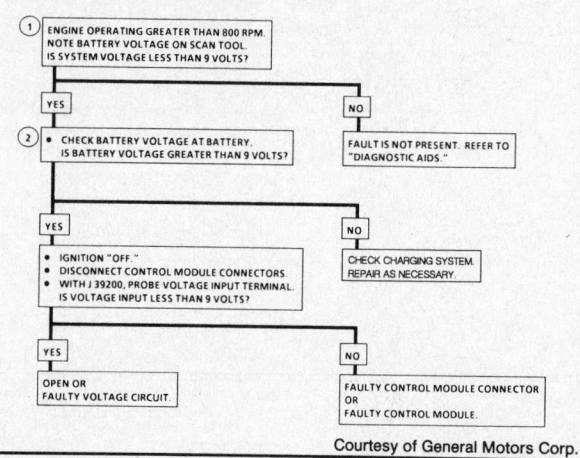

Courtesy of General Motors Corp.

DTC 79, TRANSMISSION FLUID TEMPERATURE SENSOR CIRCUIT (HIGH TEMPERATURE INDICATED) 1994

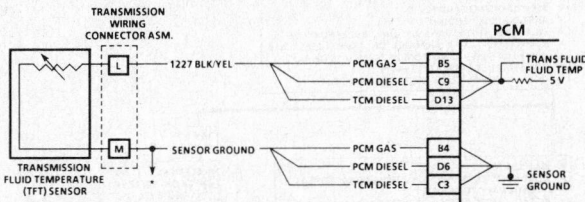

The transmission fluid temperature sensor is a thermistor which controls the signal voltage to the PCM/TCM. The PCM/TCM supplies a 5 volt reference signal to the sensor on circuit No. 1227. When transmission fluid is cold, sensor resistance is high and PCM/TCM will sense high signal voltage. As transmission fluid temperature warms to normal operating temperature of 212°F (100°C), sensor resistance becomes less and voltage decreases to approximately 1.5 to 2 volts. DTC 79 will set when DTC 58 is not present and signal voltage indicates temperature greater than 295°F (146°C) for 30 seconds.

NOTE: Test numbers refer to numbers on diagnostic chart.

1) This test checks for short to ground or faulty sensor.
2) This test simulates DTC 59.

DIAGNOSTIC AIDS

Check harness routing for potential short to ground in circuit No. 1227. Scan tool displayed temperature should rise steadily to about 212°F (100°C), then stabilize. Test transmission sensor at various temperature levels to determine if sensor is out of calibration. See TEMPERATURE-TO-RESISTANCE VALUES (DTC 79) table. An out-of-calibration sensor could result in firm shifts or TCC enable complaint.

TEMPERATURE-TO-RESISTANCE VALUES [1] (DTC 79)

Temperature °F (°C)	Ohms
300 (150)	43-52
248 (120)	90-110
212 (100)	158-196
160 (70)	410-524
104 (40)	1260-1660
70 (20)	2981-4018
15 (-10)	13,366-18,770
0 (-18)	23,458-33,524
-40 (-40)	80,965-120,123

[1] – Measure resistance across sensor terminals.

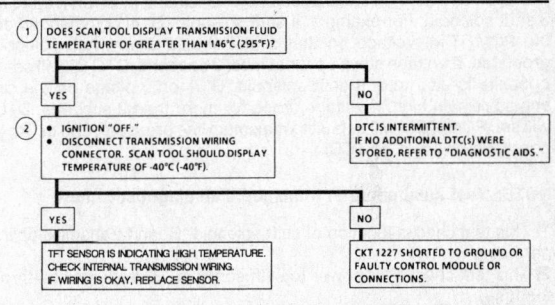

94H38387 94I38388

Courtesy of General Motors Corp.

DTC 81, SOLENOID "B" CIRCUIT FAULT (1993)

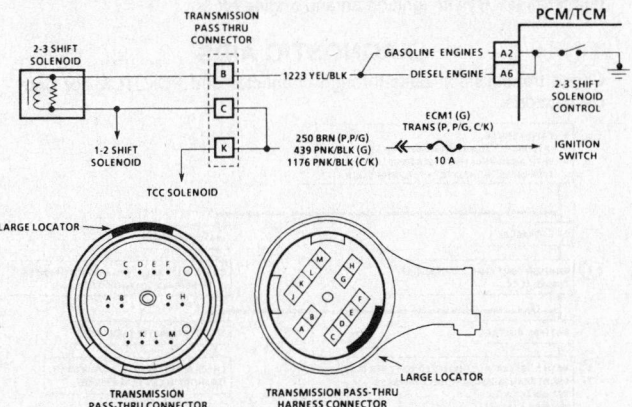

The PCM/TCM continually monitors voltage on each circuit connected to the quad-driver, looking for either low or high voltage, depending on the commanded state of the devices connected to it. DTC 81 will set if a fault has been detected on the shift solenoid "B" circuit, also referred to as 2-3 shift solenoid. For example, if shift solenoid "B" is commanded on by the PCM/TCM, voltage on that circuit should drop when solenoid is grounded. If voltage remains high for at least 2 seconds, DTC 81 will set. The opposite is also true. If shift solenoid "B" is off, voltage on the circuit should remain high. If voltage drops for greater than 2 seconds, DTC 81 will set.

NOTE: Test numbers refer to numbers on diagnostic chart.

1) This step checks shift solenoid "B" and circuits inside transmission for shorts.
2) Battery voltage should be present at shift solenoid "B".
3) This step checks circuit No. 1223 for short to ground.

4) This step checks if PCM/TCM can control solenoid "B". If bidirectional scan tool is not available, solenoid may be activated by grounding ALDL test terminal "B" with ignition on and engine off.
5) This determines whether circuit No. 1223 is open or PCM/TCM is faulty.

DIAGNOSTIC AIDS

Check transmission pass-through connector and PCM/TCM for poor connections.

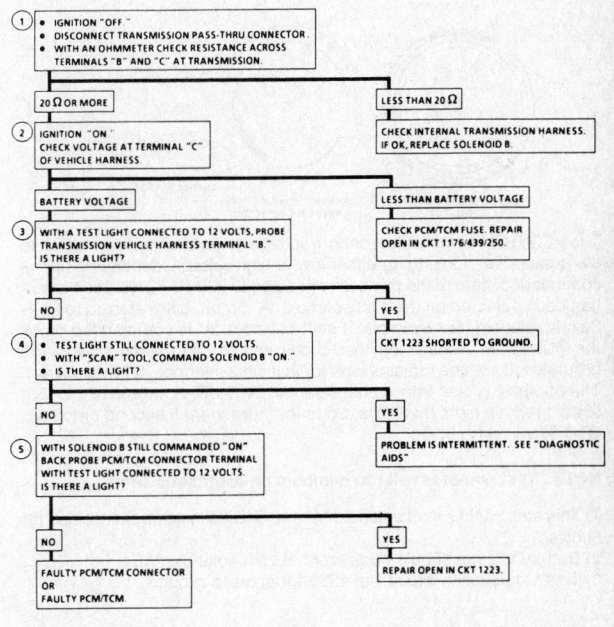

93C76309 91J13689

Courtesy of General Motors Corp.

DTC 81, SOLENOID "B" CIRCUIT FAULT (1994)

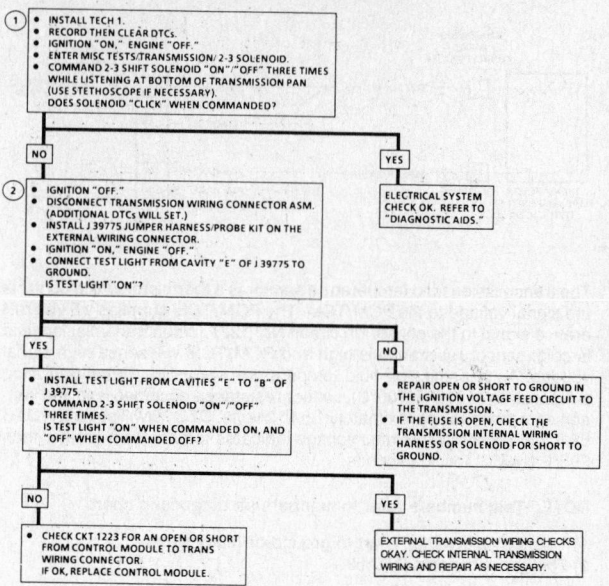

DIAGNOSTIC AIDS

Check all connections, especially at transmission pass-thru connector. An open in the ignition feed circuit may cause multiple DTC's to set.

The PCM/TCM continually monitors voltage on each circuit connected to the quad-driver, looking for either low or high voltage, depending on the commanded state of the devices connected to it. DTC 81 will set if a fault has been detected on the shift solenoid "B" circuit, also referred to as 2-3 shift solenoid. For example, if shift solenoid "B" is commanded on by the PCM/TCM, voltage on that circuit should drop when solenoid is grounded. If voltage stays up for at least 2 seconds, DTC 81 will set. The opposite is also true. If shift solenoid "B" is off, voltage on the circuit should remain high. If voltage drops for more than 2 seconds, DTC 81 will set. PCM/TCM will default to maximum line pressure, 2nd or 3rd gear operation only and no TCC.

NOTE: Test numbers refer to numbers on diagnostic chart.

1) This test checks function of shift solenoid "B" and transmission internal wiring.
2) This test checks for power to shift solenoid "B" from ignition through the fuse.

94G38360 94J38389 94C38390

Courtesy of General Motors Corp.

DTC 82, SOLENOID "A" CIRCUIT FAULT (1993)

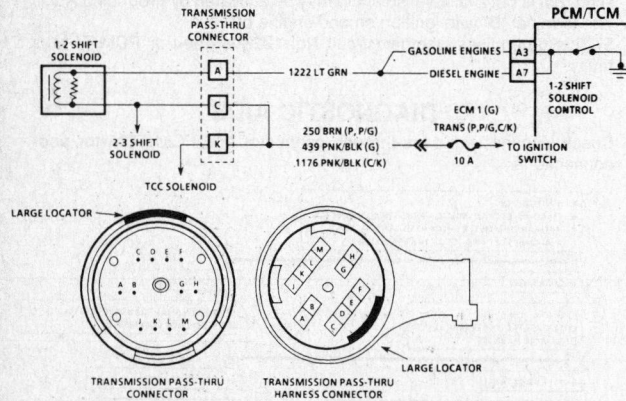

The PCM/TCM continually monitors voltage on each circuit connected to the quad-driver, looking for either low or high voltage, depending on the commanded state of the devices connected to it. DTC 82 will set if a fault has been detected on the shift solenoid "A" circuit, also referred to as 1-2 shift solenoid. For example, if shift solenoid "A" is commanded on by the PCM/TCM, voltage on that circuit should drop when solenoid is grounded. If voltage remains high for at least 2 seconds, DTC 82 will set. The opposite is also true. If shift solenoid "A" is off, voltage on the circuit should remain high. If voltage drops for more than .5 second or longer, DTC 82 will set.

NOTE: Test numbers refer to numbers on diagnostic chart.

1) This step checks shift solenoid "A" and circuits inside transmission for shorts.
2) Battery voltage should be present at shift solenoid "A".
3) This step checks circuit No. 1222 for short to ground.

4) This step checks if PCM/TCM can control solenoid "A". If bidirectional scan tool is not available, solenoid may be activated by grounding ALDL test terminal "B" with ignition on and engine off.

DIAGNOSTIC AIDS

Check transmission pass-through connector and PCM/TCM for poor connections.

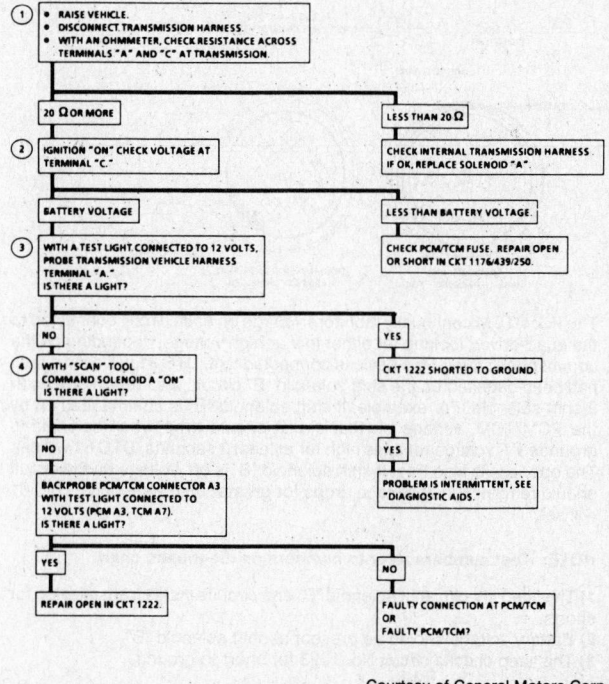

93F76310 91C13690

Courtesy of General Motors Corp.

DTC 82, SOLENOID "A" CIRCUIT FAULT (1994)

DIESEL

GASOLINE

The PCM/TCM continually monitors voltage on each circuit connected to the quad-driver, looking for either low or high voltage, depending on the commanded state of the devices connected to it. DTC 82 will set if a fault has been detected on the shift solenoid "A" circuit, also referred to as 1-2 shift solenoid. For example, if shift solenoid "A" is commanded on by the PCM/TCM, voltage on that circuit should drop when solenoid is grounded. If voltage stays up for at least 2 seconds, DTC 82 will set. The opposite is also true. If shift solenoid "A" is off, voltage on the circuit should remain high. If voltage drops for greater than 2 seconds, DTC 82 will set. PCM/TCM will default to maximum line pressure, 2nd or 3rd gear operation, or 1st and 4th gear operation only.

NOTE: Test numbers refer to numbers on diagnostic chart.

94H38361 94D38391 94E38392

1) This test checks function of shift solenoid "A" and transmission internal wiring.

2) This test checks for power to shift solenoid "A" from ignition through the fuse.

DIAGNOSTIC AIDS

Check all connections, especially at transmission pass-thru connector. An open in the ignition feed circuit may cause multiple DTC's to set.

Courtesy of General Motors Corp.

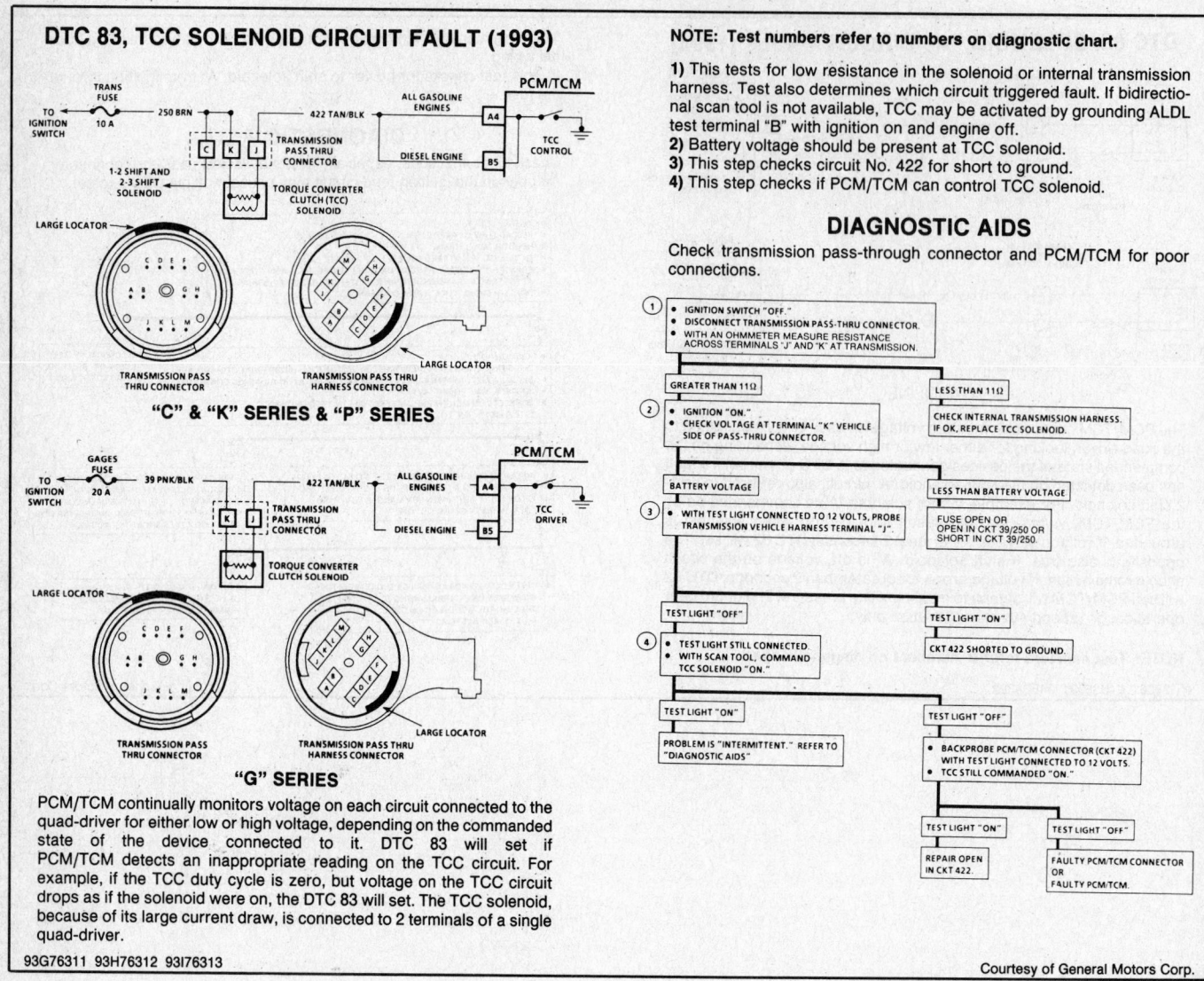

DTC 83, TCC SOLENOID CIRCUIT FAULT (1993)

"C" & "K" SERIES & "P" SERIES

"G" SERIES

PCM/TCM continually monitors voltage on each circuit connected to the quad-driver for either low or high voltage, depending on the commanded state of the device connected to it. DTC 83 will set if PCM/TCM detects an inappropriate reading on the TCC circuit. For example, if the TCC duty cycle is zero, but voltage on the TCC circuit drops as if the solenoid were on, the DTC 83 will set. The TCC solenoid, because of its large current draw, is connected to 2 terminals of a single quad-driver.

93G76311 93H76312 93I76313

NOTE: Test numbers refer to numbers on diagnostic chart.

1) This tests for low resistance in the solenoid or internal transmission harness. Test also determines which circuit triggered fault. If bidirectional scan tool is not available, TCC may be activated by grounding ALDL test terminal "B" with ignition on and engine off.
2) Battery voltage should be present at TCC solenoid.
3) This step checks circuit No. 422 for short to ground.
4) This step checks if PCM/TCM can control TCC solenoid.

DIAGNOSTIC AIDS

Check transmission pass-through connector and PCM/TCM for poor connections.

Courtesy of General Motors Corp.

DTC 83, TCC SOLENOID CIRCUIT FAULT (1994)

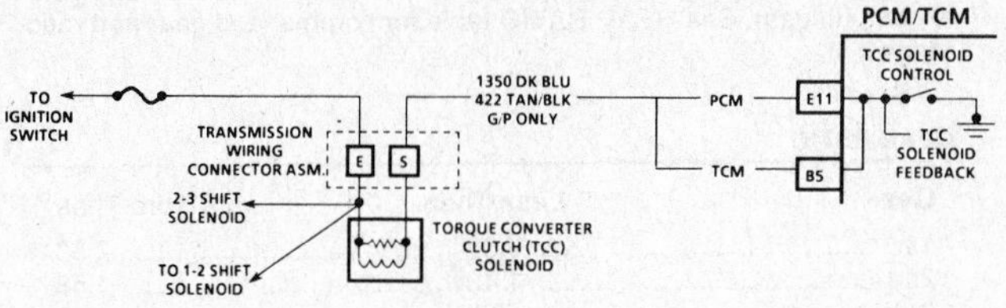

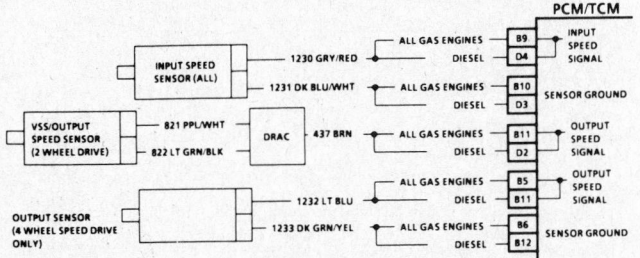

DIESEL

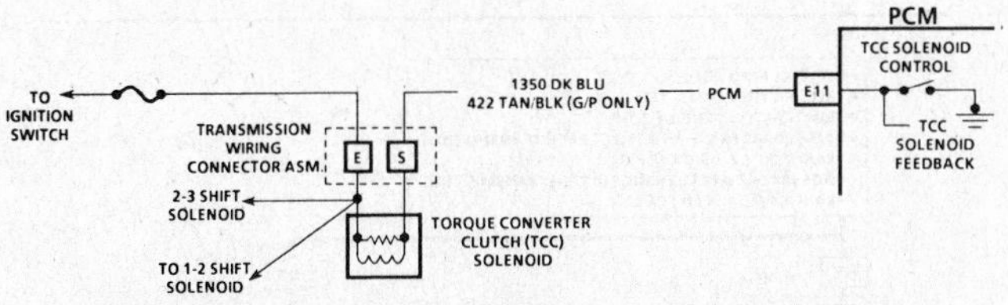

GASOLINE

The PCM/TCM supplies a ground through an internal quad-driver module, allowing current to flow through the solenoid coil according to the duty cycle (percentage of on and off time). This current flow through the solenoid coil creates a magnetic field that magnetizes the solenoid core. The magnetized core attracts the check ball to seat against spring pressure. This blocks the exhaust for the TCC signal fluid and allows 2-3 drive fluid to feed the TCC signal circuit. The TCC signal fluid pressure acts on the TCC regulator valve to regulate line pressure and to apply fluid pressure to the TCC shift valve. When the TCC shift valve is in the apply position, regulated apply fluid pressure is directed through the TCC valve to apply the torque converter clutch.

The PCM/TCM continually monitors voltage on each circuit connection to the quad-driver for either low or high voltage, depending on the commanded state of the device connected to it. DTC 83 will set if PCM/TCM commands the solenoid on and voltage remains high (battery voltage), or PCM/TCM commands solenoid off and voltage remains low (zero volts). Condition must be met for 2 seconds. PCM/TCM will default to inhibit TCC operation and 4th gear operation if in hot mode.

NOTE: Test numbers refer to numbers on diagnostic chart.

94I38362 94F38393 94G38394

1) This test checks if PCM/TCM is commanding the TCC solenoid on.
2) This test will check for voltage to the solenoid.

DIAGNOSTIC AIDS

Check all connections, especially those at the transmission pass-thru connector.

(1)
- INSTALL TECH 1.
- RECORD THEN CLEAR DTCs.
- RAISE AND SUPPORT DRIVE WHEELS.
- ENTER MISC TESTS/TRANSMISSION/TCC PWM SOLENOID.
- WITH ENGINE AT NORMAL OPERATING TEMPERATURE, SELECT "D4" AND ACCELERATE TO 25 mph.
- COMMAND THE TCC PWM SOLENOID "ON," AND THEN "OFF." WHILE OBSERVING TCC, SLIP SPEED ON TECH 1 DISPLAY. IS TCC SLIP SPEED LESS THAN 10 RPM WHILE COMMANDED "ON," AND IS TCC SLIP SPEED GREATER THAN 10 RPM WHILE COMMANDED "OFF"?

NO → (2)
- IGNITION "OFF."
- DISCONNECT TRANSMISSION WIRING CONNECTOR ASM. (ADDITIONAL DTCs WILL SET.)
- INSTALL J 39775 JUMPER HARNESS/PROBE KIT ON THE EXTERNAL WIRING CONNECTOR.
- IGNITION "ON," ENGINE "OFF."
- CONNECT TEST LIGHT FROM CAVITY "E" OF J 39775 TO GROUND. IS TEST LIGHT "ON"?

YES → ELECTRICAL SYSTEM CHECK OK. REFER TO "DIAGNOSTIC AIDS."

YES →
- INSTALL TEST LIGHT FROM CAVITIES "E" TO "S" (4L80E) OF J 39775.
- COMMAND TCC PWM SOLENOID "ON"/"OFF" THREE TIMES.
- IS TEST LIGHT "ON" WHEN COMMANDED "ON" AND "OFF" WHEN COMMANDED "OFF"?

NO → REPAIR OPEN OR SHORT TO GROUND IN THE IGNITION VOLTAGE FEED CIRCUIT TO THE TRANSMISSION. IF THE FUSE IS OPEN, CHECK THE TRANSMISSION INTERNAL WIRING HARNESS OR SOLENOID FOR SHORT TO GROUND.

NO → CHECK CKT 1350 (4L80E) FOR AN OPEN OR SHORT FROM THE CONTROL MODULE TO THE TRANSMISSION WIRING CONNECTOR. IF OKAY, REPLACE CONTROL MODULE.

YES → EXTERNAL TRANSMISSION WIRING CHECKS OKAY. CHECK INTERNAL TRANSMISSION WIRING AND REPAIR AS NECESSARY.

Courtesy of General Motors Corp.

DTC 85, UNDEFINED GEAR RATIO (1993)

While in each gear, PCM/TCM calculates actual gear ratio from input and output speed readings, also referred to as vehicle speed, then compares these to what gear ratio should be, taking into consideration selected gear range. This monitor includes reverse gear, but does not include overdrive gear.

NOTE: Test numbers refer to numbers on diagnostic chart.

1) This step checks operation of input sensor.
2) This step checks operation of output sensor.

DIAGNOSTIC AIDS

The PCM/TCM relies on Vehicle Speed Sensor Buffer Module (DRAC) to indicate what gear range has been selected. DRAC must be functioning properly or DTC 85 may be set. Check all connections, especially those at the transmission pass-thru connector. Compare scan tool gear ratio reading to specifications in GEAR RATIO table.

GEAR RATIO

Gear	Less Than	More Than
1st	2.38	2.63
2nd	1.43	1.58
3rd	.95	1.05
Reverse	1.97	2.17

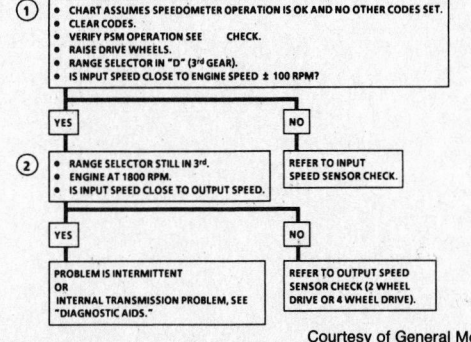

(1)
- CHART ASSUMES SPEEDOMETER OPERATION IS OK AND NO OTHER CODES SET.
- CLEAR CODES.
- VERIFY PSM OPERATION SEE   CHECK.
- RAISE DRIVE WHEELS.
- RANGE SELECTOR IN "D" (3rd GEAR).
- IS INPUT SPEED CLOSE TO ENGINE SPEED ± 100 RPM?

NO → REFER TO INPUT SPEED SENSOR CHECK.

YES → (2)
- RANGE SELECTOR STILL IN 3rd.
- ENGINE AT 1800 RPM.
- IS INPUT SPEED CLOSE TO OUTPUT SPEED.

NO → REFER TO OUTPUT SPEED SENSOR CHECK (2 WHEEL DRIVE OR 4 WHEEL DRIVE).

YES → PROBLEM IS INTERMITTENT OR INTERNAL TRANSMISSION PROBLEM, SEE "DIAGNOSTIC AIDS."

91E13692 92J14125

Courtesy of General Motors Corp.

DTC 85, UNDEFINED GEAR RATIO (1994)

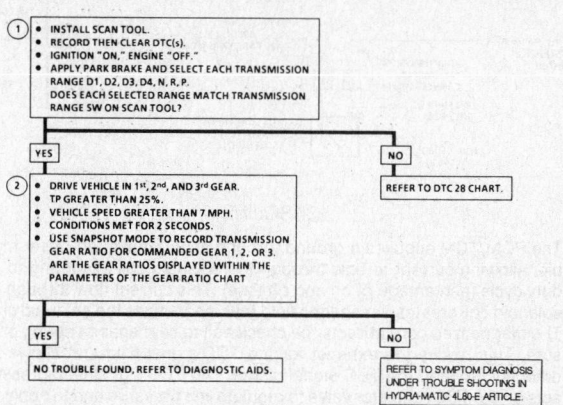

DIESEL

GASOLINE

While in each gear, PCM/TCM calculates actual gear ratio from input and output speed sensor readings, also referred to as the vehicle speed, then compares these to what gear ratio should be, taking into consideration selected gear range. This monitor includes reverse gear, but does not include overdrive gear.

DTC 85 will set when DTC(s) 21, 22, 24, 28, 71, 72 or 87 is not present, throttle position is greater than 25 percent, transmission is not in Park, Neutral or 4th gear, engine speed is greater than 300 RPM and vehicle speed is greater than 7 MPH. All conditions must be met for 2 seconds. PCM/TCM will default to maximum line pressure and inhibit TCC operation.

NOTE: Test numbers refer to numbers on diagnostic chart.

1) An out-of-range transmission fluid pressure switch could falsely indicate the actual transmission range.
2) This test checks the calculated ratio to determine if the ratio is within parameters.

94J38363 94H38395 94I38396

DIAGNOSTIC AIDS

DTC 85 will set when an unknown gear ratio is detected for any gear except 4th gear. See GEAR RATIO table for commanded gear and ratio range.

GEAR RATIO

Gear	Less Than	More Than
1st	2.38	2.63
2nd	1.43	1.58
3rd	.95	1.05
4th	1.97	2.17

① • INSTALL SCAN TOOL.
• RECORD THEN CLEAR DTC(s).
• IGNITION "ON," ENGINE "OFF."
• APPLY PARK BRAKE AND SELECT EACH TRANSMISSION RANGE D1, D2, D3, D4, N, R, P.
DOES EACH SELECTED RANGE MATCH TRANSMISSION RANGE SW ON SCAN TOOL?

YES

NO → REFER TO DTC 28 CHART.

② • DRIVE VEHICLE IN 1st, 2nd, AND 3rd GEAR.
• TP GREATER THAN 25%.
• VEHICLE SPEED GREATER THAN 7 MPH.
• CONDITIONS MET FOR 2 SECONDS.
• USE SNAPSHOT MODE TO RECORD TRANSMISSION GEAR RATIO FOR COMMANDED GEAR 1, 2, OR 3.
ARE THE GEAR RATIOS DISPLAYED WITHIN THE PARAMETERS OF THE GEAR RATIO CHART

YES → NO TROUBLE FOUND, REFER TO DIAGNOSTIC AIDS.

NO → REFER TO SYMPTOM DIAGNOSIS UNDER TROUBLE SHOOTING IN HYDRA-MATIC 4L80-E ARTICLE.

WHEN ALL DIAGNOSIS AND REPAIRS ARE COMPLETED, CLEAR DTC(s) AND VERIFY PROPER OPERATION.

Courtesy of General Motors Corp.

DTC 86, LOW GEAR RATIO (1993)

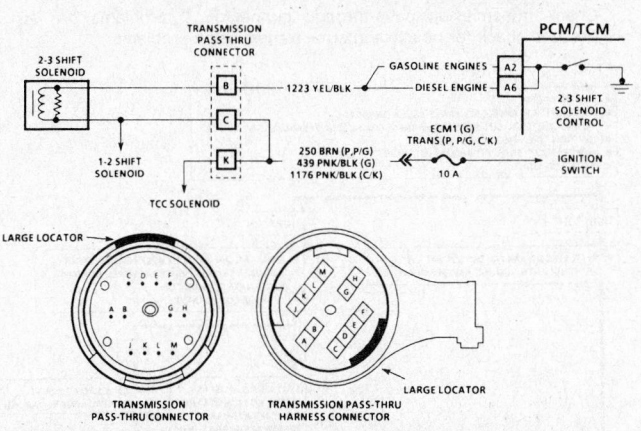

Shift solenoids are used inside valve body to control spool valves, which determine the transmission gear. Fused ignition power is supplied to solenoid "B", also referred to as 2-3 shift solenoid. PCM/TCM engages solenoid "B" by grounding circuit No. 1223. DTC 86 will set under following conditions: vehicle speed is greater than 7 MPH, TPS value is greater than 25 percent of total TPS travel, 1st or 2nd gear operation is requested by PCM/TCM, and transmission ratio indicates 3rd or 4th gear. All conditions must be met for 6 seconds.

93C76309 92B14127

NOTE: Test number refers to number on diagnostic chart.

1) This step checks if PCM/TCM can control solenoid "B".

DIAGNOSTIC AIDS

Check transmission pass-through connector. If problems are still present, check for possible internal transmission problems.

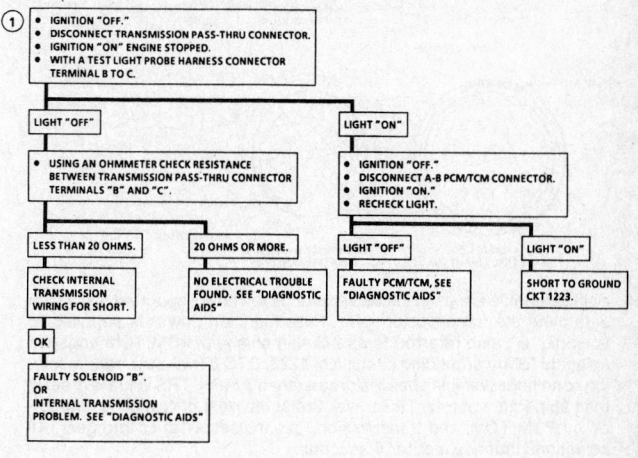

Courtesy of General Motors Corp.

DTC 86, LOW GEAR RATIO (1994)

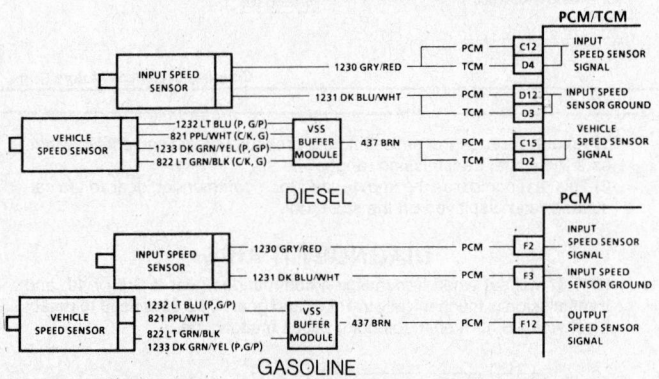

While in each gear, PCM/TCM calculates actual gear ratio from input and output speed sensor readings, also referred to as the vehicle speed, then compares these to what gear ratio should be, taking into consideration selected gear range.

DTC 86 will set when DTC(s) 21, 22, 24, 28, 71, 72 or 74 is not present, throttle position is greater than 25 percent, transmission is not in Park, Neutral or Reverse, engine speed is greater than 300 RPM, vehicle speed is greater than 7 MPH and transmission gear ratio is less than 1.06 in 1st or 2nd gear. All conditions must be met for 2 seconds. PCM/TCM will default to maximum line pressure, 2nd gear and inhibit TCC operation.

NOTE: Test numbers refer to numbers on diagnostic chart.

94J38363 94H38395 94J38397

1) An out-of-range transmission fluid pressure switch could falsely indicate the actual transmission range.
2) This test compares the known ratio for a commanded gear to the calculated ratio displayed on the scan tool.

DIAGNOSTIC AIDS

DTC 86 will set when transmission commanded gear is 1st or 2nd and transmission is mechanically in 3rd or 4th gear. DTC 81 is used to detect a solenoid "B" (2-3 shift solenoid) circuit malfunction.

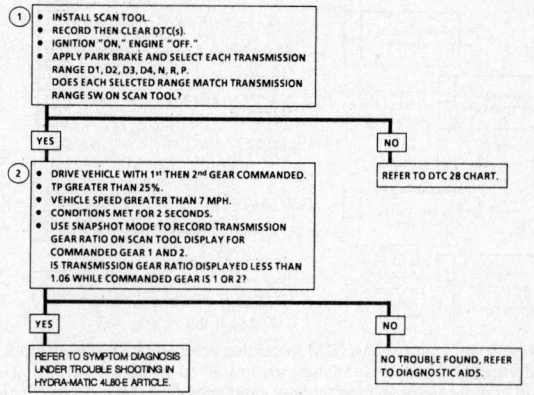

WHEN ALL DIAGNOSIS AND REPAIRS ARE COMPLETED, CLEAR DTC(s) AND VERIFY PROPER OPERATION.

Courtesy of General Motors Corp.

DTC 87, HIGH GEAR RATIO (1993)

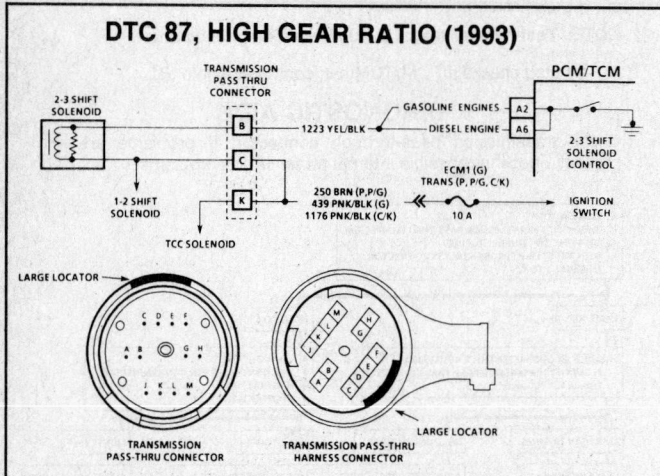

TRANSMISSION PASS-THRU CONNECTOR

TRANSMISSION PASS-THRU HARNESS CONNECTOR

Shift solenoids are used inside valve body to control spool valves, which determine the transmission gear. Fused ignition power is supplied to solenoid "B", also referred to as 2-3 shift solenoid. PCM/TCM engages solenoid "B" by grounding circuit No. 1223. DTC 87 will set under following conditions: vehicle speed is greater than 7 MPH, TPS value is greater than 25 percent of total TPS travel, 3rd or 4th gear operation is requested by PCM/TCM, and transmission ratio indicates 1st or 2nd gear. All conditions must be met for 6 seconds.

NOTE: Test numbers refer to numbers on diagnostic chart.

1) This step checks if PCM/TCM can control solenoid "B". If bidirectional scan tool is not available, solenoid may be activated by grounding ALDL test terminal 'B' with ignition on and engine off.
2) Battery supply should be present at PCM/TCM.
3) This step checks shift solenoid "B" and circuits inside transmission for shorts.

93C76309 92D14129

DIAGNOSTIC AIDS

Check transmission pass-through connector. If problems are still present, check for possible internal transmission problems.

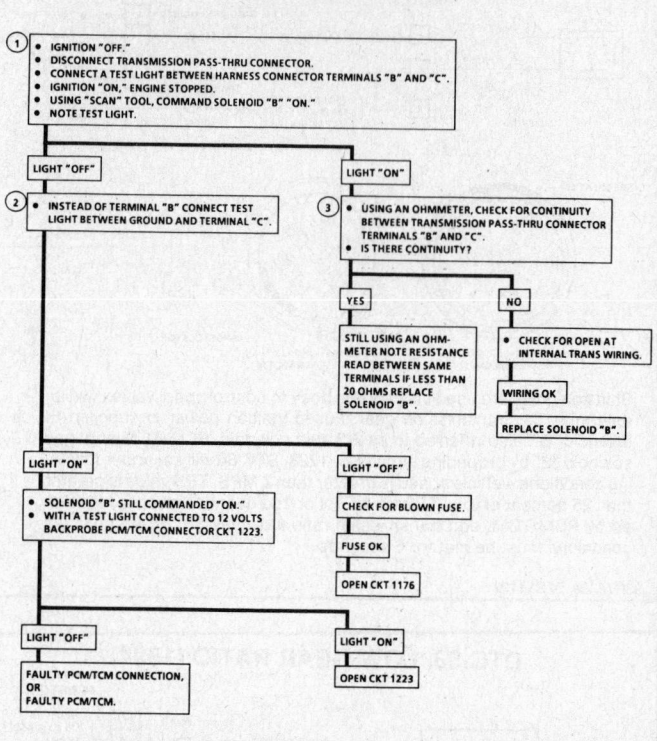

Courtesy of General Motors Corp.

DTC 87, HIGH GEAR RATIO (1994)

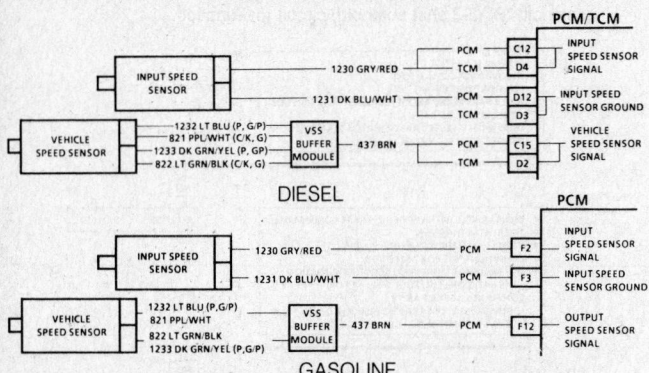

DIESEL

GASOLINE

While in each gear, PCM/TCM calculates actual gear ratio from input and output speed sensor readings, also referred to as the vehicle speed, then compares these to what gear ratio should be, taking into consideration selected gear range.

DTC 87 will set when DTC(s) 21, 22, 24, 28, 71, 72 or 74 is not present, throttle position is greater than 25 percent, transmission is not in Park, Neutral or Reverse, engine speed is greater than 300 RPM, transmission fluid temperature is greater than (20°C), vehicle speed is greater than 7 MPH and transmission gear ratio is greater than 1.42 in 3rd or 4th gear. All conditions must be met for 2 seconds. PCM/TCM will default to maximum line pressure, 2nd gear and inhibit TCC operation.

NOTE: Test numbers refer to numbers on diagnostic chart.

94J38363 94H38395 94A38398

1) An out-of-range transmission fluid pressure switch could falsely indicate the actual transmission range.
2) This test compares the known ratio for a commanded gear to the calculated ratio displayed on the scan tool.

DIAGNOSTIC AIDS

DTC 87 will set when transmission commanded gear is 3rd or 4th and transmission is mechanically in 1st or 2nd gear. DTC 81 is used to detect a solenoid "B" (2-3 shift solenoid) circuit malfunction.

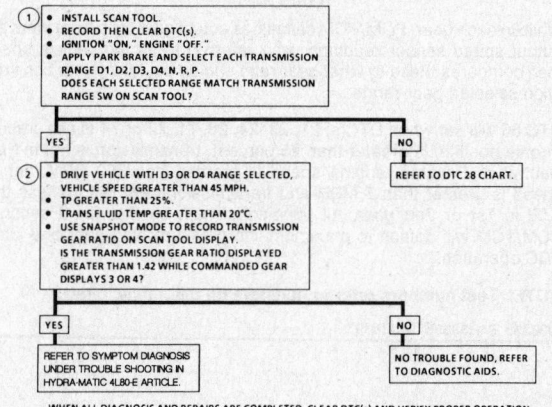

WHEN ALL DIAGNOSIS AND REPAIRS ARE COMPLETED, CLEAR DTC(s) AND VERIFY PROPER OPERATION.

Courtesy of General Motors Corp.

ELECTRONIC TESTING

NOTE: *If self-diagnostics are not used, following charts may help diagnose electronic transmission controls.*

CLUTCH & BAND APPLICATION CHART
CLUTCH & BAND APPLICATION CHART

Selector Lever Position	Solenoid Positions	Elements In Use
"D" (Overdrive)		
1st Gear	"A" ON/"B" OFF	[1] Overdrive Roller Clutch, Forward Clutch, [2] Intermediate Sprag Clutch & Low Roller Clutch
2nd Gear	"A" OFF/"B" OFF	[1] Overdrive Roller Clutch, Forward Clutch, [1] Intermediate Sprag Clutch, Intermediate Clutch & [3] Low Roller Clutch
3rd Gear	"A" OFF/"B" ON	[1] Overdrive Roller Clutch, Forward Clutch, Direct Clutch, [3] Intermediate Sprag Clutch, Intermediate Clutch & [3] Low Roller Clutch
Overdrive	"A" ON/"B" ON	4th Clutch, [3] Overdrive Roller Clutch, Forward Clutch, Direct Clutch, [3] Intermediate Sprag Clutch, Intermediate Clutch & [3] Low Roller Clutch
"D" (Manual 3rd)		
1st Gear	"A" ON/"B" OFF	Overrun Clutch, [1] Overdrive Roller Clutch, Forward Clutch, [2] Intermediate Sprag Clutch & [1] Low Roller Clutch
2nd Gear	"A" OFF/"B" OFF	Overrun Clutch, [1] Overdrive Roller Clutch, Forward Clutch, [1] Intermediate Sprag Clutch, Intermediate Clutch & [3] Low Roller Clutch
3rd Gear	"A" OFF/"B" ON	Overrun Clutch, [1] Overdrive Roller Clutch, Forward Clutch, Direct Clutch, [3] Intermediate Sprag Clutch, Intermediate Clutch & [3] Low Roller Clutch
"2" (Manual 2nd)		
1st Gear	"A" ON/"B" OFF	Overrun Clutch, [1] Overdrive Roller Clutch, Forward Clutch, [2] Intermediate Sprag Clutch & [1] Low Roller Clutch
2nd Gear	"A" OFF/"B" OFF	Overrun Clutch, [1] Overdrive Roller Clutch, Forward Clutch, Front Band [1] Intermediate Sprag Clutch, Intermediate Clutch & [3] Low Roller Clutch
"1" (Manual Low)		
1st Gear	"A" ON/"B" OFF	Overrun Clutch, [1] Overdrive Roller Clutch, Forward Clutch, [2] Intermediate Sprag Clutch, [1] Low Roller Clutch & Rear Band
2nd Gear	"A" OFF/"B" OFF	Overrun Clutch, [1] Overdrive Roller Clutch, Forward Clutch, Front Band [1] Intermediate Sprag Clutch, Intermediate Clutch & [3] Low Roller Clutch
"R" (Reverse)	"A" ON/"B" OFF	[1] Overdrive Roller Clutch, Direct Clutch & Rear Band
"N" Or "P" (Neutral Or Park)	"A" ON/"B" OFF	[1] Overdrive Roller Clutch, All Other Clutches & Bands Released Or Ineffective

[1] – Holding.
[2] – Applied but not effective.
[3] – Overrunning.

COMPONENT TEST CHARTS (NO CODES)

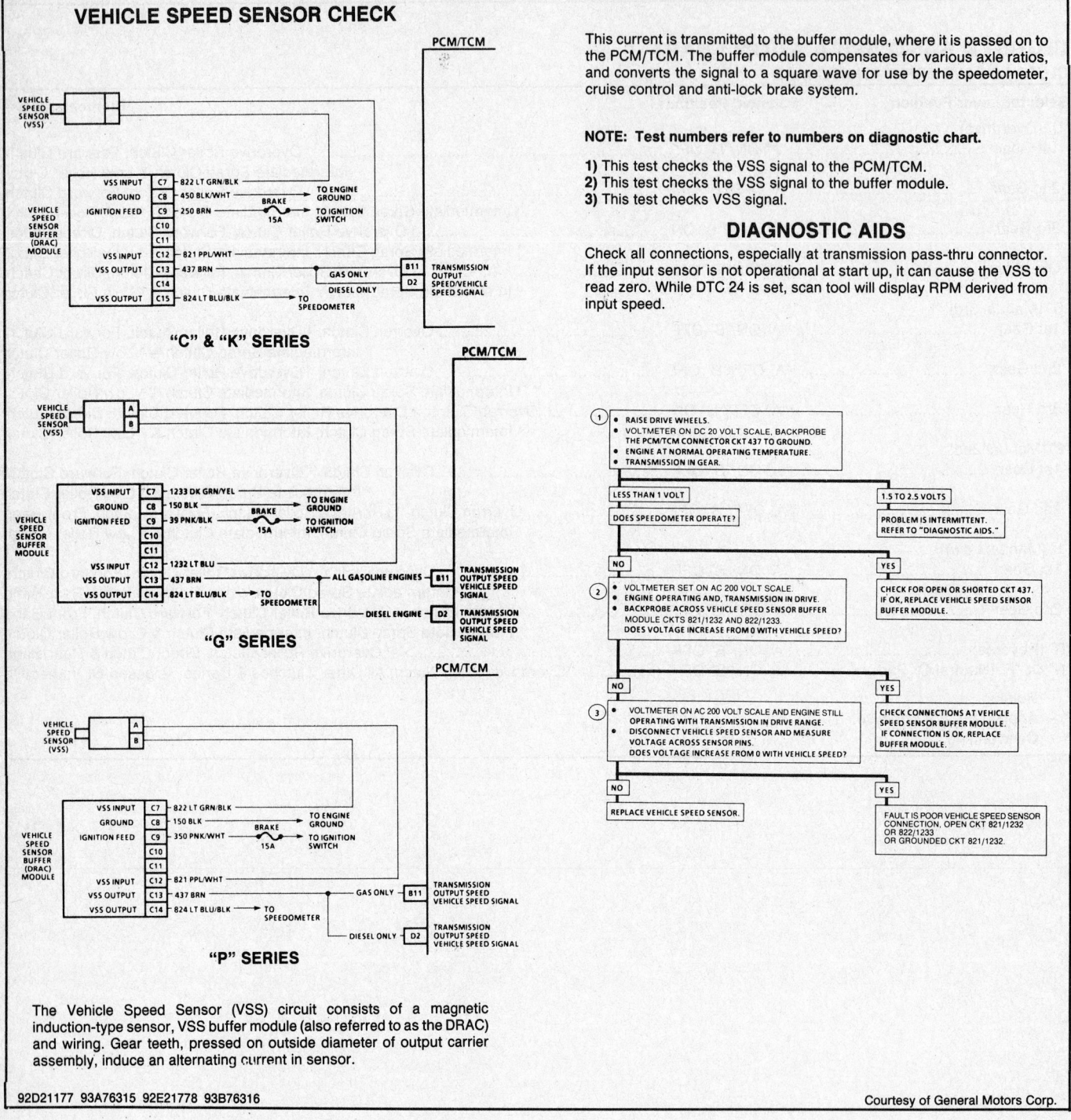

VEHICLE SPEED SENSOR CHECK

"C" & "K" SERIES

"G" SERIES

"P" SERIES

This current is transmitted to the buffer module, where it is passed on to the PCM/TCM. The buffer module compensates for various axle ratios, and converts the signal to a square wave for use by the speedometer, cruise control and anti-lock brake system.

NOTE: Test numbers refer to numbers on diagnostic chart.

1) This test checks the VSS signal to the PCM/TCM.
2) This test checks the VSS signal to the buffer module.
3) This test checks VSS signal.

DIAGNOSTIC AIDS

Check all connections, especially at transmission pass-thru connector. If the input sensor is not operational at start up, it can cause the VSS to read zero. While DTC 24 is set, scan tool will display RPM derived from input speed.

① • RAISE DRIVE WHEELS.
• VOLTMETER ON DC 20 VOLT SCALE, BACKPROBE THE PCM/TCM CONNECTOR CKT 437 TO GROUND.
• ENGINE AT NORMAL OPERATING TEMPERATURE.
• TRANSMISSION IN GEAR.

LESS THAN 1 VOLT

DOES SPEEDOMETER OPERATE?

1.5 TO 2.5 VOLTS

PROBLEM IS INTERMITTENT. REFER TO "DIAGNOSTIC AIDS."

NO

② • VOLTMETER SET ON AC 200 VOLT SCALE.
• ENGINE OPERATING AND, TRANSMISSION IN DRIVE.
• BACKPROBE ACROSS VEHICLE SPEED SENSOR BUFFER MODULE CKTS 821/1232 AND 822/1233. DOES VOLTAGE INCREASE FROM 0 WITH VEHICLE SPEED?

YES

CHECK FOR OPEN OR SHORTED CKT 437. IF OK, REPLACE VEHICLE SPEED SENSOR BUFFER MODULE.

NO

③ • VOLTMETER ON AC 200 VOLT SCALE AND ENGINE STILL OPERATING WITH TRANSMISSION IN DRIVE RANGE.
• DISCONNECT VEHICLE SPEED SENSOR AND MEASURE VOLTAGE ACROSS SENSOR PINS. DOES VOLTAGE INCREASE FROM 0 WITH VEHICLE SPEED?

YES

CHECK CONNECTIONS AT VEHICLE SPEED SENSOR BUFFER MODULE. IF CONNECTION IS OK, REPLACE BUFFER MODULE.

NO

REPLACE VEHICLE SPEED SENSOR.

YES

FAULT IS POOR VEHICLE SPEED SENSOR CONNECTION, OPEN CKT 821/1232 OR 822/1233 OR GROUNDED CKT 821/1232.

The Vehicle Speed Sensor (VSS) circuit consists of a magnetic induction-type sensor, VSS buffer module (also referred to as the DRAC) and wiring. Gear teeth, pressed on outside diameter of output carrier assembly, induce an alternating current in sensor.

INPUT SPEED SENSOR CIRCUIT (1993)

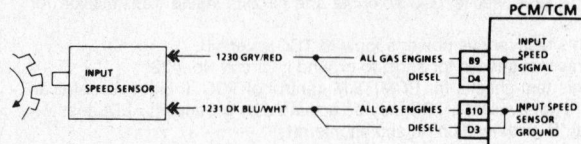

The input speed sensor is of the magnetic induction type and is located on the left side of the transmission, forward of center. Serrations in the forward clutch housing induce a small A/C current as they pass by the input speed sensor. While there is no specific code for an input speed sensor problem, the PCM/TCM uses input speed sensor readings to calculate gear ratio, turbine speed and TCC slip, and determine if engine is running.

NOTE: Test numbers refer to numbers on diagnostic chart.

1) This test checks input sensor circuit to PCM/TCM.
2) This test checks input speed sensor output.

91G13702 91H13703

DIAGNOSTIC AIDS

Check transmission pass-through connector and PCM/TCM for poor connections.

Courtesy of General Motors Corp.

BRAKE SIGNAL CIRCUIT (1993)

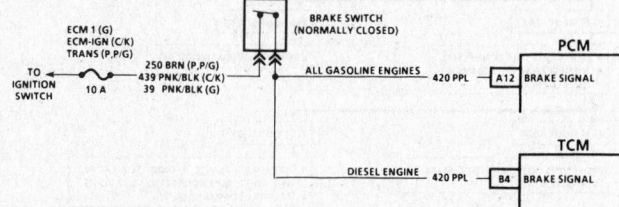

The normally closed brake switch supplies a 12-volt signal on circuit No. 420 to the PCM/TCM. The signal voltage is removed when brakes are applied. An incorrect brake signal may affect TCC operation.

NOTE: Test numbers refer to numbers on diagnostic chart. Display may vary depending on manufacturer of scan tool. Display may read APPLIED, RELEASED, ON or OFF.

1) This test checks for voltage at brake switch.
2) This test simulates closed brake switch (brakes off).
3) This test checks circuit No. 420 from brake switch to PCM/TCM.
4) This test opens circuit No. 420 and simulates condition of brakes being applied.

DIAGNOSTIC AIDS

Check for problem with one or more of following components: fuse, power supply circuit, brake switch or wire before splice. Check for wire or circuit problem between splice and PCM/TCM, poor connection to PCM/TCM or faulty PCM/TCM.

93C76317 91J13705

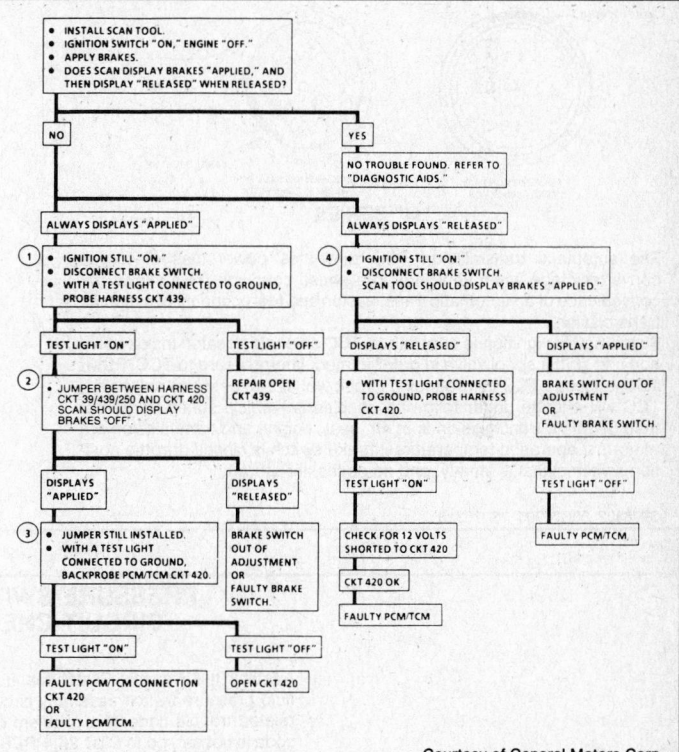

Courtesy of General Motors Corp.

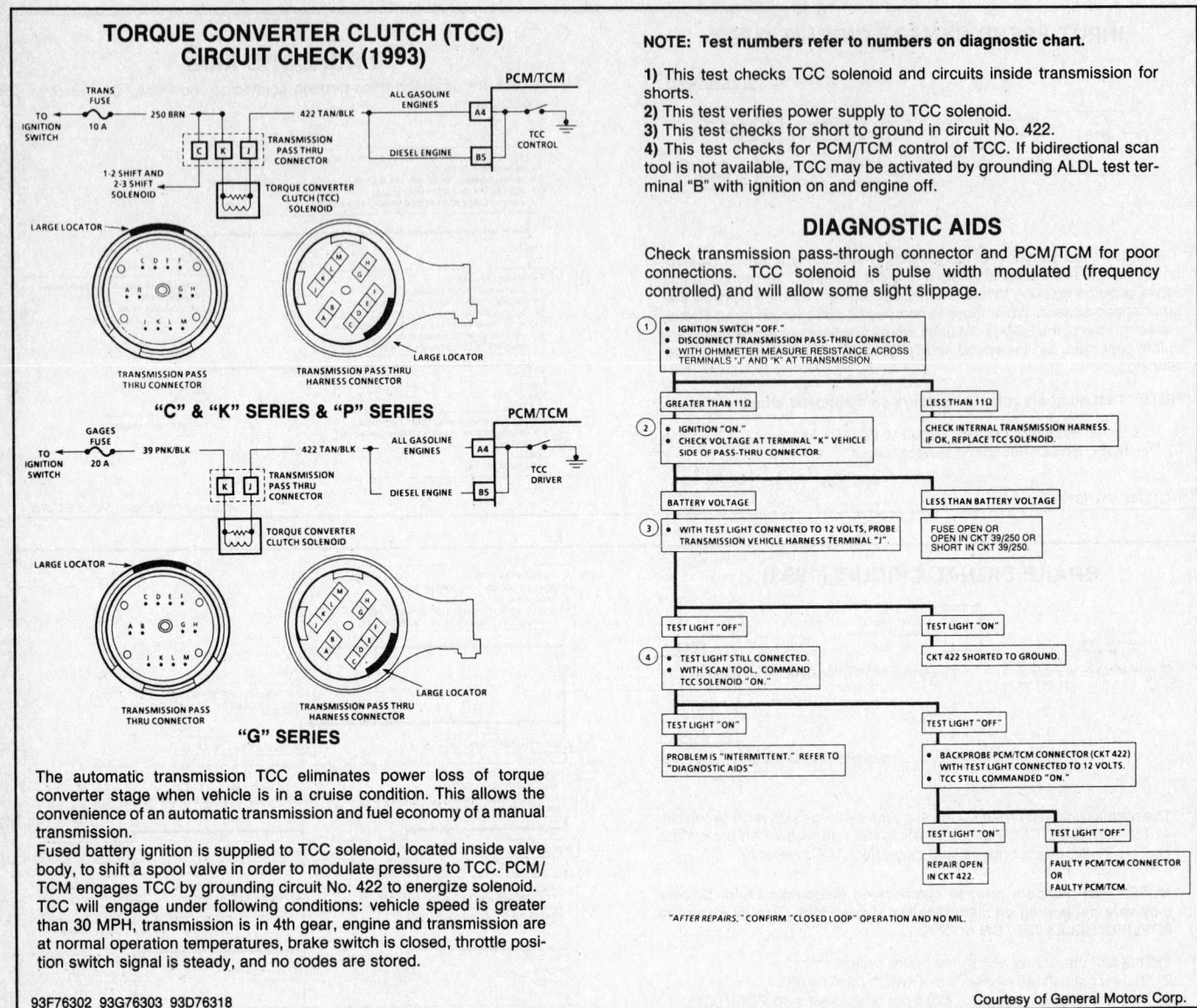

TORQUE CONVERTER CLUTCH (TCC) CIRCUIT CHECK (1993)

"C" & "K" SERIES & "P" SERIES

"G" SERIES

The automatic transmission TCC eliminates power loss of torque converter stage when vehicle is in a cruise condition. This allows the convenience of an automatic transmission and fuel economy of a manual transmission.

Fused battery ignition is supplied to TCC solenoid, located inside valve body, to shift a spool valve in order to modulate pressure to TCC. PCM/TCM engages TCC by grounding circuit No. 422 to energize solenoid. TCC will engage under following conditions: vehicle speed is greater than 30 MPH, transmission is in 4th gear, engine and transmission are at normal operation temperatures, brake switch is closed, throttle position switch signal is steady, and no codes are stored.

93F76302 93G76303 93D76318

NOTE: Test numbers refer to numbers on diagnostic chart.

1) This test checks TCC solenoid and circuits inside transmission for shorts.

2) This test verifies power supply to TCC solenoid.

3) This test checks for short to ground in circuit No. 422.

4) This test checks for PCM/TCM control of TCC. If bidirectional scan tool is not available, TCC may be activated by grounding ALDL test terminal "B" with ignition on and engine off.

DIAGNOSTIC AIDS

Check transmission pass-through connector and PCM/TCM for poor connections. TCC solenoid is pulse width modulated (frequency controlled) and will allow some slight slippage.

"AFTER REPAIRS," CONFIRM "CLOSED LOOP" OPERATION AND NO MIL.

Courtesy of General Motors Corp.

PRESSURE SWITCH MANIFOLD CIRCUIT CHECK (1993-94)

A fault in the Pressure Switch Manifold (PSM) circuit, also referred to as fluid pressure switch assembly circuit, should result in the setting of a related trouble code. If a problem is suspected with this circuit and a code is not set, go to DTC 28, PRESSURE SWITCH MANIFOLD FAULT chart.

SHIFT SOLENOID "A" CIRCUIT CHECK (1993)

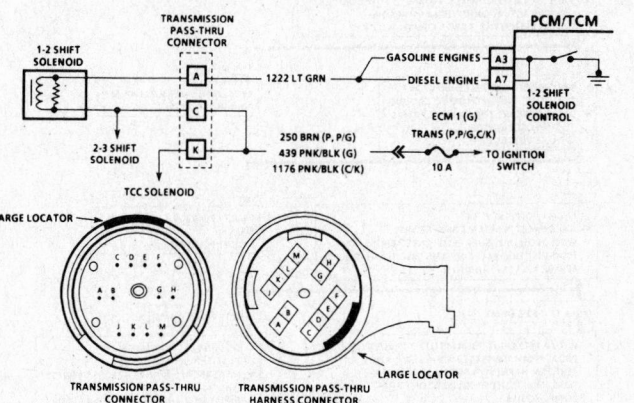

Shift solenoid "A", also referred to as 1-2 shift solenoid, is attached to the valve body and is a normally open exhaust valve. The PCM/TCM activates the solenoid by grounding it through an internal quad-driver. Solenoid "A" (Gray) is on in 1st and 4th gears, but is off in 2nd and 3rd gears. When solenoid is on, it redirects fluid to act on the shift valves.

NOTE: Test numbers refer to numbers on diagnostic chart.

1) This test checks shift solenoid "A" and circuits inside transmission for shorts.
2) Battery voltage should be present at shift solenoid "A".
3) This test checks circuit No. 1222 for short to ground.

93F76310 91B13707

4) This test checks if PCM/TCM can control solenoid "A". If bidirectional scan tool is not available, solenoid may be activated by grounding ALDL test terminal "B" with ignition on and engine off.

DIAGNOSTIC AIDS

Check transmission pass-through connector and PCM/TCM for poor connections.

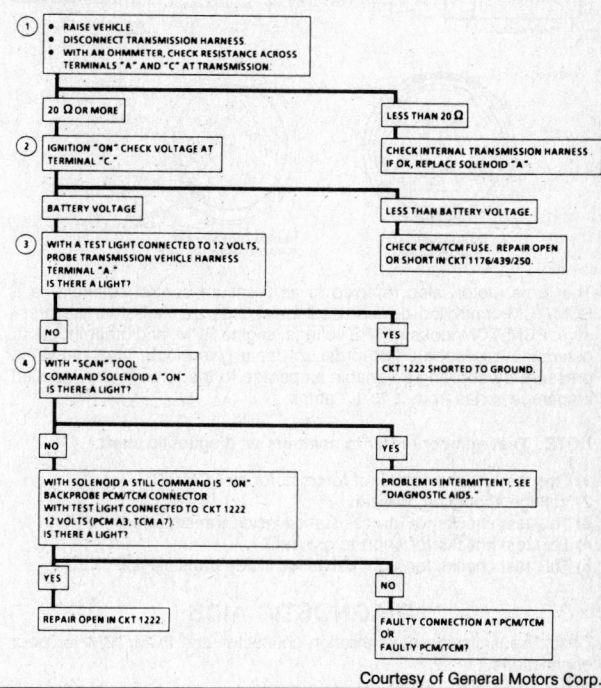

Courtesy of General Motors Corp.

SHIFT SOLENOID "B" CIRCUIT CHECK (1993)

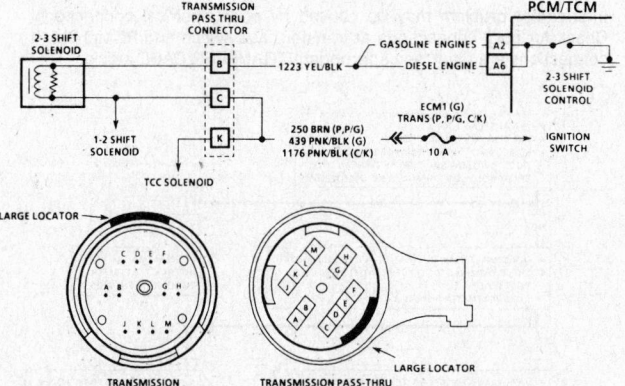

Shift solenoid "B", also referred to as 2-3 shift solenoid, is attached to the valve body and is a normally open exhaust valve, which determines the transmission gear. Solenoid "B" (Green) is on in 3rd and 4th gears, but is off in 1st and 2nd gears. Fused ignition voltage is supplied to solenoid "B". PCM/TCM engages solenoid "B" by grounding circuit No. 1223.

NOTE: Test numbers refer to numbers on diagnostic chart.

1) This test checks shift solenoid "B" and circuits inside transmission for shorts.
2) Battery voltage should be present at shift solenoid "B".
3) This test checks circuit No. 1223 for short to ground.
4) This test checks if PCM/TCM can control solenoid "B". If bidirectional scan tool is not available, solenoid may be activated by grounding ALDL test terminal "B" with ignition on and engine off.

93C76309 91C13708

5) This determines whether circuit No. 1223 is open or PCM/TCM is faulty.

DIAGNOSTIC AIDS

Check transmission pass-through connector and PCM/TCM for poor connections.

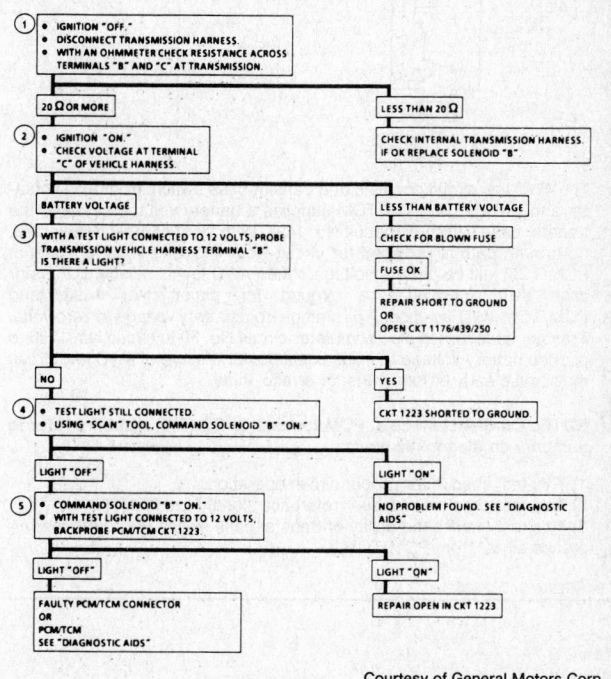

Courtesy of General Motors Corp.

FORCE MOTOR CIRCUIT CHECK (1993)

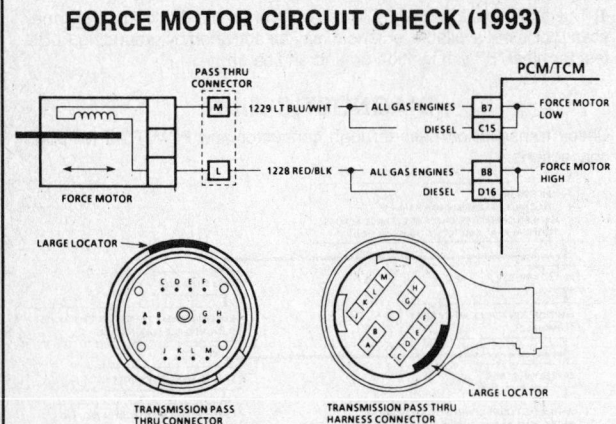

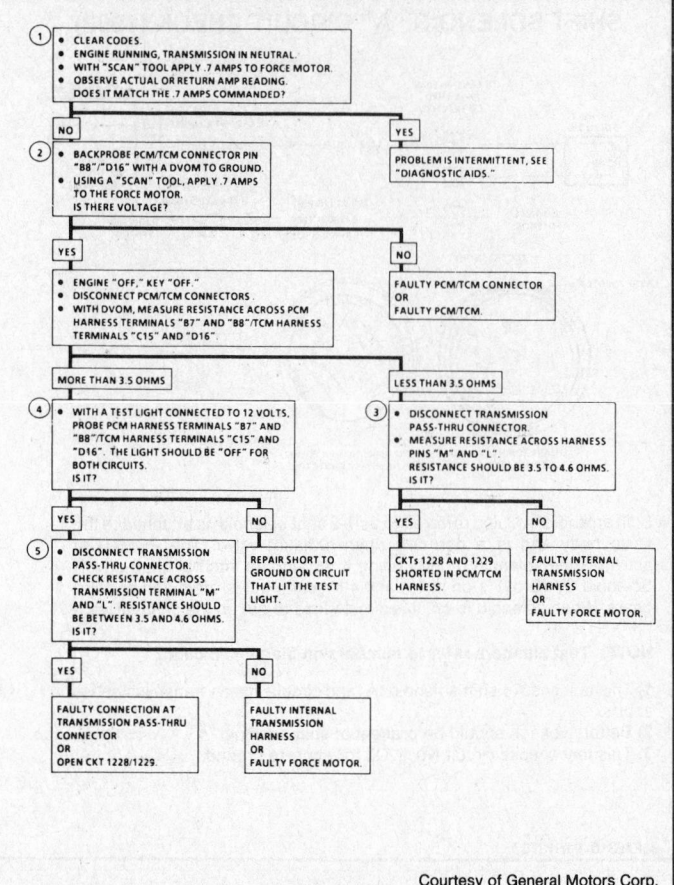

The force motor, also referred to as pressure control solenoid, is a PCM/TCM-controlled device used to regulate transmission line pressure. PCM/TCM looks at TPS voltage, engine RPM, and other inputs to determine appropriate line pressure for a given load, then regulates pressure by applying a variable amperage to the force motor. Applied amperage varies from .1 to 1.1 amps.

NOTE: Test numbers refer to numbers on diagnostic chart.

1) This test checks control of force motor by PCM/TCM.
2) Voltage should be present.
3) This test checks for low resistance inside transmission.
4) This test checks for short to ground.
5) This test checks for high resistance inside transmission.

DIAGNOSTIC AIDS

Check transmission pass-through connector and PCM/TCM for poor connections.

91E13684 92F21779

Courtesy of General Motors Corp.

4WD LOW SWITCH SIGNAL CHECK (1994)

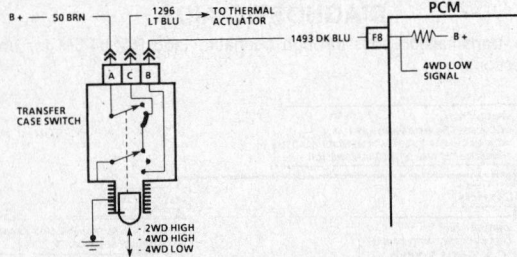

The 4WD low circuit consists of a transfer case switch, front axle actuator and wiring. The PCM/TCM supplies a battery voltage signal to the transfer case switch on circuit No. 1493. With 2WD or 4WD HI selected, no ground path is provided for circuit No. 1493, and voltage signal at PCM/TCM will be battery voltage. When 4WD low is selected, transfer case switch provides a ground for circuit No. 1493, and PCM/TCM 4WD low signal will change from battery voltage to zero volts. Transfer case switch also completes circuit No. 50 to circuit No. 1296 to provide battery voltage to front axle actuator. Failure of 4WD low circuit may cause early or late shifts, or erratic shifts.

NOTE: On diesel models, PCM terminal is E2. Test numbers refer to numbers on diagnostic chart.

1) This test checks for proper circuit operation.
2) This test checks for proper reference signal from PCM/TCM.
3) This test checks the ability of transfer case switch to ground the reference signal from PCM/TCM.

DIAGNOSTIC AIDS

Intermittent problem may be caused by poor electrical connections. Check for poor connections at transfer case switch and PCM/TCM. If connections are okay, see appropriate TRANSFER CASE article.

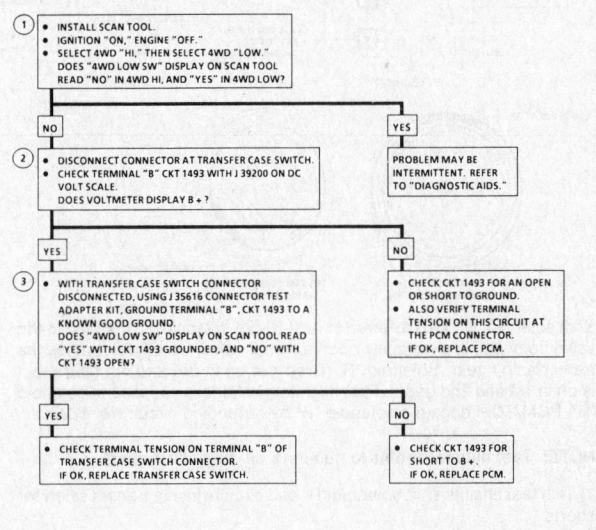

94A38364 94B38365

Courtesy of General Motors Corp.

WIRING DIAGRAMS

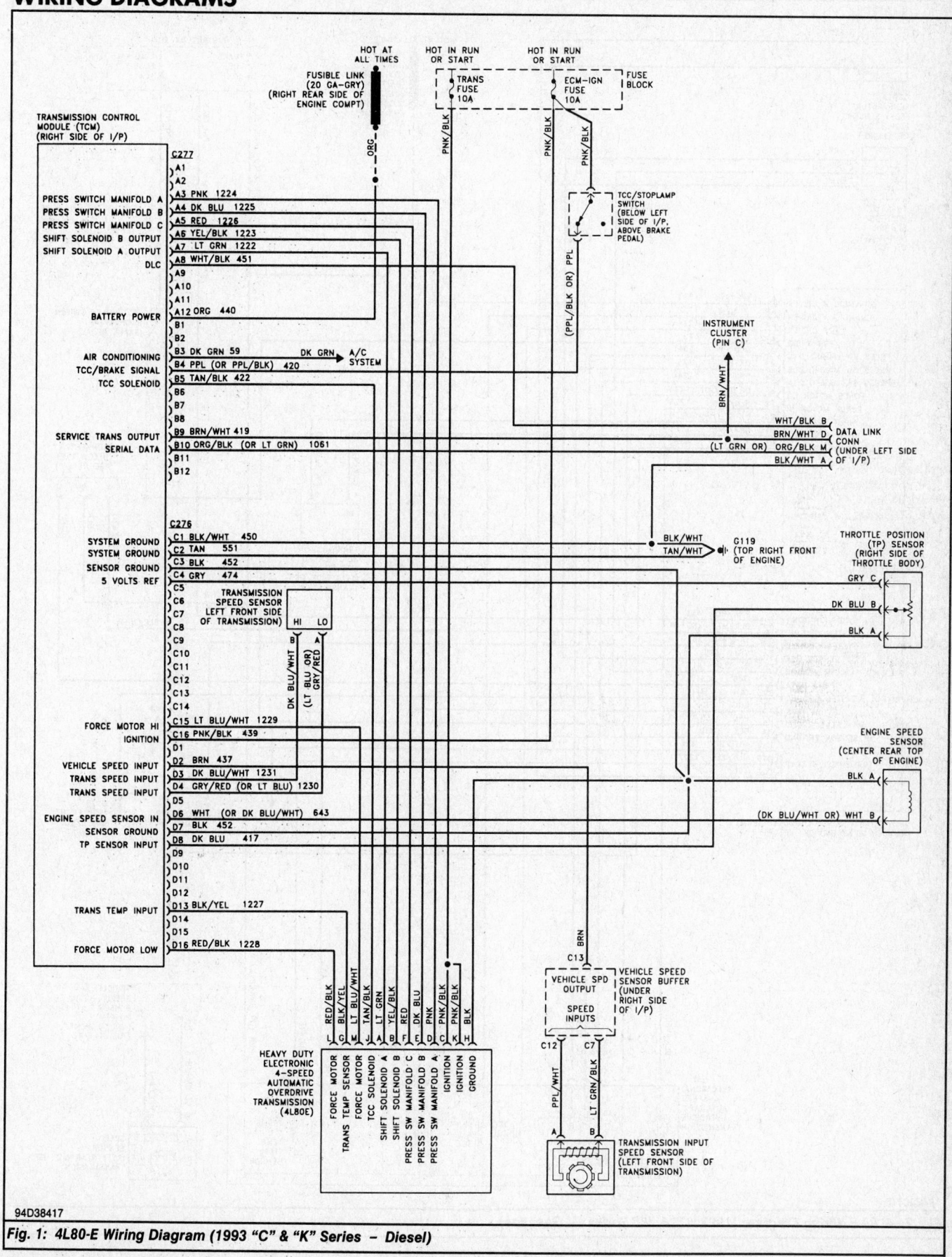

94D38417

Fig. 1: 4L80-E Wiring Diagram (1993 "C" & "K" Series – Diesel)

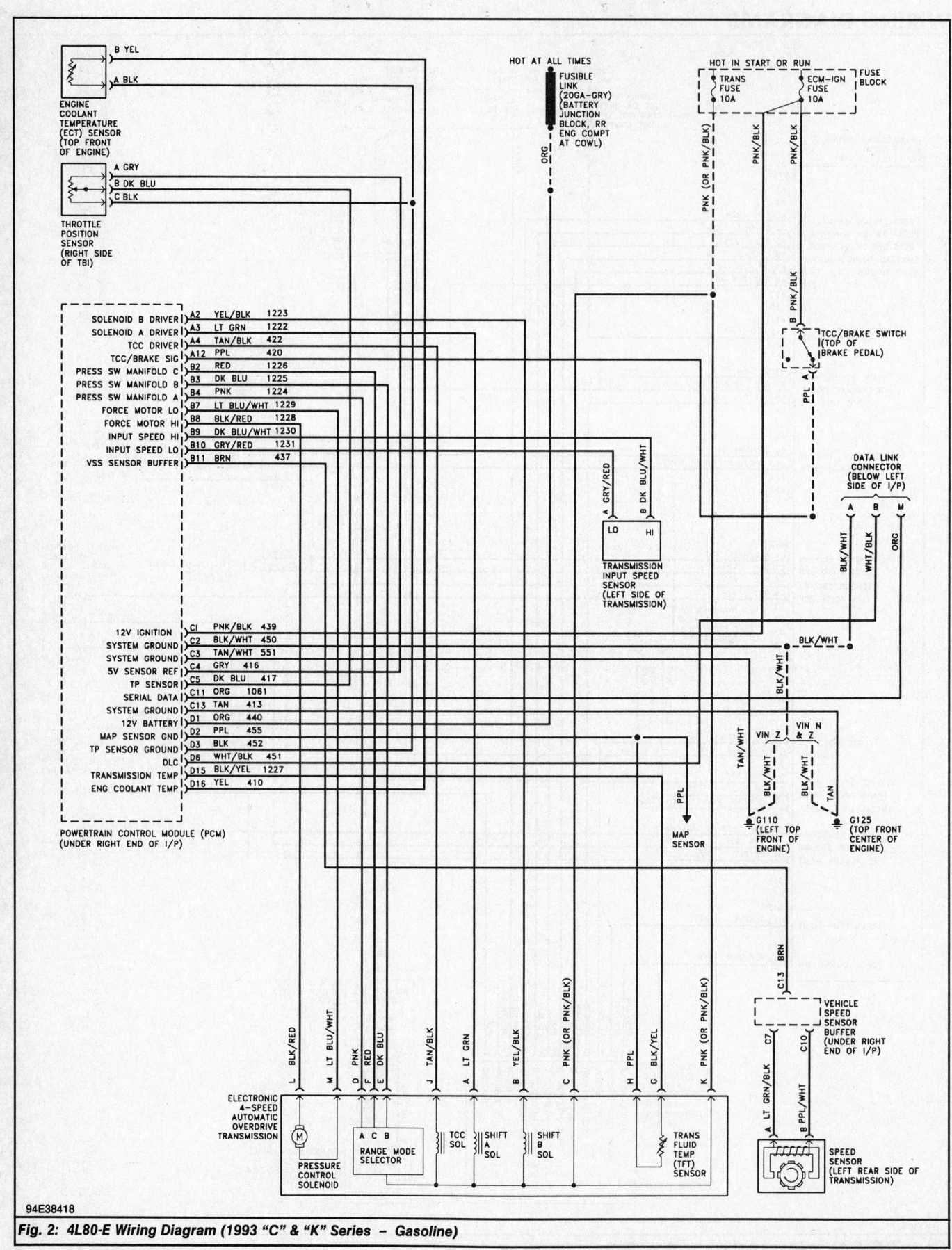

94E38418

Fig. 2: 4L80-E Wiring Diagram (1993 "C" & "K" Series – Gasoline)

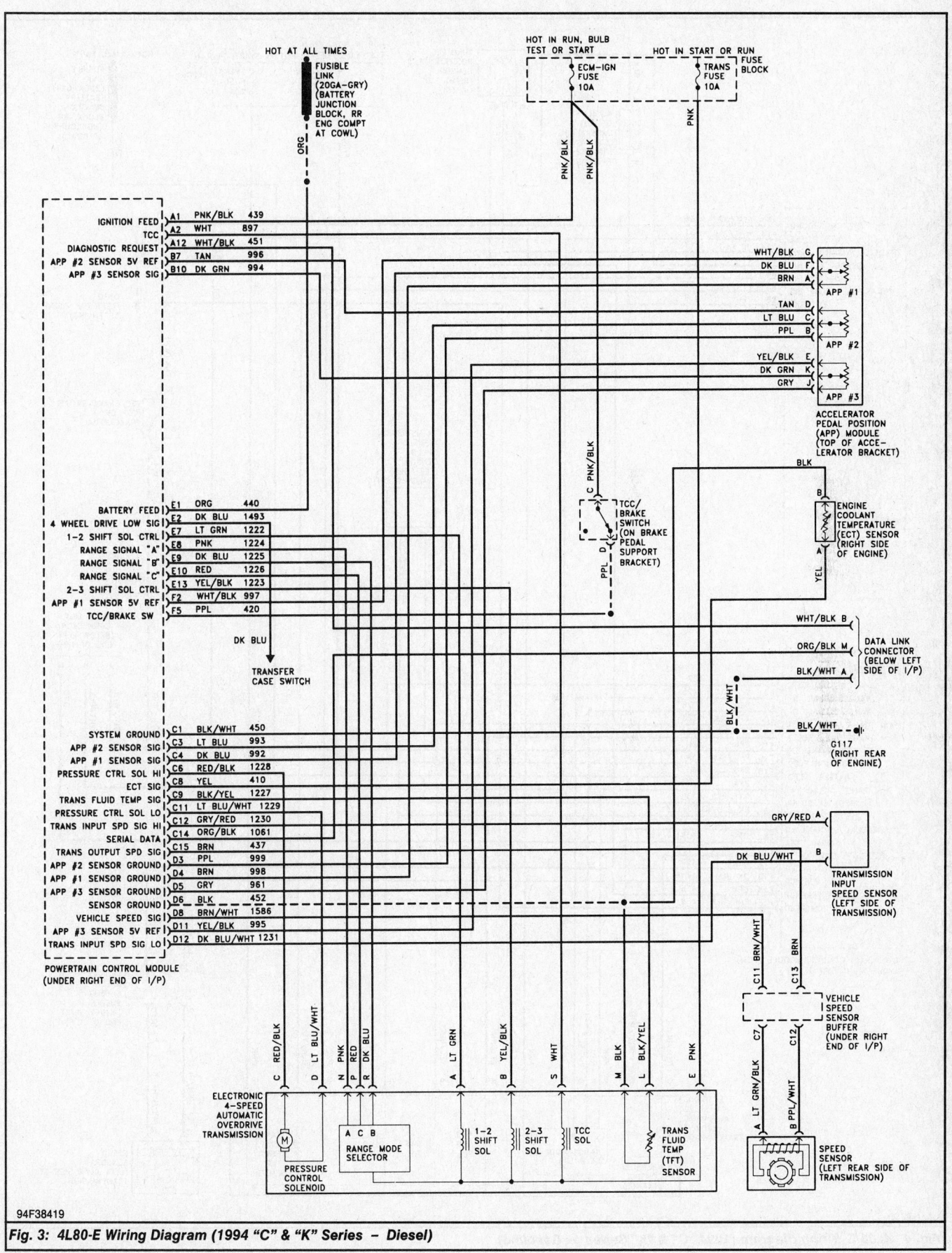

94F38419

Fig. 3: 4L80-E Wiring Diagram (1994 "C" & "K" Series – Diesel)

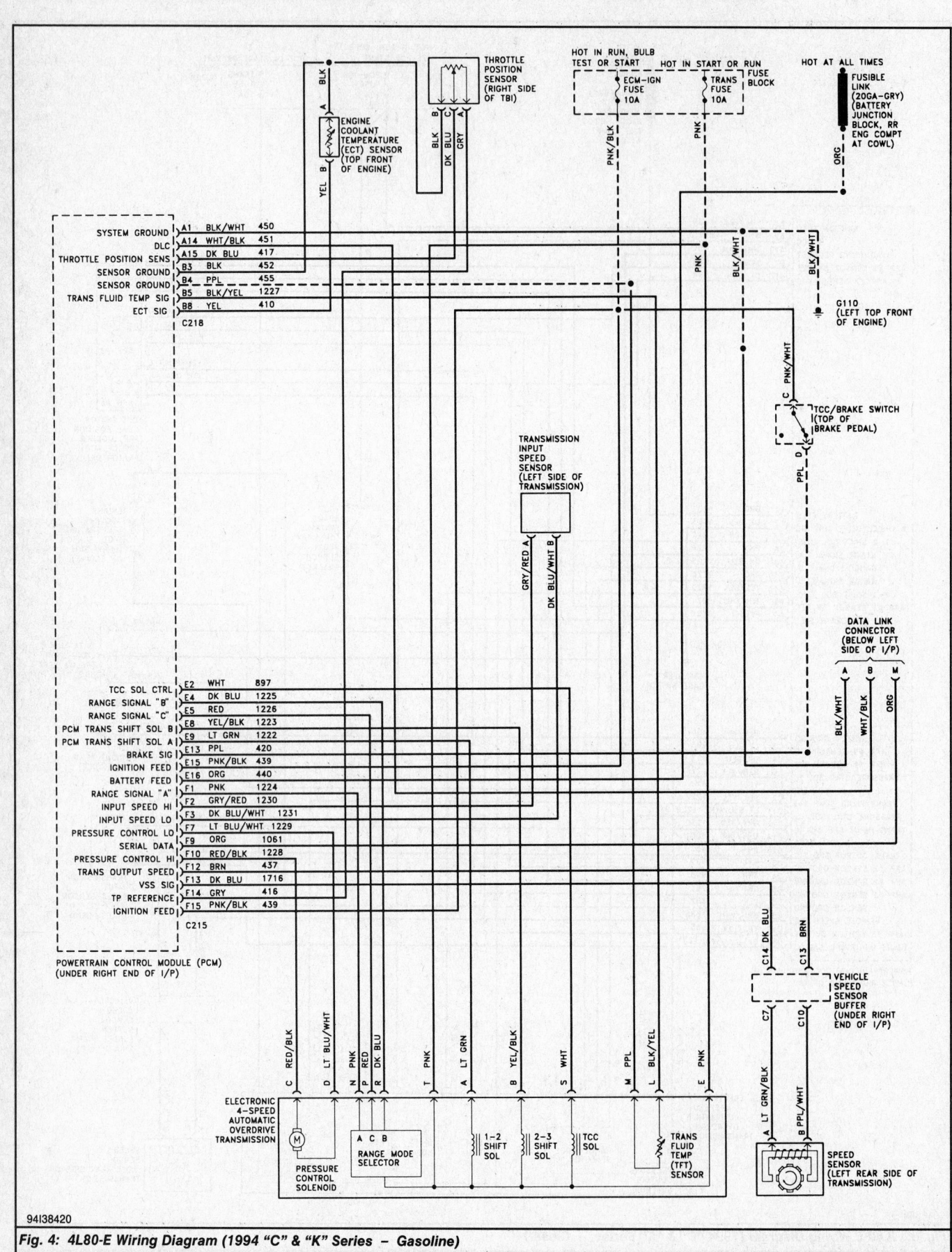

94I38420

Fig. 4: 4L80-E Wiring Diagram (1994 "C" & "K" Series – Gasoline)

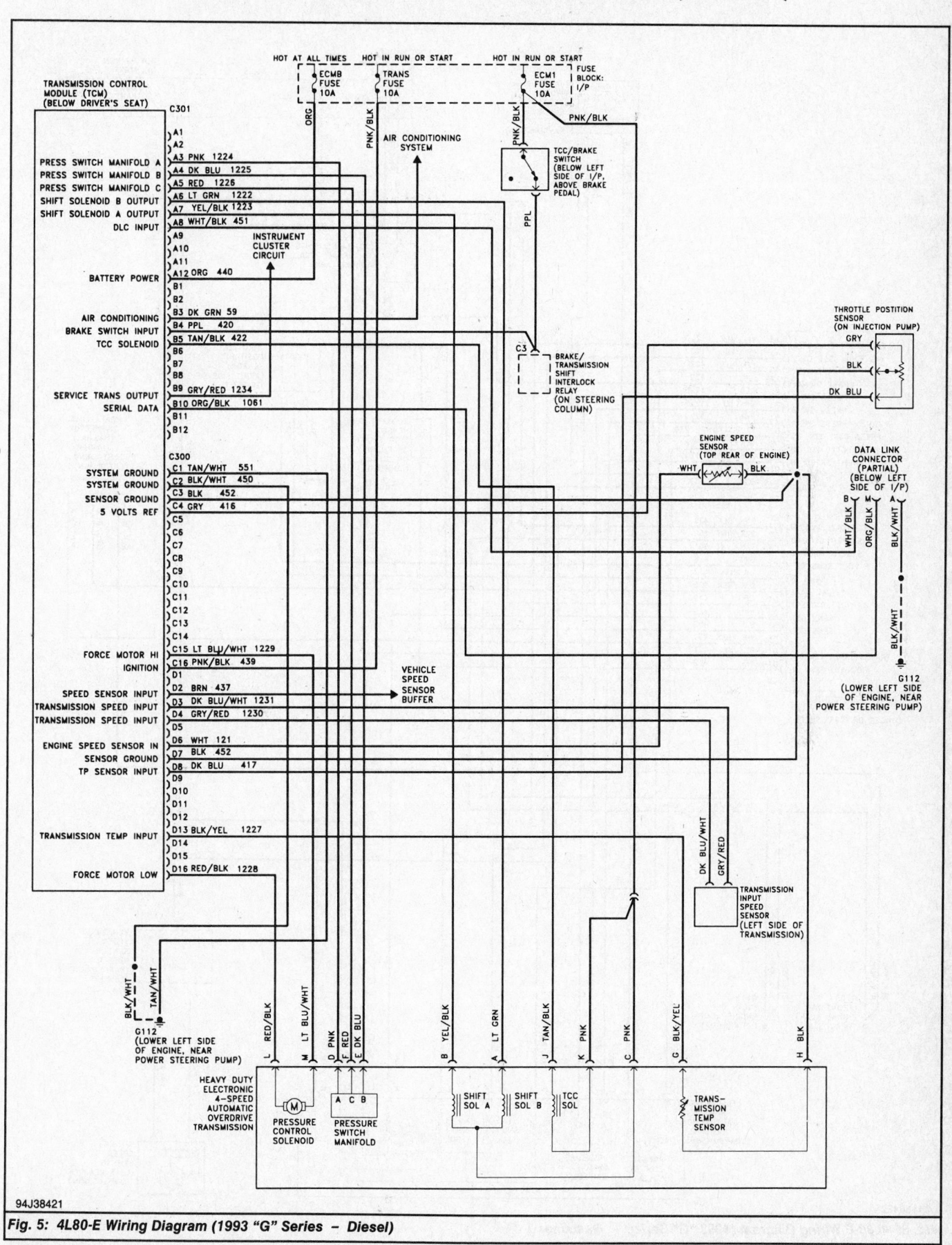

94J38421

Fig. 5: 4L80-E Wiring Diagram (1993 "G" Series – Diesel)

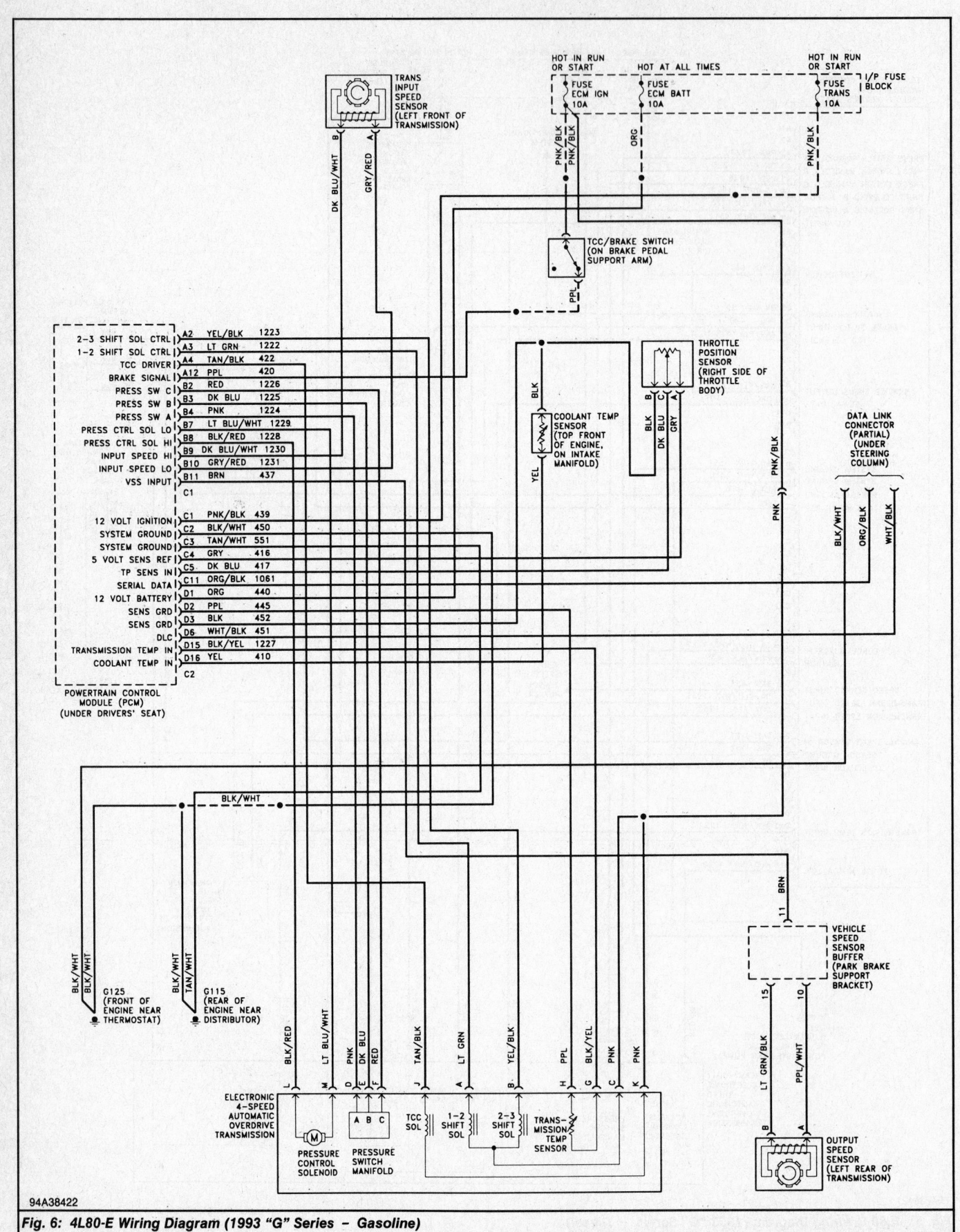

Fig. 6: 4L80-E Wiring Diagram (1993 "G" Series – Gasoline)

94A38422

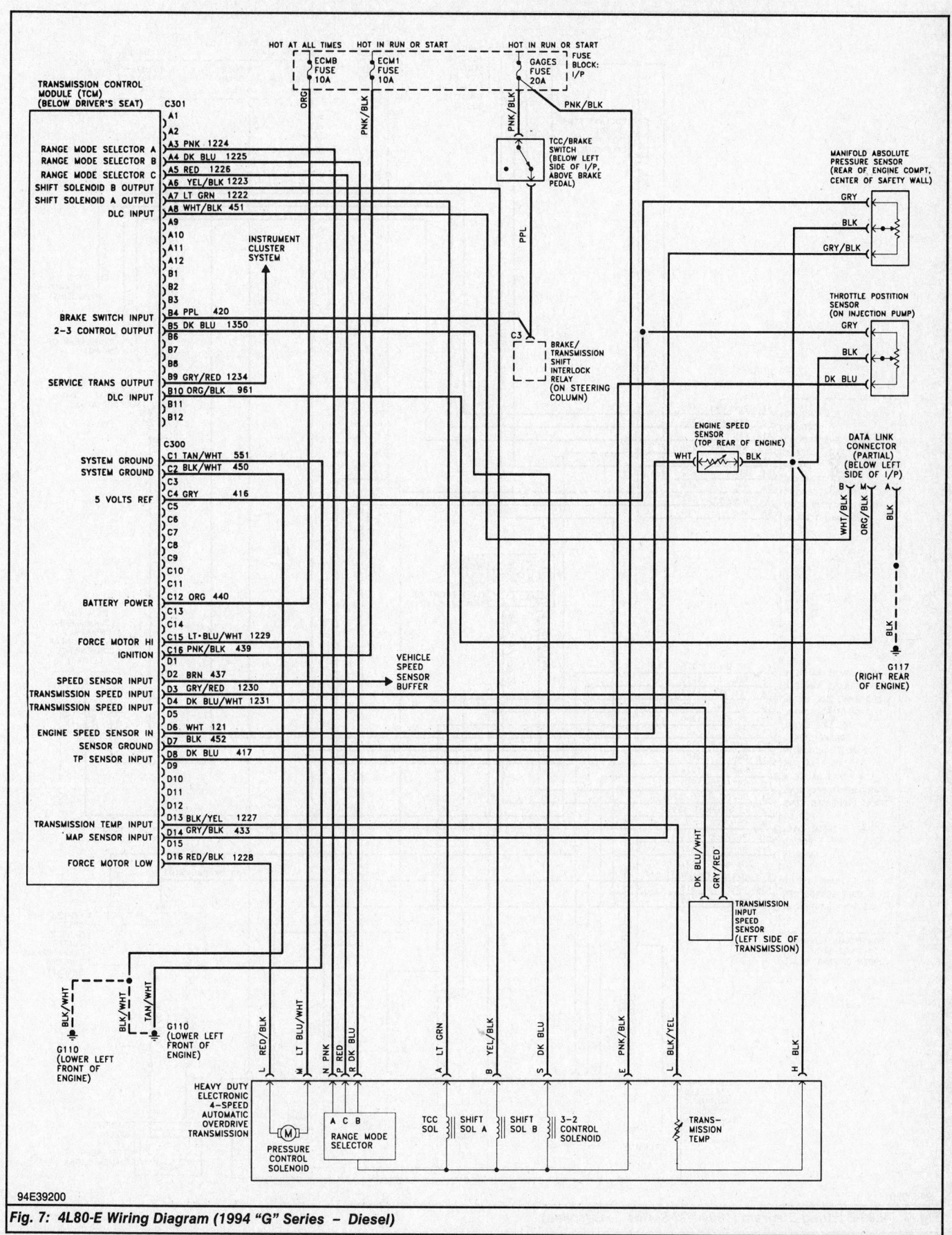

Fig. 7: 4L80-E Wiring Diagram (1994 "G" Series – Diesel)

94E39200

AUTOMATIC TRANSMISSIONS
4L80-E Electronic Controls (Cont.)

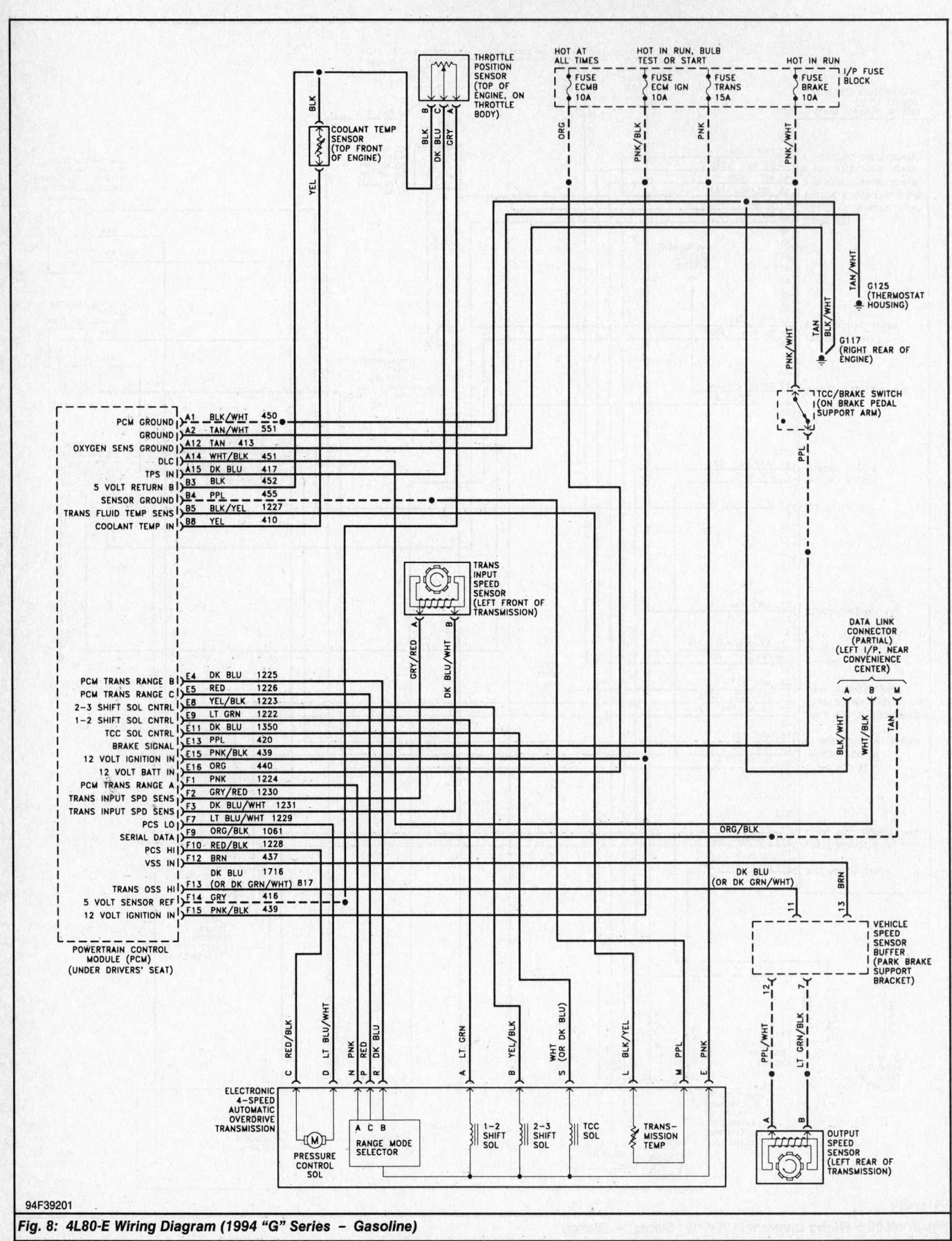

94F39201

Fig. 8: 4L80-E Wiring Diagram (1994 "G" Series – Gasoline)

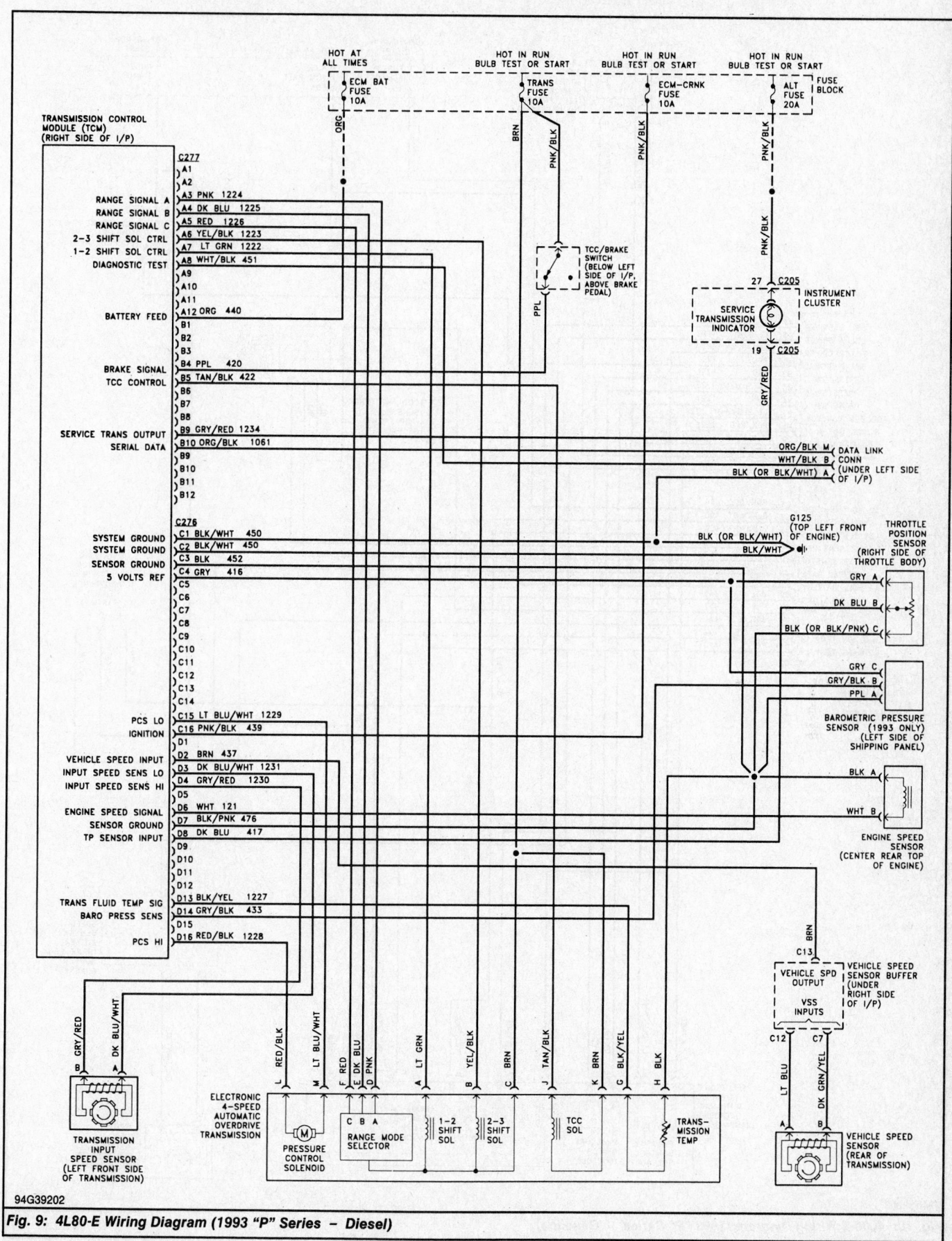

94G39202

Fig. 9: 4L80-E Wiring Diagram (1993 "P" Series – Diesel)

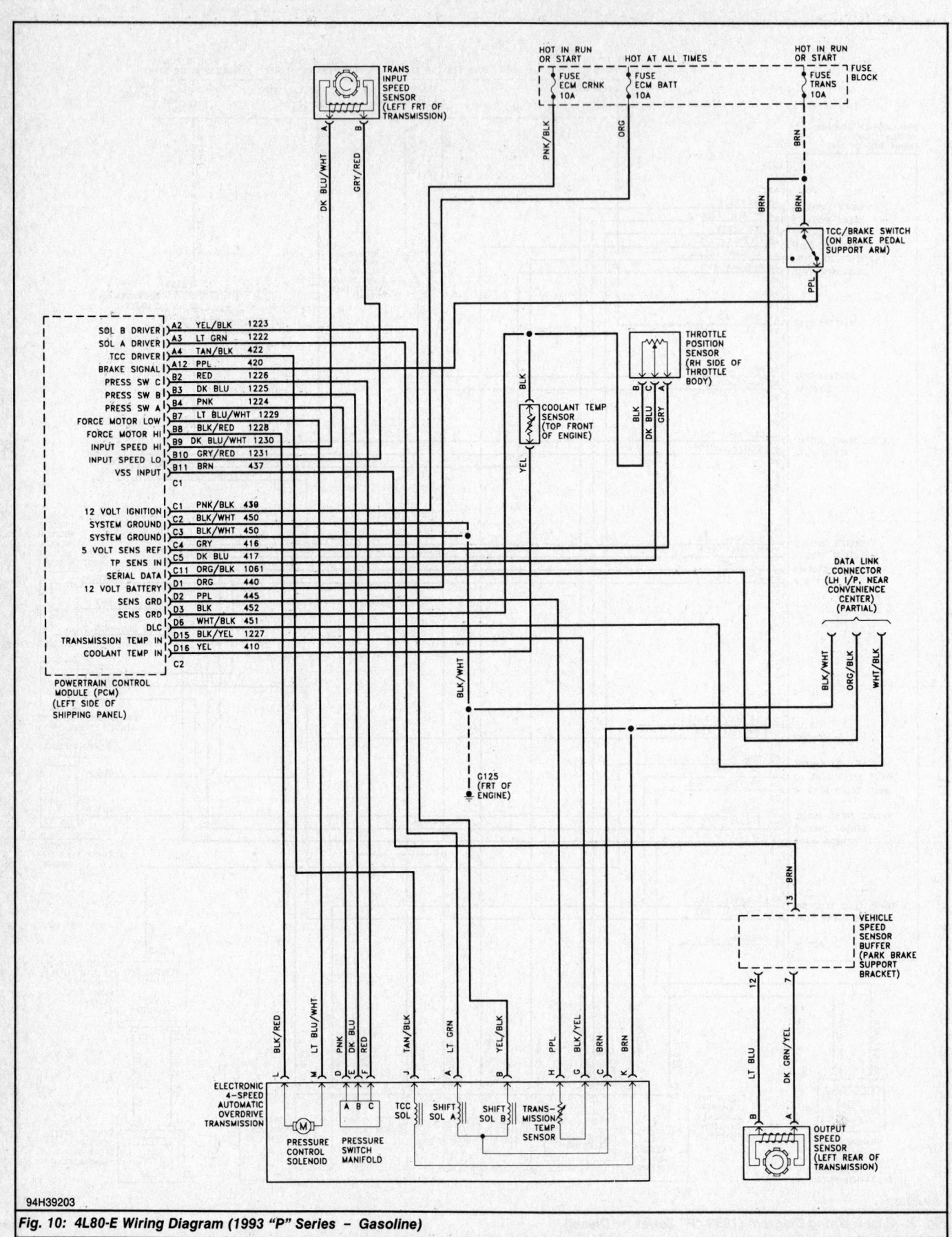

Fig. 10: 4L80-E Wiring Diagram (1993 "P" Series – Gasoline)

94H39203

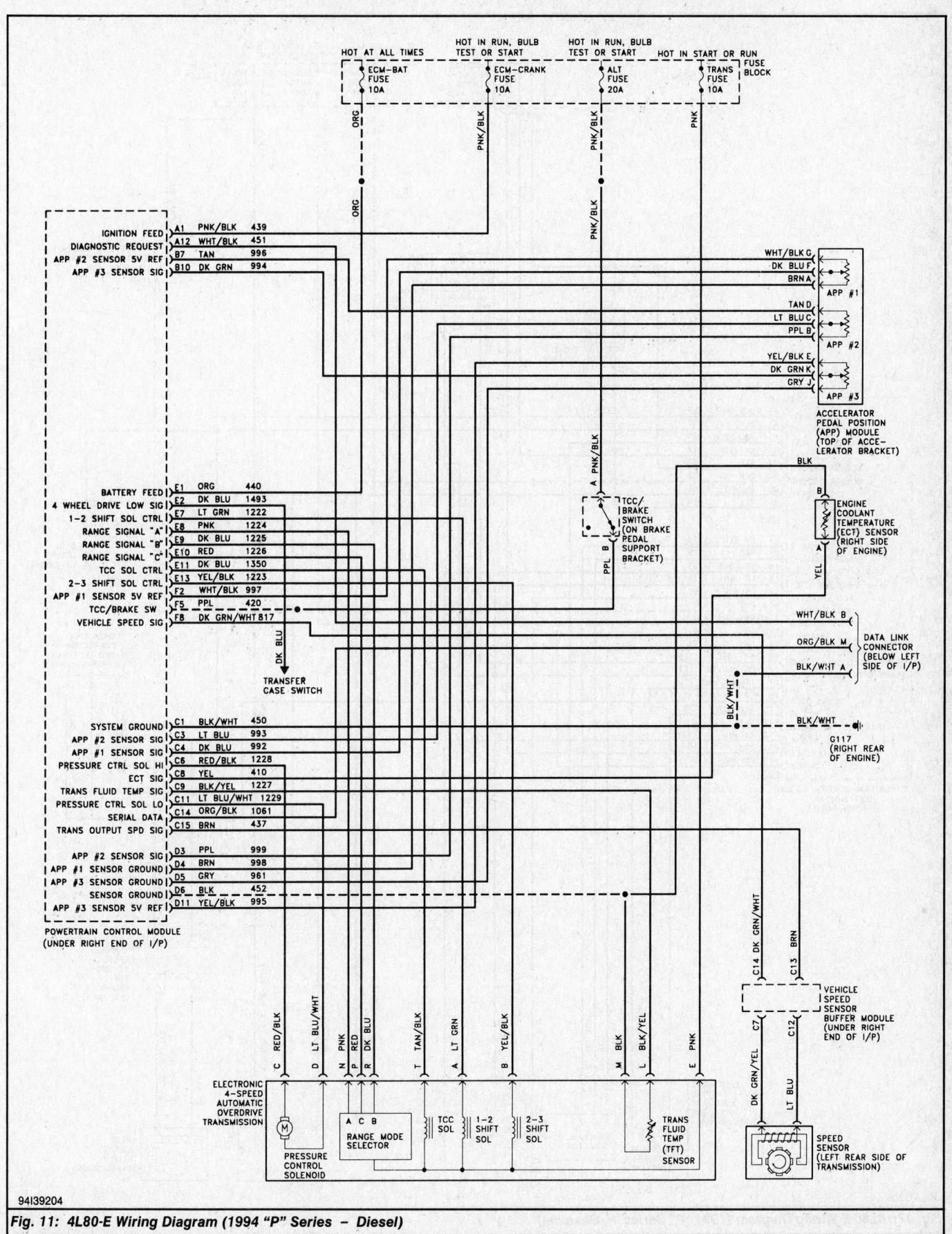

Fig. 11: 4L80-E Wiring Diagram (1994 "P" Series – Diesel)

94I39204

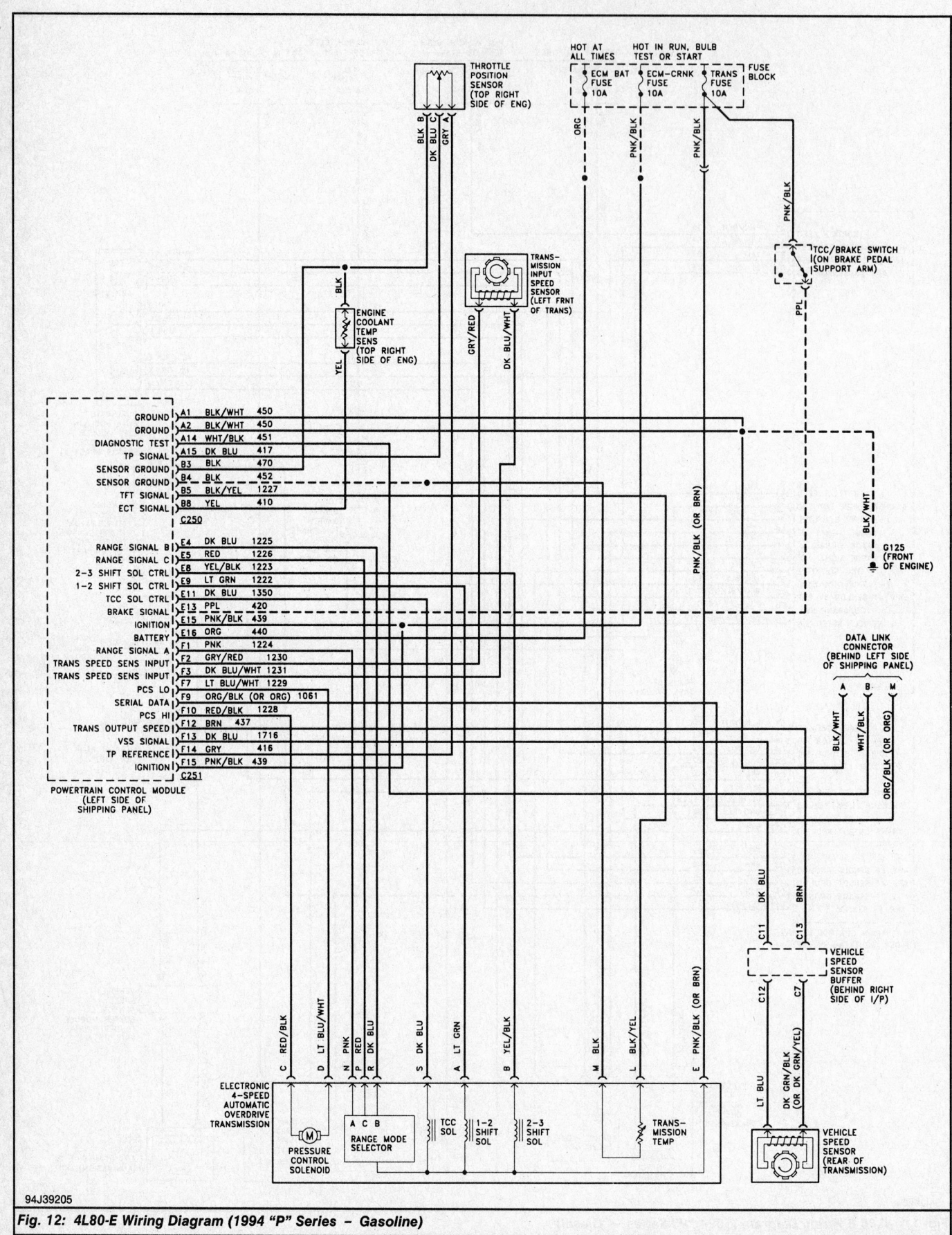

Fig. 12: 4L80-E Wiring Diagram (1994 "P" Series – Gasoline)

94J39205

NOTE: For testing and diagnostic procedures of electronic components, see 4T80-E ELECTRONIC CONTROLS article in AUTOMATIC TRANSMISSIONS.

APPLICATION & LABOR TIMES

APPLICATION & LABOR TIMES

Vehicle Application	Labor Times		Engine Size
	[1] R & I	[2] Overhaul	
Cadillac			
DeVille Concours	8.3	9.0	[3] 4.6L
Eldorado	8.3	9.0	[3] 4.6L
Seville	8.3	9.0	[3] 4.6L

[1] – Removal and installation of transaxle from vehicle chassis.
[2] – Bench overhaul time for transaxle and differential. DOES NOT include removal and installation.
[3] – Engines code "Y" (8th digit of VIN), use a viscous clutch converter. Engines code "9" (8th digit of VIN), use a torque converter clutch.

BODY CODE DESIGNATIONS

Body Designation	Model
"E" Body	Eldorado
"K" Body	Seville
"K" Special Body [1]	DeVille Concours

[1] – Applies to 1994 models.

IDENTIFICATION

All transaxles have a nameplate attached to the rear face of transaxle case. A transaxle VIN number is also stamped into right rear surface of case. *See Fig. 1.*

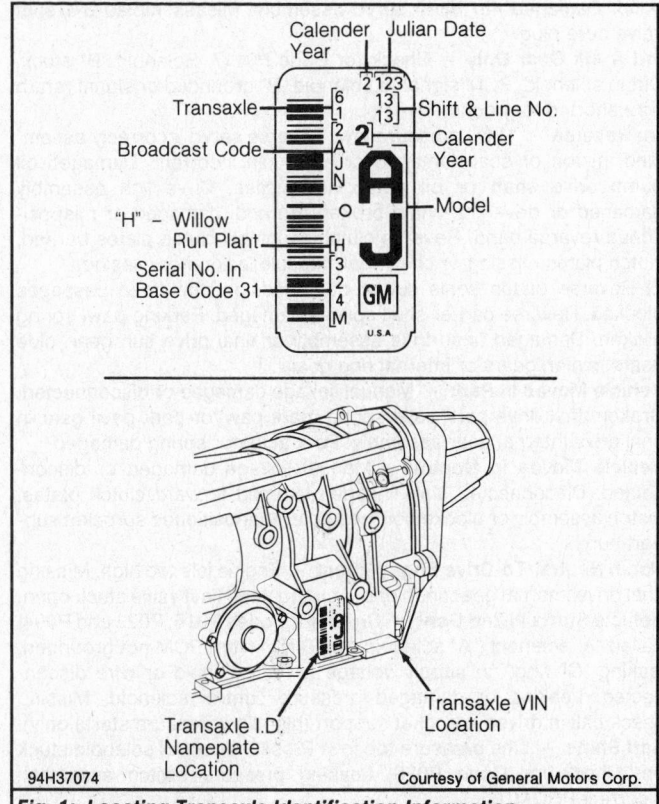

94H37074   Courtesy of General Motors Corp.

Fig. 1: Locating Transaxle Identification Information

DESCRIPTION

The Hydra-Matic 4T80-E transaxles are fully automatic 4-speed units consisting primarily of a 3-element hydraulic torque converter and converter clutch. Some models use a viscous converter clutch and other models use a torque converter clutch for converter lock-up.

Transaxle uses 3 gear-type pumps to supply all hydraulic pressure needed for operation. A scavenge pump removes oil from the lower oil pan. This oil is pumped into the side oil pan. A primary oil pump takes oil from the side oil pan and supplies line pressure oil. A secondary oil pump takes oil from the side oil pan and supplies remaining oil for initial clutch apply, forced downshifts, wide open throttle and reverse gear operations.

The multiplied torque from torque converter is transferred to the transaxle by a sprocket and drive link assembly. Other internal components consist of 4 multiple disc clutches, a roller clutch, 2 sprag clutches, 2 bands and 2 planetary gear sets. The final drive gear and differential assemblies are bolted on end of transaxle.

The 4T80-E uses 2 electronic shift valves controlled by the Powertrain Control Module (PCM). Transaxles also use a transaxle pressure control solenoid (force motor) solenoid to control line pressure, transaxle temperature sensor, pressure switch assembly, 2 speed sensors (Vehicle Speed Sensor – VSS and Transaxle Input Sensor – TIS), and a lock-up control solenoid for Torque/Viscous Converter Clutch (TCC or VCC) operation.

LUBRICATION & ADJUSTMENTS

See appropriate AUTOMATIC TRANSMISSION SERVICING article in TRANSMISSION SERVICING.

TROUBLE SHOOTING

NOTE: For testing and diagnostic procedures of electronic components, see 4T80-E ELECTRONIC CONTROLS article in AUTOMATIC TRANSMISSIONS.

NOTE: For clutch and band applications, see appropriate CLUTCH & BAND APPLICATION CHART.

QUICK CHECK

1) Check level and condition of transaxle fluid. Check PCM memory for stored codes. See 4T80-E ELECTRONIC CONTROLS article in AUTOMATIC TRANSMISSIONS. If no codes are present, go to next step. If codes are present, diagnose and repair all PCM-related codes. Clear PCM code memory.
2) Perform road test. See ROAD TEST under TESTING. Enter PCM data mode to monitor throttle angle. See 4T80-E ELECTRONIC CONTROLS article in AUTOMATIC TRANSMISSIONS. During road test, record shift points. If shift point timing or shifting is incorrect, go to 4T80-E ELECTRONIC CONTROLS article.
3) If shift(s) is too harsh or too soft, see HYDRAULIC PRESSURE TESTS under TESTING.
4) For specific complaints, see appropriate condition(s) listed under TRANSAXLE in TROUBLE SHOOTING.

SYMPTOMS

Oil Out Of Vent Or Foaming – Transaxle overfilled. Oil contaminated with antifreeze or engine overheating. Oil filter "O" ring damaged or missing. Scavenger oil pump screens blocked.
High Or Low Line Pressure – Incorrect oil level. Scavenge, primary or secondary oil pump assembly seals or gears damaged. Pump drive shaft damaged. Pressure regulator valve spring damaged or pressure regulator valve nicked or scored. Pressure relief valve spring damaged or ball missing. Problem with transaxle pressure control solenoid oil feed or valve stuck. Pressure switch assembly loose. Check balls missing in control valve body. Pump or case cover leaking (bolts loose). Actuator feed limit valve stuck open.
Delayed Engagement – Low fluid level. Pressure regulator valve stuck in bore. Faulty pressure switch assembly, throttle position switch or vehicle speed sensor.
No Drive In "D" – **1)** Low oil level or pressure. Faulty torque converter. Manual linkage misadjusted or disconnected. Manual valve stuck. Blocked valve body channels or spacer plate. Damaged oil pump drive shaft or pump assemblies. Torque converter stator roller clutch damaged. Drive link assembly damaged, drive link chain broken or sprockets and bearings damaged.

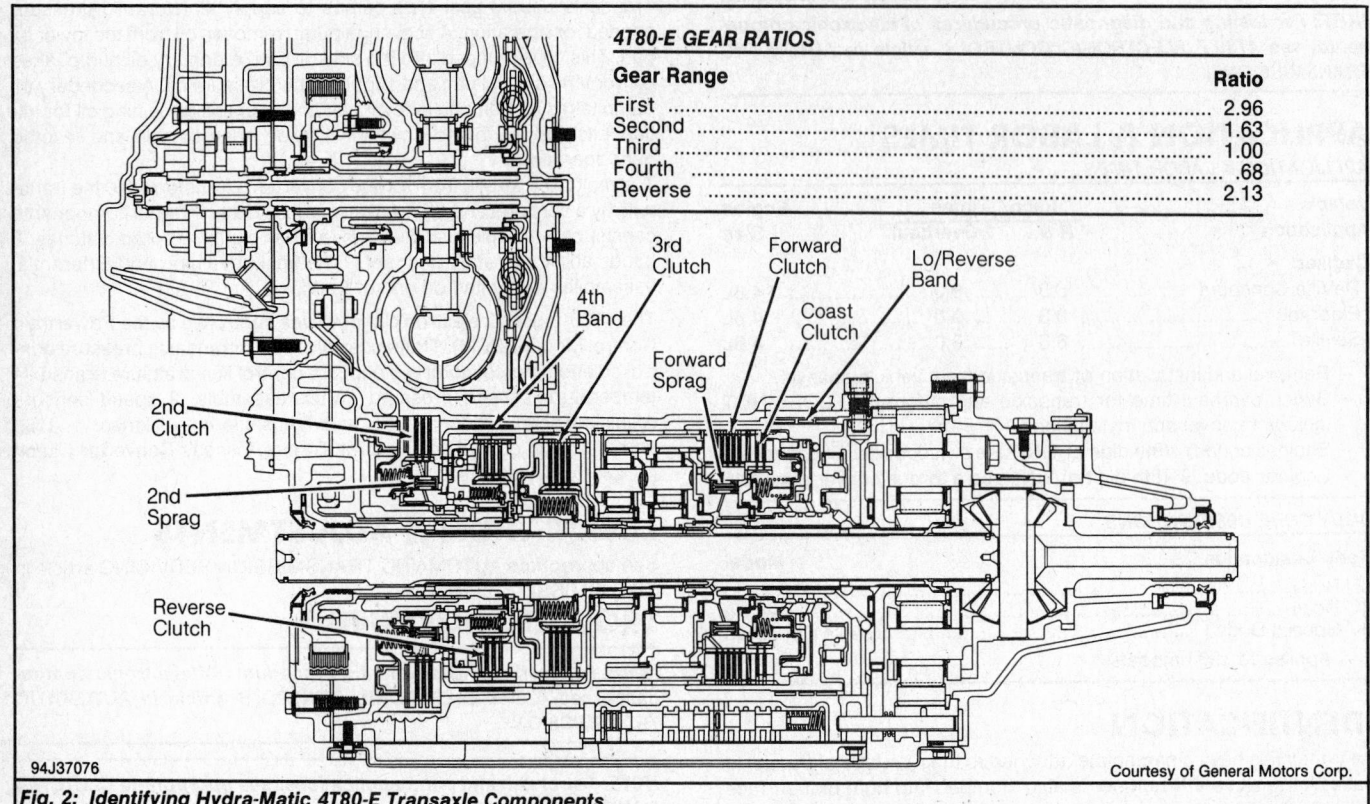

4T80-E GEAR RATIOS

Gear Range	Ratio
First	2.96
Second	1.63
Third	1.00
Fourth	.68
Reverse	2.13

94J37076

Courtesy of General Motors Corp.

Fig. 2: Identifying Hydra-Matic 4T80-E Transaxle Components

2) Forward clutch assembly clutch plates burned, clutch plates missing, check ball capsule leaking or missing. Forward piston seals cut or damaged, or shaft feed passages blocked. Damaged or incorrectly assembled forward roller sprag or sun gear assembly.

3) Output shaft damaged or drive axles incorrectly assembled into differential. damged or loose channel plates. Parking pawl spring broken. Damaged final drive assembly or final drive sun gear, side gears, pinion gears or internal ring gear.

Slips In "R" – Low fluid level. Low line pressure. Oil pump assemblies seals or gears damaged. Damaged reverse clutch assembly or leaking servo piston seal. Oil filter screen plugged. Leaking or damaged lo/reverse band servo seals. Damaged lo/reverse band.

No 1st Gear – Misadjusted manual valve. Damaged lo roller clutch, forward sprag or forward clutch assembly. Leaking oil transfer sleeve. Check for Codes P016, P029 and P094. Check solenoid circuits "A" and "B" for loose, open or shorted wires. Check PCM for loose grounds, loose or corroded connections. Leaking 3rd clutch housing check ball. Broken splines at 3rd clutch housing or forward clutch splined shaft.

No 1st Gear (In "2", "3", Or "D") – Missing check ball No. 6 or inoperative coast clutch. Damaged lo/reverse servo apply pin. Stuck 1-2 shift valve. Damaged or broken coast clutch splined shaft or broken support studs. Damaged or worn lo roller clutch or forward clutch piston. Leaking support housing seal rings. Forward sprag damaged. Check for trouble Code 94. Problem with solenoid circuit "A".

No 2nd Gear (In "2" Or "3") – Solenoid "A" stuck on. Dirt in solenoid, PCM signal to solenoid "A" grounded or signal return wire shorted to ground. Stuck 1-2 shift valve. Damaged 2nd clutch housing seals, piston or piston check ball. Burned 2nd clutch housing clutches. Mispositioned rollers or broken springs on 2nd sprag.

No 3rd Gear (In "3") – Check for Codes P019, P094 or P117. Solenoid "A" or "B" stuck. Dirt in solenoid, PCM signal to solenoid "B" grounded or signal return wire shorted to ground. Leaking or missing 3rd clutch check ball. Damaged 3rd clutch housing seals, piston or piston check ball. Burned 3rd clutch housing clutches. Exhaust valve cup plug or valve improperly installed in driven sprocket support.

No 4th Gear – Check for Code P094. Failed "A" solenoid ("A" solenoid off). Dirt in filter, PCM not grounded, leaking "O" ring, no supply voltage to "A" solenoid or wire disconnected. Burned or damaged 4th

band. Damaged 4th band servo assembly. Misassembled 3-4 shift valve bore plug.

3rd & 4th Gear Only – Check for Code P0117. Solenoid "B" stuck. Dirt in solenoid, PCM signal to solenoid "B" grounded or signal return wire shorted to ground.

No Reverse – **1)** Oil pressure low. Reverse servo incorrectly assembled, piston or seal damaged or apply pin incorrect. Damaged oil pump drive shaft or oil pump assemblies. Drive link assembly damaged or drive link chain broken. Burned, damaged or mispositioned reverse band. Reverse clutch assembly clutch plates burned, clutch plates missing or check ball capsule leaking or missing.

2) Reverse piston seals cut or damaged, or shaft feed passages blocked. Reverse carrier shell splines damaged. Parking pawl spring broken. Damaged final drive assembly or final drive sun gear, side gears, pinion gears or internal ring gear.

Vehicle Moves In Park – Manual linkage damaged or disconnected. Broken final drive park pawl spring, park pawl or park pawl gear in final drive internal gear assembly. Park actuator spring damaged.

Vehicle Moves In Neutral – Manual linkage damaged or disconnected. Disconnected shift linkage. Jammed forward clutch plates, piston assembly or blocked oil feed hole. Mispositioned sprocket support hub.

Harsh Neutral-To-Drive Engagement – Engine idle too high. Missing final drive internal gear snap ring. Actuator feed limit valve stuck open.

Vehicle Starts In 2nd Gear – Check for Codes P016, P029 and P094. Failed "A" solenoid ("A" solenoid off). Dirt in filter, PCM not grounded, leaking "O" ring, no supply voltage to "A" solenoid or wire disconnected. Leaking or damaged pressure control solenoid. Missing check ball in driven sprocket support (high line pressure starts only).

Soft Shifts – Line pressure too low. Pressure control solenoid stuck on. Check for Code P028. Leaking pressure switch assembly. Incorrect PROM.

Erratic Shifts – Leaking or damaged "O" rings at "A" or "B" solenoids.

No Engine Breaking – Misaligned oil transfer sleeve. Broken or slipping drive chain. Damaged sprockets or drive splines.

No Overrun Breaking In "3" – Oil level too low. Burned or damaged coast clutch assembly. Damaged or cracked forward clutch housing. Stuck 3-4 shift valve. Check for trouble Code P094. Stuck "A" solenoid or dirt in filter.

No Overrun Breaking In "2" – Stuck, broken or burned 4th band. Damaged 4th band servo assembly. Burned or damaged coast clutch assembly. Damaged or missing coast clutch support seal rings. Check for Code P028. Pressure switch assembly not working.

No Engine Breaking In "1" – Check for Code P028. Pressure switch assembly not working. Burned or damaged coast clutch assembly. Damaged or missing coast clutch support check ball. Stuck, broken or burned lo/reverse band. Damaged lo/reverse band servo assembly. Missing No. 6 check ball.

No TCC/VCC – Verify proper PCM operation and vehicle wiring. Check for possible Codes P016, P029, P039, P088, P090 or P117. Check the following solenoids and switches for faulty operation, dirt or binding: TCC/VCC solenoid, brake switch, PRNDL ("P"/"N" switch) and coolant temperature sensor. Also check the same solenoid and switch circuits for open or shorted wires between voltage supply or PCM. Converter clutch shift valve of control valve assembly stuck. Converter clutch apply valve stuck. Solenoid "O" ring leaking or screen blocked. Turbine shaft seals damaged. Blocked oil pressure screen. Damaged or missing TCC/VCC "O" ring.

Converter Clutch Does Not Release – Check for Code P039. TCC/VCC solenoid stuck on. TCC/VCC solenoid does not exhaust. Control valve assembly converter clutch apply valve stuck open. Turbine shaft splines damaged.

Converter Ballooning – Stuck converter feed valve.

Converter Clutch Apply With Cold Engine – Check for Code P059. Transaxle temperature sensor shorted.

Converter Clutch Apply Too Soft – Fluid level too low. Converter clutch feed valve stuck. Turbine shaft seals damaged or missing. Faulty TCC/VCC solenoid. Seals damaged or missing. Defective converter clutch.

ELECTRONIC SELF-DIAGNOSTICS & ELECTRONIC TESTING

NOTE: See 4T80-E ELECTRONIC CONTROLS article in AUTOMATIC TRANSMISSIONS.

TESTING

ROAD TEST

NOTE: Before road testing vehicle, engine and transmission must be at operating temperature. TCC/VCC will not engage if engine coolant has not reached 140°F (60°C).

Gear Selector Position "D" (Overdrive) – **1)** Enter PCM data mode to monitor throttle angle. See 4T80-E ELECTRONIC CONTROLS article in AUTOMATIC TRANSMISSIONS. With gear selector in "D" (overdrive) position, steadily increase throttle pressure to accelerate vehicle. Note shift speed engagement points in 2nd gear, 3rd gear and

overdrive gear. Use chart as a reference for proper shift speeds. *See Figs. 3-10.* Also note Torque/Viscous Converter Clutch (TCC/VCC) engagement point while in 3rd gear or Overdrive.

NOTE: Ensure TCC engages in 3rd gear or overdrive during the following steps. On vehicles with VCC, engagement point may be hard to feel. Use climate control panel to indicate TCC/TCC engagement and release points.

2) At vehicle speeds of 40-50 MPH, quickly depress accelerator to half-open position (part throttle detent downshift). TCC/VCC should release, and transaxle should immediately downshift to 3rd gear. DEFOG on display changes from on to off.

3) At vehicle speeds of 40-50 MPH, quickly depress accelerator to wide open position (full throttle detent downshift). TCC/VCC should release, and transaxle should immediately downshift to 2nd gear. DEFOG and ECON on display changes from on to off.

4) At vehicle speeds of 40-55 MPH, release accelerator pedal while moving gear selector to the "3" (third gear) position. The TCC/VCC should release, transaxle should downshift into 3rd gear.

5) Move gear selector to the "D" (overdrive) position, and accelerate to 40-45 MPH. Release accelerator pedal while moving gear selector to the "2" (2nd gear) position. The TCC/VCC should release, transaxle should downshift to 2nd gear immediately, and engine braking should slow vehicle.

6) Move gear selector to the "D" (overdrive) position, and accelerate to 30 MPH. Release accelerator pedal while moving gear selector to "1" (1st gear) position. TCC/VCC should release, transaxle should downshift to 1st gear and engine braking should slow vehicle.

7) With gear selector in the "D" (overdrive) position, accelerate vehicle to overdrive gear with TCC/VCC applied. Release accelerator pedal, and lightly apply brakes. The TCC/VCC should release. Note speeds at which vehicle downshifts. *See Figs. 3-10.*

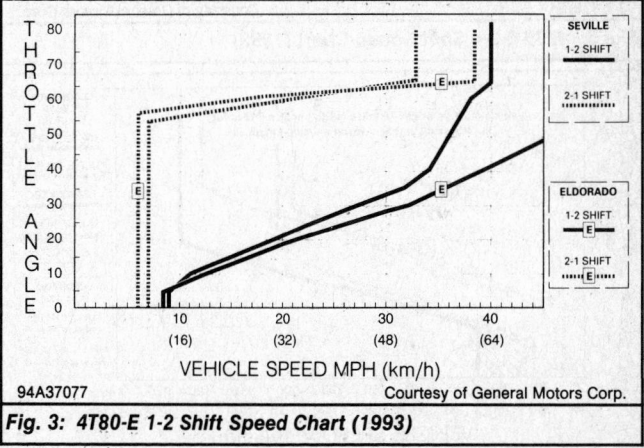

94A37077   Courtesy of General Motors Corp.

Fig. 3: 4T80-E 1-2 Shift Speed Chart (1993)

CLUTCH & BAND APPLICATION CHART (4T80-E)

Selector Lever Position	Solenoid Positions	Elements In Use
"D" (Drive)		
1st Gear	"A" ON/"B" OFF	Forward Clutch, Lo/Reverse Band, [1] Lo Roller & [1] Forward Sprag
2nd Gear	"A" OFF/"B" OFF	Forward Clutch, 2nd Clutch, [1] 2nd Sprag & [1] Forward Sprag
3rd Gear	"A" OFF/"B" ON	Forward Clutch, 2nd Clutch, 3rd Clutch & [1] Forward Sprag
Overdrive	"A" ON/"B" ON	Forward Clutch, 2nd Clutch, 3rd Clutch & 4th Band
"3" (Manual 3rd)		
3rd Gear	"A" OFF/"B" ON	Forward Clutch, Coast Clutch, 2nd Clutch, 3rd Clutch & [1] Forward Sprag
2nd Gear	"A" OFF/"B" OFF	Forward Clutch, Coast Clutch, 2nd Clutch, [1] 2nd Sprag & [1] Forward Sprag
1st Gear	"A" ON/"B" OFF	Forward Clutch, Coast Clutch, Lo/Reverse Band, [1] Lo Roller & [1] Forward Sprag
"2" (Manual 2nd)		
2nd Gear	"A" OFF/"B" OFF	Forward Clutch, Coast Clutch, 2nd Clutch, 4th Band, [1] 2nd Sprag & [1] Forward Sprag
1st Gear	"A" ON/"B" OFF	Forward Clutch, Coast Clutch, Lo/Reverse Band, [1] Lo Roller & [1] Forward Sprag
"1" (Manual Low)		
2nd Gear	"A" OFF/"B" OFF	Forward Clutch, Coast Clutch, 2nd Clutch, 4th Band, [1] 2nd Sprag & [1] Forward Sprag
1st Gear	"A" ON/"B" OFF	Forward Clutch, Coast Clutch, Lo/Reverse Band, [1] Lo Roller & [1] Forward Sprag
"R" (Reverse)	"A" ON/"B" OFF	Reverse Band & Lo/Reverse Band
"N"/"P" (Neutral/Park)	"A" ON/"B" OFF	All Clutches & Bands Released Or Ineffective

[1] – Holding

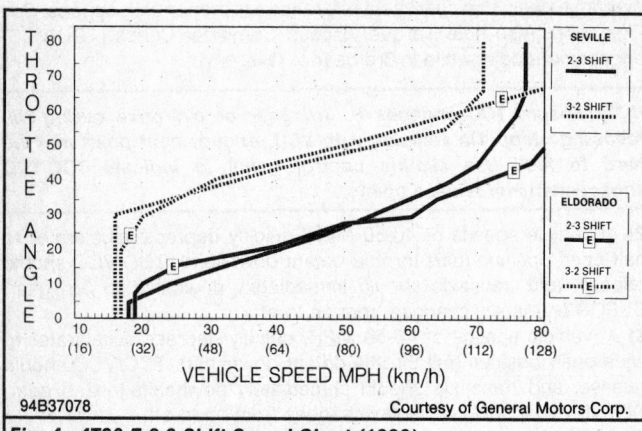

94B37078   Courtesy of General Motors Corp.

Fig. 4: 4T80-E 2-3 Shift Speed Chart (1993)

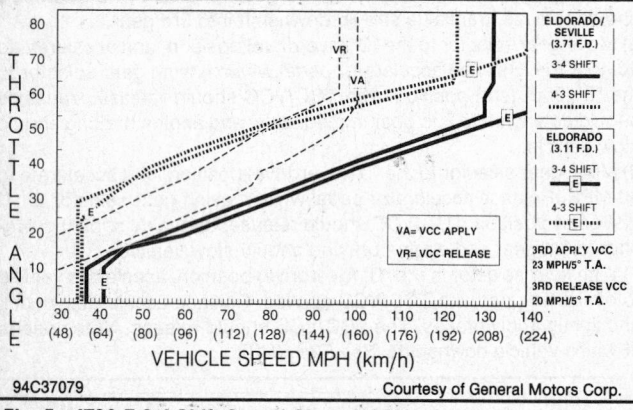

94C37079   Courtesy of General Motors Corp.

Fig. 5: 4T80-E 3-4 Shift Speed Chart (1993)

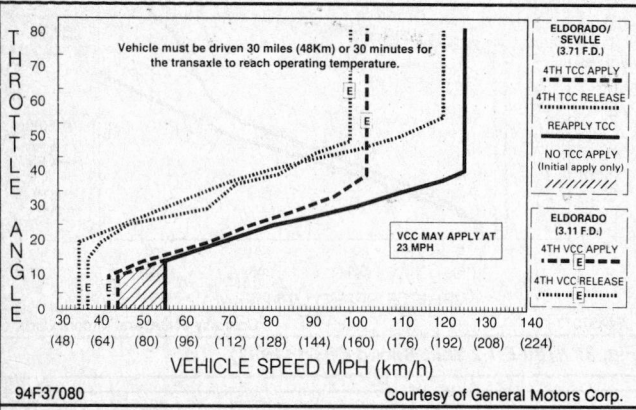

94F37080   Courtesy of General Motors Corp.

Fig. 6: 4T80-E TCC/VCC Shift Speed Chart (1993)

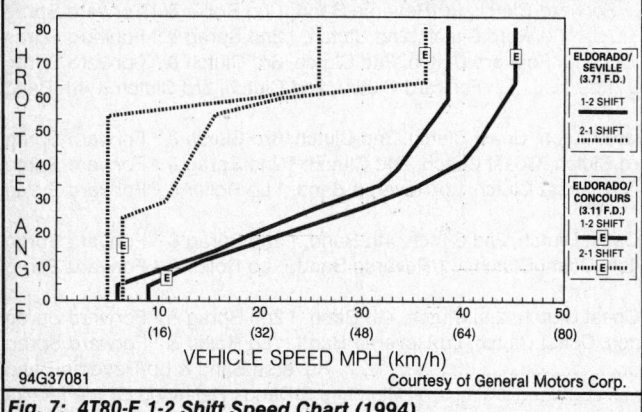

94G37081   Courtesy of General Motors Corp.

Fig. 7: 4T80-E 1-2 Shift Speed Chart (1994)

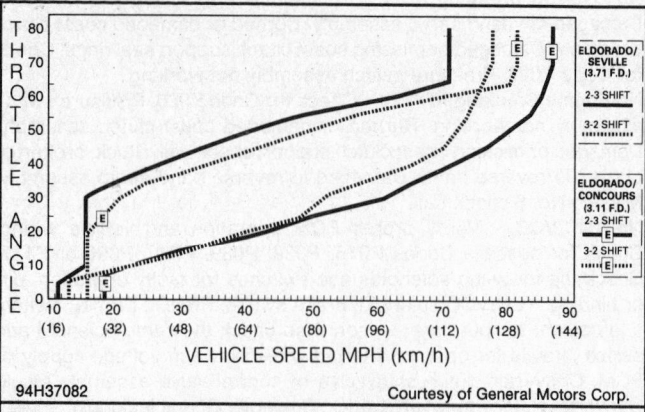

94H37082   Courtesy of General Motors Corp.

Fig. 8: 4T80-E 2-3 Shift Speed Chart (1994)

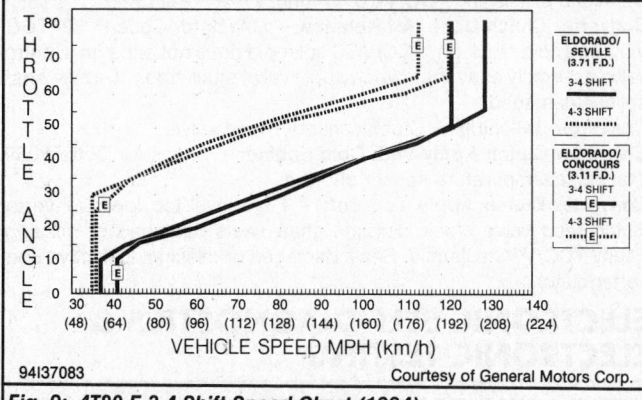

94I37083   Courtesy of General Motors Corp.

Fig. 9: 4T80-E 3-4 Shift Speed Chart (1994)

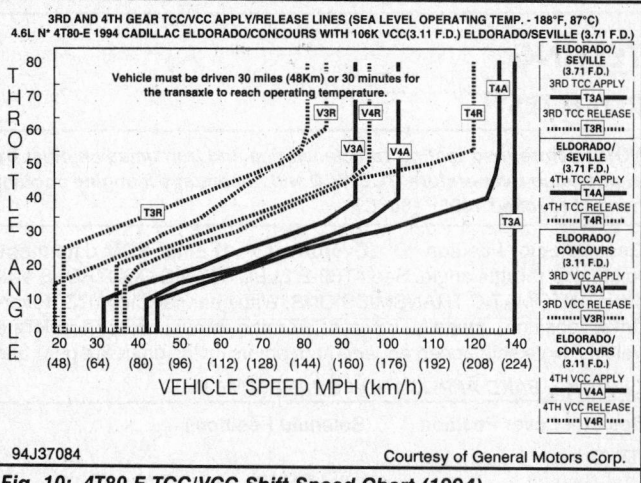

94J37084   Courtesy of General Motors Corp.

Fig. 10: 4T80-E TCC/VCC Shift Speed Chart (1994)

Gear Selector Position "3" (3rd Gear) – With vehicle stopped, move gear selector to "3" (3rd gear) position and steadily increase throttle pressure to accelerate vehicle. Note speeds at which vehicle goes into 2nd and 3rd gears. *See Figs. 3-10.* Also note when TCC/VCC engages while in 3rd gear.

Gear Selector Position "2" (2nd Gear) – With vehicle stopped, move gear selector to the "2" (2nd gear) position. Accelerate vehicle and note speed at which vehicle shifts from 1st gear to 2nd gear. Accelerate vehicle to 25 MPH. Transaxle should not shift into 3rd gear, and TCC/VCC should not engage.

Gear Selector Position "1" (1st Gear) – With vehicle stopped, move gear selector to the "1" (1st gear) position. Accelerate vehicle to 15 MPH. Transaxle should not upshift, and TCC/VCC should not engage.

PCM DATA – Enter the following modes on climate control panel and watch operation of sensors and transaxle. Repeat the same test steps as during road test. See ROAD TEST under TESTING:

- **PD74 "A" Current** – Line pressure should be low with over 1 amp current. Line pressure should be high with less than 1 amp current.
- **PD72 Turbine** – Signal should be close to engine RPM.
- **PD73 Slip Speed** – When TCC/VCC is release, numbers around 100 should be displayed. With TCC/VCC applied, numbers around 10 should be displayed.
- **PD76 Ratio** – Should display transaxle ratios while in specific gear range (1st - 2.96, 2nd - 1.63, 3rd - 1.00, 4th - .68, "R" - 2.13).
- **PD77 Transaxle Temperature** – Displays transaxle temperature in centrigrade.
- **PD82 Shift Time** – Displays shift time. Shift time is usually about .25 second (except for first gear).

HYDRAULIC PRESSURE TESTS

CAUTION: Parking and service brakes must be applied throughout hydraulic pressure test. Total time for testing with vehicle in any driving gear should not exceed 2 minutes.

Before performing hydraulic pressure tests, check fluid level and condition. Check manual control linkages for correct adjustment. Connect oil pressure gauge to line pressure test port. *See Fig. 11.*

NOTE: Hydraulic pressure is controlled by pump output and regulated by transaxle pressure control solenoid. Line pressure is boosted to 90-300 psi 6.2-20.7 kg/cm² in "R" position. Line pressure should increase when PCM commands less duty cycle (less current) to transaxle pressure control solenoid.

1) Enter PCM data mode to monitor throttle angle. See 4T80-E ELECTRONIC CONTROLS article in AUTOMATIC TRANSMISSIONS. Check for stored trouble Code P076. Repair vehicle as necessary.
2) Start engine and set parking brake. Select PCM OUTPUT OVERRIDE level on display panel. Access transaxle pressure control solenoid override (PS20). Increase PCM pressure signal to transaxle pressure control solenoid. Record line pressure readings.
3) Line pressure should gradually increase after each increase in command signal. Line pressure should be 50 psi (3.4 kg/cm²) at zero percent command and about 240 psi (16.5 kg/cm²) at 100 percent command. If recorded pressure is incorrect, see HIGH OR LOW LINE PRESSURE under TROUBLE SHOOTING.

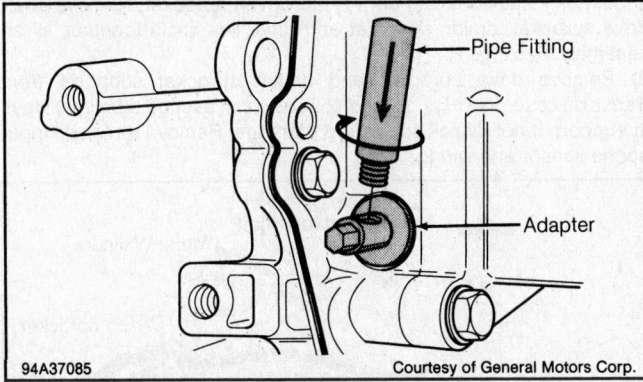

94A37085   Courtesy of General Motors Corp.

Fig. 11: Installing Line Pressure Gauge

ON-VEHICLE SERVICE

The following components can be serviced without removing transaxle from vehicle:
- Case Side Cover Pan
- Converter-To-Flexplate Bolts
- Cooler Lines
- Drive Axles
- Final Drive Assembly
- Fluid Level Indicator
- Reverse Servo
- Scavenger Oil Scoop
- Manual Control Cable

- Output Shaft
- Solenoids "A" & "B"
- Transaxle Input Speed Sensor
- Transaxle Temperature Switch
- Transaxle Pan
- Transaxle Filter
- Valve Body
- Vehicle Speed Sensor
- Transaxle Wiring Harness
- 4th Servo
- 1-2, 3-4, Forward & Reverse Accumulator Assemblies
- Oil Pressure Switch Assembly

VALVE BODY

See OIL PUMP & VALVE BODY under TRANSAXLE DISASSEMBLY.

DRIVE AXLE SHAFTS

See appropriate AXLE SHAFTS article in AXLE SHAFTS & TRANSFER CASES.

OIL COOLER FLUSHING

1) If available, fill Line Flusher (J-35944) with solution, and install oil cooler and line flusher to top transaxle cooler line on transaxle. Follow manufacturer instructions to flush oil cooler and cooler lines.
2) If line flusher is not available, flush cooler and cooler lines with a mixture of clean solvent and water. Flush cooler in both directions until all old fluid and debris are removed. If necessary, replace plugged or damaged cooler and/or lines.

REMOVAL & INSTALLATION

See appropriate AUTOMATIC TRANSMISSION REMOVAL article in TRANSMISSION SERVICING.

TORQUE CONVERTER

INSPECTION

Torque converter must be replaced for any of the following reasons.
- Damage To Pump Assembly
- Metal Particles Present In Oil
- Leaks In Hub Weld Area
- Crankshaft Pilot Broken Or Damaged
- Hub Scored Or Damaged
- Stator Failure
- Torque Converter Imbalance
- Engine Coolant Contamination
- Excessive End Play

TRANSAXLE DISASSEMBLY

CASE ASSEMBLY

Remove torque converter, turbine shaft "O" ring, oil pump drive shaft, vehicle (output) speedometer sensor and oil cooler fitting. Remove 4th servo from case.

FINAL DRIVE END PLAY CHECK & ASSEMBLY PROCEDURE

1) Mount Dial Indicator Post (J-39687) and Dial Gauge (J-8001-3) to check end play. Pry up on speed sensor rotor through speedometer sensor hole. End play should be .006-.025" (.15-.65 mm). *See Fig. 12.* Record this measurement for reassembly.
2) Remove case extension, washers and seal. Remove scavenge tube and seal from transaxle case. Lock parking gear with park actuator. Remove 4 differential bolts and differential carrier.
3) Push on output shaft and remove snap ring. Remove differential gear and remove output shaft from front end of transaxle. Remove final drive carrier, thrust bearing, final drive sun gear and internal gear.

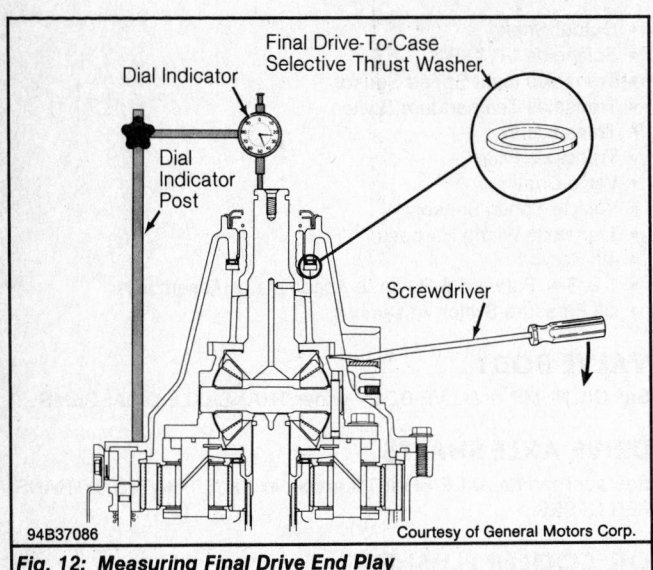

Fig. 12: Measuring Final Drive End Play

LOWER TRANSAXLE ASSEMBLY

Remove bottom oil pan and oil scavenger screens. Disconnect manual valve link and wiring harness connectors. Remove control valve and accumulator cover assembly. See Fig. 13.

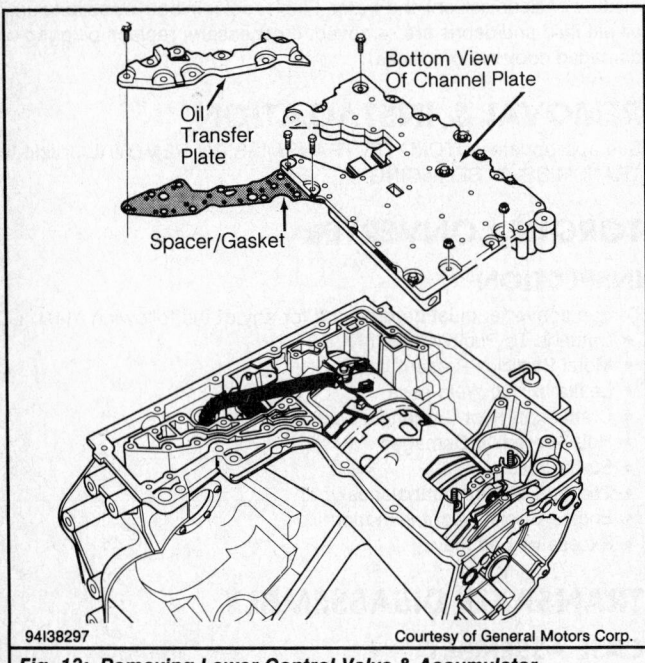

Fig. 13: Removing Lower Control Valve & Accumulator Cover Assembly

INPUT SHAFT END PLAY CHECK

Install Input Shaft End Play Fixture (J-39686) to front side of transaxle. Ensure "J" tab on fixture rests on input shaft. Mount Dial Indicator Post (J-25025-7A) and Dial Gauge (J-8001-3) to check end play. Push down on handle to raise input shaft. End play should be .004-.034" (.10-.85 mm). See Fig. 14. Record this measurement for reassembly.

SIDE COVER, OIL PUMP & UPPER VALVE BODY

1) Remove side cover, filter and seals. Disconnect wiring harness from transaxle temperature sensor, transaxle pressure control and TCC/VCC solenoid and case connector. Remove wiring harness.

2) Remove oil pump assembly cover bolts and remove pump assemblies. Remove upper valve body and separate gasket and spacer plate.

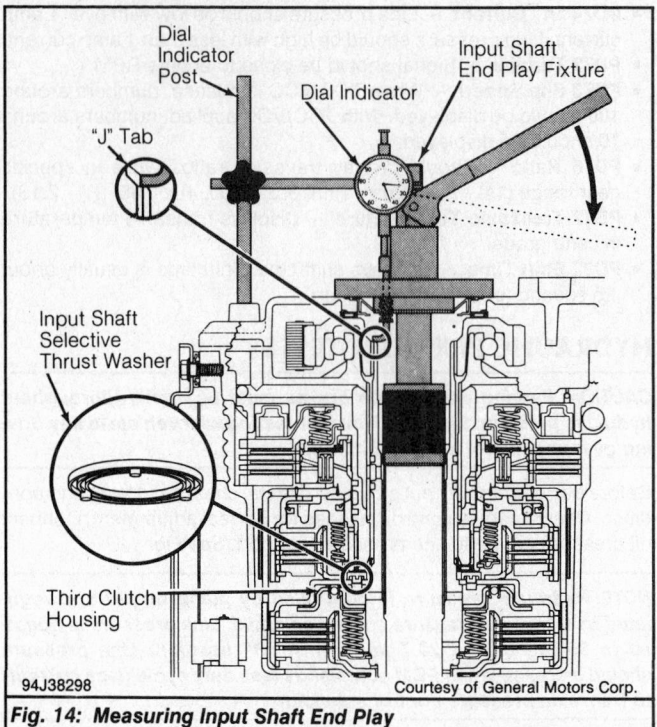

Fig. 14: Measuring Input Shaft End Play

3) Remove 2 check balls between spacer plate and transaxle case cover. Remove transaxle case cover and gaskets from transaxle case.

DRIVE LINK ASSEMBLY

NOTE: See COMPONENT DISASSEMBLY & REASSEMBLY for exploded views of all internal components. See Fig. 43 for thrust washer and bearing locations. See Fig. 44 for lip seal locations.

1) Remove thrust washers. Mark position of link on drive link chain; it should be installed facing up. Pry up driven sprocket. Remove shaft drive sprocket, driven sprocket and drive link chain together as an assembly. See Fig. 15.

2) Remove drive sprocket and driven sprocket supports from transaxle case. See Figs. 15 and 16. Ensure scavenge tube seal stays in support. If not, check support for damage. Remove transaxle input speed sensor and wiring.

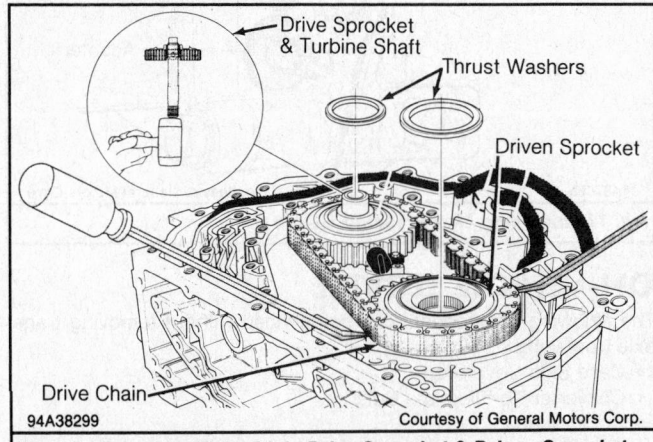

Fig. 15: Removing Drive Link, Drive Sprocket & Driven Sprocket

CLUTCH & BAND ASSEMBLIES

1) Remove 2nd clutch plate assembly. See Fig. 20. Remove reverse clutch support thrust washer. Remove reverse clutch housing and 2nd sprag assembly. Remove 4th band, 3rd clutch and reaction carrier assemblies. See Fig. 20. Remove reaction carrier shell.

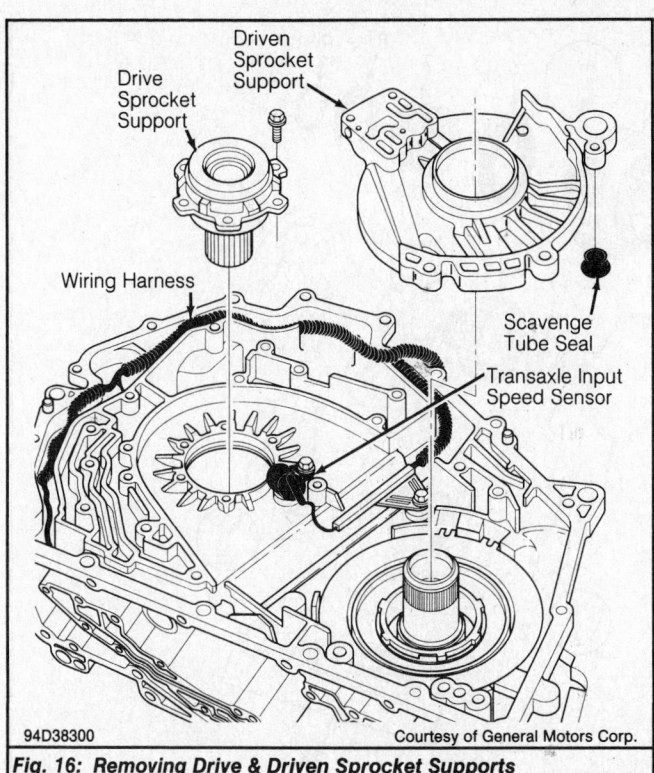

94D38300 Courtesy of General Motors Corp.

Fig. 16: Removing Drive & Driven Sprocket Supports

2) Move manual control shaft from "P" position. Remove parking pawl and pivot pin assembly. Remove 2 forward and coast clutch support bolts from transaxle case. Remove oil cooler return fitting to forward and coast clutch support.

3) Using Forward/Coast Clutch Puller (J-39053), remove clutch assemblies. *See Fig. 17*. Remove lo/reverse band and fretting ring. Remove manual shaft assembly, spring and case seals. Remove detent lever if necessary.

CAUTION: If oil cooler return fitting is NOT removed from forward and coast clutch support, damage to transaxle case may result.

NOTE: If detent lever is removed, detent lever must be replaced.

COMPONENT DISASSEMBLY & REASSEMBLY

TRANSAXLE CASE

Cleaning & Inspection – Clean transaxle case thoroughly with solvent, and then air dry. Inspect transaxle case for damage to band lugs, snap ring grooves and drive sprocket bearings. Check for interconnected or damaged oil passages and servo bores. Inspect case for stripped threads in bolt holes or casting porosity. Repair or replace case if necessary.

3RD CLUTCH & REACTION CARRIER

Disassembly & Inspection – 1) Remove carrier assembly. Remove clutch plates. Compress spring assembly and remove snap ring. Remove piston. Inspect reaction carrier and sun gear for damaged teeth, scoring or warpage.

2) Check thrust bearing for damage. Check reaction carrier pinion gear end play. End play should be .004-.035" (.10-.90 mm). Check for damage to reaction carrier internal gear. *See Fig. 18*.

Reassembly – 1) Using seal ring expander, install both seal rings. Using Seal Ring Sizer (J-34741-3), compress seal rings and leave tool in place until input housing is installed.

2) Install reaction sun gear-to-final drive internal gear thrust bearing, positioning inner race against internal gear. Assemble reaction sun gear and drum assembly onto final drive internal gear.

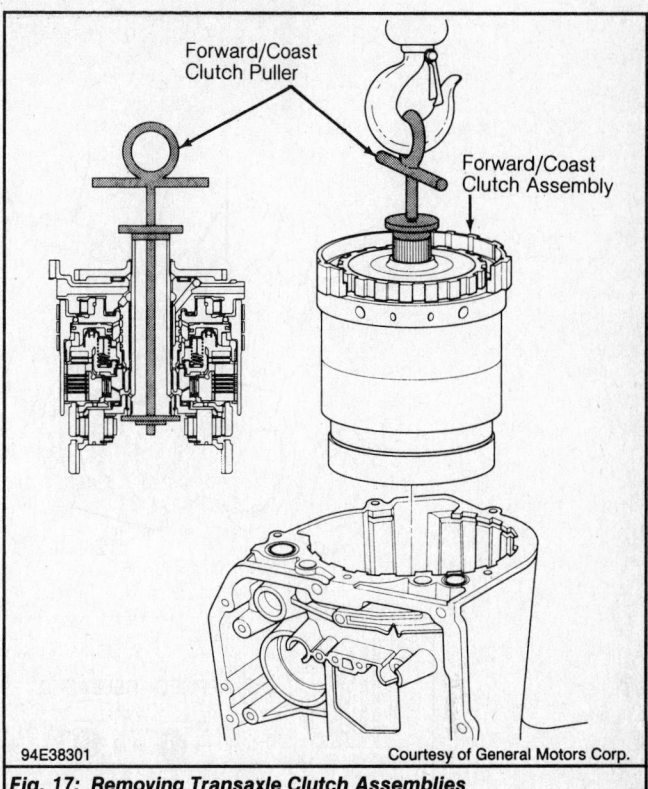

94E38301 Courtesy of General Motors Corp.

Fig. 17: Removing Transaxle Clutch Assemblies

3) Install reaction carrier-to-sun gear thrust bearing, positioning inner race against reaction carrier. Retain bearing with petroleum jelly. Install reaction carrier, rotating carrier until pinions engage sun gear.

4) Install piston, springs and clutch plate assembly. Install backing plate with stepped side up. Install snap ring, thrust washer, 3rd clutch hub assembly and thrust washers. Assemble and install reaction carrier. Assemble remaining parts. *See Fig. 18*.

4TH BAND ASSEMBLY

Inspection – DO NOT wash 4th band in solvent. Inspect 4th band assembly for heat damage, lining cracks and separation. Check band stop for damage and replace if necessary.

REVERSE CLUTCH & 2ND SPRAG

Disassembly & Inspection – Disassemble clutch plates. Remove apply piston. *See Fig. 19*. If necessary, remove 2nd sprag. Spiral snap ring must be replaced if removed from 2nd sprag. Inspect clutches for wear and piston for cracks or damaged check ball. Inspect 2nd sprag for damage.

Reassembly – Assemble removed parts. Ensure 2nd sprag rotates in correct direction. *See Fig. 19*. Install a new 2nd sprag spiral snap ring, if removed.

2ND CLUTCH

Disassembly & Inspection – Set clutch plates on bench. Remove apply piston. *See Fig. 20*. Remove 3rd clutch exhaust valve from driven sprocket support. Inspect clutches for wear and piston for cracks or damaged check ball. Inspect driven sprocket support for damage.

Reassembly – To reassemble, reverse disassembly procedures.

FORWARD & COAST CLUTCH

Disassembly & Inspection – 1) Remove parking pawl gear and thrust washer. Remove clutch support assembly with low roller clutch. Separate clutch housing from coast clutch hub and thrust washers. Remove final drive sun gear shaft. *See Figs. 21 and 22*.

2) Remove coast and forward clutch plates from housing. Compress spring retainer and remove snap ring. Remove coast piston, apply ring, forward clutch piston and seals. *See Fig. 21*. Inspect clutches for wear and piston for cracks or damaged check ball.

Reassembly – To reassemble, reverse disassembly procedures.

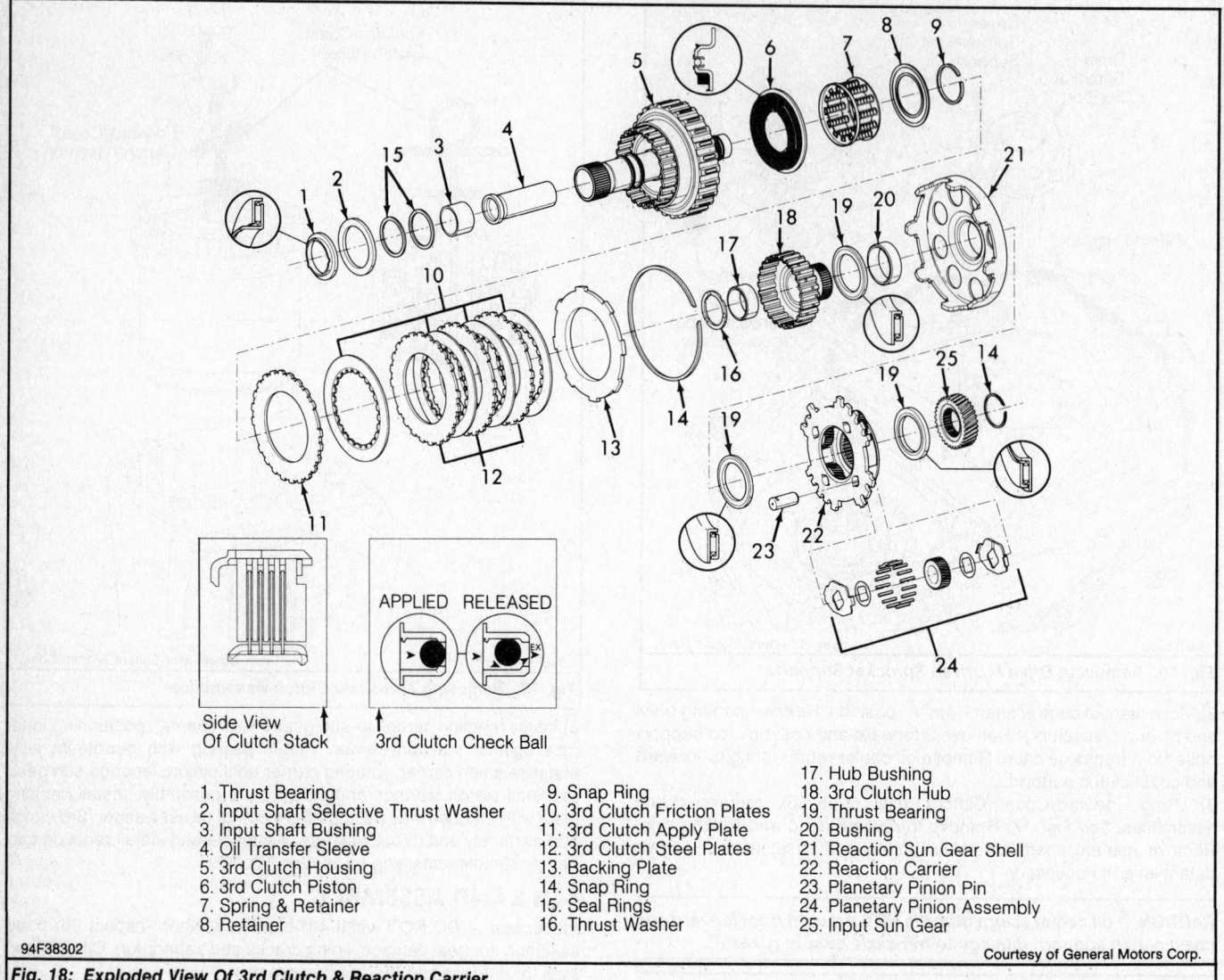

Side View
Of Clutch Stack

APPLIED   RELEASED

3rd Clutch Check Ball

1. Thrust Bearing
2. Input Shaft Selective Thrust Washer
3. Input Shaft Bushing
4. Oil Transfer Sleeve
5. 3rd Clutch Housing
6. 3rd Clutch Piston
7. Spring & Retainer
8. Retainer
9. Snap Ring
10. 3rd Clutch Friction Plates
11. 3rd Clutch Apply Plate
12. 3rd Clutch Steel Plates
13. Backing Plate
14. Snap Ring
15. Seal Rings
16. Thrust Washer
17. Hub Bushing
18. 3rd Clutch Hub
19. Thrust Bearing
20. Bushing
21. Reaction Sun Gear Shell
22. Reaction Carrier
23. Planetary Pinion Pin
24. Planetary Pinion Assembly
25. Input Sun Gear

94F38302

Courtesy of General Motors Corp.

Fig. 18: Exploded View Of 3rd Clutch & Reaction Carrier

REACTION PLANETARY & LO/REVERSE BAND

Disassembly, Inspection & Reassembly – 1) Remove snap rings and separate reaction gear, planetary carrier and coast clutch hub from final drive sun gear shaft. *See Fig. 22.* Inspect reaction gear, coast input hub, final drive sun gear shaft and related parts for damaged teeth and distortion.

2) Check thrust bearing for damage. Check planetary carrier pinion gear end play. End play should be .004-.035" (.10-.90 mm). Check for damage to input internal gear flange. *See Fig. 22.*

3) DO NOT wash lo/reverse band in solvent. Inspect lo/reverse band assembly for damage and replace if necessary. *See Fig. 23.* To reassemble, reverse disassembly procedures. Ensure forward sprag and outer race are installed correctly. *See Fig. 22.*

FORWARD & COAST CLUTCH SUPPORT

Disassembly & Inspection – Disassemble clutch support. Remove and discard oil seal rings and oil cooler return seal. *See Fig. 23.* Inspect all parts for damage or wear. Replace worn bushing.

Reassembly – Install new seals to clutch support. Install lo roller clutch. *See Fig. 23.* Turn counterclockwise as far as possible. Ensure tabs on clutch rest on face of clutch support. Ensure lo roller clutch turns in correct direction and locks in opposite direction. *See Fig. 24.*

FINAL DRIVE ASSEMBLY

Disassembly & Inspection – 1) Inspect final drive internal gear for damaged teeth, worn bearing surfaces, or damage to differential and pinion gears. Inspect sun gear, thrust bearings and speed sensor ring gear for wear or damage.

2) Check final drive carrier pinion gears for excessive end play. Measure end play between carrier and pinion gear thrust washer. End play should be .008-.012" (.20-.30 mm).

3) Using a pin punch, drive differential pinion shaft retainer pin from carrier. Remove pinion shaft, pinion and side gears, and thrust washers. *See Fig. 25.* Inspect all parts for damage or abnormal wear. Inspect final drive sun gear shaft for damaged splines or journals.

Reassembly – 1) Assemble differential side gears and thrust washers into carrier. Using petroleum jelly, stick thrust washers onto pinion gears. Assemble pinion gears and washers into carrier.

2) Rotate pinion gears into position, then install pinion shaft. Tap retaining pin into position using a plastic hammer. Assemble remaining thrust washers, spacers and snap rings. Install final drive sun gear seal into sun gear with seal lip facing forward clutch. Install sun gear.

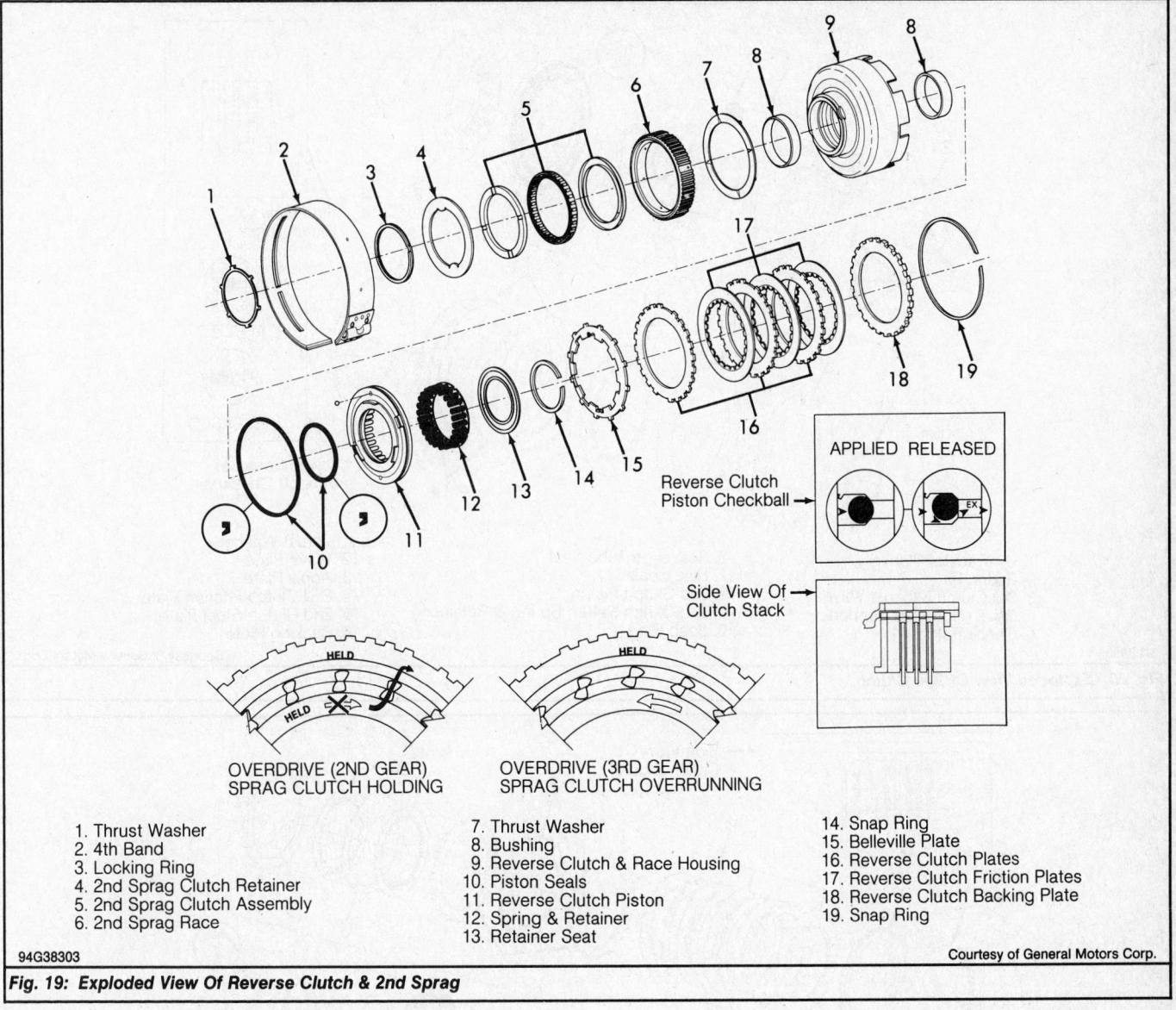

94G38303

Courtesy of General Motors Corp.

Fig. 19: Exploded View Of Reverse Clutch & 2nd Sprag

1. Thrust Washer
2. 4th Band
3. Locking Ring
4. 2nd Sprag Clutch Retainer
5. 2nd Sprag Clutch Assembly
6. 2nd Sprag Race
7. Thrust Washer
8. Bushing
9. Reverse Clutch & Race Housing
10. Piston Seals
11. Reverse Clutch Piston
12. Spring & Retainer
13. Retainer Seat
14. Snap Ring
15. Belleville Plate
16. Reverse Clutch Plates
17. Reverse Clutch Friction Plates
18. Reverse Clutch Backing Plate
19. Snap Ring

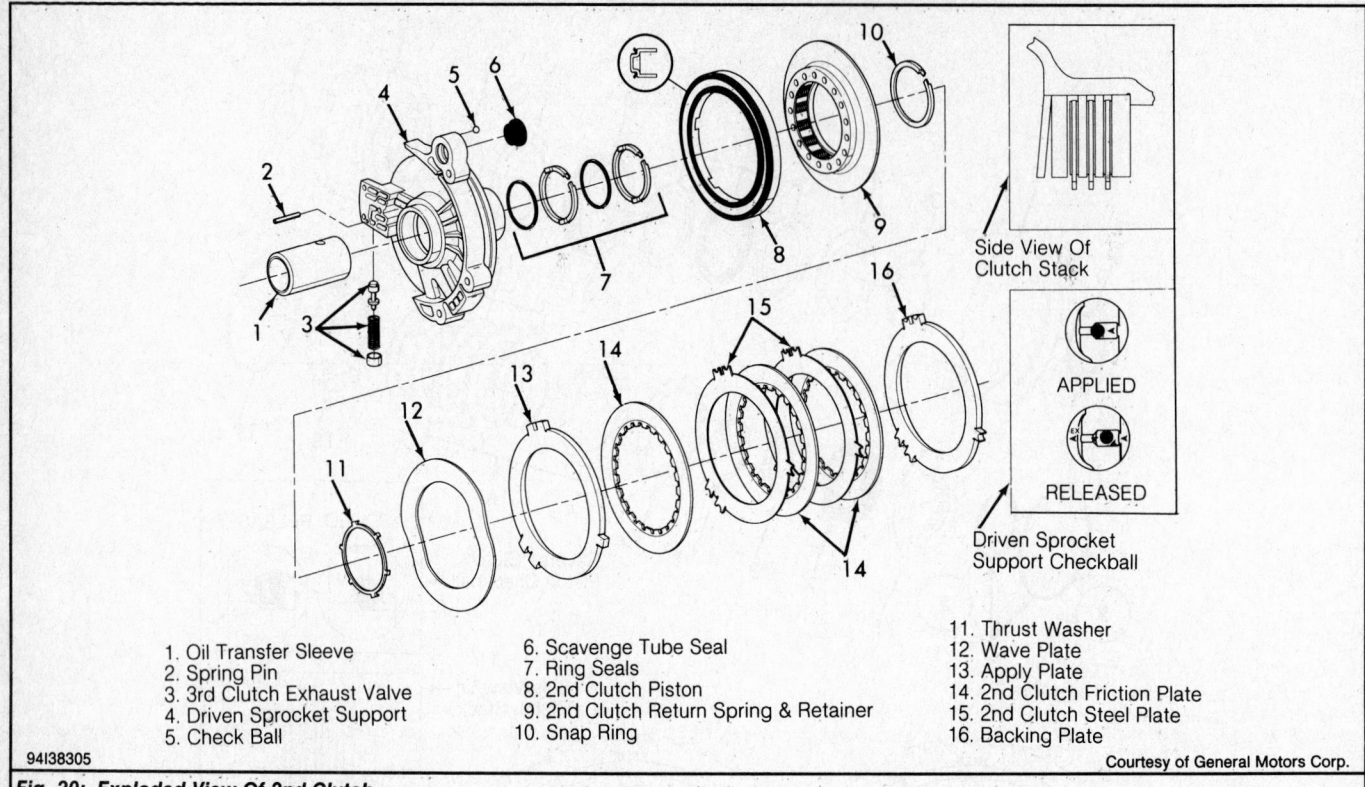

Side View Of Clutch Stack

APPLIED

RELEASED

Driven Sprocket Support Checkball

1. Oil Transfer Sleeve
2. Spring Pin
3. 3rd Clutch Exhaust Valve
4. Driven Sprocket Support
5. Check Ball
6. Scavenge Tube Seal
7. Ring Seals
8. 2nd Clutch Piston
9. 2nd Clutch Return Spring & Retainer
10. Snap Ring
11. Thrust Washer
12. Wave Plate
13. Apply Plate
14. 2nd Clutch Friction Plate
15. 2nd Clutch Steel Plate
16. Backing Plate

94I38305

Courtesy of General Motors Corp.

Fig. 20: Exploded View Of 2nd Clutch

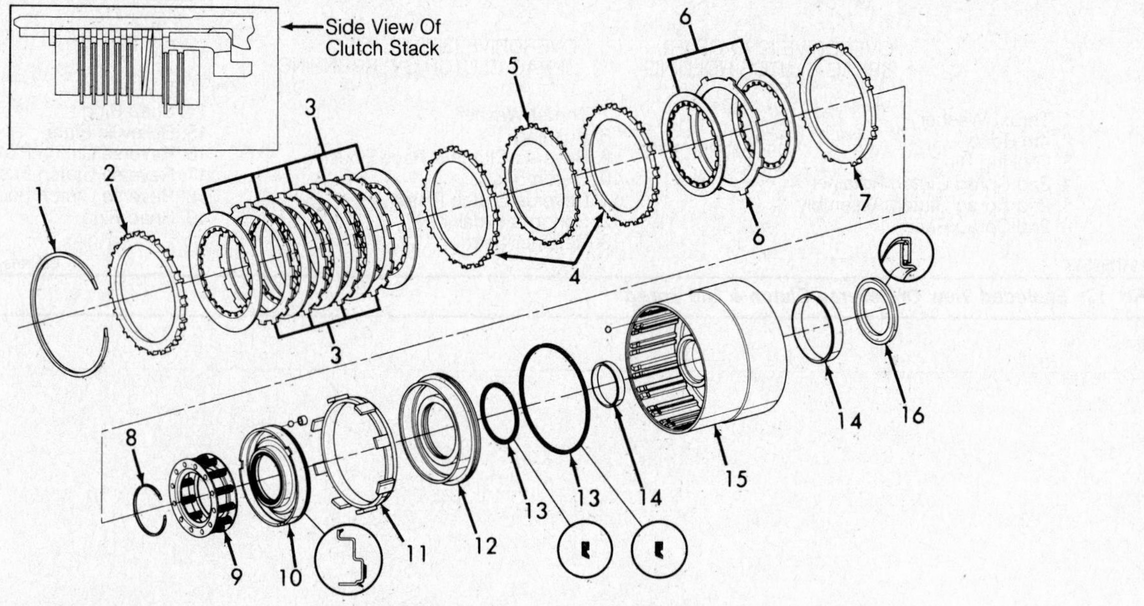

Side View Of Clutch Stack

1. Snap Ring
2. Backing Plate
3. Forward Clutch Plates
4. Forward/Coast Plate
5. Belleville Plate
6. Coast Clutch Plates
7. Apply Plate
8. Snap Ring
9. Spring Assembly
10. Coast Clutch Piston
11. Forward Apply Ring
12. Forward Clutch Piston
13. Piston Seals
14. Bushing
15. Forward/Coast Clutch Housing
16. Thrust Bearing

94I38305

Courtesy of General Motors Corp.

Fig. 21: Exploded View Of Coast & Forward Clutches

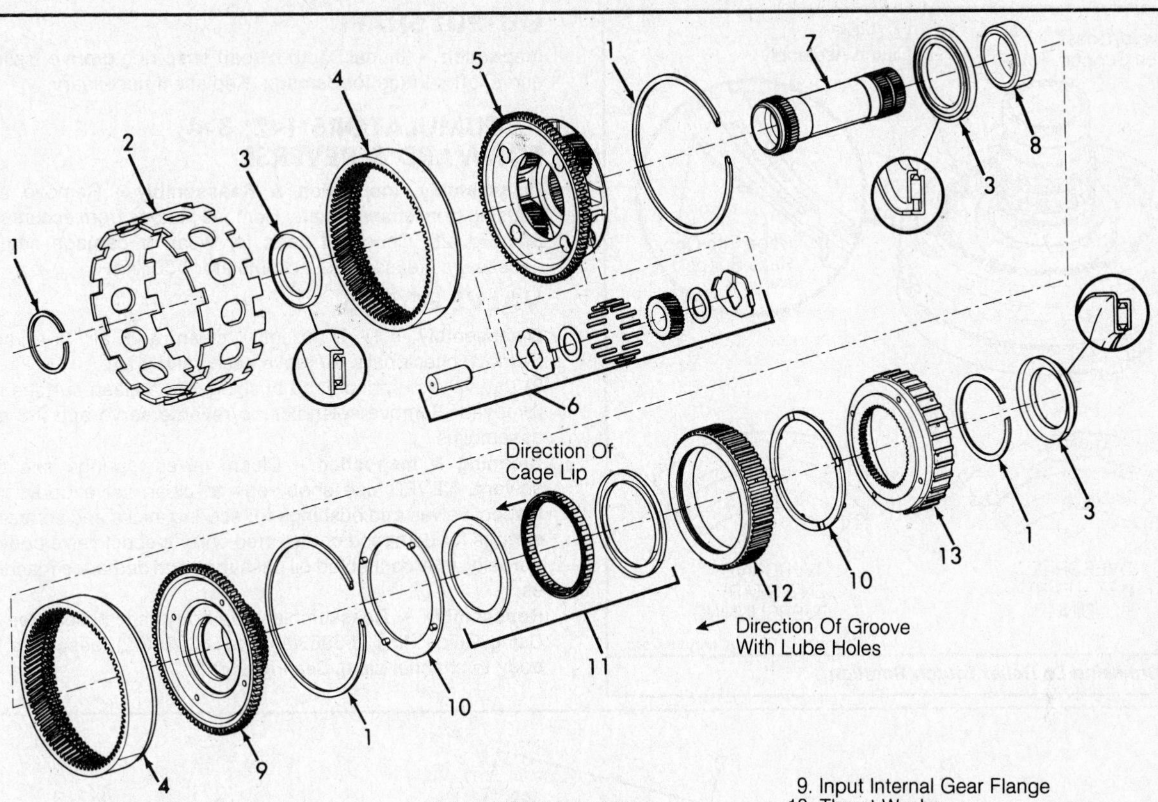

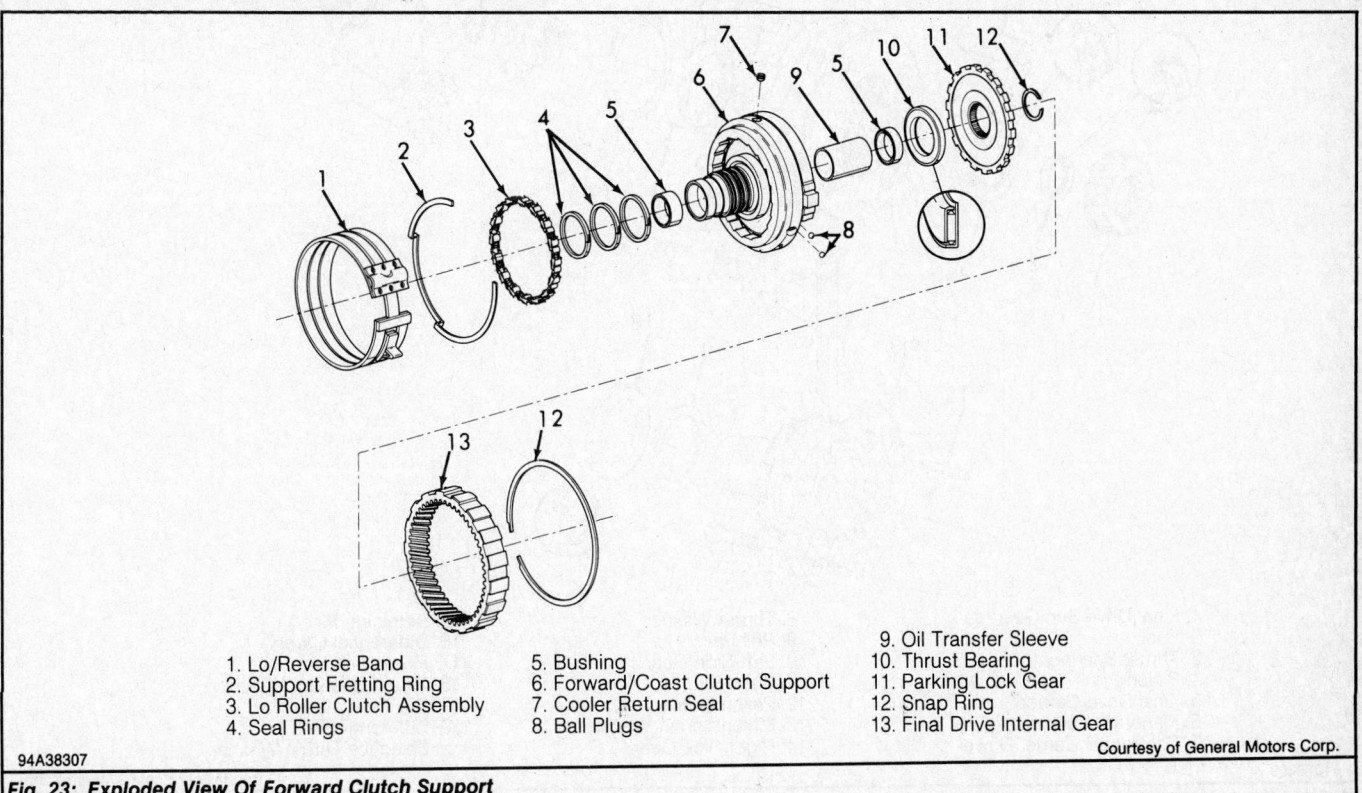

Direction Of Cage Lip

Direction Of Groove With Lube Holes

1. Snap Ring
2. Reaction Carrier Shell
3. Thrust Bearing
4. Reaction/Input Gear
5. Input Carrier Assembly
6. Pinion Assembly
7. Final Drive Sun Gear Shaft
8. Input Flange Bushing
9. Input Internal Gear Flange
10. Thrust Washer
11. Forward Clutch Sprag Assembly
12. Forward Sprag Race
13. Coast Clutch Hub

94J38306

Courtesy of General Motors Corp.

Fig. 22: Exploded View Of Reaction Planetary Assembly

1. Lo/Reverse Band
2. Support Fretting Ring
3. Lo Roller Clutch Assembly
4. Seal Rings
5. Bushing
6. Forward/Coast Clutch Support
7. Cooler Return Seal
8. Ball Plugs
9. Oil Transfer Sleeve
10. Thrust Bearing
11. Parking Lock Gear
12. Snap Ring
13. Final Drive Internal Gear

94A38307

Courtesy of General Motors Corp.

Fig. 23: Exploded View Of Forward Clutch Support

Forward/Coast
Clutch Support
Lo Roller
Clutch Assembly
Cage Sits On
Race Support
STATIONARY
HELD
STATIONARY
OVERDRIVE
(1ST GEAR)
HOLDING
OVERDRIVE
(2ND GEAR)
OVERRUNNING
94B38308
Courtesy of General Motors Corp.

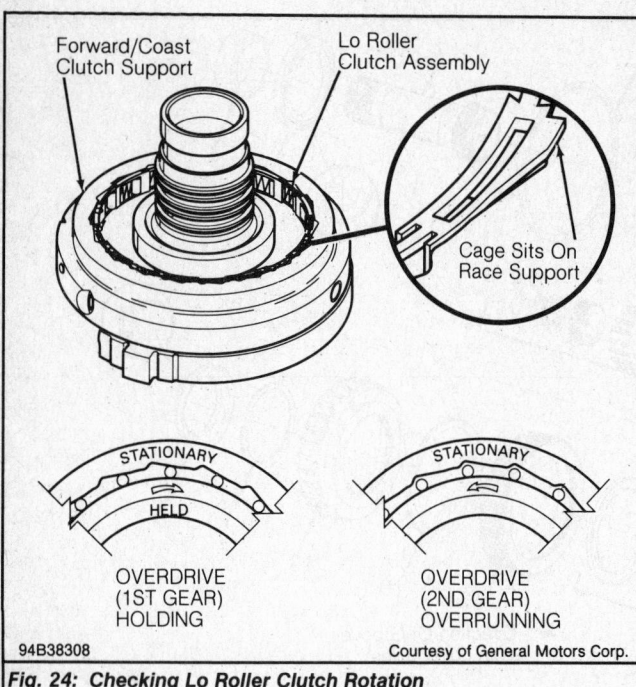

Fig. 24: Checking Lo Roller Clutch Rotation

OUTPUT SHAFT

Inspection – Inspect output shaft snap ring groove, splines, journal and shaft surface for damage. Replace if necessary.

ACCUMULATORS 1-2, 3-4, FORWARD & REVERSE

Disassembly, Inspection & Reassembly – Remove accumulator housing from channel plate. Remove pistons from accumulator bores. *See Fig. 26.* Check all parts for wear or damage and replace as necessary. Reassemble accumulator housing.

VALVE BODIES

Disassembly – 1) Thoroughly clean and air dry valve bodies. Remove check balls. Remove each valve train.

2) Lay valves, springs and bushings on a clean surface in the order removed. Remove solenoids, lo/reverse servo and 2-3 accumulator assemblies.

Cleaning & Inspection – Clean valves, springs and bushings in solvent. NEVER use shop rags to clean valve body components. Inspect valves and bushings for scoring, nicks and scratches. Inspect springs for damaged or distorted coils. Inspect valve body casting for porosity, interconnected oil passages and damaged machined surfaces.

Reassembly – Reassemble valve body assemblies. *See Figs. 27-29.* Using Guide Pins (J-39630-1 and J-39068-2), assemble lower valve body to channel plate. *See Figs. 30-32.*

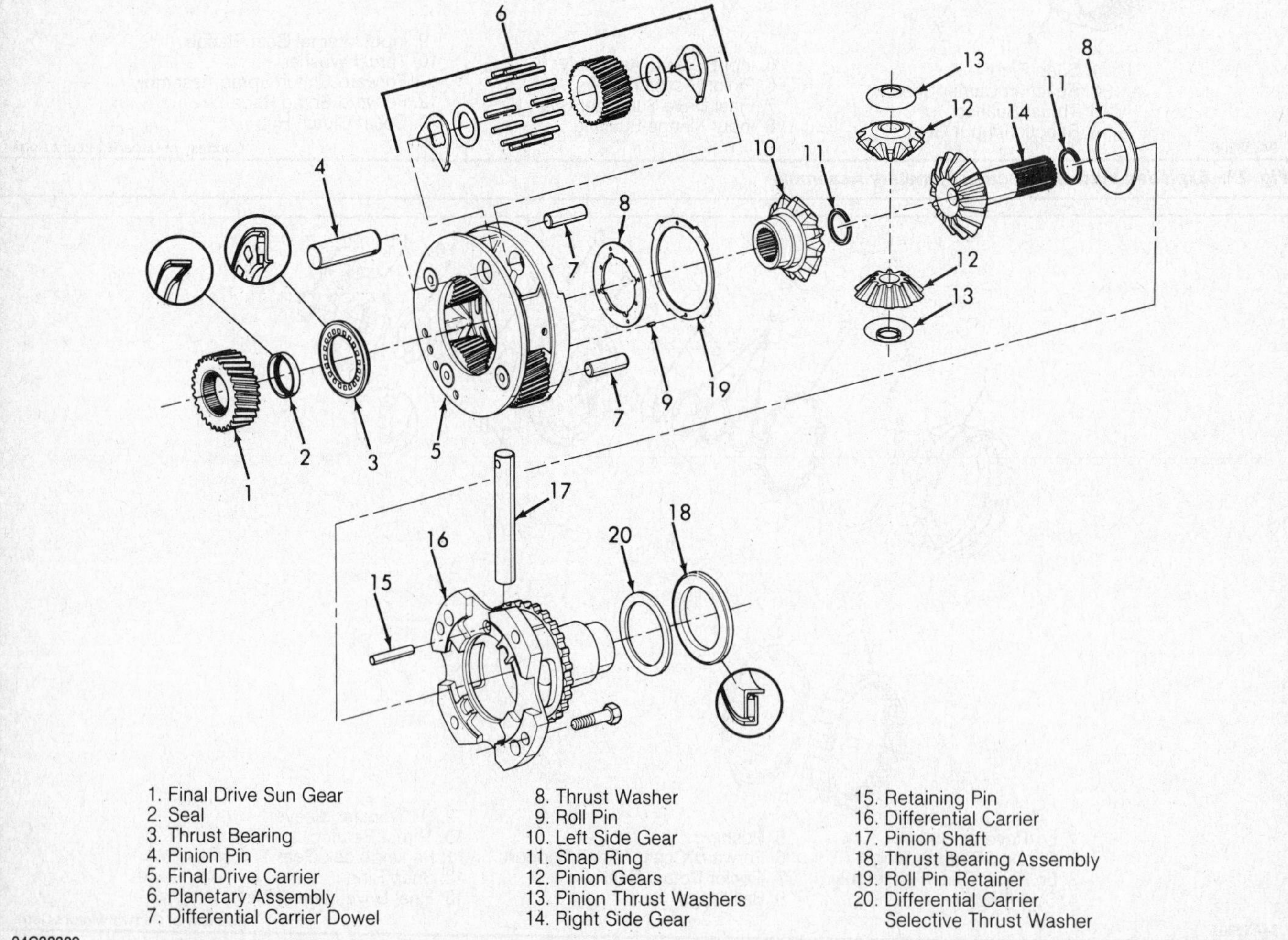

1. Final Drive Sun Gear
2. Seal
3. Thrust Bearing
4. Pinion Pin
5. Final Drive Carrier
6. Planetary Assembly
7. Differential Carrier Dowel
8. Thrust Washer
9. Roll Pin
10. Left Side Gear
11. Snap Ring
12. Pinion Gears
13. Pinion Thrust Washers
14. Right Side Gear
15. Retaining Pin
16. Differential Carrier
17. Pinion Shaft
18. Thrust Bearing Assembly
19. Roll Pin Retainer
20. Differential Carrier
Selective Thrust Washer
94C38309
Courtesy of General Motors Corp.

Fig. 25: Exploded View Of Final Drive & Differential Assembly

NOTE: Install oil pressure switch assembly to lower valve body. Illustration of oil pressure switch assembly is not available from the manufacturer.

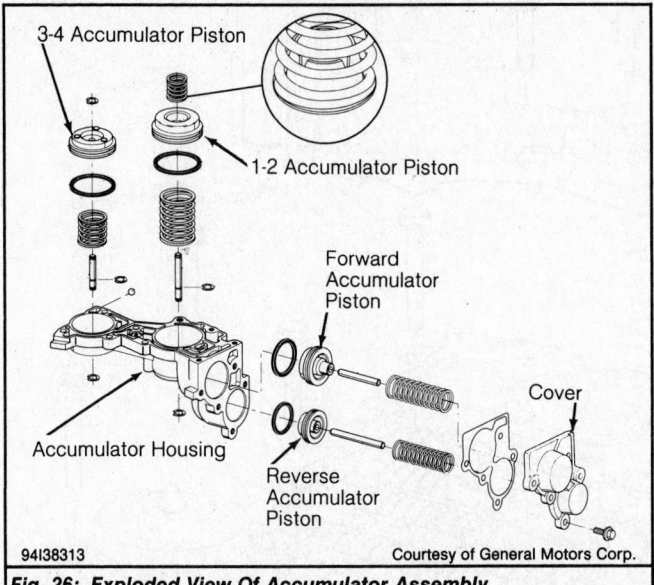

94I38313   Courtesy of General Motors Corp.

Fig. 26: Exploded View Of Accumulator Assembly

(labels in figure: 3-4 Accumulator Piston; 1-2 Accumulator Piston; Forward Accumulator Piston; Cover; Accumulator Housing; Reverse Accumulator Piston)

OIL PUMP ASSEMBLY

Disassembly – Clean and air dry oil pump. Remove scavenge oil pump cover and secondary oil pump body from scavenge oil pump body. See Fig. 34. Remove oil pump gears. Remove shaft and roll pins. Remove retainer pins. Remove pressure regulator valve and sleeve, and boost valve assembly. See Fig. 33.

Cleaning & Inspection – Inspect pump body for porosity, interconnected oil passages, or damaged inner pump area surface or machine facing. Check oil pump gears for damage. Check oil pump shaft and thrust washer for wear or damage. Check valve parts for damage.

Reassembly – Install valve train assemblies into pump body. Install and align oil pump gears with punch marks up. Assemble scavenge oil pump cover and secondary oil pump body to scavenge oil pump body.

LO/REVERSE SERVO & 4TH SERVO

For lo/reverse servo information, see VALVE BODIES under COMPONENT DISASSEMBLY & REASSEMBLY. See Fig. 28. For 4th servo information, see CASE ASSEMBLY under TRANSAXLE DISASSEMBLY.

TRANSAXLE REASSEMBLY

NOTE: All selective snap ring and thrust washer measurements taken during disassembly must be rechecked at appropriate reassembly stage.

1) Install manual shaft, detent lever assembly and parking pawl, if removed. Install drive sprocket support, transaxle input speed sensor and wiring harness. See Fig. 16. Install torque converter seal.

2) Install lo/reverse band and ensure anchor engages band. Install fretting ring with open end at bottom. Install oil cooler return fitting "O" ring to coast and forward clutch assembly. Using Forward/Coast Clutch Puller (J-39053), install coast and forward clutch assembly into case. See Fig. 17. Make sure anchor holes in support align with holes in case.

3) Install final drive internal gear with groove up. Install snap ring with open end in scavenge tube area. Rotate support counterclockwise against spline. See Fig. 35.

4) Install reaction shell and 3rd clutch housing. Install input shaft selective washer and thrust bearing on 3rd clutch housing. See Fig. 14.

Install 4th band and reverse clutch assembly. See Fig. 36. Make sure band pin seat engages servo pin. Install reverse clutch housing and thrust washer.

5) Install seal on drive sprocket support. Using Sizer (J-39064-2), size seal. Install backing plate, 2nd clutch plates, apply plate and waved plate.

6) Place scavenge tube seal on driven sprocket support and install driven sprocket support. Install drive chain (in same direction as removed) to drive sprocket support. Tap sprockets until seated. Place thrust roller bearings on sprockets.

7) To air check reverse, 2nd and 3rd clutches at drive sprocket support, go to next step. Install island gasket and case cover gasket. Install case cover allowing wiring harness connector to pass through opening in case cover. Install bolts in correct position and hand tighten only. See Fig. 38.

8) Using 40 psi (2.7 kg/cm²) of air pressure, air check clutches and servos. Reverse, 2nd and 3rd clutches may be checked at driven sprocket support. Coast and forward clutches may be checked through passage in lower case. See Fig. 39. To check Reverse clutch, 3rd clutch or 4th servo, fabricate an air checking plate. See Fig. 40.

9) Trace template as shown. See Fig. 40. Using 3/8-1/2" thick aluminum or plastic, cut out an air checking plate to match template. Mark and drill holes in plate. Bolt plate to case. Air check clutches and 4th servo.

NOTE: About 90-100 psi (6.2-6.9 kg/cm²) of air pressure are required to apply the 3rd clutch.

10) Check input shaft end play. See Fig. 14. Install Input Shaft End Play Fixture (J-39686) to front side of transaxle. Make sure "J" tab on fixture rests on input shaft. Mount Dial Indicator Post (J-25025-7A) and Dial Gauge (J-8001-3) to check end play. Push down on handle. End play should be .004-.034" (.10-.85 mm). Input shaft thrust washers size range is .089-.195" (2.27-4.97 mm) in increments of .012" (.30 mm).

11) Tighten case cover bolts and studs in a criss-cross pattern. Install 2 check balls. See Fig. 38. Install upper valve body. See Fig. 41. Tighten bolts starting with center ones and working to outside ones. Install side filter.

12) Install TCC/VCC solenoid and transaxle pressure control solenoid. Install oil pump assembly. Tighten bolts starting with center ones and working to outside ones. Install oil pan and tighten bolts in a star pattern. Install 4th servo. See Fig. 37. Make sure tab on servo piston aligns with slot in case (some models).

13) Using a long thin piece of .025" (.60 mm) shim stock, slide lo/reverse band into position. Install lower valve body and channel plate. See Fig. 42. Install bolts and tighten by hand. Remove shim stock.

14) Install oil transfer plate and hand tighten bolts. See Fig. 42. Connect wiring harness and manual valve. Tighten channel plate and oil transfer plate bolts in a criss-cross pattern. Install scavenge screens. See Fig. 37. Install pan gasket and tighten bolts in a star pattern.

15) Assemble and install final carrier, output shaft and differential carrier. See Fig. 37. Engage parking pawl to hold final drive unit. Tighten differential carrier bolts.

16) Install scavenge tube and seal. Install selective thrust washer and roller thrust bearing onto output shaft. See Fig. 37. Install extension housing and hand tighten bolts.

17) Mount Dial Indicator Post (J-39687) and Dial Gauge (J-8001-3) to check end play. Pry up on speed sensor rotor through speed sensor hole. End play should be .006-.025" (.15-.65 mm). See Fig. 12.

18) If necessary, adjust end play with selective final drive-to-case thrust washer. See FINAL DRIVE-TO-CASE SELECTIVE THRUST WASHER SIZES table. Tighten extension housing bolts. Install oil cooler return fitting to forward and coast clutch support. Install axle seals, oil pump drive shaft, torque converter and vehicle speed sensor.

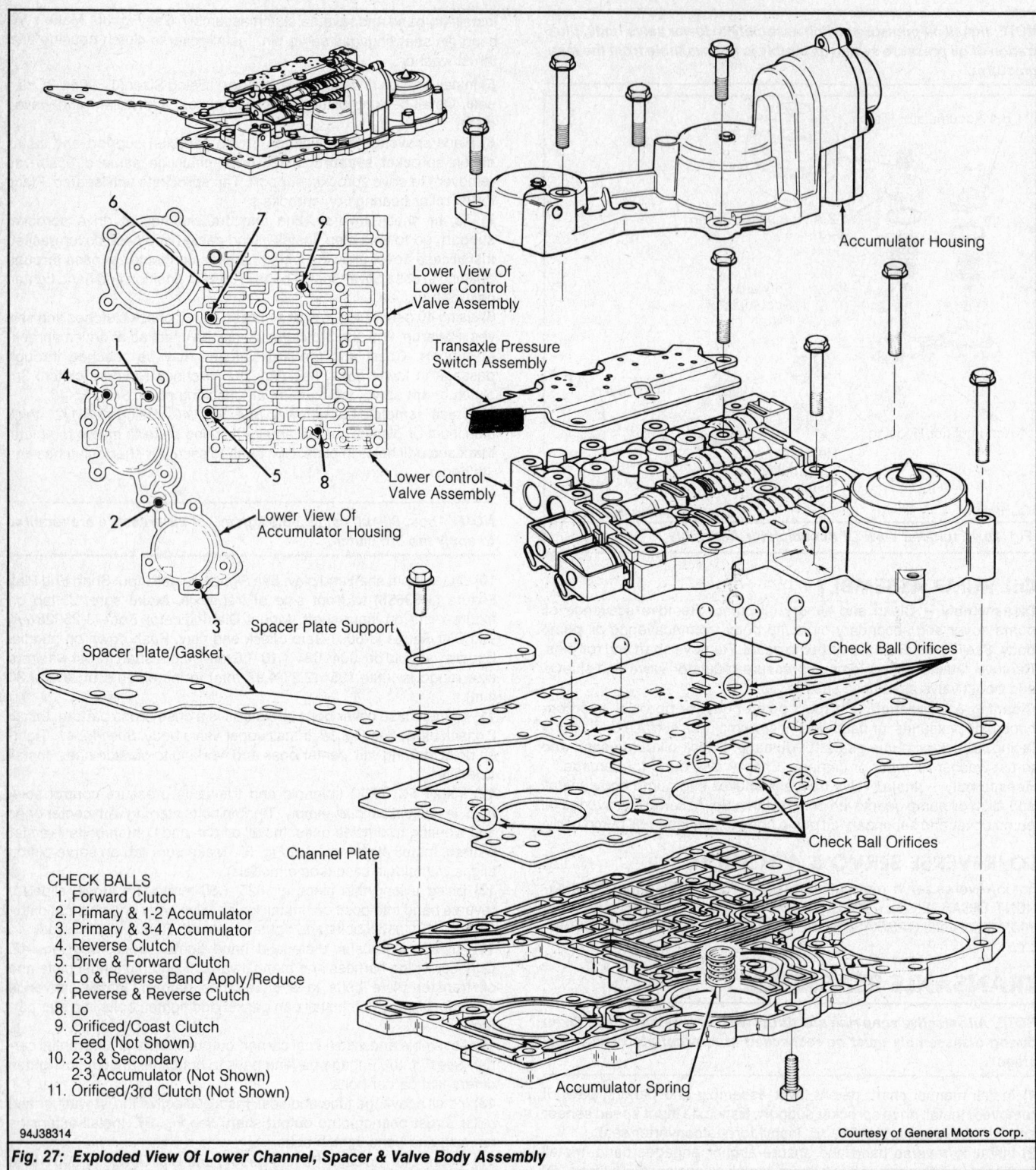

Accumulator Housing

Lower View Of Lower Control Valve Assembly

Transaxle Pressure Switch Assembly

Lower Control Valve Assembly

Lower View Of Accumulator Housing

Spacer Plate Support

Spacer Plate/Gasket

Check Ball Orifices

Check Ball Orifices

Channel Plate

CHECK BALLS
1. Forward Clutch
2. Primary & 1-2 Accumulator
3. Primary & 3-4 Accumulator
4. Reverse Clutch
5. Drive & Forward Clutch
6. Lo & Reverse Band Apply/Reduce
7. Reverse & Reverse Clutch
8. Lo
9. Orificed/Coast Clutch Feed (Not Shown)
10. 2-3 & Secondary 2-3 Accumulator (Not Shown)
11. Orificed/3rd Clutch (Not Shown)

Accumulator Spring

94J38314

Courtesy of General Motors Corp.

Fig. 27: Exploded View Of Lower Channel, Spacer & Valve Body Assembly

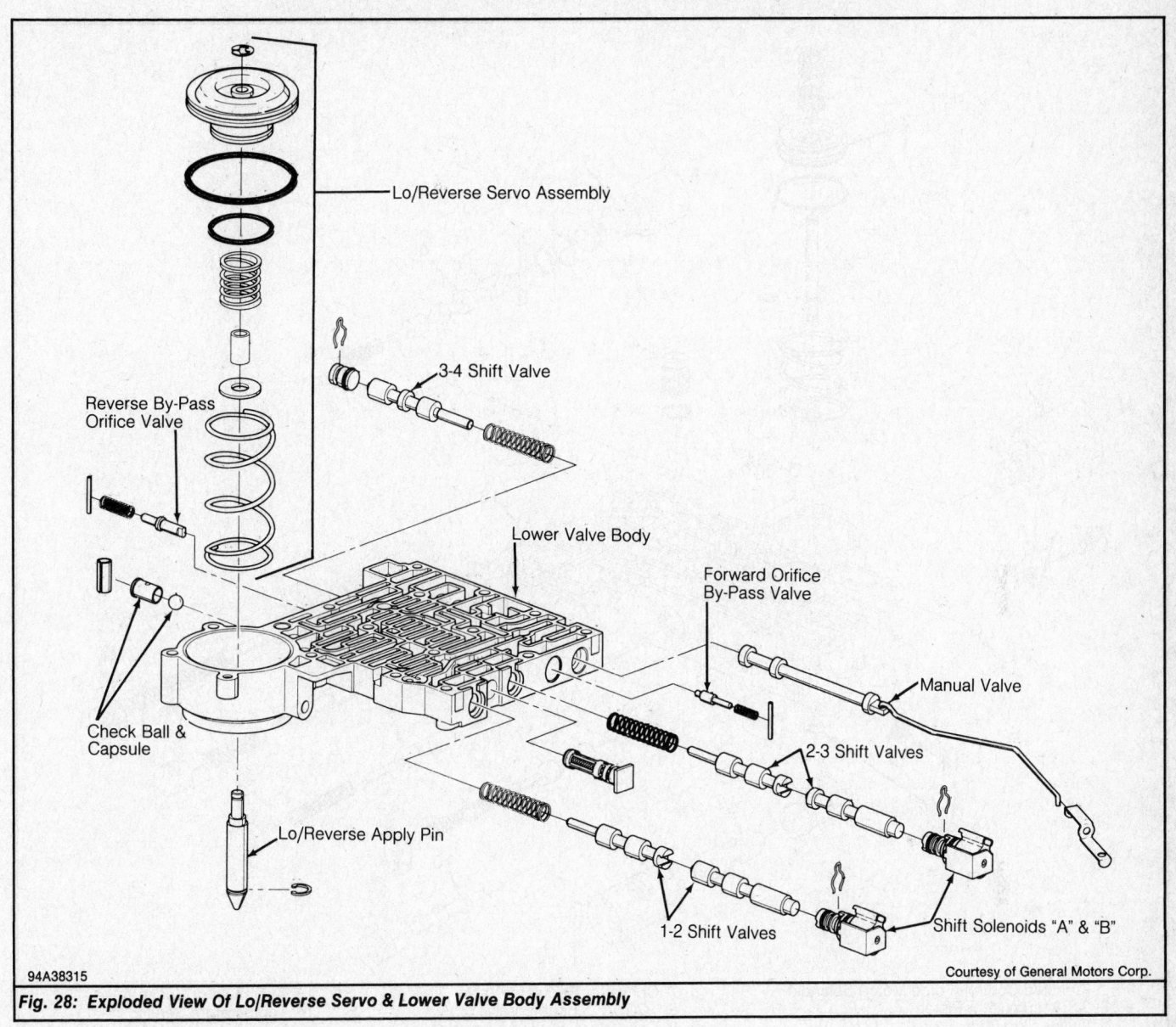

Lo/Reverse Servo Assembly

3-4 Shift Valve

Reverse By-Pass Orifice Valve

Lower Valve Body

Forward Orifice By-Pass Valve

Manual Valve

Check Ball & Capsule

2-3 Shift Valves

Lo/Reverse Apply Pin

1-2 Shift Valves

Shift Solenoids "A" & "B"

94A38315

Courtesy of General Motors Corp.

Fig. 28: Exploded View Of Lo/Reverse Servo & Lower Valve Body Assembly

AUTOMATIC TRANSMISSIONS
Hydra-Matic 4T80-E (Cont.)

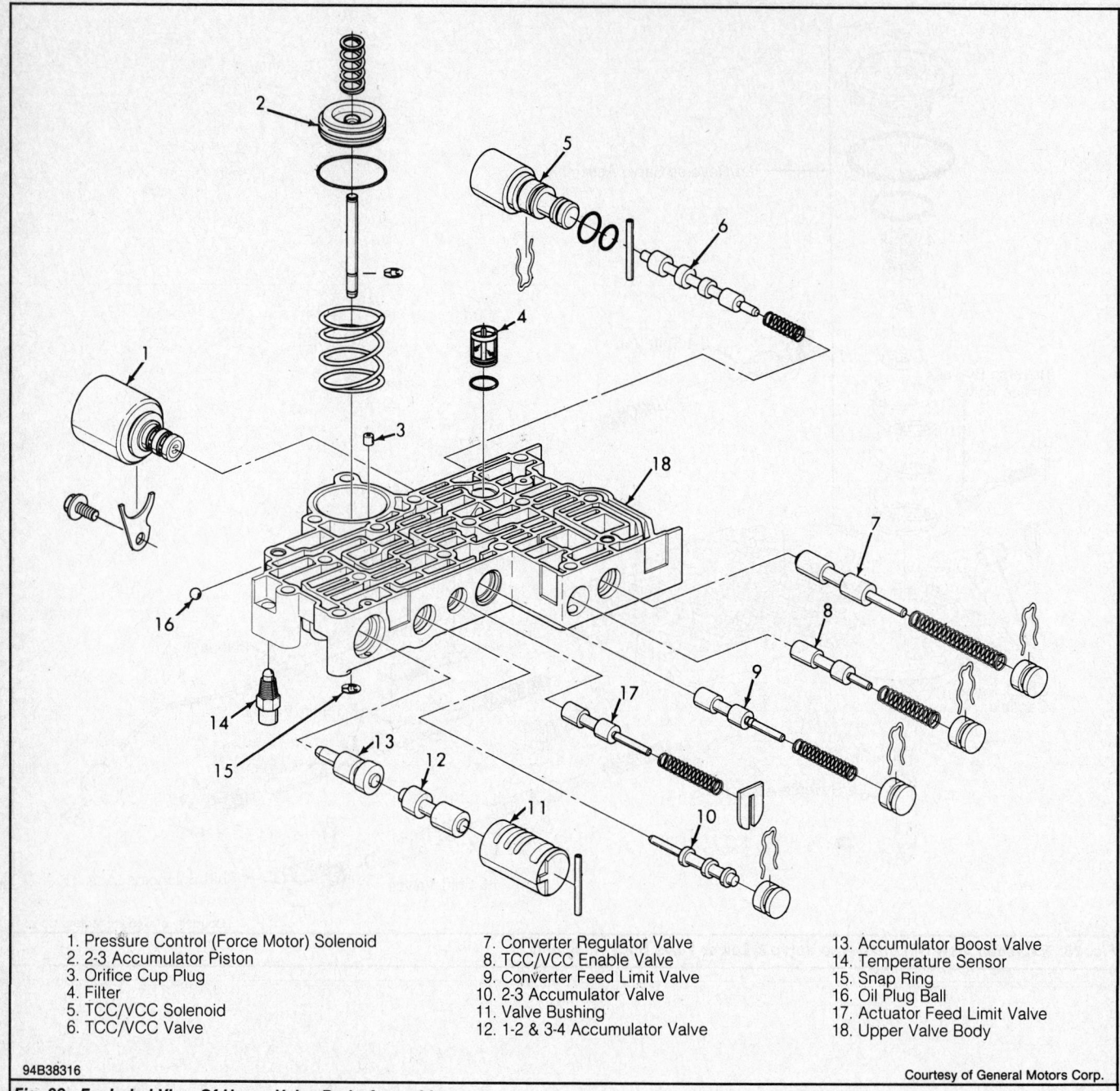

1. Pressure Control (Force Motor) Solenoid
2. 2-3 Accumulator Piston
3. Orifice Cup Plug
4. Filter
5. TCC/VCC Solenoid
6. TCC/VCC Valve

7. Converter Regulator Valve
8. TCC/VCC Enable Valve
9. Converter Feed Limit Valve
10. 2-3 Accumulator Valve
11. Valve Bushing
12. 1-2 & 3-4 Accumulator Valve

13. Accumulator Boost Valve
14. Temperature Sensor
15. Snap Ring
16. Oil Plug Ball
17. Actuator Feed Limit Valve
18. Upper Valve Body

94B38316

Courtesy of General Motors Corp.

Fig. 29: Exploded View Of Upper Valve Body Assembly

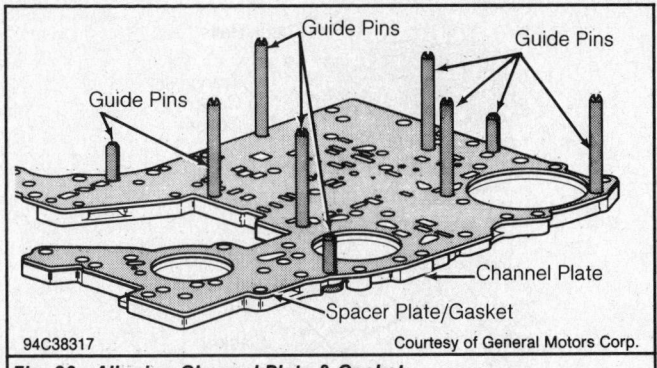

94C38317 Courtesy of General Motors Corp.

Fig. 30: Aligning Channel Plate & Gasket

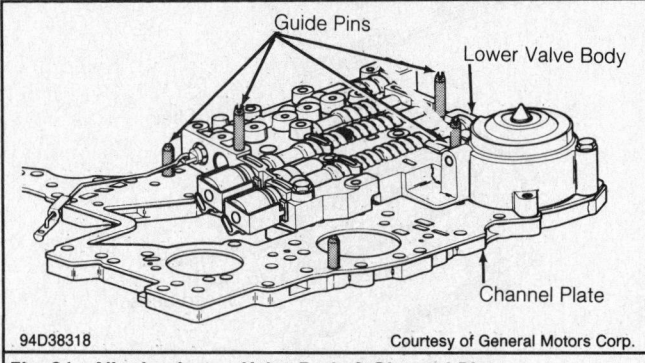

94D38318 Courtesy of General Motors Corp.

Fig. 31: Aligning Lower Valve Body & Channel Plate

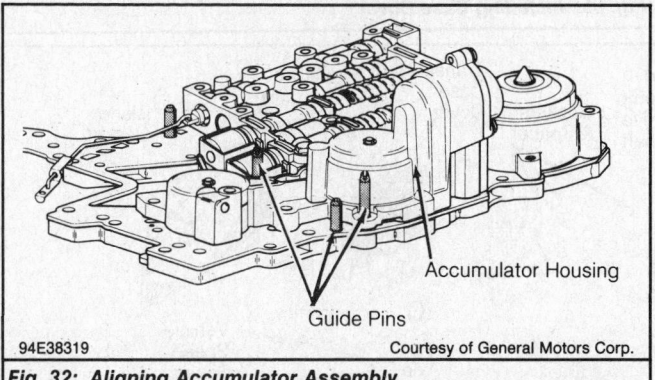

94E38319 Courtesy of General Motors Corp.

Fig. 32: Aligning Accumulator Assembly

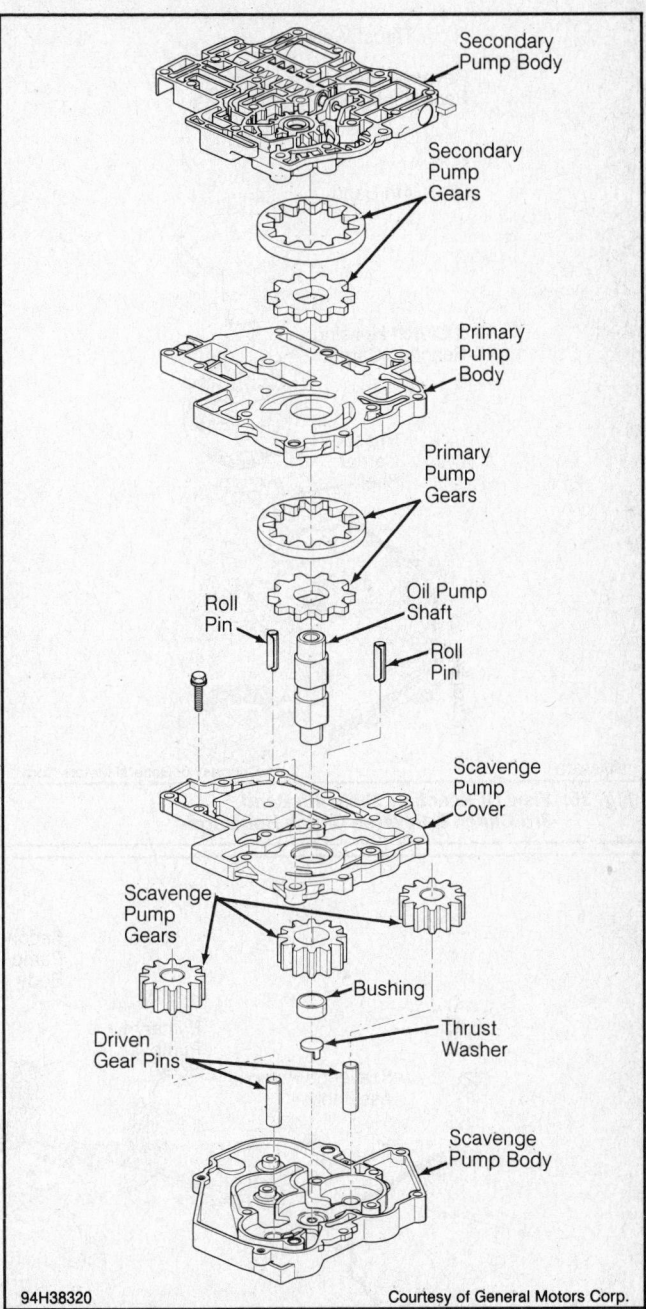

94H38320 Courtesy of General Motors Corp.

Fig. 34: Exploded View Of Oil Pump Assemblies

94I38321 Courtesy of General Motors Corp.

Fig. 33: View Of Oil Pressure Regulator Valve Assembly

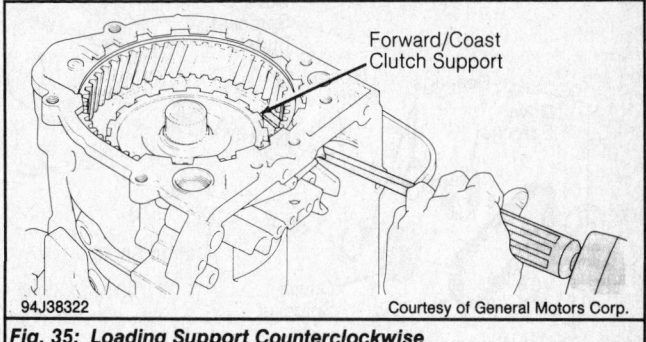

94J38322 Courtesy of General Motors Corp.

Fig. 35: Loading Support Counterclockwise

AUTOMATIC TRANSMISSIONS
Hydra-Matic 4T80-E (Cont.)

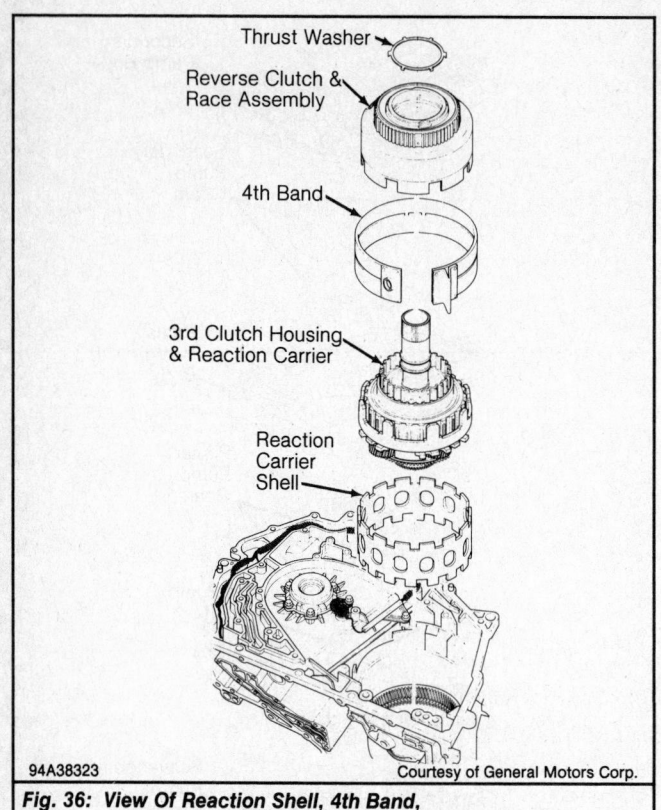

Thrust Washer

Reverse Clutch & Race Assembly

4th Band

3rd Clutch Housing & Reaction Carrier

Reaction Carrier Shell

94A38323

Courtesy of General Motors Corp.

Fig. 36: View Of Reaction Shell, 4th Band, 3rd Clutch & Reverse Clutch Housings

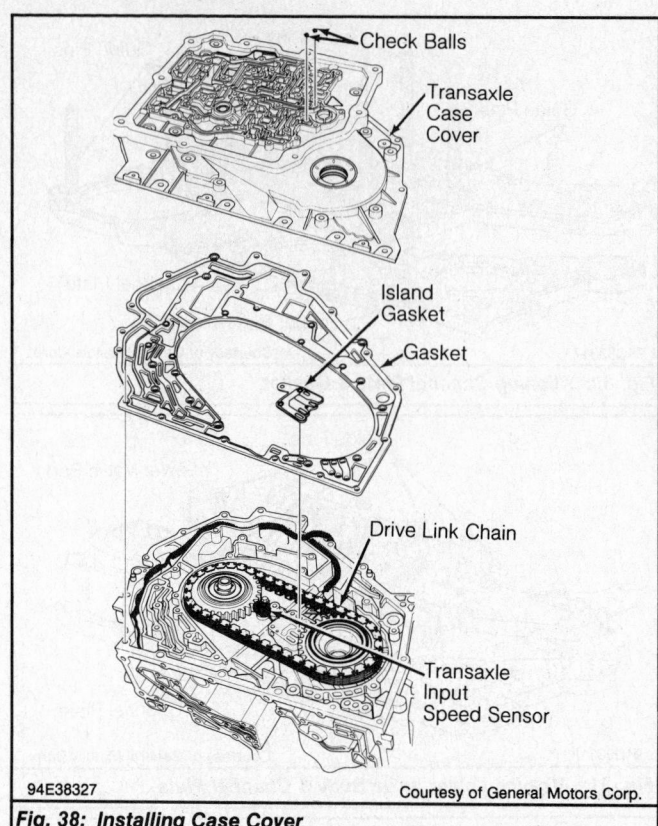

Check Balls

Transaxle Case Cover

Island Gasket

Gasket

Drive Link Chain

Transaxle Input Speed Sensor

94E38327

Courtesy of General Motors Corp.

Fig. 38: Installing Case Cover

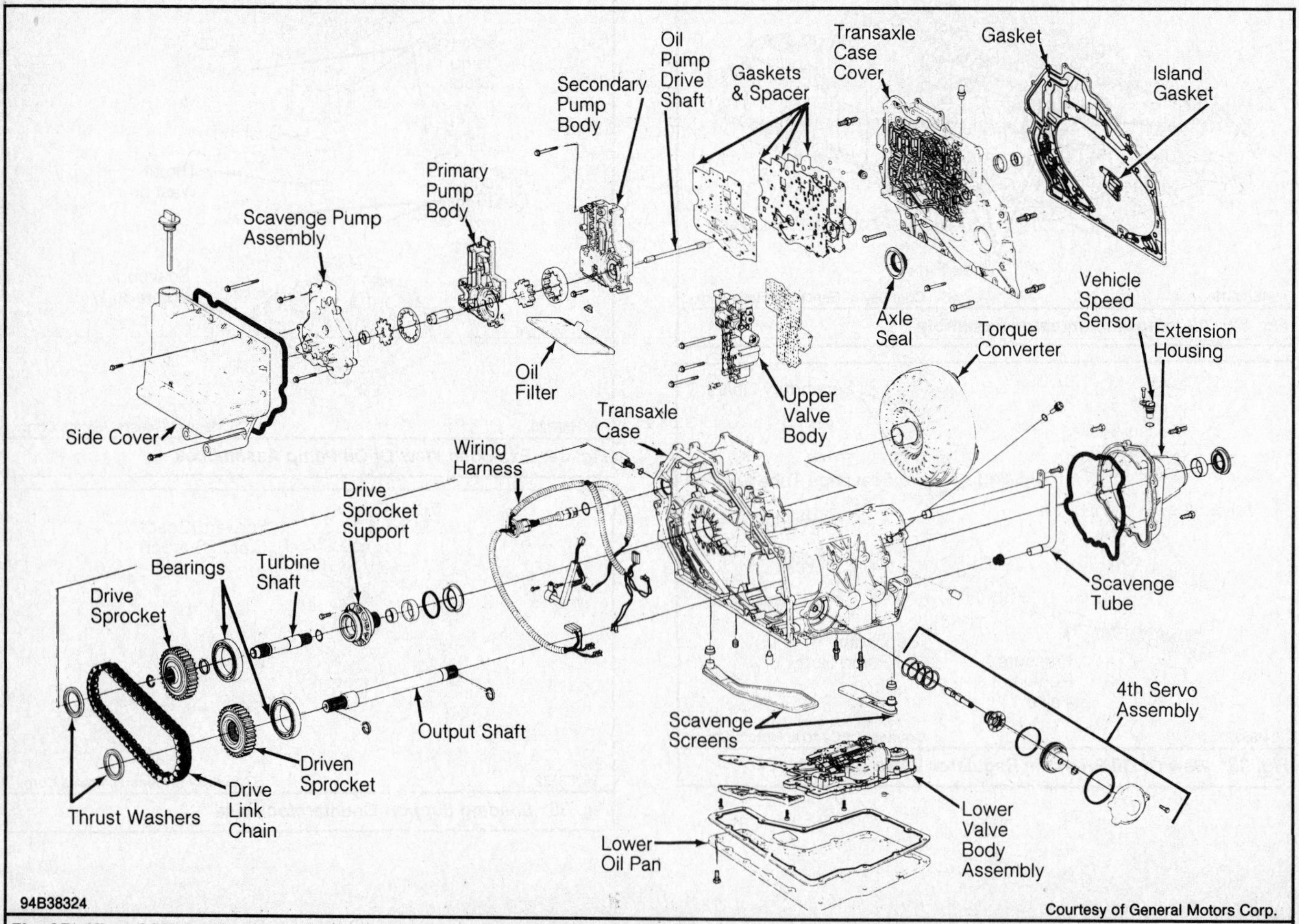

Oil Pump Drive Shaft

Secondary Pump Body

Gaskets & Spacer

Transaxle Case Cover

Gasket

Island Gasket

Primary Pump Body

Scavenge Pump Assembly

Oil Filter

Axle Seal

Torque Converter

Vehicle Speed Sensor

Extension Housing

Side Cover

Upper Valve Body

Transaxle Case

Wiring Harness

Scavenge Tube

Drive Sprocket Support

Bearings

Turbine Shaft

Drive Sprocket

Output Shaft

Scavenge Screens

4th Servo Assembly

Thrust Washers

Drive Link Chain

Driven Sprocket

Lower Oil Pan

Lower Valve Body Assembly

94B38324

Courtesy of General Motors Corp.

Fig. 37: View Of Valve Bodies, Oil Pump, Sprockets & Drive Chain Assemblies

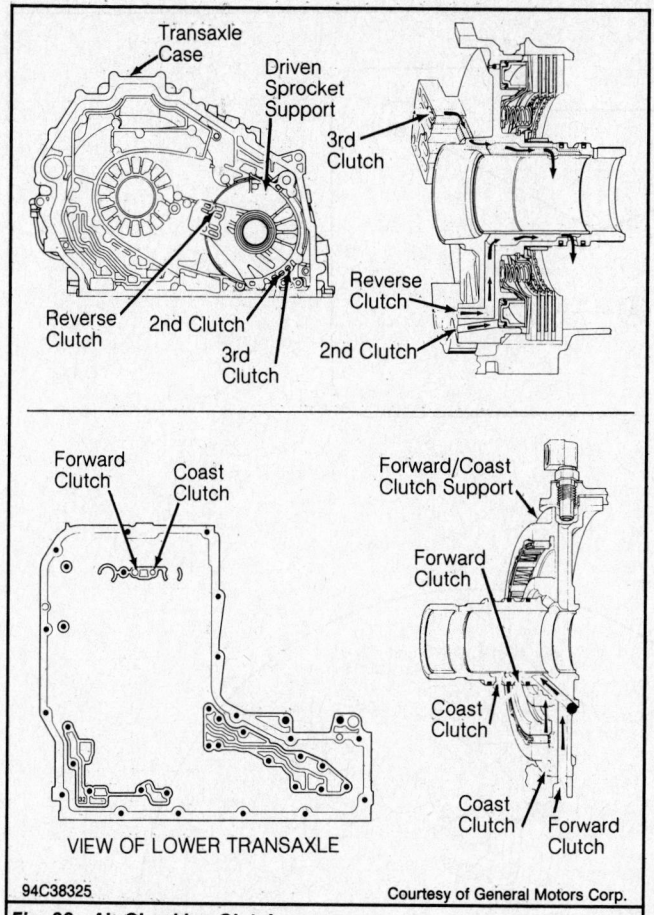

94C38325

Courtesy of General Motors Corp.

Fig. 39: Air Checking Clutches

FINAL DRIVE-TO-CASE SELECTIVE THRUST WASHER SIZES

Washer Identification Color	Thickness In. (mm)
Orange	.137-.141 (3.49-3.59)
White	.131-.136 (3.35-3.46)
Blue	.126-.130 (3.21-3.32)
Pink	.120-.125 (3.07-3.18)
Brown	.115-.119 (2.93-3.04)
Green	.110-.114 (2.79-2.90)
Black	.104-.109 (2.65-2.77)

TORQUE SPECIFICATIONS
TORQUE SPECIFICATIONS

Application	Ft. Lbs. (N.m)
Accumulator Assembly Bolts	9 (12)
Case Cover Bolts/Studs	22 (30)
Case Extension (Large Bolts)	39 (52)
Case Extension (Small Bolts)	20 (27)
Channel Plate Bolts	9 (12)
Coast & Forward Clutch Support Studs	18 (24)
Final Drive-To-Differential Bolts	54 (73)
Lower Oil Pan Bolts	9 (12)
Lower Valve Body Bolts	9 (12)
Pump Assembly Bolts	9 (12)
Side Oil Pan-To-Case Cover (13 mm Bolt)	18 (24)
Side Oil Pan-To-Case Cover (15 mm Bolts)	39 (52)
Transfer Plate Bolts	9 (12)
Upper Valve Body Bolts	9 (12)

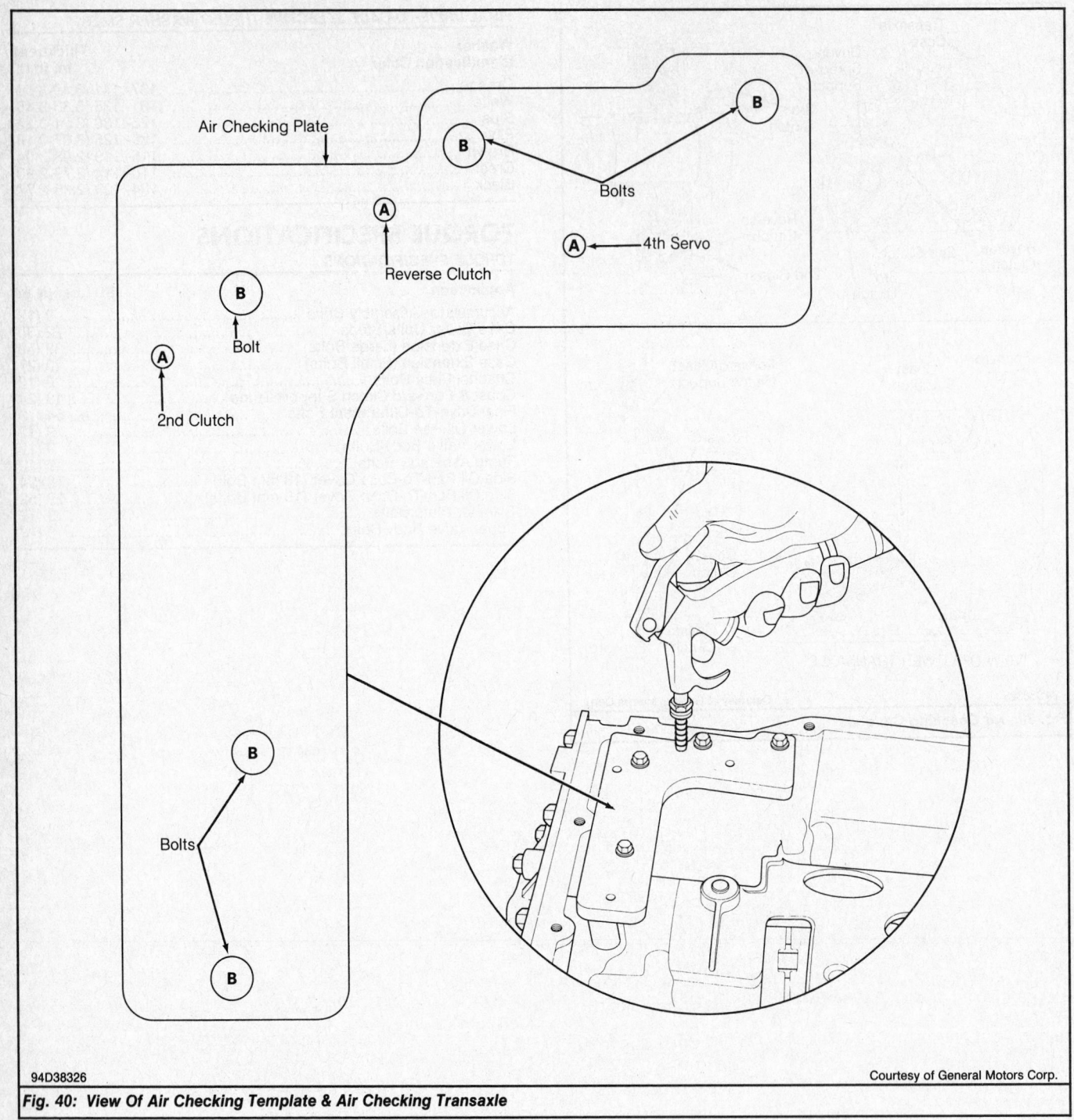

Air Checking Plate

B

B

Bolts

A Reverse Clutch

A 4th Servo

B Bolt

A 2nd Clutch

B

Bolts

B

94D38326

Courtesy of General Motors Corp.

Fig. 40: View Of Air Checking Template & Air Checking Transaxle

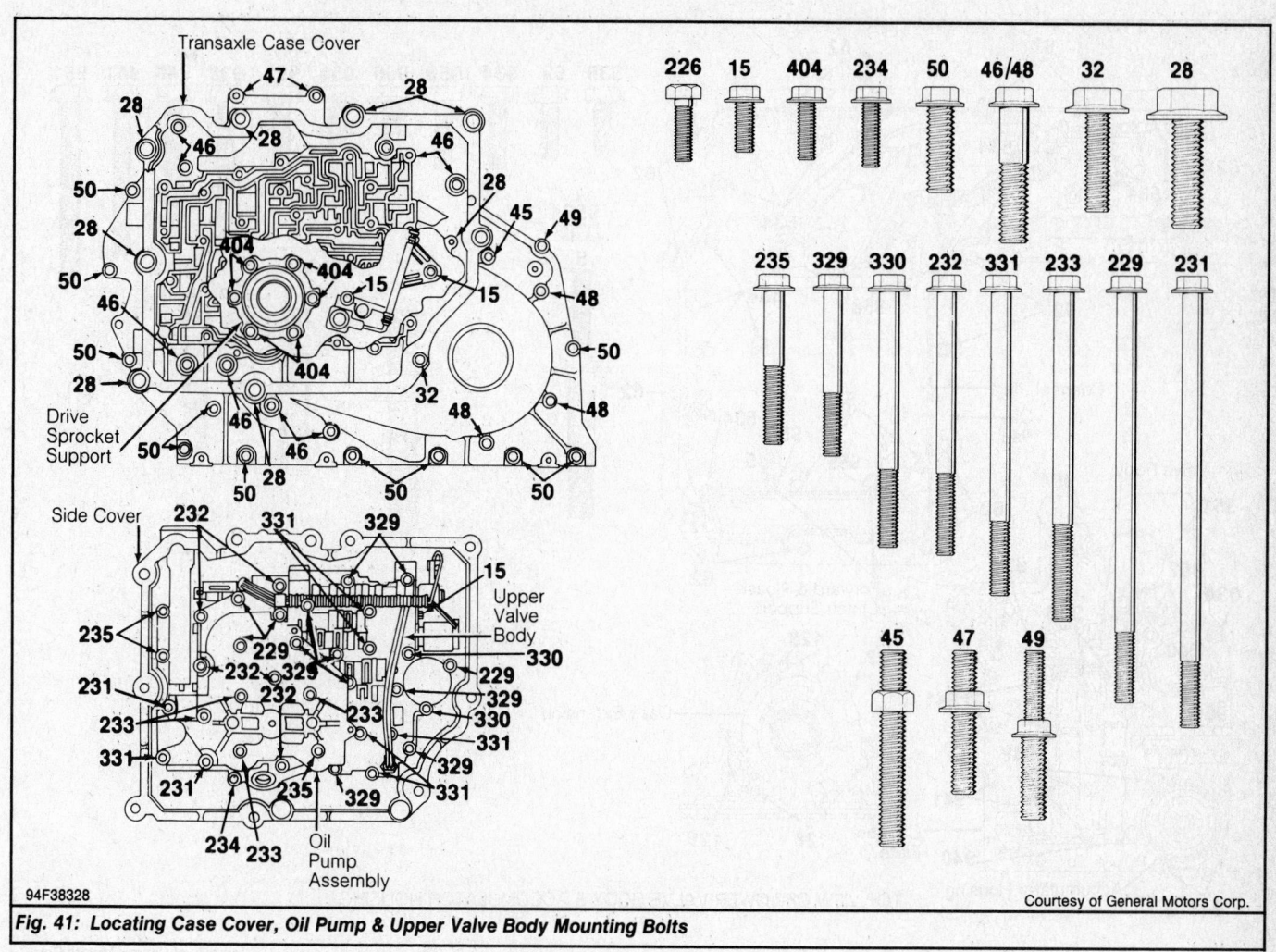

Fig. 41: Locating Case Cover, Oil Pump & Upper Valve Body Mounting Bolts

94F38328

Courtesy of General Motors Corp.

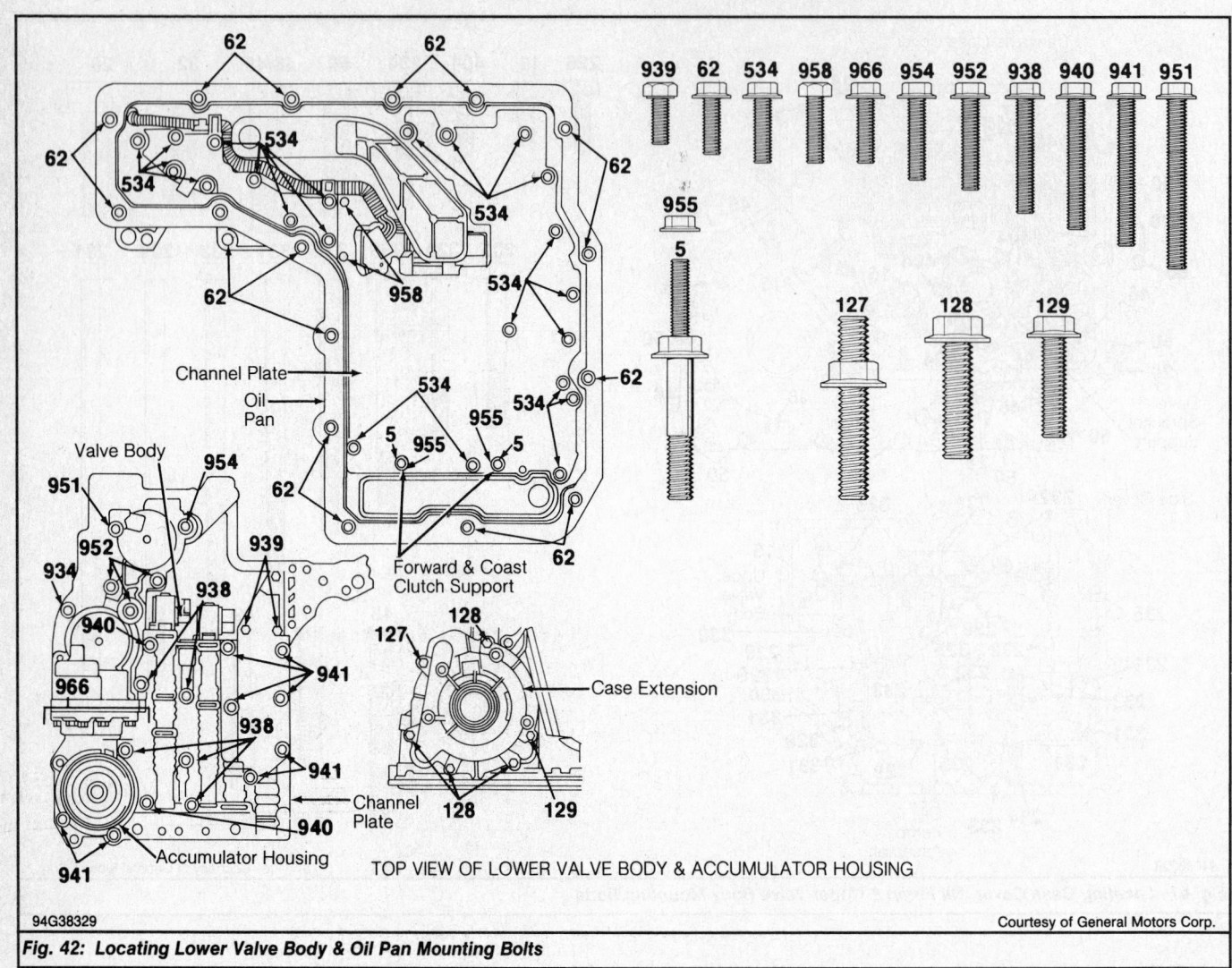

94G38329

Courtesy of General Motors Corp.

Fig. 42: Locating Lower Valve Body & Oil Pan Mounting Bolts

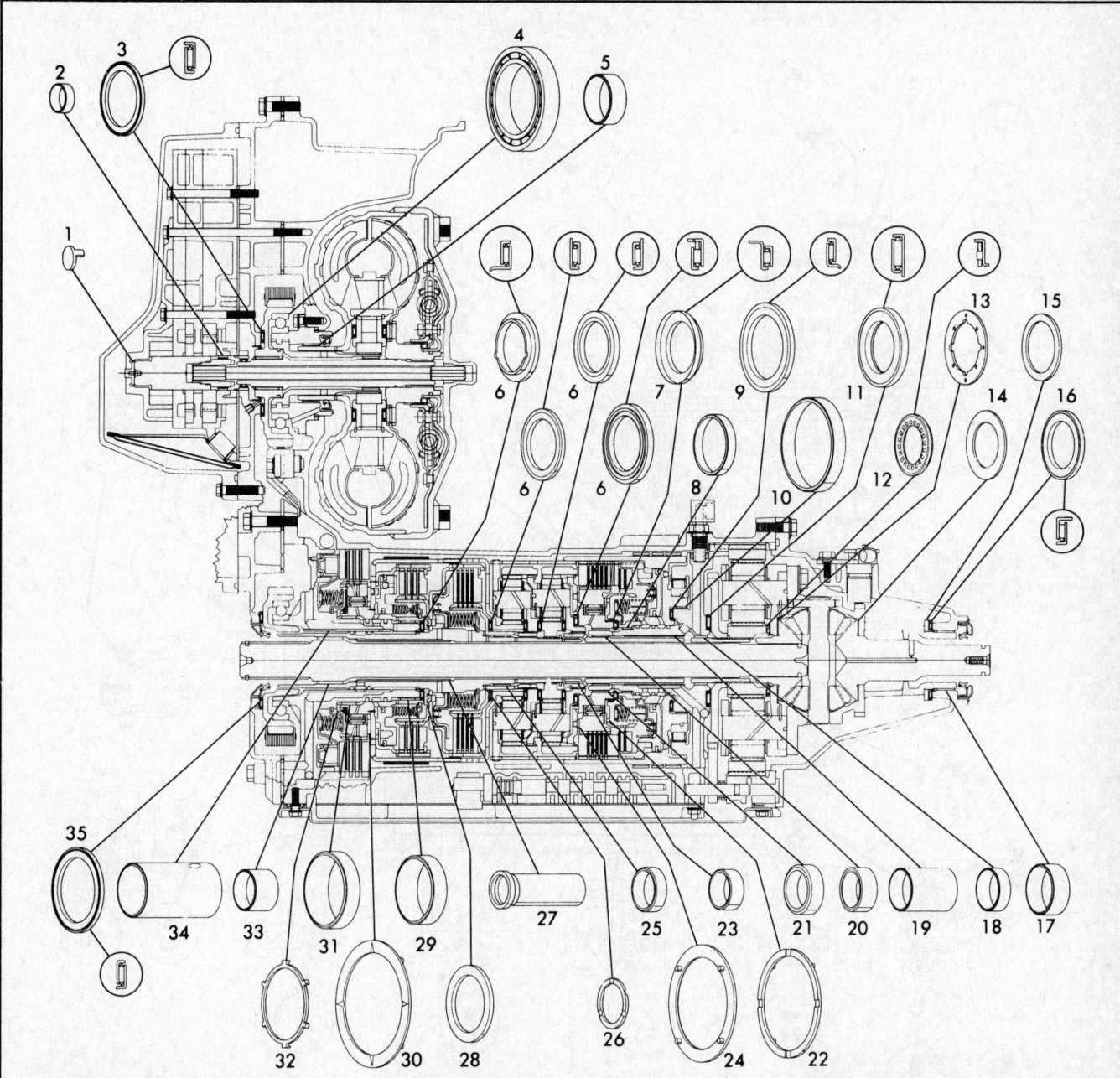

94J38330

Fig. 43: Identifying Hydra-Matic 4T80-E Thrust Washers & Bearing Locations

1. Oil Pump Shaft Thrust Washer
2. Stator Shaft Bushing
3. Thrust Bearing Assembly
4. Sprocket Bearing
5. Converter Hub Bushing
6. Thrust Bearings
7. Forward Clutch Housing Thrust Bearing
8. Housing Bushing (Small)
9. Forward Clutch Housing/Parking Gear Thrust Bearing
10. Housing Bushing (Large)
11. Forward Clutch Housing/Parking Gear Thrust Bearing
12. Sun Gear Thrust Bearing
13. Differential Thrust Washer (Left)
14. Differential Thrust Washer (Right)
15. Differential Carrier Selective Thrust Washer
16. Thrust Bearing
17. Extension Housing Bushing
18. Shaft Support Bushing (Right)
19. Oil Transfer Sleeve
20. Shaft Support Bushing (Left)
21. Input Flange Bushing
22. Coast Clutch Hub Thrust Washer
23. Hub Bushing
24. Input Internal Gear Flange Thrust Washer
25. Reaction Sun Gear Bushing
26. 3rd Hub Thrust Washer
27. Input Shaft Oil Transfer Sleeve
28. Driven Sprocket Support Selective Thrust Washer
29. Reverse Clutch Housing Bushing (Small)
30. 2nd Clutch Outer Race Washer
31. Reverse Clutch Housing Bushing (Large)
32. Reverse Clutch Support Thrust Washer
33. Input Shaft Bushing
34. Oil Transfer Sleeve
35. Forward Clutch Support Parking Gear Thrust Bearing

AUTOMATIC TRANSMISSIONS
Hydra-Matic 4T80-E (Cont.)

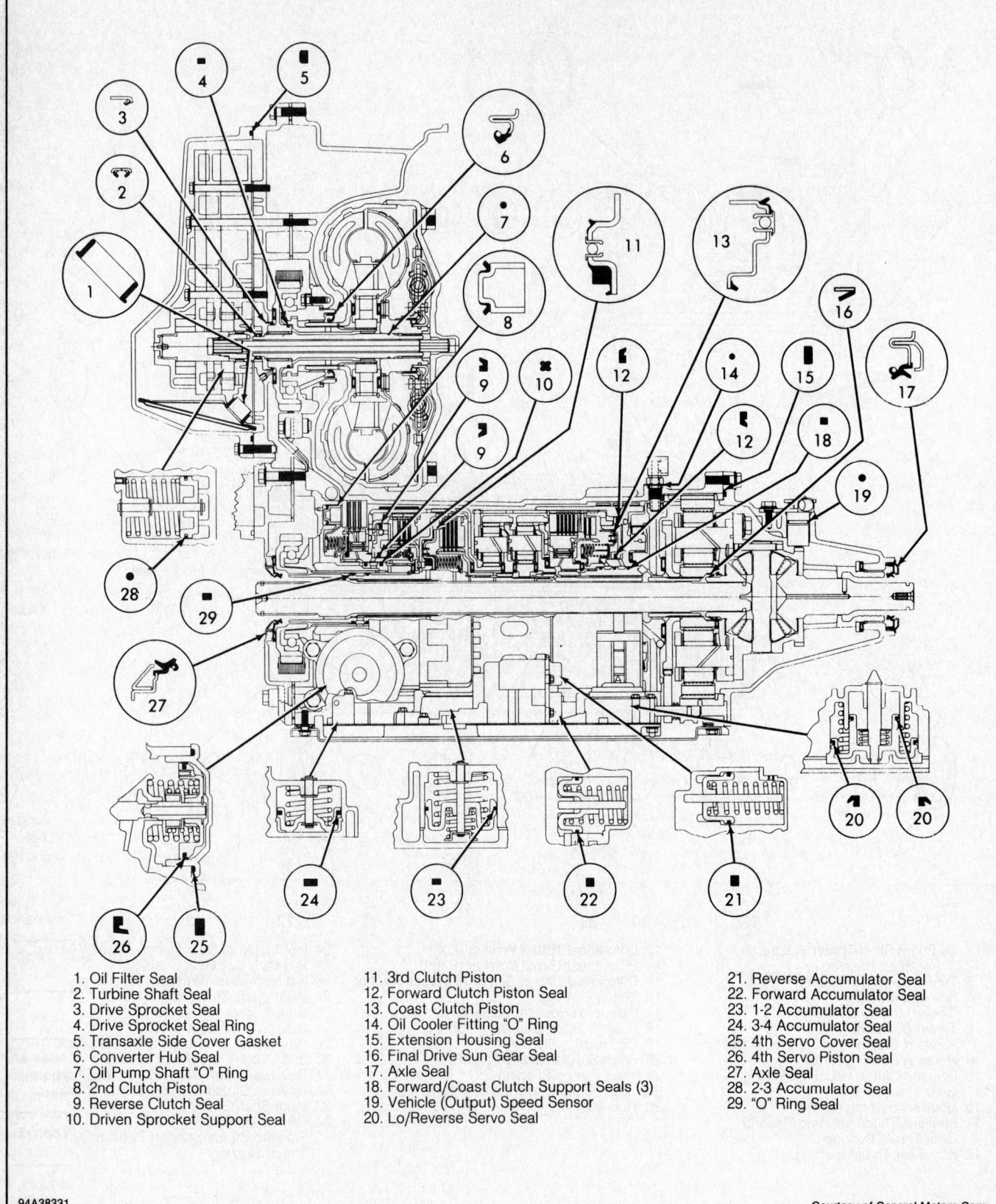

1. Oil Filter Seal
2. Turbine Shaft Seal
3. Drive Sprocket Seal
4. Drive Sprocket Seal Ring
5. Transaxle Side Cover Gasket
6. Converter Hub Seal
7. Oil Pump Shaft "O" Ring
8. 2nd Clutch Piston
9. Reverse Clutch Seal
10. Driven Sprocket Support Seal

11. 3rd Clutch Piston
12. Forward Clutch Piston Seal
13. Coast Clutch Piston
14. Oil Cooler Fitting "O" Ring
15. Extension Housing Seal
16. Final Drive Sun Gear Seal
17. Axle Seal
18. Forward/Coast Clutch Support Seals (3)
19. Vehicle (Output) Speed Sensor
20. Lo/Reverse Servo Seal

21. Reverse Accumulator Seal
22. Forward Accumulator Seal
23. 1-2 Accumulator Seal
24. 3-4 Accumulator Seal
25. 4th Servo Cover Seal
26. 4th Servo Piston Seal
27. Axle Seal
28. 2-3 Accumulator Seal
29. "O" Ring Seal

94A38331

Courtesy of General Motors Corp.

Fig. 44: Identifying Hydra-Matic 4T80-E Lip Seal Locations

APPLICATION

THM 4T80-E APPLICATION

Application	Engine
Cadillac	
DeVille Concours, Eldorado & Seville .... [1] 4.6L	

[1] – Engines code "Y" (eighth digit of VIN), use a viscous clutch converter. Engines code "9" (eighth digit of VIN), use a torque converter clutch.

BODY CODE DESIGNATIONS

Body Designation	Model
"E" Body	Eldorado
"K" Body	Seville
"K" Special Body [1]	DeVille Concours

[1] – Applies to 1994 models.

DESCRIPTION

The 4T80-E transaxle uses 2 electric solenoids to control transaxle upshifts and downshifts. Each solenoid is turned on or off by the Powertrain Control Module (PCM). The PCM also includes on-board self-diagnostics. This helps identify which parts or circuits may need further testing.

OPERATION

Each solenoid either holds hydraulic pressure (solenoid on) or releases hydraulic pressure (solenoid off). This action controls the shift valves inside valve body. By switching one or both solenoids on or off, different combinations of clutches, sprags and bands are operated. See CLUTCH & BAND APPLICATION CHART (4T80-E) under ELECTRONIC TESTING.

COMPONENT DESCRIPTION

PCM

The PCM is located under right side of dash near glove box. PCM controls ignition, fuel and emission devices related to the engine and transaxle upshifts and downshifts.

The PCM receives electronic signals from sensors and switches. These signals help the PCM determine when to operate various relays and solenoids related to engine and transaxle control.

The PCM is connected to additional computers, which operate the climate control system, anti-lock brake system, driver information center and supplemental restraint system.

SENSORS & SWITCHES

The PCM controls upshifts and downshifts based on coolant temperature, throttle position, PRNDL switch position, pressure switch assembly, transaxle input speed sensor, vehicle speed sensor and brake pedal switch. The system includes several other switches and sensors which are used for engine control. These are covered in ENGINE PERFORMANCE in appropriate MITCHELL® manual.

SOLENOIDS

Transaxle is shifted up or down by 2 electric solenoids. Both solenoids are located on the valve body. Ignition power is supplied to each solenoid by fuse D1.

The 4T80-E uses 2 electronic shift valves controlled by the Powertrain Control Module (PCM). Transaxles also use a transaxle pressure control solenoid (force motor) to control line pressure, and a lock-up control solenoid for Torque Converter Clutch (TCC) or Viscous Converter Clutch (VCC) operation.

ON-BOARD SELF-DIAGNOSTICS

These vehicles are capable of retrieving trouble codes and computer data from the PCM on the Electronic Climate Control Panel (ECCP). The information is similar to what a scan tool can provide. Several lights on the ECCP are used to indicate operating status of transaxle related functions.

PCM STATUS LIGHTS

While in SYSTEM LEVEL of DIAGNOSTIC SERVICE MODE, mode indicators on ECCP are used to indicate status of certain operating modes. Different modes of operation are indicated by status light being on or off. Following is a description of various status lights.

- **AUTO A/C Status Indicator** – This indicator is used to signify operating mode of PCM. If AUTO is on, PCM is in close loop. If AUTO is off, PCM is in open loop.
- **AUTO Fan Status Indicator** – This displays status of Park/Neutral switch. When Park/Neutral switch is closed, AUTO fan symbol is on. When Park/Neutral switch is open, AUTO fan symbol is off.
- **ECON Status Indicator** – This displays status of transaxle shift solenoid "B". When ECON is on, transaxle shift solenoid "B" is energized. When ECON is off, transaxle shift solenoid "B" is not energized.
- **"E" Temperature Status Indicator** – This displays status of shift adapt status. When the "E" symbol is on, transaxle shift adapts are disabled. When the "E" symbol is off, transaxle shift adapts are enabled.
- **DEFOG Status Indicator** – This displays status of transaxle shift solenoid "A". When DEFOG is on, transaxle shift solenoid "A" is energized. When DEFOG is off, transaxle shift solenoid "A" is not energized.
- **Front Defogger Status Indicator** – This indicator is used for A/C clutch command. See Fig. 1. Light should only be on when A/C clutch is engaged.
- **LO Fan Speed Status Indicator** – This indicator is used to indicate status of the throttle position switch. When the throttle position switch is closed, the LO fan symbol is on. When the throttle position switch is open, the LO fan symbol is off.
- **Rear Defogger Status Indicator** – This indicator is used for the Torque Converter Clutch (TCC) or Viscous Converter Clutch (VCC). See Fig. 1. Light only indicates TCC/VCC solenoid status requested by PCM; actual operation depends on condition of TCC/VCC system.

ELECTRONIC SELF-DIAGNOSTICS

PCM constantly monitors all electrical circuits. If PCM detects circuit problems or sensors out of range, it will record trouble codes. If problem continues for a predetermined time, SERVICE ENGINE SOON light will glow.

If the SERVICE ENGINE SOON light is on all the time, trouble code(s) are currently being detected. If the SERVICE ENGINE SOON light is off, but PCM had detected a circuit or sensor problem, trouble code(s) will be stored in computer memory.

Stored trouble codes may be retrieved from PCM memory. On these models, trouble codes may be retrieved through the instrument panel.

NOTE: For complete PCM testing and diagnosis, see ENGINE PERFORMANCE in appropriate MITCHELL® manual.

RETRIEVING CODES

NOTE: These vehicles are capable of displaying trouble codes and computer data on the instrument panel. The information is similar what a scan tool can provide. Use the following information to access transaxle-related trouble codes and to erase them from computer memory. If available, a bidirectional scan tool (Tech 1) can also be used on these vehicles.

In order to access and control the PCM self-diagnostic features, 2 electronic components are used, the Drivers Information Center (DIC) and the Electronic Climate Control Panel (ECCP). See Fig. 1. The SERVICE MODE for diagnostic information incorporates odometer/trip odometer as Driver Information Center (DIC) display. When a malfunction is sensed by the PCM, the SERVICE ENGINE SOON (SES) light will glow on DIC and stay on (with engine running) until code is cleared from PCM.

ELECTRONIC TESTING
CLUTCH & BAND APPLICATION CHART (4T80-E)

Selector Lever Position	Solenoid Position	Elements In Use
"D" (Drive)		
1st Gear	"A" ON/"B" OFF	Forward Clutch, Lo/Reverse Band, ¹ Lo Roller & ¹ Forward Sprag
2nd Gear	"A" OFF/"B" OFF	Forward Clutch, 2nd Clutch, ¹ 2nd Sprag & ¹ Forward Sprag
3rd Gear	"A" OFF/"B" ON	Forward Clutch, 2nd Clutch, 3rd Clutch & ¹ Forward Sprag
Overdrive	"A" ON/"B" ON	Forward Clutch, 2nd Clutch, 3rd Clutch & 4th Band
"3" (Manual 3rd)		
3rd Gear	"A" OFF/"B" ON	Forward Clutch, Coast Clutch, 2nd Clutch, 3rd Clutch & ¹ Forward Sprag
2nd Gear	"A" OFF/"B" OFF	Forward Clutch, Coast Clutch, 2nd Clutch, ¹ 2nd Sprag & ¹ Forward Sprag
1st Gear	"A" ON/"B" OFF	Forward Clutch, Coast Clutch, Lo/Reverse Band, ¹ Lo Roller & ¹ Forward Sprag
"2" (Manual 2nd)		
2nd Gear	"A" OFF/"B" OFF	Forward Clutch, Coast Clutch, 2nd Clutch, 4th Band, ¹ 2nd Sprag & ¹ Forward Sprag
1st Gear	"A" ON/"B" OFF	Forward Clutch, Coast Clutch, Lo/Reverse Band, ¹ Lo Roller & ¹ Forward Sprag
"1" (Manual Low)		
2nd Gear	"A" OFF/"B" OFF	Forward Clutch, Coast Clutch, 2nd Clutch, 4th Band, ¹ 2nd Sprag & ¹ Forward Sprag
1st Gear	"A" ON/"B" OFF	Forward Clutch, Coast Clutch, Lo/Reverse Band, ¹ Lo Roller & ¹ Forward Sprag
"R" (Reverse)	"A" ON/"B" OFF	Reverse Band & Lo/Reverse Band
"N" Or "P" (Neutral Or Park)	"A" ON/"B" OFF	All Clutches & Bands Released Or Ineffective

¹ – Holding.

The ECCP becomes the controller by which to enter and access self-diagnostics. By pressing the appropriate buttons on the ECCP, data messages can be sent to the PCM, requesting specific diagnostic features. This process allows PCM to transfer any of its available diagnostic information to instrument panel DIC display during service mode operation.

ENTERING SELF-DIAGNOSTICS

CAUTION: Accessing self-diagnostics for 30 minutes or longer without running engine will cause battery to discharge, resulting in a possible no-start condition and faulty diagnostic readings. To ensure proper operation, attach battery charger to battery.

1) Turn ignition switch on. Simultaneously depress OFF and WARMER buttons on the Electronic Climate Control Panel (ECCP). *See Fig. 1.*
2) Continue to depress OFF and WARMER buttons until all segments and bulbs of the DIC and ECCP illuminate. When all segments are lit, system has entered self-diagnostic mode. Release OFF and WARMER button.
3) If all segments of the DIC and ECCP glow, go to step **4)**. Failure of any segment to glow may result in inaccurate test results. All inoperative segments of the display must be made to operate before proceeding with self-diagnostic procedures.
4) Powertrain Control Module (PCM) trouble codes are automatically displayed after system enters self-diagnostics. Trouble codes (3-digit) appear in numerical order and are prefixed with letter "P". If no PCM trouble codes are stored, NO PCM CODES message will be displayed.
5) All PCM trouble codes are followed by letter "C" or "H". Letter "C" stands for current and indicates fault presently exists.

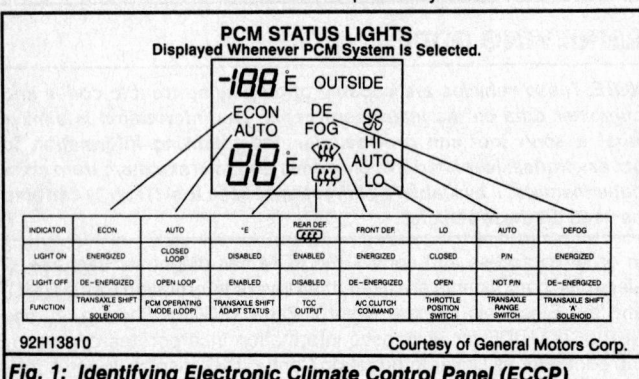

Fig. 1: Identifying Electronic Climate Control Panel (ECCP)

6) The letter "H" stands for history and indicates system failure was not present during last key cycle, but was present during one of previous

50 key cycles. For example: Code P024H is PCM Code 024, set in response to a malfunction that occurred in the past (history).

NOTE: After all trouble codes have been displayed, depressing OFF button on ECCP will activate a repeat of trouble code display.

CLEARING CODES

To clear codes, depress LO button on the ECCP 4 times or until ECCP displays PCM CLEAR CODES. Press HI button on ECCP. PCM will clear codes within 3 seconds. Press LO button on ECCP to return to PCM DATA display. If ignition switch is turned to OFF position, trouble codes are not erased.

EXITING SELF-DIAGNOSTICS

To exit self-diagnostics, press BI-LEV button on ECCP. Another way to exit self-diagnostics is to turn ignition to OFF position. Trouble codes will not be cleared by exiting self-diagnostics.

NOTE: Faulty engine sensors and actuators may cause transmission related fault codes or driveability problems. Engine faults and related trouble codes must be diagnosed and repaired before transmission codes are repaired. For additional information on diagnosing and repairing engine related PCM fault codes, see ENGINE PERFORMANCE section of appropriate MITCHELL® manual.

PCM TROUBLE CODES ¹

Code	Circuit Affected
P012 ¹ ²	No Ignition Module Signal
P021	Shorted Throttle Position (TP) Circuit
P022	Open Throttle Position (TP) Circuit
P024	Vehicle Speed Sensor (VSS) Circuit
P028	Pressure Switch Circuit
P029	Shift Solenoid "B" Circuit
P039	TCC Or VCC Problem
P056	Transaxle Input Speed Sensor Circuit
P057	Shorted Temperature Sensor Circuit
P059	Open Temperature Sensor Circuit
P075	Vehicle Speed Sensor (VSS) Circuit Interrupt
P076	Pressure Control Solenoid Circuit
P086	Undefined Gear Ratio
P088	TCC Or VCC Not Disengaging
P089	Long Shift & Maximum Adapt
P091	Range Switch Circuit
P094	Shift Solenoid "A" Circuit
P096	TCC Or VCC Overstress
P117	Shift Solenoid "A" Or "B" Circuit

¹ – For all other trouble codes, see ENGINE PERFORMANCE in appropriate MITCHELL® manual.
² – Code P012 is normal when no reference pulses are received by control module (engine not running).

DIAGNOSTIC CODES

CODE P021
SHORTED THROTTLE POSITION (TP) SENSOR

The TP sensor is a variable potentiometer. The PCM detects throttle position by monitoring TP sensor input circuit. When throttle is closed or nearly closed, input circuit voltage will be low. If PCM detects an input voltage that is too high, Code P021 will be set. PCM also locks transaxle in current gear, and disables TCC/VCC and transaxle pressure control.

1) Turn ignition on and enter self-diagnostics. When PCM DATA appears, press HI on ECCP to display PD01 (throttle position). If -14 to 84 is displayed, fault is not present at this time.

2) If display reads 85-94, disconnect TP connector. If display reads -14 to -7, go to step **4)**. If display reads -6 to 94, backprobe terminal 1B15 at Red PCM connector and measure voltage.

3) If voltage is greater than .5 volts are present, repair short to voltage in Dark Blue wire. If voltage is less than .5 volts are present, check for weak contact at PCM terminal 1B15. If terminal is okay, replace PCM.

4) Measure voltage between TP harness terminals "A" and "B". If less than 4.5 volts are present, repair open in Black or Black/Pink wire between TP and PCM. See Fig. 2 or 3. If more than 5.4 volts are present, repair short to voltage in Gray wire. If voltage is 4.6-5.4, check for weak terminals at TP sensor. If TP sensor terminals are okay, replace TP sensor.

CODE P022
OPEN THROTTLE POSITION (TP) SENSOR

The TP sensor is a variable potentiometer. The PCM detects throttle position by monitoring TP sensor input circuit. When throttle is closed or nearly closed, input circuit voltage will be low. If PCM detects an input voltage that is too low, Code P022 will be set. PCM also locks transaxle in current gear, and disables TCC/VCC.

NOTE: If Codes P032, P036 and/or P103 are also set, repair Gray wire for open or shorted to ground problem.

1) Turn ignition on and enter self-diagnostics. When PCM DATA appears, press HI on ECCP to display PD01 (throttle position). Move accelerator to part throttle. If -4 to 94 is displayed, fault is not present at this time.

2) If display reads -14 to -5, disconnect TP connector. Using a jumper wire, connect TP harness terminals "A" to "C". If display reads -14 to 84, go to step **3)**. If display reads 85 to 94, check for weak contact at TP sensor. If TP sensor terminals are okay, replace TP sensor.

3) Measure voltage at jumper wire. If voltage is less than .5 volt go to step **5)**. If voltage is greater than .5 volt, backprobe terminal 1B15 at Red PCM connector and measure voltage.

4) If voltage is greater than .5 volt, check for weak contact at PCM connector. If terminal is okay, replace PCM. If less than .5 volt are present, repair open in Dark Blue wire between TP harness and PCM terminal 1B15.

5) Remove jumper wire. Measure voltage between TP harness terminals "A" and ground. If less than 4.5 volts are present, repair open in Gray wire between TP and PCM splice connection. See Fig. 2 or 3. If more than 4.5 volts are present, repair short to ground in Dark Blue wire.

CODE P024
VEHICLE SPEED SENSOR (VSS)

The speed sensor, which is a Permanent Magnet (PM) generator, provides the control module with vehicle speed information. The PM generator, mounted in the transaxle, produces a pulsing voltage signal whenever the vehicle speed is more than 5 MPH. The voltage level and pulses increase with vehicle speed. The control module converts the pulsing voltage to MPH, which is used by the control module in calculations to determine vehicle adjustments.

A Code P024 will set when MPH reads zero to 5, transmission is not in Park or Neutral, transaxle input speed sensor indicates 3000 RPM or more and transaxle pressure switch is not in "R". All of these condi-

tions must be met for 2-5 seconds. The PM generator only produces a voltage signal if drive wheels are turning faster than 5 MPH.

NOTE: DO NOT use this test procedure if vehicle is connected to a battery charger.

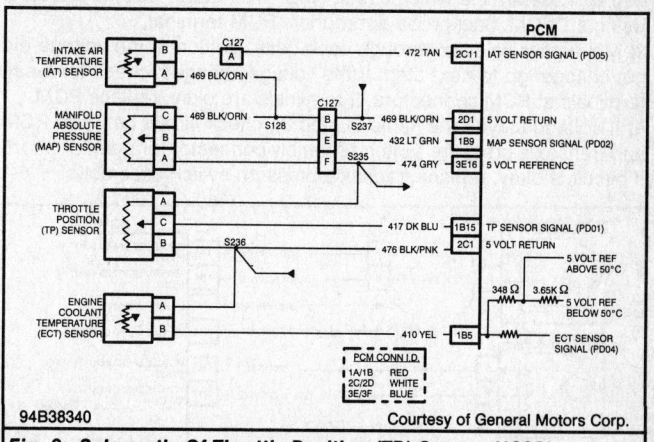

Fig. 2: Schematic Of Throttle Position (TP) Sensor (1993)

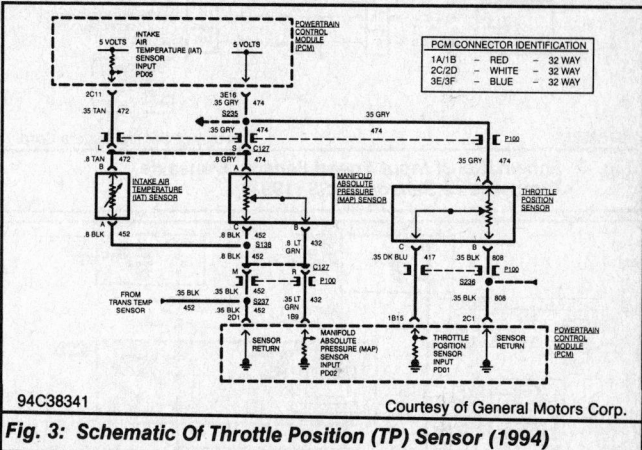

Fig. 3: Schematic Of Throttle Position (TP) Sensor (1994)

1) If code P024 is not present, go to Code P075. If Code P024 is present, lift drive wheels and place transaxle in Neutral. Set a DVOM on 400mV AC. Turn ignition on. Backprobe PCM terminals 1A10 and 1B10. See Fig. 4 or 5.

2) Rotate either wheel by hand. If no volts are present, go to step **4)**. If more than .2 volt is present, note if speedometer indicated speed. If vehicle speed was indicated, no problem is present at this time. If no vehicle speed was indicated, check for weak connections at PCM terminals 1A10 and 1B10. If connections are okay, replace PCM.

3) If less than .2 volts are present at PCM, check connections at VSS. If connections are okay, replace VSS.

4) If no volts are present at PCM terminals, check both circuits between VSS and PCM for open or short. See Fig. 4 or 5. Repair circuits as necessary. If no problems are found, check connections at VSS. If connections are okay, replace VSS.

CODE P028
TRANSAXLE PRESSURE SWITCH

The transaxle pressure switch assembly informs PCM of gear engagement based on hydraulic pressure detected inside valve body. The transaxle pressure switch assembly contains 5 switches. These switches are connected internally to operate 3 circuits connected to the PCM. These 3 circuits provide a code which the PCM uses to determine transaxle gear engagement.

If either code 000 or 010 appears for 5 seconds with engine running, PCM will set Code P028. PCM will also set Code P028 if the transaxle pressure switch assembly indicates a specific gear range while the actual gear ratio does not match.

1) With engine running, enter self-diagnostics. Wait until ECCP displays PCM DATA. Press HI on ECCP until PCM parameter PD71 is displayed. Move gear selector through each gear position and record value. *See Fig. 6 or 7.*

2) If all columns do not stay at 0 or 1, go to step **5)**. If any column stays at 0 or 1, determine which circuit (1A6, 1A7 and/or 1B6) is affected. Using a DVOM, backprobe appropriate PCM terminal.

3) Move gear selector through each gear position. If the voltage did not change, go to next step. If the voltage changed, check for weak terminals at PCM connectors. If terminals are okay, replace PCM.

4) If voltage stayed the same in step **3)**, check circuit between PCM and transaxle pressure switch assembly connector for open or short. If circuit is okay, replace transaxle pressure switch assembly.

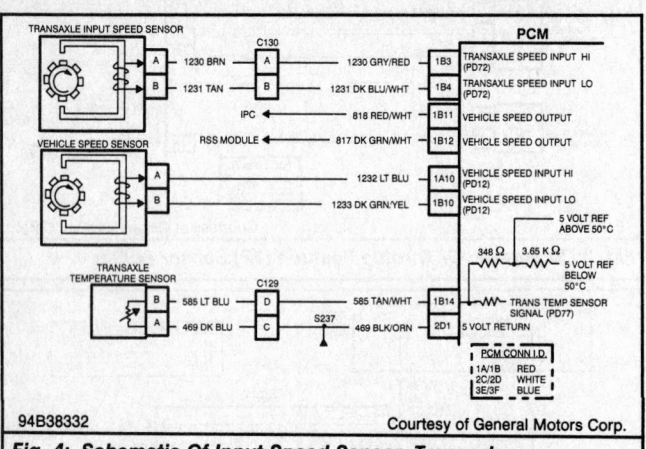

Fig. 4: Schematic Of Input Speed Sensor, Transaxle Temperature Sensor & VSS (1993)

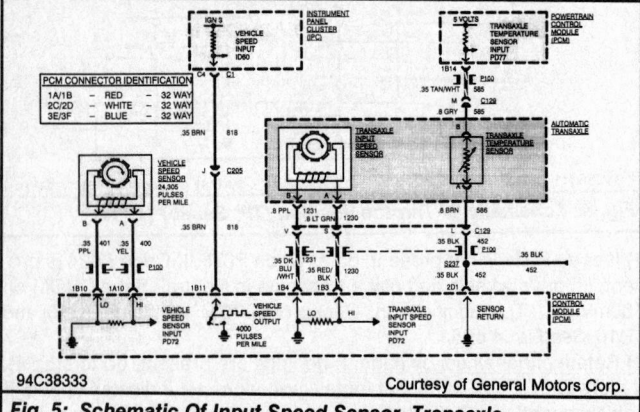

Fig. 5: Schematic Of Input Speed Sensor, Transaxle Temperature Sensor & VSS (1994)

5) If all columns from PD71 do not match with known transaxle pressure switch assembly values, check terminals at PCM connection. *See Fig. 6 or 7.* If PCM terminals are okay, replace transaxle pressure switch assembly.

6) If all columns from PD71 match with known transaxle pressure switch assembly values, select PCM snapshot data PD76 (transaxle gear ratio). This checks to see if the failure occurred with vehicle in reverse.

7) If PD76 value is not 2.02 to 2.23, go to next step. If PD76 value is between 2.02 and 2.23, select PCM snapshot data PD71. If PD71 value is 110, check circuit 1225 for a short to ground or weak connections. If PD71 value is 000, check circuit 1226 for a short to ground or weak connections. *See Fig. 6 or 7.*

8) If PD76 value is not 2.02 to 2.23, select PCM snapshot data PD71. Note value and check appropriate circuit(s) for intermittent open or short. See GEAR RANGE CIRCUIT PROBLEM chart. If no problems are found, check all circuits for weak connections. After repairs, clear code and check operation.

GEAR RANGE CIRCUIT PROBLEM

PD71 Value	Circuit & Condition
100	1224 For Short
100	1225 For Short
101	1226 For Open
101	1225 For Short
101	1224 For Open
000	1224 For Short
010	1226 For Short
010	1224 For Short

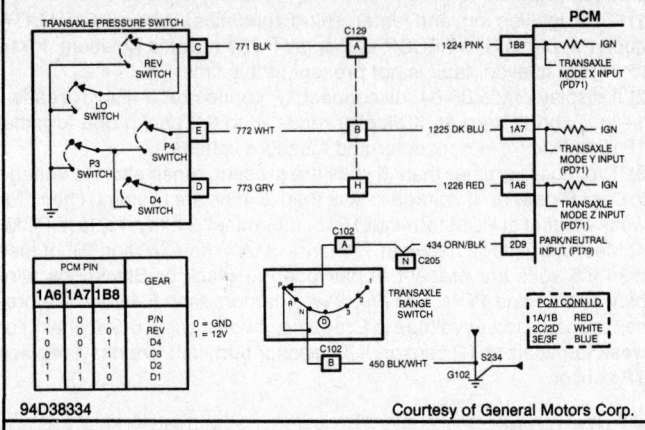

Fig. 6: Schematic Of Transaxle Pressure Switch (1993)

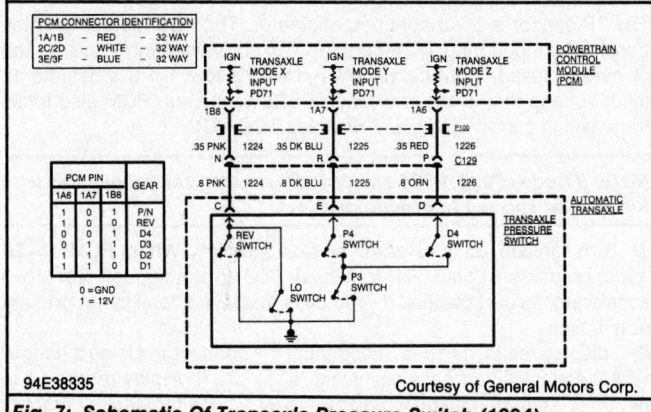

Fig. 7: Schematic Of Transaxle Pressure Switch (1994)

CODE P029
SHIFT SOLENOID "B"

1) Turn ignition key on. Enter self-diagnostics. If Code P117 is also present, diagnose Code P117 first. If only Code P029 is present, move gear selector to "D".

2) Press LO 3 times on ECCP until PCM OVERRIDES appears. Press HI until PS11 (transaxle shift) is selected. Using COOLER and WARMER buttons, shift transaxle through all gear ranges while watching fault status "B" of PD17.

3) If fault status is high (1) in 1st and 2nd gear, go to next step. If fault status is high (1) in 3rd and 4th gear, go to step **8)**. If fault status is low (0) in all gears, go to step **12)**.

4) Using a DVOM, backprobe terminal 3E5 at PCM connector. *See Fig. 8 or 9.* Cycle shift solenoid "B". If voltage changes from zero to 12 volts, check for weak terminal at PCM connector. If terminal is okay, replace PCM.

5) If voltage is less than 10 volt, disconnect 14-pin connector at upper transaxle oil pan. Check voltage at Pink/Black (1993) or Brown (1994) wire on engine side of harness. If voltage is less than 10 volts, check for open circuit from harness to fuse block.

6) If voltage is greater than 10 volt, remove Blue PCM connector. Check for open or short in Yellow/Black wire between PCM and transaxle connector. Repair wire as necessary.

7) If Yellow/Black wire is okay, measure resistance between terminals "F" and "G" (1993) or "E" and "B" (1994) at transaxle harness connector. If resistance is 100 ohms or more, check transaxle harness and shift solenoid "B" for an open. If resistance is less than 100 ohms, check Black/Yellow wire between transaxle and PCM for an intermittent short.

8) Using a DVOM, backprobe terminal 3E5 at PCM connector. Press LO on ECCP until "PCM OUTPUTS" appear. Press HI until PO11 (shift solenoid "B") is selected. Shift solenoid "B" will start cycling on and off.

9) If voltage cycles between zero and 12 volts, check for a weak connection at PCM terminal 3E5. *See Fig. 8 or 9.* If connection is okay, replace PCM. If voltage is over 10 volts, disconnect transaxle connector and check voltage at terminal "G" (1993) or "B" (1994) of transaxle connector.

10) If voltage is at least 10 volts, check Yellow/Black wire between transaxle connector and shift solenoid "B" for short to voltage. If voltage is less than 10 volts, disconnect PCM connector. Check voltage at terminal "G" (1993) or "B" (1994) of engine side of transaxle harness.

11) If 10 or more volts are present, repair short to voltage in harness. If less than 10 volts are present, check for weak connection at PCM terminal 3E5. If connection is okay, replace PCM.

12) Press LO on ECCP until PCM SNAPSHOT appears. Press HI 2 times and enter snapshot data PO29. Note PD76 (transaxle gear ratio). Depending on recorded ratio, check mechanical parts of transaxle for cause of wrong gear range. See WRONG GEAR RATIO & CODE P029 chart.

WRONG GEAR RATIO & CODE P029

Gear Ratio	Possible Cause
.65-.71	Shift Solenoid "B" Checkball Stuck Or 2-3 Shift Valve Stuck (Applied)
.95-1.05	Shift Solenoid "B" Checkball Stuck, 2-3 Shift Valve Stuck (Applied) Or 2-3 Accumulator Faulty
1.54-1.71	Shift Solenoid "B" Leaking, 2-3 Shift Valve Stuck (Released) Or 2-3 Accumulator Leaking
2.87-3.11	Shift Solenoid "B" Leaking Or 2-3 Shift Valve Stuck (Released)

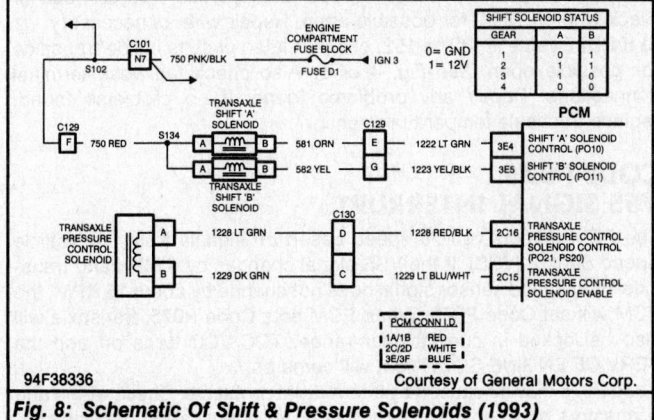

94F38336   Courtesy of General Motors Corp.

Fig. 8: Schematic Of Shift & Pressure Solenoids (1993)

CODE P039
TCC/VCC ENGAGEMENT

NOTE: DO NOT use this procedure if Codes P016, P024, P051 or P059 are current codes in PCM.

The converter clutch is controlled by holding or releasing hydraulic fluid. PCM monitors TCC/VCC operation by detecting transaxle slippage. When TCC/VCC is released, a slip speed of 50-300 RPM is normal under most driving conditions. When TCC/VCC is applied, slip speed is near zero (during vehicle cruise speed). The slip speed is determined by the PCM; based on transaxle input speed sensor and vehicle speed sensor inputs. If engine RPM is too high during TCC/VCC application, PCM sets Code P039.

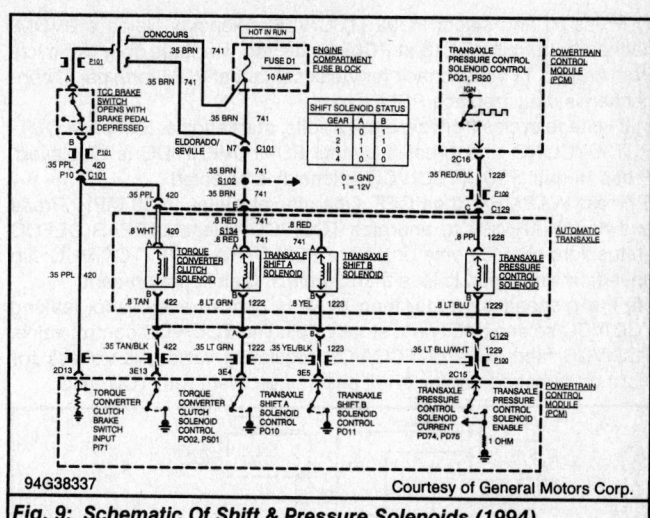

94G38337   Courtesy of General Motors Corp.

Fig. 9: Schematic Of Shift & Pressure Solenoids (1994)

1) Turn ignition key on. From PCM DATA, press LO to enter PCM INPUTS. Press HI and select PI71. Press brake pedal and release. If PI71 cycles HI to LO, go to step 3). If PI71 stays HI, check for short to voltage between brake switch and PCM or faulty brake switch. Repair circuit or replace brake switch as necessary.

2) If PI71 stays LO, check related circuits for cause of no voltage to or from brake switch (open wire, weak connection, bad brake switch or burned fuse). *See Fig. 10 or 11.* Repair or replace parts as necessary.

3) Check for an open in Purple wire between terminal "E" (1993) or "U" (1994) of transaxle connector and brake switch. Repair Purple wire as required. If Purple wire is okay, check resistance between terminals "E" and "F" (1993) or "U" and "T" (1994) of transaxle connector.

4) If resistance is greater than 40 ohms or less than 10 ohms, check internal transaxle wiring for open or short, or replace TCC/VCC solenoid. If resistance is 10-40 ohms, check for short to ground in terminals "E" and "T" (1993) or "U" and "T" (1994) of transaxle connector.

5) Repair any wire found shorted to ground. If wires are not shorted to ground, turn ignition key off. Disconnect Blue PCM connector. Check for open (measure resistance) in Tan/Black wire between transaxle connector and PCM connector. *See Fig. 10 or 11.*

6) If resistance is greater than 10 ohms, repair open in wire. If resistance is less than 10 ohms, reconnect Blue PCM connector and transaxle connector. Turn ignition key on. Enter self-diagnostics and press HI to display PCM DATA. Press LO until PCM OUTPUT CYCLING is displayed.

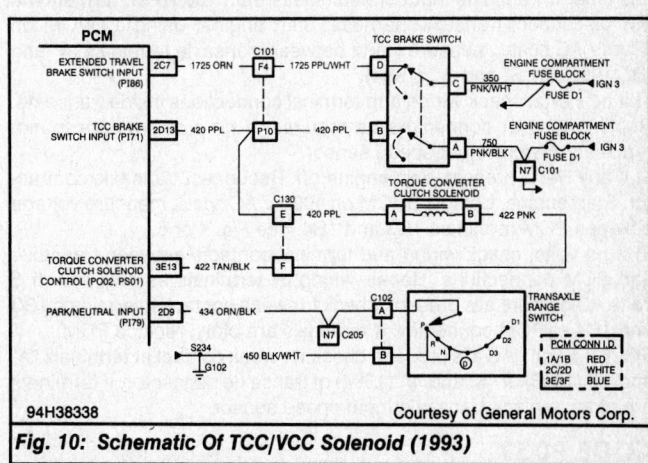

94H38338   Courtesy of General Motors Corp.

Fig. 10: Schematic Of TCC/VCC Solenoid (1993)

NOTE: Wiring schematic in Fig. 10 also applies to 1994 transaxle range switch circuits.

7) Press HI and select PO02 (TCC/VCC solenoid). Using a DVOM, backprobe terminal 3E13 at PCM connector. If voltage does not cycle from zero to 12 volts, check for weak contact at PCM terminal. If connection is okay, replace PCM.

8) If voltage cycles from zero to 12 volts, start engine. Exit PCM OUTPUT CYCLING and press LO until PCM OVERRIDE is displayed. Press HI until PS01 (TCC/VCC solenoid) is selected.

9) Press WARMER, then OFF. Operate vehicle at 40-60 MPH. Press and hold WARMER to energize TCC/VCC solenoid (REAR DEFOG status light should come on). Note PCM DATA PD73 (TCC/VCC slip speed). If slip speed is less than 10 MPH, fault is not present.

10) If slip speed is greater than 10 MPH, check transaxle for leaking TCC/VCC solenoid "O" ring, stuck or binding TCC/VCC control valve, TCC/VCC feed valve or TCC/VCC regulating valve. Also check for worn or damaged turbine shaft seals or problem with TCC/VCC.

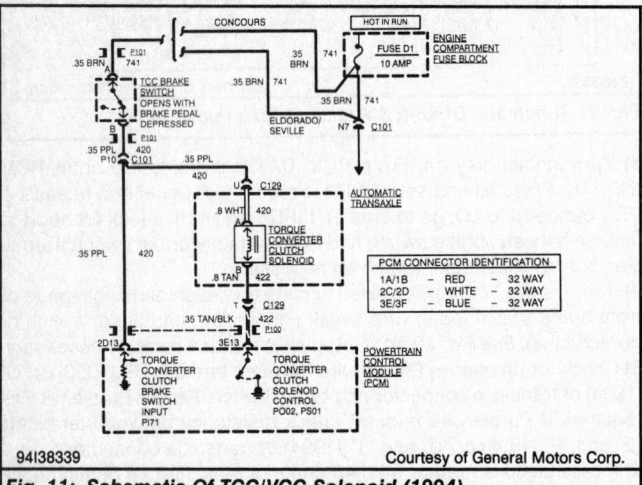

94I38339   Courtesy of General Motors Corp.

Fig. 11: Schematic Of TCC/VCC Solenoid (1994)

CODE P056
TRANSAXLE INPUT SPEED SENSOR

Transaxle input speed sensor detects turbine shaft speed. The PCM uses this data to monitor shift speed adapts and slip speed (TCC/VCC operation). If turbine speed is less than 50 RPM and vehicle speed is 10 MPH or more, PCM will set Code P056.

1) Start engine and place transaxle in Park or Neutral. Enter self-diagnostics. Wait until ECCP displays PCM DATA. Press HI on ECCP until PCM parameter PD72 (transaxle input speed) is displayed.

2) If transaxle input speed is 100 RPM or more, fault is not present at this time. If transaxle input speed is less than 100 RPM, turn engine off. Disconnect transaxle harness. Start engine. Using a DVOM on 400mV AC scale, measure Hertz between transaxle terminals "A" and "B" (1993) or "S" and "V" (1994).

3) If no Hertz, check wiring and terminal connections inside transaxle. Repair wiring or connectors as required. If no problems are found, replace transaxle input speed sensor.

4) If any Hertz present, turn engine off. Reconnect transaxle connector. Start engine. Using a DVOM on 400mV AC scale, measure voltage between PCM terminals 1B3 and 1B4. See Fig. 4 or 5.

5) If no volts, check wiring and terminal contacts between transaxle and PCM connections. Repair wiring or terminals as required. If 5 volts AC or more are present, check for weak contact at terminals 1B3 and 1B4 of PCM connector. If terminals are okay, replace PCM.

6) If 1-4.5 volts AC are present, check for weak contact at terminals "A" and "B" (1993) or "S" and "V" (1994) of transaxle connector. If terminals are okay, replace transaxle input speed sensor.

CODE P057
SHORTED TEMPERATURE SENSOR

The transaxle temperature sensor is a thermistor. As the temperature increases, the resistance of thermistor (sensor) goes down. If transaxle temperature is high, a low voltage signal will be detected by PCM. If PCM detects a transaxle temperature over 298°F (148°C), Code P057 will be set.

1) Turn ignition on. Enter self-diagnostics. Wait until ECCP displays PCM DATA. Press HI on ECCP until PCM parameter PD77 (transaxle oil temperature) is displayed.

2) If PD77 value is -40 to 147, fault is not present at this time. If PD77 value is 148 to 152, disconnect transaxle harness. If PD77 value is -28 to 152, check Tan/White wire between transaxle harness connector and PCM connector for short to ground. See Fig. 4 or 5.

3) If wire is okay, check for weak contact at terminal 1B14 of PCM connector. If no problem is found, replace PCM.

4) If PD77 value is -40 to -29, check terminal "D" (1993) or "M" (1994) of transaxle harness connector for possible short to ground inside transaxle. Repair any problems found. If no problems found, replace transaxle temperature sensor.

CODE P059
OPEN TEMPERATURE SENSOR

The transaxle temperature sensor is a thermistor. As the temperature increases, the resistance of thermistor (sensor) goes down. If transaxle temperature is low, a high voltage signal will be detected by PCM. If PCM detects a transaxle temperature below -31°F (-35°C), Code P059 will be set.

1) Turn ignition on. Enter self-diagnostics. Wait until ECCP displays PCM DATA. Press HI on ECCP until PCM parameter PD77 (transaxle oil temperature) is displayed.

2) If PD77 value is -34 to 152, fault is not present at this time. If PD77 value is -40 to -35, disconnect transaxle harness. Using a jumper wire, connect transaxle harness terminal "D" (1993) or "M" (1994) to ground. If PD77 value is -34 to 152, go to step **4)**. If PD77 value is -40 to -35, use a jumper wire to connect PCM terminal 1B14 to ground.

3) If PD77 value is -40 to -35, check for weak contact at terminal 1B14 of PCM connector. If no problem is found, replace PCM. If PD77 value changed to -34 to 152, check Tan/White wire between PCM and transaxle harness connector for open wire. See Fig. 4 or 5. Repair wire as necessary.

4) If PD77 value from end of test step **2)** is -34 to 152, connect terminals "C" and "D" (1993) or "L" and "M" (1994) of transaxle harness connector together. If PD77 value is -40 to -35, check ground side of transaxle temperature sensor circuit (Black/Green wire on 1993 or Black wire on 1994) for possible open. Repair wire as necessary.

5) If PD77 value is -32 to 152, check related circuits inside transaxle for possible open. See Fig. 4 or 5. Also check for weak terminal connections. Repair any problems found. If no problems found, replace transaxle temperature sensor.

CODE P075
VSS SIGNAL INTERRUPT

The PCM detects vehicle speed based on signals from the Vehicle Speed Sensor (VSS). If the VSS signal changes by 4 MPH and transaxle input speed sensor signal does not change by about 15 RPM, the PCM will set Code P075. When PCM sets Code P075, transaxle will also be locked in current gear range, TCC/VCC turns off and the SERVICE ENGINE SOON light will come on.

Code P075 may be caused by intermittent problems. Check wiring and connectors between the VSS and PCM for opens, short or weak contact at harness connections. See Fig. 4 or 5. Also check for Electromagnetic Interference (EMI) from spark plug wires or high power transmitters (mobile phones).

CODE P076
PRESSURE CONTROL SOLENOID

The pressure control solenoid is used to modulate line pressure based on operating conditions. The PCM controls the pressure control solenoid by varying the duty cycle signal (pulse width modulated). Current draw is proportional to transaxle line pressure. The PCM monitors current draw on internal circuit to detect any problems with pressure control solenoid operation. If actual and commanded current varies by more than .16 amps for 1 second or pressure control solenoid is operated at 100 percent duty cycle for more than 3 minutes, PCM will set Code P076.

1) Disconnect White PCM connector. Measure resistance across terminals 2C15 and 2C16. If 3-8 ohms are present, go to step **3)**. If 3 ohms or less are present, check circuits between PCM and transaxle connector, and internal transaxle wiring and connectors for possible short. *See Fig. 8 or 9.* Repair circuits as necessary. If circuits are okay, replace pressure control solenoid.

2) If 8 or more ohms are present, check circuits between PCM and transaxle connector, and internal transaxle wiring and connectors for possible open wire. Repair circuits as necessary. If circuits are okay, replace pressure control solenoid.

3) If 3-8 ohms are present (from first step), measure resistance between PCM terminal 2C16 and ground. If more than 100 ohms are present, reconnect PCM connector. Clear code and start engine. If Code P076 does not reset, fault is not present. If Code P076 does reset, check PCM connector for weak terminals. If terminals are okay, replace PCM.

4) If 100 ohms or less are present, check circuits between PCM and transaxle connector, and internal transaxle wiring and connectors for possible short to ground. *See Fig. 8 or 9.* Repair circuits as necessary. If circuits are okay, replace pressure control solenoid.

CODE P086
UNDEFINED GEAR RATIO

The PCM determines transaxle gear ratio based on transaxle input speed sensor and VSS input data. If a gear ratio that is not possible for the transaxle operating conditions is detected, the PCM will set Code P086.

1) Turn ignition on. Enter self-diagnostics. If Codes P028, P029, P076, P089 or P094 are present, diagnosis them first. If only Code P086 is present, turn ignition off.

2) Install Oil Pressure Adapter (J-21867-93) and pressure gauge to transaxle. Start engine and enter self-diagnostics. After PCM DATA is displayed, press LO until PCM OVERRIDE appears. Press HI until PS20 (transaxle pressure control) is displayed.

3) Press WARMER to command line pressure to increase. If oil pressure does increase, go to next step. If oil pressure does not increase, check fluid level, scavenge pump and pickup tube for damage, clogged oil screens, gasket leakage at primary or secondary oil pumps or stuck pressure regulator valve.

4) If oil pressure stayed high, check for stuck pressure regulator valve or faulty pressure control solenoid. If oil pressure did not increase, exit PCM OVERRIDE. Press LO until PCM SNAPSHOT is displayed.

PRESSURE SWITCH VS. GEAR RATIO

PD71 Pressure Sw.	PD76 Gear Ratio	Possible Cause
100	2.22 Or More	Slipping Reverse Clutch Or Lo/Rev Band
100	2.02 Or Less	Pressure Switch Assembly Or Valve Body Problem
001	.65 Or Less	VSS Or Transaxle Input Speed Sensor Problem
011	.71-.95	Slipping 4th Band, 3rd Clutch Or Forward Clutch, Or Failed Forward Sprag
001/011/111	1.05-1.54	Slipping 3rd Clutch, Forward Clutch, Or Failed Forward Sprag
001/011/111	1.71-2.87	Slipping 2nd Or Forward Clutch, Or Failed 2nd Or Forward Sprag
110	3.11 Or More	Slipping Forward Clutch, Failed Forward Sprag Or Lo Roller Clutch
110	2.87 Or Less	Valve Body Or Clutch Not Releasing
111	1.54 Or Less	Valve Body Or Clutch Not Releasing
011	.95 Or Less	Valve Body Or Clutch Not Releasing

5) Press HI to select P086. Record values shown for PD71 (transaxle pressure switch assembly) and PD76 (gear ratio). Depending on values recorded by PCM, determine possible cause of wrong gear ratio. See PRESSURE SWITCH VS. GEAR RATIO chart.

CODE P088
TCC/VCC NOT DISENGAGING

The converter clutch is controlled by holding or releasing hydraulic fluid. PCM monitors TCC/VCC operation by detecting transaxle slippage. When TCC/VCC is released, a slip speed of 50-300 RPM is normal under most driving conditions. When TCC/VCC is applied, slip speed is near zero (during vehicle cruise speed). The slip speed is determined by the PCM; based on transaxle input speed sensor and vehicle speed sensor inputs. If no slippage is detected under certain conditions, PCM sets Code P088.

1) Turn ignition key on and enter self-diagnostics. From PCM DATA, press LO to enter PCM INPUTS. Press HI and select PI71. Press brake pedal and release. If PI71 cycles HI to LO, go to step **3)**. If PI71 stays HI, check for short to voltage between brake switch and PCM or faulty brake switch. *See Fig. 10 or 11.* Repair circuit or replace brake switch as necessary.

2) If PI71 stays LO, check related circuits for cause of no voltage to or from brake switch (open wire, weak connection, bad brake switch or burned fuse). Repair or replace parts as necessary.

3) Backprobe Purple wire at transaxle connector and measure voltage. *See Fig. 10 or 11.* If voltage is less than 10 volts, check transaxle harness for possible short to ground or faulty TCC/VCC solenoid. Repair circuits as necessary.

4) If more than 10 volts are present at Purple wire, backprobe Tan/Black wire at transaxle connector and measure voltage. Enter self-diagnostics and press HI to display PCM DATA. Press LO until PCM OUTPUT CYCLING is displayed.

5) Press HI until PO02 (TCC/VCC solenoid) is selected. If voltage cycles from zero to 12 volts, check TCC/VCC solenoid for damage or a stuck (applied) TCC/VCC control valve.

6) If voltage stays at zero, turn ignition key off. Disconnect Blue PCM connector. Turn ignition key on. Measure voltage at terminal 3E13 of PCM connector. *See Fig. 10 or 11.* If 10 or more volts are present, check for weak contact at PCM terminal. If connection is okay, replace PCM. If less than 10 volts are present, check for open circuit in Tan/Black wire between PCM and transaxle connectors.

CODE P089
LONG SHIFT & MAXIMUM ADAPT

The PCM monitors and varies shift time. This is called adaptive modifier. If a shift takes more than .55 seconds, PCM increases line pressure to shorten shift time. If the shift time cannot be shorten to less than .55 seconds, PCM will set Code P089.

1) Turn ignition on. Enter self-diagnostics. If Codes P028, P029, P076, P086 or P094 are present, diagnosis them first. If only Code P089 is present, turn ignition off.

2) Install Oil Pressure Adapter (J-21867-93) and pressure gauge to transaxle. Start engine and enter self-diagnostics. After PCM DATA is displayed, press LO until PCM OVERRIDE appears. Press HI until PS20 (transaxle pressure control) is displayed.

3) Press WARMER to command line pressure to increase. If oil pressure does increase, go to next step. If oil pressure does not increase, check fluid level, scavenge pump and pickup tube for damage, clogged oil screens, gasket leakage at primary or secondary oil pumps or stuck pressure regulator valve.

4) If oil pressure stayed high, check for stuck pressure regulator valve or faulty pressure control solenoid. If oil pressure did not increase, exit PCM OVERRIDE. Press LO until PCM SNAPSHOT is displayed.

5) Press HI to select P089. Display will show values for PD01, PD02, PD12 and PD82. Drive vehicle and record values shown for PD82 (transaxle shift time). Depending on shift time and when Code P089 reset, determine possible cause of long shift time. See LONG SHIFT TROUBLE SHOOTING chart. If Code P089 did not reset, fault is not present at this time.

LONG SHIFT TROUBLE SHOOTING

Shift	Possible Cause
1-2 Shift	Leaking 2nd Accumulator Seals, Burned Clutches, Damaged Piston, Broken Springs, Leaking Seals, Damaged Driven Support, Missing Support Seals, Damaged 3rd Clutch Piston Or Rear Stator Support, Damaged 2nd Or Forward Sprag
2-3 Shift	Leaking 3rd Accumulator Seals, Damaged Coast Clutch Piston Or Seals, Damaged 3rd Clutch Plates, Cut 3rd Clutch Seals Or Missing Check Ball
3-4 Shift	Leaking 4th Accumulator Seals, Slipping 4th Band, Damaged 4th Servo Assembly Or Reversed Sprag

CODE P091
TRANSAXLE RANGE SWITCH

Normally the transaxle range switch is closed in Park and Neutral only. When the transaxle is placed in any other gear, the transaxle range switch is open. If PCM detects an input from transaxle range switch that conflicts with transaxle or vehicle operating conditions, PCM sets Code P091.

1) Place gear shift lever in Park or Neutral. Turn ignition key on and enter self-diagnostics. If AUTO fan status light is on, go to step **4)**. If AUTO status fan light is off, jumper transaxle range switch terminals "A" and "B" together.

2) If status light is on, adjust or replace transaxle range switch. If status light stays off, jumper transaxle range switch terminal "A" to ground. If status light is on, repair open Black/White ground wire.

3) If status light stays off, jumper Orange/Black wire at terminal (backprobe wire) 2D9 at White PCM connector to ground. See Fig. 10. If status light is on, repair open Orange/Black wire between PCM and transaxle range switch connector. If status light stays off, check for weak contact at PCM terminal 2D9. If terminal is okay, replace PCM.

4) If AUTO fan status light was on in step **1)**, move gear shift lever to any drive position. If status light is off, fault is not present at this time. If status light stays on, disconnect transaxle range switch.

5) If status light is off, adjust or replace transaxle range switch. If status light stays on, turn ignition off. Check Orange/Black wire between PCM and transaxle range switch for short to ground. See Fig. 10. Repair wire as necessary. If wire is okay, check PCM connector. If connector is okay, replace PCM.

CODE P094
SHIFT SOLENOID "A"

1) Turn ignition key on. Enter self-diagnostics. If Code P117 is also present, diagnose Code P117 first. If only Code P094 is present, move gear selector to "D".

2) Press LO 3 times on ECCP until PCM OVERRIDES appears. Press HI until PS11 (transaxle shift) is selected. Using COOLER and WARMER buttons, shift transaxle through all gear ranges while watching fault status "B" of PD17.

3) If fault status is high (1) in 1st and 2nd gear, go to next step. If fault status is high (1) in 1st and 4th gear, go to step **8)**. If fault status is low (0) in all gears, go to step **12)**.

4) Using a DVOM, backprobe terminal 3E4 at PCM connector. Cycle shift solenoid "A". If voltage changes from zero to 12 volts, check for weak terminal at PCM connector. If terminal is okay, replace PCM.

5) If less than 10 volts are present, disconnect 14-pin connector at upper transaxle oil pan. Check voltage at Pink/Black (1993) or Brown (1994) wire on engine side of harness. See Fig. 8 or 9. If voltage is less than 10 volts, check for open circuit from harness to fuse block.

6) If voltage is 10 volts or more, remove Blue PCM connector. Check for open or short in Light Green wire between PCM and transaxle connector. Repair wire as necessary.

7) If Light Green wire is okay, measure resistance between terminals "F" and "E" (1993) or "E" and "A" (1994) at transaxle harness connector. If resistance is 100 ohms or more, check transaxle harness and shift solenoid "A" for an open. If resistance is less than 100 ohms, check Light Green wire between transaxle and PCM for an intermittent short.

8) Using a DVOM, backprobe terminal 3E4 at PCM connector. Press LO on ECCP until PCM OUTPUTS appear. Press HI until PO11 (shift solenoid "A") is selected. Shift solenoid "A" will start cycling on and off.

9) If voltage cycles between zero and 12 volts, check for a weak connection at PCM terminal 3E4. If connection is okay, replace PCM. If voltage is greater than 10 volts, disconnect transaxle connector and check voltage at terminal "E" (1993) or "A" (1994) of transaxle connector.

10) If voltage is at least 10 volts, check Light Green wire between transaxle connector and shift solenoid "A" for short to voltage. See Fig. 8 or 9. If voltage is less than 10 volts, disconnect PCM connector. Check voltage at terminal "E" (1993) or "B" (1994) of engine side of transaxle harness.

11) If 10 or more volts are present, repair short to voltage in harness. If less than 10 volts are present, check for weak connection at PCM terminal 3E4. If connection is okay, replace PCM.

12) Press LO on ECCP until PCM SNAPSHOT appears. Press HI 2 times and enter snapshot data P094. Note PD76 (transaxle gear ratio). Depending on recorded ratio, check mechanical parts of transaxle for cause of wrong gear range. See WRONG GEAR RATIO & CODE P094 chart.

WRONG GEAR RATIO & CODE P094

Gear Ratio	Possible Cause
.65-.71	Shift Solenoid "A" Checkball Stuck Or 2-3 Shift Valve Stuck (Applied)
.95-1.05	Shift Solenoid "A" Checkball Stuck, 2-3 Shift Valve Stuck (Applied) Or 2-3 Accumulator Faulty
1.54-1.71	Shift Solenoid "A" Leaking, 2-3 Shift Valve Stuck (Released) Or 2-3 Accumulator Leaking
2.87-3.11	Shift Solenoid "A" Leaking Or 2-3 Shift Valve Stuck (Released)

CODE 096
TORQUE CONVERTER OVERSTRESS

During braking, the throttle will usually be closed. If the brakes are applied and the throttle held open (as during a stall speed test), this may cause damage to the torque converter. If this condition is present for more than 12 seconds with transaxle in Drive or Reverse, the PCM turns SERVICE ENGINE SOON light on and records Code 096.

Check operation of the brake switch. Check TP operation. See CODE 021 and 022. Check for VSS and MPH display on instrument panel. See CODE 024. Check transaxle range switch. See CODE 091.

CODE P117
SHIFT SOLENOID "A" OR "B" CIRCUIT FAULTS

When PCM commands a shift to take place, the pressure switch assembly detects hydraulic pressure changes. PCM monitors this change and compares intended shift with actual shift. If any shift does not match with intended shift, PCM records this. If an incorrect shift occurs 10 times in a row, the PCM sets Code P117.

1) Enter self-diagnostics. If Code P029 is also set, go to step **6)**. If only Code P117 is set, go to step **10)**. If Code P094 is also set, press HI on ECCP until PCM DATA parameter PD76 is displayed.

2) If PD76 is .95-1.71, check Light Green wire between transaxle connector and PCM for short to voltage. Repair circuits as necessary. If circuits are okay, check for a shorted shift solenoid "A". Replace as necessary.

3) If PD76 is .65-.71 or 2.87-3.11, disconnect transaxle harness connector. Turn ignition on. Check voltage at terminal "F" (1993) or "E" (1994) on harness side of connector. See Fig. 8 or 9.

4) If less than 10 volts exist, repair circuit back to fuse block or replace fuse. If at least 10 volts exist, measure resistance across transaxle harness connector "E" and "F" (1993) or "A" and "E" (1994).

5) If resistance is greater than 100 ohms, check for open circuit inside transaxle or open shift solenoid "A". If resistance is less than 100 ohms, check for short circuit inside transaxle (including internal circuit for shift solenoid "B").

6) If Code P029 is also set, press HI on ECCP until PCM DATA parameter PD76 is displayed. If PD76 is 1.54-3.11, check Yellow/Black wire between transaxle connector and PCM for short to voltage. *See Fig. 8 or 9.* Repair circuits as necessary. If circuits are okay, check for a shorted shift solenoid "B". Replace as necessary.

7) If PD76 is .65-1.05, disconnect transaxle harness connector. Turn ignition on. Check voltage at terminal "F" (1993) or "E" (1994) on harness side of connector.

8) If less than 10 volts exist, repair circuit back to fuse block or replace fuse. If at least 10 volts exist, measure resistance across transaxle harness connector "G" and "F" (1993) or "B" and "E" (1994).

9) If resistance is greater than 100 ohms, check for open circuit inside transaxle or open shift solenoid "B". If resistance is less than 100 ohms, check for short circuit inside transaxle (including internal circuit for shift solenoid "A").

10) With engine running, enter self-diagnostics. Wait until ECCP displays PCM DATA. Press LO until PCM OVERRIDE appears. Press HI on ECCP until PCM parameter PD71 is displayed. Move gear selector through each gear position and record fault status "B" of parameter PD17.

11) If status light stays low in all gears, go to step **15)**. If status light stays high when 1st and 2nd gear are commanded, repair open or shorted circuits related to shift solenoid "B". *See Fig. 8 or 9.* If circuits are okay, replace shift solenoid "B".

12) If status light stays high when 1st and 4th gear are commanded, repair short to voltage circuit between shift solenoid "B" and PCM. If circuit is okay, replace shift solenoid "A".

13) If status light stays high when 2nd and 3rd gear are commanded, repair open or shorted circuits related to shift solenoid "A". If circuits are okay, replace shift solenoid "A".

14) If status light stays high when 3rd and 4th gear are commanded, repair short to voltage circuit between shift solenoid "B". If circuits are okay, replace shift solenoid "B".

15) If status light stays low in all gears from step **11)**, exit from PCM OVERRIDE. Press LO on ECCP until PCM OUTPUT appears. Press HI on ECCP until PCM parameter PO10 is displayed. Note DEFOG light on ECCP.

16) If DEFOG light stays on, check for weak contact at PCM connector. If connector is okay, replace PCM. If DEFOG light cycles on and off, go to step **20)**. If DEFOG light is off, check for voltage by backprobing Blue PCM connector terminal 3E4. *See Fig. 8 or 9.*

17) If voltage cycles zero to 12 volts, check for weak contact at PCM terminal 3E4. If terminal is okay, replace PCM. If voltage is less than 10 volts, disconnect transaxle harness connector. Measure voltage at terminal "F" (1993) or "E" (1994). *See Fig. 8 or 9.*

18) If voltage is less than 10 volts, repair circuit back to fuse block or replace fuse. If voltage is greater than 10 volts, measure resistance across transaxle harness connector "G" and "F" (1993) or "B" and "E" (1994).

19) If resistance is greater than 100 ohms, check for open circuit inside transaxle or open shift solenoid "A". If resistance is less than 100 ohms, check for short circuit inside transaxle or problem in Light Green wire between transaxle harness connector and PCM.

20) If DEFOG light cycles on and off, from step **16)**, press HI on ECCP to display PO11. Note ECON light on ECCP. If ECON cycles on and off, fault is not present at this time. If ECON light stays on, check for weak contact at PCM terminal E35. If terminal is okay, replace PCM.

21) If ECON light is off, check for voltage by backprobing Blue PCM connector terminal 3E5. *See Fig. 8 or 9.* If voltage cycles zero to 12 volts, check for weak contact at PCM terminal 3E5. If terminal is okay, replace PCM.

22) If voltage is less than 10 volts, disconnect transaxle harness connector. Measure resistance between terminals "F" and "G" (1993) or "B" and "E" (1994).

23) If more than 100 ohms exist, check for open circuit inside transaxle or open shift solenoid "B". If less than 100 ohms are present, check for short circuit inside transaxle or problem in Yellow/Black wire between transaxle harness connector and PCM.

COMPONENT TESTS

INPUT SENSORS

Pressure Switch Assembly – Component testing for pressure switch assembly is not available. See CODE P028.

Transaxle Input Speed Sensor – Measure resistance across appropriate terminals of transaxle harness connector C130 (1993) or C129 (1994). *See Fig. 4 or 5.* Resistance of each circuit and sensor at room temperature should be 1260-1540 ohms. If resistance is not 1260-1540 ohms, replace transaxle input speed sensor.

Transaxle Temperature Sensor – Measure voltage across appropriate terminals of transaxle harness connector C130 (1993) or C129 (1994). *See Fig. 4 or 5.* Voltage of sensor should match known values. See TRANSAXLE TEMPERATURE SENSOR VALUES chart. If voltages do not match chart, replace transaxle temperature sensor.

TRANSAXLE TEMPERATURE SENSOR VALUES

Temperature	Volts
-18°F (-28°C)	4.6
24°F (-4°C)	3.8
66°F (19°C)	2.5
104°F (40°C) [1]	1.3
131°F (55°C) [1]	3.3
176°F (80°C)	2.2
239°F (115°C)	1.3

[1] – Internal shunt changes resistance between 104-131°F (40-55°C).

VSS – Measure resistance across terminals of VSS connector. *See Fig. 4 or 5.* Resistance of sensor at room temperature should be 1260-1540 ohms. If resistance is not 1260-1540 ohms, replace VSS.

OUTPUT DEVICES

Shift Solenoids "A" & "B" – Measure resistance across appropriate terminals of transaxle harness connector. *See Fig. 8 or 9.* Resistance of each circuit and solenoid at room temperature should be 20-30 ohms. If resistance is not 20-30 ohms, check resistance at each solenoid. If resistance at solenoid is correct, repair circuit as necessary. If not, replace shift solenoid.

TCC/VCC Solenoid – Measure resistance across appropriate terminals of transaxle harness connector. *See Fig. 10 or 11.* Resistance of circuit and solenoid at room temperature should be 10-15 ohms. If resistance at solenoid is correct, repair circuit as necessary. If resistance is not 10-15 ohms, check resistance at solenoid. If not, replace TCC/VCC solenoid.

Transaxle Pressure Control Solenoid – Measure resistance across appropriate terminals of transaxle harness connector. *See Fig. 8 or 9.* Resistance of circuit and solenoid at room temperature should be 3.5-4.6 ohms. If resistance is not 3.5-4.6 ohms, check resistance at solenoid. If resistance at solenoid is correct, repair circuit as necessary. If not, replace transaxle pressure control solenoid.

WIRING DIAGRAMS

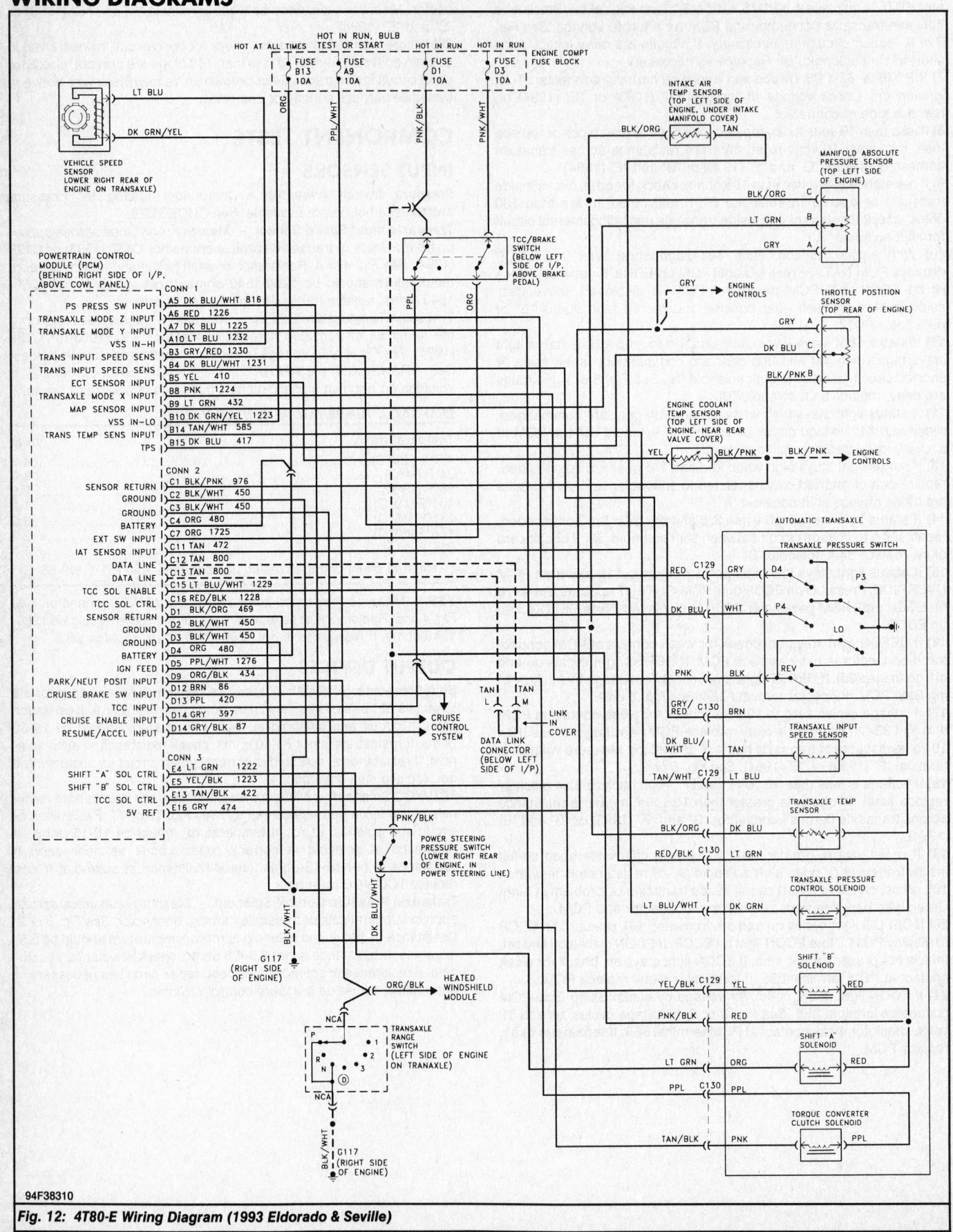

Fig. 12: 4T80-E Wiring Diagram (1993 Eldorado & Seville)

94F38310

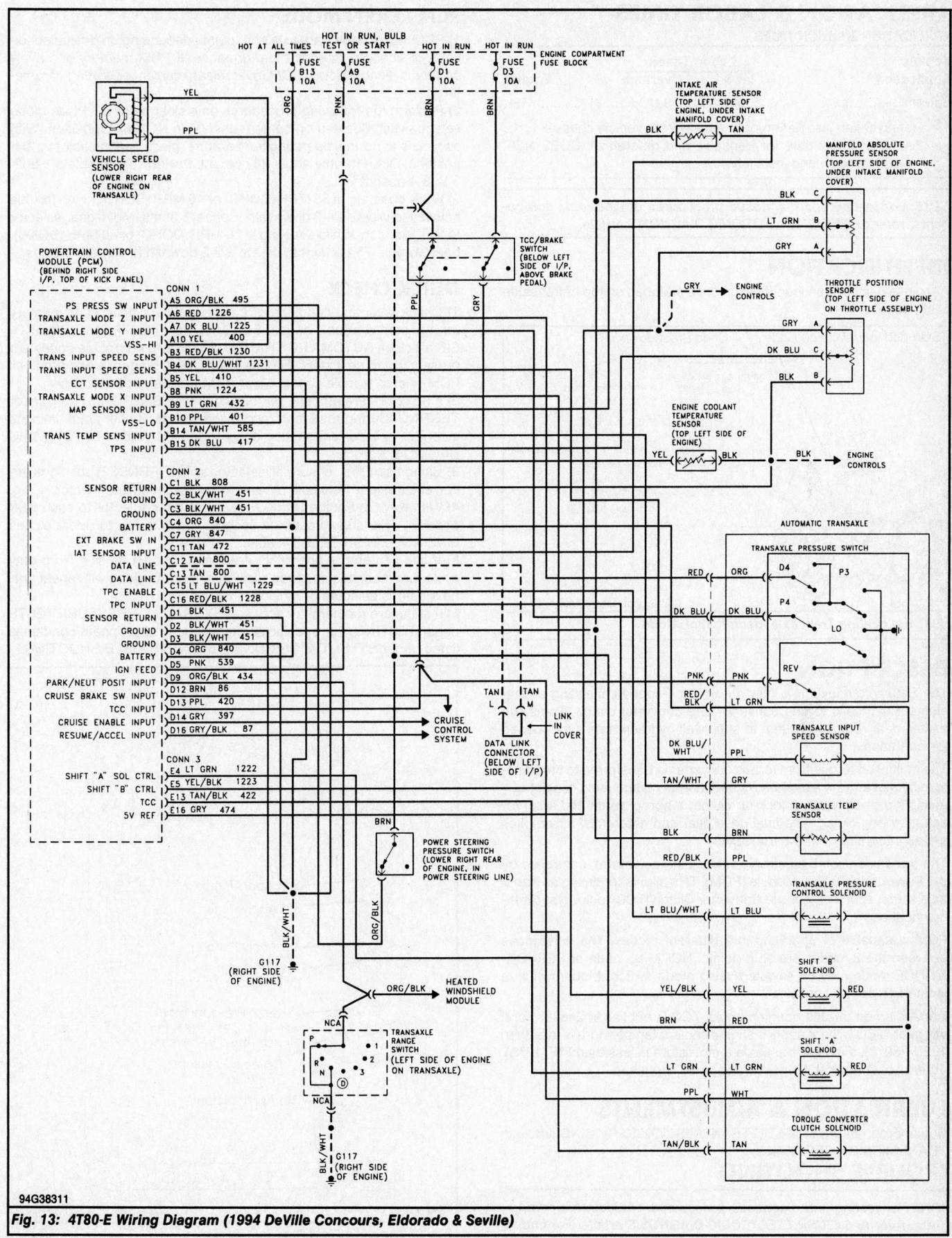

Fig. 13: 4T80-E Wiring Diagram (1994 DeVille Concours, Eldorado & Seville)

94G38311

APPLICATION & LABOR TIMES

APPLICATION & LABOR TIMES

Vehicle Application	Labor Times		Engine
	¹ R & I	² Overhaul	
Saturn	7.4	9.0	1.9L

¹ – Removal and installation of transaxle from vehicle chassis.

² – Bench overhaul time for transaxle and differential. DOES NOT include removal and installation.

NOTE: For testing and diagnostic procedures of electronic components, refer to SATURN ELECTRONIC DIAGNOSIS article.

IDENTIFICATION

All transaxles have an identification code stamped on top of transaxle case. See Fig. 1.

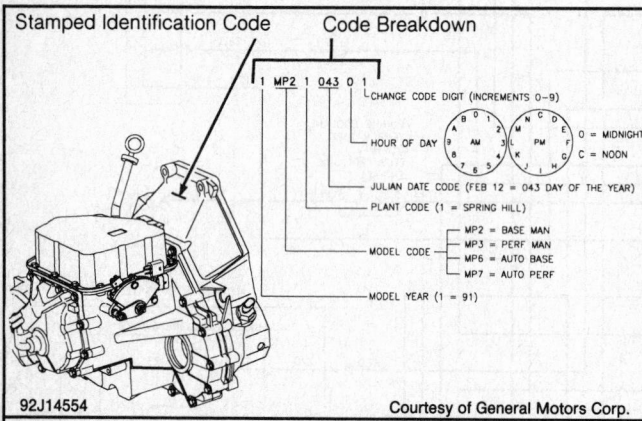

Fig. 1: Locating Transaxle Identification Code

DESCRIPTION

The Saturn transaxle is a fully automatic 4-speed consisting of a 4-element hydraulic torque converter and converter clutch. Transaxle uses a gear rotor-type pump to supply all hydraulic pressure needed for operation.

The multiplied torque from torque converter is transferred to the transaxle by a gear train assembly. Other internal components consist of 4 multiple disc clutches, a lock-up clutch, a sprag clutch and a servo-actuated dog clutch. The final drive gear and differential assemblies are an integral part of the transaxle.

The transaxle uses 5 electronic valves (line actuators), controlled by the Powertrain Control Module (PCM). This allows for timing all transaxle shifts, shift feel, Torque Converter Clutch (TCC) lock-up and self-diagnostics.

PCM is capable of operating in 2 different modes. The differences between the 2 modes are shift points. NORMAL mode or PERFORMANCE mode may be selected using mode switch. Mode switch is located on center console.

Depending on throttle opening angle, TCC is applied in 2nd, 3rd and 4th gear. TCC will not apply if engine coolant temperature is less than 122°F (50°C), if air and transaxle temperature is less than 7°F (10°C), during coast downshifts or if brake pedal is pushed.

LUBRICATION & ADJUSTMENTS

See appropriate AUTOMATIC TRANSMISSION SERVICING article in TRANSMISSION SERVICING.

TROUBLE SHOOTING

NOTE: For testing and diagnostic procedures of electronic components, refer to SATURN ELECTRONIC DIAGNOSIS article. For clutch and actuator applications, see CLUTCH & ACTUATOR APPLICATION table.

PCM LEARN MODE

1) PCM will change transaxle shift points depending on driving conditions or changes in engine performance. If PCM memory or vehicle battery is disconnected, PCM must relearn current operating parameters.

2) Perform the following procedures on a clear highway. Place mode select switch (located on center console) in NORMAL position. With transaxle at normal operating temperature, place gear selector in "D4" position. Open throttle about 30 percent. Perform 10 complete 1-2, 2-3 to 3-4 upshifts.

3) While coasting at 35 MPH (DOHC) or 40 MPH (SOHC), open throttle halfway to create a 4-3 downshift. Repeat 5 times. Move gear selector to "D3" position. While coasting at 20 MPH (DOHC) or 30 MPH (SOHC), open throttle 75 percent to create a 3-2 downshift. Repeat 5 times.

QUICK CHECK

1) Check level and condition of transaxle fluid. Check PCM memory for any stored trouble codes. See SATURN ELECTRONIC DIAGNOSIS article in AUTOMATIC TRANSMISSIONS. If no trouble codes are present, go to next step. If codes are present, diagnose and repair all PCM-related trouble codes. Clear PCM trouble code memory.

2) If no codes are present, perform road test. See ROAD TEST under TESTING. During road test, record shift points. If shift point timing is incorrect or incorrect shifting occurs, go to SATURN ELECTRONIC DIAGNOSIS article.

3) Using scan tool, ensure all selector switch (PRND32) positions are correct. Jumper terminals "A" and "B" of diagnostic connector.

4) With Key On Engine Off (KOEO), move gear selector to each gear position. This should cause a specific line actuator to operate. See LINE ACTUATOR SELECT table.

5) If line actuator is operating, it will audibly operate at a fixed duty cycle for 6 seconds and then click on and off. Clicking will repeat until next gear is selected or ignition is turned off.

6) If shifts are too harsh or soft, see HYDRAULIC PRESSURE TESTS under TESTING. For specific complaints, see appropriate conditions listed under SYMPTOM DIAGNOSIS under TROUBLE SHOOTING.

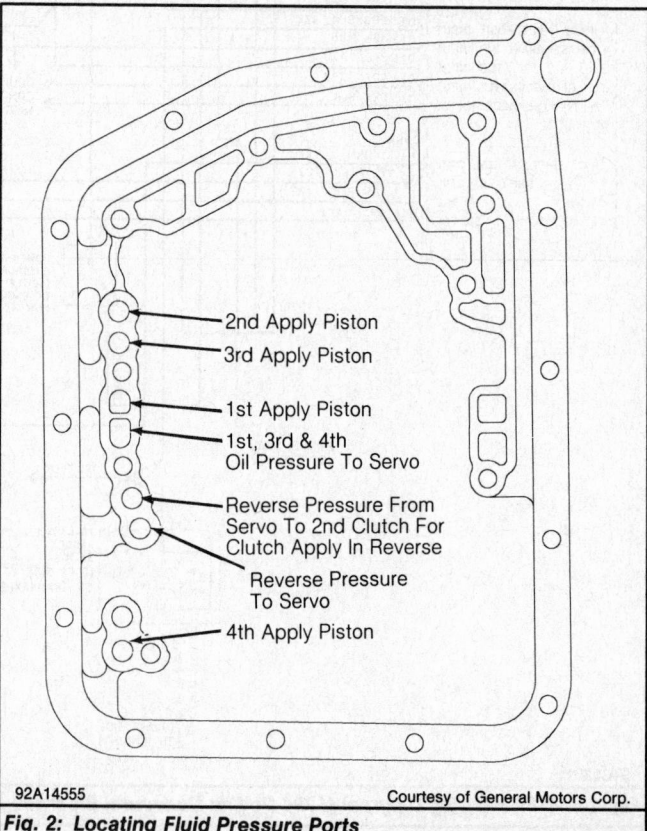

Fig. 2: Locating Fluid Pressure Ports

LINE ACTUATOR SELECT

Selected Gear	Actuator
"D2"	2nd
"D3"	3rd
"D4"	4th
"R"	TCC
"N" Or "P"	Line

SYMPTOM DIAGNOSIS

NOTE: Saturn transaxle uses a Powertrain Control Module (PCM) computer. This computer controls TCC, line pressure and clutch or servo shifting solenoids. Because most transaxle operations are PCM-controlled, only a few hydraulic or mechanical problems can cause problems with transaxle operations. For more symptom diagnosis, see SATURN ELECTRONIC DIAGNOSIS article in AUTOMATIC TRANSMISSIONS.

Fluid Out Of Vent Or Foaming – Transaxle overfilled. Fluid contaminated with antifreeze. Engine overheating. Problem with clutch assemblies.

No Reverse – 1) Low fluid level. Low fluid pressure. High clutch dragging. Check transaxle for 2nd gear operation. If no 2nd gear, refer to DTC 22. See SATURN ELECTRONIC DIAGNOSIS article. If 2nd gear is possible, ensure flat surface of manual valve is facing up.

2) If manual valve is okay, remove valve body. Block off 2nd clutch feed hole. Using a rag, cover 1st apply piston port to prevent fluid spray. See Fig. 2. Apply air pressure to reverse pressure to servo apply port.

3) If servo does not move, check servo piston for stuck condition and damaged seal. If servo motor moves, repair faulty dog clutch or oil tube hub seal rings.

Harsh Upshifts – 1) If a new transaxle has been installed, perform test drive to reset PCM adaptive memory. If upshifts are still harsh, quick check line actuator. If line actuators are stuck, replace stuck actuators.

2) If line actuators are okay, check hydraulic pressure in each gear. If line pressure is out of range in any gear, check for a sticking line pressure regulator valve, faulty line actuator in affected range and damaged clutch plates in affected range.

Vehicle Moves In Park – Manual control cable damaged or disconnected. Broken final drive parking pawl spring, parking pawl or parking pawl gear in final drive internal gear assembly. Park actuator spring damaged.

Vehicle Stuck In Park – Problem with shift interlock system. Broken parking pawl assembly. Park actuator lever rod damaged.

NOTE: Following problems may be related to PCM controls or inputs. If a mechanical or hydraulic problem is not found, go to SATURN ELECTRONIC DIAGNOSIS article in AUTOMATIC TRANSMISSIONS.

High Line Pressure – Check for a stuck line actuator or faulty pressure regulator valve.

Low Line Pressure – Check for a stuck line actuator, faulty pressure regulator valve or plugged oil filter. If transaxle has reverse only, check 1st clutch for leak and damage. If transaxle will not move in reverse or forward, check input and output shafts for damage.

No 1st Gear – Faulty 1st clutch assembly. Damaged servo piston, problem with piston seals or rear cover seal leaks. Damaged 1st sprag clutch, broken output shaft or blocked fluid passages. See Fig. 2.

2nd Gear Stuck ON – Check for a stuck line actuator. Faulty 2nd clutch assembly. Damaged servo piston or problem in piston seals or valve body. Damaged clutch return springs or blocked fluid passages. See Fig. 2.

No 2nd Gear – Check for a stuck line actuator. Faulty 2nd clutch assembly. Damaged servo piston or problem in piston seals or valve body. Damaged dog clutch or blocked fluid passages. See Fig. 2.

No 3rd Gear – Check for a stuck line actuator. Faulty 3rd clutch assembly. Damaged servo piston or problem in piston seals or valve body. Blocked fluid passages. See Fig. 2.

No 4th Gear – Check for a stuck line actuator. Faulty 4th clutch assembly. Damaged servo piston or problem in piston seals or valve body. Blocked fluid passages. See Fig. 2.

No Drive In Any Gear – 1) Low fluid level. Low fluid pressure. Manual linkage misadjusted or disconnected. Drive axles disengaged. Damaged oil pump drive shaft or complete pump assembly. Torque converter stator roller clutch damaged.

2) Clutch assembly plates burned or clutch plates missing. Clutch piston seals cut or damaged or blocked fluid passages. See Fig. 2. Problem with valve body.

NOTE: Saturn transaxles use a Powertrain Control Module (PCM) computer. This computer controls TCC application.

No TCC Apply – Check for a stuck line actuator. Leaking or missing torque converter, input shaft or stator shaft seals. Damaged torque converter.

TCC Stuck On (Engine Stops) – Check for a stuck line actuator. Leaking or missing input shaft seals. Damaged torque converter.

CLUTCH & ACTUATOR APPLICATION

Selector Lever Position	Elements In Use
Drive	
1st Gear	[1] TCC Actuator, 1st Clutch, [2] Dog Clutch & 1st Sprag
2nd Gear	[1] 2nd Actuator, 1st Clutch, 2nd/Reverse Clutch & [2] Dog Clutch
3rd Gear	[1] 3rd Actuator, 1st Clutch, 3rd Clutch & [2] Dog Clutch
4th Gear	[1] 4th Actuator, 1st Clutch, 4th Clutch & [2] Dog Clutch
"R" (Reverse)	[1] 2nd/Reverse & [1] TCC Actuator, 2nd/Reverse Clutch & [3] Dog Clutch
"N" Or "P" (Neutral Or Park)	[1] Line Actuator, All Clutches Released Or Ineffective

[1] – Listed actuators off, all others are on.
[2] – Applied to 2nd driven gear.
[3] – Applied to reverse driven gear.

ELECTRONIC SELF-DIAGNOSTICS & ELECTRONIC TESTING

NOTE: See SATURN ELECTRONIC DIAGNOSIS article.

TESTING
ROAD TEST

NOTE: Before road testing vehicle, engine and transaxle must be at operating temperature. Torque converter clutch will not engage if transaxle temperature has not reached operating temperature.

Gear Selector Position "D4" (Overdrive) – 1) With gear selector in "D4" (overdrive) position, accelerate vehicle using steadily increasing throttle pressure. Note shift speed engagement points in 2nd, 3rd and overdrive gear. Use upshift charts as a reference for proper shift speeds. See Figs. 3 and 5. Also note when Torque Converter Clutch (TCC) applies while in 2nd, 3rd and overdrive gear.

2) At cruising speeds, quickly push accelerator pedal to half open position (part throttle detent downshift). TCC should release and transaxle should immediately downshift. Note downshift speeds into 1st, 2nd and 3rd gear. Use downshift charts as a reference for proper shift speeds. See Figs. 4 and 6.

3) Move gear selector to "D4" (overdrive) position and accelerate to 40-45 MPH. Release accelerator pedal while moving gear selector to "3" (3rd gear) position. TCC should release, transaxle should downshift immediately and engine braking should slow vehicle.

4) Repeat step 3) at slower initial speeds for "2" (2nd gear) position. Note downshift speeds into lower gear. Use downshift charts as a reference for proper shift speeds. See Figs. 4 and 6.

5) With gear selector in "D4" (overdrive) position, accelerate vehicle to overdrive gear with TCC applied. Release accelerator pedal and lightly apply brakes. TCC should release. Note speeds at which vehicle downshifts. See Figs. 4 and 6.

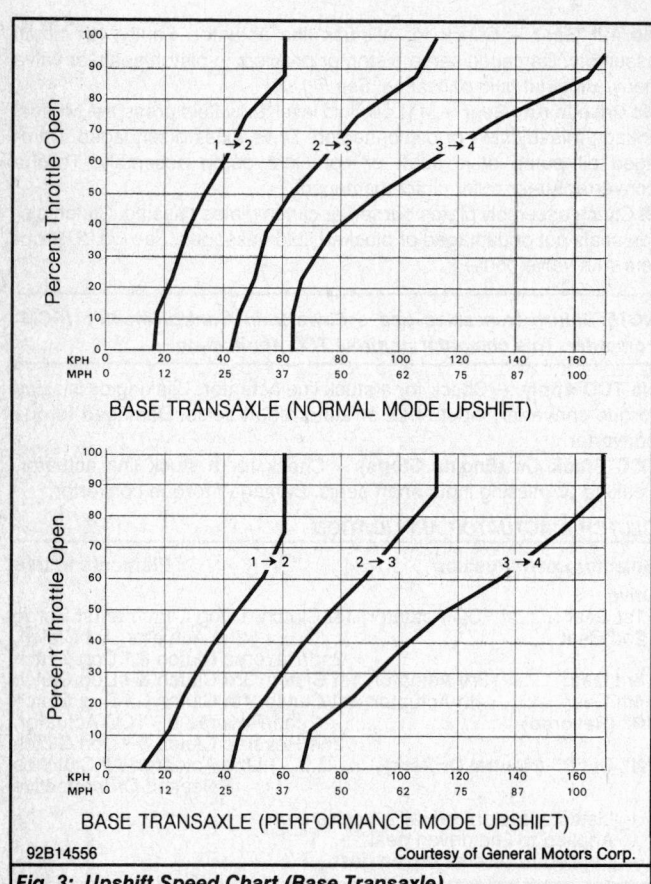

BASE TRANSAXLE (NORMAL MODE UPSHIFT)

BASE TRANSAXLE (PERFORMANCE MODE UPSHIFT)

92B14556   Courtesy of General Motors Corp.

Fig. 3: Upshift Speed Chart (Base Transaxle)

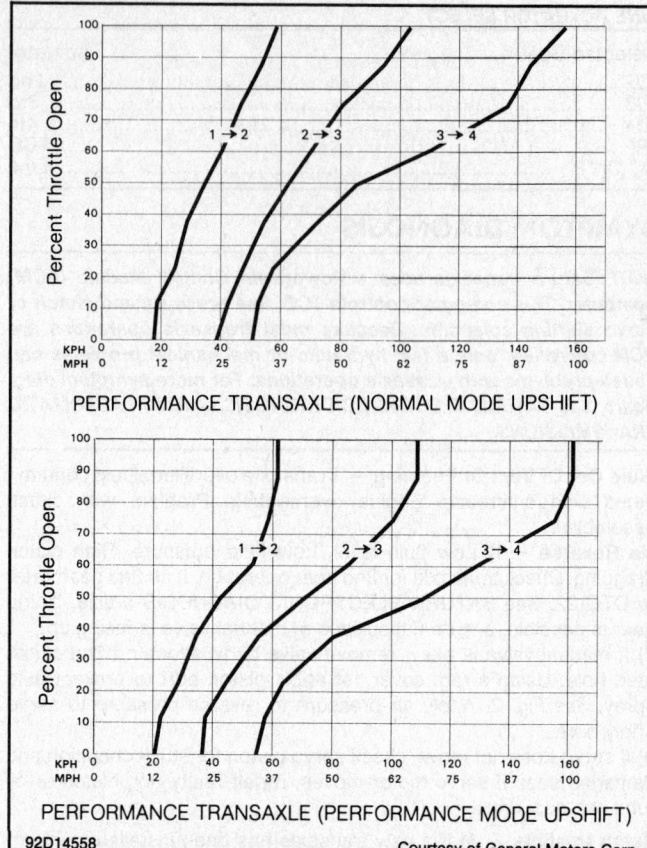

PERFORMANCE TRANSAXLE (NORMAL MODE UPSHIFT)

PERFORMANCE TRANSAXLE (PERFORMANCE MODE UPSHIFT)

92D14558   Courtesy of General Motors Corp.

Fig. 5: Upshift Speed Chart (Performance Transaxle)

BASE TRANSAXLE (NORMAL MODE DOWNSHIFT)

BASE TRANSAXLE (PERFORMANCE MODE DOWNSHIFT)

92C14557   Courtesy of General Motors Corp.

Fig. 4: Downshift Speed Chart (Base Transaxle)

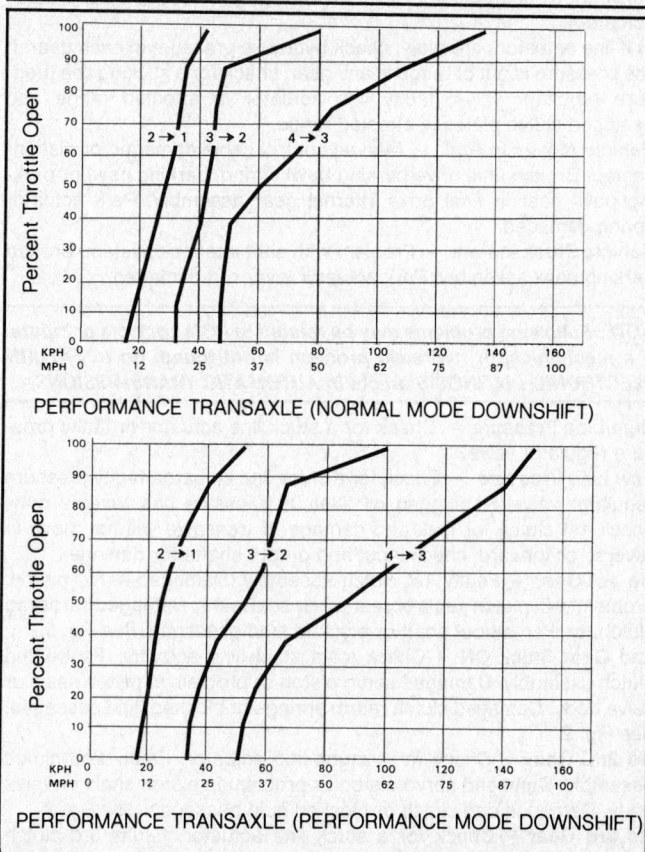

PERFORMANCE TRANSAXLE (NORMAL MODE DOWNSHIFT)

PERFORMANCE TRANSAXLE (PERFORMANCE MODE DOWNSHIFT)

92E14559   Courtesy of General Motors Corp.

Fig. 6: Downshift Speed Chart (Performance Transaxle)

STALL SPEED TEST

NOTE: Stall speed test information and specifications are not available.

HYDRAULIC PRESSURE TESTS

With Saturn Portable Diagnostic Tool (PDT) – 1) Remove transaxle temperature sensor, and install pressure gauge. *See Fig. 7.* Connect PDT to vehicle.

2) With transaxle at operating temperature, turn engine off and ignition to ON position. Go to MENU SELECTION on PDT. Select SPECIAL TEST. On next screen, select LINE PRESSURE.

3) PDT will request that engine be started. Select RUN on PDT; test will begin. PDT will operate engine at 1500 RPM and command line pressure from 58-220 psi (400-1518 kPa) in 15 psi (100 kPa) increments.

4) Ensure actual pressure is within range of that commanded by PDT. See LINE PRESSURE SPECIFICATIONS table. If line pressure is too high or too low, see SYMPTOM DIAGNOSIS under TROUBLE SHOOTING. Using Sealant (21485278) on transaxle temperature sensor threads, install sensor to transaxle case. Clear PCM memory to remove any stored codes.

LINE PRESSURE SPECIFICATIONS

PDT Commanded psi (kPa)	Actual Pressure psi (kPa)
58 (400)	58-72 (400-500)
72 (500)	61-80 (425-550)
87 (600)	72-98 (500-675)
102 (702)	87-116 (600-800)
117 (804)	101-134 (700-925)
131 (906)	116-154 (800-1050)
146 (1008)	130-170 (900-1175)
161 (1110)	145-188 (1000-1300)
175 (1212)	159-203 (1100-1400)
191 (1314)	174-218 (1200-1500)
205 (1416)	188-240 (1300-1650)
220 (1518)	218-268 (1500-1850)

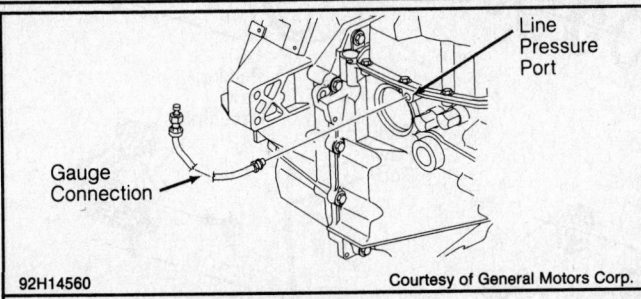

Fig. 7: Locating Line Pressure Port

Without Saturn Portable Diagnostic Tool (PDT) – 1) Remove temperature sensor. Connect an oil pressure gauge to line pressure test port (temperature sensor connection). *See Fig. 7.* With engine idling in Park and transaxle at operating temperature, line pressure should be 58-72 psi (400-500 kPa).

2) Remove line actuator fuse (TRS LP). With engine idling in Park, line pressure should be 218-245 psi (1500-1690 kPa). If line pressure is too high or too low, see SYMPTOM DIAGNOSIS under TROUBLE SHOOTING. Using Sealant (21485278) on transaxle temperature sensor threads, install sensor to transaxle case. Clear PCM memory to remove any stored codes.

TORQUE CONVERTER

NOTE: For diagnosing torque converter clutch, refer to SATURN ELECTRONIC DIAGNOSIS article.

STALL SPEED TEST

NOTE: Stall speed test information and specifications are not available.

INSPECTION

Torque converter must be replaced for any of following problems.
- Damage To Pump Assembly
- Metal Particles Present In Fluid
- Leaks In Hub Weld Area
- Crankshaft Pilot Broken Or Damaged
- Hub Scored Or Damaged
- Stator Failure
- Torque Converter Imbalance
- Engine Coolant Contamination
- Excessive End Play

END PLAY CHECK

Install End Play Tool (SA9163T) to converter splines. Install dial indicator. *See Fig. 8.* Lift tool handle and measure end play. If end play is greater than .026" (.60 mm), replace torque converter.

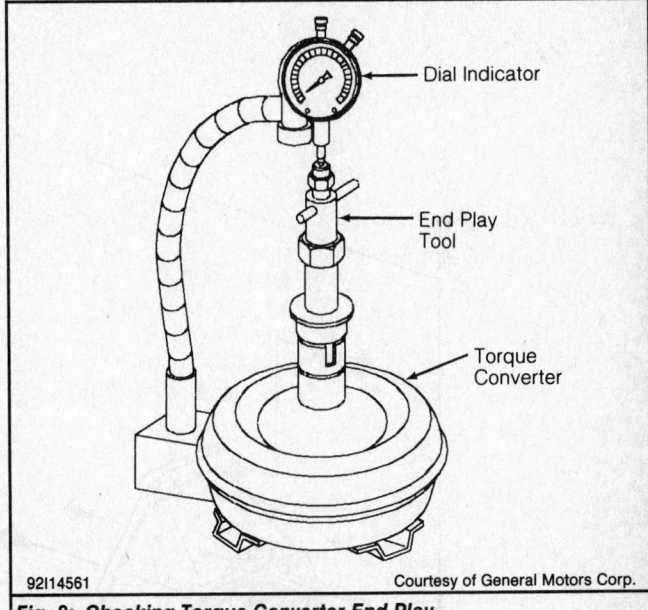

Fig. 8: Checking Torque Converter End Play

ON-VEHICLE SERVICE

Following components can be serviced without removing transaxle from vehicle.
- Converter-To-Flexplate Bolts
- Cooler Lines
- Drive Axle Seals
- End Cover
- Dipstick Tube
- Neutral Safety Switch
- Shift Control Cable
- Shift Solenoids
- Temperature Sensor
- Transaxle Pan
- Transaxle Filter
- Turbine Speed Sensor
- Valve Body
- Vehicle Speed Sensor
- Wiring Harness

VALVE BODY

See TRANSAXLE DISASSEMBLY.

DRIVE AXLE SHAFTS

See appropriate AXLE SHAFTS article in AXLE SHAFTS & TRANSFER CASES.

AUTOMATIC TRANSMISSIONS
Saturn (Cont.)

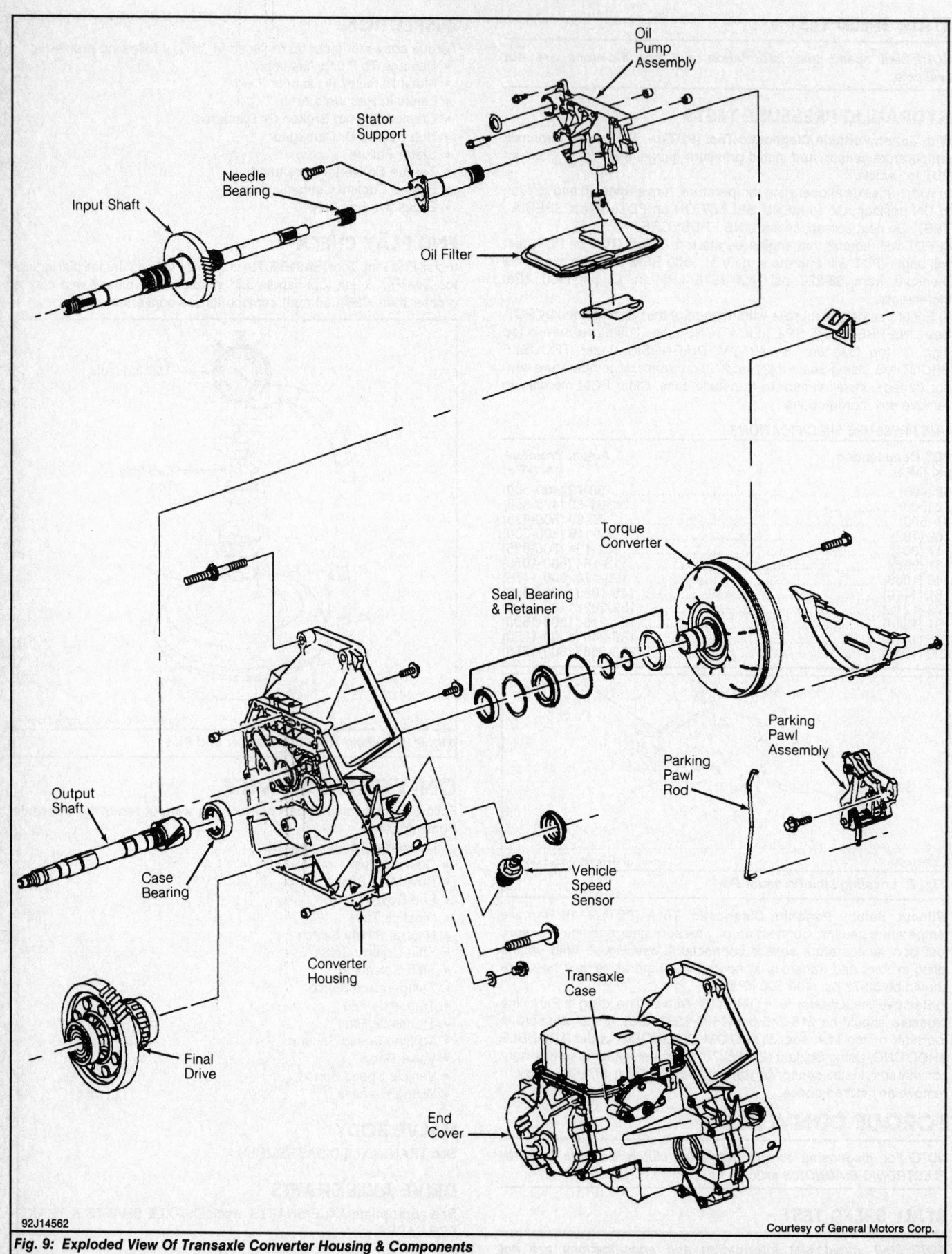

Oil Pump Assembly

Stator Support

Needle Bearing

Input Shaft

Oil Filter

Torque Converter

Seal, Bearing & Retainer

Parking Pawl Assembly

Parking Pawl Rod

Output Shaft

Case Bearing

Converter Housing

Vehicle Speed Sensor

Final Drive

Transaxle Case

End Cover

92J14562

Fig. 9: Exploded View Of Transaxle Converter Housing & Components

OIL COOLER FLUSHING

1) If Line Flusher (J-35944) is available, fill it with solution, and install oil cooler and line flusher to top transaxle cooler line on transaxle. Follow manufacturer instructions to flush oil cooler and cooler lines.

2) If line flusher is not available, flush cooler and cooler lines with a mixture of clean solvent and water. Flush cooler in both directions until all old fluid and debris is removed. Use compressed air to dry cooler and lines. If necessary, replace plugged or damaged cooler and/or lines.

REMOVAL & INSTALLATION

See appropriate AUTOMATIC TRANSMISSION REMOVAL article in TRANSMISSION SERVICING.

TRANSAXLE DISASSEMBLY

1) Thoroughly clean transaxle exterior. Drain fluid, and remove torque converter. Remove 2 bolts behind torque converter. Remove pressure filter, temperature sensor, turbine speed sensor, vehicle speed sensor and dipstick tube. *See Fig. 9.*

2) Remove valve body pan and valve body assembly. *See Fig. 10.* Remove 2nd/reverse fork bolt. Remove manual detent lever assembly. *See Fig. 11.* Remove end cover. *See Fig. 12.*

3) Using Input Shaft Holding Tool (SA9119T), hold input shaft and remove input shaft lock nut. *See Fig. 13.* Remove tool. Lock output shaft using parking pawl. Remove output shaft lock nut.

4) Remove 1st clutch housing and 1st drive gear from input shaft. *See Fig. 14.* Remove 1st driven gear and sprag clutch from output shaft. *See Fig. 15.* Remove 2nd/reverse servo assembly. Remove 2nd/reverse clutch fork. *See Fig. 16.*

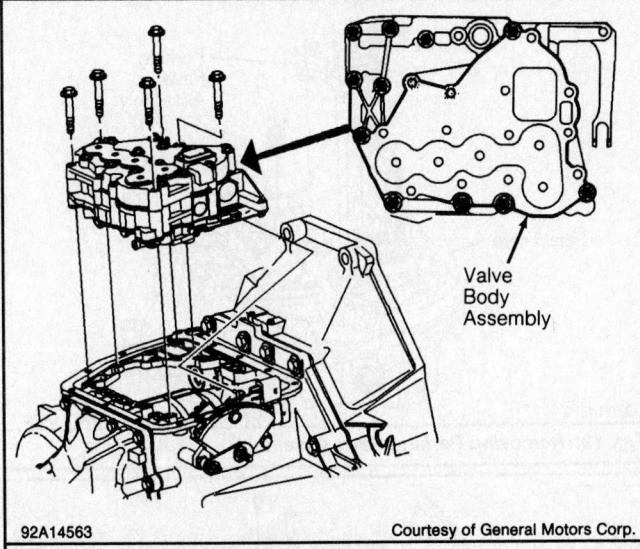

92A14563   Courtesy of General Motors Corp.

Fig. 10: Removing Valve Body Assembly

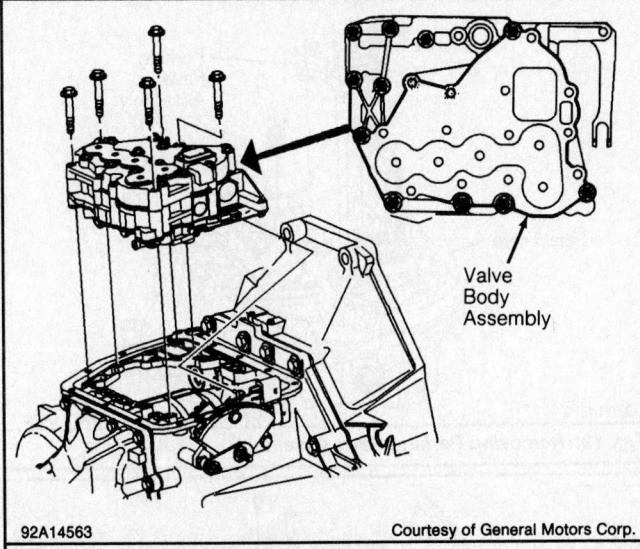

92B14564   Courtesy of General Motors Corp.

Fig. 11: Removing Manual Detent Lever & Fork Bolt

5) Remove converter housing bolts. If necessary, pry converter housing from case. *See Fig. 17.* Rotate, and at same time, pull input shaft, output shaft and final drive assembly from case. *See Fig. 18.*

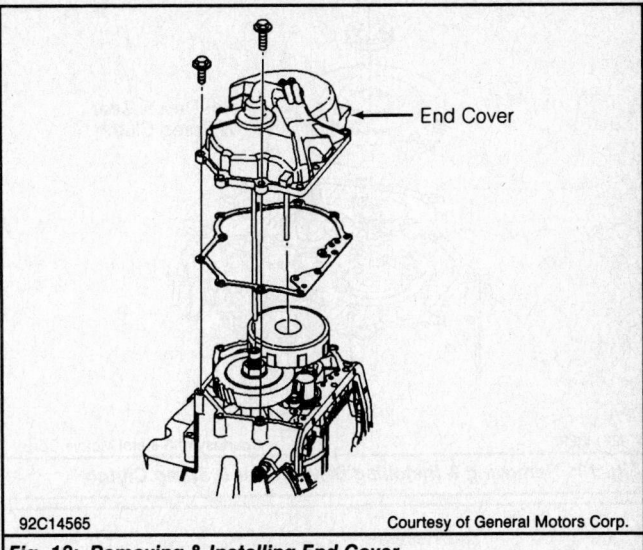

92C14565   Courtesy of General Motors Corp.

Fig. 12: Removing & Installing End Cover

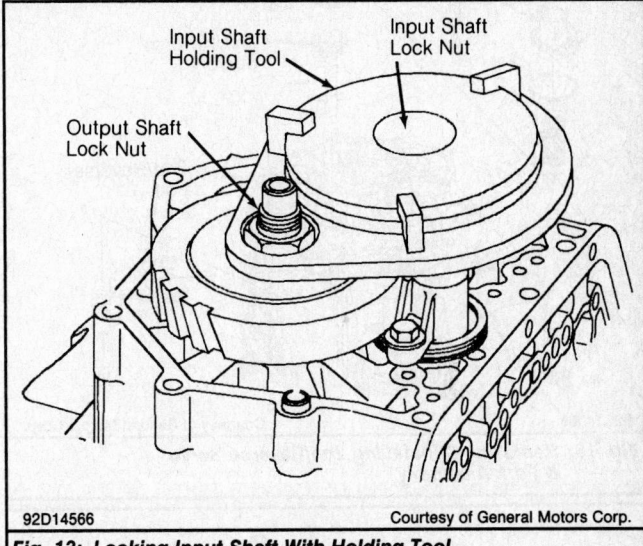

92D14566   Courtesy of General Motors Corp.

Fig. 13: Locking Input Shaft With Holding Tool

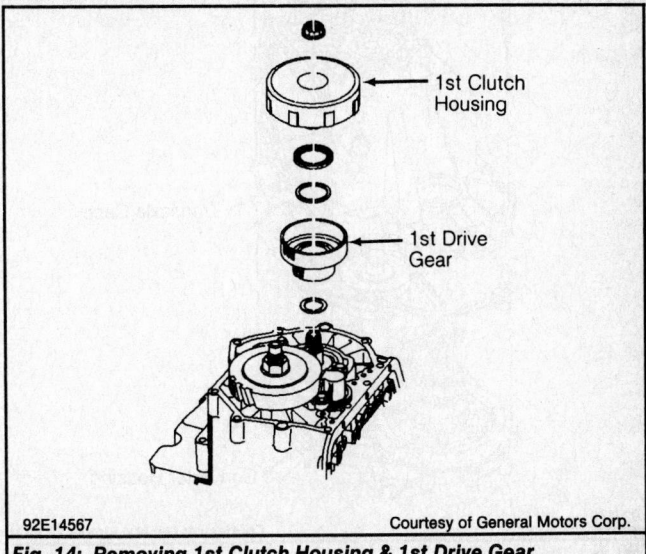

92E14567   Courtesy of General Motors Corp.

Fig. 14: Removing 1st Clutch Housing & 1st Drive Gear

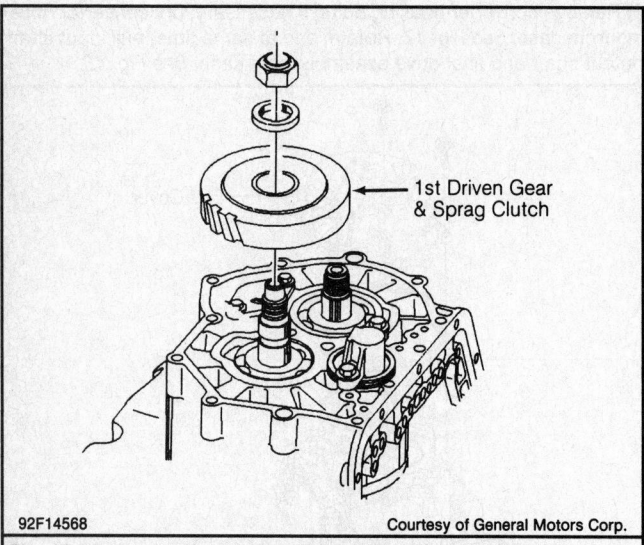

92F14568   Courtesy of General Motors Corp.

Fig. 15: Removing & Installing Driven Gear & Sprag Clutch

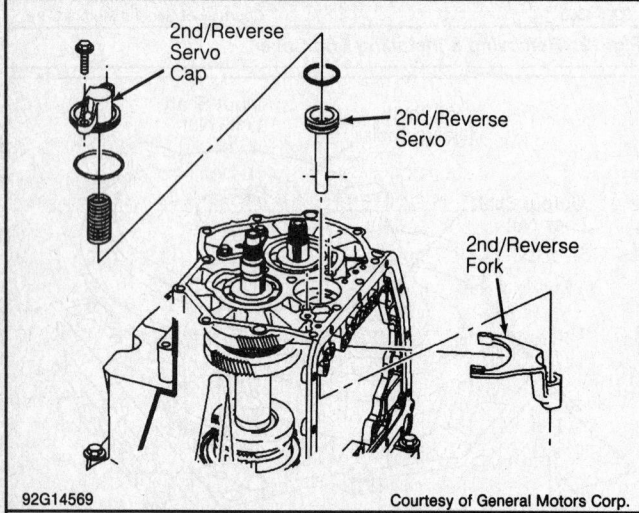

92G14569   Courtesy of General Motors Corp.

Fig. 16: Removing & Installing 2nd/Reverse Servo & Fork Assembly

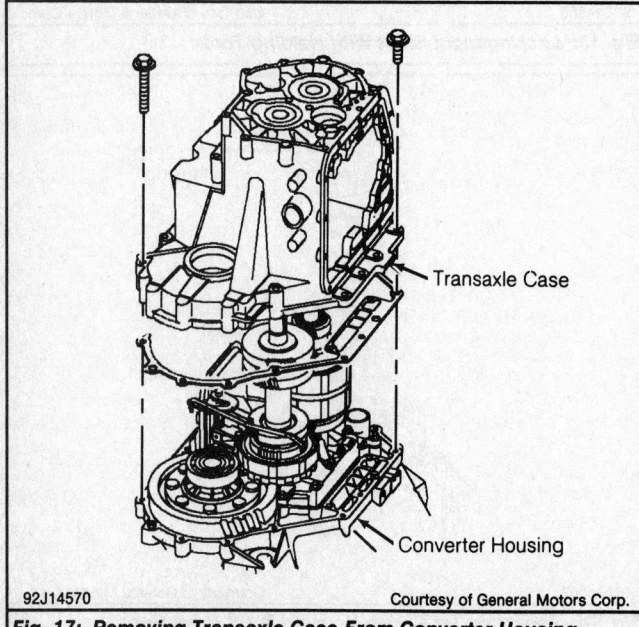

92J14570   Courtesy of General Motors Corp.

Fig. 17: Removing Transaxle Case From Converter Housing

6) Remove parking pawl assembly and oil pump assembly from case. *See Figs. 9, 19 and 20.* Remove case bearings. Remove reverse idler gear assembly. *See Fig 21.* Check lube relief valve. If valve is not damaged, DO NOT remove. If necessary, use Remover (SA9103E) to remove lube relief valve. *See Fig. 22.*

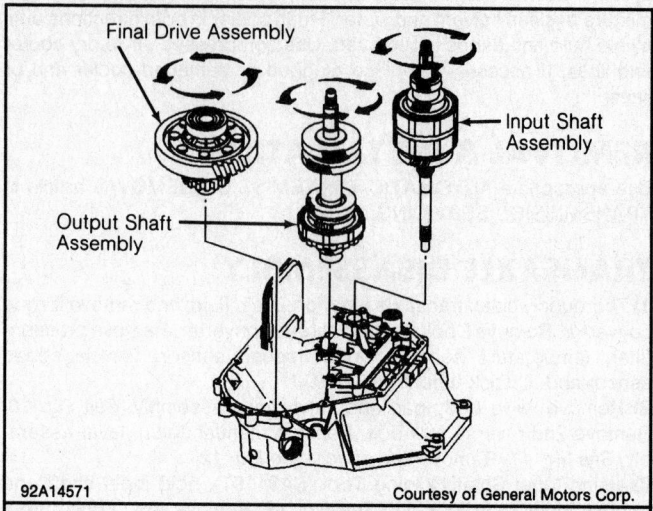

92A14571   Courtesy of General Motors Corp.

Fig. 18: Removing Input & Output Shafts & Final Drive Assembly

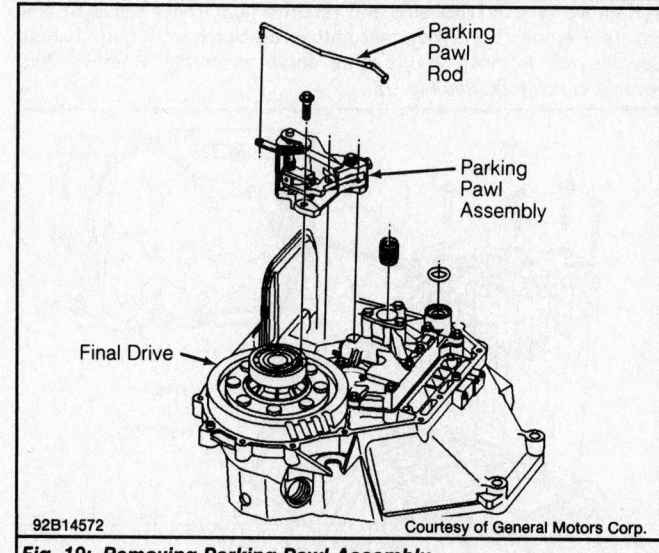

92B14572   Courtesy of General Motors Corp.

Fig. 19: Removing Parking Pawl Assembly

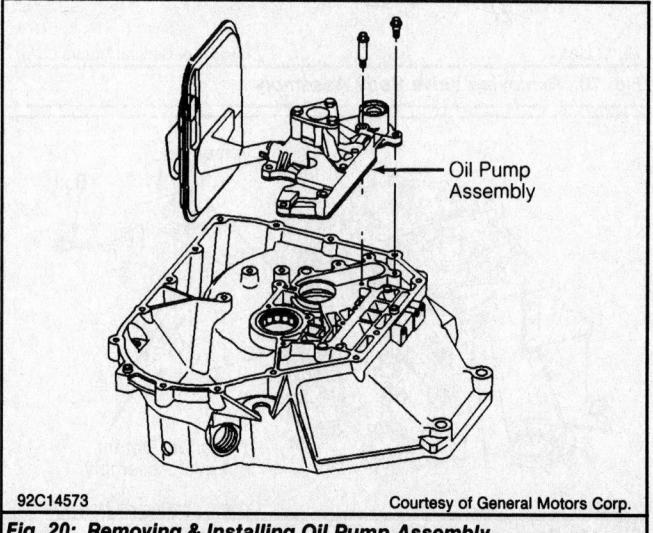

92C14573   Courtesy of General Motors Corp.

Fig. 20: Removing & Installing Oil Pump Assembly

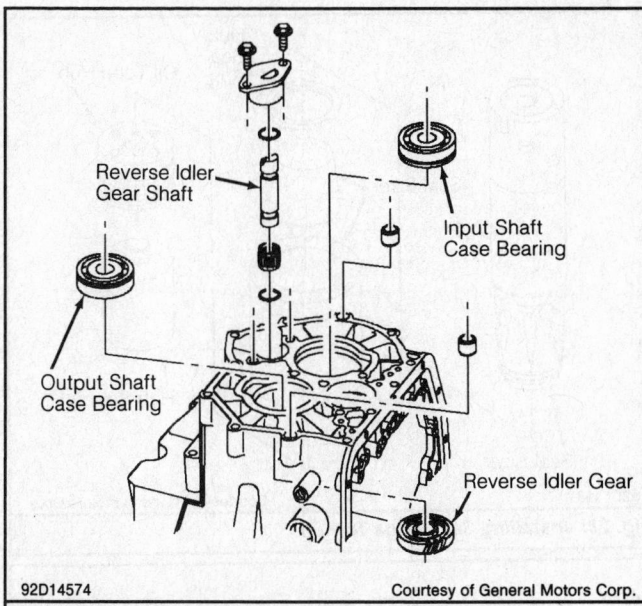

Fig. 21: Exploded View Of Input/Output Shaft Bearings & Idler Gear Assembly

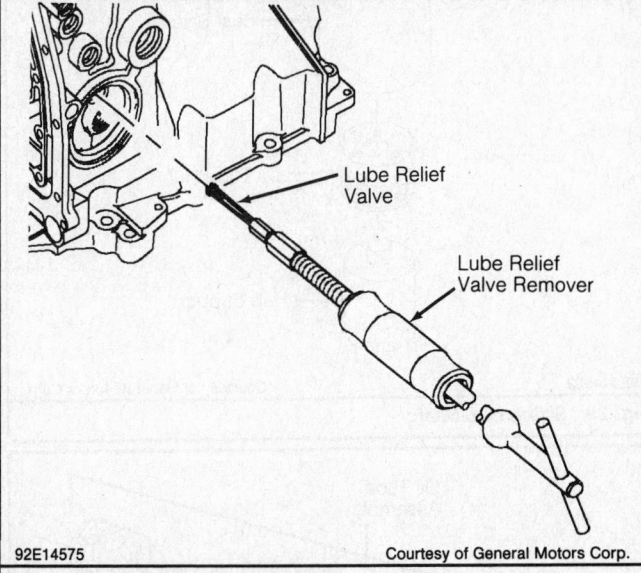

Fig. 22: Removing Lube Relief Valve

COMPONENT DISASSEMBLY & REASSEMBLY

NOTE: Exploded views of internal components, thrust washer and bearing locations can be found in Figs. 9, 21, 36 and 50.

TRANSAXLE CASE

Cleaning & Inspection – Clean transaxle case thoroughly, and air dry. Inspect transaxle case for damage to bearing seats, snap ring grooves and interconnected or damaged fluid passages and servo bores. *See Figs. 2 and 9.* Inspect case for stripped threads in bolt holes and casting porosity. Repair or replace case if necessary.

NOTE: DO NOT remove bearings and seals unless replacement is necessary.

Bearing & Seals – **1)** Using Bearing Puller (SA91113T) and Slide Hammer (SA9173G), remove converter retaining ring, seal and bearing. *See Figs. 23 and 24.* Remove axle shaft seals.

2) Replace all worn or damaged parts. Press converter bearing into case. Ensure bearing is flush or below converter housing surface. Install new output shaft and converter seals.

3) Install output and input shaft bearing snap rings into transaxle case. Ensure output shaft bearing snap ring groove faces up and input shaft bearing snap ring groove faces down. Install input and output shaft bearings to transaxle case. *See Fig. 21.*

Parking Pawl Assembly – Disassembly and reassembly information is not available.

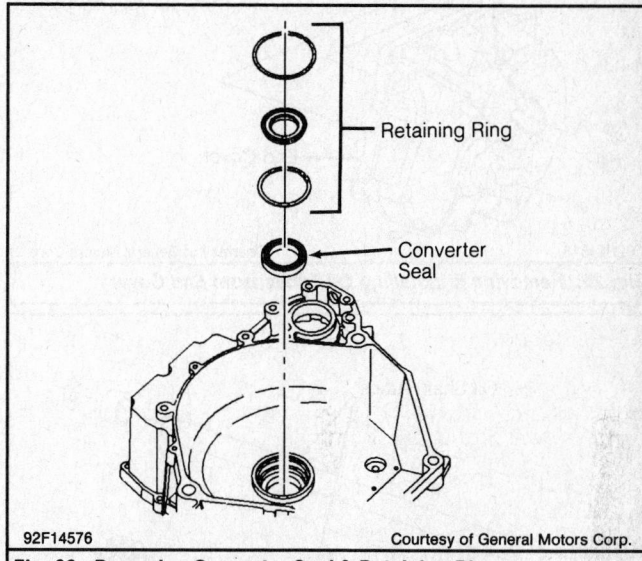

Fig. 23: Removing Converter Seal & Retaining Ring

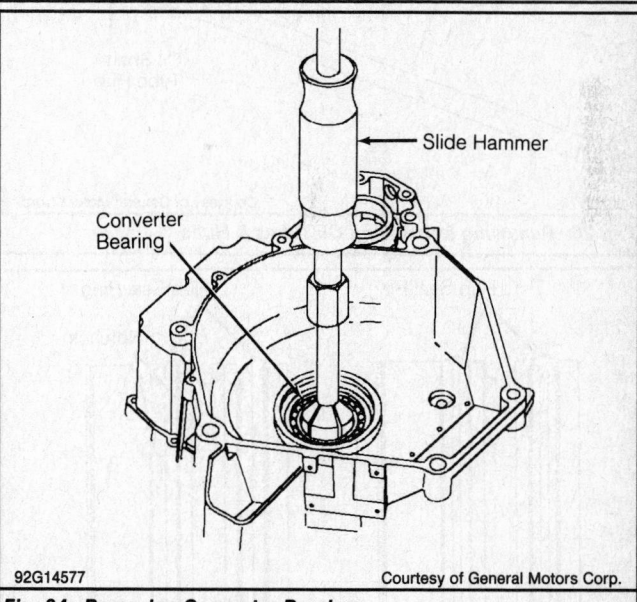

Fig. 24: Removing Converter Bearing

END COVER

Disassembly & Reassembly – **1)** Remove input and output shaft oil tubes and hubs. Separate oil tubes from hubs. Inspect all parts for wear and damage. *See Figs. 25 and 26.*

2) Ensure hub seal rings are not rolled. *See Fig. 27.* If necessary, remove seals from hub. Lubricate new seals with ATF prior to installation. Using Seal Sizer Tools (SA9136T-1, SA9136T-4, SA9136T-2 and SA9143T), install and size seals. *See Figs. 28 and 29.*

3) Install input oil tube to hub. *See Fig. 30.* Ensure roll pin aligns with slot in hub. Install gasket to hub. Lube seal, and install it in end cover. Tighten hub mounting bolts to 106 INCH lbs. (12 N.m). Install output shaft to output shaft hub. Ensure roll pin aligns with slot in hub. Lube seal, and install it in transaxle case. *See Fig. 25.*

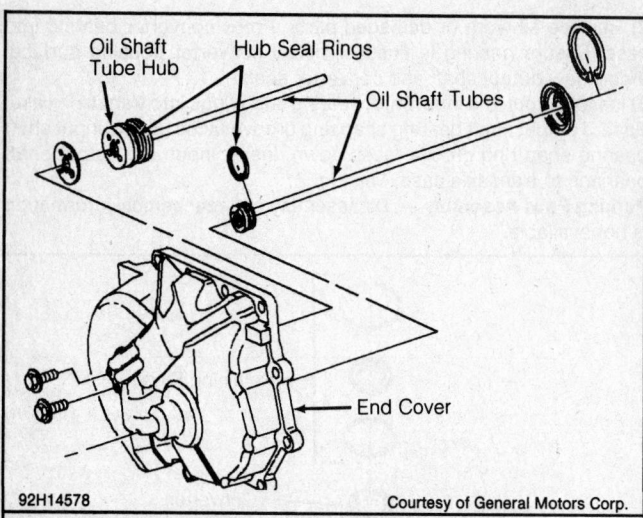

Fig. 25: *Removing & Installing Oil Tubes from End Cover*

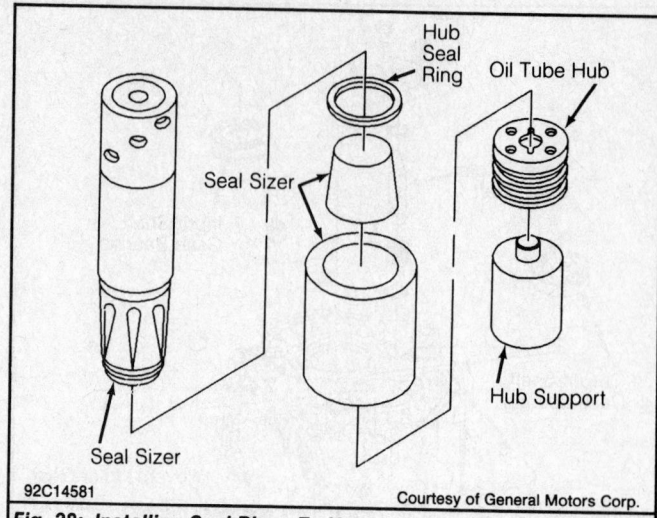

Fig. 28: *Installing Seal Rings To Hub*

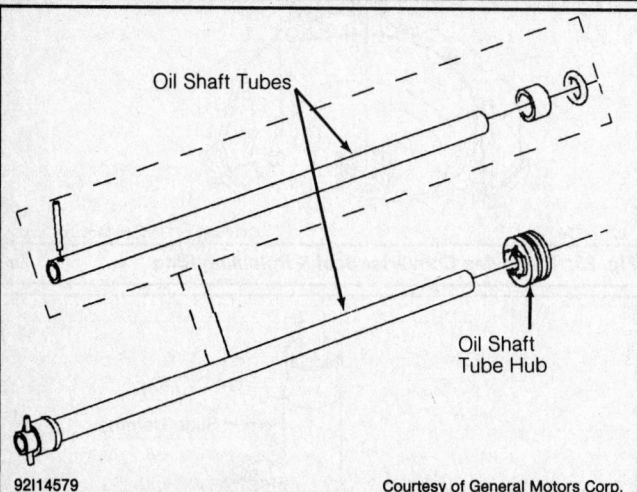

Fig. 26: *Removing & Installing Oil Tubes & Hubs*

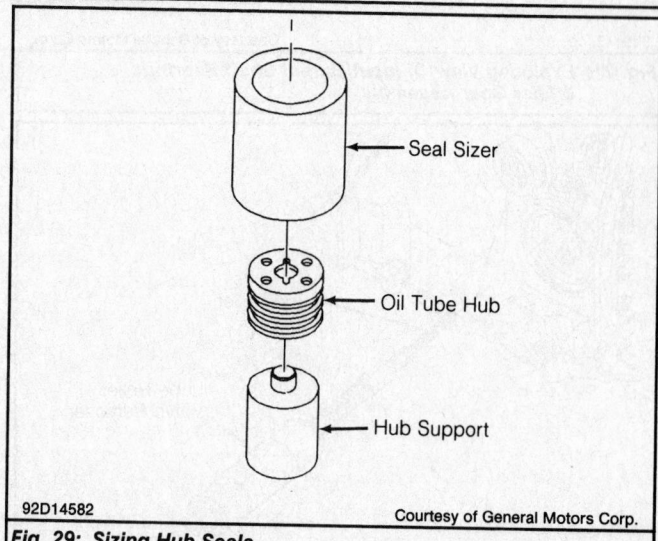

Fig. 29: *Sizing Hub Seals*

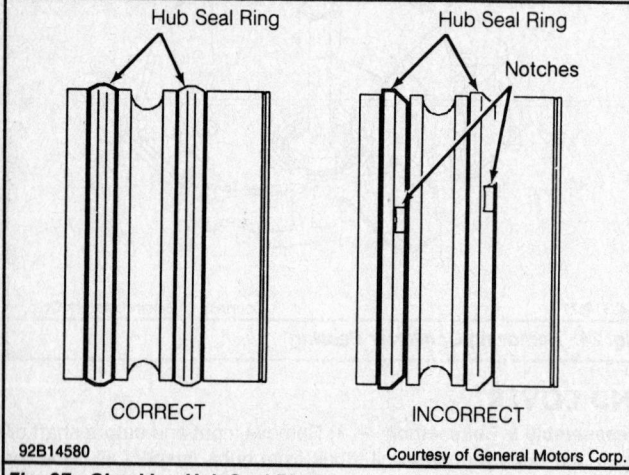

Fig. 27: *Checking Hub Seal Rings*

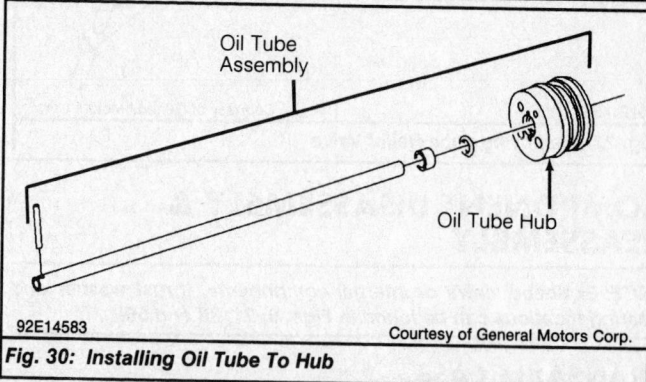

Fig. 30: *Installing Oil Tube To Hub*

FINAL DRIVE ASSEMBLY

Disassembly & Inspection – 1) Inspect final drive gear for damaged teeth and worn bearing surfaces. Inspect thrust bearings for wear and damage. If necessary, remove differential side bearings. *See Fig. 31.* Check differential pinion gears for excessive backlash. Backlash specification is not available.

2) If necessary, replace thrust washers. Using a pin punch, drive cross pin locking pin from case. *See Fig. 32.* Remove pinion shaft, pinion and side gears, and thrust washers. Inspect all parts for damage and abnormal wear.

Reassembly – 1) Assemble differential side gears and thrust washers into case. Set thrust washers onto pinion gears. Assemble pinion gears and washers into case. *See Fig. 32.*

2) Slide cross pin through both pinion gears for alignment, and then remove pin. Rotate side gears into position, and then install cross pin. Tap cross pin locking pin into position. Install side bearings to differential (if removed).

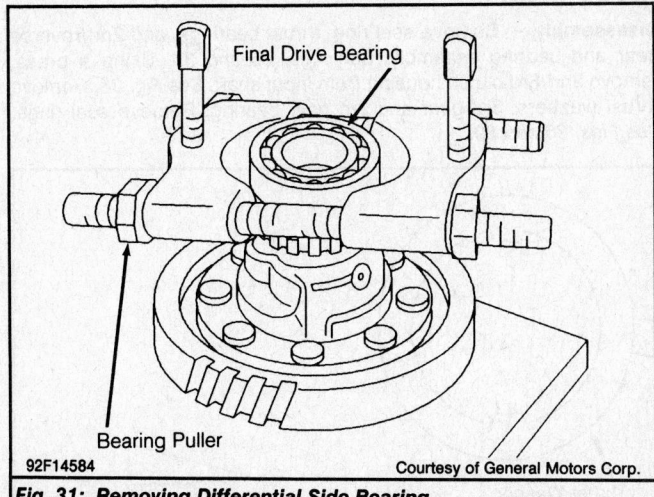

92F14584

Final Drive Bearing

Bearing Puller

Courtesy of General Motors Corp.

Fig. 31: Removing Differential Side Bearing

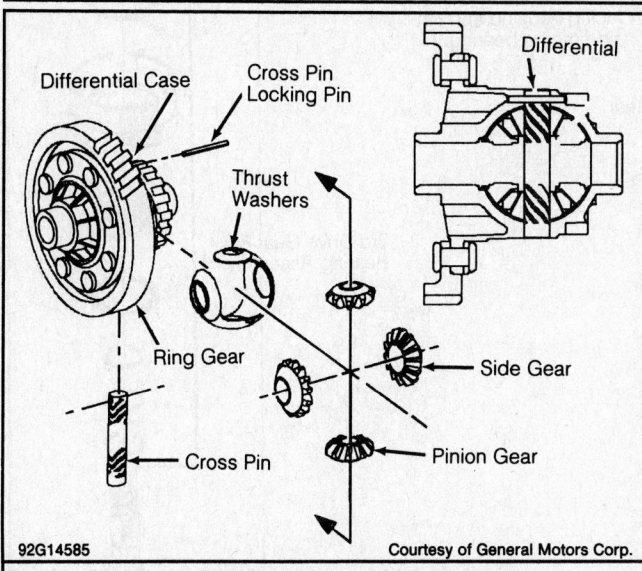

92G14585

Differential Case

Cross Pin
Locking Pin

Differential

Thrust
Washers

Ring Gear

Side Gear

Cross Pin

Pinion Gear

Courtesy of General Motors Corp.

Fig. 32: Identifying Final Drive Assembly Components

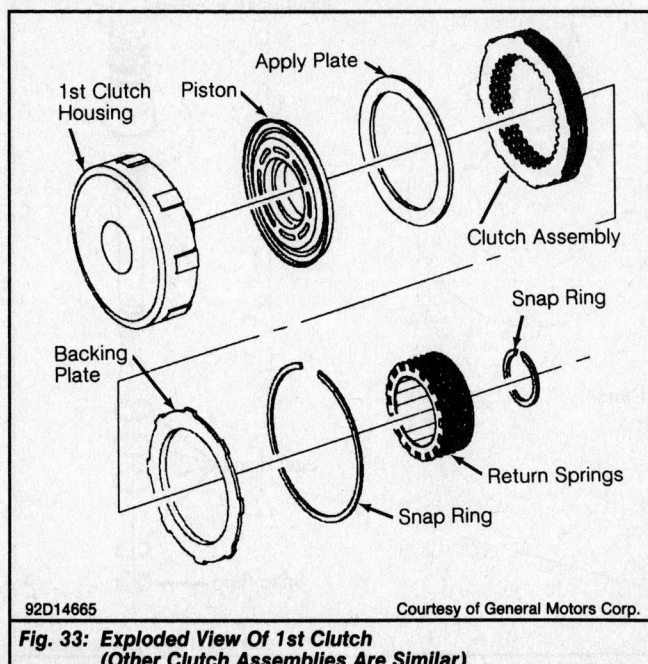

92D14665

1st Clutch
Housing

Piston

Apply Plate

Clutch Assembly

Snap Ring

Backing
Plate

Return Springs

Snap Ring

Courtesy of General Motors Corp.

**Fig. 33: Exploded View Of 1st Clutch
(Other Clutch Assemblies Are Similar)**

1ST CLUTCH

Disassembly & Inspection – 1) Remove large snap ring. Lift out backing plate, clutch plates and apply plate (Belleville spring). *See Fig. 33.* Compress clutch spring retainer to remove small snap ring, spring retainer and clutch return springs.

2) Apply air pressure to clutch fluid passage to remove piston. Remove and discard piston seal rings. If necessary, remove needle bearing by separating bearing from inner race. Remove 1st gear thrust washer. Inspect for wear and damage. If 1st clutch housing is replaced, install a new needle bearing and race. *See Fig. 34.*

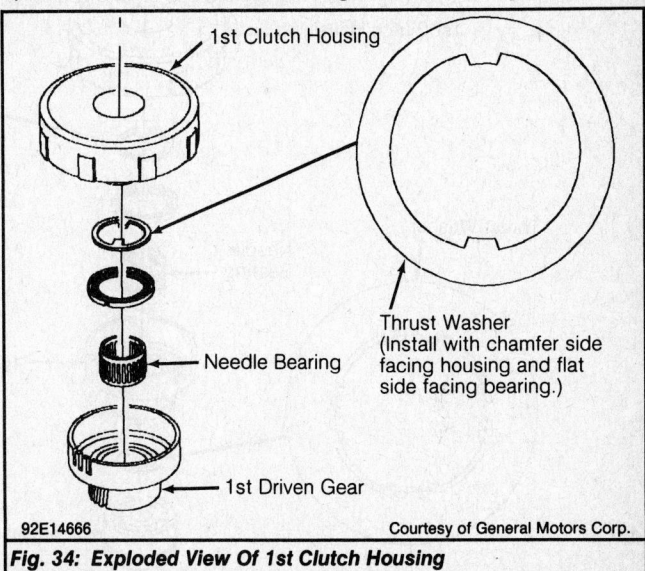

92E14666

1st Clutch Housing

Needle Bearing

Thrust Washer
(Install with chamfer side
facing housing and flat
side facing bearing.)

1st Driven Gear

Courtesy of General Motors Corp.

Fig. 34: Exploded View Of 1st Clutch Housing

Reassembly – 1) Install 1st gear thrust washer. Ensure flat side faces bearing and chamfer side faces housing. Ensure thrust washer tabs line up with slots on hub. Install thrust bearing (roller faces thrust washer) and 1st gear needle bearing. *See Fig. 34.*

2) Lubricate new piston oil seals. Install Clutch Housing Seal Protector (SA9117T-3) in clutch housing. Using Seal Installer Set (SA9117T), install clutch piston in clutch housing. Install return springs and spring retainer.

3) Compress return spring retainer and install snap ring. Install apply plate (Belleville spring) with convex side toward piston. *See Fig. 33.* Install 3 internal tanged and 3 external tanged clutch plates. Install clutch plates with fiber side up. Starting with external tanged plate, alternate external and internal tanged plates. Install backing plate and snap ring. *See Fig. 33.*

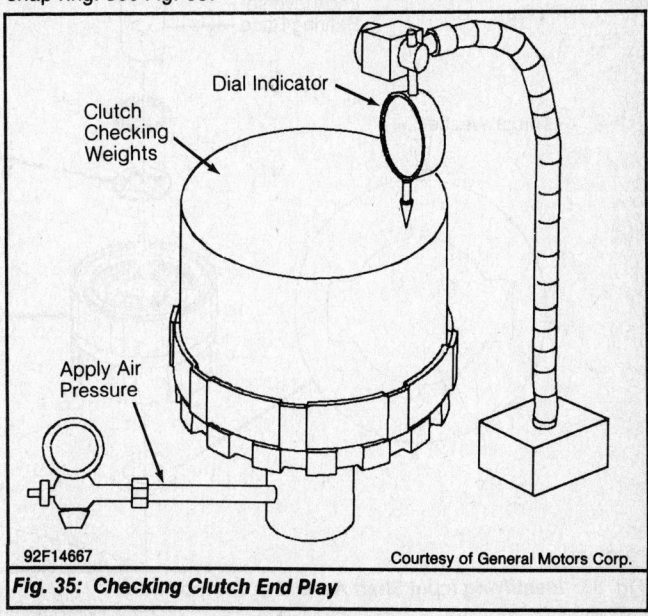

92F14667

Dial Indicator

Clutch
Checking
Weights

Apply Air
Pressure

Courtesy of General Motors Corp.

Fig. 35: Checking Clutch End Play

4) Using both Clutch Checking Weights (SA9111T-1 and SA9111T-2), place weights on top of clutch backing plate. *See Fig. 35.* Apply 60 psi (415 kPa) of compressed air to each clutch fluid passage and check operation. Using a dial indicator, check clutch end play.

5) End play for 1st clutch should be .038-.055" (.96-1.40 mm). If end play is not as specified, selective size snap rings are available from .063-.113" (1.60-2.87 mm) in .007" (.18 mm) increments.

INPUT SHAFT

Disassembly – Remove seal ring, thrust bearings, and 2nd/reverse gear and bearing assembly. *See Figs. 36 and 37.* Using a press, remove 2nd/3rd clutch housing from input shaft. *See Fig. 38.* Remove thrust washers, 3rd gear and 3rd gear bearing. Remove seal rings. *See Figs. 36 and 39.*

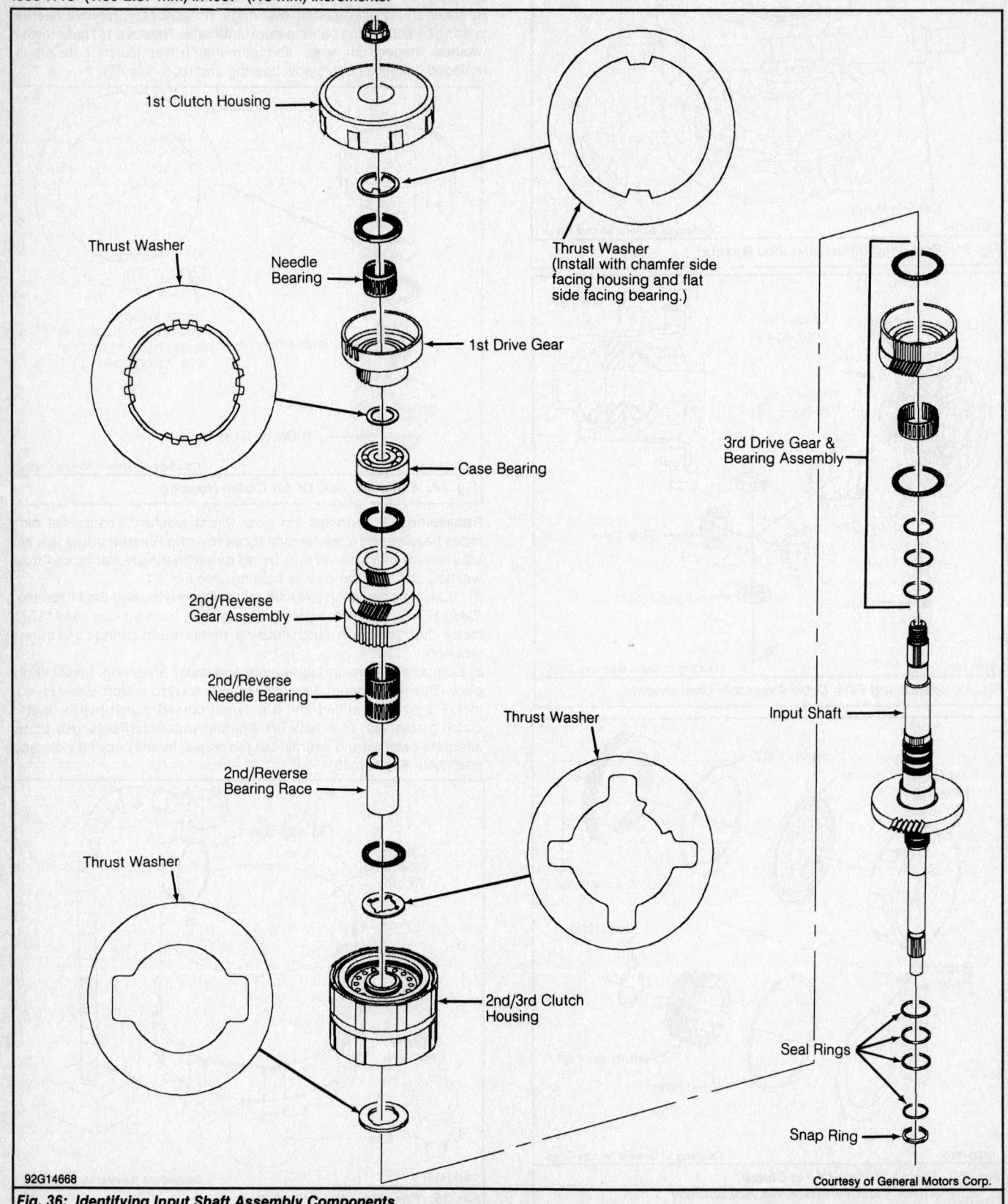

1st Clutch Housing

Thrust Washer

Needle Bearing

Thrust Washer
(Install with chamfer side facing housing and flat side facing bearing.)

1st Drive Gear

Case Bearing

3rd Drive Gear & Bearing Assembly

2nd/Reverse Gear Assembly

2nd/Reverse Needle Bearing

2nd/Reverse Bearing Race

Thrust Washer

Input Shaft

Thrust Washer

2nd/3rd Clutch Housing

Seal Rings

Snap Ring

92G14668

Courtesy of General Motors Corp.

Fig. 36: Identifying Input Shaft Assembly Components

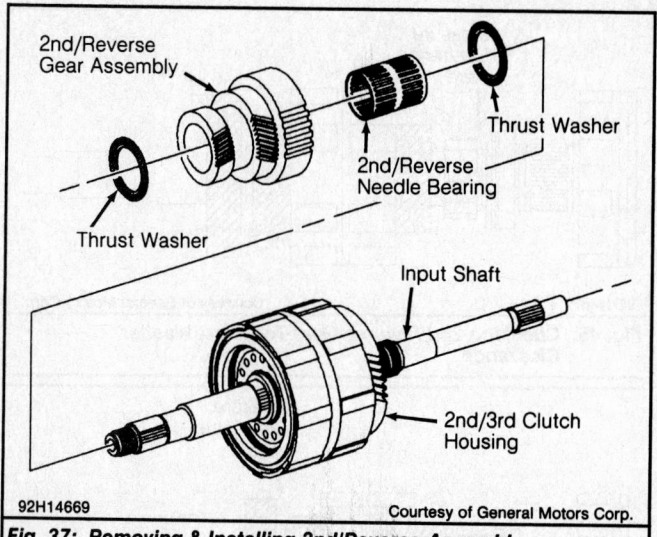

Fig. 37: Removing & Installing 2nd/Reverse Assembly

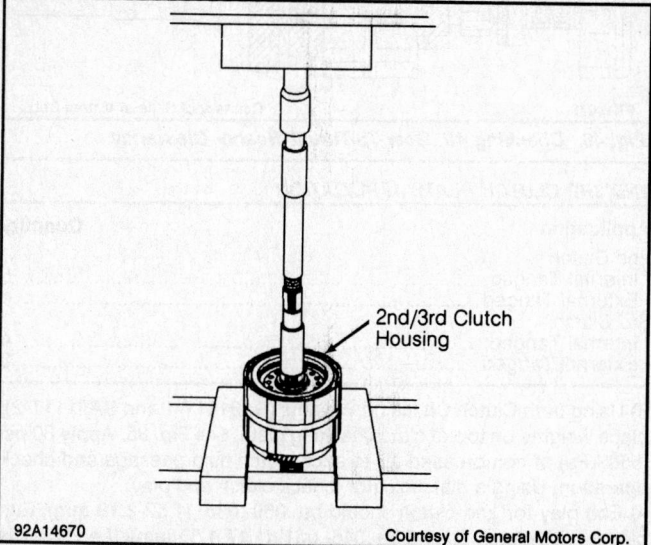

Fig. 38: Pressing Off 2nd/3rd Clutch Housing

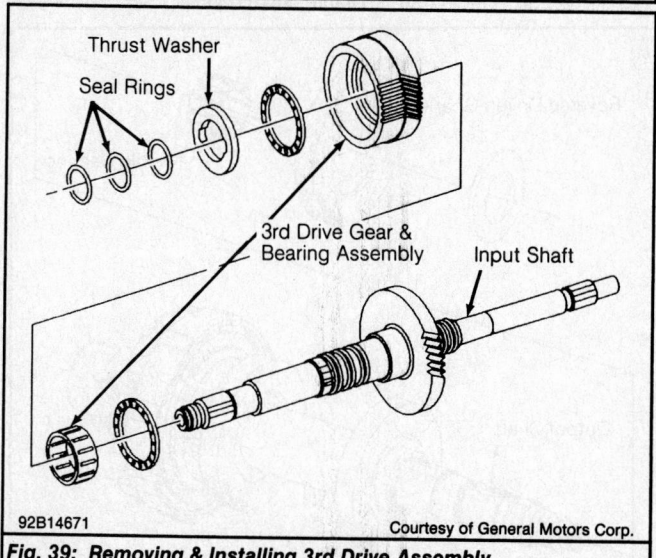

Fig. 39: Removing & Installing 3rd Drive Assembly

Reassembly – 1) Using Seal Sizer Set (SA9144T), size input shaft seal rings. *See Fig. 40.* Lubricate and install 3rd gear bearing. Lubricate and install seal rings. *See Fig. 41.*

2) Using petroleum jelly, install thrust washers to clutch hub and 2nd/3rd clutch housing. *See Fig. 36.* Install washer on 3rd gear side of clutch housing. Ensure washer slots line up with clutch housing tangs.

3) Twist input shaft while installing it into 3rd gear clutch assembly. Ensure 3rd gear contacts 4th gear. Line up 2nd/reverse thrust washer internal tang with lube slot on shaft, and install thrust washer.

4) Using a heat gun, heat 2nd/reverse needle bearing race and install race. Install 2nd/reverse gear assembly. *See Fig. 42.* Ensure all clutch tangs are aligned to gear. Ensure 2nd/reverse thrust bearing is installed with tab toward gear.

INPUT SHAFT CLEARANCE SPECIFICATIONS

Application	Clearance
1st Gear-To-Thrust Washer	.003-.017" (.08-.43 mm)
2nd/Reverse-To-Thrust Washer	.001-.006" (.03-.15 mm)
4th Gear-To-Thrust Washer	.002-.009" (.05-.23 mm)

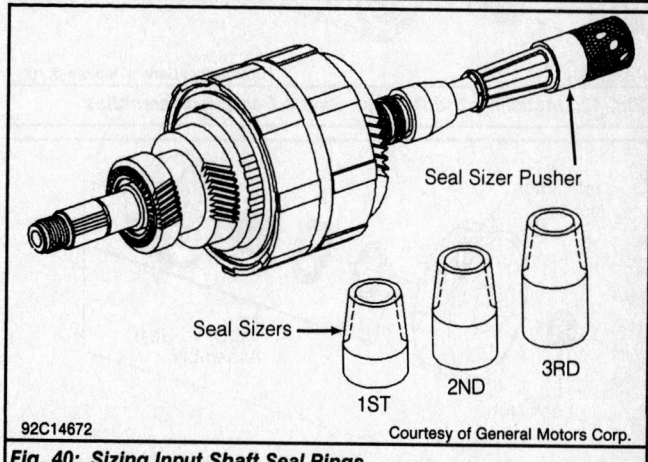

Fig. 40: Sizing Input Shaft Seal Rings

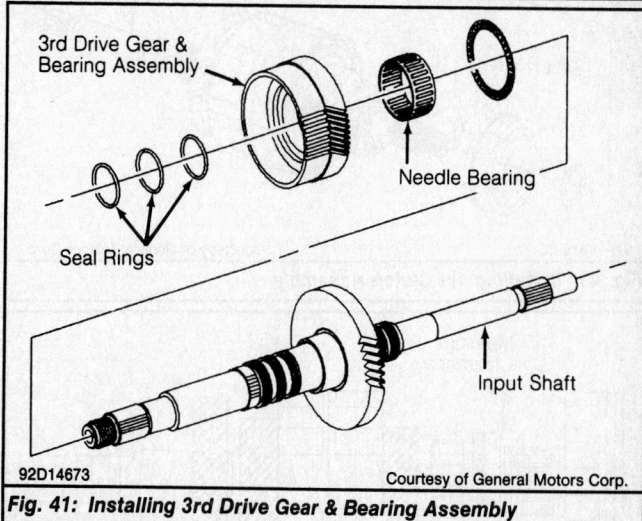

Fig. 41: Installing 3rd Drive Gear & Bearing Assembly

5) Install case bearing, 1st gear thrust washer, 1st gear and 1st clutch assembly onto input shaft. Install and tighten input shaft lock nut to 110 ft. lbs. (150 N.m). *See Fig. 43.*

6) Using a feeler gauge, measure clearance between gears and thrust washers. *See Figs. 44-46.* If clearance is not as specified, check for correct reassembly. See INPUT SHAFT CLEARANCE SPECIFICATIONS table. Remove input shaft nut and 1st clutch assembly. Remove thrust washer and input shaft case bearing.

2ND/3RD CLUTCH

Disassembly & Inspection – Remove large snap ring. Lift out backing plate, clutch plates and apply plate. Compress clutch spring retainer to remove small snap ring, spring retainer and clutch return springs. *See Fig. 33.* Apply air pressure to each clutch fluid passage to remove piston. Remove and discard piston seal rings. Inspect for wear and damage.

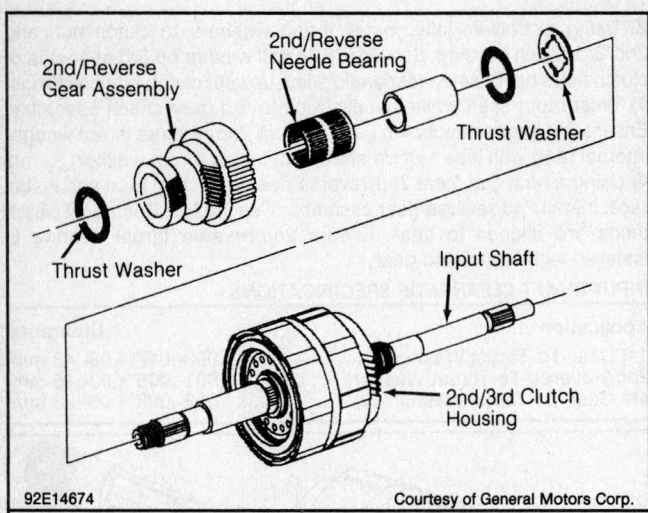

Fig. 42: Installing 2nd/Reverse Gear & Bearing Assemblies

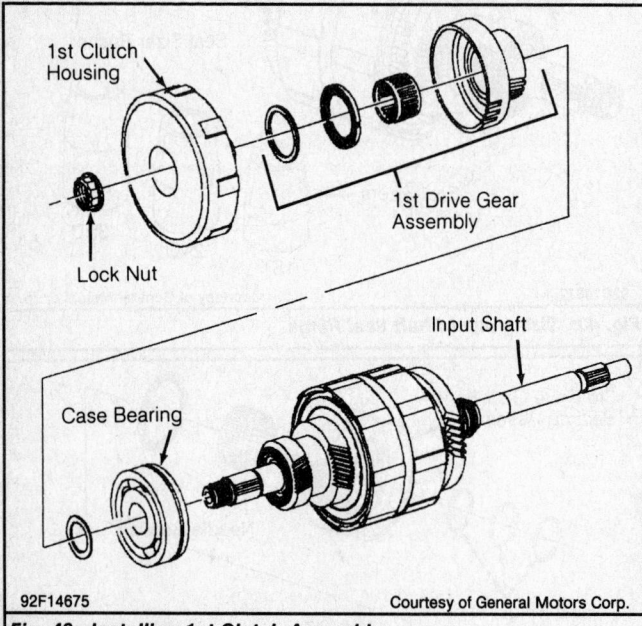

Fig. 43: Installing 1st Clutch Assembly

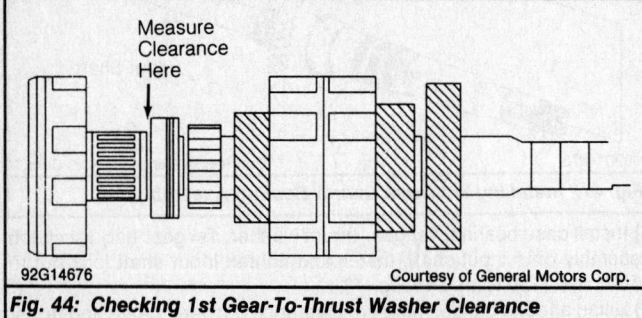

Fig. 44: Checking 1st Gear-To-Thrust Washer Clearance

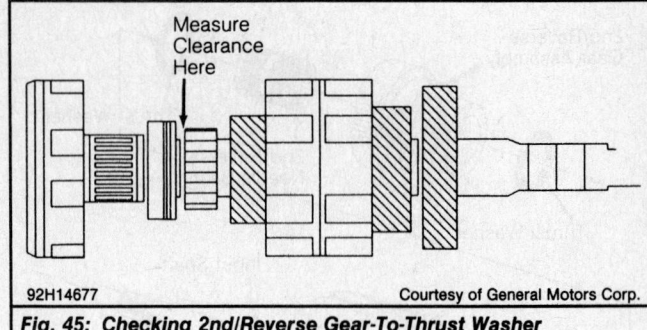

Fig. 45: Checking 2nd/Reverse Gear-To-Thrust Washer Clearance

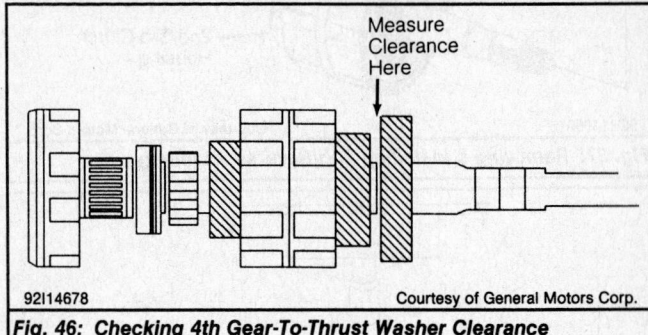

Fig. 46: Checking 4th Gear-To-Thrust Washer Clearance

2ND/3RD CLUTCH PLATE APPLICATION

Application	Quantity
2nd Clutch	
Internal Tanged	5
External Tanged	4
3rd Clutch	
Internal Tanged	4
External Tanged	3

3) Using both Clutch Checking Weights (SA9111T-1 and SA9111T-2), place weights on top of clutch backing plate. *See Fig. 35.* Apply 80 psi (550 kPa) of compressed air to each clutch fluid passage and check operation. Using a dial indicator, check clutch end play.

4) End play for 2nd clutch should be .060-.086" (1.52-2.18 mm). End play for 3rd clutch should be .046-.061" (1.17-1.55 mm). If end play is not as specified, selective size snap rings are available from .063-.113" (1.60-2.87 mm) in .007" (.18 mm) increments.

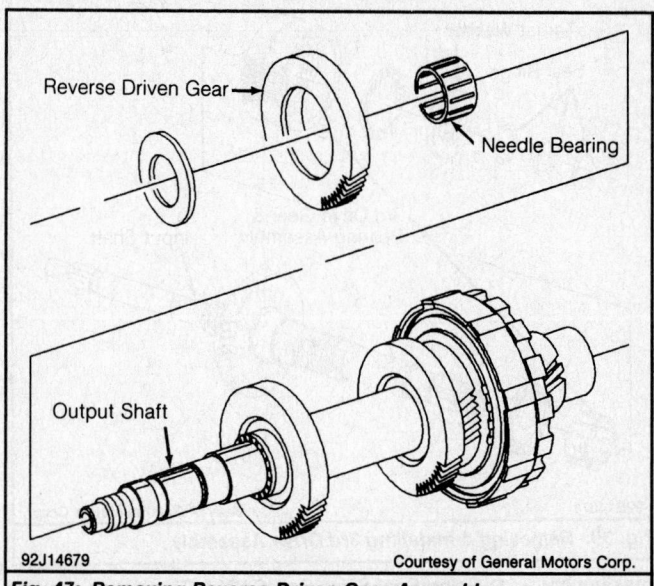

Fig. 47: Removing Reverse Driven Gear Assembly

Reassembly – 1) Lubricate new piston oil seals. Install Clutch Housing Step (SA9117T-2) and Seal Protector (SA9117T-3) in clutch housing. Using Seal Installers from (SA9117T), install clutch piston in clutch housing. Install return springs and spring retainer.

2) Compress return spring retainer and install snap ring. Install apply plate. Install clutch plates with fiber side up. Starting with internal tanged plate, alternate internal and external tanged plates. See 2ND/3RD CLUTCH PLATE APPLICATION table. Install backing plate and snap ring.

OUTPUT SHAFT

Disassembly – 1) Remove reverse driven gear assembly. *See Fig. 47.* Using a press, remove dog clutch sleeve and hub and 2nd/reverse gear assembly. *See Fig. 48.*

2) Remove 2nd/3rd gear spacer. If necessary, use a gear puller to remove 3rd gear. Remove 3rd gear split thrust washer. *See Fig. 49.* Remove 4th gear assembly. Remove 4th clutch assembly. *See Figs. 49 and 50.* Remove shaft seals from output shaft.

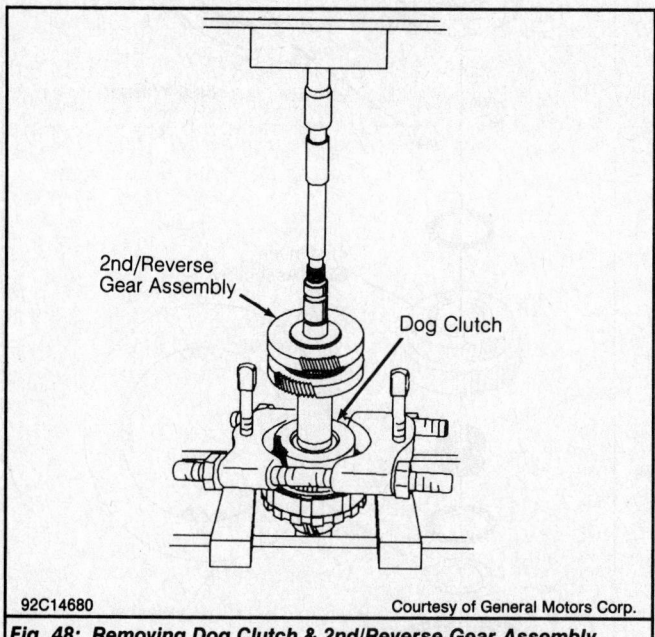

92C14680 Courtesy of General Motors Corp.

Fig. 48: Removing Dog Clutch & 2nd/Reverse Gear Assembly

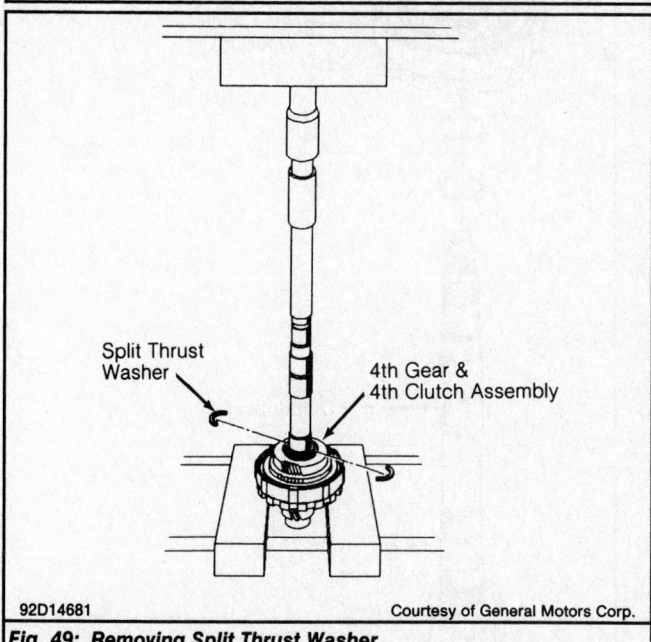

92D14681 Courtesy of General Motors Corp.

Fig. 49: Removing Split Thrust Washer

Reassembly – 1) Lubricate and install shaft seal rings to output shaft. Install 4th clutch assembly and 4th gear assembly. Install bearings, washers and 3rd gear assembly. *See Figs. 50 and 51.*

2) Using a heat gun, heat 2nd gear bearing race. Install race. Install bearing and 2nd gear assembly. Install dog clutch hub with wide slots facing 2nd gear. *See Fig. 52.* Install dog clutch sleeve with groove on outside of sleeve facing reverse gear.

3) Heat and install reverse 2nd gear bearing race. Assemble and install remaining parts on output shaft. *See Figs. 50 and 52.* Reassemble 1st gear and sprag clutch assembly. *See Fig. 53.*

4) Install case bearing, 1st gear thrust washer, 1st gear and sprag clutch assembly onto output shaft. *See Fig. 50.* Install and tighten output shaft nut to 110 ft. lbs. (150 N.m).

5) Using a feeler gauge, measure clearance between gears and thrust washers. *See Figs. 54-57.* If clearance is not as specified, check for correct reassembly. See OUTPUT SHAFT CLEARANCE SPECIFICATIONS table. Remove output shaft nut, 1st gear and sprag clutch assembly. Remove thrust washer and output shaft case bearing. *See Fig. 50.*

OUTPUT SHAFT CLEARANCE SPECIFICATIONS

Application	Clearance
1st Gear-To-Thrust Washer	.004-.016" (.10-.40 mm)
2nd Gear-To-Dog Clutch Hub	.002-.006" (.05-.15 mm)
3rd Gear-To-Thrust Washer	.007-.018" (.18-.46 mm)
Reverse Gear-To-Thrust Washer	.003-.007" (.08-.18 mm)

4TH CLUTCH

Disassembly & Inspection – Remove large snap ring. Lift out backing plate, clutch plates and apply plate. Compress clutch spring retainer to remove small snap ring, spring retainer and clutch return springs. *See Fig. 33.* Apply air pressure to each clutch fluid passage to remove piston. Remove and discard piston seal rings. Inspect for wear and damage.

Reassembly – 1) Lubricate new piston oil seals. Install Clutch Housing Step (SA9117T-2) and Seal Protector (SA9117T-3) in clutch housing. Using Seal Installers from Installer Kit (SA9117T), install clutch piston in clutch housing. Install return springs and spring retainer.

2) Compress return spring retainer and install snap ring. Install apply plate. Install 3 internal tanged and 2 external tanged clutch plates. Install clutch plates with fiber side up. Starting with internal tanged plate, alternate internal and external tanged plates. Install backing plate and snap ring.

3) Using both Clutch Checking Weights (SA9111T-1 and SA9111T-2), place weights on top of clutch backing plate. *See Fig. 35.* Apply 80 psi (550 kPa) of compressed air to clutch fluid passage and check operation. Using a dial indicator, check clutch end play.

4) End play should be .036-.046" (0.91-1.17 mm). If end play is not as specified, selective size snap rings are available from .063-.113" (1.60-2.87 mm) in .007" (.18 mm) increments.

REVERSE IDLER GEAR

Inspection – Inspect gear and bearing for wear and damage. *See Fig. 21.* Replace all worn parts as necessary.

VALVE BODY

Disassembly – 1) Remove line actuator cover bolts. *See Fig. 58.* Carefully remove cover and connector plate. Remove line actuators by twisting line actuator as it is pulled from valve body. *See Fig. 58.*

2) Remove through bolts. Separate valve body and separator plate. Remove check balls. *See Fig. 59.* Remove manual valve. Remove each valve assembly. Retain in proper order for reassembly. *See Figs. 60 and 61.*

Inspection – Inspect valves for scoring, nicks and scratches. Inspect springs for damaged or distorted coils. Using a No. 43 (2.25 mm) drill bit, insert drill bit shank into connector plate terminals. Ensure drill bit drags slightly in each terminal. If bit does not drag slightly, replace connector plate. Inspect valve body casting for porosity, interconnected fluid passages and damaged machined surfaces. *See Figs. 60 and 61.*

Reassembly – 1) To reassemble, reverse disassembly procedures. Assemble each valve, spring, plug and key. *See Figs. 60 and 61.* DO NOT push in using too much force. Install separator plate, gaskets and check balls to valve body. *See Fig. 59.* Install line actuator housing to valve body. Install one valve body bolt. *See Fig. 63.*

2) Lubricate line actuators. Using a twisting motion, install line actuators. Ensure line actuator terminals line up with connector plate. Install connector plate. Install cover. *See Fig. 58.* Ensure dowel bolts are installed in correct positions. *See Figs. 63 and 64.* Finger-tighten cover bolts.

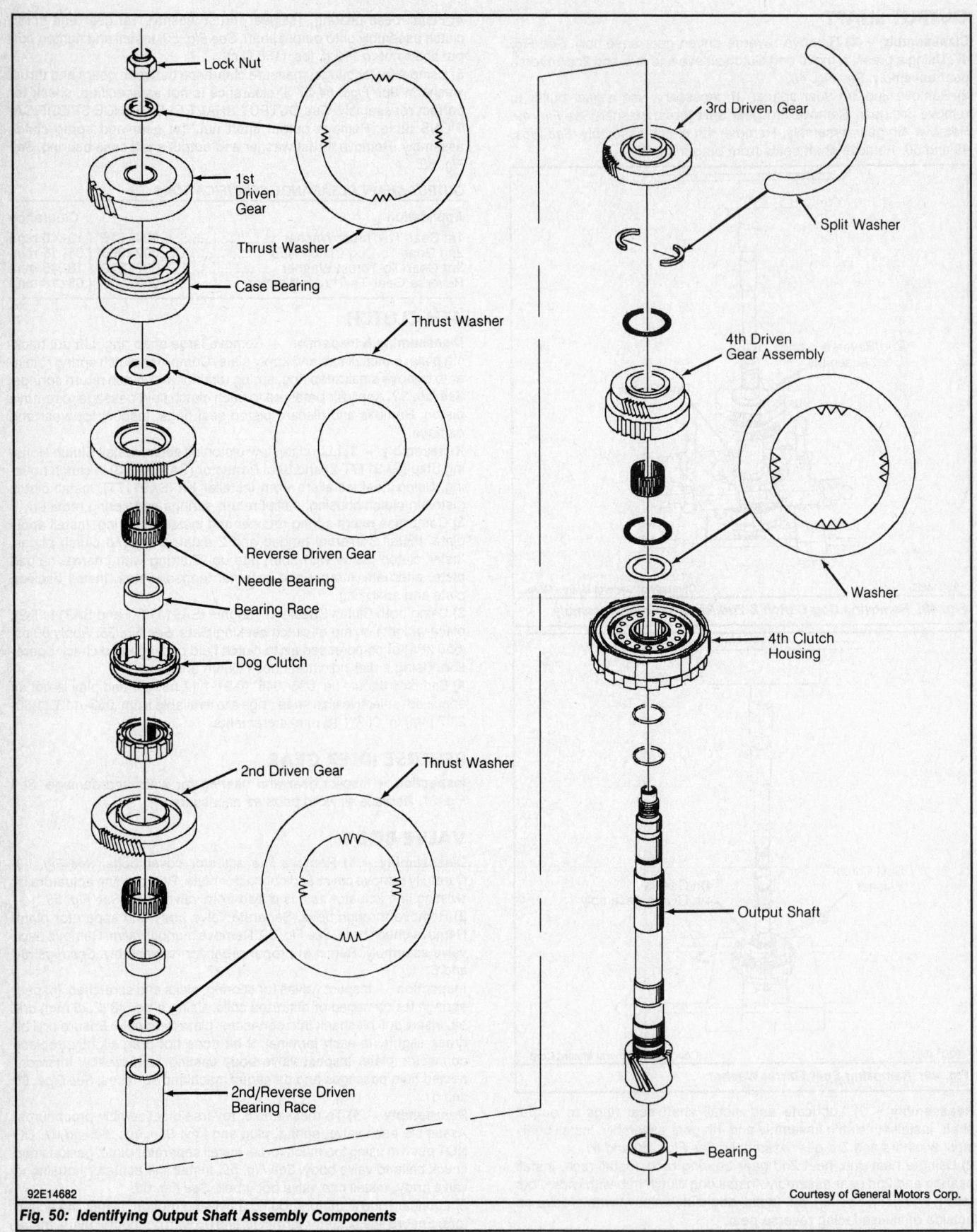

Lock Nut

1st Driven Gear

Thrust Washer

Case Bearing

Thrust Washer

Reverse Driven Gear

Needle Bearing

Bearing Race

Dog Clutch

2nd Driven Gear

Thrust Washer

2nd/Reverse Driven Bearing Race

3rd Driven Gear

Split Washer

4th Driven Gear Assembly

Washer

4th Clutch Housing

Output Shaft

Bearing

92E14682

Courtesy of General Motors Corp.

Fig. 50: Identifying Output Shaft Assembly Components

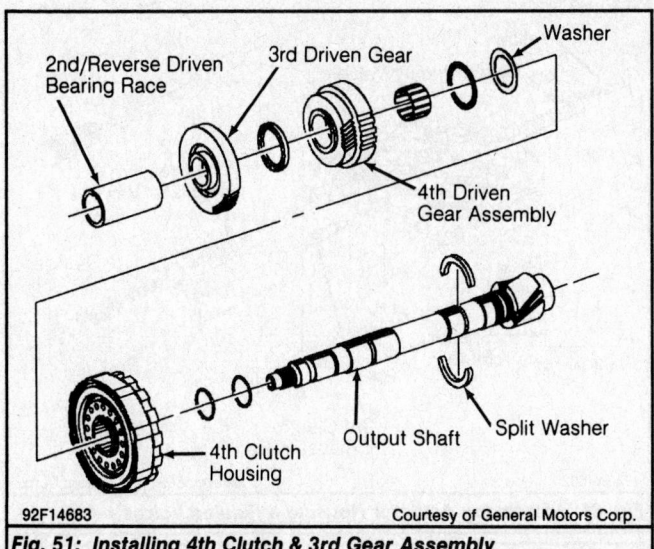

Fig. 51: Installing 4th Clutch & 3rd Gear Assembly

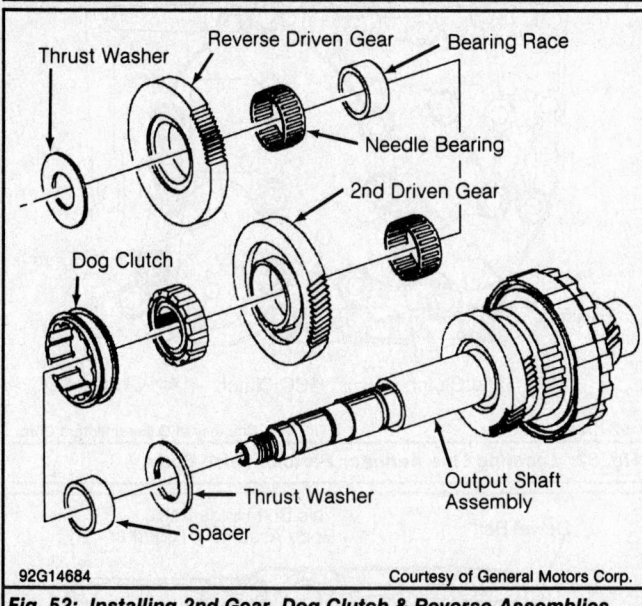

Fig. 52: Installing 2nd Gear, Dog Clutch & Reverse Assemblies

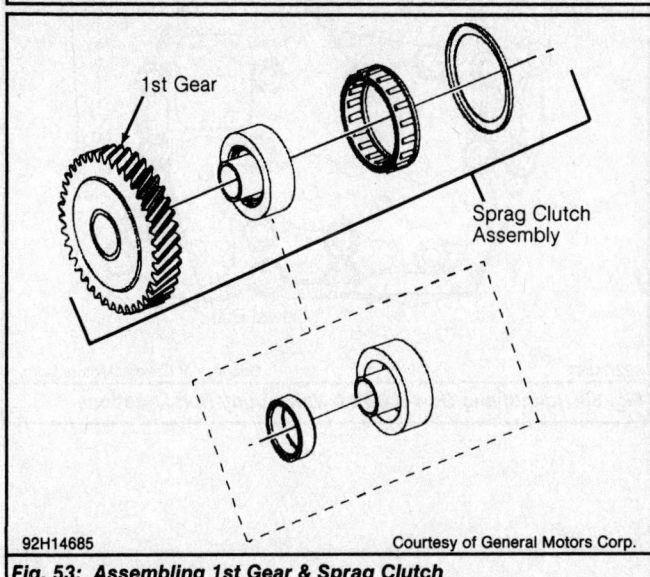

Fig. 53: Assembling 1st Gear & Sprag Clutch

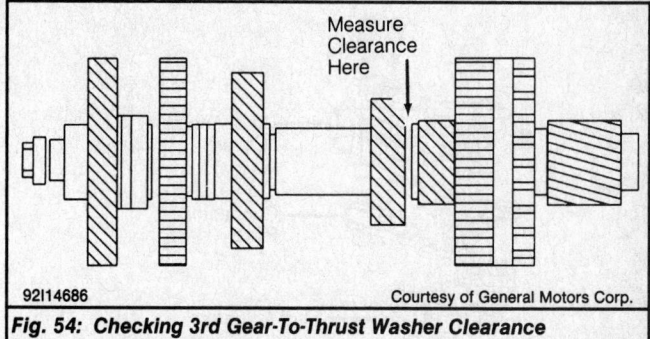

Fig. 54: Checking 3rd Gear-To-Thrust Washer Clearance

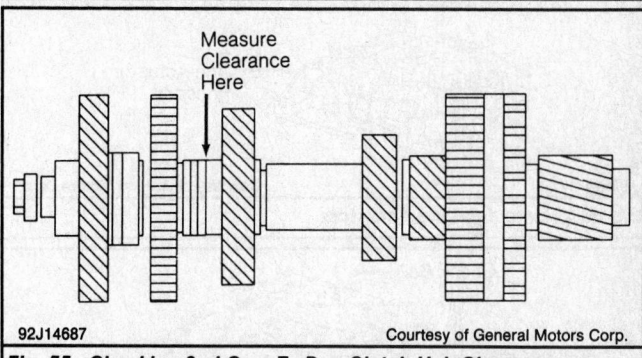

Fig. 55: Checking 2nd Gear-To-Dog Clutch Hub Clearance

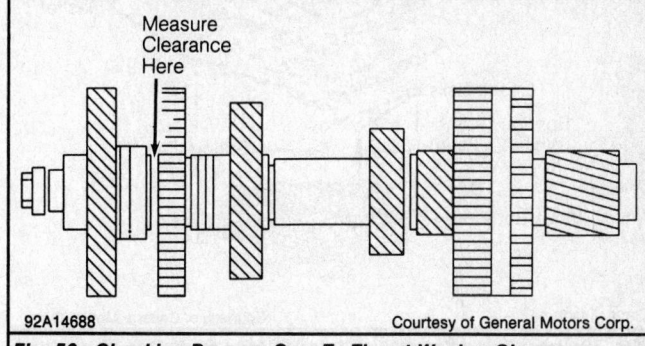

Fig. 56: Checking Reverse Gear-To-Thrust Washer Clearance

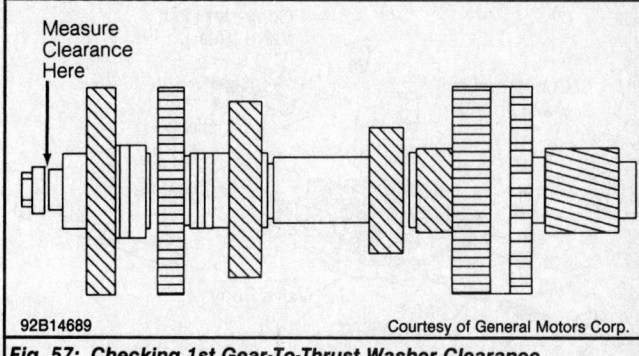

Fig. 57: Checking 1st Gear-To-Thrust Washer Clearance

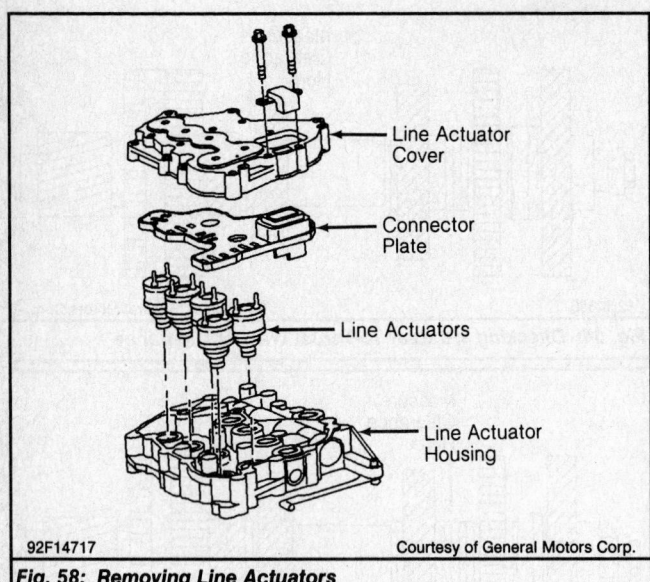

Line Actuator Cover

Connector Plate

Line Actuators

Line Actuator Housing

92F14717   Courtesy of General Motors Corp.

Fig. 58: Removing Line Actuators

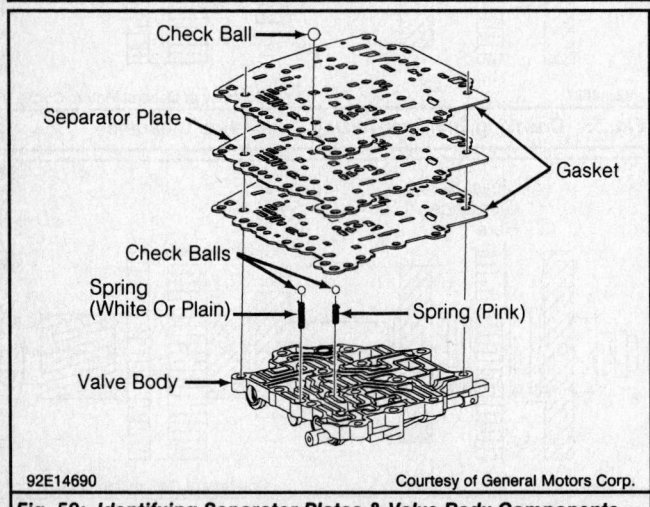

Check Ball

Separator Plate

Gasket

Check Balls

Spring (White Or Plain)

Spring (Pink)

Valve Body

92E14690   Courtesy of General Motors Corp.

Fig. 59: Identifying Separator Plates & Valve Body Components

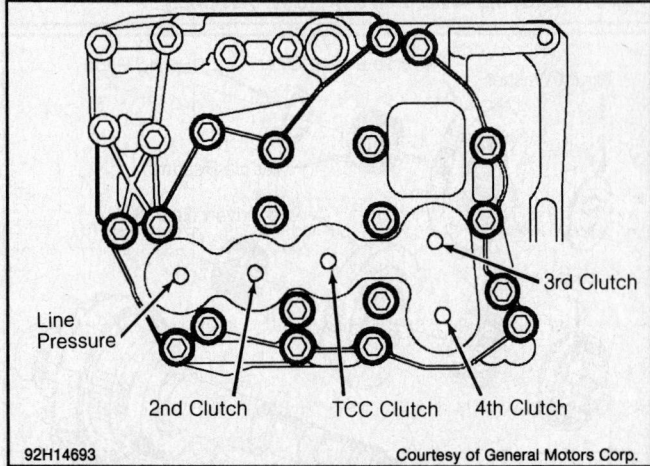

Converter Limit Valve (Rear)

Converter Limit Valve (Front)

Black

Manual Valve

Violet

Servo Apply Valve

Valve Body

Lt. Blue

94E38483   Courtesy of General Motors Corp.

Fig. 60: Identifying Valve Body & Related Valves

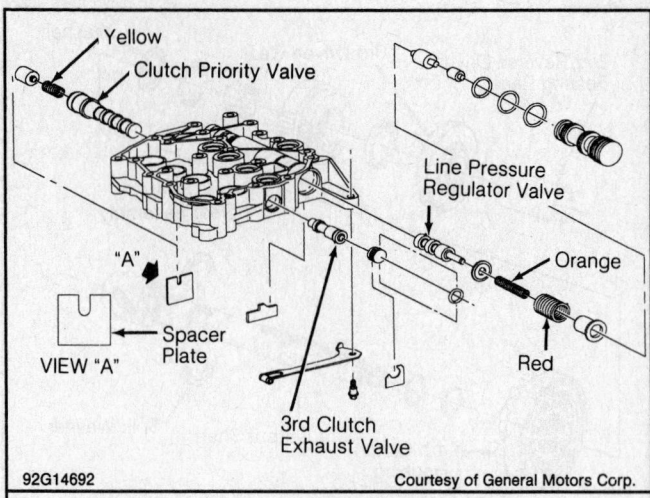

Yellow

Clutch Priority Valve

Line Pressure Regulator Valve

"A"

Orange

Spacer Plate

VIEW "A"

Red

3rd Clutch Exhaust Valve

92G14692   Courtesy of General Motors Corp.

Fig. 61: Identifying Actuator Housing & Related Valves

3rd Clutch

Line Pressure

2nd Clutch   TCC Clutch   4th Clutch

92H14693   Courtesy of General Motors Corp.

Fig. 62: Locating Line Actuator Ports In Valve Body

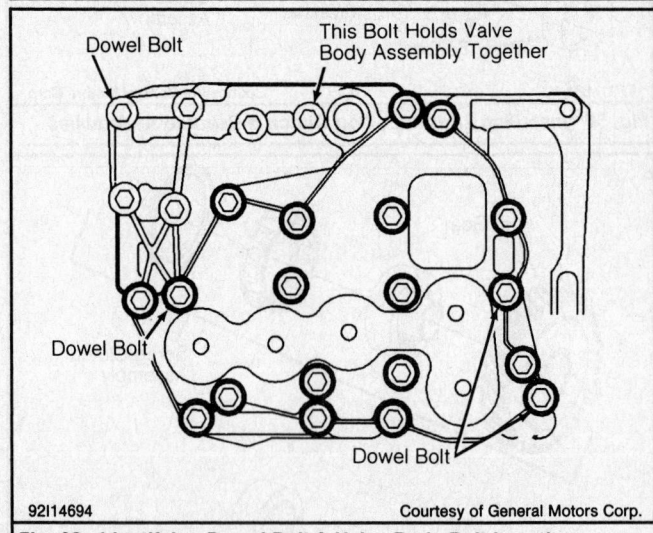

Dowel Bolt

This Bolt Holds Valve Body Assembly Together

Dowel Bolt

Dowel Bolt

92I14694   Courtesy of General Motors Corp.

Fig. 63: Identifying Dowel Bolt & Valve Body Bolt Locations

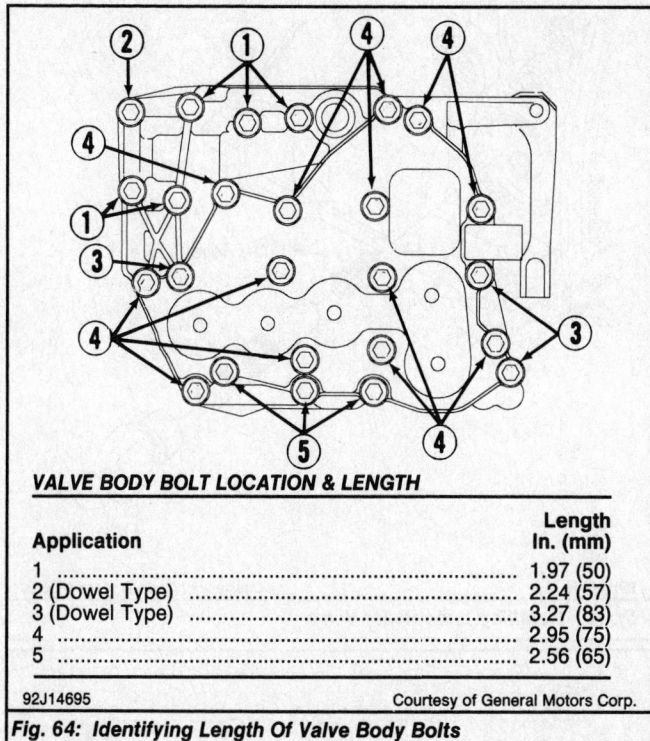

VALVE BODY BOLT LOCATION & LENGTH

Application	Length In. (mm)
1	1.97 (50)
2 (Dowel Type)	2.24 (57)
3 (Dowel Type)	3.27 (83)
4	2.95 (75)
5	2.56 (65)

92J14695   Courtesy of General Motors Corp.

Fig. 64: Identifying Length Of Valve Body Bolts

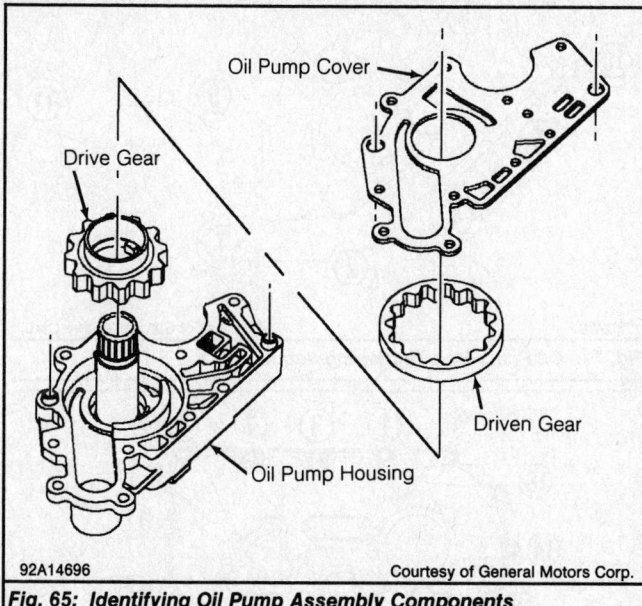

92A14696   Courtesy of General Motors Corp.

Fig. 65: Identifying Oil Pump Assembly Components

OIL PUMP ASSEMBLY

Disassembly – Remove oil pump cover from oil pump housing. *See Fig. 65.* Remove drive gear, driven gear and pressure relief valve assembly.

Inspection – Inspect drive and driven gear surfaces and bushings for wear and damage. Replace any defective part. Measure oil pump clearances. Using straight edge and feeler gauge, measure drive and driven gear side clearance. *See Fig. 66.* Measure driven gear-to-oil pump housing clearance. *See Fig. 67.* Use feeler gauge to measure between each gear and crescent. *See Figs. 68 and 69.* See OIL PUMP SPECIFICATIONS table. Replace any part not within specification.

Reassembly – To reassemble, reverse disassembly procedures. Lubricate all parts.

OIL PUMP SPECIFICATIONS

Application	Clearance In. (mm)
Drive Gear Side Clearance	.0005-.0016 (.012-.041)
Driven Gear Side Clearance	.0005-.0016 (.012-.041)
Driven Gear-To-Housing	.0025-.0055 (.064-.139)
Driven Gear-To-Crescent	.0075-.0134 (.191-.341)
Drive Gear-To-Crescent	.0050-.0109 (.128-.278)

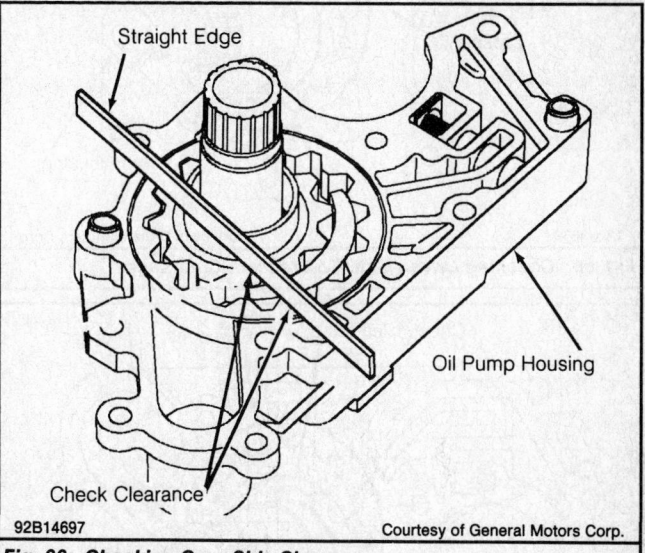

92B14697   Courtesy of General Motors Corp.

Fig. 66: Checking Gear Side Clearance

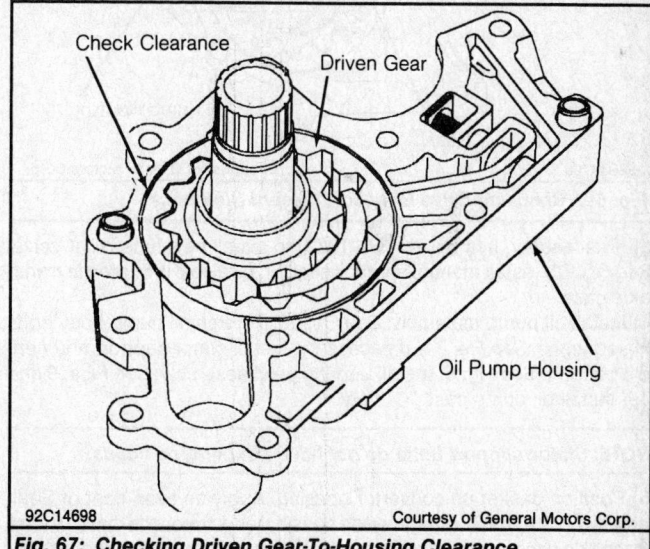

92C14698   Courtesy of General Motors Corp.

Fig. 67: Checking Driven Gear-To-Housing Clearance

TRANSAXLE REASSEMBLY

NOTE: *Exploded views of internal components, thrust washer and bearing locations can be found in Figs. 9, 21, 36 and 50.*

Case Assembly – 1) Apply petroleum jelly to output shaft bearing, and install bearing on output shaft. With another technician, align input shaft, output shaft and final drive assemblies. Carefully install assemblies into converter housing.

CAUTION: *If shaft assemblies are not installed at same time, output shaft bearing or bearing race may be damaged.*

2) Lubricate and install reverse idler gear, shaft and bearing assembly. *See Fig. 21.* Ensure chamfer side of gear faces rear of transaxle case. Install reverse idler gear cap housing, and tighten bolts to 15 ft. lbs. (20 N.m).

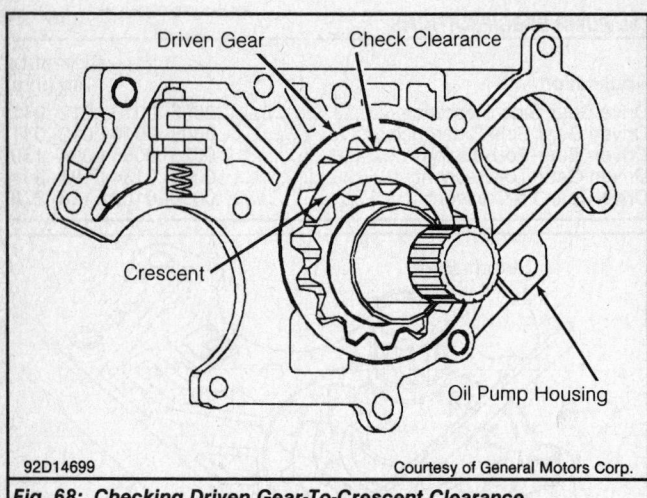

Fig. 68: Checking Driven Gear-To-Crescent Clearance

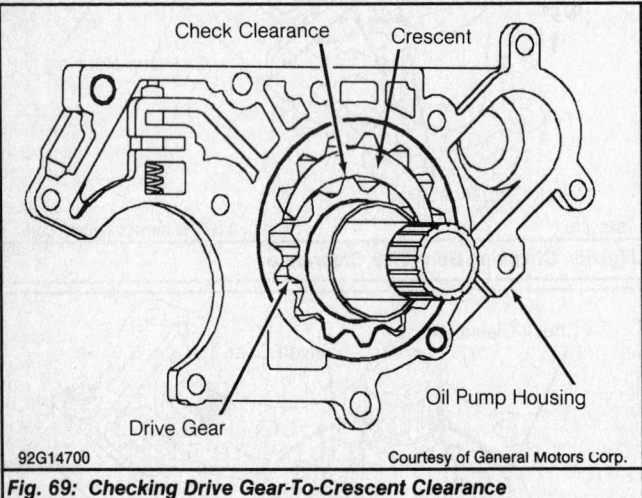

Fig. 69: Checking Drive Gear-To-Crescent Clearance

3) If necessary, use Driver (SA9103E) to install new lube relief valve. *See Fig. 70.* Install manual shaft oil seal. Ensure seal is seated in transaxle case.

4) Install oil pump assembly. *See Fig. 20.* Tighten oil pump body bolts in sequence. *See Fig. 71.* If necessary, install stator support and needle bearing. *See Fig. 9.* Install parking pawl assembly. *See Figs. 9 and 19.* Install oil pump case "O" ring.

NOTE: Stator support bolts do not have washer-type heads.

5) Position gasket on converter housing. Apply an even coat of Sealant 515 (21005993) to converter housing and transaxle case. Install transaxle case over converter housing. If necessary, turn reverse idler gear to allow transaxle case to clear.

6) Lightly lubricate case bolts. Install bolts, and tighten in sequence. *See Fig. 72.* Remaining 2 case bolts are installed after end cover is installed. Ensure both shafts still rotate.

Differential End Play – 1) Differential end play is not specified. If possible, install old snap ring into transaxle case. Using feeler gauge(s), measure clearance between case and differential side bearing outer race. *See Fig. 73.*

2) Record clearance. Select a snap ring which provides smallest possible end play. Selective snap rings are available from dealer. Install axle shaft seal and retaining ring. *See Fig. 74.*

End Cover – 1) If necessary, use Seal Sizer Set (SA9137T) to install and size 2nd/reverse servo piston seal. Slide 2nd/reverse fork on dog clutch sleeve. *See Figs. 16, 75 and 76.*

2) Install servo piston. Align servo shaft with 2nd/reverse fork. Apply Loctite 242 to bolt. Install and tighten bolt in 2nd/reverse fork. *See Fig. 16.* Install servo spring and cover and tighten servo cover bolts.

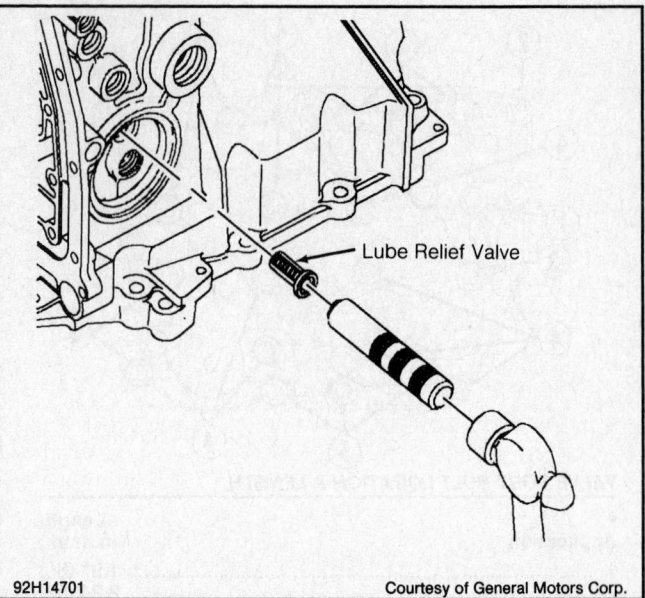

Fig. 70: Installing Lube Relief Valve

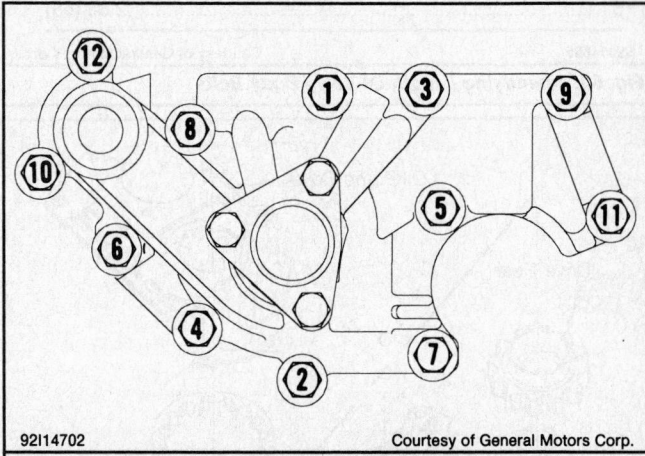

Fig. 71: Oil Pump Bolt Tightening Sequence

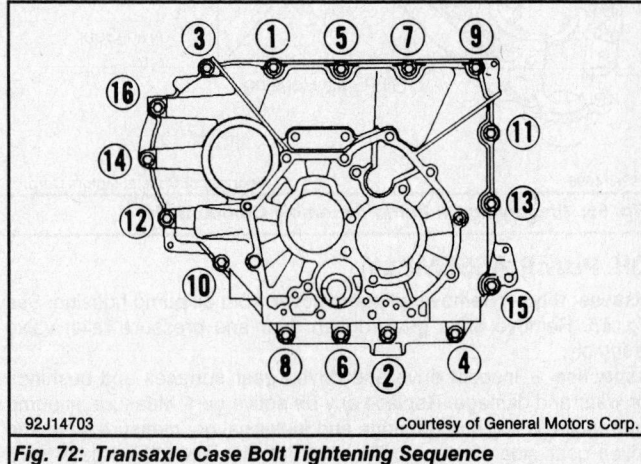

Fig. 72: Transaxle Case Bolt Tightening Sequence

3) Install 1st driven gear and sprag assembly. *See Fig. 15.* Ensure threads on input shaft are clean. Engage parking pawl to hold shaft. Tighten new input shaft lock nut to 110 ft. lbs. (150 N.m).

4) Install 1st drive gear and hub assembly. *See Fig. 77.* Ensure hub tangs and clutch tangs line up. Install Input Shaft Holder (SA9119T) to 1st drive gear. Ensure threads on output shaft are clean. Tighten a new output shaft lock nut to 110 ft. lbs. (150 N.m). *See Fig. 13.*

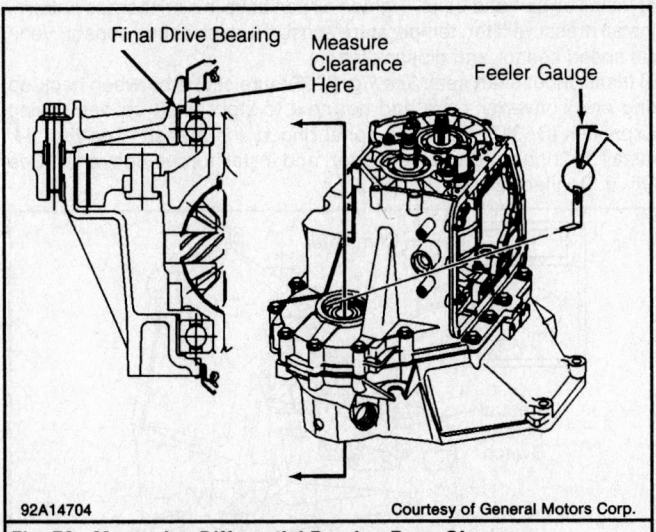

Fig. 73: Measuring Differential Bearing Race Clearance

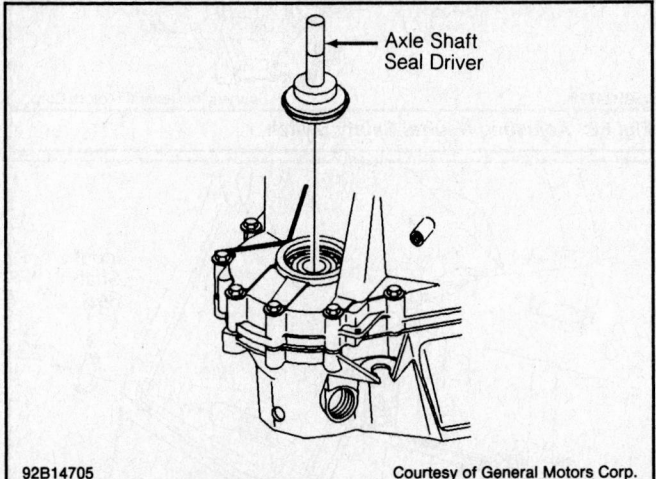

Fig. 74: Installing Axle Shaft Seal

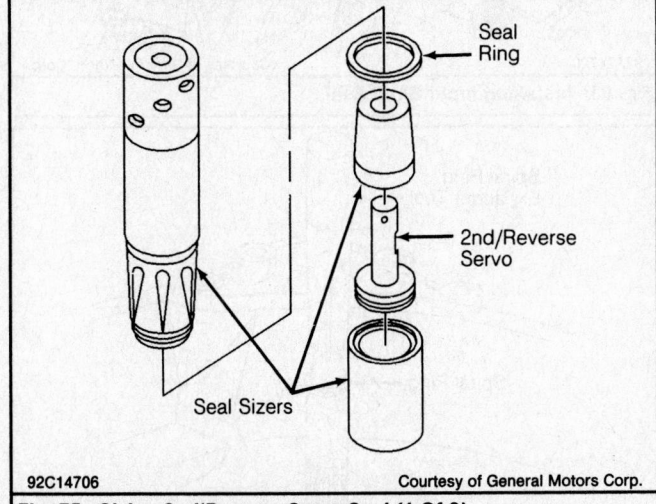

Fig. 75: Sizing 2nd/Reverse Servo Seal (1 Of 2)

5) Check clearance between 1st drive gear and 1st thrust washer. Clearance should be .003-.017" (.08-.43 mm). If clearance is not as specified, check position of 1st clutch, gear and hub assembly.

6) Disengage parking pawl. Rotate 1st clutch. Ensure all drive gears on input shaft rotate. If all drive gears do not rotate, clutch plates may not be positioned correctly.

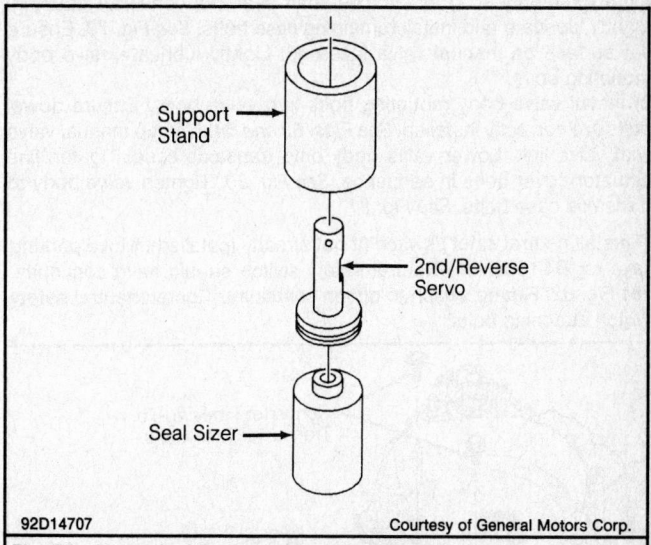

Fig. 76: Sizing 2nd/Reverse Servo Seal (2 Of 2)

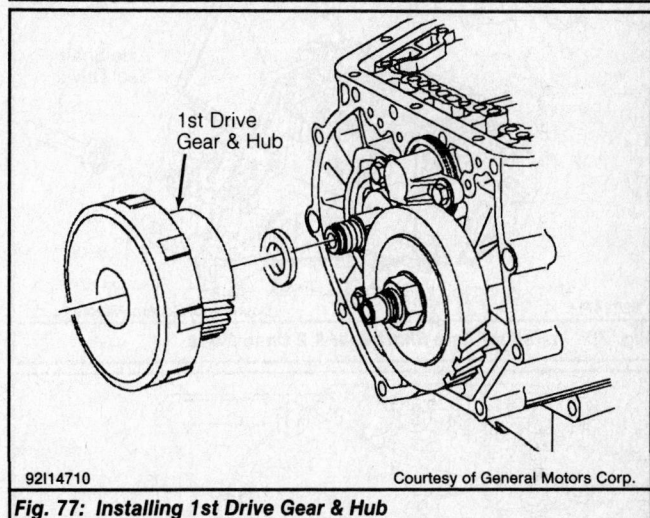

Fig. 77: Installing 1st Drive Gear & Hub

7) Line up and install manual valve link assembly. Assemble detent lever to lever shaft. Install new roll pin or nut to detent lever assembly. See Fig. 11. Install, but DO NOT tighten, neutral safety switch.

8) Install end cover gasket. See Fig. 12. Line up and insert shaft oil tubes into both shafts. DO NOT force tubes into shafts. Lightly lubricate end cover bolts. Install bolts. Tighten end cover bolts in sequence. See Fig. 78.

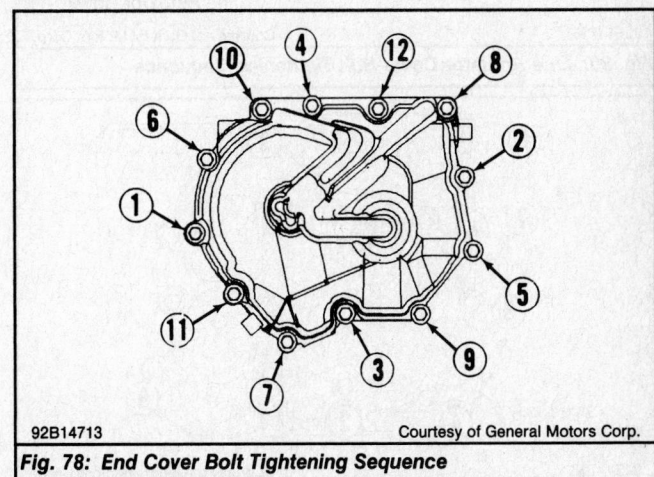

Fig. 78: End Cover Bolt Tightening Sequence

Final Assembly – 1) Install axle shaft seal into converter housing. Lightly lubricate and install remaining case bolts. *See Fig. 79.* Ensure flat surface on manual valve faces up. Lightly lubricate valve body mounting bolts.

2) Install valve body mounting bolts into valve body. Ensure dowel bolts are correctly installed. *See Figs. 63 and 64.* Line up manual valve with valve link. Lower valve body onto transaxle case. Tighten line actuator cover bolts in sequence. *See Fig. 80.* Tighten valve body to transaxle case bolts. *See Fig. 81.*

3) Install neutral safety switch (if not already installed). Move parking pawl to "D4" position. Neutral safety switch should have continuity. *See Fig. 82.* Rotate switch to obtain continuity. Tighten neutral safety switch attaching bolts.

4) Install oil pan and bolts. Tighten oil pan bolts in a crisscross pattern. Install pressure filter, temperature sensor, turbine speed sensor, vehicle speed sensor and dipstick tube.

5) Install input shaft seal. *See Fig. 83.* Ensure seal is between back-up ring and converter case and not next to input shaft splines. Using Expander (SA9135T), install spiral ring to input shaft. *See Fig. 84.* Install "O" ring to torque converter, and install torque converter. *See Fig. 9.* Recheck converter end play.

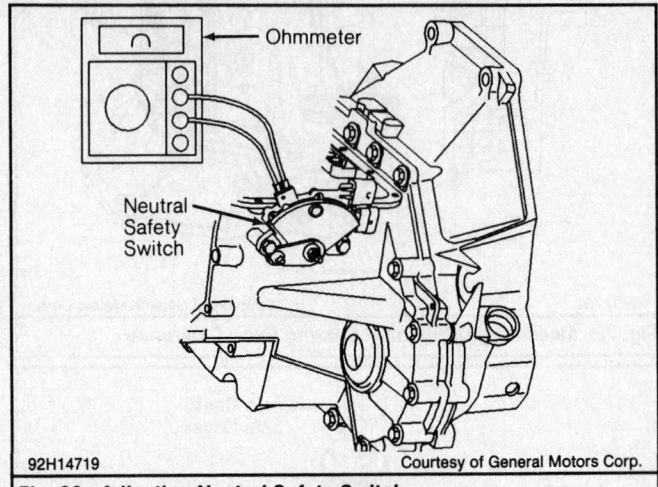

Fig. 82: *Adjusting Neutral Safety Switch*

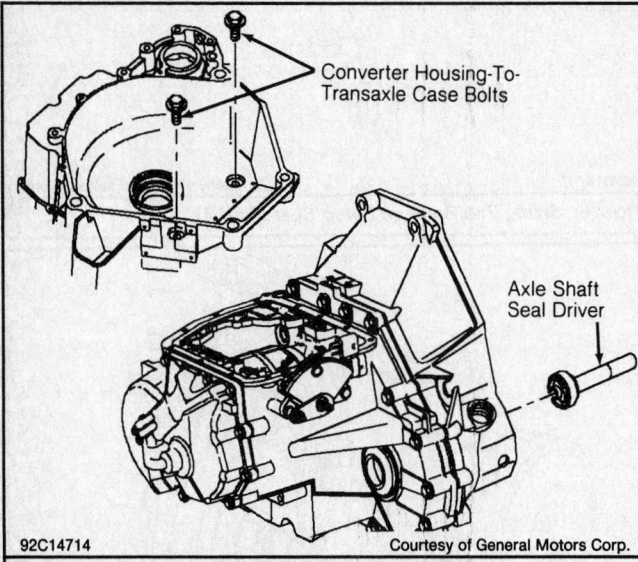

Fig. 79: *Installing Axle Shaft Seal & 2 Case Bolts*

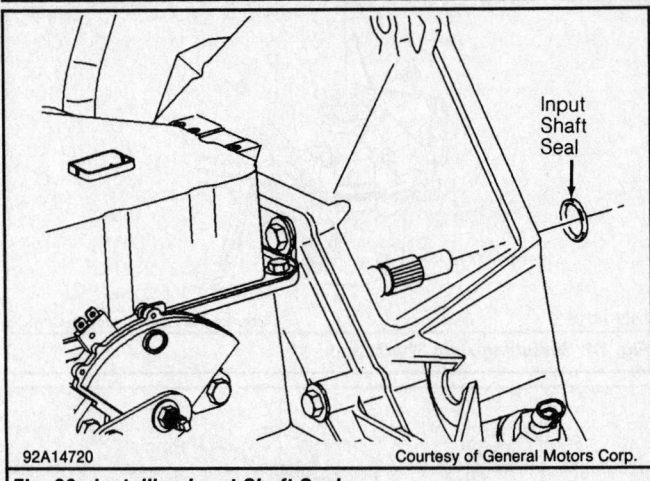

Fig. 83: *Installing Input Shaft Seal*

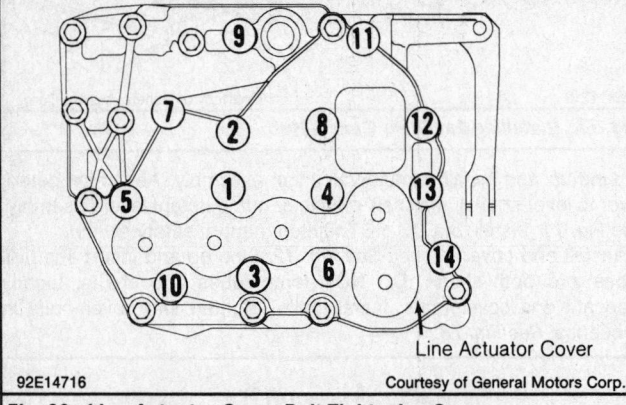

Fig. 80: *Line Actuator Cover Bolt Tightening Sequence*

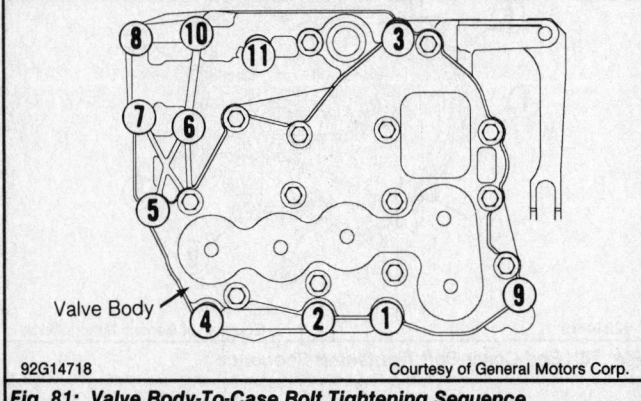

Fig. 81: *Valve Body-To-Case Bolt Tightening Sequence*

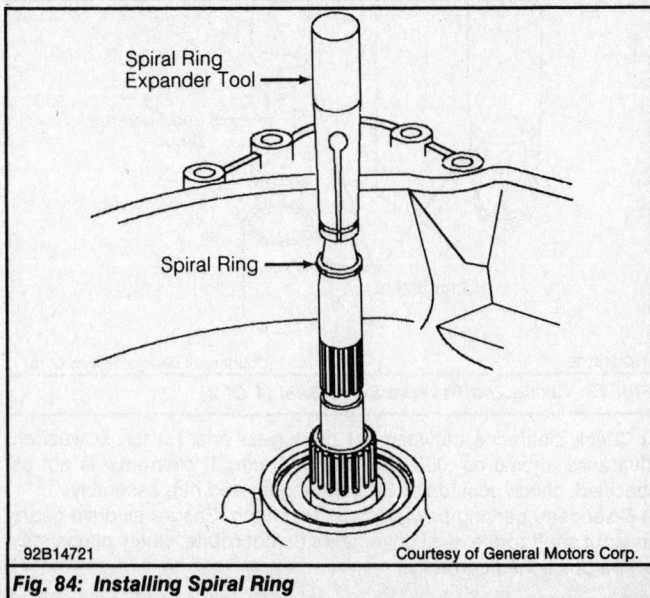

Fig. 84: *Installing Spiral Ring*

TORQUE SPECIFICATIONS

TORQUE SPECIFICATIONS

Application	Ft. Lbs. (N.m)
End Cover Bolt	21 (28)
Input Shaft Lock Nut	110 (149)
Oil Pan Drain Plug	
With Aluminum Washer	33 (45)
With Rubber Washer	22 (30)
Output Shaft Lock Nut	110 (149)
Parking Pawl Assembly Bolt	22 (30)
Reverse Idler Gear Cap Housing Bolt	15 (20)
Speed Sensors	19 (26)
Stator Support Bolt	22 (30)
Torque Converter Housing-To-Transaxle Case Bolt	
Short	18 (25)
Long	21 (28)
Transaxle Filter Tube Bolt	23 (31)
2nd/Reverse Servo Cover Bolt	15 (20)

Application	INCH Lbs. (N.m)
Dipstick Tube-To-Case Bolt	106 (12)
Line Actuator Cover Bolt	97 (11)
Manual Detent Shaft Nut	106 (12)
Neutral Safety Switch Bolt	124 (14)
Oil Pan Bolt	89 (10)
Oil Pump Bolt	106 (12)
Temperature Sensor	71 (8)
Valve Body-To-Case Bolt	97 (11)
2nd/Reverse Fork Lock Bolt	89 (10)

TRANSAXLE SPECIFICATIONS

TRANSAXLE SPECIFICATIONS

Application	In. (mm)
Clearance	
Input Shaft	
1st Gear-To-Thrust Washer	.003-.017 (.08-.43)
2nd/Reverse-To-Thrust Washer	.001-.006 (.03-.15)
4th Gear-To-Thrust Washer	.002-.009 (.05-.23)
Oil Pump	
Drive Gear Side	.0005-.0016 (.012-.041)
Driven Gear Side	.0005-.0016 (.012-.041)
Driven Gear-To-Housing	.0025-.0055 (.064-.139)
Drive Gear-To-Crescent	.0050-.0109 (.128-.278)
Driven Gear-To-Crescent	.0075-.0134 (.191-.341)
Output Shaft	
1st Gear-To-Thrust Washer	.004-.016 (.10-.40)
2nd Gear-To-Dog Clutch	.002-.006 (.05-.15)
3rd Gear-To-Thrust Washer	.00008-.018 (.0020-.46)
Reverse Gear-To-Thrust Washer	.003-.007 (.08-.18)
End Play	
Torque Converter (Maximum)	.026 (.60)
1st Clutch	.038-.055 (0.96-1.40)
2nd Clutch	.060-.086 (1.52-2.18)
3rd Clutch	.046-.061 (1.17-1.55)
4th Clutch	.036-.046 (0.91-1.17)

WIRING DIAGRAM

NOTE: For wiring diagram, see SATURN ELECTRONIC DIAGNOSIS article.

IDENTIFICATION

An identification code is stamped on top of transaxle case.

DESCRIPTION & OPERATION

Saturn vehicles use a 4-speed, fully automatic, electronically controlled transaxle with shift mode select function and self-diagnostic function.

The transaxle uses 5 electronic valves (line actuators), controlled by the Powertrain Control Module (PCM). The PCM controls all transaxle shifts, shift feel, Torque Converter Clutch (TCC) lock-up and self-diagnostics. PCM is located behind right side of dash. PCM has two 32-pin connectors and one 24-pin connector.

If an electrical circuit problem occurs, MALFUNCTION INDICATOR LIGHT (MIL) or LOW COOLANT/HOT light may come on or start flashing. PCM will store Diagnostic Trouble Codes (DTC's) or information flags in memory. A stored trouble code indicates PCM has detected a fault in engine or transaxle circuits. Information flags help diagnose current or intermittent trouble codes.

PCM is capable of operating in 2 different modes. The differences between the 2 modes are shift points. NORMAL mode or PERFORMANCE mode may be selected using mode switch. Mode switch is located on center console.

PCM INPUT SENSORS

ATF Temperature Sensor – Automatic Transaxle Fluid (ATF) temperature sensor is a thermistor mounted in line pressure port. PCM supplies a 5 volt reference signal to ATF temperature sensor through a resistor inside PCM and uses a signal line to measure voltage. Signal voltage will be high when transaxle fluid is cold and low when transaxle fluid is warm.

Brake Switch – Brake switch includes a normally closed contact. PCM uses this switch to determine when to apply or release TCC.

Ignition Signal – Ignition signal is supplied to PCM. PCM uses this signal to determine when TCC lock-up should occur.

Master Enable Relay – When ignition is on, PCM provides a ground to master enable relay. When relay is energized, battery voltage is connected to the line actuators and PCM. This signal allows PCM to monitor operation of master enable relay.

Mode Switch – Mode switch allows driver to select NORMAL mode or PERFORMANCE mode. When depressed, switch provides a signal to PCM. PCM will adjust shift points and TCC lock-up for mode selected.

Neutral Safety Switch Signal – This signal is used by PCM to detect what position transaxle selector lever is in. If selector lever is misadjusted, shifting of transaxle will be affected. For adjustment procedures, see TRANSAXLE REASSEMBLY in overhaul article.

PCM Diagnostic Connector – The diagnostic connector is located under instrument panel. PCM will indicate engine and transaxle related faults by turning on MALFUNCTION INDICATOR LIGHT (MIL) or LOW COOLANT/HOT light.

Turbine Speed Signal – Turbine shaft speed (RPM) signal is supplied to PCM by transaxle mounted PM generator. This signal is created when turbine shaft speed is above 250 RPM.

Vehicle Speed Sensor – Vehicle Speed Sensor (VSS) sends a pulse voltage signal to PCM. PCM uses this signal to determine shift points and TCC engagement. Signal for VSS is supplied by a transaxle mounted PM generator.

ECU OUTPUT CONTROLLED DEVICES

Line Actuators – Line actuators are controlled by PCM. Line actuators (duty-cycle type) open or close valve body ports inside the valve body. PCM controls line pressure with (duty-cycle type) line actuator to regulate transaxle line pressure for smooth shifting of transaxle.

Master Enable Relay – When ignition is on, PCM provides a ground to master enable relay. When relay is energized, battery voltage is connected to the line actuators and PCM.

MALFUNCTION INDICATOR LIGHT (MIL) – MALFUNCTION INDICATOR LIGHT (MIL) is controlled by PCM. The light will be on if a problem is present when ignition is on, or light will flicker on and off to indicate a problem has occurred. MALFUNCTION INDICATOR LIGHT (MIL) is also used to flash engine related trouble codes when cavity "A" and "B" of PCM diagnostic connector are jumpered. *See Fig. 1.*

LOW COOLANT/HOT Light – LOW COOLANT/HOT light is controlled by PCM. The light will be on if any of the following conditions are present when ignition is on: vehicle system voltage too low, PCM detection of faulty line actuator operation, vehicle speed too low in high gear, TCC stuck on or data communication missing. LOW COOLANT/HOT light is also used to flash transaxle related trouble codes and information flags when cavity "A" and "B" of PCM diagnostic connector are jumpered. *See Fig. 1.*

SELF-DIAGNOSTICS

PCM includes a self-diagnostic system. When a malfunction occurs, PCM will illuminate MALFUNCTION INDICATOR LIGHT (MIL) or LOW COOLANT/HOT light located on instrument panel. When a problem is detected and light is turned on, a corresponding trouble code will be stored in PCM memory. Problems are recorded as hard failures or as intermittent failures.

PCM will also store other problems as information flags in malfunction history. Information flags will not turn on MALFUNCTION INDICATOR LIGHT (MIL) or LOW COOLANT/HOT light. Information flags are used as a diagnostic tool to help technician when hard failures or intermittent failures occur.

Hard Failures – Hard failures cause MALFUNCTION INDICATOR LIGHT (MIL) and/or LOW COOLANT/HOT light to glow and remain on until problem is repaired. If light comes on and remains on (light may flash) during vehicle operation, determine cause of problem by using diagnostic (code) charts.

Intermittent Failures – Intermittent failures cause MALFUNCTION INDICATOR LIGHT (MIL) and/or LOW COOLANT/HOT light to flicker or glow and go out about 10 seconds after intermittent fault goes away. Corresponding trouble code, however, will be retained in PCM memory. If related fault does not reoccur within 50 engine starts, related trouble code will be erased from PCM memory. Intermittent failures may be caused by sensor, connector or wiring related problems.

Malfunction History & Information Flags – Engine information flags will not cause MALFUNCTION INDICATOR LIGHT (MIL) or LOW COOLANT/HOT light to glow. Unlike hard failures and intermittent failures, information flags and malfunction history will not be erased from PCM memory after 50 engine restarts.

Malfunction history includes data from the 4 most likely sensors which can cause a trouble code or information flag to be stored in PCM memory. When a malfunction occurs, the PCM records the appropriate sensor data. Information flag and malfunction history information can only be retrieved and cleared from PCM memory using a Saturn Portable Diagnostic Tool (PDT).

READING TROUBLE CODES

NOTE: Only hard codes, intermittent codes and information flags may be retrieved without using Saturn PDT. Malfunction history information can only be retrieved by using Saturn PDT.

PCM stores component failure information under a related trouble code which can be recalled for diagnosis and repair. Trouble codes may be read by counting flashes of MALFUNCTION INDICATOR LIGHT (MIL) or LOW COOLANT/HOT light.

For example, "FLASH, FLASH, pause, FLASH, longer pause" identifies DTC 21. The first series of flashes represents first digit of trouble code. The second series of flashes represents second digit of trouble code. Thus; "FLASH, FLASH, FLASH, FLASH, FLASH, pause, FLASH, FLASH, longer pause" identifies DTC 52.

The first code will always be DTC 12, followed by all other stored trouble codes. Each code will be repeated 3 times. Record all stored codes. MALFUNCTION INDICATOR LIGHT (MIL) will flash DTC 11 three times to indicate end of engine related trouble codes and start of transaxle related trouble codes.

LOW COOLANT/HOT light will start flashing transaxle related codes and information flags. See appropriate table under TROUBLE CODES & INFORMATION FLAGS. Stored transaxle DTC's and information flags are read by counting flashes of LOW COOLANT/HOT light. If MALFUNCTION INDICATOR LIGHT (MIL) does not flash DTC 11, no transaxle trouble codes or information flags are stored in PCM memory.

NOTE: Trouble codes will be recorded at various operating times. In order to set some trouble codes, vehicle may require road testing (up to 5 minutes or longer for some sensors or switches).

RETRIEVING CODES

NOTE: The Saturn PDT is used to display all self-diagnostic information stored in PCM memory. For information on retrieving codes with Saturn PDT, see manufacturer's information.

1) Turn ignition on. DO NOT start engine. MALFUNCTION INDICATOR LIGHT (MIL) should glow. Insert jumper wire from terminal "B" (diagnostic test terminal) to terminal "A" (ground) of PCM diagnostic connector. *See Fig. 1.*

2) MALFUNCTION INDICATOR LIGHT (MIL) should begin to flash codes. To exit diagnostic mode, turn ignition off and remove jumper wire from PCM diagnostic connector.

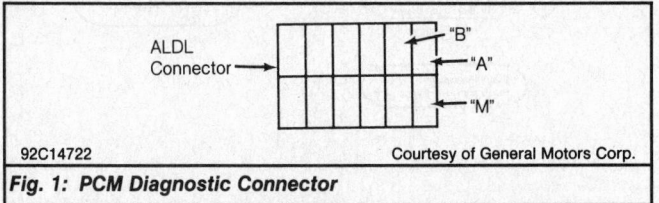

92C14722   Courtesy of General Motors Corp.

Fig. 1: PCM Diagnostic Connector

TROUBLE CODES & INFORMATION FLAGS

DIAGNOSTIC TROUBLE CODES (DTC)

DTC No.	Fault
11	Transaxle Codes Present
13	High Line Pressure
14	Low Line Pressure
16	No 1st Gear
18	No Forward Gears
21	2nd Gear Stuck On
22	No 2nd Gear
23	No 3rd Gear
24	No 4th Gear
25	No TCC
26	TCC Stuck On
31	Transaxle Temperature Cold (Circuit Open)
32	Transaxle Temperature Hot (Circuit Grounded)
34	PCM Data Communication Failed
35	No Turbine Speed Input
36	Noise On Turbine Speed Input
41	Vehicle Speed Sensor Input Not Present
42	Noise On Vehicle Speed Sensor Input
43	Master Enable Relay Grounded/Open
44	Master Enable Relay Shorted To Voltage
45	Selector Switch No Data
46	Selector Switch Incorrect Data
49	Selector Switch Incorrect Data
54	Data Error (PCM Failure)
55	Transaxle Temperature Resistor (PCM Failure)
56	Output Driver Error (PCM Failure)
75	3rd Gear Stuck On
78	4th Gear Stuck On

INFORMATION FLAGS

Information Flag No.	Fault
15	HOT Light On
47	PCM Data Communication Failure (PCM Failure)
51	PCM Serial Data Link Error (PCM Failure)
57	Non-Volatile RAM Error (PCM Failure)
61	PROM Error (PCM Failure)
62	PCM Error (PCM Failure)
63	PCM RAM Error (PCM Failure)
64	PCM EE PROM Error (PCM Failure)
65	Battery Voltage Too High Or Too Low
68	Line Actuator Circuit Grounded/Open
69	Line Actuator Circuit Shorted To Voltage
71	2nd Gear Actuator Circuit Grounded/Open
72	2nd Gear Actuator Circuit Shorted To Voltage
73	3rd Gear Actuator Circuit Grounded/Open
74	3rd Gear Actuator Circuit Shorted To Voltage
76	4th Gear Actuator Circuit Grounded/Open
77	4th Gear Actuator Circuit Shorted To Voltage
79	TCC Actuator Circuit Grounded/Open
81	TCC Actuator Circuit Shorted To Voltage
83	Low Transaxle Temperature
84	Brake Switch Stuck Open
85	Brake Switch Stuck Closed
86	Engine Speed Signal Error (PCM Failure)
89	Master Enable Relay Stuck On
94	Possible Master Enable Relay Failure (1993)
95	Possible Line Actuator Failure
96	Possible TCC Actuator Failure
97	Possible 2nd Actuator Failure
98	Possible 3rd Actuator Failure
99	Possible 4th Actuator Failure

CLEARING CODES

To clear trouble codes, turn ignition switch to ON position and jumper connector test terminal "B" to ground terminal "A" at PCM diagnostic connector 3 times within 5 seconds. *See Fig. 1.* Trouble codes will also clear automatically if they do not reoccur within 50 engine starts. Malfunction history codes and information flags can only be cleared using a Saturn PDT.

PCM LEARN MODE

1) The PCM will change transaxle shift points depending on driving conditions or changes in engine performance. If the PCM memory or vehicle battery is disconnected, the PCM must relearn the current operating parameters.

2) Perform the following procedure on a clear highway. Place mode select switch (located on center console) in NORMAL position. With transaxle at normal operating temperature, place gear selector in "D4" position. Open throttle about 30 percent. Perform 10 complete 1-2, 2-3 to 3-4 upshifts.

3) While coasting at 35 MPH (DOHC engine) or 40 MPH (SOHC engine), open throttle halfway to create a 4-3 downshift. Repeat 5 times. Move gear selector to "D3" position. While coasting at 20 MPH (DOHC engine) or 30 MPH (SOHC engine), open throttle 75 percent to create a 3-2 downshift. Repeat 5 times.

ACTUATOR QUICK CHECK

1) Check level and condition of transaxle fluid. Check PCM memory for any stored trouble codes. If no trouble codes are present, go to next step. If codes are present, diagnose and repair all PCM related trouble codes. Clear PCM trouble code memory.

2) If no codes are present, use Saturn PDT to ensure all selector switch (PRND32) positions are correct. Jumper terminals "A" and "B" of the diagnostic connector. *See Fig. 1.*

3) With key on and engine off, move gear selector to each gear position. This should cause a specific line actuator to operate. See LINE ACTUATOR SELECT table.

4) If the line actuator is operating, it will audibly operate at a fixed duty cycle for 6 seconds and then click on and off. Clicking will repeat until the next gear is selected or ignition turned off.

LINE ACTUATOR SELECT

Selected Gear	Actuator
"D2"	2nd Actuator
"D3"	3rd Actuator
"D4"	4th Actuator
"R"	TCC Actuator
"N" or "P"	Line Actuator

DTC CHARTS

NOTE: Several steps included in code charts require the use of a Saturn PDT. If these steps are followed without the PDT, false testing results may occur.

Diagnostic Charts – The following charts include related electrical circuits, flow charts and testing information. For complete wiring diagram, see WIRING DIAGRAM.

Diagnostic Aids – DIAGNOSTIC AIDS (located in many code charts) are additional tips used to help diagnose codes when circuit checks do not find a problem.

DTC 13, HIGH LINE PRESSURE

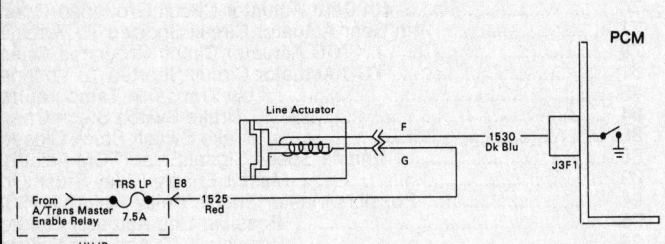

The PCM modulates line pressure by grounding line pressure actuator. As duty cycle decreases (circuit is opened more), line pressure increases. As duty cycle is increased (circuit is grounded more), line pressure decreases. When PCM lowers line pressure, gear shifts take more time. A DTC 13 will set if transaxle oil temperature is above 104°F (40°C) and PCM detects that shifts occur too fast even though line pressure has been commanded low.

NOTE: Test numbers refer to numbers on diagnostic chart.

1) If present, go to information flag listed. Using flow charts, check for possible causes of trouble code.
2) See ACTUATOR QUICK CHECK under SELF-DIAGNOSTICS.
3) See HYDRAULIC PRESSURE TESTS in overhaul article.
4) If line pressure does not change or only changes a little, regulator valve is stuck. If necessary, see HYDRAULIC PRESSURE TESTS in overhaul article.

92E14724 92F14725

DIAGNOSTIC AIDS

Problem is intermittent at this time. Check all terminals, connections and harness for possible loose or corroded condition. The PCM is protected from damage by internal circuit design.

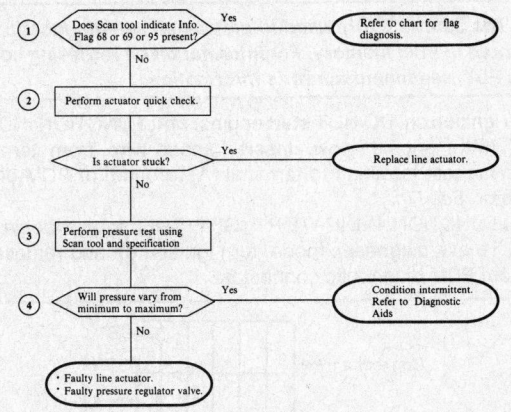

Courtesy of General Motors Corp.

DTC 14, LOW LINE PRESSURE

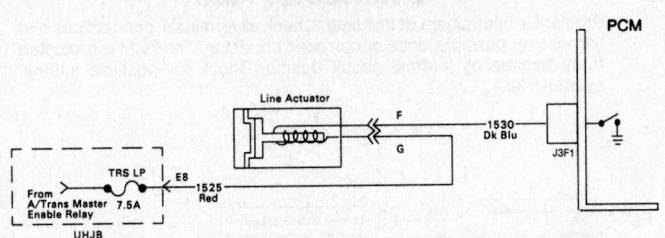

The PCM modulates line pressure by grounding line pressure actuator. As duty cycle decreases (circuit is opened more), line pressure increases. As duty cycle increases (circuit is grounded more), line pressure decreases. When PCM raises line pressure, gear shifts take less time. An DTC 14 will be set if transaxle DTC's 16, 22, 23 and 24 are detected, and PCM detects that shifts occur too slowly even though line pressure has been commanded high. If transaxle DTC's 16, 22, 23 and 24 are set, forward gears may not be present.

NOTE: Test numbers refer to numbers on diagnostic chart.

1) If present, go to information flag listed. Using flow charts, check for possible causes of information flag.
2) See ACTUATOR QUICK CHECK under SELF-DIAGNOSTICS. If line actuator noise is the same, check for damaged pressure regulator valve or oil pump assembly.
3) See HYDRAULIC PRESSURE TESTS in overhaul article.
4) This step checks if output shaft may be broken. If no forward gears are available, DTC 18 will probably set. Ensure pressure increases in correct increments during pressure test. If pressure changes erratically and moves in large increments, pressure regulator valve is probably stuck.
5) This step checks for problem with oil pump pick-up or if pressure regulator valve is stuck. If necessary, see HYDRAULIC PRESSURE TESTS in overhaul article.

92E14724 92B14762

DIAGNOSTIC AIDS

Problem is intermittent at this time. Check all terminals, connections and harness for possible loose or corroded condition. The PCM is protected from damage by internal circuit design.

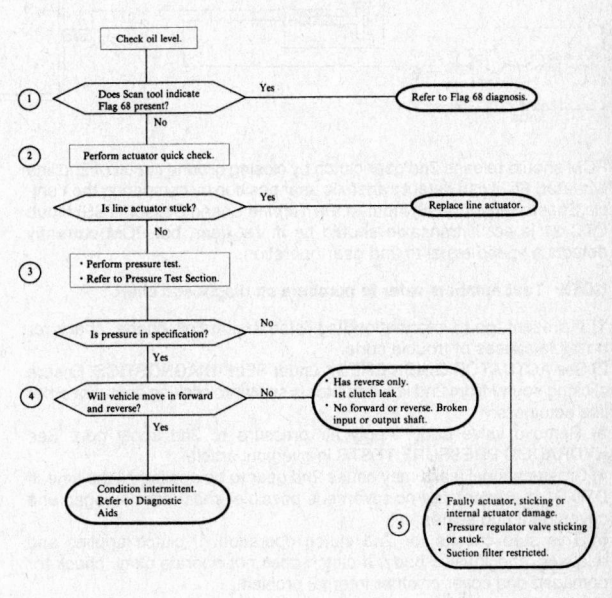

Courtesy of General Motors Corp.

DTC 16, NO 1ST GEAR

Manual shift valve controls hydraulic pressure to 1st gear clutch housing. First gear clutch is engaged in all forward gears. If PCM detects 1st gear clutch slipping, PCM will increase line pressure. If clutch is still slipping, PCM will set DTC 16.

NOTE: Test numbers refer to numbers on diagnostic chart.

1) If present, go to DTC 14. Using flow chart, check for possible causes of low line pressure.
2) See HYDRAULIC PRESSURE TESTS in overhaul article.
3) Remove valve body. Apply air pressure to 1st apply port. See HYDRAULIC PRESSURE TESTS in overhaul article.
4) This step checks for hydraulic or mechanical problems. See overhaul article.

DIAGNOSTIC AIDS

First gear is controlled by manual shift valve and line pressure. If 1st gear is slipping, ensure manual valve, selector linkage and internal components are okay. Other than line pressure, PCM does not control 1st gear operation.

94F38484

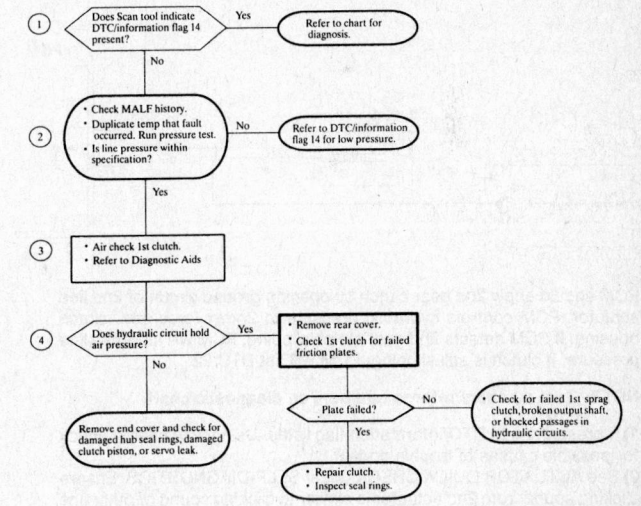

Courtesy of General Motors Corp.

DTC 18, NO FORWARD GEARS

For each gear position (except 1st), PCM controls hydraulic pressure to appropriate clutch housing. If PCM does not detect correct turbine shaft speed for any forward gear, and vehicle speed is zero, PCM will set DTC 18.

NOTE: Test numbers refer to numbers on diagnostic chart.

1) If DTC 18 is present, ensure VSS and TSS are working correctly. See DTC 14 and test system for low line pressure.
2) Ensure selector switch is operating properly and selector switch wiring is correct. Check for misadjusted shift cable and/or disconnected manual valve.

Courtesy of General Motors Corp.

DTC 21, 2ND GEAR STUCK ON

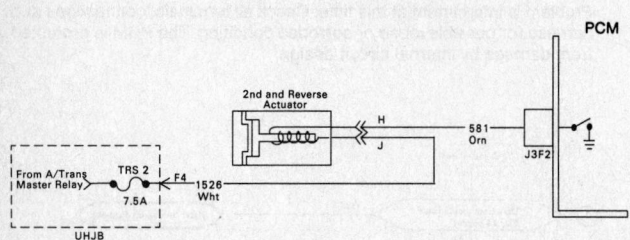

PCM should release 2nd gear clutch by closing ground circuit of 2nd line actuator. PCM can detect transaxle gear position by comparing the Vehicle Speed Sensor (VSS) input to the Turbine Speed Sensor (TSS) input. DTC 21 is set if transaxle should be in 1st gear, but PCM currently detects a speed equal to 2nd gear operation.

NOTE: Test numbers refer to numbers on diagnostic chart.

1) If present, go to information flag listed. Using flow charts, check for possible causes of trouble code.
2) See ACTUATOR QUICK CHECK under SELF-DIAGNOSTICS. Ensure clicking sound from 2nd line actuator is similar to clicking sound of other line actuators.
3) Remove valve body. Apply air pressure to 2nd apply port. See HYDRAULIC PRESSURE TESTS in overhaul article.
4) Cross-channel leaks may cause 2nd gear to be applied all the time. If DTC 21 is present and no reverse is possible, check for damaged end cover input hub seals.
5) This step checks for 2nd clutch operation. If clutch applies and releases, check valve body. If clutch does not operate okay, check for damaged end cover or other internal problem.

92H14727 92I14728

DIAGNOSTIC AIDS

Problem is intermittent at this time. Check all terminals, connections and harness for possible loose or corroded condition. The PCM is protected from damage by internal circuit design. Check for possible internal hydraulic leak.

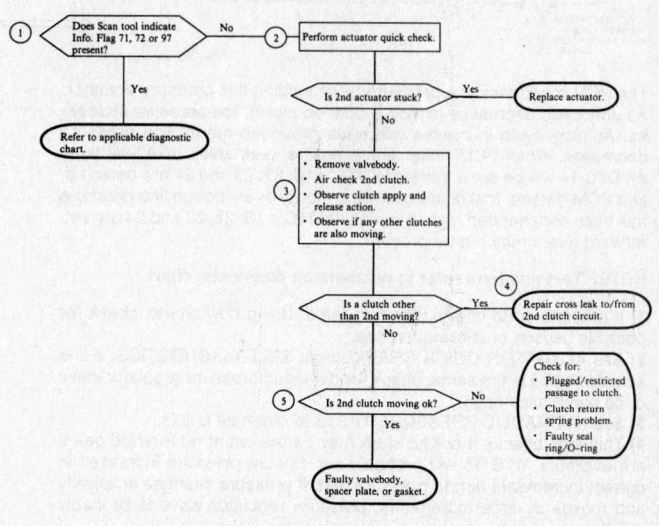

Courtesy of General Motors Corp.

DTC 22, NO 2ND GEAR

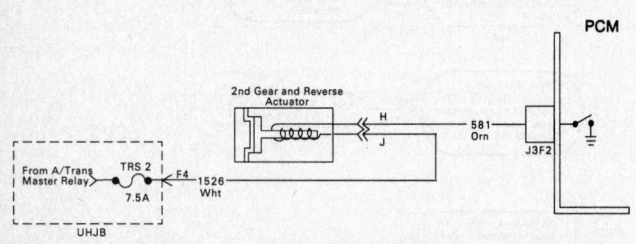

PCM should apply 2nd gear clutch by opening ground circuit of 2nd line actuator. PCM controls hydraulic pressure to 2nd/reverse gear clutch housing. If PCM detects 2nd gear clutch slipping, PCM will increase line pressure. If clutch is still slipping, PCM will set DTC 22.

NOTE: Test numbers refer to numbers on diagnostic chart.

1) If present, go to DTC/information flag listed. Using flow charts, check for possible causes of trouble code.
2) See ACTUATOR QUICK CHECK under SELF-DIAGNOSTICS. Ensure clicking sound from 2nd actuator is similar to clicking sound of other line actuators.
3) See HYDRAULIC PRESSURE TESTS in overhaul article. If line pressure does not change or only changes a little, regulator valve is stuck.
4) Remove valve body. Apply air pressure to 2nd apply port. See HYDRAULIC PRESSURE TESTS in overhaul article.
5) Cross-channel leaks may cause other clutches to be applied. If PCM detects other gears are stuck on, other DTC's will be present. This may help locate cross-channel leak.
6) This step checks for 2nd clutch operation. If clutch applies and releases, check valve body for damage. If clutch does not operate, check for failed clutch plates.

92H14727 94G38485

DIAGNOSTIC AIDS

Problem is intermittent at this time. Check all terminals, connections and harness for possible loose or corroded condition. The PCM is protected from damage by internal circuit design.

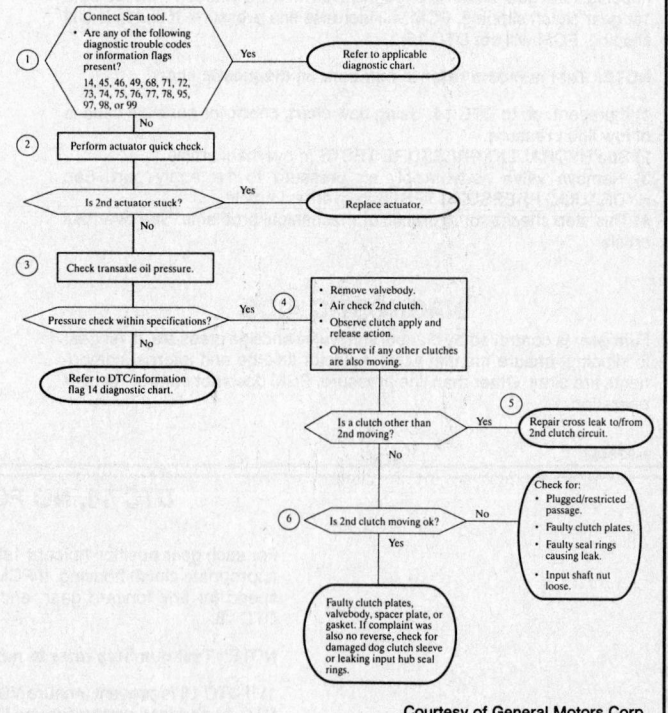

Courtesy of General Motors Corp.

DTC 23, NO 3RD GEAR

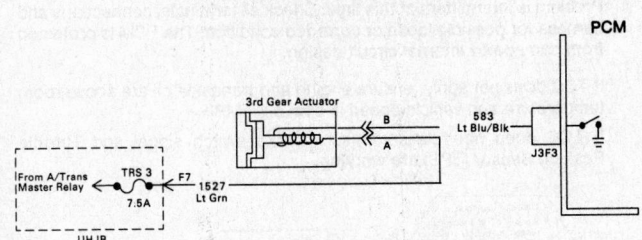

PCM should apply 3rd gear clutch by opening ground circuit of 3rd line actuator. PCM also controls hydraulic pressure to 3rd gear clutch housing. If PCM detects 3rd gear clutch slipping, PCM will increase line pressure. If clutch is still slipping, PCM will set DTC 23.

NOTE: Test numbers refer to numbers on diagnostic chart.

1) If present, go to DTC/information flag listed. Using flow charts, check for possible causes of trouble code.
2) See ACTUATOR QUICK CHECK under SELF-DIAGNOSTICS. Ensure clicking sound from 3rd line actuator is similar to clicking sound of other line actuators.
3) See HYDRAULIC PRESSURE TESTS in overhaul article. If line pressure does not change or only changes a little, regulator valve is stuck.
4) Remove valve body. Apply air pressure to 3rd apply port. See HYDRAULIC PRESSURE TESTS in overhaul article.
5) Cross-channel leaks may cause other clutches to be applied. If PCM detects other gears are stuck on, other DTC's will be present. This may help locate cross-channel leak.
6) This step checks for 3rd clutch operation. If clutch applies and releases, check valve body for damage. If clutch does not operate okay, check for failed clutch plates.

92D14731 94H38486

DIAGNOSTIC AIDS

Problem is intermittent at this time. Check all terminals, connections and harness for possible loose or corroded condition. The PCM is protected from damage by internal circuit design.

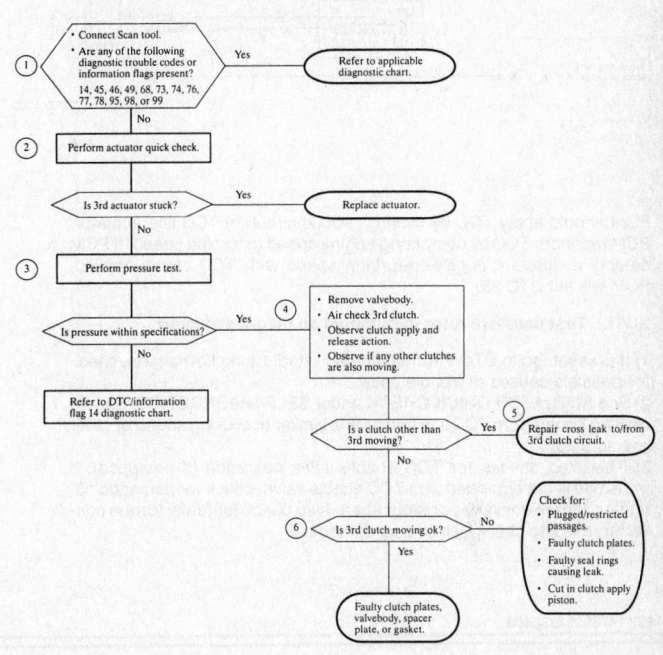

Courtesy of General Motors Corp.

DTC 24, NO 4TH GEAR

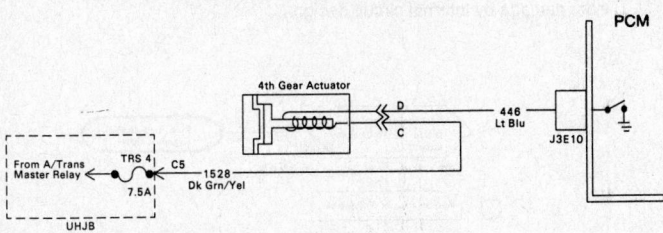

PCM should apply 4th gear clutch by opening ground circuit of 4th line actuator. PCM controls hydraulic pressure to 4th gear clutch housing. If PCM detects 4th gear clutch slipping, PCM will increase line pressure. If clutch is still slipping, PCM will set DTC 24.

NOTE: Test numbers refer to numbers on diagnostic chart.

1) If present, go to DTC/information flag listed. Using flow charts, check for possible causes of trouble code.
2) See ACTUATOR QUICK CHECK under SELF-DIAGNOSTICS. Ensure clicking sound from 4th line actuator is similar to clicking sound of other line actuators.
3) See HYDRAULIC PRESSURE TESTS in overhaul article. If line pressure does not change or only changes a little, regulator valve is stuck.
4) Remove valve body. Apply air pressure to 4th apply port. See HYDRAULIC PRESSURE TESTS in overhaul article.
5) Cross-channel leaks may cause other clutches to be applied. If PCM detects other gears are stuck on, other DTC's will be present. This may help locate cross-channel leak.
6) This step checks for 4th clutch operation. If clutch applies and releases, check valve body for damage. If clutch does not operate, check for failed clutch plates.

92F14733 94I38487

DIAGNOSTIC AIDS

Problem is intermittent at this time. Check all terminals, connections and harness for possible loose or corroded condition. The PCM is protected from damage by internal circuit design.

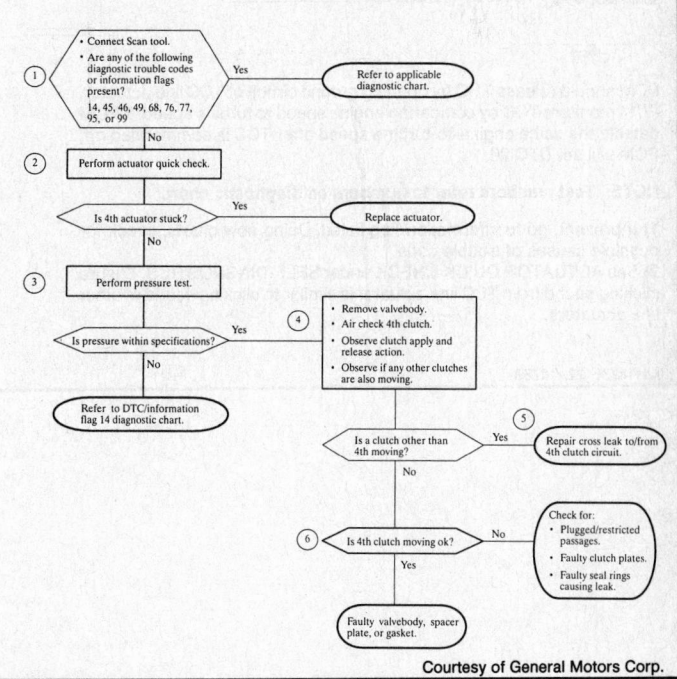

Courtesy of General Motors Corp.

DTC 25, NO TCC

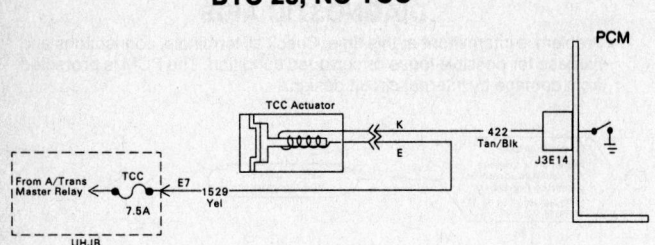

PCM should apply TCC by closing ground circuit of TCC line actuator. PCM monitors TCC by comparing engine speed to turbine speed. If PCM detects a different engine-to-turbine speed with TCC clutch applied, PCM will set DTC 25.

NOTE: Test numbers refer to numbers on diagnostic chart.

1) If present, go to DTC/information flag listed. Using flow charts, check for possible causes of trouble code.
2) See ACTUATOR QUICK CHECK under SELF-DIAGNOSTICS. Ensure clicking sound from TCC line actuator is similar to clicking sound of other line actuators.
3) This step checks for TCC enable valve operation (if equipped). If transaxle is not equipped with TCC enable valve, check for damaged "O" ring on torque converter or input shaft. Also check for faulty torque converter, missing check ball or seal damage.

92H14735 94J38488

DIAGNOSTIC AIDS

Problem is intermittent at this time. Check all terminals, connections and harness for possible loose or corroded condition. The PCM is protected from damage by internal circuit design.

If TCC does not apply, ensure engine and transaxle oil are above room temperature and vehicle speed is above 16 MPH.

If TCC does not release, ensure brake switch signal and Throttle Position Sensor (TPS) are working.

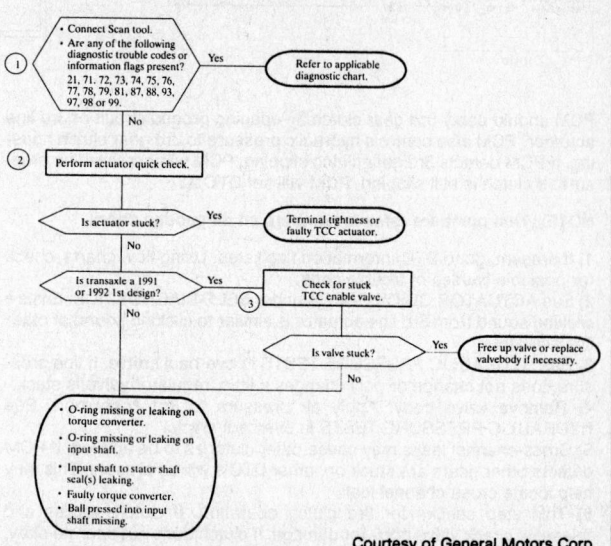

Courtesy of General Motors Corp.

DTC 26, TCC STUCK ON

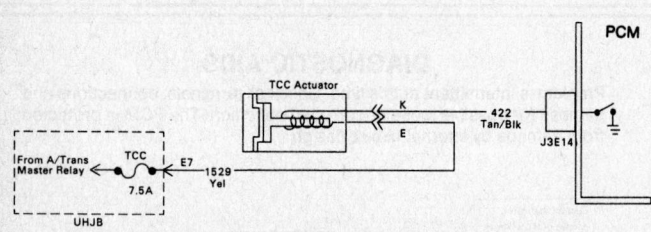

PCM should release TCC by opening ground circuit of TCC line actuator. PCM monitors TCC by comparing engine speed to turbine speed. If PCM detects the same engine-to-turbine speed after TCC is commanded off, PCM will set DTC 26.

NOTE: Test numbers refer to numbers on diagnostic chart.

1) If present, go to information flag listed. Using flow charts, check for possible causes of trouble code.
2) See ACTUATOR QUICK CHECK under SELF-DIAGNOSTICS. Ensure clicking sound from TCC line actuator is similar to clicking sound of other line actuators.

92H14735 92A14738

DIAGNOSTIC AIDS

Problem is intermittent at this time. Check all terminals, connections and harness for possible loose or corroded condition. The PCM is protected from damage by internal circuit design.

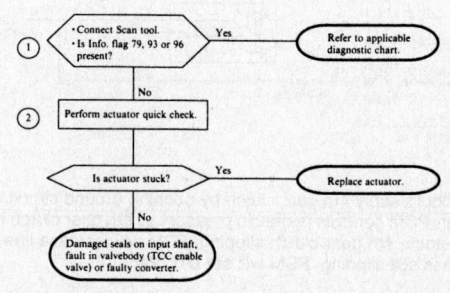

Courtesy of General Motors Corp.

DTC 31, TRANSAXLE TEMPERATURE COLD (CIRCUIT OPEN)

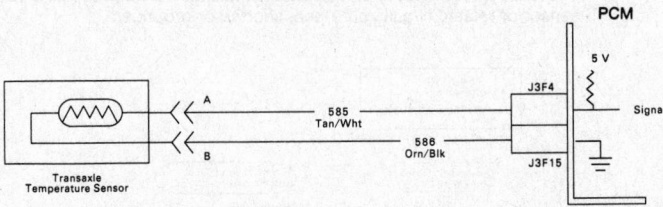

PCM supplies a 5 volt signal to transaxle temperature sensor. As transaxle temperature increases, sensor value should decrease. PCM monitors the voltage change on an internal circuit. If engine is running for at least 3 1/2 minutes, and PCM detects a transaxle temperature less than -35°F (-37°C), PCM will set DTC 31.

NOTE: Test numbers refer to numbers on diagnostic chart.

1) This step checks if DTC 31 is still present. If scan tool temperature reading is above -35°F (-37°C), problem is intermittent.
2) This step duplicates conditions for DTC 32. If PCM does not set a DTC 32, go to next step. If PCM sets DTC 32 and/or scan tool reads greater than 284°F (140°C), PCM and wiring are okay. If PCM and wiring are okay, replace sensor.
3) This step also duplicates conditions for DTC 32. If PCM does not set DTC 32, Orange/Black wire is open or PCM is faulty. If Orange/Black wire is okay, replace PCM.

DIAGNOSTIC AIDS

PCM should detect high sensor resistance with low transaxle temperature. Problem is intermittent at this time. Check all terminals, connections and harness for possible loose or corroded condition.

92B14739 94A38489

TEMPERATURE SENSOR TEMPERATURE TO RESISTANCE

Degrees C	Degrees F	Sensor Resistance
−40	−40	93630
−29	−20	46352
−18	0	24094
−7	20	13111
4	40	7436
16	60	4180
27	80	2554
38	100	1609
49	120	1043
60	140	693
72	160	456
83	180	318
94	200	226
105	220	165
120	248	109
140	284	65

Courtesy of General Motors Corp.

DTC 32, TRANSAXLE TEMPERATURE HOT (CIRCUIT GROUNDED)

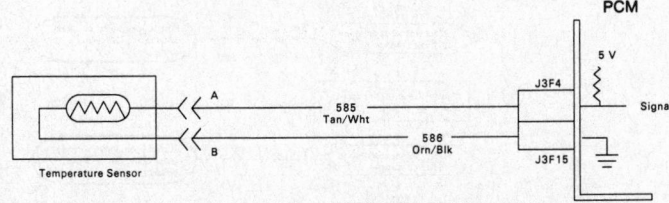

PCM supplies a 5 volt signal to transaxle temperature sensor. As transaxle temperature increases, sensor value should decrease. PCM monitors the voltage change on an internal circuit. If engine is running for at least 1/2 minute, and PCM detects a transaxle temperature greater than 284°F (140°C) with engine coolant temperature below 212°F (100°C), PCM will set DTC 32.

NOTE: Test numbers refer to numbers on diagnostic chart.

1) This step checks if DTC 31 is still present. If scan tool temperature reading is less than 284°F (140°C), problem is intermittent.
2) This step duplicates conditions for DTC 31. If PCM sets a DTC 31 and/or scan tool reads less than -35°F (-37°C), PCM and wiring are okay. If PCM and wiring are okay, replace sensor. If PCM does not set DTC 31 and/or scan tool reads greater than -35°F (-37°C), check for shorted circuits or replace PCM.

92B14739 92G14742

DIAGNOSTIC AIDS

PCM should detect high sensor resistance with low transaxle temperature. Problem is intermittent at this time. Check all terminals, connections and harness for possible loose or corroded condition.

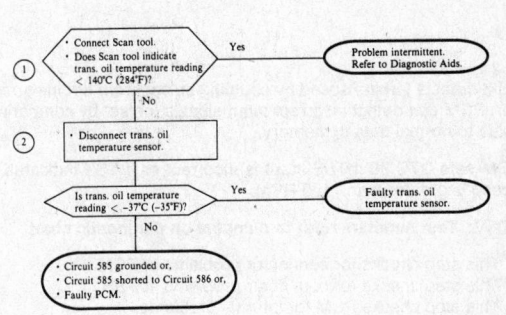

Courtesy of General Motors Corp.

DTC 34, COMMUNICATIONS ERROR

If PCM sets DTC 34, an internal communication problem is present.
Replace PCM.

Courtesy of General Motors Corp.

DTC 35, NO TURBINE SPEED INPUT

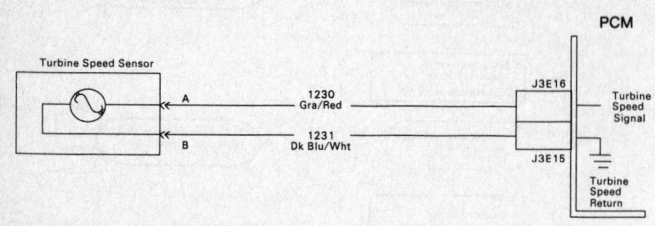

DIAGNOSTIC AIDS

Problem is intermittent at this time. Check all terminals, connections and harness for possible loose or corroded condition. PCM will set DTC 35 if sensor or related circuits are open, shorted or grounded.

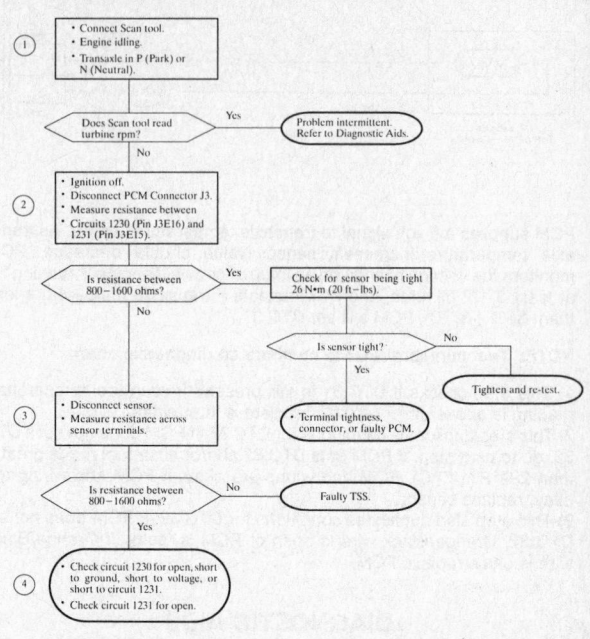

When turbine shaft speed is greater than 250 RPM, Turbine Speed Sensor (TSS) produces 8 electrical pulses per turbine shaft revolution. PCM detects turbine speed by counting pulses from turbine speed sensor. PCM sets DTC 35 if TSS input is zero and engine speed is greater than 3472 RPM. PCM also sets DTC 35 if TSS input is zero, engine speed is greater than 980 RPM and vehicle speed is greater than 6 MPH.

NOTE: Test numbers refer to numbers on diagnostic chart.

1) This step checks if code is still present.
2) This step checks if a wiring or sensor problem is present. If not, PCM may be faulty.
3) This step checks for a bad sensor.
4) This step checks each circuit for short or ground condition.

92H14743 94D38490 | Courtesy of General Motors Corp.

DTC 36, NOISE ON TURBINE SPEED INPUT

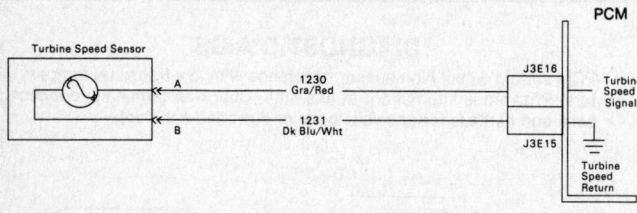

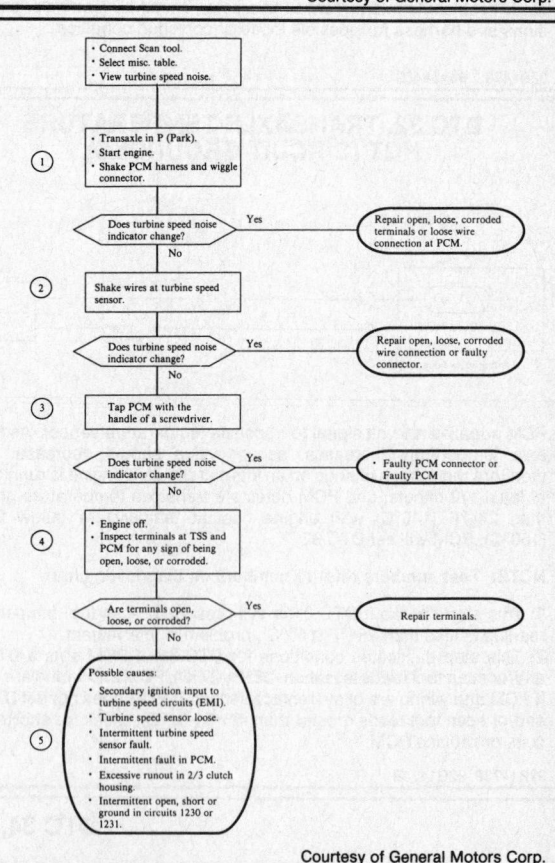

PCM detects turbine speed by counting pulses from turbine speed sensor. PCM can detect incorrect input signals (noise) by comparing input value to normal data in memory.

PCM sets DTC 36 if TSS input is incorrect or if TSS indicates turbine speed is greater than 1400 RPM.

NOTE: Test numbers refer to numbers on diagnostic chart.

1) This step checks for connector problems at PCM.
2) This step checks for connector problems at TSS.
3) This step checks PCM for internal problems.
4) This step checks each circuit for any visual problems.
5) This step lists other possible causes of DTC 36.

DIAGNOSTIC AIDS

Problem is intermittent at this time. Check all terminals, connections and harness for possible loose or corroded condition. PCM will set DTC 36 if sensor or related circuits are open, shorted or grounded.

92H14743 92A14746 | Courtesy of General Motors Corp.

DTC 41, VEHICLE SPEED SENSOR INPUT NOT PRESENT

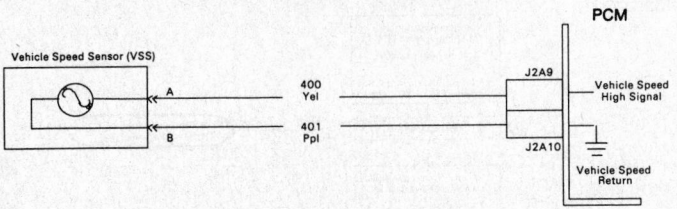

When vehicle speed is greater than 3 MPH, Vehicle Speed Sensor (VSS) produces 16 electrical pulses per turbine shaft revolution. PCM detects vehicle speed by counting pulses from VSS. PCM sets DTC 41 if VSS input is zero, turbine speed is greater than 1400 RPM and throttle is held at a moderate opening.

NOTE: Test numbers refer to numbers on diagnostic chart.

1) This step checks if DTC is still present.
2) This step checks if a wiring or sensor problem is present. If not, PCM may be faulty.
3) This step checks for a bad sensor.
4) This step checks each circuit for short or ground condition.

92B14747 92C14748

DIAGNOSTIC AIDS

Problem is intermittent at this time. Check all terminals, connections and harness for possible loose or corroded condition. PCM will set DTC 41 if sensor or related circuits are open, shorted or grounded.

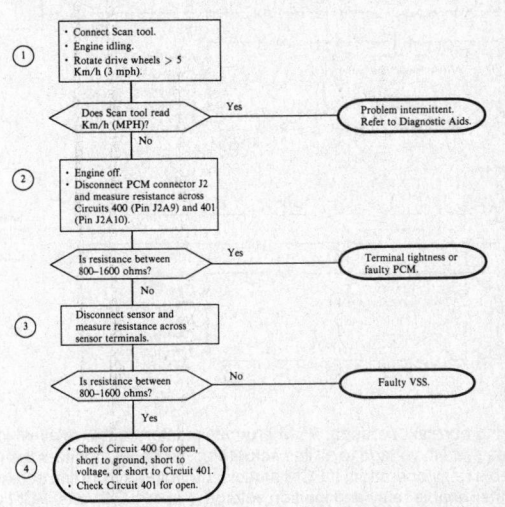

Courtesy of General Motors Corp.

DTC 42, NOISE ON VEHICLE SPEED SENSOR INPUT

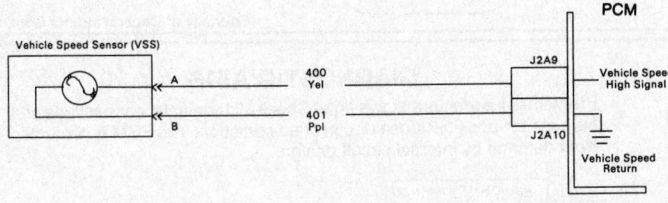

PCM detects vehicle speed by counting pulses from Vehicle Speed Sensor (VSS). PCM can detect incorrect input signals (noise) by comparing input value to normal data in memory. PCM sets DTC 42 if VSS input is incorrect or if VSS indicates vehicle speed is greater than 15 MPH.

NOTE: Test numbers refer to numbers on diagnostic chart.

1) This step checks for connector problems at PCM.
2) This step checks PCM for internal problems.
3) This step checks for connector problems at VSS.
4) This step checks each circuit for any visual problems.
5) This step lists other possible causes of DTC 42.

DIAGNOSTIC AIDS

Problem is intermittent at this time. Check all terminals, connections and harness for possible loose or corroded condition. PCM will set DTC 36 if sensor or related circuits are open, shorted or grounded.

92B14747 92H14750

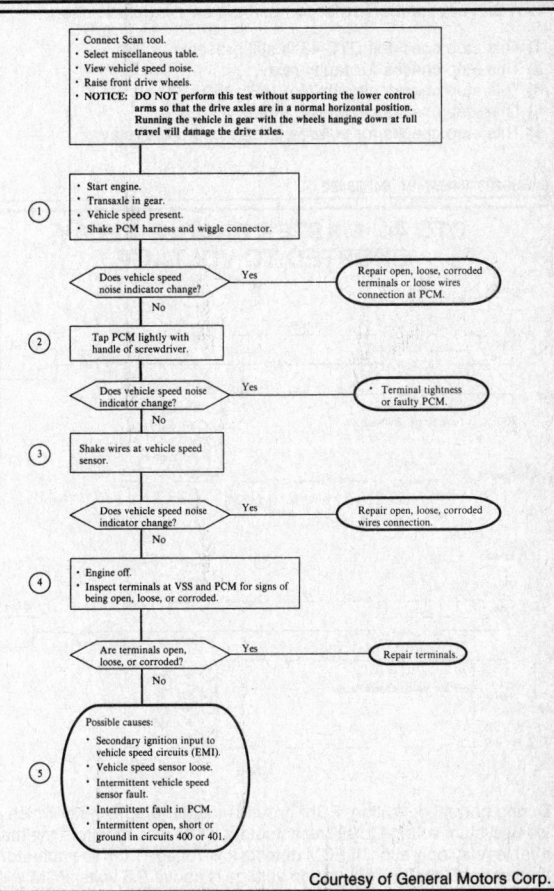

Courtesy of General Motors Corp.

DTC 43, MASTER ENABLE RELAY GROUNDED/OPEN

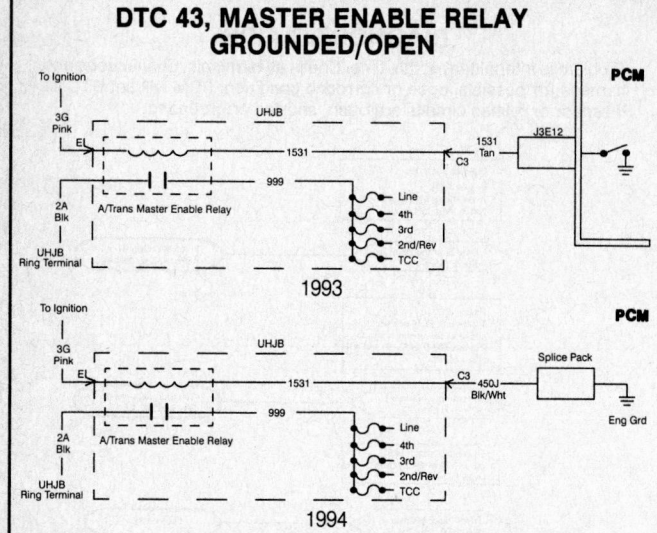

1993

1994

During normal operation, PCM grounds master enable relay which provides system voltage to all line actuators. PCM also monitors the master enable relay operation. If PCM detects low voltage from line actuators or master enable relay and ignition voltage is above 9.5 volts, PCM will set DTC 43.

NOTE: Test numbers refer to numbers on diagnostic chart.

1) This step checks if DTC 43 is still present.
2) This step checks for faulty relay.
3) This step checks circuits No. 1531/450J.
4) This step checks circuit No. 999.
5) This step checks for voltage to master enable relay.

94G38493 94E38491 94F38492

DIAGNOSTIC AIDS

Problem is intermittent at this time. Check all terminals, connections and harness for possible loose or corroded condition. The PCM is protected from damage by internal circuit design.

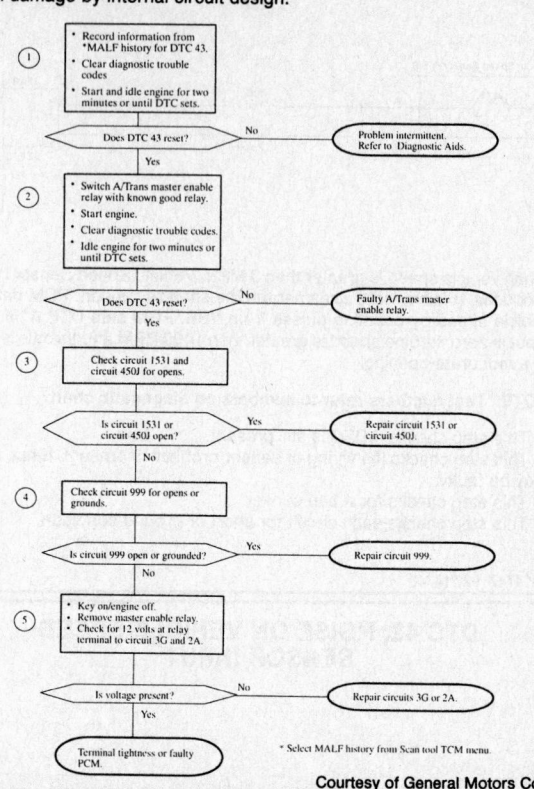

Courtesy of General Motors Corp.

DTC 44, MASTER ENABLE RELAY SHORTED TO VOLTAGE

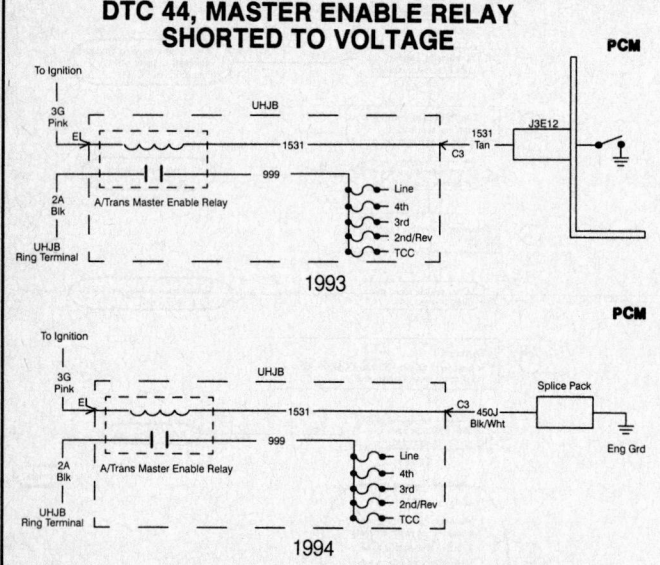

1993

1994

During normal operation, PCM grounds master enable relay which provides system voltage to all line actuators. PCM also monitors the master enable relay operation. If PCM detects low voltage from line actuators or master enable relay and ignition voltage is above 9.5 volts, PCM will set DTC 43.

NOTE: Test numbers refer to numbers on diagnostic chart.

1) This step checks if DTC 44 is still present.
2) This step checks for faulty relay.
3) This step checks circuit No. 1531.

94G38493 94E38491 94H38494

DIAGNOSTIC AIDS

Problem is intermittent at this time. Check all terminals, connections and harness for possible loose or corroded condition. The PCM is protected from damage by internal circuit design.

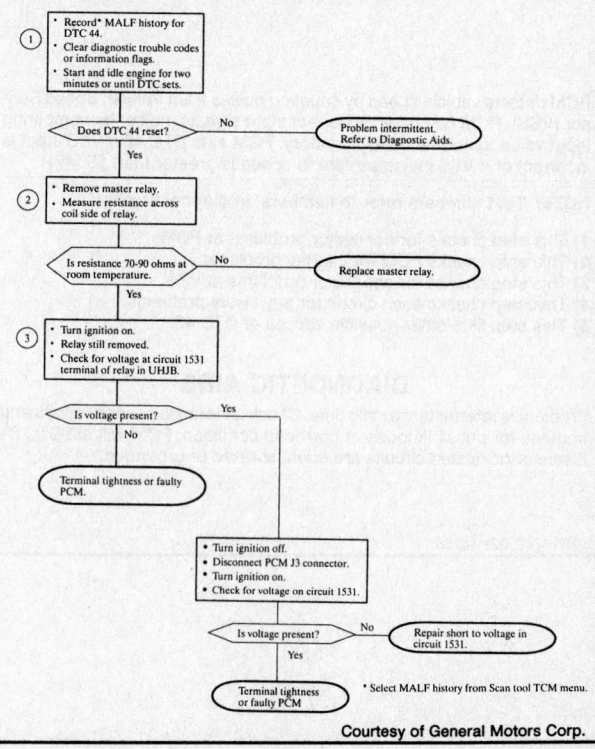

Courtesy of General Motors Corp.

DTC 45, SELECTOR SWITCH NO DATA

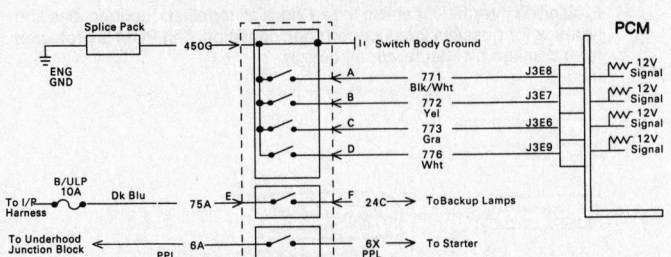

The selector switch uses 4 switches to signal PCM which gear position has been selected. See SELECTOR SWITCH POSITION (DTC 45) table. If all 4 circuits are open at the same time, PCM will set DTC 45.

NOTE: Test numbers refer to numbers on diagnostic chart.

1) This step checks if DTC 45 is still present.
2) This step checks for connector problems at selector switch.
3) This step checks selector switch for a good ground.
4) Use scan tool to ensure wiring and connections are okay. If all circuits are open, PCM will set DTC 45.
5) Check for open circuits by checking each terminal at selector switch for 12 volts.

SELECTOR SWITCH POSITION (DTC 45)

Gear Selected	Selector Switch Terminals
"P"	"A" & "D"
"R"	"A" & "B"
"N"	"B" & "D"
"D4"	"B" & "C"
"D3"	"C" & "D"
"D2"	"A" & "C"

92I14751 92J14752

DIAGNOSTIC AIDS

Problem is intermittent at this time. Check all terminals, connections and harness for possible loose or corroded condition.

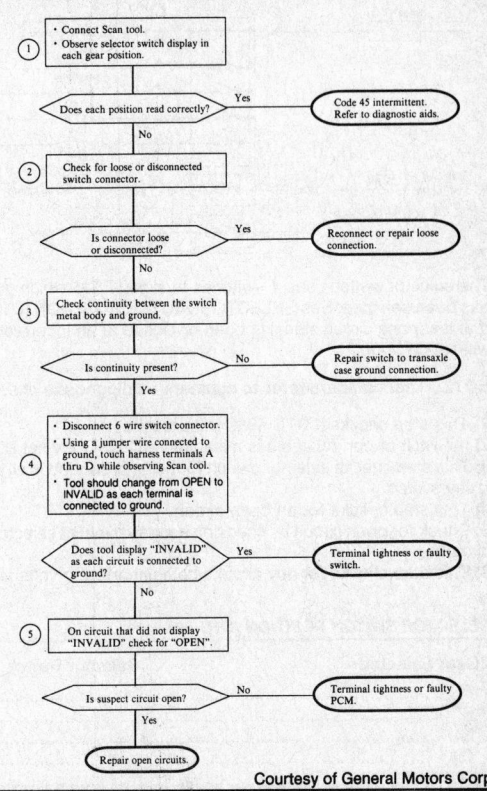

Courtesy of General Motors Corp.

DTC 46, SELECTOR SWITCH INCORRECT DATA

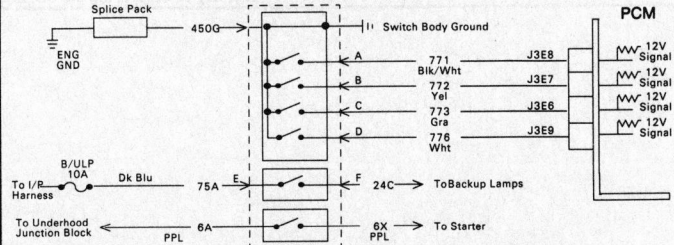

The selector switch uses 4 switches to signal PCM which gear position has been selected. See SELECTOR SWITCH POSITION (DTC 46) table. If at least one circuit signal is open or closed at an incorrect time, PCM will set DTC 46.

NOTE: Test numbers refer to numbers on diagnostic chart.

1) This step checks if DTC 46 is still present.
2) This step checks for a grounded or invalid input signal.
3) This step checks selector switch for being grounded in all positions or faulty switch.
4) This step checks for 2 circuits being grounded or faulty switch.
5) Check for open circuits by checking each terminal at selector switch for 12 volts.

SELECTOR SWITCH POSITION (DTC 46)

Gear Selected	Selector Switch Terminals
"P"	"A" & "D"
"R"	"A" & "B"
"N"	"B" & "D"
"D4"	"B" & "C"
"D3"	"C" & "D"
"D2"	"A" & "C"

92I14751 92B14754

DIAGNOSTIC AIDS

Problem is intermittent at this time. Check all terminals, connections and harness for possible loose or corroded condition. The PCM is protected from damage by internal circuit design.

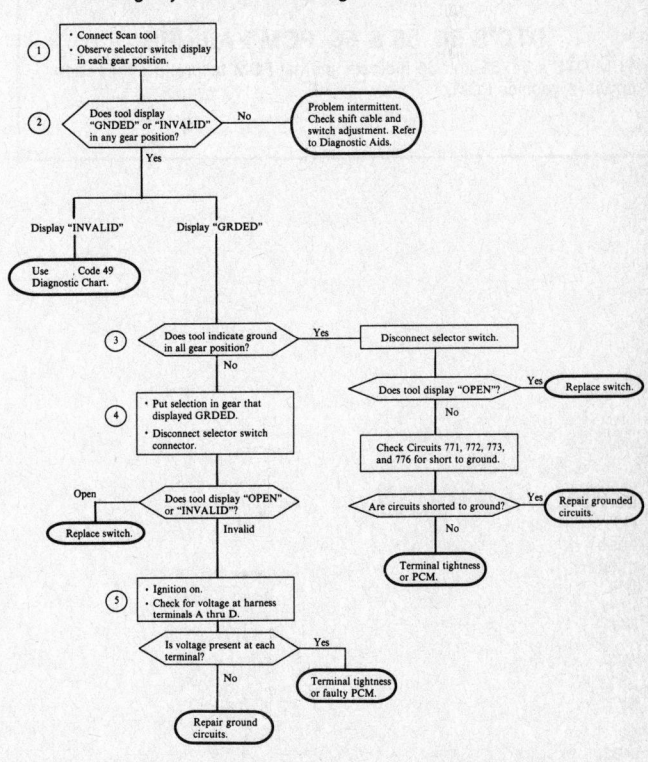

Courtesy of General Motors Corp.

DTC 49, SELECTOR SWITCH INCORRECT DATA

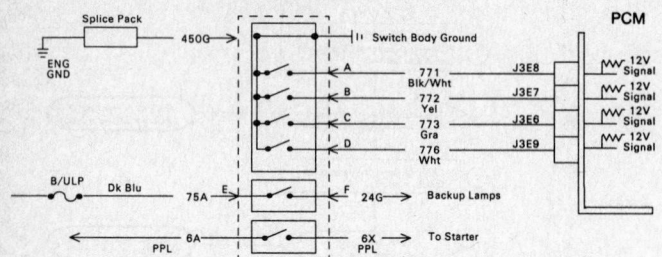

The selector switch uses 4 switches to signal PCM which gear position has been selected. See SELECTOR SWITCH POSITION (DTC 49) table. If at least one circuit signal is open or closed at an incorrect time, PCM will set DTC 49.

NOTE: Test numbers refer to numbers on diagnostic chart.

1) This step checks if DTC 49 is still present.
2) If switch or control cable is misadjusted, PCM may set DTC 45.
3) This step checks selector switch for being grounded in all positions or faulty switch.
4) This step checks for an open circuit.
5) Check for open circuit by checking each terminal at selector switch for 12 volts.
6) This step checks for any circuits being shorted to voltage.

SELECTOR SWITCH POSITION (DTC 49)

Gear Selected	Selector Switch Terminals
"P"	"A" & "D"
"R"	"A" & "B"
"N"	"B" & "D"
"D4"	"B" & "C"
"D3"	"C" & "D"
"D2"	"A" & "C"

92I14751 92F14758

DIAGNOSTIC AIDS

Problem is intermittent at this time. Check all terminals, connections and harness for possible loose or corroded condition. The PCM is protected from damage by internal circuit design.

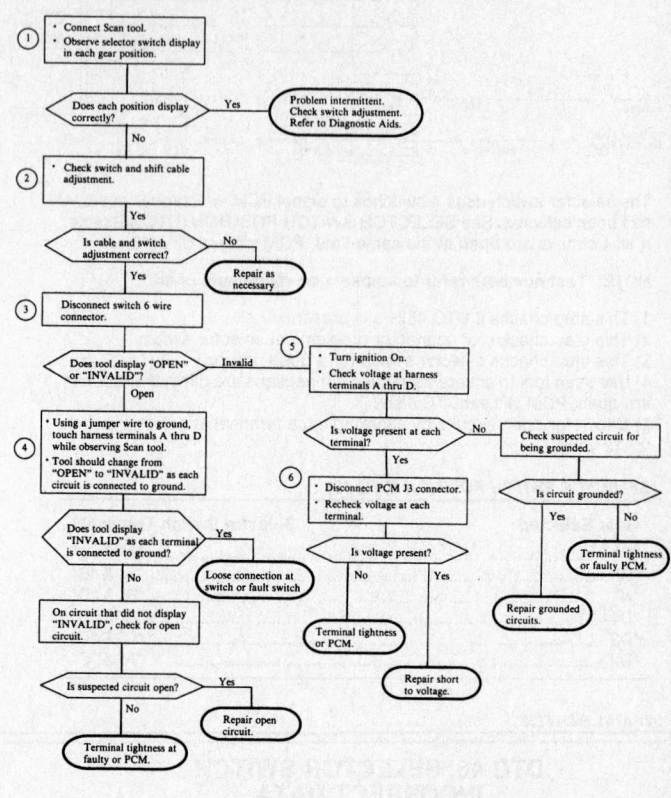

Courtesy of General Motors Corp.

DTC'S 54, 55 & 56, PCM FAILURE

PCM DTC's 54, 55 and 56 indicate internal PCM failure. If either code appears, replace PCM.

DTC 75, 3RD GEAR STUCK ON

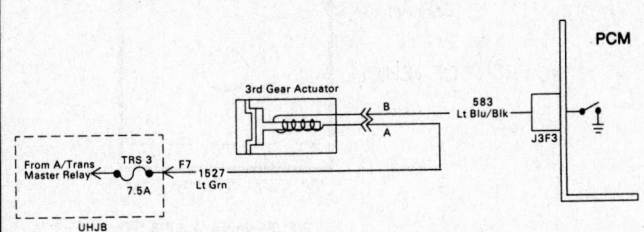

PCM should release 3rd gear clutch by closing ground circuit of 3rd line actuator. PCM can detect transaxle gear position by comparing the Vehicle Speed Sensor (VSS) input to the Turbine Speed Sensor (TSS) input. DTC 75 is set if transaxle should be in 1st gear, but PCM detects a speed equal to 3rd gear operation is present.

NOTE: Test numbers refer to numbers on diagnostic chart.

1) If present, go to information flag listed. Using flow charts, check for possible causes of information flag.
2) See ACTUATOR QUICK CHECK under SELF-DIAGNOSTICS. Ensure clicking sound from 3rd line actuator is similar to clicking sound of other line actuators.
3) Remove valve body. Apply air pressure to 3rd apply port. See HYDRAULIC PRESSURE TESTS in overhaul article.
4) Cross-channel leaks may cause 3rd gear to be applied all the time.
5) This step checks for 3rd clutch operation. If clutch applies and releases, check valve body. If clutch does not operate okay, check for damaged end cover or other internal problem.

92D14731 92D14780

DIAGNOSTIC AIDS

Problem is intermittent at this time. Check all terminals, connections and harness for possible loose or corroded condition. The PCM is protected from damage by internal circuit design. Check for possible internal hydraulic leak.

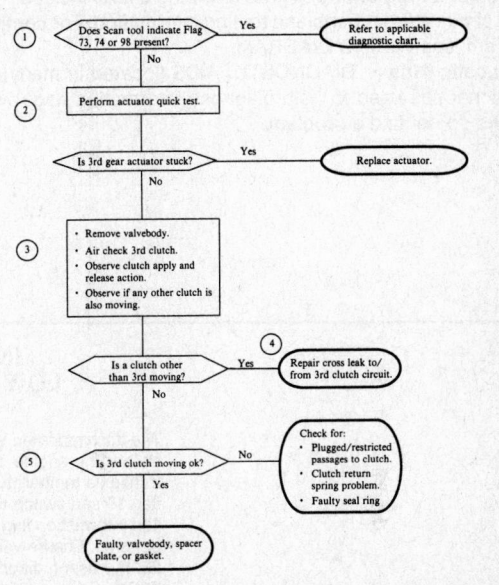

Courtesy of General Motors Corp.

DTC 78, 4TH GEAR STUCK ON

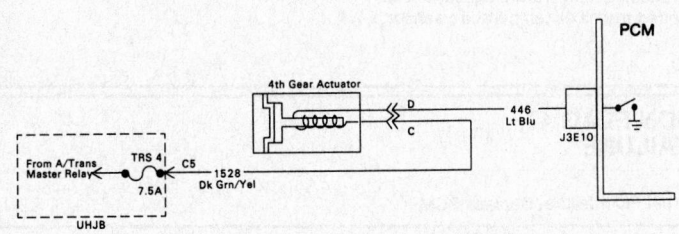

PCM should release 4th gear clutch by closing ground circuit of 4th line actuator. PCM can detect transaxle gear position by comparing the Vehicle Speed Sensor (VSS) input to the Turbine Speed Sensor (TSS) input. DTC 78 is set if transaxle should be in 1st gear, but PCM detects a speed equal to 4th gear operation is present.

NOTE: Test numbers refer to numbers on diagnostic chart.

1) If present, go to information flag listed. Using flow charts, check for possible causes of information flag.
2) See ACTUATOR QUICK CHECK under SELF-DIAGNOSTICS. Ensure clicking sound from 4th line actuator is similar to clicking sound of other line actuators.
3) Remove valve body. Apply air pressure to 4th apply port. See HYDRAULIC PRESSURE TESTS in overhaul article.
4) Cross-channel leaks may cause 4th gear to be applied all the time.
5) This step checks for 4th clutch operation. If clutch applies and releases, check valve body. If clutch does not operate okay, check for damaged end cover or other internal problem.

92F14733 94I38495

DIAGNOSTIC AIDS

Problem is intermittent at this time. Check all terminals, connections and harness for possible loose or corroded condition. The PCM is protected from damage by internal circuit design. Check for possible internal hydraulic leak.

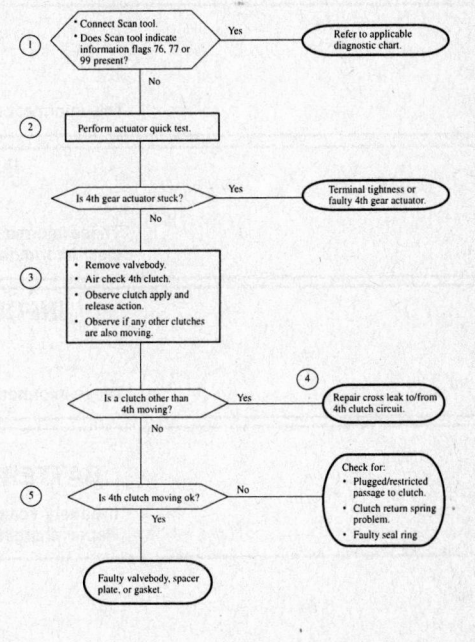

Courtesy of General Motors Corp.

INFORMATION FLAG CHARTS

NOTE: Several steps included in information flag charts require the use of a Saturn PDT. Saturn PDT must be used to obtain MALF history. If these steps are followed without the PDT, false testing results may occur.

Information Flag Charts – The following charts include related electrical circuits, flow charts and testing information. For complete wiring diagram, see WIRING DIAGRAM.

Diagnostic Aids – DIAGNOSTIC AIDS (located in many charts) are additional tips used to help diagnose information flags when circuit checks do not find a problem.

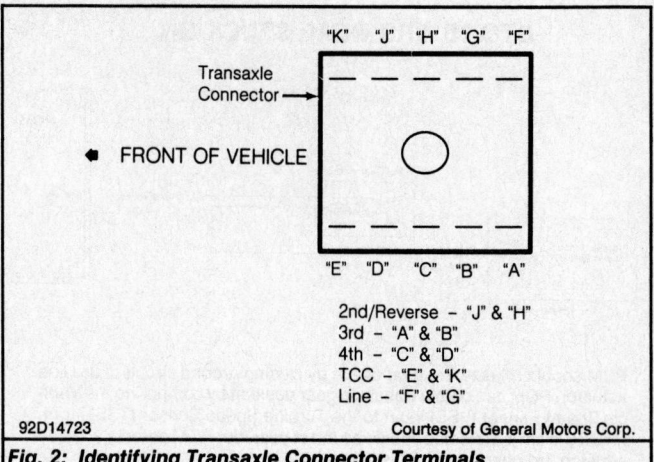

2nd/Reverse – "J" & "H"
3rd – "A" & "B"
4th – "C" & "D"
TCC – "E" & "K"
Line – "F" & "G"

92D14723   Courtesy of General Motors Corp.

Fig. 2: Identifying Transaxle Connector Terminals

INFORMATION FLAG 15,
LOW COOLANT/HOT LIGHT ON

The dash mounted LOW COOLANT/HOT light communicates to the driver that the engine or transaxle is overheating. If the PCM detects the transaxle temperature is over 284°F (140°C), PCM will set information flag 15 and switch the LOW COOLANT/HOT light on.
1) If information flag 15 is present, check the following systems and components. Ensure vehicle is not overloaded. Check PCM for stored DTC 25. If present, diagnose and repair as required.
2) Check for restricted oil cooler or cooler lines, restricted radiator airflow, inoperative radiator fan, low transaxle oil level or overheating engine.

DIAGNOSTIC AIDS

This information flag will not set if transaxle temperature sensor circuit is grounded. If PCM detects a grounded transaxle temperature sensor, DTC 32 will be set.

INFORMATION FLAG 47,
PCM FAILURE

This information flag indicates internal PCM failure. Replace PCM.

INFORMATION FLAGS 51 & 57,
PCM FAILURE

These information flags indicate internal PCM failure. Using Saturn PDT, clear information flags. If either information flag resets, replace PCM.

INFORMATION FLAGS 61, 62, 63 & 64,
PCM FAILURE

These information flags indicate internal PCM failure. Replace PCM.

INFORMATION FLAG 65,
BATTERY VOLTAGE TOO HIGH OR TOO LOW

If battery voltage is not 9.5-17 volts, PCM will set information flag 65. Repair charging system or repair source of PCM battery voltage.

INFORMATION FLAG 68, LINE ACTUATOR CIRCUIT GROUNDED/OPEN

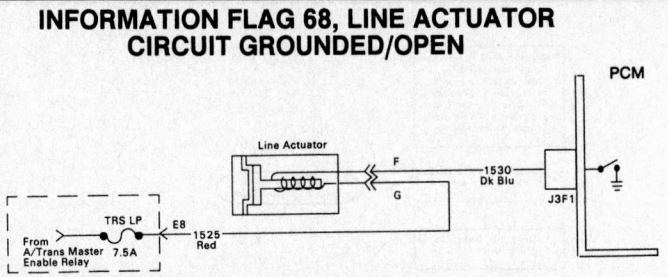

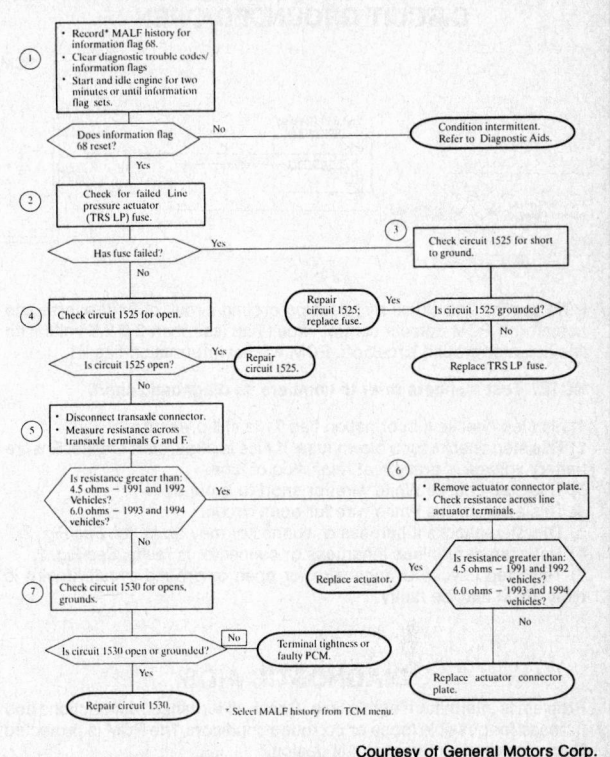

PCM controls hydraulic pressure by modulating ground circuit of line actuator. As duty cycle decreases (circuit is more open), line pressure increases. As duty cycle is increased (circuit is grounded more), line pressure decreases. If PCM detects control circuit has less than 2.0-2.5 volts with duty cycle decreasing, PCM will set information flag 68.

NOTE: Test numbers refer to numbers on diagnostic chart.

1) This step checks if information flag 68 is still present.
2) This step checks for a blown fuse. If fuse is okay, start engine. Ensure battery voltage is present at relay side of fuse.
3) This step checks Red wire for short to ground.
4) This step checks Red wire for open circuit.
5) This step checks if harness or connector may be faulty. *See Fig. 2.*
6) This step determines if harness or connector is faulty. *See Fig. 2.*
7) This step checks Dark Blue wire for open or ground circuit. If wire is okay, PCM may be faulty.

DIAGNOSTIC AIDS

Problem is intermittent at this time. Check all terminals, connections and harness for possible loose or corroded condition. The PCM is protected from damage by internal circuit design.

92E14724 94J38496

Courtesy of General Motors Corp.

INFORMATION FLAG 69, LINE ACTUATOR CIRCUIT SHORTED TO VOLTAGE

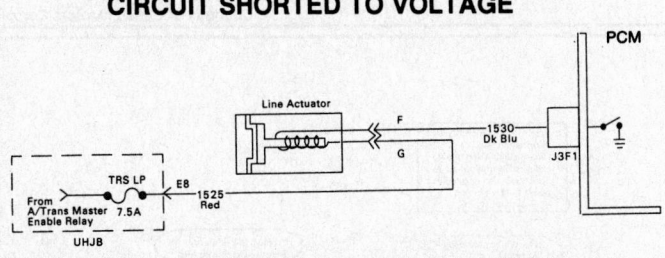

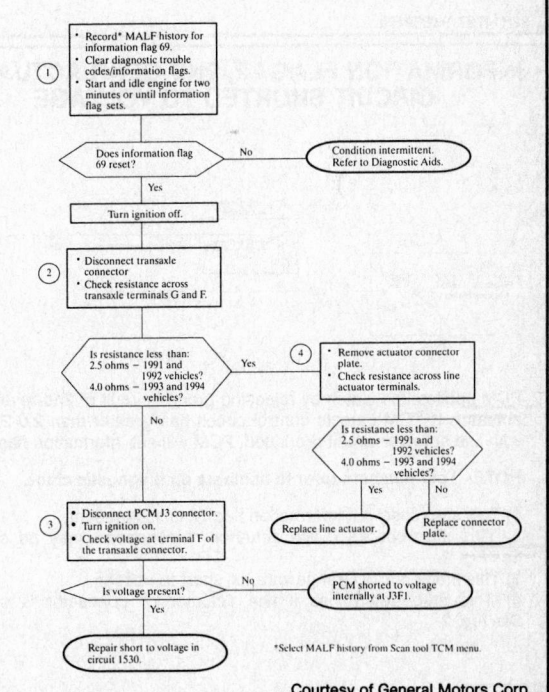

PCM controls hydraulic pressure by modulating ground circuit of line actuator. As duty cycle decreases (circuit is more open), line pressure increases. As duty cycle is increased (circuit is grounded more), line pressure decreases. If PCM detects control circuit is greater than 2.0-2.5 volts with duty cycle increasing, PCM will set information flag 69.

NOTE: Test numbers refer to numbers on diagnostic chart.

1) This step checks if information flag 69 is still present.
2) This step checks if line actuator or connector may be shorted. *See Fig. 2.*
3) This step checks Dark Blue wire for short to voltage.
4) This step determines if line actuator or connector is shorted. *Seo Fig. 2.*

DIAGNOSTIC AIDS

Problem is intermittent at this time. Check all terminals, connections and harness for possible loose or corroded condition. The PCM is protected from damage by internal circuit design.

92E14724 94A38497

Courtesy of General Motors Corp.

INFORMATION FLAG 71, 2ND GEAR ACTUATOR CIRCUIT GROUNDED/OPEN

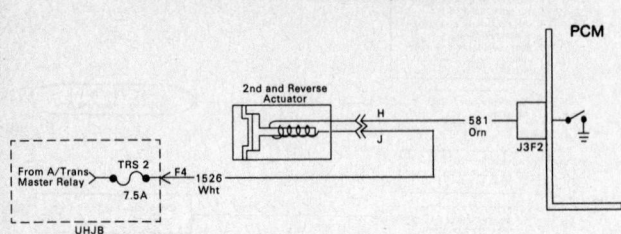

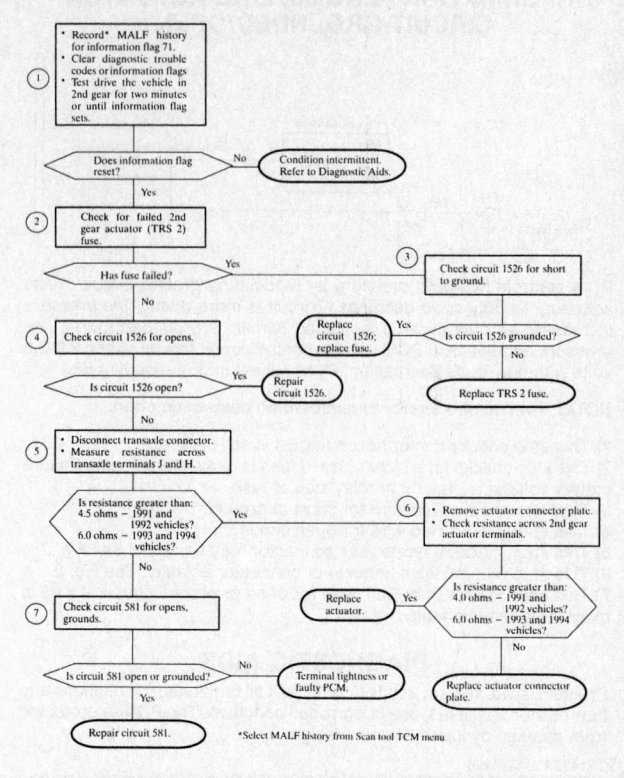

PCM applies 2nd clutch by releasing ground circuit of 2nd/reverse line actuator. If PCM detects control circuit has less than 2.0-2.5 volts with line actuator ground circuit off, PCM will set information flag 71.

NOTE: Test numbers refer to numbers on diagnostic chart.

1) his step checks if information flag 71 is still present.
2) This step checks for a blown fuse. If fuse is okay, start engine. Ensure battery voltage is present at relay side of fuse.
3) This step checks White wire for short to ground.
4) This step checks White wire for open circuit.
5) This step checks if harness or connector may be faulty. See Fig. 2.
6) This step determines if harness or connector is faulty. See Fig. 2.
7) This step checks Orange wire for open or ground circuit. If wire is okay, PCM may be faulty.

DIAGNOSTIC AIDS

Problem is intermittent at this time. Check all terminals, connections and harness for possible loose or corroded condition. The PCM is protected from damage by internal circuit design.

92H14727 94B38498   **Courtesy of General Motors Corp.**

INFORMATION FLAG 72, 2ND GEAR ACTUATOR CIRCUIT SHORTED TO VOLTAGE

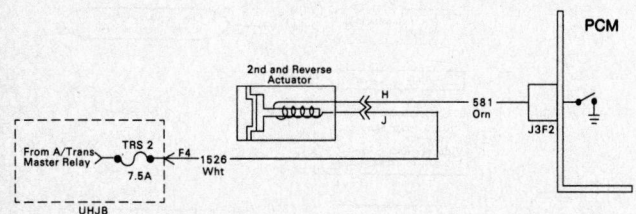

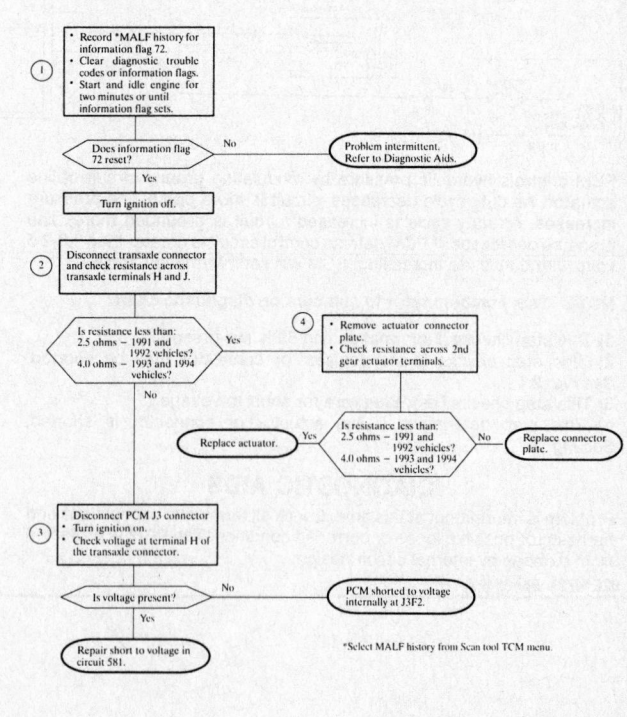

PCM applies 2nd clutch by releasing ground circuit of 2nd/reverse line actuator. If PCM detects control circuit has greater than 2.0-2.5 volts with line actuator circuit grounded, PCM will set information flag 72.

NOTE: Test numbers refer to numbers on diagnostic chart.

1) This step checks if information flag 72 is still present.
2) This step checks if line actuator or connector may be shorted. See Fig. 2.
3) This step checks Orange wire for short to voltage.
4) This step determines if line actuator or connector is shorted. See Fig. 2.

DIAGNOSTIC AIDS

Problem is intermittent at this time. Check all terminals, connections and harness for possible loose or corroded condition. The PCM is protected from damage by internal circuit design.

92H14727 94C38499   **Courtesy of General Motors Corp.**

INFORMATION FLAG 73, 3RD GEAR ACTUATOR CIRCUIT GROUNDED/OPEN

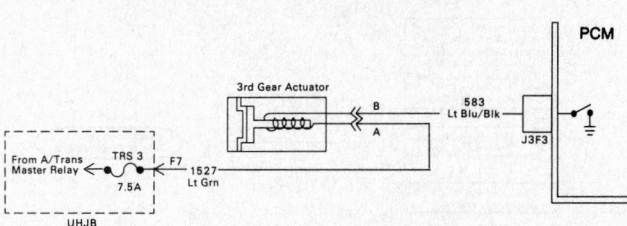

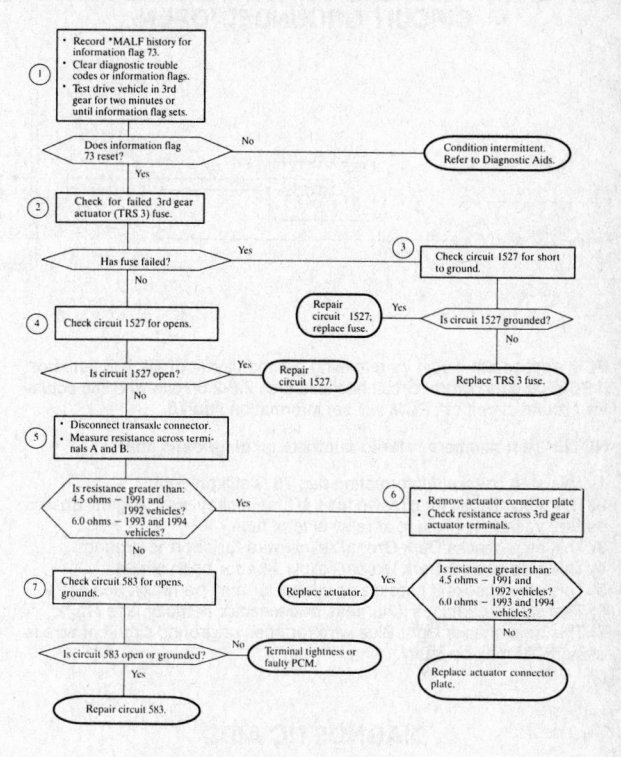

PCM applies 3rd clutch by releasing ground circuit of 3rd line actuator. If PCM detects control circuit has less than 2.0-2.5 volts with line actuator ground circuit off, PCM will set information flag 73.

NOTE: Test numbers refer to numbers on diagnostic chart.

1) This step checks if information flag 73 is still present.
2) This step checks for a blown fuse. If fuse is okay, start engine. Ensure battery voltage is present at relay side of fuse.
3) This step checks Light Green wire for short to ground.
4) This step checks Light Green wire for open circuit.
5) This step checks if harness or connector may be faulty. *See Fig. 2.*
6) This step determines if harness or connector is faulty. *See Fig. 2.*
7) This step checks Light Blue/Black wire for open or ground circuit. If wire is okay, PCM may be faulty.

DIAGNOSTIC AIDS

Problem is intermittent at this time. Check all terminals, connections and harness for possible loose or corroded condition. The PCM is protected from damage by internal circuit design.

* Select MALF history from Scan tool TCM menu.

92D14731 94F38500

Courtesy of General Motors Corp.

INFORMATION FLAG 74, 3RD GEAR ACTUATOR CIRCUIT SHORTED TO VOLTAGE

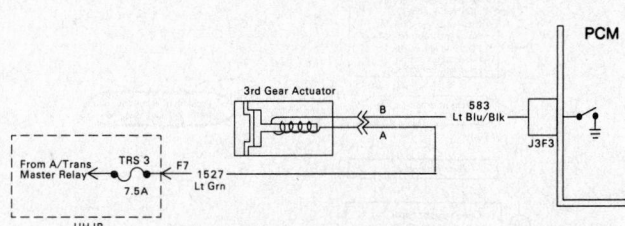

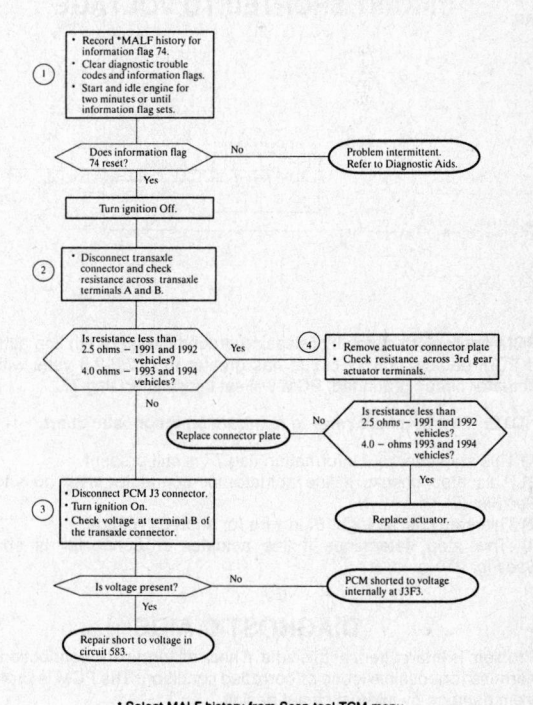

PCM applies 3rd clutch by releasing ground circuit of 3rd line actuator. If PCM detects control circuit has greater than 2.0-2.5 volts with line actuator circuit grounded, PCM will set information flag 74.

NOTE: Test numbers refer to numbers on diagnostic chart.

1) This step checks if information flag 74 is still present.
2) This step checks if line actuator or connector may be shorted. *See Fig. 2.*
3) This step checks Light Blue/Black wire for short to voltage.
4) This step determines if line actuator or connector is shorted. *See Fig. 2.*

DIAGNOSTIC AIDS

Problem is intermittent at this time. Check all terminals, connections and harness for possible loose or corroded condition. The PCM is protected from damage by internal circuit design.

* Select MALF history from Scan tool TCM menu.

92D14731 94G38501

Courtesy of General Motors Corp.

INFORMATION FLAG 76, 4TH GEAR ACTUATOR CIRCUIT GROUNDED/OPEN

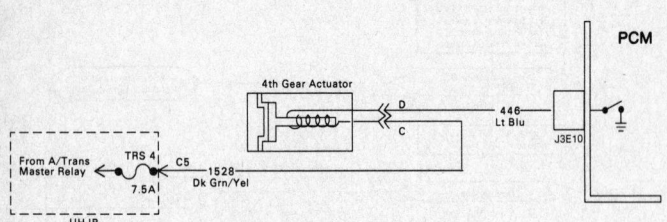

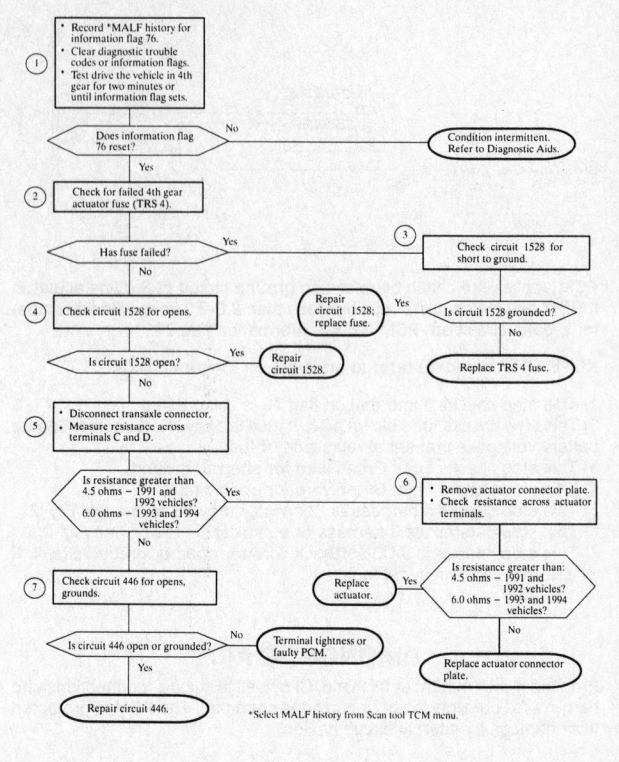

PCM applies 4th clutch by releasing ground circuit of 4th line actuator. If PCM detects control circuit has less than 2.0-2.5 volts with line actuator ground circuit off, PCM will set information flag 76.

NOTE: Test numbers refer to numbers on diagnostic chart.

1) This step checks if information flag 76 is still present.
2) This step checks for a blown fuse. If fuse is okay, start engine. Ensure battery voltage is present at relay side of fuse.
3) This step checks Dark Green/Yellow wire for short to ground.
4) This step checks Dark Green/Yellow wire for open circuit.
5) This step checks if harness or connector may be faulty. *See Fig. 2.*
6) This step determines if harness or connector is faulty. *See Fig. 2.*
7) This step checks Light Blue wire for open or ground circuit. If wire is okay, PCM may be faulty.

DIAGNOSTIC AIDS

Problem is intermittent at this time. Check all terminals, connections and harness for possible loose or corroded condition. The PCM is protected from damage by internal circuit design.

92F14733 94H38502

Courtesy of General Motors Corp.

INFORMATION FLAG 77, 4TH GEAR ACTUATOR CIRCUIT SHORTED TO VOLTAGE

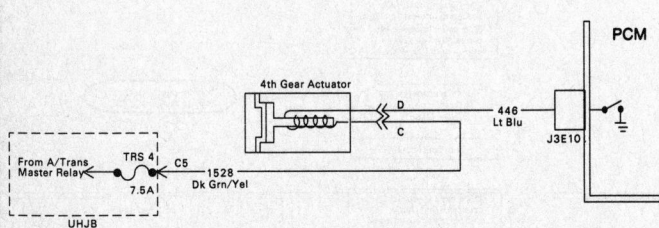

PCM applies 4th clutch by releasing ground circuit of 4th line actuator. If PCM detects control circuit has greater than 2.0-2.5 volts with line actuator circuit grounded, PCM will set information flag 77.

NOTE: Test numbers refer to numbers on diagnostic chart.

1) This step checks if information flag 77 is still present.
2) This step checks if line actuator or connector may be shorted. *See Fig. 2.*
3) This step checks Light Blue wire for short to voltage.
4) This step determines if line actuator or connector is shorted. *See Fig. 2.*

DIAGNOSTIC AIDS

Problem is intermittent at this time. Check all terminals, connections and harness for possible loose or corroded condition. The PCM is protected from damage by internal circuit design.

92F14733 94I38503

Courtesy of General Motors Corp.

INFORMATION FLAG 79, TCC ACTUATOR CIRCUIT GROUNDED/OPEN

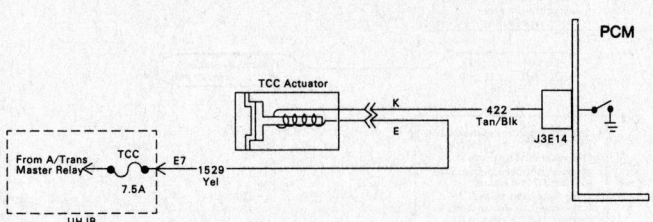

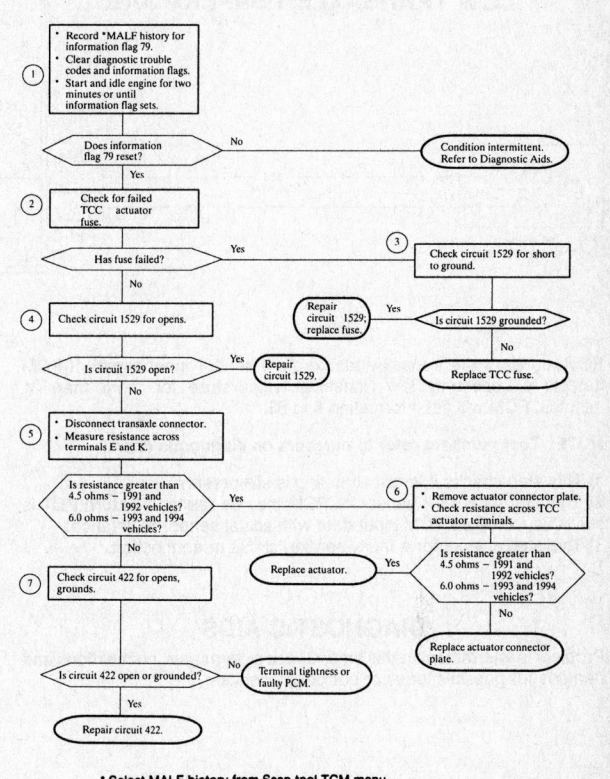

PCM applies TCC by grounding circuit of TCC line actuator. If PCM detects control circuit has less than 2.0-2.5 volts with line actuator ground circuit off, PCM will set information flag 79.

NOTE: Test numbers refer to numbers on diagnostic chart.

1) This step checks if information flag 79 is still present.
2) This step checks for a blown fuse. If fuse is okay, start engine. Ensure battery voltage is present at relay side of fuse.
3) This step checks Yellow wire for short to ground.
4) This step checks Yellow wire for open circuit.
5) This step checks if harness or connector may be faulty. *See Fig. 2.*
6) This step determines if harness or connector is faulty. *See Fig. 2.*
7) This step checks Tan/Black wire for open or ground circuit. If wire is okay, PCM may be faulty.

DIAGNOSTIC AIDS

Problem is intermittent at this time. Check all terminals, connections and harness for possible loose or corroded condition. The PCM is protected from damage by internal circuit design.

* Select MALF history from Scan tool TCM menu.

92H14735 94J38504

Courtesy of General Motors Corp.

INFORMATION FLAG 81, TCC ACTUATOR CIRCUIT SHORTED TO VOLTAGE

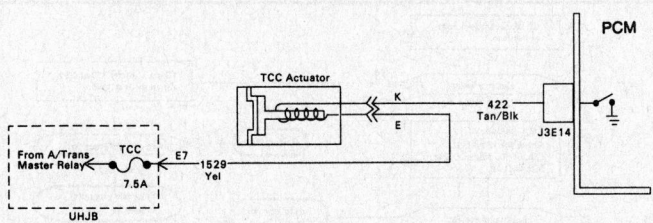

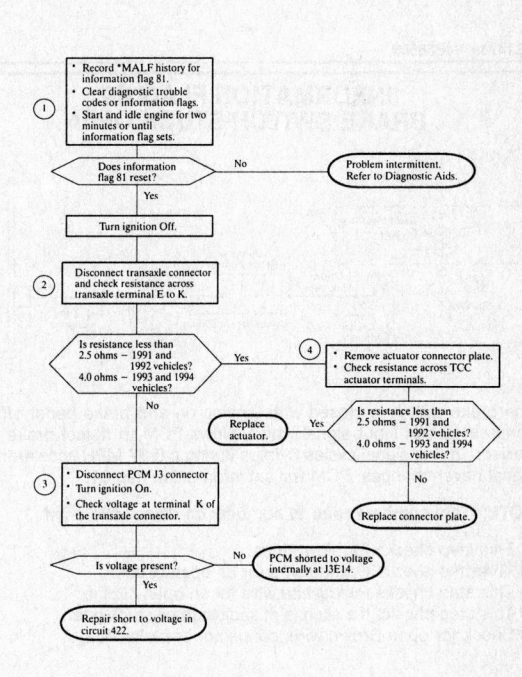

PCM applies TCC by grounding circuit of TCC line actuator. If PCM detects control circuit has greater than 2.0-2.5 volts with line actuator circuit grounded, PCM will set information flag 81.

NOTE: Test numbers refer to numbers on diagnostic chart.

1) This step checks if information flag 81 is still present.
2) This step checks if line actuator or connector may be shorted. *See Fig. 2.*
3) This step checks Tan/Black wire for short to voltage.
4) This step determines if line actuator or connector is shorted. *See Fig. 2.*

DIAGNOSTIC AIDS

Problem is intermittent at this time. Check all terminals, connections and harness for possible loose or corroded condition. The PCM is protected from damage by internal circuit design.

* Select MALF history from Scan tool TCM menu.

92H14735 94A38505

Courtesy of General Motors Corp.

INFORMATION FLAG 83, LOW TRANSAXLE TEMPERATURE

PCM

Transaxle Temperature Sensor

A — 585 Tan/Wht — J3F4 — Signal — 5 V

B — 586 Orn/Blk — J3F15

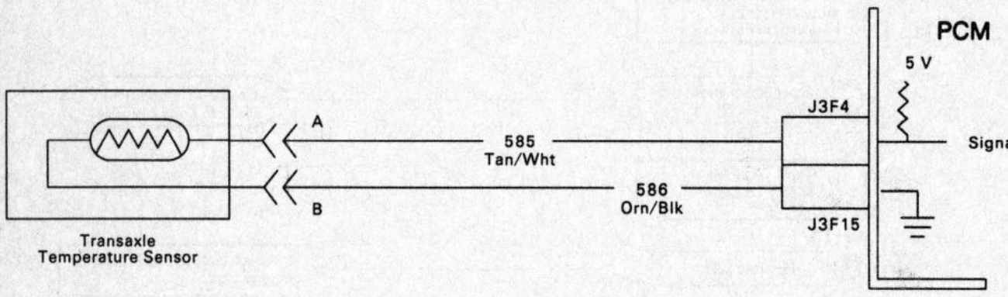

PCM monitors the transaxle temperature sensor input signal. If PCM detects a constantly low transaxle temperature for more than 21 minutes, PCM will set information flag 83.

NOTE: Test numbers refer to numbers on diagnostic chart.

1) This step checks if information flag is still present.
2) This step checks if sensor or PCM may be faulty. If Saturn PDT is available, compare PCM input data with actual sensor resistance.
3) This step checks for a faulty sensor, circuit or connection.

DIAGNOSTIC AIDS

Problem is intermittent at this time. Check all terminals, connections and harness for possible loose or corroded condition.

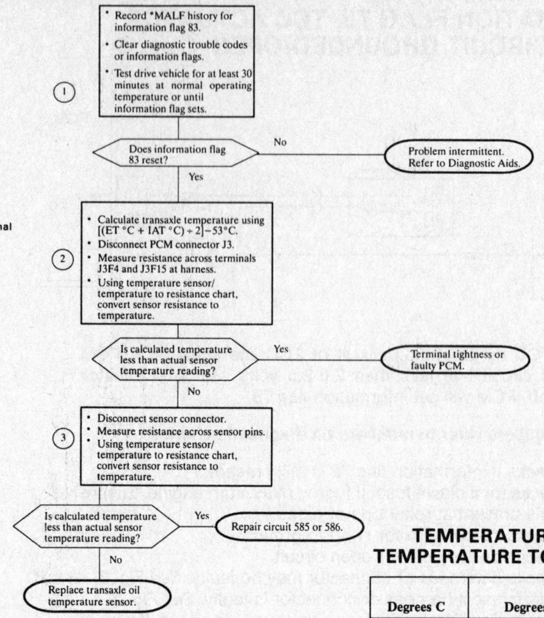

(1)
- Record *MALF history for information flag 83.
- Clear diagnostic trouble codes or information flags.
- Test drive vehicle for at least 30 minutes at normal operating temperature or until information flag sets.

Does information flag 83 reset? → No → Problem intermittent. Refer to Diagnostic Aids.
↓ Yes

(2)
- Calculate transaxle temperature using [(ET °C + IAT °C) + 2] − 53°C.
- Disconnect PCM connector J3.
- Measure resistance across terminals J3F4 and J3F15 at harness.
- Using temperature sensor/temperature to resistance chart, convert sensor resistance to temperature.

Is calculated temperature less than actual sensor temperature reading? → Yes → Terminal tightness or faulty PCM.
↓ No

(3)
- Disconnect sensor connector.
- Measure resistance across sensor pins.
- Using temperature sensor/temperature to resistance chart, convert sensor resistance to temperature.

Is calculated temperature less than actual sensor temperature reading? → Yes → Repair circuit 585 or 586.
↓ No

Replace transaxle oil temperature sensor.

* Select MALF history from Scan tool TCM menu.

TEMPERATURE SENSOR TEMPERATURE TO RESISTANCE

Degrees C	Degrees F	Sensor Resistance
−40	−40	93630
−29	−20	46352
−18	0	24094
−7	20	13111
4	40	7436
16	60	4180
27	80	2554
38	100	1609
49	120	1043
60	140	693
72	160	456
83	180	318
94	200	226
105	220	165
120	248	109
140	284	65

92B14739 94B38506

Courtesy of General Motors Corp.

INFORMATION FLAG 84, BRAKE SWITCH STUCK OPEN

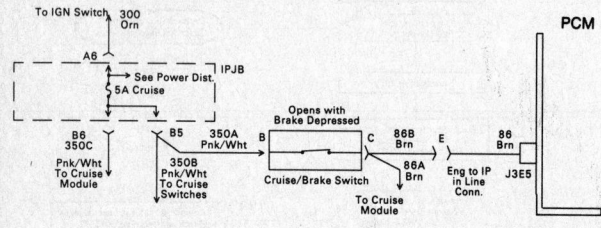

PCM

To IGN Switch — 300 Orn

A6

IPJB — See Power Dist. — 5A Cruise

B6 350C Pnk/Wht To Cruise Module

B5 350A Pnk/Wht — 350B Pnk/Wht To Cruise Switches

Opens with Brake Depressed — Cruise/Brake Switch — B — 86B Brn — C — 86A Brn To Cruise Module — E — 86 Brn Eng to IP in Line Conn. — J3E5

The brake switch is closed with ignition on and brake pedal off. This sends a 12 volt input signal which allows PCM to detect brake pedal position. If this signal cycles 5 times during a 0-37 MPH acceleration or signal never changes, PCM will set information flag 84.

NOTE: Test numbers refer to numbers on diagnostic chart.

1) This step checks for blown fuse.
2) This step checks Orange wire for an open circuit.
3) This step checks Pink/White wire for an open circuit.
4) This step checks if switch is misadjusted or stuck open.
5) Check for open Brown wire, connector or faulty PCM.

DIAGNOSTIC AIDS

Problem is intermittent at this time. Check all terminals, connections and harness for possible loose or corroded condition.

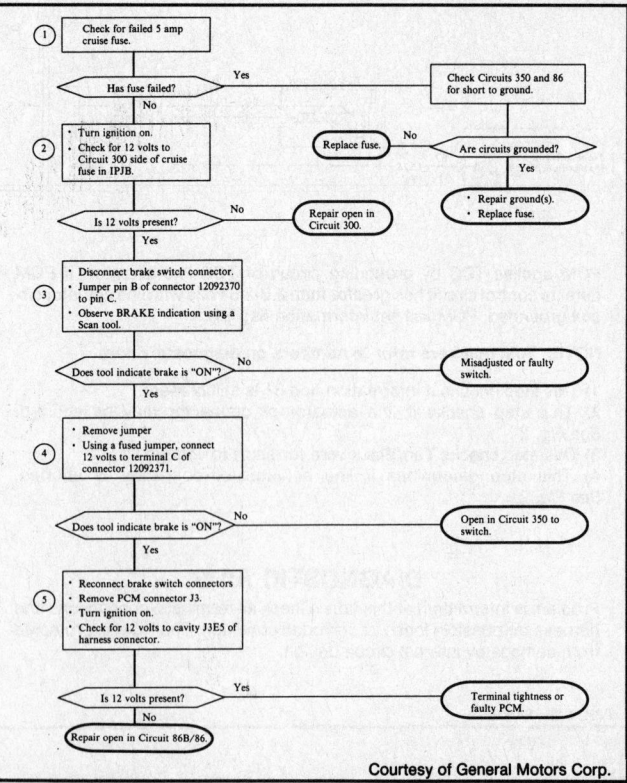

(1)
- Check for failed 5 amp cruise fuse.

Has fuse failed? → Yes → Check Circuits 350 and 86 for short to ground.
↓ No

(2)
- Turn ignition on.
- Check for 12 volts to Circuit 300 side of cruise fuse in IPJB.

Is 12 volts present? → No → Repair open in Circuit 300.
↓ Yes

(3)
- Disconnect brake switch connector.
- Jumper pin B of connector 12092370 to pin C.
- Observe BRAKE indication using a Scan tool.

Does tool indicate brake is "ON"? → No → Misadjusted or faulty switch.
↓ Yes

(4)
- Remove jumper
- Using a fused jumper, connect 12 volts to terminal C of connector 12092371.

Does tool indicate brake is "ON"? → No → Open in Circuit 350 to switch.
↓ Yes

(5)
- Reconnect brake switch connectors.
- Remove PCM connector J3.
- Turn ignition on.
- Check for 12 volts to cavity J3E5 of harness connector.

Is 12 volts present? → Yes → Terminal tightness or faulty PCM.
↓ No

Repair open in Circuit 86B/86.

Check Circuits 350 and 86 for short to ground. → Are circuits grounded? → No → Replace fuse.
↓ Yes
- Repair ground(s).
- Replace fuse.

92A14795 92B14796

Courtesy of General Motors Corp.

INFORMATION FLAG 85, BRAKE SWITCH STUCK CLOSED

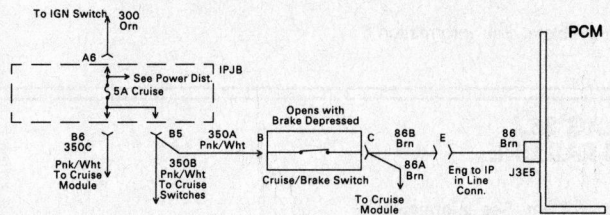

The brake switch is closed with ignition on and brake pedal off. This sends a 12 volt input signal which allows PCM to detect brake pedal position. If this signal cycles 5 times during a 0-37 MPH acceleration or 12 volt signal is always on, PCM will set information flag 85.

NOTE: Test numbers refer to numbers on diagnostic chart.

1) This step checks for faulty brake switch.
2) This step checks Brown wire for short to voltage or a faulty PCM.

92A14795 92D14798

DIAGNOSTIC AIDS

Problem is intermittent at this time. Check all terminals, connections and harness for possible loose or corroded condition.

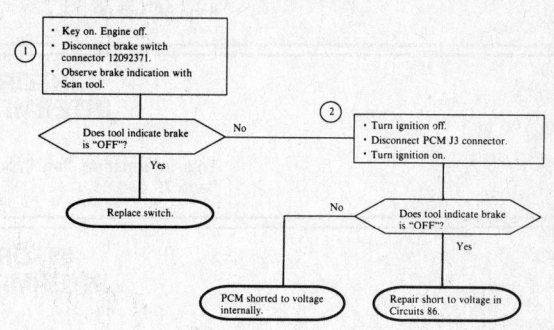

Courtesy of General Motors Corp.

INFORMATION FLAG 86, PCM FAILURE

This information flag indicates internal PCM failure. Replace PCM.

INFORMATION FLAG 89, MASTER ENABLE RELAY STUCK ON

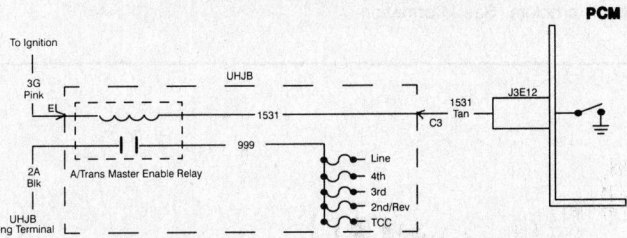

During normal operation, PCM grounds master enable relay which provides system voltage to all line actuators. PCM also monitors the master enable relay operation. If PCM detects more than 3 volts present on master enable relay detect circuit and PCM has commanded master enable relay off, PCM will set information flag 89.

NOTE: Test numbers refer to numbers on diagnostic chart.

1) If present, go to information flag listed.
2) This step checks if information flag is still present.
3) This step checks for a faulty relay.
4) This step determines if relay circuit No. 1531 is at fault.
5) This step checks for short to voltage in circuit No. 999.
6) This step checks for short to ground in circuit No. 1531 or faulty PCM.

DIAGNOSTIC AIDS

Problem is intermittent at this time. Check all terminals, connections and harness for possible loose or corroded condition. The PCM is protected from damage by internal circuit design.

94G38493 94C38507

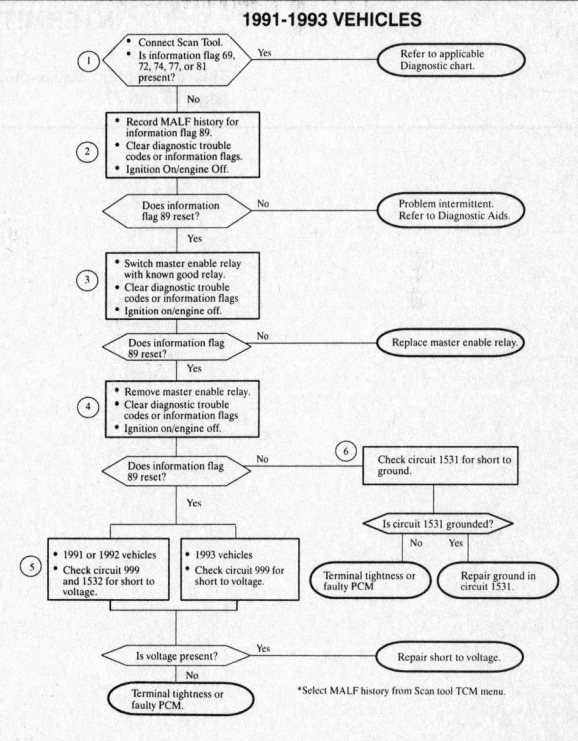

Courtesy of General Motors Corp.

INFORMATION FLAG 94, (1993) INTERMITTENT PCM FAILURE

This information flag indicates intermittent problem. See information flags 43 and 44.

INFORMATION FLAG 95, INTERMITTENT PCM FAILURE

This information flag indicates intermittent problem. See information flags 68 and 69.

INFORMATION FLAG 96, INTERMITTENT PCM FAILURE

This information flag indicates intermittent problem. See information flags 79 and 81.

INFORMATION FLAG 97, INTERMITTENT PCM FAILURE

This information flag indicates intermittent problem. See information flags 71 and 72.

INFORMATION FLAG 98, INTERMITTENT PCM FAILURE

This information flag indicates intermittent problem. See information flags 73 and 74.

INFORMATION FLAG 99, INTERMITTENT PCM FAILURE

This information flag indicates intermittent problem. See information flags 76 and 77.

WIRING DIAGRAM

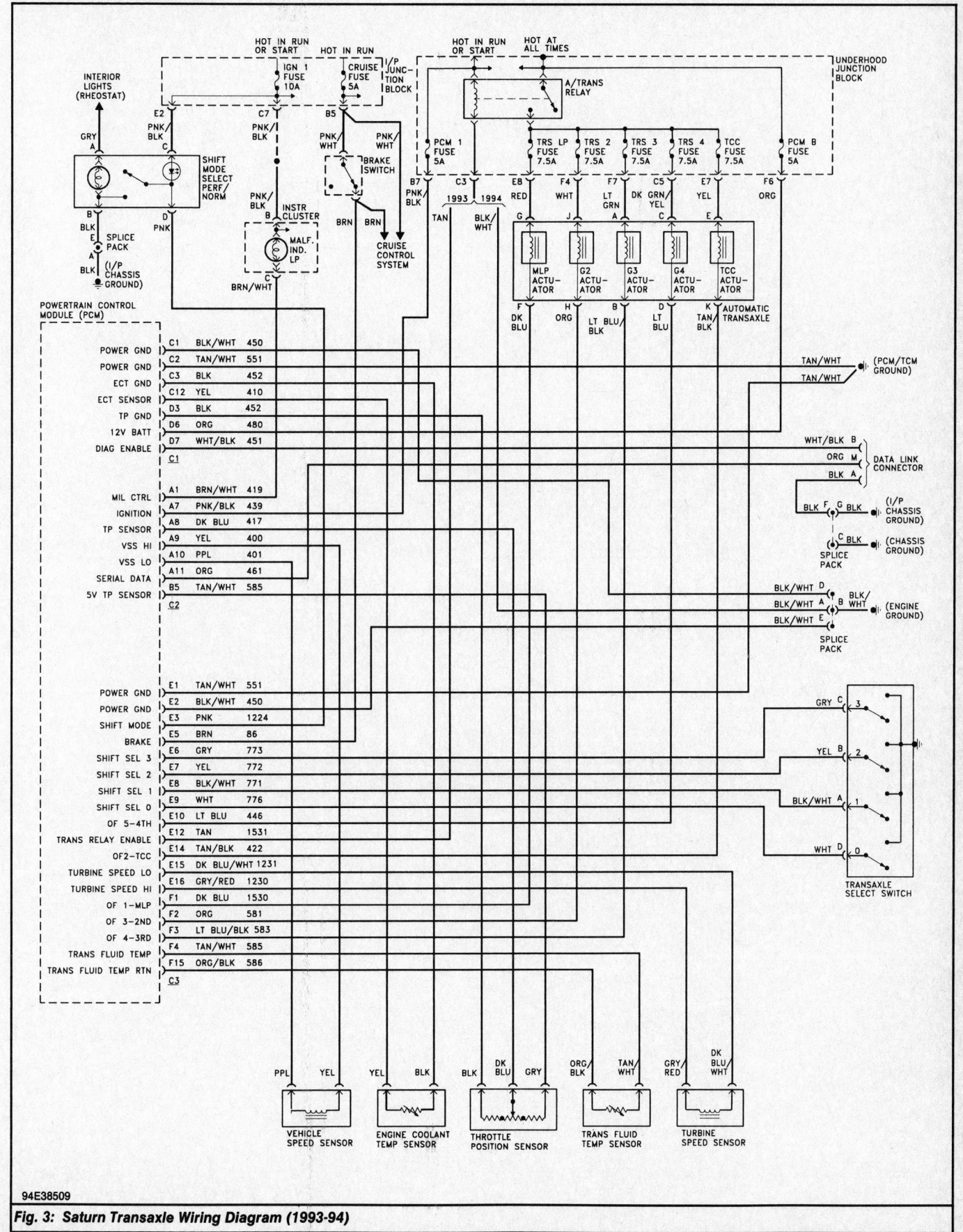

Fig. 3: Saturn Transaxle Wiring Diagram (1993-94)

SECTION 4

MANUAL TRANSMISSIONS

MANUAL TRANSMISSIONS
General Trouble Shooting

INTRODUCTION

There are many times when the transmission is incorrectly blamed for shifting problems or noises that are actually caused by other reasons. Shift difficulties are frequently caused by conditions outside the transmission or transaxle. Typical conditions include: shift linkage, shift cables, alignment of engine to transmission, worn engine mounts, or clutch problems.

Drive train noises may come from many sources such as tires, road surfaces, wheel bearings, differentials, engine, or exhaust system. Repairing or overhauling the transmission will not cure these problems.

No manufacturer makes a perfectly quiet transmission. Gear rollover noise is present in most constant mesh transmissions and will tend to disappear when the clutch is disengaged or the transmission is placed in gear. Clutch release bearing noise will disappear when the release bearing is moved enough to slide the release bearing away from the pressure plate, if clutch is properly adjusted.

Trouble shooting can be helped by driving the vehicle on a smooth level road to help eliminate tire and body noises. Note whether noise occurs on acceleration, coasting, deceleration, or steady driving conditions. Some problems may only occur when transmission is either hot or cold. Gear lubricant that is too thick can cause hard shifting on cold mornings before the engine is warm and vehicle has been driven.

MANUAL TRANSMISSION/TRANSAXLE TROUBLE SHOOTING

Condition	Possible Cause
Noisy In Forward Gears	Low Gear Oil Level, Loose Bellhousing Bolts, Worn Bearings Or Gears
Clunk On Deceleration (FWD Only)	Loose Engine Mounts, Worn Inboard CV Joints, Worn Differential Pinion Shaft, Side Gear Hub Counterbore In Case Worn Oversize
Gear Clash When Shifting Forward Gears	Clutch Out Of Adjustment, Shift Linkage Damaged Or Out Of Adjustment, Gears Or Synchronizers Damaged, Low Gear Oil Level
Transmission Noisy When Moving (RWD Only), Quiet In Neutral With Clutch Engaged	Worn Rear Output Shaft Bearing
Gear Rattle	Worn Bearings, Wrong Gear Oil, Low Gear Oil, Worn Gears
Steady Ticking At Idle (Increases With RPM)	Broken Tooth On A Gear
Gear Clash When Shifting Forward Gears	Worn Or Broken Synchronizers, Faulty Clutch
Loud Whine In Reverse	[1] Normal condition
Noise When Stepping On Clutch	Bad Release Bearing, Worn Pilot Bearing
Ticking Or Screeching As Clutch Is Engaged	Faulty Release Bearing, Uneven Pressure Plate Fingers
Click Or Snap When Clutch Is Engaged	Worn Clutch Fork, Worn Pivot Ball, Worn Or Broken Front Bearing Retainer
Transmission Shifts Hard	Clutch Not Releasing, Incorrect Gear Oil, Shift Mechanism Binding, Clutch Installed Backward
Will Not Shift Into One Gear, Shifts Into All Others	Bent Shift Ford, Worn Detent Balls
Locked Into Gear, Cannot Shift	Clutch Adjustment, Worn Detent Balls
Transmission Jumps Out Of Gear	Pilot Bearing Worn, Bent Shift Fork, Worn Gear Teeth or Face, Excessive Gear Train End Play, Worn Synchronizers, Missing Detent Ball Spring, Shift Mechanism Worn Or Out Of Adjustment, Engine Or Transmission Mount Bolts Loose, Transmission Not Aligned
Shift Lever Rattle	Worn Detents Or Shift Lever, Worn Shift Fork, Worn Synchronizers Sleeve
Shift Lever Hops Under Acceleration	Worn Engine Or Transmission Mounts

[1] – Most units use spur cut gears in reverse and are naturally noisy

Jeep: Cherokee, Wrangler

IDENTIFICATION

The identification codes used on AX5 transmissions are stamped on the bottom surface of transmission case next to intermediate plate. First number of code is year of manufacture, 2nd and 3rd numbers are month of manufacture. Remaining numbers indicate transmission serial number in sequence.

DESCRIPTION

The AX5 is a 5-speed manual transmissions. AX5 has 5th gear as an overdrive gear with a 0.85:1 ratio. An integral shift mechanism mounts in adapter housing. AX5 is used with 2.5L engines.

LUBRICATION & ADJUSTMENTS

See appropriate MANUAL TRANSMISSION SERVICING article in TRANSMISSION SERVICING.

TROUBLE SHOOTING

See GENERAL TROUBLE SHOOTING article in MANUAL TRANSMISSIONS.

ON-VEHICLE SERVICE

EXTENSION HOUSING SEAL

Removal & Installation – Mark and remove propeller shaft and rear axle pinion yoke. Remove extension housing seal using slide hammer and internal puller. Clean oil and build-up from around housing bore. Install extension housing seal. Align and install propeller shaft and tighten propeller shaft "U" bolts.

SPEEDOMETER GEAR & SEAL

Removal – Remove speedometer/distance sensor, speedometer adapter and retainer. Pull speedometer adapter and pinion gear out of transmission case. Discard adapter "O" ring. Slide pinion gear off of speedometer cable and out of adapter. Replace adapter oil seal if fluid is found inside of cable cover.

Installation – 1) Install speedometer pinion gear into adapter. Ensure speedometer gear shaft is properly engaged with speedometer cable. Lubricate replacement "O" ring and install. Count the number of teeth on pinion gear and locate the number that corresponds to number of teeth on adapter face.

2) Rotate adapter until desired number of teeth that is stamped on adapter face lines up with extension housing index mark. Numbers should be positioned in the 6 o'clock position when aligned. Insert assembled adapter, cable and pinion gear in case until fully seated. Install speedometer adapter retainer and tighten to specification. Install distance sensor on adapter.

REMOVAL & INSTALLATION

See appropriate MANUAL TRANSMISSION REMOVAL article in TRANSMISSION SERVICING.

TRANSMISSION DISASSEMBLY

1) Remove release fork and bearing. Remove clutch housing bolts. Separate clutch housing from transmission case.

2) Use Torx bit to remove detent plug. Use pencil magnet to remove detent spring and ball. *See Figs. 1 and 2.* Remove 5 bolts and the nut holding adapter housing to intermediate plate.

3) Remove shift arm set bolt and lock plate. Remove shift arm pivot shaft plug from back of adapter housing. Using a large magnet, remove shift arm pivot shaft. Use plastic hammer to tap and remove extension or adapter housing from intermediate plate.

4) Remove front bearing retainer snap rings. Use plastic hammer to tap and remove intermediate plate and front bearing retainer. Remove transmission case.

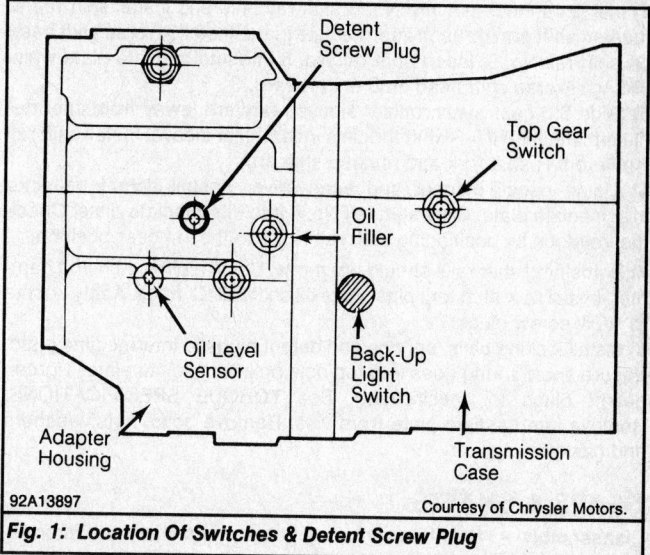

Fig. 1: Location Of Switches & Detent Screw Plug
92A13897 — Courtesy of Chrysler Motors.

COMPONENT DISASSEMBLY & REASSEMBLY

NOTE: Replace all oil seals, lock nuts, roll pins and snap rings when transmission repair is made.

SHIFT RAILS & COMPONENTS

Disassembly – 1) Install 2 clutch housing bolts, washers and suitable nuts in intermediate plate. *See Fig. 2.* Increase or decrease number of washers used so that bolt tip and outer surface of nut are aligned.

2) Clamp bolts in jaws of vise. Ensure machined surfaces of intermediate plate are protected from damage to sealing surfaces. Remove detent screw plugs. Using a Torx bit and pencil magnet, remove detent balls and springs from side and bottom of intermediate plate.

NOTE: Detent balls in intermediate housing will usually fall out when plugs or shift rails are removed. Ensure detent balls, springs and interlock pins are not lost. Use a pencil magnet to remove parts that do not come out easily.

3) Using a hammer and punch, drive out 5 shift fork pins and remove 2 "C" rings from the shift rails. Pull shift rail No. 4 from intermediate plate and catch detent balls and pin. Remove shift rail No. 4 and 5-R shift fork. *See Fig. 3.*

4) Remove shift rail No. 5 from intermediate plate with reverse shift head attached. Remove shift rail No. 3 from intermediate plate, catching interlock pins. Remove shift rail No. 1 from intermediate plate.

5) Remove shift rail No. 2 along with 1-2 and 3-4 shift forks. Remove reverse idler gear and shaft. Remove reverse shift arm from reverse shift fork.

Reassembly – 1) Before reassembling shift rails and components, ensure all gear and shaft repairs are complete. Install reverse shift arm. Seat reverse shift fork in bracket. Put reverse idler gear onto shaft. Install reverse idler gear shaft assembly into intermediate plate. Install reverse idler gear shaft lock plate and tighten to specification. See TORQUE SPECIFICATIONS.

2) Install 1-2 and 3-4 shift forks into groove of synchronizer sleeves. Slide shift rail No. 2 through intermediate plate into shift forks. Coat detent balls and interlock pins with grease. Using a pencil magnet and screwdriver, install detent ball into intermediate plate. Ensure interlock pins and balls are installed in correct locations. *See Fig. 4.*

3) Using pencil magnet and screwdriver, install interlock pin into intermediate plate. Install smaller interlock pin into No. 1 shift rail hole. Install shift rail No. 1 to 1-2 shift fork through intermediate plate. Install largest interlock pin between No. 1 and 3 shift rails.

4) Install interlock pin into No. 3 shift rail hole and install shift rail to reverse shift arm through intermediate plate. Install reverse shift head on shift rail No. 5. Insert shift rail No. 5 into intermediate plate while sliding reverse shift head onto shift rail No. 3.

5) Slide 5th gear synchronizer sleeve rearward, away from intermediate plate. Install 5-R shift fork in synchronizer sleeve. Install shift rail No. 4 to 5-R shift fork and reverse shift arm.

6) Using pencil magnet and screwdriver, install detent ball into intermediate plate. Slide shift rail No. 4 into intermediate plate. Check the interlock by positioning shift rail No. 1 to the 1st gear position.

7) Remaining shift rails should not move. Using a pin punch and hammer, install new shift fork pins. Install 2 shift rail "C" rings. Apply Loctite to NEW screw plugs.

8) Install locking balls, springs and detent plugs to intermediate plate. Ensure short spring goes into top hole on intermediate plate. Tighten detent plugs to specification. See TORQUE SPECIFICATIONS. Remove intermediate plate from vise. Remove bolts, nuts, washers and gasket.

GEARS & SHAFTS

Disassembly – 1) Before removing gears and shafts from intermediate plate, thrust clearance should be measured. Measure between 5th gear on countershaft and rear countergear bearing spacer. Ensure clearance is .004-.012" (.10-.30 mm). If not, check 5th gear components for wear or damage.

2) Engage any 2 gears so that output shaft is locked up. Remove countergear lock nut and disengage gears. Using 2-jaw puller, remove countershaft 5th gear, needle bearing, synchronizer ring and gear spline piece No. 5. Remove spacer and lock ball underneath spacer with pencil magnet. Remove reverse shift arm bracket.

3) Remove rear output shaft bearing retainer Torx bolts and retainer. Remove snap ring from rear output shaft bearing. See Fig. 5. Remove output shaft, countergear and input shaft as a unit by tapping on intermediate plate while holding countergear. Remove countergear rear bearing from intermediate plate.

4) Remove input shaft, and 14 needle roller bearings from output shaft. With shaft removed from intermediate plate, measure thrust clearance of each gear. Ensure clearance is .004-.012" (.10-.30 mm).

5) Using 2 screwdrivers, remove small snap ring from output shaft. Using a press, remove 5th gear (if applicable), rear bearing, 1st gear and inner race from output shaft. Remove needle roller bearing. Remove synchronizer ring and locking ball with pencil magnet.

6) Using a press, remove 1-2 synchronizer and 2nd gear. Remove needle roller bearing. Remove 3-4 synchronizer snap ring. Using press, remove 3-4 synchronizer and 3rd gear. Remove needle roller bearing.

Inspection – 1) Check output shaft and 1st gear inner race for wear or damage. Measure shaft dimensions and replace shafts that are below minimum sizes. See SHAFT SPECIFICATIONS table.

SHAFT SPECIFICATIONS

Area Measured	Minimum Size
Output Shaft	
Flange	.189" (4.80 mm)
Inner Race	1.535" (38.99 mm)
Inner Race Flange	.157" (3.99 mm)
2nd Gear Journal	1.495" (37.97 mm)
3rd Gear Journal	1.377" (34.98 mm)

2) Mount output shaft in "V" blocks or lathe. Mount dial indicator with tip on portion of shaft where 1st gear inner race seats. Rotate output shaft and measure runout. Maximum runout allowed is .002" (.05 mm).

3) Oil clearance between gears and bearing races must be measured. Install 1st gear needle bearing and inner race into 1st gear. Hold gear securely. With tip of indicator on inner race, move race up and down to measure oil clearance. See Fig. 6. Ensure clearance is .0004-.0013" (.010-.033 mm).

4) Measure oil clearance of 2nd, 3rd and countershaft 5th gears. Install gear on shaft with needle roller bearing in place. Position dial indicator tip on tooth of gear to be measured. With shaft held securely, move gear up and down to measure clearance. Ensure clearance for 2nd, 3rd and countershaft 5th gears is .0004-.0013" (.010-.033 mm).

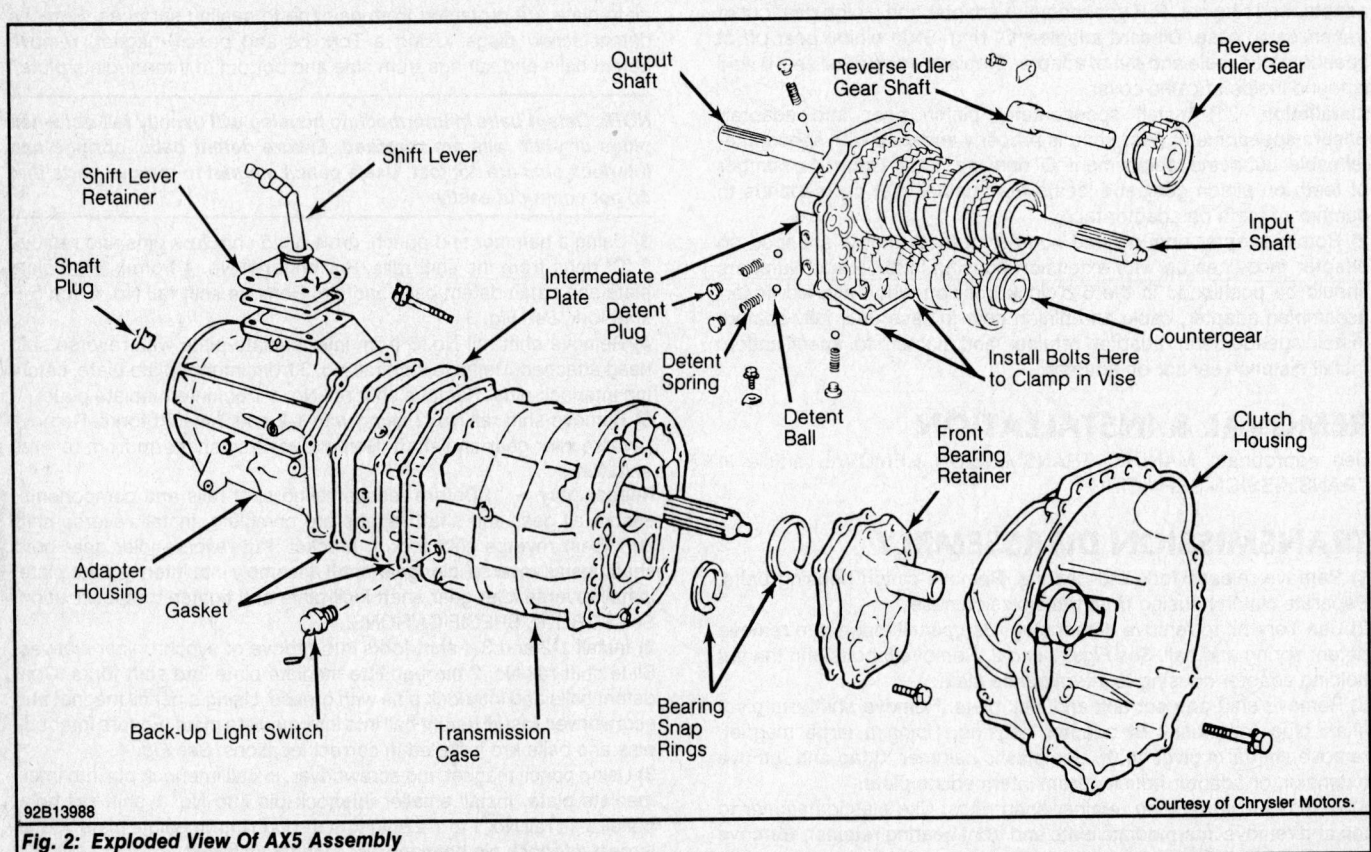

Courtesy of Chrysler Motors.

Fig. 2: Exploded View Of AX5 Assembly

92B13988

5) Measure synchronizer-to-gear face clearance with feeler gauge while ring is firmly pushed toward gear on cone. Ensure clearance does not exceed .078" (1.98 mm). If clearance exceeds .078" (1.98 mm) replace synchronizer ring.

6) Measure clearance between synchronizer sleeve and face of shift fork. Maximum clearance is .039" (.99 mm). Replace shift fork if necessary. Inspect transmission case for cracks, porosity, or damaged bearing or gear bores. Replace case if necessary.

7) Check input shaft, countergear and countergear bearing for wear or damage. Check front bearing retainer and adapter housing for any damage or wear. Replace as necessary.

Reassembly – 1) If input shaft bearing is replaced, press new bearing in place. Select snap ring that allows minimum axial play of bearing. There are 6 snap rings available. See BEARING SNAP RING SIZES table.

2) If countergear front bearing is to be replaced, press new bearing and inner race in place. Select snap ring which will allow minimal axial play. There are 6 snap rings available. See BEARING SNAP RING SIZES table.

3) Press NEW seal into front bearing retainer. Oil seal should be installed so that top edge of seal is .441-.480" (11.20-12.19 mm) from bearing retainer mating surface.

4) Reverse pin must be replaced if worn or damaged. Remove screw plug and drive out roll pin. Remove shift arm and slide out shift arm pivot shaft. Install shift arm with new reverse pin. Install NEW roll pin and tighten shaft plug to specification.

5) Replace adapter housing oil seal. Assemble 1-2 and 3-4 synchronizer assemblies. Install synchronizer inserts into synchronizer hub and slide synchronizer sleeve over hub and inserts. Install hub springs, ensuring spring gaps are not in line. Install insert springs under insert keys. *See Fig. 7.*

BEARING SNAP RING SIZES

Input Gear Snap Ring Mark	Countergear Snap Ring Mark	Thickness In. (mm)
0	1	.0807-.0827 (2.05-2.10)
1	2	.0827-.0846 (2.10-2.15)
2	3	.0846-.0866 (2.15-2.20)
3	4	.0866-.0886 (2.20-2.25)
4	5	.0886-.0906 (2.25-2.30)
5	6	.0906-.0925 (2.30-2.35)

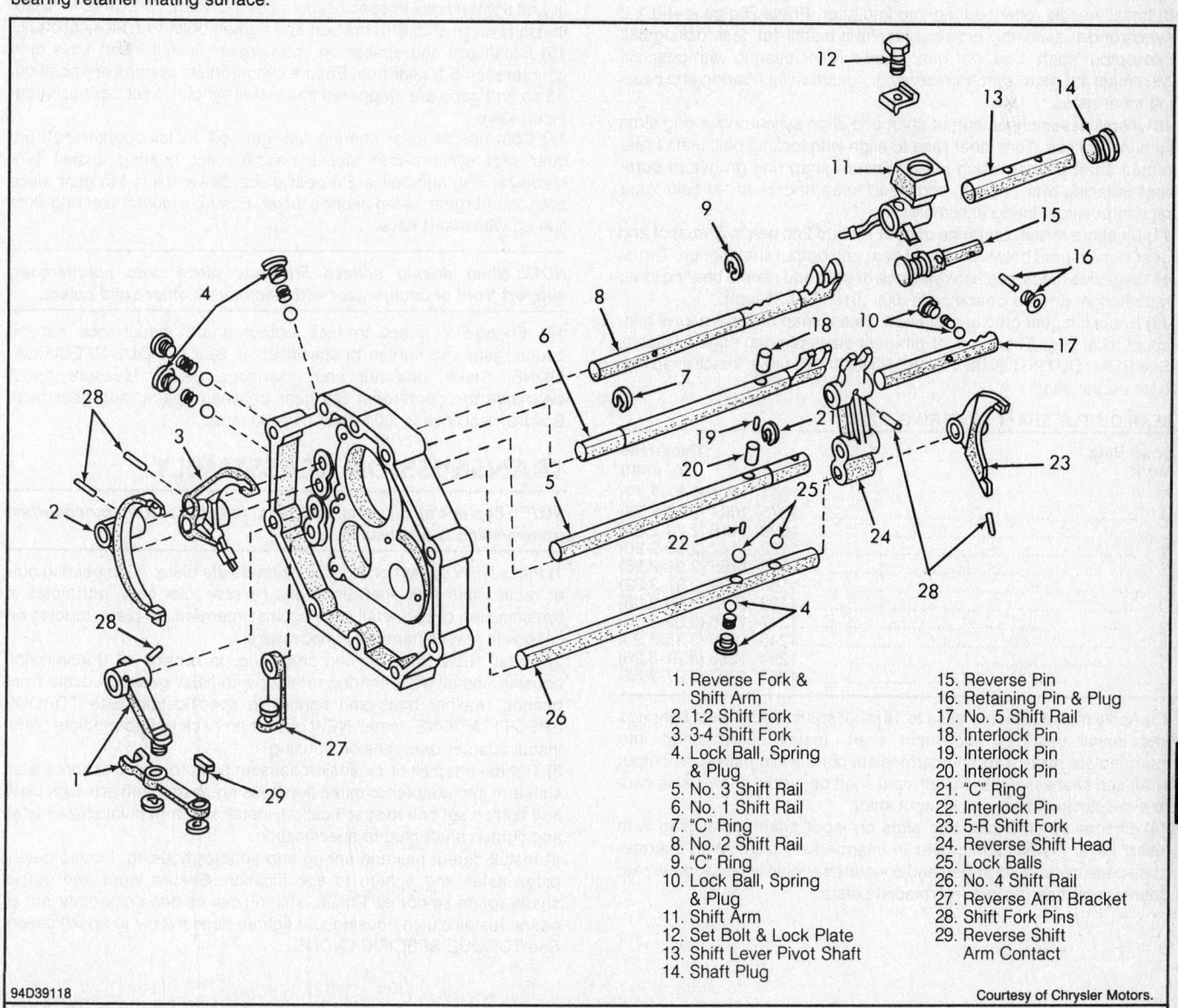

1. Reverse Fork & Shift Arm
2. 1-2 Shift Fork
3. 3-4 Shift Fork
4. Lock Ball, Spring & Plug
5. No. 3 Shift Rail
6. No. 1 Shift Rail
7. "C" Ring
8. No. 2 Shift Rail
9. "C" Ring
10. Lock Ball, Spring & Plug
11. Shift Arm
12. Set Bolt & Lock Plate
13. Shift Lever Pivot Shaft
14. Shaft Plug
15. Reverse Pin
16. Retaining Pin & Plug
17. No. 5 Shift Rail
18. Interlock Pin
19. Interlock Pin
20. Interlock Pin
21. "C" Ring
22. Interlock Pin
23. 5-R Shift Fork
24. Reverse Shift Head
25. Lock Balls
26. No. 4 Shift Rail
27. Reverse Arm Bracket
28. Shift Fork Pins
29. Reverse Shift Arm Contact

94D39118

Courtesy of Chrysler Motors.

Fig. 3: Exploded View Of Shift Rails & Forks

6) Lubricate output shaft and 3rd gear needle roller bearing. Install needle roller bearing into 3rd gear and synchronizer hub. Place 3rd gear and 3-4 synchronizer assembly on output shaft.

7) Press 3rd gear and 3-4 synchronizer assembly into place on output shaft. Install new snap ring selected to allow minimal axial play. Snap rings are available in 7 thicknesses. See 3RD GEAR SNAP RINGS SIZES table.

3RD GEAR SNAP RING SIZES

Snap Ring Mark	Thickness In. (mm)
C-1	.0689-.0709 (1.75-1.80)
D	.0709-.0728 (1.80-1.85)
D-1	.0728-.0748 (1.85-1.90)
E	.0748-.0768 (1.90-1.95)
E-1	.0768-.0787 (1.95-2.00)
F	.0788-.0807 (2.01-2.05)
F-1	.0807-.0827 (2.05-2.10)

8) Measure 3rd gear thrust clearance between gear face and output shaft flange. Ensure clearance is .004-.010" (.10-.25 mm). Coat output shaft and 2nd gear needle bearing with gear oil. Place 2nd gear synchronizer ring on 2nd gear. Align slots in ring with inserts in hub.

9) Install needle roller bearing into 2nd gear. Press 2nd gear and 1-2 synchronizer assembly onto output shaft. Install 1st gear locking ball into output shaft. Coat 1st gear needle roller bearing with gear oil. Assemble 1st gear, synchronizer ring, needle roller bearing and bearing inner race.

10) Install assembly on output shaft and align synchronizer ring slots with insert keys. Turn inner race to align with locking ball. Install rear output shaft bearing using press. Ensure snap ring groove of outer race is facing rear of shaft, and install snap ring. Hold 1st gear inner race in position during assembly.

11) Measure thrust clearance of both 1st and 2nd gears. Thrust of 2nd gear is measured between face of gear and output shaft flange. Thrust of 1st gear is measured between face of gear and needle bearing inner race flange. Ensure clearance is .004-.010" (.10-25 mm).

12) Press 5th gear onto output shaft. Select snap ring that allows minimum axial play. There are 11 different sizes of snap rings available. See REAR OUTPUT SHAFT SNAP RING SIZES table. Install snap ring onto output shaft.

REAR OUTPUT SHAFT SNAP RING SIZES

Snap Ring Mark	Thickness In. (mm)
A	.1051-.1071 (2.67-2.72)
B	.1075-.1094 (2.73-2.78)
C	.1098-.1118 (2.79-2.84)
D	.1122-.1142 (2.85-2.90)
E	.1146-.1165 (2.91-2.96)
F	.1169-.1189 (2.97-3.02)
G	.1193-.1213 (3.03-3.08)
H	.1217-.1236 (3.09-3.14)
J	.1240-.1260 (3.15-3.20)
K	.1264-.1283 (3.21-3.26)
L	.1287-.1307 (3.27-3.32)

13) Apply multipurpose grease to 14 input shaft needle roller bearings and install bearings into input shaft. Install output shaft into intermediate plate. Tap on intermediate plate while pulling on output shaft and seat assembly. Install input shaft on output shaft, using care to avoid cocking bearings in input shaft.

14) Ensure synchronizer ring slots on input shaft are aligned with insert keys. Install countergear in intermediate plate. With intermediate plate securely clamped and countergear held in place, drive rear countergear bearing into intermediate plate.

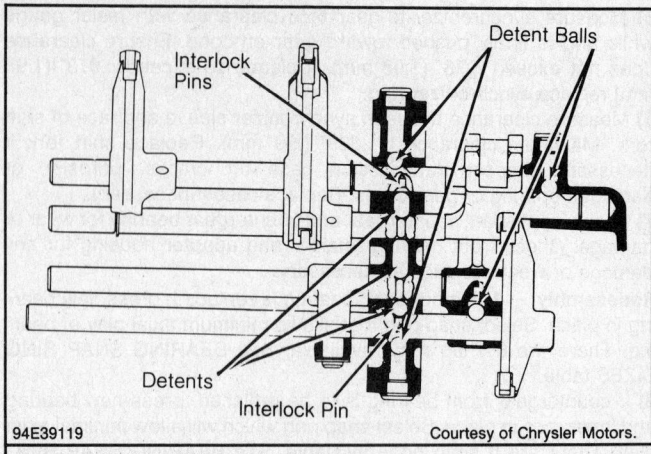

Fig. 4: Installing Detents & Interlocks

15) Install small snap ring for rear countergear bearing. Ensure snap ring is flush with intermediate plate surface. Install rear bearing retainer and tighten bolts to specification. See TORQUE SPECIFICATIONS. Install reverse shift arm bracket and tighten bolts to specification.

16) Install ball and spacer on countergear. Install insert keys onto countershaft 5th gear hub. Ensure synchronizer springs are positioned so end gaps are staggered and install synchronizer springs under insert keys.

17) Coat needle roller bearing with gear oil. Install countershaft 5th gear with synchronizer sleeve needle roller bearing. Install synchronizer ring and spline 5th gear piece. Drive spline 5th gear piece onto countergear, using bearing driver. Ensure synchronizer ring slots line up with insert keys.

NOTE: *When driving splined 5th gear piece onto countergear, support front of countergear with hammer or other solid object.*

18) Engage 2 gears to lock output shaft. Install lock nut on countergear and tighten to specification. See TORQUE SPECIFICATIONS. Stake lock nut and disengage gears. Measure thrust clearance of countergear 5th gear between spacer and gear face. Ensure clearance is .004-.012" (.10-.30 mm).

TRANSMISSION REASSEMBLY

NOTE: *Replace all oil seals, lock nuts, roll pins and snap rings when transmission is overhauled.*

1) Place NEW gasket on front of intermediate plate. Align bearing outer races, shift fork shaft ends and reverse idler gear with holes in transmission case. Install case against intermediate plate, tapping on case with plastic hammer (if necessary).

2) Install NEW front bearing snap ring on outside of transmission housing. Install front bearing retainer with NEW gasket. Loctite front bearing retainer bolts and tighten to specification. See TORQUE SPECIFICATIONS. Install NEW gasket on back of intermediate plate. Install adapter or extension housing.

3) Tighten adapter or extension housing bolts to specification. Install shift arm into adapter or extension housing. Install shift arm lock plate and tighten set bolt to specification. Install shift arm pivot shaft. Install and tighten shaft plug to specification.

4) Install detent ball and spring into adapter housing. Loctite detent plug, install and tighten to specification. Ensure input and output shafts rotate smoothly. Ensure shifting can be done smoothly into all gears. Install clutch housing and tighten bolts evenly to specification. See TORQUE SPECIFICATIONS.

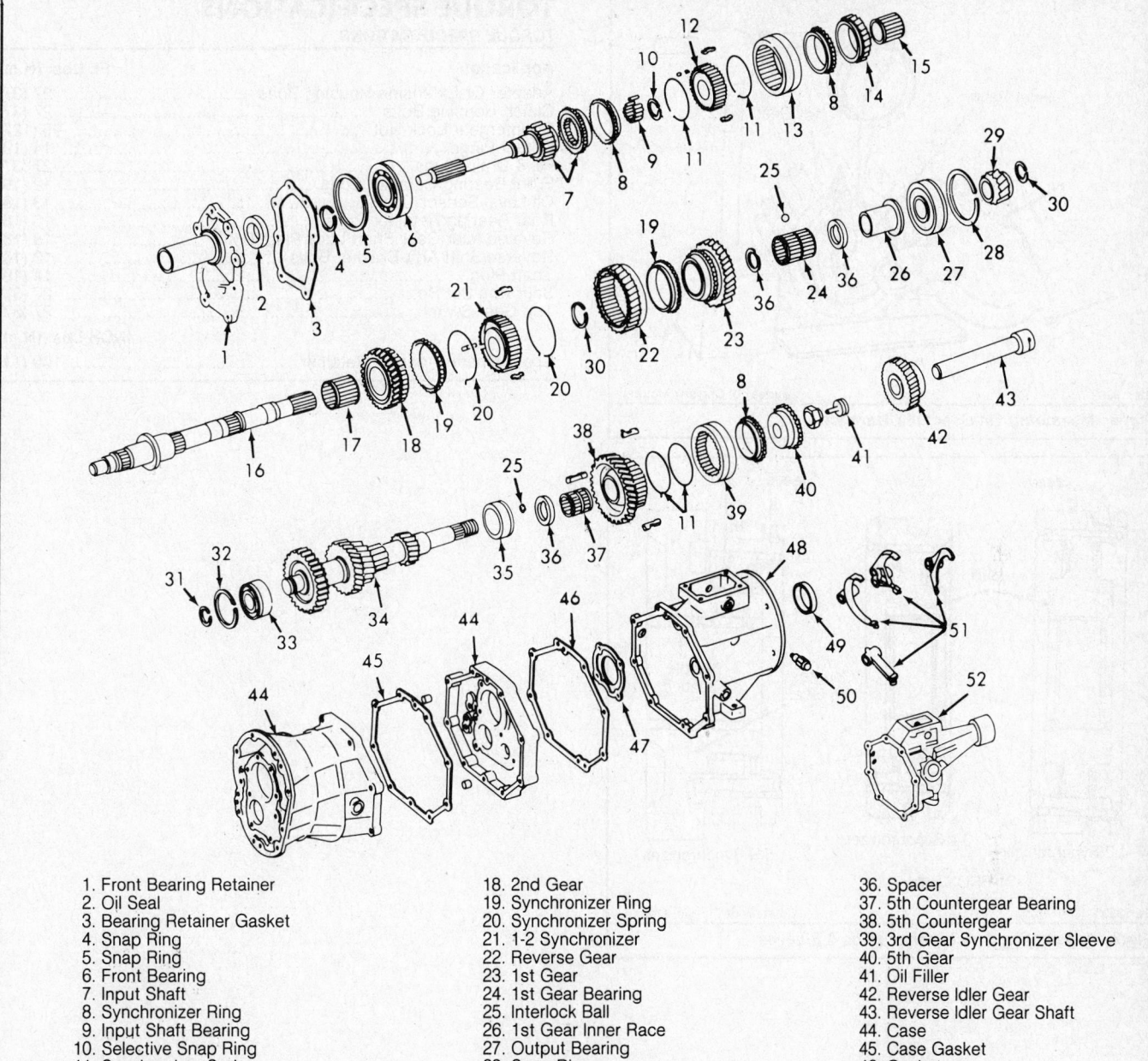

1. Front Bearing Retainer	18. 2nd Gear	36. Spacer
2. Oil Seal	19. Synchronizer Ring	37. 5th Countergear Bearing
3. Bearing Retainer Gasket	20. Synchronizer Spring	38. 5th Countergear
4. Snap Ring	21. 1-2 Synchronizer	39. 3rd Gear Synchronizer Sleeve
5. Snap Ring	22. Reverse Gear	40. 5th Gear
6. Front Bearing	23. 1st Gear	41. Oil Filler
7. Input Shaft	24. 1st Gear Bearing	42. Reverse Idler Gear
8. Synchronizer Ring	25. Interlock Ball	43. Reverse Idler Gear Shaft
9. Input Shaft Bearing	26. 1st Gear Inner Race	44. Case
10. Selective Snap Ring	27. Output Bearing	45. Case Gasket
11. Synchronizer Spring	28. Snap Ring	46. Gasket
12. 3-4 Synchronizer	29. 5th Gear	47. Rear Retainer
13. Synchronizer Sleeve	30. Selective Snap Ring	48. Adapter Housing
14. 3rd Gear	31. Selective Snap Ring	49. Oil Seal
15. 3rd Gear Bearing	32. Snap Ring	50. Reverse Pin
16. Output Shaft	33. Front Countergear Bearing	51. Shift Forks
17. 2nd Gear Bearing	34. Countergear	52. Extension Housing
	35. Rear Countergear Bearing	

94H39120

Courtesy of Chrysler Motors.

Fig. 5: Exploded View Of AX5 Transmission

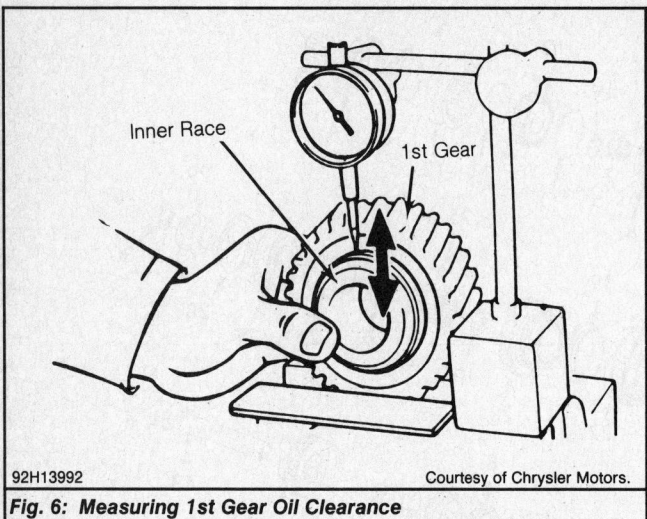

92H13992

Courtesy of Chrysler Motors.

Fig. 6: Measuring 1st Gear Oil Clearance

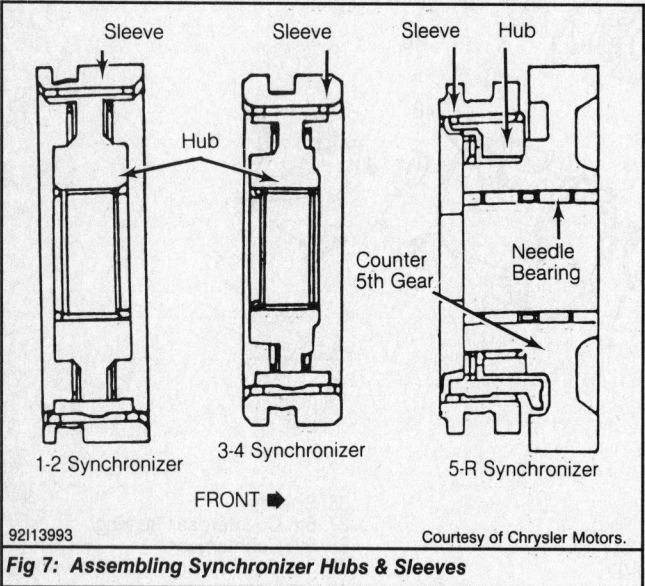

92I13993

Courtesy of Chrysler Motors.

Fig 7: Assembling Synchronizer Hubs & Sleeves

TORQUE SPECIFICATIONS
TORQUE SPECIFICATIONS

Application	Ft. Lbs. (N.m)
Adapter Or Extension Housing Bolts	27 (37)
Clutch Housing Bolts	27 (37)
Countergear Lock Nut	90 (122)
Detent Plugs	14 (19)
Fill & Drain Plugs	27 (37)
Front Bearing Retainer Bolts	12 (16)
Oil Level Sensor	13 (18)
Rear Bearing Retainer Bolts	13 (18)
Reverse Idler Gear Shaft Lock Plate Bolts	13 (18)
Reverse Shift Arm Bracket Bolts	13 (18)
Shaft Plug	14 (19)
Shift Arm Set Bolt	27 (37)
Top Gear Switch	27 (37)
	INCH Lbs. (N.m)
Speedometer Adapter Retainer	100 (11)

Jeep: Cherokee, Grand Cherokee, Wrangler

IDENTIFICATION

The identification code numbers are stamped on the bottom surface of the transmission gear case. *See Fig. 1.* The 1st number is year of manufacture; 2nd and 3rd numbers are month of manufacture. The next series of numbers is the transmission serial number.

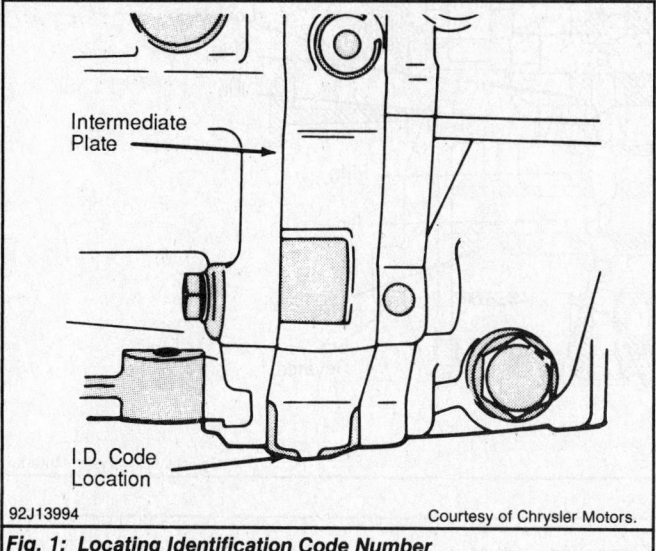

92J13994   Courtesy of Chrysler Motors.

Fig. 1: Locating Identification Code Number

DESCRIPTION

The AX15 is a 5-speed manual transmission. AX15 has 5th gear as an overdrive gear with a 0.79:1 ratio. AX15 unit has integral shift mechanism mounted in adapter or extension housings.

LUBRICATION & ADJUSTMENT

See appropriate MANUAL TRANSMISSION SERVICING article in TRANSMISSION SERVICING.

TROUBLE SHOOTING

See GENERAL TROUBLE SHOOTING article in MANUAL TRANSMISSIONS.

ON-VEHICLE SERVICE

EXTENSION HOUSING SEAL

Removal & Installation – Mark propeller shaft and rear axle pinion yoke for reassembly reference. Remove drive shaft. Remove extension housing seal. Clean oil and grease build-up from around housing bore. Install extension housing seal using seal driver. Align and install propeller shaft. Tighten propeller shaft "U" bolts to specification.

REMOVAL & INSTALLATION

See appropriate MANUAL TRANSMISSION REMOVAL article in TRANSMISSION SERVICING.

TRANSMISSION DISASSEMBLY

1) Remove hydraulic release bearing, clutch housing and shift lever. Remove extension housing seal on 2WD models.
2) Remove 4 shift tower bolts. Remove tower and gasket from adapter or extension housing.
3) Remove shift arm retainer bolt. Loosen and remove 2 restrictor pins and shift arm pivot shaft plug.

4) Remove shift arm shaft with a large magnet, and lift out shift arm. Remove reverse shift head lock plug. Using a pencil magnet, remove lock-ball spring and lock-ball.
5) Remove back-up light switch. On 2WD models, remove speedometer driven gear assembly. Remove adapter/extension housing bolts and loosen housing by tapping with a rubber mallet. Remove housing and pry out housing oil seal.
6) Remove front bearing retainer bolts and retainer. Remove retainer oil seal.
7) Remove input shaft bearing snap ring and cluster gear front bearing snap ring. Loosen gear case by tapping with a rubber mallet. Remove transmission case from geartrain and intermediate plate. On 2WD models, remove speedometer gear snap ring, gear and spacer from output shaft.
8) On 2WD and 4WD models, remove 3 lock-ball plugs from intermediate plate. Using a pencil magnet, remove lock-ball springs, and lock-balls.
9) Mount intermediate plate and geartrain assembly in a vise by inserting 2 clutch housing bolts, washers and suitable nuts in both bottom bolt holes of intermediate plate. Insert bolts from opposite sides. Increase or decrease number of washers used so that bolt tip and outer surface of nut are aligned. Clamp vise jaws securely against bolt heads. DO NOT clamp vise jaws on intermediate plate. *See Fig. 2.*

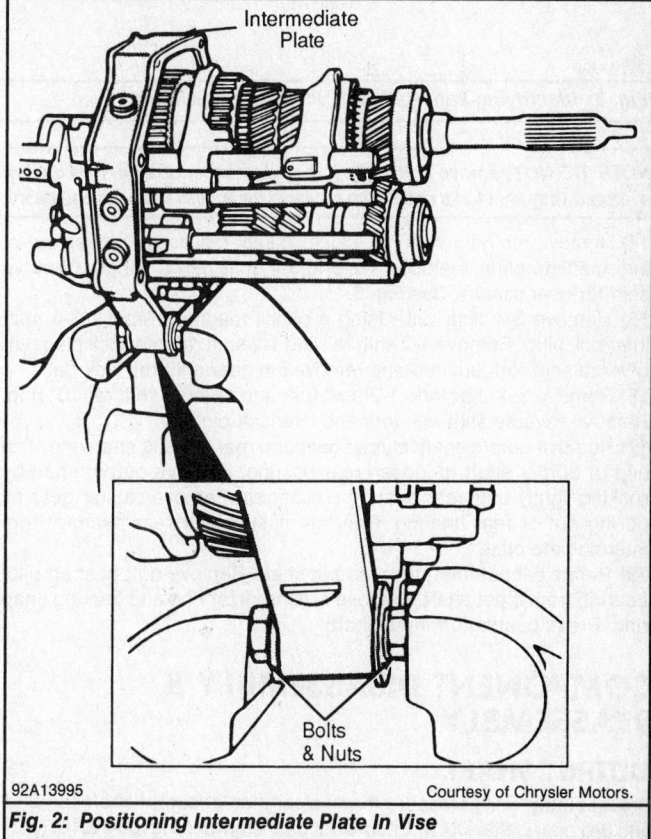

92A13995   Courtesy of Chrysler Motors.

Fig. 2: Positioning Intermediate Plate In Vise

10) Remove 5th gear selective snap ring, reverse shift arm "E" ring, reverse shift arm bracket bolts and bracket. Remove reverse shift arm and shoe.
11) Remove 5th gear shift fork set screw and move shift rail forward until shift rail clears shift fork. Remove shift fork. Remove reverse shift rail and shift head as an assembly. *See Fig. 3.*
12) Measure thrust clearance between counter 5th gear and thrust ring. Ensure clearance is .004-.016" (.10-.40 mm). If not, gear and ring should be replaced.
13) Loosen 5th spline gear with a 2-jaw puller positioned behind 5th counter gear. Remove 5th spline gear, 5th gear synchronizer ring, 5th gear synchronizer and sleeve assembly. Remove counter 5th gear thrust ring. Using a pencil magnet, remove thrust ring lock-ball.

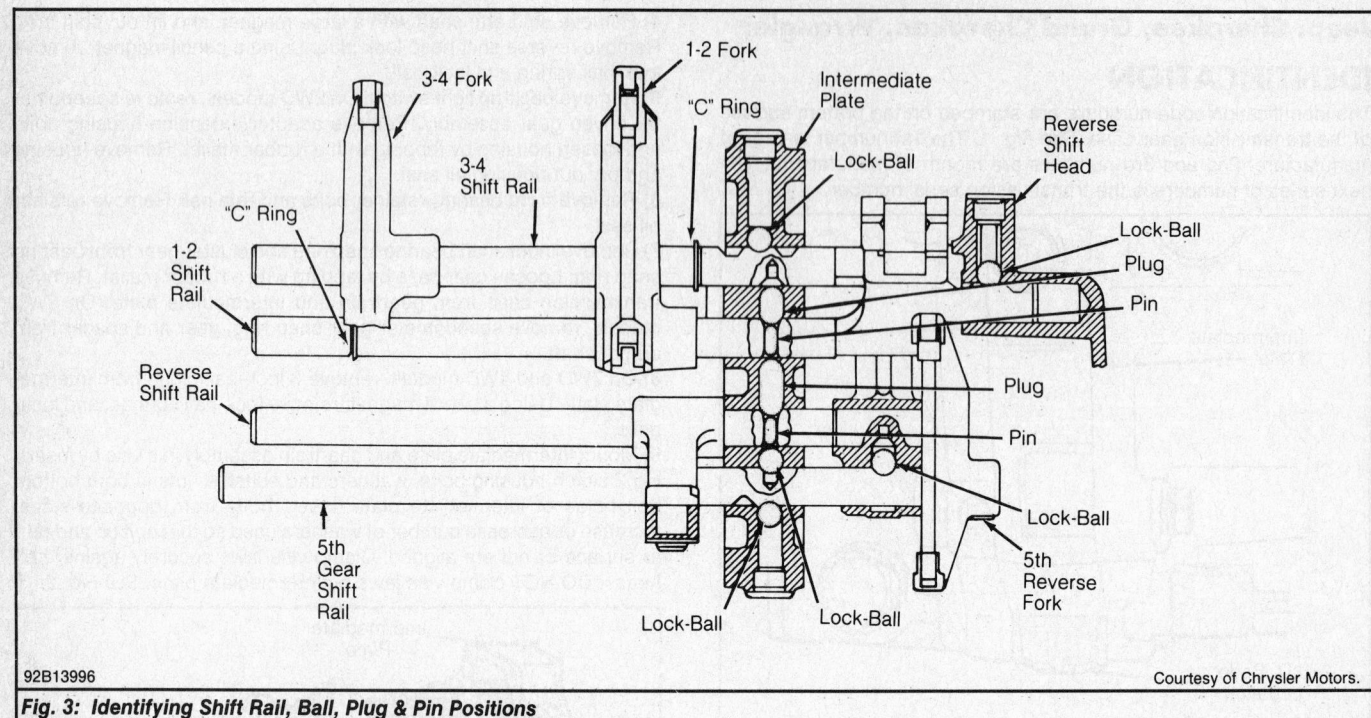

Fig. 3: Identifying Shift Rail, Ball, Plug & Pin Positions

92B13996   Courtesy of Chrysler Motors.

NOTE: DO NOT remove shift rails if they do not require service during overhaul. Only shift forks need to be removed for access to shafts and gears.

14) Remove 5th gear shift rail, catching lock-ball as rail comes out of intermediate plate. Remove 1-2 and 3-4 shift rail "C" rings. Remove shift fork set screws. *See Fig. 3.*

15) Remove 3-4 shift rail. Using a pencil magnet, remove 3-4 shift interlock plug. Remove 1-2 shift rail and 1-2 shift rail interlock plug. Lift reverse shift fork upward and remove 5th gear shift rail lock-ball.

16) Remove 3-4 shift fork, 1-2 shift fork and reverse shift rail "C" ring. Remove reverse shift rail, fork and interlock pin.

17) Remove output shaft, cluster gear and rear bearing snap ring. Tap end of output shaft to loosen rear bearing. Remove output shaft by rocking lightly until rear bearing comes out. Remove cluster gear by pulling out of rear bearing. Remove cluster gear rear bearing from intermediate plate.

18) Remove input shaft from output shaft. Remove output shaft pilot bearing from input shaft. Remove synchronizer ring and bearing snap ring. Press bearing off input shaft.

COMPONENT DISASSEMBLY & REASSEMBLY

OUTPUT SHAFT

Disassembly – **1)** Measure thrust clearance of output shaft 1st, 2nd and 3rd gears. *See Fig. 4.* Ensure 1st gear clearance is .004-.016" (.10-.40 mm). Ensure 2nd and 3rd gear clearance is .004-.012" (.10-.30 mm). If 1st gear thrust clearance is incorrect, replace gear and thrust washer. If 2nd or 3rd gear clearance is incorrect, gear and/or bearing are worn or output shaft is worn.

2) Press 5th gear and rear bearing off output shaft. Remove thrust washer, pin and 1st gear with bearing. Remove 1st-reverse hub snap ring. Remove synchronizer ring.

3) Press reverse gear and 1st-reverse hub off shaft as an assembly. Remove synchronizer ring, 2nd gear and bearing.

4) Remove front snap ring. Press off 3-4 hub and sleeve as an assembly. Remove synchronizer ring. Remove 3rd gear and needle bearing. *See Fig. 5.*

Inspection – **1)** Measure output shaft flange thickness. Ensure minimum thickness is .185" (4.70 mm). If output shaft flange thickness is okay, but 2nd and 3rd gear thrust clearance was incorrect, replace gear and needle bearing as an assembly.

2) Check diameter of 1st, 2nd and 3rd gear bearing surfaces of shaft. See OUTPUT SHAFT BEARING SURFACE table.

3) Check shaft runout. Ensure maximum runout is .002" (.05 mm).

OUTPUT SHAFT BEARING SURFACE

Application	In. (mm)
1st Gear Surface	1.530 (38.86)
2nd Gear Surface	1.845 (46.86)
3rd Gear Surface	1.491 (37.86)

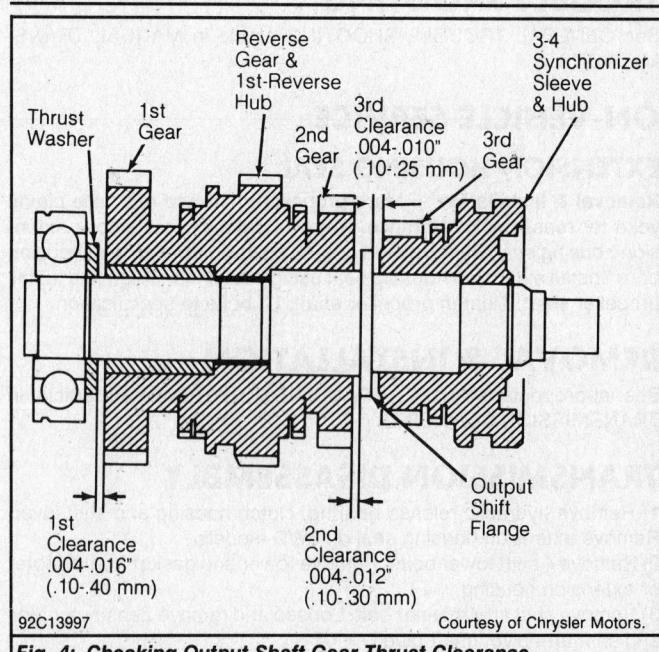

92C13997   Courtesy of Chrysler Motors.

Fig. 4: Checking Output Shaft Gear Thrust Clearance

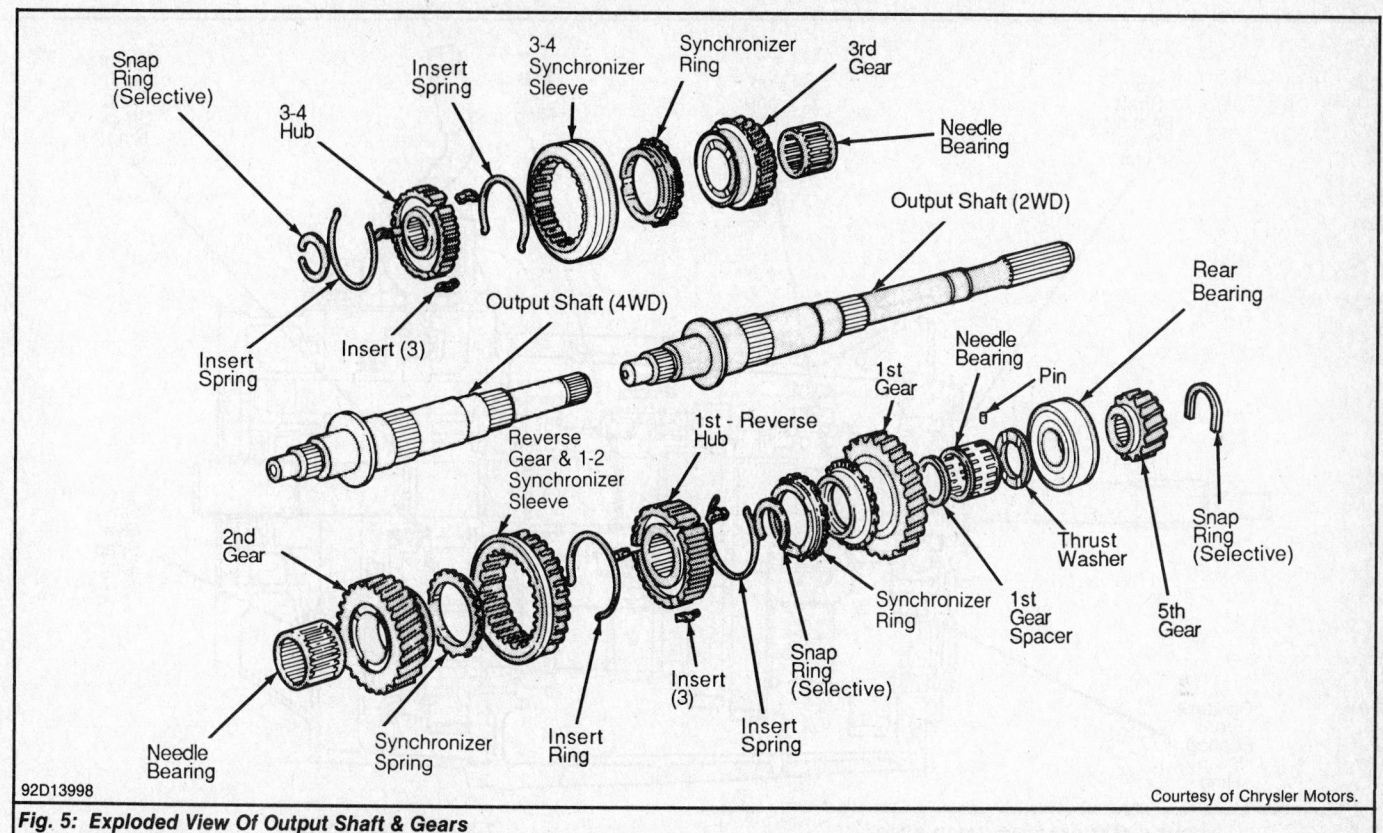

Fig. 5: Exploded View Of Output Shaft & Gears

92D13998

Courtesy of Chrysler Motors.

Reassembly – **1)** Lubricate output shaft journals, gears and needle bearings with 75W-90 gear lubricant. Install 3rd gear and needle bearing. Install synchronizer ring onto the 3rd gear.

2) Reassemble 1-2 and 3-4 synchronizer hubs and sleeves. Install inserts and springs in synchronizer sleeves ensuring open ends of springs are 180 degrees apart. Install 3-4 synchronizer hub and sleeve. Install 3-4 synchronizer hub selective snap ring using thickest snap ring that will seat in shaft groove. See Fig. 6. Check thrust clearance. See Fig. 4.

3) Install 2nd gear and needle bearing. Install synchronizer ring on 2nd gear. Reassemble 1st-reverse hub, insert springs, inserts and reverse gear and 1-2 sleeve. Install hub so that chamfered side faces front of output shaft and press into place. Install selective snap ring using thickest snap ring that will seat in shaft groove. See Fig. 6.

4) Install synchronizer ring on 1st gear. Install 1st gear spacer, 1st gear and needle bearing, locating pin and thrust washer on shaft. Press rear bearing on shaft. Check 1st and 2nd gear thrust clearance. See Fig. 4. Press 5th gear onto shaft. Install selective snap ring using thickest snap ring that will seat in shaft groove. See Fig. 6.

TRANSMISSION REASSEMBLY

1) Press front bearing onto input shaft. See Fig. 7. Secure bearing with thickest snap ring that will fit in shaft groove. See Fig. 6. Press front bearing on cluster gear. Secure bearing with thickest snap ring that will fit in ring groove on shaft. See Fig. 6.

2) Install new oil seals in front bearing retainer and adapter housing. Installation depth of front bearing retainer seal is .413-.453" (10.5-11.5 mm). Install reverse shaft and shaft retaining pin in adapter housing. Install access hole plug.

3) Lubricate reverse shaft and gear components. Mount intermediate plate in a vise. See Fig. 2. Lubricate and install cluster gear rear bearing (snap ring groove rearward) in intermediate plate. Start cluster gear into bearing, hold bearing and push gear into place.

4) Install output shaft rear bearing in intermediate plate. Start output shaft into bearing and push rearward. Install snap rings on cluster and output shaft rear bearings. Install reverse idler gear and shaft.

5) Position rear bearing retainer over output shaft with retainer tab engaged in reverse idler gear shaft notch. Install rear bearing retainer bolts and tighten to specification. See TORQUE SPECIFICATIONS.

6) Coat intermediate plate shift rail bores and interlock-balls, pins and plugs with a thick covering of petroleum jelly before assembly. Install reverse rail interlock pin in reverse shift rail and install rail into intermediate plate. Install reverse shift rail "C" ring.

7) Position 1-2 and 3-4 shift fork in synchronizer sleeves. Tilt reverse shift fork upward and insert reverse rail lock-ball in intermediate plate. Install 1-2 shift rail interlock plug in intermediate plate bore.

8) Install 1-2 shift rail interlock pin in shift rail and shift rail in intermediate plate and 1-2 shift fork. Install 3-4 shift rail interlock plug in intermediate plate. See Fig. 3.

9) Install 3-4 shift rail in intermediate plate and 1-2 and 3-4 shift forks on rail. Verify interlock-balls, plugs, or pins were not displaced during shift rail installation. Install shift fork set screws and tighten to specification. See TORQUE SPECIFICATIONS.

10) Install 1-2 and 3-4 shift rail "C" rings. Insert 5th gear shift rail through reverse shift fork and slide rail into intermediate plate just far enough to secure interlock-ball. DO NOT fully install at this time.

11) Install thrust ring lock-ball in cluster gear journal. Install 5th gear thrust ring with notch fitting over lock-ball. Assemble counter 5th gear, synchronizer sleeve, inserts and insert springs.

12) Install 2-piece bearing in counter 5th gear and then install counter 5th gear and synchronizer assembly on cluster gear journal. Install synchronizer ring in synchronizer sleeve.

13) Install 5th spline gear on cluster journal. Tap into place with a plastic mallet if necessary. Install 5th gear selective snap ring using thickest snap ring that will seat in shaft groove.

14) Install reverse shift head and rail. Install lock-ball in shift head. Position 5th gear shift fork in synchronizer sleeve. Install 5th gear shift rail by sliding rail through fork, shift head, intermediate plate and reverse shift fork. Ensure interlock-ball is not displaced. See Fig. 3.

15) Align screw holes in shift fork and rail and install set screw. Tighten screw to specifications. Install lock-balls and springs in intermediate plate. Install and tighten lock-ball plugs to specification. See TORQUE SPECIFICATIONS.

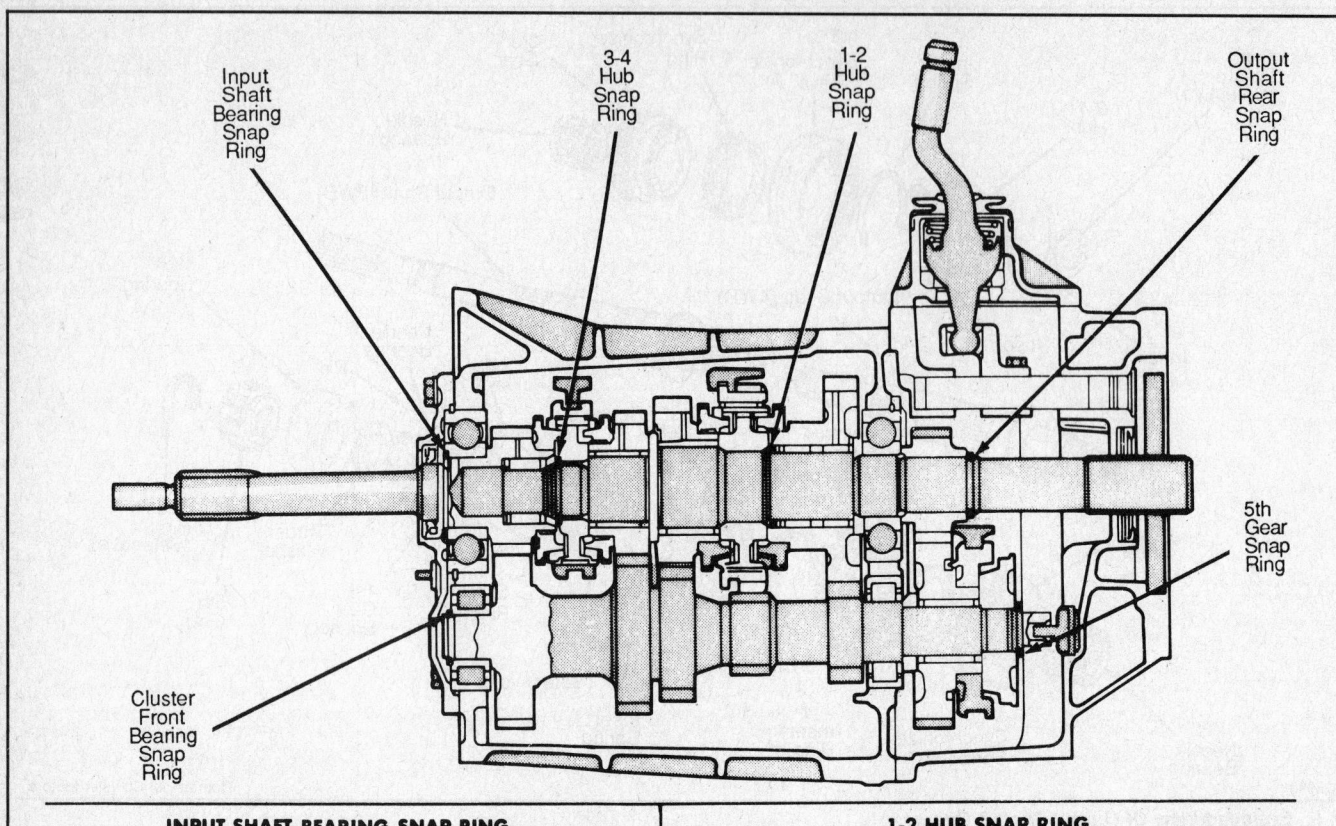

92J14000

Courtesy of Chrysler Motors.

Fig. 6: Identifying Selective Snap Ring Locations & Sizes

INPUT SHAFT BEARING SNAP RING

I.D. MARK	THICKNESS	
A	0.0827 - 0.0846 in.	(2.10 - 2.15 mm)
B	0.0846 - 0.0866 in.	(2.15 - 2.20 mm)
C	0.0866 - 0.0886 in.	(2.20 - 2.25 mm)
D	0.0886 - 0.0906 in.	(2.25 - 2.30 mm)
E	0.0906 - 0.0925 in.	(2.30 - 2.35 mm)
F	0.0925 - 0.0945 in.	(2.35 - 2.40 mm)
G	0.0945 - 0.0965 in.	(2.40 - 2.45 mm)

1-2 HUB SNAP RING

I.D. MARK	THICKNESS	
B	0.0925 - 0.0945 in..	(2.35 - 2.40 mm)
C	0.0945 - 0.0965 in.	(2.40 - 2.45 mm)
D	0.0965 - 0.0984 in.	(2.45 - 2.50 mm)
E	0.0984 - 0.1004 in.	(2.50 - 2.55 mm)
F	0.1004 - 0.1024 in.	(2.55 - 2.60 mm)
G	0.1024 - 0.1043 in.	(2.60 - 2.65 mm)

CLUSTER FRONT BEARING SNAP RING

I.D. MARK	THICKNESS	
A	0.0787 - 0.0807 in.	(2.00 - 2.05 mm)
B	0.0807 - 0.0827 in.	(2.05 - 2.10 mm)
C	0.0827 - 0.0846 in.	(2.10 - 2.15 mm)
D	0.0846 - 0.0866 in.	(2.15 - 2.20 mm)
E	0.0866 - 0.0886 in.	(2.20 - 2.25 mm)

OUTPUT SHAFT REAR SNAP RING

I.D. MARK	THICKNESS	
A	0.1083 - 0.1102 in.	(2.75 - 2.80 mm)
B	0.1102 - 0.1122 in.	(2.80 - 2.85 mm)
C	0.1122 - 0.1142 in.	(2.85 - 2.90 mm)
D	0.1142 - 0.1161 in.	(2.90 - 2.95 mm)
E	0.1161 - 0.1181 in.	(2.95 - 3.00 mm)
F	0.1181 - 0.1201 in.	(3.00 - 3.05 mm)
G	0.1201 - 0.1220 in.	(3.05 - 3.10 mm)
H	0.1220 - 0.1240 in.	(3.10 - 3.15 mm)
I	0.1240 - 0.1260 in.	(3.15 - 3.20 mm)
J	0.1260 - 0.1280 in.	(3.20 - 3.25 mm)
K	0.1280 - 0.1299 in.	(3.25 - 3.30 mm)
L	0.1299 - 0.1319 in.	(3.30 - 3.35 mm)

3-4 HUB SNAP RING

I.D. MARK	THICKNESS	
A	0.0709 - 0.0728 in.	(1.80 - 1.85 mm)
B	0.0728 - 0.0748 in.	(1.85 - 1.90 mm)
C	0.0748 - 0.0768 in.	(1.90 - 1.95 mm)
D	0.0768 - 0.0787 in.	(1.95 - 2.00 mm)
E	0.0787 - 0.0807 in.	(2.00 - 2.05 mm)
F	0.0807 - 0.0827 in.	(2.05 - 2.10 mm)
G	0.0827 - 0.0846 in.	(2.10 - 2.15 mm)

FIFTH GEAR SNAP RING

I.D. MARK	THICKNESS	
A	0.1122 - 0.1142 in.	(2.80 - 2.85 mm)
B	0.1142 - 0.1161 in.	(2.85 - 2.90 mm)
C	0.1161 - 0.1181 in.	(2.90 - 2.95 mm)
D	0.1181 - 0.1201 in.	(2.95 - 3.00 mm)
E	0.1201 - 0.1220 in.	(3.00 - 3.05 mm)
F	0.1220 - 0.1240 in.	(3.05 - 3.10 mm)
G	0.1240 - 0.1260 in.	(3.10 - 3.15 mm)
H	0.1260 - 0.1280 in.	(3.15 - 3.20 mm)

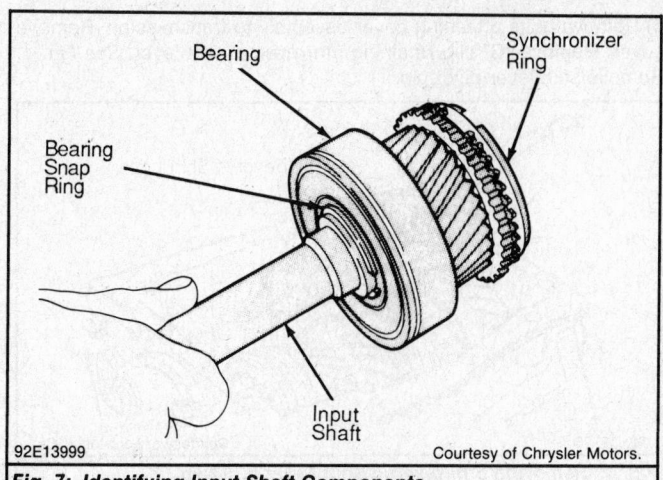

Fig. 7: Identifying Input Shaft Components

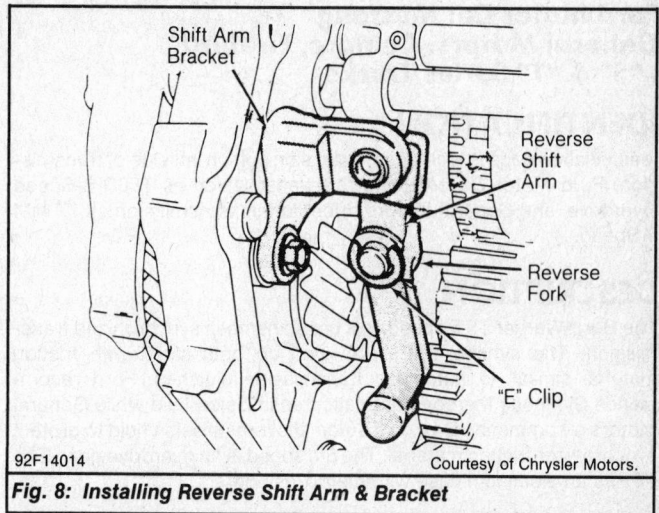

Fig. 8: Installing Reverse Shift Arm & Bracket

16) Install reverse shift arm bracket and tighten bracket bolts to specification. Install reverse shift arm by positioning arm on reverse fork pin and engage with pin on shift arm bracket. Ensure shift arm shoe is engaged in reverse idler gear. Secure shift arm to reverse fork pin with an "E" clip. *See Fig. 8.*

17) Remove intermediate plate and gear assemblies from vise and clean mating surfaces of plate and transmission case. Apply a 1/8" bead of silicone sealer to mating surface of transmission case, keeping sealer bead inside bolt holes.

18) Install transmission case by aligning shift rails and bearings, tapping into place and seating case on intermediate plate dowel pins. Install front bearing snap rings. Clean transmission case and front bearing retainer sealing surfaces.

19) Install a new seal in front bearing retainer at a depth of .413-.453" (10.5-11.5 mm). Lubricate seal lip with petroleum jelly. Apply a 1/8" bead of silicone sealer to front bearing retainer sealing surface. Align and seat on case and bearings. Install front bearing retainer bolts and tighten to specification. See TORQUE SPECIFICATIONS.

20) On 2WD models, install speedometer gear, lock-ball and retaining rings. Inspect reverse pin in adapter/extension housing. If okay, proceed to next step. If worn or damaged, remove roll pin access plug, tap out roll pin and remove old reverse pin. Install NEW reverse pin and secure with roll pin. Install and tighten access plug to specification.

21) Clean sealing surfaces of adapter/extension housing and intermediate plate. Apply a 1/8" bead of silicone sealer to surface of adapter/extension housing. Keep sealer bead inside bolt holes.

22) Align and install adapter/extension housing on intermediate plate. Ensure housing is fully seated on plate dowel pins. Install housing attaching bolts coated with silicone sealer and tighten to specification.

23) Install shift arm shaft detent ball, spring and access plug. Tighten plug to specification. Install shift arm shaft in adapter housing, engaging shift rails. Align shift arm with shaft and push shaft onto arm.

24) Rotate shift arm shaft and align set screw holes in arm and shaft. Install and tighten set screw to specification. Install restrictor pins and shift arm shaft access plug and tighten to specification.

25) Position shift tower gasket on adapter housing and install shift tower and attaching bolts. Tighten bolts to specification. Install gasket on back-up light switch and install switch. Tighten to specification.

26) Install washers on drain plug and fill plug. Install drain plug and tighten to specification. Place transmission in a level position and fill with 75W-90, grade GL-5 gear lubricant. Install fill plug and tighten to specification. Install shift lever, clutch housing and hydraulic throw-out bearing.

TORQUE SPECIFICATIONS
TORQUE SPECIFICATIONS

Applications	Ft. Lbs. (N.m)
Access Plugs	14 (19)
Back-Up Light Switch	27 (37)
Drain & Fill Plugs	27 (37)
Front Bearing Retainer Bolts	12 (16)
Gear Case-To-Adaptor Housing Bolts	27 (37)
Interlock & Detent Ball Plugs	14 (19)
Rear Bearing Retainer Bolts	13 (18)
Restrictor Pins	14 (19)
Reverse Shift Arm Bracket Bolts	13 (18)
Shift Arm Set Screw	28 (38)
Shift Fork Set Screws	15 (20)
Shift Tower Bolts	13 (18)

Ford Motor Co: Mustang
General Motors: Camaro, Firebird,
"S" & "T" Series Trucks

IDENTIFICATION

Identification code is located on extension bolt on left side of transmission. Ford Motor Co. refers to this transmission as T50D 5-Speed Overdrive, and General Motors refers to this transmission as 77 MM 5-Speed.

DESCRIPTION

The Borg-Warner T5 5 speed, is a constant mesh synchronized transmission. The synchronizers are lined on both sides with friction material similar to automatic transmission clutches. Ford recommends Synthetic Mercon automatic transmission fluid while General Motors recommends Dexron II automatic transmission fluid to protect synchronizer friction material. The 5th speed is an overdrive gear. The T5 has an aluminum case with metric fasteners.

LUBRICATION & ADJUSTMENTS

See appropriate MANUAL TRANSMISSION SERVICING article in TRANSMISSION SERVICING.

TROUBLE SHOOTING

See GENERAL TROUBLE SHOOTING article in MANUAL TRANSMISSIONS.

ON-VEHICLE SERVICE

GEARSHIFT LEVER

Removal & Installation – 1) Remove 4 bolts attaching shift boot to floor pan. Remove shift lever-to-transmission bolts. To install, reverse removal procedure. On Ford vehicles, shift lever bolts must only be installed from left side of shift lever.
2) On General Motors vehicles, the upper and lower shift levers are bonded together. Separation of the levers will damage shifter and will require replacement of shifter assembly.

EXTENSION HOUSING BUSHING & OIL SEAL

Removal & Installation – Remove drive shaft. Pry out oil seal with screwdriver. Insert bushing puller into extension housing until it grips front side of bushing. Turn clockwise until bushing is free. Drive NEW bushing into extension housing. Install NEW oil seal, and install drive shaft.

REMOVAL & INSTALLATION

See appropriate MANUAL TRANSMISSION REMOVAL article in TRANSMISSION SERVICING.

TRANSMISSION DISASSEMBLY

CAUTION: If replacing bolts, use only those of same size and length as originals.

NOTE: See Fig. 4 for exploded view of transmission.

1) Drain lubricant and position shift lever in Neutral. Remove turret cover attaching bolts. Using a pry bar, break seal between turret cover and extension housing. Remove turret cover.
2) Remove back-up light switch and external components. DO NOT remove offset lever while extension housing is bolted in place.
3) Using a pin punch and hammer, remove roll pin attaching offset lever to shift rail. Remove damper sleeve. Remove extension housing-to-transmission bolts, and remove housing and offset lever as an assembly by sliding rearward.
4) Remove offset lever from assembly. Remove roll pin, detent spring and detent ball from extension housing detent plate.

5) Remove bolts attaching cover assembly to transmission. Remove cover. Remove "C" clip retaining 5th/reverse shift lever. *See Fig. 1.* Remove shift lever pivot pin.

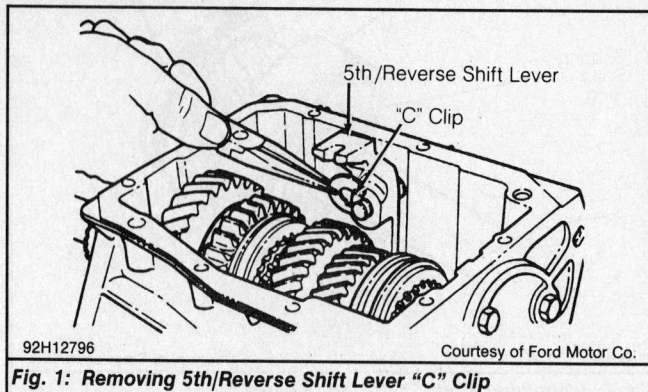

92H12796   Courtesy of Ford Motor Co.
Fig. 1: Removing 5th/Reverse Shift Lever "C" Clip

6) Remove 5th gear synchronizer snap ring. Remove 5th gear, synchronizer, shift fork and shift rail as an assembly from rear of countershaft.
7) Press downward on speedometer gear retaining clip and slide gear off shaft. Remove retaining clip. Mark front bearing retainer for reassembly reference. Remove front bearing retainer bolts. Remove front bearing retainer.
8) Rotate input shaft until flat surface on main drive gear faces countershaft. Remove input shaft from transmission. Remove 4th gear synchronizer ring from 3rd/4th synchronizer. Remove output shaft rear bearing race. Tilt output shaft upward and remove through top of transmission case. *See Fig. 2.*

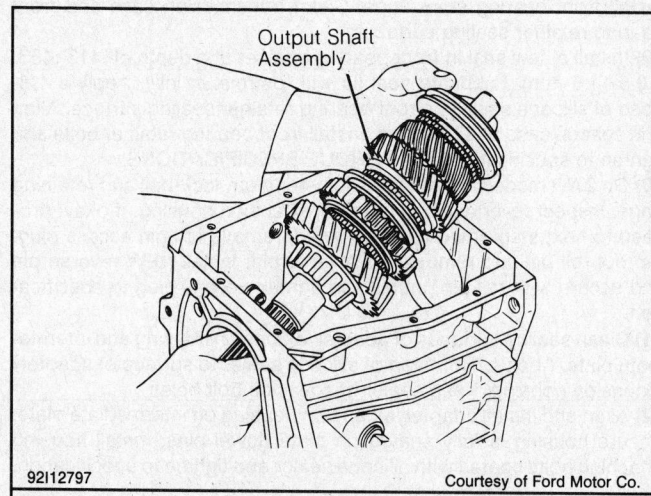

92I12797   Courtesy of Ford Motor Co.
Fig. 2: Removing & Installing Output Shaft Assembly

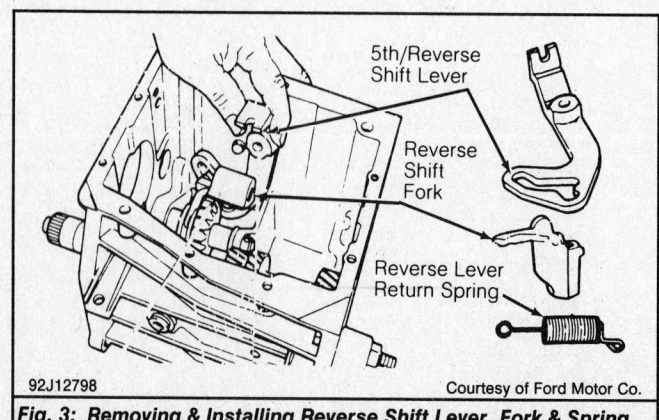

92J12798   Courtesy of Ford Motor Co.
Fig. 3: Removing & Installing Reverse Shift Lever, Fork & Spring

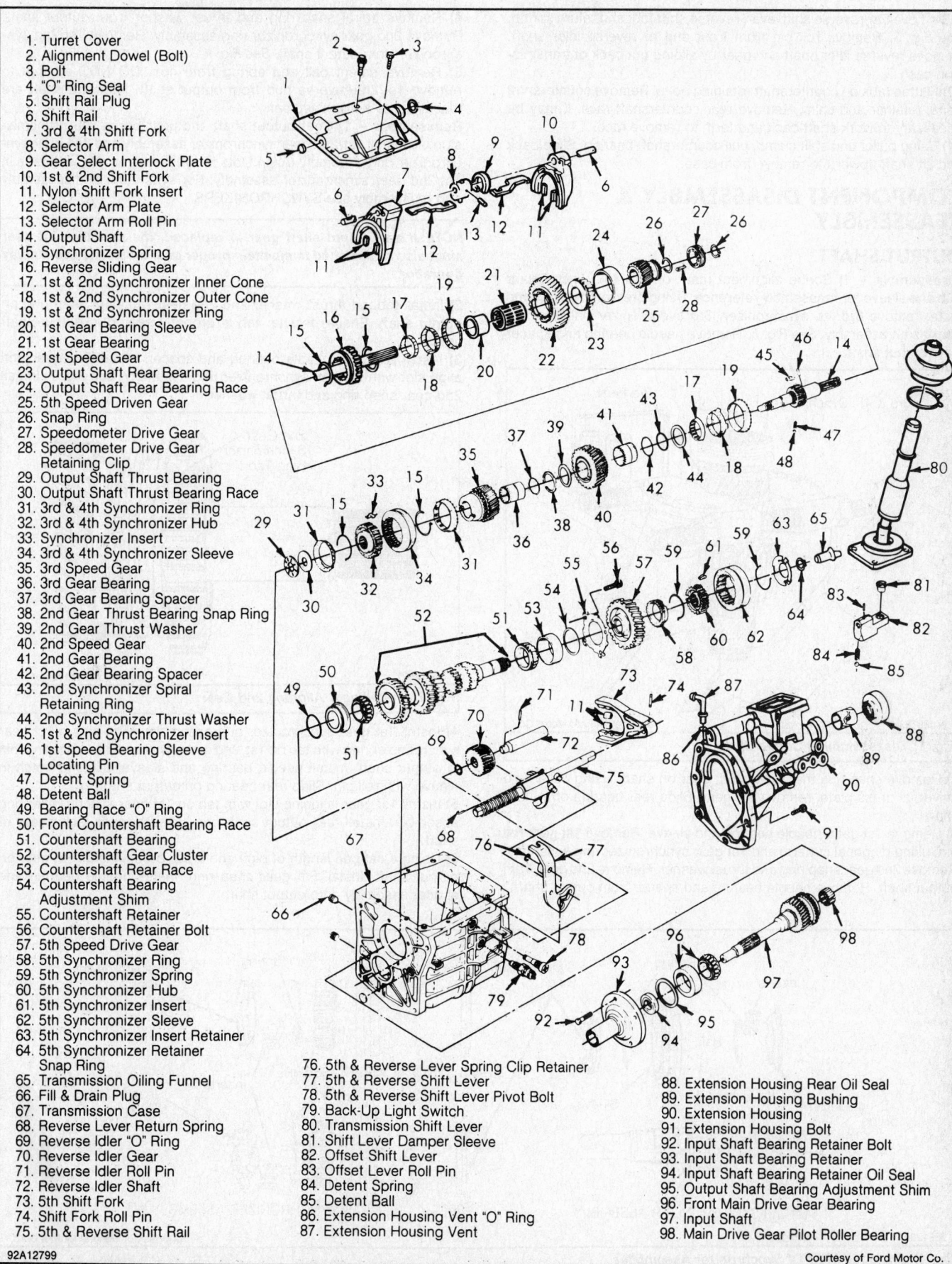

1. Turret Cover
2. Alignment Dowel (Bolt)
3. Bolt
4. "O" Ring Seal
5. Shift Rail Plug
6. Shift Rail
7. 3rd & 4th Shift Fork
8. Selector Arm
9. Gear Select Interlock Plate
10. 1st & 2nd Shift Fork
11. Nylon Shift Fork Insert
12. Selector Arm Plate
13. Selector Arm Roll Pin
14. Output Shaft
15. Synchronizer Spring
16. Reverse Sliding Gear
17. 1st & 2nd Synchronizer Inner Cone
18. 1st & 2nd Synchronizer Outer Cone
19. 1st & 2nd Synchronizer Ring
20. 1st Gear Bearing Sleeve
21. 1st Gear Bearing
22. 1st Speed Gear
23. Output Shaft Rear Bearing
24. Output Shaft Rear Bearing Race
25. 5th Speed Driven Gear
26. Snap Ring
27. Speedometer Drive Gear
28. Speedometer Drive Gear Retaining Clip
29. Output Shaft Thrust Bearing
30. Output Shaft Thrust Bearing Race
31. 3rd & 4th Synchronizer Ring
32. 3rd & 4th Synchronizer Hub
33. Synchronizer Insert
34. 3rd & 4th Synchronizer Sleeve
35. 3rd Speed Gear
36. 3rd Gear Bearing
37. 3rd Gear Bearing Spacer
38. 2nd Gear Thrust Bearing Snap Ring
39. 2nd Gear Thrust Washer
40. 2nd Speed Gear
41. 2nd Gear Bearing
42. 2nd Gear Bearing Spacer
43. 2nd Synchronizer Spiral Retaining Ring
44. 2nd Synchronizer Thrust Washer
45. 1st & 2nd Synchronizer Insert
46. 1st Speed Bearing Sleeve Locating Pin
47. Detent Spring
48. Detent Ball
49. Bearing Race "O" Ring
50. Front Countershaft Bearing Race
51. Countershaft Bearing
52. Countershaft Gear Cluster
53. Countershaft Rear Race
54. Countershaft Bearing Adjustment Shim
55. Countershaft Retainer
56. Countershaft Retainer Bolt
57. 5th Speed Drive Gear
58. 5th Synchronizer Ring
59. 5th Synchronizer Spring
60. 5th Synchronizer Hub
61. 5th Synchronizer Insert
62. 5th Synchronizer Sleeve
63. 5th Synchronizer Insert Retainer
64. 5th Synchronizer Retainer Snap Ring
65. Transmission Oiling Funnel
66. Fill & Drain Plug
67. Transmission Case
68. Reverse Lever Return Spring
69. Reverse Idler "O" Ring
70. Reverse Idler Gear
71. Reverse Idler Roll Pin
72. Reverse Idler Shaft
73. 5th Shift Fork
74. Shift Fork Roll Pin
75. 5th & Reverse Shift Rail

76. 5th & Reverse Lever Spring Clip Retainer
77. 5th & Reverse Shift Lever
78. 5th & Reverse Shift Lever Pivot Bolt
79. Back-Up Light Switch
80. Transmission Shift Lever
81. Shift Lever Damper Sleeve
82. Offset Shift Lever
83. Offset Lever Roll Pin
84. Detent Spring
85. Detent Ball
86. Extension Housing Vent "O" Ring
87. Extension Housing Vent

88. Extension Housing Rear Oil Seal
89. Extension Housing Bushing
90. Extension Housing
91. Extension Housing Bolt
92. Input Shaft Bearing Retainer Bolt
93. Input Shaft Bearing Retainer
94. Input Shaft Bearing Retainer Oil Seal
95. Output Shaft Bearing Adjustment Shim
96. Front Main Drive Gear Bearing
97. Input Shaft
98. Main Drive Gear Pilot Roller Bearing

92A12799

Fig. 4: Exploded View Of Borg-Warner T5 5-Speed Overdrive Transmission

9) Remove 5th/reverse shift lever, reverse shift fork and return spring. *See Fig. 3.* Remove roll pin from front end of reverse idler shaft. Remove reverse idler shaft and gear by sliding out back of transmission case.

10) Flatten tabs on countershaft retaining bolts. Remove countershaft bolts, retainer and shim. Remove rear countershaft race. It may be necessary to work shaft back and forth to remove race.

11) Using puller and split clamp, pull countershaft bearing. Slide back and tilt shaft upward to remove from case.

COMPONENT DISASSEMBLY & REASSEMBLY

OUTPUT SHAFT

Disassembly – 1) Scribe alignment mark on 3rd/4th synchronizer hub and sleeve for reassembly reference. Using press and split clamp plate, remove 3rd/4th synchronizer, 3rd synchronizer ring and 3rd gear as an assembly. *See Fig. 5.* Remove needle bearing and spacer from output shaft.

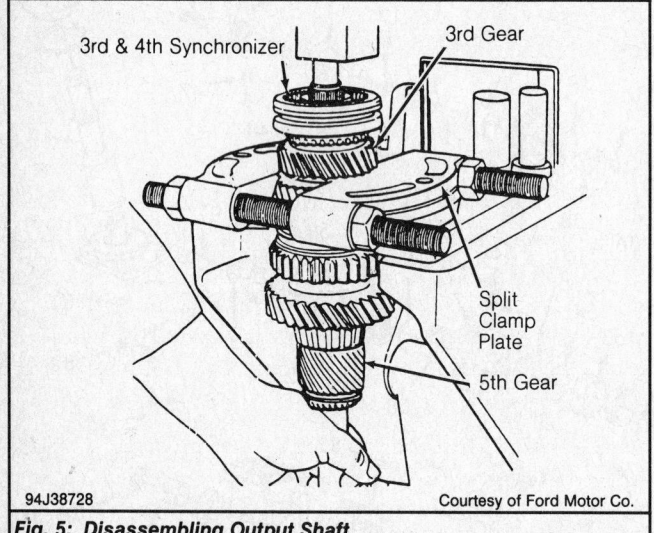

94J38728   Courtesy of Ford Motor Co.

Fig. 5: Disassembling Output Shaft

2) Remove snap ring that retains 5th gear on shaft. Using puller and universal press plate, remove 5th gear. Slide rear bearing off output shaft.

3) Remove 1st gear, needle bearing and sleeve. Remove 1st gear roll pin (using diagonal cutters) and 1st gear synchronizer ring assembly. Remove 2nd gear snap ring and thrust washer. Remove 2nd gear from output shaft. Remove needle bearing and spacer from output shaft.

4) Remove spiral snap ring and thrust washer from output shaft. Remove 2nd gear synchronizer ring assembly. Remove 1st/2nd synchronizer from output shaft. *See Fig. 4.*

5) Remove detent ball and spring from hub. DO NOT attempt to remove 1st/2nd/reverse hub from output shaft. Hub and shaft are machined as a machined set.

Reassembly – 1) Coat output shaft and gear bores with transmission oil. Install 1st/2nd gear synchronizer assembly and 2nd gear synchronizer ring assembly. Align slots in synchronizer ring with tabs in 1st/2nd gear synchronizer assembly. For synchronizer disassembly and reassembly see SYNCHRONIZERS.

NOTE: If any output shaft gear is replaced, the countershaft gear must also be replaced to maintain proper gear mesh and avoid noisy operation.

---

2) Install tabbed thrust washer and 2nd gear retaining snap ring on output shaft. Ensure washer tab is properly seated in output shaft notch.

3) Install 2nd gear needle bearing and spacer. Install 2nd gear and align slot with tabs on synchronizer ring assembly. *See Fig. 7.* Install 2nd gear snap ring and thrust washer.

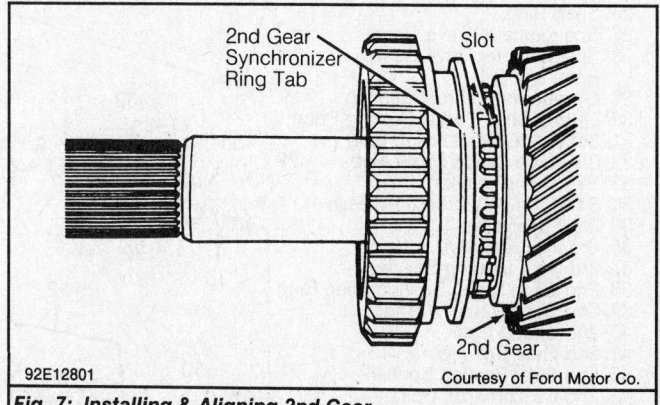

92E12801   Courtesy of Ford Motor Co.

Fig. 7: Installing & Aligning 2nd Gear

4) Install 1st gear synchronizer ring assembly. Align slot in 1st gear synchronizer ring with tab on 1st/2nd gear synchronizer. Install roll pin in output shaft. Install needle bearing and sleeve, aligning notch in sleeve with roll pin. Slide rear bearing on output shaft.

5) Install 1st gear, aligning slot with tab on 1st gear synchronizer ring assembly. Install rear output shaft bearing with taper facing rear of shaft.

6) Using a capped length of pipe and arbor press, install 5th gear on output shaft. Install 5th gear snap ring. Install needle bearing and spacer assembly onto output shaft.

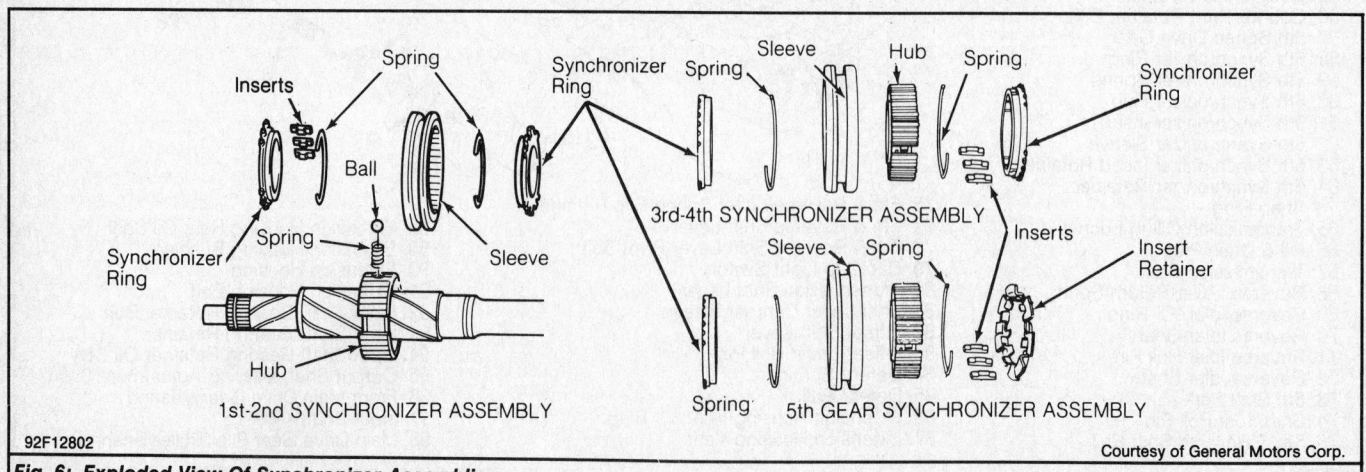

92F12802   Courtesy of General Motors Corp.

Fig. 6: Exploded View Of Synchronizer Assemblies

7) Using press, install 3rd/4th gear synchronizer, 3rd synchronizer ring and 3rd gear as an assembly on output shaft. Hub offset must face forward. Hold 3rd gear against synchronizer to maintain synchronizer ring alignment.

SYNCHRONIZERS

Disassembly – Before disassembling, scribe alignment marks on sleeve and hub for reassembly reference. Remove insert retainer (5th gear synchronizer only). *See Fig. 6.* Remove retaining springs and inserts. On 1st/2nd synchronizer, sleeve should be removed to prevent loss of detent ball and spring.

NOTE: The 1st/2nd gear synchronizer is available only as an assembly with the output shaft. DO NOT attempt to separate hub from shaft.

Reassembly – Assemble inserts and synchronizer retaining springs onto sleeve and hub. Retaining springs engage same insert but rotate in opposite directions. Install insert retainer on 5th gear synchronizer and ensure retainer tabs are positioned over synchronizer inserts. *See Fig. 6.* On 1st/2nd gear synchronizer, install detent ball and spring into hub on output shaft, and assemble retaining springs, inserts and sleeve onto hub.

SHIFT COVER ASSEMBLY

Disassembly – **1)** Place selector arm plates and shift rail in Neutral. Rotate shift rail counterclockwise until selector arm disengages from selector arm plates and selector arm roll pin is accessible.

2) Pull shift rail rearward until selector arm contacts 1st/2nd shift fork. Using a punch, remove selector arm roll pin. *See Fig. 8.* Remove shift rail.

3) Remove shift forks, selector arm plates, selector arm, roll pin and interlock plate. Using a screwdriver, remove shift rail oil seal and "O" ring. Using a hammer and punch, remove shift rail plug.

4) Remove nylon inserts and selector arm plates from shift forks. Note position of inserts and plates for reassembly reference.

Reassembly – **1)** Install nylon inserts and selector arm plates in shift forks. Apply sealer to edge of shift rail plug and install plug. Coat shift rail and bore with petroleum jelly. Install shift rail in cover with end of rail flush with inside edge of cover.

2) Position 1st/2nd shift fork in cover with fork offset facing rear of cover. Push shift rail through fork. Position selector arm and "C" shaped interlock plate in cover, and insert shift rail. Widest part of interlock plate must face away from cover, and selector arm roll pin hole must face downward and toward rear of cover.

3) Position 3rd/4th shift fork in cover with fork offset facing rear of cover. Fork selector arm plate must be positioned under 1st/2nd shift fork selector arm plate. Insert shift rail through 3rd/4th shift fork and into shift rail bore in cover. Rotate shift rail until selector arm plate faces away from cover. *See Fig. 4.*

4) Align roll pin holes in selector arm and shift rail. Install roll pin. Failure to install roll pin below surface may cause interference during shifts. Install "O" ring in groove of shift rail oil seal. Install shift rail oil seal in cover.

INPUT SHAFT BEARING

Disassembly & Reassembly – Using a press and split clamp plate, remove input shaft bearing. Use a press and a capped length of pipe to install bearing.

INPUT SHAFT BEARING RETAINER SEAL

Disassembly & Reassembly – Remove bearing race and end play shim. Using a screwdriver, carefully pry out seal from bearing retainer. Using bearing retainer seal installer, install NEW seal. Install end play shim and bearing race.

NOTE: If seal is replaced as part of a transmission overhaul, DO NOT install end play shim.

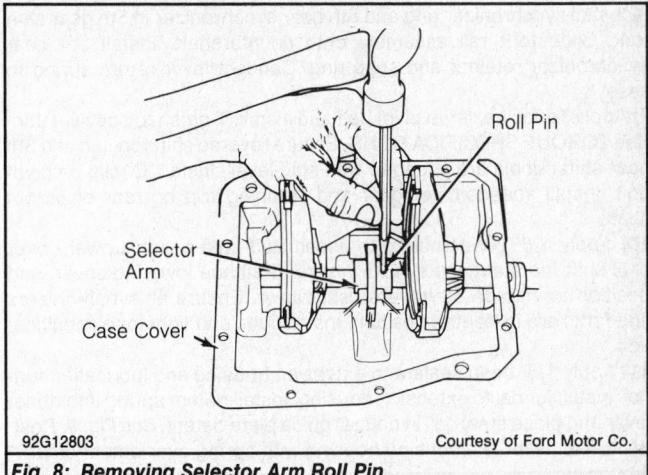

92G12803   Courtesy of Ford Motor Co.

Fig. 8: Removing Selector Arm Roll Pin

CLEANING & INSPECTION

1) Wash all parts in solvent. Dry all parts except bearings with compressed air. Allow bearings to air dry or wipe dry with a clean shop cloth. Clean needle, thrust and roller bearings.

2) Inspect transmission case, cover and extension housing. Replace transmission case, cover or extension housing if there are cracks in bores, sides, bosses or bolt holes. Replace case if there are stripped bolt holes, nicks, burrs, or rough surfaces in shaft bores or on gasket surfaces.

3) Inspect gear train and shift mechanism. Replace any parts exhibiting wear, chips, galling, distortion or bending. Check for worn bearings and bores. Check for weak snap rings and stripped offset lever.

TRANSMISSION REASSEMBLY

1) Coat countershaft front bearing outer cage with Loctite 601. Using a press, install countershaft front bearing flush with case.

CAUTION: Failure to properly support countershaft during bearing installation can result in permanent damage to transmission case.

2) Place transmission case on end, and install countershaft in front bearing. Support countershaft with 2 pieces of 1/4" bar stock under front gear. Using bearing installer and press, install countershaft rear bearing onto countershaft. Install rear race onto countershaft.

3) Install countershaft retainer without shims to transmission case. Tighten to specification. See TORQUE SPECIFICATIONS. Measure end play using dial indicator. Remove retainer and install necessary shims. Ensure end play is .001-.005" (.025-.127 mm).

4) Place reverse idler gear in case with shift lever groove facing case. Install reverse idler shaft from rear of case. Install retaining roll pin. Place reverse shift fork and 5th/reverse shift lever in case. *See Fig. 3.*

5) Install assembled output shaft in transmission case. Coat input shaft roller bearings, thrust bearing and race with petroleum jelly, and install inside input shaft. Install synchronizer ring, aligning notches with inserts in 3rd/4th synchronizer.

6) Install input shaft, aligning flat on synchronizer with countershaft. Install front bearing race in bearing retainer without shims. Temporarily install bearing retainer. Tighten bolts to specification.

7) Install output shaft rear bearing race. Tap into place with plastic-tip hammer, if necessary. Install 5th speed gear on countershaft. Slide shift rail, 5th gear shift fork assembly into case. Align shift fork and slide rail through fork. Position lever return spring in case, and slide shift rail the remaining distance through spring.

NOTE: Long end of spring must face rear of case.

8) Install synchronizer ring and 5th gear synchronizer in 5th gear shift fork. Slide fork rail assembly onto countershaft. Install 5th gear synchronizer retainer and snap ring. Connect lever return spring to case.

9) Apply Teflon sealer to pivot bolt and install. Tighten to specification. See TORQUE SPECIFICATIONS. Ensure reverse shift fork pin and 5th gear shift rail pin are engaged with shift lever. Install "C" clip on pivot bolt. Install speedometer gear and retaining clip on rear of output shaft.

10) Apply 1/8" bead sealant to assembled shift cover. Lower cover until shift forks engage synchronizers. Continue lowering cover, and position to engage 5th/reverse shift lever. Ensure all synchronizers and forks are in Neutral position. Install bolts and tighten to specification.

11) Apply 1/8" bead sealant to extension housing and lubrication funnel. Install funnel to extension housing. Install detent spring into offset lever and place steel ball in neutral guide plate detent. See Fig. 9. Position offset lever in extension housing with spring over detent ball.

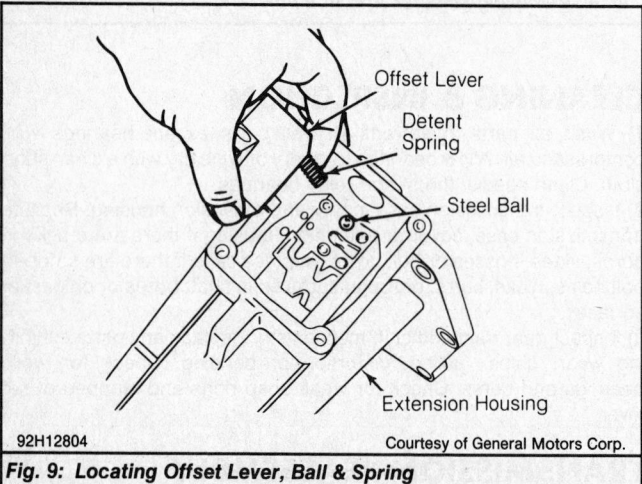

92H12804   Courtesy of General Motors Corp.

Fig. 9: Locating Offset Lever, Ball & Spring

12) Slide offset lever and extension housing to transmission case. Apply pressure to steel ball with detent spring and offset lever, pushing lever and housing into position. See Fig. 9. Install and tighten housing bolts to specification.

13) Align roll pin hole in shift rail and offset lever, and install pin. Install damper sleeve in offset lever. Turn transmission case on end and mount dial indicator on extension housing with indicator pointer on end of output shaft. Rotate clutch and output shaft and zero dial indicator. Pull upward on output shaft and read end play on dial indicator. See Fig. 10.

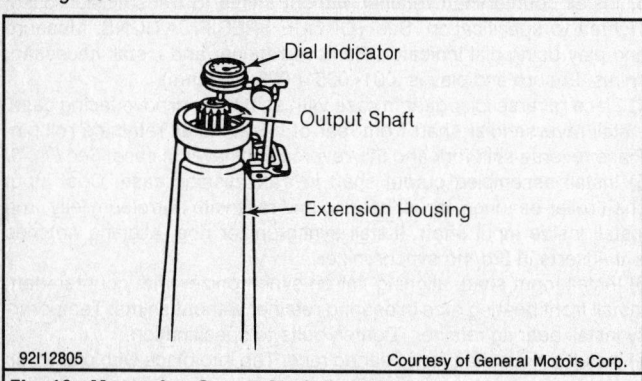

92I12805   Courtesy of General Motors Corp.

Fig. 10: Measuring Output Shaft End Play

14) Select a shim pack equal to measurement on dial indicator. Remove front bearing retainer and race. Add shims to cap and install bearing race in cap. Apply silicone sealant to front bearing retainer and install on transmission case. Tighten to specification. Ensure no end play exists.

CAUTION: Ideal end play specification is zero. Acceptable tolerance is up to .002" (.051 mm). DO NOT overload bearings with excessive shims.

15) Apply bead of silicone sealant to turret cover. Install cover on extension housing and tighten bolts to specification. Coat back-up light switch threads with silicone sealant, and install switch.

TORQUE SPECIFICATIONS

TORQUE SPECIFICATIONS – FORD MOTOR CO.

Application	Ft. Lbs. (N.m)
Back-Up Light Switch	20-35 (27-47)
Bearing Retainer Bolt	11-20 (15-27)
Drain Plug	15-22 (20-30)
Extension Housing Bolt	30-45 (41-61)
Flywheel Housing Bolt	45-65 (61-88)
Neutral Sensing Switch	20-35 (27-47)
Shift Lever Bolt	23-32 (31-43)
Transmission Support Bolt	36-50 (49-68)
Turret Cover Bolt	12-15 (16-20)
5th/Reverse Shift Lever Pivot Pin	25-35 (34-47)
	INCH Lbs. (N.m)
Reverse Positioning Spring Anchor Pin Bolt	54-115 (6-13)
Shift Boot Floor Pan Bolts	36-84 (4-9.5)
Shift Cover Bolts	72-132 (8-15)
Speedometer Cable Retaining Bolt	54-115 (6-13)

TORQUE SPECIFICATIONS – GENERAL MOTORS

Application	Ft. Lbs. (N.m)
Back-Up Light Switch	28 (38)
Countershaft Retainer	15 (20)
Drain & Fill Plug	20 (27)
Extension Housing	22 (30)
Flywheel Housing Bolt	55 (75)
Front Bearing Retainer	15 (20)
Reverse Pivot Bolt	20 (27)
Transmission Cover Bolt	10 (14)
Transmission Support Bolt	40 (54)
Transmission Support Nut	35 (47)
	INCH Lbs. (N.m)
Shift Boot Floor Pan Bolt	53 (6)
Speed Sensor Retainer Bolt	89 (10)

SERVICE BULLETINS

SQUAWK NOISE IN 5TH GEAR – COLD

General Motors Corp. (93-274-7B – July 24, 1993) – Description – Squawk noise occurs cold for first 5-10 miles in 5th gear. Squawk noise can be caused by input shaft synchronizer ring vibrating on shaft.

Repair – Refer to TRANSMISSION DISASSEMBLY to disassemble unit and add an input shaft synchronizer ring wave spring (Part No. GM 12545629). The wave spring should be installed between input shaft clutch tool face and synchronizer ring.

5TH GEAR WHINE

General Motors Corp. (93-172-7B – April 13, 1993) – Description – Whine or gear noise occurs mostly at freeway speed. Noise is caused by normal internal transmission workings being transmitted and amplified through shift lever.

Repair – Refer to ON-VEHICLE SERVICE to remove gear shift lever. Cut off top of shifter stub shaft (non-threaded portion). Replace shifter with updated design, (Part No. GM 15965641).

RATTLING, 2ND GEAR NOISE

Ford Motor Co. (TSB 92-4-8 – February 12, 1992) – Description – Rattling noise while in 2nd gear. Condition occurs after reverse lever pivot bolt is removed mistakenly for fill plug, causing reverse shift lever return spring to fall into case.

Repair – Refer to TRANSMISSION DISASSEMBLY to disassemble unit and remount reverse shift lever return spring.

Ford Motor Co (1993): Bronco, F-150, F-250

IDENTIFICATION

The identification tag is located on top right side of transmission, on bolt retaining housing assembly to case. Tag has serial number, build date code and manufacturer's identification number.

DESCRIPTION

The Borg-Warner Model T18 4-speed has spur gears in 1st-reverse position. All other gears are helical cut and are synchronized engagement design. *See Fig. 1.*

LUBRICATION & ADJUSTMENTS

See appropriate MANUAL TRANSMISSION SERVICING article in TRANSMISSION SERVICING.

TROUBLE SHOOTING

See GENERAL TROUBLE SHOOTING article in MANUAL TRANSMISSIONS.

ON-VEHICLE SERVICE

SHIFT LEVER

Removal – **1)** If shift lever ball removal is required, remove ball prior to shift lever removal. Warm shift lever ball with a heat gun to 140-180°F (60-82°C). Remove shift lever ball by tapping with a block of wood.

2) For shift lever removal, remove carpet, rubber boot and floor pan cover. Shift transmission into 2nd gear. Pull outer trim cover boot down off upper shift lever to expose 2 attaching bolts. Remove both bolts and remove upper shift lever.

3) Remove outer trim boot, inner boot and vapor seal. Remove splash boot. Remove trunnion pin and remove lower shift lever from shifter housing assembly. *See Fig. 2.*

Installation – Install lower shift lever in shifter housing assembly so that slot in lever aligns with tab in housing. Install trunnion pin. *See Fig. 2.* To complete installation, reverse removal procedure. Warm shift lever ball with a heat gun to 140-180°F (6082°C) and tap onto lever with a socket and mallet (if removed).

REMOVAL & INSTALLATION

See appropriate MANUAL TRANSMISSION REMOVAL article in TRANSMISSION SERVICING.

TRANSMISSION DISASSEMBLY

Disassembly – **1)** Place transmission into a holding fixture. Place in 2nd gear, drain fluid and remove shifter housing assembly. Lock transmission into 2 gears. Remove "U" joint flange (if equipped) and oil seal. Remove speedometer driven gear and bearing assembly (if equipped).

2) Remove extension housing and speedometer drive gear snap ring retainer. Slide drive gear off shaft. Remove annular bearing snap ring retainers from shaft and bearing. Remove flat washer and annular bearing.

3) Remove input shaft bearing retainer and input bearing snap ring from input shaft and from bearing. Remove input shaft bearing. *See Fig. 1.*

4) Remove output shaft assembly from transmission case. Remove input shaft assembly with 22 pilot bearing rollers from inner end of shaft. Remove reverse idler shaft and countershaft lock plate. Remove reverse idler shaft and gear from case. Remove countershaft.

5) Install a suitable dummy shaft in cluster gear assembly. Remove cluster gear assembly from transmission case. Guide cluster gear assembly (with dummy shaft installed) out of case so needle bearings and spacers that remain in cluster gear assembly are not lost.

COMPONENT DISASSEMBLY & REASSEMBLY

OUTPUT SHAFT

Disassembly – **1)** Remove 3rd-4th speed synchronizer hub snap ring from output shaft, and slide synchronizer assembly and 3rd speed gear off. Remove synchronizer sleeve and synchronizer inserts from hub. *See Fig. 1.*

2) Before removing 2 snap rings from ends of hub, check end play of 2nd speed gear. Ensure end play is .005-.024" (.13-.61 mm). Make an index mark on gear and hub before disassembly to insure same hub and gear alignment at reassembly. Slide 1st-2nd speed gear off shaft.

3) Remove snap ring from behind synchronizer hub, and pull hub from shaft. Remove blocking ring. Remove snap ring from behind 2nd speed gear, and remove gear and thrust washer from output shaft. For cleaning and inspection of components, see CLEANING & INSPECTION.

Reassembly – **1)** Position output shaft with threaded end up in a soft-jawed vise. Install 2nd speed gear against thrust washer flange on shaft, then install snap ring in groove behind gear. Install blocking ring on 2nd speed gear.

2) Install 2nd speed synchronizer assembly over splines of output shaft, aligning 3 blocking ring cutouts with synchronizer inserts. Ensure 1st-2nd gear shift fork groove is located to rear of transmission case.

3) Install snap ring in groove behind clutch hub. Turn shaft over and install 3rd speed gear and blocking ring. Install 3rd-4th synchronizer assembly over output shaft splines. Align 3 blocking ring slots with synchronizer inserts. Position end of hub with long chamfer to front of transmission. Install snap ring in output shaft groove in front of 3rd-4th synchronizer assembly. Install spacer on shaft.

COUNTERSHAFT GEAR

Disassembly – Remove dummy shaft, needle bearings, bearing spacers and center spacer from countershaft gear. For cleaning and inspection of components, see CLEANING & INSPECTION.

Reassembly – **1)** Slide center spacer into countershaft gear bore and insert dummy shaft in spacer. *See Fig. 1.* Apply a film of petroleum jelly to countershaft gear bore, and install one of the bearing spacers. Position the 22 needle bearing rollers in gear bore.

2) Place a spacer in gear bore. Hold a large thrust washer against end of countershaft gear to prevent rollers from dropping out. Turn assembly over and install bearing spacer, 22 needle bearing rollers and spacer.

GEARSHIFT HOUSING

Disassembly – **1)** Remove 3 expansion plugs from forward end of shifter housing assembly. Using a pin punch, remove 3 lock pins from shift forks and 3 lock pins from shift gates. *See Fig. 2.*

2) Tap shift rails forward out of housing while holding a towel over poppet balls and springs to prevent loss of ball and springs. Remove interlock pin from 3rd-4th shift rail. Remove shift forks and shift gates. Remove poppet balls and springs from housing. Remove interlock plunger from housing.

Reassembly – **1)** Install spring and plunger in reverse gate. Press plunger through gate and fasten plunger in place with clip. Install poppet spring and ball in reverse shift rail hole in gear shift housing. Insert rail part way into the housing.

2) Install reverse shift fork on rail. Press down on poppet ball and spring with a long thin drift and position reverse shift ball notch so reverse shift fork does not slide over ball.

3) Slide reverse gate onto rail (long end forward), and drive rail into housing until ball snaps into groove of rail. Install lock pin that fastens gate to rail.

4) Insert 2 interlocking plungers in pockets between shift rail holes. Place poppet spring and ball in 1st-2nd shift rail hole. Press down on poppet ball and spring with a long thin drift, and insert shift rail part way into housing.

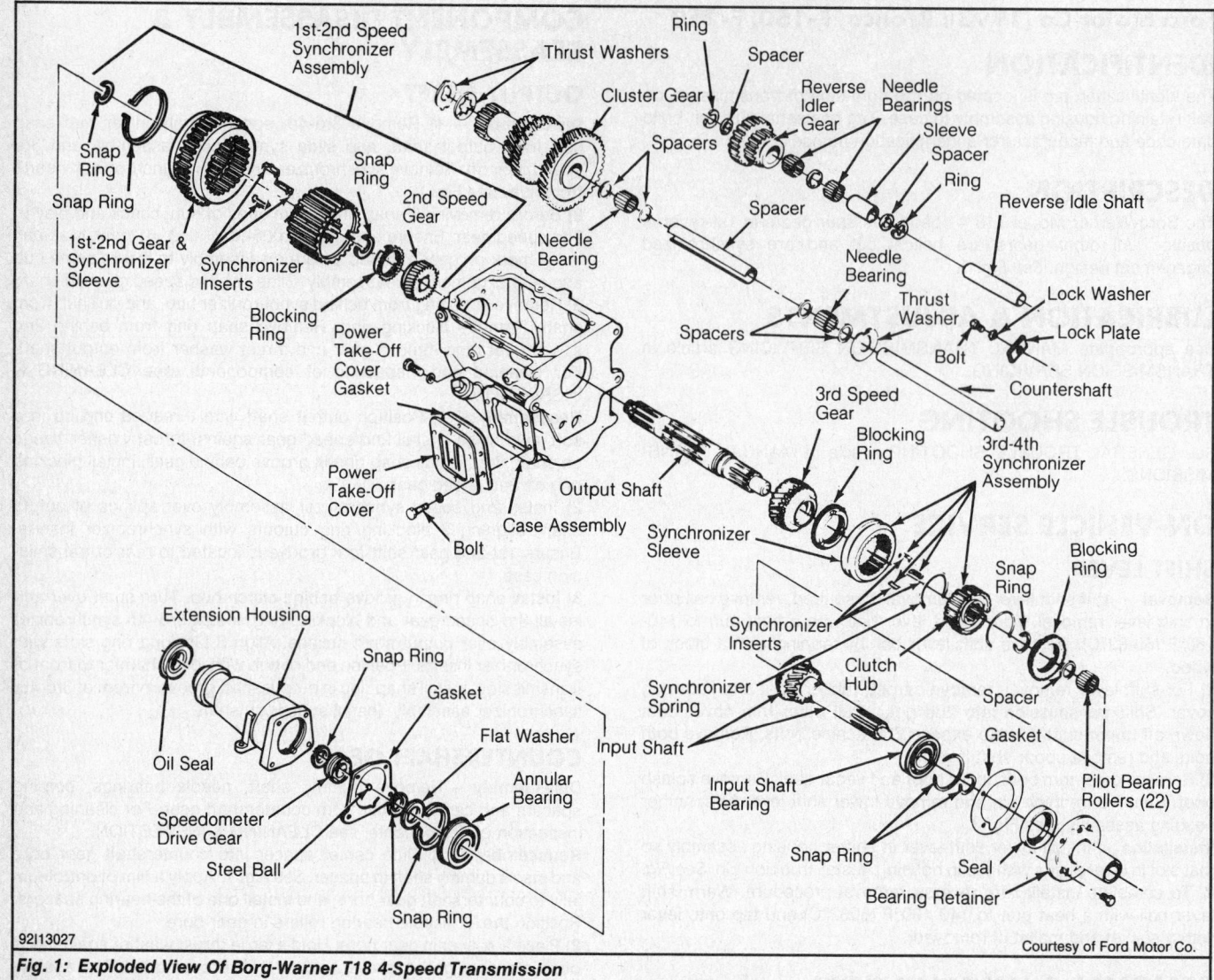

Fig. 1: Exploded View Of Borg-Warner T18 4-Speed Transmission

92I13027

Courtesy of Ford Motor Co.

5) Slide 1st-2nd head assembly onto rail, and install 1st-2nd shift fork on rail so offset of fork is toward rear of housing. Push rail into housing until poppet ball snaps into rail groove. Install lock pins that fastens fork and gate to rail.

6) Insert 3rd-4th shift rail through center rear hole of housing. Insert interlock pin into interlock pin hole in shift rail.

NOTE: *Apply petroleum jelly to interlock pin to hold it in position during assembly.*

---

7) Apply a coating of petroleum jelly to interlock plungers and insert them into their respective holes in housing. Place poppet spring and ball in center shift rail hole in housing. Press down on poppet ball with a long thin drift, and carefully push shift rail into housing over poppet ball and spring. Position 3rd-4th shift gate onto shift rail. Spring-loaded ball tang should be installed facing rear of transmission.

NOTE: *It is extremely important that shift gate be installed on shift rail with long flat tang end of gate area facing forward of gear shift housing. To insure proper installation, measure 2 flat tangs of shift gate, and identify longer .718" (18.24 mm) tang. This tang should be installed facing forward on shift rail.*

---

8) Position 3-4 shift fork on shift rail so that lock pin hole in shift fork is toward rear of housing. Push shift rail into housing until poppet ball seats into 2nd detent (Neutral). Install lock pins attaching shift fork and shift gate to shift rail.

9) Install shift gate lock pin so pin is flush with bottom of notch in shift gate. Install NEW expansion plugs in front and rear of transmission housing.

CLEANING & INSPECTION

CLEANING

Wash all parts except seals, in cleaning solvent. Dry all parts with compressed air. DO NOT spin bearings with compressed air.

INSPECTION

Bearings – Inspect bearings and replace if broken, worn or rough. Lubricate cleaned bearing. Hold bearing vertically by inner race and spin outer race by hand. DO NOT spin bearings with compressed air. If roughness or vibration is noticed, bearing should be cleaned and lubricated again and retested. If roughness or vibration is noticed after 3 tests, replace bearing.

Cluster Gear Assembly – Inspect splines and gear teeth for damage or wear. Replace cluster gear assembly if bent, damaged or worn. Inspect needle bearing surface in bore for wear or damage. Replace components as necessary.

Input Shaft – Replace input shaft if splines are damaged, needle bearing surface in bore of bearing is worn or rough, or if cone surface is damaged. DO NOT spin bearings with compressed air.

Output Shaft – Inspect splines for damage or wear. Replace output shaft if bent or worn.

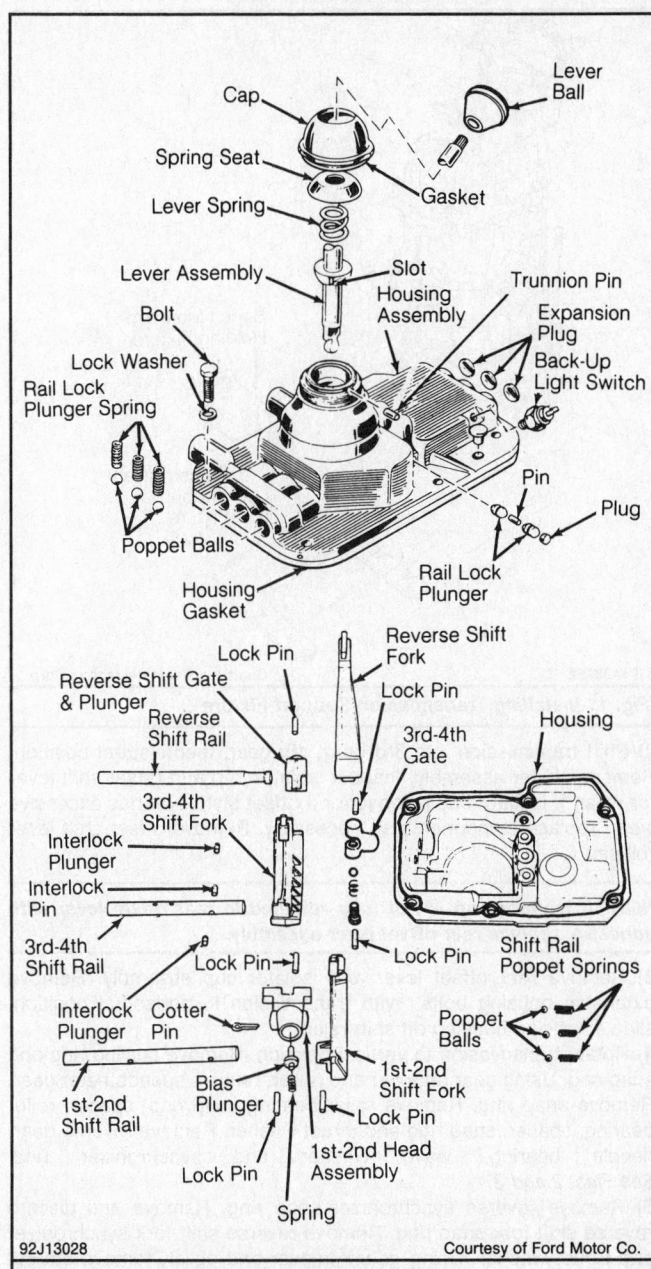

Fig. 2: Exploded View Of Gearshift Housing

92J13028   Courtesy of Ford Motor Co.

Synchronizers – If teeth on blocking ring are chipped, broken or worn, replace blocking ring.

TRANSMISSION REASSEMBLY

NOTE: If a dummy bearing is not used, ensure a protector is used over 3rd-4th synchronizer to prevent jamming 4th blocking ring into cone seat.

Reassembly – 1) Lubricate all parts with transmission fluid prior to installation. Position cluster gear assembly thrust washers in transmission case. Install cluster gear assembly (with dummy shaft) into transmission case.

2) Drive out cluster gear assembly dummy shaft by installing countershaft from rear of transmission. Position slot in rear of countershaft so it can be engaged by shaft retainer.

3) Position reverse idler gear inside case, and install reverse idler shaft from rear of transmission case. Position slot in rear of reverse idler shaft so it can be engaged by shaft retainer.

4) Install countershaft and reverse idler shaft lock plate. Tighten bolt to specification. See TORQUE SPECIFICATIONS. Install 22 pilot bearing rollers in inner end of input shaft. Install input shaft assembly in transmission case, and install blocking ring onto input shaft.

5) Install output shaft assembly in transmission case. Ensure pilot bearing rollers do not drop out of input shaft. Install a dummy bearing onto input shaft.

6) Install locating snap ring into outer race of annular bearing groove. Install annular bearing, flat washer and snap ring onto output shaft. Remove dummy bearing from input shaft.

7) Install input shaft bearing, snap ring, spacer, retainer gasket and retainer. Tighten bolts to specification. Install speedometer drive gear, and spacer (if used) on output shaft over lock ball, and install speedometer drive gear retaining snap ring.

8) Install extension housing with NEW gasket. Tighten bolts to specification. Lubricate extension housing bushing, seal and "U" joint flange (if equipped).

9) Lock transmission into 2 gears, and install "U" joint flange. Tighten flange nut to specification. See TORQUE SPECIFICATIONS. Unlock transmission and place into second gear. Install gear shift housing assembly onto transmission, and tighten bolts to specifications.

10) Install drain plug and tighten to specification. Fill transmission to proper level with Mercon automatic transmission fluid. Install fill plug and tighten to specification. See TORQUE SPECIFICATIONS. Fill rear transmission extension housing through speedometer cable hole (if equipped), with approximately 1/2 pint of lubricant.

TORQUE SPECIFICATIONS
TORQUE SPECIFICATIONS

Application	Ft. Lbs. (N.m)
Countershaft Retainer Bolt	25-35 (34-47)
Drain & Fill Plug	25-40 (34-54)
Extension Housing Bolts	
3/8"	25-35 (34-47)
1/2"	40-50 (54-68)
Housing Assembly Bolt	25-35 (34-47)
Input Shaft Bearing Retainer Bolt	10-15 (14-20)
Output Shaft Flange Nut	75-110 (102-149)
PTO Cover Bolt	25-35 (34-47)
Reverse Idler Shaft & Countershaft Lock Plate Bolt	25-35 (34-47)

MANUAL TRANSMISSIONS
Borg-Warner T56 6-Speed

General Motors: Camaro, Firebird

IDENTIFICATION

Transmission has 2 identification labels, located on lower left side of case. One label contains a VIN derivative. Other label is transmission identification information, giving model type and date of manufacturer.

DESCRIPTION

The Borg-Warner T56 transmission is a fully synchronized 6-speed gear box. GM also identifies it as 85-mm 6-speed. Transmission is used in vehicles equipped with a 5.7L engine. The transmission has an aluminum case with internal shift rail mechanism. Manufacturer recommends Dexron II automatic transmission fluid to protect synchronizer friction material.

Transmission is equipped with a solenoid which operates a reverse lock-out assembly. Solenoid prevents operator from shifting transmission into Reverse when vehicle is moving forward.

To enhance fuel economy, transmission also is equipped with a gear select solenoid, which inhibits 2nd and 3rd gears when shifting from 1st gear. Solenoid is activated when engine coolant temperature is greater than 162°F (77°C), vehicle speed is between 15-21 MPH and throttle is opened 35 percent or less.

LUBRICATION & ADJUSTMENTS

See appropriate MANUAL TRANSMISSION SERVICING article in TRANSMISSION SERVICING.

TROUBLE SHOOTING

See GENERAL TROUBLE SHOOTING article in MANUAL TRANSMISSIONS.

ON-VEHICLE SERVICE

EXTENSION HOUSING OIL SEAL

Removal & Installation – Raise and support vehicle. Remove drive shaft. Using appropriate seal remover, remove seal. Lubricate inside lip of NEW oil seal prior to installation. Using appropriate seal installer, install seal Install drive shaft and tighten bolts to specification. See TORQUE SPECIFICATIONS. Check fluid level.

REVERSE LOCK-OUT SOLENOID

Removal & Installation – Raise and support vehicle. Remove harness connector. Remove reverse lock-out solenoid from reverse lock-out assembly, located on left side of transmission. To install, reverse removal procedure. Install NEW "O" ring. Tighten solenoid to specification. See TORQUE SPECIFICATIONS.

VEHICLE SPEED SENSOR

Removal & Installation – Raise and support vehicle. Remove harness connector and retainer bolt. Remove vehicle speed sensor. Remove "O" ring from sensor. To install, reverse removal procedure. Install NEW "O" ring. Tighten sensor retainer bolt to specification. See TORQUE SPECIFICATIONS.

REMOVAL & INSTALLATION

See appropriate MANUAL TRANSMISSION REMOVAL article in TRANSMISSION SERVICING.

TRANSMISSION DISASSEMBLY

1) Ensure exterior of transmission is free of dirt and grease prior to disassembly. Remove vent tube, clutch housing, clutch fork and clutch fork pivot "T" handle. Mount Support Fixture (J-39430) to transmission and install on Bench Holding Fixture (J-32289-20). *See Fig. 1.* Rotate transmission to horizontal position with shifter up. Drain transmission fluid.

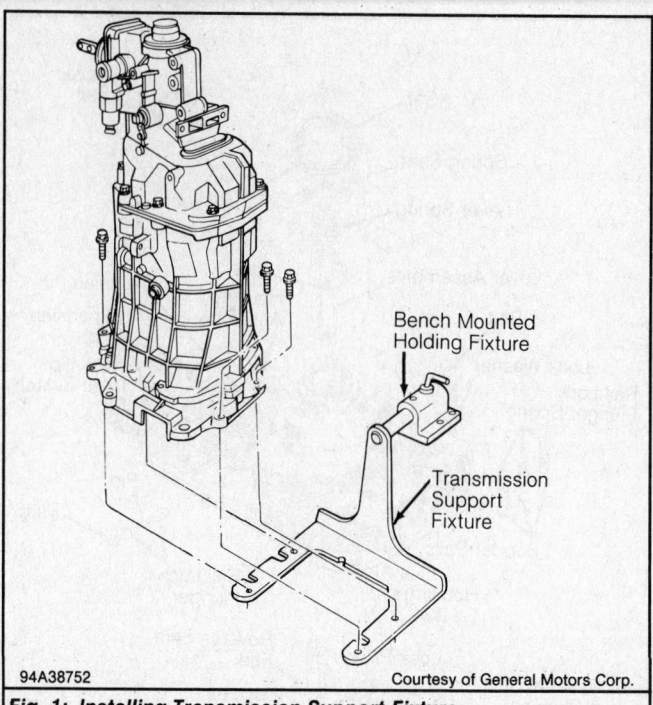

Courtesy of General Motors Corp.

Fig. 1: Installing Transmission Support Fixture

2) Shift transmission into 3rd gear, 4th gear, then Neutral position. Remove shifter assembly. Inspect isolator cup and offset shift lever for wear. If isolator cup is loose, or if offset shift lever has excessive wear, replace components as necessary. Remove offset shift lever roll pin.

NOTE: If isolator cup is not fully retained in rear offset lever with adhesive, replace rear offset lever assembly.

3) Remove rear offset lever and isolator cup assembly. Remove extension housing bolts. With transmission in horizontal position, slide extension housing off shift rails.

4) Rotate transmission to vertical position. Remove sealing ring and snap ring. Using gear remover and puller, remove speedometer gear. Remove snap ring. Remove roller bearing snap ring, spacer, roller bearing, spacer, snap ring and thrust washer. Remove reverse gear, needle bearing, wave washer and synchronizer ring. *See Figs. 2 and 3.*

5) Remove reverse synchronizer snap ring. Remove and discard reverse shift fork snap ring. Remove reverse shift fork synchronizer and thrust washer. Using gear remover and puller, remove 5th-6th driven gear. Remove 5th-6th shift fork snap ring.

6) Rotate transmission to horizontal position with guide plate up. Remove countershaft extension assembly with 5th-6th shift fork. Remove gear select solenoid. Remove cover plate bolts and cover plate. Remove shift detent assembly, front offset lever roll pin and shift guide plate bolts. *See Figs. 2 and 3.*

7) Remove guide plate and front offset lever. Hold guide plate and front offset lever together while sliding off shift rail to prevent spring release of detent ball and spring. Remove solenoid lever. Rotate front offset lever to clear case during removal.

8) Remove front offset lever, roll pin, shift detent spring, detent ball and shift guide plate. Remove 8 of 10 adapter plate-to-transmission bolts. Rotate transmission to vertical position. Remove 2 remaining adapter plate bolts. Remove shift lever guide bolts. *See Figs. 2 and 3.* Remove case magnet. Slide transmission case up off of gear clusters and shift rail components. Remove transmission case.

9) Remove 5th-6th and reverse shift rail levers from shift interlock plate. Remove 5th-6th and reverse shift rail assembly. Lift up mainshaft enough to remove countershaft. Remove mainshaft and shift rail assembly as complete assemblies. *See Fig. 4.* Remove shift rail assembly from mainshaft. Remove 4th gear synchronizer ring. Remove input shaft.

MANUAL TRANSMISSIONS
Borg-Warner T56 6-Speed

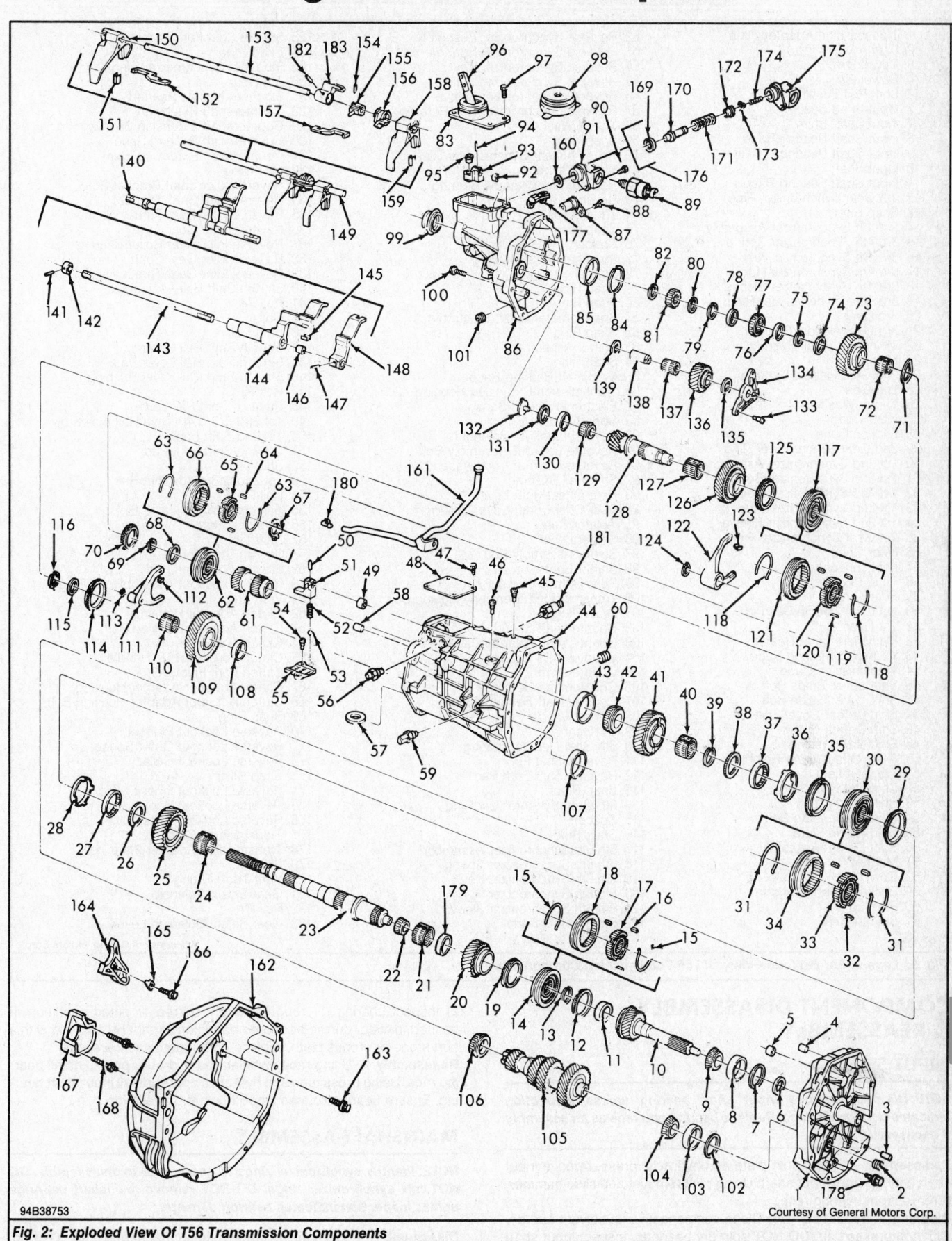

94B38753

Courtesy of General Motors Corp.

Fig. 2: Exploded View Of T56 Transmission Components

MANUAL TRANSMISSIONS
Borg-Warner T56 6-Speed

1. Transmission Adapter Plate
2. Plug
3. Dowel Pin
4. Dowel Pin
5. Shift Rail Bushing
6. Input Shaft Seal
7. Input Shaft Shim
8. Input Shaft Bearing Race
9. Input Shaft Bearing
10. Input Shaft
11. Input Shaft Bearing Race
12. 4th Gear Synchronizer Ring
13. Snap Ring
14. 3rd-4th Synchronizer Assembly
15. 3rd-4th Synchronizer Spring
16. 3rd-4th Synchronizer Key
17. 3rd-4th Synchronizer Hub
18. 3rd-4th Synchronizer Sleeve
19. 3rd Gear Synchronizer Ring
20. 3rd Gear
21. 3rd Gear Needle Bearing
22. Mainshaft Small Bearing
23. Mainshaft
24. 2nd Gear Needle Bearing
25. 2nd Gear
26. Thrust Washer
27. Inner Cone
28. Friction Cone
29. 2nd Gear Synchronizer Ring
30. 1st-2nd Synchronizer Assembly
31. 1st-2nd Synchronizer Spring
32. 1st-2nd Synchronizer Key
33. 1st-2nd Synchronizer Hub
34. 1st-2nd Synchronizer Sleeve
35. 1st Gear Synchronizer Ring
36. Inner Cone
37. Friction Cone
38. Thrust Washer
39. Snap Ring
40. 1st Gear Needle Bearing
41. 1st Gear
42. Mainshaft Large Bearing
43. Mainshaft Bearing Race
44. Transmission Case
45. Shift Lever Guide Bolt
46. Shift Lever Guide Bolt
47. Shift Detent Cover Bolt
48. Shift Detent Cover
49. Shift Rail Bushing
50. Front Offset Lever Roll Pin
51. Front Offset Lever
52. Shift Detent Spring
53. Shift Detent Ball
54. Shift Guide Plate Bolt
55. Shift Guide Plate
56. Shift Detent Assembly
57. Magnet
58. Dowel Pin
59. Back-Up Light Switch
60. Fill Plug
61. 5th-6th Gear

62. Reverse Synchronizer Assembly
63. Reverse Synchronizer Spring
64. Reverse Synchronizer Key
65. Reverse Synchronizer Hub
66. Reverse Synchronizer Sleeve
67. Reverse Synchronizer Key Retainer
68. Thrust Washer
69. Snap Ring
70. Reverse Gear Synchronizer Ring
71. Wave Washer
72. Reverse Gear Needle Bearing
73. Reverse Gear
74. Thrust Washer
75. Snap Ring
76. Spacer
77. Mainshaft Rear Bearing
78. Spacer
79. Snap Ring
80. Snap Ring
81. Speedometer Gear (Electronic)
82. Snap Ring
83. Shifter Assembly
84. Snap Ring
85. Mainshaft Bearing Race
86. Transmission Extension Housing
87. Electronic Speed Sensor
88. Speed Sensor Bolt
89. Reverse Lockout Solenoid
90. Reverse Lockout Assembly Bolt
91. Reverse Lockout Body Assembly
92. Shift Rail Bushing
93. Rear Offset Shift Lever
94. Rear Offset Shift Lever Roll Pin
95. Isolator Cup
96. Shifter Lever
97. Shifter Assembly Bolt
98. Shifter Boot
99. Rear Output Seal & Boot
100. Transmission Extension Housing Bolt
101. Drain Plug
102. Countershaft Shim
103. Countershaft Bearing Race
104. Countershaft Bearing
105. Countershaft
106. Countershaft Bearing
107. Countershaft Bearing Race
108. Thrust Washer
109. 6th Gear
110. 6th Gear Needle Bearing
111. Reverse Shift Fork
112. Reverse Shift Fork Pad
113. Snap Ring
114. 6th Gear Synchronizer Ring
115. Spacer
116. Snap Ring
117. 5th-6th Synchronizer Assembly
118. 5th-6th Synchronizer Spring
119. 5th-6th Synchronizer Key
120. 5th-6th Synchronizer Hub
121. 5th-6th Synchronizer Sleeve
122. 5th-6th Shift Fork

123. 5th-6th Shift Fork Pad
124. Snap Ring
125. 5th Gear Synchronizer Ring
126. 5th Gear
127. 5th Gear Needle Bearing
128. Countershaft Extension
129. Countershaft Extension Bearing
130. Countershaft Bearing Race
131. Countershaft Extension Shim
132. Oil Funnel
133. Reverse Idler Shaft Bracket Bolt
134. Reverse Idler Shaft Bracket
135. Reverse Idler Gear Thrust Washer
136. Reverse Idler Gear
137. Reverse Idler Gear Roller Bearing
138. Reverse Idler Gear Shaft
139. Reverse Idler Gear Thrust Washer
140. 5th-6th Shift Rail Assembly
141. Roll Pin
142. Collar
143. Shift Rail
144. 5th-6th Shift Rail Lever
145. 5th-6th Shift Rail Lever Pad
146. 5th-6th Shift Rail Lever Bushing
147. Roll Pin
148. Reverse Shift Rail Lever
149. 1st-2nd & 3rd-4th Shift Rail Assembly
150. 1st-2nd Shift Fork
151. 1st-2nd Shift Fork Pad
152. Shift Link
153. 1st-2nd & 3rd-4th Shift Rail
154. Roll Pin
155. Selector Pin
156. Interlock Plate
157. Shift Link
158. 3rd-4th Shift Fork
159. 3rd-4th Shift Fork Pad
160. Reverse Lockout Assembly "O" Ring
161. Vent Tube
162. Clutch Adapter Housing
163. Clutch Adapter Housing Bolt
164. Clutch Fork
165. Clutch Fork Pivot "T" Handle
166. Clutch Fork Pivot Bolt
167. Clutch Actuator Adapter Housing
168. Clutch Actuator Adapter Housing Bolt
169. Snap Ring
170. Reverse Lockout Plunger
171. Reverse Lockout Outer Spring
172. Reverse Lockout Collar
173. Snap Ring
174. Reverse Lockout Inner Spring
175. Reverse Lockout Body
176. Reverse Lockout Assembly
177. Transmission Bumper
178. Transmission Adapter Plate Bolt
179. Spacer
180. Vent Tube Fitting
181. Gear Select Solenoid
182. Roll Pin
183. Gear Select Solenoid Lever

94C38754

Courtesy of General Motors Corp.

Fig. 3: Legend For Exploded View Of T56 Transmission Components

COMPONENT DISASSEMBLY & REASSEMBLY

INPUT SHAFT

NOTE: DO NOT remove input shaft bearing unless inspection indicates bearing damage. Replace bearing and race as an assembly if necessary.

Disassembly – Using split plate and hydraulic press, remove input shaft bearing from input shaft. Using race remover and slide hammer, remove input bearing race.
Cleaning & Inspection – 1) Clean components with solvent and dry with compressed air. DO NOT spin dry bearings. Inspect input shaft and spline for excessive wear or cracks. Inspect gear teeth for excessive wear, pitting, scoring, spalling or breaks.

2) Inspect bearing for rough rotation, burred or pitted condition. If scuffed, nicked, burred or scored condition cannot be repaired with a soft stone or crocus cloth, replace components as necessary.
Reassembly – Using race installer and hydraulic press, install bearing race. Using press tube and hydraulic press, install input shaft bearing. Ensure bearing rotates smoothly after installation.

MAINSHAFT ASSEMBLY

NOTE: Identify synchronizer rings to gears prior to disassembly. DO NOT mix synchronizer rings. DO NOT remove mainshaft bearings unless inspection indicates bearing damage.

Disassembly – 1) Remove large mainshaft bearing and "O" ring. Remove 1st gear and 1st gear needle bearing. Remove snap ring, thrust washer, inner cone, friction cone and synchronizer ring. Using

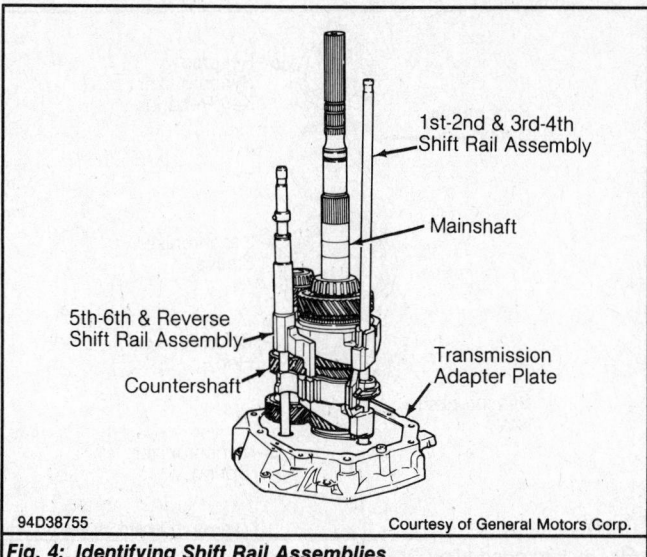

1st-2nd & 3rd-4th
Shift Rail Assembly

Mainshaft

5th-6th & Reverse
Shift Rail Assembly

Countershaft

Transmission
Adapter Plate

94D38755   Courtesy of General Motors Corp.

Fig. 4: Identifying Shift Rail Assemblies

split plate and hydraulic press, remove 1st-2nd synchronizer assembly, 2nd gear synchronizer ring, friction cone, 2nd gear inner cone, thrust washer and 2nd gear. *See Fig. 5.*

2) Remove 2nd gear needle bearing. Remove 3rd-4th gear synchronizer snap ring. Using split plate, "V" blocks and hydraulic press, remove 3rd gear synchronizer assembly, 3rd gear synchronizer ring and 3rd gear. Remove spacer and 3rd gear needle bearing. Using press adapter, split plate and hydraulic press, remove and discard small mainshaft bearing (if necessary).

Cleaning & Inspection – Clean components with solvent and dry with compressed air. Inspect mainshaft and spline for excessive wear or cracks. Inspect gear teeth for excessive wear, pitting, scoring, spalling or breaks. Inspect bearings for rough rotation, burred or pitted conditions. If scratches, grooves or nicks cannot be removed using a soft stone or crocus cloth, replace component as necessary.

NOTE: For synchronizer disassembly and reassembly, see SYNCHRONIZERS under COMPONENT DISASSEMBLY & REASSEMBLY.

Reassembly – 1) Using bearing installer, "V" blocks and hydraulic press, install NEW mainshaft small bearing (if removed). Install 3rd gear needle bearing, spacer and 3rd gear. Install 3rd gear synchronizer ring. Using press tube, press tube adapter and hydraulic press, press 3rd-4th gear synchronizer assembly onto mainshaft.

2) Install 3rd-4th gear synchronizer assembly with inside diameter groove on sleeve facing 3rd gear. Start hydraulic press operation but stop before synchronizer keys engage synchronizer ring slots. Lift and rotate 3rd gear to engage keys of synchronizer ring. Continue to press until fully seated.

3) Install 3rd-4th synchronizer snap ring. Install 2nd gear needle bearing, 2nd gear and thrust washer. Install 2nd gear inner cone, friction cone and 2nd gear synchronizer ring. Using split plate and hydraulic press, press 1st-2nd gear synchronizer assembly onto mainshaft.

4) Install 1st-2nd gear synchronizer assembly with inside diameter groove on sleeve facing 1st gear. Start hydraulic press operation but stop before synchronizer keys engage synchronizer ring slots. Lift and rotate 2nd gear to engage keys of synchronizer ring. Continue to press until fully seated.

5) Install 1st gear synchronizer ring, friction cone, inner cone and thrust washer. Install snap ring and 1st gear needle bearing. Install 1st gear, mainshaft large bearing and "O" ring.

COUNTERSHAFT ASSEMBLY

NOTE: DO NOT remove countershaft bearings unless inspection indicates bearing damage. Replace bearing and race as an assembly if necessary.

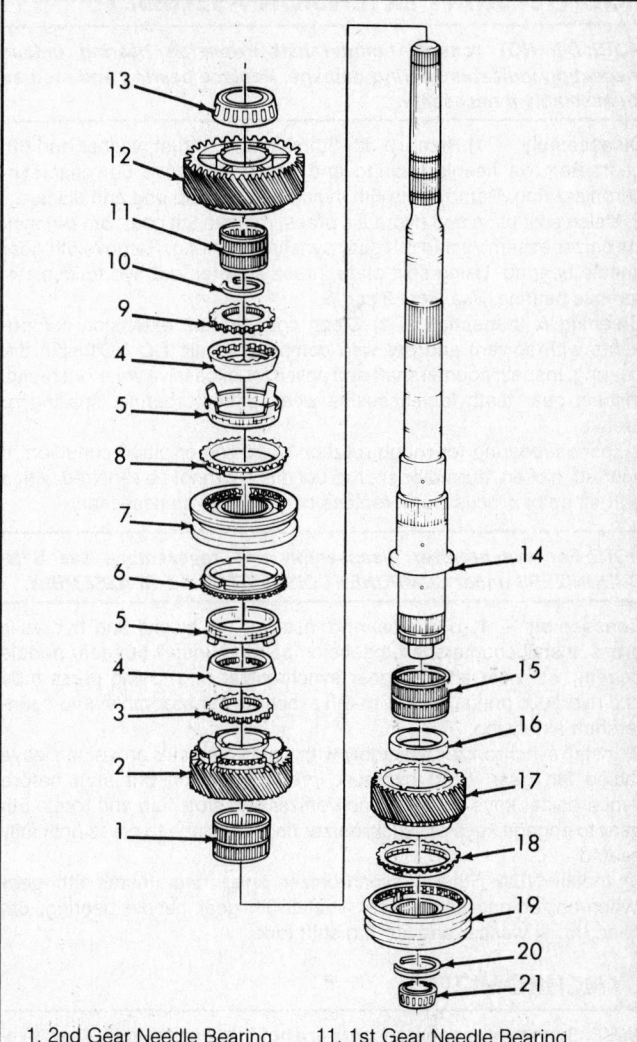

1. 2nd Gear Needle Bearing	11. 1st Gear Needle Bearing
2. 2nd Gear	12. 1st Gear
3. Thrust Washer	13. Mainshaft Large Bearing
4. Inner Cone	14. Mainshaft
5. Friction Cone	15. 3rd Gear Needle Bearing
6. 2nd Gear Synchronizer Ring	16. Spacer
7. 1st-2nd Synchronizer Assembly	17. 3rd Gear
8. 1st Gear Synchronizer Ring	18. 3rd Gear Synchronizer Ring
9. Thrust Washer	19. 3rd-4th Synchronizer Assembly
10. Snap Ring	20. Snap Ring
	21. Mainshaft Small Bearing

94E38756   Courtesy of General Motors Corp.

Fig. 5: Exploded View Of Mainshaft Assembly

Disassembly – Using split plate and hydraulic press, remove small countershaft bearing from countershaft (if necessary). Using split plate, press adapter and hydraulic press, remove large countershaft bearing from countershaft (if necessary). *See Fig. 2.*

Cleaning & Inspection – 1) Clean components with solvent and dry with compressed air. DO NOT spin dry bearings. Inspect countershaft for excessive wear or cracks. Inspect gear teeth for excessive wear, pitting, scoring, spalling or breaks.

2) Inspect bearings for rough rotation or burred or pitted condition. If scuffed, nicked, burred or scored condition cannot be repaired with a soft stone or crocus cloth, replace components as necessary.

Reassembly – Using bearing installer and hydraulic press, install bearings. Ensure bearings rotate smoothly after installation.

MANUAL TRANSMISSIONS
Borg-Warner T56 6-Speed

COUNTERSHAFT EXTENSION ASSEMBLY

NOTE: DO NOT remove countershaft extension bearing unless inspection indicates bearing damage. Replace bearing and race as an assembly if necessary.

Disassembly – 1) Remove 5th-6th shift fork, thrust washer and 6th gear. Remove needle bearing and spacer. Remove 6th gear synchronizer ring. Remove 5th-6th synchronizer snap ring and discard.
2) Using split plate and hydraulic press, remove 5th gear, 5th-6th synchronizer assembly and 5th gear synchronizer ring. Remove 5th gear needle bearing. Using split plate, press adapter and hydraulic plate, remove bearing. *See Figs. 2 and 3.*

Cleaning & Inspection – 1) Clean countershaft extension components with solvent and dry with compressed air. DO NOT spin dry bearing. Inspect countershaft and spline for excessive wear or cracks. Inspect gear teeth for excessive wear, pitting, scoring, spalling or breaks.
2) Inspect bearing for rough rotation or burred or pitted condition. If scuffed, nicked, burred or scored condition cannot be repaired with a soft stone or crocus cloth, replace components as necessary.

NOTE: For synchronizer disassembly and reassembly, see SYNCHRONIZERS under COMPONENT DISASSEMBLY & REASSEMBLY.

Reassembly – 1) Using bearing installer, "V" blocks and hydraulic press, install countershaft extension bearing. Install 5th gear needle bearing, 5th gear and 5th gear synchronizer ring. Using press tube and hydraulic press, press 5th-6th synchronizer assembly onto countershaft extension.
2) Install synchronizer assembly with inside diameter grove on sleeve facing 5th gear. Start hydraulic press operation but stop before synchronizer keys engage synchronizer ring slots. Lift and rotate 5th gear to engage keys of synchronizer ring. Continue to press until fully seated.
3) Install NEW 5th-6th synchronizer snap ring. Install 6th gear synchronizer ring and spacer. Install 6th gear needle bearing, 6th gear, thrust washer and 5th-6th shift fork.

SYNCHRONIZERS

NOTE: Synchronizer components are not interchangeable. Keep synchronizer components separate. Hubs and sleeve are a matched set and should be kept together as originally assembled.

Disassembly – Using small screwdriver, remove synchronizer springs. Remove keys and synchronizer sleeve from hub. On reverse synchronizer, remove key retainer and discard. *See Fig. 6.*

Cleaning & Inspection – 1) Clean components with solvent and dry with compressed air. Inspect synchronizer teeth for wear, nicked, burred or broken teeth. Replace hub and sleeve if excessive wear exists. Inspect keys and springs for wear, cracks or distortion. If scuffed, nicked or burred conditions cannot be repaired with a soft stone or crocus cloth, replace components as necessary.
2) Inspect synchronizer rings for excessive wear. Using a feeler gauge, measure clearance between each synchronizer ring and gear. Ensure rings and gears are matched correctly and rings are fully seated on gear. If clearance for all rings except reverse is less than .015" (.38 mm), replace appropriate synchronizer ring.
3) If clearance for reverse synchronizer ring is less than .030" (.75 mm) when measured without wave washer between gear and ring, replace reverse synchronizer ring.

Reassembly – 1) Install synchronizer sleeve to hub. Align key openings in hub with cuts in synchronizer sleeve. Install keys with slots facing hub. Install one synchronizer spring, locating spring tang to one key slot.
2) Turn synchronizer assembly over. Install other synchronizer spring, locating spring tang on same key but wind in opposite direction. Install NEW synchronizer key retainer on reverse synchronizer with retainer tangs over synchronizer keys. *See Fig. 6.*

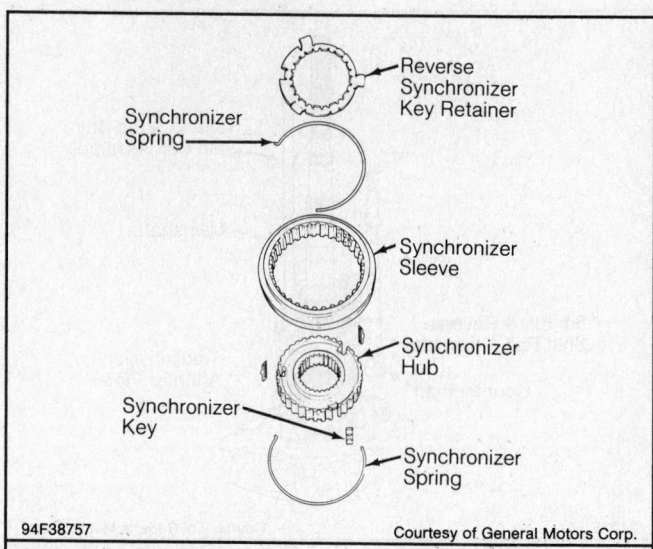

94F38757   Courtesy of General Motors Corp.

Fig. 6: Exploded View Of Reverse Synchronizer Assembly (Others Are Similar)

SHIFT RAIL ASSEMBLIES

Disassembly (1st-2nd & 3rd-4th Shift Rail) – Rotate selector pin until opposite shift links. Remove 1st-2nd and 3rd-4th shift forks with shift links from rail. Remove interlock plate from rail. Remove selector pin roll pin. Remove selector pin. *See Fig. 7.*

Cleaning & Inspection – Clean components with solvent and dry with compressed air. Inspect shift rail for excessive wear or burrs. Inspect shift forks and shift links for excessive wear, breaks or distortion. Inspect shift fork nylon inserts for excessive wear. Replace components as necessary.

Reassembly – Install selector pin, roll pin and interlock plate to shift rail. Install 1st-2nd and 3rd-4th shift fork with shift link to rail. Align selector pin with slots in shift links.

Disassembly (5th-6th & Reverse Shift Rail) – Remove collar roll pin and collar. Remove 5th-6th shift rail lever from rail. Using slide hammer and bushing remover, remove shift rail lever bushings. DO NOT remove bushings unless inspection indicates bushing damage. Remove reverse shift rail lever roll pin and shift rail lever from shift rail. *See Fig. 7.*

Cleaning & Inspection – Clean components with solvent and dry with compressed air. Inspect shift rail for excessive wear or burrs. Inspect shift fork nylon insert for excessive wear. Inspect shift rail levers for excessive wear, fracture or distortion. Inspect shift rail lever bushings for excessive wear. Replace components as necessary.

Reassembly – Install reverse shift rail lever to rail. Locate reverse shift rail lever to roll pin hole at opposite end of rail from snap ring groove. Notched edge of reverse shift rail lever should face toward other roll pin hole. Install reverse shift rail lever roll pin. Install 5th-6th shift rail lever bushings. Install 5th-6th shift rail lever to shift rail. Install collar and collar roll pin.

TRANSMISSION ADAPTER PLATE

Disassembly– Remove input shaft and counter shaft bearing races and shims. Remove adapter plate plug and input shaft seal. Using bushing remover and slide hammer, remove 1st-2nd and 3rd-4th shift rail bushings. DO NOT remove bushings unless inspection indicates bushing damage. Remove dowel pins. *See Figs. 2 and 3.*

Cleaning & Inspection – Clean components with solvent and dry with compressed air. Inspect bearing races and bores for wear, scratches or grooves. Inspect bushings for excessive wear or burrs. Inspect case for cracks and replace if necessary. Inspect sealing surfaces for nicks, burrs or scratches. If scratches, grooves or nicks cannot be removed using a soft stone or crocus cloth, replace component as necessary.

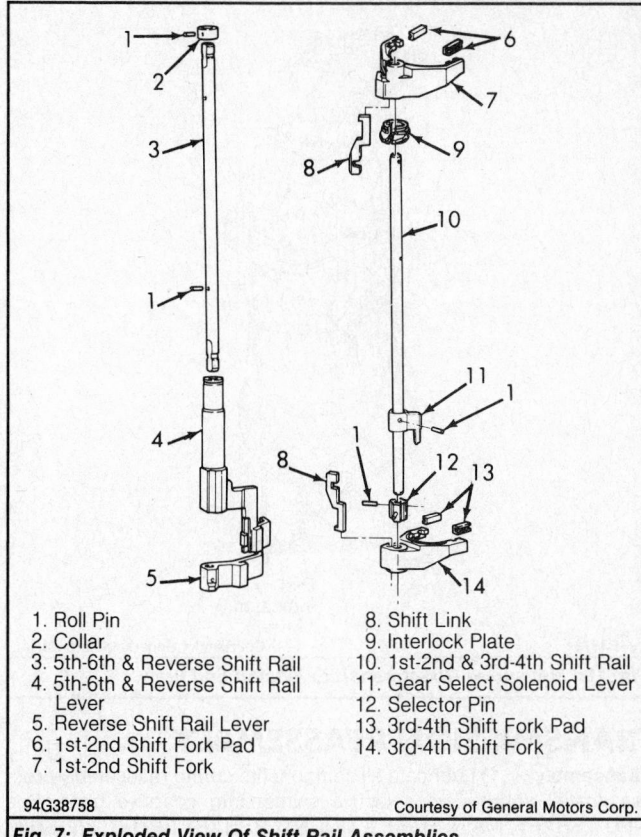

1. Roll Pin
2. Collar
3. 5th-6th & Reverse Shift Rail
4. 5th-6th & Reverse Shift Rail Lever
5. Reverse Shift Rail Lever
6. 1st-2nd Shift Fork Pad
7. 1st-2nd Shift Fork
8. Shift Link
9. Interlock Plate
10. 1st-2nd & 3rd-4th Shift Rail
11. Gear Select Solenoid Lever
12. Selector Pin
13. 3rd-4th Shift Fork Pad
14. 3rd-4th Shift Fork

94G38758   Courtesy of General Motors Corp.

Fig. 7: Exploded View Of Shift Rail Assemblies

Reassembly – 1) Install dowel pins. Using bushing installer, install 1st-2nd and 3rd-4th shift rail bushings. Using seal installer, install input shaft seal. If end play measurement procedure has been performed, install selected shims in appropriate positions.
2) If end play procedure has not been performed, see INPUT SHAFT, MAINSHAFT & COUNTERSHAFT SELECTIVE SHIM PROCEDURE and COUNTERSHAFT EXTENSION SELECTIVE SHIM PROCEDURE under REASSEMBLY ADJUSTMENTS. Install countershaft and input shaft bearing races.

TRANSMISSION CASE

Disassembly – Remove fill plug. Remove back-up light switch and dowel pins. Using race remover, removing countershaft and mainshaft bearing races. DO NOT remove bearing races unless inspection indicates bearing race damage. Using bushing remover and drive handle, remove 1st-2nd and 3rd-4th shift rail bushing. *See Figs. 2 and 3.*
Cleaning & Inspection – Clean components with solvent and dry with compressed air. Inspect bearing races and bores for wear, scratches or grooves. Inspect bushing for excessive wear. Inspect transmission case for cracks and replace if necessary. Inspect for damaged threads, sealing surfaces for nicks, burrs or scratches. If scratches, grooves or nicks cannot be removed using a soft stone or crocus cloth, replace component as necessary.
Reassembly – Using bushing installer, install 1st-2nd and 3rd-4th shift rail bushing. Install mainshaft and countershaft bearing races. Install dowel pins. Install back-up light switch and fill plug and tighten to specification. See TORQUE SPECIFICATIONS.

EXTENSION HOUSING

Disassembly – 1) Remove reverse idler shaft bracket bolts and bracket. Remove revere idler gear thrust washer, idler gear and roller bearing. Remove thrust washer and reverse idler shaft. Remove countershaft extension bearing race and shim. Remove funnel, plug and reverse lockout assembly bolt. *See Figs. 2 and 3.*

CAUTION: *Reverse lockout assembly is under spring pressure. Exercise caution when removing snap ring to prevent injury.*

2) Remove reverse lockout solenoid from reverse lockout body. Remove "O" ring and snap ring from lockout body. Remove reverse lockout inner spring. Compress reverse lockout plunger and collar in vise and remove snap ring. Remove reverse lockout plunger, outer spring and collar. Remove vehicle speed sensor bolt and sensor. Remove "O" ring from sensor. Remove rear seal and boot.
3) Remove mainshaft bearing race snap ring. Using bearing race remover and drive handle, remove mainshaft bearing race. DO NOT remove bearing race unless inspection indicates bearing race damage. Using bushing remover and drive handle, remove shift rail bushing. DO NOT remove bushing unless inspection indicates bushing damage.
Cleaning & Inspection – Clean components with solvent and dry with compressed air. Inspect bearing races and bores for wear, scratches or grooves. Inspect bushing for excessive wear or burrs. Inspect housing for cracks and sealing surfaces for nicks, burrs or scratches. If scratches, grooves or nicks cannot be removed using a soft stone or crocus cloth, replace component as necessary.
Reassembly – 1) Using bushing installer and drive handle, install shift rail bushing (if necessary). Using bearing race installer and drive handle, install mainshaft bearing race (if necessary). Install mainshaft bearing race snap ring. Install rear seal and boot with drain hole down. Install NEW "O" ring on speed sensor and install speed sensor. Tighten bolt to specification. See TORQUE SPECIFICATIONS.
2) Install reverse lockout plunger, outer spring and collar to reverse lockout body assembly. Compress reverse lockout plunger collar and outer spring in vise and install snap ring. Install reverse lockout inner spring. Install reverse lockout components into reverse lockout body and install snap ring.
3) Install reverse lockout solenoid to reverse lockout body assembly. Tighten solenoid to specification. Install NEW "O" ring to body assembly and install reverse lockout assembly to extension housing. Tighten lockout assembly bolt to specifications. See TORQUE SPECIFICATIONS. Install sealant to plug threads and install plug. Tighten plug to specification.
4) If end play measurement procedure has been performed, install selected shim in appropriate locations. If end play procedure has not been performed, see INPUT SHAFT, MAINSHAFT & COUNTERSHAFT SELECTIVE SHIM PROCEDURE and COUNTERSHAFT EXTENSION SELECTIVE SHIM PROCEDURE under REASSEMBLY ADJUSTMENTS.

REASSEMBLY ADJUSTMENTS

INPUT SHAFT, MAINSHAFT & COUNTERSHAFT SELECTIVE SHIM PROCEDURE

1) Position transmission in vertical position. Install input shaft to adapter plate. Install mainshaft to input shaft. Lift mainshaft enough to install countershaft and install countershaft. Install transmission case to adapter plate and install bolts. Tighten bolts to 26 ft. lbs. (35 N.m).
2) Place tip of dial indicator on end of mainshaft. *See Fig. 8.* Measure input shaft/mainshaft end play by moving input shaft up and down. End play should be 0-.002" (0-.05 mm). Select appropriate shim to obtain specification. Remove dial indicator and place tip of dial indicator on end of countershaft.
3) Install Countershaft End Play Measuring Tool (J-39444-1) through adapter plate plug hole. *See Fig. 9.* Measure countershaft end play by moving countershaft up and down. End play should be 0-.002" (0-.05 mm). Select appropriate shim to obtain specification.
4) Remove adapter plate-to-transmission case bolts. Remove transmission case and countershaft. Remove mainshaft from input shaft. Remove input shaft from adapter plate. Remove input shaft and countershaft bearing race. Install selective shim.

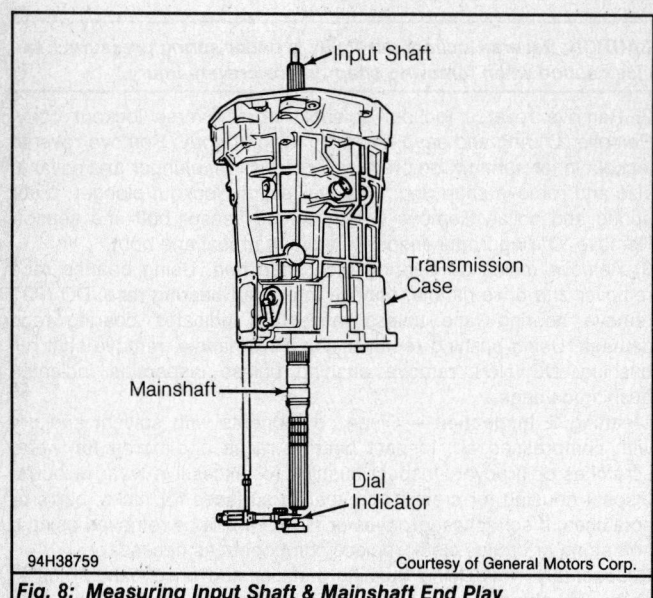

94H38759   Courtesy of General Motors Corp.

Fig. 8: Measuring Input Shaft & Mainshaft End Play

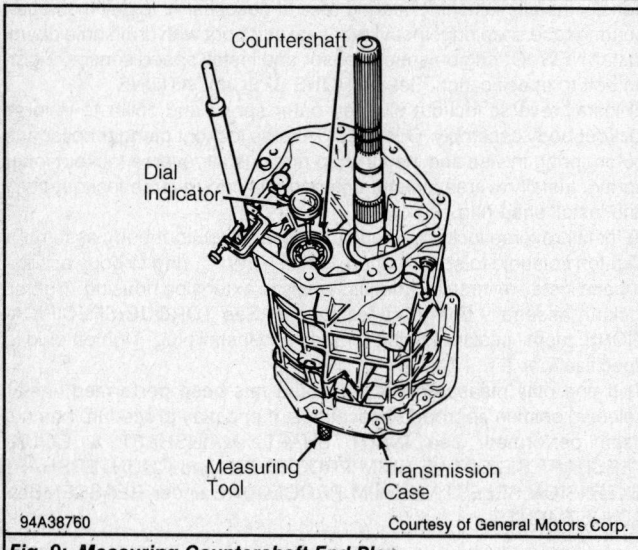

94A38760   Courtesy of General Motors Corp.

Fig. 9: Measuring Countershaft End Play

COUNTERSHAFT EXTENSION SELECTIVE SHIM PROCEDURE

NOTE: This procedure cannot be performed accurately until countershaft selective shim procedure has been performed, and transmission has been assembled to point of installing countershaft extension.

1) Position transmission in horizontal position. Install countershaft extension to countershaft, ensuring splines fully engage. Install extension housing and bolts. Tighten bolts to 26 ft. lbs. (35 N.m). Install Countershaft Extension End Play Measuring Rod (J-39444-2) through adapter plate plug hole, and screw rod into countershaft extension. *See Fig. 10.*

2) Install dial indicator with tip on end of measuring rod. Position transmission in a vertical position. Measure countershaft end play using rod to move countershaft extension up and down. End play should be .002-.005" (.05-.13 mm). Select appropriate shim to obtain specification.

3) Remove dial indicator and measuring rod. Apply sealant to plug threads and install adapter plate plug. Tighten plug to specification. See TORQUE SPECIFICATIONS. Remove extension housing bolts and extension housing. Remove countershaft extension and countershaft extension bear race. Install selective shim.

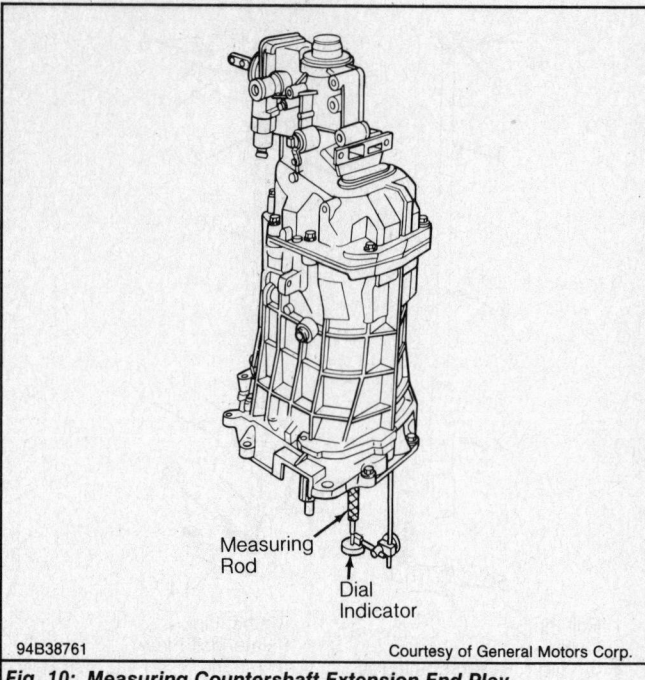

94B38761   Courtesy of General Motors Corp.

Fig. 10: Measuring Countershaft Extension End Play

TRANSMISSION REASSEMBLY

Reassembly – 1) Lubricate all components during reassembly process. Install appropriate selective shims onto adaptive plate. See INPUT SHAFT, MAINSHAFT & COUNTERSHAFT SELECTIVE SHIM PROCEDURE under REASSEMBLY ADJUSTMENTS. Install input shaft and countershaft bearing races. Install input shaft and 4th gear synchronizer assembly.

2) Install shift rail assembly to mainshaft assembly. Install mainshaft assembly with shift rail assembly. Lift mainshaft assembly enough to install countershaft assembly. Install countershaft assembly. Lift mainshaft assembly enough to rotate input shaft to engage synchronizer keys with 4th gear synchronizer ring.

3) Install 5th-6th and reverse shift rail. Align slots of shift rail levers with interlock plate. Install sealant at transmission case to adapter plate mating surface. Assemble ball detent in offset lever. Ensure transmission is in Neutral position to keep 3rd-4th shift rail from engaging. Install solenoid lever. *See Figs. 2 and 3.*

4) Slide transmission case onto gear clusters and shift rail components. Apply anaerobic sealer to threads of 2 shift lever guide bolts and install guide bolts. Pull up on 5th-6th and reverse shift rail assembly enough to align slot of shift interlock plate with guide hole. Tighten guide bolts to specification. See TORQUE SPECIFICATIONS.

5) Install adapter plate to transmission case bolts and tighten to specification. Install shift detent ball in neutral detent groove of shift guide plate. Install shift detent spring into front offset lever. Install front offset lever and spring to shift guide plate and ball. *See Figs. 2 and 3.*

6) Install guide plate and front offset lever together. Lubricate shift rail with assembly lube. Compress guide plate and front offset lever together while sliding onto shift rail to prevent spring release of inner components.

7) Install shift guide plate bolts and tighten to specification. Install front offset lever roll pin and shift detent assembly. Apply anaerobic sealer to threads of shift detent assembly. Tighten shift detent assembly to specification. See TORQUE SPECIFICATIONS.

8) Apply sealant to mating surface of cover plate and install cover plate. Install cover plate bolts and tighten bolts to specification. Install gear select solenoid. Install countershaft extension assembly and 5th-6th shift fork with transmission in horizontal position. Ensure splines of countershaft extension engage splines of countershaft. Install 5th-6th shift fork snap ring. *See Figs. 2 and 3.*

9) Using gear installer assembly, install 5th-6th gear with smaller outside diameter of gear facing down. Engage splines of 5th-6th gear to shaft splines prior to pressing gear onto shaft. Install reverse shift fork, synchronizer and thrust washer. Install NEW reverse shift fork snap ring. Install reverse synchronizer snap ring.

10) Install reverse gear synchronizer ring. Install wave washer so concave side faces synchronizer ring. Install needle bearing, reverse gear, thrust washer and snap ring. Install spacer, roller bearing, spacer and roller bearing snap ring.

11) Install one speedometer gear snap ring. Install speedometer gear using gear installer assembly. Install other speedometer gear snap ring. Install sealing ring. Install funnel to extension housing.

12) Install appropriate countershaft extension selective shim. See COUNTERSHAFT EXTENSION SELECTIVE SHIM PROCEDURE under REASSEMBLY ADJUSTMENTS. Install countershaft extension bearing race. Install reverse idler shaft and thrust washer.

13) Install roller bearing, reverse idler gear and thrust washer. Install reverse idler shaft bracket. Apply sealant to shift bracket bolt threads and install bolts. Tighten bolts to specification. Apply sealant at extension housing to transmission case mating surface. Align 5th-6th and reverse shift rail with extension housing bore and install extension housing. *See Figs. 2 and 3.*

14) Apply sealant to bolt threads retaining transmission bumper. Install extension housing bolts and transmission bumper. Tighten bolts to specification. Install rear offset shift lever and isolator cup. Install rear offset shift lever roll pin.

15) Apply sealant at extension housing to shifter mating surface and install shifter. Tighten bolts to specification. Remove transmission from support fixture and holding fixture. Install clutch fork and "T" handle.

16) Apply sealant to clutch fork bolt threads and install bolt. Install clutch housing and clutch housing bolts. Tighten bolts to specification. Install vent tube.

TORLQUE SPECIFICATIONS
TORQUE SPECIFICATIONS

Application	Ft. Lbs. (N.m)
Adapter Plate Plug	13 (17)
Adapter Plate-To-Trans. Bolt	26 (35)
Back-Up Light Switch	20 (27)
Clutch Fork Bolt	18 (24)
Clutch Housing-To-Adapter Plate Bolt	26 (35)
Cover Plate Bolt	15 (20)
Drive Shaft Bolt	16 (22)
Extension Housing Plug	13 (18)
Extension Housing-To-Trans. Bolt	26 (35)
Reverse Idler Shaft Bracket Bolt	18 (24)
Reverse Lockout Assembly Bolt	13 (18)
Reverse Lockout Solenoid	30 (41)
Shift Detent Assembly	25 (34)
Shift Guide Plate Bolt	16 (22)
Shift Lever Guide Bolt	20 (27)
Shifter Bolt	15 (20)
Transmission Case Fill Plug	13 (18)

	INCH Lbs. (N.m)
Speed Sensor Retainer Bolt	89 (10)

MANUAL TRANSMISSIONS
Chrysler A-523, A-543 & A-568 5-Speed

Chrysler: LeBaron
Dodge: Caravan, Daytona, Shadow, Spirit
Plymouth: Acclaim, Sundance, Voyager

IDENTIFICATION

The A-523, A-543 and A-568 model transaxle assembly number, build date, and final-drive ratio are stamped on an identification tag. The tag is located on top of transaxle housing. The last 8 digits of the Vehicle Identification Number (VIN) are stamped on a raised boss on top of clutch housing area.

DESCRIPTION

The A-523, A-543 and A-568 model transaxles are fully synchronized 5-speed manual transaxles. These units all have die-cast aluminum cases. A-523 is used in light 4-cylinder applications. A-543 is used in V6 applications and A-568 is used in turbocharged applications.

LUBRICATION & ADJUSTMENTS

See appropriate MANUAL TRANSMISSION SERVICING article in TRANSMISSION SERVICING.

TROUBLE SHOOTING

See GENERAL TROUBLE SHOOTING article in MANUAL TRANSMISSIONS.

ON-VEHICLE SERVICE

SPEEDOMETER PINION GEAR

NOTE: Speedometer pinion gear is located in right extension housing. Speedometer pinion must be removed before removing right-side drive axle shaft.

Removal – Remove bolt and washer securing speedometer pinion adapter in extension housing. With cable housing connected, carefully remove adapter and pinion from extension housing. Remove retainer and remove pinion from adapter.

Seal Replacement – If transmission oil is found in cable housing, install a new speedometer pinion and seal assembly. If oil is found between cable and adapter, replace small "O" ring on cable.

Installation – Before installing pinion, adapter and cable assembly, ensure adapter flange and its mating areas on extension housing are clean. Dirt or sand will cause misalignment, resulting in speedometer pinion gear damage. Install and tighten bolt to specification. See TORQUE SPECIFICATIONS.

DRIVE AXLE SHAFTS

See appropriate AXLE SHAFTS article in AXLE SHAFTS & TRANSFER CASES.

INTERNAL TRANSMISSION PARTS

The following components can be serviced and/or repaired without transaxle removal from vehicle:
- Gearshift Selector Housing
- Synchronizers
- Intermediate Shaft Gears
- Input Shaft
- Reverse Idler Gear And Shaft
- Shift Forks And Pads
- Shift Rails
- Speedometer Pinion

To repair these components, refer to TRANSAXLE DISASSEMBLY steps 2) through 9).

NOTE: Differential assembly can only be serviced by removing complete assembly from vehicle because bearing preload must be reset.

REMOVAL & INSTALLATION

See appropriate MANUAL TRANSMISSION REMOVAL article in TRANSMISSION SERVICING.

TRANSAXLE DISASSEMBLY

1) Remove differential cover by removing 2 extension housing bolts and 3 differential bearing retainer bolts that thread into differential cover. Remove extension housing and differential bearing retainer. Remove differential assembly. *See Fig. 1.*

2) Remove rear end cover bolts and nuts. Using a screwdriver, pry up on cover and remove end cover. Remove 5th gear shift fork roll pin. Mark 5th gear synchronizer hub and sleeve for reassembly reference. Remove 5th gear synchronizer sleeve and shift fork. *See Figs. 2 and 3.*

3) Remove 5th gear synchronizer strut retainer and snap ring. Remove 5th gear synchronizer hub and struts from intermediate shaft using gear puller. Using Tool (6252), remove input shaft nut from 5th gear. Pull 5th gear from input shaft.

4) Remove bearing retainer plate (tap with plastic hammer as needed). Remove interlock shuttles and plate. *See Fig. 5.*

NOTE: Before removing gearshift selector housing turn over lock pin in same hole. This will save time installing gearshift selector housing.

5) Remove 6 gearshift selector housing bolts and housing assembly. *See Fig. 4.* Using pencil magnet, remove roller detents and springs. *See Fig. 5.* Remove 1-2 shift lug and shift fork roll pins.

6) Remove reverse shift lever "E" clip and reverse shift lever. Remove 5th shift rail snap ring. Slide 5th shift rail from case and remove 5-R shift lug. Slide 3-4 shift rail from case and remove 3-4 shift lug. Slide 1-2 shift rail from case. *See Fig. 5.*

7) Remove intermediate shaft rear bearing snap ring. Remove 2 bearing support plate bolts and pry off support plate. Only pry at slot openings at sides of bearing support plate and case.

8) Remove reverse idler gear shaft, idler gear and plastic stop as an assembly. *See Fig. 6.* Rotate 1-2 shift fork (rail end) towards input shaft to aid shaft assembly removal.

9) Grasp intermediate shaft assembly and input shaft assembly together and remove from transaxle case. Remove shift forks and pads from intermediate shaft assembly.

10) Remove input shaft seal retainer bolts. Remove seal retainer and selective shim. Measure shim thickness for transaxle reassembly reference. *See Fig. 7.*

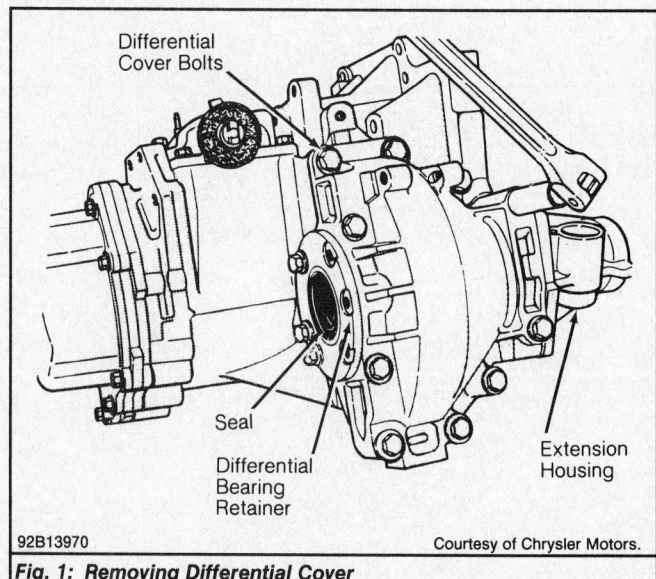

92B13970   Courtesy of Chrysler Motors.

Fig. 1: Removing Differential Cover

MANUAL TRANSMISSIONS
Chrysler A-523, A-543 & A-568 5-Speed (Cont.)

4-31

COMPONENT DISASSEMBLY & REASSEMBLY

INTERMEDIATE SHAFT ASSEMBLY

NOTE: Synchronizer rings are NOT interchangeable. The 1-2 synchronizer rings are larger diameter than other rings.

Disassembly – 1) Remove intermediate shaft rear bearing snap ring. Using a bearing puller, remove rear bearing and 4th gear as an assembly. Remove 3-4 synchronizer hub snap ring. Using a puller, remove 3-4 synchronizer hub and 3rd gear as an assembly.
2) Remove 2nd gear retaining rings, split thrust washer, 2nd gear and 2nd gear synchronizer ring. Remove 1-2 synchronizer hub snap ring. Using a press, press shaft out of synchronizer assembly. See Fig. 8.
3) Remove 1-2 synchronizer assembly, 1st gear synchronizer ring and 1st gear. Remove 1st gear thrust washer and anti-spin pin.

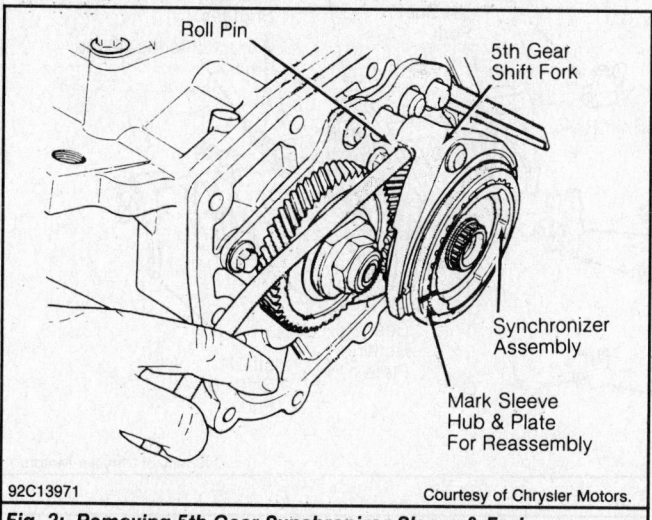

92C13971   Courtesy of Chrysler Motors.

Fig. 2: Removing 5th Gear Synchronizer Sleeve & Fork

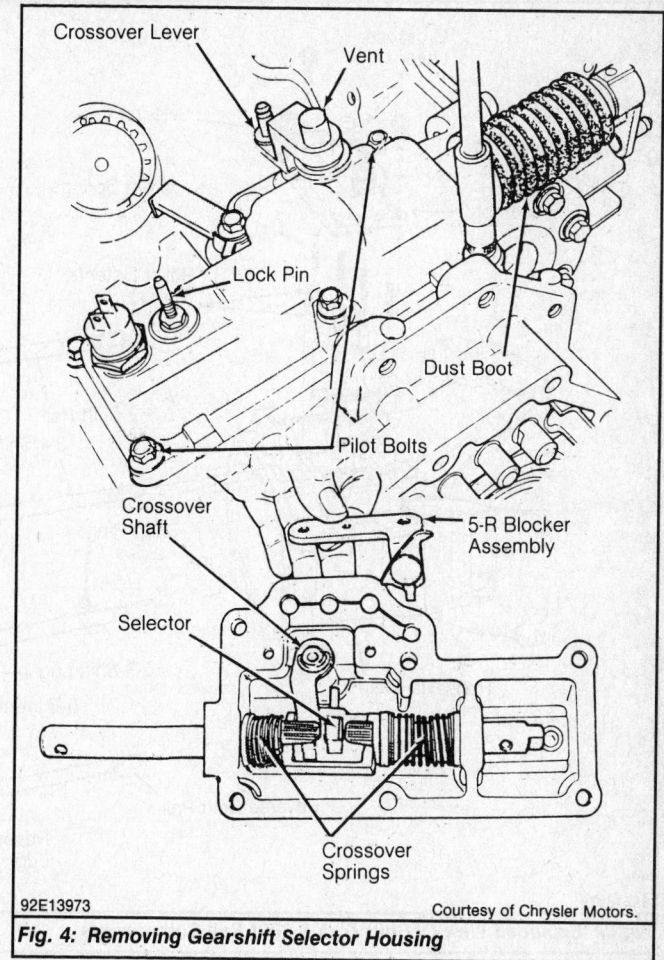

92E13973   Courtesy of Chrysler Motors.

Fig. 4: Removing Gearshift Selector Housing

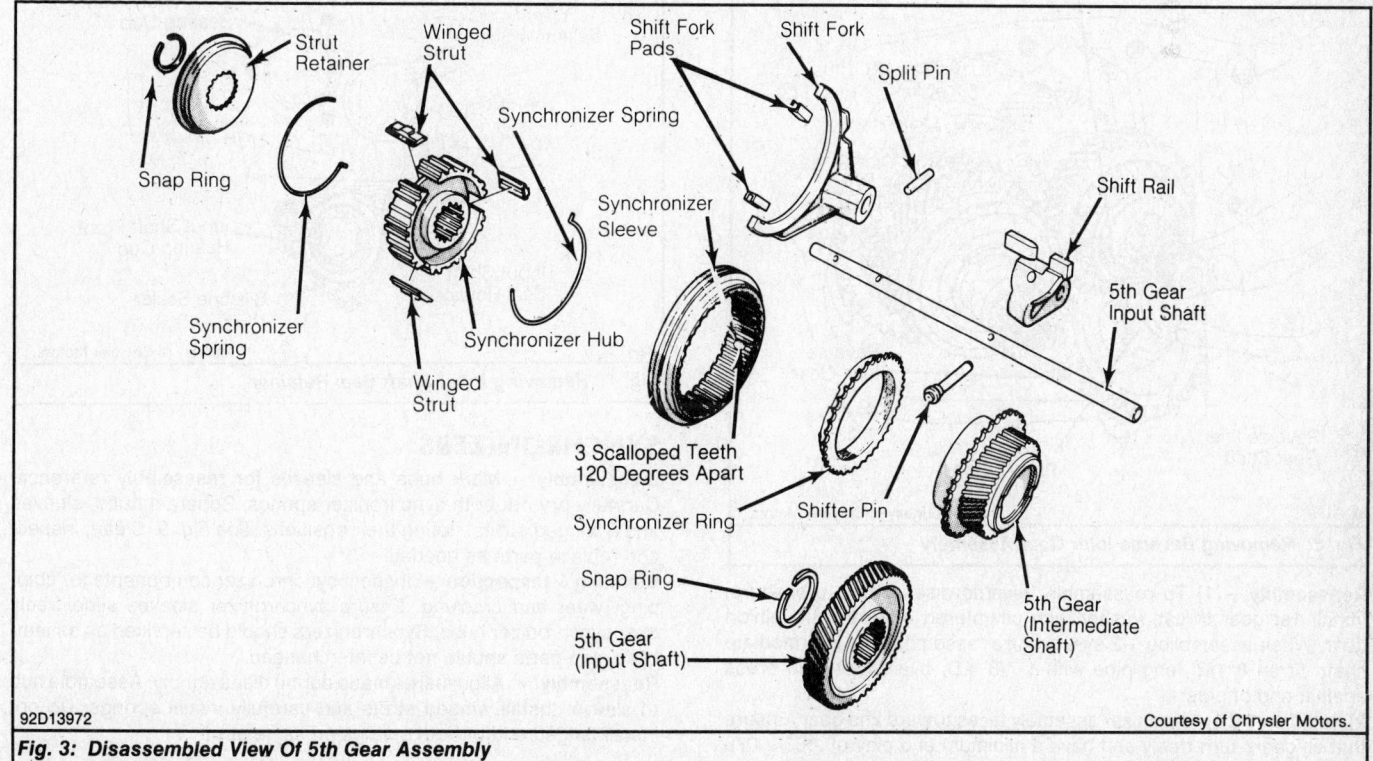

92D13972   Courtesy of Chrysler Motors.

Fig. 3: Disassembled View Of 5th Gear Assembly

4-32

MANUAL TRANSMISSIONS
Chrysler A-523, A-543 & A-568 5-Speed (Cont.)

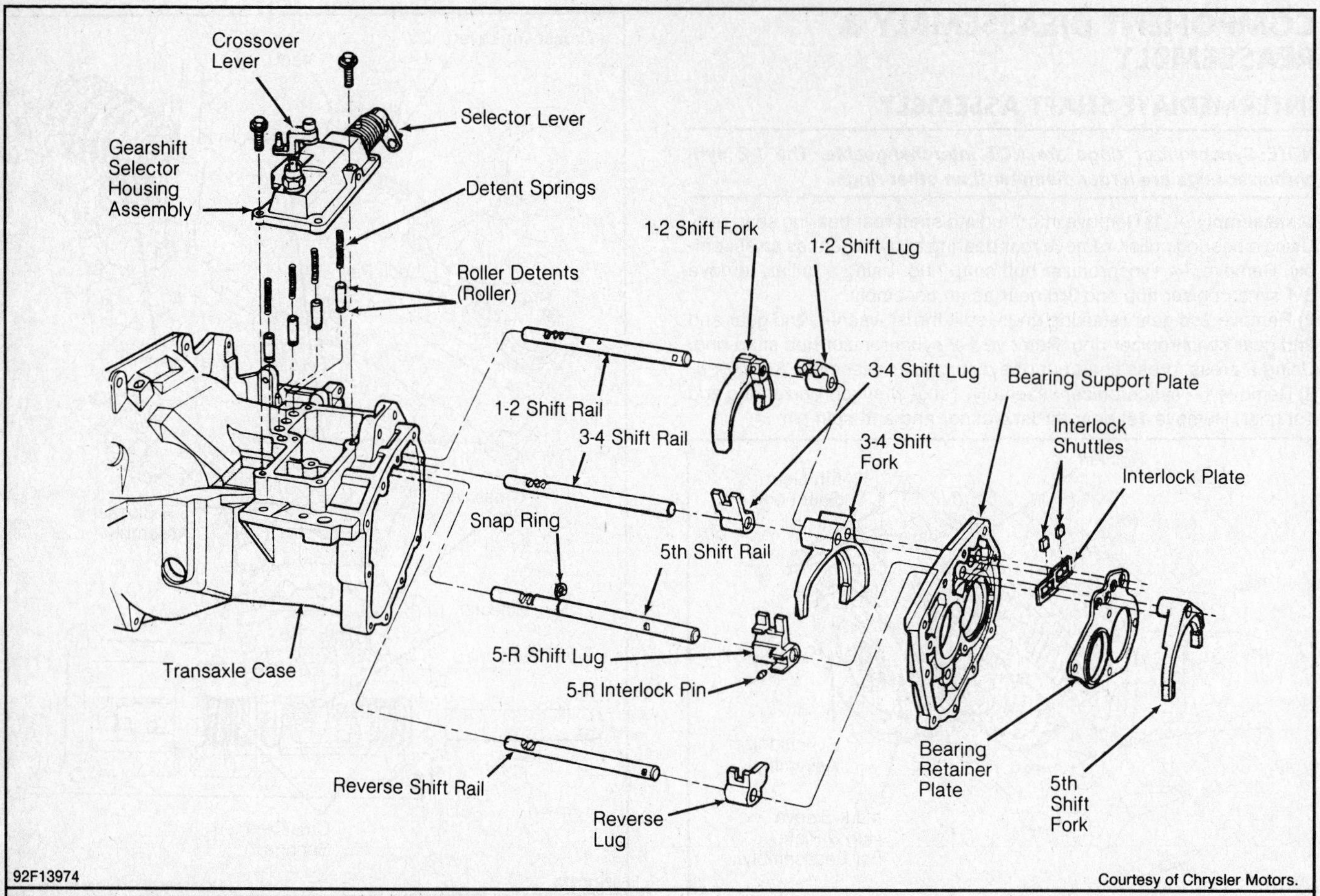

Fig. 5: Exploded View Of Shift Fork & Shift Rail Components

Labels: Crossover Lever, Selector Lever, Gearshift Selector Housing Assembly, Detent Springs, Roller Detents (Roller), 1-2 Shift Fork, 1-2 Shift Lug, 3-4 Shift Lug, Bearing Support Plate, Interlock Shuttles, Interlock Plate, 1-2 Shift Rail, 3-4 Shift Rail, 3-4 Shift Fork, 3-4 Shift Fork, Snap Ring, 5th Shift Rail, Transaxle Case, 5-R Shift Lug, 5-R Interlock Pin, Bearing Retainer Plate, 5th Shift Fork, Reverse Shift Rail, Reverse Lug, 92F13974, Courtesy of Chrysler Motors.

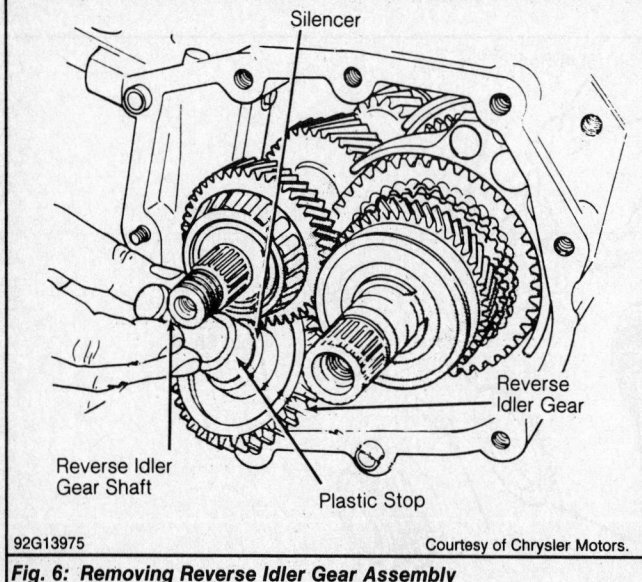

Fig. 6: Removing Reverse Idler Gear Assembly

Labels: Silencer, Reverse Idler Gear, Reverse Idler Gear Shaft, Plastic Stop, 92G13975, Courtesy of Chrysler Motors.

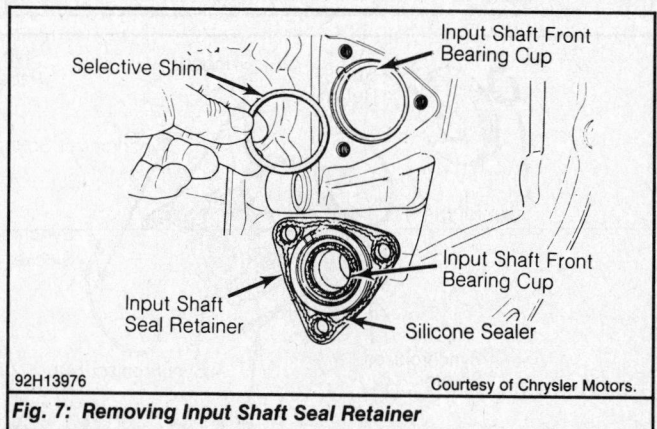

Fig. 7: Removing Input Shaft Seal Retainer

Labels: Selective Shim, Input Shaft Front Bearing Cup, Input Shaft Seal Retainer, Input Shaft Front Bearing Cup, Silicone Sealer, 92H13976, Courtesy of Chrysler Motors.

Reassembly – 1) To reassemble, reverse disassembly procedure. Install 1st gear thrust washer with chamfered edge toward pinion gear. When assembling 1-2 synchronizer assembly and intermediate shaft, fit an 8 1/2" long pipe with 1 7/8" I.D. over shaft, and press against end of pipe.

2) Relief on 1-2 synchronizer assembly faces toward 2nd gear. Ensure that all gears turn freely and have a minimum end play of .003" (.076 mm). Using press, install rear bearing.

SYNCHRONIZERS

Disassembly – Mark hubs and sleeves for reassembly reference. Carefully pry out both synchronizer springs. Separate hubs, sleeves and 3 winged struts, noting their positions. See Fig. 9. Clean, inspect and replace parts as needed.

Cleaning & Inspection – Inspect synchronizer components for chipping, wear and cracking. Ensure synchronizer sleeves slide freely over synchronizer hubs. Synchronizers should be serviced as assemblies, and parts should not be interchanged.

Reassembly – Align marks made during disassembly. Assemble hub to sleeve. Install winged struts and carefully install springs. Do not install tanged end of both springs on same strut.

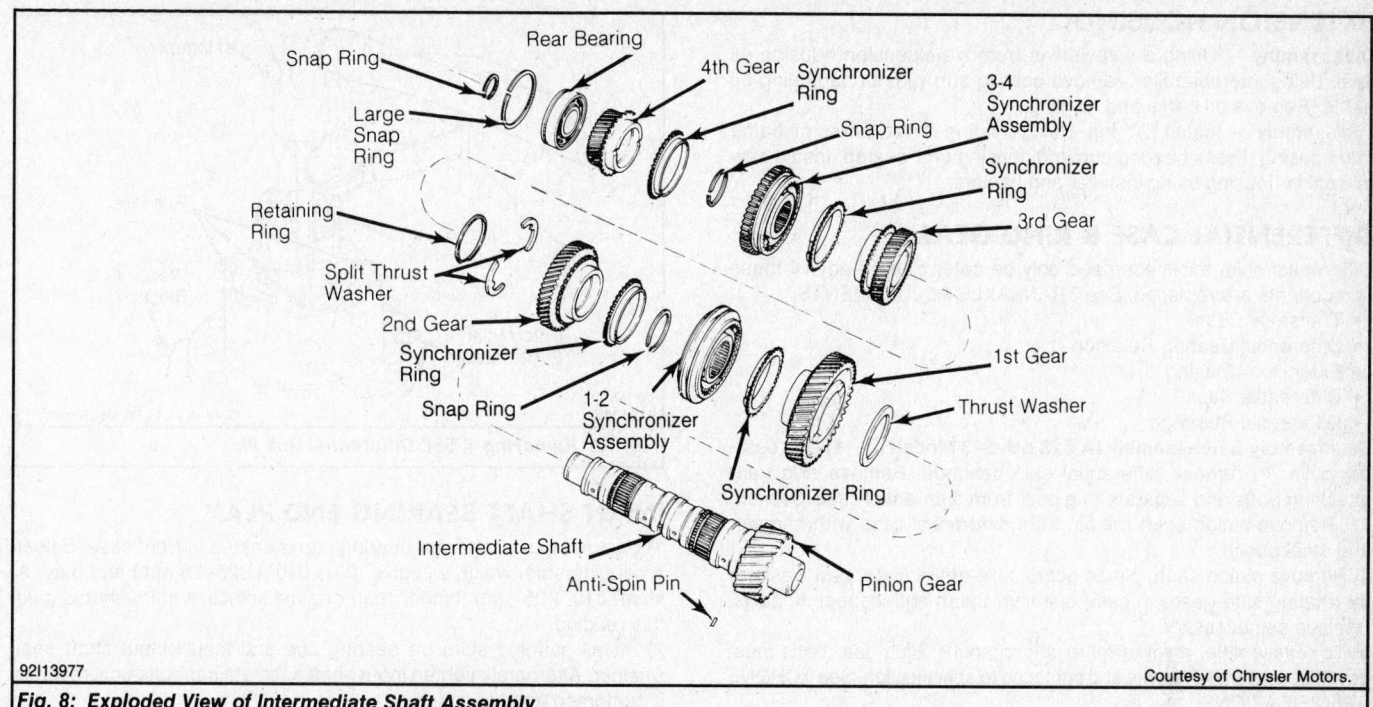

Courtesy of Chrysler Motors.

Fig. 8: Exploded View of Intermediate Shaft Assembly

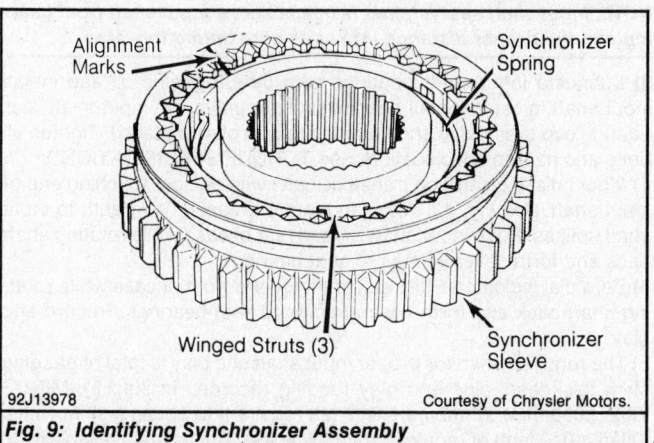

Courtesy of Chrysler Motors.

Fig. 9: Identifying Synchronizer Assembly

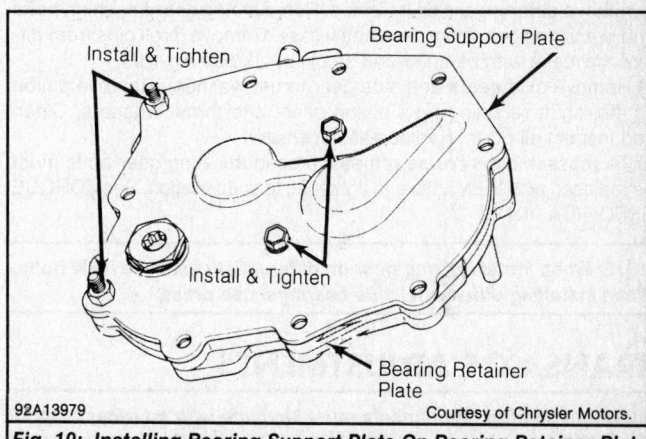

Courtesy of Chrysler Motors.

Fig. 10: Installing Bearing Support Plate On Bearing Retainer Plate

INPUT SHAFT ASSEMBLY

Input shaft shim thickness need only be determined if any of these components are replaced. See TRANSAXLE ADJUSTMENTS.

- Transaxle Case
- Input Shaft Seal Retainer
- Bearing Retainer Plate
- Rear End Cover
- Input Shaft
- Input Shaft Bearings

Disassembly – Using a bearing puller, remove input shaft rear bearing and front bearing. Place bearing retainer plate on wooden blocks. Using a press, press out rear bearing cup from bearing retainer plate.

Reassembly – Press front and rear bearings onto input shaft. Install bearing support plate on bearing retainer plate. See Fig. 10. Press bearing cup into plate until cup bottoms on support plate.

TRANSAXLE CASE

Disassembly – Using a press, press out input shaft front bearing cup. Remove intermediate shaft front bearing retaining strap bolts and strap. Press intermediate shaft front bearing from case. Remove bearing and oil feeder.

Reassembly – Install oil feeder and intermediate shaft front bearing in case. Press bearing into position with letters on bearing facing upward. Install bearing retaining strap and bolts. Using press, install input shaft front bearing cup.

GEARSHIFT SELECTOR HOUSING

Disassembly – **1)** Remove dust boot, snap ring and dust boot. Using a screwdriver, pry oil seal off selector shaft. Remove lock pin, back-up light switch and gasket. Remove vent cap and crossover lock pin. See Fig. 4.

2) Remove 5-R blocker assembly and crossover shaft. Slide 1-2 crossover spring back with screwdriver and remove selector shaft "C" clip. Slide 5-R crossover spring back with screwdriver and remove selector shaft "C" clip.

3) Using hammer and drift, drive selector assembly roll pin out far enough to allow selector shaft removal. Carefully remove selector shaft from shaft housing bore. Remove selector, inhibitor and crossover springs.

Reassembly – For reassembly, reverse disassembly procedure. Using a hammer and driver, drive in NEW seal. Ensure selective shaft is installed prior to seal installation. "C" clip grooves will damage new seal.

4-34

MANUAL TRANSMISSIONS
Chrysler A-523, A-543 & A-568 5-Speed (Cont.)

EXTENSION HOUSING

Disassembly – Using a screwdriver, remove extension housing oil seal. Using internal puller, remove bearing cup without damaging oil baffle. Remove oil baffle and "O" ring.

Reassembly – Install "O" ring. Using bearing driver, press oil baffle into housing. Press bearing cup into housing until seated. Install new oil seal in housing using installer and hammer.

DIFFERENTIAL CASE & RING GEAR

Differential shim thickness need only be determined if any of these components are replaced. See TRANSAXLE ADJUSTMENTS.

- Transaxle Case
- Differential Bearing Retainer
- Extension Housing
- Differential Case
- Differential Bearings

Disassembly & Reassembly (A-523 & A-543 Models) – **1)** Use bearing puller to remove differential side bearings. Remove ring gear attaching bolts and separate ring gear from differential case. *See Fig. 11.* Remove pinion shaft roll pin from differential case with hammer and steel punch.

2) Remove pinion shaft, pinion gears, side gears and thrust washers by rotating side gears to case opening. Clean and inspect all parts. Replace as necessary.

3) To reassemble, reverse removal procedure. Ring gear bolts must be replaced with NEW bolts and tightened to specification. See TORQUE SPECIFICATIONS.

Disassembly & Reassembly (A-568 Models) – **1)** Use bearing puller to remove differential side bearings. Remove ring gear attaching bolts and press ring gear from differential case. Remove 3 roll pins from differential case with hammer and steel punch. *See Fig. 12.*

2) Remove side gears and side gear thrust washers. Remove pinion shafts, shaft retaining ring, pinion gears and thrust washers. Clean and inspect all parts. Replace as necessary.

3) To reassemble, reverse removal procedure. Ring gear bolts must be replaced with NEW bolts and tightened to specification. See TORQUE SPECIFICATIONS.

NOTE: When installing ring gear on differential case, use NEW bolts. When installing differential side bearings, use press.

TRANSAXLE ADJUSTMENTS

NOTE: All bearing adjustments must be made with no other component interference or gear inter-mesh. Replace bearings in pairs. Bearing cups MUST be replaced if removed. Turning torque readings should be obtained while smoothly rotating (break-away reading does not indicate true turning torque.)

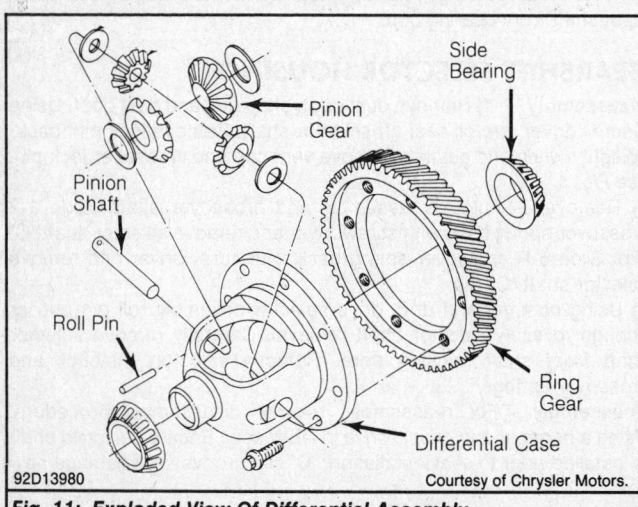

92D13980   Courtesy of Chrysler Motors.
Fig. 11: Exploded View Of Differential Assembly

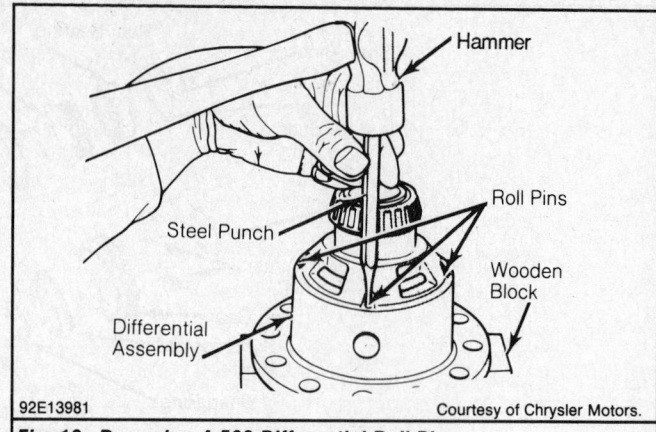

92E13981   Courtesy of Chrysler Motors.
Fig. 12: Removing A-568 Differential Roll Pin

INPUT SHAFT BEARING END PLAY

1) Ensure input shaft front bearing cup is seated in front case. Select a gauging shim which will give .001-.010" (.025-.25 mm) end play. A shim .010" (.25 mm) thinner than original selective shim should give this reading.

2) Install gauging shim on bearing cup and install input shaft seal retainer. Alternately tighten input shaft seal retainer bolts until retainer is bottomed against case.

NOTE: Input shaft seal retainer is used to draw input shaft front bearing cup the proper distance into case bore during this step.

3) Lubricate input shaft bearings with 5W-30 engine oil and install input shaft in case. Install bearing retainer plate with input shaft rear bearing cup pressed in and bearing support plate installed. Tighten all bolts and nuts to specification. See TORQUE SPECIFICATIONS.

4) Mount dial indicator on transaxle case with plunger touching end of input shaft. *See Fig. 13.* Apply moderate pressure, by hand, to input shaft splines. Push input shaft toward rear of case while rotating shaft back and forth several times to seat bearings.

5) Zero dial indicator. Pull input shaft toward front of case while rotating shaft back and forth several times to seat bearings. Record end play.

6) The required shim for proper input shaft end play is total of gauging shim thickness, plus end play reading recorded in step **5)**, MINUS .002" (.050 mm). Combine shims (as required) to obtain a shim within .0016" (.040 mm) of required shim thickness. Shims are available in 30 thicknesses ranging from .024-.069" (.60-1.75 mm). Remove dial indicator.

7) Remove input shaft seal retainer and gauging shim. Install required shim(s). Apply a 1/16" bead of silicone sealer to input shaft seal retainer and install. Tighten bolts alternately until retainer is bottomed against case and torque specification has been reached.

NOTE: Do not allow silicone sealant to obstruct in oil slot.

8) Using Adapter (L-4508) and an INCH-pound torque wrench, check input shaft turning torque. Turning torque for new bearings should be 1-5 INCH lbs. (.11-.56 N.m). Turning torque for old bearings should be one INCH lb. (.11 N.m) minimum. If turning torque is too high, install a .0016" (.040 mm) THINNER shim. If torque is too low, install a .0016" (.040 mm) THICKER shim.

9) If shims require replacement after initial torque reading check, repeat step **1)** to ensure input shaft front bearing cup is properly seated. Repeat step **8)** until proper bearing turning torque is obtained.

DIFFERENTIAL SIDE GEAR END PLAY

1) With differential assembled out of transaxle case, install Adapter (C-4996) into differential bearing. Mount dial indicator to ring gear with plunger resting against adapter. Using fingers or screwdriver, move side gear up and down. Record end play. *See Fig. 14.*

MANUAL TRANSMISSIONS
Chrysler A-523, A-543 & A-568 5-Speed (Cont.)

4-35

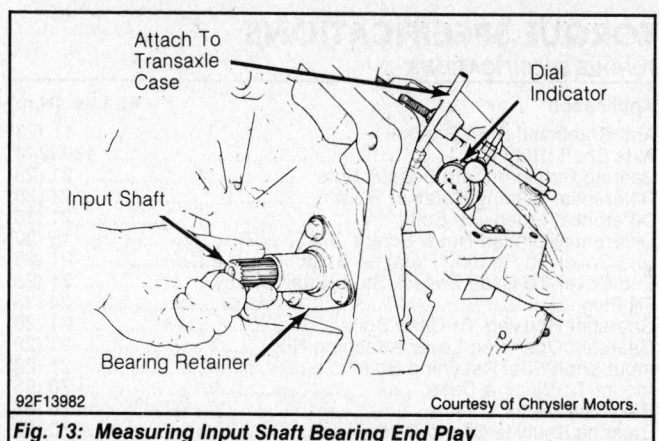

Fig. 13: Measuring Input Shaft Bearing End Play

2) Ensure side gear end play is .001-.013" (.03-.33 mm). Thrust washers are available in the 4 following sizes: .032", .037", .042" and .047" (.81 mm, .94 mm, 1.07 mm and 1.19 mm). Install thrust washers as necessary. Repeat procedure for opposite side gear.

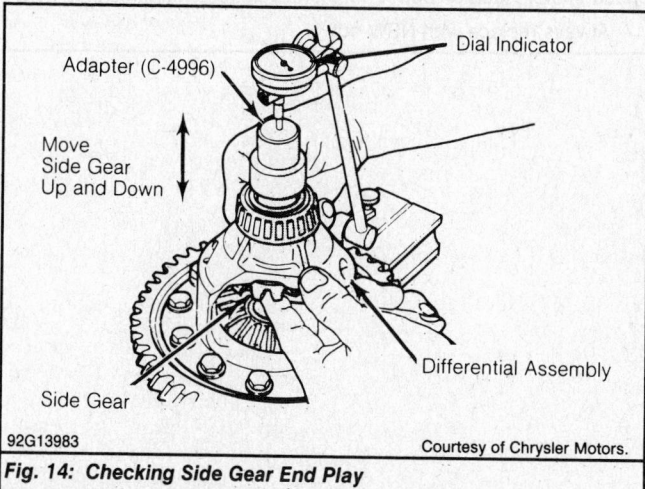

Fig. 14: Checking Side Gear End Play

DIFFERENTIAL BEARING PRELOAD

1) Remove bearing cup and existing shim from differential bearing retainer. *See Fig 15.* Select a gauging shim which will give .001-.010" (.025-.25 mm) end play. A shim .015" (.38 mm) thinner than original selective shim should give this reading. Install gauging shim in differential bearing retainer and press in bearing cup.

NOTE: Do not install oil baffle when checking differential end play.

2) Lubricate differential bearings with 5W-30 engine oil and install differential assembly in transaxle case. Apply 1/16" bead of silicone sealer to extension housing flange, install extension housing and bearing retainer. Tighten bolts to specification. See TORQUE SPECIFICATIONS table at end of article. Mount transaxle case on workbench with "C" clamps (clutch housing facing down). Mount dial indicator with plunger touching differential case. *See Fig. 16.*

3) Apply medium pressure to ring gear, with "T" Handle and Adapter (C-4995), in downward direction while rolling differential assembly back and forth several times to seat bearings. Zero dial indicator. Apply medium pressure in upward direction while rotating differential several times to seat bearings. Record end play.

4) The required shim to obtain proper bearing preload is the total of gauging shim thickness, plus end play reading recorded in step **3)**, PLUS .010" (.25 mm). Combine shims (as required) to obtain a shim within .002" (.05 mm) of required shim thickness. Shims are available in 29 thicknesses ranging from .020-.083". Remove dial indicator.

5) Remove differential bearing retainer. Remove bearing cup and gauging shim. Install oil baffle, using care not to damage baffle. Install required shim(s). Press bearing cup into differential bearing retainer.

6) Check bearing retainer "O" ring for damage and replace if necessary. Apply 1/16" bead of silicone sealer to bearing retainer and install. Tighten bolts to specification. See TORQUE SPECIFICATIONS.

7) Using Adapter (C4995) and an INCH-pound torque wrench, check rotating torque of differential assembly. Rotating torque should be 9-14 INCH lbs. (1.0-1.6 N.m) for new bearings, or 6 INCH lbs. (.68 N.m) minimum for used bearings. If rotating torque is too high, install a .002" (.05 mm) THINNER shim. If torque is too low, install a .002" (.05 mm) THICKER shim. Recheck rotating torque and repeat procedure until proper torque is obtained.

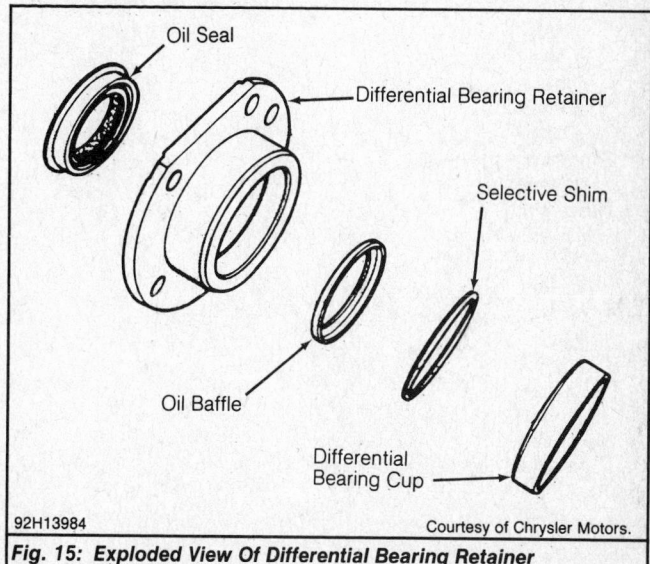

Fig. 15: Exploded View Of Differential Bearing Retainer

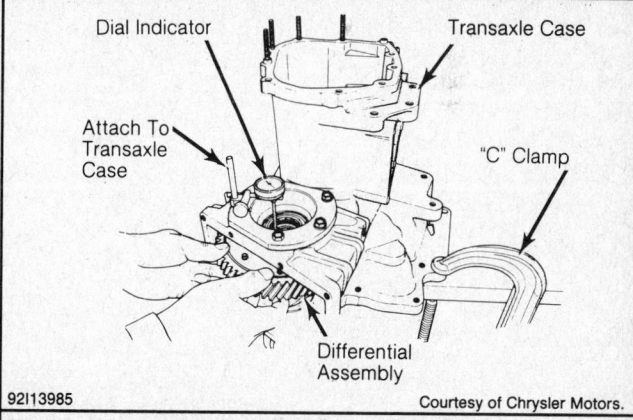

Fig. 16: Measuring Differential Bearing End Play

TRANSAXLE REASSEMBLY

To assemble transaxle, reverse disassembly procedure. Use silicone sealer on components as indicated in TRANSAXLE REASSEMBLY SILICONE USAGE table. Install NEW seal in input shaft seal retainer.

TRANSAXLE REASSEMBLY SILICONE USAGE

Component	Bead Size
Bearing Retainer Plate	1/8"
Extension Housing	1/16"
Input Shaft Differential Cover	1/8"
Rear Cover	1/8"
Seal Retainer	1/16"
Selector Shaft Housing	1/16"

4-36

MANUAL TRANSMISSIONS
Chrysler A-523, A-543 & A-568 5-Speed (Cont.)

NOTE: *When installing reverse idler gear assembly, align roll pin on idler gear with notch in transaxle case. Press 5th gear onto input shaft with Installer (C-4810). Press 5th gear synchronizer assembly onto intermediate shaft with Installer (C-4888).*

TORQUE SPECIFICATIONS
TORQUE SPECIFICATIONS

Application	Ft. Lbs. (N.m)
Anti-Rotational Strut Bracket	17 (23)
Axle Shaft (Hub) Nut [1]	180 (244)
Bearing Retainer Plate Bolts & Nuts	21 (28)
Differential Bearing Retainer Bolts	21 (28)
Differential Extension Bolts	21 (28)
Differential Oil Pan Nut & Screw	15 (20)
End Cover-To-Bearing Retainer Bolts	21 (28)
End Cover-To-Case Bolts & Stud Nuts	21 (28)
Fill Plug	24 (33)
Gearshift Housing-To-Case Bolts	21 (28)
Gearshift Operating Lever Attaching Nut [1]	21 (28)
Input Shaft Seal Retaining Bolt	21 (28)
Mount-To-Block & Case	70 (95)
Ring Gear Bolts	70 (95)
Steering Knuckle Clamp Bolt	70 (95)
Strut-To-Block & Case Bolts	70 (95)
Transaxle Case-To-Engine Block Bolts	70 (95)

	INCH Lbs. (N.m)
Intermediate Shaft Bearing Strap Screw	108 (12)
Shift Linkage Adjusting Pin	108 (12)
Speedometer Adaptor Bolt	60 (7)

[1] – Always replace with NEW nut.

Dodge: 1993 Pickup 5.9L (Diesel)

IDENTIFICATION

Transmission identification number is stamped on tag attached to passenger's side of transmission case, near the oil fill plug.

DESCRIPTION

Getrag G360 transmission is a heavy-duty 5-speed fully synchronized transmission with a fifth gear which provides an overdrive range. Gearshift lever, mounted in the shift cover, operates the shift rails and shift forks for transmission shifting.

LUBRICATION & ADJUSTMENTS

See appropriate MANUAL TRANSMISSION SERVICING article in TRANSMISSION SERVICING.

TROUBLE SHOOTING

See GENERAL TROUBLE SHOOTING article in MANUAL TRANSMISSIONS.

REMOVAL & INSTALLATION

See appropriate MANUAL TRANSMISSION REMOVAL article in TRANSMISSION SERVICING.

TRANSMISSION DISASSEMBLY

1) Place gearshift in Neutral. Remove shift cover bolts. Using pry bars, pry upward evenly on each side of shift cover until shift cover is free of alignment dowels. Alignment dowels are located on each side of transmission case, near front of shift cover.

2) Remove shift cover and gasket (if equipped). See Fig. 1. Early production transmissions do not use gasket between shift cover and transmission case. Manufacturer recommends using gasket for all models during reassembly. Remove bolts and front bearing retainer. See Fig. 1.

3) On 2WD models, remove yoke nut and yoke. On all models, remove bolts, rear bearing retainer and shims located on output shaft and countershaft. See Fig. 1.

4) On 2WD models, remove spacers and speedometer gear from output shaft. Remove oil seal from rear bearing retainer (if necessary).

5) On all models, remove rear bearing races for output shaft and countershaft from transmission case by tapping on face of transmission case with soft-faced hammer until races are free. Remove bearing race for input shaft bearing from transmission case.

6) Rotate input shaft until flat area on teeth of input shaft are facing downward. Pull input shaft forward until it is clear of output shaft.

7) Remove output shaft and gear train assembly from transmission case. Remove input shaft with bearing from transmission case. Press bearing from input shaft if replacement is required.

8) For removal of countershaft assembly, use hammer to unseat cap from front of transmission case. See Fig. 1. DO NOT use excessive force or cap may damage front bearing on the countershaft.

9) Remove snap ring that retains bearing race for bearing on the countershaft bearing from front of transmission case. Remove bearing race for countershaft from front of transmission case.

10) Remove snap ring from rear of countershaft. See Fig. 3. Using hammer and Brass drift, tap countershaft toward front of transmission case and remove.

11) Press bearings from countershaft if replacement is required. Position transmission case in vertical position with input shaft opening facing upward.

NOTE: Two styles of transmission cases are used in 1993. On early style transmissions, countershaft gear cannot be removed from transmission case until reverse idler gear is removed. On later style transmissions, countershaft gear can be rotated past reverse idler gear and removed from transmission case.

12) On later style transmissions, rotate countershaft gear past reverse idler gear and remove from transmission case. On early style transmissions, reverse idler gear must be removed and then remove countershaft gear from transmission case.

13) On early style transmissions, to remove reverse idler gear, remove shaft pin from front of idler gear shaft. Slide reverse idler gear and thrust washer forward. Remove shaft pin from rear of idler gear shaft. DO NOT reuse shaft pins.

14) Remove idler shaft bolt from transmission case . Slide idler gear shaft forward. Remove reverse idler gear and thrust washer from transmission case. It may be necessary to rotate countershaft gear during removal of reverse idler gear. Remove countershaft gear from transmission case (if necessary).

15) On later style transmissions, to remove reverse idler gear, remove shaft pins. Shaft pins are located on each end of reverse idler gear and extend through the idler gear shaft. See Fig. 3. DO NOT reuse shaft pins.

16) Remove idler gear shaft bolt from side of transmission case, near PTO cover. Mark idler gear shaft retaining bolt for reassembly reference so proper bolt is installed for retaining idler gear shaft.

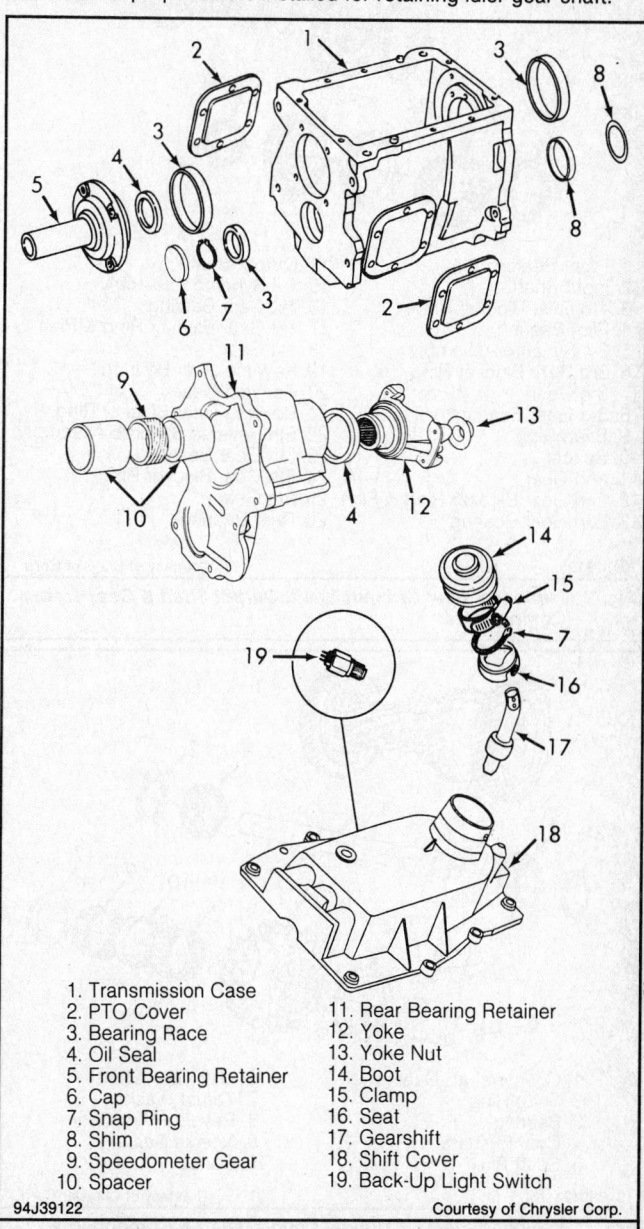

1. Transmission Case
2. PTO Cover
3. Bearing Race
4. Oil Seal
5. Front Bearing Retainer
6. Cap
7. Snap Ring
8. Shim
9. Speedometer Gear
10. Spacer
11. Rear Bearing Retainer
12. Yoke
13. Yoke Nut
14. Boot
15. Clamp
16. Seat
17. Gearshift
18. Shift Cover
19. Back-Up Light Switch

94J39122   Courtesy of Chrysler Corp.

Fig. 1: Exploded View Of Typical 2WD Transmission Case & Components

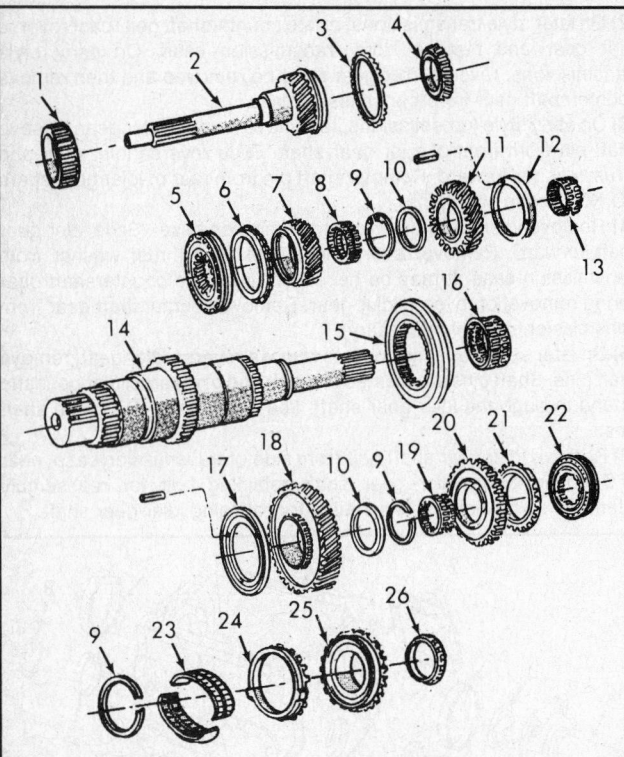

1. Front Bearing
2. Input Shaft
3. 4th Gear Blocker Ring
4. Pilot Bearing
5. 3-4 Synchro Assembly
6. 3rd Gear Blocker Ring
7. 3rd Gear
8. 3rd Gear Bearing
9. Snap Ring
10. Spacer
11. 2nd Gear
12. 2nd Gear Blocker Ring & Pins
13. 2nd Gear Bearing
14. Output Shaft
15. 1-2 Synchro Assembly
16. 1st Gear Bearing
17. 1st Gear Blocker Ring & Pins
18. 1st Gear
19. Reverse Gear Bearing
20. Reverse Gear
21. Reverse Gear Blocker Ring
22. 5th-Reverse Synchro Assembly
23. 5th Gear Bearing
24. 5th Gear Blocker Ring
25. 5th Gear
26. Rear Bearing

94A39123   Courtesy of Chrysler Corp.

Fig. 2: Exploded View Of Input Shaft, Output Shaft & Gear Train Components

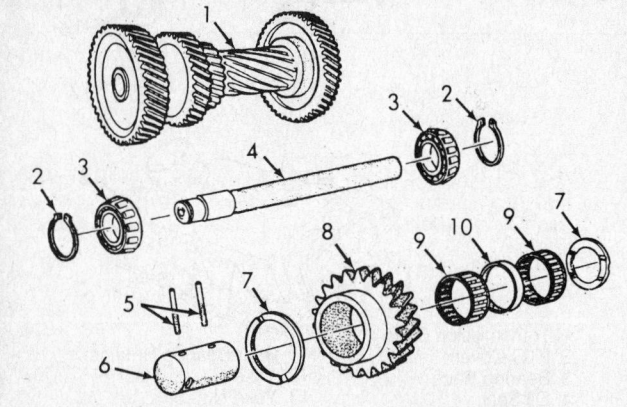

1. Countershaft Gear
2. Snap Ring
3. Bearing
4. Countershaft
5. Shaft Pin
6. Idler Gear Shaft
7. Thrust Washer
8. Reverse Idler Gear
9. Needle Bearing
10. Spacer

94B39124   Courtesy of Chrysler Corp.

Fig. 3: Exploded View Of Typical Countershaft & Components

17) Remove idler gear shaft from transmission case. Remove reverse idler gear with thrust washers, bearings and spacer as an assembly. *See Fig. 3.*

COMPONENT DISASSEMBLY & REASSEMBLY

OUTPUT SHAFT & GEAR TRAIN

NOTE: DO NOT disassemble 1-2, 3-4 and 5th-reverse synchro assemblies. Synchros are serviced as an assembly.

Disassembly – 1) Using press, press 5th gear and rear bearing off output shaft. Remove snap ring and 5th gear blocker ring from output shaft. *See Fig. 2.*

2) Remove both halves of 5th gear bearing. Using 2 screwdrivers, pry reverse gear with 5th-reverse synchro assembly from output shaft. Pry between each side of 1st gear for removal of reverse gear with 5th-reverse synchro assembly.

3) Remove reverse gear bearing from output shaft or reverse gear. Remove snap ring from output shaft, located next to the 1st gear. Press 1st gear from output shaft.

4) Remove 1st gear bearing from output shaft or 1st gear. Place reference mark on 1-2 synchro assembly and output shaft for reassembly reference. Remove 1-2 synchro assembly from output shaft.

5) Using press and bearing splitter, press 3rd gear with pilot bearing and 3-4 synchro assembly from output shaft as an assembly. Remove 3rd gear bearing from output shaft or 3rd gear.

6) Remove snap ring retaining 2nd gear on output shaft. DO NOT reuse this snap ring, as NEW snap ring must be installed during reassembly. Press spacer and 2nd gear from output shaft. Remove 2nd gear bearing from 2nd gear or output shaft.

7) If removing 1st gear blocker ring from 1st gear, tap pins through 1st gear blocker ring. Remove 1st gear blocker ring from 1st gear. DO NOT reuse the pins.

8) If removing 2nd gear blocker ring from 2nd gear, tap pin 3/4 the way out of 2nd gear blocker ring. Pry 2nd gear blocker ring from 2nd gear. Replace 2nd gear blocker ring if excessive force was required to remove 2nd gear blocker ring from 2nd gear. Remove pins from 2nd gear. DO NOT reuse pins.

Cleaning & Inspection – 1) Clean all parts in solvent. Dry all components except bearings with compressed air. Use shop towels to dry bearings. Inspect output shaft for wear or damage.

2) Inspect for chipped or worn gears. Inspect blocker rings for cracks or signs of clutch material on the rings. Place blocker rings on flat surface and check for distortion. Replace damaged components.

3) Inspect 1-2, 3-4 and 5th-reverse synchro assemblies for damage. Synchros are serviced as an assembly.

NOTE: Manufacturer recommends using NEW snap rings when reassembling output shaft and gear train.

Reassembly – 1) Lubricate output shaft and gear train components with 5W-30 engine oil. Install 1st gear and 2nd gear blocker ring on 1st gear and 2nd gears (if removed).

2) Install NEW pins through blocker ring and into the gear. DO NOT reuse old pins. Using hammer and punch, drive pins into the gear until end of pin is even with surface of blocker ring. DO NOT drive pin below surface of blocker ring.

3) Install 2nd gear bearing in 2nd gear. Install 2nd gear on output shaft. Spacer that fits on output shaft, next to 2nd gear is a tight fit on output shaft and must be heated before installing on output shaft.

CAUTION: DO NOT heat spacer for more that 5 minutes at 200°F (93°C).

4) Heat spacer in an oven for 5 minutes at 200°F (93°C). Install spacer on output shaft. Ensure spacer fully seats against the 2nd gear. Install NEW snap ring on output shaft, next to the spacer. This snap ring is a select fit. Use the thickest snap ring that will fit. Install 3rd gear bearing in the 3rd gear. Install 3rd gear on output shaft.

CAUTION: Ensure 3-4 synchro assembly is installed on output shaft so longest shoulder on synchro hub fits into the 3rd gear. Ensure the 3-4 synchro assembly alignes with splines on 3rd gear blocker ring before pressing onto output shaft or blocker ring may be damaged.

5) Install 3-4 synchro assembly on output shaft so longest shoulder on synchro hub fits into the 3rd gear. Ensure 3-4 synchro assembly is aligned with splines on 3rd gear blocker ring. Using suitable diameter pipe, drive 3-4 synchro assembly on output shaft.
6) Using bearing installer, install pilot bearing on output shaft. It may be necessary to heat pilot bearing before installing on output shaft.

NOTE: If installing NEW 1-2 synchro assembly on output shaft, synchro assembly can be installed in either direction. If installing original 1-2 synchro assembly, synchro assembly must be installed so reference marks made during disassembly are aligned.

7) Position output shaft with rear of shaft facing upward. Install 1-2 synchro assembly on output shaft. Install 1st gear bearing on output shaft. Install 1st gear on output shaft. Rotate 1st gear back and forth until blocker ring seats in 1-2 synchro assembly.
8) Install spacer on output shaft, next to 1st gear. It may be necessary to use a press and suitable diameter pipe to press spacer on the output shaft.
9) Install NEW snap ring on output shaft, next to the spacer. DO NOT over expand snap ring during installation. Ensure snap ring is fully seated.
10) Install reverse gear bearing in reverse gear. Install reverse gear on output shaft. Install reverse gear blocker ring on reverse gear.

CAUTION: Ensure 5th-reverse synchro assembly is aligned with reverse gear blocker ring before pressing onto output shaft or blocker ring may be damaged.

11) Install 5th-reverse synchro assembly on output shaft. Ensure 5th-reverse synchro assembly aligns with splines on reverse gear blocker ring. Using suitable diameter pipe, press 5th-reverse synchro assembly on output shaft.
12) Install snap ring on output shaft, next to 5th-reverse synchro assembly. This snap ring is a select fit. Use the thickest snap ring that will fit.
13) Using petroleum jelly to hold bearing halves in place, install both halves of 5th gear bearing on output shaft. Install 5th gear blocker ring on output shaft and engage in 5th-reverse synchro assembly.
14) Install 5th gear and rear bearing on output shaft. Ensure output shaft and gear train components are correctly installed. *See Fig. 4.*

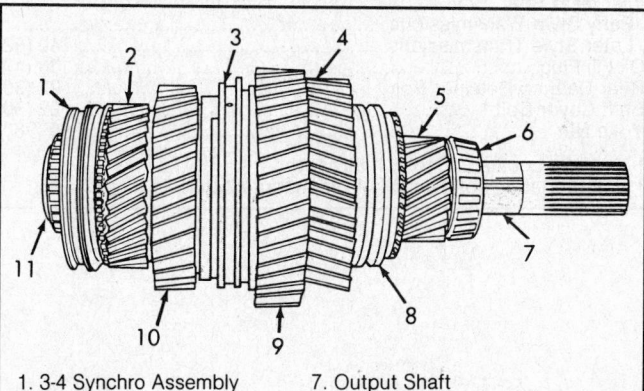

1. 3-4 Synchro Assembly	7. Output Shaft
2. 3rd Gear	8. 5th-Reverse Synchro Assembly
3. 1-2 Synchro Assembly	9. 1st Gear
4. Reverse Gear	10. 2nd Gear
5. 5th Gear	11. Pilot Bearing
6. Rear Bearing	

94C39125   Courtesy of Chrysler Corp.

Fig. 4: Identifying Output Shaft & Gear Train Locations

TRANSMISSION REASSEMBLY

CAUTION: Manufacturer recommends using NEW snap rings

NOTE: Two styles of transmission cases are used in 1993. On early style transmissions, countershaft gear must be installed in transmission case before reverse idler gear is installed. On later style transmissions, countershaft gear can be installed with reverse idler gear installed in transmission case.

1) Position transmission case in vertical position with input shaft opening facing upward. Install countershaft gear in transmission case. Install bearing and NEW snap ring on front end of countershaft.
2) Install countershaft with bearing in transmission case. Install bearing race for front bearing on countershaft in front side of transmission case.

CAUTION: Ensure sealant is applied on outer edge of cap before installing in transmission case.

3) Install snap ring that retains bearing race in front of transmission case. Apply sealant on outer edge of cap and install in transmission case. Install bearing and snap ring on rear of countershaft. On early style transmissions, proceed to step **4**). On later style transmissions, proceed to step **7**).
4) On early style transmissions, install idler gear shaft part way in transmission case from the front side of transmission case. Install reverse idler gear assembly and thrust washers.

NOTE: Used shaft pins are installed until correct thrust washer clearance is obtained. Once correct thrust washer clearance is obtained, used shaft pins must be replaced with NEW shaft pins.

5) Push idler gear shaft into reverse idler gear. Install used shaft pins by installing rear shaft pin first and then the front shaft pin. Using feeler gauge, check thrust washer clearance between each thrust washer and reverse idler gear.
6) Thrust washer clearance should be .002-.010" (.05-.25 mm). Replace thrust washers if thrust washer clearance exceeds specification. Once correct thrust washer clearance is obtained, remove used shaft pins and replace with NEW shaft pins. Install idler shaft bolt in transmission case.
7) On later style transmissions, install idler gear shaft part way in transmission case from the front of transmission case. Ensure spacer is installed between needle bearings and install in reverse idler gear.

CAUTION: Thrust washers must be installed on each end of reverse idler gear with slots on thrust washer facing away from reverse idler gear so shaft pins can be installed.

8) Install thrust washers on each end of reverse idler gear with slots on thrust washers facing away from reverse idler gear. Slots must be positioned away from reverse idler gear, so shaft pins can be installed.

NOTE: Used shaft pins are installed until correct thrust washer clearance is obtained. Once correct thrust washer clearance is obtained, used shaft pins must be replaced with NEW shaft pins.

9) Install reverse idler gear in transmission case. Align shaft pin holes in idler shaft with slots in thrust washers and fully install idler gear shaft. Install used shaft pins part way in idler gear shaft to hold thrust washers in place.
10) Using feeler gauge, check thrust washer clearance between each thrust washer and reverse idler gear. Thrust washer clearance should be .002-.010" (.05-.25 mm). Replace thrust washers if thrust washer clearance exceeds specification. Once correct thrust washer clearance is obtained, remove used shaft pins and replace with NEW shaft pins.
11) Install and tighten idler gear shaft bolt to specification. See TORQUE SPECIFICATIONS.

12) On all transmissions, install NEW oil seal in front bearing retainer. Ensure lip on oil seal faces toward the transmission case side of front bearing retainer. Coat lip on oil seal with oil.

13) Install bearing on input shaft (if removed). Rotate input shaft until flat area on teeth of input shaft is facing downward. Install input shaft in transmission case.

14) Install output shaft and gear train in transmission case. Install bearing race for input shaft bearing in transmission case. Apply sealant on front bearing retainer-to-transmission case surface.

15) Install front bearing retainer. Apply Loctite 242 to threads of front bearing retainer bolts. Install and tighten bolts to specification. Install bearing races for rear bearing on countershaft and output shaft in transmission case.

16) Place transmission case in vertical position with output shaft facing upward. Support transmission case with wooden blocks positioned on each side of front bearing retainer.

17) Ensure bearings races are seated on rear bearings on countershaft and output shaft. Using depth gauge, measure and record bearing race protrusion from top of bearing race to the transmission case on countershaft and output shaft bearing races. See Fig. 5. Bearing race protrusion is required for determining proper shim thickness.

18) Using depth gauge, measure and record depth of output shaft and countershaft bearing shim bores in rear bearing retainer. See Fig. 6.

19) To determine proper shim thickness, subtract bearing race protrusion measurement from bearing shim bore measurement. Then add an extra .006-.008'' (.15-.20 mm) to the result to obtain correct thickness of shim to be installed. These shims are used to control the bearing preload.

20) Using petroleum jelly to hold shims in place, install shims in rear bearing retainer. Thinnest shims should installed at rear of shim pack so shims will seat in rear bearing retainer.

21) On 2WD models, install NEW oil seal in rear bearing retainer. Install spacers and speedometer gear on output shaft. On all models, apply Loctite 518 on rear bearing retainer-to-transmission case sealing surface.

22) Install rear bearing retainer on transmission case. Ensure shims remain in place on rear bearing retainer. Apply Loctite 242 to threads of rear bearing retainer bolts. Install and tighten bolts to specification. See TORQUE SPECIFICATIONS.

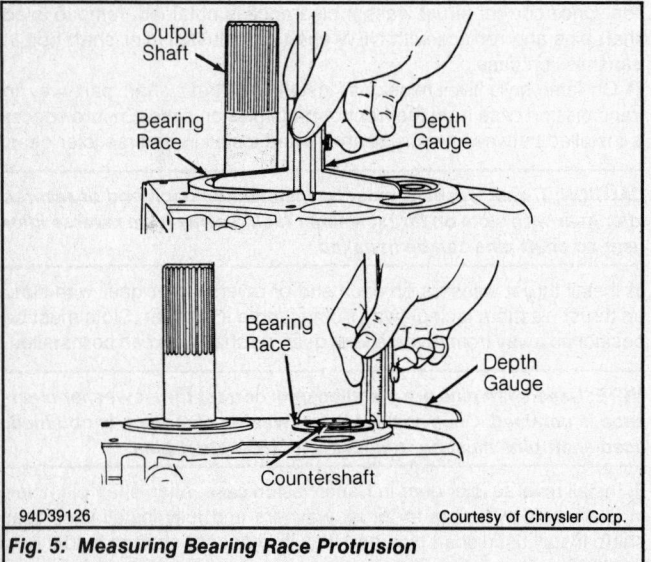

94D39126   Courtesy of Chrysler Corp.

Fig. 5: Measuring Bearing Race Protrusion

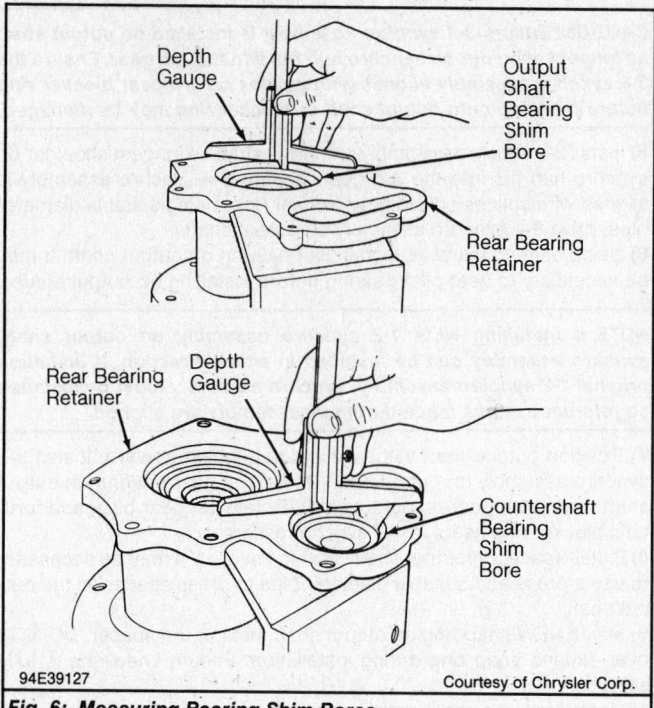

94E39127   Courtesy of Chrysler Corp.

Fig. 6: Measuring Bearing Shim Bores

23) On 2WD models, lube lip of oil seal with petroleum jelly. Install yoke. Install and tighten NEW yoke nut to specification.

24) On all models, apply sealant to NEW gasket for shift cover and install on transmission case. Early production transmissions did not use gasket between shift cover and transmission case. Manufacturer recommends installing gasket during reassembly.

25) Ensure sleeves on synchro assemblies are in the centered (neutral) position. Install shift cover, ensuring shift forks align with sleeves on synchro assemblies. Apply Loctite 242 to threads of shift cover bolts. Install and tighten bolts to specification.

TORQUE SPECIFICATIONS
TORQUE SPECIFICATIONS

Application	Ft. Lbs. (N.m)
Drain Plug	35 (47)
Front Bearing Retainer Bolt [1]	22 (30)
Idler Gear Shaft Bolt	
Early Style Transmissions	[2]
Later Style Transmissions	40 (52)
Oil Fill Plug	35 (47)
Rear Bearing Retainer Bolt [1]	22 (30)
Shift Cover Bolt [1]	22 (30)
Yoke Nut	280 (380)

[1] – Apply Loctite 242 to bolt threads.
[2] – Information not available from manufacturer.

Aspire (1994), Festiva (1993)

IDENTIFICATION

Transaxle can be identified by a safety compliance label, located on driver's door lock pillar below latch striker. Transaxle code on label for manual 5-speed transaxle is "D".

DESCRIPTION

Transaxle is designed with split cases. One half of case forms the clutch housing and contains clutch release components, speedometer driven gear, input shift shaft and 3rd-4th detent plug. The other half forms the transaxle case and contains input and mainshaft assemblies. *See Fig. 1.*

Transaxle is installed transversely in engine compartment with clutch housing facing right side of vehicle. Two rubber-insulated mounts secure transaxle to a crossmember and also serve as rear engine mounts.

LUBRICATION & ADJUSTMENTS

See appropriate MANUAL TRANSMISSION SERVICING article in TRANSMISSION SERVICING.

TROUBLE SHOOTING

See GENERAL TROUBLE SHOOTING article in MANUAL TRANSMISSIONS.

ON-VEHICLE SERVICE

SHIFT LEVER & LINKAGE

NOTE: The manual shift mechanism and linkage are not adjustable. No adjustments are required before or after installation.

Removal – 1) Remove shift lever knob. Remove 6 console screws. Remove console and boot assembly. *See Fig. 2.* Remove nuts and plastic retainers attaching shift lever housing to floor pan.
2) Raise and support vehicle. Disconnect shift rod from transaxle and shift lever. If necessary for replacement, remove bushings from shift lever and/or input shift shaft.
3) Disconnect stabilizer rod from transaxle stud. Remove shift lever housing and stabilizer rod. It may be necessary to pry down on exhaust system for clearance.
Installation – To install, reverse removal procedure. Ensure all bushings and washers are in place. Coat inside of bushings with a light coating of multi-purpose grease. Tighten all bolts and nuts to specification. See TORQUE SPECIFICATIONS.

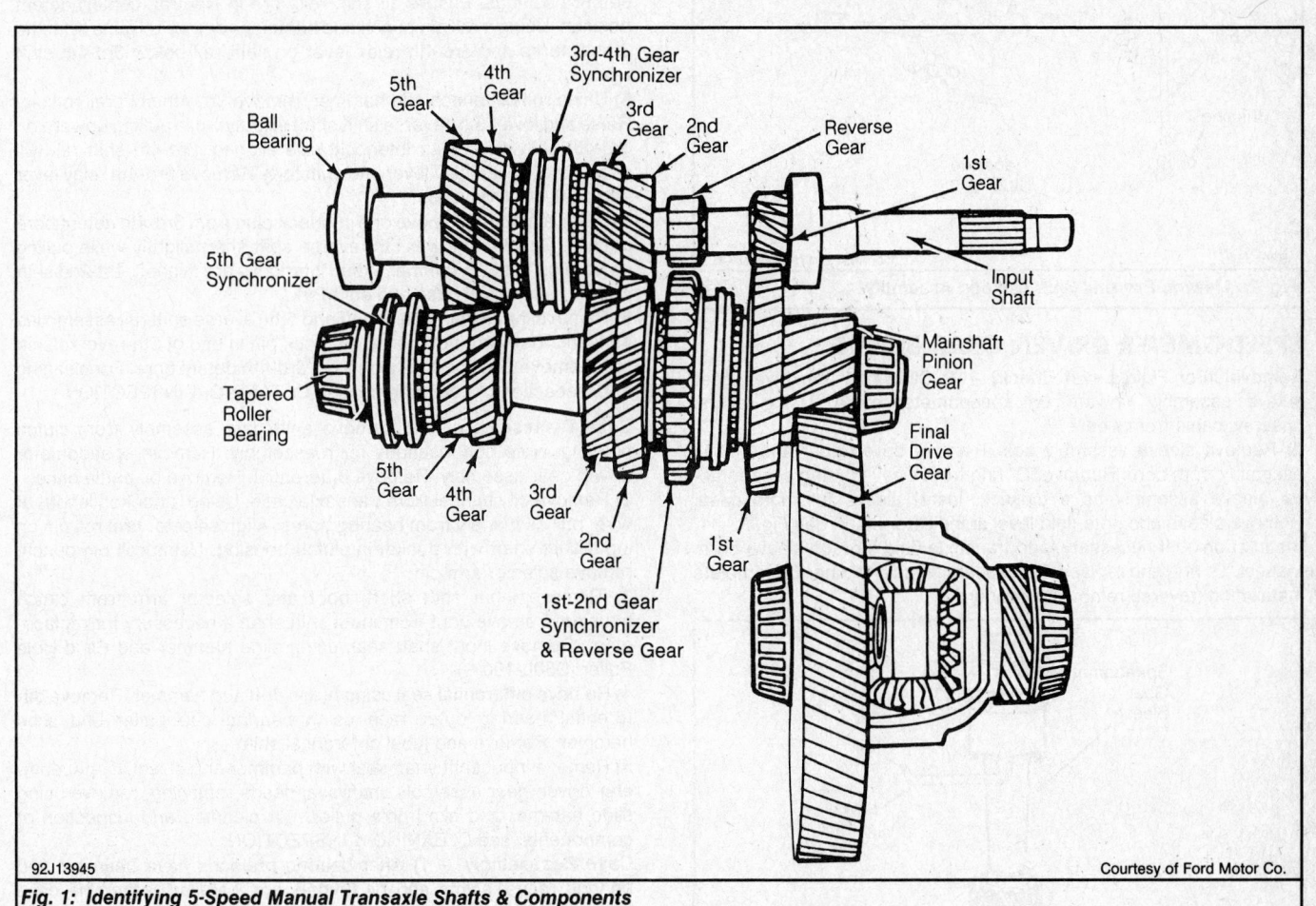

92J13945   Courtesy of Ford Motor Co.

Fig. 1: Identifying 5-Speed Manual Transaxle Shafts & Components

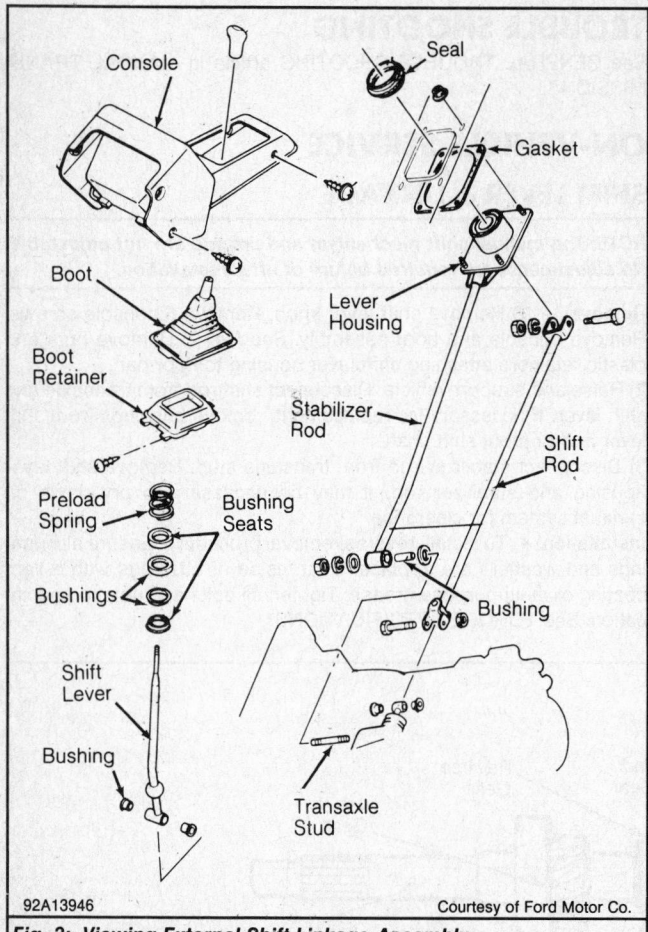

Console
Seal
Gasket
Boot
Lever Housing
Boot Retainer
Stabilizer Rod
Shift Rod
Preload Spring
Bushing Seats
Bushings
Bushing
Shift Lever
Bushing
Transaxle Stud

92A13946   Courtesy of Ford Motor Co.

Fig. 2: Viewing External Shift Linkage Assembly

SPEEDOMETER DRIVEN GEAR SLEEVE

Removal (For Fluid Level Check) – 1) Slide boot on driven gear sleeve assembly upward on speedometer cable. Using pliers, unscrew cable from sleeve.
2) Remove sleeve assembly bolt. Remove driven gear and sleeve assembly from bore. Remove "O" ring from sleeve. Using speedometer sleeve assembly as a dipstick, insert sleeve fully into case. Remove sleeve and note fluid level at indicator mark. *See Fig. 3.*
Installation – If necessary, add transaxle fluid through sleeve bore. Inspect "O" ring and replace if necessary. Install "O" ring. To complete installation, reverse removal procedure.

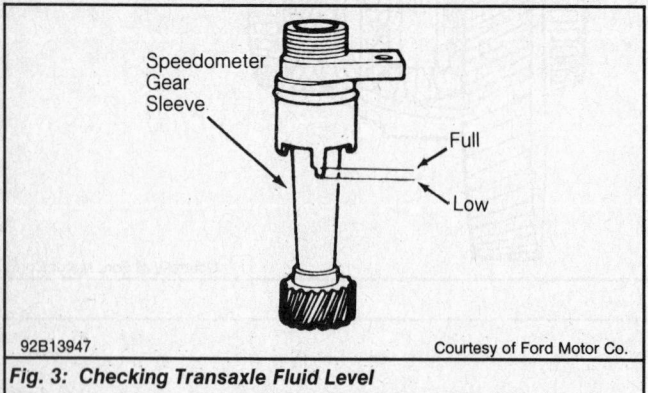

Speedometer Gear Sleeve
Full
Low

92B13947   Courtesy of Ford Motor Co.

Fig. 3: Checking Transaxle Fluid Level

DRIVE AXLE SHAFTS

See appropriate AXLE SHAFTS article in AXLE SHAFTS & TRANSFER CASES.

REMOVAL & INSTALLATION

See appropriate MANUAL TRANSMISSION REMOVAL article in TRANSMISSION SERVICING.

TRANSAXLE DISASSEMBLY

1) Place transaxle in Neutral. Remove drain plug from transaxle case. Drain transaxle fluid. Set transaxle into a bench mounting fixture. Remove transaxle mount from case. Remove 1st-2nd detent plug, spring and ball. If necessary, use magnet to remove ball and/or spring. *See Fig. 4.*
2) Remove 5th-Reverse detent plug, spring and ball. Remove back-up light switch. Remove 14 transaxle case bolts. Rotate transaxle so input shaft faces downward. Separate transaxle case from clutch housing. If necessary, tap case with plastic-tipped hammer.
3) Remove and label input and mainshaft adjustment shims for reassembly reference. It may be necessary to remove bearing outer races from transaxle case bores to obtain adjustment shims. Label shims and races for reassembly reference.
4) Remove case magnet. Remove reverse shift lever detent plate from below reverse shift lever pivot. Remove reverse idler gear and shaft. Remove retaining pin from reverse shift lever pivot. Remove pivot pin and reverse shift lever.
5) Remove 3rd-4th detent plug, spring and ball. Each shift rail has 3 detent positions. Ensure all shift rails are in Neutral (center) detent position. Using a roll pin punch and hammer, remove roll pins from the 3 shift forks and 3rd-4th relay lever on shift rail below 3rd-4th shift fork.
6) Using roll pin punch and hammer, remove 3rd-4th shift rail roll pin. Raise and lower 5th-reverse shift shaft slightly while pulling upward on 3rd-4th shift rail. When interlocks are aligned, 3rd-4th shift rail will slide out of case, relay lever and shift fork. Remove 3rd-4th relay lever and shift fork from case.
7) Using a magnet, remove one interlock plug from 3rd-4th detent bore in case. Raise and lower 5th-reverse shift shaft slightly while pulling upward on 1st-2nd shift rail. When interlocks are aligned, 1st-2nd shift rail will slide out of case and shift fork.
8) Remove input shaft, mainshaft and 5th-reverse shift rail assemblies as a unit. Use care not to lose interlock pin in end of 5th-reverse shift rail. Remove 2nd interlock plug from 3rd-4th detent bore. For cleaning and inspection of components, see CLEANING & INSPECTION.

Case Disassembly – **1)** Remove shift gate assembly from clutch housing. Note bolt locations for reassembly. Remove speedometer driven gear assembly. Remove differential. Remove oil baffle plate.
2) Remove oil channel from transaxle case. Using a hooked length of wire, pull oil funnels from bearing bores. Align selector arm roll pin on input shift shaft with pocket in clutch housing. Using roll pin punch, remove selector arm pin.
3) Remove input shift shaft, boot and selector arm from clutch housing. Remove boot from input shift shaft if necessary for replacement. Remove input shaft seal, using slide hammer and Blind Hole Puller (D80L-100-S).
4) Remove differential seal using brass drift and hammer. Remove differential bearing outer race using bearing cup puller and slide hammer. Remove and label differential shim.
5) Remove input shift shaft seal with hammer and chisel. If speedometer driven gear assembly shaft seal needs replacing, remove using slide hammer and blind hole puller. For cleaning and inspection of components, see CLEANING & INSPECTION.
Case Reassembly – **1)** After bearing preloads have been set and bearing races, shims and oil funnels are installed, assemble case components as follows: If speedometer driven gear assembly shaft seal is being replaced, install NEW seal using hammer and an appropriate sized socket as a driver.
2) Install input shift shaft seal with a plastic-tipped hammer. Install differential seal with differential seal replacer. Install boot onto shift input shaft.

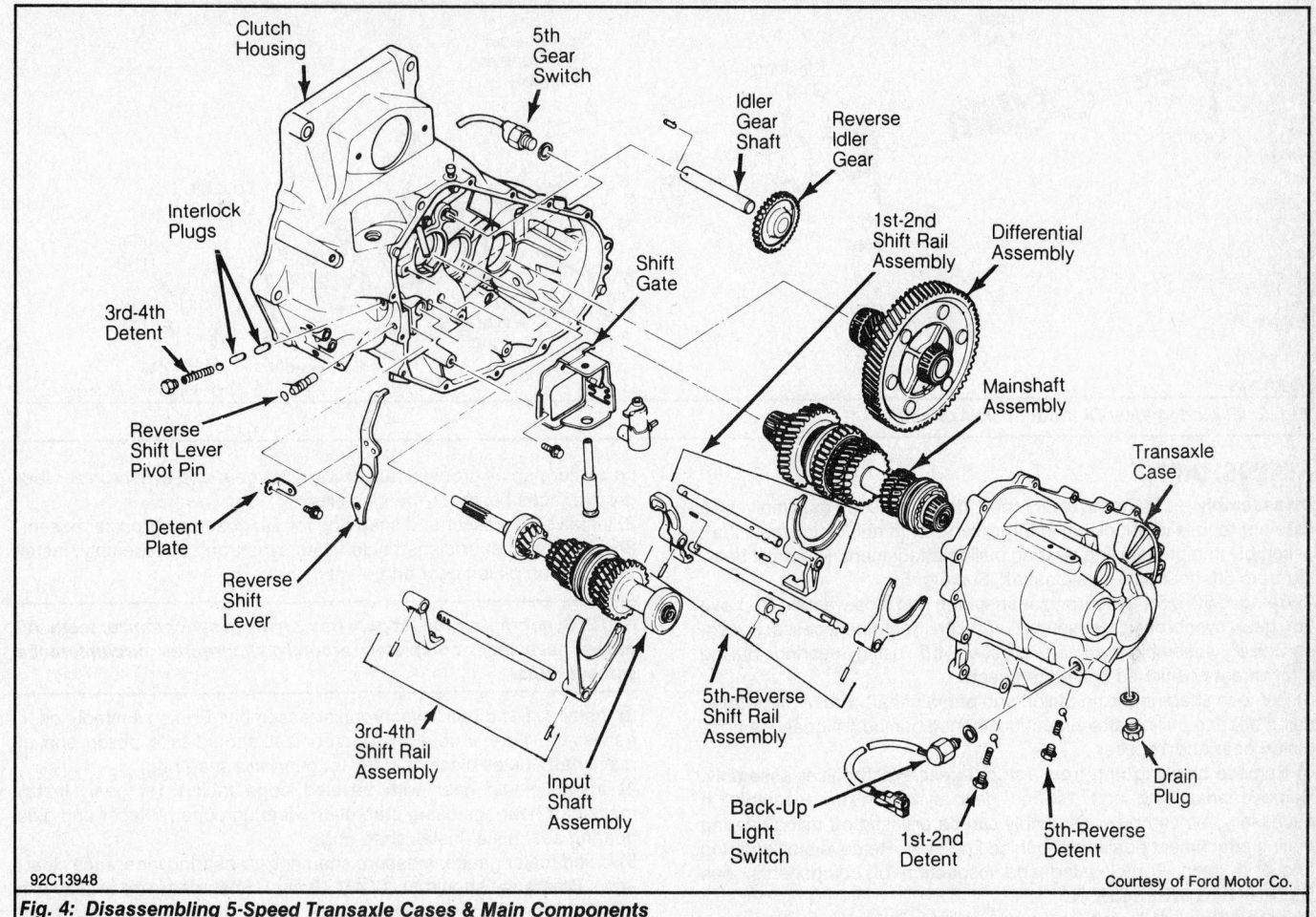

Fig. 4: Disassembling 5-Speed Transaxle Cases & Main Components

92C13948   Courtesy of Ford Motor Co.

3) Install oil channel into transaxle case and baffle plate into clutch housing. Install shift input shaft into case and selector arm. Face selector arm outward from case and install roll pin. Pull boot over input shift shaft seal. Ensure drain tube faces downward.

4) Install differential with speedometer gear facing toward clutch housing. Install shift gate assembly. Tighten shift gate frame bolts to specification. See TORQUE SPECIFICATIONS. Install speedometer driven gear assembly into clutch housing. Proceed to TRANSAXLE REASSEMBLY.

COMPONENT DISASSEMBLY & REASSEMBLY

DIFFERENTIAL ASSEMBLY

Disassembly – 1) Remove side gears and thrust washers from differential case by rotating gears toward case windows. Using punch, drive out differential pinion gear shaft retaining pin. Remove pinion shaft, pinion gears and thrust washers from case.

2) Using puller, remove differential roller bearings from differential case. On speedometer gear side, use bearing puller attachment to remove bearing. Alternately tighten puller nuts until puller is seated under bearing inner race. Remove speedometer drive gear from case.

Reassembly – To reassemble differential, reverse disassembly procedure. Using transmission fluid, lubricate all thrust washers and thrust surfaces on gears and in case. Install speedometer gear on case. Install differential bearings using bearing cone replacer and driver.

INPUT SHAFT

Disassembly – 1) Remove snap ring from 5th gear end of input shaft. See Fig. 5. Install input shaft assembly into press, using Bearing Pulling Attachment (D84L-1123-A). Press off bearing. Remove spacer, 5th gear and 4th gear.

2) Using magnet, remove locator ball. Remove blocking ring from 3rd-4th gear synchronizer assembly. Remove snap ring from 3rd-4th gear synchronizer assembly.

3) Remove 3rd-4th gear synchronizer assembly and blocking ring. If necessary synchronizer assembly can be pressed off using bearing pulling attachment positioned behind 3rd gear. Remove 3rd gear. Use bearing puller attachment to press off bearing from input end of shaft. For cleaning and inspection of components, see CLEANING & INSPECTION.

Reassembly – 1) Install 3rd gear. Install blocking ring and 3rd-4th gear synchronizer assembly. Press assembly on, if necessary. Ensure synchronizer hub oil grooves face toward 3rd gear.

2) Install snap ring for 3rd-4th gear synchronizer assembly. Install blocking ring. Install 4th and 5th gear. Install locator ball and spacer. Using an appropriate driver, install both input shaft bearings. Install snap ring on 5th gear end.

3) Using feeler gauge, measure snap ring-to-bearing inner race clearance. Clearance should be .004" (.10 mm). Snap rings are available in .004" (.10 mm) increments from .080-.100" (2.00-2.40 mm). Select and install appropriate size snap ring.

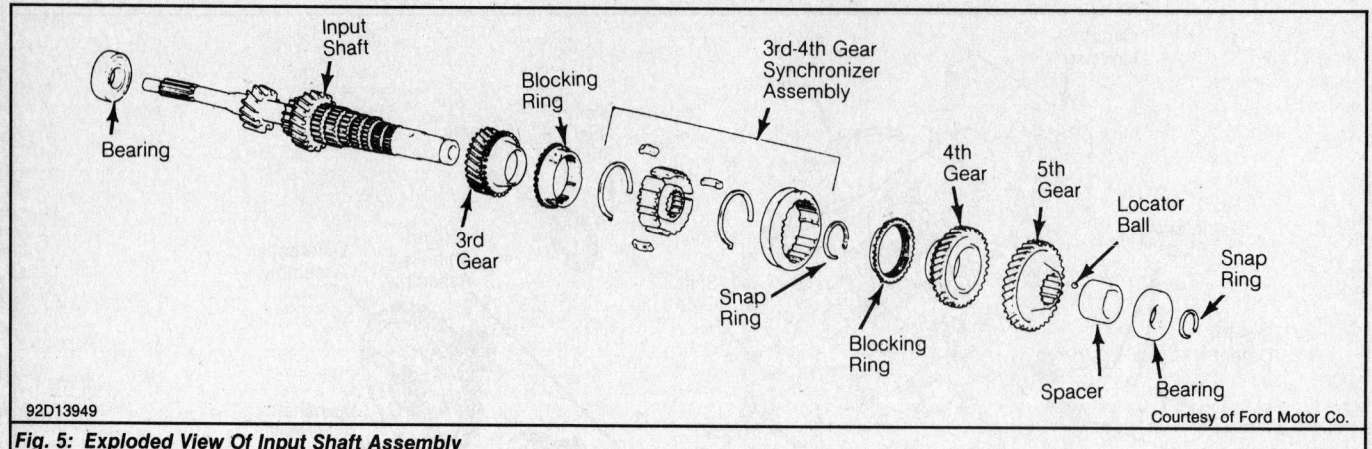

Fig. 5: Exploded View Of Input Shaft Assembly

MAINSHAFT

Disassembly – 1) Remove shift forks from mainshaft assembly. Use care not to lose interlock pin in 5th-reverse shift rail. Install mainshaft assembly into press using bearing pulling attachment. Press off bearing from 5th gear side of mainshaft. See Fig. 6.

2) Remove 5th gear synchronizer snap ring and stop washer. Remove 5th gear synchronizer assembly and 5th gear. If necessary, synchronizer assembly can be pressed off using bearing pulling attachment positioned behind 5th gear.

3) Remove snap ring from pinion end of mainshaft. Press off bearing using bearing pulling attachment positioned behind 1st gear. Remove pinion gear and 1st gear.

4) Remove blocking ring from 1st-2nd gear synchronizer assembly. Remove snap ring and 1st-2nd gear synchronizer assembly. If necessary, synchronizer assembly can be pressed off using bearing pulling attachment positioned behind 2nd gear. Remove blocking ring and 2nd gear. For cleaning and inspection of components, see CLEANING & INSPECTION.

Reassembly – 1) Install 5th gear. Install blocking ring and 5th gear synchronizer assembly. Press assembly on, if necessary. Ensure synchronizer hub oil grooves face toward 5th gear and synchronizer fork groove faces bearing (when installed).

2) Install stop washer and snap ring for 5th gear synchronizer assembly. Ensure washer dished side faces synchronizer assembly. Install 2nd gear on pinion gear end of mainshaft.

NOTE: Synchronizer for 1st gear has 3 gaps in synchronizer teeth. All others have teeth completely around synchronizer circumference without gaps.

3) Install 1st-2nd gear synchronizer assembly. Press assembly on, if necessary. Fork groove in synchronizer should face pinion end of mainshaft. Install blocking ring, 1st gear and snap ring.

4) Install pinion gear with beveled edge facing 1st gear. Install mainshaft bearings using step plate, bearing cone replacer and axle bearing seal plate. Install snap ring.

5) Using feeler gauge, measure snap ring-to-bearing inner race clearance. Clearance should be .004" (.10 mm). Snap rings are available in .004" (.10 mm) increments from .080-.100" (2.00-2.40 mm). Select and install appropriate size snap ring.

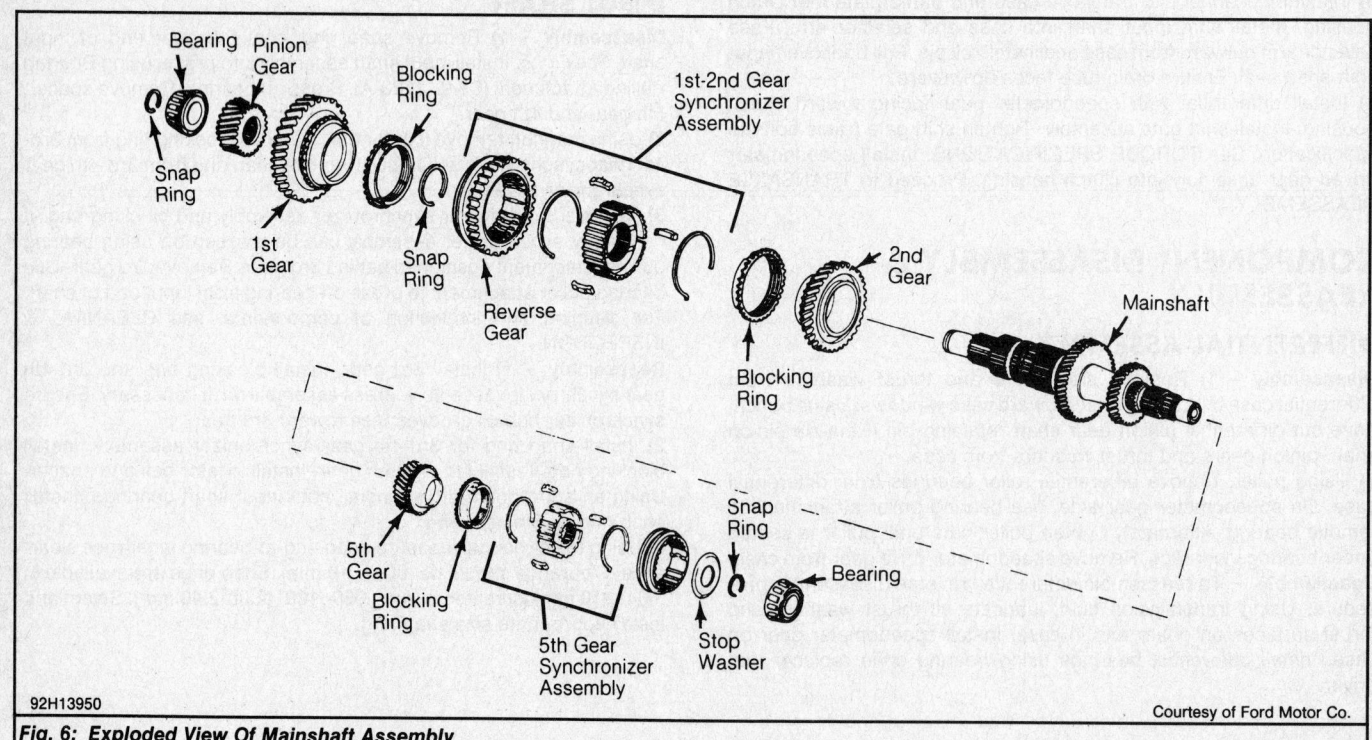

Fig. 6: Exploded View Of Mainshaft Assembly

SHIFT GATE

Disassembly & Reassembly – **1)** Remove "C" clip retaining selector lever pin. Remove selector lever pin and selector lever from gate frame. *See Fig. 4.*

2) To assemble, reverse disassembly procedure. Ensure return spring is properly positioned on reverse lockout pawl. Install selector lever pin and "C" clip.

SYNCHRONIZER ASSEMBLIES

NOTE: Before disassembling synchronizer, mark sleeve and hub with index marks for reassembly reference. Synchronizer components are matched at factory and should not be interchanged.

Disassembly – Note position of index marks. Slide hub and sleeve apart. Remove springs from hub with small screwdriver. DO NOT compress springs any more than necessary. Remove 3 hub inserts. Hub inserts are 2 different sizes. *See Fig. 7.* For cleaning and inspection of components, see CLEANING & INSPECTION.

Reassembly – **1)** Align index marks on synchronizer sleeve and hub. On 1st-2nd and 5th gear synchronizers, oil grooves inside hub must be installed facing away from shouldered side of sleeve. *See Fig. 8.* Synchronizer hub oil groove for 3rd-4th gear can face either way.

2) Install insert spring. Ensure each spring engages hole in hub and rotates away in opposite directions (clockwise and counterclockwise) from hole in hub. *See Fig. 9.*

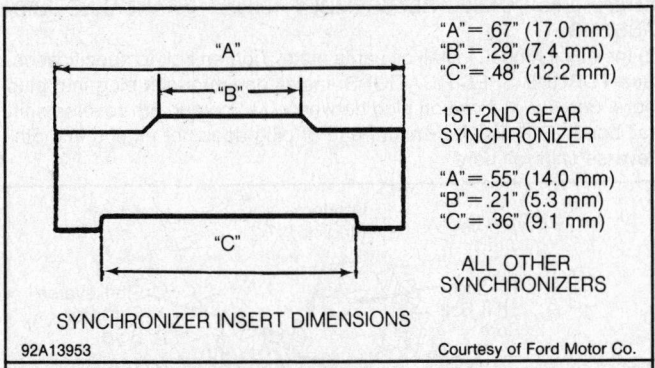

"A" = .67" (17.0 mm)
"B" = .29" (7.4 mm)
"C" = .48" (12.2 mm)

1ST-2ND GEAR SYNCHRONIZER

"A" = .55" (14.0 mm)
"B" = .21" (5.3 mm)
"C" = .36" (9.1 mm)

ALL OTHER SYNCHRONIZERS

SYNCHRONIZER INSERT DIMENSIONS

92A13953   Courtesy of Ford Motor Co.

Fig. 7: Identifying Synchronizer Inserts

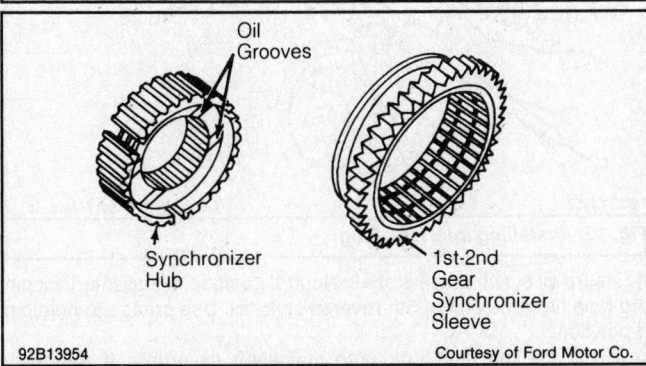

92B13954   Courtesy of Ford Motor Co.

*Fig. 8: Installing Synchronizer Hub into Sleeve
(1st-2nd Gear Synchronizer Shown; 5th Gear Is Similar)*

5TH GEAR SHIFT FORK RAIL

Disassembly & Reassembly – Slide 5th gear shift fork from rail. Remove roll pin from 5th-reverse relay arm. Remove arm from rail. To install, reverse disassembly procedure. Note direction of installation. *See Fig. 10.* Install 5th-reverse relay arm pin. Shift fork pin is installed during TRANSAXLE REASSEMBLY.

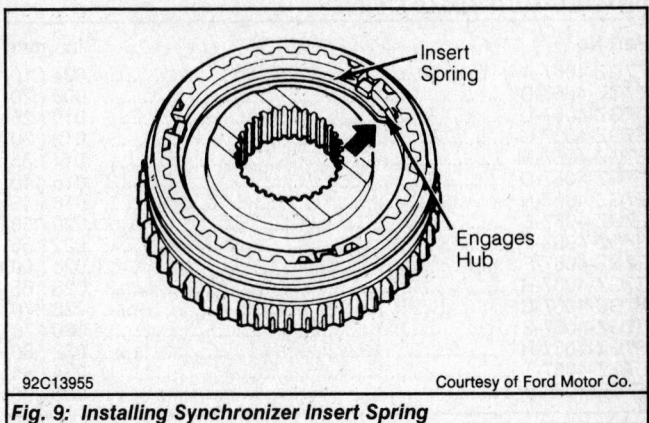

92C13955   Courtesy of Ford Motor Co.

Fig. 9: Installing Synchronizer Insert Spring

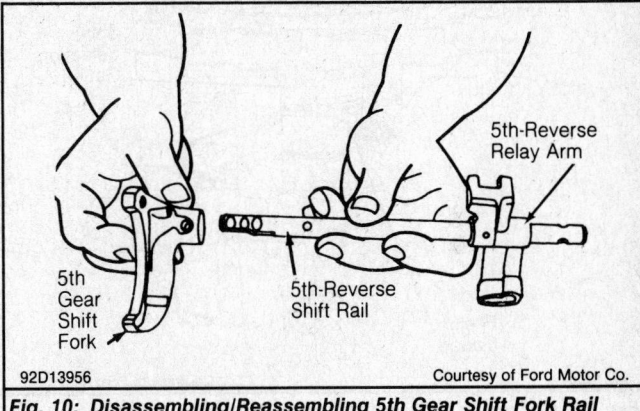

92D13956   Courtesy of Ford Motor Co.

Fig. 10: Disassembling/Reassembling 5th Gear Shift Fork Rail

ADJUSTMENTS

DIFFERENTIAL BEARING PRELOAD

1) Install differential front bearing outer race into clutch housing. Position differential assembly in clutch housing. Place rear bearing outer race on differential rear bearing cone.

2) Install Shim Selection Gauge, (T87C-77000-J) over rear bearing outer race. *See Fig. 11.* Place 11 collars from shim selection kit on clutch housing.

3) Turn gauge halves to eliminate any gap between them. Place transaxle case on collars. Install washers and retaining bolts supplied with shim selection kit. Tighten retaining bolts to 14-19 ft. lbs. (19-26 N.m).

4) Adjust gauge, using pins provided, until all free play is removed and bearing outer race is seated in case. Turn gauge halves back together until gap between gauge halves is eliminated.

5) Insert Differential Rotator (T88C-77000-L) through transaxle case and engage pinion shaft. Using a torque wrench on differential rotator, turn selector gauge halves apart until a reading of 4.4 INCH lbs. (.5 N.m) is obtained. Remove differential rotator. Using a feeler gauge, measure gap in shim selection gauge. *See Fig. 11.*

6) Take measurements at 90-degree intervals. Average measurement obtained is thickness of shim required to obtain specified differential bearing preload. Use no more than 2 shims. Refer to DIFFERENTIAL PRELOAD SHIMS table.

7) Separate transaxle case from clutch housing and remove measuring tools. Do not remove bearing outer races in clutch housing. Install selected shim(s) and bearing race. Assemble transaxle case and recheck preload. If preload is not 4.4-6.3 INCH lbs. (.5-.7 N.m), perform adjustment procedure again.

DIFFERENTIAL PRELOAD SHIMS

Part No.	In. (mm)
E7GZ-4067-A	.004 (.10)
E7GZ-4067-B	.008 (.20)
E7GZ-4067-L	.010 (.25)
E7GZ-4067-C	.012 (.30)
E7GZ-4067-M	.014 (.35)
E7GZ-4067-D	.016 (.40)
E7GZ-4067-N	.018 (.45)
E7GZ-4067-E	.020 (.50)
E7GZ-4067-P	.022 (.55)
E7GZ-4067-F	.024 (.60)
E7GZ-4067-R	.026 (.65)
E7GZ-4067-G	.028 (.70)
E7GZ-4067-S	.030 (.75)
E7GZ-4067-H	.032 (.80)
E7GZ-4067-T	.034 (.85)
E7GZ-4067-J	.036 (.90)

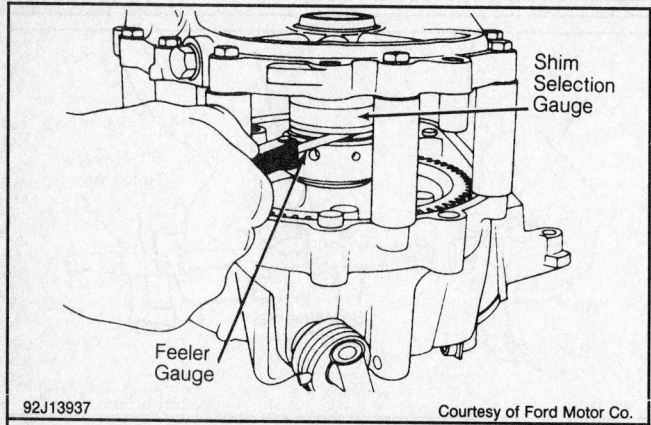

92J13937   Courtesy of Ford Motor Co.

Fig. 11: Measuring Differential Bearing Preload

INPUT SHAFT BEARING PRELOAD

1) Install input shaft bearing outer races (without shim) and oil funnel into clutch housing and transaxle case. Install assembled input shaft into clutch housing.

2) Place transaxle case on clutch housing and input shaft assembly. Install washers and bolts. Tighten transaxle case bolts to 14-19 ft. lbs. (19-26 N.m).

3) Tap end of input shaft lightly with a plastic-faced hammer to seat bearing race. Mount dial indicator to check end play of input shaft. Rotate shaft several times to ensure seating of bearings. Zero dial indicator at lowest point on end of input shaft. Lift shaft by hand, and read end play. Correct end play is .0002-.004" (.005-.10 mm).

4) Preload shims are available in thicknesses of .012" (.30 mm), .016" (.40 mm) and .020" (.50 mm). Select shim that is closest to or slightly smaller than dial indicator reading. Use no more than 2 shims.

5) Remove measuring tools. Separate transaxle case from clutch housing. DO NOT remove bearing outer race in clutch housing. Proceed to mainshaft preload procedure.

MAINSHAFT BEARING PRELOAD

1) Install input shaft bearing outer races (with shim) and oil funnel into clutch housing and transaxle case. Install input shaft. Install assembled mainshaft, bearing races (without shim) and oil funnel into clutch housing.

2) Shift 3rd-4th gear synchronizer into 4th gear position. Place transaxle case on clutch housing and shaft assemblies. Install washers and bolts. Tighten transaxle case bolts to 14-19 ft. lbs. (19-26 N.m).

3) Rotate shaft several times to ensure seating of bearings. Using Rotating Torque Adapter (T88C-7025-E) and torque wrench, turn input shaft. Install shim(s) as necessary to obtain a torque reading of .5 - 4.4 INCH lbs. (.06-.5 N.m). Use no more than 2 shims.

4) Install selected shim(s) and bearing race. If preloads have all been adjusted, assemble transaxle case, shafts and differential. See TRANSAXLE REASSEMBLY.

CLEANING & INSPECTION

1) DO NOT clean, wash or soak transaxle seals in cleaning solvent. Inspect transaxle case and clutch housing case for cracks, worn or damaged bearing bores or damaged threads. Inspect mating surfaces on cases for small nicks or burrs that could cause misalignment of case halves. Remove all small nicks or burrs with a fine stone or file.

2) Check reverse idler gear for chipped, broken or bent teeth. Check reverse idler gear for bushing damage. Check wear of reverse idler gear shaft.

3) Check teeth, splines and journals of mainshaft for damage. Check all other gears for chipped, broken or worn teeth. Check for eroded synchronizer teeth and damaged bearing surfaces. Synchronizer teeth will usually show rounding on points, which does not interfere with normal operation.

4) Check synchronizer sleeves for smooth and free movement on hubs. Check for damaged teeth. Check for proper positioning of springs.

5) Inspect synchronizer blocker rings for wear marks on back face, which indicates ring was bottoming on gear face due to excessive blocker ring wear.

TRANSAXLE REASSEMBLY

1) Perform bearing preload adjustments. See DIFFERENTIAL BEARING PRELOAD, MAINSHAFT BEARING PRELOAD and INPUT SHAFT BEARING PRELOAD under ADJUSTMENTS. Assemble case components. See CASE REASSEMBLY under TRANSAXLE DISASSEMBLY.

2) Install oil funnel. Install oil baffle plate. Tighten bolt to specification. See TORQUE SPECIFICATIONS. Install one interlock plug into plug bore. See Fig. 4. Position plug between 1st-2nd and 5th-reverse shift rail bores. See Fig. 12. Ensure end of plug does not extend into 5th-reverse shift rail bore.

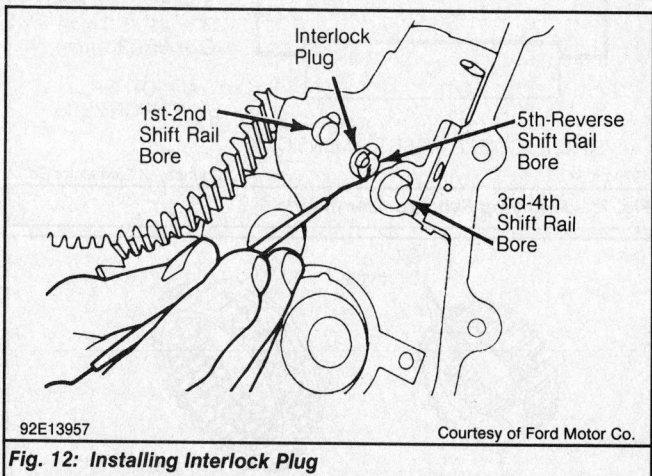

92E13957   Courtesy of Ford Motor Co.

Fig. 12: Installing Interlock Plug

3) Ensure all synchronizers are in Neutral position. Install interlock pin into hole near the end of 5th-reverse shift rail. Use grease to hold pin in position.

4) Install 1st-2nd shift fork onto mainshaft assembly. If removed, install 5th gear shift fork onto shift rail. Install 5th-reverse gear shift rail assembly onto mainshaft.

5) Mesh input shaft assembly and mainshaft assembly. Install as a unit. See Fig. 13. Use a small thin tool to push interlock plug back into it's bore while slightly raising and lowering 5th-reverse shift rail. The 5th-reverse shift rail is properly positioned when interlock plug no longer extends into 1st-2nd shift rail bore.

6) Install 1st-2nd shift rail through shift fork and into shift rail bore. Detents in shift rail should face away from mainshaft. If 1st-2nd shift rail won't enter bore, slightly lift and lower 5th-reverse shift rail while pushing down on 1st-2nd shift rail.

7) Install 3rd-4th shift fork and shift rail. Detents in 3rd-4th shift rail should be facing directly away from 5th-reverse shift shaft. Hold 3rd-

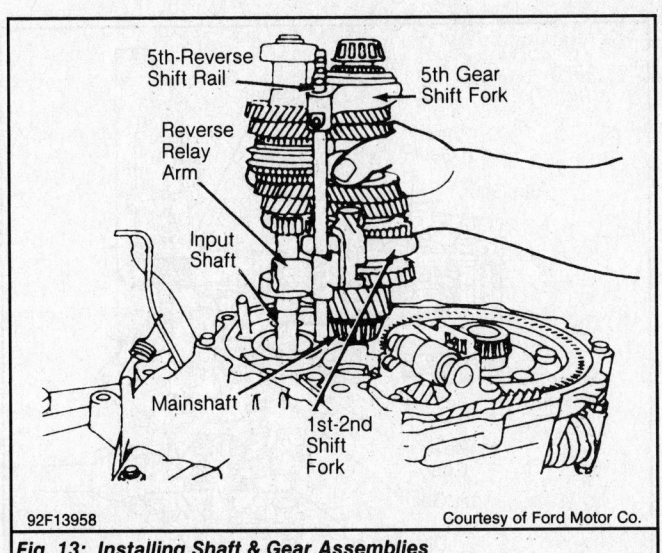

5th-Reverse Shift Rail

5th Gear Shift Fork

Reverse Relay Arm

Input Shaft

Mainshaft

1st-2nd Shift Fork

92F13958   Courtesy of Ford Motor Co.

Fig. 13: Installing Shaft & Gear Assemblies

4th relay arm in position while installing shift rail.

8) Rest 3rd-4th gear shift rail on mating surface of clutch housing while slightly lifting and lowering 5th-reverse shift rail and pushing interlock plug back into its bore. The 5th-reverse shift rail is properly positioned when plug no longer extends into 3rd-4th shift rail bore. Pivot 3rd-4th shift rail into position and install in shift rail bore.

9) Install roll pins into shift forks, relay arm and shift rail ends. All shift fork and 3rd-4th shift rail end roll pins are .87" (22 mm) in length. Roll pin for 5th-reverse shift rail end is .79" (20.0 mm) in length. Both roll pin types are .20" (5.0 mm) diameter.

10) Install NEW "O" ring on reverse relay lever pivot pin and install through case and reverse relay lever. Install retaining pin into reverse lever pivot. Install reverse idler gear onto idler gear shaft so that idler gear sleeve faces roll pin hole in idler gear shaft.

11) Raise reverse shift lever and install reverse idler gear and shaft assembly. Install detent plate under reverse shift lever. Tighten bolt to specification. See TORQUE SPECIFICATIONS.

12) Install case magnet. Apply 1/16" (1.5 mm) bead of gasket eliminator on clutch housing mating surface. Ensure sealer encircles clutch housing bolt holes. Install transaxle case onto clutch housing. Tighten bolts to specification.

13) Install detent springs and balls. Detent springs for transaxle case are .89" (22.6 mm) in length. Detent spring for clutch housing is 1.31" (33.3 mm) in length. Both springs are .28" (7.1 mm) diameter.

14) Coat threads with pipe sealant and install detent plugs and back-up light switch. Install transaxle mount onto case. Tighten components to specification. See TORQUE SPECIFICATIONS. Ensure input shift shaft bushings are installed. Shift transaxle through all gears to ensure operation.

TORQUE SPECIFICATIONS
TORQUE SPECIFICATIONS

Application	Ft. Lbs. (N.m)
Back-Up Light Switch	[1] 15-22 (20-30)
Detent Plugs	[1] 11-15 (15-20)
Preload Checking Tool Bolt	14-19 (19-26)
Transaxle Case Bolt	14-19 (19-26)
Transaxle-To-Engine Bolt	47-66 (64-89)
Transaxle Mount Bolt	14-19 (19-26)
	INCH Lbs. (N.m)
Baffle Plate Bolt	72-96 (8-11)
Detent Plate Bolt	72-96 (8-11)
Shift Gate Frame Bolt	72-96 (8-11)

[1] – Apply pipe sealer to threads prior to installation.

MANUAL TRANSMISSIONS
Ford (Mazda) "F" & "G" 5-Speed

APPLICATION

TRANSAXLE APPLICATIONS

Application	Transaxle
Capri	
Non-Turbo	Type "F"
Turbo	Type "G"
Escort & Tracer	
1.8L	Type "G"
1.9L	Type "F"
Probe	
2.0L & 2.5L	Type "G"

IDENTIFICATION

Ford vehicles have a vehicle certification label, located on driver's door lock pillar. Transaxle code on label for Capri, Escort and Tracer is the letter "W". Code for Probe is No. 445.

DESCRIPTION

Transaxle and differential assembly are located in an aluminum alloy housing. All forward gears are helical cut for quiet operation and synchronized for ease in shifting.

Engine power is transferred from clutch disc to input shaft. Input shaft gears are in constant mesh with corresponding mainshaft gears. Power is transmitted from selected gear on input shaft to matching mainshaft gear. Power is then transmitted through mainshaft to pinion gear, through differential assembly to axle shafts and wheels. See Figs. 1 and 2.

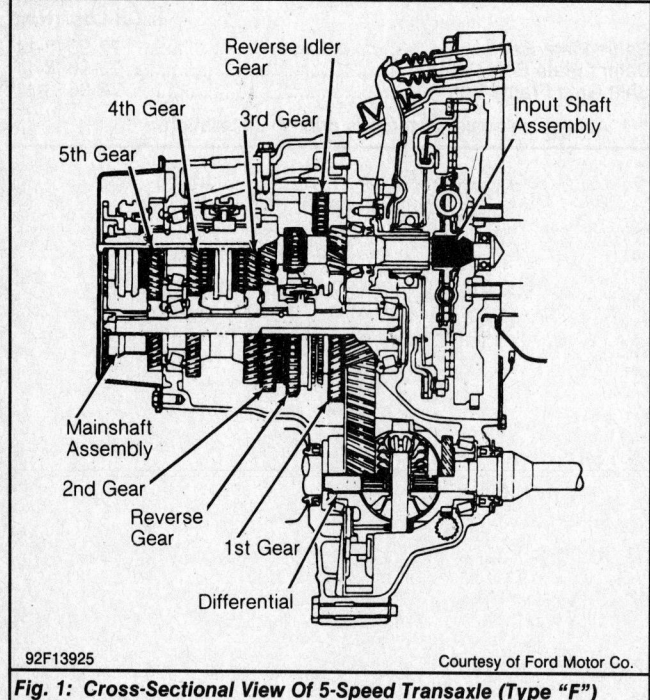

92F13925   Courtesy of Ford Motor Co.

Fig. 1: Cross-Sectional View Of 5-Speed Transaxle (Type "F")

LUBRICATION & ADJUSTMENTS

See appropriate MANUAL TRANSMISSION SERVICING article in TRANSMISSION SERVICING.

TROUBLE SHOOTING

See GENERAL TROUBLE SHOOTING article in MANUAL TRANSMISSIONS.

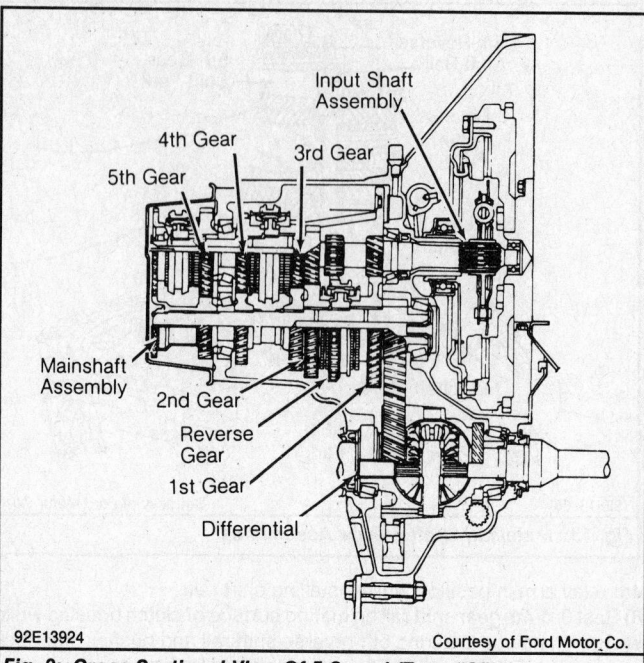

92E13924   Courtesy of Ford Motor Co.

Fig. 2: Cross-Sectional View Of 5-Speed (Type "G")

ON-VEHICLE SERVICE

DIFFERENTIAL OIL SEALS

NOTE: If both axle shafts are removed from transaxle, differential plugs should be installed in differential side gears to prevent misalignment. If side gears become misaligned, differential will have to be removed to realign gears.

Removal (Capri) – 1) Remove front wheels and splash shields. Drain transaxle fluid. Remove stabilizer link. Remove bolts and nuts from lower control arm ball joints. Pull lower control arms down to separate from steering knuckles.
2) Pull outward on steering knuckle and brake assembly to separate halfshaft from transaxle. If necessary, insert pry bar between shaft and case. Remove halfshafts and support with wire. Remove differential oil seals with flat-tip screwdriver.

NOTE: Manufacturer recommends removal of halfshaft from vehicle on Escort and Tracer.

Removal (Escort & Tracer) – 1) Remove front wheels and splash shields. Drain transaxle fluid. Unstake and remove nut from outer end of halfshaft. Remove tie-rod cotter pins and nuts. Disconnect tie-rod ends.
2) Remove bolts from lower control arm ball joints. Pull lower control arms down to separate from steering knuckles. Pull outward on steering knuckle and brake assembly to separate from halfshaft.
3) If left side halfshaft is being removed, support transaxle with transmission jack and remove crossmember. For both right and left sides, insert pry bar between shaft and case. Remove halfshafts. Remove differential oil seals with flat-tip screwdriver.
Removal (Probe) – 1) Remove front wheels and splash shields. Drain transaxle fluid. Remove tie-rod cotter pins and nuts. Disconnect tie-rod ends.
2) Remove stabilizer link. Remove retaining bolts and nuts from lower control arm ball joints. Pull lower control arms down to separate from steering knuckles.
3) Remove right side bearing support (if necessary). Insert pry bar between shaft and case. Remove halfshafts and support with wire. Remove differential oil seals with flat-tip screwdriver.

Installation (All Models) – **1)** Using appropriate seal installer, tap in NEW seals. Install NEW circlip on halfshafts. Install halfshafts with circlip gap at 12 o'clock position. A snap should be felt as circlip seats in differential side gears. To complete installation, reverse removal procedure. Install NEW halfshaft outer end nut on Escort and Tracer models.

2) To install stabilizer link assemblies on Capri, turn nuts on link assemblies until 7/16" (11.1 mm) of bolt thread is exposed. On all models, tighten nuts and bolts to specification. See TORQUE SPECIFICATIONS. Add specified fluid and check for leaks.

GEAR SHIFT LINKAGE

Removal (Capri) – **1)** Remove gearshift knob and boot from center console. See Fig. 3. Remove center console. Remove bolt, nut and washer from shift control rod at gearshift lever.

2) Use screwdriver to pry out spring retaining gearshift lever. Remove spring and mounting boot from gearshift lever. Pull gearshift up and remove. From under vehicle, remove shift control rod bolts, nuts and washers.

3) Remove upper ball seat from gearshift lever. Remove boot, lower ball seat and retainer from gearshift lever. From inside vehicle, remove housing assembly nuts. From under vehicle, remove nut, washers, bushing and spacer from extension bar. Remove extension bar and housing assembly from vehicle.

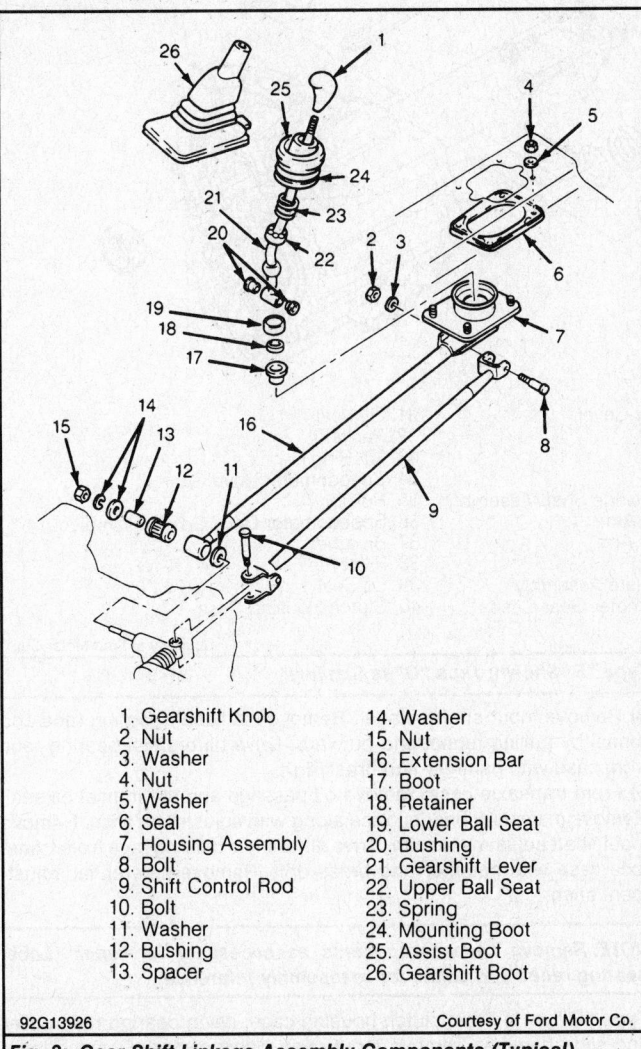

1. Gearshift Knob
2. Nut
3. Washer
4. Nut
5. Washer
6. Seal
7. Housing Assembly
8. Bolt
9. Shift Control Rod
10. Bolt
11. Washer
12. Bushing
13. Spacer
14. Washer
15. Nut
16. Extension Bar
17. Boot
18. Retainer
19. Lower Ball Seat
20. Bushing
21. Gearshift Lever
22. Upper Ball Seat
23. Spring
24. Mounting Boot
25. Assist Boot
26. Gearshift Boot

92G13926   Courtesy of Ford Motor Co.

Fig. 3: Gear Shift Linkage Assembly Components (Typical)

Removal (Escort & Tracer) – **1)** From under vehicle, remove gearshift lever-to-control rod bolt, nut and washer. See Fig. 3. From inside vehicle, remove gearshift knob. Remove center console. Remove shift lever boot from center console.

2) Remove gasket and using a screwdriver, pry out spring retaining upper ball seat. Remove shift lever and ball seats. Remove nuts and washers from housing assembly.

3) Remove nut, washers, bushing and spacer from extension bar. Remove extension bar. Remove housing assembly. Remove shift control rod bolt and nut. Remove shift control rod.

Removal (Probe) – **1)** Remove gearshift knob and boot from center console. See Fig. 3. Remove center console, assist boot and mounting boot.

2) From under vehicle, remove shift control rod shield, bolts, nut and washer. Lift out control rod. From inside vehicle, remove insulation covering housing assembly. Remove control housing nuts. Using a screwdriver, pry out spring retaining upper ball seat.

3) Remove upper ball seat. Pull gearshift up and remove. Remove bushings, boot, lower ball seat and retainer from gearshift lever. Remove nut, washers, bushing and spacer from extension bar. Remove extension bar.

Installation (All Models) – Apply lithium grease to change lever ball, ball seats and to all moveable joints. To install, reverse removal procedure. Ensure spring is properly seated in bracket groove. Tighten bolts/nuts to specification. See TORQUE SPECIFICATIONS.

REMOVAL & INSTALLATION

See appropriate MANUAL TRANSMISSION REMOVAL article in TRANSMISSION SERVICING.

TRANSAXLE DISASSEMBLY

NOTE: During disassembly, all gaskets must be removed and discarded. Thoroughly clean all traces of gasket material from mating surfaces of transaxle case.

TRANSAXLE

1) Remove drain plug from transaxle case and drain transaxle fluid. Position transaxle with rear cover facing upward. Remove rear cover bolts. Loosen rear cover gasket seal with a plastic mallet and remove rear cover. See Figs. 4 and 5.

2) Shift to 1st gear. Use Torque Adapter (T87C-7025-A) to lock-up input shaft. Uncrimp tabs and remove mainshaft lock nut, input shaft lock nut and sleeve.

3) Remove input reverse synchronizer gear and mainshaft reverse synchronizer gear. Using punch, remove shift fork roll pin. Remove shift fork, synchronizer ring and clutch hub. Remove synchronizer ring and input 5th gear.

4) Remove gear sleeve. Using a magnet, remove ball from input shaft. Remove mainshaft 5th gear. Remove lock bolts, washers, guide bolt, springs and balls. See Figs. 4 and 5. Remove back-up light switch. Remove transaxle case bolts. Tap transaxle case lightly with a plastic hammer to loosen gasket seal and remove case.

5) Remove magnet from case. Remove reverse idler shaft and gear. On Type "F", remove roll pin from crank lever shaft and remove crank lever shaft and assembly. Remove 5th gear shift rod end. Insert pin punch through 5th gear shift rod end, and remove 5th gear shift rod.

6) On Type "G", remove lock bolt from 5th gear shift rod gate. Remove clip and shift rod (5th and reverse). Remove gate. Remove crank lever shaft pin. Remove crank lever shaft and assembly.

7) On both transaxles, align ends of interlock sleeve and control lever on shift rod shaft. Turn shift rod counterclockwise. On Type "F", remove breather cover and gasket. Remove input shaft and mainshaft assemblies.

8) On Type "G", raise both shift forks and shift clutch hub sleeves. Lift shaft control end and remove steel ball. Remove shift fork and shift rod assembly. On both transaxles, remove input shaft and mainshaft assemblies. Remove differential and neutral switch.

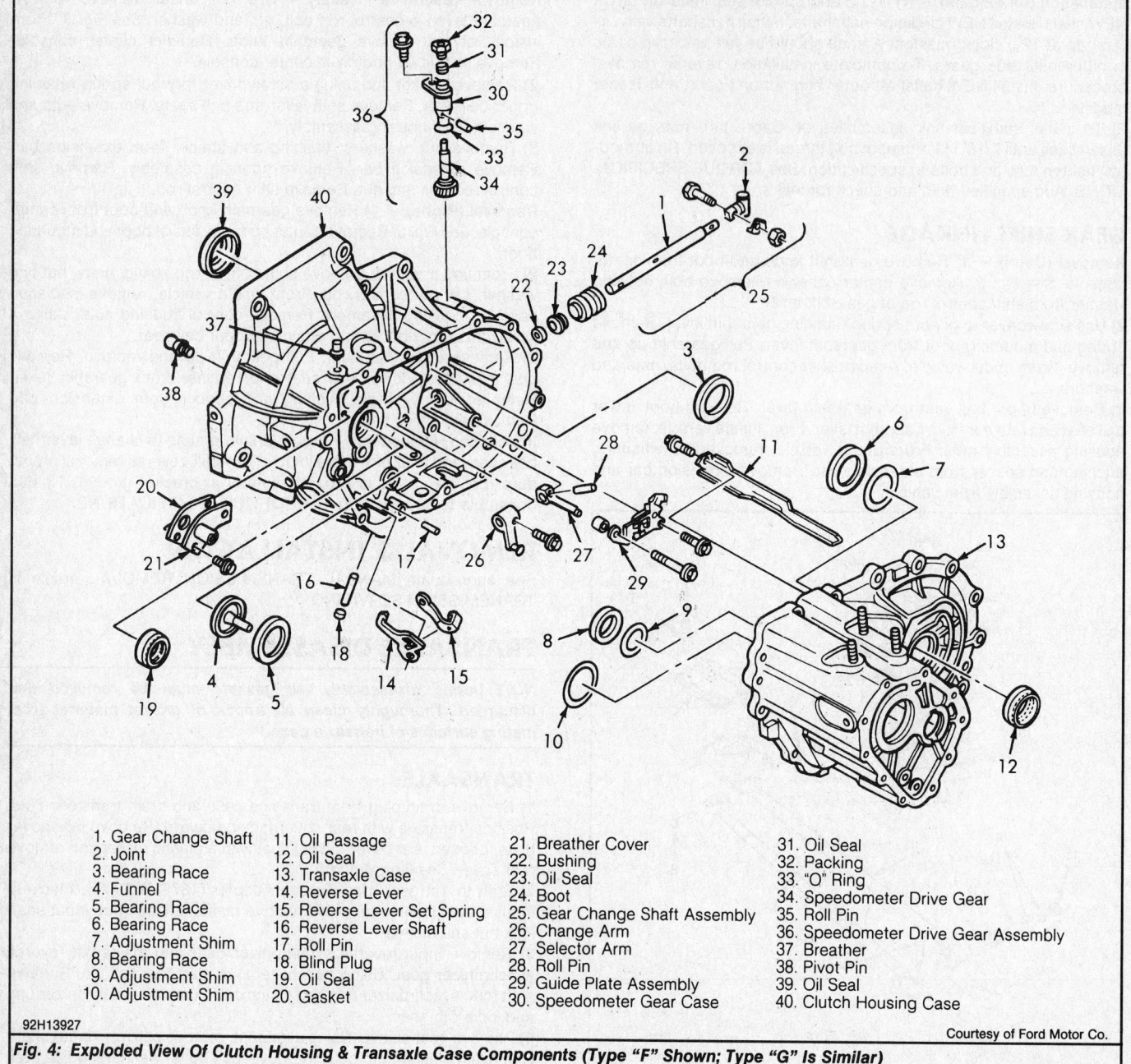

1. Gear Change Shaft
2. Joint
3. Bearing Race
4. Funnel
5. Bearing Race
6. Bearing Race
7. Adjustment Shim
8. Bearing Race
9. Adjustment Shim
10. Adjustment Shim
11. Oil Passage
12. Oil Seal
13. Transaxle Case
14. Reverse Lever
15. Reverse Lever Set Spring
16. Reverse Lever Shaft
17. Roll Pin
18. Blind Plug
19. Oil Seal
20. Gasket
21. Breather Cover
22. Bushing
23. Oil Seal
24. Boot
25. Gear Change Shaft Assembly
26. Change Arm
27. Selector Arm
28. Roll Pin
29. Guide Plate Assembly
30. Speedometer Gear Case
31. Oil Seal
32. Packing
33. "O" Ring
34. Speedometer Drive Gear
35. Roll Pin
36. Speedometer Drive Gear Assembly
37. Breather
38. Pivot Pin
39. Oil Seal
40. Clutch Housing Case

92H13927

Courtesy of Ford Motor Co.

Fig. 4: Exploded View Of Clutch Housing & Transaxle Case Components (Type "F" Shown; Type "G" Is Similar)

CASE

NOTE: Remove case components as necessary for repair. Label bearing races and shims for reassembly reference.

Type "F" – 1) From clutch housing, remove blind plug and reverse lever shaft. *See Fig. 4.* Remove reverse lever set spring and reverse lever. Remove speedometer driven gear assembly. Remove differential seal, breather assembly and clutch arm pivot stud.

2) To disassemble case-mounted gear change assembly, remove 2 bolts, guide plate (with cut-outs) and spacer. Drive roll pin from selector mounted on gear change shaft.

3) Remove bolt from change arm mounted on end of gear change shaft. Remove gear change shaft, boot, selector and change arm from case. If necessary for repair, remove gear change shaft oil seal and bushing. *See Fig. 4.*

4) Remove input shaft oil seal. Remove mainshaft bearing race and funnel by pulling funnel end outward. Drive differential bearing race from case with hammer and brass drift.

5) From transaxle case, remove oil passage and differential oil seal. Remove mainshaft bearing race along with adjustment shim. Remove input shaft adjustment shim. Drive differential bearing race from transaxle case with hammer and brass drift. Remove differential adjustment shim.

NOTE: Remove case components as necessary for repair. Label bearing races and shims for reassembly reference.

Type "G" – 1) From clutch housing case, using bearing race puller and slide hammer, remove input shaft bearing race. Remove input shaft oil seal. Remove mainshaft bearing race and funnel by pulling funnel end outward.

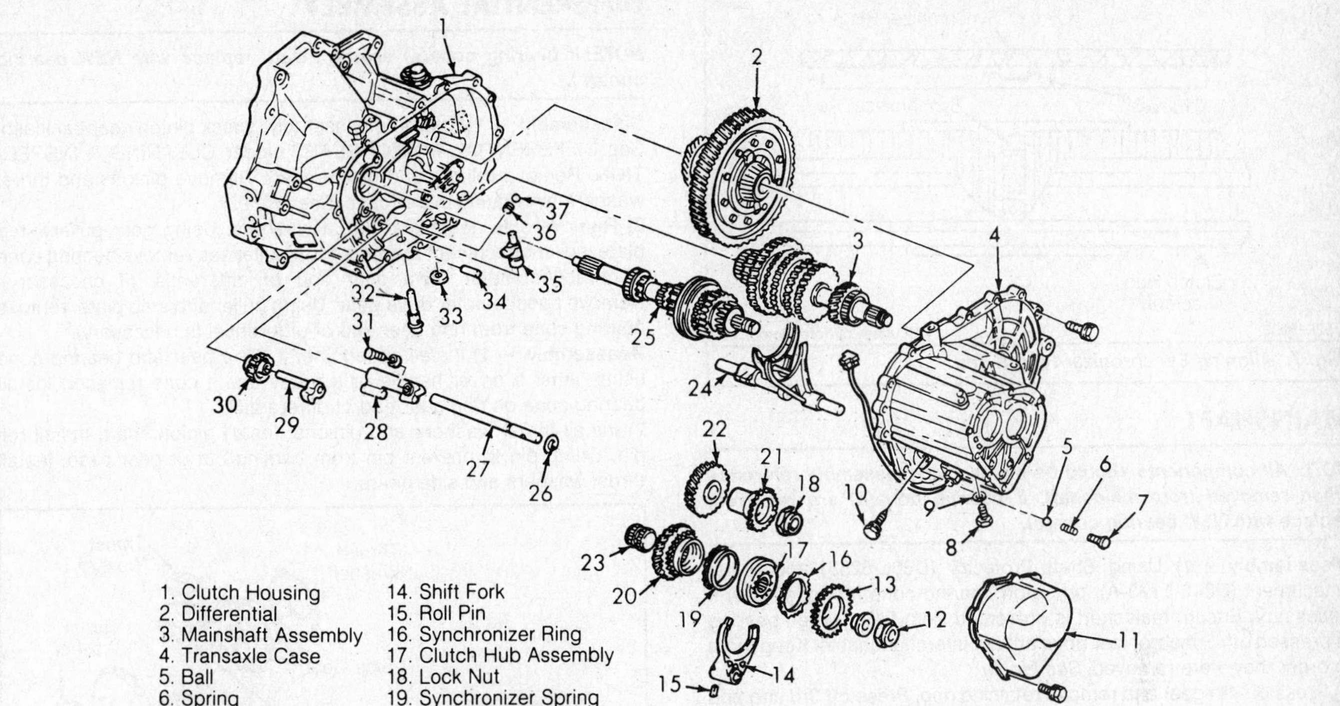

1. Clutch Housing
2. Differential
3. Mainshaft Assembly
4. Transaxle Case
5. Ball
6. Spring
7. Lock Bolt
8. Guide Bolt
9. Washer
10. Lock Bolt
11. Rear Cover
12. Lock Nut
13. Input Reverse Synchronizer Gear
14. Shift Fork
15. Roll Pin
16. Synchronizer Ring
17. Clutch Hub Assembly
18. Lock Nut
19. Synchronizer Spring
20. Input 5th Gear
21. Mainshaft Reverse Synchronizer Gear
22. Mainshaft 5th Gear
23. Gear Sleeve
24. Shift Fork and Shift Rod Assembly
25. Input Shaft Assembly
26. Clip
27. Shift Rod (5th & Reverse)
28. Gate
29. Reverse Idler Shaft
30. Reverse Idler Gear
31. Lock Bolt
32. Crank Lever Shaft
33. Magnet
34. Pin
35. Crank Lever Assembly
36. Spring
37. Ball

92J13929

Courtesy of Ford Motor Co.

Fig. 5: Exploded View Of Transaxle (Type "G" Shown; Type "F" Is Similar)

2) To disassemble case-mounted gear change assembly, remove 3 bolts, guide plate (with cut-outs) and spacer. Align selector retaining pin with groove in clutch housing case. Drive pin from selector.

3) Remove bolt from change arm mounted at end of gear change shaft. Remove gear change shaft, boot and change arm from case. Remove spring, reverse gate and selector from case.

4) Using Collet (D80L-100-Q), actuator pin and slide hammer, remove gear change shaft oil seal. Remove breather cover, turn breather and remove from case. *See Fig. 5.* Remove speedometer drive gear assembly (analog cluster) or vehicle speed sensor (digital cluster) from case.

5) If not removed previously, remove reverse lever shaft. Remove reverse lever set spring and lever. Using bearing remover, puller and slide hammer, remove differential bearing races from both cases. Remove adjustment shim.

6) Using bearing race puller and slide hammer, remove transaxle case input shaft and mainshaft bearing races. Remove diaphragm springs and adjustment shims. Using bearing race puller and slide hammer, remove differential oil seals.

COMPONENT DISASSEMBLY & REASSEMBLY

INPUT SHAFT

NOTE: All components should be marked for reassembly reference when removed from input shaft. If bearing cone(s) are removed, replace with NEW bearing cone(s).

Disassembly – 1) Using Shaft Protector (D80L-625-3 for Type "F" or D80L-625-4 for Type "G") and Puller Attachment (D84L-1123-A), press off bearing cone (if necessary). Ensure input shaft is prevented from falling when bearing is removed.

2) Remove 4th gear, synchronizer ring and retaining ring. *See Fig. 6.* Using shaft protector and bearing puller attachment, press off clutch hub, synchronizer ring and 3rd gear.

3) Press off bearing cone (3rd gear end) if necessary. Remove synchronizer springs and keys from clutch hub. Remove clutch hub from sleeve. For component cleaning and inspection, see INPUT SHAFT under CLEANING & INSPECTION.

Reassembly – 1) Lubricate bearing bore and press on bearing cone (3rd gear end). Slide clutch hub into sleeve. Install synchronizer keys and springs. When installing synchronizer ring and clutch hub, align synchronizer ring groove and key. *See Fig. 7.*

2) Ensure ridge and oil grooves are facing 3rd gear when installing clutch hub. *See Fig. 6.* Using shaft protector, bearing plate and cone replacer, press on 3rd gear, synchronizer ring and clutch hub. Install retaining ring. Using shaft protector, bearing plate and cone replacer, press on synchronizer ring, 4th gear and bearing cone.

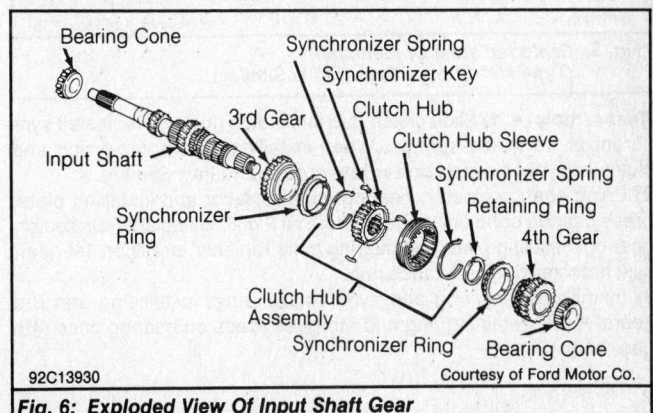

92C13930

Courtesy of Ford Motor Co.

Fig. 6: Exploded View Of Input Shaft Gear

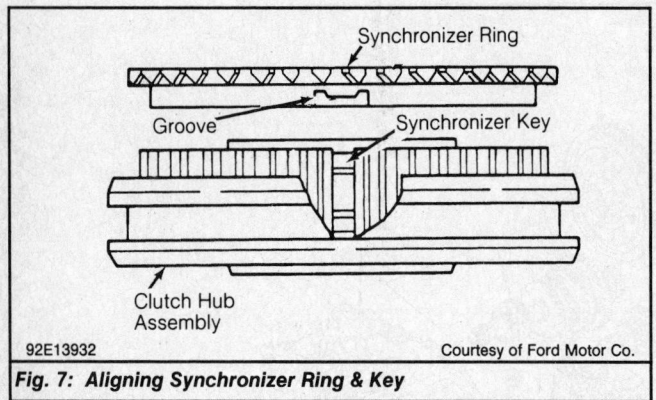

Fig. 7: Aligning Synchronizer Ring & Key

MAINSHAFT

NOTE: All components should be marked for reassembly reference when removed from mainshaft. If bearing cone(s) are removed, replace with NEW bearing cone(s).

Disassembly – 1) Using Shaft Protector (D80L-6253) and Puller Attachment (D84L-1123-A), press off bearing cone (4th gear end) if necessary. Ensure mainshaft is prevented from falling when bearing is pressed off. Synchronizer rings are not interchangeable. Keep them in order they were removed. See Fig. 8.

2) Press off 4th gear and remove retaining ring. Press off 3rd and 2nd gears. Remove synchronizer ring and retaining ring. See Fig. 8. Using shaft protector and seal plate, remove clutch hub, synchronizer ring and 1st gear.

3) Press off bearing cone (1st gear end) if necessary. Remove synchronizer springs and keys from clutch hub. Remove clutch hub from sleeve. For component cleaning and inspection, see MAINSHAFT under CLEANING & INSPECTION.

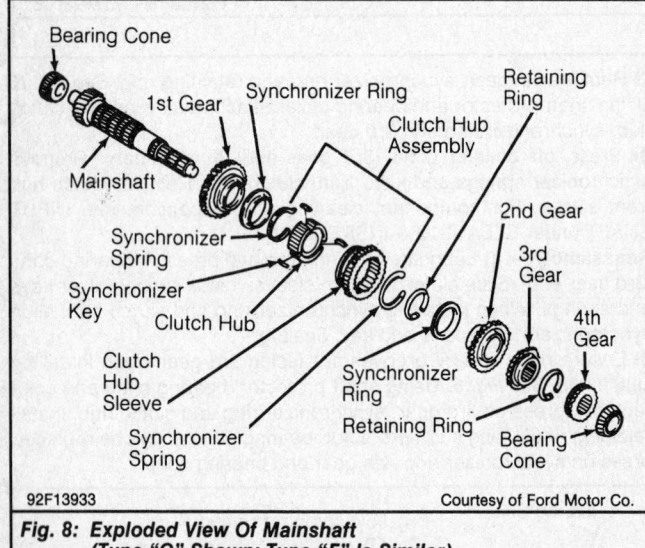

Fig. 8: Exploded View Of Mainshaft (Type "G" Shown; Type "F" Is Similar)

Reassembly – 1) Slide clutch hub into clutch hub sleeve. Install synchronizer keys and springs. When installing synchronizer ring and clutch hub, align synchronizer ring groove and key. See Fig. 7.

2) Using shaft protector, bearing cone replacer and installing plate, press bearing cone on 1st gear end. See Fig. 8. Using shaft protector, bearing installing plate and bearing cone replacer, press on 1st gear, synchronizer ring and clutch hub.

3) Install retaining ring and synchronizer ring. Install 2nd and 3rd gears. Install retaining ring and 4th gear. Press on bearing cone (4th gear end).

DIFFERENTIAL ASSEMBLY

NOTE: If bearing cone(s) are removed, replace with NEW bearing cone(s).

Disassembly – 1) Prior to disassembly, check pinion gear backlash. See DIFFERENTIAL PINION GEARS under CLEANING & INSPECTION. Remove roll pin and pinion shaft. Remove pinions and thrust washers by rotating out of case. See Fig. 9.

2) Remove side gears and thrust washers. Using gear puller, step plate, puller attachment and legs from puller set, remove bearing cone from speedometer drive gear end of differential (if necessary). Remove speedometer drive gear. Using puller and step plate, remove bearing cone from ring gear end of differential (if necessary).

Reassembly – 1) Install speedometer drive gear and bearing cone using either a driver handle or a press and a cone replacer. Install bearing cone on ring gear end of differential.

2) Install thrust washers and pinions. Install pinion shaft. Install roll pin. Crimp pin to prevent pin from coming out of gear case. Install thrust washers and side gears.

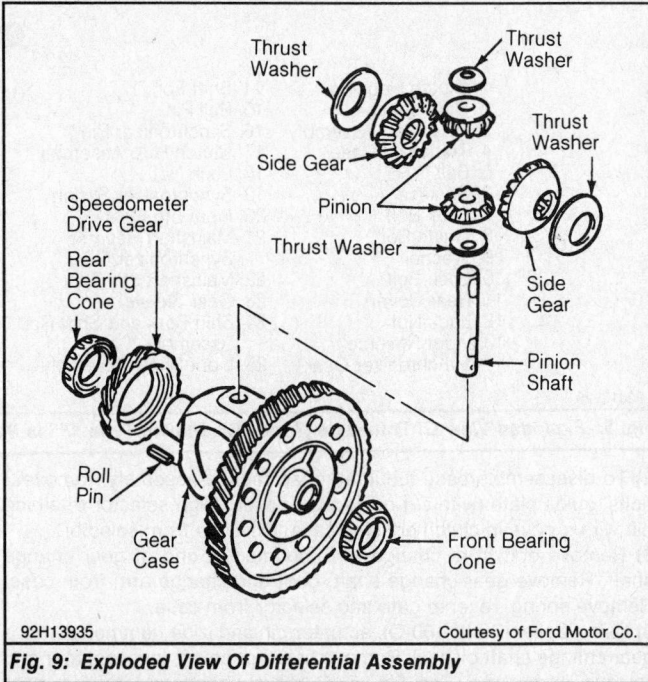

Fig. 9: Exploded View Of Differential Assembly

MAINSHAFT & INPUT SHAFT BEARING PRELOAD

NOTE: Whenever transaxle is disassembled, bearing preload must be adjusted. Adjustment is made by selecting shims to insert between rear bearing outer races and transaxle case.

TYPE "F"

Input Shaft – 1) Install input shaft bearing outer races into clutch housing and transaxle case. Install assembled input shaft into clutch housing. Place transaxle case on clutch housing and input shaft assembly. Install washers and bolts. Tighten transaxle case bolts to 14-19 ft. lbs. (19-26 N.m).

2) Mount dial indicator to check end play of input shaft. Rotate shaft several times to ensure seating of bearings. Zero dial indicator at lowest point on end of input shaft. Lift shaft equally on both sides by hand, and read end play.

3) Preload shims for input shaft are available in thicknesses of .004-.024" (.10-.61 mm) in .004" (.10 mm) increments. Select shim that is closest to or slightly smaller than dial indicator reading. Final input shaft end play should be .0002-.0039" (.005-.100 mm).

4) Remove measuring tools. Separate transaxle case from clutch housing. DO NOT remove bearing outer race in clutch housing. Proceed to mainshaft preload procedure.

Mainshaft – 1) Install funnel and mainshaft outer bearing race in clutch housing. Install assembled mainshaft into clutch housing. Install rear mainshaft bearing outer race into transaxle case. Place transaxle case on clutch housing. Install transaxle bolts. Tighten to 14-19 ft. lbs. (19-26 N.m).

2) Mount a dial indicator to check end play of shaft. Rotate shaft several times to ensure seating of bearings. Zero dial indicator at lowest point on end of mainshaft. Lift shaft equally on both sides by hand, and read end play.

3) Add .0012" (.030 mm) to end play reading obtained in step **2)**, to establish minimum clearance. Add .0031" (.080 mm) to end play reading obtained in step **2)**, to establish maximum clearance.

4) Preload shims for mainshaft are available in thicknesses of .006-.028" (.15-.70 mm) in .002" (.05 mm) increments. Select a shim thickness that when added to the end play reading in step **2)** will be more than the minimum dimension obtained in step **3)** and closest to the maximum dimension obtained in step **3)**.

5) Remove measuring tools. Separate transaxle case from clutch housing. DO NOT remove bearing outer races in clutch housing. Proceed to DIFFERENTIAL BEARING PRELOAD.

TYPE "G"

Input & Mainshaft – 1) Starting with input shaft, install assembled shaft into clutch housing. Place rear bearing outer race on shaft bearing cone. Position Shim Selection Gauge (T88C-77000-CH3) on top of shaft. Place 6 collars (part of T87C-77000-J) on clutch housing. See Fig. 10.

2) Place transaxle case on collars. Install washers and retaining bolts supplied with preload checking tools. Tighten retaining bolts to 13-14 ft. lbs. (18-19 N.m). Mount a dial indicator to check end play of shaft. Rotate shaft several times to ensure bearings are seated. Zero dial indicator at lowest point on end of shaft.

3) Lift shaft equally on both sides by hand, and read end play. Turn shaft until reading returns to zero. Repeat procedure to obtain at least 3 readings within .004" (.10 mm) of each other. Average the readings.

4) Subtract .028" (.70 mm) from average end play reading to account for thickness of diaphragm spring. Dimension obtained is thickness of shim needed to obtain specified shaft bearing preload.

5) Using Shim Kit (E92Z-7L172-A), select shim(s) that is closest to or slightly smaller than dimension obtained in step **4)** for final shim size. Use no more than 2 shims.

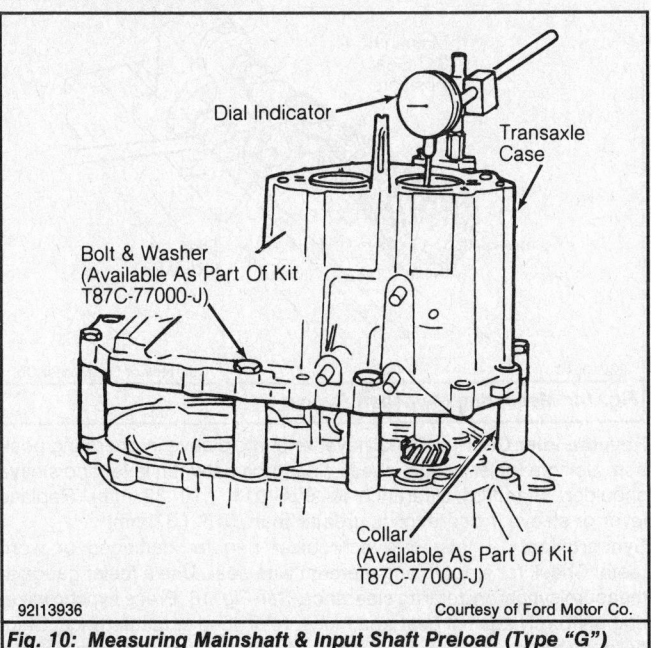

Fig. 10: Measuring Mainshaft & Input Shaft Preload (Type "G")

6) Separate transaxle case from clutch housing and remove measuring tools. DO NOT remove bearing outer race in clutch housing. Repeat procedure for mainshaft.

7) After completing input shaft and mainshaft bearing preload procedure, remove measuring tools. Separate transaxle case from clutch housing. DO NOT remove bearing outer races in clutch housing. Proceed to DIFFERENTIAL BEARING PRELOAD.

DIFFERENTIAL BEARING PRELOAD CHECKS

PRELIMINARY CHECK

All Models – 1) Install differential front bearing outer race into clutch housing. Position differential assembly in clutch housing. Place rear bearing outer race on differential rear bearing cone.

2) Install Shim Selection Gauge (T88C-77000-J for Type "F" or T88C-77000-CH1 for Type "G") on top of rear bearing outer race. See Fig. 11. On both transaxles, place 6 collars from Shim Selection Kit (T87C-77000-J) on clutch housing.

3) Turn gauge halves to eliminate any gap between them. Place transaxle case on collars. Install washers and retaining bolts supplied with shim selection kit. Tighten retaining bolts to 14-19 ft. lbs. (19-26 N.m) for Type "F" or 13-14 ft. lbs. (18-19 N.m) for Type "G".

4) On both transaxles, adjust gauge, using pins provided, until all free play is removed and bearing outer race is seated in case. Turn gauge halves back together until gap between gauge halves is eliminated.

5) Insert Differential Rotator (T90P-7025-BH for Type "F" or T88C-77000-L for Type "G") through transaxle case and engage pinion shaft. Using a torque wrench on differential rotator, turn selector gauge halves apart until a reading of 4.4 INCH lbs. (.5 N.m) is obtained. Remove differential rotator. Using a feeler gauge, measure gap in shim selection gauge. See Fig. 11.

6) Take measurements at 90-degree intervals. Largest measurement obtained is thickness of shim required to obtain specified differential bearing preload. On Type "G", add .006" (.15 mm) to measured clearance. On both transaxles, use no more than 2 shims.

7) On Capri, shims are available in thicknesses of .008-.022" (.20-.55 mm), in .002" (.05 mm) increments. On all other models, shims are available in thicknesses of .004-.047" (.10-1.20 mm), in .002" (.05 mm) increments.

8) Separate transaxle case from clutch housing and remove measuring tools. DO NOT remove bearing outer races in clutch housing. Install selected shim(s) and bearing race.

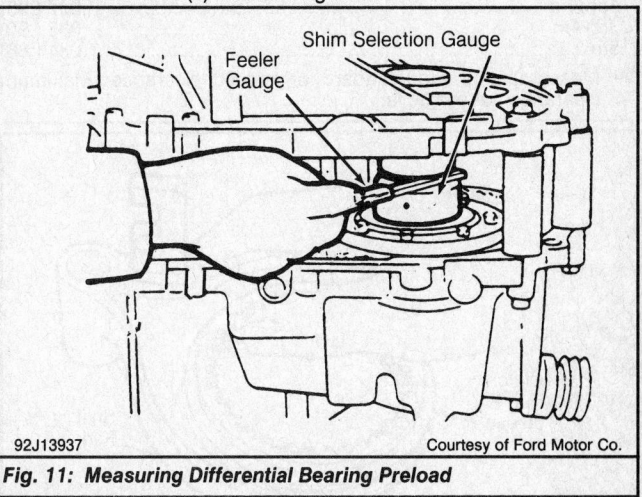

Fig. 11: Measuring Differential Bearing Preload

FINAL CHECK

1) Install selected input and mainshaft shims, bearing races and diaphragm springs. Install differential. Assemble transaxle case and clutch housing. Tighten transaxle case bolts to specification. See TORQUE SPECIFICATIONS.

2) Recheck differential bearing preload using differential rotator and torque wrench. Preload should be .26-6.60 INCH lbs. (.03-.75 N.m). If differential assembly is not within preload specification, repeat differential bearing preload adjustment procedures. When preload is correct, assemble transaxle. See TRANSAXLE REASSEMBLY.

CLEANING & INSPECTION

CLEANING

Wash all parts in cleaning solvent, except sealed bearings, "O" rings and seals. Use scraper or brush for heavy deposits. Rotate bearings by hand in cleaning solvent.

Dry all parts with compressed air. Hold bearings while drying to prevent bearing from spinning. DO NOT spin dry bearings. Lubricate clean bearings with multi-purpose grease and wrap in lint-free cloth until ready to install.

INSPECTION

Clutch Hub Assembly – **1)** Check for worn or damaged splines, synchronizer key groove or shift fork groove. Check for smooth operation as clutch hub sleeve is manually engaged and disengaged with clutch hub.

2) Using a feeler gauge, check for excessive clearance between clutch hub sleeve and shift fork. See Fig. 12. See CLUTCH HUB SLEEVE-TO-SHIFT FORK MAXIMUM CLEARANCE table. Replace as necessary.

CLUTCH HUB SLEEVE-TO-SHIFT FORK MAXIMUM CLEARANCE

Application	In. (mm)
Type "F"	
Capri	
1st-2nd	.018 (.46)
3rd-4th	.024 (.61)
5th	.034 (.86)
Escort & Tracer	
1st-2nd	.034 (.86)
3rd-4th	.039 (1.00)
5th	.049 (1.25)
Type "G"	
Capri	
All	.020 (.51)
Escort & Tracer [1]	
1st-2nd	.003-.009 (.08-.23)
3rd-4th	.004-.020 (.10-.51)
5th	.006-.018 (.15-.46)
Probe	
1st-2nd	.037 (.95)
3rd-4th	.035 (.90)
5th	.034 (.86)

[1] – Measurements are standard or rebuild clearance. Maximum clearance not available.

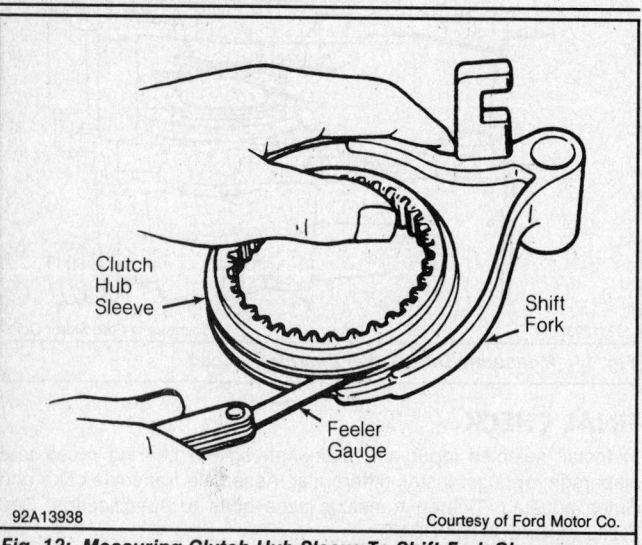

92A13938   Courtesy of Ford Motor Co.

Fig. 12: Measuring Clutch Hub Sleeve-To-Shift Fork Clearance

Differential Pinion Gears – Before disassembly, measure side gear and pinion backlash. Install left and right halfshafts. Support halfshafts on "V" blocks. Using a dial indicator with magnetic base and flex arm, measure backlash of both pinion gears. Backlash should be 0-.004" (0-.10 mm). If measurement is not within limits, replace differential assembly. See Fig. 13.

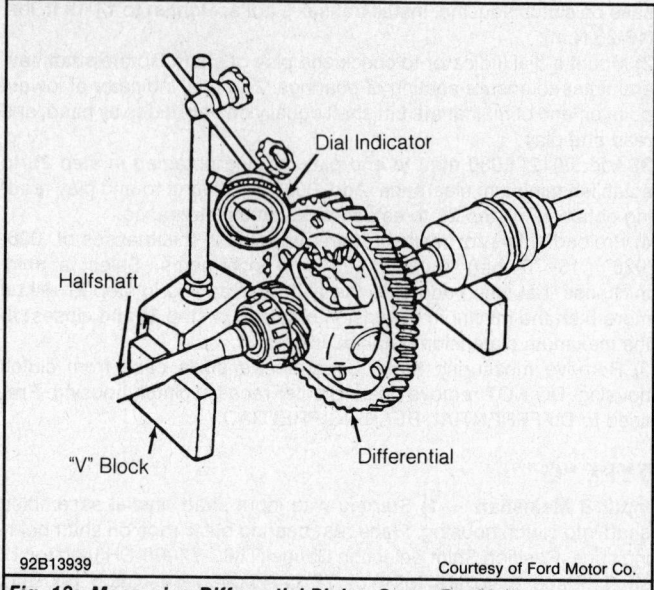

92B13939   Courtesy of Ford Motor Co.

Fig. 13: Measuring Differential Pinion Gears Backlash

Input Shaft – Inspect gear teeth for wear or damage. Inspect shaft for heat discoloring or gear or bearing surface damage. Measure input shaft runout by mounting input shaft in lathe or "V" blocks. Measure runout at 3rd gear installation point. Maximum allowable runout is .002" (.050 mm).

Mainshaft – **1)** Mount mainshaft in a lathe or "V" block. Measure runout at point shown. See Fig. 14. Maximum allowable runout is .0006" (.015 mm).

2) Measure diameter of mainshaft at point where gear is installed. Measure inside diameter of gear. Subtract shaft diameter from inside gear diameter. Difference between 2 measurements is oil clearance. Standard clearance is .001-.003" (.03-.08 mm). See Fig. 15.

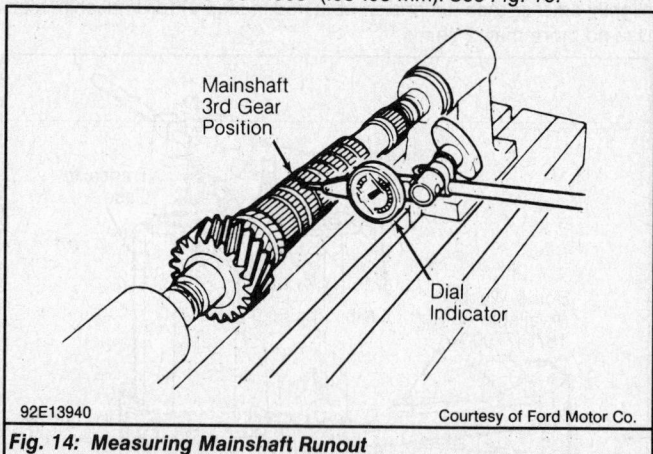

92E13940   Courtesy of Ford Motor Co.

Fig. 14: Measuring Mainshaft Runout

Reverse Idler Gear – Install lever end into sleeve in operating position. Using a feeler gauge, check clearance between lever and sleeve shoulder. Standard clearance is .004-.013" (.10-.32 mm). Replace lever or sleeve if clearance is greater than .015" (.37 mm).

Synchronizers – Inspect synchronizer ring for damaged or worn teeth. Check for smooth engagement with gear. Use a feeler gauge to measure synchronizer ring clearance. See Fig. 16. Press synchronizer ring uniformly against gear and measure around circumference. Standard clearance is .059" (1.50 mm). Minimum allowable clearance is .031" (.80 mm).

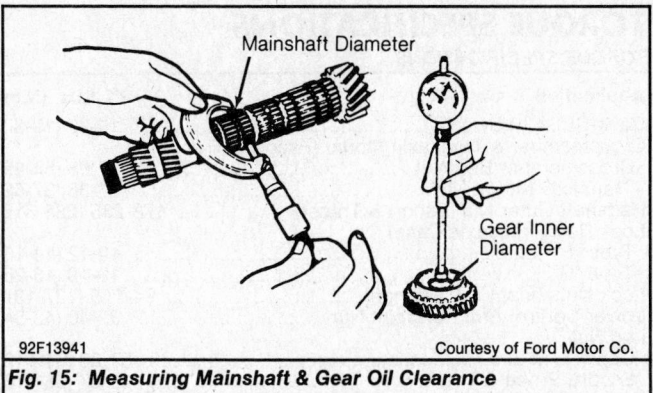

92F13941   Courtesy of Ford Motor Co.

Fig. 15: Measuring Mainshaft & Gear Oil Clearance

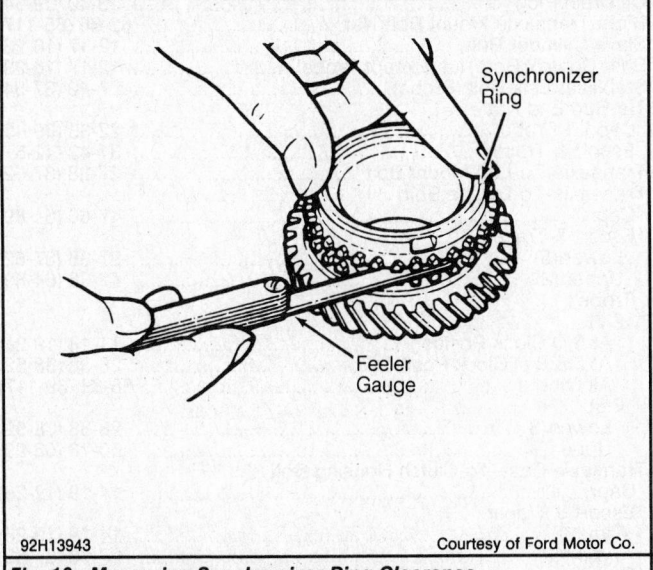

92H13943   Courtesy of Ford Motor Co.

Fig. 16: Measuring Synchronizer Ring Clearance

TRANSAXLE REASSEMBLY

PRELIMINARY ASSEMBLY

All Models – 1) Adjust bearing preloads and install selected shims, bearing outer races and related parts. See MAINSHAFT & INPUT SHAFT BEARING PRELOAD and DIFFERENTIAL BEARING PRELOAD.

2) Install breather and breather cover. Install oil passage and tighten to specification. See TORQUE SPECIFICATIONS. Using pilot bearing installer, install gear change shaft seal.

3) Install neutral switch, oil drain plug and back-up light switch. Tighten to specification. Using seal installer, install differential oil seals. Using seal replacer and driver, install input shaft seal.

4) Install change shaft and boot, spring, reverse gate and selector. Install NEW selector pin. Install change arm and tighten to specification. See TORQUE SPECIFICATIONS.

5) Install guide plate. Tighten bolts to specification. Install reverse lever and shaft. Install NEW roll pin. Install speedometer driven gear (analog cluster) or vehicle speed sensor (digital cluster) to case. Install magnet. Install differential. On Type "G", install mainshaft and input shaft assemblies into clutch housing case.

6) On Type "F", assemble mainshaft, input shaft and shift fork assemblies as a single unit. Install complete assembly into clutch housing case. Keep assembly in vertical position during installation.

FINAL ASSEMBLY

Type "F" – 1) Install steel ball and spring into reverse lever shaft. Install shaft through clutch housing, reverse lever and spring. Using a small screwdriver, compress spring into shaft. Align holes and install NEW roll pin. Use soft-faced hammer to tap in blind plug. See Fig. 4.

2) Install NEW "O" ring onto crank lever shaft. See Fig. 5. Install crank lever between change arm and shift fork shaft control end in clutch housing case. Align crank lever shaft and case holes. Install NEW roll pin.

3) Install 5th and reverse shift rod end and shift rod into clutch housing case. Ensure shift rod and rod end holes are aligned. Tighten bolt to specification. See TORQUE SPECIFICATIONS. Install reverse idler shaft and gear.

4) Bring end of shift rod interlock sleeve even with shift rod control lever. Align reverse idler shaft screw hole with alignment mark (if equipped) or case dowel. See Fig. 17.

5) Apply liquid gasket to both case contact surfaces and bolt case halves together. Install lock bolt into transaxle case. Tighten all bolts to specification. Install 2 Transaxle Plugs (T87C-7025-C) to prevent side gears from being displaced during installation procedures.

6) Install 5th gear onto mainshaft. Install gear sleeve, 5th gear and synchronize ring onto input shaft. Install 5th gear synchronizer assembly, shift fork and clutch hub together onto input shaft. Install NEW roll pin into shift fork. Install lock plate.

7) Lock input shaft with Input Torque Adapter (T87C-7025-A). Install NEW input shaft and mainshaft lock nuts. Tighten nuts to specification. See TORQUE SPECIFICATIONS table. Using dial indicator, measure 5th gear end play. End play should be .002-.012" (.06-.30 mm). Apply sealant, install rear cover.

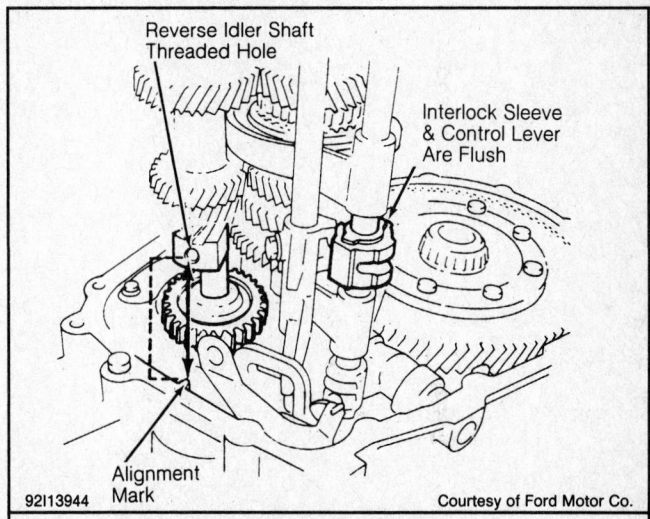

92I13944   Courtesy of Ford Motor Co.

Fig. 17: Aligning Reverse Idler Shaft & Interlock Sleeve (Type "G" Shown; Type "F" Is Similar)

Type "G" – 1) Install reverse lever into clutch housing. Install reverse lever shaft through clutch housing and reverse lever. Install NEW roll pin.

2) Shift to 2nd and 4th gear and position shift fork and rod on case. Insert spring seat and springs into reverse lever shaft. Install ball and hold in place with gasket scraper. Push control end toward scraper. Ball should go into shaft.

3) Set each clutch hub sleeve to Neutral position and tap shift rod from above until steel ball goes into center groove. Swivel control end until ball goes into groove detent.

4) Install NEW "O" ring onto crank lever shaft. Install crank lever into case. Align crank lever shaft and case holes. Install NEW roll pin. Install reverse idler shaft and gear.

5) Install 5th-Reverse gate and shift rod. Ensure shift rod and gate holes are aligned. Tighten bolt to specification. Install reverse idler shaft and gear.

6) Bring end of shift rod interlock sleeve even with shift rod control lever. Align reverse idler shaft screw hole with alignment mark (if equipped) or case dowel. See Fig. 17.

7) Apply a thin coat of liquid gasket to both case contact surfaces and bolt case halves together. Install lock bolt and guide bolt into transaxle case. Install ball, spring and lock bolt. See Fig. 5. Tighten all bolts to specification. Install 2 Transaxle Plugs (T88C-7025-AH) to prevent side gears from being displaced during installation procedures.

8) Install 5th gear onto mainshaft. Install gear sleeve and 5th gear and synchronizer ring onto input shaft. Install 5th gear synchronizer assembly, shift fork and clutch hub together onto input shaft. Install NEW roll pin into shift fork. Install mainshaft reverse synchronizer gear. Install input shaft reverse synchronizer gear.

9) Shift transaxle into 1st gear. Lock input shaft with Torque Adapter (T88C-7025-GH). Install lock nuts. Tighten nuts to specification. Stake lock nuts in place. Apply sealant and install rear cover.

TORQUE SPECIFICATIONS
TORQUE SPECIFICATIONS

Application	Ft. Lbs. (N.m)
Back-Up Light Switch	14-22 (19-30)
Crossmember & Transaxle Mount (Escort & Tracer)	
Crossmember Bolt/Nut	47-66 (64-89)
Transaxle Mount Nut	27-38 (37-52)
Halfshaft Outer Nut (Escort & Tracer)	173-235 (235-319)
Lock Bolt (Transaxle Case)	
Type "F"	10-12 (14-16)
Type "G"	13-19 (18-26)
Lock Nuts (Input & Mainshaft)	94-145 (127-197)
Lower Control Arm Ball Joint Nut	32-40 (43-54)
Lug Nut	
Capri	67-88 (91-119)
Escort, Probe & Tracer	65-87 (88-118)
Neutral Switch	14-18 (19-24)
Oil Drain Plug	29-40 (39-54)
Right Transaxle Mount Bolt/Nut	63-86 (85-117)
Slave Cylinder Bolt	12-17 (16-23)
Shift Control Rod Nut (Except Probe)	12-17 (16-23)
Stabilizer Link Bolt (Probe)	27-40 (37-54)
Tie-Rod End Nut	
Capri & Probe	22-33 (30-45)
Escort & Tracer	31-42 (42-57)
Transaxle-To-Left Mount Bolt	27-38 (37-52)
Transaxle-To-Engine Bolt	
Capri	47-66 (64-89)
Escort & Tracer	
Lower (5)	27-38 (37-52)
Upper (2)	47-66 (64-89)
Probe	
2.0L	
At 6 O'Clock Position	14-18 (19-24)
At 5 & 8 O'Clock Position	28-38 (38-52)
All Others	66-86 (89-117)
2.5L	
Lower (3)	28-38 (38-52)
Upper (7)	50-73 (68-99)
Transaxle Case-To-Clutch Housing Bolt	
Capri	14-19 (19-26)
Escort & Tracer	
Type "F"	14-19 (19-26)
Type "G"	27-38 (37-52)
Probe	27-38 (37-52)

	INCH Lbs. (N.m)
Breather Cover	
Type "F"	96-115 (11-13)
Type "G"	71-96 (8-11)
Change Arm	104-122 (12-14)
Flywheel Inspection Cover	71-96 (8-11)
Guide Bolt	78-122 (9-14)
Guide Plate Bolt	
Long	204-300 (23-34)
Short	71-96 (8-11)
Gearshift Housing (Escort & Tracer)	96-132 (11-15)
Gearshift Housing (Except Escort & Tracer)	60-84 (7-9)
Oil Passage	71-96 (8-11)
Rear Cover	71-96 (8-11)
Shift Control Rod Nut (Probe)	60-84 (7-9)
5th-Reverse Shift Rod Bolt	104-122 (12-14)
Vehicle Speed Sensor Bolt	8-12 (71-104)

Taurus SHO (3.0L), Tempo, Topaz

APPLICATION

MTX III and IV are manual 5-speed transaxles. MTX III and IV are similar, with MTX IV used for heavy duty applications. MTX IV is equipped with a 4-pinion differential, heavy duty gears and bearings. While procedures and gear train layout are similar for both types, parts may not be interchanged. See TRANSAXLE APPLICATION table.

TRANSAXLE APPLICATION

Application	Transaxle
Taurus 3.0 SHO	MTX IV
Tempo/Topaz	
2.3L Engine	MTX III
3.0L Engine	MTX IV

IDENTIFICATION

The MTX 5-speed manual transaxles can be identified by tag affixed to top of transaxle case. Top line of tag identifies transaxle model, next line identifies transaxle assembly, third line shows build date code, and bottom line is transaxle serial number.

DESCRIPTION

Transaxle is a of split case design. One half of case forms the clutch housing and support for one side of differential assembly, input cluster shaft assembly, mainshaft assembly, 5th gear shaft assembly and bearings. The other transaxle case half houses transaxle gears and supports other side of differential assembly, shaft assemblies and bearings. *See Fig. 1.*

Engine torque is transferred from clutch disc to input cluster shaft gears. Input cluster shaft gears are in constant mesh with mainshaft gears. Movement of shift lever transmits motion through external linkages to an internal selector rod assembly. Motion is then transmitted to one or more shift rails and forks. Shift forks engage and/or disengage gears from mainshaft through synchronizers. Power then flows from input cluster shaft through selected gear on mainshaft or 5th gear shaft, through mainshaft or 5th gear shaft to pinion gear and differential final drive gear to drive axle shafts and wheels.

LUBRICATION & ADJUSTMENTS

See appropriate MANUAL TRANSMISSION SERVICING article in TRANSMISSION SERVICING.

TROUBLE SHOOTING

See GENERAL TROUBLE SHOOTING article in MANUAL TRANSMISSIONS.

ON-VEHICLE SERVICE

BACK-UP LIGHT SWITCH

CAUTION: DO NOT shift transaxle with back-up light switch removed from transaxle case.

Removal & Installation – 1) Disconnect electrical lead to back-up light switch. Place transaxle in reverse. Remove switch from transaxle case using 22 mm wrench. To prevent internal problems, do not shift transaxle until NEW back-up light switch is installed.

2) Wrap switch threads with Teflon tape in clockwise direction. To complete installation, reverse removal procedure. Tighten to specification. See TORQUE SPECIFICATIONS.

EXTERNAL SHIFT LINKAGE

The manual shift mechanism and linkage is not adjustable. No adjustments are required before or after installation. *See Fig. 2.*

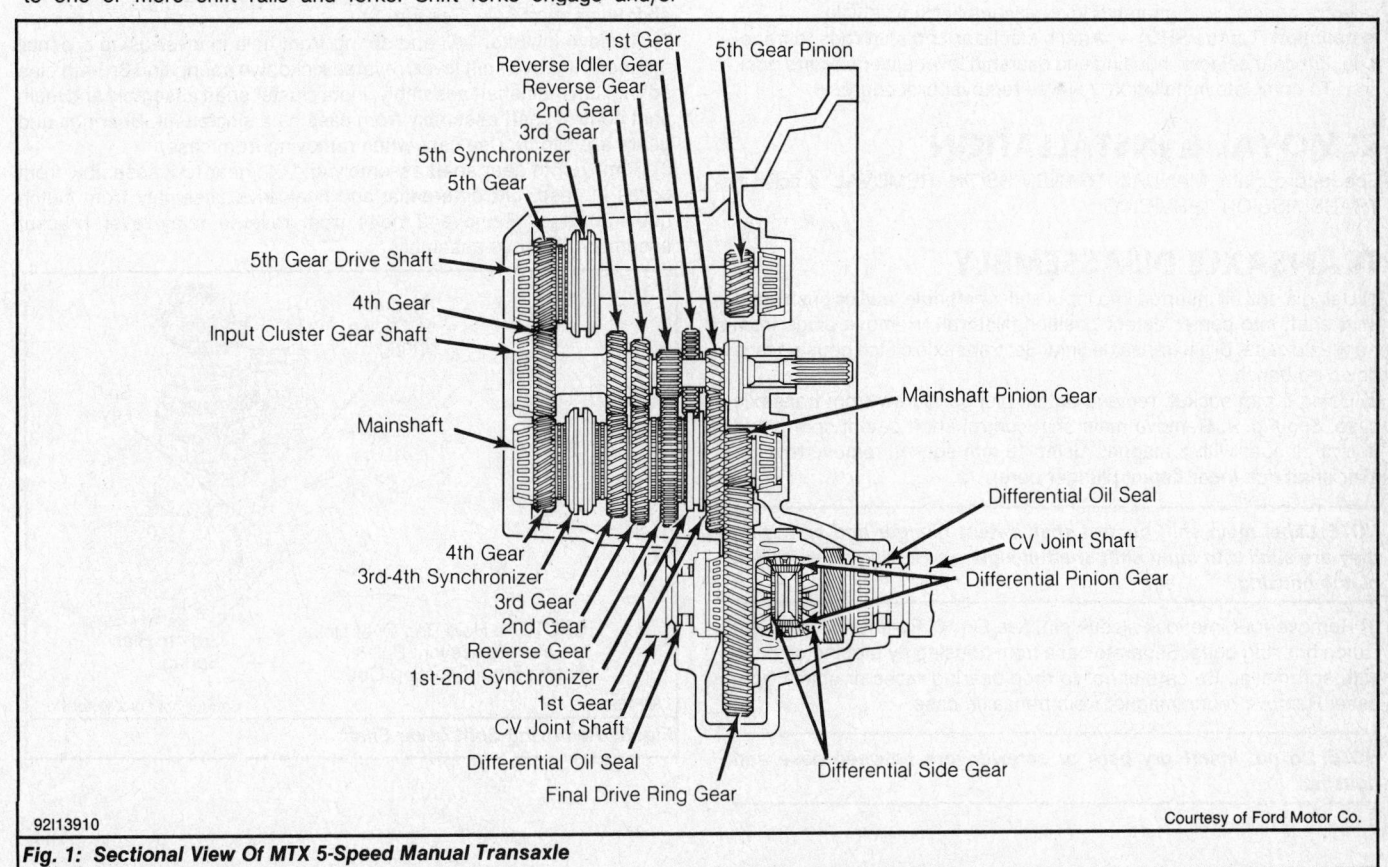

92I13910

Courtesy of Ford Motor Co.

Fig. 1: Sectional View Of MTX 5-Speed Manual Transaxle

SPEEDOMETER CABLE RETAINER & DRIVEN GEAR

Removal & Installation – **1)** Clean off top of retainer. Remove bolt from driven gear retainer assembly with 7 mm wrench. Pull up on speedometer cable, pulling cable retainer and driven gear assembly from its bore. Unscrew cable from retainer.

2) Clean and inspect case bore and all parts. Lightly grease "O" ring on retainer. Using 13/16" deep-well socket, gently tap retainer and gear assembly into case bore while aligning groove in retainer with hole in case. Install speedometer cable retainer bolt. Tighten to specification. See TORQUE SPECIFICATIONS.

DRIVE AXLE SHAFTS

See appropriate AXLE SHAFTS article in AXLE SHAFTS & TRANSFER CASES.

GEARSHIFT LEVER

Removal (Tempo & Topaz) – **1)** Remove console. Remove bolts holding boot and knob assembly to floor pan. Lift boot and knob assembly from floor pan to gain access to gearshift lever bolts. Remove gearshift lever bolts.

2) Remove boot, knob and gearshift lever as an assembly. Do not separate unless component replacement is necessary. If replacement is necessary, hold gearshift lever in vise while pulling boot and knob assembly from lever.

Installation (Tempo & Topaz) – If knob and boot were removed, place boot on shift lever. Using rubber mallet, lightly tap shift knob onto gearshift lever. To complete installation, reverse removal procedure.

Removal (Taurus SHO) – **1)** Remove knob by unscrewing counterclockwise. Slide console and boot assembly off gearshift lever. Raise and support vehicle. Remove resonator pipe.

2) Disconnect stabilizer and shift rods from transaxle. Remove nuts securing gear selector housing to vehicle. Pull down and remove gear selector housing and gearshift lever assembly from vehicle.

Installation (Taurus SHO) – Attach stabilizer and shift rods to transaxle. Lift gear selector housing and gearshift lever assembly into position. To complete installation, reverse removal procedure.

REMOVAL & INSTALLATION

See appropriate MANUAL TRANSMISSION REMOVAL article in TRANSMISSION SERVICING.

TRANSAXLE DISASSEMBLY

1) Using a drill bit inserted into input shift shaft hole, pull or push input shift shaft into center detent position (Neutral). Remove plugs from transaxle case. Drain transaxle fluid. Set transaxle clutch housing face down on bench.

2) Using 8 mm socket, remove detent plunger screw from transaxle case. See Fig. 4. Remove main shift control shaft detent spring and detent plunger with a magnet. Using 13 mm socket, remove reverse idler shaft bolt (near detent plunger bore).

NOTE: Label main shift control shaft detent plunger and spring as they are similar to input shift shaft plunger and spring contained in clutch housing.

3) Remove fork interlock sleeve pin. See Fig. 4. Remove 15 case-to-clutch housing bolts. Separate case from housing by tapping on case with soft mallet. Be careful not to drop bearing races or shims from case. Remove round magnet from transaxle case.

NOTE: Do not insert pry bars or screwdrivers between case and housing.

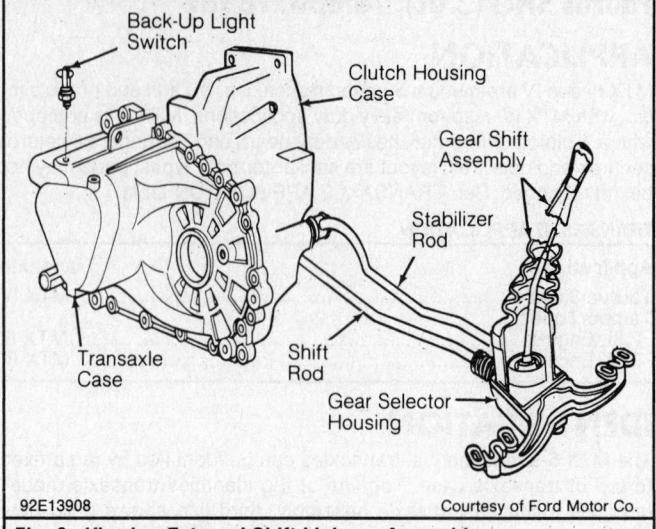

Fig. 2: Viewing External Shift Linkage Assembly
(Tempo/Topaz Shown)

4) Remove "C" clip from 5th gear relay lever pivot pin. Remove 5th gear relay lever. Remove reverse idler shaft and reverse idler gear from case by lifting straight up.

5) Use punch to drive roll pin from case and shift lever shaft. Gently pry on shift lever shaft to move it out of case, so that hole in shift lever shaft is exposed.

NOTE: When prying on shift lever shaft, use care not to damage mainshaft gear teeth or other components.

6) Hold rag over hole in shift lever to prevent inhibitor ball and spring from shooting out and remove shift lever shaft using a drift in exposed shift lever shaft hole. See Fig. 3.

7) Remove inhibitor ball and spring from hole in lever using a pencil magnet. Remove shift lever, reverse kickdown spring and 3rd-4th bias spring. Lift mainshaft assembly, input cluster shaft assembly and main shift control shaft assembly from case as a single unit. Bearings and gears are slip fit. Use care when removing from case.

8) Remove 5th gear shaft assembly and 5th gear fork assembly from bores in case. Lift differential and final drive assembly from clutch housing case. Remove 2 bolts from reverse relay lever bracket assembly. Remove assembly.

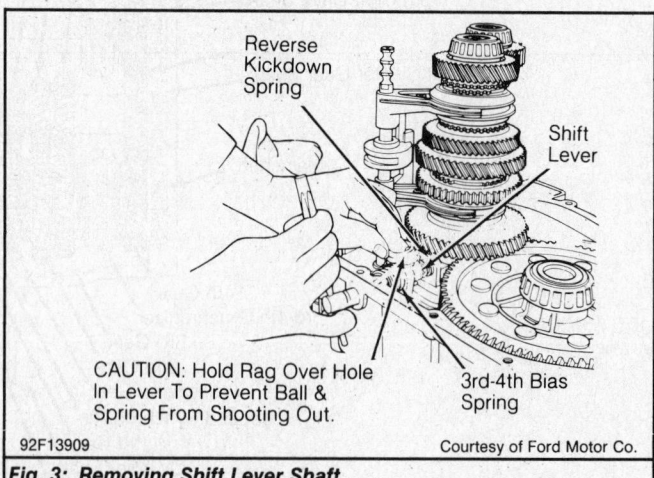

CAUTION: Hold Rag Over Hole In Lever To Prevent Ball & Spring From Shooting Out.

Fig. 3: Removing Shift Lever Shaft

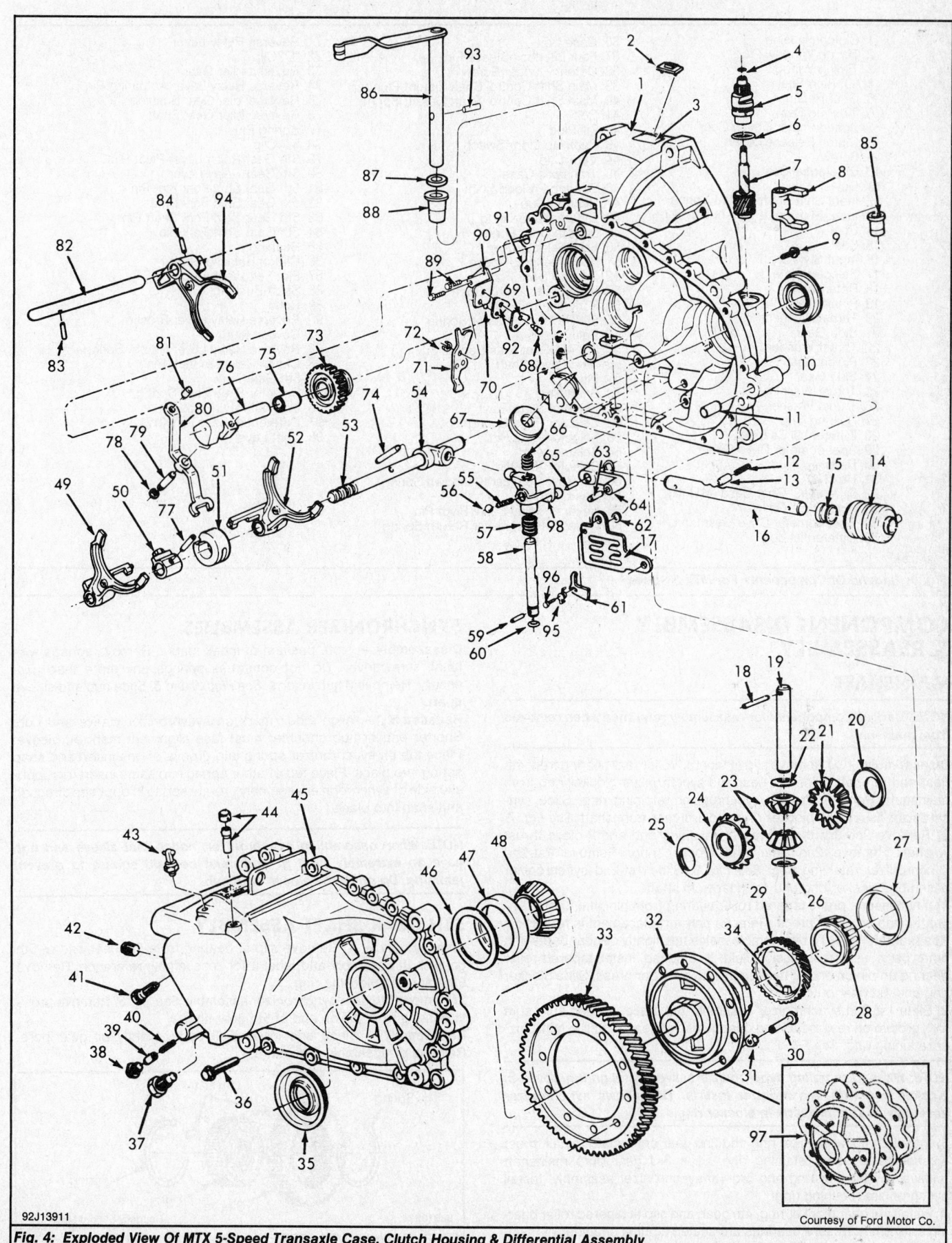

92J13911

Courtesy of Ford Motor Co.

Fig. 4: Exploded View Of MTX 5-Speed Transaxle Case, Clutch Housing & Differential Assembly

1. Clutch Housing	36. Case Bolt	71. Reverse Relay Lever
2. Timing Window Plug	37. Fork Interlock Sleeve Pin	72. "C" Clip
3. Timing Window	38. Detent Plunger Screw	73. Reverse Idler Gear
4. "O" Ring Seal	39. Main Shift Control Shaft Detent Plunger	74. Reverse Relay Lever Actuating Pin
5. Gear Retainer	40. Main Shift Control Shaft Detent Spring	75. Reverse Idler Gear Bushing
6. "O" Ring Seal	41. Bolt	76. Reverse Idler Gear Shaft
7. Speedometer Driven Gear	42. Fill Plug	77. Spring Pin
8. Clutch Release Lever	43. Back-Up Light Switch	78. "C" Clip
9. Screw	44. Vent Cap	79. 5th Gear Relay Lever Pivot Pin
10. Differential Seal	45. Transaxle Case	80. 5th Gear Relay Lever
11. Dowel	46. Bearing Preload Shim	81. 5th Gear Shift Fork Slot Pin
12. Input Shift Shaft Detent Spring	47. Bearing Cup	82. 5th Gear Shift Fork Shaft
13. Input Shift Shaft Detent Plunger	48. Differential Bearing	83. 5th Gear Shift Fork Shaft Pin
14. Boot	49. 3rd-4th Gear Fork	84. 5th Gear Shift Fork Pin
15. Seal	50. Fork Selector Arm	85. Bushing
16. Input Shift Shaft	51. Fork Interlock Sleeve	86. Clutch Release Shaft
17. Selector Plate	52. 1st-2nd Gear Fork	87. Flat Felt Washer
18. Retaining Pin	53. Main Shift Control Shaft	88. Shaft Bushing
19. Pinion Gear Shaft	54. Fork Control Block	89. Bolts
20. Thrust Washer	55. 5th-Reverse Inhibitor Spring	90. Reverse Relay Lever Bracket
21. Side Gear	56. Ball	91. Dowel Mount
22. Thrust Washer	57. 3rd-4th Gear Bias Spring	92. Reverse Relay Lever Return Spring
23. Pinion Gear	58. Shift Lever Shaft	93. Clutch Release Shaft Pin
24. Side Gear	59. Pin	94. 5th Gear Fork
25. Thrust Washer	60. Shaft Seal	95. Selector Plate Pawl Spring
26. Thrust Washer	61. Selector Plate Pawl	96. Lockout Pawl Pivot Pin
27. Bearing Cup	62. Selector Plate Spring	97. Differential Case (MTX IV)
28. Differential Bearing	63. Selector Plate Pin	98. Shift Lever
29. Speedometer Drive Gear	64. Selector Arm	
30. Rivet	65. Selector Arm Pin	
31. Hex Nut	66. 5th-Reverse Gear Kickdown Spring	
32. Differential Gear Case (MTX III)	67. Case Magnet	
33. Final Drive Gear	68. Reverse Relay Lever Pivot Pin	
34. Speedometer Drive Gear Lock	69. Reverse Relay Lever Return Spring	
35. Differential Seal	70. Ball	

92A13912

Fig. 5: Legend Of Components For MTX 5-Speed

COMPONENT DISASSEMBLY & REASSEMBLY

MAINSHAFT

NOTE: Mark all components for reassembly reference when removed from mainshaft.

Disassembly – 1) Remove slip fit tapered roller rear bearing from 4th gear end of shaft. Slide 4th gear and synchronizer blocker ring from mainshaft. Remove 3rd-4th synchronizer retaining ring. Slide synchronizer assembly, blocker ring and 3rd gear from shaft. See Fig. 7.
2) Remove 2nd-3rd thrust washer retaining ring and 2-piece thrust washer. Remove 2nd gear and blocker ring. Remove 1st-2nd synchronizer retaining ring. See Fig. 8. Slide 1st-2nd synchronizer assembly, blocker ring and 1st gear from shaft.
3) If necessary, press tapered roller bearing from pinion end of mainshaft using an arbor press. Remove only if replacement is required.
Reassembly – 1) To reassemble mainshaft, lightly oil gear bores and other parts with transmission fluid. If removed, install tapered roller bearing on pinion end of mainshaft with an arbor press. Slide blocker ring and 1st gear onto shaft.
2) Slide 1st-2nd synchronizer assembly into place, making sure shift fork groove on reverse sliding gear faces 1st gear. Install synchronizer retaining ring. See Fig. 7.

NOTE: When assembling synchronizer assembly, align 3 grooves in blocker ring with synchronizer inserts. This allows synchronizer assembly to seat properly in blocker ring.

3) Install 2nd gear blocker ring and 2nd gear onto shaft. Install thrust washer halves and retaining ring. Slide 3rd gear onto mainshaft followed by blocker ring and 3rd-4th synchronizer assembly. Install synchronizer retaining ring.
4) Install 4th gear blocker ring, 4th gear, and slip fit tapered roller bearing onto shaft. Ensure bearings are seated against shoulder of mainshaft. Ensure synchronizer sleeves are in Neutral position.

SYNCHRONIZER ASSEMBLIES

Disassembly – Note position of index marks. Remove springs with small screwdriver. Do not compress springs any more than necessary. Remove 3 hub inserts. See Figs. 6 and 8. Slide hub and sleeve apart.
Reassembly – Align index mark on synchronizer sleeve and hub. Shorter end of hub shoulder must face alignment mark on sleeve. Place tab on synchronizer spring into groove of one insert and snap spring into place. Place tab of other spring into same insert (on opposite side of synchronizer assembly), rotate spring in opposite direction and snap into place.

NOTE: When assembling synchronizer, notice that sleeve and hub have an extremely tight fit and must be held square to prevent jamming. Do not force sleeve onto hub.

5TH GEAR SHAFT ASSEMBLY

Disassembly – 1) Remove slip fit bearing from 5th gear end of 5th gear shaft assembly and label it for reassembly reference. Remove 5th gear and blocking ring.
2) Remove 5th gear synchronizer assembly. See Fig. 8. Remove press fit bearing from pinion end of 5th gear shaft.
Reassembly – Clean and inspect all parts. Lightly oil gear bore. Reverse disassembly procedure.

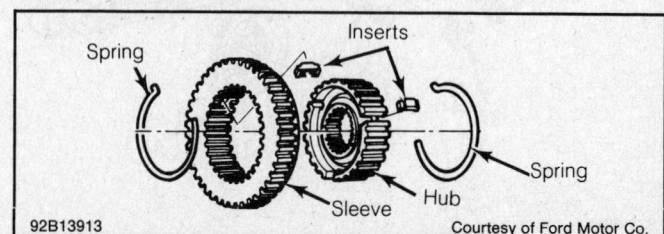

92B13913   Courtesy of Ford Motor Co.

Fig. 6: Exploded View Of Synchronizer Assembly (Typical)

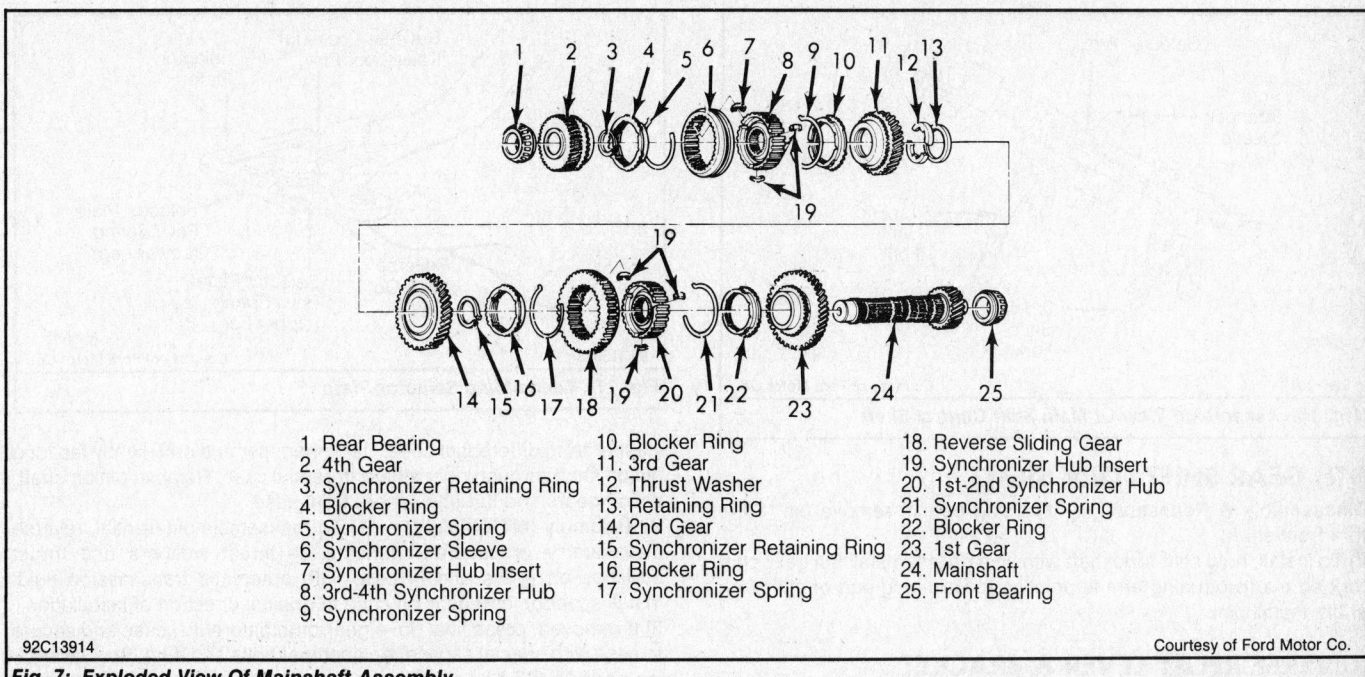

1. Rear Bearing
2. 4th Gear
3. Synchronizer Retaining Ring
4. Blocker Ring
5. Synchronizer Spring
6. Synchronizer Sleeve
7. Synchronizer Hub Insert
8. 3rd-4th Synchronizer Hub
9. Synchronizer Spring

10. Blocker Ring
11. 3rd Gear
12. Thrust Washer
13. Retaining Ring
14. 2nd Gear
15. Synchronizer Retaining Ring
16. Blocker Ring
17. Synchronizer Spring

18. Reverse Sliding Gear
19. Synchronizer Hub Insert
20. 1st-2nd Synchronizer Hub
21. Synchronizer Spring
22. Blocker Ring
23. 1st Gear
24. Mainshaft
25. Front Bearing

92C13914

Courtesy of Ford Motor Co.

Fig. 7: Exploded View Of Mainshaft Assembly

NOTE: *The 5th gear synchronizer assembly is positioned on 5th gear shaft with plastic spacer and retainer facing 5th drive gear.*

INTERNAL SHIFT LINKAGE

Disassembly – 1) Remove 2 bolts and selector plate from transaxle case. Place input shift shaft in center detent position. Drive selector arm pin through selector arm and input shift shaft into recess in clutch housing case. Remove input shift shaft boot.

2) Using a drift as a lever, rotate input shift shaft 90 degrees. Depress input shift shaft detent plunger out of notches inside housing and pull input shift shaft out. Remove shift shaft selector arm and selector plate pin. Place rag over plunger bore to prevent detent plunger and spring from flying out. *See Fig. 9.*

3) Using magnet, remove input shift shaft detent plunger and spring from case. Label for reassembly reference. Remove input shift shaft oil seal with slide hammer.

Reassembly – 1) Coat NEW input shift shaft oil seal lip with grease and install seal in case. Install input shift shaft detent spring and plunger in clutch housing case bore.

2) Using small drift, compress spring and plunger. Slide input shift shaft into its bore and over plunger. Be careful not to cut seal when installing shift shaft.

3) Install selector arm in its working position and slide input shift shaft through selector arm. Align hole in selector arm with hole in input shift shaft and install selector arm pin. Install input shift shaft boot.

4) Install selector plate and tighten bolts to specification. See TORQUE SPECIFICATIONS. Ensure pin in selector arm rides in cut-out of gate in selector plate. Move input shift shaft through selector plate positions to ensure proper operation.

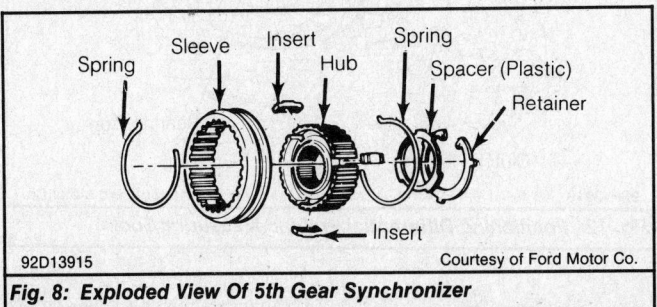

92D13915

Courtesy of Ford Motor Co.

Fig. 8: Exploded View Of 5th Gear Synchronizer

NOTE: *Ensure notches in input shift shaft face input shift shaft detent plunger.*

MAIN SHIFT CONTROL SHAFT

Disassembly – 1) Rotate 3rd-4th shift fork on main shift control shaft until notch in fork is positioned over fork interlock sleeve. *See Fig. 10.* Rotate 1st-2nd shift fork on main shift control shaft until notch in fork is positioned over selector arm finger.

2) With forks in this position, slide 3rd-4th fork and fork interlock sleeve off shaft. Drive out selector arm spring pin using a punch. Remove selector arm and 1st-2nd shift fork from shaft. Drive out fork control block pin and remove from shaft.

Reassembly – 1) Clean and inspect all parts. Lightly oil all parts. Position fork control block onto main shift control shaft with offset of fork control block facing toward near end of shaft. Align pin holes and install pin.

2) Install 1st-2nd fork and selector arm on main shift control shaft. Note that 1st-2nd fork is thinner than 3rd-4th fork. Align holes in fork selector arm and shaft. Install spring pin. Position 1st-2nd fork notch over selector arm finger.

3) Position slot in 3rd-4th fork over fork interlock sleeve. Slide 3rd-4th fork and fork interlock sleeve onto shaft. Align fork interlock sleeve slot with spline on fork selector arm and slide into position. When assembled properly, forks should be aligned.

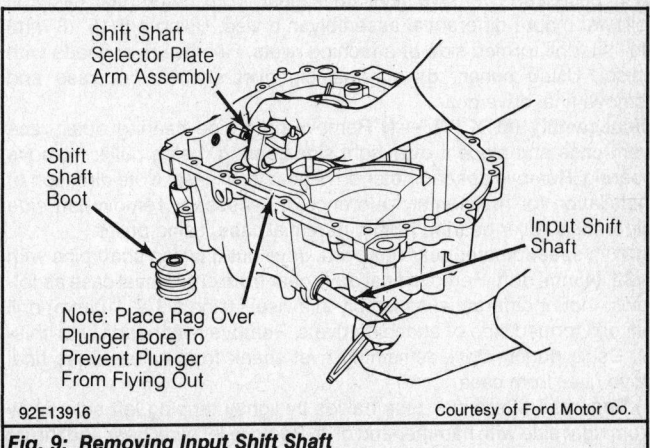

92E13916

Courtesy of Ford Motor Co.

Fig. 9: Removing Input Shift Shaft

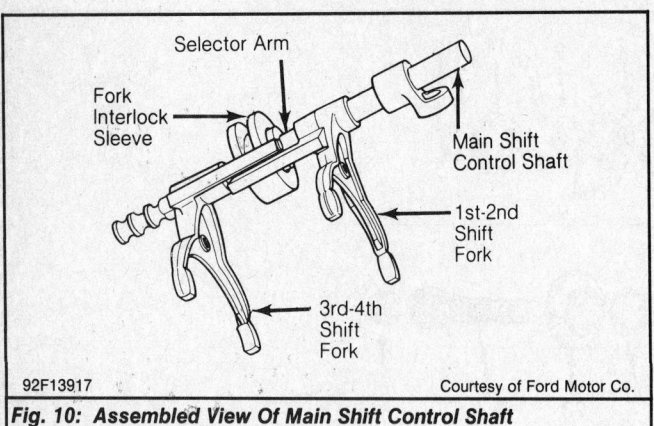

Fig. 10: Assembled View Of Main Shift Control Shaft

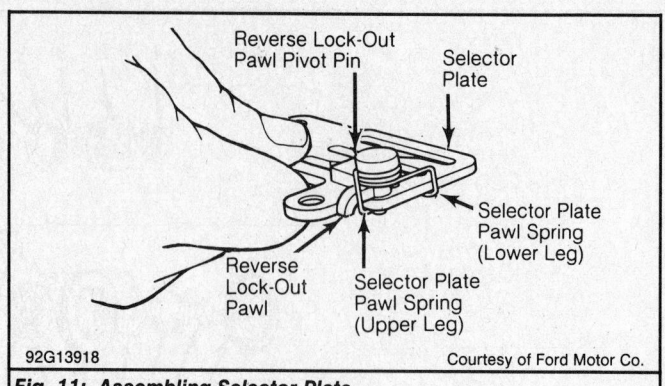

Fig. 11: Assembling Selector Plate

5TH GEAR SHIFT FORK SHAFT

Disassembly & Reassembly – 1) Using punch, remove pin. Slide fork from shaft.

2) To install, hold shift fork shaft with hole on left. Install 5th gear shift fork so that protruding arm is pointing toward long end of shift fork shaft. Install pin.

REVERSE RELAY LEVER & BRACKET

Disassembly & Reassembly – 1) Remove "C" clip from bracket. Slide relay lever off pivot pin. See Fig. 5. Remove steel ball and 2 springs between lever and bracket.

2) To install, place steel ball in dimple provided in bracket. Slide relay lever and springs onto bracket pivot pin, aligning steel ball with dimples on relay lever.

3) Install "C" clip. Ensure bend in lever is towards bracket when installed.

SELECTOR PLATE

Disassembly & Reassembly – Remove "C" clip retaining reverse lock-out pawl pivot pin to selector plate. Remove reverse lock-out pawl, pin and spring. To assemble, reverse disassembly procedures. See Fig. 11. Install "C" clip.

DIFFERENTIAL ASSEMBLY

Disassembly (MTX III) – 1) Using puller, remove left side differential roller bearings from differential case. Remove right side bearing outer race from case and place it over right side bearing. Using puller, remove bearing. Remove speedometer drive gear from case. Note direction of installation for reassembly reference.

2) Remove side gears and thrust washers from differential case by rotating gears toward case windows. Using punch, drive out differential pinion gear shaft retaining pin. Remove pinion shaft, pinion gears and thrust washers from case.

3) If necessary, remove final drive gear from differential case as follows: mount differential assembly in a vise. Using a 5/16" (8 mm) drill bit, drill formed side of attaching rivets. Remove rivet heads with chisel. Using punch, drive remaining rivet shank from case and remove final drive gear.

Disassembly (MTX IV) – 1) Remove right side bearing outer race from case and place it over right side bearing. Using puller, remove bearing. Remove speedometer drive gear from case. Note direction of installation for reassembly reference. If necessary, remove left side differential roller bearing from differential case, using puller.

2) With speedometer gear removed, drive out 3 pinion shaft pins with 5/32" (4 mm) drift. Remove final drive gear from differential case as follows: mount differential assembly in a vise. Using a 3/8" (10 mm) drill bit, drill formed side of attaching rivets. Remove rivet heads with chisel. Using punch, drive remaining rivet shank from case. Press final drive gear from case.

3) Separate differential case halves by lightly tapping left side away from right side with hammer and drift. Remove left side gear and thrust

washer from differential case. Using hammer and drift, lightly tap long pinion shaft through right side differential case. Remove pinion shaft, pinion gears and thrust washers from case.

Reassembly (MTX III & IV) – 1) To reassemble differential, reverse disassembly procedure. Lubricate all thrust washers and thrust surfaces on gears and in case with automatic transmission fluid. Install speedometer gear on case in original direction of installation.

2) If removed, press final drive gear onto differential case and secure to case with special service replacement bolts and nuts. Special service parts MUST be used to provide proper clearance with transmission case. Install bolts with heads on final drive gear side of case and nuts on differential side. Partially tighten nuts. Using standard circular pattern sequence, tighten bolts to specification. See TORQUE SPECIFICATIONS.

ADJUSTMENTS

DIFFERENTIAL BEARING PRELOAD

1) Differential bearing preload is set at factory and need not be checked or adjusted unless one of the following components is replaced: transaxle case, differential case, differential side bearings or clutch housing.

2) To check and adjust preload, remove differential seal from transaxle case. Drive differential bearing outer race from case and remove preload adjusting shim located under race.

3) Position differential assembly in clutch housing. Install Height Gauge Spacers (T81P-4451-B2 and T83P-4451-AH2) on clutch housing dowels. Position bearing outer race removed from transaxle case on differential bearing. Install Shim Selector (T83P-4451-B1) for MTX III or (T83P-4451-AH1) for MTX IV, over race. See Fig. 12.

4) Place transaxle case in position on clutch housing and install 4 bolts supplied with preload checking tools. Tighten bolts to 17-21 ft. lbs. (23-28 N.m). Rotate differential several times to ensure setting of differential bearing.

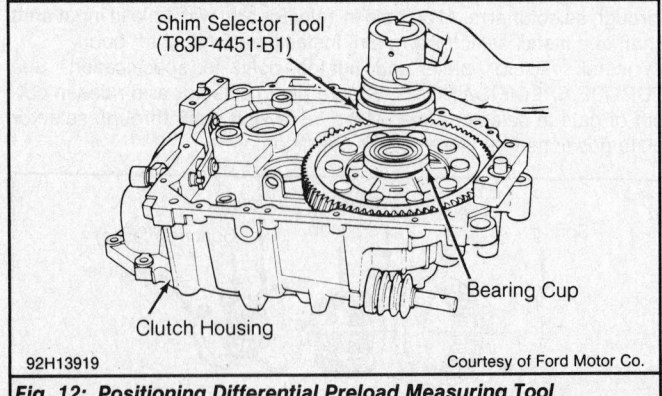

Fig. 12: Positioning Differential Preload Measuring Tool

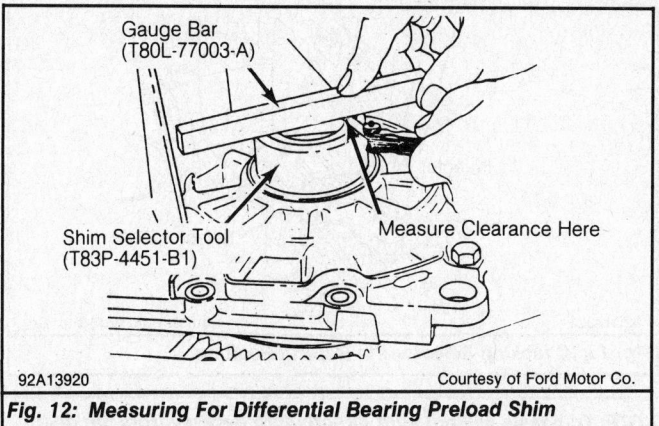

Fig. 12: Measuring For Differential Bearing Preload Shim

5) Place Gauge Bar (T80L-77003-A) across shim selector tool. Using feeler gauge or depth micrometer, measure clearance between gauge bar and shim selector tool. *See Fig. 13.* Record measurements from 3 positions around tool and average the readings.

6) Average measurement obtained in preceding step is thickness of shim needed to obtain specified differential bearing preload. Differential bearing preload shims are available in thicknesses of .012-.049" (.30-1.24 mm) in .002" (.05 mm) increments.

NOTE: If preload adjusting shim required is not available, always use next thinner shim.

7) Separate transaxle case from clutch housing and remove measuring tools. Install selected preload shim in transaxle case. Lubricate bearing bores and press outer race into case until fully seated. Install NEW differential oil seal in transaxle case.

MAINSHAFT, INPUT CLUSTER SHAFT & 5TH GEAR DRIVE SHAFT BEARING PRELOAD

NOTE: When replacing bearing or bearing race, the use of a standard thickness service shim (provided with bearing) eliminates need for measuring mainshaft, input cluster shaft and 5th gear drive shaft bearing clearances and is acceptable by factory standards.

1) Preload of mainshaft, input cluster shaft and 5th gear drive shaft bearings is maintained by shims located behind bearing outer races in transaxle case.

2) When bearing or bearing race is replaced, a replacement bearing preload shim will be provided for service and should be installed in place of original shim as outlined in PRELOAD SHIM SELECTION CHART. *See Fig. 14.*

3) The following points should be noted when replacing shaft bearing preload shims. When repairs require use of service replacement shim, discard original shim. DO NOT use more than one shim per shaft.

4) If parts are replaced other than parts shown in selection chart, original shim should be re-used. Preload shims must be installed only under bearing races at transaxle case end of each shaft as indicated.

CAUTION: It is important to label bearing races as they are removed from transaxle case or clutch housing. Maintaining proper race-to-shim relationship and proper race labeling will ensure correct bearing preload when transaxle is assembled.

CLEANING & INSPECTION

1) Inspect transaxle case and clutch housing case for cracks, worn or damaged bearing bores or damaged threads. Inspect mating surfaces on cases for small nicks or burrs that could cause misalignment of case halves. Remove all small nicks or burrs with a fine stone or file.

2) Check reverse idler gear and sliding gear for chipped, broken or bent teeth. Check reverse idler gear for bushing damage. Check wear of reverse idler gear shaft. It is normal for front of teeth to show wear; this does not interfere with proper function.

Parts Replaced	Shims Replaced with Service Shims		
	Input Cluster Shaft	Main Shaft	5th Gear Shaft
1 Input Cluster Bearing	Yes	No	No
2 Input Cluster Bearings	Yes	No	No
1 Input Cluster Bearing 1 Mainshaft Bearing 1 5th Gear Shaft Bearing	Yes Yes Yes	Yes Yes Yes	Yes Yes Yes
2 Input Cluster Bearings 2 Mainshaft Bearings 2 5th Gear Shaft Bearings	Yes Yes Yes	Yes Yes Yes	Yes Yes Yes
1 Mainshaft Bearing	No	Yes	No
2 Mainshaft Bearings	No	Yes	No
1 5th Gear Shaft Bearing	No	No	Yes
2 5th Gear Shaft Bearings	No	No	Yes
Clutch Housing Assembly	Yes	Yes	Yes
Transaxle Case Assembly	Yes	Yes	Yes

92B13921   Courtesy of Ford Motor Co.

Fig. 14: Preload Shim Selection Chart

3) Check teeth, splines and journals of mainshaft for damage. Check all other gears for chipped, broken or worn teeth. Check for eroded clutch teeth and damaged bearing surfaces. Clutch teeth will usually show rounding on points which does not interfere with normal operation.

4) Check synchronizer sleeves for smooth and free movement on hubs. Ensure index marks are properly aligned. Check for damaged clutching teeth. Check for proper positioning of springs.

5) Inspect synchronizer blocker rings for wear marks on spline end back face, which indicates ring was bottoming on gear face due to excessive blocker ring wear.

TRANSAXLE REASSEMBLY

NOTE: Lightly oil all bores with Synthetic Mercon automatic transmission fluid or equivalent prior to assembly.

1) Install reverse relay lever bracket assembly into case. Position differential assembly in clutch housing case. Align differential gears for later installation of half-shafts. Install 5th gear shaft assembly and fork shaft assembly in case. Place main shift control shaft assembly on mainshaft so that shift forks engage in appropriate synchronizer sleeves. *See Fig. 15.*

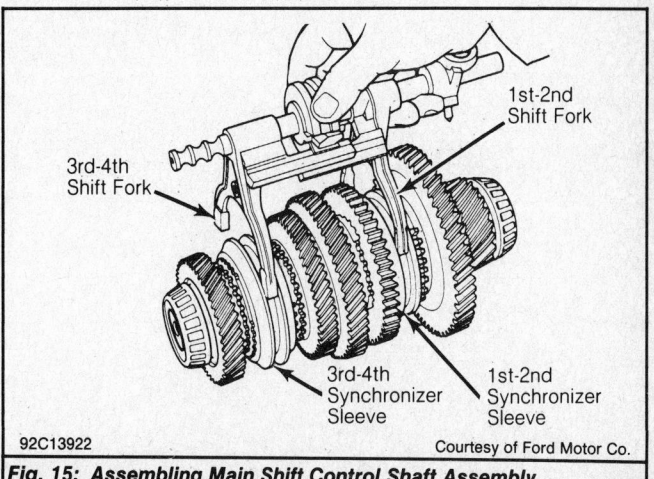

Fig. 15: Assembling Main Shift Control Shaft Assembly

2) Mesh mainshaft assembly with input cluster shaft. Hold shaft assemblies together in their respective working positions and lower them into bores in clutch housing case as a unit. Use care not to damage input cluster shaft oil seal or mainshaft oil funnel.

3) Position shift lever, 3rd-4th bias spring and kickdown spring in their working positions. One shift lever ball should be in socket of input shift shaft selector plate arm assembly. The other ball should be in socket of fork control block on main shift control shaft.

4) Install inhibitor spring and ball in 5th and reverse shift inhibitor lever hole. Depress inhibitor ball and spring using a drift and slide shift lever shaft (notch down) through shift lever. Tap shift lever shaft into its bore in clutch housing. Align shift lever shaft pin bore with case pin bore and tap in pin. Ensure that pin is slightly below case surface.

5) Before continuing with transaxle reassembly, verify the following: selector pin should be in Neutral (center) position in selector plate. *See Fig. 16.* Finger of fork selector arm should be partially engaged with 1st-2nd shift fork and 3rd-4th shift fork.

6) Place groove in reverse idler gear in engagement with pin at end of reverse relay lever. Slide reverse idler shaft through gear and into clutch housing bore. Clean and install magnet in pocket of clutch housing case.

7) Install 5th gear relay lever onto reverse idler shaft. Align it with 5th gear fork interlock sleeve and fork slot, and install "C" clip.

8) Install detent spring and plunger in their bore in case. Apply a 1/16" wide bead of Sealer (E1FZ-19562-A) or equivalent between clutch housing and transaxle case mating surface.

9) Carefully lower transaxle case over clutch housing case. Gently lower case until shift control shaft, mainshaft, input cluster shaft and 5th gear shaft align with bores in transaxle case.

10) Gently slide transaxle case over dowels. Case should sit flush on clutch housing, without binding on magnet. Apply pipe sealant with Teflon to threads of fork interlock sleeve pin. Align slot in fork interlock sleeve with hole in transaxle case using a drift. Install and tighten fork interlock sleeve pin to specification. See TORQUE SPECIFICATIONS.

NOTE: If hole in case does not align with slot in fork interlock sleeve, remove case half and check for proper installation of fork interlock sleeve.

---

11) Install transaxle case bolts. Tighten to specification. Use drift to align bore in reverse idler shaft with bolt hole in transaxle case. Install and tighten reverse idler shaft bolt.

12) Apply Teflon tape to threads of detent plunger screw. Install and tighten screw. Install differential oil seal. Place transaxle upright and position drift through hole in input shift shaft. Shift transaxle through all gears to ensure operation.

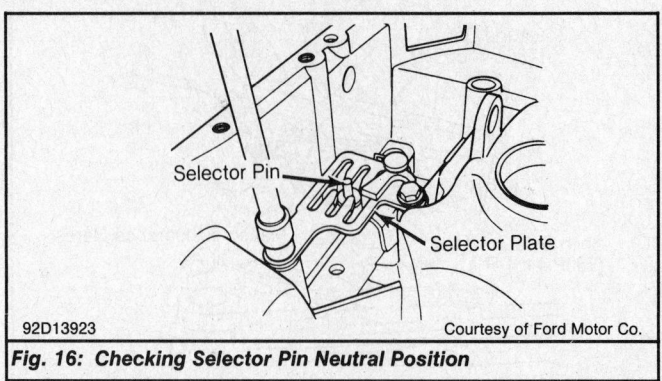

92D13923   Courtesy of Ford Motor Co.

Fig. 16: Checking Selector Pin Neutral Position

NOTE: Transaxle will not shift directly into Reverse from 5th gear.

TORQUE SPECIFICATIONS
TORQUE SPECIFICATIONS

Application	Ft. Lbs. (N.m)
Back-Up Light Switch	[1] 12-15 (16-20)
Fork Interlock Sleeve Pin	[1] 12-15 (16-20)
Final Drive Gear Bolt	
MTX III & MTX IV (Tempo & Topaz)	55-70 (75-95)
MTX IV (Taurus SHO)	80-100 (108-136)
Preload Checking Tool Bolt	17-21 (23-28)
Reverse Idler Shaft Bolt	16-20 (22-27)
Transaxle Case Bolt	13-17 (18-23)
Transaxle-To-Engine Bolt	
MTX III	25-35 (34-47)
MTX IV	34-36 (46-62)
	INCH Lbs. (N.m)
Detent Plunger Screw	[1] 68-96 (8-11)
Gearshift Assembly	53-68 (6-8)
Reverse Relay Lever Bracket Bolt	68-96 (8-11)
Selector Plate Bolt	68-96 (8-11)
Speedometer Cable Retainer Bolt	18-26 (2-3)
Transaxle Filler Plug	108-180 (12-20)

[1] – Apply pipe sealant with Teflon to threads prior to installation and tightening.

Thunderbird Super Coupe

IDENTIFICATION

The 5-speed manual transmission can be identified by a safety compliance (or vehicle certification) label. Label is located on driver's door lock pillar below latch striker. Transmission code on label is located at bottom of label under designation TR. First character of series denotes type of transmission. Code for manual 5-speed transmission is "W".

Manual transmissions are equipped with service identification tags. M5R2 transmission service identification tag is located on left side of transmission.

DESCRIPTION

The M5R2 is a top shift, fully synchronized, 5-speed transmission with an overdrive 5th gear ratio. Transmission is constructed of aluminum alloy with steel bearing race inserts.

All gear shifts are accomplished through the use of synchronizers. The extension housing contains a non-serviceable bronze bushing. If bushing requires replacement, housing must be replaced as a unit.

LUBRICATION & ADJUSTMENTS

See appropriate MANUAL TRANSMISSION SERVICING article in TRANSMISSION SERVICING.

TROUBLE SHOOTING

See GENERAL TROUBLE SHOOTING article in MANUAL TRANSMISSIONS.

ON-VEHICLE SERVICE

EXTENSION HOUSING SEAL

NOTE: To replace extension housing seal, extension housing must remain installed on transmission. If any other service is required, extension housing must be replaced as a unit.

Removal – Raise and support vehicle. Remove underbody covers as necessary. Remove drive shaft. Note index marks on drive shaft flange and drive shaft yoke. DO NOT remove extension housing. Remove seal using extension housing seal remover. *See Fig. 1.*

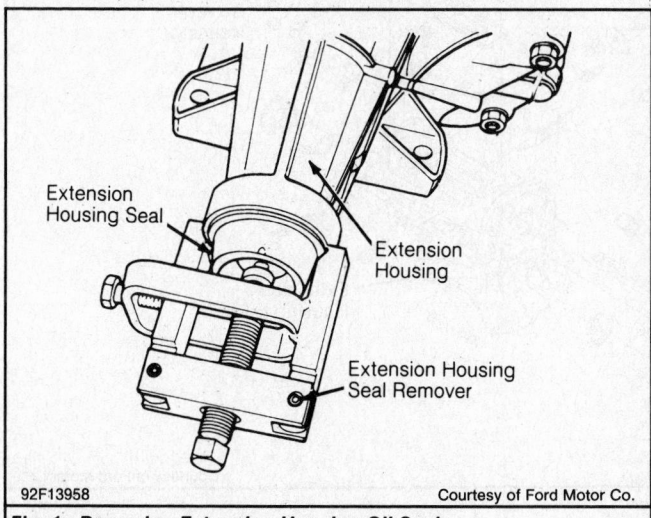

92F13958   Courtesy of Ford Motor Co.

Fig. 1: Removing Extension Housing Oil Seal

Installation – Install seal using appropriate seal installer. Ensure oil seal drain hole is located at 6 o'clock position. To complete installation, reverse removal procedure. Ensure drive shaft index marks are aligned. Tighten bolts to specification. See TORQUE SPECIFICATIONS.

NOTE: Manufacturer does not supply on-vehicle procedures for extension housing removal. See TRANSMISSION DISASSEMBLY and TRANSMISSION REASSEMBLY for extension housing removal and installation procedures.

REMOVAL & INSTALLATION

See appropriate MANUAL TRANSMISSION REMOVAL article in TRANSMISSION SERVICING.

TRANSMISSION DISASSEMBLY

1) Remove drain plug and drain transmission. Remove shift control housing. *See Fig. 2.* Remove offset lever pin using a 5/32" punch. *See Fig. 3.* Use care not to lose pin.

2) Remove extension housing seal. See EXTENSION HOUSING SEAL under ON-VEHICLE SERVICE. Remove extension housing bolts and gently pry extension housing away from transmission case. Remove countershaft oil funnel from countershaft bore in extension housing. Remove back-up light and neutral start switches.

3) Remove top cover assembly. From behind gear box portion of transmission, remove shift rail and selector finger from case. Remove offset lever and control selector spring from extension housing. *See Fig. 3.*

4) If necessary for repair or replacement, remove the following components.

- Gearshift lever guide (inside extension housing)
- 5th-reverse inhibitor assembly (outside of extension housing)
- Shift rod bushings and retaining rings (inside extension housing)
- Rear oil trough (in front of extension housing)

5) Remove and discard anti-spill oil seal from output shaft. Remove speedometer snap ring, drive gear and steel ball. Record speedometer drive color for reassembly.

CAUTION: Staked areas of lock nuts MUST BE fully released or damage to shaft threads will result.

6) Lock transmission into 1st and 3rd gears. Using chisel, release staked areas of lock nut. Using appropriate wrench and remover tube, remove and discard output shaft lock nut. Using 32 mm socket, remove and discard countershaft rear bearing lock nut. Remove countershaft bearing and thrust washer.

7) Remove reverse idler shaft fixing bolt and washer. *See Fig. 4.* Remove reverse idler gear assembly by grasping and pulling rearward. To remove output shaft rear bearing from output shaft, use remover/replacer tube, TOD Forcing Screw (T84T-7025-B), bearing puller, and puller ring. *See Fig. 5.*

8) Remove reverse gear and sleeve from output shaft. Remove countershaft reverse gear with 2 needle bearings and reverse synchronizer ring. Remove thrust washer and split washer from countershaft.

9) From left rear portion of transmission case, remove 5th-reverse gear shift rod fixing bolt. From the same area of transmission case, remove counter lever fixing bolt and inner circlip. Remove counter lever assembly.

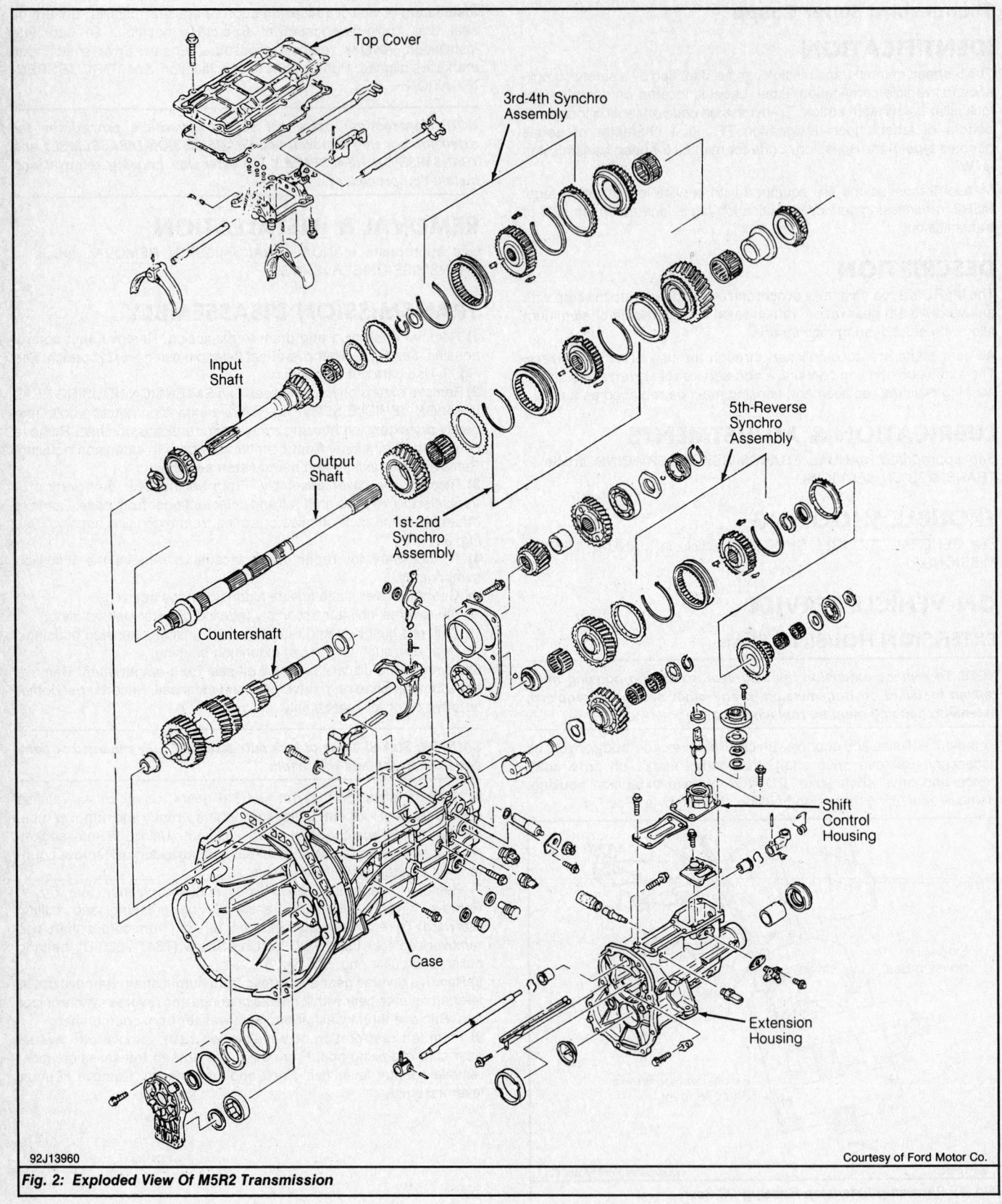

Top Cover

3rd-4th Synchro Assembly

Input Shaft

Output Shaft

1st-2nd Synchro Assembly

5th-Reverse Synchro Assembly

Countershaft

Shift Control Housing

Case

Extension Housing

92J13960

Courtesy of Ford Motor Co.

Fig. 2: Exploded View Of M5R2 Transmission

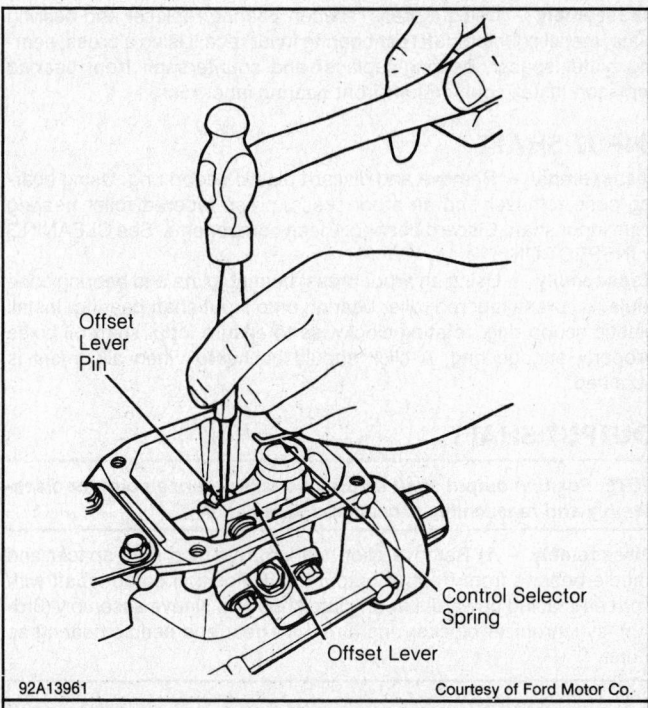

Offset Lever Pin

Control Selector Spring

Offset Lever

92A13961   Courtesy of Ford Motor Co.

Fig. 3: Removing & Installing Offset Lever Pin

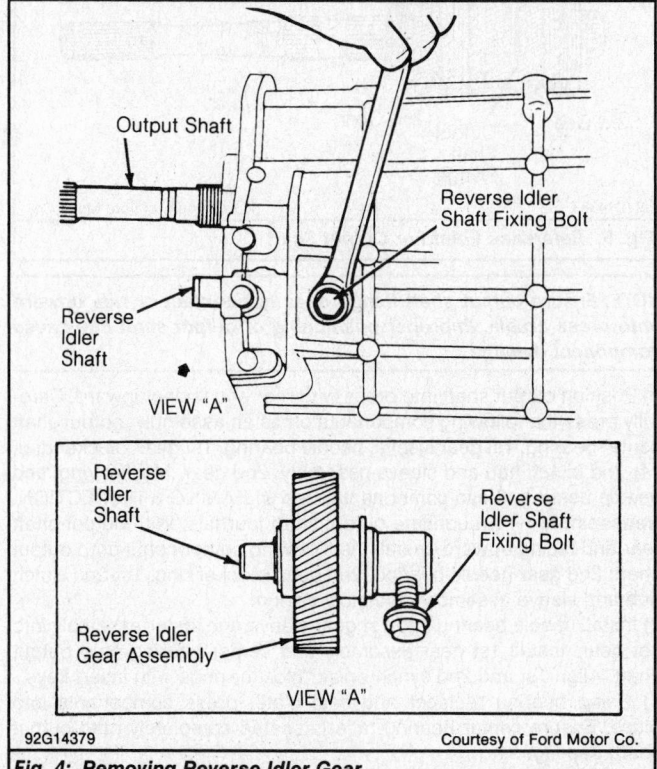

Output Shaft

Reverse Idler Shaft Fixing Bolt

Reverse Idler Shaft

VIEW "A"

Reverse Idler Shaft

Reverse Idler Shaft Fixing Bolt

Reverse Idler Gear Assembly

VIEW "A"

92G14379   Courtesy of Ford Motor Co.

Fig. 4: Removing Reverse Idler Gear

NOTE: DO NOT remove Torx nut retaining counter lever pin at this time.

---

10) Remove the following assemblies:
- Countershaft 5th-reverse synchronizer hub and sleeve
- 5th-reverse shift fork and rod
- 5th gear, bearing assembly and fiber-lined blocker ring

NOTE: DO NOT separate steel ball and spring from shift fork groove unless necessary.

---

11) Remove 5th gear sleeve. Use a magnet to remove ball. Remove 5th gear. For reassembly reference, ensure longer 5th gear collar faces forward. At rear of transmission, remove center bearing cover retaining bolts. See Fig. 6.

12) At front of transmission, remove front bearing cover bolts. See Fig. 7. Thread 2 bolts into front bearing service bolt locations, at 3 and 9 o'clock. Tighten bolts until cover can be lifted by hand.

13) Do not remove plastic scoop ring from input shaft unless input shaft bearing is to be replaced. If removed, replace with NEW ring. Use appropriate seal remover/installer to remove front cover seal (if necessary).

14) Remove front oil trough from upper transmission case. Pull input shaft forward and remove input shaft bearing outer race. Pull output shaft rearward and remove output shaft bearing outer race.

15) Remove countershaft bearing outer races by pulling countershaft forward and rearward. Pull countershaft rearward to permit bearing puller clearance.

NOTE: Tap gently during bearing removal. Forceful blows can damage bearing or transmission case.

---

16) Using bearing race puller and slide hammer, remove countershaft bearings (if necessary). Separate input shaft from output shaft. To gain clearance, pull input shaft forward with flats on flange located at top and bottom (6 and 12 o'clock).

17) Lift output shaft through upper opening of case. Remove input shaft and 4th gear blocker ring from case. Remove countershaft. Clean components. See CLEANING & INSPECTION.

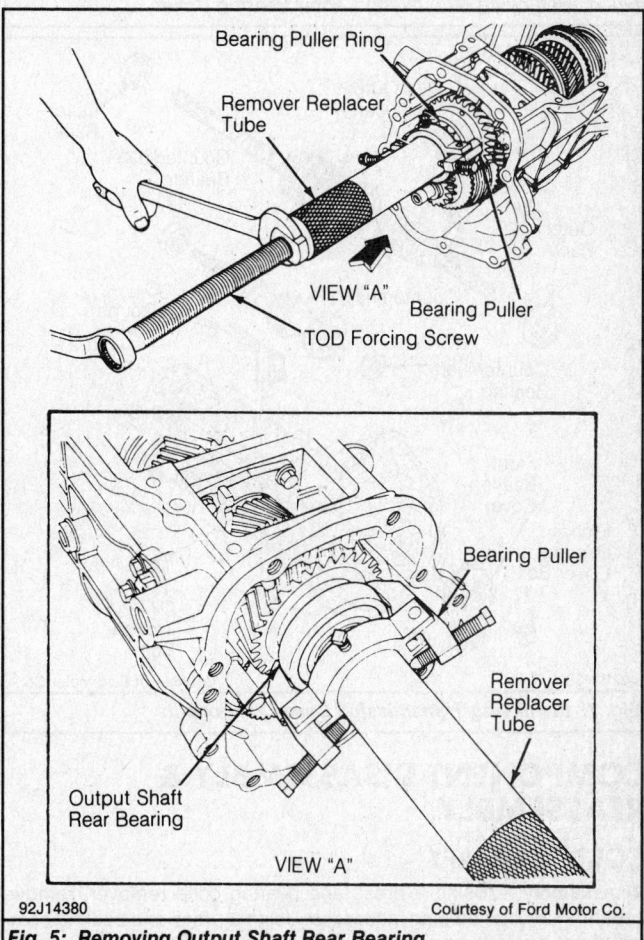

Bearing Puller Ring

Remover Replacer Tube

VIEW "A"

Bearing Puller

TOD Forcing Screw

Bearing Puller

Output Shaft Rear Bearing

Remover Replacer Tube

VIEW "A"

92J14380   Courtesy of Ford Motor Co.

Fig. 5: Removing Output Shaft Rear Bearing

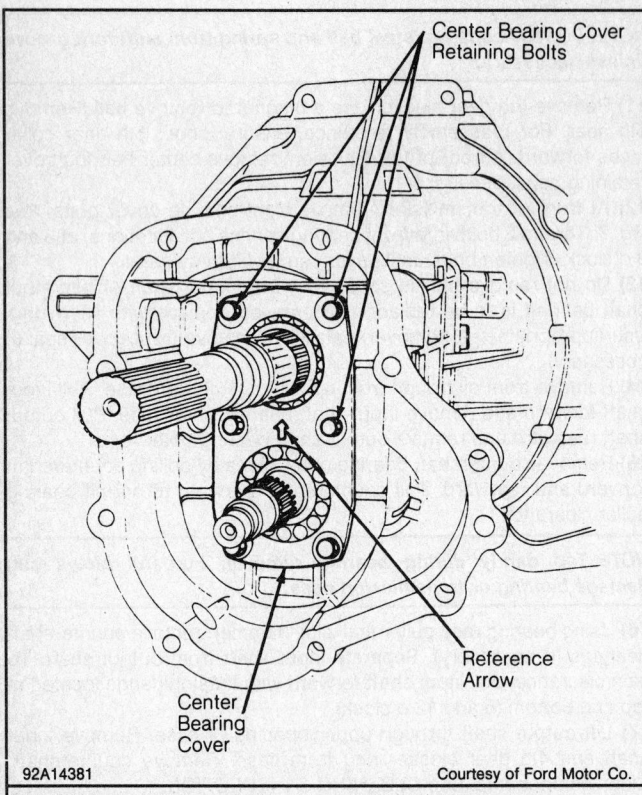

Fig. 6: Removing & Installing Center Bearing Cover

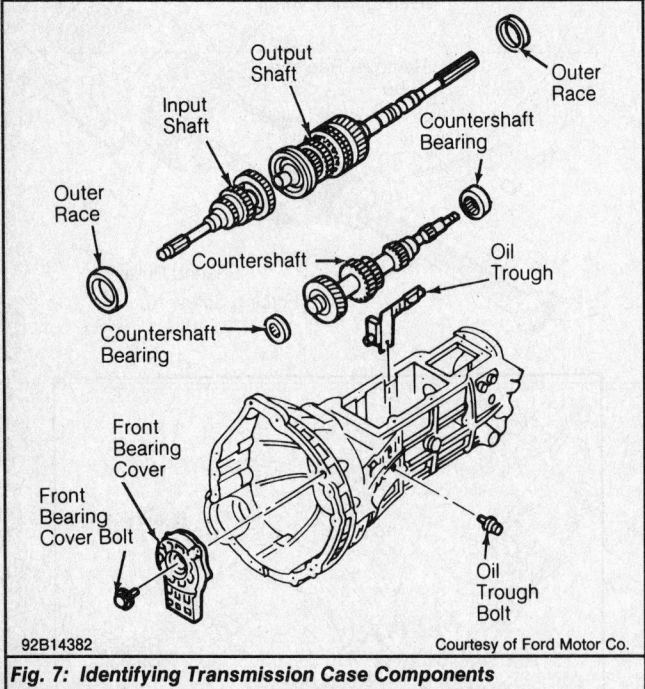

Fig. 7: Identifying Transmission Case Components

COMPONENT DISASSEMBLY & REASSEMBLY

COUNTERSHAFT

Disassembly – Using a press and bearing cone remover, remove countershaft rear bearing inner race. Using a press and bearing splitter, remove countershaft front bearing inner race. Clean components. See CLEANING & INSPECTION.

Reassembly – Using a press, spacer, bearing replacer and bearing plate, install countershaft rear bearing inner race. Using a press, bearing plate, spacer, bearing replacer and countershaft front bearing replacer, install countershaft front bearing inner race.

INPUT SHAFT

Disassembly – Remove and discard plastic scoop ring. Using bearing cone remover and an arbor press, press tapered roller bearing from input shaft. Discard bearing. Clean components. See CLEANING & INSPECTION.

Reassembly – Using an arbor press, bearing plate and bearing cone replacer, press tapered roller bearing onto input shaft bearing. Install plastic scoop ring, rotating clockwise to ensure input shaft oil holes properly engage ring. A click should be heard when alignment is obtained.

OUTPUT SHAFT

NOTE: Position output shaft as directional reference point for disassembly and reassembly procedures. See Fig. 8.

Disassembly – **1)** Remove pilot bearing, retaining ring, spacer and needle bearing from front of output shaft. Position output shaft with front end facing upward. Lift off clutch hub and sleeve assembly (3rd-4th), synchronizer blocker ring (3rd), 3rd gear and needle bearing as a unit.

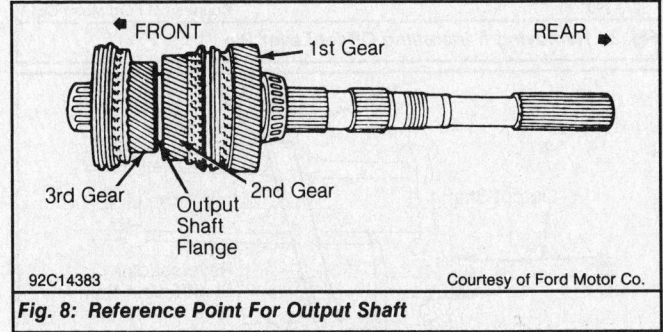

Fig. 8: Reference Point For Output Shaft

NOTE: Ensure output shaft flange does not contact or ride upward onto press cradle. Improper positioning of output shaft can cause component damage.

2) Position output shaft into press with rear end facing upward. Carefully press the following components off as an assembly: output shaft center bearing, 1st gear sleeve, needle bearing, 1st gear, blocker ring, 1st-2nd clutch hub and sleeve assembly, 2nd gear, blocker ring, and needle bearing. Clean components. See CLEANING & INSPECTION.

Reassembly – **1)** Lubricate output shaft journals. With output shaft rear end facing upward, install the following components onto output shaft: 2nd gear needle bearing, 2nd gear, blocker ring, 1st-2nd clutch hub and sleeve assembly, and blocker ring.

2) Install needle bearing into 1st gear sleeve and install assembly into 1st gear. Install 1st gear assembly and center bearing onto output shaft. Align 1st and 2nd synchronizer blocker rings with insert keys.

3) Using bearing replacer and seal plate, press components into place. Ensure center bearing race is seated completely onto output shaft. *See Fig. 9.*

4) Position output shaft with front end facing upward. Install needle bearing, 3rd gear and blocker ring. Install clutch hub and sleeve. Ensure reference mark and synchronizer key are aligned and that hub is installed in proper direction. *See Fig. 10.*

5) Install spacer, needle bearing (rollers upward or visible) and original retaining ring. Using a feeler gauge, measure end play between 3rd-4th clutch hub and retaining ring. End play should be .00-.002" (.00-.05 mm). If end play is not as specified, replace retaining ring. Retaining rings are available in thicknesses of .059-.077" (1.50-1.95 mm), in .002" (.05 mm) increments.

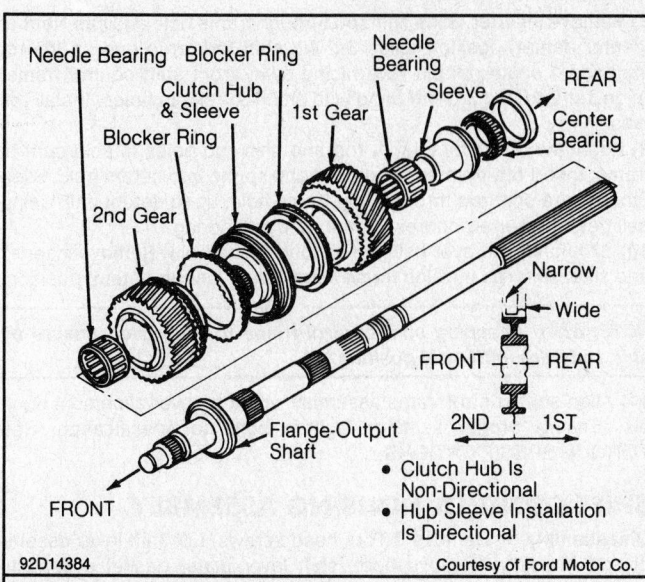

Fig. 9: Reassembly Of Output Shaft

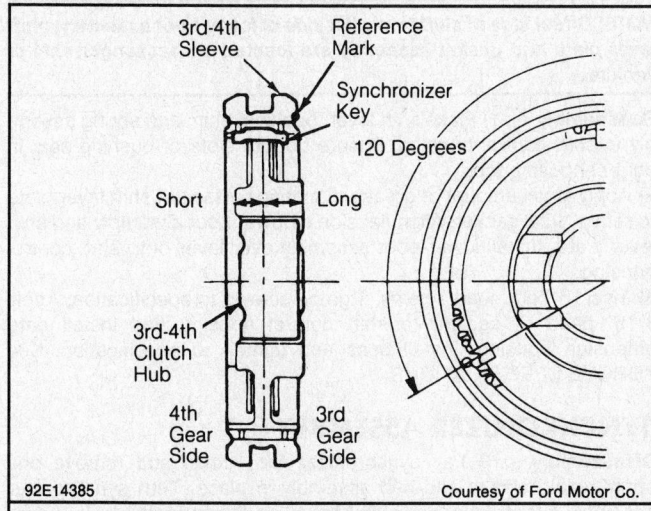

Fig. 10: Installing 3rd-4th Clutch Hub & Sleeve

REVERSE IDLER GEAR SHAFT

Disassembly – Remove retaining ring, spacer, reverse idler gear, needle bearings and thrust washer. Clean components. See CLEANING & INSPECTION.

Reassembly – **1)** Install idler gear shaft into transmission case. Use sealant on reverse idler shaft fixing bolt threads. Install and tighten fixing bolt to specification. See TORQUE SPECIFICATIONS.

2) Install thrust washer onto shaft, with brass side toward gear. Ensure tab mates with groove on reverse idler shaft. Install needle bearings onto shaft.

NOTE: Remaining steps are to be performed after installation of countershaft and input shaft assemblies.

3) Install reverse idler gear and spacer with brass side toward gear. Install original retaining ring onto idler shaft. Using a feeler gauge, measure end play. *See Fig. 11.* End play should be .004-.008" (.10-.20 mm). If end play is not as specified, replace retaining ring. Retaining rings are available in thicknesses of .059-.075" (1.5-1.9 mm), in .004" (.10 mm) increments.

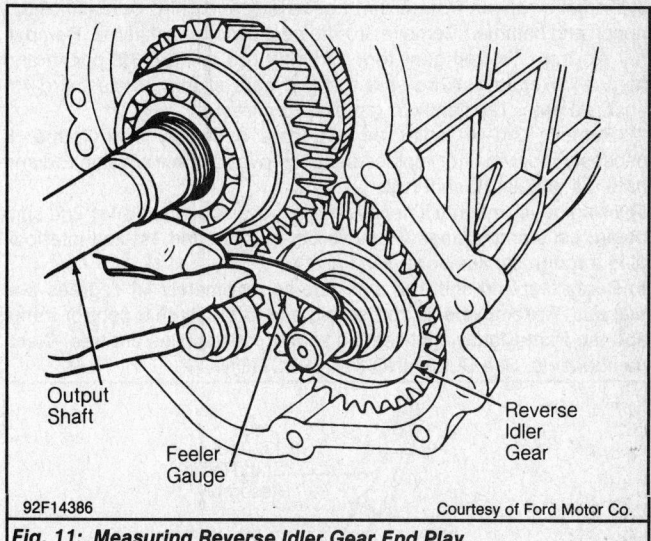

Fig. 11: Measuring Reverse Idler Gear End Play

SHIFT CONTROL FRAME ASSEMBLY

Disassembly – **1)** Ensure shift rods are in Neutral position. If necessary for repair or component replacement, remove top cover-to-shift control frame bolts. See Fig. 12. Remove shift control frame assembly from top cover.

CAUTION: Perform shift rod removal procedures with care. Wear safety glasses. Firmly cover detent ball bores with shop cloth to prevent component loss when tension is released on detent balls, springs and spring seats.

2) With clean cloth held tightly over lock ball bore, carefully remove 5th-reverse shift rod from shift control frame assembly. *See Fig. 13.* Using pencil magnet if necessary, remove 5th-reverse shift rod detent ball and spring.

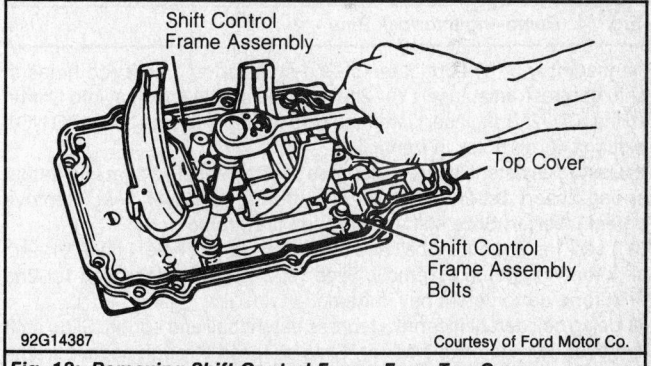

Fig. 12: Removing Shift Control Frame From Top Cover

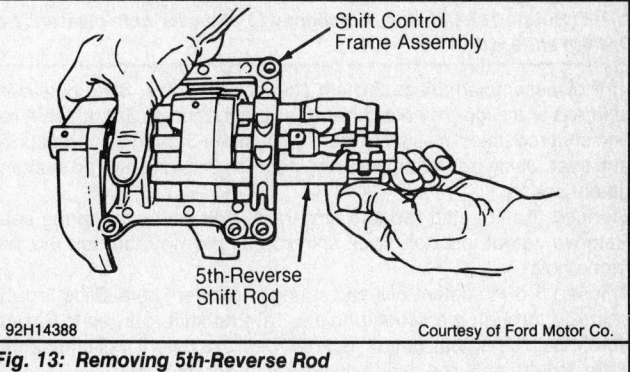

Fig. 13: Removing 5th-Reverse Rod

3) Remove roll pin from 3rd-4th gear fork and shift rod using 5/32" punch and hammer. Remove 3rd-4th gear fork from shift rod. Remove roll pin from 1st-2nd gear fork and shift rod using 5/32" punch and hammer. Rotate 1st-2nd shift rod and gate slightly to clear 3rd-4th shift rod gate. Tap lightly to remove from frame.

4) Remove 3rd-4th shift rod and gate assembly from frame. If necessary for repair or replacement, remove roll pin from shift rod and gate. Slide gate off shift rod.

5) Using pencil magnet if necessary, remove 3rd-4th and 1st-2nd shift detent balls and springs. Remove 5th-reverse and 1st-2nd interlock pins through service bore. See Fig. 14.

6) Rotate 1st-2nd shift rod and gate approximately 45 degrees and pull out. To remove shift rod spring and seat, tilt shift control frame and tap frame lightly until seat and spring assemblies are free. Clean components. See CLEANING & INSPECTION.

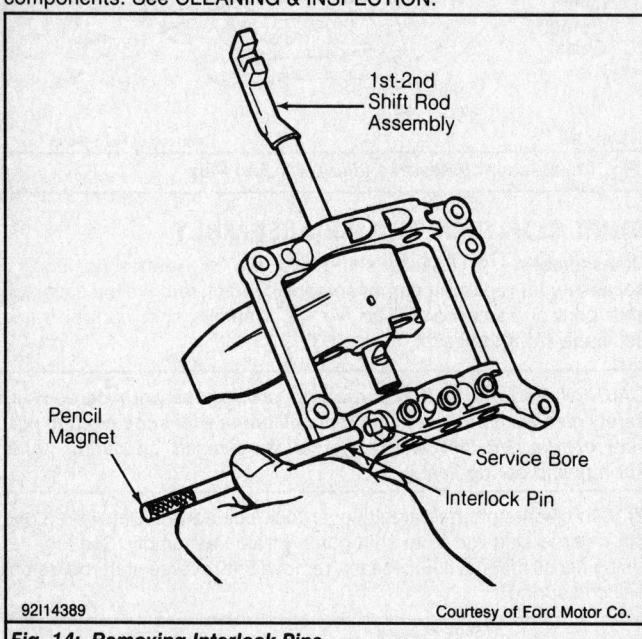

1st-2nd Shift Rod Assembly

Pencil Magnet

Service Bore

Interlock Pin

92I14389   Courtesy of Ford Motor Co.

Fig. 14: Removing Interlock Pins

Reassembly – 1) Lubricate 1st-2nd shift rod and shift rod holes in shift control frame. Insert 1st-2nd shift rod spring and seat into frame. Using a 5/32" drift, insert interlock pins through service bore. DO NOT block shift rod holes in frame.

2) Using ball detent inserter, depress 1st-2nd shift rod seat and detent spring. Insert 1st-2nd shift rod into frame hole over seat. Remove detent inserter. Slide shift rod through first frame hole.

3) Insert 1st-2nd detent ball and spring into detent hole. Install 1st-2nd shift fork into frame assembly. Slide 1st-2nd shift rod through 1st-2nd shift fork, up to detent ball in frame.

4) Using ball detent inserter, depress detent ball and spring. Slide shift rod over ball. Remove inserter. Slide shift rod through second frame hole and into Neutral (center detent) position.

NOTE: Rotate 1st-2nd shift rod slightly to allow for gate clearance of 3rd-4th shift rod.

5) If disassembled, place 3rd-4th shift rod in a vise. Slide gate onto shift rod and align pin holes. Install roll pin. Lubricate 3rd-4th shift rod and shift rod holes in shift control frame. Insert 3rd-4th shift rod spring and seat. Using ball detent inserter, depress 3rd-4th shift rod seat and detent spring.

6) Insert 3rd-4th shift rod into first frame hole and over spring seat. Remove detent inserter. Slide shift rod all the way through the first frame hole.

7) Insert 3rd-4th detent ball and spring into detent hole. Slide 3rd-4th shift rod through the second hole in 1st-2nd shift fork, up to 3rd-4th detent ball. Using ball detent inserter, depress detent ball and spring. Slide 3rd-4th shift rod over ball into second frame hole.

8) Remove inserter. Slide shift rod through frame hole and into Neutral (center detent) position. Slide 3rd-4th shift fork onto end of 3rd-4th shift rod. Locate roll pin hole facing away from shift control frame. Align 1st-2nd and 3rd-4th forks with shift rod roll pin holes. Install roll pins.

9) Lubricate 5th-reverse shift rod and shift rod holes in shift control frame. Insert 5th-reverse detent ball and spring into detent hole. Slide 5th-reverse shift rod through first frame hole, up to detent ball. Using ball detent inserter, depress detent ball and spring.

10) Slide shift rod over ball into second frame hole. Remove inserter and slide shift rod through frame into Neutral (center detent) position.

NOTE: When attaching shift control frame to top cover, ensure all shift rods are in Neutral position.

11) Align shift control frame assembly with top cover alignment dowels. Ensure proper seating. Tighten bolts to specification. See TORQUE SPECIFICATIONS.

SHIFT CONTROL HOUSING ASSEMBLY

Disassembly – Remove 3 Torx head screws. Lift shift lever assembly off housing. Remove boot, shift lever plate, gasket assembly, spring, shim and bushing from shift lever.

NOTE: Offset side of shift lever, flat side of lower boot assembly, shift lever plate and gasket assembly are located on passenger side of vehicle.

Reassembly – 1) Place shift lever, bushing, shim and spring assembly in shift control housing. Ensure bottom slots of bushing seat in control housing tabs.

2) Apply small amount of grease to mating surface of shift lever plate to retain NEW gasket. Align flat side of lower boot assembly and shift lever plate. Install lower boot assembly over lever onto shift control housing.

3) Insert 3 Torx head screws. Tighten screws to specification. Apply 1/16" bead of sealant to shift control housing and install onto extension housing. Install bolts and tighten to specification. See TORQUE SPECIFICATIONS.

SYNCHRONIZER ASSEMBLY

Disassembly – 1) Lay synchronizer face down and remove one spring. Hold sleeve and hub assembly in place. Turn synchronizer assembly over to opposite side and lay on flat surface.

2) Remove second spring and 3 insert keys. Slide sleeve and hub apart. See Fig. 15. Clean components. See CLEANING & INSPECTION.

Reassembly – 1) Locate dot reference mark on shoulder of one side of sleeve. Note direction of clutch hub-to-sleeve assembly. See Fig. 16. Insert hub into sleeve with one of 3 insert key slots of hub aligned with reference mark. Ensure hub moves freely on sleeve.

2) Lay hub and sleeve assembly face down on a flat surface. Install insert keys into hub slots. Insert synchronizer spring into clip hole on inner shoulder of sleeve. Install spring under protruding edges of insert keys.

3) Turn assembly over and repeat procedure using second spring. Springs install in opposite directions (clockwise and counterclockwise).

4) Use care during installation of synchronizer assembly onto shaft. Excessive movement between hub and sleeve may cause insert keys to pop out of hub slots, requiring reassembly.

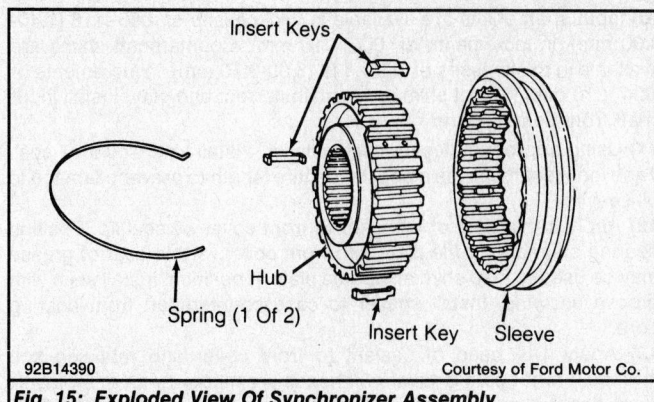

92B14390   Courtesy of Ford Motor Co.

Fig. 15: Exploded View Of Synchronizer Assembly

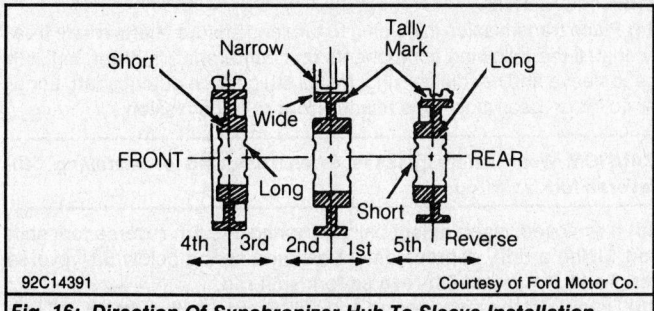

92C14391   Courtesy of Ford Motor Co.

Fig. 16: Direction Of Synchronizer Hub-To-Sleeve Installation

CLEANING & INSPECTION

CLEANING

Wash all parts in cleaning solvent except sealed bearings, "O" rings and seals. Use scraper or brush for heavy deposits. Rotate bearings by hand in cleaning solvent.

Dry all parts with compressed air. Hold bearings while drying to prevent bearing from spinning. To prevent damage to components, DO NOT spin dry bearings. Lubricate clean bearings with Mercon ATF and wrap in lint-free cloth until ready to install.

INSPECTION

Bearings – Inspect bearings and replace if broken, worn or rough. Lubricate cleaned bearing. Hold bearing vertically by inner race and spin outer race by hand. To prevent personal injury and/or damage to components, DO NOT spin bearings with compressed air. If roughness or vibration is noticed, bearing should be cleaned and lubricated again and retested. If roughness or vibration is noticed after 3 tests, replace bearing.

Bell Housing, Case & Extension Housing – Check transmission case and housings for cracks, worn or damaged bores or any other damage. Check machined mating surfaces for burrs, nicks or any other damage that could cause case or housing misalignment.

If extension housing bushing requires service, extension housing must be replaced as a unit.

Countershaft – Check gear teeth and splines for wear or damage. Replace countershaft if worn, scored or bent.

Gears – Inspect teeth on each gear. If teeth are chipped, worn or broken, replace individual gear. Carefully inspect any gear mating with damaged gear for signs of wear or damage. Replace as necessary.

Output Shaft – Check output shaft for runout by mounting shaft between "V"-blocks and applying dial indicator to several places along shaft. Runout should be less than .002" (.05 mm). Check splines for damage. Check needle bearing surface and bore of bearing for wear or roughness.

Shift Forks – Inspect shift fork fingers for wear or damage. Install shift fork into synchronizer sleeve. Using feeler gauge, check fork-to-sleeve clearance. Maximum clearance is .031" (.80 mm). Replace sleeve and/or fork if clearance exceeds specification.

Synchronizers – Inspect teeth on synchronizer ring. If teeth are chipped or excessively worn, replace ring. Measure clearance between side faces of synchronizer ring and gear. If clearance is less than .031" (.80 mm) replace ring and/or gear.

Inspect fiber-lined blocker ring for evidence of damaged, burned or missing lining material. Inspect synchronizer insert keys and insert grooves on clutch hub for wear. Ensure synchronizer sleeve slides easily on hub.

TRANSMISSION REASSEMBLY

1) Install countershaft assembly into transmission case through top opening. Ensure needle bearing is installed on input shaft. Position input shaft flange flats at top and bottom (6 and 12 o'clock).

2) Install input shaft into case through top opening. Install 4th gear synchronizer ring onto input shaft. Holding synchronizer blocker ring in place, position output shaft into case.

3) Angle input and output shaft assemblies upward. Carefully lower while assembling them as one unit. At rear of transmission, install output shaft center bearing outer race using a brass drift.

4) Seat output shaft bearing outer race. Install countershaft center bearing. See Fig. 17. Maintain correct bearing race protrusion above case surface. Protrusion should be approximately .078" (2.0 mm) for output shaft bearing outer race and .039" (1.0 mm). for countershaft bearing. See Fig. 18.

NOTE: Ensure center bearing outer races are squarely positioned in bores.

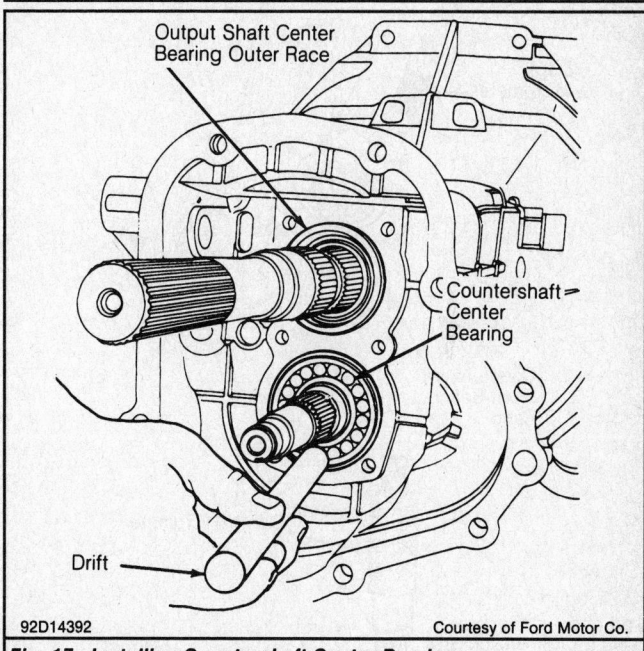

92D14392   Courtesy of Ford Motor Co.

Fig. 17: Installing Countershaft Center Bearing

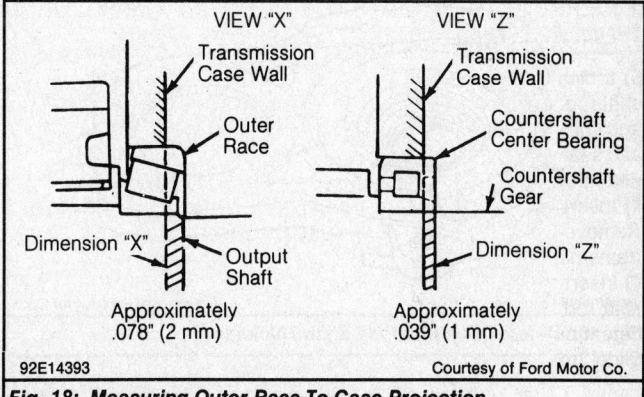

92E14393   Courtesy of Ford Motor Co.

Fig. 18: Measuring Outer Race-To-Case Projection

5) Install output shaft bearing cone. Install center bearing cover. Ensure cover reference arrow points upward. Center bearing cover bolts are marked with an "8". Tighten bolts to specification. See TORQUE SPECIFICATIONS.

6) Position transmission with input shaft and clutch housing facing upward. At front of transmission, use a brass drift to install input shaft front bearing outer race. Ensure outer race is squarely positioned in bore and input and output shafts turn freely. Install countershaft front bearing.

NOTE: If any input shaft, output shaft or countershaft related parts are replaced, end play must be readjusted.

7) If input shaft, output shaft or countershaft related parts have been replaced, measure dimensions "A", "B", and "C". *See Fig. 19.* Perform indicated calculations.

8) For Dimension "A", measure height of input shaft bearing outer race above transmission front bearing cover mating surface. For Dimension "B", measure depth of front cover outer race bore (input shaft). For Dimension "C", measure depth of countershaft front bearing race (transmission case to front cover mating surface).

9) For input shaft end play shim thickness, measure Dimension "B" minus Dimension "A" plus .002-.006 (.05-.15 mm). For countershaft end play shim thickness, measure Dimension "C" minus .006-.010" (.15-.25 mm).

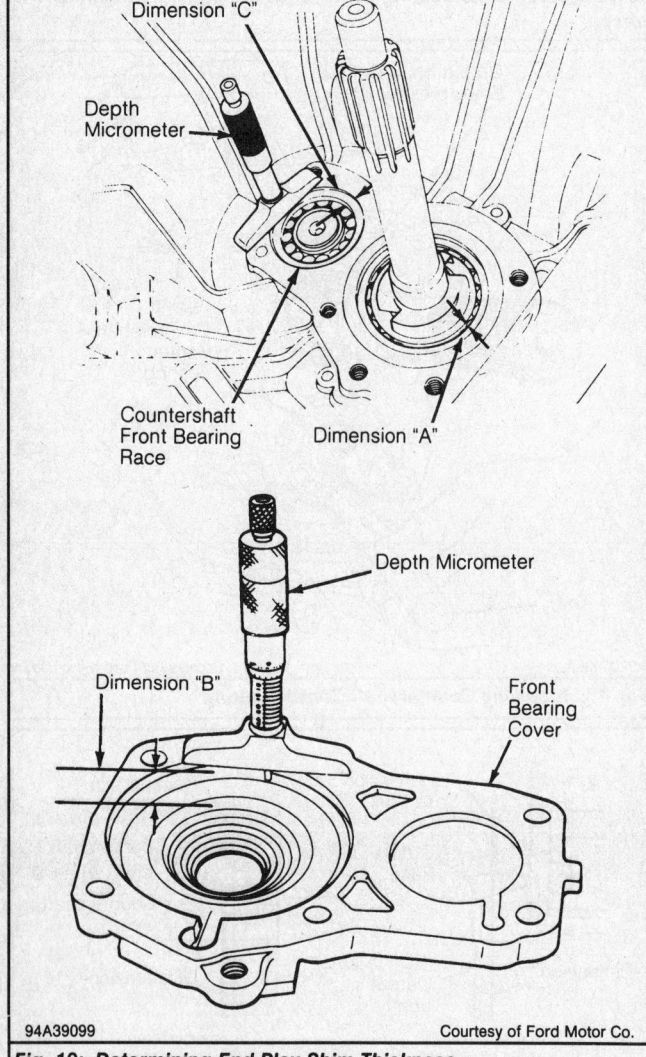

Fig. 19: Determining End Play Shim Thickness

10) Input shaft shims are available in thicknesses of .055-.118 (1.40-3.00 mm), in increments of .004" (.10 mm). Countershaft shims are available in thicknesses of .118-.146 (3.00-3.70 mm), in increments of .004" (.10 mm). Select shim to maintain correct end play. Install input shaft front bearing cone.

11) Using appropriate cover seal installer, install front cover oil seal. Tape input shaft splines along their entire length to prevent damage to oil seal lip.

12) Apply a thin coat of lubricant to front cover oil seal lip. Position bearing shim and baffle plate into front cover. A thin coat of grease may be used to hold shim and baffle plate in position. Install shim with groove showing. Install spacer to case countershaft front bearing bore.

13) Apply 1/8" bead of sealant to front cover and retaining bolt threads. Front bearing cover bolt heads are marked with a "6". Install front bearing cover. Tighten bolts to specification. See TORQUE SPECIFICATIONS.

14) Place transmission in holding fixture and ensure shafts rotate freely. Install the following components on countershaft in order: ball, 5th gear sleeve and needle bearing. Install 5th gear on output shaft. Longer collar on gear must face toward front of transmission.

CAUTION: Wear safety glasses when removing or installing 5th-reverse fork shift rod.

15) If removed, insert detent ball and spring into 5th-reverse fork shift rod. Using a drift, depress detent ball and spring below 5th-reverse fork rod bore. Install 5th-reverse fork shift rod.

16) Detent notches face spring and ball. Spring, ball and shift rod bolt hole face toward front of transmission. Remove drift and push rod completely through fork bore until detent ball locks into first detent notch.

17) Assemble 5th-reverse synchronizer hub, sleeve and 5th gear synchronizer blocker ring, to 5th-reverse shift fork and rod assembly. *See Fig. 20.* Reference mark must face reverse gear side.

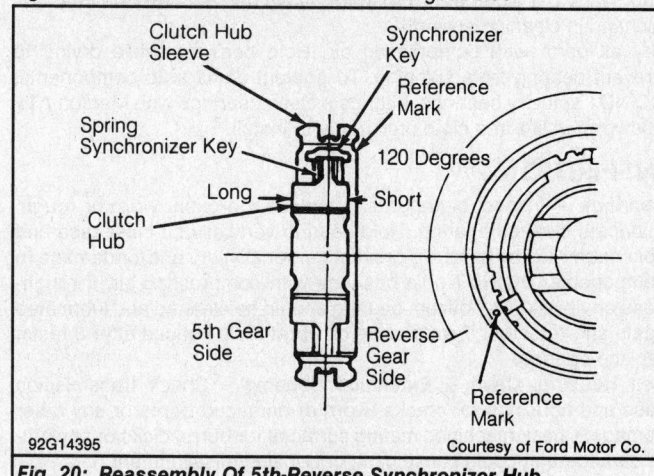

Fig. 20: Reassembly Of 5th-Reverse Synchronizer Hub

18) Install 5th-reverse shift fork, shift rod and synchronizer assembly to countershaft. Longer side of hub must face toward front of transmission. Mate shift fork gate to 5th-reverse counter lever end.

NOTE: To aid installation of shift rod, 5th-reverse shift fork can be shifted to rearward position. Reset to Neutral (center) position after installation.

19) Align fixing bolt holes in rod and transmission case. Apply sealant to 5th-reverse shift rod fixing bolt threads. Install rod fixing bolt. Tighten bolt to specification. See TORQUE SPECIFICATIONS.

20) Install split washer onto countershaft. Use a feeler gauge to measure end play. End play should be .0-.002 (.0-.05 mm). Split washers are available in thicknesses of .118-.137" (3.00-3.50 mm), in .004" (.10 mm) increments.

21) Install reverse gear thrust washer over countershaft with thrust washer groove facing toward split washer. Install blocker ring and needle bearings on countershaft as an assembly. Ensure blocker ring aligns with insert keys.

22) Install second thrust washer to countershaft. Press thrust washer forward against shoulder on countershaft reverse gear. Measure end play between thrust washer and countershaft reverse gear.

23) End play should be .010-.014" (.25-.35 mm). Replace thrust washer behind countershaft reverse gear, to obtain correct end play. Thrust washers are available in thicknesses of .295-.307" (7.5-7.8 mm), in .004" (.10 mm) increments.

24) Install selected thrust washer, countershaft reverse gear and second thrust washer. Install a temporary spacer onto countershaft in place of countershaft rear bearing.

25) Spacer should have an inner diameter larger than .83" (21.0 mm), an outer diameter smaller than 1.42" (36.0 mm), and an overall length of .59-.79" (15.0-20.0 mm). Loosely install countershaft lock nut to retain components.

26) Install reverse idler gear assembly. See REVERSE IDLER GEAR SHAFT under COMPONENT DISASSEMBLY & REASSEMBLY. Install sleeve and reverse gear onto output shaft. Ensure large flange faces toward rear of transmission.

27) Install counter lever assembly into transmission and align with slot in shift fork. Install thrust washer and retaining ring. Apply sealant to counter lever fixing bolt threads. Tighten counter lever fixing bolt to specification. See TORQUE SPECIFICATIONS.

28) Using gear installing spacer, shaft adapter, shaft adapter screw, remover/replacer tube, nut and washer, install output shaft rear bearing. *See Fig. 21.*

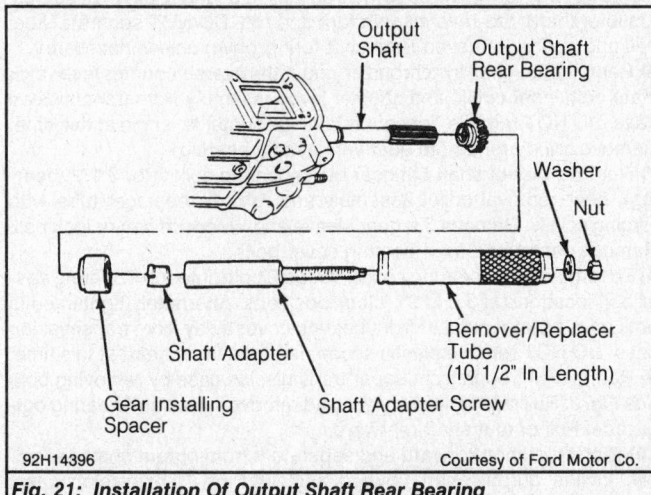

Fig. 21: Installation Of Output Shaft Rear Bearing

29) Remove temporary spacer from countershaft. Install countershaft rear bearing. Ensure bearing is fully seated before tightening shaft lock nuts. Lock transmission in 1st and 3rd gears.

30) Install NEW output shaft and countershaft lock nuts. Tighten nuts to specification. See TORQUE SPECIFICATIONS. Using chisel, stake lock nuts into shaft groove. Apply sealant to rear oil trough bolt. Install rear oil trough to transmission case. Tighten bolt to specification.

NOTE: If replacing speedometer drive gear, ensure replacement gear is same color code as original. Standard color is Green. Part number is E8TZ-17285-C (8 teeth RH).

31) Install speedometer drive gear and steel ball to output shaft. Steel ball can be installed in any of the 3 detents in drive gear. Install snap ring. Install countershaft oil funnel into extension housing. Ensure tabs are in correct slots.

32) Insert shift rail and selector finger assembly into rear hole of transmission case. Apply sealant to transmission case mating surface. Guiding shift rail through extension housing, position housing approximately 3-4" from case.

33) Install offset lever and guide spring into extension housing. Move extension housing toward transmission while guiding shift rail into offset lever and spring. *See Fig. 22.*

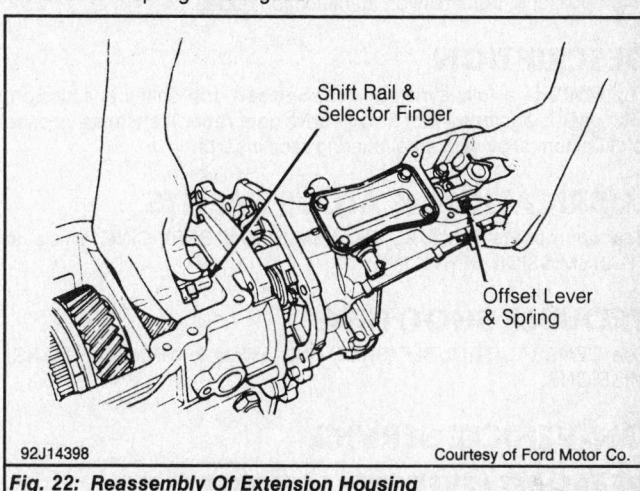

Fig. 22: Reassembly Of Extension Housing

34) Seat extension housing assembly to transmission case and install bolts. Tighten bolts to specification. Ensure transmission shafts rotate freely.

35) Install roll pin into offset lever and shift rail holes. *See Fig. 3.* Ensure synchronizers, top cover shift forks and shift rail selector finger are in Neutral position. Ensure gasket seats properly on top cover.

36) Position top cover to transmission case. Engage selector finger with shift forks and shift forks with synchronizers. Install top cover bolts. Tighten bolts to specification.

37) Install drain plug and washer. Tighten plug to specification. Using seal replacer, install extension housing seal. Ensure oil seal drain hole faces downward. Install back-up light switch and neutral start switch. Check operation of transmission. Ensure transmission shafts rotate freely. Manually shift transmission through all gears.

TORQUE SPECIFICATIONS
TORQUE SPECIFICATIONS

Application	Ft. Lbs. (N.m)
Back-Up Light Switch	18-26 (24-35)
Bell Housing Bolt	28-38 (38-52)
Center Bearing Cover Bolt	14-19 (19-26)
Countershaft Lock Nut	94-144 (127-195)
Crossmember Bolt	35-50 (47-68)
Drain Plug	29-43 (39-58)
Drive Shaft Bolt	71-95 (96-129)
Extension Housing Bolt	24-34 (33-46)
Filler Plug	29-43 (39-58)
Front Bearing Cover Bolt	10-12 (14-16)
Neutral Start Switch	18-26 (24-35)
Output Shaft Lock Nut	160-202 (217-274)
Reverse Idler Shaft Fixing Bolt	58-86 (79-117)
Shift Lever Bolt	18-24 (24-33)
Top Cover Bolt	12-16 (16-22)
5th-Reverse Shift Rod Bolt	16-22 (22-30)

	INCH Lbs. (N.m)
Counter Lever Fixing Bolt	70-90 (8-10)
Extension Housing Cover Bolt	70-90 (8-10)
Gearshift Lever Guide Bolt	70-90 (8-10)
Oil Trough Bolt (Front & Rear)	70-90 (8-10)
Shift Lever Plate Torx Screw	70-90 (8-10)
Shift Control Frame Bolt	7-9 (.8-1)
Shift Control Housing Bolt	70-90 (8-10)
Shift Lever Plate Torx Screw	70-90 (8-10)
5th-Reverse Inhibitor Assembly Bolt	70-90 (8-10)

MANUAL TRANSMISSIONS
Ford (Mazda) M50D 5-Speed

**Aerostar, Bronco, Explorer,
"F" Series, Ranger**

IDENTIFICATION

The M50D identification tag is located on left side of transmission main case. Certification label, located on left side door lock pillar, also lists applicable transmission identification codes.

DESCRIPTION

The M50D is a fully synchronized, 5-speed, top shift transmission. Fifth gear is equipped with an overdrive gear ratio. Transmission case is aluminum alloy with steel bearing race inserts.

LUBRICATION & ADJUSTMENTS

See appropriate MANUAL TRANSMISSION SERVICING article in TRANSMISSION SERVICING.

TROUBLE SHOOTING

See GENERAL TROUBLE SHOOTING article in MANUAL TRANSMISSIONS.

ON-VEHICLE SERVICE

GEARSHIFT LEVER REPLACEMENT

Removal – Shift transmission to Neutral position. Remove transfer case shift lever knob (if equipped). Remove carpet or floor mat to expose transmission shift lever boot screws. Remove transmission shift lever boot screws. Slide boot upward on shift lever to expose transmission shift lever nut and bolt. Remove shift lever nut, bolt and shift lever.

Installation – Install transmission shift lever. Ensure flat on transmission shift lever aligns with flat on transmission stub shaft so that shift lever bolt installs fully. Tighten bolt/nut to specification. See TORQUE SPECIFICATIONS. To complete installation, reverse removal procedure.

EXTENSION HOUSING SEAL

Removal & Installation – Remove drive shaft. Using appropriate seal remover, remove extension housing seal. Using appropriate seal installer, install NEW seal on extension housing. Lubricate oil seal lip prior to installation. Ensure oil seal drain hole faces downward. Install drive shaft.

EXTENSION HOUSING BUSHING

Extension housing bushing cannot be serviced. If bushing requires service or replacement, extension housing must be replaced as a unit.

REMOVAL & INSTALLATION

See appropriate MANUAL TRANSMISSION REMOVAL article in TRANSMISSION SERVICING.

TRANSMISSION DISASSEMBLY

1) Remove transmission drain plug and drain transmission. Remove top cover assembly and extension housing. Remove speedometer drive gear and steel ball (if equipped). If necessary, remove rear oil passage.

2) Lock transmission into 1st and 3rd gears. Release staked areas securing output shaft and countershaft lock nuts. Remove and discard countershaft rear bearing lock nut. Remove countershaft rear bearing and thrust washer.

3) Remove and discard output shaft lock nut. Remove reverse idler shaft attaching bolt. See Fig. 1. Remove reverse idler gear assembly by grasping and pulling rearward. Using remover/replacer tube, forcing screw and bearing puller, remove output shaft rear bearing from output shaft.

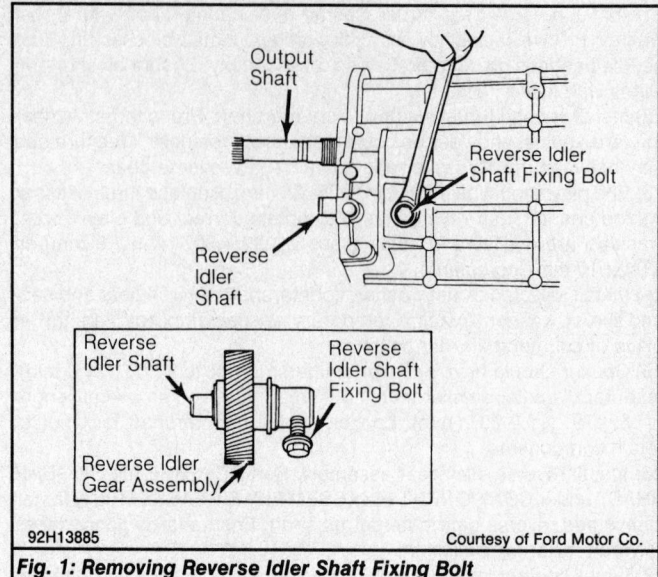

92H13885   Courtesy of Ford Motor Co.

Fig. 1: Removing Reverse Idler Shaft Fixing Bolt

4) Using brass drift and hammer, drive reverse gear from output shaft. Remove output shaft sleeve. See Fig. 2. Remove countershaft reverse gear with 2 needle bearings and reverse synchronizer ring.

5) Remove thrust washer and split washer from countershaft. Remove 5th and reverse shift rod attaching bolt. Remove the following parts as an assembly: 5th-reverse synchronizer hub and sleeve assembly (countershaft), 5th-reverse shift fork and rod. DO NOT separate steel ball and spring (removed from shift fork groove) unless necessary.

6) Remove 5th gear synchronizer ring, 5th-reverse counter lever lock plate bolt, inner circlip and counter lever assembly from transmission case. DO NOT remove Torx nut retaining counter lever pin at this time. Remove countershaft 5th gear with needle bearing.

7) Remove output shaft 5th gear using bearing collet (for 3 1/2" bearing), gear removal collet assembly and remover/replacer tube with forcing screw. Remove 5th gear sleeve and Woodruff key or lock ball. Remove center and front bearing cover bolts.

8) To remove front bearing cover, thread 2 bolts into front bearing cover bolt locations at 3 and 9 o'clock positions. Alternately tighten bolts until bolts bottom out. Lift front bearing cover away from transmission case. DO NOT remove plastic scoop ring from input shaft at this time.

9) Remove oil trough from upper transmission case by removing bolt. See Fig. 3. Pull input shaft forward and remove input shaft bearing outer race. Pull output shaft rearward.

10) Pull input shaft forward and separate it from output shaft assembly. Incline output shaft upward and lift from transmission case. Remove input shaft from transmission case.

11) Remove countershaft front and center bearing outer races by moving countershaft forward and rearward. Pull countershaft rearward to permit clearance for bearing puller behind countershaft front bearing. Remove countershaft front bearing. Remove countershaft through top of transmission case.

COMPONENT DISASSEMBLY & REASSEMBLY

INPUT SHAFT

Disassembly – Remove and discard plastic scoop ring. Using bearing cone remover/installer and arbor press, press tapered roller bearing from input shaft. See Fig. 4. For cleaning and inspection of components, see CLEANING & INSPECTION.

Reassembly – Using a press and bearing cone remover/installer, install input shaft bearing onto input shaft. Install NEW plastic scoop ring onto input shaft. Manually rotate ring clockwise to ensure input shaft holes properly engage scoop ring. A click should be heard as scoop ring notches align with input shaft holes.

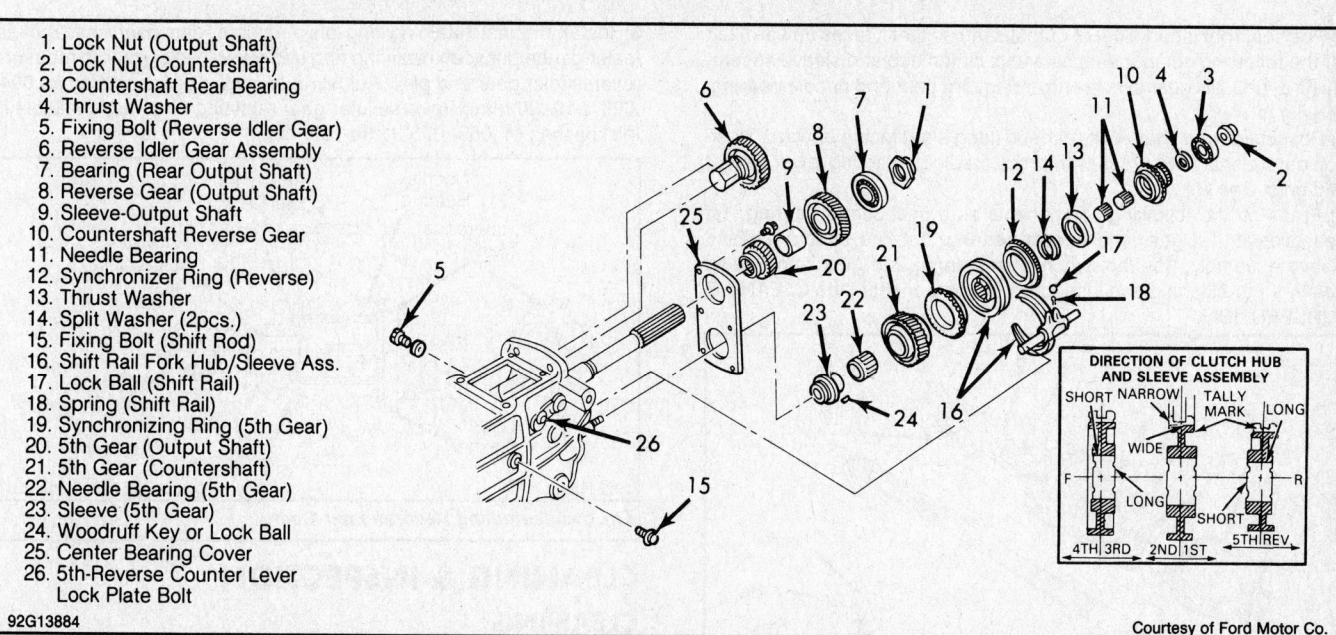

1. Lock Nut (Output Shaft)
2. Lock Nut (Countershaft)
3. Countershaft Rear Bearing
4. Thrust Washer
5. Fixing Bolt (Reverse Idler Gear)
6. Reverse Idler Gear Assembly
7. Bearing (Rear Output Shaft)
8. Reverse Gear (Output Shaft)
9. Sleeve-Output Shaft
10. Countershaft Reverse Gear
11. Needle Bearing
12. Synchronizer Ring (Reverse)
13. Thrust Washer
14. Split Washer (2pcs.)
15. Fixing Bolt (Shift Rod)
16. Shift Rail Fork Hub/Sleeve Ass.
17. Lock Ball (Shift Rail)
18. Spring (Shift Rail)
19. Synchronizing Ring (5th Gear)
20. 5th Gear (Output Shaft)
21. 5th Gear (Countershaft)
22. Needle Bearing (5th Gear)
23. Sleeve (5th Gear)
24. Woodruff Key or Lock Ball
25. Center Bearing Cover
26. 5th-Reverse Counter Lever
    Lock Plate Bolt

92G13884

Courtesy of Ford Motor Co.

Fig. 2: Exploded View Of Rear Housing Components

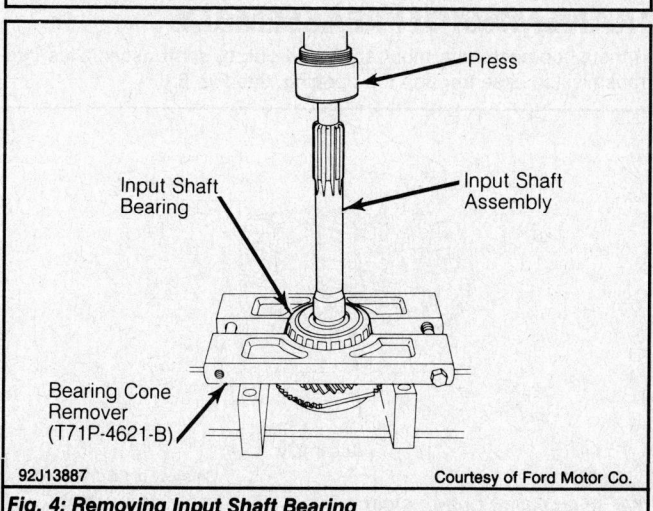

92I13886

Courtesy of Ford Motor Co.

Fig. 3: Exploded View Of Transmission Main Case Components

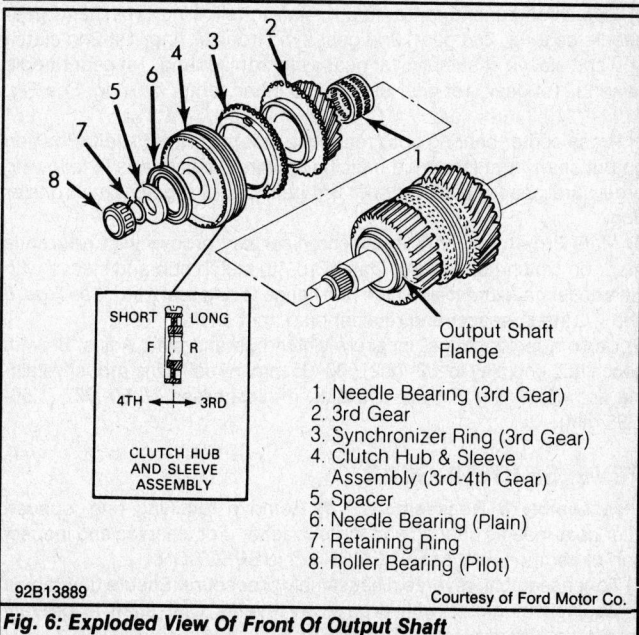

92J13887

Courtesy of Ford Motor Co.

Fig. 4: Removing Input Shaft Bearing

OUTPUT SHAFT

Disassembly – 1) Note location of output shaft flange. *See Fig. 5.* Use this flange as reference point and dividing line during assembly procedure. Remove pilot bearing, retaining ring, needle bearing (plain) and spacer from front of output shaft. *See Fig. 6.*

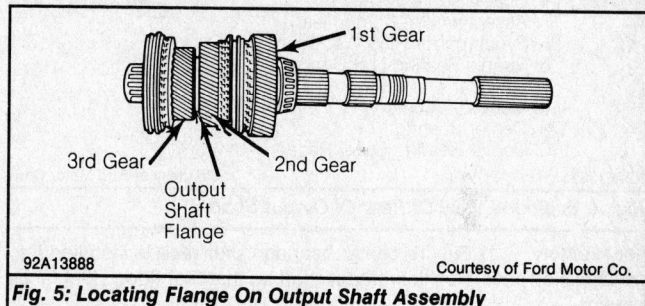

92A13888

Courtesy of Ford Motor Co.

Fig. 5: Locating Flange On Output Shaft Assembly

1. Needle Bearing (3rd Gear)
2. 3rd Gear
3. Synchronizer Ring (3rd Gear)
4. Clutch Hub & Sleeve
   Assembly (3rd-4th Gear)
5. Spacer
6. Needle Bearing (Plain)
7. Retaining Ring
8. Roller Bearing (Pilot)

92B13889

Courtesy of Ford Motor Co.

Fig. 6: Exploded View Of Front Of Output Shaft

2) Position front (short side) of output shaft so that it faces upward. Lift off the following components as a unit: clutch hub and sleeve assembly (3rd-4th), 3rd gear synchronizer ring, 3rd gear and needle bearing. See Fig. 6.

3) Position output shaft with rear end (long side) facing upward. Position output shaft into press with press cradle contacting lower part of 2nd gear. See Fig. 7.

4) Press off the following components as a unit: center bearing, 1st gear sleeve, 1st gear and needle bearing, 1st-2nd clutch hub and sleeve assembly, 1st-2nd synchronizer rings, 2nd gear and needle bearing. For cleaning and inspection of components, see CLEANING & INSPECTION.

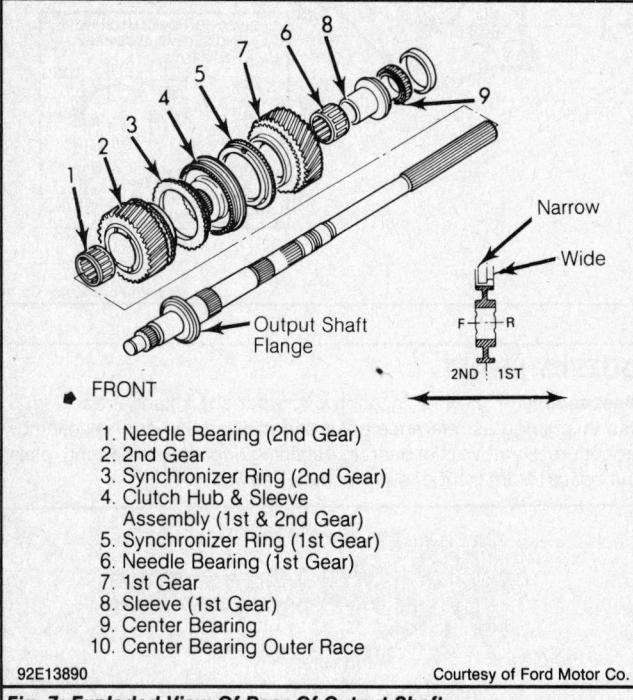

FRONT

1. Needle Bearing (2nd Gear)
2. 2nd Gear
3. Synchronizer Ring (2nd Gear)
4. Clutch Hub & Sleeve
   Assembly (1st & 2nd Gear)
5. Synchronizer Ring (1st Gear)
6. Needle Bearing (1st Gear)
7. 1st Gear
8. Sleeve (1st Gear)
9. Center Bearing
10. Center Bearing Outer Race

92E13890   Courtesy of Ford Motor Co.

Fig. 7: Exploded View Of Rear Of Output Shaft

Reassembly – 1) Ensure center bearing outer race is installed into transmission case. Position output shaft so that rear (long side) faces upward.

2) Install components onto output shaft in following order: 2nd gear needle bearing, 2nd gear, 2nd gear synchronizer ring, 1st-2nd clutch hub and sleeve assembly, 1st gear synchronizer ring, 1st gear needle bearing, 1st gear, 1st gear sleeve and inner center bearing. See Fig. 7.

3) Press center bearing onto rear (long side) of output shaft. Position output shaft front (short side) facing upward. Install parts in following order: 3rd gear needle bearing, 3rd gear and 3rd gear synchronizer ring.

4) Mate 3rd-4th clutch hub synchronizer key groove with reference mark on clutch hub sleeve. Install 3rd-4th clutch hub and sleeve with reference mark and long clutch hub flange facing rearward. See Figs. 6 and 11. Install spacer and retainer on output shaft.

5) Using a feeler gauge, measure clutch hub end play. Adjust 3rd-4th clutch hub end play to .00-.002" (.00-.05 mm) by selecting proper retaining ring. Retaining ring are available in thicknesses of .59-.077 (1.50-1.95 mm).

REVERSE IDLER GEAR

Disassembly & Reassembly – 1) Remove retaining ring, spacer, idler gear, needle bearing and thrust washer. For cleaning and inspection of components, see CLEANING & INSPECTION.

2) To reassemble, reverse disassembly procedure. Ensure that tab on thrust washer mates with groove on reverse idler shaft to prevent rotation of thrust washer. See Fig. 8.

3) Install original retaining ring onto reverse idler gear shaft. Insert feeler gauge between retaining ring and reverse idler gear to measure reverse idler gear end play. Adjust reverse idler gear end play to .004-.008" (.10-.20 mm). Reverse idler gear retaining rings are available in thicknesses of .059-.075" (1.50-1.90 mm).

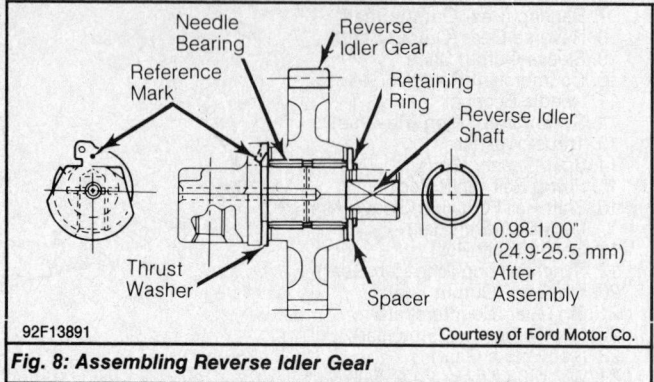

92F13891   Courtesy of Ford Motor Co.

Fig. 8: Assembling Reverse Idler Gear

CLEANING & INSPECTION
CLEANING

Wash all parts except seals, in cleaning solvent. Dry all parts with compressed air. DO NOT spin bearings with compressed air.

INSPECTION

Bearings – Inspect bearings and replace if broken, worn or rough. Lubricate cleaned bearing. Hold bearing vertically by inner race and spin outer race by hand. DO NOT spin bearings with compressed air. If roughness or vibration is noticed, bearing should be cleaned and lubricated again and retested. If roughness or vibration is noticed after 3 tests, replace bearing.

Countershaft – Inspect splines and gear teeth for damage or wear. Replace countershaft if bent, damaged or worn.

Input Shaft – Replace input shaft if splines are damaged, needle bearing surface in bore of bearing is worn or rough, or if cone surface is damaged. DO NOT spin bearings with compressed air.

Output Shaft – Mount output shaft in V-blocks. Check runout on shaft at several locations. If runout exceeds .002" (.05 mm), replace output shaft.

Synchronizers – If teeth on synchronizer ring are chipped, broken or worn, replace synchronizer ring. Note that 3rd gear synchronizer is different from others. To check for wear, mount synchronizer to mating gear and measure clearance between gear and synchronizer side faces using a feeler gauge. If clearance is less than .031" (.80 mm), replace synchronizer ring or mating gear.

TRANSMISSION REASSEMBLY

1) Install countershaft, input shaft and output shaft assemblies into transmission case through top opening. See Fig. 9.

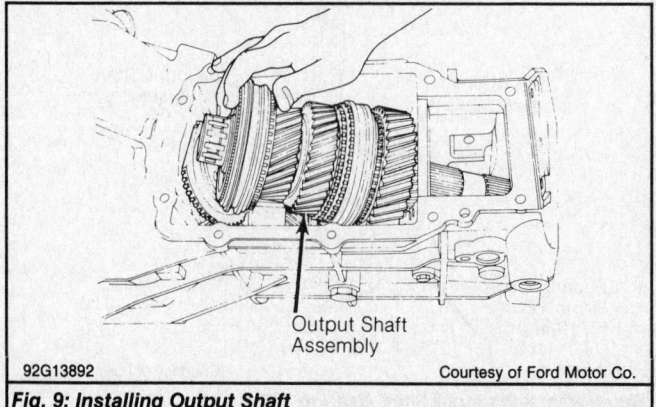

92G13892   Courtesy of Ford Motor Co.

Fig. 9: Installing Output Shaft

NOTE: Ensure that needle roller bearing is installed into input shaft and 4th gear synchronizer ring is installed at this time.

2) Mate input and output shaft assemblies by positioning them at an upward angle and setting them together. Install output shaft center bearing outer race using a brass drift. Seat center bearing outer races. Install countershaft center bearing. Ensure center bearing outer races are squarely positioned in bores.

3) Position center bearing cover to transmission case with reference arrow pointing upward. Ensure all center bearing cover bolt heads are marked with an "8". Tighten center bearing cover bolts to specification. See TORQUE SPECIFICATIONS.

4) Install countershaft front bearing by hand. Apply grease to shim, bearing cover and oil baffle to retain them in position during assembly. Install shim with groove showing. Install spacer to transmission case countershaft front bearing bore.

5) Install Woodruff key or lock ball, 5th gear sleeve and 5th gear needle bearing onto 5th gear countershaft. To install 5th gear assembly, use Gear Installing Spacer (T88T-7025-F). When tool bottoms, add Gear Installing Spacer (T88T-7025-G) and press 5th gear assembly all the way into position.

6) Position counter lever assembly on transmission and install thrust washer and retaining ring. If removed, position 5th-reverse shift fork and shift rail to top cover. See Fig. 10. Insert 5th-reverse shift rail through top cover bore and 5th-reverse shift fork. Install spring and detent ball to lower part of rod.

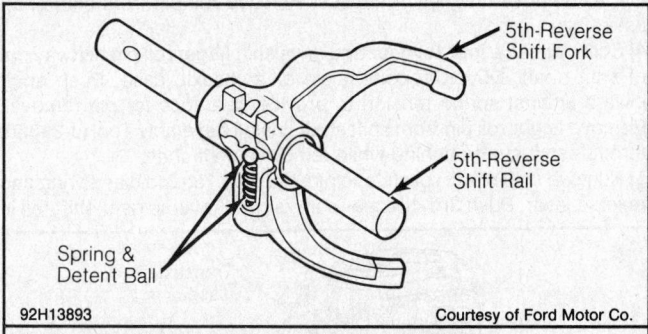

Fig. 10: Installing 5th-Reverse Shift Fork & Rail

7) Assemble 5th-reverse synchronizer hub, sleeve and 5th gear synchronizer ring to 5th-reverse shift fork and rod assembly. Install longer flange, on 5th-reverse hub, sleeve and synchronizer assembly, toward front of transmission. Reference mark on synchronizer sleeve must be installed toward reverse gear. See Figs. 2 and 11.

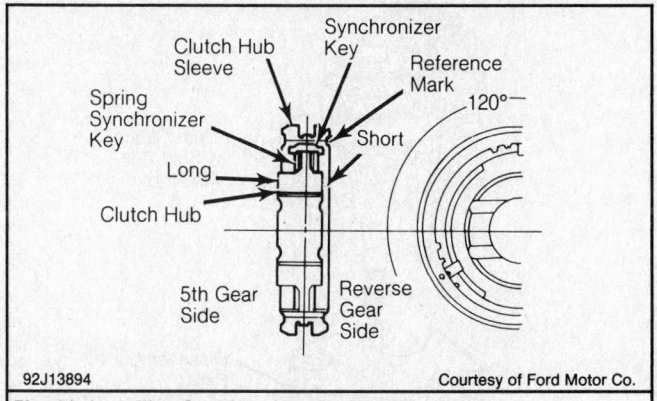

Fig. 11: Installing Synchronizer Assembly

8) Install and mate 5th-reverse shift fork and shift rail assembly to counter lever end. Install assembly in case, aligning threaded fixing bolt bores, in rail and transmission case. Tighten bolt to specification. See TORQUE SPECIFICATIONS. Position oil passage to transmission case and install bolt.

9) If original clutch hub and/or counter reverse gear are being used, install original split washers onto countershaft and go to step 11). If synchronizer hub has been replaced, install original split washers. Using a feeler gauge, measure 5th-reverse synchronizer hub end play between synchronizer hub and split washers.

10) End play should be 0-0.002" (0-.05 mm). Replace split washers to obtain proper end play. Split washers are available in thicknesses of .12-.14" (3.0-3.5 mm). Ensure NEW split washers are same thickness. Go to next step.

11) Install reverse synchronizer ring and needle bearing into reverse gear. Install counter reverse gear and needle bearings onto counter shaft as an assembly. Install thrust washer and press forward by hand against shoulder on countershaft.

12) Maintain forward pressure and measure end play with feeler gauge between counter reverse gear and thrust washer. Counter reverse gear end play should be .010-.014" (.25-.36 mm). Replace thrust washer to obtain proper end play. Thrust washers are available in thicknesses of .293-.305" (7.45-7.75 mm).

13) Temporarily install a spacer in place of countershaft bearing. Loosely install countershaft lock nut to retain components. Install reverse idler gear assembly.

14) Drive sleeve and reverse gear assembly onto output shaft. Install reverse gear with longer flange facing forward. Install output shaft rear bearing.

15) Remove temporary spacer from countershaft. Install countershaft rear bearing by hand. Ensure bearing is fully seated to avoid damage to output shaft threads.

16) Lock transmission into 1st and 3rd gear. Install NEW output and countershaft lock nuts by hand. Tighten nuts to specification. See TORQUE SPECIFICATIONS. Stake lock nuts to bottom of shaft.

17) Install speedometer drive gear (if equipped). Install transmission extension housing and top cover. Tighten bolts to specification. See TORQUE SPECIFICATIONS. Fill transmission with Mercon automatic transmission fluid.

TORQUE SPECIFICATIONS
TORQUE SPECIFICATIONS

Application	Ft. Lbs. (N.m)
Center Bearing Cover Bolt	14-19 (19-26)
Countershaft Lock Nut	94-144 (127-195)
Drain Plug	29-43 (39-58)
Extension Housing Bolt	24-34 (33-46)
Filler Plug	29-43 (39-58)
Front Bearing Cover Bolt	12-17 (16-23)
Gear Shift Lever Bolt/Nut	12-18 (16-24)
Output Shaft Lock Nut	160-203 (217-275)
Reverse Idler Shaft Fixing Bolt	58-86 (79-117)
Top Cover Bolt	12-16 (16-22)
5th-Reverse Shift Rail Bolt	16-22 (22-30)

	INCH Lbs. (N.m)
Front Oil Passage Bolt	72-96 (8-11)
Rear Oil Passage Bolt	60-84 (7-9)

MANUAL TRANSMISSIONS
GM GETRAG 284 5-Speed

Chevrolet: Lumina (1993)
Oldsmobile: Cutlass Supreme (1993)
Pontiac: Grand Prix (1993)

IDENTIFICATION

Transaxle is identified by identification tags located on left rear side and lower left side of transaxle below left side axle. *See Fig. 1.*

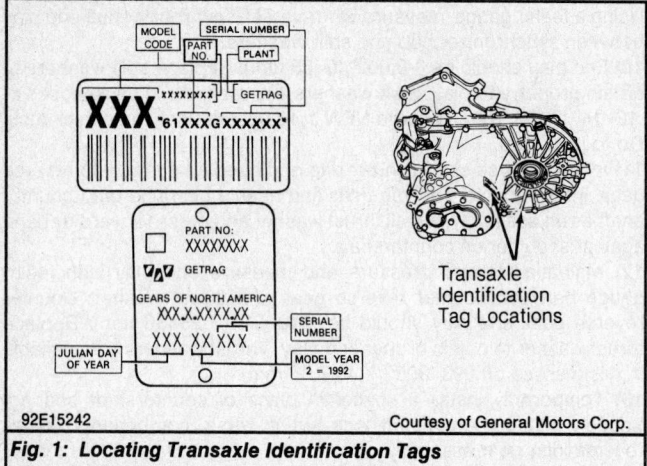

Fig. 1: Locating Transaxle Identification Tags

DESCRIPTION

Getrag 284 transaxle is a 5-speed constant-mesh transaxle. All forward gears, reverse gear and differential output are combined in the assembly. Gear selection and shifting is accomplished by a combination of synchronizers and sliding shift forks.

LUBRICATION & ADJUSTMENTS

See appropriate MANUAL TRANSMISSION SERVICING article in TRANSMISSION SERVICING.

TROUBLE SHOOTING

See GENERAL TROUBLE SHOOTING article in MANUAL TRANSMISSIONS.

ON-VEHICLE SERVICE

WARNING: When battery is disconnected, vehicle computer and memory systems may lose memory data. Driveability problems may exist until computer systems have completed a relearn cycle. See COMPUTER RELEARN PROCEDURES article in APPLICATIONS & IDENTIFICATION before disconnecting battery.

SHIFT CABLES

Removal & Installation – 1) Disconnect negative battery cable. Disconnect cables from transaxle. Remove nut and retaining clamp securing shift and select cables to transaxle. Remove console assembly. Disconnect cables at shifter. Pull carpet back to expose cables. **2)** Remove shift cables cover. Remove cable grommet retainer and nuts and grommet at floor panel. Raise and support vehicle. Push cable through dash mat. Lower vehicle and remove cables. To install, reverse removal procedure.

DRIVE AXLE OIL SEAL

Removal & Installation – Raise and support vehicle. Remove wheel and drive axle. See DRIVE AXLE SHAFTS. Pry out oil seal with screwdriver. Lubricate NEW oil seal lip and install seal using seal installer. Install drive axle. To complete installation, reverse removal procedure. Tighten nuts to specification. See TORQUE SPECIFICATIONS. Check fluid level.

DRIVE AXLE SHAFTS

See appropriate article in AXLE SHAFTS & TRANSFER CASES.

REMOVAL & INSTALLATION

See appropriate MANUAL TRANSMISSION REMOVAL article in TRANSMISSION SERVICING.

TRANSAXLE DISASSEMBLY

1) Remove shift lever and selector lever retainer from transaxle. Remove dipstick and speedometer signal assembly. Puncture detent holder cover in middle and pry it off. Remove bolts, detent holder, springs and interlock pins. Remove detent balls, and pry loose reverse shift rail bushing. Remove shift shaft detent snap ring and cover. *See Fig. 3.*

CAUTION: Use caution when removing 5th-reverse bias spring outer spring seat and screw. Components are under pressure.

2) Remove screw, detent outer spring seat, 5th-reverse bias spring and detent inner spring seat. Shift transaxle to Neutral position. Place transaxle on bench with clutch housing facing upward. Remove bolts retaining clutch housing to transaxle case. Remove clutch housing.
3) Remove differential output shaft by inserting a punch through differential case onto output shaft. Tap on output shaft to free shaft from transaxle case. Remove differential gear assembly from case. *See Fig. 4.* Remove magnet from case. Remove roll pin from shift shaft assembly.
4) Shift transaxle into 1st gear and drive shift finger roll pin halfway out of shift shaft. DO NOT bottom pin on transaxle case. Push shaft inward against spring tension to provide clearance for pin removal. Remove finger roll pin from shift shaft. Install Assembly Tool (J-39366) through shift shaft opening while removing shift shaft.
5) Remove shift shaft, rollers and pin. Remove 1st-2nd bias spring and reverse lever. Push 3rd-4th gear shift rail and reverse gear shift rail in

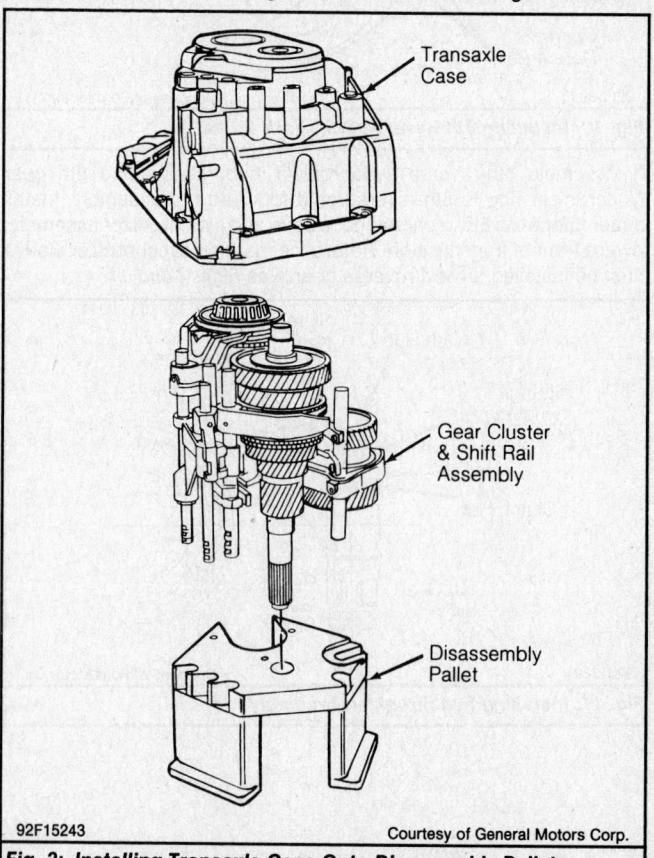

Fig. 2: Installing Transaxle Case Onto Disassembly Pallet

to engage transaxle in 4th and Reverse gears. Ensure gears are engaged to lock shaft. Remove case end plate retaining bolts and case end plate.

6) Remove input and output oil delivery tubes, selective shim and retainer. *See Fig. 4.* Using Hex socket, remove retainers, input cluster

gear and shaft assembly. Shift transaxle to Neutral position. Position transaxle case onto Disassembly Pallet (J-39367). *See Fig. 2.* Align shift rail and shaft pilots to fixture. Remove transaxle case from gear cluster and shift rail assembly.

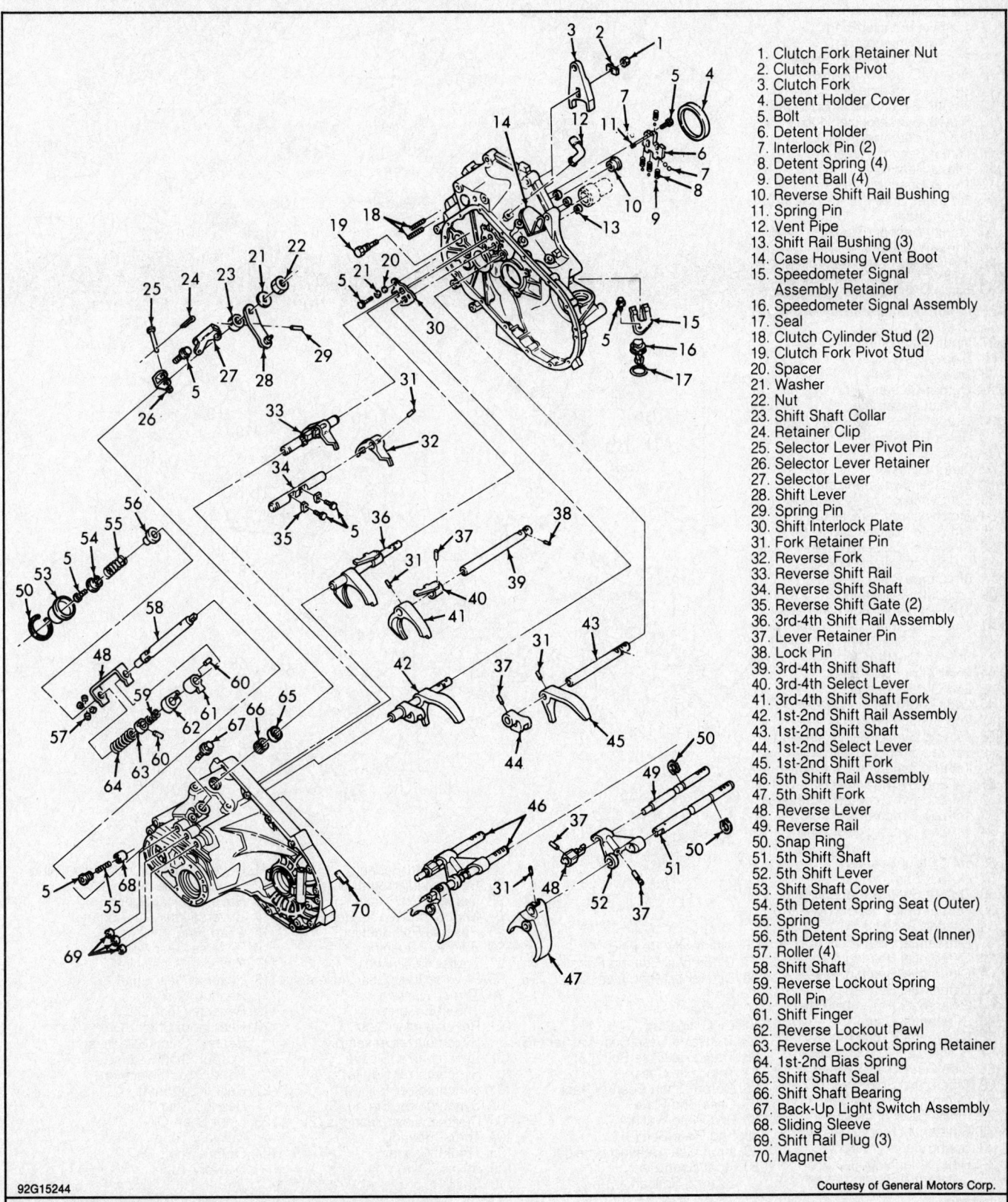

1. Clutch Fork Retainer Nut
2. Clutch Fork Pivot
3. Clutch Fork
4. Detent Holder Cover
5. Bolt
6. Detent Holder
7. Interlock Pin (2)
8. Detent Spring (4)
9. Detent Ball (4)
10. Reverse Shift Rail Bushing
11. Spring Pin
12. Vent Pipe
13. Shift Rail Bushing (3)
14. Case Housing Vent Boot
15. Speedometer Signal Assembly Retainer
16. Speedometer Signal Assembly
17. Seal
18. Clutch Cylinder Stud (2)
19. Clutch Fork Pivot Stud
20. Spacer
21. Washer
22. Nut
23. Shift Shaft Collar
24. Retainer Clip
25. Selector Lever Pivot Pin
26. Selector Lever Retainer
27. Selector Lever
28. Shift Lever
29. Spring Pin
30. Shift Interlock Plate
31. Fork Retainer Pin
32. Reverse Fork
33. Reverse Shift Rail
34. Reverse Shift Shaft
35. Reverse Shift Gate (2)
36. 3rd-4th Shift Rail Assembly
37. Lever Retainer Pin
38. Lock Pin
39. 3rd-4th Shift Shaft
40. 3rd-4th Select Lever
41. 3rd-4th Shift Shaft Fork
42. 1st-2nd Shift Rail Assembly
43. 1st-2nd Shift Shaft
44. 1st-2nd Select Lever
45. 1st-2nd Shift Fork
46. 5th Shift Rail Assembly
47. 5th Shift Fork
48. Reverse Lever
49. Reverse Rail
50. Snap Ring
51. 5th Shift Shaft
52. 5th Shift Lever
53. Shift Shaft Cover
54. 5th Detent Spring Seat (Outer)
55. Spring
56. 5th Detent Spring Seat (Inner)
57. Roller (4)
58. Shift Shaft
59. Reverse Lockout Spring
60. Roll Pin
61. Shift Finger
62. Reverse Lockout Pawl
63. Reverse Lockout Spring Retainer
64. 1st-2nd Bias Spring
65. Shift Shaft Seal
66. Shift Shaft Bearing
67. Back-Up Light Switch Assembly
68. Sliding Sleeve
69. Shift Rail Plug (3)
70. Magnet

92G15244

Courtesy of General Motors Corp.

Fig. 3: *Exploded View Of Shift Assemblies & Case Components*

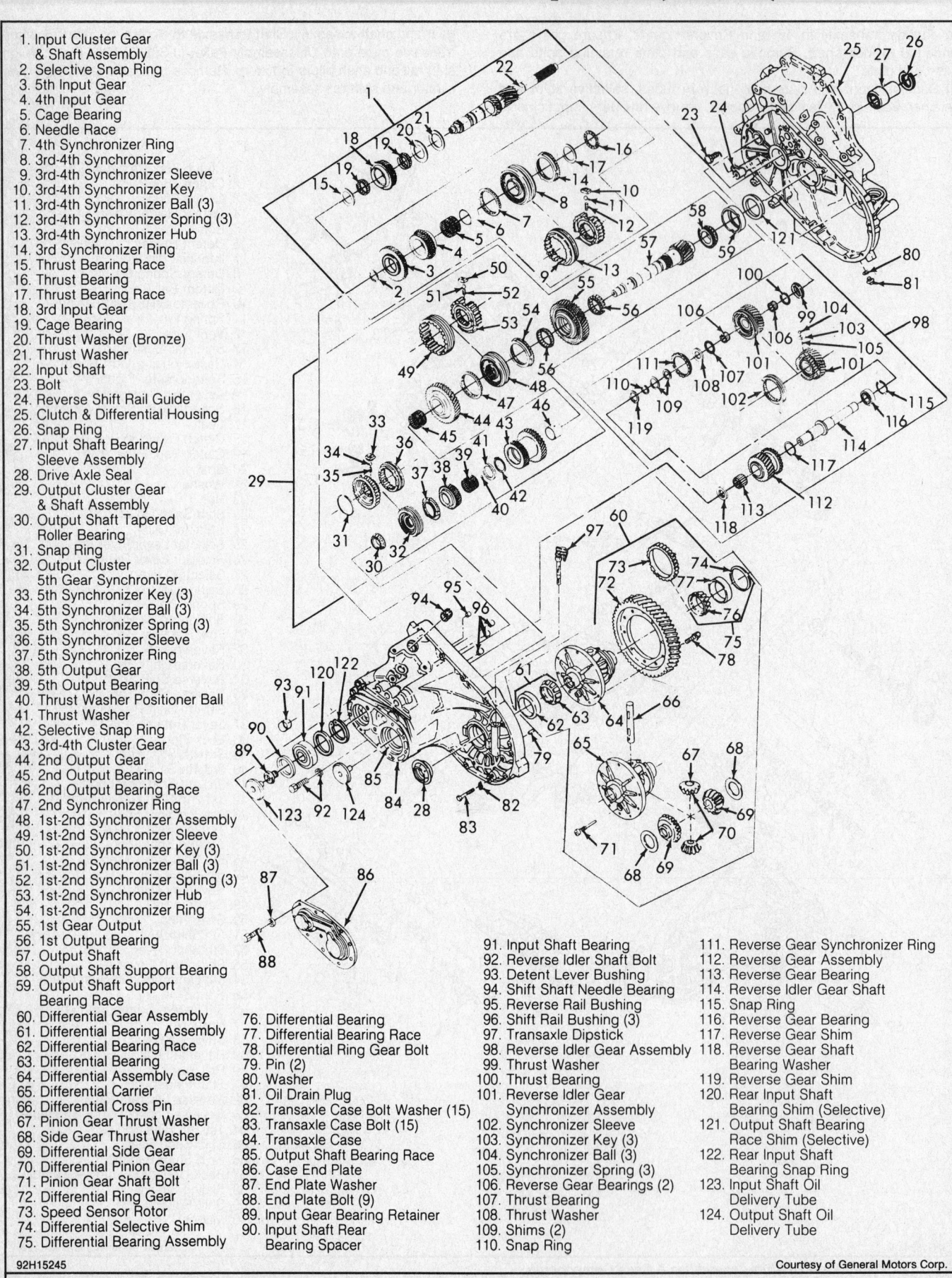

1. Input Cluster Gear & Shaft Assembly
2. Selective Snap Ring
3. 5th Input Gear
4. 4th Input Gear
5. Cage Bearing
6. Needle Race
7. 4th Synchronizer Ring
8. 3rd-4th Synchronizer
9. 3rd-4th Synchronizer Sleeve
10. 3rd-4th Synchronizer Key
11. 3rd-4th Synchronizer Ball (3)
12. 3rd-4th Synchronizer Spring (3)
13. 3rd-4th Synchronizer Hub
14. 3rd Synchronizer Ring
15. Thrust Bearing Race
16. Thrust Bearing
17. Thrust Bearing Race
18. 3rd Input Gear
19. Cage Bearing
20. Thrust Washer (Bronze)
21. Thrust Washer
22. Input Shaft
23. Bolt
24. Reverse Shift Rail Guide
25. Clutch & Differential Housing
26. Snap Ring
27. Input Shaft Bearing/ Sleeve Assembly
28. Drive Axle Seal
29. Output Cluster Gear & Shaft Assembly
30. Output Shaft Tapered Roller Bearing
31. Snap Ring
32. Output Cluster 5th Gear Synchronizer
33. 5th Synchronizer Key (3)
34. 5th Synchronizer Ball (3)
35. 5th Synchronizer Spring (3)
36. 5th Synchronizer Sleeve
37. 5th Synchronizer Ring
38. 5th Output Gear
39. 5th Output Bearing
40. Thrust Washer Positioner Ball
41. Thrust Washer
42. Selective Snap Ring
43. 3rd-4th Cluster Gear
44. 2nd Output Gear
45. 2nd Output Bearing
46. 2nd Output Bearing Race
47. 2nd Synchronizer Ring
48. 1st-2nd Synchronizer Assembly
49. 1st-2nd Synchronizer Sleeve
50. 1st-2nd Synchronizer Key (3)
51. 1st-2nd Synchronizer Ball (3)
52. 1st-2nd Synchronizer Spring (3)
53. 1st-2nd Synchronizer Hub
54. 1st-2nd Synchronizer Ring
55. 1st Gear Output
56. 1st Output Bearing
57. Output Shaft
58. Output Shaft Support Bearing
59. Output Shaft Support Bearing Race
60. Differential Gear Assembly
61. Differential Bearing Assembly
62. Differential Bearing Race
63. Differential Bearing
64. Differential Assembly Case
65. Differential Carrier
66. Differential Cross Pin
67. Pinion Gear Thrust Washer
68. Side Gear Thrust Washer
69. Differential Side Gear
70. Differential Pinion Gear
71. Pinion Gear Shaft Bolt
72. Differential Ring Gear
73. Speed Sensor Rotor
74. Differential Selective Shim
75. Differential Bearing Assembly

76. Differential Bearing
77. Differential Bearing Race
78. Differential Ring Gear Bolt
79. Pin (2)
80. Washer
81. Oil Drain Plug
82. Transaxle Case Bolt Washer (15)
83. Transaxle Case Bolt (15)
84. Transaxle Case
85. Output Shaft Bearing Race
86. Case End Plate
87. End Plate Washer
88. End Plate Bolt (9)
89. Input Gear Bearing Retainer
90. Input Shaft Rear Bearing Spacer

91. Input Shaft Bearing
92. Reverse Idler Shaft Bolt
93. Detent Lever Bushing
94. Shift Shaft Needle Bearing
95. Reverse Rail Bushing
96. Shift Rail Bushing (3)
97. Transaxle Dipstick
98. Reverse Idler Gear Assembly
99. Thrust Washer
100. Thrust Bearing
101. Reverse Idler Gear Synchronizer Assembly
102. Synchronizer Sleeve
103. Synchronizer Key (3)
104. Synchronizer Ball (3)
105. Synchronizer Spring (3)
106. Reverse Gear Bearings (2)
107. Thrust Bearing
108. Thrust Washer
109. Shims (2)
110. Snap Ring

111. Reverse Gear Synchronizer Ring
112. Reverse Gear Assembly
113. Reverse Gear Bearing
114. Reverse Idler Gear Shaft
115. Snap Ring
116. Reverse Gear Bearing
117. Reverse Gear Shim
118. Reverse Gear Shaft Bearing Washer
119. Reverse Gear Shim
120. Rear Input Shaft Bearing Shim (Selective)
121. Output Shaft Bearing Race Shim (Selective)
122. Rear Input Shaft Bearing Snap Ring
123. Input Shaft Oil Delivery Tube
124. Output Shaft Oil Delivery Tube

92H15245

Courtesy of General Motors Corp.

Fig. 4: Exploded View Of Gear Assemblies

COMPONENT DISASSEMBLY & REASSEMBLY

INPUT SHAFT

Disassembly – 1) Remove snap ring from end of shaft. Before removing any synchronizer rings, ensure rings and gears are labeled for reassembly. DO NOT mix rings. *See Fig. 5.* Using bearing remover, press adapter and hydraulic press, remove 5th gear. Remove 4th gear and 4th gear bearing.

2) Label and remove 4th gear synchronizer ring, 3rd-4th gear synchronizer and 4th gear bearing race. Remove 3rd gear synchronizer ring, upper thrust bearing race, thrust bearing and lower thrust bearing race, 3rd gear bearing and 3rd gear from input shaft. Remove bronze thrust washer and thrust washer from input shaft. *See Fig. 5.*

Cleaning & Inspection – 1) Clean all parts in solvent and blow dry with compressed air. Inspect input shaft splines for wear or cracks and replace if necessary. Inspect all gears for scuffed, nicked or broken teeth.

2) Inspect bearings for rough rotation, burred or pitting conditions. Replace bearings if necessary. Check bearing races and input shaft races for scoring, wear or overheating conditions.

3) Inspect snap ring for nicks, wear or distortion. Check synchronizer for wear, scuffed, nicked, burred or broken teeth. If defects cannot be repaired by using a soft stone or crocus cloth, replace component.

1. Selective Snap Ring
2. 5th Gear
3. 4th Gear
4. 4th Gear Bearing
5. 4th Gear Bearing Race
6. 4th Gear Synchronizer Ring
7. 3rd-4th Gear Synchronizer
8. 3rd Gear Synchronizer Ring
9. Thrust Bearing Race
10. Thrust Bearing
11. 3rd Gear Bearing
12. 3rd Gear
13. Thrust Washer (Bronze)
14. Thrust Washer
15. Input Shaft

92I15246   Courtesy of General Motors Corp.

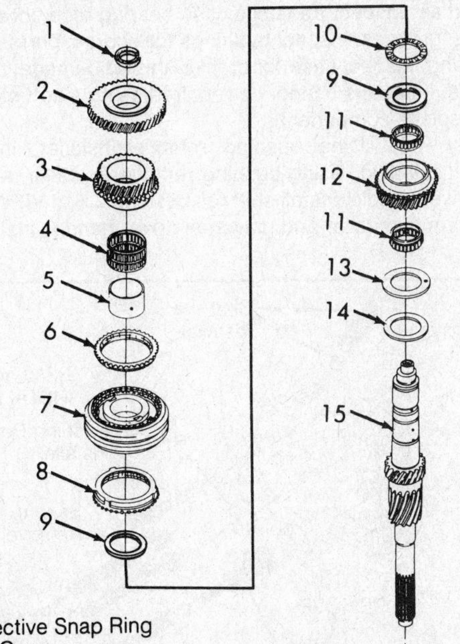

Fig. 5: Exploded View Of Input Shaft Assembly

Reassembly – 1) Lubricate all components prior to reassembly. Heat bearing race and 5th gear to 250°F (120°C) for 7-10 minutes to properly expand components prior to reassembly.

2) Install thrust washer. Install bronze thrust washer with bronze side facing down. Install 3rd gear bearing onto input shaft. Install 3rd gear with cone facing up. Install 3rd gear synchronizer ring. *See Fig. 5.*

3) Install thrust bearing and thrust bearing races with groove on race facing down. Using press tube, press tube adapter, input traft support tube and hydraulic press, install 3rd-4th synchronizer onto input shaft. Install 3rd-4th gear synchronizer with flat side of inner hub facing 3rd gear.

4) Start hydraulic press operation to press on 3rd-4th gear synchronizer, but stop before tangs engage. DO NOT allow tangs to engage. Lift and rotate 3rd gear and 3rd gear synchronizer ring into synchronizer tangs. Press until synchronizer is seated properly. Ensure any metal shavings are removed.

5) Install 4th gear bearing race and bearing onto input shaft. Install 4th gear synchronizer ring. Install 4th gear with cone facing down. Using press tube, press tube adapter and shaft support tube, press 5th gear onto input shaft. Ensure grooved side of gear faces down. Select and install NEW selective snap ring. See 5TH GEAR-TO-INPUT SHAFT SELECTIVE SNAP RING PROCEDURE.

OUTPUT SHAFT

Disassembly – 1) Before removing any synchronizer rings, ensure rings and gears are labeled for reassembly. DO NOT mix rings. Using gear remover, press adapter and hydraulic press, remove 5th gear and 5th gear bearing from output shaft. Output shaft bearing, 5th gear synchronizer and 5th gear synchronizer ring will press off with 5th gear. *See Fig. 6.*

2) Remove thrust washer and positioning ball from shaft. Remove selective snap ring. Using gear remover, press adapter and hydraulic press, remove 3rd-4th gear. Remove 2nd gear bearing, 2nd gear and synchronizer ring.

3) Using gear remover, press adapter and hydraulic press, remove 1st gear. 2nd gear bearing race, 1st-2nd synchronizer, synchronizer ring and 1st gear bearing will press off with 1st gear. Remove 1st gear bearing. Press off output shaft support bearing and replace if necessary.

Cleaning & Inspection – 1) Clean all parts in solvent and blow dry with compressed air. Inspect output shaft splines for wear and/or cracks. Inspect all gears for scuffing, nicks, burrs or broken teeth. Inspect bearing races for scoring, wear or overheating.

2) Inspect bearings for rotation roughness, burrs or pits. Check synchronizer for wear, scuffed, nicked, burred or broken teeth. If defects cannot be repaired by using a soft stone or crocus cloth, replace component.

3) Check synchronizer for wear, scuffed, nicked, burred or broken teeth. If defects cannot be repaired by using a soft stone or crocus cloth, replace component.

Reassembly – 1) Lubricate all components prior to reassembly. Heat 2nd gear bearing race to 250°F (120°C) for 7-10 minutes. Heat 3rd-4th gear to 250°F (120°C) for a minimum of 20 minutes.

2) Using bearing installer and hydraulic press, install output shaft support bearing. Install 1st gear bearing with larger plastic side of bearing facing center of 1st gear. Install 1st gear with cone facing up. Install 1st gear bearing with larger plastic side of bearing facing center of 1st gear. Install 1st gear synchronizer ring. *See Fig. 6.*

3) Using press tube, press tube adapter, bearing installer, and hydraulic press, install 1st-2nd gear synchronizer with synchronizer sleeve extension facing 1st gear. Install 2nd gear bearing race.

4) Start hydraulic press operation to press on 1st-2nd gear synchronizer, but stop before tangs engage. DO NOT allow tangs to engage. Lift and rotate 1st gear and 1st gear synchronizer ring to engage synchronizer ring tangs. Continue to press until synchronizer is properly seated. Ensure any metal shavings are removed. Install 2nd gear bearing race, bearing and 2nd gear. Using press tube, press tube adapter and bearing installer, install 3rd-4th gear with large outside diameter down.

5) Select and install NEW selective snap ring. See 3RD-4TH GEAR-TO-OUTPUT SHAFT SELECTIVE SNAP RING PROCEDURE. Install thrust washer with positioner ball and slotted thrust washer. Retain ball with lubricant. *See Fig. 6.* Align inside diameter slot of thrust washer with positioner ball.

6) Install 5th gear bearing and 5th gear with cone facing up. Install 5th gear synchronizer ring. Using press tube and press tube adapter, press 5th gear synchronizer onto output shaft. Snap ring on synchronizer must face away from 5th gear.

7) Start hydraulic press operation to press on reverse-5th gear synchronizer, but stop before tangs engage. DO NOT allow tangs to engage. Lift and rotate 5th gear and 5th gear synchronizer ring until

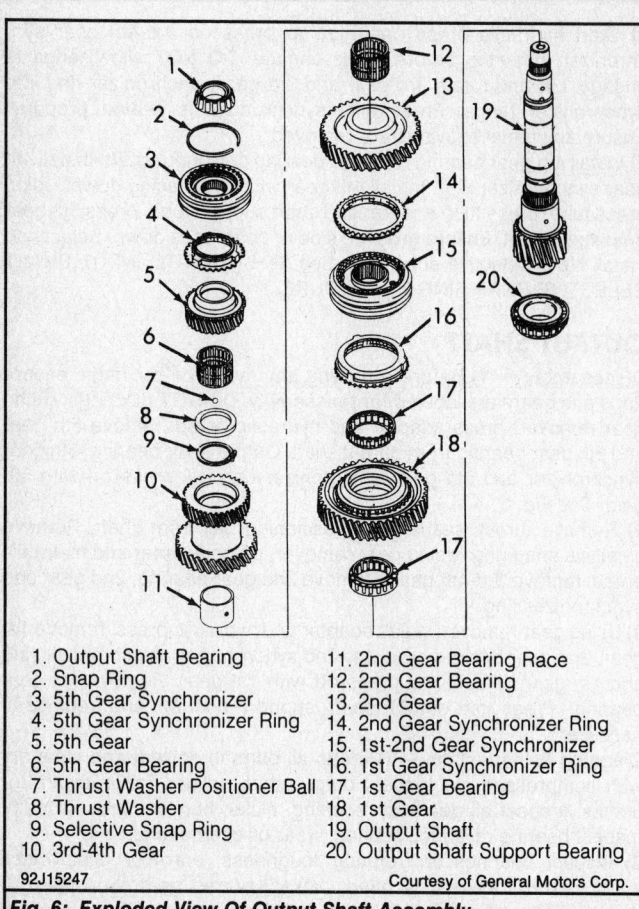

1. Output Shaft Bearing
2. Snap Ring
3. 5th Gear Synchronizer
4. 5th Gear Synchronizer Ring
5. 5th Gear
6. 5th Gear Bearing
7. Thrust Washer Positioner Ball
8. Thrust Washer
9. Selective Snap Ring
10. 3rd-4th Gear
11. 2nd Gear Bearing Race
12. 2nd Gear Bearing
13. 2nd Gear
14. 2nd Gear Synchronizer Ring
15. 1st-2nd Gear Synchronizer
16. 1st Gear Synchronizer Ring
17. 1st Gear Bearing
18. 1st Gear
19. Output Shaft
20. Output Shaft Support Bearing

92J15247   Courtesy of General Motors Corp.

Fig. 6: Exploded View Of Output Shaft Assembly

tangs engage. Ensure thrust washer stays down. Continue to press together until synchronizer is properly seated. Ensure all metal shavings are removed. Using bearing press adapter, bearing installer and hydraulic press, install output shaft bearing.

TRANSAXLE CASE

Disassembly – 1) Remove bearings or bushings only if there is evidence of damage, or a mating part is being replaced. Using a punch, remove shift rail plugs. Using bushing remover/installer, remove small reverse shift rail plug. Using bushing remover/installer, adapter and universal driver handle, remove shift rail bushings. See VIEW "B" in *Fig. 7*.

2) Use a screwdriver to remove shift shaft seal. Using bearing remover and universal driver handle, remove shift shaft bearing. See VIEW "A" in *Fig. 7*. Remove bolt, spring and sliding sleeve. *See Fig. 3.* Remove detent lever snap ring, spacer and lever assembly.

3) Using bushing remover/installer and universal driver handle, remove detent lever bushing. See VIEW "C" in *Fig. 7*. Using bushing remover/installer and universal driver handle, remove sliding sleeve bushing.

4) Remove snap ring retaining input shaft bearing. Using bearing race remover and slide hammer, remove differential bearing race. Drive out axle shaft seal. Using bearing race remover/installer and universal driver handle, remove output shaft bearing race. See VIEW "B" in *Fig. 7*. Remove input shaft bearing shim ring and input shaft bearing.

Cleaning & Inspection – Clean all parts in solvent and blow dry with compressed air. Inspect transaxle case bearing race bores for wear, scratches or grooves. Inspect bushings for scores, burrs, roundness or overheating. Inspect case for cracks, thread damage, nicks, burrs or scratches. If defects cannot be repaired using a soft stone or crocus cloth, replace component.

Reassembly – 1) Using bushing remover/installer, install small reverse shift rail plug. Using bushing remover/installer, adapter and universal driver handle, install shift rail bushings. See VIEW "B" in *Fig. 7*. Using bearing installer and universal driver handle, install shift rail plugs.

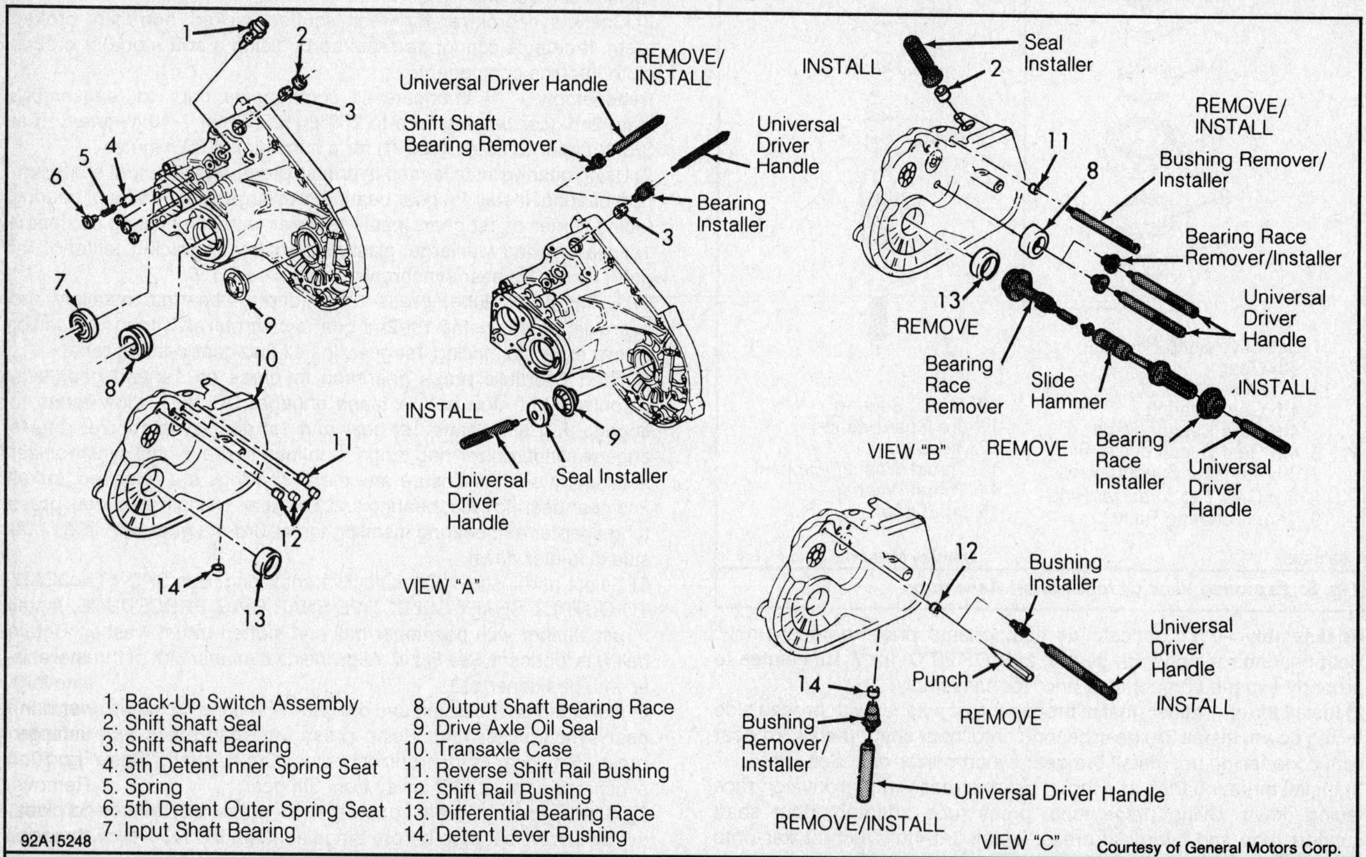

1. Back-Up Switch Assembly
2. Shift Shaft Seal
3. Shift Shaft Bearing
4. 5th Detent Inner Spring Seat
5. Spring
6. 5th Detent Outer Spring Seat
7. Input Shaft Bearing
8. Output Shaft Bearing Race
9. Drive Axle Oil Seal
10. Transaxle Case
11. Reverse Shift Rail Bushing
12. Shift Rail Bushing
13. Differential Bearing Race
14. Detent Lever Bushing

92A15248   Courtesy of General Motors Corp.

Fig. 7: Removing & Installing Transaxle Case Components

2) Using bearing installer and universal driver handle, install shift shaft bearing. See VIEW "A" in *Fig. 7*. Using seal installer, install shift shaft seal. See VIEW "B" in *Fig. 7*. Using remover/installer and universal driver handle, install detent lever bushing. See VIEW "C" in *Fig. 7*. Using bushing remover/installer and universal driver handle, install sliding sleeve bushing.

3) Install detent lever assembly, spacer and snap ring. Install sliding sleeve, spring and bolt. Install Teflon thread sealant to bolt prior to installation. Tighten bolt to specification. See TORQUE SPECIFICATIONS. Install snap ring retaining input shaft bearing. Using bearing race installer and universal driver handle, install differential bearing race. See VIEW "B" in *Fig. 7*.

4) Using seal installer and universal driver handle, install axle seal. Using bearing race installer and universal driver handle, install output shaft bearing race. See VIEW "B" in *Fig. 7*. Install input shaft bearing and bearing shim ring.

REVERSE IDLER GEAR

Disassembly – **1)** Remove outer thrust washer, thrust bearing and reverse gear synchronizer. Remove thrust bearing, inner thrust washer and reverse gear bearings. Remove shims and reverse idler gear synchronizer ring. Remove washer and cage bearing. Remove snap ring and shim. *See Fig. 8.*

2) Remove reverse gear bearing snap ring. Remove reverse idler gear and shim. Using bearing remover/installer and hydraulic press, remove reverse gear bearing.

Cleaning & Inspection – Wash all parts in solvent and blow dry with compressed air. Inspect all parts for scuffing, nicks, burrs and broken teeth. Inspect bushings for burrs, scoring, roundness or overheating. Check shaft for scoring, nicks, burrs or overheating. If defects cannot be repaired by using a soft stone or crocus cloth, replace component.

Reassembly – **1)** Lubricate all components prior to reassembly. Select appropriate reverse gear bearing shim. See REVERSE BEARING-TO-REVERSE GEAR SELECTIVE SHIM PROCEDURE. Using bearing remover/installer and hydraulic press, install reverse gear bearing onto reverse gear shaft. Install washer and select appropriate NEW snap ring. See REVERSE BEARING-TO-REVERSE GEAR SHAFT SELECTIVE SNAP RING PROCEDURE. Install shim and reverse idler gear.

2) Install reverse gear bearing snap ring. Install reverse gear cage bearing and washer. Install reverse gear synchronizer ring. Install 2 shims with large outside diameter shim over snap ring. *See Fig. 8.*

3) Install thrust washer, thrust bearing and reverse gear bearings. Install reverse gear synchronizer and thrust bearing. Select and install appropriate thrust washer. See REVERSE GEAR THRUST WASHER SELECTION PROCEDURE.

SYNCHRONIZERS

Disassembly – Wrap 1st-2nd, 3rd-4th and 5th gear synchronizer assemblies in separate clean shop towels. Press against inner hub until assembly comes apart.

Cleaning & Inspection – Clean all parts in solvent and blow dry with compressed air. Inspect synchronizer for wear, scuffing, nicks, burrs or broken teeth. Check balls and springs for distortion, cracks or wear. If defects cannot be repaired using a soft stone or crocus cloth, replace component.

Reassembly – **1)** Install 1st-2nd gear sleeve with sleeve extension facing opposite inner hub extension. Install 5th gear sleeve with small outside diameter groove positioned over wider side of hub. Install springs into keys. Install spring and key assemblies with bevel cut on keys facing toward sleeve. *See Fig. 9.*

2) Position assembly as shown. See VIEW "A" in *Fig. 9*. Install balls. Push ball and key into sleeve using screwdriver. By centering hub, the keys and balls should click into position. See VIEW "B" in *Fig. 9*.

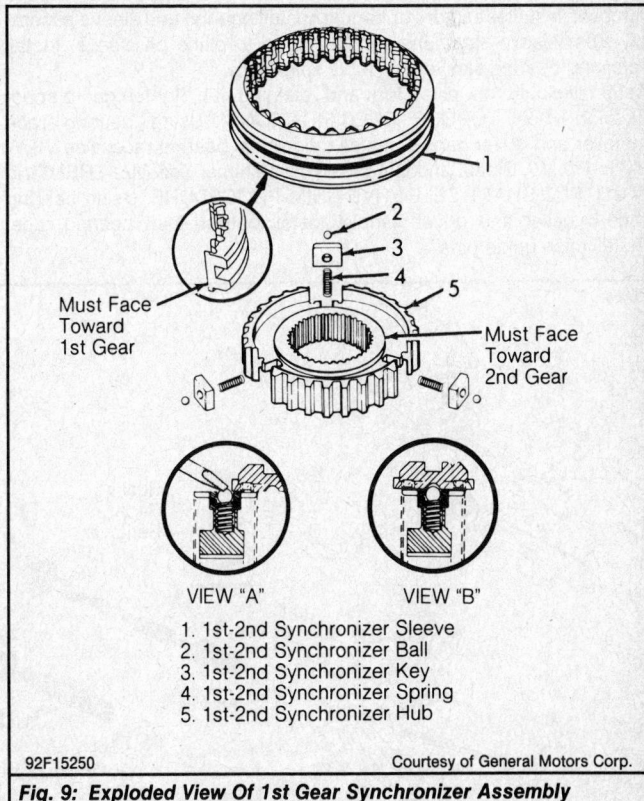

VIEW "A"   VIEW "B"

1. 1st-2nd Synchronizer Sleeve
2. 1st-2nd Synchronizer Ball
3. 1st-2nd Synchronizer Key
4. 1st-2nd Synchronizer Spring
5. 1st-2nd Synchronizer Hub

92F15250   Courtesy of General Motors Corp.

Fig. 9: Exploded View Of 1st Gear Synchronizer Assembly (Others Are Similar)

CLUTCH & DIFFERENTIAL HOUSING

Disassembly – **1)** Remove bearings or bushings only if there is evidence of damage, or a mating part is being replaced. Remove 3 bolts retaining shift rail interlock spacers and plate. Using driver handle adapter and universal driver handle, remove shift rail bushings. Remove 5th and reverse shift rail guide bolt and guide. *See Fig. 10.*

2) Remove clutch cylinder studs. Pry out transaxle vent pipe. Remove housing vent boot. Remove clutch fork retaining nut, fork and pivot. Remove clutch fork pivot bolt. Pivot bolt has left hand threads. Remove input shaft bearing sleeve assembly snap ring.

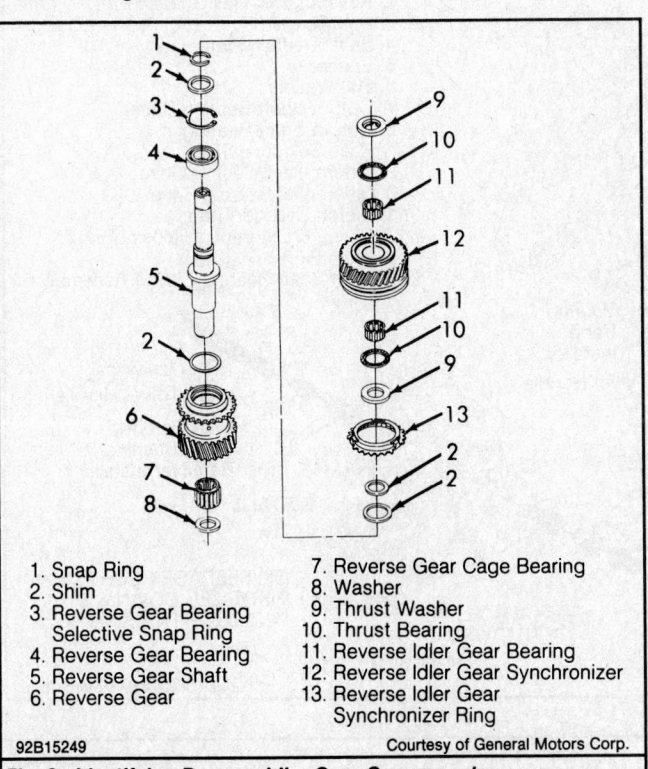

1. Snap Ring
2. Shim
3. Reverse Gear Bearing Selective Snap Ring
4. Reverse Gear Bearing
5. Reverse Gear Shaft
6. Reverse Gear
7. Reverse Gear Cage Bearing
8. Washer
9. Thrust Washer
10. Thrust Bearing
11. Reverse Idler Gear Bearing
12. Reverse Idler Gear Synchronizer
13. Reverse Idler Gear Synchronizer Ring

92B15249   Courtesy of General Motors Corp.

Fig. 8: Identifying Reverse Idler Gear Components

3) Using bearing remover/installer, bearing and sleeve remover/installer and universal driver handle, remove bearing and sleeve assembly. See VIEW "B" in *Fig. 10*. Drive out assembly by tapping on bearing side.

4) Using bearing race remover and slide hammer and adapter, remove differential bearing race. Remove selective shim from differential housing. Using bearing race remover and slide hammer, remove output shaft bearing race. See VIEW "A" in *Fig. 10*. Remove selective shim from differential housing. Using a punch, remove case guide pins.

Cleaning & Inspection – Clean all parts in solvent and blow dry with compressed air. Check bearing race bores for wear, scratches or grooves. Inspect bushings for scores, burrs, roundness or overheating. Check case for cracks, thread damage, nicks, burrs, scratches or scoring. If defects cannot be repaired using a soft stone or crocus cloth, replace component.

Reassembly – **1)** Using bushing installer and driver handle, install shift rail bushings. Install shift rail interlock plate, spacers and bolts. Install reverse shift rail guide and bolt. Apply Loctite to bolt threads prior to installation. Install clutch cylinder studs. Tighten bolts and studs to specification. See TORQUE SPECIFICATIONS.

2) Apply small amount of sealant to transaxle vent pipe and install pipe into transaxle case. Install clutch housing vent boot. Apply Loctite to clutch fork assembly pivot bolt and install pivot bolt. Pivot bolt has left hand threads. Tighten bolt to specification. See TORQUE SPECIFICATIONS.

3) Lubricate bearing and sleeve. Using bearing and sleeve remover/installer and driver handle, install bearing and sleeve assembly from sleeve side. Ensure "O" ring is in place on sleeve. Install retaining bearing sleeve assembly snap ring.

4) Install clutch fork pivot, fork and retaining nut. Tighten nut to specification. See TORQUE SPECIFICATIONS. Using bearing race installer and driver handle, install differential bearing race. See VIEW "A" in *Fig. 10*. Select and install selective shims. See DIFFERENTIAL & OUTPUT SHAFT SELECTIVE SHIM PROCEDURE. Using bearing race installer and driver handle, install output shaft bearing race. Install case guide pins.

DIFFERENTIAL & RING GEAR

Disassembly – **1)** Remove ring gear retaining bolts and ring gear. Using bearing remover, adapter and hydraulic press, remove differential side bearings.

2) Remove speed sensor rotor. Remove differential cross pin bolt and washer. Remove differential cross pin. Remove differential side gears, pinion gears and washers. *See Fig. 4*.

Cleaning & Inspection – Clean all parts in solvent and blow dry with compressed air. Inspect gears and thrust washers for wear, scuffing, nicks, burrs or broken teeth. Check carrier for distortion, out-of-round bores or scoring. Check bearing for rotation roughness, burrs or pits. If defects cannot be repaired using a soft stone or crocus cloth, replace component.

Reassembly – **1)** Heat NEW speed sensor rotor prior to assembly. Rotor must be preheated to 250°F (120°C) for 7-10 minutes. Install preheated speed sensor rotor and allow it to cool. Using bearing installer and hydraulic press, install differential side bearings. Install differential side gear, pinion gear and thrust washers. *See Fig. 4*.

2) Install differential cross pin. Install differential cross pin bolt. Install ring gear on differential assembly using NEW bolts. Tighten bolts to specification. See TORQUE SPECIFICATIONS. Apply sealant to bolt threads prior to installation.

DIFFERENTIAL & OUTPUT SHAFT SELECTIVE SHIM PROCEDURE

NOTE: This procedure must be performed with gear assemblies, shift fork assemblies and differential installed in transaxle case.

1) Install output shaft support bearing race onto output shaft bearing. Install differential bearing race onto differential bearing. Remove shims from clutch and differential housing. Install measuring base and dial indicator assembly into clutch and differential case where differential bearing race seats. See VIEW "A" in *Fig. 11*.

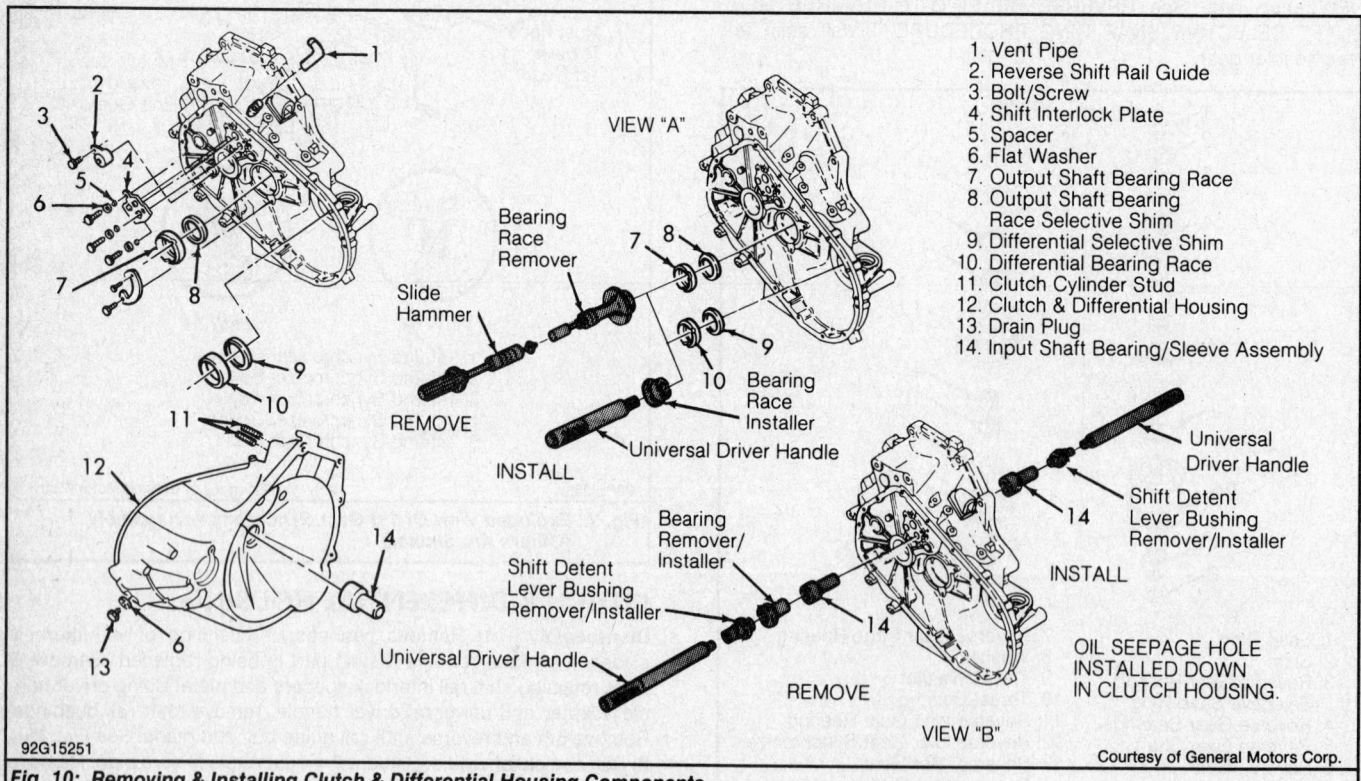

1. Vent Pipe
2. Reverse Shift Rail Guide
3. Bolt/Screw
4. Shift Interlock Plate
5. Spacer
6. Flat Washer
7. Output Shaft Bearing Race
8. Output Shaft Bearing Race Selective Shim
9. Differential Selective Shim
10. Differential Bearing Race
11. Clutch Cylinder Stud
12. Clutch & Differential Housing
13. Drain Plug
14. Input Shaft Bearing/Sleeve Assembly

VIEW "A"

Bearing Race Remover

Slide Hammer

REMOVE

Bearing Race Installer

Universal Driver Handle

INSTALL

Shift Detent Lever Bushing Remover/Installer

Bearing Remover/Installer

Universal Driver Handle

Universal Driver Handle

Shift Detent Lever Bushing Remover/Installer

INSTALL

REMOVE

OIL SEEPAGE HOLE INSTALLED DOWN IN CLUTCH HOUSING.

VIEW "B"

92G15251

Courtesy of General Motors Corp.

Fig. 10: *Removing & Installing Clutch & Differential Housing Components*

2) Place dial indicator measuring tip on transaxle case mating surface and set dial indicator to .050" (1.27 mm). Remove measuring base and dial indicator as a unit, and install measuring base to mating surface of transaxle case and dial indicator tip to top of differential bearing race. See VIEW "B" in *Fig. 11*.

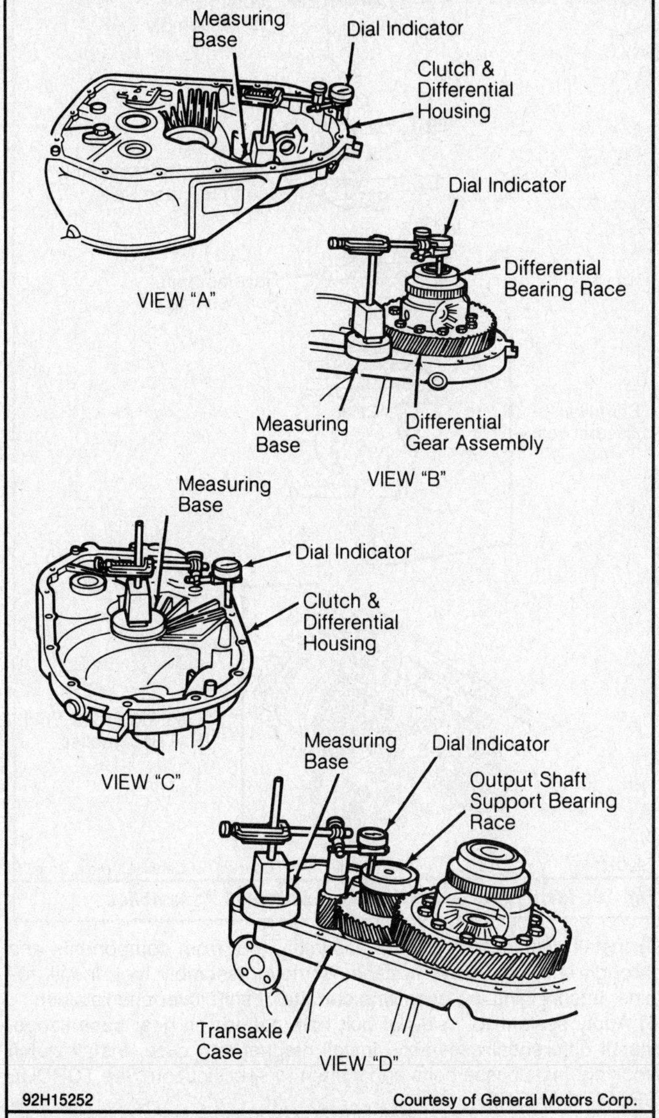

3) Calculate difference between .050" (1.27 mm) at transaxle case mating surface and reading to bearing race. Choose shim to obtain a bearing preload of .012-.014" (.30-35 mm). Repeat procedure for output shaft bearing preload. See VIEW "C" and VIEW "D" in *Fig. 11*. Shims are available in thicknesses of .012-.024" (.30-.60 mm) in increments of .004" (.10 mm).

INPUT SHAFT BEARING SELECTIVE SHIM PROCEDURE

Assemble snap ring into transaxle case. Install input shaft bearing into case. Install spacer. Ensure bearing and spacer are seated against snap ring. Using a Dial Depth Gauge, measure between transaxle case end plate mating surface and spacer. *See Fig. 12*. Select appropriate shim to obtain zero clearance. Shims are available in thicknesses of .012-.020" (.30-.50 mm) in increments of .004" (.10 mm).

REVERSE BEARING-TO-REVERSE GEAR SELECTIVE SHIM PROCEDURE

Assemble reverse gear bearing to reverse idler gear. Install snap ring. *See Fig. 8*. Using a feeler gauge, measure between reverse gear bearing and snap ring. Select appropriate shim to obtain zero clearance. Shims are available in thicknesses of .012-.20" (.30-.50 mm) in increments of .004" (.10 mm)

REVERSE BEARING-TO-REVERSE GEAR SHAFT SELECTIVE SNAP RING PROCEDURE

When shimming reverse gear bearing, start by choosing smallest snap ring available in shim kit. Install snap ring in groove on reverse gear shaft above reverse gear bearing. *See Fig. 13*. Install largest snap ring that fits in groove. Snap rings are available in thicknesses of .079-.091" (2.01-2.31 mm) in increments of .004" (.10 mm).

REVERSE GEAR THRUST WASHER SELECTION PROCEDURE

NOTE: This procedure must be performed with reverse gear assembly installed in transaxle case.

1) Set Measuring Base (J-39457) and dial indicator assembly on mating surface of clutch and differential housing. *See Fig. 14*. Place tip of dial indicator on surface of transaxle case where reverse gear thrust washer seats and set dial indicator to .050" (1.27 mm).

2) Remove measuring base and dial indicator as a unit. Place measuring base on mating surface of transaxle case and dial indicator on top of reverse gear thrust washer. Calculate difference between .050" (1.27 mm) at transaxle case mating surface and reading at thrust washer. Choose thrust washer to obtain axial play of .006-010" (.15-25 mm). Thrust washers are available in thicknesses of .138-.158" (3.51-4.01 mm) in increments of .004" (.10 mm).

3RD-4TH GEAR-TO-OUTPUT SHAFT SELECTIVE SNAP RING PROCEDURE

When shimming 3rd-4th gear, start by choosing smallest snap ring available in shim kit. Install largest snap ring that fits in groove. *See Fig. 15*. Snap rings are available in thicknesses of .067-.079" (1.70-2.01 mm) in increments of .004" (.10 mm).

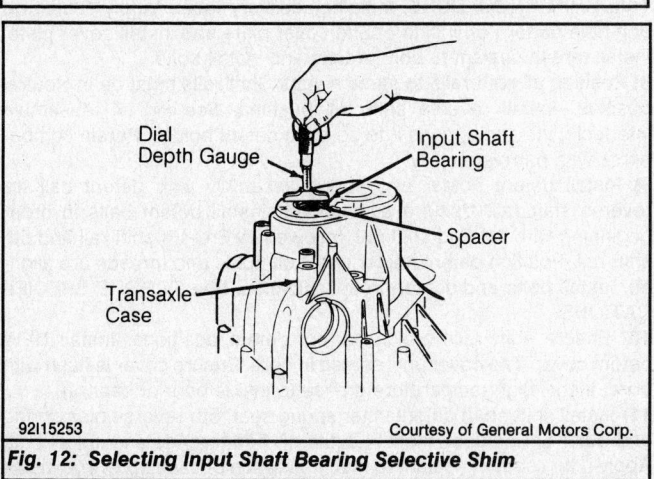

92H15252   Courtesy of General Motors Corp.

Fig. 11: Selecting Differential & Output Shaft Shim

92I15253   Courtesy of General Motors Corp.

Fig. 12: Selecting Input Shaft Bearing Selective Shim

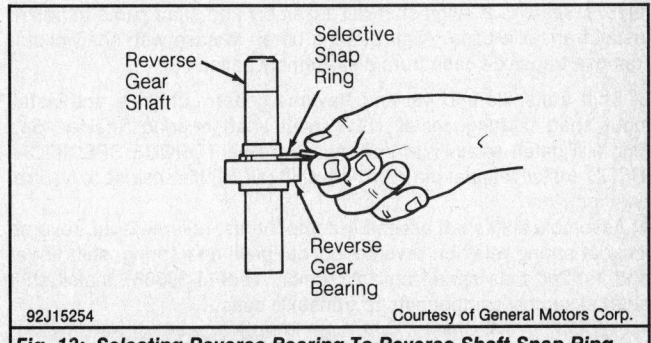

92J15254   Courtesy of General Motors Corp.

Fig. 13: Selecting Reverse Bearing-To-Reverse Shaft Snap Ring

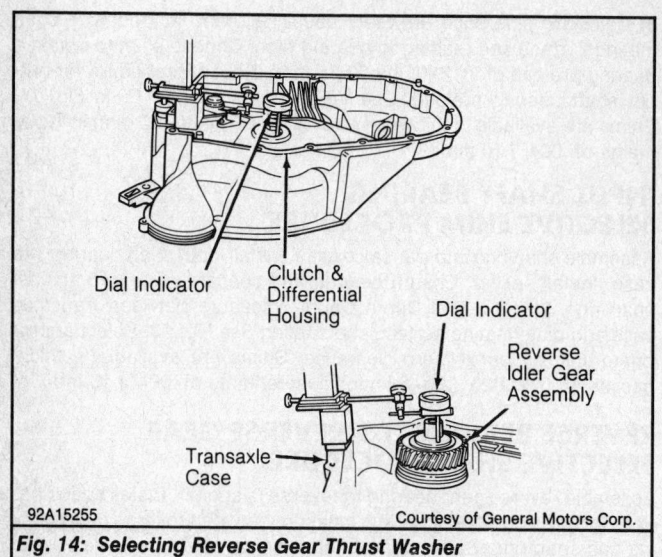

92A15255   Courtesy of General Motors Corp.

Fig. 14: Selecting Reverse Gear Thrust Washer

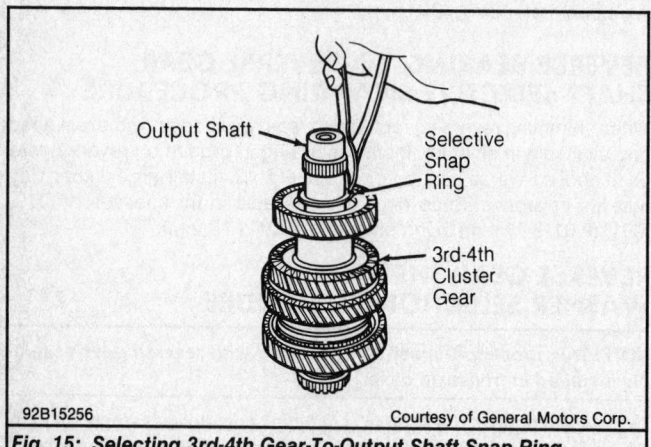

92B15256   Courtesy of General Motors Corp.

Fig. 15: Selecting 3rd-4th Gear-To-Output Shaft Snap Ring

5TH GEAR-TO-INPUT SHAFT SELECTIVE SNAP RING PROCEDURE

When shimming 5th gear, start by choosing smallest snap ring available in shim kit. Install largest snap ring that will fit in groove located above 5th gear on input shaft. Snap rings are available in thicknesses of .067-.079" (1.70-2.01 mm) in increments of .002" (.05 mm).

TRANSAXLE REASSEMBLY

1) Assemble input and output shaft assemblies. Install 1st-2nd shift rail assembly. Install interlock pin. Retain pin using petroleum jelly. Install 3rd-4th shift rail assembly. *See Fig. 16.* Install 5th shift rail assembly. Install reverse shift rail assembly. Install shift gate.

2) Position gear cluster/shift rail assembly on Disassembly Pallet (J-39367). *See Fig. 2.* Align shift rail assembly and shaft pilots to pallet. Install transaxle case. Align bearing bores in case with shaft pilots. Remove transaxle case from disassembly pallet.

3) Shift transaxle into 4th and Reverse gears. Lubricate and install input shaft bearing. Install NEW input shaft bearing retainer. *See Fig. 4.* Tighten retainer to specification. *See TORQUE SPECIFICATIONS.* Install retainer pin in 3rd-4th shift rail. Shift transaxle to Neutral position.

4) Assemble shift shaft assembly components, reverse lever, reverse lockout spring retainer, reverse lockout pawl and spring, shift finger and 1st-2nd bias spring onto Assembly Tool (J-39366). Install shift shaft assembly components to transaxle case.

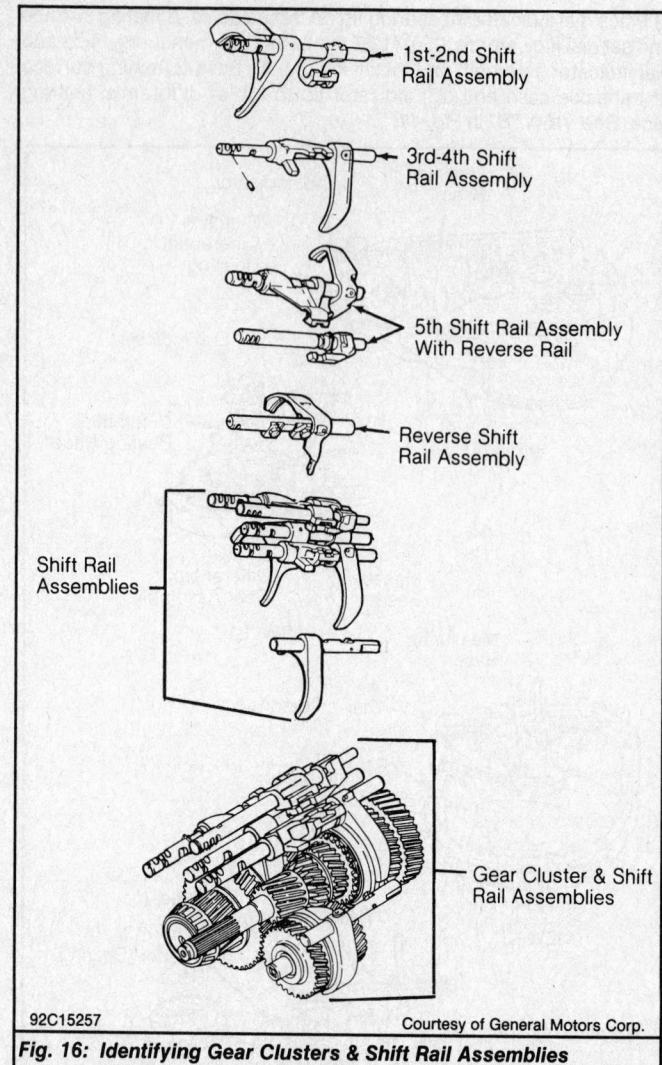

92C15257   Courtesy of General Motors Corp.

Fig. 16: Identifying Gear Clusters & Shift Rail Assemblies

5) Install shift shaft, pushing assembly tool from components and through shift shaft hole in case. Remove assembly tool. Install roll pins. Ensure pins are even with surface of shift lever and retainer.

6) Apply sealant to inside of bolt hole pattern on gear case flange. Install differential assembly. Install magnet into case. Install clutch housing. Install case bolts and tighten to specification. See TORQUE SPECIFICATIONS.

7) Install shim previously selected in INPUT SHAFT BEARING SELECTIVE SHIM PROCEDURE. Install oil delivery tubes. Apply sealant to bolt hole pattern on inside of end cover plate and install cover plate. Install thread sealant to bolt threads and install bolts.

8) Position all shift rails to same height. Shift rails must be in Neutral position. Install reverse shift rail bushing. *See Fig. 7.* Assemble interlock pins and springs into bores in detent holder. Retain components with petroleum jelly.

9) Install detent holder and spring assembly with detent ball for reverse shift rail. Using a screwdriver, install detent balls in order beginning with 1st-2nd shift rail, followed by 3rd-4th shift rail and 5th shift rail. Position detent holder until bolt holes and threads are aligned. Install bolts and tighten to specification. See TORQUE SPECIFICATIONS.

10) Ensure shift rails are in correct detent positions. Install NEW detent cover. Tap cover until seated in bore. Ensure cover is flush with bore. Install high temperature grease to inside bore of bearing.

11) Install shift shaft detent inner spring seat, 5th-reverse bias spring and outer spring seat. Install Loctite on bolt threads and install bolt. Apply a thin coat of sealant to mating surface of case bore, and install NEW shift shaft cover. Install snap ring. *See Fig. 3.*

CAUTION: Ensure shift shaft cover is not caved in. Caved-in cover may cause a hard shift into 1-2 gate by not allowing full travel of shift shaft.

12) Install selector lever bracket and bolts. Use sealant on bolt threads. Install shift shaft collar and NEW spring pin. Apply a thin coat of high temperature grease to slot in collar. Install selector pivot and NEW pivot pin. Install shift lever, washer and nut. Apply Loctite to shift shaft threads.

13) Install dipstick. Coat NEW seal with transaxle fluid and install seal on speed sensor assembly. Install speed sensor assembly, retainer and bolt. Tighten bolt to specification.

TORQUE SPECIFICATIONS
TORQUE SPECIFICATIONS

Application	Ft. Lbs. (N.m)
Clutch Cylinder Studs	23 (31)
Clutch Fork Pivot Nut	17 (23)
Clutch Fork Pivot Stud	24 (33)
Clutch Housing-To-Case Housing Bolt	20 (27)
Differential Gear Bolt	63 (85)
Differential Pinion Shaft Bolt	17 (23)
Drain Plug	18 (24)
Drive Axle Shaft Nut	184 (249)
End Plate-To-Gear Housing Bolt	20 (27)
Input Shaft Bearing Retainer Bolt	42 (57)
Interlock Plate Bolt	15 (20)
Reverse Idler Shaft Retaining Bolt	21 (28)
Shift Lever Bracket Bolt	17 (23)
Shift Lever Nut	63 (85)
Sliding Sleeve Bolt	18 (24)
Wheel Lug Nut	103 (140)

	INCH Lbs. (N.m)
Cable Grommet Nut	27 (3)
Cable Retaining Clamp Nut	89 (10)
Clutch Actuator Stud	115 (13)
Detent Holder Bolt	80 (9)
Reverse Shift Rail Guide Bolt	44 (5)
Shift Shaft Detent Bolt	80 (9)
Speed Sensor Retainer Bolt	80 (9)

MANUAL TRANSMISSIONS
GM NVT550 5-Speed

Chevrolet: Beretta, Cavalier, Corsica
Oldsmobile: Achieva
Pontiac: Grand Am, Sunbird

IDENTIFICATION

Transaxle can be identified by a code stamped on forward side of transaxle case where it mates with clutch housing. First digit, "H", identifies transaxle type. Second digit identifies model year.

DESCRIPTION

NVT550 5-speed transaxle is a fully synchronized transaxle combined with the differential assembly. Reverse uses a sliding idler gear arrangement. Output gear turns differential ring gear, providing power to drive axles.

LUBRICATION & ADJUSTMENTS

See appropriate MANUAL TRANSMISSION SERVICING article in TRANSMISSION SERVICING.

TROUBLE SHOOTING

See GENERAL TROUBLE SHOOTING article in MANUAL TRANSMISSIONS.

ON-VEHICLE SERVICE

SHIFT CABLES

Removal & Installation – 1) Remove clamp and nut from each shifting lever at transaxle. Remove shifter knob, console and shift boot. Disconnect cables from ball stud on control assembly by twisting a screwdriver between cable socket and control assembly.
2) Remove spring clips retaining cables to control assembly. Pull right side carpet back to gain access to shift cables. Remove shift cable grommet cover screws and cable cover at floor pan. Remove cables. To install, reverse removal procedure.

DRIVE AXLE OIL SEAL

Removal & Installation – 1) Raise and support vehicle. Remove wheel. Remove stabilizer shaft from control arm. Remove ball joint from steering knuckle. Place Seal Protector (J-34754) over axle shaft. Remove drive axle from transaxle case. Remove drive axle oil seal.
2) Install drive axle oil seal using seal installer and driver handle. Install drive axle to transaxle case. Install ball joint to steering knuckle. To complete installation, reverse removal procedure. Tighten nuts and bolts to specification. See TORQUE SPECIFICATIONS.

DRIVE AXLE SHAFTS

See appropriate FWD AXLE SHAFTS article in AXLE SHAFTS & TRANSFER CASES.

REMOVAL & INSTALLATION

See appropriate MANUAL TRANSMISSION REMOVAL article in TRANSMISSION SERVICING.

TRANSAXLE DISASSEMBLY

1) Remove shift lever and selector lever bracket from transaxle. DO NOT allow shift lever to move during removal of nut. Hold shift lever at shift cable mounting stud. Remove fluid level indicator and speedometer signal assembly.
2) Remove clutch release bearing. Puncture detent holder cover in middle and pry it off. Remove bolts, detent holder, springs and interlock pins. Remove detent balls, and pry loose reverse shift rail bushing.
3) Remove shift shaft detent snap ring and cover. Remove screw, outer spring seat, 5th-reverse bias spring and inner spring seat. Shift transaxle to Neutral position.

4) Place transaxle on bench with clutch housing facing upward. Remove bolts retaining clutch housing to transaxle case. Remove clutch housing. Remove differential gear assembly from case. Remove magnet from bottom of case. Remove output shaft bearing. Remove pin from shift shaft assembly.
5) Remove shift shaft, rollers and pin. Remove 3rd-4th bias spring, shift lever and reverse lever. See Figs. 3 and 12. Push in 3rd-4th gear shift rail and reverse gear shift rail to engage transaxle into 4th and Reverse gears. Ensure gears are engaged to lock mainshaft. Remove end plate retaining bolts and end plate. Remove oil slinger washer, selective shim and retainer.
6) Using bearing retainer socket, remove retainers, input shaft, output shaft and gear cluster. Shift transaxle to Neutral position. Place Disassembly Pallet (J-36182-1) and Adapters (J-36182-2) on hydraulic press bed. See Fig. 1.
7) Position transaxle case onto Disassembly Pallet (J-36182-1). Align shift rail and shaft pilots to fixture. Position gear cluster remover on support shaft bearings and pilots. See Fig 1. Using press, separate shaft and gear cluster from transaxle case.
8) Remove 1st-2nd shift rail assembly and lock pin. See Fig. 3. Remove 3rd-4th shift rail assembly. Remove 5th gear shift rail assembly. Remove reverse shift rail assembly, shift gate and gear disengage roller. See Fig. 3.

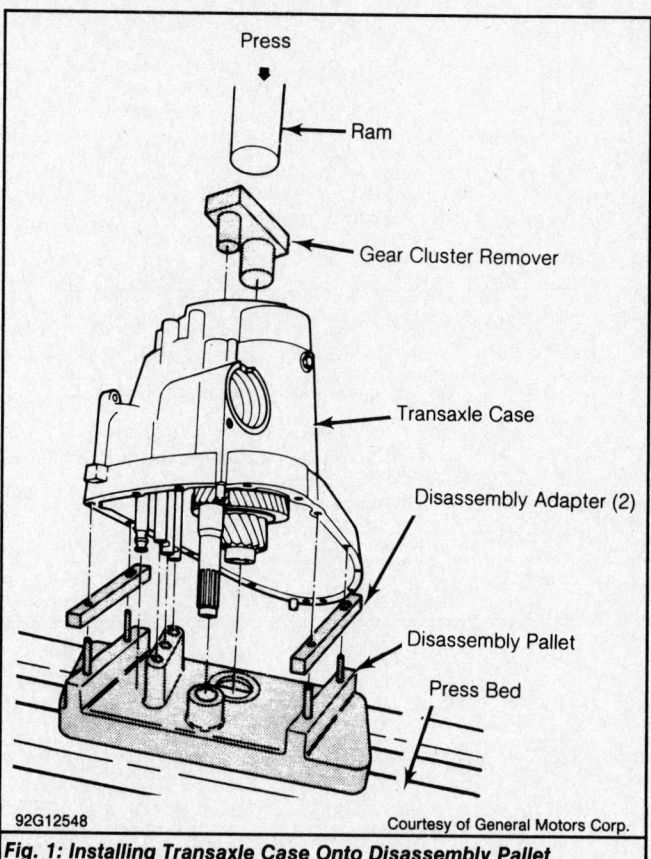

92G12548   Courtesy of General Motors Corp.

Fig. 1: Installing Transaxle Case Onto Disassembly Pallet

COMPONENT DISASSEMBLY & REASSEMBLY

INPUT SHAFT

Disassembly – 1) Remove snap ring from end of shaft. Label synchronizer rings for gear location prior to removal for reassembly reference. DO NOT mix rings. See Fig. 4. Using hydraulic press, shaft gear press tube and reducer, remove 5th gear, 4th gear, 4th gear bearing and bearing race.
2) Label and remove 4th gear synchronizer ring, 3rd-4th synchronizer assembly, 3rd gear synchronizer ring and 3rd gear from input shaft. Remove 2 halves of 3rd gear bearing from Input shaft. See Fig. 4.

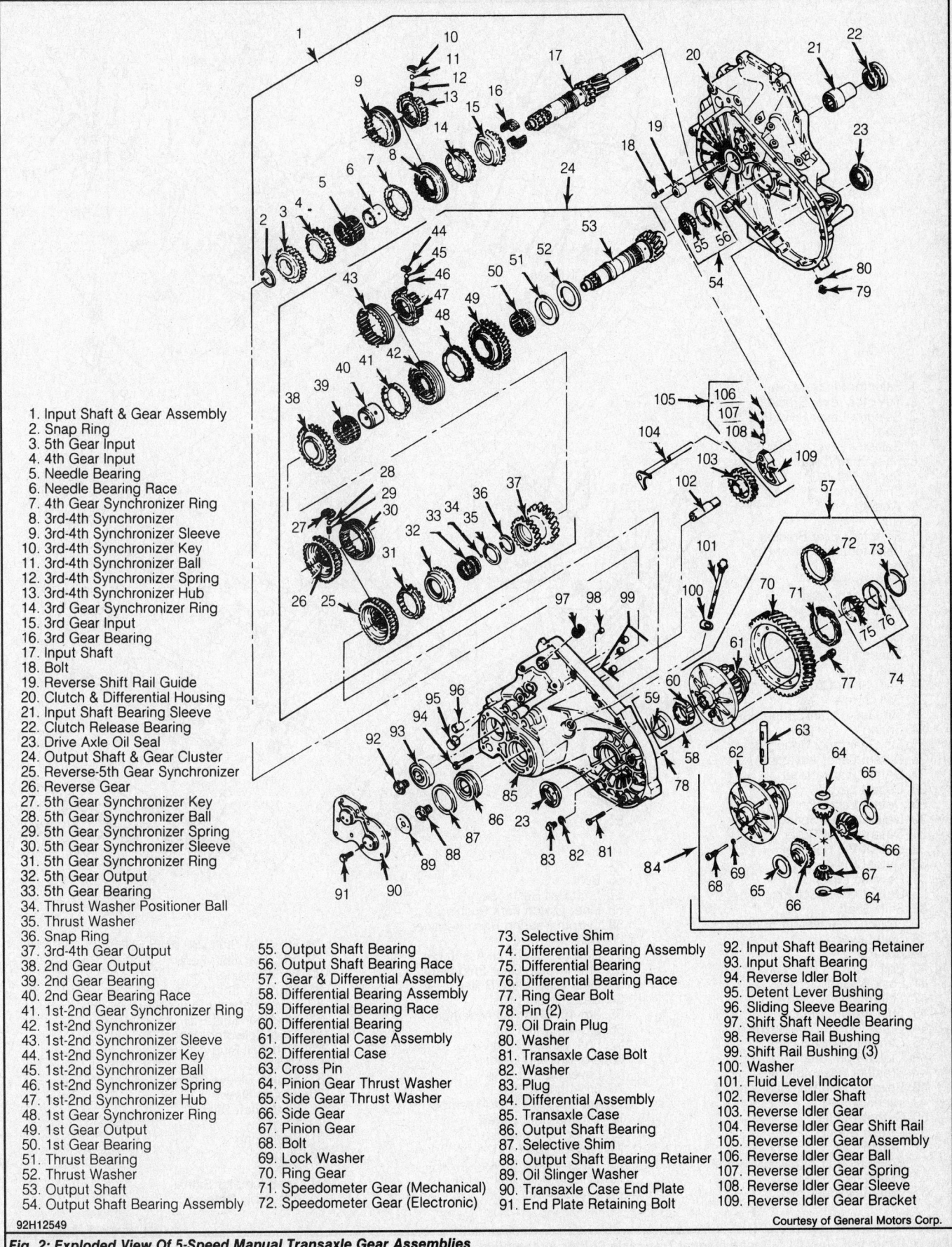

1. Input Shaft & Gear Assembly
2. Snap Ring
3. 5th Gear Input
4. 4th Gear Input
5. Needle Bearing
6. Needle Bearing Race
7. 4th Gear Synchronizer Ring
8. 3rd-4th Synchronizer
9. 3rd-4th Synchronizer Sleeve
10. 3rd-4th Synchronizer Key
11. 3rd-4th Synchronizer Ball
12. 3rd-4th Synchronizer Spring
13. 3rd-4th Synchronizer Hub
14. 3rd Gear Synchronizer Ring
15. 3rd Gear Input
16. 3rd Gear Bearing
17. Input Shaft
18. Bolt
19. Reverse Shift Rail Guide
20. Clutch & Differential Housing
21. Input Shaft Bearing Sleeve
22. Clutch Release Bearing
23. Drive Axle Oil Seal
24. Output Shaft & Gear Cluster
25. Reverse-5th Gear Synchronizer
26. Reverse Gear
27. 5th Gear Synchronizer Key
28. 5th Gear Synchronizer Ball
29. 5th Gear Synchronizer Spring
30. 5th Gear Synchronizer Sleeve
31. 5th Gear Synchronizer Ring
32. 5th Gear Output
33. 5th Gear Bearing
34. Thrust Washer Positioner Ball
35. Thrust Washer
36. Snap Ring
37. 3rd-4th Gear Output
38. 2nd Gear Output
39. 2nd Gear Bearing
40. 2nd Gear Bearing Race
41. 1st-2nd Gear Synchronizer Ring
42. 1st-2nd Synchronizer
43. 1st-2nd Synchronizer Sleeve
44. 1st-2nd Synchronizer Key
45. 1st-2nd Synchronizer Ball
46. 1st-2nd Synchronizer Spring
47. 1st-2nd Synchronizer Hub
48. 1st Gear Synchronizer Ring
49. 1st Gear Output
50. 1st Gear Bearing
51. Thrust Bearing
52. Thrust Washer
53. Output Shaft
54. Output Shaft Bearing Assembly

55. Output Shaft Bearing
56. Output Shaft Bearing Race
57. Gear & Differential Assembly
58. Differential Bearing Assembly
59. Differential Bearing Race
60. Differential Bearing
61. Differential Case Assembly
62. Differential Case
63. Cross Pin
64. Pinion Gear Thrust Washer
65. Side Gear Thrust Washer
66. Side Gear
67. Pinion Gear
68. Bolt
69. Lock Washer
70. Ring Gear
71. Speedometer Gear (Mechanical)
72. Speedometer Gear (Electronic)

73. Selective Shim
74. Differential Bearing Assembly
75. Differential Bearing
76. Differential Bearing Race
77. Ring Gear Bolt
78. Pin (2)
79. Oil Drain Plug
80. Washer
81. Transaxle Case Bolt
82. Washer
83. Plug
84. Differential Assembly
85. Transaxle Case
86. Output Shaft Bearing
87. Selective Shim
88. Output Shaft Bearing Retainer
89. Oil Slinger Washer
90. Transaxle Case End Plate
91. End Plate Retaining Bolt

92. Input Shaft Bearing Retainer
93. Input Shaft Bearing
94. Reverse Idler Bolt
95. Detent Lever Bushing
96. Sliding Sleeve Bearing
97. Shift Shaft Needle Bearing
98. Reverse Rail Bushing
99. Shift Rail Bushing (3)
100. Washer
101. Fluid Level Indicator
102. Reverse Idler Shaft
103. Reverse Idler Gear
104. Reverse Idler Gear Shift Rail
105. Reverse Idler Gear Assembly
106. Reverse Idler Gear Ball
107. Reverse Idler Gear Spring
108. Reverse Idler Gear Sleeve
109. Reverse Idler Gear Bracket

92H12549

Courtesy of General Motors Corp.

Fig. 2: Exploded View Of 5-Speed Manual Transaxle Gear Assemblies

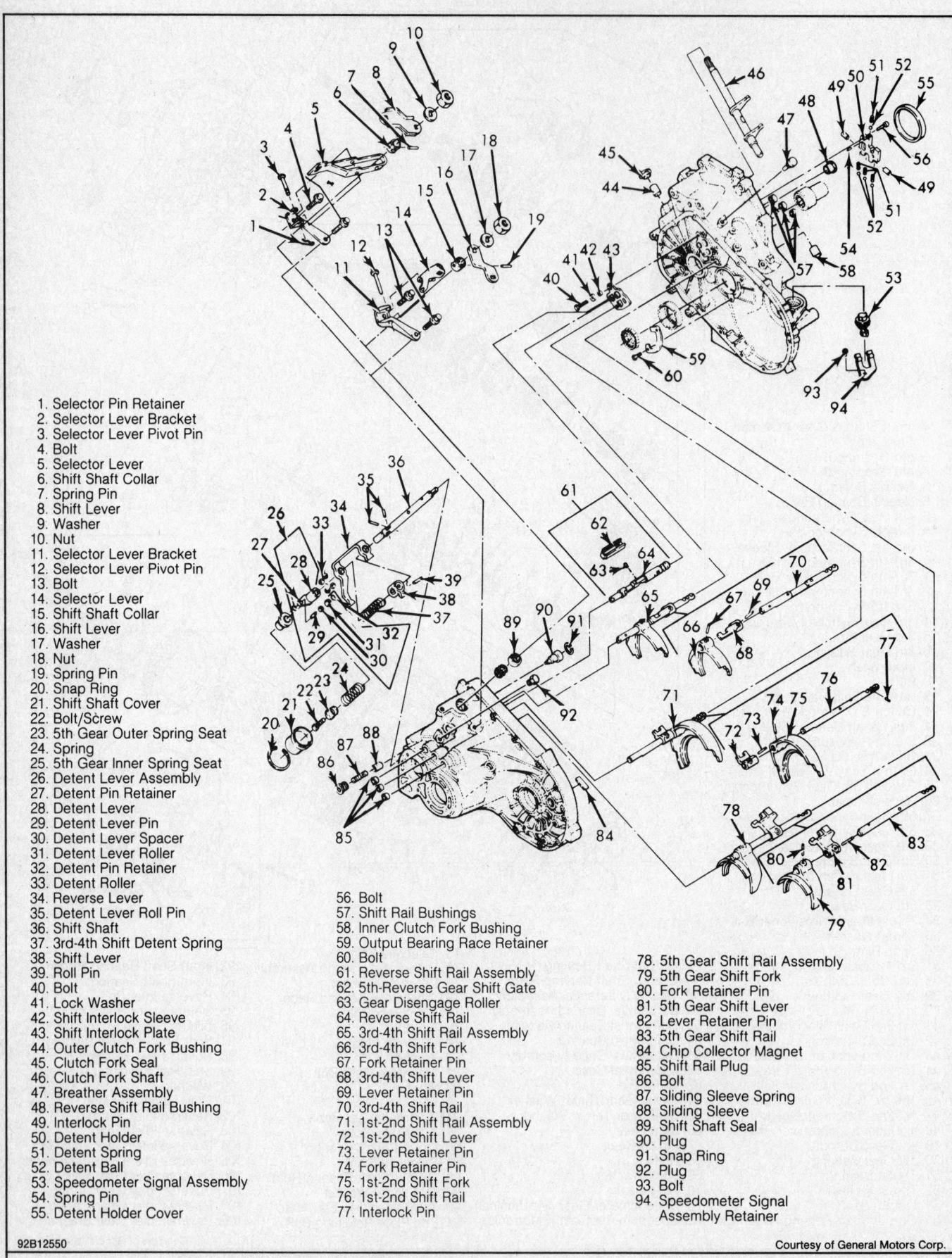

1. Selector Pin Retainer
2. Selector Lever Bracket
3. Selector Lever Pivot Pin
4. Bolt
5. Selector Lever
6. Shift Shaft Collar
7. Spring Pin
8. Shift Lever
9. Washer
10. Nut
11. Selector Lever Bracket
12. Selector Lever Pivot Pin
13. Bolt
14. Selector Lever
15. Shift Shaft Collar
16. Shift Lever
17. Washer
18. Nut
19. Spring Pin
20. Snap Ring
21. Shift Shaft Cover
22. Bolt/Screw
23. 5th Gear Outer Spring Seat
24. Spring
25. 5th Gear Inner Spring Seat
26. Detent Lever Assembly
27. Detent Pin Retainer
28. Detent Lever
29. Detent Lever Pin
30. Detent Lever Spacer
31. Detent Lever Roller
32. Detent Pin Retainer
33. Detent Roller
34. Reverse Lever
35. Detent Lever Roll Pin
36. Shift Shaft
37. 3rd-4th Shift Detent Spring
38. Shift Lever
39. Roll Pin
40. Bolt
41. Lock Washer
42. Shift Interlock Sleeve
43. Shift Interlock Plate
44. Outer Clutch Fork Bushing
45. Clutch Fork Seal
46. Clutch Fork Shaft
47. Breather Assembly
48. Reverse Shift Rail Bushing
49. Interlock Pin
50. Detent Holder
51. Detent Spring
52. Detent Ball
53. Speedometer Signal Assembly
54. Spring Pin
55. Detent Holder Cover

56. Bolt
57. Shift Rail Bushings
58. Inner Clutch Fork Bushing
59. Output Bearing Race Retainer
60. Bolt
61. Reverse Shift Rail Assembly
62. 5th-Reverse Gear Shift Gate
63. Gear Disengage Roller
64. Reverse Shift Rail
65. 3rd-4th Shift Rail Assembly
66. 3rd-4th Shift Fork
67. Fork Retainer Pin
68. 3rd-4th Shift Lever
69. Lever Retainer Pin
70. 3rd-4th Shift Rail
71. 1st-2nd Shift Rail Assembly
72. 1st-2nd Shift Lever
73. Lever Retainer Pin
74. Fork Retainer Pin
75. 1st-2nd Shift Fork
76. 1st-2nd Shift Rail
77. Interlock Pin

78. 5th Gear Shift Rail Assembly
79. 5th Gear Shift Fork
80. Fork Retainer Pin
81. 5th Gear Shift Lever
82. Lever Retainer Pin
83. 5th Gear Shift Rail
84. Chip Collector Magnet
85. Shift Rail Plug
86. Bolt
87. Sliding Sleeve Spring
88. Sliding Sleeve
89. Shift Shaft Seal
90. Plug
91. Snap Ring
92. Plug
93. Bolt
94. Speedometer Signal
Assembly Retainer

92B12550

Courtesy of General Motors Corp.

Fig. 3: Exploded View Of 5-Speed Manual Transaxle Shifter Assemblies

Cleaning & Inspection – 1) Clean all parts in solvent and blow dry with compressed air. Inspect input shaft splines for wear or cracks and replace if necessary. Inspect all gears for scuffed, nicked or broken teeth.

2) Check bearings for rough rotation, burred or pitting conditions. Replace bearings if necessary. Check bearing races and input shaft races for scoring, wear or overheating conditions.

3) Inspect snap ring for nicks, wear or distortion. Check synchronizer for wear, scuffed, nicked, burred or broken teeth. If defects cannot be repaired by using a soft stone or crocus cloth, replace component.

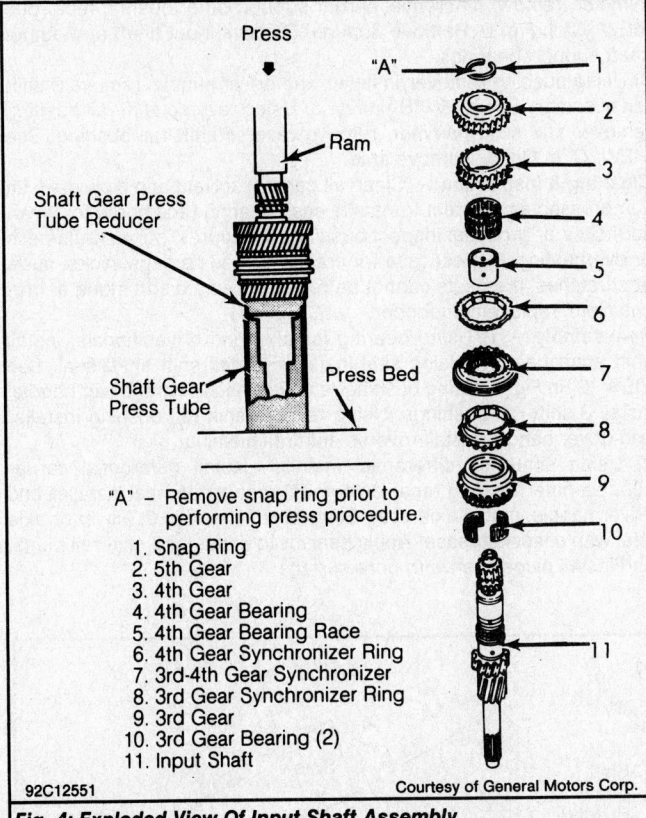

"A" – Remove snap ring prior to performing press procedure.

1. Snap Ring
2. 5th Gear
3. 4th Gear
4. 4th Gear Bearing
5. 4th Gear Bearing Race
6. 4th Gear Synchronizer Ring
7. 3rd-4th Gear Synchronizer
8. 3rd Gear Synchronizer Ring
9. 3rd Gear
10. 3rd Gear Bearing (2)
11. Input Shaft

92C12551　　Courtesy of General Motors Corp.

Fig. 4: Exploded View Of Input Shaft Assembly

Reassembly – 1) Prior to reassembly, lubricate all components. Heat bearing race and 5th gear to 250°F (120°C) for 7-10 minutes to properly expand components prior to reassembly. Install 3rd gear bearing halves onto input shaft. Install 3rd gear with cone facing up. Install 3rd gear synchronizer ring. *See Fig. 4.*

2) Using shaft gear remover/installer, tube, tube reducer and press, install 3rd-4th gear synchronizer onto input shaft with small outside diameter groove of sleeve facing 3rd gear.

3) Start hydraulic press operation to press on 3rd-4th gear synchronizer, but stop before tangs engage. DO NOT allow tangs to engage with each other. Lift and rotate 3rd gear and 3rd gear synchronizer ring to engage synchronizer ring tangs. Continue to press until synchronizer is properly seated. Ensure all metal shavings are removed.

4) Install 4th gear synchronizer ring. Install 4th gear with cone facing down. Install 4th gear bearing race and bearing onto input shaft. Using shaft gear press tube and shaft gear press tube reducer, press 5th gear onto input shaft. Ensure flat side of gear faces down. Install NEW snap ring.

OUTPUT SHAFT

Disassembly – 1) Using shaft gear remover/installer and hydraulic press, remove reverse-5th gear synchronizer from output shaft. Remove 5th gear synchronizer ring, 5th gear and 5th gear bearing. *See Fig. 5.* Before removing any synchronizer rings, ensure rings are labeled as to which gear they go with. DO NOT mix rings.

2) Remove thrust washer and positioning ball from shaft. Remove snap ring. Using shaft gear press tube and press, remove 1st gear, 1st gear bearing, thrust bearing and thrust washer from shaft. *See Fig. 5.*

3) When 1st gear is pressed off output shaft, 2nd gear, 2nd gear bearing and race, 1st-2nd gear synchronizer, 1st and 2nd gear synchronizer rings and 3rd-4th gear will also be removed. *See Fig. 5.*

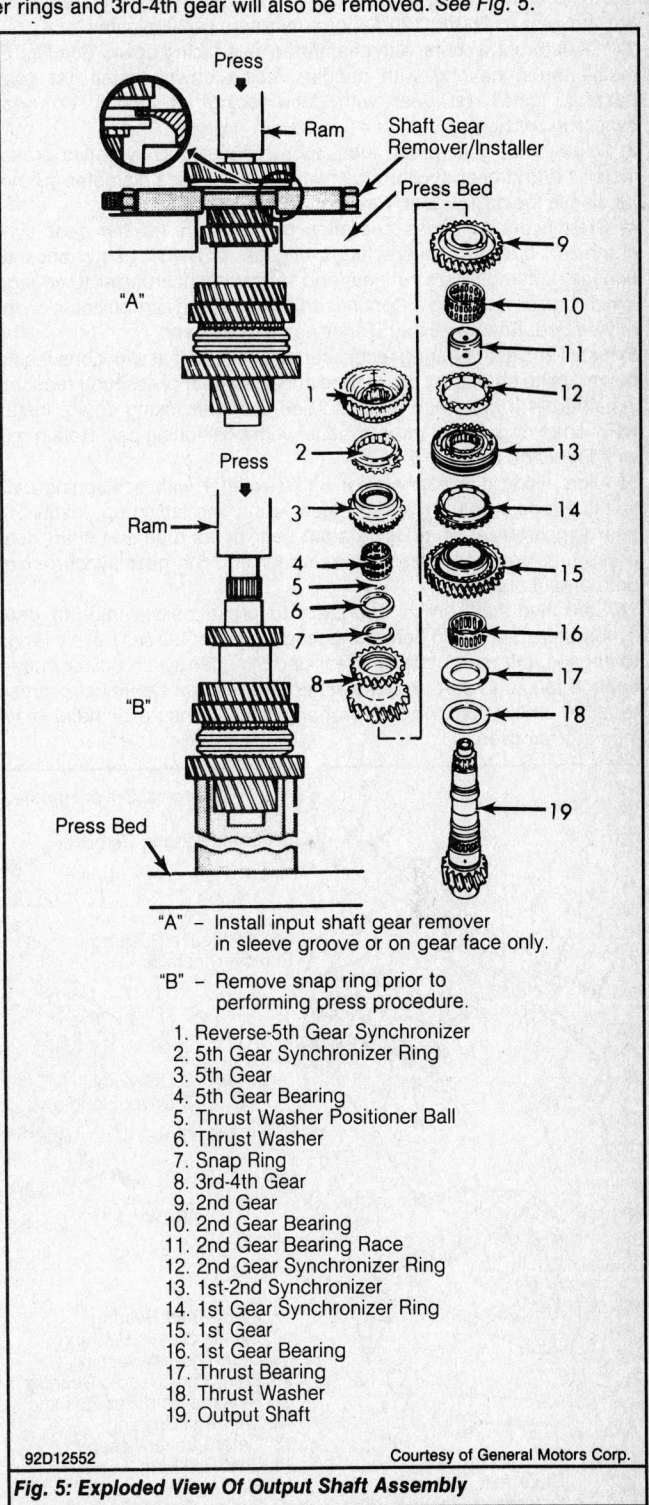

"A" – Install input shaft gear remover in sleeve groove or on gear face only.

"B" – Remove snap ring prior to performing press procedure.

1. Reverse-5th Gear Synchronizer
2. 5th Gear Synchronizer Ring
3. 5th Gear
4. 5th Gear Bearing
5. Thrust Washer Positioner Ball
6. Thrust Washer
7. Snap Ring
8. 3rd-4th Gear
9. 2nd Gear
10. 2nd Gear Bearing
11. 2nd Gear Bearing Race
12. 2nd Gear Synchronizer Ring
13. 1st-2nd Synchronizer
14. 1st Gear Synchronizer Ring
15. 1st Gear
16. 1st Gear Bearing
17. Thrust Bearing
18. Thrust Washer
19. Output Shaft

92D12552　　Courtesy of General Motors Corp.

Fig. 5: Exploded View Of Output Shaft Assembly

Cleaning & Inspection – 1) Clean all parts in solvent and blow dry with compressed air. Inspect output shaft splines for wear or cracks. Check all gears for scuffing, nicks, burrs or broken teeth. Inspect bearing races for scoring, wear or overheating.

2) Inspect bearings for rotation roughness, burrs or pits. Check synchronizer for wear, scuffed, nicked, burred or broken teeth. If defects cannot be repaired by using a soft stone or crocus cloth, replace component.

Reassembly – 1) Prior to reassembly, lubricate all components, and heat 2nd gear bearing race to 250°F (120°C) for 7-10 minutes. Heat 3rd-4th gear to 250°F (120°C) for a minimum of 20 minutes.

2) Install thrust washer with chamfered side facing down. *See Fig. 5.* Install thrust bearing with needles facing down. Install 1st gear bearing. Install 1st gear with cone facing up. Install 1st gear synchronizer ring.

3) Using shaft gear press tube, tube reducer and hydraulic press, install 1st-2nd gear synchronizer with small outside diameter groove on sleeve facing 1st gear. *See Fig. 5.*

4) Start hydraulic press operation to press on 1st-2nd gear synchronizer, but stop before tangs engage. DO NOT allow tangs to engage. Lift and rotate 1st gear and 1st gear synchronizer to engage synchronizer ring tangs. Continue to press until synchronizer is properly seated. Ensure all metal shavings are removed.

5) Install 2nd gear bearing race, bearing and 2nd gear with cone facing down. Using shaft gear press tube and shaft gear press tube reducer, install 3rd-4th gear with large outside diameter facing down. Install NEW snap ring. Install thrust washer with positioning ball. Retain ball with lubricant. *See Fig. 5.*

6) Align inside diameter slot of thrust washer with positioning ball. Install 5th gear bearing and 5th gear with cone facing up. Install 5th gear synchronizer ring. Using shaft gear press tube and shaft gear press tube reducer, press reverse gear and 5th gear synchronizer onto output shaft.

7) Start hydraulic press operation to press on reverse-5th gear synchronizer, but stop before the tangs engage. DO NOT allow tangs to engage. Lift and rotate 5th gear and 5th gear synchronizer ring to engage tangs. Ensure thrust washer stays down. Continue to press together until synchronizer is properly seated. Ensure all metal shavings are removed.

TRANSAXLE CASE

Disassembly – 1) Remove bearing or bushings only if there is evidence of damage, or a mating part is being replaced. Remove snap ring and plug. Using bushing remover/installer and driver handle, remove plug, spring and sliding sleeve. See VIEW "A" in *Fig. 6.*

2) Remove detent lever. Using bushing remover/installer and driver handle, remove shift detent lever bushing. See VIEW "B" in *Fig. 6.* Remove shift shaft seal. Using shift shaft bearing remover, remove shaft bearing. See VIEW "A" in *Fig. 6.*

3) Remove axle seal. Using seal/race differential remover and slide hammer, remove differential carrier support outer bearing race. See VIEW "C" in *Fig. 6.* Remove 3 plugs. Remove input shaft and output shaft support bearings.

4) Using bushing remover/installer and driver handle, remove 3 shift rail bushings. See VIEW "B" in *Fig. 6.* Using reverse shift rail bushing remover and slide hammer, remove reverse shift rail bushing. See VIEW "C" in *Fig. 6.* Remove stud.

Cleaning & Inspection – Clean all parts in solvent and blow dry with compressed air. Inspect transaxle case bearing race bores for wear, scratches or grooves. Inspect bushings for scores, burrs, roundness or overheating. Inspect case for cracks, thread damage, nicks, burrs or scratches. If defects cannot be repaired using a soft stone or crocus cloth, replace component.

Reassembly – 1) Using bearing installer and driver handle, install shift shaft bearing. Using seal installer, install shift shaft seal. See VIEW "C" in *Fig. 6.* Using bushing remover/installer and driver handle, install 3 shift rail bushings. Using reverse shift rail bushing installer and driver handle, install reverse shift rail bushing.

2) Using seal/race differential installer, install differential carrier support outer bearing race. Using seal/race differential installer and driver handle, install axle seal. See VIEW "A" in *Fig. 6.* Fill lip of axle seal with chassis grease. Apply sealant to edges of 3 shift rail plugs, and install plugs even with bore surface.

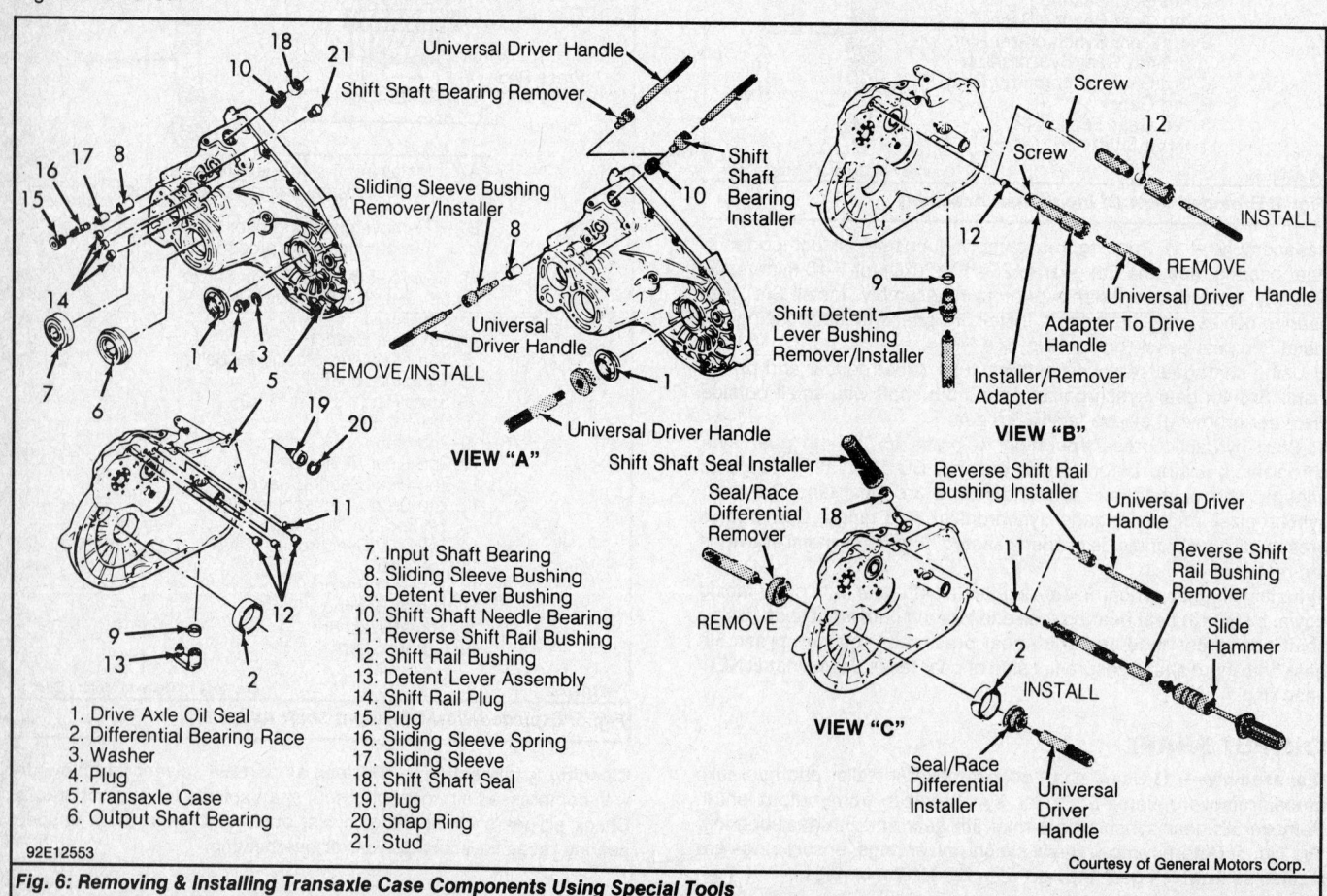

1. Drive Axle Oil Seal
2. Differential Bearing Race
3. Washer
4. Plug
5. Transaxle Case
6. Output Shaft Bearing
7. Input Shaft Bearing
8. Sliding Sleeve Bushing
9. Detent Lever Bushing
10. Shift Shaft Needle Bearing
11. Reverse Shift Rail Bushing
12. Shift Rail Bushing
13. Detent Lever Assembly
14. Shift Rail Plug
15. Plug
16. Sliding Sleeve Spring
17. Sliding Sleeve
18. Shift Shaft Seal
19. Plug
20. Snap Ring
21. Stud

92E12553

Courtesy of General Motors Corp.

Fig. 6: Removing & Installing Transaxle Case Components Using Special Tools

3) Using shift detent lever bushing remover/installer and driver handle, install detent lever bushing. Install detent lever. Using sliding sleeve bushing remover/installer and driver handle, install sliding sleeve bushing.

4) Install sleeve, spring and plug. Apply sealant to edge of plug prior to installation. Install stud so chamfered end faces out. Tighten stud to specification. See TORQUE SPECIFICATIONS.

REVERSE IDLER GEAR

Disassembly – Remove reverse idler bolt, shift rail and reverse idler gear. *See Fig. 7*. Remove shaft and bracket. When removing bracket from shift rail, DO NOT lose detent ball and spring from behind bracket (if equipped).

Cleaning & Inspection – Wash all parts in solvent and blow dry with compressed air. Inspect all parts for scuffing, nicks, burrs and broken teeth. Inspect bushings for burrs, scoring, roundness or overheating. Check shaft for scoring, nicks, burrs or overheating. If defects cannot be repaired by soft stone or crocus cloth, replace component.

Reassembly – Lubricate all components prior to assembly. Install spring and detent ball (if equipped) into bracket and place bracket over shift rail. *See Fig. 7*. Assemble reverse idler gear onto shaft with slot of gear facing threaded hole in shaft. Install reverse idler assembly into case. Apply Teflon sealant to bolt threads and install bolt. Tighten bolt to specification. See TORQUE SPECIFICATIONS.

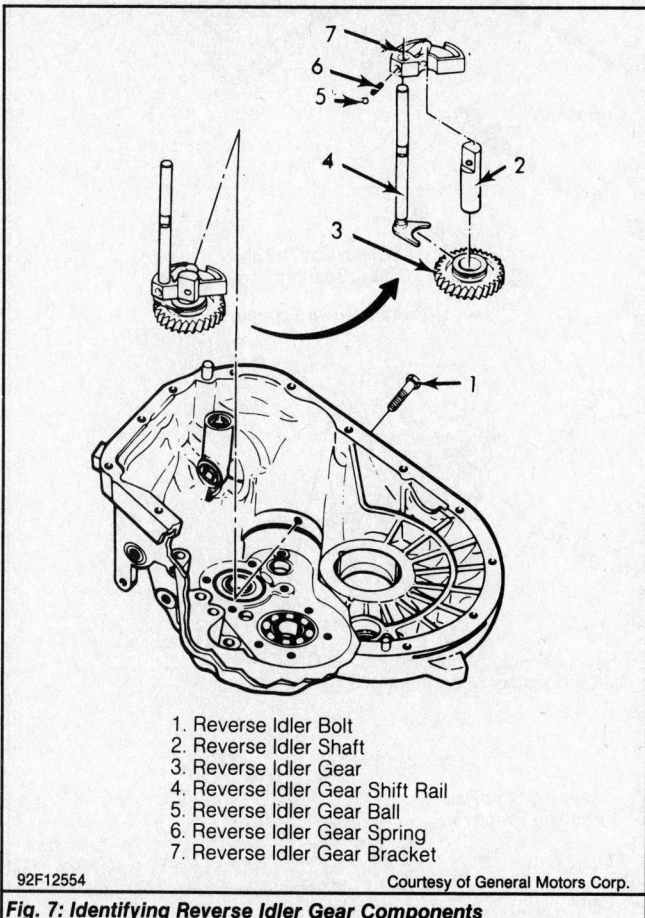

1. Reverse Idler Bolt
2. Reverse Idler Shaft
3. Reverse Idler Gear
4. Reverse Idler Gear Shift Rail
5. Reverse Idler Gear Ball
6. Reverse Idler Gear Spring
7. Reverse Idler Gear Bracket

92F12554   Courtesy of General Motors Corp.

Fig. 7: Identifying Reverse Idler Gear Components

SYNCHRONIZERS

Disassembly – Wrap 1st-2nd, 3rd-4th and 5th gear synchronizer assemblies in separate clean shop towels. Press against inner hub until assembly comes apart.

Cleaning & Inspection – Clean all parts in solvent and blow dry with compressed air. Inspect synchronizer for wear, scuffing, nicks, burrs or broken teeth. Check balls and springs for distortion, cracks or wear. If defects cannot be repaired using a soft stone or crocus cloth, replace component.

Reassembly – 1) Install 1st-2nd gear sleeve with small outside diameter groove positioned over thinner side of hub. Install 3rd-4th gear sleeve with small outside diameter groove positioned over wider side of hub. Install springs into keys. Install spring and key assemblies with bevel cut on keys facing toward sleeve. *See Fig. 8*.

2) Position assembly as shown. See VIEW "A" in *Fig. 8*. Install balls. Push ball and key into sleeve using screwdriver. By centering hub, the keys and balls should click into position. See VIEW "B" in *Fig. 8*.

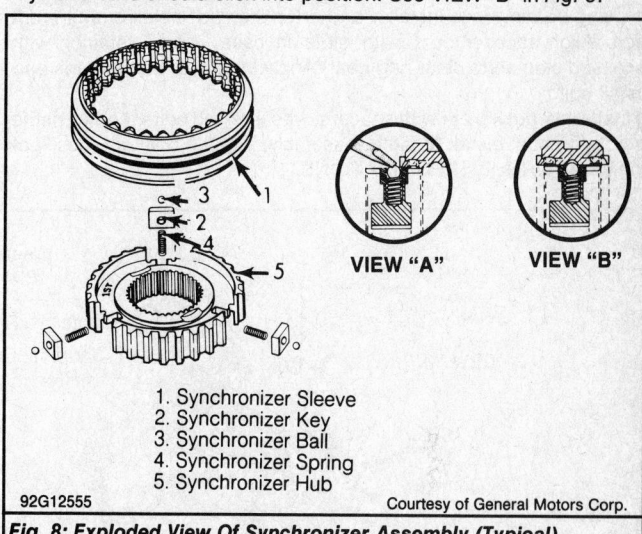

1. Synchronizer Sleeve
2. Synchronizer Key
3. Synchronizer Ball
4. Synchronizer Spring
5. Synchronizer Hub

92G12555   Courtesy of General Motors Corp.

Fig. 8: Exploded View Of Synchronizer Assembly (Typical)

CLUTCH & DIFFERENTIAL HOUSING

Disassembly – 1) Remove bearing or bushings only if there is evidence of damage, or a mating part is being replaced. Remove 2 output shaft retainer bolts and retainer. Using bearing race remover and slide hammer, remove output shaft bearing race. *See Fig. 9*.

2) Remove 3 interlock plate retaining bolts and plate. Remove retaining bolt and reverse rail guide. Remove axle seal. Using seal/race differential remover and slide hammer, remove differential bearing race and selective shim.

3) Pry out clutch shaft seal. *See Fig. 9*. Using bearing remover/installer, remove clutch shaft outer bearing. Remove clutch shaft. Using bushing remover and driver handle, remove clutch shaft inner bearing.

4) Using bearing remover/installer, press out input bearing sleeve assembly. Using bushing remover/installer, remove 3 shift rail bushings. Remove drain plug and washer. Remove breather assembly. DO NOT remove metal tube from case.

Cleaning & Inspection – Clean all parts in solvent and blow dry with compressed air. Check bearing race bores for wear, scratches or grooves. Inspect bushings for scores, burrs, roundness or overheating. Check case for cracks, thread damage, nicks, burrs, scratches or scoring. If defects cannot be repaired using a soft stone or crocus cloth, replace component.

Reassembly – 1) Install drain plug and NEW washer. *See Fig. 9*. Using bushing remover/installer and driver handle, install 3 shift rail bushings.

CAUTION: Shift rail bushing must not protrude into case side of housing. DO NOT install differential bearing race, axle seal or shim. These components are installed after differential assembly selective shimming procedure has been completed. See DIFFERENTIAL ASSEMBLY SELECTIVE SHIM PRELOAD PROCEDURE and OUTPUT SHAFT SUPPORT BEARING SELECTIVE SHIM PROCEDURE.

---

2) Using bearing remover/installer, install input shaft bearing sleeve with oil seepage hole facing down in clutch housing. See VIEW "B" in *Fig. 9*. Using bushing installer and driver, install clutch shaft inner bearing.

3) Install clutch shaft. Apply high temperature grease to clutch shaft fingers and inner bearing end. Using bearing installer/remover, install clutch shaft outer bearing. Ensure bearing is flush with bottom of seal bore.

4) Install clutch shaft seal. Install clutch release lever and bolt. Ensure clutch release lever bolt hole is aligned with slot in clutch shaft. Install reverse rail guide with short side in bore. Tighten bolt to specification. See TORQUE SPECIFICATIONS.

5) Using bearing race installer and driver handle, install output shaft race. Align race cutouts with slots in case. Install retainer with recessed side up to clear ring gear. Apply Loctite to bolt threads and install bolts.

6) Install interlock plate with spacers, washers and bolts. Apply Loctite to bolt threads. Install breather assembly. Tighten bolts to specification. See TORQUE SPECIFICATIONS.

DIFFERENTIAL & RING GEAR

Disassembly – Remove ring gear retaining bolts and ring gear. Using bearing puller and bearing remover, remove differential side bearings. Remove speedometer gear. Remove differential cross pin bolt and washer. Remove differential cross pin. Remove differential side gears, pinion gears and washers.

Cleaning & Inspection – Clean all parts in solvent and blow dry with compressed air. Inspect gears and thrust washers for wear, scuffing, nicks, burrs or broken teeth. Check carrier for distortion, out-of-round bores or scoring. Check bearings for rotation roughness, burrs or pits. If defects cannot be repaired using a soft stone or crocus cloth, replace component.

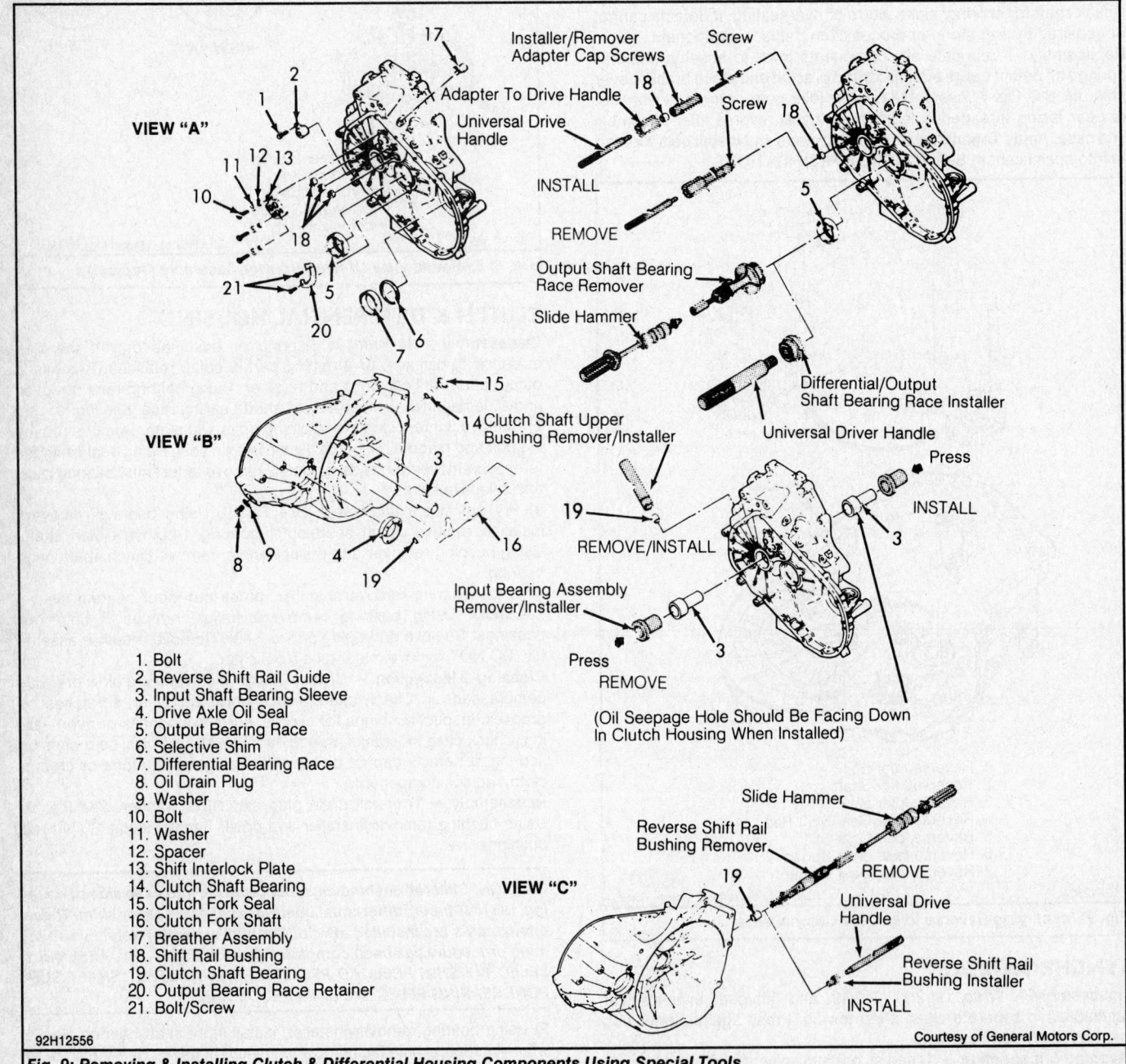

1. Bolt
2. Reverse Shift Rail Guide
3. Input Shaft Bearing Sleeve
4. Drive Axle Oil Seal
5. Output Bearing Race
6. Selective Shim
7. Differential Bearing Race
8. Oil Drain Plug
9. Washer
10. Bolt
11. Washer
12. Spacer
13. Shift Interlock Plate
14. Clutch Shaft Bearing
15. Clutch Fork Seal
16. Clutch Fork Shaft
17. Breather Assembly
18. Shift Rail Bushing
19. Clutch Shaft Bearing
20. Output Bearing Race Retainer
21. Bolt/Screw

92H12556

Courtesy of General Motors Corp.

Fig. 9: Removing & Installing Clutch & Differential Housing Components Using Special Tools

Reassembly – 1) Heat NEW electronic speedometer gear prior to assembly. Gear must be preheated to 250°F (120°C) for 7-10 minutes. Install preheated speedometer gear and allow it to cool. Using bearing installer, press on differential side bearings. Install differential side gears, pinion gears and thrust washers. *See Fig. 2.*

2) Install differential cross pin. Install differential cross pin bolt. Tighten bolt to specification. See TORQUE SPECIFICATIONS. Install ring gear on differential assembly using NEW bolts. Tighten bolts to specification and then tighten them an additional 45 degrees.

DIFFERENTIAL ASSEMBLY SELECTIVE SHIM PRELOAD PROCEDURE

CAUTION: Perform preload procedure when one or more of the following components are replaced: transaxle case, clutch and differential case, differential carrier and differential bearing assemblies.

1) Install Shim Selection Set (J-26935) to clutch housing and transaxle housing. Measure Dimension "U", and use shim that is 2 sizes larger. See PRELOAD SHIM SELECTION TABLE. *See Fig. 10.*

2) Install selected shim. Using seal/race installer and driver, install differential bearing race. Using seal/race installer and driver, install axle seal. Fill lip of axle seal with chassis grease.

PRELOAD SHIM SELECTION TABLE

Shim Part No.	¹ Dimension "U" In. (mm)	Color	Stripes
14082132	.012 (.30)	Orange	1
14082133	.014 (.35)	Orange	2
14082134	.016 (.40)	Orange	3
14082135	.018 (.45)	Orange	4
14082136	.020 (.50)	Yellow	1
14082137	.022 (.55)	Yellow	2
14082138	.024 (.60)	Yellow	3
14082139	.026 (.65)	Yellow	4
14082140	.028 (.70)	White	1
14082141	.030 (.75)	White	2
14082142	.031 (.80)	White	3
14082143	.033 (.85)	White	4
14082144	.035 (.90)	Green	1
14082145	.037 (.95)	Green	2
14082146	.039 (1.00)	Green	3
14082147	.041 (1.05)	Green	4
14082148	.043 (1.10)	Blue	1
14082149	.045 (1.15)	Blue	2
14082150	.047 (1.20)	Blue	3
14082151	.049 (1.25)	Blue	4
14082152	.051 (1.30)	Red	1

¹ – Measure Dimension "U", and use shim that is 2 sizes larger.

OUTPUT SHAFT SUPPORT BEARING SELECTIVE SHIM PROCEDURE

1) Ensure output bearing is properly seated in its bore. Ensure bearing retainer is tightened properly. Measure dimension "A", which is distance between end plate mounting surface and outer race of output shaft bearing. *See Fig. 11.*

2) Select appropriate shim based on measured dimension "A". See OUTPUT SHAFT SHIM SELECTION TABLE. Selected shim can be .001" (.03 mm) greater than or .004" (.12 mm) less than measured dimension "A".

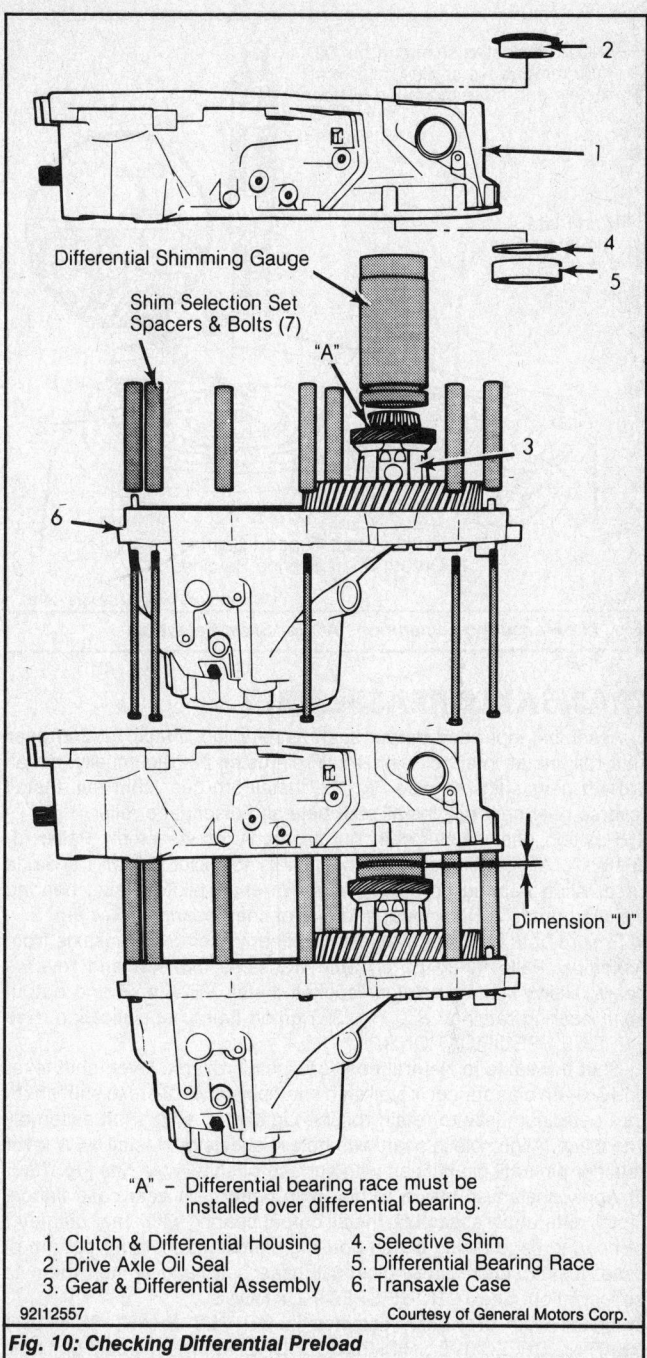

"A" – Differential bearing race must be installed over differential bearing.

1. Clutch & Differential Housing
2. Drive Axle Oil Seal
3. Gear & Differential Assembly
4. Selective Shim
5. Differential Bearing Race
6. Transaxle Case

92I12557
Courtesy of General Motors Corp.

Fig. 10: Checking Differential Preload

OUTPUT SHAFT SHIM SELECTION TABLE ¹

Part No.	Dimension "A" In. (mm)
14092067	.179 (4.54)
14092068	.183 (4.64)
14092069	.187 (4.74)
14092070	.191 (4.84)
14092071	.194 (4.94)
14092072	.198 (5.04)
14092073	.202 (5.14)

¹ – Selected shim can be .001" (.03 mm) greater than or .004" (.12 mm) less than measured dimension "A".

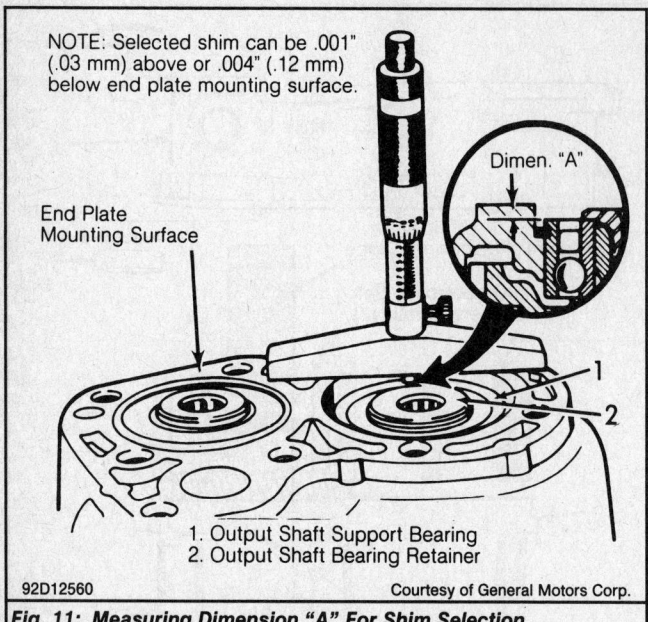

NOTE: Selected shim can be .001"
(.03 mm) above or .004" (.12 mm)
below end plate mounting surface.

Dimen. "A"

End Plate
Mounting Surface

1. Output Shaft Support Bearing
2. Output Shaft Bearing Retainer

92D12560   Courtesy of General Motors Corp.

Fig. 11: Measuring Dimension "A" For Shim Selection

TRANSAXLE REASSEMBLY

1) Assemble input and output shaft assemblies. Install 1st-2nd gear shift rail. Install interlock pin. Retain pin using petroleum jelly. Install 3rd-4th gear shift rail. See Fig. 12. Install 5th gear shift rail. Install reverse gear shift rail. Install shift gate and disengage roller.

2) Position gear cluster/shift rail assembly on Assembly Pallet (J-36182-1). Align shift rail and shaft pilots to pallet. Install transaxle case. Align bearing bores in case with shaft pilots. Using bearing installer, press in NEW input and output shaft bearings. See Fig. 2.

3) Ensure both bearings are seated properly. Remove transaxle from Assembly Pallet (J-36182-1). Shift transaxle into 4th and reverse gears. Using bearing retainer socket, install NEW input and output shaft bearing retainer. See Fig. 2. Tighten bolt to specification. See TORQUE SPECIFICATIONS.

4) Shift transaxle to Neutral position. Install reverse lever, shift lever and 3rd-4th bias spring. Install shift shaft pins and rollers to shift shaft. Use petroleum jelly to retain rollers. Lightly tap shift shaft assembly into place. Align hole in shaft with hole in shift lever. Install NEW lever retainer pin until pin is flush with surface of shift lever. See Fig. 13.

5) Apply sealant to inside of bolt hole pattern on gear case flange. Install differential assembly. Install output bearing with small diameter of bearing cage facing clutch housing. Install magnet into bottom of case. Install clutch housing. Install case bolts and tighten them to specification. See TORQUE SPECIFICATIONS.

6) Install shim previously selected in OUTPUT SHAFT SUPPORT BEARING SELECTIVE SHIM PROCEDURE. Apply sealant to bolt hole pattern on inside of plate, and install transaxle case end plate. Install thread sealant to end plate bolt threads and install bolts.

7) Position shift rails so that 5th gear shift rail is 1/4" below other shift rails. Shift rails must be in Neutral position. Install reverse bushing. See Fig. 3. Assemble interlock pins and springs into bores in detent holder. Retain components with petroleum jelly.

8) Install detent holder and spring assembly with detent ball for reverse shift rail. Using a screwdriver, install detent balls. Position holder until bolt holes and threads are aligned. Install bolts and tighten them to specification. See TORQUE SPECIFICATIONS.

9) Ensure shift rails are in correct detent positions. Install NEW detent cover. Tap cover until seated in bore. Ensure cover is flush with bore. Install clutch release bearing. Install high temperature grease to inside bore of bearing.

10) Install shift shaft detent inner spring seat, 5th-reverse bias spring and outer spring seat. Install Loctite on bolt threads and install bolt. Apply a thin coat of sealant to mating surface of case bore, and install NEW shift shaft cover. Install snap ring. See Fig. 3.

CAUTION: Ensure shift shaft cover top is not caved in. Caved-in cover may cause a hard shift into 1-2 gate by not allowing full travel of shift shaft.

---

11) Install selector lever bracket and bolts. Use sealant on bolt threads. Install shift shaft collar and NEW spring pin. Apply a thin coat of high temperature grease to slot in collar. Install selector lever and NEW pivot pin. Install shift lever, washer and nut. Apply Loctite to shift shaft threads.

12) DO NOT allow lever to move during installation of nut. Hold shift lever at shift cable mounting stud. Install fluid level indicator. Coat NEW seal with transaxle fluid and install seal on speedometer signal assembly. Install speedometer signal assembly and bolt. Tighten bolt to specification. See TORQUE SPECIFICATIONS.

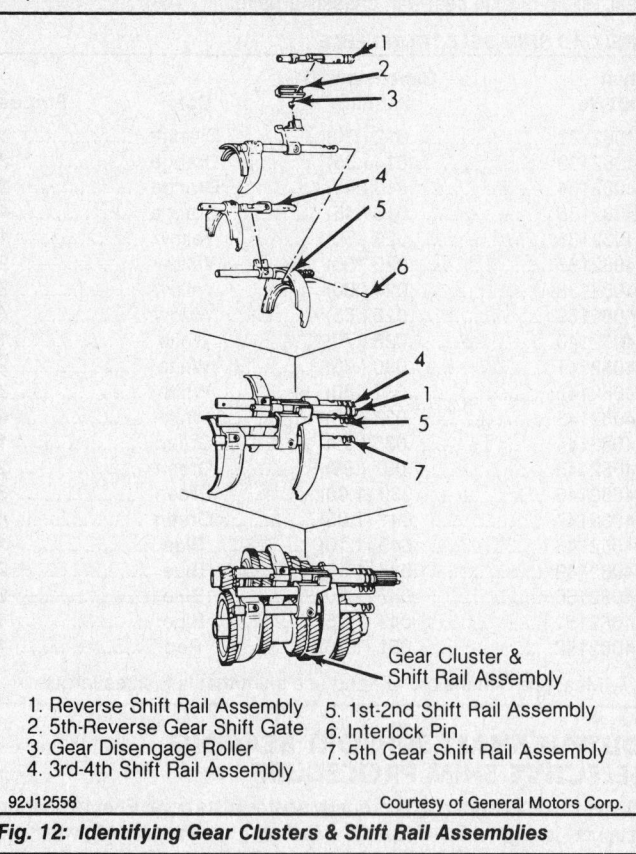

1. Reverse Shift Rail Assembly
2. 5th-Reverse Gear Shift Gate
3. Gear Disengage Roller
4. 3rd-4th Shift Rail Assembly
5. 1st-2nd Shift Rail Assembly
6. Interlock Pin
7. 5th Gear Shift Rail Assembly

Gear Cluster &
Shift Rail Assembly

92J12558   Courtesy of General Motors Corp.

Fig. 12: Identifying Gear Clusters & Shift Rail Assemblies

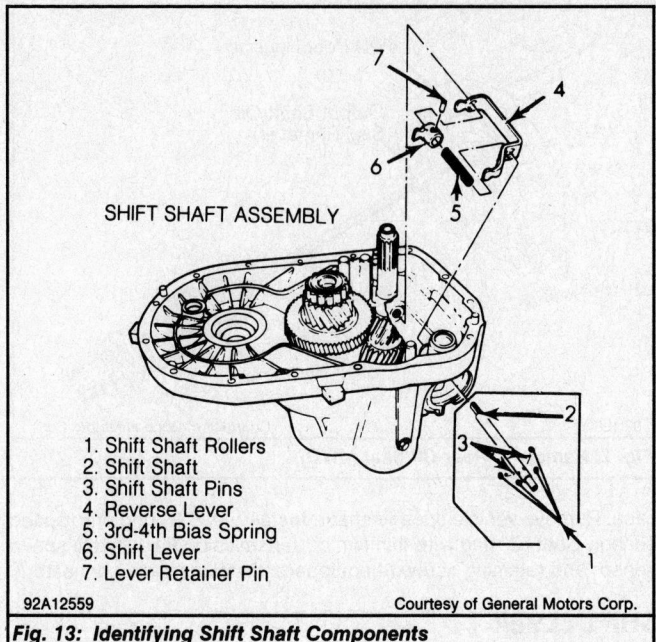

SHIFT SHAFT ASSEMBLY

1. Shift Shaft Rollers
2. Shift Shaft
3. Shift Shaft Pins
4. Reverse Lever
5. 3rd-4th Bias Spring
6. Shift Lever
7. Lever Retainer Pin

92A12559 Courtesy of General Motors Corp.

Fig. 13: Identifying Shift Shaft Components

TORQUE SPECIFICATIONS

TORQUE SPECIFICATIONS

Application	Ft. Lbs. (N.m)
Ball Joint Nut	48-63 (65-85)
Clutch Housing-To-Case Housing Bolt	15 (20)
Differential Ring Gear Bolt	[1] 22 (30)
Drive Axle Shaft Nut	192 (260)
End Plate-To-Gear Housing Bolt	15 (20)
Engine-To-Transaxle Bolt	55 (75)
Fill & Drain Plug	18 (24)
Input Shaft Bearing Retainer	50 (68)
Interlock Plate Bolt	15 (20)
Output Bearing Race Retainer Bolt	15 (20)
Output Shaft Bearing Retainer	50 (68)
Reverse Idler Gear Bracket Bolt	15 (20)
Shift Lever Nut	61 (83)
Shift Pivot Bracket Bolt	17 (23)
Sliding Sleeve Screw	32 (44)
Stabilizer Shaft-To-Control Arm Nut	13 (17)
Stabilizer Shaft-To-Suspension Support Nut	15 (20)
Stud	15 (20)
Transaxle Mount Nut	24 (33)
Transaxle Mounting Bolt	41 (56)
Wheel Lug Nut	100 (136)

	INCH Lbs. (N.m)
Detent Spring Retaining Bolt	80 (9)
Differential Cross Pin Bolt	80 (9)
Reverse Shift Rail Bolt	53 (6)
Shift Rail Detent Bolt	80 (9)
Shift Shaft Bolt	80 (9)
Speedometer Signal Retainer Bolt	80 (9)

[1] – Tighten bolt to specification and then tighten it an additional 45 degrees.

MANUAL TRANSMISSIONS
GM 5LM60 5-Speed

"C" & "K" Series, "S" & "T" Series
1993-94 SERIES CODE DESIGNATIONS

Model	Designation
Blazer	
2WD	"S" Series
4WD	"K" & "T" Series
Jimmy & Sonoma	
2WD	"S" Series
4WD	"T" Series
Pickup	
2WD	"C" & "S" Series
4WD	"K" & "T" Series
Sierra	
2WD	"C" Series
4WD	"K" Series
Yukon	"K" Series

IDENTIFICATION

Transmission identification code is stamped on right side of transmission at front and rear housing joint. First digit "P" identifies 5LM60 type transmission. Second digit represents model year.

LUBRICATION & ADJUSTMENTS

See appropriate MANUAL TRANSMISSION SERVICING article in TRANSMISSION SERVICING.

TROUBLE SHOOTING

See GENERAL TROUBLE SHOOTING article in MANUAL TRANSMISSIONS.

ON-VEHICLE SERVICE

REAR HOUSING OIL SEAL

Removal – Raise and support vehicle. Drain transmission fluid. Remove drive shaft. On 2WD models, use Oil Seal Remover (J-26941) to remove oil seal. See Fig. 1. On 4WD models, use Oil Seal Remover (J-36825). See Fig. 2.

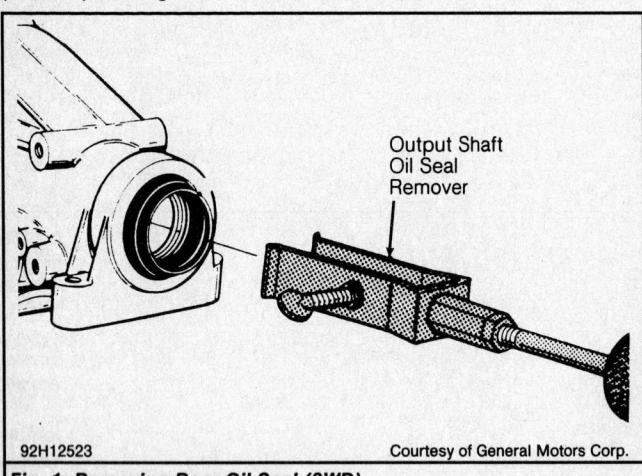

92H12523   Courtesy of General Motors Corp.
Fig. 1: Removing Rear Oil Seal (2WD)

Installation – **1)** Apply sealant on outside area of NEW seal. On 2WD models, install seal using appropriate oil seal installer. On 4WD models, use Seal Protector (J-36502-2A) and oil seal installer.
2) On all models, fill lip of oil seal with chassis grease. Install oil seal and drive shaft. Tighten drive shaft bolts to specification. See TORQUE SPECIFICATIONS. Fill transmission and lower vehicle.

VEHICLE SPEED SENSOR

Removal & Installation – Raise and support vehicle. Remove harness connector and retaining screw (if equipped) holding sensor in

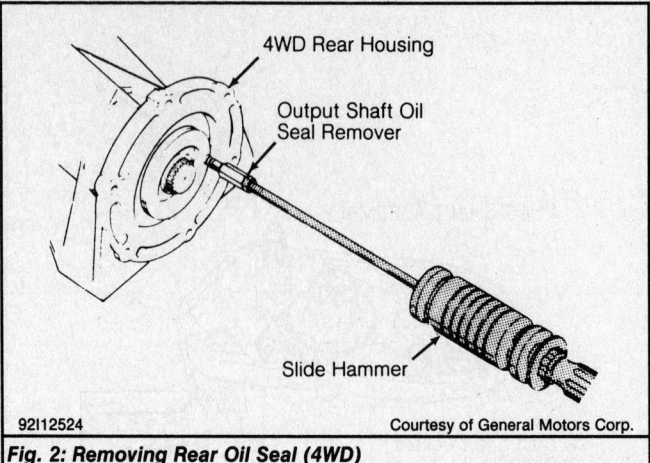

92I12524   Courtesy of General Motors Corp.
Fig. 2: Removing Rear Oil Seal (4WD)

case. Remove vehicle speed sensor. Install NEW "O" ring onto speed sensor. Coat "O" ring with thin film of transmission fluid. Install speed sensor and retaining screw (if equipped). Install harness connector.

SHIFT LEVER

Removal & Installation – Remove shift lever boot, retainer and cover plate. Loosen jam nut on shift lever and remove lever. To install, reverse removal procedure. Ensure shift pattern on lever knob is horizontal.

REMOVAL & INSTALLATION

See appropriate MANUAL TRANSMISSION REMOVAL article in TRANSMISSION SERVICING.

TRANSMISSION DISASSEMBLY

1) Remove idler shaft support bolt and 2 bottom bolts holding rear housing to main case. Mount Holding Fixtures (J-8763-21, J-8763-02 and J-36824) onto transmission. Remove back-up light switch and vehicle speed sensor assembly (if equipped). Remove shift shaft block out bushing bolt, located on top of front housing near breather assembly (if equipped).
2) Using Detent Plug Remover (J-36509) and slide hammer, remove detent plug, spring and plunger from front housing. See Fig. 3. On rear housing of 1993 transmission, remove 2 bolts on shift rail detent spring cover. Remove cover, springs and balls (if equipped). See Fig. 4.
3) On both transmissions, remove output shaft oil seal. With transmission in vertical position, remove input shaft bearing retainer. Remove snap ring and selective shim. Position transmission horizontally and remove front housing-to-rear housing bolts.
4) Drive dowels into front housing and remove front housing. Remove countershaft bearing and bearing race. Snap out idler shaft support. Remove 4 rollers and roll pin. Pull shift rail forward.
5) Support shift rail end while driving out shift finger roll pin. Remove shift rail socket assembly roll pin. DO NOT apply excessive force, or pin will peen shift rail and damage the rear housing shift rail bearing.
6) On 1993 transmissions, remove shift rail, shift rail socket assembly and finger. See Figs. 5 and 12. Pry out 3rd-4th shift fork roll pin. Remove 3rd-4th rail plug and rail. Ensure 1st-2nd, and 5th-reverse rails are in Neutral position. Drive rail through plug hole. Expose roll pin hole, and insert a 3/8" punch through roll pin hole. Pull out shift rail. Remove 2 detent balls. See Fig. 6.

NOTE: *1994 transmission has only one shift rail. All shift forks are attached to shift rail. See Fig. 13.*

7) On 1994 transmissions, remove shift rail, shift forks, shift rail socket, anti-rotation bracket, bias spring, shift lever and shift rail block-out bushing. *See Fig. 13.* Rotate 3rd-4th shift fork counterclockwise and remove shift fork.

8) On both transmissions, position rear housing onto Holding Fixture (J-36515) and Adapters (J-36516-15 and J-36516-15). Remove Holding Fixtures (J-36824 and J-8763-02).

9) On 2WD models, remove rear housing. Remove output shaft bearing retainer and bearing. Slide snap ring away from speed sensor for clearance. Remove speed sensor rotor using speedometer gear puller adapter and gear puller. DO NOT reuse rotor.

10) Remove 2 snap rings and output shaft bearing assembly. On 4WD models, remove rear housing assembly and bearing. On all models, remove reverse idler gear assembly, countershaft, 1st-2nd shift rail assembly, 5th-reverse shift rail assembly and 3rd-4th shift fork (if equipped). Remove mainshaft assembly, input shaft and pilot bearing.

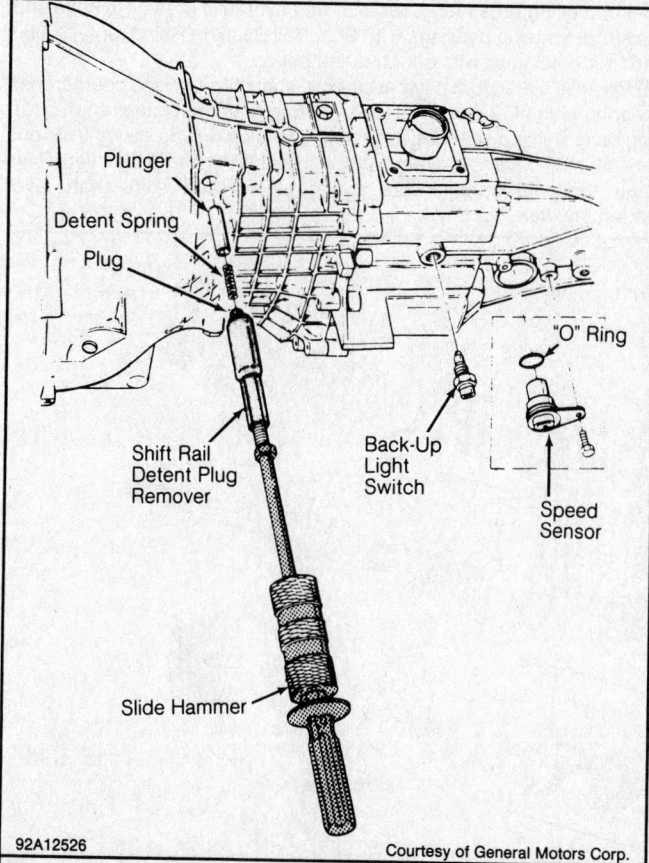

92A12526   Courtesy of General Motors Corp.

Fig. 3: Removing External Components

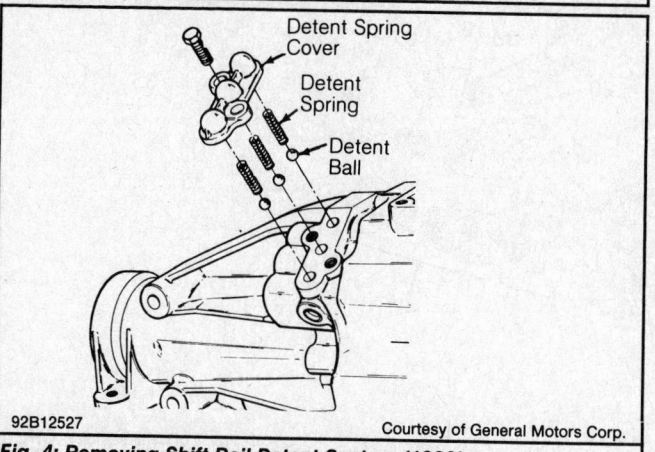

92B12527   Courtesy of General Motors Corp.

Fig. 4: Removing Shift Rail Detent System (1993)

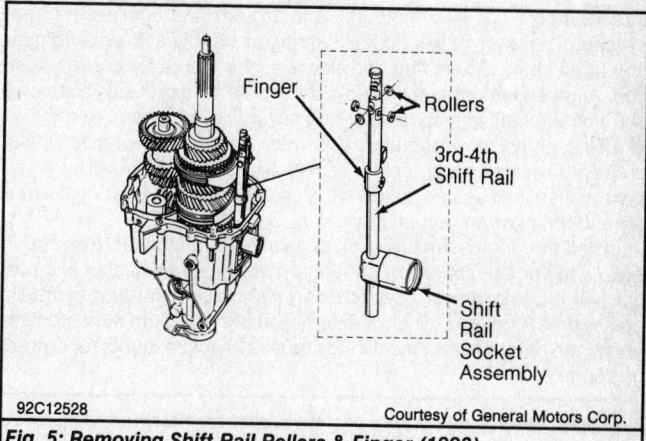

92C12528   Courtesy of General Motors Corp.

Fig. 5: Removing Shift Rail Rollers & Finger (1993)

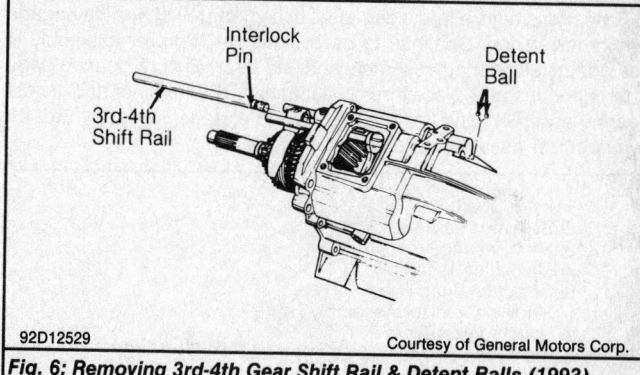

92D12529   Courtesy of General Motors Corp.

Fig. 6: Removing 3rd-4th Gear Shift Rail & Detent Balls (1993)

COMPONENT DISASSEMBLY & REASSEMBLY

MAINSHAFT

Disassembly – 1) Using Gear and Bearing Separator Plate (J-36513) and hydraulic press, remove snap ring, 3rd-4th synchronizer assembly, synchronizer rings and 3rd gear from mainshaft. *See Fig. 7.* Scribe marks on hub and sleeve for installation reference.

NOTE: Leave synchronizer rings on all synchronizer assemblies to prevent synchronizer detent balls from popping out.

---

2) Remove 3rd gear bearing, retainer ring and 2-piece thrust washer. Remove 2nd gear and 2nd gear bearing assembly using Gear and Bearing Separator Plate (J-36513) and hydraulic press. Remove 1st gear and 1st-2nd synchronizer assembly using gear and bearing separator plate and hydraulic press.

3) Scribe marks on hub and sleeve for installation reference. Remove 1st gear bearing assembly, 5th gear and 5th gear bearing assembly. Remove snap ring. *See Fig. 7.*

4) Remove reverse gear and 5th-reverse synchronizer assembly using gear and bearing separator plate and hydraulic press. Scribe marks on hub and sleeve for installation reference. Remove reverse gear bearing assembly.

5) Place 1st-2nd, 3rd-4th and 5th-reverse gear synchronizers in separate shop towels. Wrap assemblies and press against inner hub. Disassemble synchronizer assemblies. DO NOT mix parts.

Cleaning & Inspection – 1) Wash all parts in solvent and air dry. DO NOT spin dry bearings. Check gears and synchronizers for cracks, chipped gear teeth, excess wear and other damage.

2) The Black phosphate coating on gears will develop wear patterns. This is a normal condition. Check bearings and bearing surfaces for nicks, burrs, bent cages and wear. Lubricate all bearings and check for rough rotation. Lubricate all components during reassembly.

Reassembly – 1) Assemble 1st-2nd, 3rd-4th and 5th-reverse gear synchronizer assemblies. Install bearing assembly and reverse gear on output shaft. Check hub and sleeve scribe marks for correct position. Align and engage splines of 5th-reverse synchronizer assembly and output shaft with spiral lock ring toward reverse gear. See Fig. 7.

2) Using press tube, reducer, separator plate and hydraulic press, press 5th-reverse synchronizer assembly with synchronizer ring onto output shaft until seated. Install NEW snap ring. Install bearing assembly and 5th gear on output shaft.

3) Install bearing assembly and 1st gear on output shaft. See Fig. 7. Align and engage splines of 1st-2nd synchronizer assembly and output shaft. Using press tube, reducer, separator plate and hydraulic press, press 1st-2nd synchronizer assembly with both synchronizer rings onto output shaft. Check hub and sleeve scribe marks for correct position.

CAUTION: Groove on outside of sleeve must face toward 2nd gear to prevent gear clash during 1st-2nd gear shifts.

4) Stop press before tangs engage. Lift and rotate 1st gear to engage synchronizer ring. Continue to press until synchronizer assembly is seated. Install bearing assembly and 2nd gear. Ensure bearing cage is together. Install 2-piece thrust washer and NEW retainer ring. Install bearing assembly and 3rd gear. Align and engage splines of 3rd-4th synchronizer assembly and output shaft.

5) Using press tube, reducer, separator plate and hydraulic press, press 3rd-4th synchronizer assembly with both synchronizer rings onto output shaft. Stop press before tangs engage. Lift and rotate 3rd gear to engage synchronizer ring. Continue to press until synchronizer assembly is seated. Install NEW snap ring.

REVERSE IDLER GEAR

Disassembly & Reassembly – Remove snap ring, thrust washer, reverse gear and bearing assembly. See Fig. 7. Clean all parts in solvent and air dry. Check gear teeth, bearing assembly and idler shaft for damage. Replace as necessary. To reassemble, reverse disassembly procedure. Lubricate all components during reassembly. Install NEW snap ring.

FRONT HOUSING ASSEMBLY

Disassembly – 1) Remove spacer (if equipped). Press out input shaft bearing using press tube, reducer and hydraulic press. Remove shift rail front housing bearings with Shift Rail Bushing Remover (J-36800) and slide hammer with pilot bearing puller.

2) Remove clutch fork pivot assembly, shift rail plugs and countershaft bearing plug (if equipped). Remove snap ring and countershaft bearing race. Using a screwdriver, release tension of bias spring from end of shift shaft lever pin. Remove bolt, bias spring and sleeve seat, bias load torsional spring, bias spring sleeve and shift shaft lever assembly. See Fig. 8.

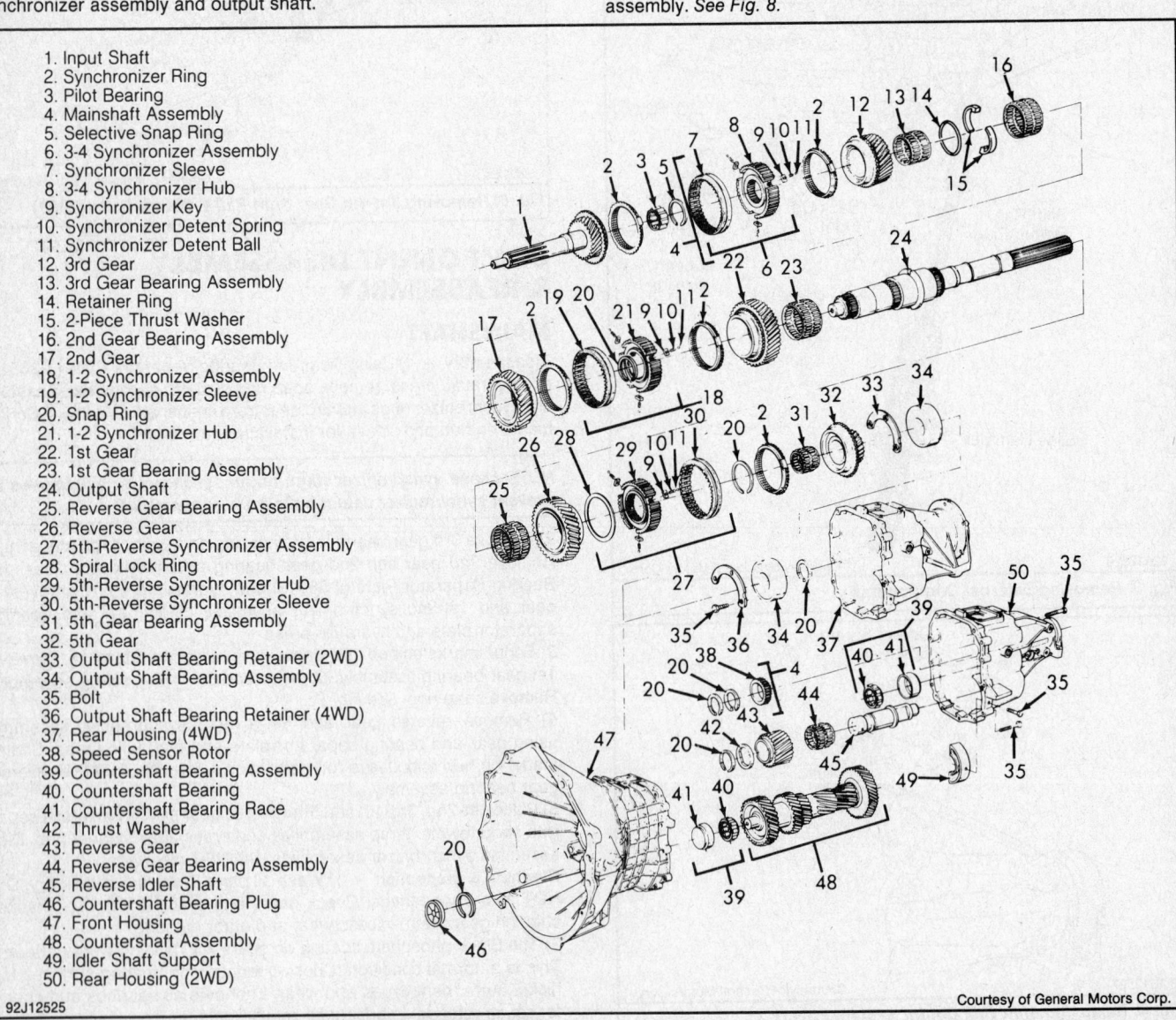

1. Input Shaft
2. Synchronizer Ring
3. Pilot Bearing
4. Mainshaft Assembly
5. Selective Snap Ring
6. 3-4 Synchronizer Assembly
7. Synchronizer Sleeve
8. 3-4 Synchronizer Hub
9. Synchronizer Key
10. Synchronizer Detent Spring
11. Synchronizer Detent Ball
12. 3rd Gear
13. 3rd Gear Bearing Assembly
14. Retainer Ring
15. 2-Piece Thrust Washer
16. 2nd Gear Bearing Assembly
17. 2nd Gear
18. 1-2 Synchronizer Assembly
19. 1-2 Synchronizer Sleeve
20. Snap Ring
21. 1-2 Synchronizer Hub
22. 1st Gear
23. 1st Gear Bearing Assembly
24. Output Shaft
25. Reverse Gear Bearing Assembly
26. Reverse Gear
27. 5th-Reverse Synchronizer Assembly
28. Spiral Lock Ring
29. 5th-Reverse Synchronizer Hub
30. 5th-Reverse Synchronizer Sleeve
31. 5th Gear Bearing Assembly
32. 5th Gear
33. Output Shaft Bearing Retainer (2WD)
34. Output Shaft Bearing Assembly
35. Bolt
36. Output Shaft Bearing Retainer (4WD)
37. Rear Housing (4WD)
38. Speed Sensor Rotor
39. Countershaft Bearing Assembly
40. Countershaft Bearing
41. Countershaft Bearing Race
42. Thrust Washer
43. Reverse Gear
44. Reverse Gear Bearing Assembly
45. Reverse Idler Shaft
46. Countershaft Bearing Plug
47. Front Housing
48. Countershaft Assembly
49. Idler Shaft Support
50. Rear Housing (2WD)

92J12525

Courtesy of General Motors Corp.

Fig. 7: Exploded View Of Transmission Components (2WD & 4WD)

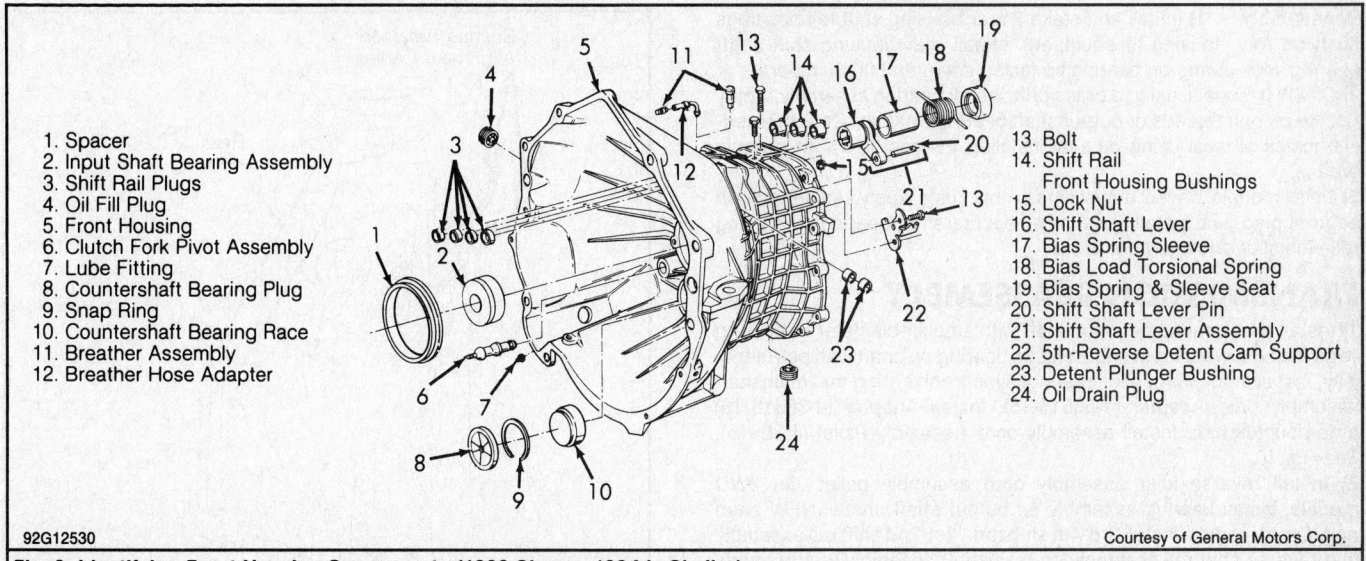

1. Spacer
2. Input Shaft Bearing Assembly
3. Shift Rail Plugs
4. Oil Fill Plug
5. Front Housing
6. Clutch Fork Pivot Assembly
7. Lube Fitting
8. Countershaft Bearing Plug
9. Snap Ring
10. Countershaft Bearing Race
11. Breather Assembly
12. Breather Hose Adapter

13. Bolt
14. Shift Rail
    Front Housing Bushings
15. Lock Nut
16. Shift Shaft Lever
17. Bias Spring Sleeve
18. Bias Load Torsional Spring
19. Bias Spring & Sleeve Seat
20. Shift Shaft Lever Pin
21. Shift Shaft Lever Assembly
22. 5th-Reverse Detent Cam Support
23. Detent Plunger Bushing
24. Oil Drain Plug

92G12530

Courtesy of General Motors Corp.

Fig. 8: Identifying Front Housing Components (1993 Shown; 1994 Is Similar)

CAUTION: Use caution when removing spring. Spring is under high tension.

3) Remove detent cam support bolt and cam. Remove 2 detent plunger bushings individually. Remove breather assembly. DO NOT remove metal tube from case. Remove oil fill plug and oil drain plug.

Cleaning & Inspection – 1) Remove gasket material from case with liquid gasket remover. Clean all parts in solvent and air dry. Inspect all parts for damage, wear and cracks. Check mating surfaces for flatness. If scratches, grooves or scoring cannot be removed, replace component.

2) If countershaft bearing race is worn or damaged, rear housing must be replaced. Measure countershaft bearing race bore in 2 places diagonally 0.157" (4 mm) in from inside of transmission housing. Replace housing if bore is not 2.283-2.284" (58.006-58.024 mm).

Reassembly – 1) Press in input shaft bearing using press tube, reducer and hydraulic press. Install spacer (if equipped). Install shift rail front housing bushings flush to housing, and stake bushings (if equipped) using Installer (J-36798-1 and J-36798-2). DO NOT stake tabs on bushings. Install clutch fork pivot assembly using Installer (J-36510) and universal driver handle.

2) Grease clutch fork pivot assembly after installation through lube fitting. Install 2 detent plunger bushings. Align lube slot in race with groove in housing and install countershaft bearing race using Countershaft Bearing Cup Shimming Tool (J-38884) and universal driver handle. Install snap ring.

3) Apply sealant to outside edge of NEW countershaft bearing plug, and install plug (if equipped). Stake plug in 3 places spaced evenly apart. Install detent cam support and bolt (if equipped). Install shift shaft lever assembly into housing. Install bias spring sleeve, bias load torsional spring, bias spring and sleeve seat and bolt. (if equipped).

4) Install bias load torsional spring end back into shift shaft lever pin. Install breather assembly. Apply sealant to threads of oil fill and drain plugs and install plugs. Apply sealant to edge of shift rail plugs, and install plugs flush on housing.

REAR HOUSING ASSEMBLY

Disassembly – 1) Remove 3 rear housing shift rail bushings and shift shaft bearing (if equipped). Drive out dowel pins. On 4WD models, remove 3 output shaft bearing retainer bolts.

2) Using a brass drift, drive out bearing assembly. On 2WD models, remove oil seal. On all models, remove plug above rear housing shift rail bearing. Remove countershaft bearing race. See Fig. 9.

Cleaning & Inspection – 1) Remove gasket material from case with liquid gasket remover. Wash parts in solvent and air dry. Inspect bearing race bore for wear, scratches or grooves. If countershaft bearing race is worn or damaged, rear housing must be replaced.

2) Inspect bushings for scores, burrs, roundness or evidence of overheating. On 2WD models, output shaft bushing cannot be serviced. Rear housing MUST be replaced if bushing shows signs of wear or damage. Using straightedge, check machined mating surfaces for flatness.

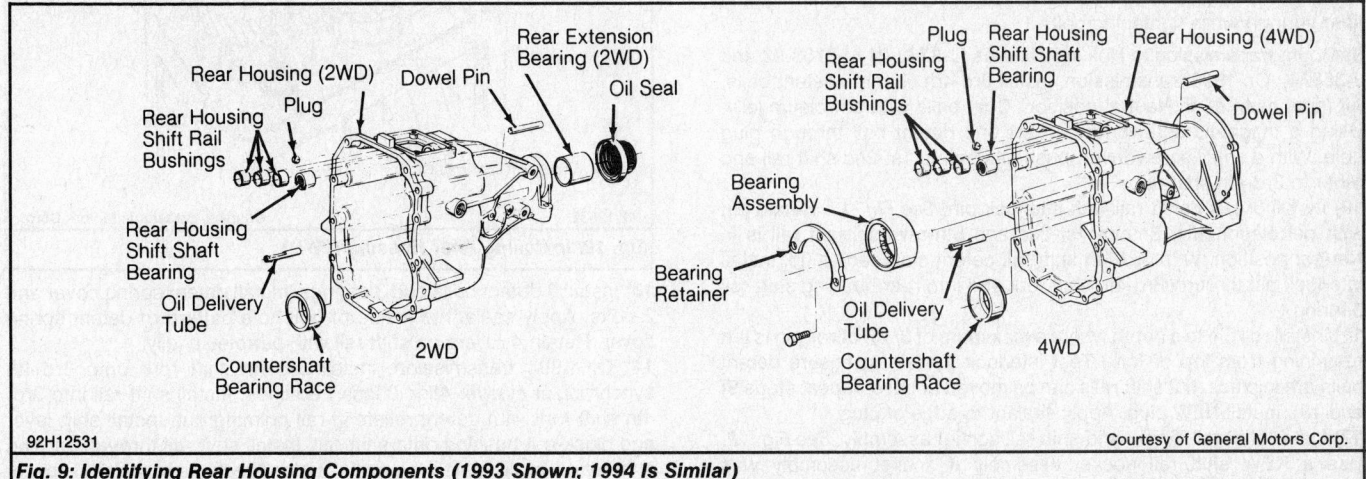

92H12531

Courtesy of General Motors Corp.

Fig. 9: Identifying Rear Housing Components (1993 Shown; 1994 Is Similar)

Reassembly – 1) Install and stake 3 rear housing shift rail bushings flush on rear housing (if equipped). Install rear housing shift shaft bearing with writing on bearing lip facing down and flush in bore.

2) On 4WD models, using a brass drift, install bearing assembly. Apply Loctite on bolt threads of output shaft bearing retainer. On 2WD models, install oil seal using oil seal installer. Fill seal lips with chassis grease.

3) On all models, drive 2 dowel pins in until flush. Apply sealant around edge of plug, and install plug. Install countershaft bearing race using race installer and hydraulic press.

TRANSMISSION REASSEMBLY

1) Install pilot bearing on input shaft with smaller diameter of bearing cage facing toward input shaft. Retain bearing on shaft with petroleum jelly. Install input shaft, pilot bearing, synchronizer ring and mainshaft assembly onto Adapter (J-36515-15). Install Adapter (J-36516-16) onto countershaft. Install assembly onto Assembly Pallet (J-36515). *See Fig. 10.*

2) Install reverse idler assembly onto assembly pallet. On 2WD models, install bearing assembly on output shaft. Install NEW snap ring. On all models, install 3rd-4th shift fork, 1st-2nd shift rail assembly and reverse shift rail assembly on mainshaft assembly (if equipped). Ensure taper on shift fork is facing toward 3rd gear. On 2WD models, install NEW snap ring at bearing assembly.

3) Install second snap ring on output shaft. Install NEW speed sensor rotor. Heating is required on speed sensor rotor prior to installation. Heat 7-10 minutes to a temperature of 250°F (120°C) and install on mainshaft. Heat rear housing output shaft bearing bore 3-5 minutes with heat gun before assembly.

4) Install Bearing Retainer Alignment Cables (J-36515-10) to output shaft bearing retainer. *See Fig. 10.* Ensure notch in output shaft bearing retainer is facing towards oil delivery tube assembly.

5) On all models, install bearing assembly into rear housing bearing race with small diameter of bearing cage into bearing race. Retain with petroleum jelly. Press each roller towards race to secure for easier assembly.

6) Install rear housing assembly. *See Figs. 10 and 11.* Ensure reverse idler shaft is lined up with holes in case. Rotate case back and forth while pulling down. On 2WD models, pull up on Bearing Retainer Alignment Cables while installing rear housing assembly. DO NOT force rear housing assembly down.

7) Apply Loctite to rear housing assembly bolts and install bolts into output shaft bearing retainer. Apply pipe sealant with Teflon to bolt holes of rear housing. On 4WD models, install seal protector on output shaft. Fill seal lips with chassis grease, and install oil seal. Remove seal protector from output shaft.

8) On all models, lay transmission on workbench. Remove Adapters (J-36515-15 and J-36516-16) and Assembly Pallet (J-36515). Install idler shaft support. Apply pipe sealant with Teflon to bolt holes of rear housing and Loctite to bolt threads. Hold reverse idler shaft against idler support while tightening bolts.

9) Mount transmission to Holding Fixtures (J-8763-21, J-8763-02 and J-36824). On 1993 transmission, install 3rd-4th shift rail detent balls. All forks must be in Neutral position. Coat balls with petroleum jelly. Using a magnetic screwdriver, insert one detent ball through plug hole. With a small screwdriver, push one ball to 1st-2nd shift rail and other to 3rd-4th shift rail.

10) Install 3rd-4th shift rail with interlock pin. *See Fig. 12.* Retain pin with petroleum jelly. Ensure 1st-2nd and 5th-reverse shift rail is in Neutral position. With 3rd-4th shift rail detent slots facing up, install interlock pin through 3rd-4th shift fork and into rear housing shift rail bearing.

11) Install roll pin to a depth where a maximum of 3/16" of roll pin is left remaining from top of fork. Test interlock system to ensure detent balls are in place. If 2 shift rails can be moved at once, repeat steps **9)** and **10)**. Install NEW plug. Apply sealant to edge of plug.

12) Install shift rail, finger and shift rail socket assembly. *See Fig. 12.* Use a NEW shift rail socket assembly if socket assembly was previously staked. DO NOT reuse a staked socket assembly. Install roll pins.

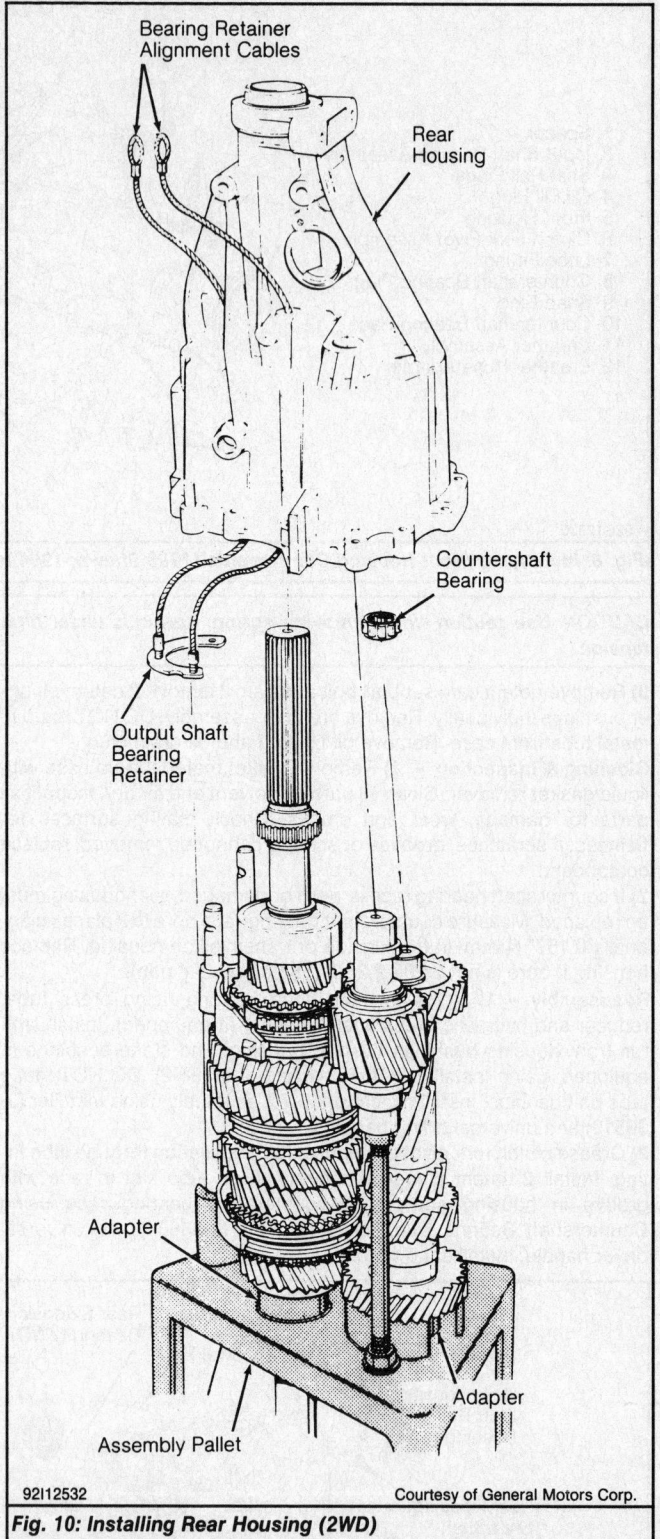

92I12532   Courtesy of General Motors Corp.

Fig. 10: Installing Rear Housing (2WD)

13) Install 3 detent balls and 3 springs. Install detent spring cover and 2 bolts. Apply sealant to inside of bolt hole pattern of detent spring cover. Retain 4 rollers on shift rail with petroleum jelly.

14) On 1994 transmission, install 3rd-4th shift fork onto 3rd-4th synchronizer sleeve. Align 3 insert notches. Install shift rail into 3rd-4th shift fork with detent reliefs in rail pointing out. Install shift lever and block-out bushing onto shift rail. Install shift rail through 1st-2nd shift fork. Install bias spring, anti-rotation bracket and shift rail socket on shift rail. *See Fig. 13.* Slide shift rail into case.

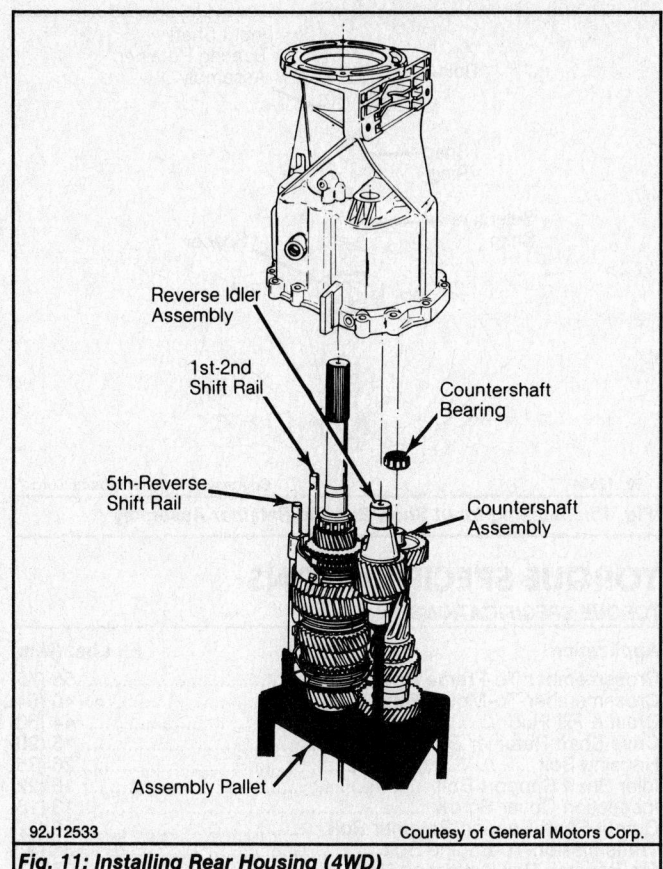

92J12533   Courtesy of General Motors Corp.

Fig. 11: Installing Rear Housing (4WD)

15) Install NEW roll pin into shift lever until pin is flush with shift lever. Rotate shift rail counterclockwise until shift lever is almost into 5th-Reverse insert notch. Install detent spring and ball into shift lever. Rotate shift rail until shift lever aligns with 3-4 insert.

16) Install shift rail socket to shift rail roll pin. *See Fig. 13.* Drive in roll pin until it is flush with bottom of shift rail socket. If transmission is in "C" or "K" series vehicle, use middle roll pin hole. If transmission is in "S" or "T" series vehicle, use rear roll pin hole. Using a screwdriver, install bias spring tangs to anti-rotation bracket.

17) Ensure shifter is in neutral and anti-rotation bracket rollers are level with machined surface of case opening. Lubricate both sides of anti-rotation roller plate and install to case opening. Install anti-rotation roller retainer with thin side of retainer toward left side of transmission.

18) On both transmissions, install countershaft bearing into front housing race with smaller diameter of bearing cage facing bearing race. Retain with petroleum jelly. Press each roller toward race to secure them for easier assembly.

19) Bring front housing straight down. *See Fig. 14.* Install 2 dowels and bolts. DO NOT tighten bolts at this time. Tip transmission vertically. Install NEW snap ring. Apply sealant to inside of bolt hole pattern. Install shim into input shaft bearing retainer assembly. Install input shaft bearing retainer assembly. *See Fig. 15.* Ensure oil drain back hole is lined up with hole in housing.

20) Install shift rail detent plunger, detent spring and plug. On 2WD models, install NEW "O" ring on speed sensor. Lubricate "O" ring with transmission fluid. Install speed sensor. On all models, install back-up light assembly. Remove transmission from holding fixture.

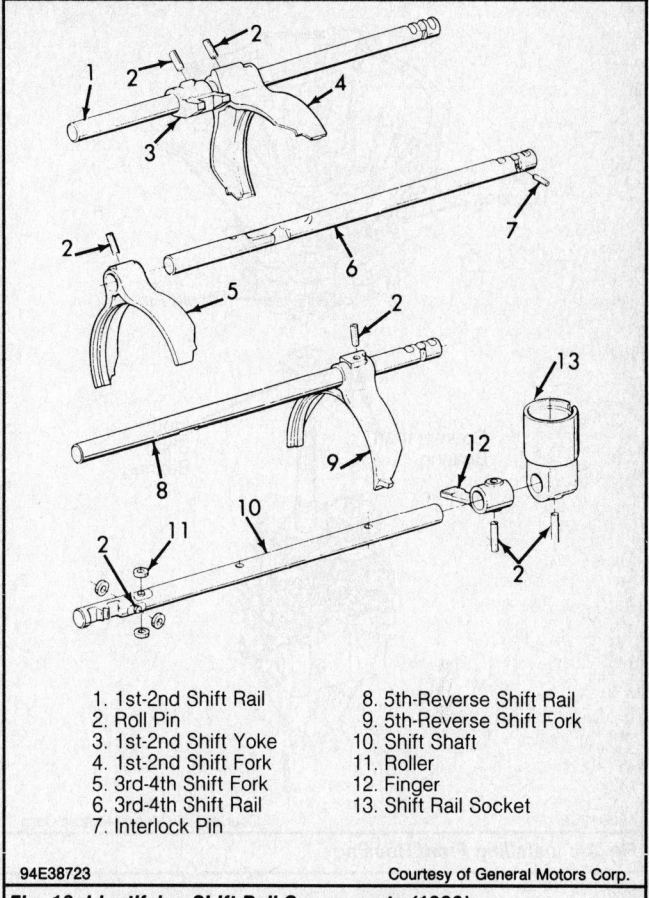

1. 1st-2nd Shift Rail	8. 5th-Reverse Shift Rail
2. Roll Pin	9. 5th-Reverse Shift Fork
3. 1st-2nd Shift Yoke	10. Shift Shaft
4. 1st-2nd Shift Fork	11. Roller
5. 3rd-4th Shift Fork	12. Finger
6. 3rd-4th Shift Rail	13. Shift Rail Socket
7. Interlock Pin	

94E38723   Courtesy of General Motors Corp.

Fig. 12: Identifying Shift Rail Components (1993)

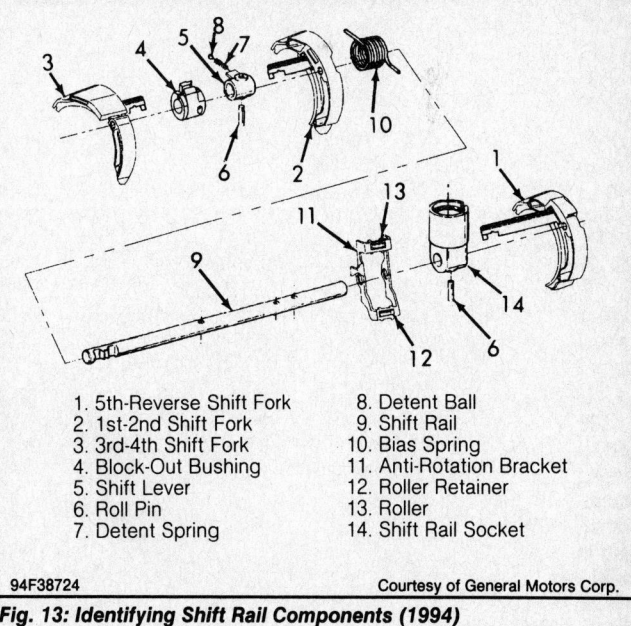

1. 5th-Reverse Shift Fork	8. Detent Ball
2. 1st-2nd Shift Fork	9. Shift Rail
3. 3rd-4th Shift Fork	10. Bias Spring
4. Block-Out Bushing	11. Anti-Rotation Bracket
5. Shift Lever	12. Roller Retainer
6. Roll Pin	13. Roller
7. Detent Spring	14. Shift Rail Socket

94F38724   Courtesy of General Motors Corp.

Fig. 13: Identifying Shift Rail Components (1994)

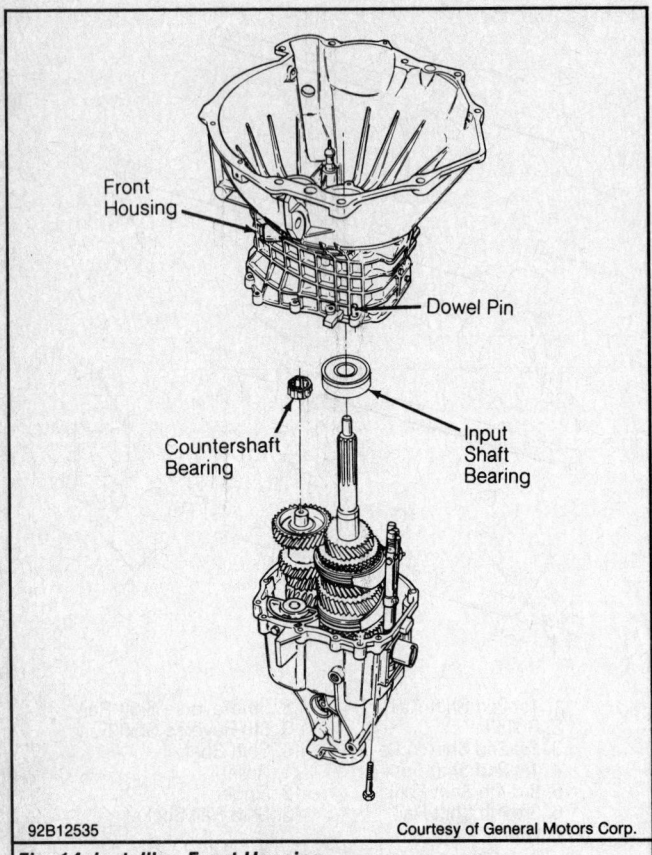

Front Housing

Dowel Pin

Countershaft Bearing

Input Shaft Bearing

92B12535

Courtesy of General Motors Corp.

Fig. 14: Installing Front Housing

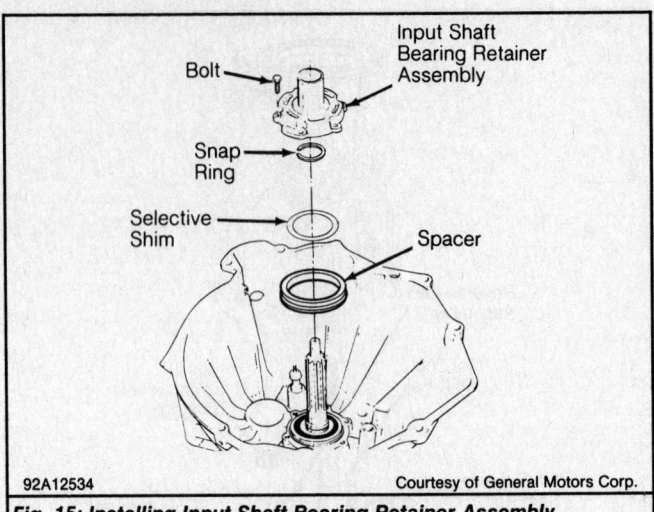

Bolt

Input Shaft Bearing Retainer Assembly

Snap Ring

Selective Shim

Spacer

92A12534

Courtesy of General Motors Corp.

Fig. 15: Installing Input Shaft Bearing Retainer Assembly

TORQUE SPECIFICATIONS
TORQUE SPECIFICATIONS

Application	Ft. Lbs. (N.m)
Crossmember-To-Frame Bolt	55 (75)
Crossmember-To-Mount Bolt	40 (54)
Drain & Fill Plug	44 (60)
Drive Shaft Retainer Bolts	15 (20)
Housing Bolt	26 (35)
Idler Shaft Support Bolt	16 (22)
Inspection Cover Screw	13 (18)
Output Shaft Bearing Retainer Bolt	16 (22)
Transmission-To-Engine Bolt	35 (47)
5th-Reverse Rail Deflection Bolt	27 (37)

	INCH Lbs. (N.m)
Back-Up Light Switch	80 (9)
Bias Spring & Sleeve Seat Bolt	75 (8.5)
Detent Cam Bolt	75 (8.5)
Input Shaft Retainer Bolt	75 (8.5)
Shift Lever Housing Assembly Bolt	75 (8.5)
Vehicle Speed Sensor Screw	80 (9)

Metro

IDENTIFICATION

Transaxle identification number plate is located on upper surface of transaxle case. *See Fig. 1.* The identification number begins with a letter followed by a 6-digit serial number. The letter "O" indicates 1993 model transaxle. The letter "P" indicates 1994 model.

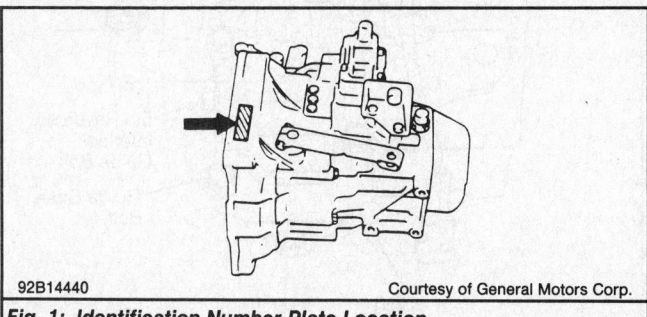

92B14440   Courtesy of General Motors Corp.

Fig. 1: Identification Number Plate Location

DESCRIPTION

Transaxle provides 5 forward gears and one reverse gear. Transaxle uses 3 synchronizers to engage forward gears. The low speed synchronizer is mounted on the countershaft, and engages 1st or 2nd gear. The high speed synchronizer is mounted on the input shaft, and engages 3rd or 4th gear. The 5th gear synchronizer is mounted on the input shaft, and engages 5th gear. Reverse gear is unsynchronized, and utilizes an idler gear supported by a sliding spindle idler gear shaft.

Power is transmitted through input shaft to countershaft. From countershaft, power is transmitted through differential final drive gear to drive axles and wheels.

LUBRICATION & ADJUSTMENTS

See appropriate MANUAL TRANSMISSION SERVICING article in TRANSMISSION SERVICING.

TROUBLE SHOOTING

See GENERAL TROUBLE SHOOTING article in MANUAL TRANSMISSIONS.

ON-VEHICLE SERVICE

WARNING: When battery is disconnected, vehicle computer and memory systems may lose memory data. Driveability problems may exist until computer systems have completed a relearn cycle. See COMPUTER RELEARN PROCEDURES article in APPLICATIONS & IDENTIFICATION before disconnecting battery.

BACK-UP LIGHT SWITCH

Removal & Installation – Disconnect negative battery cable. Disconnect switch electrical connector and remove wire from clamp. Remove switch from case. To install, reverse removal procedure. Tighten switch to 15 ft. lbs. (20 N.m)

DRIVE AXLE SHAFTS

See appropriate FWD AXLE SHAFTS article in AXLE SHAFTS & TRANSFER CASES.

DRIVE AXLE SHAFT SEAL

Removal – Raise and support vehicle. Drain transaxle fluid. Install Drive Axle Shaft Boot Protector (J28712). Remove drive axle shaft. See appropriate FWD AXLE SHAFTS article in AXLE SHAFTS & TRANSFER CASES. Remove drive axle shaft seal by prying out or using seal remover and slide hammer.

Installation – Using Axle Shaft Seal Installer (J35538), install seal with spring side facing outward. Inspect axle shaft for damage that may have caused seal failure. If okay, install axle shaft. To complete installation, reverse removal procedure. Refill transaxle with fluid.

SPEEDOMETER DRIVEN GEAR ASSEMBLY

Removal – Slice speedometer cable boot up speedometer cable. Remove speedometer case clip and disconnect speedometer cable from case. Remove bolt and speedometer driven gear case assembly.
Disassembly – Drive out spring pin and remove speedometer driven gear. *See Fig. 2.* Hold driven gear case and remove oil seal using slide hammer, adapter and pinion bearing remover. Remove "O" ring.
Reassembly – Install oil seal with spring side down using shift shaft seal installer. Install speedometer driven gear into case and drive in spring pin. Check driven gear for smooth rotation. Install "O" ring.
Installation – Apply grease to "O" ring and install case assembly into transaxle. Install bolt and tighten to 53 INCH lbs. (6 N.m). Connect speedometer cable and install clip and boot.

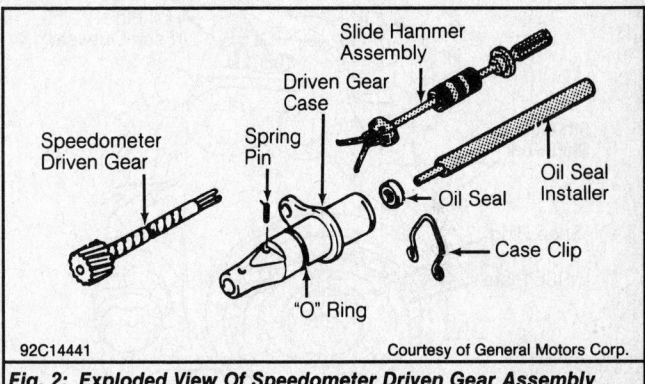

92C14441   Courtesy of General Motors Corp.

Fig. 2: Exploded View Of Speedometer Driven Gear Assembly

GEARSHIFT LEVER

Removal – **1)** Unscrew gearshift lever knob. Remove upper gearshift lever boot from lever. Remove 6 console screws and console. Remove 4 gearshift housing nuts from studs.
2) Raise and support vehicle. Disconnect gearshift lever from gearshift control shaft. *See Fig. 3.* Remove guide plate bolts, and disconnect extension rod from guide plate. Remove gearshift lever assembly from vehicle.
Disassembly – Remove gearshift boot cover, lower boot, snap ring, shim and gearshift lever upper seat from gearshift lever. Remove gearshift lever housing-to-guide plate nuts and separate guide plate from gearshift housing. Remove gearshift lever lower seat from gearshift lever.
Reassembly & Installation – To reassemble, reverse disassembly procedure. Tighten bolts to specification. See TORQUE SPECIFICATIONS. To install, reverse removal procedure.

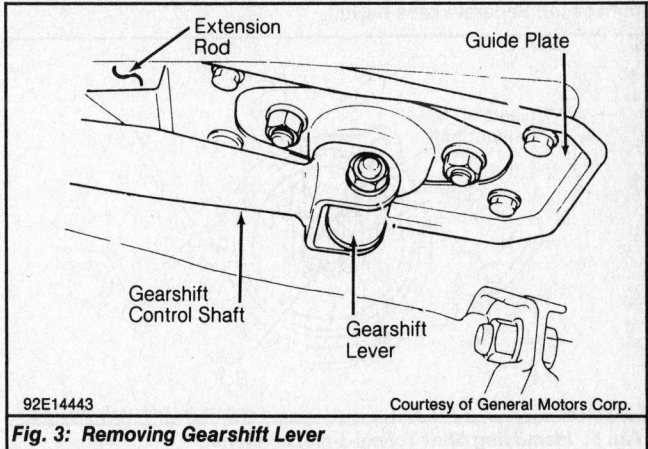

92E14443   Courtesy of General Motors Corp.

Fig. 3: Removing Gearshift Lever

REMOVAL & INSTALLATION

See appropriate MANUAL TRANSMISSION REMOVAL article in TRANSMISSION SERVICING.

TRANSAXLE DISASSEMBLY

1) Drain transaxle fluid. Remove transaxle side cover. Use rubber mallet to free cover, if necessary. Remove snap ring and hub plate. See Fig. 4.

2) Push in on input shift shaft and engage transaxle gear. Move 5th gear shift fork so 5th gear is also engaged. Unstake countershaft nut. With transaxle locked in 2 gears, countershaft nut can be removed.

3) Remove shift fork plug and guide ball (a magnet may be necessary). Return shift shaft to Neutral position. Drive out 5th gear shift fork roll pin. Using a gear puller on input shaft, remove 5th gear, shift fork, sleeve, hub and synchronizer as a complete assembly.

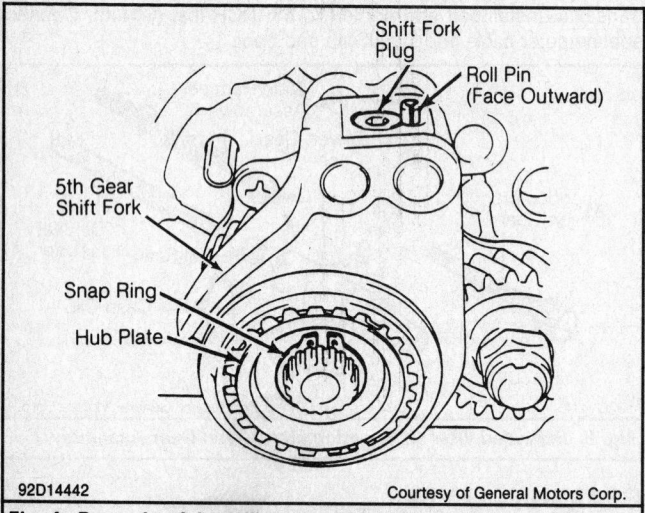

Fig. 4: Removing & Installing Input Shaft 5th Gear Assemblies

4) Using gear puller, remove countershaft 5th gear. Remove screws, left case plate and bearing shim. Remove bolts, "O" ring and left case cap. Remove shift yoke bolt. See Fig. 5.

5) From right case, remove 3 shift fork shaft bolts with washers, springs and balls. See Fig. 6. Remove bolts, wiring harness clamp and shift guide case.

NOTE: Springs are color coded. Note spring color and location for reassembly reference.

6) Remove shift interlock bolt with washer. Remove gearshift and select shaft assembly. Remove back-up light switch. Remove reverse idler shaft bolt with washer. See Fig. 7. Remove 11 case bolts from transaxle side of case (left case) and 2 bolts from clutch housing side (right case). Separate case halves.

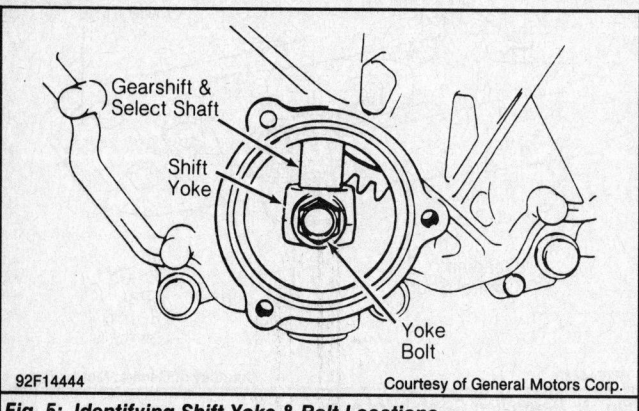

Fig. 5: Identifying Shift Yoke & Bolt Locations

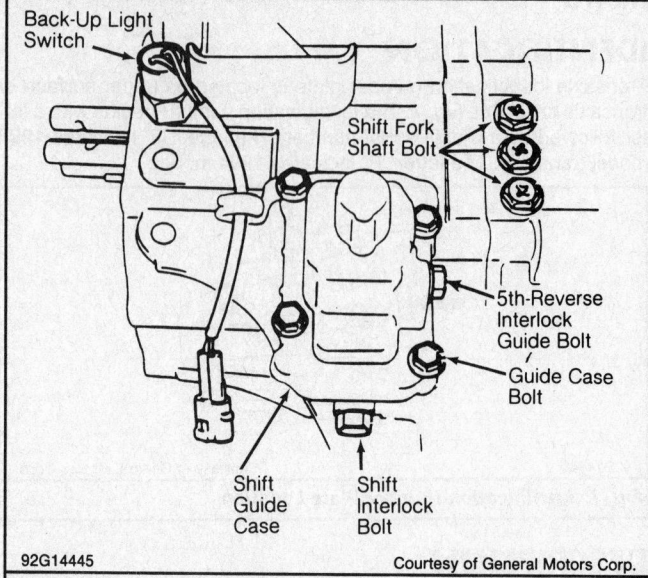

Fig. 6: Identifying Shift Guide Case & Bolt Locations

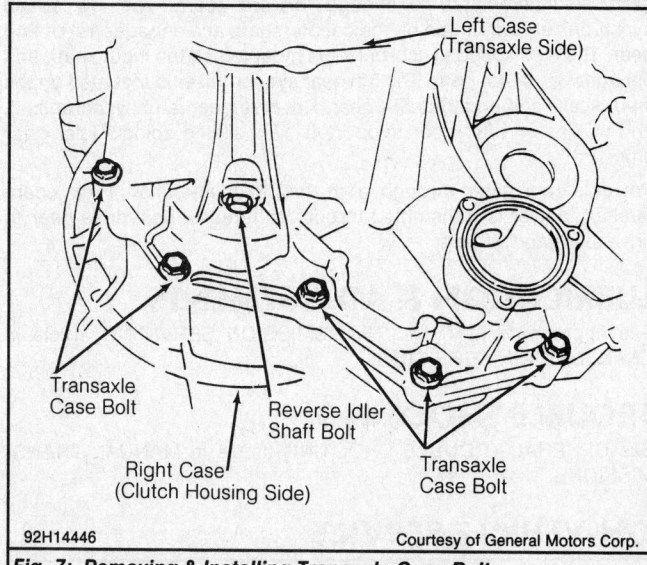

Fig. 7: Removing & Installing Transaxle Case Bolts

7) Remove shift yoke. Remove reverse idler gear shaft with washer and reverse idler gear. See Fig. 8. Push in high speed shift fork shaft (shifting to 4th gear). Remove 5th-reverse guide shaft together with 5th-reverse shift fork shaft.

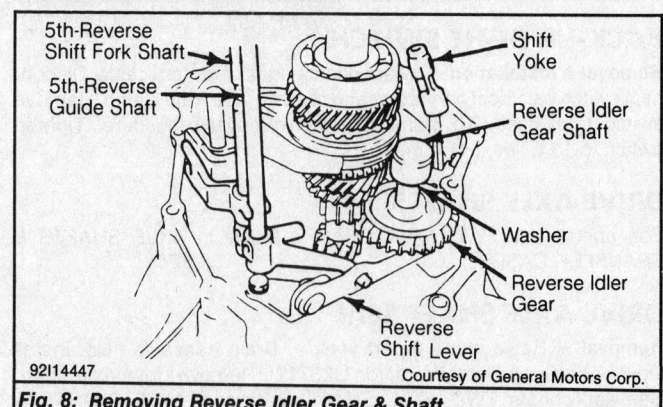

Fig. 8: Removing Reverse Idler Gear & Shaft

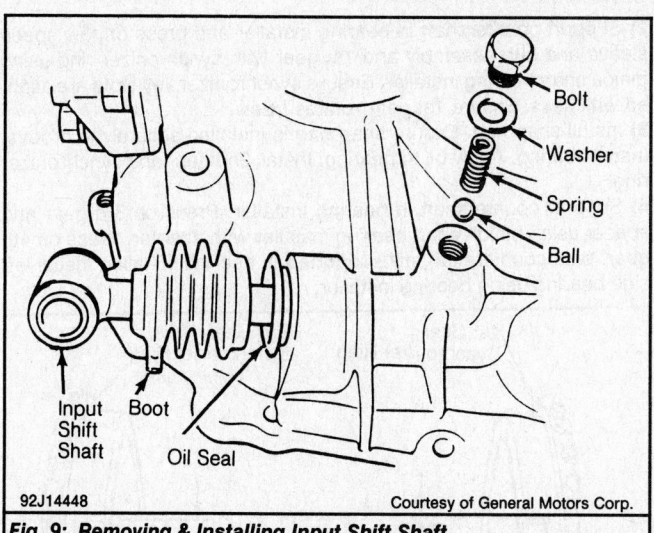

Input Shift Shaft — Boot — Oil Seal

Bolt — Washer — Spring — Ball

92J14448   Courtesy of General Motors Corp.

Fig. 9: Removing & Installing Input Shift Shaft

8) Remove input shaft assembly, countershaft assembly, high speed shift fork shaft and low speed shift fork shaft as an assembly. Remove differential gear assembly and speedometer driven gear case.

9) Remove input shaft oil seal using slide hammer. Remove countershaft right case bearing race using bearing race remover with slide hammer. Remove input shaft right case bearing race using remover and slide hammer (if necessary). Remove magnet.

10) Remove shift arm from input shift shaft. Remove input shift shaft bolt with washer, spring and ball. *See Fig. 9.* Remove input shift shaft, boot and oil seal. Remove differential oil seal from right case. Remove reverse shift lever. *See Fig. 8.* Remove bolt and oil gutter from case, if necessary.

COMPONENT DISASSEMBLY & REASSEMBLY

INPUT SHAFT ASSEMBLY

Disassembly – 1) Remove right side bearing. *See Fig. 10.* Assemble input shaft and bearing puller with puller flat side facing upward into press. Press off right side bearing. DO NOT exceed 11,000 lbs. (4990 kg).

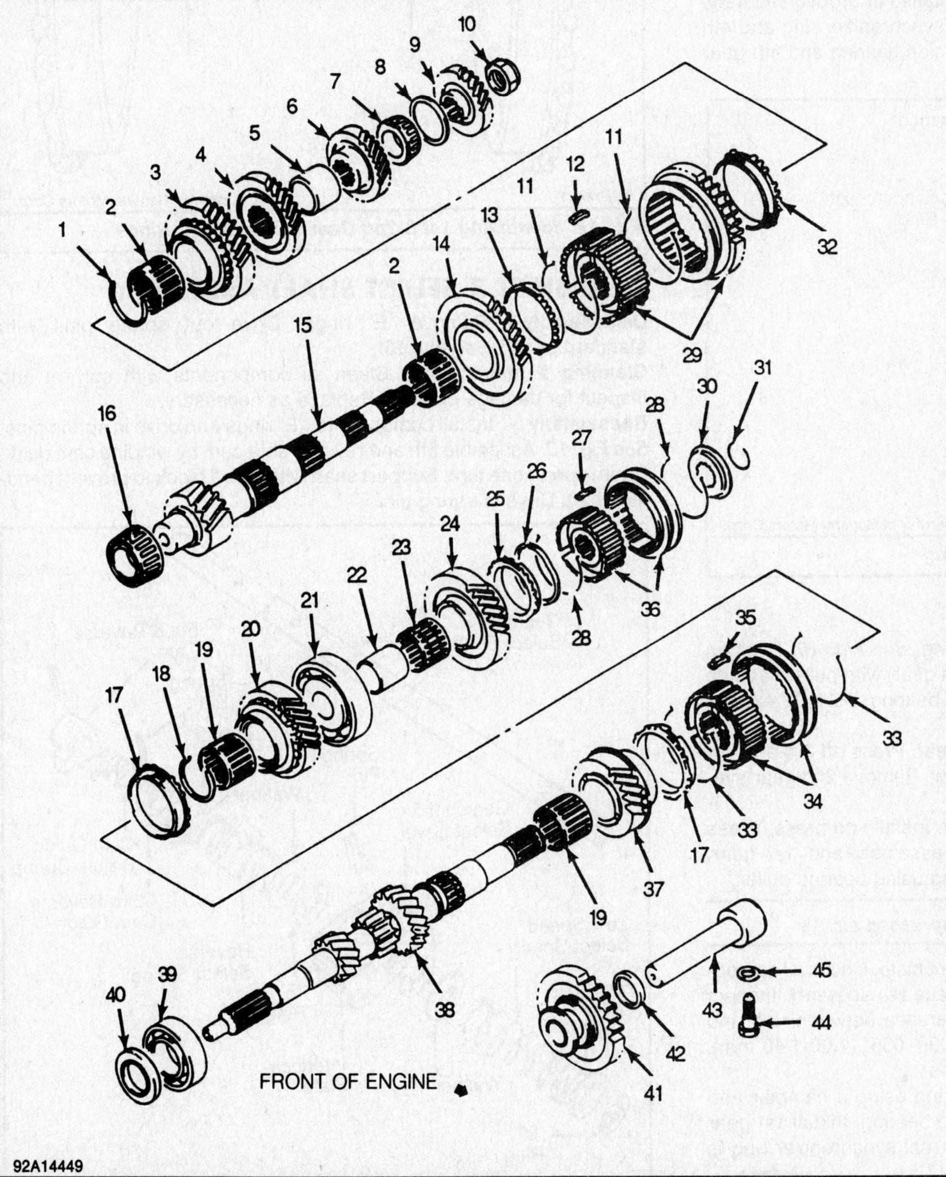

1. Snap Ring
2. 1st & 2nd Gear Bearing
3. Countershaft 2nd Gear
4. Countershaft 3rd Gear
5. 3rd & 4th Gear Spacer
6. Countershaft 4th Gear
7. Countershaft Left Side Bearing
8. Bearing Set Shim
9. Countershaft 5th Gear
10. Countershaft Nut
11. Low Speed Synchronizer Spring
12. Low Speed Synchronizer Key
13. 1st Gear Synchronizer Ring
14. Countershaft 1st Gear
15. Countershaft
16. Countershaft Right Side Bearing
17. High Speed Synchronizer Ring
18. Snap Ring
19. 3rd & 4th Gear Bearing
20. Input Shaft 4th Gear
21. Input Shaft Left Side Bearing
22. 5th Gear Spacer
23. 5th Gear Bearing
24. Input Shaft 5th Gear
25. 5th Gear Synchronizer Ring
26. Synchronizer Ring Spring
27. 5th Gear Synchronizer Key
28. 5th Gear Synchronizer Spring
29. Low Speed Sleeve & Hub
30. 5th Gear Synchronizer Hub Plate
31. Snap Ring
32. 2nd Gear Synchronizer Ring
33. High Speed Synchronizer Spring
34. High Speed Sleeve & Hub
35. High Speed Synchronizer Key
36. 5th Gear Sleeve & Hub
37. Input Shaft 3rd Gear
38. Input Shaft
39. Input Shaft Right Side Bearing
40. Oil Seal
41. Reverse Idler Gear
42. Washer
43. Reverse Idler Gear Shaft
44. Bolt
45. Washer

FRONT OF ENGINE

92A14449   Courtesy of General Motors Co.

Fig. 10: Exploded View Of Input Shaft, Countershaft & Reverse Idler Shaft Assemblies

2) Turn input shaft over and reassemble bearing puller behind 4th gear. Press off 5th gear spacer, left side bearing and 4th gear together. Remove 4th gear needle bearing, high speed synchronizer ring and snap ring.

3) Assemble bearing puller behind 3rd gear. Install into press. Press off high speed synchronizer sleeve, hub assembly and 3rd gear. Remove 3rd gear bearing.

WARNING: DO NOT spin dry bearings. Never spin bearings with compressed air.

Cleaning & Inspection – Check all components for wear, broken teeth or cracks. Replace as necessary. Inspect synchronizer assemblies and measure clearance between synchronizer ring and gear. *See Fig. 11.* Standard clearance is .039-.055" (1.00-1.40 mm). Replace if clearance is .020" (.50 mm) or less.

Reassembly – **1)** Press on right side bearing using bearing installer. Install 3rd gear bearing. Apply oil to bearing and press on 3rd gear and synchronizer ring.

2) Using bearing installer, press on high speed sleeve and hub assembly. Ensure synchronizer ring slots are aligned with keys in sleeve and hub assembly. Ensure free rotation of 3rd gear.

3) Install snap ring. Ensure snap ring is installed in groove securely. Install bearing. Apply oil to bearing. Install synchronizer ring and 4th gear. Using bearing installer, press on left side bearing and 5th gear spacer.

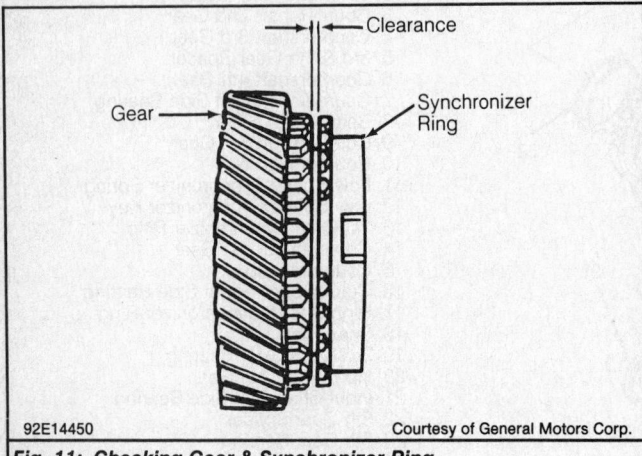

92E14450   Courtesy of General Motors Corp.
Fig. 11: Checking Gear & Synchronizer Ring

COUNTERSHAFT ASSEMBLY

Disassembly – **1)** Remove left side bearing. *See Fig. 10.* Position bearing puller onto countershaft (behind 4th gear) with puller flat side facing upward into press. Press off left side bearing. DO NOT exceed 11,000 lbs. (4990 kg).

2) Reassemble bearing puller behind 2nd gear. Press off 3rd and 4th gear spacer, 3rd gear and 2nd gear together. Remove 2nd gear synchronizer ring and snap ring.

3) Assemble bearing puller behind 1st gear. Install into press. Press off low speed synchronizer sleeve, hub assembly and 1st gear. Remove bearing. Press off right side bearing using bearing puller.

WARNING: DO NOT spin bearings with compressed air.

Cleaning & Inspection – Ensure oil holes are clear. Check all components for wear, broken teeth or cracks. Replace as necessary. Inspect synchronizer assemblies and measure clearance between ring and gear. *See Fig. 11.* Standard clearance is .039-.055" (1.00-1.40 mm). Replace if clearance is .020" (.50 mm) or less.

Reassembly – **1)** Drive on right side bearing using a hammer and bearing installer. Install bearing. Apply oil to bearing. Install 1st gear and 1st gear synchronizer ring. Ensure correct synchronizer ring is used. *See Fig. 12.*

2) Support countershaft in bearing installer and press on low speed sleeve and hub assembly and 1st gear with synchronizer ring using pinion shaft bearing installer. Ensure synchronizer key slots are aligned with keys. Ensure 1st gear rotates freely.

3) Install snap ring. Ensure snap ring is installed securely in groove. Install bearing. Apply oil to bearing. Install 2nd gear and synchronizer ring.

4) Support countershaft in bearing installer. Press on 3rd gear and spacer using pinion shaft bearing installer with adapter. Press on 4th gear. With countershaft still supported in bearing installer, install left side bearing using bearing installer.

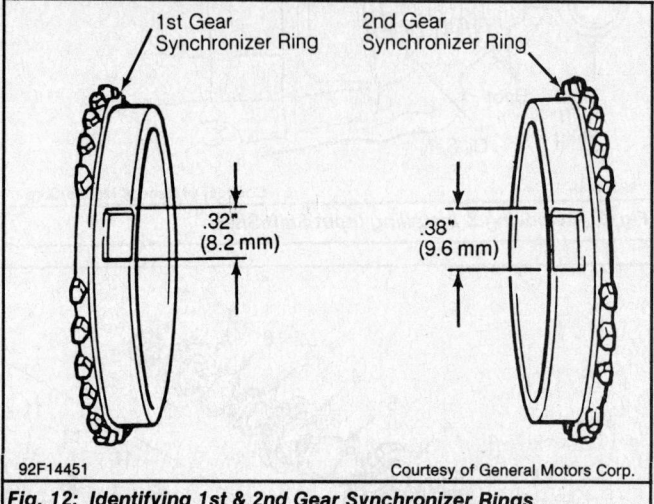

92F14451   Courtesy of General Motors Corp.
Fig. 12: Identifying 1st & 2nd Gear Synchronizer Rings

GEARSHIFT & SELECT SHAFT ASSEMBLY

Disassembly – Remove "E" rings. Drive out spring pins with standard punch. *See Fig. 13.*

Cleaning & Inspection – Clean all components with solvent and inspect for damage or wear. Replace as necessary.

Reassembly – Install components, "E" rings and drive in spring pins. *See Fig. 13.* Assemble 5th and reverse shift cam by winding cam guide return spring one turn. Support shaft with wood block to prevent bending shaft. Drive in spring pin.

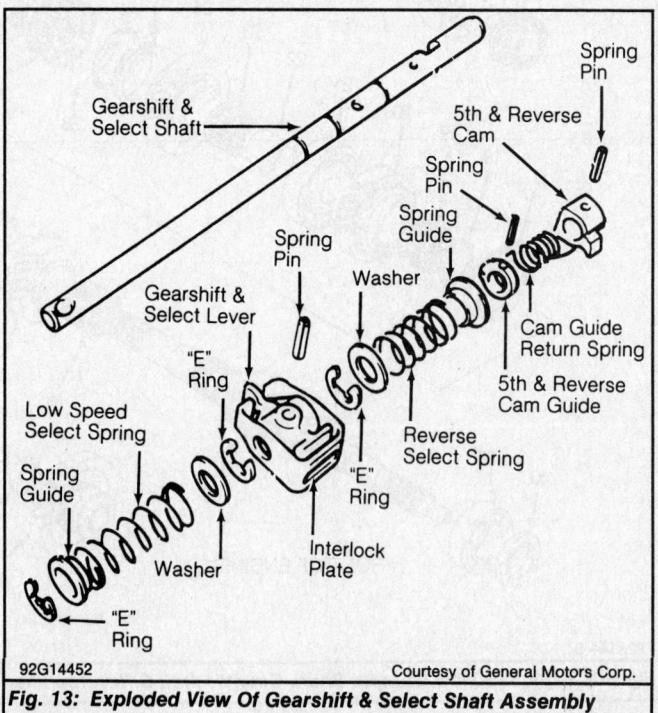

92G14452   Courtesy of General Motors Corp.
Fig. 13: Exploded View Of Gearshift & Select Shaft Assembly

LOW SPEED & HIGH SPEED SHIFT FORK ASSEMBLIES

Disassembly – Drive out spring pins. Remove forks and yokes from shaft. See Fig. 14.

Cleaning & Inspection – Clean all parts with solvent. Inspect shafts for flat spots, wear or damage. Inspect shift fork contact areas for bending, cracks, damage or wear. Measure clearance between shift fork fingers and synchronizer sleeve groove. Replace fork and sleeve if clearance exceeds .039" (1.0 mm).

Reassembly – Install forks and yokes on shaft. Support shafts with wood block to prevent bending shafts. Drive in spring pins.

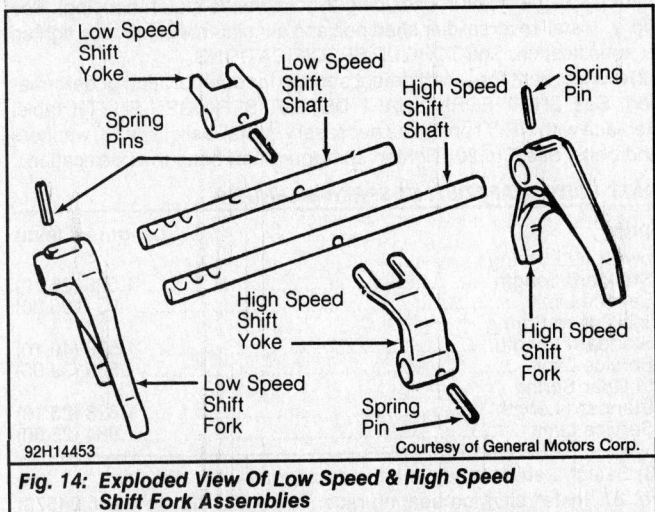

Fig. 14: Exploded View Of Low Speed & High Speed Shift Fork Assemblies

5TH & REVERSE SHIFT SHAFT ASSEMBLY

Disassembly – Drive out spring pins. Remove yoke, arm, balls and spring. See Fig. 15.

Cleaning & Inspection – Clean all parts with solvent. Inspect shafts for flat spots, wear or damage. Inspect contact areas shift arm and yoke for cracks, damage or wear.

Reassembly – For reassembly, reverse disassembly procedure. Ensure 2 balls are installed in reverse shift arm, and that spring pin slit is installed toward front. See Fig. 15.

DIFFERENTIAL ASSEMBLY

Disassembly – Remove left and right side bearings using universal bearing puller with Differential Side Bearing Puller Attachment (J34851). Remove speedometer drive gear. Remove bolts and ring gear from differential case. Drive out pinion shaft roll pin. Remove pinion shaft, pinion gears with thrust washers and side gears with thrust washers.

Cleaning & Inspection – Clean all components with solvent. Inspect all gear teeth for cracks, chips or other damage. Check differential bearings for roughness or wear. Inspect differential case and bearing surface for cracks or discoloration due to overheating. Replace as necessary.

Reassembly – 1) Install thrust washers and side gears. Install pinion gears and thrust washers. Install pinion shaft. Install differential case in soft-jawed vise. Place measuring tip of dial indicator on top surface of side gears. Move side gears up and down. See Fig. 16.

2) End play should be .002-.013" (.05-.33 mm). Select and install thrust washers to obtain specified end play. Thrust washers are available in thicknesses from .035-.047" (.90-1.20 mm) in .002" (.05 mm) increments.

3) Drive in pinion shaft roll pin until flush with case. Using driver, install left bearing using Differential Side Bearing Puller Attachment (J34851) for support. Install speedometer drive gear. Support differential case to prevent damage to left side bearing and install right side bearing using bearing installer with driver. Install ring gear and bolts. Tighten bolts to specification. See TORQUE SPECIFICATIONS.

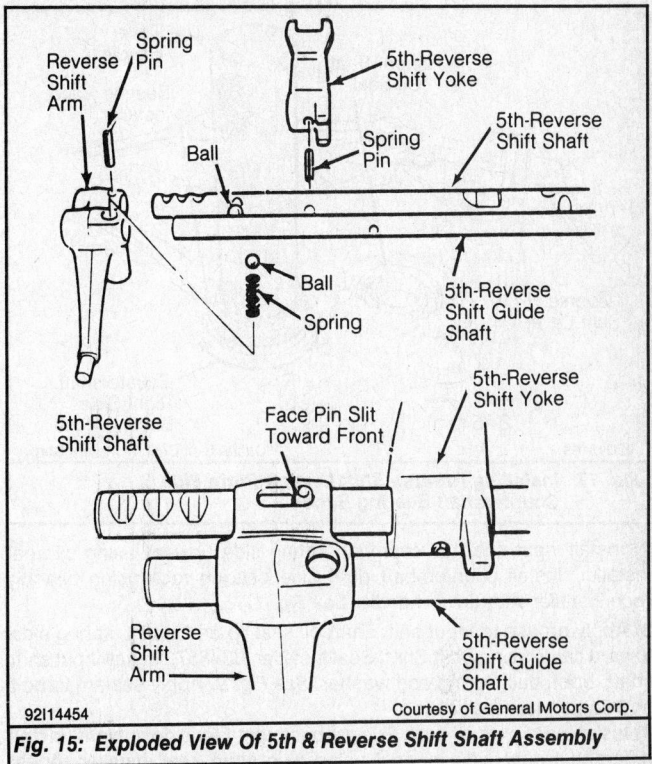

Fig. 15: Exploded View Of 5th & Reverse Shift Shaft Assembly

TRANSMISSION REASSEMBLY

1) If removed, install reverse shift lever into right side case. Apply Loctite to bolts and install bolts loosely. Measure and set lever end .2" (5 mm) from reverse gear shaft bore. See Fig. 17. Tighten bolts to specification. See TORQUE SPECIFICATIONS.

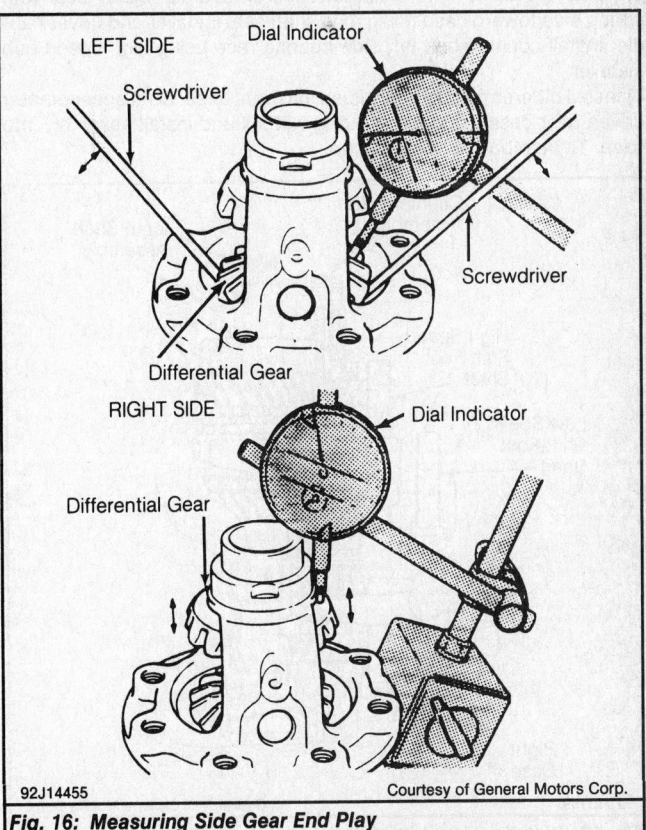

Fig. 16: Measuring Side Gear End Play

MANUAL TRANSMISSIONS
Geo MM5 5-Speed (Cont.)

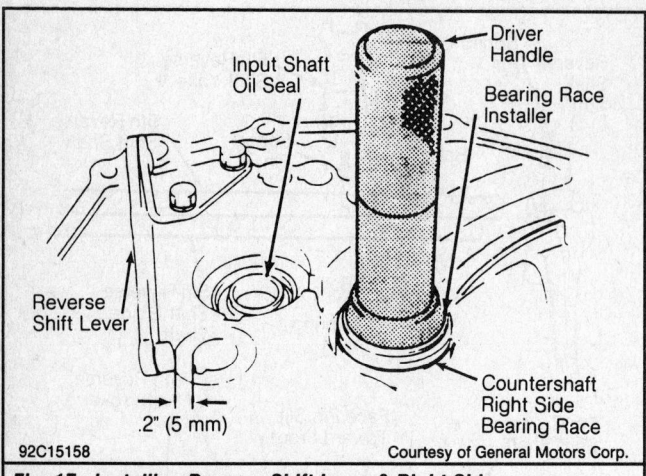

Fig. 17: Installing Reverse Shift Lever & Right Side Countershaft Bearing Race

2) Install input shaft oil seal with spring side upward using oil seal installer. Install countershaft right side bearing race using bearing race installer with driver handle. See Fig. 17.

3) Apply grease to input shift shaft oil seal lip and install, spring side toward case, using Shift Shaft Seal Installer (J34857). Install input shift shaft, boot, ball, spring and washer. See Fig. 9. Apply sealant to bolt and tighten to specification.

4) Install boot over oil seal. Ensure boot vent faces downward. Install differential right side oil seal using axle shaft seal installer. Apply grease to seal lip.

5) Install shift arm onto input shift shaft. Tighten bolt to specification. See TORQUE SPECIFICATIONS. Install magnet to case. If removed, install oil gutter. Coat bolt threads with Loctite and tighten to specification. Install countershaft left side bearing race into case using bearing and seal installer.

6) Apply grease to differential left side oil seal lip. Install seal with spring side toward case using axle shaft seal installer and driver handle. Install countershaft left side bearing race using high speed hub installer.

7) Install differential assembly flush into right case. Coat speedometer driven gear case assembly "O" ring with oil and install assembly into case. Tighten bolt to specification.

8) Assemble input shaft and countershaft together with high and low speed shift fork shaft assemblies. Install into right case. See Fig. 18. Ensure countershaft is engaged to final drive gear.

9) Install 5th and reverse shift shaft assembly and 5th and reverse shift guide shaft assembly into case. See Fig. 8. Join reverse shift arm on guide shaft to reverse shift lever.

10) Install reverse idler gear shaft through idler gear and washer into case. Align shaft mark with case mark. See Fig. 19. Engage shift yoke with input shift shaft arm.

11) Clean mating surfaces of case halves. Coat mating surface of left case with sealant and install onto right case. Install case bolts and tighten to specification (including 2 bolts inside clutch housing). See Fig. 7. Install reverse idler shaft bolt and aluminum washer, and tighten to specification. See TORQUE SPECIFICATIONS.

12) Inspect shift shaft detent springs for deterioration or deformation. See SHIFT FORK SHAFT DETENT SPRINGS LENGTH table. Replace with NEW springs as necessary. Install balls, spring, washers and bolts. See Fig. 20. Tighten shift fork shaft bolts to specification.

SHIFT FORK SHAFT DETENT SPRINGS LENGTH

Spring	Length In. (mm)
Low Speed Spring	
Standard Length	1.028 (26.10)
Service Limit	.984 (25.00)
High Speed Spring	
Standard Length	1.579 (40.10)
Service Limit	1.535 (39.00)
5th Gear Spring	
Standard Length	1.028 (26.10)
Service Limit	.984 (25.00)

13) Select a shim to adjust left side countershaft clearance "A". See Fig. 21. Install shim on bearing race. Place Flat Gauge Bar (J34673) onto top of shim. Measure dimension "A" using feeler gauge. Clearance should be .003-.005" (.08-.12 mm).

14) Install left case plate by inserting tab in groove of shift guide shaft.

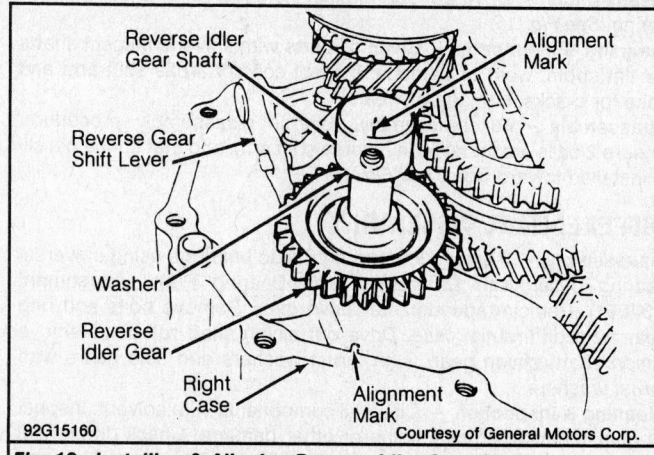

Fig. 19: Installing & Aligning Reverse Idler Gear Shaft

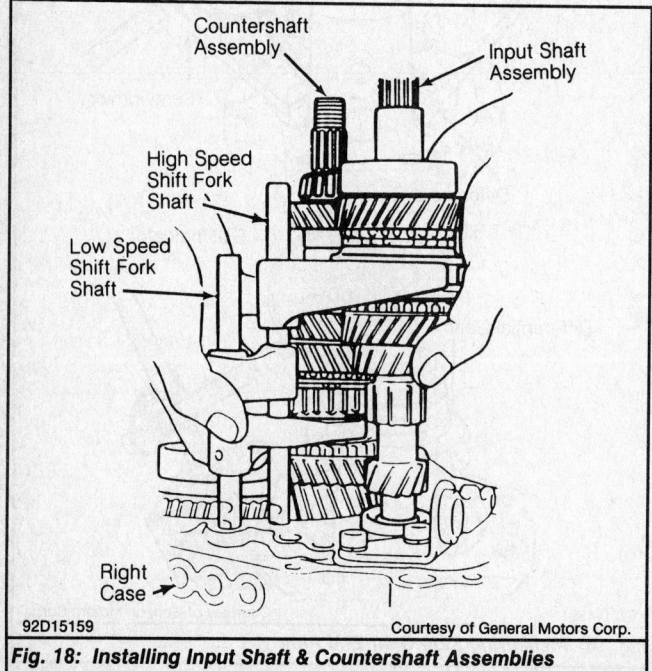

Fig. 18: Installing Input Shaft & Countershaft Assemblies

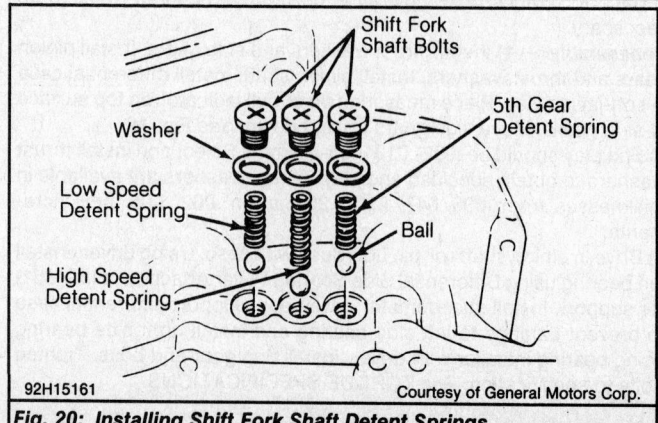

Fig. 20: Installing Shift Fork Shaft Detent Springs

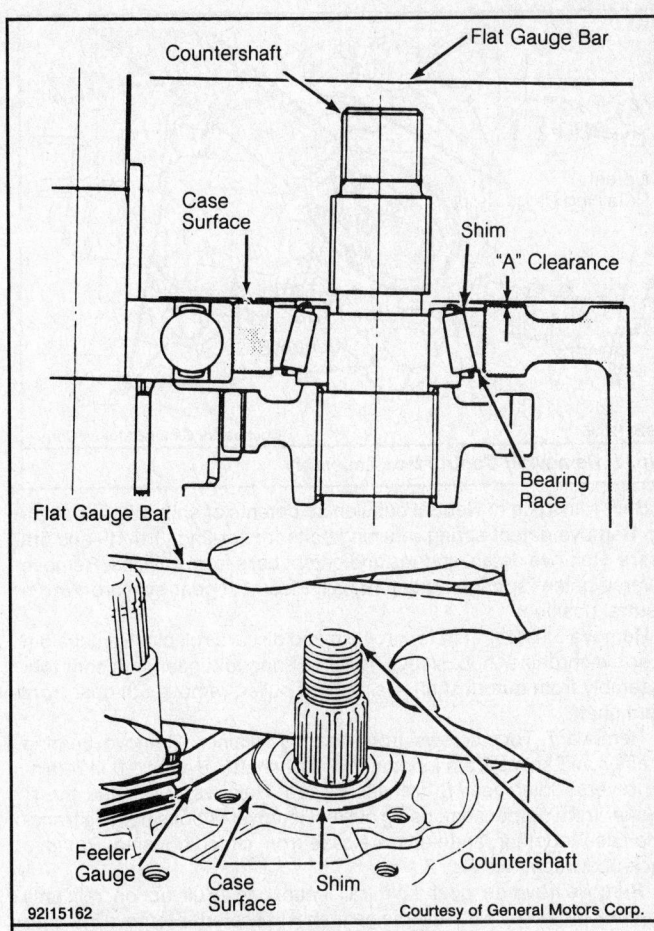

Fig. 21: Selecting Countershaft Bearing Shim

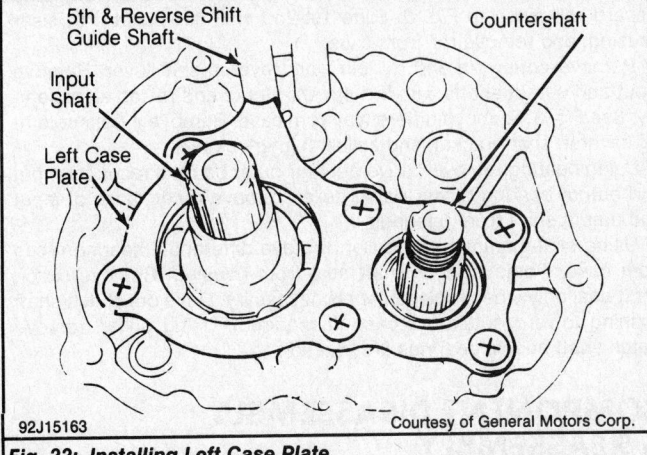

Fig. 22: Installing Left Case Plate

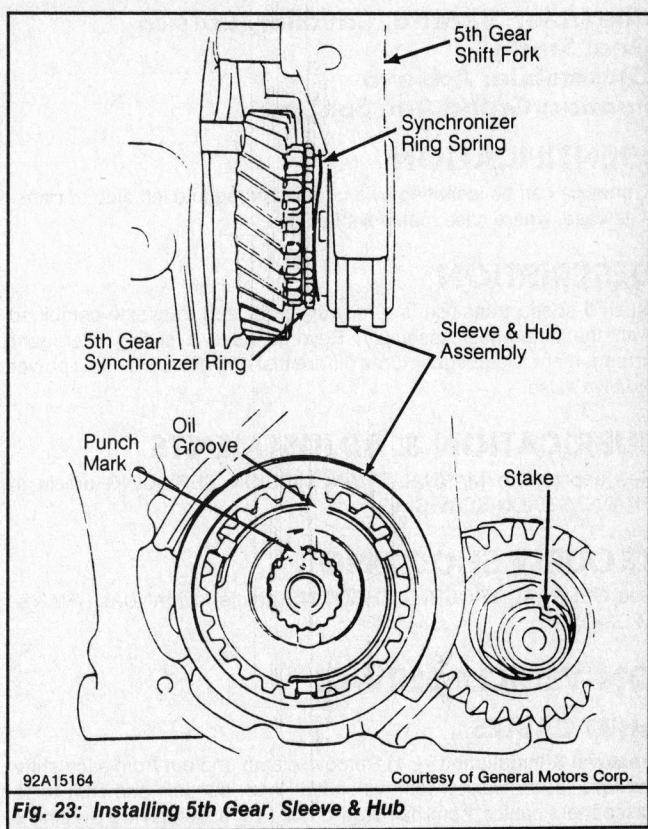

Fig. 23: Installing 5th Gear, Sleeve & Hub

See Fig. 22. Apply Loctite to screws. Tighten screws to specification. Ensure countershaft can be rotated by hand.

15) Install 5th gear onto countershaft facing machined boss inward. Install bearing onto input shaft. Apply oil to bearing. Install 5th gear. Install countershaft lock nut. Lock transaxle into 2 gears. Tighten lock nut to specification. See TORQUE SPECIFICATIONS. Stake lock nut.

16) Install synchronizer ring and ring spring. See Fig. 23. Install 5th gear shift fork to sleeve and hub assembly. Install onto input shaft, No. 1 shift shaft and shift guide shaft, aligning hub oil groove with shaft punch mark. See Fig. 23.

17) Drive in roll pin facing slit in pin outward. See Fig. 4. Install shift fork guide ball and apply Loctite lightly to shift fork plug threads. Install plug and tighten to specification. Install hub plate and snap ring. Ensure snap ring is installed securely.

18) Apply sealer to case and install left cover to case. Install shift yoke. See Fig. 5. Install gearshift and select shaft assembly and join its bottom end to shift yoke. Apply Loctite to shift yoke bolt threads and tighten to specification. Install shift interlock bolt with washer and tighten to specification.

19) Clean mating surfaces of left case and shift guide case. Apply sealant to shift guide case. Install shift guide case with wiring harness clamp and tighten to specification. See Fig. 6. Install back-up light switch and wire harness. Clean left case cap and left case mating surfaces. Install cap with ring and tighten to specification.

TORQUE SPECIFICATIONS
TORQUE SPECIFICATIONS

Application	Ft. Lbs. (N.m)
Back-Up Light Switch	15 (20)
Countershaft Lock Nut	52 (71)
Drain Plug	21 (28)
Extension Rod Nut	30 (41)
Filler Plug	40 (54)
Gearshift Control Shaft Bolt	15 (20)
Input Shift Shaft Bolt	10 (14)
Reverse Idler Shaft Bolt	10 (14)
Reverse Shift Lever Bolt	17 (23)
Ring Gear Bolt	63 (85)
Shift Interlock Bolt	17 (23)
Shift Fork Shaft Bolt	10 (14)
Shift Yoke Bolt	17 (23)
Transaxle Case Bolt	16 (22)
5th Gear Shift Fork Plug	10 (14)
5th-Reverse Interlock Guide	17 (23)

	INCH Lbs. (N.m)
Gearshift Housing Nut	53 (6)
Guide Plate Bolt	89 (10)
Left Case Cap Bolt	89 (10)
Left Case Plate Screw	62 (7)
Left Cover Bolt	89 (10)
Oil Gutter Bolt	53 (6)
Shift Arm Bolt	89 (10)
Shift Guide Case Bolt	89 (10)
Speedometer Case Bolt	53 (6)

MANUAL TRANSMISSIONS
Isuzu 76 MM 5-Speed

Chevrolet: Beretta, Cavalier, Corsica
Geo: Storm
Oldsmobile: Achieva
Pontiac: Grand Am, Sunbird

IDENTIFICATION

Transaxle can be identified by a code stamped into left side of transaxle case, where case mates with engine.

DESCRIPTION

Isuzu 5-speed transaxle is a fully synchronized transaxle combined with the differential assembly. Reverse uses a sliding idler gear arrangement. Output gear turns differential ring gear, providing power to drive axles.

LUBRICATION & ADJUSTMENTS

See appropriate MANUAL TRANSMISSION SERVICING article in TRANSMISSION SERVICING.

TROUBLE SHOOTING

See GENERAL TROUBLE SHOOTING article in MANUAL TRANSMISSIONS.

ON-VEHICLE SERVICE

SHIFT CABLES

Removal & Installation – 1) Remove clamp and nut from each shifting lever at transaxle. Remove shifter knob, console and shift boot. Disconnect cables from ball stud on control assembly by twisting a screwdriver between cable socket and control assembly.
2) Remove spring clips retaining cables to control assembly. Pull right side carpet back to gain access to shift cables. Remove shift cable grommet cover screws and cable cover at floor pan. Remove cables. To install, reverse removal procedure.

DRIVE AXLE OIL SEAL

Removal & Installation – 1) Raise and support vehicle. Remove wheel. Remove stabilizer shaft from control arm. Remove ball joint from steering knuckle. Place Seal Protector (J-34754) over axle shaft. Remove drive axle from transaxle case. Remove drive axle oil seal.
2) Install drive axle oil seal using seal installer and driver handle. Install drive axle to transaxle case. Install ball joint to steering knuckle. To complete installation, reverse removal procedure. Tighten nuts and bolts to specification. See TORQUE SPECIFICATIONS.

DRIVE AXLE SHAFTS

See appropriate FWD AXLE SHAFTS article in AXLE SHAFTS & TRANSFER CASES.

REMOVAL & INSTALLATION

See appropriate MANUAL TRANSMISSION REMOVAL article in TRANSMISSION SERVICING.

TRANSAXLE DISASSEMBLY

1) Remove clutch release bearing. Place transaxle assembly into Holding Fixture (J-33366) and attach holding fixture to Base Plate (J-3289). Remove 7 bolts retaining rear cover assembly to transaxle case. Remove rear cover assembly.
2) Remove 4 bolts retaining control box assembly to transaxle case. See Figs. 1 and 3. Shift transaxle into gear. Remove 5th gear drive and driven gear retaining nuts from input and output shaft. Discard retaining nuts.

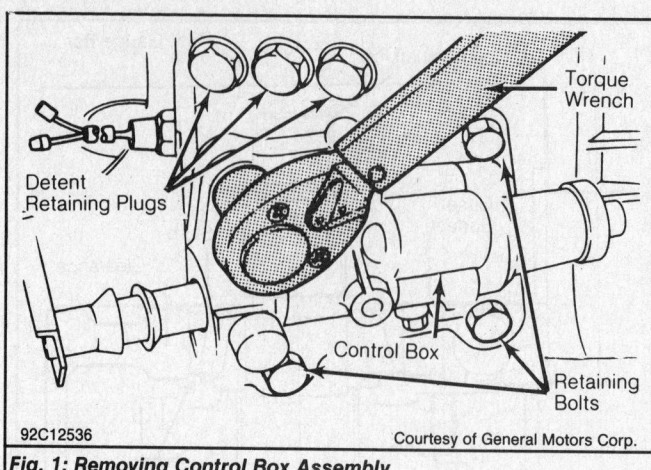

Fig. 1: Removing Control Box Assembly

92C12536   Courtesy of General Motors Corp.

3) Shift transaxle to Neutral position so detents of shift rails are aligned. Remove detent spring retaining bolts for 1st-2nd, 3rd-4th and 5th gears. Remove detent springs and detent balls from cavities. Remove reverse detent spring and detent ball. Place 5th gear synchronizer in Neutral position.
4) Remove 5th gear shift fork roll pin and discard roll pin. Remove 5th gear synchronizer hub, sleeve, roller bearing and gear with shift fork assembly from output shaft. Using gear puller, remove 5th gear from input shaft.
5) Remove 7 Torx screws from bearing retainer. Remove bearing retainer and shims from input and output shafts. Remove bolt retaining reverse idler gear to transaxle case. Remove collar and thrust washer from output shaft using puller. Remove 14 bolts holding transaxle case together, and separate case from clutch housing. Remove back-up switch. See Fig. 2.
6) Remove reverse gear shift rail snap ring. Pull up on rail until interlock pin aligns with reverse gear shift rail detent. Remove 5th gear shift rail and reverse gear shift rail. Remove reverse idler gear and reverse idler shaft. Remove roll pin from 1st-2nd shift fork, and discard roll pin. See Fig. 3. Slide 1st-2nd shift rail upward to clear housing, and remove rail from case.
7) Remove cotter pin and roll pin from reverse shift lever. Remove input and output shafts with 3rd-4th shift forks and rail as an assembly. See Fig. 3. Remove differential from case. Remove 4 bolts retaining reverse shift bracket, and collect 3 interlock pins.
8) Using bearing remover, drive out rear outer bearing races for input and output bearing races. Using puller, remove outer races of input and output shaft front bearings.
9) Using slide hammer and puller, remove differential bearing races from case. Remove input shaft seal from housing. Remove clutch shaft seal only when replacement is necessary. Drive out clutch shaft bushing toward outside of case (if required). Using puller, remove clutch shaft needle bearings (if required).

COMPONENT DISASSEMBLY & REASSEMBLY

NOTE: For component cleaning and inspection procedures, see CLEANING & INSPECTION after DIFFERENTIAL CASE & RING GEAR reassembly.

INPUT SHAFT

Disassembly – Support front bearing on hydraulic press bed with split plate. Press end of input shaft through bearing. Using split plate and press, push input shaft through 4th gear, 3rd-4th synchronizer assembly and 3rd gear in one step. See Fig. 4. Remove remaining parts from input shaft.

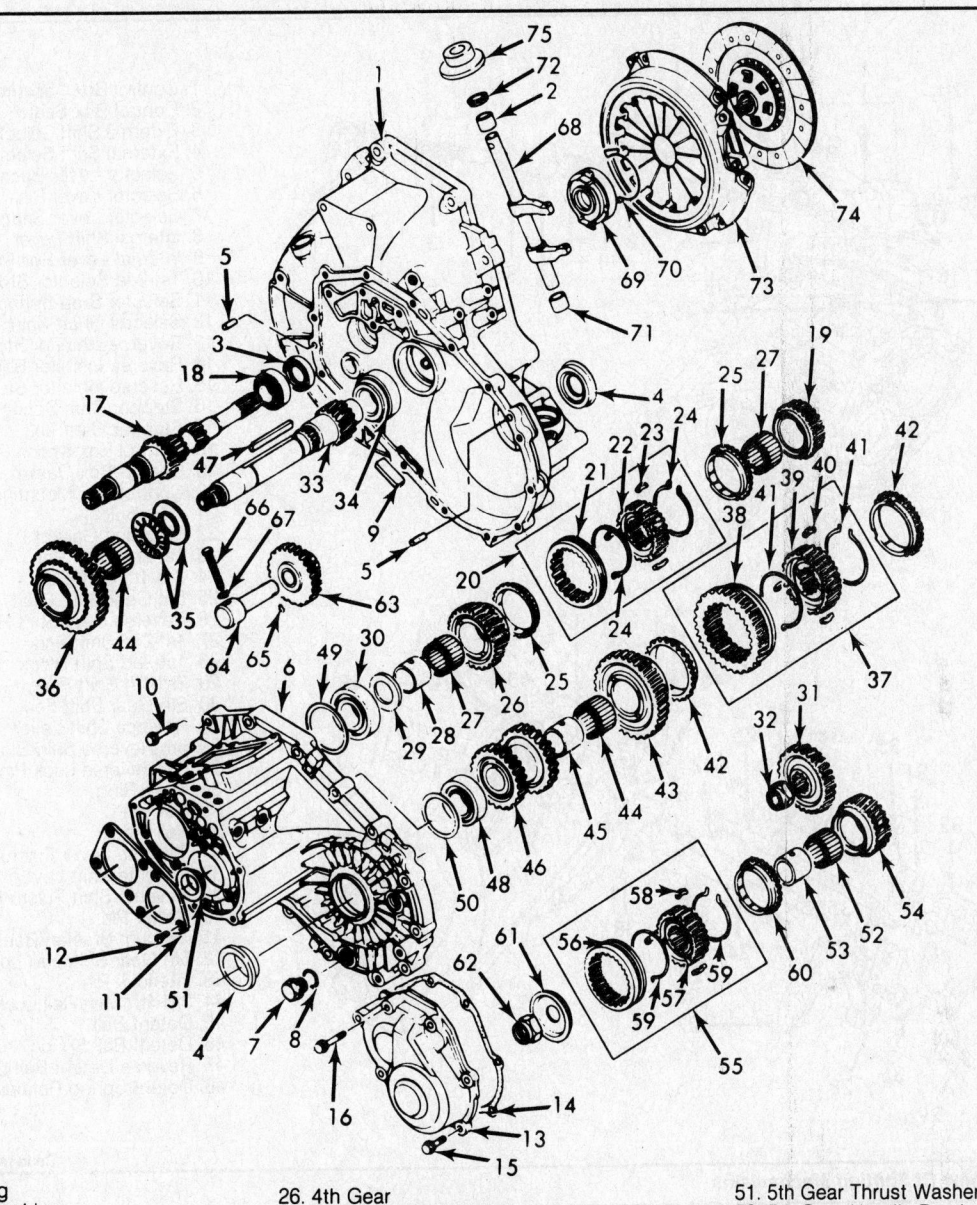

1. Clutch Housing
2. Clutch Shaft Bushing
3. Input Shaft Seal
4. Drive Shaft Oil Seal
5. Straight Pin
6. Transaxle Case
7. Drain Plug
8. Drain Plug "O" Ring
9. Magnet
10. Bolt
11. Bearing Retainer
12. Screw
13. Rear Cover
14. Gasket
15. Rear Cover Bolt
16. Rear Cover Bolt
17. Input Shaft
18. Input Shaft Front Bearing
19. 3rd-Gear
20. 3rd-4th Synchronizer Assembly
21. 3rd-4th Synchronizer Sleeve
22. 3rd-4th Synchronizer Hub
23. 3rd-4th Synchronizer Insert (Key)
24. 3rd-4th Synchronizer Spring
25. 3rd-4th Synchronizer Ring

26. 4th Gear
27. 3rd-4th Needle Bearing
28. 4th Gear Needle Bearing Collar
29. 4th Gear Thrust Washer
30. Rear Input Shaft Bearing
31. 5th Gear
32. 5th Gear Retaining Nut
33. Output Shaft
34. Output Shaft Front Bearing
35. Output Shaft Thrust Needle Bearing
36. 1st Gear
37. 1st-2nd Synchronizer Assembly
38. Reverse Synchronizer Sleeve & Gear
39. Reverse Clutch Hub
40. 1st-2nd Synchronizer Insert (Key)
41. 1st-2nd Insert Spring
42. 1st-2nd Synchronizer Ring
43. 2nd Gear
44. 1st-2nd Needle Bearing
45. 2nd Gear Needle Bearing Collar
46. 3rd-4th Gear
47. Output Shaft Key
48. Output Shaft Rear Bearing
49. Input Shaft Bearing Shim
50. Output Shaft Bearing Shim

51. 5th Gear Thrust Washer
52. 5th Gear Needle Bearing
53. 5th Gear Needle Bearing Collar
54. 5th Gear
55. 5th Gear Synchronizer Assembly
56. 5th Gear Synchronizer Sleeve
57. 5th Gear Synchronizer Hub
58. 5th Gear Synchronizer Insert (Key)
59. 5th Gear Synchronizer Spring
60. 5th Gear Synchronizer Ring
61. Plate Stopper Insert
62. Retaining Nut
63. Reverse Idler Gear
64. Reverse Idler Gear Shaft
65. Straight Pin
66. Reverse Idler Shaft Bolt
67. Idler Shaft Bolt Gasket
68. Clutch Fork Shaft Assembly
69. Clutch Release Bearing
70. Release Bearing Spring
71. Clutch Shaft Bearing
72. Clutch Shaft Seal
73. Clutch Pressure Plate Assembly
74. Clutch Disc
75. Clutch Shaft Cap

92D12537

Fig. 2: Exploded View Of Isuzu 5-Speed Manual Transaxle

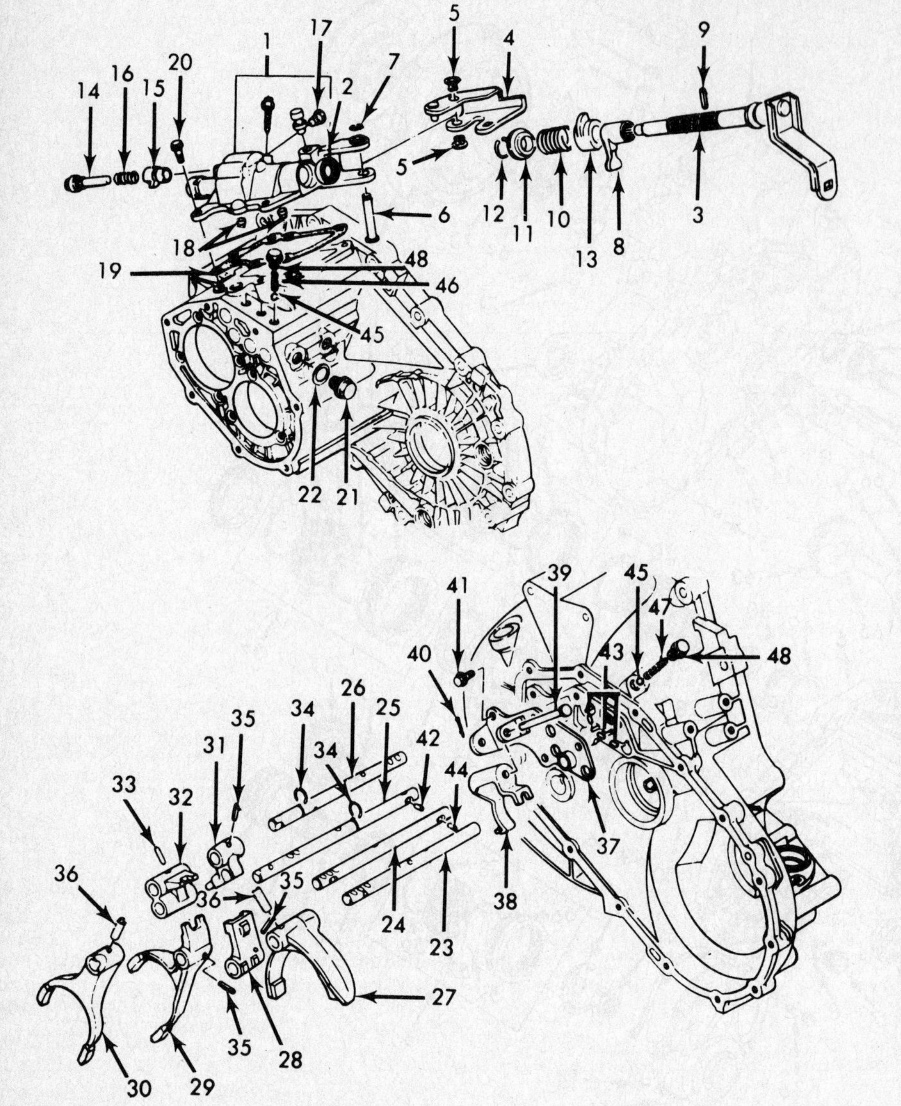

1. Control Box Assembly
2. Control Box Seal
3. External Shift Selector Shaft
4. External Shift Selector Lever
5. Selector Lever Bushing
6. Selector Lever Pin
7. Selector Lever Snap Ring
8. Internal Shift Lever
9. Internal Lever Roll Pin
10. 1st-2nd Selector Stop Spring
11. Selector Stop Spring Seat
12. Selector Shaft Snap Ring
13. Reverse Inhibitor Stopper
14. Reverse Inhibitor Bolt
15. Reverse Inhibitor Stopper Cam
16. Stopper Cam Spring
17. Stopper Cam Bolt
18. Control Box Knock Pin
19. Control Box Gasket
20. Control Box Mounting Bolt
21. Plug Bolt
22. Plug Bolt Gasket
23. 1st-2nd Shift Rail
24. 3rd-4th Shift Rail
25. 5th Gear Shift Rail
26. Reverse Gear Shift Rail
27. 1st-2nd Shift Fork
28. 1st-2nd Shift Block
29. 3rd-4th Shift Fork
30. 5th Gear Shift Fork
31. Reverse Shift Lever
32. 5th-Reverse Shift Block
33. 5th-Reverse Lock Pin
34. Snap Ring
35. Roll Pin
36. Roll Pin
37. Reverse Lever Fulcrum Bracket
38. Reverse Shift Lever
39. Reverse Shift Fulcrum Bracket Pin
40. Cotter Pin
41. Fulcrum Bracket Bolt
42. 5th Gear Shift Rail Lock Pin
43. Interlock Pin
44. 3rd-4th Shift Rail Lock Pin
45. Detent Ball
46. Detent Ball Spring
47. Reverse Detent Ball Spring
48. Detent Spring Retaining Plug

92E12538

Courtesy of General Motors Corp.

Fig. 3: Exploded View Of Shifting Mechanisms

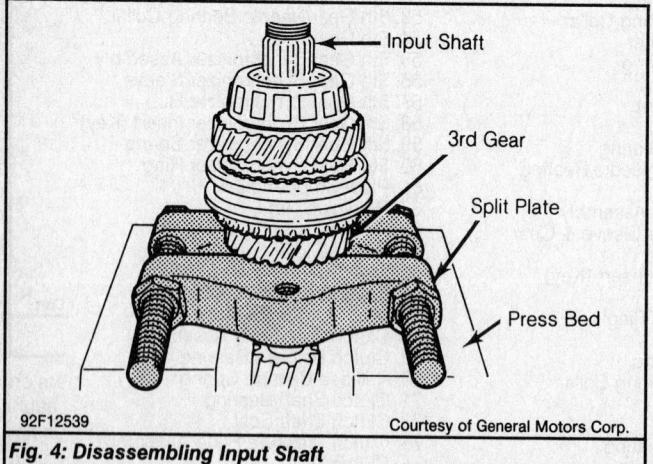

92F12539   Courtesy of General Motors Corp.

Fig. 4: Disassembling Input Shaft

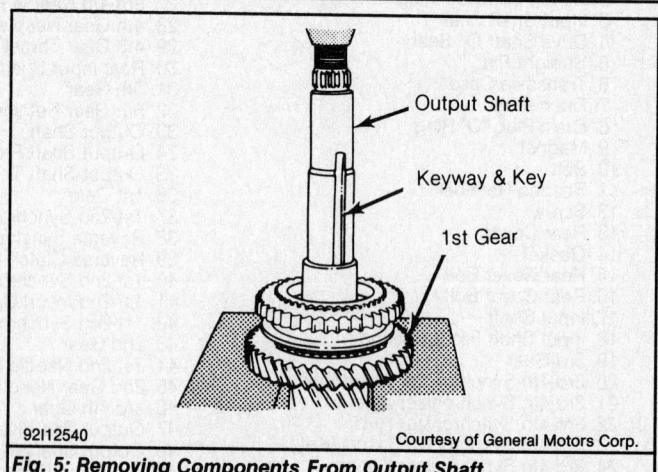

92I12540   Courtesy of General Motors Corp.

Fig. 5: Removing Components From Output Shaft

Reassembly – 1) Prior to reassembly, lubricate all components. Install needle bearing and 3rd gear and install synchronizer ring. Using bearing/collar installer and a press, carefully press 3rd-4th synchronizer sleeve and hub assembly together. Apply lubricant to entire circumference of collar hub interiors.

2) Ensure that insert springs do not interfere with hub after installation. Install synchronizer ring, needle bearing, 4th gear and thrust washer. See Fig. 2. Install thrust washer with recessed area facing 4th gear. Apply lubricant and using bearing/collar installer, press on front and rear bearing until firmly seated.

OUTPUT SHAFT

Disassembly – **1)** Remove front bearing using bearing remover, pilot and a press. Remove rear bearing and 3rd-4th gear simultaneously using split plate and a press.

2) Remove collar, needle bearing, 2nd gear, 1st-2nd synchronizer assembly, 1st gear and key from output shaft using a press. *See Figs. 2 and 5.* Remove 1st-2nd needle bearing and thrust needle bearing.

Reassembly – **1)** Apply lubricant to thrust surfaces and bearings of all gears. Install thrust needle bearing, needle bearing, 1st gear and synchronizer ring on output shaft. Mate grooves of synchronizer ring with inserts in sleeve and hub assembly.

2) Press collar, sleeve and hub assembly together using collar installer and pilot. Apply lubricant to entire assembly before and after reassembly. Ensure insert springs do not interfere with hub after installation. Install synchronizer ring, needle bearing and 2nd gear.

3) Install key into groove on output shaft. Apply lubricant to interior of 3rd-4th gear and install on output shaft while aligning key with keyway. Fit key together with rear bearing. Using bearing installer, press rear bearing into place on output shaft. Using bearing installer, press front bearing onto shaft.

DIFFERENTIAL CASE & RING GEAR

Disassembly – **1)** Using puller and pilot, remove differential side bearing. Remove 10 bolts retaining ring gear to differential case. *See Fig. 6.* Discard ring gear bolts.

2) Using a screwdriver, pry speedometer drive gear or rotor from differential case. DO NOT reuse speedometer drive gear or rotor. Drive out lock pin, and pull cross pin from its bore. Remove pinion gears and thrust washers. Remove side gears and thrust washers.

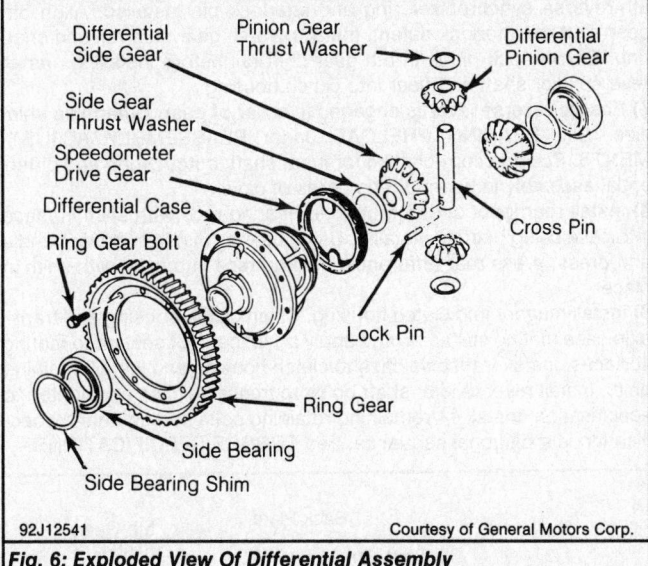

92J12541   Courtesy of General Motors Corp.

Fig. 6: Exploded View Of Differential Assembly

NOTE: Prior to reassembly, lubricate all inner and outer bearing surfaces. Apply lubricant to cross pin, differential gears and side gears.

Reassembly – **1)** Install 2 side gears in differential case together with thrust washers. Position thrust washers and pinion gears opposite each other. Insert cross pin into bore. Using a feeler gauge, check side gear backlash. Backlash should be .001-.003" (.03-.08 mm).

2) If backlash is not within specified range, install larger or smaller thrust washers depending on reading. Install lock pin into cross pin. Heat NEW speedometer gear or rotor to about 200°F (95°C). DO NOT use hot water or open flame. Install speedometer gear or rotor on differential case. Heat ring gear to 122-212°F (50-100°C). Apply lubricant on outside diameter of ring gear and position ring gear onto differential case.

3) Apply a small amount of lubricant on bottom side only of 10 NEW ring gear bolts. Install bolts and tighten to specification in a diagonal pattern. See TORQUE SPECIFICATIONS. Press side bearings onto differential case using bearing installer.

CLEANING & INSPECTION

1) Wash all parts thoroughly in solvent. Apply compressed air to each oil feed port and channel in each side of case. Inspect all gear teeth for signs of excessive wear, distortion or damage. Remove minor nicks or scratches with an oil stone.

2) Inspect all thrust washers for excessive wear, distortion or damage. Inspect case halves for cracks, porosity, damaged mating surfaces, stripped bolt threads or distortion. Inspect all needle, roller and thrust bearings for rough operation, excessive wear or damage. DO NOT spin bearings when drying with compressed air.

3) Inspect synchronizers for worn or broken parts. When reassembling synchronizer assemblies, each insert spring should support all 3 keys and each opening portion of insert spring should face opposite direction from other insert spring.

4) Measure clearance between synchronizer ring and inserts. Clearance should be .15" (3.9 mm) for 1st-2nd gear and .14" (3.7 mm) for 3rd-4th and 5th gear. If clearance is not as specified, replace components as necessary. Measure clearance between synchronizer ring and gear. Minimum clearance should be .031" (.80 mm). If clearance is not as specified, replace components as necessary.

5) Measure detent spring length. Length for reverse detent spring should be greater than 2.43" (61.7 mm). Length for all other detent springs should be greater than 1.00" (25.5 mm). Replace springs as necessary.

6) Measure shift fork pad thickness. Thickness for Reverse shift fork should be .29" (7.4 mm). Thickness for all other shift forks should be .30" (7.5 mm). Replace as necessary.

NOTE: Keep all synchronizer parts together with their original sleeve and hub.

REASSEMBLY ADJUSTMENTS

BEARING PRELOAD

1) Position outer bearing races on input, output and differential assembly bearings. Install gauges on bearing races. *See Fig. 7.* Place 7 Spacers (J-33373) evenly around perimeter of clutch housing. Install bearing and shim retainer on transaxle case. Tighten bearing and shim retainer bolts to 13 ft. lbs. (17 N.m).

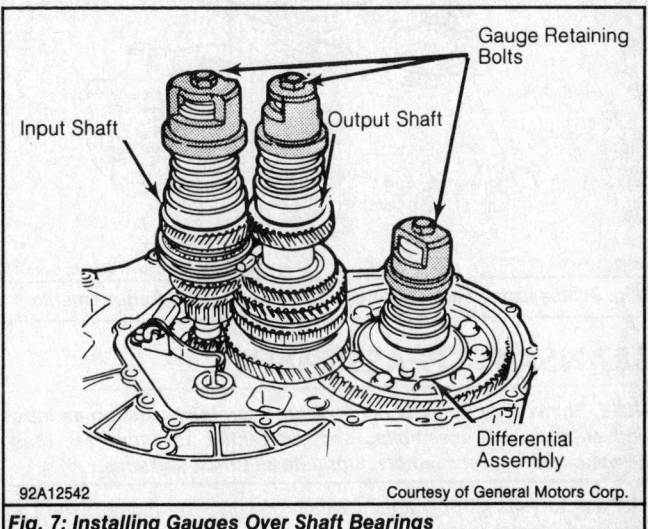

92A12542   Courtesy of General Motors Corp.

Fig. 7: Installing Gauges Over Shaft Bearings

2) Carefully position transaxle case over gauges and onto spacers on clutch housing. *See Fig. 8.* Install bolts and tighten bolts alternately to gradually draw transaxle case to spacers on clutch housing. Tighten bolts to 10 ft. lbs. (13 N.m). Rotate each gauge to seat bearings.

3) Rotate differential assembly 3 revolutions in each direction. With gauges compressed, measure gap between outer sleeve and base pad of each shaft. This will provide shim thickness required for proper bearing preload at each shaft. *See Fig. 9.*

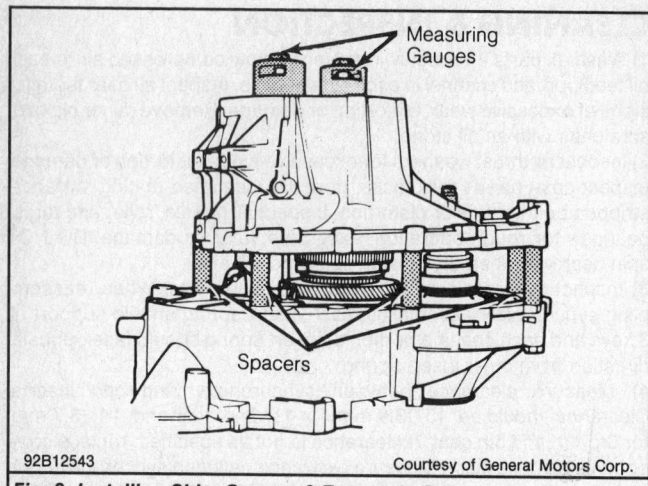

Measuring Gauges

Spacers

92B12543   Courtesy of General Motors Corp.

Fig. 8: Installing Shim Gauges & Transaxle Case

4) On output shaft, use largest shim size that can be placed into gap and drawn through without binding. On input shaft, use a shim 2 sizes smaller than largest shim that will fit in gap. See Fig. 9.

5) On differential assembly use a shim 3 sizes larger than shim that will fit smoothly in gap. See Fig. 9. When shims are selected, remove clutch housing, spacers and gauges. Install shims into their respective race bores in clutch housing.

6) Shims for input shaft are available in thicknesses of .039-.098" (1.00-2.48 mm), in increments of .0016" (.040 mm). Shims for output shaft are available in thicknesses of .046-.096" (1.16-2.44 mm), in increments of .0031" (.080 mm). Shims for differential assembly are available in thicknesses of .043-.079" (1.08-2.00 mm), in increments of .0016" (.040 mm).

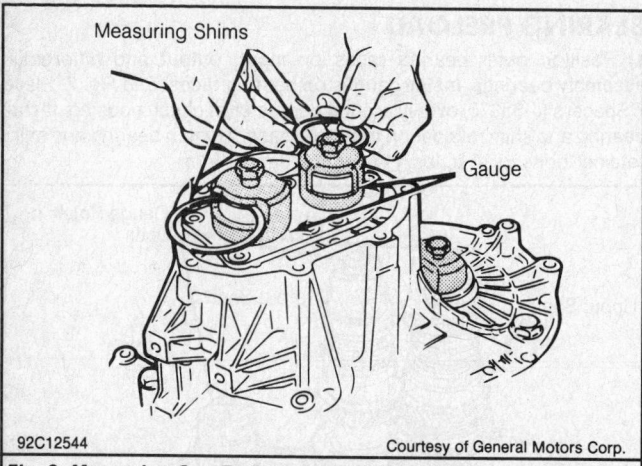

Measuring Shims

Gauge

92C12544   Courtesy of General Motors Corp.

Fig. 9: Measuring Gap To Determine Preload Shim Requirements

TRANSAXLE REASSEMBLY

NOTE: Shims may be selected for proper preload as soon as input and output shaft assemblies and differential assembly are reassembled. During reassembly, lubricate all thrust surfaces.

1) Prior to reassembly, attach clutch housing to holding fixture (if removed). Install holding fixture into base plate. Install NEW input shaft oil seal using oil seal installer.

2) Install outer bearing races for input shaft, output shaft and differential into clutch housing. Apply lubricant to bearing races prior to installation. Use bearing race installer and driver handle to install input and output shaft bearing race.

3) Use bearing race installer and driver handle to install differential bearing race. Apply grease to interlock pins, and install pins into clutch housing. See Fig. 10. Install reverse shift bracket on clutch housing.

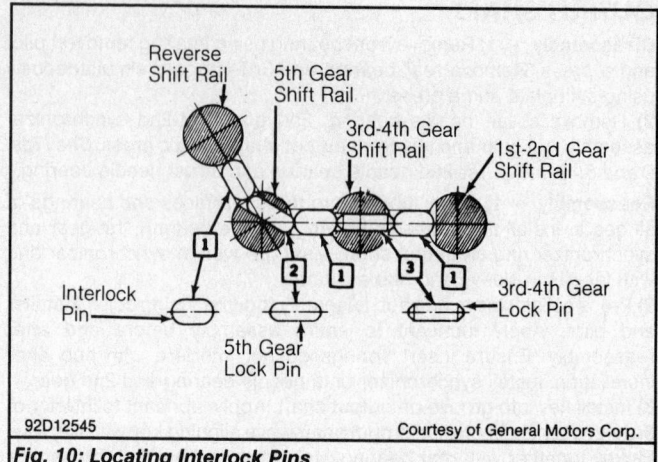

Reverse Shift Rail
5th Gear Shift Rail
3rd-4th Gear Shift Rail
1st-2nd Gear Shift Rail

Interlock Pin

1   2   1   3   1

5th Gear Lock Pin

3rd-4th Gear Lock Pin

92D12545   Courtesy of General Motors Corp.

Fig. 10: Locating Interlock Pins

4) Use 3rd-4th shift rail to align shift bracket with housing. Install reverse shift bracket retaining bolts and tighten to specification. See TORQUE SPECIFICATIONS. Ensure shift rail operates smoothly. Install differential case assembly. Install input shaft, output shaft and 3rd-4th shift fork and shift rail as an assembly into clutch housing.

5) Ensure lock pins are in 3rd-4th shift rail prior to installation. The 3rd-4th shift rail is installed into raised collar of reverse shift lever bracket. Install 1st-2nd gear shift fork onto synchronizer sleeve, and insert shift rail into reverse shift lever bracket. Align hole in fork with rail, and install NEW roll pin.

6) Install reverse lever onto shift bracket. Install 5th gear shift rail with 5th-reverse synchronizer ring and interlock pin installed. Align 5th gear shift rail interlock detent. Install reverse gear shift rail and snap ring. Ensure lock pin is in 5th gear shift rail before installing. Install reverse idler shaft and gear into clutch housing .

7) Ensure reverse lever is engaged in collar of gear. Determine shim size. See BEARING PRELOAD under REASSEMBLY ADJUSTMENTS. Position correct shim for input shaft, output shaft and differential assembly in bearing race bores of case.

8) Install rear input and output shaft bearing race with shim in place into case using bearing installer. Using bearing installer, driver handle and press, press rear differential bearing race into case with shim in place.

9) Install magnet into clutch housing. Clean clutch housing and transaxle case mating surfaces, and apply a 1/8" bead of sealant to mating surfaces. Install transaxle case to clutch housing and install retaining bolts. Install reverse idler shaft bolt into transaxle case and tighten to specification. Install 14 remaining retaining bolts and tighten to specification in a diagonal sequence. See TORQUE SPECIFICATIONS.

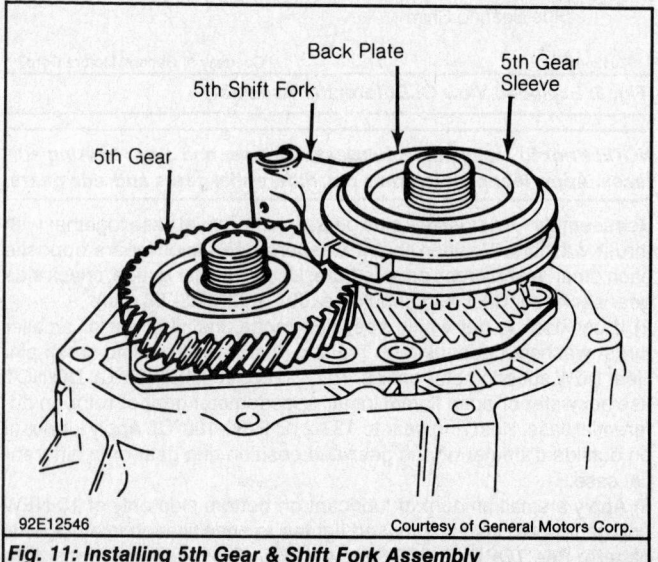

Back Plate
5th Gear Sleeve
5th Shift Fork
5th Gear

92E12546   Courtesy of General Motors Corp.

Fig. 11: Installing 5th Gear & Shift Fork Assembly

10) Install drive axle seals. Lubricate and install thrust washer and collar to output shaft, using bearing installer. Install 5th gear on input shaft. Install needle bearing, 5th gear, synchronizer ring, sleeve and hub assembly with shift fork in its groove and back plate on output shaft. *See Fig. 11.*

11) Align shift fork on shift rail and install NEW roll pin. Install detent balls and springs for reverse, 1st-2nd, 3rd-4th and 5th gears. Install detent spring retaining bolts and tighten to specification. See TORQUE SPECIFICATIONS. Wipe lubricant from input and output shafts, and apply Loctite to threads of both shafts. DO NOT allow Loctite to flow on to 5th gear splines or splines of input shaft.

12) Install NEW input and output shaft retaining nuts and tighten to specification. See TORQUE SPECIFICATIONS. Stake nuts in place after reaching final torque. To assemble control box, install stopper cam onto internal control lever. Ensure serrations on stopper cam and lever are aligned. *See Fig. 12.* Install stopper cam and internal lever to shift lever assembly.

13) Align stopper cam alignment mark with center of internal lever. *See Fig. 12.* Ensure reverse inhibitor mechanism is operating properly. Use NEW roll pin to attach internal lever during assemble. Install control box assembly with NEW gasket to transaxle case. Install 4 retaining bolts and tighten to specification. See TORQUE SPECIFICATIONS.

14) Ensure transaxle shifts properly before installing rear cover. Install rear cover with NEW gasket, and install 7 retaining bolts. Tighten retaining bolts to specification. Install clutch fork assembly (if removed). If removed, install NEW clutch shaft bushing using bushing installer.

15) Install NEW shaft seal. Install clutch shaft cap. Install clutch release bearing. Measure input shaft rotating torque. When measuring input shaft rotating torque, position transaxle with input shaft facing upward and differential section of transaxle to lower side. Rotating torque should be less than 7 INCH lbs. (.8 N.m).

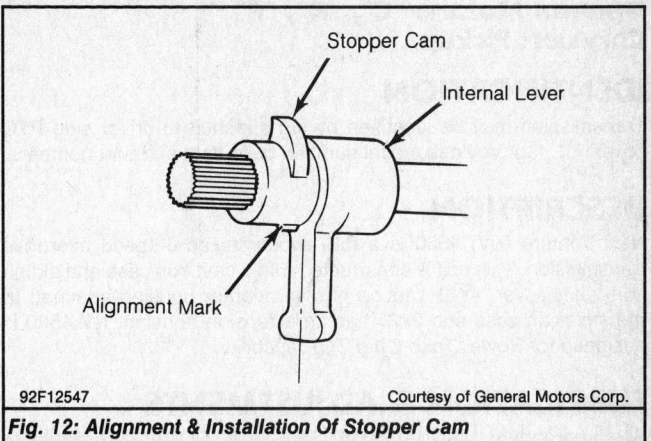

92F12547   Courtesy of General Motors Corp.

Fig. 12: Alignment & Installation Of Stopper Cam

TORQUE SPECIFICATIONS
TORQUE SPECIFICATIONS

Application	Ft. Lbs. (N.m)
Back-Up Switch	22 (33)
Ball Joint Nut	48-63 (65-85)
Bearing & Shim Retainer Bolt	13 (17)
Clutch Housing Bolt	28 (38)
Clutch Shaft Release Lever Bolt	37 (50)
Control Box-To-Case Bolt	13 (17)
Detent Spring Retaining Bolt	18 (25)
Drive Axle Shaft Nut	192 (260)
Engine-To-Transaxle Bolt	55 (75)
Input & Output Shafts Retaining Nut	94 (128)
Mount-To-Engine Bolt	55 (75)
Rear Cover Bolt	13 (17)
Reverse Idler Shaft Bolt	28 (38)
Reverse Shift Bracket Retaining Bolt	13 (17)
Ring Gear Bolt	72-79 (98-107)
Stabilizer Shaft-To-Control Arm Nut	15 (21)
Stabilizer Shaft-To-Suspension Support Nut	15 (21)
Wheel Lug Nut	100 (136)

MANUAL TRANSMISSIONS
New Venture 4500 5-Speed

General Motors: "C", "K", "P"
Chrysler: Pickup

IDENTIFICATION

Transmission may be identified by tag attached to driver side PTO cover. I.D. tag provides model number, build date and part number.

DESCRIPTION

New Venture (NV) 4500 is a fully synchronized 5-speed overdrive transmission. This unit is constructed with a cast iron case and aluminum shift cover. 4WD version has an adapter housing attached to transmission case and 2WD has an extension housing. NV 4500 is designed for Power Take-Off (PTO) capability.

LUBRICATION & ADJUSTMENTS

See appropriate MANUAL TRANSMISSION SERVICING article in TRANSMISSION SERVICING.

TROUBLE SHOOTING

See GENERAL TROUBLE SHOOTING article in MANUAL TRANSMISSIONS.

ON-VEHICLE SERVICE

EXTENSION HOUSING SEAL

Removal & Installation – Drain transmission oil. Remove drive shaft, yoke nut and washer. Remove yoke and seal. Using appropriate seal installer, install NEW seal. To complete installation, reverse removal procedure. Tighten drive shaft bolts to specification. See TORQUE SPECIFICATIONS.

REMOVAL & INSTALLATION

See appropriate MANUAL TRANSMISSION REMOVAL article in TRANSMISSION SERVICING.

TRANSMISSION DISASSEMBLY

1) Remove shift cover bolts and pry shift cover loose. Ensure only slots provided in shift cover are used to pry cover loose. Tilt front of shift cover up and lift off transmission case.

NOTE: Use only 10mm 12-point socket on extension/adapter housing bolts. Any other size will damage bolt head splines.

---

2) Remove extension or adapter housing bolts. Tap extension or adapter housing with plastic hammer to loosen and remove housing. Remove spline seal from end of mainshaft. On 2WD models, remove extension housing seal.

CAUTION: On some 4WD models there is a vibration damper on mainshaft. If transmission is equipped with vibration damper on mainshaft, step 4) must be performed before step 3). See Fig. 1. Remove vibration damper before performing step 3).

---

3) Remove snap ring from countershaft 5th gear. Remove countershaft 5th clutch gear, synchronizer ring and bearing spacer. Remove synchronizer inserts and springs from synchronizer hub and sleeve.

4) Remove mainshaft 5th gear nut and washer. Ensure mainshaft does not rotate during removal. Mainshaft 5th gear nut is secured with Loctite and may require several blows with hammer on nut wrench to loosen.

5) Drive out 5th gear shift fork roll pins from bottom. Remove 5th gear shift fork and synchronizer as assembly. Remove countershaft 5th gear and synchronizer hub assembly. Remove 5th gear needle bearing, cone shaped rear bearing thrust washer and locating pin from countershaft.

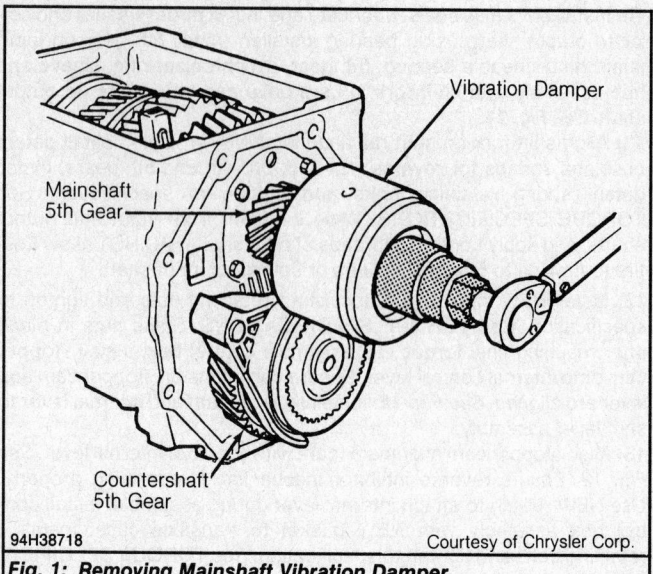

94H38718   Courtesy of Chrysler Corp.

Fig. 1: Removing Mainshaft Vibration Damper

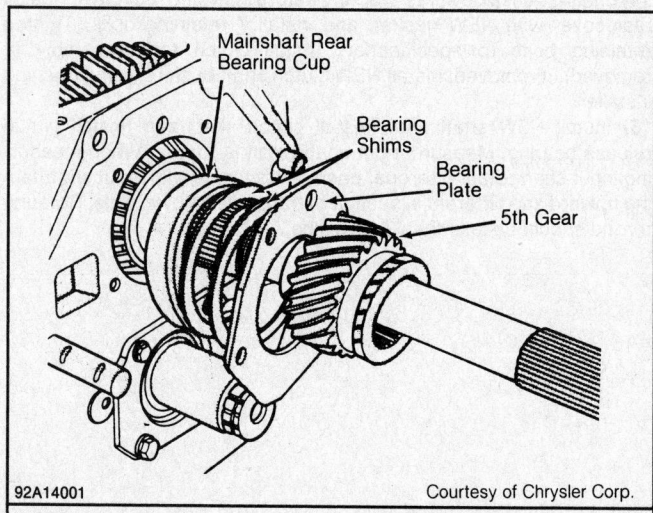

92A14001   Courtesy of Chrysler Corp.

Fig. 2: Removing Mainshaft 5th Gear & Components

6) Remove mainshaft 5th gear with Puller Tool Set (6444). Remove mainshaft rear bearing plate bolts, rear bearing plate, end play shims and bearing cup. See Fig. 2.

7) Remove front bearing retainer bolts. Tap front bearing retainer with plastic hammer and remove retainer from recess in transmission case. Use screwdriver to remove seal from front bearing retainer. Pull bearing cup from front bearing retainer using internal puller.

8) Remove input shaft by tilting shaft downward and out of transmission case. Remove input shaft pilot bearing and press input bearing from shaft. See Fig. 3.

9) Remove countershaft rear bearing plate, end play shims and rear bearing cup. Remove reverse idler shaft by screwing bolt into end of shaft and pulling shaft from transmission case.

10) Shift 1-2 and 3-4 synchronizer sleeves into Neutral position. Remove input shaft thrust bearing from end of mainshaft. Remove 4th clutch gear and synchronizer ring from mainshaft. See Fig. 4.

11) Separate reverse idler gear from mainshaft gears. Raise front of mainshaft and hold mainshaft rear splines. Rotate spline end of mainshaft counterclockwise and lift mainshaft from transmission case.

12) Separate reverse idler gear from countershaft and remove gear through input shaft bore in front of transmission case. Insert reverse idler shaft through gear bearings to hold assembly together. Remove reverse idler gear thrust washers from transmission case and install on reverse idler shaft.

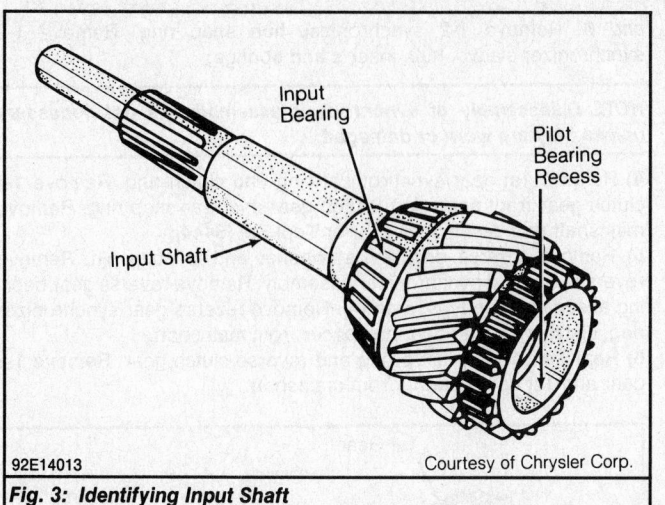

Fig. 3: Identifying Input Shaft

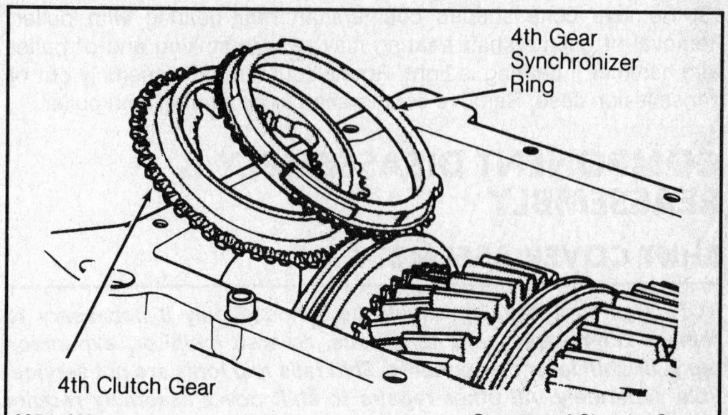

92E14013

Courtesy of Chrysler Corp.

Fig. 4: Removing 4th Clutch Gear & Synchronizer Ring

92B14002

Courtesy of Chrysler Corp.

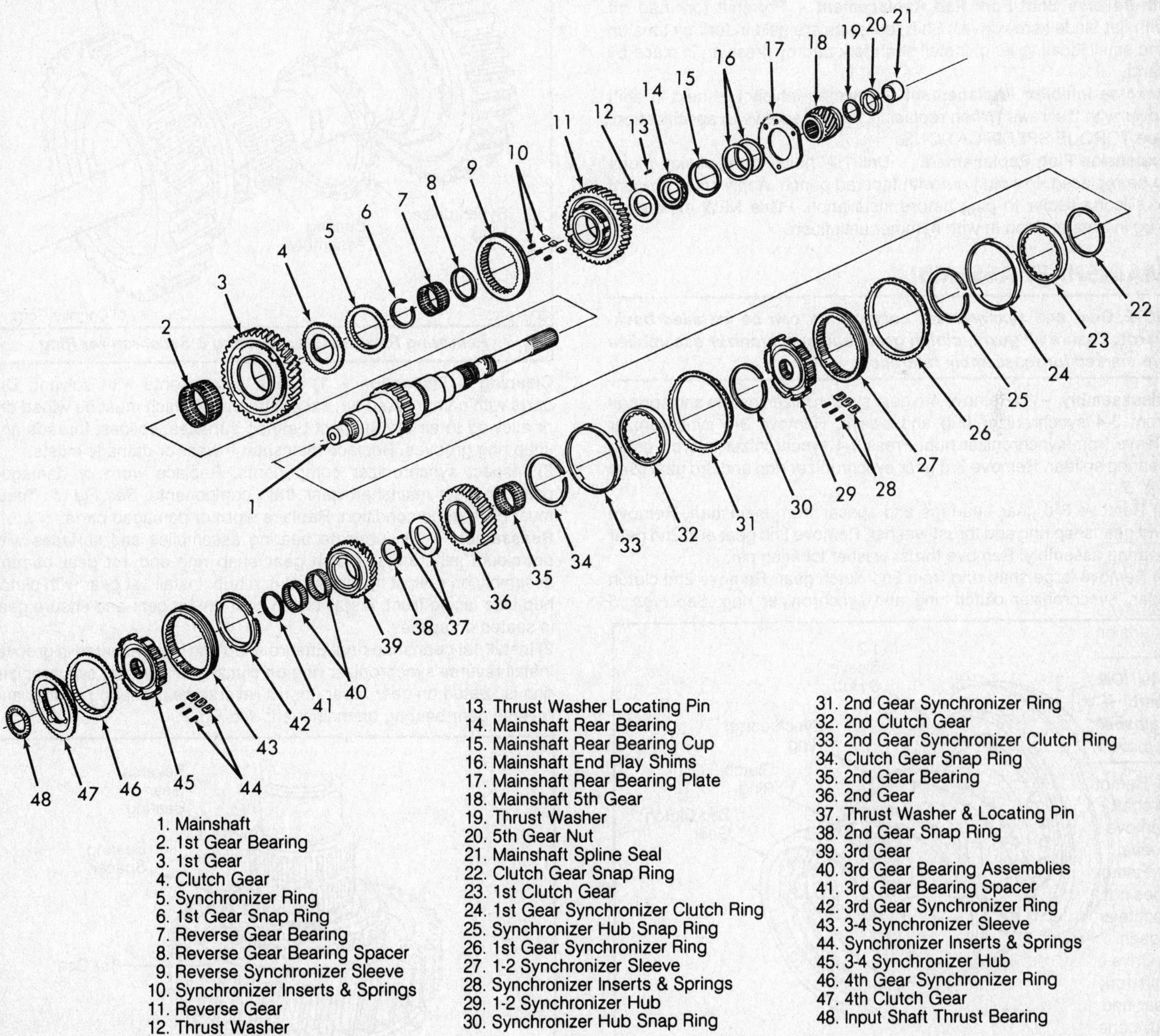

1. Mainshaft
2. 1st Gear Bearing
3. 1st Gear
4. Clutch Gear
5. Synchronizer Ring
6. 1st Gear Snap Ring
7. Reverse Gear Bearing
8. Reverse Gear Bearing Spacer
9. Reverse Synchronizer Sleeve
10. Synchronizer Inserts & Springs
11. Reverse Gear
12. Thrust Washer
13. Thrust Washer Locating Pin
14. Mainshaft Rear Bearing
15. Mainshaft Rear Bearing Cup
16. Mainshaft End Play Shims
17. Mainshaft Rear Bearing Plate
18. Mainshaft 5th Gear
19. Thrust Washer
20. 5th Gear Nut
21. Mainshaft Spline Seal
22. Clutch Gear Snap Ring
23. 1st Clutch Gear
24. 1st Gear Synchronizer Clutch Ring
25. Synchronizer Hub Snap Ring
26. 1st Gear Synchronizer Ring
27. 1-2 Synchronizer Sleeve
28. Synchronizer Inserts & Springs
29. 1-2 Synchronizer Hub
30. Synchronizer Hub Snap Ring
31. 2nd Gear Synchronizer Ring
32. 2nd Clutch Gear
33. 2nd Gear Synchronizer Clutch Ring
34. Clutch Gear Snap Ring
35. 2nd Gear Bearing
36. 2nd Gear
37. Thrust Washer & Locating Pin
38. 2nd Gear Snap Ring
39. 3rd Gear
40. 3rd Gear Bearing Assemblies
41. 3rd Gear Bearing Spacer
42. 3rd Gear Synchronizer Ring
43. 3-4 Synchronizer Sleeve
44. Synchronizer Inserts & Springs
45. 3-4 Synchronizer Hub
46. 4th Gear Synchronizer Ring
47. 4th Clutch Gear
48. Input Shaft Thrust Bearing

92C14003

Courtesy of Chrysler Corp.

Fig. 5: Exploded View Of Mainshaft Assembly

13) Remove cone shaped countershaft rear bearing with puller. Removal of countershaft bearing may require striking end of puller with hammer if bearing is tight. Rotate countershaft assembly out of transmission case. Remove countershaft front bearing with puller.

COMPONENT DISASSEMBLY & REASSEMBLY

SHIFT COVER ASSEMBLY

NOTE: Gearshift housing should be serviced only if necessary to replace 5th-reverse shift fork pads, reverse inhibitor, expansion plugs or shift lever components. Shift rails and forks are not serviceable separately. All other repairs to shift cover assembly require assembly replacement.

Cleaning & Inspection – Clean components with solvent and dry with compressed air. Examine housing for cracks or other damage. Inspect shift forks and pads for wear and/or distortion. Inspect shift rails for case fit. If loose, replace cover assembly. Inspect expansion plugs for leakage or looseness.

5th-Reverse Shift Fork Pad Replacement – Pry shift fork pad off with flat blade screwdriver. Shift fork pads are held in fork by tension and small locating tang. Install shaft fork pad by pressing in place by hand.

Reverse Inhibitor Replacement – Reverse inhibitor is held in shift cover with 2 screws. When replacing, tighten screws to specification. See TORQUE SPECIFICATIONS.

Expansion Plug Replacement – Drill 1/4" holes in expansion plugs to be replaced. Pry plug out with tapered punch. Apply small amount of silicone sealer to plug before installation. Place NEW expansion plug in bore and tap in with hammer until flush.

MAINSHAFT ASSEMBLY

NOTE: Gear and synchronizer components can be installed backwards. Ensure all gears, clutch gears and synchronizer assemblies are marked for reassembly reference.

Disassembly – 1) Remove 4th gear synchronizer inserts and springs from 3-4 synchronizer hub and sleeve. Remove 3-4 synchronizer sleeve from synchronizer hub. Press 3-4 synchronizer hub off using bearing splitter. Remove 3rd gear synchronizer ring and 3rd gear. *See Fig. 5.*

2) Remove 3rd gear bearings and spacer from mainshaft. Remove 2nd gear snap ring and thrust washer. Remove 2nd gear and 2nd gear bearing assembly. Remove thrust washer locating pin.

3) Remove large snap ring from 2nd clutch gear. Remove 2nd clutch gear, synchronizer clutch ring and synchronizer ring. *See Figs. 5*

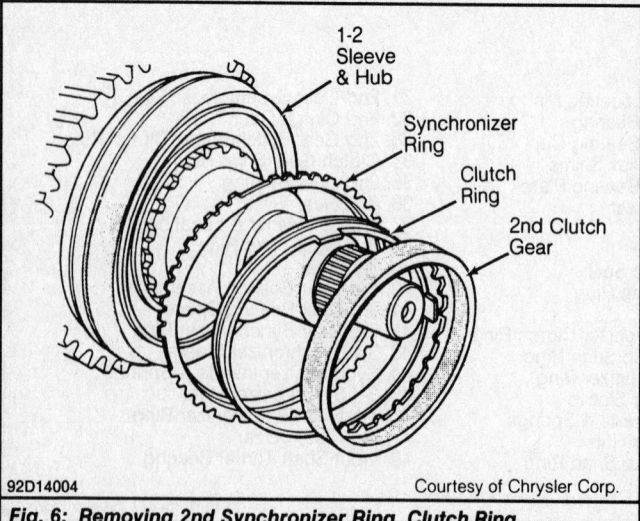

92D14004   Courtesy of Chrysler Corp.

Fig. 6: Removing 2nd Synchronizer Ring, Clutch Ring & Clutch Gear

and 6. Remove 1-2 synchronizer hub snap ring. Remove 1-2 synchronizer sleeve, hub, inserts and springs.

NOTE: Disassembly of synchronizer assemblies is not necessary unless they are worn or damaged.

4) Remove 1st gear synchronizer ring and clutch ring. Remove 1st clutch gear front snap ring, clutch gear and rear snap ring. Remove mainshaft rear bearing with Puller Tool Set (6444).

5) Remove reverse gear thrust washer and locating pin. Remove reverse gear and synchronizer assembly. Remove reverse gear bearing assembly. *See Figs. 5 and 7.* Remove reverse gear synchronizer ring, clutch gear and bearing spacer from mainshaft.

6) Remove 1st gear snap ring and reverse clutch gear. Remove 1st gear and 1st gear bearing from mainshaft.

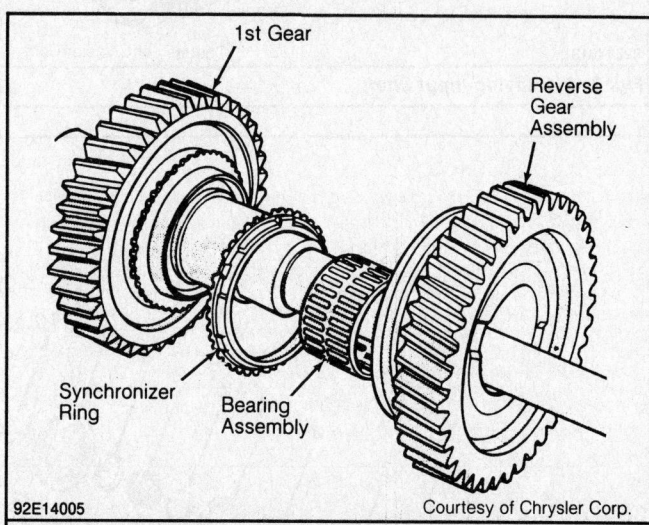

92E14005   Courtesy of Chrysler Corp.

Fig. 7: Removing Reverse Gear, Bearing & Synchronizer Ring

Cleaning & Inspection – 1) Clean components with solvent. Dry parts with compressed air, except bearings which must be wiped dry or allowed to air dry. Inspect bearing surfaces, splines, threads and snap ring grooves. Replace mainshaft if wear or damage exists.

2) Inspect synchronizer components. Replace worn or damaged parts. Inspect mainshaft gear train components. *See Fig. 5.* Teeth must be in good condition. Replace worn or damaged parts.

Reassembly – 1) Lubricate bearing assemblies and surfaces with petroleum jelly. Install clutch gear snap ring and 1st gear bearing assembly on rear of mainshaft clutch hub. Install 1st gear with clutch hub side facing front. Install clutch gear on 1st gear and ensure gear is seated on splines.

2) Install 1st gear snap ring. Ensure snap ring is fully seated in groove. Install reverse synchronizer ring on clutch gear. Ensure synchronizer ring is seated on gear taper. Install reverse gear bearing spacer and reverse gear bearing on mainshaft. *See Fig. 8.*

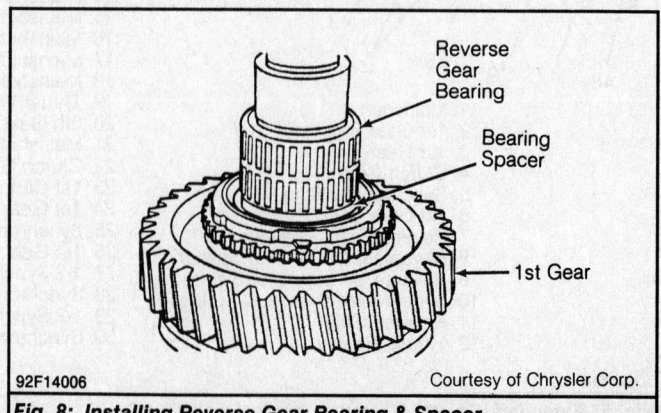

92F14006   Courtesy of Chrysler Corp.

Fig. 8: Installing Reverse Gear Bearing & Spacer

3) Install reverse synchronizer sleeve on hub portion of reverse gear and position sleeve taper facing rear. Align teeth on sleeve and hub portion of reverse gear. Install synchronizer springs in hub portion of reverse gear. Slide synchronizer spring back with screwdriver and install synchronizer inserts. Center synchronizer sleeve over inserts.

4) Install reverse gear synchronizer assembly on mainshaft. Rotate assembly to align hub portion of reverse gear with synchronizer ring lugs and seat reverse gear assembly. Install reverse gear thrust washer locating pin and thrust washer.

5) Install rear bearing on mainshaft with press. Turn mainshaft over and install 1st clutch gear on mainshaft synchronizer hub, ensuring recessed side of clutch gear faces front. Secure 1st clutch gear with snap ring. Assemble 1st gear synchronizer and clutch ring. Install assembled 1st gear synchronizer and clutch ring on 1st clutch gear.

6) Assemble 1-2 synchronizer assembly. *See Fig. 9.* Install hub weights in synchronizer hub with retainer springs. Ensure flat spring goes in front side of synchronizer hub. Ensure ends of retainer springs are securely installed in weight slots.

7) Align and install 1-2 synchronizer sleeve on hub, ensuring reference marks from disassembly are aligned. Space synchronizer hub off work bench enough to allow synchronizer sleeve to drop down, allowing access to install synchronizer springs and inserts.

8) Slide 1-2 synchronizer sleeve into Neutral position, ensuring synchronizer inserts are seated and synchronizer springs are not displaced. Install 1st gear synchronizer ring in 1-2 synchronizer hub and sleeve.

9) Install 1-2 synchronizer assembly on mainshaft. Ensure tapered side of 1-2 synchronizer assembly faces front, and tapered side of reverse synchronizer assembly faces rear.

10) Remove flat weight spring from front side of 1-2 synchronizer hub to ease installation of 1-2 synchronizer snap ring. Install 1-2 synchronizer snap ring. Reinstall flat weight spring in 1-2 synchronizer hub.

11) Assemble 2nd clutch gear, clutch ring and synchronizer ring. Install assembly on mainshaft in 1-2 synchronizer hub. Install 2nd clutch gear snap ring, ensuring snap ring is fully seated in groove.

12) Install 2nd gear bearing and 2nd gear on mainshaft. Install thrust washer locating pin and 2nd gear thrust washer. Install 2nd gear thrust washer snap ring, ensuring snap ring is fully seated in groove.

13) Install 3rd gear bearing spacer and seat against thrust washer snap ring. Install 3rd gear bearings and 3rd gear. Install synchronizer ring on 3rd gear, ensuring synchronizer ring is fully seated on gear taper.

14) Assemble 3-4 synchronizer assembly. Install 3-4 synchronizer sleeve on hub, ensuring narrow groove machined on synchronizer hub faces front. Install synchronizer springs in synchronizer hub and sleeve slot of assembly. Slide synchronizer spring back with screwdriver and install synchronizer inserts.

15) Slide 3-4 synchronizer assembly onto mainshaft, aligning synchronizer ring with sleeve and hub. Ensure grooved side of synchronizer hub faces forward. Drive or press synchronizer assembly remaining distance until seated. Approximately 1/8" of shaft spline is visible when 3-4 synchronizer assembly is seated.

16) Install 4th synchronizer ring in 3-4 synchronizer sleeve. Install 4th clutch gear in synchronizer ring. Mainshaft assembly is now ready for reassembly into transmission case.

TRANSMISSION CASE

Disassembly – 1) Remove countershaft front bearing cap with hammer from inside transmission case. Remove countershaft front bearing cup with bearing driver.

2) Remove shift lug roll pin from shift lug and rail in transmission case. Use modified pin punch for removal of shift lug roll pin. *See Fig. 10.* Drive shift rail from case with drift. Remove shift lug rail bushings with bushing driver. Remove magnet from bottom of transmission case.

Cleaning & Inspection – 1) Clean transmission case with solvent and dry with compressed air. Inspect condition of transmission case. Ensure alignment dowels are round and tight.

2) Inspect threaded holes for stripped or clogged threads and repair as necessary. Ensure all sealing surfaces are smooth. Replace transmission case if broken or cracked.

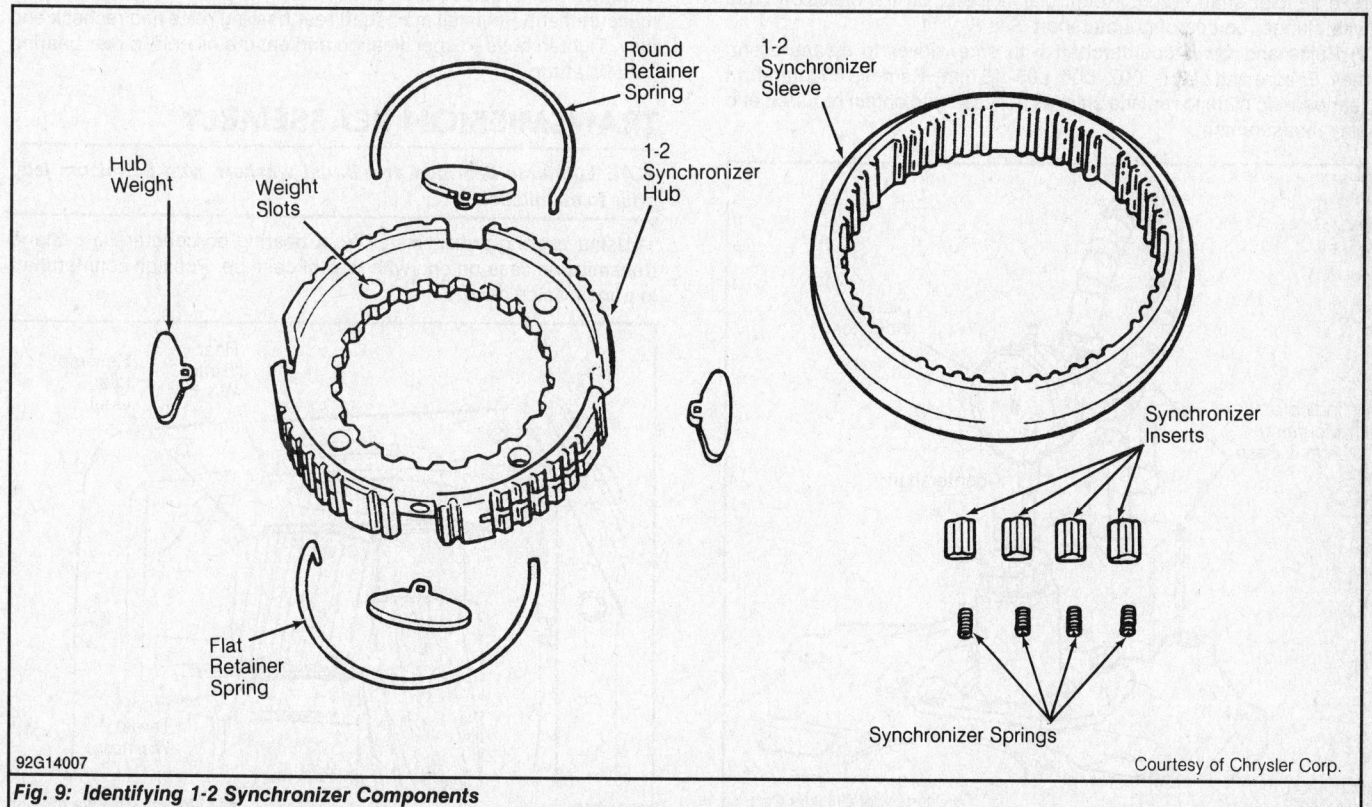

92G14007

Courtesy of Chrysler Corp.

Fig. 9: Identifying 1-2 Synchronizer Components

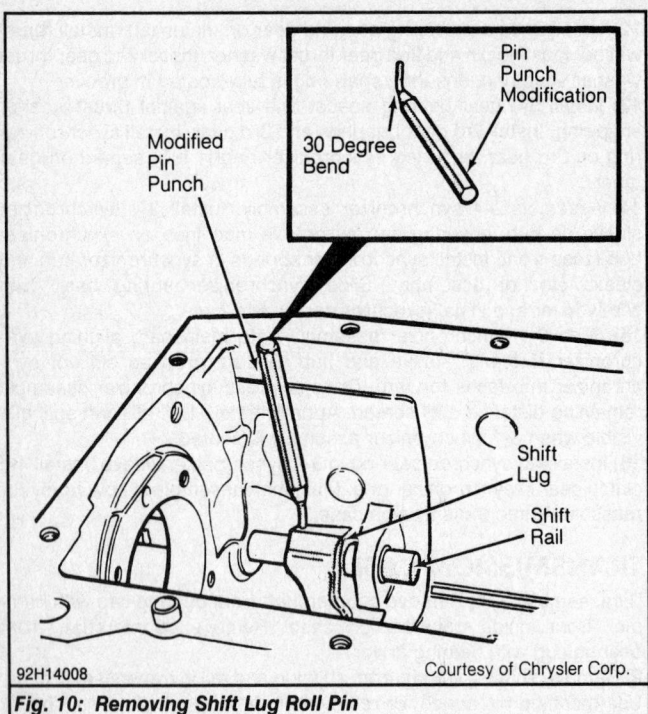

Fig. 10: Removing Shift Lug Roll Pin

Reassembly – Install countershaft front bearing cup with bearing driver. Install NEW shift lug rail bore bushings. Seat bushings flush with case. Install magnet and secure under clip at bottom of case.

ADJUSTMENTS

COUNTERSHAFT END PLAY

1) Install countershaft rear bearing plate, ensuring plate is seated in reverse idler shaft notch. Mount dial indicator on transmission case with plunger on end of countershaft. *See Fig. 11.*
2) Raise and lower countershaft with screwdriver to measure end play. Ensure end play is .002-.006" (.05-.15 mm). Remove countershaft rear bearing plate to replace shim as necessary to obtain required end play measurement.

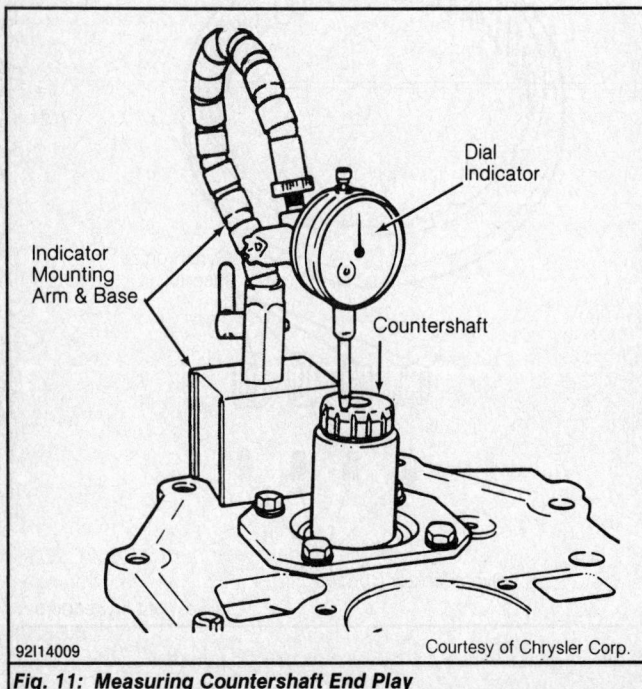

Fig. 11: Measuring Countershaft End Play

3) Reinstall countershaft rear bearing plate and recheck end play. Loctite countershaft rear bearing plate bolts and tighten to specification. See TORQUE SPECIFICATIONS.

MAINSHAFT END PLAY

1) Install mainshaft rear bearing cup and tap into place with plastic hammer. Install rear bearing plate without any shims. Stand transmission case in upright position. Slide input shaft and front retainer through hole in work bench to stand transmission case flat.
2) Mount dial indicator on rear of transmission case with plunger on rear bearing inner race. *See Fig. 12.* Raise and lower mainshaft with screwdriver between input shaft and transmission case to measure end play.
3) Ensure end play is .002-.006" (.05-.15 mm). Remove mainshaft rear bearing plate to replace shim as necessary to obtain required end play measurement. Reinstall mainshaft rear bearing plate and recheck end play. Tighten bolts to specification and ensure oil hole in rear bearing plate is at top.

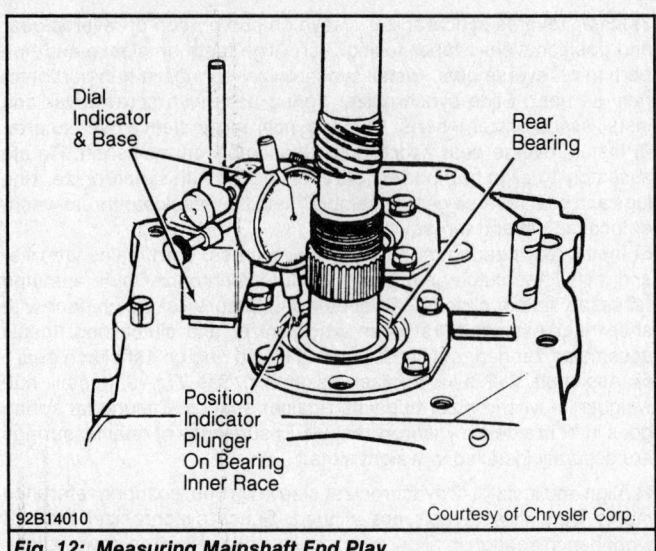

Fig. 12: Measuring Mainshaft End Play

TRANSMISSION REASSEMBLY

NOTE: Lubricate bearings and thrust washers with petroleum jelly prior to installation.

1) Using bearing driver, install front bearing on countershaft. Stand transmission case on end with rear of case up. Position countershaft in transmission case.

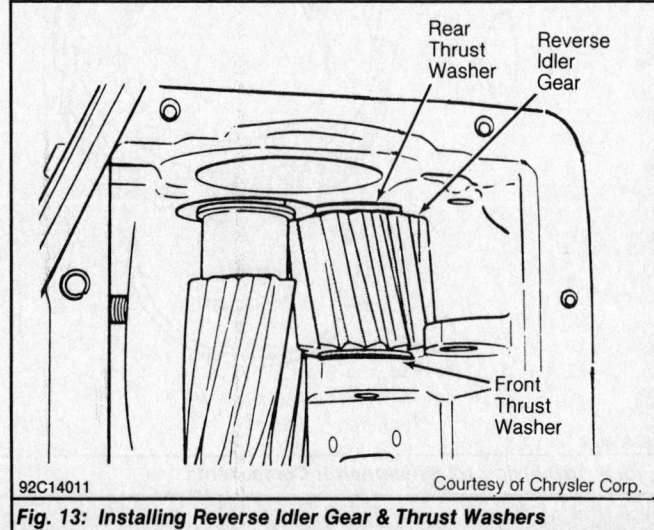

Fig. 13: Installing Reverse Idler Gear & Thrust Washers

2) Install idler shaft bearings and spacer. Install idler gear front thrust washer on boss in transmission case. See Fig. 13. Install reverse idler gear on top of thrust washer.

3) Install reverse idler gear rear thrust washer between transmission case and reverse idler gear. See Fig. 13. Install reverse idler gear shaft aligning gear and thrust washers as necessary with drift. Ensure notch in idler shaft faces countershaft.

4) Support front of countershaft with wooden block between transmission case and countershaft. Using bearing driver, install rear bearing cone on countershaft. Remove wooden block from front of countershaft.

5) Install NEW front bearing cap in transmission case. Apply silicone sealer to flange and lip of bearing cup, and seat with wooden block and hammer. Install countershaft rear bearing cup in transmission case. Tap into place with plastic hammer if necessary.

6) Adjust countershaft end play. See COUNTERSHAFT END PLAY under ADJUSTMENTS. Insert shift lug rail through front bushing in transmission case. Install shift lug on rail and slide shift lug rail remainder of distance. Ensure roll pin notches are facing 5 o'clock position. Install shift lug roll pin.

7) Position transmission case with case opening up. Lift mainshaft assembly tilting rear of mainshaft downward into case. Guide rear of mainshaft through rear bearing bore of transmission case. Holding front of mainshaft, lift slightly, align gears and seat in case. Ensure 4th clutch gear and synchronizer ring were not knocked out of alignment during installation.

8) Install input shaft thrust bearing on mainshaft. Using bearing driver, install bearing on input shaft. Install pilot bearing in input shaft bore. See Fig. 3.

9) Install input shaft on mainshaft and work input shaft rearward until mainshaft is seated in pilot bearing. Install bearing cup in front bearing retainer with bearing driver.

10) Install NEW oil seal in front bearing retainer. Apply silicone sealer to flange of front bearing retainer and install over input shaft. Install front bearing retainer in transmission case. Ensure lube channel is in 12 o'clock position. See Fig. 14.

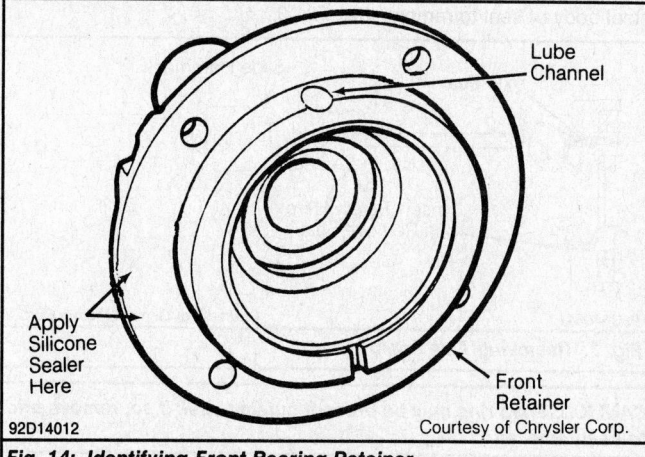

Fig. 14: Identifying Front Bearing Retainer

11) Align front bearing retainer holes, and tap retainer into place with plastic hammer. Install front bearing retainer bolts and tighten to specification. See TORQUE SPECIFICATIONS. Adjust mainshaft end play. See MAINSHAFT END PLAY under ADJUSTMENTS.

12) Install mainshaft 5th gear, seating gear with long pipe and hammer. Install 5th gear coned nut washer, ensuring coned side faces end of mainshaft.

CAUTION: On some 4WD models there is a vibration damper on mainshaft. See Fig. 1. If transmission is equipped with vibration damper on mainshaft, steps 14-17) must be performed before step 13). Install vibration damper before performing step 13).

13) Loctite nut threads on mainshaft. Install 5th gear nut with nut wrench. Lock all synchronizers into engaged position, and place breaker bar on end of mainshaft with spline socket. Position breaker bar against workbench to restrict mainshaft rotation. Tighten 5th gear nut to specification. See TORQUE SPECIFICATIONS.

14) Install thrust washer locating pin in countershaft and install thrust washer. Cone side of thrust washer faces front. Install 5th gear bearings and spacer on countershaft.

15) Install synchronizer sleeve on countershaft 5th gear synchronizer hub. Install 5th gear shift fork in synchronizer sleeve. Install assembled 5th gear synchronizer/shift fork assembly. Tap fork and gear into place with plastic hammer.

16) Align notches in shift lug rail with roll pin holes in shift fork and install roll pins. Install synchronizer springs in synchronizer hub. Pull synchronizer spring back with screwdriver and install synchronizer inserts.

17) Assemble and install 5th clutch gear and synchronizer ring in 5th gear hub. Ensure parts are seated in hub. Install 5th clutch gear snap ring.

18) Remove extension housing bushing, if necessary. Using tapered punch in slot at end of bushing, collapse and remove bushing. Install NEW extension housing bushing using bearing driver. Install NEW extension housing seal.

19) Ensure alignment dowels in transmission case are seated and in position. Apply silicone sealer to mating surfaces and install extension/adapter housing to transmission case. Loctite and install extension/adapter housing bolts. Tighten bolts to specification. See TORQUE SPECIFICATIONS.

NOTE: Use only 10-mm 12-point socket on extension/adapter housing bolts. Any other size will damage bolt head splines.

20) Apply small bead of silicone sealer to mating surface of shift cover assembly. Lubricate synchronizer sleeves with gear oil, and shift fork contact points with petroleum jelly.

21) Shift 1-2 and 3-4 synchronizer sleeves and shift forks into Neutral position. Align and install shift cover assembly. Loctite and install shift cover bolts. Tighten bolts to specification. Install drain and fill plugs and tighten to specification.

TORQUE SPECIFICATIONS
TORQUE SPECIFICATIONS

Application	Ft. Lbs. (N.m)
Countershaft Rear Bearing Plate Bolt	14-19 (19-26)
Drain & Fill Plug	25-35 (34-47)
Drive Shaft Bolt	15 (20)
Extension/Adapter Housing Bolt	30-50 (41-68)
Front Bearing Retainer Bolt	20-25 (27-34)
Mainshaft Rear Bearing Plate Bolt	14-19 (19-26)
PTO Cover Bolt	20-40 (27-54)
Shift Cover Bolt	20-23 (27-31)
Yoke Nut	325 (441)
5th Gear Nut	250-350 (339-475)
	INCH Lbs. (N.m)
Reverse Inhibitor Screw	75-115 (8.5-13)

TECHNICAL SERVICE BULLETINS

3RD GEAR JUMP-OUT, 2ND GEAR CLASH & 1ST/2ND GEAR BLOCK-OUT

Chrysler Corp. Technical Service Bulletin No. 21-12-92 – Mainshaft and bearing plate of NV4500 transmission may move rearward if retaining bolts become loose. See Fig. 2. This may cause 3rd gear jump-out when accelerating, 2nd gear clash and/or 1st and 2nd gear block-out.

Remove transmission rear adapter or extension housing. Examine mainshaft bearing retainer plate bolts. If retainer is not damaged, replace bolts (p/n 4728934). Replace bearing plate (4637784) and synchronizer ring (4723007) as needed if damaged. See TRANSMISSION DISASSEMBLY and TRANSMISSION REASSEMBLY.

Saturn: Coupe, Sedan

IDENTIFICATION

Transaxle can be identified by stamp code on top of bellhousing. See Fig. 1. First number on stamp shows model year. Next group of numbers shows transaxle model, followed by plant code and Julian production date and hour. Always refer to this number when ordering parts.

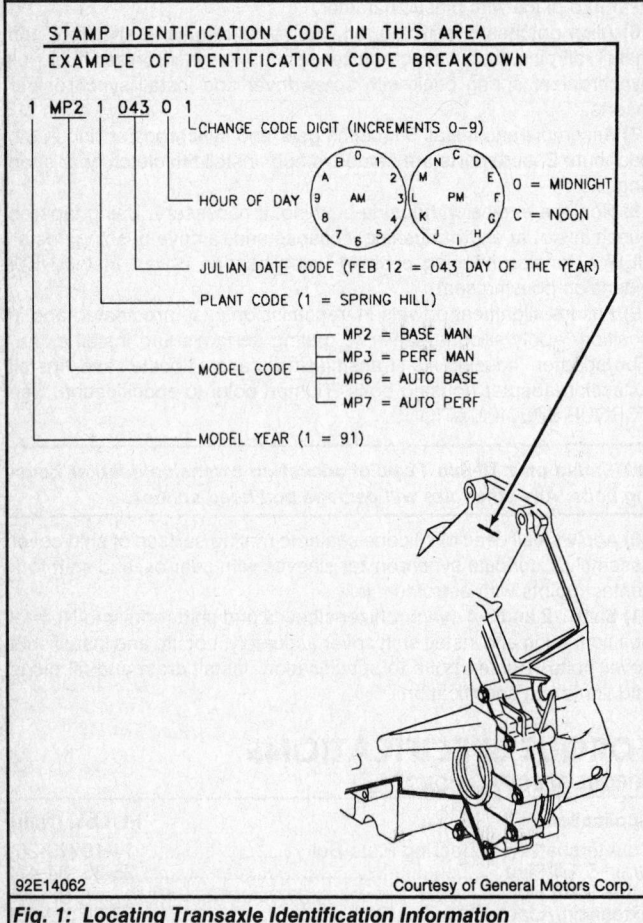

Fig. 1: Locating Transaxle Identification Information

DESCRIPTION

Transaxle is a fully synchronized 5-speed overdrive unit. Differential and transaxle are housed within same aluminum case. Transaxle is equipped with sliding idler gear for reverse gear operation.

LUBRICATION & ADJUSTMENTS

See appropriate MANUAL TRANSMISSION SERVICING article in TRANSMISSION SERVICING.

TROUBLE SHOOTING

See GENERAL TROUBLE SHOOTING article in MANUAL TRANS-MISSIONS.

ON-VEHICLE SERVICE

DRIVE AXLE SHAFTS

See appropriate FWD AXLE SHAFTS article in AXLE SHAFTS & TRANSFER CASES.

AXLE SEALS

Removal – 1) Raise and support vehicle. Remove wheels and drain fluid. Remove ball joint and tie rod cotter pins and nuts. Separate ball joint from steering knuckle with ball joint separating tool. Separate tie rod from steering knuckle with tie rod separating tool.

2) On right axle seal, remove starter bracket to intermediate shaft support bolt. Remove intermediate shaft-to-engine block bolts. See Fig. 2. Slide out intermediate shaft.

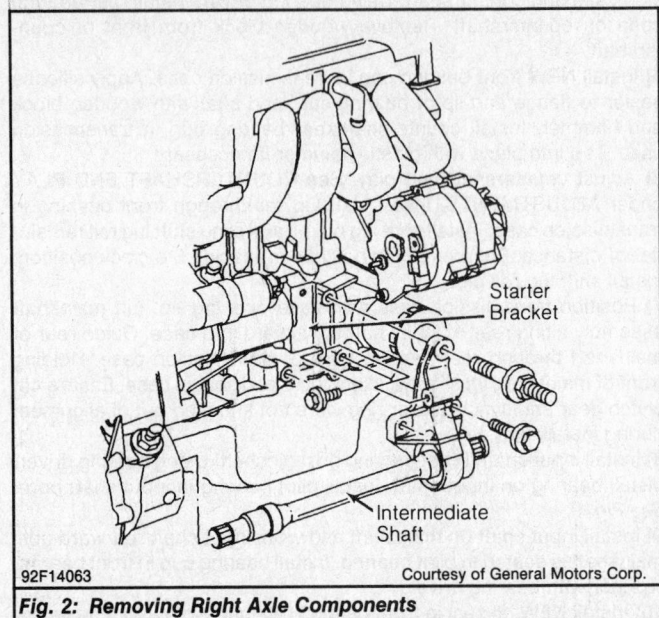

Fig. 2: Removing Right Axle Components

3) On left axle seal, remove left inner splash shield. Remove axle from transaxle using a pry bar or large screwdriver. Remove axle seals with slide hammer equipped with screw attachment. Thread screw through steel body of seal to remove. See Fig. 3.

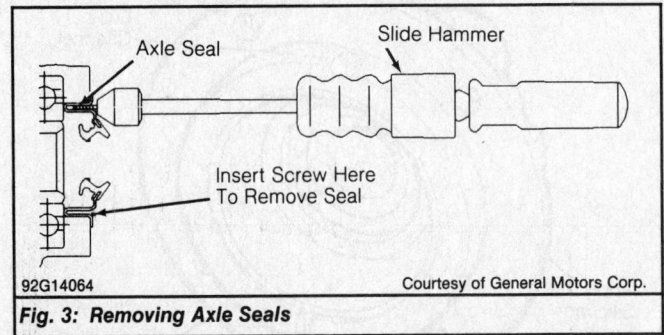

Fig. 3: Removing Axle Seals

CAUTION: Snap ring may be present outside seal; if so, remove prior to seal removal.

Installation – To install, reverse removal procedure. Ensure seal area is clean prior to installation. Tighten bolts and nuts to specification. See TORQUE SPECIFICATIONS. Use new cotter pins after tightening nuts. Fill transaxle with fluid.

SHIFT CONTROL HOUSING

Removal – Remove battery shield and battery. Remove battery tray retaining bolts from fender well. Remove top battery tray bolt and battery tray. Remove back-up light switch connector. Shift transaxle to "N" position. Remove shift control housing bolts and cover. See Fig. 4.

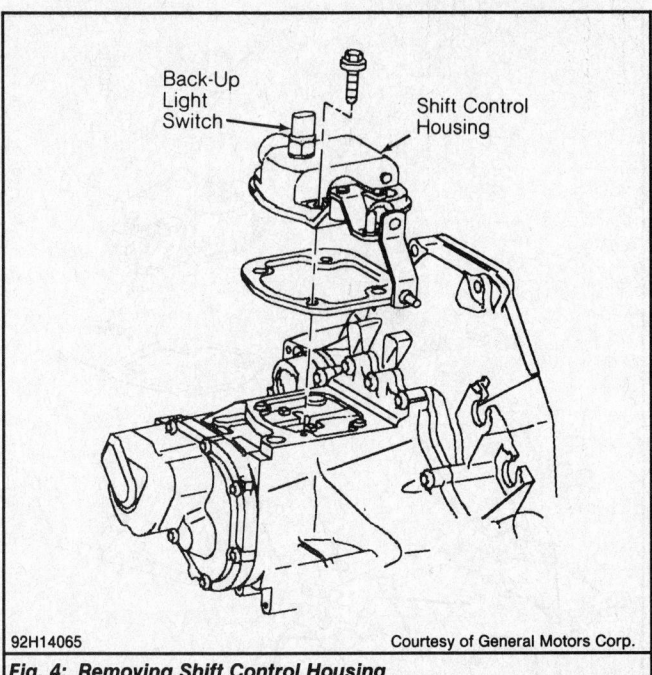

92H14065   Courtesy of General Motors Corp.

Fig. 4: Removing Shift Control Housing

Installation – To install, reverse removal procedure. Install NEW gasket. Tighten bolts to specification. See TORQUE SPECIFICATIONS. Ensure shift control housing is flush with case before tightening bolts.

REAR COVER

Removal – Raise and support vehicle. Remove left front wheel and drain fluid. Remove left inner fender splash shield to gain access to rear cover bolts. Remove rear cover bolts and rear cover.

Installation – To install, reverse removal procedure. Install NEW gasket. Tighten bolts to specification using crisscross pattern. See TORQUE SPECIFICATIONS.

5TH GEAR & 5TH-REVERSE SYNCHRONIZER ASSEMBLY

Removal – **1)** Remove rear cover. See REAR COVER. Shift transaxle into 1st gear. Remove 5th-reverse fork retaining clip. Retaining clip can be either 2 retaining rings or one clip with bridge between 2 rings.
2) Shift 5th-reverse shift fork and lock transaxle into 5th gear. See Fig. 5. Remove input and output shaft nuts. Remove washer, reverse cone and reverse synchronizer ring. Remove 5th-reverse shift fork.
3) Remove 5th-reverse synchronizer assembly, 5th synchronizer ring and 5th gear. Remove 5th driven gear with puller, if necessary. If puller is necessary, remove bearing retainer snap ring to allow shaft and gear assembly to raise up enough to permit puller jaws access under gear.

Installation – **1)** Install 5th input and output shaft gears. Install 5th gear synchronizer ring and spring to 5th gear. Install 5th-reverse shift fork on synchronizer assembly sleeve.
2) Install 5th-reverse synchronizer assembly while sliding shift fork over shift rail. Ensure synchronizer ring tabs align with slots in synchronizer hub. Install new 5th-reverse shift fork retaining clip.
3) Install synchronizer spring on reverse synchronizer ring and install assembly on 5th-reverse synchronizer sleeve. Install reverse cone and washer. Shift transaxle into 1st gear and shift 5th-reverse fork into reverse position. Transaxle is now in 2 gears.
4) Install input and output shaft nuts and tighten to specification. Move all shift forks to neutral position. To complete installation, reverse removal procedure. See REAR COVER.

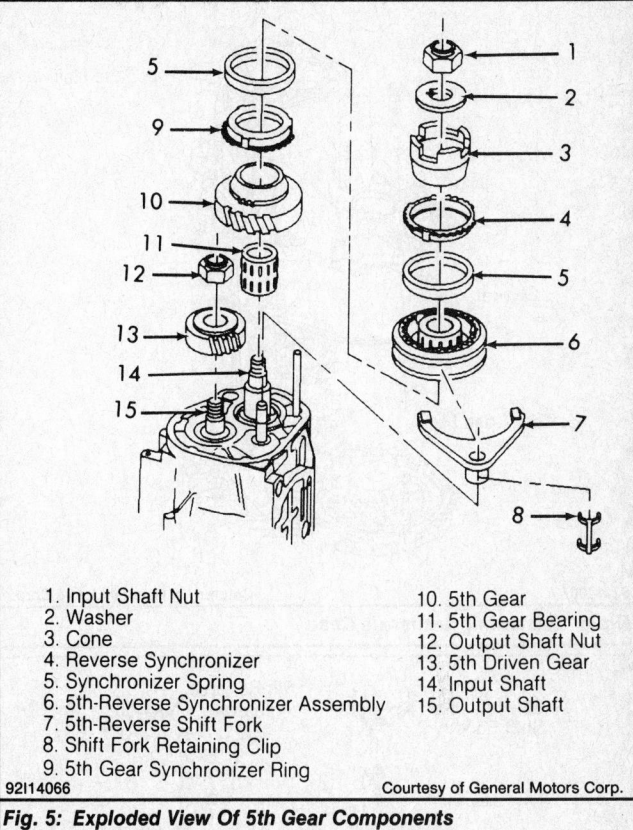

1. Input Shaft Nut
2. Washer
3. Cone
4. Reverse Synchronizer
5. Synchronizer Spring
6. 5th-Reverse Synchronizer Assembly
7. 5th-Reverse Shift Fork
8. Shift Fork Retaining Clip
9. 5th Gear Synchronizer Ring
10. 5th Gear
11. 5th Gear Bearing
12. Output Shaft Nut
13. 5th Driven Gear
14. Input Shaft
15. Output Shaft

92I14066   Courtesy of General Motors Corp.

Fig. 5: Exploded View Of 5th Gear Components

REMOVAL & INSTALLATION

See appropriate MANUAL TRANSMISSION REMOVAL article in TRANSMISSION SERVICING.

TRANSAXLE DISASSEMBLY

1) Remove clutch arm and bearing assembly. Remove shift control housing. Remove rear cover and vehicle speed sensor. Lock transaxle into 2 gears with shift forks. Remove input and output shaft nuts.
2) Remove washer, reverse cone and reverse synchronizer ring. Remove 5th-reverse fork retaining clip. Retaining clip can be 2 retaining rings or one clip with bridge between 2 rings.
3) Remove 5th-reverse shift fork. Remove 5th-reverse synchronizer assembly, 5th synchronizer ring and 5th gear. See Figs. 5 and 18. Remove 5th driven gear with puller, if necessary. If puller is necessary, remove bearing retainer snap ring to allow shaft and gear assembly to raise up enough to permit puller jaws access under gear.
4) Remove case half bolts. Spread input and output shaft bearing snap rings to allow both bearings to fall below top case half. Use pry bar or large screwdriver in pry slots to separate case halves. Remove top case half. See Fig. 6.
5) Remove shift rail retaining clip and remove shift rail. Remove 1-2, 3-4 shift fork and 5th-reverse actuator. See Figs. 7 and 8. Remove oil flow tube. Remove reverse shift lever bolts and reverse idler gear shift lever assembly.
6) Remove reverse idler gear and thrust washer. Remove reverse idler gear shaft. See Fig. 17. Lift input and output shaft assemblies out of bottom case half. Lift differential assembly out of bottom case half. See Fig. 9. Remove case magnet from bottom case half.

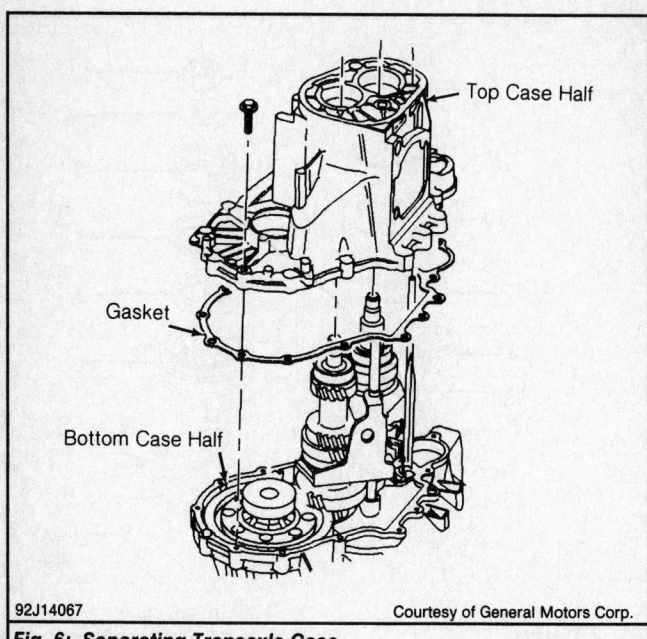

92J14067   Courtesy of General Motors Corp.

Fig. 6: Separating Transaxle Case

Top Case Half

Gasket

Bottom Case Half

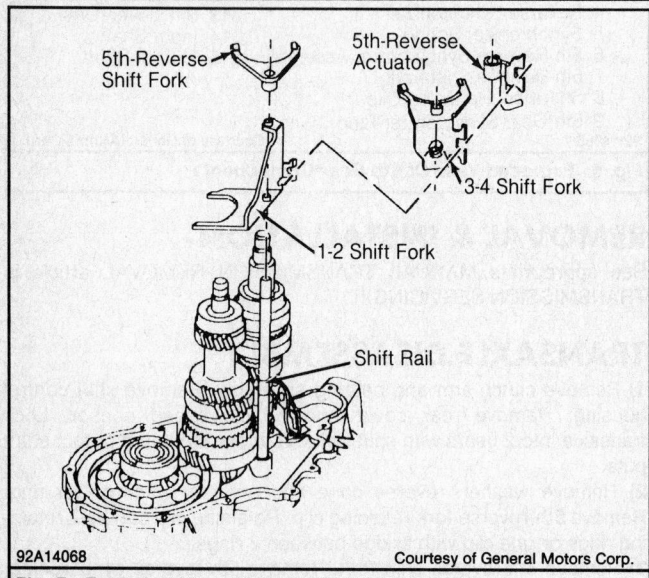

92A14068   Courtesy of General Motors Corp.

Fig. 7: Exploded View Of Shift Fork Components

5th-Reverse Shift Fork

5th-Reverse Actuator

3-4 Shift Fork

1-2 Shift Fork

Shift Rail

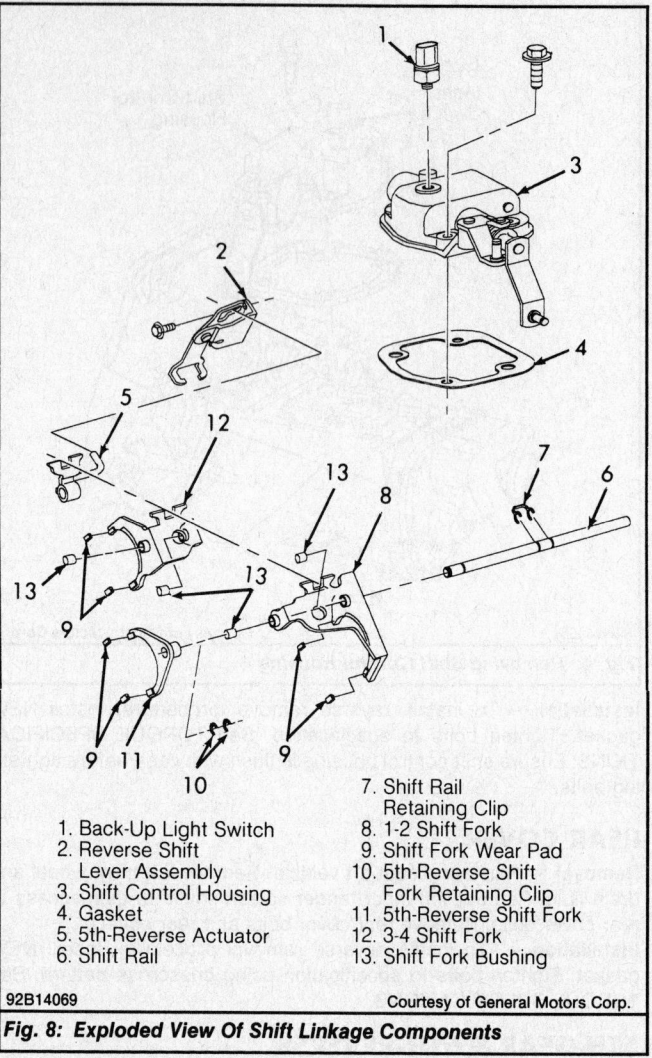

92B14069   Courtesy of General Motors Corp.

Fig. 8: Exploded View Of Shift Linkage Components

1. Back-Up Light Switch
2. Reverse Shift Lever Assembly
3. Shift Control Housing
4. Gasket
5. 5th-Reverse Actuator
6. Shift Rail
7. Shift Rail Retaining Clip
8. 1-2 Shift Fork
9. Shift Fork Wear Pad
10. 5th-Reverse Shift Fork Retaining Clip
11. 5th-Reverse Shift Fork
12. 3-4 Shift Fork
13. Shift Fork Bushing

COMPONENT DISASSEMBLY & REASSEMBLY

DIFFERENTIAL ASSEMBLY

Disassembly – Drive out pinion shaft lock pin from differential housing and slide out pinion shaft. Remove pinion gears by rotating out of housing. *See Fig. 10.* Remove side gears and thrust liner from housing. Remove differential side bearings with 2-jaw puller. Shield bearing to protect against bearing breakage.

Reassembly – 1) Press side bearings onto case. Ensure bearings are seated. Roll thrust liner into differential housing. Hold side gears in position in housing.

2) Install 1st pinion gear on tabbed side of thrust liner and pull thrust liner over to hold pinion gear in place. Place 2nd pinion gear opposite 1st and pull thrust liner out until pinion shaft hole in cover and pinion gears line up.

3) Rotate thrust liner and pinion gears into housing until they line up with pinion shaft bore in housing. Install pinion shaft and drive in pinion shaft roll pin. Ensure pin is flush with case.

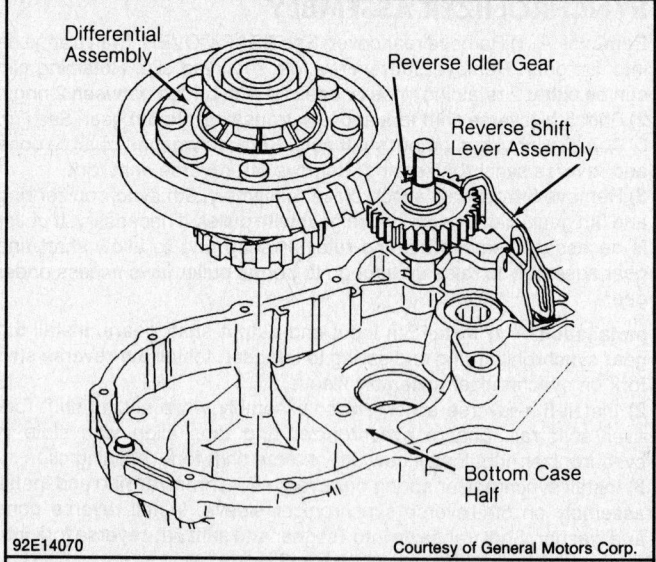

92E14070   Courtesy of General Motors Corp.

Fig. 9: Removing Differential Assembly From Case

Differential Assembly

Reverse Idler Gear

Reverse Shift Lever Assembly

Bottom Case Half

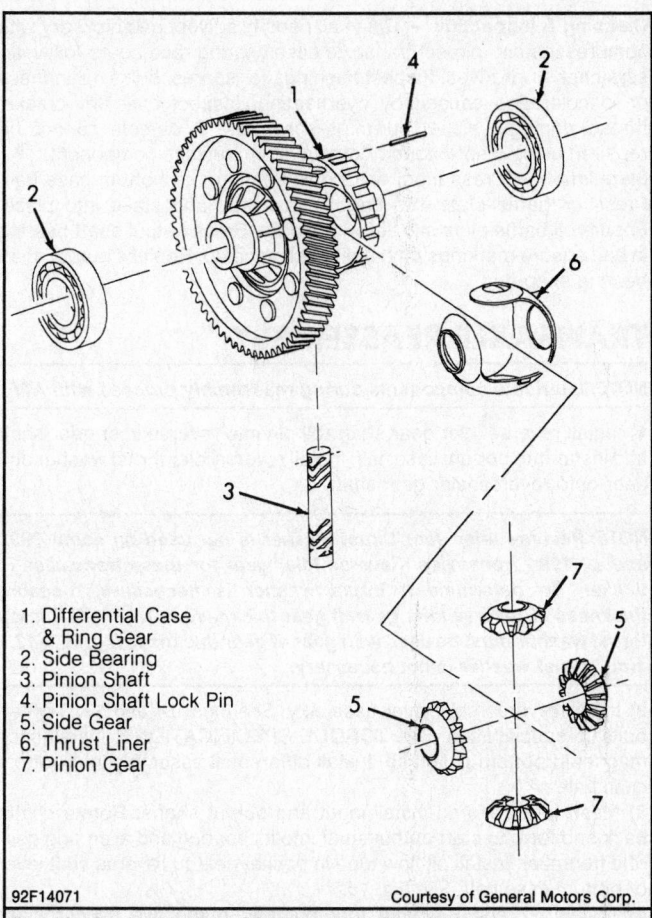

1. Differential Case
   & Ring Gear
2. Side Bearing
3. Pinion Shaft
4. Pinion Shaft Lock Pin
5. Side Gear
6. Thrust Liner
7. Pinion Gear

92F14071   Courtesy of General Motors Corp.

Fig. 10: Exploded View Of Differential Assembly

OUTPUT SHAFT ASSEMBLY

Disassembly – Using a press, remove the following components in order. *See Fig. 18.*
1) Output shaft bearing
2) 3-4 driven gear
3) 2nd driven gear
4) 2nd gear driven bearing
5) 2nd gear synchronizer ring and 1-2 synchronizer sleeve
6) 1-2 synchronizer hub
7) 1st gear synchronizer ring
8) 1st driven gear
9) 1st driven gear bearing
10) 1st driven gear thrust bearing/washer

NOTE: On 1994 transaxles, 1st driven gear thrust bearing has been replaced with a thrust washer.

Cleaning & Inspection – 1) Wash all parts in solvent and air dry. DO NOT spin dry bearings. Check gears and synchronizers for cracks, chipped gear teeth, excessive wear and other damage.
2) Install synchronizer ring on matching gear and measure clearance between ring and gear in 4 places. *See Fig. 11.* Ensure synchronizer minimum clearance is .016" (.40 mm). If clearance is less, replace synchronizer ring.
3) Check bearings and bearing surfaces for nicks, burrs, bent cages and/or wear. Lubricate all bearings and check for rough rotation. Lubricate all components during reassembly process with ATF.

NOTE: Keep all synchronizer parts together with their original sleeve and hub. Soak all new synchronizer rings in ATF for 15 minutes before assembly.

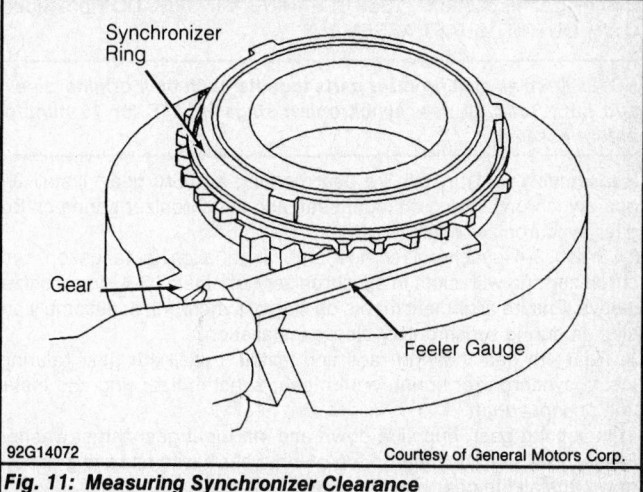

92G14072   Courtesy of General Motors Corp.

Fig. 11: Measuring Synchronizer Clearance

Reassembly – 1) Install 1st driven gear thrust bearing/washer with Black side down. Install 1st driven gear bearing and gear. Install 1st synchronizer ring and spring.
2) Press 1-2 synchronizer hub onto shaft, aligning tangs on synchronizer ring with slots in synchronizer hub. Install 1-2 synchronizer sleeve with gear side down. Ensure alignment marks on side of synchronizer assembly are aligned during synchronizer sleeve installation.
3) Inspect synchronizer sleeve and check movement of 1st and 2nd gears. Install synchronizer spring on 2nd gear synchronizer ring and install unit on output shaft. Heat and install 2nd gear bearing race.
4) Install 2nd gear bearing and 2nd driven gear. Install 3-4 driven gear with larger gear down. Press output shaft bearing on top of output shaft with snap ring groove up.

Measurements – 1) Install output shaft nut and tighten to specification. Measure clearance with feeler gauge between 3-4 driven gear and 2nd driven gear. *See Fig. 12.* Ensure clearance is .008-.014" (.20-.35 mm).
2) Measure clearance with feeler gauge between 1st driven gear and 1st driven gear thrust bearing. Ensure clearance is .008-.019" (.20-.48 mm). If clearances are not within specification, replace thrust bearing or necessary output shaft components.

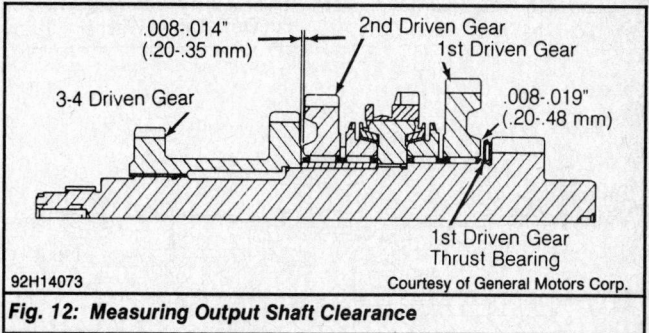

92H14073   Courtesy of General Motors Corp.

Fig. 12: Measuring Output Shaft Clearance

INPUT SHAFT ASSEMBLY

Disassembly – Using a press, remove the following components in order. *See Fig. 18.*
1) 5th gear bearing, bearing race and thrust washer
2) Input shaft bearing
3) 4th gear thrust washer
4) 4th gear
5) 4th gear synchronizer ring and spring
6) 4th gear bearing
7) 4th gear bearing race
8) 3-4 synchronizer sleeve
9) 3-4 synchronizer hub
10) 3rd gear synchronizer ring and spring
11) 3rd gear and 3rd gear bearing

Cleaning & Inspection – See CLEANING & INSPECTION procedure under OUTPUT SHAFT ASSEMBLY.

NOTE: Keep all synchronizer parts together with their original sleeve and hub. Soak all new synchronizer rings in ATF for 15 minutes before assembly.

Reassembly – 1) Install 3rd gear bearing and 3rd gear. Install 3rd gear synchronizer ring on input shaft and synchronizer spring on 3rd gear synchronizer ring.

2) Press 3-4 synchronizer hub onto shaft aligning tangs on synchronizer ring with slots in synchronizer hub. Install 3-4 synchronizer sleeve. Ensure alignment marks on side of synchronizer assembly are aligned during synchronizer sleeve installation.

3) Heat 4th gear bearing race and install. Install 4th gear bearing. Install synchronizer spring on 4th gear synchronizer ring and install unit on input shaft.

4) Install 4th gear, hub side down and 4th input gear thrust washer. Press input shaft bearing on top of input shaft with snap ring groove down. Install 5th gear bearing race and thrust washer.

Measurements – 1) Install 5th gear bearing, 5th gear, 5th-reverse synchronizer assembly, reverse cone and washer. Install input shaft nut and tighten to specification. Measure clearance with feeler gauge between 5th gear and 5th gear thrust washer. *See Fig. 13.* Ensure clearance is .008-.014" (.20-.35 mm).

2) Using a feeler gauge, measure clearance between 4th gear and 4th gear thrust washer. Ensure clearance is .008-.014" (.20-.35 mm). Using a feeler gauge, measure clearance between 3rd gear and input shaft. Ensure clearance is .008-.014" (.20-.35 mm). If clearances are not within specification replace thrust washer or necessary input shaft components.

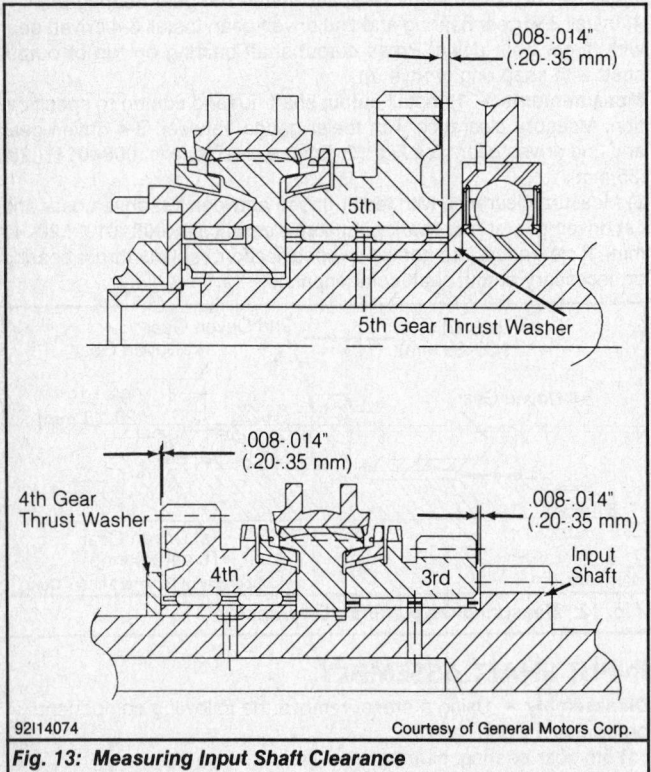

Fig. 13: Measuring Input Shaft Clearance

TRANSAXLE CASE

Removal – Remove output shaft bearing snap ring and using internal puller, remove output shaft bearing. Remove staking at oil baffle plate. Thread rear cover bolt into oil baffle plate and pull plate out. *See Fig. 17.* Press input shaft quill bearing from bottom case half.

Cleaning & Inspection – Clean all parts in solvent and blow dry with compressed air. Inspect transaxle case bearing race bores for wear, scratches or grooves. Inspect bushings for scores, burrs, roundness or discoloration caused by overheating. Inspect case for cracks, thread damage, nicks, burrs or scratches. If defects cannot be repaired using a soft stone or crocus cloth, replace component.

Installation – Press input shaft quill bearing into bottom case half. Press oil baffle plate into bottom case half and stake into place. Ensure oil baffle plate sits flat within bore. Press output shaft bearing in and ensure markings on bearing side face up. Replace output shaft bearing snap ring.

TRANSAXLE REASSEMBLY

NOTE: Lubricate components during reassembly process with ATF.

1) Install reverse idler gear shaft roll pin into reverse idler gear shaft and install into bottom case half. Install reverse idler thrust washer and gear onto reverse idler gear shaft.

NOTE: Reverse idler gear thrust washer is not used on some 1993 and all 1994 transaxles. Reverse idler gear for these transaxles is thicker. To determine if thrust washer is necessary, measure thickness of reverse idler gear. If gear thickness is 1.38" (35.0 mm), thrust washer must be used with gear. If gear thickness is 1.66" (42.2 mm), thrust washer is not necessary.

2) Install reverse shift lever assembly. *See Figs. 14 and 17.* Tighten bolts to specification. See TORQUE SPECIFICATIONS. Install case magnet in bottom case half. Install differential assembly into bottom case half.

3) Mesh together and install input and output shafts. Rotate shafts back and forth to start output shaft into its bearing and align ring gear of differential. Install oil flow tube in pocket next to reverse shift lever of bottom case half. *See Fig. 15.*

4) Install 1-2 and 3-4 shift fork on their respective synchronizer sleeves. Install 5th-reverse actuator into slot of reverse shift lever. Align forks and actuator and install shift rail. Ensure shift rail retaining groove is up. Install 5th-reverse actuator retaining clip.

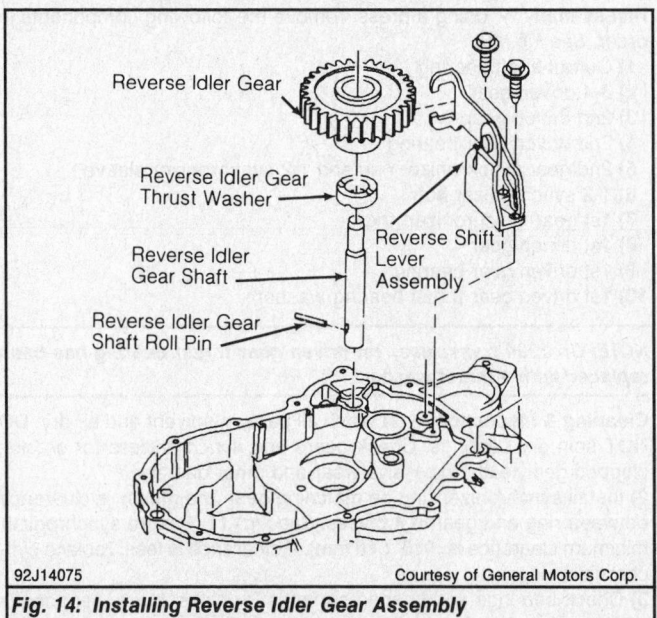

Fig. 14: Installing Reverse Idler Gear Assembly

NOTE: Ensure 5th-reverse actuator and shift forks are aligned properly to expose retaining clip grooves. Attempting to install prior to alignment will bend retaining clip, requiring replacement.

Oil Flow Tube
92A14076
Courtesy of General Motors Corp.

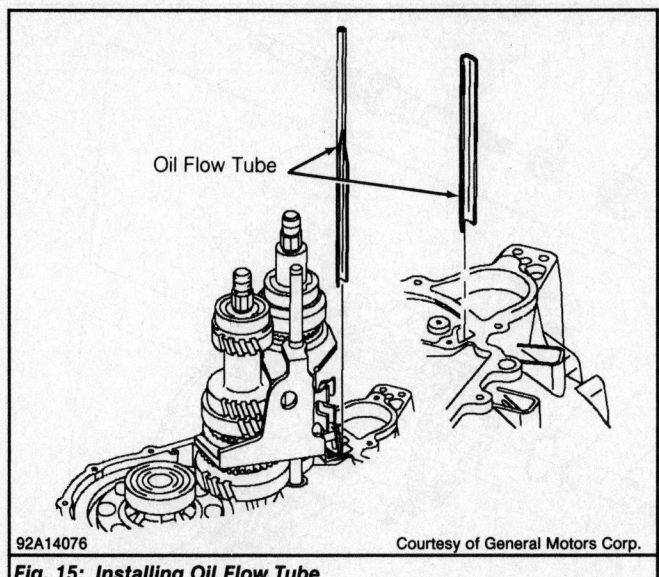

Fig. 15: Installing Oil Flow Tube

5) Apply anaerobic sealer to both sides of transaxle case gasket. Place gasket over dowel pins of bottom case half and lower top case half over gear train.

NOTE: On 1993 transaxles built after and including VIN PZ160920, and all 1994 transaxles, transaxle case gasket has been eliminated. Apply a bead of Loctite 515 sealant .04-.12" (1-3 mm) wide, down center of mating surface on bottom case half. Sealant must go completely around 5 bolt holes near differential assembly.

12
3
1
14
15
5
10
7
8
6
9
2
11
4
13
92B14077
Courtesy of General Motors Corp.

Fig. 16: Transaxle Case Bolt Tightening Sequence

6) Spread input and output shaft bearing snap rings to allow snap rings to slide over bearings. Seat top case half and install case half bolts. Tighten bolts in sequence to specification. *See Fig. 16.* Ensure both shafts rotate freely during tightening process.

7) Measure differential end play between side bearing and case using Differential End Play Tool (SA9112T). Install differential selective shim to set end play to zero. Ensure shim is positioned into groove.

8) Apply anaerobic sealer to top case half axle seal bore and drive in axle seal. Install snap ring, if equipped. Install 5th driven and 5th gear. Install 5th gear synchronizer ring and spring to 5th gear. *See Figs. 5 and 18.* Install 5th-reverse shift fork on synchronizer assembly sleeve.

1. Clutch Fork Retainer
2. Clutch Fork
3. Clutch Fork Stabilizer
4. Axle Seal
5. Vehicle Speed Sensor
6. Dowel Pin
7. Oil Baffle Plate
8. Output Shaft Bearing
9. Snap Ring
10. Reverse Idler Gear Shaft Roll Pin
11. Reverse Idler Gear Shaft
12. Reverse Idler Thrust Washer
13. Reverse Idler Gear
14. Oil Flow Tube
15. Bottom Case Half
16. Quill Bearing

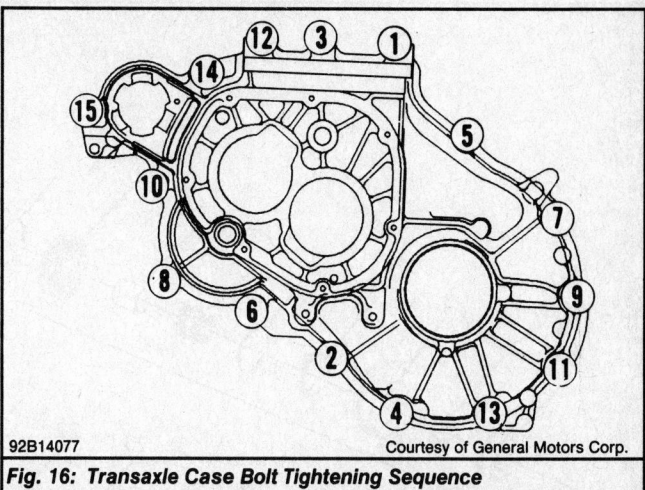

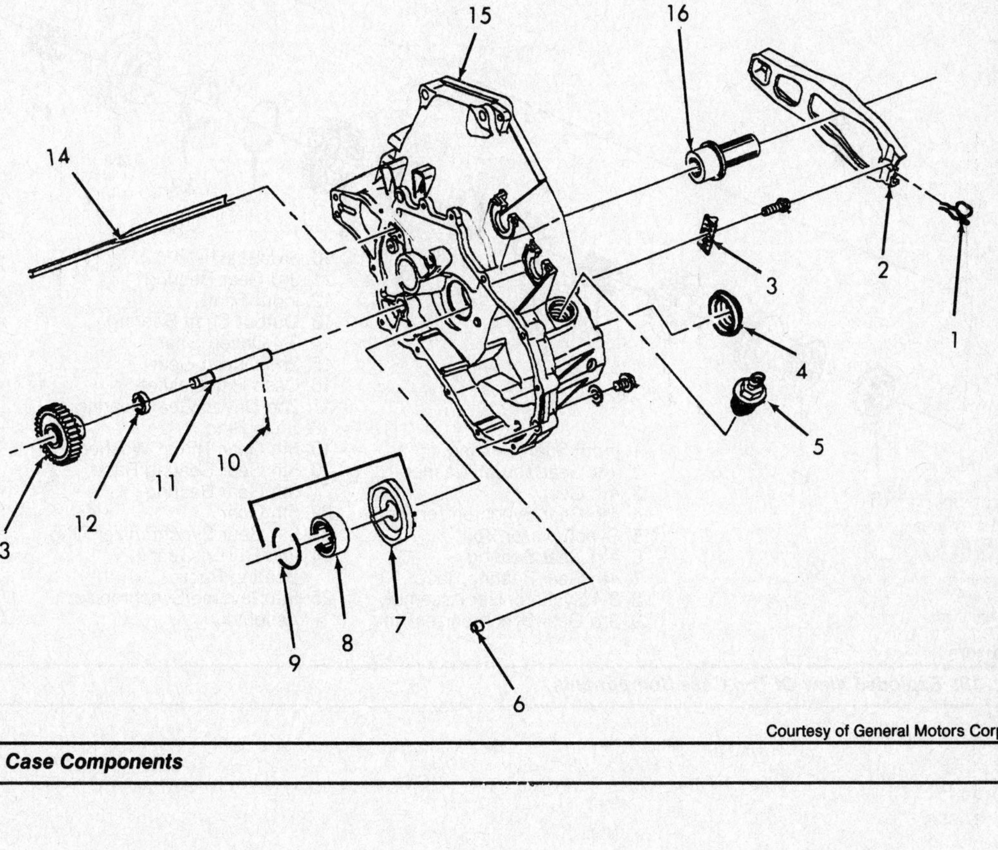

15
16
14
3
2
1
4
5
10
11
12
13
7
8
9
6
92C14078
Courtesy of General Motors Corp.

Fig. 17: Exploded View Of Bottom Case Components

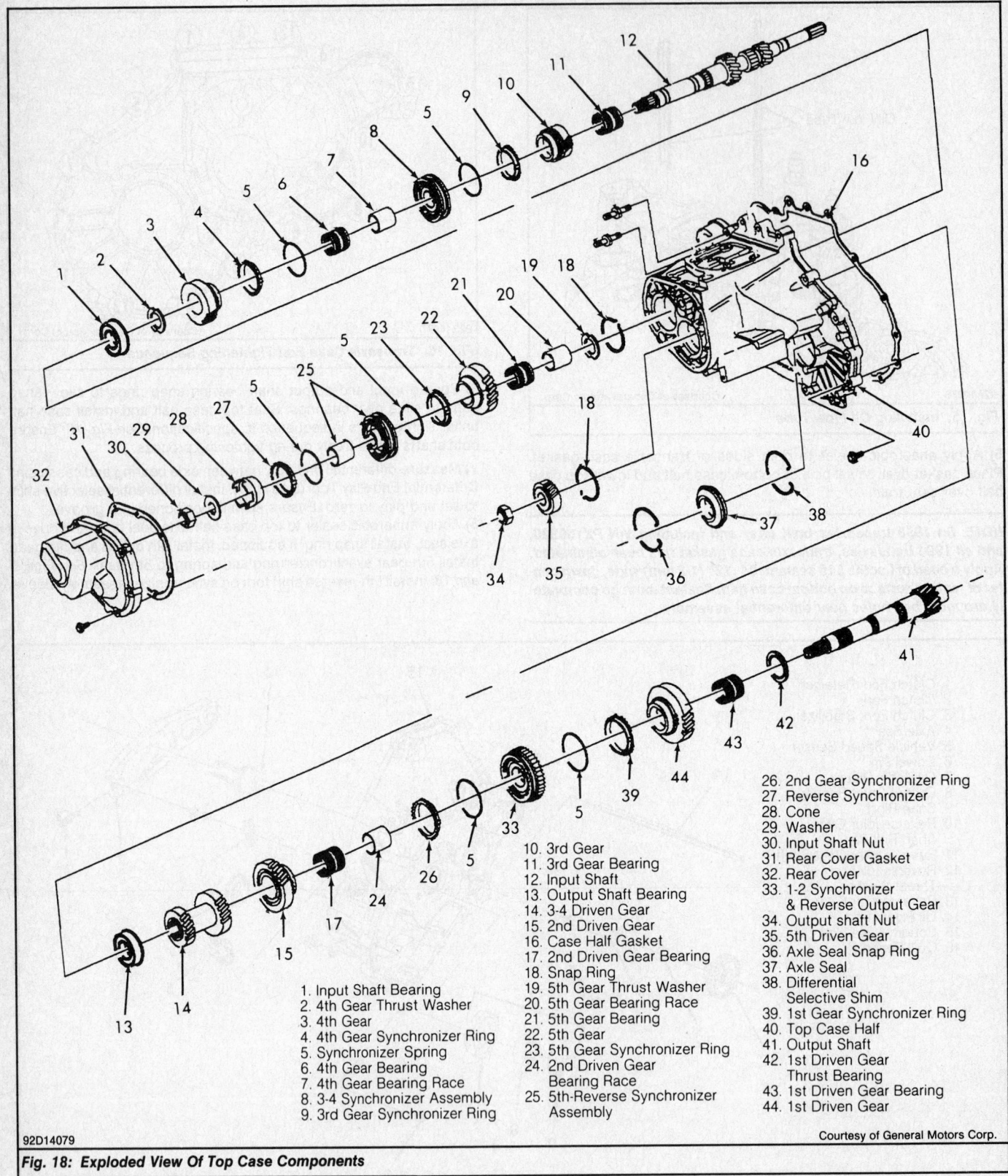

1. Input Shaft Bearing
2. 4th Gear Thrust Washer
3. 4th Gear
4. 4th Gear Synchronizer Ring
5. Synchronizer Spring
6. 4th Gear Bearing
7. 4th Gear Bearing Race
8. 3-4 Synchronizer Assembly
9. 3rd Gear Synchronizer Ring
10. 3rd Gear
11. 3rd Gear Bearing
12. Input Shaft
13. Output Shaft Bearing
14. 3-4 Driven Gear
15. 2nd Driven Gear
16. Case Half Gasket
17. 2nd Driven Gear Bearing
18. Snap Ring
19. 5th Gear Thrust Washer
20. 5th Gear Bearing Race
21. 5th Gear Bearing
22. 5th Gear
23. 5th Gear Synchronizer Ring
24. 2nd Driven Gear Bearing Race
25. 5th-Reverse Synchronizer Assembly
26. 2nd Gear Synchronizer Ring
27. Reverse Synchronizer
28. Cone
29. Washer
30. Input Shaft Nut
31. Rear Cover Gasket
32. Rear Cover
33. 1-2 Synchronizer & Reverse Output Gear
34. Output shaft Nut
35. 5th Driven Gear
36. Axle Seal Snap Ring
37. Axle Seal
38. Differential Selective Shim
39. 1st Gear Synchronizer Ring
40. Top Case Half
41. Output Shaft
42. 1st Driven Gear Thrust Bearing
43. 1st Driven Gear Bearing
44. 1st Driven Gear

Courtesy of General Motors Corp.

Fig. 18: Exploded View Of Top Case Components

92D14079

9) Install 5th-reverse synchronizer assembly while sliding shift fork over shift rail. Ensure synchronizer ring tabs align with slots in synchronizer hub. Install new 5th-reverse shift fork retaining clip.

10) Install synchronizer spring on reverse synchronizer ring to form assembly. Install assembly on 5th-reverse synchronizer sleeve. Install reverse cone and thrust washer. Shift transaxle into 1st gear and shift 5th-reverse shift fork into reverse position. Transaxle is now in 2 gears.

11) Install input and output shaft nuts and tighten to specification. See TORQUE SPECIFICATIONS. Move all shift forks to neutral position. Install rear cover gasket and cover. Install bolts and tighten to specification using crisscross pattern.

12) Install shift control housing gasket and shift control housing assembly on case. Install bolts and tighten to specification. See TORQUE SPECIFICATIONS. Ensure shift control housing is flush with case before tightening bolts.

13) Install vehicle speed sensor and tighten to specification. Apply anaerobic sealer to bottom case half axle seal bore and drive in axle seal. Install snap ring, if equipped. Install drain plug and tighten to specification. See TORQUE SPECIFICATIONS. Install clutch arm and bearing assembly. Apply light film of grease on input shaft spline.

TORQUE SPECIFICATIONS
TORQUE SPECIFICATIONS

Application	Ft. Lbs. (N.m)
Ball Joint Nut	55 (75)
Drain Plug	
With Aluminum Washer	40 (54)
With Rubber Seal	22 (30)
Input Shaft Nut	110 (150)
Intermediate Shaft Support Bolt	40 (54)
Output Shaft Nut	110 (150)
Shift Control Housing Bolt	21 (28)
Starter Bracket Bolt	22 (30)
Tie Rod End Nut	33 (45)
Transaxle Case Bolt	21 (28)
Vehicle Speed Sensor	19 (26)
Wheel Lug Nut	103 (140)

	INCH Lbs. (N.m)
Rear Cover Bolt	107 (12)
Reverse Shift Lever Assembly Bolt	124 (14)

MANUAL TRANSMISSIONS
ZF S5-42 5-Speed

Ford Motor Co: "F" Series

IDENTIFICATION

Identification label is located on left side of case. Label contains information for transmission ratio, part number, oil grade and capacity.

DESCRIPTION

Model number for the ZF transmission is S5-42. The ZF S5-42 has an aluminum case and is designed for Power Take-Off (PTO) capability. The "S" designates a synchronized transmission, "5" designates number of forward gears and "42" is the approximate maximum input torque capacity in tens of ft. lbs.

LUBRICATION & ADJUSTMENTS

See appropriate MANUAL TRANSMISSION SERVICING article in TRANSMISSION SERVICING.

TROUBLE SHOOTING

See GENERAL TROUBLE SHOOTING article in MANUAL TRANSMISSIONS.

ON-VEHICLE SERVICE

REAR OIL SEAL

Removal – 1) Disconnect drive shaft from output flange. On 4WD vehicles, remove transfer case. On "F" Series Super Duty vehicles, remove transmission-mounted parking brake. On 2WD vehicles, remove output flange from output end of mainshaft.

2) On all models, insert seal remover over output shaft and tighten into rear seal. Assemble forcing screw into seal remover. Turn forcing screw to remove seal.

Installation – 1) Position output shaft seal on output seal installer, and position seal over output end of mainshaft. Using soft hammer, gently tap seal until it seats properly.

2) On 4WD vehicles, install transfer case. On "F" Series Super Duty vehicles, install transmission mounted parking brake. On 2WD vehicles, install output shaft flange on output end of mainshaft. Connect driveshaft.

REMOVAL & INSTALLATION

See appropriate MANUAL TRANSMISSION REMOVAL article in TRANSMISSION SERVICING.

TRANSMISSION DISASSEMBLY

1) Place transmission in vertical position with front case pointing downward on holding fixture. Attach companion flange holding tool, and loosen hex nut holding output flange to mainshaft.

2) Remove PTO equipment (if equipped). Remove shift housing assembly. Remove complete gearshift lever and tower as an assembly.

3) Remove interlock plate and compression spring, which serves as a reverse gear interlock. Ensure parts do not fall into transmission.

WARNING: Sealing cap is under spring pressure. Always wear eye protection when performing the following procedure.

---

4) Remove detent bolt sealing cap. Hold drift punch at an angle so it is off center on the cap. Drive cap inward until spring pressure against its underside forces the cap out of its hole. Repeat procedure for 2 other detent bolt sealing caps in front case. See Fig. 1.

5) Remove springs from sealing cap holes. Drive out sealing caps for reverse idler shaft cap screws (2). Remove reverse idler shaft cap screws. See Fig. 2. Remove back-up light switch, located near identification label.

6) Remove 2 dowel pins from the 2 upper corners of rear case-to-front case mating surfaces. Drive out dowel pins towards rear of transmission. Remove remaining hex bolts from rear case.

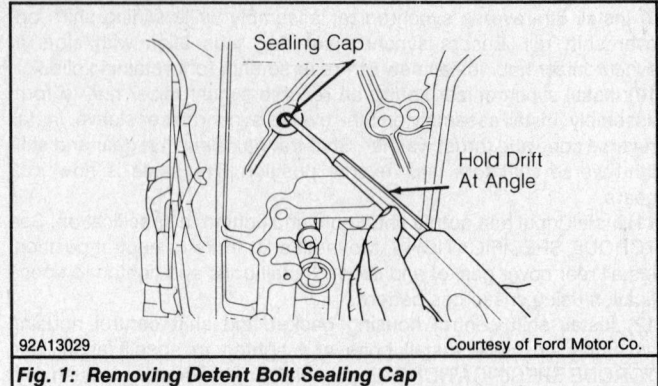

Fig. 1: Removing Detent Bolt Sealing Cap

7) Lift front case off rear case. Ensure central shift rail is not lifted off together with front case. DO NOT pry or force housings apart. Remove central shift rail and shift finger assembly. See Fig. 3. Lift the shaft out of the reverse idler gear, and remove gear and 2 caged roller bearings from rear case.

8) Remove 3 cap screws retaining shift interlock to rear case. With transmission in vertical position, use Nylon Lifting Sling (D87L-1000-A) to strap Gear Pack Holding Fixture (T87T-7025-HH) to mainshaft and output shaft assemblies. Pass sling over shift rails. See Fig. 4.

9) Carefully rotate transmission to horizontal position. Remove flange from output shaft. Pull gear pack, shift rails and their holding fixtures forward to dislodge them from rear case.

10) Remove speedometer drive gear from mainshaft (if equipped). Remove sling from shift rails, gear pack and holding fixture. Turn gearshift rails approximately 45 degrees to release from shift hubs.

11) Using support tool, lift gearshift rails, forks and interlocks off the mainshaft. Remove interlock from shift rails. Mark each shift fork, shift rail, and position in the holding fixture for reassembly. Lift shift rails from support tool. Separate input shaft from mainshaft.

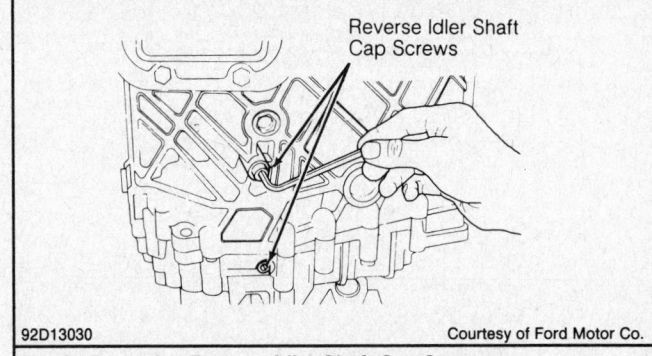

Fig. 2: Removing Reverse Idler Shaft Cap Screws

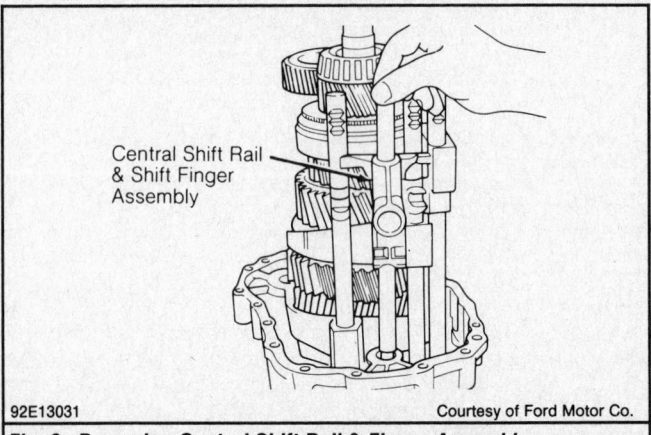

Fig. 3: Removing Central Shift Rail & Finger Assembly

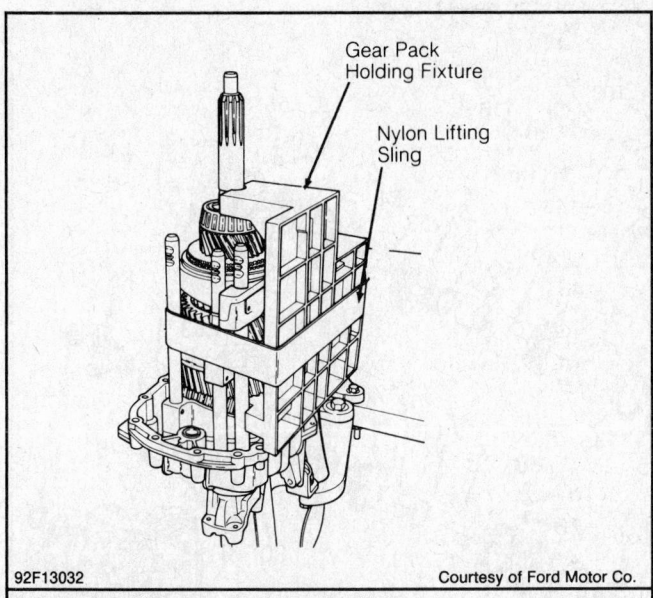

92F13032   Courtesy of Ford Motor Co.

Fig. 4: Installing Gear Pack Holding Fixture

COMPONENT DISASSEMBLY & REASSEMBLY

MAINSHAFT

Disassembly – 1) Clamp output end of mainshaft in vise. Remove 4th synchronizer ring from 3rd-4th synchronizer assembly. *See Fig. 6.* Pull bearing from mainshaft.

2) Wrap synchronizer assembly with shop towel to catch compression springs, pressure pieces and balls that will be released when 3rd-4th gear synchronizer sleeves are removed from mainshaft.

3) Remove snap ring retaining 3rd-4th synchronizer body to mainshaft. Pull synchronizer body from main shaft. Remove synchronizer ring from mainshaft 3rd gear.

4) Remove 3rd gear and 3rd gear caged needle bearings from mainshaft. Lift 1st-2nd gear synchronizer sleeve up. Pull 1st-2nd synchronizer sleeve, 2nd gear, thrust washer and 3rd gear bearing inner race from mainshaft. *See Fig. 5.*

5) Remove snap ring retaining 1st-2nd synchronizer body to mainshaft. Reposition mainshaft in vise so output end of shaft is now facing up. On 4WD and "F" Series Super Duty vehicles, remove snap ring retaining taper roller bearing inner race. Use bearing puller to pull bearing assembly.

6) Remove 5th gear and 5th gear caged needle bearing from mainshaft. Remove 5th synchronizer and 5th-reverse synchronizer body from reverse gear. Remove reverse gear from mainshaft.

7) Remove reverse gear caged needle bearings from mainshaft. With a press, press out 1st gear and 1st-2nd gear synchronizer body from mainshaft. Remove 1st gear caged needle bearing from mainshaft.

NOTE: Synchronizer rings have a molybdenum coating on grooved surface which provides a very hard surface. This coating causes different wear patterns on the friction taper cone of gear. To determine if replacement is required, see CLEANING & INSPECTION.

Cleaning & Inspection – 1) Before installing original synchronizer ring and synchronizer body, check internal surface for contact pattern. Contact pattern should be same on entire internal circumference of ring.

2) Check synchronizer ring clearance. Position synchronizer ring on synchronizer body, and measure clearance at 2 opposite points. *See Fig. 7.* If clearance is less than .024" (.6 mm) for 1st-2nd, 3rd-4th and 5th synchronizer assemblies and .016" (.4 mm) for reverse synchronizer assemblies, replace synchronizer ring, synchronizer body or both (if required) to bring clearance within specification.

3) Inspect friction taper cone on gears and check for wear patterns. Sporadic slightly burnt patches on otherwise evenly smoothed circumference is acceptable. Patches will appear Black and will vary in degree and surface area. Signs of excessive heat will appear burnt to a Red-Blue color, mainly on edges of the cone. Replace gears showing excessive burn spots. Selector teeth may also be damaged.

Reassembly – 1) Clamp input end of mainshaft in vise. Install caged needle bearings onto mainshaft. Install reverse gear over needle bearings on mainshaft. Clutching teeth on reverse gear must face upwards.

2) Position reverse gear synchronizer ring on taper of reverse gear. Heat 5th-reverse synchronizer body to 320°F (160°C). DO NOT heat for more than 15 minutes.

3) Position synchronizer body on mainshaft splines with deeper hub facing down and short lugs on synchronizing ring engaged in gaps in synchronizer body. Push or lightly tap synchronizer body down until it stops.

4) Install snap rings on mainshaft next to 5th-reverse synchronizer body. Clearance between snap ring and synchronizer body should not be greater than .004" (.1 mm). Check reverse gear end play.

5) Reverse gear end play must be .006-.014" (.15-.35 mm). With grooves on 5th-reverse synchronizer sleeve facing up, position synchronizer sleeve over synchronizer body. Align areas of synchronizer sleeve where teeth are cut away with lugs on synchronizer rings and gaps on synchronizer body. Insert 3 compression springs with pressure pieces in recesses of synchronizer body.

6) Push in balls with screwdriver and slide pressure piece so it rests against ball. *See Fig. 8.* Install 5th gear synchronizer ring with short lugs over gaps in 5th-reverse synchronizer body.

7) Push 5th gear synchronizer ring downwards while pulling the synchronizer sleeve into the center position. Place both 5th gear caged needle bearings on mainshaft and install 5th gear.

8) Heat inner race of mainshaft rear taper roller bearing to 320°F (160°C). Drive bearing in until it seats against its stop on the mainshaft. Check 5th gear end play. End play must be .006-.014" (.15-.35 mm). On 4WD and "F" Super Duty vehicles, fit an additional retaining ring in the annular groove adjacent to the taper roller bearing inner race. End play is .0-.004" (.006-.014 mm).

9) Turn mainshaft over and clamp it at the output end. Install 1st gear needle bearings. Install 1st gear over needle bearings on mainshaft with taper facing up. Install 1st gear synchronizer ring on taper side of 1st gear.

10) Heat 1st-2nd synchronizer body to 320°F (160°C). DO NOT heat for more than 15 minutes. Short lugs on synchronizer ring must engage in gaps on synchronizer body. When proper installation is made, the word ENGINE will be visible on the synchronizer body.

11) Install NEW snap ring. Clearance between snap ring and synchronizer body should not be greater than .004" (.1 mm). The 1st gear end play must be .006-.014" (.15-.35 mm).

12) Position synchronizer sleeve over synchronizer body with tapered collar facing down (toward output end of mainshaft). Align areas of synchronizer sleeve where teeth are cut away with lugs on synchronizer rings and gaps on synchronizer body.

13) Insert 3 compression springs with pressure pieces in the recesses of synchronizer body. Raise pressure pieces with screwdriver. Push in balls with screwdriver and slide pressure piece so it rests against ball. *See Fig. 9.* Install 2nd gear synchronizer rings with short lugs positioned over the gaps in the 1st-2nd synchronizer body.

14) Install 2nd gear needle bearings. Install 2nd gear over needle bearings with taper of 2nd gear facing down on the mainshaft. Heat thrust washer to 320°F (160°C) and seat washer against its stop on the shaft.

15) Heat 3rd gear bearing inner race to 320°F (160°C) and seat race against its stop on the shaft. DO NOT heat for more than 15 minutes. Check 2nd gear end play. End play must be .006-.017 (.15-.45 mm). Install 3rd gear caged needle bearings over bearing inner race after race has fully cooled down.

16) Install 3rd gear over needle bearing on mainshaft with taper facing up. Place 3rd gear synchronizer ring on taper of 3rd gear. Heat 3rd-4th synchronizer body to 320°F (160°C). Position body over mainshaft splines. Gaps must line up with lugs on 3rd gear synchronizer ring. Install NEW snap ring on mainshaft.

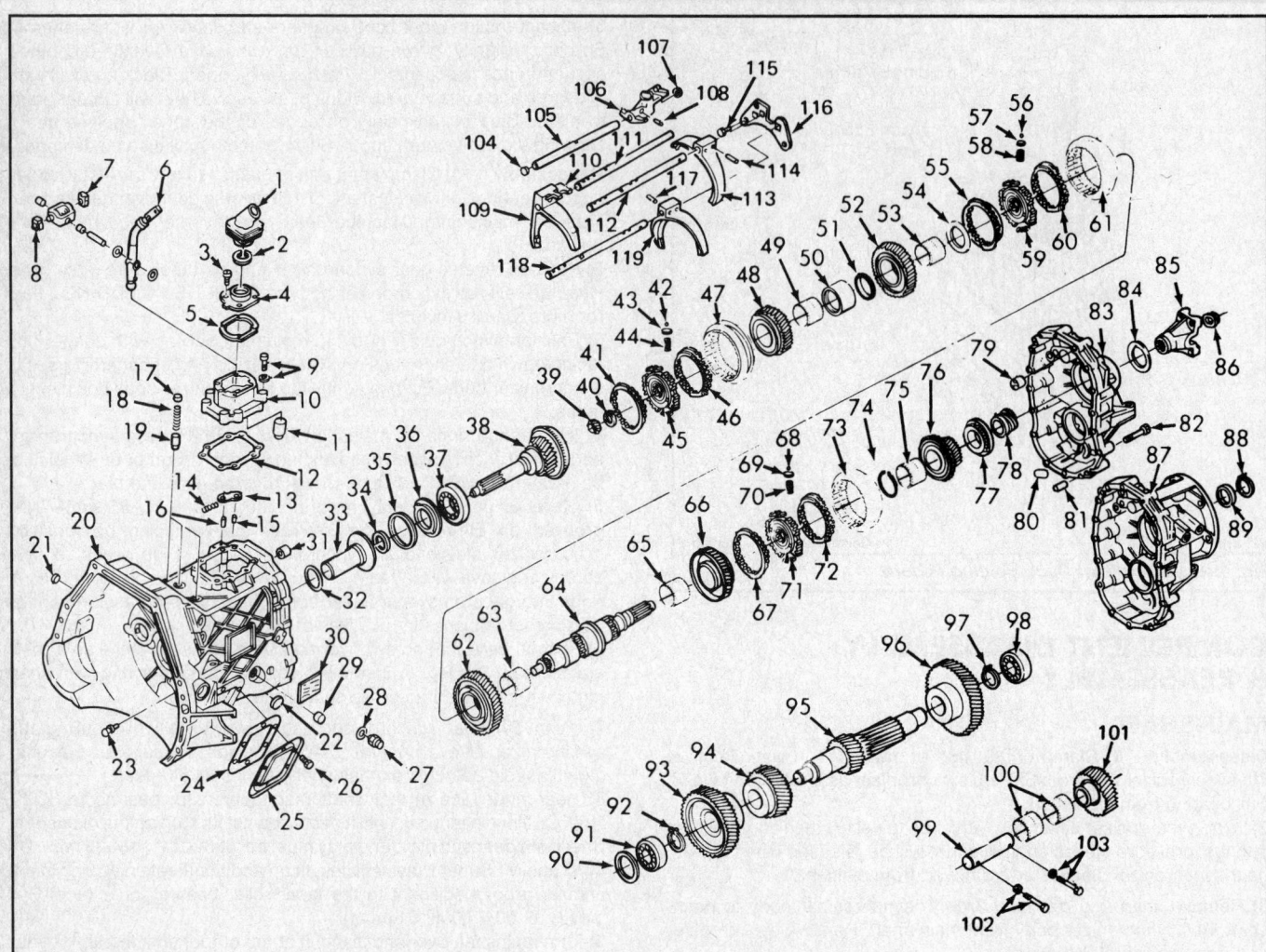

1. Shift Lever Boot	31. Central Shift Rail Bearing	61. 1st-2nd Synchronizer Sleeve	91. Front Countershaft Bearing
2. Snap Ring	32. "O" Ring	62. 1st Gear	92. Snap Ring
3. Cap Screw	33. Quill	63. Needle Bearings	93. Countershaft Drive Gear
4. Shift Tower	34. Oil Seal	64. Mainshaft	94. Countershaft 3rd Gear
5. Gasket	35. Shim	65. Caged Needle Bearings	95. Countershaft
6. Lower Shift Lever	36. Baffle	66. Reverse Gear	96. Countershaft 5th Gear
7. Guide Piece	37. Input Shaft Bearing	67. Reverse Gear Synchronizer Ring	97. Snap Ring
8. Guide Piece	38. Input Shaft	68. Ball	98. Countershaft Rear Bearing
9. Hex Bolts	39. Mainshaft Bearing	69. Pressure Piece	99. Reverse Idler Shaft
10. Shift Housing	40. Snap Ring	70. Spring	100. Caged Needle Bearings
11. Shift Detent	41. 4th Gear Synchronizer Ring	71. 5th-Reverse Synchronizer Body	101. Reverse Idler Gear
12. Gasket	42. Ball	72. 5th Gear Synchronizer Ring	102. Screw & Sealing Ring
13. 5th-Reverse Interlock	43. Pressure Piece	73. 5th-Reverse Synchronizer Sleeve	103. Screw & Sealing Ring
14. Interlock Spring	44. Spring	74. Snap Ring	104. Plug
15. Interlock Roll Pin	45. 3rd-4th Synchronizer Body	75. Caged Needle Bearings	105. Central Shift Rail
16. Interlock Roll Pin	46. 3rd Gear Synchronizer Ring	76. 5th Gear	106. Shift Finger
17. Sealing Cap	47. 3rd-4th Synchronizer Sleeve	77. Mainshaft Bearing	107. Plug
18. Spring	48. 3rd Gear	78. Speedometer Drive Gear (2WD)	108. Roll Pin
19. Shift Rail Detent	49. Caged Needle Bearings	79. Central Shift Rail Bearing	109. Roll Pin
20. Front Case	50. Bearing Race	80. Magnet	110. Shift Fork
21. Sealing Cap	51. Thrust Washer	81. Dowel	111. Shift Rail
22. Drain Plug	52. 2nd Gear	82. Bolt	112. Shift Rail
23. Bolt	53. Caged Needle Bearings	83. Rear Case (2WD)	113. Shift Fork
24. Gasket	54. Snap Ring	84. Rear Oil Seal (2WD)	114. Roll Pin
25. PTO Cover	55. 2nd. Gear Synchronizer Ring	85. Output Yoke (2WD)	115. Bolt
26. Bolt	56. Ball	86. Lock Nut (2WD)	116. Interlock Plate
27. Back-Up Light Switch	57. Pressure Piece	87. Rear Case (4WD)	117. Roll Pin
28. Sealing Ring	58. Spring	88. Snap Ring (4WD)	118. Shift Rail
29. Filler Plug	59. 1st-2nd Synchronizer Body	89. Oil Seal (4WD)	119. Shift Fork
30. Identification Plate	60. 1st Gear Synchronizer Ring	90. Shim	

92G13033

Courtesy of Ford Motor Co.

Fig. 5: Exploded View Of Transmission Case & Components

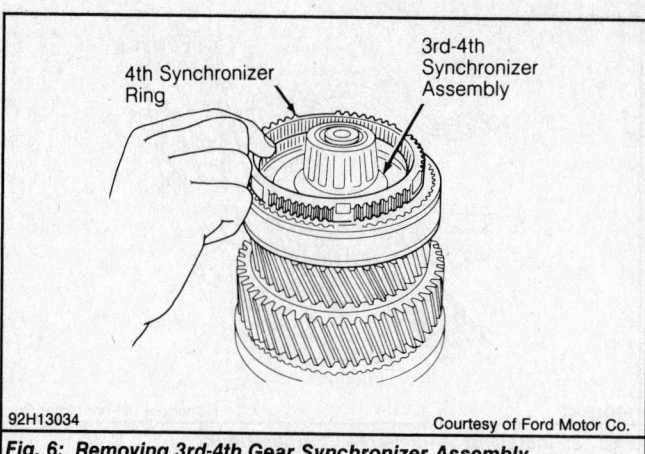

4th Synchronizer Ring

3rd-4th Synchronizer Assembly

92H13034

Courtesy of Ford Motor Co.

Fig. 6: Removing 3rd-4th Gear Synchronizer Assembly

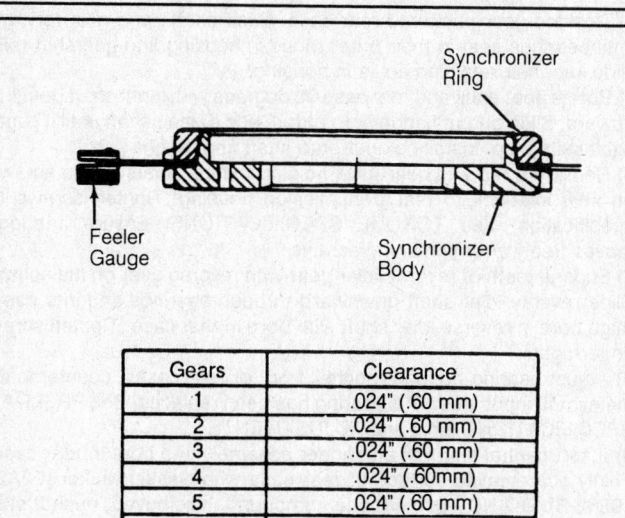

Synchronizer Ring

Feeler Gauge

Synchronizer Body

Gears	Clearance
1	.024" (.60 mm)
2	.024" (.60 mm)
3	.024" (.60 mm)
4	.024" (.60mm)
5	.024" (.60 mm)
Reverse	.016" (.40 mm)

92I13035

Courtesy of Ford Motor Co.

Fig. 7: Measuring Synchronizer Ring Clearance

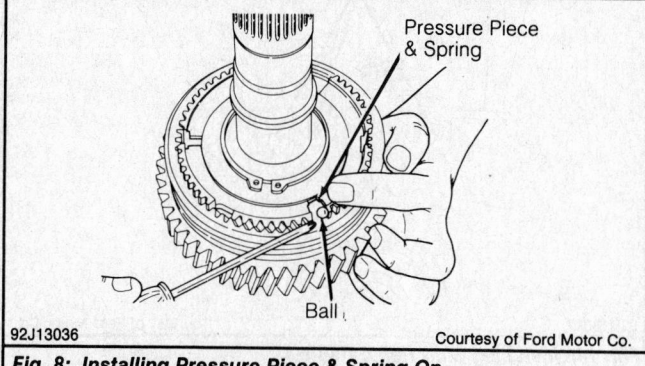

Pressure Piece & Spring

Ball

92J13036

Courtesy of Ford Motor Co.

Fig. 8: Installing Pressure Piece & Spring On 5th-Reverse Synchronizer

17) Clearance between snap ring and synchronizer body should not be greater than .004" (.1 mm). Check 3rd gear end play. End play must be .006-.014" (.15-.35 mm).

18) Position synchronizer sleeve over synchronizer body with smaller of the 2 grooves facing down. Align areas of synchronizer sleeve where teeth are cut away with gaps on synchronizer body and lugs on synchronizer ring.

19) Insert 3 compression springs with pressure pieces in the recesses of the synchronizer body. Install 4th gear synchronizer ring with short lugs positioned over the gaps in the 3rd-4th synchronizer body.

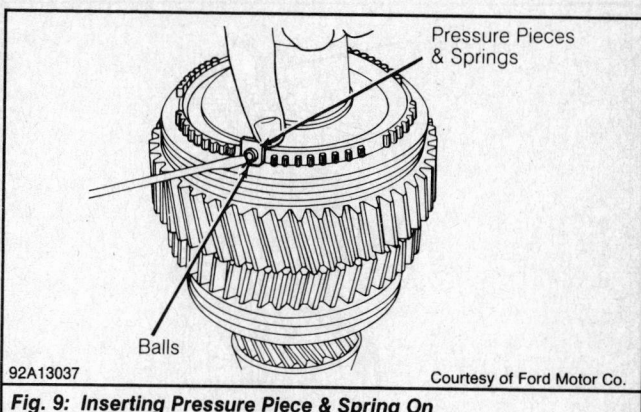

Pressure Pieces & Springs

Balls

92A13037

Courtesy of Ford Motor Co.

Fig. 9: Inserting Pressure Piece & Spring On 1st-2nd Synchronizer

20) Push synchronizing ring downward while pulling up on synchronizer sleeve. Heat front taper roller bearing inner race to 320°F (160°C). DO NOT heat for more than 15 minutes. Install mainshaft front taper roller bearing on the mainshaft.

INPUT SHAFT

Disassembly & Reassembly – Using universal bearing remover set, pull input shaft bearing from input shaft . Ensure pocket bearing oil baffle is fully installed and not damaged. Install bearing on input shaft.

COUNTERSHAFT

NOTE: Countershaft is serviced as an assembly; components are not available separately. Gears are heated and shrunk fit to shaft.

ADJUSTMENTS

INPUT SHAFT & MAINSHAFT BEARING PRELOAD

1) With transmission output flange facing upward, attach dial indicator gauge with a magnetic base to output flange and indicator bar resting on output end of mainshaft. *See Fig. 10.*

2) Zero dial indicator. Using pry bar, gently pry up on input shaft and mainshaft. Note reading. Shim and baffle to be fitted must have a combined thickness equal to dial indicator reading plus .0008-.004" (.02-.11 mm). See COUNTERSHAFT BEARING PRELOAD.

NOTE: Shims and baffle must be removed prior to preload measurement. Baffle is part of shim package under the bearing race. Ensure baffle lip is recessed .24" (6 mm) below synchronizer cone edge and fits tightly.

COUNTERSHAFT BEARING PRELOAD

1) Attach dial indicator to PTO mounting flange in the front case. *See Fig. 11.* Position dial indicator measurement bar against the flat face of the 4th speed helical gear on countershaft.

2) Zero dial indicator. Insert pry bars through each of 2 PTO openings and position them beneath 4th speed helical gear on countershaft. Pry up on countershaft. Check and adjust preload with shims. See PRELOAD SPECIFICATIONS table.

PRELOAD SPECIFICATIONS

Application	In. (mm)
Countershaft	.0008-.004 (.02-.11)
Input & Main Shaft	.0008-.004 (.02-.11)
Mainshaft Reverse Gear	.006-.014 (.15-.35)
Mainshaft 1st Gear	.006-.014 (.15-.35)
Mainshaft 2nd Gear	.006-.018 (.15-.45)
Mainshaft 3rd Gear	.006-.014 (.15-.35)
Mainshaft 4th Gear	.006-.014 (.15-.35)
Mainshaft Synchronizer Body Retention Rings	0-.004 (0-.1)

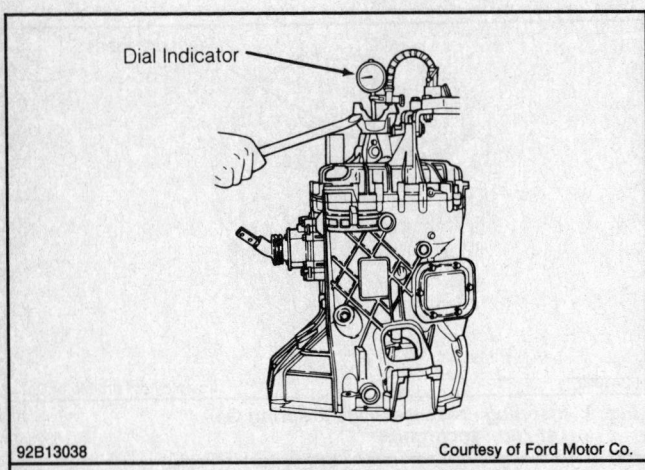

Fig. 10: Measuring Input Shaft & Mainshaft Preload

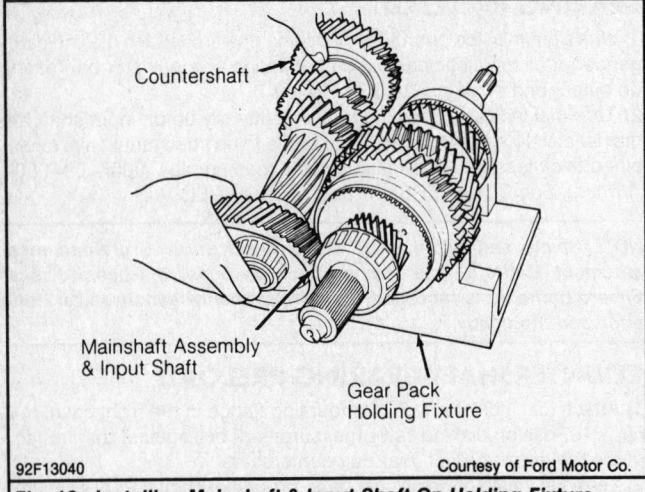

Fig. 11: Measuring Countershaft Preload

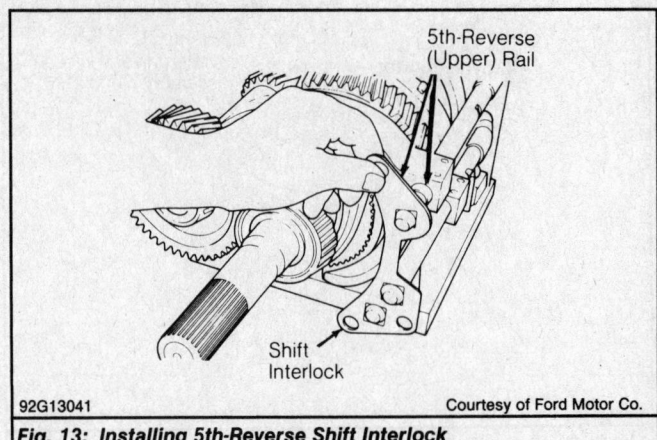

Fig. 13: Installing 5th-Reverse Shift Interlock

4) Position gear pack into rear case. Push shafts and rails forward until bearings seat in their outer races in housing and gearshift rails slide into their retaining holes in housing.

5) Rotate gear pack and rear case 90 degrees with input shaft pointing upward. Slide output flange onto output end of mainshaft until it seats against its stop. Install hex nut onto shaft finger-tight.

6) Remove strap and gear pack holding fixture. Attach 3 cap screws on shift interlock to rear transmission housing. Tighten screws to specification. See TORQUE SPECIFICATIONS. Ensure interlock moves freely after tightening screws.

7) Engage teeth of reverse idler gear with reverse gear on mainshaft. Slide reverse idler shaft downward through bearings and into case. Align bore in reverse idler shaft with bore in rear case. Tighten screw finger-tight.

8) Adjust bearing preload if either front or rear cases, countershaft, mainshaft, input shaft or a bearing has been replaced. See PRELOAD SPECIFICATIONS table and ADJUSTMENTS.

9) Insert central shift rail and finger assembly into bore in rear case. Thinly coat sealing surface of rear case with Gasket Maker (E2AZ-19562-B). DO NOT use silicone compound. If removed, push 3 shift rail detents back into their holes in front case. Ensure detents do not obstruct entry of shift rails. See Fig. 14.

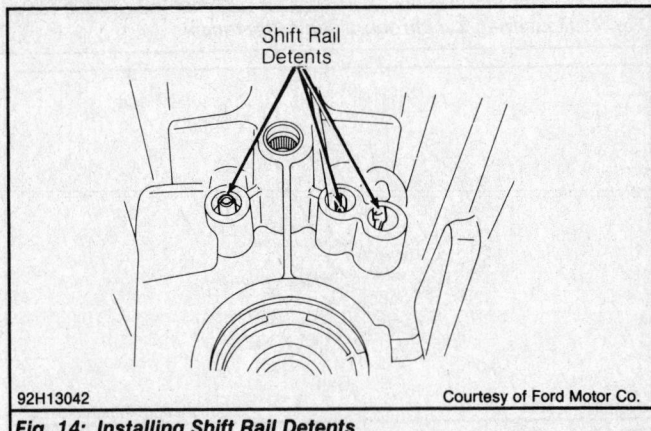

Fig. 14: Installing Shift Rail Detents

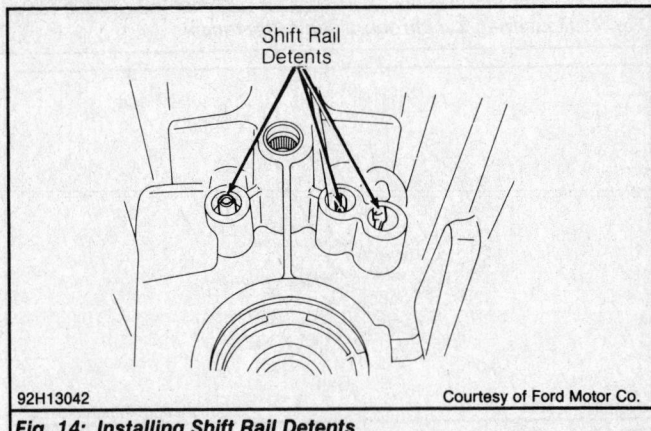

Fig. 12: Installing Mainshaft & Input Shaft On Holding Fixture

TRANSMISSION REASSEMBLY

1) Place input shaft and synchronizer ring assembly over the tapered roller bearing on input end of mainshaft. Place mainshaft and input shaft on gear pack holding fixture and place countershaft on fixture and mesh the gears of the 2 shafts. See Fig. 12.

2) Place 3 shift rails and fork assemblies into the shift rod support tool in the position from which they were removed. Position the 3 shift rails assemblies together with the shift rod so shift forks engage in correct mainshaft synchronizer sleeves.

3) Place shift interlock on 3 gearshift rails and engage it in interlock grooves in 5th-reverse (upper) rail. See Fig. 13. Slide speedometer worm gear (if equipped) onto mainshaft.

10) Drive in 2 dowels aligning rear case and front case. Tighten hex screws finger-tight. After any preload adjustments are made, tighten hex screws to specifications.

11) Fit sealing ring to reverse idler shaft retaining cap screws. Install screws in front and rear cases. Tighten screws to specification. Push caps into cap screws until they are flush with screw head surface.

12) Rotate transmission so input shaft is pointing down. Install speedometer drive gear (if equipped) on mainshaft. Install rear oil seal. See REAR OIL SEAL under ON-VEHICLE SERVICE.

13) Position 5th-reverse gear interlock plate in installed position. Ensure stop plate moves freely and gasket does not interfere with it. Place spring above nose in interlock plate, and move both parts into their installed positions. See Fig. 15.

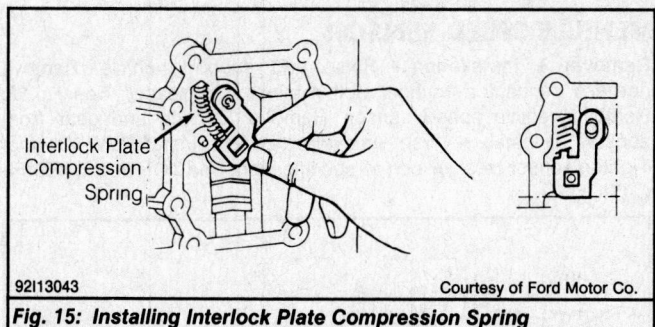

Interlock Plate
Compression
Spring

92I13043

Courtesy of Ford Motor Co.

Fig. 15: Installing Interlock Plate Compression Spring

14) Install shift tower assembly. Nose on gearshift finger must point toward interlock plate. Check interlock function. Interlock function is operating properly if transmission cannot be shifted into 5th and Reverse. Check interlock plate compression spring length and install over each of 3 detent bolts. Springs have an unloaded length of 1.736" (44.1 mm).

15) Install NEW sealing caps over detents in front case. Drive caps until they seat 3/64" (1 mm) below surface of housing. Deeper installation will cause high shift efforts.

TORQUE SPECIFICATIONS
TORQUE SPECIFICATIONS

Application	Ft. Lbs. (N.m)
Drain & Filler Plugs	37 (50)
End Yoke-To-Mainshaft Nut	184 (250)
Extension Housing-To-Main Case Bolt	16 (22)
Front Case-To-Rear Case Screw	16 (22)
Idler Shaft Retention Screw	16 (22)
PTO Cover Plate Bolt	28 (38)
Shift Cover-To-Main Case Bolt	16 (22)

	INCH Lbs. (N.m)
Shift Cover-To-Tower Cover Bolts	84 (10)
Shift Interlock Screws	84 (10)
Shift Rail Plate Bolt	84 (10)

MANUAL TRANSMISSIONS
ZF S6-40 6-Speed

General Motors: Corvette

IDENTIFICATION

Identification label is located on right side of case. Label contains information for transmission ratio, type and oil grade.

DESCRIPTION

The ZF S6-40 transmission is a fully synchronized 6-speed gear box. GM also identifies it as 95-mm 6-speed. The ZF S6-40 has an aluminum case with internal shift rail mechanism. There is a reverse idler gear and shaft located between the mainshaft and countershaft. Input torque rating 450 ft. lbs. (610 N.m).

LUBRICATION & ADJUSTMENTS

See appropriate MANUAL TRANSMISSION SERVICING article in TRANSMISSION SERVICING.

TROUBLE SHOOTING

See GENERAL TROUBLE SHOOTING article in MANUAL TRANS-MISSIONS.

ON-VEHICLE SERVICE

EXTENSION HOUSING OIL SEAL

Removal & Installation – Raise and support vehicle. Remove complete exhaust system. Remove drive shaft. Work around outer edge of seal with screwdriver, and tap out seal. To install, reverse removal procedure and check fluid level.

REVERSE IDLER GEAR COVER GASKET

Removal – Raise and support vehicle, drain fluid. Remove reverse idler gear cover bolts including shaft bolt and seal. See Fig. 1. Remove cover and gasket.

NOTE: Reverse idler shaft bolt must be reinstalled after cover removal to prevent shaft rotation.

Installation – Clean surfaces and install NEW cover gasket and shaft bolt seal. To complete installation, reverse removal procedure. Tighten bolts to specification. See TORQUE SPECIFICATIONS.

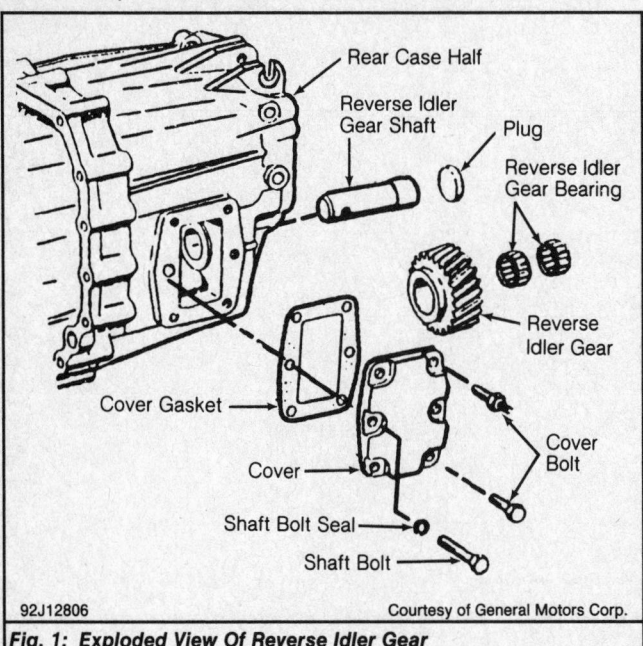

Rear Case Half
Reverse Idler Gear Shaft
Plug
Reverse Idler Gear Bearing
Reverse Idler Gear
Cover Gasket
Cover
Cover Bolt
Shaft Bolt Seal
Shaft Bolt

92J12806   Courtesy of General Motors Corp.

Fig. 1: Exploded View Of Reverse Idler Gear

VEHICLE SPEED SENSOR

Removal & Installation – Raise and support vehicle. Remove harness connector, retainer bolt retainer and spacer. See Fig. 2. Remove vehicle speed sensor. Remove "O" ring and gear from sensor. To install, reverse removal procedure. Install NEW "O" ring. Tighten sensor retainer bolt to specification. See TORQUE SPECIFICATIONS.

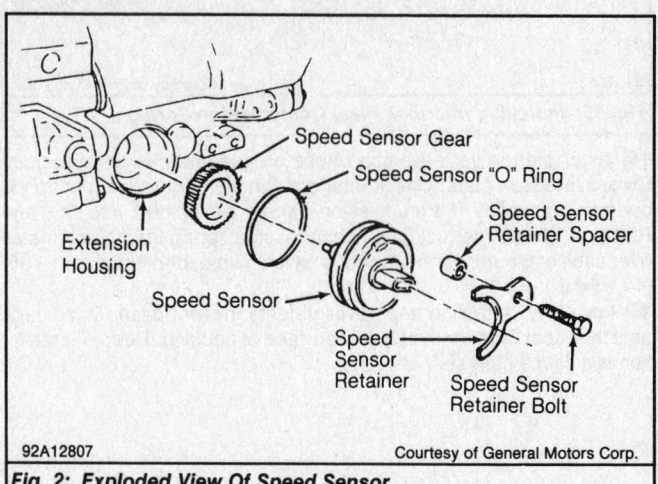

Speed Sensor Gear
Speed Sensor "O" Ring
Speed Sensor Retainer Spacer
Extension Housing
Speed Sensor
Speed Sensor Retainer
Speed Sensor Retainer Bolt

92A12807   Courtesy of General Motors Corp.

Fig. 2: Exploded View Of Speed Sensor

REMOVAL & INSTALLATION

See appropriate MANUAL TRANSMISSION REMOVAL article in TRANSMISSION SERVICING.

TRANSMISSION DISASSEMBLY

1) Mount transmission to holding fixture using Front Plate (J-37337-1) and Arbor (J-37337-2). Prior to disassembly, shift transmission into 1st gear.

2) Remove cable tie at lower front of shift boot, and pull boot back to expose gearshift rod. See Fig. 3. Remove snap ring and shaft pin from gearshift rod. Remove support bracket and gearshift control arm bolt. Remove gearshift assembly from transmission.

3) Remove speed sensor and extension housing bolts. See Fig. 4. Note position of short bolt. Remove extension housing and selective shim. Depress clip and remove speed sensor drive gear, clip and washer. Drive out roll pin and remove support ring from extension housing. Remove extension housing rear seal and bushing.

4) Remove reverse idler gear cover and bolts. Note position and length of bolts. Remove reverse idler shaft plug. Thread bolt into back of reverse idler gear shaft, and remove shaft. Remove reverse idler gear and bearing assembly. Remove bearing assembly from gear. See Fig. 1.

5) Rotate transmission so input shaft is up. Pull countershaft seal from case using slide hammer and adapter. Remove countershaft nut and washer while holding main drive gear. Remove bearing retainer bolts and assembly. Remove gasket and selective shim.

6) Separate retainer flange from bearing retainer assembly. Remove "O" ring from bearing retainer flange and input shaft seal from retainer tube. Remove snap ring from front case.

7) Remove gearshift shaft detent bolt, inner-outer springs and detent. Remove gear select solenoid assembly. Remove back-up light switch and pin. See Fig. 5. Rotate transmission so output shaft is up.

8) Remove gearshift rail detent plugs, springs and pins in rear case half. Remove snap ring and washer from mainshaft. Remove attaching bolts and stud between case halves. Pull rear case half from front case using puller and Long Bolts (J-38129). Magnet may fall from case during separation.

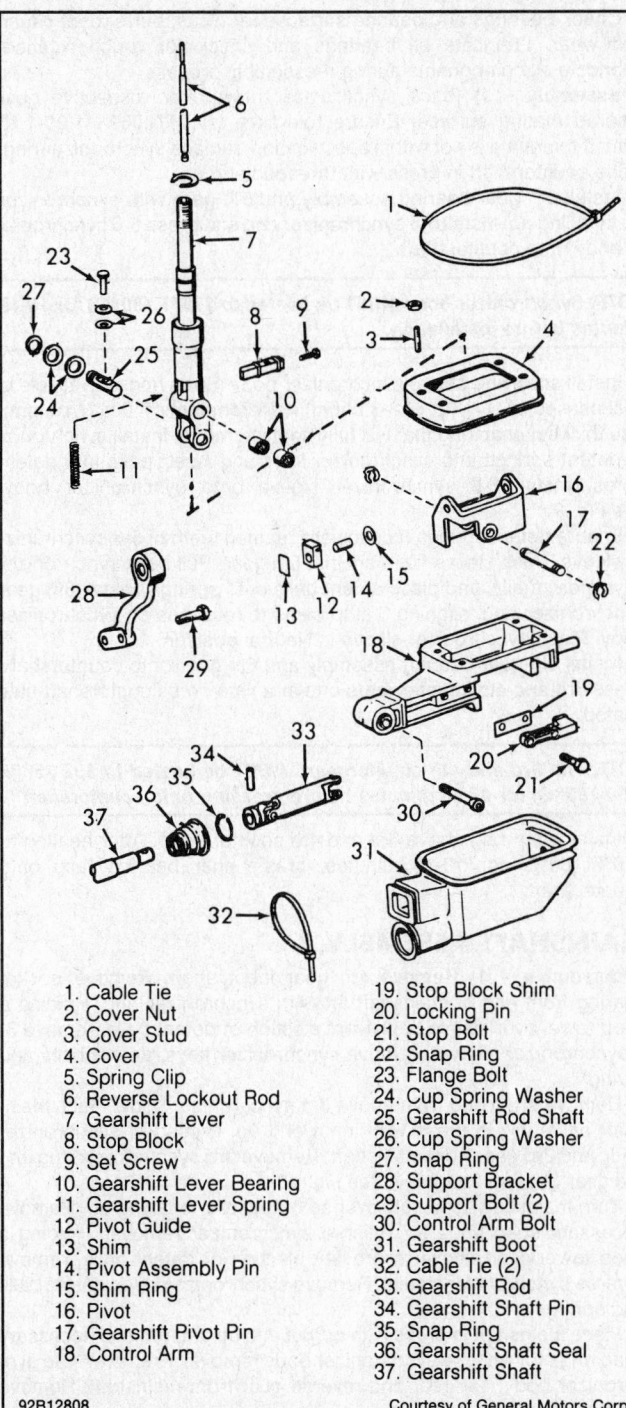

1. Cable Tie
2. Cover Nut
3. Cover Stud
4. Cover
5. Spring Clip
6. Reverse Lockout Rod
7. Gearshift Lever
8. Stop Block
9. Set Screw
10. Gearshift Lever Bearing
11. Gearshift Lever Spring
12. Pivot Guide
13. Shim
14. Pivot Assembly Pin
15. Shim Ring
16. Pivot
17. Gearshift Pivot Pin
18. Control Arm
19. Stop Block Shim
20. Locking Pin
21. Stop Bolt
22. Snap Ring
23. Flange Bolt
24. Cup Spring Washer
25. Gearshift Rod Shaft
26. Cup Spring Washer
27. Snap Ring
28. Support Bracket
29. Support Bolt (2)
30. Control Arm Bolt
31. Gearshift Boot
32. Cable Tie (2)
33. Gearshift Rod
34. Gearshift Shaft Pin
35. Snap Ring
36. Gearshift Shaft Seal
37. Gearshift Shaft

92B12808   Courtesy of General Motors Corp.

Fig. 3: Exploded View Of Gear Shifter

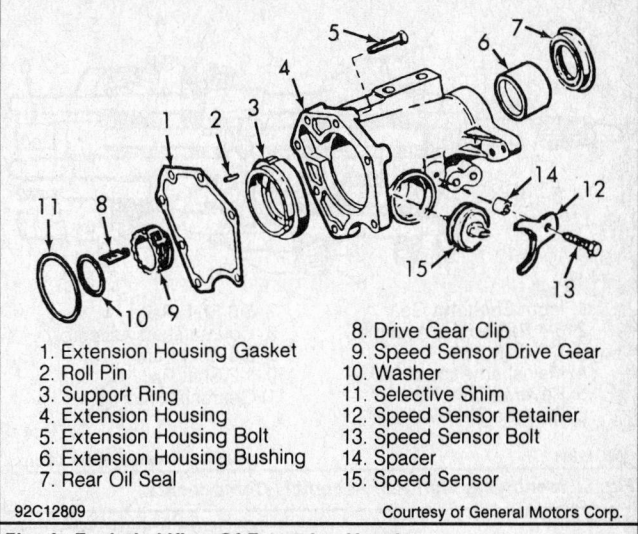

1. Extension Housing Gasket
2. Roll Pin
3. Support Ring
4. Extension Housing
5. Extension Housing Bolt
6. Extension Housing Bushing
7. Rear Oil Seal
8. Drive Gear Clip
9. Speed Sensor Drive Gear
10. Washer
11. Selective Shim
12. Speed Sensor Retainer
13. Speed Sensor Bolt
14. Spacer
15. Speed Sensor

92C12809   Courtesy of General Motors Corp.

Fig. 4: Exploded View Of Extension Housing

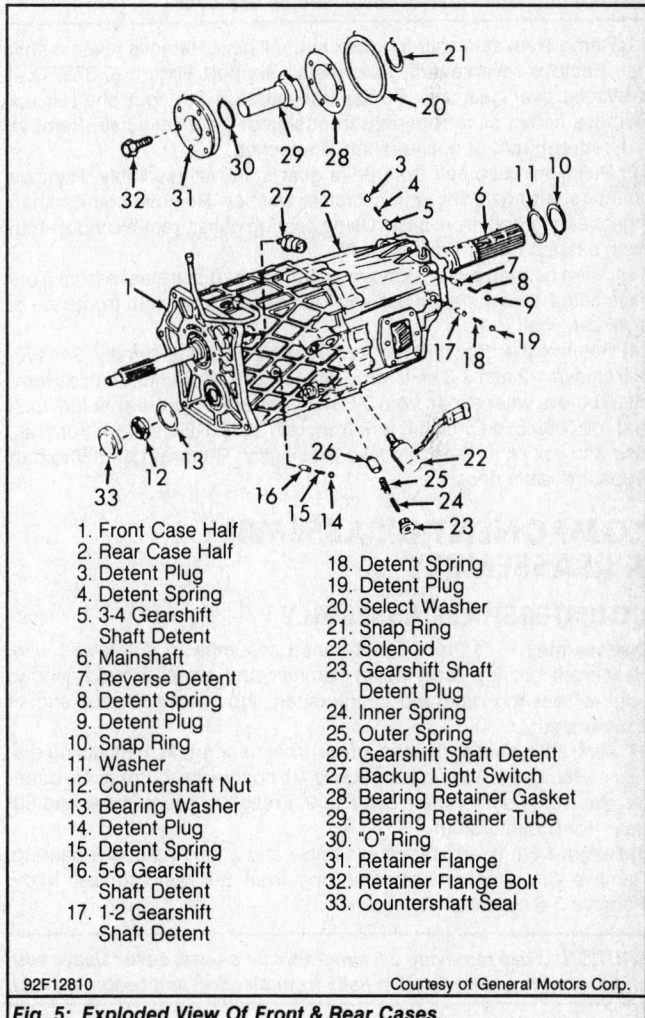

1. Front Case Half
2. Rear Case Half
3. Detent Plug
4. Detent Spring
5. 3-4 Gearshift Shaft Detent
6. Mainshaft
7. Reverse Detent
8. Detent Spring
9. Detent Plug
10. Snap Ring
11. Washer
12. Countershaft Nut
13. Bearing Washer
14. Detent Plug
15. Detent Spring
16. 5-6 Gearshift Shaft Detent
17. 1-2 Gearshift Shaft Detent
18. Detent Spring
19. Detent Plug
20. Select Washer
21. Snap Ring
22. Solenoid
23. Gearshift Shaft Detent Plug
24. Inner Spring
25. Outer Spring
26. Gearshift Shaft Detent
27. Backup Light Switch
28. Bearing Retainer Gasket
29. Bearing Retainer Tube
30. "O" Ring
31. Retainer Flange
32. Retainer Flange Bolt
33. Countershaft Seal

92F12810   Courtesy of General Motors Corp.

Fig. 5: Exploded View Of Front & Rear Cases

9) Remove mainshaft output bearing from rear case. Bearing should slide out. Pull countershaft rear bearing using bearing race remover and adapter from rear of case. Pry out gearshift shaft seal with screwdriver. Remove shaft bearing assembly from rear case using bearing remover.

10) Remove gearshift rail detent plug, spring and pin in left front side of front case half. Remove gearshift shaft, rotating shaft back and forth while pulling up to clear shift forks. *See Figs. 6-8.* Remove lock and roll pins from 1-2 shift fork. Slide 1-2 shift rail out until rail end clears front case half rail boss.

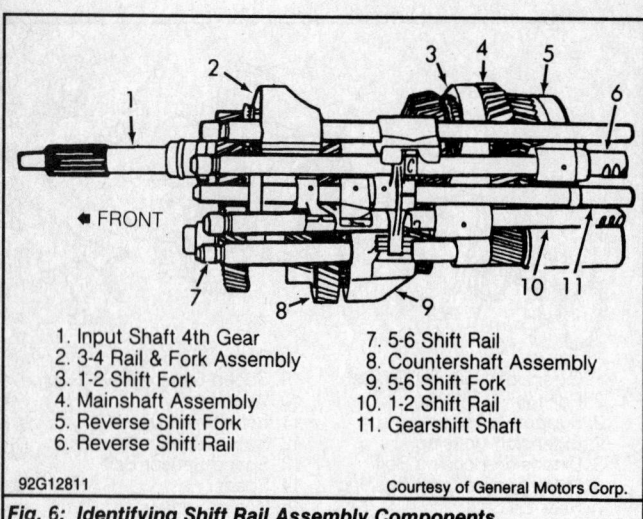

1. Input Shaft 4th Gear
2. 3-4 Rail & Fork Assembly
3. 1-2 Shift Fork
4. Mainshaft Assembly
5. Reverse Shift Fork
6. Reverse Shift Rail
7. 5-6 Shift Rail
8. Countershaft Assembly
9. 5-6 Shift Fork
10. 1-2 Shift Rail
11. Gearshift Shaft

92G12811   Courtesy of General Motors Corp.

Fig. 6: Identifying Shift Rail Assembly Components

CAUTION: Hold reverse synchronizer sleeve during reverse shift rail removal to prevent loss of keys, springs and balls.

11) Remove reverse shift fork lock and roll pins. Remove reverse shift rail. Remove reverse shift fork. Install Support Fixture (J-37337), if available, over gear set. Rotate transmission so input shaft is up. Remove detent plug from right front side of front case half. Remove fixture from front of countershaft, if attached.

12) Pull front case half from drive gear/shift rail assembly. Remove countershaft snap ring and selective washer. Remove countershaft input bearing from front case. Using bearing puller, remove input shaft main bearing from front case half.

13) Using bearing puller, remove gearshift shaft ball sleeve from front case half. Remove detent ball and locking pins from right front side of front case half.

14) Remove 3-4 gearshift fork/rail from mainshaft assembly. *See Fig. 6.* Remove 1-2 and 5-6 shift rails, with forks from countershaft assembly. Remove wear shoes from 5-6 shift fork. Remove 5-6 shift fork lock and roll pins. Slide 5-6 shift fork from rail. Slide 1-2 shift fork from rail, lock and roll pins were removed previously. Remove gearshift shaft stops and snap rings.

COMPONENT DISASSEMBLY & REASSEMBLY

COUNTERSHAFT ASSEMBLY

Disassembly – 1) Place countershaft assembly in soft-jawed vise. Heat front bearing race. Using hammer and chisel around flanged edge of bearing race and countershaft, move race toward end of countershaft.

2) Using split plate and press, press front bearing race remaining distance. Remove snap ring from above 4th countergear. Press 4th countergear from countershaft. *See Fig. 9.* Press 3rd countergear and 6th gear from countershaft.

3) Remove 6th gear bearing assembly and snap ring below bearing. Remove 6th gear synchronizer ring from 5-6 synchronizer body. Remove 5-6 synchronizer sleeve.

CAUTION: When removing 5-6 synchronizer sleeve, cover sleeve with shop towel to prevent detent balls from ejecting and becoming lost.

4) Remove 5-6 synchronizer keys, detent balls and springs. Press 5-6 synchronizer body from countershaft. Remove 5th gear synchronizer ring and 5th gear bearing assembly.

Cleaning & Inspection – 1) Wash all parts in solvent and air dry. DO NOT spin dry bearings. Check gears and synchronizers for cracks, chipped gear teeth, excess wear and other damage. Whenever transmission is disassembled, manufacturer recommends replacing synchronizer rings.

2) Check bearings and bearing surfaces for nicks, burrs, bent cages and wear. Lubricate all bearings and check for rough rotation. Lubricate all components during reassembly process.

Reassembly – 1) Place synchronizer rings over respective gear tapered mating surface. Ensure tolerance is .047-.069" (1.20-1.75 mm). If tolerance is not within specification, replace synchronizer ring. Place countershaft in press with threaded end up.

2) Install 5th gear bearing assembly and 5th gear with synchronizer teeth facing up. Install 5-6 synchronizer ring and press 5-6 synchronizer body onto countershaft.

NOTE: Synchronizer body MUST be heated to 176°F (80°C) for 10-15 minutes before installation.

3) Install snap ring above synchronizer body. Snap ring is available in thicknesses of .11-.12" (2.8-3.0 mm) in increments of .004" (.10 mm). Use thickest snap ring that will fully seat in groove. Install synchronizer detent springs into synchronizer keys and insert pairs into detent bores. Install 5-6 synchronizer sleeve onto synchronizer body. *See Fig. 9.*

4) Ensure detent springs face toward reamed teeth of 5-6 synchronizer sleeve. Push sleeve flush against 5th gear. Pull back synchronizer keys individually, and place detent balls onto springs. Install 6th gear synchronizer ring, aligning 3 stop cams to recesses on synchronizer body. Place synchronizer sleeve in Neutral position.

5) Install 6th gear bearing assembly and 6th gear onto countershaft. Press 3rd and 4th countergears one at a time onto countershaft until seated.

NOTE: The 3rd and 4th countergears MUST be heated to 302-356°F (150-180°C) for 45-50 minutes before pressing onto countershaft.

6) Install snap ring above 3rd and 4th countergears. After heating to 176°F (80°C) for 10-15 minutes, press inner bearing race onto countershaft.

MAINSHAFT ASSEMBLY

Disassembly – 1) Remove 4th gear input shaft. Remove pocket bearing from end of mainshaft and 4th synchronizer ring. Holding a shop towel over sleeve to prevent ejection of detent balls, remove 3-4 synchronizer sleeve. Remove synchronizer keys, detent balls and springs.

2) Remove snap ring from above 3-4 synchronizer body. Place mainshaft assembly in press with input end up. Press 3-4 synchronizer body and 3rd gear from mainshaft. Remove 3rd synchronizer ring and 3rd gear bearing assembly. *See Fig. 10.*

3) Turn mainshaft assembly over so output end is facing up. Remove necessary snap rings for reverse synchronizer removal. Holding a shop towel over sleeve to prevent ejection of detent balls, remove reverse synchronizer sleeve. Remove synchronizer keys, detent balls and springs.

4) Place mainshaft in press with output end up and remove necessary snap rings for reverse synchronizer body removal. Press reverse synchronizer body, 1st gear and reverse gear from mainshaft. Remove reverse synchronizer ring.

5) Remove reverse gear bearing and race. Remove thrust washer and 1st gear bearing assembly. Remove 1st gear synchronizer internal and intermediate rings. Remove 1st gear synchronizer ring.

6) Holding a shop towel over sleeve to stop ejection of detent balls remove 1-2 synchronizer sleeve. Remove synchronizer keys, detent balls and springs. Remove snap ring above 1-2 synchronizer body. Press 1-2 synchronizer body and 2nd gear from mainshaft. Remove 2nd gear synchronizer ring, intermediate ring and internal ring. Remove 2nd bearing assembly.

Cleaning & Inspection – Wash all parts in solvent and air dry. Check gears and synchronizers for cracks, chipped gear teeth, excess wear and other damage. Whenever transmission is disassembled, manufacturer recommends replacing synchronizer rings. Lubricate all components during reassembly process.

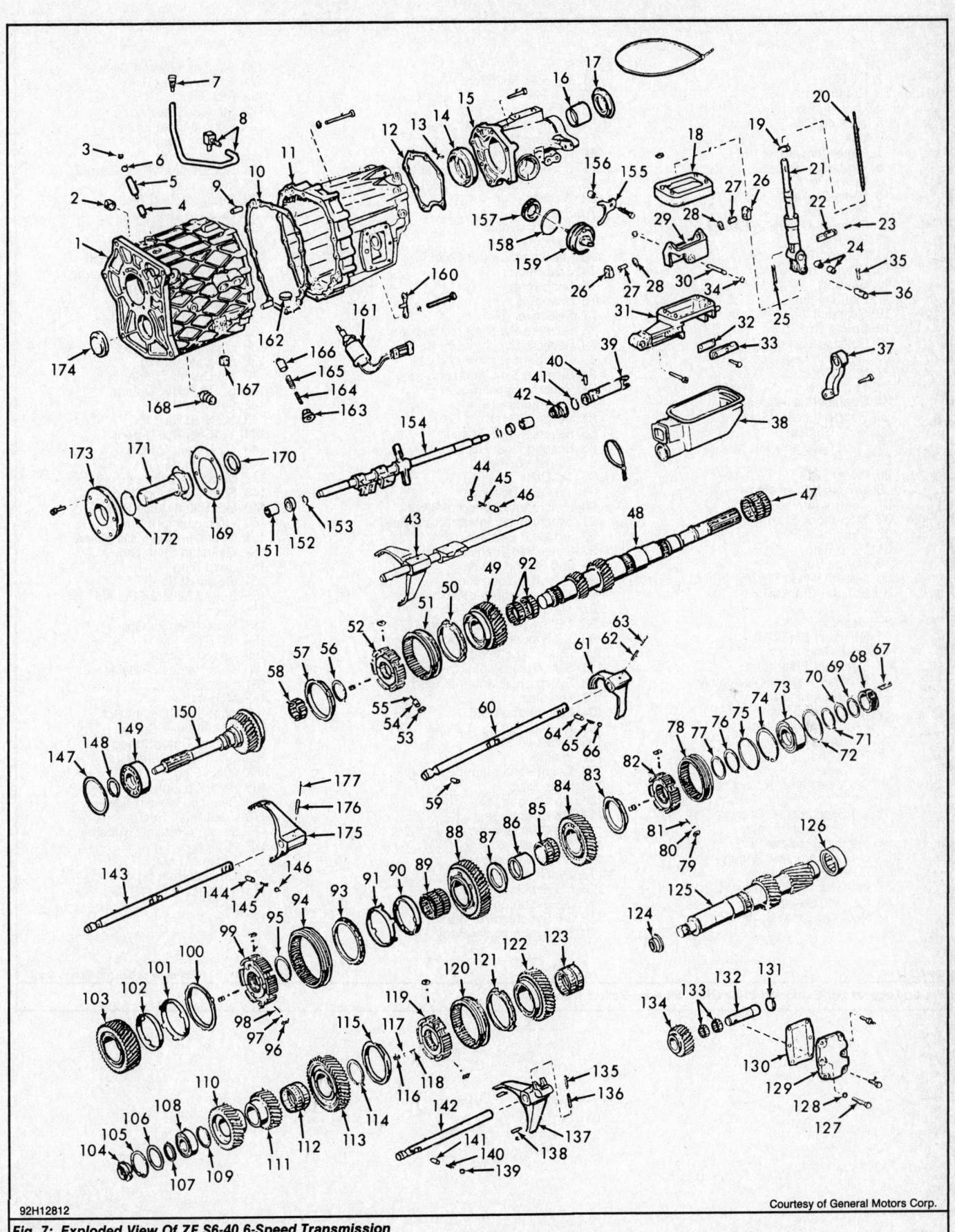

92H12812

Fig. 7: Exploded View Of ZF S6-40 6-Speed Transmission

MANUAL TRANSMISSIONS
ZF S6-40 6-Speed (Cont.)

1. Front Case
2. Fill Plug
3. Detent Cap
4. Locking Pin
5. Locking Pin
6. Ball
7. Ventilator Cap
8. Ventilator Tube
9. Dowel Pin
10. Case Gasket
11. Rear Case
12. Extension Housing Gasket
13. Roll Pin
14. Support Ring
15. Extension Housing
16. Bushing
17. Rear Oil Seal
18. Gearshift Cover
19. Spring Clip
20. Reverse Lockout Rod
21. Gearshift Lever
22. Stop Block
23. Set Screw
24. Gearshift Lever Bearing
25. Gearshift Lever Spring
26. Pivot Guides
27. Pivot Assembly Pin
28. Shim
29. Pivot
30. Gearshift Pivot Pin
31. Control Arm
32. Stop Block Shim
33. Stop Block Pin
34. Snap Ring
35. Flange Bolt
36. Gearshift Rod Shaft
37. Support Bracket
38. Gearshift Boot
39. Gearshift Rod
40. Gearshift Shaft Pin
41. Snap Ring
42. Gearshift Shaft Seal
43. 3-4 Shift Rail-Fork Assembly
44. 3-4 Detent Plug
45. 3-4 Detent Spring
46. 3-4 Shift Rail Detent
47. 2nd Gear Bearing
48. Mainshaft
49. 3rd Gear
50. 3rd Gear Synchronizer Ring
51. 3-4 Synchronizer Sleeve
52. 3-4 Synchronizer Body
53. 3-4 Synchronizer Key
54. 3-4 Synchronizer Ball
55. 3-4 Synchronizer Spring
56. Selective Snap Ring
57. 4th Gear Synchronizer Ring
58. Pocket Bearing
59. Back-Up Lamp Switch Pin

60. Reverse Shift Rail
61. Reverse Shift Fork
62. Roll Pin
63. Lock Pin
64. Reverse Shift Rail Detent
65. Reverse Detent Spring
66. Reverse Detent Plug
67. Speedometer Drive Gear Clip
68. Speedometer Drive Gear
69. Washer
70. Snap Ring
71. Selective Shim
72. Selective Shim
73. Mainshaft Output Bearing
74. Snap Ring
75. Snap Ring
76. Snap Ring
77. Selective Shim
78. Reverse Synchronizer Sleeve
79. Reverse Synchronizer Key
80. Reverse Synchronizer Ball
81. Reverse Synchronizer Spring
82. Reverse Synchronizer Body
83. Synchronizer Ring
84. Reverse Gear
85. Reverse Gear Bearing
86. Bearing Inner Race
87. Thrust Washer
88. 1st Gear
89. 1st Gear Bearing
90. Synchronizer Internal Ring
91. Synchronizer Intermediate Ring
92. 3rd Gear Bearing
93. Outer Synchronizer
94. 2nd Sliding Sleeve
95. Selective Snap Ring
96. 1-2 Synchronizer Key
97. 1-2 Synchronizer Ball
98. 1-2 Synchronizer Spring
99. 1-2 Synchronizer Body
100. Outer Synchronizer Ring
101. Synchronizer Intermediate Ring
102. Synchronizer Internal Ring
103. 2nd Gear
104. Countershaft Nut
105. Snap Ring
106. Selective Shim
107. Washer
108. Countershaft Input Bearing
109. Snap Ring
110. 4th Countergear
111. 3rd Countergear
112. 6th Gear Bearing
113. 6th Gear
114. Selective Snap Ring
115. Synchronizer Ring
116. 5-6 Synchronizer Key
117. 5-6 Synchronizer Ball
118. 5-6 Synchronizer Spring
119. 5-6 Synchronizer Body

120. 5-6 Synchronizer Sleeve
121. Synchronizer Ring
122. 5th Gear
123. 5th Gear Bearing
124. Countershaft Front Bearing Race
125. Countershaft
126. Countershaft Rear Bearing
127. Idler Retaining Bolt
128. Retaining Bolt Seal
129. Reverse Idler Cover
130. Cover Gasket
131. Plug
132. Reverse Idler Gear Shaft
133. Reverse Idler Gear Bearing
134. Reverse Idler Gear
135. Lock Pin
136. Roll Pin
137. 5-6 Shift Fork
138. 5-6 Shift Fork Shoe
139. 5-6 Detent Plug
140. 5-6 Detent Spring
141. 5-6 Shift Rail Detent
142. 5-6 Shift Rail
143. 1-2 Shift Rail
144. 1-2 Shift Rail Detent
145. 1-2 Detent Spring
146. 1-2 Detent Plug
147. Selective Shim
148. Selective Snap Ring
149. Input Shaft Main Bearing
150. 4th Gear Input Shaft
151. Gearshift Shaft Ball Sleeve
152. Gearshift Shaft Stop
153. Snap Ring
154. Gearshift Shaft
155. Speed Sensor Retainer
156. Spacer
157. Speed Sensor Gear
158. "O" Ring
159. Speed Sensor
160. Wire Harness Retainer
161. Solenoid
162. Magnet
163. Shift Shaft Detent Bolt
164. Detent Inner Spring
165. Detent Outer Spring
166. Shift Shaft Detent
167. Drain Plug
168. Back-Up Light Switch
169. Bearing Retainer Gasket
170. Input Shaft Seal
171. Bearing Retainer Tube
172. "O" Ring
173. Retainer Flange
174. Countershaft Seal
175. 1-2 Shift Fork
176. Roll Pin
177. Lock Pin

92I12813

Fig. 8: Legend For Exploded View Of ZF S6-40 6-Speed Transmission

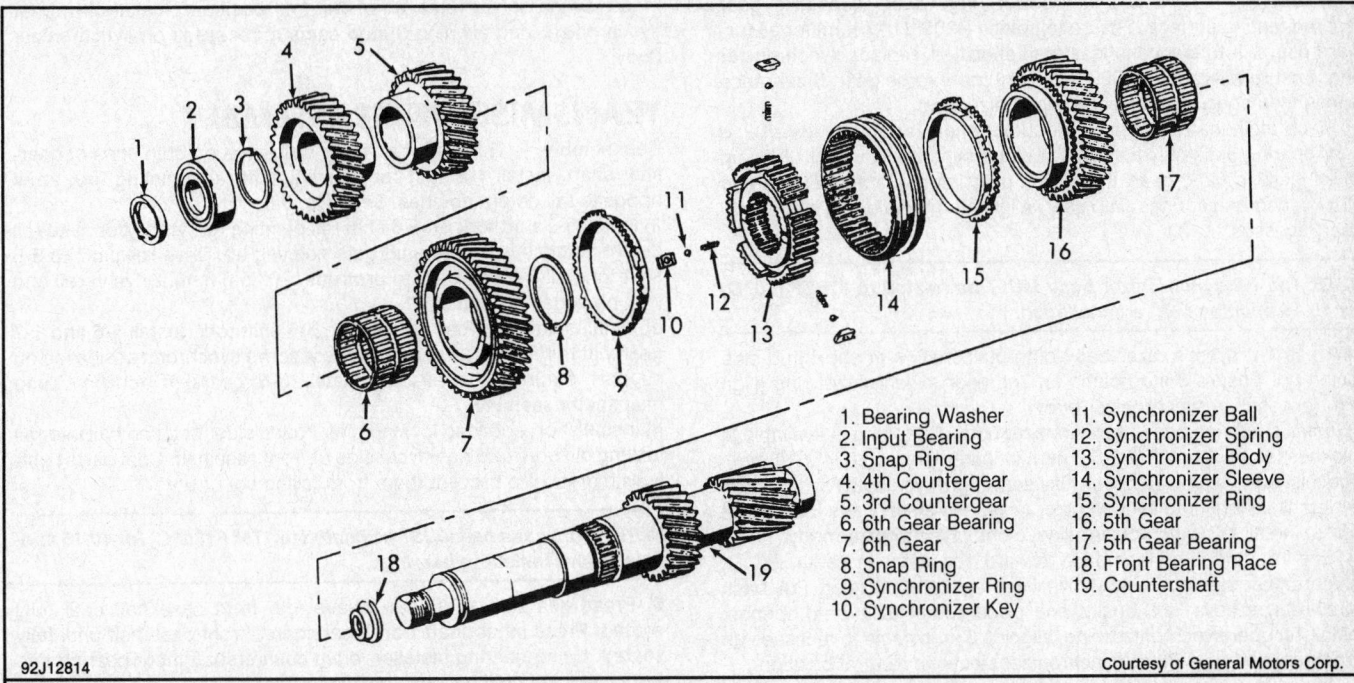

92J12814

Courtesy of General Motors Corp.

Fig. 9: Exploded View Of Countershaft Assembly

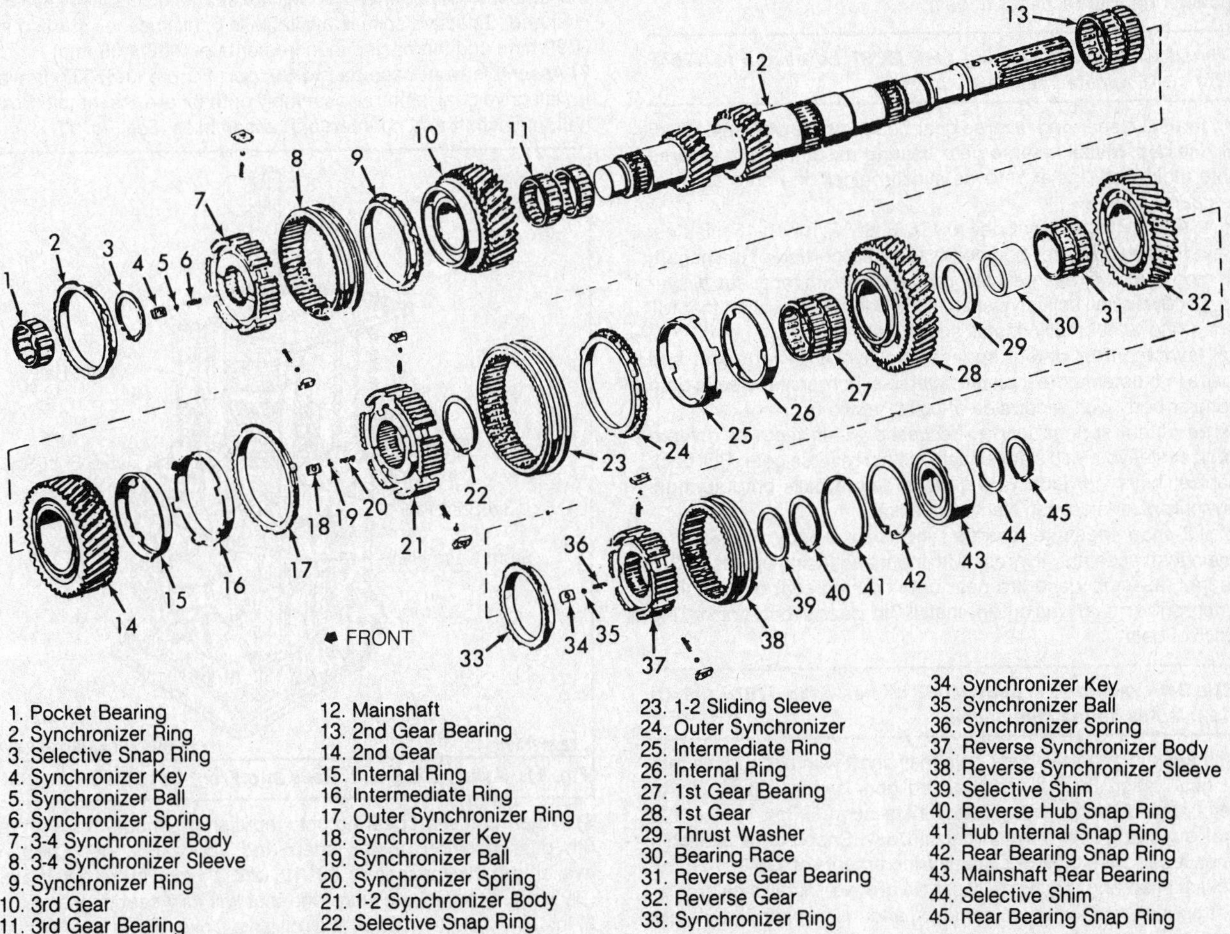

1. Bearing Washer
2. Input Bearing
3. Snap Ring
4. 4th Countergear
5. 3rd Countergear
6. 6th Gear Bearing
7. 6th Gear
8. Snap Ring
9. Synchronizer Ring
10. Synchronizer Key
11. Synchronizer Ball
12. Synchronizer Spring
13. Synchronizer Body
14. Synchronizer Sleeve
15. Synchronizer Ring
16. 5th Gear
17. 5th Gear Bearing
18. Front Bearing Race
19. Countershaft

◄ FRONT

1. Pocket Bearing
2. Synchronizer Ring
3. Selective Snap Ring
4. Synchronizer Key
5. Synchronizer Ball
6. Synchronizer Spring
7. 3-4 Synchronizer Body
8. 3-4 Synchronizer Sleeve
9. Synchronizer Ring
10. 3rd Gear
11. 3rd Gear Bearing
12. Mainshaft
13. 2nd Gear Bearing
14. 2nd Gear
15. Internal Ring
16. Intermediate Ring
17. Outer Synchronizer Ring
18. Synchronizer Key
19. Synchronizer Ball
20. Synchronizer Spring
21. 1-2 Synchronizer Body
22. Selective Snap Ring
23. 1-2 Sliding Sleeve
24. Outer Synchronizer
25. Intermediate Ring
26. Internal Ring
27. 1st Gear Bearing
28. 1st Gear
29. Thrust Washer
30. Bearing Race
31. Reverse Gear Bearing
32. Reverse Gear
33. Synchronizer Ring
34. Synchronizer Key
35. Synchronizer Ball
36. Synchronizer Spring
37. Reverse Synchronizer Body
38. Reverse Synchronizer Sleeve
39. Selective Shim
40. Reverse Hub Snap Ring
41. Hub Internal Snap Ring
42. Rear Bearing Snap Ring
43. Mainshaft Rear Bearing
44. Selective Shim
45. Rear Bearing Snap Ring

92A12815

Courtesy of General Motors Corp.

Fig. 10: Exploded View Of Mainshaft Assembly

Reassembly – 1) Place synchronizer rings over respective gear tapered mating surface. Ensure tolerance is .05" (1.27 mm) for all forward gears. If tolerance is less then specified, replace synchronizer ring. Ensure tolerance is .028" (.71 mm) for reverse gear. If tolerance is less then specified, replace synchronizer ring.

2) Place mainshaft in press with output shaft facing up. Install 2nd gear bearing assembly and gear. Ensure synchronizer teeth face up when installing 2nd gear. Install 2nd gear internal, intermediate and outer synchronizer rings onto gear. Align intermediate ring cones with gear recesses.

NOTE: The 1-2 synchronizer body MUST be heated to 176°F (80°C) for 10-15 minutes before installation.

---

3) Press 1-2 synchronizer body onto mainshaft with short hub side facing up. Ensure 3 stop cams on 2nd gear synchronizer ring align with recesses in synchronizer body.

4) Install snap ring above synchronizer body. Snap ring is available in thicknesses of .11-.12" (2.8-3.0 mm) in increments of .004" (.10 mm). Use thickest snap ring that will fully seat in groove. Install synchronizer detent springs into synchronizer keys, and insert pairs into detent bores. Install 1-2 synchronizer sleeve onto synchronizer body.

5) Ensure detent springs face toward recesses in teeth of 1-2 synchronizer sleeve. Push sleeve flush against 2nd gear. Pull back synchronizer keys individually, and place detent balls onto springs. Install 1st gear synchronizer ring, aligning 3 stop cams to recesses on synchronizer body. Place synchronizer sleeve in Neutral position.

6) Install 1st gear synchronizer intermediate ring into taper of synchronizer ring and internal ring into taper of intermediate ring. Install 1st gear bearing assembly and 1st gear aligning notches in intermediate ring with recesses in gear.

NOTE: Thrust washer and bearing race MUST be heated to 176°F (80°C) for 10-15 minutes before installation.

---

7) Press thrust washer and reverse gear bearing race onto mainshaft until fully seated. Install reverse gear bearing assembly and reverse gear onto mainshaft. Install reverse synchronizer ring onto taper of reverse gear.

8) Heat reverse synchronizer body to 176°F (80°C) for 10-15 minutes. Press reverse synchronizer body onto serrated portion of mainshaft, aligning stop cams on reverse synchronizer ring with recesses in synchronizer body. Install selective shim, choosing thickest shim that will allow snap ring to seat fully. Install snap ring.

9) Install synchronizer detent springs into synchronizer keys, and insert pairs into detent bores. Install reverse synchronizer sleeve onto synchronizer body with wider side of collar facing up.

10) Ensure detent springs face to recesses within teeth of reverse synchronizer sleeve. Push sleeve flush against reverse gear. Pull back synchronizer keys individually, and place detent balls onto springs. Place synchronizer sleeve in Neutral position.

11) Install 2 snap rings into reverse synchronizer body. *See Fig. 10.* Place mainshaft assembly in press with input end facing up. Install 3rd gear bearing assembly and 3rd gear onto bearing seat of mainshaft with synchronizer teeth facing up. Install 3rd gear synchronizer ring onto taper of gear.

NOTE: The 3-4 synchronizer body MUST be heated to 176°F (80°C) for 10-15 minutes before installation.

---

12) Press 3-4 synchronizer body onto mainshaft with flat surface facing 3rd gear. Align 3 stop cams of 3rd gear synchronizer ring to recesses on synchronizer body during installation.

13) Install snap ring above synchronizer body. Snap ring is available in thicknesses of .09-.10" (2.3-2.5 mm) in increments of .004" (.10 mm). Use thickest snap ring that will fully seat in groove. Install synchronizer detent springs into synchronizer keys, and insert pairs into detent bores. Install 3-4 synchronizer sleeve onto synchronizer body.

14) Ensure detent springs face to recesses within teeth of 3-4 synchronizer sleeve. Push sleeve flush against 3rd gear. Pull back synchronizer keys individually, and place detent balls onto springs.

Place synchronizer sleeve in Neutral position. Install 4th gear synchronizer ring aligning 3 stop cams to recesses on synchronizer body.

TRANSMISSION REASSEMBLY

Reassembly – 1) Install snap rings and stops on both ends of gearshift shaft. Install 1-2 shift fork on 1-2 shift rail, pointing fork arms opposite rail detent notches. *See Figs. 6-8.*

2) Install 5-6 shift fork on 5-6 shift rail pointing fork arms opposite rail detent notches with fork shift gate pointing up. Drive roll pin into 5-6 shift fork, allowing roll pin to protrude .20" (5.0 mm). Drive in roll and lock pin together until flush.

3) Install shift fork wear shoes onto 5-6 shift fork. Install 5-6 and 1-2 gearshift rail/fork assembles onto respective synchronizer sleeves on support fixture, if available. Install 3-4 gearshift fork/rail onto mainshaft assembly.

4) Install short and long locking pins, round side first, and ball into rail locking pin bore into right front side of front case half. Coat parts lightly with grease to prevent them from falling out of bore.

NOTE: Front case half MUST be heated to 176°F (80°C) for 10-15 minutes before installing bearings.

---

5) Press gearshift shaft ball sleeve into front case half until fully seated. Press input shaft front bearing into front case half until fully seated. Using bearing installer, drive countershaft input bearing into front case half until fully seated.

6) Install countershaft selective shim onto countershaft input bearing. Install snap ring above shim, ensuring no axial movement of shim. If movement exists or snap ring will not seat, the selective shim must be changed. Selective shim is available in 6 thicknesses starting at .075" (1.90 mm) and increasing in increments of .002" (.05 mm).

7) Assemble front case half to Support Fixture (J-37337) if available. Install drive gear/shift rail assembly onto fixture. Assemble front case half, mainshaft and countershaft assemblies. *See Fig. 11.*

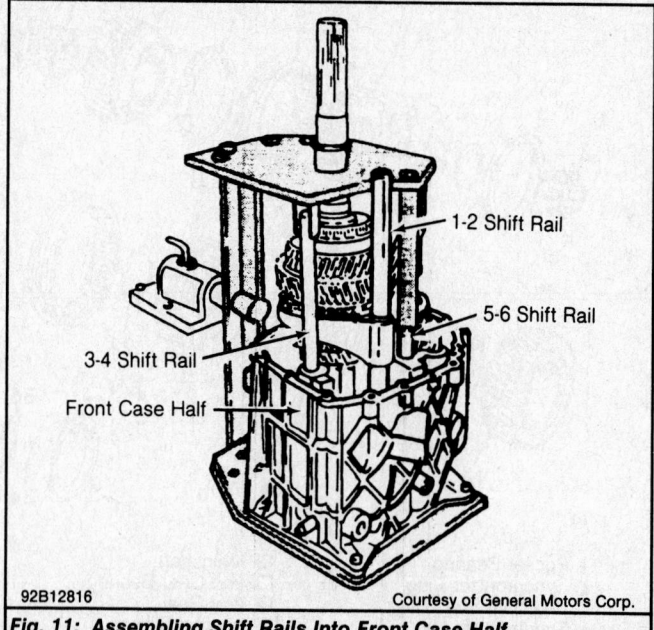

92B12816   Courtesy of General Motors Corp.

Fig. 11: Assembling Shift Rails Into Front Case Half

8) Press input shaft bearing onto input shaft. Ensure 5-6 shift rail is in 6th gear position. Install snap ring above bearing. Snap ring is available in thicknesses of .09-.10" (2.3-2.5 mm) in increments of .004" (.10 mm). Use thickest snap ring that will fully seat in groove.

9) Install 1-2 shift fork lock and roll pins. Drive roll pin into 1-2 shift fork, allowing roll pin to protrude .20" (5.0 mm). Drive in roll and lock pin together until flush.

10) Install reverse shift fork on reverse synchronizer sleeve with fork offset to rear. Slide reverse shift rail through reverse shift fork with detent notches toward output shaft. Install reverse shift fork lock and roll pin. Drive roll pin into reverse shift fork, allowing roll pin to protrude .20" (5.0 mm). Drive in roll and lock pin together until flush.

11) Install 5-6 shift rail detent and spring into detent bore on left front side of case. *See Fig. 5*. Install 5-6 detent sealing cap flush with case surface. Install gearshift shaft onto front case with detent facing away from gears.

12) Install front case half gasket. Install rear case half over gears ensuring position of gearshift shaft and seal. Install rear case half bolts and stud. Tighten bolts to specification. See TORQUE SPECIFICATIONS.

NOTE: Inner ring of rear mainshaft bearing MUST be heated to 176°F (80°C) before installing bearing.

---

13) Press mainshaft rear bearing onto mainshaft with roller bearing side facing forward. Install selective shim and snap ring. Ensure there is no axial movement of shim. If movement exists or snap ring will not seat, the selective shim must be changed. Selective shim is available in 7 thicknesses starting at .099" (2.50 mm) and increasing in .002" (.05 mm) increments.

14) Install NEW extension housing bushing using bushing installer. After heating extension housing to 176°F (80°C) for 10-15 minutes, press support ring into housing. Ensure support ring groove is aligned before pressing. *See Fig. 4*. Drive in support ring roll pin.

15) Install extension housing rear oil seal. Choose proper selective shim by measuring depth of mainshaft bearing from top of rear case half and subtracting depth of support ring from sealing surface of extension housing with NEW gasket in place. *See Fig. 12*. It is necessary to subtract .002-.004" (.05-.10 mm) from previously calculated number for gasket crush. Use this measurement for selective shim dimension.

16) Install selective shim and washer onto mainshaft. Install speed sensor drive gear clip and gear onto mainshaft. Install extension housing and bolts with NEW gasket. Tighten bolts to specification. See TORQUE SPECIFICATIONS. Install speed sensor, spacer, retainer and bolt. *See Fig. 4*. Install gearshift assembly.

17) Install reverse idler gear bearing assembly into reverse idler gear. Install reverse idler gear and bearing assembly into rear case half. Install reverse idler shaft into rear case half with smaller end first. It may be necessary to rotate reverse idler shaft to install shaft bolt. *See Fig. 1*. Install NEW reverse idler cover gasket, cover, shaft bolt with seal and cover bolts. Tighten bolts to specification. See TORQUE SPECIFICATIONS. Install reverse idler shaft plug flush with rear case.

18) Install 3 sets of shift rail detents, detent springs and plugs into rear case half. Shortest detent spring is for reverse detent bore located at upper left rear side of rear case half. Install 2 sets of shift rail detents, detent springs and plugs into front case half. *See Fig. 5*. Tighten plugs to specification. See TORQUE SPECIFICATIONS. Apply sealer to detent caps and drive in flush with case.

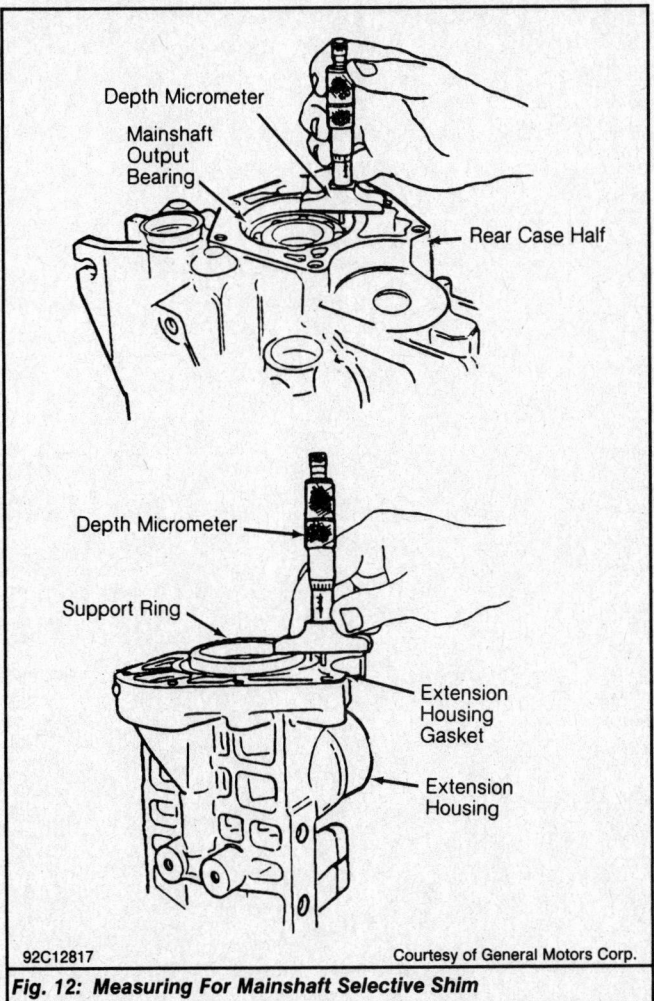

92C12817   Courtesy of General Motors Corp.

Fig. 12: *Measuring For Mainshaft Selective Shim*

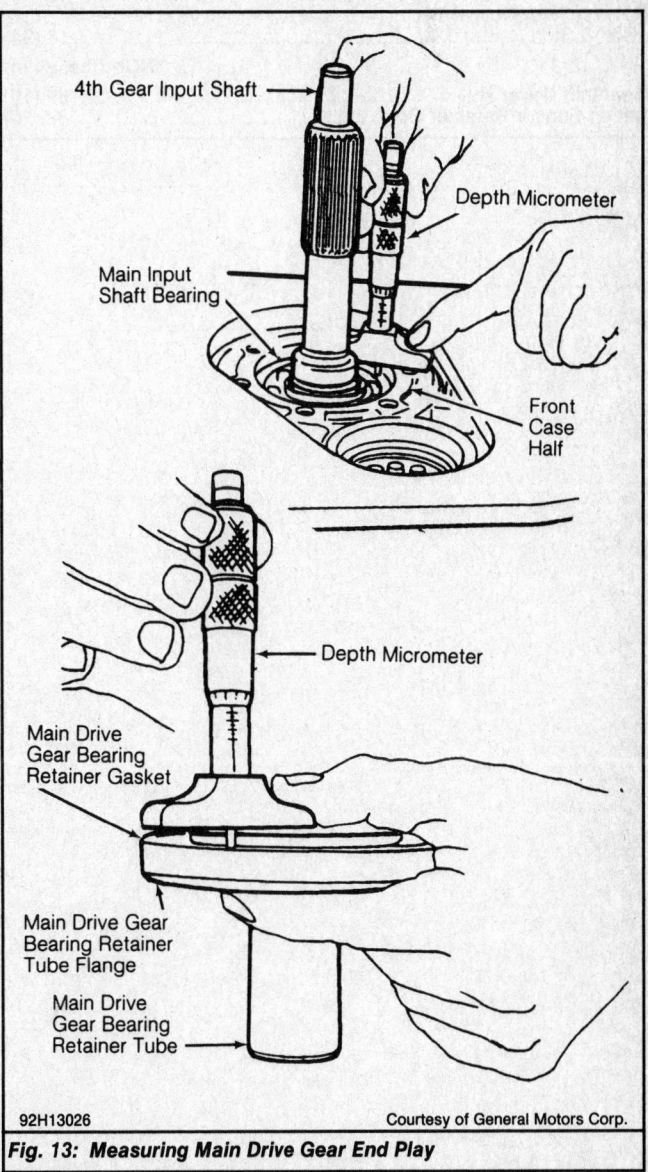

92H13026   Courtesy of General Motors Corp.

Fig. 13: *Measuring Main Drive Gear End Play*

19) Install back-up light pressure pin and switch. Install drain and fill plugs. Tighten both to specification. Rotate transmission to input shaft up position.

20) Measure depth to main drive gear bearing outer race from sealing surface of front case half. Measure depth from main drive gear retainer flange gasket surface with NEW gasket to retainer tube selective shim surface. Subtract smaller number from larger and subtract an additional .002-.004" (.05-.10 mm) to compensate for gasket crush. This figure is selective shim dimension. *See Fig. 13.*

21) Install selective shim, bearing retainer gasket, bearing retainer assembly and bolts. Tighten bolts to specification. Tighten countershaft nut to specification while holding main drive gear. Peen countershaft nut onto threads in 2 places using drift. Install countershaft seal into front case half.

TORQUE SPECIFICATIONS

TORQUE SPECIFICATIONS

Application	Ft. Lbs. (N.m)
Back-Up Light Switch	35 (47)
Countershaft Nut	162 (220)
Drain & Fill Plug	26 (35)
Extension Housing Bolt	18 (24)
Gearshift Control Arm Bolt	18 (24)
Gearshift Shaft Detent Plug	26 (35)
Rear Case Bolt & Stud	18 (24)
Rear Support Bracket Bolt	18 (24)
Reverse Idler Gear Cover Bolt & Stud	18 (24)
	INCH Lbs. (N.m)
Gearshift Cover Nut	89 (10)
Speed Sensor Retainer Bolt	89 (10)

TECHNICAL SERVICE BULLETIN

TRANSMISSION WHINE, LOSS OF GEARS

1993 Corvette (GM TSB 377140) December 1993 – 1) ZF S6-40 transmission may have a whine in neutral or all gears when clutch is engaged. A loss of all gears may also occur. If vehicle was built between VIN No. 110966-113902, and clutch housing has a casting date of January, February or March 1993, clutch housing may be cause of condition. Casting date is located on right side of clutch housing, above transmission identification number.

NOTE: Suspect housing will have no more than 3 dots in casting date.

2) Transmission to clutch housing pilot bore may be misaligned. Misaligned pilot bore may side load input shaft, causing whine. This condition may cause clutch disc rivets to loosen or shear, disengaging clutch disc friction facing from splined hub. If vehicle requires replacement of clutch disc due to sheared rivets, clutch housing MUST also be replaced.

SECTION 5

AXLE SHAFTS & TRANSFER CASES

AXLE SHAFTS & TRANSFER CASES
Drive Axle Noise Diagnosis

UNRELATED NOISES

Some driveline trouble symptoms are also common to the engine, transmission, wheel bearings, tires, and other parts of the vehicle. Ensure cause of trouble actually is in the drive axle before adjusting, repairing, or replacing any of its parts.

NON-DRIVE AXLE NOISES

A few conditions can sound just like drive axle noise and have to be considered in pre-diagnosis. The 4 most common noises are exhaust, tires, CV/universal joints and wheel trim rings.

In certain conditions, the pitch of the exhaust gases may sound like gear whine. At other times, it may be mistaken for a wheel bearing rumble.

Tires, especially radial and snow, can have a high-pitched tread whine or roar, similar to gear noise. Also, some non-standard tires with an unusual tread construction may emit a roar or whine.

Defective CV/universal joints may cause clicking noises or excessive driveline play that can be improperly diagnosed as drive axle problems.

Trim and moldings also can cause a whistling or whining noise. Ensure none of these components are causing the noise before disassembling the drive axle.

GEAR NOISE

A "howling" or "whining" noise from the ring and pinion gear can be caused by an improper gear pattern, gear damage, or improper bearing preload. It can occur at various speeds and driving conditions, or it can be continuous.

Before disassembling axle to diagnose and correct gear noise, make sure that tires, exhaust, and vehicle trim have been checked as possible causes.

CHUCKLE

This is a particular rattling noise that sounds like a stick against the spokes of a spinning bicycle wheel. It occurs while decelerating from 40 MPH and usually can be heard until vehicle comes to a complete stop. The frequency varies with the speed of the vehicle.

A chuckle that occurs on the driving phase is usually caused by excessive clearance due to differential gear wear, or by a damaged tooth on the coast side of the pinion or ring gear. Even a very small tooth nick or a ridge on the edge of a gear tooth is enough the cause the noise.

This condition can be corrected simply by cleaning the gear tooth nick or ridge with a small grinding wheel. If either gear is damaged or scored badly, the gear set must be replaced. If metal has broken loose, the carrier and housing must be cleaned to remove particles that could cause damage.

KNOCK

This is very similar to a chuckle, though it may be louder, and occur on acceleration or deceleration. Knock can be caused by a gear tooth that is damaged on the drive side of the ring and pinion gears. Ring gear bolts that are hitting the carrier casting can cause knock. Knock can also be due to excessive end play in the axle shafts.

CLUNK

Clunk is a metallic noise heard when an automatic transmission is engaged in Reverse or Drive, or when throttle is applied or released. It is caused by backlash somewhere in the driveline, but not necessarily in the axle. To determine whether driveline clunk is caused by the axle, check the total axle backlash as follows:

1) Raise vehicle on a frame or twinpost hoist so that drive wheels are free. Clamp a bar between axle companion flange and a part of the frame or body so that flange cannot move.

2) On conventional drive axles, lock the left wheel to keep it from turning. On all models, turn the right wheel slowly until it is felt to be in Drive condition. Hold a chalk marker on side of tire about 12" from center of wheel. Turn wheel in the opposite direction until it is again felt to be in Drive condition.

3) Measure the length of the chalk mark, which is the total axle backlash. If backlash is one inch or less, drive axle is not the source of clunk noise.

BEARING WHINE

Bearing whine is a high-pitched sound similar to a whistle. It is usually caused by malfunctioning pinion bearings. Pinion bearings operate at drive shaft speed. Roller wheel bearings may whine in a similar manner if they run completely dry of lubricant. Bearing noise will occur at all driving speeds. This distinguishes it from gear whine, which usually comes and goes as speed changes.

BEARING RUMBLE

Bearing rumble sounds like marbles being tumbled. It is usually caused by a malfunctioning wheel bearing. The lower pitch is because the wheel bearing turns at only about 1/3 of drive shaft speed.

CHATTER ON TURNS

This is a condition where the entire front or rear of vehicle vibrates when vehicle is moving. The vibration is plainly felt as well as heard. Extra differential thrust washers installed during axle repair can cause a condition of partial lock-up that creates this chatter.

AXLE SHAFT NOISE

Axle shaft noise is similar to gear noise and pinion bearing whine. Axle shaft bearing noise will normally distinguish itself from gear noise by occurring in all driving modes (Drive, cruise, coast and float), and will persist with transmission in Neutral while vehicle is moving at problem speed.

If vehicle displays this noise condition, remove suspect axle shafts, replace wheel seals and install a new set of bearings. Re-evaluate vehicle for noise before removing any internal components.

VIBRATION

Vibration is a high-frequency trembling, shaking or grinding condition (felt or heard) that may be constant or variable in level and can occur during the total operating speed range of the vehicle.

The types of vibrations that can be felt in the vehicle can be divided into 3 main groups:

- Vibrations of various unbalanced rotating parts of the vehicle.
- Resonance vibrations of the body and frame structures caused by rotating of unbalanced parts.
- Tip-in moans of resonance vibrations from stressed engine or exhaust system mounts or driveline flexing modes.

DESCRIPTION

Except Laser & Talon – Drive shaft assemblies are 3-piece units consisting of outer Constant Velocity (CV) joint, connecting shaft, and inner tripod joint. Removal, repair and installation procedures for the models covered are generally the same, however, some repair procedures vary according to specific model of axle.

Axle shafts are identified by configuration and manufacturer. Axle shaft configurations are equal length, or unequal length. *See Fig 1.* Axle shafts are manufactured by either GKN or Saginaw. Each manufacturer has several models. *See Fig. 2.* All LH body vehicles use Saginaw axles.

Laser & Talon – The axle shafts use a Birfield-type outer joint and a Tripod-type inner joint. The outer joint is not serviceable and cannot be disassembled.

FWD models have unequal length axles, AWD models have equal length axles with intermediate shaft and support bearing. The inner joint is splined into the transaxle and retained by a circlip.

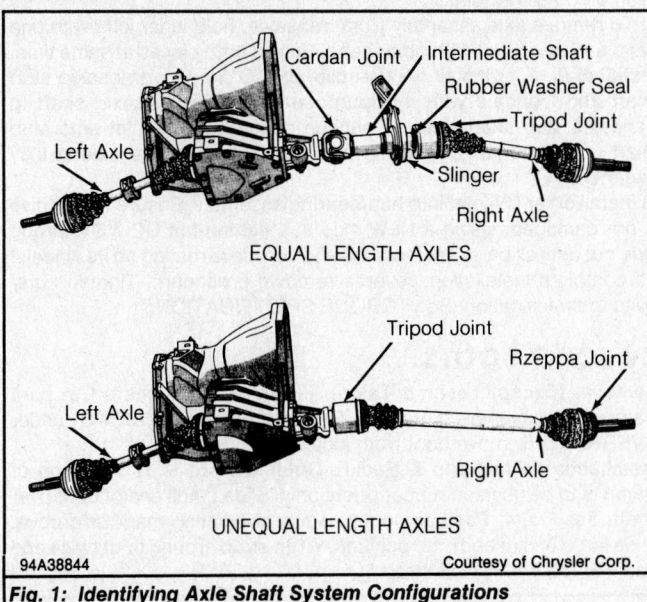

Fig. 1: Identifying Axle Shaft System Configurations

TROUBLE SHOOTING

NOTE: See DRIVE AXLE NOISE DIAGNOSIS article in AXLE SHAFTS & TRANSFER CASES.

LUBRICATION

CV joints require special lubrication. CV joints are enclosed in a boot to contain lubricant and prevent contamination. Periodic lubrication of CV joints is not required, but boots should be inspected at regular intervals.

ADJUSTMENTS

AXLE SHAFT POSITIONING

NOTE: On all models except Laser, LH body and Talon, check axle shaft positioning if engine/transaxle is loosened or moved or if front structural damage has occurred. Incorrect axle shaft positioning may result in premature failure of components.

Except Laser, LH Body & Talon – 1) Engine mount bolt holes are slotted for side-to-side positioning of engine. With vehicle completely assembled, ensure front wheels are in straight ahead position. Vehicle should be on platform hoist or alignment rack.

2) Using a tape measure, measure distance from inner edge of outer boot to inner edge of inner boot on both axle shafts. *See Fig. 3.* This measurement must be taken at bottom of axle shaft only.

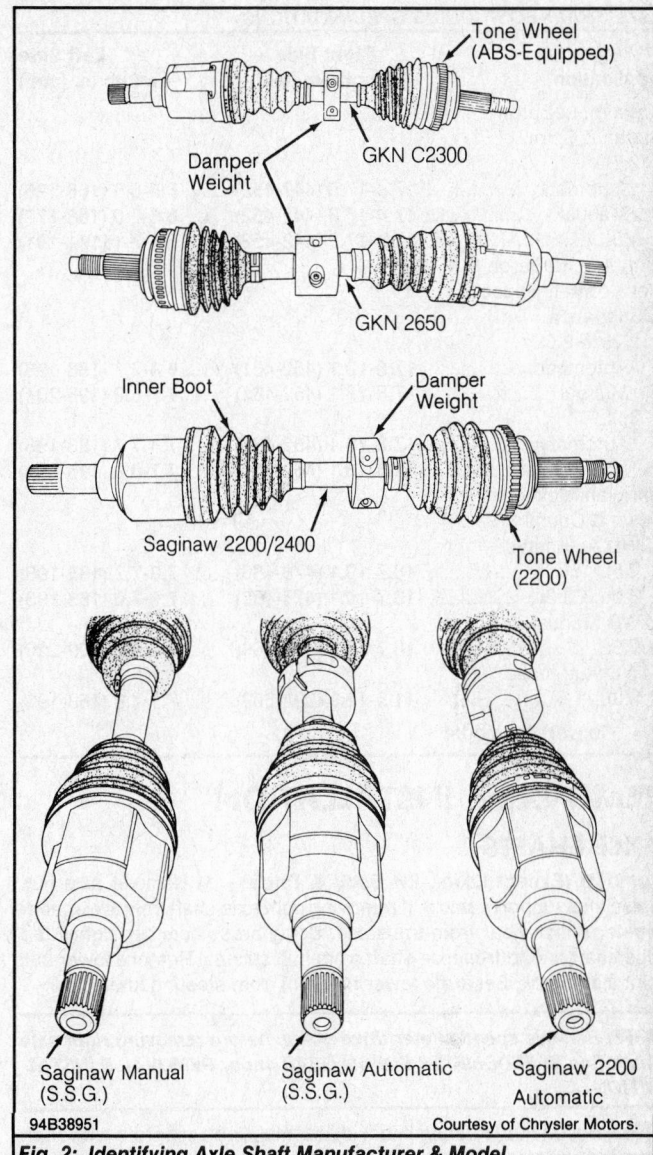

Fig. 2: Identifying Axle Shaft Manufacturer & Model

3) If both axle shafts are within specification, no further service is necessary. See AXLE SHAFT POSITIONING SPECIFICATIONS table. If either left or right axle shaft is not within specification, support engine/transaxle assembly using a floor jack.

4) Loosen right engine mount fasteners, front engine mount bracket and front crossmember fasteners. Pry engine right or left as required to obtain correct axle shaft length.

5) Tighten mounting bolts/nuts to specification. Recheck axle shaft length. Install damper weights (if equipped), and tighten to specification. See TORQUE SPECIFICATIONS.

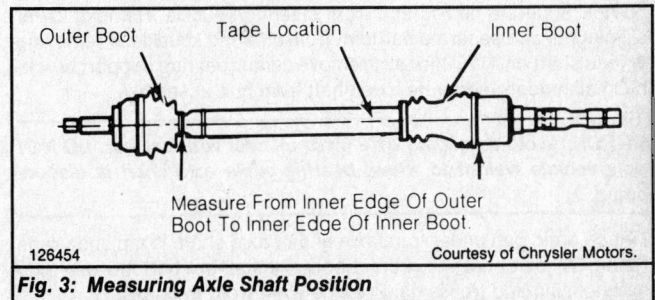

Fig. 3: Measuring Axle Shaft Position

5-4

AXLE SHAFTS
Chrysler Corp. FWD Passenger Cars & Vans (Cont.)

AXLE SHAFT POSITIONING SPECIFICATIONS

Application	Right Side Length In. (mm)	Left Side Length In. (mm)
Acclaim, LeBaron Sedan & Spirit		
2.5L		
Automatic	17.4-17.8 (442-452)	6.5-6.9 (166-176)
Manual	17.4-17.8 (442-452)	6.6-7.0 (168-178)
3.0L	17.4-17.8 (442-452)	6.7-7.1 (171-181)
Fifth Ave, LeBaron [1] New Yorker, Shadow & Sundance		
2.2L & 2.5L		
Automatic	17.8-18.1 (452-461)	7.4-7.7 (188-196)
Manual	17.8-18.1 (452-461)	7.7-8.0 (196-204)
3.0L		
Automatic	17.8-18.1 (452-461)	7.4-7.7 (188-196)
Manual	17.8-18.1 (452-461)	7.7-8.0 (196-204)
Caravan, Voyager Town & Country		
2WD Automatic		
2.5L	18.7-19.1 (476-486)	7.3-7.7 (185-196)
3.0L & 3.3L	18.7-19.1 (476-486)	7.2-7.6 (183-193)
2WD Manual		
2.5L	18.7-19.1 (476-486)	8.2-8.6 (209-220)
4WD Automatic		
3.3L	11.5-11.9 (292-302)	7.2-7.6 (183-193)

[1] – Convertible model.

REMOVAL & INSTALLATION

AXLE SHAFTS

Removal (Except Laser, LH Body & Talon – 1) Remove axle nut. Raise and support vehicle. If removing right axle shaft, remove speedometer pinion gear from transaxle. Using brass hammer, lightly tap axle shaft end to free axle shaft from hub splines. Remove lower ball joint clamp bolt. Separate lower ball joint from steering knuckle.

NOTE: Remove speedometer drive pinion before removing right axle shaft. See SPEEDOMETER PINION GEAR under REMOVAL & INSTALLATION.

2) Pull out on hub/steering knuckle assembly, and separate axle shaft from hub. If removing axle with support bearing, remove support bearing bolts. On all axles, grasp both CV joints at outer housings to prevent separation, and pull axle shaft out of transaxle or intermediate shaft. Remove axle shaft from vehicle.
Installation – Grasp both CV joints at outer housings, and insert inner CV joint into transaxle or intermediate shaft. To complete installation, reverse removal procedure. Using multipurpose lubricant, lubricate seal and wear sleeve. To complete installation, reverse removal procedure. Tighten all bolts and nuts to specifications. See TORQUE SPECIFICATIONS.
Removal (Laser & Talon) – 1) With vehicle on ground and brakes applied, remove axle nut. Raise and support vehicle. Remove tie rod end nut. Separate tie rod end from steering knuckle. Remove lower ball joint nut and separate ball joint from steering knuckle. If removing left axle shaft on AWD models, remove center bearing support bracket. On all models, separate axle shaft from hub assembly.

CAUTION: Avoid damaging axle shaft oil seal with pry bar. DO NOT apply vehicle weight to wheel bearing while axle shaft is disconnected.

2) Place drain pan under transaxle end of axle shaft. Wrap shop rags around CV joint boots to protect boots. Install pry bar between axle shaft housing and transaxle. Pry axle shaft from transaxle.

Installation – To install, reverse removal procedure. Use a soft mallet to tap inner CV joints until fully seated. DO NOT damage CV boots. Check fluid level and add fluid as necessary.

Removal (LH Body) – 1) Raise and support vehicle. Remove front wheel. Remove brake caliper, and wire aside. Remove brake rotor. Remove speed sensor cable routing bracket from strut assembly. Remove axle nut. Using a pry bar, dislodge inner tripod joint from transaxle. Disengage inner CV joint from transaxle, DO NOT remove axle shaft from transaxle at this time.

CAUTION: Bolts attaching strut assembly to steering knuckle are serrated. When removing bolts, turn nuts off of bolts. DO NOT turn bolts in steering knuckle.

2) Remove 2 strut-to-steering knuckle bolts. Separate steering knuckle from strut assembly. Separate outer CV joint from hub/bearing assembly, being careful not to damage flinger disc (hub bearing seal) on outer CV joint.
3) To remove axle assembly from transaxle, hold inner joint with one hand and axle shaft with other hand. Pull on both pieces at same time.
Installation – 1) Install NEW circlip and "O" ring on transaxle stub shaft and lubricate with multipurpose grease. Install axle shaft to transaxle stub shaft spline. Continue pushing tripod joint onto stub shaft until it bottoms. Pull on inner CV joint to ensure axle is fully engaged.
2) Install outer CV joint into hub/bearing assembly. Ensure flinger disc is not damaged. Using a NEW axle nut, tighten but DO NOT torque axle nut until all parts are installed and vehicle is resting on its wheels. To complete installation, reverse removal procedure. Tighten nuts/bolts to specification. See TORQUE SPECIFICATIONS.

CV JOINT BOOTS

Removal (Except Laser & Talon) – Remove axle shaft. Cut boot clamps. Disassemble CV joint. See appropriate CV JOINT under OVERHAUL. Remove boot from axle shaft.
Installation (With Strap & Buckle Outer Clamp) – 1) This type of clamp is to be used on rubber boots only. Slide small end of boot over shaft. See Fig. 4. Position boot to edge of locating mark or groove. Slide large end of boot into position. Wrap strap around boot twice and add 2.5" (63.5 mm). Cut strap.

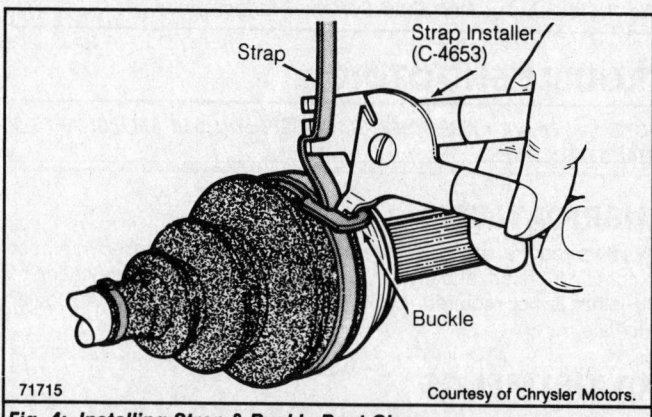

71715   Courtesy of Chrysler Motors.

Fig. 4: Installing Strap & Buckle Boot Clamp

2) Remove strap from CV joint. Install buckle on strap, and fold strap back about 1.25" (31.75 mm) on inside of buckle. Wrap strap around CV joint twice, passing strap through buckle on each wrap. Using Strap Installer (C-4653), tighten strap.
3) DO NOT pull installer downward to tighten strap, as strap can break. If necessary, disconnect and reinstall installer to retighten strap. With strap tightened sufficiently, move installer to side and cut strap .125" (3.18 mm) beyond buckle. Complete by folding strap under buckle.

AXLE SHAFTS
Chrysler Corp. FWD Passenger Cars & Vans (Cont.)

5-5

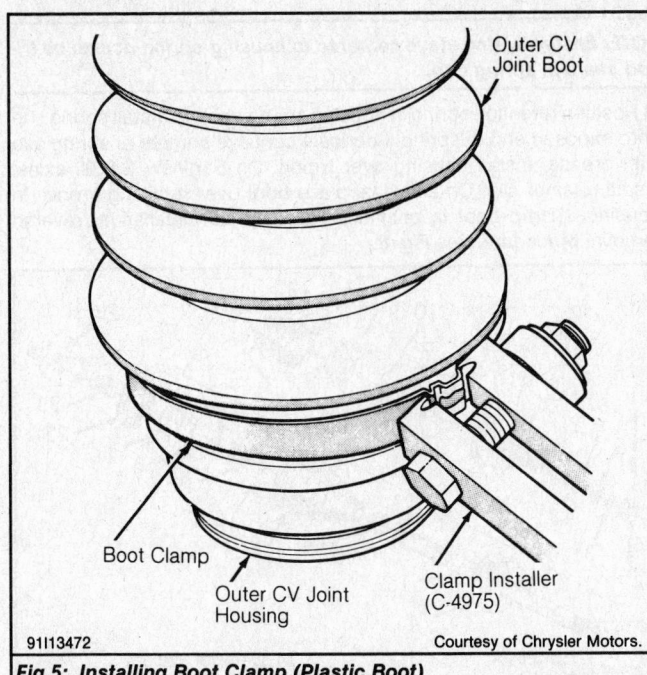

Fig 5: *Installing Boot Clamp (Plastic Boot)*

Installation (Crimp Type Clamp) – Slide small diameter boot clamp onto axle shaft. Slide boot onto axle shaft until small end of boot is seated in boot groove on shaft. Position boot clamp evenly in clamp groove on boot. Position tabs on boot clamp in jaws of Crimper (C-4975) for plastic boots, or plier type crimper for rubber boots. *See Fig. 5.* Tighten crimper until clamp is sufficiently tight (plastic boot clamps need to be much tighter than rubber boot clamps).

Installation (Ratchet Lock Clamp) – Slide small diameter boot clamp onto axle shaft. Slide large end of boot onto CV joint. Position large boot clamp evenly in groove on boot. Position prongs of Clamp Locking Tool (YA-3050) in holes of clamp. *See Fig. 6.* Squeeze until tight.

Removal (Laser & Talon) – 1) Remove axle from vehicle. Cut inner boot band clamps. Slide boot back and remove tripod joint housing.

NOTE: *Outer CV joint does not detach from axle shaft. Outer boot must be removed from inner end of axle.*

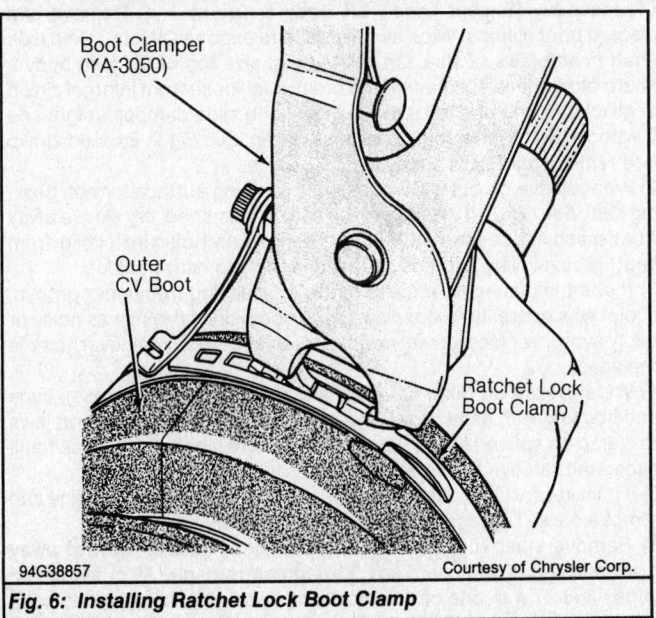

Fig. 6: *Installing Ratchet Lock Boot Clamp*

2) Remove snap ring retaining spider assembly. Remove spider assembly from axle shaft. *See Fig. 8.* Do not hammer on spider assembly bearings.

3) Clean splined end of axle shaft. Wrap splines on end of axle shaft with tape. Slide inner boot off shaft. If replacing outer boot, cut band clamps and slide boot off toward inboard end of shaft.

Installation – **1)** Ensure axle shaft is clean. Wrap tape on splined end of axle shaft. If removed, slide outer boot in to position on axle. Position small outer boot clamp on boot (DO NOT tighten).

2) Install CV grease supplied with boot kit. Distribute grease equally between boot and joint. Bleed off any excess air in boot. Check boot length. See CV BOOT LENGTH table. While boot is at specified length, install large outer boot clamp and tighten small outer boot clamp. Repeat procedure for inner joint.

INNER CV BOOT LENGTH [1]

Application	In. (mm)
Laser & Talon	
1.8L	
Left	2.8-3.1 (72-78)
Right	3.2-3.5 (82-88)
2.0L	
AWD	3.2-3.5 (82-88)
2WD	3.0-3.3 (77-83)

[1] – Distance measured between CV boot clamps.

Removal – Inner Boot (LH Body) – **1)** Remove axle shaft. Remove both clamps from inner CV boot. Remove CV boot from tripod housing, and slide boot down axle shaft.

2) Separate axle shaft from tripod joint housing. When removing tripod joint from housing, hold tripod rollers in place to prevent rollers and needle bearings from falling off. Remove snap ring that retains tripod joint to axle shaft. Remove tripod joint from axle shaft. Remove CV boot from axle.

Inspection – Clean and inspect tripod assembly, tripod joint housing and axle shaft. If any part shows excessive wear, replace axle shaft as an assembly.

Installation – **1)** Slide NEW CV boot and boot clamp on axle shaft. Install tripod joint onto axle shaft. Install tripod joint snap ring. Ensure snap ring is fully seated into axle shaft groove. Using grease provided in CV boot service package, distribute 1/2 of grease into tripod housing. DO NOT use any other type of grease. Put remaining grease into CV boot. Slide tripod joint into tripod joint housing.

2) Position small end of CV boot over boot retaining grove on axle shaft. Install boot clamp evenly over boot. Position large end of CV boot into tripod housing retaining groove. Before crimping CV boot clamp, check inner tripod joint stroke position. *See Fig. 7.*

3) Failure to correctly position tripod joint will result in CV boot failure. After tripod joint is positioned correctly, crimp boot clamp. If installing plastic boot, Crimp boot clamp using Clamp Installer (C-4975). *See Fig. 5.* To complete installation, reverse removal procedure. Tighten nuts/bolts to specification. See TORQUE SPECIFICATIONS.

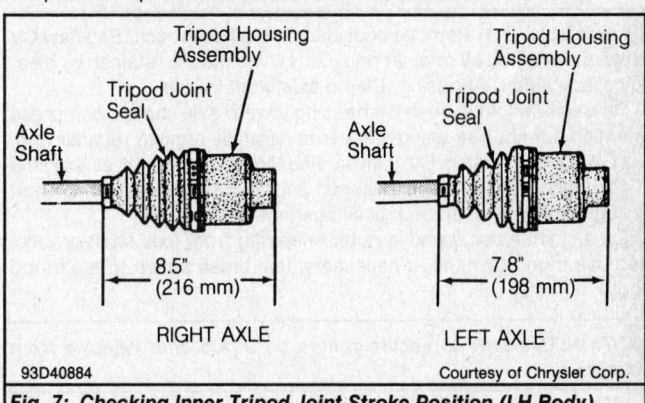

Fig. 7: *Checking Inner Tripod Joint Stroke Position (LH Body)*

5-6

AXLE SHAFTS
Chrysler Corp. FWD Passenger Cars & Vans (Cont.)

Removal – Outer Boot (LH Body) – Remove axle shaft. See FWD AXLE SHAFTS. Cut clamps from outer CV boot and remove boot from outer housing. Slide boot down axle shaft. Wipe away grease to expose snap ring that retains outer CV joint to axle shaft. Remove snap ring. Slide outer CV joint assembly off end of axle shaft. Remove CV boot.

Inspection – Clean and inspect outer CV joint assembly and axle shaft. If any part shows excessive wear, replace axle shaft as an assembly.

Installation – 1) Slide NEW CV boot and boot clamp on axle shaft. Install outer CV joint assembly onto axle shaft. CV joint is installed on axle shaft by pushing axle shaft into outer CV joint until snap ring is seated in groove on axle shaft.

2) Using grease provided in CV boot service package, distribute 1/2 of grease into outer CV joint housing. DO NOT use any other type of grease. Put remaining grease into CV boot.

3) Position small end of CV boot over boot retaining grove on axle shaft. Install boot clamp evenly over boot. Crimp boot clamp. If installing plastic boot, use Clamp Installer (C-4975). See Fig. 5. Position large end of CV boot into outer CV joint housing retaining groove.

4) Install boot clamp evenly over boot. Using clamp installer, crimp boot clamp. To complete installation, reverse removal procedure. Tighten nuts/bolts to specification. See TORQUE SPECIFICATIONS.

SPEEDOMETER PINION GEAR

Removal (Except Laser, LH Body & Talon) – Disconnect speed sensor connector. Remove sensor assembly retaining bolt. Gently remove sensor and pinion gear from housing.

Installation – To install, reverse removal procedure. Ensure adapter and transaxle housing area are clean. Install and tighten retaining bolt.

AXLE SHAFT DAMPER WEIGHTS

Removal & Installation – Damper weights are split in 2 pieces and are attached by 2 bolts to left axle shaft between inner and outer CV joints. Damper weights should be removed from axle shaft during axle shaft positioning procedure. Ensure damper weight bolts are tightened to specification. See TORQUE SPECIFICATIONS.

OVERHAUL

NOTE: On Laser and Talon, outer joint cannot be disassembled and is serviced with axle shaft. Replacement inner joint is available. On LH Bodies, axle assembly is not serviceable (except boots), and must be replaced as an assembly.

INNER CV JOINT

NOTE: On Laser & Talon, see INNER CV JOINT BOOT for inner joint replacement procedure.

Disassembly – 1) Remove boot clamps. Pull boot back. Saginaw CV joints are retained by retainer ring. GKN CV joints are retained by plastic collar inside CV housing. Clamp axle shaft in vise.

2) On Saginaw joints, push CV housing toward axle shaft to compress retention spring. Use a screwdriver to carefully remove retainer ring. On GKN joints, clamp CV joint in vise. Move axle shaft at extreme angle until one of the tripod bearings pops out. Continue holding shaft at angle and pull on shaft until all bearings are free.

3) On all joint types, remove outer snap ring from axle shaft groove. Remove tripod by hand. If necessary, use brass punch to tap tripod body.

CAUTION: Use tape to secure rollers on tripod after removal from housing.

Reassembly – 1) Install NEW axle boot on axle shaft. Slide tripod onto axle shaft, chamfered side first. Flat side of tripod should be next to retaining ring groove. Using grease supplied in boot kit, distribute 1/2 of the grease into boot and 1/2 of the grease into CV housing.

NOTE: Ensure spring stays centered in housing spring pocket as tripod seats in spring cup.

2) Position retention spring in housing spring pocket. Install spring cup onto exposed end of spring. Lubricate concave surface of spring cup with grease. Install housing over tripod. On Saginaw S.S.G. axles, install retainer clip. On all axles, place boot over retaining groove in housing. Clamp boot in position. To complete installation, reverse removal procedure. See Fig. 8.

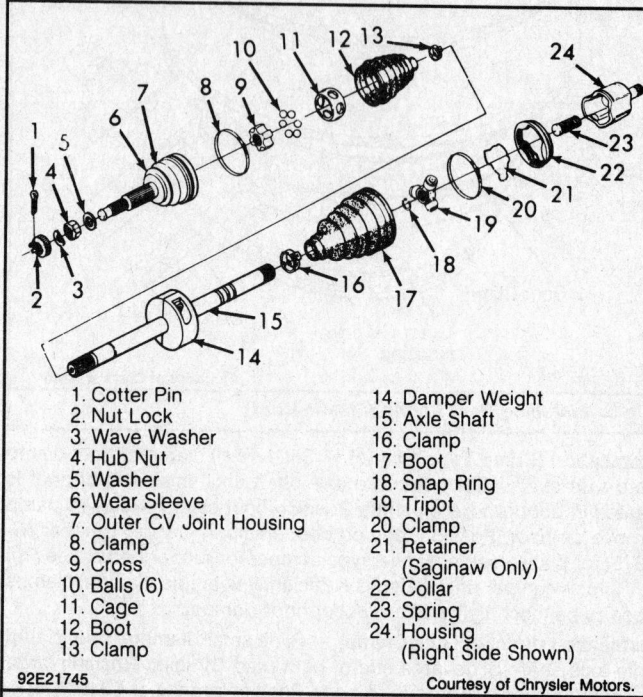

1. Cotter Pin	14. Damper Weight
2. Nut Lock	15. Axle Shaft
3. Wave Washer	16. Clamp
4. Hub Nut	17. Boot
5. Washer	18. Snap Ring
6. Wear Sleeve	19. Tripot
7. Outer CV Joint Housing	20. Clamp
8. Clamp	21. Retainer
9. Cross	(Saginaw Only)
10. Balls (6)	22. Collar
11. Cage	23. Spring
12. Boot	24. Housing
13. Clamp	(Right Side Shown)

92E21745   Courtesy of Chrysler Motors.

Fig. 8: Exploded View Of Axle Assembly

OUTER CV JOINT

NOTE: On Laser, LH Body & Talon, DO NOT attempt to overhaul outer CV joint.

Disassembly (Except Laser, LH Body & Talon) – 1) Remove and discard boot clamps. Wipe away grease to expose CV joint. Hold axle shaft in soft jaws of vise. On GKN joints, give top of CV joint body a sharp blow with a soft hammer to break joint loose from internal circlip in groove at end of shaft. On Saginaw joint, slide damper weight and CV boot toward inner joint to expose circlip. See Fig 9. Expand circlip and remove joint from shaft.

2) Wear sleeve on outer CV housing is a wiping surface for hub bearing seal. See Fig. 8. If wear sleeve is bent or damaged, pry sleeve away from machined ledge of CV joint. Remove and discard circlip from shaft groove. New circlip is supplied in replacement boot kit.

3) If shaft is damaged, remove heavy spacer ring from inner groove. If joint was operating properly, replace boots only. If joint was noisy or badly worn, replace complete joint. Replace boot whenever joint is replaced.

4) Wipe grease off outer CV joint, and mark inner race (cross), cage and housing with paint. Position joint vertically in vise, using soft jaws to clamp on splined shaft. Press down on one side of inner race to tilt cage, and remove ball from opposite side. Remove all balls.

5) If joint is very tight, use brass drift and hammer to tap inner race and remove balls. Tilt cage and inner race assembly to vertical.

6) Remove inner race and cage assembly by pulling upward away from housing. Turn inner race 90 degrees to cage. Align elongated cage window with one of spherical lands on race. Raise land to cage window, and remove inner race by swinging it out of cage. See Fig. 10.

AXLE SHAFTS
Chrysler Corp. FWD Passenger Cars & Vans (Cont.)

5-7

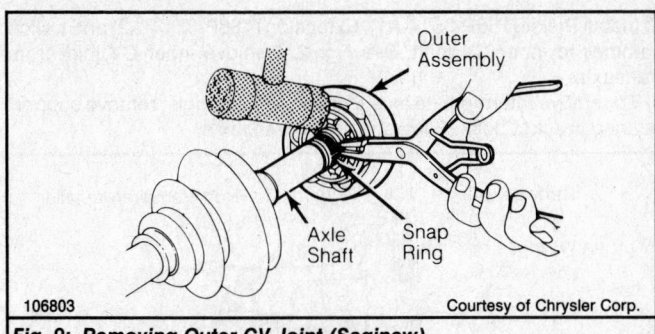

Fig. 9: Removing Outer CV Joint (Saginaw)

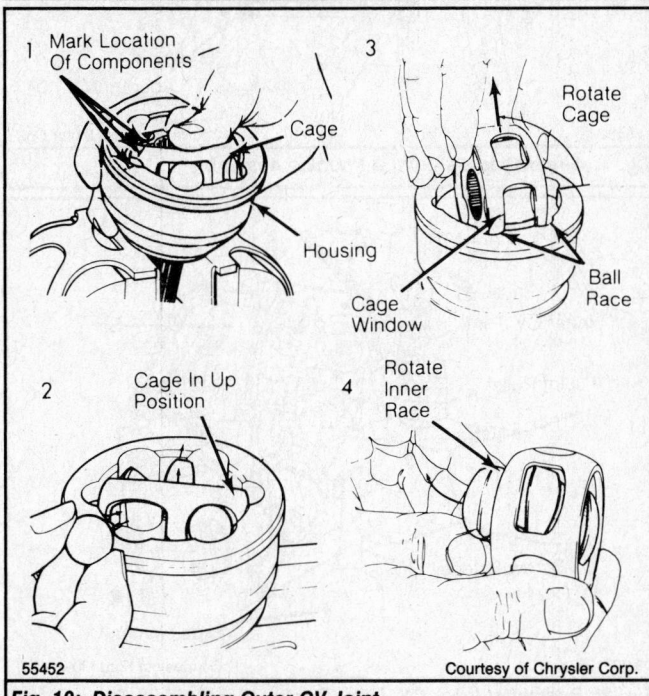

Fig. 10: Disassembling Outer CV Joint

Inspection – Check grease for contamination. Wash all parts except boots in solvent, and dry with compressed air. Inspect races, splined shaft and nut threads for damage. Inspect balls and cage for excessive wear or damage. If excessive wear or damage is found, replace CV joint.

Reassembly – 1) Position new wear sleeve on joint housing machined ledge. Lightly oil all components before reassembly. Align parts according to paint markings.

2) Insert one inner race (cross) into cage window, and feed race into cage. Pivot inner race to fully assemble cage and race. Align opposing elongated cage windows with housing land. Feed cage assembly into housing. Pivot cage 90 degrees to complete installation.

3) Counterbore of inner race should face outward from joint. Apply lubricant to ball races from packet in boot kit.

4) Distribute grease equally between all sides of ball grooves. Insert balls into raceways by tilting cage and inner race assembly. Fasten boot to shaft. Insert NEW circlip from shaft groove kit.

5) Position outer joint on splined end of axle shaft. Put hub nut on stub axle. Engage splines, and tap sharply on hub nut using mallet. Ensure circlip is properly seated by trying to pull joint off shaft.

6) Install large end of boot over joint housing, ensuring boot is not twisted. Clamp boot to housing. See CV JOINT BOOTS under REMOVAL & INSTALLATION

TORQUE SPECIFICATIONS

TORQUE SPECIFICATIONS

Application	Ft. Lbs. (N.m)
Except Laser, LH Body & Talon	
Axle Hub Nut	180 (244)
Ball Joint Clamp Nut	70 (95)
Damper Weight Bolts	21 (28)
Engine Mount Bolts	
Front Mount	50 (68)
Timing Belt Side	75-98 (102-133)
Transaxle Mount	50 (68)
Wheel Lug Nut	95 (129)
Laser & Talon	
Axle Nut	148-192 (200-260)
Brake Caliper Mounting Bolts	59-74 (80-100)
Center Bearing Support Bracket (AWD)	27-34 (37-46)
Lower Ball Joint Nut	44-53 (60-72)
Steering Knuckle-To-Strut	81-103 (110-140)
Wheel Lug Nuts	89-103 (120-140)
LH Body	
Axle Nut	70-90 (95-122)
Brake Caliper Guide Pin Bolts	14 (19)
Steering Knuckle-To-Strut Nuts	125 (169)
Wheel Lug Nuts	95 (129)

AXLE SHAFTS
Ford Motor Co. FWD Passenger Cars

Aspire, Capri, Continental, Escort, Festiva, Probe, Sable, Taurus, Tempo, Topaz, Tracer, Villager

DESCRIPTION & OPERATION

Power from transaxle is transferred to driving wheels by 2 axle shafts. Both axle shafts use CV joints at inner and outer ends. CV joints are enclosed in CV joint boots, and connected by an interconnecting shaft. CV boots maintain proper lubrication and prevent contaminants from entering joint. Interconnecting shaft is splined on both ends.

Circlips retain interconnecting shaft in the inner and outer CV joints. A circlip retains the inner CV joint stub shaft in differential side gear. Outer CV joint stub shaft is splined into the wheel hub, and secured by a spindle nut. All outer CV joints are fixed position type, and inner CV joints are plunge (movable) type.

LUBRICATION

The CV joints require CV Joint Grease (E43Z-19590-A). After servicing axles, ensure transmission is filled with proper lubricant. See appropriate TRANSMISSION SERVICING article.

REMOVAL & INSTALLATION

ASPIRE, CAPRI, FESTIVA & PROBE

Removal – 1) Remove front wheels and inner fender splash guards. Carefully raise staked portion of axle nut. Apply brakes and loosen, but DO NOT remove, axle nut. Remove stabilizer bar-to-control arm nut, spacer and bolt.

2) Remove lower control arm ball joint clamp bolt. Pry downward on lower control arm to separate control arm from knuckle. Remove knuckle-to-strut attaching bolts. Slide knuckle assembly off axle shaft. On Capri turbo models, remove bolts securing intermediate shaft bearing bracket to engine.

NOTE: If removing right drive axle, disconnect dynamic damper support from engine block.

---

3) On all models, insert a pry bar between transaxle case and axle flange. Carefully apply force to pry bar until axle circlip is disengaged.
4) Carefully withdraw axle assembly from transaxle, and quickly install Transaxle Plug (T87C-7025-C). Remove and discard axle nut. Pull axle from hub.
Installation – 1) Install a NEW circlip on transaxle end of axle. Replace oil seal (if necessary). Remove transaxle plug, and carefully install axle into transaxle. Ensure circlip snaps into retaining groove.
2) Install axle into hub. Install NEW axle nut. Tighten all bolts and nuts to specifications. See TORQUE SPECIFICATIONS. Stake NEW axle nut with blunt-nose chisel. To complete installation, reverse removal procedure.

CONTINENTAL, SABLE & TAURUS

Removal – 1) Remove wheel assembly and hub nut retainer. Remove bolt attaching brake hose to strut.
2) Remove lower ball joint pinch bolt and nut, and discard. Remove ABS sensor, and move aside (if equipped). Pry down on control arm assembly to separate ball joint from steering knuckle. If necessary, disconnect stabilizer bar at control arm.

CAUTION: If both axles are removed, Shipping Plugs (T81P-1177-B) must be installed to prevent differential side gears from moving. If side gears move, transaxle must be removed to realign side gears.

---

3) Install Hub Remover/Installer (T81P-1104-C) assembly, and push CV joint out of hub assembly. *See Fig. 1.* Remove axle shaft from vehicle.

4) Install Puller (T86P-3514-A1), Extension (T86P-3514-A2) and a slide hammer to inner CV joint. *See Fig. 2.* Remove inner CV joint from transaxle.
5) To remove intermediate axle shaft on MTX models, remove support bearing bracket bolts. Slide shaft from transaxle.

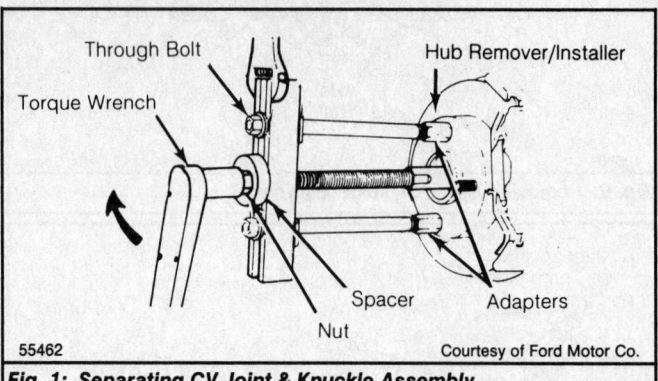

Fig. 1: Separating CV Joint & Knuckle Assembly

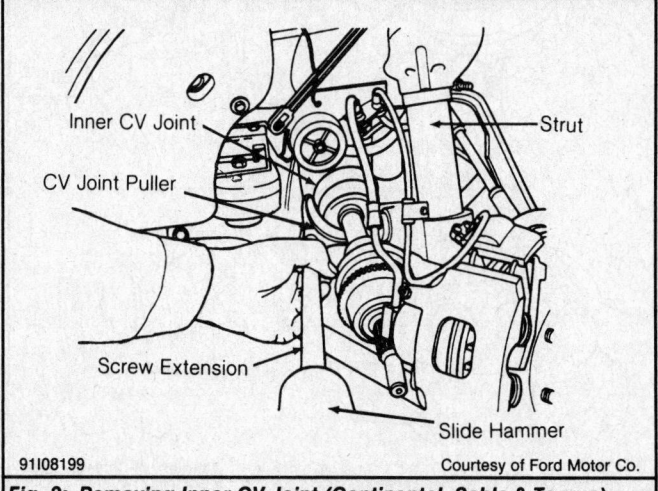

Fig. 2: Removing Inner CV Joint (Continental, Sable & Taurus)

Installation – 1) Replace circlip on transaxle end of axle shaft. Insert axle shaft into transaxle. Ensure circlip is fully engaged in transaxle. If difficulty is encountered engaging axle shaft into transmission, tap on outer CV joint with plastic or rubber mallet.
2) Feed outer CV joint stub shaft into hub as far as possible. Install NEW hub retainer nut on end of axle shaft. Tighten retainer nut to specification. See TORQUE SPECIFICATIONS.

ESCORT & TRACER

Removal – 1) Remove wheel assembly and hub nut retainer. Remove splash shield. Remove bolt attaching brake hose to strut. Remove and discard bolt and nut retaining lower ball joint to steering knuckle.
2) Separate tie rod end from steering knuckle. Pry down on control arm assembly to separate ball joint from steering knuckle. Pull out on steering knuckle, and remove outer CV joint from hub assembly.
3) Support outer axle shaft assembly with wire to keep axle shaft straight during inner CV joint removal. Put drain pan under transaxle. To remove right axle on 1.9L models, pry outward between inner CV joint and transaxle. After axle disengages from differential side gears, remove axle assembly.
4) To remove right axle on 1.8L models, remove support bearing mounting bolts. pry outward between dynamic damper bearing support bracket and starter motor. After axle disengages from differential side gears, remove axle assembly.

CAUTION: If both axles are removed, Shipping Plugs (T81P-1177-B) must be installed to prevent differential side gears from moving. If side gears move, transaxle must be removed to realign side gears.

5) On all models, to remove left axle, use jack to support transaxle. Remove transaxle-to-crossmember nuts. Remove crossmember rear and front attaching bolts, respectively. To remove left axle, pry outward between inner CV joint and transaxle. DO NOT damage differential oil seal, case or CV joint boot. Install Shipping Plugs (T81P-1177-B) to prevent side gears from moving.

Installation – Replace inner CV joint circlip. To install axle shaft, reverse removal procedure. Ensure circlip is fully seated in transaxle. Install NEW axle retaining nut and tighten to specifications. See TORQUE SPECIFICATIONS. Ensure one lock tab is positioned in axle shaft slot. Replace nut if cracks occur in staked portion of nut after nut is staked.

TEMPO & TOPAZ

Removal – 1) Remove wheel assembly and hub nut retainer. Remove bolt attaching brake hose to strut. Remove and discard bolt and nut retaining lower ball joint to steering knuckle.

2) Remove stabilizer bar link. Move brake rotor shield aside, and pry down on control arm assembly to separate ball joint from steering knuckle.

NOTE: On Tempo and Topaz with automatic transmission, right axle shaft must be removed from transaxle before left axle shaft.

3) Install Hub Remover/Installer (T81P-1104-C) assembly, and push CV joint out of hub assembly. See Fig. 1.

4) Pry axle shaft out of transaxle. DO NOT damage differential oil seal, case or CV joint boot. Install Shipping Plugs (T81P-1177-B) to prevent side gears from moving.

CAUTION: If both axles are removed, Shipping Plugs (T81P-1177-B) must be installed to prevent differential side gears from moving. If side gears move, transaxle must be removed to realign side gears.

CAUTION: DO NOT reuse hub nut retainers, circlips, snap rings or lower ball joint pinch bolt and nut.

Installation – Replace inner CV joint circlip. To install axle shaft, reverse removal procedure. Ensure circlip is fully seated in transaxle. During hub nut retainer installation, an click should be heard. Replace nut retainer if no click is heard or if any tabs are broken. Tighten nut retainer to specifications, and ensure one tab is staked in axle shaft slot. See TORQUE SPECIFICATIONS.

VILLAGER

Removal – 1) Raise and support vehicle. Remove front wheels. Remove splash shields. Remove and discard cotter pin from half-shaft. Remove castellated nut and insulator. Remove steering knuckle/wheel hub assembly nut. Remove flat washer.

2) Remove and discard cotter pin from ball joint. Loosen ball joint nut until it contacts outer CV joint. Strike steering knuckle on outside of ball joint taper with a hammer, while pulling down on control arm, until ball joint breaks free. Remove nut.

3) Remove stabilizer link-to-control arm nut. Using a pry bar, separate stabilizer link from control arm. Pry down on control arm and separate ball joint from steering knuckle. Separate half-shaft from hub/bearing assembly. Position drain pan under transaxle.

CAUTION: Ensure pry bar does not damage transaxle case, oil seal, outer race or boot.

4) When removing left side half-shaft, position 2 pry bars, one on either side of outer race, between outer race and transaxle case. Pry gently outward to unseat circlip.

NOTE: When removing right side half-shaft, it is not necessary to remove half-shaft support bearing bracket from engine block.

5) Remove 3 half-shaft support bearing retainer-to-bracket bolts. Pull right side half-shaft assembly from differential side gear. Support half-shaft assemblies and slide out of vehicle. DO NOT damage CV joint boots.

Installation – 1) Inspect differential seals and replace if leakage is evident. Install new circlip on left inner CV joint. To complete installation, reverse removal procedure. Tighten bolts to specification. See TORQUE SPECIFICATIONS.

DISASSEMBLY, OVERHAUL & REASSEMBLY

NOTE: Use CV JOINT TYPE APPLICATION chart to determine which disassembly procedure to follow.

CV JOINT TYPE APPLICATION

Application	Inner Joint	Outer Joint
Aspire	Tripod	Birfield
Capri		
Non-Turbo	Tripod	Birfield
Turbo	[1] DOJ	Birfield
Continental	Triplan	Rzeppa
Escort & Tracer	Tripod	Birfield
Festiva	Tripod	Birfield
Probe		
A/T	Tripod	Birfield
M/T	[1] DOJ	Birfield
Sable & Taurus		
3.0L Non-ABS	T&C Design	Rzeppa
3.0L W/ABS	GKN Trilobe	Rzeppa
3.0 SHO	Tripod	Rzeppa
3.2 SHO	Triplan	Rzeppa
3.8L	GKN Trilobe	Rzeppa
Tempo/Topaz		
A/T		
2.3L Left	Tripod	Birfield
2.3L Right	Tripod	Birfield
3.0L Left	[1] DOJ	Birfield
3.0L Right	Tripod	Birfield
M/T		
2.3L Left	[1] DOJ	Birfield
2.3L Right	Tripod	Birfield
3.0L Left	[1] DOJ	Birfield
3.0L Right	Tripod	Birfield
Villager	[1] DOJ	Rzeppa

[1] – Double Offset Joint

BIRFIELD TYPE OUTER JOINT

The Birfield type outer CV joint cannot be removed from axle interconnecting shaft, or overhauled. Birfield joints are serviced as an assembly with halfshaft. Outer boot replacement is accomplished by removing inner joint. Follow appropriate inner joint DISASSEMBLY, OVERHAUL & REASSEMBLY procedure.

RZEPPA TYPE OUTER JOINT

Disassembly – 1) Remove axle shaft from vehicle. Clamp axle shaft horizontally in vise with protected jaws. Cut large boot clamp, and pull boot back over axle shaft. Reposition axle shaft in vise to expose inner race. See Fig. 3.

2) Use hammer and brass drift to tap inner bearing race sharply and dislodge internal circlip. DO NOT drop CV joint. Using a small screwdriver, remove and discard circlip and stop ring at end of axle shaft.

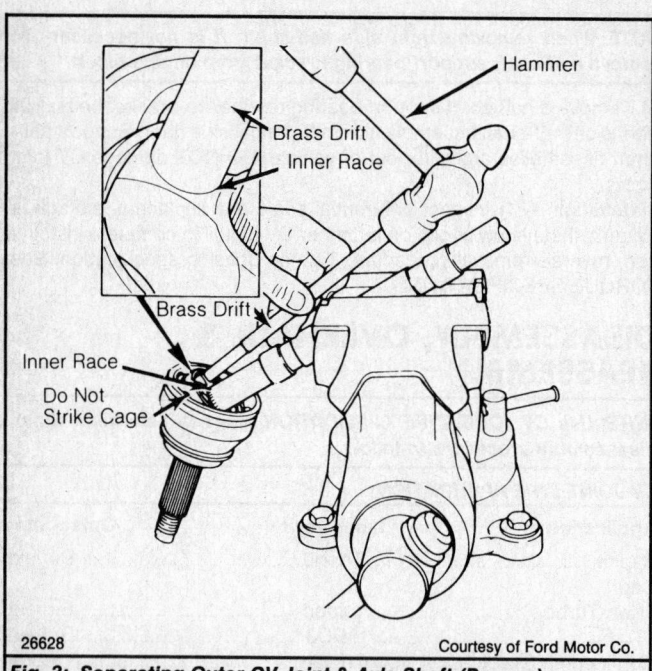

26628   Courtesy of Ford Motor Co.

Fig. 3: Separating Outer CV Joint & Axle Shaft (Rzeppa)

3) Remove boot (if replacing). Place CV joint stub shaft, bearing facing up, in vise. Press down on inner race enough to tilt cage, and remove ball. *See Fig. 4.* Using a hammer and wooden drift, tap on inner race to tilt cage (if necessary).

4) Tilt cage enough to obtain clearance to remove ball. If ball(s) are difficult to remove, use screwdriver with blunted edges to assist removal. Repeat procedure for remaining balls. Pivot cage and inner race assembly until it is vertical in outer race. Align cage windows with outer race lands while pivoting cage.

5) Lift cage assembly from outer race. With cage assembly removed, pivot inner race until it is straight (vertical) in cage. Align one inner race land with one cage window, and position race through window. Rotate inner race up and out of cage.

NOTE: Components are factory matched and cannot be interchanged, mixed or substituted.

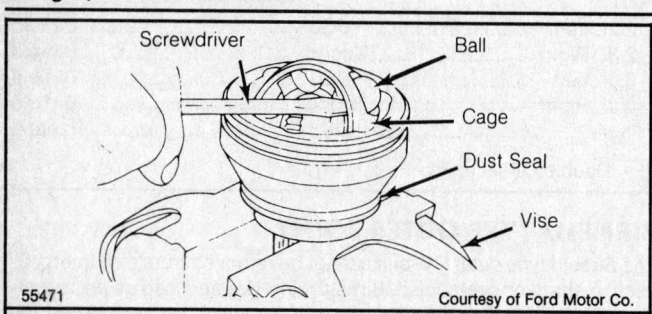

55471   Courtesy of Ford Motor Co.

Fig. 4: Removing CV Joint Balls (Rzeppa)

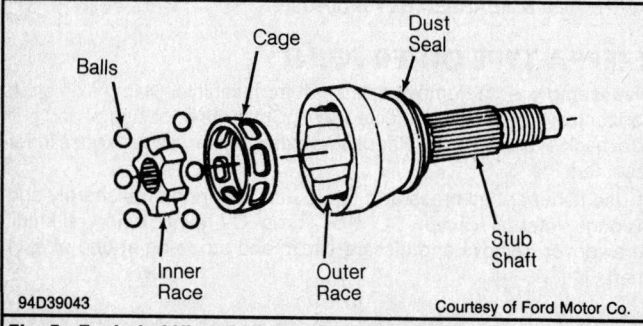

94D39043   Courtesy of Ford Motor Co.

Fig. 5: Exploded View Of Outer Joint (Rzeppa)

Reassembly – 1) If components are cracked, broken, pitted or worn, replace complete assembly. Apply CV Joint Grease on inner and outer races.

2) To reassemble cage and balls, reverse disassembly procedure. *See Fig. 5.* Install boot on axle shaft (if removed) and seat in groove. Securely tighten, but DO NOT overtighten, clamp. Install stop ring, and ensure ring is properly seated.

3) Install new circlip. Pack CV joint and boot with specified CV joint grease. See LUBRICATION. Fill CV joint first, and place remaining amount of grease in boot. Replace dust seal if damaged. To complete reassembly, reverse disassembly procedure.

Disassembly & Reassembly – ABS Wheel Sensor Ring – 1) Separate outer CV joint from axle shaft. Place stub shaft assembly on Remover/Installer (T88P-20202-A) with splined end of stub shaft up. Press anti-lock brake sensor ring off stub shaft assembly.

2) Place anti-lock brake sensor ring on remover/installer. Position stub shaft through anti-lock brake sensor ring (splined end of stub shaft down). Press stub shaft through ring until fully seated.

DOUBLE OFFSET INNER JOINT (DOJ)

Disassembly – 1) Mount half-shaft in soft-jawed vise. Using Boot Clamp Pliers (D87P-1090-A), remove boot clamps and discard. If half-shaft is removed to replace damaged boot, inspect grease for contamination by rubbing between fingers. If grease is contaminated, replace joint.

NOTE: DO NOT remove wheel speed sensor rotors. Speed sensor rotors are serviced as a separate item.

2) Remove wire retaining ring from outer race. *See Fig. 6.* Slide inboard CV joint boot back and clean grease out of joint assembly and boot. Slide outer race off axle assembly. Remove 6 ball bearings from cage and clean in solvent.

3) Using snap-ring pliers, remove snap ring from end of half-shaft. On Villager, remove inner race using a 2-jaw puller. *See Fig. 7.* On all models, remove inner race from half-shaft. Slide cage off. Slide boot off half-shaft. *See Fig. 8.*

NOTE: If boot is to be reused, wrap half-shaft splines with tape before removing boot from shaft.

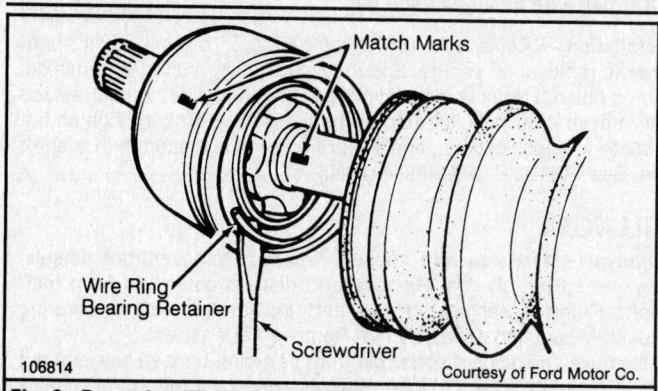

106814   Courtesy of Ford Motor Co.

Fig. 6: Removing Wire Retaining Ring

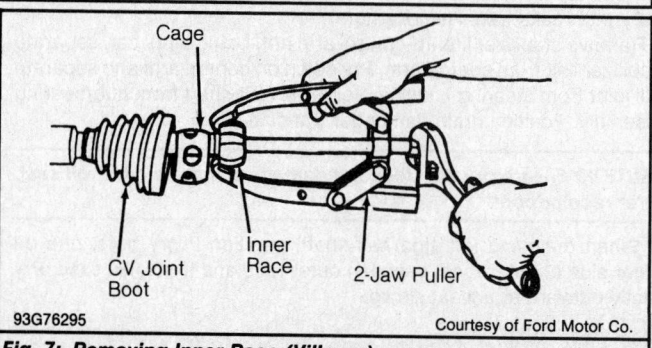

93G76295   Courtesy of Ford Motor Co.

Fig. 7: Removing Inner Race (Villager)

Reassembly – 1) Slide boot and small boot clamp onto half-shaft. Using a soft-faced hammer, gently tap inner race onto shaft. Slide cage onto half-shaft. Using snap-ring pliers, seat snap ring onto end of half-shaft.

2) Install 6 ball bearings into cage. Lubricate with a small amount of CV joint grease to hold bearings in cage. Slide outer race (joint housing) onto end of half-shaft, over ball bearings. *See Fig. 8.*

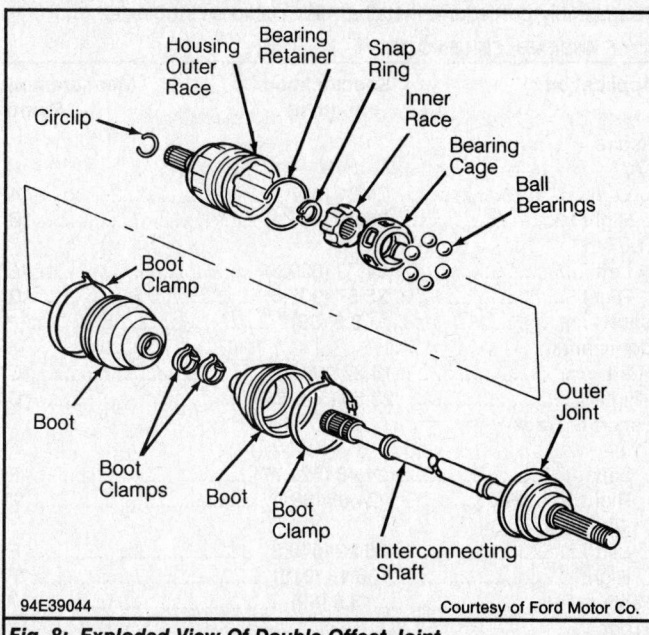

94E39044   Courtesy of Ford Motor Co.

Fig. 8: Exploded View Of Double Offset Joint

3) Fill boot with 7.43-8.31 oz. (210-235g) High-Temp Constant Velocity Joint Grease E43Z-19590-A (ESP-M1C207-A). Position boot on outer race. Ensure boot is fully seated in shaft grooves and outer race. Insert blunt screwdriver between boot and outer race to allow trapped air to escape.

4) Using Boot Clamp Pliers (D87P-1090-A), install 2 NEW boot clamps on inboard boot. Extend or compress inner joint to obtain specified axle length. See AXLE ASSEMBLED LENGTH table. Wrap clamps around boot in clockwise direction and tighten securely (DO NOT overtighten clamp). Work CV joint through its full range of travel at various angles. Joint should flex, extend and compress smoothly without stress on boot. For installation, reverse removal procedure.

GNK TRILOBE INNER JOINT

NOTE: If replacing inner CV boot, outer joint must be removed. Trilobe joint cannot be completely disassembled.

Disassembly – 1) Remove axle shaft from vehicle. Cut and remove both boot clamps. Slide boot back away from inner CV joint housing. Slide outer race (joint housing) off halfshaft assembly. Remove trilobe insert from inner CV joint housing.

2) When replacing damaged boots, check grease for contamination. If grease is contaminated, replace joint and halfshaft assembly. Do not attempt to remove spider as it is permanently attached to axle interconnecting shaft. To replace inner boot, remove outer joint. See RZEPPA TYPE OUTER JOINT disassembly procedure.

Reassembly – 1) Slide inner boot off axle interconnecting shaft. Slide new inner boot and small boot clamp on axle interconnecting shaft.

2) Install trilobe insert on inner joint housing until engaged in groove. Fill inner CV joint housing and boot with 9 oz. (250 grams) CV joint grease (E43Z-19590-A).

3) Position boot over housing. Extend or compress axle shaft to achieve specified length of CV joint. Ensure boot is properly seated in groove. Wipe excess grease from external surfaces. Remove trapped air by lifting boot off housing with a dull screwdriver. Ensure axle shaft is specified length and boot properly seated.

4) Install boot clamp. Tighten, but DO NOT overtighten, clamp. Install low profile type clamps. See Fig. 9. To complete reassembly, reverse disassembly procedure.

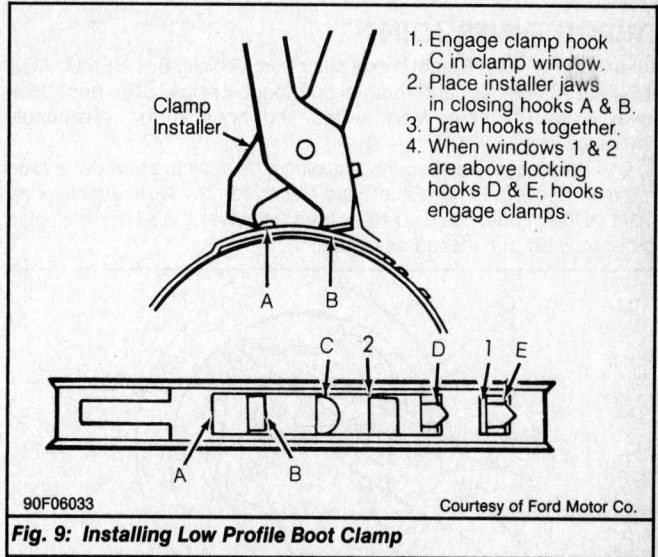

1. Engage clamp hook C in clamp window.
2. Place installer jaws in closing hooks A & B.
3. Draw hooks together.
4. When windows 1 & 2 are above locking hooks D & E, hooks engage clamps.

90F06033   Courtesy of Ford Motor Co.

Fig. 9: Installing Low Profile Boot Clamp

T & C DESIGN INNER JOINT

The T & C type inner joint cannot be removed from axle interconnecting shaft. The joint cannot be disassembled or serviced in any way (except boot replacement). If any servicing is necessary, replace joint and halfshaft assembly. Inner boot replacement is accomplished by removing outer joint. Extend or compress inner joint to obtain specified axle length. See AXLE ASSEMBLED LENGTH table.

TRIPLAN TYPE INNER JOINT

The triplan type inner joint can be removed from axle interconnecting shaft but cannot be disassembled or overhauled. Replace joint assembly if movement is not smooth, or noise exists.

Removal & Installation – 1) Remove axle assembly. Mount axle by interconnecting shaft in vise. Cut both boot clamps. Pull boot back and wipe away grease to expose snap ring on axle interconnecting shaft.

2) Using snap ring pliers, expand snap ring and pull joint from shaft. Remove snap ring from axle interconnecting shaft. Remove boot (if necessary).

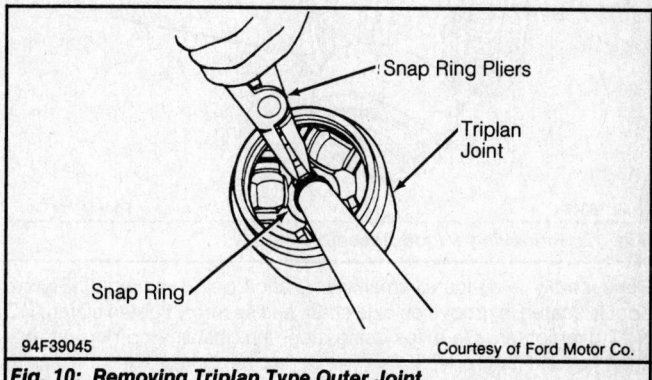

94F39045   Courtesy of Ford Motor Co.

Fig. 10: Removing Triplan Type Outer Joint

3) To install, slide boot with small boot clamp, on axle shaft. Position triplan joint on axle shaft splines. Tap on inner joint with soft-faced mallet to engage snap ring. Distribute 17.3 oz. (490 grams) of CV joint grease (E43-1950-A) equally between joint and boot.

4) Position boot over housing. Extend or compress axle shaft to achieve specified length of CV joint. See AXLE ASSEMBLED LENGTH table. Ensure boot is properly seated in groove. Wipe excess grease from external surfaces. Remove trapped air by lifting boot off housing with a dull screwdriver. Ensure axle shaft is specified length and boot properly seated.

5) Install low profile type clamps (DO NOT overtighten). *See Fig. 9.* To complete reassembly, reverse disassembly procedure. Install a NEW circlip.

TRIPOD INNER JOINT

Disassembly – 1) Remove axle shaft from vehicle. See REMOVAL & INSTALLATION. Cut and remove both boot clamps. Slide boot back away from CV joint. Mark tripod and housing for reassembly reference.

2) On Tempo and Topaz, bend retaining tabs back to allow outer race removal. *See Fig. 11.* On Escort and Tracer, remove wire retaining ring from inside of outer race, to allow tripod removal. On all models, slide outer race off of halfshaft assembly.

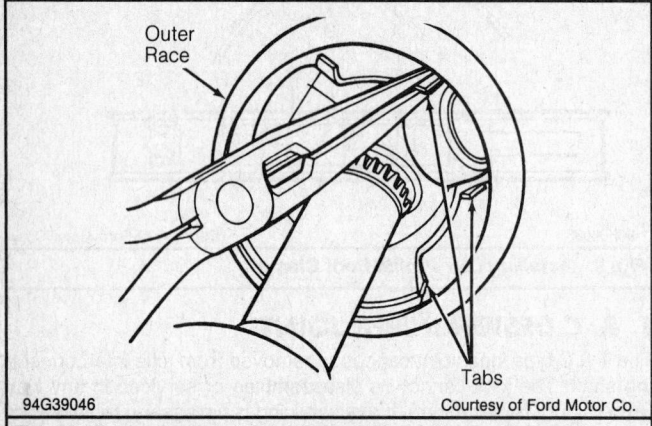

94G39046   Courtesy of Ford Motor Co.

Fig. 11: Removing Tripod Joint Outer Race (Tempo & Topaz)

3) On models using stop ring on backside of tripod, move stop ring up axle shaft. *See Fig. 12.* Move tripod assembly back, and remove circlip. On models without stop ring, remove snap ring from end of axle interconnecting shaft. On all models, slide tripod off assembly axle interconnecting shaft. Remove boot (if necessary).

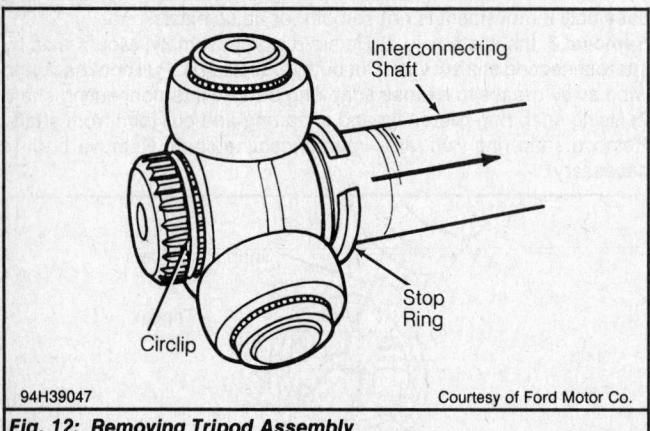

94H39047   Courtesy of Ford Motor Co.

Fig. 12: Removing Tripod Assembly

Reassembly – 1) Install small clamp and boot (if removed). Ensure boot is seated in groove on axle shaft, and securely tighten clamp. DO NOT overtighten. On axles using stop ring, install stop ring on axle shaft beyond its groove.

2) On all models, slide tripod assembly on axle shaft with chamfered side inward. Install snap ring or circlip and stop ring (if equipped). Slide tripod/axle shaft assembly into outer race. On Tempo and Topaz, bend retaining tabs back to original position. On Escort and Tracer, install retaining ring. On all models, position boot over housing.

3) Ensure boot is properly seated in groove. Wipe excess grease from external surfaces. Extend or compress axle shaft to achieve specified length of CV joint. Ensure axle shaft is specified length and boot properly seated. See AXLE ASSEMBLED LENGTH table. Remove trapped air from boot.

4) Install boot clamp. Tighten, but DO NOT overtighten, clamp. Install low profile type clamps. *See Fig. 9.* To complete reassembly, reverse disassembly procedure. Install a NEW circlip on stub axle.

AXLE ASSEMBLED LENGTHS

Application	Specification In. (mm)	[1] Measurement Points
Aspire		
A/T		
Left	24.31 (617.4)	"A"
Right	36.04 (915.4)	"B"
M/T		
Left	24.79 (629.6)	"A"
Right	35.57 (903.6)	"B"
Capri	3.5 (89)	[2]
Continental		
Left	18.27 (463.65)	"C"
Right	23.58 (598.55)	"D"
Escort & Tracer		
1.8L		
Left	24.48 (621.7)	"E"
Right	24.85 (631)	"F"
1.9L		
Left	25.22 (640.0)	"E"
Right	36.16 (918)	"F"
Festiva	3.5 (89)	[2]
Probe		
A/T		
Left	25.7 (652.8)	"A"
Right	23.8 (604.5)	"B"
M/T		
Left	25.8 (654.1)	"A"
Right	23.8 (605.2)	"B"
Sable & Taurus		
3.0L		
Left	18.70 (475.0)	"C"
Right	23.74 (603)	"D"
3.0 SHO		
Left	21.40 (544.0)	"C"
Right	21.81 (554.0)	"D"
3.2 SHO		
Left	18.70 (475.0)	"C"
Right	23.85 (606)	"D"
3.8L		
Left	18.70 (475.0)	"C"
Right	23.74 (603)	"D"
Tempo/Topaz		
A/T		
2.3L Left	16.93 (430.0)	"G"
2.3L Right	29.92 (760.0)	"G"
3.0L Left	16.02 (406.9)	"G"
3.0L Right	29.92 (760.0)	"G"
M/T		
2.3L Left	16.02 (407.0)	"G"
2.3L Right	29.92 (760.0)	"G"
3.0L Left	16.93 (429.9)	"G"
3.0L Right	29.92 (760.0)	"G"
Villager	[3]	[3]

[1] – See Fig. 13, for measurement points.

[2] – When installing inner boots, measure from center of small boot clamp to center of large boot clamp (both on inner boot).

[3] – Information not available from manufacturer.

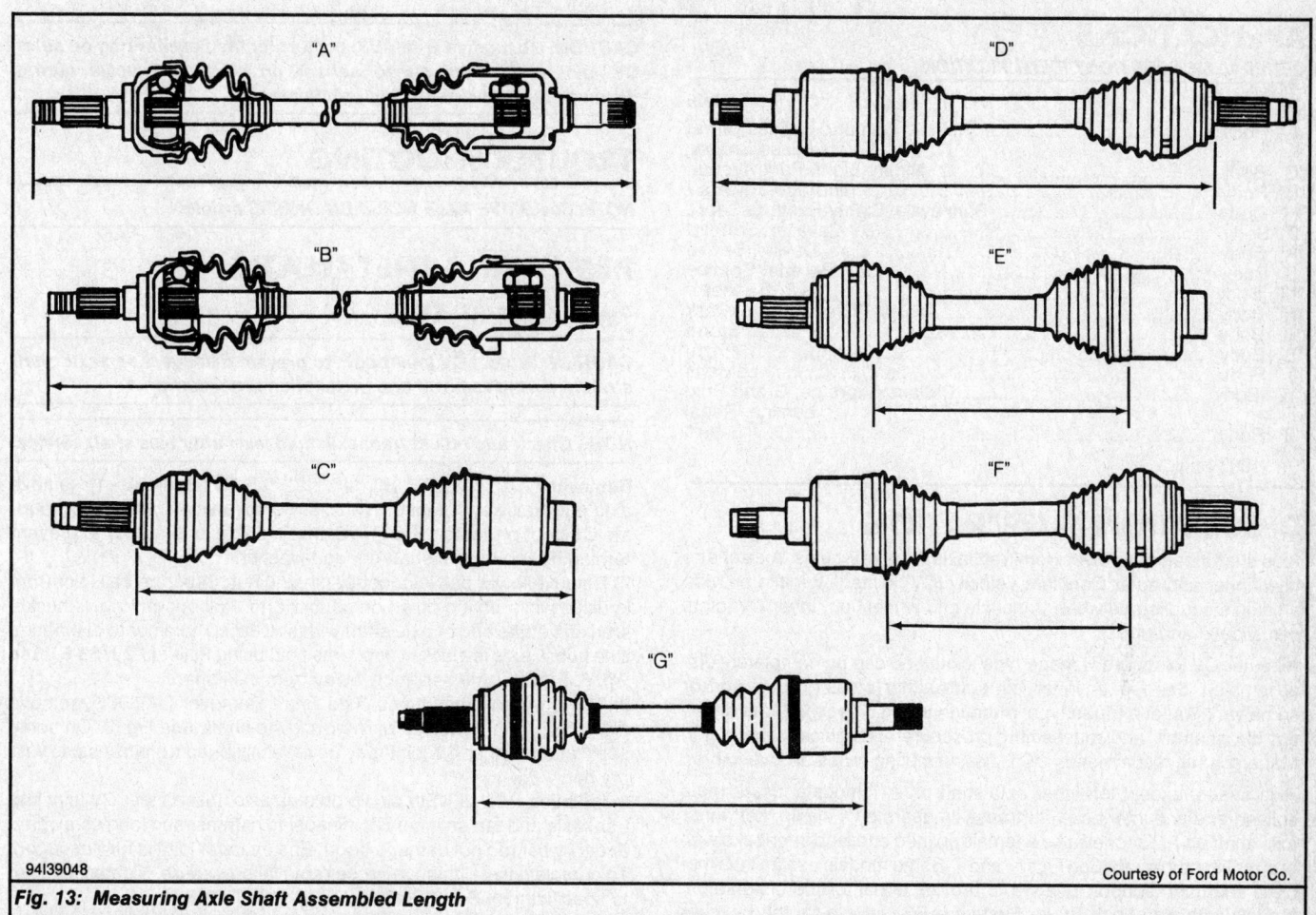

94I39048

Courtesy of Ford Motor Co.

Fig. 13: Measuring Axle Shaft Assembled Length

TORQUE SPECIFICATIONS
TORQUE SPECIFICATIONS

Application	Ft. Lbs. (N.m)
Axle Nut	
Aspire & Capri	166-174 (225-236)
Escort, Probe & Tracer	174-235 (236-319)
All Others	180-200 (244-271)
Ball Joint Pinch Bolt	
Aspire, Capri,	
Escort & Tracer	32-43 (43-59)
Continental, Sable & Taurus	40-55 (54-75)
Brake Caliper Bolts	58-72 (79-98)
Dynamic Damper	
Bearing Support Bracket Bolt	31-46 (42-62)
Intermediate Shaft Bearing Bolt	16-23 (22-31)
Stabilizer Bar Link Nut	35-48 (47-65)
Strut-To-Knuckle Nut	
Probe	69-86 (94-117)
All Others	55-80 (75-108)
Tie Rod-To-Steering Knuckle Nut	31-42 (42-57)
Wheel Lug Nut	
Aspire, Capri & Probe	65-87 (88-118)
All Others	80-105 (108-142)

APPLICATIONS

GENERAL MOTORS BODY IDENTIFICATION

Car Line	Models
"A" Body	Century, Cutlass Ciera, Cutlass Cruiser
"C" Body	Ninety-Eight, Park Avenue
"E" Body	Eldorado, Riviera [1]
"H" Body	Bonneville, Eighty-Eight, LeSabre
"J" Body	Cavalier, Sunbird
"K" Body	Deville, Seville
"L" Body	Beretta, Corsica
"M" Body	Metro
"N" Body	Achieva, Grand Am, Skylark
"R" Body	Storm
"S" Body	Prizm
"T" Body	LeMans
"W" Body	Cutlass Supreme, Grand Prix, Lumina, Regal
"Z" Body	Saturn

[1] – 1993 only.

DESCRIPTION & OPERATION

Axle shafts transfer power from transaxle to drive wheels. Axle shafts have inner and outer Constant Velocity (CV) joints. CV joints provide a flexible coupling between transaxle and wheel hub. Inner CV joints can slide in and out.

All outer CV joints are Rzeppa type joints and can be completely disassembled. *See Fig. 1.* Inner joints are either cross-groove type or some variation of a tripod type. Although tripod types may look different, disassembly and reassembly procedure are basically the same. Manufacturer recommends NOT disassembling cross-groove joints.

Axle shafts, except left inner axle shaft on A/T models, use a male splined end and interlock with transaxle gears by a circlip. Left inner axle shaft on A/T models use a female splined end, and interlocks with protruding stub shaft. *See Figs. 1 and 7.* Some models use an intermediate shaft and support bearing to provide equal torque distribution. Models with Anti-Lock Brake System (ABS) have a toothed exciter ring on outer CV joint housing.

CAUTION: On models with ABS, protect toothed exciter ring on outer CV joint and wheel speed sensor on steering knuckle during disassembly and reassembly procedures.

TROUBLE SHOOTING

NOTE: See DRIVE AXLE NOISE DIAGNOSIS article.

REMOVAL & INSTALLATION

FWD AXLE SHAFTS

CAUTION: Protect CV joint boots to prevent damage. Keep axle shaft straight during removal and installation procedures.

NOTE: Check and adjust transaxle fluid level after axle shaft service.

Removal ("A", "C", "E", "H", "J", "K", "L", "N" Bodies) –1) Remove axle nut. Raise and support vehicle. Remove wheel. Install appropriate CV boot protector. *See Fig. 2.* Insert drift in brake rotor to prevent turning. Remove axle shaft nut and washer.

2) Remove lower ball joint cotter pin and nut. Separate ball joint from knuckle while prying down on control arm. Pull out on lower knuckle area and strike end of axle shaft with soft-faced hammer to disengage axle hub. If axle is stuck in hub, press out using Puller (J-28733-B). *See Fig. 3.* Pull knuckle assembly away from axle shaft.

3) Using slide hammer and Axle Shaft Remover (J-33008), remove axle shaft from transaxle or intermediate shaft. *See Fig. 2.* On some applications, inner CV joint may be carefully pried from transaxle with pry bar.

Installation – Use NEW circlip on stub axle. Insert inner CV joint into transaxle and tap on inner CV joint using hammer and long screwdriver or pry bar (do not damage boot). Ensure Inner joint is fully engaged. To complete installation, reverse removal procedure. Tighten axle nut to specification. See TORQUE SPECIFICATIONS.

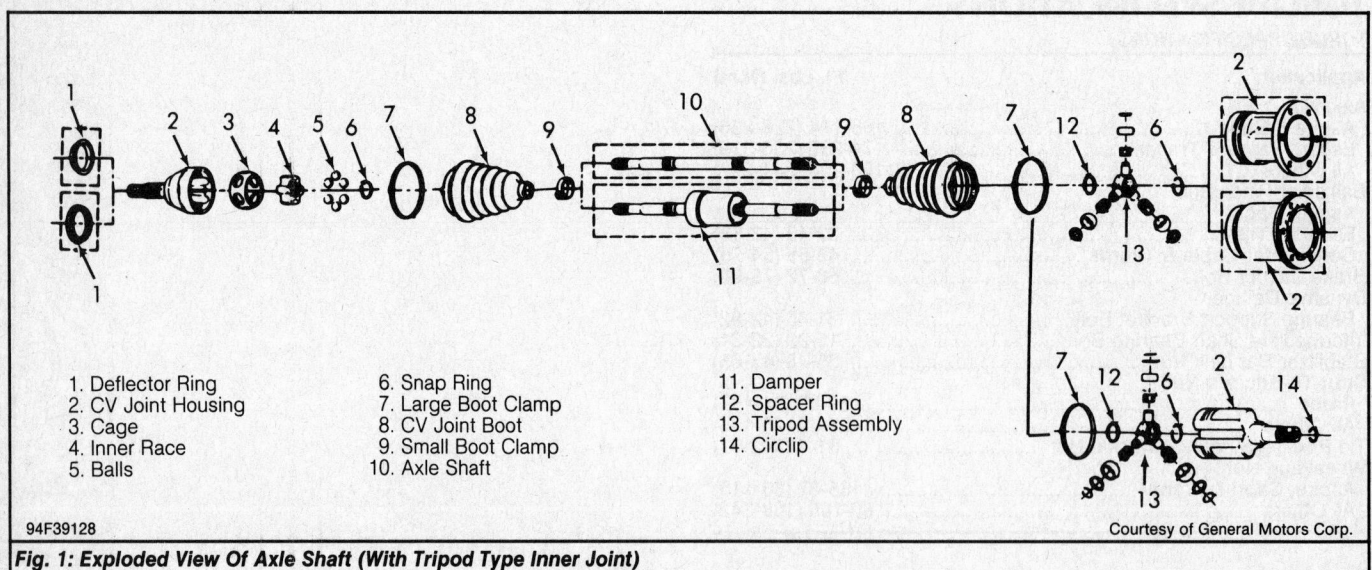

1. Deflector Ring	6. Snap Ring
2. CV Joint Housing	7. Large Boot Clamp
3. Cage	8. CV Joint Boot
4. Inner Race	9. Small Boot Clamp
5. Balls	10. Axle Shaft

11. Damper	
12. Spacer Ring	
13. Tripod Assembly	
14. Circlip	

94F39128

Courtesy of General Motors Corp.

Fig. 1: Exploded View Of Axle Shaft (With Tripod Type Inner Joint)

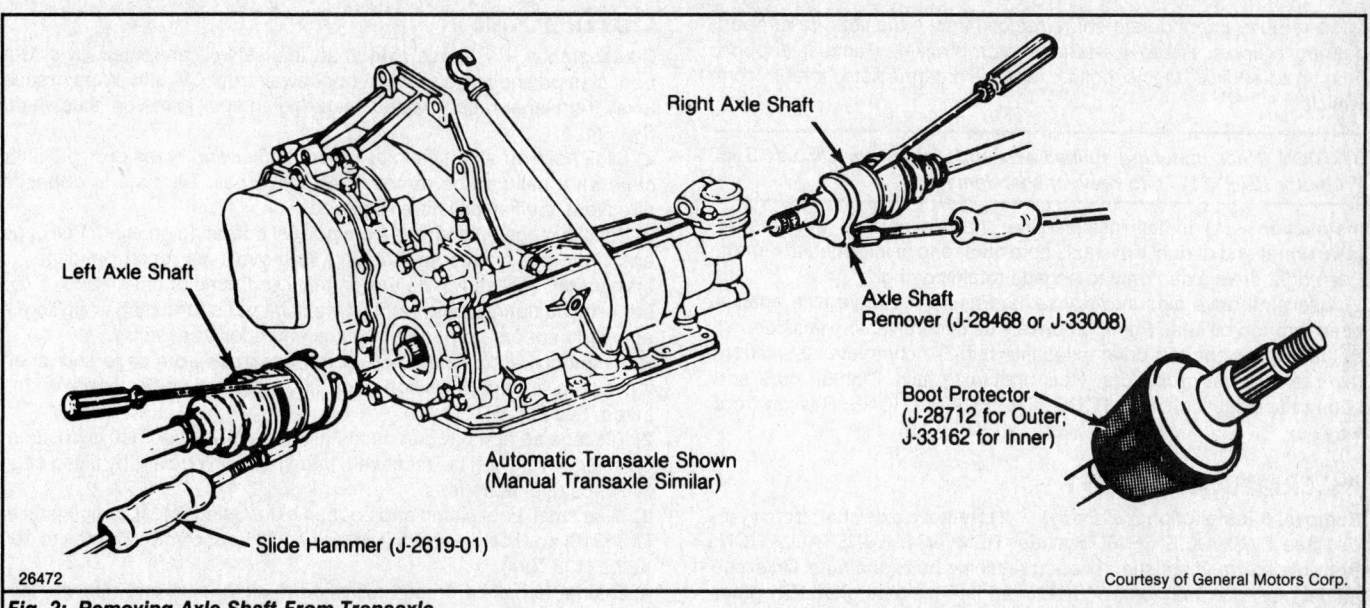

Right Axle Shaft

Left Axle Shaft

Axle Shaft Remover (J-28468 or J-33008)

Boot Protector (J-28712 for Outer; J-33162 for Inner)

Automatic Transaxle Shown (Manual Transaxle Similar)

Slide Hammer (J-2619-01)

26472

Courtesy of General Motors Corp.

Fig. 2: Removing Axle Shaft From Transaxle

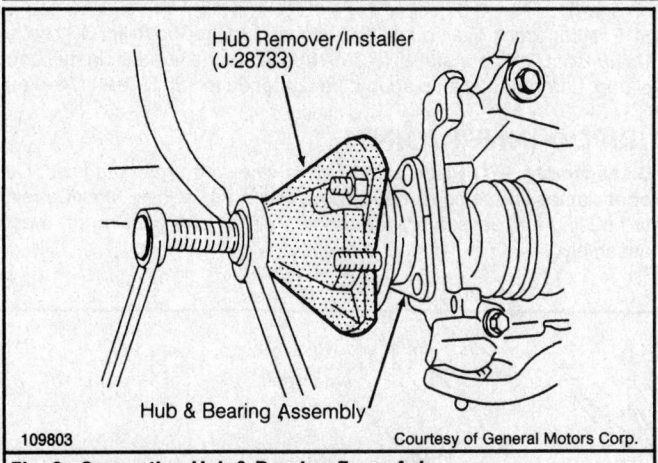

Hub Remover/Installer (J-28733)

Hub & Bearing Assembly

109803

Courtesy of General Motors Corp.

Fig. 3: Separating Hub & Bearing From Axle

Removal & Installation ("M", "R", "S", "T" Bodies) – **1)** Raise and support vehicle. Unstake axle nut. Remove axle nut from axle shaft. Disconnect outer tie rod end from steering knuckle.
2) Remove ball joint nut and separate ball joint from steering knuckle. Pull steering knuckle outward, off of axle shaft.
3) Using a pry bar, disengage inner CV joint from transaxle. If axle shaft has a intermediate shaft with support bearing, tap on inner joint to disengage from support bearing. Remove axle from vehicle. To install, reverse removal procedure. Tighten nuts and bolts to specification. See TORQUE SPECIFICATIONS.
Removal ("W" Body) – **1)** Remove axle nut. Raise and support vehicle. Remove wheel. Remove brake caliper and rotor. Remove 4 hub-to-steering knuckle bolts. Using Puller (J-28733-A), separate axle shaft from hub. See Fig. 3. Remove hub.
2) On right axle shaft, use slide hammer and Axle Shaft Remover (J-33008) to remove axle shaft from transaxle or intermediate shaft. See Fig. 2. On left axle shaft, pry axle shaft from transaxle at groove on inner CV joint. Remove axle shaft through steering knuckle.
Installation – **1)** Slide axle shaft through steering knuckle into transaxle. Install hub and bearing assembly in steering knuckle. Loosely tighten hub and bearing assembly-to-knuckle bolts and nuts. Ensure axle shaft snap ring is engaged by prying on inner CV joint groove. Pry against frame cradle or lower control arm.
2) Grip inner CV joint housing and pull outward, away from transaxle. DO NOT pull on axle shaft. If snap ring is seated, axle shaft will remain intact. To complete installation, reverse removal procedure. Check and adjust transaxle fluid level.

Removal ("Z" Body) – **1)** With vehicle on ground, depress brake pedal and loosen drive axle nut. Raise and support vehicle with hoist. Remove wheel. Remove axle nut.

CAUTION: Use of incorrect tool to separate ball joint from steering knuckle can cause damage to ABS sensor ring.

2) Remove front inner splash shield. Remove ball joint cotter pin and loosen castle nut. Using Ball Joint Separator (SA9132S), separate ball joint from steering knuckle. See Fig. 4.

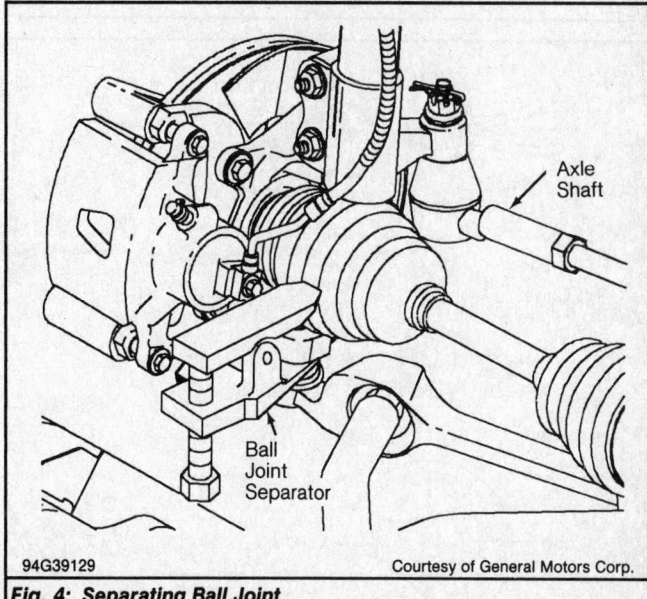

Axle Shaft

Ball Joint Separator

94G39129

Courtesy of General Motors Corp.

Fig. 4: Separating Ball Joint

3) Remove outer tie rod end-to-steering knuckle nut. Using Tie Rod End Remover (SA91100C), separate tie rod end from steering knuckle. Remove ball joint nut.
4) To disengage left axle, insert screwdriver between left drive axle and transaxle. Carefully separate left drive axle from transaxle. Remove axle.
5) To disengage right axle, carefully tap inner CV joint from support bearing using soft mallet. Separate right drive axle from intermediate shaft. Remove axle.

6) To remove intermediate shaft, remove intake manifold-to-support bearing bracket. Remove starter motor bracket. Remove support bearing-to-engine block bolts. remove intermediate shaft from vehicle.

CAUTION: When installing splined axle ends into transaxle, use Seal Protector (SA91112T), to prevent seal damage.

Installation – 1) Install intermediate shaft in reverse of removal. Insert inner end of right drive axle onto outer end of intermediate shaft. Push right drive axle firmly to engage retaining ring.

2) Insert left drive axle into transaxle. Ensure left drive axle splines pass through oil seal. Push left drive axle securely into transaxle.

3) Insert right and left drive axles into hub. To complete installation, reverse removal procedure. Refill transaxle fluid. Tighten nuts and bolts to specification. See TORQUE SPECIFICATIONS. Realign front wheels.

INTERMEDIATE SHAFT

Removal & Installation ("J" Body) – 1) Remove axle shaft from vehicle. See FWD AXLE SHAFTS under REMOVAL & INSTALLATION. Remove intermediate shaft bracket retaining bolts and nuts. On some models, bracket may be removed from intermediate shaft. On other models, bracket is removed with intermediate shaft assembly.

2) On some models, intermediate shaft is bolted to transaxle. On other models, intermediate shaft is retained in transaxle by bracket near axle shaft. Remove intermediate shaft-to-transaxle bolts (if equipped). On all models, carefully pull intermediate shaft out of transaxle. To install, reverse removal procedure.

OVERHAUL

NOTE: Models with Anti-Lock Brake System (ABS) have a speed sensor ring. Speed sensor ring and joint must be replaced as a unit. Speed sensor ring must be checked whenever work is done on axle.

OUTER JOINT

Disassembly – 1) Place axle shaft in vise with protected jaws. Cut boot clamps and remove. Slide boot away from CV joint. Wipe grease away from inner race. Expand snap ring and pull joint from axle shaft. *See Fig. 5.*

2) Slide boot off axle shaft. Using a hammer and brass drift, tilt inner cage so a ball can be removed. Remove ball. Tilt cage in opposite directions until all balls are removed.

3) Position cage 90 degrees from normal operating position. Pull cage and inner race from outer housing. Remove inner race from cage.

Inspection – Clean parts thoroughly. No traces of old grease or dirt are allowed during reassembly. Check all parts for pitting or galling. If any parts appear damaged, replace entire joint assembly.

Reassembly – 1) Hold inner race 90 degrees from cage and insert inner race in cage. Position cage 90 degrees to outer housing and insert. *See Fig. 5.*

2) Tilt cage so first ball can be installed. Ensure inner race is positioned so snap ring can be accessed. Install remaining balls by tilting cage in opposite directions.

3) Slide small boot clamp and boot on axle. Using Boot Clamp Installer (J-35910) and torque wrench, install small boot clamp. Tighten to 100 ft. lbs (136 N.m).

4) Distribute half of grease provided in kit in joint, and remainder in boot. Install CV joint onto axle shaft. Ensure joint is securely engaged on shaft.

5) Position boot over outer housing and locate boot lip in groove. Using Boot Clamp Installer (J-35910) and torque wrench, install boot clamp. Large boot clamp should be tightened to 130 ft. lbs. (176 N.m)

TRIPOD INNER JOINT

Disassembly – 1) Place axle shaft in vise with protected jaws. Cut boot clamps and remove. Slide boot away from CV joint. Mark CV joint to housing for reassembly reference. Pull CV joint housing off tripod assembly.

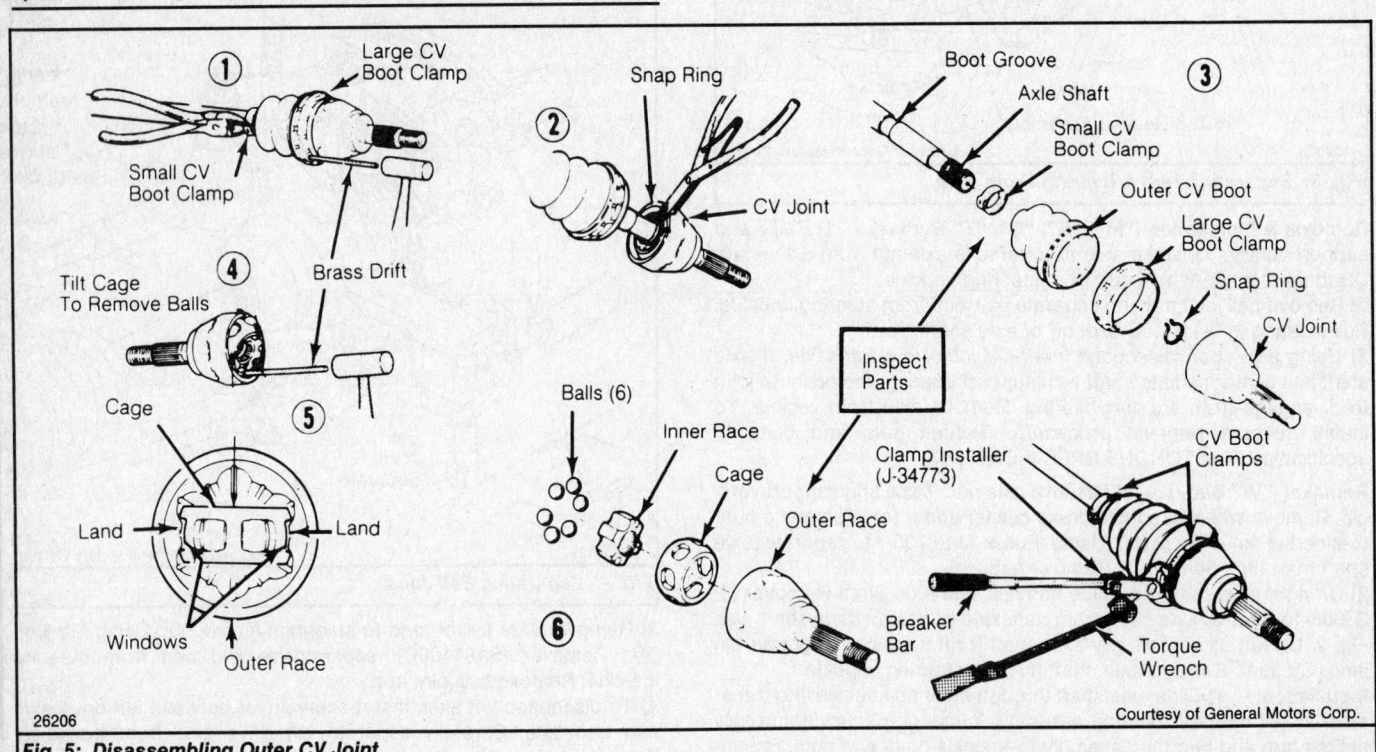

26206

Courtesy of General Motors Corp.

Fig. 5: Disassembling Outer CV Joint

2) Expand spacer ring and slide spacer ring up axle shaft. *See Fig. 6.* Move tripod up shaft. Remove tripod retaining ring. Mark tripod to axle shaft for installation reference. Slide tripod off axle shaft. Remove spacer ring. Remove boot (if replacing).

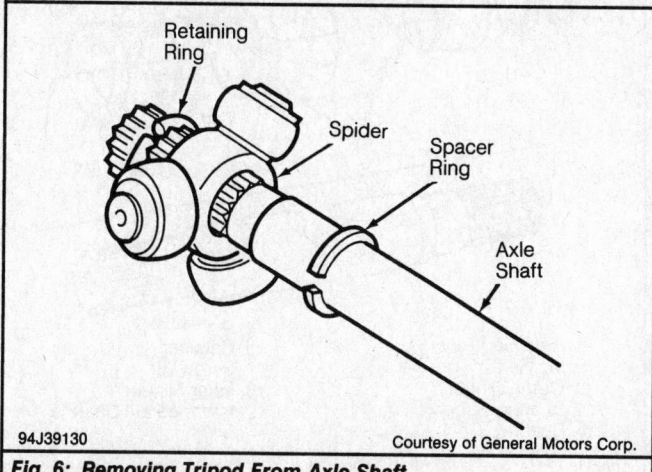

94J39130   Courtesy of General Motors Corp.

Fig. 6: Removing Tripod From Axle Shaft (Tripod Joint Shown, S-Plan Joint Similar)

WARNING: Wear safety glasses when using compressed air to dry parts.

Inspection – Wash all parts (except boots) in solvent and dry with compressed air. Wash boots with soap and water. Inspect races for excessive wear and scoring. Inspect splined areas of shafts for wear, cracks and twists. Inspect balls for pitting, cracking or scoring. Check for cracks, chips or heavy dents on cage windows.

Reassembly – 1) Pack CV joint housing with approximately one-half amount of grease supplied in kit. Apply remaining grease in boot. Install small clamp and boot on axle shaft (if removed). Slide spacer ring on axle shaft past groove. Slide tripod on axle shaft. Install tripod in original location (marked during disassembly).

2) Install tripod retaining snap ring. Slide tripod against snap ring and install spacer ring in groove. Slide CV joint housing on tripod assembly. Position boot over housing. Remove trapped air by using a blunt screwdriver to lift large end of boot off sealed area.

3) Measure length of boot. *See Fig. 7.* Ensure length is 5.1" (130 mm) before clamping boot clamps. Move CV joint housing in or out as necessary. When length is within specification, position clamps on boot. Use Boot Clamp Installer (J-35910) and torque wrench to install boot clamps.

4) Large boot clamp should be tightened to 130 ft. lbs. (176 N.m). Small boot clamps should be tightened to 100 ft. lbs (136 N.m). Recheck boot length. To complete reassembly, reverse disassembly procedure.

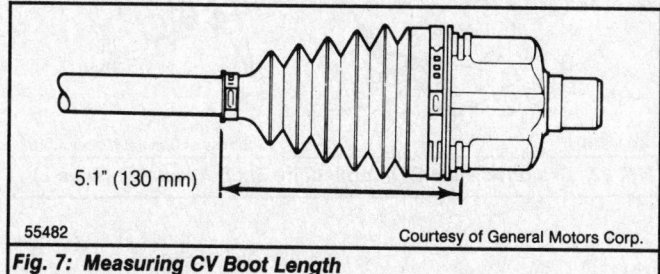

5.1" (130 mm)

55482   Courtesy of General Motors Corp.

Fig. 7: Measuring CV Boot Length

S-PLAN TRIPOD JOINT

Disassembly – 1) Cut boot clamps and discard. Separate boot from outer housing. Pull outer race off of axle assembly.

2) Expand spacer ring and move it up the axle shaft. *See Fig. 6.* Move tripod assembly up axle shaft. Remove retaining ring from end of axle shaft.

3) Slide spider assembly off shaft. Remove spacer ring and boot from axle.

Inspection – Inspect boot, spider, housing and bearing blocks for damage or wear. For cleaning purposes bearing blocks may be removed from spider. *See Fig. 8.*

Reassembly – 1) Install small boot clamp on neck of boot. DO NOT crimp. Slide boot onto shaft, and position neck of boot in seal groove on axle shaft. Crimp retaining clamp with Boot Clamp Installer (J-35910) to 100 ft. lbs. (136 N.m).

2) Position spacer ring beyond it's groove on shaft. Apply small amount of grease to inside of bearing blocks before assembling. Align flats on opening in bearing block, with flats on spider. Rotate 90 degrees to secure block to spider. *See Fig. 8.*

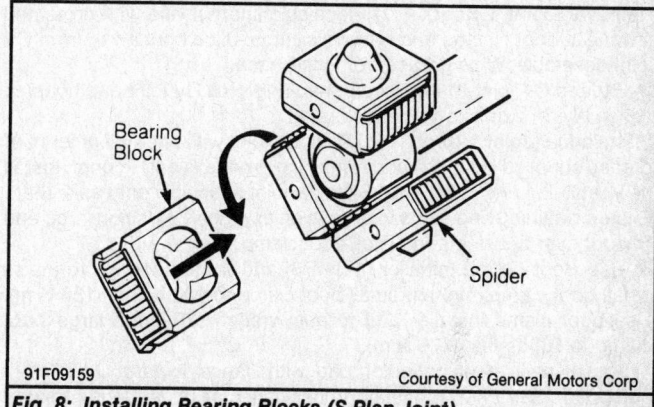

91F09159   Courtesy of General Motors Corp

Fig. 8: Installing Bearing Blocks (S-Plan Joint)

NOTE: Ensure counterbored face of spider faces end of shaft.

3) Slide spider against spacer ring on shaft. Install shaft retaining ring in groove at end of shaft. Slide spider towards end of shaft and seat spacer ring in groove on shaft. Pack CV joint housing with approximately one-half amount of grease supplied in kit. Apply remaining grease in boot.

4) Place slotted, 6" square metal sheet between boot and bearing blocks to maintain proper bearing block alignment during reassembly. *See Fig. 9.* Install tripod assembly in outer housing. Position large clamp on boot. Slide housing over spider assembly and shaft; remove slotted metal sheet. Slide large end of boot, with clamp in place, over outer housing. Locate lip of boot in groove.

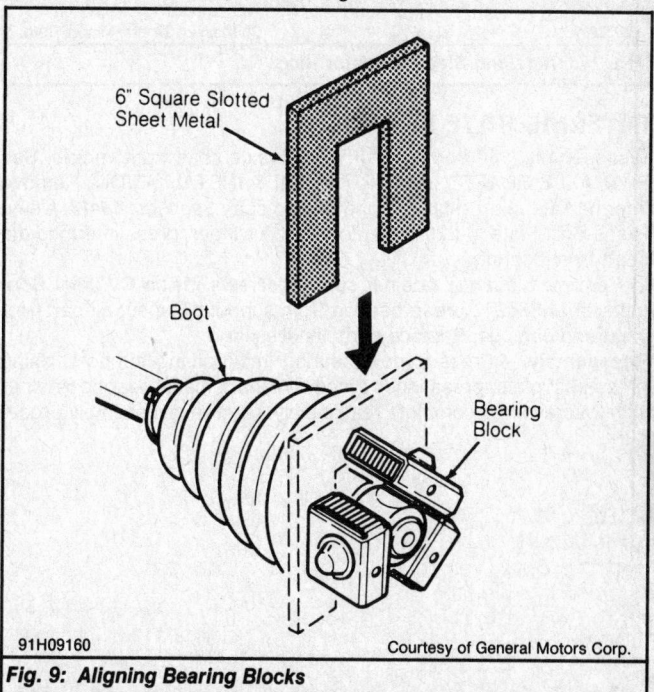

6" Square Slotted Sheet Metal

Boot

Bearing Block

91H09160   Courtesy of General Motors Corp.

Fig. 9: Aligning Bearing Blocks

5) Position joint assembly at installed length. Ensuring boot is not dimpled, stretched or out of shape in any way, crimp large diameter retaining clamp with Boot Clamp Installer (J-35566) to 130 ft. lbs (176 N.m).

NOTE: Ensure boot, housing and clamp remain aligned while crimping.

CROSS GROOVE INNER JOINT

NOTE: DO NOT disassemble cross-groove type CV joint. Complete inner joint must be replaced.

Removal (Joint & Boot) – 1) Place axle shaft in vise with protected jaws. Cut boot clamps and remove clamps. Slide boot away from CV joint assembly. Wipe grease from inner race.
2) Expand CV joint-to-axle shaft snap ring. Pull CV joint and housing assembly off axle shaft. Remove boot.
Installation (Joint & Boot) – 1) Pack CV joint with one-half amount of grease supplied in kit. Spread remaining grease evenly in boot. Install new retaining ring in CV joint. Slide CV joint assembly onto axle shaft. Ensure retaining ring seats in groove on axle shaft. Position large end of boot over housing and install boot clamp.
3) Use Boot Clamp Installer (J-34773) and torque wrench to install small boot clamp. Tighten small boot clamp to 100 ft. lbs. (136 N.m). Use boot clamp installer and torque wrench to tighten large boot clamp to 130 ft. lbs. (176 N.m).
4) Install new steel deflector ring with flange toward CV joint (if equipped). See Fig. 10. Install rubber deflector rings (flange toward hub assembly) by stretching ring over housing and seating in groove. To complete reassembly, reverse disassembly procedure.

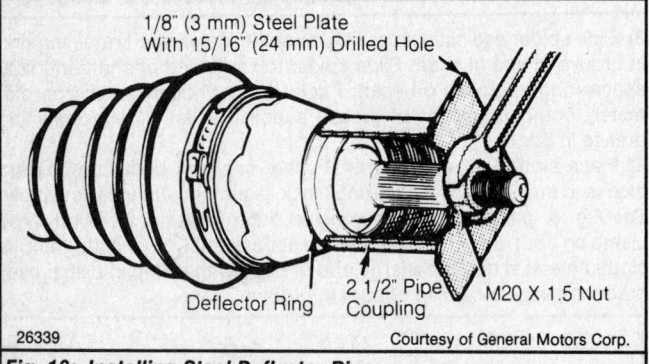

1/8" (3 mm) Steel Plate
With 15/16" (24 mm) Drilled Hole

Deflector Ring

2 1/2" Pipe Coupling

M20 X 1.5 Nut

26339   Courtesy of General Motors Corp.

Fig. 10: Installing Steel Deflector Ring

INTERMEDIATE SHAFT

Disassembly ("J" Body) – 1) Remove axle shaft from vehicle. See FWD AXLE SHAFTS under REMOVAL & INSTALLATION. Remove intermediate shaft retaining ring and lip seal. See Figs. 11-13. Using Press-Split Plate (J-22912-01) to support slinger, press intermediate shaft from bearing.
2) Remove 3 bearing retainer support screws. Using CV Joint Boot Installer (J-23694), press bearing from support. Inspect all parts for wear and damage. Replace parts if necessary.
Reassembly – Press a new bearing into bearing support. Using press-split plate, press inner slinger on shaft. Install bearing retainer with 3 screws. To complete reassembly, reverse disassembly procedure.

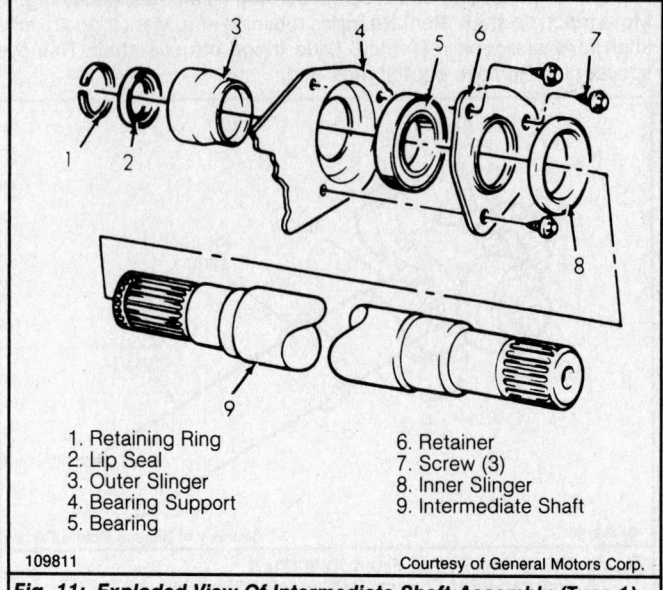

1. Retaining Ring	6. Retainer
2. Lip Seal	7. Screw (3)
3. Outer Slinger	8. Inner Slinger
4. Bearing Support	9. Intermediate Shaft
5. Bearing	

109811   Courtesy of General Motors Corp.

Fig. 11: Exploded View Of Intermediate Shaft Assembly (Type 1)

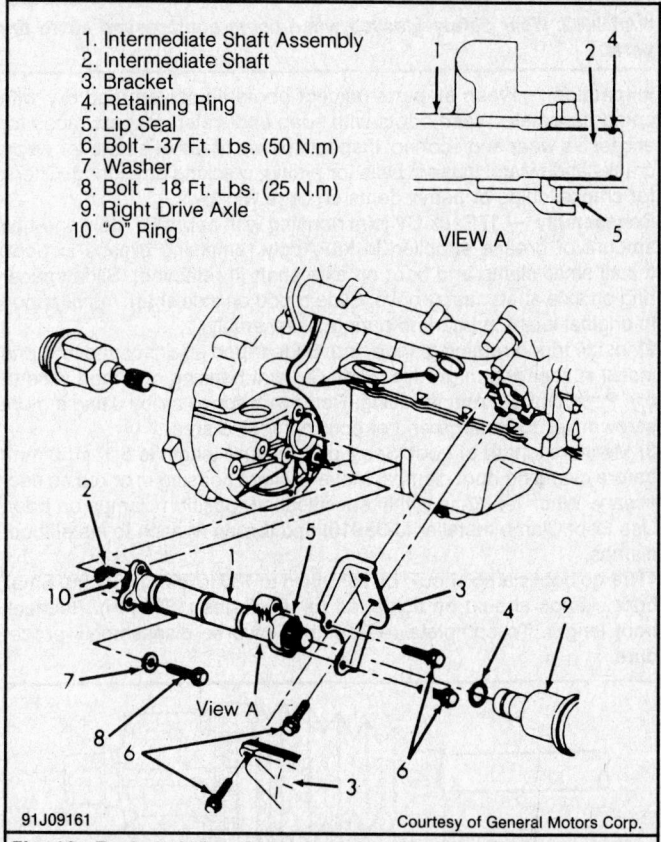

1. Intermediate Shaft Assembly
2. Intermediate Shaft
3. Bracket
4. Retaining Ring
5. Lip Seal
6. Bolt – 37 Ft. Lbs. (50 N.m)
7. Washer
8. Bolt – 18 Ft. Lbs. (25 N.m)
9. Right Drive Axle
10. "O" Ring

VIEW A

View A

91J09161   Courtesy of General Motors Corp.

Fig. 12: Exploded View Of Intermediate Shaft Assembly (Type 2)

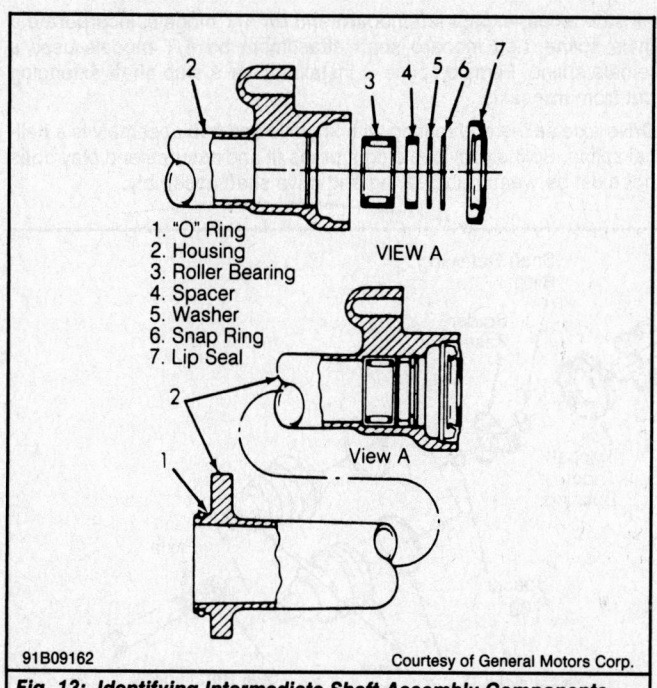

1. "O" Ring
2. Housing
3. Roller Bearing
4. Spacer
5. Washer
6. Snap Ring
7. Lip Seal

VIEW A

View A

91B09162

Courtesy of General Motors Corp.

Fig. 13: Identifying Intermediate Shaft Assembly Components (Type 2)

TORQUE SPECIFICATIONS
TORQUE SPECIFICATIONS

Application	Ft. Lbs. (N.m)
Axle Nut	
"A" Body	192 (260)
"C" & "W" Bodies	180 (244)
"E", "K", "M" & "R" Bodies	129 (175)
"H" Bodies	107 (145)
"S" Bodies	159 (216)
"T" Bodies	74 (100)
"J", "L" & "N" Bodies	185 (251)
Intermediate Shaft Bracket-To-Engine Bolt	41 (56)
Lower Ball Joint-To-Control Arm Bolt	50 (68)
Lower Ball Joint-To-Steering Knuckle Nut	
"A" Body	33 (45)
"C", "E" & "H" Bodies	[1] [2]
"J","M", "N", "R" & "S" Bodies	42-45 (57-61)
"L" & "Z" Body	55 (75)
Tie Rod End Nut	
"C" & "H" Bodies	[3] 35 (47)
"E" & "K" Bodies	[4]
All Others	35 (47)
Wheel Lug Nut	
Except "M", "R" & "S"	100 (136)
"M", "R" & "S"	44 (60)

[1] – Tighten to 88 INCH lbs. (10 N.m), then turn nut additional 120 degrees. Minimum torque of 37 ft. lbs. (50 N.m) must be obtained.

[2] – On replacement ball joint, tighten nut to 81 ft. lbs. (110 N.m) at initial installation only.

[3] – Maximum of 52 ft. lbs. (71 N.m) to align cotter key.

[4] – Tighten to 88 INCH lbs. (10 N.m), then turn nut additional 1/3 turn. Minimum torque of 33 ft. lbs. (45 N.m) must be obtained.

AXLE SHAFTS
General Motors FWD Vans

Lumina APV, Silhouette, Trans Sport
DESCRIPTION

Drive axles on FWD vans consist of an inner and an outer Constant Velocity (CV) joint connected by an axle shaft. *See Fig. 1.* Inner tripot CV joint is capable of moving in and out. Outer ball/cage CV joint is flexible but cannot move in and out.

All stub axles, except left inboard end on A/T models, incorporate a male spline. Left inboard shaft attachment on A/T models uses a female spline. Female spline is installed over a stub shaft extending out from transaxle.

Drive axle spline end mating with knuckle and hub assembly is a helical spline. Spline provides a tight press fit and assures end play does not exist between hub bearing and drive shaft assembly.

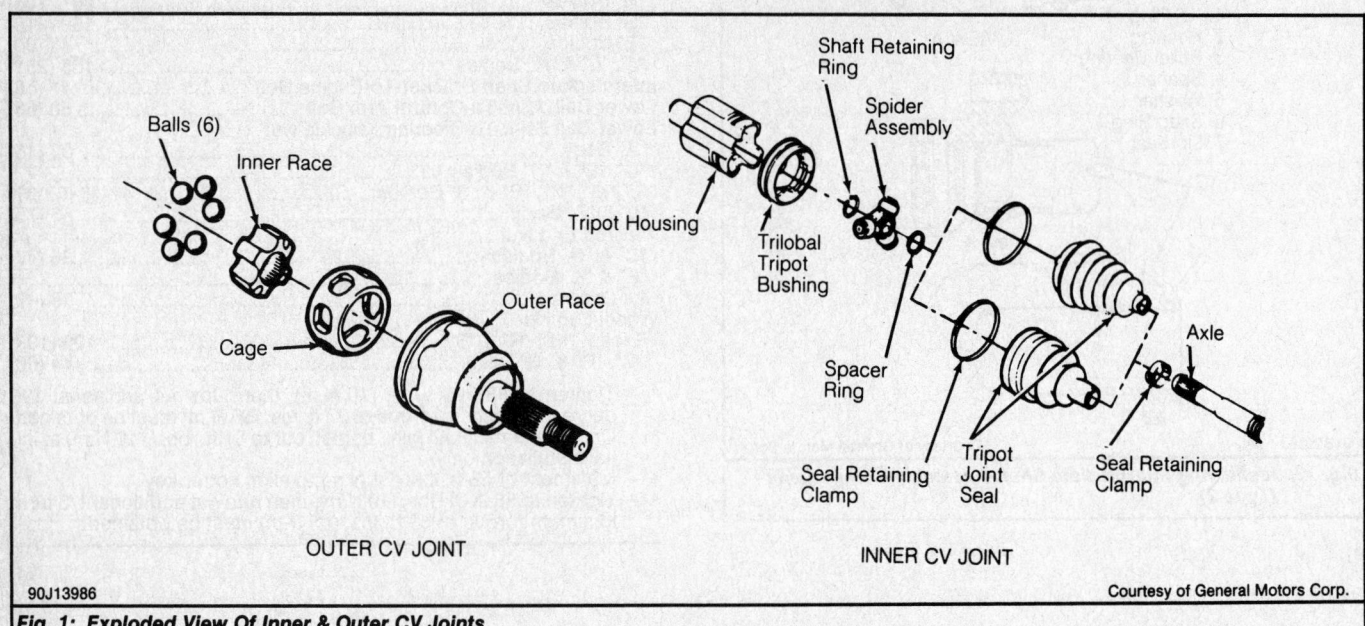

90J13986

Fig. 1: Exploded View Of Inner & Outer CV Joints

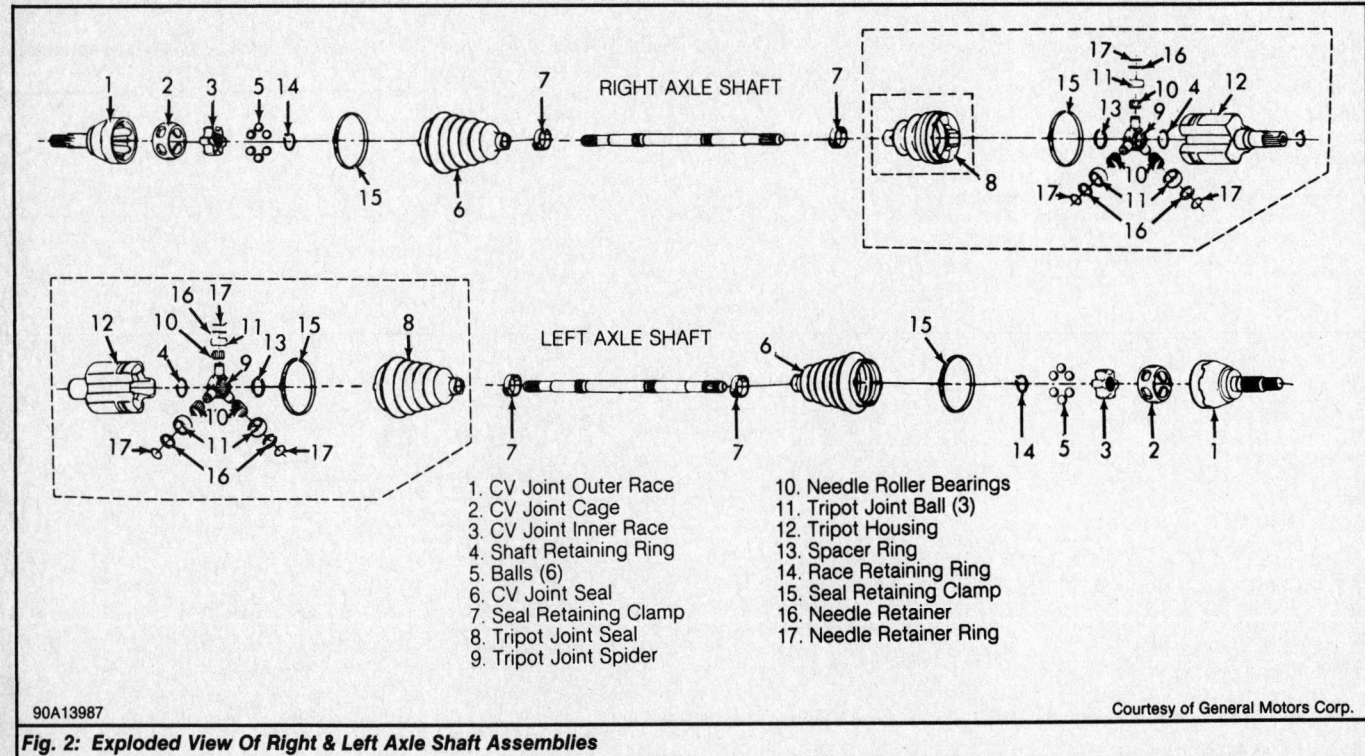

1. CV Joint Outer Race
2. CV Joint Cage
3. CV Joint Inner Race
4. Shaft Retaining Ring
5. Balls (6)
6. CV Joint Seal
7. Seal Retaining Clamp
8. Tripot Joint Seal
9. Tripot Joint Spider
10. Needle Roller Bearings
11. Tripot Joint Ball (3)
12. Tripot Housing
13. Spacer Ring
14. Race Retaining Ring
15. Seal Retaining Clamp
16. Needle Retainer
17. Needle Retainer Ring

90A13987

Fig. 2: Exploded View Of Right & Left Axle Shaft Assemblies

REMOVAL & INSTALLATION

DRIVE AXLES

Removal & Installation – 1) Raise and support vehicle. Remove tire and wheel assembly. Remove tie rod end cotter pin and tie rod nut. Separate tie rod end from steering knuckle.

2) Remove axle nut and washer. Insert a long punch through brake caliper and into brake rotor fins to aid in axle nut removal. Discard axle nut. Remove lower ball joint pinch bolt. Install modified (inner tabs removed) Seal Protector (J-34754) over drive axle seal.

NOTE: Drive Axle Seal Protector (J-34754) should be modified and installed on any drive axle before performing services on or near drive axle. Failure to do so may result in seal damage and possible future joint failure.

3) Separate ball joint from steering knuckle. To remove axle shaft from hub/bearing assembly, press axle shaft inward using Axle Remover (J-28733). DO NOT allow axle shaft to drop or hang freely when removing from hub/bearing assembly.

4) Remove axle remover. Remove axle shaft from transaxle using slide hammer. To install axle shaft, reverse removal procedure. Seat drive axle into transaxle by placing screwdriver into groove on joint housing and tapping until axle is seated. Use a NEW axle shaft nut. Tighten all nuts and bolts to specification. See TORQUE SPECIFICATIONS.

DISASSEMBLY, OVERHAUL & REASSEMBLY

OUTER JOINT

Disassembly – 1) Remove axle assembly from vehicle. Cut both boot clamps. Slide boot back away from joint. Wipe grease away from inner race. Expand snap ring retaining inner race. *See Fig. 2.* Remove joint and boot from axle shaft.

2) Tilt cage enough to remove at least one ball. Tilt cage in other directions until all balls are removed. When all balls are removed, position cage 90 degrees from normal operating position. Remove cage and inner race from outer race.

Reassembly – 1) Coat all internal parts with CV joint grease, to ease assembly. Install cage and inner race in reverse of disassembly procedure. Ensure inner race is positioned so snap ring can be accessed. Install balls one at a time until all balls are installed.

2) Slide small boot clamp, and boot on axle shaft. Install CV joint assembly on axle shaft by tapping on outer joint with soft faced mallet. Ensure boot is engaged in grooves, tighten clamps.

INNER JOINT

Disassembly – 1) Remove axle shaft from vehicle. Cut and remove both boot clamps. Slide boot back away from CV joint. Mark tripod and housing for reassembly reference. Slide outer race off axle shaft assembly.

2) Move stop ring up axle shaft. Move tripod assembly up axle shaft, and remove circlip. Slide tripod off axle interconnecting shaft. Remove boot.

Reassembly – 1) Install small clamp and boot (if removed). Install stop ring on axle shaft beyond its groove. Slide tripod assembly (spider) on axle shaft with chamfered side inward. Install circlip and stop ring. Slide axle assembly into outer race. Position boot over housing.

2) Ensure boot is properly seated in groove. Wipe excess grease from external surfaces. Extend or compress axle shaft to achieve an overall boot length of 4.9" (125 mm). Remove trapped air from boot. Install boot clamp. Tighten, but DO NOT overtighten, clamp.

TORQUE SPECIFICATIONS
TORQUE SPECIFICATIONS

Application	Ft. Lbs (N.m)
Axle Shaft (Hub) Nut	185 (250)
Ball Joint Pinch Bolt	33 (45)
Brake Caliper Bolts	38 (51)
Hub & Bearing Bolts	62 (84)
Large Seal Clamp	[1] 130 (176)
Small Seal Clamp	[1] 100 (136)
Wheel Lug Nuts	100 (136)

[1] – These specifications apply only when using Seal Clamp Installer (J-35910 & J-35566).

TRANSFER CASES
Borg-Warner 1354 & 1356

Ford Motor Co: Bronco, Explorer, "F" Series, Ranger

DESCRIPTION

TRANSFER CASE

The Explorer and Ranger are equipped with model 1354 transfer case and Bronco and "F" Series are equipped with model 1356 transfer case. All models are chain-driven, part-time 4WD units. Some models are equipped with electronic shift controls, which are activated by push-button controls on instrument panel. System allows vehicle to be shifted from 2WD high range to 4WD high range at any speed.

OPERATION

ELECTRONIC SHIFT CONTROL SYSTEM

Electronic Shift Operation – System consists of a push-button control, electronic control module, electric shift motor with integral shift position sensor and a speed sensor.

Transfer case is equipped with a magnetic clutch, located inside case next to the 2WD/4WD shift collar. Clutch is used to spin-up front drive system from zero to vehicle speed in less than a second. This spin-up allows the 2WD to 4WD shift to be made at any speed.

When transfer case rear and front output shafts reach the same rotating speed, spring-loaded shift collar mechanically engages mainshaft hub to chain drive sprocket. Magnetic clutch is then deactivated. Shifts between 4WD high and 4WD low only occur with clutch interlock or transmission safety switch closed. Explorer and Ranger models require vehicle speed to be 3 MPH or less. Bronco and "F" Series vehicles must be at full stop.

When operator selects 4WD or 2WD mode, actual shifting is carried out by electric motor mounted on the transfer case.

Electronic Control Module – This module controls operation of transfer case, using inputs from push button controls, speed sensor and shift position sensor. On Bronco and "F" Series, module is located in right kick panel. On Explorer, module is located in driver-side rear compartment trim panel over rear wheel. On Ranger, module is located behind driver's seat. Module is equipped with a self-test capability.

When either of the 2 switches on instrument panel are depressed, electronic control module will analyze information from transfer case shift position sensor to verify its current position. Module also receives data from speed sensor and clutch interlock switch, or neutral safety switch depending on application.

If all conditions are met, electronic control module will signal electric shift motor to shift gear positions. After shift takes place, module will read input from shift position sensor to determine if transfer case is in desired position. Control module will then illuminate push button and dash indicator light.

Speed Sensor – Mounted on the rear of transfer case, speed sensor tells electronic control module correct speed to shift transfer case. Speed sensor picks up rotating speed of output shaft from 2 notches cut in opposite sides of outer ring of clutch housing assembly. *See Fig. 1.*

Shift Position Sensor – The shift position sensor tells electronic control module shift position of transfer case. It is an integral part of the electric shift motor. *See Fig. 1.*

Electric Shift Motor – Mounted externally on rear of transfer case, this motor is responsible for shifting between 4WD and 2WD. Motor drives a rotary helical cam which moves the 2WD/4WD shift fork and 4H-4L reduction shift fork to selected drive position.

Clutch Interlock Switch – The clutch interlock switch is located on clutch pedal bracket. On manual transmission vehicles with electronic shift transfer cases, clutch pedal must be fully depressed with vehicle stopped in order to make 4H-to-4L or 4L-to-4H shift change.

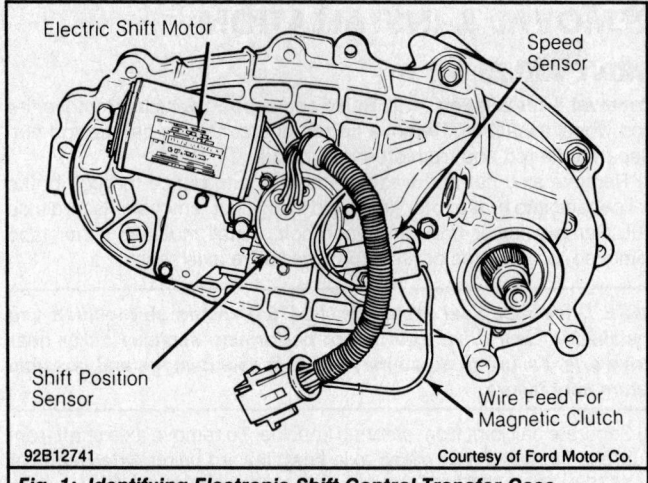

92B12741   Courtesy of Ford Motor Co.

Fig. 1: Identifying Electronic Shift Control Transfer Case Components (1356 Shown; 1354 Similar)

ADJUSTMENTS

1) Raise shift boot to expose cam plate. Loosen bolts "A" and "B" approximately one turn. Move transfer case shift lever to "4L" position. *See Fig. 2.*

2) Move cam plate rearward until bottom chamfered corner of neutral lug just contacts forward right edge of shift lever (point "C"). Hold in this position and tighten bolt "A" to specification. Tighten bolt "B" to specification.

3) Move transfer case shift lever to all shift positions to check for positive engagement and cam plate clearances. *See Fig. 2.* Install shift boot.

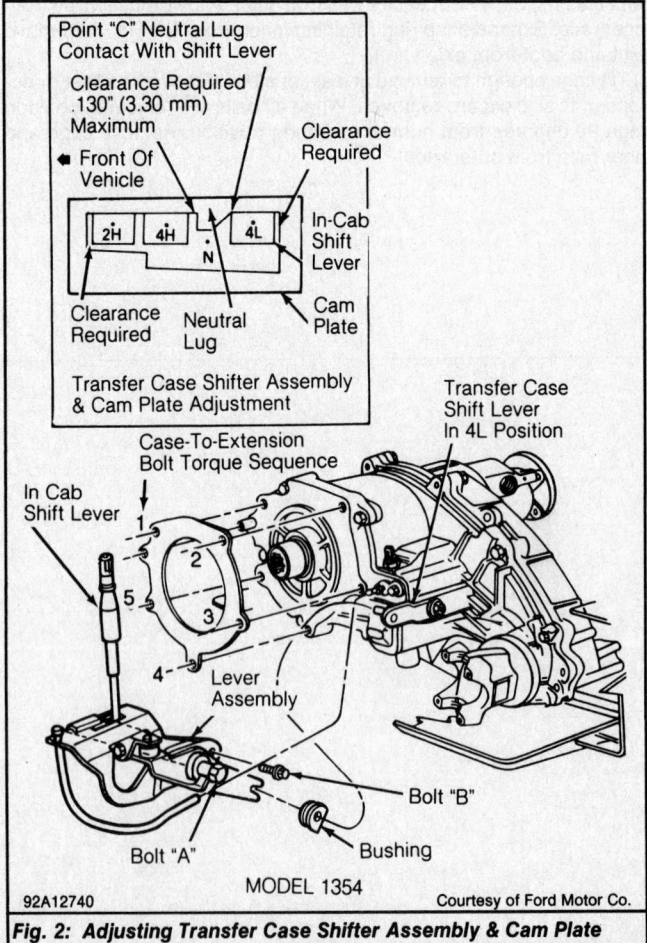

92A12740   Courtesy of Ford Motor Co.

Fig. 2: Adjusting Transfer Case Shifter Assembly & Cam Plate

TESTING

ELECTRONIC SHIFT TRANSFER CASE

Circuit Protection – The battery feed circuit, through a circuit breaker, provides memory capability for electronic control module. Ignition RUN and ACC circuits, through a fuse, supply power for switches and electric shift motor. The circuits supply power for illumination of instrument panel switches.

Control Module Self-Test – **1)** To perform electronic control module self-test, remove 5-wire connector and 8-wire connector from module. Turn ignition switch to RUN position.

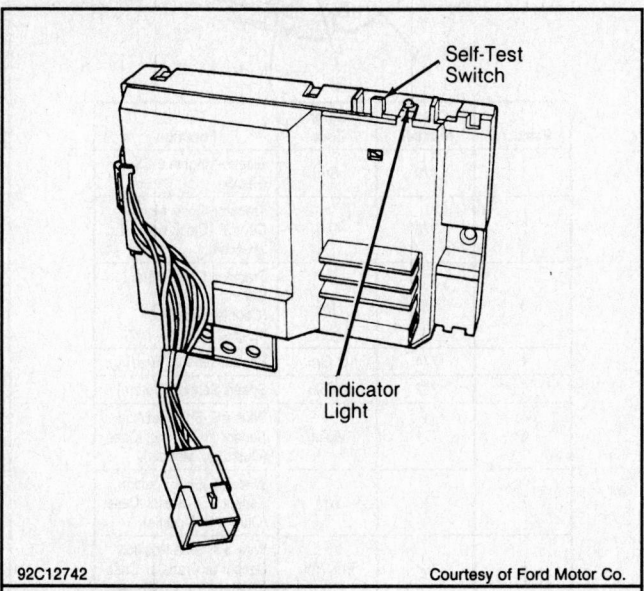

92C12742   Courtesy of Ford Motor Co.

Fig. 3: Identifying Control Module

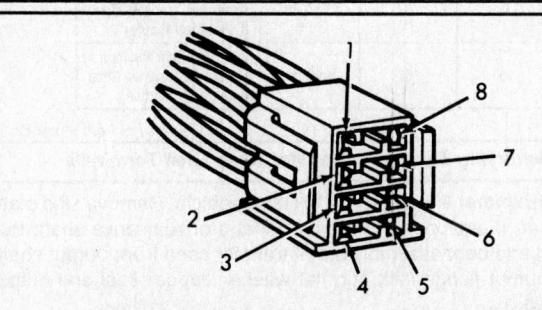

Position	Circuit Number	Color Code	Function
1			Open
2	57	Blk	Ground
3	396	Blk/Org	Logic Ground
4	778	Org	Transfer Case Motor Control (Clockwise) 2H-4H-4L
5	777	Yel	Transfer Case Motor Control (Counterclockwise) 4L-4H-2H
6	779	Brn	Electromagnetic Clutch (Feed)
7	296	Wht/Ppl	Ignition Run and Crank (Start) Feed (Fused)
	517	Blk/Wht	Battery Feed (Circuit Breaker)
8	704	DG/LG	20A Maxi-Fuse in Power Network Box

94J39155   Courtesy of Ford Motor Co.

Fig. 4: 8-Wire Pigtail Connector & Function Chart

2) Activate self-test switch and note result. If LED flashes 4 times control module is okay. No illumination indicates a dead module and module must be replaced. A steady indicator light indicates control module is inoperative and must be replaced. *See Fig. 3.*

Speed Sensor – Ensure speed sensor resistance is 225-275 ohms at module connection with vehicle stopped.

8-Wire Pigtail Connector Test – **1)** With ignition off, unplug the 8-wire connector from module. Connect voltmeter between terminal No. 8 and ground. Battery voltage should be present. *See Fig. 4.*

2) Connect voltmeter between terminal No. 7 and ground. Turn ignition to RUN position. Battery voltage should be present.

CAUTION: Disconnect battery cable before proceeding with ohmmeter tests. Never connect an ohmmeter to powered circuit.

---

3) Connect ohmmeter between terminal No. 6 and ground. Resistance should be less than 10 ohms. Connect ohmmeter between terminals No. 4 and 5 of connector. Resistance should be less than 10 ohms.

4) Connect ohmmeter between terminal No. 3 and ground. Resistance should be zero ohms. Resistance between terminal No. 2 and ground should be zero ohms.

5-Wire Harness Connector Test – **1)** Connect ohmmeter between terminals No. 1 and 2. Depress and hold 4WD switch; resistance should be less than 50 ohms. *See Fig. 5.*

2) Connect ohmmeter between terminals No. 1 and 3. Depress LOW RANGE switch. Resistance should be less than 50 ohms with switch depressed.

3) Connect jumper wire between terminal No. 4 and ground. Turn ignition switch to RUN position. Light in instrument panel and low range bar should illuminate. Turn ignition off and remove jumper wire.

4) Connect jumper wire between terminal No. 5 and ground. Turn ignition to RUN position. The light in the instrument panel and 4WD bar should illuminate.

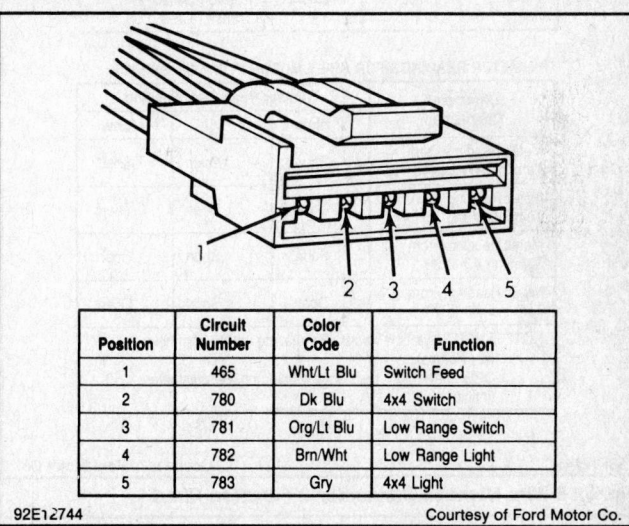

Position	Circuit Number	Color Code	Function
1	465	Wht/Lt Blu	Switch Feed
2	780	Dk Blu	4x4 Switch
3	781	Org/Lt Blu	Low Range Switch
4	782	Brn/Wht	Low Range Light
5	783	Gry	4x4 Light

92E12744   Courtesy of Ford Motor Co.

Fig. 5: 5-Wire Harness Connector & Function Chart

8-Wire Harness Connector Test – **1)** Turn ignition off. Connect ohmmeter between terminal No. 1 and ground. On manual transmission, depress clutch pedal and observe ohmmeter. Resistance should be less than 50 ohms.

2) On automatic transmission, shift transmission into Neutral and observe ohmmeter. Resistance should be less than 50 ohms.

3) To check speed sensor continuity, measure resistance between terminals No. 2 and 3. *See Fig. 6.* There should be 200-350 ohms. Connect ohmmeter between terminal No. 8 and, in turn, terminals No. 4, 5, 6 and 9. Resistance should be as specified.

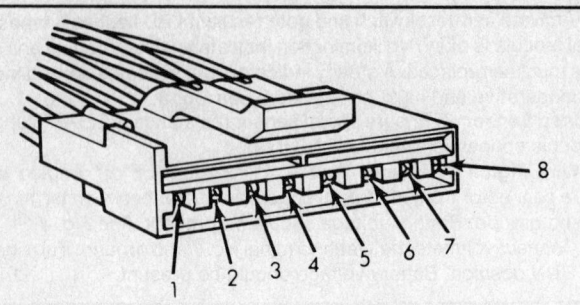

Position	Circuit Number	Color Code	Function
1	32	Red/Lt Blu	Manual Transmission Clutch Interlock Switch
1	463	Red/Wht	Automatic Transmission Neutral Safety Switch
2	774	Lt Grn	Speed Sensor (Feed)
3	772	Lt Blu	Speed Sensor Return
4	771	Violet	Wire #5, Contact Plate Position Sensor in Transfer Case
5	770	Wht	Wire #4, Contact Plate Position Sensor in Transfer Case
6	764	Brn/Wht	Wire #3, Contact Plate Position Sensor in Transfer Case
7	763	Org/Wht	Wire #2, Contact Plate Position Sensor in Transfer Case
8	762	Yel/Wht	Wire#1, Contact Plate Position Sensor in Transfer Case

OHMMETER READINGS FOR SHIFT MOTOR POSITION SENSOR

Ohmmeter Connection	Transfer Case Gear Position		
	2 High	4 High	4 Low
Meter Reading From Terminal #8 to #4	Short	Open	Short
Meter Reading From Terminal #8 to #5	Open	Open	Short
Meter Reading From Terminal #8 to #6	Short	Short	Open
Meter Reading From Terminal #8 to #7	Open	Short	Open

NOTE: SHORT is a "low" resistance reading on the ohmmeter (zero ohms).
OPEN is a "high" resistance reading on the ohmmeter (infinity).

92F12745   Courtesy of Ford Motor Co.

Fig. 6: 8-Wire Harness Connector & Function Chart

Electronic Transfer Case Feed – For functions of transfer case feed terminals, *See Fig. 7.* Ensure battery voltage is always present at terminals No. 1 and 4. Test remaining terminals for continuity to locations listed in function chart. See WIRING DIAGRAMS.

ON-VEHICLE SERVICE

FRONT & REAR OUTPUT SHAFT OIL SEAL

Removal (Bronco & "F" Series) – Raise vehicle. Remove front and/or rear drive shaft from transfer case yoke. Wire drive shafts out of way. Remove yoke lock nut, flat washer, rubber seal and output shaft flange. Using seal remover and slide hammer, remove oil seal.
Installation – Ensure housing face and bore are free from nicks and burrs. Lubricate seals with ATF or multipurpose grease. Using oil seal installer, install NEW oil seal. To complete installation, reverse removal procedure. Tighten to specification. See TORQUE SPECIFICATIONS.

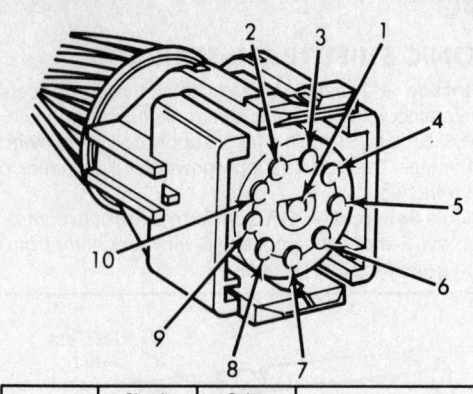

Position	Circuit Number	Color Code	Function
1	779	Brn	Electro-Magnetic Clutch (Feed)
2	778	Org	Transfer Case Motor Control (Clockwise) 2H-4H-4L
3	777	Yel	Transfer Case Motor Control (Counterclockwise) 4L-4H-2H
4	774	Lt Grn	Speed Sensor (Feed)
5	772	Lt Blu	Speed Sensor (Return)
6	771	Violet	Wire #5, Shift Position Sensor in Transfer Case (Output to Module)
7	770	Wht	Wire #4, Shift Position Sensor in Transfer Case (Output to Module)
8	764	Brn/Wht	Wire #3, Shift Position Sensor in Transfer Case (Output to Module)
9	763	Org/Wht	Wire #2, Shift Position Sensor in Transfer Case (Output to Module)
10	762	Yel/Wht	Wire #1, Shift Position Sensor in Transfer Case (Input from Module)

92J12749   Courtesy of Ford Motor Co.

Fig. 7: Identifying Electronic Transfer Case Feed Terminals

Removal (Explorer & Ranger) – 1) Raise vehicle. Remove skid plate and damper, if equipped. Remove front and/or rear drive shaft. Pull drive shaft and boot assembly out of transfer case front output shaft. Remove output flange lock nut, flat washer, rubber seal and output shaft flange.
2) Place a drain pan under transfer case, remove drain plug and drain fluid from case. Remove oil seals by prying out or screwing into metal portion of seal and using slide hammer.
Installation – 1) Ensure housing face and bore are free from nicks and burrs. Coat oil seal with multipurpose grease or ATF. Position oil seal into front output housing bore. Ensure oil seal is not cocked in bore. Drive oil seal into bore with appropriate driver.
2) Install flanges, rubber seals, flat washers, and flange lock nuts. Tighten to specification. See TORQUE SPECIFICATIONS. Install drain plug and tighten. Remove fill plug and fill transfer case with Mercon ATF. Install fill plug and tighten to specification.

REMOVAL & INSTALLATION

TRANSFER CASE

Removal – 1) Raise vehicle on hoist. Remove skid plate and damper (if equipped). Remove drain plug and drain transfer case lubricant. Disconnect 4WD indicator switch wire at transfer case (if equipped).

2) On electronic shift models, disconnect wiring harness plug at rear of transfer case and remove connector from shift motor mounting bracket. Disconnect drive shafts from transfer case. Wire drive shaft out of way. Disconnect speedometer driven gear or cable from case rear cover (if equipped).

3) Disconnect vent hose from transfer case. On manual shift models (1354), loosen or remove large and small bolts retaining shifter to extension housing. Pull on control lever until bushing slides off transfer case shift lever pin. If necessary, unscrew shift lever from control lever. On manual shift models (1356) disconnect control rod between shift lever and control lever assembly. On all models, remove heat shield (if equipped).

4) Support transfer case with a transmission jack. Remove transfer case-to-transmission bolts. Slide transfer case rearward off transmission, and lower case from vehicle. Remove gasket from between transfer case and extension housing.

Installation – **1)** Install new transfer case-to-extension housing gasket. Position transfer case so input shaft splines align with transmission output shaft. Slide case forward onto transmission output shaft and dowel pin.

2) Install transfer case-to-transmission bolts in sequence. See Fig. 8. Tighten bolts to specification. See TORQUE SPECIFICATIONS. Remove jack from transfer case. To complete installation, reverse removal procedure. On manual shift models (1354), install shifter assembly and adjust. See ADJUSTMENTS. See Fig. 2.

3) Install vent assembly so White marking on hose is in position in notch on shifter. On Explorer and Ranger, vent hose should be positioned so that upper end of hose is about 2" above top of shifter and inside shift boot.

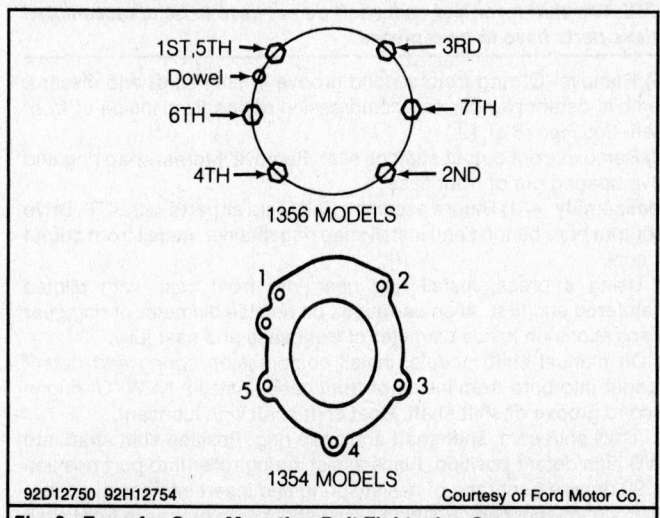

Fig. 8: Transfer Case Mounting Bolt Tightening Sequence

OVERHAUL

TRANSFER CASE (MODEL 1354)

Disassembly – **1)** Remove transfer case. See REMOVAL & INSTALLATION. Remove rear output flange lock nut, flat washer, rubber seal and yoke. Remove front output flange lock nut, flat washer, rubber seal and yoke.

2) On electronic shift models remove speed sensor bracket. Fabricate tool by forming small hook at tip of paper clip or safety pin. Remove Red locking sleeve from connector by hooking with tool and pulling from bottom.

3) Remove Brown wire (center), Green (No. 4) wire and Blue (No. 5) wire by pulling from back of connector. See Fig. 9. Remove speed sensor and shift motor, noting position of triangular shaft in case and slot in motor. See Fig. 10.

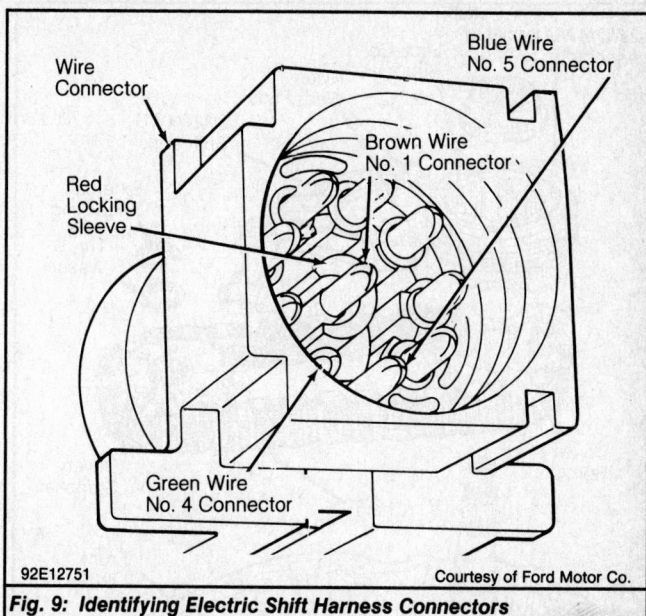

Fig. 9: Identifying Electric Shift Harness Connectors

4) On all models remove case-to-cover bolts and pry front case and rear cover apart. Ensure rear cover is facing up. If speedometer drive gear or ball bearing assembly is to be replaced, remove rear output shaft oil seal. Remove internal snap ring and drive bearing assembly from outside case.

5) If required, remove front output shaft caged needle bearings from rear cover. Remove clutch coil assembly, "O" rings and Brown wire from cover of electronic shift model. Remove 2WD-4WD shift fork return spring. Remove lock-up hub from output shaft. See Fig. 11.

6) Remove 2WD-4WD lock-up assembly and 2WD-4WD shift fork together as an assembly. Remove shift fork from lock-up assembly. If required, disassemble 2WD-4WD lock-up assembly. Remove internal snap ring and pull lock-up and spring from collar.

7) On electronic shift models remove helical cam assembly from case. If required, remove helical cam, torsion spring and sleeve from shaft.

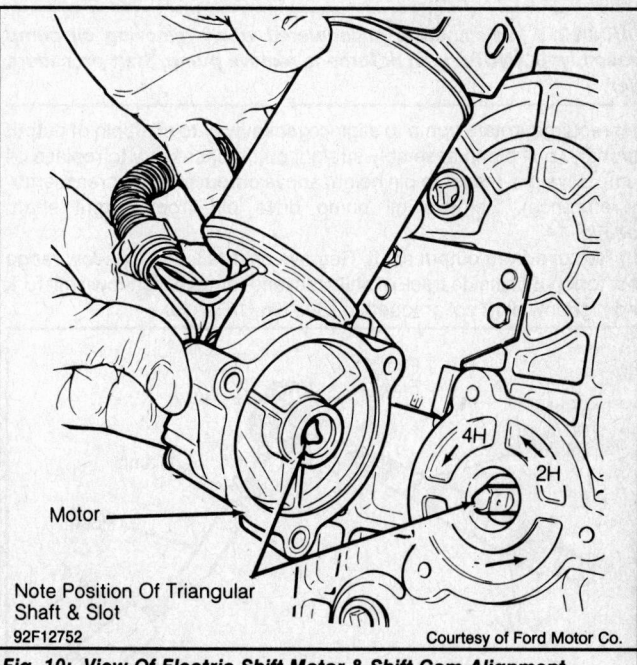

Fig. 10: View Of Electric Shift Motor & Shift Cam Alignment

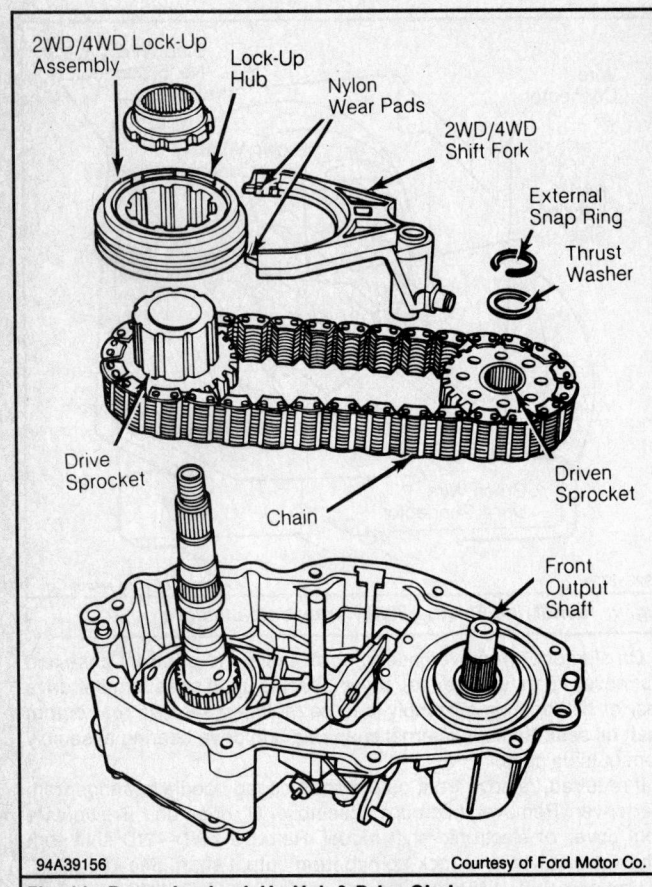

Fig. 11: Removing Lock-Up Hub & Drive Chain

94A39156   Courtesy of Ford Motor Co.

8) On all models, remove front output shaft snap ring and thrust washer. Remove chain, driven sprocket and drive sprocket as an assembly. Remove collector magnet. Remove rear output shaft and oil pump as an assembly. See Figs. 11, 18 or 19.

WARNING: If resistance is encountered when removing oil pump assembly, DO NOT pound or force to remove pump. Start procedure over.

---

9) If required, rotate pump to align cover keyway to shaft pin of output shaft and pull pump assembly straight out. If necessary to replace oil pump drive pin, measure pin height above output shaft (for reassembly reference). Remove oil pump drive pin from output shaft. See Fig. 14.

10) Remove front output shaft. Remove shift rail. Slip high-low range shift fork out of inside track of shift cam and remove high-low shift fork and high-low shift collar together. See Fig. 18 or 19.

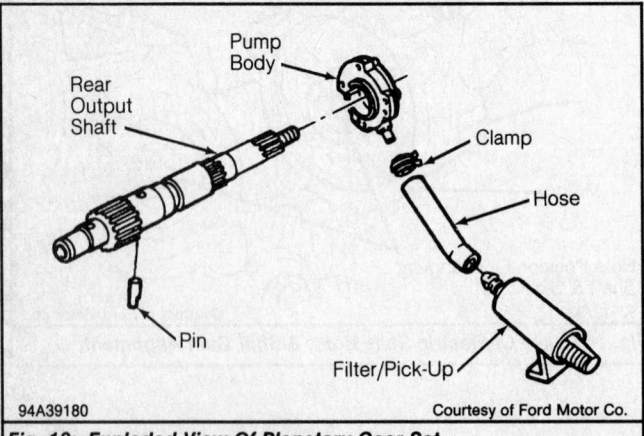

94A39180   Courtesy of Ford Motor Co.

Fig. 12: Exploded View Of Planetary Gear Set

11) On manual shift models push and pull out anchor end of assist spring from locking post in front case half. Remove spring and roller out of shift cam. See Fig. 19.

12) On all models, turn front case over, remove main drive gear bearing retainer, input shaft and planetary gear set as an assembly from front case half. Expand tangs of large snap ring in main drive gear bearing retainer, push adapter down and slide adapter off bearing. See Fig. 12.

13) Lift input shaft and planetary gear set from main drive gear bearing retainer. If required, remove oil seal from main drive gear bearing retainer. See Fig. 12.

14) Remove snap ring from planetary carrier and separate planetary gear set from input shaft assembly. Remove snap ring from input shaft. Press off bearing from input shaft. Remove thrust washer, thrust plate and sun gear from input shaft. See Fig. 12, 18 or 19.

15) Remove ring gear from front case using a press as necessary. Note relationship of serrations to chamfered pilot diameter during removal. Remove snap ring retaining front output shaft bearing using drift. See Fig. 18 or 19.

16) On manual shift models, move shift lever down to 4L then up 2 detents to 4H position. Mark a line on outside of case using side of shift lever and a grease pencil. Remove 2 Torx head set screws from front case and from shift cam. See Fig. 19.

NOTE: DO NOT pound the external snap ring during removal.

---

17) Turn front case over and remove external clip. Using a screwdriver, pry shift shaft out of front case and shift cam.

NOTE: The shift lever and cam shaft do not have to be disassembled unless parts have to be replaced.

---

18) Remove "O" ring from second groove in shift shaft and discard. Remove detent plunger and compression spring from inside of front case. See Fig. 18 or 19.

19) Remove front output shaft oil seal. Remove internal snap ring and drive bearing out of front case.

Reassembly – 1) Before assembly, lubricate all parts with ATF. Drive in output bore bearing and install snap ring retainer. Install front output oil seal.

2) Using a press, install ring gear into front case with piloted chamfered end first. Align serrations on outside diameter of ring gear to serrations on inside diameter of front case and seat fully.

3) On manual shift models, install compression spring and detent plunger into bore from inside of front case. Install a NEW "O" ring in second groove of shift shaft. Coat shift shaft with lubricant.

4) Install shift cam, shift shaft and snap ring. Position shift shaft into 4WD high detent position. Place assist spring roller into port position on 90 degree bent tang of assist spring and insert into assist spring-roller slot of shift cam. Position assist spring into groove in front case and push-to-lock upper end of spring behind front case spring anchor tab. See Fig. 13 and 19.

5) Install Torx head set screws in front case and in shift cam. Torque screws to specification. On all models slide sun gear, thrust plate and thrust washer onto input shaft. Press on bearing and install snap ring onto input shaft. See Fig. 18 or 19.

NOTE: Sun gear recessed face and snap ring groove on bearing race should be toward rear of transfer case. Stepped face of thrust washer should face towards bearing.

---

6) Install planetary gear set to sun gear and input shaft assembly. Install snap ring to planetary carrier. Install oil seal into main drive gear bearing retainer bore.

7) Place tanged snap ring in main drive gear bearing retainer groove. Install input shaft and planetary gear set in main drive gear bearing retainer and expand tanged snap ring while pushing inward until planetary assembly and input shaft assembly are seated. Snap ring will snap into groove.

8) Apply a bead of RTV gasket sealant on surface of front case. Position main drive gear bearing retainer on front case and install bolts. Tighten to specification. See TORQUE SPECIFICATIONS.

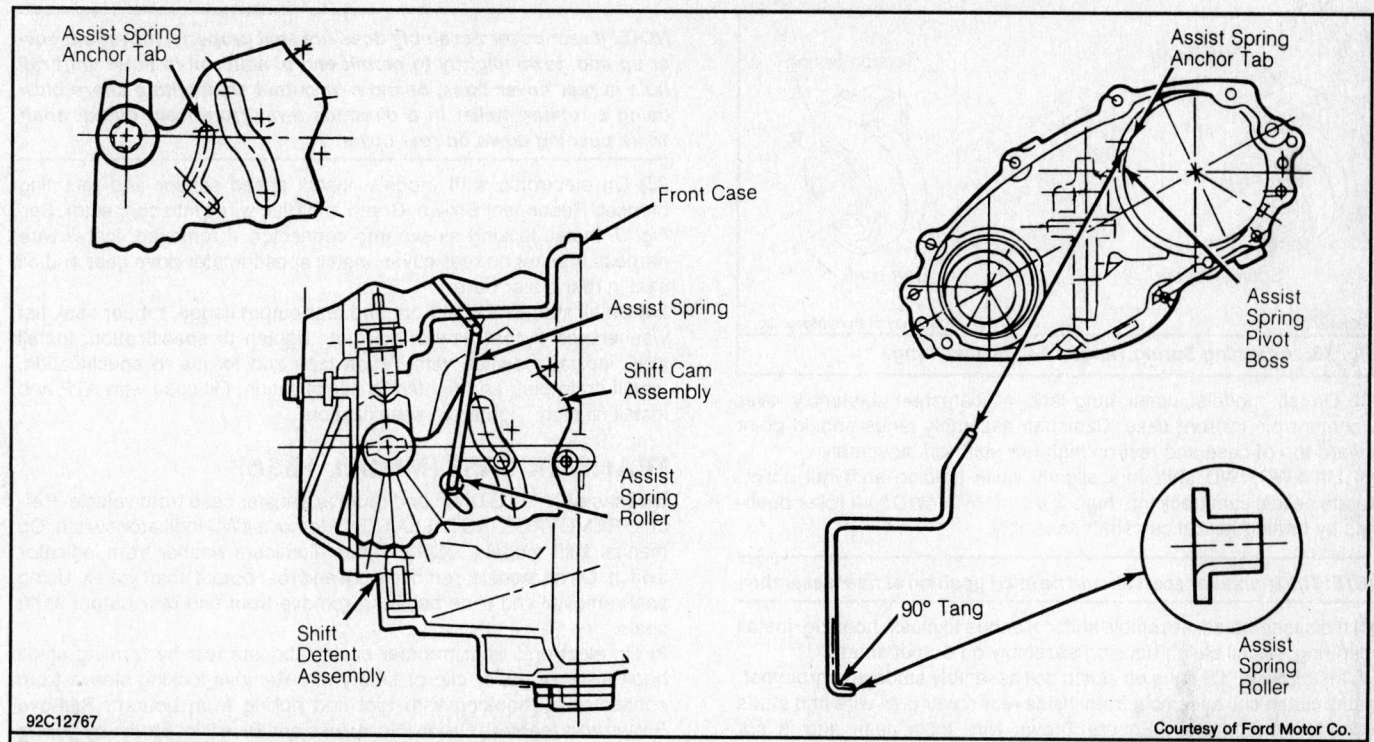

Fig. 13: Installing Assist Spring On Manual Shift Models

92C12767

Courtesy of Ford Motor Co.

9) Install high-low shift fork and shift collar on output shift shaft together into front planet. Install a new pin, roller, retainer assembly to high-low shift fork. Install nylon wear pads onto shift fork. Ensure dots on pads are installed in fork holes.

10) If removed, press pin into rear output and 5th gear shaft. Ensure pin is installed at same height as removal height or a minimum height of .040" (1.0 mm).

11) On manual shift models install shift rail through high-low fork and ensure shift rail is seated in bore in front case. Using shift lever, position high-low shift fork in 4H position.

NOTE: Prime pump through oil filter pick-up tube while turning output shaft. Output shaft must turn freely within oil pump. If binding occurs, re-align cover keyway to pin of rear output shaft and jiggle pump until it fully seats and rotates freely.

12) Inspect oil pump outside surfaces and bore for discoloration. Replace assembly if discolored. Align keyways and bores of housing, gear and cover and slide pump onto rear output and 5th gear driveshaft pin with retaining arm of cover toward rear of case. *See Fig. 14.*

13) Install output shaft and oil pump assembly in input shaft. Ensure splines of output shaft engage splines of high-low shift collar, and oil pump retainer and oil filter leg are in groove and notch of front case.

14) Install collector magnet and front output shaft into front case. Install chain, drive sprocket and driven sprocket as an assembly over shafts. *See Figs. 11, 18 or 19.*

NOTE: Driven sprocket must be installed with REAR mark facing toward rear cover.

15) Install thrust washer and new snap ring on front output shaft to retain driven sprocket.

16) Assemble 2WD/4WD lock-up assembly. Install spring in lock-up collar, place lock-up hub over spring and engage hub in notches in collar. Retain hub in collar with an internal snap ring. *See Figs. 15, 18 or 19.*

17) On electronic shift models, assemble spring spacer on camshaft. Slide spring spacer and spring onto camshaft. Position first spring tang to left side of drive tang. Wind second spring tang back to right

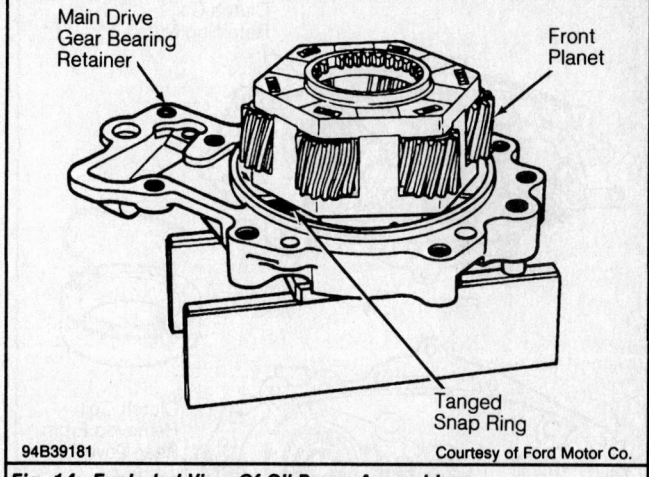

Fig. 14: Exploded View Of Oil Pump Assembly

94B39181

Courtesy of Ford Motor Co.

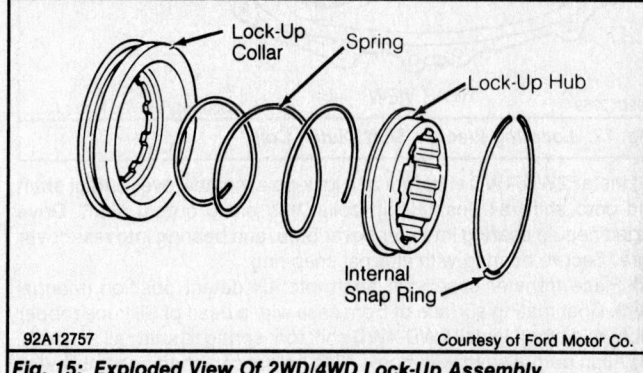

Fig. 15: Exploded View Of 2WD/4WD Lock-Up Assembly

92A12757

Courtesy of Ford Motor Co.

side of drive tang. Slide spring and spacer in as far as possible. Install helical cam onto camshaft with cam tang in between spring tangs. *See Fig. 16.*

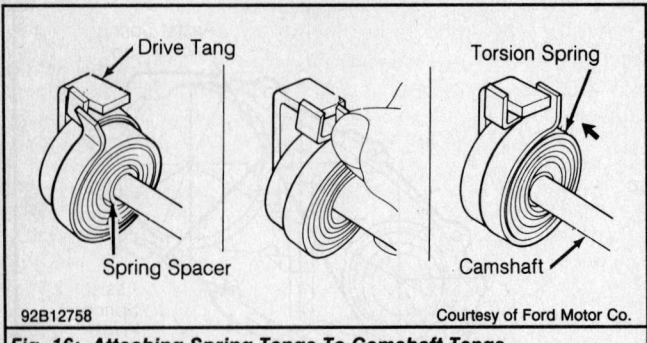

92B12758   Courtesy of Ford Motor Co.

Fig. 16: Attaching Spring Tangs To Camshaft Tangs

18) On all models install tang end of camshaft assembly over alignment pin in front case. Camshaft assembly tangs should point toward top of case and rest on high-low shift fork assembly.

19) Lift 2WD/4WD shift fork slightly while holding shift rail down. Rotate helical cam track into high-low and 2WD/4WD fork roller bushings by turning helical camshaft assembly.

NOTE: The triangular shaft should be in 2H position at final assembly.

20) If disassembled, assemble shift collar hub to clutch housing. Install snap ring. Install clutch housing assembly on output shaft.

21) Install NEW "O" rings on clutch coil assembly studs and grommet. Install clutch coil assembly from inside rear cover until wire and studs extend through cover. Ensure Brown wire exits case and is not pinched. *See Fig. 17.*

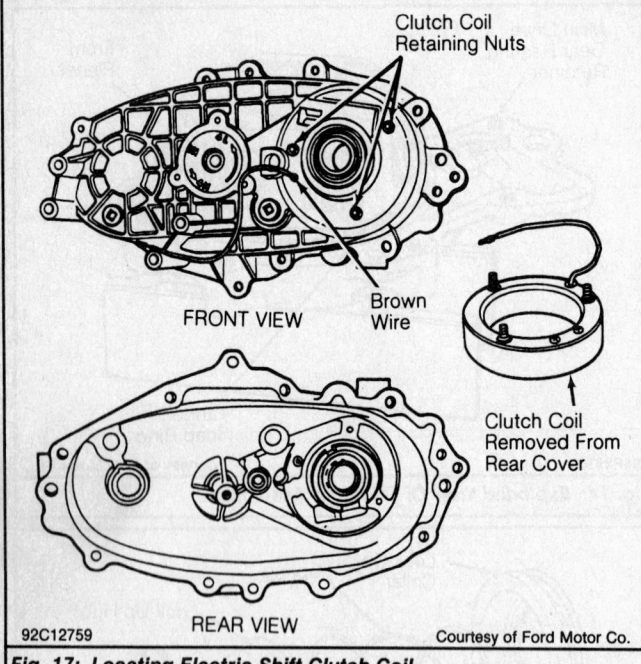

92C12759   Courtesy of Ford Motor Co.

Fig. 17: Locating Electric Shift Clutch Coil

22) Install 2WD/4WD shift fork and lock-up assembly over output shaft and onto shift rail. Install shift collar hub on to output shaft. Drive caged needle bearing into rear cover bore, and bearing into rear cover bore. Secure bearing with internal snap ring.

23) Place transfer case shift shaft into 4H detent position (manual shift). Coat mating surface of front case with a bead of Silicone rubber (Non-acid type). Install 2WD-4WD shift fork spring to shift rail and fork.

24) Align output shaft with bore. Align helical camshaft assembly with bore (electronic shift). Position rear cover so that spring boss engages 2WD/4WD shift fork spring and shift rail. Install 9 bolts (starting with bolts on rear cover) and tighten to specification. See TORQUE SPECIFICATIONS.

NOTE: If rear cover assembly does not seat properly, move rear cover up and down slightly to permit end of shift rail to enter shift rail hole in rear cover boss, or tap rear output shaft with a sharp blow using a rubber mallet in a direction away from front output shaft while pushing down on rear cover.

25) On electronic shift models, install speed sensor and retaining bracket. Reconnect Brown, Green and Blue wires into connector. *See Fig. 9.* Install locking sleeve into connector. If removed, install wire harness bracket on rear cover. Install speedometer drive gear and oil seal in rear cover bore.

26) On all models install front and rear output flange, rubber seal, flat washer and output flange lock nut. Tighten to specification. Install 4WD indicator switch with Teflon tape and torque to specification. Install drain plug and tighten to specification. Fill case with ATF and install fill plug. Tighten to specification.

TRANSFER CASE (MODEL 1356)

Disassembly – 1) Drain and remove transfer case from vehicle. Refer to REMOVAL & INSTALLATION. Remove 4WD indicator switch. On manual shift models, DO NOT lose aluminum washer from indicator switch. On all models, remove front and rear output shaft yokes. Using seal remover and slide hammer, remove front and rear output shaft seals.

2) On electronic shift transfer case, fabricate tool by forming small hook at tip of paper clip or safety pin. Remove locking sleeve from connector by hooking with tool and pulling from bottom. Remove Brown wire (center), Green (No. 4) wire and Blue (No. 5) wire by pulling from back of connector. *See Fig. 9.* On all models, remove rear bearing retainer.

3) On all electronic shift models, remove speed sensor. Remove 4 electric shift motor mount bolts and motor. Note position of triangular shaft in case and triangular slot in electric shift motor. *See Fig. 10.*

4) On all models, remove upper rear bearing snap ring. Remove 12 case half bolts. Separate case halves. Remove front output shaft inner needle bearing. Remove rear output shaft bearing from case half. On electronic shift models, remove clutch coil assembly, "O" ring and Brown wire. Remove shift shaft bushing and seal.

5) On all models, remove clutch housing retaining snap ring from output shaft. Remove clutch housing and/or 4WD hub. Remove spring from shift shaft. Lift mode shift fork and shift collar from upper rear output shaft sprocket. Carefully remove 2WD/4WD lock-up assembly snap ring. *See Fig. 11.*

6) Remove lock-up hub, spring and collar. Remove lower sprocket snap ring from lower output shaft. Remove sprockets and chain as an assembly. Remove shift rail. Remove collecting magnet from case. Remove output shaft and oil pump as an assembly.

7) If disassembling oil pump, remove 4 bolts from pump body. Note position of pump front body, pins, springs, rear cover and retainer before disassembling. *See Fig. 20 or 21.*

8) Rotate high-low shift fork until it disengages from cam. Remove fork from shifting hub. On electronic shift models, remove helical cam assembly from front case.

CAUTION: If disassembling helical cam assembly, use care when sliding cam rearward from spring. Spring is energized and can release violently.

9) Spring must be removed from helical cam and shaft finger by rotating spring ends 180 degrees apart. DO NOT get your fingers in way when disengaging spring.

10) On all models, remove high-low shift hub. Remove front output shaft. Turn case over and remove front oil seal. Reaching through front opening of case, remove snap ring from input shaft and carrier assembly. Input shaft and carrier should only be serviced as an assembly. Needle bearing or bushing may be replaced separately.

11) Remove ring gear retaining snap ring. Remove ring gear. Remove power take-off drive gear from input shaft and carrier assembly (if equipped). Remove snap ring and front input shaft bearing. Remove snap ring and front output shaft bearing. *See Fig. 20 or 21.*

12) On manual shift models, place shift lever in neutral. Remove set screw through 4WD indicator switch hole. Slide shift lever out of case. On all models, remove shift shaft seals. Remove shift cam, spring and bushing from case.

Reassembly – 1) Lubricate all parts with Mercon ATF. Install input shaft bearing and snap ring. Install front output shaft bearing and snap ring. Install front output shaft seal. Install front output shaft through lower bearing. Install front yoke to retain front output shaft. Install rubber seal, flat washer and lock nut. Tighten to specification. See TORQUE SPECIFICATIONS.

2) Install needle bearing and Bronze bushing in input shaft, if removed. Press power take-off drive gear onto input shaft (if equipped). Position ring gear in case. Install snap ring and ensure ring gear is fully seated. Install input shaft and carrier assembly. Support input shaft and carrier assembly in case. See Fig. 20 or 21.

3) Install NEW snap ring on front side of input shaft bearing. Ensure snap ring is fully seated. Install upper input shaft oil seal. On manual shift models, install NEW shift shaft seal, bushing, spring and cam. Secure shift cam with retaining clip or set screw as required.

4) On electronic shift models, engage one end of spring on helical cam assembly shaft finger. Install other end on cam finger. Place shaft finger in a soft-jawed vise. Turn cam to wind up spring until fingers of cam and shaft are aligned. Slide cam forward to lock spring in cocked position. Install cam assembly, with shaft vertical, into small hole in case.

5) On all models, place oil pump cover with TOP facing front of case. Install 2 pins, with flats facing upward and springs between them, in oil pump bore on output shaft. Place oil pump body and pick-up tube over shaft. Ensure pins are riding against inside of pump body.

6) Place oil pump rear cover, with TOP REAR facing rear of case. Install pump retainer with tabs facing front of case. While rotating output shaft, tighten oil pump bolts to specification. See TORQUE SPECIFICATIONS.

NOTE: If binding occurs while tightening oil pump bolts, loosen and retighten.

---

7) Install high-low shift hub. Install high-low shift fork by engaging it with shift hub flange and rotating it until roller engages with lower groove of helical cam (electronic) or shift cam (manual). Install shift rail through high-low fork bore and rail bore.

8) Install output shaft and oil pump assembly in input shaft. Ensure output shaft external splines and internal splines of high-low shift hub are engaged. Oil pump retainer and oil filter leg should be in case groove and notch.

9) Install collecting magnet. Install driven sprocket into chain with REAR on sprocket facing up. Install sprockets and chain as an assembly. Install thrust washer and snap ring on front output shaft sprocket. Install lock-up collar. Install tapered compression spring in lock-up collar, small end first. Place lock-up hub over spring. See Figs. 15, 20 or 21.

10) Compress spring and install snap ring. Install lock-up assembly and shift fork over output shaft sprocket and shift rail. Clutch face (electronic) should be facing rearward and long boss of shift rail facing forward. Place 4WD return spring over shift rail, against shift fork. Install 4WD hub over output shaft. On manual shift models, install snap ring. See Fig. 20.

11) On electronic shift models, install clutch housing and snap ring. On all models, install front output shaft inner needle bearing. Install rear output shaft bearing. On electronic shift models, install NEW shift shaft bushing. Install NEW "O" rings on clutch coil assembly studs. Install clutch coil assembly from inside rear cover until wire and studs extend through cover. See Fig. 17.

NOTE: DO NOT kink or pinch wire while seating clutch coil assembly.

---

12) On all models, install rear output shaft oil seal until fully seated. Apply thin bead of silicone sealant to case half mating surface, (non-acid type). Install case halves and bolts. Ensure output shaft, shift shaft and shift rails are aligned. Tighten to specification. See TORQUE SPECIFICATIONS.

13) Install rear bearing snap ring. Ensure snap ring is fully seated. Apply silicone sealant to rear bearing retainer mating surface. Install rear bearing retainer and bolts. On electronic shift models, install speed sensor. Ensure Brown wire does not get pinched under retainer. On all models, install rear output shaft yoke. Tighten to specification.

14) On manual shift models, install 4WD indicator switch and aluminum washer. Install fill and drain plugs. On electronic shift models, apply silicone sealant to motor mating surface. Note position of triangular shaft in case and triangular slot in electric shift motor. Align triangular slot. Install motor and washer (if equipped). See Fig. 10

15) If shaft will not stay in 4H position, rotate shaft clockwise to 2H position. Install motor and rotate counterclockwise until mounting holes are aligned. Install wiring in connector. Install drain plug and refill transfer case with 2 qts. Mercon ATF. Install fill plug.

TORQUE SPECIFICATIONS
TORQUE SPECIFICATIONS (MODEL 1354)

Application	Ft. Lbs. (N.m)
Breather Vent	6-14 (8-19)
Case-To-Cover Bolts	23-30 (31-41)
Damper Bolts	25-35 (34-47)
Drain & Fill Plug	14-22 (19-30)
4WD Indicator Switch	25-35 (34-47)
Front Drive Shaft Bolts	12-16 (16-22)
Rear Drive Shaft Flange Bolts	61-87 (83-118)
Shift Control Bolts (Mechanical Shift)	
Large (A)	70-90 (95-122)
Small (B)	33-42 (45-57)
Shift Shaft & Shift Cam	
Set Screw	5-7 (6.8-9.5)
Shift Lever Nut	19-26 (25-35)
Skid Plate-To-Frame Bolts	
Electronic Shift	22-30 (30-41)
Manual Shift	15-20 (20-27)
Transfer Case-To-Transmission	25-35 (34-47)
Front/Rear Yoke/Flange Nut	150-180 (203-244)

	INCH Lbs. (N.m)
Motor Mount, Motor Bracket	
Bolt & Clutch Coil Nuts	72-97 (8.1-11)
Motor Bracket Nuts	24-30 (2.7-3.4)
Speedometer Screw	20-25 (2.3-2.8)

TORQUE SPECIFICATIONS (MODEL 1356)

Application	Ft. Lbs. (N.m)
Case Half Bolts	22-36 (30-49)
4WD Indicator Switch	25-35 (34-47)
Front & Rear Output Yoke-To-Transfer Case	120-150 (163-203)
Drain & Fill Plug	7-17 (9-23)
Transfer Case-To-Transmission	25-35 (34-47)
Heat Shield-To-Transfer Case	40-45 (54-61)
Skid Plate-To-Frame Bolt	15-20 (20-27)
Front Drive Shaft-To-Front Output Yoke	8-15 (11-20)
Rear Drive Shaft-To-Rear Output Yoke	
Bolt (Bronco)	20-28 (27-33)
Rear Drive Shaft-To-Rear Output Yoke	
Nut (F150/350 4WD)	8-15 (11-20)

	INCH Lbs. (N.m)
Oil Pump Bolts	36-40 (4-4.5)

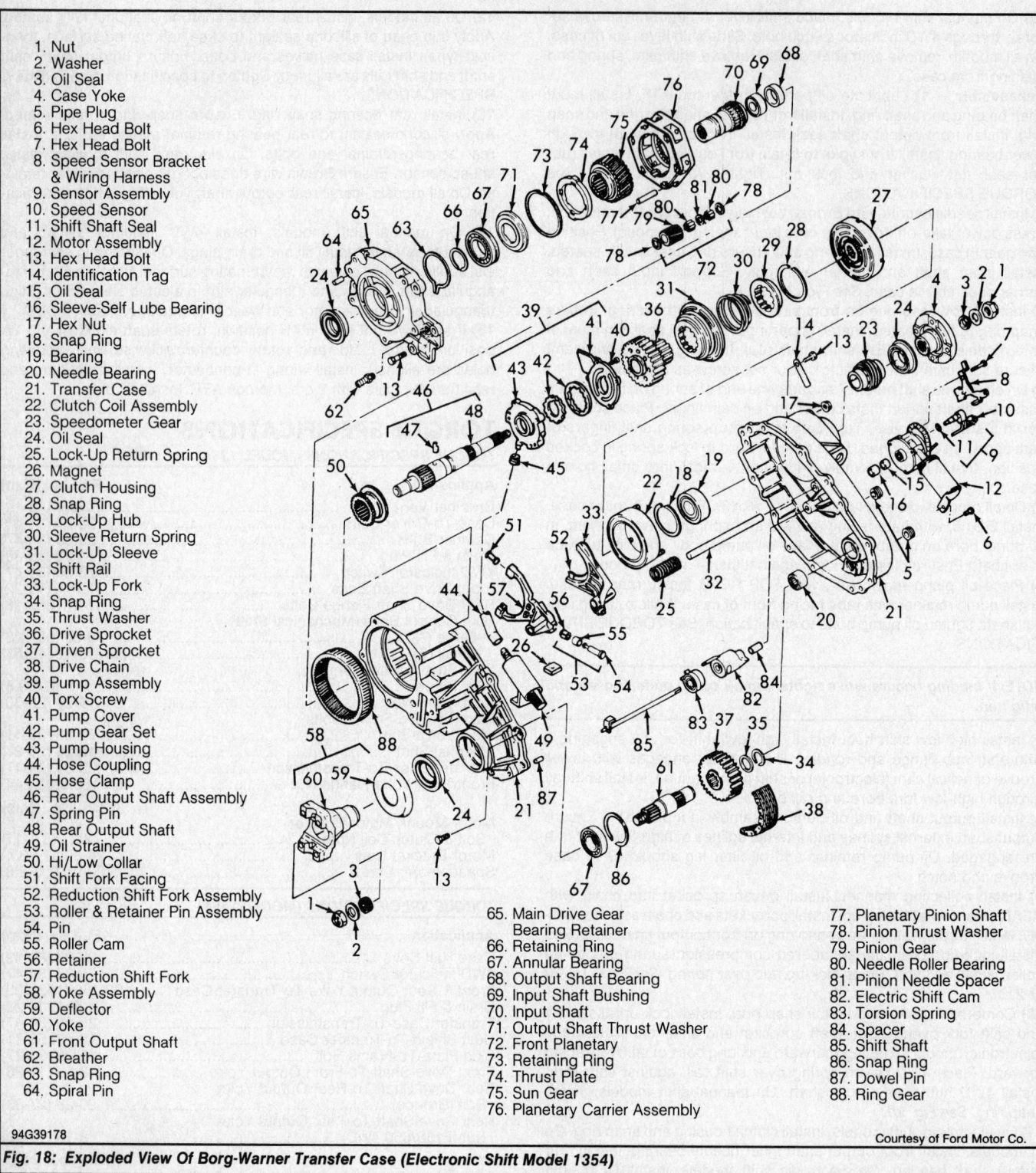

1. Nut
2. Washer
3. Oil Seal
4. Case Yoke
5. Pipe Plug
6. Hex Head Bolt
7. Hex Head Bolt
8. Speed Sensor Bracket & Wiring Harness
9. Sensor Assembly
10. Speed Sensor
11. Shift Shaft Seal
12. Motor Assembly
13. Hex Head Bolt
14. Identification Tag
15. Oil Seal
16. Sleeve-Self Lube Bearing
17. Hex Nut
18. Snap Ring
19. Bearing
20. Needle Bearing
21. Transfer Case
22. Clutch Coil Assembly
23. Speedometer Gear
24. Oil Seal
25. Lock-Up Return Spring
26. Magnet
27. Clutch Housing
28. Snap Ring
29. Lock-Up Hub
30. Sleeve Return Spring
31. Lock-Up Sleeve
32. Shift Rail
33. Lock-Up Fork
34. Snap Ring
35. Thrust Washer
36. Drive Sprocket
37. Driven Sprocket
38. Drive Chain
39. Pump Assembly
40. Torx Screw
41. Pump Cover
42. Pump Gear Set
43. Pump Housing
44. Hose Coupling
45. Hose Clamp
46. Rear Output Shaft Assembly
47. Spring Pin
48. Rear Output Shaft
49. Oil Strainer
50. Hi/Low Collar
51. Shift Fork Facing
52. Reduction Shift Fork Assembly
53. Roller & Retainer Pin Assembly
54. Pin
55. Roller Cam
56. Retainer
57. Reduction Shift Fork
58. Yoke Assembly
59. Deflector
60. Yoke
61. Front Output Shaft
62. Breather
63. Snap Ring
64. Spiral Pin

65. Main Drive Gear Bearing Retainer
66. Retaining Ring
67. Annular Bearing
68. Output Shaft Bearing
69. Input Shaft Bushing
70. Input Shaft
71. Output Shaft Thrust Washer
72. Front Planetary
73. Retaining Ring
74. Thrust Plate
75. Sun Gear
76. Planetary Carrier Assembly

77. Planetary Pinion Shaft
78. Pinion Thrust Washer
79. Pinion Gear
80. Needle Roller Bearing
81. Pinion Needle Spacer
82. Electric Shift Cam
83. Torsion Spring
84. Spacer
85. Shift Shaft
86. Snap Ring
87. Dowel Pin
88. Ring Gear

94G39178

Courtesy of Ford Motor Co.

Fig. 18: Exploded View Of Borg-Warner Transfer Case (Electronic Shift Model 1354)

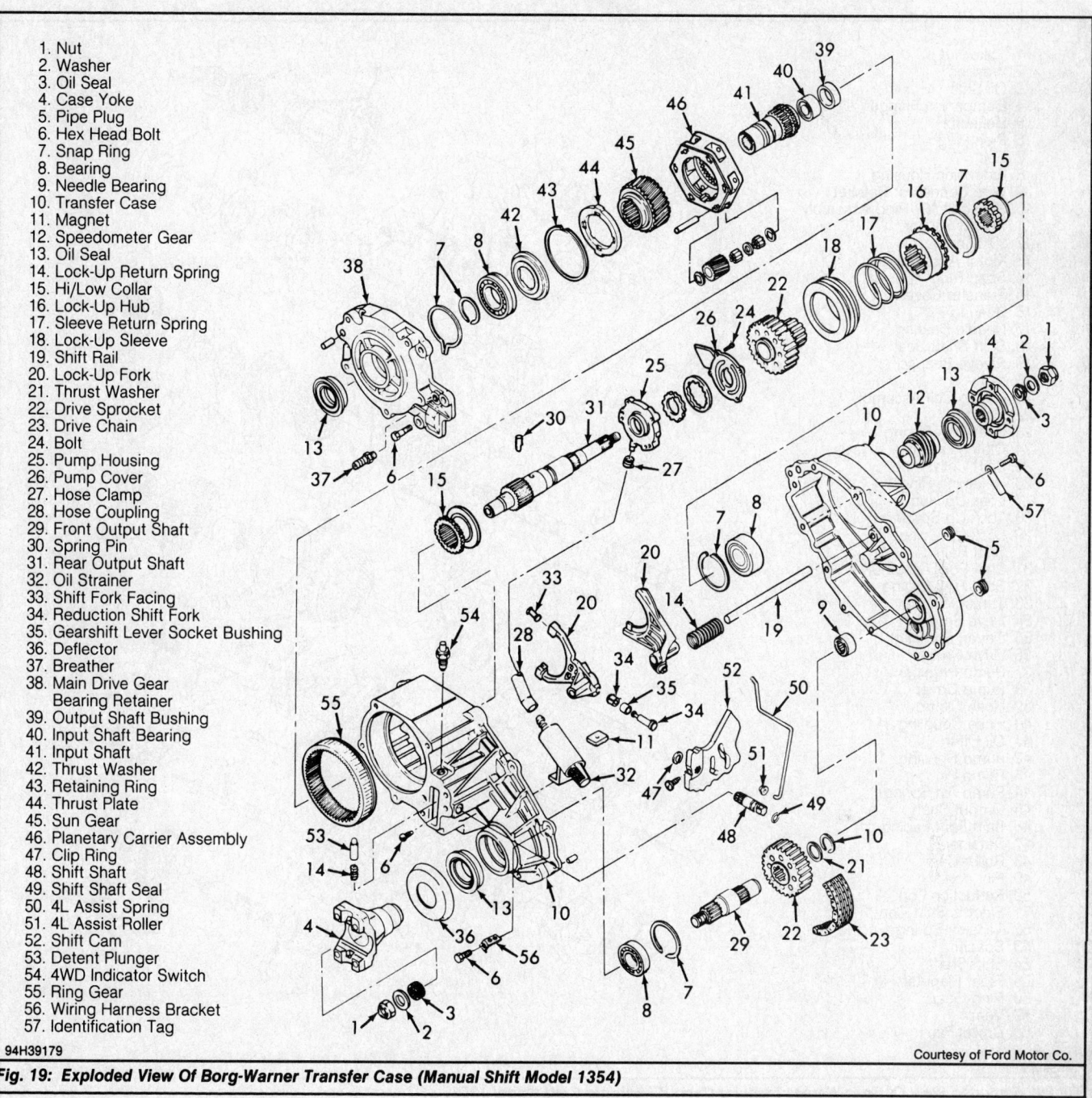

1. Nut
2. Washer
3. Oil Seal
4. Case Yoke
5. Pipe Plug
6. Hex Head Bolt
7. Snap Ring
8. Bearing
9. Needle Bearing
10. Transfer Case
11. Magnet
12. Speedometer Gear
13. Oil Seal
14. Lock-Up Return Spring
15. Hi/Low Collar
16. Lock-Up Hub
17. Sleeve Return Spring
18. Lock-Up Sleeve
19. Shift Rail
20. Lock-Up Fork
21. Thrust Washer
22. Drive Sprocket
23. Drive Chain
24. Bolt
25. Pump Housing
26. Pump Cover
27. Hose Clamp
28. Hose Coupling
29. Front Output Shaft
30. Spring Pin
31. Rear Output Shaft
32. Oil Strainer
33. Shift Fork Facing
34. Reduction Shift Fork
35. Gearshift Lever Socket Bushing
36. Deflector
37. Breather
38. Main Drive Gear
    Bearing Retainer
39. Output Shaft Bushing
40. Input Shaft Bearing
41. Input Shaft
42. Thrust Washer
43. Retaining Ring
44. Thrust Plate
45. Sun Gear
46. Planetary Carrier Assembly
47. Clip Ring
48. Shift Shaft
49. Shift Shaft Seal
50. 4L Assist Spring
51. 4L Assist Roller
52. Shift Cam
53. Detent Plunger
54. 4WD Indicator Switch
55. Ring Gear
56. Wiring Harness Bracket
57. Identification Tag

94H39179

Courtesy of Ford Motor Co.

Fig. 19: Exploded View Of Borg-Warner Transfer Case (Manual Shift Model 1354)

1. Yoke Nut
2. Washer
3. Oil Seal
4. Companion Flange
5. Deflector
6. Pipe Plug
7. Bolt
8. Extension Housing
9. Wire Connector Bracket
10. Sensor & "O" Ring Assembly
11. Speed Sensor
12. "O" Ring
13. Motor Assembly
14. Snap Ring
15. Transfer Case
16. Bearing
17. Needle Bearing
18. Shift Shaft Seal
19. Sleeve Bearing
20. Nut
21. Clutch Coil Assembly
22. Magnet
23. Shift Fork Spring
24. Clutch Housing
25. Shift Collar Hub
26. Retaining Ring
27. Lock-Up Hub
28. Lock-Up Spring
29. Lock-Up Collar
30. Shift Rail
31. Shift Fork Assembly
32. Shift Fork Facing
33. Thrust Washer
34. Drive Sprocket
35. Driven Sprocket
36. Drive Chain
37. Pump Retainer
38. Pump Cover
39. Hose Clamp
40. Hose Coupling
41. Oil Filter
42. Pump Housing
43. Pump Pin
44. Pump Pin Spring
45. Output Shaft
46. Shift Fork Facing
47. Retainer
48. Roller Cam
49. Pin
50. Reduction Fork
51. Electric Shift Cam
52. Tension Spring
53. Spacer
54. Shift Shaft
55. Front Planetary
56. Ring Gear
57. Vent
58. Dowel Pin

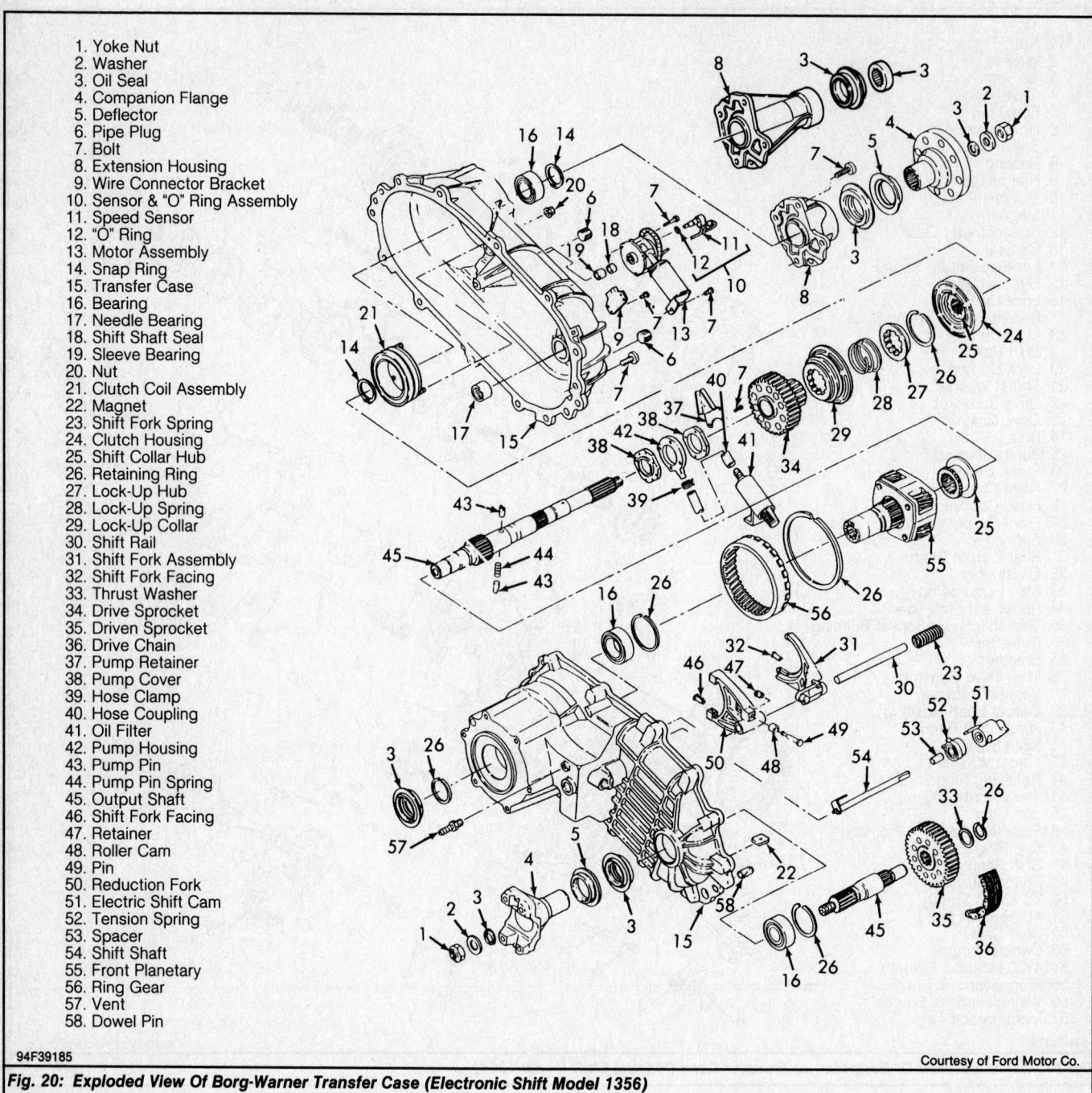

94F39185

Courtesy of Ford Motor Co.

Fig. 20: Exploded View Of Borg-Warner Transfer Case (Electronic Shift Model 1356)

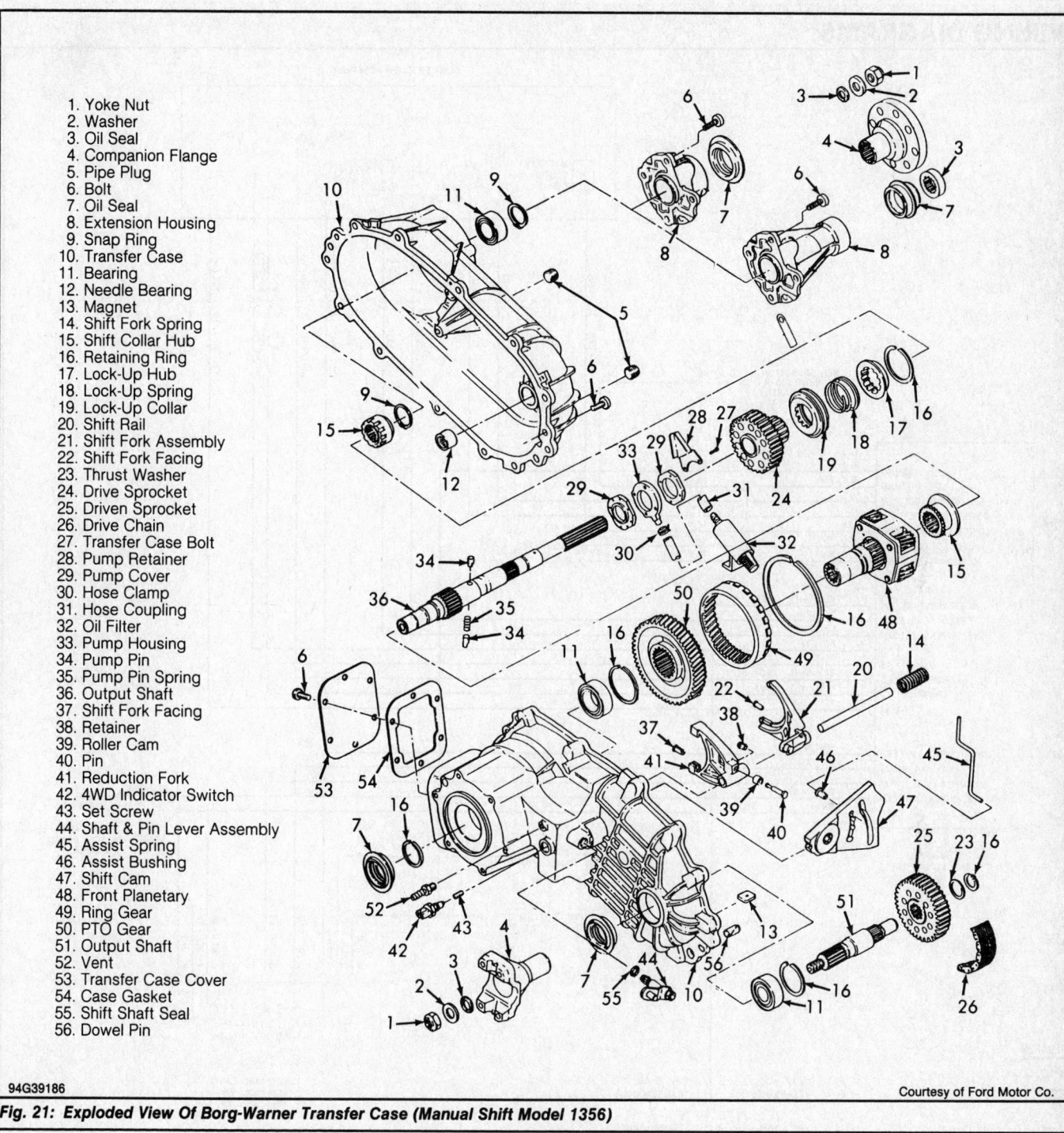

1. Yoke Nut
2. Washer
3. Oil Seal
4. Companion Flange
5. Pipe Plug
6. Bolt
7. Oil Seal
8. Extension Housing
9. Snap Ring
10. Transfer Case
11. Bearing
12. Needle Bearing
13. Magnet
14. Shift Fork Spring
15. Shift Collar Hub
16. Retaining Ring
17. Lock-Up Hub
18. Lock-Up Spring
19. Lock-Up Collar
20. Shift Rail
21. Shift Fork Assembly
22. Shift Fork Facing
23. Thrust Washer
24. Drive Sprocket
25. Driven Sprocket
26. Drive Chain
27. Transfer Case Bolt
28. Pump Retainer
29. Pump Cover
30. Hose Clamp
31. Hose Coupling
32. Oil Filter
33. Pump Housing
34. Pump Pin
35. Pump Pin Spring
36. Output Shaft
37. Shift Fork Facing
38. Retainer
39. Roller Cam
40. Pin
41. Reduction Fork
42. 4WD Indicator Switch
43. Set Screw
44. Shaft & Pin Lever Assembly
45. Assist Spring
46. Assist Bushing
47. Shift Cam
48. Front Planetary
49. Ring Gear
50. PTO Gear
51. Output Shaft
52. Vent
53. Transfer Case Cover
54. Case Gasket
55. Shift Shaft Seal
56. Dowel Pin

94G39186

Courtesy of Ford Motor Co.

Fig. 21: Exploded View Of Borg-Warner Transfer Case (Manual Shift Model 1356)

TRANSFER CASES
Borg-Warner 1354 & 1356 (Cont.)

WIRING DIAGRAMS

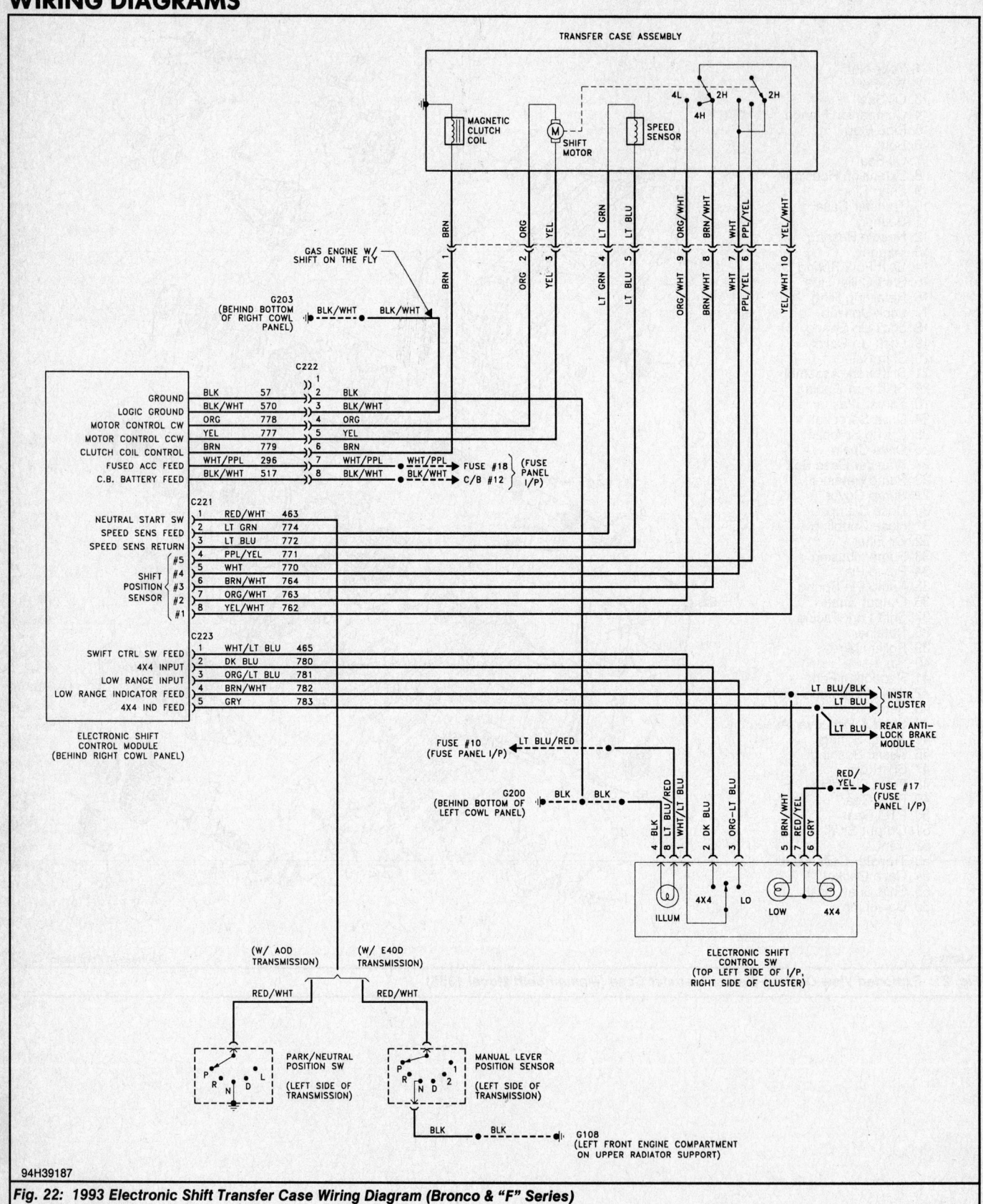

94H39187

Fig. 22: *1993 Electronic Shift Transfer Case Wiring Diagram (Bronco & "F" Series)*

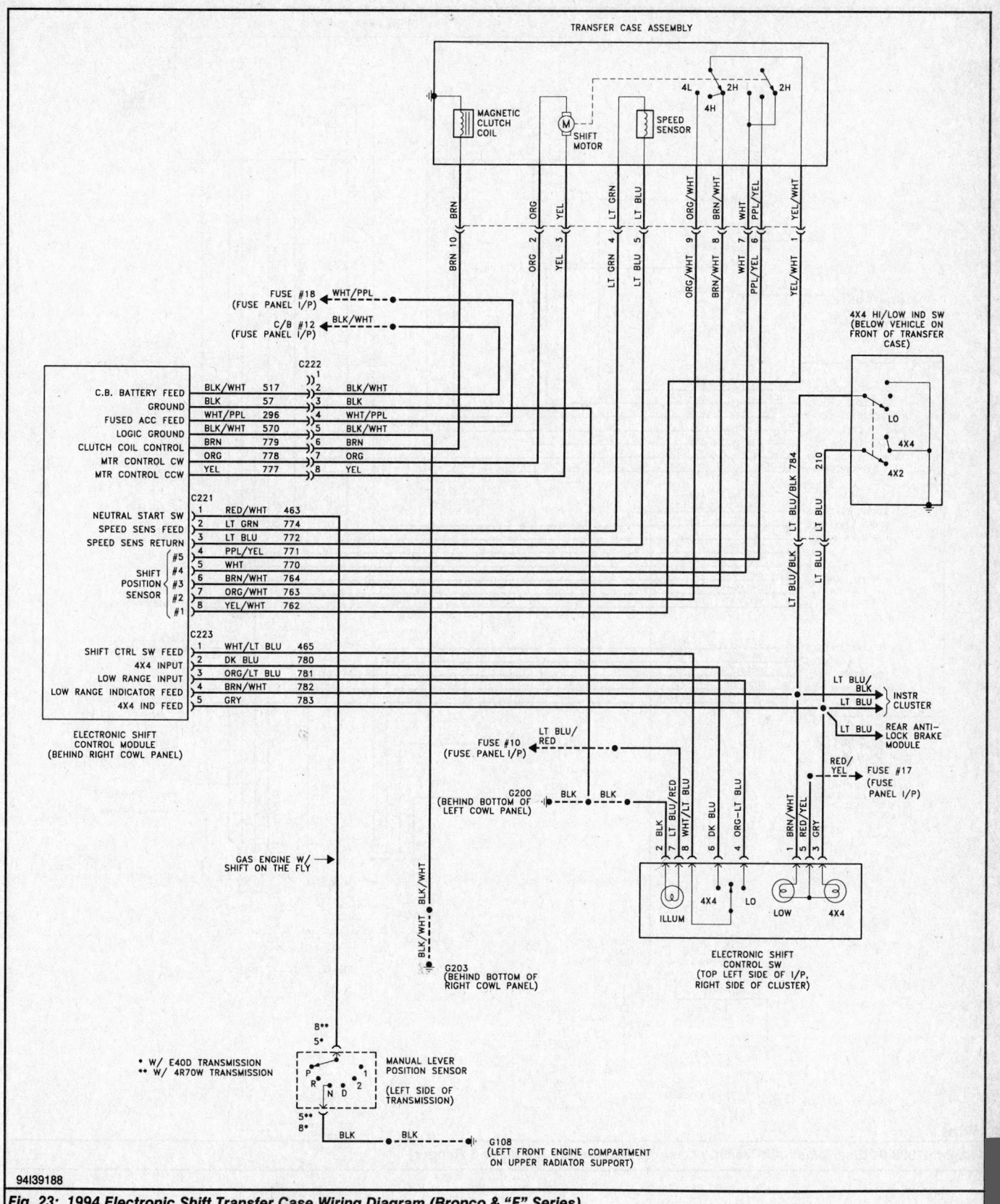

94I39188

Fig. 23: 1994 Electronic Shift Transfer Case Wiring Diagram (Bronco & "F" Series)

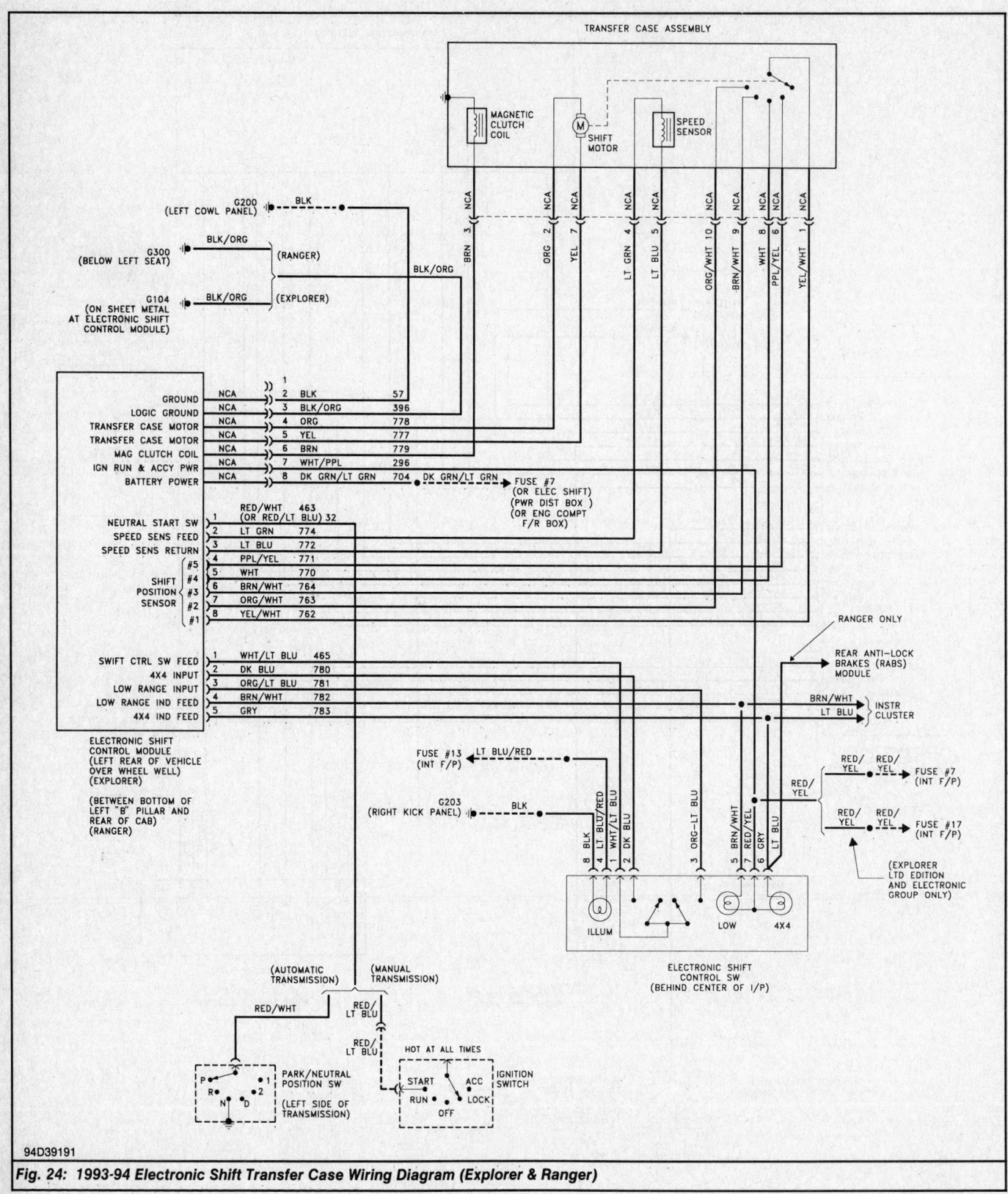

Fig. 24: *1993-94 Electronic Shift Transfer Case Wiring Diagram (Explorer & Ranger)*

94D39191

General Motors: K30

IDENTIFICATION

Identification tag is an aluminum tag attached under self-tapping extension housing bolts. This tag provides model number, serial number and build date.

DESCRIPTION

The Borg-Warner Model 4401 and 4470 transfer cases are part time 4-Wheel Drive (4WD) units. They are chain-driven and have a 2-piece aluminum case. The case has provisions for Power Take-Off (PTO) and uses an electronic synchronizer for shifting into 4WD.

TROUBLE SHOOTING

Will Not Shift Into 4WD – Check for blown A/C-HTR fuse. Faulty transfer case switch. Transfer case linkage improperly adjusted. Internal transfer case mechanical problem.

Noisy In All Gears – Check fluid level. Ensure correct fluid is used. Low tire pressure. Check for possible internal mechanical fault.

Jumps Out Of Gear Or Noisy In 4WD – Transfer case not completely in gear; check shift linkage for looseness or binding. Range fork damaged, fork inserts are worn or shift fork binding on shift rail. Low range gear worn or damaged.

Fluid Leaking From Vent Or Seals – Transfer case overfilled. Vent plugged. Output shaft seals are damaged or not installed properly.

ELECTRONIC TESTING

The electronic synchronizer is used to provide smoother shifting. The system consists of a relay, electromagnetic clutch coil, front axle switch and an indicator light.

The clutch coil receives power through transfer case switch. See WIRING DIAGRAM. When energized, the clutch coil provides synchronization. When shift is complete, front axle switch energizes transfer case relay. Relay is normally closed, when relay is energized, power is cut to clutch coil. When transfer case is shifted to 2WD, power to indicator light is cut. For specific part location see ELECTRONIC COMPONENT LOCATION table.

ELECTRONIC COMPONENT LOCATION

Component	Component Location
Synchronizer Coil	In Transfer Case
Front Axle Actuator	Right Side Of Differential Case
Front Axle Switch	Front Axle Housing
Indicator Light	Above Shifter
Transfer Case Relay	Left Side Of Firewall
Transfer Case Switch	Threaded Into Transfer Case At Linkage

NOTE: For all electronic test procedures, refer to WIRING DIAGRAM at end of article.

SYMPTOM DIAGNOSIS

4WD Will Not Disengage – Check for faulty front axle switch. Replace switch if faulty. Check wiring to switch, if switch checks okay. Front axle shifting mechanism faulty. Check front axle for mechanical problem in shifting mechanism.

4WD Indicator Light Will Not Shut Off In 2WD – Check for faulty front axle switch. Disconnect axle switch connector at front of engine. If indicator light goes out, replace front axle switch. If not, repair short to voltage between front axle switch and indicator light.

4WD Will Not Engage – 1) Test power to transfer case switch. With ignition on, connect test light to ground and backprobe Brown wire terminal at transfer case switch connector. Test light should light. If so, proceed to next step. If not, inspect 25-amp 4WD fuse in fuse block. If fuse is okay, attach test light to ground and backprobe Pink/White terminal at convenience center. Test light should light. If so, repair open in Brown wire between convenience center and transfer case switch. If not, repair open in Pink/White wire between convenience center and 4WD fuse in fuse block.

2) Test transfer case switch. With transfer case shift selector in 4WD position and ignition on, attach test light to ground and backprobe Light Blue wire terminal at transfer case switch. Test light should light. If so, proceed to next step. If not, replace transfer case switch.

NOTE: Remainder of transfer case electronic testing and diagnosis is performed with transfer case gear selector in 4WD position and ignition on.

3) Test front axle solenoid power circuit. Attach test light to ground and backprobe Light Blue wire terminal of disconnected front axle solenoid. Test light should light. If so, proceed to next step. If not, repair open in Light Blue wire between front axle solenoid and transfer case switch.

4) Test front axle solenoid. Attach test light between Light Blue wire terminal and Black wire terminal of connected front axle solenoid. If test light lights, replace front axle solenoid and proceed to next step. If test light does not light, repair open in Black wire between front axle solenoid and ground. If no opens in circuit are found, replace transfer case relay.

4WD Engages But 4WD Indicator Light Will Not Light – Check 25-amp 4WD fuse and 5-amp PANEL LAMPS fuse. If okay, test indicator light power circuit. Remove bulb from 4WD indicator light. Attach test light to ground and backprobe White wire terminal of indicator light. If test light lights, replace bulb. If test light does not light, check front axle switch.

ON-VEHICLE SERVICE

FRONT & REAR OUTPUT SHAFT OIL SEALS

Disassembly – Raise vehicle and remove front and rear drive shafts. Remove yoke flanges, washers and nuts. Remove seal shield, if equipped. Pry out seals with screwdriver.

Reassembly – Ensure seal lips are lubricated with ATF. Install seals with appropriate seal installer. Reverse disassembly procedures for reassembly. Tighten yoke/flange nuts to specification. Refill fluid as necessary. *See Fig. 1.*

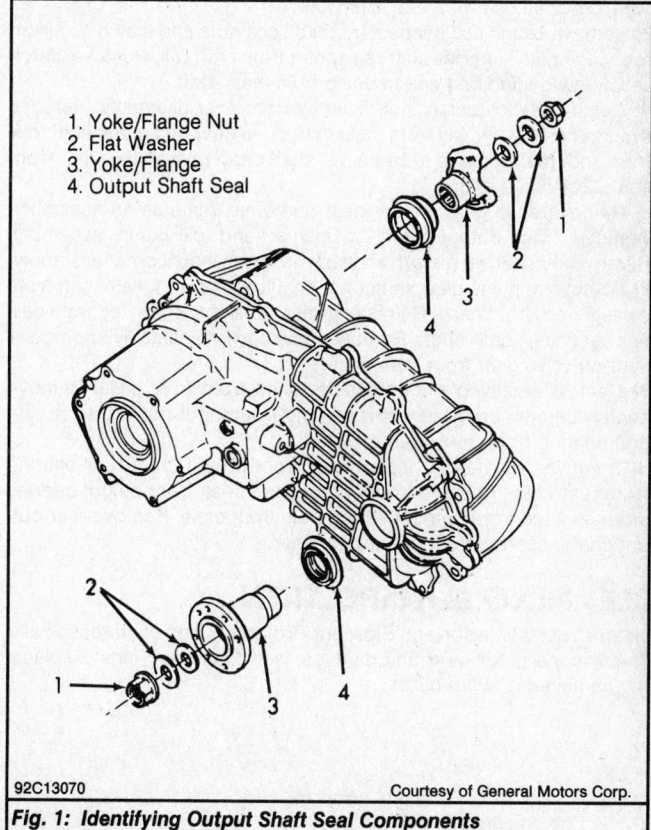

1. Yoke/Flange Nut
2. Flat Washer
3. Yoke/Flange
4. Output Shaft Seal

92C13070   Courtesy of General Motors Corp.

Fig. 1: Identifying Output Shaft Seal Components

TRANSFER CASES
Borg-Warner 4401 & 4470 (Cont.)

TRANSFER CASE LINKAGE ADJUSTMENT

Place shift lever in 4H position. Raise vehicle and remove linkage from shift lever. Move shift lever on transfer case fully forward. Adjust shift linkage with swivel to align with shift lever. Reattach linkage and lower vehicle.

REMOVAL & INSTALLATION

TRANSFER CASE

Removal – 1) Disconnect negative battery cable. Raise vehicle. Drain lubricant from transfer case. Remove cotter pin from shift lever linkage. Mark transfer case front and rear output shafts and yokes, for assembly alignment reference. Remove left strut rod. Remove shafts.

2) Disconnect electrical wires and speed sensor wire (if equipped). Disconnect parking brake cable guide from pivot located on right frame rail. On automatic transmission models, remove engine strut rod from transfer case (if equipped).

3) Remove skid plate. Place support under transfer case and remove transfer case-to-transmission bolts. Move transfer case assembly rearward until free of transmission output shaft and remove assembly. Remove all gasket material from rear of transmission adapter housing.

Installation – To install, reverse removal procedure. Install new gasket and tighten bolts to specification. See TORQUE SPECIFICATIONS.

TRANSFER CASE DISASSEMBLY

1) Remove front and rear output flange nuts, washers and flanges from front and rear output shafts. Remove speed sensor, 4WD indicator switch, rear bearing retainer bolts and retainer. See Fig. 2 or 3.

NOTE: Case-half screws are self-tapping screws and aluminum shavings are common when removed.

2) Remove speedometer tone wheel, tone wheel snap ring and rear output bearing snap ring from mainshaft. Remove case screws and pry front case half from rear case half.

3) Remove clutch coil connector, clutch coil nuts and clutch coil from rear case half. Remove shift rail spring from shift rail. Remove clutch coil housing snap ring and housing from mainshaft.

4) Remove synchronizer hub from synchronizer assembly. Remove synchronizer assembly from mainshaft drive gear and mode shift fork from shift rail. Remove front output shaft snap ring and washer from shaft. See Fig. 2 or 3.

5) Remove drive gear, driven gear and drive chain as an assembly. Remove front output shaft, mainshaft and oil pump assembly. Remove shift rail, range fork and shift hub from input carrier assembly.

6) Remove annulus gear snap ring, annulus gear and mainshaft front oil seal from front case. Remove carrier assembly snap ring from carrier assembly input shaft. Remove input carrier assembly and power take-off drive gear from front case.

7) Remove retaining clip and sector shaft from front case. Remove sector, detent spring, detent roller and front input bearing snap ring and bearing from front case.

8) Remove rear output bearing and front output shaft rear bearing from rear case. Remove front output shaft seal, front output bearing snap ring and front output bearing from front case. Remove rear output shaft seal from rear bearing retainer.

CLEANING & INSPECTION

Clean all parts with solvent. Blow out all oil ports with compressed air. Check all parts for wear and damage, including snap rings. Replace any damaged or worn part.

COMPONENT DISASSEMBLY & REASSEMBLY

OIL PUMP (MODEL 4401)

Disassembly – 1) Remove oil pump retainer bolts and retainer from oil pump rear cover. See Fig. 2 or 4. Remove oil pump body and pick-up tube assembly from mainshaft. Remove oil pump pins and spring from mainshaft.

2) Remove oil pump front cover from mainshaft. Remove pick-up tube clamp. Remove pick-up tube and oil pump pick-up from oil pump body. Inspect oil pump housing, pins and pin bores for wear, galling or cracks. If visible, replace oil pump assembly.

NOTE: Ensure moving parts are lubricated with ATF before assembly.

Reassembly – 1) Install oil pump pick-up on pick-up tube. Install pick-up tube and clamp on housing. Install oil pump front cover with TOP marking on edge, readable from front case side. Install oil pump spring between oil pump pins and assembly into mainshaft bore. Ensure flats of oil pump pins are facing rear case half.

2) Install oil pump housing and ensure pins are riding against inside of pump housing. Install oil pump rear cover with TOP marking on edge, readable from rear case side. The words TOP on front and rear oil pump covers are on same side of assembled pump housing. Install oil pump retainer and bolts with tabs facing front case half. Rotate mainshaft while tightening bolts to ensure oil pump turns freely. Tighten bolts to specification. See TORQUE SPECIFICATIONS.

OIL PUMP (MODEL 4470)

Disassembly – 1) Remove oil pump cover screws and cover from oil pump body. See Fig. 3. Remove oil pump drive gear and driven gear from oil pump body. Remove pick-up tube clamp.

2) Remove pick-up tube and oil pump pick-up from oil pump body. Inspect oil pump gears and housing for wear, galling or cracks. If visible, replace oil pump assembly.

NOTE: Ensure moving parts are lubricated with ATF before assembly.

Reassembly – 1) Assemble needle bearings to mainshaft. Install pick-up tube and clamp on oil pump body. Install oil pump drive and driven gear into oil pump body.

2) Install oil pump cover and cover screws to oil pump body. Rotate mainshaft while tightening screws to ensure oil pump turns freely. Tighten bolts to specification. See TORQUE SPECIFICATIONS.

TRANSFER CASE REASSEMBLY

1) Lubricate all internal parts with ATF. Install rear output shaft seal to rear bearing retainer. Install front output bearing, snap ring and front output shaft seal to front case. See Fig. 2 or 3.

2) Install rear output bearing to rear case, and front input bearing and snap ring to front case. Install front output shaft seal to front case. Install rear output bearing to rear case.

3) Install front input bearing and snap ring to front case half. Install sector detent spring and roller into front case. Install sector shaft through case, align with spline on sector and install retainer clip.

4) Install power take-off drive gear and input carrier assembly to front case. Install input carrier snap ring to input carrier, and mainshaft front oil seal to front case. Install annulus gear and annulus gear snap ring to front case.

5) Install range fork and shaft hub, aligning shift hub to carrier assembly and shift fork pin to slot in sector. Install shift rail through range fork and into boss in front case.

6) Install mainshaft and oil pump assembly. Install front output shaft to front output bearing. Install drive gear, driven gear, and drive chain as an assembly to mainshaft and front output shaft. Install flat washer and output shaft snap ring to front output shaft.

1. Speedometer Tone Wheel
2. Tone Wheel Snap Ring
3. Rear Output Bearing Snap Ring
4. Clutch Coil Wire Connector
5. Clutch Coil Nut
6. Clutch Coil
7. Shift Rail Spring
8. Shift Rail
9. Clutch Coil Housing Snap Ring
10. Clutch Coil Housing
11. Synchronizer Assembly
12. Mode Shift Fork
13. Front Output Shaft
14. Drive Gear
15. Needle Bearing
16. Drive Chain
17. Front Output Bearing
18. Mainshaft
19. Oil Pump Assembly
20. Input Carrier Assembly
21. Oil Pump Pick-Up
22. Range Fork
23. Shift Hub
24. Annulus Gear Snap Ring
25. Front Case
26. Annulus Gear
27. Mainshaft Front Oil Seal
28. Carrier Assembly Snap Ring
29. PTO Drive Gear
30. Retainer Clip
31. Sector Shaft
32. Sector
33. Detent Spring
34. Front Output Bearing Snap Ring
35. Front Output Shaft Seal
36. Front Input Bearing Snap Ring
37. Front Input Bearing
38. Rear Output Bearing
39. Rear Case
40. Rear Output Shaft Seal
41. Shift Lever
42. Detent Roller
43. Rear Bearing Retainer
44. Synchronizer Hub Snap Ring
45. Lock-Up Hub
46. Compression Spring
47. Lock-Up Collar
48. Synchronizer Hub
49. Flat Washer
50. Rubber Sealing Washer
51. Front Output Flange
52. Speed Sensor
53. Transfer Case Switch
54. Rear Bearing Retainer Bolts
55. Case Bolt
56. Oil Pump Cover Screw
57. Oil Pump Body
58. Deflector
59. Cover
60. Oil Pump Cover
61. Pick-Up Tube Clamp
62. Pick-Up Tube
63. Rear Output Yoke Nut
64. Front Output Flange Nut
65. Identification Tag (Not Shown)
66. Vent
67. Rear Output Yoke
68. PTO Cover
69. PTO Bolt
70. Magnet
71. Dowel Pin
72. Drain & Fill Plug
73. Front Output Shaft Rear Bearing
74. Spacer Washer
75. Snap Ring

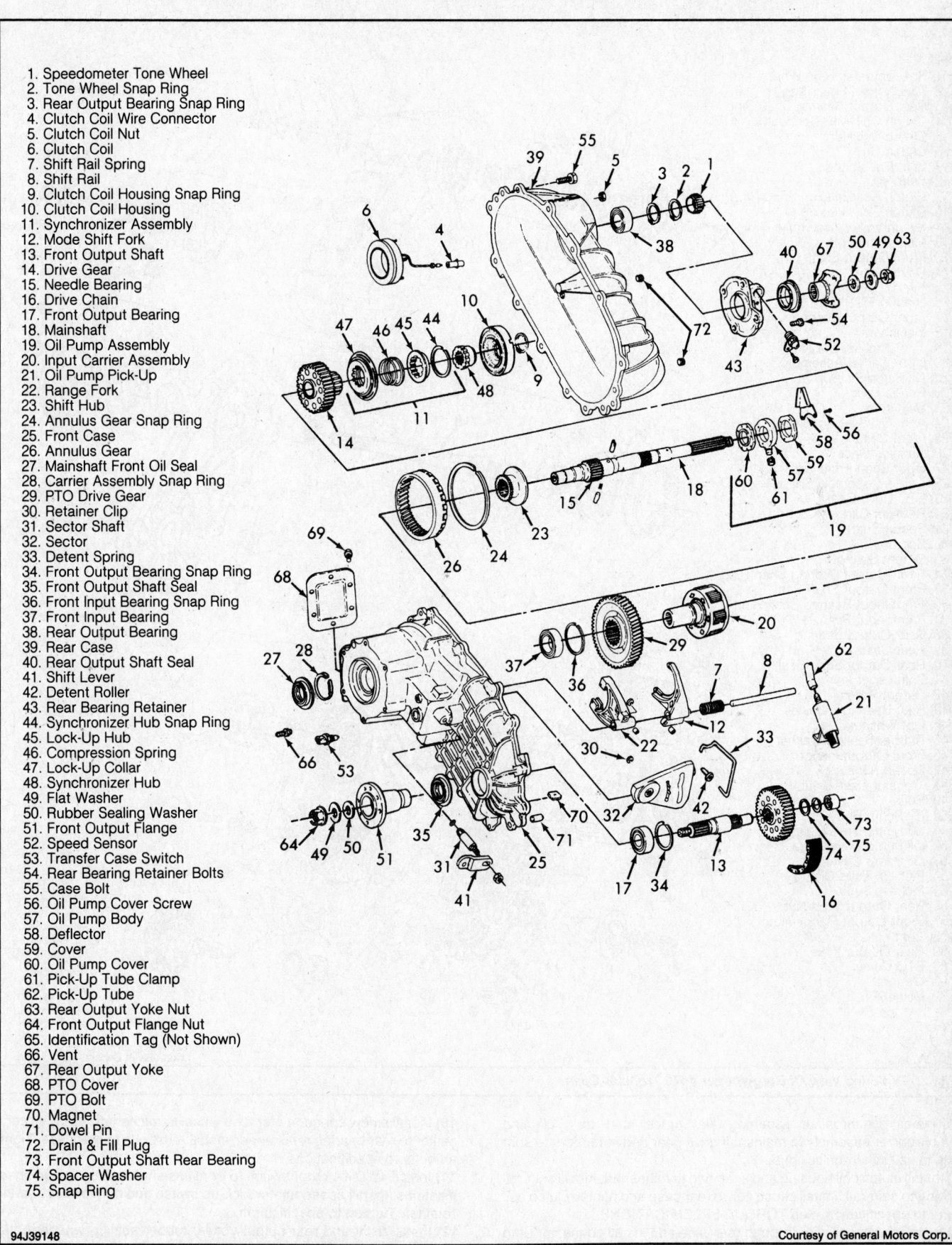

94J39148

Fig. 2: Exploded View Of Borg-Warner 4401 Transfer Case

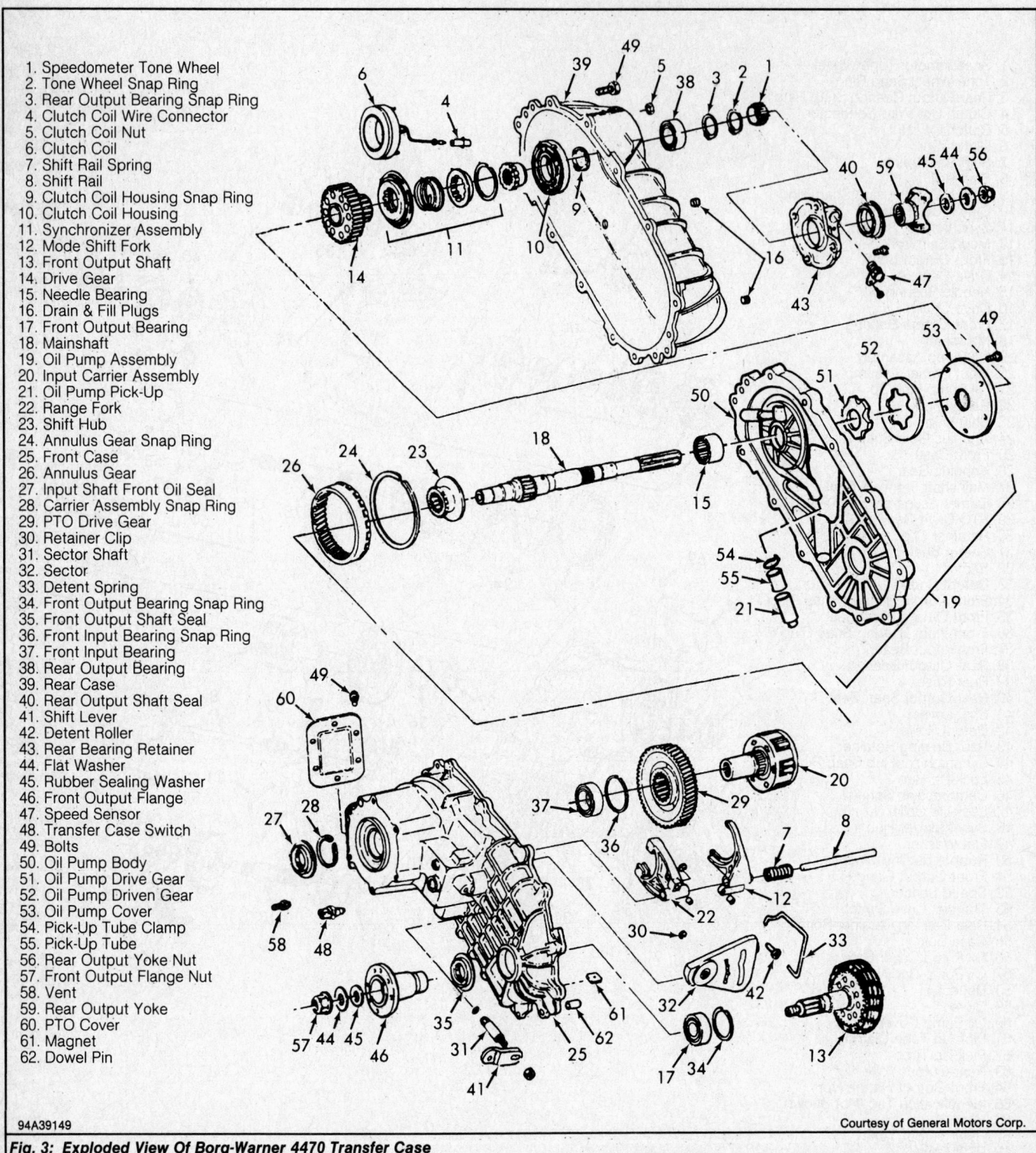

1. Speedometer Tone Wheel
2. Tone Wheel Snap Ring
3. Rear Output Bearing Snap Ring
4. Clutch Coil Wire Connector
5. Clutch Coil Nut
6. Clutch Coil
7. Shift Rail Spring
8. Shift Rail
9. Clutch Coil Housing Snap Ring
10. Clutch Coil Housing
11. Synchronizer Assembly
12. Mode Shift Fork
13. Front Output Shaft
14. Drive Gear
15. Needle Bearing
16. Drain & Fill Plugs
17. Front Output Bearing
18. Mainshaft
19. Oil Pump Assembly
20. Input Carrier Assembly
21. Oil Pump Pick-Up
22. Range Fork
23. Shift Hub
24. Annulus Gear Snap Ring
25. Front Case
26. Annulus Gear
27. Input Shaft Front Oil Seal
28. Carrier Assembly Snap Ring
29. PTO Drive Gear
30. Retainer Clip
31. Sector Shaft
32. Sector
33. Detent Spring
34. Front Output Bearing Snap Ring
35. Front Output Shaft Seal
36. Front Input Bearing Snap Ring
37. Front Input Bearing
38. Rear Output Bearing
39. Rear Case
40. Rear Output Shaft Seal
41. Shift Lever
42. Detent Roller
43. Rear Bearing Retainer
44. Flat Washer
45. Rubber Sealing Washer
46. Front Output Flange
47. Speed Sensor
48. Transfer Case Switch
49. Bolts
50. Oil Pump Body
51. Oil Pump Drive Gear
52. Oil Pump Driven Gear
53. Oil Pump Cover
54. Pick-Up Tube Clamp
55. Pick-Up Tube
56. Rear Output Yoke Nut
57. Front Output Flange Nut
58. Vent
59. Rear Output Yoke
60. PTO Cover
61. Magnet
62. Dowel Pin

94A39149

Courtesy of General Motors Corp.

Fig. 3: Exploded View Of Borg-Warner 4470 Transfer Case

7) Install synchronizer assembly and mode shift fork, aligning synchronizer assembly to mainshaft drive gear and mode fork to shift rail. Install synchronizer hub.

8) Install clutch coil housing and snap ring to mainshaft. Install shift rail spring to shift rail. Install clutch coil to rear case and tighten clutch coil nuts to specification. See TORQUE SPECIFICATIONS.

9) Install clutch coil wire through rear case and install connector onto wire. Apply silicone sealer to case sealing surfaces and install rear case half to front case half. Install case screws and tighten to specification.

10) Install a new speedometer tone wheel to mainshaft. Apply silicone sealer to rear bearing retainer and install with bolts to rear case. Tighten bolts to specifications.

11) Install 4WD indicator switch to front case half and tighten to specifications. Install speedometer pick-up switch and bolt to rear bearing retainer. Tighten to specification.

12) Install front and rear output yokes, rubber sealing washers, flat washers and front and rear output yoke nuts to front and rear output shafts. Tighten to specification.

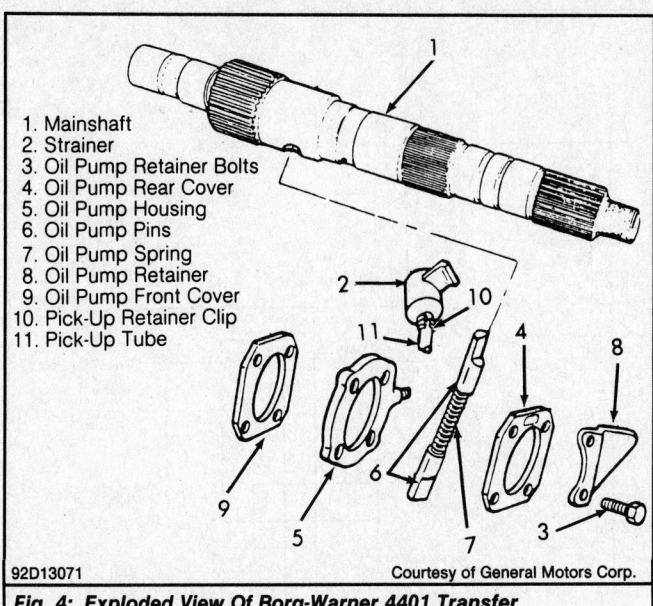

1. Mainshaft
2. Strainer
3. Oil Pump Retainer Bolts
4. Oil Pump Rear Cover
5. Oil Pump Housing
6. Oil Pump Pins
7. Oil Pump Spring
8. Oil Pump Retainer
9. Oil Pump Front Cover
10. Pick-Up Retainer Clip
11. Pick-Up Tube

92D13071   Courtesy of General Motors Corp.

Fig. 4: Exploded View Of Borg-Warner 4401 Transfer Case Mainshaft & Oil Pump Assembly

TORQUE SPECIFICATIONS
TORQUE SPECIFICATIONS

Application	Ft. Lbs. (N.m)
Case Screws	30 (41)
Drain & Fill Plugs	18 (24)
Front Output Flange Nut	165 (224)
PTO Cover Bolts	20 (27)
Rear Bearing Retainer	30 (41)
Rear Output Flange Nut	125 (169)
Speed Sensor Bolts	12 (16)
Transfer Case Switch	30 (41)
Transfer Case-To-Transmission Bolts	24 (33)

	INCH Lbs. (N.m)
Clutch Coil Nuts	84 (9.5)
Oil Pump Retaining Bolts Or Screws	
4401	54 (6.1)
4470	22 (2.5)

WIRING DIAGRAMS

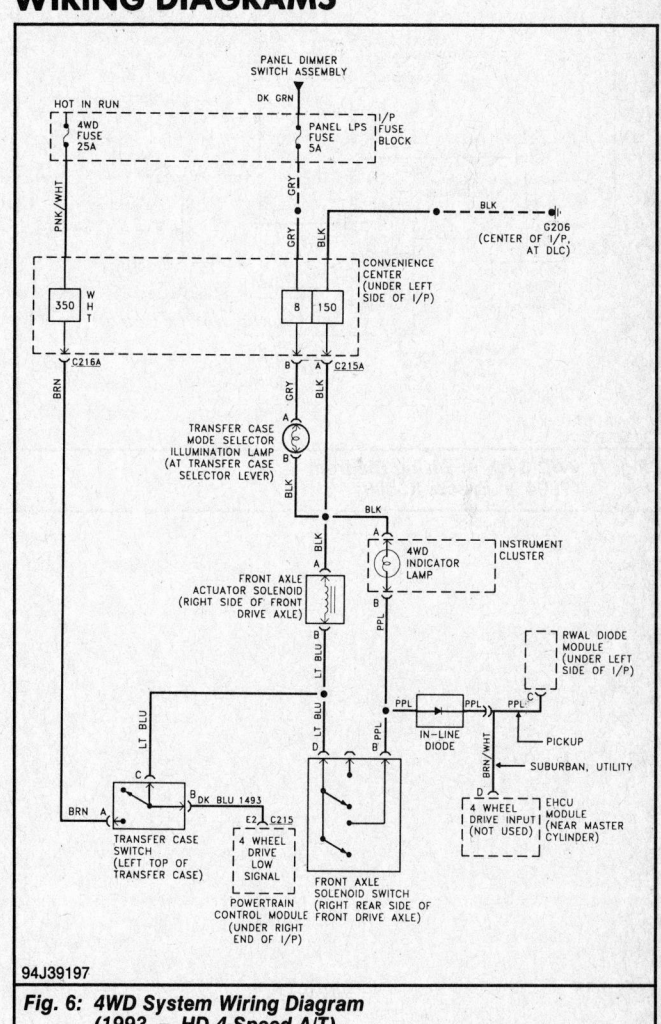

94J39197

Fig. 6: 4WD System Wiring Diagram (1993 – HD 4-Speed A/T)

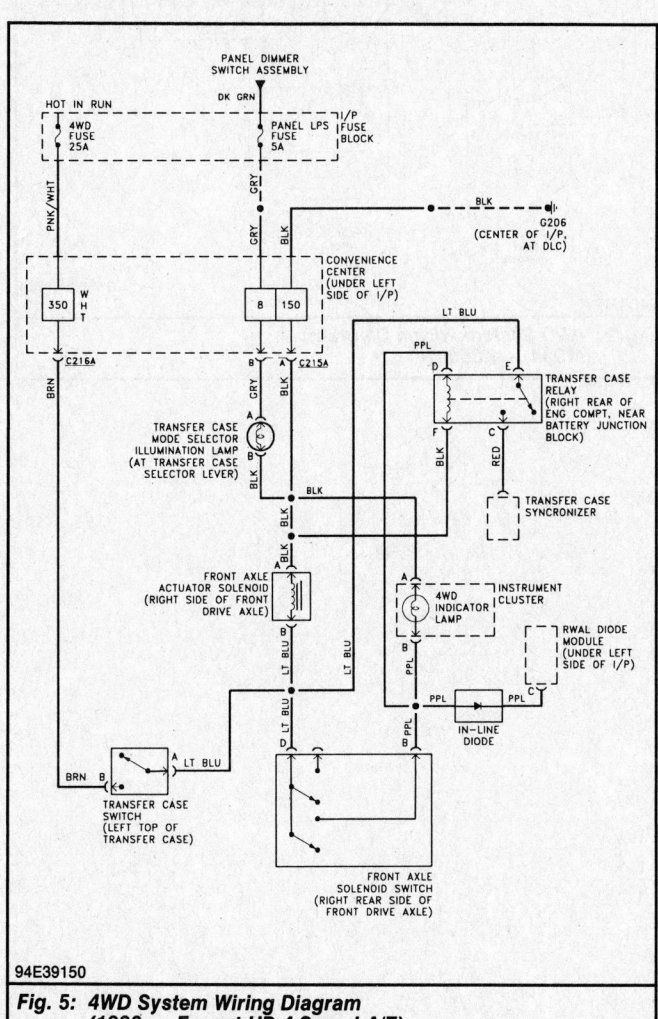

94E39150

Fig. 5: 4WD System Wiring Diagram (1993 – Except HD 4-Speed A/T)

TRANSFER CASES
Borg-Warner 4401 & 4470 (Cont.)

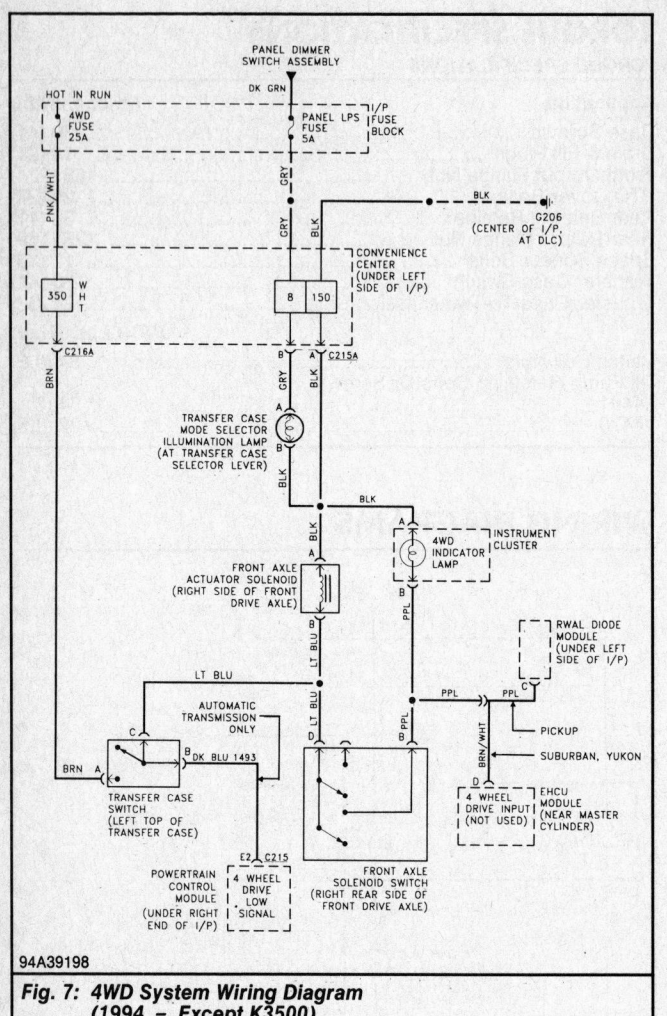

94A39198

Fig. 7: 4WD System Wiring Diagram (1994 – Except K3500)

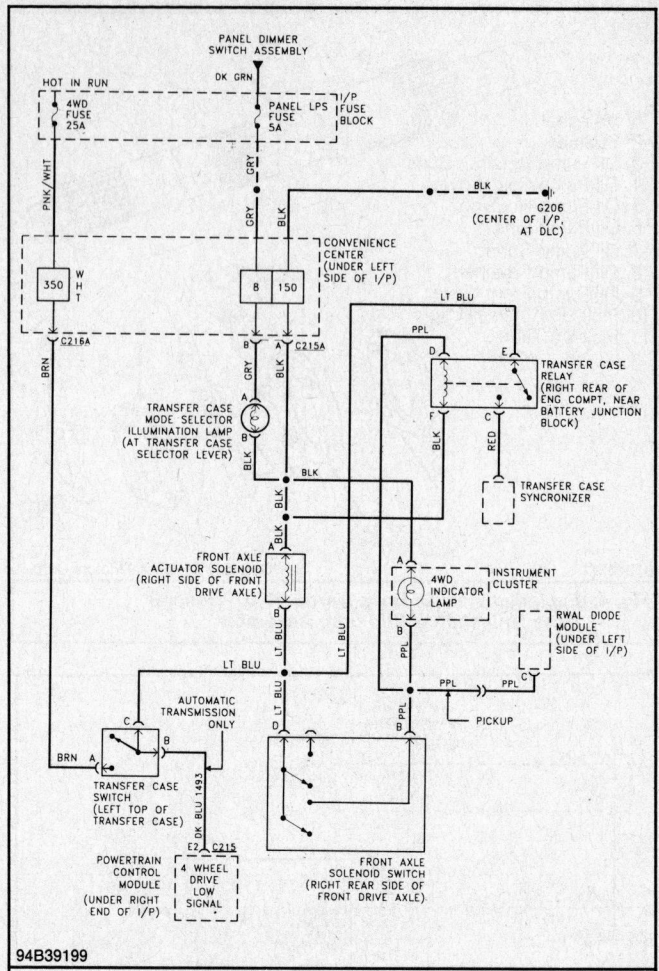

94B39199

Fig. 8: 4WD System Wiring Diagram (1994 – K3500)

TRANSFER CASES
Borg-Warner 4472

General Motors: Astro, Bravada, Safari, Typhoon

IDENTIFICATION

An aluminum identification tag is attached under a self-tapping case bolts at bottom of transfer case. This tag provides part number, serial number and build date.

DESCRIPTION

The Borg-Warner Model 4472 transfer case is a full-time All-Wheel Drive (AWD) unit. It is chain-driven and has a 3-piece aluminum case. Torque distribution is by viscous clutch. Torque is divided at a ratio of 1:3 to the front and 2:3 to the rear.

ON-VEHICLE SERVICE

FRONT & REAR OUTPUT SHAFT OIL SEALS

Removal – Raise vehicle, and disconnect front and/or rear drive shaft. Remove front output shaft flange nut and steel flat washer. Remove rubber sealing washer and front output flange. Pry out output shaft oil seals using screwdriver. DO NOT damage seal bore.

Installation – 1) Lubricate seals with ATF. Install front oil seal using Output Shaft Seal Installer (J-37668). Install rear oil seal by aligning water drain hole in output shaft oil seal with drain groove in extension housing.

2) Install front output shaft flange and rubber sealing washer. Install steel flat washer and flange nut. Tighten nut to specification. See TORQUE SPECIFICATIONS. Reconnect drive shafts, and check fluid level.

REMOVAL & INSTALLATION

TRANSFER CASE

Removal & Installation – 1) Raise vehicle, and drain transfer case. Remove front and rear drive shafts. Disconnect breather hose and electrical connections at transfer case.

2) Support transfer case with suitable jack. Remove transfer case support brace and adapter-to-transfer case bolts. Remove transfer case mount nuts and washers.

3) To install, reverse removal procedures. Ensure mating surfaces are clean, and install new gasket. Tighten bolts and nuts to specification. See TORQUE SPECIFICATIONS.

OVERHAUL

TRANSFER CASE

Disassembly – 1) Remove front output flange nut. Remove steel flat washer, rubber sealing washer and output flange from front output shaft. Remove speed sensor bolt and speed sensor from extension housing. *See Fig. 1.*

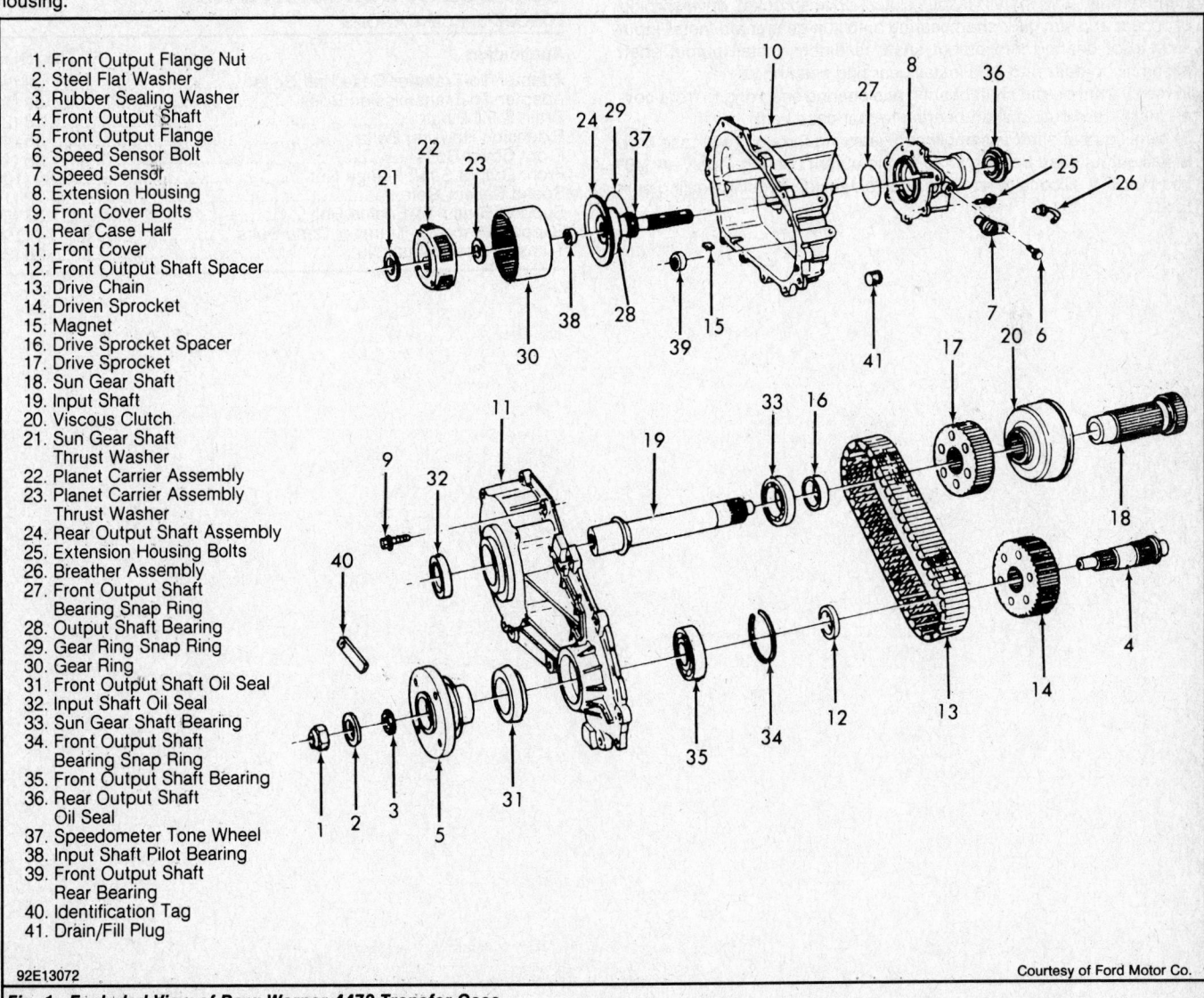

1. Front Output Flange Nut
2. Steel Flat Washer
3. Rubber Sealing Washer
4. Front Output Shaft
5. Front Output Flange
6. Speed Sensor Bolt
7. Speed Sensor
8. Extension Housing
9. Front Cover Bolts
10. Rear Case Half
11. Front Cover
12. Front Output Shaft Spacer
13. Drive Chain
14. Driven Sprocket
15. Magnet
16. Drive Sprocket Spacer
17. Drive Sprocket
18. Sun Gear Shaft
19. Input Shaft
20. Viscous Clutch
21. Sun Gear Shaft Thrust Washer
22. Planet Carrier Assembly
23. Planet Carrier Assembly Thrust Washer
24. Rear Output Shaft Assembly
25. Extension Housing Bolts
26. Breather Assembly
27. Front Output Shaft Bearing Snap Ring
28. Output Shaft Bearing
29. Gear Ring Snap Ring
30. Gear Ring
31. Front Output Shaft Oil Seal
32. Input Shaft Oil Seal
33. Sun Gear Shaft Bearing
34. Front Output Shaft Bearing Snap Ring
35. Front Output Shaft Bearing
36. Rear Output Shaft Oil Seal
37. Speedometer Tone Wheel
38. Input Shaft Pilot Bearing
39. Front Output Shaft Rear Bearing
40. Identification Tag
41. Drain/Fill Plug

92E13072

Courtesy of Ford Motor Co.

Fig. 1: Exploded View of Borg-Warner 4472 Transfer Case

2) Remove front cover bolts from rear case half, and remove front cover by prying case tabs apart. Remove front output shaft, drive chain and driven sprocket from rear case half. Remove input shaft from sun gear shaft.

3) Remove, as an assembly, sun gear shaft, sun gear shaft bearing, drive sprocket spacer, drive sprocket, viscous clutch and sun gear shaft thrust washer from planet carrier assembly. Remove planet carrier assembly and thrust washer from output shaft assembly.

4) Remove extension housing bolts and breather assembly from extension housing. Remove extension housing from rear case half. Remove output shaft snap ring from output shaft bearing.

5) Remove gear ring snap ring and output shaft assembly from gear ring. Remove front output shaft oil seal, input shaft oil seal, output shaft bearing snap ring and output shaft bearing from front cover. Remove rear output shaft oil seal from extension housing.

6) Press sun gear shaft bearing from sun gear shaft. Remove drive sprocket spacer, drive sprocket and viscous clutch from sun gear shaft.

7) Remove input shaft pilot bearing from output shaft assembly. Remove output shaft rear bearing from rear case half.

Cleaning & Inspection – Clean all parts with solvent and dry with compressed air. Replace all oil seals, "O" rings and snap rings. Check all parts for wear or damage. Replace all worn or damaged parts.

NOTE: Apply ATF to all parts before installing.

Reassembly – 1) Install viscous clutch, drive sprocket, drive sprocket spacer and sun gear shaft bearing onto sun gear shaft. Install input shaft pilot bearing into output shaft assembly. Install output shaft assembly to gear ring, and install gear ring snap ring.

2) Install front output shaft bearing and bearing snap ring to front cover. Install rear output shaft bearing to rear case half.

3) Install output shaft assembly and gear ring through rear case half. Install output shaft bearing snap ring to output bearing. Apply an 1/8" bead of RTV silicone to rear case half extension housing sealing surface.

4) Install extension housing and bolts to rear case half. Tighten bolts to specification. Install speed sensor and speed sensor bolt into extension housing. Tighten to specification. See TORQUE SPECIFICATIONS.

5) Align water drain hole in rear output shaft oil seal with drain groove in extension housing, and press seal into extension housing.

6) Using petroleum jelly, install planet carrier assembly thrust washer to output shaft assembly and align with input shaft pilot bearing. Install planet carrier assembly into gear ring. Install sun gear shaft thrust washer to planet carrier assembly.

7) Install sun gear shaft assembly into planet carrier assembly planet gears, and align viscous clutch teeth with gear ring spline. Install input shaft into input shaft pilot bearing, aligning input shaft with sun gear shaft thrust washer and planet carrier assembly thrust washer.

8) Install driven sprocket onto front output shaft, and install drive chain onto driven sprocket. Install drive chain over drive sprocket, and install front output shaft into output shaft rear bearing. Install front output shaft spacer and magnet.

9) Apply 1/8" bead of RTV silicone to rear case half front cover sealing surface. Install front cover and bolts to rear case. Tighten bolts to specification. See TORQUE SPECIFICATIONS.

10) Install front output shaft oil seal and input shaft oil seal. Install front output flange, rubber washer, steel flat washer and a new front output flange nut. Tighten flange nut to specification.

TORQUE SPECIFICATIONS
TORQUE SPECIFICATIONS

Application	Ft. Lbs. (N.m)
Adapter-To-Transfer Case Half Bolts	38 (52)
Adapter-To-Transmission Bolts	38 (52)
Drain & Fill Plugs	18 (24)
Extension Housing Bolts	35 (47)
Front Cover Bolts	35 (47)
Front Output Shaft Flange Nut	80 (108)
Speed Sensor Bolt	12 (16)
Support Brace-To-Engine Bolt	37 (50)
Support Brace-To-Transfer Case Bolts	74 (100)
Transfer Case Mount Nuts	26 (35)

Colt Vista, Laser, Summit Wagon, Talon

DESCRIPTION & IDENTIFICATION

The All-Wheel Drive (AWD) transfer case is a full-time unit. Transfer case can be removed from transaxle and serviced separately. AWD transaxles are identified by vehicle identification plate, located on center of firewall. AWD transaxle (with transfer case) model numbers are as follows: W4A32 (A/T), W4A33 (A/T) and W5M33 (M/T).

ON-VEHICLE SERVICE

OIL SEAL REPLACEMENT

Removal – Remove oil filler plug. *See Fig. 1.* Remove oil drain plug, and drain transfer case oil. Remove drive shaft. Using a flat-tip screwdriver, remove oil seal.

Installation – Coat seal with gear oil and install into extension housing using appropriate oil seal installer. Install drive shaft. Install drain plug and tighten to specification. See TORQUE SPECIFICATIONS. Fill transfer case with .6 qt. (.6L) of SAE 75W-90/75W-85 GL-4 or equivalent gear oil. Install filler plug and tighten to specification.

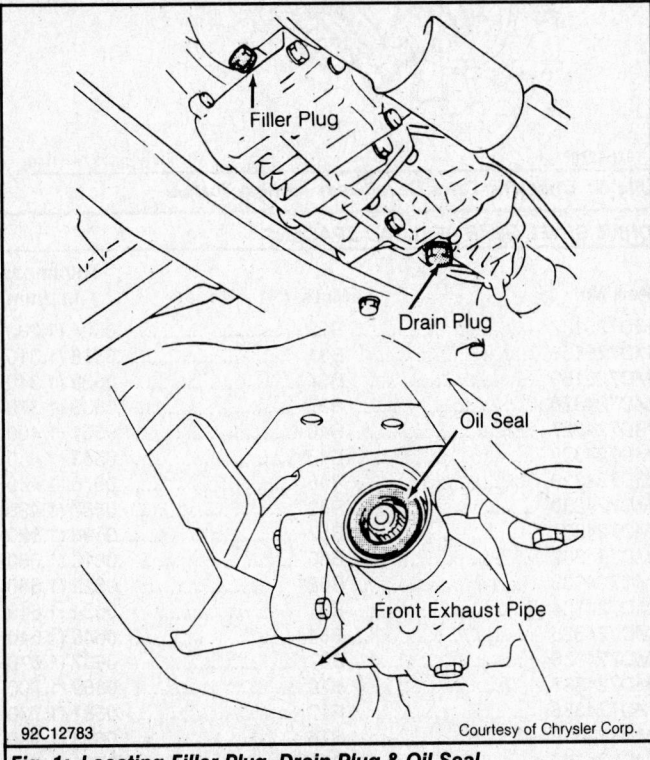

Fig. 1: Locating Filler Plug, Drain Plug & Oil Seal

REMOVAL & INSTALLATION

NOTE: On Laser and Talon, transfer case may be removed from vehicle with transaxle in chassis. Manufacturer does not give removal and installation procedure for Colt Vista and Summit Wagon. See appropriate TRANSMISSION REMOVAL article in TRANSMISSION SERVICING, if necessary.

TRANSFER CASE

Removal & Installation (Laser & Talon) – 1) Remove exhaust manifold flange self-locking nuts and front exhaust pipe mounting bracket bolts. *See Fig. 2.* Remove exhaust pipe gasket, and tie exhaust pipe to left.

2) Remove transfer case bolts, move transfer case to the left, and lower front side. Remove drive shaft, and cover transfer output opening to prevent oil loss. *See Fig. 3.* Tie drive shaft off to side. Remove transfer case assembly.

3) To install, remove transfer output shaft cover, and install drive shaft. Install transfer case and bolts to transaxle case. Tighten bolts to specification. See TORQUE SPECIFICATIONS.

4) Connect front exhaust pipe and gasket to exhaust manifold. Install self-locking nuts and front exhaust pipe mounting bracket bolts. Tighten bolts and self-locking nuts to specification. See TORQUE SPECIFICATIONS.

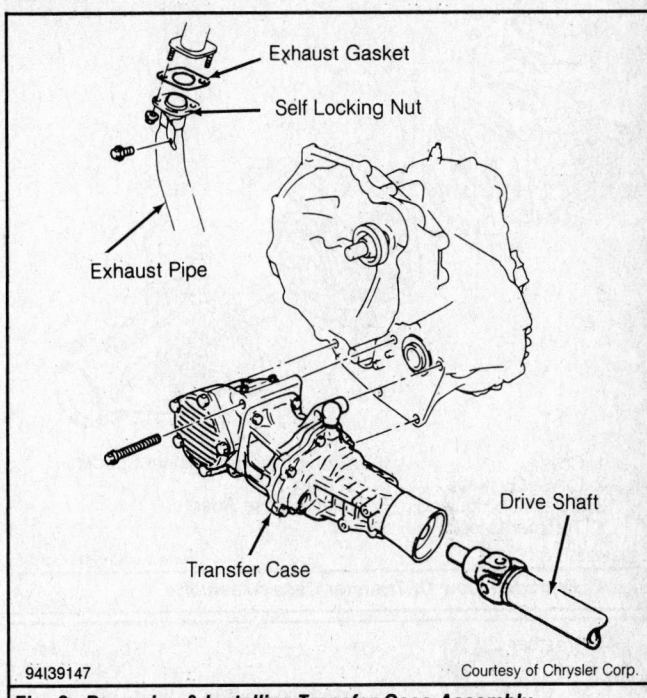

Fig. 2: Removing & Installing Transfer Case Assembly

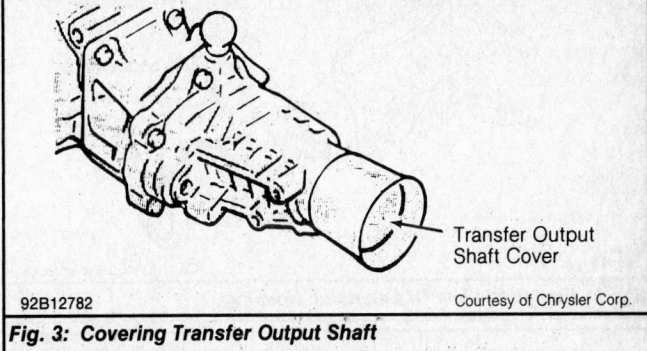

Fig. 3: Covering Transfer Output Shaft

COMPONENT DISASSEMBLY & REASSEMBLY

EXTENSION HOUSING

Disassembly – Remove extension housing from transfer case. *See Fig. 4.* Remove air breather and dust seal guard. *See Fig. 5.* Remove oil seal using a flat-tip screwdriver.

Reassembly – Install oil seal using oil seal installer and hammer. Install dust seal guard. Apply weatherstrip adhesive to air breather port and install air breather.

TRANSFER CASE

Disassembly – Remove transfer case from transfer case adapter. *See Fig. 4.* Remove bolts, transfer cover, "O" ring, drive bevel gear mount spacer and outer race. *See Fig. 6.* Remove drive bevel gear assembly, outer race, drive bevel gear preload spacer and oil seal.

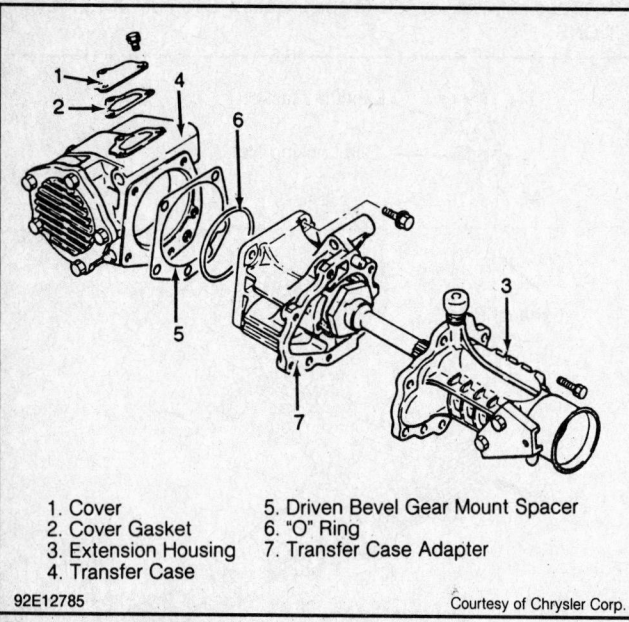

1. Cover
2. Cover Gasket
3. Extension Housing
4. Transfer Case
5. Driven Bevel Gear Mount Spacer
6. "O" Ring
7. Transfer Case Adapter

92E12785   Courtesy of Chrysler Corp.

Fig. 4: Exploded View Of Transfer Case Assembly

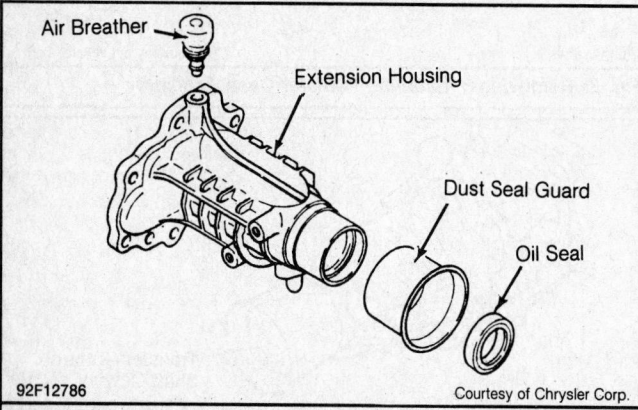

Air Breather
Extension Housing
Dust Seal Guard
Oil Seal

92F12786   Courtesy of Chrysler Corp.

Fig. 5: Exploded View Of Extension Housing

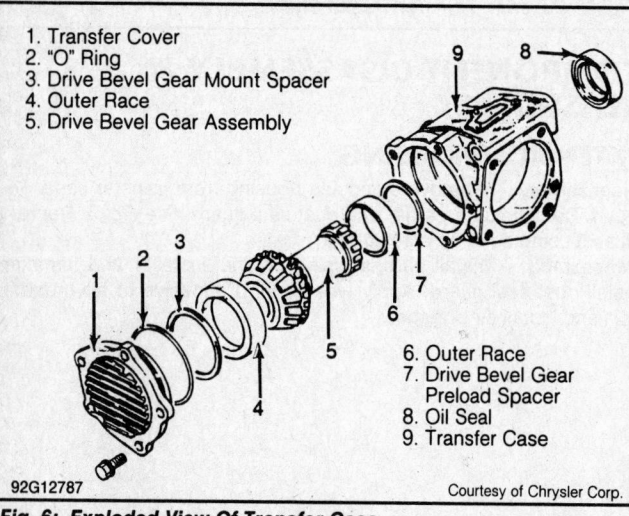

1. Transfer Cover
2. "O" Ring
3. Drive Bevel Gear Mount Spacer
4. Outer Race
5. Drive Bevel Gear Assembly
6. Outer Race
7. Drive Bevel Gear Preload Spacer
8. Oil Seal
9. Transfer Case

92G12787   Courtesy of Chrysler Corp.

Fig. 6: Exploded View Of Transfer Case

Reassembly – Using seal installer and hammer, install oil seal. Install drive bevel gear preload spacer, outer race, drive bevel gear assembly, outer race and drive bevel gear mount spacer. Install "O" ring and transfer cover. Tighten bolts to specification. See TORQUE SPECIFICATIONS.

Inspection – Using Wrench Adapter (MD991144) and torque wrench, check turning torque of drive bevel gear assembly. *See Fig. 7.* Turning torque should be 15-22 INCH lbs. (1.7-2.5 N.m). If turning torque is out of specification, select and install adjusting spacers. See DRIVE BEVEL GEAR PRELOAD SPACERS and DRIVE BEVEL GEAR MOUNT SPACERS tables. Select spacers of nearly equal thickness for both sides.

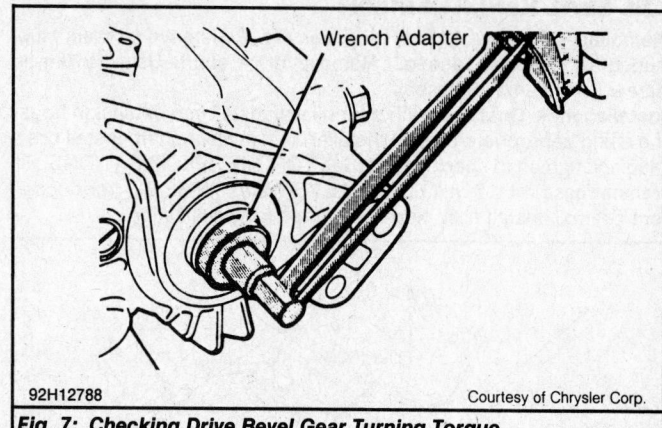

Wrench Adapter

92H12788   Courtesy of Chrysler Corp.

Fig. 7: Checking Drive Bevel Gear Turning Torque

DRIVE BEVEL GEAR PRELOAD SPACERS

Part No.	Mark	Thickness In. (mm)
MD726167	B28	.0504 (1.280)
MD726168	B31	.0516 (1.310)
MD726169	B34	.0528 (1.340)
MD724326	B37	.0539 (1.370)
MD724327	B40	.0551 (1.400)
MD724328	B43	.0563 (1.430)
MD724329	B46	.0575 (1.460)
MD724330	B49	.0587 (1.490)
MD724331	B52	.0598 (1.520)
MD724332	B55	.0610 (1.550)
MD724333	B58	.0622 (1.580)
MD724334	B61	.0634 (1.610)
MD724335	B64	.0646 (1.640)
MD724336	B67	.0657 (1.670)
MD724337	B70	.0669 (1.700)
MD724338	B73	.0681 (1.730)
MD724339	B76	.0693 (1.760)
MD724340	B79	.0705 (1.790)
MD724341	B82	.0717 (1.820)
MD724342	B85	.0728 (1.850)

DRIVE BEVEL GEAR MOUNT SPACERS

Part No.	Mark	Thickness In. (mm)
MD723600	34	.0528 (1.340)
MD723601	37	.0539 (1.370)
MD723602	40	.0551 (1.400)
MD723603	43	.0563 (1.430)
MD723604	46	.0575 (1.460)
MD723605	49	.0587 (1.490)
MD723606	52	.0598 (1.520)
MD723607	55	.0610 (1.550)
MD723608	58	.0622 (1.580)
MD723609	61	.0634 (1.610)
MD726170	64	.0646 (1.640)
MD726171	67	.0657 (1.670)

DRIVE BEVEL GEAR ASSEMBLY

Disassembly – Remove shaft taper roller bearing from drive bevel gear shaft using bearing remover and press. *See Fig. 8.* Remove gear taper roller bearing from drive bevel gear shaft using bearing remover and press. Remove drive bevel gear using bearing remover and press.

Reassembly – Using press and bearing installer, press on drive bevel gear, ensure mating marks on gear and shaft align. Press on gear taper roller bearing using drive handle and bearing installer. *See Fig. 9.* Press on shaft taper roller bearing using bearing installer.

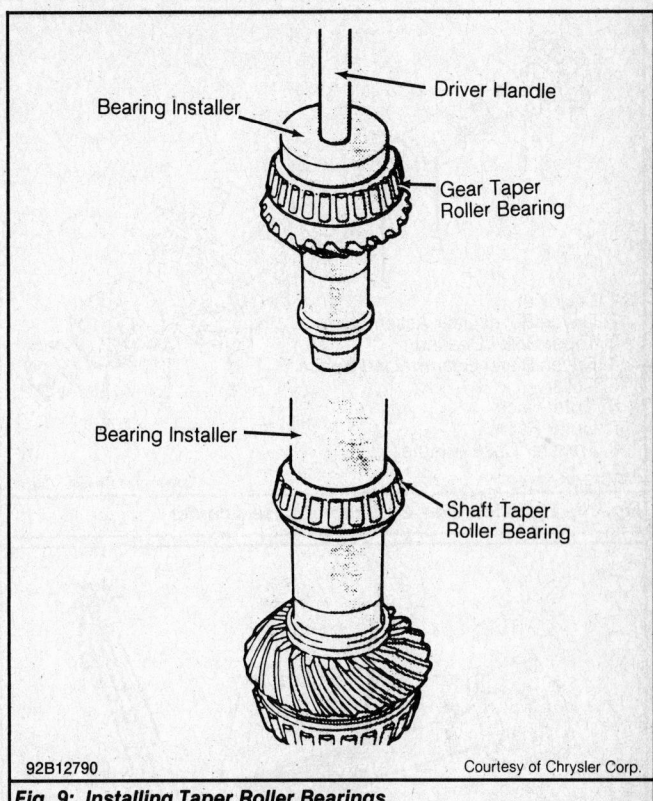

Fig. 9: *Installing Taper Roller Bearings*

Reassembly – Tap in each outer race until fully seated. Install collar and driven bevel gear preload spacer onto driven bevel gear assembly. Using bearing installer, press taper roller bearing into transfer case adapter. Install driven bevel gear assembly, and align mating marks. Tighten lock nut to specification using appropriate wrench. See TORQUE SPECIFICATIONS. Stake lock nut in 2 places.

DRIVEN BEVEL GEAR PRELOAD SPACERS

Part No.	Mark	Thickness In. (mm)
MD726172	19	.0469 (1.190)
MD722081	22	.0480 (1.220)
MD722082	25	.0492 (1.250)
MD722083	28	.0504 (1.280)
MD722084	31	.0516 (1.310)
MD722085	34	.0528 (1.340)
MD722086	37	.0539 (1.370)
MD722087	40	.0551 (1.400)
MD722088	43	.0563 (1.430)
MD722089	46	.0575 (1.460)
MD722090	49	.0587 (1.490)
MD722091	52	.0598 (1.520)
MD722092	55	.0610 (1.550)
MD722093	58	.0622 (1.580)
MD722094	61	.0634 (1.610)
MD722095	64	.0646 (1.640)
MD722096	67	.0657 (1.670)
MD722097	70	.0669 (1.700)
MD722098	73	.0681 (1.730)
MD722099	76	.0693 (1.760)
MD722100	79	.0705 (1.790)
MD722101	82	.0717 (1.820)
MD722102	85	.0728 (1.850)
MD722103	88	.0740 (1.880)
MD722104	91	.0752 (1.910)
MD722105	94	.0764 (1.940)

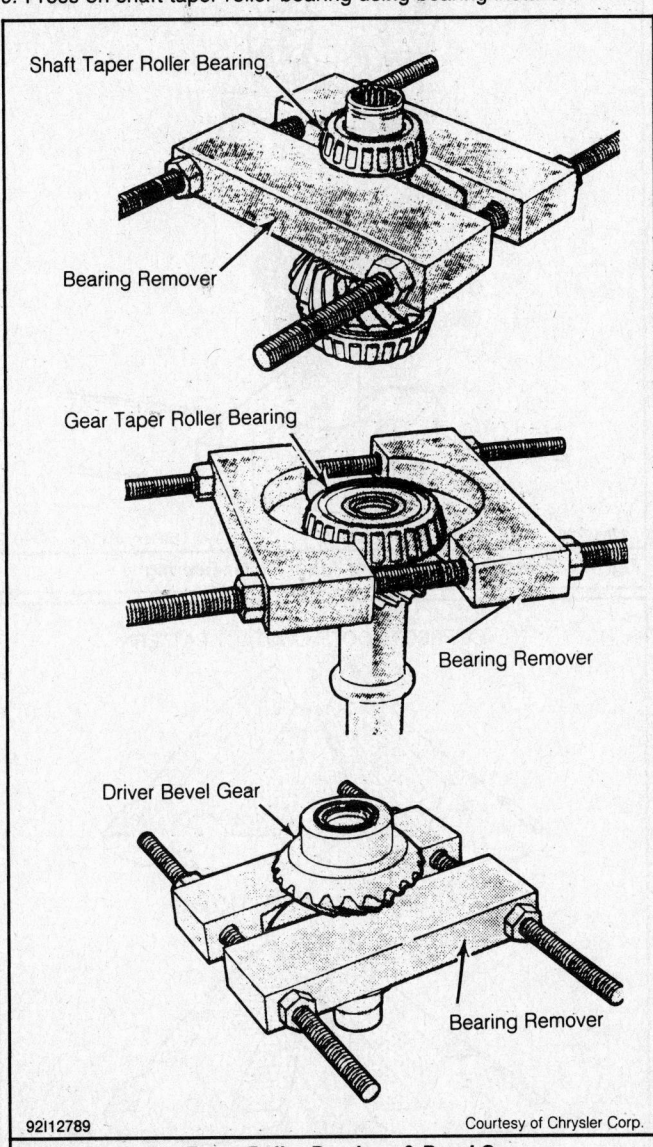

Fig. 8: *Removing Taper Roller Bearings & Bevel Gear*

TRANSFER CASE ADAPTER

Disassembly – Unstake and remove lock nut. Press out driven bevel gear assembly. Remove taper roller bearing, driven bevel gear preload spacer and collar. *See Fig. 10.* Using a flat-tip screwdriver, tap out each outer race from inside transfer case adapter.

Inspection – Using Wrench Adapter (MD998806) and torque wrench, check turning torque of driven bevel gear. *See Fig. 11.* Turning torque should be 9-15 INCH lbs. (1.0-1.7 N.m). If turning torque is out of specification, select and install adjusting driven bevel gear preload spacer. See DRIVEN BEVEL GEAR PRELOAD SPACERS table.

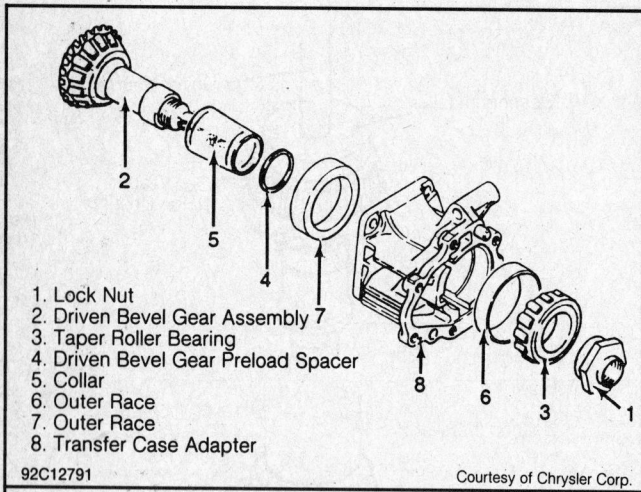

1. Lock Nut
2. Driven Bevel Gear Assembly
3. Taper Roller Bearing
4. Driven Bevel Gear Preload Spacer
5. Collar
6. Outer Race
7. Outer Race
8. Transfer Case Adapter

92C12791   Courtesy of Chrysler Corp.

Fig. 10: Exploded View Of Transfer Case Adapter

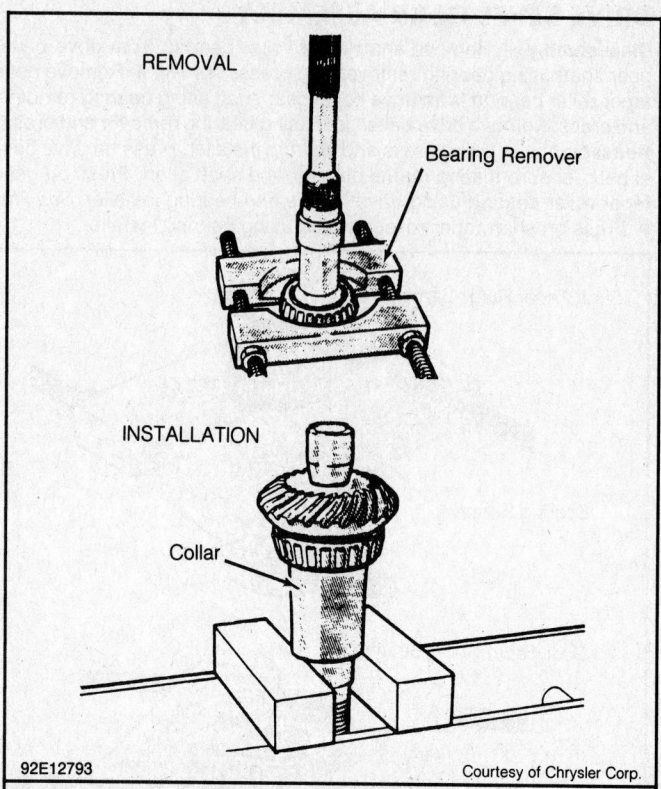

92E12793   Courtesy of Chrysler Corp.

Fig. 12: Removing & Installing Taper Roller Bearing

Wrench Adapter

92D12792   Courtesy of Chrysler Corp.

Fig. 11: Checking Driven Bevel Gear Turning Torque

DRIVEN BEVEL GEAR ASSEMBLY

Disassembly & Reassembly – Press off taper roller bearing using bearing remover. *See Fig. 12.* Press on taper roller bearing using collar.

TRANSFER CASE
DISASSEMBLY & REASSEMBLY

Disassembly – Transfer case is disassembled as individual components. See COMPONENT DISASSEMBLY & REASSEMBLY.

Reassembly – **1)** Evenly apply thin coat of Prussian Blue to both tooth surfaces of driven bevel gear. Install "O" ring and driven bevel gear mount spacer to transfer case. *See Fig. 4.* Install transfer case adapter to transfer case, and align mating marks. Tighten bolts to specification. See TORQUE SPECIFICATIONS.

2) Using Wrench Adapter (MD991144) and spinner handle, turn driven bevel gear shaft one full turn clockwise and counterclockwise. Remove bolts and transfer case adapter. Check contact pattern of driven bevel gear teeth. *See Fig. 13.*

3) If tooth contact pattern shows that driven bevel gear is too high, select and install thicker spacer for driven bevel gear mount adjustment. If tooth contact pattern shows that driven bevel gear is too low, select and install thinner spacer for driven bevel gear mount adjustment. See DRIVEN BEVEL GEAR MOUNT SPACERS table. Repeat steps **1)** through **3)** until correct tooth contact pattern is obtained.

4) If driven bevel gear is still too high when thickest spacer for mount adjustment is used, change drive bevel gear mount spacer to next thinner spacer and drive bevel gear preload spacer to next thicker spacer. See DRIVE BEVEL GEAR ASSEMBLY under COMPONENTS DISASSEMBLY & REASSEMBLY. Repeat steps **1)** through **3)** until correct tooth contact pattern is obtained.

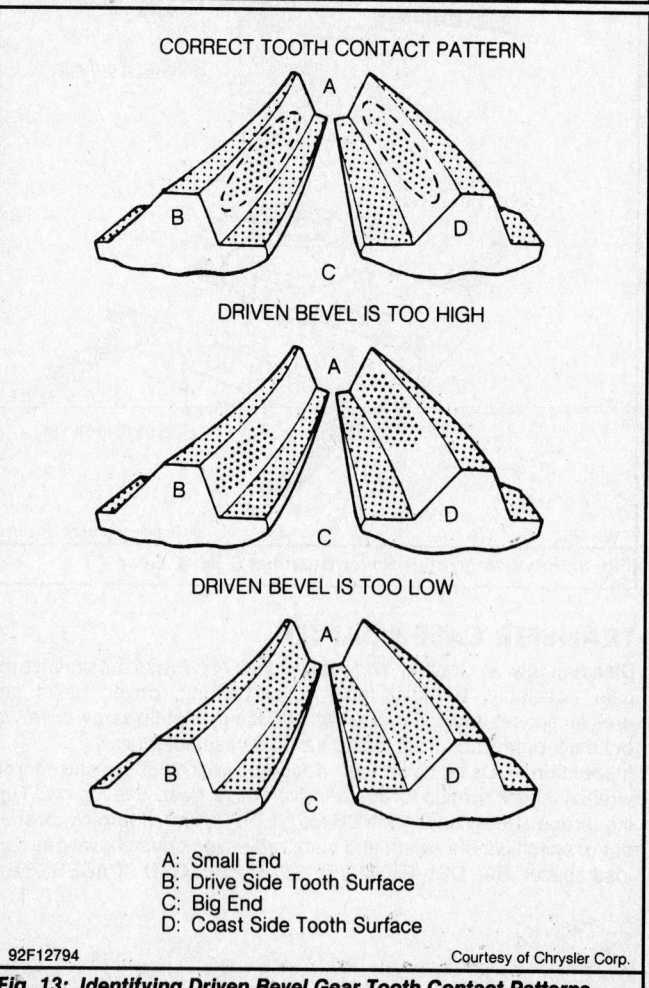

CORRECT TOOTH CONTACT PATTERN

DRIVEN BEVEL IS TOO HIGH

DRIVEN BEVEL IS TOO LOW

A: Small End
B: Drive Side Tooth Surface
C: Big End
D: Coast Side Tooth Surface

92F12794   Courtesy of Chrysler Corp.

Fig. 13: Identifying Driven Bevel Gear Tooth Contact Patterns

5) If driven bevel gear is still too low when thinnest spacer for mount adjustment is used, change drive bevel gear mount spacer to next thicker spacer and drive bevel gear preload spacer to next thinner spacer. See DRIVE BEVEL GEAR ASSEMBLY under COMPONENTS DISASSEMBLY & REASSEMBLY. Repeat steps **1)** through **3)** until correct tooth contact pattern is obtained.

6) Using dial indicator, measure backlash between drive and driven bevel gears. *See Fig. 14.* Backlash should be .0031-.0051" (.080-.130 mm).

7) Clean extension housing mating surfaces, and apply bond-type sealant to transfer case adapter flange. Install extension housing, and tighten bolts to specification. See TORQUE SPECIFICATIONS. Apply bond-type sealant to both sides of case cover gasket. Install case cover gasket and case cover. Tighten bolts to specification.

DRIVEN BEVEL GEAR MOUNT SPACERS

Part No.	Mark	Thickness In (.mm)
MD720353	13	.0051 (.130)
MD720354	16	.0063 (.160)
MD720355	19	.0075 (.190)
MD720356	22	.0087 (.220)
MD720357	25	.0098 (.250)
MD720358	28	.0110 (.280)
MD720359	31	.0122 (.310)
MD720360	34	.0134 (.340)
MD720361	37	.0146 (.370)
MD720362	40	.0157 (.400)
MD720363	43	.0169 (.430)
MD720364	46	.0181 (.460)
MD720365	49	.0193 (.490)
MD720366	52	.0205 (.520)

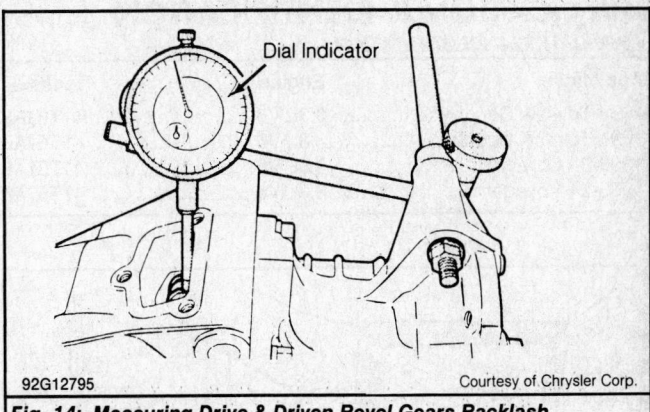

92G12795 Courtesy of Chrysler Corp.

Fig. 14: Measuring Drive & Driven Bevel Gears Backlash

TORQUE SPECIFICATIONS
TORQUE SPECIFICATIONS

Application	Ft. Lbs. (N.m)
Drain & Fill Plug	22-26 (30-35)
Driven Bevel Gear Lock Nut	103-118 (140-160)
Extension Housing Bolt	11-16 (15-22)
Front Exhaust Pipe Mounting Bracket Bolt	15-22 (20-30)
Front Exhaust Pipe Self-Locking Nut	22-30 (30-40)
Transfer Case Adapter Bolt	26-31 (35-42)
Transfer Side Cover Bolt	26-31 (35-42)
Transfer Case Assembly Mounting Bolt	40-43 (54-58)
	INCH Lbs. (N.m)
Case Cover Bolt	71-89 (8-10)

APPLICATION & IDENTIFICATION

APPLICATION & IDENTIFICATION

Application	Engine	Transaxle
1993 Town & Country	3.3L V6	41TE/AE
1994 Town & Country	3.8L V6	41TE/AE
1993-94 Caravan	3.3L V6	41TE/AE
1993-94 Voyager	3.3L V6	41TE/AE

DESCRIPTION

The All-Wheel Drive (AWD) transfer case is attached where right axle shaft extension housing would be located on a 2WD vehicle. This unit is identified by Chrysler Motors as a Power Transfer Unit (PTU). PTU is a full-time operational unit. PTU is available with 4-speed automatic overdrive transaxle vehicles only. It is sealed from transaxle and has its own lubrication sump.

REMOVAL & INSTALLATION

See appropriate AUTOMATIC TRANSMISSION REMOVAL article in TRANSMISSION SERVICING.

TROUBLE SHOOTING

Leak Diagnosis – **1)** The PTU has 2 weep holes to aid in leak diagnosis. *See Fig. 1.* If fluid leak is found at either weep hole, seal replacement is necessary.

2) If fluid is leaking from transaxle side weep hole, color of fluid determines which seal is replaced. Red fluid leaking (transmission fluid) indicates transaxle differential carrier seal needs replacement. *See Fig. 2.* Brown fluid leaking (gear oil) indicates input seal of PTU needs replacement.

3) If fluid is leaking from axle shaft side weep hole, color of fluid determines which seal is replaced. Red fluid leaking (transmission fluid) indicates input shaft end seal needs replacement.

4) Brown fluid leaking (gear oil) indicates PTU input shaft cover seal and axle shaft inner seal need replacement. For replacement of these seals, see COMPONENT DISASSEMBLY & REASSEMBLY and ON-VEHICLE SERVICE.

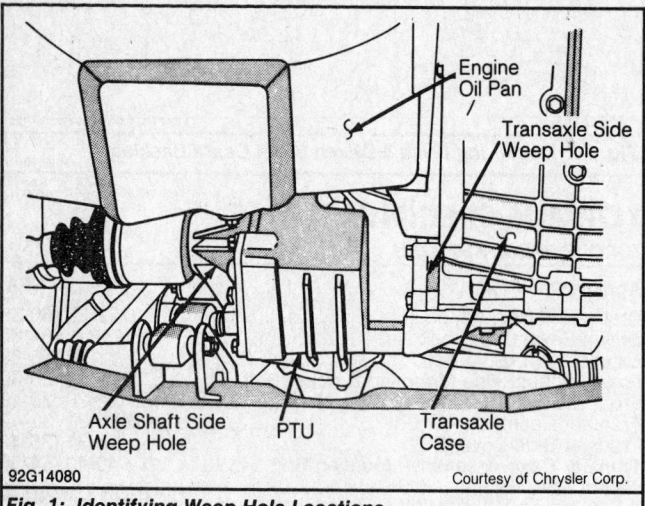

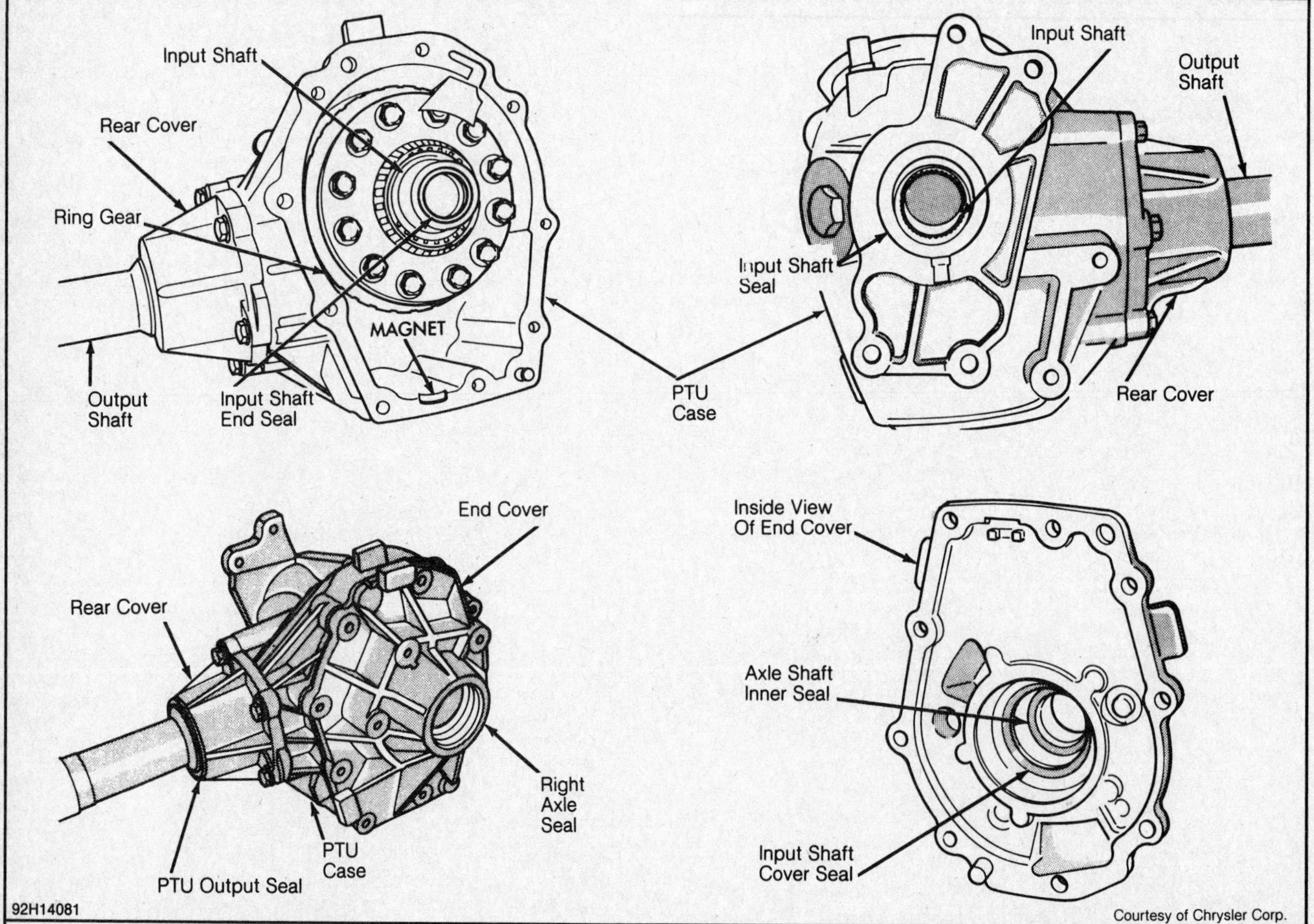

92G14080   Courtesy of Chrysler Corp.

Fig. 1: Identifying Weep Hole Locations

92H14081   Courtesy of Chrysler Corp.

Fig. 2: Identifying PTU Seal Locations

TRANSFER CASES
Chrysler Corp. Power Transfer Unit (Cont.)

5-51

ON-VEHICLE SERVICE

DRIVE AXLE SHAFTS

See appropriate AXLE SHAFTS article in AXLE SHAFTS & TRANSFER CASES.

RIGHT AXLE SEAL

Removal – Raise and support vehicle. Remove right axle shaft. See appropriate AXLE SHAFTS article in AXLE SHAFTS & TRANSFER CASES. Using a chisel or flat-tip screwdriver, remove axle seal. *See Fig. 3.*

Installation – Coat seal with gear oil and tap it into end cover using appropriate oil seal installer. *See Fig. 4.* Install right axle shaft. Check fluid level and refill as necessary.

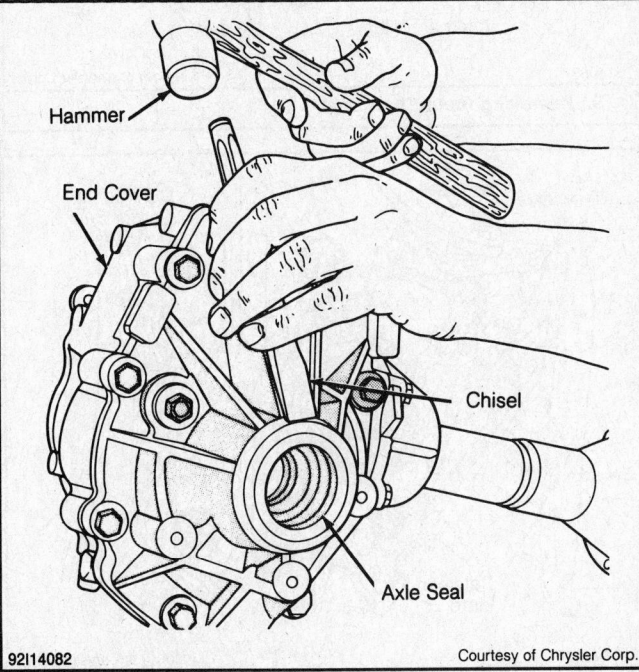

Fig. 3: Removing Right Axle Seal

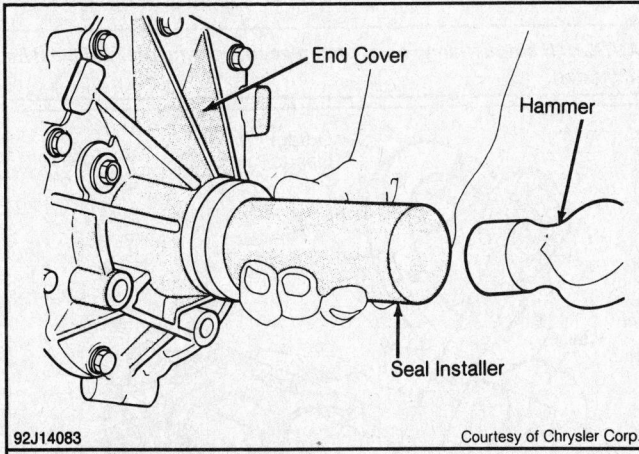

Fig. 4: Installing Right Axle Seal

REAR COVER "O" RING

Removal & Installation – Raise and support vehicle. Remove drive shaft. Scribe alignment mark between rear cover and case. Remove rear cover retaining bolts. Remove rear cover from PTU case and remove cover "O" ring. *See Fig. 5.* To install, reverse removal procedures. Align rear cover to case alignment mark. Tighten bolts to specification. See TORQUE SPECIFICATIONS.

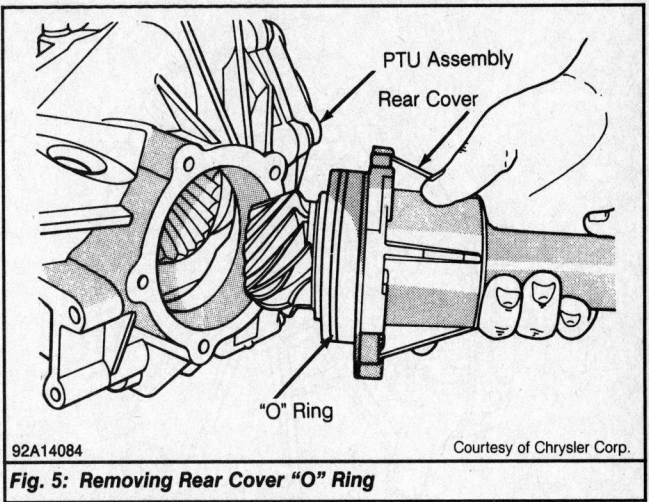

Fig. 5: Removing Rear Cover "O" Ring

END COVER BALL BEARING

Removal – Raise and support vehicle. Remove right axle shaft. See appropriate AXLE SHAFTS article in AXLE SHAFTS & TRANSFER CASES. Using a flat-tip screwdriver, remove axle seal. *See Fig. 3.* Remove bearing retainer snap ring. Using bearing puller, pull end cover ball bearing. *See Fig. 6.*

Installation – Using appropriate bearing installer, drive end cover ball bearing into place. Install retainer snap ring. Index snap ring to ensure bearing oil passage is not covered. Coat NEW axle seal with gear oil and tap it into end cover. Install right axle shaft. Check fluid level and refill as necessary.

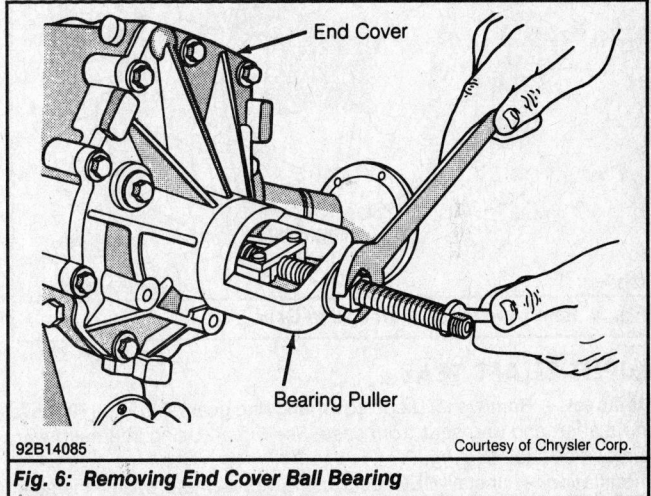

Fig. 6: Removing End Cover Ball Bearing

TRANSFER CASE DISASSEMBLY & REASSEMBLY

NOTE: Repair of PTU is limited to end cover ball bearing, seals and gaskets. All other repairs require unit replacement. For exploded view of PTU assembly, see Fig. 17.

COMPONENT DISASSEMBLY & REASSEMBLY

END COVER SEAL

Disassembly & Reassembly – Remove PTU end cover bolts and tap on end cover ears to remove cover from case. Apply anaerobic sealer to both mating surfaces. Install end cover and retaining bolts. Tighten bolts to specification in sequence. See TORQUE SPECIFICATIONS. *See Fig. 7.*

5-52

TRANSFER CASES
Chrysler Corp. Power Transfer Unit (Cont.)

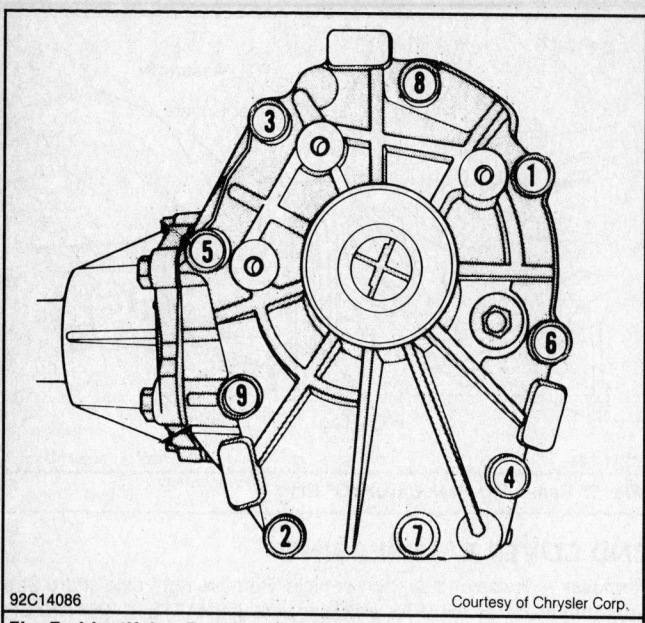

92C14086　　Courtesy of Chrysler Corp.

Fig. 7: Identifying End Cover Bolt Sequence

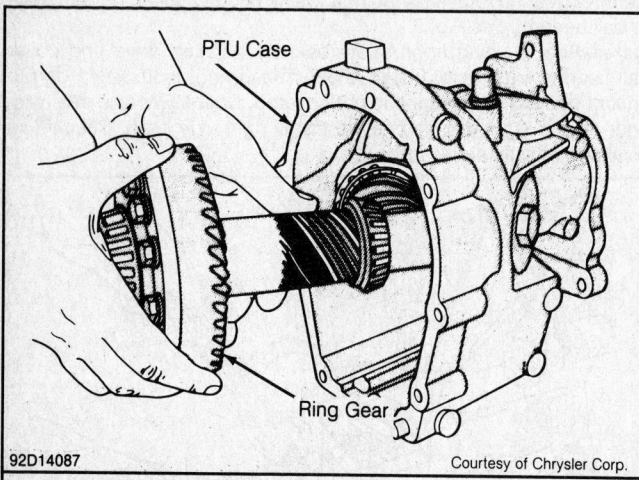

92D14087　　Courtesy of Chrysler Corp.

Fig. 8: Removing Input Shaft & Ring Gear

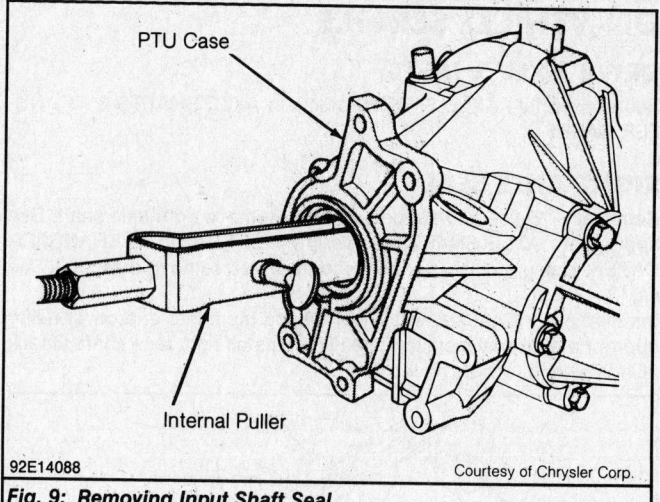

92E14088　　Courtesy of Chrysler Corp.

Fig. 9: Removing Input Shaft Seal

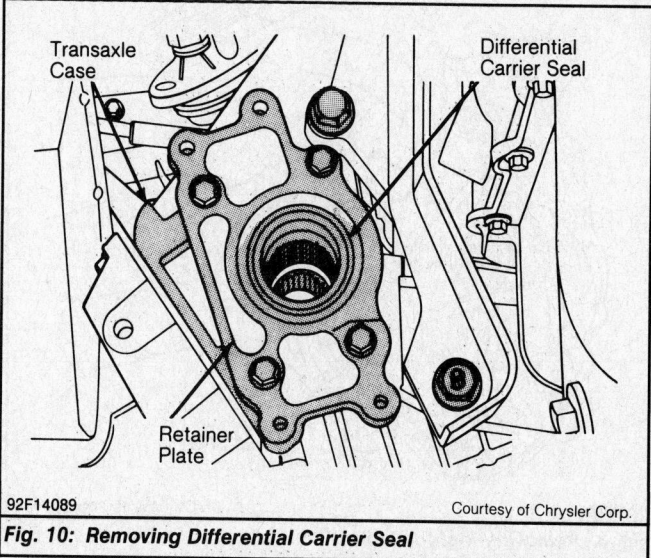

92F14089　　Courtesy of Chrysler Corp.

Fig. 10: Removing Differential Carrier Seal

INPUT SHAFT SEAL

Removal – Remove PTU end cover and ring gear oil trough. Remove input shaft and ring gear from case. See Fig. 8. Using internal puller, remove oil seal. See Fig. 9.

Installation – Install NEW seal using appropriate sealer installer. Install seal with spring facing ring gear. Ensure seal is driven in flush with case shoulder. Install input shaft and ring gear. Install oil trough on case. Apply anaerobic sealer to both mating surfaces. Install end cover and retaining bolts. Tighten bolts to specification in sequence. See TORQUE SPECIFICATIONS. See Fig. 7.

TRANSAXLE DIFFERENTIAL CARRIER SEAL

Removal & Installation – Using a large flat-tip screwdriver or pry bar, remove seal from retainer plate. See Fig. 10. Install NEW seal using appropriate sealer installer. Ensure seal is installed with spring facing transaxle. Check fluid level and refill as necessary.

OUTPUT SEAL

Removal – 1) Raise and support vehicle. Remove drive shaft and scribe an alignment mark between rear cover and case. Remove rear cover from PTU case and remove cover "O" ring.

2) Remove output flange nut from opposite end of output shaft. Scribe an alignment mark between pinion and flange. See Figs. 11 and 12. Press output flange from pinion. Using a flat-tip screwdriver, remove output flange seal.

CAUTION: If output flange must be replaced, bearing preload must be readjusted.

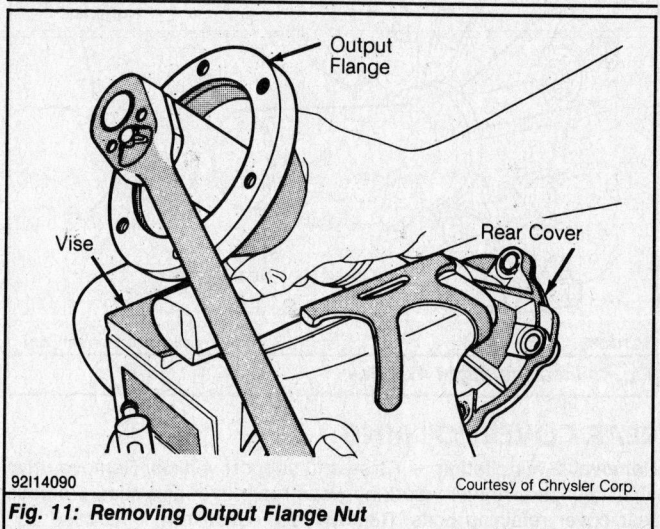

92I14090　　Courtesy of Chrysler Corp.

Fig. 11: Removing Output Flange Nut

TRANSFER CASES
Chrysler Corp. Power Transfer Unit (Cont.)

5-53

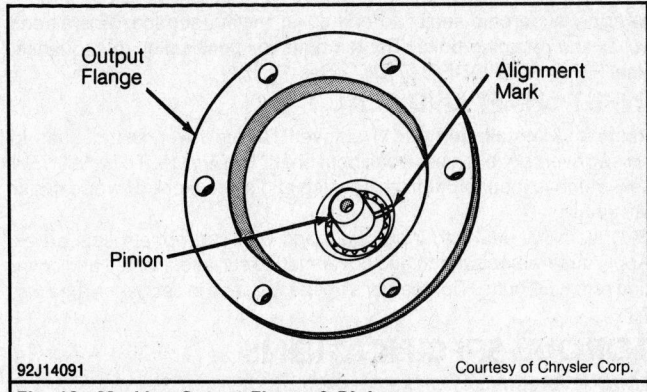

Fig. 12: Marking Output Flange & Pinion

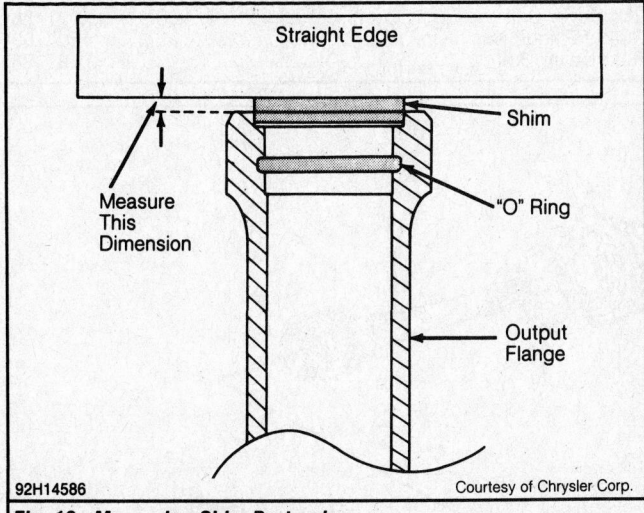

Fig. 13: Measuring Shim Protrusion

Installation – 1) Install NEW seal using appropriate seal installer. Press flange onto pinion, ensuring marks are aligned. Install flange nut and tighten to specification. See TORQUE SPECIFICATIONS.
2) Install rear cover with NEW "O" ring. Align rear cover to case alignment mark. Tighten bolts to specification. Install drive shaft and refill fluid as necessary.

Preload Adjustment – 1) Preload adjustment is required when output flange is replaced. Shim measurement is taken from prior shim protrusion above output flange. See Fig. 13. Take measurement with original output flange and compare measurement with same shim and NEW output flange.
2) If measurement with NEW flange is larger, reduce shim thickness to equal original measurement. If measurement with NEW flange is smaller, increase shim thickness to equal original measurement.
3) For available shim thickness, see PRELOAD SHIM THICKNESS table. Measure pinion turning torque prior to rear cover installation. Ensure pinion turning torque is 22-27 INCH Lbs. (2.5-3.1 N.m). Adjust shim thickness as necessary.

PRELOAD SHIM THICKNESS

Part No.	[1] Thickness
4641-430	.202" (5.13 mm)
4641-431	.204" (5.17 mm)
4641-432	.205" (5.21 mm)
4641-433	.207" (5.25 mm)
4641-434	.208" (5.29 mm)
4641-435	.210" (5.33 mm)
4641-436	.211" (5.37 mm)
4641-437	.213" (5.41 mm)
4641-438	.215" (5.45 mm)
4641-439	.216" (5.49 mm)

[1] – Preload shim thicknesses have a .001" (.03 mm) tolerance.

INPUT SHAFT COVER & AXLE SHAFT INNER SEAL

Removal & Installation – 1) Larger seal in end cover is input shaft cover seal; smaller seal is axle shaft inner seal. Remove PTU end cover. Using a flat-tip screwdriver, drive axle shaft inner seal from outside end cover. See Fig. 14.
2) To remove input shaft cover seal, using Puller (6514), remove differential bearing race and shim from inside of PTU end cover. Using internal puller and slide hammer, remove input shaft cover seal.
3) Drive in NEW seals from inside PTU end cover. Ensure seals are installed with spring facing up. See Fig. 15. Install differential bearing race and shim. Ensure race is seated in end cover.

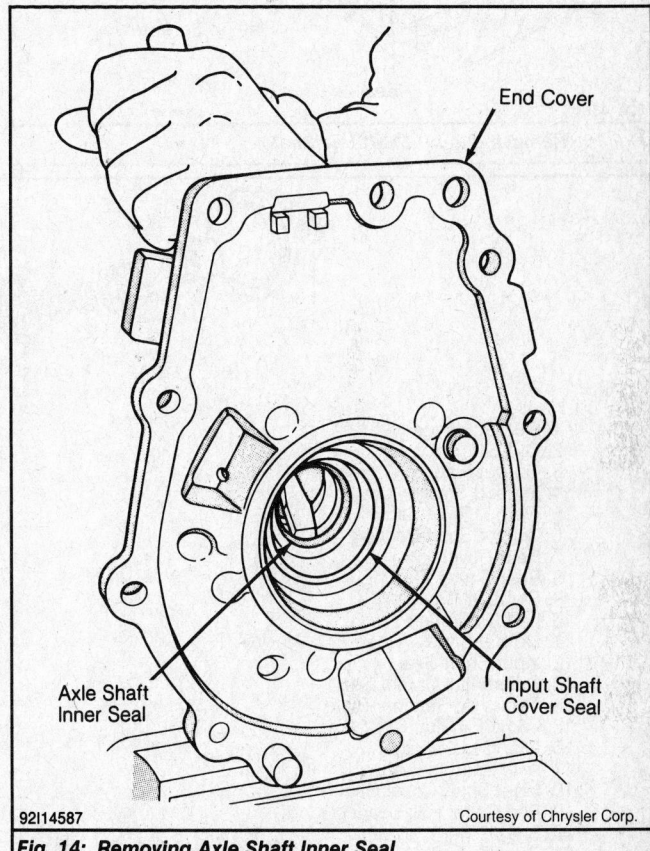

Fig. 14: Removing Axle Shaft Inner Seal

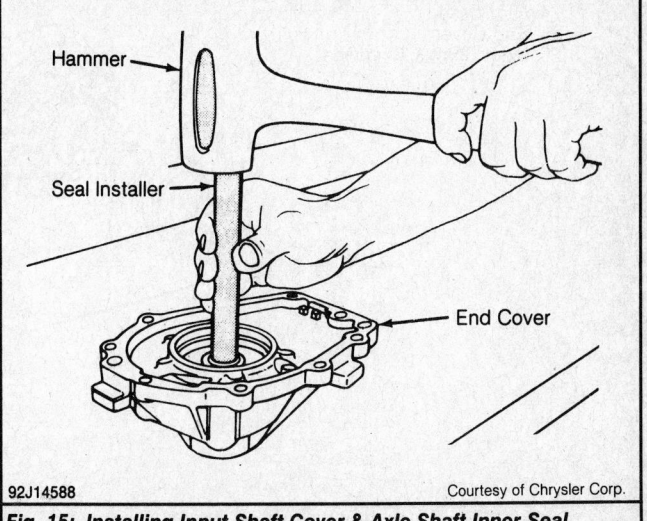

Fig. 15: Installing Input Shaft Cover & Axle Shaft Inner Seal

5-54

TRANSFER CASES
Chrysler Corp. Power Transfer Unit (Cont.)

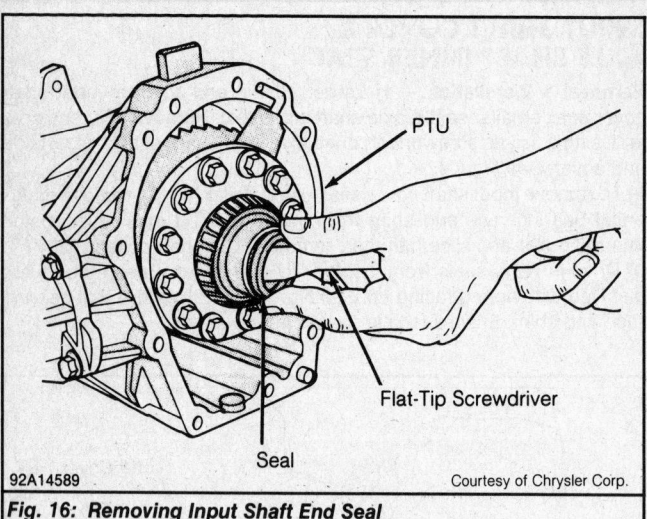

92A14589   Courtesy of Chrysler Corp.

Fig. 16: Removing Input Shaft End Seal

4) Apply anaerobic sealer to end cover mating surfaces. Install end cover and retaining bolts. Tighten bolts to specification in sequence. See TORQUE SPECIFICATIONS. See Fig. 7.

INPUT SHAFT END SEAL

Removal & Installation – 1) Remove PTU end cover. Using a flat-tip screwdriver, pry end seal from input shaft. See Fig. 16. To install NEW seal, remove input shaft from housing and place block of wood under assembly.

2) Drive NEW seal into input shaft end with appropriate seal driver. Apply anaerobic sealer to end cover mating surfaces. Install end cover and retaining bolts. Tighten bolts to specification in sequence. See Fig. 7.

TORQUE SPECIFICATIONS

TORQUE SPECIFICATIONS

Application	Ft. Lbs. (N.m)
End Cover Bolt	21 (28)
Output Flange Nut	120 (163)
Rear Cover Bolt	21 (28)

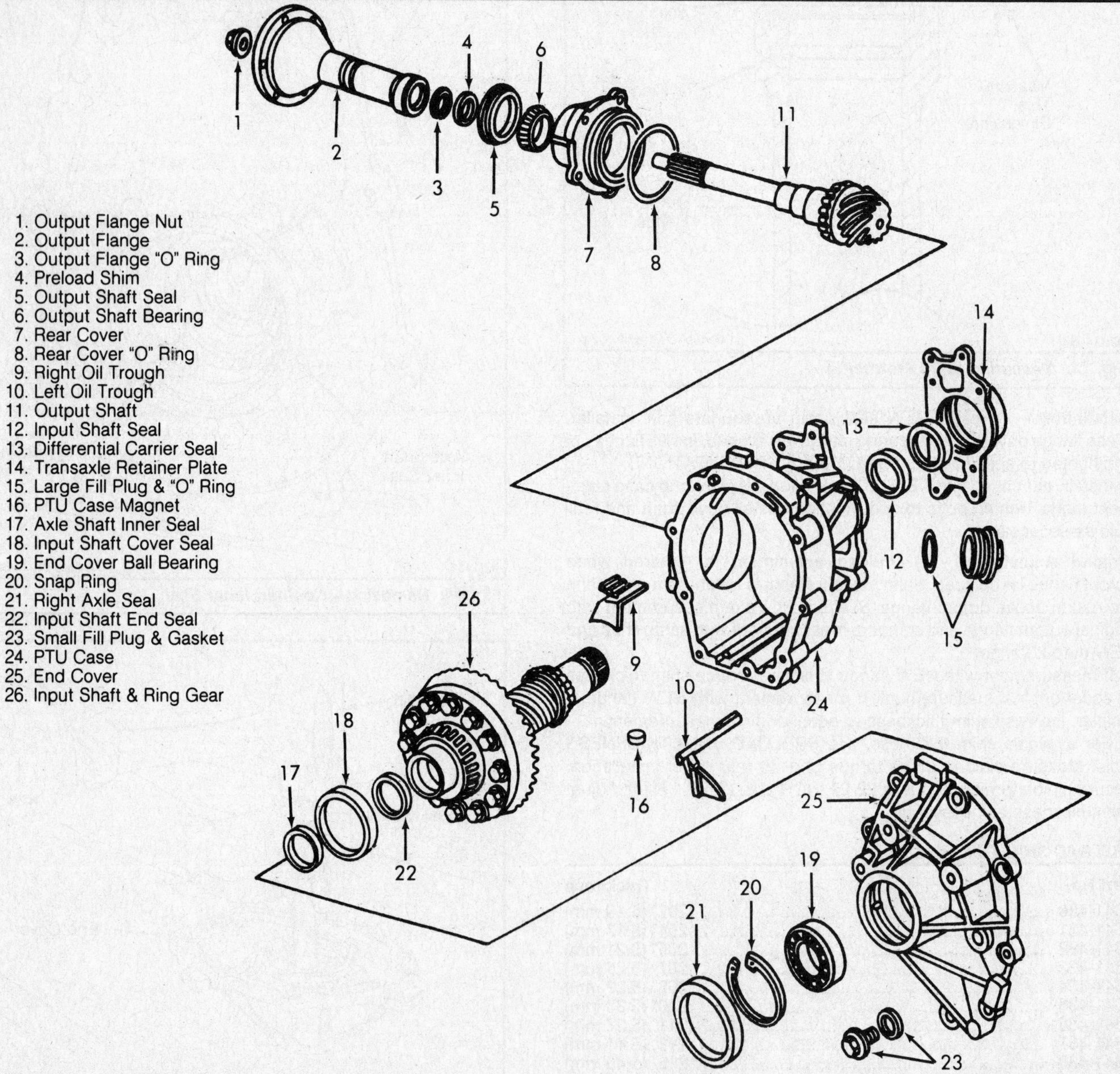

1. Output Flange Nut
2. Output Flange
3. Output Flange "O" Ring
4. Preload Shim
5. Output Shaft Seal
6. Output Shaft Bearing
7. Rear Cover
8. Rear Cover "O" Ring
9. Right Oil Trough
10. Left Oil Trough
11. Output Shaft
12. Input Shaft Seal
13. Differential Carrier Seal
14. Transaxle Retainer Plate
15. Large Fill Plug & "O" Ring
16. PTU Case Magnet
17. Axle Shaft Inner Seal
18. Input Shaft Cover Seal
19. End Cover Ball Bearing
20. Snap Ring
21. Right Axle Seal
22. Input Shaft End Seal
23. Small Fill Plug & Gasket
24. PTU Case
25. End Cover
26. Input Shaft & Ring Gear

92D14590   Courtesy of Chrysler Corp.

Fig. 17: Exploded View Of Chrysler Motors PTU Assembly

Ford Motor Co: Aerostar AWD

DESCRIPTION

The Dana TC-28, also called E-4WD, is a full-time transfer case mounted on rear of the A4LD transmission. It has electronic controls that actuate the transfer case clutch under adverse conditions. The control unit senses wheel slip and locks up the differential through an electromagnetic clutch. The control unit has self-diagnostic capability.

OPERATION

TRANSFER CASE

The Dana TC-28 distributes torque through a planetary gear differential. The planetary gear differential distributes 2/3 of torque to rear wheels and 1/3 to front wheels. The planetary gear differential allows both axles to turn at different speeds.

ELECTRONIC CONTROL SYSTEM

The system consists of a control module, speed sensors and a electromagnetic clutch. The control module monitors signals from brake switch, park/neutral position switch and axle sensors. The control module will not allow clutch to engage if brakes are applied, vehicle speed is over 35 MPH or transmission selector is in "P" or "N" position.

When the control module senses wheel slip it engages the electromagnetic clutch. When clutch is engaged, front and rear wheels rotate at same speed and planetary gear does not operate. The control module engages the electromagnetic clutch for 3.3 seconds and releases. If wheel slip still exists clutch will re-engage after 1/2 second and continue to cycle until wheel slip is gone.

TROUBLE SHOOTING

INITIAL CHECKS

Many symptoms may occur with continuous transfer case clutch engagement. Noise, vibration, harshness and wheel hop that occur while driving straight or during tight turns may be caused by the electromagnetic clutch. When electromagnetic clutch does not disengage, a binding condition occurs causing these symptoms.

1) Ensure rear axle ratio is 3.73. Inspect wiring for added aftermarket devices. Inspect the following electrical connectors:
- Control module 14-pin plug under drivers seat.
- 8-pin (8-way) plug at transfer case.
- Sensor plugs (2) at transfer case, front and rear pick-ups.
- Electromagnetic clutch wiring plug at transfer case.

2) If symptoms can be duplicated on road test, unplug control module under seat and re-road test. See Fig. 1. If symptom stops, problem is in wiring, plug connectors or sensors.

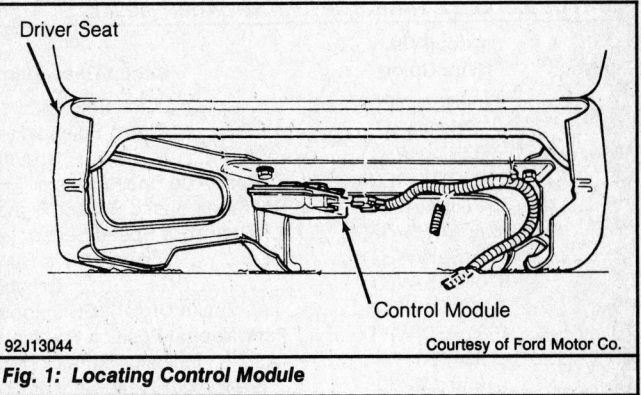

Driver Seat

Control Module

92J13044   Courtesy of Ford Motor Co.

Fig. 1: Locating Control Module

SELF-DIAGNOSTICS

If a problem is detected by control module, a code will flash on 4WD indicator light. The number of flashes must be counted between pauses. If key is turned off before code is counted, codes 9-16 will be lost. Codes 1-8 will reappear when key is turned back on. For specific tests, see TESTING. For description of codes and diagnostic action, see ELECTRONIC TRANSFER CASE CODES table.

TESTING

NOTE: For all procedures under TESTING, see Fig. 2 for connector identification. For pin No. and circuit description reference, see CONTROL MODULE CONNECTOR IDENTIFICATION table and WIRING DIAGRAMS.

CONTROL MODULE CONNECTOR IDENTIFICATION (1993)

Pin No.	Circuit No. (Wire Color)	Circuit Description
1	150 (DK. GRN/WHT)	Front Axle Speed Sensor (−)
2	349 (DK. BLU)	Front Axle Speed Sensor Signal
3	350 (GRY)	Front Axle Speed Sensor (+)
4	994 (WHT)	Indicator Light Control
5	463 (RED/WHT)	Park/Neutral Position Sw. Input
6	810 (RED/LT. GRN)	Brake On/Off (BOO) Input
7	570 (BLK/WHT)	Ground
8	972 (BLK/WHT)	Switched Power
9	518 (LT. GRN/RED)	Rear Axle Speed Sensor (−)
10	351 (BRN/WHT)	Rear Axle Speed Sensor Signal
11	359 (GRY/WHT)	Rear Axle Speed Sensor (+)
12	570 (BLK/WHT)	Ground
13	976 (ORG)	Clutch Solenoid (−)
14	975 (BRN/YEL)	Clutch Solenoid (+)

ELECTRONIC TRANSFER CASE CODES

Code	Description	Diagnostic Action
....	Inoperative Or Erratic System Errors	Tests A Through D
1	Microprocessor RAM Access Error	Replace Control Module
2	Clutch Connector/Coil Open	TEST F1
3	Front Output Sensor Or Sensor Connector Open	TEST E1
4	Rear Output Sensor Or Sensor Connector Open	TEST E1
5	Front & Rear Sensor &/Or Sensor Connectors Open	TEST E1
6	Clutch Connector/Coil & Front Output Sensor &/Or Sensor Connector Open	TEST F1, Then E1
7	Clutch Connector/Coil & Rear Output Sensor &/Or Sensor Connector Open	TEST F1, Then E1
8	Clutch Connector/Coil & Both Output Sensors &/Or Sensor Connectors Open	TEST F1, Then E1
9	Mechanical Problem Allowing Clutch Slippage Or Bad Sensor Output Signal	TEST F1, Then E1
10	Both Codes 2 & 9	TEST F1, Then E1
11	Both Codes 3 & 9	TEST F1, Then E1
12	Both Codes 4 & 9	TEST F1, Then E1
13	Both Codes 5 & 9	TEST F1, Then E1
14	Both Codes 6 & 9	TEST F1, Then E1
15	Both Codes 7 & 9	TEST F1, Then E1
16	Both Codes 8 & 9	TEST F1, Then E1

CONTROL MODULE CONNECTOR IDENTIFICATION (1994)

Pin No.	Circuit No. (Wire Color)	Circuit Description
1	975 (BRN/YEL)	Clutch Solenoid (+)
2	976 (ORG)	Clutch Solenoid (−)
3	570 (BLK/WHT)	Ground
4	359 (GRY/RED)	Rear Axle Speed Sensor (+)
5	351 (BRN/WHT)	Rear Axle Speed Sensor Signal
6	518 (LT. GRN/RED)	Rear Axle Speed Sensor (−)
7	972 (BLK/WHT)	Ignition (Hot In Run)
8	570 (BLK/WHT)	Ground
9	511 (LT. GRN)	Brake On/Off (BOO) Input
10	463 (RED/WHT)	Park/Neutral Position Sw. Input
11	994 (WHT)	Indicator Light Control
12	350 (GRY)	Front Axle Speed Sensor (+)
13	349 (DK. BLU)	Front Axle Speed Sensor Signal
14	150 (DK. GRN/WHT)	Front Axle Speed Sensor (−)

PINPOINT TESTS

Pinpoint tests are labeled "A" through "F". If system fault is not defined, testing should begin at TEST A1 and continue in order until fault is identified. See ELECTRONIC TRANSFER CASE PINPOINT TESTS table.

ELECTRONIC TRANSFER CASE PINPOINT TESTS

Test	Pinpoint Test Title
A	Power & Grounds
B	4WD Indicator Light
C	Brake Switch Input
D	Park/Neutral Position Switch
E	Speed Sensors
F	Clutch

Test A1, Intermittent Or No Power To Control Module – Check for open circuit No. 972 between module harness connector and positive battery terminal: Check voltage between disconnected module harness connector and ground. If voltage is steady and greater than 9 volts, proceed to TEST A2. If voltage is intermittent or less than 9 volts, repair power supply line.

Test A2, Faulty Control Module Ground – Check for intermittent or poor module ground: With battery disconnected, check resistance in both circuits No. 570 between module harness connector and chassis ground. If resistance is steady and less than one ohm, replace control module. If resistance fluctuates or is greater than one ohm, repair ground circuit No. 570. See WIRING DIAGRAMS.

Test B1, 4WD Indicator Light Not Functioning Properly – Check voltage of circuit No. 994 at module harness connector: Test voltage with key off and module harness connector in place. Backprobe module harness connector at pin to chassis ground. If voltage is less than 3 volts, proceed to TEST B2. If voltage is greater than 3 volts, repair short in circuit No. 275 between 4WD indicator light and module harness connector.

Test B2, 4WD Indicator Light Not Functioning – Check voltage at control module circuit No. 994 using same procedure as TEST B1 with key on: If voltage is steady and greater than 9 volts, proceed to TEST B3. If voltage is less than 9 volts, replace control module.

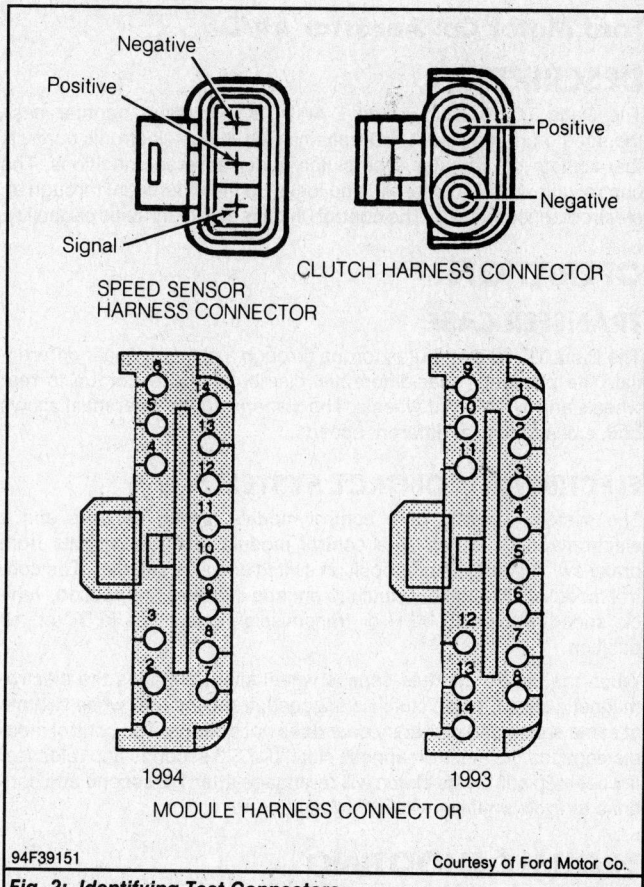

Fig. 2: Identifying Test Connectors

Speed Sensor Harness Connector — Negative, Positive, Signal. Clutch Harness Connector — Positive, Negative. 1994 / 1993 Module Harness Connector.

94F39151   Courtesy of Ford Motor Co.

Test B3, 4WD Indicator Light Circuit Open – Check for open in circuit No. 994 between module harness connector and 4WD indicator light: With key off and module harness connector disconnected, check resistance of circuit No. 994 between module harness connector and chassis ground. If resistance is greater than 15 ohms, replace 4WD indicator light or repair open circuit No. 275 (Yellow wire) or No. 994 (White wire). If resistance is less than 4 ohms, repair short to ground between module harness connector and 4WD indicator light.

Test C1, Stoplight Operation – Apply brakes and observe rear stoplights. If stoplights are inoperative, repair stoplight circuit. If stoplights operate properly, proceed to TEST C2.

Test C2, Intermittent Or No Brake Switch Input – Check for intermittent open in control module brake switch circuit: Measure voltage in circuits No. 810 or 511 between disconnected module harness connector and chassis ground while brake is depressed. Shake and wiggle module harness and retest. If voltage is steady and greater than 9 volts, replace control module. If voltage is less than 9 volts or intermittent, repair break in module to brake switch circuits No. 810 or 511. See WIRING DIAGRAMS.

Test D1, Park/Neutral Position Switch Input – Check for intermittent short in control module park/neutral position switch circuit: Measure voltage in circuit No. 463 between disconnected module harness connector and chassis ground, while key is on and transmission is in "N" position. If voltage is less than one volt, proceed to TEST D2. If voltage is greater than one volt, repair short in park/neutral position switch circuit No. 463 or replace park/neutral position switch. See WIRING DIAGRAMS.

Test D2, Faulty Park/Neutral Position Switch Or Circuit – Check for short in control module park/neutral position switch circuit: Measure resistance in circuit No. 463 between disconnected module harness connector and chassis ground while key is off and transmission is in "D" position. If resistance is greater than 100 ohms, proceed to TEST D3. If resistance is less than 100 ohms, repair short to ground in park/neutral position switch circuit No. 463 or replace park/neutral position switch. See WIRING DIAGRAMS.

Test D3, Park/Neutral Position Switch Open – Check for open between module harness connector and park/neutral position switch: Measure resistance in circuit No. 463 between disconnected module harness connector and chassis ground with key off and transmission in "N" position. If resistance is less than 50 ohms, replace control module. If resistance is greater than 50 ohms, repair open in park/neutral position switch circuit No. 463 or replace park/neutral position switch. See WIRING DIAGRAMS.

Test E1, Speed Sensor Power Supply – Check for voltage at speed sensor: Measure voltage between positive pin of each disconnected speed sensor harness connector and chassis ground (circuits No. 350 and 359) with key on. If voltage is steady and greater than 4 volts, proceed to TEST E2. If voltage is less than 4 volts, repair open in speed sensor circuits. See WIRING DIAGRAMS.

Test E2, Speed Sensor Circuit Continuity Test – Check continuity of speed sensor signal and grounds: With key off and speed sensor and module harness connector disconnected, measure resistance between module harness connector and speed sensor harness connector. See CONTROL MODULE CONNECTOR IDENTIFICATION table. If resistance is greater than one ohm, repair open circuit. If resistance is less than one ohm, proceed to TEST E3.

Test E3, Speed Sensor Ground Testing – Check for short to ground in speed sensor signal circuit: With key off and speed sensor and module harness connector disconnected, measure resistance between speed sensor harness connector signal pin and chassis ground. Shake connector during test. If resistance is greater than one ohm replace speed sensor. Retest; if fault reappears, replace control module. If resistance is less than one ohm, repair short to ground in speed sensor signal circuit. See WIRING DIAGRAMS.

Test F1, Intermittent Or No Power To Clutch – Check voltage at clutch connector: With key on and clutch harness connector disconnected, measure battery voltage between positive pin and chassis ground. If no voltage is measured, go to TEST F2. If voltage is measured, repair short to battery in clutch circuit or replace control module. See WIRING DIAGRAMS.

Test F2, Clutch Circuit Ground Testing – Check for short to ground in clutch circuit: With key off and module harness connector disconnected, measure resistance in circuit No. 975 between module harness connector and chassis ground. Shake connector during test. If resistance is greater than one ohm, proceed to TEST F3. If resistance is less than one ohm, repair short-to-ground in clutch circuit No. 975. See WIRING DIAGRAMS.

Test F3, Clutch Circuit Continuity Test – Check for open in clutch circuit: With key off and module harness connector disconnected, measure resistance in circuit No. 975 between module harness connector and chassis ground. If resistance is less than 1.5 ohms or greater than 4 ohms, repair open clutch circuit. If resistance is 1.5-4 ohms proceed to TEST F4.

Test F4, Verify Electronic Clutch Engagement – Check clutch by powering circuit: Disconnect module harness connector, and ground circuit No. 976. Jumper circuit No. 972 to circuit No. 975 at module harness connector. On road test if clutch engages (driveline wind-up) replace control module. If clutch does not engage (no driveline wind-up), replace clutch or identify a mechanical fault in system.

ON-VEHICLE SERVICE

FRONT & REAR OUTPUT SHAFT OIL SEAL

Removal – Raise vehicle. Remove front and/or rear drive shaft from transfer case yoke. Wire drive shaft out of way. Remove yoke lock nut. On front yoke, hold nut with holding tool and turn splines of front output shaft with nut wrench to remove lock nut. Remove steel bushing from front output shaft. Using seal remover tool and slide hammer, remove oil seals.

Installation – Lubricate seals with ATF. Using oil seal installer, install NEW oil seals. To complete installation, reverse removal procedure. Tighten bolts and nuts to specification. See TORQUE SPECIFICATIONS.

REMOVAL & INSTALLATION

TRANSFER CASE

Removal – 1) Raise vehicle on hoist. Remove drain plug, and drain transfer case lubricant. Disconnect transfer case harness connector, and disconnect drive shafts from transfer case.

2) Remove transfer case strut. *See Fig. 3.* Support transfer case with a transmission jack. Remove transfer case-to-extension housing bolts. Slide transfer case rearward off transmission, and lower case from vehicle. Remove gasket from between transfer case and extension housing.

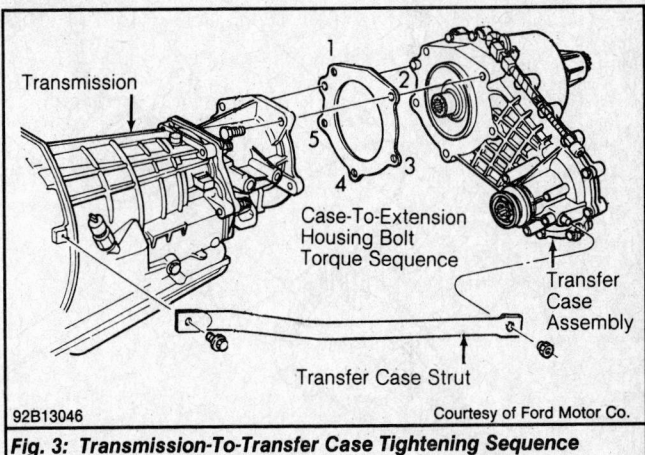

Transmission

Case-To-Extension Housing Bolt Torque Sequence

Transfer Case Assembly

Transfer Case Strut

92B13046   Courtesy of Ford Motor Co.

Fig. 3: Transmission-To-Transfer Case Tightening Sequence

Installation – 1) Install NEW transfer case-to-extension housing gasket. Position transfer case so input shaft splines align with transmission output shaft. Slide case forward onto transmission output shaft and dowel pins.

2) Install transfer case-to-extension housing bolts in sequence. *See Fig. 3.* Tighten bolts to specification. See TORQUE SPECIFICATIONS. Remove jack from transfer case. To complete installation, reverse removal procedure.

TRANSFER CASE DISASSEMBLY

Disassembly – 1) Remove transfer case. See TRANSFER CASE under REMOVAL & INSTALLATION. Remove sensors from rear case half. *See Fig. 5.* Remove yoke lock nut with Front Output Shaft Nut Wrench (T90T-7127-E) and Front Output Shaft Holding Tool (T90T-7127-F).

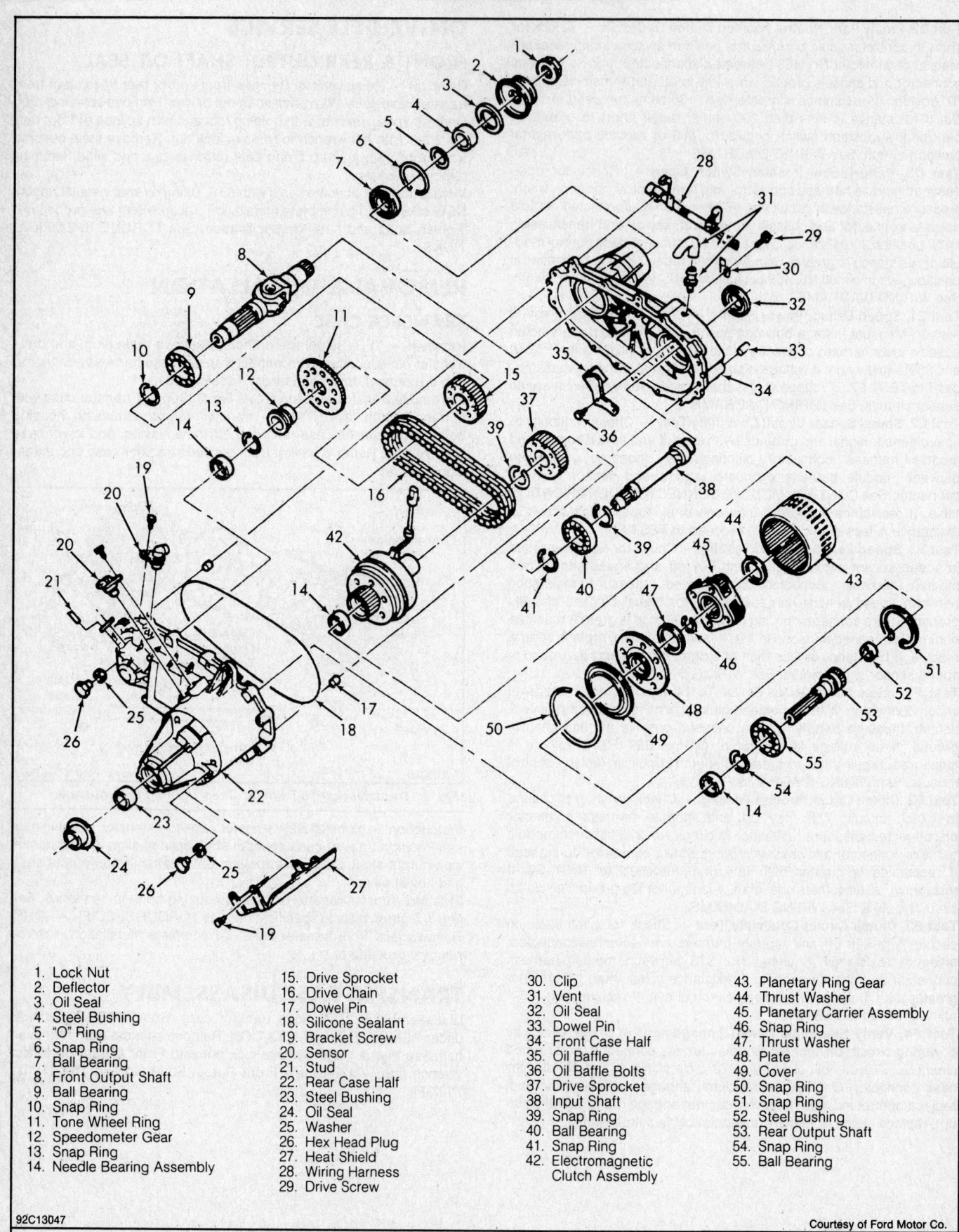

92C13047

Fig. 4: Exploded View Of TC-28 Transfer Case

1. Lock Nut
2. Deflector
3. Oil Seal
4. Steel Bushing
5. "O" Ring
6. Snap Ring
7. Ball Bearing
8. Front Output Shaft
9. Ball Bearing
10. Snap Ring
11. Tone Wheel Ring
12. Speedometer Gear
13. Snap Ring
14. Needle Bearing Assembly

15. Drive Sprocket
16. Drive Chain
17. Dowel Pin
18. Silicone Sealant
19. Bracket Screw
20. Sensor
21. Stud
22. Rear Case Half
23. Steel Bushing
24. Oil Seal
25. Washer
26. Hex Head Plug
27. Heat Shield
28. Wiring Harness
29. Drive Screw

30. Clip
31. Vent
32. Oil Seal
33. Dowel Pin
34. Front Case Half
35. Oil Baffle
36. Oil Baffle Bolts
37. Drive Sprocket
38. Input Shaft
39. Snap Ring
40. Ball Bearing
41. Snap Ring
42. Electromagnetic
   Clutch Assembly

43. Planetary Ring Gear
44. Thrust Washer
45. Planetary Carrier Assembly
46. Snap Ring
47. Thrust Washer
48. Plate
49. Cover
50. Snap Ring
51. Snap Ring
52. Steel Bushing
53. Rear Output Shaft
54. Snap Ring
55. Ball Bearing

2) Hold nut with holding tool, and turn splines of front output shaft with nut wrench to remove lock nut. Remove steel bushing from front output shaft. Using seal remover and slide hammer, remove oil seal. Remove "O" ring from front output shaft if it did not come out with steel bushing.

3) Mark position of harness clips for reassembly purposes. Remove case half flange screws, and place large screwdriver in pry slots to separate case halves. *See Fig. 6.*

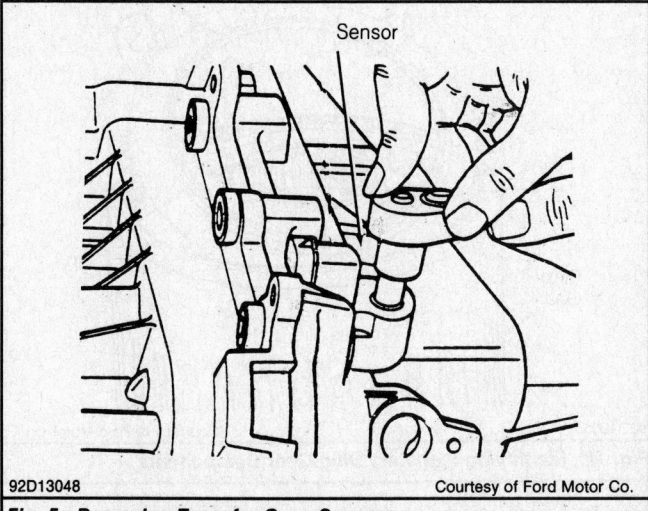

Fig. 5: **Removing Transfer Case Sensors**

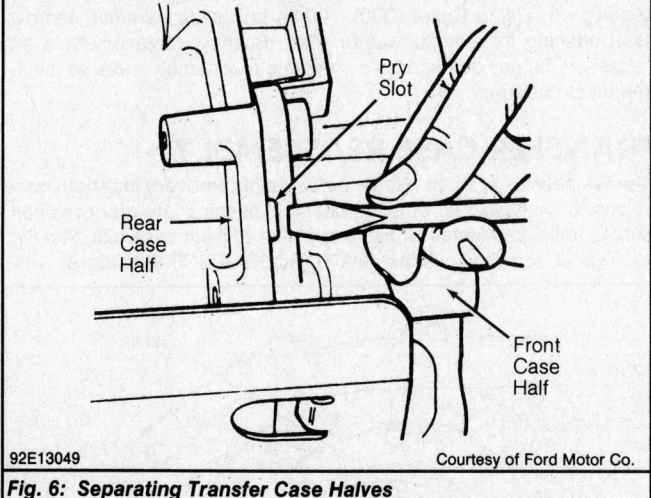

Fig. 6: **Separating Transfer Case Halves**

NOTE: Magnesium filings may fall into case when case is separated. This is a normal condition. Ensure all filings are removed before reassembly.

---

4) Remove front output shaft and chain assembly. *See Figs. 4 and 7.* It may be necessary to tap on end of shaft to separate from case. Remove snap ring and drive out bearing for front output shaft in nose of front case half. Using seal remover tool and slide hammer, remove oil seal from front case half for input shaft.

5) Remove electromagnetic clutch and planetary gear assembly from rear case half. *See Fig. 8.* Ensure clutch wiring is removed from slot. Remove thrust washer from bottom of ring gear in rear case half.

6) Turn over rear case half, and tap case on bench to remove ring gear. Using seal remover tool and slide hammer, remove oil seal from rear case half for rear output shaft. Remove snap ring retaining rear output shaft inside rear case half. *See Figs. 4 and 9.*

7) Remove output shaft from rear case half. It may be necessary to tap on end of shaft to separate from case. Using Collet Puller (T87P-7120-D), remove bushing from rear case half. Using hammer and drift,

remove rear output shaft needle bearing in rear case half. Using collet puller and slide hammer, remove front output shaft needle bearing in rear case half. Remove oil baffle from front case half.

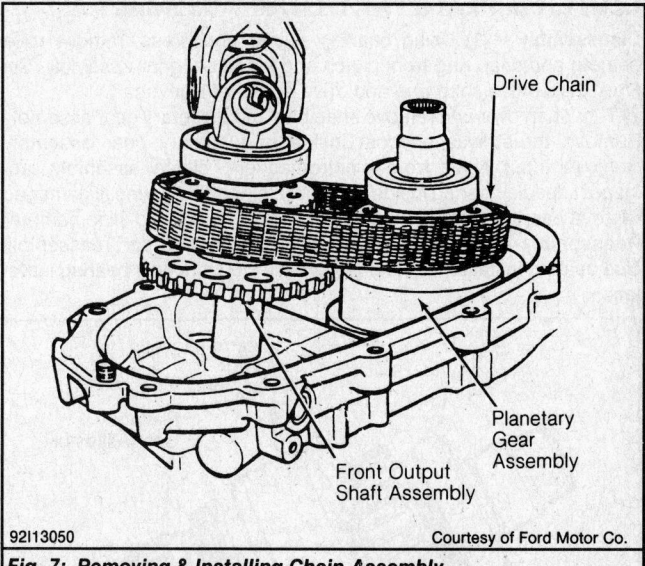

Fig. 7: **Removing & Installing Chain Assembly**

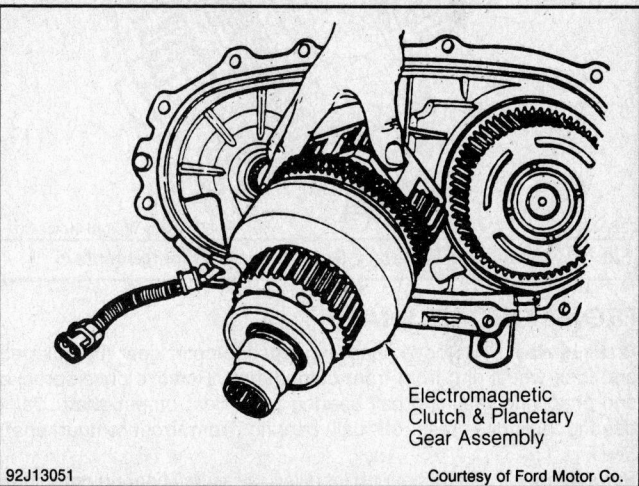

Fig. 8: **Removing Planetary Gear Assembly**

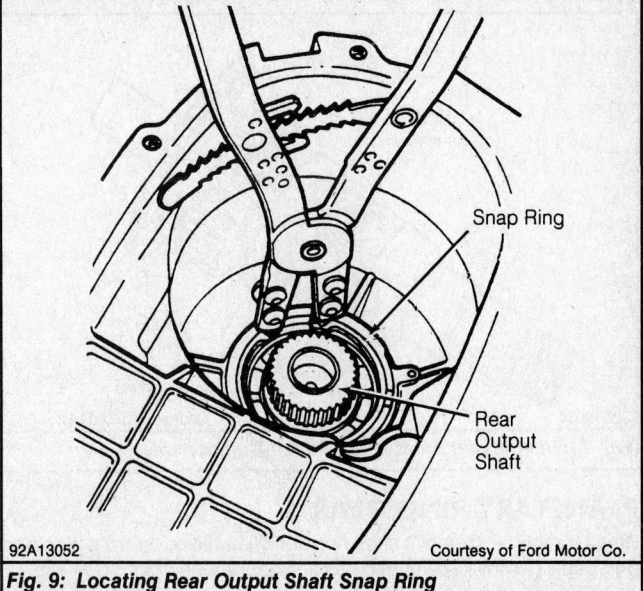

Fig. 9: **Locating Rear Output Shaft Snap Ring**

COMPONENT DISASSEMBLY & REASSEMBLY

CLUTCH & PLANETARY GEAR ASSEMBLY

Disassembly – 1) Using bearing splitter and press, remove roller bearing and snap ring from clutch and planetary gear assembly. *See Fig. 10.* Remove snap ring and drive sprocket from shaft.

2) Turn shaft over and remove snap ring and planetary gear assembly. Remove thrust washer from inside of planetary gear assembly. Remove input shaft from electromagnetic clutch assembly, and inspect needle bearing inside assembly. If needle bearing is damaged, remove bearing using Collet Puller (T87P-7120-D) and slide hammer.

Reassembly – Reverse disassembly procedures for reassembly. Use bearing installer for electromagnetic clutch needle bearing installation.

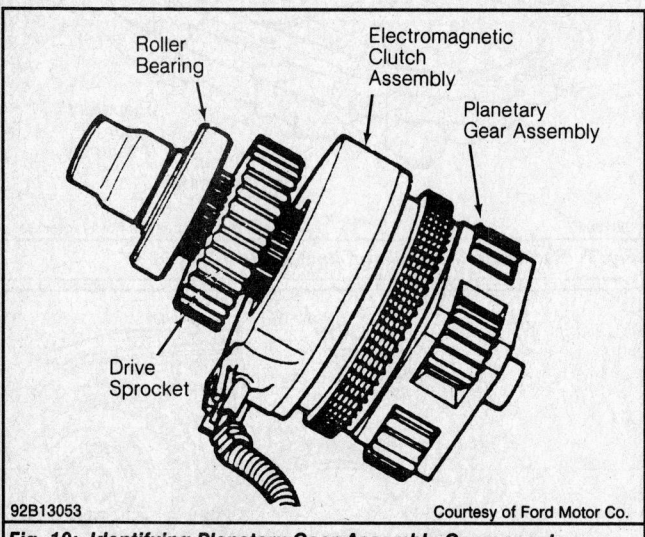

Fig. 10: Identifying Planetary Gear Assembly Components

FRONT OUTPUT SHAFT

Disassembly – Remove snap ring, speedometer gear (if equipped) and tone wheel ring from front output shaft. Remove drive sprocket and snap ring retaining ball bearing from front output shaft. Using bearing splitter, press off ball bearing from front output shaft. *See Fig. 11.*

Reassembly – Using bearing installer, press ball bearing onto shaft. To complete reassembly, reverse disassembly procedures. Ensure raised boss on tone wheel is installed toward drive sprocket.

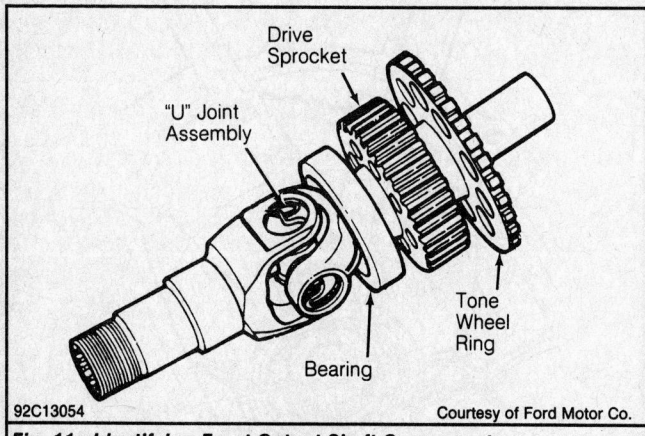

Fig. 11: Identifying Front Output Shaft Components

PLANETARY RING GEAR

Disassembly – Remove snap ring and oil baffle cover from planetary ring gear. Remove spline plate from planetary ring gear. *See Fig. 12.*

Reassembly – Install spline plate in planetary ring gear with hub toward top of gear. Install baffle plate in planetary ring gear with lip toward groove on snap ring. Install snap ring. Ensure snap ring is fully seated in groove.

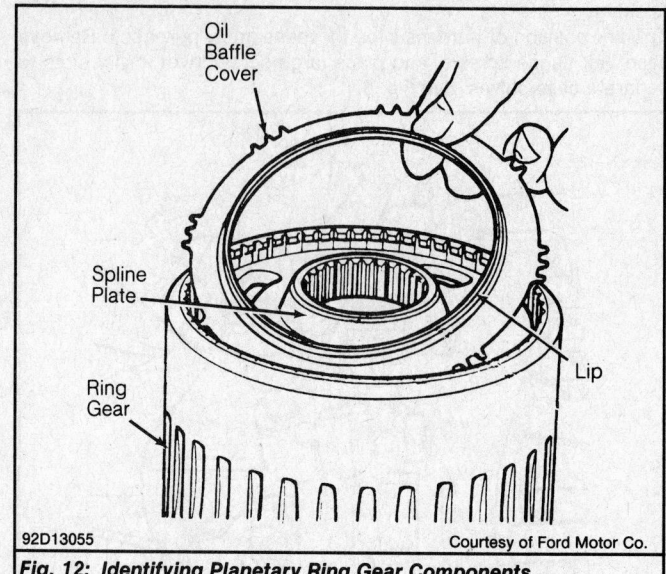

Fig. 12: Identifying Planetary Ring Gear Components

REAR OUTPUT SHAFT

Disassembly & Reassembly – Remove snap ring, and press roller bearing off. Using Collet (D80L-100-H) and slide hammer, remove steel bushing from inside output shaft. Bushing replacement is not necessary unless damaged. To complete reassembly, reverse disassembly procedures.

TRANSFER CASE REASSEMBLY

Reassembly – 1) Drive needle bearings (if removed) into both case halves. Drive NEW rear output shaft steel bushing into rear case half. Loctite bolts, and install oil baffle to inside of front case half. *See Fig. 13.* Tighten to specifications. See TORQUE SPECIFICATIONS.

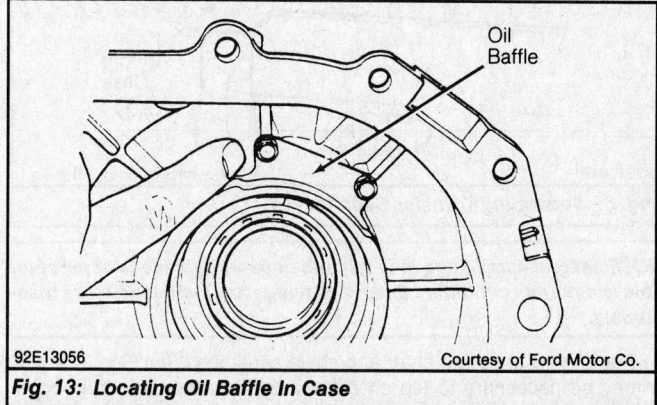

Fig. 13: Locating Oil Baffle In Case

2) Before reassembly, lubricate all parts with ATF. Mount rear case half in soft-jawed vise. Install rear output shaft assembly and snap ring in rear case half. Install planetary ring gear over rear output shaft splines. Install thrust washer in bottom of planetary ring gear.

3) Install chain and sprockets over front output shaft assembly, and over electromagnetic clutch and planetary gear assembly. *See Fig. 7.* Install wires for electromagnetic clutch assembly in slot of rear case half.

4) Install roller bearing and snap ring in front case half; if necessary, press bearing into place. Apply 1/8-1/4" bead of silicone sealant (non-acid type) to rear case half mating surface, in pattern shown. *See Fig. 14.* Install front case half on rear case half, and place harness clips in marked positions. *See Fig. 15.*

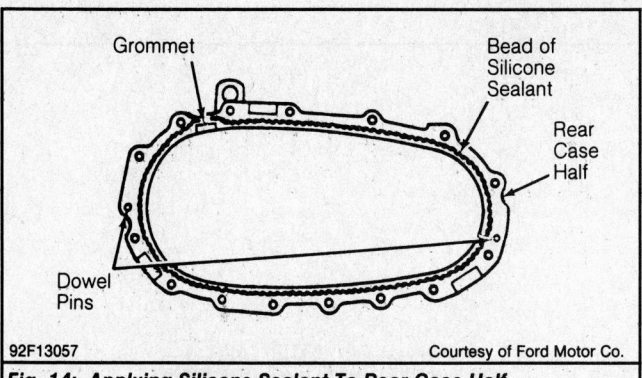

92F13057   Courtesy of Ford Motor Co.

Fig. 14: Applying Silicone Sealant To Rear Case Half

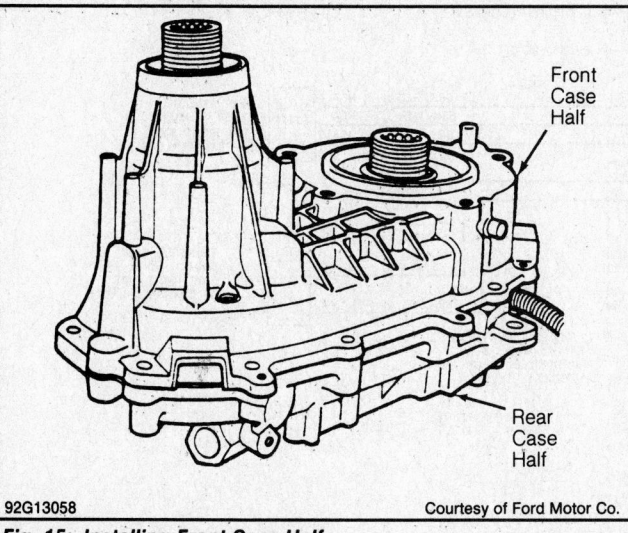

92G13058   Courtesy of Ford Motor Co.

Fig. 15: Installing Front Case Half

5) Loctite case half screws and tighten to specifications. Install front output shaft bearing snap ring in front case half. Install front output shaft "O" ring and seal.

6) Install steel bushing on front output shaft with "O" ring groove down. Install oil deflector on front output shaft. Loctite threads of NEW front output shaft lock nut, and using front output shaft wrench and holding tool, tighten to specifications.

7) Mark position of blind spline of front output shaft on oil deflector. This mark is used for installing front drive shaft. Lubricate lips and install NEW rear output shaft seal using seal installer. Ensure slot in tool is over tab on the seal and hole in seal is installed at 6 o'clock position (transfer case installed).

8) Lubricate lips and install NEW input shaft oil seal in front case half. Install wiring harness in clips on transfer case. Connect harness to both sensors in rear case half and electromagnetic clutch harness connector. Install transfer case assembly. See REMOVAL & INSTALLATION.

SERVICE BULLETINS

NOISE & VIBRATION

Ford Motor Co. (TSB 91-5-12) – Description – Noise or vibration may be caused by poor snap ring retention in planetary ring gear. *See Fig. 16.*

Repair – Planetary ring gear snap ring has been updated. Refer to COMPONENT DISASSEMBLY & REASSEMBLY for replacement procedure. Ensure round design snap ring is replaced with square design (F19Z-7C122-A).

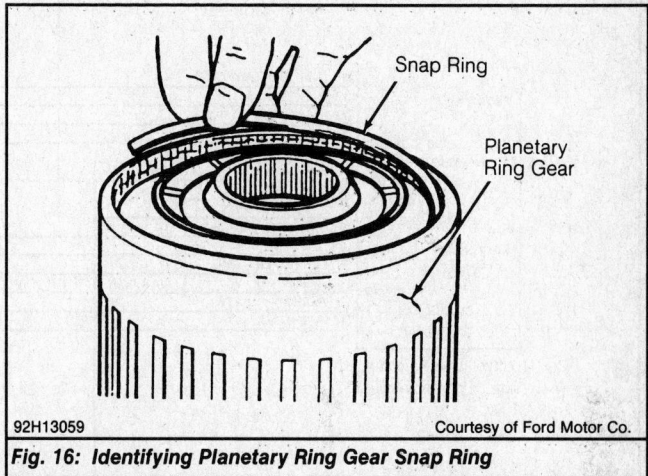

92H13059   Courtesy of Ford Motor Co.

Fig. 16: Identifying Planetary Ring Gear Snap Ring

NOISE, VIBRATION, HARSHNESS & WHEEL HOP

Ford Motor Co. (TSB 91-16-14) – Description – Symptoms may occur while turning, due to repeated engagement of electromagnetic clutch.

Diagnosis – Follow procedures in INITIAL CHECKS under TROUBLE SHOOTING and then go to next repair step.

Repair – Replace front speed sensor and road test. If symptoms reoccur replace rear speed sensor. Ensure updated front and rear sensors (FO9Z-7F293-A) are used. Updated sensors have welded connections and withstand heat build-up better. If symptoms reoccur, repeat INITIAL CHECKS. If repairs at this point have not corrected symptoms, the cause could be a grounded wire from dash to control module or mechanical problem in front suspension or transfer case. Inspect further and repair as required.

TORQUE SPECIFICATIONS
TORQUE SPECIFICATIONS

Application	Ft. Lbs. (N.m)
Case Half Flange Screws	25-35 (34-47)
Drain & Fill Plugs	10-20 (14-27)
Front Drive Shaft-To-Front Axle Flange Bolts	22-29 (30-39)
Output Shaft Assembly Nut	130-150 (176-203)
Rear Drive Shaft-To-Rear Axle Flange Bolts	61-87 (83-118)
Sensor Retaining Screws	12-16 (16-22)
Speedometer Cable Retaining Stud	8-12 (11-16)
Transfer Case-To-Extension Bolts	25-35 (34-47)
Transfer Case Strut Bolt	45-60 (61-81)
Transfer Case Strut Nut	55-65 (75-88)
	INCH Lbs. (N.m)
Oil Baffle Bolts	25-35 (3-4)

TRANSFER CASES
Dana TC-28 (Cont.)

WIRING DIAGRAMS

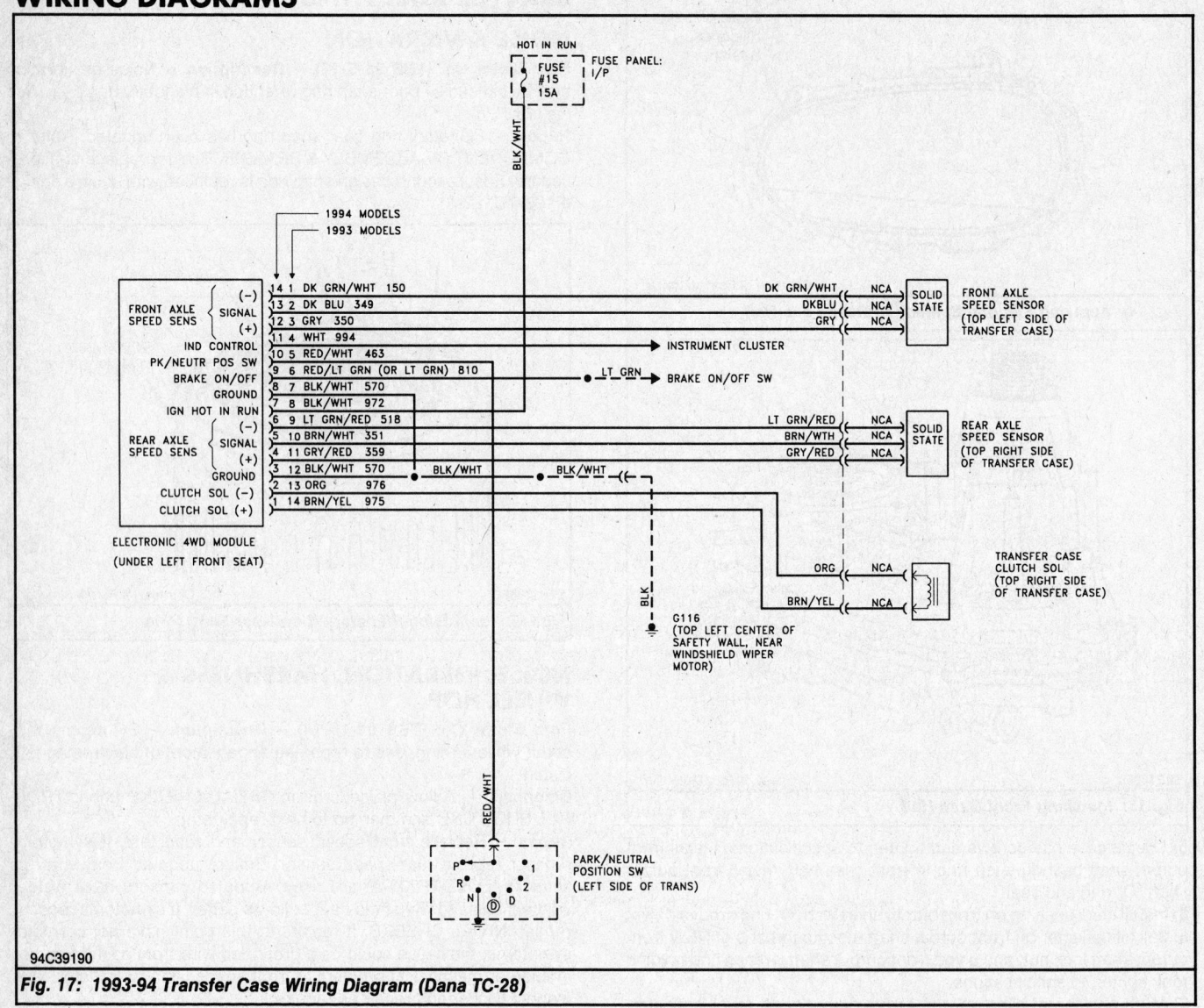

Fig. 17: 1993-94 Transfer Case Wiring Diagram (Dana TC-28)

Chrysler Corp:
1993 4WD Pickup (W250/350)

IDENTIFICATION

An identification tag is located on driver's side of transfer case, on power take-off cover. Information on tag consists of model number, low range reduction ratio and assembly number.

DESCRIPTION

The New Process Model 205 is a heavy duty, part-time unit with constant mesh, helical gears. Gears are mounted in a one-piece cast iron case.

ON-VEHICLE SERVICE

SHIFT LINKAGE ADJUSTMENT

Shift transfer case to Neutral position. Remove shift boot screws. Raise shift boot for access to shift bracket bolts. Loosen shift bracket bolts, and move bracket forward as far as possible. Tighten bolts and check shift linkage operation. Install shift boot.

REMOVAL & INSTALLATION

TRANSFER CASE

Removal – 1) Raise vehicle, and drain transfer case fluid. Disconnect vehicle speed sensor wires. Remove skid plate, crossmember and strut rods as needed. Disconnect drive shafts and wire aside. DO NOT allow drive shafts to hang free, as damage to "U" joints may result.
2) Disconnect shift lever rod from range lever. Support transfer case. Remove nuts attaching transfer case to transmission adapter. Move transfer case to rear until input shaft clears adapter. Lower transfer case from vehicle.
Installation – 1) Install NEW transfer case-to-transmission gasket. Apply sealer to both sides of gasket. Ensure transfer case input splines align with transmission output shaft. Align splines by rotating output yoke.

NOTE: DO NOT install transfer case-to-transmission nuts until transfer case is completely seated.

---

2) To complete transfer case installation, reverse removal procedure. Ensure all attaching bolts are tightened to specification. See TORQUE SPECIFICATIONS. Fill transfer case with lubricant.

OVERHAUL

NOTE: For exploded view of transfer case assembly, see Fig. 4.

TRANSFER CASE

Disassembly – 1) Loosen rear output shaft yoke nut. *See Fig. 4.* Remove rear output shaft housing and retainer from case. Remove yoke nut, washer, seal washer and rear yoke from shaft. Remove rear retainer, rear output shaft and gears as an assembly from housing. Remove rear seal retainer from bearing retainer. Remove and discard snap ring.
2) Remove rear bearing retainer. Remove rear output shaft bearing, speedometer gear, shaft support bearing, thrust washer pin and low gear from rear output shaft. Remove lock ring, thrust washer and pilot bearing rollers from rear output shaft. *See Fig. 4.*
3) Remove front yoke nut, washer and flange. Remove front seal retainer and gasket. Remove power take-off cover and gasket. Remove detent plug and 4WD indicator light switch from case. Remove shift rail detent springs and balls. Use pencil magnet to remove as necessary.
4) Remove bolts attaching front bearing retainer to case. Tap front output shaft with plastic mallet to loosen. Remove shaft, retainer and gears. *See Fig. 1.* Remove shaft snap ring. Remove thrust washer, gear, bearings and spacer.

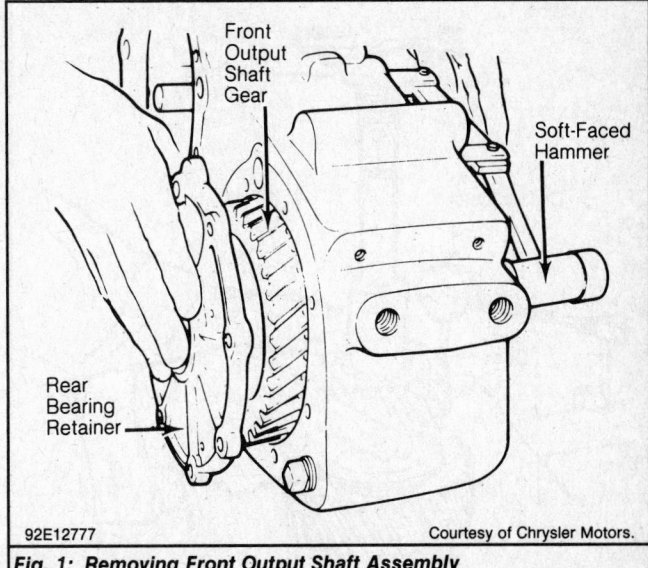

Front Output Shaft Gear

Soft-Faced Hammer

Rear Bearing Retainer

92E12777 — Courtesy of Chrysler Motors.

Fig. 1: Removing Front Output Shaft Assembly

5) Remove transfer case adapter and gasket. Remove idler shaft nut and washer. Remove idler shaft cover and gasket. Remove cup plugs at top of case for access to shift fork lock pins. Use small punch to remove plugs. Place shift rails in Neutral position.
6) Remove lock pins from shift forks with long handle easy out. Remove pins attaching shift rail link and remove link. Remove shift forks and sliding clutches. Remove snap ring, thrust washer and bearing from front output shaft. Remove front output shaft and high gear.
7) Remove input gear, bearings, seals and washer. Loosen and remove idler shaft with soft-faced mallet. Tilt case, roll idler gear toward front output shaft opening in case, and remove gear through opening. Remove and retain idler gear shims. Keep shims together.
8) Remove bearing races and bearings from idler gear. Remove interlock pins from inside case. Remove pins through power take-off cover opening. If front output shaft rear bearing must be replaced, replace bearing and retainer as an assembly.
Cleaning & Inspection – 1) Clean all parts with solvent, and blow parts dry with compressed air. DO NOT spin dry bearings. Remove all traces of gaskets from surfaces.
2) Inspect teeth of all gears for excessive wear or damage. Replace gear(s) if these conditions exist. Check for sliding clutch wear on engagement side. If wear exists, use opposite side of clutch in reassembly. Both sides of clutch are identical.
3) Carefully examine splines and shaft for scoring or evidence of wear. Sliding clutch gears must move freely on splines. Parts should be replaced if spline or shaft is scored or heavily worn.

NOTE: For exploded view of transfer case assembly, see Fig. 4.

Reassembly – 1) Lubricate transfer case gears and shafts with gear oil during reassembly. Use petroleum jelly to lubricate and hold bearings in place during installation. Use NEW gaskets and seals. Replace snap rings if distorted or damaged. Use NEW yoke lock nuts to secure yoke and flange.
2) Using a press, install bearing races in idler gear. Assemble idler gear, gear bearings, bearing spacer and shims on dummy shaft with bore facing up. Check idler gear end play. *See Fig. 2.* End play should be 0-.002" (0-.005 mm).
3) Press shift rail oil seals into case. Seals should be installed with seal lip facing outward. Install idler gear assembly and dummy shaft into case. Insert assembly through front shaft bore, large end first. Tilt case at 45 degree angle to ease bearing installation.
4) Install idler shaft. Insert shaft from large bore side and tap shaft into gear and bearings with soft-faced hammer. Remove dummy shaft as idler shaft pushes shaft out of gear and case. Install idler shaft washer and NEW lock nut. Check for end play and free rotation. Tighten lock nut to specification. See TORQUE SPECIFICATIONS.

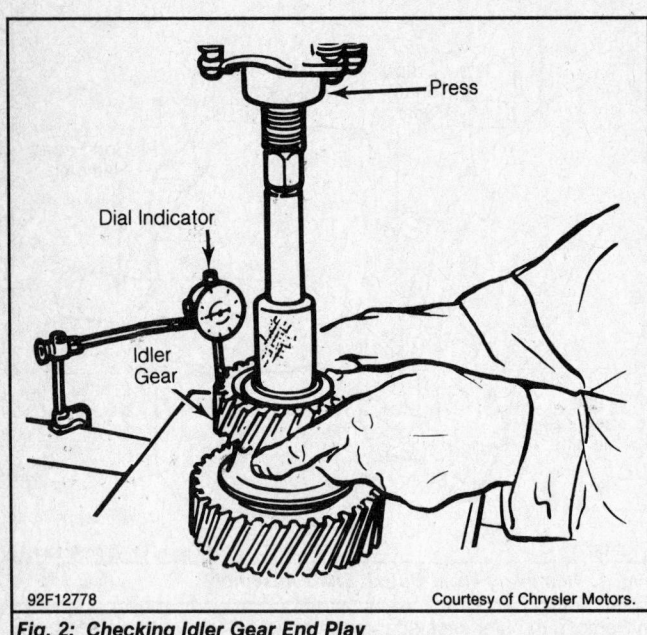

92F12778   Courtesy of Chrysler Motors.

Fig. 2: Checking Idler Gear End Play

5) Install front bearing and lock ring on input shaft. Assemble front output shaft. Install gear, sliding clutch, bearings, thrust washer pin, thrust washers, snap ring and retainer on front output shaft. *See Fig. 4*. Install interlock pins through large bore of power take-off opening. Install input gear into case.

6) Install sliding clutch on input gear and position shift fork in sliding clutch. Install rear wheel shift rail into case with slotted end first and detent notches facing up. Push rail through shift fork and into opposite end of case. Install front output shaft into case. Install front wheel shift fork in sliding clutch on front output shaft.

7) Install front wheel shift rail into case and through shift fork. Secure shift forks to shift rails with NEW lock pins. Install pins through small bores at top of case. Install front output shaft bearing retainers. *See Fig. 4*. Prior to tightening retainer bolts, ensure oil drain slot in bearing retainer is aligned with drain hole in case. Use NEW gaskets and apply sealant to retainer bolts threads. Tighten bolts to specification. See TORQUE SPECIFICATIONS.

8) Install flange on front output shaft. Install seal washer on shaft and install flange lock nut finger tight. Install washer, seal, gasket and adapter on input shaft. Install shift link and link retaining pins and clips.

9) Assemble rear output shaft. Install gear, bearings and spacers. *See Fig. 4*. Install NEW snap ring. Tap snap ring to seat and check end play. End play should be .002-.027" (.51-.69 mm). Grease pilot bearing bore of rear output shaft. Install pilot bearing rollers (15) in rear output shaft. Use petroleum jelly to secure rollers.

10) Install pilot bearing thrust washer and NEW lock ring. Install retainer on rear output shaft. Install speedometer gear and spacer. *See Fig. 3*. Install rear output shaft support bearing. Install retainer and shaft assembly. Ensure oil drain slot in retainer is aligned with drain hole in case. Tighten retainer bolts to specification.

11) Install seals in front and rear retainers. Position gaskets on case and install retainers over shafts against case. Tighten retainer bolts to specification. Install yoke and flange. Install NEW lock nuts and tighten to specification.

12) Install detent balls, springs, plugs, cup plugs and 4WD indicator light switch. Install drain plug. Fill transfer case to bottom edge of fill plug hole with appropriate lubricant. Install fill plug.

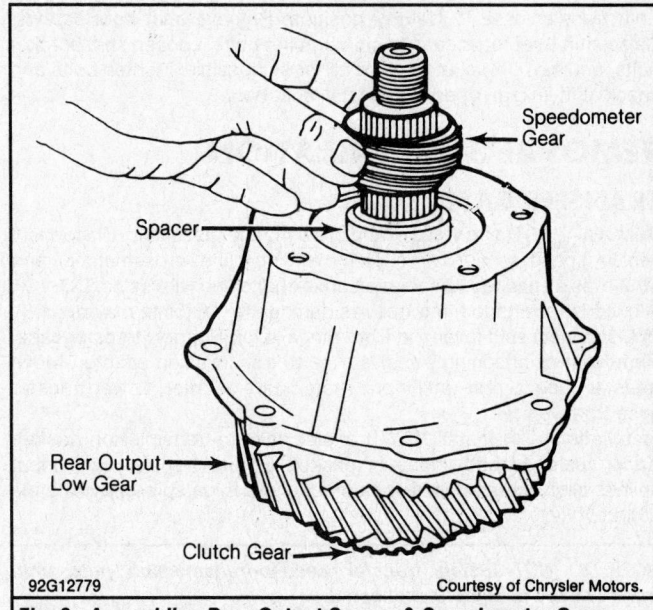

92G12779   Courtesy of Chrysler Motors.

Fig. 3: Assembling Rear Output Spacer & Speedometer Gear

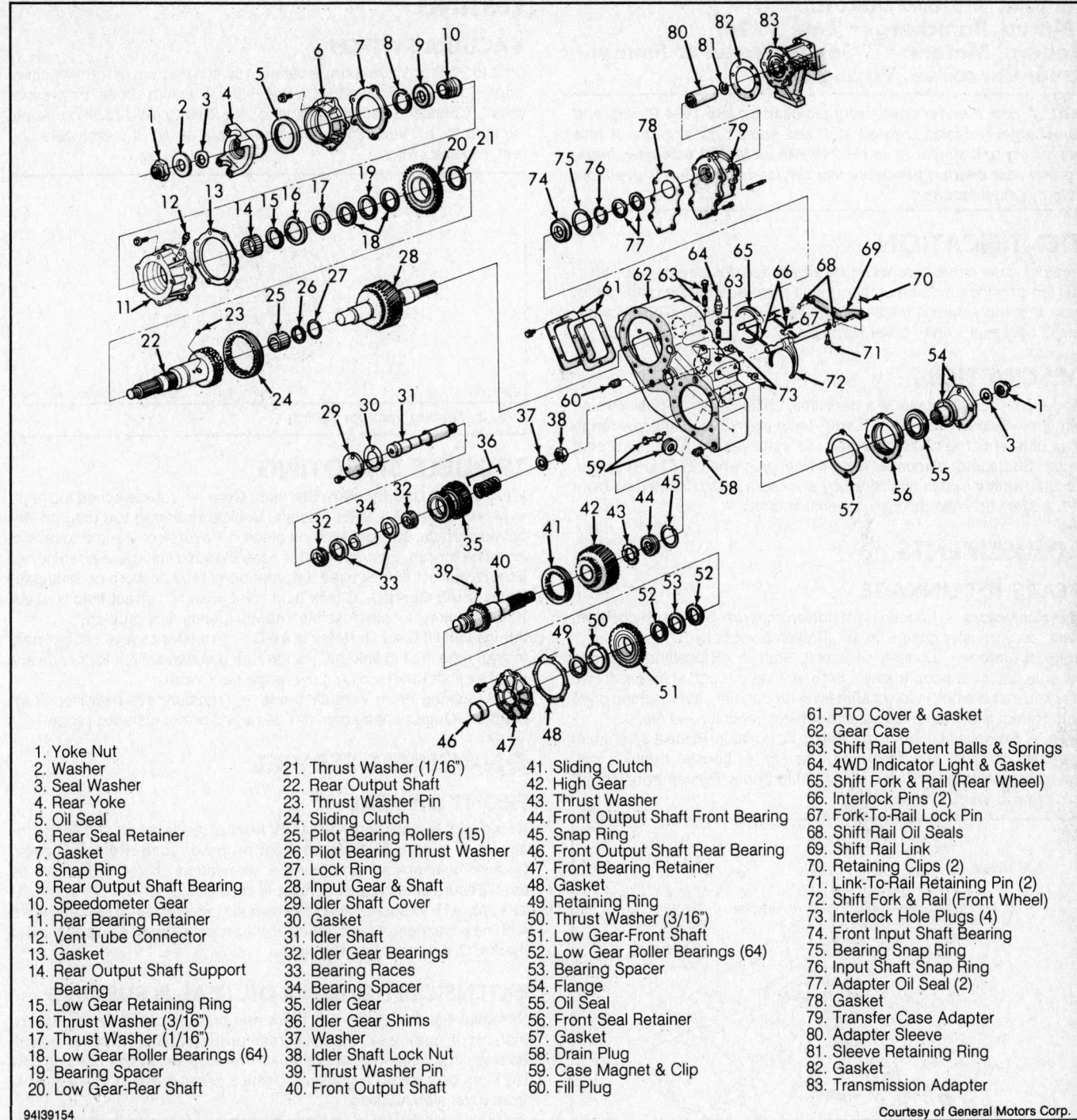

94I39154

Fig. 4: Exploded View Of Transfer Case Assembly

1. Yoke Nut
2. Washer
3. Seal Washer
4. Rear Yoke
5. Oil Seal
6. Rear Seal Retainer
7. Gasket
8. Snap Ring
9. Rear Output Shaft Bearing
10. Speedometer Gear
11. Rear Bearing Retainer
12. Vent Tube Connector
13. Gasket
14. Rear Output Shaft Support Bearing
15. Low Gear Retaining Ring
16. Thrust Washer (3/16")
17. Thrust Washer (1/16")
18. Low Gear Roller Bearings (64)
19. Bearing Spacer
20. Low Gear-Rear Shaft
21. Thrust Washer (1/16")
22. Rear Output Shaft
23. Thrust Washer Pin
24. Sliding Clutch
25. Pilot Bearing Rollers (15)
26. Pilot Bearing Thrust Washer
27. Lock Ring
28. Input Gear & Shaft
29. Idler Shaft Cover
30. Gasket
31. Idler Shaft
32. Idler Gear Bearings
33. Bearing Races
34. Bearing Spacer
35. Idler Gear
36. Idler Gear Shims
37. Washer
38. Idler Shaft Lock Nut
39. Thrust Washer Pin
40. Front Output Shaft
41. Sliding Clutch
42. High Gear
43. Thrust Washer
44. Front Output Shaft Front Bearing
45. Snap Ring
46. Front Output Shaft Rear Bearing
47. Front Bearing Retainer
48. Gasket
49. Retaining Ring
50. Thrust Washer (3/16")
51. Low Gear-Front Shaft
52. Low Gear Roller Bearings (64)
53. Bearing Spacer
54. Flange
55. Oil Seal
56. Front Seal Retainer
57. Gasket
58. Drain Plug
59. Case Magnet & Clip
60. Fill Plug
61. PTO Cover & Gasket
62. Gear Case
63. Shift Rail Detent Balls & Springs
64. 4WD Indicator Light & Gasket
65. Shift Fork & Rail (Rear Wheel)
66. Interlock Pins (2)
67. Fork-To-Rail Lock Pin
68. Shift Rail Oil Seals
69. Shift Rail Link
70. Retaining Clips (2)
71. Link-To-Rail Retaining Pin (2)
72. Shift Fork & Rail (Front Wheel)
73. Interlock Hole Plugs (4)
74. Front Input Shaft Bearing
75. Bearing Snap Ring
76. Input Shaft Snap Ring
77. Adapter Oil Seal (2)
78. Gasket
79. Transfer Case Adapter
80. Adapter Sleeve
81. Sleeve Retaining Ring
82. Gasket
83. Transmission Adapter

TORQUE SPECIFICATIONS
TORQUE SPECIFICATIONS

Application	Ft. Lbs. (N.m)
Drain & Fill Plug	40 (54)
Idler Shaft Cover Bolt	20 (27)
Idler Shaft Lock Nut	150 (203)
Input & Output Bearing Retainer Bolt	40 (54)
Output Yoke Lock Nut	130 (176)
Power Take-Off Cover Bolt	15 (20)
Transfer Case-To-Adapter Bolt	35 (47)
	INCH Lbs. (N.m)
Shift Boot Screw	35 (4)

Chrysler Motors: Dakota, Pickup, Ramcharger (Late 1994)
General Motors: "T" Series (Blazer & Jimmy)
Jeep: Cherokee, Wrangler

NOTE: A new transfer case design is used on late 1994 Pickup and Ramcharger vehicles with all 3.9L and some 5.2L engines. It is a heavy duty unit similar to an NP 241 with an NP 231 extension housing and rear bearing assembly. No service information is available from the manufacturer.

IDENTIFICATION

Transfer case can be identified by an I.D. tag, located on rear case. I.D. tag provides model number, serial number and low range ratio. Date of manufacture is the serial number (I.D. number). This information is necessary when ordering parts.

DESCRIPTION

Model 231 transfer case is a part time, chain-driven, 4-position unit with 2-piece aluminum case. Torque input in 4WD high and low range is undifferentiated. 2WD operation is achieved by a vacuum shift motor. Shift motor disconnects right front axle when 2WD is selected. Vacuum shift motor is controlled by a vacuum switch located on front of transfer case and actuated by shift sector.

ADJUSTMENTS

GEARSHIFT LINKAGE

Chrysler Motors – Loosen pivot bolt on shift rod. Shift to 4H position. Make sure transfer case is in 4H. Tighten pivot bolt.
General Motors – Loosen pivot bolt. Shift to 4H position. Remove console. Lift shift boot. Install a 5/16" drill bit through shifter and into bracket. Install a bolt in lower shift lever on transfer case. Tighten pivot bolt. Remove drill bit. Install shift boot and console. *See Fig. 1.*
Jeep – Remove shift boot and shift to 4L position. Place a 3/16" shim between gearshift and shift gate. *See Fig. 1.* Loosen trunnion nut. Adjust trunnion and shift rod until rod fits freely. Tighten trunnion nut and remove shim.

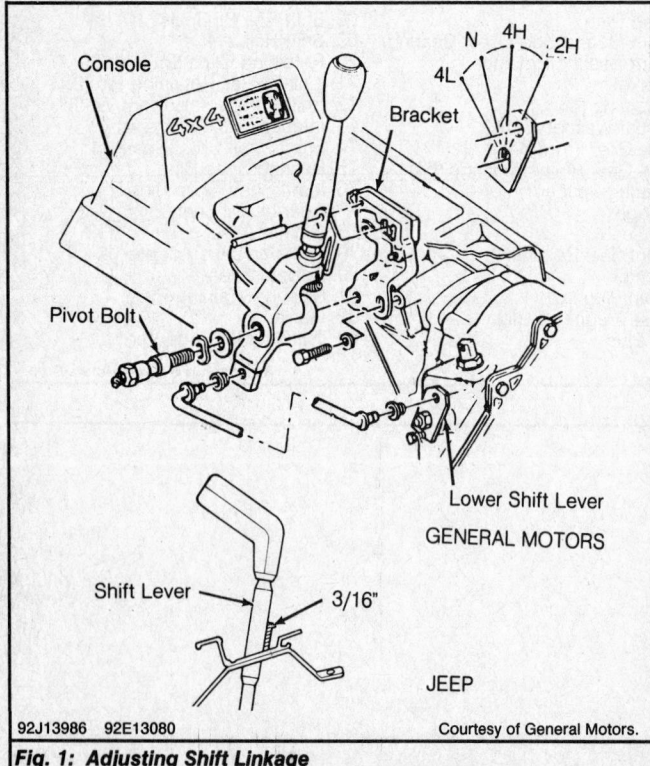

92J13986 92E13080   Courtesy of General Motors.

Fig. 1: Adjusting Shift Linkage

TESTING

VACUUM SWITCH

Shift to 2WD position. Locate vacuum switch on front of transfer case. Apply 15 in. Hg vacuum to "L". *See Fig. 2.* Vacuum should be present at "M". Connect a vacuum gauge to "N". Shift to 4WD position. Apply vacuum to "L". Vacuum should be present at "N". If switch fails any test, replace switch.

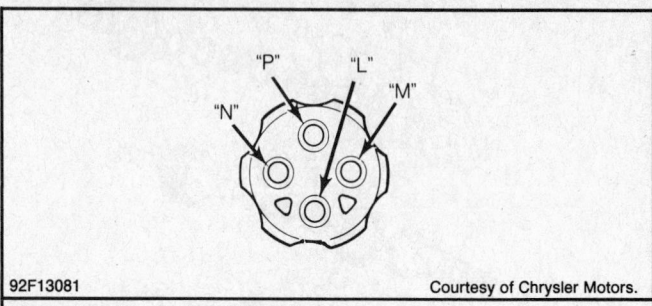

92F13081   Courtesy of Chrysler Motors.

Fig. 2: Testing Vacuum Switch

TROUBLE SHOOTING

Will Not Shift Or Difficult To Shift Into Gear – Vehicle speed too high; slow vehicle to 2-3 MPH to shift. Vehicle operated too long on dry paved surface; stop vehicle and place in Reverse or Neutral to relieve driveline torque. Ensure transfer case external linkage is not binding. Ensure correct fluid is used. Internal parts may be worn or damaged.
Noisy In All Gears – Check fluid level. Ensure correct fluid is used. If fluid is okay, locate possible internal mechanical problem.
Jumps Out Of Gear Or Noisy In 4WD – Transfer case not completely in gear; check shift linkage. Range fork damaged. Shift fork pads are worn or shift fork binding. Low range gear worn.
Fluid Leaking From Vent Or Seals – Transfer case overfilled. Vent plugged. Output shaft seals are damaged or not installed properly.

ON-VEHICLE SERVICE

FRONT OIL SEAL

Removal & Installation – **1)** Mark front propeller shaft and flange for alignment purposes. Remove front propeller shaft. Remove flange. Discard washer and nut. Using a screwdriver, carefully remove oil seal. Ensure seal contact surface is clean.
2) Apply ATF to seal lip and yoke seal surface. Install oil seal and yoke with new washer and nut. Install front propeller shaft using alignment marks. Check transfer case fluid.

EXTENSION HOUSING OIL SEAL & BUSHING

Removal & Installation – **1)** Mark rear propeller shaft and flange for installation purposes. Remove rear propeller shaft. Tap extension housing in a clockwise direction and remove extension housing. DO NOT pry on extension housing. Using a screwdriver, remove oil seal from extension housing.
2) Using bushing driver, replace bushing in extension housing. Install new extension housing oil seal. Apply silicone sealant to extension housing mating surface. Install extension housing. Reverse removal procedure to complete installation.

REMOVAL & INSTALLATION

TRANSFER CASE

Removal – **1)** Shift transfer case into 4H and disconnect battery negative cable. Raise vehicle, remove skid plate and drain fluid.
2) Mark front and rear output shaft yokes to propeller shafts for reassembly reference. Support transfer case and remove rear crossmember. Remove propeller shafts.
3) Disconnect speedometer cable and vacuum (hoses) harness at transfer case. Remove shift lever or linkage rod from case. Remove transfer case attaching bolts. Remove transfer case from vehicle.

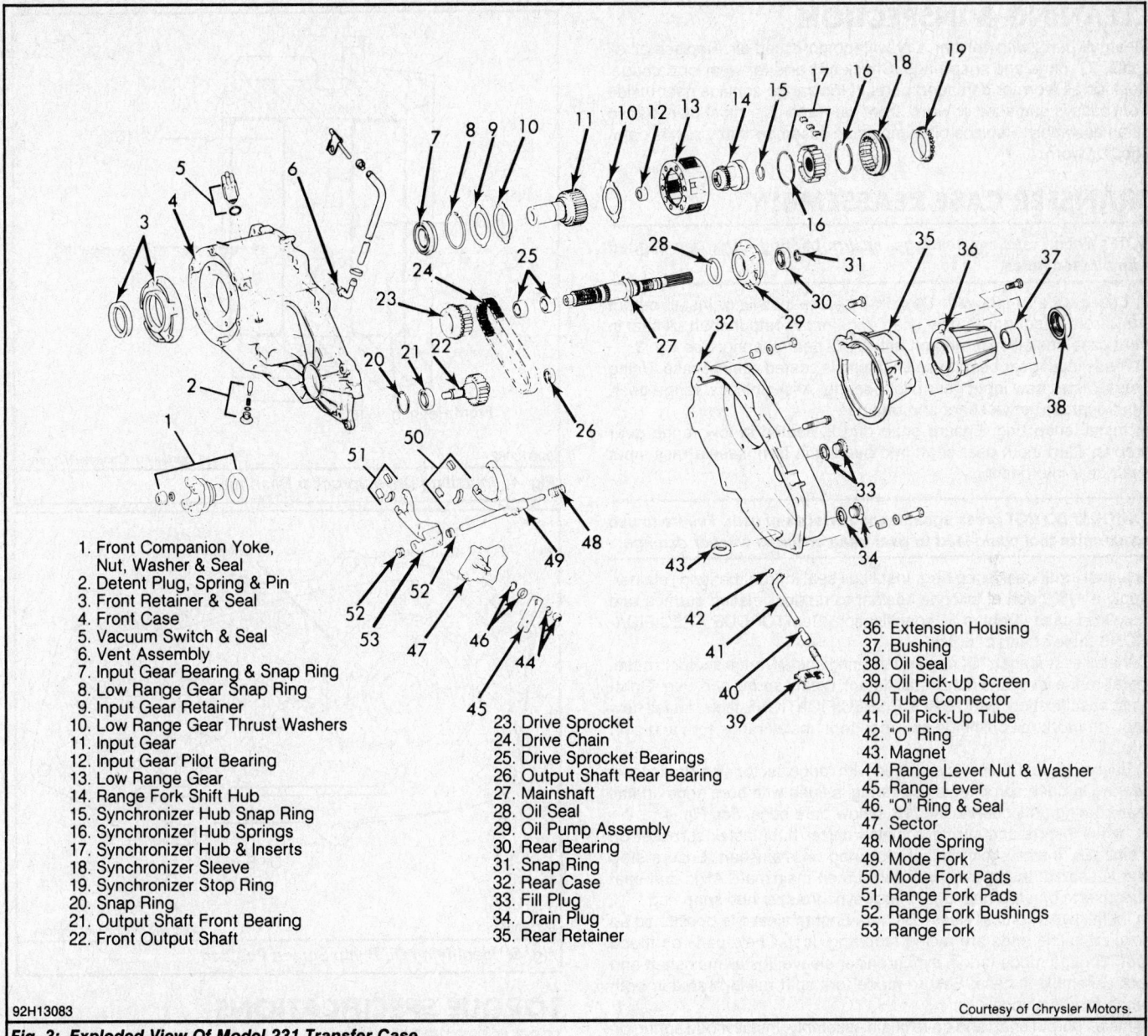

1. Front Companion Yoke, Nut, Washer & Seal
2. Detent Plug, Spring & Pin
3. Front Retainer & Seal
4. Front Case
5. Vacuum Switch & Seal
6. Vent Assembly
7. Input Gear Bearing & Snap Ring
8. Low Range Gear Snap Ring
9. Input Gear Retainer
10. Low Range Gear Thrust Washers
11. Input Gear
12. Input Gear Pilot Bearing
13. Low Range Gear
14. Range Fork Shift Hub
15. Synchronizer Hub Snap Ring
16. Synchronizer Hub Springs
17. Synchronizer Hub & Inserts
18. Synchronizer Sleeve
19. Synchronizer Stop Ring
20. Snap Ring
21. Output Shaft Front Bearing
22. Front Output Shaft

23. Drive Sprocket
24. Drive Chain
25. Drive Sprocket Bearings
26. Output Shaft Rear Bearing
27. Mainshaft
28. Oil Seal
29. Oil Pump Assembly
30. Rear Bearing
31. Snap Ring
32. Rear Case
33. Fill Plug
34. Drain Plug
35. Rear Retainer

36. Extension Housing
37. Bushing
38. Oil Seal
39. Oil Pick-Up Screen
40. Tube Connector
41. Oil Pick-Up Tube
42. "O" Ring
43. Magnet
44. Range Lever Nut & Washer
45. Range Lever
46. "O" Ring & Seal
47. Sector
48. Mode Spring
49. Mode Fork
50. Mode Fork Pads
51. Range Fork Pads
52. Range Fork Bushings
53. Range Fork

92H13083

Courtesy of Chrysler Motors.

Fig. 3: Exploded View Of Model 231 Transfer Case

Installation – 1) Clean all old gasket material from transmission and transfer case mating surfaces. Position new gasket on transfer case with orientation tab at upper left bolt hole.

2) Install transfer case, aligning splines of input shaft with transmission. Slide transfer case forward until seated against transmission. Install transfer case attaching bolts and tighten to specification. See TORQUE SPECIFICATIONS. Install rear crossmember.

3) Attach shift lever and connect speedometer and vacuum harness at transfer case. Using reference marks made during removal, reinstall front and rear propeller shafts. Refill transfer case. Install skid plate and lower vehicle. Connect negative battery cable. Road test vehicle.

TRANSFER CASE DISASSEMBLY

1) Remove front companion yoke. *See Fig. 3.* Discard lock nut. Shift transfer case to 4L and remove extension housing. Remove rear bearing snap ring. Using 2 screwdrivers under each tab, remove retainer housing. Remove rear case and oil pump as an assembly.

2) Remove oil pump pick-up screen and tube from rear case. Remove oil pump. Remove "O" ring from oil pump and discard. Mark pump housing position for reassembly purposes. Separate oil pump halves. Record gear positions and remove them from housing.

3) Remove mode spring. Using a soft hammer, tap front output shaft upward and remove with drive chain as an assembly. Remove mainshaft, mode fork and shift rail as an assembly. Remove mode fork and shift rail from synchronizer sleeve.

4) Mark synchronizer sleeve position for reassembly purposes. Remove synchronizer sleeve from mainshaft. Remove synchronizer hub snap ring. Remove synchronizer hub, stop ring and drive sprocket. Slide range fork pin out of sector.

5) Remove range fork and shift hub as an assembly. Remove range lever from sector shaft. Remove shift sector, bushing and "O" ring. Remove shift detent pin, spring and plug. Remove front bearing retainer. Remove input gear snap ring.

6) Press input and low range gear assembly from input gear bearing. Remove low range gear snap ring. Remove input gear retainer, thrust washers and input gear from low range gear.

7) Remove all oil seals. Remove magnet from front case. Remove front bearing snap ring. Using a plastic hammer, remove front bearing. Press input gear bearing from front case.

8) Using slide hammer and internal puller, remove input gear pilot bearing. Press bearings from drive sprocket. Using internal puller and slide hammer, remove output shaft rear bearing.

CLEANING & INSPECTION

Clean all parts with solvent. Dry with compressed air. Replace all oil seals, "O" rings and snap rings. Check all parts for wear or damage. Replace all worn or damaged parts. If low range annulus gear inside front case is damaged or worn, front case and gear must be replaced as an assembly. Replace oil pump as an assembly if any part is damaged or worn.

TRANSFER CASE REASSEMBLY

NOTE: When installing bearings, ensure bearing bores are aligned with oil feed holes.

1) Lubricate all parts with Dexron II before installing. Install output shaft front bearing with new snap ring. Install output shaft oil seal in front case. Install snap ring on new input gear bearing. See Fig. 3.
2) Press input gear bearing so snap ring is seated against case. Using press, install new input gear pilot bearing. Assemble low range gear, input gear, thrust washers and retainer.
3) Install snap ring. Ensure snap ring is seated in low range gear groove. Start input gear shaft into bearing in front case. Press input shaft gear into bearing.

CAUTION: DO NOT press against end surfaces of gear. Failure to use proper size tool could lead to gear case or thrust washer damage.

4) Install input gear snap ring. Install oil seal in front bearing retainer. Apply a 1/8" bead of silicone sealant to retainer mating surface and install on case. Tighten to specification. See TORQUE SPECIFICATIONS table at end of article.
5) Install sector shaft "O" ring and bushing. Install range sector in case. Install range lever and nut. Install detent, detent spring and plug. Tighten to specification. See TORQUE SPECIFICATIONS table. Install new pads and fork rail bushings on range fork. Install range fork and shift hub.
6) Ensure range fork pin is engaged with range sector slot. Press front bearing in drive sprocket until bearing is flush with bore edge. Install rear bearing until bearing is 3/16" below bore edge. See Fig. 4.
7) Install inserts and spring in synchronizer hub. Install sprocket on mainshaft. Install synchronizer stop ring on mainshaft. Ensure stop ring is seated. Install synchronizer hub on mainshaft. Align and seat hub inserts on stop ring lugs. Install synchronizer hub snap ring.
8) Install synchronizer sleeve on hub. Ensure sleeve is positioned so beveled spline ends are facing stop ring. Install new pads on mode fork. Engage mode fork in synchronizer sleeve. Install mainshaft and fork assembly in case. Ensure mode fork shift rail is seated in both range fork bushings.
9) Install output shaft and drive chain assembly. Install mode spring on shift rail. Using bearing driver, install output shaft rear bearing. Lubricate bearing after installation. Install seal in oil pump feed housing. Assemble oil pump and install in housing. Tighten to specification.
10) Install oil pick-up tube "O" ring in oil pump. Install oil pump and pick-up tube in case. Ensure screen is properly positioned. See Fig. 5. Install magnet in front case. Apply 1/8" bead of silicone sealer to front case. Install rear case. Tighten to specification. See TORQUE SPECIFICATIONS. Ensure mainshaft splines are engaged with oil pump inner gear and a washer is used on bolts at dowel locations.
11) Install rear bearings in retainer. Apply 1/8" bead of silicone sealer and install retainer to case. Install rear retainer snap ring. Install extension housing. Install front companion yoke. Install new gasket on vacuum switch. Install vacuum switch in case. Fill transfer case with Dexron II.

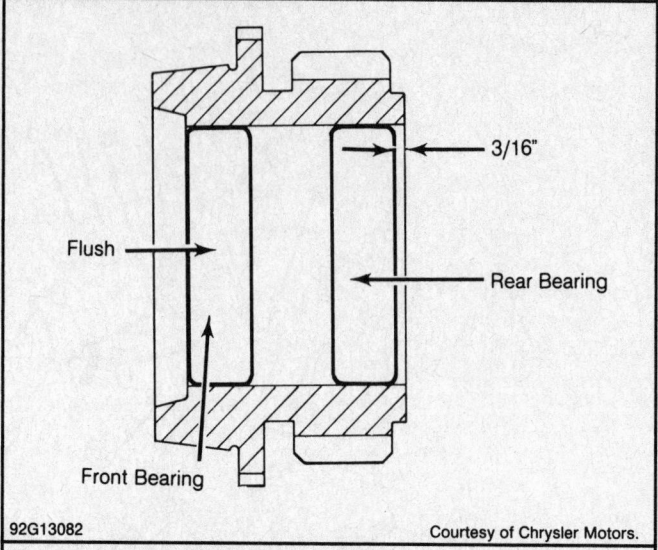

92G13082   Courtesy of Chrysler Motors.

Fig. 4: Installing Drive Sprocket Bearings

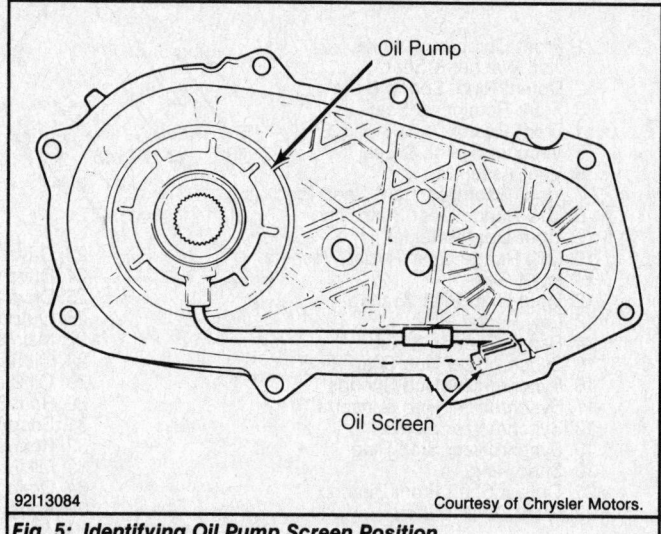

92I13084   Courtesy of Chrysler Motors.

Fig. 5: Identifying Oil Pump Screen Position

TORQUE SPECIFICATIONS
TORQUE SPECIFICATIONS

Application	Ft. Lbs. (N.m)
Companion Yoke Nut	90-130 (122-176)
Detent Plug	
General Motors	23 (31)
Chrysler Motors & Jeep	12-18 (16-24)
Drain & Fill Plug	30-40 (41-54)
Extension Housing Bolt	26-34 (35-46)
Front & Rear Bearing Retainer Bolt	15-20 (20-27)
Front Case-to-Rear Case Bolt	
General Motors	23 (31)
Chrysler Motors & Jeep	26-34 (35-46)
Range Lever Nut	20-25 (27-34)
Rear Crossmember	30 (41)
Shift Lever	
Adjusting Bolt	30 (41)
Bracket Bolt	55 (75)
Pivot Bolt	96 (130)
"U" Bolt Clamp Bolt	35 (47)
Transfer Case-to-Transmissions Nuts	26 (35)
Vacuum Switch	15-25 (20-34)

	INCH Lbs. (N.m)
Oil Pump Screw	12-15 (1.4-1.7)

General Motors: "T" Series

IDENTIFICATION

Transfer case can be identified by an I.D. tag, located on rear case. *See Fig. 1.* I.D. tag provides model number, assembly number and low range ratio. This information is necessary when ordering parts.

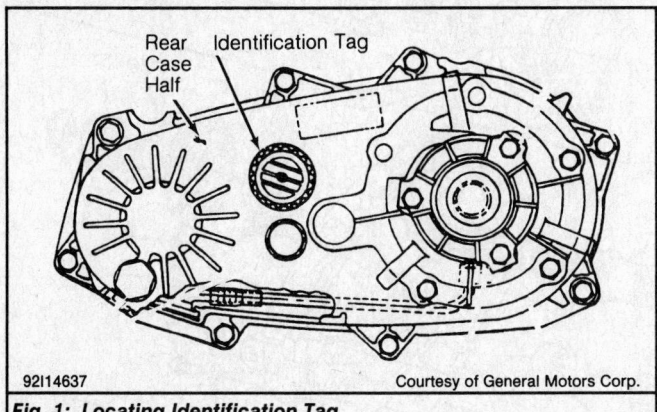

92I14637   Courtesy of General Motors Corp.

Fig. 1: Locating Identification Tag

DESCRIPTION

Model 233 transfer case is a chain drive, 2-piece aluminum case, 3-position unit. Transfer case uses an electronic control system and a shift motor to shift the transfer case.

ADJUSTMENTS

GEARSHIFT LINKAGE

Model 233 uses a electronic control system for transfer case shifting and is not equipped with transfer case gearshift linkage.

TESTING

ELECTRONIC SYSTEM

For testing of electronic system and components, see NEW PROCESS 233 ELECTRONIC CONTROLS article.

TROUBLE SHOOTING

Will Not Shift Or Difficult To Shift Into Gear – Vehicle speed too high. Slow vehicle to 2-3 MPH to shift. Vehicle operated too long on dry paved surface. Stop vehicle. Place transmission in Reverse or Neutral to relieve drive line torque. Ensure correct fluid is used. Internal parts may be worn or damaged.

Noisy In All Gears – Check fluid level. Ensure correct fluid is used. If fluid is okay, locate possible internal mechanical problem.

Jumps Out Of Gear Or Noisy In 4WD – Transfer case internal shift mechanism faulty. Range fork damaged. Fork pads are worn. Shift fork binding. Low range gear worn.

Fluid Leaking From Vent Or Seals – Transfer case overfilled. Vent plugged. Output shaft seals are damaged or not installed properly.

ON-VEHICLE SERVICE

FRONT OIL SEAL

Removal – Mark front drive shaft and flange for alignment purposes. Remove front drive shaft. Remove flange. Discard washer and nut. Using a screwdriver, carefully remove oil seal. Ensure seal contact surface is clean.

Installation – Apply ATF to seal lip and yoke seal surface. Install oil seal and yoke with NEW washer and nut. Install front drive shaft using alignment marks. Check transfer case fluid.

EXTENSION HOUSING OIL SEAL & BUSHING

Removal – Mark rear drive shaft and flange for installation purposes. Remove rear drive shaft. Tap extension housing clockwise and remove extension housing. DO NOT pry on extension housing. Using a screwdriver, remove oil seal from extension housing.

Installation – Using bushing driver, replace bushing in extension housing. Install NEW extension housing oil seal. Apply silicone sealant to extension housing mating surface. Install extension housing. To complete installation, reverse removal procedure.

REMOVAL & INSTALLATION

TRANSFER CASE

WARNING: When battery is disconnected, vehicles equipped with computers may lose memory data. When battery power is restored, driveability problems may exist on some vehicles. These vehicles may require a relearn procedure. See COMPUTER RELEARN PROCEDURES in APPLICATION & IDENTIFICATION.

Removal – **1)** Shift transfer case into 4H and disconnect battery negative cable. Raise vehicle, remove skid plate and drain fluid.

2) Mark front and rear output shaft yokes to drive shafts for reassembly reference. Support transfer case and remove rear crossmember. Remove drive shafts.

3) Disconnect speedometer cable, electrical connections and vacuum (hoses) harness at transfer case. Remove transfer case attaching bolts. Remove transfer case from vehicle.

Installation – **1)** Clean all old gasket material from transmission and transfer case mating surfaces. Position NEW gasket on transfer case with orientation tab at upper left bolt hole.

2) Install transfer case, aligning splines of input shaft with transmission. Slide transfer case forward until seated against transmission. Install transfer case attaching bolts and tighten to specification. See TORQUE SPECIFICATIONS. Install rear crossmember.

3) Attach speedometer cable, electrical connections and vacuum harness at transfer case. Using reference marks made during removal, reinstall front and rear drive shafts. Refill transfer case. Install skid plate and lower vehicle. Connect negative battery cable. Road test vehicle.

TRANSFER CASE DISASSEMBLY

NOTE: See Fig. 2 for exploded view of transfer case.

1) Remove front output yoke. Discard lock nut. Remove encoder motor, vacuum switch and speed sensor. Remove extension housing and rear output bearing retainer snap ring. Using 2 screwdrivers under each tab, remove pump retainer housing. Remove speedometer tone wheel from mainshaft. Remove rear case and oil pump as an assembly.

2) Remove pump pick-up screen and tube from rear case. *See Fig. 3.* Remove oil pump. Remove "O" ring from oil pump and discard. Mark pump housing position for reassembly purposes. Separate oil pump halves. Note gear positions for reassembly reference and remove them from housing.

3) Remove mode shift fork spring. Using a soft hammer, tap front output shaft upward and remove with drive chain as an assembly. Remove mainshaft, mode fork and shift rail as an assembly. Remove mode fork and shift rail from synchronizer sleeve.

4) Mark synchronizer sleeve position for reassembly purposes. Remove synchronizer sleeve from mainshaft. Remove synchronizer hub snap ring. Remove synchronizer hub, synchronizer ring and drive sprocket. Slide range fork pin out of shift sector.

5) Remove range shift fork and range shift hub as an assembly. Remove shift sector, bushing and "O" ring. Remove shift detent pin, spring and plug. Remove front bearing retainer. Remove input gear snap ring.

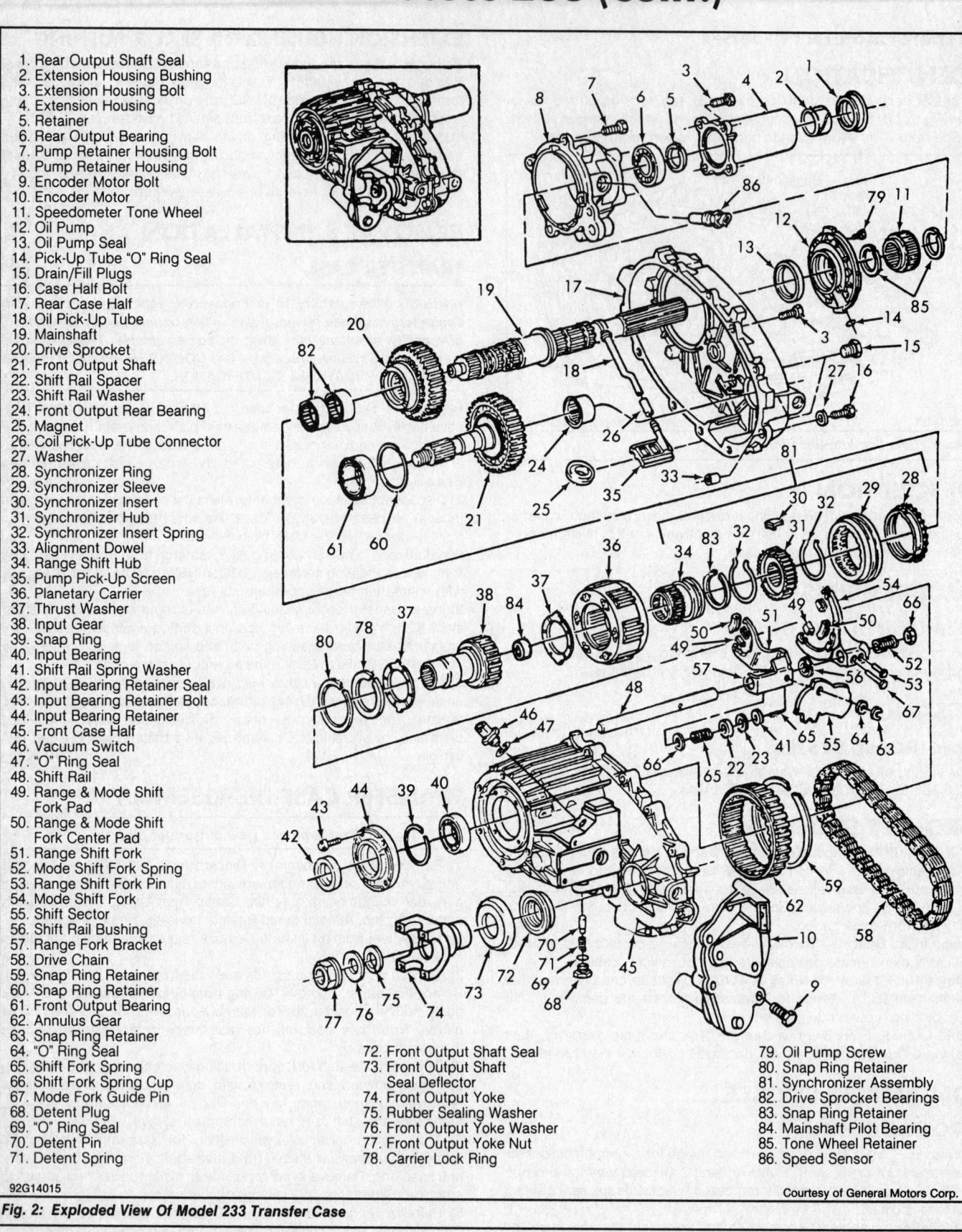

1. Rear Output Shaft Seal
2. Extension Housing Bushing
3. Extension Housing Bolt
4. Extension Housing
5. Retainer
6. Rear Output Bearing
7. Pump Retainer Housing Bolt
8. Pump Retainer Housing
9. Encoder Motor Bolt
10. Encoder Motor
11. Speedometer Tone Wheel
12. Oil Pump
13. Oil Pump Seal
14. Pick-Up Tube "O" Ring Seal
15. Drain/Fill Plugs
16. Case Half Bolt
17. Rear Case Half
18. Oil Pick-Up Tube
19. Mainshaft
20. Drive Sprocket
21. Front Output Shaft
22. Shift Rail Spacer
23. Shift Rail Washer
24. Front Output Rear Bearing
25. Magnet
26. Coil Pick-Up Tube Connector
27. Washer
28. Synchronizer Ring
29. Synchronizer Sleeve
30. Synchronizer Insert
31. Synchronizer Hub
32. Synchronizer Insert Spring
33. Alignment Dowel
34. Range Shift Hub
35. Pump Pick-Up Screen
36. Planetary Carrier
37. Thrust Washer
38. Input Gear
39. Snap Ring
40. Input Bearing
41. Shift Rail Spring Washer
42. Input Bearing Retainer Seal
43. Input Bearing Retainer Bolt
44. Input Bearing Retainer
45. Front Case Half
46. Vacuum Switch
47. "O" Ring Seal
48. Shift Rail
49. Range & Mode Shift
   Fork Pad
50. Range & Mode Shift
   Fork Center Pad
51. Range Shift Fork
52. Mode Shift Fork Spring
53. Range Shift Fork Pin
54. Mode Shift Fork
55. Shift Sector
56. Shift Rail Bushing
57. Range Fork Bracket
58. Drive Chain
59. Snap Ring Retainer
60. Snap Ring Retainer
61. Front Output Bearing
62. Annulus Gear
63. Snap Ring Retainer
64. "O" Ring Seal
65. Shift Fork Spring
66. Shift Fork Spring Cup
67. Mode Fork Guide Pin
68. Detent Plug
69. "O" Ring Seal
70. Detent Pin
71. Detent Spring

72. Front Output Shaft Seal
73. Front Output Shaft
   Seal Deflector
74. Front Output Yoke
75. Rubber Sealing Washer
76. Front Output Yoke Washer
77. Front Output Yoke Nut
78. Carrier Lock Ring

79. Oil Pump Screw
80. Snap Ring Retainer
81. Synchronizer Assembly
82. Drive Sprocket Bearings
83. Snap Ring Retainer
84. Mainshaft Pilot Bearing
85. Tone Wheel Retainer
86. Speed Sensor

92G14015

Courtesy of General Motors Corp.

Fig. 2: Exploded View Of Model 233 Transfer Case

6) Press input gear and planetary carrier assembly from annulus gear. Remove planetary carrier snap ring. Remove input gear snap ring, thrust washers and input gear from planetary carrier.

7) Remove all oil seals. Remove magnet from front case. Remove front bearing snap ring. Using a plastic hammer, remove front bearing. Press input gear bearing from front case.

8) Using slide hammer and internal puller, remove input gear pilot bearing. Press bearings from drive sprocket. Using internal puller and slide hammer, remove output shaft rear bearing.

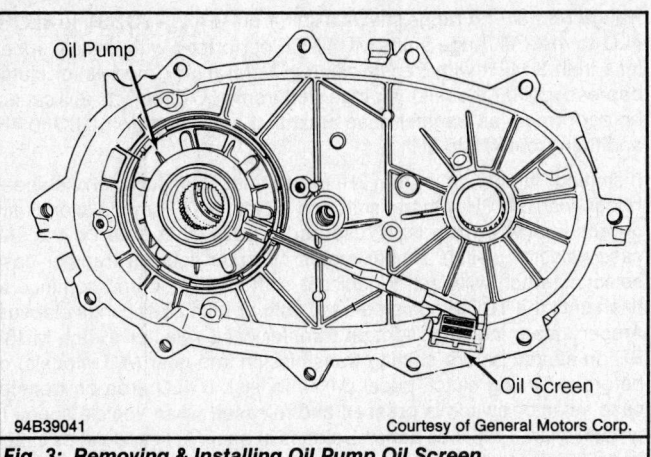

94B39041   Courtesy of General Motors Corp.

Fig. 3: Removing & Installing Oil Pump Oil Screen

CLEANING & INSPECTION

Clean all parts with solvent. Dry all parts with compressed air, except bearings. Bearings must be wiped dry or allowed to air dry. Replace all oil seals, "O" rings and snap rings. Check all parts for wear or damage. Replace all worn or damaged parts. If annulus gear, inside front case, is damaged or worn, front case and gear must be replaced as an assembly. Replace oil pump as an assembly if any part is damaged or worn.

TRANSFER CASE REASSEMBLY

NOTE: See Fig. 2 for exploded view of transfer case. When installing bearings, ensure bearing bores are aligned with oil feed holes.

1) Lubricate all parts with Dexron-II before installing. Install output shaft front bearing with NEW snap ring. Install output shaft oil seal in front case. Install snap ring on NEW input gear bearing.
2) Press input gear bearing so snap ring is seated against case. Using press, install NEW input gear pilot bearing. Assemble planetary carrier, input gear, thrust washers and lock ring.
3) Install snap ring. Ensure snap ring is seated in annulus gear groove. Start input gear shaft into bearing in front case. Press input shaft gear into bearing.

CAUTION: DO NOT press against end surfaces of gear. Failure to use proper size tool could lead to gear case or thrust washer damage.

4) Install input gear snap ring. Install oil seal in front bearing retainer. Apply a 1/8" bead of silicone sealant to retainer mating surface and install on case. Tighten bolts to specification. See TORQUE SPECIFICATIONS.
5) Install sector shaft "O" ring and bushing. Install range sector in case. Install detent, detent spring and plug. Tighten to specification. Install NEW pads and fork rail bushings on range fork. Install range fork and shift hub.
6) Ensure range fork pin is engaged with range sector slot. Press bearings into drive sprocket until bearings are flush with bore edge.
7) Install inserts and spring in synchronizer hub. Install sprocket on mainshaft. Install synchronizer ring on mainshaft. Ensure synchronizer ring is seated. Install synchronizer hub on mainshaft. Align and seat hub inserts on synchronizer ring lugs. Install synchronizer hub snap ring.
8) Install synchronizer sleeve on hub. *See Fig. 4.* Ensure sleeve is positioned so beveled spline ends are facing synchronizer ring. Install NEW pads on mode fork. Engage mode fork in synchronizer sleeve. Install mainshaft and fork assembly in case. Ensure mode fork shift rail is seated in both range fork bushings.
9) Install output shaft and drive chain assembly. *See Fig. 5.* Install mode shift fork spring on shift rail. Using bearing driver, install output shaft rear bearing. Lubricate bearing after installation. Install seal in oil pump feed housing. Assemble oil pump and install in housing. Tighten to specification.

10) Install oil pick-up tube "O" ring in oil pump. Install oil pump and pick-up tube in case. Ensure screen is properly positioned. *See Fig. 3.* Install magnet in front case. Apply 1/8" bead of silicone sealer to front case.
11) Install rear case and tighten bolts to specification. See TORQUE SPECIFICATIONS. Ensure mainshaft splines are engaged with oil pump inner gear and a washer is used on bolts at dowel locations. Install rear bearings in retainer. Apply 1/8" bead of silicone sealer and install retainer to case. Install rear retainer snap ring.
12) Install oil seal in extension housing. Install extension housing. Install encoder motor, vacuum switch and speed sensor. Install front companion yoke. Install NEW gasket on vacuum switch. Install vacuum switch in case. Fill transfer case with Dexron-II.

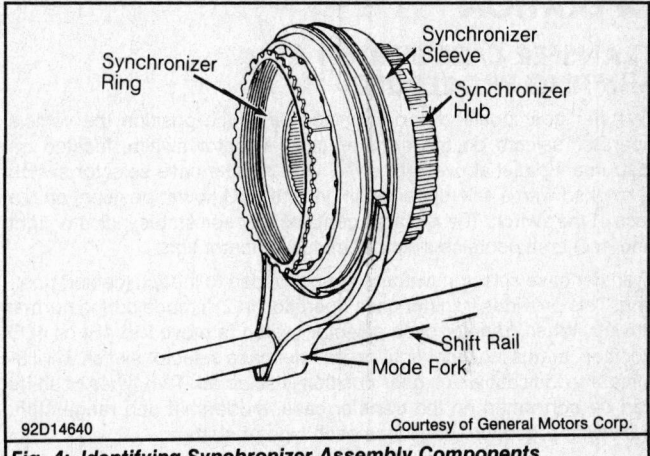

92D14640   Courtesy of General Motors Corp.

Fig. 4: Identifying Synchronizer Assembly Components

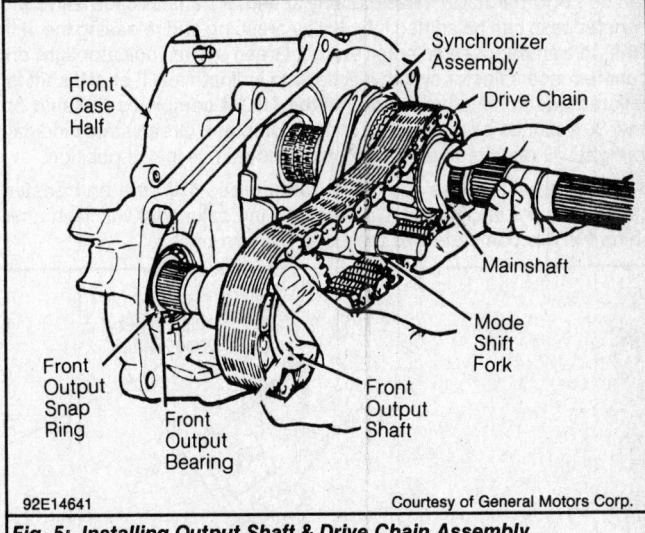

92E14641   Courtesy of General Motors Corp.

Fig. 5: Installing Output Shaft & Drive Chain Assembly

TORQUE SPECIFICATIONS
TORQUE SPECIFICATIONS

Application	Ft. Lbs. (N.m)
Detent Plug	11 (15)
Drain & Fill Plug	35 (47)
Extension Housing Bolt	23 (31)
Front & Rear Bearing Retainer Bolt	14 (19)
Front Case-To-Rear Case Bolts	23 (31)
Oil Pump Housing Screw	23 (31)
Output Yoke Nut	110 (152)
Range Lever Nut	23 (31)
Shift Motor Bolts	13 (18)
Transfer Case-To-Transmission Nuts	26 (35)
Vacuum Switch	15-25 (20-34)
Vehicle Speed Sensor	23 (31)

TRANSFER CASES
New Process 233 Electronic Controls

General Motors: "T" Series
(1993 Pickup & 1993-94 Blazer & Jimmy)

NOTE: Information for 1994 Pickup not available.

DESCRIPTION

The New Process 233 transfer case shifting is electronically controlled by the Transfer Case Control Module (TCCM). The TCCM controls shift motor operation in response to various inputs signals. Shift motor is located on the transfer case and rotates the sector shaft to shift the transfer case.

OPERATION

TRANSFER CASE SWITCH & SHIFTING PROCEDURE

Transfer gear position is determined by which position the vehicle operator selects on the transfer case selector switch, located on instrument panel above light switches. Transfer case selector switch is marked with a 4HI (upper position) and 4LO (lower position) on the face of the switch. The 4HI area contains a Green status indicator light and 4LO area contains a Amber status indicator light.

Transfer case selector switch is spring-loaded to the 2HI (center) position. This provides transfer case operation in 2HI mode during normal driving. When transfer case selector switch is moved to 4HI or 4LO position, status indicator light on transfer case selector switch will illuminate to indicate which gear position is selected. Two types of shifts can be performed on the transfer case, mode shift and range shift. Following procedure describes each type of shift.

Mode Shifts – A mode shift is a shift from 2HI to 4HI or 4HI to 2HI and can be performed with vehicle at any speed. If transfer case is in 2HI, transfer case can be shifted into 4HI by pressing and releasing the 4HI area on transfer case selector switch. Green status indicator light on transfer case selector switch will flash to indicate a 2HI or 4HI shift is initiated and continue to flash until the TCCM completes the shift or until 30 seconds elapses. After shift is complete, Green status indicator light will remain on to indicate transfer case is in 4HI position.

If shifting transfer case from 4HI to 2HI, press 4HI area on transfer case selector switch again. Green status indicator light will flash until shift to 2HI is complete and then light will turn off.

Range Shifts – A range shift is a shift from 2HI to 4LO, 4HI to 4LO or 4LO to 4HI. All range shifts MUST BE performed with vehicle speed less than 3 MPH with transmission in Neutral (A/T models) or clutch depressed (M/T models). A range shift from 4LO directly to 2HI cannot be performed, as transfer case must first be shifted from 4LO to 4HI and then from 4HI to 2HI.

If shifting transfer case from 2HI or 4HI to 4LO, ensure vehicle speed is less than 3 MPH with transmission in Neutral (A/T models) or clutch depressed (M/T models). Press and release 4LO area on transfer case selector switch. Amber status indicator light on transfer case selector switch will flash to indicate shift is initiated and continue to flash until the TCCM completes the shift or until 30 seconds elapses. Amber status indicator light on transfer case selector switch MUST BE on steady before shifting transmission into gear (A/T models) or before releasing clutch pedal (M/T models). If 4LO area on transfer case selector switch is pressed and released when vehicle speed is greater than 3 MPH or transmission is in gear (A/T models) or clutch pedal is released (M/T models), Amber status indicator light on transfer case selector switch will flash for 30 seconds and the shift will not be completed.

If shifting transfer case from 4LO to 4HI, ensure vehicle speed is less than 3 MPH with transmission in Neutral (A/T models) or clutch depressed (M/T models). Press and release 4HI area on transfer case selector switch. Green status indicator light on transfer case selector switch will flash to indicate shift is initiated and continue to flash until the TCCM completes the shift. Green status indicator light on transfer case selector switch MUST BE on steady before shifting transmission into gear (A/T models) or before clutch pedal is released (M/T models). If 4HI area on transfer case selector switch is pressed and released when vehicle speed is greater than 3 MPH or transmission is shifted into gear (A/T models) or clutch pedal is released (M/T models), Green status indicator light on transfer case selector switch will flash for 30 seconds and the shift will not be completed.

TRANSFER CASE CONTROL MODULE (TCCM)

The TCCM controls shift motor operation for transfer case shifting. The TCCM is located behind passenger's side of instrument panel and contains a White 32-pin connector. *See Fig. 1.*

The TCCM uses input and output devices for controlling transfer case operation. See INPUT DEVICES and OUTPUT DEVICES for additional information on various controlling devices.

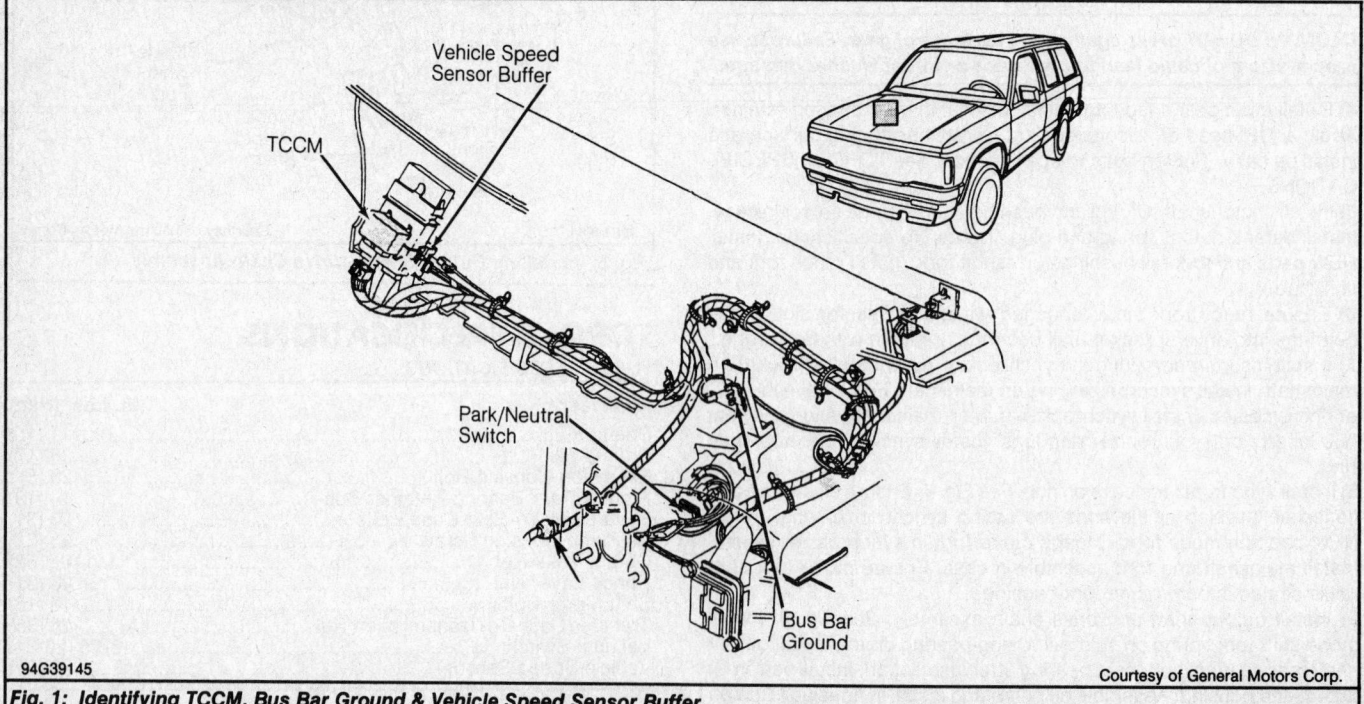

94G39145

Fig. 1: Identifying TCCM, Bus Bar Ground & Vehicle Speed Sensor Buffer

The TCCM memory receives constant battery voltage through the TCCM (5-amp) fuse in the fuse block, located near driver's side lower corner of instrument panel. The TCCM receives battery voltage from the ignition switch, through the RADIO (15-amp) fuse in the fuse block. The TCCM is grounded at the bus bar ground, located on steering column bracket. See Fig. 1.

Every time ignition is turned on, the TCCM checks the system for a failure or problem in the transfer case control system. If a failure or problem exists, the TCCM self-diagnostic system will store a Diagnostic Trouble Code (DTC) in the memory. Diagnostic trouble code can be retrieved for diagnosis of transfer case control system. See SYSTEM DIAGNOSIS under SELF-DIAGNOSTIC SYSTEM.

INPUT DEVICES

CLUTCH SWITCH (M/T MODELS)

NOTE: Clutch switch may be referred to as neutral start switch.

Clutch switch delivers an input signal to the TCCM indicating when clutch pedal is fully depressed or released. The TCCM uses input signal for controlling range shifts. When clutch pedal is released, clutch switch contacts open and a battery voltage signal is delivered to pin D16 on TCCM. The TCCM uses battery voltage signal to determine clutch pedal is released. When clutch pedal is depressed, clutch switch contacts close and low or no voltage is delivered to pin D16 on TCCM. The TCCM uses low or no voltage signal to determine clutch pedal is depressed. Clutch switch is located on bracket, near clutch pedal.

DATA LINK CONNECTOR

Data link connector can be used to provide an input signal to the TCCM to display the diagnostic trouble codes when proper terminals are grounded. Data link connector is located below instrument panel on the steering columns. See Fig. 3.

ENCODER SWITCH

NOTE: Encoder switch may be referred to as electric shift transfer case position switch.

Encoder switch is located internally in the shift motor mounted on transfer case. Encoder switch delivers an input signal to the TCCM, indicating current transfer case mode and range positions. TCCM reads the 4 channels of the encoder switch to determine range and mode in which transfer case is operating or if transfer case is shifting between modes and/or ranges.

Encoder switch consists of an inner ground ring in contact with a 3-contact wiper arm. Contacts on wiper arm are spaced 120° degrees apart. When any contact makes contact with conductive area of any channel, a path to ground is provided by the inner ground ring. This provides an input signal to the TCCM.

PARK/NEUTRAL SWITCH (A/T MODELS)

NOTE: Park/neutral switch may also be referred to as park/neutral position switch.

Park/neutral switch delivers an input signal to TCCM, indicating which gear position transmission is in. The TCCM uses input signal for controlling range shifts. Park/neutral switch is located on the steering column. See Fig. 1. Electrical connector must be properly installed on park/neutral switch. If electrical connector is installed in reversed position (up side down) on park/neutral switch, this would not provide a voltage supply to the park switch section of park/neutral switch. The TCCM would not receive voltage at pins D2 and D16, resulting in a range shift in park as well as neutral.

TRANSFER CASE SELECTOR SWITCH

Transfer case selector switch, located on instrument panel above light switches, provides input signals to TCCM to indicate which transfer case gear position is selected by the vehicle operator. The TCCM then operates the shift motor to obtain the correct gear selection.

VEHICLE SPEED SENSOR BUFFER

Vehicle speed sensor delivers a vehicle speed input signal to the TCCM. The TCCM uses input signal to prevent range shifts with vehicle speed greater than 3 MPH. Vehicle speed sensor buffer is located behind passenger's side of instrument panel. See Fig. 1.

OUTPUT DEVICES

SHIFT MOTOR

The TCCM provides an output signal to the shift motor, located on transfer case. Shift motor operation is obtained by energizing the 2 relays in the TCCM. TCCM operates shift motor in one direction by energizing one relay while de-energizing the other relay. To reverse shift motor operation, the relay operation is reversed.

STATUS INDICATOR LIGHTS

The TCCM controls operation of status indicator lights in transfer case selector switch to indicate transfer case mode and range operation. TCCM will also control status indicator lights to display diagnostic trouble codes.

SELF-DIAGNOSTIC SYSTEM

SYSTEM DIAGNOSIS

The TCCM monitors transfer case operation along with input and output information. If TCCM self-diagnostic system senses a failure or problem in the transfer case control system, a Diagnostic Trouble Code (DTC) will be stored in TCCM memory. Diagnostic trouble code can be retrieved for diagnosis of transfer case control system.

DIAGNOSTIC PROCEDURE

When performing transfer case diagnosis, perform the following:
- Start by performing functional test. See FUNCTIONAL TEST under TROUBLE SHOOTING CHARTS.
- Proceed to appropriate chart as instructed from functional test. If instructed to read diagnostic trouble codes, see RETRIEVING DIAGNOSTIC TROUBLE CODES under SELF-DIAGNOSTIC SYSTEM. It may be necessary to verify TCCM terminals and circuit numbers when diagnosing the system. See Fig. 2.
- Proceed to appropriate diagnostic trouble code chart as instructed. See TROUBLE SHOOTING CHARTS.
- Perform repair procedures to correct diagnostic trouble code.
- Clear diagnostic trouble code from TCCM memory. See CLEARING DIAGNOSTIC TROUBLE CODES under SELF-DIAGNOSTIC SYSTEM.

RETRIEVING DIAGNOSTIC TROUBLE CODES

1) Locate Data Link Connector (DLC) near right side of steering column. See Fig. 3. Install jumper wire between terminals "A" and "J" of data link connector. See Fig. 4.

NOTE: Jumper wire can also be installed between terminal "J" and proper body ground for retrieving diagnostic trouble codes.

2) Turn ignition on. Wait approximately 3 seconds and note operation of status indicator lights on transfer case selector switch.
3) Status indicator lights on transfer case selector switch will flash to indicate a stored diagnostic trouble code. If only one diagnostic trouble code exists, status indicator lights will flash repeatedly with approximately a 3 second delay between the displays. See Fig. 4.

CIRCUIT NO.	WIRE SIZE	COLOR	CAVITY	DESCRIPTION
1694	.8	GRA/BLK 1	C1	PCM
			C2	NOT USED
1559	.5	DK GRN/WHT 2	C3	4 LO REQUEST
			C4	NOT USED
1564	.5	GRA/BLK	C5	2HI/4HI REQUEST
140	.8	ORN/BLK 3	C6	12V BATTERY
			C7	NOT USED
141	.8	BRN/WHT	C8	12V IGNITION
1554	.5	BLK/WHT 4	C9	ENCODER SIGNAL GROUND
150	.8	BLK	C10	POWER GROUND
			C11	NOT USED
1566	.5	TAN/BLK	C12	4 HI STATUS LAMP
			C13	NOT USED
1565	.5	PPL/WHT	C14	4 LO STATUS LAMP
			C15	NOT USED
1552	2.0	BLK	C16	MOTOR CONTROL A
1553	2.0	RED	D1	MOTOR CONTROL B
1569	.5	DK GRN	D2	PARK SWITCH (AUTO TRANS)
1568	.5	ORN	D3	DATA LINK CONNECTOR
1555	.5	BRN/WHT	D4	ENCODER CHANNEL P
1556	.5	RED/WHT	D5	ENCODER CHANNEL C
1557	.5	DK BLU/WHT	D6	VEHICLE SPEED SENSOR
1558	.5	YEL/BLK	D7	ENCODER CHANNEL B
1567	.5	BRN	D8	ENCODER CHANNEL A
			D9	NOT USED
			D10	NOT USED
			D11	NOT USED
150	1	BLK	D12	MOTOR GROUND
150	1	BLK	D13	MOTOR GROUND
60	1	ORN 1	D14	12V MOTOR SUPPLY
60	1	ORN 1	D15	12V MOTOR SUPPLY
434	.5	ORN/BLK	D16	PARK/NEUTRAL POSITION SWITCH (AUTO)
5	1	YEL	DI6	NEUTRAL/START SWITCH (MAN)

1 – May be ORG/BLK.
2 – May be DK BLU/WHT.
3 – May be ORG.
4 – May be BLK/YEL.

94B39157

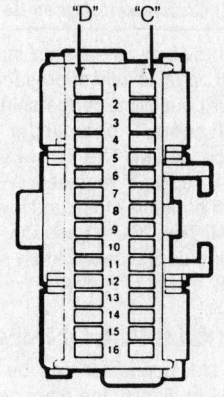

Courtesy of General Motors Corp.

Fig. 2: Identifying TCCM Terminals & Circuits

4) If more than one diagnostic trouble code exists, status indicator lights will flash the first diagnostic trouble code once, wait 3 seconds and then flash the next diagnostic trouble code. *See Fig. 4.* Diagnostic trouble code displays will continue until jumper wire is disconnected.
5) Using the diagnostic trouble code, determine the problem area of transfer case control system. See DIAGNOSTIC TROUBLE CODE IDENTIFICATION table.

DIAGNOSTIC TROUBLE CODE IDENTIFICATION

DTC Displayed	Problem Area
1	RAM Standby Power Lost
2	Encoder Fault
3	Shift Motor Circuit
4	RAM/ROM Failure

6) Once diagnostic trouble code is obtained, proceed to appropriate DTC chart under TROUBLE SHOOTING CHARTS. After repairs are performed, clear diagnostic trouble codes from the TCCM memory. See CLEARING DIAGNOSTIC TROUBLE CODES under SELF-DIAGNOSTIC SYSTEM.

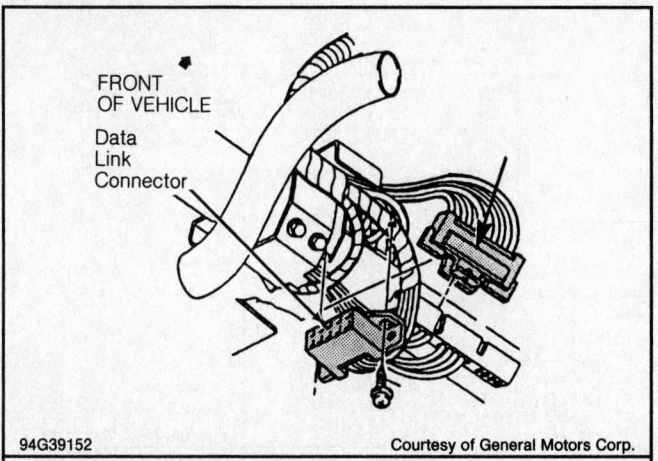

94G39152   Courtesy of General Motors Corp.

Fig. 3: Identifying Data Link Connector

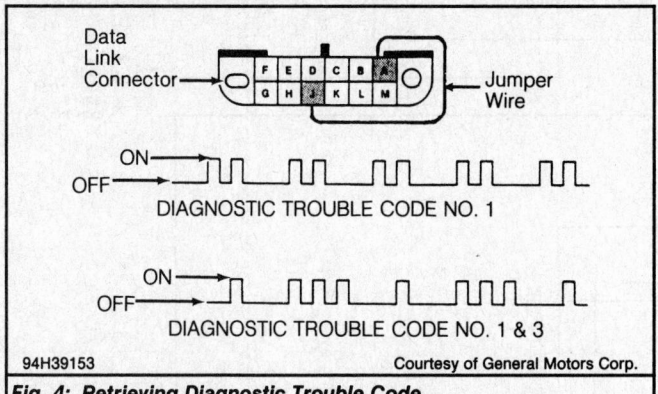

94H39153   Courtesy of General Motors Corp.

Fig. 4: Retrieving Diagnostic Trouble Code

CLEARING DIAGNOSTIC TROUBLE CODES

1) Turn ignition off. Remove jumper wire. Remove TCCM (5-amp) fuse from fuse block, located near driver's side lower corner of instrument panel.

2) Wait at least approximately 2 1/2 minutes and reinstall fuse. Fuse must be removed from fuse block for at least 2 1/2 minutes before diagnostic trouble code will cleared from TCCM memory. Cycle ignition on and off 5 times.

REMOVAL & INSTALLATION

CAUTION: When battery is disconnected, vehicle computer and memory systems may lose memory data. Driveability problems may exist until computer systems have completed a relearn cycle.

CLUTCH SWITCH

Removal & Installation – Remove panel located below instrument panel for access to clutch switch, located on bracket, near clutch pedal. Disconnect electrical connector from clutch switch. Remove clutch switch from bracket. To install, reverse removal procedure.

PARK/NEUTRAL SWITCH

Removal – Remove panel located below steering column. Disconnect electrical connector from park/neutral switch, located on the steering column. *See Fig. 1.* Pull park/neutral switch outward from steering column.

Installation – **1)** To install, apply parking brake. Place gearshift in Neutral. Align actuator on park/neutral switch with holes in shift tube on steering column. Press downward on front of park/neutral switch until tangs on the switch engage with rectangular holes on steering column.

2) To adjust park/neutral switch, place gearshift in Park. Main housing on park/neutral switch should ratchet, providing proper switch adjustment. Install electrical connector on park/neutral switch.

3) Ensure engine starts with gearshift in Park and Neutral to verify proper park/neutral switch adjustment. If park/neutral switch adjustment is required, readjust by moving housing on park/neutral switch toward the low gearshift position. Recheck park/neutral switch operation. Reinstall panel below steering column.

SHIFT MOTOR

Removal – **1)** Disconnect negative battery cable. Raise and support vehicle. Remove covers for access to transfer case. Disconnect electrical connector from shift motor, located on side of transfer case.

2) Remove front drive shaft. Remove yoke nut, washer, rubber washer and front drive shaft fork from transfer case. Remove shift motor-to-transfer case bolts. Remove shift motor.

Installation – **1)** Install shift motor. Install and tighten shift motor bolts to specification. See TORQUE SPECIFICATIONS. Install front drive shaft yoke, rubber washer, washer and yoke nut. Ensure rubber washer is installed between yoke and washer on front drive shaft yoke before installing the yoke nut.

2) Install and tighten yoke nut to specification. Install front drive shaft. Install and tighten front drive shaft flange-to-transfer case bolts to specification.

TRANSFER CASE SELECTOR SWITCH

Removal & Installation – **1)** Disconnect negative battery cable. Remove screws and trim panel, located on front side of transfer case selector switch. Disconnect electrical connector from transfer case selector switch.

2) Remove transfer case selector switch. To install, reverse removal procedure.

TRANSFER CASE CONTROL MODULE (TCCM)

Removal & Installation – **1)** Disconnect negative battery cable. The TCCM is located behind passenger's side of instrument panel and contains a White 32-pin connector. *See Fig. 1.*

2) Disconnect electrical connector from TCCM. Remove TCCM. To install, reverse removal procedure.

TORQUE SPECIFICATIONS

TORQUE SPECIFICATIONS

Application	Ft. Lbs. (N.m)
Front Drive Shaft Flange-To-Transfer Case Bolt	92 (125)
Shift Motor Bolt	13 (18)
Yoke Nut	150 (203)

TROUBLE SHOOTING CHARTS

NOTE: The following trouble shooting charts and illustrations are courtesy of General Motors Corp. It may be necessary to consult wiring diagram or verify TCCM terminals and circuit numbers when diagnosing the system. See WIRING DIAGRAMS or Fig. 2.

TRANSFER CASES
New Process 233 Electronic Controls (Cont.)

WIRING DIAGRAMS

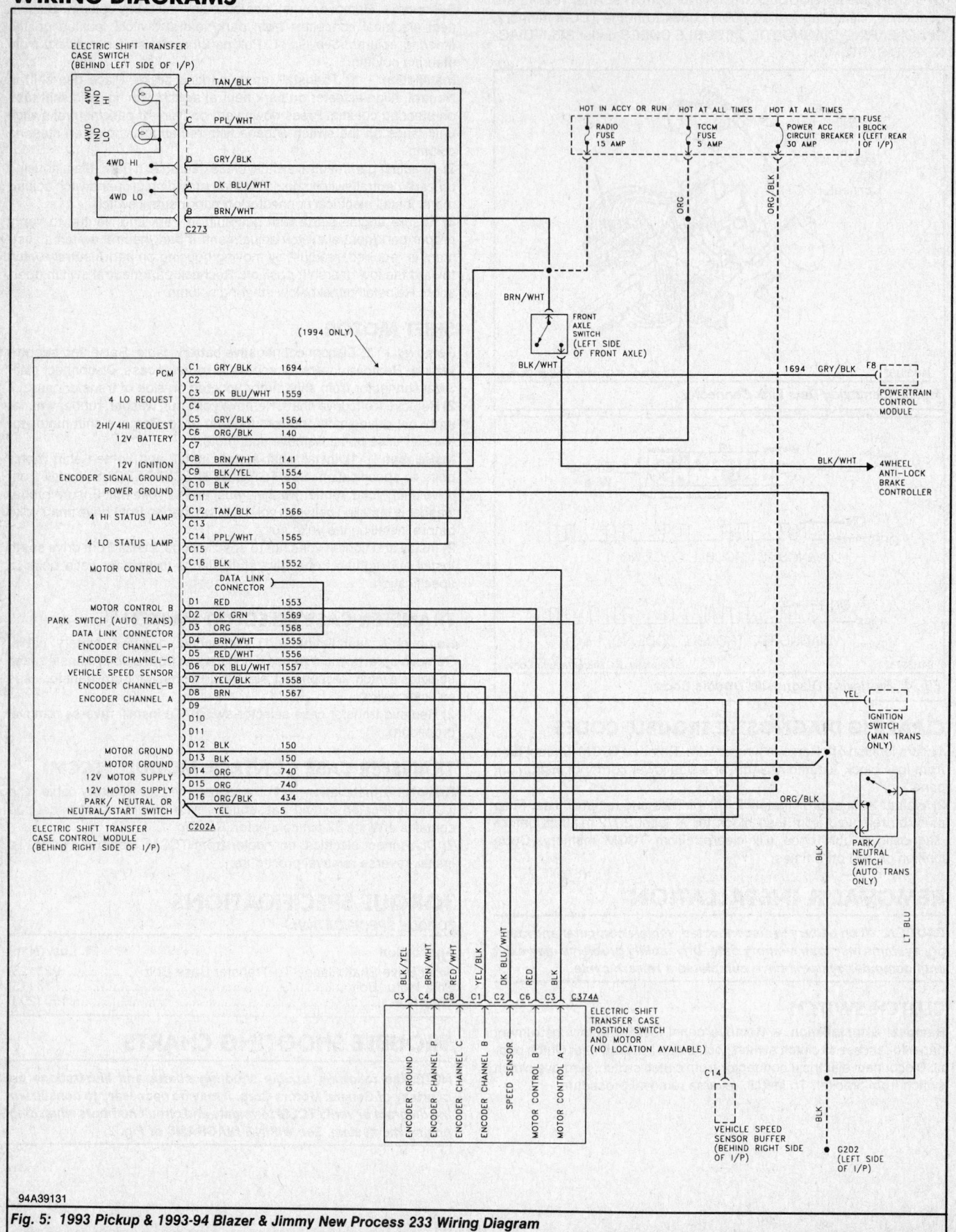

Fig. 5: 1993 Pickup & 1993-94 Blazer & Jimmy New Process 233 Wiring Diagram

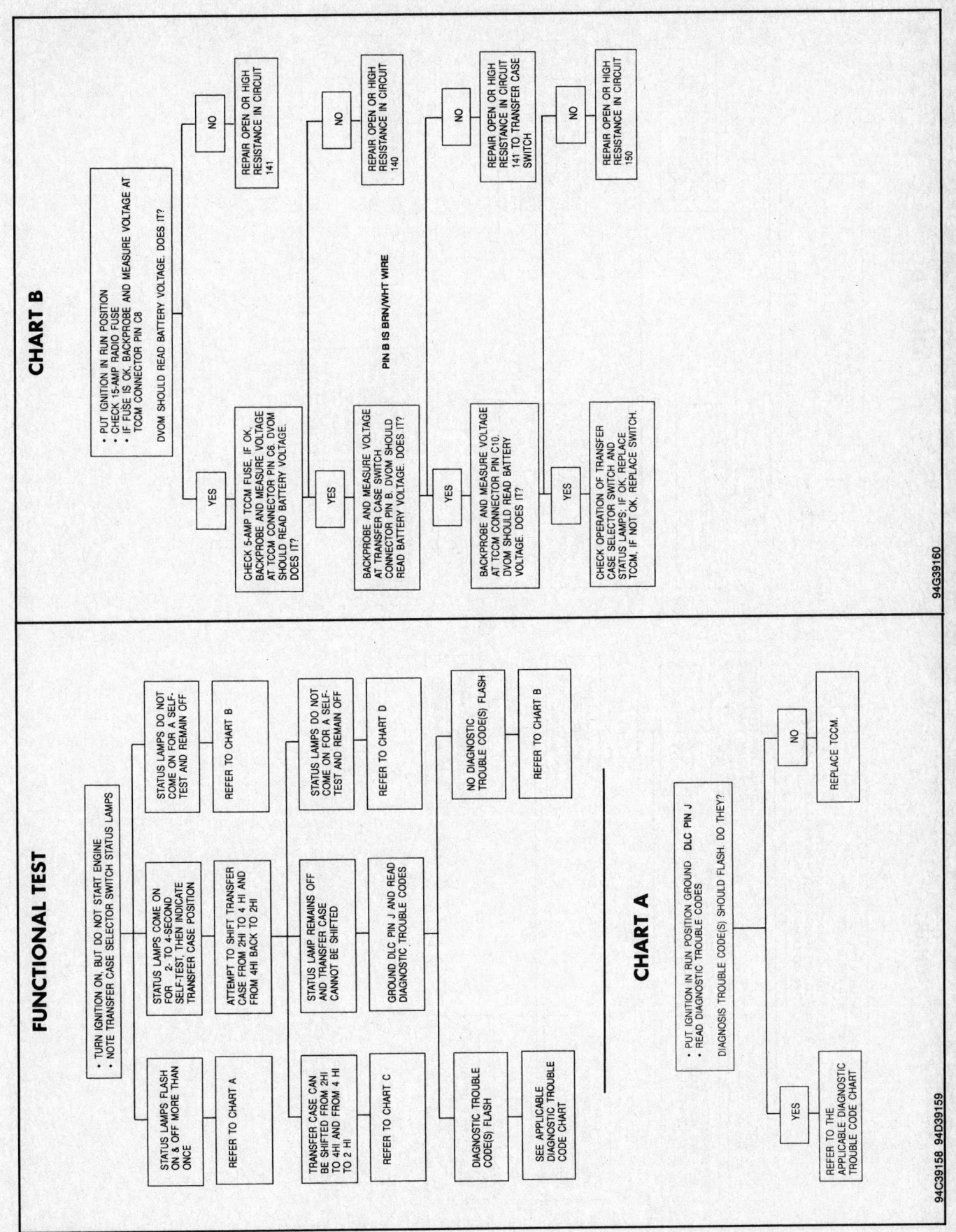

CHART B

- PUT IGNITION IN RUN POSITION
- CHECK 15-AMP RADIO FUSE
- IF FUSE IS OK, BACKPROBE AND MEASURE VOLTAGE AT TCCM CONNECTOR PIN C8

DVOM SHOULD READ BATTERY VOLTAGE. DOES IT?

YES → CHECK 5-AMP TCCM FUSE. IF OK, BACKPROBE AND MEASURE VOLTAGE AT TCCM CONNECTOR PIN C6. DVOM SHOULD READ BATTERY VOLTAGE. DOES IT?

NO → REPAIR OPEN OR HIGH RESISTANCE IN CIRCUIT 141

YES → BACKPROBE AND MEASURE VOLTAGE AT TRANSFER CASE SWITCH CONNECTOR PIN B. DVOM SHOULD READ BATTERY VOLTAGE. DOES IT?

NO → REPAIR OPEN OR HIGH RESISTANCE IN CIRCUIT 140

PIN B IS BRN/WHT WIRE

YES → BACKPROBE AND MEASURE VOLTAGE AT TCCM CONNECTOR PIN C10. DVOM SHOULD READ BATTERY VOLTAGE. DOES IT?

NO → REPAIR OPEN OR HIGH RESISTANCE IN CIRCUIT 141 TO TRANSFER CASE SWITCH

YES → CHECK OPERATION OF TRANSFER CASE SELECTOR SWITCH AND STATUS LAMPS: IF OK, REPLACE TCCM, IF NOT OK, REPLACE SWITCH.

NO → REPAIR OPEN OR HIGH RESISTANCE IN CIRCUIT 150

94G39160

FUNCTIONAL TEST

- TURN IGNITION ON, BUT DO NOT START ENGINE
- NOTE TRANSFER CASE SELECTOR SWITCH STATUS LAMPS

STATUS LAMPS FLASH ON & OFF MORE THAN ONCE → REFER TO CHART A

STATUS LAMPS COME ON FOR 2- TO 4-SECOND SELF-TEST, THEN INDICATE TRANSFER CASE POSITION

STATUS LAMPS DO NOT COME ON FOR A SELF-TEST AND REMAIN OFF → REFER TO CHART B

ATTEMPT TO SHIFT TRANSFER CASE FROM 2HI TO 4 HI AND FROM 4HI BACK TO 2HI

TRANSFER CASE CAN BE SHIFTED FROM 2HI TO 4HI AND FROM 4 HI TO 2 HI → REFER TO CHART C

STATUS LAMP REMAINS OFF AND TRANSFER CASE CANNOT BE SHIFTED

STATUS LAMPS DO NOT COME ON FOR A SELF-TEST AND REMAIN OFF → REFER TO CHART D

GROUND DLC PIN J AND READ DIAGNOSTIC TROUBLE CODES

DIAGNOSTIC TROUBLE CODE(S) FLASH → SEE APPLICABLE DIAGNOSTIC TROUBLE CODE CHART

NO DIAGNOSTIC TROUBLE CODE(S) FLASH → REFER TO CHART B

CHART A

- PUT IGNITION IN RUN POSITION GROUND DLC PIN J
- READ DIAGNOSTIC TROUBLE CODES

DIAGNOSIS TROUBLE CODE(S) SHOULD FLASH. DO THEY?

YES → REFER TO THE APPLICABLE DIAGNOSTIC TROUBLE CODE CHART

NO → REPLACE TCCM.

94C39158 94D39159

TRANSFER CASES
New Process 233 Electronic Controls (Cont.)

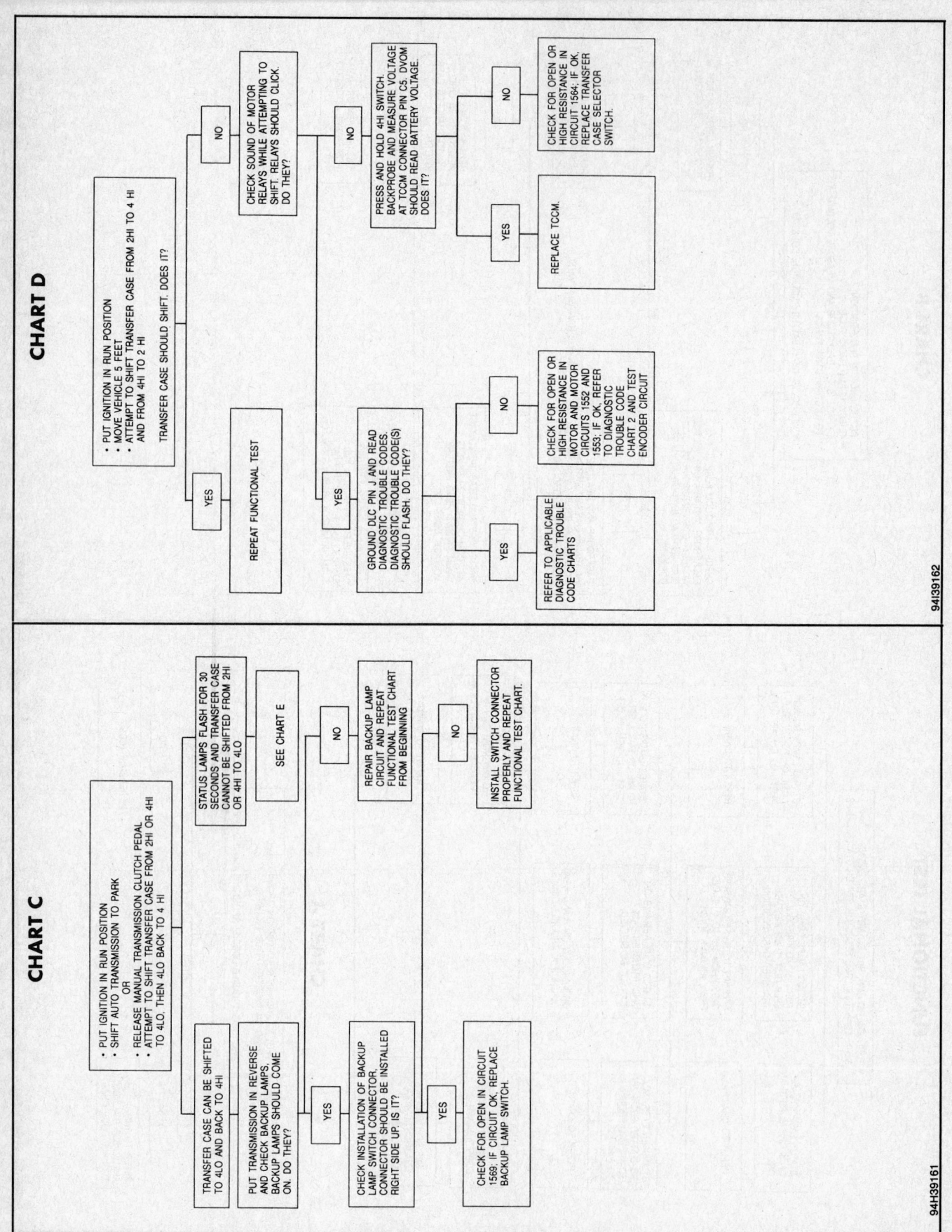

CHART D

- PUT IGNITION IN RUN POSITION
- MOVE VEHICLE 5 FEET
- ATTEMPT TO SHIFT TRANSFER CASE FROM 2HI TO 4 HI AND FROM 4HI TO 2 HI

TRANSFER CASE SHOULD SHIFT. DOES IT?

NO → CHECK SOUND OF MOTOR RELAYS WHILE ATTEMPTING TO SHIFT. RELAYS SHOULD CLICK. DO THEY?

NO → PRESS AND HOLD 4HI SWITCH. BACKPROBE AND MEASURE VOLTAGE AT TCCM CONNECTOR PIN C5. DVOM SHOULD READ BATTERY VOLTAGE. DOES IT?

NO → CHECK FOR OPEN OR HIGH RESISTANCE IN CIRCUIT 1564: IF OK. REPLACE TRANSFER CASE SELECTOR SWITCH.

YES → REPLACE TCCM.

YES → REPEAT FUNCTIONAL TEST

YES → GROUND DLC PIN J AND READ DIAGNOSTIC TROUBLE CODES. DIAGNOSTIC TROUBLE CODE(S) SHOULD FLASH. DO THEY?

NO → CHECK FOR OPEN OR HIGH RESISTANCE IN MOTOR AND MOTOR CIRCUITS 1552 AND 1553; IF OK. REFER TO DIAGNOSTIC TROUBLE CODE CHART 2 AND TEST ENCODER CIRCUIT

YES → REFER TO APPLICABLE DIAGNOSTIC TROUBLE CODE CHARTS

94J39162

CHART C

- PUT IGNITION IN RUN POSITION
- SHIFT AUTO TRANSMISSION TO PARK
  OR
- RELEASE MANUAL TRANSMISSION CLUTCH PEDAL
- ATTEMPT TO SHIFT TRANSFER CASE FROM 2HI OR 4HI TO 4LO, THEN 4LO BACK TO 4 HI

TRANSFER CASE CAN BE SHIFTED TO 4LO AND BACK TO 4HI

PUT TRANSMISSION IN REVERSE AND CHECK BACKUP LAMPS, BACKUP LAMPS SHOULD COME ON. DO THEY?

STATUS LAMPS FLASH FOR 30 SECONDS AND TRANSFER CASE CANNOT BE SHIFTED FROM 2HI OR 4HI TO 4LO

SEE CHART E

YES → CHECK INSTALLATION OF BACKUP LAMP SWITCH CONNECTOR. CONNECTOR SHOULD BE INSTALLED RIGHT SIDE UP. IS IT?

NO → REPAIR BACKUP LAMP CIRCUIT AND REPEAT FUNCTIONAL TEST CHART FROM BEGINNING

YES → CHECK FOR OPEN IN CIRCUIT 1569. IF CIRCUIT OK. REPLACE BACKUP LAMP SWITCH.

NO → INSTALL SWITCH CONNECTOR PROPERLY AND REPEAT FUNCTIONAL TEST CHART.

94H39161

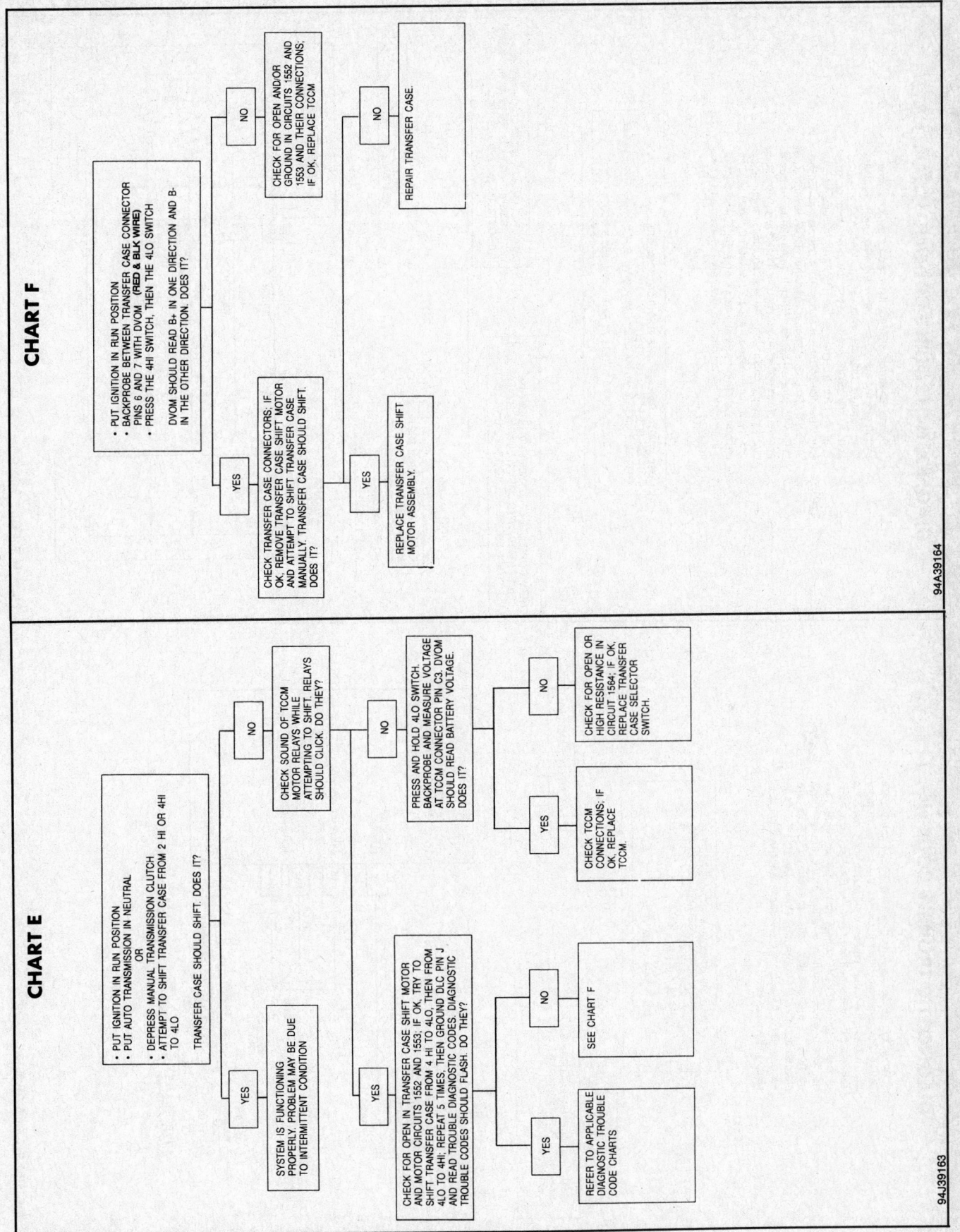

CHART F

- PUT IGNITION IN RUN POSITION
- BACKPROBE BETWEEN TRANSFER CASE CONNECTOR PINS 6 AND 7 WITH DVOM **(RED & BLK WIRE)**
- PRESS THE 4HI SWITCH, THEN THE 4LO SWITCH

DVOM SHOULD READ B+ IN ONE DIRECTION AND B- IN THE OTHER DIRECTION. DOES IT?

YES → CHECK TRANSFER CASE CONNECTORS; IF OK, REMOVE TRANSFER CASE SHIFT MOTOR AND ATTEMPT TO SHIFT TRANSFER CASE MANUALLY. TRANSFER CASE SHOULD SHIFT. DOES IT?

YES → REPLACE TRANSFER CASE SHIFT MOTOR ASSEMBLY.

NO → CHECK FOR OPEN AND/OR GROUND IN CIRCUITS 1552 AND 1553 AND THEIR CONNECTIONS; IF OK, REPLACE TCCM

NO → REPAIR TRANSFER CASE.

94J39164

CHART E

- PUT IGNITION IN RUN POSITION
- PUT AUTO TRANSMISSION IN NEUTRAL
  OR
- DEPRESS MANUAL TRANSMISSION CLUTCH
- ATTEMPT TO SHIFT TRANSFER CASE FROM 2 HI OR 4HI TO 4LO

TRANSFER CASE SHOULD SHIFT. DOES IT?

YES → SYSTEM IS FUNCTIONING PROPERLY. PROBLEM MAY BE DUE TO INTERMITTENT CONDITION

NO → CHECK SOUND OF TCCM MOTOR RELAYS WHILE ATTEMPTING TO SHIFT. RELAYS SHOULD CLICK. DO THEY?

YES → CHECK FOR OPEN IN TRANSFER CASE SHIFT MOTOR AND MOTOR CIRCUITS 1552 AND 1553; IF OK, TRY TO SHIFT TRANSFER CASE FROM 4 HI TO 4LO, THEN FROM 4LO TO 4HI; REPEAT 5 TIMES, THEN GROUND DLC PIN J AND READ TROUBLE DIAGNOSTIC CODES. DIAGNOSTIC TROUBLE CODES SHOULD FLASH. DO THEY?

YES → REFER TO APPLICABLE DIAGNOSTIC TROUBLE CODE CHARTS

NO → SEE CHART F

NO → PRESS AND HOLD 4LO SWITCH. BACKPROBE AND MEASURE VOLTAGE AT TCCM CONNECTOR PIN C3. DVOM SHOULD READ BATTERY VOLTAGE. DOES IT?

YES → CHECK TCCM CONNECTIONS; IF OK, REPLACE TCCM.

NO → CHECK FOR OPEN OR HIGH RESISTANCE IN CIRCUIT 1584; IF OK, REPLACE TRANSFER CASE SELECTOR SWITCH.

94J39163

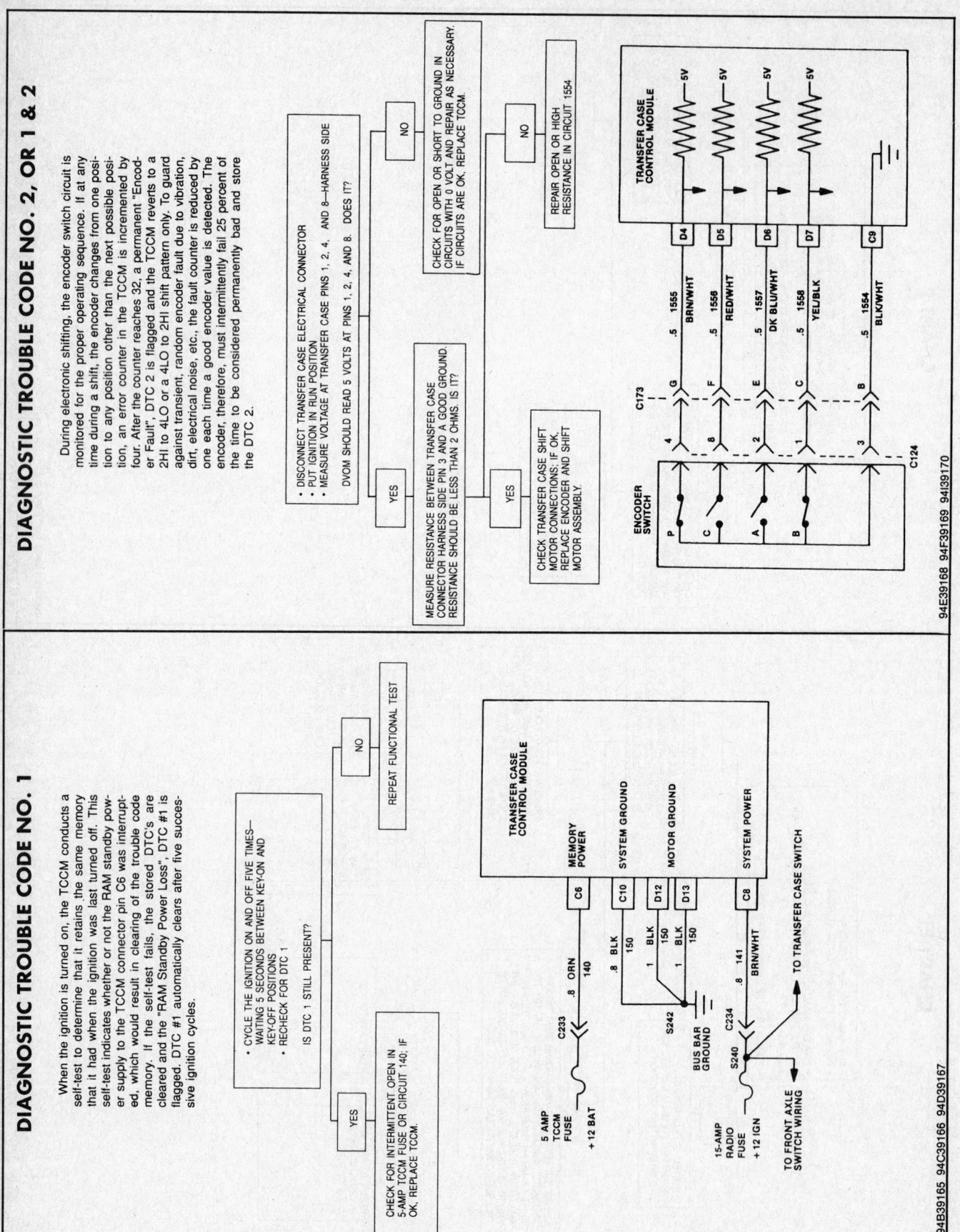

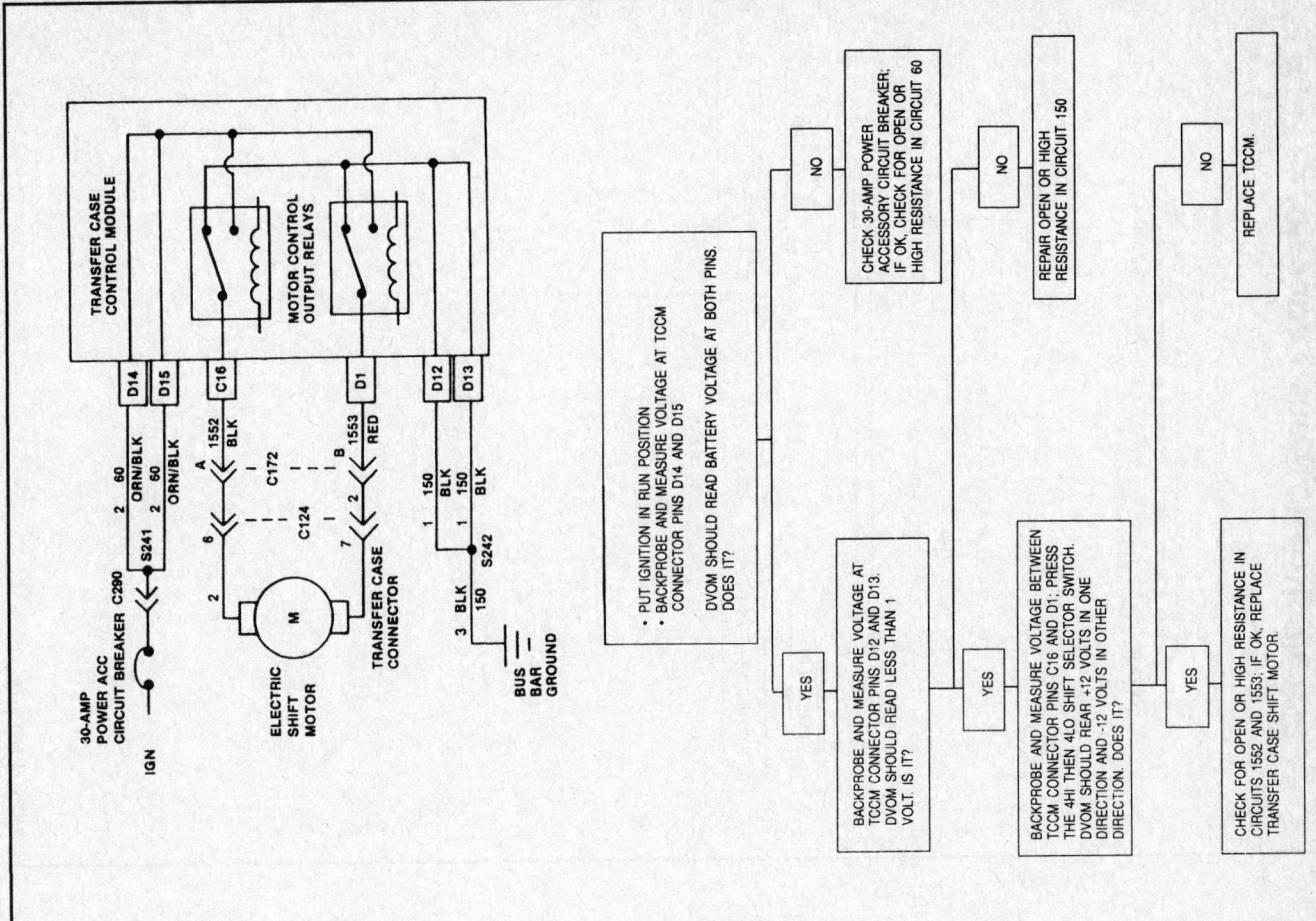

DIAGNOSTIC TROUBLE CODE NO. 3, OR 1 & 3

Each time the electric-shift motor is turned on or off, it and its electrical circuits are tested, both in the de-energized and energized conditions. If the motor circuits are not functioning properly, one of the following exists:

- An open or short circuit in one or more of the following:
  - Motor supply circuit 60
  - Motor ground circuit 150
  - Motor circuit 1552
  - Motor circuit 1553
  - Motor circuit connections
- A short and/or open within the motor itself
- A malfunctioning motor relay (not energizing or not de-energizing)

If one or both of the relays fail to detect the proper voltage after energizing, the shift is aborted and the fault counter counts in 4 part increments, when the fault counter reaches 16 increments the "TCCM Motor Circuit" DTC 3 is flagged. After the condition that caused the fault code to be flagged has been corrected, the fault code must be cleared by removing the 5-amp TCCM fuse for 2 minutes and 30 seconds.

If one or both relays fail to detect the proper voltage after de-energizing (condition 4), both relays are turned on even with the ignition turned off to prevent the motor from running. The TCCM then flags a "TCCM Motor Circuit" DTC 3, and flashes the status lamps to inform the vehicle driver that a condition that must be corrected immediately exists. This condition also causes the battery to drain when the ignition is off.

94J39171 94A39172 94B39173

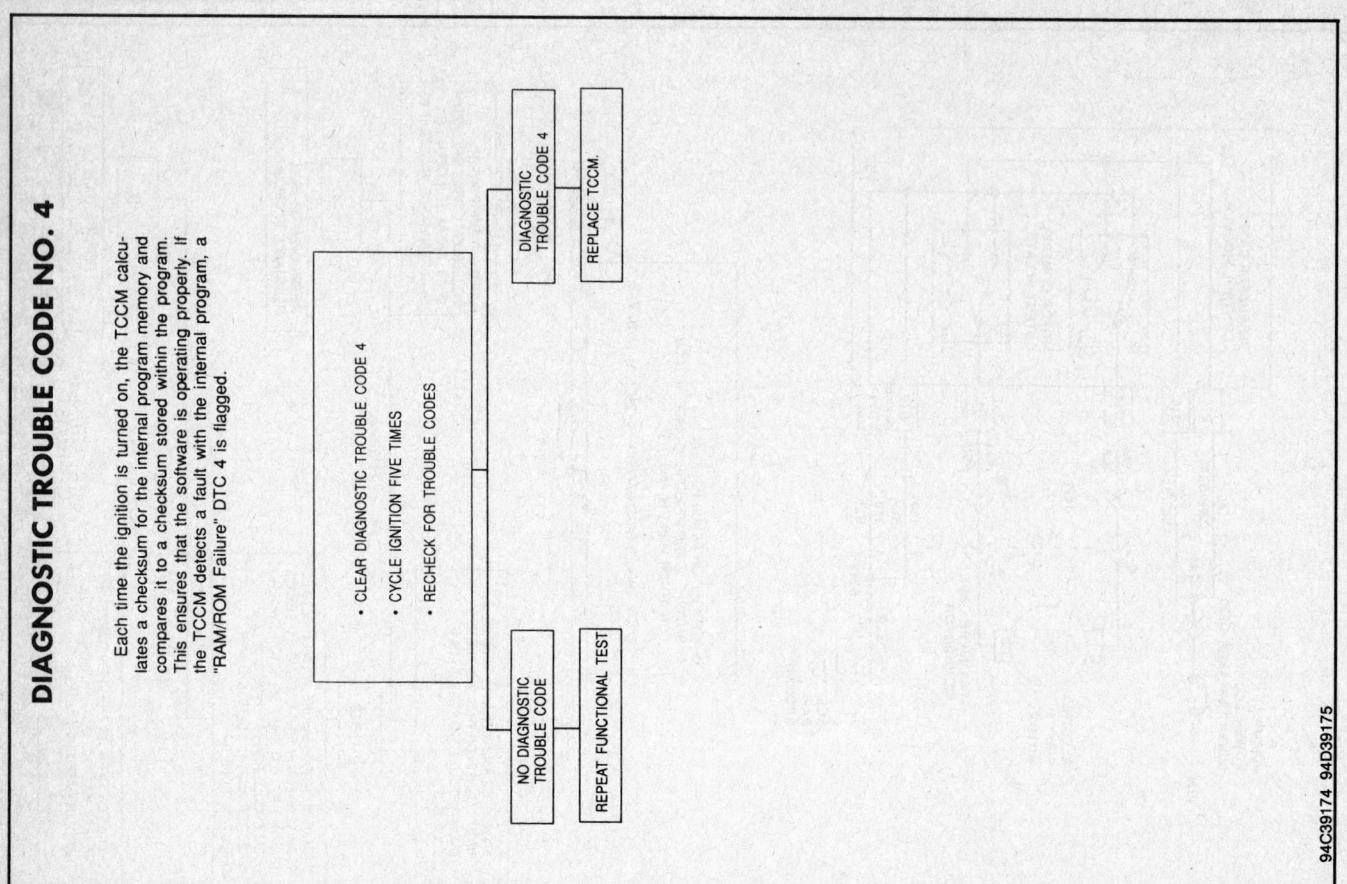

DIAGNOSTIC TROUBLE CODE NO. 4

Each time the ignition is turned on, the TCCM calculates a checksum for the internal program memory and compares it to a checksum stored within the program. This ensures that the software is operating properly. If the TCCM detects a fault with the internal program, a "RAM/ROM Failure" DTC 4 is flagged.

- CLEAR DIAGNOSTIC TROUBLE CODE 4
- CYCLE IGNITION FIVE TIMES
- RECHECK FOR TROUBLE CODES

NO DIAGNOSTIC TROUBLE CODE

REPEAT FUNCTIONAL TEST

DIAGNOSTIC TROUBLE CODE 4

REPLACE TCCM.

94C39174 94D39175

APPLICATION

MODEL APPLICATION

Model Year	Application
1993-94	Dodge "BR" Series
1993-94	GM "K" Series (Under 9200 Lbs GVW)
1993-94	Suburban & Yukon

IDENTIFICATION

Transfer case can be identified by an I.D. tag, located on rear case. I.D. tag provides model number, serial number and low range ratio. Date of manufacture is the serial number (I.D. number). This information is necessary when ordering parts.

DESCRIPTION

Model 241 transfer case is a part time, chain-driven, 4-position unit with 2-piece aluminum case. Torque input in 4WD high and low range is undifferentiated.

ADJUSTMENTS

GEARSHIFT LINKAGE

Remove shifter boot. Place shift lever in 4H position. Raise vehicle and remove linkage from shift lever. Move transfer case shift lever fully forward. Adjust shift linkage with swivel to align with shift lever. Reattach linkage and lower vehicle.

TROUBLE SHOOTING

Will Not Shift Or Difficult To Shift Into Gear – Vehicle speed too high; slow vehicle to 2-3 MPH to shift. Vehicle operated too long on dry paved surface; stop vehicle and place in Reverse or Neutral to relieve driveline torque. Ensure transfer case external linkage is not binding. Ensure correct fluid is used. Worn or damaged internal parts.

Noisy In All Gears – Check fluid level. Ensure correct fluid is used. If fluid is okay, locate noise and check for possible internal mechanical problem.

Jumps Out Of Gear Or Noisy In 4WD – Transfer case not completely in gear; check shift linkage. Engine or transmission mounts loose. Range fork damaged. Fork pads are worn. Shift fork binding on shift rail. Low range gear worn or damaged.

Fluid Leaking From Vent Or Seals – Transfer case overfilled. Vent plugged. Output shaft seals are damaged or not installed properly.

ON-VEHICLE SERVICE

OUTPUT SHAFT SEALS REPLACEMENT

Removal & Installation – **1)** Mark propeller shafts and flanges for alignment purposes during installation. Remove front or rear propeller shaft. Remove flange. Discard nut and washers. Using a screwdriver, carefully remove oil seal. Ensure seal contact surface is clean.

2) Apply ATF to seal lip and flange seal surface. Install oil seal and flange with new washer and nut. Install front and rear propeller shafts using alignment marks. Check transfer case fluid.

REMOVAL & INSTALLATION

TRANSFER CASE

Removal – **1)** Shift transfer case into 4H and disconnect battery negative cable. Raise vehicle and drain fluid. Remove cotter pin from shift lever swivel. Mark transfer case front and rear output shaft flanges and propeller shafts for assembly alignment reference. Remove shafts.

2) Disconnect speedometer cable, indicator switch wires, vacuum (hoses) harness at transfer case and speed sensor wire (if equipped). On General Motors automatic transmission models, remove engine strut rod from transfer case (if equipped).

3) On all models, remove skid plate. Support transfer case and remove rear crossmember. Remove transfer case-to-transmission adapter bolts. Move transfer case assembly rearward until free of transmission output shaft and remove assembly. Remove all gasket material from rear of transmission adapter housing.

Installation – To install, reverse removal procedure. Install new gasket and tighten bolts to specification. See TORQUE SPECIFICATIONS.

TRANSFER CASE DISASSEMBLY

1) Remove front companion flange, nut and washer. Remove 4WD indicator switch. Remove speedometer sensor. Remove poppet screw, spring and range selection plunger. *See Fig. 1.*

2) Remove rear extension housing. Remove rear bearing retainer housing from mainshaft. Remove snap ring and bearing from housing. Remove speedometer gear snap ring and gear from mainshaft. Remove oil pump. Separate rear case from front case. Remove oil pump pick-up tube, filter and magnetic washer. Remove mode fork spring.

3) Remove snap ring from driven sprocket. Remove mainshaft, drive chain and driven sprocket as a unit from front case. Mode fork and shift rail will come out with mainshaft. Remove synchronizer retaining snap ring. Remove synchronizer assembly and drive sprocket from mainshaft. Remove drive sprocket needle bearing.

NOTE: It is NOT necessary to disassemble synchronizer assembly unless wear or damage is visible.

---

4) Remove synchronizer stop ring and insert springs. Separate synchronizer sleeve from synchronizer hub. Ensure synchronizer inserts are not lost when synchronizer sleeve is removed. Remove range fork, range sector, mode fork and range shift hub. Remove range shift lever, washer and nut.

5) Remove input bearing retainer bolts and retainer. Remove retainer oil seal. Remove input gear lock ring. Remove planetary assembly and input gear. Remove input gear snap ring, carrier lock ring, thrust washer and bearing.

6) Remove mainshaft pilot bearing from input gear. Remove front output bearing snap ring and bearing. Remove front output shaft oil seal. Remove oil seal from extension housing. Remove rear case needle bearing.

CLEANING & INSPECTION

Clean all parts with solvent. Blow out all oil ports with compressed air. Replace all oil seals, "O" rings and snap rings. Check all parts for wear or damage. Replace oil pump as an assembly if any part is damaged or worn.

TRANSFER CASE REASSEMBLY

NOTE: When installing bearings, ensure bearing bores are aligned with oil feed holes.

---

1) Lubricate all internal parts with Dexron II ATF or equivalent. Install needle bearing into drive sprocket and rear case. Ensure drive sprocket bearing is flush on synchronizer side. Install input gear bearing. *See Fig. 1.*

2) Install bearing in front case and oil pump. Install mainshaft pilot bearing in input shaft. Install thrust washer and carrier lock ring on input gear. Install input gear bearing and snap ring. Install input gear, bearing and planetary assembly in annulus gear. Install input gear lock ring.

3) Install extension housing oil seal. Install front case oil seal. Apply bead of silicone sealer to input shaft bearing retainer mating surface. Install input shaft bearing retainer and oil seal. Apply Loctite to bearing retainer bolt threads before installing. Tighten to specification. See TORQUE SPECIFICATIONS. Install range shift hub, mode fork, range selector and range fork. Install shift lever, washer and nut.

4) Install synchronizer insert springs on synchronizer hub. Install synchronizer inserts on synchronizer hub and slide synchronizer sleeve over assembly. Install synchronizer stop ring on synchronizer sleeve.

TRANSFER CASES
New Process 241 (Cont.)

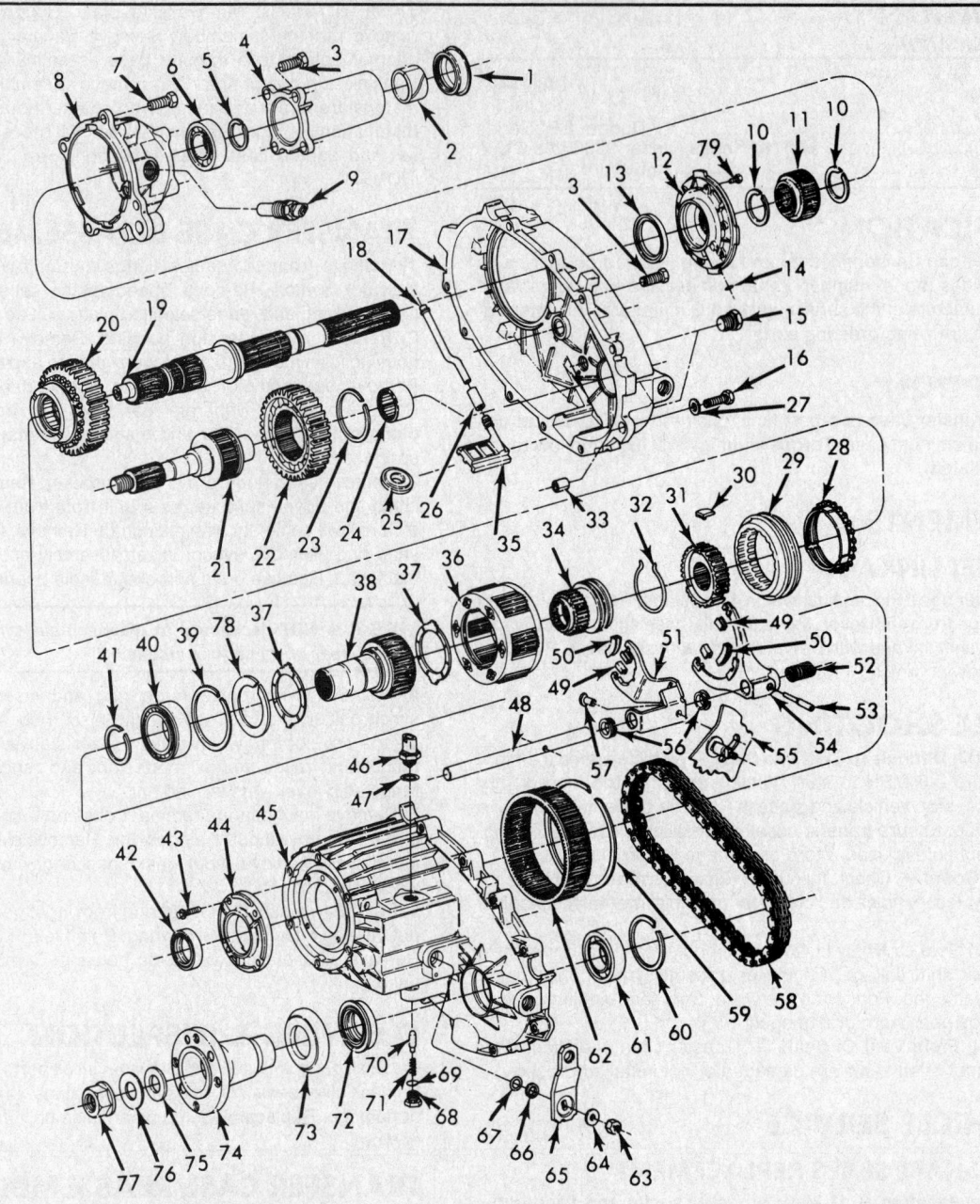

1. Oil Seal	21. Front Output Shaft	41. Snap Ring	61. Front Output Shaft Bearing
2. Extension Housing Bushing	22. Driven Sprocket	42. Oil Seal	62. Annulus Gear
3. Bolt	23. Snap Ring	43. Screw	63. Nut
4. Extension Housing	24. Front Output Shaft Rear Bearing	44. Input Bearing Retainer	64. Washer
5. Snap Ring	25. Magnetic Washer	45. Front Case	65. Lever
6. Output Shaft Bearing	26. Connector	46. 4WD Indicator Switch	66. Retainer
7. Bolt	27. Washer	47. Seal	67. Oil Seal
8. Rear Bearing Retainer Housing	28. Synchronizer Stop Ring	48. Shift Rail	68. Plug
9. Speedometer Sensor	29. Synchronizer Sleeve	49. Mode Shift Fork Pad	69. "O" Ring
10. Snap Ring	30. Synchronizer Insert	50. Range Shift Fork Pad	70. Poppet Plunger
11. Speedometer Gear	31. Synchronizer Hub	51. Range Fork	71. Poppet Spring
12. Oil Pump	32. Synchronizer Insert Spring	52. Mode Fork Spring	72. Oil Seal
13. Oil Pump Seal	33. Dowel	53. Fork Pin	73. Oil Deflector
14. "O" Ring	34. Range Shift Hub	54. Mode Fork	74. Companion Flange
15. Fill Plug	35. Screen	55. Range Sector	75. Washer
16. Bolt	36. Planet Carrier	56. Bushing	76. Washer
17. Rear Case	37. Input Gear Thrust Washer	57. Range Fork Pin	77. Nut
18. Oil Pick-Up Tube	38. Input Gear	58. Drive Chain	78. Carrier Lock Ring
19. Mainshaft	39. Lock Ring	59. Planetary Gear Retaining Ring	79. Screw
20. Drive Sprocket	40. Input Gear Bearing	60. Snap Ring	

92J13085

Fig. 1: Exploded View Of Model 241 Transfer Case

5) Install drive sprocket on mainshaft. Install synchronizer assembly on mainshaft. Install sector with shaft, range shift lever, washer and nut. Tighten to specification. Install range fork and range shift hub.

6) Install front output shaft. Install mainshaft, drive chain and driven sprocket as a unit in front case. Install driven sprocket snap ring. Install mode shift fork and pin on shift rail. Install mode shift fork assembly through range shift fork onto synchronizer sleeve. Install mode fork spring.

7) Install oil pick-up tube, screen and magnetic washer to rear case. Apply silicone sealant to oil pump housing mating surface. Install oil pump with new "O" ring. Apply bead of silicone sealer to case mating surfaces. Install rear case on front case. Install bolts and tighten to specification. See TORQUE SPECIFICATIONS. Install snap ring, speedometer gear and snap ring onto mainshaft.

8) Install rear bearing retainer housing. Apply Loctite to rear bearing retainer bolt threads before installing. Install snap ring on mainshaft above rear bearing. Apply silicone sealant to extension housing mating surface. Install extension housing. Apply Loctite to extension housing bolt threads before installing and tighten bolts to specification.

9) Install range selector plunger, spring and poppet screw. Install speedometer sensor. Install indicator switch. Install front companion flange, washer and nut. Tighten nut to specification.

TORQUE SPECIFICATIONS

TORQUE SPECIFICATIONS

Application	Ft. Lbs. (N.m)
Case Half Bolts	23 (31)
Extension Housing Bolt	
Chrysler	32 (43)
General Motors	23 (31)
Input Shaft Retainer Bolt	14 (19)
Transfer Case-To-Transmission	24 (33)
Shift Selector Lever Nut (General Motors)	23 (31)
Shift Selector Light Switch	17 (23)
Speedometer Pick-Up Switch	23 (31)
Yoke Nut	165 (224)
	INCH Lbs. (N.m)
Oil Pump Screws (Chrysler)	12-15 (1.4-1.8)

Jeep: Cherokee, Grand Cherokee

IDENTIFICATION

Transfer case can be identified by an I.D. tag, located on rear case. I.D. tag provides model number, serial number and low range ratio. Date of manufacture is the serial number (I.D. number). This information is necessary when ordering parts.

DESCRIPTION

Model 242 transfer case is a chain-driven, 2-piece aluminum case, with full time operation. Torque input in 4WD high and low range is undifferentiated.

ADJUSTMENTS

GEARSHIFT LINKAGE

Remove shift boot and shift to 4L position. Place a 3/16" shim between gearshift and shift gate. *See Fig. 1.* Loosen trunnion nut. Adjust trunnion and shift rod until rod fits freely. Tighten trunnion nut and remove shim.

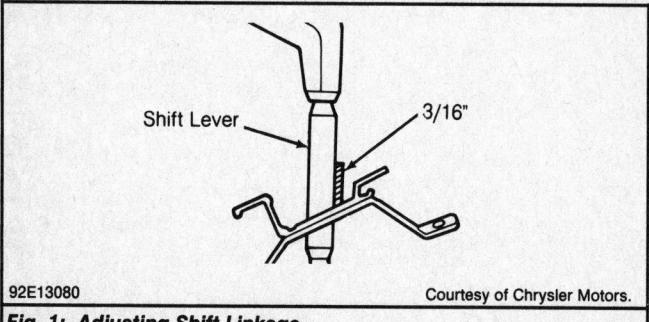

92E13080   Courtesy of Chrysler Motors.

Fig. 1: Adjusting Shift Linkage

TROUBLE SHOOTING

Will Not Shift Or Difficult To Shift Into Gear – Vehicle speed too high; slow vehicle to 2-3 MPH to shift. Vehicle operated too long on dry paved surface; stop vehicle and place in Reverse or Neutral to relieve driveline torque. Ensure transfer case external linkage is not binding. Ensure correct fluid is used. Internal parts may be worn or damaged.

Noisy In All Gears – Check fluid level. Ensure correct fluid is used. If fluid is okay, locate noise and check for possible internal mechanical problem.

Jumps Out Of Gear Or Noisy In 4WD – Transfer case not completely in gear; check shift linkage. Range fork damaged. Inserts are worn. Shift fork binding on shift rail. Low range gear worn or damaged.

Fluid Leaking From Vent Or Seals – Transfer case overfilled. Vent plugged. Output shaft seals are damaged or not installed properly.

Transfer Case Will Not Shift Through High Lock Range – Incomplete shift due to driveline torque load; momentarily release accelerator pedal to complete shift. Check tire pressure and tire wear. Vehicle overloaded; remove load and check shifting.

ON-VEHICLE SERVICE

FRONT OIL SEAL

Removal & Installation – **1)** Mark front propeller shaft and flange for alignment purposes. Remove front propeller shaft. Remove flange. Discard washer and nut. Using a screwdriver, carefully remove oil seal. Ensure seal contact surface is clean.

2) Apply ATF to seal lip and yoke seal surface. Install oil seal and flange with new washer and nut. Install front propeller shaft using alignment marks. Check transfer case fluid.

EXTENSION HOUSING OIL SEAL & BUSHING

NOTE: When replacing oil seal, do not remove extention housing.

Removal & Installation – **1)** Mark rear propeller shaft and flange for installation purposes. Remove rear propeller shaft. Remove bolts and tap extension housing in a clockwise direction and remove extension housing. DO NOT pry on extension housing. Using a screwdriver, remove oil seal from extension housing.

2) Using bushing driver, replace bushing in extension housing. Install new extension housing oil seal. Apply silicone sealant to extension housing mating surface. Install extension housing. Reverse removal procedure to complete installation.

REMOVAL & INSTALLATION

TRANSFER CASE

Removal & Installation – **1)** Shift transfer case into Neutral position and drain fluid. Mark front and rear propeller shaft for installation purposes. Remove front and rear propeller shafts. Disconnect vacuum lines and speedometer cable. Remove rear crossmember.

2) Disconnect shift linkage. Support transfer case with a jack. Separate transfer case from transmission. Remove transfer case. To install, reverse removal procedure. Tighten bolts to specification. See TORQUE SPECIFICATIONS. Adjust shift linkage, if necessary.

TRANSFER CASE DISASSEMBLY

1) Remove drain and fill plugs. *See Fig. 2.* Remove front companion flange, washer and seal. Place transfer case in LO LOCK position. Remove extension housing. See EXTENSION HOUSING OIL SEAL & BUSHING under ON-VEHICLE SERVICE. Remove rear bearing snap ring. Remove rear retainer. Separate rear case from front case. DO NOT pry against mating surfaces.

2) Remove oil pump, pick-up tube and screen from rear case. Remove pick-up tube "O" ring from oil pump. Mark oil pump housing for reassembly purposes. Disassemble oil pump. Remove magnet from front case. Remove drive sprocket snap ring. Remove drive sprocket and drive chain.

3) Remove front output shaft. Remove shift lever from sector shaft. Remove shift detent plug, spring and plunger. Remove plug from low range fork lock pin access hole. Move shift sector until lock pin is aligned with hole. Remove lock pin with No. 1 screw extractor.

4) Remove shift rail from fork assembly. Remove mode fork and mainshaft as an assembly. Record mode sleeve position. Remove mode shift sleeve and mode fork assembly. Remove sleeve from fork. Remove intermediate clutch shaft snap ring from mainshaft.

5) Remove clutch shaft thrust ring. Remove intermediate clutch shaft. Remove differential retaining snap ring. Remove differential assembly. Remove differential needle bearings and thrust washers from mainshaft. Remove low range fork and hub.

6) Remove shift sector. Remove shift sector bushing and "O" ring. Remove front bearing retainer. Remove input gear snap ring. Using a press, remove input and low range gear assembly from input gear bearing. Remove low range gear snap ring.

7) Remove input gear retainer, thrust washers and input gear. Mark differential halves for reassembly purposes. Separate differential halves. Remove planetary gear and thrust washers.

8) Record mainshaft gear and sprocket gear position. Remove gears. Remove front output shaft front bearing oil seal, snap ring and front bearing. Using a press, remove input gear bearing.

9) Using slide hammer and internal puller, remove input gear pilot bearing. If necessary, install a longer 1/4" x 20 bolt in adapter to clear top edge of gear. Using slide hammer and internal puller, remove front output shaft rear bearing.

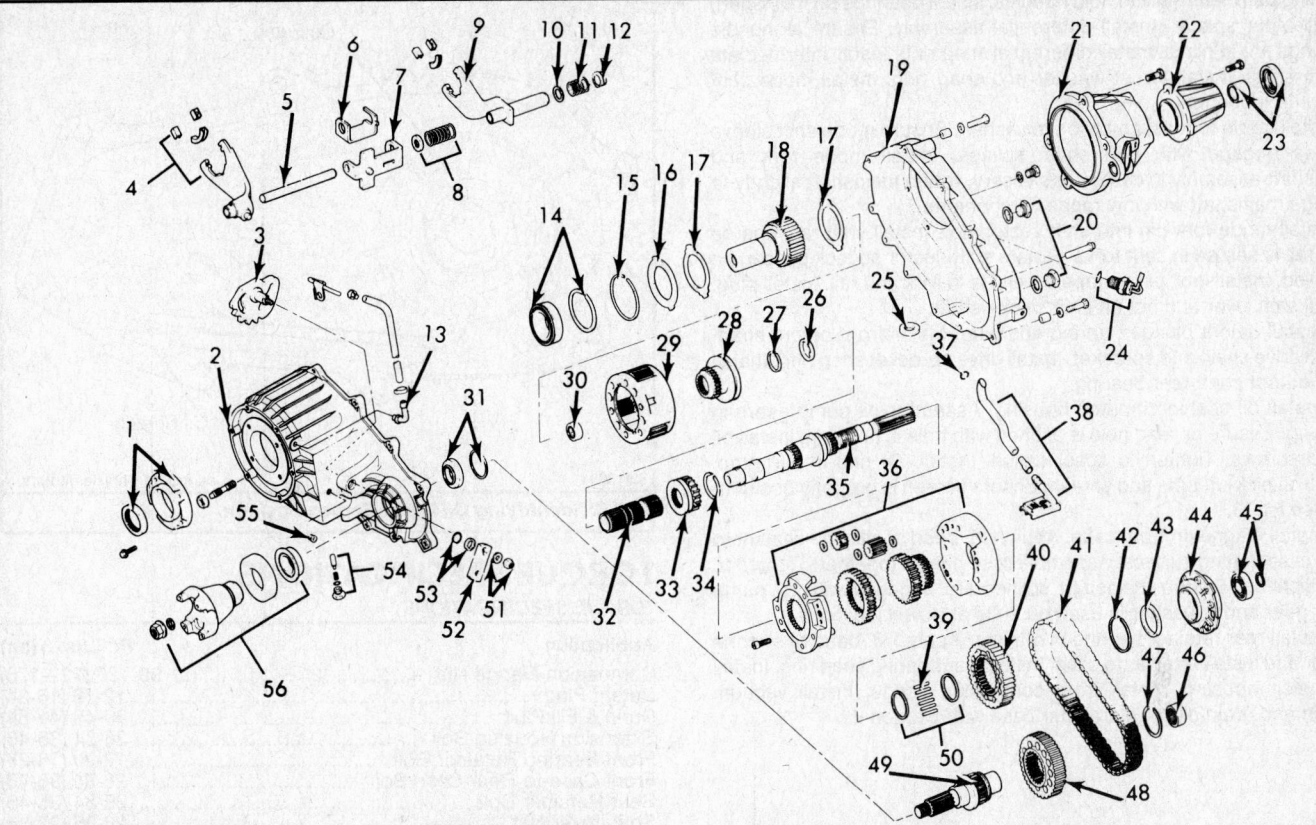

1. Front Bearing Retainer & Seal
2. Front Case
3. Shift Sector
4. Low Range Fork & Inserts
5. Shift Rail
6. Shift Bracket
7. Slider Bracket
8. Bushing & Spring
9. Mode Fork & Inserts
10. Bushing
11. Fork Spring
12. Bushing
13. Vent Tube
14. Input Gear Bearing & Snap Ring
15. Low Range Gear Snap Ring
16. Low Range Gear Retainer
17. Low Range Gear Thrust Washer
18. Input Gear
19. Rear Case
20. Drain & Fill Plugs
21. Rear Bearing Retainer
22. Extension Housing
23. Bushing & Oil Seal
24. Vacuum Switch
25. Magnet
26. Thrust Ring
27. Snap Ring
28. Shift Sleeve
29. Low Range Gear
30. Pilot Bushing
31. Front Output Shaft Front Bearing & Snap Ring
32. Intermediate Clutch Shaft
33. Shift Sleeve
34. Snap Ring
35. Mainshaft
36. Differential Assembly
37. Oil Pick-Up Tube "O" Ring
38. Oil Pick-Up Tube & Screen
39. Mainshaft Bearing Rollers
40. Drive Sprocket
41. Drive Chain
42. Snap Ring
43. Oil Pump Seal
44. Oil Pump
45. Rear Bearing & Snap Ring
46. Front Output Shaft Rear Bearing
47. Snap Ring
48. Driven Sprocket
49. Front Output Shaft
50. Mainshaft Bearing Spacers
51. Shift Lever Washer & Nut
52. Shift Lever
53. Sector "O" Ring & Seal
54. Detent Pin, Spring & Plug
55. Seal Plug
56. Companion Flange, Nut, Seal, Washer & Oil Slinger

92A13086

Fig. 2: Exploded View Of Model 242 Transfer Case

CLEANING & INSPECTION

1) Clean all parts with solvent. Dry with compressed air. Replace all oil seals, "O" rings and snap rings. Check all parts for wear or damage. Replace all worn or damaged parts. Apply Dexron II to all parts before installing.
2) Inspect low range annulus gear inside front case. If gear is worn or damaged, replace case and gear as an assembly. Replace oil pump as an assembly if any part is damaged or worn.

NOTE: When installing bearings, ensure bearing bores are aligned with oil feed holes.

TRANSFER CASE REASSEMBLY

1) Install front output shaft front bearing, snap ring and oil seal. Install snap ring on input gear bearing. Using a wooden block and press, install input gear bearing until snap ring is against case.
2) Install input gear pilot bearing. Assemble low range gear, thrust washers, input gear and retainer. Install low range gear snap ring. Ensure snap ring is seated properly in groove.

3) Start input gear shaft through the bearing in front case. Using a press, install input gear shaft through bearing. Ensure adapter is positioned properly before pressing shaft.

NOTE: Ensure proper size tool is used to press input gear shaft; wrong size tool can damage case and thrust washers and will move pilot bearing too far into gear bore.

4) Install input gear snap ring. Install front bearing retainer oil seal. Apply 1/8" bead of silicone sealant to front bearing retainer mating surface. Install front bearing retainer on front case. Install sector shaft "O" ring and bushing. Install shift sector.
5) Install detent pin, spring and plug. Install low range fork pads. Assemble low range fork and hub. Ensure low range fork pin is engaged in shift sector slot. Install differential sprocket gear in lower differential case. Install planet gears and new thrust washers on lower case pins.
6) Ensure thrust washers are positioned on top and bottom of each gear. Install mainshaft gear. Align marks on upper and lower differential case. Install bolts and tighten to specifications. See TORQUE SPECIFICATIONS. Install needle bearing spacer on mainshaft.

7) Using petroleum jelly to hold needles, install bearings on mainshaft. Install other spacer. Install differential assembly. Ensure all needle bearings are in place. Install differential snap ring. Install intermediate clutch shaft. Install thrust washer and snap ring. Install mode shift sleeve in mode fork.

8) Install mode fork assembly on mainshaft. Ensure mode shift sleeve splines engage with differential splines. Install mode fork and mainshaft assembly in case. If necessary, rotate mainshaft slightly to engage mainshaft with low range components.

9) Install mode fork pin into shift sector slot. Install shift rail. Ensure shift rail is seated in shift forks. Rotate shift sector so lock pin can be installed. Install lock pin so tapered end is in fork and rail. Install plug. Install shift lever and nut on shift sector shaft.

10) Install detent plunger, spring and plug. Install front output shaft. Install drive chain and sprocket. Install drive sprocket snap ring. Install front output shaft rear bearing.

11) Install oil seal in oil pump housing. Assemble oil pump gears in housing. Ensure oil feed hole is aligned with hole in housing. Install oil pump screws. Tighten to specification. Install "O" ring in oil pump. Install oil pick-up tube and screen. Ensure screen is properly positioned. See Fig. 3.

12) Install magnet in front case. Apply 1/8" bead of silicone sealant to front case mating surface. Assemble case halves together. Tighten to specification. Ensure mainshaft splines are engaged with oil pump inner gear and a washer is used on bolts at dowel locations.

13) Install rear retainer bearing in retainer. Apply 1/8" bead of silicone sealer and install retainer to case. Install rear bearing snap ring. Install extension housing. Install front companion flange. Install vacuum switch and drain plug. Fill transfer case with Dexron II.

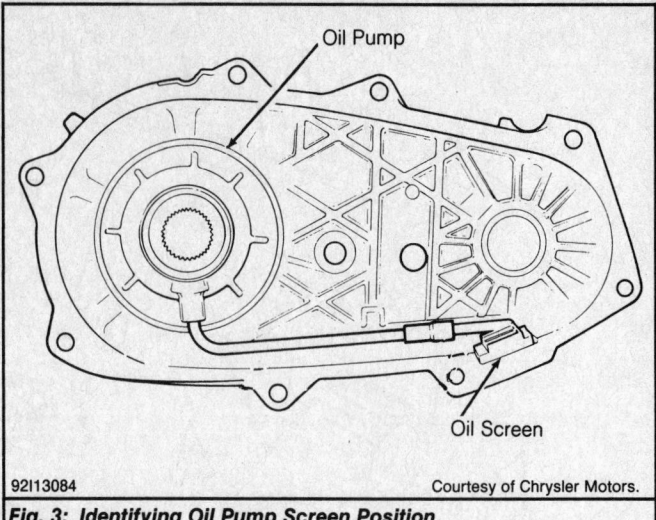

92I13084   Courtesy of Chrysler Motors.

Fig. 3: Identifying Oil Pump Screen Position

TORQUE SPECIFICATIONS
TORQUE SPECIFICATIONS

Application	Ft. Lbs. (N.m)
Companion Flange Nut	90-130 (122-176)
Detent Plug	12-18 (16-24)
Drain & Fill Plug	30-40 (41-54)
Extension Housing Bolt	26-34 (35-46)
Front Bearing Retainer Bolt	12-20 (16-27)
Front Case-to-Rear Case Bolt	26-34 (35-46)
Rear Retainer Bolt	26-34 (35-46)
Shift Lever Nut	20-25 (27-34)
Transfer Case-to-Transmission	26 (35)
Vacuum Switch	15-25 (20-34)

	INCH Lbs. (N.m)
Oil Pump Screw	12-15 (1.4-1.7)

TRANSFER CASES
New Venture PTO 021

Chrysler Motors: BR2500/3500 (2WD)

IDENTIFICATION

Transfer case can be identified by a round I.D. tag, located on rear case. I.D. tag provides model number, serial number and ratio. This information is necessary when ordering parts.

DESCRIPTION

Model 021 Power Take Off (PTO) is used on some 2WD vehicles with automatic transmission. With PTO shift lever in "D", engine torque is available to the rear wheels (PTO output gear also turns). With PTO shift lever in "N", driveshaft is disengaged and engine torque is available to PTO only.

ADJUSTMENTS

GEARSHIFT LINKAGE

Remove shifter boot. Place shift lever in "D" position. Raise vehicle and loosen nut on shift rod. Move PTO shift lever fully to "D" position. Tighten shift rod nut.

TROUBLE SHOOTING

Will Not Shift Or Difficult To Shift – PTO misaligned or low fluid level. Ensure external linkage is not binding. Ensure correct fluid is used. Worn or damaged internal parts.

Noisy In All Gears – Loose or misadjusted shifting mechanism. Check fluid level. Ensure correct fluid is used. If fluid is okay, locate noise and check for possible internal mechanical problem.

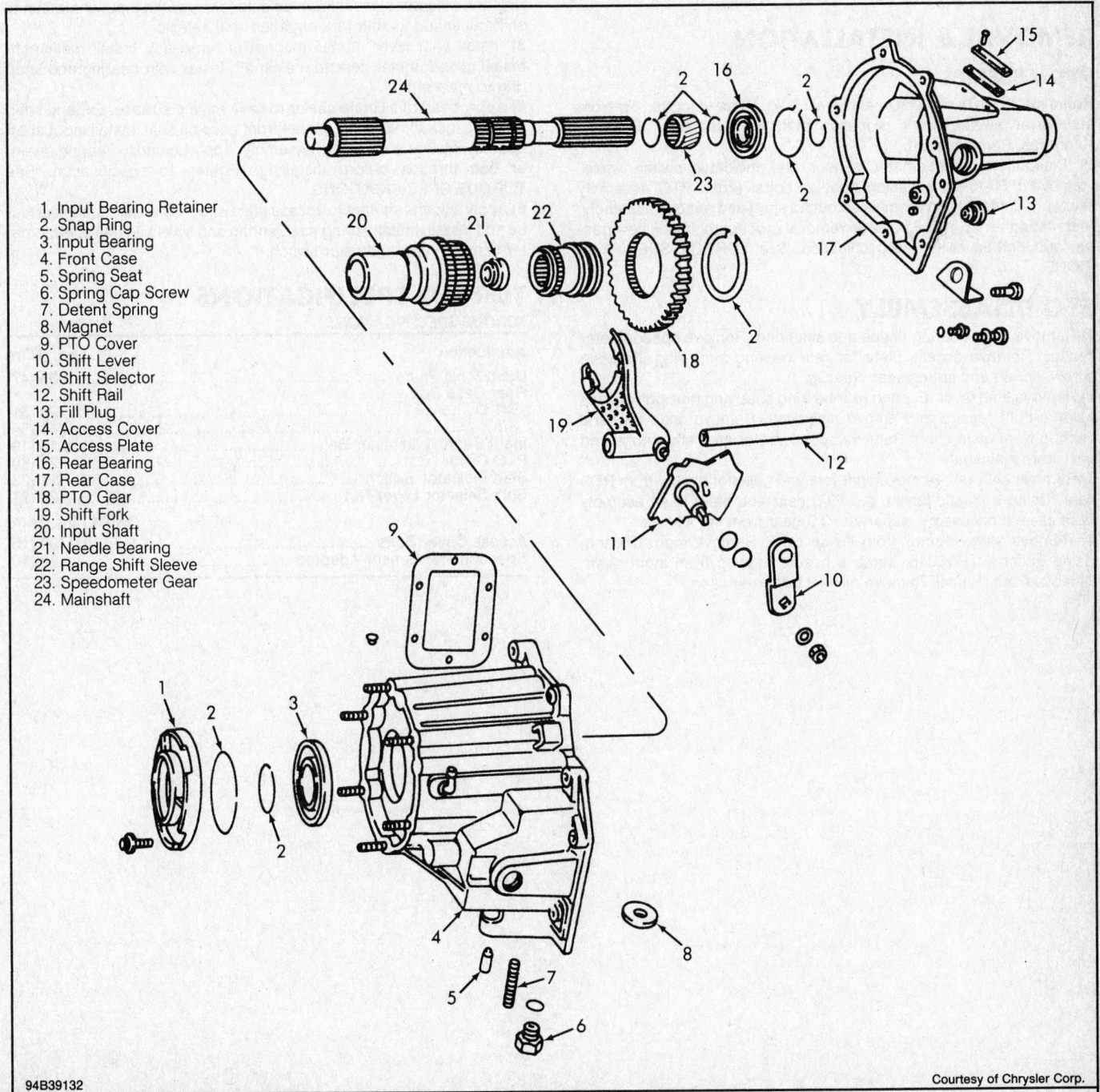

1. Input Bearing Retainer
2. Snap Ring
3. Input Bearing
4. Front Case
5. Spring Seat
6. Spring Cap Screw
7. Detent Spring
8. Magnet
9. PTO Cover
10. Shift Lever
11. Shift Selector
12. Shift Rail
13. Fill Plug
14. Access Cover
15. Access Plate
16. Rear Bearing
17. Rear Case
18. PTO Gear
19. Shift Fork
20. Input Shaft
21. Needle Bearing
22. Range Shift Sleeve
23. Speedometer Gear
24. Mainshaft

94B39132

Fig. 1: Exploded View Of PTO NV 021

PTO Unit Inoperative – PTO case not completely in gear; check shift linkage. Range fork damaged. Fork pads are worn. Shift fork binding on shift rail. PTO loose or misaligned. PTO gears not meshing. Internal splines on PTO gear stripped.

Fluid Leaking From Vent Or Seals – PTO overfilled. Vent plugged. Output shaft seals are damaged or not installed pr operly.

ON-VEHICLE SERVICE

OUTPUT SHAFT SEALS REPLACEMENT

Removal & Installation – **1)** Mark propeller shaft for alignment purposes during installation. Remove propeller shaft. Carefully remove oil seal. Ensure seal contact surface is clean.

2) Apply ATF to seal lip and flange seal surface. Install oil seal and flange with new washer and nut. Install propeller shaft using alignment marks. Check PTO fluid.

REMOVAL & INSTALLATION

PTO ASSEMBLY

Removal – **1)** Raise vehicle and drain fluid. Remove cotter pin from shift lever swivel. Mark propeller shaft for assembly alignment reference. Remove shaft.

2) Disconnect speedometer sensor and indicator switch wires. Remove PTO-to-transmission adapter bolts. Move PTO assembly rearward until free of transmission output shaft and remove assembly.

Installation – To install, reverse removal procedure. Install new gasket and tighten bolts to specification. See TORQUE SPECIFICATIONS.

PTO DISASSEMBLY

1) Remove input bearing flange and snap ring. Remove speedometer sensor. Remove access plate for rear bearing snap ring. Remove screw, spring and spring seat. *See Fig. 1.*

2) Remove shift lever. Expand rear bearing snap ring (through access hole) and lift rear case. Remove mainshaft. Remove snap ring and bearing from main shaft. Remove speedometer gear snap rings and gear from mainshaft.

3) Remove shift rail. Remove shift fork and selector sleeve from PTO gear. Using a plastic mallet, tap PTO gear and input shaft asembly from case. If necessary, separate PTO gear from input shaft.

4) Remove shift selector from inside case. Remove input bearing. Using Puller (MD998346), remove needle bearing from input shaft. Remove front oil seal. Remove oil seal from rear case.

CLEANING & INSPECTION

Clean all parts with solvent. Blow out all oil ports with compressed air. Replace all oil seals, "O" rings and snap rings. Check all parts for wear or damage. Replace oil pump as an assembly if any part is damaged or worn.

PTO REASSEMBLY

NOTE: When installing bearings, ensure bearing bores are aligned with oil feed holes.

1) Lubricate all internal parts with ATF. Install needle bearing into input shaft. Install bearing and snap ring in front case. Install shift selector in case. Assemble PTO gear and input shaft (if removed). Install PTO gear assembly in front case.

2) Install snap ring to input shaft in front of bearing. Assemble shift fork and selector sleeve. Align selector sleeve with input shaft. Install shift rail ensuring shift fork engages shift selector.

3) Install shift lever. Install magnet (if removed). Install mainshaft. Install speedometer gear to mainshaft. Install rear bearing and snap ring to main shaft.

4) Apply bead of silicone sealer to case mating surface. Expand snap ring and install rear case. Install front case oil seal. Install input shaft bearing retainer and oil seal assembly. Apply Loctite to bearing retainer bolt threads before installing. Tighten to specification. See TORQUE SPECIFICATIONS.

5) Apply silicone sealant to access plate and PTO cover mating surfaces and install. Install spring seat, spring and screw. Install speedometer sensor. Install indicator switch.

TORQUE SPECIFICATIONS
TORQUE SPECIFICATIONS

Application	Ft. Lbs. (N.m)
Drain & Fill Plugs	35 (47)
Rear Case Bolt	
5/16"	23 (31)
3/8"	40 (54)
Input Bearing Retainer Bolt	14 (19)
PTO Cover	22 (30)
Shift Indicator Switch	17 (23)
Shift Selector Lever Nut	20 (27)
	INCH Lbs. (N.m)
Access Cover Bolts	90 (10)
Speedometer Sensor Adapter	90 (10)

NOTES

NOTES

NOTES

NOTES

NOTES

English-Metric Conversion Chart

CONVERSION FACTORS

Unit	To	Unit	Multiply By
LENGTH			
Millimeters	Inches		.03937
Inches	Millimeters		25.4
Meters	Feet		3.28084
Feet	Meters		.3048
Kilometers	Miles		.62137
Miles	Kilometers		1.60935
AREA			
Square Centimeters	Square Inches		.155
Square Inches	Square Centimeters		6.45159
VOLUME			
Cubic Centimeters	Cubic Inches		.06103
Cubic Inches	Cubic Centimeters		16.38703
Liters	Cubic Inches		61.025
Cubic Inches	Liters		.01639
Liters	Quarts		1.05672
Quarts	Liters		.94633
Liters	Pints		2.11344
Pints	Liters		.47317
Liters	Ounces		33.81497
Ounces	Liters		.02957

Unit	To	Unit	Multiply By
WEIGHT			
Grams	Ounces		.03527
Ounces	Grams		28.34953
Kilograms	Pounds		2.20462
Pounds	Kilograms		.45359
WORK			
Centimeter Kilograms	Inch Pounds		.8676
Inch Pounds	Centimeter Kilograms		1.15262
Meter Kilograms	Foot Pounds		7.23301
Foot Pounds	Newton Meters		1.3558
PRESSURE			
Kilograms/Sq. Centimeter	Pounds/Sq. Inch		14.22334
Pounds/Sq. Inch	Kilograms/Sq. Centimeter		.07031
Bar	Pounds/Sq. Inch		14.504
Pounds/Sq. Inch	Bar		.06895
Atmosphere	Pounds/Sq. Inch		14.696
Pounds/Sq. Inch	Atmosphere		.06805
TEMPERATURE			
Centigrade Degrees	Fahrenheit Degrees		$(C° \times {}^9/_5) + 32$
Fahrenheit Degrees	Centigrade Degrees		$(F° - 32) \times {}^5/_9$

Inches	Decimals	MM
1/64	.016	.397
1/32	.031	.794
3/64	.047	1.191
1/16	.063	1.588
5/64	.078	1.984
3/32	.094	2.381
7/64	.109	2.778
1/8	.125	3.175
9/64	.141	3.572
5/32	.156	3.969
11/64	.172	4.366
3/16	.188	4.763
13/64	.203	5.159
7/32	.219	5.556
15/64	.234	5.953
1/4	.250	6.350
17/64	.266	6.747
9/32	.281	7.144
19/64	.297	7.541
5/16	.313	7.938
21/64	.328	8.334
11/32	.344	8.731
23/64	.359	9.128
3/8	.375	9.525
25/64	.391	9.922
13/32	.406	10.319
27/64	.422	10.716
7/16	.438	11.113
29/64	.453	11.509
15/32	.469	11.906
31/64	.484	12.303
1/2	.500	12.700

Inches	Decimals	MM
33/64	.516	13.097
17/32	.531	13.494
35/64	.547	13.891
9/16	.563	14.288
37/64	.578	14.684
19/32	.594	15.081
39/64	.609	15.478
5/8	.625	15.875
41/64	.641	16.272
21/32	.656	16.669
43/64	.672	17.066
11/16	.687	17.463
45/64	.703	17.859
23/32	.719	18.256
47/64	.734	18.653
3/4	.750	19.050
49/64	.766	19.447
25/32	.781	19.844
51/64	.797	20.241
13/16	.813	20.638
53/64	.828	21.034
27/32	.844	21.431
55/64	.859	21.828
7/8	.875	22.225
57/64	.891	22.622
29/32	.906	23.019
59/64	.922	23.416
15/16	.938	23.813
61/64	.953	24.209
31/32	.969	24.606
63/64	.984	25.003

METRIC CONVERSIONS

Metric conversions are making life more difficult for the mechanic. In addition to doubling the number of tools required, metric-dimensioned nuts and bolts are used alongside English components in many new vehicles. The mechanic has to decide which tool to use, slowing down the job. The tool problem can be solved by trial and error, but some metric conversions aren't so simple.

Converting temperature, lengths or volumes requires a calculator and conversion charts, or else a very nimble mind. Conversion charts are only part of the answer though, because they don't help you "think" metric, or "visualize" what you are converting. The following examples are intended to help you "see" metric sizes:

LENGTH

Meters are the standard unit of length in the metric system. The smaller units are 10ths (decimeter), 100ths (centimeter), and 1000ths (millimeter) of a meter. These common examples might help you to visualize the metric units:

* A meter is slightly longer than a yard (about 40 inches).
* An aspirin tablet is about one centimeter across (.4 inches).
* A millimeter is about the thickness of a dime.

VOLUME

Cubic meters and centimeters are used to measure volume, just as we normally think of cubic feet and inches. Liquid volume measurements include the liter and milliliter, like the English quarts or ounces.

* One teaspoon is about 5 cubic centimeters.
* A liter is about one quart.
* A liter is about 61 cubic inches.

WEIGHT

The metric weight system is based on the gram, with the most common unit being the kilogram (1000 grams). Our comparable units are ounces and pounds:

* A kilogram is about 2.2 pounds.
* An ounce is about 28 grams.

TORQUE

Torque is somewhat complicated. The term describes the amount of effort exerted to turn something. A chosen unit of weight or force is applied to a lever of standard length. The resulting leverage is called torque. In our standard system, we use the weight of one pound applied to a lever a foot long– resulting in the unit called a foot-pound. A smaller unit is the inch-pound (the lever is one inch long). Metric units include the meter kilogram (lever one meter long with a kilogram of weight applied) and the Newton-meter (lever one meter long with force of one Newton applied). Some conversions are:

* A meter kilogram is about 7.2 foot pounds.
* A Newton-meter is about 1.4 foot pounds.
* A centimeter kilogram (cmkg) is equal to .9 inch pounds.

PRESSURE

Pressure is another complicated measurement. Pressure is described as a force or weight applied to a given area. Our common unit is pounds per square inch. Metric units can be expressed in several ways. One is the kilogram per square centimeter (kg/cm²). Another unit of pressure is the Pascal (force of one Newton on an area of one square meter), which equals about 4 ounces on a square yard. Since this is a very small amount of pressure, we usually see the kiloPascal, or kPa (1000 Pascals). Another common automotive term for pressure is the bar (used by German manufacturers), which equals 10 Pascals. Thoroughly confused? Try the examples below:

* Atmospheric pressure at sea level is about 14.7 psi.
* Atmospheric pressure at sea level is about 1 bar.
* Atmospheric pressure at sea level is about 1 kg/cm².
* One pound per square inch is about 7 kPa.

COMMENTS AND SUGGESTIONS

Please let us know if you have any comments or recommended changes to this book. Mail this postage-paid card today. We'd like to hear from you!

☐ Domestic Cars ☐ Imported Cars & Trucks ☐ Domestic Light Trucks ☐ Medium & Heavy Duty Trucks
☐ Engine Performance ☐ Electrical ☐ Engine ☐ Chassis ☐ Transmission
☐ Air Conditioning ☐ Electrical Component Locators ☐ Other _____

Section No. _____ Page No. _____ Vehicle Model & Year _____

Comments: _____
_____
_____
_____

Name _____ Company _____
Address _____ City _____ State _____ Zip _____
Phone (___) _____ Date _____ THANK YOU

TD94

COMMENTS AND SUGGESTIONS

Please let us know if you have any comments or recommended changes to this book. Mail this postage-paid card today. We'd like to hear from you!

☐ Domestic Cars ☐ Imported Cars & Trucks ☐ Domestic Light Trucks ☐ Medium & Heavy Duty Trucks
☐ Engine Performance ☐ Electrical ☐ Engine ☐ Chassis ☐ Transmission
☐ Air Conditioning ☐ Electrical Component Locators ☐ Other _____

Section No. _____ Page No. _____ Vehicle Model & Year _____

Comments: _____
_____
_____
_____

Name _____ Company _____
Address _____ City _____ State _____ Zip _____
Phone (___) _____ Date _____ THANK YOU

TD94

COMMENTS AND SUGGESTIONS

Please let us know if you have any comments or recommended changes to this book. Mail this postage-paid card today. We'd like to hear from you!

☐ Domestic Cars ☐ Imported Cars & Trucks ☐ Domestic Light Trucks ☐ Medium & Heavy Duty Trucks
☐ Engine Performance ☐ Electrical ☐ Engine ☐ Chassis ☐ Transmission
☐ Air Conditioning ☐ Electrical Component Locators ☐ Other _____

Section No. _____ Page No. _____ Vehicle Model & Year _____

Comments: _____
_____
_____
_____

Name _____ Company _____
Address _____ City _____ State _____ Zip _____
Phone (___) _____ Date _____ THANK YOU

TD94

Be sure to fill out this form completely.

BUSINESS   REPLY   MAIL

FIRST CLASS   PERMIT NO. 3701   SAN DIEGO, CA

POSTAGE WILL BE PAID BY ADDRESSEE

MITCHELL INTERNATIONAL
P.O. Box 26260
San Diego, California 92196-9984

BUSINESS   REPLY   MAIL

FIRST CLASS   PERMIT NO. 3701   SAN DIEGO, CA

POSTAGE WILL BE PAID BY ADDRESSEE

MITCHELL INTERNATIONAL
P.O. Box 26260
San Diego, California 92196-9984

BUSINESS   REPLY   MAIL

FIRST CLASS   PERMIT NO. 3701   SAN DIEGO, CA

POSTAGE WILL BE PAID BY ADDRESSEE

MITCHELL INTERNATIONAL
P.O. Box 26260
San Diego, California 92196-9984